D1412080

EDITOR & PUBLISHER®

97th Annual

Newspaper DATABOOK™

The Encyclopedia of the Newspaper Industry

BOOK 2: WEEKLIES

2018

Editorial: 18475 Bandilier Circle, Fountain Valley, CA 92708 – (949) 660-6150; Fax (949) 660-6172
Customer Service: (888) 732-7323

97th ANNUAL
Newspaper
DATABOOK®

Published annually by Editor & Publisher®, the oldest publishers' and advertisers' periodical in the United States

With which has been merged: ***The Journalist***, establisher March 22, 1884; ***Newspaperdom***, March 22, 1892; ***The Fourth Estate***, March 1, 1894; ***Editor & Publisher***, June 29, 1901; ***Advertising***, January 22, 1925.

CORPORATE OFFICES (949) 660-6150
FAX (949) 660-6172

EDITOR-IN-CHIEF *Jeff Fleming*
jeff@editorandpublisher.com

MANAGING EDITOR *Nu Yang*
nu@editorandpublisher.com

ART DIRECTOR *Meredith Ewell*
meredith@editorandpublisher.com

SALES & MARKETING CONSULTANT *Wendy MacDonald*, ext. 231
wendy@editorandpublisher.com

SUBSCRIPTION SERVICES (888) 732-7323

CIRCULATION MANAGER *Rick Avila*, ext. 254
rick@editorandpublisher.com

CIRCULATION ASSISTANTS *Emily Wells*, ext. 225
Dustin Nguyen, ext. 255

ACCOUNTING *Kym Bashford*, ext. 213
kym@editorandpublisher.com

EDITORIAL & ADVERTISING MAILING ADDRESS
18475 BANDILIER CIRCLE, FOUNTAIN VALLEY, CA 92708

WWW.EDITORANDPUBLISHER.COM

Editor & Publisher is printed in the U.S.A.

dMcI
duncan mcintosh co. inc.

DUNCAN McINTOSH CO.
FOUNDED BY:

Editor and Publisher • *Duncan McIntosh Jr.*
Co-Publisher • *Teresa Ybarra McIntosh (1942-2011)*

18475 Bandilier Circle, Fountain Valley, CA 92708, (949) 660-6150; fax (949) 660-6172; www.editorandpublisher.com;

ISBN 1-930732-69-4 (Book 1) ISBN 1-930732-70-8 (Book 2)

Letter from the Publisher...

Welcome to the *2018 Editor & Publisher Newspaper DataBook-Book 2.* Inside you will find a wealth of information concerning the nondaily, community and free paper industry, including listings of weekly (three or fewer days a week) newspapers, shopper publications, specialty and niche publications, and organizations supporting the industry

The listings in this directory are designed to give you the information you need about nondaily newspapers--fast. This directory is also available electronically on the web, enabling you to search, retrieve, and export data in seconds for your own personal use.

This directory is divided into sections for U.S. and Canadian publications, organizations and support companies: Community Weekly Newspapers; Shopper/TMC Publications; Specialty and Niche Publications; College and University Newspapers and Journalism Schools; Weekly Newspaper Groups and Other Organizations and Industry Services.

Specific facts and figures on the paid and free community newspaper industry are found in charts at the front of the book. The chart, "Circulation of the U.S. Community Weekly Newspapers by Type of Publication" shows 3,377 paid community newspapers and 1,189 free community newspapers. It also displays total community newspaper circulation in the United States as 16.8 million paid and 28.6 million free, for a total of 45.4 million as of January 1, 2018.

E&P defines a weekly newspaper as any publication printing one to three times a week. A shopper is defined as a publication with less than 25 percent editorial content. A paid community newspaper has more than 95 percent paid circulation while the reverse is true for free publications. Anything else is a combined newspaper. For the purpose of *E&P* data charts, papers that publish two or three times a week are averaged to find one paid and one free circulation number.

You will find the Who's Where contact directory of industry professionals with phone numbers, titles, and company names in the back of Book 1. We thank our many friends and colleagues who have helped make the *Newspaper DataBook - Book 2* the authoritative reference of the nondaily newspaper industry. As always, we welcome feedback from our subscribers and listees as we continue our efforts to provide the most useful and reliable information possible. Please continue to direct your comments and suggestions to us at rick@editorandpublisher.com.

Sincerely,

Duncan McIntosh
Publisher

TABLE OF CONTENTS
2018 EDITOR & PUBLISHER® NEWSPAPER DATABOOK®

BOOK 2: WEEKLIES

FRONT PAGES

Letter from the Publisher ii
Sample listing iv
Audit service companies iv
Top 50 Paid Community Weekly Newspapers in the U.S. by Circulation Category.. v
Top 50 Free Community Weekly Newspapers in the U.S. by Circulation Category.. v
Top 50 Combined Community Weekly Newspapers in the U.S. by Circulation Category v
Top 50 U.S. Shopper Publications in the U.S. vi
Circulation of U.S. Community Weekly Newspapers vii
Circulation of U.S. Community Weekly Newspapers by Day of Publication viii
Circulation of U.S. Community Weekly Newspapers by Circulation Groups ix
Circulation of Canadian Community Weekly Newspapers ix
Circulation of Canadian Community Weekly Newspapers by Day of Publication x
Circulation of Canadian Community Weekley Newspapers by Circulation Group x
Circulation of U.S. Shopper/TMC Publications xi
Circulation of Canadian Shopper/TMC Publications xii
Circulation Totals for All Publications xii
Mechanical Equipment-Abbreviations xiii

I COMMUNITY NEWSPAPERS PUBLISHED IN THE UNITED STATES AND CANADA

Community Newspapers in the U.S. 2
Community Newspapers in Canada 451

II SHOPPER AND TMC PUBLICATIONS PUBLISHED IN THE UNITED STATES AND CANADA

Shopper/TMC Publications in the U.S. 2
Shopper/TMC publications in Canada 75

III SPECIALTY AND NICHE PUBLICATIONS PUBLISHED IN THE UNITED STATES AND CANADA

Specialty

Alternative Newspapers in the U.S 2
Black Newspapers in the U.S. 12
Schools and Departments of Journalism 22
Schools and Departments of Journalism - Foreign 51
College and University Newspapers 53
Ethnic Newspapers in the U.S. 99
Gay & Lesbian Newspapers in the U.S. 108
Hispanic Newspapers in the U.S. 110
Jewish Newspapers in the U.S. 121
Military Newspapers in the U.S. 127
Religious Newspapers in the U.S. 133
Alternative Newspapers in Canada 141
Ethnic Newspapers in Canada 142

Niche

Parenting Publications in the U.S. 146
Real Estate Publications in the U.S. 151
Senior Publications in the U.S. 154

IV WEEKLY NEWSPAPER GROUPS AND OTHER ORGANIZATIONS AND INDUSTRY SERVICES

Weekly Newspaper and Shopper Publication Groups in the U.S. 2
Weekly Newspaper and Shopper Publication Groups in Canada 21
Alternate Delivery Services 24
Associations and Clubs-National and International 26
Associations and Clubs-City, State and Regional 30
Newspaper Brokers and Appraisers 33
Newspaper Representatives-National 35
Newspaper Representatives-State 37
Newspaper Distributed Magazines and TMC publications 38

BOOK 1: DAILIES
FRONT PAGES

Letter from the Publisher ii
Basic Data for Space Buyers iv
Ready Reckoners of Advertising Rates and Circulations for Canada iv
Ready Reckoners of Advertising Rates and Circulations for the United States v
Circulation of U.S. Daily Newspapers by Circulation Groups vi
Annual Newspaper Advertising Totals vi
Circulation of Daily Newspapers in Canada by Circulation Groups vii
U.S. Multi-Newspaper Cities vii
Canadian Multi-Newspaper Cities vii
Top One Hundred U.S. Daily newspapers viii
Top Ten Canadian Daily Newspapers viii
Top One Hundred U.S. Sunday Newspapers ix
Top Ten Canadian Sunday newspapers ix
Mechanical Equipment-Abbreviations x
Daily Newspapers Sold in 2017 xi

I DAILY NEWSPAPERS PUBLISHED IN THE UNITED STATES AND CANADA
II U.S. AND CANADIAN DAILY NEWSPAPER GROUPS AND SPECIAL SERVICES
III NEWS, PICTURES AND SYNDICATE SERVICES
IV MECHANICAL AND INTERACTIVE EQUIPMENT, SUPPLIES AND SERVICES
V OTHER ORGANIZATIONS AND INDUSTRY SERVICES
VI E&P'S WHO'S WHERE DIRECTORY OF NEWSPAPER PEOPLE

E&P NEWSPAPER DATABOOK® - SAMPLE LISTING

Community (communities) served → **Evansville**

Street address (city and zip code if different); PO Box, city, state, zip code, telephone number, fax number, e-mail address and web site (if applicable)

Advertising per column inch rate (modular rate in Canada). Comb avail refers to the special advertising rate available in conjunction with one or more other publications.

Insert rate is per 1,000 pieces. Year of establishment for publication follows. Parent company appears, when applicable. In this example, Thrifty Nickel is published by American Classifieds LLC.

Equipment includes hardware, software and press equipment owned by the publisher and used in publishing of the paper. Number of units precedes the hardware and presses. The version follows software, if available. Delivery method(s) listed refer to the means of the paper's distribution – mail, newsstand, racks, and/or private carrier.

Evansville

Thrifty Nickel (thur)
1301 E. Morgan Ave., Evansville, IN 47711-4715; tel (812) 428-8484; fax (812) 428-8491; web site http://www.americanclassifieds.com.
Circulation: 26,000fr; Estimate.
Advertising: Open inch rate $7.00 (comb avail).
Insert Rate: $35.00/M. Established: 1981.
Parent Co.: American Classifieds LLC
Editions (circ.): 4 total — Carmi American Classifieds; Evansville American Classifieds; Henderson American Classifieds; Princeton American Classifieds.

PERSONNEL

Pub. . . . . James Hall
Adv. Mgr. . . . . James Hall
Circ. Mgr. . . . . Judy Smith
Ed. . . . . James Hall
Prodn. Mgr. Kristy Kerley

Mechanical specifications: Format page 10 1/4" x 15"; E - 8 cols, 1 3/16", 1/8" between; A - 8 cols, 1 3/16", 1/8" between; C - 8 cols, 1 3/16", 1/8" between.
Equipment: Hardware — 9-APP/Power Mac, APP/Mac G3, APP/Mac G4; Software — Adobe/PageMaker 6.0.
Delivery method — Newsstand.

Name of publication (day(s) published).

Circulation for each day of publication. If no day(s) is listed, circulation numbers provided are for each day published. Audit type follows.

Edition information (if applicable). Total number of editions is followed by the name of each edition (and the edition's circulation). Sum of circulation figures may or may not equal circulation amount listed above.

Personnel information. Title and name.

Mechanical information. Format size is the image area of one page. Following are the number of columns, column width and space between columns for Editorial (E), Display advertising (A) and Classified advertising (C).

CIRCULATION AUDIT SERVICES

ALLIANCE FOR AUDITED MEDIA (AAM)
(Est. 1914)— 900 N. Meacham Rd., Schaumburg, IL 60173-4968; tel (847) 879-8294; fax (847) 605-0483; web site http://www.accessabc.com.
Chrmn. — Merle Davidson
Pres./MD — Michael J. Lavery
Sr. Vice Pres., Accounting — Paul Fajnor
Sr. Vice Pres., Auditing/Technical Review — Mike Moran
Sr. Vice Pres., Centralized/Electronic Auditing — Scott Hanson
Sr. Vice Pres., Publisher Rel./Field Auditing — Teresa Perry
Sr. Vice Pres., Mktg./Sales — Mark Wachowicz
Vice Pres., HR — Laura Claybaugh
Vice Pres., Meetings — Sue Thomas
Vice Pres., Info Systems — Kaydene Stachelski
Commun. Mgr. — Kammi Altig
ABC Coupon Verification Service
Audit Bureau of Verification Services Inc. (ABVS)

BPA WORLDWIDE
(Est. 1930)— 2 Corporate Dr. 9th Fl, Shelton, CT 06484; tel (203) 447-2800; fax (203) 447-2900; web site http://www.bpaww.com.
Pres./CEO — Glenn Hansen
Sr. Vice Pres., Bus. Devel. — Peter D. Black
Sr. Vice Pres., Auditing — Richard J. Murphy

CANADIAN CIRCULATION AUDIT BOARD
(CCAB, INC.)
(Est. 1937)— 1 Concord Gate Ste. 800, Toronto, ON M3C 3N6; tel (416) 487-2418; fax (416) 487-6405; web site http://www.bpaww.com.
Vice Pres. — Timothy Peel
Mktg. Mgr. — Neil Ta
Bulk Distribution Audit
Select Distribution Audit

CANADIAN COMMUNITY NEWSPAPER ASSOCIATION
(Est. 1919)— 8 Market St., Ste. 300, Toronto, ON M5E 1M6; tel (416) 482-1090; fax (416) 482-1908; e-mail info@ccna.ca; web site http://www.ccna.ca.
Pres. — John Hinds
MD — Tina Ongkeko

CERTIFIED AUDIT OF CIRCULATIONS, INC.
(Est. 1956)— 155 Willowbrook Blvd., 4th Fl., Wayne, NJ 07470-7032; tel (973) 785-3000; fax (973) 785-8341; web site http://www.certifiedaudit.com.
CEO — Mark Stoecklin
Audit Mgr. — Debbie Maragoudakis
Dir., Mktg. — Evelina Sodt
Dir., Opns. — David Roe

CIRCULATION VERIFICATION COUNCIL
(Est. 1992)— PO Box 31523, Saint Louis, MO 63131-0523; tel (314) 966-7711; fax (314) 822-0666; e-mail info@cvcaudit.com; web site http://www.cvcaudit.com.
Pres./CEO — Tim A. Bingaman
Audit Mgr. — Jim Kennedy
Audit Coord. — Lisa Funken
Audit Coord. — Deborah Tata
Audit Coord. — Karen Wood
Office Mgr. — Darlene Lucy

VERIFIED AUDIT CIRCULATION (VAC) (Est.
1951)— 900 Larkspur Landing Cir., Ste. 295, Larkspur, CA 94939; tel (415) 461-6006; fax (415) 461-6007; e-mail support@verifiedaudit.com; web site http://www.verifiedaudit.com.
CEO — Tim Prouty
Dir., Market Research — Mike Lynch

TOP FIFTY COMMUNITY WEEKLY NEWSPAPERS IN THE UNITED STATES BY CIRCULATION CATEGORY

PAID

Rahway (NJ) NJTODAY.NET....140000
Cleveland (OH) Sun News....137284
Swarthmore (PA) News of Delaware County, Town Talk, Garnet Valley Press, Springfield Press, County Press....137214
Midlothian (IL) Oak Lawn Independent....76700
Ephrata (PA) Lancaster Farming....59983
Melbourne (FL) Best - North....55000
Melbourne (FL) Best - South....55000
Patchogue (NY) Suffolk County News....53000
New York (NY) The New York Observer....52000
Mobile (AL) Press-Register....48619
Menlo Park (CA) Palo Alto Daily News....47585
Melbourne (FL) Best - Central....45000
Dodge City (KS) High Plains Journal....44232
Chino (CA) Chino Hills Champion....40697
Leesburg (FL) South Lake Press....40000
Huntsville (AL) The Huntsville Times....36709
Naples (FL) Bonita Springs Florida Weekly....35646
Fort Myers (FL) Fort Myers Florida Weekly....35646
Naples (FL) Naples Florida Weekly....35646
Palm Beach Gardens (FL) Palm Beach Gardens Florida Weekly....35646
Punta Gorda (FL) Punta Gorda/Port Charlotte Florida Weekly....35646
Houston (TX) Houston Forward Times....35089
Ventura (CA) Ventura County Reporter....33000
Lincoln (NE) Neighborhood Extra....33000
Birmingham (AL) The Birmingham News....30136
Denham Springs (LA) The Livingston Parish News....30000
Port Isabel (TX) Port Isabel-South Padre Press..30000
Elkton (VA) The Valley Banner....29896
Daly City (CA) Philippines Today....29855
New York (NY) Forward Newspaper....29479
Thompson Falls (MT) Sanders County Ledger....28700
Chatham (MA) The Cape Cod Chronicle....28125
Detroit (MI) Westland Observer....28007
Pearland (TX) Pearland Reporter News....28000
Salem (OR) Capital Press....27535
Puyallup (WA) The Puyallup Herald....27000
Eau Claire (WI) The Country Today....26124
Middleburg (PA) Snyder County Times....26000
Alameda (CA) The Montclarion....25858
Dothan (AL) Dothan Progress....25000
Kansas City (MO) The Olathe News....25000
Maspeth (NY) The Leader-Observer of Woodhaven....25000
Bangor (ME) The Weekly....24775
Homestead (FL) South Dade News Leader....24000
Huntington (NY) The Long-Islander News....24000
Orland Park (IL) The Orland Park Prairie....22580
Northport (AL) The Northport Gazette....22000
Winter Garden (FL) The West Orange Times & Observer....22000
Dorchester (MA) The Dorchester Reporter....22000
Raynham (MA) Canton Journal....21894

FREE

Coupeville (WA) Whidbey Crosswind....322397
Honolulu (HI) MidWeek Oahu....267859
Bensalem (PA) The Midweek Wire....178628
Ballston Spa (NY) Ballston Journal....151000
Tempe (AZ) East Valley Tribune....149308
Whitestone (NY) Queens Tribune....149000
Clinton Township (MI) The Advisor & Source...115389
Neptune (NJ) Toms River Observer-Reporter....115000
Bensalem (PA) Northeast Times....110099
San Francisco (CA) San Francisco Examiner....108753
Sterling (VA) Fairfax County Times....102157
Santa Monica (CA) Brentwood News....100000
Santa Monica (CA) Century City News....100000
Santa Monica (CA) LA Pride....100000
Santa Monica (CA) Santa Monica Mirror....100000
Santa Monica (CA) Westside Today....100000
Santa Monica (CA) Yo Venice....100000
Atlanta (GA) Reporter Newspapers....100000
Tekamah (NE) Midwest Messenger....100000
New Port Richey (FL) The Suncoast News....90433
Bel Air (MD) The Weekender....87000
Detroit (MI) Lake Orion Eccentric....86387
White Plains (NY) Northern Westchester Express....86008
Fort Lauderdale (FL) Deerfield and Pompano Forum....85704
Sacramento (CA) Inside Publications....82900
Fort Lauderdale (FL) Boynton Forum....77744
Godfrey (IL) AdVantage News....77000
Chapel Hill (NC) The Durham News....75594
Florence (AL) Courier Journal....75531
Raleigh (NC) Midtown Raleigh News....75189
Goodyear (AZ) West Valley View....73876
Raleigh (NC) North Raleigh News....73782
Las Vegas (NV) Nifty Nickel....72000
Brooklyn (NY) Caribbean Life....71500
Lowell (MA) Broadcaster....68364
Fair Lawn (NJ) Community News....66888
Delavan (WI) Janesville Messenger....64640
Beaverton (OR) Beaverton Leader....64397
New Providence (NJ) Suburban News....63986
Cherry Hill (NJ) Philadelphia Weekly....62958
Apple Valley (MN) Thisweek Newspapers....62000
Falmouth (ME) The Forecaster....60000
Saint Paul (MN) Villager....59799
Clinton Township (MI) The Armada Times....59500
White Plains (NY) Rockland County Express....59176
Fort Lauderdale (FL) Plantation/Davie Forum....58872
South Williamsport (PA) Webb Weekly....57940
Cherry Hill (NJ) South Philly Review....56585
Raleigh (NC) The Cary News....56003
Dundalk (MD) The Avenue News....55423

COMBINED

Las Vegas (NV) View Neighborhood Newspapers....600557
Town And Country (MO) Louisiana Press Journal........ 315722
Portland (OR) Sustainable Life....177000
Des Plaines (IL) Mount Prospect Journal....90996
Bayside (NY) The Queens Courier....76000
Southgate (MI) Heritage Sunday....71995
Golden (CO) Arvada Press....71803
Madison (WI) The Capital Times....69000
Pell City (AL) The Saint Clair Times....68000
Tampa (FL) Brandon News & Tribune....58000
Detroit (MI) Observer & Eccentric Media....54888
Mechanicsburg (PA) The Patriot-News....54629
Southgate (MI) News-Herald....50339
Tampa (FL) Carrollwood News & Tribune....48651
Harlan (IA) News-Advertiser....47000
Saint Petersburg (FL) South Tampa News & Tribune....45014
Bellevue (WA) Mercer Island Reporter....42362
Bourbonnais (IL) The Herald/Country Market....42000
Barberton (OH) The Barberton Herald....41418
Dallas (TX) Lone Star Outdoor News....40761
New Milford (CT) New Milford Spectrum....40369
Frankfort (KY) Kentucky Monthly....40000
Plainfield (IL) The Enterprise....39700
Bartlett (IL) Examiner Publications, Inc....37800
Troy (MO) The Lincoln County Journal....37700
Merced (CA) Merced County Times....35000
Hastings (MI) The Hastings Banner....34998
Needham (MA) Needham Times....34856
Needham (MA) Watertown TAB....34856
Saint Louis (MO) St. Louis/Southern Illinois Labor Tribune....33311
Derry (NH) Derry News....33000
Columbiana (AL) Alabaster Reporter....32497
Columbiana (AL) Pelham Reporter....32497
Columbiana (AL) Shelby County Reporter....32497
Southbridge (MA) The Webster Times....32200
Red Bank (NJ) The Two River Times....32000
Avon (IN) Hendricks County Flyer....31550
Georgetown (SC) The Georgetown Times....31223
Santa Ana (CA) Fullerton News-Tribune....31056
Mena (AR) The Mena Star....30700
Ann Arbor (MI) Ann Arbor Observer....30659
Framingham (MA) Hudson Sun....30355
Needham (MA) Medfield Press....30355
Framingham (MA) Weston Town Crier....30355
Gaffney (SC) The Gaffney Ledger....30200
Vidalia (GA) The Advance....30000
Williamsville (NY) Amherst Bee....30000
Merced (CA) Atwater Signal....29944
Tampa (FL) South Shore News....29695
Fenton (MI) Tri-County Times....29681

TOP FIFTY SHOPPER PUBLICATIONS IN THE U.S.

Oak Brook (IL) Shoplocal	4600000
Tampa (FL) The Flyer, Inc.	1600000
Westborough (MA) Headliners	1200000
Germantown (MD) The Merchandiser Magazine	1122000
Melville (NY) Newsday Hometown Shopper	951993
Hanover (MD) Maryland Pennysaver	840992
Melville (NY) This Week Pennysaver	836778
Lewis Center (OH) The Bag	811248
Miami (FL) Herald Values	787390
Warren (MI) C & G Newspapers	614210
Lebanon (PA) Merchandiser	599028
Pittsburgh (PA) Pennysaver	506754
Mount Joy (PA) Engle Printing & Publishing Co., Inc.	444397
Lansing (MI) The Source Sampler	332725
Hicksville (NY) Pennysaver/town Crier	325000
Poulsbo (WA) Sound Publishing, Inc.	322397
Hamburg (PA) Northern Berks Merchandiser	310256
Cheektowaga (NY) Metro Community News	279152
White Plains (NY) Lohud Express	272000
Syracuse (NY) Scotsman Community Publication	260000
Kansas City (MO) American Classifieds	250000
Hoffman Estates (IL) Dollar Wise	236580
Edgewood (NY) Pennysaver News	220000
East Rochester (NY) The Shopping Bag Advertiser	205402
Carroll (OH) Lancaster/fairfield Advertiser	201749
Elmsford (NY) Pennysaver	188350
Albany (NY) Pennysaver/moneysaver/advertiser	187000
Yorktown Heights (NY) Pennysaver	176091
Round Lake (NY) The Pennysaver	173000
Avon (NY) Genesee Valley Pennysaver	171677
Clifton Park (NY) Capital Region Weekly Newspaper Group	171388
Canandaigua (NY) Community News	160000
Staten Island (NY) Staten Island Pennysaver	150000
Syosset (NY) North Shore Today	147903
Springfield (MO) Pennypower Shopping News	145000
Brownsville (TX) Bargain Book	144976
Mechanicsburg (PA) Guide News	141500
Portland (ME) Saving Source	140000
Farmingdale (NY) South Bay's Neighbor	138617
Cherry Hill (NJ) Newspaper Media Group	129287
Portage (WI) Shopper Stopper	129021
Syracuse (NY) Pennysaver/pennywise	120126
Pontiac (MI) Greater Detroit Ads	114110
Ormond Beach (FL) Volusia Pennysaver, Inc.	112300
Mount Joy (PA) Shopper	106726
Concord (MA) Action Unlimited	103892
Garden City (NY) Primetime	102138
Santa Clarita (CA) Scv Express	100571
Springfield (VA) The Buyer's Guide	100000
Bensalem (PA) Northeast Times	100000

CIRCULATION OF U.S. COMMUNITY WEEKLY NEWSPAPERS BY TYPE OF PUBLICATION*

6,033 weekly newspapers (3,377 paid, 1,189 free, 1,467 combined paid and free)

Number of newspapers as of Jan. 1, 2018 with circulation as reported for six months primarily ending on Sept. 30, 2017

STATE	FREQUENCY					TYPE OF NEWSPAPER AND CIRCULATION											
						Paid Weeklies*			Free Weeklies*			Combined Weeklies*			Total		
	Number of Weeklies	Published 1 x Week	Published 2 x Week	Published 3 x Week	Total Days Published	Number of Weeklies	Paid Circulation	Associated Free Content	Number of Weeklies	Free Circulation	Associated Paid Content	Number of Weeklies	Paid Circulation	Free Circulation	Paid Circulation	Free Circulation	Total Circulation
Alabama	94	75	14	5	118	71	430,537	1,614	1	75,509	22	22	103,868	173,607	534,427	250,730	785,157
Alaska	15	14	0	1	17	8	21,320	139	1	30,000	0	6	6,719	2,384	28,039	32,523	60,562
Arizona	75	62	10	3	91	28	107,738	1,363	3	65,808	616	14	25,442	46,560	133,796	113,731	247,527
Arkansas	87	80	7	0	94	70	219,308	1,283	23	643,784	298	24	24,896	34,551	244,502	679,618	924,120
California	295	253	31	11	348	124	825,345	1,705	89	2,189,276	8,760	82	293,142	460,215	1,127,247	2,651,196	3,778,443
Colorado	86	80	5	1	93	50	137,824	1,186	13	173,674	484	23	84,153	73,074	222,461	247,934	470,395
Connecticut	81	75	6	0	87	21	86,578	579	46	574,403	99	14	39,347	41,180	126,024	616,162	742,186
Delaware	14	13	1	0	15	2	14,393	0	5	65,610	41	1	13,332	14,302	27,766	79,912	107,678
District of Columbia	6	6	0	0	6	0	0	0	9	147,608	1,439	3	2,205	2,753	3,644	150,361	154,005
Florida	165	147	15	3	186	52	585,044	288	70	1,539,107	3,280	43	165,241	287,577	753,565	1,826,972	2,580,537
Georgia	130	107	15	8	161	85	419,266	2,462	26	609,758	744	19	46,032	44,763	466,042	656,983	1,123,025
Hawaii	7	7	0	0	7	1	1,798	0	4	350,643	0	2	300	3,500	2,098	354,143	356,241
Idaho	29	27	2	0	31	22	44,088	643	5	76,912	751	66	66,044	185,843	110,883	263,398	374,281
Illinois	322	295	15	12	361	184	607,342	2,950	3	43,955	25	4	6,627	13,100	613,994	60,005	673,999
Indiana	110	101	8	1	120	74	210,129	1,294	40	608,101	1,838	98	258,279	338,280	470,246	947,675	1,417,921
Iowa	235	215	16	4	259	164	294,498	1,071	12	209,689	0	24	61,398	118,655	355,896	329,415	685,311
Kansas	159	141	12	6	183	103	230,635	1,496	6	64,471	120	50	34,090	28,990	264,845	94,957	359,802
Kentucky	117	101	11	5	138	80	338,289	2,130	5	76,108	145	32	128,743	139,853	467,177	218,091	685,268
Louisiana	75	60	9	6	96	45	183,696	434	5	59,080	43	25	51,289	123,349	235,028	182,863	417,891
Maine	50	48	1	1	53	26	127,742	637	46	530,258	482	63	154,158	200,284	282,382	731,179	1,013,561
Maryland	56	49	6	1	64	20	155,613	224	24	586,997	2,574	12	33,683	39,127	191,870	626,348	818,218
Massachusetts	214	210	3	1	219	105	347,229	2,904	8	201,992	0	16	22,435	9,347	369,664	214,243	583,907
Michigan	199	177	21	1	222	83	344,757	1,875	78	1,789,783	3,000	38	201,459	249,876	549,216	2,041,534	2,590,750
Minnesota	301	289	12	0	313	186	367,558	2,707	76	983,517	4,877	39	70,587	127,675	443,022	1,113,899	1,556,921
Mississippi	83	70	7	6	102	65	265,634	3,062	14	322,725	228	58	278,345	463,424	544,207	789,211	1,333,418
Missouri	187	169	14	4	209	115	321,776	2,099	1	8,500	0	17	50,174	54,377	371,950	64,976	436,926
Montana	64	58	6	0	70	49	129,441	1,569	5	51,800	0	10	8,965	14,428	138,406	67,797	206,203
Nebraska	140	134	6	0	146	117	217,335	1,512	21	658,560	540	37	109,562	93,913	327,437	753,985	1,081,422
Nevada	26	19	6	1	34	12	39,183	231	2	41,348	0	15	14,512	6,412	53,695	47,991	101,686
New Hampshire	39	35	3	1	44	12	62,707	408	1	100,000	0	22	51,737	69,334	114,444	169,742	284,186
New Jersey	165	161	4	0	169	42	273,529	4,781	20	264,268	126	7	9,687	26,231	283,342	295,280	578,622
New Mexico	26	20	4	2	34	17	65,923	346	82	1,624,754	2,304	41	89,697	61,356	157,924	1,686,456	1,844,380
New York	329	315	10	4	347	148	959,837	3,056	3	59,500	1,000	6	12,755	18,524	973,592	81,080	1,054,672
North Carolina	122	86	26	10	168	64	340,670	3,137	9	231,144	453	5	101,754	502,986	442,877	737,267	1,180,144
North Dakota	84	84	0	0	84	67	98,167	774	80	1,494,371	4,477	101	248,277	270,335	350,921	1,765,480	2,116,401
Ohio	195	181	12	2	211	65	333,644	1,409	83	1,214,089	3,470	47	187,873	231,846	524,987	1,447,344	1,972,331
Oklahoma	120	102	15	3	141	96	209,345	1,533	1	1,974	1	23	45,162	59,313	254,508	62,820	317,328
Oregon	88	73	12	3	106	58	211,830	3,343	7	199,152	1,008	23	117,319	159,512	330,157	362,007	692,164
Pennsylvania	184	171	11	2	199	88	538,983	3,307	52	1,296,873	2,429	44	183,168	112,978	724,580	1,413,158	2,137,738
Rhode Island	30	27	3	0	33	7	17,624	114	10	102,001	175	13	33,451	12,304	51,250	114,419	165,669
South Carolina	64	51	8	5	82	46	227,377	1,015	10	180,673	491	8	34,423	107,706	262,291	289,394	551,685
South Dakota	103	103	0	0	103	91	113,525	1,080	3	47,144	320	9	11,854	18,628	125,699	66,852	192,551
Tennessee	88	70	13	5	111	59	319,418	1,708	10	188,221	1,703	19	84,983	111,062	406,104	300,991	707,095
Texas	453	391	59	3	518	286	768,398	5,350	69	1,192,925	6,322	98	168,239	172,551	942,959	1,370,826	2,313,785
Utah	14	11	3	0	17	7	27,300	400	1	32,633	0	6	12,855	27,875	40,155	60,908	101,063
Vermont	27	26	1	0	28	11	47,325	610	28	370,514	695	24	24,561	22,655	72,581	393,779	466,360
Virginia	97	84	7	6	116	45	295,831	2,062	12	126,681	763	4	0	0	296,594	128,743	425,337
Washington	117	108	7	2	128	40	171,926	720	32	783,915	19,609	45	100,300	167,242	291,835	951,877	1,243,712
West Virginia	45	37	4	4	57	36	137,155	739	33	515,579	943	53	105,809	71,456	243,907	587,774	831,681
Wisconsin	193	167	25	1	220	107	381,906	3,846	1	20,000	0	8	26,287	32,997	408,193	56,843	465,036
Wyoming	28	23	5	0	33	23	66,023	268	1	25,000	600	4	5,675	2,735	72,298	28,003	100,301
TOTALS	6,033	5,408	491	134	6,792	3,377	12,742,539	77,463	1,189	22,850,387	77,295	1,467	4,010,893	5,651,025	16,830,727	28,578,875	45,409,602

*Editor & Publisher defines a weekly newspaper as any publication printing less than 4 times a week. A paid community newspaper has more than ninety-five percent of the total circulation as paid (i.e. 100pd 5fr); the opposite for free publications. Anything in the middle is a combination newspaper.

CIRCULATION OF U.S. COMMUNITY WEEKLY NEWSPAPERS BY DAY OF PUBLICATION*

6,792 weekly newspaper editions (Highest 2,645 Thursday; Lowest 159 Monday)

Number of newspapers as of Jan. 1, 2018 with circulation as reported for six months primarily ending on Sept. 30, 2017

STATE	MONDAY CIRCULATION			TUESDAY CIRCULATION			WEDNESDAY CIRCULATION			THURSDAY CIRCULATION			FRIDAY CIRCULATION			SATURDAY CIRCULATION			SUNDAY CIRCULATION			TOTAL CIRCULATION		
	Number of Editions	Paid	Free	Number of Editions	Paid	Free	Number of Editions	Paid	Free	Number of Editions	Paid	Free	Number of Editions	Paid	Free	Number of Editions	Paid	Free	Number of Editions	Paid	Free	Number of Editions	Paid	Free
Alabama	2	9,000	0	4	15,703	178	52	310,241	184,874	33	190,186	65,393	10	136,853	375	13	64,373	10,348	4	118,964	0	118	845,320	261,168
Alaska	0	0	0	0	0	0	3	4,420	30,732	12	23,619	1,791	1	2,400	732	0	0	0	1	2,400	732	17	32,839	33,987
Arizona	0	0	0	4	15,454	406	60	178,070	54,367	21	52,373	13,974	5	13,697	20,149	2	21,831	0	2	4,638	25,000	94	286,063	113,896
Arkansas	1	0	0	5	19,396	299	50	96,635	449,642	13	14,346	34,361	15	31,953	31,249	2	4,094	20,025	5	10,472	161,970	91	176,896	697,546
California	2	7,431	38,017	27	112,477	737,233	88	367,222	412,682	114	445,223	840,208	89	341,607	1,253,222	21	162,439	108,728	7	16,216	204,119	348	1,452,615	3,594,209
Colorado	0	0	0	3	8,398	80	23	58,581	68,754	49	126,992	135,238	14	22,258	48,072	1	7,003	0	3	17,895	30,500	93	241,127	282,644
Connecticut	1	1,170	7,856	0	0	0	5	7,634	29,376	61	75,800	480,681	20	45,748	136,723	0	0	0	0	0	0	87	130,352	654,636
Delaware	1	13,332	14,302	0	0	0	4	41	45,610	0	0	0	1	0	20,000	0	0	0	0	0	0	6	13,373	79,912
District of Columbia	0	0	0	2	12,000	18,921	7	5,291	59,971	2	700	14,843	4	12,046	56,626	0	0	0	0	0	0	15	30,037	150,361
Florida	1	5,000	9,050	7	27,000	55,775	59	406,840	852,704	76	315,929	729,414	26	67,087	144,861	13	32,468	283,857	4	31,583	25,500	186	885,907	2,101,161
Georgia	2	7,500	500	2	293	50,500	85	313,654	311,818	37	135,384	190,928	14	48,766	101,871	10	51,891	29,859	11	65,202	14,574	161	622,690	700,050
Hawaii	0	0	0	0	0	0	4	2,098	294,785	1	0	0	2	0	59,358	0	0	0	0	0	0	7	2,098	354,143
Idaho	5	4,689	23,000	29	48,110	62,494	96	152,543	85,788	105	149,438	48,359	14	28,646	91,265	10	29,737	23,000	0	0	0	259	413,163	333,906
Illinois	1	2,600	75	1	0	10,500	17	32,343	37,827	10	15,797	9,296	1	11	28,394	0	0	0	1	1,660	50	31	52,411	86,142
Indiana	10	26,722	40,835	18	46,255	94,092	116	278,501	433,731	169	535,670	349,819	34	65,306	233,462	9	24,916	38,848	5	12,561	64,995	361	989,931	1,255,782
Iowa	5	25,479	494	16	50,864	19,611	51	110,422	239,550	35	78,819	73,725	9	20,203	398	4	13,244	44,800	0	0	0	120	299,031	378,578
Kansas	9	57,926	12,769	18	43,908	18,779	57	85,543	53,552	78	96,506	22,708	16	31,710	10,667	5	12,390	705	0	0	0	183	327,983	119,180
Kentucky	5	35,474	34,900	9	30,624	5,950	47	206,218	82,218	56	229,315	82,645	12	63,236	28,210	7	30,270	35,902	2	9,536	0	138	604,673	269,825
Louisiana	2	3,311	2,380	4	5,046	11,259	32	98,533	90,077	40	131,188	87,380	6	18,576	10,500	3	15,000	0	9	46,231	41,825	96	317,885	243,421
Maine	3	929	8,353	2	0	20,500	33	65,682	122,246	107	281,713	311,493	72	171,887	337,031	1	4,852	24	1	0	18,168	219	525,063	817,815
Maryland	1	12,163	0	1	292	187	22	92,144	149,343	21	61,021	315,507	16	83,220	162,346	2	19,925	919	1	0	0	64	268,765	628,302
Massachusetts	2	2,242	23,234	1	2,500	0	11	39,755	61,609	29	99,880	115,541	9	8,300	116,592	1	0	15,000	0	0	0	53	152,677	331,976
Michigan	10	9,609	104,304	4	14,358	16,571	67	243,661	702,349	75	238,218	553,365	9	34,863	64,678	8	15,844	87,910	49	218,531	823,194	222	775,084	2,352,371
Minnesota	16	15,263	87,458	29	37,392	96,051	103	171,453	284,938	117	181,642	378,435	20	33,875	45,532	22	31,659	182,241	6	14,367	61,814	313	485,651	1,136,469
Mississippi	2	7,606	1,530	9	35,678	51,940	102	361,131	539,487	63	171,189	109,165	23	59,031	139,529	7	60,583	20,954	3	0	82,600	209	695,218	945,205
Missouri	0	0	0	7	35,745	5,529	31	130,712	48,609	46	168,579	17,158	8	37,002	17,790	7	41,119	3,429	3	12,635	106	102	425,792	92,621
Montana	0	0	0	3	2,486	4,564	33	66,598	62,051	25	65,122	1,133	6	10,502	4,672	1	4,551	108	2	5,392	20	70	154,651	72,548
Nebraska	8	43,300	424	9	52,765	39,716	66	218,528	586,007	42	197,273	110,155	19	81,609	63,520	5	31,809	23,279	19	55,569	483,588	168	680,853	1,306,689
Nevada	8	16,375	3,100	2	4,750	0	34	41,650	41,785	24	27,271	656	12	14,633	593	4	8,000	2,400	0	0	0	84	112,679	48,534
New Hampshire	1	3,900	200	6	26,510	23,978	61	105,428	20,786	69	100,904	117,657	7	26,690	20,125	2	36,000	5,200	0	0	0	146	299,432	187,946
New Jersey	0	0	0	5	20,237	330	8	22,913	16,348	21	42,862	186,538	9	4,545	87,921	0	0	0	1	4,525	0	44	95,082	291,137
New Mexico	1	0	0	1	423	15,151	38	30,445	391,741	92	174,821	896,249	28	154,472	289,454	2	5,797	48,256	7	9,350	72,159	169	375,308	1,713,010
New York	0	0	0	2	4,895	5,300	8	24,044	16,701	11	37,904	12,589	8	23,774	25,626	3	10,195	60	2	3,850	23,500	34	104,662	83,776
North Carolina	1	365	9,874	3	97,924	510,633	8	117,117	508,647	9	14,808	29,484	10	23,213	132,306	1	3,650	0	2	6,100	54,523	34	263,177	1,245,467
North Dakota	9	12,072	24,519	13	17,298	110,887	76	238,165	214,865	153	613,637	944,154	70	318,676	341,872	15	18,762	130,468	11	27,284	84,754	347	1,245,894	1,851,519
Ohio	8	4,535	104,029	15	29,029	79,117	54	190,173	320,298	81	301,882	502,816	7	12,364	2,732	17	28,235	125,815	29	20,484	443,240	211	586,702	1,578,047
Oklahoma	2	789	3,056	8	28,301	13,003	39	85,563	26,499	68	134,376	20,166	12	36,767	355	5	19,597	9,300	7	17,732	50	141	323,125	72,429
Oregon	3	5,799	261	4	14,044	300	52	146,747	174,969	23	126,217	140,118	18	73,191	38,842	6	19,945	32,485	0	0	0	106	385,943	386,975
Pennsylvania	3	2,460	15,675	10	92,940	39,170	70	145,710	1,056,082	69	379,669	217,450	15	55,702	33,331	5	88,677	32,438	27	105,489	112,652	199	870,647	1,506,798
Rhode Island	0	0	0	2	19,239	9,400	6	6,026	17,004	20	37,542	95,457	5	9,602	2,130	0	0	0	0	0	0	33	72,409	123,991
South Carolina	4	28,923	46,000	4	19,985	0	41	156,656	238,727	18	87,535	35,542	12	76,007	82,625	1	0	250	2	12,896	18,600	82	382,002	421,744
South Dakota	1	3,200	0	6	8,727	186	47	61,697	24,959	44	45,621	6,182	4	5,579	35,499	1	875	26	0	0	0	103	125,699	66,852
Tennessee	3	13,609	16,945	14	62,250	28,387	45	240,953	190,499	27	106,872	73,398	15	86,868	57,419	1	5,775	3,308	6	38,187	53,794	111	554,514	423,750
Texas	4	8,575	3,446	17	39,536	38,741	139	367,086	508,978	240	429,128	639,600	54	115,377	81,882	21	67,546	89,014	43	98,558	158,572	518	1,125,806	1,520,233
Utah	0	0	0	2	1,805	2,675	9	35,550	17,500	5	8,100	47,033	0	0	0	1	7,800	300	0	0	0	17	53,255	67,508
Vermont	8	28,618	3,493	3	7,175	5,325	45	211,250	70,861	40	102,985	184,149	11	32,432	138,278	7	42,477	5,380	2	5,058	1,500	116	429,995	408,986
Virginia	1	7,425	0	1	2,700	28	9	20,287	58,991	14	24,925	41,033	1	0	15,000	1	176	12,239	1	0	0	28	55,513	127,291
Washington	2	1,600	20,600	9	32,057	23,964	47	143,216	228,354	44	104,834	453,594	20	39,701	229,114	3	18,507	749	3	6,811	20,249	128	346,726	976,624
West Virginia	6	14,953	14,570	13	53,303	23,320	50	214,311	252,589	112	221,116	65,976	11	41,537	21,746	20	21,933	82,405	8	5	285,853	220	567,158	746,459
Wisconsin	4	14,568	20	4	19,071	6,231	24	92,696	13,746	11	39,770	1,015	6	22,168	120	8	30,605	38,894	0	0	0	57	218,878	60,026
Wyoming	1	0	0	4	14,850	73	9	26,618	27,710	13	34,080	220	5	13,650	143	0	0	0	1	4,475	2,600	33	93,673	30,746
TOTALS	159	458,512	675,269	362	1,233,793	2,257,334	2,243	6,828,795	10,813,336	2,645	7,278,781	9,803,791	815	2,657,340	4,864,937	278	1,114,550	1,548,923	290	1,004,656	3,370,801	6,792	20,576,427	33,334,391

*Editor & Publisher defines a weekly newspaper as any publication printing less than 4 times a week.

CIRCULATION OF U.S. COMMUNITY WEEKLY NEWSPAPERS BY CIRCULATION GROUPS*

6,033 weekly newspapers (3,377 paid, 1,189 free, 1,467 combined paid and free)

Number of newspapers as of Jan. 1, 2018 with circulation as reported for six months primarily ending on Sept. 30, 2017

	NUMBER OF COMMUNITY WEEKLIES				PAID WEEKLY CIRCULATION*			FREE WEEKLY CIRCULATION*			COMBINED WEEKLY CIRCULATION*			TOTAL CIRCULATION		
Circulation	Paid Weeklies	Free Weeklies	Combined Weeklies	Total	Paid Circulation	Associated Free Circulation	Total Circulation	Free Circulation	Associated Paid Circulation	Total Circulation	Paid Circulation	Free Circulation	Total Circulation	Paid Circulation	Free Circulation	Total Circulation
More than 100,000	3	11	3	17	411,154	3,344	414,498	1,753,171	16,419	1,769,590	267,646	825,633	1,093,279	695,219	2,582,148	3,277,367
50,001 - 100,000	6	50	10	66	350,454	1,229	351,683	3,549,876	1,444	3,551,320	321,106	344,544	665,650	673,004	3,895,649	4,568,653
35,001 - 50,000	13	60	12	85	516,161	0	516,161	2,471,751	2,567	2,474,318	172,289	330,486	502,775	691,017	2,802,237	3,493,254
20,001 - 35,000	34	252	75	361	870,489	4,024	874,513	6,729,649	23,244	6,752,893	585,648	1,387,146	1,972,794	1,479,381	8,120,819	9,600,200
10,001 - 20,000	96	390	177	663	1,308,941	4,233	1,313,174	5,686,022	21,060	5,707,082	930,079	1,615,487	2,545,566	2,260,080	7,305,742	9,565,822
5,001 - 10,000	482	290	246	1,018	3,217,185	20,968	3,238,153	2,235,184	10,702	2,245,886	900,059	881,328	1,781,387	4,127,946	3,137,480	7,265,426
1,001 - 5,000	2,264	122	363	2,749	5,738,007	41,427	5,779,434	418,120	1,859	419,979	788,934	257,366	1,046,300	6,528,800	716,913	7,245,713
1,000 or less	479	14	581	1,074	330,148	2,238	332,386	6,614	0	6,614	45,132	9,035	54,167	375,280	17,887	393,167
TOTAL	3,377	1,189	1,467	6,033	12,742,539	77,463	12,820,002	22,850,387	77,295	22,927,682	4,010,893	5,651,025	9,661,918	16,830,727	28,578,875	45,409,602

*Editor & Publisher defines a weekly newspaper as any publication printing less than 4 times a week. A paid community newspaper has more than ninety-five percent of the total circulation as paid (i.e. 100pd 5fr); the opposite for free publications. Anything in the middle is a combination newspaper. Papers that publish two or three times a week are averaged for one paid number and one free number.

CIRCULATION OF CANADIAN COMMUNITY WEEKLY NEWSPAPERS BY TYPE OF PUBLICATION*

893 weekly newspapers (241 paid, 500 free and 152 combined paid and free)

Number of newspapers as of Jan. 1, 2018 with circulation as reported for six months primarily ending on Sept. 30, 2017

PROVINCE	FREQUENCY					TYPE OF NEWSPAPER AND CIRCULATION											
						Paid Weeklies*			Free Weeklies*			Combined Weeklies*			Total		
	Number of Weeklies	Published 1 x Week	Published 2 x Week	Published 3 x Week	Total Days Published	Number of Weeklies	Paid Circulation	Associated Free Content	Number of Weeklies	Free Circulation	Associated Paid Content	Number of Weeklies	Paid Circulation	Free Circulation	Paid Circulation	Free Circulation	Total Circulation
Alberta	107	105	2	0	109	27	54,564	427	47	543,860	1,887	33	41,731	189,836	98,182	734,123	832,305
British Columbia	112	76	28	8	156	25	172,810	316	59	1,526,354	655	28	28,958	104,099	202,423	1,630,769	1,833,192
Manitoba	46	44	2	0	48	12	21,368	215	20	280,928	1,574	14	16,455	38,640	39,397	319,783	359,180
New Brunswick	15	13	2	0	17	9	26,881	147	5	29,094	0	1	3,500	500	30,381	29,741	60,122
Newfoundland	14	14	0	0	14	14	20,579	0	0	0	0	0	0	0	20,579	0	20,579
Northwest Territories	7	6	1	0	8	0	0	0	2	1,583	0	5	9,856	7,667	9,856	9,250	19,106
Nova Scotia	27	27	0	0	27	15	39,907	312	6	147,904	0	6	20,282	39,951	60,189	188,167	248,356
Nunavut	3	3	0	0	3	0	0	0	3	10,484	0	0	0	0	0	10,484	10,484
Ontario	273	252	19	2	296	81	403,297	3,350	152	4,132,682	2,647	40	121,799	192,778	527,743	4,328,810	4,856,553
Prince Edward Island	4	4	0	0	4	2	6,260	216	1	5,733	121	1	752	625	7,133	6,574	13,707
Quebec	211	204	7	0	218	10	107,379	1,144	188	5,998,804	4,244	13	58,739	49,315	170,362	6,049,263	6,219,625
Saskatchewan	73	72	1	0	74	46	57,933	765	17	183,985	528	10	6,209	21,519	64,670	206,269	270,939
Yukon Territory	1	0	1	0	2	0	0	0	0	0	0	1	1,729	2,537	1,729	2,537	4,266
TOTALS	893	820	63	10	976	241	910,978	6,892	500	12,861,411	11,656	152	310,010	647,467	1,232,644	13,515,770	14,748,414

*Editor & Publisher defines a weekly newspaper as any publication printing less than 4 times a week. A paid community newspaper has more than ninety-five percent of the total circulation as paid (i.e. 100pd 5fr); the opposite for free publications. Anything in the middle is a combination newspaper.

CIRCULATION OF CANADIAN COMMUNITY WEEKLY NEWSPAPERS BY DAY OF PUBLICATION*

976 weekly newspaper editions (Highest 360 Wednesday; Lowest 14 Sunday)

Number of newspapers as of Jan. 1, 2018 with circulation as reported for six months primarily ending on Sept. 30 2017

PROVINCE	MONDAY CIRCULATION			TUESDAY CIRCULATION			WEDNESDAY CIRCULATION			THURSDAY CIRCULATION			FRIDAY CIRCULATION			SATURDAY CIRCULATION			SUNDAY CIRCULATION			TOTAL CIRCULATION		
	Number of Editions	Paid	Free	Number of Editions	Paid	Free	Number of Editions	Paid	Free	Number of Editions	Paid	Free	Number of Editions	Paid	Free	Number of Editions	Paid	Free	Number of Editions	Paid	Free	Number of Editions	Paid	Free
Alberta	4	60	18,507	30	22,811	92,862	38	39,684	300,411	23	15,908	172,016	13	19,719	156,733	1	1,652	24,879	0	0	0	109	99,834	765,408
British Columbia	1	0	32,454	12	81,235	348,430	56	108,577	735,745	40	97,272	706,995	42	126,170	841,263	2	60	71,381	3	29,884	72,000	156	443,198	2,808,268
Manitoba	2	593	876	8	12,167	162	9	2,400	200,612	13	15,186	91,936	16	10,263	26,235	0	0	0	0	0	0	48	40,609	319,821
New Brunswick	1	3,768	13	4	6,658	110	5	14,162	519	2	0	19,140	3	9,693	58	2	2,561	9,970	0	0	0	17	36,842	29,810
Newfoundland	5	8,159	0	3	5,890	0	1	312	0	5	6,218	0	0	0	0	0	0	0	0	0	0	14	20,579	0
Northwest Territories	1	1,922	2,167	0	0	0	3	7,733	5,210	2	201	998	2	2,077	1,838	0	0	0	0	0	0	8	11,933	10,213
Nova Scotia	1	0	5,900	5	17,567	228	10	19,578	42,867	9	17,685	138,818	2	5,359	354	0	0	0	0	0	0	27	60,189	188,167
Nunavut	1	0	4,161	0	0	0	1	0	935	0	0	0	1	0	5,388	0	0	0	0	0	0	3	0	10,484
Ontario	7	23,692	78,065	21	38,819	229,937	91	229,592	583,414	146	280,625	3,615,320	28	170,819	833,792	0	0	0	3	8,200	39,125	296	751,747	5,379,653
Prince Edward Island	0	0	0	0	0	0	3	6,381	5,949	0	0	0	1	752	625	0	0	0	0	0	0	4	7,133	6,574
Quebec	1	0	1,700	23	1,351	805,296	127	49,308	3,429,821	18	31,779	423,835	19	7,688	552,369	22	79,463	773,222	8	831	335,653	218	170,420	6,321,896
Saskatchewan	17	19,361	8,790	9	7,436	16,298	15	19,798	29,342	17	11,657	76,528	16	6,418	89,200	0	0	0	0	0	0	74	64,670	220,158
Yukon Territory	0	0	0	0	0	0	1	1,729	2,537	0	0	0	1	1,729	2,537	0	0	0	0	0	0	2	3,458	5,074
TOTALS	41	57,555	152,633	115	193,934	1,493,323	360	499,254	5,337,362	275	476,531	5,245,586	144	360,687	2,510,392	27	83,736	879,452	14	38,915	446,778	976	1,710,612	16,065,526

*Editor & Publisher defines a weekly newspaper as any publication printing less than 4 times a week.

CIRCULATION OF CANADIAN COMMUNITY WEEKLY NEWSPAPERS BY CIRCULATION GROUPS*

893 weekly newspapers (241 paid, 500 free, 152 combined paid and free)

Number of newspapers as of Jan. 1, 2018 with circulation as reported for six months primarily ending on Sept. 30, 2017

Circulation	NUMBER OF COMMUNITY WEEKLIES				PAID WEEKLY CIRCULATION*			FREE WEEKLY CIRCULATION*			COMBINED WEEKLY CIRCULATION*			TOTAL CIRCULATION		
	Paid Weeklies	Free Weeklies	Combined Weeklies	Total	Paid Circulation	Associated Free Circulation	Total Circulation	Free Circulation	Associated Paid Circulation	Total Circulation	Paid Circulation	Free Circulation	Total Circulation	Paid Circulation	Free Circulation	Total Circulation
More than 100,000	2	8	0	10	227,602	1,200	228,802	1,113,489	0	1,113,489	0	0	0	227,602	1,114,689	1,342,291
50,001 - 100,000	1	52	2	55	54,193	875	55,068	3,288,485	1,371	3,289,856	9,813	98,122	107,935	65,377	3,387,482	3,452,859
35,001 - 50,000	1	62	2	65	43,046	0	43,046	2,617,690	1,731	2,619,421	40,381	32,345	72,726	85,158	2,650,035	2,735,193
20,001 - 35,000	4	116	8	128	102,555	39	102,594	3,173,028	2,265	3,175,293	73,208	163,437	236,645	178,028	3,336,504	3,514,532
10,001 - 20,000	6	129	17	152	82,579	657	83,236	1,922,229	2,736	1,924,965	52,172	192,782	244,954	137,487	2,115,668	2,253,155
5,001 - 10,000	8	85	22	115	60,006	359	60,365	651,950	2,669	654,619	48,021	101,728	149,749	110,696	754,037	864,733
1,001 - 5,000	158	28	50	236	299,361	3,286	302,647	88,220	863	89,083	71,420	55,132	126,552	371,644	146,638	518,282
1,000 or less	61	20	51	132	41,636	476	42,112	6,320	21	6,341	14,995	3,921	18,916	56,652	10,717	67,369
TOTAL	241	500	152	893	910,978	6,892	917,870	12,861,411	11,656	12,873,067	310,010	647,467	957,477	1,232,644	13,515,770	14,748,414

*Editor & Publisher defines a weekly newspaper as any publication printing less than 4 times a week. A paid community newspaper has more than ninety-five percent of the total circulation as paid (i.e. 100pd 5fr); the opposite for free publications. Anything in the middle is a combination newspaper. Papers that publish two or three times a week are averaged for one paid number and one free number.

CIRCULATION OF U.S. SHOPPER/TMC PUBLICATIONS

1,209 shopper publications with 2,318 zoned editions**

Number of newspapers as of Jan. 1, 2018 with circulation as reported for six months primarily ending on Sept. 30, 2017

STATE	TOTAL NUMBER OF PUBLICATIONS, ZONED EDITIONS AND CIRCULATION					PUBLICATIONS APPEARING ONCE A WEEK				PUBLICATIONS APPEARING AT LEAST TWICE A WEEK*				PUBLICATIONS APPEARING LESS THAN ONCE A WEEK			
	Number of Publications	Number of Editions	Paid Circulation	Free Circulation	Total Circulation	Published 1x Week	Paid Circulation	Free Circulation	Total Circulation	Published More Than 1x Week	Paid Circulation	Free Circulation	Total Circulation	Published Less Than 1x Week	Paid Circulation	Free Circulation	Total Circulation
Alabama	10	10	17,969	151,064	169,033	10	17,969	151,064	169,033	0	0	0	0	0	0	0	0
Alaska	0	0	0	0	0	0	0	0	0	0	0	0	0	0	0	0	0
Arizona	14	16	29,213	217,902	247,115	13	18,841	209,048	227,889	0	0	0	0	1	10,372	8,854	19,226
Arkansas	7	7	1,872	74,594	76,466	7	1,872	74,594	76,466	0	0	0	0	0	0	0	0
California	29	37	45,051	768,682	813,733	26	24,916	655,841	680,757	2	0	112,571	112,571	1	20,135	270	20,405
Colorado	12	13	24,100	199,813	223,913	10	24,100	154,322	178,422	1	0	24,500	24,500	1	0	20,991	20,991
Connecticut	8	23	56,114	202,004	258,118	7	33,000	202,004	235,004	1	23,114	0	23,114	0	0	0	0
Delaware	1	1	1,580	1,939	3,519	1	1,580	1,939	3,519	0	0	0	0	0	0	0	0
District of Columbia	0	0	0	0	0	0	0	0	0	0	0	0	0	0	0	0	0
Florida	29	136	566	3,260,222	3,260,788	26	4	3,102,953	3,102,957	2	561	152,426	152,987	1	1	4,843	4,844
Georgia	24	27	75,363	435,204	510,567	22	75,363	375,754	451,117	1	0	34,000	34,000	1	0	25,450	25,450
Hawaii	0	0	0	0	0	0	0	0	0	0	0	0	0	0	0	0	0
Idaho	12	12	13	210,800	210,813	12	13	210,800	210,813	0	0	0	0	0	0	0	0
Illinois	57	230	55,638	5,813,976	5,869,614	53	53,387	1,185,155	1,238,542	3	2,233	4,620,388	4,622,621	1	18	8,433	8,451
Indiana	43	54	24,877	724,619	749,496	39	21,127	661,894	683,021	3	300	52,738	53,038	1	3,450	9,987	13,437
Iowa	74	130	50,659	1,058,119	1,108,778	67	46,509	915,879	962,388	5	4,150	94,908	99,058	2	0	47,332	47,332
Kansas	23	30	10,060	304,281	314,341	21	10,060	269,935	279,995	0	0	0	0	2	0	34,346	34,346
Kentucky	18	51	16,209	293,174	309,383	17	9,209	270,174	279,383	1	7,000	23,000	30,000	0	0	0	0
Louisiana	11	11	3,200	209,820	213,020	11	3,200	209,820	213,020	0	0	0	0	0	0	0	0
Maine	1	1	0	140,000	140,000	1	0	140,000	140,000	0	0	0	0	0	0	0	0
Maryland	5	53	0	2,065,992	2,065,992	4	0	943,992	943,992	0	0	0	0	1	0	1,122,000	1,122,000
Massachusetts	12	16	0	1,534,016	1,534,016	11	0	1,465,506	1,465,506	0	0	0	0	1	0	68,510	68,510
Michigan	75	92	138	2,594,997	2,595,135	73	138	2,191,361	2,191,499	1	0	332,725	332,725	1	0	70,911	70,911
Minnesota	74	90	79,790	1,092,303	1,172,093	67	61,990	998,259	1,060,249	4	17,800	46,892	64,692	3	0	47,152	47,152
Mississippi	8	8	0	187,838	187,838	7	0	154,487	154,487	1	0	33,351	33,351	0	0	0	0
Missouri	31	44	26,930	772,018	798,948	30	10,930	764,693	775,623	1	16,000	7,325	23,325	0	0	0	0
Montana	11	16	40	195,797	195,837	9	40	165,597	165,637	1	0	7,200	7,200	1	0	23,000	23,000
Nebraska	26	28	155	359,083	359,238	25	155	352,483	352,638	0	0	0	0	1	0	6,600	6,600
Nevada	0	0	0	0	0	0	0	0	0	0	0	0	0	0	0	0	0
New Hampshire	3	3	9	66,221	66,230	3	9	66,221	66,230	0	0	0	0	0	0	0	0
New Jersey	6	6	46,156	324,686	370,842	3	0	114,147	114,147	2	46,156	128,939	175,095	1	0	81,600	81,600
New Mexico	7	7	8,800	118,739	127,539	5	0	113,139	113,139	1	8,800	5,600	14,400	1	0	0	0
New York	146	454	194,259	7,201,444	7,395,703	142	190,733	7,155,829	7,346,562	3	3,526	37,615	41,141	1	0	8,000	8,000
North Carolina	24	29	50,911	415,578	466,489	23	50,911	398,078	448,989	0	0	0	0	1	0	17,500	17,500
North Dakota	7	7	0	141,100	141,100	7	0	141,100	141,100	0	0	0	0	0	0	0	0
Ohio	49	120	77,811	1,844,119	1,921,930	46	61,911	1,760,231	1,822,142	2	0	66,888	66,888	1	15,900	17,000	32,900
Oklahoma	12	12	7,342	173,344	180,686	10	42	166,344	166,386	1	4,200	5,500	9,700	1	3,100	1,500	4,600
Oregon	16	20	4	366,271	366,275	15	4	356,271	356,275	0	0	0	0	1	0	10,000	10,000
Pennsylvania	61	136	72,446	3,612,435	3,684,881	54	58,150	2,374,554	2,432,704	5	69	1,161,330	1,161,399	2	14,227	76,551	90,778
Rhode Island	6	6	13,465	86,448	99,913	5	1,920	73,961	75,881	0	0	0	0	1	11,545	12,487	24,032
South Carolina	9	10	26,004	147,351	173,355	9	26,004	147,351	173,355	0	0	0	0	0	0	0	0
South Dakota	16	18	2,454	342,059	344,513	14	2,426	281,241	283,667	1	0	52,310	52,310	1	28	8,508	8,536
Tennessee	24	24	11,817	503,076	514,893	23	17	495,076	495,093	1	11,800	8,000	19,800	0	0	0	0
Texas	62	92	15,100	1,443,481	1,458,581	58	15,100	1,363,318	1,378,418	3	0	55,163	55,163	1	0	25,000	25,000
Utah	4	5	0	44,800	44,800	4	0	44,800	44,800	0	0	0	0	0	0	0	0
Vermont	5	9	0	114,400	114,400	5	0	114,400	114,400	0	0	0	0	0	0	0	0
Virginia	8	11	0	181,450	181,450	6	0	79,050	79,050	0	0	0	0	2	0	102,400	102,400
Washington	18	20	17,294	558,895	576,189	18	17,294	558,895	576,189	0	0	0	0	0	0	0	0
West Virginia	5	8	0	83,772	83,772	5	0	83,772	83,772	0	0	0	0	0	0	0	0
Wisconsin	104	183	27,550	2,120,424	2,147,974	99	27,550	1,973,496	2,001,046	4	0	112,928	112,928	1	0	34,000	34,000
Wyoming	2	2	0	39,722	39,722	2	0	39,722	39,722	0	0	0	0	0	0	0	0
TOTALS	1,209	2,318	1,090,959	42,798,072	43,889,031	1,125	866,474	33,728,550	34,595,024	50	145,709	7,176,297	7,322,006	34	78,776	1,893,225	1,972,001

*Shopper/TMC Publications that publish two or three times a week are averaged for one paid number and one free number.

**Editor & Publisher defines a publication with zoned editions as one with press runs allowing the editorial and/or advertising department to place specific material within different distribution areas.

Any publication not having zoned editions is counted as one in both the number of publications column and number of editions column.

CIRCULATION OF CANADIAN SHOPPER/TMC PUBLICATIONS

66 shopper publications with 134 zoned editions**

Number of newspapers as of Jan. 1, 2018 with circulation as reported for six months primarily ending on Sept. 30, 2017

PROVINCE	TOTAL NUMBER OF PUBLICATIONS, ZONED EDITIONS AND CIRCULATION					PUBLICATIONS APPEARING ONCE A WEEK				PUBLICATIONS APPEARING AT LEAST TWICE A WEEK*				PUBLICATIONS APPEARING LESS THAN ONCE A WEEK			
	Number of Publications	Number of Editions	Paid Circulation	Free Circulation	Total Circulation	Published 1x Week	Paid Circulation	Free Circulation	Total Circulation	Published More Than 1x Week	Paid Circulation	Free Circulation	Total Circulation	Published Less Than 1x Week	Paid Circulation	Free Circulation	Total Circulation
Alberta	10	11	2,589	164,257	166,846	10	2,589	164,257	166,846	0	0	0	0	0	0	0	0
British Columbia	10	17	0	154,038	154,038	9	0	133,038	133,038	1	0	21,000	21,000	0	0	0	0
Nova Scotia	1	1	0	20,479	20,479	1	0	20,479	20,479	0	0	0	0	0	0	0	0
Ontario	35	43	30,465	1,177,515	1,207,980	33	30,465	1,113,265	1,143,730	2	0	64,250	64,250	0	0	0	0
Quebec	2	2	11	52,973	52,984	1	0	18,500	18,500	1	11	34,473	34,484	0	0	0	0
Saskatchewan	8	60	0	91,335	91,335	7	0	85,055	85,055	0	0	0	0	1	0	6,280	6,280
TOTALS	66	134	33,065	1,660,597	1,693,662	61	33,054	1,534,594	1,567,648	4	11	119,723	119,734	1	0	6,280	6,280

*Shopper/TMC Publications that publish two or three times a week are averaged for one paid number and one free number.

**Editor & Publisher defines a publication with zoned editions as one with press runs allowing the editorial and/or advertising department to place specific material within different distribution areas.

Any publication not having zoned editions is counted as one in both the number of publications column and number of editions column.

CIRCULATION TOTALS FOR ALL PUBLICATIONS BY CATEGORY*

9,387 total publications (6,926 community, 1,275 shoppers and 1,186 specialty/niche)

Number of newspapers as of Jan. 1, 2018 with circulation as reported for six months primarily ending on Sept. 30, 2017

CATEGORY	TOTAL NUMBER OF PUBLICATIONS, ZONED EDITIONS AND CIRCULATION					PUBLICATIONS APPEARING ONCE A WEEK				PUBLICATIONS APPEARING AT LEAST TWICE A WEEK				PUBLICATIONS APPEARING LESS THAN ONCE A WEEK			
	Number of Publications	Number of Editions**	Paid Circulation	Free Circulation	Total Circulation	Published 1x Week	Paid Circulation	Free Circulation	Total Circulation	Published More Than 1x Week	Paid Circulation	Free Circulation	Total Circulation	Published Less Than 1x Week	Paid Circulation	Free Circulation	Total Circulation
UNITED STATES																	
Alternative	129	246	801,397	5,889,402	6,690,799	120	221,475	5,724,088	5,945,563	2	578,512	12,739	591,251	7	1,410	152,575	153,985
Black	168	255	1,988,807	2,103,551	4,092,358	149	1,890,821	1,906,750	3,797,571	5	52,856	103,240	156,096	14	45,130	93,561	138,691
Community	6,033	8,064	16,830,727	28,578,875	45,409,602	5,408	13,925,358	24,338,279	38,263,637	625	2,905,369	4,240,596	7,145,965	0	0	0	0
Ethnic	122	307	1,720,257	1,273,773	2,994,030	59	757,542	274,468	1,032,010	18	501,272	85,119	586,391	45	461,443	914,186	1,375,629
Gay & Lesbian	31	32	4,432	350,951	355,383	20	202	225,618	225,820	1	0	10,000	10,000	10	4,230	115,333	119,563
Hispanic	174	203	1,753,892	7,514,275	9,268,167	140	892,937	4,577,090	5,470,027	19	850,705	2,646,325	3,497,030	15	10,250	290,860	301,110
Jewish	98	173	1,007,256	593,969	1,601,225	58	812,549	351,050	1,163,599	1	1,200	50	1,250	39	193,507	242,869	436,376
Military	89	92	101,436	1,067,644	1,169,080	78	87,086	935,410	1,022,496	5	14,350	95,734	110,084	6	0	36,500	36,500
Parenting	89	212	2,049	4,062,968	4,065,017	3	0	50,000	50,000	0	0	0	0	86	2,049	4,012,968	4,015,017
Real Estate	54	61	137,832	855,000	992,832	8	93,886	169,000	262,886	0	0	0	0	46	43,946	686,000	729,946
Religious	121	366	3,349,702	515,975	3,865,677	70	1,737,673	91,095	1,828,768	1	0	1,000	1,000	50	1,612,029	423,880	2,035,909
Senior	46	114	39,673	2,059,905	2,099,578	0	0	0	0	0	0	0	0	46	39,673	2,059,905	2,099,578
Shoppers	1,209	2,318	1,090,959	42,798,072	43,889,031	1,125	866,474	33,728,550	34,595,024	50	145,709	7,176,297	7,322,006	34	78,776	1,893,225	1,972,001
TOTAL	8,363	12,443	28,828,419	97,664,360	126,492,779	7,238	21,286,003	72,371,398	93,657,401	727	5,049,973	14,371,100	19,421,073	398	2,492,443	10,921,862	13,414,305
CANADA																	
Alternative	13	13	13	394,712	394,725	6	13	224,132	224,145	0	0	0	0	7	0	170,580	170,580
Community	893	1,375	1,232,644	13,515,770	14,748,414	803	811,052	10,960,903	11,771,955	73	290,756	2,383,080	2,673,836	17	130,836	171,787	302,623
Ethnic	52	58	193,489	313,596	507,085	34	159,097	276,373	435,470	3	105	12,200	12,305	15	34,287	25,023	59,310
Shoppers	66	72	33,065	1,660,597	1,693,662	61	33,054	1,534,594	1,567,648	4	11	119,723	119,734	1	0	6,280	6,280
TOTAL	1,024	1,518	1,459,211	15,884,675	17,343,886	904	1,003,216	12,996,002	13,999,218	80	290,872	2,515,003	2,805,875	40	165,123	373,670	538,793
GRAND TOTAL	9,387	13,961	30,287,630	113,549,035	143,836,665	8,142	22,289,219	85,367,400	107,656,619	807	5,340,845	16,886,103	22,226,948	438	2,657,566	11,295,532	13,953,098

*Shopper/TMC Publications that publish two or three times a week are averaged for one paid number and one free number.

**Editor & Publisher defines a publication with zoned editions as one with press runs allowing the editorial and/or advertising department to place specific material within different distribution areas.

Any publication not having zoned editions is counted as one in both the number of publications column and number of editions column.

MECHANICAL EQUIPMENT — ABBREVIATIONS

COMPOSITION

TYPESETTERS

AG — Agfa-Gevaert
AU — Autologic
AX — Automix
Bg — Bobst Graphic
COM — Compugraphic
Dy — Dymo
F — Fairchild
Fi — Filmotype
Fo — Fotosetter
Fr — Friden
HCM — Hell/HCM
Hd — Headliner
HI — Harris
Ik — Itek
Jus — Justowriter
L — Lanston
LC — Linofilm Composer
M — Mergenthaler
Ma — Morisawa
MGD — MGD-Rockwell
MON — Monotype
Ph — Photon
Pr — Protype
Pt — Photo Typositor
So — Simmons-Owega
SP — Star Parts
Sr — Singer
ST — Stripprinter
TC — Titus Communications
V — Varityper
Va — Varisystems
VG — Visual Graphics

FRONT-END HARDWARE & SOFTWARE

ACT — Automated Complete Typesetting
AG — Agfa-Gevaert
AP — Associated Press
APP — Apple
AT — Atex
AU — Autologic
AX — Automix
BD — Berthold NA
Bee — Beehive
BF — Basic 4
Bg — Bobst Graphic
BR — Bunker Ramo
Bs — Burroughs
C — Chemco
CD — Crosfield Data Systems
CDS — Computer Double Screen
CJ — Collier-Jackson
CM — Cincinnati Milacron
COM — Compugraphic
CPU — Computext
Cp — CompuScan
CS — Computer Services
CSI — Computer Systems Inc.
Cx — Camex
Da — Datapoint
DD — Delta Data
DEC — Digital Equipment Corp.
DL — Data Logic
DS — Data Disc
DTI — Digital Technology International
Dy — Dymo
ECR — ECRM
EKI — Electric Knowledge Inc.
En — Entrex
ES — Evans & Southerland
ESE — Editorial System Engineering Co.
FSI — Freedom Systems Integrators
Gn — Genisis
HAS — Hastech
Hel — Hell
HI — Harris
HP — Hewlett Packard
Hw — Honeywell
Hx — Hendrix
Hz — Hazeltine
IBM — International Business Machines
III — Information International Inc.
Ik — Itek
In — Infotron
INS — Independent Network Services
ISSI — Integrated Software Systems Inc.
KC — Key Corp.
Kk — Kodak
Lf — Leaf Systems
LIP — Logicon-Intercomp
Lk — Lektromedia
LNS — Lee Newspapers Services
LS — Lear-Siegler
M — Mergenthaler
Mac — Macintosh
MD — Micro Data
MeD — Mega Data
MGD — MGD-Rockwell
Mh — Mohr
Mk — Mycro-Tek
MON — Monotype
MPS — Morris Publishing Systems
Mx — Memorex
NEC — Newspaper Electronics Corp.
NW — Neasi-Weber
Omn — Omnitext
Omo — Omron
On — Ontel
Op — Omptimix
OS — One Systems
PBS — Publishing Business Systems
PEP — Perception Electronic

PUBLISHING

PS — Peripheral Systems
QPS — Quark Publishing Systems
Ra — Raytheon
RSK — Radio Shack
RZ — Royal Zenith
SCS — Software Consulting Services
SII — System Integrators Inc.
SMS — Stauffer Media Systems
Syc — Sycor
SyD — Systems Development
TC — Titus Communications
Te — Telcom
TI — Texas Instruments
TM — Teleram
Tr — Teleray
TRW — TRW-Fujitsu
TS — Tal-Star
Tt — Teleterm
Tx — Telex
Uni — Univac
V — Varityper
Va — Varisystems
X — Xerox
XIT — Xitron
ZC — Zentec Corp.

AUDIOTEX

DJ — Dow Jones
TEDS — Toronto Star Edition Design System
TMS — Tribune Media Services
VNN — Voice News Network

OCR READERS

APP — Apple
COM — Compugraphic
Cp — CompuScan
Da — Datatype
Di — Digitek
ECR — ECRM
Hx — Hendrix
M — Mergenthaler
MGD — MGD-Rockwell

PLATE-MAKING

PLATE SYSTEMS

AU — Autologic
B — Brown
CD — Crosfield Data Systems
DiL — DiLitho
DP — DuPont
Dyn — Dynaflex
ECM — EOCOM
F — Fairchild
He — Hercules (Merigraph)
LE — LogEtronics
LP — Laser-Plate
LX — Grace (Letterflex)
Mag — Magnesium
Na — Napp
Nat — National
Rf — Richflex
WL — Western Litho
Z — Zinc

PLATE PROCESSORS

B — Brown
Be — Beach
BM — Ball Metal
CEM — Chemcut
Dow — Dow Chemical
DP — DuPont
Dyn — Dynaflex
He — Hercules (Merigraph)
Ic — Iconics
LG — Laser Graphics
LX — Grace (Letterflex)
MAS — Master
Na — Napp
Nat — National
Nu — nuArc
Ny — Nyloprint
Tas — TasopeSearch
Wd — Wood
WL — Western Litho

CAMERAS

AG — Agfa-Gevaert
B — Brown
Bo — Borrowdale
Br — Bruning
C — Chemco
CL — Clydedale
Co — Consolidated
COM — Compugraphic
DAI — Dainippon
DSA — D.S. America (SCREEN)
ECR — ECRM
Go — Goodkin
Ik — Itek
K — Kenro
Kk — Kodak
Kl — Klimsch
L — Lanston
LE — LogEtronics
MG — ModiGraphic
Nu — nuArc
R — Robertson
Sm — Statmaster
VG — Visual Graphics
W — Western

AUTOMATIC FILM PROCESSORS

AG — Agfa-Gevaert
AU — Autologic
C — Chemo
DP — DuPont
Kk — Kodak
Kr — Kreonite
LE — LogEtronics
P — Pako
WL — Western Litho

COLOR SEPARATION SYSTEMS

AG — Agfa-Gevaert
BKY — Berkey
C — Chemco
Ca — Carlson
Eh — Ehrenreich
Hel — Hell
KFM — K&F Printing Systems International
Kk — Kodak
Lf — Leaf Systems
RZ — Royal Zenith
WDS — Warner MDS

PRESSROOM

DILITHO SYSTEMS

DI — Dahlgren
G — Goss
HI — Harris
In — Inland
RPM — Smith RPM Co.
Ry — Ryco Graphic
T — Taft
Wd — Wood

PRESSES

Bk — Babcock
Cb — Crabtree
FAU — Faustel
Fin — Fincor
FOL — Flex-O-Line
G — Goss
GE — General Electric
H — Hoe
Ha — Hantscho
HAR — Hoe-Aller
HI — Heidleberg-Harris
KB — Koenig & Bauer
KP — King Press
MAN — MAN/Roland USA
MHI — Mitsubishi Heavy Ind.
MOT — Motter
SC — Scott
SLN — Solna
TKS — Tokyo Kikai Seisakusho
Tp — Thatcher-Pacer
Wd — Wood
WPC — Web Press Corp.

PRESS CONVERSION SYSTEMS

KDS — Kidder Stacy
KFM — K&F Printing Systems International
PEC — Publishers Equip. Corp.
PMC — Press Machinery Corp.
RKW — Rockwell
RPM — Smith RPM Co.

REPROPORTIONING SYSTEMS

CS — Combined Services
FLS — Flurographic Services

MAILROOM

STACKERS

BG — Baldwin-Gegenheimer
CH — Cutler-Hammer
DG — Didde Glaser
Fg — Ferag
HI — Heidelberg-Harris
HL — Hall
Id — IDAB
KAN — Kansa
MM — Muller-Martini
MRS — Mailroom Systems
NJP — Nolan Jampol
PPK — Pace Pack
QWI — Quipp
RKW — Rockwell
SH — Sta-Hi
St — Stepper

INSERTERS/STUFFERS

D — Dexter
DG — Didde Glaser
Fg — Ferag
G — Goss
Gr — Graphicart
HI — Harris
I — Insertomatic
KAN — Kansa
KR — Kirk-Rudy
LEG — Leger Inc.
M — Mergenthaler
Mc — McCain
Mg — Magnacraft
MM — Muller-Martini
S — Sheridan
SH — Sta-Hi
St — Stepper

BUNDLE TYERS

AMP — Ampag
Bu — Bunn
Ca — Carlson
Cn — Cranston
Cr — Crawford
CYP — Cypack
Eb — Ebby
Gd — Gerrard
Gs — General Strapping
HL — Hall
Id — IDAB
In — Inland
It — Interlake
J — Jampol
Mc — McCain
Md — MidStates
MLN — Signode
MM — Muller-Martini
MVP — Metaveppa
NJP — Nolan Jampol
OVL — Ovalstrapping
PM — Paper Man
QWI — Quipp
S — Sheridan
Sa — Saxmayer
SHt — SatoHit
Si — Parker-Signode
St — Stepper
Ty — Tyler
Us — USSteel
Ws — Walla Star
WT — Wire-Tyer

ADDRESSERS

Am — Addressograph-Multigraph
AVY — Avery
BH — Bell & Howell
Ch — Cheshire
Dm — Dick Mailer
El — Elliott
Gd — Gerrard
GL — Galley List
Gp — Graphotype
Hw — Honeywell
IBM — International Business Machines
KAN — Kansa
KR — Kirk-Rudy
Mg — Magnacraft
Pa — Pollard-Alling
PB — Pitney-Bowes
Rp — Roto-Strip Printer
RSK — Radio Shack
SC — Scriptomatic
Sp — Speedomat
SRC — Standard Register Co.
St — Stepper
Wm — Wing Mailer

DELIVERY SYSTEMS

CBM — Custom Built Machinery
EDS — EDS-IDAB
Fg — Ferag
FMC — FMC Corp.
KAN — Kansa
RKW — Rockwell
SIH — SI Handling

LIBRARY SYSTEMS

AT — Atex
ATT — AT&T
BH — Bell & Howell
CCC — Capital Cities Communications
DDC — Documaster
DEC — Digital Equipment
GE — General Electric
IBM — International Business Machines
IFK — Info-Ky
IXA — Infotex Assoc.
LIP — Logicon-Intercomp
MED — Mead
QLS — QL Systems
SII — System Integrators Inc.
SMS — Stauffer Media Systems

COMMUNICATIONS

FACSIMILE EQUIPMENT

ABD — AB Dick
Ao — Apeco
AP — Associated Press
ATT — AT&T
CD — Crosfield Digital Systems
CP — Canadian Press
DF — Data Fax
Dm — Daycom
ECM — EOCOM
Hel — Hell
Ho — Hogan
IBM — International Business Machines
III — Information International Inc.
LI — Litcom
Mag — Magnavox
Mh — Muirhead
Px — Pressfax
Q — Quickfax
QWI — Quipp
Rem — Remington
SN — Scanatron
SW — Stewart Warner
Uf — Unifax
UPI — United Press International
VI — Vistatype
Wr — Warwick
Wx — Westrex
X — Xerox

DATA COMMUNICATIONS

AMS — American Satellite
DTG — Datalog
EPT — Epic Technology
GAN — Gandalf Data
Mot — Motorola
XIT — Xitron

BUSINESS COMPUTERS

ALR — Advanced Logic Research
APP — Apple
AT — Atex
ATT — AT&T
Bs — Burroughs
CJ — Collier-Jackson
DEC — Digital Equipment Corp.
DG — Data General
EKI — Electric Knowledge Inc.
HP — Hewlett Packard
Hw — Honeywell
IBM — International Business Machines
Mac — Macintosh
Mk — Mycro-Tek
NEC — Newspaper Electronics Corp.
PBS — Publishing Business Systems
RSK — Radio Shack
TI — Texas Instruments
Uni — Univac
Wa — Wang

The table of abbreviations is for major equipment manufacturers listed in section I & III. Companies not found in the above list are entered in full.

Section I

Community Newspapers Published in the United States and Canada

United States

Alabama.................................2
Alaska...................................9
Arizona.................................11
Arkansas...............................16
California..............................23
Colorado...............................42
Connecticut..........................49
Delaware..............................55
District of Columbia.........57
Florida..................................57
Georgia................................70
Hawaii...................................79
Idaho.....................................81
Illinois..................................84
Indiana................................104
Iowa.....................................112
Kansas.................................126
Kentucky.............................137
Louisiana.............................145
Maine...................................151
Maryland..............................156
Massachusetts....................160
Michigan..............................175
Minnesota............................188
Mississippi..........................207
Missouri...............................213
Montana...............................226
Nebraska.............................231
Nevada.................................240
New Hampshire..................243
New Jersey..........................246
New Mexico.........................257
New York.............................260
North Carolina....................281
North Dakota.......................290
Ohio.....................................296
Oklahoma............................312
Oregon.................................320
Pennsylvania......................327
Rhode Island......................342
South Carolina....................345
South Dakota......................351
Tennessee...........................359
Texas....................................368
Utah......................................402
Vermont...............................405
Virginia.................................408
Washington........................416
West Virginia.......................426
Wisconsin............................430
Wyoming.............................445

Canada

Alberta..................................449
British Columbia.................456
Manitoba..............................464
New Brunswick....................467
Newfoundland.....................469
Nova Scotia..........................469
Northwest Territories.....471
Nunavut................................472
Ontario.................................472
Prince Edward Island....488
Quebec.................................489
Saskatchewan....................498
Yukon...................................503

COMMUNITY NEWSPAPERS IN THE UNITED STATES

ALABAMA

ABBEVILLE

ABBEVILLE HERALD (THUR)
135 Kirkland St, Abbeville, AL, 36310-2113, Henry, USA; gen tel (334) 585-2331; gen fax (334) 585-6835; disp adv e-mail heraldadv@centurytel.net; ed e-mail heraldnews@centurytel.net; web site No Website
Circulation: 2,350pd,; Sworn/Estimate/Non-Audited
Advertising rate: Open inch rate $ 6.11
Established: 1912
Ed. .... J. Edward Dodd
Delivery Method: Mail, Racks
Areas Served: 36310, 36345, 36353, 36373, 36319

ALBERTVILLE

SAND MOUNTAIN REPORTER (TUES, THUR, SAT)
1603 Progress Dr, Albertville, AL, 35950-8547, Marshall, USA; gen tel (256) 840-3000; adv tel (256) 840-3000 x120; ed tel (256) 840-3000 x115; gen fax (256) 840-2987; adv fax 256-840-2987; ed fax 256-840-2987; disp adv e-mail advertising@sandmountainreporter.com; class adv e-mail advertising@sandmountainreporter.com; ed e-mail news@sandmountainreporter.com; web site www.sandmountainreporter.com
Circulation: 5,403pd, 178fr; CAC
Advertising rate: Open inch rate $10.00
Established: 1955
Group: Southern Newspapers Inc.
Account Executive .... Jessica Patterson
Advertising Assistant .... Elliot Andrews
Business Manager .... Michelle Rowell
Managing Editor .... Michael Treadwell
Staff Writer .... Taylor Beck
Staff Writer .... Jay Beard
Sports Editor .... Shannon Allen
Classifieds .... Linda Allen
Staff Photographer .... Brittney Hannah
Advertising Director .... Kathy Register
Account Executive .... Sherrie Hall
Cir. Mgr .... Tammy Walker
Managing Ed .... Melissa Cooper
Mechanical Specifications: Type page 11 9/16 x 21 1/2; E - 6 cols, 1/8 between; A - 6 cols, 1/8 between; C - 9 cols, 1/16 between.Equipment & Software: Hardware — Baseview; Presses — Web Leader; Software — QPS/QuarkXPress 6.0.
Delivery Method: Mail, Carrier, Racks
Areas Served: Marshall County, DeKalb County and Etowah County

ALEXANDER CITY

DADEVILLE RECORD (THUR)
548 Cherokee Rd, Alexander City, AL, 35010-2503, Tallapoosa, USA; gen tel (256) 234-4281; adv tel (256) 234-4281 x15; ed tel (256) 234-4281 x22; gen fax (256) 234-6550; disp adv e-mail tippy.hunter@alexcityoutlook.com; class adv e-mail linda.ewing@alexcityoutlook.com; ed e-mail virginia.spears@alexcityoutlook.com; web site www.alexcityoutlook.com
Circulation: 1,600pd,; Sworn/Estimate/Non-Audited
Advertising rate: Open inch rate $9.65
Group: Boone Newspapers, Inc.
Pub. .... Kenneth Boone
Bookkeeper .... Mary Lyman
Adv. Rep. .... Tippy Hunter
David Kendrick
Sports Ed. .... Cathy Higgins
Delivery Method: Mail, Racks

THE WETUMPKA HERALD (WED)
548 CHEROKEE RD, Alexander City, AL, 35010-2503, Elmore, USA; gen tel (334) 567-7811; gen fax (334) 567-3284; disp adv e-mail tippy.hunter@alexcityoutlook.com; class adv e-mail tippy.hunter@alexcityoutlook.com; ed e-mail david.granger@alexcityoutlook.com; web site www.thewetumpkaherald.com
Circulation: 5,700pd, 100fr; Sworn/Estimate/Non-Audited
Advertising rate: Open inch rate $9.75
Established: 1898
Group: Boone Newspapers, Inc.
President/Publisher .... Steve Baker
Managing Editor .... David Granger
Advertising Director .... Tippy Hunter
Mechanical Specifications: Type page 13 x 21 1/2; E - 6 cols, 2, 3/16 between; A - 6 cols, 2, 3/16 between; C - 6 cols, 2, 3/16 between. Equipment & Software: Hardware — APP/Mac Quadra 700, APP/Power Mac G3; Presses — H/Multilith 1250; Software — QPS/QuarkXPress 3.3.
Delivery Method: Mail, Newsstand

ANNISTON

PIEDMONT JOURNAL (TUES)
4305 McClellan Blvd, Anniston, AL, 36206-2812, Calhoun, USA; gen tel (256) 235-3563; adv tel (256) 235-9238; gen fax (256) 241-1990; disp adv e-mail smartin@annistonstar.com; web site annistonstar.com/piedmont_journal
Circulation: 3,300pd,; Sworn/Estimate/Non-Audited
Advertising rate: Open inch rate $6.13
Established: 1907
Group: Consolidated Publishing Co.
Pub. .... John Alred
Adv. Dir. .... Shannon Martin
News Ed. .... Laura Johnson

THE JACKSONVILLE NEWS (TUES)
4305 McClellan Blvd, Anniston, AL, 36206-2812, Calhoun, USA; gen tel (256) 435-5021; gen fax (256) 435-1028; disp adv e-mail news@jaxnews.com; web site www.jaxnews.com
Circulation: 3,300pd,; Sworn/Estimate/Non-Audited
Advertising rate: Open inch rate $9.45
Established: 1936
Group: Consolidated Publishing Co.
Pub. .... Phillip A. Sanguinetti
Adv. Mgr. .... Shannon Martin
Ed. .... John Alred
Mechanical Specifications: Type page 11 9/16 x 21 1/4; E - 6 cols, 1 13/16, between; A - 6 cols, 1 13/16, between; C - 10 cols, 1 2/25, between.Equipment & Software: Hardware — APP/Mac; Software — Adobe/PageMaker 6.5, Microsoft/Word 5.1, QPS/QuarkXPress 4.1.
Areas Served: 36265

ARAB

THE ARAB TRIBUNE (WED, SAT)
619 S Brindlee Mountain Pkwy, Arab, AL, 35016-1502, Marshall County, USA; gen tel (256) 586-3188; gen fax (256) 586-3190; disp adv e-mail tribads@otelco.net; ed e-mail tribnews@otelco.net; web site www.thearabtribune.com
Circulation: 6,500pd,; Sworn/Estimate/Non-Audited
Advertising rate: Open inch rate $7.10
Established: 1958
Pub. .... Edwin H. Reed
Ed. .... Charles Whisenant
VP/OPs .... Marcus Johnson
Class. Ads Mgr .... RayeLynne Wingrove
Sports Ed. .... Donna Matuszak
Mechanical Specifications: 21.29 x 10.96 inches; 6 columns; column = 1.69 inches x 1 inch deep
Equipment & Software: Hardware — APP/Mac, PC; Presses — G.
Delivery Method: Mail, Carrier, Racks
Areas Served: Marshall County, Blount County, Cullman County, Morgan County

ATMORE

ATMORE ADVANCE (WED)
301 S Main St, Atmore, AL, 36502-2436, Escambia, USA; gen tel (251) 368-2123; gen fax (251) 368-2124; disp adv e-mail newsroom@atmoreadvance.com; class adv e-mail advertising@atmoreadvance.com; web site www.atmoreadvance.com
Circulation: 3,100pd, 6,000fr; Sworn/Estimate/Non-Audited
Advertising rate: Open inch rate $10.95
Group: Boone Newspapers, Inc.
Circ. Mgr. .... Allison Knowles
Editor .... Andrew Garner
Pres./Pub. .... Blake Bell
Mechanical Specifications: Type page 13 x 21 1/2; E - 6 cols, 2, 3/25 between; A - 6 cols, 2, 3/25 between; C - 10 cols, 1 1/5, 1/10 between.Equipment & Software: Hardware — APP/Mac G3, APP/Mac 7100, APP/Mac 6100; Software — QPS/QuarkXPress 3.3, Adobe/Photoshop.

ATMORE NEWS (WED)
128 S Main St, Atmore, AL, 36502-2446, Escambia, USA; gen tel (251) 368-6397; gen fax (251) 368-3397; disp adv e-mail myrna@atmorenews.com; class adv e-mail myrna@atmorenews.com; ed e-mail sherry@atmorenews.com; web site www.atmorenews.com
Circulation: 1,500pd, 50fr; Sworn/Estimate/Non-Audited
Advertising rate: Open inch rate $6.00
Established: 2005
Digital Platform - Mobile: Apple, Android
Digital Platform - Tablet: Apple iOS, Android
Co-owner. .... Myrna Monroe
Co-Pub. .... Sherry Digmon
Staff Writer .... Don Fletcher
Delivery Method: Mail, Carrier, Racks
Areas Served: Escambia County

AUBURN

AUBURN VILLAGER (THUR)
687 N Dean Rd, Auburn, AL, 36830-4044, Lee, USA; gen tel (334) 501-0600; adv tel (334) 501-0600; gen fax (334) 826-7700; adv fax (334) 826-7700; disp adv e-mail dawn@auburnvillager.com; ed e-mail editorial@auburnvillager.com; web site www.auburnvillager.com
Circulation: 3,000pd, 1,000fr; Sworn/Estimate/Non-Audited
Advertising rate: Open rate: $20
Established: 2006
Assoc. Ed. .... Allison Blankenship
Assoc Ed .... Brian Woodham
Accts. Mgr. .... Rhonda Fields
Advert. Mgr .... Lance Radermacher
Mechanical Specifications: 21" x 11.625" — 6 cols (1 1/2" x 1 1/2" each)
Delivery Method: Mail, Racks
Areas Served: Auburn

BESSEMER

THE WESTERN STAR (WED)
1709 3rd Ave N, Bessemer, AL, 35020-0900, USA; gen tel (205) 424-7827; gen fax (205) 424-8118; disp adv e-mail bessemercutoff@gmail.com; ed e-mail editor@thewesternstarnews.com
Circulation: 4,200pd,; Sworn/Estimate/Non-Audited
Advertising rate: Open inch rate $8.30
Pub. .... Matt Bryant
Ed. .... Matthew McCrary
Office Mgr. .... Michelle Lambert
Mechanical Specifications: Type page 12 x 21 1/2; E - 6 cols, 1 7/8, 1/6 between; A - 6 cols, 1 7/8, 1/6 between; C - 6 cols, 1 7/8, 1/6 between.Equipment & Software: ; Software — QPS/QuarkXPress 4.1.

BIRMINGHAM

ALABAMA MESSENGER (WED, SAT)
205 20th St N, 706 Frank Nelson Bldg. Ste 706, Birmingham, AL, 35203-3673, Jefferson County, USA; gen tel (205) 252-3672; gen fax (205) 252-3679; disp adv e-mail alamsgr@bellsouth.net; ed e-mail alamsgr@bellsouth.net; web site www.alabamamessenger.com
Circulation: 1,500pd, 75fr; Sworn/Estimate/Non-Audited
Advertising rate: Open inch rate $7.50
Established: 1918
Pub. / Gen. Mgr. .... Karen W. Abercrombie
Mng. Ed. .... Traci Smeraglia

BIRMINGHAM BUSINESS JOURNAL (FRI)
2140 11th Ave S Ste 205, Ste. 205, Birmingham, AL, 35205-2840, Jefferson, USA; gen tel (205) 443-5600; adv tel (205) 443-5617; gen fax (205) 322-0040; disp adv e-mail jwelker@bizjournals.com; ed e-mail ccrawford@bizjournals.com; web site www.bizjournals.com/birmingham/
Group: American City Business Journals
Pres./Pub. .... Joel Welker
Editor .... Cindy Crawford
Ed.-in-chief .... Ty West
Digital Prod. .... Ryan Phillips
Research Dir. .... Dan Bagwell
Prod. Dir. .... Derek Morrow
Audience Dev Dir .... Ginger Gardner Aarons
Events Mgr .... Courtney Sanak
Business Mgr. .... Jana Branch
Credit Mgr. .... Beth Hoff
Mng. Ed. .... Stephanie Rebman
Delivery Method: Mail

THE BIRMINGHAM NEWS (WED, FRI, SUN)
1731 1st Ave N, Birmingham, AL, 35203-2055, Jefferson, USA; gen tel (205) 325.4444; adv tel (205) 325-2261; gen fax (205) 325-2283; adv fax (205) 325-3217; ed fax (205) 325-2283; disp adv e-mail advertise@al.com; web site www.al.com/birmingham - 64,000,000(views) 4,200,000(visitors)
Circulation: 30,136pd,; AAM
Advertising rate: Open inch rate $190.00
Group: Advance Publications, Inc.
Digital Platform - Mobile: Apple, Android, Windows, Blackberry
Digital Platform - Tablet: Apple iOS, Android, Windows 7, Blackberry Tablet OS, Kindle, Nook, Kindle Fire
Adv. Dir., Bus. Devel. .... Carl Bates
Circ./Vice Pres. .... Troy Niday
President .... Pam Siddall
VP, Digital Solutions .... Dee Dee Mathis
VP, Content .... Michelle Holmes
VP, Sales/Mktg. .... Kurt Vantosky
Nat'l Coord. .... Elaine Jackson
Nat'l Classifieds Adv. Rep. .... Kelley Kilgore
Mechanical Specifications: Type page 12 1/2 x

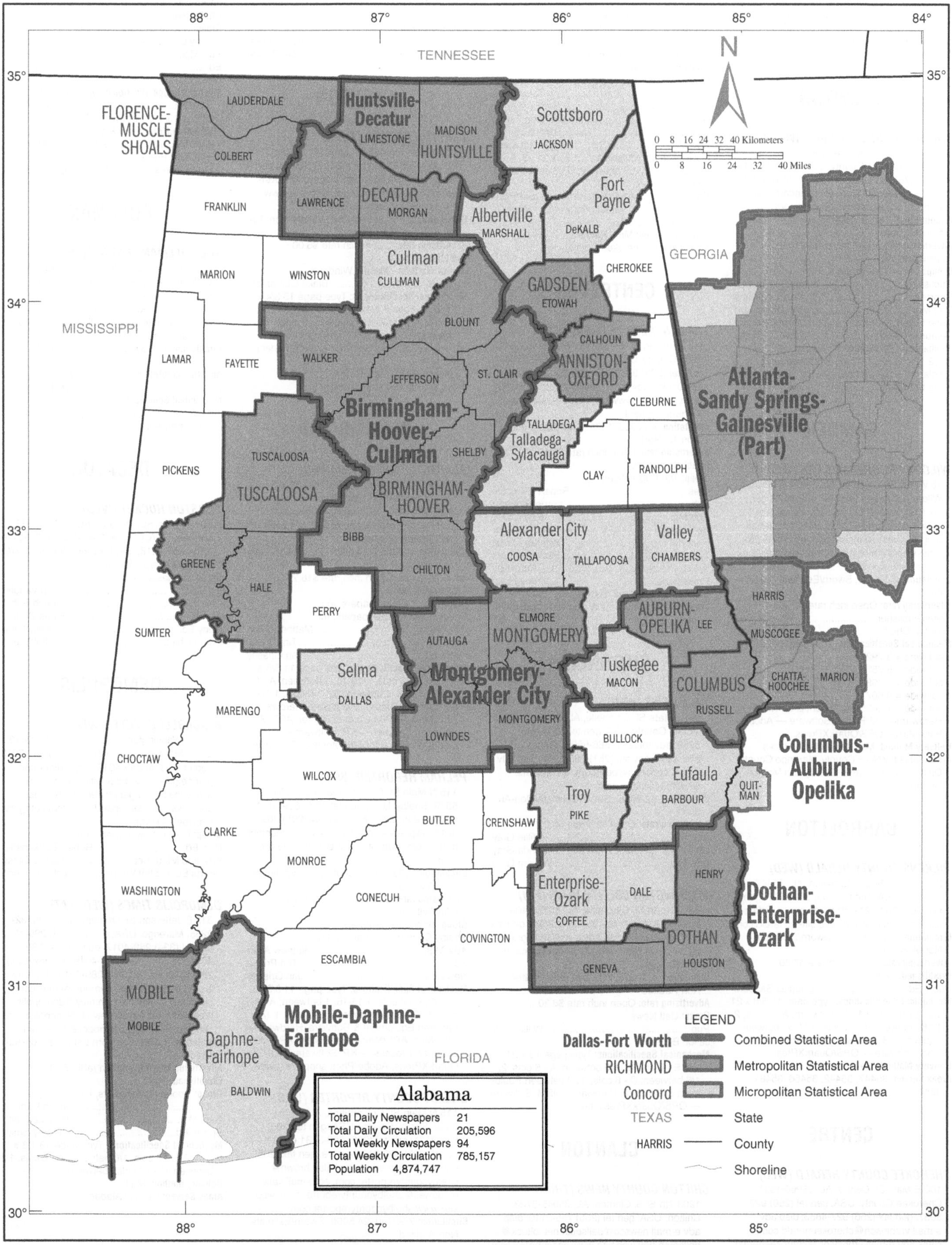
TENNESSEE
MISSISSIPPI
GEORGIA
FLORIDA
N
0 8 16 24 32 40 Kilometers
0 8 16 24 32 40 Miles
FLORENCE-MUSCLE SHOALS
LAUDERDALE
COLBERT
Huntsville-Decatur
LIMESTONE
MADISON
HUNTSVILLE
DECATUR
MORGAN
LAWRENCE
FRANKLIN
Scottsboro
JACKSON
Fort Payne
DeKALB
Albertville
MARSHALL
Cullman
CULLMAN
MARION
WINSTON
GADSDEN
ETOWAH
CHEROKEE
BLOUNT
CALHOUN
ANNISTON-OXFORD
LAMAR
FAYETTE
WALKER
JEFFERSON
ST. CLAIR
CLEBURNE
Birmingham-Hoover-Cullman
TALLADEGA
Talladega-Sylacauga
SHELBY
BIRMINGHAM-HOOVER
PICKENS
TUSCALOOSA
TUSCALOOSA
CLAY
RANDOLPH
Atlanta-Sandy Springs-Gainesville (Part)
Alexander City
COOSA
TALLAPOOSA
Valley
CHAMBERS
BIBB
CHILTON
GREENE
HALE
PERRY
SUMTER
ELMORE
MONTGOMERY
AUTAUGA
AUBURN-OPELIKA
LEE
HARRIS
MUSCOGEE
Selma
DALLAS
Montgomery-Alexander City
MONTGOMERY
LOWNDES
Tuskegee
MACON
COLUMBUS
RUSSELL
CHATTA-HOOCHEE
MARION
MARENGO
BULLOCK
CHOCTAW
WILCOX
Columbus-Auburn-Opelika
Troy
PIKE
Eufaula
BARBOUR
QUIT-MAN
BUTLER
CRENSHAW
CLARKE
MONROE
Enterprise-Ozark
COFFEE
DALE
HENRY
Dothan-Enterprise-Ozark
WASHINGTON
CONECUH
COVINGTON
ESCAMBIA
DOTHAN
HOUSTON
GENEVA
MOBILE
MOBILE
Mobile-Daphne-Fairhope
Daphne-Fairhope
BALDWIN
LEGEND
Dallas-Fort Worth — Combined Statistical Area
RICHMOND — Metropolitan Statistical Area
Concord — Micropolitan Statistical Area
TEXAS — State
HARRIS — County
Shoreline
Alabama
Total Daily Newspapers 21
Total Daily Circulation 205,596
Total Weekly Newspapers 94
Total Weekly Circulation 785,157
Population 4,874,747
88°
87°
86°
85°
84°
35°
34°
33°
32°
31°
30°

21 3/4; E - 6 cols, 2 1/16, 1/8 between; A - 6 cols, 2 1/16, 1/8 between; C - 10 cols, 1 3/8, 1/16 between.
Delivery Method: Carrier, Racks
Areas Served: Central Alabama

BREWTON

THE BREWTON STANDARD (WED, SAT)
407 Saint Nicholas Ave, Brewton, AL, 36426-1847, Escambia County, USA; gen tel (251) 867-4876; gen fax (251) 867-4877; disp adv e-mail newsroom@brewtonstandard.com; web site www.brewtonstandard.com
Circulation: 3,180pd, 150fr; Sworn/Estimate/Non-Audited
Advertising rate: Open inch rate $10.95
Established: 1906
Group: Boone Newspapers, Inc.
Publisher............................... Stephanie Nelson
Sports Ed.................................. Corey Williams
Circ Mgr.................................. Jennifer Howard
Advert. Rep.................................. Amy Booker
Features Report.......................... Lydia Grimes
Mechanical Specifications: Type page 12 x 21 1/2; E - 6 cols, 1 13/16, 1/8 between; A - 6 cols, 1 13/16, 1/8 between; C - 10 cols, 1 1/4, 1/8 between.

CAMDEN

WILCOX PROGRESSIVE ERA (WED)
16 Water St, Camden, AL, 36726-2111, Wilcox, USA; gen tel (334) 682-4422; gen fax (334) 682-5163; disp adv e-mail progressiveera@mchsi.com; class adv e-mail progressiveera@mchsi.com; ed e-mail progressiveera@mchsi.com; web site thewilcoxprogressiveera.com
Circulation: 2,000pd,; Sworn/Estimate/Non-Audited
Advertising rate: Open inch rate $5.90
Editor/Publisher............................ Glenda Curl
Editor in Chief.......................... Ethan Van Sice
Mechanical Specifications: 1 col wide = 1.833"
2 col wide = 3.792"
3 col wide = 5.75"
4 col wide = 7.708"
5 col wide = 9.667"
6 col wide = 11.625"Equipment & Software: Hardware — APP/Mac; Software — Adobe/PageMaker, QPS/QuarkXPress.
Delivery Method: Mail, Newsstand, Racks
Areas Served: Wilcox County, Marengo County, Dallas County, Clarke County and Monroe County

CARROLLTON

PICKENS COUNTY HERALD (WED)
215 REFORM ST, Carrollton, AL, 35447, Pickens, USA; gen tel (205) 367-2217; gen fax (205) 367-2217; disp adv e-mail pickenscnty@centurytel.net; web site pcherald.com
Circulation: 4,000pd, 27fr; Sworn/Estimate/Non-Audited
Advertising rate: Open inch rate $7.20
Established: 1848
Pub. / Ed............................. Douglas Sanders
Mechanical Specifications: Type page 11 5/8 x 21 1/2; E - 6 cols, 2 1/16, between; A - 6 cols, 2 1/16, between; C - 9 cols, 2 1/16, between. Equipment & Software: Hardware — APP/Mac; Software — QPS/QuarkXPress.
Delivery Method: Mail, Racks
Areas Served: 35447, 35442, 35466, 35481, 35461, 35471

CENTRE

CHEROKEE COUNTY HERALD (WED)
100 E Main St, Centre, AL, 35960-1517, Cherokee County, USA; gen tel (256) 927-5037; gen fax (256) 927-4853; disp adv e-mail vrobinson@cherokeeherald.com; class adv e-mail vrobinson@cherokeeherald.com; ed e-mail tdean@cherokeeherald.com; web site www.cherokeeherald.com
Circulation: 2,594pd, 5,872fr; Sworn/Estimate/Non-Audited
Advertising rate: Open inch rate $12.64
Established: 1938
Group: Rome News-Tribune
Pub./Ed... Terry Dean
Layout Ed.................................. Buddie Norton
Sports Ed............................... Shannon Fagan
Classified/Legal......................... Brenda Burger
Adv. Mgr................................. Vickie Robinson
Mechanical Specifications: 10.625 x 21.25; A - 6 cols, 1.6667, 1/8 between; C - 8 cols, 1.181, 6pts between
Equipment & Software: Hardware — IBM/PC, ACT; Presses — Gault; Software — Microsoft/Windows 3.0.
Delivery Method: Mail, Racks
Areas Served: Cherokee County

CENTREVILLE

THE CENTREVILLE PRESS (WED)
32 Court Sq W, Centreville, AL, 35042-2232, Bibb County, USA; gen tel (205) 926-9769; adv tel (205) 926-9769; gen fax (205) 926-9760; disp adv e-mail billy@centrevillepress.com; web site www.centrevillepress.com/Community.html
Circulation: 4,200pd, 157fr; Sworn/Estimate/Non-Audited
Advertising rate: Open inch rate $7.10
Established: 1880
Group: Trib Publications
Pres...................................... Robert E. Tribble
Pub.. Lorrie Rinehart
Adv. Mgr... Billy Colley
Bookkeeper................................ Carol Belcher
Reporter................................. Deborah Martin
Typist.. Essie Sanders
Typist, Proofer.................................. Ann Riley
Pressman.................................... Jimmy Huett
Delivery Method: Mail, Racks
Areas Served: Bibb County and surrounding areas

CITRONELLE

CALL NEWS (WED)
7870 State St, Citronelle, AL, 36522-2486, Mobile County, USA; gen tel (251) 866-5998; adv tel (251) 866-5998; gen fax (251) 866-5981; adv fax (251) 866-5981; disp adv e-mail callnews@bellsouth.net; web site www.thecallnews.com
Circulation: 4,550pd,; Sworn/Estimate/Non-Audited
Advertising rate: Open inch rate $6.00
Pub.. Willie Gray
Office Mgr.................................. Rhonda Gray
Adv. Mgr...................................... William Gray

WASHINGTON COUNTY NEWS (FRI)
8350 North St, Citronelle, AL, 36522-4008, Mobile, USA; gen tel (251) 847-2599; gen fax (251) 847-3847; disp adv e-mail williegray@thecallnews.com; web site www.washcountynews.com
Circulation: 4,000pd, 75fr; Sworn/Estimate/Non-Audited
Advertising rate: Open inch rate $6.30
Group: Call News
Pub.. Willie Gray
Jason Boothe
Mechanical Specifications: Type page 13 x 21 1/2; E - 6 cols, 2, 1/6 between; A - 6 cols, 2, 1/6 between; C - 8 cols, 3/20 between.Equipment & Software: Hardware — IBM; Software — QPS/QuarkXPress 4.0.

CLANTON

CHILTON COUNTY NEWS (THUR)
1203 7th St S, Clanton, AL, 35045-3723, Chilton, USA; gen tel (205) 755-0110; disp adv e-mail newscc@bellsouth.net; oltuck@bellsouth.net; web site www.beachbecky.com
Circulation: 3,000pd,; Sworn/Estimate/Non-Audited
Advertising rate: Open inch rate $6.50
Ed... Robert M. Tucker
Adv. Mgr... Ben Tucker

CLAYTON

CLAYTON RECORD (THUR)
12 Eufaula Avenue, Clayton, AL, 36016, Barbour, USA; gen tel (334) 775-3254; gen fax (334) 775-8554; disp adv e-mail advertising@claytonrecord.com; web site www.theclaytonrecordonline.com
Circulation: 2,500pd,; Sworn/Estimate/Non-Audited
Advertising rate: Open inch rate $6.00
Established: 1870
Digital Platform - Mobile: Windows
Ed./Pub............................... Blake Gumprecht
Mechanical Specifications: Type page 13 3/4 x 21; E - 6 cols, 2 1/12, 1/2 between; A - 6 cols, 2 1/12, 1/2 between; C - 6 cols, 2 1/12, 1/2 between.Equipment & Software: Hardware — IBM, Compaq; Software — WordPerfect, Ventura.
Delivery Method: Mail, Racks
Areas Served: Barbour County

COLUMBIANA

ALABASTER REPORTER (WED)
115 N Main St, Columbiana, AL, 35051-5359, USA; gen tel (205) 669-3131; gen fax (205) 669-4217; disp adv e-mail news@shelbycountyreporter.com; web site www.alabasterreporter.com
Circulation: 7,997pd, 24,500fr; Sworn/Estimate/Non-Audited
Advertising rate: Open inch rate $16.75
Established: 1843
Group: Boone Newspapers, Inc.
Shelby County Newspapers, Inc
Adv. Mgr.................................... Matthew Allen
Ed... Tim Prince
News Ed....................................... Jan Grissey
Mechanical Specifications: Type page 11 5/8 x 21 1/2; E - 6 cols, 1 13/16, 1 between; A - 6 cols, 1 13/16, 1 between; C - 10 cols, 1 1/2, between.Equipment & Software: Hardware — APP/Mac, APP/Mac Laser Printer, APP/Mac Scanner; Presses — KP; Software — QPS/QuarkXPress, Adobe/Photoshop, Baseview.

PELHAM REPORTER (WED)
115 N Main St, Columbiana, AL, 35051-5359, Shelby, USA; gen tel (205) 669-3131; adv tel (205) 280-5667; gen fax (205) 669-4217; disp adv e-mail news@shelbycountyreporter.com; web site www.pelhamreporter.com
Circulation: 7,997pd, 24,500fr; Sworn/Estimate/Non-Audited
Advertising rate: Open inch rate $16.75
Established: 1843
Group: Boone Newspapers, Inc.
Shelby County Newspapers, Inc
Adv. Mgr.................................... Matthew Allen
Ed... Tim Prince
News Ed....................................... Jan Grissey
Mechanical Specifications: Type page 11 5/8 x 21 1/2; E - 6 cols, 1 13/16, 1 between; A - 6 cols, 1 13/16, 1 between; C - 10 cols, 1 1/2, between.Equipment & Software: Hardware — APP/Mac, APP/Mac Laser Printer, APP/Mac Scanner; Presses — KP; Software — QPS/QuarkXPress, Adobe/Photoshop, Baseview.

SHELBY COUNTY REPORTER (WED)
115 N Main St, Columbiana, AL, 35051-5359, Shelby County, USA; gen tel (205) 669-3131; adv tel (205) 669-3131 ext. 11; ed tel (205) 669-3131 ext. 19; gen fax (205) 669-4217; disp adv e-mail alan.brown@shelbycountyreporter.com; ed e-mail katie.mcdowell@shelbycountyreporter.com; web site www.shelbycountyreporter.com
Circulation: 7,997pd, 24,500fr; Sworn/Estimate/Non-Audited
Advertising rate: Open inch rate $16.75
Established: 1843
Group: Boone Newspapers, Inc.
Shelby County Newspapers, Inc
Adv. Mgr.................................... Matthew Allen
Ed... Tim Prince
News Ed....................................... Jan Grissey
Mechanical Specifications: Type page 11 5/8 x 21 1/2; E - 6 cols, 1 13/16, 1 between; A - 6 cols, 1 13/16, 1 between; C - 10 cols, 1 1/2, between.Equipment & Software: Hardware — APP/Mac, APP/Mac Laser Printer, APP/Mac Scanner; Presses — KP; Software — QPS/QuarkXPress, Adobe/Photoshop, Baseview.

CULLMAN

THE CULLMAN TRIBUNE (THUR)
219 2nd Ave SE, Cullman, AL, 35055-3513, Cullman, USA; gen tel (256) 739-1351; gen fax (256) 739-4422; disp adv e-mail news@culltrib.com; class adv e-mail news@culltrib.com; ed e-mail news@culltrib.com; web site cullmansense.com
Circulation: 13,400pd,; Sworn/Estimate/Non-Audited
Advertising rate: Open inch rate $8.00
Ed... Delton Blalock
Mechanical Specifications: Type page 13 x 21; E - 6 cols, 2 1/16, between; A - 6 cols, 2 1/16, between.

DECATUR

REDSTON ROCKET (WED)
201 1st Ave SE, Decatur, AL, 35601-2333, Morgan, USA; gen tel (256) 340-2463; adv tel (256) 260-2218; gen fax (256) 260-2211; web site www.theredstonerocket.com
Group: Tennessee Valley Media Co., Inc.
Ed.. Skip Vaughn
Gen. Mgr.................................... French Salter
Adv. Rep..................................... Donna Counts
Copy Ed.. Kelly Lane
Ed.-in-Chief....................................... Bill Marks

DEMOPOLIS

BLACKBELT GAZETTE (WED)
115 E Washington St, Demopolis, AL, 36732-2101, Marengo, USA; gen tel (334) 289-2013 ; gen fax (334) 289-4019; disp adv e-mail jeanne.glass@demopolistimes.com; class adv e-mail clara.gary@demopolistimes.com; web site demopolistimes.com/category/blackbelt-gazette
Group: Boone Newspapers, Inc.
Pub. Ed............................ Robert Bankenship
Adv. and Mktg. Rep.................... Jeanne Glass
Sports Ed. & Staff Writer........... Nicholas Finch

DEMOPOLIS TIMES (WED, SAT)
315 E Jefferson St, Demopolis, AL, 36732-2255, Marengo, USA; gen tel (334) 289-4017; adv tel (334) 289-4017; ed tel (334) 289-4017; gen fax (334) 289-4019; adv fax (334) 289-4019; ed fax (334) 289-4019; disp adv e-mail hannah.riley@demopolistimes.com; class adv e-mail hannah.riley@demopolistimes.com; ed e-mail news@demopolistimes.com; web site www.demopolistimes.com
Circulation: 2,850pd,; Sworn/Estimate/Non-Audited
Advertising rate: Open inch rate $8.01
Established: 1887
Group: Boone Newspapers, Inc.
Pub.. Jason Cannon
Gen. Mgr................................... Bernice Smith
Sports Ed.................................. Jeremy Smith
Mechanical Specifications: Type page 13 1/3 x 21 1/2; E - 6 cols, 1/6 between; A - 6 cols, 1/6 between; C - 10 cols, between.
Delivery Method: Mail
Areas Served: Central Alabama

DOTHAN

DOTHAN PROGRESS (THUR)

227 N Oates St, Dothan, AL, 36303-4555, Houston, USA; gen tel (334) 792-3141; adv tel (334) 702-2600; ed tel (334) 792-3141; gen fax (334) 702-6043; adv fax (334) 712-7975; ed fax (334) 712-7979; disp adv e-mail advertising@dothaneagle.com; class adv e-mail classifieds@dothaneagle.com; ed e-mail news@dothaneagle.com; web site www.dothaneagle.com
Circulation: 25,000pd,; Sworn/Estimate/Non-Audited
Advertising rate: Open inch rate $11.50
Group: BH Media Group
Pub. .... James Whittum
Regl. Sales Mgr. .... Jerry Morgan
Ed. .... Elaine Brackin
Prodn. Mgr. .... Kelly Bexley
Adv. Rep. .... Misty Webb
Mechanical Specifications: Type page 13 1/2 x 21 1/2; E - 6 cols, 2 1/16, between; A - 6 cols, 2 1/16, between; C - 6 cols, 2 1/6, between.Equipment & Software: Hardware — APP/Power Mac; Presses — G/Urbanite; Software — QPS/QuarkXPress 3.31, Adobe/Multi-Ad Creator.
Areas Served: 36302

ELBA

THE ELBA CLIPPER (THUR)

417 Buford St, Elba, AL, 36323-1753, Coffee, USA; gen tel (334) 897-2823; gen fax (334) 897-3434; disp adv e-mail clipper@alaweb.com; ed e-mail clipperace@alaweb.com; web site www.elba-clipper.com
Circulation: 2,650pd,; Sworn/Estimate/Non-Audited
Advertising rate: Open inch rate $5.50
Established: 1897
Group: HF Enterprises, Inc.
Digital Platform - Mobile: Apple
Digital Platform - Tablet: Apple iOS
Pub. .... John Ferrin Cox
Ed. .... Linda Hodge
Mechanical Specifications: 21.5 X 10 wide - 6 column format
Delivery Method: Mail, Racks
Areas Served: Coffee County

EUFAULA

EUFAULA TRIBUNE (WED, SUN)

514 E Barbour St, Eufaula, AL, 36027-1704, Barbour, USA; gen tel (334) 687-3506; gen fax (334) 687-3229; disp adv e-mail dshelley@alsmg.com; class adv e-mail dshelley@alsmg.com; ed e-mail editor@eufaulatribune.com; web site www.eufaulatribune.com
Circulation: 3,500pd,; Sworn/Estimate/Non-Audited
Advertising rate: Open inch rate $7.50
Established: 1929
Group: BH Media Group
World Media Enterprises Inc.
Digital Platform - Mobile: Apple, Android, Blackberry
Adv. Sales Rep. .... Dennis Shelley
Gen. Mgr. .... Kyle Mooty
Mechanical Specifications: Full Page 9.88 x 19.75
Delivery Method: Mail, Racks
Areas Served: Barbour County Alabama
Quitman County Georgia

EUTAW

GREENE COUNTY INDEPENDENT (WED)

106 Main St, Eutaw, AL, 35462-1104, Greene, USA; gen tel (205) 372-2232; gen fax (205) 372-2232; disp adv e-mail greenecoind@aol.com; web site www.facebook.com/Greene-County-Independent-Inc-233365326677345/
Circulation: 1,500pd, 19fr; Sworn/Estimate/Non-Audited
Advertising rate: Open inch rate $5.75
Established: 1986
Ed. .... Betty C. Banks
Special Reporter .... J. William McFarland
Delivery Method: Mail, Newsstand, Racks
Areas Served: 35462

EVERGREEN

EVERGREEN COURANT (THUR)

114 Rural St, Evergreen, AL, 36401-2834, Conecuh, USA; gen tel (251) 578-1492; gen fax (251) 578-1496; disp adv e-mail courantpublisher@earthlink.net; class adv e-mail evergreencourant@earthlink.net; ed e-mail courantpublisher@earthlink.net
Circulation: 3,460pd, 185fr; Sworn/Estimate/Non-Audited
Advertising rate: Open inch rate $4.50
Established: 1895
Ed. / Pub. / Adv. Mgr. .... Robert Bozeman
Mechanical Specifications: Type page 13 x 21 1/2; E - 6 cols, 2 1/16, 1/8 between; A - 6 cols, 2 1/16, 1/8 between; C - 6 cols, 2 1/16, 1/8 between.

FAIRHOPE

THE FAIRHOPE COURIER (WED, FRI)

420 Fairhope Ave, Fairhope, AL, 36532-2110, Baldwin, USA; gen tel (251) 928-2321; adv tel (251) 928-2321; ed tel (251) 928-2321; gen fax (251) 928-9963; adv fax (251) 928-9963; ed fax (251) 928-9963; disp adv e-mail pjohnson@gulfcoastnewspapers.com; ed e-mail courier@gulfcoastnewspapers.com; web site www.thefairhopecourier.com
Circulation: 1,752pd,; Sworn/Estimate/Non-Audited
Advertising rate: Open inch rate $10.00
Established: 1894
Group: Gulf Coast Newspapers
Adv. Mgr. .... Pat Johnson
Ed. .... Mike Odom
Pub. .... Jessie Patterson
Mechanical Specifications: Type page 13 x 21 1/2; E - 6 cols, 1 7/8, 1/8 between; A - 6 cols, 1 7/8, 1/6 between; C - 9 cols, 1 1/4, between.Equipment & Software: Hardware — APP/Macs; Presses — 9-G/Community; Software — QPS/QuarkXPress, Adobe/Photoshop.
Areas Served: 36526, 36532, 36533, 36559, 36564

FAYETTE

THE TIMES-RECORD (WED)

106 1st St SE, Fayette, AL, 35555-2702, Fayette, USA; gen tel (205) 932-6271; gen fax (205) 932-6998; disp adv e-mail tradvertising@centurytel.net; ed e-mail trnews@centurytel.net; web site www.mytrpaper.com
Circulation: 5,000pd,; Sworn/Estimate/Non-Audited
Advertising rate: Open inch rate $10.35
Established: 1977
Pub. .... Horace Moore
Adv. Mgr. .... Gina Lynn
Gen. Mgr. .... Jerrie Elliott
Ed. .... Crystal Foster
Mng. Ed. .... Michael Palmer
Delivery Method: Mail, Carrier, Racks
Areas Served: Fayette County

FLOMATON

THE TRI-CITY LEDGER (THUR)

20766 Hwy 31, Flomaton, AL, 36441, Escambia, USA; gen tel (251) 296-3491; gen fax (251) 296-0010; disp adv e-mail newsroom@tricityledger.com; web site No Website
Circulation: 5,300pd,; Sworn/Estimate/Non-Audited
Advertising rate: Open inch rate $5.25
Ed. .... Joe Thomas

FLORALA

THE FLORALA NEWS (WED)

1155 5th St, Florala, AL, 36442-3243, Covington, USA; gen tel (334) 858-3342; gen fax (334) 858-3786; disp adv e-mail floralanews@fairpoint.net; class adv e-mail windham@gtcom.net; web site No Website
Circulation: 1,700pd,; Sworn/Estimate/Non-Audited
Advertising rate: Open inch rate $4.50
Established: 1900
Adv. Mgr. .... Lisa Windham
Pub. .... Gary Woodham
Mechanical Specifications: 10" x 21"
Delivery Method: Mail, Racks
Areas Served: 36442

FLORENCE

COURIER JOURNAL (WED)

219 W Tennessee St, Florence, AL, 35630-5440, Lauderdale, USA; gen tel (256) 764-4268; adv tel (256) 740-4701; ed tel (256) 740-4701; gen fax (256) 760-9618; adv fax (256) 760-9618; ed fax (256) 760-9618; disp adv e-mail advertising@courierjournal.net; class adv e-mail classified@courierjournal.net; ed e-mail editor@courierjournal.net; web site www.courierjournal.net
Circulation: 22pd, 75,509fr; VAC
Advertising rate: Open inch rate $19.50
Established: 1884
Group: Tennessee Valley Media Co., Inc.
Digital Platform - Mobile: Apple, Android, Windows, Blackberry
Digital Platform - Tablet: Apple iOS, Android, Windows 7, Blackberry Tablet OS, Kindle, Nook, Kindle Fire
Pub./Ed. .... Thomas V. Magazzu
Adv. Mgr. .... Sadonna B. Magazzu
Circ. Mgr. .... Jane Brasfield
Mechanical Specifications: Type page 13 x 21 1/2; E - 6 cols, 1 7/8, 1/8 between; A - 6 cols, 1 7/8, 1/6 between; C - 9 cols, 1 1/4, between.Equipment & Software: Hardware — APP/Macs; Presses — 9-G/Community; Software — QPS/QuarkXPress, Adobe/Photoshop.
Delivery Method: Mail
Areas Served: Lauderdale County

FOLEY

THE BALDWIN TIMES INDEPENDENT (THUR)

901 N McKenzie St, Foley, AL, 36535-3546, Baldwin, USA; gen tel (251) 928-2321; adv tel (251) 928-2321; gen fax (251) 928-9963; adv fax (251) 928-9963; disp adv e-mail bcuddy@gulfcoastnewspapers.com; ed e-mail timeseditor@gulfcoastnewspapers.com; web site www.gulfcoastnewstoday.com/baldwin-times/
Circulation: 3,200pd, 4,500fr; Sworn/Estimate/Non-Audited
Advertising rate: Open inch rate $6.30
Established: 1890
Group: Gulf Coast Newspapers
Pub. .... Sudie Gambrell
Prod. Dir. .... Ken Hilton
News Ed. .... Cathy Higgins
Adv. Mgr. .... Bruce Cuddy
Mechanical Specifications: Type page 13 x 21 1/2; E - 6 cols, 2 1/16, 1/8 between; A - 6 cols, 2 1/16, 1/8 between; C - 9 cols, between.Equipment & Software: Hardware — APP/Mac; Presses — 9-G/Community; Software — QPS/QuarkXPress.
Areas Served: Baldwin

THE ISLANDER (WED, FRI)

901 N McKenzie St, Foley, AL, 36535-3546, Baldwin, USA; gen tel (251) 968-6414; adv tel (251) 943-2151; ed tel (251) 968-6414; gen fax (251) 943-3441; adv fax (251) 943-3441; ed fax (251) 943-3441; disp adv e-mail hclarke@gulfcoastnewspapers.com; ed e-mail theislander@gulfcoastnewspapers.com; web site www.gulfcoastnewstoday.com/the-islander
Circulation: 1,737pd,; Sworn/Estimate/Non-Audited
Advertising rate: Open inch rate $7.35
Established: 1977
Group: Gulf Coast Newspapers
Pub. .... Sudie Gambrell
Ed. .... John Mullen
Adv. Mgr. .... Harry Clarke
Areas Served: 36547, 36542, 36561; Gulf Shores, Orange Beach, Fort Morgan

THE ONLOOKER (WED, SAT)

901 N McKenzie St, Foley, AL, 36535-3546, Baldwin, USA; gen tel (251) 943-2151; adv tel (251) 943-2151; ed tel (251) 943-2151; gen fax (251) 943-3441; adv fax (251) 943-3441; ed fax (251) 943-3441; disp adv e-mail jbouzan@gulfcoastnewspapers.com; ed e-mail onlooker@gulfcoastnewspapers.com; web site www.gulfcoastnewstoday.com/the-onlooker
Circulation: 4,600pd,; Sworn/Estimate/Non-Audited
Advertising rate: Open inch rate $7.35
Established: 1907
Group: Gulf Coast Newspapers
Pub. .... Jim Walther
Ed. .... Cathy Higgins
Adv. Consultant .... Jeniece Bouzan
Mechanical Specifications: Type page 13 x 21 1/2; E - 6 cols, 2 1/16, between; A - 6 cols, 2 1/16, between; C - 6 cols, 2 1/16, between.

FORT DEPOSIT

LOWNDES SIGNAL (THUR)

118 Ellis Street, Fort Deposit, AL, 36032, Lowndes, USA; gen tel (334) 382-3111; gen fax (334) 382-7104; disp adv e-mail tracy.salter@greenvilleadvocate.com/; class adv e-mail tracy.branum@greenvilleadvocate.com; ed e-mail andy.brown@greenvilleadvocate.com; web site www.lowndessignal.com
Circulation: 1,900pd,; Sworn/Estimate/Non-Audited
Advertising rate: Open inch rate $4.50
Group: Boone Newspapers, Inc.
Office Mgr. .... Lea Fennell
Adv. Mgr. .... Tracy Salter
Managing Ed. .... Andy Brown

GADSDEN

GADSDEN MESSENGER (FRI)

408 Broad St, Gadsden, AL, 35901-3718, Etowah, USA; gen tel (256) 547-1049; gen fax (256) 547-1011; disp adv e-mail cmccarthy@gadsdenmessenger.com; ed e-mail info@gadsdenmessenger.com; web site www.gadsdenmessenger.com
Circulation: 8,000pd,; Sworn/Estimate/Non-Audited
Advertising rate: Open inch rate $8.65
Adv. Dir. .... Art Segers
Ed. .... Keith Reason
Areas Served: Gadsden, Attalla, Rainbow City, Southside, Glencoe, Hokes Bluff

GARDENDALE

NORTH JEFFERSON NEWS (WED)

1110 Main St., Gardendale, AL, 35071, Jefferson, USA; gen tel (205) 631-8716; adv tel (205) 631-8716; ed tel (205) 631-8716; gen fax (205) 631-9902; disp adv e-mail sadams@njeffersonnews.com; ed e-mail editor@njeffersonnews.com; web site www.njeffersonnews.com
Circulation: 2,310pd,; Sworn/Estimate/Non-Audited

Advertising rate: Open inch rate $8.45
Established: 1970
Group: Community Newspaper Holdings, Inc.
Pub. .... Bill Morgan
Circ. Mgr. .... Sam Mazzara
Gen. Mgr. .... Danielle Cater
Ed. .... Melanie Patterson
Sales .... Stephen Adams
Ed. .... Rachel Davis
Delivery Method: Mail, Racks
Areas Served: 35071, 35068, 35180, 35172, 35117, 35116, 35091, 35097

GENEVA

GENEVA COUNTY REAPER (WED)

506 S Commerce St, Geneva, AL, 36340-2421, Geneva, USA; gen tel (334) 684-2280; gen fax (334) 684-3099; disp adv e-mail ads@genevareaper.com; ed e-mail news@genevareaper.com; web site www.oppnewsonline.com
Circulation: 2,500pd,; Sworn/Estimate/Non-Audited
Advertising rate: Open inch rate $5.00
Established: 1899
Pub. .... Brenda Pujol
Ed. .... Jay Felsberg
Mechanical Specifications: Type page 13 x 21 1/2; E - 6 cols, 2, 1/8 between; A - 6 cols, 2, 1/8 between; C - 6 cols, 2, 1/8 between. Equipment & Software: Hardware — APP/Mac SE, APP/Mac Performa, PCs; Presses — G/Community; Software — Adobe/PageMaker 5.0.
Delivery Method: Racks
Areas Served: Geneva County

HARTFORD NEWS-HERALD (WED)

506 S Commerce St, Geneva, AL, 36340-2421, Geneva, USA; gen tel (334) 684-2280; gen fax (334) 684-3099; disp adv e-mail ads@genevareaper.com; ed e-mail news@genevareaper.com; web site www.oppnewsonline.com
Circulation: 2,500pd,; Sworn/Estimate/Non-Audited
Advertising rate: Open inch rate $5.00
Pub. .... Brenda Pujol
Ed. .... Jay Felsberg
Delivery Method: Mail, Racks
Areas Served: artford, Slocomb, Malvern and the surrounding communities of eastern Geneva County

SAMSON LEDGER (WED)

506 S Commerce St, Geneva, AL, 36340-2421, Geneva, USA; gen tel (334) 684-2280; gen fax (334) 684-3099; disp adv e-mail ads@genevareaper.com; ed e-mail news@genevareaper.com; web site www.oppnewsonline.com
Advertising rate: Open inch rate $5.00
Pub. .... Brenda Pujol
Ed. .... Jay Felsberg
Delivery Method: Racks

GILBERTOWN

CHOCTAW SUN-ADVOCATE (WED)

PO Box 269, 13440 Choctaw Ave, Gilbertown, AL, 36908-0269, Choctaw, USA; gen tel (251) 843-6397; gen fax (251) 843-3233; disp adv e-mail choctawsun@millry.net; web site www.choctawsun.com - 55,000(views) 18,500(visitors)
Circulation: 4,800pd,; Sworn/Estimate/Non-Audited
Advertising rate: Open inch rate $9.00
Established: 1890
Publisher/Advertising Manager .... Tommy Campbell
Editor .... Dee Ann Campbell
Delivery Method: Mail, Newsstand, Racks
Areas Served: 36904-36925, 39301, 39367, 36558

GREENSBORO

GREENSBORO WATCHMAN (THUR)

1005 Market St, Greensboro, AL, 36744-1509, Hale, USA; gen tel (334) 624-8323; gen fax (334) 624-8327; disp adv e-mail gwatchman@bellsouth.net; class adv e-mail gwatchman@bellsouth.net; ed e-mail gwatchman@bellsouth.net; web site https://www.facebook.com/pages/The-Greensboro-Watchman/114189515350998
Circulation: 2,700pd, 95fr; Sworn/Estimate/Non-Audited
Advertising rate: Open inch rate $6.30
Established: 1876
Ed. .... Willie Jean Lowry Arrington
Pub. .... Becky Johnson
Adv. Dir. .... Waymon Johnson
John Clark
Mechanical Specifications: Type page 13 x 22 1/2; E - 3 cols, 4 1/4, 1/8 between; A - 6 cols, 2, 1/8 between; C - 6 cols, 2, 1/8 between. Equipment & Software: Hardware — APP/Macs; Presses — 3-KP/News King.
Areas Served: Hale County

GREENVILLE

BUTLER COUNTY NEWS (THUR)

103 Hickory St, Greenville, AL, 36037-2609, Butler, USA; gen tel (334) 382-3111; gen fax (334) 382-7104; ed e-mail editor@greenvilleadvocate.com; web site www.greenvilleadvocate.com
Circulation: 900pd, 28fr; Sworn/Estimate/Non-Audited
Advertising rate: Open inch rate $5.50
Group: Boone Newspapers, Inc.
Pub. .... Ashley Vansant
Ed. .... Kevin Pearcey

THE GREENVILLE ADVOCATE (WED, SAT)

103 Hickory St, Greenville, AL, 36037-2609, Butler, USA; gen tel (334) 382-3111; gen fax (334) 382-7104; disp adv e-mail news@theclintonjournal.com; web site www.greenvilleadvocate.com
Circulation: 3,000pd, 9,700fr; Sworn/Estimate/Non-Audited
Advertising rate: Open inch rate $12.45
Established: 1865
Group: Civitas Media, LLC-OOB
Ohio Newspaper Services, Inc.
Boone Newspapers, Inc.
Pub. .... Tracy Salter
Mng. Ed. .... Jonathan Bryant
Mktg. Coord. .... April Gregory
Mktg. Consult. .... Courtney Neese
Luverne Journal Ed. .... Beth Hyatt
Bus. and Circ. .... Tammy Edwards

GROVE HILL

CLARKE COUNTY DEMOCRAT (THUR)

261 N Jackson St, Grove Hill, AL, 36451-3073, Clarke, USA; gen tel (251) 275-3375; gen fax (251) 275-3060; disp adv e-mail jimcox@tds.net; ed e-mail jimcox@tds.net; web site www.clarkecountydemocrat.com
Circulation: 3,700pd,; Sworn/Estimate/Non-Audited
Advertising rate: Open inch rate $7.50
Established: 1856
Ed. .... James A. Cox
Pub. .... Jim Cox
Mechanical Specifications: Type page 10 inches x 21
6 cols. per pageEquipment & Software: Hardware — APP/Mac; Presses — KP/News King; Software — QPS/QuarkXPress.
Delivery Method: Mail, Racks
Areas Served: Clarke County

GUNTERSVILLE

THE ADVERTISER-GLEAM (WED, SAT)

2218 Taylor St, Guntersville, AL, 35976-1126, Marshall, USA; gen tel (256) 582-3232; gen fax (256) 582-3231; disp adv e-mail ads@advertisergleam.com; class adv e-mail ads@advertisergleam.com; ed e-mail news@advertisergleam.com; web site www.advertisergleam.com
Circulation: 8,140pd,; Sworn/Estimate/Non-Audited
Advertising rate: Open inch rate $8.30
Group: Tennessee Valley Printing
Circ. Mgr. .... Taunya Buchanan
Editor .... Anthony Campbell
Reporter .... Joe Cagle
Reporter .... Cindy McGregor
Gen. Mgr .... Kim Fitch
Advert. Sales .... Christy Graves
Advert. Sales .... Stephanie Lemke
Mechanical Specifications: Type page 13 x 21 1/2; E - 6 cols, 2 1/16, 1/8 between; A - 6 cols, 2 1/16, 1/8 between; C - 6 cols, 2 1/16, 1/8 between.
Delivery Method: Mail, Newsstand, Racks
Areas Served: Marshall County

HALEYVILLE

JOURNAL RECORD (WED, SAT)

PO Box 430, Haleyville, AL, 35565-0430, Marion, USA; gen tel (205) 921-3104; gen fax (205) 921-3105; disp adv e-mail jrads@centurytel.net; ed e-mail jrpaper@centurytel.net; web site www.myjrpaper.com
Circulation: 8,500pd, 79fr; Sworn/Estimate/Non-Audited
Advertising rate: Open inch rate $5.90
Pub. .... Horace Moore
Adv. Mgr. .... Kristi White
Circ. Mgr. .... Tammy Hall
Ed. .... Tracy Estes
Mgn. Ed. .... Les Walters
Mechanical Specifications: Type page 13 1/8 x 21 1/2; E - 6 cols, 1 1/16, 1/8 between; A - 6 cols, 2 1/16, 1/8 between; C - 6 cols, 2 1/16, 1/8 between.Equipment & Software: Hardware — APP/Mac; Presses — WCD/Atlas; Software — QPS/QuarkXPress.

NORTHWEST ALABAMIAN (WED, SAT)

1530 21st St, Haleyville, AL, 35565-2099, Winston, USA; gen tel (205) 486-9461; gen fax (205) 486-4849; disp adv e-mail nwaads@centurytel.net; class adv e-mail nwamoore@centurytel.net; ed e-mail nwanews@centurytel.net; web site mynwapaper.com
Circulation: 7,500pd, 78fr; Sworn/Estimate/Non-Audited
Advertising rate: Open inch rate $6.00
Established: 1915
Gen. Mgr. .... Mike Moore
Adv. Mgr. .... Roger Carden
Editor/Publisher .... Horace Moore
Mng. Ed. .... Shelly Hess
Prodn. Mgr. .... Phillip Brooks
Mechanical Specifications: Type page 13 1/4 x 21 1/4; E - 6 cols, 2 1/16, 1/8 between; A - 6 cols, 2 1/16, 1/8 between; C - 6 cols, 2 1/16, 1/8 between.Equipment & Software: Hardware — APP/Mac; Presses — 2-WPC/Atlas; Software — QPS/QuarkXPress.
Delivery Method: Mail, Racks
Areas Served: All of Winston County, Alabama. Portions of Marion, Franklin, Walker and Cullman counties in Alabama

HARTSELLE

HARTSELLE ENQUIRER (THUR)

407 Chesthut St NW, Hartselle, AL, 35640-2407, Morgan, USA; gen tel (256) 773-6566; gen fax (256) 773-1953; disp adv e-mail randy.garrison@hartselleenquirer.com; class adv e-mail classifieds@hartselleenquirer.com; ed e-mail news@hartselleenquirer.com; web site www.hartselleenquirer.com - 83,949(views) 19,300(visitors)
Circulation: 3,100pd, 3,500fr; Sworn/Estimate/Non-Audited
Advertising rate: Open inch rate $11.95
Established: 1933
Group: Boone Newspapers, Inc.
Digital Platform - Mobile: Apple, Android, Windows, Blackberry
Digital Platform - Tablet: Apple iOS, Android, Windows 7, Blackberry Tablet OS, Kindle, Nook, Kindle Fire
Pub. .... Randy Cox
Delivery Method: Mail, Newsstand, Racks
Areas Served: 35640, 35619, 35622, 35670, 35601, 35603

HEFLIN

THE CLEBURNE NEWS (MON, THUR)

926 Ross St, Heflin, AL, 36264-1134, Cleburne, USA; gen tel (256) 463-2872; gen fax (256) 463-7127; disp adv e-mail mpointer@cleburnenews.com; ed e-mail news@cleburnenews.com; web site www.annistonstar.com/cleburne_news
Circulation: 3,000pd,; Sworn/Estimate/Non-Audited
Advertising rate: Open inch rate $10.92
Established: 1906
Group: Consolidated Publishing Co.
Pub. .... John Alred
Ed. .... Laura Camper
Adv. Mgr. .... Misty Pointer

HUNTSVILLE

THE HUNTSVILLE TIMES (WED, FRI, SUN)

200 Westside Sq, Ste 100, Huntsville, AL, 35801-4894, Madison, USA; gen tel (256) 532-4000; adv tel (256) 532-4250; ed tel (256) 532-4400; gen fax (256) 532-4420; adv fax (256) 532-4183; ed fax (256) 532-4420; disp adv e-mail sheila.runnels@htimes.com; class adv e-mail bill.joyner@htimes.com; ed e-mail htimes@htimes.com; web site www.al.com/huntsville
Circulation: 36,709pd,; AAM
Advertising rate: Open inch rate $80.73; $106.34 (Sun)
Group: Advance Publications, Inc.
Mktg. Mgr. .... Carol Casey
City Desk Ed. .... Shelly Haskins
Pub .... Tom Bates
Pres./Pub. .... Robert D. Ludwig
Adv. Mgr., Retail .... Steve Wilson
Asst. Controller .... Anita McCain
Controller .... Robert Carothers
Adv. Mgr., Classified .... Sheila Runnels
Adv. Mgr., Major Accts. .... Joe Bagwell
Circ. Dir. .... Frank Maier
Design Ed. .... Doug Mendenhall
Editorial Page Ed. .... John Ehinger
Entertainment/Leisure Ed. .... Deborah Storey
Health Ed. .... Kenneth Kesner
Asst. News Ed. .... Stephen Lomax
Outdoors Ed. .... Alan Clemons
Chief Photographer .... Mike Mercier
Regl. Ed. .... Mike Hollis
Religion Ed. .... Yvonne Betowt
News Ed. .... Joe Duncan
Mechanical Specifications: Type page 12 x 21; E - 6 cols, 2, 3/16 between; A - 6 cols, 2, 3/16 between; C - 10 cols, 1 1/4, 1/6 between.

JACKSON

THE SOUTH ALABAMIAN (THUR)

1525 College Ave, Jackson, AL, 36545-2418, Clarke, USA; gen tel (251) 246-4494; gen fax (251) 246-7486; disp adv e-mail Ads@thesouthalabamian.com; ed e-mail News@thesouthalabamian.com; web site www.southalabamian.com
Circulation: 4,200pd, 58fr; USPS
Advertising rate: Open inch rate $6.60
Ed. .... Evan Carden

Pub. .... Jerry Turner
Adv. Mgr. .... Travis Matthews
Mechanical Specifications: Type page 13 x 21; E - 6 cols, 2, 3/8 between; A - 6 cols, 2, 3/8 between; C - 6 cols, 2, 3/8 between.Equipment & Software: Hardware — APP/Mac; Software — QPS/QuarkXPress.

JASPER

THE CORRIDOR MESSENGER (WED)

1903 3rd Ave S, Jasper, AL, 35501-5315, Walker, USA; gen tel (205) 282-4569; adv tel (2; gen fax (205) 572-4621; disp adv e-mail ken@corridormessenger.com; class adv e-mail nicole@corridormessenger.com; ed e-mail tanya@corridormessenger.com; web site www.corridormessenger.com
Circulation: 2,546pd,; Sworn/Estimate/Non-Audited
Advertising rate: Open inch rate $6.20
Digital Platform - Mobile: Apple
Digital Platform - Tablet: Apple iOS
Pub./Ed. .... David Lazenby
Mng. Ed. .... Tanya Guin
Delivery Method: Mail, Newsstand
Areas Served: 35549

LAFAYETTE

LAFAYETTE SUN (WED)

116 S Lafayette St, Lafayette, AL, 36862-2044, Chambers, USA; gen tel (334) 864-8885; gen fax (334) 864-8310; disp adv e-mail advertising@thelafayettesun.com; class adv e-mail ledge@thelafayettesun.com; ed e-mail mhand@thelafayettesun.com; web site www.thelafayettesun.com
Circulation: 2,605pd, 33fr; Sworn/Estimate/Non-Audited
Advertising rate: Open inch rate $4.95
Established: 1880
Ed. / Pub. .... Michael D. Hand
Gen. Mgr. .... Lisa Edge
Adv. Mgr. .... Kendra Gilmore
Mechanical Specifications: Type page 13 x 21 1/2; E - 6 cols, 2, between; A - 6 cols, 2, between.Equipment & Software: Hardware — APP/Mac; Software — QPS/QuarkXPress 3.32.

LINEVILLE

CLAY TIMES-JOURNAL (THUR)

60132 Hwy 49, Lineville, AL, 36266, Clay, USA; gen tel (256) 396-5760; gen fax (256) 396-5760; disp adv e-mail timesjournal@centurytel.net; ed e-mail timesjournal@centurytel.net; web site www.theclaytimes-journal.com
Circulation: 3,800pd, 99fr; Sworn/Estimate/Non-Audited
Advertising rate: Open inch rate $7.00
Gen. Mgr. .... Linda D. McDonald
Ed. .... David Proctor
Mechanical Specifications: Type page 13 x 21 1/2; E - 6 cols, 2 1/16, 1/8 between; A - 6 cols, 2 1/16, 1/8 between; C - 6 cols, 2 1/16, 1/8 between.

LIVINGSTON

SUMTER COUNTY RECORD-JOURNAL (THUR)

210 S Washington St, Livingston, AL, 35470, Sumter, USA; gen tel (205) 652-6100; gen fax (205) 652-4466; disp adv e-mail scrjmedia@yahoo.com; web site www.recordjournal.net
Circulation: 5,200pd, 200fr; Sworn/Estimate/Non-Audited
Advertising rate: Open inch rate $6.44
Ed. .... Gena Doggett Robbins
Mng. Ed. .... Tommy McGraw
Assoc. Ed. .... Herman B. Ward
Mechanical Specifications: Type page 13 x 21 1/2; E - 6 cols, 2, 1/6 between; A - 6 cols, 2, 1/6 between; C - 6 cols, 2, 1/6 between. Equipment & Software: Hardware — APP/Macs; Software — QPS/QuarkXPress 3.2.

LUVERNE

THE LUVERNE JOURNAL (THUR)

506 S Forest Ave, Luverne, AL, 36049-1902, Crenshaw, USA; gen tel (334) 335-3541; adv tel (334) 382-3111; ed tel (334) 335-3541; gen fax (334) 335-4299; disp adv e-mail tracy.salter@greenvilleadvocate.com; class adv e-mail tracy.hadley@greenvilleadvocate.com; ed e-mail kendra.bolling@luvernejournal.com; web site www.luvernejournal.com
Circulation: 2,400pd,; Sworn/Estimate/Non-Audited
Advertising rate: Open inch rate $7.90
Established: 1890
Group: Boone Newspapers, Inc.
Pub. .... Tracy Salter
Regina Grayson
Ed. .... Beth Hyatt
Mechanical Specifications: Type page 13 1/2 x 23 1/3; E - 6 cols, 2 1/4, 1/4 between; A - 6 cols, 2 1/4, 1/4 between; C - 6 cols, 2 1/4, 1/4 between.Equipment & Software: Hardware — APP/Power Mac, APP/iMac; Software — QPS/QuarkXPress 4.0, Adobe/Photoshop 4.0, Microsoft/Word, Archetype/Corel Draw 8.
Areas Served: Crenshaw County

MADISON

THE MADISON RECORD (WED)

14 Main St, Ste C, Madison, AL, 35758-2084, Madison, USA; gen tel (256) 772-6677; gen fax (256) 772-6655; class adv e-mail classifieds@themadisonrecord.com; web site www.themadisonrecord.com
Group: Boone Newspapers, Inc.
Customer Service Rep. .... Tammy Overman
Pub. .... Randy Cox
Mktg. Consult. .... Ashley Davis
Class. Consult. .... Kari George

MARION

MARION TIMES-STANDARD (WED)

424 Washington St, Marion, AL, 36756-2334, Perry, USA; gen tel (334) 683-6318; adv tel (334) 683-6318; gen fax (334) 683-4616; ed e-mail mariontimesnews@qwestoffice.net; web site www.facebook.com/MarionTimes-Standard
Circulation: 2,000pd, 25fr; Sworn/Estimate/Non-Audited
Advertising rate: Open inch rate $5.75
Established: 1839
Group: Trib Publications
Pres. .... Robert E. Tribble
Pub. .... Lorrie Rinehart
Adv. Mgr. .... Kimberly Clements
Mechanical Specifications: Type page 13 x 21 1/2; E - 4 cols, 3, between; A - 6 cols, 2 1/16, between; C - 6 cols, 2 1/16, between.Equipment & Software: Hardware — APP/Mac; Software — Adobe/PageMaker 6.5.

MILLPORT

WEST ALABAMA GAZETTE (WED)

PO Box 249, Millport, AL, 35576-0249, Lamar, USA; gen tel (205) 759-3091; gen fax (205) 759-5449; disp adv e-mail gazettenews@frontiernet.net; web site www.facebook.com/pg/The-West-Alabama-Gazette-110067155713008
Circulation: 3,000pd, 500fr; Sworn/Estimate/Non-Audited
Advertising rate: Open inch rate $5.50
Established: 1967
Areas Served: Lamar, Fayette and Pickens Counties

MOBILE

PRESS-REGISTER (WED, FRI, SUN)

18 S ROYAL ST, Mobile, AL, 36602, Mobile, USA; gen tel (251) 219-5400; adv tel (251) 219-5545; ed tel (251) 219-5632; gen fax (251) 219-5799; adv fax (251) 219-5068; ed fax (251) 219-5799; disp adv e-mail adservices@press-register.com; class adv e-mail classnational@mobileregister.com; ed e-mail news@press-register.com; newsroom@mobileregister.com; web site www.al.com/mobile 3,902,000(visitors)
Circulation: 48,619pd,; AAM
Advertising rate: Open inch rate $111.97; $130.97 (Sun)
Group: Advance Publications, Inc.
Digital Platform - Mobile: Apple, Android, Blackberry
Digital Platform - Tablet: Apple iOS, Android
Controller/Treasurer .... Vicki Catlett
Dir., HR .... Lee Stringfellow
Adv. Mgr., Classified .... Britt Pickett
Adv. Mgr., Nat'l. .... Wanda Jacobs
Adv. Mgr., Retail .... Steve Hall
Dir., Mktg./Promo. .... Randy Granger
Circ. Dir. .... George Markevicz
Circ. Mgr., Home Delivery .... Wayne Carrier
Circ. Mgr., Opns. .... Bill Van Hook
Circ. Mgr., Single Copy .... Jim McKeel
Vice Pres., News/Ed. .... Michael Marshall
Mng. Ed. .... Dewey English
Bus./Finance Ed. .... K.A. Turner
Editorial Page Ed. .... Frances Coleman
Environmental Reporter .... Ben Raines
Farm/Agriculture Ed. .... Charles Croft
Features Ed. .... Debbie Lord
Graphics Ed. .... Thom Dudgeon
Growth/Environmental Ed. .... Bill Finch
Health/Medical Reporter .... Monique Curet
Mechanical Specifications: Type page 11 3/5 x 20 1/2; E - 6 cols, 1 4/5, 1/8 between; A - 6 cols, 1 4/5, 1/8 between; C - 10 cols, 1 9/32, 1/32 between.

MONROEVILLE

THE MONROE JOURNAL (THUR)

49 Hines St, Monroeville, AL, 36460-1833, Monroe, USA; gen tel (251) 575-3282; gen fax (251) 575-3284; disp adv e-mail advertising@monroejournal.com; ed e-mail news@monroejournal.com; web site www.monroejournal.com
Circulation: 7,800pd, 11,900fr; Sworn/Estimate/Non-Audited
Advertising rate: Open inch rate $9.42
Pub. .... Bo Bolton
Ed. .... Mike Qualls
Art Dir. .... Jodie Bolton
Adv. Mgr. .... Michael Lambeth
Areas Served: Monroe County and surrounding areas

MOULTON

THE MOULTON ADVERTISER (THUR)

659 Main St, Moulton, AL, 35650-1512, Lawrence, USA; gen tel (256) 974-1114; gen fax (256) 974-3097; disp adv e-mail teresa@moultonadvertiser.com; class adv e-mail classified@moultonadvertiser.com; ed e-mail editor@moultonadvertiser.com; web site www.moultonadvertiser.com
Circulation: 4,123pd, 9,550fr; Sworn/Estimate/Non-Audited
Advertising rate: Open inch rate $9.20
Established: 1828
Group: Tennessee Valley Media Co., Inc.
Adv. Mgr. .... Teresa Woodruff
Ad Rep. .... Misty Alexander
Staff Writer .... Jeff Edwards
Staff Writer .... J.R. Tidewell
Mechanical Specifications: Type page 10.25 x 21; E - 6 cols, between; A - 6 cols, between; C - 6 cols, between.Equipment & Software: Hardware — APP/Power Macs; Presses — 6-KP/Color King; Software — Indesign, Adobe/Photoshop.
Delivery Method: Mail, Newsstand, Carrier, Racks
Areas Served: 35650,35673,35651,35672,35619,35618,35643

MOUNDVILLE

MOUNDVILLE TIMES (WED)

46 2ND AVE, Moundville, AL, 35474, Hale, USA; gen tel (205) 371-2488; gen fax (205) 371-2788; ed fax (205) 371-9010; disp adv e-mail times@mound.net; web site moundvilletimes.net
Circulation: 1,300pd,; Sworn/Estimate/Non-Audited
Advertising rate: Open inch rate $6.00
Pub. .... Larry Taylor
Ed. .... Cindy Bolling

NORTHPORT

THE NORTHPORT GAZETTE (WED)

401 20th Ave, Ste 2, Northport, AL, 35476-5045, Tuscaloosa, USA; gen tel (205) 759-3091; gen fax (205) 759-5449; disp adv e-mail northportgazette@northportgazette.com; web site www.northportgazette.com
Circulation: 22,000pd,; Sworn/Estimate/Non-Audited
Advertising rate: Open inch rate $9.75
Established: 1998
Delivery Method: Mail, Newsstand, Racks
Areas Served: Northport, Coker, Elrod, Buhl, Echola and Fosters.

ONEONTA

THE BLOUNT COUNTIAN (WED)

217 3rd St S, Oneonta, AL, 35121-2189, Blount, USA; gen tel (205) 625-3231; gen fax (205) 625-3239; disp adv e-mail countian@otelco.net; web site www.blountcountian.com
Circulation: 6,900pd, 13,000fr; Sworn/Estimate/Non-Audited
Advertising rate: Open inch rate $7.00
Pub. .... Molly Howard Ryan
Owner/Ed. .... Rob Rice
Circ. Mgr. .... Jenna Wood
Advert. Dir. .... Kim Hipp
Mechanical Specifications: Type page 13 x 21 1/2; E - 4 cols, 3 1/8, 1/8 between; A - 6 cols, 2 1/16, 1/8 between; C - 6 cols, 2 1/16, 1/8 between.Equipment & Software: Hardware — 4-APP/Mac, 2-PC; Software — Adobe/Photoshop 2.5, QPS/QuarkXPress 3.2.

OPP

THE OPP NEWS (THUR)

200 W Covington Ave, Opp, AL, 36467-2046, Covington, USA; gen tel (334) 493-3595; gen fax (334) 493-4901; disp adv e-mail opppublisher@centurytel.net; ed e-mail oppnews@centurytel.net; web site www.oppnewsonline.com
Circulation: 5,300pd,; Sworn/Estimate/Non-Audited
Advertising rate: Open inch rate $7.10
Pub. .... Moe Pujol
Adv. Mgr. .... Wanda Sasser
Ed. .... Jay Thomas
Ed. .... Josh Richards

OZARK

THE OZARK SOUTHERN STAR (WED)

373 Ed Lisenby Dr, Ozark, AL, 36360-1473, Dale, USA; gen tel (334) 774-2715; gen fax (334) 774-9619; disp adv e-mail southstar@centurytel.net; web site www.thesouthern-

staronline.com
Circulation: 4,900pd,; Sworn/Estimate/Non-Audited
Advertising rate: Open inch rate $6.00
Adv. Mgr. .... Charlie Dawkins
Ed. .... Joseph H. Adams
Mechanical Specifications: Type page 13 x 21 1/2.

PELL CITY

ST. CLAIR NEWS-AEGIS (THUR)

1820 2nd Ave N, Pell City, AL, 35125-1616, Saint Clair, USA; gen tel (205) 884-2310; adv tel (205) 884-2310; ed tel (205) 884-2310; gen fax (205) 884-2312; disp adv e-mail ads@newsaegis.com; ed e-mail editor@newsaegis.com; web site www.newsaegis.com
Circulation: 5,500pd,; Sworn/Estimate/Non-Audited
Advertising rate: Open inch rate $8.05
Group: Community Newspaper Holdings, Inc.
Ed. .... Gordon Roberts
Pub. .... Terry Conner
Circ. Mgr. .... Sam Mazarra
Areas Served: St. Clair County

THE SAINT CLAIR TIMES (THUR)

1911 Martin St S, Ste 7, Pell City, AL, 35128-2372, Saint Clair, USA; gen tel (205) 884-3400; adv tel (205) 884-3400; ed tel (205) 884-3400; gen fax (205) 814-9194; disp adv e-mail dhalpin@dailyhome.com; ed e-mail wheath@thestclairtimes.com; web site www.annistonstar.com/the_st_clair_times
Circulation: 34,000pd, 34,000fr; Sworn/Estimate/Non-Audited
Advertising rate: Open inch rate $8.12
Established: 2000
Group: Consolidated Publishing Co.
Pub. .... Ed Fowler
Ed. .... Will Heath
Assoc. Ed. .... Gary Hanner
Adv. Sales .... Dale Halpin
Classifed Adv. Sales .... Polly T. Ramsey
Delivery Method: Mail, Carrier
Areas Served: St. Clair County, Trussville, Leeds

PHENIX CITY

THE CITIZEN OF EAST ALABAMA (THUR)

2401 Sportsman Dr, Phenix City, AL, 36867-5402, Russell, USA; gen tel (334) 664-0145; gen fax (334) 664-0154; ed e-mail ddubois@citizenea.com; web site www.citizenofeastalabama.com
Circulation: 13,500pd,; Sworn/Estimate/Non-Audited
Advertising rate: Open inch rate $9.00
Established: 1954
Executive Editor .... Denise DuBois
Mechanical Specifications: Type page 11 5/8 x 21; E - 6 cols, 1 2/3, between; A - 6 cols, 1 2/3, between; C - 6 cols, 1 2/3, between. Equipment & Software: ; Software — QPS/QuarkXPress 4.1, Adobe/Photoshop 4.0.
Delivery Method: Mail, Racks
Areas Served: Phenix City, Russell County, Lee County

PRATTVILLE

PRATTVILLE PROGRESS (SAT)

152 W 3rd St, Prattville, AL, 36067-3046, Autauga, USA; gen tel (334) 365-6739; gen fax (334) 365-1400; disp adv e-mail info@prattvilleprogress.com; web site www.montgomeryadvertiser.com/news/prattville
Circulation: 8,500pd, 88fr; Sworn/Estimate/Non-Audited
Advertising rate: Open inch rate $14.95
Group: Gannett
Pub. .... Scott Brown
Ed. .... Jess Nicholas

RED BAY

THE RED BAY NEWS (WED)

120 4th Ave SE, Red Bay, AL, 35582-4191, Franklin, USA; gen tel (256) 356-2148; gen fax (256) 356-2787; disp adv e-mail rbaynews@gmail.com; class adv e-mail rbaynews@gmail.com; ed e-mail rbaynews@gmail.com; web site www.trbnews.net
Circulation: 2,600pd, 0fr; Sworn/Estimate/Non-Audited
Advertising rate: Open inch rate $6.00
Established: 1963
Publisher Emeritus .... LaVale Mills
Advertising Manager .... Angel Gasaway
Managing Ed. .... Bridget Berry
Delivery Method: Mail, Newsstand, Racks
Areas Served: 35582,35593,38827,38847

ROANOKE

THE RANDOLPH LEADER (WED)

524 Main St, Roanoke, AL, 36274-1440, Randolph, USA; gen tel (334) 863-2819; gen fax (334) 863-4006; disp adv e-mail peggy@therandolphleader.com; ed e-mail vanessa@therandolphleader.com; web site www.therandolphleader.com
Circulation: 7,000pd,; Sworn/Estimate/Non-Audited
Advertising rate: Open inch rate $7.20
Established: 1892
Ed. / Pub. .... John W. Stevenson
Adv. Mgr. .... Peggy Seabolt
News Ed. .... Vanessa Sorrell Burnside
Mechanical Specifications: Type page 13 x 21 1/4; E - 6 cols, 2 1/20, between; A - 6 cols, 2 1/20, between; C - 6 cols, 2 1/20, between. Equipment & Software: Hardware — APP/Power Mac 7300s; Software — QPS/QuarkXPress, Adobe/Photoshop.
Delivery Method: Mail, Racks
Areas Served: Randolph County and surrounding areas

ROCKFORD

COOSA COUNTY NEWS (FRI)

10 Main St, Rockford, AL, 35136, Coosa, USA; gen tel (256) 377-2525; gen fax (256) 377-2422; ed e-mail editor@coosanews.com; web site www.facebook.com/coosacountynews
Circulation: 1,400pd, 300fr; Sworn/Estimate/Non-Audited
Advertising rate: Open inch rate $4.50
Owner .... Lewis Scarbrough
Pub. / Mgn. Ed. / Adv. mgr. .... Carlton Jones

ROGERSVILLE

EAST LAUDERDALE NEWS (THUR)

1617 Lee St, Rogersville, AL, 35652-7606, Lauderdale, USA; gen tel (256) 247-5565; gen fax (256) 247-1902; disp adv e-mail elnewsrog@aol.com; web site https://www.facebook.com/eastlauderdalenews
Circulation: 4,500pd,; Sworn/Estimate/Non-Audited
Advertising rate: Open inch rate $6.50
Co-Pub. .... Phyllis D. Cox
Ed. .... James B. Cox
Mechanical Specifications: Type page 17 x 21 1/2; E - 8 cols, 1 3/4, between; A - 8 cols, 1 3/4, between; C - 8 cols, 1 3/4, between.
Areas Served: Lauderdale County

RUSSELLVILLE

FRANKLIN COUNTY TIMES (WED)

14131 Highway 43, Russellville, AL, 35653-2847, Franklin, USA; gen tel (256) 332-1881; adv tel (256) 332-1881 ext. 19; ed tel (256) 332-1881 ext. 16; gen fax (256) 332-1883; disp adv e-mail nicole.pell@franklincountytimes.com; class adv e-mail nicole.pell@franklincountytimes.com; ed e-mail kellie.singleton@franklincountytimes.com; web site www.franklincountytimes.com
Circulation: 3,800pd,; Sworn/Estimate/Non-Audited
Advertising rate: Open inch rate $12.07
Established: 1879
Group: Boone Newspapers, Inc.
Ed. .... Kellie Singleton
Adv. Mgr. .... Peggy Hyde
General Manager .... Nicole Pell
Delivery Method: Mail, Racks
Areas Served: Franklin County

STEVENSON

NORTH JACKSON PROGRESS (MON, THUR)

128 Oak Hill Cir, Stevenson, AL, 35772-5411, Jackson, USA; gen tel (256) 437-2395; gen fax (256) 437-2592; disp adv e-mail njprogresslog@aol.com; web site No Website
Circulation: 6,000pd,; Sworn/Estimate/Non-Audited
Advertising rate: Open inch rate $6.90
Ed. / Pub. .... Larry O. Glass
News Ed. .... Faye Glass

SULLIGENT

LAMAR LEADER (WED)

55071 Highway 17, Sulligent, AL, 35586-3800, Lamar, USA; gen tel (205) 698-8148; gen fax (205) 698-8146; disp adv e-mail news@lamarleader.com; class adv e-mail news@lamarleader.com; ed e-mail news@lamarleader.com; web site www.facebook.com/lamar.leader
Circulation: 3,000pd,; Sworn/Estimate/Non-Audited
Advertising rate: Open inch rate $8.40
Established: 1973
Group: Lamar Publishing, Inc.
Digital Platform - Mobile: Apple, Android
Ed. .... Stephanie Minor
Publisher, News Editor .... Keith Bryson
Delivery Method: Mail, Racks
Areas Served: Lamar County, Alabama; plus news additional racks in Marion and Fayette Counties, Alabama

TALLASSEE

THE TALLASSEE TRIBUNE (WED)

301 Gilmer Ave, Tallassee, AL, 36078-1211, Tallapoosa, USA; gen tel (334) 283-6568; gen fax (334) 283-6569; disp adv e-mail jayne.carr@alexcityoutlook.com; class adv e-mail heather.glenn@alexcityoutlook.com; ed e-mail editor@tallasseetribune.com; web site www.tallasseetribune.com
Circulation: 4,200pd,; Sworn/Estimate/Non-Audited
Advertising rate: Open inch rate $4.25
Established: 1899
Group: Boone Newspapers, Inc.
Advertising Director .... Tippy Hunter
Reporter .... Carmen Rodgers
Managing Editor .... David Granger
Mechanical Specifications: Type page 13 x 21 1/2.
Delivery Method: Mail, Newsstand, Racks

THOMASVILLE

THE THOMASVILLE TIMES (TUES, THUR, SAT)

24 W. Front St., Thomasville, AL, 36784, Clarke, USA; gen tel (334) 636-2214; gen fax (334) 636-9822; disp adv e-mail aloflin@hpe.com; class adv e-mail terri@thethomasvilletimes.net; ed e-mail editor@tvilletimes.com; web site www.thethomasvilletimes.com
Circulation: 3,700pd,; Sworn/Estimate/Non-Audited
Advertising rate: Open inch rate $16.09
Established: 1921
Sales, Book Keeping .... Renee Campbell
Mechanical Specifications: Type page 13 x 21 1/2; E - 6 cols, 2, 1/6 between; A - 6 cols, 2, 1/6 between; C - 6 cols, 2, 1/6 between. Equipment & Software: Hardware — APP/Power Mac; Software — QPS/QuarkXPress.
Areas Served: Clarke, south Marengo and west Wilcox Counties

TUSCUMBIA

COLBERT COUNTY REPORTER (FRI)

106 W 5th St, Tuscumbia, AL, 35674-2412, Colbert, USA; gen tel (256) 383-8471; gen fax (256) 383-8476; disp adv e-mail colbertcountyreporter@earthlink.net; web site www.facebook.com/thecolbertcountyreporter
Circulation: 4,500pd,; Sworn/Estimate/Non-Audited
Advertising rate: Open inch rate $4.95
Adv. Mgr. .... Charlie Crawford
Ed. .... Jim Crawford
Mng. Ed. .... Estelle Crawford-Whitehead

STANDARD & TIMES (SAT)

106 W 5th St, Tuscumbia, AL, 35674-2412, Colbert, USA; gen tel (256) 383-8471; gen fax (256) 383-8476; disp adv e-mail estelle0601@yahoo.com; web site No website
Circulation: 1,000pd,; Sworn/Estimate/Non-Audited
Advertising rate: Open inch rate $6.95
Pub. .... Jim Crawford
Adv. Mgr. .... Charlie Crawford
Mng. Ed. .... Estelle Crawford-Whitehead
Mechanical Specifications: Type page 13 x 21; E - 6 cols, 2 1/16, 1/8 between; A - 6 cols, 2 1/16, 1/8 between.

TUSKEGEE

THE TUSKEGEE NEWS (THUR)

103 S Main St, Tuskegee, AL, 36083-1801, Macon, USA; gen tel (334) 727-3020; adv tel same; ed tel same; gen fax (334) 727-3020; adv fax (334) 727-3020; disp adv e-mail tuskegeenews@bellsouth.net; class adv e-mail tuskegeenews@bellsouth.net; ed e-mail tuskegeenews@bellsouth.net; web site www.thetuskegeenews.com
Circulation: 2,800pd,; Sworn/Estimate/Non-Audited
Advertising rate: Open inch rate $7.95
Established: 1865
Assistant to the Publisher .... Scott Richardson
Editor/Publisher .... Guy Rhodes
Mechanical Specifications: 1 Column 1.555"
2 Columns 3.222"
3 Columns 4.888"
4 Columns 6.555"
5 Columns 8.222"
6 Columns 9.888"
Depth 20"Equipment & Software: Hardware — APP/Mac G3; Presses — G/Community; Software — QPS/QuarkXPress, Adobe/Photoshop.
Delivery Method: Mail, Newsstand, Carrier, Racks
Areas Served: 36083, 36075, 36088, 36866, 36087

WETUMPKA

ECLECTIC OBSERVER (THUR)

300 Green St, Wetumpka, AL, 36092-2507, Elmore, USA; gen tel (334) 567-7811; gen fax (334) 567-3284; disp adv e-mail advertising@thewetumpkaherald.com; class adv e-mail shannon.elliott@wetumpkaherald.com; ed e-mail kim.price@thewetumpkaherald.com; web site thewetumpkaherald.com/theeclecticobserver
Circulation: 1,200pd, 100fr; Sworn/Estimate/

Non-Audited
Advertising rate: Open inch rate $9.75
Group: Boone Newspapers, Inc.
Pub.. Kim Price
Mng. Ed................................ Peggy Blackburn
Ed. ....David Goodwin
Classified Adv. Mgr...................Shannon Elliott
Areas Served: Elmore County

ALASKA

ANCHORAGE

THE ARCTIC SOUNDER (THUR)
500 W Intl Airport Rd, Ste F, Anchorage, AK, 99518-1175, Anchorage, USA; gen tel (907) 770-0820; adv tel (907) 770-0820; ed tel (907) 770-0820; gen fax (907) 770-0822; disp adv e-mail ads@reportalaska.com; class adv e-mail ads@reportalaska.com; ed e-mail crestino@reportalaska.com; web site www.thearcticsounder.com
Circulation: 2,000pd,; Sworn/Estimate/Non-Audited
Advertising rate: Open inch rate $26.00
Group: Alaska Media LLC
Pub... Jason Evans
News Ed. .... Carey Restino
Mechanical Specifications: Type page 10 3/16 x 15 1/2; E - 5 cols, 1 15/16, between; A - 5 cols, 1 15/16, between; C - 5 cols, 1 15/16, between.
Areas Served: Northwest Arctic

THE BRISTOL BAY TIMES (THUR)
500 W Intl Airport Rd, Ste F, Anchorage, AK, 99518-1175, Anchorage, USA; gen tel (907) 770-0820; adv tel (907) 770-0820; ed tel (907) 770-0820; gen fax (907) 770-0822; disp adv e-mail ads@reportalaska.com; class adv e-mail ads@reportalaska.com; ed e-mail crestino@reportalaska.com; web site www.thebristolbaytimes.com
Circulation: 2,000pd, 552fr; Sworn/Estimate/Non-Audited
Advertising rate: Open inch rate $26.00
Group: Alaska Media LLC
Pub... Jason Evans
News Ed. .... Carey Restino
Areas Served: Bristol Bay

THE DUTCH HARBOR FISHERMAN (THUR)
500 W Intl Airport Rd, Ste F, Anchorage, AK, 99518-1175, Anchorage, USA; gen tel (907) 770-0820; adv tel (907) 770-0820; ed tel (907) 770-0820; gen fax (907) 770-0822; disp adv e-mail ads@reportalaska.com; class adv e-mail ads@reportalaska.com; ed e-mail crestino@reportalaska.com; web site www.thedutchharborfisherman.com
Circulation: 2,000pd, 74fr; Sworn/Estimate/Non-Audited
Advertising rate: Open inch rate $26.00
Group: Alaska Media LLC
Pub... Jason Evans
News Ed. .... Carey Restino
Areas Served: Dutch Harbor, AK

CORDOVA

THE CORDOVA TIMES (THUR)
110 Nicholoff Way, Cordova, AK, 99574, Valdez Cordova, USA; gen tel (907) 424-7181; adv tel (907) 350-3993; ed tel (907) 424-7181; gen fax (907) 424-5799; adv fax (907) 222-7706; disp adv e-mail lnewton@thecordovatimes.com; class adv e-mail lnewton@thecordovatimes.com; ed e-mail editor@thecordovatimes.com; web site www.thecordovatimes.com
Circulation: 919pd, 50fr; Sworn/Estimate/Non-Audited
Advertising rate: Open inch rate $26.50
Established: 1906
Group: Alaska Newspapers, Inc. (OOB)
Pub./Pres. .... Margaret Nelson
Adv. Rep.................................. Mary Beth Carr
Mng. Ed.. Tony Hall
News Ed. ....Joy Landaluce
Adv. Mgr. .... Linda Newton
Delivery Method: Mail, Racks
Areas Served: Prince William Sound; Cordova, AK

EAGLE RIVER

ALASKA STAR (THUR)
11401 Old Glenn Hwy, Ste 105, Eagle River, AK, 99577-7747, Anchorage, USA; gen tel (907) 694-2727; gen fax (907) 694-1545; disp adv e-mail jada.nowling@morris.com; ed e-mail cinthia.ritchie@alaskastar.com; web site www.alaskastar.com
Circulation: 4,800pd,; Sworn/Estimate/Non-Audited
Advertising rate: Open inch rate $52.00
Ed. ....Cinthia Ritchie
Adv. Media Consultant................ Jada Nowling
Mechanical Specifications: Type page 11 1/4 x 17 1/2; E - 5 cols, 1 11/12, 1/6 between; A - 6 cols, 1 7/12, 1/6 between; C - 6 cols, 1 7/12, 1/6 between.Equipment & Software: Hardware — IBM/PC; Software — Adobe/PageMaker, WordPerfect 6.0.

HAINES

CHILKAT VALLEY NEWS (THUR)
PO Box 630, Haines, AK, 99827-0630, Haines, USA; gen tel (907) 766-2688; adv tel (907) 766-2688; disp adv e-mail cvn@chilkatvalleynews.com; class adv e-mail cvn@chilkatvalleynews.com; ed e-mail cvn@chilkatvalleynews.com; web site www.chilkatvalleynews.com
Circulation: 1,200pd, 11fr; Sworn/Estimate/Non-Audited
Advertising rate: Open inch rate $14.00
Established: 1966
Pub...Bonnie Hedrick
Mechanical Specifications: Type page 10 x 15; E - 5 cols, 1 5/6, 3/16 between; A - 5 cols, 1 5/6, 3/16 between; C - 5 cols, 1 5/6, 3/16 between.
Delivery Method: Mail, Carrier, Racks
Areas Served: 99827

HOMER

HOMER NEWS (THUR)
3482 Landings St, Homer, AK, 99603-7948, Kenai Peninsula, USA; gen tel (907) 235-7767; gen fax (907) 235-4199; ed e-mail news@homernews.com; web site www.homernews.com
Circulation:; Sworn/Estimate/Non-Audited
Established: 1964
Group: GateHouse Media, Inc.
Digital Platform - Mobile: Apple
Ed. ....Michael Armstrong
Reporter ....Megan Pacer
Delivery Method: Mail, Newsstand, Racks
Areas Served: Kenai Peninsula Borough

JUNEAU

CAPITAL CITY WEEKLY (WED)
3100 Channel Dr, Ste 1, Juneau, AK, 99801-7837, Juneau, USA; gen tel (907) 789-4144; gen fax (907) 789-0987; disp adv e-mail editor@capweek.com; ed e-mail editor@capweek.com; web site www.capitalcity-weekly.com
Circulation: 30,000fr; Sworn/Estimate/Non-Audited
Established: 1980
Adv. Mgr. .... Karen Wright
Classified Adv. Specialist..........Laura Newsom
Deedie McKenzie
Mechanical Specifications: Tabloid size.Equipment & Software: Hardware — APP/Mac; Presses — Web offset; Software — DOS, Adobe/PageMaker, Adobe/Photoshop.
Delivery Method: Mail, Racks
Areas Served: Juneau, Douglas, Ketchikan, Sitka, Wrangell, Skagway, Elfin Cove, Tenakee Springs, Metlakatla, Kake, Petersburg, Craig, Klawock, Pelican, Yakutat, Gustavus, Angoon, Hoonah, Whale Pass, Coffman Cove, Kaukati, Thorne Bay, Hydaburg, Hyder

NOME

THE NOME NUGGET (THUR)
304 Front St, Nome, AK, 99762, Nome, USA; gen tel (907) 443-5235; adv tel (907) 443-5235; ed tel (907) 443-5235; gen fax (907) 443-5112; adv fax (907) 443-5112; ed fax (907) 443-5112; disp adv e-mail ads@nomenugget.com; class adv e-mail ads@nomenugget.com; ed e-mail nugget@nomenugget.com; web site www.nomenugget.net
Circulation: 6,000pd,; Sworn/Estimate/Non-Audited
Advertising rate: Open inch rate $24.00
Established: 1897
Ed./Pub. .... Nancy L. McGuire
Adv. Mgr. .... Nadja Cavin
Mechanical Specifications: Type page 9 3/4 x 15 1/2; E - 5 cols, 1 3/4, 1/25 between; A - 5 cols, 1 3/4, 1/25 between; C - 5 cols, 1 3/4, between.Equipment & Software: Hardware — APP/Mac; Software — QPS/QuarkXPress 3.3, Adobe/Acrobat.
Delivery Method: Mail, Carrier
Areas Served: 997-995

PETERSBURG

PETERSBURG PILOT (THUR)
207 N Nordic Dr, Petersburg, AK, 99833, Petersburg, USA; gen tel (907) 772-9393; gen fax (907) 772-4871; disp adv e-mail pilotpub@gmail.com; class adv e-mail pilotpub@gmail.com; web site www.petersburgpilot.com
Circulation: 1,800pd, 34fr; Sworn/Estimate/Non-Audited
Advertising rate: Open inch rate $13.50
Established: 1974
Co-Owner/Pub. ....Anne Loesch
Co-Owner/Pub./Ed............... Ronald J. Loesch
Mechanical Specifications: Type page 9 7/8 x 16 1/2.Equipment & Software: Hardware — ECR, AG/Multi-Scan; Presses — 4-G/Community; Software — QPS/QuarkXPress 3.6, Adobe/PageMaker 6.0, Adobe/Photoshop 4.0.
Delivery Method: Mail, Newsstand, Racks
Areas Served: 998, 999, 981, 980, 982, 983, 985, 986, 970-973, 500, 799, 800, 969

SEWARD

THE SEWARD PHOENIX LOG (THUR)
232 4th Ave, Seward, AK, 99664, Kenai Peninsula, USA; gen tel (907) 224-4888; adv tel (907) 224-4888; ed tel (907) 224-4888; gen fax (907) 224-7016; disp adv e-mail advertising@TheSewardPhoenixLOG.com; class adv e-mail advertising@TheSewardPhoenixLOG.com; ed e-mail editor@TheSewardPhoenixLOG.com; web site www.TheSewardPhoenixLOG.com
Circulation: 700pd, 50fr; Sworn/Estimate/Non-Audited
Advertising rate: Open inch rate $21.00
Established: 1966
Group: All Alaska News Unlimited
Digital Platform - Mobile: Apple
Digital Platform - Tablet: Apple iOS
Publisher...............................Annette Shacklett
Mechanical Specifications: Type page 10 1/4 x 15 1/2; E - 5 cols, 1 14/15, 1/6 between; A - 5 cols, 1 14/15, 1/6 between; C - 5 cols, 1 14/15, 1/6 between.Equipment & Software: Hardware — Macintosh; Software — Adobe Creative Suite 5.5
Delivery Method: Mail, Newsstand
Areas Served: 99664 99631 99572 99605

THE TUNDRA DRUMS (THUR)
232 4th Ave, Seward, AK, 99664, Kenai Peninsula, USA; gen tel (907) 224-4888; adv tel (907) 224-4888; ed tel (907) 224-4888; gen fax (907) 224-4888; disp adv e-mail advertising@TheTundraDrums.com; class adv e-mail advertising@TheTundraDrums.com; ed e-mail editor@TheTundraDrums.com; web site www.TheTundraDrums.com
Circulation: 700pd, 1,000fr; Sworn/Estimate/Non-Audited
Advertising rate: Open inch rate $21.00
Established: 1974
Group: All Alaska News Unlimited
Digital Platform - Mobile: Apple
Digital Platform - Tablet: Apple iOS
Pub......................................Annette Shacklett
Mechanical Specifications: Type page 10 1/4 x 15; E - 5 cols, 1 11/12, 1/6 between; A - 5 cols, 1 11/12, 1/6 between; C - 5 cols, 1 11/12, 1/6 between.Equipment & Software: Hardware — APP/Mac; Software — Adobe Creative Suite 5.5
Delivery Method: Mail, Racks
Areas Served: 99557 99581 99575 99578 99581 99589 99604 99609 99614 99545 99620 99621 99622 99626 99585 99630 99632 99634 99559 99559 99690 99666 99641 99650 99655 99657 99658 99662 99668 99557 99637 99679 99680 99681 99607

VALDEZ

VALDEZ STAR (WED)
310 Pioneer St, Valdez, AK, 99686, Valdez-Cordova, USA; gen tel (907) 835-2405; disp adv e-mail editor@valdezstar.net; ed e-mail editor@valdezstar.net; web site www.valdezstar.net
Circulation: 2,020pd,; Sworn/Estimate/Non-Audited
Advertising rate: Open inch rate $14.39
Ed. .... Lee Revis
Office/Business Mgr............ Marilyn Braighboy
Graphics ....Mark Dickman

WASILLA

FRONTIERSMAN (WED, FRI, SUN)
5751 E Mayflower Ct, Wasilla, AK, 99654-7880, Matanuska-Susitna Borough, USA; gen tel (907) 352-2250; adv tel (907) 352-2291; ed tel (907) 352-2268; gen fax (907) 352-2277; disp adv e-mail addirector@frontiersman.com; ed e-mail news@frontiersman.com; web site www.frontiersman.com - 400,000(views) 125,000(visitors)
Circulation: 2,400pd, 732fr; AAM
Advertising rate: 1/8 Pg $332.00
Established: 1947
Group: Wick Communications
Sports Ed.................................Jeremiah Bartz
Circ. Mgr................................ Christy Pinkerton
Pub./ Adv. Dir. ..... Dennis AndersonEquipment & Software: Hardware — APP/Mac; Software — QPS/QuarkXPress 4.04.
Delivery Method: Mail, Racks
Areas Served: 99654

WRANGELL

WRANGELL SENTINEL (THUR)
205 Front St, Wrangell, AK, 99929, Wrangell, USA; gen tel (907) 874-2301; gen fax (907) 874-2303; disp adv e-mail wrgsent@gmail.com; ed e-mail wrgsent@gmail.com; web site www.wrangellsentinel.com
Circulation: 1,500pd, 20fr; Sworn/Estimate/Non-Audited
Advertising rate: Open inch rate $10.00
Established: 1902
Group: Jade River Publishing
Co-Owner/Pub. ....Anne Loesch

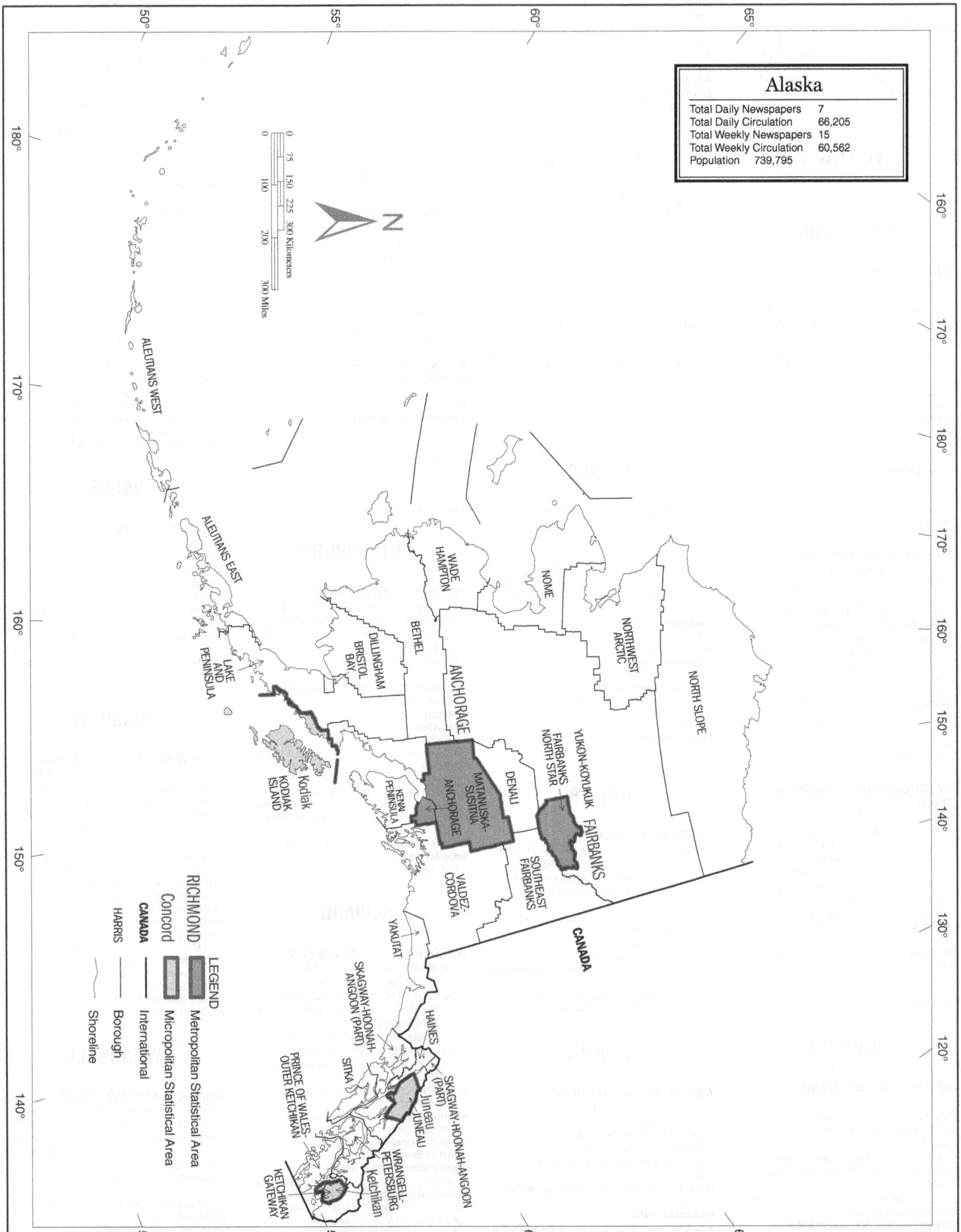
Alaska
Total Daily Newspapers 7
Total Daily Circulation 66,205
Total Weekly Newspapers 15
Total Weekly Circulation 60,562
Population 739,795
0 75 150 225 300 Kilometers
0 100 200 300 Miles
N
LEGEND
RICHMOND Metropolitan Statistical Area
Concord Micropolitan Statistical Area
CANADA International
HARRIS Borough
Shoreline
ALEUTIANS WEST
ALEUTIANS EAST
LAKE AND PENINSULA
Kodiak
KODIAK ISLAND
DILLINGHAM
BRISTOL BAY
BETHEL
WADE HAMPTON
NOME
NORTHWEST ARCTIC
NORTH SLOPE
YUKON-KOYUKUK
FAIRBANKS NORTH STAR
FAIRBANKS
SOUTHEAST FAIRBANKS
DENALI
ANCHORAGE
MATANUSKA-SUSITNA
KENAI PENINSULA
VALDEZ-CORDOVA
YAKUTAT
SKAGWAY-HOONAH-ANGOON (PART)
HAINES
SITKA
Juneau
JUNEAU
PRINCE OF WALES-OUTER KETCHIKAN
WRANGELL-PETERSBURG
Ketchikan
KETCHIKAN GATEWAY
CANADA
50°
55°
60°
65°
180°
170°
160°
150°
140°
130°
120°

Co-Owner/Pub./Ed......................... Ron Loesch
Adv. Mgr.......................... Chris Reed
Mechanical Specifications: Type page 9 4/5 x 14 1/4; E - 5 cols, 1 5/6, 1/6 between; A - 5 cols, 1 5/6, 1/6 between.Equipment & Software: Hardware — APP/Mac; Software — Adobe/ PageMaker 6.0, Claris.

ARIZONA

AJO

AJO COPPER NEWS (TUES)

10 W Pajaro St, Ajo, AZ, 85321-2435, Pima, USA; gen tel (520) 387-7688; adv tel (520) 387-7688; gen fax (520) 387-7505; disp adv e-mail cunews@cunews.info; class adv e-mail advertising@cunews.info; ed e-mail editor@cunews.info; web site www.cunews.info
Circulation: 1,000pd, 45fr; Sworn/Estimate/ Non-Audited
Advertising rate: Open inch rate $5.00
Established: 1916
Group: ANA Advertising Services, Inc. (Arizona Newspaper Association)
Pub....................................... H.J. David
Off. Mgr. .... Michelle Pacheco
Ed. .... Gabrielle David
Mechanical Specifications: Type page 9 5/6 x 16; E - 5 cols, 1 4/5, 1/6 between; A - 5 cols, 1 4/5, 1/6 between; C - 5 cols, 1 4/5, 1/6 between.Equipment & Software: Hardware — APP/Macs; Software — Microsoft/Word 98, Macromedia/Freehand 7.0, Adobe/Photoshop 4.0, Adobe/Acrobat.
Delivery Method: Mail, Newsstand
Areas Served: 85321

APACHE JUNCTION

QUEEN CREEK INDEPENDENT (WED)

2066 W Apache Trl, Ste 110, Apache Junction, AZ, 85120-3733, Maricopa, USA; gen tel (480) 982-7799; gen fax (480) 671-0016; disp adv e-mail qcnews@newszap.com; class adv e-mail evads@newszap.com; ed e-mail qcnews@newszap.com; web site www.queencreekindependent.com
Circulation: 0pd, 10,000fr; CAC
Advertising rate: Open inch rate $20.00
Established: 2004
Group: Independent Newsmedia Inc. Usa
Ed. .... Wendy Miller
Pub.. Bret McKeand
Mng. Ed.. Richard Dyer
Adv. Consultant...................... Deb Richardson
Delivery Method: Carrier
Areas Served: 85120

THE APACHE JUNCTION/GOLD CANYON NEWS (MON)

1075 S Idaho Rd, Ste 102, Apache Junction, AZ, 85119-6497, Pinal, USA; gen tel (480) 982-6397; gen fax (480) 982-3707; disp adv e-mail ajnews@ajnews.com; web site www.ajnews.com
Advertising rate: Open inch rate $19.75
Established: 1997
Group: Foothills Publishing, Inc.
Co-Publisher.............................. Chuck Baker
Areas Served: 85119

BENSON

SAN PEDRO VALLEY NEWS-SUN (WED)

200 S Ocotillo Ave, Benson, AZ, 85602-6407, Cochise, USA; gen tel (520) 586-3382; adv tel (520) 586-3382; gen fax (520) 586-2382; adv fax (520) 586-2382; disp adv e-mail newssun@bensonnews-sun.com; class adv e-mail sara.brown@bensonnews-sun.com; ed e-mail chris.dabovich@bensonnews-sun.com; web site www.bensonnews-sun.com
Circulation: 1,466pd,; VAC
Advertising rate: Open inch rate $12.00
Established: 1900
Group: Wick Communications
Mng. Ed.................................. Chris Dabovich
Bus. Mgr.................................. Joan Hancock
Adv. Rep...................................... Adam Tanner
Classifieds Adv. Mgr.................. Kendra Tanner
Circ. Dir. .... Donna Fenn
Publisher...................................... Francis Wick
Mechanical Specifications: Type page 11 1/2 x 21 1/2; E - 6 cols, 1 5/6, 3/16 between; A - 6 cols, 1 5/6, 3/16 between; C - 6 cols, 1 5/6, 3/16 between.Equipment & Software: Hardware — APP/Mac; Software — Adobe/ PageMaker 6.5, QPS/QuarkXPress 4.0, Adobe/Photoshop 6.0.
Areas Served: 85602

BISBEE

THE BISBEE OBSERVER (THUR)

7 Bisbee Rd Ste L, Ste. L, Bisbee, AZ, 85603-1140, Cochise, USA; gen tel (520) 432-7254; gen fax (520) 432-4192; disp adv e-mail bisbeeobserver@cableone.net; web site www.thebisbeeobserver.com
Circulation: 2,100pd, 45fr; Sworn/Estimate/ Non-Audited
Advertising rate: $6.50
Established: 1985
Group: ANA Advertising Services, Inc. (Arizona Newspaper Association)
Circ. Mgr... Paul Lewis
Prodn. Mgr. .... Laura Swan
Mechanical Specifications: Type page 10 1/4 x 15 1/2; E - 5 cols, 1 19/20, 1/8 between; A - 5 cols, 1 19/20, 1/8 between; C - 5 cols, 1 19/20, 1/8 between.Equipment & Software: Hardware — APP/Mac; Software — Adobe/In Design, APP/Works, Adobe/Photoshop.
Delivery Method: Mail, Newsstand
Areas Served: 85603

BUCKEYE

BUCKEYE VALLEY NEWS (THUR)

122 S 4th St, Buckeye, AZ, 85326, Maricopa, USA; gen tel (623) 386-4426; gen fax (623) 386-4199; disp adv e-mail bvalnews@qwestoffice.net; class adv e-mail bvalnews@qwestoffice.net; ed e-mail bvalnews@qwestoffice.net; web site buckeyevalleynews.net
Circulation: 3,000pd, 8,000fr; Sworn/Estimate/ Non-Audited
Advertising rate: Open inch rate $8.42
Owner,Publisher .... Marlene Turner
Editor, CFO.................................. Sharon Torres
Areas Served: 85326

THE BUCKEYE STAR (WED, BI-MTHLY)

108 N 4th St, Buckeye, AZ, 85326-2402, Maricopa, USA; gen tel (623) 374-4303; gen fax (623) 322-9686; disp adv e-mail publisher@thebuckeyestar.net; web site www.thebuckeyestar.net
Advertising rate: Open inch rate $16.04
Established: 2010
Pub... Jonathan Stein
Areas Served: 85326

BULLHEAD CITY

BULLHEAD CITY BOOSTER (WED, SUN)

2435 Miracle Mile, Bullhead City, AZ, 86442-7311, Mohave, USA; gen tel (928) 763-2505; ed tel (928) 763-2505 x 5144; gen fax (928) 763-6752; disp adv e-mail mvdnews@mohavedailynews.com; ed e-mail bmcmillen@mohavedailynews.com; web site www.mohavedailynews.com
Circulation: 12,500fr; Sworn/Estimate/Non-Audited
Advertising rate: Open inch rate $13.04
Group: Brehm Communications, Inc.
News West Publishing Company Inc. (OOB)
Pub... Gary Milks
News Ed. .... Bill McMillen
Delivery Method: Carrier, Racks
Areas Served: 86442

LAUGHLIN ENTERTAINER (WED)

2435 Miracle Mile, Bullhead City, AZ, 86442-7311, Mohave County, USA; gen tel (928) 763-2505; adv tel 9287632505 x7238; ed tel 9287632505 x7232; gen fax (928) 763-2232; disp adv e-mail laughlin.entertainer@gmail.com; ed e-mail entertainereditor@gmail.com; web site laughlinentertainer.com
Circulation: 55,000fr
Established: 1985
Group: Brehm Communications, Inc.
Ed. .... Alan Marciocchi

LAUGHLIN NEVADA TIMES (WED)

2435 Miracle Mile, Bullhead City, AZ, 86442-7311, Mohave, USA; gen tel (928) 763-2505; gen fax (928) 763-6752; disp adv e-mail nwpad@nwppub.com; class adv e-mail classifieds@nwppub.com; ed e-mail LaughlinTimes @gmail.com; web site www.laughlintimes.com
Circulation: 4,300pd,; Sworn/Estimate/Non-Audited
Advertising rate: Open inch rate $18.05
Established: 1990
Group: Brehm Communications, Inc.
News West Publishing Company Inc. (OOB)
Pub... Gary Milks
Ed. .... Julie FarimanEquipment & Software: Hardware — APP/Macs; Presses — WPC/Web Leader; Software — Baseview/ Class Act.
Delivery Method: Newsstand, Carrier, Racks
Areas Served: 89029

CAMP VERDE

CAMP VERDE BUGLE (WED, FRI, SUN)

283 3rd St, Camp Verde, AZ, 86322, Yavapai, USA; gen tel (928) 634-2241; adv tel (928) 634-2241; ed tel (928) 634-2241; gen fax (928) 634-2312; adv fax (928) 634-2312; ed fax (928) 634-2312; disp adv e-mail advertising@verdenews.com; class adv e-mail classified@verdenews.com; ed e-mail dengler@verdenews.com; web site www.cvbugle.com
Circulation: 824pd,; VAC
Advertising rate: Open inch rate $14.00
Established: 1947
Group: Western News&Info, Inc.
Digital Platform - Mobile: Apple
Digital Platform - Tablet: Apple iOS
Pub... Pam Miller
Ed. .... Dan Engler
Delivery Method: Mail, Newsstand
Areas Served: Yavapai County

THE CAMP VERDE JOURNAL (WED)

406 S. First St., Camp Verde, AZ, 86322, Yavapai, USA; gen tel (928) 567-3341; gen fax (928) 567-2373; disp adv e-mail bob@redrocknews.com; ed e-mail editor@larsonnewspapers.com; web site www.journalaz.com
Circulation: 2,000pd, 125fr; Sworn/Estimate/ Non-Audited
Advertising rate: Open inch rate $10.85
Established: 1980
Group: Larson Newspapers
Adv. Mgr... David Zarn
Pub.. Robert B. Larson
Adv. Dir .... Kyle Larson
Ed. .... Trista Steers
Mechanical Specifications: Type page 13 x 21; E - 6 cols, 2, 1/6 between; A - 6 cols, 2, 1/6 between; C - 6 cols, 2, 1/6 between.Equipment & Software: Hardware — IBM; Presses — WPC/Web Leader; Software — ACT.
Areas Served: 86322

CAVE CREEK

SONORAN NEWS (WED)

6702 E Cave Creek Rd, Ste 3, Cave Creek, AZ, 85331-8659, Maricopa, USA; gen tel (480) 488-2021; gen fax (480) 488-6216; disp adv e-mail sales@sonorannews.com; ed e-mail editorial@sonorannews.com; web site www.sonorannews.com/new/
Circulation: 62pd, 43,000fr; Sworn/Estimate/ Non-Audited
Advertising rate: Open inch rate $24.00
Ed. .... Don Sorchych
Mechanical Specifications: Type page 11 5/8 x 21; E - 6 cols, 1 4/5, between; A - 6 cols, 1 4/5, between; C - 6 cols, 1 4/5, between. Equipment & Software: Hardware — APP/ Mac; Software — QPS/QuarkXPress.
Delivery Method: Mail
Areas Served: 85327, 85377, 85331, 85255, 85262

CHINO VALLEY

CHINO VALLEY REVIEW (WED)

110 W Center St, Ste A2, Chino Valley, AZ, 86323-5961, Yavapai, USA; gen tel (928) 636-2653; adv tel (928) 636-2653; ed tel (928) 636-2653; gen fax (928) 636-1334; disp adv e-mail theitzman@prescottaz.com; ed e-mail hdfoster@prescottaz.com; web site www.cvrnews.com
Circulation: 51pd, 6,691fr; VAC
Advertising rate: Open inch rate $12.70
Group: Western News&Info, Inc.
Ed. .... Heidi Dahms Foster
Adv. Dir.. Babette Cubitt
Adv. Mgr.. Fred Ellison
Classified Adv. Mgr.......................... Teri Bryant
Circ. Mgr..................................... David Russell
Co-Pub... Kit Atwell
Mechanical Specifications: Type page 11 5/8 x 21 1/2; E - 6 cols, 2 1/16, 1/4 between; A - 6 cols, 2 1/16, 1/4 between; C - 6 cols, 2 1/16, 1/4 between.
Delivery Method: Newsstand, Carrier
Areas Served: 86323

PRESCOTT VALLEY TRIBUNE (WED)

PO Box 370, Chino Valley, AZ, 86323-0370, Yavapai, USA; gen tel (928) 445-3333; adv tel (928) 776-8122; ed tel (928) 445-3333 x 1020; gen fax (928) 772-3393; disp adv e-mail bcubitt@prescottaz.com; class adv e-mail classifieds@prescottaz.com; ed e-mail hdfoster@prescottaz.com; web site www.prescottvalleytribune.com
Circulation: 131pd, 15,389fr; VAC
Advertising rate: Open inch rate $17.40
Group: ANA Advertising Services, Inc. (Arizona Newspaper Association)
Western News&Info, Inc.
Pub.. Kelly Soldwedel
Ed. Mgr........................... Heidi Dahms Foster
Adv. Mgr...................................... Will Campbell
Adv. Dir...................................... Babette Cubitt
Classified Coord. .... Teri Bryant
Areas Served: 86314

COOLIDGE

COOLIDGE EXAMINER (WED)

353 W Central Ave, Coolidge, AZ, 85128-4706, Pinal, USA; gen tel (520) 723-5441; gen fax (520) 723-7899; disp adv e-mail coolidgeexaminer@yahoo.com; web site pinalcentral.com/coolidge_examiner
Circulation: 1,943pd,; Sworn/Estimate/Non-Audited
Advertising rate: Open inch rate $6.72
Group: Casa Grande Valley Newspapers Inc.
County Team Ed. .... Adam Gaub
Adv. Mgr... Kelli Kent
Mechanical Specifications: Type page 13 x 21 1/2; E - 6 cols, 2 1/16, 1/8 between; A - 6 cols, 2 1/16, 1/8 between; C - 6 cols, 2 1/16, 1/8 between.
Areas Served: 85128

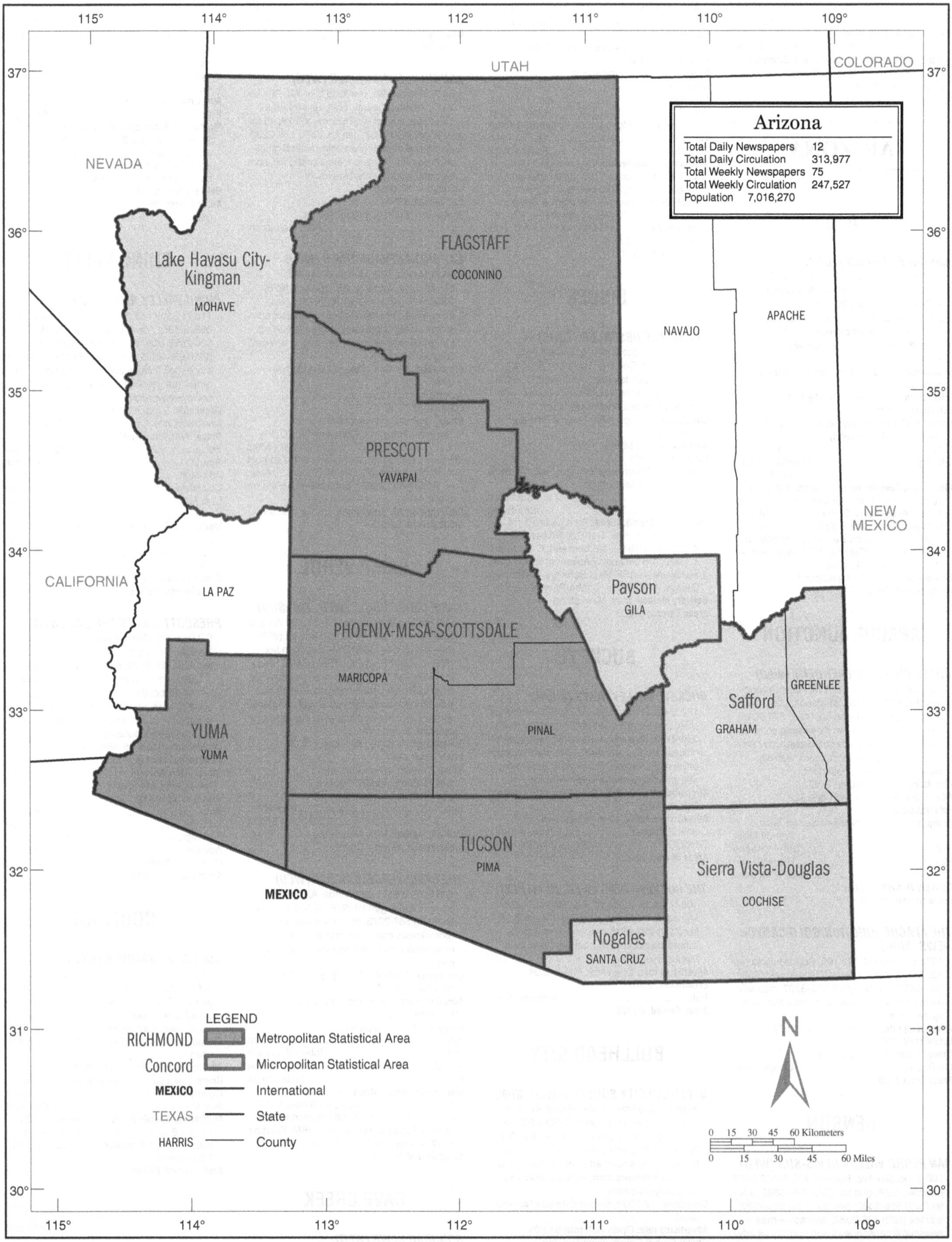
Arizona
Total Daily Newspapers 12
Total Daily Circulation 313,977
Total Weekly Newspapers 75
Total Weekly Circulation 247,527
Population 7,016,270
UTAH
COLORADO
NEVADA
CALIFORNIA
NEW MEXICO
MEXICO
Lake Havasu City-Kingman
MOHAVE
FLAGSTAFF
COCONINO
NAVAJO
APACHE
PRESCOTT
YAVAPAI
LA PAZ
Payson
GILA
PHOENIX-MESA-SCOTTSDALE
MARICOPA
PINAL
Safford
GRAHAM
GREENLEE
YUMA
YUMA
TUCSON
PIMA
Sierra Vista-Douglas
COCHISE
Nogales
SANTA CRUZ
LEGEND
RICHMOND Metropolitan Statistical Area
Concord Micropolitan Statistical Area
MEXICO International
TEXAS State
HARRIS County
N
0 15 30 45 60 Kilometers
0 15 30 45 60 Miles

COTTONWOOD

COTTONWOOD JOURNAL EXTRA (WED)

830 S Main St, Ste 1E, Cottonwood, AZ, 86326-4621, Yavapai, USA; gen tel (928) 634-8551; gen fax (928) 634-0823; disp adv e-mail bob@redrocknews.com; web site www.journalaz.com

Circulation: 548pd, 8,500fr; Sworn/Estimate/Non-Audited
Advertising rate: Open inch rate $8.50
Group: Larson Newspapers
Pub.......... Robert Larson
Adv. Mgr.......... David Zarin
Ed.......... Greg Ruland
Mechanical Specifications: Type page 13 x 21; E - 6 cols, 2, 1/6 between; A - 6 cols, 2, 1/6 between; C - 6 cols, 2, 1/6 between.Equipment & Software: Hardware — IBM; Presses — WPC/Web Leader; Software — ACT.
Areas Served: 86326

THE VERDE INDEPENDENT (WED, FRI, SUN)

116 S Main St, Cottonwood, AZ, 86326-3998, Yavapai, USA; gen tel (928) 634-2241; adv tel (928) 634-2241 ext. 6024; ed tel (928) 634-2241 ext. 6032; gen fax (928) 634-2312; adv fax (928) 634-2312; ed fax (928) 634-2312; disp adv e-mail advertising@verdenews.com; class adv e-mail classified@verdenews.com; ed e-mail dengler@verdenews.com; web site www.verdenews.com

Circulation: 2,522pd,; VAC
Advertising rate: Open inch rate $200.00
Established: 1947
Group: Western News&Info, Inc.
Digital Platform - Mobile: Apple, Android
Digital Platform - Tablet: Apple iOS, Android
Ed.......... Dan Engler
Pres.......... Edward Dulin
VP.......... Bret McKeand
Delivery Method: Mail, Newsstand, Racks
Areas Served: 86326

DOUGLAS

THE DOUGLAS DISPATCH (WED)

530 E 11th St, Douglas, AZ, 85607-2014, Cochise, USA; gen tel (337)365-6773; adv tel (520) 220-8775; ed tel (520) 234-0145; gen fax (520) 364-6750; adv fax (520) 364-6750; ed fax (520) 364-6750; disp adv e-mail newsroom@douglasdispatch.com; class adv e-mail advertising@douglasdispatch.com; ed e-mail editor@douglasdispatch.com; web site www.douglasdispatch.com

Circulation: 1,435pd,; VAC
Advertising rate: Open inch rate $7.95(wknd)
Established: 1902
Group: Wick Communications
Bookkeeper.......... Kimberly Hicks
Adv. Mgr.......... David Dominguez
Circ. Mgr.......... Francisco Barrios
Managing Ed.......... Bruce Whetten
Pub.......... Nancy Wykle
Mechanical Specifications: Type page 13 x 21; E - 6 cols, 2 1/16, 1/8 between; A - 6 cols, 2 1/16, 1/8 between; C - 6 cols, 2 1/16, 1/8 between.

FLAGSTAFF

FLAGSTAFF LIVE! (THUR)

1751 S Thompson St, Flagstaff, AZ, 86001-8716, Coconino, USA; gen tel (928) 774-4545; adv tel (928) 556-2287; ed tel (928) 556-2262; gen fax (928) 773-1934; disp adv e-mail cbrady@azdailysun.com; class adv e-mail cbrady@azdailysun.com; ed e-mail mchase@flaglive.com; web site www.flaglive.com

Circulation: 8,300fr; Sworn/Estimate/Non-Audited
Advertising rate: Modular
Established: 1995
Group: Flagstaff Publishing
Lee Enterprises, Inc.Editions: (1)
Man. Ed.......... Nancy Wiechec
Staff Writer.......... MacKenzie Chase
Staff Writer.......... Gabriel Granillo
Delivery Method: Racks
Areas Served: Northern Arizona

FLORENCE

ELOY ENTERPRISE (THUR)

190 N Main St, Florence, AZ, 85132, Pinal, USA; gen tel (520) 868-5897; gen fax (520) 868-5898; disp adv e-mail ahowell@pinalcentral.com; ed e-mail news@florencereminder.com; web site pinalcentral.com/florence_reminder_blade_tribune

Circulation: 1,623pd, 8fr; Sworn/Estimate/Non-Audited
Advertising rate: Open inch rate $6.25
Established: 1947
Group: ANA Advertising Services, Inc. (Arizona Newspaper Association)
Casa Grande Valley Newspapers Inc.
Editor.......... Andy Howell
Mechanical Specifications: Type page 13 x 21 1/2; E - 6 cols, 2 1/16, 1/8 between; A - 6 cols, 2 1/16, 1/8 between; C - 6 cols, 2 1/16, 1/8 between.
Areas Served: 85131 85141

FLORENCE REMINDER & BLADE-TRIBUNE (THUR)

190 N Main St, Florence, AZ, 85132, Pinal, USA; gen tel (520) 868-5897; gen fax (520) 868-5898; disp adv e-mail info@florencereminder.com; class adv e-mail ads@florencereminder.com; ed e-mail news@florencereminder.com; web site pinalcentral.com/florence_reminder_blade_tribune

Circulation: 1,623pd, 8fr; Sworn/Estimate/Non-Audited
Advertising rate: Open inch rate $6.25
Group: Casa Grande Valley Newspapers Inc.
Ed.......... Mark Cowling
Mechanical Specifications: Type page 13 x 21 1/2; E - 6 cols, 2 1/16, 1/8 between; A - 6 cols, 2 1/16, 1/8 between; C - 6 cols, 2 1/16, 1/8 between.
Delivery Method: Mail, Newsstand
Areas Served: 85132

FOUNTAIN HILLS

LET'S GO (THUR, MTHLY)

16508 E Laser Dr, Ste 101, Fountain Hills, AZ, 85268-6512, Maricopa, USA; gen tel (480) 837-1925; gen fax (480) 837-1951; disp adv e-mail brent@fhtimes.com; ed e-mail mike@fhtimes.com; web site fhtimes.com/lets_go

Circulation: 17,000fr; Sworn/Estimate/Non-Audited
Advertising rate: Open inch rate $9.00
Established: 1999
Group: Western States Publishers, Inc.
Digital Platform - Mobile: Windows
Pub.......... L. Alan Cruikshank
Ed.......... Michael Scharnow
Delivery Method: Mail, Newsstand
Areas Served: 85268

THE FOUNTAIN HILL TIMES (WED)

16508 E Laser Dr, Ste 101, Fountain Hills, AZ, 85268-6512, Maricopa, USA; gen tel (480) 837-1925; adv tel (480) 837-1925; gen fax (480) 837-1951; adv fax (480) 837-1951; disp adv e-mail brent@fhtimes.com; class adv e-mail Tammie@fhtimes.com; ed e-mail mike@fhtimes.com; web site www.fhtimes.com

Circulation: 5,300pd,; USPS
Advertising rate: Open inch rate $9.00
Established: 1974
Group: Western States Publishers, Inc.Editions: fhtimes.com
Digital Platform - Mobile: Windows
Pub.......... L. Alan Cruikshank
Ed.......... Michael G. Scharnow
Bus. Mgr.......... Kip Kirkendoll
Circ. Mgr.......... Jennifer Gentry
Delivery Method: Mail, Newsstand, Carrier
Areas Served: Fountain Hills, Verde Communities and Fort McDowell

GLENDALE

PEORIA TIMES (FRI)

7122 N 59th Ave, Glendale, AZ, 85301-2436, Maricopa, USA; gen tel (623) 842-6000; adv tel (623) 847-4601; ed tel (623) 847-4604; gen fax (623) 842-6013; disp adv e-mail sales@star-times.com; class adv e-mail notices@star-times.com; ed e-mail cdryer@star-times.com; web site www.peoriatimes.com

Circulation: 4,200pd, 800fr; USPS
Advertising rate: Open inch rate $7.20
Established: 1952
Group: Pueblo Publishers, Inc.
Pub./Gen. Mng.......... William E. Toops
Bus. Mgr.......... Roger W. Toops
Adv. Mgr.......... Connie Williams
Ed.......... Carolyn Dryer
Mechanical Specifications: Type page 10 5/16 x 16; E - 6 cols, 1 9/16, 1/6 between; A - 6 cols, 1 9/16, 1/6 between; C - 6 cols, 1 9/16, 1/6 between.Equipment & Software: Hardware — PC; Presses — G/Community; Software — Adobe/PageMaker 6.5.
Delivery Method: Mail, Newsstand
Areas Served: 85345, 85381, 85382, 85383

THE GLENDALE STAR (THUR)

7122 N 59th Ave, Glendale, AZ, 85301-2436, Maricopa, USA; gen tel (623) 842-6000; adv tel (623) 847-4601; ed tel (623) 847-4604; gen fax (623) 842-6013; disp adv e-mail wtoops@star-times.com; class adv e-mail sales@star-times.com; ed e-mail cdryer@star-times.com; web site www.glendalestar.com

Circulation: 6,000pd, 1,000fr; USPS
Advertising rate: Open inch rate $8.50
Established: 1978
Group: Pueblo Publishers, Inc.
Pub./Gen.Mng.......... William E. Toops
Mng. Ed.......... Carolyn Dryer
Bus. Mgr.......... Roger W. Toops
Mechanical Specifications: Type page 10 5/16 x 16; E - 6 cols, 1 9/16, 1/6 between; A - 6 cols, 1 9/16, 1/6 between; C - 6 cols, 1 9/16, 1/6 between.Equipment & Software: Hardware — PC; Presses — G/Community; Software — Adobe/PageMaker 6.5, Adobe/Photoshop 4.0.
Delivery Method: Mail, Newsstand
Areas Served: 85301-85312

GLOBE

ARIZONA SILVER BELT (WED)

298 N Pine St, Globe, AZ, 85501-2516, Gila, USA; gen tel (928) 425-7121; adv tel (928) 425-7121; ed tel (928) 425-7121; gen fax (928) 425-7001; disp adv e-mail sherri@silverbelt.com; class adv e-mail sherri@silverbelt.com; ed e-mail news@silverbelt.com; web site www.silverbelt.com

Circulation: 1,800pd,; Sworn/Estimate/Non-Audited
Advertising rate: Open inch rate $5.50
Established: 1878
Group: News Media Corp.
Ed.......... Holly Sow
Gen. Mgr..........
Sherri DavisEquipment & Software: ; Presses — 4-G; Software — Adobe/PageMaker 6.0, Adobe/Photoshop 4.0.
Areas Served: 85501

COPPER COUNTRY NEWS (WED)

298 N Pine St, Globe, AZ, 85501-2516, Gila, USA; gen tel (928) 425-0355; ed tel (928) 425-0355; gen fax (928) 425-6535; disp adv e-mail globeccn@yahoo.com; ed e-mail ed@coppercountrynews.com; web site www.coppercountrynews.com

Circulation: 19,000fr; Sworn/Estimate/Non-Audited
Advertising rate: Open inch rate $12.95
Established: 1984
Group: News Media Corp.
Pub.......... Marc Martin
Ed.......... Ed Kuehneman
Adv. Sales.......... Vicki Ross
Mechanical Specifications: Type page 10 x 16; E - 5 cols, 1 5/6, 1/6 between; A - 5 cols, 1 5/6, 1/6 between; C - 5 cols, 1 5/6, 1/6 between. Equipment & Software: Hardware — APP/Mac G3; Software — QPS/QuarkXPress 4.0.
Areas Served: 85501

SAN CARLOS APACHE MOCCASIN (WED)

298 N Pine St, Globe, AZ, 85501-2516, Gila, USA; gen tel (928) 425-7121; gen fax (928) 425-7001; disp adv e-mail publisher@silverbelt.com; web site silverbelt.com

Circulation: 1,973pd,; Sworn/Estimate/Non-Audited
Advertising rate: Open inch rate $5.35
Pub.......... Marc Marin
Ed.......... Andrea MarcandiEquipment & Software: Hardware — APP/Power Mac G3; Presses — G/Community; Software — Adobe/PageMaker 6.5, Adobe/Photoshop 4.0.
Areas Served: 85501

GOODYEAR

WEST VALLEY VIEW (WED)

250 N Litchfield Rd, Ste 130, Goodyear, AZ, 85338-1380, Maricopa, USA; gen tel (623) 535-8439; gen fax (623) 935-2103; disp adv e-mail advertising@westvalleyview.com; class adv e-mail classifieds@westvalleyview.com; ed e-mail news1@westvalleyview.com; web site www.westvalleyview.com - 149,122(views) 59,092(visitors)

Circulation: 9pd, 73,867fr; Sworn/Estimate/Non-Audited
Advertising rate: Open inch rate $44.00 Modular
Established: 1986
Pub.......... Steve Strickbine
Mng. Ed.......... Cary Hines
Mechanical Specifications: Type page 10" x 16"; Editorial - 4 cols, 2 1/4, 1/6 between; Advertising - 6 cols, 1 1/2, 1/6 between; Classified - 6 cols, 1 1/2, 1/6 between.Equipment & Software: Hardware — PC; Presses — 12 unit DGM 430 (Goss Community Equivalent), InDesign Creative Suite 5.5; Software — Adobe/InDesign CS3, Adobe/Acrobat 8.0, Photoship CS3, Illustrator CS3
Delivery Method: Mail, Newsstand, Carrier, Racks
Areas Served: 85322,85323,85392,85326,85396,85329,85307,85309,85338,85395,85340,85343,85037,85353,85354,85355

GREEN VALLEY

GREEN VALLEY NEWS & SAHUARITA SN (WED, SUN)

18705 S I 19 Frontage Rd, Ste 125, Green Valley, AZ, 85614-5014, Pima, USA; gen tel (520) 625-5511; adv tel (520) 547-9757; ed tel (520) 547-9770; gen fax (520) 625-8046; disp adv e-mail asaenz@gvnews.com; class adv e-mail classifieds@gvnews.com; ed e-mail editorial@gvnews.com; web site www.gvnews.com

Circulation: 7,126pd, 162fr; VAC
Advertising rate: Open inch rate $49.50
Group: Wick Communications
Ed.......... Dan Shearer
Adv. Mgr.......... Andrew Saenz
Production Mgr.......... Graham Harrington
Ops./Circ Dir.......... Laura Kurtz
Business Manager.......... Lynda Chambers
Pub.......... Dru Sanchez
Mechanical Specifications: Type page 11 5/8 x 21; E - 6 cols, 1 5/6, 1/8 between; A - 6 cols, 1 5/6, 1/8 between; C - 6 cols, 1 5/6, 1/8 between.Equipment & Software: Hardware — APP/Mac; Software — QPS/QuarkXPress 4.1.
Delivery Method: Carrier, Racks
Areas Served: 85614, 85622, 85629, 85629, 85646, 85645

SAHUARITA SUN (WED)
18705 S I 19 Frontage Rd, Ste 125, Green Valley, AZ, 85614-5014, Pima, USA; gen tel (520) 625-5511; adv tel (520) 547-9757; ed tel (520) 547-9770; gen fax (520) 625-8046; disp adv e-mail asaenz@gvnews.com; class adv e-mail classifieds@gvnews.com; ed e-mail dshearer@gvnews.com; web site www.sahuaritasun.com
Circulation: 813pd, 8,141fr; VAC
Advertising rate: Open inch rate $62.00 (3.22"x2.5")
Established: 2005
Group: Wick Communications
Digital Platform - Mobile: Apple, Android
Digital Platform - Tablet: Apple iOS, Android, Blackberry Tablet OS, Kindle
Ed. .... Dan Shearer
Publisher .... Rebecca Bradner
Areas Served: 85629, 85614, 85622

HOLBROOK

SILVER CREEK HERALD (WED, FRI)
200 E Hopi Dr, Holbrook, AZ, 86025-2628, Navajo, USA; gen tel (928) 524-6203; gen fax (928) 524-3541; disp adv e-mail mbarger@cableone.net; class adv e-mail rbarger@cableone.net; ed e-mail franciepayne@cableone.net; web site tribunenewsnow.com
Circulation: 3,200fr; Sworn/Estimate/Non-Audited
Advertising rate: Open inch rate $9.85
Established: 1909
Pub. .... Matthew Barger
Ed./Gen. Mgr. .... Francie Payne
Off. Mgr. .... Debbie Barger
Delivery Method: Mail, Racks
Areas Served: 86025

THE TRIBUNE-NEWS (WED, FRI)
200 E Hopi Dr, Holbrook, AZ, 86025-2628, Navajo, USA; gen tel (928) 524-6203; gen fax (928) 524-3541; disp adv e-mail mikenilsson.adv@gmail.com; class adv e-mail mbarger@cableone.net; ed e-mail franciepayne@cableone.net; web site tribunenewsnow.com
Circulation: 2,490pd, 1,538fr; Sworn/Estimate/Non-Audited
Advertising rate: Open inch rate $9.85
Group: Navajo County Publishers, Inc.
Pub. .... Matthew Barger
Ed./Gen. Mgr. .... Francie Payne
Mechanical Specifications: Type page 9.8889 x 21; E - 6 cols, .1111 between; A - 6 cols, .1111 between; C - 6 cols, .1111 between. Equipment & Software: Hardware — APP/Mac; Software — Microsoft/Word, QPS/QuarkXPress.
Delivery Method: Mail, Newsstand
Areas Served: 86025 86047 85942 86029 85939 85937 86032 86047 86034 86042 86031 86505 86028

KEARNY

COPPER BASIN NEWS (WED)
366 W Alden Rd, Kearny, AZ, 85137-1208, Pinal and Gila, USA; gen tel (520) 363-5554; gen fax (520) 363-9663; disp adv e-mail michaelc@minersunbasin.com; web site www.copperarea.com
Circulation: 2,403pd, 23fr; Sworn/Estimate/Non-Audited
Advertising rate: Open inch rate $5.60
Established: 1958
Adv. Mgr. .... James Carnes
Mng. Ed. .... Jennifer Carnes
Adv. Prodn. .... Michael Carnes
Mechanical Specifications: Type page 13 x 20 3/4.Equipment & Software: ; Software — MacSoft/PhotoMaker, Adobe/PageMaker.
Areas Served: 85237

SAN MANUEL MINER (WED)
366 W Alden Rd, Kearny, AZ, 85137-1208, Pinal, USA; gen tel (520) 385-2266; gen fax (520) 385-4666; web site www.copperarea.com
Circulation: 3,310pd, 36fr; Sworn/Estimate/Non-Audited
Advertising rate: Open inch rate $5.70
Group: ANA Advertising Services, Inc. (Arizona Newspaper Association)
Pub. .... James Carnes
Adv. Mgr. .... Pat Hernandez
Circ. Mgr. .... Jan Carlson
Mng. Ed. .... Gayle Carnes
Areas Served: 85631, 85623, 85618

THE PINAL NUGGET (WED)
366 W Alden Rd, Kearny, AZ, 85137-1208, Pinal, USA; gen tel (520) 385-2266; gen fax (520) 385-4666; disp adv e-mail michaelc@minersunbasin.com; web site www.copperarea.com
Advertising rate: Open inch rate $14
Established: 2007
Areas Served: Copper Corridor, Apache Junction, Gold Canyon, Catalina

KINGMAN

THE STANDARD (WED)
221 E Beale St, Kingman, AZ, 86401-5829, Mohave, USA; gen tel (928) 753-1143; gen fax (928) 753-1312; disp adv e-mail ads@thestandardnewspaper.net; class adv e-mail classifiedads@thestandardnewspaper.net; web site www.thestandardnewspaper.net
Advertising rate: Open inch rate $12.31
Established: 1990
Ed. .... Erin Clark
Areas Served: 86401

MARICOPA

MARICOPA MONITOR (TUES, FRI)
21300 N John Wayne Pkwy, Ste 103, Maricopa, AZ, 85139-8964, Pinal, USA; gen tel (520) 568-4198; adv tel (520) 568-4198; ed tel (520) 568-4198; gen fax (520) 560-2831; disp adv e-mail kdodge@trivalleycentral.com; class adv e-mail dcortez@trivalleycentral.com; ed e-mail agaub@trivalleycentral.com; web site pinalcentral.com/maricopa_monitor
Advertising rate: Open inch rate $12.47
Established: 2003
Group: Casa Grande Valley Newspapers Inc.
Mng. Ed. .... Adam Guab
News Ed. .... Brian Wright
Areas Served: 85139

NEW RIVER

FOOTHILLS FOCUS (WED)
46641 N Black Canyon Hwy, Ste 1, New River, AZ, 85087-6941, Maricopa, USA; gen tel (623) 465-5808; gen fax (623) 465-1363; disp adv e-mail foothillsfocus@qwestoffi ce.net; ed e-mail ffeditorial@hotmail.com; web site www.thefoothillsfocus.com
Advertising rate: Open inch rate $25.00
Established: 2002
Publisher & Editor .... John Alexander
Areas Served: 85087

NOGALES

NOGALES INTERNATIONAL (TUES, FRI)
268 W View Point Dr, Nogales, AZ, 85621-4114, Santa Cruz, USA; gen tel (337)365-6773; adv tel (520) 375-5764; ed tel (520) 375-5767; gen fax (520) 761-3115; disp adv e-mail graphics@nogalesinternational.com; class adv e-mail classifieds@nogalesinternational.com; ed e-mail editorial@nogalesinternational.com; web site www.nogalesinternational.com
Circulation: 1,736pd, 68fr; CVC
Advertising rate: Open inch rate $50.00 (3.22" x 2.5")
Established: 1925
Group: Wick Communications
Pub. .... Manuel Coppola
Mng. Ed. .... Jonathan Clark
Circ. Mgr. .... Ricardo Villarreal
Adv. Mgr. .... Debbie Keller
Int. Gen. Mgr. .... Andrew Saenz
Areas Served: 85621

SANTA CRUZ VALLEY SUN (WED)
268 W View Point Dr, Nogales, AZ, 85621-4114, Santa Cruz, USA; gen tel (520) 375-5760; adv tel (520) 625-5511; gen fax (520) 761-3115; disp adv e-mail webmaster@nogalesinternational.com; web site www.nogalesinternational.com/santa_cruz_valley_sun
Circulation: 0pd, 18,079fr; VAC
Advertising rate: Open inch rate $40.00 (3.22"x2.5")
Pub. .... Manuel Coppola
Mng. Ed. .... Jonathan Clark
Circ. Mgr. .... Ricardo Villarreal
Adv. Mgr. . Debbie KellerEquipment & Software: Hardware — APP/Mac
Areas Served: 85621

THE WEEKLY BULLETIN (WED)
268 W View Point Dr, Nogales, AZ, 85621-4114, Santa Cruz, USA; gen tel (520) 375-5760; adv tel (520) 375-5764; ed tel (520) 375-5767; gen fax (520) 761-3115; disp adv e-mail carmen.torres@nogalesinternational.com; class adv e-mail classifieds@nogalesinternational.com; ed e-mail editorial@nogalesinternational.com; web site www.nogalesinternational.com/the_bulletin/
Circulation: 515pd,; VAC
Advertising rate: Open inch rate $45.00
Established: 1991
Digital Platform - Mobile: Apple, Android
Digital Platform - Tablet: Apple iOS, Android
Pub. .... Manuel Coppola
Ed. .... Jonathan Clark
Areas Served: 85621

PAGE

LAKE POWELL CHRONICLE (WED)
PO Box 1716, Page, AZ, 86040-1716, Coconino, USA; gen tel (928) 645-8888; gen fax (928) 645-2209; disp adv e-mail ed@lakepowellchronicle.com; ed e-mail editor@lakepowellchronicle.reporter@lakepowellchronicle.com; web site www.lakepowellchronicle.com
Advertising rate: Open inch rate $15.25
Established: 1965
Group: News Media Corp.
Ed./Pub. .... David Rupkalvis
Office Mgr. .... Kim Clark
Sales Rep. .... Mary Chilton
Areas Served: 86040

PARKER

THE PARKER PIONEER (WED)
1317 S Joshua Ave, Ste L, Parker, AZ, 85344-5768, La Paz, USA; gen tel (928) 669-2275; gen fax (928) 669-9624 ; disp adv e-mail sales@havasunews.com; ed e-mail bbowers@havasunews.com; web site www.parkerpioneer.net
Circulation: 2,075pd, 32fr; VAC
Advertising rate: Open inch rate $12.85
Group: Wick Communications Western News&Info, Inc.
Pub. .... Michael E. Quinn
Adv. Mgr. .... Christine Hammers
Circ. Mgr. .... Alexis Christensen
Prod. Mgr. .... Cindy Taylor
Areas Served: 85344

PAYSON

THE PAYSON ROUNDUP (TUES, WED, FRI)
708 N Beeline Hwy, Payson, AZ, 85541-3770, Gila, USA; gen tel (928) 474-5251; adv tel (928) 474-5251 x 104; ed tel (928) 474-5251 x 115; gen fax (928) 474-1893; adv fax (928) 474-1893; ed fax (928) 474-1893; disp adv e-mail gtackett@payson.com; class adv e-mail classads@payson.com; ed e-mail paleshire@payson.com; web site www.payson.com
Circulation: 5,166pd, 169fr; USPS
Advertising rate: Open inch rate $15.00
Established: 1937
Group: White Mountain Publishing
Digital Platform - Mobile: Apple
Ed. .... Peter Aleshire
Circ. Mgr. .... Patty Behm
Opns. Mgr. .... Julie Williams
Director of Sales .... Gary Tackett
Mechanical Specifications: Type page 12 19/20 x 21 1/2; A - 6 cols, between; C - 8 cols, between.Equipment & Software: Hardware — APP/Mac; Presses — 5-G/Community; Software — QPS/QuarkXPress 5.0 & 6.0, Adobe/PageMaker, Macromedia/Freehand, Microsoft/Word, Adobe/Photoshop.
Delivery Method: Mail, Newsstand, Carrier, Racks
Areas Served: 85541, 85547

PHOENIX

APACHE JUNCTION/GOLD CANYON INDEPENDENT (WED)
23043 N 16th Ln, Phoenix, AZ, 85027-1331, Pinal, USA; gen tel (480) 982-7799; gen fax (480) 671-0016; disp adv e-mail evads@newszap.com; class adv e-mail iniclassads@newszap.com; ed e-mail ajeditor@newszap.com; web site www.apachejunctionindependent.com
Circulation: 0pd, 20,000fr; CAC
Advertising rate: Open inch rate $20.00
Established: 1959
Group: Independent Newsmedia Inc. Usa
Pub. .... Bret McKeand
Mng. Ed. .... Richard Dyer
General Manager .... Deb Richardson
Delivery Method: Carrier, Racks
Areas Served: 85120

ARIZONA BUSINESS GAZETTE (THUR)
200 E Van Buren St, Phoenix, AZ, 85004-2238, Maricopa, USA; gen tel (602) 444-8838; gen fax (602) 444-7312; web site www.abgnews.com
Advertising rate: Full run display open rate $186.30
Group: Gannett

ARIZONA CAPITOL TIMES (FRI)
1835 W Adams St, Phoenix, AZ, 85007-2603, Maricopa, USA; gen tel (602) 258-7026; adv tel (602) 258-7026; ed tel (602) 258-7026; gen fax (602) 258-2504; adv fax (602) 258-2504; ed fax (602) 258-2504; disp adv e-mail jschanfeldt@azcapitoltimes.com; ed e-mail tom.spratt@azcapitoltimes.com; web site www.azcapitoltimes.com
Circulation: 1,675pd, 26fr; Sworn/Estimate/Non-Audited
Advertising rate: 1/16 Pg $130.00; 1/8 Pg $258.00; 1/4 Pg $531.00
Established: 1906
Group: GateHouse Media, Inc.
Pub. .... Kent Johnson
Reg. Bus. Mgr. .... Gina Brignac
Mng. Ed. .... Tom Spratt
Adv. Acc. Exec. .... Jay Schanfelt
Mechanical Specifications: Type page 10 1/4 x 12 1/4; E - 4 cols, 2 3/8, 1/4 between; A - 4 cols, 2 3/8, 1/4 between; C - 4 cols, 2 3/8, 1/4 between.Equipment & Software: Hardware — APP/Mac; Software — QPS/QuarkXPress, Adobe/Photoshop, Adobe/Illustrator, InDesign.
Delivery Method: Mail, Newsstand, Racks
Areas Served: 85007

ARIZONA INFORMANT (WED)
1301 E Washington St, Ste 101, Phoenix,

AZ, 85034-1173, Maricopa, USA; gen tel (602) 257-9300; gen fax (602) 257-0547; disp adv e-mail aznewspaper@questoffice.net; web site www.azinformant.com
Circulation: 15,000pd,; Sworn/Estimate/ Non-Audited
Advertising rate: Open inch rate $32.00
Established: 1971
Pub....................................... Roland Campbell
Ed.......................................Clovis C. Campbell
Areas Served: 85034

SCOTTSDALE INDEPENDENT (WED)
23043 N 16th Ln, Phoenix, AZ, 85027-1331, Maricopa, USA; gen tel (623) 445-2777; gen fax (623) 445-2740; disp adv e-mail neads@newszap.com; class adv e-mail iniclassads@newszap.com; ed e-mail scottsdalenews@newszap.com; web site www.scottsdaleindependent.com
Circulation: 0pd, 10,000fr; CAC
Advertising rate: $20 pci
Established: 1984
Group: Independent Newsmedia Inc. Usa
Publisher/President .... Bret McKeand
Ed. ....Terrance Thornton
Adv. Mgr.................................... Jan McKinney
Pub....................................... Charlene Bisson
Pres. ....Edward Dulin
Mechanical Specifications: Full page: 10" wide by 10.625" high
Delivery Method: Carrier, Racks
Areas Served: 85266, 85262, 85255, 85259, 85254, 85258, 85250, 85251, 85257

THE BUSINESS JOURNAL (FRI)
101 N 1st Ave Ste 2300, Suite 2300, Phoenix, AZ, 85003-1903, Maricopa, USA; gen tel (602) 230-8400; adv tel (602) 308-6525; ed tel (602) 308-6513; gen fax (602) 230-0955; disp adv e-mail sdenison@bizjournals.com; ed e-mail ilowery@bizjournals.com; web site www.bizjournals.com/phoenix
Advertising rate: Open inch rate $2215
Pub...Ray Schey
Ed.-in-Chief................................... Llana Lwery
Mng. Ed...................................Patrick O'Grady
Prod. Dir.................................. David Hostetler
Adv. Dir.................................. Rhonda Pringle
Areas Served: 85003

THE CATHOLIC SUN (THUR)
400 E Monroe St, Phoenix, AZ, 85004-2336, Maricopa, USA; gen tel (602) 354-2139; adv tel (602) 354-2136; ed tel (602) 354-2131; gen fax (602) 354-2429; disp adv e-mail advertising@catholicsun.org; class adv e-mail akearns@catholicsun.org; ed e-mail jdlgarcia@catholicsun.org; web site www.catholicsun.org
Advertising rate: Open inch rate $42.00
Established: 1985
Adv. Rep...Jennifer Ellis
Adv. Sales.................................. Alana Kearns
Ed. ....Tony Gutiérrez
Areas Served: 85002

TOWN OF PARADISE VALLEY INDEPENDENT (WED)
23043 N 16th Ln, Phoenix, AZ, 85027-1331, Maricopa, USA; gen tel (623) 445-2777; gen fax (623) 445-2740; disp adv e-mail neads@newszap.com; class adv e-mail iniclassads@newszap.com; ed e-mail pvalleynews@newszap.com; web site www.paradisevalleyindependent.com
Circulation: 0pd, 8,500fr; CAC
Advertising rate: Open inch rate $20.00
Established: 1984
Group: Independent Newsmedia Inc. Usa
VP... Bret McKeand
Ed. ....Terrance Thornton
Adv. Mgr.................................... Jan McKinney
Pres. ....Edward Dulin
Pub....................................... Charlene Bisson
Mechanical Specifications: Full page: 10" wide by 10.625" high
Delivery Method: Mail
Areas Served: 85253

SAFFORD

EASTERN ARIZONA COURIER (WED, SAT)
301 E Hwy 70, Ste A, Safford, AZ, 85546, Graham, USA; gen tel (928) 428-2560; gen fax (928) 428-5396; disp adv e-mail mwatson@eacourier.com; class adv e-mail classi@eacourier.com; ed e-mail editor@eacourier.com; web site www.eacourier.com
Circulation: 4,094pd, 25fr; VAC
Advertising rate: Open inch rate $12.00
Established: 1889
Group: Wick Communications
Mng. Ed...David Bell
Circulation Manager ....James Copeland
Pub... Monica Watson
Mechanical Specifications: Type page 11 5/8 x 21 1/2; E - 6 cols, 1 13/16, 1/8 between; A - 6 cols, 1 13/16, 1/8 between; C - 6 cols, 1 13/16, 1/8 between.Equipment & Software: Hardware — APP/Mac G3, APP/Mac G4; Software — Macromedia/Freehand 8.0, Adobe/PageMaker 6.5.
Delivery Method: Mail, Newsstand, Carrier, Racks
Areas Served: 85546, 85552, 85551, 85536, 85550, 85548

THE COPPER ERA (WED)
301 E Hwy 70, Ste A, Safford, AZ, 85546, Graham, USA; gen tel (928) 428-2560; gen fax (928) 428-5396; disp adv e-mail mwatson@eacourier.com; class adv e-mail classi@eacourier.com; ed e-mail business@eacourier.com; web site eacourier.com/copper_era
Circulation: 871pd,; VAC
Advertising rate: Open inch rate $10.00
Established: 1899
Group: Wick Communications
Digital Platform - Mobile: Apple, Android, Windows, Other
Digital Platform - Tablet: Apple iOS, Windows 7, Kindle
Pub... Monica Watson
Mng. Ed...David Bell
Mechanical Specifications: Type page 9.88 x 21 1/2; E - 6 cols, 1 13/16, 1/8 between; A - 6 cols, 1 13/16, 1/8 between; C - 6 cols, 1 13/16, 1/8 between.Equipment & Software: Hardware — APP/Power Macmini, APP/Power Mac G4; Software — CS5
Delivery Method: Mail, Newsstand, Carrier, Racks
Areas Served: 85533, 85540, 85534

SCOTTSDALE

AU-AUTHM ACTION NEWS (THUR)
10005 E Osborn Rd, Scottsdale, AZ, 85256-4019, Maricopa, USA; gen tel (480) 362-7750; adv tel (480) 362-6699; gen fax (480) 362-5592; disp adv e-mail dustin.hughes@srpmic-nsn.gov; ed e-mail Dodie.Manuel@srpmic-nsn.gov; web site www.srpmic-nsn.gov
Advertising rate: Open inch rate $75.00 (3.5'x2')
Mng. Ed...Dodie Manuel
Ad Sales .... Jessica Joaquin
Areas Served: 85256

SEDONA

SEDONA RED ROCK NEWS (WED, FRI)
298 Van Deren Rd, Sedona, AZ, 86336-4826, Coconino, USA; gen tel (928) 282-5580; adv tel (928) 282-5580; ed tel (928) 282-7795 x129; gen fax (928) 282-6011; disp adv e-mail bob@redrocknews.com; ed e-mail Editor@LarsonNewspapers.com; web site www.redrocknews.com
Advertising rate: Open inch rate $14.10
Established: 1963
Group: Larson Publishing, Inc.
Copy Ed................................. George Werner
Pub... Robert Larson
Adv. Dir.. Kyle Larson
Ed. ....Trista Steers
Areas Served: 86336

SHOW LOW

WHITE MOUNTAIN INDEPENDENT (TUES, FRI)
3191 S White Mountain Rd, Ste 3, Show Low, AZ, 85901-7409, Navajo, USA; gen tel (928) 537-5721; adv tel (928) 537-5721 x 234; ed tel (928) 537-5721 x 228; gen fax (928) 537-1780; disp adv e-mail krippy@wmicentral.com; class adv e-mail classifieds@wmicentral.com; ed e-mail sdieterich@wmicentral.com; web site www.wmicentral.com
Circulation: 11,494pd, 17fr; Sworn/Estimate/ Non-Audited
Advertising rate: Open inch rate $200.00
Established: 1888Editions: (2) 2 total ; Apache; Navajo;
Ed. .... Sean Dieterich
Pub....................................... Charlene Bisson
VP... Bret McKeand
Pres. ....Edward Dulin
Mechanical Specifications: Type page 13 x 21 1/2; E - 6 cols, 2 1/16, 1/8 between; A - 6 cols, 2 1/16, 1/8 between; C - 6 cols, 2 1/16, 1/8 between.Equipment & Software: Hardware — APP/Mac; Software — QPS/QuarkXPress, Multi-Ad/Creator, In Design, News Edit, In Copy, Photoshop, Excel, Microsoft Word,
Delivery Method: Mail, Newsstand, Racks
Areas Served: 85901

SIERRA VISTA

ARIZONA RANGE NEWS (WED)
333 W Wilcox Dr, Ste 302, Sierra Vista, AZ, 85635-1791, Cochise, USA; gen tel (520) 384-3571; gen fax (520) 384-3572; disp adv e-mail steve.reno@willcoxrangenews.com; class adv e-mail deedee.hicks@willcoxrangenews.com; ed e-mail ainslee.wittig@willcoxrangenews.com; web site www.willcoxrangenews.com
Circulation: 1,514pd,; VAC
Advertising rate: Open inch rate $11.75
Established: 1884
Group: Wick Communications
Digital Platform - Tablet: Apple iOS, Windows 7
Mng. Ed....................................... Ainslee Wittig
Adv. Rep.. Steve Reno
Pub....................................... Rebecca Bradner
Mechanical Specifications: Type page 9.88 x 21.5 inches
6 column - 1.55; 3.22; 4.88; 6.55; 8.22; 9.88 inchesEquipment & Software: Hardware — APP/Mac; Software — QPS/QuarkXPress 6.52, Microsoft/Word.
Delivery Method: Mail, Newsstand, Racks
Areas Served: 85643, 85610, 85609, 85606, 85605, 85632, 85625

SUN CITY

GLENDALE TODAY (FRI)
17220 N Boswell Blvd, Ste 101, Sun City, AZ, 85373-2065, Maricopa, USA; gen tel (623) 977-8351; adv tel (623) 876-2566; ed tel (623) 876-2534; gen fax (623) 876-2589; disp adv e-mail paslandes@yourwestvalley.com; class adv e-mail sunclassads@yourwestvalley.com; ed e-mail dmccarthy@yourwestvalley.com; web site www.yourwestvalley.com - 130,000(views) 60,000(visitors)
Circulation: 1pd, 22,384fr; CAC
Advertising rate: Open inch rate $16.93
Established: 1995
Group: Independent Newsmedia Inc. Usa
Digital Platform - Mobile: Apple, Android, Windows
Digital Platform - Tablet: Apple iOS, Android, Windows 7
Pub..Marji Ranes
Exec. Ed....................................Dan McCarthy
Mechanical Specifications: Type page 10" x 12.75"; 6 colsEquipment & Software: Hardware — SVM; Presses — G/Urbanite; Software — DTI.
Delivery Method: Mail, Newsstand, Carrier, Racks
Areas Served: 85301, 85303, 85304, 85305, 85306, 85308, 85310, 85381, 85382, 85383

PEORIA INDEPENDENT (WED)
17220 N Boswell Blvd, Ste 101, Sun City, AZ, 85373-2065, Maricopa, USA; gen tel (623) 972-6101; adv tel (623) 445-2807; gen fax (623) 445-2720; disp adv e-mail azmajoraccounts@newszap.com; ed e-mail aznews@newszap.com; web site www.yourwestvalley.com
Circulation: 6pd, 16,340fr; CAC
Advertising rate: call for special discount rates
Established: 1999
Group: Independent Newspapers, Inc. (Arizona)
News Ed. .... Rusty Bradshaw
Mechanical Specifications: Special ROP ad prices discounts for NON contract of 1X-6X runs:
2-4 markets we can offer the 26 week rate Plus 50% off each additional market (Discount applies to less-expensive markets) with $25 for color per market.
Five market buy: (**receive 20,000 impressions for a month, per run**
Full pg $500 per market + $50 color = $2,500 B/W + $250 = $2,750 for a 5 market buy per run
½ pg $325 per market + $25 color = $1,625 B/W + $125 = $1,750 for a 5 market buy per run
¼ pg $200 per market + $25 color = $1,000 B/W + $125 = $1,125 for a 5 market buy per run
Delivery Method: Carrier, Racks

SUN CITY INDEPENDENT (WED)
17220 N Boswell Blvd, Ste 101, Sun City, AZ, 85373-2065, Maricopa, USA; gen tel (623) 972-6101; gen fax (623) 974-6004; disp adv e-mail wvads@newszap.com; class adv e-mail iniclassads@newszap.com; ed e-mail wvnews@newszap.com ; web site YourWestValley.com - 22,000(views)
Circulation: 19,850pd, 699fr; CAC
Advertising rate: Open inch rate $100.00
Established: 1960
Group: ANA Advertising Services, Inc. (Arizona Newspaper Association)
Independent Newsmedia Inc. UsaEditions: (22,000)
Pub....................................... Charlene Bisson
Pres. ....Edward Dulin
VP... Bret McKeand
Mechanical Specifications: 10 by 11 compactEquipment & Software: ; Presses — Web
Delivery Method: Carrier, Racks
Areas Served: 85351, 85373,

SUN CITY WEST INDEPENDENT (WED)
17220 N Boswell Blvd, Ste 101, Sun City, AZ, 85373-2065, Maricopa, USA; gen tel (623) 972-6101; adv tel 623-876-2569; gen fax (623) 974-6004; disp adv e-mail kmahoney@newszap.com; ed e-mail aznews@newszap.com; web site www.yourwestvalley.com
Circulation: 5pd, 11,986fr; CAC
Advertising rate: call for special discount rates
Established: 1978
Group: Independent Newspapers, Inc. (Arizona)
News Ed .... Rusty Bradshaw
Mechanical Specifications: Special ROP ad prices discounts for NON contract of 1X-6X runs:
2-4 markets we can offer the 26 week rate Plus 50% off each additional market (Discount applies to less-expensive markets) with $25 for color per market.
Five market buy: (**receive 20,000 impressions for a month, per run**
Full pg $500 per market + $50 color = $2,500 B/W + $250 = $2,750 for a 5 market buy per run
½ pg $325 per market + $25 color = $1,625 B/W + $125 = $1,750 for a 5 market buy per run
¼ pg $200 per market + $25 color = $1,000 B/W + $125 = $1,125 for a 5 market buy per run
Delivery Method: Carrier, Racks

SURPRISE INDEPENDENT (WED)
17220 N Boswell Blvd, Ste 101, Sun City, AZ, 85373-2065, Maricopa, USA; gen tel (623) 972-6101; gen fax (623) 974-6004; disp adv e-mail wvads@newszap.com; class adv e-mail iniclassads@newszap.com; ed e-mail wvnews@newszap.com; web site YourValley.nete
Circulation: 32,000fr; CAC
Advertising rate: Modular pricing
Established: 1997
Group: Independent Newspapers, Inc. (Arizona)
ANA Advertising Services, Inc. (Arizona Newspaper Association)
Independent Newsmedia Inc. Usa
Publisher........................ Charlene Patti-Bisson
VP., Opns.................................. Bret McKeand
Pres... Edward Dulin
Mechanical Specifications: Full page: 11 inches by 12.4 inches
Delivery Method: Carrier
Areas Served: 85374, 85375, 85379,

TEMPE

AHWATUKEE FOOTHILLS NEWS (WED)
1620 W Fountainhead Pkwy, Ste 219, Tempe, AZ, 85282-1848, Maricopa, USA; gen tel (480) 898-5940; adv tel (480) 898-7900; ed tel (480) 898-7913; gen fax (480) 898-6329; disp adv e-mail kmays@ahwatukee.com; class adv e-mail ecota@ahwatukee.com; ed e-mail Pmaryniak@ahwatukee.com; web site www.ahwatukee.com
Circulation: 27,800fr; CAC
Advertising rate: Open inch rate $21.25
Established: 1978
Group: Times Media Group
Pub.................................... Steve Strickbine
Ops. Mgr.................................. Chuck Morales
Circ. Dir.................................... Aaron Kolodny
Adv. Admin................................... Lori Dionisio
Class Mgr...................................... Elaine Cota
Mechanical Specifications: Type page 10" x 13.75"; 6 cols
Delivery Method: Mail, Carrier, Racks
Areas Served: 85044

EAST VALLEY TRIBUNE (SUN)
1620 W Fountainhead Pkwy, Ste 219, Tempe, AZ, 85282-1848, Maricopa, USA; gen tel (480) 898-6500; adv tel (480) 898-6415; ed tel (480) 898-6512; gen fax (480) 898-6463; ed fax (480) 898-6362; disp adv e-mail national@evtrib.com; class adv e-mail golocal@evtrib.com; ed e-mail newstips@evtrib.com; newstips@evtrib.com; web site www.eastvalleytribune.com
Circulation: 0pd, 149,308fr; VAC
Advertising rate: open inch rate $39.10; $47.60 (Sun)
Established: 1891
Group: Times Media Group
Adv. Mgr....................................... Lori Dionisio
Pub. Mgr...................................... Steven Pope
Dir., Nat'l Accts................................ Tom Legg
Nat'l Acct. Coord......................... Patricia Dixie
Circ. Mgr.............................. Brandi Rodriguez
Mechanical Specifications: Type page 10 x 13.75; 6 cols
Delivery Method: Carrier, Racks
Areas Served: 85119, 85120, 85201,85202, 85203, 85204, 85205, 85206, 85207, 85208, 85209, 85210, 85212, 85213, 852245, 85225, 85226, 85248, 85249, 85233, 85234, 85282, 85282, 85283, 85295, 85296, 85297, 85298, 85140, 85142, 85143, 85146, 85541

WRANGLER NEWS (SAT)
2145 E Warner Rd Ste 102, Ste 102, Tempe, AZ, 85284-3497, Maricopa, USA; gen tel (480) 966-0845; adv tel (480) 966-0837; gen fax NA; disp adv e-mail tracy.doren@wranglernews.com; class adv e-mail tracy.doren@wranglernews.com; ed e-mail editor@wranglernews.com; web site www.wranglernews.com
Circulation: 20,000fr; Sworn/Estimate/Non-Audited
Advertising rate: Open inch rate $85.00
Established: 1991
Pub.. Tracy Doren
Don Kirkland
Delivery Method: Carrier, Racks
Areas Served: TEMPE AZ/MARICOPA/85284, 85283, 85281
CHANDLER AZ/MARICOPA/85226

TOMBSTONE

THE TOMBSTONE NEWS (FRI)
525 E Allen St, # 4, Tombstone, AZ, 85638, Cochise, USA; gen tel (520) 457-3086; gen fax (520) 457-3126; ed e-mail editor@thetombstonenews.com; web site www.thetombstonenews.com
Advertising rate: Open inch rate $2.80
Established: 2005
Areas Served: 85638

TUCSON

EXPLORER (WED)
7225 N Mona Lisa Rd, Ste 125, Tucson, AZ, 85741-2581, Pima, USA; gen tel (520) 797-4384; adv tel (520) 797-4384; ed tel (520) 797-4384; gen fax (520) 575-8891; adv fax (520) 575-8891; ed fax (520) 575-8891; disp adv e-mail ads@explorernews.com; class adv e-mail expclassifieds@explorernews.com; ed e-mail editor@explorernews.com; web site www.explorernews.com
Circulation: 33pd, 43,440fr; VAC
Advertising rate: Open inch rate $35.16
Established: 1993
Gen. Mgr.. Jamie Hood
Ed... Mari Herreras
News Ed.. Jim Nintzel
Web Ed.. Chelo Grubb
Circulation Manager.................. Laura Horvath
Pres./Pub.................................... Jason Joseph
Mechanical Specifications: Type page 10" x 12.75"; 5 colsEquipment & Software: Hardware — APP/Mac; Software — QPS/QuarkXPress 4.1, Adobe/Photoshop 5.0.
Delivery Method: Newsstand, Racks
Areas Served: 85704, 85737, 85739, 85741, 85742, 85743, 85623, 85718

FOOTHILLS NEWS (MTHLY)
7225 N Mona Lisa Rd, Ste 125, Tucson, AZ, 85741-2581, Pima, USA; gen tel (520) 797-4384; gen fax (520) 575-8891; disp adv e-mail Kristin@tucsonlocalmedia.com; web site tucsonlocalmedia.com/foothillsnews
Pres.?Pub.................................... Jason Joseph
Gen. Mgr.. Jaime Hood
Adv. Dir................................. Casey Anderson
Circ. Mgr..................................... Laura Horvath

INSIDE TUCSON BUSINESS (FRI)
7225 N Mona Lisa Rd Ste 125, Ste. 125, Tucson, AZ, 85741-2581, Pima, USA; gen tel (520) 294-1200; gen fax (520) 294-4040; disp adv e-mail jahearn@azbiz.com; ed e-mail mevans@azbiz.com; web site www.insidetucsonbusiness.com
Circulation: 1,845pd, 3,047fr; VAC
Advertising rate: Open inch rate $80.00
Group: ANA Advertising Services, Inc. (Arizona Newspaper Association)
Ed... Mark Evans
Pres./Pub.................................... Jason Joseph
Circ... Laura Horvath
Sales Admin................................. Grace Heike
Ed... Mari Herreras
Mechanical Specifications: Type page 10 1/4 x 16; A - 4 cols, 2 1/2, 1/6 between; C - 6 cols, 1 3/5, 1/6 between.Equipment & Software: Hardware — APP/Mac; Presses — 8-HI/V-15A, 8-Atlas/Web Leader; Software — Adobe/PageMaker 6.0, Adobe/Photoshop 3.0, Adobe/Illustrator 7.0.
Areas Served: 85706

MARANA NEWS (THUR, MTHLY)
7225 N Mona Lisa Rd, Ste 125, Tucson, AZ, 85741-2581, Pima, USA; gen tel (520) 797-4384; adv tel (520) 578-1505 ext.19; gen fax (520) 908-0455; disp adv e-mail carolyn@newsmediacorp.com; ed e-mail news@maranaweeklynews.com; web site www.themarananews.com
Advertising rate: Open inch rate $35.16
Established: 2007
General Manager/Editor......... Tonja Greenfield
Dir., Nat'l Sales................................ Tom Legg
Nat'l Acct. Coord......................... Patricia Dixie
Pres./Pub.................................... Jason Joseph
Delivery Method: Mail, Racks
Areas Served: 85713

WICKENBURG

WICKENBURG SUN (WED)
180 N Washington St, Wickenburg, AZ, 85390-2263, Maricopa, USA; gen tel (928) 684-5454; adv tel (928) 684-5454; gen fax (928) 684-3185; adv fax (928) 684-3185; disp adv e-mail publisher@wickenburgsun.com; class adv e-mail vic44@wickenburgsun.com; ed e-mail editor@wickenburgsun.com; web site www.wickenburgsun.com
Circulation: 4,000pd, 3,400fr; Sworn/Estimate/Non-Audited
Advertising rate: Open inch rate $18.55
Established: 1934
Group: Brehm Communications, Inc.
News West Publishing Company Inc. (OOB)
Prodn. Mgr................................. Juan Jimenez
Pub... Jeanie Hankins
Delivery Method: Mail, Newsstand, Racks
Areas Served: 85390

WILLIAMS

WILLIAMS-GRAND CANYON NEWS (WED)
118 S 3rd St, Williams, AZ, 86046-2404, Coconino, USA; gen tel (928) 635-4426; ed tel (928) 635-4426 ; gen fax (928) 635-4887; disp adv e-mail advertising@williamsnews.com; class adv e-mail advertising@williamsnews.com; ed e-mail editorial@williamsnews.com; web site www.williamsnews.com
Circulation: 3,000pd,; Sworn/Estimate/Non-Audited
Advertising rate: Open inch rate $14.23
Established: 1889
Group: ANA Advertising Services, Inc. (Arizona Newspaper Association)
Western News&Info, Inc.
Adv. Mgr................................ Connie Hiemenz
Pub... Madeline Keith
Ed.. Yerian Loretta
Mechanical Specifications: Type page 12 1/2 x 22 3/4; E - 6 cols, 1 5/6, 1/6 between; A - 6 cols, 1 5/6, 1/6 between; C - 6 cols, 1 5/6, 1/6 between.Equipment & Software: Hardware — APP/Mac; Software — Microsoft/Word, Microsoft/Excel, Adobe/InDesign, Adobe/Photoshop.
Delivery Method: Mail, Racks
Areas Served: 86046, 86023

ARKANSAS

AMITY

THE STANDARD (THUR)
132 W Thompson St, Amity, AR, 71921-9135, Clark, USA; gen tel (870) 342-5007; disp adv e-mail southernstandard@yahoo.com; web site www.thesouthernstandard.com
Advertising rate: Open inch rate $3.00
Established: 1996
Delivery Method: Mail, Racks
Areas Served: Clark, Pike and Hot Spring Counties

ARKADELPHIA

THE GURDON TIMES (WED)
205 S 26th St, Arkadelphia, AR, 71923-5423, Clark, USA; gen tel (870) 353-4482; adv tel (870) 353-4482; ed tel (870) 353-4482; gen fax (870)887-2949; adv fax (870)887-2949; ed fax (870)887-2949; disp adv e-mail lmartin@picayune-times.com; ed e-mail wledbetter@siftingsherald.com; web site www.thegurdontimes.com
Circulation: 1,200pd,; Sworn/Estimate/Non-Audited
Advertising rate: Open inch rate $5.20
Group: GateHouse Media, Inc.
Pub... John Tucker
Ed... Wendy Ledbetter
Circ. Mgr...................................... Donnie Hollis
Reporter...................................... Sherry Kelley
Delivery Method: Mail, Carrier, Racks
Areas Served: Gurdon and surrounding communities of Clark county

ASHDOWN

LITTLE RIVER NEWS (WED)
614 E Wood St, Ashdown, AR, 71822-3648, Little River County, USA; gen tel (870) 898-3462; gen fax (870) 898-6213; disp adv e-mail jamie.lrnews@gmail.com; ed e-mail editor.lrnews@gmail.com; web site www.thelrnews.com
Circulation: 3,000pd,; Sworn/Estimate/Non-Audited
Advertising rate: Open inch rate $7.05
Established: 1898
Group: Red River Media
Gen. Mgr.................................. Quinton Bagley
Composing/Layout.................... Melanie Rhyne
Jamie Bagley
Mechanical Specifications: Type page 15 x 21; E - 7 cols, 2 1/16, between; A - 7 cols, 2 1/16, between; C - 7 cols, 2 1/16, between.Equipment & Software: Hardware — Pentium/CTX; Presses — KP/News King; Software — Microsoft/Windows 95, Archetype/Corel Draw 7.0, Microsoft/Works, Microsoft/Publisher.
Delivery Method: Mail, Newsstand

ATKINS

ATKINS CHRONICLE (WED)
204 Avenue 1 NE, Atkins, AR, 72823-4233, Pope, USA; gen tel (479) 641-7161; gen fax (479) 641-1604; disp adv e-mail advertise@atkinschronicle.com; class adv e-mail advertise@atkinschronicle.com; ed e-mail news@atkinschronicle.com; web site www.atkinschronicle.com
Circulation: 2,200pd, 201fr; Sworn/Estimate/Non-Audited
Advertising rate: Open inch rate $5.75
Established: 1897
Digital Platform - Mobile: Apple
Digital Platform - Tablet: Apple iOS, Windows 7, Kindle, Kindle Fire
Pub... Ginnie Tyson
Ed.. Van A. Tyson
Managing. Ed................................ Beckie Tyson
Circ. Mgr..................................... Beverly Davis
Mechanical Specifications: Type page 13 x 21 1/2; E - 6 cols, 1 5/6, 1/6 between; A - 6 cols, 1 5/6, 1/6 between; C - 6 cols, 1 5/6, 1/6 between.Equipment & Software: Hardware — 1-HPPavillion Elite HPE, 2-custom HP computers, 1-HP laptop, Brother printer; Presses — None; Software — Microsoft Office 365, AdobeCeative Suite 5.5
Delivery Method: Mail, Racks
Areas Served: 72823,72822, 72837, 72843, 72080, 72801,72858

THE DOVER TIMES (WED)
204 Avenue 1 NE, Atkins, AR, 72823-4233, Pope, USA; gen tel (479) 331-3875; gen fax (479) 331-4728; disp adv e-mail dovertimes@hotmail.com; ed e-mail dovertimes@hotmail.com; web site www.atkinschronicle.

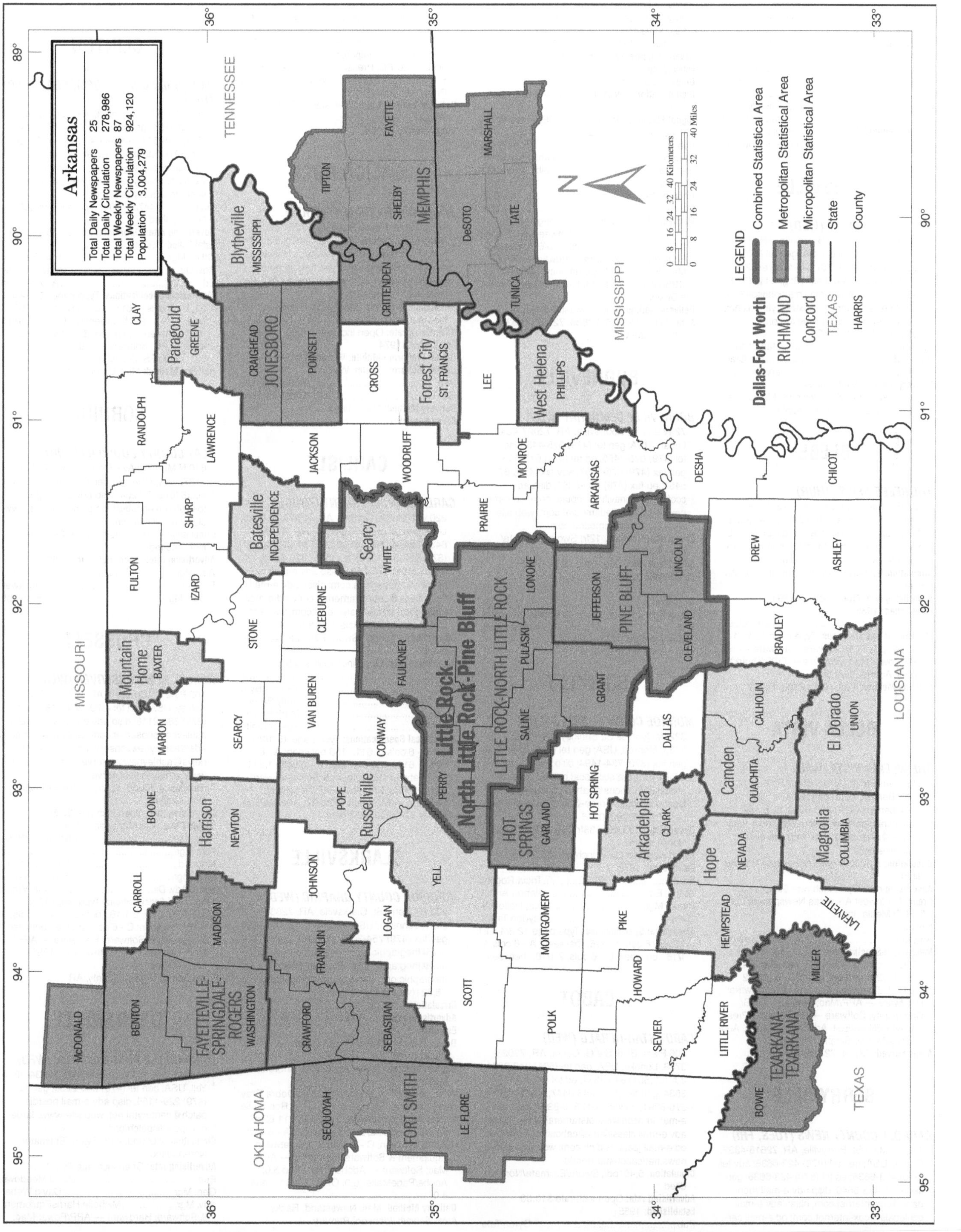
Arkansas
Total Daily Newspapers 25
Total Daily Circulation 278,986
Total Weekly Newspapers 87
Total Weekly Circulation 924,120
Population 3,004,279
LEGEND
Dallas-Fort Worth Combined Statistical Area
RICHMOND Metropolitan Statistical Area
Concord Micropolitan Statistical Area
TEXAS State
HARRIS County
0 8 16 24 32 40 Kilometers
0 8 16 24 32 40 Miles
N
TENNESSEE
MISSISSIPPI
MISSOURI
OKLAHOMA
TEXAS
LOUISIANA
Blytheville
MISSISSIPPI
Paragould
GREENE
CLAY
CRAIGHEAD
JONESBORO
POINSETT
CRITTENDEN
MEMPHIS
TIPTON
SHELBY
FAYETTE
MARSHALL
DeSOTO
TATE
TUNICA
CROSS
Forrest City
ST. FRANCIS
LEE
West Helena
PHILLIPS
RANDOLPH
LAWRENCE
JACKSON
WOODRUFF
MONROE
Batesville
INDEPENDENCE
SHARP
FULTON
IZARD
STONE
Mountain Home
BAXTER
MARION
SEARCY
Searcy
WHITE
PRAIRIE
ARKANSAS
DESHA
CHICOT
DREW
ASHLEY
LINCOLN
PINE BLUFF
JEFFERSON
CLEVELAND
LONOKE
LITTLE ROCK-NORTH LITTLE ROCK
Little Rock-North Little Rock-Pine Bluff
PULASKI
SALINE
GRANT
FAULKNER
CLEBURNE
VAN BUREN
CONWAY
PERRY
HOT SPRINGS
GARLAND
HOT SPRING
DALLAS
BRADLEY
CALHOUN
Camden
OUACHITA
El Dorado
UNION
Magnolia
COLUMBIA
Arkadelphia
CLARK
Hope
NEVADA
LAFAYETTE
HEMPSTEAD
MILLER
TEXARKANA-TEXARKANA
BOWIE
LITTLE RIVER
SEVIER
HOWARD
PIKE
MONTGOMERY
POLK
SCOTT
YELL
Russellville
POPE
JOHNSON
LOGAN
FRANKLIN
SEBASTIAN
CRAWFORD
FORT SMITH
SEQUOYAH
LE FLORE
BOONE
Harrison
NEWTON
CARROLL
MADISON
FAYETTEVILLE-SPRINGDALE-ROGERS
WASHINGTON
BENTON
McDONALD
36°
35°
34°
33°
89°
90°
91°
92°
93°
94°
95°

com
Circulation: 1,600pd,; Sworn/Estimate/Non-Audited
Advertising rate: Open inch rate $4.25
Established: 1926
Pub.. Van A. Tyson
Bus. Mgr...................................... Ginnie Tyson
Gen. Mgr.......................... Gail Tyson Murdoch
Circ. Mgr..................................... Beverly Davis
Ed.. Elizabeth Brown
Delivery Method: Mail, Carrier, Racks
Areas Served: Pope, Yell and Johnson Counties

BATESVILLE

ARKANSAS WEEKLY (WED)

920 Harrison St, # C, Batesville, AR, 72501-6949, Independence, USA; gen tel (870) 793-4196; adv tel (870) 793-4196 ext.21; ed tel (870) 793-4196 ext.13; gen fax (870) 793-5222; disp adv e-mail mattjohnson21@swbell.net; ed e-mail rgmax99@yahoo.com; web site www.arkansasweekly.com
Circulation: 21,012fr; CAC
Sales Mgr................................... Matt Johnson
Pres./Ed.. Rob Grace
Gen Mgr................................... Gary Bridgman
Delivery Method: Mail, Racks
Areas Served: Batesville, Newport, Melbourne and all of Independence County

BEEBE

THE BEEBE NEWS (THUR)

107 E Center St, Beebe, AR, 72012-3011, White, USA; gen tel (501) 882-5414; gen fax (501) 882-3576; disp adv e-mail tbn@beebe-news.com; ed e-mail tbn@beebenews.com; web site www.beebenews.com
Circulation: 2,500pd,; Sworn/Estimate/Non-Audited
Advertising rate: Open inch rate $9.00
Established: 1935
Ed. / Pub...................................... Lee McLane
Mechanical Specifications: Type page 13 x 21 1/2.Equipment & Software: Hardware — APP/Power Mac; Software — QPS/QuarkXPress, Adobe/Photoshop.
Delivery Method: Mail, Newsstand, Racks

BELLA VISTA

THE WEEKLY VISTA (WED)

313 Town Ctr W, Bella Vista, AR, 72714-2442, Benton, USA; gen tel (479) 855-3724; gen fax (479) 855-6992; disp adv e-mail bpaulos@nwaonline.com; ed e-mail tthrone@nwaonline.com; web site bvwv.nwaonline.com
Circulation: 5,000pd,; Sworn/Estimate/Non-Audited
Advertising rate: Open inch rate $9.95
Group: Northwest Arkansas Newspapers LLC
WEHCO Media, Inc.
NAN LLC
Adv. Mgr..................................... Dani Beeman
Mechanical Specifications: Type page 10 5/8 x 16; E - 5 cols, 2 1/24, 1/12 between; A - 5 cols, 2 1/24, 1/12 between; C - 5 cols, 2 1/24, 1/12 between.Equipment & Software: Hardware — APP/Mac; Presses — 8-G/Community; Software — QPS/QuarkXPress, Baseview/NewsEdit, Adobe/Photoshop, Adobe/PageMaker, Simple Text.
Areas Served: 72714, 72715

BERRYVILLE

CARROLL COUNTY NEWS (TUES, FRI)

1105 S Main St, Berryville, AR, 72616-4332, Carroll, USA; gen tel (870) 423-6636; adv tel (870) 423-6636; ed tel (870) 423-6636; gen fax (870) 423-6640; disp adv e-mail rhonda.w@cox-internet.com; class adv e-mail ccnlegals@cox-internet.com; ed e-mail carrollcountynews@cox-internet.com; web site www.carrollconews.com - 220,000(views) 29,000(visitors)
Circulation: 2,797pd, 215fr; USPS
Advertising rate: Open inch rate $14.50
Established: 1871
Group: Rust Communications
Digital Platform - Mobile: Apple, Android, Windows
Digital Platform - Tablet: Apple iOS, Android, Windows 7
Pub.. Bob Moore
Associate Ed......................... Samantha Jones
Reporter .... Kelby Newcomb
Mng Ed .... Scott Loftis
Photograher....................................... Tavi Ellis
Sports...Ty Loftis
Mechanical Specifications: Type page 10.25 x 21 1/2; E - 6 cols, 1 5/6, between; A - 6 cols, 1 5/6, between; C - 6 cols, 1 5/6, between. Equipment & Software: Hardware — APP/Mac; Presses — G/Community; Software — QPS/QuarkXPress, Multi-Ad, DTI/Ad Builder. InDesign
Delivery Method: Mail, Newsstand, Racks
Areas Served: 72616, 72638, 72632, 72631, 72611, 72660

BOONEVILLE

BOONEVILLE DEMOCRAT (WED)

72 W 2nd St, Booneville, AR, 72927-4043, Logan, USA; gen tel (479) 675-4455; adv tel (479) 675-4455; ed tel (479) 675-4455; gen fax (479) 675-5457; adv fax (479) 675-5457; ed fax (479) 675-5457; disp adv e-mail ccoffee@boonevilledemocrat.com; ed e-mail news@boonevilledemocrat.com; web site www.boonevilledemocrat.com
Circulation: 2,900pd, 12fr; Sworn/Estimate/Non-Audited
Advertising rate: Open inch rate $10.85
Established: 1899
Ed.. Glenn M. Parrish
Circ. Mgr................................. Christina Coffee
Office Mgr. .... Christina Holmes
Pub.. Kristyn Sims
Delivery Method: Mail, Racks

BRINKLEY

MONROE COUNTY HERALD (FRI)

322 W Cypress St, Brinkley, AR, 72021-2733, Monroe, USA; gen tel (870) 734-1056; gen fax (870) 734-1494; disp adv e-mail brinkleyargus@sbcglobal.net; ed e-mail argussubmissions@yahoo.com; web site facebook.com/Monroe-County-Herald-Shopper-108283809210276
Circulation: 2,300pd, 138fr; Sworn/Estimate/Non-Audited
Advertising rate: Open inch rate $5.25
Established: 1877
Ed... Tricia Rogers
Assoc. Ed.................................. Glenda Arnett
Prodn. Mgr. .... Doug Holloway
Owner....................................... Hayden Taylor
Mechanical Specifications: Type page 12 3/4 x 21 1/2; E - 6 cols, 2 1/16, between; A - 6 cols, 2 1/16, between; C - 6 cols, 2 1/16, between.

CABOT

CABOT STAR-HERALD (WED)

206 Plaza Blvd, Ste G, Cabot, AR, 72023-3748, Lonoke, USA; gen tel (501) 843-3534; adv tel (501) 843-3534; ed tel (501) 843-3534; gen fax (501) 843-6447; adv fax (501) 370-8391; ed fax (501) 370-8391; disp adv e-mail tmason@cabotstarherald.com; class adv e-mail classifieds@cabotstarherald.com; ed e-mail jpappas@nlr.com; web site lonokenews.net/cabot-star-herald
Circulation: 5,461pd,; Sworn/Estimate/Non-Audited
Advertising rate: Open inch rate $10.50
Established: 1955
Pub.. Byron Tate
Retail Adv. Mgr.......................... Teresa Mason
Mechanical Specifications: Type page 10 1/2 x 21; E - 6 cols, 1.611, .166 between; A - 6 cols, 1.611, .166 between; C - 6 cols, 1.611, .166 between.Equipment & Software: Hardware — 20-PC; Presses — 6-KP/News King; Software — Adobe/Photoshop, QPS/QuarkXPress, Microsoft/Word.
Delivery Method: Mail, Newsstand, Carrier, Racks
Areas Served: 72023

CALICO ROCK

WHITE RIVER CURRENT (THUR)

15 W 1st St, Calico Rock, AR, 72519-9099, Izard, USA; gen tel (870) 297-3010; disp adv e-mail wrcnews@centurytel.net; class adv e-mail wrcnews@centurytel.net; ed e-mail news@whiterivercurrent.com; web site www.whiterivercurrent.com
Circulation: 1,500pd, 75fr; Sworn/Estimate/Non-Audited
Advertising rate: Open inch rate $8.00
Established: 1974
Digital Platform - Mobile: Windows
Digital Platform - Tablet: Windows 7
Pub.. Charles Francis
Ed. .... Cindy Stewart
Delivery Method: Mail, Racks
Areas Served: 72519/Izard

CARLISLE

CARLISLE INDEPENDENT (THUR)

220 W Main St, Carlisle, AR, 72024, Lonoke, USA; gen tel (870) 552-3111; adv tel (501) 843-3534; ed tel (501) 843-3534; gen fax (870) 552-3111; adv fax (501) 370-8391; ed fax (501) 370-8391; disp adv e-mail ascott@arkansasnews.com; class adv e-mail classifieds@cabotstarherald.com; ed e-mail mdougherty@arkansasnews.com; web site lonokenews.net/carlisle-independent
Circulation: 1,063pd,; Sworn/Estimate/Non-Audited
Advertising rate: Open inch rate $7.25
Pub... Byron Tate
Exec. Ed...................................... Dennis Byrd
Gen. Mgr.................................... Emily Billings
Ed. .... Mark Buffalo
Adv. Mgr...................................... Susan Smith
Mechanical Specifications: Type page 10 1/2 x 21; E - 6 cols, 1.611, .166 between; A - 6 cols, 1.611, .166 between; C - 6 cols, 1.611, .166 between.Equipment & Software: Hardware — PCs; Presses — KP/News King; Software — Microsoft/Word 97, Adobe/PageMaker, QPS/QuarkXPress 4.0.

CLARKSVILLE

JOHNSON COUNTY GRAPHIC (WED)

203 E Cherry St, Clarksville, AR, 72830-3101, Johnson, USA; gen tel (479) 754-2005; gen fax (479) 754-2098; disp adv e-mail ads@thegraphic.org; class adv e-mail ads@thegraphic.org; ed e-mail news@thegraphic.org; web site www.thegraphic.org - 8,221(views) 1,687(visitors)
Circulation: 6,200pd, 0fr; USPS
Advertising rate: Open inch rate $12.00
Established: 1877
Digital Platform - Mobile: Apple, Android, Blackberry
Digital Platform - Tablet: Apple iOS, Android, Windows 7
Asst. Adv. Mgr. .... Debra Gray
Publisher/Mng. Ed............................ Ron Wylie
Mechanical Specifications: Type page 11.62 x 21 1/2; E - 6 cols, 2, 1/6 between; A - 6 cols, 2, 1/6 between; C - 6 cols, 2, 1/6 between. Equipment & Software: Hardware — APP/Mac; Software — Adobe/Photoshop 5.0, Adobe/PageMaker 6.0, QPS/QuarkXPress 4.0.
Delivery Method: Mail, Newsstand, Racks
Areas Served: Johnson, Primary
Logan, Franklin, Newton & Pope

CLINTON

VAN BUREN COUNTY DEMOCRAT (WED, THUR)

197 COURT ST, Clinton, AR, 72031, Van Buren, USA; gen tel (501) 745-5175; adv tel (501) 745-5175; ed tel (501) 745-5175; gen fax (501) 745-8865; disp adv e-mail ads@vanburencountydem.com; ed e-mail editor@vanburencountydem.com; web site www.vanburencountydem.com
Circulation: 3,447pd, 30fr; Sworn/Estimate/Non-Audited
Advertising rate: Open inch rate $8.75
Established: 1909
Office Mgr. .... Carrie Ramsey
Adv. Dir...................................... Megan Bailey
Ed. .... Alex Kienlen
Mechanical Specifications: Type page 10 1/2 x 21; E - 6 cols, 1.611, .166 between; A - 6 cols, 1.611, .166 between; C - 6 cols, 1.611, .166 between.Equipment & Software: Hardware — PC; Software — Adobe/PageMaker 5.0, XYQUEST/XyWrite.
Delivery Method: Mail, Carrier, Racks

CORNING

CLAY COUNTY COURIER (THUR)

810 N Missouri Ave, Corning, AR, 72422-7187, Clay, USA; gen tel (870) 857-3531; gen fax (870) 857-5204; disp adv e-mail jmcintosh@corningpublishing.com; web site www.claycountyliving.com
Circulation: 4,000pd, 60fr; Sworn/Estimate/Non-Audited
Advertising rate: Open inch rate $5.82
Adv. Mgr.. Fred Martin
Ed./Pub....................................... J.V. Rockwell
Prodn. Mgr. .... Bill Cobb

CROSSETT

ASHLEY NEWS OBSERVER (WED)

102 Pine St, Crossett, AR, 71635-2906, Ashley, USA; gen tel (870) 364-5186; gen fax (870) 364-2116; disp adv e-mail kcaldwell@ashleynewsobserver.com; class adv e-mail ads@ashleynewsobserver.com; ed e-mail news@ashleynewsobserver.com; web site www.ashleynewsobserver.com
Circulation: 4,300pd, 151fr; Sworn/Estimate/Non-Audited
Advertising rate: Open inch rate $6.50
Group: Lancaster Management, Inc.
Pub....................................... Barney W. White
Adv. Mgr.. Pat Tullos
Mng. Ed.................................... Vershal Hogan
Gen. Mgr. .... Whitney White
Mktg./Adv. Dir................................ Kelly White
Mechanical Specifications: Type page 13 x 21 1/2; E - 6 cols, 2 1/16, between; A - 6 cols, 2 1/16, between; C - 6 cols, 2 1/16, between. Equipment & Software: Hardware — APP/Mac; Presses — G; Software — QPS/QuarkXPress.
Areas Served: Ashley County, AR

DARDANELLE

DARDANELLE POST-DISPATCH (WED)

218 N Front St, Dardanelle, AR, 72834-3824, Yell, USA; gen tel (479) 229-2250; gen fax (479) 229-1159; disp adv e-mail postdispatch@centurytel.net; web site www.dardanellepostdispatch.com
Circulation: 2,000pd, 44fr; Sworn/Estimate/Non-Audited
Advertising rate: Open inch rate $6.30
Pub... David Meadows
Gen. Mgr. .... David Weber
Adv. Mgr.................. Michelle HarrisEquipment & Software: Hardware — APP/Power Mac;

Software — Baseview, QPS/QuarkXPress.

DE QUEEN

DEQUEEN BEE (THUR)

404 W Dequeen Ave, De Queen, AR, 71832-2834, Sevier, USA; gen tel (870) 642-2111; adv tel (870) 642-2111; gen fax (870) 642-3138; disp adv e-mail ads@dequeenbee.com; ed e-mail editor@dequeenbee.com; web site www.dequeenbee.com
Circulation: 3,600pd,; Sworn/Estimate/Non-Audited
Advertising rate: Open inch rate $8.55
Established: 1897
Group: Lancaster Management, Inc.
Pub./Ed. .... Clark Smith
Sports Ed. .... Doug Dunson
Office Manager .... Linda Russell
Advertising .... Cindy Evans
Advertising Director .... Linda Dollar
Marty Bachman
Mechanical Specifications: Type page 16 x 21; E - 7 cols, 2 1/16, 1/6 between; A - 7 cols, 2 1/16, 1/6 between; C - 7 cols, 2 1/16, 1/6 between.Equipment & Software: Hardware — APP/Mac, HP/LaserPrinter; Presses — HI/Cotrell V-15A; Software — Microsoft/Word, Adobe/PageMaker, Multi-Ad.
Delivery Method: Mail, Newsstand, Racks
Areas Served: DeQueen/Sevier/71832

DE WITT

DE WITT ERA-ENTERPRISE (THUR)

140 Court Sq, De Witt, AR, 72042-2049, Arkansas, USA; gen tel (870) 946-3933; gen fax (870) 946-3934; disp adv e-mail manager@dewitt-ee.com; class adv e-mail graphics@dewitt-ee.com; ed e-mail editor@dewitt-ee.com; web site www.dewitt-ee.com
Circulation: 2,700pd, 16fr; Sworn/Estimate/Non-Audited
Advertising rate: Open inch rate $5.50
Established: 1882
Group: Kingsett, LLC
Graphic Designer .... Haley Watkins
Manager/Ad Sales .... Dawn Deane
Ed. .... Kaley WebbEquipment & Software: Hardware — Macintosh computers, Xante printers; Presses — 4-unit News King; Software — Adobe CS5 (Indesign, Photoshop)
Delivery Method: Mail, Newsstand, Racks
Areas Served: 72042, 72055, 72038, 72140, 72003, 72160

DUMAS

DUMAS CLARION (WED)

136 E Waterman St, Dumas, AR, 71639-2227, Desha, USA; gen tel (870) 382-4925; adv tel (870) 382-4925; ed tel (870) 382-4925; gen fax (870) 382-6421; adv fax (870) 382-6421; ed fax (870) 382-6421; disp adv e-mail ads@dumas-clarion.com; class adv e-mail ads@dumas-clarion.com; ed e-mail editorial@dumas-clarion.com; web site www.facebook.com/dumas.clarion.5
Circulation: 2,600pd,; Sworn/Estimate/Non-Audited
Advertising rate: Open inch rate $8.05
Established: 1930
Group: Emmerich Newspapers, Inc.
Pub. .... Terry G. Hawkins
Office Mgr. / Circ. .... Heather Lawrence
Prod. Mgr. .... Debra Conard
Ed. .... Linda Lambert
Mechanical Specifications: Type page 14 1/8 x 21 1/2; E - 6 cols, 2, between; A - 6 cols, 2, between; C - 6 cols, 2, between.Equipment & Software: Hardware — IBM/PC, APP/Mac; Presses — HI/V-15A; Software — Microsoft, Adobe/PageMaker, QPS/QuarkXPress, Lotus/1-2-3.
Delivery Method: Mail, Newsstand, Carrier, Racks
Areas Served: Dumas and Desha County 71639
Gould 71643
McGehee 71654

ENGLAND

ENGLAND DEMOCRAT (WED)

121 E Haywood St, England, AR, 72046-1841, Lonoke, USA; gen tel (501) 842-3111; gen fax (501) 842-3081; disp adv e-mail englanddemo@centurytel.net; web site No Website
Circulation: 1,800pd,; Sworn/Estimate/Non-Audited
Advertising rate: Open inch rate $5.00
Established: 1989
Ed. .... Jerry M. Jackson
Areas Served: England and Lonoke County

EUREKA SPRINGS

LOVELY COUNTY CITIZEN (THUR)

3022 E Van Buren, Ste H, Eureka Springs, AR, 72632-9800, Carroll, USA; gen tel (479) 253-0070 ; adv tel (479) 253-0070; ed tel (479) 981-9419; gen fax (479) 253-0080 ; disp adv e-mail b.moore@cox-internet.com; class adv e-mail citizendesk@cox-internet.com; ed e-mail citizen.editor.eureka@gmail.com; web site www.lovelycitizen.com - 64,000(views) 21,000(visitors)
Circulation: 5,200pd,; CAC
Advertising rate: 1/8 P $80 1/4 P $130 1/2 $230 Full $400
Established: 1999
Group: Rust Communications
Digital Platform - Mobile: Apple, Android, Windows
Digital Platform - Tablet: Apple iOS, Android, Windows 7
Pub./Adv. Dir. .... Bob Moore
Mng Ed .... Scott Loftis
Adv. Mgr. .... Karen Horst
Design Dir. .... Melody Rust
Associate Ed. .... Samantha Jones
Delivery Method: Mail, Carrier, Racks
Areas Served: Carroll County

FAIRFIELD BAY

LAKE AREA WEEKLY (WED)

PO Box 1370, Fairfield Bay, AR, 72088-1370, Van Buren, USA; gen tel (501) 884-6012; gen fax (501) 884-6019; disp adv e-mail editor@lakeareaweekly.com; class adv e-mail volunteers@lakeareaweekly.com; ed e-mail editor@lakeareaweekly.com; web site www.lakeareaweekly.com
Circulation: 1,200pd, 0fr; Sworn/Estimate/Non-Audited
Advertising rate: Open inch rate $7.50
Established: 1967
Group: Fairfield Bay Community Club
Mng. Ed. .... Dan Feuer
Mechanical Specifications: 10" x 21"Equipment & Software: Hardware — 3 iMac Computers; Software — Quark
Photoshop
MultiAd Creator Pro
Adobe Acrobat Professional
Delivery Method: Mail, Racks
Areas Served: 72088,72031,72028,72013,72067,72044,72153,
72560,72137,72131,72543,72545

FARMINGTON

WASHINGTON COUNTY ENTERPRISE-LEADER (WED)

128 Southwinds Rd, Ste 1, Farmington, AR, 72730-8652, Washington, USA; gen tel (479) 571-6418; adv tel (479) 841-6541; gen fax (501) 399-3681; disp adv e-mail wcel@nwaonline.net; class adv e-mail wcel@nwaonline.com; ed e-mail wcel@nwaonline.com; web site wcel.nwaonline.com
Advertising rate: Open inch rate $6.23
Group: Northwest Arkansas Newspapers LLC
WEHCO Media, Inc.
Pub. .... Rusty Turner
Delivery Method: Mail, Carrier, Racks
Areas Served: Farmington and the surrounding communities of Washington County

FLIPPIN

THE MOUNTAINEER ECHO (THUR)

1277 Highway 178 N, Flippin, AR, 72634-9653, Marion, USA; gen tel (870) 453-3731; gen fax (870) 453-3071; disp adv e-mail estesd@suddenlinkmail.com; web site www.flippinonline.com
Circulation: 2,100pd,; Sworn/Estimate/Non-Audited
Advertising rate: Open inch rate $6.53
Group: Jade Media, Inc.
Adv. Mgr. .... Dale Estes
Ed. .... Jane Estes
Delivery Method: Mail, Racks
Areas Served: Marion County, AR

FORDYCE

FORDYCE NEWS-ADVOCATE (WED)

304 N Spring St, Fordyce, AR, 71742-3318, Dallas, USA; gen tel (870) 352-3144; adv tel (870) 352-3144; gen fax (870) 352-8091; disp adv e-mail newsadvo@windstream.net; web site No Website
Circulation: 2,993pd, 98fr; Sworn/Estimate/Non-Audited
Advertising rate: Open inch rate $7.00
Adv. Mgr. .... Ann Mathews
Ed. .... W.R. Whitehead
Mechanical Specifications: Type page 13 x 21 1/2; E - 6 cols, 2 1/6, 1/8 between; A - 6 cols, 2 1/6, 1/8 between; C - 6 cols, 2 1/6, 1/8 between.Equipment & Software: Hardware — PC 386s, Pentium; Presses — 3-KP/News King; Software — Adobe/PageMaker 6.0, Archetype/Corel Draw.
Areas Served: Dallas County

GLENWOOD

GLENWOOD HERALD (THUR)

209 E Broadway, Glenwood, AR, 71943-9200, Pike, USA; gen tel (870) 356-2111; gen fax (870) 356-4400; disp adv e-mail gwherald@alltel.windstream.net; web site www.swarkansasnews.com/glenwood_herald
Circulation: 2,439pd,; Sworn/Estimate/Non-Audited
Advertising rate: Open inch rate $6.00
Established: 1926
Group: Nashville Leader Publishing Company
Pub. .... Mike Graves
Adv. Mgr. .... Kareth Baber
Ed. .... P.J. Tracey IV
Comptroller .... Donna Harwell
Production .... Kenny Jackson
Advert./Web Mgr. .... Natasha Worley
Office Mgr .... Nikkole Vines
Areas Served: Glenwood, Pike and Montgomery County

GREENWOOD

CHARLESTON EXPRESS (WED)

38 TOWN SQ, Greenwood, AR, 72936, Franklin, USA; gen tel (479) 965-7368; gen fax (479) 965-7206; disp adv e-mail ksims@charlestonexpress.com; ed e-mail pgramlich@charlestonexpress.com; web site www.charlestonexpress.com
Circulation: 2,050pd,; Sworn/Estimate/Non-Audited
Advertising rate: Open inch rate $10.07
Pub. .... Kristyn Sims
Inside Sales .... Rachel Henley
Multi-Media Sales Exec. .... Lindsey Neel
Ed. .... Paul Gramlich
Delivery Method: Mail, Racks
Areas Served: Franklin County

GREENWOOD DEMOCRAT (WED)

38 TOWN SQ, Greenwood, AR, 72936, Sebastian, USA; gen tel (479) 996-4494; adv tel (479) 996-4494; ed tel (479) 996-4494; gen fax (479) 996-4122; adv fax (479) 996-4122; ed fax (479) 996-4122; disp adv e-mail info@greenwooddemocrat.com; class adv e-mail info@greenwooddemocrat.com; ed e-mail info@greenwooddemocrat.com; web site www.greenwooddemocrat.com
Circulation: 2,280pd,; Sworn/Estimate/Non-Audited
Advertising rate: Open inch rate $8.15
Established: 1881
Pub. .... Summer Aina
Adv. Mgr. .... Pam Nutter
News Desk .... Michael Stromley
Mechanical Specifications: Type page 11 5/8 x 21; E - 6 cols, 1 5/6, 1/8 between; A - 6 cols, 1 5/6, 1/8 between; C - 9 cols, 1 1/8, 1/16 between.
Delivery Method: Newsstand, Carrier, Racks
Areas Served: City of Greenwood and Sebastian county

HELENA

THE HELENA ARKANSAS DAILY WORLD (TUES, FRI)

417 YORK ST, HELENA, AR, 72342-3232, Phillips, USA; gen tel (870) 338-9181; gen fax (870) 338-9184; disp adv e-mail advertising1@helena-arkansas.com; class adv e-mail advertising1@helena-arkansas.com; ed e-mail editorial@helena-arkansas.com; web site www.helena-arkansas.com
Circulation: 2,157pd,; Sworn/Estimate/Non-Audited
Advertising rate: Open inch rate $14.50
Group: GateHouse Media, Inc.
Gen. Mgr. .... Renee Durham
Adv. Exec. .... Philly Rains
Mechanical Specifications: Type page 12 17/20 x 21 1/2; E - 6 cols, 2 1/16, 1/8 between; A - 6 cols, 2 1/16, 1/8 between; C - 8 cols, 1 9/16, 1/8 between.
Delivery Method: Mail, Racks

HAMBURG

ASHLEY COUNTY LEDGER (WED)

PO Box 471, Hamburg, AR, 71646-0471, Ashley, USA; gen tel (870) 853-2424; adv tel (870) 853-2424; gen fax (870) 853-8203; disp adv e-mail ledgerads@att.net; class adv e-mail acledger@att.net; ed e-mail editor@ashleycountyledger.com; web site www.ashleycountyledger.com
Circulation: 3,072pd,; Sworn/Estimate/Non-Audited
Advertising rate: Open inch rate $5.00
Group: Ashley Publishing Inc.
Ed. .... Whitney White
Areas Served: Ashley County

HARRISBURG

THE MODERN NEWS (WED)

206 N Main St, Harrisburg, AR, 72432-1932, Poinsett, USA; gen tel (870) 578-2121; gen fax (870) 578-9415; disp adv e-mail modernnews@pcsii.com; web site www.themodernnews.com
Circulation: 1,865pd, 30fr; Sworn/Estimate/Non-Audited
Advertising rate: Open inch rate $6.25
Established: 1888
Ed. .... Charles D. Nix
Editor .... Curtis Sanders
Mechanical Specifications: Type page 11 5/8 x 21 1/2; E - 6 cols, 1 3/4, between; A - 6 cols, 1 3/4, between; C - 6 cols, 1 3/4, between. Equipment & Software: Hardware — IBM/PC; Software — Adobe/PageMaker 6.5, Adobe/

Photoshop.
Areas Served: 72432

HAZEN

HERALD PUBLISHING CO. (WED)
PO Box 370, Hazen, AR, 72064-0370, Prairie, USA; gen tel (870) 255-4538; adv tel (870) 255-4538; ed tel (870) 255-4538; gen fax (870) 255-4538; adv fax (870) 255-4538; ed fax (870) 255-4538; disp adv e-mail heraldpublishing@gmail.com; class adv e-mail heraldpublishing@gmail.com; ed e-mail heraldpublishing@gmail.com; web site www.herald-publishing.com
Circulation: 1,000pd, 50fr; Sworn/Estimate/Non-Audited
Advertising rate: Open inch rate $11.00
Established: 1900
Group: Herald Publishing Co.
Owner/Pub.............................Roxanne Bradow
Circulation.................................Trudy Johnson
Mechanical Specifications: Type page 13 x 21; E - 6 cols, 2 1/10, 1/6 between; A - 6 cols, 2 1/10, 1/6 between; C - 6 cols, 2 1/10, 1/6 between.Equipment & Software: Hardware — PC 486, Pentium/PC; Presses — Lithographic/Multilith 1250; Software — QPS/QuarkXPress 3.3, Adobe/Photoshop 5.0, DOS 6.2.
Delivery Method: Mail, Racks
Areas Served: Hazen, DeValls Bluff, and Prairie County

HEBER SPRINGS

THE SUN-TIMES (WED, FRI)
107 N 4th St, Heber Springs, AR, 72543-3061, Cleburne, USA; gen tel (501) 362-2425; adv tel (501) 362-2425; ed tel (501) 362-2425; gen fax (501) 362 5877; disp adv e-mail advertising@thesuntimes.com; class adv e-mail advertising@thesuntimes.com; ed e-mail publisher@thesuntimes.com; web site www.thesuntimes.com
Circulation: 5,827pd,; Sworn/Estimate/Non-Audited
Advertising rate: Open inch rate $7.75
Group: GateHouse Media, Inc.
Sr. Grp. Pub.....................................Ed Graves
Ed. ....James Jackson
Adv. Mgr.................................Regina Cantrell
Delivery Method: Mail, Carrier, Racks
Areas Served: Heber Springs and Cleburne County

HOPE

NEVADA COUNTY PICAYUNE (WED)
522 W 3rd St, Hope, AR, 71801-5001, Hempstead, USA; gen tel (870) 777-1501; adv tel (870) 777-1501; ed tel (870) 777-1501; gen fax (870) 777-3311; adv fax (870) 777-3311; ed fax (870) 777-3311; disp adv e-mail lmartin@picayune-times.com; ed e-mail ccobbs@thegurdontimes.com; web site www.picayune-times.com
Circulation: 2,200pd,; Sworn/Estimate/Non-Audited
Advertising rate: Open inch rate $6.20
Established: 1899
Group: GateHouse Media, Inc.
Reporter ....Cherith Cobbs
Bus. Mgr.......................................Marcia Hunt
Class. Mgr......................................Lisa Martin
Sr. Group Publisher ....Ed Graves
Mechanical Specifications: Type page 13 1/4 x 21 1/2; E - 6 cols, 2 1/16, 1/6 between; A - 6 cols, 2 1/16, 1/6 between; C - 6 cols, 2 1/16, 1/6 between.
Delivery Method: Mail, Carrier, Racks
Areas Served: Prescott Area

HORSESHOE BEND

PACESETTING TIMES (WED)
703 S Bend Dr, Horseshoe Bend, AR, 72512-3740, Izard, USA; gen tel (870) 670-6397; adv tel (870) 670-6397; ed tel (870) 670-6397; gen fax (870) 670-7223; adv fax (870) 670-7223; ed fax (870) 670-7223; disp adv e-mail pacesetting@centurytel.net; class adv e-mail pacesetting@centurytel.net; ed e-mail pacesetting@centurytel.net; web site www.pacesettingtimesonline.com
Circulation: 2,400pd,; Sworn/Estimate/Non-Audited
Advertising rate: Open inch rate $5.00
Digital Platform - Mobile: Apple, Android
Digital Platform - Tablet: Apple iOS, Android
Pub./Ed..................................Karen Johnson
Mechanical Specifications: Type page 13 x 21.Equipment & Software: Hardware — IBM; Software — QPS/QuarkXPress 3.32.
Delivery Method: Mail, Newsstand
Areas Served: Horseshoe Bend, Melbourne, Calico Rock, Franklin, Violet Hill, Oxford, Salem, Glencoe, Ash Flat, Hardy, Highland, Cherokee Village, Mammoth Spring, and other communities in Fulton, Sharp, and Izard County

HOT SPRINGS VILLAGE

HOT SPRINGS VILLAGE VOICE (TUES)
3576 N Highway 7, Hot Springs Village, AR, 71909-9608, Garland, USA; gen tel (501) 623-6397; adv tel (501) 623-6397; ed tel (501) 623-6397; gen fax (501) 623-3131; disp adv e-mail jallen@hsvvoice.com; class adv e-mail jkegley@hsvvoice.com; ed e-mail hdaste@hsvvoice.com; web site www.hsvvoice.com
Circulation: 7,600pd, 132fr; Sworn/Estimate/Non-Audited
Advertising rate: Open inch rate $11.33
Established: 1990
Pub...Byron Tate
Adv. Mgr...................................Jennifer Allen
Gen. Mgr....................................Emily Billings
Circ. Dir.......................................David Singer
Exec. Ed......................................Dennis Byrd
Managing Ed..................................Jeff Meek
Mechanical Specifications: Type page 13 x 21 1/2; E - 6 cols, 2 1/16, 1/8 between; A - 6 cols, 2 1/16, 1/8 between; C - 6 cols, 2 1/16, 1/8 between.
Delivery Method: Mail, Carrier, Racks
Areas Served: Hot Springs Village

HUNTSVILLE

THE MADISON COUNTY RECORD (THUR)
201 Church St, Huntsville, AR, 72740, Madison, USA; gen tel (479) 738-2141; gen fax (479) 738-1250; disp adv e-mail loripollock@mcrecordonline.com; web site www.mcrecordonline.com
Circulation: 3,000pd, 4,600fr; Sworn/Estimate/Non-Audited
Advertising rate: Open inch rate $8.25
Established: 1879
Group: Boone Newspapers, Inc.
The Madison County Record, Inc.
Mng. Ed..................................Preston Tolliver
Office Mgr...............................Shannon Hahn
Ed. Asst.......................................Debbie Diver
Adv. Mgr.................................Johnna Cornett
Pub..............Randy CoxEquipment & Software: ; Software — Adobe/Photoshop 5.0, Adobe/PageMaker 6.5, Microsoft/Word 97.
Delivery Method: Mail, Newsstand, Carrier, Racks
Areas Served: Madison County, Washington County

JACKSONVILLE

THE LEADER (WED, SAT)
404 Graham Rd, Jacksonville, AR, 72076-3813, Lonoke, USA; gen tel (501) 982-9421; adv tel (501) 982-9421; ed tel (501) 982-9421; gen fax (501) 985-0026; adv fax (501) 985-0026; ed fax (501) 985-0026; disp adv e-mail johnhenderson@arkansasleader.com; class adv e-mail johnhenderson@arkansasleader.com; ed e-mail leadernews@arkansasleader.com; web site www.arkansasleader.com
Circulation: 16,251pd,; Sworn/Estimate/Non-Audited
Advertising rate: Open inch rate $17.50
Established: 1987
Ed. / Pub. ....Garrick Feldman
Exec. Ed...................................Eileen Feldman
Ed. ....Aliya Feldman
Gen. Mgr...............................John Henderson
Adv. Rep..Susan Swift
Delivery Method: Mail, Carrier, Racks
Areas Served: Sherwood, Jacksonville, Cabot, Ward, Austin, Beebe, Lonoke, Carlisle

LAKE VILLAGE

CHICOT SPECTATOR (WED)
105 N Court St, Lake Village, AR, 71653-1917, Chicot, USA; gen tel (870) 265-2071; gen fax (870) 265-2807; disp adv e-mail news@chicotnewspaper.com; class adv e-mail ads@chicotnewspaper.com; web site No Website
Circulation: 1,250pd,; Sworn/Estimate/Non-Audited
Advertising rate: Open inch rate $5.00
Group: Lancaster Management, Inc.
Circ. Mgr.................................Gloria Emerson
Areas Served: Lake Village and Chicot County

EUDORA ENTERPRISE (WED)
105 N Court St, Lake Village, AR, 71653-1917, Chicot, USA; gen tel (870) 265-2071; gen fax (870) 265-2807; disp adv e-mail news@chicotnewspapers.com; class adv e-mail ads@chicotnewspapers.com; web site No Website
Circulation: 1,250pd,; Sworn/Estimate/Non-Audited
Advertising rate: Open inch rate $5.00
Group: Lancaster Management, Inc.
Pub...Barney White
Circ. Mgr.................................Gloria Emerson
Ed. ....Whitney White
Reporter ....Justin Mazzanti
Areas Served: Eudora and Chicot County

LITTLE ROCK

ARKANSAS FREE PRESS (SUN)
324 Carpenter Dr, Little Rock, AR, 72205-4727, Pulaski, USA; gen tel (501) 224-4256; disp adv e-mail arkansasfreepress@gmail.com; class adv e-mail arkansasfreepress@gmail.com; ed e-mail arkansasfreepress@gmail.com; web site www.arkansasfreepress.net
Circulation: 25,000fr; Sworn/Estimate/Non-Audited
Advertising rate: Open inch rate $48.00
Established: 2011Editions: (120)
Circ. Mgr...................................Glen Schwarz
Prodn. Mgr. ....Dotty Oliver
Publisher, Editor ....Tracy Crain
Mechanical Specifications: Type page 10 1/2 x 12 1/2; E - 4 cols, between; A - 4 cols, between; C - 6 cols, between.Equipment & Software: Hardware — APP/Mac; Software — Adobe/PageMaker.
Areas Served: Arkansas

ARKANSAS TIMES (FRI)
201 E Markham St Ste 200, Suite 200, Little Rock, AR, 72201-1696, Pulaski, USA; gen tel (501) 375-2985; adv tel (501) 3752985; ed tel (501) 3752985; gen fax (501) 375-3623; disp adv e-mail phyllis@arktimes.com; class adv e-mail luis@arktimes.com; ed e-mail lindseymillar@arktimes.com; web site www.arktimes.com
Circulation: 616pd, 19,796fr; VAC
Advertising rate: $3,080 open rate full page four color
Established: 1974
Group: Arkansas Times Limited PartnershipEditions: (52) same circ all editions
Digital Platform - Mobile: Apple, Android
Pub.......................................Alan Leveritt
Adv. Mgr..................................Phyllis Britton
Circ. Mgr..................................Anitra Hickman
Ed. ....Max Brantley
Editor ....Lindsey Millar
Mechanical Specifications: 9 1/4W X 12HEquipment & Software: Hardware — APP/Macs, APP/Macs G4; Presses — Magazine Heat Press; Software — Adobe/PageMaker 6.5, QPS/QuarkXPress 4.x, Adobe/Illustrator 8.0, Adobe/InDesign.
Delivery Method: Newsstand, Racks
Areas Served: Central Arkansas

LONOKE

LONOKE DEMOCRAT (THUR)
402 N Center St, Lonoke, AR, 72086-2851, Lonoke, USA; gen tel (501) 676-2463; adv tel (501) 843-3534; ed tel (501) 843-3534; gen fax (501) 676-6231; adv fax (501) 370-8391; ed fax (501) 370-8391; disp adv e-mail ascott@arkansasnews.com; class adv e-mail classifieds@lonokedemocrat.com; ed e-mail mdougherty@arkansasnews.com; web site lonokenews.net/lonoke-democrat
Circulation: 1,929pd, 100fr; Sworn/Estimate/Non-Audited
Advertising rate: Open inch rate $7.25
Established: 1872
Pub..Byron Tate
Exec. Ed......................................Dennis Byrd
Adv. Mgr......................................Susan Smith
Gen. Mgr...................................Emily Billings
Jeremy Peppas
Mechanical Specifications: Type page 10 1/2 x 21; E - 6 cols, 1.611, .166 between; A - 6 cols, 1.611, .166 between; C - 6 cols, 1.611, .166 between.
Equipment & Software: Hardware — PCs; Presses — 6-KP/News King; Software — Microsoft/Word 97, Adobe/PageMaker, QPS/QuarkXPress 4.0.
Areas Served: 72086

MANILA

THE TOWN CRIER (TUES)
100 W LAKE ST, Manila, AR, 72442, Mississippi, USA; gen tel (870) 561-4634; gen fax (870) 561-3602; ed e-mail towncrier@centurytel.net; web site www.thetown-crier.com
Circulation: 2,900pd, 59fr; Sworn/Estimate/Non-Audited
Advertising rate: Open inch rate $12.50
Group: Rust Communications
Pub..Ron Kemp
Ed. ....Kaye Farrow
Mechanical Specifications: Type page 13 x 21; E - 6 cols, 2 1/4, 1/8 between; A - 6 cols, 2 1/4, 1/8 between; C - 6 cols, 2 1/4, 1/8 between. Equipment & Software: ; Software — Microsoft/Windows 95.
Delivery Method: Mail, Carrier, Racks
Areas Served: Manila and surrounding communities of Mississippi County

MARIANNA

COURIER INDEX (THUR)
31 S Poplar St, Marianna, AR, 72360-2319, Lee, USA; gen tel (870) 295-2521; gen fax (870) 295-9662; disp adv e-mail cinews@sbcglobal.net; web site No Website
Circulation: 2,500pd, 13fr; Sworn/Estimate/Non-Audited
Advertising rate: Open inch rate $10.02
Established: 1872
Group: Argent Arkansas News Media
Pub.....................................Weston M. Lewey
Ed. ....Amanda Vondran
Mechanical Specifications: Type page 11 5/8 x

21; E - 6 cols, 1 5/6, between; A - 6 cols, 1 5/6, between; C - 9 cols, between.
Areas Served: Lee County

MARSHALL

MARSHALL MOUNTAIN WAVE (THUR)

215 Highway 27 S, Marshall, AR, 72650-7781, Searcy, USA; gen tel (870) 448-3321; gen fax (870) 448-5659; disp adv e-mail mmw@windstream.net; web site emountainwave.com
Circulation: 3,200pd,; Sworn/Estimate/Non-Audited
Advertising rate: Open inch rate $8.00
Established: 1891
Adv. Mgr. .... Leisa Younger
Publisher/Editor .... Jane Estes
Mechanical Specifications: Type page 13 1/4 x 21; A - 6 cols, 2, between; C - 8 cols, 1 1/2, 1/4 between.Equipment & Software: Hardware — APP/Mac.

MC CRORY

WOODRUFF COUNTY MONITOR-LEADER-ADVOCATE (WED)

112 W 2nd St, Mc Crory, AR, 72101-8062, Woodruff, USA; gen tel (870) 731-2263; adv tel (870) 731-2263; ed tel (870) 731-2263; gen fax (870) 731-5899; disp adv e-mail wcm@centurytel.net; web site www.wcmla.net
Circulation: 2,000pd, 156fr; Sworn/Estimate/Non-Audited
Advertising rate: Open inch rate $10.00
Established: 1923
Adv. Mgr. .... Maryln Moody
Ed. .... Paula Barnett
Delivery Method: Mail, Racks
Areas Served: Woodruff County

MC GEHEE

MCGEHEE DERMOTT TIMES/NEWS (WED)

211 N 2nd St, Mc Gehee, AR, 71654-2201, Desha, USA; gen tel (870) 222-3922; adv tel (870) 222-3922; ed tel (870) 222-3922; gen fax (870) 222-3726; adv fax (870) 222-3726; ed fax (870) 222-3726; disp adv e-mail advertising@themcgeheetimes.com; class adv e-mail advertising@themcgeheetimes.com; ed e-mail editor@themcgeheetimes.com; web site www.themcgeheetimes.com
Circulation: 3,400pd,; Sworn/Estimate/Non-Audited
Advertising rate: Open inch rate $6.50
Group: McGehee Publishing Company Inc.
Circ. Mgr. .... Brenda Denton
Pub./Ed. .... Rachel Freeze
Areas Served: Desha and Chicot County

MENA

THE MENA STAR (WED)

501 Mena St, Mena, AR, 71953-3337, Polk, USA; gen tel (479) 394-1900; gen fax (479) 394-1908; disp adv e-mail clark@menastar.com; class adv e-mail sales@menastar.com; ed e-mail editor@menastar.com; web site www.menastar.com
Circulation: 4,700pd, 26,000fr; Sworn/Estimate/Non-Audited
Advertising rate: Open inch rate $8.90
Established: 1898
Group: Lancaster Management, Inc.Editions: (52)
Digital Platform - Mobile: Apple
Digital Platform - Tablet: Apple iOS
Pub. .... Clark Smith
Business Mgr. .... Jessica Laws
Account Rep. .... Vicki Agee
Advertising Director .... Linda Dollar
Composing Manager .... Cheyenne Blake
Editor .... Jeri Pearson
Press Foreman .... Carlos Duck
Mechanical Specifications: Type page 1-11/16 per col. 6 column format, depth 21"Equipment & Software: Hardware — Mac, NEWSmatic CTP; Presses — G/Community
7 units with 4 High; Software — QPS/QuarkXPress 7.0.
Delivery Method: Mail, Newsstand, Racks
Areas Served: Polk County

MONTICELLO

ADVANCE-MONTICELLONIAN (WED)

314 N Main St, Monticello, AR, 71655-4359, Drew, USA; gen tel (870) 367-5325; gen fax (870) 367-6612; disp adv e-mail advertising@monticellonews.net; class adv e-mail classified@monticellonews.net; ed e-mail editor@monticellonews.net; web site www.mymonticellonews.net
Circulation: 3,027pd,; Sworn/Estimate/Non-Audited
Advertising rate: Open inch rate $7.80
Established: 1870
Group: Smith Newspapers
Adv. Mgr.
Publisher .... Tom White
Ed. .... Harold Coggins
Ad Manager .... Vicki Kelly
Mechanical Specifications: Type page 11.625 x 21 1/2; E - 6 cols, 1.833 per column. PASSEquipment & Software: Hardware — APP/Mac; Presses — G/Community; Software — Creative Suite 6
Delivery Method: Mail, Newsstand, Racks
Areas Served: 71655-71675

MORRILTON

CONWAY COUNTY PETIT JEAN COUNTRY HEADLIGHT (WED)

908 W Broadway St, Morrilton, AR, 72110-3329, Conway, USA; gen tel (501) 354-2451; gen fax (501) 354-4225; disp adv e-mail pjch@fuddenlinkmail.com; web site www.headlightnews.com
Circulation: 6,200pd,; Sworn/Estimate/Non-Audited
Advertising rate: Open inch rate $13.00
Established: 1876
Digital Platform - Mobile: Apple
Pub. .... David Fisher
Adv. Mgr. .... Sharon Judkins
Circ. Mgr. .... Donna Ferren
Ed. .... Larry Miller
Mechanical Specifications: Type page 11 5/8 x 21 1/2; E - 6 cols, 1 5/6, 1/8 between; A - 6 cols, 1 5/6, 1/8 between; C - 6 cols, 1 5/6, 1/8 between.Equipment & Software: Hardware — APP/Mac; Software — Multi-Ad.
Delivery Method: Mail, Racks
Areas Served: Conway County

PERRY COUNTY PETIT JEAN COUNTRY HEADLIGHT (WED)

908 W Broadway St, Morrilton, AR, 72110-3329, Conway, USA; gen tel (501) 354-2451; adv tel (501) 889-2331; ed tel (501) 889-2331; gen fax (501) 354-4225; adv fax (501) 889-2331; ed fax (501) 889-2331; disp adv e-mail pjch@suddenlinkmail.com; class adv e-mail pjch@suddenllinkmail.com; ed e-mail pjch@suddenlinkmail.com; web site www.headlightnews.com
Circulation: 1,900pd,; Sworn/Estimate/Non-Audited
Advertising rate: Open inch rate $9
Established: 1874
Group: Yell County Publishing, Inc.
Ed. .... Lary Miller
Mechanical Specifications: Type page 11 5/8 x 21 1/2; E - 6 cols, 1 5/6, 1/8 between; A - 6 cols, 1 5/6, 1/8 between; C - 6 cols, 1 5/6, 1/8 between.
Delivery Method: Mail, Racks
Areas Served: 72125. 72126. 72001, 72025,72070,72016,

MOUNT IDA

MONTGOMERY COUNTY NEWS (THUR)

154 S George St, Mount Ida, AR, 71957, Montgomery, USA; gen tel (870) 867-2821; adv tel (870) 867-2821; ed tel (870) 867-2821; gen fax (870) 867-2010; adv fax (870) 867-2010; ed fax (870) 867-2010; disp adv e-mail montcnews2@windstreme.net; web site swarkansasnews.com
Circulation: 1,850pd, 45fr; Sworn/Estimate/Non-Audited
Advertising rate: Open inch rate $6.67
Established: 1951
Group: Nashville Leader Publishing Company
Pub. .... Lawrence Graves
Adv. Mgr. .... Barbara Ingami
Ed. .... Danielle Cummings
Areas Served: Montgomery County

MOUNTAIN VIEW

STONE COUNTY LEADER (WED)

104 W Main St, Mountain View, AR, 72560-6388, Stone, USA; gen tel (870) 269-3841; gen fax (870) 269-2171; disp adv e-mail leaderads@mvtel.net; class adv e-mail pam@stonecountyleader.com; ed e-mail lori@stonecountyleader.com; web site www.stonecountyleader.com
Circulation: 3,746pd, 62fr; USPS
Advertising rate: Open inch rate $8.00
Established: 1952
Digital Platform - Mobile: Apple
Digital Platform - Tablet: Apple iOS
Pub., Owner .... James R. Fraser
Circ. Mgr. .... Karen Younger
Mng. Ed. .... Lori Freeze
Mechanical Specifications: col. width 1.563 inches 6 cols
20" cutoff
Delivery Method: Mail, Newsstand, Racks
Areas Served: 72560

MURFREESBORO

MURFREESBORO DIAMOND (WED)

201 S Washington Ave, Murfreesboro, AR, 71958-9025, Pike, USA; gen tel (870) 285-2723; adv tel (870) 285-2723; ed tel (870) 285-2723; gen fax (870) 285-3820; disp adv e-mail mdiamond@windstream.net; web site swarkansasnews.com
Circulation: 1,700pd,; Sworn/Estimate/Non-Audited
Advertising rate: Open inch rate $6.00
Pub. .... Mike Graves
Adv. Mgr. .... Heather Grabin
Areas Served: Pike County

NASHVILLE

THE NASHVILLE NEWS-LEADER (WED)

119 N Main St, Nashville, AR, 71852-2002, Howard, USA; gen tel (870) 845-0600; gen fax (870) 845-5091; disp adv e-mail tracy@nashvilleleader.com; ed e-mail jrs@nashvilleleader.com; web site swarkansasnews.com
Circulation:; Sworn/Estimate/Non-Audited
Group: Nashville Leader Publishing Company
Ed. .... John Schirmer
Tracy Denny-Bailey
Office Mgr. .... Pam McAnelly
Assoc. Ed. .... John Balch
Co-Pub. .... Louie Graves
Co-Pub .... Jane GravesEquipment & Software: Hardware — CTP; Presses — King
Delivery Method: Mail, Newsstand

NEWPORT

NEWPORT INDEPENDENT (THUR)

2408 Highway 367 N, Newport, AR, 72112-2324, Jackson, USA; gen tel (870) 523-5855; adv tel (870) 523-5855; ed tel (870) 523-5855; gen fax (870) 523-6540; adv fax (870) 523-6540; ed fax (870) 523-6540; disp adv e-mail ads@newportindependent.com; class adv e-mail ads@newportindependent.com; ed e-mail gslagley@newportindependent.com; web site www.newportindependent.com
Circulation: 2,300pd,; Sworn/Estimate/Non-Audited
Advertising rate: Open inch rate $9.00
Established: 1907
Group: GateHouse Media, Inc.
Ed./Pub. .... Gina Stagley
Reporter .... Tristan Mount
Office Mgr./Classifieds/Circ. Mgr. .... Jodi Arnold
Mechanical Specifications: Type page 13 x 21 1/2; E - 5 cols, 2 3/5, 1/8 between; A - 6 cols, 2 1/16, 1/8 between; C - 6 cols, 2 1/16, 1/8 between.Equipment & Software: Hardware — APP/Mac, APP/Mac II, APP/Super Mac; Software — Baseview/Class Manager Plus, QPS/QuarkXPress, Microsoft/Word.
Delivery Method: Mail, Carrier, Racks
Areas Served: City of Newport and Jackson County

NORTH LITTLE ROCK

JACKSONVILLE PATRIOT (WED)

1 Riverfront Pl, Ste 615, North Little Rock, AR, 72114-5650, Pulaski, USA; gen tel (501) 370-8300; adv tel (501) 843-3534; ed tel (501) 370-8318; gen fax (501) 370-8391; disp adv e-mail advertising@jacksonville-patriot.com; class adv e-mail ksatterfield@arkansasnews.com; ed e-mail news@jacksonvillepatriot.com; web site pulaskinews.net/jacksonville-patriot
Circulation: 911pd, 10fr; Sworn/Estimate/Non-Audited
Advertising rate: Open inch rate $8.30
Established: 1958
Gen. Mgr. .... Emily Billings
Pub. .... Byron Tate
Circ. Dir. .... David Singer
Adv. Mgr. .... Susan Smith
Ed. .... Jeremy Peppas
Mechanical Specifications: Type page 10 1/2 x 21; E - 6 cols, 1.611, .166 between; A - 6 cols, 1.611, .166 between; C - 6 cols, 1.611, .166 between.
Delivery Method: Mail, Carrier, Racks
Areas Served: 72076, 72078

MAUMELLE MONITOR (WED)

1 Riverfront Pl, Ste 615, North Little Rock, AR, 72114-5650, Pulaski, USA; gen tel (501) 370-8300; adv tel (501) 370-8317; ed tel (501) 370-8356; gen fax (501) 370-8391; disp adv e-mail advertising@maumellemonitor.com; class adv e-mail ksatterfield@arkansasnews.com; ed e-mail editor@maumellemonitor.com; web site pulaskinews.net/maumelle-monitor
Circulation: 2,906pd, 15fr; Sworn/Estimate/Non-Audited
Advertising rate: Open inch rate $14.00
Pub. .... Byron Tate
Gen. Mgr. .... Emily Billings
managing Ed. .... Bill Lawson
Circ. Dir. .... David Singer
Adv. Mgr. .... Susan Smith
Mechanical Specifications: Type page 10 1/2 x 21; E - 6 cols, 1.611, .166 between; A - 6 cols, 1.611, .166 between; C - 6 cols, 1.611, .166 between.
Delivery Method: Mail, Carrier, Racks
Areas Served: 72113, 72118

SHERWOOD VOICE (THUR)

1 Riverfront Pl, Ste 615, North Little Rock, AR, 72114-5650, Pulaski, USA; gen tel (501) 370-8300; adv tel (501) 370-8309; ed tel (501) 370-8318; gen fax (501) 370-8391; disp adv e-mail advertising@sherwoodvoice.com; class adv e-mail ksatterfield@arkansasnews.com; ed e-mail news@sherwoodvoice.com; web site pulaskinews.net/sherwood-voice
Circulation: 1,964pd, 15fr; Sworn/Estimate/Non-Audited
Advertising rate: Open inch rate $19.50
Gen Mgr. .... Emily Billings

Pub..Byron Tate
Circ. Dir...David Singer
Adv. Mgr.......................................Susan Smith
Ed...Jeremy Peppas
Mechanical Specifications: Type page 10 1/2 x 21; E - 6 cols, 1.611, .166 between; A - 6 cols, 1.611, .166 between; C - 6 cols, 1.611, .166 between.
Delivery Method: Mail, Carrier, Racks
Areas Served: 72120

THE NORTH LITTLE ROCK TIMES (THUR)
1 Riverfront Pl, Ste 615, North Little Rock, AR, 72114-5650, Pulaski, USA; gen tel (501) 370-8300; adv tel (501) 370-8309; ed tel (501) 370-8318; gen fax (501) 370-8391; disp adv e-mail advertising@nlrtimes.com; class adv e-mail ksatterfield@arkansasnews.com; ed e-mail editor@nlrtimes.com; web site pulaskinews.net/north-little-rock-times
Circulation: 4,081pd, 20fr; Sworn/Estimate/Non-Audited
Advertising rate: Open inch rate $17.60
Established: 1898
Pub..Byron Tate
Gen. Mgr......................................Emily Billings
Circ. Dir...David Singer
Adv. Mgr.......................................Susan Smith
Ed...Jeremy Peppas
Mechanical Specifications: Type page 10 1/2 x 21; E - 6 cols, 1.611, .166 between; A - 6 cols, 1.611, .166 between; C - 6 cols, 1.611, .166 between.
Delivery Method: Carrier
Areas Served: 72114, 72115, 72116, 72117, 72118, 72120

OSCEOLA

THE OSCEOLA TIMES (THUR)
112 N Poplar St, Osceola, AR, 72370-2637, Mississippi, USA; gen tel (870) 563-2615; adv tel (870) 563-2615; ed tel (870) 563-2615; gen fax (870) 563-2616; adv fax (870) 563-2616; ed fax (870) 563-2616; disp adv e-mail timesads@osceolatimes.com; class adv e-mail timesads@osceolatimes.com; ed e-mail brand@osceolatimes.com; web site www.osceolatimes.com
Circulation: 3,000pd, 9,000fr; Sworn/Estimate/Non-Audited
Advertising rate: Open inch rate $7.50
Group: Rust Communications
Tennyson Publishing Co.
Pub...................................David Tennyson
Adv. Mgr...Steve Knox
Ed...Sandra Brand
Areas Served: Mississippi County

OZARK

THE SPECTATOR (WED)
207 W Main St, Ozark, AR, 72949-3231, Franklin, USA; gen tel (479) 667-2136; gen fax (479) 667-4365; disp adv e-mail spectator@centurytel.net; web site www.ozark-spectator.net
Circulation: 5,800pd,; Sworn/Estimate/Non-Audited
Advertising rate: Open inch rate $5.25
Established: 1911
Digital Platform - Mobile: Windows
Pub..Bob Bevil
Adv. Mgr.................................Tracey Kendrick
Circ. Mgr...Pat Bevil
Ed...Jo Eveld
Mechanical Specifications: full page 10x21 inches
Delivery Method: Mail, Racks
Areas Served: Franklin County

PARIS

PARIS EXPRESS (WED)
22 S Express St, Paris, AR, 72855-3816, Logan, USA; gen tel (479) 963-2901; adv tel (479) 963-2901; ed tel (479) 963-2901; gen fax (479) 963-3062; disp adv e-mail ads@paris-express.com; class adv e-mail ads@paris-express.com; ed e-mail news@paris-express.com; web site www.paris-express.com
Circulation: 3,600pd,; Sworn/Estimate/Non-Audited
Advertising rate: Open inch rate $9.01
Established: 1980
Pub...Vickey Wiggins
Ed...Pat McHughes
Mechanical Specifications: Type page 13 x 21 1/2; E - 6 cols, between; A - 6 cols, between; C - 9 cols, between.
Delivery Method: Mail, Carrier, Racks
Areas Served: Paris, AR and Logan County

PEA RIDGE

THE TIMES OF NORTHEAST BENTON COUNTY (WED)
981 N Curtis Ave, Pea Ridge, AR, 72751-2907, Benton, USA; gen tel (479) 451-1196; ed tel (479) 445-4081 ; gen fax (479) 451-9456; disp adv e-mail prtnews@nwaonline.com; web site tnebc.nwaonline.com
Circulation: 1,500pd,; Sworn/Estimate/Non-Audited
Advertising rate: Open inch rate $4.24
Established: 1966
Group: WEHCO Media, Inc.
Weeklies Ed. & Gen. Mgr.................Kent Marts
Mng. Ed.....................................Annette Beard
Delivery Method: Mail, Racks
Areas Served: northeast Benton County

PIGGOTT

CLAY COUNTY TIMES-DEMOCRAT (WED)
270 W Court St, Piggott, AR, 72454-2640, Clay, USA; gen tel (870) 598-2201; adv tel (870) 598-2201; ed tel (870) 598-2201; gen fax (870) 598-5189; disp adv e-mail ronkemp@centurytel.net; ed e-mail ronkemp@centurytel.net; web site www.cctimesdemocrat.com
Circulation: 1,900pd, 86fr; Sworn/Estimate/Non-Audited
Advertising rate: Open inch rate $6.75
Established: 2011
Group: Rust Communications
Co-Pub., Co-Ed..........................Nancy Kemp
Co-Pub., Co-Ed.............................Ron Kemp
Office Mgr...............................Dianna Risinger
Delivery Method: Mail, Carrier, Racks
Areas Served: Piggott and surrounding communities of Clay County

THE PIGGOTT TIMES (WED)
270 W Court St, Piggott, AR, 72454-2640, USA; gen tel (870) 598-2201; gen fax (870) 598-5189; disp adv e-mail piggotttimes@centurytel.net; web site www.piggotttimes.com
Circulation: 3,186pd, 130fr; Sworn/Estimate/Non-Audited
Advertising rate: Open inch rate $6.90
Ed...Ronald E. Kemp
Mechanical Specifications: Type page 13 x 21; E - 6 cols, 2 1/16, 1/8 between; A - 6 cols, 2 1/16, 1/8 between; C - 6 cols, 2 1/16, 1/8 between.Equipment & Software: Hardware — IBM/PC; Software — Adobe/PageMaker.

POCAHONTAS

POCAHONTAS STAR HERALD (WED)
109 N Van Bibber St, Pocahontas, AR, 72455-3319, Randolph, USA; gen tel (870) 892-4451; adv tel (870) 892-4451; gen fax (870) 892-4453; disp adv e-mail starheraldads@yahoo.com; ed e-mail anita@starheraldnews.com; web site starheraldnews.com
Circulation: 4,500pd,; Sworn/Estimate/Non-Audited
Advertising rate: Open inch rate $5.50
Pub...Jan V. Rockwell
Editor...Anita Murphy
Adv. Mgr.......................................Tonya Long
Mechanical Specifications: Type page 13 x 21 1/2; E - 6 cols, 2, 1/6 between; A - 6 cols, 2, 1/6 between; C - 6 cols, 2, 1/6 between.

RISON

CLEVELAND COUNTY HERALD (WED)
215 N MAIN ST, Rison, AR, 71665, Cleveland, USA; gen tel (870) 325-6412; adv tel (870) 325-6412; ed tel (870) 325-6412; gen fax (870) 325-6127; adv fax (870) 325-6127; ed fax (870) 325-6127; disp adv e-mail ccherald@tds.net; class adv e-mail ccherald@tds.net; ed e-mail ccherald@tds.net; web site www.clevelandcountyherald.com
Circulation: 2,200pd, 30fr; USPS
Advertising rate: Open inch rate $4.85
Established: 1888
Group: Talent Publishing LLC
Ed..Britt Talent
Circulation Manager/Graphic Arts.......Douglas Boultinghouse
Delivery Method: Mail, Newsstand
Areas Served: Cleveland County

SALEM

THE NEWS (THUR)
388 Highway 62 E, Salem, AR, 72576-8074, Fulton, USA; gen tel (870) 895-3207; adv tel (417) 264-3085; gen fax (870) 895-4277; disp adv e-mail news@areawidenews.com; web site www.areawidenews.com
Group: Rust Communications
Circ. Mgr.................................Debra Perryman
Prodn. Mgr.................................Patti Sanders
Pub..Ron Kemp
Adv. Exec. ....Kacey HollinsEquipment & Software: Hardware — APP/Mac; Presses — 6-KP; Software — Multi-Ad, Microsoft/Word 4.0.
Delivery Method: Mail, Newsstand

SHERIDAN

SHERIDAN HEADLIGHT (WED)
101 N Rose St, Sheridan, AR, 72150-2137, Grant, USA; gen tel (870) 942-2142; adv tel (870) 942-2142; ed tel (870) 942-2142; gen fax (870) 942-8823; disp adv e-mail ads@thesheridanheadlight.com; ed e-mail kristin@thesheridanheadlight.com; web site www.thesheridanheadlight.com
Circulation: 4,050pd,; Sworn/Estimate/Non-Audited
Advertising rate: Open inch rate $5.50
Established: 1881
Prodn. Mgr................................LeAnn McTigrit
Pub..Byron Tate
Mng. Ed......................................Millie McClain
Adv. Dir./Graphic Dsgn...............LeAnn Brown
Bus. Mgr.......................Kathi WebbEquipment & Software: Hardware — APP/Mac; Software — Microsoft/Word, Aldus/PageMaker.
Areas Served: Grant County

SILOAM SPRINGS

THE HERALD-LEADER (WED, SUN)
101 N Mount Olive St, Siloam Springs, AR, 72761-3156, Benton, USA; gen tel (479) 524-5144; adv tel (479) 524-5144; ed tel (479) 524-5144; gen fax (479) 524-3612; ed e-mail hleader@nwanews.com; web site www.hl.nwaonline.com
Circulation: 4,638pd,; Sworn/Estimate/Non-Audited
Advertising rate: Open inch rate $9.06
Group: Northwest Arkansas Newspapers LLC
Pub...Kent Marts
Delivery Method: Mail, Carrier, Racks
Areas Served: Siloam Springs community and areas of East Oklahoma such as Watts, Colcord, Kansas and West Siloam Springs

WESTSIDE EAGLE OBSERVER (WED)
101 N Mount Olive St, Siloam Springs, AR, 72761-3156, Benton, USA; gen tel (479) 524-5144; adv tel (479) 549-8148; disp adv e-mail rturner@nwaonline.net; class adv e-mail rturner@nwaonline.net; ed e-mail rturner@nwaonline.net; web site www.eagleobserver.com
Advertising rate: Open inch rate $6.23
Established: 2010
Group: WEHCO Media, Inc.
Digital Platform - Mobile: Apple, Android
Digital Platform - Tablet: Apple iOS, Android
Pub..Rusty Turner
Mng. Ed...Randy Moll
Delivery Method: Mail, Racks
Areas Served: Benton County

STAMPS

LAFAYETTE COUNTY PRESS (WED)
221 Main St, Stamps, AR, 71860-2827, Lafayette, USA; gen tel (870) 533-4708; adv tel (870) 533-4708; ed tel (870) 533-4708; gen fax (870) 533-1368; disp adv e-mail lcpress@sbcglobal.net; web site www.lafayettecountypress.com
Circulation: 1,550pd,; Sworn/Estimate/Non-Audited
Advertising rate: Open inch rate $5.20
Pub...Lucy Goodwin
Ed...Tommy Goodwin
Areas Served: Lafayette County

STAR CITY

LINCOLN LEDGER (WED)
216 W Bradley St, Star City, AR, 71667-5116, Lincoln, USA; gen tel (870) 628-4161; adv tel (870) 628-4161; ed tel (870) 628-4161; gen fax (870) 628-3802; disp adv e-mail lincolnledger@centurytel.net; web site www.lincolnledger.weebly.com
Circulation: 3,500pd,; Sworn/Estimate/Non-Audited
Advertising rate: Open inch rate $4.00
Established: 1876
Adv. Mgr.....................................Peggy Mason
Ed...Joe V. Mason
Areas Served: Lincoln County

TRUMANN

POINSETT COUNTY DEMOCRATE TRIBUNE (WED)
201 Highway 463 N, Trumann, AR, 72472-3503, Poinsett, USA; gen tel (870) 483-6317; gen fax (870) 483-6031; disp adv e-mail poinsettdteditor@centurytel.net; web site www.democratetribune.com
Circulation: 2,500pd,; Sworn/Estimate/Non-Audited
Advertising rate: Open inch rate $7.90
Pub...Ron Kemp

VAN BUREN

ALMA JOURNAL (WED)
100 N 11th St, Van Buren, AR, 72956-4306, Crawford, USA; gen tel (479) 474-5215; gen fax (479) 471-5607; disp adv e-mail info@pressargus.com; web site www.pressargus.com
Circulation: 210pd,; Sworn/Estimate/Non-Audited
Advertising rate: Open inch rate $11.90
Group: GateHouse Media, Inc.
Circ. Mgr..................................Tawana Wright
Ed...Ken Fry
Publisher.....................................Kim Hattaway
Multi-Media Account Executive....Lacey Nietert
Delivery Method: Mail, Carrier, Racks
Areas Served: 72921, 72935, 72947, 72952

PRESS ARGUS COURIER (WED, SAT)
100 N 11th St, Van Buren, AR, 72956-4306, Crawford, USA; gen tel (479) 474-5215; adv tel (479) 474-5215; ed tel (479) 474-5215; gen fax (479) 471-5607; disp adv e-mail jweese@pressargus.com; class adv e-mail jweese@pressargus.com; ed e-mail kfry@pressargus.com; web site www.pressargus.com
Circulation: 5,580pd,; Sworn/Estimate/Non-Audited
Advertising rate: Open inch rate $11.66
Established: 1858
Areas Served: Crawford County

WALDRON

THE CITIZEN (WED)
200 S MAIN ST, Waldron, AR, 72958, Scott, USA; gen tel (479) 637-4161; gen fax (479) 637-4162; disp adv e-mail carla@waldronnews.com; web site www.waldronnews.com
Circulation: 1,875pd,; Sworn/Estimate/Non-Audited
Advertising rate: Open inch rate $6.85
Adv. Dir. .... Don Jones
Ed. .... Joe Ben Oller
Prodn. Dir. .... Carla Harrison

THE WALDRON NEWS (WED)
200 S MAIN ST, Waldron, AR, 72958, Scott, USA; gen tel (479) 637-4161; gen fax (479) 637-4162; disp adv e-mail ads@waldronnews.com; class adv e-mail office@waldronnews.com; ed e-mail editor@waldronnews.com; web site www.waldronnews.com
Circulation: 2,670pd, 6,000fr; Sworn/Estimate/Non-Audited
Advertising rate: Open inch rate $7.00
Established: 1964
Group: Lancaster Management, Inc.
Delivery Method: Mail, Carrier, Racks
Areas Served: Waldron and Scott Counties

WALNUT RIDGE

THE TIMES DISPATCH (WED)
225 W Main St, Walnut Ridge, AR, 72476-1934, Lawrence, USA; gen tel (870) 886-2464; adv tel (870) 886-2464; ed tel (870) 886-2464; gen fax (870) 886-9369; disp adv e-mail advertising@thetd.com; class adv e-mail advertising@thetd.com; ed e-mail editor@thetd.com; web site www.thetd.com
Circulation: 4,800pd,; Sworn/Estimate/Non-Audited
Advertising rate: Open inch rate $6.50
Adv. Mgr. .... Janice Hibbard
Ed. .... John A. Bland
Mng. Ed. .... Gretchen Hunt
Mechanical Specifications: Type page 13 x 21; E - 6 cols, 2, 1/8 between; A - 6 cols, 2, 1/8 between; C - 6 cols, 2, 1/8 between.Equipment & Software: Hardware — APP/Mac; Software — Adobe/PageMaker.
Areas Served: Lawrence County

WARREN

THE EAGLE DEMOCRAT (WED)
200 W Cypress St, Warren, AR, 71671-2743, Bradley, USA; gen tel (870) 226-5831; adv tel (870) 226-5831; ed tel (870) 226-5831; gen fax (870) 226-6601; disp adv e-mail eagledemocrat@hotmail.com; web site www.facebook.com/timkesslerEditor
Circulation: 3,600pd,; Sworn/Estimate/Non-Audited
Advertising rate: Open inch rate $6.25
Established: 1885
Adv. Mgr. .... Danny Cook
Circ. Mgr. .... Deborah Rawls
Ed. .... Zack Plair
Mechanical Specifications: Type page 13 x 21; E - 2 cols, 4 1/4, 1/8 between; A - 6 cols, 2 1/8, 1/8 between; C - 6 cols, 2 1/8, 1/8 between. Equipment & Software: Hardware — APP/Mac G4 cube, Minolta/2060 printer; Software — QPS/QuarkXPress 4.1, Adobe/Photoshop, Microsoft/Office 98.
Areas Served: Bradley County

WHITE HALL

WHITE HALL JOURNAL (WED)
7400 Dollarway Rd, Ste E, White Hall, AR, 71602-3067, Jefferson, USA; gen tel (870) 247-4700; adv tel (870) 247-4700; ed tel (870) 247-4700; gen fax (870) 247-4755; adv fax (870) 247-4755; ed fax (870) 247-4755; disp adv e-mail vkelly@whitehalljournal.com; ed e-mail tbennett@whitehalljournal.com; web site www.whitehalljournal.com
Circulation: 1,800pd,; Sworn/Estimate/Non-Audited
Advertising rate: Open inch rate $7.36
Established: 1983
Group: GateHouse Media, Inc.
Sr. Grp. Pub. .... Ed Graves
Mng. Ed. .... John Worthen
Adv. Sales .... Keanon Reep
Stephanie Tiner
Reporter and Columnist .... Dawn Teer
Mechanical Specifications: Type page 13 x 21; E - 6 cols, 2 1/12, 3/20 between; A - 6 cols, 2 1/12, between; C - 6 cols, 2 1/12, between. Equipment & Software: Hardware — IBM/PC; Software — Adobe/PageMaker 6.5, Adobe/Photoshop 5.0, XYQUEST/XyWrite 4 Plus.
Delivery Method: Mail, Racks
Areas Served: Jefferson county

WYNNE

WYNNE PROGRESS (WED)
702 Falls Blvd N, Wynne, AR, 72396-2209, Cross, USA; gen tel (870) 238-2375; adv tel (870) 238-2375; ed tel (870) 238-2375; gen fax (870) 238-4655; disp adv e-mail ads@wynneprogressinc.com; ed e-mail news@wynneprogressinc.com; web site www.facebook.com/WynneProgress
Circulation: 2,775pd, 250fr; Sworn/Estimate/Non-Audited
Advertising rate: Open inch rate $14.00
Group: Wynne Progress
Pub. .... David M. Boger
Adv. Mgr. .... Brandon Boger
Ed. .... James Jennings
Prodn. Mgr. .... Sandra Boger
David Owens
Mechanical Specifications: Type page 13 x 21; E - 6 cols, 2, 1/4 between; A - 6 cols, 2, 1/4 between; C - 8 cols, 1 1/2, 1/8 between. Equipment & Software: Hardware — APP/Super Macs; Software — QPS/QuarkXPress, Multi-Ad/Creator.
Areas Served: Cross County

CALIFORNIA

AGOURA HILLS

SIMI VALLEY ACORN (FRI)
30423 Canwood St, Ste 108, Agoura Hills, CA, 91301-4313, Los Angeles, USA; gen tel (805) 367-8232; adv tel (818) 706-0266; gen fax (805) 367-8237; ed fax (805) 367-8237; disp adv e-mail AdRep@theacorn.com; class adv e-mail classads@theacorn.com; ed e-mail newstip@theacorn.com; web site www.theacorn.com
Circulation: 34,041fr; VAC
Advertising rate: Open inch rate $17.00
Group: J. Bee NP Publishing, Ltd.
Ed. .... Darleen Principe
Mechanical Specifications: Type page 10 1/4 x 16 3/4; E - 5 cols, 1 7/8, 1/3 between; A - 5 cols, 1 7/8, 1/3 between; C - 6 cols, 1 3/16, 1/3 between.
Areas Served: 91361

THE ACORN (FRI)
30423 Canwood St, Ste 108, Agoura Hills, CA, 91301-4313, Los Angeles, USA; gen tel (818) 706-0266; gen fax (818) 706-8468; ed fax (818) 671-1873; disp adv e-mail info@theacorn.com; web site www.theacorn.com
Circulation: 26,650fr; VAC
Advertising rate: Open inch rate $17.00
Group: J. Bee NP Publishing, Ltd.
Gen. Mgr. .... Lisa Rule
Ed. .... John Loesing
Mechanical Specifications: Type page 10 1/4 x 16 3/4; E - 5 cols, 1 7/8, 1/3 between; A - 5 cols, 1 7/8, 1/3 between; C - 6 cols, 1 3/16, 1/3 between.
Areas Served: 91361

THOUSAND OAKS ACORN (THUR)
30423 Canwood St, Ste 108, Agoura Hills, CA, 91301-4313, Los Angeles, USA; gen tel (805) 367-8232; adv tel (818) 706-0266; gen fax (805) 764-4432; ed fax (805) 367-8237; disp adv e-mail AdRep@theacorn.com; class adv e-mail classads@theacorn.com; ed e-mail newstip@theacorn.com; web site www.toacorn.com
Circulation: 40,072fr; VAC
Advertising rate: Open inch rate $17.00
Group: J. Bee NP Publishing, Ltd.
Ed. .... Kyle Jorrey
Mechanical Specifications: Type page 10 1/4 x 16 3/4; E - 5 cols, 1 7/8, 1/3 between; A - 5 cols, 1 7/8, 1/3 between; C - 6 cols, 1 3/16, 1/3 between.
Areas Served: 91301

ALAMEDA

ALAMEDA JOURNAL (TUES, FRI)
1516 Oak St, Ste 105, Alameda, CA, 94501-2953, Alameda, USA; gen tel (510) 748-1658; gen fax (510) 748-1680; disp adv e-mail jkohler@bayareanewsgroup.com; class adv e-mail classads@bayareanewsgroup.com; ed e-mail dhatfield@bayareanewsgroup.com; web site www.insidebayarea.com
Circulation: 11,469pd,; AAM
Advertising rate: Open inch rate $21.00
Group: Digital First Media
Asst. Mng. Ed. .... Frankel Mike
Red. News Ed. .... Ken McLaughlin
News Ed. .... Chris Walker
Areas Served: Almeda County

PIEDMONTER (FRI)
1516 Oak St, Alameda, CA, 94501-2947, Alameda, USA; gen tel (510) 748-1666; ed tel (510) 748-1658; gen fax (510) 748-1680; web site www.insidebayarea.com/piedmont
Circulation: 4,929pd,; AAM
Advertising rate: Open inch rate $20.10
Group: Digital First Media
Reg. news editor .... Ken McLaughlin
Asst. Mng. Ed. – Reg. .... Frankel Mike
News Ed. .... Chris Walker
Areas Served: 94501

THE MONTCLARION (TUES, FRI)
1516 Oak St, Alameda, CA, 94501-2947, Contra Costa, USA; gen tel (510) 748-1666; gen fax (510) 748-1680; disp adv e-mail drounds@bayareanewsgroup.com; web site www.insidebayarea.com/montclair
Circulation: 25,858pd,; AAM
Advertising rate: Open inch rate $21.00
Group: Digital First Media
Hills Ed. .... Jon Kawamoto
Pub. .... David Rounds
Reg. News Ed. .... Chris Walker
Ken McLaughlin
Areas Served: 94598

ALPINE

ALPINE SUN (THUR)
2144 Alpine Blvd, Alpine, CA, 91901-2113, San Diego, USA; gen tel (619) 445-3288; gen fax (619) 445-6776; disp adv e-mail editor@thealpinesun.com; web site www.thealpinesun.com
Circulation: 4,400pd, 2,800fr; Sworn/Estimate/Non-Audited
Advertising rate: Open inch rate $8.00
Pub. .... Vonne Sanchez
Ed. .... Lori Bledsoe
Adv. Mgr. .... Jennifer Tshida
Areas Served: San Diego County

ALTURAS

THE MODOC COUNTY RECORD (THUR)
201 W Carlos St, Alturas, CA, 96101-3919, Modoc, USA; gen tel (530) 233-2632; gen fax (530) 233-5113; disp adv e-mail record1@modocrecord.com; class adv e-mail classifieds@modocrecord.com; ed e-mail rick@modocrecord.com; web site www.modocrecord.com
Circulation: 4,500pd,; Sworn/Estimate/Non-Audited
Advertising rate: Open inch rate $4.75
Established: 1892
Jane Holloway
Rick HollowayEd.s
Mechanical Specifications: Type page 11 5/8 x 21; E - 6 cols, 1 7/8, 1/6 between; A - 6 cols, 1 7/8, 1/6 between; C - 8 cols, 1 1/3, 1/6 between.Equipment & Software: Hardware — APP/Mac; Software — Microsoft/Word.
Delivery Method: Mail, Racks
Areas Served: 96101

ATASCADERO

ATASCADERO NEWS (WED, FRI)
PO Box 6068, Atascadero, CA, 93423-6068, San Luis Obispo, USA; gen tel (805) 466-2585; adv tel (805) 466-2585 x 116; ed tel (805) 466-2585 x 203; gen fax (805) 466-2714; disp adv e-mail publisher@atascaderonews.com; ed e-mail editor@atascaderonews.com; web site www.atascaderonews.com
Circulation: 12,500pd, 5,800fr; Sworn/Estimate/Non-Audited
Advertising rate: Open inch rate $13.50
Established: 1916
Group: News Media Corp.
Ed. .... Ryan Cronk
Ad. Mgr. .... Adriana Novack
Pub. .... John Bartlett
Gen. Mgr. .... Michael bartlett
Office Mgr. .... Autumn ThayerEquipment & Software: ; Presses — KP/News King.
Areas Served: San Luis Obispo County

AVALON

THE CATALINA ISLANDER (FRI)
635 Crescent Ave, Ste A, Avalon, CA, 90704, Los Angeles, USA; gen tel (310) 510-0500; adv tel (310) 510-0500 x 250; ed tel (310) 510-0500; gen fax (310) 510-2882; disp adv e-mail advertising@thecatalinaislander.com; class adv e-mail advertising@thecatalinaislander.com; ed e-mail editor@thecatalinaislander.com; web site www.thecatalinaislander.com
Circulation: 3,015pd, 2,000fr; Sworn/Estimate/Non-Audited
Advertising rate: Open inch rate $16.25
Established: 1914
Group: CommunityMedia Co.
Digital Platform - Mobile: Blackberry
Digital Platform - Tablet: Other
Exec. Pub. .... Vince Bodiford
Editor .... Dixie Redfearn
General Manager .... Jon Remy

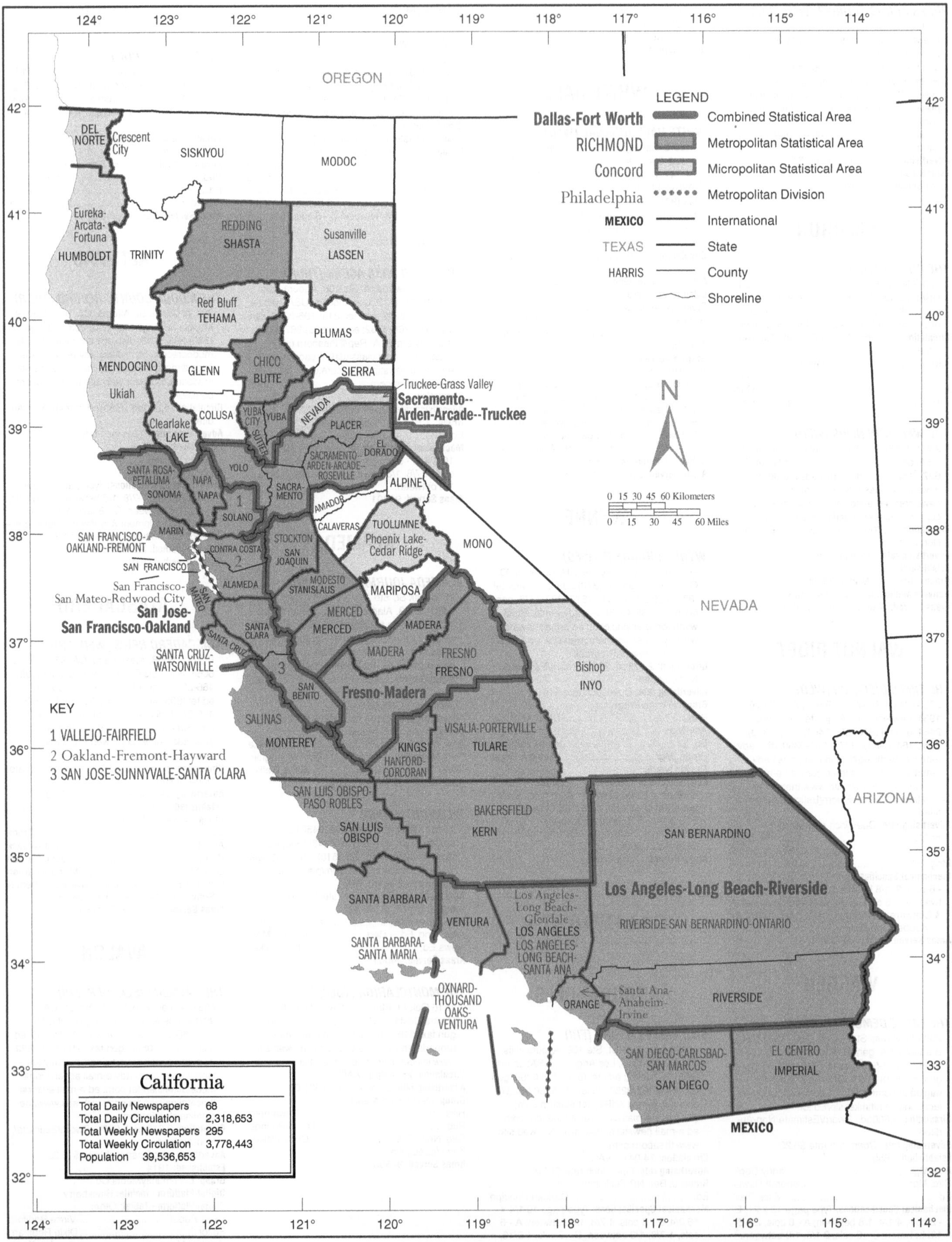
OREGON
NEVADA
ARIZONA
MEXICO
LEGEND
Dallas-Fort Worth Combined Statistical Area
RICHMOND Metropolitan Statistical Area
Concord Micropolitan Statistical Area
Philadelphia Metropolitan Division
MEXICO International
TEXAS State
HARRIS County
Shoreline
N
0 15 30 45 60 Kilometers
0 15 30 45 60 Miles
DEL NORTE
Crescent City
SISKIYOU
MODOC
Eureka-Arcata-Fortuna
HUMBOLDT
TRINITY
REDDING
SHASTA
Susanville
LASSEN
Red Bluff
TEHAMA
PLUMAS
MENDOCINO
Ukiah
GLENN
CHICO
BUTTE
SIERRA
Truckee-Grass Valley
Sacramento--Arden-Arcade--Truckee
Clearlake
LAKE
COLUSA
YUBA CITY
YUBA
SUTTER
NEVADA
PLACER
EL DORADO
SACRAMENTO--ARDEN-ARCADE--ROSEVILLE
YOLO
SANTA ROSA-PETALUMA
SONOMA
NAPA
NAPA
SOLANO
SACRAMENTO
ALPINE
AMADOR
CALAVERAS
TUOLUMNE
Phoenix Lake-Cedar Ridge
MONO
MARIN
SAN FRANCISCO-OAKLAND-FREMONT
CONTRA COSTA
STOCKTON
SAN JOAQUIN
SAN FRANCISCO
San Francisco-San Mateo-Redwood City
ALAMEDA
MODESTO
STANISLAUS
MARIPOSA
SAN MATEO
San Jose-San Francisco-Oakland
MERCED
MERCED
SANTA CLARA
MADERA
MADERA
SANTA CRUZ
SANTA CRUZ-WATSONVILLE
FRESNO
FRESNO
Bishop
INYO
SAN BENITO
Fresno-Madera
KEY
1 VALLEJO-FAIRFIELD
2 Oakland-Fremont-Hayward
3 SAN JOSE-SUNNYVALE-SANTA CLARA
SALINAS
MONTEREY
VISALIA-PORTERVILLE
TULARE
KINGS
HANFORD-CORCORAN
SAN LUIS OBISPO-PASO ROBLES
SAN LUIS OBISPO
BAKERSFIELD
KERN
SAN BERNARDINO
SANTA BARBARA
Los Angeles-Long Beach-Glendale
LOS ANGELES
LOS ANGELES-LONG BEACH-SANTA ANA
Los Angeles-Long Beach-Riverside
RIVERSIDE-SAN BERNARDINO-ONTARIO
VENTURA
SANTA BARBARA-SANTA MARIA
OXNARD-THOUSAND OAKS-VENTURA
ORANGE
Santa Ana-Anaheim-Irvine
RIVERSIDE
SAN DIEGO-CARLSBAD-SAN MARCOS
SAN DIEGO
EL CENTRO
IMPERIAL
California
Total Daily Newspapers 68
Total Daily Circulation 2,318,653
Total Weekly Newspapers 295
Total Weekly Circulation 3,778,443
Population 39,536,653

Mechanical Specifications: Type page 10 1/4 x 16; E - 5 cols, 1 11/12, 1/6 between; A - 5 cols, 1 11/12, 1/6 between; C - 5 cols, 1 11/12, 1/6 between.
Delivery Method: Mail, Newsstand, Racks
Areas Served: 90704

BAKERSFIELD

SHAFTER PRESS (WED)

1508 Corte Perito, Bakersfield, CA, 93309-7155, Kern, USA; gen tel (661) 746-4942; adv tel (661) 303-7465; ed tel (661) 746-4942; gen fax (661) 746-5571; disp adv e-mail shafterpress@earthlink.net; ed e-mail shafterpress@earthlink.net; web site www.shafterpress.net
Circulation: 2,300pd, 4,000fr; Sworn/Estimate/Non-Audited
Advertising rate: Open inch rate $6.50
Established: 1927
Pub.. Donald L. Reed
Pub.. Frank W. Reed
Circ. Mgr..................................... Diane Givens
Ed. .... Jamie Stewart
Areas Served: 93263, 93206, 93312

BANNING

RECORD GAZETTE (FRI)

218 N Murray St, Banning, CA, 92220-5512, Riverside, USA; gen tel (951) 849-4586; adv tel (951) 849-4586; gen fax (951) 849-2437; adv fax (951) 849-2437; disp adv e-mail advertising@recordgazette.net; class adv e-mail advertising@recordgazette.net; web site www.recordgazette.net
Circulation: 1,537pd, 18,178fr; VAC
Advertising rate: Open inch rate $18.50
Group: Century Group Newspapers
Gen. Mgr... Art Reyes
Ed. .... Ron Smith
Areas Served: 92220

BEVERLY HILLS

BEVERLY HILLS COURIER (FRI)

499 Cañon Drive Suite 100, Beverly Hills, CA, 90210, Los Angeles, USA; gen tel (310) 278-1322; adv tel (310) 278-1322 x 116; gen fax (310) 271-5118; disp adv e-mail eportugal@bhcourier.com; class adv e-mail advertising@bhcourier.com; ed e-mail editorial@bhcourier.com; web site www.bhcourier.com
Circulation: 39,975fr; VAC
Advertising rate: $48.50
Established: 1965
Digital Platform - Mobile: Apple, Android, Windows
Digital Platform - Tablet: Apple iOS, Android, Windows 7, Blackberry Tablet OS, Kindle, Kindle Fire
Pub.. Clifton S. Smith
Associate Pub./Circ. Mgr Marcia Wilson Hobbs
Sr. Sales Exec................................ Ron Pingul
Prod. Mgr........................... Ferry Simanjuntak
Mechanical Specifications: Type page 10" x 14"; 5 colsEquipment & Software: Hardware — Mac OS 10; Presses — urbanite; Software — Quark
Delivery Method: Carrier
Areas Served: 90210, 90211, 90212, 90024, 90025, 90035, 90049, 90067, 90077, 92260, 92262, 92270

BEVERLY HILLS WEEKLY (THUR)

140 S Beverly Dr, Ste 201, Beverly Hills, CA, 90212-3050, Los Angeles, USA; gen tel (310) 887-0788; gen fax (310) 887-0789; disp adv e-mail editor@bhweekly.com; web site www.bhweekly.com
Circulation: 30pd, 14,920fr; VAC
Advertising rate: 1/8 Pg $700.00; 1/4 Pg $1000.00; 1/2 Ph $1600.00
Established: 1999
Pub. Mgr .... Josh Gross
Ed. .... Olivia Anderson
Ad. .... Yasi Pedram
Mechanical Specifications: Type page 10 x 13; E - 4 cols, between; A - 4 cols, between; C - 4 cols, between.Equipment & Software: Hardware — APP/Mac.
Areas Served: 90035, 90210, 90211, 90212

BIG BEAR LAKE

BIG BEAR GRIZZLY (WED)

42007 Fox Farm Rd, Ste 3, Big Bear Lake, CA, 92315, San Bernardino, USA; gen tel (909) 866-3456; adv tel (909) 866-3456; ed tel (909) 866-3003 x 137; gen fax (909) 866-2302; disp adv e-mail mweaver@bigbeargrizzly.net; class adv e-mail classified@bigbeargrizzly.net; ed e-mail jbowers.grizzly@gmail.com; web site www.bigbeargrizzly.net - 129,975(views) 16,200(visitors)
Circulation: 4,500pd, 0fr; Sworn/Estimate/Non-Audited
Advertising rate: Modular
Established: 1941
Group: Brehm Communications, Inc.
Digital Platform - Mobile: Apple, Android, Windows
Digital Platform - Tablet: Apple iOS, Android, Windows 7, Blackberry Tablet OS, Kindle, Nook, Kindle Fire
Pub... Judi Bowers
Sports Ed.................................... Kathy Portie
Business Manager Karen Osuna-Sharamitaro
Mechanical Specifications: Tall tabloid format, incremental ad sizes from 1/16 to full page. Full page 10 5/16" wide x 15 3/4" high.Equipment & Software: Hardware — APP/Mac; Software — InDesign, MultiAd Creator, Pre1 Smart Publisher
Delivery Method: Mail, Newsstand
Areas Served: 92314, 92315, 92333, 92386

GRIZZLY WEEKENDER (SAT)

42007 Fox Farm Rd, Ste 3, Big Bear Lake, CA, 92315, San Bernardino, USA; gen tel (909) 866-3456; gen fax (909) 866-2302; disp adv e-mail mweaver@bigbeargrizzly.net; class adv e-mail classified@bigbeargrizzly.net; ed e-mail jbowers.grizzly@gmail.com; web site www.bigbeargrizzly.net
Circulation: 6,500fr; Sworn/Estimate/Non-Audited
Advertising rate: Modular
Established: 1993
Group: Brehm Communications, Inc.
Digital Platform - Mobile: Blackberry
Digital Platform - Tablet: Other
General Manager.......................... Judi Bowers
Business Manager....................... Karen Osuna
Marketing Director....................... Mike Weaver
Mechanical Specifications: Tall tabloid format. Full page 10 5/16" wide by 15 3/4" high. Equipment & Software: Hardware — MacKintosh; Software — In Design, Multiad Creator, Pre1 Smart Publisher
Delivery Method: Carrier, Racks
Areas Served: 92315, 92314, 92386, 92333

BISHOP

INYO REGISTER (TUES, THUR, SAT)

407 W Line St, Ste 8, Bishop, CA, 93514-3321, Inyo, USA; gen tel (760) 873-3535; adv tel (760) 873-3535 x 207; ed tel (760) 873-3535 x 211; gen fax (760) 873-3591; disp adv e-mail terry@inyoregister.com; class adv e-mail classy@inyoregister.com; ed e-mail tvestal@inyoregister.com; web site www.inyoregister.com
Circulation: 3,688pd, 2,400fr; Sworn/Estimate/Non-Audited
Advertising rate: Open inch rate $13.24
Established: 1870
Group: Horizon Publications Inc.
Publisher..................................... Rena Mlodecki
Managing Editor .... Terrance Vestal
Publisher.................................... Rena Mlodecki
Associate Editor................ Michael Chacanaca
Mechanical Specifications: regular page; 11.25 x 20.5 inchesEquipment & Software: Hardware — PC, APP/Macs, ECR/Imagesetter; Presses — G/Community; Software — Baseview, QPS/QuarkXPress 4.1, Adobe/Photoshop 5.5, ECR/PostScript Level II.
Delivery Method: Mail, Newsstand, Carrier, Racks
Areas Served: Inyo County

BLYTHE

PALO VERDE VALLEY TIMES (WED, FRI)

400 W Hobsonway, Blythe, CA, 92225-1509, Riverside, USA; gen tel (760) 922-3181; gen fax (760) 922-3184; disp adv e-mail advertising@pvvt.com; class adv e-mail classifieds@pvvt.com; ed e-mail editor@pvvt.com; web site www.paloverdevalleytimes.com
Circulation: 1,770pd, 55fr; VAC
Advertising rate: Open inch rate $14.70
Established: 1925
Group: Western News&Info, Inc.
Pub.. Debbie Hoel
Adv. Rep.. Jill Madsen
Assoc. Ed.................................. Jaclyn Randall
Classified Adv. Mgr............... Sylvia Rubalcaba
Circ. Mgr.................................. Robin Echardt
Mechanical Specifications: Type page 14 1/4 x 21 1/2; E - 6 cols, 2 1/6, 1/4 between; A - 6 cols, 2 1/16, 1/4 between.Equipment & Software: Hardware — Mac.
Areas Served: 92225

QUARTZSITE TIMES (WED)

153 S Broadway, Blythe, CA, 92225-2501, Riverside, USA; gen tel (760) 922-3181; adv tel (760) 922-3181; ed tel (760) 922-3181; gen fax (760) 922-3184; disp adv e-mail advertising@pvvt.com; class adv e-mail advertising@pvvt.com; ed e-mail mbachman@pvvt.com; web site www.paloverdevalleytimes.com
Circulation: 78pd,; VAC
Advertising rate: Open inch rate $13.98
Established: 1925
Group: Western News&Info, Inc.
Publisher...................................... Debbie Hoel
Adv. Rep.. Jill Madsen
Mng. Ed..................................... Jaclyn Randall
Mechanical Specifications: Type page 14 1/4 x 21 1/2; E - 6 cols, 2 1/6, 1/4 between; A - 6 cols, 2 1/16, 1/4 between.Equipment & Software: Hardware — Mac.
Areas Served: 92226

BOONVILLE

ANDERSON VALLEY ADVERTISER (WED)

PO Box 459, Boonville, CA, 95415-0459, Mendocino, USA; gen tel (707) 895-3016; gen fax (707) 895-3355; disp adv e-mail ava@pacific.net; web site www.theava.com
Circulation: 3,000pd,; Sworn/Estimate/Non-Audited
Advertising rate: Open inch rate $3.50
Ed. .... Bruce Anderson
Areas Served: Mendocino County

BRENTWOOD

THE PRESS

248 Oak St, Brentwood, CA, 94513-1337, USA; gen tel (925) 634-1441

BURNEY

THE INTERMOUNTAIN NEWS (WED)

PO Box 1030, Burney, CA, 96013-1030, Shasta, USA; gen tel (530) 725-0925; gen fax (530) 303-1528; disp adv e-mail news@northstate.news; class adv e-mail katie@northstate.news; ed e-mail craig@northstate.news; web site www.northstate.news
Circulation: 2,300pd,; Sworn/Estimate/Non-Audited
Advertising rate: Open inch rate $13.70
Established: 1957
Group: Cright, Inc.
Pres./Pub.............................. Craig Harrington
Mgr....................................... Katie Harrington
Mechanical Specifications: Type page 11 5/8 x 21; E - 6 cols, 1 13/16, 1/8 between; A - 6 cols, 1 13/16, 1/8 between; C - 6 cols, 1 13/16, 1/8 between.Equipment & Software: Hardware — APP/Mac, PCs; Software — Microsoft/Word 2001, Adobe/PageMaker 6.5, Adobe/Photoshop 5.5, Adobe/Illustrator 9.0, Archetype/Corel Draw 9.0, QPS/QuarkXPress, Macromedia/Freehand 8.0.
Delivery Method: Mail, Racks
Areas Served: 96013, 96028, 96056, 96009, 96006

CALIFORNIA CITY

MOJAVE DESERT NEWS (THUR)

8148 California City Blvd, California City, CA, 93505-2662, Kern, USA; gen tel (760) 373-4812; gen fax (760) 373-2941; disp adv e-mail admin@desertnews.com; class adv e-mail classified@desertnews.com; ed e-mail sales@desertnews.com; web site www.desertnews.com
Circulation: 5,500pd, 500fr; Sworn/Estimate/Non-Audited
Advertising rate: Open inch rate $8.65
Established: 1938
Group: Times Media Group
Co-Pub./Ed. .... James Quiggle
Co-Pub... Linda Love
Mechanical Specifications: 6 cols. Total; 1.625"; 2 cols. 3.375"; 3 cols. 5.125"; 4 cols. 6.875"; 5 cols. 8.625"; 6 cols. 10.39"; 1/8 betw cols. Inches Charged full depth ; col. 21.5; pg 129, dbl truck 258. Classified Pages 9 cols. Total; 1 col. 1.0625"; 2 cols. 2.25" 3 cols 3.375"; 4 cols. 4.50"; 5 cols. 5.75"; 6 cols. 6.875"; 7 cols. 8.125"; 8 cols. 9.25"; 9 cols10.39": 1/8" betw cols.
Delivery Method: Mail, Newsstand, Racks
Areas Served: 93505, 93504, 93501, 93502, 93560, 93516, 93523

CALISTOGA

THE WEEKLY CALISTOGAN (THUR)

PO Box 385, Calistoga, CA, 94515-0385, Napa, USA; gen tel (707) 942-4035; adv tel (707) 967-6815; ed tel (707) 942-4035; disp adv e-mail nkostecka@napanews.com; class adv e-mail classified@napanews.com; ed e-mail editor@weeklycalistogan.com; web site www.napavalleyregister.com/calistogan/
Circulation: 250pd,; Sworn/Estimate/Non-Audited
Advertising rate: Open inch rate $16.94
Established: 1877
Group: Lee Enterprises, Inc.
Ed. .... Anne Ernst
Areas Served: 94515

CAMARILLO

CAMARILLO ACORN (FRI)

1203 Flynn Rd, Unit 140, Camarillo, CA, 93012-6202, Ventura, USA; gen tel (818)706-0266; gen fax (805) 484-2313; disp adv e-mail camarillo@theacorn.com; ed e-mail newstip@theacorn.com; web site thecamarilloacorn.com
Circulation: 26,628fr; VAC
Advertising rate: Open inch rate $76.08
Group: J. Bee NP Publishing, Ltd.
Ed. .... Daniel Wolowicz
Areas Served: Ventura County

MOORPARK ACORN (FRI)

1203 Flynn Rd, Unit 140, Camarillo, CA, 93012-6202, Ventura, USA; gen tel (818) 706-0266; gen fax (818) 706-8468; del fax (818) 671-1873; disp adv e-mail AdRep@theacorn.com; class adv e-mail classads@theacorn.com; ed e-mail newstip@theacorn.com; web site www.mpacorn.com

Circulation: 11,530fr; VAC
Group: J. Bee NP Publishing, Ltd.
ed.. Daniel Wolowicz

CAMBRIA

THE CAMBRIAN (THUR)

2068 Main St, Cambria, CA, 93428-3014, San Luis Obispo, USA; gen tel (805) 927-8652; adv tel (805) 927-8652; ed tel (805) 927-8896; gen fax (805) 927-4708; ed fax (805) 927-4708; disp adv e-mail cambrianads@thetribunenews.com; class adv e-mail classifiedsells@thetribunenews.com; ed e-mail cambrian@thetribunenews.com; web site www.sanluisobispo.com/northcoast/
Circulation: 1,069pd,; Sworn/Estimate/Non-Audited
Advertising rate: Open inch rate $14.23
Established: 1931
Group: The McClatchy Company
Digital Platform - Mobile: Apple
Pres & Pub .... Tom Cullinan
VP/Exec Ed .... Sandra Duerr
Mng Ed .... Steve Provost
Local Media Consultant/Office Mgr ..... Jennifer Perryman
Mechanical Specifications: 6 col x 10" Tab (1 col = 1.542")Equipment & Software: Hardware — APP/Macs; Presses — WPC/Web Leader; Software — Claris/Works, QPS/QuarkXPress, Adobe/Photoshop.
Delivery Method: Mail, Newsstand, Racks
Areas Served: 93428, 93452, 93435

CAMPBELL

CAMPBELL EXPRESS (WED)

334 E Campbell Ave, Frnt, Campbell, CA, 95008-2094, Santa Clara, USA; gen tel (408) 374-9700; adv tel (408) 206-4720; gen fax (408) 374-0813; disp adv e-mail info@campbellexpress.com; news@campbellexpress.com; web site www.campbellexpress.com
Circulation: 2,200pd,; Sworn/Estimate/Non-Audited
Advertising rate: Open inch rate $9.50
Co Ed.. Roberta Howe
Co-Ed .... Matthew Howe
Areas Served: Santa Clara County

CANYON LAKE

THE FRIDAY FLYER (FRI)

31558 Railroad Canyon Rd, Canyon Lake, CA, 92587-9427, Riverside, USA; gen tel (951)244-1966; adv tel (951) 244-1966; ed tel (951) 244-1966; gen fax (951) 244-2748; adv fax (951) 244-2748; ed fax (951) 244-2748; disp adv e-mail greg@goldingpublications.com; class adv e-mail greg@goldingpublications.com; ed e-mail news@goldingpublications.com; web site fridayflyer.com - 45,417(views) 8,888(visitors)
Circulation: 4,041pd, 1,116fr; USPS
Advertising rate: 5.07
Established: 1990
Group: Golding Publications
Digital Platform - Mobile: Apple, Android, Windows
Digital Platform - Tablet: Apple iOS, Android, Windows 7
Pub... Chuck Golding
Adv. Mgr..................................... Greg Golding
Classified Mgr................................ Gina Wells
Editor .... Donna Ritchie
Mechanical Specifications: Mechanical Specifications
Width .... Depth
Full Page.. 10 5/16" 15 5/8"
3/4 Page .... 10 5/16" 11 21/32"
1/2 Page Hor....................................... 10 5/16" 7 11/16"
1/2 Page Vert. .... 5 3/32" 15 5/8"
1/4 Page Hor.. 10 5/16" 3 23/32"
1/4 Page Vert. .... 5 3/32" 7 11/16"
1/8 Page .... 5 3/32" 3 23/32"
Delivery Method: Mail, Newsstand
Areas Served: 92587

CAPISTRANO BEACH

DANA POINT TIMES (FRI)

34932 Calle Del Sol, Ste B, Capistrano Beach, CA, 92624-1664, Orange, USA; gen tel (949) 388-7700; gen fax (949) 388-9977; disp adv e-mail lloynes.picketfencemedia.com; web site danapointtimes.com
Group: Picket Fence MediaMatt Cortina
Norb Garrett
Lauralyn Loynes
Prod. and Circ. Mgr........................ Tricia Zines
Bus. Ops. Mgr............................ Alyssa Garrett

SAN CLEMENTE TIMES (THUR)

34932 Calle Del Sol, Ste B, Capistrano Beach, CA, 92624-1664, Orange, USA; gen tel (949) 388-7700; gen fax (949) 388-9977; disp adv e-mail slantz@picketfencemedia.com; ed e-mail kpritchett@picketfencemedia.com; web site sanclementetimes.com
Group: Picket Fence Media
Grp. Mng. Ed................................ Matt Cortina
CEO/pUB..................................... Norb Garrett
Sales Associate .... Susie Lantz
M.E. .... Rachel Mattice

THE CAPISTRANO DISPATCH (FRI, BI-MTHLY)

34932 Calle Del Sol, Ste B, Capistrano Beach, CA, 92624-1664, Orange, USA; gen tel (949) 388-7700; gen fax (949) 388-9977; disp adv e-mail kpritchett@picketfencemedia.com; class adv e-mail dwells@picketfence-media.com; web site thecapistranodispatch.com
Group: Picket Fence MediaNorb Garrett
Matt Cortina
Lauralyn Loynes
Tricia Zines
Alyssa Garrett

CARMICHAEL

CARMICHAEL TIMES (FRI)

7144 Fair Oaks Blvd, Ste 5, Carmichael, CA, 95608-6464, Sacramento, USA; gen tel (916) 773-1111; adv tel (916) 773-1111; ed tel (916) 773-1111; gen fax (916) 773-2999; disp adv e-mail Publisher@MPG8.com; class adv e-mail Publisher@MPG8.com; ed e-mail Publisher@MPG8.com; web site www.CarmichaelTimes.com - 5,903(views) 3,177(visitors)
Circulation: 250pd, 8,500fr; Sworn/Estimate/Non-Audited
Advertising rate: Open inch rate $17.00
Established: 1981
Group: Messenger Publishing Group
Pub.. Paul Scholl
Delivery Method: Mail, Newsstand, Carrier, Racks
Areas Served: 95608

PAUL V SCHOLL (FRI)

7144 Fair Oaks Blvd, Ste 5, Carmichael, CA, 95608-6464, Sacramento, USA; gen tel (916)773-1111; adv tel (916) 773-1111; ed tel (916) 773-1111; gen fax (916) 773-2999; adv fax (916) 773-2999; disp adv e-mail Publisher@MPG8.com; class adv e-mail Publisher@MPG8.com; ed e-mail Publisher@MPG8.com; web site www.placersentinel.com
Circulation: 8,000fr; Sworn/Estimate/Non-Audited
Advertising rate: Open inch rate $17.00
Established: 1987
Group: Messenger Publishing Group
Owner/Pub...................................... Paul Scholl
Mechanical Specifications: Type page 11.5 x 20.5 - 6 colsEquipment & Software: Hardware — PC; Software — Adobe/InDesign
Delivery Method: Newsstand, Carrier, Racks
Areas Served: 95602, 95603, 95650, 95658, 95703, 95713, 95722

CARPINTERIA

COASTAL VIEW NEWS (THUR)

4856 Carpinteria Ave, Carpinteria, CA, 93013-1935, Santa Barbara, USA; gen tel (805) 684-4428; gen fax (805) 684-4655; disp adv e-mail dan@coastalview.com; ed e-mail news@coastalview.com; web site www.coastalview.com
Circulation: 7,000pd, 7,000fr; CVC
Advertising rate: Open inch rate $18.50
Established: 1994
Group: RMG VENTURES, LLC
Digital Platform - Mobile: Apple, Android
Digital Platform - Tablet: Apple iOS, Android, Windows 7, Blackberry Tablet OS
Pub.. Michael Van Stry
Ed. .... Lea Boyd
Advertising Manager......................... Dan Terry
Mechanical Specifications: Type page 10 x 16; E - 4 cols, 2 1/4, 1/4 between; A - 4 cols, 2 1/4, 1/4 between; C - 5 cols, 1 3/4, 1/4 between. Equipment & Software: Hardware — MAC; Software — Adobe/InDesign
Areas Served: 93013, 93014, 93067, 93101

CHESTER

CHESTER PROGRESSIVE (WED)

135 MAIN ST, Chester, CA, 96020, Plumas, USA; gen tel (530) 283-0800; gen fax (530) 283-3952; disp adv e-mail ccurran@plumasnews.com; class adv e-mail mnewhouse@plumasnews.com; ed e-mail dmoore@plumasnews.com; web site www.plumasnews.com
Circulation: 2,150pd, 2,150fr; Sworn/Estimate/Non-Audited
Advertising rate: Open inch rate $5.50 net (all six $10.50 inch)
Established: 1946
Group: Feather Publishing Co., Inc.
Pub .... Michael C. Taborski
Ed .... Debra Moore
Mechanical Specifications: Page 12 1/4 x 21 1/2; E - 6 cols, 1 5/6, 1/6 between; A - 6 cols, 1 5/6, 1/6 between; C - 9 cols, 1 1/4, 1/6 between.Equipment & Software: Hardware — APP/Macs; Presses — G/Community; Software — QPS/QuarkXPress.
Delivery Method: Mail, Newsstand
Areas Served: 96020, 96137

CHINO

CHINO CHAMPION (SAT)

13179 9th St, Chino, CA, 91710-4216, San Bernardino, USA; gen tel (909) 628-5501; adv tel (909) 628-5501 x22; ed tel (909) 628-5501 x31; gen fax (909) 590-1217; adv fax (909) 591-6296; ed fax (909) 590-1217; disp adv e-mail ads@ChampionNewspapers.com; class adv e-mail Classified@ChampionNewspapers.com; ed e-mail News@ChampionNewspapers.com; web site www.ChampionNewspapers.com - 39,090(views) 16,991(visitors)
Circulation: 210pd, 39,405fr; CAC
Advertising rate: Open inch rate $38.25.
Established: 1887
Group: Champion NewspapersEditions: (2) Chino Champion; Chino Hills Champion
Digital Platform - Mobile: Apple, Android, Windows
Pub./Adv. Dir. .... Bruce M. Wood
Mng. Ed... Mel Ewald
Prodn. Mgr. .... Lynn Haws
IT/Business Manager..................... Tom Hebert
Pub. Emeritus .... Allen McCombs
Pres./CEO .... William Fleet
Mechanical Specifications: Type page 10.0" x 21.0"; Display - 6 cols, 1 col: 1.58; 2 cols 3.25; 3 cols 4.94; 4 cols 6.63; 5 cols 8.32; 6 cols 10.0; Classified - 10 cols, 1 col .87; 2 cols 1.89; 3 cols 2.90; 4 cols 3.91; 5 cols 4.92; 6 cols 5.93; 7 cols 6.94; 8 cols 7.96; 9 cols 8.96; 10 cols 10.0.Equipment & Software: Hardware — PCs, Macs, HP/LaserJets.; Presses — We use a contract printer.; Software — Adobe Creative Suites 4, QuarkXPress 6.5, AdPerfect/Classified; Microsoft Office.
Delivery Method: Mail, Newsstand, Carrier, Racks
Areas Served: Chino (91708, 91710); Chino Hills (91709) and Ontario (91761, 91762)

CHINO HILLS CHAMPION (SAT)

13179 9th St, Chino, CA, 91710-4216, San Bernardino, USA; gen tel (909) 628-5501; adv tel (909) 628-5501 x22; ed tel (909) 628-5501 x31; gen fax (909) 590-1217; adv fax (909) 591-6296; ed fax (909) 590-1217; disp adv e-mail ads@ChampionNewspapers.com; class adv e-mail Classified@ChampionNewspapers.com; ed e-mail News@ChampionNewspapers.com; web site www.ChampionNewspapers.com
Circulation: 40,697pd,; CAC
Advertising rate: Open inch rate $38.25.
Established: 1887
Group: Champion Newspapers
Pub./Adv. Dir. .... Bruce M. Wood
Mng. Ed... Mel Ewald
Prodn. Mgr. .... Lynn Haws
IT/Business Manager..................... Tom Hebert
Pub. Emeritus .... Allen McCombs
Pres./CEO .... William Fleet
Delivery Method: Mail, Newsstand, Carrier, Racks
Areas Served: Chino (91708, 91710); Chino Hills (91709) and Ontario (91761, 91762)

EASTVALE COMMUNITY NEWS (THUR, MTHLY)

14144 Central Ave, Ste H, Chino, CA, 91710-5763, Riverside, USA; gen tel (909) 464-1200; gen fax (909) 464-1257; disp adv e-mail diane@anapr.com; ed e-mail editor@anapr.com; web site www.anapr.com
Advertising rate: 1/8 P $150 1/4 P $300 1/2 P $600 Full $1200
Group: Armijo News
Ed. .... Michael Armijo
Asst. Ed....................................... Sarah Armijo
Adv. Sales.................................. Joe A. Merica

CHULA VISTA

THE STAR-NEWS (FRI)

296 3rd Ave, Chula Vista, CA, 91910-2701, San Diego, USA; gen tel (619) 427-3000; adv tel (619) 427-3000 x 270; ed tel (619) 427-3000 x 220; gen fax (619) 426-6346; disp adv e-mail legals@thestarnews.com; class adv e-mail classified@thestarnews.com; ed e-mail carlos@thestarnews.com; web site www.thestarnews.com
Circulation: 270pd, 35,000fr; Sworn/Estimate/Non-Audited
Advertising rate: Open inch rate $14.00
Established: 1954
Group: Community Media Group
Ed. .... Carlo Davalos
Pub.. John Moreno
Circ. Mgr.................................... Jo Delgadillo
Business Mgr. .... Jutta Vanderhayden
Areas Served: 91910

CLAREMONT

CLAREMONT COURIER (WED, SAT)

114 Olive St, Ste 205B, Claremont, CA, 91711-4924, Los Angeles, USA; gen tel (909) 621-4761; gen fax (909) 621-4072; disp adv e-mail maryrose@claremont-courier.com; class adv e-mail classified@claremont-courier.com; ed e-mail editor@claremont-courier.com; web site www.claremont-courier.com
Circulation: 5,600pd,; Sworn/Estimate/Non-Audited

Advertising rate: Open inch rate $8.25
Established: 1908
Pub....................................... Peter Weinberger
Ed. .... Kathryn Dunn
Mechanical Specifications: Type page 10 1/4 x 14; E - 6 cols, 1 3/8, 1/8 between; A - 6 cols, 1 3/8, 1/8 between; C - 7 cols, 1 3/8, 1/6 between.Equipment & Software: Hardware — APP/Mac G3; Software — Adobe/Photoshop, QPS/QuarkXPress, Adobe/Illustrator.
Areas Served: 91711

COLFAX

COLFAX RECORD (THUR)

233 S Auburn St, Ste 205, Colfax, CA, 95713-9753, Placer, USA; gen tel (916)774-7910; adv tel (530) 852-0225; ed tel (530) 346-2232; gen fax (530) 346-2700; ed fax (530) 346-2700; disp adv e-mail mjh@goldcountrymedia.com; class adv e-mail classifieds@goldcountrymedia.com; ed e-mail marthag@goldcountrymedia.com; web site www.colfaxrecord.com
Circulation: 736pd, 0fr; VAC
Advertising rate: Open inch rate $10.85
Established: 1937
Group: Brehm Communications, Inc.
Gold Country Media
Pub....................................... Carol Feineman
Ed. .... Martha Garcia
Business Develop. .... Linda Shuman-Prins
Areas Served: 95602

CORCORAN

THE CORCORAN JOURNAL (THUR)

1012 Hale Ave, Corcoran, CA, 93212-2309, Kings, USA; gen tel (559) 992-3115; gen fax (559) 992-5543; disp adv e-mail tbotill@hotmail.com; web site www.thecorcoranjournal.net
Circulation: 2,450pd,; Sworn/Estimate/Non-Audited
Advertising rate: Open inch rate $7.00
Established: 1908
Adv. Mgr.. Rob Atilano
Ed. .... Jeanette Todd
Areas Served: 93212

CORONADO

CORONADO EAGLE & JOURNAL (WED)

1116 10th St, Coronado, CA, 92118-3402, San Diego, USA; gen tel (619) 437-8800; gen fax (619) 437-8635; disp adv e-mail editor@eaglenewsca.com; ed e-mail editor@eaglenewsca.com; web site www.coronadonewsca.com
Circulation: 12,496fr; CVC
Advertising rate: 1/40 Pg $58.00; 1/20 Pg $94.00; 1/10 Pg $181.00
Established: 1912
Group: Eagle Newspapers
Pub....................................... Dean Eckenroth
Assoc. Pub........................ Dean Eckenroth, Jr.
Adv. Dir.................................. Daniel Teonnies
Mechanical Specifications: Type page 10 1/4 x 15 1/2; E - 5 cols, 1 15/16, 1/8 between; A - 5 cols, 1 15/16, 1/8 between; C - 6 cols, 1 19/32, 1/8 between.Equipment & Software: Hardware — APP/Mac; Software — Adobe/PageMaker 6.5.
Delivery Method: Mail, Newsstand, Carrier, Racks
Areas Served: San Diego County

IMPERIAL BEACH EAGLE & TIMES (THUR)

1116 Teneth Street, Coronado, CA, 92118, San Diego, USA; gen tel (619) 437-8800; gen fax (619) 437-8635; disp adv e-mail sarah@eaglenewsca.com; ed e-mail editorial@eaglenewsca.com; web site www.imperialbeachnewsca.com
Circulation: 7,500fr; Sworn/Estimate/Non-Audited

Advertising rate: 1/4 P $105 1/2 P $168 Full $326
Pub./Ed. .... Dean Eckenroth
Mechanical Specifications: Type page 10 1/4 x 15 1/2; E - 5 cols, 1 15/16, 1/8 between; A - 5 cols, 1 15/16, 1/8 between; C - 6 cols, 1 5/8, 1/8 between.Equipment & Software: Hardware — APP/Mac; Software — Adobe/PageMaker 8.5.
Areas Served: 91933

CRESCENT CITY

THE DEL NORTE TRIPLICATE (TUES, THUR, SAT)

312 H St, Crescent City, CA, 95531-4018, Del Norte, USA; gen tel (707) 464-2141; gen fax (707) 464-5102; disp adv e-mail tripads@triplicate.com; ed e-mail mdurkee@triplicate.com; web site www.triplicate.com - 233,973(views) 24,540(visitors)
Circulation: 3,905pd, 114fr; CVC
Advertising rate: Open inch rate $11.75
Established: 1879
Group: Western Communications, Inc.
Operations Manager .... Kyle Curtis
Regional Pub. .... Cindy Vosburg
Ed. .... Matt Durkee
Circ. Dir. .... David Jeffcoat
Production Mgr........................ David DeLonge
Circ District Mgr..................... Elizabeth Carter
Ops. Mgr. .... Kyle Curtis
Sports Ed.................................. Michael Zogg
Adv Acct Mgr .... Emily Reed
Mechanical Specifications: Type page 11.83" x 21.50"; 6 cols
Delivery Method: Mail, Carrier, Racks
Areas Served: 95531

DAVIS

THE DAVIS ENTERPRISE (WED, FRI, SUN)

315 G ST, DAVIS, CA, 95616-4119, Yolo, USA; gen tel (530) 756-0800; adv tel (530) 756-0800; ed tel (530) 756-0800; gen fax (530) 756-7504; adv fax (530) 756-6707; ed fax (530) 756-1668; disp adv e-mail nhannell@davisenterprise.net; class adv e-mail classads@davisenterprise.net; ed e-mail newsroom@davisenterprise.net; web site www.davisenterprise.com
Circulation: 5,478pd, 67fr; CAC
Advertising rate: Open inch rate $25.00 (National - Wed & Fri)
Established: 1897
Group: McNaughton Newspapers
McNaughton Newspapers
Digital Platform - Mobile: Apple, Android, Windows
Digital Platform - Tablet: Apple iOS, Android, Windows 7, Blackberry Tablet OS, Kindle Fire, Other
Pub./Vice Pres./Sec. .... Burt McNaughton
Adv. Dir.................................. Nancy Hannell
Educ./Schools Ed. .... Jeff Hudson
Photo Ed.................................. Wayne Tilcock
Political/Gov't Ed......................... Debbie Davis
Mechanical Specifications: Type page 11 9/10 x 21; E - 6 cols, 1 7/8, 1/8 between; A - 6 cols, 1 7/8, 1/8 between; C - 10 cols, 1 3/16, 1/16 between.
Delivery Method: Carrier, Racks
Areas Served: 95616, 95618, 95695, 95776

DALY CITY

PHILIPPINES TODAY (WED)

6454 Mission St, Suite 227, Daly City, CA, 94014-2013, San Mateo, USA; gen tel (650) 872-3200; adv tel (650) 8723200; ed tel same; gen fax (650) 8723208; adv fax (650) 8723208; ed fax same; disp adv e-mail advertising@philippinestodayus.com; class adv e-mail advertising@philippinestodayus.com; ed e-mail editor@philippinestodayus.com; web site www.philippinestodayus.com
Circulation: 29,855pd,; CAC

Advertising rate: 1/4P $250, 1/2P $500, Full 900
Established: 2008
VP, Sales .... Marilyn King
Delivery Method: Racks
Areas Served: whole Northern California

DINUBA

THE DINUBA SENTINEL (THUR)

145 S L St, Dinuba, CA, 93618-2324, Tulare, USA; gen tel (559) 591-4632; gen fax (559) 591-1322; disp adv e-mail vanessa@midvalleypublishing.com; class adv e-mail classifieddinubasentinel@yahoo.com; ed e-mail editor@thedinubasentinel.com; web site www.thedinubasentinel.com
Circulation: 3,000pd,; Sworn/Estimate/Non-Audited
Advertising rate: Open inch rate $11.50
Established: 1909
Group: Mid Valley Publishing
Ed. .... Linda Renn
Sports Writer............................ Keven Geaney
Reporter .... Jackson Moore
Mechanical Specifications: Type page 11 3/4 x 21; E - 6 cols, 1 13/16, 1/6 between; A - 6 cols, 1 13/16, 1/6 between; C - 9 cols, 1 3/16, 1/6 between.Equipment & Software: Hardware — APP/Mac; Software — Adobe/PageMaker 6.5.
Delivery Method: Mail
Areas Served: 93618

DIXON

DIXON TRIBUNE (WED, FRI, SUN)

145 E A St, Dixon, CA, 95620-3599, Solano, USA; gen tel (707) 678-5594; gen fax (707) 678-5404; ed e-mail editor@dixontribune.com; web site www.facebook.com/dixontribunesocialmedia
Circulation: 5,500pd, 2,000fr; Sworn/Estimate/Non-Audited
Advertising rate: Open inch rate $8.00
Pub... David L. Payne
Adv. Mgr...................................... Sarah Villec
Ed. .... Brianna Boyd
Mechanical Specifications: Type page 13 x 21.Equipment & Software: ; Presses — G/Community.
Areas Served: Solano County

DIXON'S INDEPENDENT VOICE (FRI)

1275 W H St, Dixon, CA, 95620-2621, Solano, USA; gen tel (707) 678-8917; disp adv e-mail staff@independentvoice.com; class adv e-mail staff@independentvoice.com; ed e-mail staff@independentvoice.com; web site www.independentvoice.com
Circulation: 280pd, 4,200fr; Sworn/Estimate/Non-Audited
Advertising rate: Open inch rate $6.95
Established: 1992
Pub/Ed...................................... David J. Scholl
Mechanical Specifications: Type page 10 1/2 x 20; E - 6 cols, 2, 1/8 between; A - 6 cols, 2, 1/8 between; C - 9 cols, 1 1/2, 1/8 between. Equipment & Software: Hardware — PC; Software — Microsoft/Publisher.
Delivery Method: Mail, Newsstand, Carrier, Racks
Areas Served: 95620

EL CAJON

THE EAST COUNTY CALIFORNIAN (THUR)

119 N Magnolia Ave, El Cajon, CA, 92020-3903, San Diego, USA; gen tel (619) 441-0400; gen fax (619) 441-0020; disp adv e-mail info@eccalifornian.com; ed e-mail editor@eccalifornian.com; web site www.eccalifornian.com
Circulation: 1,450pd, 32,500fr; Sworn/Estimate/Non-Audited
Advertising rate: Open inch rate $25.80
Established: 1887
Ed. .... Albert Fulcher

Mechanical Specifications: Type page 13 x 21 1/2; E - 5 cols, 1 9/10, 1/8 between; A - 5 cols, 1 9/10, 1/8 between; C - 7 cols, 1 1/3, 1/8 between.Equipment & Software: Hardware — 35-CText, 5-APP/Mac; Presses — 8-G/Urbanite, 7-DEV/1400.
Areas Served: 92020

EL CENTRO

ADELANTE VALLE (FRI)

205 N 8th St, El Centro, CA, 92243-2301, Imperial, USA; gen tel (760) 335-4646; adv tel (760) 337-3443; ed tel (760) 337-3446; gen fax (760) 353-3003; disp adv e-mail advertising@ivpressonline.com; class adv e-mail classified@ivpressonline.com; ed e-mail pdale@ivpressonline.com; web site www.ivpressonline.com
Circulation: 6,003pd, 5,378fr; CAC
Advertising rate: Open inch rate $14.00
Group: Imperial Valley Press
Pub... Belinda Mills
Adv. Dir... Alexis Singh
Dist. Mgr...................................... Julio Navarro
Delivery Method: Mail

EL SEGUNDO

EL SEGUNDO HERALD (THUR)

500 Center St, El Segundo, CA, 90245-3201, Los Angeles, USA; gen tel (310) 322-1830; gen fax (310) 322-2787; disp adv e-mail classifieds@heraldpublishers.com; class adv e-mail classifieds@heraldpublications.com; web site www.heraldpublications.com
Circulation: 16,000fr; Sworn/Estimate/Non-Audited
Advertising rate: Open inch rate $200.00
CEO/Pub.................................... Heidi Maerker
Classified Adv. Mgr....................... Martha Prieto
Areas Served: Los Angeles County

ELK GROVE

ELK GROVE CITIZEN (WED)

8970 Elk Grove Blvd, Elk Grove, CA, 95624-1971, Sacramento, USA; gen tel (209)745-1551; adv tel (916) 685-5533; gen fax (916) 686-6675; disp adv e-mail advertising@herburger.net; class adv e-mail classified@herburger.net; ed e-mail cameronjmacdonald@gmail.com; web site www.egcitizen.com
Circulation: 5,434pd,; VAC
Advertising rate: Open inch rate $12.00
Established: 1903
Group: Herburger Publications, Inc.
Gen. Mgr. .... David Herburger
Adv. Mgr...................................... Jim O'Donnell
News Ed. .... Cameron Macdonald
Pub... Roy Herburger
Mechanical Specifications: Type page 11 1/2 x 21; E - 6 cols, 1 3/4, 1/6 between; A - 6 cols, 1 3/4, 1/6 between; C - 9 cols, 1 1/2, 1/12 between.Equipment & Software: Hardware — APP/Macs, PC; Presses — 10-G/Suburban; Software — Adobe/PageMaker.
Areas Served: Sacramento County

ENCINITAS

RANCHO SANTA FE NEWS (FRI)

315 S Coast Highway 101 Ste W, Ste W, Encinitas, CA, 92024-3555, San Diego, USA; gen tel (760) 436-9737; gen fax (760) 943-0850; disp adv e-mail advertising@coastnewsgroup.com; class adv e-mail classifieds@coastnewsgroup.com; ed e-mail jgillette@coastnewsgroup.com; web site www.coastnewsgroup.com
Circulation: 9,935fr; CVC
Advertising rate: CP
Established: 2004
Group: Coast News Group, Inc.
Managing Ed.......................... Anthony Cagala

Pub. Mgr .... Jim Kydd
Adv. Mgr./Assc. Pub. .... Chris Kydd
Circ. Mgr .... Becky Roland
Prod. Mgr .... Charles Steinman
Mechanical Specifications: Mechanical Requirements - Printed web offset on regular newsprint. Full Page
Image Area: 10.25" wide by 14.5" tall.
E-mail: Mac compatible art to: advertising@coastnewsgroup.
com.
ROP and Classified Ad Width by Columns: 1.625" columns, .0.10" gutters. 2-col.
3.35", 3 col. 5.075", 4 col. 6.8", 5 col. 8.525", 6 col., 10.25".Equipment & Software: Hardware — Mac; Presses — Web Offset; Software — Quark
Delivery Method: Mail, Racks
Areas Served: 92067, 92091, 92130, 92127, RR011, CR 52, 53

THE COAST NEWS (FRI)

315 S Coast Highway 101, Ste W, Encinitas, CA, 92024-3555, San Diego, USA; gen tel (760) 436-9737; gen fax (760) 943-0850; disp adv e-mail advertising@thecoastnewsgroup.com; class adv e-mail advertising@thecoastnewsgroup.com; ed e-mail editor@coastnewsgroup.com; web site www.coastnewsgroup.com
Circulation: 206pd, 29,903fr; VAC
Advertising rate: CP
Established: 1987
Group: Coast News Group, Inc.
Pub./Own. .... James Kydd
Mng. Ed .... Tony Cagala
Adv. Mgr./Assoc. Pub. .... Chris Kydd
Circ. Mgr .... Becky Roland
Mechanical Specifications: Mechanical Requirements - Printed web offset on regular newsprint. Full Page
Image Area: 10.25" wide by 14.5" tall. E-mail: Mac compatible art to: advertising@coastnewsgroup.
com. ROP and Classified Ad Width by Columns: 1.625" columns, .0.10" gutters. 2-col.
3.35", 3 col. 5.075", 4 col. 6.8", 5 col. 8.525", 6 col., 10.25".Equipment & Software: Hardware — 11-APP/Macs; Presses — Web Offset; Software — QPS/QuarkXPress 6.0.
Delivery Method: Mail, Racks
Areas Served: 92007, 92008, 92009, 92010, 92011, 92014, 92024, 92054, 92055, 92056, 92057, 92058, 92069, 92075, 92078, 92081, 92083, 92084, 92130

ESCONDIDO

TIMES-ADVOCATE (THUR)

720 N Broadway, Ste 108, Escondido, CA, 92025-1870, San Diego, USA; gen tel (760) 546-4000; adv tel (760) 546-4000; ed tel (760) 546-4000; web site times-advocate.com
Circulation:; Sworn/Estimate/Non-Audited
Group: Roadrunner Publications, Inc.
Editor In Chief .... David Ross
Editor .... Doug Green
Publisher .... Justin Salter
Advertising Account Manager.... Andrew Leyva
Delivery Method: Mail, Racks
Areas Served: Escondido, CA

EUREKA

NORTH COAST JOURNAL (THUR)

310 F St, Eureka, CA, 95501-1006, Humboldt, USA; gen tel (707) 442-1400; gen fax (707) 442-1401; disp adv e-mail ncjournal@northcoastjournal.com; class adv e-mail classified@northcoastjournal.com; web site www.northcoastjournal.com
Circulation: 76pd, 20,328fr; VAC
Advertising rate: $75 (smallest modular rate)
Established: 1990
Group: C-VILLE Holdings LLC
Pub. Mgr .... Judy Hodgson
Ed. .... Henk Sims
Prodn. Mgr. .... Linda Schwend
Adv. Mgr .... Chuck Leishman
Circ. Mgr .... Carolyn Fernandez
Reporter .... Kimberley Wear
Mechanical Specifications: Type page 10" x 10.75"; 4 cols
Areas Served: 95501

THE HUMBOLDT BEACON (THUR)

930 6th St, Eureka, CA, 95501-1112, Humboldt, USA; gen tel (707) 441-0563; adv tel (707) 441-0599; ed fax (707) 441-0501; disp adv e-mail kmaynard@times-standard.com; class adv e-mail class@times-standard.com; ed e-mail news@humboldtbeacon.com; web site www.humboldtbeacon.com
Circulation: 2,500pd,; Sworn/Estimate/Non-Audited
Advertising rate: Open inch rate $8.50
Established: 1903
Group: Media news
Ed. .... Franklin Stover
Mechanical Specifications: Type page 13 x 21; E - 6 cols, 2, 1/6 between; A - 6 cols, 2, 1/6 between; C - 9 cols, 1 1/3, 1/12 between. Equipment & Software: Hardware — APP/Mac; Software — QPS/QuarkXPress.
Delivery Method: Mail
Areas Served: 95501

TRI-CITY WEEKLY (TUES)

930 6th St, Eureka, CA, 95501-1112, CA - California, USA; gen tel (707) 441-0500; adv tel (707) 441-0556; ed tel (707) 441-0520; gen fax (707) 441-0565; adv fax (707) 441-0565; ed fax (707) 441-0501; disp adv e-mail ads@times-standard.com; class adv e-mail class@times-standard.com; ed e-mail mvalles@times-standard.com; web site www.tricityweekly.com
Circulation: 0pd, 32,050fr; Sworn/Estimate/Non-Audited
Advertising rate: Open inch rate $20.00
Established: 1970
Group: Digital First Media
Digital Platform - Mobile: Apple, Android, Windows
Digital Platform - Tablet: Apple iOS, Android, Windows 7
Pub .... Paula Patton
Prod. Mgr. .... Carmel Bonitatibus
Mechanical Specifications: 1 col = 1.6"
2 col = 3.34"
3 col = 5.08"
4 col = 6.8"
5 col = 8.57"
6 col = 10.313"
12 col Dub.Trk = 20.826"
Delivery Method: Carrier, Racks
Areas Served: 95501, 95503, total, Zone 2, ZIP CODE, 95519, 95521, 95524, 95525, 95546, 95548, 95549, 95555, 95570, 95573, 95563, total, Zone 3, ZIP CODE, 95536, 95540, 95542, 95551, 95560, 95562, 95526, 95528, 95547, 95553, 95559, 95565, 95569, 95514, 95526

EXETER

THE FOOTHILLS SUN-GAZETTE (WED)

PO Box 7, Exeter, CA, 93221-0007, Tulare, USA; gen tel (559) 592-3171; gen fax (559) 592-4308; disp adv e-mail ads@thesungazette.com; class adv e-mail ads@thesungazette.com; web site fsgnews.com
Circulation: 3,000pd, 20,000fr; Sworn/Estimate/Non-Audited
Advertising rate: Open inch rate $11.70
Established: 1901
Group: Mineral King Publishing, Inc.
Pub .... Reggie Ellis
Mechanical Specifications: Type page 12 1/2 x 22 1/4; E - 6 cols, 1 3/4, 1/4 between; A - 6 cols, 1 7/8, 1/4 between; C - 9 cols, 1 1/8, 3/16 between.Equipment & Software: Hardware — APP/Mac; Software — QPS/QuarkXPress.
Areas Served: 93221

FALL RIVER MILLS

THE MOUNTAIN ECHO (TUES)

43152 State Highway 299 E, Fall River Mills, CA, 96028-9811, Shasta, USA; gen tel (530) 336-6262; gen fax (530) 336-6262; disp adv e-mail mtecho@shasta.com; web site www.mountainecho.com
Circulation: 3,000pd, 500fr; Sworn/Estimate/Non-Audited
Advertising rate: Open inch rate $7.90
Established: 1977
Pub .... Donna Caldwell
Ed. .... Walt Caldwell
Adv. Mgr. .... Katie CliftEquipment & Software: Hardware — PC; Software — Archetype/Corel Draw, QPS/QuarkXPress, Caere/OmniPage Pro. InDesign
Delivery Method: Mail, Racks
Areas Served: 96006, 96101, 96009, 96011, 96013, 96028, 96015, 96016, 96040, 96053, 96054, 96056, 96065, 96068, 96071, 96084, 96068, 96071, 96084

FERNDALE

THE FERNDALE ENTERPRISE (THUR)

207 Francis St, Ferndale, CA, 95536, Humboldt, USA; gen tel (707) 786-3068; adv tel (707) 786-3068; gen fax (707) 786-4311; adv fax (707) 786-4311; disp adv e-mail editor@ferndaleenterprise.us; ed e-mail editor@ferndaleenterprise.us; web site www.ferndaleenterprise.us
Circulation: 1,500pd,; Sworn/Estimate/Non-Audited
Advertising rate: Open inch rate $5.95
Established: 1878
Group: Cages Publishing, Inc.
Ed./Pub. .... Caroline Titus
Circ. Dir. .... Donna Mays
Areas Served: 95536

FONTANA

FONTANA HERALD NEWS (FRI)

16981 Foothill Blvd Ste F, Suite F, Fontana, CA, 92335-3566, San Bernardino, USA; gen tel (909) 822-2231; adv tel (909) 797-9101; gen fax (909) 355-9358; adv fax (909) 355-9358; disp adv e-mail advertising@fontanaheraldnews.com; class adv e-mail classifieds@fontanaheraldnews.com; ed e-mail ringold@fontanaheraldnews.com; web site www.fontanaheraldnews.com
Circulation: 266pd, 181fr; VAC
Advertising rate: Open inch rate $18.50
Group: Century Group Newspapers
Pub .... Grace Barnett
Ed. .... Russell Ingold
Areas Served: San Bernardino County

FORT BRAGG

FORT BRAGG ADVOCATE-NEWS (THUR)

690 S Main St, Fort Bragg, CA, 95437-5108, Mendocino, USA; gen tel (707) 964-5642; ed tel (707) 964-5642 x96094; gen fax (707) 964-0424; disp adv e-mail mrham@advocate-news.com; class adv e-mail classads@advocate-news.com; ed e-mail editor@advocate-news.com; web site www.advocate-news.com
Circulation: 3,800pd,; Sworn/Estimate/Non-Audited
Advertising rate: Open inch rate $10.75
Established: 1889
Group: Digital First Media
Digital Platform - Mobile: Apple, Android
Digital Platform - Tablet: Apple iOS, Android, Kindle, Kindle Fire
Pub .... Sharon DiMauro
Editor
Chris Calder
Circulation Manager .... Kate Lee
Mechanical Specifications: Type page 12 x 21; E - 6 cols, 2 7/8, between; A - 6 cols, 1 7/8, between; C - 10 cols, 1 1/16, between. Equipment & Software: Hardware — APP/Power Mac 7300; Software — Baseview/NewsEdit Pro, Adobe/Photoshop.
Delivery Method: Mail, Newsstand, Racks
Areas Served: 95437

THE MENDOCINO BEACON (THUR)

690 S Main St, Fort Bragg, CA, 95437-5108, Mendocino, USA; gen tel (707) 964-5642; adv tel (707) 964-5642; ed tel (707) 964-5642; gen fax (707) 964-0424; disp adv e-mail mrharm@advocate-news.com; class adv e-mail classads@advocate-news.com; ed e-mail editor@advocate-news.com; web site www.mendocinobeacon.com
Circulation: 1,600pd, 3fr; Sworn/Estimate/Non-Audited
Advertising rate: Open inch rate $9.75
Established: 1877
Group: Digital First Media
Digital Platform - Mobile: Apple, Android, Other
Digital Platform - Tablet: Apple iOS, Android, Kindle, Kindle Fire
Adv. Mgr. .... Sharon DiMauro
Ed .... Chris Calder
Circulation Mgr .... Kate Lee
Office Mgr .... Cathy Stanley
Mechanical Specifications: Type page 6col x 21 E - 6 cols, 1 7/8, 1/6 between; A - 6 cols, 1 7/8, 1/6 between; C - 10 cols, 1 1/16, 1/6 between.Equipment & Software: Hardware — APP/Mac, APP/Power Mac 7300; Software — QPS/QuarkXPress, Baseview/NewsEdit Pro, Adobe/Photoshop.
Delivery Method: Mail, Newsstand, Racks
Areas Served: 95437; 95460

FOUNTAIN VALLEY

THE LOG NEWSPAPER (FRI)

18475 Bandilier Cir, Fountain Valley, CA, 92708-7000, Orange, USA; gen tel (949) 660-6150; adv tel (949) 660-6150 ext. 230; ed tel (949) 660-6150 ext. 226; gen fax (949) 660-6172; disp adv e-mail susanne@thelog.com; class adv e-mail classifieds@thelog.com; ed e-mail ambrosia@thelog.com; web site www.thelog.com
Circulation: 265pd, 40,000fr; Sworn/Estimate/Non-Audited
Established: 1971
Group: Duncan McIntosh Co., Inc.
Digital Platform - Mobile: Android
Digital Platform - Tablet: Android, Other
Pub .... Duncan McIntosh
Vice Pres./General Mgr .... Jeff Fleming
Mgr. of Fullfillment .... Rick Avila
Regional Adv. Mgr........ Susanne Kirkham-Diaz
National Adv. Mgr.................. Annabelle Zabala
Managing Ed .... Parimal M. Rohit
Delivery Method: Mail, Newsstand, Racks
Areas Served: Orange, LA, Ventura, San Diego Counties

FREMONT

TRI-CITY VOICE (TUES, FRI)

39737 Paseo Padre Pkwy, Frnt, Fremont, CA, 94538-2997, Alameda, USA; gen tel (510) 494-1999; gen fax (510) 796-2462; disp adv e-mail tricityvoice@aol.com; web site www.tricityvoice.com
Advertising rate: Open inch rate $80.00
Pub .... William Marshak
Areas Served: 94538

FRESNO

THE BUSINESS JOURNAL (FRI)

1315 Van Ness Ave, Ste 200, Fresno, CA, 93721-1729, Fresno, USA; gen tel (559) 490-3400; adv tel (559) 490-3422; ed tel (559) 490-3467; gen fax (559) 490-3526; adv fax (559) 490-3526; ed fax (559) 490-3526; disp adv e-mail kaysi@thebusinessjournal.com; class adv e-mail gordon@thebusinessjournal.com; ed e-mail gabriel@thebusinessjournal.com; web site www.thebusinessjournal.com
Circulation: 1,028pd, 5,359fr; VAC
Advertising rate: Open inch rate $3,222.00

(Full-Page)
Established: 1886
Group: Pacific Publishing Group, Inc.
Digital Platform - Mobile: Apple, Android, Windows, Blackberry
Digital Platform - Tablet: Apple iOS, Android, Windows 7, Blackberry Tablet OS, Kindle, Nook, Kindle Fire
Pub....Gordon Webster
Mng. Ed....Gabriel Dillard
Adv. Mgr....Kaysi Coelho
Delivery Method: Mail, Newsstand, Racks
Areas Served: Fresno County

THE CLOVIS INDEPENDENT (FRI)
1626 E St, Fresno, CA, 93786-0001, Fresno, USA; gen tel (559) 441-6111; gen fax (559) 441-6740; disp adv e-mail jcollings@fresnobee.com; ed e-mail jrich@fresnobee.com; web site www.clovisindependent.com
Circulation: 13,688pd,; AAM
Advertising rate: Open inch rate $34.11
Established: 1905
Group: The McClatchy Company
Pub./Pres....Tom Cullinan
Exec. Ed./Sen. VP....Jim Boren
Mechanical Specifications: Type page 13 x 21; E - 6 cols, 2, between; A - 6 cols, 2, between; C - 10 cols, 1 1/4, between.Equipment & Software: Hardware — 150-HP/Vectra VE8, 12-Sun/Enterprise 450, Tandem/K1004; Software — Unisys Hermes 5.5.
Areas Served: 93611, 93612, 93613

GALT

LAGUNA CITIZEN (THUR)
604 N Lincoln Way, Galt, CA, 95632-8601, Sacramento, USA; gen tel (209) 745-1551; gen fax (209) 745-4492; disp adv e-mail news@herburger.com; web site www.herburger.net
Circulation: 12,593fr; VAC
Advertising rate: Open inch rate $9.00
Group: Herburger Publications, Inc.
Pub....David Herburger
Areas Served: 95632

RIVER VALLEY TIMES (WED)
604 N Lincoln Way, Galt, CA, 95632-8601, Sacramento, USA; gen tel (209) 745-1551; adv tel (209) 745-1551 x 112; gen fax (209) 745-4492; disp adv e-mail advertising@herburger.net; web site www.herburger.net
Circulation: 256pd, 5,600fr; Sworn/Estimate/Non-Audited
Advertising rate: Open inch rate $9.50
Group: Herburger Publications, Inc.
Pub....David Herburger
Adv. Mgr....Jim O'Donnell
Areas Served: 95632

THE GALT HERALD (WED)
604 N Lincoln Way, Galt, CA, 95632-8601, Sacramento, USA; gen tel (209) 745-1551; gen fax (209) 745-4492; disp adv e-mail advertising@herburger.net; class adv e-mail classified@herburger.net; ed e-mail editor_galtherald@herburger.net; web site www.galtheraldonline.com
Circulation: 2,453pd,; VAC
Advertising rate: Open inch rate $9.50
Group: Herburger Publications, Inc.
Pub....David Herburger
Adv. Mgr....Jim O'Donnell
Mng. Ed....Bonnie Rodriguez
Areas Served: 95632

GARDEN GROVE

WESTMINSTER HERALD (THUR)
7441 Garden Grove Blvd, Ste G, Garden Grove, CA, 92841-4209, Orange, USA; gen tel (714) 893-4501; gen fax (714) 893-4502; disp adv e-mail westmherald@aol.com; ed e-mail editor@westminsterheraldnews.com; web site www.westminsterheraldnews.com/
Circulation: 5,000pd,; Sworn/Estimate/Non-Audited
Advertising rate: Open inch rate $9.80
Established: 1946
Ed....Lloyd W. Thomas
Areas Served: 92683

GARDENA

GARDENA VALLEY NEWS (THUR)
15005 S Vermont Ave, Gardena, CA, 90247-3004, Los Angeles, USA; gen tel (310) 329-6351; ed tel (310) 329-6351 x 121; gen fax (310) 329-7501; disp adv e-mail gvneditorial@gardenavalleynews.org; web site www.gardenavalleynews.org
Circulation: 10,000pd,; Sworn/Estimate/Non-Audited
Advertising rate: Open inch rate $7.30
Established: 1895
Pub....Alan Moskal
Ed....Gary Kohatsu
Areas Served: 90247

GEORGETOWN

GEORGETOWN GAZETTE (THUR)
2775 Miners Flat Rd, Georgetown, CA, 95634-9345, El Dorado, USA; gen tel (530) 333-4481; gen fax (530) 333-0152; disp adv e-mail editor@gtgazette.com; class adv e-mail kay@gtgazette.com; ed e-mail editor@gtgazette.com; web site gtgazette.com
Circulation: 1,600pd, 6,700fr; Sworn/Estimate/Non-Audited
Advertising rate: 1/8 Pg $250.00; 1/4 Pg $460.00; 1/2 Pg $840.00
Established: 1880
Group: McNaughton Media
Ed....Wendy Thompson
Mechanical Specifications: Type page 10 x 12 1/2.Equipment & Software: Hardware — APP/Mac; Software — Adobe/PageMaker.
Delivery Method: Mail, Newsstand, Racks

GILROY

THE GILROY DISPATCH (TUES, FRI)
64 W 6th St, Gilroy, CA, 95020-6102, Santa Clara, USA; gen tel (408) 842-6400; ed tel (408) 847-7010; gen fax (408) 842-2206; adv fax (408) 842-7105; disp adv e-mail sstaloch@mainstreetmg.com; class adv e-mail cgault@svnewspapers.com; ed e-mail mderry@gilroydispatch.com; web site www.gilroydispatch.com
Circulation: 4,800pd, 15,600fr; Sworn/Estimate/Non-Audited
Advertising rate: Open inch rate $14.00 (Tue); $16.15 (Fri)
Established: 1868
Group: Mainstreet Media Group, LLC
Prodn./IT Mgr....Chuck Gibbs
Pub....Steve Staloch
Adv. Dir....Deborah Garcia
Editor....Jack Foley
Sports Ed....Erin Redmond
Mechanical Specifications: Type page 13 x 21 1/2; E - 6 cols, 2 1/16, 1/6 between; A - 6 cols, 2 1/16, 1/6 between; C - 10 cols, 1 7/32, 1/6 between.Equipment & Software: Hardware — APP/Power Mac, Dewar/Sys IV; Presses — 8-G/Community, 3-DEV/Color-Stack Unit, 1-ATF/Davidson-Chief 17 Offset; Software — QPS/QuarkXPress 4.03, Adobe/Photoshop.
Delivery Method: Newsstand, Carrier
Areas Served: 95020

GREENVILLE

INDIAN VALLEY RECORD (WED)
PO Box 469, Greenville, CA, 95947-0469, Plumas, USA; gen tel (530) 283-0800; gen fax (530) 283-3952; disp adv e-mail ccurran@plumasnews.com; class adv e-mail mnewhouse@plumasnews.com; ed e-mail dmoore@plumasnews.com; web site www.plumasnews.com
Circulation: 1,175pd,; Sworn/Estimate/Non-Audited
Advertising rate: Open inch rate $4.50
Established: 1930
Group: Feather Publishing Co., Inc.
Pub....Michael C. Taborski
Classified and Circ. Mgr....Mary Newhouse
Mng. Ed....Debra Moore
Mechanical Specifications: Full page 12 1/4 x 21; E - 6 cols, 1 5/6, 1/6 between; A - 6 cols, 1 5/6, 1/6 between; C - 9 cols, 1 1/4, 1/6 between.Equipment & Software: Hardware — APP/Macs; Presses — G/Community; Software — Microsoft/Word.
Delivery Method: Mail, Newsstand
Areas Served: 95947;95934;95923;95983

GRIDLEY

THE GRIDLEY HERALD (WED, FRI)
650 Kentucky St, Gridley, CA, 95948-2118, Butte, USA; gen tel (530) 846-3661; gen fax (530) 846-4519; disp adv e-mail jcalcagno@gridleyherald.com; class adv e-mail ajohnson-cooper@gridleyherald.com; ed e-mail lvandehey@gridleyherald.com; web site www.gridleyherald.com
Circulation: 2,900pd, 95fr; Sworn/Estimate/Non-Audited
Advertising rate: Open inch rate $13.00
Group: GateHouse Media, Inc.
Pub./Ed....Lisa Hey
Areas Served: 95948

GUALALA

INDEPENDENT COAST OBSERVER (FRI)
PO Box 1200, Gualala, CA, 95445-1200, Mendocino, USA; gen tel (707) 884-3501; adv tel (707) 884-3501; gen fax (707) 884-1710; adv fax (707) 884-1710; disp adv e-mail display@mendonoma.com; class adv e-mail classads@mendonoma.com; ed e-mail editor@mendonoma.com; web site www.mendonoma.com
Circulation: 3,500pd, 10fr; Sworn/Estimate/Non-Audited
Advertising rate: Open inch rate $12.00
Established: 1969
Adv. Mgr....Greg Oliver
Pub./Ed....J. Stephen McLaughlin
Mechanical Specifications: Type page 10 x 15; E - 6 cols, 1 7/12, 1/6 between; A - 6 cols, 1 7/12, 1/6 between; C - 6 cols, 1 7/12, 1/6 between.
Areas Served: 95445, 95468, 95497, 95459, 95480, 95412

HALF MOON BAY

HALF MOON BAY REVIEW (WED)
714 Kelly St, Half Moon Bay, CA, 94019-1919, San Mateo, USA; gen tel (650) 726-4424; gen fax (650) 726-7054; disp adv e-mail linda@hmbreview.com; class adv e-mail liners@hmbreview.com; ed e-mail clay@hmbreview.com; web site www.hmbreview.com - 350,000(views)
Circulation: 5,600pd,; Sworn/Estimate/Non-Audited
Advertising rate: Open inch rate $17.25
Established: 1898
Group: Wick Communications
Pub....Bill Murray
Business, Circ. Mgr....Barbara Anderson
Adv. Mgr....Linda Pettengil
Ed....Clay Lambert
Mechanical Specifications: Type page 11.5 x 21.Equipment & Software: Hardware — Apple; Software — InDesign, Photoshop.
Delivery Method: Mail, Newsstand, Racks
Areas Served: 94019, 94037, 94038, 94018

HANFORD

THE KINGSBURG RECORDER (WED)
300 W 6th St, Hanford, CA, 93230-4518, Kings, USA; gen tel (559) 582-0471; adv tel (559) 583-2420; ed tel (559) 583-2421; gen fax (559) 582-2341; disp adv e-mail jvikjord@HanfordSentinel.com; class adv e-mail jvikjord@HanfordSentinel.com; ed e-mail jmcgill@kingsburgrecorder.com; web site www.hanfordsentinel.com/kingsburg_recorder/
Circulation: 1,289pd,; AAM
Advertising rate: Open inch rate $14.80
Group: Lee Enterprises, Inc.
Digital Platform - Mobile: Apple, Android, Windows
Digital Platform - Tablet: Apple iOS, Android, Windows 7
Pub....Davis Taylor
Ed....Jenny Mcgill
Circulation Manager....Gordon Weaver
Mechanical Specifications: Type page 13 x 21 1/2; E - 6 cols, between; A - 6 cols, between; C - 9 cols, between.
Delivery Method: Mail, Newsstand, Carrier, Racks
Areas Served: 93631

THE SELMA ENTERPRISE (WED)
300 W 6th St, Hanford, CA, 93230-4518, Fresno, USA; gen tel (559) 896-1976; adv tel (559) 583-2402; ed tel (559) 896-1976 x 1013; gen fax (559) 896-9160; disp adv e-mail mdaniel@HanfordSentinel.com; class adv e-mail mdaniel@HanfordSentinel.com; ed e-mail jmcgill@selmaenterprise.com; web site www.selmaenterprise.com
Circulation: 5,000pd, 1,650fr; Sworn/Estimate/Non-Audited
Advertising rate: Open inch rate $16.00
Established: 1851
Pub....Davis Taylor
Ed....Jenny Mcgill
Mechanical Specifications: Type page 13 x 21 1/2; E - 6 cols, 2, between; A - 6 cols, 2, between; C - 9 cols, 1 1/2, between.Equipment & Software: Hardware — APP/Mac, PCs, AG/Imagesetter, SCREEN/Drum Scanner; Presses — G/Community; Software — Adobe/PageMaker 6.5, QPS/QuarkXPress 4.0.
Areas Served: 93662

HEALDSBURG

SONOMA WEST TIMES AND NEWS (THUR)
230 Center St, Healdsburg, CA, 95448-4402, Sonoma, USA; gen tel (707) 823-7845; web site www.sonomawest.com
Circulation: 3,800pd,; USPS
Group: Sonoma West Publishers
Digital Platform - Mobile: Apple
Assoc. Pub....Sarah Bradbury
Sports Ed....Greg Clementi
Laura Hager-Rush
Bleys Rose
Reporter....Elizabeth Hillin
Mgr. Editor....Eay Holley
Areas Served: Sonoma County

THE WINDSOR TIMES (THUR)
230 Center St, Healdsburg, CA, 95448-4402, Sonoma, USA; gen tel (707) 838-9211; gen fax (707) 838-7791; disp adv e-mail sales@hbgtrib.com; class adv e-mail sales@hbgtrib.com; ed e-mail editor@wdsrtimes.com; web site sonomawest.com/the_windsor_times
Circulation: 3,600fr; Sworn/Estimate/Non-Audited
Advertising rate: Open inch rate $33.44
Group: Sonoma West Publishers
Digital Platform - Mobile: Apple
Digital Platform - Tablet: Apple iOS
Pub....Rollie Atkinson
Assoc. Pub....Sarah Bradbury
Mgr. editor....Ray Holley
Mechanical Specifications: Type page 13 x 21; E - 6 cols, 2 1/16, 1/8 between; A - 6 cols, 2 1/16, 1/8 between; C - 6 cols, 2 1/16, 1/8

between.
Delivery Method: Mail, Newsstand
Areas Served: 95492

HEMET

THE VALLEY CHRONICLE (THUR)

227 E Florida Ave, Hemet, CA, 92543-4205, Riverside, USA; gen tel (951) 652-6529; adv tel (951) 318-2908; gen fax (951) 652-4009; disp adv e-mail knichols@thevalleychronicle.com; ed e-mail jself@thevalleychronicle.com; web site www.thevalleychronicle.com
Circulation: 2,029pd, 23,152fr; VAC
Advertising rate: 1/12 Pg $145.00; 1/8 Pg $195.00; 1/4 Pg $350.00
Group: Verican, Inc.
Pub....Eric Buskirk
Ed. ....Mary Ann Morris
Sales & Adv....Kathy McNeeley
Sales & Adv....David Burlison
Sales & Adv. ....Leo Monreal
Sales & Adv. ....Rocky Zharp
Journalist....Rusty Strait
Corey Evan
Mng. Ed....Jessica Self
Journalist....Debbie Mulvena
Journalist....Halima Haider
Journalist....Kyle Selby
Operations Dir....R.A. Calderon
Areas Served: 92543

HESPERIA

APPLE VALLEY NEWS (FRI)

16925 Main St, Hesperia, CA, 92345-6097, San Bernardino, USA; gen tel (760) 242-1930; gen fax (760) 244-6609; disp adv e-mail valleywide@valleywidenews.com; web site www.valleywidenews.com
Circulation: 24,000fr; Sworn/Estimate/Non-Audited
Advertising rate: Open inch rate $10.25
Group: Valley Wide Newspapers
Ed. ....Raymond Pryke
Mechanical Specifications: Type page 12 1/2 x 20 1/2; E - 6 cols, 2, between; A - 6 cols, 2, between; C - 9 cols, 1 1/4, between.
Delivery Method: Mail, Newsstand, Carrier, Racks
Areas Served: 92307

HESPERIA RESORTER (THUR)

16925 Main St, Ste A, Hesperia, CA, 92345-6038, San Bernardino, USA; gen tel (760) 244-0021; gen fax (760) 244-6609; disp adv e-mail valleywide@valleywidenews.com; web site www.valleywidenewspaper.com
Circulation: 20,000fr; Sworn/Estimate/Non-Audited
Advertising rate: Open inch rate $10.25
Established: 1959
Group: Valley Wide Newspapers
Pub....Raymond Pryke
Mechanical Specifications: Type page 12 1/2 x 20 1/2; E - 6 cols, 2, between; A - 6 cols, 2, between; C - 9 cols, 1 1/4, between.
Delivery Method: Mail, Newsstand, Carrier, Racks
Areas Served: 92345,92344&92340

HIGHLAND

HIGHLAND COMMUNITY NEWS (FRI)

27000 Baseline St Ste G, Suite G, Highland, CA, 92346-3169, San Bernardino, USA; gen tel (909) 862-1771; adv tel (909) 797-9101; gen fax (909) 862-1787; disp adv e-mail advertising@highlandnews.net; class adv e-mail classifieds@highlandnews.net; ed e-mail editor@highlandnews.net; web site www.highlandnews.net
Circulation: 496pd, 14,248fr; VAC
Advertising rate: Open inch rate $18.50
Established: 1994
Group: Century Group Newspapers
Ed. ....Charles Roberts
Office Mgr. ....Florina Ybarra
Gen. Mgr. ....Doris Diaz
Mechanical Specifications: Full Page 5 Col. wide x 14" high (9.833" w x 14" h)
4 Col. - 7.833" wide
3 col. - 5.833" wide
2 Col. - 3.833" wide
1 Col. - 1.833" wide
Equipment & Software: Hardware — APP/Mac; Presses — WPC; Software — Adobe/PageMaker, Adobe/Photoshop, Claris/Works, QPS/Quark XPress 5.1.
Delivery Method: Mail, Newsstand, Carrier, Racks
Areas Served: 92346

HILMAR

HILMAR TIMES (THUR)

19920 1st St, Hilmar, CA, 95324-9096, Merced, USA; gen tel (209) 358-5311; gen fax (209) 358-7108; disp adv e-mail midvalleypub@aol.com; web site hilmartimes.weebly.com
Circulation: 4,000pd,; Sworn/Estimate/Non-Audited
Advertising rate: Open inch rate $11.95
Established: 1962
Group: Mid Valley Publishing
Pres. ....Fran Sodini
Pub....John M. Derby
Mechanical Specifications: Type page 13 x 21.
Areas Served: 95324

HOLLISTER

HOLLISTER FREE LANCE (FRI)

350 6th St Ste 102, Suite 102, Hollister, CA, 95023-3882, San Benito, USA; gen tel (831) 637-5566; adv tel (831) 637-5566; gen fax (831) 637-4104; adv fax (831) 637-4104; disp adv e-mail info@freelancenews.com; class adv e-mail classified@freelancenews.com; ed e-mail editor@freelancetoday.com; web site www.sanbenitocountytoday.com
Circulation: 3,221pd, 9,000fr; Sworn/Estimate/Non-Audited
Advertising rate: Open inch rate $14.75
Established: 1873
Group: New SV Media, Inc
Circ. Mgr....Robert Rodriguez
Ed. ....Kollin Kosmicki
Publisher....Jeff Mitchell
Mechanical Specifications: Type page 13 x 21 1/2; E - 6 cols, 2 1/16, 1/8 between; A - 6 cols, 2 1/16, 1/8 between; C - 10 cols, 1 7/32, 1/8 between.Equipment & Software: Hardware — APP/Mac G3; Presses — 8-G/Community; Software — QPS/QuarkXPress 4.0, Adobe/Photoshop 5.0.
Areas Served: 95023

HOLTVILLE

CALEXICO CHRONICLE (THUR)

128 W 5th St, Holtville, CA, 92250-1214, Imperial, USA; gen tel (760) 356-2995; gen fax (760) 356-4915; disp adv e-mail holtvillenews@aol.com; web site www.tribwekchron.com
Circulation: 1,500pd, 11,000fr; Sworn/Estimate/Non-Audited
Advertising rate: Open inch rate $15.00
Established: 1904
Pub./Bus. Mgr./Adv. Mgr....Brenda Torres
Office Mgr. ....Rosa Nogueda
Mechanical Specifications: Type page 9 7/8 x 12; E - 5 cols, 1 7/8, 1/8 between.Equipment & Software: Hardware — APP/Power Mac 7100-80, APP/Mac IICX, APP/Mac Performa 405, APP/Mac Classic, APP/Power Mac 9300, APP/Power Mac 603e; Software — Adobe/PageMaker 6.5, Adobe/Photoshop 3.0, Microsoft/Word 6.0.
Delivery Method: Mail, Newsstand, Carrier, Racks
Areas Served: 92250

HOLTVILLE TRIBUNE (THUR)

128 W 5th St, Holtville, CA, 92250-1214, Imperial, USA; gen tel (760) 356-2995; gen fax (760) 356-4915; disp adv e-mail holtvillenews@aol.com; class adv e-mail holtvillenews@aol.com; web site www.tribwekchron.com
Circulation: 2,013pd,; Sworn/Estimate/Non-Audited
Advertising rate: Open inch rate $15.00
Established: 1904
Pub....Brenda Torres
Mechanical Specifications: Type page 10 x 21; 5c x 21Equipment & Software: Hardware — APP/Power Mac 7100-80, APP/Mac IIcx, APP/Mac Performa 405, APP/Mac Classic, APP/Power Mac 7300, APP/Power Mac 603; Software — Adobe/PageMaker 6.5, Adobe/Photoshop 3.0, Microsoft/Word 6.0.
Delivery Method: Mail, Newsstand, Carrier, Racks
Areas Served: 92250

HUGHSON

HUGHSON CHRONICLE-DENAIR DISPATCH (TUES)

7012 Pine St., STE 1, Hughson, CA, 95326, Stanislaus, USA; gen tel (209) 883-9215; gen fax (209) 358-7108; disp adv e-mail info@midvalleypub.com; web site hughsonchronicle-denairdispatch.weebly.com
Circulation: 7,500pd,; Sworn/Estimate/Non-Audited
Advertising rate: Open inch rate $11.95
Group: Mid Valley Publishing
Office Mgr. ....Kelly Thomas
Chief Ed./Sales/Mktg. ....Wendy Krier
Areas Served: Merced County

IDYLLWILD

IDYLLWILD TOWN CRIER (THUR)

54405 North Circle Dr, Idyllwild, CA, 92549, Riverside, USA; gen tel (951) 659-2145; gen fax (951) 659-2071; disp adv e-mail grace@towncrier.com; class adv e-mail dolores@towncrier.com; ed e-mail becky@towncrier.com; web site www.towncrier.com
Circulation: 4,200pd, 700fr; Sworn/Estimate/Non-Audited
Advertising rate: 9.80
Established: 1946
Group: Idyllwild House Publishing Co., Ltd.
Digital Platform - Mobile: Apple
Ed. ....J.P. Crumrine
Publisher-Editor....Becky Clark
Mechanical Specifications: Type page 10 1/4 x 13; E - 6 cols, 1 7/12, 1/6 between; A - 3 cols, 2 2/3, 1/6 between; C - 6 cols, 1 7/12, 1/4 between.Equipment & Software: Hardware — APP/Mac; Software — Adobe/InDesign 3.01.
Delivery Method: Mail, Newsstand
Areas Served: 92549, 92561,92706

INVERNESS

POINT REYES LIGHT (THUR)

12781 Sir Francis Drake Blvd, Inverness, CA, 94937-9736, Marin, USA; gen tel (415) 669-1200; adv tel (415) 669-1200; ed tel (415) 669-1200; gen fax (415) 669-1216; adv fax (415) 669-1216; ed fax (415) 669-1216; disp adv e-mail editor@ptreyeslight.com; class adv e-mail renee@ptreyeslight.com; ed e-mail editor@ptreyeslight.com; web site www.ptreyeslight.com
Circulation: 4,256pd, 26fr; Sworn/Estimate/Non-Audited
Advertising rate: Open inch rate $10.00
Established: 1948
Accounting....Donna Blum
Adv. Mgr. ....Renee Shannon
Ed. ....Tess Elliott
Pub....Lys Plotkin
Circ. Mgr....Missy Patterson
Mechanical Specifications: Type page 10 5/16 x 13; E - 4 cols, 2 3/8, 3/16 between; A - 6 cols, 1 9/16, 3/16 between; C - 6 cols, 1 9/16, 3/16 between.Equipment & Software: Hardware — APP/Mac; Software — Microsoft/Word 5.0, Claris/FileMaker Pro, Abbott Systems/Ready, Set, Go 6.0, QPS/QuarkXPress 4.1, Microsoft/Excel 4.0, Adobe/Photoshop.
Delivery Method: Mail, Newsstand, Racks
Areas Served: 94924, 94933, 94937, 94938, 94940, 94946, 94950, 94956, 94963, 94970, 94973

JACKSON

AMADOR LEDGER-DISPATCH (TUES, FRI)

10776 ARGONAUT LN, Jackson, CA, 95642, Amador, USA; gen tel (209) 223-1767; gen fax (209) 223-1264; disp adv e-mail jmitchell@ledger-dispatch.com; web site www.ledger-dispatch.com
Circulation: 6,000pd, 193fr; VAC
Advertising rate: Open inch rate $11.00
Established: 1855
Group: Amador Hometown Media, LLC
Mainstreet Media Group, LLCEditions: Ledger Dispatch - 6,000, Gold Mine 34,000
Digital Platform - Mobile: Apple, Android, Windows, Blackberry
Digital Platform - Tablet: Apple iOS, Android, Windows 7, Blackberry Tablet OS, Kindle, Nook, Kindle Fire
Pub....Jack Mitchell
Adv. Dir....Beth Bernard
Ed. ....Caitlyn Schaap
Circ. Coord....Joe Svec
Mechanical Specifications: Tabloid publication; Full Page 65", Half Page 32", Quarter Page 16.5", Eighth Page 8.25"Equipment & Software: Hardware — IBM/486, APP/Mac Quadra 800, APP/Power Mac; Presses — 8-HI/V-15D; Software — Archetype/Corel Draw 5.0, Adobe/Photoshop 3.4, QPS/QuarkXPress 3.31.
Delivery Method: Mail, Newsstand, Carrier, Racks
Areas Served: 95232, 95245, 95255, 95257, 95249, 95252, 95246, 95248, 95601, 95629, 95640, 95642, 95665, 95666, 95669, 95675, 95685, 95689, 95699

JULIAN

JULIAN NEWS (WED)

1453 Hollow Glen Rd, Julian, CA, 92036, San Diego, USA; gen tel (760) 765-2231; adv tel (760) 765-2231; gen fax (760) 765-2231; adv fax (760) 765-2231; disp adv e-mail publisher@juliannews.com; ed e-mail editor@juliannews.com; web site www.juliannews.com
Circulation: 1,200pd, 400fr; Sworn/Estimate/Non-Audited
Advertising rate: Open inch rate $15.00
Established: 1984
Ed/Columnist....Michele Harvey
Pub/ Produc Mgr....Michael Hart
Mechanical Specifications: Type page 13 x 21; E - 6 cols, 2, 1/8 between; A - 6 cols, 2, 1/8 between; C - 6 cols, 2, 1/8 between.Equipment & Software: Hardware — PC windows based ; Presses — out sourced; Software — Adobe Creative Suite
MS Word
Delivery Method: Mail, Newsstand, Racks
Areas Served: 92036, 92070, San Diego County

KERMAN

THE KERMAN NEWS (WED)

652 S Madera Ave, Kerman, CA, 93630-1737, Fresno, USA; gen tel (559) 846-6689; gen fax (559) 846-8045; disp adv e-mail kerwest@msn.com; web site www.kerwestnewspapers.com
Circulation: 2,000pd, 6,050fr; Sworn/Estimate/Non-Audited
Advertising rate: Open inch rate $15.00
Established: 1906
Ed. ....Mark Kilen
Areas Served: Northwest Fresno County

KING CITY

GONZALES TRIBUNE (WED)

522 Broadway St, Ste B, King City, CA, 93930-3243, Monterey, USA; gen tel (831) 385-4880; gen fax (831) 385-4799; disp adv e-mail soledadb@redshift.com; web site www.gonzalestribune.com
Circulation: 650pd,; Sworn/Estimate/Non-Audited
Advertising rate: Open inch rate $17.00
Group: News Media Corp.
Adv. Mgr....................................Sheryl Bailey
Ed./Gen. Mgr............................Tricia Bergeron
Areas Served: 93930

GREENFIELD NEWS (WED)

522 Broadway St, Ste A, King City, CA, 93930-3243, Monterey, USA; gen tel (831) 385-4880; gen fax (831) 385 4799; ed e-mail editor@southcountynewspapers.com; web site www.greenfieldnews.com
Circulation: 1,400pd,; Sworn/Estimate/Non-Audited
Advertising rate: Open inch rate $17.00
Group: News Media Corp.
Adv. Mgr....................................Sheryl Bailey
Ed./Gen Mgr..............................Tricia Bergeron
Areas Served: 93930

SOLEDAD BEE (WED)

522 Broadway St, Ste B, King City, CA, 93930-3243, Monterey, USA; gen tel (831) 385-4880; gen fax (831) 385-4799; disp adv e-mail sheryl@southcountynewspapers.com; class adv e-mail sheryl@southcountynewspapers.com; ed e-mail editor@southcountynewspapers.com; web site www.soledadbee.com
Circulation: 1,500pd,; Sworn/Estimate/Non-Audited
Advertising rate: Open inch rate $15.50
Group: News Media Corp.
Ed.......................................Aaron Crutchfield
Areas Served: 93930

THE RUSTLER (WED)

522 Broadway St, Ste A, King City, CA, 93930-3243, Monterey, USA; gen tel (831) 385-4880; adv tel (831) 385-4880 x 15; ed tel (831) 385-4880 x 21; gen fax (831) 385-4799; disp adv e-mail sheryl@southcountynewspapers.com; class adv e-mail sheryl@southcountynewspapers.com; ed e-mail editor@southcountynewspapers.com; web site www.kingcityrustler.com
Circulation: 3,820pd,; Sworn/Estimate/Non-Audited
Advertising rate: Open inch rate $17.00
Group: News Media Corp.
Pub...Jeremy Burke
Gen. Mgr.................................Tricia Bergeron
Mechanical Specifications: Type page 13 x 21; E - 6 cols, 2 1/16, between; A - 6 cols, 2 1/16, between.Equipment & Software: Hardware — APP/Mac, PC; Software — QPS/QuarkXPress, Multi-Ad/Creator, Adobe/PageMaker.
Areas Served: 93930

LA JOLLA

LA JOLLA LIGHT (THUR)

565 Pearl St, Ste 300, La Jolla, CA, 92037-5051, San Diego, USA; gen tel (858) 459-4201; adv tel (858) 875-5954; ed tel (858) 875-5950; gen fax (858) 459-5250; adv fax (858) 459-0977; ed fax (858) 459-5250; disp adv e-mail donp@lajollalight.com; class adv e-mail mwilliams@mainstreetsd.com; ed e-mail editor@lajollalight.com; web site www.lajollalight.com - 83,195(views) 42,676(visitors)
Circulation: 17,931pd,; AAM
Advertising rate: 1/8 Pg $425.00; 1/4 Pg $770.00
Established: 1913
Group: Mainstreet Media Group, LLC
La Jolla Light, an edition of The San Diego Union Tribune
Digital Platform - Mobile: Apple, Android
Digital Platform - Tablet: Apple iOS, Android
President/Gen Mgr ....Phyllis Pfeiffer
Graphics Mgr. ....John Feagans
Exec. Ed...............................Susan DeMaggio
Adv. Mgr.......................................Don Parks
Circ. Mgr......................................Dara Elstein
Classified Adv. Mgr......................Sandra Hood
Mechanical Specifications: Type page 10.33" x 12.25"; 6 cols
Delivery Method: Mail, Racks
Areas Served: 92037, 92122, 92109

LAKE ARROWHEAD

MOUNTAIN NEWS & CRESTLINE COURIER-NEWS (THUR)

PO Box 2410, PO Box 2410, Lake Arrowhead, CA, 92352-2410, San Bernardino, USA; gen tel (909) 337-6145; adv tel (909) 337-6145; ed tel (909) 337-6145; gen fax (909) 337-6145; adv fax (909) 337-6145; ed fax (909) 337-6145; disp adv e-mail hbradley@mountain-news.com; class adv e-mail classified@mountain-news.com ; ed e-mail hbradley@mountain-news.com; web site www.mountain-news.com - 90,000(views) 30,000(visitors)
Circulation: 5,000pd, 500fr; Sworn/Estimate/Non-Audited
Advertising rate: Open inch rate $25
Established: 1924
Group: Brehm Communications, Inc.
Publisher...................................Harry Bradley
Mechanical Specifications: Type page 10 x 21; E - 6 cols, 2, between; A - 6 cols, 2, between.
Delivery Method: Mail, Newsstand, Racks
Areas Served: 92352

LAKE ISABELLA

KERN VALLEY SUN (WED)

6416 LAKE ISABELLA BLVD, Lake Isabella, CA, 93240, Kern, USA; gen tel (760) 379-3667; ed tel (760) 379-3667 x 14; gen fax (760) 379-4343; disp adv e-mail michelel@kvsun.com; ed e-mail editor@kvsun.com; web site www.kvsun.com
Circulation: 6,500pd, 10,500fr; Sworn/Estimate/Non-Audited
Advertising rate: Open inch rate $9.50
Established: 1959
Pub...Marsha Smith
Ed. ....Susan Barr
Mechanical Specifications: Type page 13 x 21 1/2; E - 6 cols, 2 1/4, 1/6 between; A - 6 cols, 2 1/4, 1/6 between; C - 6 cols, 2 1/4, 1/6 between.Equipment & Software: Hardware — APP/Mac IIci; Software — Photoshop 10.0
Quark 7.5
Adobe Acrobat 7
Areas Served: 93240

LAKEPORT

CLEAR LAKE OBSERVER-AMERICAN (WED)

2150 S Main St, Lakeport, CA, 95453-5620, Lake, USA; gen tel (707) 263-5636 ; adv tel (707) 263-5636 ; ed tel (707) 263-5636; disp adv e-mail ahansmith@record-bee.com; class adv e-mail advertising@record-bee.com ; web site www.record-bee.com
Circulation: 6,000pd,; Sworn/Estimate/Non-Audited
Advertising rate: Open inch rate $9.90
Established: 1961
Group: Digital First Media
Pub.......................Kevin McConnellEquipment & Software: Hardware — APP/Mac; Software — NewsEditPro.
Delivery Method: Mail, Newsstand, Carrier, Racks
Areas Served: Lake County

SOUTH COUNTY NEWS (WED)

2150 S Main St, Lakeport, CA, 95453-5620, Lake, USA; gen tel (707) 263-5636; class adv e-mail advertising@record-bee.com ; web site www.record-bee.com
Circulation: 5,700fr; USPS
Advertising rate: Open inch rate varies - please call
Group: Digital First Media
Delivery Method: Carrier

LAYTONVILLE

MENDOCINO COUNTY OBSERVER (THUR)

50 Ramsey Rd, Laytonville, CA, 95454-9900, Mendocino, USA; gen tel (707) 984-6223; gen fax (707) 984-8118; disp adv e-mail observer@pacific.net; web site No Website
Circulation: 3,000pd,; Sworn/Estimate/Non-Audited
Advertising rate: Open inch rate $7.00
Established: 1978
Adv. Mgr....................................Susan Shields
Ed. ....Jim Shields
Mechanical Specifications: Type page 13 x 21; E - 6 cols, 2 2/5, between; A - 6 cols, 2 2/5, between.Equipment & Software: Hardware — APP/Mac; Software — Adobe/PageMaker, Microsoft/Word.
Areas Served: 95454, 95417, 95585, 95528, 95482

LINCOLN

LINCOLN NEWS MESSENGER (THUR)

553 F St, Lincoln, CA, 95648-1849, Placer, USA; gen tel (916) 645-7733 ; adv tel (916) 774-7971; ed tel (916) 774-7972; gen fax (916) 645-2776 ; disp adv e-mail jenniferp@goldcountrymedia.com; class adv e-mail lizd@goldcountrymedia.com; ed e-mail carolf@goldcountrymedia.com; web site www.lincolnnewsmessenger.com
Circulation: 3,777pd, 0fr; VAC
Advertising rate: Open inch rate $10.45
Established: 1891
Group: Brehm Communications, Inc.
Gold Country Media
Ed..Carol Feineman
Mechanical Specifications: 6 col tabloid
Delivery Method: Mail, Newsstand, Carrier
Areas Served: 95648

LIVERMORE

THE INDEPENDENT (THUR)

2250 1st St, Livermore, CA, 94550-3143, Alameda, USA; gen tel (925) 447-8700; adv tel (925) 243-8010; ed tel (925) 243-8013; gen fax (925) 447-0212; disp adv e-mail editmail@compuserve.com; class adv e-mail ramona@independentnews.com; ed e-mail editmail@compuserve.com; web site www.independentnews.com
Circulation: 48,000fr; Sworn/Estimate/Non-Audited
Advertising rate: Open inch rate $29.10
Established: 1963
Pub.............................Joan Kinney Seppala
Assoc. Pub...............................David T. Lowell
Adv. Mgr...Tina Rose
Ed./Prod. Mgr........................Janet Armantrout
Mechanical Specifications: Type page 13 x 21; E - 6 cols, 2 1/16, 1/8 between; A - 6 cols, 2 1/6, 1/8 between; C - 10 cols, between. Equipment & Software: Hardware — PCs; Software — Aldus/PageMaker.
Areas Served: 94550

LONG BEACH

DOWNTOWN GAZETTE (FRI)

5225 E 2nd St, Long Beach, CA, 90803-5326, Los Angeles, USA; gen tel (562) 433-2000; gen fax (562) 434-8826; disp adv e-mail advertising@gazettes.com; class adv e-mail classifieds@gazettes.com; ed e-mail editor@gazettes.com; web site www.gazettes.com
Circulation: 0pd, 17,975fr; CVC
Advertising rate: Open inch rate $15.00
Established: 1978
Group: MediaNews Group
Digital Platform - Mobile: Apple
Digital Platform - Tablet: Apple iOS
Pub./Adv. Mgr.............................Simon Grieve
Exec. Ed................................Henry Saltzgaver
Circ. Mgr................................Michelle Shearer
Circ. Mgr ....Julie Mckibben
Areas Served: 90802

GRUNION GAZETTE (THUR)

5225 E 2nd St, Long Beach, CA, 90803-5326, Los Angeles, USA; gen tel (562) 433-2000; gen fax (562) 434-8826; disp adv e-mail jchandler@gazettes.com; ed e-mail hsalt@gazettes.com; web site www.gazettes.com
Circulation: 39,021fr; VAC
Advertising rate: Open inch rate $18.50
Established: 1977
Group: Digital First Media
Digital Platform - Mobile: Apple
Digital Platform - Tablet: Apple iOS
Pub./Adv. Mgr.............................Simon Grieve
Exec. Ed................................Henry Saltzgaver
Circ. Mgr................................Michelle Shearer
Circ. Mgr ....Julie Mckibben
Mechanical Specifications: full page - 10" across by 15.5" vertical
Delivery Method: Carrier, Racks
Areas Served: 90803, 90814, 90815,

UPTOWN GAZETTE (FRI)

5225 E 2nd St, Long Beach, CA, 90803-5326, Los Angeles, USA; gen tel (562) 433-2000; gen fax (562) 434-8826; disp adv e-mail advertising@gazettes.com; class adv e-mail classifieds@gazettes.com; ed e-mail editor@gazettes.com; web site www.gazettes.com
Circulation: 17,975fr; CVC
Established: 2008
Pub..Simon Grieve
Exec. Ed................................Harry Saltzgaver
Areas Served: 90805, 90807

LOOMIS

LOOMIS NEWS (THUR)

3550 Taylor Rd, Loomis, CA, 95650-9501, Placer, USA; gen tel (916) 786-8746; adv tel (916) 783-1183; ed tel (916) 652-7939; gen fax (916) 783-1183; disp adv e-mail paulc@goldcountrymedia.com; class adv e-mail lizd@goldcountrymedia.com; ed e-mail carolf@goldcountrymedia.com; web site www.theloomisnews.com
Circulation: 771pd, 195fr; VAC
Advertising rate: Open inch rate $10.00
Established: 1940
Group: Brehm Communications, Inc.
Circulation Mgr ....Kelly Leibold
Delivery Method: Mail, Newsstand, Racks
Areas Served: 95650

LOS ALTOS

LOS ALTOS TOWN CRIER (WED)

138 Main St, Los Altos, CA, 94022-2905, Santa Clara, USA; gen tel (650) 948-9000; adv tel (650) 948-9000 x 307; gen fax (650) 948-9213; disp adv e-mail info@latc.com; class adv e-mail jt@latc.com; web site www.latc.com
Circulation: 8,598pd, 7,355fr; Sworn/Estimate/Non-Audited
Advertising rate: Open inch rate $16.40
Established: 1947
Pub...Paul Nyberg
Circ. Mgr................................Howard Bischoff
Ed. ....Bruce Barton
HR Dir...Liz Nyberg
Circulation Mgr ....Howard Bischoff
Mechanical Specifications: Type page 10 x 13;

E - 5 cols, 1 7/8, 3/16 between; A - 5 cols, 1 7/8, 3/16 between; C - 7 cols, 1 5/16, 1/8 between.Equipment & Software: Hardware — APP/Macs; Software — QPS/QuarkXPress, Adobe/Photoshop.
Delivery Method: Mail, Newsstand
Areas Served: 94022

LOS ANGELES

BURBANK LEADER (WED, SAT)

202 W 1st St, 2nd Floor, Los Angeles, CA, 90012-4299, Los Angeles, USA; gen tel (818) 637-3200; adv tel (818) 637-3200; gen fax (818) 241-1975; disp adv e-mail jeffrey.young@latimes.com; class adv e-mail tcnclassifieds@latimes.com; web site www.burbankleader.com
Circulation: 15,020pd, 10,387fr; VAC
Advertising rate: Open inch rate $18.72
Established: 1901
Group: Times Community News (TCN)
Ed. .... Dan Evans
Pub. .... Scott Pompe
Sales Dir. .... Hector Cabral
Classified Supervisor.............. Carlin Chesney
Areas Served: 91523

LA CANADA VALLEY SUN (THUR)

202 W 1st St Fl 2nd, 2nd Floor, Los Angeles, CA, 90012-4299, Los Angeles, USA; gen tel (818) 495-4440; adv tel (818) 637-3200; ed tel (818) 495-4161; gen fax (818) 790-5690; adv fax (213) 237-6065; disp adv e-mail marissa.contreras@latimes.com; class adv e-mail gil.cormaci@latimes.com; ed e-mail lcnews@valleysun.net; web site www.lacanadaonline.com
Circulation:; Sworn/Estimate/Non-Audited
Established: 1946
Group: Times Community News (TCN)
Mechanical Specifications: Type page 10 1/4 x 16; E - 6 cols, 1 9/16, between; A - 6 cols, 1 9/16, between; C - 6 cols, 1 9/16, between. Equipment & Software: Hardware — APP/Mac; Software — Adobe/Photoshop, Adobe/Illustrator, QPS/QuarkXPress, APP/AppleWorks.
Delivery Method: Carrier, Racks
Areas Served: 91011

LOS ANGELES DOWNTOWN NEWS (MON)

1264 W 1st St, Los Angeles, CA, 90026-5831, Los Angeles, USA; gen tel (213) 481-1448; adv tel (213) 481-1448; ed tel (213) 481-1448; gen fax (213) 250-4617; adv fax (213) 250-4617; ed fax (213) 250-4617; disp adv e-mail realpeople@downtownnews.com; class adv e-mail catherine@downtownnews.com; ed e-mail regardie@downtownnews.com; web site www.downtownnews.com
Circulation: 31pd, 37,670fr; VAC
Advertising rate: Open inch rate $45.00
Established: 1972
Digital Platform - Mobile: Apple
Gen. Mgr. .... Dawn Eastin
Mechanical Specifications: Type page 10 1/4 x 15 1/2; A - 6 cols, 1 1/2, 1/4 between; C - 7 cols, 1 5/16, 1/4 between.Equipment & Software: Hardware — APP/Mac; Software — InDesign, Adobe/Illustrator, Adobe/Photoshop.
Delivery Method: Mail, Newsstand, Racks
Areas Served: Downtown Los Angeles 90012 90013 90017 90014 and many more

LOS ANGELES WAVE (SUN)

3731 Wilshire Blvd Ste 840, Suite 840, Los Angeles, CA, 90010-2851, Los Angeles, USA; gen tel (323) 556-5720; adv tel (323) 556-5720 x 245; gen fax (213) 835-0584; disp adv e-mail dwanless@wavepublication.com; web site www.wavenewspapers.com
Circulation: 49,900fr; CAC
Advertising rate: Open inch rate $22.25
Pub. .... Pluria Marshall
Circ. Mgr. .... Farras Shamuon
Prodn. Mgr. .... Jorge Infante
Ed .... Don Wanlass
Mechanical Specifications: Type page 11 1/2 x 21; E - 6 cols, 1 3/4, 1/6 between; A - 6 cols, 1 3/4, 1/6 between; C - 11 cols, 1 1/16, 1/8 between.Equipment & Software: Hardware — APP/Mac; Software — Adobe/Illustrator 5.5, QPS/QuarkXPress 4.0, Adobe/Photoshop 5.0.
Areas Served: 90010

PARK LABREA NEWS & BEVERLY PRESS (THUR)

5150 Wilshire Blvd Ste 330, Suite 330, Los Angeles, CA, 90036-4480, Los Angeles, USA; gen tel (323) 933-5518; web site beverlypress.com
Group: Times Community News (TCN)

THE ARGONAUT (THUR)

5355 McConnell Ave, Los Angeles, CA, 90066-7025, Los Angeles, USA; gen tel (310) 822-1629; gen fax (310) 822-2089; disp adv e-mail Renee@Argonautnews.com; class adv e-mail Chantal@Argonautnews.com; ed e-mail Vince@ArgonautNews.com; web site argonautnews.com - 32,904(views) 10,764(visitors)
Circulation: 13pd, 29,962fr; CVC
Advertising rate: 1/4 Pg $475.00; 1/2 Pg $895.00
Established: 1971
Group: Southland Publishing, Inc.
Pub. .... David Comden
David Maury
Circ. Mgr. .... Tom Ponton
Mechanical Specifications: Type page 10.25 x 16; 5 colsEquipment & Software: Hardware — APP/Mac, PC; Software — QPS/QuarkXPress, Adobe/PageMaker, Adobe/Photoshop, Adobe/Illustrator, Microsoft/Word, APT.
Delivery Method: Mail, Carrier, Racks
Areas Served: 90291, 90292, 90293, 90066, 90045, 90401, 90405

LOS BANOS

LOS BANOS ENTERPRISE (FRI)

907 6th St, Los Banos, CA, 93635-4215, Merced, USA; gen tel (209) 704-3831; adv tel (209) 704-3831; ed tel (209) 385-2482; gen fax (209) 826-2005; adv fax (209) 826-8888; ed fax (209) 826-2005; disp adv e-mail glieb@losbanosenterprise.com; class adv e-mail glieb@losbanosenterprise.com; ed e-mail glieb@losbanosenterprise.com; web site www.losbanosenterprise.com - 70,000(views)
Circulation: 1,890pd, 6fr; AAM
Advertising rate: Open inch rate $11.00
Established: 1891
Group: The McClatchy Company
Outside Adv. Sales .... Gene Lieb
Sports Reporter............................. David Witte
Reporter .... Corey Pride
Reporter .... Thaddeus Miller
Admin./Sales Asst.......................... Beth Smith
Managing. Ed................................ Victor Patton
Pres./Pub. .... Ken Riddick
Adv. Dir........... Deanna WhitmoreEquipment & Software: Hardware — PC/Mac; Presses — Flexo; Software — Adobe/Photoshop, Uniysis
Delivery Method: Mail, Newsstand, Carrier, Racks
Areas Served: 93635, 93620, 93622

MADERA

THE MADERA TRIBUNE (WED, SAT)

2591 Mitchell Ct, Ste 107, Madera, CA, 93637-3807, Madera, USA; gen tel (559) 674-2424; ed tel (559) 674-8134; gen fax (559) 673-0944; adv fax (559) 673-6526; disp adv e-mail maderatribune@maderatribunet.net; ed e-mail cdoud@maderatribune.net; web site www.maderatribune.com
Circulation: 4,213pd,; Sworn/Estimate/Non-Audited
Advertising rate: Open inch rate $14.00
Established: 1892
Digital Platform - Mobile: Apple
CFO .... Nancy Simpson
Ed. .... Charles P. Doud
Dir., Opns.................................... Leonard Soliz
Pres./Pub. .... Doug Caldwell
Mechanical Specifications: Type page 13 x 21; E - 6 cols, 2 1/16, 1/8 between; A - 6 cols, 2 1/16, 1/8 between; C - 9 cols, 1 3/8, 1/16 between.
Delivery Method: Mail, Newsstand, Racks
Areas Served: City of Madera and outlying areas

MALIBU

THE MALIBU SURFSIDE NEWS (WED)

PO Box 6854, Malibu, CA, 90264-6854, Los Angeles, USA; gen tel (708) 326-9170; gen fax (708) 326-9179; disp adv e-mail m.vinci@22ndcenturymedia.com; class adv e-mail m.vinci@22ndcenturymedia.com; ed e-mail news@malibusurfsidenews.com; web site www.malibusurfsidenews.com
Circulation: 6,770fr; CAC
Advertising rate: Open inch rate $26.47
Adv. Dir./Nat'l Adv. Mgr..................... Mike Vinci
Adv. Dir.. Andrew Nicks
Circ. Mgr..................................... Hillary Carroll
Areas Served: 90265

THE MALIBU TIMES (THUR)

3864 Las Flores Canyon Rd, Malibu, CA, 90265-5239, Los Angeles, USA; gen tel (310) 456-5507; adv tel (310) 456-5507; ed tel (310) 456-5507 ; gen fax (310) 456-8986; adv fax (310) 456-8986; disp adv e-mail barbara@malibutimes.com; class adv e-mail classads@malibutimes.com; ed e-mail editoral@malibutimes.com; web site www.malibutimes.com
Circulation: 500pd, 11,500fr; Sworn/Estimate/Non-Audited
Advertising rate: Starting from $157.00
Established: 1946
Pub./Gen. Mgr............................ Arnold G. York
Mechanical Specifications: Type page 13 x 20 1/2; E - 6 cols, 2, 3/16 between; A - 6 cols, 2 1/16, 1/8 between; C - 6 cols, 2, 3/16 between.Equipment & Software: Hardware — APP/Mac Quadra 650; Software — QPS/QuarkXPress 3.2.
Delivery Method: Mail, Racks
Areas Served: 90265

MAMMOTH LAKES

MAMMOTH TIMES (THUR)

501 Old Mammoth Rd, Unit 9, Mammoth Lakes, CA, 93546, Mono, USA; gen tel (760) 934-3929; adv tel 7609343929 x 107; ed tel 7609343929 x 116; gen fax (760) 934-3951; disp adv e-mail ads@mammothtimes.com; class adv e-mail classifieds@mammoth-times.com; ed e-mail editor@mammothtimes.com; web site www.mammothtimes.com
Circulation: 4,200pd,; USPS
Advertising rate: Open Inch Rate $6.85
Established: 1987
Group: Horizon Publications Inc.
Managing Ed................................ Mike Gervais
Staff Writer........................... Wendi Grasseschi
Sales Rep................................ Blake Martines
Classifieds/Circ......................... Josh Haywood
Delivery Method: Mail, Carrier, Racks
Areas Served: Topaz, Coleville, Walker, Bridgeport, June Lake, Lee Vining, Mono City, Mammoth Lakes, Benton, Chalfant, Bishop, Toms Place, Crowley Lake

MARIPOSA

MARIPOSA GAZETTE (THUR)

5801 State Highway 140, Ste B, Mariposa, CA, 95338-9249, Mariposa, USA; gen tel (209) 966-2500; gen fax (209) 966-3384; disp adv e-mail ads@mariposagazette.com; class adv e-mail ads@mariposagazette.com; ed e-mail editor@mariposagazette.com; web site www.mariposagazette.com
Circulation: 5,109pd, 80fr; Sworn/Estimate/Non-Audited
Advertising rate: Open inch rate $13.00
Established: 1854
Digital Platform - Mobile: Apple, Android, Windows, Blackberry
Digital Platform - Tablet: Apple iOS, Kindle Fire
Pub. .... R.D. Tucker
Greg Little
Mechanical Specifications: Type page 13 x 21 1/2; E - 6 cols, 2 1/16, 1/8 between; A - 6 cols, 2 1/16, 1/8 between; C - 6 cols, 2 1/16, 1/8 between.
Delivery Method: Mail, Newsstand, Racks
Areas Served: Mariposa County

MARTINEZ

MARTINEZ NEWS-GAZETTE (TUES, THUR, SUN)

802 Alhambra Ave, Martinez, CA, 94553-1604, Contra Costa, USA; gen tel (925) 228-6400; gen fax (925) 228-1536; disp adv e-mail gazette_ads@yahoo.com; web site www.martinezgazette.com
Circulation: 2,550pd, 8,399fr; VAC
Advertising rate: Open inch rate $6.95
Ed. in Chief .... David L. Payne
Gen. Mgr. .... Samuel Li-Ron
Ed. .... Yael Li-Ron
Erin Clark
Mechanical Specifications: Type page 12 3/8 x 21; E - 6 cols, 1 7/8, 3/16 between; A - 6 cols, 1 7/8, 3/16 between; C - 8 cols, 1 7/16, 3/16 between.Equipment & Software: Hardware — AG, COM, APP/Mac; Presses — G/Community, H; Software — Adobe/PageMaker, QPS/QuarkXPress.
Areas Served: 94553

MARYSVILLE

COLUSA COUNTY SUN-HERALD (WED)

1530 Ellis Lake Dr, Marysville, CA, 95901-4258, Colusa, USA; gen tel (530) 458-2121; adv tel (530) 934-6800; ed tel (530) 749-4767; gen fax (530) 458-5711; disp adv e-mail dbaggett@appealdemocrat.com; class adv e-mail nbrown@appealdemocrat.com; web site www.colusa-sun-herald.com
Circulation: 5,000pd, 3,151fr; Sworn/Estimate/Non-Audited
Advertising rate: 1/16 Pg $92.00; 1/8 Pg $150.00
Group: Times Media Group
Pub. .... Paula Patton
Ed. .... Steve Miller
nat'l Adv. Mgr. .... Jamie Keith
Adv./Retail/Mktg Mgr............... Debbie Baggett
Classified Adv. Mgr...................... Nancy Brown
Mechanical Specifications: Type page 13 x 21 1/2; E - 6 cols, 2, between; A - 6 cols, 2, between; C - 9 cols, 1 1/2, between.Equipment & Software: Hardware — APP/iMac; Presses — 8-G/Community.
Areas Served: Colusa County

CORNING OBSERVER (WED, SAT)

1530 Ellis Lake Dr, Marysville, CA, 95901-4258, Yuba, USA; gen tel (530) 824-5464; adv tel (530) 934-6800; ed tel (530) 749-4767; gen fax (530) 824-4804; disp adv e-mail dbaggett@appealdemocrat.com; class adv e-mail smiller@appealdemocrat.com; web site www.corning-observer.com
Circulation: 1,500pd,; Sworn/Estimate/Non-Audited
Advertising rate: 1/16 Pg $92.00; 1/8 Pg $150.00
Group: Times Media Group
Pub. .... Paula Patton
Ed. .... Steve Miller
Nat'l Adv. Mgr. .... Jamie Keith
Adv./Retail/Mktg Dir. .... Debbie Baggett
Mechanical Specifications: Type page 13 x 21; E - 6 cols, between; A - 6 cols, between; C - 9 cols, between.Equipment & Software: ; Presses — 8-G/Community.
Areas Served: Tehama County

MENLO PARK

PALO ALTO DAILY NEWS (WED, FRI, SAT)

255 Constitution Dr, Menlo Park, CA, 94025-1108, San Mateo, USA; gen tel (650) 391-1000; adv tel (650) 391-1028; ed tel (650) 391-1337; gen fax (650) 391-1001; adv fax (650) 391-1011; disp adv e-mail letters@bayareanewsgroup.com; class adv e-mail adsales@dailynewsgroup.com; ed e-mail news@paloaltodailynews.com; web site www.paloaltodailynews.com
Circulation: 47,585pd,; AAM
Advertising rate: Open inch rate $20.00 (Wed/Fri); $25.00 (Sat)
Group: Digital First Media
Exec. Ed....................................... Mario Dianda
City Ed.. Jason Green
Copydesk Chief ....Kevin Kelly
Sports Editor.................................. Bud Geracie
Opns. Mgr. .... Paulo Pereira
Prodn./Creative Servs. Mgr .... Christine Eng
Adv. Sales Mgr......................... Jennifer Belton
Mechanical Specifications: Type page 13 x 21.
Areas Served: 94070, 94061, 94063, 94025, 94027, 94062, 94028, 94022, 94305, 94301, 94303, 94306, 94043, 94041, 94040

THE ALMANAC (WED)

3525 Alameda De Las Pulgas, Menlo Park, CA, 94025-6544, San Mateo, USA; gen tel (650) 854-2626; adv tel (650) 223-6570; ed tel (650) 223-6507; gen fax (650) 854-0677; disp adv e-mail ads@almanacnews.com; ed e-mail editor@almanacnews.com; web site www.almanacnews.com
Circulation: 17,000fr; USPS
Advertising rate: Open inch rate $45.00
Established: 1965
Group: Embarcadero Media
Real Estate Sales Manager...............Neal Fine
Editor .... Richard Hine
Major Accounts Sales Mgr.... Connie Jo Cotton
Mechanical Specifications: Type page 10 x 13 13/16; E - 5 cols, 1 15/16, 1/8 between; A - 5 cols, 1 15/16, 1/8 between; C - 6 cols, 1 9/16, 1/8 between.Equipment & Software: Hardware — APP/Mac; Presses — 17-SLN; Software — QPS/QuarkXPress, Multi-Ad.
Delivery Method: Mail, Newsstand, Carrier, Racks
Areas Served: 94025, 94027, 94028, 94062, 94061

MERCED

ATWATER SIGNAL (TUES)

3033 G St, Merced, CA, 95340-2108, Merced, USA; gen tel (209) 722-1511; gen fax (209) 384-2226; disp adv e-mail rperes@mercedsunstar.com; ed e-mail editor@mercedsun-star.com; web site www.mercedsunstar.com
Circulation: 14,944pd, 15,000fr; Sworn/Estimate/Non-Audited
Advertising rate: Open inch rate $10.80
Established: 1869
Group: The McClatchy Company
Pub./Adv. Direc. ....Jason Cross
Areas Served: Merced County

MERCED COUNTY TIMES (THUR)

2221 K St, Merced, CA, 95340-3868, Merced, USA; gen tel (209) 358-5311; gen fax (209) 358-7108; disp adv e-mail midvalley-pub@aol.com; web site www.mercedcountytimes.net
Circulation: 10,000pd, 25,000fr; Sworn/Estimate/Non-Audited
Advertising rate: Open inch rate $11.95
Established: 1962
Group: Mid Valley Publishing
Ed. .... John Whitaker
Areas Served: 95340

THE CHOWCHILLA NEWS (WED)

3033 G St, Merced, CA, 95340-2108, Madera, USA; gen tel (559) 665-5751; adv tel (209) 385-2463; ed tel (559) 665-5751 x 101; gen fax (559) 665-5462; disp adv e-mail lswanson@mercedsun-star.com; class adv e-mail lswanson@mercedsun-star.com; ed e-mail pmandrell@mercedsun-star.com; web site www.thechowchillanews.com
Circulation: 760pd, 4fr; AAM
Advertising rate: Open inch rate $7.25
Group: The McClatchy Company
Mng. Ed....................................... Patty Mandrell
Adv. Dir.................................. Deanna Whitmore
Mechanical Specifications: Type page 12 15/16 x 21; E - 6 cols, 2, between; A - 6 cols, 2, between; C - 9 cols, 1 5/16, between.
Areas Served: 93610

MILPITAS

FREMONT BULLETIN (SAT)

59 Marylinn Dr, Milpitas, CA, 95035-4311, Santa Clara, USA; gen tel (408) 262-2454; gen fax (408) 263-9710; disp adv e-mail news@themilpitaspost.com; web site www.mercurynews.com/fremont
Circulation: 500pd, 29,400fr; Sworn/Estimate/Non-Audited
Advertising rate: Open inch rate $28.00
Group: Digital First Media
Bus. Mgr...................................... Gloria Guillen
Sales Rep.. Liz Pollock
Ed. .... Robert J. Devincenzi
Areas Served: Santa Clara County

MONROVIA

AZUSA HERALD HIGHLANDER (THUR)

605 E Huntington Dr Ste 100, Suite 100, Monrovia, CA, 91016-6353, Los Angeles, USA; gen tel (626) 962-8811; adv tel (626) 544-0888; ed tel (626) 422-4305; gen fax (626) 854-8719; disp adv e-mail mark.welches@sgvn.com; web site www.sgvtribune.com/highlanders
Circulation: 3,490fr; Sworn/Estimate/Non-Audited
Advertising rate: Open inch rate $3.70
Pres./Pub. .... Ron Hasse
Exec. Ed./VP......................... Michael Anastasi
Mechanical Specifications: Type page 9 3/4 x 11 3/4; E - 5 cols, 2, 3/16 between; A - 5 cols, 2, 3/16 between; C - 10 cols, 2, 3/16 between.
Areas Served: Los Angeles County

COVINA PRESS COURIER HIGHLANDER (THUR)

605 E Huntington Dr Ste 101, Suite 101, Monrovia, CA, 91016-6353, Los Angeles, USA; gen tel (626) 962-8811; adv tel (626) 962-8811; ed tel (626) 544-0811; gen fax (626) 854-8719; disp adv e-mail jim.maurer@sgvn.com; ed e-mail steve.hunt@sgvn.com; web site www.sgvtribune.com/highlanders
Circulation: 13,075fr; Sworn/Estimate/Non-Audited
Advertising rate: Open inch rate $12.95
Sen. Ed. .... Steve Hunt
Mechanical Specifications: Type page 9 3/4 x 11 3/4; E - 5 cols, 2, 3/16 between; A - 5 cols, 2, 3/16 between; C - 10 cols, 2, 3/16 between.
Areas Served: Los Angeles County

DIAMOND BAR HIGHLANDER (SAT)

605 E Huntington Dr Ste 100, Suite 100, Monrovia, CA, 91016-6353, Los Angeles, USA; gen tel (626) 962-8811; adv tel (626) 962-8811; ed tel (626) 544-0811; gen fax (626) 854-8719; disp adv e-mail malfonso@scng.com; ed e-mail fpine@scng.com; web site www.sgvtribune.com
Circulation: 1,183fr; Sworn/Estimate/Non-Audited
Advertising rate: Open inch rate $13.15
Group: Southern California News Group
Advertising Vice President....... Melene Alfonso
Classified Advertising Manager.............. Carla Asmundson
Delivery Method: Carrier
Areas Served: 91765

GLENDORA PRESS HIGHLANDER (THUR)

605 E Huntington Dr Ste 102, Suite 102, Monrovia, CA, 91016-6353, Los Angeles, USA; gen tel (626) 962-8811; adv tel (626) 544-0888; ed tel (626) 422-4305; gen fax (666) 338-9157; disp adv e-mail mark.welches@sgvn.com; class adv e-mail Carla.asmundson@sgvn.com; ed e-mail michael.anastasi@langnews.com; web site www.sgvtribune.com/highlanders
Circulation: 500pd, 12,450fr; Sworn/Estimate/Non-Audited
Advertising rate: Open inch rate $12.95
Pres./Pub. .... Ron Hasse
Exec. Ed./VP......................... Michael Anastasi
Mechanical Specifications: Type page 9 3/4 x 11 3/4; E - 5 cols, 2, 3/16 between; A - 5 cols, 2, 3/16 between; C - 5 cols, 2, 1/8 between.
Areas Served: 91790

LA PUENTE HIGHLANDER (SAT)

605 E Huntington Dr, Ste 100, Monrovia, CA, 91016-6353, Los Angeles, USA; gen tel (626) 962-8811; adv tel (626) 544-0888; ed tel (626) 422-4305; gen fax (626) 856-2758; disp adv e-mail malfonso@scng.com; class adv e-mail Casmundson@scng.com; ed e-mail fpine@scng.com; web site www.sgvtribune.com/highlanders
Circulation: 2,437fr; Sworn/Estimate/Non-Audited
Group: Southern California News Group
VP Advertising......................... Melene Alfonso
Classified Advertising Manager.............. Carla Asmundson
Mechanical Specifications: Type page 9 3/4 x 11 3/4; E - 5 cols, 2, 3/16 between; A - 5 cols, 2, 3/16 between; C - 10 cols, 2, 3/16 between.
Delivery Method: Carrier
Areas Served: 91744, 91746, 91706, 91731, 91732, 91733

ROWLAND HEIGHTS HIGHLANDER (SAT)

605 E Huntington Dr Ste 104, Suite 104, Monrovia, CA, 91016-6353, Los Angeles, USA; gen tel (626) 962-8811; adv tel (626) 544-0888; ed tel (626) 422-4305; gen fax (666) 338-9157; disp adv e-mail highlanders@sgvn.com; class adv e-mail casmundson@scng.com; ed e-mail news.tribune@sgvn.com; web site www.sgvtribune.com/highlanders
Circulation: 1,910fr; Sworn/Estimate/Non-Audited
Group: Southern California News Group
VP Advertising......................... Melene Alfonso
Classified Advertising Manager.............. Carla Asmundson
Mechanical Specifications: Type page 9 3/4 x 11 3/4; E - 5 cols, 2, 1/6 between; A - 5 cols, 2, 1/6 between; C - 5 cols, 2, 1/6 between.
Delivery Method: Carrier
Areas Served: 91790

THE HIGHLANDER - GLENDORA EDITION (THUR)

605 E Huntington Dr Ste 105, Suite 105, Monrovia, CA, 91016-6353, Los Angeles, USA; gen tel (626) 962-8811; adv tel (626) 962-8811; ed tel (626) 544-0811; gen fax (626) 854-8719; disp adv e-mail malfonso@scng.com; class adv e-mail malfonso@scng.com; web site www.sgvtribune.com/highlanders
Circulation: 2,909fr; Sworn/Estimate/Non-Audited
Group: San Gabriel Valley News Group (Digital First Media)
VP, Advertising......................... Melene Alfonso
Mechanical Specifications: Type page 9 3/4 x 11 3/4; E - 5 cols, 2, 3/16 between; A - 5 cols, 2, 3/16 between; C - 10 cols, 2, 3/16 between.
Areas Served: Glendora Edition: 91740, 91741, 91750, 91773

THE HIGHLANDER - LA PUENTE EDITION (THUR)

605 E Huntington Dr Ste 100, Suite 100, Monrovia, CA, 91016-6353, Los Angeles, USA; gen tel (626) 962-8811; adv tel (626) 962-8811; ed tel (626) 544-0811; gen fax (626) 854-8719; disp adv e-mail malfonso@scng.com; ed e-mail malfonso@scng.com; web site www.sgvtribune.com
Circulation: 2,837fr; Sworn/Estimate/Non-Audited
Group: San Gabriel Valley News Group (Digital First Media)
VP, Advertising......................... Melene Alfonso
Delivery Method: Carrier
Areas Served: La Puente Edition: 91744, 91748, 91706, 91731, 91732, 91733

THE HIGHLANDER - ROWLAND HEIGHTS EDITION (THUR)

605 E Huntington Dr, Ste 100, Monrovia, CA, 91016-6353, Los Angeles, USA; gen tel (626) 962-8811; adv tel (626) 962-8811; ed tel (626) 544-0990; gen fax (626) 854-8719; disp adv e-mail malfonso@scng.com; class adv e-mail malfonso@scng.com; ed e-mail fpine@scng.com; web site www.sgvtribune.com/highlanders
Circulation: 1,910fr; Sworn/Estimate/Non-Audited
Group: San Gabriel Valley News Group (Digital First Media)
Pres./Pub. .... Ron Hasse
Frank Pine
Mechanical Specifications: Type page 9 3/4 x 11 3/4; E - 5 cols, 2, 3/16 between; A - 5 cols, 2, 3/16 between; C - 10 cols, 2, 3/16 between.
Delivery Method: Carrier
Areas Served: Rowland Heights Edition: 91748, 91745, 91789, 91765

MONTEREY

SALINAS VALLEY WEEKLY (SUN)

8 Upper Ragsdale Dr, Monterey, CA, 93940-5730, Monterey, USA; gen tel (831) 646-4301; adv tel (831) 646-4395; ed tel (831) 646-4381; gen fax (831) 372-8401; disp adv e-mail rpowell@montereyherald.com; ed e-mail rcalkins@montereyherald.com; web site www.montereyherald.com
Circulation: 35,000fr; Sworn/Estimate/Non-Audited
Advertising rate: Open inch rate $10.00
Group: The McClatchy Company
Pub... Gary Omnerick
Ed. .... Royal Calkins
Prod. Coord.................Lucia FernandezEquipment & Software: Hardware — APP/Mac, PC; Software — QPS/QuarkXPress 3.3.2, Adobe/Illustrator 8.0, Adobe/Photoshop 4.0, Adobe/Acrobat 2.0.
Areas Served: 93940

MORGAN HILL

MORGAN HILL TIMES (FRI)

17500 Depot St Ste 140, Ste 140, Morgan Hill, CA, 95037-3886, Santa Clara, USA; gen tel (408) 779-4106; adv tel (408) 842-2206; ed tel (408) 847-7010; gen fax (408) 779-3886; adv fax (408) 779-3886; disp adv e-mail editor@morganhilltimes.com; ed e-mail editor@morganhilltimes.com; web site www.morganhilltimes.com
Circulation: 1,375pd, 9,000fr; Sworn/Estimate/Non-Audited
Advertising rate: Open inch rate $14.75
Group: New SV Media, Inc
Publisher.. Jeff Mitchell
Editor .... Michael Moore
Ad Director............................ Deborah Garcia
Mechanical Specifications: Type page 13 x 21; E - 6 cols, 2, 1/6 between; A - 6 cols, 2, 1/6 between; C - 10 cols, 1 1/5, 1/6 between.
Areas Served: 95020

MOUNT SHASTA

DUNSMUIR NEWS (WED)

924B N MOUNT SHASTA BLVD, Mount Shasta, CA, 96067-8700, Siskiyou, USA; gen tel (530) 926-5214; gen fax (530) 926-4166; disp adv e-mail news@mtshastanews.com;

class adv e-mail legals@mtshastanews.com; web site www.mtshastanews.com
Circulation: 1,000pd, 800fr; Sworn/Estimate/Non-Audited
Advertising rate: Open inch rate $11.50
Established: 1887
Group: GateHouse Media, Inc.
Pub....Matt Guthrie
Ed. ....Steve Gerace
Mechanical Specifications: Type page 11 1/2 x 21 1/2; E - 6 cols, 1/6 between; A - 6 cols, 1/6 between.Equipment & Software: ; Presses — G
Areas Served: 96017, 96067, 96025

MT. SHASTA HERALD (WED)

924 N Mount Shasta Blvd, Mount Shasta, CA, 96067-8700, Siskiyou, USA; gen tel (530) 926-5214; adv tel (530) 926-5214; gen fax (530) 926-4166; disp adv e-mail mguthrie@siskiyoudaily.com; class adv e-mail classifieds@mtshastanews.com; ed e-mail sgerace@mtshastanews.com; web site www.mtshastanews.com
Circulation: 6,000pd,; Sworn/Estimate/Non-Audited
Advertising rate: Open inch rate $11.50
Established: 1934
Group: GateHouse Media, Inc.
Pub....Matt Guthrie
Ed. ....Steve GeraceEquipment & Software: ; Software — QPS/QuarkXPress 4.1.
Areas Served: 96067

WEED PRESS (WED)

924 N Mount Shasta Blvd, Mount Shasta, CA, 96067-8700, Siskiyou, USA; gen tel (530) 926-5214; gen fax (530) 926-4166; disp adv e-mail news@mtshastanews.com; class adv e-mail classifieds@mtshastanews.com; ed e-mail sgerace@mtshastanews.com; web site www.mtshastanews.com
Circulation: 1,600pd, 900fr; Sworn/Estimate/Non-Audited
Advertising rate: Open inch rate $25.00
Group: GateHouse Media, Inc.
Pub....Matt Guthrie
Ed. ....Steve Gerace
Mechanical Specifications: Type page 11 x 21 1/2; E - 6 cols, 1/6 between; A - 6 cols, 1/6 between; C - 8 cols, 1 5/16, 1/6 between. Equipment & Software: Hardware — Mac; Presses — G/Community with Panther Imagesetter; Software — QPS/QuarkXPress 4.1.
Areas Served: 96067

NAPA

AMERICAN CANYON EAGLE (THUR)

1615 Soscol Ave, Napa, CA, 94559-1901, Napa, USA; gen tel (707) 256-2269; gen fax (707) 224-3963; ed e-mail editor@americancanyoneagle.com; web site http://napavalleyregister.com/eagle/
Circulation: 200pd, 6,000fr; Sworn/Estimate/Non-Audited
Advertising rate: Open inch rate $8.85
Pub....Brenda Speth
Disp. Dir....Norma Kostecka
Ed. ....Noel Brinkerhoff
Dir of News Content ....Sean Scully
Areas Served: Napa County

NEEDLES

NEEDLES DESERT STAR (WED)

800 W Broadway St, Ste E, Needles, CA, 92363-2755, San Bernadino, USA; gen tel (760) 326-2222; adv tel (928) 763-2505; ed tel (760) 326-2222; gen fax (760) 326-3480; disp adv e-mail needlesdesertstar@citlink.net; web site www.thedesertstar.com
Circulation: 1,800pd, 500fr; Sworn/Estimate/Non-Audited
Advertising rate: Open inch rate $15.54
Established: 1888
Group: Brehm Communications, Inc.
News West Publishing Company Inc. (OOB)
Digital Platform - Mobile: Apple, Android, Windows, Blackberry
Digital Platform - Tablet: Apple iOS, Android, Windows 7, Blackberry Tablet OS, Kindle, Nook, Kindle Fire
Ed ....Robin Richards
Circulation Mgr ....Don Orth
Mechanical Specifications: Type page 11 9/16 x 21; E - 6 cols, 1 13/16, 3/16 between; A - 6 cols, 1 13/16, 3/16 between; C - 8 cols, 1 1/2, 3/16 between.Equipment & Software: Hardware — APP/Mac G4; Presses — 1-WPC/4 High, 6-Atlas/PC Units, 4-WPC/Marc 25's, 2-WPC/Leader Folders - 22 3/4 Cut Off; Software — QPS/QuarkXPress 4.0, Multi-Ad/Creator, Adobe/Illustrator 9.0.
Delivery Method: Mail, Newsstand, Carrier, Racks
Areas Served: 92363 , 86440 , 86442

NEWMAN

MATTOS NEWSPAPERS, INC. (THUR)

PO Box 878, Newman, CA, 95360-0878, Stanislaus, USA; gen tel (209) 604-8105; adv tel (209) 243-8170; ed tel (209) 243-8104; gen fax (209) 862-4133; disp adv e-mail smattos@mattosnews.com; web site Website
Circulation: 7,500pd,; Sworn/Estimate/Non-Audited
Advertising rate: Open inch rate $8.00
Pub....Susan Mattos
Ed. ....Dean Harris
Mechanical Specifications: Type page 13 x 21; E - 6 cols, 2, 1/6 between; A - 6 cols, 2, 1/6 between; C - 8 cols, 1 1/12, 4/5 between. Equipment & Software: Hardware — APP/Mac Quadra, APP/Mac IIci, APP/Power Mac; Software — QPS/QuarkXPress 4.0.
Delivery Method: Mail
Areas Served: 95360 & 95322

TUESDAY REVIEW (TUES)

1021 Fresno St, Newman, CA, 95360-1303, Stanislaus, USA; gen tel (209) 862-2222; adv tel (209) 862-2222; gen fax (209) 862-4133; disp adv e-mail advertising@mattosnews.com; class adv e-mail advertising@mattosnews.com; ed e-mail dharris@mattosnews.com; web site www.mattosnews.com
Circulation: 6,500fr; Sworn/Estimate/Non-Audited
Advertising rate: Open inch rate $8.00
Pub....Susan Mattos
Adv. Mgr....Mary Beth Merin
Ed. ....Dean Harris
Mechanical Specifications: Type page 13 x 21; E - 6 cols, 2, 1/6 between; A - 6 cols, 2, 1/6 between; C - 6 cols, 2, 1/6 between.Equipment & Software: Hardware — APP/Mac Quadra, APP/Mac IIci, APP/Power Mac; Software — QPS/QuarkXPress 4.0.
Areas Served: 95360

NOVATO

MILL VALLEY HERALD (WED)

1301B Grant Ave, Novato, CA, 94945-3143, Marin, USA; gen tel (415) 892-1516; adv tel (415) 892-1516 x 15; ed tel (415) 892-1516 x 31; gen fax (415) 897-0940; disp adv e-mail mmckellips@marinscope.com; class adv e-mail mmckellips@marinscope.com; ed e-mail shemmila@marinscope.com; web site www.marinscope.com/mill_valley_herald/news/
Circulation: 121pd, 4,977fr; CVC
Advertising rate: Open inch rate $29.00
Established: 1994
Group: Marinscope Community Newspapers
Ed. ....Soren Hemmila
Mechanical Specifications: Type page 11" x 21"; 6 cols
Delivery Method: Mail, Newsstand, Carrier, Racks
Areas Served: 94945

NOVATO ADVANCE (WED)

1301B Grant Ave, # B, Novato, CA, 94945-3143, USA; gen tel (415) 892-1516; adv tel (415) 892-1516 x15; ed tel (415) 892-1516 x 13; gen fax (415) 897-0940; disp adv e-mail scope@marinscope.com; class adv e-mail mmckellips@marinscope.com; ed e-mail nbaptista@marinscope.com; web site www.marinscope.com/novato_advance/
Circulation: 3,725pd, 3,848fr; CVC
Advertising rate: Open inch rate $25.75
Established: 1922
Group: Marinscope Community Newspapers
Pub....Sherman Frederick
Ed. ....Nicole Baptista
Managing Ed ....Joe Wolfcale
Southern Marin Editor ....Soren Hemmila
Central Marin Ed....Derek Wilson
Mechanical Specifications: Type page 11" x 21"; 6 colsEquipment & Software: Hardware — APP/Mac; Software — QPS/QuarkXPress, Adobe/Photoshop, Adobe/Illustrator.
Delivery Method: Mail, Carrier, Racks
Areas Served: 94945, 94947, 94949

PACIFICA TRIBUNE (WED)

1301B Grant Ave, Novato, CA, 94945-3143, San Mateo, USA; gen tel (650) 359-6666; gen fax (650) 359-3821; disp adv e-mail elarsen@bayareanewsgroup.com; class adv e-mail cschivo@bayareanewsgroup.com; ed e-mail elarsen@bayareanewsgroup.com; web site pacificatribune.com
Circulation: 3,697pd, 160fr; AAM
Advertising rate: Open inch rate $13.00
Established: 1959
Group: MediaNews Group
Ed./Pub. ....Horace Hinshaw
Classifieds Adv. Mgr....Carol Schivo
Circ. Mgr....Marcus Scofield
Adv. Mgr....Jennifer Belton
Mechanical Specifications: Type page 12 x 20 1/4; E - 6 cols, 2 1/16, between; A - 6 cols, 2 1/16, between; C - 10 cols, 1 3/16, between.
Delivery Method: Mail, Carrier, Racks
Areas Served: 94044

ROSS VALLEY REPORTER (WED)

1301B Grant Ave, Novato, CA, 94945-3143, Marin, USA; gen tel (415) 892-1516; adv tel (415) 892-1516 x 15; ed tel (415) 892-1516 x 38; gen fax (415) 897-0940; disp adv e-mail mmckellips@marinscope.com; class adv e-mail mmckellips@marinscope.com; ed e-mail jwolfcale@marinscope.com; web site www.marinscope.com
Circulation: 54pd, 5,421fr; CVC
Advertising rate: $29.00
Established: 1922
Pub....Paul Hutcheson
Ed. ....Joe Wolfcale
Mechanical Specifications: Type page 11" x 21"; 6 cols
Delivery Method: Mail, Carrier, Racks
Areas Served: Marin County

SAN RAFAEL NEWS POINTER (WED)

1301B Grant Ave, Novato, CA, 94945-3143, Marin, USA; gen tel (415) 892-1516; adv tel (415) 892-1516 x 15; ed tel (415) 892-1516 x 19; gen fax (415) 897-0940; disp adv e-mail mmckellips@marinscope.com; class adv e-mail mmckellips@marinscope.com; ed e-mail gandersen@marinscope.com; web site www.marinscope.com
Circulation: 65pd, 4,661fr; CVC
Advertising rate: $29.00
Established: 1922
Group: Marinscope Community Newspapers
Pub....Paul Hutcheson
Ed. ....Greg Andersen
Mechanical Specifications: Type page 11.0" x 21"; 6 cols
Delivery Method: Mail, Carrier, Racks
Areas Served: Marin County

SAUSALITO MARINSCOPE (WED)

1301B Grant Ave, Novato, CA, 94945-3143, Marin, USA; gen tel (415) 892-1516; adv tel (415) 892-1516 x 15; ed tel (415) 892-1516 x 31; gen fax (415) 897-0940; disp adv e-mail phutcheson@marinscope.com; class adv e-mail phutcheson@marinscope.com; ed e-mail shemmila@marinscope.com; web site www.marinscope.com
Circulation: 867pd, 311fr; CVC
Advertising rate: Open inch rate $29.00
Established: 1922
Group: Marinscope Community Newspapers
Pub./Adv. Mgr....Paul Hutcheson
Ed. ....Soren Hemmila
Circ. Mgr....Linda Mallin
Mechanical Specifications: Type page 11" x 21"; 6 cols
Delivery Method: Mail, Carrier, Racks
Areas Served: Marin County

TWIN CITIES TIMES (WED)

1301B Grant Ave, Novato, CA, 94945-3143, Marin, USA; gen tel (415) 892-1516; adv tel (415) 892-1516 x 15; ed tel (415) 892-1516 x 19; gen fax (415) 897-0940; disp adv e-mail mmckellips@marinscope.com; class adv e-mail mmckellips@marinscope.com; ed e-mail gandersen@marinscope.com; web site www.marinscope.com
Circulation: 71pd, 7,351fr; CVC
Advertising rate: 25.00
Established: 1922
Group: Marinscope Community Newspapers
Pub....Paul Hutcheson
Ed. ....Greg Andersen
Circ. Mgr....Linda Mallin
Mechanical Specifications: Broadsheet full page 10.5" x 21"
Delivery Method: Carrier, Racks
Areas Served: Marin County

OAKDALE

ESCALON TIMES (WED)

122 S 3rd Ave, Oakdale, CA, 95361-3935, Stanislaus, USA; gen tel (209) 847-3021; adv tel (209) 847-3021; gen fax (209) 847-9750; adv fax (209) 847-9750; disp adv e-mail ads@oakdaleleader.com; class adv e-mail mkendig@oakdaleleader.com; ed e-mail mjackson@escalontimes.com; web site www.escalontimes.com
Circulation: 11,000pd, 2,800fr; Sworn/Estimate/Non-Audited
Established: 1926
Group: Morris Multimedia, Inc.
Pub....Hank Veen
Ed. ....Marg Jackson
Circ. Mgr....Teresa Hammond
Areas Served: Stanislaus County

OAKDALE LEADER (WED)

122 S 3rd Ave, Oakdale, CA, 95361-3993, Stanislaus, USA; gen tel (209) 847-3021; adv tel (209) 847-3021; ed tel (209) 847-3021; gen fax (209) 847-9750; adv fax (209) 847-9750; ed fax (209) 847-9750; disp adv e-mail mjackson@oakdaleleader.com; class adv e-mail ads@oakdaleleader.com; ed e-mail mjackson@oakdaleleader.com; web site www.oakdaleleader.com
Circulation: 6,000pd, 5,000fr; Sworn/Estimate/Non-Audited
Advertising rate: Open inch rate $18.18
Group: Morris Multimedia, Inc.
Pub....Hank Veen
Ed. ....Marg Jackson
Circ. Mgr....Teresa Hammond
Asst. Adv. Dir....Corey Rogers
Mechanical Specifications: Type page 13 1/4 x 21; E - 6 cols, 1 7/8, 1/2 between; A - 6 cols, 1 7/8, between; C - 10 cols, 1 1/8, between. Equipment & Software: Hardware — APP/Mac; Presses — H; Software — Adobe/PageMaker.
Areas Served: 95361

THE RIVERBANK NEWS (WED)

122 S 3rd Ave, Oakdale, CA, 95361-3935, Stanislaus, USA; gen tel (209) 847-3021; adv tel (209) 847-3021; ed tel (209) 847-3021; gen fax (209) 847-9750; adv fax (209) 847-9750; ed fax (209) 847-9750; disp adv e-mail ads@oakdaleleader.com; class adv e-mail mkendig@oakdaleleader.com; ed e-mail mjackson@oakdaleleader.com; web site www.theriverbanknews.com
Circulation: 1,100pd, 6,800fr; Sworn/Estimate/Non-Audited
Advertising rate: Open inch rate $13.55

Group: Morris Multimedia, Inc.
Pub..Hank Veen
Circ. Mgr...............................Teresa Hammond
Ed. ....Marg Jackson
Mechanical Specifications: Type page 13 1/4 x 21; E - 6 cols, 2 1/16, 1/2 between; A - 6 cols, 2 1/16, between; C - 8 cols, 1 1/2, between. Equipment & Software: Hardware — APP/Mac; Presses — H; Software — Adobe/PageMaker.
Areas Served: 95361

OAKHURST

SIERRA STAR (THUR)
49165 Crane Valley Rd [426], Oakhurst, CA, 93644, Madera, USA; gen tel (559) 683-4464; gen fax (559) 683-8102; disp adv e-mail blinn@sierrastar.com; class adv e-mail class@sierrastar.com; ed e-mail editor@sierrastar.com; web site www.sierrastar.com
Circulation: 2,605pd, 288fr; AAM
Advertising rate: Open inch rate $14.50
Established: 1957
Group: The McClatchy Company
Digital Platform - Mobile: Apple, Android, Windows
Digital Platform - Tablet: Apple iOS, Android
Pub...Betty E. Linn
Ed. ....Brian Wilkinson
Mechanical Specifications: Type page 11 x 21 1/2; E - 6 cols, between; A - 6 cols, between; C - 6 cols, 1 5/6, between.Equipment & Software: Hardware — APP/Mac; Software — QPS/QuarkXPress, Multi-Ad/Creator.
Delivery Method: Mail, Newsstand
Areas Served: 93644, 93614, 93604

OAKLAND

JOINT FORCES JOURNAL (FRI, BI-MTHLY)
PO Box 13283, Oakland, CA, 94661-0283, Alameda, USA; gen tel (510) 428-2000; gen fax (510) 595-7777; disp adv e-mail info@jointforcesjournal.com; class adv e-mail jointforcesjournal@aol.com; web site www.jointforcesjournal.com
Circulation: 42,000fr; Sworn/Estimate/Non-Audited
Advertising rate: Open inch rate $11.00
Established: 1995
Pub.. Ken Krause
Ed. ....Jan Miller
Areas Served: 94610

MARIN COUNTY POST (FRI, SAT)
405 14th St, Ste 1215, Oakland, CA, 94612-2707, Alameda, USA; gen tel (510) 287-8200; adv tel (510) 287-8220; gen fax (510) 287-8247; class adv e-mail ads@postnewsgroup.net; web site https://marinpost.org/
Circulation: 0pd, 417fr; VAC
Advertising rate: Open inch rate $50.00
Established: 1963
Group: Post News Group
Pub... Paul Cobbs
Chief Operating Officer.............Maxine Ussery
Production Manager........................Jack Naidu
Associate Editor...................Ashley Chambers
Associate Editor................... Taison Kwamilele
Editor......................................Kenneth Epstein
Mechanical Specifications: Type page 12 3/4 x 21 1/2; C - 9 cols, 1 3/8, between.
Delivery Method: Carrier

OJAI

OJAI VALLEY NEWS (FRI)
101 Vallerio Ave, Ojai, CA, 93023-3631, Ventura, USA; gen tel (805) 646-1476; adv tel (805) 646-1476; ed tel (805) 646-1476; gen fax (805) 646-4281; disp adv e-mail editor@ojaivalleynews.com; class adv e-mail classified@ojaivalleynews.com; ed e-mail editor@ojaivalleynews.com; web site www.ojaivalleynews.com

Circulation: 3,800pd,; Sworn/Estimate/Non-Audited
Advertising rate: Open inch rate $12.00
Established: 1891
Group: Downhome Publishing LLC
Pub..Tim Dewar
Mechanical Specifications: Type page 13 x 21 1/2; E - 6 cols, 2/3 between; A - 6 cols, between; C - 8 cols, between.Equipment & Software: Hardware — APP/Mac; Presses — Hamada; Software — QPS/QuarkXPress
Delivery Method: Mail, Newsstand, Carrier, Racks
Areas Served: 93023, 93024, 93022, 93060

PACIFIC PALISADES

PALISADIAN-POST (THUR)
881 Alma Real Dr, Ste 213, Pacific Palisades, CA, 90272-3737, Los Angeles, USA; gen tel (310) 454-1321; gen fax (310) 454-1078; disp adv e-mail info@palipost.com; class adv e-mail kendy@palipost.com; ed e-mail editor@palipost.com; web site www.palipost.com
Circulation: 4,950pd, 24fr; VAC
Advertising rate: Open inch rate $33.00
Established: 1928
Pub...................................... Roberta Donohue
Mechanical Specifications: Type page 12 3/4 x 21; E - 6 cols, 1 15/16, 1/6 between; A - 6 cols, 1 15/16, 1/6 between; C - 6 cols, 1 15/16, 1/6 between.Equipment & Software: Hardware — APP/Power Macs; Presses — G/Community; Software — QPS/QuarkXPress, Adobe/Photoshop.
Delivery Method: Mail, Racks
Areas Served: 90272

PALM DESERT

DESERT ENTERTAINER (THUR)
41995 Boardwalk, Ste L2, Palm Desert, CA, 92211-9065, USA; gen tel (760) 776-5181; gen fax (760) 776-5733; disp adv e-mail ads@desertentertainer.com; class adv e-mail ads@desertentertainer.com; ed e-mail news@desertentertainer.com; web site http://desertentertainer.com
Established: 2003
Group: Brehm Communications, Inc.
Hi-Desert Publishing Co., Inc.
Ed ....Jose De La Cruz
Delivery Method: Racks
Areas Served: Riverside county

PALO ALTO

MOUNTAIN VIEW VOICE (FRI)
450 Cambridge Ave, Palo Alto, CA, 94306-1507, Santa Clara, USA; gen tel (650) 964-6300; adv tel (650) 223-6570; ed tel (650) 223-6537; gen fax (650) 223-7507; disp adv e-mail ads@mv-voice.com; class adv e-mail ads@mv-voice.com; ed e-mail editor@mv-voice.com; web site www.mv-voice.com
Circulation: 15,000fr; Sworn/Estimate/Non-Audited
Advertising rate: Open Modular Rate $34.00
Established: 1992
Group: Embarcadero Media
Ed...Andrea Gemmet
VP, Sales/Mktg......................Connie Jo Cotton
Delivery Method: Mail, Racks
Areas Served: 94306

PARADISE

PARADISE POST (WED, SAT)
PO Box 70, Paradise, CA, 95967-0070, Butte, USA; gen tel (530) 877-4413; gen fax (530) 877-1326; disp adv e-mail jurban@paradisepost.com; class adv e-mail jurban@paradisepost.com; web site www.paradisepost.com

Circulation: 2,902pd,; AAM
Advertising rate: Open inch rate $23.90
Established: 1945
Circ. Mgr..Jean Chirsty
Mng. Ed.. Rick Silva
Prodn. Mgr. .... Jeri Luce
Rowland Rebele
Pub......................................Gregg McConnell
Adv. Dir...Jerry Urban
Advertising..............................Darren Holden
Mechanical Specifications: Type page 12 1/4 x 21; E - 6 cols, 1 7/8, 1/8 between; A - 6 cols, 1 7/8, 1/8 between; C - 9 cols, 1 1/4, 1/8 between.Equipment & Software: Hardware — IBM; Presses — DEV/Tensor; Software — QPS/QuarkXPress 4.1.
Areas Served: 95969, 95967, 95954

PARAMOUNT

THE PARAMOUNT JOURNAL (THUR)
8007 Somerset Blvd, Paramount, CA, 90723-4334, Los Angeles, USA; gen tel (800) 540-1870; adv tel (562) 833-1234 x 310; gen fax (562) 630-8141; disp adv e-mail info@paramountjournal.org; ed e-mail ckelly@paramountjournal.org; web site www.paramountjournal.org
Circulation: 4,500pd,; Sworn/Estimate/Non-Audited
Advertising rate: Open inch rate $10.00
Established: 2003
Pub..Vince Bodiford
Ed. ....Charles Kelly
Mechanical Specifications: Type page 10 x 15; E - 5 cols, 2, 1/9 between; A - 5 cols, 2, 1/9 between; C - 5 cols, 2, 1/9 between.
Areas Served: 90723

PASADENA

PASADENA WEEKLY (THUR)
50 S De Lacey Ave Ste 200, Ste 200, Pasadena, CA, 91105-3806, Los Angeles, USA; gen tel (626) 584-1500; gen fax (626) 795-0149; disp adv e-mail jon@pasadenaweekly.com; ed e-mail kevinu@pasadenaweekly.com; web site www.pasadenaweekly.com
Circulation: 26,691fr; VAC
Advertising rate: 1/20 Pg $100.00; 1/10 Pg $195.00; 1/8 Pg $240.00
Established: 1985
Group: Southland Publishing, Inc.
Pub..Jon Guynn
Ed. ....Kevin Uhrich
Mechanical Specifications: Type page 9 13/16 x 12 5/8.
Areas Served: Los Angeles County

PASO ROBLES

PASO ROBLES PRESS (TUES, FRI)
829 10th St, Ste B, Paso Robles, CA, 93446-2507, San Luis Obispo, USA; gen tel (805) 237-6060; adv tel (805) 237-6060 x 211; ed tel (805) 237-6060 x 203; gen fax (805) 237-6066; disp adv e-mail news@pasoroblespress.com; class adv e-mail bkoyak@pasoroblespress.com; ed e-mail news@pasoroblespress.com; web site www.pasoroblespress.com
Circulation: 2,821pd, 12,379fr; Sworn/Estimate/Non-Audited
Advertising rate: Open inch rate $19.81
Group: News Media Corp.
Pub...John Bartlett
Adv. Mgr.. Joe Harris
Circ. Mgr...................................Autumn Thayer
Ed. ....Ryan Cronk
Gen. Mgr. ....Michael bartlett
Mechanical Specifications: Type page 13 x 21; E - 6 cols, 2 1/16, 1/8 between; A - 6 cols, 2 1/16, 1/8 between; C - 9 cols, 1 3/8, 1/16 between.Equipment & Software: Hardware — APP/Mac G3-300, PC 486; Presses — Synaptic Micro; Software — Microsoft/Word, QPS/QuarkXPress 4.0, GoldDisk/Professional Draw, WinFaxPro, HCE Maker Pro, Adobe/Photoshop 3.0.
Areas Served: 93446

PATTERSON

PATTERSON IRRIGATOR (THUR)
26 N 3rd St, Patterson, CA, 95363-2507, Stanislaus, USA; gen tel (209) 892-6187; adv tel (209) 892-6187; gen fax (209) 892-3761; adv fax (209) 892-3761; disp adv e-mail news@pattersonirrigator.com; class adv e-mail marybeth@pattersonirrigator.com; ed e-mail jenifer@pattersonirrigator.com; web site www.pattersonirrigator.com
Circulation: 8,700pd, 7,000fr; Sworn/Estimate/Non-Audited
Advertising rate: Open inch rate $8.50
Established: 1911
Pub......................................Robert Matthews
Mechanical Specifications: Type page 12 7/8 x 21; E - 5 cols, 1 5/6, 1/6 between; C - 6 cols, 1 1/2, between.Equipment & Software: Hardware — IBM Compatibles; Software — Adobe/PageMaker, Microsoft/Word 97, Archetype/Corel Draw 5.
Delivery Method: Mail, Carrier
Areas Served: 95363, 95387

PERRIS

PERRIS PROGRESS (WED, FRI)
277 E 4th St, Ste F, Perris, CA, 92570-2256, Riverside, USA; gen tel (951) 737-9784; gen fax (951) 737-9785; disp adv e-mail SentinelWeekly@aol.com; class adv e-mail PerrisCityNews@aol.com; web site www.theperrisprogress.com/
Circulation: 5,000fr; Sworn/Estimate/Non-Audited
Advertising rate: Open inch rate $6.00
Established: 1900
Ed. ....Gary Lendennie
Mechanical Specifications: Type page 13 x 21; E - 6 cols, 2 1/16, 1/8 between; A - 6 cols, 2 1/16, 1/8 between; C - 9 cols, 1 5/16, 1/16 between.
Delivery Method: Mail, Newsstand
Areas Served: 92570 & 92571

PETALUMA

PETALUMA ARGUS-COURIER (THUR)
719 Southpoint Blvd, Ste C, Petaluma, CA, 94954-8004, Sonoma, USA; gen tel (707) 762-4541; adv tel (707) 526-8551; ed tel (707) 776-8458; disp adv e-mail john.burns@arguscourier.com; class adv e-mail john.burns@arguscourier.com; ed e-mail matt.brown@arguscourier.com; web site www.petaluma360.com
Circulation: 5,538pd,; AAM
Advertising rate: Open inch rate $20.00
Established: 1855
Group: Sonoma Media Investments LLC
Pub..John Burns
Ed. ....Matt Brown
Mechanical Specifications: Type page 13 x 15; E - 5 cols, 2, 1/6 between; A - 5 cols, 2, 1/6 between; C - 7 cols, 1 1/3, 1/6 between.Equipment & Software: ; Presses — G/Urbanite; Software — QPS/QuarkXPress.
Delivery Method: Carrier, Racks
Areas Served: 94952, 94954

PLACERVILLE

MOUNTAIN DEMOCRAT (MON, WED, FRI)
2889 Ray Lawyer Dr, Placerville, CA, 95667-3914, El Dorado, USA; gen tel (530) 622-1255; gen fax (530) 622-7894; disp adv e-mail mtdemo@mtdemocrat.net; class adv e-mail adorders@mtdemocrat.com; web site www.mtdemocrat.com
Circulation: 7,400pd, 347fr; CAC
Advertising rate: Open inch rate $22.10

Established: 1851
Group: McNaughton Newspapers
Pub.....Richard B. Esposito
Adv. Dir.....Ian Balentine
Circ. Mgr.....Gerry Ulm
Editor.....Noel Stack
Lifestyle Ed.....Mimi Escabar
Sports Ed.....Jerry Heinzer
Graphics Manager.....Letty Baumgardner
Mechanical Specifications: Type page 12 x 21; E - 6 cols, 1 15/16, 1/8 between; A - 6 cols, 1 15/16, 1/8 between; C - 10 cols, 1 1/4, 1/8 between.
Delivery Method: Mail, Newsstand, Carrier, Racks

VILLAGE LIFE (WED)

2889 Ray Lawyer Dr, Placerville, CA, 95667-3914, El Dorado, USA; gen tel (530) 622-1255; adv tel (530) 344-5048; ed tel (530) 344-5073; gen fax (530) 622-7894; disp adv e-mail ibalentine@mtdemocrat.net; class adv e-mail ibalentine@mtdemocrat.net; ed e-mail editor@villagelife.com; web site www.villagelife.com
Circulation: 12,000pd,; Sworn/Estimate/Non-Audited
Advertising rate: Open inch rate $13.80
Group: McNaughton Newspapers
Mng. Ed.....Noel Stack
Pub.....Richard Esposito
Areas Served: 95630

PLEASANTON

PLEASANTON WEEKLY (FRI)

5506 Sunol Blvd, Ste 100, Pleasanton, CA, 94566-7779, Alameda, USA; gen tel (925) 600-0840; gen fax (925) 600-9559; disp adv e-mail ads@pleasantonweekly.com; class adv e-mail ads@pleasantonweekly.com; ed e-mail editor@pleasantonweekly.com; web site www.pleasantonweekly.com - 200,000(views) 60,000(visitors)
Circulation: 14,000fr; USPS
Established: 2000
Group: Embarcadero MediaEditions: (1)
Digital Platform - Mobile: Apple, Android, Windows
Pres.....Gina Channell
Ed.....Jeremy Walsh
Adv. Acct. Exec.....Carol Cano
Adv. Acct. Exec.....Karen Klein
Delivery Method: Mail, Newsstand, Racks
Areas Served: 95488 94566 94526 94583 94582 94550 94551 94568

PORTOLA

PORTOLA REPORTER (WED)

96 E Sierra St, Portola, CA, 96122-8436, Plumas, USA; gen tel (530) 832-4646; gen fax (530) 832-5319; disp adv e-mail ccurran@plumasnews.com; class adv e-mail mnewhouse@plumasnews.com; ed e-mail dmoore@plumasnews.com; web site www.plumasnews.com
Circulation: 2,270pd,; Sworn/Estimate/Non-Audited
Advertising rate: Open inch rate $5.50
Established: 1927
Group: Feather Publishing Co., Inc.
Pub.....Michael Taborski
Mng Ed.....Debra Moore
Mechanical Specifications: Full page 14 1/8 x 21; E - 6 cols, 1 11/12, 1/6 between; A - 6 cols, 1 11/12, 1/6 between; C - 9 cols, 1 11/12, 1/6 between.Equipment & Software: Hardware — APP/Mac; Presses — G/Community; Software — Microsoft/Word, QPS/QuarkXPress.
Delivery Method: Mail, Newsstand
Areas Served: 96122,96106,96105,96106,96129,96133

POWAY

POWAY NEWS CHIEFTAIN (THUR)

14023 Midland Rd, Poway, CA, 92064-3959, San Diego, USA; gen tel (858) 748-2311; gen fax (858) 748-7695; disp adv e-mail ppfeiffer@lajollalight.com; ed e-mail editor@pomeradonews.com; web site sandiegouniontribune.com/pomerado-news
Circulation: 14,732pd,; AAM
Advertising rate: 1/16 Pg $190.00
Established: 2004
Group: Mainstreet Communications LLC
Digital Platform - Mobile: Blackberry
Digital Platform - Tablet: Other
Ed.....Steve Dreyer
Pub.....Douglas F. Manchester
VP, Adv.....Phyllis Pfeiffer
Adv. Dir.....Don Parks
Mechanical Specifications: Type page: 10.33" x 12.25"; 6 cols
Delivery Method: Mail, Carrier, Racks
Areas Served: 92064

RANCHO BERNARDO NEWS-JOURNAL (FRI)

14023 Midland Rd, Poway, CA, 92064-3959, San Diego, USA; gen tel (858) 748-2311; adv tel (858) 218-7205; ed tel (858) 218-7207; gen fax (858) 513-7203; disp adv e-mail donp@rsfreview.com; class adv e-mail mwilliams@mainstreetsd.com; ed e-mail editor@pomeradonews.com; web site sandiegouniontribune.com/pomerado-news
Circulation: 16,561pd,; AAM
Advertising rate: 1/16 Pg $190.00
Established: 2004
Group: Mainstreet Media Group, LLC Mainstreet Communications LLC
Digital Platform - Mobile: Blackberry
Exec. Ed.....Steve Dreyer
VP, Adv.....Phyllis Pfeiffer
Adv. Dir.....Don Parks
Pub.....Douglas F. Manchester
Mechanical Specifications: Type page: 10.33" x 12.25"; 6 cols
Delivery Method: Carrier, Racks
Areas Served: 92064

QUINCY

FEATHER RIVER BULLETIN (WED)

287 Lawrence St, Quincy, CA, 95971-9477, Plumas, USA; gen tel (530) 283-0800; adv tel (530) 283-0800; ed tel (530) 283-0800; gen fax (530) 283-3952; disp adv e-mail ccurran@plumasnews.com; class adv e-mail mnewhouse@plumasnews.com; ed e-mail dmoore@plumasnews.com; web site www.plumasnews.com
Circulation: 2,505pd,; Sworn/Estimate/Non-Audited
Advertising rate: Open inch rate $5.50
Established: 1866
Group: Feather Publishing Co., Inc.
Pub.....Michael C. Taborski
Mng Ed.....Debra Moore
Mechanical Specifications: Type page 12 1/4 x 21 1/2; E - 6 cols, 1 5/6, 1/6 between; A - 6 cols, 1 5/6, 1/6 between; C - 9 cols, 1 1/4, 1/6 between.Equipment & Software: Hardware — APP/Macs; Presses — G/Community, G; Software — Microsoft/Word, QPS/QuarkXPress.
Delivery Method: Mail, Newsstand
Areas Served: 95971, 95956, 95984, 96103

REDDING

ANDERSON VALLEY POST (WED)

1101 Twin View Blvd, Redding, CA, 96003-1531, Shasta, USA; gen tel (530) 365-2797; adv tel (530) 225-8205; gen fax (530) 225-8275; disp adv e-mail christina.gutierrez@redding.com; class adv e-mail classifieds@andersonvalleypost.com; ed e-mail gwinship@andersonvalleypost.com; web site www.andersonvalleypost.com
Circulation: 0pd, 6,400fr; Sworn/Estimate/Non-Audited
Advertising rate: Open inch rate $14.00
Established: 1882
Group: E. W. Scripps Co.Editions: (1) Anderson Valley PostWi/Post-Adviser (10,850);
Ed.....George Winship
Mechanical Specifications: Type page 13 x 21 1/2; E - 6 cols, 2 1/16, between; A - 6 cols, 2 1/16, between; C - 9 cols, 1 3/8, between. Equipment & Software: Hardware — PC; Software — Adobe/Incopy, Adobe/Indesign, Microsoft/Word, Adobe/Photoshop.
Delivery Method: Carrier
Areas Served: 99007, 96022, 96080, 96047, 96088, 96002, 96001

REEDLEY

THE REEDLEY EXPONENT (THUR)

PO Box 432, 1130 G Street, Reedley, CA, 93654-0432, Fresno, USA; gen tel (559) 638-2244; gen fax (559) 638-5021; disp adv e-mail janie@midvalleypublishing.com; ed e-mail editor@reedleyexponent.com; web site http://www.reedleyexponent.com/
Established: 1891
Editor.....Jon Earnest
Publisher.....Fred Hall
Areas Served: Reedley, CA 93654

RICHMOND

THE BERKELEY VOICE (FRI)

1050 Marina Way S, Richmond, CA, 94804-3741, Contra Costa, USA; gen tel (510) 262-2784; gen fax (510) 748-1680; web site www.insidebayarea.com/berkeley
Circulation: 7,268pd,; AAM
Advertising rate: Open inch rate $22.34
Group: Digital First Media
Asst. Mng. Ed. – Reg.....Mike Frankel
Reg. News Ed.....Ken McLaughlin
Reg. News Ed.....Chris Walker
Areas Served: Alameda County

THE JOURNAL - ALBANY, EL CERRITO, KENSINGTON (FRI)

1050 Marina Way S, Richmond, CA, 94804-3741, Contra Costa, USA; gen tel (510) 293-2624; web site www.insidebayarea.com/albany
Circulation: 369pd, 3,982fr; VAC
Group: Digital First Media
Delivery Method: Carrier, Racks
Areas Served: 94804

RIDGECREST

THE NEWS REVIEW (WED)

109 N Sanders St, Ridgecrest, CA, 93555-3848, Kern, USA; gen tel (760) 371-4301; gen fax (760) 371-4304; disp adv e-mail newsreview@iwvisp.com; web site news-ridgecrest.com
Circulation: 7,500pd, 10,728fr; Sworn/Estimate/Non-Audited
Advertising rate: Open inch rate $8.50
Pub.....Patricia Farris
Adv. Mgr.....Christine Scrivner
Mng. Ed.....Patti Farris Cosner
Prodn. Mgr.....Rebecca Neipp
Graphics.....Laura Auspin
Mechanical Specifications: Type page 13 x 21 1/2; E - 6 cols, 2 1/12, 1/6 between; A - 6 cols, 2 1/12, 1/6 between; C - 8 cols, 1 7/12, between.Equipment & Software: Hardware — APP/Macs, PCs; Software — QPS/QuarkXPress, Adobe/Photoshop.
Areas Served: 93555

RIO VISTA

THE RIVER NEWS-HERALD & ISLETON JOURNAL (WED)

21 S Front St, Rio Vista, CA, 94571-1822, Solano, USA; gen tel (707) 374-6431; adv tel (707) 374-6431; gen fax (707) 374-6322; adv fax (707) 374-6322; disp adv e-mail rvads@citlink.net; class adv e-mail rvads@citlink.net; ed e-mail rveditor@citlink.net; web site www.rivernewsherald.org
Circulation: 3,900pd, 1,008fr; VAC
Advertising rate: Open inch rate $6.50
Established: 1890
Pub.....David L. Payne
Ed.....Galen Kusic
Areas Served: 94571

ROCKLIN

PLACER HERALD (THUR)

5055 Pacific St, Rocklin, CA, 95677-2707, Placer, USA; gen tel (916) 624-9713; adv tel 916) 351-3570; ed tel (916) 774-7955; gen fax (916) 783-1183; ed fax (916) 624-7469; disp adv e-mail suzannes@goldcountrymedia.com; class adv e-mail classifieds@goldcountrymedia.com; ed e-mail placerherald@goldcountrymedia.com ; web site www.placerherald.com
Circulation: 722pd, 4,537fr; VAC
Advertising rate: Open inch rate $24.00
Group: Brehm Communications, Inc.
Ed.....Krissi Khokhobashvili
Business Develop.....Linda Shuman-Prins
Areas Served: 95677

ROHNERT PARK

THE COMMUNITY VOICE (FRI)

100 Professional Center Dr Ste 110, Ste 110, Rohnert Park, CA, 94928-2137, Sonoma, USA; gen tel (707) 584-2222; adv tel (707) 584-2222 x10; ed tel (707) 584-2222; gen fax (707) 584-2233; adv fax (707) 584-2233; ed fax (707) 584-2233; disp adv e-mail publisher@thecommunityvoice.com; class adv e-mail ads@thecommunityvoice.com; ed e-mail news@thecommunityvoice.com; web site www.thecommunityvoice.com
Circulation: 2,400pd, 5,600fr; Sworn/Estimate/Non-Audited
Advertising rate: Open inch rate $24.00
Established: 1993
Pub.....Yatin Shah
Delivery Method: Mail, Newsstand, Carrier, Racks
Areas Served: 94928,94931&94951

ROLLING HILLS ESTATES

PALOS VERDES PENINSULA NEWS (THUR)

609 Deep Valley Dr, Ste 200, Rolling Hills Estates, CA, 90274-3614, Los Angeles, USA; gen tel (310) 372-0388; gen fax (310) 372-6113; disp adv e-mail ed.pilolla@pvnews.com; web site pvnews.com
Circulation: 13,444pd,; AAM
Group: Digital First Media
Ed.in Chief.....Ed Pilolla
Sales Exec.....Caren Weiner

ROSEVILLE

EL DORADO HILLS TELEGRAPH (WED)

188 Cirby Way, Roseville, CA, 95678-6481, Placer, USA; gen tel (916) 774-7910; adv tel (916) 351-3750; ed tel (916) 351-3753; gen fax (916) 985-0720; disp adv e-mail lindas@goldcountrymedia.com; class adv e-mail classifieds@goldcountrymedia.com; ed e-mail donc@goldcountrymedia.com; web site www.edhtelegraph.com
Circulation: 0pd, 0fr; VAC
Advertising rate: Open inch rate $8.50
Established: 2001

Group: Brehm Communications, Inc.
Gold Country MediaEditions: (1)
Sports Ed..Matt Long
Pub..Ken Larson
Business Develop. .... Linda Shuman-Prins
Ed. ....Lydia McNabb
Delivery Method: Newsstand, Racks
Areas Served: El Dorado County

FOLSOM TELEGRAPH (WED)
188 Cirby Way, Roseville, CA, 95678-6481, Placer, USA; gen tel (916)774-7910; adv tel (916) 351-3750; ed tel (916) 351-3753; gen fax (916) 985-0720; disp adv e-mail ryans@goldcountrymedia.com; class adv e-mail classifieds@goldcountrymedia.com; ed e-mail donc@goldcountrymedia.com; web site www.folsomtelegraph.com
Circulation: 2,275pd, 11,593fr; VAC
Advertising rate: Open inch rate $23.10
Established: 1856
Group: Brehm Communications, Inc.
Gold Country Media
Pub..Ryan Schuyler
Ed. ....Lydia McNabb
National Advert........................Sandy Stockton
Advert. ....Bill Sullivan
Mechanical Specifications: Type page 10 x 21; E - 6 cols, between; A - 6 cols, 1 7/8, 1/8 between; C - 9 cols, 1 3/8, 1/8 between.Equipment & Software: ; Presses — G/Community.
Delivery Method: Newsstand, Carrier
Areas Served: 95630

PRESS TRIBUNE (FRI)
188 Cirby Way, Roseville, CA, 95678-6481, Placer, USA; gen tel (916) 786-8746; adv tel (916) 774-7910; ed tel (916) 774-7955; gen fax (916) 783-1183; disp adv e-mail suzannes@goldcountrymedia.com; class adv e-mail classifieds@goldcountrymedia.com; ed e-mail pteditor@goldcountrymedia.com; web site www.thepresstribune.com
Circulation: 1,418pd, 11,280fr; CVC
Ed. ....Krissi Khokhobashvili
Delivery Method: Mail
Areas Served: 95678

THE PRESS-TRIBUNE (FRI)
188 Cirby Way, Roseville, CA, 95678-6481, Placer, USA; gen tel (916) 786-8746; adv tel (916) 774-7921; ed tel (916) 774-7955; gen fax (916) 783-1183; ed fax (916) 783-1183; disp adv e-mail jlove@goldcountrymedia.com; class adv e-mail classifieds@goldcountrymedia.com; ed e-mail pteditor@goldcountrymedia.com; web site www.thepresstribune.com
Circulation: 1,500pd, 10,500fr; VAC
Group: Gold Country Media, Inc.
Brehm Communications, Inc.
GCM Circulation Director..............Kelly Leibold
Publisher..Gary Milks
Mechanical Specifications: Type page 13 x 21; A - 6 cols, 2 1/12, 1/6 between; C - 6 cols, 21 1/2, 1/6 between.
Delivery Method: Newsstand, Carrier, Racks
Areas Served: Roseville and Granite Bay

SACRAMENTO

INSIDE EAST SACRAMENTO (MTHLY)
3104 O St, # 120, Sacramento, CA, 95816-6519, Sacramento, USA; gen tel (916) 443-5087; disp adv e-mail at@insidepublications.com; ed e-mail mbbizjak@aol.com; web site www.insidepublications.com
Circulation: 241pd, 17,210fr; Sworn/Estimate/Non-Audited
Advertising rate: 1/4P Color $396, 1/2P Color $609 Full P Color $924
Established: 1996
Group: Inside Publications
Digital Platform - Mobile: Apple, Windows, Blackberry
Digital Platform - Tablet: Apple iOS, Android, Windows 7, Blackberry Tablet OS, Kindle, Nook, Kindle Fire, Other
Pub.. Cecily Hastings
Acc. Rep..Ann Tracy
Delivery Method: Mail, Newsstand
Areas Served: 95816, 95817, 95819, 95820, 95815

INSIDE LAND PARK (MTHLY)
3104 O St, # 120, Sacramento, CA, 95816-6519, Sacramento, USA; gen tel (916) 443-5087; disp adv e-mail aj@insidepublications.com; ed e-mail mbbizjak@aol.com; web site www.insidepublications.com
Circulation: 210pd, 17,863fr; Sworn/Estimate/Non-Audited
Advertising rate: 1/4P Color $396, 1/2P Color $609 Full P Color $924
Established: 1998
Group: Inside Publications
Pub.. Cecily Hastings
Acc. Rep... A J Holm
Delivery Method: Mail, Newsstand
Areas Served: 95822, 95818, 95814, 95811

INSIDE POCKET (MTHLY)
3104 O St, # 120, Sacramento, CA, 95816-6519, Sacramento, USA; gen tel (916) 443-5087; disp adv e-mail dk@insidepublications.com; ed e-mail mbbizjak@aol.com; web site www.insidepublications.org
Circulation: 250pd, 14,000fr; Sworn/Estimate/Non-Audited
Advertising rate: 1/4P $396, 1/2P $609 Full $924
Established: 1996
Group: Inside Publications
Digital Platform - Mobile: Apple, Windows
Digital Platform - Tablet: Apple iOS, Windows 7, Blackberry Tablet OS, Kindle Fire
Pub.. Cecily Hastings
Delivery Method: Mail, Newsstand
Areas Served: Sacramento County,95831

INSIDE PUBLICATIONS (MTHLY)
3104 O St, # 120, Sacramento, CA, 95816-6519, Sacramento, USA; gen tel (916) 443-5087; adv tel (916) 443-5087; ed tel (916) 443-5087; disp adv e-mail dk@insidepublications.com; class adv e-mail dk@insidepublications.com; ed e-mail mbbizjak@aol.com; web site www.insidepublications.com
Circulation: 900pd, 82,000fr; USPS
Advertising rate: 1/4P Color $396, 1/2P Color $609 Full P Color $924
Established: 1996
Group: Inside Publications
Digital Platform - Mobile: Apple, Android, Windows, Blackberry, Other
Digital Platform - Tablet: Apple iOS, Android, Windows 7, Blackberry Tablet OS, Kindle, Nook, Kindle Fire, Other
Pub.. Cecily Hastings
Acc. Rep..Duffy Kelly
Delivery Method: Mail, Newsstand, Racks
Areas Served: 95608, 95821, 95825, 95864, 95833, 95816, 95819, 95825, 95864, 95821, 95814, 95811

SACRAMENTO BUSINESS JOURNAL (FRI)
555 Capitol Mall, Ste 200, Sacramento, CA, 95814-4557, Sacramento, USA; gen tel (916) 447-7661; gen fax (916) 558-7898; disp adv e-mail sacramento@bizjournals.com; web site www.bizjournals.com/sacramento
Advertising rate: Open inch rate $115.00
Established: 1984
Pub.. David Lichtman
Ed. in Chief .... Adam Steinhauer
Areas Served: 95818

SACRAMENTO GAZETTE (FRI)
770 L St Ste 950, Ste. 950, Sacramento, CA, 95814-3361, Sacramento, USA; gen tel (916) 567-9654; adv tel (916) 567-9654; gen fax (888) 567-1193; disp adv e-mail sacgazette@aol.com; web site Sacramento Gazette
Circulation: 1,700pd,; Sworn/Estimate/Non-Audited
Advertising rate: Open inch rate $17.75
Established: 1996
Ed. ....David A. Fong
Areas Served: 95814

SAINT HELENA

ST HELENA STAR (THUR)
1200 Main St, Ste C, Saint Helena, CA, 94574-1901, Napa, USA; gen tel (707) 963-2731; adv tel (707) 256-2228; ed tel (707) 967-6800; gen fax (707) 963-8957; disp adv e-mail nkostecka@napanews.com; class adv e-mail rschwanz@napanews.com; ed e-mail editor@sthelenastar.com; web site www.StHelenaStar.com
Circulation: 2,400pd,; Sworn/Estimate/Non-Audited
Advertising rate: Open inch rate $17.65
Established: 1874
Group: Napa Valley Publishing
Editor .... David Stoneberg
Staff writer ....Jesse Duarte
Delivery Method: Mail, Newsstand, Carrier, Racks
Areas Served: 94574 94515

SALINAS

THE SALINAS CALIFORNIAN (WED, FRI, SAT)
123 W Alisal St, Salinas, CA, 93901-4800, Monterey County, USA; gen tel (831) 424-2221; adv tel (831) 754-4133; ed tel (831) 754-4260; gen fax (831) 754-4104; adv fax (831) 754-4104; ed fax (831) 754-4104; disp adv e-mail chymovitz@thecalifornian.com; class adv e-mail chymovitz@thecalifornian.com; ed e-mail newsroom@thecalifornian.com; web site www.thecalifornian.com
Circulation: 6,854pd,; AAM
Advertising rate: Open inch rate $63.93
Established: 1871
Group: Gannett
Digital Platform - Mobile: Apple, Android, Windows
Digital Platform - Tablet: Apple iOS, Android, Windows 7
Publisher & President............Paula Goudreau
Adv. Sales Mgr..........................Craig Hymovitz
Digital Ed. .... Katharine Ball
Major/Nat'l Sales .... Paul Young
Regional Publisher .... Karen Ferguson
Exec. Ed...Silas Lyons
Mechanical Specifications: Type page 11 5/8 x 21; E - 6 cols, 2 1/16, 1/6 between; A - 6 cols, 2 1/16, 1/12 between; C - 9 cols, 1 3/8, 1/12 between.
Delivery Method: Mail, Carrier, Racks
Areas Served: Monterey County

SAN ANDREAS

CALAVERAS CALIFORNIAN (WED)
15 MAIN ST, San Andreas, CA, 95249, USA; gen tel (209) 754-3861; adv tel (209) 754-3863; ed tel (209) 498-2078; gen fax (209) 754-1805; ed fax (209) 754-4396; disp adv e-mail jmetzger@calaverasenterprise.com; class adv e-mail advertising@calacerasenterprise.com; web site www.calaverasenterprise.com
Circulation: 12,973fr; Sworn/Estimate/Non-Audited
Advertising rate: Open inch rate $12.00
Established: 1923
Pub... Ralph Alldredge
Ed./Pres.......................................Joel Metzger
Mechanical Specifications: Type page 13 x 21; E - 6 cols, 12 1/6, 1/6 between; A - 6 cols, 12 1/6, 1/6 between; C - 10 cols, 8 1/6, 1/6 between.Equipment & Software: Hardware — PC; Presses — G/Community; Software — Microsoft/Windows NT, QPS/QuarkXPress 4.0, Adobe/PageMaker 6.5, Adobe/Photoshop 4.0.
Areas Served: 95221, 95222, 95223, 95228, 95247

CALAVERAS ENTERPRISE (THUR)
15 Main St, 15 N. Main St., San Andreas, CA, 95249-9548, Calaveras, USA; gen tel (209) 754-3861; adv tel (209) 754-3863; ed tel (209) 498-2078; gen fax (209) 754-1805; ed fax (209) 754-4396; disp adv e-mail advertising@calaverasenterprise.com; class adv e-mail class@calaverasenterprise.com; ed e-mail editor@calaverasenterprise.com; web site www.calaverasenterprise.com
Circulation: 4,500pd,; Sworn/Estimate/Non-Audited
Advertising rate: Open inch rate $12.60
Established: 1960
Group: Calaveras First Co.
Gen. Mgr. ....Talibah Al-Rafiq
Circ. Sup. ....Monty Wright
Adv. Mgr. ....Jock Piel
Ed .... Sean ThomasEquipment & Software: Hardware — PC; Software — Microsoft/Windows NT, QPS/QuarkXPress 4.0, Adobe/Photoshop 4.0.
Delivery Method: Mail, Newsstand, Carrier, Racks
Areas Served: 95249, 95252, 95255, 95222, 952221, 95228, 95223, 95247

SAN DIEGO

BEACH & BAY PRESS (THUR)
1621 Grand Ave, Ste C, San Diego, CA, 92109-4458, San Diego, USA; gen tel (858) 270-3103; adv tel (858) 270-3103 x 106; ed tel (858) 270-3103 x133; gen fax (858) 270-9325; adv fax (858) 713-0095; disp adv e-mail julie@sdnews.com; class adv e-mail julie@sdnews.com; ed e-mail bbp@sdnews.com; web site www.sdnews.com
Circulation: 29pd, 18,549fr; Sworn/Estimate/Non-Audited
Advertising rate: Open inch rate $18.25
Established: 1988
Group: San Diego Community Newspaper Group, publishers of La Jolla Today, Peninsula Beacon and Beach & Bay Press
Pub..Julie Main
Ed. ....Tom Melville
Mechanical Specifications: Type page 10 1/4 x 15 1/2; E - 5 cols, 1 15/16, 5/32 between; A - 5 cols, 1 15/16, 5/32 between; C - 6 cols, 1 1/2, 3/16 between.Equipment & Software: Hardware — APP/Mac; Software — Adobe/Photoshop, Adobe/Illustrator, QPS/QuarkXPress,
Delivery Method: Mail, Newsstand, Carrier, Racks
Areas Served: 92109

LA JOLLA VILLAGE NEWS (FRI, BI-MTHLY)
1621 Grand Ave, Ste C, San Diego, CA, 92109-4458, San Diego, USA; gen tel (858) 270-3103; adv tel (858) 270-3103 x 106; ed tel (858) 270-3103 x 133; gen fax (858) 713-0095; adv fax (858) 713-0095; disp adv e-mail julie@sdnews.com; class adv e-mail kim@sdnews.com; ed e-mail Tom@sdnews.com; web site www.sdnews.com
Circulation: 25pd, 22,149fr; Sworn/Estimate/Non-Audited
Advertising rate: Open inch rate $80.00
Established: 1988
Group: San Diego Community Newspaper Group, publishers of La Jolla Today, Peninsula Beacon and Beach & Bay PressEditions: (3) La Jolla Village News, Beach & Bay Press, Peninsula Beacon
Publisher..Julie Main
Editor in Chief..............................Tom Melville
Mechanical Specifications: Type page 10 1/4 x 15 1/2; E - 5 cols, 1 15/16, 5/32 between; A - 5 cols, 1 15/16, 5/32 between; C - 6 cols, 1 1/2, 3/16 between.Equipment & Software: Hardware — APP/Mac; Software — Multi-Ad/Creator, Adobe/Photoshop, QPS/QuarkXPress, Adobe/Illustrator, Adobe/InDesign.
Delivery Method: Mail, Newsstand, Carrier, Racks
Areas Served: 92037, 92121, 92122

PENINSULA BEACON (THUR)
1621 Grand Ave, Ste C, San Diego, CA, 92109-4458, San Diego, USA; gen tel (858) 270-3103; adv tel (858) 270-3103 x 106; ed tel (858) 270-3103 x 131; gen fax (858) 713-0095; adv fax (858) 713-0095; disp adv

e-mail heather@sdnews.com; class adv e-mail kim@sdnews.com; ed e-mail mail@sdnews.com; web site www.sdnews.com
Circulation: 21pd, 20,000fr; Sworn/Estimate/Non-Audited
Advertising rate: 1/40 Pg $92.00; 1/20 Pg $167.00; 1/10 Pg $311.00
Established: 1989
Group: San Diego Community Newspaper Group, publishers of La Jolla Today, Peninsula Beacon and Beach & Bay Press
Pub....................Julie Main
Ad Manager....................Heather Long
Editor....................Tom Melville
Mechanical Specifications: Type page 10 1/4 x 15 1/2; E - 5 cols, 1 15/16, 5/32 between; A - 5 cols, 1 15/16, 5/32 between; C - 6 cols, 1 1/2, 3/16 between.Equipment & Software: Hardware — APP/Mac; Software — Quark, Photoshop,
Delivery Method: Mail, Newsstand, Carrier, Racks
Areas Served: 92106, 92107, 92110

SAN DIEGO UPTOWN NEWS (FRI)
123 Camino De La Reina, Ste 202, San Diego, CA, 92108-3002, San Diego, USA; gen tel (619) 519-7775; adv tel (619) 961-1951; disp adv e-mail david@sdcnn.com; ed e-mail john@sdcnn.com; web site www.sdcnn.com
Circulation: 23,011fr; CVC
Established: 2009
Group: San Diego Community News Netwrok
Digital Platform - Mobile: Apple, Android, Windows, Blackberry
Digital Platform - Tablet: Apple iOS, Android, Windows 7, Blackberry Tablet OS, Kindle, Nook, Kindle Fire
Pub./Circ. Mgr....................David Mannis
Adv. Mgr....................Mike Rosensteel
Mechanical Specifications: Type page 10" x 14.5"; 5 cols
Delivery Method: Mail, Newsstand, Carrier, Racks
Areas Served: San Diego County

UPTOWN SAN DIEGO EXAMINER (WED, FRI)
3601 30th St, San Diego, CA, 92104-3508, San Diego, USA; gen tel (619) 955-8960; adv tel (619) 955-8960; gen fax (619) 955-8962; adv fax (619) 955-8962; disp adv e-mail kevin@uptownexaminer.com; web site www.uptownexaminer.com
Circulation: 50pd, 15,000fr; Sworn/Estimate/Non-Audited
Advertising rate: Open inch rate $6.50
Established: 1937
Pub....................Gary Shaw
Mng. Ed....................Manny Cruz
Legal Notice Rep....................Kevin Specht
Mechanical Specifications: Type page 7 1/2 x 10; E - 3 cols, 2 3/8, 1/4 between; A - 3 cols, 2 3/8, 1/4 between.Equipment & Software: ; Presses — Risograph; Software — QPS/QuarkXPress.
Areas Served: 92164

SAN FRANCISCO

EAST BAY BUSINESS TIMES (FRI)
275 Battery St, Ste 940, San Francisco, CA, 94111-3332, San Francisco, USA; gen tel (415) 989-2522; gen fax (415) 398-2494; web site www.bizjournals.com/eastbay
Advertising rate: Open inch rate $115
Pub....................Mary Huss
Mng. Ed....................Jim Gardner
Areas Served: San Francisco County

SAN FRANCISCO EXAMINER (WED, THUR, SUN)
835 Market St., Suite 550, San Francisco, CA, 94103, South of Market, USA
Circulation: 0pd, 108,753fr; CVC
Group: Black Press Group Ltd.

SAN JOSE

ALMADEN RESIDENT (FRI)
1095 the Alameda, San Jose, CA, 95126-3142, Santa Clara, USA; gen tel (408) 200-1000; gen fax (408) 200-1011; disp adv e-mail almadenresident@svcn.com; web site www.mercurynews.com
Circulation: 5,969pd,; AAM
Advertising rate: 1/10 Pg $145.00; 3/20 Pg $217.00
Established: 2003
Group: The McClatchy Company
Pres./Pub....................Sharon Ryan
Circ. Dir....................Dan Smith
David Butler
Adv. Mgr....................Jeannette Close
Mechanical Specifications: Type page 10 x 12 3/4.
Areas Served: 95120

CAMPBELL REPORTER (FRI)
1095 the Alameda, San Jose, CA, 95126-3142, Santa Clara, USA; gen tel (408) 200-1000; adv tel (408) 200-1003; gen fax (408) 200-1011; disp adv e-mail jclose@community-newspapers.com; ed e-mail bbabcock@community-newspapers.com; web site mercurynews.com/campbell
Circulation: 9,250pd,; AAM
Advertising rate: 1/10 Pg $145.00; 3/20 Pg $217.00; 1/5 Pg $297.00
Group: The McClatchy Company
Pres./Pub....................Sharon Ryan
Ed./VP....................David Butler
Adv. Mgr....................Jeannette Close
Mechanical Specifications: Type page 10 x 12 3/4; E - 5 cols, 2 1/16, 3/16 between; A - 5 cols, 2 1/16, 3/16 between; C - 8 cols, 1 1/4, 1/16 between.
Areas Served: Santa Clara County

ROSE GARDEN RESIDENT (FRI)
1095 the Alameda, San Jose, CA, 95126-3142, Santa Clara, USA; gen tel (408) 200-1000; gen fax (408) 200-1101; disp adv e-mail rgr@svcn.com; web site www.community-newspapers.com
Circulation: 5,170pd,; AAM
Advertising rate: Open inch rate $36.50
Established: 2003
Group: The McClatchy Company
Circ. Mgr....................Mark Tomasz
Mechanical Specifications: Type page 10 x 12 3/4.
Areas Served: 95126, 95128

SAN JOSE BUSINESS JOURNAL (FRI)
125 S Market St, Fl 11th, San Jose, CA, 95113-2292, Santa Clara, USA; gen tel (408) 295-5028; adv tel (408) 299-1814; ed tel (408) 299-1828; disp adv e-mail wkupiec@bizjournals.com; class adv e-mail wkupiec@bizjournals.com; ed e-mail gbaumann@bizjournals.com; web site www.bizjournals.com/sanjose/
Advertising rate: 1/8 P $715 1/4 P $1,350 1/2 P $2230 Full $9100
Established: 1983
Pub....................James MacGregor
Ed....................Scott Ard
Areas Served: Santa Clara County

SARATOGA NEWS (FRI)
1095 the Alameda, San Jose, CA, 95126-3142, Santa Clara, USA; gen tel (408) 200-1000; gen fax (408) 200-1013; disp adv e-mail sn@svcn.com; web site mercurynews.com/saratoga
Circulation: 11,372pd,; AAM
Advertising rate: 1/10 Pg $145.00; 3/20 Pg $217.00; 1/5 Pg $297.00
Group: The McClatchy Company
Pres./Pub....................Sharon Ryan
Ed./VP....................David Butler
Adv. Mgr....................Jeannette Close
Mechanical Specifications: Type page 10 x 12 3/4; E - 5 cols, 2 1/16, 3/16 between; A - 5 cols, 2 1/16, 3/16 between; C - 8 cols, 1 1/4, 1/16 between.
Areas Served: 95126

THE CUPERTINO COURIER (FRI)
1095 the Alameda, San Jose, CA, 95126-3142, Santa Clara, USA; gen tel (408) 200-1000; gen fax (408) 200-1011; disp adv e-mail jkohler@bayareanewsgroup.com; web site www.mercurynews.com/cupertino
Circulation: 3,446pd,; AAM
Advertising rate: 1/10 Pg $145.00; 3/20 Pg $217.00; 1/5 Pg $297.00
Established: 1947
Group: The McClatchy Company
Pres./Pub....................Sharon Ryan
Ed./VP....................David Butler
Adv. Mgr....................Jeannette Close
Mechanical Specifications: Type page 10 x 12 3/4; E - 5 cols, 2 1/16, 3/16 between; A - 5 cols, 2 1/16, 3/16 between; C - 8 cols, 1 1/4, 1/16 between.
Areas Served: 95126

THE SUNNYVALE SUN (FRI)
1095 the Alameda, San Jose, CA, 95126-3142, Santa Clara, USA; gen tel (408) 200-1000; adv tel (408) 200-1009; ed tel (408) 200-1039; gen fax (408) 200-1011; disp adv e-mail etaloma@bayareanewsgroup.com; ed e-mail cvongsarath@community-newspapers.com; web site www.mercurynews.com/sunnyvale
Circulation: 12,015pd,; AAM
Advertising rate: 1/10 Pg $145.00; 3/20 Pg $217.00; 1/5 Pg $297.00
Group: The McClatchy Company
Ed....................Chris Vongsarath
Adv. Mgr....................Jeannette Close
Mechanical Specifications: Type page 10 x 12 3/4; E - 4 cols, 2 5/16, 1/4 between; A - 4 cols, 2 5/16, 1/4 between; C - 8 cols, 1 1/4, 1/16 between.
Areas Served: 95126

SANGER

SANGER HERALD (THUR)
740 N St, Sanger, CA, 93657-3114, Fresno, USA; gen tel (559) 875-2511; gen fax (559) 875-2521; disp adv e-mail mvpsanger@yahoo.com; class adv e-mail mvpsanger@yahoo.com; ed e-mail sangerherald@yahoo.com; web site www.thesangerherald.com
Circulation: 3,100pd, 14,300fr; Sworn/Estimate/Non-Audited
Advertising rate: Open inch rate $11.50
Group: Mid Valley Publishing
Pub....................Fred Hall
Editor....................Dick SheppardEquipment & Software: ; Software — Adobe/PageMaker 7.0, Microsoft/Word 5.0, QPS/QuarkXPress 4.0, Adobe/Illustrator 1, Adobe/Photoshop 6.0, Adobe/Acrobat 5.0.
Areas Served: 93657

SANTA ANA

ALISO VIEJO NEWS (THUR)
625 N Grand Ave, Santa Ana, CA, 92701-4347, Orange, USA; gen tel (949) 454-7300; gen fax (949) 454-7354; disp adv e-mail alisoviejonews@ocregister.com; class adv e-mail nationalads@ocregister.com; ed e-mail letters@ocregister.com; web site www.ocregister.com/alisoviejo
Circulation: 1,611pd,; AAM
Advertising rate: Open inch rate $35.00
Group: Times Media Group
Pub....................Aaron Kushner
Ed....................Ken Brusic
Ed....................Susan Verdon
Areas Served: Orange County

ANAHEIM BULLETIN (THUR)
625 N Grand Ave, Santa Ana, CA, 92701-4347, Orange, USA; gen tel (714) 634-1567; gen fax (714) 704-3714; disp adv e-mail anaheimhillsnews@ocregister.com; class adv e-mail nationalads@ocregister.com; retailads@ocregister.com; classifiedads@ocregister.com; ed e-mail letters@ocregister.com; web site www.ocregister.com
Circulation: 12,749pd, 14,143fr; AAM
Advertising rate: Open inch rate $35.00
Group: Times Media GroupAaron Kushner
City Ed....................Heather McRea
Ed....................Ken Brusic
Exec. Ed....................Frank Pine
Sr. Ed....................Todd Harmonson
Areas Served: Orange County

BREA-LA HABRA STAR-PROGRESS (FRI)
625 N Grand Ave, Santa Ana, CA, 92701-4347, Orange, USA; gen tel (877) 469-7344; adv tel (714) 796-3844; gen fax (949) 454-7354; disp adv e-mail customerservice@ocregister.com; class adv e-mail ebrunelli@ocregister.com; ed e-mail kbrusic@ocregister.com; web site www.ocregister.com
Circulation: 4,652pd, 16,000fr; AAM
Advertising rate: Open inch rate $35.00
Group: Times Media Group
Pub....................Chris Anderson
Pub....................Aaron Kushner
Ed....................Ken Brusic
Adv. Mgr....................Nick Lapaceia
Ed....................Tom Graves
Areas Served: Orange County

CAPISTRANO VALLEY NEWS (THUR)
625 N Grand Ave, Santa Ana, CA, 92701-4347, Orange, USA; gen tel (877) 469-7344; adv tel (714) 796-3844; gen fax (949) 454-7354; disp adv e-mail customerservice@ocregister.com; class adv e-mail ebrunelli@ocregister.com; ed e-mail kbrusic@ocregister.com; web site www.ocregister.com/sections/city-pages/sanjuancapistrano/
Circulation: 2,726pd,; AAM
Advertising rate: Open inch rate $35.00
Group: Times Media Group
Pub....................Aaron Kushner
Ed....................Ken Brusic
Areas Served: Orange County

CURRENT (FRI)
625 N Grand Ave, Santa Ana, CA, 92701-4347, Orange, USA; gen tel (877) 469-7344; adv tel (714) 796-3844; gen fax (949) 454-7354; disp adv e-mail customerservice@ocregister.com; class adv e-mail ebrunelli@ocregister.com; ed e-mail kbrusic@ocregister.com; web site www.ocregister.com/
Circulation: 9,014pd,; AAM
Advertising rate: Open inch rate $35.00
Pub....................Aaron Kushner
Ed....................Ken Brusic
Areas Served: Orange County

DANA POINT NEWS (THUR)
625 N Grand Ave, Santa Ana, CA, 92701-4347, Orange, USA; gen tel (877) 469-7344; adv tel (714) 796-3844; gen fax (949) 454-7354; disp adv e-mail customerservice@ocregister.com; class adv e-mail ebrunelli@ocregister.com; ed e-mail kbrusic@ocregister.com; web site www.ocregister.com/sections/city-pages/danapoint/
Circulation: 3,138pd,; AAM
Advertising rate: Open inch rate $35.00
Group: Times Media Group
Pub....................Aaron Kushner
Ed....................Ken Brusic
Areas Served: Orange County

FOUNTAIN VALLEY VIEW (THUR)
625 N Grand Ave, Santa Ana, CA, 92701-4347, Orange, USA; gen tel (877) 469-7344; adv tel (714) 796-3844; gen fax (949) 454-7354; disp adv e-mail customerservice@ocregister.com; class adv e-mail ebrunelli@ocregister.com; ed e-mail letters@ocregister.com; web site www.ocregister.com/sections/city-pages/fountainvalley/
Circulation: 3,522pd,; AAM
Advertising rate: Open inch rate $35.00
Group: Times Media Group
Pub....................Aaron Kushner
Ed....................Ken Brusic
Areas Served: Orange County

FULLERTON NEWS-TRIBUNE (THUR)
625 N Grand Ave, Santa Ana, CA, 92701-

4347, Orange, USA; gen tel (877) 469-7344; adv tel (714) 796-3844; gen fax (949) 454-7354; disp adv e-mail fullertonnewstribune@ocregister.com; class adv e-mail ebrunelli@ocregister.com; web site www.ocregister.com
Circulation: 9,056pd, 22,000fr; AAM
Advertising rate: Open inch rate $35.00
Group: Times Media Group
Pub.....Terry Horne
Pub.....Aaron Kushner
Ed.....Ken Brusic
City Ed.....Bob Ziebell
Areas Served: Orange County

HUNTINGTON BEACH WAVE (THUR)
625 N Grand Ave, Santa Ana, CA, 92701-4347, Orange, USA; gen tel (877) 469-7344; adv tel (714) 796-3844; gen fax (949) 454-7354; disp adv e-mail customerservice@ocregister.com; class adv e-mail ebrunelli@ocregister.com; ed e-mail letters@ocregister.com; web site www.ocregister.com/sections/city-pages/huntingtonbeach/
Circulation: 14,073pd,; AAM
Advertising rate: Open inch rate $35.00
Group: Times Media Group
Pub.....Aaron Kushner
Ed.....Ken Brusic
Areas Served: Orange County

IRVINE WORLD NEWS (THUR)
625 N Grand Ave, Santa Ana, CA, 92701-4347, Orange, USA; gen tel (877) 469-7344; adv tel (714) 796-3844; gen fax (949) 454-7354; disp adv e-mail customerservice@ocregister.com; class adv e-mail ebrunelli@ocregister.com; ed e-mail letters@ocregister.com; web site www.ocregister.com/sections/city-pages/irvine/
Circulation: 8,026pd,; AAM
Advertising rate: Open inch rate $35.00
Group: Times Media Group
Pub.....Aaron Kushner
Ed.....Ken Brusic
Areas Served: Orange County

LAGUNA BEACH NEWS POST (THUR)
625 N Grand Ave, Santa Ana, CA, 92701-4347, Orange, USA; gen tel (877) 469-7344; adv tel (714) 796-3844; gen fax (949) 454-7354; disp adv e-mail customerservice@ocregister.com; class adv e-mail ebrunelli@ocregister.com; ed e-mail letters@ocregister.com; web site www.ocregister.com/sections/city-pages/lagunabeach/
Circulation: 9,643fr; Sworn/Estimate/Non-Audited
Advertising rate: Open inch rate $35.00
Pub.....Aaron Kushner
Ed.....Ken Brusic
Areas Served: Orange County

LAGUNA NEWS-POST (THUR)
625 N Grand Ave, Santa Ana, CA, 92701-4347, Orange, USA; gen tel (714) 796-7954; gen fax (949) 454-7354; disp adv e-mail lagunanewspost@ocregister.com; web site www.ocregister.com
Circulation: 2,170pd,; AAM
Advertising rate: Open inch rate $16.41
Group: Times Media Group
Ed.....Rob Vardon
Events Ed.....Chris Boucly

LAGUNA NIGUEL NEWS (THUR)
626 N Grand Ave, Santa Ana, CA, 92701-4348, Orange, USA; gen tel (714) 796-7954; adv tel (714) 796-3844; gen fax (949) 454-7354; disp adv e-mail customerservice@ocregister.com; class adv e-mail ebrunelli@ocregister.com; ed e-mail letters@ocregister.com; web site www.ocregister.com/sections/city-pages/alisoviejo-lagunaniguel
Circulation: 3,768pd,; AAM
Advertising rate: Open inch rate $18.54
Group: Times Media Group
Pub.....Aaron Kushner
Ed.....Ken Brusic
Areas Served: Orange County

LAGUNA WOODS GLOBE (THUR)
625 N Grand Ave, Santa Ana, CA, 92701-4347, Orange, USA; gen tel (714) 796-3860; adv tel (714) 796-3844; gen fax (714) 796-3852; disp adv e-mail customerservice@ocregister.com; class adv e-mail ebrunelli@ocregister.com; ed e-mail letters@ocregister.com; web site www.ocregister.com/lagunawoods
Circulation: 6,747pd, 619fr; AAM
Advertising rate: Open inch rate $49.86
Group: Times Media Group
Pub.....Aaron Kushner
Ed.....Ken Brusic
VP, Circ.....Bruce Blair
Areas Served: Orange County

ORANGE CITY NEWS (WED)
625 N Grand Ave, Santa Ana, CA, 92701-4347, Orange, USA; gen tel (714) 796-7954; gen fax (714) 704-3714; disp adv e-mail orangecitynews@ocregister.com; web site www.ocregister.com/sections/city-pages/orange-villapark/
Circulation: 6,959pd,; AAM
Advertising rate: Open inch rate $16.75
Group: Times Media Group
Pub.....Aaron Kushner
Ed.....Ken Brusic
Areas Served: Orange County

PLACENTIA NEWS TIMES (THUR)
625 N Grand Ave, Santa Ana, CA, 92701-4347, Orange, USA; gen tel (877) 469-7344; adv tel (714) 796-3844; gen fax (949) 454-7354; disp adv e-mail customerservice@ocregister.com; class adv e-mail ebrunelli@ocregister.com; ed e-mail letters@ocregister.com; web site www.ocregister.com/sections/city-pages/placentia-yorbalinda/
Circulation: 3,092pd,; AAM
Advertising rate: Open inch rate $35.00
Group: Times Media Group
Pub.....Aaron Kushner
Ed.....Ken Brusic
Areas Served: Orange County

SADDLEBACK VALLEY NEWS (FRI)
627 N Grand Ave, Santa Ana, CA, 92701-4347, Orange, USA; gen tel (714) 796-7955; adv tel (714) 796-2205; gen fax (949) 454-7355; disp adv e-mail customerservice@ocregister.com; class adv e-mail ebrunelli@ocregister.com; ed e-mail letters@ocregister.com; web site www.ocregister.com/sections/city-pages/lakeforest-lagunahills
Circulation: 5,276pd,; AAM
Advertising rate: Open inch rate $38.00
Group: Times Media Group
Pub.....Aaron Kushner
Ed.....Ken Brusic
Areas Served: Orange County

SADDLEBACK VALLEY NEWS - MISSION VIEJO (FRI)
625 N Grand Ave, Santa Ana, CA, 92701-4347, Orange, USA; gen tel (877) 469-7344; adv tel (714) 796-2205; gen fax (949) 454-7354; disp adv e-mail customerservice@ocregister.com; class adv e-mail ebrunelli@ocregister.com; ed e-mail letters@ocregister.com; web site www.ocregister.com/sections/city-pages/missionviejo/
Circulation: 6,291pd,; AAM
Advertising rate: Open inch rate $35.00
Group: Times Media Group
Pub.....Aaron Kushner
Ed.....Ken Brusic
Areas Served: Orange County

SAN CLEMENTE SUN POST (THUR)
625 N Grand Ave, Santa Ana, CA, 92701-4347, Orange, USA; gen tel (877) 469-7344; adv tel (714) 796-2205; gen fax (949) 454-7354; disp adv e-mail customerservice@ocregister.com; class adv e-mail ebrunelli@ocregister.com; ed e-mail letters@ocregister.com; web site www.ocregister.com/sections/city-pages/sanclemente/
Circulation: 6,133pd,; AAM
Advertising rate: Open inch rate $35.00
Group: Times Media Group
Pub.....Aaron Kushner
Ed.....Ken Brusic
Areas Served: Orange County

SUN-POST NEWS (TUES, THUR, SAT)
625 N Grand Ave, Santa Ana, CA, 92701-4347, Orange, USA; gen tel (949) 492-4316; adv tel (714) 796-3844; ed tel (949) 492-4316; gen fax (714) 796-7000; disp adv e-mail sunpostnews@ocregister.com; ed e-mail nteubner@ocregister.com; web site www.ocregister.com/sanclemente
Circulation: 9,296pd,; Sworn/Estimate/Non-Audited
Advertising rate: Open inch rate $14.50
Group: Times Media Group
Ed.....Nellene Teubner
Areas Served: Orange County

THE TUSTIN NEWS (THUR)
625 N Grand Ave, Santa Ana, CA, 92701-4347, Orange, USA; gen tel (877) 469-7344; adv tel (714) 796-3844; gen fax (949) 553-2925; disp adv e-mail customerservice@ocregister.com; class adv e-mail ebrunelli@ocregister.com; ed e-mail kbrusic@ocregister.com; web site www.ocregister.com/sections/city-pages/tustin/
Circulation: 6,528pd,; AAM
Advertising rate: Open inch rate $11.33
Group: Times Media Group
Pub.....Aaron Kushner
City Ed.....Theresa Cisneros
Ed.....Ken BrusicEquipment & Software: ; Software — QPS/QuarkXPress 3.3.
Areas Served: Orange County

YORBA LINDA STAR (THUR)
625 N Grand Ave, Santa Ana, CA, 92701-4347, Orange, USA; gen tel (714) 634-1567; ed tel (714) 796-2226; gen fax (714) 704-3714; disp adv e-mail yorbalindastar@ocregister.com; web site www.ocregister.com/sections/city-pages/placentia-yorbalinda/
Circulation: 5,047pd,; AAM
Advertising rate: Open inch rate $16.68
Group: Times Media Group
Aaron Kushner
Ken Brusic
Heather McReaEd.s
Areas Served: Orange County

SANTA CLARITA

CONNECT SCV (WED)
24000 Creekside Rd, Santa Clarita, CA, 91355-1726, Los Angeles, USA; gen tel (661) 259-1234; gen fax (661) 254-8068; adv fax (661) 259-2081; ed fax (661) 255-9689; disp adv e-mail info@the-signal.com; web site www.the-signal.com
Circulation: 8,824pd, 159fr; VAC
Advertising rate: Open inch rate $39.90
Established: 1919
Pub.....Russ Briley
Executive Editor.....Jason Schaff
Lila Littlejohn
Asst. Mng. Ed./Sports Ed.....Cary Osborne
Senior Writer.....Jim Holt
Mechanical Specifications: Type page 12 x 21 1/4; E - 6 cols, 1 7/8, 1/8 between; A - 6 cols, 1 7/8, 1/8 between; C - 10 cols, 1, 1/8 between.

SANTA MARIA

ADOBE PRESS (FRI)
3200 Skyway Dr, Santa Maria, CA, 93455-1824, Santa Barbara, USA; gen tel (805) 925-2691; gen fax (805) 473-0571; disp adv e-mail dchavez@leecentralcoastnews.com; web site www.theadobepress.com
Circulation: 7,500pd,; Sworn/Estimate/Non-Audited
Advertising rate: Open inch rate $9.60
Pub.....Cynthia Schur
Mng. Ed.....Emily Slater
Areas Served: Santa Luis Obispo County

THE LOMPOC RECORD (WED, SUN)
3200 Skyway Dr, Santa Maria, CA, 93455-1824, Santa Barbara, USA; gen tel (805) 736-2313; adv tel (805) 739-2150; ed tel (805) 739-2143; gen fax (805) 736-5654; adv fax (805) 736-5654; ed fax (805) 736-5654; disp adv e-mail zchavez@lompocrecord.com; class adv e-mail sedwards@lompocrecord.com; ed e-mail mcooley@lompocrecord.com; web site www.lompocrecord.com
Circulation: 2,688pd,; AAM
Advertising rate: Open inch rate $15.00
Established: 1979
Group: Lee Enterprises, Inc.
Pub.....Cynthia Schur
Exec. Ed.....Tom Bolton
City Ed.....Bo Poertner
Sports Ed.....Elliott Stern
IT/Web Admin.....Braxton Carroll
Prodn. Mgr.....George Fischer
Bus. Mgr.....Donna Dimock
Circ. Dir.....Rich Macke
Mechanical Specifications: Type page 13 x 21 1/2; E - 6 cols, 2 1/16, 1/8 between; A - 6 cols, 2 1/16, 1/8 between; C - 8 cols, 1 1/2, 1/8 between.
Delivery Method: Mail, Newsstand, Carrier, Racks
Areas Served: 93436

SANTA MONICA

BRENTWOOD NEWS (TUES, FRI)
2116 Wilshire Blvd, Ste 260, Santa Monica, CA, 90403-5750, Los Angeles, USA; gen tel (310) 310-2637; gen fax (424) 744-8821; disp adv e-mail advertising@smmirror.com ; class adv e-mail advertising@smmirror.com; ed e-mail editor@smmirror.com ; web site www.westsidetoday.com
Circulation: 0pd, 100,000fr; Sworn/Estimate/Non-Audited
Advertising rate: N/A
Established: 1990
Group: Mirror Media Group
President/Publisher.....TJ Montemer
Sales Mgr.....Judy Swartz
Delivery Method: Newsstand, Carrier, Racks
Areas Served: Santa Monica, Pacific Palisades, West LA, Brentwood, Westwood, Century City, Beverly Hills, Cheviot Hills, Beverlywood, Venice, West Hollywood, Hollywood, Downtown LA, Echo Park, Silverlake

CENTURY CITY NEWS (TUES, FRI)
2116 Wilshire Blvd, Ste 260, Santa Monica, CA, 90403-5750, Los Angeles, USA; gen tel (310) 310-2637; gen fax (424) 744-8821; disp adv e-mail advertising@smmirror.com ; class adv e-mail advertising@smmirror.com; ed e-mail editor@smmirror.com ; web site www.westsidetoday.com
Circulation: 0pd, 100,000fr; Sworn/Estimate/Non-Audited
Advertising rate: N/A
Established: 1990
Group: Mirror Media Group
President/Publisher.....TJ Montemer
Sales Mgr.....Judy Swartz
Delivery Method: Newsstand, Carrier, Racks
Areas Served: Santa Monica, Pacific Palisades, West LA, Brentwood, Westwood, Century City, Beverly Hills, Cheviot Hills, Beverlywood, Venice, West Hollywood, Hollywood, Downtown LA, Echo Park, Silverlake

LA PRIDE (TUES, FRI)
2116 Wilshire Blvd, Ste 260, Santa Monica, CA, 90403-5750, Los Angeles, USA; gen tel (310) 310-2637; gen fax (424) 744-8821; disp adv e-mail advertising@smmirror.com ; class adv e-mail advertising@smmirror.com; ed e-mail editor@smmirror.com ; web site www.westsidetoday.com
Circulation: 0pd, 100,000fr; Sworn/Estimate/Non-Audited
Advertising rate: N/A
Established: 1990
Group: Mirror Media Group

President/Publisher ....TJ Montemer
Sales Mgr.......................................Judy Swartz
Delivery Method: Newsstand, Carrier, Racks
Areas Served: Santa Monica, Pacific Palisades, West LA, Brentwood, Westwood, Century City, Beverly Hills, Cheviot Hills, Beverlywood, Venice, West Hollywood, Hollywood, Downtown LA, Echo Park, Silverlake

SANTA MONICA MIRROR (TUES, FRI)

2116 Wilshire Blvd, Ste 260, Santa Monica, CA, 90403-5750, Los Angeles, USA; gen tel (310) 310-2637; gen fax (424) 744-8821; disp adv e-mail advertising@smmirror.com ; class adv e-mail advertising@smmirror.com; ed e-mail editor@smmirror.com ; web site www.westsidetoday.com
Circulation: 0pd, 100,000fr; Sworn/Estimate/Non-Audited
Advertising rate: N/A
Established: 1990
Group: Mirror Media Group
President/Publisher ....TJ Montemer
Sales Mgr.......................................Judy Swartz
Delivery Method: Newsstand, Carrier, Racks
Areas Served: Santa Monica, Pacific Palisades, West LA, Brentwood, Westwood, Century City, Beverly Hills, Cheviot Hills, Beverlywood, Venice, West Hollywood, Hollywood, Downtown LA, Echo Park, Silverlake

WESTSIDE TODAY (TUES, FRI)

2116 Wilshire Blvd, Ste 260, Santa Monica, CA, 90403-5750, Los Angeles, USA; gen tel (310) 310-2637; gen fax (424) 744-8821; disp adv e-mail advertising@smmirror.com ; class adv e-mail advertising@smmirror.com; ed e-mail editor@smmirror.com ; web site www.westsidetoday.com
Circulation: 0pd, 100,000fr; Sworn/Estimate/Non-Audited
Advertising rate: N/A
Established: 1990
Group: Mirror Media Group
President/Publisher ....TJ Montemer
Sales Mgr.......................................Judy Swartz
Delivery Method: Newsstand, Carrier, Racks
Areas Served: Santa Monica, Pacific Palisades, West LA, Brentwood, Westwood, Century City, Beverly Hills, Cheviot Hills, Beverlywood, Venice, West Hollywood, Hollywood, Downtown LA, Echo Park, Silverlake

YO VENICE (TUES, FRI)

2116 Wilshire Blvd, Ste 260, Santa Monica, CA, 90403-5750, Los Angeles, USA; gen tel (310) 310-2637; gen fax (424) 744-8821; disp adv e-mail advertising@smmirror.com ; class adv e-mail advertising@smmirror.com; ed e-mail editor@smmirror.com ; web site www.westsidetoday.com
Circulation: 0pd, 100,000fr; Sworn/Estimate/Non-Audited
Advertising rate: N/A
Established: 1990
Group: Mirror Media Group
President/Publisher ....TJ Montemer
Sales Mgr.......................................Judy Swartz
Delivery Method: Newsstand, Carrier, Racks
Areas Served: Santa Monica, Pacific Palisades, West LA, Brentwood, Westwood, Century City, Beverly Hills, Cheviot Hills, Beverlywood, Venice, West Hollywood, Hollywood, Downtown LA, Echo Park, Silverlake

SAUSALITO

ROSS VALLEY REPORTER (THUR)

1050 Bridgeway, Sausalito, CA, 94965-2173, Marin, USA; gen tel (415) 339-8510; gen fax (415) 331-1882; disp adv e-mail mscope@marinscope.com; web site www.marinscope.com/ross_valley_reporter/
Circulation: 14,000pd,; Sworn/Estimate/Non-Audited
Advertising rate: Open inch rate $32.00
Group: Marinscope Community Newspapers
Pub..Paul Hutcheson
Ed. ....Joe Wolfcale
Areas Served: 94965

SCOTTS VALLEY

PRESS BANNER (FRI)

5215 Scotts Valley Dr, Ste F, Scotts Valley, CA, 95066-3522, Santa Cruz, USA; gen tel (831) 438-2500; adv tel 831-438-2500; ed tel 831-438-2500; gen fax (831) 438-4114; adv fax (831) 438-4114; ed fax (831) 438-4114; disp adv e-mail pbads@pressbanner.com; class adv e-mail pbads@pressbanner.com; ed e-mail pbeditor@pressbanner.com; web site www.pressbanner.com
Circulation: 70pd, 12,780fr; Sworn/Estimate/Non-Audited
Advertising rate: Open inch rate $14.00 (b/w) add $3 for color
Established: 1960
Group: TankTown Media
Editor ....Barry Holtzclaw
Advertising Director..............Cherie Anderson
Mechanical Specifications: Type page 13 x 21; E - 6 cols, between; A - 6 cols, between; C - 6 cols, between.Equipment & Software: Hardware — APP/Mac; Software — Adobe/Pagemaker.
Delivery Method: Mail, Racks
Areas Served: 95066

SEAL BEACH

LEISURE WORLD GOLDEN RAIN NEWS (THUR)

13533 Seal Beach Blvd., Amphitheater Bldg., 13533 Seal Beach Blvd., Amphitheater Bldg., Seal Beach, CA, 90740, Orange, USA; gen tel (562) 430-0534; adv tel (562) 472-1275; ed tel (562) 472-1278; gen fax (562) 598-1617; disp adv e-mail davesaunders@lwsbnews.com; class adv e-mail davesaunders@lwsbnews.com; ed e-mail davesaunders@lwsbnews.com; web site www.lwsb.com/newspaper
Circulation: 7,000pd, 2,000fr; Sworn/Estimate/Non-Audited
Advertising rate: Open inch rate $15.45
Established: 1963
Mng. Ed.................................Dave Saunders
Adv. Sales...............................Karen McElwain
Mechanical Specifications: Type page 10 7/16 x 16; E - 5 cols, 1 15/16, 1/8 between; A - 5 cols, 1 15/16, 1/8 between; C - 5 cols, 1 15/16, 1/8 between.Equipment & Software: Hardware — APP/Mac; Software — Microsoft, InDesign, PDF
Delivery Method: Carrier
Areas Served: 90740

NEWS ENTERPRISE (WED)

216 Main St, Seal Beach, CA, 90740-6318, Orange, USA; gen tel (562) 431-1397; adv tel (562) 431-1397; ed tel (562) 431-1397 x 220; gen fax (562) 493-2310; disp adv e-mail info@newsenterprise.net ; class adv e-mail publisher@newsenterprise.net ; ed e-mail editor@newsenterprise.net; web site www.newsenterprise.net
Circulation: 1,400pd, 30,000fr; Sworn/Estimate/Non-Audited
Advertising rate: Open inch rate: $17.00
Established: 1923
Group: CommunityMedia Co.
Pub...Vince Bodiford
Ed. ....Ted Apodaca
Advert. Acct Mgr.......................Alice Melamed
Sports Ed.......................................Jesus Ruiz
Mechanical Specifications: 1 Column = 1.9"
2 Columns = 3.9"
3 Columns = 6.1"
4 Columns = 8.1"
5 Columns = 10.25" Equipment & Software: Hardware — APP/Mac; Software — InDesign, Microsoft/Word, Adobe/Illustrator, Adobe/Photoshop.
Delivery Method: Mail, Newsstand, Carrier, Racks
Areas Served: 90720, 90740, 90630, 90808, 90623

SOLANA BEACH

CARMEL VALLEY NEWS (THUR)

380 Stevens Ave Ste 316, Suite 316, Solana Beach, CA, 92075-2069, San Diego, USA; gen tel (858) 756-1403; adv tel (858) 459-4201; ed tel (858) 756-1451; gen fax (858) 756-9912; disp adv e-mail donp@rsfreview.com; ed e-mail editor@delmartimes.net; web site delmartimes.net/carmel-valley
Circulation: 17,421pd,; AAM
Advertising rate: 1/8 Pg $315.00; 1/4 Pg $545.00
Group: Mainstreet Media Group, LLC
Pub..Phyllis Pfeiffer
Exec. Ed....................................Lorine Wright
Adv. VP ....Don Parks
Circ. Mgr..Dara Elstein
Mechanical Specifications: Type page 10 1/4 x 15 1/2; E - 5 cols, 2, between; A - 5 cols, 2, between; C - 5 cols, 2, between.Equipment & Software: Hardware — APP/Mac; Software — QPS/QuarkXPress 7.0, Adobe/Photoshop.
Areas Served: 92130

DEL MAR TIMES (THUR)

380 Stevens Ave Ste 316, Suite 316, Solana Beach, CA, 92075-2069, San Diego, USA; gen tel (858) 756-1403; adv tel (858) 459-4201; ed tel (858) 756-1451; gen fax (858) 756-9912; disp adv e-mail ashleyo@lajollalight.com; class adv e-mail donp@rsfreview.com; ed e-mail editor@delmartimes.net; web site www.delmartimes.net
Circulation: 7,032pd,; AAM
Advertising rate: 1/8 Pg $315.00; 1/4 Pg $545.00
Established: 1995
Group: ManinStreet Media Group
Mainstreet Media Group, LLC
Pub..Phyllis Pfeiffer
Exec. Ed....................................Lorine Wright
VP, Adv...Don Parks
Circ. Mgr..Dara Elstein
Mechanical Specifications: Type page: 10.33" x 12.25"; 6 cols
Delivery Method: Mail, Newsstand, Racks
Areas Served: 92014

ENCINITAS ADVOCATE (THUR)

380 Stevens Ave Ste 316, Suite 316, Solana Beach, CA, 92075-2069, San Diego, USA; gen tel (858) 876-7997; adv tel (858) 876-8853; gen fax (858) 756-9912; ed e-mail editor@rsfreview.com; web site delmartimes.net/encinitas-advocate
Circulation: 17,931pd,; AAM
President and General ManagerPhyllis Pfeiffer
Executive Editor..........................Lorine Wright
Publisher and Editor ....Jeff Light

RANCHO SANTA FE REVIEW (THUR)

380 Stevens Ave Ste 316, Suite 316, Solana Beach, CA, 92075-2069, San Diego, USA; gen tel (858) 876-7997; adv tel (858) 459-4201; ed tel (858) 756-1451; gen fax (858) 756-9912; disp adv e-mail donp@rsfreview.com; ed e-mail editor@rsfreview.com; web site www.ranchosantafereview.com - 24,966(views) 9,411(visitors)
Circulation: 6,987pd,; AAM
Advertising rate: 1/8 Pg $315.00; 1/4 Pg $535.00; 1/2 Pg $935.00
Established: 1983
Group: Mainstreet Media Group, LLC
VP/Gen. Mgr. ....Phyllis Pfeiffer
Exec. Ed....................................Lorine Wright
VP, Adv...Don Parks
Circ. Mgr..Dara Elstein
Mechanical Specifications: Type page 10.33" x 12.25"; 6 colsEquipment & Software: Hardware — APP/Mac; Software — QPS/QuarkXPress, Adobe/Photoshop, Microsoft/Word.
Delivery Method: Mail, Carrier, Racks
Areas Served: 92067, 92091, 92014, 92024

SOLANA BEACH SUN (THUR)

380 Stevens Ave Ste 316, Suite 316, Solana Beach, CA, 92075-2069, San Diego, USA; gen tel (858) 756-1403; adv tel (858) 459-4201; ed tel (858) 756-1451; gen fax (858) 756-9912; disp adv e-mail donp@rsfreview.com; ed e-mail editor@delmartimes.net; web site www.delmartimes.net/solana-beach-sun
Circulation: 4,325pd,; AAM
Advertising rate: 1/8 Pg $315.00; 1/4 Pg $545.00
Established: 2004
Group: Mainstreet Media Group, LLC
Pub..Phyllis Pfeiffer
Exec. Ed....................................Lorine Wright
VP, Adv...Don Parks
Circ. Mgr..Dara Elstein
Mechanical Specifications: Type page: 10.33" x 12.25"; 6 cols
Delivery Method: Mail, Carrier, Racks
Areas Served: 92014

SOLVANG

SANTA YNEZ VALLEY NEWS/EXTRA (TUES, THUR)

423 2nd St, Solvang, CA, 93463-3711, Santa Barbara, USA; gen tel (805) 688-5522; adv tel (805) 688-5522 x 6003; ed tel (805) 739-2143; gen fax (805) 688-7685; disp adv e-mail cdelgado@syvnews.com; class adv e-mail sedwards@syvnews.com; ed e-mail mcooley@syvnews.com; web site www.syvnews.com
Circulation: 13,500fr; Sworn/Estimate/Non-Audited
Advertising rate: Open inch rate $13.48
Established: 1925
Pub..Cynthia Schur
Mng. Ed......................................Marga Cooley
Mechanical Specifications: Type page 12 x 21; E - 6 cols, 1 7/8, 1/6 between; A - 6 cols, 1 7/8, 1/6 between; C - 9 cols, 1 1/4, 3/20 between.
Areas Served: 93643

SONOMA

THE SONOMA INDEX-TRIBUNE (TUES, FRI)

117 W Napa St, Ste D, Sonoma, CA, 95476-6691, Sonoma, USA; gen tel (707) 938-2111; adv tel (707) 933-2749; ed tel (707) 933-2737; gen fax (707) 938-1600; disp adv e-mail robert.lee@sonomanews.com; class adv e-mail joanne.herrfeldt@pressdemocrat.com; ed e-mail jason.walsh@sonomanews.com; web site www.sonomanews.com
Circulation: 5,618pd,; AAM
Advertising rate: Open inch rate $32.00
Established: 1879
Group: Sonoma Media Investments
Mng. Ed...Bill Hoban
Editor-in-chief ....Jason Walsh
Pub..John Burns
Photo Ed..Robbi Pengelly
Mechanical Specifications: Type page 12 1/4 x 21; E - 6 cols, 1 5/8, 9/50 between; A - 6 cols, 1 5/8, 9/50 between; C - 6 cols, 1 5/8, 9/50 between.Equipment & Software: Hardware — APP/Macs; Software — Adobe CS
Microsoft Word
Delivery Method: Mail, Newsstand, Carrier, Racks
Areas Served: 95476, 95409, 95442

WINE COUNTRY THIS WEEK (FRI)

669 Broadway, Ste B, Sonoma, CA, 95476-7085, Sonoma, USA; gen tel (707) 938-3494; gen fax (707) 938-3674; web site http://www.winecountrythisweek.com
Group: Brehm Communications, Inc.
Ed. ....Chandra Grant

SOUTH LAKE TAHOE

TAHOE DAILY TRIBUNE (WED, FRI, SAT)

3079 Harrison Ave, South Lake Tahoe, CA, 96150-7976, El Dorado, USA; gen tel (530) 541-3880; adv tel (530) 541-3880; ed tel (530) 541-3880; gen fax (530) 541-0373; adv fax (530) 541-0373; ed fax (530) 541-0373; class adv e-mail classifieds@sierranevada-

media.com; ed e-mail editor@tahoedailytribune.com; web site www.tahoedailytribune.com
Circulation: 7,078pd,; CAC
Advertising rate: 1/32 Pg $50.00; 1/16 Pg $70.00; 1/12 Pg $90.00
Established: 1952
Group: Swift Communications, Inc.
Digital Platform - Mobile: Apple, Android, Windows
Digital Platform - Tablet: Apple iOS, Android, Blackberry Tablet OS, Kindle
Ed. .... Trisha Leonard
Adv. Sales .... Ben Rogers
Distribution .... Lisa Ronhovdee
Circ. Mgr. .... Wyatt Gardiner
Adv. Dir./Pub. .... Natasha Schue
Mechanical Specifications: Type page 12 7/8 x 21 1/2; E - 6 cols, 2, 1/8 between; A - 6 cols, 2, 1/8 between; C - 9 cols, 1 1/3, 1/9 between.
Delivery Method: Newsstand, Carrier, Racks
Areas Served: 96150+

SOUTH PASADENA

SOUTH PASADENA REVIEW (WED)
1020 Mission St, Unit C, South Pasadena, CA, 91030-3172, Los Angeles, USA; gen tel (626) 799-1161; gen fax (626) 799-2404; disp adv e-mail advertising@southpasadenareview.com; class adv e-mail advertising@southpasadenareview.com; ed e-mail bglazier@southpasadenareview.com; web site www.south.pasadenanow.com
Circulation: 4,000pd,; Sworn/Estimate/Non-Audited
Advertising rate: Open inch rate $8.00
Established: 1888
Pub. .... William Ericson
Adv. Mgr. .... Nancy Lem
Ed. .... Bill Glazier
Mechanical Specifications: Type page 13 x 21; E - 6 cols, 2 1/16, 1/8 between; A - 6 cols, 2 1/16, 1/8 between; C - 6 cols, 2 1/16, 1/8 between.Equipment & Software: Hardware — APP/Macs; Software — QPS/QuarkXPress, Adobe/Photoshop.
Areas Served: 91030

SUSANVILLE

LASSEN COUNTY TIMES (TUES)
100 Grand Ave, Susanville, CA, 96130-4451, Lassen, USA; gen tel (530) 257-5321; adv tel (530) 257-5321; ed tel (530) 257-5321; gen fax (530) 257-0408; disp adv e-mail ltew@lassennews.com; class adv e-mail rmeadows@lassennews.com; ed e-mail swilliams@lassennews.com; web site www.lassennews.com
Circulation: 6,128pd, 3,598fr; Sworn/Estimate/Non-Audited
Advertising rate: Open inch rate $6.00
Established: 1976
Group: Feather Publishing Co., Inc.
Pub .... Michael C. Taborski
Mgr. Ed .... Sam Williams
Class .... Rashelle Meadows
Mechanical Specifications: Full page 12 1/4 x 21 1/2; E - 6 cols, 1 5/6, 1/6 between; A - 6 cols, 1 5/6, 1/6 between; C - 9 cols, 1 1/4, 1/6 between.Equipment & Software: Hardware — APP/Macs; Presses — G/Community; Software — Microsoft/Word, QPS/QuarkXPress.
Delivery Method: Mail, Newsstand, Carrier
Areas Served: 96130, 96127, 96114, 96117, 96128, 96113

WESTWOOD PINEPRESS (WED)
100 Grand Ave, Susanville, CA, 96130-4451, Lassen, USA; gen tel (530) 257-5321; adv tel (530) 257-5321; ed tel (530) 257-5321; gen fax (530) 257-0408; adv fax (530) 257-0408; ed fax (530) 257-0408; disp adv e-mail jatkinson@lassennews.com; class adv e-mail rmeadows@lassennews.com; ed e-mail swilliams@lassennews.com; web site www.lassennews.com
Circulation: 750fr; Sworn/Estimate/Non-Audited
Advertising rate: Open inch rate $6.00
Established: 1977
Group: Feather Publishing Co., Inc.
Pub .... Michael Taborski
Mgr. Ed .... Sam Williams
Adv. Mgr. .... Jill Atkinson
Mechanical Specifications: Full page 12 1/4 x 21 1/2; E - 6 cols, 1 5/6, 1/6 between; A - 6 cols, 1 5/6, 1/6 between; C - 9 cols, 1 1/4, 1/6 between.Equipment & Software: Hardware — APP/Macs; Presses — G/Community; Software — Microsoft/Word, QPS.
Delivery Method: Racks
Areas Served: 96137

TAFT

DAILY MIDWAY DRILLER (TUES, FRI)
800 Center St, Taft, CA, 93268-3129, Kern, USA; gen tel (661) 763-3171; gen fax (661) 763-5638; disp adv e-mail cthompson@taftmidwaydriller.com; ed e-mail editor@bay.rr.com; web site www.taftmidwaydriller.com
Circulation: 4,900pd,; Sworn/Estimate/Non-Audited
Advertising rate: Open inch rate $10.00
Established: 1916
Group: GateHouse Media, Inc.
Office Mgr. .... Deanna Long
Circ. Mgr. .... Melissa Robertson
Pub .... John Watkins
Ed. .... Doug Keeler
Sports Ed. .... Sara Mitchell
Adv. Rep. .... Christine Thompson
Classified Adv. Mgr. .... Kim Coker
Production Mgr. .... Roseanne Noble
Mechanical Specifications: Type page 13 x 21 1/2; E - 6 cols, 2 1/16, 1/8 between; A - 6 cols, 2 1/16, 1/8 between; C - 6 cols, 2 1/16, 1/8 between.

TEHACHAPI

TEHACHAPI NEWS (WED)
411 N Mill St, Tehachapi, CA, 93561-1351, Kern, USA; gen tel (661) 822-6828; gen fax (661) 822-4053; disp adv e-mail advertise@tehachapinews.com; class adv e-mail classifieds@tehachapinews.com; ed e-mail editorial@tehachapinews.com; web site www.tehachapinews.com
Circulation: 8,300pd, 5,200fr; Sworn/Estimate/Non-Audited
Established: 1899
Group: TBC Media
Bus. Mgr .... Stephanie Ursua
Mechanical Specifications: Type page 13 x 21; E - 6 cols, 2 1/16, between; A - 6 cols, 2 1/16, between; C - 10 cols, 1 1/4, between. Equipment & Software: Hardware — APP/Mac; Software — Multi-Ad/Creator 3.6, QPS/QuarkXPress 3.3, Adobe/PageMaker 5.0.
Delivery Method: Mail, Carrier, Racks
Areas Served: 93561, 93531

TIBURON

THE ARK (WED)
1550 Tiburon Blvd, Ste D, Tiburon, CA, 94920-2537, Marin, USA; gen tel (415) 435-2652; adv tel (415) 435-1190; ed tel (415) 435-2652; gen fax (415) 435-0849; adv fax (415) 435-0849; ed fax (415) 435-0849; disp adv e-mail ads@thearknewspaper.com; class adv e-mail ark.manager@thearknewspaper.com; ed e-mail editor@thearknewspaper.com; web site www.thearknewspaper.com
Circulation: 2,750pd, 50fr; Sworn/Estimate/Non-Audited
Advertising rate: Open inch rate $48.00
Established: 1973
Group: AMMI Publishing Co Inc
Owner-publisher .... Alison Gray
Executive editor .... Kevin Hessel
Owner/pub. .... Arthur Kern
Dir. of Bus & Adv. .... Henriette Corn
Assist ed & Strawberry reporter .... Emily Lavin
Belvedere & public safety reporter .... Matthew Hose
Prod ed & youth reporter .... Jeff Dempsey
Tiburon reporter .... Deirdre McCrohan
Accounts mgr .... Leigh Pagan
Copy ed. & calendar ed .... Diana Goodman
Delivery Method: Mail, Racks
Areas Served: Belvedere-Tiburon, CA 94920

TRACY

TRACY PRESS (FRI)
145 W 10th St, Tracy, CA, 95376-3903, San Joaquin, USA; gen tel (209) 835-3030; adv tel (209) 830-4260; gen fax (209) 835-0655; adv fax (209) 832-5383; disp adv e-mail tpads@tracypress.com; class adv e-mail tpads@tracypress.com; ed e-mail mlangley@tracypress.com; web site www.tracypress.com
Circulation: 19,000pd,; Sworn/Estimate/Non-Audited
Advertising rate: Open inch rate $26.00
Established: 1898
Co-Pub. .... Ralph Alldredge
Ed. .... Michael Langley
Adv. Sales .... Vanessa Alfaro
Mktg. Mgr. .... Lisa Carcraft
Adv. Rep. .... Diane LopezEquipment & Software: Hardware — APP/Mac, MS/NT Server; Presses — 8-G/Community, G/SC; Software — QPS, Baseview.
Areas Served: 95378

TRUCKEE

SIERRA SUN (WED, FRI)
10775 Pioneer Trl, Ste 101, Truckee, CA, 96161-0233, Nevada, USA; gen tel (530) 587-6061; adv tel (530) 550-9696; ed tel (530) 587-6061; gen fax (530) 587-3763; disp adv e-mail editor@sierrasun.com; class adv e-mail classifieds@sierranevadamedia.com; ed e-mail editor@sierrasun.com; web site www.sierrasun.com
Circulation: 0pd, 5,852fr; CAC
Advertising rate: 1/32 Pg $50.00; 1/16 Pg $70.00; 1/12 Pg $90.00
Established: 1869
Group: Swift Communications, Inc.
Major Accts. Rep. .... Howard Young
Ed. .... Jamie Bate
Distribution .... Lisa Ronhovdee
Circ. Mgr. .... Josh Sweigert
Co-Gen. Mgr. .... Ben Rogers
Co-Gen. Mgr. .... Kevin MacMillan
Mechanical Specifications: Type page 11 3/5 x 20 1/2; E - 6 cols, 1 4/5, 3/5 between; A - 6 cols, 1 4/5, 3/5 between; C - 9 cols, 1 3/10, 1/10 between.
Areas Served: 96160, 96161

TURLOCK

THE CERES COURIER (WED)
138 S Center St, Turlock, CA, 95380-4508, Stanislaus, USA; gen tel (209) 537-5032; adv tel (209) 537-5032; ed tel (209) 537-5032; gen fax (209) 632-8813; adv fax (209) 847-9750; ed fax (209) 632-8813; disp adv e-mail tphillips@turlockjournal.com; class adv e-mail tphillips@turlockjournal.com; ed e-mail jbenziger@cerescourier.com; web site www.cerescourier.com
Circulation: 4,062pd, 19,500fr; Sworn/Estimate/Non-Audited
Advertising rate: Open inch rate $12.95
Established: 1910
Group: Morris Multimedia, Inc.
Ed. .... Jeff Benziger
Pub .... Hank Veen
Circ. Mgr. .... Kelli Wilson
Mechanical Specifications: Type page 12 x 21; E - 6 cols, 2 1/3, 1/6 between; A - 6 cols, 2 1/3, 1/6 between; C - 9 cols, 1 1/2, between. Equipment & Software: ; Software — Baseview.
Areas Served: 95380

TURLOCK JOURNAL (WED, SAT)
138 S Center St, Turlock, CA, 95380-4508, Stanislaus, USA; gen tel (209) 634-9141; adv tel (209) 634-9141; ed tel (209) 634-9141; gen fax (209) 632-8813; adv fax (209) 632-8813; ed fax (209) 632-8813; disp adv e-mail adinfo@turlockjournal.com; class adv e-mail classifieds@turlockjournal.com; ed e-mail news@turlockjournal.com; web site www.turlockjournal.com
Circulation: 6,030pd, 14,500fr; Sworn/Estimate/Non-Audited
Advertising rate: Open inch rate $13.91
Established: 1904
Group: Morris Multimedia, Inc.
Pub .... Hank Veen
Ed. .... Kristina Hacker
Adv. Sales .... Victoria Batesole
Adv. Mgr. .... Taylor Phillips
Mechanical Specifications: Type page 13 x 21 1/2; E - 6 cols, 2 1/16, 1/8 between; A - 6 cols, 2 1/16, 1/8 between; C - 9 cols, 1 5/16, 1/8 between.Equipment & Software: Hardware — 2-APP/Power Mac, 1-APP/Mac IIci, APP/Mac G4; Presses — 8-G/Community; Software — Adobe/PageMaker 6.5, QPS/QuarkExpress 3.04, Adobe/Photoshop 5.0, Baseview/NewsEdit Pro, Adobe/Illustrator, Multi-Ad/Creator.
Areas Served: 95380, 95381, 95382, 95315, 95324, 95316, 95326, 95328

TWENTYNINE PALMS

DESERT TRAIL (THUR)
6396 Adobe Rd, Twentynine Palms, CA, 92277-2648, San Bernardino, USA; gen tel (760) 367-3577; gen fax (760) 367-1798; disp adv e-mail advertising@hidesertstar.com; class adv e-mail advertising@hidesertstar.com; ed e-mail news@deserttrail.com; web site www.hidesertstar.com/the_desert_trail/
Circulation: 3,500pd,; Sworn/Estimate/Non-Audited
Advertising rate: Open inch rate $16.50
Established: 1935
Group: Brehm Communications, Inc.
Hi-Desert Publishing Co., Inc.
Pub .... Cindy Melland
Ed./Gen. Mgr. .... Kurt Schauppner
Areas Served: 92277

VALLEY CENTER

VALLEY ROADRUNNER (THUR)
29115 Valley Center Rd, Ste L, Valley Center, CA, 92082-6553, San Diego, USA; gen tel (760) 749-1112; gen fax (760) 749-1688; disp adv e-mail advertising@valleycenter.com; class adv e-mail advertising@valleycenter.com; ed e-mail editor@valleycenter.com; web site www.valleycenter.com
Circulation: 3,600pd, 42fr; Sworn/Estimate/Non-Audited
Advertising rate: Open inch rate $14.00
Established: 1974
Group: Verican, Inc.
Digital Platform - Mobile: Apple, Android
Ed .... David Ross
Acct. Exec. .... Kimberly Nichols
Publisher .... Justin Salter
Delivery Method: Mail, Newsstand, Racks
Areas Served: 92082, 92061, 92060, 92059, 92026

VENTURA

VENTURA COUNTY REPORTER (THUR)
700 E Main St, Ventura, CA, 93001-2906, Ventura, USA; gen tel (805) 648-2244; adv tel (805) 648-2244 x 237; gen fax (805) 648-2245; disp adv e-mail diane@vcreporter.com; class adv e-mail tori@vcreporter.com; ed e-mail editor@vcreporter.com; web site www.vcreporter.com
Circulation: 33,000pd,; Sworn/Estimate/Non-Audited
Advertising rate: Open inch rate $35.00

Established: 1976
Group: Southland Publishing, Inc.
Pub. .... David Comden
Ed. .... Michael Sullivan
Mechanical Specifications: Type page 10 x 13; E - 5 cols, 1 5/8, between; A - 5 cols, 1 5/8, between; C - 6 cols, between.
Delivery Method: Racks
Areas Served: 93001, 93002, 93003, 93004, 93030, 93033, 93035, 93041, 93023, 93010, 93012, 91320, 91360, 91361, 91362

VICTORVILLE

HESPERIA STAR (TUES)
13891 Park Ave, Victorville, CA, 92392-2435, San Bernardino, USA; gen tel (760) 956-7827; adv tel (760) 956-7827; ed tel (760) 956-7827 x 224; gen fax (760) 956-6803; ed e-mail editor@hesperiastar.com; web site www.hesperiastar.com
Circulation: 20,000fr; Sworn/Estimate/Non-Audited
Advertising rate: Open inch rate $11.50
Group: Times Media Group
Ed. .... Peter Day
Areas Served: 92345

LUCERNE VALLEY LEADER (WED)
13891 Park Ave, Victorville, CA, 92392-2435, San Bernardino, USA; gen tel (760) 248-7878; gen fax (760) 248-2042; disp adv e-mail leader@lucernevalley.net; web site www.lucernevalleyleader.com
Circulation: 4,400pd,; Sworn/Estimate/Non-Audited
Advertising rate: Open inch rate $11.75
Established: 1956
Pub. .... Stephen Wringert
Adv. Mgr. .... Sheila Johnson
Ed. .... Kate Rosenburg
Mechanical Specifications: Type page 13 x 21 1/2; E - 6 cols, 2 1/16, between; A - 6 cols, 2 1/16, between; C - 6 cols, 2 1/16, between. Equipment & Software: Hardware — IBM; Software — Microsoft/Windows 98, Microsoft/Publisher.

WALNUT CREEK

LAMORINDA SUN (THUR)
2640 Shadelands Dr, Walnut Creek, CA, 94598-2513, Contra Costa, USA; gen tel (925) 935-2525; adv tel (925) 943-8119; ed tel (925) 943-8241; gen fax (925) 933-0239; adv fax (925) 933-0239; ed fax (925) 933-0239; disp adv e-mail ccretailads@cctimes.com; class adv e-mail dsmith@bayareanewsgroup.com; ed e-mail dbutler@bayareanewsgroup.com; web site www.contracostatimes.com/lafayette
Circulation: 11,000pd, 10fr; Sworn/Estimate/Non-Audited
Advertising rate: Open inch rate $25.85
Established: 1857
Group: The McClatchy Company
Digital Platform - Mobile: Apple, Android, Windows, Blackberry
Digital Platform - Tablet: Apple iOS, Android, Windows 7, Blackberry Tablet OS
Exec. Ed. .... Dave Butler
Ed. .... Samuel Richards
Editorial Asst. .... Lisa HerendeenEquipment & Software: Hardware — APP/Macs; Software — Microsoft/Word, QPS/QuarkXPress.
Delivery Method: Mail, Racks
Areas Served: 94549, 94556, 94563

WATERFORD

WATERFORD NEWS (TUES)
12717 Bentley St, Waterford, CA, 95386-9012, Stanislaus, USA; gen tel (209) 874-1927; gen fax (209) 358-7108; disp adv e-mail midvalleypub@aol.com; info@yahoo.com; web site waterfordnews.weebly.com
Circulation: 7,000fr; Sworn/Estimate/Non-Audited
Advertising rate: Open inch rate $11.95
Group: Mid Valley Publishing
Pub. .... John M. Derby
Ed. .... Paul Kelly
Areas Served: 95386

WEAVERVILLE

TRINITY JOURNAL (WED)
500 Main St, Weaverville, CA, 96093, Trinity, USA; gen tel (530) 623-2055; gen fax (530) 623-5382; disp adv e-mail tjads@trinityjournal.com; class adv e-mail tjads@trinityjournal.com; ed e-mail editor@trinityjournal.com; web site www.trinityjournal.com
Circulation: 3,730pd, 35fr; Sworn/Estimate/Non-Audited
Advertising rate: Open inch rate $10.25
Established: 1856
Group: WRA Enterprises, Inc.
Ed./Pub. .... Wayne Agner
Mechanical Specifications: Type page 11 x 20.5; E - 6 cols, 1 3/4, 1/6 between; A - 6 cols, 1 3/4, 1/6 between; C - 8 cols, 1 5/16, 1/6 between.Equipment & Software: Hardware — PCs; Software — InDesign CC PhotoShop CC
Delivery Method: Mail, Racks
Areas Served: Trinity County, CA

WEST COVINA

WEST COVINA HIGHLANDER (THUR)
1210 N Azusa Canyon Rd, West Covina, CA, 91790-1003, Los Angeles, USA; gen tel (626) 854-8700; adv tel (626) 962-8811; ed tel (626) 544-0990; gen fax (626) 854-8719; disp adv e-mail lauree.sierra@sgvn.com; class adv e-mail Carla.asmundson@sgvn.com; ed e-mail michael.anastasi@langnews.com; web site www.sgvtribune.com/highlanders
Circulation: 18,450fr; Sworn/Estimate/Non-Audited
Advertising rate: Open inch rate $17.65
Pres./Pub. .... Ron Hasse
Exec. Ed./VP .... Michael Anastasi
Mechanical Specifications: Type page 9 3/4 x 11 3/4; E - 5 cols, 2, 3/16 between; A - 5 cols, 2, 3/16 between; C - 10 cols, 2, 3/16 between.
Areas Served: 91790

WEST SACRAMENTO

THE NEWS-LEDGER (WED)
1040 W Capitol Ave, Ste B, West Sacramento, CA, 95691-2701, Yolo, USA; gen tel (916) 371-8030; adv tel (916) 371-8030; gen fax (916) 371-8055; web site www.news-ledger.com
Circulation: 2,100pd,; Sworn/Estimate/Non-Audited
Advertising rate: Open inch rate $5.75
Established: 1964
Editor...... Monica StarkEquipment & Software: Hardware — PC.
Delivery Method: Mail, Newsstand, Racks
Areas Served: 95691 95605

WILLITS

THE WILLITS NEWS (WED, FRI)
PO Box 628, Willits, CA, 95490-0628, Mendocino, USA; gen tel (707) 459-4643; adv tel (707) 456-9520; ed tel (707) 456-9520; gen fax (707) 459-1664; disp adv e-mail advertising@willitsnews.com; class adv e-mail classifieds@willitsnews.com; ed e-mail editorial@willitsnews.com; web site www.willitsnews.com
Circulation: 2,700pd,; Sworn/Estimate/Non-Audited
Advertising rate: Open inch rate $9.98
Established: 1903
Group: Digital First Media
Pub Emeritus .... Debbie Clark
Ed. .... KC Meadows
Kevin McConnell
Mechanical Specifications: Type page 11 5/8 x 21; E - 6 cols, 1 7/8, 1/8 between; A - 6 cols, 1 7/8, 1/8 between; C - 10 cols, 1, 1/8 between.Equipment & Software: ; Software — QPS/QuarkXPress 4.1, Adobe/InDesign 4.0.
Delivery Method: Mail, Newsstand, Racks
Areas Served: 95490, 95437, 95417, 95454, 95429

WINTERS

WINTERS EXPRESS (THUR)
13 Russell St, Winters, CA, 95694-1730, Yolo, USA; gen tel (530) 795-4551; disp adv e-mail ads@wintersexpress.com; class adv e-mail ads@wintersexpress.com; ed e-mail news@wintersexpress.com; web site www.wintersexpress.com
Circulation: 2,000pd, 100fr; Sworn/Estimate/Non-Audited
Advertising rate: Open inch rate $6.50
Established: 1884
Group: McNaughton Newspapers
Pub. .... Charles R. Wallace
Ed. .... Debra DeAngelo
Mechanical Specifications: Type page 11 15/16 x 21 1/2; E - 6 cols, 1 3/4, 1/6 between; A - 6 cols, 1 3/4, between; C - 10 cols, 1 1/6, 1/32 between.
Delivery Method: Mail, Newsstand, Carrier, Racks
Areas Served: 95694

WINTON

WINTON TIMES (THUR)
6950 Gerard Ave, Winton, CA, 95388, Merced, USA; gen tel (209) 358-5311; gen fax (209) 358-7108; disp adv e-mail info@midvalleypub.com
Circulation: 2,500pd, 50fr; Sworn/Estimate/Non-Audited
Advertising rate: Open inch rate $11.75
Group: Mid Valley Publishing
Pub. .... John M. Derby
Bookkeeper .... Kelly Thomas
Areas Served: 95388

WRIGHTWOOD

MOUNTAINEER PROGRESS (THUR)
3407 State Highway 2, Wrightwood, CA, 92397-9687, San Bernardino, USA; gen tel (760) 249-3245; gen fax (760) 249-4021; disp adv e-mail editorial@mtprogress.net; class adv e-mail displayads@mtprogress.net; ed e-mail newsroom@mtprogress.net; web site www.mtprogress.net
Circulation: 3,500pd, 1,200fr; Sworn/Estimate/Non-Audited
Advertising rate: Open inch rate $14.95
Established: 1961
Pub. .... Steve Rinek
Ed. .... Vicky Rinek
Areas Served: 92397, 92372, 92371, 92329

YUCAIPA

YUCAIPA & CALIMESA NEWS-MIRROR (FRI)
35154 Yucaipa Blvd, Yucaipa, CA, 92399-4339, San Bernardino, USA; gen tel (909) 797-9101; adv tel (909) 797-9101; gen fax (909) 797-0502; adv fax (909) 797-0502; disp adv e-mail advertising@newsmirror.net; class adv e-mail advertising@newsmirror.net; ed e-mail cteeters@newsmirror.net; web site www.newsmirror.net
Circulation: 0pd, 15,327fr; CVC
Advertising rate: Open inch rate $16.00
Group: Century Group Newspapers
Pub./VP .... Toebe Bush
Ed. .... Claire Teeters
Delivery Method: Mail, Newsstand, Carrier, Racks
Areas Served: 92399, 92320

YUCCA VALLEY

HI-DESERT STAR (WED, SAT)
56445 29 Palms Hwy, Yucca Valley, CA, 92284-2861, San Bernardino, USA; gen tel (760) 365-3315; gen fax (760) 365-8686; disp adv e-mail advertising@hidesertstar.com; class adv e-mail advertising@hidesertstar.com; ed e-mail editor@hidesertstar.com; web site www.hidesertstar.com
Circulation: 7,361pd, 75fr; Sworn/Estimate/Non-Audited
Advertising rate: Open inch rate $18.50
Group: Brehm Communications, Inc.
Hi-Desert Publishing Co., Inc.
Mktg. Dir. .... Cindy Melland
Mng. Ed. .... Stacy Moore
Mechanical Specifications: Type page 11 1/2 x 21 1/2; E - 6 cols, 2 1/16, 1/8 between; A - 6 cols, 2 1/16, 1/8 between; C - 9 cols, 1 1/4, 1/4 between.Equipment & Software: Hardware — APP/Mac; Presses — 8-G/Community; Software — QPS/QuarkXPress.
Areas Served: 92284, 92252, 92277, 92285

COLORADO

AKRON

AKRON NEWS-REPORTER (WED)
69 Main Ave, Akron, CO, 80720-1439, Washington, USA; gen tel (970) 345-2296; gen fax (970) 345-6638; disp adv e-mail mmcmahill@akronnewsreporter.com; class adv e-mail mmcmahill@akronnewsreporter.com; ed e-mail jbusing@akronnewsreporter.com; web site www.akronnewsreporter.com
Circulation: 2,000pd,; Sworn/Estimate/Non-Audited
Advertising rate: Open inch rate $5.75
Group: Digital First Media
Prairie Mountain Publishing
Pub. .... Iva Horner
Ed. .... JoAnne Busing
Mechanical Specifications: Type page 11 13/16 x 21 1/2; E - 6 cols, 1 13/16, 1/6 between; A - 6 cols, 1 13/16, 1/6 between; C - 9 cols, 1 13/16, 1/8 between.Equipment & Software: Hardware — APP/Mac; Software — 10-QPS/QuarkXPress 4.1, Adobe/InDesign, Adobe/Photoshop, Adobe/Illustrator.
Areas Served: 80720

ASPEN

SNOWMASS SUN (WED)
314 E Hyman Ave, Aspen, CO, 81611-1918, Pitkin, USA; gen tel (970) 923-5829; gen fax (970) 923-2571; disp adv e-mail afreitas@aspentimes.com; class adv e-mail classifieds@cmnm.org; ed e-mail news@snowmasssun.com; web site aspentimes.com/news/snowmass
Circulation: 2,000pd, 2,000fr; Sworn/Estimate/Non-Audited
Advertising rate: 1/16 Pg $52.75; 1/8 Pg $116.05; 1/4 Pg $237.38
Group: Swift Communications, Inc.
Adv. Acct. Mgr. .... Louise Walker
Ed. .... Laura Glendenning
Mng. Ed. .... Rick Carroll
Distrib. Mgr. .... Maria WimmerEquipment & Software: Hardware — APP/Power Mac; Software — Microsoft/Word, QPS/QuarkXPress.
Areas Served: 81615, 81611, 81612, 81656

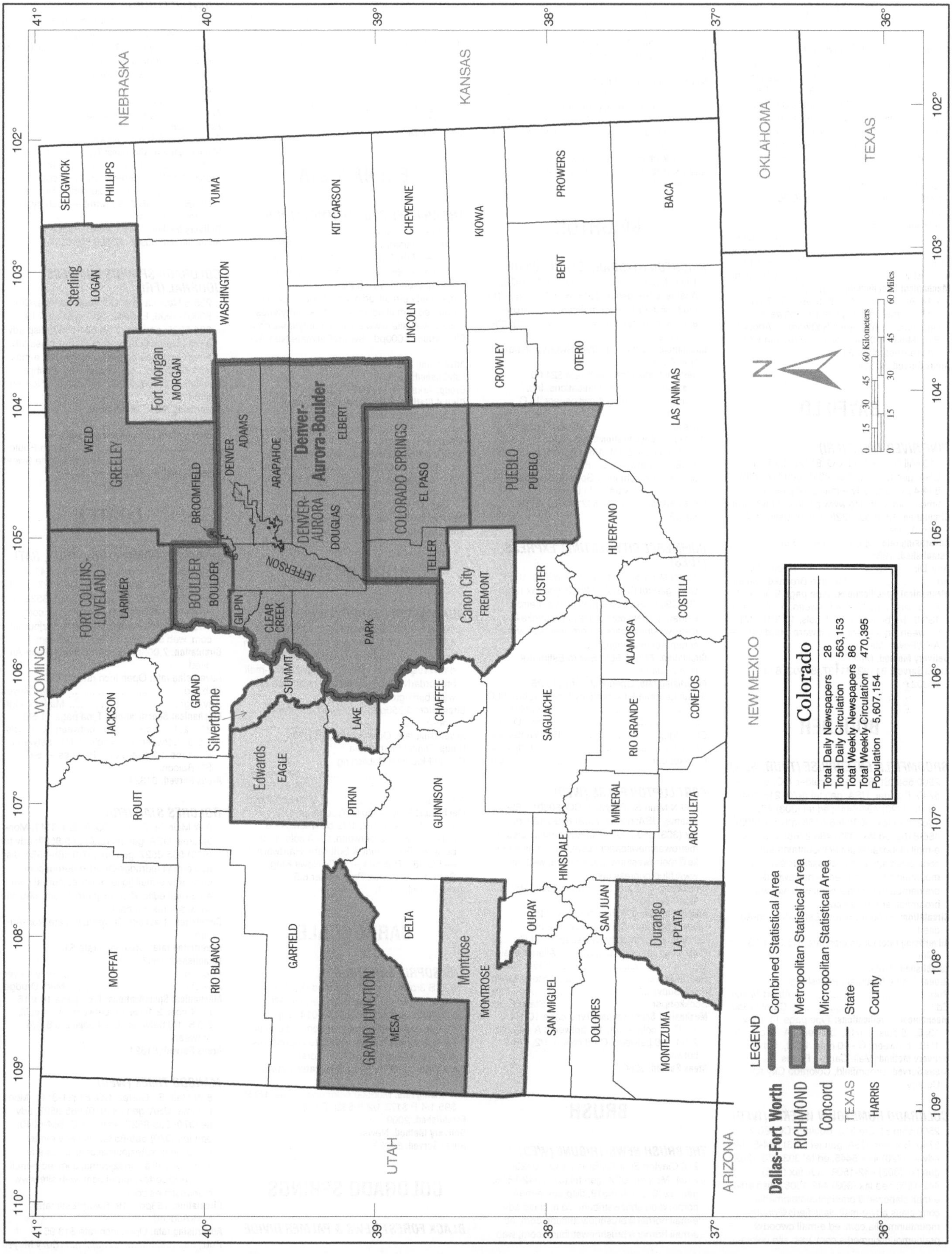
Colorado
Total Daily Newspapers 28
Total Daily Circulation 563,153
Total Weekly Newspapers 86
Total Weekly Circulation 470,395
Population 5,607,154
LEGEND
Dallas-Fort Worth Combined Statistical Area
RICHMOND Metropolitan Statistical Area
Concord Micropolitan Statistical Area
TEXAS State
HARRIS County
0 15 30 45 60 Kilometers
0 15 30 45 60 Miles
N
WYOMING
NEBRASKA
KANSAS
OKLAHOMA
TEXAS
NEW MEXICO
ARIZONA
UTAH
SEDGWICK
PHILLIPS
YUMA
KIT CARSON
CHEYENNE
KIOWA
PROWERS
BACA
Sterling
LOGAN
WASHINGTON
LINCOLN
BENT
Fort Morgan
MORGAN
CROWLEY
OTERO
LAS ANIMAS
WELD
GREELEY
BROOMFIELD
DENVER
ADAMS
ARAPAHOE
Denver-Aurora-Boulder
ELBERT
DENVER-AURORA
DOUGLAS
COLORADO SPRINGS
EL PASO
PUEBLO
PUEBLO
FORT COLLINS-LOVELAND
LARIMER
BOULDER
BOULDER
JEFFERSON
TELLER
Canon City
FREMONT
CUSTER
HUERFANO
COSTILLA
GILPIN
CLEAR CREEK
PARK
ALAMOSA
JACKSON
GRAND
SUMMIT
Silverthorne
LAKE
CHAFFEE
SAGUACHE
RIO GRANDE
CONEJOS
Edwards
EAGLE
ROUTT
PITKIN
GUNNISON
MINERAL
ARCHULETA
HINSDALE
MOFFAT
RIO BLANCO
GARFIELD
DELTA
Montrose
MONTROSE
OURAY
SAN JUAN
Durango
LA PLATA
GRAND JUNCTION
MESA
SAN MIGUEL
DOLORES
MONTEZUMA
41°
40°
39°
38°
37°
36°
102°
103°
104°
105°
106°
107°
108°
109°
110°

AURORA

AURORA SENTINEL (THUR)
12100 E Iliff Ave Ste 102, Suite 102, Aurora, CO, 80014-1277, Arapahoe, USA; gen tel (303) 750-7555; adv tel (303) 750-7555; ed tel (303) 750-7555; gen fax (303) 750-7699; adv fax (303) 750-7699; ed fax (720) 449-9033; disp adv e-mail advertising@aurorasentinel.com; class adv e-mail advertise@aurorasentinel.com; web site www.aurorasentinel.com
Circulation: 7,055pd,; CVC
Advertising rate: Modular 2x2 $240.00; 3x2 & 5x1 $359.00; 2x3 $480.00
Established: 1908
Pub...James Gold
Ed. ....Dave Perry
Mktg. Dir.....................................Melanie Coker
Mktg. Mgr. ....Lindsay Nicoletti
Mechanical Specifications: Type page 10 3/16 x 14; A - 5 cols, 1 7/8, between; C - 7 cols, 1 1/3, between.Equipment & Software: Hardware — APP/Mac; Software — Adobe/PageMaker 5.0, Macromedia/Freehand 3.0, Adobe/Photoshop 3.0.
Areas Served: 80014

BAYFIELD

PINE RIVER TIMES (FRI)
110 Mill St, Bayfield, CO, 81122, La Plata, USA; gen tel (970) 884-2331; gen fax (970) 884-4385; disp adv e-mail prt@pinerivertimes.com; web site www.pinerivertimes.com
Circulation: 1,800pd, 122fr; Sworn/Estimate/Non-Audited
Advertising rate: Open inch rate $8.00
Established: 1985
Adv. Dir.......................................Robert Mazur
Ed. ....Melanie Brubaker Mazur
Mechanical Specifications: Type page 9 3/4 x 13; E - 5 cols, 1 13/16, 1/4 between; A - 5 cols, 1 13/16, 1/4 between; C - 5 cols, 1 13/16, 1/4 between.Equipment & Software: Hardware — APP/Power Mac
Delivery Method: Mail
Areas Served: 81122, 81137, 81303, 81302, 81302

BOULDER

BROOMFIELD ENTERPRISE (THUR, SUN)
2500 55th St, Ste 210, Boulder, CO, 80301-5740, Boulder, USA; gen tel (970) 215-4943; adv tel (720) 494-5445; ed tel (303) 473-1362; gen fax (303) 466-8168; adv fax (303) 466-8168; ed fax (303) 466-8168; disp adv e-mail clabozan@prairiemountainmedia.com; class adv e-mail classifieds@prairiemountainmedia.com; ed e-mail cwood@prairiemountainmedia.com; web site www.broomfieldenterprise.com
Circulation: 20,000fr; Sworn/Estimate/Non-Audited
Advertising rate: Open inch rate $15.34 + $3 color
Established: 1975
Group: Prairie Mountain Publishing
Pub..Albert Manzi
Ed. ....Carol Wood
Mechanical Specifications: Type page 11 1/4 x 13; E - 5 cols, 2 1/18, between; A - 5 cols, 2 1/18, between; C - 10 cols, 1 1/3, between.
Delivery Method: Mail, Carrier, Racks
Areas Served: Broomfield, Colorado City and County

COLORADO HOMETOWN WEEKLY (WED)
2500 55th St, Ste 210, Boulder, CO, 80301-5740, Boulder, USA; gen tel (303) 684-5218; adv tel (720) 494-5445; ed tel 303-473-1362; gen fax (303) 442-1508 ; adv fax (303) 442-1508 ; ed fax (303) 442-1508 ; disp adv e-mail clabozan@prairiemountainmedia.com; class adv e-mail classifieds@prairiemountainmedia.com; ed e-mail cwood@prairiemountainmedia.com; web site coloradohometownweekly.com
Circulation: 6,000pd,; Sworn/Estimate/Non-Audited
Advertising rate: Open inch rate $14.50
Group: Prairie Mountain Media
Editor ....Carol Wood
Mechanical Specifications: Type page 10 1/4 x 16; E - 6 cols, 1 7/12, 1/6 between; A - 6 cols, 1 7/12, 1/6 between; C - 6 cols, 1 7/12, 1/6 between.Equipment & Software: Hardware — APP/Mac; Software — QPS/QuarkXPress, Baseview.
Delivery Method: Carrier, Racks
Areas Served: Erie, Lafayette, Louisville and Superior Colorado

BRIGHTON

BRIGHTON STANDARD BLADE (WED)
139 N Main St, Brighton, CO, 80601-1626, Adams, USA; gen tel (303) 659-2522; gen fax (303) 659-2901; ed e-mail news@metrowestnewspapers.com; web site www.thebrightonblade.com
Circulation: 3,718pd, 9,109fr; Sworn/Estimate/Non-Audited
Advertising rate: Open inch rate $24.00
Group: Landmark Communications, Inc.
Landmark Community Newspapers, LLC
editor and publisher.......................Beth Potter
assistant editor ....Chad Deutschman
Mechanical Specifications: Type page 10 1/4 x 13; E - 4 cols, 2 1/4, 1/6 between; A - 5 cols, 1 7/8, 1/6 between; C - 8 cols, 1 1/4, 1/6 between.Equipment & Software: Hardware — APP/Mac; Software — In Design.
Areas Served: 80601, 80602, 80603, 80640, 80022

COMMERCE CITY SENTINEL EXPRESS (TUES)
139 N Main St, Brighton, CO, 80601-1626, USA; gen tel (303) 659-2522; gen fax (303) 659-2901; disp adv e-mail jirsik@metrowestnewspapers.com; ed e-mail kdenke@metrowestnewspapers.com; web site www.commercecitysentinel.com
Circulation: 745pd, 56fr; Sworn/Estimate/Non-Audited
Advertising rate: Open inch rate $15.25
Group: Landmark Community Newspapers, LLC
Pub...Allen Messick
Ed. ....Kevin Denke
Circ. Mgr..................................Ben Wiebesick
Graphics ....Jody Irsik
Bookkeeper ....Stacy Ervin

FORT LUPTON PRESS (WED)
139 N Main St, Brighton, CO, 80601-1626, Adams, USA; gen tel (303) 659-2522; gen fax (303) 659-2901; disp adv e-mail news@metrowestnewspapers.com; ed e-mail kdenke@metrowestnewspapers.com; web site www.ftluptonpress.com
Circulation: 4,500pd, 35fr; Sworn/Estimate/Non-Audited
Advertising rate: Open inch rate $15.25
Group: Landmark Communications, Inc.
Landmark Community Newspapers, LLC
Pub...Allen Messick
Ed. ....Kevin Denke
Sports Ed......................................Steve Smith
Prod. Supvr. ....Jody Irsik
Bookkeeper ....Stacy Ervin
Mechanical Specifications: Type page 10 1/4 x 13; E - 4 cols, 2 1/4, 1/6 between; A - 4 cols, 2 1/4, 1/6 between; C - 6 cols, 1 1/2, 1/6 between.
Areas Served: 80601

BRUSH

THE BRUSH NEWS-TRIBUNE (WED)
216 Clayton St, # 12, Brush, CO, 80723-2104, Morgan, USA; gen tel (970) 842-5516; gen fax (970) 842-5519; disp adv e-mail horner@brushnewstribune.com; class adv e-mail horner@brushnewstribune.com; ed e-mail horner@brushnewstribune.com; web site www.brushnewstribune.com
Circulation: 1,000pd,; Sworn/Estimate/Non-Audited
Advertising rate: Open inch rate $6.70
Established: 1896
Group: Digital First Media
Prairie Mountain Publishing
Pub./Ed. ....Iva Kay Horner
Delivery Method: Mail, Newsstand, Carrier, Racks
Areas Served: 80723

BUENA VISTA

THE CHAFFEE COUNTY TIMES (THUR)
209 W Main St, Buena Vista, CO, 81211-9169, Chaffee, USA; gen tel (719) 395-8621; adv tel (719) 395-8621 x11; ed tel (719) 395-8621 x14; gen fax (719) 395-8623; disp adv e-mail ckennedy@chaffeecountytimes.com; class adv e-mail judie@chaffeecountytimes.com; ed e-mail editor@chaffeecountytimes.com; web site www.chaffeecountytimes.com
Circulation: 3,000pd,; Sworn/Estimate/Non-Audited
Advertising rate: Open inch rate $8.25
Established: 1879
Group: Arkansas Valley Publishing
Digital Platform - Mobile: Apple, Android
Digital Platform - Tablet: Apple iOS
Ed. ....Dave Schiefelbein
Advertising director.................Cristie Kennedy
Mechanical Specifications: Type page 10 1/2 x 16; E - 5 cols, 2, 1/6 between; A - 5 cols, 2, 1/6 between; C - 5 cols, 2, 1/6 between. Equipment & Software: ; Software — QPS/QuarkXPress, Microsoft/Excel.
Delivery Method: Mail, Newsstand, Racks
Areas Served: Northern Chaffee County

BURLINGTON

BURLINGTON RECORD (THUR)
202 S 14th St, Burlington, CO, 80807-2322, Kit Carson, USA; gen tel (719) 346-5381; gen fax (719) 346-5514; disp adv e-mail brecordadvertising@plainstel.com; class adv e-mail brecordadvertising@plainstel.com; web site www.burlington-record.com
Circulation: 3,350pd, 15fr; Sworn/Estimate/Non-Audited
Advertising rate: Open inch rate $7.10
Group: Digital First Media
Prairie Mountain Publishing
Pub...Rol Hudler
Ed. ....Lucky Gipe
Adv. Mgr...................................Shannon Floyd
Mechanical Specifications: Type page 15 1/4 x 21; E - 8 cols, 11/12, 1/72 between; A - 8 cols, 11/12, 1/72 between; C - 8 cols, 1/72 between.Equipment & Software: Hardware — PC 486; Presses — 4-KP/News King; Software — Adobe/PageMaker 6.5.
Areas Served: 80807

CARBONDALE

THE SOPRIS SUN (THUR)
520 S 3rd St, Unit 32, Carbondale, CO, 81623-2059, Garfield, USA; gen tel (970) 510-3003; adv tel (970) 379-7014; disp adv e-mail adssales@soprissun.com; ed e-mail news@soprissun.com; web site soprissun.com - 8,900(views) 2,600(visitors)
Circulation: 4,200fr; Sworn/Estimate/Non-Audited
Advertising rate: Modular color open rates: 1/8 P $95 1/4 P $175 1/2 P $320 Full $535
Established: 2009
Delivery Method: Newsstand
Areas Served: 81623

COLORADO SPRINGS

BLACK FOREST NEWS & PALMER DIVIDE PIONEER (THUR)
6520 Shoup Rd, Colorado Springs, CO, 80908-3865, El Paso, USA; gen tel (719) 495-5924; gen fax (719) 495-4367; disp adv e-mail blackforestnews@yahoo.com; ed e-mail editor@blackforestnews-co.com; web site www.blackforestnews-co.com
Circulation: 928pd, 77fr; USPS
Advertising rate: Open inch rate $6.25
Established: 1960
Group: Poor & Piglets Newspaper
Mechanical Specifications: Type page 10 1/5 x 15; E - 5 cols, 1 11/12, 1/6 between; A - 5 cols, 1 11/12, 1/6 between; C - 5 cols, 1 11/12, 1/6 between.Equipment & Software: Hardware — IBM; Software — Archetype/Corel Ventura 4.2.
Delivery Method: Mail, Carrier, Racks
Areas Served: 80908. 80106 80918

COLORADO SPRINGS BUSINESS JOURNAL (FRI)
235 S Nevada Ave, Colorado Springs, CO, 80903-1906, El Paso, USA; gen tel (719) 634-5905; gen fax (719) 634-5157; disp adv e-mail vanessa.nagel@csbj.com; class adv e-mail vanessa.nagel@csbj.com; ed e-mail editorial@csbj.com; web site www.csbj.com
Circulation: 2,100pd,; Sworn/Estimate/Non-Audited
Advertising rate: Call for rates
Established: 1989
Group: Colorado Publishing House
Exec. Ed.....................................Ralph Routon
Ed. ....Amy Gillentine Sweet
Areas Served: Pikes Peak region

CORTEZ

CORTEZ JOURNAL (TUES, THUR, SAT)
8 W Main St, Cortez, CO, 81321-3141, Montezuma, USA; gen tel (970) 565-8527; adv tel (970) 565-8527; gen fax (970) 565-8532; disp adv e-mail mdrudge@cortezjournal.com; class adv e-mail advertising@cortezjournal.com; web site www.cortezjournal.com
Circulation: 7,003pd,; Sworn/Estimate/Non-Audited
Advertising rate: Open inch rate $13.50
Pub./Ed. ....Suzy Meyer
Adv. Mgr......................................Mark Drudge
Mechanical Specifications: Type page 11 5/8 x 21 1/2; E - 6 cols, 1 5/6, between; A - 6 cols, 1 5/6, between; C - 8 cols, 1 1/3, between. Equipment & Software: ; Presses — 5-G/SC Balcon.
Areas Served: 81321

DOLORES STAR (FRI)
8 W Main St, Cortez, CO, 81321-3141, Montezuma, USA; gen tel (970) 565-8527; adv tel (970) 565-8527; gen fax (970) 565-8532; disp adv e-mail mdrudge@cortezjournal.com; class adv e-mail jjones@cortezjournal.com; ed e-mail editor@cortezjournal.com; web site www.doloresstar.com
Circulation: 1,400pd,; Sworn/Estimate/Non-Audited
Advertising rate: Open inch rate $13.50
Established: 1897
Pub./Ed. ....Suzy Meyer
Adv. Dir..Mark Drudge
Mechanical Specifications: Type page 10 x 16; E - 4 cols, 2 1/16, 1/6 between; A - 4 cols, 2 3/8, 1/6 between; C - 4 cols, 2 3/8, 1/6 between.
Areas Served: 81321

MANCOS TIMES (WED)
8 W Main St, Cortez, CO, 81321-3141, Montezuma, USA; gen tel (970) 565-8527; adv tel (970) 565-8527; ed tel (970) 564-6040; gen fax (970) 565-8532; disp adv e-mail mdrudge@cortezjournal.com; class adv e-mail vconti@cortezjournal.com; ed e-mail smeyer@cortezjournal.com; web site www.mancostimes.com
Circulation: 753pd, 11fr; Sworn/Estimate/Non-Audited
Advertising rate: Open inch rate $13.95
Pub..Suzy Meyer

Managing Ed. .... Russell Smyth
Circ. Mgr. .... Anita Weber
Mechanical Specifications: Type page 10 1/4 x 16; E - 5 cols, 1 11/12, 1/6 between; A - 5 cols, 1 11/12, 1/6 between; C - 5 cols, 1 11/12, 1/6 between.
Areas Served: 81321

CRESTED BUTTE

CRESTED BUTTE NEWS (THUR)

301 Belleview, Unit 6A, Crested Butte, CO, 81224-8706, Gunnison, USA; gen tel (970) 349-0500; adv tel (970) 349-0500 x 111; gen fax (970) 349-9876; disp adv e-mail nolan@crestedbuttenews.com; class adv e-mail classifieds@crestedbuttenews.com; ed e-mail editorial@crestedbuttenews.com; web site www.crestedbuttenews.com
Circulation: 5,000pd,; Sworn/Estimate/Non-Audited
Advertising rate: Open inch rate $10.30
Circ. Mgr. .... Melissa Ruch
Ed. .... Mark Reaman
Prodn. Mgr. .... Tyler Hansen
Adv. Rep. .... Jeff Nolan
Adv. Rep. .... Ashley Cahir
Areas Served: 81224

DEER TRAIL

TRI-COUNTY TRIBUNE (THUR)

625 2nd Ave, Deer Trail, CO, 80105-8078, Arapahoe, USA; gen tel (303) 769-4646; gen fax (303) 769-4650; disp adv e-mail rbell357@aol.com
Circulation: 450pd,; Sworn/Estimate/Non-Audited
Advertising rate: Open inch rate $3.50
Digital Platform - Mobile: Windows
Ed. .... Harry L. Venter
Mechanical Specifications: Type page 8 1/2 x 11; E - 4 cols, 1 5/6, 1/6 between; A - 4 cols, 1 5/6, 1/6 between; C - 4 cols, 1 5/6, 1/6 between.Equipment & Software: Hardware — 2-PC, 2-HP/Laser Printer; Software — Adobe/PageMaker.
Delivery Method: Mail, Newsstand

DENVER

COLORADO STATESMAN (THUR)

1001 16th St, B-180 Pmb 113,, Denver, CO, 80265-0005, Denver, USA; gen tel (303) 837-8600; gen fax (303) 837-9015; disp adv e-mail info@coloradostatesman.com; web site www.coloradostatesman.com
Circulation: 2,139pd, 5,000fr; Sworn/Estimate/Non-Audited
Advertising rate: Open inch rate $15
Established: 1898
Ed. .... Jody Hope Strogoff
Mechanical Specifications: Type page 10 1/4 x 16; E - 4 cols, 2 1/3, 1/3 between; A - 4 cols, 2 1/3, 1/3 between; C - 4 cols, 2 1/3, 1/3 between.Equipment & Software: Hardware — APP/Mac Quadra 630; Software — QPS/QuarkXPress 3.32, Microsoft/Word 6.0, Microsoft/Excel 5.0, Claris/FileMaker Pro.
Delivery Method: Mail, Newsstand
Areas Served: 80203

DENVER BUSINESS JOURNAL (FRI)

1700 Broadway, Ste 515, Denver, CO, 80290-1700, Denver, USA; gen tel (303) 803-9200; adv tel (303) 803-9250; ed tel (303) 803-9220; gen fax (303) 803-9203; disp adv e-mail djendrusch@bizjournals.com; class adv e-mail rhesterman@bizjournals.com; ed e-mail nwestergaard@bizjournals.com; web site www.denver.bizjournals.com
Advertising rate: Open inch rate $1975
Pub. .... Scott Bemis
Ed. .... Neil Westergaard
Areas Served: Denver County

EADS

KIOWA COUNTY PRESS (FRI)

1208 Maine St, Eads, CO, 81036-9900, Kiowa, USA; gen tel (719) 438-5800; disp adv e-mail press@kiowacountypress.com; web site www.kiowacountypress.com
Circulation: 800pd,; Sworn/Estimate/Non-Audited
Advertising rate: Open inch rate $5.80
Pub. .... Chris Sorensen
Ed. .... Connie McPherson
Mechanical Specifications: Type page 8 x 10 1/2; E - 5 cols, 1 1/2, 1/10 between; A - 5 cols, 1 1/2, 1/10 between; C - 5 cols, 1 1/2, 1/10 between.Equipment & Software: Hardware — PC; Software — Archetype/Corel Ventura 10.0, Archetype/Corel Draw 8.0.
Areas Served: 81036

EATON

NORTH WELD HERALD (THUR)

216 1st St Ste H, Suite H, Eaton, CO, 80615-3598, Weld, USA; gen tel (970) 454-5551; disp adv e-mail nwh@ltbroadband.net; web site nwherald.qwestoffice.net
Circulation: 1,950pd,; Sworn/Estimate/Non-Audited
Advertising rate: Open inch rate $10.00
Gen. Mgr. .... Brenda L. Bormann
Ed. .... Bruce J. Bormann
Areas Served: 80615

ESTES PARK

ESTES PARK TRAIL-GAZETTE (WED, FRI)

251 Moraine Ave, Estes Park, CO, 80517, Larimer, USA; gen tel (970) 586-3356; gen fax (970) 586-9532; disp adv e-mail sales@eptrail.com; ed e-mail tgeditor@eptrail.com; web site www.eptrail.com
Circulation: 2,660pd, 296fr; Sworn/Estimate/Non-Audited
Advertising rate: Open inch rate $11.18 (Wed); $13.65 (Fri)
Established: 1922
Group: Digital First Media
Pub. .... Mike Romero
Adv. Mgr. .... Keith Kratochvil
Prodn. Mgr. .... Tony Wedick
Mng. Ed. .... Scott Rowen
News Ed. .... David Persons
Adv. Sales Rep. .... Mike O'Flaherty
Mechanical Specifications: Type page 11 1/2 x 20 1/2; E - 6 cols, 1 3/4, 1/6 between; A - 6 cols, 1 3/4, 1/6 between; C - 8 cols, 1 1/2, 1/6 between.Equipment & Software: Hardware — APP/Mac
Delivery Method: Mail, Newsstand, Racks
Areas Served: 80517

EVERGREEN

COLUMBINE COURIER (WED)

27902 Meadow Dr, Unit 200, Evergreen, CO, 80439-2106, Jefferson, USA; gen tel (303) 933-2233; adv tel (303) 933-2233 x 13; gen fax (303) 674-5534; disp adv e-mail columbinesales@evergreenco.com; class adv e-mail columbinesales@evergreenco.com; web site www.columbinecourier.com
Circulation: 30,000fr; Sworn/Estimate/Non-Audited
Advertising rate: Open inch rate $25.44
Established: 1989
Group: Landmark Communications, Inc.
Pub. .... Teresa Willmann
Adv. Dir. .... John Libby
Ed. .... Doug Bell
Prodn. Mgr. .... Tom Fidley
Mechanical Specifications: Type page 10 1/8 x 13 1/2; E - 5 cols, 1 7/8, 1/16 between; A - 5 cols, 2 1/16, 1/16 between; C - 6 cols, 1 1/2, 1/16 between.Equipment & Software: Hardware — APP/Macs, APP/Power Mac; Software — Macromedia/Freehand 5.0, Adobe/PageMaker 5.1.
Areas Served: 80120

THE CANYON COURIER (WED)

27902 Meadow Dr, Unit 200, Evergreen, CO, 80439-2106, Jefferson, USA; gen tel (303) 350-1039; adv tel (303) 350-1045; ed tel (303) 350-1045; gen fax (303) 674-4104 ; adv fax (303) 674-4104 ; ed fax (303) 674-4104 ; disp adv e-mail sales@evergreenco.com; class adv e-mail sales@evergreenco.com; ed e-mail circulation@canyoncourier.com; web site www.canyoncourier.com
Circulation: 9,500pd,; Sworn/Estimate/Non-Audited
Advertising rate: Open inch rate $14.65
Established: 1958
Group: Landmark Community Newspapers, LLC
Digital Platform - Mobile: Apple, Android, Blackberry
Digital Platform - Tablet: Apple iOS, Android, Blackberry Tablet OS
Pub./Ed. .... Vern Manning
Delivery Method: Mail, Racks
Areas Served: 80439

FLAGLER

VERISON (THUR)

321 Main Ave, Flagler, CO, 80815-9237, Kit Carson, USA; gen tel (719) 349-4448; adv tel (719) 349-4448; ed tel (719) 349-4448; gen fax (719) 349-4448; adv fax (719) 349-4448; ed fax (719) 349-4448; disp adv e-mail advertise@milesaver.com
Circulation: 1,400pd, 60fr; Sworn/Estimate/Non-Audited
Advertising rate: Open inch rate $2.75
Established: 1911
Group: TBP Publishing, Inc.
Ed. .... Thomas E. Bredehoft
Delivery Method: Mail, Racks
Areas Served: 80815

FLORENCE

THE FLORENCE CITIZEN (THUR)

201 E 2nd St, Florence, CO, 81226-1518, Fremont, USA; gen tel (719) 784-6383; disp adv e-mail florencecitizen@aol.com; web site facebook.com/The-Florence-Citizen-157955437616961
Circulation: 900pd, 35fr; Sworn/Estimate/Non-Audited
Advertising rate: Open inch rate $8.00
Established: 1898
Ed. .... Robert Wood
Mechanical Specifications: Type page 10 1/4 x 15 3/4; E - 6 cols, 1 1/2, 1/6 between; A - 6 cols, 1 1/2, 1/6 between; C - 6 cols, 1 1/2, 1/6 between.
Areas Served: 81226, 81212, 81240, 81244, 81253

FORT COLLINS

WINDSOR BEACON (WED, FRI)

1300 Riverside Ave, Fort Collins, CO, 80524-4353, Larimer, USA; gen tel (970) 686-9646; adv tel (970) 416-3989; ed tel (970) 224-7755; gen fax (970) 686-9647; disp adv e-mail jkurtyak@coloradoan.com; class adv e-mail jkurtyak@coloradoan.com; ed e-mail editor@windsorbeacon.com; web site www.coloradoan.com/windsor-beacon
Circulation: 0pd, 5,914fr; CAC
Advertising rate: 1/6 Pg $166.00; 1/3 Pg $325.00; 1/2 Pg $387.00
Established: 1806
Group: Gannett
Pub./Ed. .... David Persons
Adv. Rep. .... Mary Bline
Adv. Rep. .... Jack Bline
Mechanical Specifications: Type page 10 1/3 x 15 1/2; E - 6 cols, 1/8, 1/6 between; A - 6 cols, 1/8, 1/6 between; C - 10 cols, 1/5, 1/6 between.Equipment & Software: Hardware — APP/Mac; Software — QPS/QuarkXPress 4.0, Microsoft/Word 5.1, Adobe/Photoshop 5.5.
Areas Served: 80550, 80528

FORT MORGAN

MORGAN TIMES REVIEW (WED)

230 Main St, Fort Morgan, CO, 80701-2107, Morgan, USA; gen tel (970) 867-5651; gen fax (970) 867-7448; disp adv e-mail jtonsing@fmtimes.com; class adv e-mail ecpcadvertising@dailycamera.com; ed e-mail editor@fmtimes.com; web site www.fortmorgantimes.com
Circulation: 6,400fr; Sworn/Estimate/Non-Audited
Advertising rate: Open inch rate $10.75
Established: 1884
Pub. .... Julie Tonsing
Ed. .... Thomas Martinez
Circ. Mgr. .... Josephina Monsivias
Mechanical Specifications: Type page 11 5/6 x 21 1/2; E - 6 cols, 1 5/6, 1/6 between; A - 6 cols, 1 5/6, 1/6 between; C - 6 cols, 1 5/6, 1/6 between.
Areas Served: 80701

FOUNTAIN

EL PASO COUNTY ADVERTISER & NEWS (WED)

120 E Ohio Ave, Fountain, CO, 80817-2230, El Paso, USA; gen tel (719) 382-5611; gen fax (719) 382-5614; disp adv e-mail news@epcan.com; class adv e-mail ads@epcan.com; ed e-mail news@epcan.com; web site www.epcan.com
Circulation: 4,500pd, 22fr; Sworn/Estimate/Non-Audited
Advertising rate: Open inch rate $10.00
Established: 1958
Group: Shopper Press, Inc.
Mng. Ed. .... Patricia St. Louis
General Manager .... Karen Johnson
Mechanical Specifications: Type page 10 1/2 x 16; E - 7 cols, 1 5/12, between; A - 7 cols, 1 5/12, between; C - 7 cols, 1 5/12, between. Equipment & Software: Hardware — IBM; Software — Adobe/PageMaker 5.0, Microsoft/Windows.
Delivery Method: Mail, Newsstand, Carrier, Racks
Areas Served: El Paso County

FOWLER

THE FOWLER TRIBUNE (THUR)

112 E Cranston Ave, Fowler, CO, 81039-1119, Otero, USA; gen tel (719) 263-5311; adv tel (719) 384-1430; ed tel (719) 263-5311; gen fax (719) 263-5900; disp adv e-mail jason@ljtdmail.com; ed e-mail fowlereditor@ljtdmail.com; web site www.fowlertribune.com
Circulation: 1,475pd,; Sworn/Estimate/Non-Audited
Advertising rate: Open inch rate $4.95
Group: GateHouse Media, Inc.
Pub. .... Candi Hill
Multimedia Sales Exec. .... Jason Gallegos
Sports Ed. .... Ken Hamrick
Fowler Tribune Office Mgr. .... Pam Spitzer
Class. Adv. .... Rita Ojeda
Areas Served: 81039

GLENWOOD SPRINGS

CITIZEN TELEGRAM (THUR)

824 Grand Ave, Glenwood Springs, CO, 81601-3557, Garfield, USA; gen tel (970) 945-8515; ed tel (970) 384-9114; gen fax (970) 945-8518; disp adv e-mail laurie@citizentelegram.com; class adv e-mail laurie@citizentelegram.com; ed e-mail news@

citizentelegram.com; web site www.postindependent.com
Circulation: 2,858pd, 158fr; Sworn/Estimate/Non-Audited
Advertising rate: 1/32 Pg $22.26; 1/16 Pg $55.65; 1/8 Pg $122.43
Group: Swift Communications, Inc.
Pub./Ed. .... Randy Essex
Circ. Dir. .... Jake Marine
Adv. Dir. .... Brad Howard
Ed. .... Alex Zorn
Areas Served: 81650

GOLDEN

ARVADA PRESS (THUR)

722 Washington Ave Unit 210, Suite 210, Golden, CO, 80401-5876, Jefferson, USA; gen tel (303) 566-4100; adv tel (303) 566-4074; ed tel (303) 566-4127; gen fax (303) 468-2592; disp adv e-mail sales@milehighnews.com; class adv e-mail audreyb@milehighnews.com; ed e-mail mkelly@ourcoloradonews.com; web site arvadapress.com
Circulation: 37,200pd, 34,603fr; Sworn/Estimate/Non-Audited
Advertising rate: 1/16 Pg $295.00; 1/8 Pg $534.00; 1/4 Pg $961.00
Group: Colorado Community Media
Pres. / Pub. .... Jerry Healey
Circ. Mgr. .... Robin Sant
Dir, Sales/Mktg. .... Cari Witzel
Adv. Mgr. .... Barb Stolte
Mng. Ed. .... Glenn Wallace
Class. Sales .... Karen Earhart
Areas Served: 80403

GOLDEN TRANSCRIPT (THUR)

722 Washington Ave Unit 210, Unit 210, Golden, CO, 80401-5876, Jefferson, USA; gen tel (303) 566-4100; adv tel (303) 566-4074; gen fax (303) 566-4098; disp adv e-mail eaddenbrooke@coloradocommunitymedia.com; class adv e-mail kearhart@coloradocommunitymedia.com; ed e-mail gwallace@coloradocommunitymedia.com; web site www.goldentranscript.net
Circulation: 2,084pd, 1,936fr; Sworn/Estimate/Non-Audited
Established: 1866
Group: Colorado Community Media
Milehigh NewspapersKaren Earhart
Adv. Mgr. .... Mindy Nelon
Pres./Pub. .... Jerry Healey
Mng. Ed. .... Glenn Wallace
Mechanical Specifications: Type page 10 1/4 x 14; E - 5 cols, 1 7/8, 1/8 between; A - 5 cols, 1 7/8, 1/8 between; C - 6 cols, 1 5/16, 1/8 between.Equipment & Software: Hardware — APP/Mac G5, APP/Mac G4; Software — Adobe, In Design, Baseview.
Delivery Method: Mail, Carrier, Racks
Areas Served: 80401, 80403

LAKEWOOD SENTINEL (THUR)

722 Washington Ave Unit 210, Unit 210, Golden, CO, 80401-5876, Jefferson, USA; gen tel (303) 566-4100; adv tel (303) 566-4074; ed tel (303) 566-4127; gen fax (303) 468-2592; disp adv e-mail sales@milehighnews.com; class adv e-mail audreyb@milehighnews.com; ed e-mail mkelly@ourcoloradonews.com; web site www.ourcoloradonews.com
Circulation: 437pd, 14,474fr; Sworn/Estimate/Non-Audited
Advertising rate: 1/16 Pg $198.00; 1/8 Pg $347.00; 1/4 Pg $615.00
Group: Colorado Community Media
Milehigh Newspapers
Mng. Ed. .... Glenn Wallace
Pres./Pub. .... Jerry Healey
Adv. Mgr. .... Mindy Nelon
Class. Sales Mgr. .... Karen Earhart
Areas Served: 80403

WHEAT RIDGE TRANSCRIPT (THUR)

722 Washington Ave Unit 210, Unit 210, Golden, CO, 80401-5876, Jefferson, USA; gen tel (303) 566-4100; adv tel (303) 566-4074; gen fax (303) 566-4098; disp adv e-mail eaddenbrooke@coloradocommunitymedia.com; class adv e-mail kearhart@coloradocommunitymedia.com; ed e-mail gwallace@coloradocommunitymedia.com; web site www.goldentranscript.net
Circulation: 2,084pd, 1,936fr; Sworn/Estimate/Non-Audited
Established: 1866
Group: Colorado Community Media
Milehigh NewspapersKaren Earhart
Adv. Mgr. .... Mindy Nelon
Pres./Pub. .... Jerry Healey
Mng. Ed. .... Glenn Wallace
Delivery Method: Mail, Carrier, Racks
Areas Served: 80401, 80403

GRANBY

SKY-HI NEWS (WED, FRI)

424 Agate Ave E, Granby, CO, 80446, Grand, USA; gen tel (970) 887-3334; adv tel (970) 887-3334 x 13700; ed tel (970) 887-3334 x 19603; gen fax (970) 887-3204; disp adv e-mail esimmins@skyhinews.com; class adv e-mail classifieds@skyhidailynews.com; ed e-mail bmartin@skyhidailynews.com; web site www.skyhinews.com
Circulation: 5,500fr; Sworn/Estimate/Non-Audited
Group: Swift Communications, Inc.
Pub. .... Meg Boyer
Adv. Mgr. .... Emma Simmins
Areas Served: 80446

GUNNISON

GUNNISON COUNTRY TIMES (THUR)

218 N Wisconsin St, Gunnison, CO, 81230-2626, Gunnison, USA; gen tel (970) 641-1414; adv tel (970) 641-1414; ed tel (970) 641-1414; gen fax N//A; adv fax N/A; ed fax N/A; disp adv e-mail bobbie@gunnisontimes.com; class adv e-mail classifieds@gunnisontimes.com; ed e-mail editor@gunnisontimes.com; web site www.gunnisontimes.com
Circulation: 4,000pd,; Sworn/Estimate/Non-Audited
Advertising rate: Open inch rate $10.50
Established: 1865
Digital Platform - Mobile: Apple, Android, Windows
Digital Platform - Tablet: Apple iOS, Android, Windows 7, Blackberry Tablet OS, Kindle
Pub./Own. .... Chris Dickey
Ed. .... Will Shoemaker
Mechanical Specifications: Type page 10 x 16; E - 5 cols, 1 15/16, 3/16 between; A - 5 cols, 1 15/16, 3/16 between; C - 5 cols, 1 15/16, 3/16 between.
Delivery Method: Mail, Newsstand, Racks
Areas Served: 81230

GYPSUM

THE EAGLE VALLEY ENTERPRISE (THUR)

200 Lindbergh Drive, Gypsum, CO, 81637, Eagle, USA; gen tel (970) 328-6656; adv tel (970) 328-6656; ed tel (970) 328-6656; gen fax (970) 328-6393; disp adv e-mail cbukovich@vaildaily.com; class adv e-mail pschultz@eaglevalleyenterprise.com; ed e-mail pboyd@eaglevalleyenterprise.com; web site www.eaglevalleyenterprise.com
Circulation: 3,400pd, 300fr; Sworn/Estimate/Non-Audited
Advertising rate: 1/32 Pg $22.26; 1/16 Pg $55.65; 1/8 Pg $122.43
Group: Swift Communications, Inc.
Pub. .... Mark Wurzer
Adv. Dir. .... Patrick Connolly
Circ. Mgr. .... David Hakes
Ed. .... Pam Boyd
Display Adv. Rep. .... Carole Bukovich
Areas Served: 81631

HIGHLANDS RANCH

CASTLE ROCK NEWS PRESS (THUR)

9137 RIDGELINE BLVD STE 210, Suite 210, HIGHLANDS RANCH, CO, 80129-2394, Douglas, USA; gen tel (303) 566-4100; adv tel (303) 566-4092; gen fax (303) 566-4098; disp adv e-mail jherbert@ourcoloradonews.com; class adv e-mail kearhart@ourcoloradonews.com; web site castlerocknewspress.net
Circulation: 15,654fr; CVC
Advertising rate: Open inch rate $38.50
Group: Colorado Community Media
Milehigh Newspapers
Pres/ Pub. .... Jerry Healey
Mng. Ed. .... Chris Rotar
Class. Sales .... Karen Earhart
Adv. Mgr. .... Maureen Shively
Areas Served: 80104, 80108, 80109

HAXTUN

HAXTUN-FLEMING HERALD (WED)

217 S COLORADO AVE, Haxtun, CO, 80731, Phillips, USA; gen tel (970) 774-6118; gen fax (970) 774-7690; disp adv e-mail ads@hfherald.com; web site www.hfherald.com
Circulation: 1,000pd, 50fr; Sworn/Estimate/Non-Audited
Advertising rate: Open inch rate $5.75
Co-Pub./Own./Mng. Ed./ Adv. Rep. .... Candie Salyards
Co-Pub./Own./Office Mgr./Adv. Mgr. .... Spring Atchison
Mechanical Specifications: Type page 10 1/2 x 13; E - 5 cols, 2, 1/6 between; A - 5 cols, 2, 1/6 between; C - 5 cols, 2, 1/6 between. Equipment & Software: Hardware — 2-APP/Power Mac, 3-APP/iMac, 1-APP/Mac Cube; Software — Microsoft/Word 6.0, Adobe/PageMaker 6.0.
Areas Served: 80731

HIGHLANDS RANCH

CENTENNIAL CITIZEN (FRI)

9137 Ridgeline Blvd Ste 210, Suite 210, Highlands Ranch, CO, 80129-2752, Douglas, USA; gen tel (303) 566-4100; adv tel (303) 566-4074; ed tel (303) 566-4102; gen fax (303) 566-4098; disp adv e-mail eaddenbrooke@ourcoloradonews.com; class adv e-mail kearhart@ourcoloradonews.com; ed e-mail crotar@ourcoloradonews.com; web site centennialcitizen.net
Circulation: 19pd, 12,441fr; CVC
Advertising rate: 1/16 Pg $198.00; 1/8 Pg $347.00; 1/4 Pg $615.00
Group: Colorado Community Media
Mng. Ed. .... Chris Rotar
Pub. .... Jerry Healey
Class. Sales .... Karen Earhart
Adv. Mgr. .... Dawn Brandt
Delivery Method: Carrier
Areas Served: 80122, 80120, 80123

DOUGLAS COUNTY NEWS PRESS (THUR)

9137 Ridgeline Blvd Ste 210, Suite 210, Highlands Ranch, CO, 80129-2752, Douglas, USA; gen tel (303) 566-4100; adv tel (303) 566-4074; ed tel (303) 566-4102; gen fax (303) 660-4826; disp adv e-mail eaddenbrooke@ourcoloradonews.com; class adv e-mail kearhart@ourcoloradonews.com; ed e-mail crotar@ourcoloradonews.com; web site douglascountynewspress.net
Circulation: 554pd, 376fr; CVC
Advertising rate: 1/16 Pg $231.00; 1/8 Pg $407.00; 1/4 Pg $723.00
Group: Colorado Community Media
Ed. .... Chris Rotar
Adv. Dir. .... Erin Addenbrooke
Circ. Mgr. .... Sandra Arellano
Pub. .... Jerry Healey
Class. Sales .... Karen Earhart
Mechanical Specifications: Type page 11 5/8 x 22 3/4; E - 6 cols, 2, 1/6 between; A - 6 cols, 2, 1/6 between; C - 8 cols, 1 2/3, 1/6 between. Equipment & Software: Hardware — APP/Mac G4; Presses — G/Suburban; Software — QPS/QuarkXPress 5.0.
Areas Served: 80129

ELBERT COUNTY NEWS (THUR)

9137 Ridgeline Blvd Ste 210, Suite 210, Highlands Ranch, CO, 80129-2752, Douglas, USA; gen tel (303) 566-4100; adv tel (303) 566-4074; ed tel (303) 566-4102; gen fax (303) 566-4098; adv fax (303) 566-4098; disp adv e-mail eaddenbrooke@coloradocommunitymedia.com; class adv e-mail kearhart@coloradocommunitymedia.com; ed e-mail crotar@coloradocommunitymedia.com; web site www.elbertcountynews.net
Circulation: 376pd, 26fr; CVC
Group: Colorado Community Media
Mng. Ed. .... Chris Rotar
Adv. Dir. .... Erin Addenbrooke
Pub. .... Jerry Healey
Class. Sales .... Karen Earhart
Delivery Method: Mail, Carrier, Racks
Areas Served: 80107, 80117

HIGHLANDS RANCH HERALD (THUR)

9137 Ridgeline Blvd Ste 210, Suite 210, Highlands Ranch, CO, 80129-2752, Douglas, USA; gen tel (303) 566-4100; adv tel (303) 566-4078; ed tel (303) 566-4102; gen fax (303) 794-1909; disp adv e-mail eaddenbrooke@ourcoloradonews.com; class adv e-mail kearhart@ourcoloradonews.com; ed e-mail crotar@ourcoloradonews.com; web site highlandsranchherald.net
Circulation: 9pd, 27,493fr; CVC
Advertising rate: 1/16 Pg $253.00; 1/8 Pg $445.00; 1/4 Pg $792.00
Group: Colorado Community Media
Mng. Ed. .... Chris Rotar
Adv. Dir. .... Erin Addenbrooke
Class. Sales .... Karen Earhart
Adv. Mgr. .... Maureen Shively
Pub. .... Jerry Healey
Mechanical Specifications: Type page 11 5/8 x 21 1/2; E - 6 cols, 2, between; A - 6 cols, 2, between; C - 8 cols, 1 3/4, between.Equipment & Software: Hardware — APP/Mac; Software — QPS/QuarkXPress, QPS/Copy-Desk, Microsoft/Word, Adobe/Photoshop, Adobe/Illustrator.
Areas Served: 80129

LONE TREE VOICE (THUR)

9137 Ridgeline Blvd Ste 210, Suite 210, Highlands Ranch, CO, 80129-2752, Douglas, USA; gen tel (303) 566-4100; adv tel (303) 566-4074; ed tel (303) 566-4102; gen fax (303) 566-4089; disp adv e-mail eaddenbrooke@ourcoloradonews.com; class adv e-mail vortega@ourcoloradonews.com; ed e-mail crotar@ourcoloradonews.com; web site www.ourlonetreenews.com
Circulation: 7pd, 5,469fr; CVC
Advertising rate: 1/8 Pg $189.00; 1/4 Pg $331.00; 1/2 Pg $586.00
Group: Colorado Community Media
Mng. Ed. .... Chris Rotar
Adv. Mgr. .... Erin Addenbrooke
Owner .... Jerry Healey
Adv. Mgr. .... Roy Schuster
Class. Sales .... Karen Earhart
Mechanical Specifications: 6 column format - 10.25" wide
Delivery Method: Carrier, Racks
Areas Served: Douglas County

PARKER CHRONICLE (FRI)

9137 Ridgeline Blvd Ste 210, Suite 210, Highlands Ranch, CO, 80129-2752, Douglas, USA; gen tel (303) 566-4100; adv tel (303) 566-4075; ed tel (303) 566-4102; gen fax (303) 566-4098; disp adv e-mail rmitchell@ourcoloradonews.com; class adv e-mail vortega@ourcoloradonews.com; ed e-mail crotar@ourcoloradonews.com; web site parkerchronicle.net
Circulation: 12pd, 20,129fr; CVC
Advertising rate: 1/8 Pg $407.00; 1/4 Pg $723.00; 1/2 Pg $1292.00
Established: 2001

Group: Colorado Community Media
Mng. Ed....Chris Rotar
Adv. Dir....Erin Addenbrooke
Circ. Mgr....Sandra Arellano
Pub....Jerry Healey
Adv. Rep....Roy Schuster
Class. Sales....Karen Earhart
Delivery Method: Carrier
Areas Served: 80134; 80138

THE ENGLEWOOD HERALD (FRI)

9137 Ridgeline Blvd Ste 210, Suite 210, Highlands Ranch, CO, 80129-2752, Douglas, USA; gen tel (303) 566-4100; adv tel (303) 566-4074; ed tel (303) 566-4102; gen fax (303) 566-4099; disp adv e-mail eaddenbrooke@coloradocommunitymedia.com; class adv e-mail kearhart@ourcoloradonews.com; ed e-mail crotar@ourcoloradonews.com; web site www.englewoodherald.net
Circulation: 296pd, 178fr; CVC
Group: Colorado Community Media
Milehigh Newspapers
Adv. Dir....Erin Addenbrooke
Karen Earhart
Adv. Rep....Dawn Brandt
Mng. Ed....Chris Rotar
Mechanical Specifications: Type page 11 5/8 x 21 1/2; E - 6 cols, 1 5/6, between; A - 6 cols, 1 5/6, between; C - 8 cols, between. Equipment & Software: Hardware — APP/Macs; Software — Adobe/Photoshop, QPS/QuarkXPress.
Delivery Method: Mail, Carrier, Racks
Areas Served: 80110, 80113

THE LITTLETON INDEPENDENT (THUR)

9137 Ridgeline Blvd Ste 210, Suite 210, Highlands Ranch, CO, 80129-2752, Douglas, USA; gen tel (303) 566-4100; adv tel (303) 566-4073; ed tel (303) 566-4102; gen fax (303) 566-4099; disp adv e-mail cwoodman@ourcoloradonews.com; class adv e-mail vortega@ourcoloradonews.com; ed e-mail crotar@ourcoloradonews.com; web site littletonindependent.net
Circulation: 1,407pd, 236fr; CVC
Advertising rate: 1/8 Pg $189.00; 1/4 Pg $331.00; 1/2 Pg $586.00
Group: Colorado Community Media
Mng. Ed....Chris Rotar
Circ. Mgr....Sandra Arellano
Adv. Dir....Erin Addenbrooke
Jerry Healey
Adv. Rep....Dawn Brandt
Class. Sales....Karen Earhart
Mechanical Specifications: 6 column format - 10.25" wide Equipment & Software: Hardware — APP/Mac; Software — QPS/QuarkXPress 3.3, Adobe/Photoshop 4.0.
Delivery Method: Mail, Racks
Areas Served: Douglas County

HOLYOKE

HOLYOKE ENTERPRISE (THUR)

130 N Interocean Ave, Holyoke, CO, 80734-1013, Phillips, USA; gen tel (970) 854-2811; gen fax (970) 854-2232; disp adv e-mail bbholent@chase3000.com; web site www.holyokeenterprise.com
Circulation: 1,470pd, 40fr; Sworn/Estimate/Non-Audited
Advertising rate: Open inch rate $9.00
Established: 1900
Group: Johnson Publications
Digital Platform - Tablet: Kindle
Pub./Adv. Mgr....Brenda Brandt
Circ. Mgr....Ashley Sullivan
Accounting....Lori PankoninEquipment & Software: Hardware — APP/Mac; Presses — KP/News King; Software — Adobe/InDesign
Delivery Method: Mail, Newsstand
Areas Served: 80734, 80721, 80731, 80746

IDAHO SPRINGS

CLEAR CREEK COURANT (WED)

1639 Miner St., Idaho Springs, CO, 80452, Clear Creek, USA; gen tel (303) 567-4491; adv tel (303) 567-4491 x 14; ed tel (303) 567-4491; gen fax (303) 567-0520; disp adv e-mail advertising@evergreenco.com; class adv e-mail tracy@evergreenco.com; ed e-mail couranteditor@evergreenco.com; web site www.clearcreekcourant.com
Circulation: 2,000pd,; Sworn/Estimate/Non-Audited
Advertising rate: Open inch rate $8.13
Group: Landmark Community Newspapers, LLC
Ian Neligh
Doug BellEd.s
Areas Served: 80452

JOHNSTOWN

THE JOHNSTOWN BREEZE (THUR)

7 S Parish Ave, Johnstown, CO, 80534-9099, Weld, USA; gen tel (970) 587-4525; adv tel (970) 587-4525; gen fax (970) 587-5882; disp adv e-mail ads@johnstownbreeze.com; class adv e-mail ads@johnstownbreeze.com; ed e-mail editor@johnstownbreeze.com; web site www.johnstownbreeze.com 10,000(visitors)
Circulation: 1,500pd, 50fr; USPS
Advertising rate: Open inch rate $10.50
Established: 1904
Digital Platform - Tablet: Apple iOS, Android, Windows 7, Blackberry Tablet OS, Kindle, Nook, Kindle Fire, Other
Pub....Lesli Bangert
Ed....Martin B. Hamilton
Mechanical Specifications: Type page 10 3/8 x 12 1/2; E - 5 cols, 1 15/16, 3/16 between; A - 5 cols, 1 15/16, 1/6 between; C - 5 cols, 1 15/16, 1/6 between.
Delivery Method: Mail, Newsstand, Racks
Areas Served: 80534, 80543

JULESBURG

JULESBURG ADVOCATE (THUR)

114 W 1st St, Julesburg, CO, 80737-1502, Sedgwick, USA; gen tel (970) 474-3388; disp adv e-mail advertising@julesburgadvocate.com; class adv e-mail advertising@julesburgadvocate.com; ed e-mail publisher@julesburgadvocate.com; web site www.julesburgadvocate.com
Circulation: 600pd,; Sworn/Estimate/Non-Audited
Advertising rate: Open inch rate $6.75
Established: 1899
Group: Digital First Media
Prairie Mountain Publishing
Mechanical Specifications: Type page 13 x 21 1/2; E - 6 cols, 2 1/16, 1/6 between; A - 6 cols, 2 1/16, 1/6 between; C - 8 cols, 1 5/16, 1/6 between.Equipment & Software: Hardware — APP/Mac; Software — QPS/QuarkXPress 3.31, Microsoft/Word 4.0.
Delivery Method: Mail, Newsstand, Racks
Areas Served: 80737

LA JUNTA

AG JOURNAL (FRI)

422 Colorado Ave, La Junta, CO, 81050-2336, Otero, USA; gen tel (719) 384-8121; adv tel (719) 384-1430; ed tel (719) 384-1453; gen fax (719) 384-8157; disp adv e-mail jason@ljtdmail.com; class adv e-mail classifieds@ljtdmail.com; ed e-mail publisher@ljtdmail.com; web site www.agjournalonline.com
Circulation: 10,159pd, 452fr; Sworn/Estimate/Non-Audited
Advertising rate: Open inch rate $12.00
Pub./Ed....Candy Hill
Sports Ed....Ken Hamrick
Multimedia Sales Exec....Jason Gallegos
Class. Adv. Mgr....Rita Ojeda
Mechanical Specifications: Type page 10 x 13; E - 4 cols, 2 13/32, 1/6 between; A - 4 cols, 2 3/8, 1/6 between; C - 6 cols, 1 1/2, 1/6 between.Equipment & Software: Hardware — APP/Mac, Microtek/Scanner, Xante; Presses — WPC/Web Leader; Software — Adobe/PageMaker 6.5, QPS/QuarkXPress 4.11, Adobe/Illustrator 8.0, Adobe/Photoshop 5.0, Macromedia/Freehand 8.0.
Areas Served: 81050

LA VETA

THE SIGNATURE (THUR)

124 N Main St, La Veta, CO, 81055, Huerfano, USA; gen tel (719) 742-5591; adv tel (719) 742-5591; gen fax (719) 742-3183; adv fax (719) 742-3183; ed e-mail editor@signaturenewspaper.com; web site www.signaturenewspaper.com
Circulation: 2,500pd, 100fr; Sworn/Estimate/Non-Audited
Advertising rate: Open inch rate $8.00
Ed....Renee Rinehart
Mechanical Specifications: Type page 9 3/4 x 15 1/2; E - 4 cols, 2 1/4, 1/6 between; A - 4 cols, 2 1/4, 1/6 between; C - 4 cols, 2 1/4, 1/6 between.Equipment & Software: Hardware — APP/Mac.
Delivery Method: Mail, Newsstand
Areas Served: 81055, 81089

LAMAR

THE LAMAR LEDGER (WED, FRI)

222 S Main St, Lamar, CO, 81052-2833, Prowers, USA; gen tel (719) 336-2266; gen fax (719) 336-2526; disp adv e-mail rstagner@lamarledger.com, blasley@lamarledger.com; class adv e-mail tgodinez@lamarledger.com, ecpcadvertising@dailycamera.com; ed e-mail editor@lamarledger.com; web site www.lamarledger.com
Circulation: 2,000pd, 3,000fr; Sworn/Estimate/Non-Audited
Advertising rate: Open inch rate $9.50
Established: 1907
Group: Digital First Media
Gen. Mgr./Ed....Chris Frost
Sports Ed....John Contreras
Advertising Consultant....Rick Stagner
Advertising Consultant....Brenda Lasley
Mechanical Specifications: Type page 15 1/6 x 21; E - 6 cols, 2 1/16, 1/8 between; A - 6 cols, 2 1/16, 1/8 between; C - 6 cols, 2 1/16, 1/8 between.Equipment & Software: Hardware — APP/Mac; Presses — 6-WPC/Web Leader; Software — QPS/QuarkXPress, Multi-Ad/Creator.
Delivery Method: Mail, Newsstand, Carrier, Racks
Areas Served: 81052

LAS ANIMAS

BENT COUNTY DEMOCRAT (THUR)

510 Carson Ave, Las Animas, CO, 81054-1732, Bent, USA; gen tel (719) 456-1333; adv tel (719) 384-4475; ed tel (719) 456-1333; disp adv e-mail tara@ljtdmail.com; ed e-mail bcd@ljtdmail.com; web site www.bcdemocratonline.com
Circulation: 1,200pd,; Sworn/Estimate/Non-Audited
Advertising rate: Open inch rate $5.50
Group: GateHouse Media, Inc.
Office Mgr....Loreta Moss
Circ. Mgr....Adrian Hart
Pub....Candi Hill
Sports Ed....Ken Hamrick
Multimedia Sales Exec....Jason Gallegos
Multimedia Sales Exec....Tara Castaneda
Areas Served: 81054

LEADVILLE

HERALD DEMOCRAT (THUR)

717 Harrison Ave, Leadville, CO, 80461-3561, Lake, USA; gen tel (719) 486-0641; adv tel (719) 486-0641 x 11; ed tel (719) 486-0641 x 10; gen fax (719) 486-0611; disp adv e-mail advertise@leadvilleherald.com; class adv e-mail classifieds@leadvilleherald.com; ed e-mail editor@leadvilleherald.com; web site www.leadvilleherald.com
Circulation: 2,400pd,; Sworn/Estimate/Non-Audited
Advertising rate: Open inch rate $8.00
Established: 1879
Group: Arkansas Valley Publishing
Ed....Marcia Martinek
Delivery Method: Mail, Newsstand, Racks
Areas Served: 80461

LIMON

EASTERN COLORADO PLAINSMAN (THUR)

1062 Main St, Limon, CO, 80828, Lincoln, USA; gen tel (719) 775-2064; gen fax (719) 775-9082; disp adv e-mail Advertising@thelimonleader.com; class adv e-mail Classifieds@thelimonleader.com; ed e-mail Editor@thelimonleader.com; web site www.thelimonleader.com
Circulation: 1,200pd,; Sworn/Estimate/Non-Audited
Advertising rate: Open inch rate $4.75
Established: 1913
Co-Pub....Charles Hoffman
Co-Pub....Jessica Hoffman
Ed....Will Bublitz
Areas Served: 80828

THE LIMON LEADER (THUR)

1062 Main St, Limon, CO, 80828, Lincoln, USA; gen tel (719) 775-2064; gen fax (719) 775-9082; disp adv e-mail Advertising@thelimonleader.com; class adv e-mail Classifieds@thelimonleader.com; ed e-mail Editor@thelimonleader.com; web site www.thelimonleader.com
Circulation: 2,100pd,; Sworn/Estimate/Non-Audited
Advertising rate: Open inch rate $5.65
Established: 1911
Group: Hoffman Media, LLC
Ed....Will Bublitz
Pub....Fred Lister
Areas Served: 80828

LYONS

THE LYONS RECORDER (THUR)

415 Main St, Ste C, Lyons, CO, 80540, Boulder, USA; gen tel (303) 823-6625; adv tel (303) 823-6625; ed tel (303) 823-6625; gen fax n/a; adv fax n/a; ed fax n/a; disp adv e-mail ads@lyonsrecorder.com; class adv e-mail ads@lyonsrecorder.com; ed e-mail editor@lyonsrecorder.com; web site www.lyonsrecorder.com
Circulation: 400pd, 10fr; Sworn/Estimate/Non-Audited
Advertising rate: Open inch rate $8.75 grayscale/ $12.50 full color
Established: 1900
Pub....Lora Gilson
Ed....Joseph Lekarczyk
Mechanical Specifications: Type page 10 x 13; E - 5 cols, 2, 1/10 between; A - 5 cols, 2, 1/10 between; C - 5 cols, 2, 1/10 between.Equipment & Software: Hardware — Mac; Software — Adobe Creative Suites
Delivery Method: Mail, Newsstand, Racks
Areas Served: Boulder County

MEEKER

THE RIO BLANCO HERALD TIMES (THUR)

592 Main St Ste 6, Meeker, CO, 81641, Rio Blanco, USA; gen tel (970) 878-4017; adv tel (970) 878-4017; ed tel (970) 878-4017; gen fax (970) 878-4016; disp adv e-mail ads@theheraldtimes.com; class adv e-mail debbiew@theheraldtimes.com; ed e-mail editor@theheraldtimes.com; web site

www.theheraldtimes.com - 69,000(views) 8,200(visitors)
Circulation: 1,625pd,; Sworn/Estimate/Non-Audited
Established: 1885
Group: Solas Publications, Inc.
Digital Platform - Mobile: Apple
Front Office Mgr. ....Debbie Watson
Front Office.......................................Patti Hoke
Adv. Acct. Exec. ....Pat Turner
Display Adv. ....Caitlin Walker
Editor/Publisher ....Niki Turner
Sports Reporter/PhotographerBobby Gutierrez
Rangely Correspondent........................Jen Hill
Meeker Correspondent.................Reed Kelley
Mechanical Specifications: Type page 11 3/4 x 20; E - 6 cols, 1 7/8, 1/8 between; A - 6 cols, 1 7/8, 1/8 between; C - 6 cols, 1 7/8, 1/8 between.Equipment & Software: ; Software — Microsoft/Windows 95, Microsoft/Word 7.0, Adobe/Photoshop LE, Archetype/Corel Draw 7.0, Adobe/PageMaker 6.5.
Areas Served: 81641, 81648

MONTE VISTA

CENTER POST-DISPATCH (THUR)

835 1st Ave, Monte Vista, CO, 81144-1474, Rio Grande, USA; gen tel (719) 852-3531; gen fax (719) 852-3387; disp adv e-mail jfapublisher@gmail.com; class adv e-mail montevistaclass@gmail.com; ed e-mail montevistanews@gmail.com; web site www.centerpostdispatch.com/
Circulation: 315pd,; Sworn/Estimate/Non-Audited
Advertising rate: 12.75/ci
Group: News Media Corp.
Delivery Method: Mail, Racks
Areas Served: 81125

THE CONEJOS COUNTY CITIZEN (WED)

835 1st Ave, Monte Vista, CO, 81144-1474, Rio Grande, USA; gen tel (719) 852-3531; gen fax (719) 852-3387; disp adv e-mail valleypubs@amigo.net; class adv e-mail vpiclass@amigo.net; ed e-mail valleypubs@amigo.net; web site www.conejoscountycitizen.com
Circulation: 250pd, 30fr; Sworn/Estimate/Non-Audited
Advertising rate: Open inch rate $10.70
Group: News Media Corp.
Pub..Jennifer Alonzo
Circ. Mgr....................................Shasta Hunter
Ed. .... Sylvia Lobato
Class. Mgr.....................................Beth Tooker
Mechanical Specifications: Type page 10.5 x 16; E - 5 cols, 2, between; A - 5 cols, 2, between; C - 5 cols, 2, between.
Delivery Method: Mail, Newsstand
Areas Served: 81140, 81120

THE DEL NORTE PROSPECTOR (THUR)

835 1st Ave, Monte Vista, CO, 81144-1474, Rio Grande, USA; gen tel (719) 852-3531; ed tel (719) 852-3531; gen fax (719) 852-3387; disp adv e-mail vpadvertising@amigo.net; class adv e-mail vpiclass@amigo.net; ed e-mail MonteVistaNews@gmail.com; web site www.delnorteprospector.com
Circulation: 650pd,; Sworn/Estimate/Non-Audited
Advertising rate: Open inch rate $11.75
Group: News Media Corp.
Ed. ....Jennifer Alonzo
Circ. Mgr....................................Shasta Hunter
Ed. .... Sylvia Lobato
Prodn. Mgr. ....Ellie Bone
Office Mgr. ....Beth Tooker
Mechanical Specifications: Type page 10.5 x 16; E - 5 cols, 2, between; A - 5 cols, 2, between; C - 5 cols, 2, between.
Delivery Method: Mail, Newsstand
Areas Served: 81132

THE MINERAL COUNTY MINER (THUR)

835 1st Ave, Monte Vista, CO, 81144-1474, Rio Grande, USA; gen tel (719) 852-3531; ed tel (719) 852-3531; gen fax (719) 852-3387; class adv e-mail montevistaads@gmail.com; ed e-mail montevistanews@gmail.com; web site www.mineralcountyminer.com
Circulation: 650pd, 30fr; Sworn/Estimate/Non-Audited
Advertising rate: Open inch rate $11.75
Group: News Media Corp.
Ed. ....Jennifer Alonzo
Office Mgr. ....Beth Tooker
Mechanical Specifications: Type page 10.5 x 16; E - 5 cols, 2, between; A - 5 cols, 2, between; C - 5 cols, 2, between.
Delivery Method: Mail, Newsstand
Areas Served: 81130

THE MONTE VISTA JOURNAL (WED)

835 1st Ave, Monte Vista, CO, 81144-1474, Rio Grande, USA; gen tel (719) 852-3531; ed tel (719) 852-3531; gen fax (719) 852-3387; class adv e-mail montevistaads@gmail.com; ed e-mail montevistanews@gmail.com; web site www.montevistajournal.com
Circulation: 1,200pd, 30fr; Sworn/Estimate/Non-Audited
Advertising rate: Open inch rate $10.70
Group: News Media Corp.
Publisher.................................Jennifer Alonzo
Beth Tooker
Mechanical Specifications: Type page 10.5 x 16.
Delivery Method: Mail, Newsstand
Areas Served: 81144

THE SOUTH FORK TINES (THUR)

835 1st Ave, Monte Vista, CO, 81144-1474, Rio Grande, USA; gen tel (719) 852-3531; ed tel (719) 852-3531; gen fax (719) 852-3387; disp adv e-mail MonteVistaAds@gmail.com; class adv e-mail MonteVistaClass@gmail.com; ed e-mail MonteVistaNews@gmail.com; web site www.southforktines.com
Circulation: 650pd, 30fr; Sworn/Estimate/Non-Audited
Advertising rate: Open inch rate $11.75
Group: News Media Corp.
Pub./Ed.....................................Jennifer Alonzo
Office Mgr. ....Beth Tooker
Mechanical Specifications: Type page 10 1/2 x 16
Delivery Method: Mail, Newsstand
Areas Served: 81154

MONUMENT

THE TRIBUNE (WED)

153 Washington St, Monument, CO, 80132-9181, El Paso, USA; gen tel (719) 686-6447; adv tel (719) 687-306 x 111; ed tel (719) 687-306 x 111; gen fax (719) 687-3009; disp adv e-mail rcarrigan@ourcoloradonews.com; class adv e-mail vortega@ourcoloradonews.com; ed e-mail rcarrigan@ourcoloradonews.com; web site www.pikespeaknewspapers.com
Circulation: 12,000pd, 107fr; Sworn/Estimate/Non-Audited
Advertising rate: 1/16 Pg $110.00; 1/8 Pg $189.00; 1/4 Pg $250.00
Established: 1964
Group: Pikes Peak Newspapers, Inc.
pub..Rob Carrigan
News/Sports Reporter...........Danny Summers
Advertising Rep. ....David Lowe
Mechanical Specifications: Type page 11 1/16 x 21 1/2; E - 5 cols, 1 5/6, 1/6 between.Equipment & Software: Hardware — APP/Mac; Software — Adobe/PageMaker 6.0.
Delivery Method: Mail, Carrier
Areas Served: 80132, 80133, 80921, 80908

NUCLA

SAN MIGUEL BASIN FORUM (THUR)

PO Box 9, Nucla, CO, 81424-0009, Montrose, USA; gen tel (970) 864-7425; gen fax (970) 864-2298; disp adv e-mail ads@nntcwireless.com
Circulation: 1,397pd, 15fr; Sworn/Estimate/Non-Audited
Advertising rate: Open inch rate $7.10
Ed. ....Roger Culver
Delivery Method: Mail, Newsstand
Areas Served: 81424

PAGOSA SPRINGS

THE PAGOSA SPRINGS SUN (THUR)

466 Pagosa St, Pagosa Springs, CO, 81147-9955, Archuleta, USA; gen tel (970) 264-2100; gen fax (970) 264-2103; disp adv e-mail tjay@pagosasun.com; class adv e-mail classads@pagosasun.com; ed e-mail editor@pagosasun.com; web site www.pagosasun.com
Circulation: 4,645pd,; Sworn/Estimate/Non-Audited
Advertising rate: Open inch rate $8.50
Established: 1909
Owner/Pub./Ed.............................. Terri House
Adv. Mgr. .... Shari Pierce
Asst. Ed....................................... Randi Pierce
Class. Adv...................................Missy Phelan
Mechanical Specifications: Type page 13 x 21; E - 6 cols, 2 1/16, 1/6 between; A - 6 cols, 2 1/16, 1/6 between; C - 5 cols, 2 1/16, 1/6 between.Equipment & Software: Hardware — APP/Mac; Presses — G/Community.
Delivery Method: Mail, Newsstand, Racks
Areas Served: 81147, 81121, 81127, 81128

SALIDA

MOUNTAIN GUIDE (WED)

125 E 2nd St, Salida, CO, 81201-2114, Chaffee, USA; gen tel (719) 539-6691; gen fax (719) 539-6630; disp adv e-mail vickiesue@avpsalida.com; class adv e-mail classifieds@themountainmail.com; web site www.themountainmail.com
Circulation: 6,000fr; Sworn/Estimate/Non-Audited
Advertising rate: Open inch rate $7.50
Established: 1977
Digital Platform - Mobile: Apple, Windows
Pub....................................... Merle Baranczyk
Adv. Dir..Vickie Vigil
Circ. Direc. .... Sandra Christensen
Prodn. Direc... Morris ChristensenEquipment & Software: Hardware — APP/Mac; Presses — Quad Stack, Goss Community.
Delivery Method: Mail, Newsstand, Carrier, Racks
Areas Served: 81201; 81233;81222; 81223, 81242; 81211; 81236

SILVERTON

SILVERTON STANDARD AND THE MINER (THUR)

1316 Snowden St., Ste 308, Silverton, CO, 81433, San Juan, USA; gen tel (970) 387-5477; ed tel (970) 387-5477; gen fax (970) 387-5795; disp adv e-mail silvertonads@gmail.com; ed e-mail editor@silverrtonstandard.com; web site www.silvertonstandard.com
Circulation: 1,050pd,; Sworn/Estimate/Non-Audited
Advertising rate: Open inch rate $6.00
Established: 1875
Ed. .... Mark Esper
Mechanical Specifications: Type page 10 x 13; E - 5 cols, 1 11/12, 1/6 between; A - 5 cols, 1 11/12, 1/6 between; C - 5 cols, 1 11/12, 1/6 between.
Delivery Method: Mail, Racks
Areas Served: 81433

SIMLA

RANCHLAND NEWS (THUR)

115 Sioux Ave, Simla, CO, 80835, Elbert, USA; gen tel (719) 541-2288; adv tel (719) 541-2288; gen fax (719) 541-2289; adv fax (719) 541-2289; disp adv e-mail ranchland@bigsandytelco.com; web site www.ranchland-news.com
Circulation: 4,000pd,; Sworn/Estimate/Non-Audited
Advertising rate: Open inch rate $5.55
Co-Pub...Fred Lister
Co-Pub...Susan Lister
Adv. Mgr. ....Nikki Lister
Ed. ....John Hill
Areas Served: 80835

STEAMBOAT SPRINGS

STEAMBOAT PILOT (SUN)

1901 Curve Plz, Steamboat Springs, CO, 80487-4912, Routt, USA; gen tel (970) 879-1502; adv tel (970) 879-1502; ed tel (970) 879-1502; gen fax (970) 879-2888; adv fax (970) 879-7541; ed fax (970) 879-2888; disp adv e-mail advertising@steamboatToday.com; class adv e-mail advertising@SteamboatToday.com; ed e-mail news@SteamboatToday.com; web site www.steamboattoday.com
Circulation: 9,830pd, 10,500fr; Sworn/Estimate/Non-Audited
Established: 1884
Group: Swift Communications, Inc.
Pub...................................... Suzanne Schlicht
Circ. Dir. .... Steve Balgenorth
General Manager...................... Scott Stanford
Ed. ....Lisa Schlichtman
Online Devel. Mgr.........................Tyler Jacobs
Adv. Dir......................................Laura Tamucci
Delivery Method: Racks
Areas Served: 80477-80488

STRASBURG

EASTERN COLORADO NEWS (FRI)

1522 Main St, Strasburg, CO, 80136-7507, Adams, USA; gen tel (303) 622-9796; adv tel (303) 622-9796; gen fax (303) 622-9794; disp adv e-mail dclaussen@i-70scout.com; class adv e-mail jkero@i-70scout.com; ed e-mail dclaussen@i-70scout.com; web site www.i-70scout.com
Circulation: 1,012pd, 40fr; Sworn/Estimate/Non-Audited
Advertising rate: Open inch rate $11.35
Established: 1916
Ed. ....Douglas Claussen
Mng. Ed.......................................Steven Vetter
Off. Mng. ....LuAnne Stegner
Mechanical Specifications: Type page 10 x 16; E - 4 cols, 2 3/8, 1/6 between; A - 4 cols, 2 3/8, 1/6 between; C - 4 cols, 2 3/8, 1/6 between.
Areas Served: 80137, 80102, 80136, 80103, 80105, 80101

STRATTON

STRATTON SPOTLIGHT (TUES)

210 Colorado Ave., Stratton, CO, 80836, Kit Carson, USA; gen tel (719) 348-5913; gen fax (719) 348-5913; disp adv e-mail strattonspotlight@yahoo.com; web site No Website
Circulation: 650pd, 24fr; Sworn/Estimate/Non-Audited
Advertising rate: Open inch rate $5.00
Owner/Ed.......................................Nicki Lueck
Mechanical Specifications: Type page 15 3/16 x 21 1/2.
Delivery Method: Mail, Racks
Areas Served: 80836

TELLURIDE

THE NORWOOD POST (WED)

307 E Colorado Ave, Telluride, CO, 81435, San Miguel, USA; gen tel (970) 728-9788; adv tel (503) 477-2923 x 24; ed tel (503) 477-2923; gen fax (970) 728-8061; disp adv e-mail dusty@telluridedailyplanet.com; class adv e-mail dusty@telluridedailyplanet.com; ed e-mail norwoodpost@yahoo.com; web site www.telluridenews.com/norwood_post/front/

Circulation: 1,000pd,; Sworn/Estimate/Non-Audited
Advertising rate: Open inch rate $6.00Editions: (1)
Pub....Andrew Mirrington
Assoc. Pub....Dusty Atheron
Mktg./Sales Coord....Lea St. Amand
Office Mgr....Shelly Bolus
Ed....Regan Tuttle
Areas Served: San Miguel County

WALDEN

JACKSON COUNTY STAR (THUR)

PO Box 397, Walden, CO, 80480-0397, Jackson, USA; gen tel (970) 723-4404; disp adv e-mail jcstarmail@yahoo.com; web site www.jacksoncountystar.com
Circulation: 1,250pd, 30fr; Sworn/Estimate/Non-Audited
Advertising rate: Open inch rate $8.00
Established: 1913
Ed./Pub....Matt Shuler
Contrib. Ed....Jim Dustin
THE BOSS....Michelle Shuler
Mechanical Specifications: Type page 10 x 16; E - 4 cols, 2 1/2, 1/8 between; A - 6 cols, 1 5/8, 1/8 between; C - 6 cols, 1 5/8, 1/8 between. Equipment & Software: Hardware — APP/Mac; Software — QPS/QuarkXPress, Claris Works.
Delivery Method: Mail
Areas Served: 80480

WESTCLIFFE

WET MOUNTAIN TRIBUNE (THUR)

404 E Main St, Westcliffe, CO, 81252-8307, Custer, USA; gen tel (719) 783-2361; gen fax (719) 783-3725; disp adv e-mail ads@wetmountaintribune.com; class adv e-mail frontdesk@wetmountaintribune.com; ed e-mail editor@wetmountaintribune.com; web site www.wetmountaintribune.com
Circulation: 3,000pd, 0fr; Sworn/Estimate/Non-Audited
Advertising rate: Open inch rate $11.00
Established: 1883
Group: Little Publishing Company, Inc.
Ed./Pub....James A. Little
Graphic Dsgnr....Charlotte Curtis
Adv. Dir....Lynne Tabb
Admin. Asst....Blair Little
Mechanical Specifications: Type page 10 1/8 x 16; A - 6 cols, 1 2/3, 1/12 between.
Delivery Method: Mail, Newsstand, Racks
Areas Served: 81252, 81253, 81232

WESTMINSTER

NORTHGLENN-THORNTON SENTINEL (THUR)

8753 Yates Dr Ste 200, Suite 200, Westminster, CO, 80031-6946, Adams, USA; gen tel (303) 566-4100; gen fax (303) 426-4209; disp adv e-mail bstolte@coloradocommunitymedia.com; class adv e-mail kearhart@coloradocommunitymedia.com; web site northglenn-thorntonsentinel.com
Circulation: 3,124pd, 1,735fr
Group: Colorado Community Media
Opns. Mgr....Barb Stolte
Pres./Pub....Jerry Healey
Major Accts. Mgr....Erin Addenbrooke
Karen Earhart
Mng. Ed....Josh Sumner

WESTMINSTER WINDOW (THUR)

8753 Yates Dr Ste 200, Suite 200, Westminster, CO, 80031-6946, Adams, USA; gen tel (303) 566-4100; gen fax (303) 566-4098; disp adv e-mail eaddenbrooke@coloradocommunitymedia.com; class adv e-mail kearhart@coloradocommunitymedia.com; ed e-mail gwallace@coloradocommunitymedia.com; web site westminsterwindow.com
Circulation: 2,200pd, 1,150fr; Sworn/Estimate/Non-Audited
Group: Colorado Community Media
Adv. Dir....Erin Addenbrooke
Gen. Mgr./Mktg. Mgr....Barbara Stolte
Mng. Ed....Josh Sumner
Mechanical Specifications: Type page 10 1/4 x 12 3/4; E - 5 cols, 1 7/8, 1/6 between; A - 5 cols, 1 7/8, 1/6 between; C - 9 cols, 1 1/20, 1/12 between.Equipment & Software: Hardware — APP/Mac; Software — Claris/MacWrite II, QPS/QuarkXPress 3.3, Adobe/Illustrator 3.2.
Delivery Method: Mail, Carrier, Racks
Areas Served: 80031, 80021, 80030, 80221, 80234, 80260

WINDSOR

WINDSOR NOW (SUN)

423 Main St, Windsor, CO, 80550-5129, Weld, USA; gen tel (970) 674-1431; adv tel (970) 392-4406; disp adv e-mail advertising@greeleytribune.com; class adv e-mail advertising@greeleytribune.com; ed e-mail editorial@greeleytribune.com; web site www.mywindsornow.com
Circulation: 8,065pd,; CAC
Advertising rate: Open inch rate $8.00
Established: 2007
Group: Swift Communications, Inc.
Greeley Publishing Company
Pub....Bart Smith
Ed....Randy Bangert
Sales Mgr....Bruce Dennis
Acct. Mgr....Becky Colvin
Delivery Method: Mail, Newsstand
Areas Served: Windsor and Severance area

WOODLAND PARK

THE PIKES PEAK COURIER (WED)

1200 E. Hwy. 24, Suite B, Woodland Park, CO, 80863, Teller, USA; gen tel (719) 687-3006; adv tel (719) 686-6457; ed tel (719) 963-8831 x111; gen fax (719) 687-3009; disp adv e-mail eaddenbrooke@ourcoloradonews.com; class adv e-mail eaddenbrooke@ourcoloradonews.com; ed e-mail rcarrigan@ourcoloradonews.com; web site www.pikespeakcourier.net
Circulation: 2,500pd, 250fr; USPS
Advertising rate: 1/16 Pg $149.00; 1/8 pg $259.00; 1/4 Pg $456.00
Group: Pikes Peak Newspapers, Inc.
Pub....Rob Carrigan
Sports/News Reporter....Danny Summers
Adv. Rep....David Lowe
Mechanical Specifications: 6 column paper - 6 columns 10.25" wideEquipment & Software: ; Presses — 7-G/Community; Software — QPS/QuarkXPress, Adobe/Photoshop.
Delivery Method: Mail
Areas Served: 80863

CONNECTICUT

BRIDGEPORT

DARIEN NEWS (FRI)

410 State St, Bridgeport, CT, 06604-4501, Fairfield, USA; gen tel (203) 333-161; ed tel (203) 330-6581; gen fax (203) 972-4404; disp adv e-mail mmcabee@scni.com; ed e-mail avarese@bcnnew.com; web site www.dariennewsonline.com
Circulation: 784pd, 12fr; AAM
Advertising rate: Open inch rate $19.05
Group: Hearst Communications, Inc.
Ed....Jerrod Ferrari
Doreen Madden
Grp. Pub./Pres....Paul Barbetta
Circ. Dir....Bill Mason
Sports Ed....Anthony Parelli
Mechanical Specifications: Type page 10 x 16; E - 5 cols, between; A - 5 cols, between; C - 5 cols, between.

FAIRFIELD CITIZEN (WED, FRI)

410 State St, 220 Carter Henry Dr, Bridgeport, CT, 06604-4501, Fairfield, USA; gen tel (203) 337-4877; adv tel (203) 330-6409; ed tel (203) 255-4561 ext. 111; gen fax (203) 367-8158; disp adv e-mail gdoucette@hearstmediact.com; class adv e-mail classified@ctpost.com; ed e-mail jdoody@bcnnew.com; web site www.fairfieldcitizenonline.com
Circulation: 1,823pd,; AAM
Advertising rate: Open inch rate $19.75
Group: Hearst Communications, Inc.
Ed....Jerrod Ferrari
Sports Ed....Chris Elsberry
Grp. Pub....Paul Barbetta
Exec Asst to Pub....Doreen Madden
Circ. Dir....Bill Mason

NEW CANAAN NEWS (THUR)

410 State St, Bridgeport, CT, 06604-4501, Fairfield, USA; gen tel (203) 333-0161; adv tel (203) 964-2357 ; ed tel (203) 330-6581; gen fax (203) 972-4404; adv fax (203) 972-4404; ed fax (203) 972-4404; disp adv e-mail agonzalez@scni.com; class adv e-mail classifieds@ctpost.com; ed e-mail avarese@bcnnew.com; web site www.newcanaannewsonline.com
Circulation: 2,710pd,; Sworn/Estimate/Non-Audited
Advertising rate: Open inch rate $19.05
Group: Hearst Communications, Inc.
Digital Platform - Mobile: Apple
Digital Platform - Tablet: Apple iOS
Ed....Claire Racine
Sports Ed....Anthony Parelli
Ed....Jerrod Ferrari
Group Pres./Pub....Paul Barbetta
Exec. Asst. to Pub....Doreen Madden
Delivery Method: Mail, Newsstand
Areas Served: 06604

WESTPORT NEWS (WED, FRI)

410 State St, Bridgeport, CT, 06604-4501, Fairfield, USA; gen tel (203) 255-4561; adv tel (203) 964-2357; ed tel (203) 255-4561 ext. 111; gen fax (203) 255-0456; disp adv e-mail agonzalez@scni.com; ed e-mail jdoody@bcnnew.com; web site www.westport-news.com
Circulation: 2,505pd,; AAM
Advertising rate: Open inch rate $23.85
Group: Hearst Communications, Inc.
Sports Ed....Ryan Lacey
Ed....Jerrod Ferrari
Circ. Dir....Bill Mason
Grp. Pub./Pres....Paul Barbetta
Exec. Asst. to Pub....Doreen Madden
Mechanical Specifications: Type page 10 1/4 x 15 1/2; A - 5 cols, 1 7/8, between.

CHESHIRE

THE CHESHIRE HERALD (THUR)

1079 S Main St, Cheshire, CT, 06410-3414, New Haven, USA; gen tel (203) 272-5316; gen fax (203) 250-7145; disp adv e-mail ffonteyn@cheshireherald.com; ed e-mail news@cheshireherald.com; web site www.cheshireherald.com
Circulation: 7,200pd, 197fr; Sworn/Estimate/Non-Audited
Advertising rate: Open inch rate $13.40
Established: 1953
Pres./Pub....Joseph J. Jakubisyn
Treasurer....Maureen Jakubisyn
Adv. Dir....Frank Fonteyn
Circ. Mgr....Debi Reeve
Ed....John Rook
Mechanical Specifications: Type page 10 x 15.5; 5 cols, 1.875, 0.125 between
Areas Served: 06410

DARIEN

DARIEN TIMES (THUR)

10 Corbin Dr, Fl 3rd, Darien, CT, 06820-5403, Fairfield, USA; gen tel (203) 656-4230; adv tel (203) 966-9541; ed tel (203) 656-4230; gen fax (203) 656-4240; disp adv e-mail lspicehandler@hersamacorn.com; class adv e-mail class@hersamacorn.com; ed e-mail editor@darientimes.com; web site www.darientimes.com
Circulation: 6,015pd,; CAC
Advertising rate: Open inch rate $14.50
Established: 1993
Group: HAN Network
Digital Platform - Mobile: Android
Digital Platform - Tablet: Android
Ed....Susan Shultz
Acct. Exec....Lauren Spicehandler
Adv. Sales....Shelagh Barrett
Circ. Mgr....Bruce McDougall
Adv. Dir....Stephen Spinosa
Mechanical Specifications: Type page 10.75 x 21; E - 6 cols, 1 7/8, between; A - 6 cols, 1 7/8, between; C - 9 cols, 1 1/8, between.
Delivery Method: Mail, Newsstand
Areas Served: Darien (CT)

GREENWICH-POST (THUR)

10 Corbin Dr, Fl 3rd, Darien, CT, 06820-5403, Fairfield, USA; gen tel (203) 861-9191; adv tel (203) 219-0906; ed tel 2038619191 ext 112; gen fax (203) 861-0023; disp adv e-mail steves@greenwich-post.com; web site www.greenwich-post.com
Circulation: 8,820pd,; Sworn/Estimate/Non-Audited
Advertising rate: Open inch rate $14.50
Established: 1997
Ed....Ken Borsuk
Pub....Thomas B. Nash
Mechanical Specifications: Type page 10.75 x 21; E - 6 cols, 1 7/8, between; A - 6 cols, 1 7/8, between; C - 9 cols, 1 1/8, between.
Delivery Method: Mail, Newsstand
Areas Served: Greenwich

FALLS VILLAGE

THE LAKEVILLE JOURNAL (THUR)

64 Route 7 N, Falls Village, CT, 06031-1304, Litchfield, USA; gen tel (860) 435-9873; adv tel (860) 435-9873 x501; ed tel (860) 435-9873 x601; adv fax (860) 271-8282; ed fax (860) 271-8282; disp adv e-mail advertising@lakevillejournal.com; class adv e-mail classified@lakevillejournal.com; ed e-mail editor@lakevillejournal.com; web site tricornernews.com - 40,000(views) 8,000(visitors)
Circulation: 3,192pd, 38fr; CAC
Advertising rate: Open inch rate $13.00
Established: 1897
Group: The Lakeville Journal
Digital Platform - Mobile: Apple
Class Adv. Mgr....Mark Niedhammer
Pub./EIC....Janet Manko
Exec. Ed....Cynthia Hochswender
Prodn. Coord....James Clark
Adv. Mgr....Libby Hall-Abeel
Controller....Sandra Lang
Mechanical Specifications: Type page 11.5 x 21; 6 cols, 1.75"Equipment & Software: Hardware — APP/Macs; Software — Adobe/InDesign, Photoshop
Delivery Method: Mail, Newsstand, Racks
Areas Served: Canaan, Cornwall, Falls Village, Kent, Norfolk, Lakeville, Salisbury, Sharon, Winsted, Norfolk, Colebrook, Barkhamsted, New Hartford

GLASTONBURY

GLASTONBURY CITIZEN (THUR)

87 Nutmeg Ln, Glastonbury, CT, 06033-2314, Hartford, USA; gen tel (860) 633-4691; adv tel (860) 633-4691 ext. 237; ed tel (860) 633-4691 ext. 226; gen fax (860) 657-3258; disp

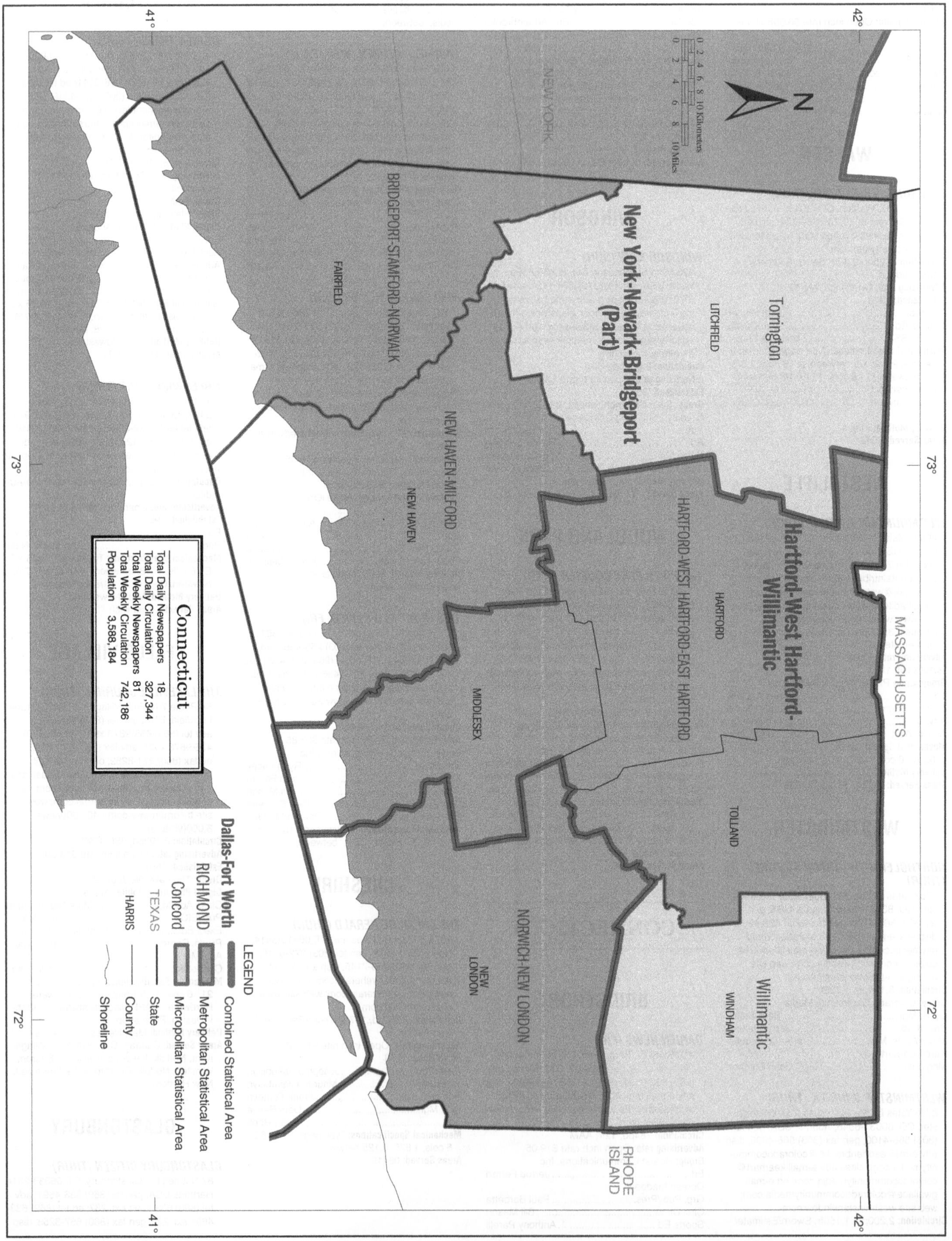
N
0 2 4 6 8 10 Kilometers
0 2 4 6 8 10 Miles
NEW YORK
MASSACHUSETTS
RHODE ISLAND
New York-Newark-Bridgeport (Part)
Torrington
LITCHFIELD
BRIDGEPORT-STAMFORD-NORWALK
FAIRFIELD
NEW HAVEN-MILFORD
NEW HAVEN
Hartford-West Hartford-Willimantic
HARTFORD-WEST HARTFORD-EAST HARTFORD
HARTFORD
MIDDLESEX
TOLLAND
Willimantic
WINDHAM
NORWICH-NEW LONDON
NEW LONDON
Connecticut
Total Daily Newspapers 18
Total Daily Circulation 327,344
Total Weekly Newspapers 81
Total Weekly Circulation 742,186
Population 3,588,184
LEGEND
Dallas-Fort Worth Combined Statistical Area
RICHMOND Metropolitan Statistical Area
Concord Micropolitan Statistical Area
TEXAS State
HARRIS County
Shoreline
41°
42°
73°
72°

adv e-mail rivereast@snet.net; ed e-mail citizen@snet.net; web site www.glcitizen.com
Circulation: 7,792pd,; Sworn/Estimate/Non-Audited
Advertising rate: Open inch rate $11.00
Group: The Glastonbury Citizen, Inc.
Adv. Mgr. .... Carole Saucier
Circ. Mgr. .... Janki Buch
Ed. & Pub. .... James Hallas
Sports Ed. .... Chris Seymour
Mechanical Specifications: Type page 10 1/2 x 15 1/2; E - 4 cols, 2 3/4, 1/6 between; A - 8 cols, 1 1/6, 1/6 between; C - 8 cols, 1 1/6, 1/6 between.Equipment & Software: Hardware — PC; Software — Adobe/PageMaker 6.5, Adobe/Photoshop 4.0.
Areas Served: Glastonbury & South Glastonbury

RIVEREAST NEWS BULLETIN (FRI)

87 Nutmeg Ln, Glastonbury, CT, 06033-2314, Hartford, USA; gen tel (860) 633-4691; adv tel (860) 633-4691 ext. 237; ed tel (860) 633-4691 ext. 225; gen fax (860) 657-3258; disp adv e-mail rivereast@snet.net; ed e-mail rivereast@snet.net; web site www.glcitizen.com
Circulation: 27,050fr; Sworn/Estimate/Non-Audited
Advertising rate: Open inch rate $10.00
Group: The Glastonbury Citizen, Inc.
Pub. .... James Hallas
Adv. Mgr. .... Carole Saucier
Ed. .... Mike Thompson
Mechanical Specifications: Type page 10 1/2 x 15 1/2; E - 8 cols, 1 3/16, between; A - 8 cols, 1 3/16, between; C - 8 cols, 1 3/16, between.
Areas Served: Andover, Cobalt, Colchester, Hebron & Amston, Middle Haddam, East Hampton, Marlborough. Portland

HAMDEN

THE HAMDEN JOURNAL (MTHLY)

17 Hesse Rd, Hamden, CT, 06517-2620, New Haven, USA; gen tel (203) 687-3075; adv tel (203) 687-3075; ed tel (203) 687-3075; disp adv e-mail sales@thehamdenjournal.com; class adv e-mail sales@thehamdenjournal.com; ed e-mail info@thehamdenjournal.com; web site www.thehamdenjournal.com
Circulation: 7,500fr; Sworn/Estimate/Non-Audited
Advertising rate: (Modular Rates) 3.5 x 2, $50 1x
Established: 2010
Group: Good News Publishing LLC
Pub / EIC .... Shala LaTorraca
Publisher / Director of Sales.... Chris LaTorraca
Mechanical Specifications: Type page 12 x 21; E - 6 cols, 1 7/8, 1/8 between; A - 6 cols, 1 7/8, 1/8 between; C - 10 cols, 1 1/8, between. Equipment & Software: Hardware — APP/Mac; Presses — G/Community; Software — Adobe/PageMaker 5.0.
Delivery Method: Carrier, Racks
Areas Served: Hamden

HARTFORD

COURANT COMMUNITY - COLCHESTER (THUR)

285 Broad St, Hartford, CT, 06105-3785, Hartford, USA; gen tel (860) 241-6200; gen fax (860) 520-6941; ed fax (860) 520-69411; disp adv e-mail lckelleher@courant.com; class adv e-mail classifieds@courant.com; ed e-mail agriffin@courant.com; web site courant.com/community/colchester-edition
Circulation: 13,620fr; CVC
Advertising rate: 1/16 Pg $327.00; 1/8 Pg $654.00; 1/4 Pg $1308.00
Group: Tronc, Inc.
Community Sales Mgr. .... Christine Neves
Adv. Sales .... Mary Lou Stoneburner
Circ. .... Brian McEnery
VP of Adv. .... Mary Lou Stoneburner
Pub. .... Andrew S. Julien
Delivery Method: Mail, Newsstand, Carrier, Racks
Areas Served: Colchester, East Hartford, Enfield, Glastonbury, Hebron, Columbia, Jewett City, Killingsly, Plainfield, Manchester, Putnam, South Windsor, Stafford, Vernon, Windham, Mansfield, Windor, Windosr Locks

COURANT COMMUNITY - EAST HARTFORD (THUR)

285 Broad St, Hartford, CT, 06105-3785, Hartford, USA; gen tel (860) 241-6200; gen fax (860) 520-6941; disp adv e-mail lckelleher@courant.com; class adv e-mail classifieds@courant.com; ed e-mail agriffin@courant.com; web site courant.com/community/east-hartford - 85,738(views) 18,205(visitors)
Circulation: 13,289fr; CVC
Advertising rate: 1/16 Pg $327.00; 1/8 Pg $654.00; 1/4 Pg $1308.00
Group: Tronc, Inc.
Adv. Sales .... Mary Lou Stoneburner
Community Sales Mgr. .... Christine Neves
Circ. Mgr .... Brian McEnery
Pub. .... Andrew S. Julien
VP of Adv. .... Mary Lou Stoneburner
Mechanical Specifications: Type page 9.875" x 11.25"; 4 cols
Delivery Method: Mail, Newsstand, Carrier, Racks
Areas Served: Colchester, East Hartford, Enfield, Glastonbury, Hebron, Columbia, Jewett City, Killingsly, Plainfield, Manchester, Putnam, South Windsor, Stafford, Vernon, Windham, Mansfield, Windor, Windosr Locks

COURANT COMMUNITY - ENFIELD (THUR)

285 Broad St, Hartford, CT, 06105-3785, Hartford, USA; gen tel (860) 241-6200; gen fax (860) 520-6941; disp adv e-mail lckelleher@courant.com; class adv e-mail classifieds@courant.com; ed e-mail agriffin@courant.com; web site courant.com/community/enfield
Circulation: 18,829fr; CVC
Advertising rate: 1/16 Pg $327.00; 1/8 Pg $654.00; 1/4 Pg $1308.00
Group: Tronc, Inc.
Adv. Sales .... Mary Lou Stoneburner
Circ. .... Brian McEnery
Community Sales Mgr. .... Christine Neves
Pub.Pub./Ed.-in-Chief .... Andrew S. Julien
VP of Adv. .... Mary Lou Stoneburner
Delivery Method: Mail, Newsstand, Carrier, Racks
Areas Served: Colchester, East Hartford, Enfield, Glastonbury, Hebron, Columbia, Jewett City, Killingsly, Plainfield, Manchester, Putnam, South Windsor, Stafford, Vernon, Windham, Mansfield, Windor, Windosr Locks

COURANT COMMUNITY - GLASTONBURY (THUR)

285 Broad St, Hartford, CT, 06105-3785, Hartford, USA; gen tel (860) 241-6200; gen fax (860) 520-6941; disp adv e-mail lckelleher@courant.com; class adv e-mail classifieds@courant.com; ed e-mail agriffin@courant.com; web site courant.com/community/glastonbury
Circulation: 9,856fr; CVC
Advertising rate: 1/16 Pg $327.00; 1/8 Pg $654.00; 1/4 Pg $1308.00
Group: Tronc, Inc.
Adv. Sales .... Mary Lou Stoneburner
Circ. .... Brian McEnery
VP of Adv. .... Mary Lou Stoneburner
Community Sales Mgr. .... Christine Neves
Pub./Ed.-in-Chief .... Andrew S. Julien
Delivery Method: Mail, Newsstand, Carrier, Racks
Areas Served: Colchester, East Hartford, Enfield, Glastonbury, Hebron, Columbia, Jewett City, Killingsly, Plainfield, Manchester, Putnam, South Windsor, Stafford, Vernon, Windham, Mansfield, Windor, Windosr Locks

COURANT COMMUNITY - HEBRON (THUR)

285 Broad St, Hartford, CT, 06105-3785, Hartford, USA; gen tel (860) 241-6200; gen fax (860) 520-6941; disp adv e-mail lckelleher@courant.com; class adv e-mail classifieds@courant.com; ed e-mail agriffin@courant.com; web site courant.com/community/hebron-edition
Circulation: 7,867fr; CVC
Advertising rate: 1/16 Pg $327.00; 1/8 Pg $654.00; 1/4 Pg $1308.00
Group: Tronc, Inc.
Adv. Sales .... Mary Lou Stoneburner
Circ. .... Brian McEnery
Community Sales Mgr. .... Christine Neves
VP of Adv. .... Mary Lou Stoneburner
Pub./Ed.-in-Chief .... Andrew S. Julien
Delivery Method: Mail, Newsstand, Carrier, Racks
Areas Served: Colchester, East Hartford, Enfield, Glastonbury, Hebron, Columbia, Jewett City, Killingsly, Plainfield, Manchester, Putnam, South Windsor, Stafford, Vernon, Windham, Mansfield, Windor, Windosr Locks

COURANT COMMUNITY - KILLINGLY (THUR)

285 Broad St, Hartford, CT, 06105-3785, Hartford, USA; gen tel (860) 241-6200; gen fax (860) 520-6941; disp adv e-mail lckelleher@courant.com; class adv e-mail classifieds@courant.com; ed e-mail agriffin@courant.com; web site courant.com/community
Circulation: 16,076fr; CVC
Advertising rate: 1/16 Pg $327.00; 1/8 Pg $654.00; 1/4 Pg $1308.00
Group: Tronc, Inc.
Adv. Sales .... Mary Lou Stoneburner
Circ. .... Brian McEnery
Community Sales Mgr. .... Christine Neves
VP of Adv. .... Mary Lou Stoneburner
Pub./Ed.-in-Chief .... Andrew S. Julien
Delivery Method: Mail, Newsstand, Carrier, Racks
Areas Served: Colchester, East Hartford, Enfield, Glastonbury, Hebron, Columbia, Jewett City, Killingsly, Plainfield, Manchester, Putnam, South Windsor, Stafford, Vernon, Windham, Mansfield, Windor, Windosr Locks

COURANT COMMUNITY - MANCHESTER (THUR)

285 Broad St, Hartford, CT, 06105-3785, Hartford, USA; gen tel (860) 241-6200; gen fax (860) 520-6941; disp adv e-mail lckelleher@courant.com; class adv e-mail classifieds@courant.com; ed e-mail agriffin@courant.com; web site courant.com/community
Circulation: 15,633fr; CVC
Advertising rate: 1/16 Pg $327.00; 1/8 Pg $654.00; 1/4 Pg $1308.00
Group: Tronc, Inc.
Adv. Sales .... Mary Lou Stoneburner
Circ. .... Brian McEnery
VP of Adv. .... Mary Lou Stoneburner
Community Sales Mgr. .... Christine Neves
Pub./Ed.-in-Chief .... Andrew S. Julien
Delivery Method: Mail, Newsstand, Carrier, Racks
Areas Served: Colchester, East Hartford, Enfield, Glastonbury, Hebron, Columbia, Jewett City, Killingsly, Plainfield, Manchester, Putnam, South Windsor, Stafford, Vernon, Windham, Mansfield, Windor, Windosr Locks

COURANT COMMUNITY - PUTNAM (THUR)

285 Broad St, Hartford, CT, 06105-3785, Hartford, USA; gen tel (860) 241-6200; gen fax (860) 520-6941; disp adv e-mail lckelleher@courant.com; class adv e-mail classifieds@courant.com; ed e-mail agriffin@courant.com; web site courant.com/community
Circulation: 9,598fr; CVC
Advertising rate: 1/16 Pg $327.00; 1/8 Pg $654.00; 1/4 Pg $1308.00
Group: Tronc, Inc.
Adv. Sales .... Mary Lou Stoneburner
Circ. .... Brian McEnery
Community Sales Mgr. .... Christine Neves
VP of Adv. .... Mary Lou Stoneburner
Pub./Ed.-in-Chief .... Andrew S. Julien
Delivery Method: Mail, Newsstand, Carrier, Racks
Areas Served: Colchester, East Hartford, Enfield, Glastonbury, Hebron, Columbia, Jewett City, Killingsly, Plainfield, Manchester, Putnam, South Windsor, Stafford, Vernon, Windham, Mansfield, Windor, Windosr Locks

COURANT COMMUNITY - SOUTH WINDSOR (THUR)

285 Broad St, Hartford, CT, 06105-3785, Hartford, USA; gen tel (860) 241-6200; gen fax (860) 520-6941; disp adv e-mail lckelleher@courant.com; class adv e-mail classifieds@courant.com; ed e-mail agriffin@courant.com; web site courant.com/community
Circulation: 7,604fr; CVC
Advertising rate: 1/16 Pg $327.00; 1/8 Pg $654.00; 1/4 Pg $1308.00
Group: Tronc, Inc.
Adv. Sales .... Mary Lou Stoneburner
Circ. .... Brian McEnery
Pub./Ed.-in-Chief .... Andrew S. Julien
Community Sales Mgr. .... Christine Neves
VP of Adv. .... Mary Lou Stoneburner
Delivery Method: Mail, Newsstand, Carrier, Racks
Areas Served: Colchester, East Hartford, Enfield, Glastonbury, Hebron, Columbia, Jewett City, Killingsly, Plainfield, Manchester, Putnam, South Windsor, Stafford, Vernon, Windham, Mansfield, Windor, Windosr Locks

COURANT COMMUNITY - STAFFORD (THUR)

285 Broad St, Hartford, CT, 06105-3785, Hartford, USA; gen tel (860) 241-6200; gen fax (860) 520-6941; disp adv e-mail lckelleher@courant.com; class adv e-mail classifieds@courant.com; ed e-mail agriffin@courant.com; web site courant.com/community
Circulation: 7,607fr; CVC
Advertising rate: 1/16 Pg $327.00; 1/8 Pg $654.00; 1/4 Pg $1308.00
Group: Tronc, Inc.
Adv. Sales .... Mary Lou Stoneburner
Circ. .... Brian McEnery
Pub./Ed.-in-Chief .... Andrew S. Julien
Community Sales Mgr. .... Christine Neves
VP of Adv. .... Mary Lou Stoneburner
Delivery Method: Mail, Newsstand, Carrier, Racks
Areas Served: Colchester, East Hartford, Enfield, Glastonbury, Hebron, Columbia, Jewett City, Killingsly, Plainfield, Manchester, Putnam, South Windsor, Stafford, Vernon, Windham, Mansfield, Windor, Windosr Locks

COURANT COMMUNITY - VALLEY (THUR)

285 Broad St, Hartford, CT, 06105-3785, Hartford, USA; gen tel (860) 241-6200; gen fax (860) 520-6941; disp adv e-mail lckelleher@courant.com; class adv e-mail classifieds@courant.com; ed e-mail agriffin@courant.com; web site courant.com/community
Circulation: 7,962fr; CVC
Advertising rate: 1/16 Pg $327.00; 1/8 Pg $654.00; 1/4 Pg $1308.00
Group: Tronc, Inc.
Adv. Sales .... Mary Lou Stoneburner
Circ. .... Brian McEnery
Pub./Ed.-in-Chief .... Andrew S. Julien
Community Sales Mgr. .... Christine Neves
VP of Adv. .... Mary Lou Stoneburner
Delivery Method: Mail, Newsstand, Carrier, Racks
Areas Served: Colchester, East Hartford, Enfield, Glastonbury, Hebron, Columbia, Jewett City, Killingsly, Plainfield, Manchester, Putnam, South Windsor, Stafford, Vernon, Windham, Mansfield, Windor, Windosr Locks

COURANT COMMUNITY - VERNON (THUR)

285 Broad St, Hartford, CT, 06105-3785, Hartford, USA; gen tel (860) 241-6200; gen fax (860) 520-6941; disp adv e-mail lckelleher@courant.com; class adv e-mail classifieds@courant.com; ed e-mail agriffin@courant.com; web site courant.com/community
Circulation: 15,816fr; CVC
Advertising rate: 1/16 Pg $327.00; 1/8 Pg $654.00; 1/4 Pg $1308.00
Group: Tronc, Inc.
Adv. Sales .... Mary Lou Stoneburner
Circ. .... Brian McEnery
Pub./Ed.-in-Chief .... Andrew S. Julien
Community Sales Mgr. .... Christine Neves
VP of Adv. .... Mary Lou Stoneburner
Delivery Method: Mail, Newsstand, Carrier, Racks
Areas Served: Colchester, East Hartford, Enfield, Glastonbury, Hebron, Columbia, Jewett

City, Killingsly, Plainfield, Manchester, Putnam, South Windsor, Stafford, Vernon, Windham, Mansfield, Windor, Windosr Locks

COURANT COMMUNITY - WEST HARTFORD (THUR)

285 Broad St, Hartford, CT, 06105-3719, Hartford, USA; gen tel (860) 241-6200; ed fax (860) 520-6941; disp adv e-mail lckelleher@courant.com; class adv e-mail classifieds@courant.com; ed e-mail agriffin@courant.com
Group: Tronc, Inc.
Community Sales Mgr.............Christine Neves
Pub./Ed.-in-Chief.................. Andrew S. Julien
Towns Ed.................................... Alaine Griffin
Sports Ed.................................... Jeff Otterbein
VP of Adv..................... Mary Lou Stoneburner
VP of Adv..................... Mary Lou Stoneburner

COURANT COMMUNITY - WETHERSFIELD (THUR)

285 Broad St, Hartford, CT, 06105-3785, Hartford, USA; gen tel (860) 241-6200; gen fax (860) 520-6941; disp adv e-mail lckelleher@courant.com; class adv e-mail classifieds@courant.com; ed e-mail agriffin@courant.com; web site courant.com/community
Group: Tronc, Inc.
Community Sales Mgr.............Christine Neves
Pub.. Andrew S. Julien
Towns Ed.................................... Alaine Griffin
Sports Ed.................................... Jeff Otterbein
VP of Adv..................... Mary Lou Stoneburner

COURANT COMMUNITY - WINDHAM (THUR)

285 Broad St, Hartford, CT, 06105-3785, Hartford, USA; gen tel (860) 241-6200; gen fax (860) 520-6941; disp adv e-mail lckelleher@courant.com; class adv e-mail classifieds@courant.com; ed e-mail agriffin@courant.com; web site courant.com/community
Circulation: 12,734fr; CVC
Advertising rate: 1/16 Pg $327.00; 1/8 Pg $654.00; 1/4 Pg $1308.00
Group: Tronc, Inc.
Adv. Sales..................... Mary Lou Stoneburner
Circ.. Brian McEnery
Pub./Ed.-in-Chief.................. Andrew S. Julien
Community Sales Mgr.............Christine Neves
VP of Adv..................... Mary Lou Stoneburner
Delivery Method: Mail, Newsstand, Carrier, Racks
Areas Served: Colchester, East Hartford, Enfield, Glastonbury, Hebron, Columbia, Jewett City, Killingsly, Plainfield, Manchester, Putnam, South Windsor, Stafford, Vernon, Windham, Mansfield, Windor, Windosr Locks

COURANT COMMUNITY - WINDSOR (THUR)

285 Broad St, Hartford, CT, 06105-3785, Hartford, USA; gen tel (860) 241-6200; gen fax (860) 520-6941; disp adv e-mail lckelleher@courant.com; class adv e-mail classifieds@courant.com; ed e-mail agriffin@courant.com; web site courant.com/community
Circulation: 9,689fr; CVC
Advertising rate: 1/16 Pg $327.00; 1/8 Pg $654.00; 1/4 Pg $1308.00
Group: Tronc, Inc.
Adv. Sales..................... Mary Lou Stoneburner
Pub./Ed.-in-Chief.................. Andrew S. Julien
Circ.. Brian McEnery
Community Sales Mgr.............Christine Neves
VP of Adv..................... Mary Lou Stoneburner
Delivery Method: Mail, Newsstand, Carrier, Racks
Areas Served: Colchester, East Hartford, Enfield, Glastonbury, Hebron, Columbia, Jewett City, Killingsly, Plainfield, Manchester, Putnam, South Windsor, Stafford, Vernon, Windham, Mansfield, Windor, Windosr Locks

COURANT COMMUNITY - WINDSOR LOCKS (THUR)

285 Broad St, Hartford, CT, 06105-3785, Hartford, USA; gen tel (860) 241-6200; gen fax (860) 520-6941; disp adv e-mail lckelleher@courant.com; class adv e-mail classifieds@courant.com; ed e-mail agriffin@courant.com; web site courant.com/community
Circulation: 9,887fr; CVC
Advertising rate: 1/16 Pg $327.00; 1/8 Pg $654.00; 1/4 Pg $1308.00
Group: Tronc, Inc.
Pub./Ed.-in-Chief.................. Andrew S. Julien
Adv. Sales..................... Mary Lou Stoneburner
Circ.. Brian McEnery
Community Sales Mgr.............Christine Neves
VP of Adv..................... Mary Lou Stoneburner
Delivery Method: Mail, Newsstand, Carrier, Racks
Areas Served: Colchester, East Hartford, Enfield, Glastonbury, Hebron, Columbia, Jewett City, Killingsly, Plainfield, Manchester, Putnam, South Windsor, Stafford, Vernon, Windham, Mansfield, Windor, Windosr Locks

HARTFORD BUSINESS JOURNAL (MON)

15 Lewis St, Ste 200, Hartford, CT, 06103-2503, Hartford, USA; gen tel (860) 236-9998; adv tel (860) 236-9998 ext. 139; ed tel (860) 236-9998 ext. 130 ; gen fax (860) 570-2493; disp adv e-mail dhartley@HartfordBusiness.com; ed e-mail gbordonaro@HartfordBusiness.com; web site www.hartfordbusiness.com
Circulation: 1,170pd, 7,856fr; Sworn/Estimate/Non-Audited
Advertising rate: 1/4 Pg $1920.00
Established: 1992
Group: New England Business Media
Ed.. Greg Bordonaro
Pub.. Gail Lebert
Senior Acct. Mgr......................... David Hartley
Pres..Joe Zwiebel
Delivery Method: Mail, Newsstand

MADISON

EAST HAVEN COURIER (THUR)

724 Boston Post Rd, Ste 202, Madison, CT, 06443-3039, New Haven, USA; gen tel (203) 245-1877; adv tel 2032451877 ext 6142; ed tel 2032451877 ext 6500; gen fax (203) 245-9773; disp adv e-mail advertising@shorepublishing.com; ed e-mail news@shorepublishing.com; web site http://www.zip06.com/section/easthaven
Circulation: 10,325fr; VAC
Advertising rate: Open inch rate $14.00
Group: The Day Publishing Co.
Pub...Robyn Collins
Ed.. Brian Boyd
Acct. Manager.......................... John McKenna
Prod. Mgr.................................... Julie Johnson
Ed... Tim Cotter
Mechanical Specifications: Type page 9.7 x 10.25; 5 cols, 1.80, 0.20 between
Delivery Method: Carrier, Racks
Areas Served: East Haven

GUILFORD COURIER (THUR)

724 Boston Post Rd, Ste 202, Madison, CT, 06443-3039, New Haven, USA; gen tel (203) 245-1877; adv tel (203) 245-1877, ext. 6142; ed tel (203) 245-1877 ext 6500; gen fax (203) 245-9773; disp adv e-mail collins@shorepublishing.com; class adv e-mail classifieds@shorepublishing.com; ed e-mail b.boyd@shorepublishing.com; web site www.zip06.com/guilford
Circulation: 8,483fr; VAC
Advertising rate: Open inch rate $14.00
Group: The Day Publishing Co.
Pub...Robyn Collins
Ed.. Brian Boyd
Prodn. Mgr. .... Alan Ellis
Prod. Mgr.................................... Julie Johnson
Classified Adv. Mgr.......................... Dave Ellis
Mechanical Specifications: Type page 9.7 x 10.25; 5 cols, 1.80, 0.20 between
Equipment & Software: Hardware — APP/Mac, PC.
Delivery Method: Carrier, Racks
Areas Served: Clinton, Westbrook, Old Saybrook

HARBOR NEWS (THUR)

724 Boston Post Rd, Ste 202, Madison, CT, 06443-3039, New Haven, USA; gen tel (203) 245-1877; adv tel 2032451877 ext 6142; ed tel 2032451877 ext 6500; gen fax (203) 245-9773; disp adv e-mail advertising@shorepublishing.com; ed e-mail news@shorepublishing.com; web site www.zip06.com
Circulation: 11,176fr; VAC
Advertising rate: Open inch rate $14.00
Group: Shore Publishing LLC
Pub...Robyn Collins
Managing Editor............................ Brian Boyd
Prodn. Mgr. .... Alan Ellis
Acct. Manager.........................Shannon Timme
Prod. Mgr.................................... Julie Johnson
Mechanical Specifications: Type page 9.7 x 10.25; 5 cols, 1.80, 0.20 between
Equipment & Software: Hardware — APP/Mac, PC.
Delivery Method: Mail, Carrier, Racks
Areas Served: Clinton, Westbrook, Old Saybrook

NORTH HAVEN COURIER (THUR)

724 Boston Post Rd, Ste 202, Madison, CT, 06443-3039, New Haven, USA; gen tel (203) 245-1877; adv tel 2032451877 ext 6142; ed tel 2032451877 ext 6500; gen fax (203) 245-9773; disp adv e-mail advertising@shorepublishing.com; ed e-mail news@shorepublishing.com; web site www.zip06.com/section/NorthHaven
Circulation: 8,518fr; VAC
Advertising rate: Open inch rate $14.00
Group: The Day Publishing Co.
Ed.. Brian Boyd
Pub...Robyn Collins
Acct. Manager.......................... John McKenna
Prod. Mgr.................................... Julie Johnson
Mechanical Specifications: Type page 9.7 x 10.25; 5 cols, 1.80, 0.20 between
Delivery Method: Carrier, Racks
Areas Served: North Haven

SOURCE (THUR)

724 Boston Post Rd, Ste 202, Madison, CT, 06443-3039, New Haven, USA; gen tel (203) 245-1877; adv tel 2032451877 ext 6142; ed tel 2032451877 ext 6500; gen fax (203) 245-9773; disp adv e-mail advertising@shorepublishing.com; ed e-mail news@shorepublishing.com; web site www.zip06.com/section/Madison
Circulation: 9,283fr; CVC
Advertising rate: Open inch rate $14.00
Established: 1996
Group: The Day Publishing Co.
Acct. Manager.......................... Denise Forrest
Pub...Robyn Collins
Mng. Ed.. Brian Boyd
Prod. Mgr.................................... Julie Johnson
Mechanical Specifications: Type page 9.7 x 10.25; 5 cols, 1.80, 0.20 between
Equipment & Software: Hardware — APP/Mac, PC.
Delivery Method: Carrier, Racks
Areas Served: Branford, North Branford, Northford

THE SOUND (THUR)

724 Boston Post Rd, Ste 202, Madison, CT, 06443-3039, New Haven, USA; gen tel (203) 245-1877; adv tel 2032451877 ext 6142; ed tel 2032451877 ext 6500; gen fax (203) 245-9773; disp adv e-mail advertising@shorepublishing.com; ed e-mail news@shorepublishing.com; web site www.zip06.com/section/Branford
Circulation: 13,625fr; VAC
Advertising rate: Open inch rate $14.00
Established: 1994
Group: The Day Publishing Co.
Pub...Robyn Collins
Managing Ed.................................. Brian Boyd
Acct. Manager................................Nikki Brinn
Prod. Mgr.................................... Julie Johnson
Mechanical Specifications: Type page 9.7 x 10.25; 5 cols, 1.80, 0.20 between
Equipment & Software: Hardware — APP/Mac, PC.
Areas Served: Madison-Killingworth

VALLEY COURIER (THUR)

724 Boston Post Rd, Ste 202, Madison, CT, 06443-3039, New Haven, USA; gen tel (203) 245-1877; adv tel 2032451877 ext 6142; ed tel 2032451877 ext 6500; gen fax (203) 245-9773; disp adv e-mail advertising@shorepublishing.com; ed e-mail news@shorepublishing.com; web site www.zip06.com
Circulation: 6,071fr; VAC
Advertising rate: Open inch rate $14.00
Group: The Day Publishing Co.
Acct. Manager........................ Hollis Romanelli
Ed.. Brian Boyd
Pub...Robyn Collins
Prodn. Mgr. .... Allan Ellis
Mechanical Specifications: Type page 9.7 x 10.25; 5 cols, 1.80, 0.20 between
Equipment & Software: Hardware — APP/Mac, PC.
Delivery Method: Carrier, Racks
Areas Served: Essex, Chester, Deep River

MERIDEN

BERLIN CITIZEN (THUR)

500 S Broad St, Ste 2, Meriden, CT, 06450-6643, New Haven, USA; gen tel (203) 235-1661; adv tel (203) 317-2312; ed tel (203) 317-2447; gen fax (203) 639-0210; adv fax (203) 235-4048; disp adv e-mail advertising@record-journal.com; ed e-mail newsroom@record-journal.com; web site www.berlincitizen.com
Circulation: 9,200fr; Sworn/Estimate/Non-Audited
Advertising rate: Open inch rate $16.45
Established: 1997
Group: The Record-Journal Publishing Co.
Pub..Eliot C. White
Adv. Dir.................................Kimberley Boath
Mng. Ed...................................... Robert Mayer
Ed.. Nick Carroll
Areas Served: Berlin, East Berlin, Kensington

THE PLAINVILLE CITIZEN (THUR)

500 S Broad St, Ste 2, Meriden, CT, 06450-6643, New Haven, USA; gen tel (203) 235-1661; adv tel (203) 317-2312; ed tel (203) 317-2449; gen fax (203) 639-0210; adv fax (203) 235-4048; disp adv e-mail kboath@record-journal.com; class adv e-mail advertising@plainvillecitizen.com; ed e-mail news@theplainvillecitizen.com; web site www.plainvillecitizen.com
Circulation: 9,200fr; Sworn/Estimate/Non-Audited
Advertising rate: Open inch rate $13.45
Established: 2002
Group: The Record-Journal Publishing Co.
Pub..Eliot C. White
Mng. Ed............................Crystal Maldonaldo
Ad. Dir...................................Kimberley Boath
Areas Served: Plainville

THE SOUTHINGTON CITIZEN (FRI)

500 S Broad St, Ste 2, Meriden, CT, 06450-6643, New Haven, USA; gen tel (203) 235-1661; adv tel (203) 317-2312; ed tel (860) 620-5960; gen fax (203) 639-0210; adv fax (203) 235-4048; disp adv e-mail kboath@record-journal.com; class adv e-mail advertising@thesouthingtoncitizen.com; ed e-mail news@thesouthingtoncitizen.com; web site www.southingtoncitizen.com
Circulation: 9,800fr; Sworn/Estimate/Non-Audited
Advertising rate: Open inch rate $9.50
Group: The Record-Journal Publishing Co.
News Editor.................................. Nick Carroll
Managing Ed......................... Carolyn Wallach
Ad. Dir...................................Kimberley Boath
Pres./Pub..Eliot White
Areas Served: Southington, Plantsville, Marion, Milldale

TOWN TIMES (THUR)

500 S Broad St, Ste 2, Meriden, CT, 06450-6643, New Haven, USA; gen tel (203) 235-1661; adv tel (203) 317-2312; ed tel (203) 317-2219; gen fax (203) 639-0210; adv fax (203) 235-4048; disp adv e-mail kboath@record-journal.com; ed e-mail news@towntimes.com; web site www.towntimes.com
Circulation: 99pd, 14,022fr; AAM
Advertising rate: Open inch rate $16.81
Established: 2002
Group: The Record-Journal Publishing Co.

Pub...Eliot C. White
Adv. Dir....................................Kimberley Boath
Managing Ed..........................Carolyn Wallach
Adv. Sales.......................................Joy Boone
Ed...Stephanie Wilcox
Areas Served: Durham, Middlefield , Rockfall

NEW BRITAIN

NEWINGTON TOWN CRIER (FRI)

1 Herald Sq, New Britain, CT, 06051-5009, Hartford, USA; gen tel (860) 225-4601; adv tel (860) 225-4601 ext 281; ed tel (860) 225-4601 ext 359; gen fax (860) 223-8171; disp adv e-mail gcurran@centralctcommunications.com; ed e-mail mbatterson@centralctcommunications.com; web site www.newingtontowncrier.com
Advertising rate: Open inch rate $12.00
Group: Central Connecticut Communications LLC
Ad. Manger..................................Gary Curran
Managing Editor...........................Daniel Kline
Owner and Publisher..........Michael Schroeder
Delivery Method: Mail
Areas Served: Newington

NEW CANAAN

NEW CANAAN ADVERTISER (THUR)

42 Vitti St, New Canaan, CT, 06840-4823, Fairfield, USA; gen tel (203) 966-9541; adv tel 2039669541 ext 106; ed tel 2039669541 ext 112; gen fax (203) 966-8006; disp adv e-mail ads@hersamacorn.com; ed e-mail editor@ncadvertiser.com; web site www.ncadvertiser.com
Circulation: 4,236pd,; CAC
Advertising rate: Open inch rate $13.50
Established: 1908
Group: HAN Network
Pub.....................................V. Donald Hersam
COO ....Martin V. Hersam
Sports Ed.................................Dave Stewart
Ed...Joshua Fisher
Account Exec............................Elizabeth Cote
VP of Sales.......................Mary Anne Hersam
Circ. Mgr...............................Bruce McDougall
Mechanical Specifications: Type page 10.75 x 21; E - 6 cols, 1 7/8, between; A - 6 cols, 1 7/8, between; C - 9 cols, 1 1/8, between.
Delivery Method: Mail, Newsstand, Racks
Areas Served: New Canaan

NEW HAVEN

FAIRFIELD MINUTEMAN (THUR)

100 Gando Dr, New Haven, CT, 06513-1049, New Haven, USA; gen tel (203) 752-2711; adv tel (203) 789-5484; ed tel (203) 789-5726; gen fax (203) 789-5309; disp adv e-mail news@fairfieldminuteman.com; class adv e-mail pwalsh@journalregister.com; ed e-mail editor@fairfieldminuteman.com; web site www.minutemannewscenter.com
Circulation: 0pd, 20,524fr; CAC
Advertising rate: Open inch rate $22.33
Group: Digital First MediaEditions: (1) 1 total; Westport (15,769);
Gen. Mgr..John Slater
Ed...Donna Saracco
Adv. Dir...Ken Kopas
Mechanical Specifications: Type page 10.25 x 15.25; 5 cols, 1.875, 0.25 betweenEquipment & Software: Hardware — PC, APP/Mac; Software — QPS/QuarkXPress 3.32, Adobe/Illustrator 6.0.
Areas Served: Fairfield County

SHORELINE TIMES (FRI)

100 Gando Dr, New Haven, CT, 06513-1049, New Haven, USA; gen tel (203) 789-5200; adv tel (203) 789-5484; gen fax (203) 789-5309; disp adv e-mail kkopas@westportminuteman.com; web site www.shorelinetimes.com
Circulation: 3,544pd,; AAM
Advertising rate: Open inch rate $18.70
Group: Digital First Media
Gen. Mgr.......................................John Slater
Editor.......................................Susan Braden
Ad. Dir...Ken Kopas
Mechanical Specifications: Type page 10 1/4 x 16; E - 4 cols, 2 3/8, 1/6 between; A - 6 cols, 1 5/8, 1/6 between; C - 6 cols, 1 5/8, 1/6 between.Equipment & Software: Hardware — APP/Power Macs, Tab/Printers 1200 dpi; Software — QPS/QuarkXPress 3.2, Adobe/Photoshop 2.5, Multi-Ad/Creator 3.1, Microsoft/Windows 95.
Areas Served: Killingworth, Clinton, Chester, Deep River, Westbrook, Essex, Old Saybrook, Old Lyme

WEST HARTFORD NEWS (FRI)

100 Gando Dr, New Haven, CT, 06513-1049, New Haven, USA; gen tel (860) 294-0157; adv tel 1 (800) 922-7066; ed tel (860) 294-0157; gen fax (860) 347-4425; disp adv e-mail jgallacher@registercitizen.com; class adv e-mail sam@middletownpress.com; ed e-mail jberry@21st-centurymedia.com; web site www.westhartfordnews.com
Circulation: 10,000fr; Sworn/Estimate/Non-Audited
Advertising rate: Open inch rate $100.76
Established: 1931
Group: Digital First Media
Exec. Ed...............................Douglas Clement
Ed..John Berry
Matt DeRienzo
Adv. Dir......................................Bob Reneson
Mechanical Specifications: Type page 11.63 x 21; 6 cols, 1.80, 0.20 between
Delivery Method: Mail, Newsstand
Areas Served: West Hartford

WESTPORT MINUTEMAN (THUR)

100 Gando Dr, New Haven, CT, 06513-1049, New Haven, USA; gen tel (203) 752-2711; adv tel (203) 789-5484; ed tel (203) 789-5750; gen fax (203) 789-5309; disp adv e-mail kkopas@westportminuteman.com; ed e-mail editor@westportminuteman.com; web site www.minutemannewscenter.com - 110,000(views)
Circulation: 0pd, 11,215fr; CAC
Advertising rate: Open inch rate $22.33
Established: 1992
Group: 21st Century Media
Gen. Mgr..John Slater
Ad. Director....................................Ken Kopas
Ed...Tom Henry
Mechanical Specifications: Type page 10.25 x 15.25; 5 cols, 1.875, 0.25 between
Delivery Method: Mail
Areas Served: Westport, Weston

NEW LONDON

NEW LONDON TIMES (THUR, FRI)

47 Eugene Oneill Dr, New London, CT, 06320-6351, New London, USA; gen tel (860) 442-2200; adv tel (860) 701-4203; ed tel (860) 701-4379; gen fax (860) 437-1176; disp adv e-mail B.Briere@theday.com; ed e-mail t.dwyer@theday.com; web site www.zip06.com
Circulation: 11,261fr; CVC
Advertising rate: Open inch rate $13.25
Group: The Day Publishing Co.
Exec. Ed..................................Timothy Dwyer
Pub...Lisa Miksis
Ed..Marisa Nadolny
Adv. Dir...Bob Briere
Pub...Gary Farrugia
Mechanical Specifications: Type page 9.7 x 10.25; 5 cols, 1.80, 0.20 between
Areas Served: New London

THE GROTON TIMES (THUR, FRI)

47 Eugene Oneill Dr, New London, CT, 06320-6306, New London, USA; gen tel (860) 442-2200; adv tel (860) 701-4203; ed tel (860) 701-4379; gen fax (860) 437-1176; disp adv e-mail B.Briere@theday.com; ed e-mail t.dwyer@theday.com; web site www.zip06.com
Circulation: 11,687fr; CVC
Advertising rate: Open inch rate $13.25
Established: 1995
Group: The Day Publishing Co.
Pub...Gary Farrugia
Exec. Ed..................................Timothy Dwyer
Ad. Dir...Bob Briere
Pub./Circ. Mgr...............................Lisa Miksis
ed...Tim Cotter
Mechanical Specifications: Type page 9.7 x 10.25; 5 cols, 1.80, 0.20 between
Areas Served: Groton, Groton City

THE LYME TIMES (THUR)

47 Eugene Oneill Dr, New London, CT, 06320-6306, New London, USA; gen tel (860) 442-2200; adv tel (860) 701-4203; ed tel (860) 701-4379; gen fax (860) 437-1176; disp adv e-mail B.Briere@theday.com; ed e-mail t.dwyer@theday.com; web site www.zip06.com
Circulation: 14,591fr; CVC
Advertising rate: Open inch rate $14.00
Group: The Day Publishing Co.
Adv. Dir..Bob Briere
Exec. Ed..................................Timothy Dwyer
Pub...Lisa Miksis
Classifieds Adv. Mgr.........................Dave Ellis
Ed..Tim Cotter
Mechanical Specifications: Type page 9.7 x 10.25; 5 cols, 1.80, 0.20 between
Areas Served: Lyme, Old Lyme, East Lyme, Niantic, Salem

THE MONTVILLE TIMES (THUR, FRI)

47 Eugene Oneill Dr, New London, CT, 06320-6306, New London, USA; gen tel (860) 442-2200; adv tel (860) 701-4203; ed tel (860) 701-4379; gen fax (860) 437-1176; disp adv e-mail B.Briere@theday.com; ed e-mail t.dwyer@theday.com; web site www.zip06.com
Circulation: 6,980fr; CVC
Advertising rate: Open inch rate $13.25
Group: The Day
Exec. Ed..................................Timothy Dwyer
Adv. Dir..Bob Briere
Pub...Lisa Miksis
Classified Adv. Mgr...........................Dave Ellis
Mechanical Specifications: Type page 9.7 x 10.25; 5 cols, 1.80, 0.20 between
Areas Served: Oakdale, Uncasville

THE MYSTIC TIMES (THUR)

47 Eugene Oneill Dr, New London, CT, 06320-6306, New London, USA; gen tel (860) 442-2200; adv tel (860) 701-4203; ed tel (860) 701-4379; gen fax (860) 437-1176; disp adv e-mail B.Briere@theday.com; ed e-mail t.dwyer@theday.com; web site www.zip06.com
Circulation: 7,465fr; CVC
Advertising rate: Open inch rate $14.00
Group: The Day Publishing Co.
Pub...Gary Farrugia
Exec. Ed..................................Timothy Dwyer
Ad. Dir...Bob Briere
Classified Adv. Mgr...........................Dave Ellis
Ed..Tim Cotter
Mechanical Specifications: Type page 9.7 x 10.25; 5 cols, 1.80, 0.20 between
Areas Served: Mystic, West Mystic, Old Mystic, Noank, Groton Long Point

THE STONINGTON TIMES (THUR)

47 Eugene Oneill Dr, New London, CT, 06320-6306, New London, USA; gen tel (860) 442-2200; adv tel (860) 701-4203; ed tel (860) 701-4379; gen fax (860) 437-1176; disp adv e-mail B.Briere@theday.com; ed e-mail t.dwyer@theday.com; web site www.zip06.com
Circulation: 8,791fr; CVC
Advertising rate: Open inch rate $14.00
Group: The Day Publishing Co.
Pub...Lisa Miksis
Adv. Dir..Bob Briere
Exec. Ed..................................Timothy Dwyer
Managing Ed...............................Brian Boyd
Ed..Tim Cotter
Mechanical Specifications: Type page 9.7 x 10.25; 5 cols, 1.80, 0.20 between
Areas Served: North Stonington, Stonington, Pawcatuck

THE THAMES RIVER TIMES (THUR)

47 Eugene Oneill Dr, New London, CT, 06320-6306, New London, USA; gen tel (860) 442-2200; adv tel (860) 701-4203; ed tel (860) 701-4379; gen fax (860) 437-1176; disp adv e-mail r.collins@shorepublishing.com; ed e-mail t.dwyer@theday.com; web site www.zip06.com
Circulation: 7,626fr; CVC
Advertising rate: Open inch rate $14.00
Established: 1986
Group: The Day
Executive Ed...........................Timothy Dwyer
Ad. Director.....................................Bob Briere
Pub...Lisa Miksis
Ed..Tim Cotter
Mechanical Specifications: Type page 9.7 x 10.25; 5 cols, 1.80, 0.20 between
Areas Served: Gales Ferry, Ledyard, Preston

WATERFORD TIMES (THUR, FRI)

47 Eugene Oneill Dr, New London, CT, 06320-6306, New London, USA; gen tel (860) 442-2200; adv tel (860) 701-4203; ed tel (860) 701-4379; gen fax (860) 437-1176; disp adv e-mail B.Briere@theday.com; ed e-mail t.dwyer@theday.com; web site www.zip06.com
Circulation: 8,546fr; CVC
Advertising rate: Open inch rate $13.25
Group: The Day Publishing Co.
Pub...Lisa Miksis
Exec. Ed..................................Timothy Dwyer
Adv. Dir..Bob Briere
Managing Ed...............................Brian Boyd
Ed..Tim Cotter
Mechanical Specifications: Type page 9.7 x 10.25; 5 cols, 1.80, 0.20 between
Areas Served: Waterford

NEW MILFORD

NEW MILFORD SPECTRUM (FRI)

45B Main St, New Milford, CT, 06776-2807, Litchfield, USA; gen tel (203) 744-5100; adv tel (203) 731-3427; ed tel (860) 355-7323; gen fax (203) 792-8730; disp adv e-mail sspinosa@hearstmediact.com; ed e-mail ncummings@newmilford.com; web site www.newmilfordspectrum.com
Circulation: 19,771pd, 20,598fr; Sworn/Estimate/Non-Audited
Advertising rate: Open inch rate $19.30
Group: Hearst Communications, Inc.
Ed.......................................Norm Cummings
Pub..Shawn Palmer
Ad. Dir..................................Stephen Spinosa

NEWTOWN

ANTIQUES & THE ARTS WEEKLY (FRI)

5 Church Hill Rd, Newtown, CT, 06470-1605, Fairfield, USA; gen tel (203) 426-3141; adv tel (203) 426-8036; gen fax (203) 426-1394; adv fax (203) 426-1394; disp adv e-mail sue@thebee.com; ed e-mail antiques@thebee.com; web site http://www.antiquesandthearts.com
Advertising rate: Open inch rate $13.45
Established: 1963
Group: Bee Publishing Co., Inc.
Pub & Ed..............................R. Scudder Smith
Mechanical Specifications: Type page 9 3/4 x 15 1/4; A - 5 cols, 1 3/4; 1/4 between
Delivery Method: Mail, Newsstand
Areas Served: 06470

THE NEWTOWN BEE (FRI)

5 Church Hill Rd, Newtown, CT, 06470-1605, Fairfield, USA; gen tel (203) 426-3141; gen fax (203) 426-5169; disp adv e-mail ellen@thebee.com; ed e-mail editor@thebee.com; web site www.newtownbee.com
Circulation: 8,000pd, 6,300fr; Sworn/Estimate/Non-Audited
Advertising rate: Open inch rate $13.10

Established: 1877
Group: Bee Publishing Co., Inc.
Publisher.............................. R. Scudder Smith
Adv. Manager.............................Ellen Therrien
Ed. .... Nancy Crevier
Delivery Method: Mail, Newsstand

NORWALK

THE WILTON VILLAGER (THUR)

1 Selleck St, Norwalk, CT, 06855-1120, Fairfield, USA; gen tel (203) 846-3281; adv tel (203) 354-1012; ed tel (203) 354-1065; gen fax (203) 846-9897; disp adv e-mail dhanson@thehour.com; class adv e-mail classified@thehour.com; ed e-mail cwright@thehour.com; web site www.wiltonvillager.com; www.thehour.com
Circulation: 800pd, 5,000fr; Sworn/Estimate/Non-Audited
Advertising rate: Open inch rate $22.00
Established: 1995
Pub./COO ....Chet Valiante
Adv. Dir.......................................Debra Hanson
Ed. .... Chase Wright
Sports Ed...John Nash
Vice Pres., Opns..........................Mark C. Koch
Prodn. Dir................................ Robert Marsala
VP Sales and marketing.................John Brozs
Circ Manager..........................Darlene Temple
Mechanical Specifications: Type page 13 x 21 1/4; E - 6 cols, between; A - 6 cols, between; C - 10 cols, between.Equipment & Software: Hardware — APP/Mac; Presses — G/Cosmo; Software — QPS/QuarkXPress, Adobe/Photoshop.
Delivery Method: Mail, Newsstand, Carrier
Areas Served: 06897

PAWCATUCK

MYSTIC RIVER PRESS (THUR)

99 Mechanic St, Pawcatuck, CT, 06379-2187, New London, USA; gen tel (860) 495-8200; gen fax (401) 348-5080; ed e-mail news@thewesterlysun.com; web site www.mysticriverpress.com
Group: Sun Publishing Company
Adv .... John Layton
Classified Advertising.................. Karen Davis
Delivery Method: Mail
Areas Served: Groton, North Stonington, Mystic, Old Mystic and West Mystic

THE EXPRESS (THUR)

99 Mechanic St, Pawcatuck, CT, 06379-2187, New London, USA; gen tel (401) 348-1000; adv tel (860) 495-8277; ed tel (860) 495-8224; gen fax (401) 348-5080; adv fax (401) 348-3080; ed fax (401) 348-3080; disp adv e-mail kdavis@thewesterlysun.com; class adv e-mail classified@thewesterlysun.com; ed e-mail editorial@thewesterlysun.com; web site www.thewesterlysun.com
Circulation: 23,680fr; VAC
Advertising rate: Open inch rate $18.00
Group: Sun Publishing Company
Associate Publisher...................Kelly Tremaine
Vice Pres./Ed......................... David Tranchida
Ass. Pub. ....Kelly Tremaine
Class. Adv. Mgr. .... Karen Davis
Delivery Method: Mail, Racks
Areas Served: Washington County

THE RESIDENT (WED)

252 S Broad St, Pawcatuck, CT, 06379-7924, New London, USA; gen tel (860) 599-1221; adv tel (860) 608-0467; gen fax (860) 599-1400; disp adv e-mail alexisinmystic@aol.com; class adv e-mail classifieds@theresident.com; ed e-mail editor@theresident.com; web site www.theresident.com
Circulation: 29,251fr; CVC
Advertising rate: Open inch rate 36.00
Established: 1990
Pub./Adv. Sales............................... Alexis Ann
Mechanical Specifications: Type page 10 x 13; E - 5 cols, 1 7/8, 1/4 between.
Delivery Method: Racks

RIDGEFIELD

EASTON COURIER (THUR)

16 Bailey Ave, Ridgefield, CT, 06877-4512, Fairfield, USA; gen tel (203) 438-1183; adv tel (203) 402-2327; ed tel (203) 894-3343; gen fax (203) 926-2091; disp adv e-mail dcosenza@hersamacorn.com; ed e-mail ndoniger@hersamacorn.com; web site www.eastoncourier.com
Circulation: 1,156pd, 99fr; CVC
Advertising rate: Open inch rate $14.50
Established: 1973
Group: HAN Network
Pub. Mgr ....Thomas Nash
Adv. Mgr...........................Mary Anne Hersam
Ed. .... Nancy Doniger
Account Exec......................... Donna Cosenza
Circ. Mgr............................... Bruce McDougall
Adv. Sales.............................. Shelagh Barrett
Classifieds Adv. Mgr.................... Rose Sayers
Prod. Mgr.. Greg Moy
Mechanical Specifications: Type page 10.75 x 21; E - 6 cols, 1 7/8, between; A - 6 cols, 1 7/8, between; C - 9 cols, 1 1/8, between.
Delivery Method: Mail, Newsstand
Areas Served: Easton

REDDING PILOT (THUR)

16 Bailey Ave, Ridgefield, CT, 06877-4512, Fairfield, USA; gen tel (203) 894-3331; adv tel (203) 894-3324; ed tel (203) 894-3337; gen fax (203) 438-3395; disp adv e-mail kforrest@hersamacorn.com; ed e-mail pilot@thereddingpilot.com; web site www.thereddingpilot.com
Circulation: 1,859pd,; CAC
Advertising rate: Open inch rate $14.50
Established: 1966
Group: HAN Network
Pub....................................... Thomas B. Nash
Gen. Mgr. ....Martin V. Hersam
VP of Sales.......................Mary Anne Hersam
Ed. ....Susan Wolf
Sports Ed.................................Rocco Valluzzo
Circ. Mgr............................... Bruce McDougall
Mechanical Specifications: Type page 10.75 x 21; E - 6 cols, 1 7/8, between; A - 6 cols, 1 7/8, between; C - 9 cols, 1 1/8, between.
Delivery Method: Mail, Newsstand
Areas Served: Redding

RIDGEFIELD PRESS (THUR)

16 Bailey Ave, Ridgefield, CT, 06877-4512, Fairfield, USA; gen tel (203) 438-6544; adv tel (203) 894-3322; ed tel (203) 894-3350; gen fax (203) 438-4269; disp adv e-mail lcampbell@hersamacorn.com; web site www.theridgefieldpress.com
Circulation: 5,528pd,; CAC
Advertising rate: Open inch rate $14.50
Established: 1875
Group: HAN Network
Pub....................................... Thomas B. Nash
COO ....Martin V. Hersam
VP of Sales.......................Mary Anne Hersam
Exec. Ed.....................................Jack Sanders
News Ed. ....Macklin K. Reid
Sports Ed.......................................Tim Murphy
Account Executive.................Laurie Campbell
Classifieds Adv. Mgr.................... Rose Sayers
Mechanical Specifications: Type page 10.75 x 21; E - 6 cols, 1 7/8, between; A - 6 cols, 1 7/8, between; C - 9 cols, 1 1/8, between.
Delivery Method: Mail, Newsstand
Areas Served: Ridgefield

WESTON FORUM (THUR)

16 Bailey Ave, Ridgefield, CT, 06877-4512, Fairfield, USA; gen tel (203) 894-3332; adv tel (203) 402-2329; ed tel (203) 894-3328; gen fax (203) 762-3120; disp adv e-mail dpross@hersamacorn.com; ed e-mail editor@thewestonforum.com; web site www.thewestonforum.com
Circulation: 1,859pd,; CAC
Advertising rate: Open inch rate $14.50
Established: 1970
Group: HAN Network
Pub....................................... Thomas B. Nash
Gen. Mgr. ....Martin V. Hersam
VP of Sales.......................Mary Anne Hersam
Ed. ....Kimberly Donnelly
Sports Ed.................................Rocco Valluzzo
Account Exec.............................. Dave Pross
Circ. Mgr............................... Bruce McDougall
Mechanical Specifications: Type page 10.75 x 21; E - 6 cols, 1 7/8, between; A - 6 cols, 1 7/8, between; C - 9 cols, 1 1/8, between.
Delivery Method: Mail, Newsstand
Areas Served: Weston

WILTON BULLETIN (THUR)

16 Bailey Ave, Ridgefield, CT, 06877-4512, Fairfield, USA; gen tel (203) 894-3330; adv tel (203) 894-3323; ed tel (203) 894-3333; gen fax (203) 762-3120; disp adv e-mail tjackse@hersamacorn.com; ed e-mail editor@wiltonbulletin.com; web site www.wiltonbulletin.com
Circulation: 2,527pd,; CAC
Advertising rate: Open inch rate $14.50
Established: 1937
Group: HAN Network
Pub....................................... Thomas B. Nash
COO ....Martin V. Hersam
VP of Sales.......................Mary Anne Hersam
Ed. .... Jeannette Ross
Sports Ed.......................................Tim Murphy
Account Exec.........................Thomas Jackse
Circ. Mgr............................... Bruce McDougall
Mechanical Specifications: Type page 10.75 x 21; E - 6 cols, 1 7/8, between; A - 6 cols, 1 7/8, between; C - 9 cols, 1 1/8, between.
Delivery Method: Mail, Newsstand, Racks
Areas Served: Wilton

SHELTON

BRIDGEPORT NEWS (THUR)

1000 Bridgeport Ave, Shelton, CT, 06484-4660, Fairfield, USA; gen tel (203) 926-2080; adv tel (203) 402-2329; ed tel (203) 402-2355; gen fax (203) 926-2091; disp adv e-mail dpross@hersamacorn.com; class adv e-mail class@hersamacorn.com; ed e-mail bridgeportnews@hersamacorn.com; web site www.thebridgeportnews.com
Circulation: 9,797pd,; Sworn/Estimate/Non-Audited
Advertising rate: Open inch rate $14.50
Established: 1985
Digital Platform - Mobile: Android
Digital Platform - Tablet: Android
Ed. ....Susan Chaves
Pub..Tom Nash
Mng. Ed.................................Nancy Doniger
Mechanical Specifications: Type page 12 x 21; E - 6 cols, 1 7/8, between; A - 6 cols, 1 7/8, between; C - 10 cols, 1 1/8, between. Equipment & Software: Hardware — APP/Mac; Presses — G/Community; Software — Adobe/PageMaker 5.0.
Areas Served: 06484

FAIRFIELD SUN (THUR)

1000 Bridgeport Ave, Shelton, CT, 06484-4660, Fairfield, USA; gen tel (203) 438-1183; adv tel (203) 402-2327; ed tel (203)894-3343; gen fax (203) 926-2091; disp adv e-mail dcosenza@hersamacorn.com; ed e-mail ndoniger@hersamacorn.com; web site www.eastoncourier.com
Circulation: 6,548fr; CVC
Advertising rate: Open inch rate $14.50
Established: 1973
Pub. Mgr ....Thomas Nash
Adv. Sales.........................Mary Anne Hersam
Ed.. Nancy Doniger
Account Exec......................... Donna Cosenza
Classified Adv. Mgr....................... Rose Sayers
Circ. Mgr............................... Bruce McDougall
Prod. Mgr.. Greg Moy
Ed .... John Kovach
Mechanical Specifications: Type page 10.75 x 21; 6 cols
Delivery Method: Mail, Newsstand
Areas Served: Easton

MILFORD MIRROR (THUR)

1000 Bridgeport Ave, Shelton, CT, 06484-4660, Fairfield, USA; gen tel (203) 926-2080; adv tel (203) 402-2335; ed tel (203) 402-2315; gen fax (203) 926-2091; disp adv e-mail ads@hersamacorn.com; web site www.milfordmirror.com
Circulation: 2,932pd, 591fr; CVC
Advertising rate: Open inch rate $14.50
Established: 1985
Group: HAN Network
Sports Ed.....................................Bill Bloxsom
Ed. ....Jill Dion
Account Exec................................Jim Chiappa
VP, Sales ....Mary Anne Hersam
Classified Adv. Mgr...................... Rose Sayers
Circ. Mgr............................... Bruce McDougall
Prod. Mgr.. Greg Moy
Mechanical Specifications: Type page 10.75 x 21; E - 6 cols, 1 7/8, between; A - 6 cols, 1 7/8, between; C - 9 cols, 1 1/8, between.
Delivery Method: Mail, Newsstand
Areas Served: Milford

MONROE COURIER (THUR)

1000 Bridgeport Ave, Shelton, CT, 06484-4660, Fairfield, USA; gen tel (203) 926-2080; adv tel (203) 402-2327; ed tel (203) 402-2313; gen fax (203) 926-2091; ed fax (203) 926-2091; disp adv e-mail mahersam@ncadvertiser.com; ed e-mail monroecourier@hersamacorn.com; web site www.monroecourier.com
Circulation: 2,372pd, 129fr; CVC
Advertising rate: Open inch rate $14.50
Established: 1962
Group: HAN Network
Pub...Thomas Nash
Sports Ed.....................................Bill Bloxsom
VP of Sales.......................Mary Anne Hersam
Account Exec......................... Donna Cosenza
Circ. Mgr............................... Bruce McDougall
Prod. Mgr.. Greg Moy
Ed ....Brad Durrell
Mechanical Specifications: Type page 10.75 x 21; E - 6 cols, 1 7/8, between; A - 6 cols, 1 7/8, between; C - 9 cols, 1 1/8, between.
Delivery Method: Mail, Newsstand
Areas Served: Monroe

SHELTON HERALD (WED)

1000 Bridgeport Ave, Shelton, CT, 06484-4660, New Haven, USA; gen tel (203) 926-2080; adv tel (203) 402-2327; ed tel (203) 402-2332; gen fax (203) 926-2091; disp adv e-mail ads@hersamacorn.com; web site www.sheltonherald.com
Circulation: 3,306pd, 125fr; CVC
Advertising rate: Open inch rate $14.50
Established: 1981
Group: HAN Network
Pub....................................... Thomas B. Nash
VP of Sales.......................Mary Anne Hersam
Ed. ....Brad Durrell
Account Exec......................... Donna Cosenza
Circ. Mgr............................... Bruce McDougall
Prod. Mgr.. Greg Moy
Ed ....Kate Czaplinski
Mechanical Specifications: Type page 10.75 x 21; E - 6 cols, 1 7/8, between; A - 6 cols, 1 7/8, between; C - 9 cols, 1 1/8, between.
Delivery Method: Mail, Newsstand
Areas Served: Shelton, Huntington

STRATFORD STAR (THUR)

1000 Bridgeport Ave, Shelton, CT, 06484-4660, Fairfield, USA; gen tel (203) 926-2080; adv tel (203) 402-2335; ed tel (203) 402-2319; gen fax (203) 926-2091; disp adv e-mail jchiappa@hersamacorn.com; ed e-mail stratfordstar@hersamacorn.com; web site www.stratfordstar.com
Circulation: 3,146pd, 607fr; CVC
Advertising rate: Open inch rate $14.50
Established: 1985
Group: HAN Network
Pub....................................... Thomas B. Nash
VP of Sales.......................Mary Anne Hersam
Account Exec................................Jim Chiappa
Circ. Mgr............................... Bruce McDougall
Prod. Mgr.. Greg Moy
Ed ....Joseph Cole
Mechanical Specifications: Type page 10.75 x 21; E - 6 cols, 1 7/8, between; A - 6 cols, 1 7/8, between; C - 9 cols, 1 1/8, between.
Delivery Method: Mail
Areas Served: Stratford

TRUMBULL TIMES (THUR)
1000 Bridgeport Ave, Shelton, CT, 06484-4660, Fairfield, USA; gen tel (203) 926-2080; adv tel (203) 402-2327; ed tel (203) 402-2311; gen fax (203) 926-2091; disp adv e-mail mahersam@ncadvertiser.com; ed e-mail trumbulltimes@hersamacorn.com; web site www.trumbulltimes.com
Circulation: 3,760pd, 136fr; CVC
Advertising rate: Open inch rate $14.50
Established: 1959
Group: HAN Network
Pub....Thomas Nash
VP of Sales....Mary Anne Hersam
Sports Ed....Bill Bloxsom
Account Executive....Donna Cosenza
Circ. Mgr....Bruce McDougall
Prod. Mgr....Greg Moy
Ed....Don Eng
Mechanical Specifications: Type page 10.75 x 21; E - 6 cols, 1 7/8, between; A - 6 cols, 1 7/8, between; C - 9 cols, 1 1/8, between.
Delivery Method: Mail, Newsstand
Areas Served: Trumbull

SIMSBURY

THE VALLEY PRESS (THUR)
540 Hopmeadow St, Ste 106, Simsbury, CT, 06070-3197, Hartford, USA; gen tel (860) 651-4700; adv tel (860) 978-1345; gen fax (860) 606-9599; disp adv e-mail Melissa@TheValleyPress.net; class adv e-mail classifieds@thevalleypress.net; ed e-mail AAlbair@TheValleyPress.net; web site turleyct.com/valley-press
Circulation: 39,500fr; Sworn/Estimate/Non-Audited
Advertising rate: Open inch rate $28.50
Group: Valley Press Publishing, Inc.
Ed.-in-Chief....Abigail Albair
Ad. Director....Melissa Friedman
Pub....Keith Turley
Mechanical Specifications: Type page 10 x 14; 5 cols, 1.875, 0.125 between
Areas Served: Avon, Burlington, Canton, Farmington, Grandy, Simsbury

THE WEST HARTFORD PRESS (THUR)
540 Hopmeadow St, Simsbury, CT, 06070-2496, Hartford, USA; gen tel (800) 651-4700; adv tel (800) 978-1345; gen fax (800) 606-9599; disp adv e-mail Melissa@TheValleyPress.net; class adv e-mail classifieds@thevalleypress.net; ed e-mail AAlbair@TheValleyPress.net; web site turleyct.com/west-hartford-press
Circulation: 12,000fr; Sworn/Estimate/Non-Audited
Advertising rate: Open inch rate $24.00
Group: Valley Press Publishing, Inc.
Ed....Abigail Albair
Ad. Director....Melissa Friedman
Pub....Keith Turley
Pub....Ed Gunderson
Mechanical Specifications: Type page 10 x 14; 5 cols, 1.875, 0.125 between
Areas Served: West Hartford

SOUTHINGTON

THE OBSERVER (FRI)
213 Spring St, Southington, CT, 06489-1542, Hartford, USA; gen tel (860) 628-9645; ed tel (860) 621-6751; gen fax (860) 621-1841; disp adv e-mail sales@StepSaver.com; ed e-mail EHarris@SouthingtonObserver.com; web site www.southingtonobserver.com
Circulation: 5,394pd, 46fr; CAC
Advertising rate: Open inch rate $13.30
Gen. Mgr....Andrew Pape
Circ. Mgr....William Malia
Ed....Ed Harris
Sports Ed....John Goralski
Prodn. Mgr....Kevin Smalley
Edition Ed....Mike Chaiken
Mechanical Specifications: Type page 13 x 22 1/2; E - 5 cols, 2 1/2, 1/6 between; A - 6 cols, 2, 1/6 between; C - 6 cols, 2, 1/6 between. Equipment & Software: Hardware — 21-APP/Mac; Presses — G/Community; Software — QPS/QuarkXPress.
Areas Served: 6489

TORRINGTON

THE FOOTHILLS TRADER (WED)
59 Field St, Torrington, CT, 06790-4942, Litchfield, USA; gen tel (860) 489-3121; disp adv e-mail dnaparstek@adtaxi.com; web site foothillstrader.com
Group: Digital First Media

THE LITCHFIELD COUNTY TIMES (FRI)
59 Field St, Torrington, CT, 06790-4942, Litchfield, USA; gen tel (860) 489-3121; adv tel 8604893121 ext 350; gen fax (860) 489-6790; disp adv e-mail ads@countytimes.com; ed e-mail news@countytimes.com; web site www.countytimes.com
Circulation: 3,335pd, 25fr; AAM
Advertising rate: Open inch rate $30.08
Established: 1981
Group: Digital First Media
Pub....Paula Walsh
Circ. Asst....Susan Dubois
Ed....Douglas Clement
Sales Dir....Dan Graziano
Mechanical Specifications: Type page 11.63 x 21; 6 cols, 1.80, 0.20 betweenEquipment & Software: Hardware — APP/Mac, PC; Software — Synaptic, QPS/QuarkXPress, Microsoft, Adobe/Illustrator, Adobe/Photoshop, Sun/SunType.
Areas Served: Litchfield County

WATERBURY

CITIZEN'S NEWS (FRI)
389 Meadow St, Waterbury, CT, 06702-1808, New Haven, USA; gen tel (203) 729-2228; adv tel (203) 729-2228 ext. 11; ed tel (203) 729-2228 ext. 20; gen fax (203) 729-9099; web site www.mycitizensnews.com
Circulation: 15,000fr; Sworn/Estimate/Non-Audited
Group: American-Republican, Incorporated
Mechanical Specifications: Type page 13 x 21 1/2; E - 6 cols, 2 1/16, 1/8 between; A - 6 cols, 2 1/16, 1/8 between; C - 9 cols, 1 3/8, 1/16 between.Equipment & Software: Hardware — Mac/PC; Software — QuarkXPress, Multi-Ad.
Delivery Method: Mail
Areas Served: Beacon Falls, Naugatuck, Prospect

WINSTED

THE WINSTED JOURNAL (FRI)
452 Main St, Winsted, CT, 06098-1537, Litchfield, USA; gen tel (860) 738-4418; gen fax (860) 738-3709; disp adv e-mail advertising@lakevillejournal.com; class adv e-mail advertising@lakevillejournal.com; ed e-mail winstedjournal@sbcglobal.net; web site www.winstedjournal.com
Circulation: 592pd,; CAC
Advertising rate: Open inch rate $11.00
Established: 1996
Group: The Lakeville Journal
Office Mgr....Lauren Dimauro
Adv. Dir....Anna Mae Kupferer
Circ. Mgr....Helen Testa
Pub. & Ed. in Chief....Janet Manko
Ed....Michael Marciano
Prodn. Coord....James Clark
Mechanical Specifications: Type page 15 7/16 x 21; E - 7 cols, 2 1/16, 1/8 between; A - 7 cols, 2 1/16, 1/8 between; C - 8 cols, 1 3/4, 1/8 between.Equipment & Software: Hardware — APP/Mac; Software — Adobe/PageMaker.
Areas Served: Barkhamsted, Colebrook, New Hartford, Norfolk, Pleasant Valley, Riverton, Winchester, Winsted, Torrington, Canaan, Litchfield

WOODSTOCK

KILLINGLY VILLAGER (FRI)
283 Route 169, Woodstock, CT, 06281-3332, Windham, USA; gen tel (860) 928-1818; adv tel (877) 888-2711; gen fax (860) 928-5940; disp adv e-mail ads@villagernewspapers.com; ed e-mail aminor@villagernewspapers.com; web site www.southbridgeeveningnews.com
Circulation: 9,418fr; Sworn/Estimate/Non-Audited
Advertising rate: Open inch rate $7.50
Ed....Adam Minor
Ad. Director....Sarah Mortensen
Mechanical Specifications: Type page 11 x 20.7; 8 cols, 1.25, 0.14 between

---

DELAWARE

BETHANY BEACH

BEACHCOMBER (FRI)
33000 Coastal Hwy, Beachcomber, Bethany Beach, DE, 19930-3712, Sussex, USA; gen tel (302) 537-1881; gen fax (302) 537-9630; disp adv e-mail wave@dmg.gannett.com; web site delmarvanow.com/news/delaware
Circulation: 25,000fr; Sworn/Estimate/Non-Audited
Group: Gannett
Gen. Mgr....Pat Purdum
Beachcomber Ed....Alyson Cunningham
Exec.Ed....Michael KilianEquipment & Software: Hardware — APP/Mac; Software — Baseview.
Areas Served: The Beachcomber covers the beach communities from Ocean City, Md. to Lewes Del.

DELAWARE COAST PRESS (WED)
33000 Coastal Hwy, Unit 3, Bethany Beach, DE, 19930-3777, Sussex, USA; gen tel (302) 537-1881; adv tel (302) 537-1881 ext.125; ed tel (302) 537-1881 ext.200; gen fax (302) 537-9705; disp adv e-mail ppurdum@smgpo.gannett.com; ed e-mail acunningh@dmg.gannett.com; web site delmarvanow.com/news/delaware
Circulation: 18,618fr; CAC
Advertising rate: Open inch rate $10.50
Established: 1897
Group: Gannett
Exec. Ed....Mike Kilian
Ed....Alyson Cunningham
Operations Dir....Ron Smith
Dir. of Sales....Robb Scott
Sales Mgr....Pat Purdum
Circ. Mgr....Lou HautEquipment & Software: Hardware — APP/Mac; Software — Baseview.

THE DELAWARE WAVE (TUES)
Route 1 Lem Hickman Plaza, Bethany Beach, DE, 19973, Sussex, USA; gen tel (302) 537-1881; adv tel (302) 537-1881 ext.125; ed tel (302) 537-1881 ext.200; gen fax (302) 537-9630; disp adv e-mail ppurdum@smgpo.gannett.com; ed e-mail acunningh@dmg.gannett.com; web site delmarvanow.com/news/delaware
Circulation: 18,921fr; CAC
Advertising rate: Open inch rate $11.30
Group: Gannett
Exec. Ed....Mike Kilian
Ed....Alyson Cunningham
Op. Dir....Ron Smith
Dir. Sales....Robb Scott
Sales Mgr....Pat Purdum
Gen Mgr....Tom ClaybaughEquipment & Software: Hardware — APP/Mac; Presses — WPC/Web Leader; Software — QPS/QuarkXPress, Microsoft/Word.
Areas Served: Southeastern Sussex County

DOVER

DOVER POST (WED)
1196 S Little Creek Rd, Dover, DE, 19901-4727, Kent, USA; gen tel (302) 678-3616; adv tel (302) 346-5434; ed tel (302) 346-5418; gen fax (302) 678-8291; disp adv e-mail brigitte.mckinney@doverpost.com; class adv e-mail brandi.ford@doverpost.com; ed e-mail jesse.chadderdon@doverpost.com; web site www.doverpost.com - 263,461(views) 66,255(visitors)
Circulation: 660pd, 21,088fr; CVC
Advertising rate: 1/16 Pg $136.00; 1/8 Pg $252.00; 1/4 Pg $461.00
Established: 1975
Group: GateHouse Media, Inc.
Exec. Ed....Jesse Chadderdon
News Ed....Jennifer Hayes
Adv. Sales Mgr....Brigitte McKinney
Prod. Dir....Jay Parsons
Adv. Sales Mgr....Amanda Johnston
Circ. Mgr....Stacey Poore
Pub. & Adv. Dir....Amy Dotson-Newton
Mechanical Specifications: Type page 10.33" x 11"; 6 cols
Delivery Method: Mail, Carrier, Racks
Areas Served: Dover, Camden, Wyoming, Hartly, Magnolia and central Kent County

MILFORD BEACON (WED)
1196 S Little Creek Rd, Dover, DE, 19901-4727, Sussex, USA; gen tel (302) 678-3616; ed tel (302) 346-5418; gen fax (302) 856-0925; disp adv e-mail kathy.mcginty@doverpost.com; class adv e-mail brandi.ford@doverpost.com; ed e-mail jesse.chadderdon@doverpost.com; web site www.milfordbeacon.com - 43,823(views) 19,890(visitors)
Circulation: 235pd, 6,149fr; CVC
Advertising rate: 1/16 Pg $75.00; 1/8 Pg $139.00; 1/4 Pg $255.00
Established: 2004
Group: GateHouse Media, Inc.
Prod. Mgr....Jay Parsons
Exec. Ed....Jesse Chadderdon
News Ed....Jennifer Hayes
Sales Mgr....Kathy McGinty
Pres./Pub....Keven Todd
Pub....Clarissa Williams
Adv. Mgr....Amanda Johnston
Adv. Mgr....Brigitte McKinney
Circ. Mgr....Stacey Poore
Mechanical Specifications: Type page 10.3125" x 11"; 6 cols
Delivery Method: Mail, Racks
Areas Served: Milford and surrounding areas

THE SUSSEX COUNTIAN (THUR)
1196 S Little Creek Rd, Dover, DE, 19901-4727, Kent, USA; gen tel (302) 678-3616; ed tel (302) 346-5418; gen fax (302) 856-0925; disp adv e-mail kathy.mcginty@doverpost.com; class adv e-mail brandi.ford@doverpost.com; ed e-mail jesse.chadderdon@doverpost.com; web site www.sussexcountian.com - 42,711(views) 23,318(visitors)
Circulation: 202pd, 1,637fr; CVC
Advertising rate: 1/16 Pg $66.00; 1/8 Pg $121.00; 1/4 Pg $220.00
Established: 1886
Group: GateHouse Media, Inc.
Prod. Dir....Jay Parsons
Exec. Ed....Jesse Chadderdon
Ed....Jennifer Hayes
Sales Mgr....Kathy McGinty
Pres./Pub....Keven Todd
Pub....Clarissa Williams
Adv. Mgr....Amanda Johnston
Adv. Mgr....Brigitte McKinney
Circ. Mgr....Stacey Poore
Mechanical Specifications: Type page 10.32" x 11"; 6 cols Equipment & Software: Hardware — APP/Mac; Software — Microsoft/Word 6.0, QPS/QuarkXPress.
Delivery Method: Mail, Carrier, Racks
Areas Served: Georgetown and central Sussex County

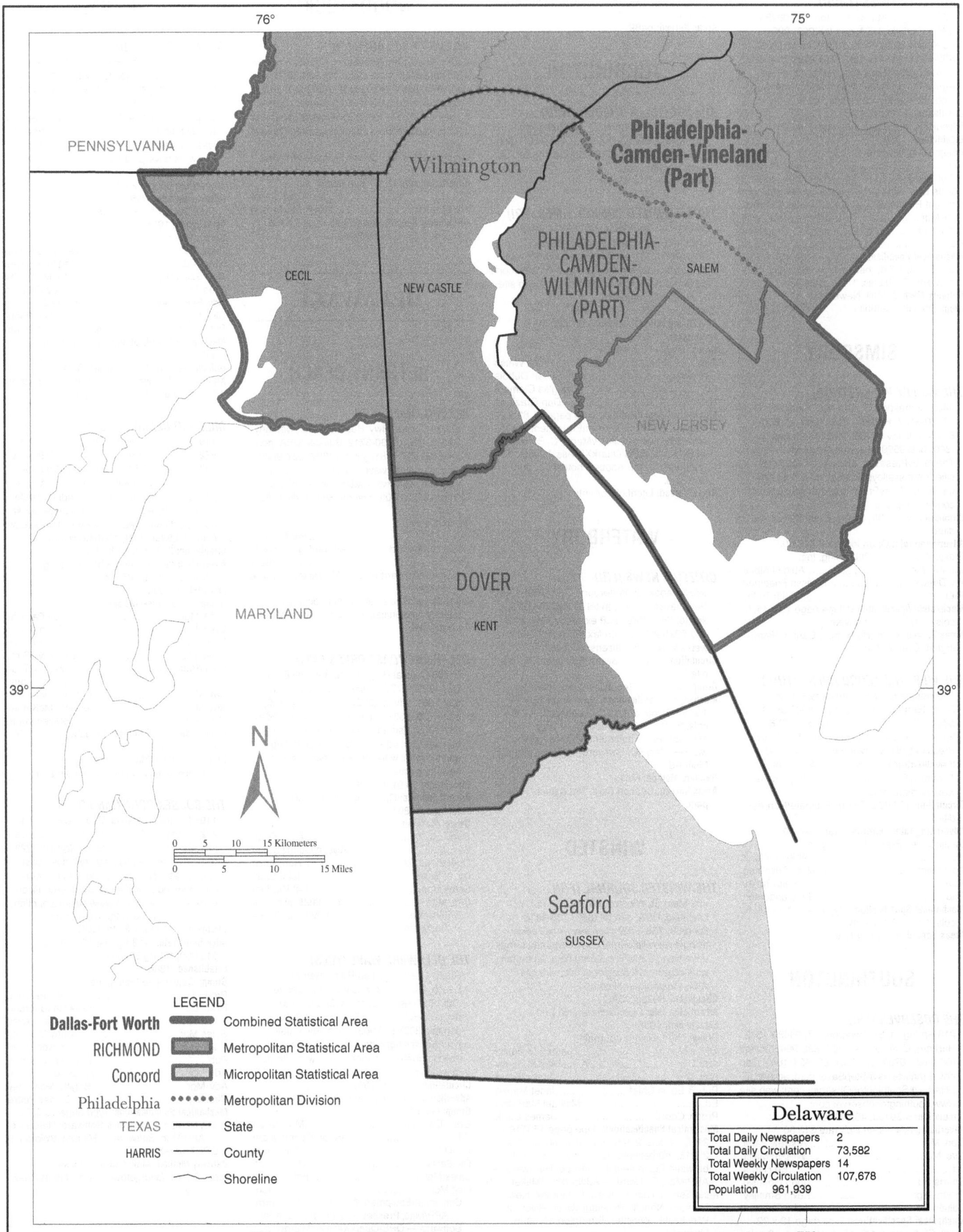

Delaware

Total Daily Newspapers	2
Total Daily Circulation	73,582
Total Weekly Newspapers	14
Total Weekly Circulation	107,678
Population	961,939

LEWES

CAPE GAZETTE (TUES, FRI)

17585 Nassau Commons Blvd, Ste 6, Lewes, DE, 19958-6286, Sussex, USA; gen tel (302) 645-7700; adv tel (302) 645-7700 ext. 307; gen fax (302) 645-1664; adv fax (302) 645-1664; disp adv e-mail adsales@capegazette.com; class adv e-mail adsales@capegazette.com; ed e-mail newsroom@capegazette.com; web site capegazette.com
Circulation: 12,000pd,; Sworn/Estimate/Non-Audited
Advertising rate: Open inch rate $12.35
Pub./Adv. Dir. ....Dennis Fourney
Ed. ....Trish Vernon
Ed. ....Laura Ritter
Prod. ....Teresa Rodriguez
Adv. Mgr. ....Cindy Bowlin
Sales Manager ....Chris Rausch
Areas Served: The Cape Region

MIDDLETOWN

HOCKESSIN COMMUNITY NEWS (FRI)

24 W Main St, Middletown, DE, 19709-1039, New Castle, USA; gen tel (302) 378-9531; adv tel (302) 378-9531 ext. 13; ed tel (302) 346-5418; gen fax (302) 378-0647; disp adv e-mail amanda.johnston@doverpost.com; class adv e-mail brandi.ford@doverpost.com; ed e-mail jesse.chadderdon@doverpost.com; web site www.hockessincommunitynews.com
Circulation: 6pd, 13,626fr; CVC
Advertising rate: 1/16 Pg $130.00; 1/8 Pg $235.00; 1/4 Pg $434.00
Established: 1983
Group: GateHouse Media, Inc.
Prod. Dir. ....Jay Parsons
Sales Mgr. ....Amanda Johnston
Exec. Ed. ....Jesse Chadderdon
Pres./Pub. ....Keven Todd
Pub. ....Clarissa Williams
Brigitte McKinney
Circ. Mgr ....Stacey Poore
Delivery Method: Mail, Carrier, Racks
Areas Served: Hockessin and Pike Creek

SMYRNA/CLAYTON SUN-TIMES (WED)

24 W Main St, Middletown, DE, 19709-1039, New Castle, USA; gen tel (302) 653-2083; adv tel (302) 346-5434; ed tel (302) 346-5418; gen fax (302) 653-8821; disp adv e-mail brigitte.mckinney@doverpost.com; class adv e-mail brandi.ford@doverpost.com; ed e-mail jesse.chadderdon@doverpost.com; web site www.scsuntimes.com - 81,641(views) 27,690(visitors)
Circulation: 1,768pd, 955fr; CVC
Advertising rate: 1/16 Pg $66.00; 1/8 Pg $121.00; 1/4 Pg $220.00
Established: 1854
Group: GateHouse Media, Inc.
Adv. Mgr. ....Brigitte McKinney
Ed. ....Ben Mace
Pres./Pub. ....Keven Todd
Pub. Mgr ....Clarissa Williams
Adv. Mgr. ....Amanda Johnston
Circ. Mgr ....Stacey Poore
Mechanical Specifications: Type page 10.33" x 11"; 6 cols
Delivery Method: Carrier, Racks
Areas Served: Smyrna and Clayton

THE MIDDLETOWN TRANSCRIPT (THUR)

24 W Main St, Middletown, DE, 19709-1039, New Castle, USA; gen tel (302) 378-9531; adv tel (302) 378-9531 ext. 13; ed tel (302) 346-5418; gen fax (302) 378-0114; disp adv e-mail amanda.johnston@doverpost.com; class adv e-mail brandi.ford@doverpost.com; ed e-mail jesse.chadderdon@doverpost.com; web site www.middletowntranscript.com - 93,391(views) 29,835(visitors)
Circulation: 498pd, 13,206fr; CVC
Advertising rate: 1/16 Pg $130.00; 1/8 Pg $235.00; 1/4 Pg $434.00
Established: 1868
Group: GateHouse Media, Inc.
Prod. Dir. ....Jay Parsons
Exec. Ed. ....Jesse Chadderdon
Ed. ....Ben Mace
Adv. Sales Mgr. ....Amanda Johnston
Pres./Pub. ....Keven Todd
Pub. ....Clarissa Williams
Adv. Sales Mgr. ....Brigitte McKinney
Circ. Mgr ....Stacey Poore
Mechanical Specifications: Type page 10.33" x 11"; 6 cols
Delivery Method: Mail, Carrier, Racks
Areas Served: Middletown, Odessa, Townsend and Delaware City

MILFORD

MILFORD CHRONICLE (WED)

37A N WALNUT ST, Milford, DE, 19963-1445, Sussex, USA; gen tel (302) 422-1200; adv tel (302) 422-1200; ed tel (302) 422-1200; gen fax (302) 422-1208; adv fax (302) 422-1208; ed fax (302) 422-1208; disp adv e-mail adsupport@newszap.com; class adv e-mail classads@newszap.com; ed e-mail mc@newszap.com; web site milfordchronicle.net
Circulation: 235pd, 161fr; CAC
Advertising rate: 1/8 Pg $279; 1/4 Pg $419; 1/2 Pg $939; Full Pg $1459
Established: 1878
Group: Independent Newsmedia Inc. Usa
Publisher ....Darel La Prade
Promotions Manager ....Heather Cregar
Major Accts. Adv. Mgr........Tim GaryEquipment & Software: Hardware — APP/Mac; Software — QPS/QuarkXPress, Adobe/Photoshop, Macromedia/Freehand, Adobe/Illustrator.
Delivery Method: Newsstand, Carrier
Areas Served: 19941, 19943, 19947, 19950, 19952, 19954, 19960, 19963, 19958

SUSSEX POST (WED)

37A N WALNUT ST, Milford, DE, 19963-1445, Sussex, USA; gen tel (302) 629-5505; adv tel (302) 629-5505; ed tel (302) 629-5505; gen fax (302) 422-1208; adv fax (302) 422-1208; disp adv e-mail adsales@newszap.com; class adv e-mail classads@newszap.com; ed e-mail sussespost@newszap.com; web site sussexpost.com
Circulation: 13,000fr; Sworn/Estimate/Non-Audited
Advertising rate: 1/8 Pg $419; 1/4 Pg $609; 1/2 Pg $1319; Full Pg $2019
Established: 1972
Group: Independent Newsmedia Inc. Usa
Pub. ....Darel LaPrade
News Ed. ....Glenn Rolfe
Promotions Manager ....Heather Cregar
Mechanical Specifications: Type page 11 5/8 x 21 1/4; E - 6 cols, 1 3/4, 1/16 between; A - 6 cols, 1 3/4, 1/16 between; C - 9 cols, 1 1/3, 1/6 between.Equipment & Software: Hardware — APP/Mac; Software — Microsoft/Word 5.0, QPS/QuarkXPress 3.3, Adobe/Photoshop 2.5.
Delivery Method: Carrier, Racks
Areas Served: 19939, 19945, 19947, 19951, 19958, 19966, 19967, 19968, 19970, 19971, 19975

THE HARRINGTON JOURNAL (WED)

37A N WALNUT ST, Milford, DE, 19963-1445, Sussex, USA; gen tel (302) 422-1200; adv tel (302) 422-1200; gen fax (302) 422-1208; adv fax (302) 422-1208; disp adv e-mail adsupport@newszap.com; class adv e-mail adsupport@newszap.com; web site delaware.newszap.com
Circulation: 2,393pd,; CAC
Advertising rate: Modular Rate: Sixteenth $110
Established: 1915
Group: Independent Newsmedia Inc. Usa
Sr. VP/Pub ....Darel La PradeEquipment & Software: Hardware — APP/Mac; Software — QPS/QuarkXPress, Adobe/Photoshop, Macromedia/Freehand, Adobe/Illustrator.
Delivery Method: Newsstand, Carrier
Areas Served: 19943, 19946, 19950, 19952, 19963, 19980

OCEAN VIEW

COASTAL POINT (FRI)

111 Atlantic Ave, Ste 2, Ocean View, DE, 19970-9166, Sussex, USA; gen tel (302) 539-1788; gen fax (302) 539-3777; disp adv e-mail susan.lyons@coastalpoint.com; class adv e-mail jane.johnson@coastalpoint.com; ed e-mail darin.mccann@coastalpoint.com; web site www.coastalpoint.com
Circulation: 40pd, 18,000fr; Sworn/Estimate/Non-Audited
Advertising rate: $11.43
Established: 2004Editions: Coastal Point
Digital Platform - Tablet: Windows 7
Pub. ....Susan Lyons
Ed. ....Darin McCann
Mechanical Specifications: column inch 2.312 x 1 inch
4 col x 13 for a full page
Delivery Method: Newsstand, Racks
Areas Served: 19930, 19939,19944,19945,19966,19967,19970,19975,19966

DISTRICT OF COLUMBIA

WASHINGTON

CAPITAL BUSINESS (MON)

1150 15th St NW, Washington, DC, 20071-0001, District Of Columbia, USA; gen tel (202) 334-6000; gen fax (202) 334-5941; disp adv e-mail washingtonpostads@washpost.com; class adv e-mail washingtonpostads@washpost.com; web site washingtonpost.com/business/capital-business
Circulation: 13,332pd, 14,302fr; CAC
Advertising rate: 1/4P $3540, 1/2P $6000, Full $8401
Group: Nash Holdings
Circ. Dir. ....Charles Love
CEO/Pub. ....Frederick J. Ryan Jr.
Delivery Method: Mail

DUPONT CURRENT (WED)

5185 MacArthur Blvd NW, Ste 102, Washington, DC, 20016-3349, District of Columbia, USA; gen tel (202) 244-7223; adv tel (202) 244-7223; gen fax (202) 363-9850; disp adv e-mail garysocha@currentnewspapers.com; class adv e-mail garysocha@currentnewspapers.com; ed e-mail newsdesk@currentnewspapers.com; web site currentnewspapers.com
Circulation: 3pd, 12,098fr; VAC
Advertising rate: Open inch rate: $45.00
Pub./Ed. ....Davis Kennedy
Adv. Dir. ....Gary Socha
Mgn. Ed. ....Chris Kain
Acct. Exec. ....Chip Py
Acct. Exec. ....Shani Madden
Service Dir./Classified Adv. Mgr. ....George Steinbrauer
Delivery Method: Mail, Carrier, Racks
Areas Served: 20005, 20009, 20036

FOGGY BOTTOM CURRENT (WED)

5185 MacArthur Blvd NW, Ste 102, Washington, DC, 20016-3349, District of Columbia, USA; gen tel (202) 244-7223; adv tel (202) 244-7223; gen fax (202) 363-9850; disp adv e-mail garysocha@currentnewspapers.com; class adv e-mail garysocha@currentnewspapers.com; ed e-mail newsdesk@currentnewspapers.com; web site currentnewspapers.com
Circulation: 2pd, 2,132fr; VAC
Advertising rate: Open inch rate: $45.00
Pub./Ed. ....Davis Kennedy
Adv. Dir. ....Gary Socha
Mgn. Ed. ....Chris Kain
Service Dir./Classified Adv. Mgr. ....George Steinbrauer
Acct. Exec. ....Chip Py
Acct. Exec. ....Shani Madden
Delivery Method: Mail, Carrier, Racks
Areas Served: 20006, 20037

GEORGETOWN CURRENT (WED)

5185 MacArthur Blvd NW, Ste 102, Washington, DC, 20016-3349, Disctrict of Columbia, USA; gen tel (202) 244-7223; adv tel (202) 244-7223; gen fax (202) 363-9850; disp adv e-mail garysocha@currentnewspapers.com; class adv e-mail garysocha@currentnewspapers.com; ed e-mail newsdesk@currentnewspapers.com; web site www.currentnewspapers.com/
Circulation: 5pd, 7,789fr; VAC
Advertising rate: Open inch rate: $45.00
Pub./Ed. ....Davis Kennedy
Adv. Mgr. ....Gary Socha
Chris Kain
Acct. Exec. ....Shani Madden
Acct. Exec. ....Chip Py
Service Dir./Classified Adv. Mgr. ....George Steinbrauer
Delivery Method: Mail, Carrier, Racks
Areas Served: 20007

NORTHWEST CURRENT (WED)

5185 MacArthur Blvd NW, Ste 102, Washington, DC, 20016-3349, District of Columbia, USA; gen tel (202) 244-7223; adv tel (202) 244-7223; gen fax (202) 363-9850; disp adv e-mail garysocha@currentnewspapers.com; class adv e-mail garysocha@currentnewspapers.com; ed e-mail newsdesk@currentnewspapers.com; web site currentnewspapers.com
Circulation: 31pd, 23,591fr; VAC
Advertising rate: Open inch rate: $45.00
Established: 1976
Pub./Ed. ....Davis Kennedy
Adv. Dir. ....Gary Socha
Mgn. Ed. ....Chris Kain
Service Dir./Classified Adv. Mgr. ....George Steinbrauer
Acct. Exec. ....Chip Py
Acct. Exec. ....Shani Madden
Delivery Method: Mail, Carrier, Racks
Areas Served: 20015, 20008, 20016, 20012, 20011, 20002, 20009

THE INTOWNER (FRI, MTHLY, OTHER)

1730B Corcoran St NW, Washington, DC, 20009-2406, District Of Columbia, USA; gen tel (202) 234-1717; adv tel (202) 234-1717; ed tel (202) 234-1717; disp adv e-mail advertising@intowner.com; class adv e-mail advertising@intowner.com; ed e-mail newsroom@intowner.com; web site www.intowner.com
Circulation: 20,000fr; Sworn/Estimate/Non-Audited
Advertising rate: Modular rate: Full page $550
Established: 1968
Group: InTowner Publishing Corp.
Mng Ed ....P.L. Wolff
Mechanical Specifications: Type page 10 x 13 7/8; E - 4 cols, 2 1/4, 1/4 between; A - 4 cols, 2 1/4, 1/4 between; C - 6 cols, 1 1/2, 1/4 between.Equipment & Software: Hardware — Compaq/Pentium; Software — Adobe/PageMaker, QPS/QuarkXPress.
Areas Served: 20001, 20004, 20005, 20006, 20008, 20009, 20010, 20011, 20036, 20037

FLORIDA

ALACHUA

ALACHUA COUNTY TODAY (THUR)

14804 Main St, Alachua, FL, 32615-8590, Alachua, USA; gen tel (386) 462-3355; gen fax (386) 462-4569; disp adv e-mail ads@alachuatoday.com; ed e-mail editor@alachuatoday.com; web site www.alachuatoday.com
Circulation: 5,000pd,; Sworn/Estimate/Non-Audited

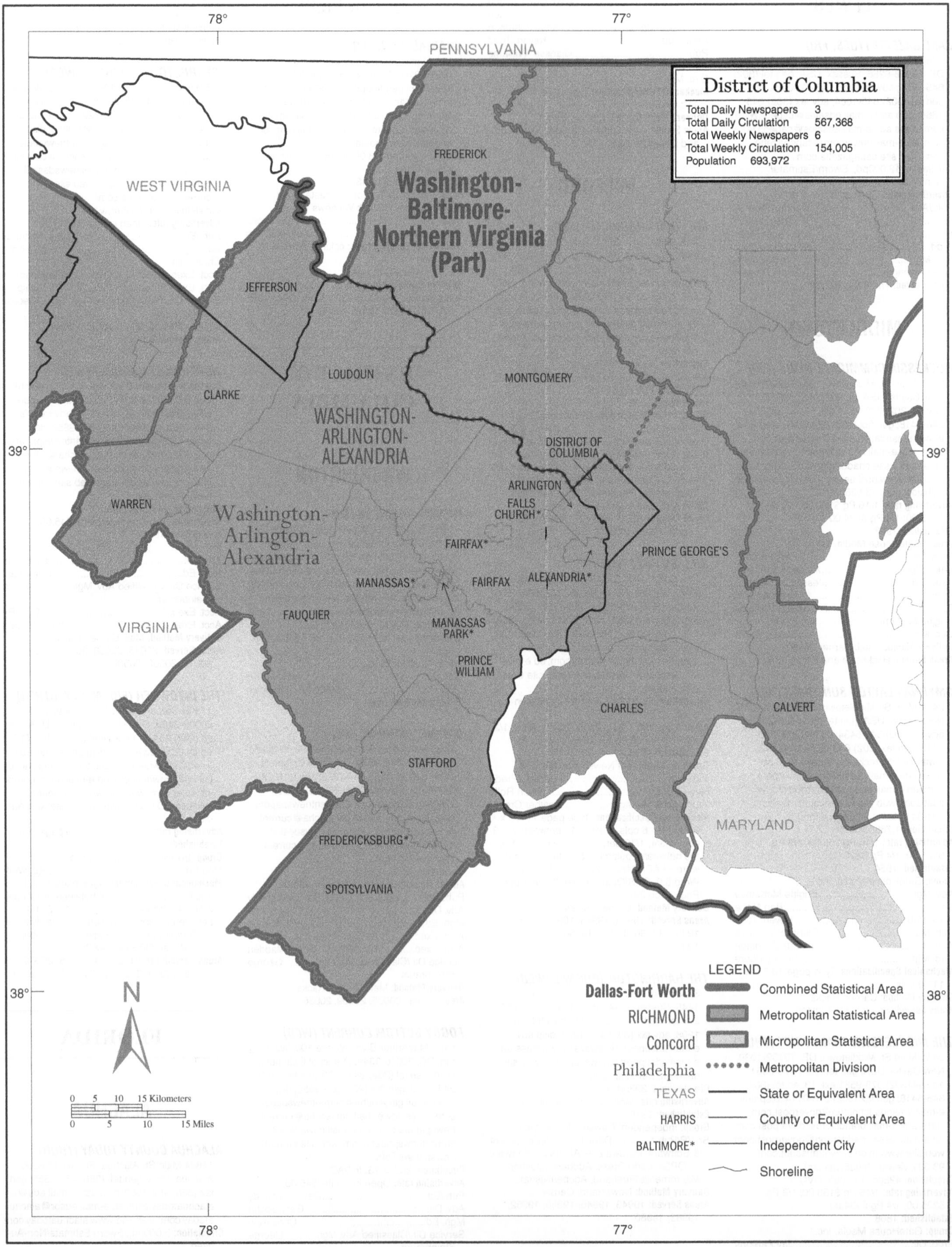
District of Columbia
Total Daily Newspapers 3
Total Daily Circulation 567,368
Total Weekly Newspapers 6
Total Weekly Circulation 154,005
Population 693,972
78°
77°
39°
38°
PENNSYLVANIA
WEST VIRGINIA
VIRGINIA
MARYLAND
Washington-Baltimore-Northern Virginia (Part)
WASHINGTON-ARLINGTON-ALEXANDRIA
Washington-Arlington-Alexandria
FREDERICK
JEFFERSON
LOUDOUN
CLARKE
MONTGOMERY
DISTRICT OF COLUMBIA
ARLINGTON
FALLS CHURCH*
WARREN
FAIRFAX*
FAIRFAX
ALEXANDRIA*
MANASSAS*
MANASSAS PARK*
PRINCE GEORGE'S
FAUQUIER
PRINCE WILLIAM
CHARLES
CALVERT
STAFFORD
FREDERICKSBURG*
SPOTSYLVANIA
N
0 5 10 15 Kilometers
0 5 10 15 Miles
LEGEND
Dallas-Fort Worth Combined Statistical Area
RICHMOND Metropolitan Statistical Area
Concord Micropolitan Statistical Area
Philadelphia Metropolitan Division
TEXAS State or Equivalent Area
HARRIS County or Equivalent Area
BALTIMORE* Independent City
Shoreline

Florida
Total Daily Newspapers 37
Total Daily Circulation 1,372,413
Total Weekly Newspapers 165
Total Weekly Circulation 2,580,537
Population 20,984,400
LEGEND
Dallas-Fort Worth Combined Statistical Area
RICHMOND Metropolitan Statistical Area
Concord Micropolitan Statistical Area
Philadelphia Metropolitan Division
TEXAS State
HARRIS County
Shoreline
0 15 30 45 60 Kilometers
0 15 30 45 60 Miles
N
GEORGIA
ALABAMA
ESCAMBIA
PENSACOLA-FERRY PASS-BRENT
SANTA ROSA
OKALOOSA
FORT WALTON BEACH-CRESTVIEW-DESTIN
WALTON
HOLMES
WASHINGTON
JACKSON
BAY
PANAMA CITY-LYNN HAVEN
CALHOUN
GULF
LIBERTY
FRANKLIN
GADSDEN
LEON
TALLAHASSEE
WAKULLA
JEFFERSON
MADISON
TAYLOR
HAMILTON
SUWANNEE
LAFAYETTE
DIXIE
COLUMBIA
Lake City
GILCHRIST
BAKER
UNION
BRADFORD
ALACHUA
GAINESVILLE
LEVY
NASSAU
DUVAL
JACKSONVILLE
CLAY
ST. JOHNS
PUTNAM
Palatka
FLAGLER
Palm Coast
Deltona-Daytona Beach-Palm Coast
DELTONA-DAYTONA BEACH-ORMOND BEACH
VOLUSIA
MARION
OCALA
The Villages
SUMTER
CITRUS
Homosassa Springs
HERNANDO
PASCO
PINELLAS
HILLSBOROUGH
TAMPA-ST. PETERSBURG-CLEARWATER
LAKE
SEMINOLE
ORANGE
ORLANDO-KISSIMMEE
Orlando-The Villages
OSCEOLA
BREVARD
PALM BAY-MELBOURNE-TITUSVILLE
POLK
LAKELAND
INDIAN RIVER
VERO BEACH
ST. LUCIE
PORT ST. LUCIE-FORT PIERCE
MARTIN
OKEECHOBEE
Okeechobee
HIGHLANDS
Sebring
HARDEE
Wauchula
DeSOTO
Arcadia
MANATEE
SARASOTA
SARASOTA-BRADENTON-VENICE
CHARLOTTE
PUNTA GORDA
GLADES
HENDRY
Clewiston
LEE
CAPE CORAL-FORT MYERS
COLLIER
NAPLES-MARCO ISLAND
PALM BEACH
West Palm Beach-Boca Raton-Boynton Beach
MIAMI-FORT LAUDERDALE-MIAMI BEACH
BROWARD
Fort Lauderdale-Pompano Beach-Deerfield Beach
MIAMI-DADE
Miami-Miami Beach-Kendall
MONROE
Key West-Marathon
31° 30° 29° 28° 27° 26° 25°
79° 80° 81° 82° 83° 84° 85° 86° 87° 88°

Advertising rate: $8.25 per column inch (PCI)
Established: 2000
Advertisement.......Robert Boukari
Publisher.......Bryan Boukari
Executive Editor.......Ellen Boukari
Associate Publisher.......Gail Luparello
Mechanical Specifications: Type page 10 x 20; A - 6 cols, 1.55
Delivery Method: Mail, Newsstand, Racks
Areas Served: Alachua, High Springs, Newberry, Jonesville, Gainsville, Archer, Hawthorne, Micanopy, Waldo, and LaCrosse

ANNA MARIA

ANNA MARIA ISLAND SUN (WED)

9801 Gulf Dr, Anna Maria, FL, 34216, Manatee, USA; gen tel (941) 778-3986; gen fax (941) 778-6988; disp adv e-mail ads@amisun.com; class adv e-mail classifieds@amisun.com; web site www.amisun.com
Circulation: 16,000fr; Sworn/Estimate/Non-Audited
Established: 2000
Publisher, Editor.......Mike Field
Co-Publisher.......Maggie Field
Advertisement.......Chantelle Lewin

APALACHICOLA

THE APALACHICOLA CARRABELLE TIMES (THUR)

129 Commerce St, Apalachicola, FL, 32320-1717, Franklin, USA; gen tel (850) 653-8868; ed tel (850) 227-7827; gen fax (850) 653-8036; disp adv e-mail rhoxie@starfl.com; web site www.apalachtimes.com
Circulation: 5,100pd,; Sworn/Estimate/Non-Audited
Advertising rate: Open inch rate $8.29
Group: GateHouse Media, Inc.
Ed.......Tim Croft

APOPKA

APOPKA CHIEF (THE) (FRI)

400 N Park Ave, Apopka, FL, 32712-4152, Orange, USA; gen tel (407) 886-2777; gen fax (407) 889-4121; disp adv e-mail news@theapopkachief.com; class adv e-mail ads@theapopkachief..com; ed e-mail news@theapopkachief..com; web site www.theapopkachief.com
Circulation: 5,000pd, 100fr; Sworn/Estimate/Non-Audited
Advertising rate: Open inch rate $8.50
Established: 1923
Pub.......John E. Ricketson
Gen. Mgr.......Neoma DeGard Knox
Mktg. & Ad. Dir.......Jackie Trefcer
Ed.......John Peery
Adv. Mgr.......Elain Gibbons
Adv. Rep.......Kathleen Jackson
Adv. Rep.......Kayla Leon
Mechanical Specifications: Type page 11 1/4 x 21 1/2; E - 6 cols, 1 13/16, 1/8 between; A - 6 cols, 1 13/16, 1/8 between; C - 9 cols, 1 3/16, 1/8 between.Equipment & Software: Hardware — APP/Mac, APP/Mac Performa 6320-CD, APP/Power Mac 6100; Software — Adobe/PageMaker 6.5, Adobe/Photoshop 5.5, Microsoft/Word Office 98, QPS/QuarkXPress 4.0, Adobe/Illustrator 8.0, Adobe/Acrobat 4.0.
Delivery Method: Mail, Newsstand, Racks
Areas Served: Apopka and NW Orange County, Florida

THE PLANTER (THUR)

400 N Park Ave, Apopka, FL, 32712-4152, Orange, USA; gen tel (407) 886-2777; gen fax (407) 889-4121; disp adv e-mail news@theapopkachief.com; class adv e-mail ads@theapopkachief..com; ed e-mail news@theapopkachief..com; web site https://www.theapopkachief.com/
Circulation: 0pd, 8,500fr; Sworn/Estimate/Non-Audited
Advertising rate: Open inch rate $11.50
Established: 1965
Pub.......John E. Ricketson
Ed.......John Peery
Mechanical Specifications: Type page 13 x 21 1/2; E - 6 cols, 2 1/16, 1/8 between; A - 6 cols, 2 1/16, 1/8 between; C - 9 cols, 1 5/16, 1/8 between.Equipment & Software: Hardware — APP/Mac Performa 6320-CD, APP/Power Mac 6100; Software — Adobe/PageMaker 5.0, Adobe/Photoshop 3.0, Microsoft/Word 3.0.
Delivery Method: Newsstand, Carrier, Racks
Areas Served: City of Apopka Fla. 32703/32712 Limited number of households in N. West Orange Co. by Adult motor route Carriers. Delivery by Thursday AM

ARCADIA

ARCADIAN (THUR)

108 S Polk Ave, Arcadia, FL, 34266-3952, DeSoto, USA; gen tel (863) 494-7600; gen fax (863) 494-3533; disp adv e-mail majoraccts@sun-herald.com; class adv e-mail gkotz@sun-herald.com; ed e-mail feedback@sun-herald.com; web site yoursun.net
Group: Sun Coast Media Group Inc
Pub.......Joe Gallimore
Ed.......Steve Bauer
Cird. Dir.......Mark Yero
Pres.......David Dunn-Rankin
Exec. Ed.......Jim Gouvellis

BELLEVIEW

VOICE OF SOUTH MARION (THUR)

5513 SE 113th St, Belleview, FL, 34420-4039, Marion, USA; gen tel (352) 245-3161; gen fax (352) 347-7444; disp adv e-mail vosm@aol.com; class adv e-mail vosminfo@aol.com; web site www.thevosm.net
Circulation: 2,800pd,; Sworn/Estimate/Non-Audited
Advertising rate: Open inch rate $8.00
Established: 1969
Digital Platform - Mobile: Apple, Android
Adv. Mgr.......Clay Waldron
Ed.......Sandy Waldron
Mechanical Specifications: Type page 10 x 16.Equipment & Software: Hardware — APP/Mac; Software — Adobe/Indesign
Delivery Method: Mail, Newsstand, Racks
Areas Served: 34420,34421,34491,34492,34470,34480,32179,32183,32195

BLOUNTSTOWN

THE COUNTY RECORD (WED)

PO Box 366, Blountstown, FL, 32424-0366, Calhoun, USA; gen tel (850) 674-5041; gen fax (850) 674-5008; disp adv e-mail displayads@thecountyrecord.net; class adv e-mail classifieds@thecountyrecord.net; ed e-mail editor@thecountyrecord.net; web site www.thecountyrecord.net
Advertising rate: Open inch rate $6.00
Established: 1907
Editor&Publisher.......Robert Turner

BOCA GRANDE

BOCA BEACON (FRI)

431 Park Ave, Boca Grande, FL, 33921, Lee, USA; gen tel (941) 964-2995; gen fax (941) 964-0372; disp adv e-mail info@bocabeacon.com; web site www.bocabeacon.com
Circulation: 3,000pd, 4,000fr; Sworn/Estimate/Non-Audited
Advertising rate: Open inch rate $8.49
Established: 1980
Publisher & General Manager...Dusty Hopkins
Office Mgr.......Karen Clark
Ad. Rep.......Julianne Greenberg
Adv. Rep.......Dizey Lindquist
Ed.......Marcy ShortuseEquipment & Software: Hardware — APP/Mac; Software — QPS/QuarkXPress 3.3, Adobe/Photoshop 6.0.

BOKEELIA

THE PINE ISLAND EAGLE (WED)

10700 Stringfellow Rd, Ste 60, Bokeelia, FL, 33922-3232, Lee, USA; gen tel (239) 283-2022; adv tel (239) 574-1110 x171; ed tel (239) 574-1110 x119 ; gen fax (239) 283-0232; disp adv e-mail cgallagher@breezenewspapers.com; ed e-mail vharring@breezenewspapers.com; web site www.pineisland-eagle.com
Circulation: 226pd, 7,797fr; CVC
Advertising rate: $12.78
Established: 1976
Group: Ogden Newspapers Inc.
Exec. Ed.......Valarie Harring
Pub.......Scott Blonde
Nat'l Acct. Mgr.......Natalie Gerreira
Adv. Dir.......Cynthia Gallagher
Circ. Mgr.......Barbara Smith
Prod. Mgr.......Cecilia Yndart

BRISTOL

THE CALHOUN LIBERTY JOURNAL (WED)

11493 NW Summers Rd, Bristol, FL, 32321-3364, Liberty, USA; gen tel (850) 643-3333; gen fax (850) 643-3334; disp adv e-mail thejournal@fairpoint.net; web site www.cljnews.com
Circulation: 5,200pd, 18fr; Sworn/Estimate/Non-Audited
Advertising rate: Open inch rate $6.00
Established: 1981
Digital Platform - Mobile: Apple
Pub.......Johnny Eubanks
Ed.......Teresa Eubanks
Mechanical Specifications: Type page 11 x 16; E - 5 cols, 2, 1/6 between; A - 5 cols, 2, 1/6 between; C - 5 cols, 2, 1/6 between.Equipment & Software: Hardware — APP/Power Mac; Software — Adobe/PageMaker 4.2.
Delivery Method: Mail, Newsstand, Racks
Areas Served: 32321

BUSHNELL

SUMTER COUNTY TIMES (THUR)

204 E McCollum Ave, Bushnell, FL, 33513-6145, Sumter, USA; gen tel (352) 793-2161; gen fax (352) 793-1486; disp adv e-mail mtaylor@sctnews.com; class adv e-mail mtaylor@sctnews.com; ed e-mail news@sctnews.com; web site www.sumtercountytimes.com
Circulation: 2,600pd,; Sworn/Estimate/Non-Audited
Advertising rate: Open inch rate $12.50
Established: 1881
Group: Landmark Communications, Inc. Landmark Community Newspapers, LLC
Pub.......Gerard Mulligan
Circ. Mgr.......Brenda Locklear
Ed.......Bob Reichman
Sales Rep.......Mike Taylor
Mgr.......John Murphy
Mechanical Specifications: Type page 11 x 21 1/2; E - 6 cols, 1.555, 1/8 between; A - 6 cols, 1.555, 1/8 between; C - 9 cols, 1, 1/8 between.Equipment & Software: ; Presses — Universal.
Delivery Method: Mail, Newsstand
Areas Served: 32162, 33513, 33514, 33538, 33585, 33597, 33618, 34484, 34785,

CALLAHAN

NASSAU COUNTY RECORD (THUR)

617317 Brandies Ave, Callahan, FL, 32011-3704, Nassau, USA; gen tel (904) 879-2727; gen fax (904) 879-5155; disp adv e-mail advertising@nassaucountyrecord.com; ed e-mail abishop@nassaucountyrecord.com; web site www.nassaucountyrecord.com
Circulation: 3,000pd,; Sworn/Estimate/Non-Audited
Advertising rate: Open inch rate $8.76
Established: 1930
Group: Community Newspapers, Inc.
Pub.......Foy Maloy
Bus. Office Mgr.......Angeline Mudd
Prodn. Dir.......Robert Fiege
Editor.......Amanda Ream
Corp. Mktg. Dir.......Joel Jenkins
Circulation Manager.......John Gaddy
Marketing Associate.......Samantha Coxwell
Delivery Method: Mail, Newsstand, Carrier, Racks
Areas Served: Nassau County, FL / 32011

CAPE CORAL

NORTH FORT MYERS NEIGHBOR (WED)

2510 Del Prado Blvd S, Cape Coral, FL, 33904-5750, Lee, USA; gen tel (239) 574-1110; adv tel (239) 220-2754; ed tel (239) 574-1110 x119 ; gen fax (239) 574-5693; disp adv e-mail mjohnson@breezenewspapers.com ; ed e-mail vharring@breezenewspapers.com; web site www.northfortmyersneighbor.com
Circulation: 6pd, 5,276fr; VAC
Advertising rate: $12.78
Established: 1999
Pub.......Scott Blonde
Ed.......Valarie Harring
Ad. Sales.......Malcolm Johnson
Adv. Mgr.......Cindy Gallagher
Circ. Mgr.......Barbara Smith
Prod. Mgr.......Cecilia Yndart

SANIBEL-CAPTIVA ISLANDER (WED)

2510 Del Prado Blvd S, Cape Coral, FL, 33904-5750, Lee, USA; gen tel (239)-574-1110 ; adv tel (239) 472-1587; gen fax (239) 472-8398; disp adv e-mail dpapoi@breezenewspapers.com; ed e-mail mcassidy@breezenewspapers.com; web site www.captivasanibel.com
Circulation: 486pd, 6,794fr; VAC
Advertising rate: $8.65
Established: 1960
Group: Ogden Newspapers Inc.
Pub.......Scott Blonde
Executive Editor.......Valarie Harring
Editor.......Mckenzie Cassidy
Ad. Sales.......Danielle Papoi
Adv. Mgr.......Cindy Gallagher
Circ. Mgr.......Barbara Smith
Prod. Mgr.......Cecilia Yndart
Mechanical Specifications: Type page 9 3/4 x 12 5/8; E - 4 cols, between; A - 6 cols, between; C - 6 cols, between.

CHATTAHOOCHEE

TWIN CITY NEWS (THUR)

314 W Washington St, Chattahoochee, FL, 32324-1434, Gadsden, USA; gen tel (850) 663-2255; disp adv e-mail tcnews@fairpoint.net
Circulation: 2,000pd,; Sworn/Estimate/Non-Audited
Advertising rate: Open inch rate $5.75
Pub.......Nick Bert
Mng. Ed.......Kathy Johnson
Mechanical Specifications: Type page 13 x 21; E - 6 cols, 2, 3/16 between; A - 6 cols, 2, 3/16 between; C - 6 cols, 2, 3/16 between.
Areas Served: 32324, 32460, 32442, 32330, 32332

CHIEFLAND

CHIEFLAND CITIZEN (THUR)

624 W Park Ave, Chiefland, FL, 32626-0430, Levy, USA; gen tel (352) 493-4796; adv tel (352) 493-4796; ed tel (352) 493-4796; gen fax (352) 493-9336; adv fax (352) 493-9336;

ed fax (352) 493-9336; disp adv e-mail circulation@chieflandcitizen.com; class adv e-mail circulation@chieflandcitizen.com; ed e-mail circulation@chieflandcitizen.com; web site www.chieflandcitizen.com
Circulation: 6,000pd,; Sworn/Estimate/Non-Audited
Advertising rate: Open inch rate $11.80
Established: 1950
Group: Landmark Community Newspapers, LLC
Digital Platform - Mobile: Apple, Android
Digital Platform - Tablet: Apple iOS, Android
Ed. ....Lou Elliott Jones
Gen. Mgr. ....Tom Broeck
Circ. Mgr. ....Marcia Vaughn
Creative ....Cheri Clark
Delivery Method: Mail, Newsstand, Racks
Areas Served: Levy, Gilchrist, and Dixie County

CHIPLEY

HOLMES COUNTY TIMES-ADVERTISER (WED)

1364 N Railroad Ave, Chipley, FL, 32428-1456, Holmes, USA; gen tel (850) 638-0212; gen fax (850) 547-9414; disp adv e-mail ssmith@chipleypaper.com; web site www.chipleypaper.com
Circulation: 4,200pd,; Sworn/Estimate/Non-Audited
Advertising rate: Open inch rate $6.50
Group: Halifax Media
Pub. ....Nicole Barefield
Ed. ....Jay Selsberg
Adv. ....Mickayla Boname
Mechanical Specifications: Type page 13 x 21 1/2; E - 6 cols, 2, 1/6 between; A - 6 cols, 2, 1/6 between; C - 9 cols, 1 1/3, 1/6 between. Equipment & Software: Hardware — APP/Power Mac, PCs; Presses — G/Community; Software — QPS/QuarkXPress, Adobe/PageMaker 6.0.

CLEARWATER

BUSINESS OBSERVER-PINELLAS (FRI)

14004 Roosevelt Blvd, Ste 604, Clearwater, FL, 33762-3850, Pinellas, USA; gen tel (727) 447-7784; adv tel (941) 726-6145; ed tel (727) 254-0976; gen fax (727) 447-3944; adv fax (727) 447-3944; ed fax (727) 447-3944; disp adv e-mail dschaefer@BusinessObserverFL.com; class adv e-mail kboothroyd@BusinessObserverFL.com; ed e-mail khughes@BusinessObserverFL.com; web site www.businessobserverfl.com
Circulation: 185pd, 696fr; VAC
Advertising rate: Modular Rate $288 (1/8P); $530 (1/4P); $1021 (1/2P)
Established: 1997
Group: Observer Media Group Inc.
Digital Platform - Mobile: Apple, Android, Windows, Blackberry
Digital Platform - Tablet: Apple iOS, Android, Windows 7, Blackberry Tablet OS
Publisher ....Matthew G. Walsh
Assoc. Pub./Adv. Dir. ....Diane Schaefer
Mechanical Specifications: 10.375" x 16"
Delivery Method: Mail, Newsstand, Racks
Areas Served: Pinellas County

CLERMONT

THE NEWS LEADER (WED)

637 8th St, Clermont, FL, 34711-2159, Lake, USA; gen tel (352) 242-9818; gen fax (352) 242-9820; disp adv e-mail jkemp@clermontnewsleader.com; class adv e-mail nlclassifieds@cfl.rr.com; ed e-mail lbriody@cfl.rr.com; web site www.clermontnewsleader.com
Circulation: 38,394fr; Sworn/Estimate/Non-Audited
Advertising rate: Modular Sizing
Established: 1982
Group: Independent Publications Inc
Lakeway Publishers, Inc.
Sun Publications of Fla.
Ed. ....Linda Briody
Adv. Dir. ....Jodi Marano
Creative Director ....Dawn Hendry
Mechanical Specifications: Type page 10 1/8 x 16; E - 6 cols, 1 3/8, 3/16 between; A - 6 cols, 1 3/8, 3/16 between; C - 6 cols, 1 3/8, 3/16 between.Equipment & Software: Hardware — APP/Mac, LaserMaster, Epson/Scanner; Software — Aldus/PageMaker 6.0.
Delivery Method: Mail
Areas Served: 34711, 34712, 34736, 34753, 34755, 34756

CRAWFORDVILLE

THE WAKULLA NEWS (THUR)

3119A Crawfordville Hwy, Crawfordville, FL, 32327-3148, Wakulla, USA; gen tel (850) 926-7102; gen fax (850) 926-3815; disp adv e-mail lkinsey@thewakullanews.net; class adv e-mail advertising@thewakullanews.net; ed e-mail editor@thewakullanews.net; web site www.thewakullanews.com
Circulation: 4,500pd,; Sworn/Estimate/Non-Audited
Advertising rate: Open inch rate $12.50
Established: 1897
Group: Landmark Community Newspapers, LLC
Ed ....William Snowden
Mechanical Specifications: Type Page 9.888 x 21.5; E - 6 cols, 1.555, .111 between; A - 6 cols, 1.555, .111 between; C - 9 cols, 1, .111 between
Delivery Method: Mail, Newsstand, Racks
Areas Served: 32326,32327,32358,32349,32351

CRESCENT CITY

PUTNAM COUNTY COURIER JOURNAL (WED)

320 N Summit St, Crescent City, FL, 32112-2300, Putnam, USA; gen tel (386) 698-1644; gen fax (386) 698-1994; disp adv e-mail ads@cjnewsfl.com; class adv e-mail classifieds@cjnewsfl.com; ed e-mail news@cjnewsfl.com; web site www.cjnewsfl.com
Circulation: 3,000pd,; Sworn/Estimate/Non-Audited
Advertising rate: 2" x 2" $38.00
Established: 1898
Group: Lakestreet Publishing Company
Ed./Pub. ....Juliette LaurieEquipment & Software: ; Software — Adobe InDesign, Adobe/Photoshop.
Delivery Method: Mail, Newsstand, Racks

CRESTVIEW

CRESTVIEW NEWS BULLETIN (WED, SAT)

638 N Ferdon Blvd, Ste 1, Crestview, FL, 32536-2170, Okaloosa, USA; gen tel (850) 682-6524; gen fax (850) 682-2246; disp adv e-mail tboni@crestviewbulletin.com; class adv e-mail sherries@crestviewbulletin.com; ed e-mail news@crestviewbulletin.com; web site www.crestviewbulletin.com - 700,000(views) 70,000(visitors)
Circulation: 4,000pd, 13,000fr; USPS
Advertising rate: Open inch rate $10.50; varies for loyal customers
Established: 1975
Group: GateHouse Media, Inc.
Digital Platform - Mobile: Apple, Android, Windows, Blackberry, Other
Ed. ....Thomas Boni
Mechanical Specifications: Type page 11 9/16 x 21; E - 6 cols, 1 29/36, 1/6 between; A - 6 cols, 1 29/36, 1/6 between; C - 10 cols, 1 1/72, 1/6 between.
Delivery Method: Mail, Carrier, Racks
Areas Served: 32536, 32539, 32537, 32531, 32564

CROSS CITY

DIXIE COUNTY ADVOCATE (THUR)

174 NE Highway 351, Cross City, FL, 32628-3120, Dixie, USA; gen tel (352) 498-3312; adv tel (352) 542-0131; gen fax (352) 507-4585; disp adv e-mail adsdcadvocate@gmail.com; class adv e-mail news@dcadvocate.net; legal@dcadvocate.net; ed e-mail editor@dcadvocate.net; web site www.dcadvocate.net
Circulation: 4,200pd, 10fr; Sworn/Estimate/Non-Audited
Advertising rate: Open inch rate $4.50
Established: 1921
Ed. ....Katherine McKinney
Ad. Rep. ....Becky Williams
Mechanical Specifications: Type page 13 3/4 x 21 1/2; E - 7 cols, 1 4/5, 1/5 between; A - 7 cols, 1 4/5, 1/5 between; C - 7 cols, 1 4/5, 1/5 between.Equipment & Software: Hardware — APP/Mac G4, PC; Software — Adobe/Photoshop 7.0, Multi-Ad, Claris, Adobe/FrontPage.

DAVIE

THE FORUM - SUNRISE & TAMARAC (WED)

6501 Nob Hill Road, Davie, FL, 33328, Broward, USA; gen tel (954) 698-6397; gen fax (954) 429-1207; disp adv e-mail placeanad.sun-sentinel.com; class adv e-mail jshalek@tribune.com; web site www.sun-sentinel.com/local
Circulation: 15,013fr
Group: Sun-Sentinel Co.
Circ. Mgr. ....Ed Wilder
Ed. ....Ruben Cueto
Adv. Mgr. ....Joann Zollo
Pres./Pub. ....Tom Adams
Circ. Mgr. ....Ed Wilder
Sr. Sales Mgr. ....Gregg Behar
Mng. Ed. ....Ruben Cueto
Circ. Mgr. ....Mark Ward
Mechanical Specifications: Type page 10.5" x 10.5"; 6 cols
Delivery Method: Carrier, Racks

DEERFIELD BEACH

OBSERVER NEWSPAPER (THUR)

201 N Federal Hwy Ste 103, Suite 103, Deerfield Beach, FL, 33441-3621, Broward, USA; gen tel (954) 428-9045; gen fax (954) 428-9096; disp adv e-mail observerart@comcast.net; class adv e-mail observerfrontdesk@comcast.net; web site www.observernewspaperonline.com
Circulation: 15,000fr; Sworn/Estimate/Non-Audited
Advertising rate: Open inch rate $10.00
Established: 1962
Vice President ....James Lust
Adv. Mgr. ....Jim Canavian
Publisher ....David Eller
Editor ....Diane Emeott
Assistant Editor ....Rachel Galvin
Mechanical Specifications: Type page 10 1/4 x 16; E - 6 cols, 1 1/2, 1/8 between; A - 6 cols, 1 1/2, 1/8 between; C - 5 cols, 1 3/4, 1/8 between.Equipment & Software: Hardware — APP/iMac, APP/Mac Performa, APP/Macs, G4/Cube; Software — Adobe/PageMaker 7.0, Adobe/Photoshop 10.0, Adobe/Acrobat 5.0, QPS/QuarkXPress 5.0.
Delivery Method: Mail, Newsstand, Racks
Areas Served: 33441, 33442, 33062, 33064

DELAND

THE WEST VOLUSIA BEACON (MON, THUR)

110 W New York Ave, Deland, FL, 32720-5416, Volusia, USA; gen tel (386) 734-4622; gen fax (386) 734-4641; disp adv e-mail adsales@beacononlinenews.com; web site www.beacononlinenews.com
Circulation: 5,000pd, 9,050fr; Sworn/Estimate/Non-Audited
Advertising rate: Open inch rate $10.00
Established: 1992
Co-Owner/Co-Pub. ....Joann Kramer
Co-Pub. ....Sammie Wiggins
Ad-Design Mgr. ....Michael Jaeckle
Co-Pub./Ed. ....Barb Shepherd
Mechanical Specifications: Type page 13 x 21 1/2; E - 6 cols, 2 1/16, 1/8 between; A - 6 cols, 2 1/16, 1/8 between; C - 8 cols, 1 1/2, 1/8 between.Equipment & Software: Hardware — APP/Mac; Software — In-Design 2.0.
Delivery Method: Mail, Newsstand

DESTIN

THE DESTIN LOG (WED, SAT)

35008 Emerald Coast Pkwy, Ste 501, Destin, FL, 32541-4753, Okaloosa, USA ; gen tel (850) 837-2828; gen fax (850) 654-8427; ed e-mail malgarin@thedestinlog.com; web site thedestinlog.com
Group: Halifax Media
Managing Ed. ....Tina Harbuck

DUNNELLON

RIVERLAND NEWS (THUR)

20441 E Pennsylvania Ave, Dunnellon, FL, 34432-6035, Marion, USA; gen tel (352) 489-2731; gen fax (352) 489-6593; disp adv e-mail editor@riverlandnews.com; web site www.riverlandnews.com
Circulation: 3,000pd,; Sworn/Estimate/Non-Audited
Advertising rate: Open inch rate $19.58
Established: 1982
Group: Landmark Communications, Inc.
Landmark Community Newspapers, LLC
Gen Mgr. ....John Murphy
Advertising sales ....Michele Northsea
Ed. ....Jeff Bryan
Pub. ....Gerry Mulligan
Gen. Mgr. ....John Provost
Mechanical Specifications: Type page 11 5/8 x 21 1/2; E - 6 cols, 1 5/6, 1/8 between; A - 6 cols, 1 5/6, 1/8 between; C - 10 cols, 1 1/16, 1/8 between.
Areas Served: 34430, 34431, 34432, 34433, 34434

FERNANDINA BEACH

NEWS-LEADER (WED, FRI)

511 Ash St, Fernandina Beach, FL, 32034-3930, Nassau, USA; gen tel (904) 261-3696; gen fax (904) 261-3698; disp adv e-mail ads@fbnewsleader.com; class adv e-mail abutler@fbnewsleader.com; ed e-mail pdavis@fbnewsleader.com; web site www.fbnewsleader.com
Circulation: 10,000pd,; USPS
Advertising rate: Open inch rate $23.76
Established: 1854
Group: Community Newspapers, Inc.
Pub. ....Foy R. Maloy
Sports Ed. ....Beth Jones
Prodn. Dir. ....Robert Fiege
Corp. Mktg. Dir. ....Joel Jenkins
Editor ....Peg Davis
Circulation/Distribution Manager ...John Gaddy
Regional Business Office Manager ....Angeline Mudd
Mechanical Specifications: Type page 11 5/8 x 21 1/4; E - 6 cols, between; A - 6 cols, between; C - 6 cols, between.Equipment & Software: Hardware — APP/Macs, PC; Software — QPS/QuarkXPress, Microsoft/Word.
Delivery Method: Mail
Areas Served: Amelia Island; Fernandina Beach; Nassau County, FL

FLEMING ISLAND

CLAY COUNTY LEADER (FRI)
3513 US Highway 17, Fleming Island, FL, 32003-7122, Clay, USA; gen tel (904) 264-3200; adv tel (904) 579-2148; ed tel (904) 579-2151; gen fax (904) 264-3285; disp adv e-mail jon@opcfla.com; class adv e-mail martha@opcfla.com; ed e-mail eric@opcfla.com; web site claytodayonline.com - 19,000(views) 12,000(visitors)
Circulation: 6,975fr; VAC
Advertising rate: Open inch rate $23.00
Established: 1987
Group: Osteen Publishing Company
Digital Platform - Tablet: Apple iOS, Android, Windows 7, Kindle, Nook, Kindle Fire
Publisher....................................... Jon Cantrell
Peg Oddy
Circ. Mgr....................................... Rob Conwell
Mechanical Specifications: full 10" x 12.75" Equipment & Software: Hardware — PC
Delivery Method: Mail, Newsstand
Areas Served: 32073, 32003, 32065, 32043, 32068, 32079

CLAY TODAY (THUR)
3513 US Highway 17, Fleming Island, FL, 32003-7122, Clay, USA; gen tel (904) 264-3200; gen fax (904) 264-3285; disp adv e-mail jon@opcfla.com; class adv e-mail martha@opcfla.com; ed e-mail eric@opcfla.com; web site www.claytodayonline.com - 19,000(views) 12,000(visitors)
Circulation: 3,637pd, 838fr; VAC
Advertising rate: Open inch rate $24.00
Established: 1950
Group: Osteen Publishing Company
Digital Platform - Mobile: Apple
Digital Platform - Tablet: Apple iOS, Android, Windows 7, Kindle, Nook, Kindle Fire
Pub.. Jon Cantrell
Circ. Mgr.. Rob Conwell
Adv. Mgr... Peg Oddy
Editor... Eric Cravey
Production .... Michele McNeil
Prod. Mgr .... Justin Freeman
Mechanical Specifications: Type page 10 x 12 3/4 E - 4 cols, 2 1/2, 1/16 between; A - 4 cols, 2 1/2, 1/16 between; C - 4 cols, 2 1/2, 1/16 between.Equipment & Software: Hardware — PC, APP/Mac; Software — QPS/QuarkXPress, Adobe/Photoshop, Adobe/Illustrator.
Delivery Method: Mail, Newsstand, Carrier, Racks
Areas Served: 32073, 32003, 32065, 32073, 32043, 32656, 32030

FORT LAUDERDALE

BOCA RATON FORUM (WED)
500 E Broward Blvd, Fort Lauderdale, FL, 33394-3000, Broward, USA; gen tel (954) 698-6397; adv tel (800) 974-7521; ed tel (954) 596-5632; gen fax (954) 429-1207; adv fax (954) 698-6719; ed fax (954) 429-1207; disp adv e-mail Kenwilliams@tribpub.com; class adv e-mail jshalek@tribune.com; ed e-mail JZizzo@tribpub.com; web site www.forumpubs.com
Circulation: 0pd, 28,193fr; CVC
Advertising rate: 2x2 $90.00; 2x3.5c $180.00
Established: 1973
Group: Forum Publishing Group
Sun-Sentinel Co.
Digital Platform - Mobile: Apple, Android, Windows, Blackberry
Digital Platform - Tablet: Apple iOS, Android, Windows 7, Blackberry Tablet OS
Pub./Gen. Mgr............................... Tom Adams
Mng. Ed.. Tracy Kolody
Adv. Mgr... Ray Daley
Prodn. Mgr. .... Stewart Cady
Circ. Mgr.. Mark Ward
Mechanical Specifications: Type page 10 3/8 x 16.
Delivery Method: Mail, Racks
Areas Served: Broward County

BOYNTON FORUM (WED)
500 E Broward Blvd, Fort Lauderdale, FL, 33394-3000, USA; gen tel (954) 698-6397; gen fax (954) 698-6719; disp adv e-mail gbehar@tribune.com; web site http://www.sun-sentinel.com/local/palm-beach/boynton-beach/
Circulation: 0pd, 77,744fr; CVC
Advertising rate: 2x2 $90.00; 2x3.5c $180.00
Group: Forum Publishing GroupLisa Goodlin
Circ. Mgr.. Mark Ward
Pub./Pres. .... Tom Adams

DEERFIELD AND POMPANO FORUM (THUR)
500 E Broward Blvd, Fort Lauderdale, FL, 33394-3000, Broward, USA; gen tel (954) 698-6397; adv tel (800) 974-7521; ed tel (954) 596-5632; gen fax (954) 429-1207; adv fax (954) 698-6719; disp adv e-mail Kenwilliams@tribpub.com; class adv e-mail jshalek@tribune.com; ed e-mail JZizzo@tribpub.com; web site www.forumpubs.com
Circulation: 0pd, 85,704fr; CVC
Group: Sun-Sentinel Co.
Senior Sales Manager................ Gregg Behar
Adv. Mgr................................. Mickie Carusos
President .... Tom Adams
Exec. Ed... Pam Doto
VP/Exec. Ed..................................... Pam Doto
Prodn. Mgr. .... Stewart Cady
Managing Editor .... Judith Zizzo
Circ. Mgr.. Mark Ward
Mechanical Specifications: Type page 10.5" x 10.5"; 6 cols
Delivery Method: Mail, Racks

DELRAY BEACH FORUM (WED)
500 E Broward Blvd, Fort Lauderdale, FL, 33394-3000, USA; gen tel (954) 356-4000; gen fax (954) 698-6719; disp adv e-mail gbehar@tribune.com; web site http://www.sun-sentinel.com/local/palm-beach/delray-beach/
Circulation: 0pd, 24,378fr; CVC
Group: Forum Publishing GroupLisa Goodlin
Circ. Mgr.. Mark Ward
Pres./Pub. .... Tom Adams
Mechanical Specifications: Type page 10.5" x 10.5"; 6 cols
Delivery Method: Mail, Carrier, Racks

EAST SIDE FORUM (THUR)
500 E Broward Blvd, Fort Lauderdale, FL, 33394-3000, Broward, USA; gen tel (954) 356-4000; gen fax (954) 698-6719; disp adv e-mail gbehar@tribune.com; web site www.sun-sentinel.com
Circulation: 26,805fr; CVC
Group: Forum Publishing GroupLisa Goodlin
Pres./Pub. .... Tom Adams
Circ. Mgr.. Mark Ward
Mechanical Specifications: Type page 10.5" x 10.5"; 6 cols
Delivery Method: Mail, Carrier, Racks

LAKE WORTH FORUM (TUES)
500 E Broward Blvd, Fort Lauderdale, FL, 33394-3000, Broward, USA; gen tel (954) 698-6397; adv tel (800) 974-7521; ed tel (954) 596-5632; gen fax (954) 429-1207; adv fax (954) 698-6719; disp adv e-mail Kenwilliams@tribpub.com; class adv e-mail jshalek@tribune.com; ed e-mail JZizzo@tribpub.com; web site www.forumpubs.com
Circulation: 12,775fr; CVC
Advertising rate: (Modular Rates) 2x2 - $63 1x
Group: Forum Publishing Group
Sun-Sentinel Co.
VP/ Exec. Ed.................................... Pam Doto
President .... Tom Adams
Senior Sales Manager................ Gregg Behar
Editor .... Kari Barnett
Mechanical Specifications: Type page 10.5" x 10.5"; 6 cols
Delivery Method: Mail, Racks
Areas Served: 33460, 33461, 33462

LIVE WELLINGTON (WED)
500 E Broward Blvd, Fort Lauderdale, FL, 33394-3000, USA; gen tel (954) 356-4000; adv tel (954) 574-5373; ed tel (954) 596-5632; gen fax (954) 429-1207; adv fax (954) 698-6719 ; disp adv e-mail TAdams@tribune.com; ed e-mail KABarnett@tribune.com; web site http://www.sun-sentinel.com/local/palm-beach/wellington/
Circulation: 16,712fr; CVC
Advertising rate: 2x2 $63.00; 2x3.5 $125.00; 6x1.5 $180.00
Group: Forum Publishing Group
The Charleston Sun-Sentinel
VP/Exec. Ed.................................... Pam Doto
President .... Tom Adams
Sr. Sales Mgr............................... Gregg Behar
Editor .... Kari Barnett
Mechanical Specifications: Type page 10.5" x 10.5"; 6 cols
Delivery Method: Mail, Racks
Areas Served: 33411, 33414, 33467

MARGATE / COCONUT CREEK FORUM (THUR)
500 E Broward Blvd, Fort Lauderdale, FL, 33394-3000, Broward, USA; gen tel (954) 574-5341; gen fax (954) 698-6719; disp adv e-mail gbehar@tribune.com; web site www.forumpubs.com
Circulation: 20,700fr; CVC
Advertising rate: 2x2 $90.00; 2x3.5c $180.00
Group: Forum Publishing Group
Circ. Mgr.. Mark Ward
Pres./Pub. .... Tom Adams
Mechanical Specifications: Type page 10.5" x 10.5"; 6 cols
Delivery Method: Mail, Carrier, Racks

PLANTATION/DAVIE FORUM (WED)
500 E Broward Blvd, Fort Lauderdale, FL, 33394-3000, Broward, USA; gen tel (954) 698-6397; gen fax (954) 429-1207; disp adv e-mail placeanad.sun-sentinel.com; class adv e-mail ewilder@tribune.com; ed e-mail JZizzo@tribpub.com; web site www.forumpubs.com
Circulation: 0pd, 58,872fr; CVC
Established: 1973
Group: Sun-Sentinel Co.Editions: (5) 5 total; Davie/Cooper City; Miramar Community News; Pembroke Pines; Plantation; Weston Community News;
Digital Platform - Mobile: Apple, Android, Windows, Blackberry
Digital Platform - Tablet: Apple iOS, Android, Windows 7, Blackberry Tablet OS
Pres./Pub. .... Tom Adams
Adv. Mgr... Ray Daley
Prodn. Mgr. .... Stewart Cady
Mechanical Specifications: Type page 10 13/16 x 13.Equipment & Software: Hardware — APP/Mac G3; Software — QPS/QuarkXPress, Adobe/Illustrator, Multi-Ad/Creator.
Delivery Method: Mail, Racks
Areas Served: Broward County

THE GAZETTE - PEMBROKE PINES & MIRAMAR (MTHLY)
500 E Broward Blvd, Fort Lauderdale, FL, 33394-3000, Broward, USA; gen tel (954) 698-6397; adv tel (800) 974-7521; ed tel (954) 596-5632; gen fax (954) 429-1207; adv fax (954) 698-6719 ; disp adv e-mail Kenwilliams@tribpub.com; class adv e-mail jshalek@tribune.com; ed e-mail JZizzo@tribpub.com; web site www.forumpubs.com
Mng. Ed... Dana Banker
Pub... Howard Saltz

WEST BOCA FORUM (WED)
500 E Broward Blvd, Ste 1710, Fort Lauderdale, FL, 33394-3012, Broward, USA; gen tel (954) 698-6397; adv tel (800) 974-7521; ed tel (954) 596-5632; gen fax (954) 429-1207; adv fax (954) 698-6719; disp adv e-mail Kenwilliams@tribpub.com; class adv e-mail jshalek@tribune.com; ed e-mail JZizzo@tribpub.com; web site www.forumpubs.com
Circulation: 0pd, 23,814fr; CVC
Advertising rate: 2x2 $90.00; 2x3.5c $180.00
Group: Forum Publishing Group
Sun-Sentinel Co.
Editor .... Kari Barnett
Sr. Sales Mgr............................... Gregg Behar
Pres./Pub. .... Tom Adams
VP/Exec. Ed..................................... Pam Doto
Circ. Mgr.. Mark Ward
Mechanical Specifications: Type page 10.5" x 10.5"; 6 cols
Delivery Method: Mail, Racks
Areas Served: 33428, 33434, 33498

WESTON GAZETTE (WED, MTHLY)
500 E Broward Blvd, Fort Lauderdale, FL, 33394-3000, Broward, USA; gen tel (954) 356-4000; adv tel (954) 698-6397; ed tel (954) 698-6397; gen fax (954) 429-1207; disp adv e-mail placeanad.sun-sentinel.com; class adv e-mail ewilder@tribune.com; ed e-mail ctouey@tribune.com; web site www.forumpubs.com
Established: 1973
Group: Sun-Sentinel Co.
Digital Platform - Mobile: Apple, Android, Windows, Blackberry
Digital Platform - Tablet: Apple iOS, Android, Windows 7, Blackberry Tablet OS
Pub./Gen. Mgr............................... Tom Adams
Mng. Ed.. Tracy Kolody
Adv. Mgr... Ray Daley
Prodn. Mgr. .... Stewart Cady
Circ. Mgr.. Mark Ward
Mechanical Specifications: Type page 10 3/8 x 16.
Delivery Method: Mail, Racks
Areas Served: Broward County

FORT MYERS

FORT MYERS FLORIDA WEEKLY (WED)
4300 Ford St, Ste 105, Fort Myers, FL, 33916-9318, Lee, USA; gen tel (239) 333-2135; gen fax (239) 333-2140 ; disp adv e-mail advertise@floridaweekly.com; class adv e-mail advertise@floridaweekly.com; ed e-mail news@floridaweekly.com; web site www.floridaweekly.com
Circulation: 35,646pd,; CAC
Advertising rate: Modular Rates: 1/8 P $250 1/4 P $625 1/2 P $940 Full $2500
Established: 2007
Pres./Pub. .... J. Pason Gaddis
Ed.. Jeffrey Cull
VP and Creative Dir. .... Jim Dickerson
Circ. Dir. .... Cameo Hinman
Delivery Method: Mail, Newsstand

LEHIGH ACRES NEWS-STAR (WED, SAT)
2442 Dr Martin Luther King Blvd, Fort Myers, FL, 33901-3904, Lee, USA; gen tel (239) 344-4721; adv tel (239) 335-0520; ed tel (239) 344-4721; adv fax (239) 945-3934; ed fax (239) 334-0708; class adv e-mail advertise@news-press.com; ed e-mail clogan@news-press.com; web site www.news-press.com
Circulation: 10,000pd, 16,000fr; Sworn/Estimate/Non-Audited
Advertising rate: Open inch rate $15.00
Established: 1957
Group: Gannett
Editorial... Casey Logan
Acct. Exec. .... Sherrie Douglas
Retail Adv. Mgr.......................... James P. Wyatt
Pub.. Carol Hudler
Dir. of Adv. Sales.......................... Barry Barlow
Delivery Method: Mail
Areas Served: 33936,33971,33972,33973,33974,33976

FORT MYERS BEACH

FORT MYERS BEACH BULLETIN (WED)
19260 San Carlos Blvd, Bldg C, Fort Myers Beach, FL, 33931-2266, USA; gen tel (239) 463-4421; ed tel (239) 765-0400; gen fax (239) 765-0846; disp adv e-mail beachbulletin@breezenewspapers.com; class adv e-mail classifieds@breezenewspapers.com; ed e-mail rpetcher@breezenewspapers.com; web site www.fortmyersbeachtalk.com
Circulation: 35pd, 6,923fr; Sworn/Estimate/Non-Audited
Advertising rate: Open inch rate $9.25
Established: 1951

Group: Ogden Newspapers Inc.
Robert Petcher
Melissa SchneiderEd.s
Mechanical Specifications: Type page 10 5/8 x 16; E - 6 cols, between; A - 6 cols, between; C - 6 cols, between.Equipment & Software: Hardware — APP/Mac.

FORT MYERS BEACH OBSERVER (WED)
19260 San Carlos Blvd, Fort Myers Beach, FL, 33931-2266, Lee, USA; gen tel (239) 463-4421; adv tel (239) 765-0400 x107; ed tel (239) 765-0400; gen fax (239) 765-0846; disp adv e-mail observer@breezenewspapers.com; class adv e-mail classifieds@breezenewspapers.com; ed e-mail rpetcher@breezenewspapers.com; web site www.fortmyersbeachtalk.com - 17,320(views) 6,410(visitors)
Circulation: 159pd, 6,998fr; VAC
Advertising rate: $15.84
Established: 1978
Group: Ogden Newspapers Inc.
Pub. .... Scott Blonde
Nat'l Sales Mgr .... Natalie Zabala
Adv. Dir. .... Jim Konig
Prod. Mgr. .... Rhonda Marble
Adv. Mgr .... Cindy Gallagher
Circ. Mgr .... Barbara Smith
Prod. Mgr .... Cecilia Yndart
Mechanical Specifications: Type page 9.875" x 13"; 6 colsEquipment & Software: Hardware — APP/Mac.
Delivery Method: Carrier, Racks

FORT PIERCE

HOMETOWN NEWS (FRI)
1102 S US Highway 1, Fort Pierce, FL, 34950-5132, Saint Lucie, USA; gen tel (772) 465-5656; gen fax (772) 465-5301; disp adv e-mail kyoung@hometownnewsol.com; web site www.hometownnewsol.com - 88,235(views) 31,162(visitors)
Circulation: 9,414fr; VAC
Advertising rate: Open inch rate $16.25-$19.25
Group: Hometown News GroupEditions: (15) Beaches (16323); Deland (16103); Deltona (16103); Ft Pierce (12002); Martin County (26166); Melbourne (17550); New Smyrna / Edgewater (17165); North Brevard / Merritt Island (20282); Ormond Beach (22108); Palm Bay (17530); Port Orange / S. Daytona (17992); Port St Lucie (17653); Sebastian (9242); Suntree / Viera (15987); Vero Beach (16789)
Pub / Gen. Mgr. .... Lee Mooty
Adv. Mgr. .... Kathy Young
Circ. Mgr. .... Dolan Hoggatt
Managing Partner .... Vernon Smith
Prod. Mgr .... Mercedes Paquette
Farris Robinson
Mechanical Specifications: Type page 11" x 20"; 6 cols
Delivery Method: Mail, Carrier, Racks

GRACEVILLE

THE GRACEVILLE NEWS (THUR)
1004 10th Ave, Graceville, FL, 32440-1906, Jackson, USA; gen tel (850) 263-6015; gen fax (850) 263-1042; disp adv e-mail gvnews@wfeca.net; web site facebook.com/thegracevillenews
Circulation: 1,750pd,; Sworn/Estimate/Non-Audited
Advertising rate: Open inch rate $3.50
Pub. .... John Ferrin Cox
Ed. .... Sharon Taylor
Mechanical Specifications: Type page 13 x 21 1/2; E - 6 cols, 2 1/16, 1/8 between; A - 6 cols, 2 1/16, 1/8 between; C - 6 cols, 2 1/16, 1/8 between.Equipment & Software: Hardware — APP/Mac.

GULF BREEZE

GULF BREEZE NEWS (THUR)
913 Gulf Breeze Pkwy, Harbourtown Suite 35, Gulf Breeze, FL, 32561-4754, Santa Rosa, USA; gen tel (850) 932-8986 ; adv tel (850) 932-8986 ext. 104; ed tel (850) 932-8986 ext. 111; gen fax (850) 932-8794 ; adv fax 850-932-8794; ed fax 850-932-8794; disp adv e-mail bob@gulfbreezenews.com; class adv e-mail class@gulfbreezenews.com; ed e-mail news@gulfbreezenews.com; web site www.gulfbreezenews.com
Circulation: 2,000pd, 1,000fr; Sworn/Estimate/Non-Audited
Advertising rate: $22.00
Established: 2001
Group: Gulf Breeze News, Inc.
Digital Platform - Mobile: Windows
Pub. .... Lisa Newell
Ad Sales .... Bob Newell
Mechanical Specifications: Display column inch: 1.799"
Classified column inch: 1.02"
Delivery Method: Mail, Newsstand
Areas Served: 32561, 32563, 32566, 32501, 32504, 32503, 32562

HAVANA

THE HERALD (THUR)
103 W 7th Ave, Havana, FL, 32333-1660, Gadsden, USA; gen tel (850) 539-6586; gen fax (850) 539-0454 ; disp adv e-mail colleen@prioritynews.net ; ed e-mail mail@prioritynews.net; web site TheHerald.onlin
Circulation: 3,500pd,; Sworn/Estimate/Non-Audited
Advertising rate: $7 ci
Established: 1947
Pub. .... Mark Pettus
Delivery Method: Mail, Newsstand, Racks
Areas Served: Gadsden County, Fla. including Quincy, Havana, Midway, Chattahoochee, Greensboro, Gretna, Florida

HOLMES BEACH

THE ISLANDER (WED)
3218 E Bay Dr, Holmes Beach, FL, 34217-2039, Manatee, USA; gen tel (941) 778-7978; gen fax (941) 778-9392; disp adv e-mail toni@islander.org; ed e-mail news@islander.org; web site www.islander.org
Circulation: 2,900pd, 15,000fr; Sworn/Estimate/Non-Audited
Advertising rate: $11.20 net
Established: 1992
Ed./Pub. .... Bonner Joy
Adv. Dir. .... Toni Lyon
Delivery Method: Mail, Newsstand, Carrier, Racks
Areas Served: Anna Maria Island, Perico Island and Cortez

HOMESTEAD

SOUTH DADE NEWS LEADER (TUES, THUR, FRI)
15 NE 1st Rd, Homestead, FL, 33030-6110, Miami-Dade, USA; gen tel (305) 245-2311; adv tel (305) 245-2315; gen fax (305) 248-0596; disp adv e-mail mdill@calkins-media.com; class adv e-mail sdnlads@calkins-media.com; ed e-mail letters@southdadenewsleader.com; web site www.southdadenewsleader.com
Circulation: 24,000pd,; Sworn/Estimate/Non-Audited
Advertising rate: Open inch rate $18.90
Established: 1912
Group: Calkins Media
Adv. Mgr. .... Tracy Lovitt
Prodn. Mgr. .... Andy Gayton
Publisher .... Dale Machesic
Mechanical Specifications: Type page 12 1/2 x 21 1/2; E - 6 cols, 2, 3/16 between; A - 6 cols, 2, 3/16 between; C - 9 cols, 1 1/4, 1/8 between.Equipment & Software: Hardware — PC, APP/Mac; Presses — HI; Software — Archetype/Corel Draw.

JACKSONVILLE

FOLIO WEEKLY (WED)
45 W Bay St, Ste 103, Jacksonville, FL, 32202-3632, Duval, USA; gen tel (904) 260-9770; gen fax (904) 260-9773; disp adv e-mail themail@folioweekly.com; web site www.folioweekly.com
Circulation: 0pd, 25,349fr; VAC
Group: C-VILLE Holdings LLC
Adv. Mgr. .... T. Farrar Martin
Circ. Mgr. .... Sam Taylor
Ed. .... Anne Schindler
Prodn. Mgr. .... Kelly Lucas
Mechanical Specifications: Type page 10 x 13; E - 4 cols, 2 3/8, between; A - 4 cols, 2 3/8, between; C - 4 cols, 2 3/8, between.

JACKSONVILLE BUSINESS JOURNAL (FRI)
200 W Forsyth St, Ste 1350, Jacksonville, FL, 32202-4349, Duval, USA; gen tel (904) 396-3502; gen fax (904) 396-5706; web site www.bizjournals.com/jacksonville
President and Publisher .... David Sillick
Delivery Method: Mail, Newsstand

MANDARIN NEWSLINE (MTHLY)
12443 San Jose Blvd, Ste 403, Jacksonville, FL, 32223-8650, Duval, USA; gen tel (904) 886-4919; gen fax (904) 379-5250; disp adv e-mail publisher@rtpublishinginc.com; ed e-mail editor@rtpublishinginc.com; web site www.mandarinnewsline.com
Circulation: 28,699fr; CVC
Advertising rate: Open inch rate $20.50
Established: 2006
Group: RT Publishing, Inc.
Digital Platform - Mobile: Apple, Android, Windows
Digital Platform - Tablet: Apple iOS, Android, Windows 7, Blackberry Tablet OS, Kindle, Nook, Kindle Fire
Pub. Mgr .... Rebecca Taus
Ed. .... Martie Thompson
Adv. Mgr. .... Heather Seay
Mechanical Specifications: 11 x 17 tabloid. visit www.rtpublishinginc.com for rate card with ad specs.
Delivery Method: Mail
Areas Served: 32223, 32257, 32258

OCEAN BREEZE (WED, BI-MTHLY)
12443 San Jose Blvd, Ste 403, Jacksonville, FL, 32223-8650, Duval, USA; gen tel (904) 886-4919; gen fax (904) 379-5250; disp adv e-mail publisher@rtpublishinginc.com; ed e-mail editor@rtpublishinginc.com; web site floridanewsline.com
Circulation: 1,800fr
Advertising rate: Open inch rate $20.00
Established: 2001
Group: RT Publishing, Inc.
Digital Platform - Mobile: Apple, Android, Windows, Blackberry
Digital Platform - Tablet: Apple iOS, Android, Windows 7, Blackberry Tablet OS, Kindle, Nook, Kindle Fire
Pub. .... Rebecca Taus
Ed. .... Martie Thompson
Adv. Mgr. .... Heather Seay
Mechanical Specifications: 11' X 14" see media kit at www.rtpublishinginc.com for ad and color specifications
Delivery Method: Mail
Areas Served: Ocean Hammock and Palm Coast

PLAYERS JOURNAL (THUR, BI-MTHLY)
12443 San Jose Blvd, Ste 403, Jacksonville, FL, 32223-8650, Duval, USA; gen tel (904) 886-4919; gen fax (904) 379-5250; disp adv e-mail publisher@rtpublishinginc.com; ed e-mail editor@rtpublishinginc.com; web site floridanewsline.com
Circulation: 1,850fr
Advertising rate: Open inch rate $20.00
Established: 2001
Group: RT Publishing, Inc.
Digital Platform - Mobile: Apple, Android, Windows, Blackberry
Digital Platform - Tablet: Apple iOS, Android, Windows 7, Blackberry Tablet OS, Kindle, Nook, Kindle Fire
Ed. .... Martie Thompson
Adv. Mgr. .... Heather Seay
Mechanical Specifications: 11" x 14". See www.rtpublishinginc.com media kit for specifications.
Delivery Method: Mail
Areas Served: Sawgrass Players Club Ponte Vedra

SOUTHSIDE NEWSLINE (MTHLY)
12443 San Jose Blvd Ste 403, Ste 403, Jacksonville, FL, 32223-8650, Duval, USA; gen tel (904) 886-4919; gen fax (904) 379-5250; disp adv e-mail publisher@rtpublishinginc.com; class adv e-mail ; ed e-mail editor@rtpublishinginc.com; web site www.southsidenewsline.com
Circulation: 23,511fr; CVC
Advertising rate: Open inch rate $19.50
Established: 2013
Group: RT Publishing, Inc.
Digital Platform - Mobile: Apple, Android, Windows, Blackberry
Digital Platform - Tablet: Apple iOS, Android, Windows 7, Blackberry Tablet OS, Kindle, Nook, Kindle Fire
Ed. .... Martie Thompson
Adv. Mgr. .... Heather Seay
Mechanical Specifications: 11" x 17" tabloid. Visit www.rtpublishinginc.com for the media kit with specifications or call 904-886-4919.
Delivery Method: Mail
Areas Served: 32256

THE CREEKLINE (MTHLY)
12443 San Jose Blvd Ste 403, Ste 403, Jacksonville, FL, 32223-8650, Duval, USA; gen tel (904) 886-4919; gen fax (904) 379-5250; disp adv e-mail publisher@rtpublishinginc.com; ed e-mail editor@rtpublishinginc.com; web site www.thecreekline.com
Circulation: 25,698fr; CVC
Advertising rate: Open inch rate $19.50
Established: 2001
Group: RT Publishing, Inc.
Digital Platform - Mobile: Apple, Android, Windows, Blackberry
Digital Platform - Tablet: Apple iOS, Android, Windows 7, Blackberry Tablet OS, Kindle, Nook, Kindle Fire
Ed. .... Martie Thompson
Adv. Mgr. .... Heather Seay
Mechanical Specifications: 11" x 17" tabloid. VIsit www.rtpublishinginc.com for the full media kit with specifications.
Delivery Method: Mail
Areas Served: 32259, 32092, 32095

JACKSONVILLE BEACH

THE BEACHES LEADER (THUR)
1372 Beach Blvd, Jacksonville Beach, FL, 32250-3447, Duval, USA; gen tel (904) 249-9033; adv tel (904) 249-9033; ed tel (904) 246-9033; gen fax (904) 249-1501; class adv e-mail classified@beachesleader.com; ed e-mail Editor@beachesleader.com; web site www.BeachesLeader.com
Circulation: 7,500pd,; Sworn/Estimate/Non-Audited
Established: 1963
Delivery Method: Mail, Newsstand, Racks
Areas Served: Duval
St. Johns

KEY BISCAYNE

ISLANDER NEWS (THUR)
104 Crandon Blvd Ste 301, Ste 301, Key Biscayne, FL, 33149-1556, Miami-Dade, USA; gen tel (305) 361-3333; gen fax (305) 361-

5051; disp adv e-mail lia@islandernews.com; ed e-mail editor@islandernews.com; web site www.islandernews.com
Circulation: 3,900pd, 690fr; Sworn/Estimate/Non-Audited
Advertising rate: (Modular Rates) 2.38"x7.88" - $295 1x
Established: 1966
Ad. Dir. .... Lia Esteban
Ed. & Pub. .... Nancye Ray
Art Dir. .... Jamie Millan

KISSIMMEE

EL OSCEOLA STAR (FRI)

220 E Monument Ave, Ste C, Kissimmee, FL, 34741-5752, Osceola, USA; gen tel (407) 933-0174; gen fax (407) 933-0190; disp adv e-mail ad@elosceolastar.com; web site www.elosceolastar.com
Circulation: 15,000fr; Sworn/Estimate/Non-Audited
Advertising rate: Open inch rate $16.00
Gen. Mgr. .... Yolanda Lopez
Ed. .... Bill Hansen
Mechanical Specifications: Type page 9 3/4 x 16; E - 2 cols, 2 1/4, 1/4 between; A - 2 cols, 4 3/4, 1/4 between; C - 3 cols, 1 1/2, 3/25 between.
Delivery Method: Racks
Areas Served: Osceola & Orange County

OSCEOLA NEWS-GAZETTE (THUR, SAT)

108 Church St, Kissimmee, FL, 34741-5055, Osceola, USA; gen tel (407) 846-7600; adv tel (454) 654-4345; gen fax (407) 846-8516; disp adv e-mail web@floridasunonline.net; web site www.oscnewsgazette.com - 92,184(views) 19,663(visitors)
Circulation: 561pd, 40,126fr; CVC
Advertising rate: Open inch rate $20.76
Established: 1897
Group: Sun Publications of Fla.
Independent Publications Inc
Lakeway Publishers, Inc.
Circ. Mgr. .... Kathy Beckham
Ed. .... Marvin Cortner
Asst. Ed. .... Rick Madewell
Prodn. Mgr. .... Ellen Johnston
Pub. Mgr .... Matt Plocha
Mechanical Specifications: Type page 11.75" x 21"; 6 colsEquipment & Software: Hardware — APP/Mac; Presses — KP/News King, G/Urbanite, HI/V-15A; Software — QPS/QuarkXPress 4.1, Adobe/Photoshop 6.0, Adobe/Illustrator 8.0, MS/Word 2000, Suitcase 8.0, Appleshare 6.3, Adobe/Acrobat 4.0.
Delivery Method: Mail, Carrier, Racks
Areas Served: 34741, 34743, 34744, 34746, 34747, 34758, 34759, 34769, 34771, 34772

LABELLE

CALOOSA BELLE (THUR)

PO Box 518, Labelle, FL, 33975-0518, USA; gen tel (863) 675-2541; web site http://caloosabelle.com
Group: Independent Newsmedia Inc. Usa
Independent Newspapers, Inc. (Florida)
Exec. Ed. .... Katrina Elsken

IMMOKALEE BULLETIN (THUR)

22 Fort Thompson Ave., Labelle, FL, 33975, Hendry, USA; gen tel (863) 675-2541; web site http://immokaleebulletin.com
Group: Independent Newsmedia Inc. Usa
Editor/Publisher .... Patty Brant
Areas Served: Immokalee, Collier County, FL

LAKE PANASOFFKEE

SUMTER EXPRESS (TUES)

3347 CR 431, Lake Panasoffkee, FL, 33538, Sumter, USA; gen tel (352) 793-1671; web site No Website
Circulation: 7,000fr; Sworn/Estimate/Non-Audited
Established: 2006
Pub./Ed. .... Rose Davis
Circ./Adv. Dir. .... Dee Dee McCaslin

LAKE WORTH

COASTAL/GREENACRES OBSERVER (THUR)

1313 Central Ter, Lake Worth, FL, 33460-1835, Palm Beach, USA; gen tel (561) 585-9387; gen fax (561) 585-5434; disp adv e-mail Adsales@lwherald.com; class adv e-mail Classifieds@lwherald.com; ed e-mail Editor@lwherald.com; web site lwherald.com
Circulation: 1,200pd, 28,000fr; Sworn/Estimate/Non-Audited
Advertising rate: Open inch rate $11.50
Established: 1912
Group: Lake Worth Herald Press, Inc.
Editor/Publisher .... Mark J. Easton
Delivery Method: Mail, Newsstand, Carrier, Racks

THE LAKE WORTH HERALD (THUR)

1313 Central Ter, Lake Worth, FL, 33460-1835, Palm Beach, USA; gen tel (561) 585-9387; gen fax (561) 585-5434; disp adv e-mail Adsales@lwherald.com; class adv e-mail Classifieds@lwherald.com; ed e-mail Editor@lwherald.com; web site lwherald.com
Circulation: 950pd, 18,000fr; Sworn/Estimate/Non-Audited
Advertising rate: Open inch rate $11.50
Established: 1912
Group: Lake Worth Herald Press, Inc.
Editor/Publisher .... Mark J. Easton
Delivery Method: Mail, Newsstand, Carrier, Racks
Areas Served: Central Palm Beach County

LAND O LAKES

LAND O LAKES LAKER (WED)

3632 Land O Lakes Blvd, Ste 102, Land O Lakes, FL, 34639-4407, Pasco, USA; gen tel (813) 909-2800; adv tel (813) 909-2800; ed tel (813) 909-2800; gen fax (813) 909-2802; adv fax (813) 909-2802; ed fax (813) 909-2802; disp adv e-mail dkortus@lakerlutznews.com; class adv e-mail classifieds@lakerlutznews.com; ed e-mail bcmanion@lakerlutznews.com; web site www.lakerlutznews.com
Circulation: 14,126fr; VAC
Advertising rate: $23.51
Established: 1981
Group: Manatee Media Inc.Editions: (1) Laker-Land O'Lakes
Pres./Pub. .... Diane Kortus
Ed .... B.C. Manion
Mechanical Specifications: Full Page: 9.916 X 15.1
1/2 Page Vertical: 4.875 X 15.5
1/2 page Horizontal: 9.916 X 7.675
1/3 Page Vertical: 4.875 X 10
1/3 Page Horizontal: 15.5 X 5
1/4 Page Vertical: 4.875 X 7.675
1/4 Page Horizontal: 9.916 X 3.75
1/6 Page Vertical: 4.75 X 3.75
1/6 Page Horizontal: 9.916 X 2.5
1/8 Page: 4.875 X 3.75
1/12 Page Horizontal: 4.875 X 2.5
Font Page Panel: 2.354 X 4
Delivery Method: Carrier, Racks
Areas Served: 34637, 34639, 34638

THE LUTZ NEWS (WED)

3632 Land O Lakes Blvd, Ste 102, Land O Lakes, FL, 34639-4407, Hillsborough, USA; gen tel (813) 909-2800; adv tel (813) 909-2800; ed tel (813) 909-2800; gen fax (813) 909-2802; adv fax (813) 909-2802; ed fax (813) 909-2802; disp adv e-mail dkortus@lakerlutznews.com; class adv e-mail classifieds@lakerlutznews.com; ed e-mail bcmanion@lakerlutznews.com; web site www.lakerlutznews.com
Circulation: 7,125fr; VAC
Advertising rate: 23.51
Established: 1965
Group: Manatee Media Inc.Editions: (1) The Lutz News
Pres./Pub./Adv. .... Diane Kortus
Ed .... B.C. Manion
Mechanical Specifications: Full Page: 9.916 X 15.1
1/2 Page Vertical: 4.875 X 15.5
1/2 page Horizontal: 9.916 X 7.675
1/3 Page Vertical: 4.875 X 10
1/3 Page Horizontal: 15.5 X 5
1/4 Page Vertical: 4.875 X 7.675
1/4 Page Horizontal: 9.916 X 3.75
1/6 Page Vertical: 4.75 X 3.75
1/6 Page Horizontal: 9.916 X 2.5
1/8 Page: 4.875 X 3.75
1/12 Page Horizontal: 4.875 X 2.5
Font Page Panel: 2.354 X 4
Delivery Method: Carrier, Racks
Areas Served: 33548, 33549, 33558, 33559, 33613

WESLEY CHAPEL LAKER (WED)

3632 Land O Lakes Blvd, Ste 102, Land O Lakes, FL, 34639-4407, Pasco, USA; gen tel (813) 909-2800; adv tel (813) 909-2800; ed tel (813) 909-2800; gen fax (813) 909-2802; adv fax (813) 909-2802; ed fax (813) 909-2802; disp adv e-mail sales@lakerlutznews.com; class adv e-mail classifieds@lakerlutznews.com; ed e-mail bcmanion@lakerlutznews.com; web site www.lakerlutznews.com
Circulation: 14,126fr; VAC
Advertising rate: Open inch rate $23.51
Established: 1981
Group: Manatee Media Inc.Editions: (1) The Laker - Wesley Chapel
Pres./Pub. .... Diane Kortus
Ed .... B.C. Manion
Mechanical Specifications: Full Page: 9.916 X 15.1
1/2 Page Vertical: 4.875 X 15.5
1/2 page Horizontal: 9.916 X 7.675
1/3 Page Vertical: 4.875 X 10
1/3 Page Horizontal: 15.5 X 5
1/4 Page Vertical: 4.875 X 7.675
1/4 Page Horizontal: 9.916 X 3.75
1/6 Page Vertical: 4.75 X 3.75
1/6 Page Horizontal: 9.916 X 2.5
1/8 Page: 4.875 X 3.75
1/12 Page Horizontal: 4.875 X 2.5
Font Page Panel: 2.354 X 4
Delivery Method: Carrier, Racks
Areas Served: 33543, 33544, 33545, 33559, 33647, 34639

ZEPHYRHILLS LAKER (WED)

3632 Land O Lakes Blvd, Ste 102, Land O Lakes, FL, 34639-4407, Pasco, USA; gen tel (813) 909-2800; adv tel (813) 909-2800; ed tel (813) 909-2800; gen fax (813) 909-2802; adv fax (813) 909-2802; ed fax (813) 909-2802; disp adv e-mail dkortus@lakerlutznews.com; class adv e-mail classifieds@lakerlutznews.com; ed e-mail bcmanion@lakerlutznews.com; web site www.lakerlutznews.com
Circulation: 8,179fr; VAC
Advertising rate: Open inch rate $23.51
Established: 1965
Group: Manatee Media Inc.Editions: (1) The Lutz News
Pres./Pub. .... Diane Kortus
Ed .... B.C. Manion
Mechanical Specifications: Full Page: 9.916 X 15.1
1/2 Page Vertical: 4.875 X 15.5
1/2 page Horizontal: 9.916 X 7.675
1/3 Page Vertical: 4.875 X 10
1/3 Page Horizontal: 15.5 X 5
1/4 Page Vertical: 4.875 X 7.675
1/4 Page Horizontal: 9.916 X 3.75
1/6 Page Vertical: 4.75 X 3.75
1/6 Page Horizontal: 9.916 X 2.5
1/8 Page: 4.875 X 3.75
1/12 Page Horizontal: 4.875 X 2.5
Font Page Panel: 2.354 X 4
Delivery Method: Carrier, Racks
Areas Served: 33523, 33525, 33540, 33541, 33542, 33543, 33574, 33576

LEESBURG

SOUTH LAKE PRESS (WED)

212 E Main St, Leesburg, FL, 34748-5227, Lake, USA; gen tel (352) 394-2183; gen fax (352) 394-8001; disp adv e-mail slpress@dailycommercial.com; web site www.southlakepress.com
Circulation: 40,000pd,; Sworn/Estimate/Non-Audited
Advertising rate: Open inch rate $14.50
Established: 1913
Group: HarborPoint Media Group (OOB)
Halifax Media
Adv. Sales Mgr. .... Vanessa Hovater
Circ. Mgr. .... Jay Gillespie
Mng. Ed. .... Dan Fields
Prodn. Mgr. .... Wayne Wicker
New Majors/Nat'l Acct. Rep. ... Melanie Randall
Steve Skaggs
Mechanical Specifications: Type page 13 x 21 1/2; E - 6 cols, 2, 3/16 between; A - 6 cols, 2, 3/16 between; C - 6 cols, 2, 3/16 between. Equipment & Software: Hardware — APP/Mac; Software — QPS/QuarkXPress, Multi-Ad/Creator, Microsoft/Word, Adobe/Photoshop.

LIVE OAK

JASPER NEWS (THUR)

521 Demorest St SE, Live Oak, FL, 32064-3320, Suwannee, USA; gen tel (386) 792-2487; gen fax (386) 792-2934; disp adv e-mail jaspernews1@windstream.net; web site www.nflaonline.com
Circulation: 1,450pd, 30fr; Sworn/Estimate/Non-Audited
Advertising rate: Open inch rate $10.00
Established: 1870
Group: Community Newspaper Holdings, Inc.
Pub. .... Myra Regan
Ad. Dir. .... Monja Robinson
Circ. Mgr. .... Angie Sparks
Ed. .... Jeff Waters
Prodn. Mgr. .... Dee Freeman
Nat'l Adv. Mgr. .... Laura Rogers
Mechanical Specifications: Type page 11 x 21 1/2; E - 6 cols, between; A - 6 cols, between; C - 10 cols, between.Equipment & Software: Hardware — APP/Mac; Presses — 8-WPC/Web Leader; Software — Adobe/PageMaker 6.0, Adobe/Photoshop, Adobe/Typestyler.

MAYO FREE PRESS (THUR)

PO Box 370, Live Oak, FL, 32064-0370, Suwannee, USA; gen tel (386) 362-1734; gen fax (386) 364-5578; disp adv e-mail mayofreepress@windstream.net; ed e-mail mayofreepress@windstream.net; web site www.suwanneedemocrat.com/mayo
Circulation: 900pd, 50fr; Sworn/Estimate/Non-Audited
Advertising rate: Open inch rate $12.30
Established: 1888
Group: Community Newspaper Holdings, Inc.
Editor .... Jeff Waters
Publisher .... Myra Regan

SUWANNEE DEMOCRAT (WED, FRI)

521 Demorest St SE, Live Oak, FL, 32064-3320, Suwannee, USA; gen tel (386) 362-1734; adv tel (386) 362-1734 x105; ed tel 386-362-1734 x131; gen fax (386) 364-5578; disp adv e-mail monja.slater@gaflnews.com; class adv e-mail louise.sheddan@gaflnews.com; ed e-mail nf.editorial@gaflnews.com; web site www.suwanneedemocrat.com
Circulation: 3,215pd,; USPS
Advertising rate: Open inch rate $11.00
Established: 1884
Group: Community Newspaper Holdings, Inc.
Pub. .... Myra Regan
Editor .... Jamie Wachter
Advertising Director .... Monja Slater
Circulation .... Jennifer Newham
Delivery Method: Mail, Newsstand, Racks
Areas Served: 32060, 32064, 32008, 32062, 32071, 32094

MACCLENNY

THE BAKER COUNTY PRESS (THUR)

104 S 5th St, Macclenny, FL, 32063-2304, Baker, USA; gen tel (904) 259-2400; gen fax (904) 259-6502; disp adv e-mail advertising@bakercountypress.com; class adv e-mail classifieds@bakercountypress.com; ed e-mail editor@bakercountypress.com; web site www.bakercountypress.com
Circulation: 5,400pd,; USPS
Advertising rate: Open inch rate $6.70
Established: 1929
Bus. Mgr....Karin Thomas
Pub./Ed....James C. McGauley
Ad. Dir....Jessica Prevatt
Mng Ed....Joel Addington
Mechanical Specifications: Type page 13 x 21; E - 6 cols, 1.95, 0.267 between.Equipment & Software: Hardware — APP/Mac; Presses — HI; Software — QPS/QuarkXPress 3.3.
Delivery Method: Mail, Racks
Areas Served: 32040, 32063, 32072, 32087, 32234

MADISON

MADISON COUNTY CARRIER (WED)

1695 S State Road 53, Madison, FL, 32340-3331, Madison, USA; gen tel (850) 973-4141; gen fax (850) 973-4121; disp adv e-mail greenepub@greenepublishing.com; ed e-mail news@greenepublishing.com; web site www.greenepublishing.com
Circulation: 3,700pd,; Sworn/Estimate/Non-Audited
Advertising rate: Open inch rate $6.00
Established: 1964
Pub....Emerald Greene
Ad....Jeanette Dunn
Editor....Jacob Bernbry
Mechanical Specifications: Type page 13 x 21 1/2; E - 6 cols, 2 1/16, between; A - 6 cols, 2 1/16, between; C - 6 cols, 2 1/16, between.

MADISON ENTERPRISE-RECORDER (FRI)

1695 S State Road 53, Madison, FL, 32340-3331, Madison, USA; gen tel (850) 973-4141; gen fax (850) 973-4121; disp adv e-mail greenepub@greenepublishing.com; ed e-mail news@greenepublishing.com; web site www.greenepublishing.com
Circulation: 3,700pd,; Sworn/Estimate/Non-Audited
Advertising rate: Open inch rate $6.25
Publisher....Emerald Greene
Editor....Jacob Bernbry
Ad....Jeanette Dunn
Mechanical Specifications: Type page 13 x 21 1/2; E - 6 cols, 2, between; A - 6 cols, 2, between; C - 6 cols, 2, between.

MARATHON

FLORIDA KEYS KEYNOTER (WED, SAT)

3015 Overseas Hwy, Marathon, FL, 33050-2236, Monroe, USA; gen tel (305) 743-5551; adv tel (305) 440-3216; ed tel (305) 440-3218; gen fax (305) 743-6397; disp adv e-mail jpulis@keynoter.com; class adv e-mail btraeger@keynoter.com; ed e-mail lkahn@keynoter.com; web site www.flkeysnews.com - 550,000(views) 175,000(visitors)
Circulation: 9,400pd, 1,250fr; Sworn/Estimate/Non-Audited
Advertising rate: Open inch rate $19.30
Established: 1953
Group: The McClatchy Company
Digital Platform - Mobile: Apple, Android
Ed....Larry Kahn
Joanne Pulis
Mechanical Specifications: Type page 10.20 x 20; ROP col 1.597-inches; Classified col 1.597-inches.Equipment & Software: Hardware — APP/Mac, PCs; Software — QPS/QuarkXPress, Adobe/Photoshop, Microsoft/Office.
Delivery Method: Mail, Newsstand, Carrier, Racks
Areas Served: Monroe County, Fl.

MARCO ISLAND

COASTAL BREEZE NEWS (FRI, OTHER)

1857 San Marco Rd, Ste C-216, Marco Island, FL, 34145-6742, Collier, USA; gen tel (239) 393-4991; gen fax (239) 393-4992; disp adv e-mail val@coastalbreezenews.com; class adv e-mail cherie@coastalbreezenews.com; ed e-mail jessica@coastalbreezenews.com; web site www.coastalbreezenews.com - 43,632(views) 13,393(visitors)
Circulation: 0pd, 17,500fr; CVC
Advertising rate: Full Page 10 X 16 open rate $800 1x annual contract $500 1x
Established: 2010
Digital Platform - Mobile: Apple, Android
Pub....Val Simon
Mechanical Specifications: Page 11" X 17" Image area 10" X 15.5"
Delivery Method: Carrier, Racks
Areas Served: Marco Island, Goodland, Isles of Capri, Naples, Everglades City, Chokoloskee

MARIANNA

JACKSON COUNTY TIMES (THUR)

2866 Madison St, Marianna, FL, 32448-4610, Jackson, USA; gen tel (850) 526-1501 ; adv tel (850) 526-1501; ed tel (850) 526-1501; gen fax (850) 526-1505; adv fax (850-526-1505; ed fax (850-526-1505; disp adv e-mail bo.jctimes@gmail.com; class adv e-mail liz@jacksoncountytimes.net; ed e-mail editor@jacksoncountytimes.net; web site www.jacksoncountytimes.net
Circulation: 2,500pd,; Sworn/Estimate/Non-Audited
Advertising rate: $5.50
Established: 2006
Group: Hatcher Publications
Pub./Adv. Mgr....Stephanie Parker
Managing Editor....Sid Riley
Advertising....Bo McMullian
Mechanical Specifications: Type page 10.25 x 21; E - 6 cols 1.596, 0.117 between
Delivery Method: Mail, Racks
Areas Served: 32420, 32423, 32426, 32431, 32440, 32442, 32443, 32445, 32446, 32447, 32448, 32460

MELBOURNE

BEST - CENTRAL (WED)

1 Gannett Plaza, Melbourne, FL, 32940, Brevard, USA; gen tel (321) 242-3500; adv tel (321) 242-3765; ed tel (321) 242-3774; gen fax (321) 242-6620; adv fax (321) 610-5152; ed fax (321) 242-6620; disp adv e-mail advertising@floridatoday.com; ed e-mail sprice@floridatoday.com; web site www.floridatoday.com
Circulation: 45,000pd,; Sworn/Estimate/Non-Audited
Advertising rate: (Modular Rates) 1/8 page 5.7 x 5 - $250 1x
Group: Gannett
President & Publisher....Jeff Kiel
Exec. Editor....Bob Stover
Editor....Shona Price
Ad. Dir....Stephanie McLoughlin
Mechanical Specifications: Type page 11 5/8 x 21; 6 cols, 1.75, 0.225 between
Delivery Method: Mail
Areas Served: 32955, 32940, 32934, 32935, 32937

BEST - NORTH (WED)

1 Gannett Plaza, Melbourne, FL, 32940, Brevard, USA; gen tel (321) 242-3500; adv tel (321) 242-3765; ed tel (321) 242-3774; gen fax (321) 242-6620; adv fax (321) 610-5152; ed fax (321) 242-6620; disp adv e-mail advertising@floridatoday.com; ed e-mail sprice@floridatoday.com; web site www.floridatoday.com
Circulation: 55,000pd,; Sworn/Estimate/Non-Audited
Advertising rate: (Modular Rates) 1/8 page 5.7 x 5 - $250 1x
Group: Gannett
President & Publisher....Jeff Kiel
Exec. Editor....Bob Stover
Editor....Shona Price
Ad. Director....Stephanie McLoughlin
Mechanical Specifications: Type page 11 5/8 x 21; 6 cols, 1.75, 0.225 between
Delivery Method: Mail
Areas Served: 32754, 32775, 32780, 32796, 32927, 32926, 32922, 32952, 32953, 32931, 32920

BEST - SOUTH (WED)

1 Gannett Plaza, Melbourne, FL, 32940, USA; gen tel (321) 242-3500; adv tel (321) 242-3765; ed tel (321) 242-3774; gen fax (321) 242-6620; adv fax (321) 610-5152; ed fax (321) 242-6620; disp adv e-mail advertising@floridatoday.com; ed e-mail sprice@floridatoday.com; web site www.floridatoday.com
Circulation: 55,000pd,; Sworn/Estimate/Non-Audited
Advertising rate: (Modular Rates) 1/8 page 5.7 x 5 - $250 1x
Group: Gannett
Ad. Dir....Stephanie McLoughlin
Editor....Shona Price
Exec. Editor....Bob Stover
President & Publisher....Jeff Kiel
Mechanical Specifications: Type page 11 5/8 x 21; 6 cols, 1.75, 0.225 between
Delivery Method: Mail
Areas Served: 32904, 32901, 32905, 32907, 32908, 32909, 32948, 32949, 32950, 32976, 32925, 32903, 32951

MIAMI

MIAMI TODAY (THUR)

2000 S Dixie Hwy Ste 100, Suite 100, Miami, FL, 33133-2451, Miami-Dade, USA; gen tel (305) 358-2663; adv tel (305) 358-1008; ed tel (305) 358-2663; gen fax (305) 358-4811 ; adv fax (305) 358-4811; ed fax (305) 358-4811; disp adv e-mail cblewis@miamitodaynews.com; class adv e-mail fgrande@miamitodaynews.com; ed e-mail editor@miamitodaynews.com; web site www.miamitodaynews.com
Circulation: 172pd, 27,229fr; BPA
Advertising rate: Modular
Established: 1983
Group: Today Enterprises Inc.
VP....Carmen Betancourt-Lewis
Delivery Method: Carrier
Areas Served: Miami-Dade County, FL

SOUTH FLORIDA BUSINESS JOURNAL (FRI)

80 SW 8th St, Ste 2710, Miami, FL, 33130-3057, Miami-Dade, USA; gen tel (954) 949-7600; adv tel (954) 949-7558; gen fax (954) 949-7591; adv fax (954) 949-7599; disp adv e-mail southflorida@bizjournals.com; web site www.bizjournals.com/southflorida
Circulation: 9,000fr; Sworn/Estimate/Non-Audited
Ed. in Chief....Mel Melendez

MILTON

SANTA ROSA PRESS GAZETTE (WED, SAT)

6576 Caroline St, Milton, FL, 32570-4759, Santa Rosa, USA; gen tel (850) 623-2120; adv tel (850) 910-5316; gen fax (850) 623-2007; ed fax (850) 623-2007; disp adv e-mail dcoon@srpressgazette.com; class adv e-mail rpratt@srpressgazette.com; ed e-mail lhough@srpressgazette.com; web site www.srpressgazette.com
Circulation: 5,000pd,; USPS
Advertising rate: Open inch rate $12.90
Established: 1908
Group: Halifax Media
Pub....Jim Fletcher
Ad. Accounts Exec....Debbie Coon
Editor....Pamela Holt
Mechanical Specifications: Type page 9.90 x 20; E - 6 cols, 2, 1/6 between; A - 6 cols, 2, 1/6 between; C - 9 cols, 1 1/3, 1/12 between. Equipment & Software: Hardware — 15-APP/Mac G4; Presses — 6-KP; Software — Adobe/PageMaker 6.5, QPS/QuarkXPress 4.1, Adobe/Photoshop 5.0, Macromedia/Freehand.
Delivery Method: Mail
Areas Served: 32570, 32583, 32571, 32572, 32565, 32530

MONTICELLO

MONTICELLO NEWS (WED, SAT)

180 W Washington St, Monticello, FL, 32344-1954, Jefferson, USA; gen tel (850) 997-3568; gen fax (850) 997-3774; disp adv e-mail glendaslater@embarqmail.com; ed e-mail monticellonews@embarqmail.com; web site www.ecbpublishing.com
Circulation: 3,000pd, 30fr; Sworn/Estimate/Non-Audited
Advertising rate: Open inch rate $6.25
Pub....Emerald Greene
Adv. Exec....Glenda Slater
Delivery Method: Mail, Racks
Areas Served: 32345

MULBERRY

POLK COUNTY PRESS (TUES)

1020 N Church Ave, Mulberry, FL, 33860-2040, Polk, USA; gen tel (863) 425-3411; adv tel same; disp adv e-mail polkcounrypress@yahoo.com; ed e-mail editor@themulberrypress.com; web site none
Circulation: 3,000pd, 3,000fr; Sworn/Estimate/Non-Audited
Advertising rate: Open inch rate $14.00
Established: 1909
Owner, Pub. & Ed....William M. Histed
Circ. Mgr....Carole M. Histed
Prodn. Mgr....Robert B. Histed
Mechanical Specifications: 8 1/4 wide by 10 1/2 inches deep
(Magazine format)Equipment & Software: ; Software — Microsoft/Windows.
Delivery Method: Mail, Newsstand, Racks
Areas Served: 33860, 33830, 33811, 33813

NAPLES

BONITA SPRINGS FLORIDA WEEKLY (THUR)

9051 Tamiami Trl N, Ste 202, Naples, FL, 34108-2520, Collier, USA; gen tel (239) 325-1960; disp adv e-mail advertise@floridaweekly.com; class adv e-mail advertise@floridaweekly.com; ed e-mail news@floridaweekly.com; web site www.floridaweekly.com
Circulation: 35,646pd,; CAC
Advertising rate: 1/8 Pg $250.00; 1/4 Pg $625.00; 1/2 Pg $940.00; Full $2500.00
Group: Florida Media Group LLC
Pres./Pub....J. Pason Gaddis
VP and Exec. Ed....Jeffrey Cull
VP and Creative Dir....Jim Dickerson
Nat'l Adv. Mgr...Shelley Hobbs **Delivery Method:** Mail, Newsstand

BUSINESS OBSERVER-COLLIER (FRI)

501 Goodlette Rd N, Ste D100, Naples, FL, 34102-5666, Collier, USA; gen tel (239) 263-0122; adv tel (941) 726-6145; ed tel (239) 275-2230; gen fax (239) 263-0112; adv fax (239) 263-0112; ed fax (239) 263-0112; disp adv e-mail dschaefer@BusinessObserverFL.com; class adv e-mail kboothroyd@BusinessObserverFL.com; ed e-mail gruss@BusinessObserverFL.com; web site www.businessobserverfl.com

Circulation: 145pd, 446fr; VAC
Advertising rate: Modular Rate $288 (1/8P); $530 (1/4P); $1021 (1/2P)
Established: 1997
Group: Observer Media Group Inc.
Digital Platform - Mobile: Apple, Android, Windows, Blackberry
Digital Platform - Tablet: Apple iOS, Android, Windows 7, Blackberry Tablet OS
Publisher.............................. Matthew G. Walsh
Assoc. Pub./Adv. Dir................ Diane Schaefer
Ed. .... Jean Gruss
Mechanical Specifications: 10.375" x 16"
Delivery Method: Mail, Newsstand, Carrier, Racks
Areas Served: 34101, 34102

MARCO EAGLE (WED, FRI, SAT)

1100 Immokalee Rd, Naples, FL, 34110-4810, Collier, USA; gen tel (239) 213-6000; adv tel (239) 213-5301; ed tel (239) 263-4863; gen fax (239) 213-5390; disp adv e-mail JLFuenmayor@Naplesnews.com; class adv e-mail classad@naplesnews.com; ed e-mail manny.garcia@naplesnews.com; web site http://www.naplesnews.com/community/marco-eagle
Circulation: 15,900fr; Sworn/Estimate/Non-Audited
Advertising rate: 1/12 Pg $196.88; 1/8 Pg $253.13; 1/4 Pg $416.25
Ad. Dir.................................... Vince Modarelli
President/Publisher ....Bill Barker
Editor ....Jay Schlichter
Delivery Method: Mail, Racks
Areas Served: Bonita Springs

NAPLES FLORIDA WEEKLY (THUR)

9051 Tamiami Trl N, Ste 202, Naples, FL, 34108-2520, Collier, USA; gen tel (239) 325-1960; gen fax (239) 325-1964; disp adv e-mail advertise@floridaweekly.com; class adv e-mail advertise@floridaweekly.com; ed e-mail news@floridaweekly.com; web site www.floridaweekly.com
Circulation: 35,646pd,; CAC
Advertising rate: 1/16 Pg $250.00; 1/8 Pg $450.00; 1/4 Pg $625.00
VP and Creative Dir. .... Jim Dickerson
VP and Exec. Ed............................Jeffrey Cull
Pres./Grp. Pub. .... J. Pason Gaddis
Pub......................................Angela Schivinski
Nat'l Adv. Mgr.............................Shelley Hobbs
Delivery Method: Mail, Newsstand

THE BANNER (WED, SAT)

1100 Immokalee Rd, Naples, FL, 34110-4810, Collier, USA; gen tel (239) 213-6000; adv tel (239) 263-4730; gen fax (239) 213-6099; disp adv e-mail salesassist@naplesnews.com; class adv e-mail classad@naplesnews.com; ed e-mail news@naplesnews.com; web site www.bonitabanner.com
Circulation: 43,000fr; Sworn/Estimate/Non-Audited
Advertising rate: (Modular Rates) 3x4.5 - $168.75 1x
Editor ....Elysa Delcorto
President/Publisher ....Bill Barker
Ad. Director............................. Vince Modarelli
Mechanical Specifications: 6 x 21
Delivery Method: Mail, Racks
Areas Served: Marco Island, Isles of Capri, East Naples

THE COLLIER CITIZEN (SAT)

1100 Immokalee Rd, Naples, FL, 34110-4810, Collier, USA; gen tel (239) 213-6000; adv tel (239) 263-4730; gen fax (239) 213-6076; disp adv e-mail salesassist@naplesnews.com; class adv e-mail classad@naplesnews.com; ed e-mail news@colliercitizen.com; web site www.colliercitizen.com
Circulation: 52,118fr; Sworn/Estimate/Non-Audited
Advertising rate: (Modular Rates) 3x4.5 - $270.00 1x
Established: 2005
Ed..Jay Schlichter
Adv. Dir................................... Vince Modarelli
Mechanical Specifications: Type page 10 1/4 x 16; E - 5 cols, 2 1/4, between; A - 5 cols, 2 1/4, between; C - 8 cols, 2 1/4, between. Equipment & Software: Hardware — PC; Software — QPS/QuarkXPress 4.0, Adobe/Acrobat 4.0.
Delivery Method: Mail, Racks
Areas Served: 34102, 34103, 34104, 34105, 34108, 34109, 34110, 34112, 34116, 34117, 34119, 34120

NAVARRE

NAVARRE PRESS (THUR)

7502 Harvest Village Ct, Navarre, FL, 32566-7319, Santa Rosa, USA; gen tel (850) 939-8040; gen fax (850) 939-4575; disp adv e-mail ads@navarrepress.com; ed e-mail news@navarrepress.com; web site www.navarrepress.com
Circulation: 4,000pd,; Sworn/Estimate/Non-Audited
Advertising rate: Open inch rate $15.00
Pub... Sandi Kemp
Ad. ....Gail Acosta
Mechanical Specifications: Type page 11 x 21; E - 6 cols, 1.55
Areas Served: 32563, 32566, 32569, 32570, 32571, 32583

NEW PORT RICHEY

THE SUNCOAST NEWS (WED, SAT)

6214 US Highway 19, New Port Richey, FL, 34652-2528, Pasco, USA; gen tel (727) 815-1000; adv tel (727) 815-1032; ed tel (727) 815-1064; gen fax (727) 815-1025; disp adv e-mail dpleus@suncoastnews.com; class adv e-mail tribisi@suncoastnews.com; ed e-mail rhibbs@suncoastnews.com; web site www.suncoastnews.com
Circulation: 90,433fr; Sworn/Estimate/Non-Audited
Advertising rate: Open inch rate $58.30
Group: BH Media Group
Media General, Inc. (OOB)Editions: (5) 5 total; Suncoast News-Holiday/Trinity (22,911); Suncoast News-Hudson/Port Richey (24,937); Suncoast News-New Port Richey (34,604); Suncoast News-Oldsmar/Safety Harbor/E. Lake (27,881); Suncoast News-Palm Harbor/Tarpon Spring/Dunedin (34,203);
Pub.................................... Duayne Chichester
Ad. Sales Manager........................ Doug Pleus
Ed. ....Robert Hibbs
Adv. Sales Mgr........................... Timothy Wahl
Mechanical Specifications: Type page 10 3/4 x 15; E - 5 cols, 2 1/16, between; A - 5 cols, 2 1/16, between; C - 9 cols, 1 1/16, between. Equipment & Software: Hardware — HP; Presses — G/Community, G/SSC; Software — QPS/QuarkXPress 4.4.
Areas Served: Pasco North, Pasco West, Pasco East, Pinellas North

NICEVILLE

THE BAY BEACON (WED)

1181 John Sims Pkwy E, Niceville, FL, 32578-2752, Okaloosa, USA; gen tel (850) 678-1080; adv tel (850) 678-1080; ed tel (850) 678-1080; disp adv e-mail info@baybeacon.com; class adv e-mail info@baybeacon.com; ed e-mail info@baybeacon.com; web site www.baybeacon.com
Circulation: 15,000fr; Sworn/Estimate/Non-Audited
Advertising rate: Open inch rate $17.45
Established: 1992
Ed. & Pub.................................. Stephen Kent
Adv. Mgr. .... Sara Kent
Mechanical Specifications: Type page 11.6" x 20"; 6 cols, 1.83", 0.167" between; C - 6 cols, 1.167", 0.167" between.
Equipment & Software: Hardware — APP/Mac; Software — QuarkXPress 8, Adobe/Acrobat 9.
Delivery Method: Carrier
Areas Served: 32578, 32588, 32580, 32439, 32542

OCEAN RIDGE

THE COASTAL STAR (MTHLY)

5114 N Ocean Blvd, Ocean Ridge, FL, 33435-7031, Palm Beach, USA; gen tel (561) 337-1553; adv tel (561) 337-1553; ed tel (561) 337-1553; gen fax (561) 337-1553; disp adv e-mail sales@thecoastalstar.com; ed e-mail editor@thecoastalstar.com; web site www.thecoastalstar.com - 16,306(views) 4,941(visitors)
Circulation: 400pd, 17,000fr; CVC
Advertising rate: 1/8 Pg $275.00
Established: 2008Editions: (2) Boca/Highland Delray/GulfStream/Manalapan
Publlisher..................................... Jerry Lower
Ed. ....Mary Kate Leming
Adv. Dir...................................... Chris Bellard
Mechanical Specifications: Full page 10" x 15.85"; 5 cols, 1.85", 0.18 betweenEquipment & Software: ; Presses — Printed by Stuart Web, Stuart FL
Delivery Method: Mail, Newsstand, Carrier, Racks
Areas Served: 33431, 33432, 33487, 33483, 33435, 33462, 33489

OKEECHOBEE

GLADES COUNTY DEMOCRAT (THUR)

107 SW 17th St, Okeechobee, FL, 34974-6110, Okeechobee, USA; gen tel (863) 763-3134; gen fax (863) 763-5901; disp adv e-mail adsales@newszap.com; class adv e-mail classads@newszap.com; web site gladescountydemocrat.com
Circulation: 1,300pd,; Sworn/Estimate/Non-Audited
Advertising rate: Modular
Established: 1915
Group: Independent Newsmedia Inc. Usa
Independent Newspapers, Inc. (Florida)
Adv. Consultant....................Suzanne Antonich
Mechanical Specifications: Type page 13 x 21 1/2; E - 6 cols, 2, 1/6 between; A - 6 cols, 2, 1/6 between; C - 9 cols, 1 2/5, 1/12 between. Equipment & Software: Hardware — APP/Power Mac; Software — QPS/QuarkXPress 3.3.1.
Delivery Method: Mail, Carrier, Racks
Areas Served: Glades County

OKEECHOBEE NEWS (WED, FRI, SUN)

107 SW 17th St, Ste D, Okeechobee, FL, 34974-6110, Okeechobee, USA; gen tel (863) 763-3134; gen fax (863) 763-5901; adv fax (863) 763-7949; disp adv e-mail adsales@newszap.com; class adv e-mail classads@newszap.com; ed e-mail okeditor@newszap.com; web site okeechobeenews.net
Circulation: 2,583pd, 4,000fr; Sworn/Estimate/Non-Audited
Advertising rate: 1/16 Pg $129.00; 1/8 Pg $252.00; 1/4 Pg $491.00
Established: 1915
Group: Independent Newsmedia Inc. Usa
Independent Newspapers, Inc. (Florida)
Digital Platform - Mobile: Apple, Android, Windows, Blackberry
Digital Platform - Tablet: Apple iOS, Android, Windows 7, Blackberry Tablet OS
Adv. Dir...................................... Judy Kasten
Circ. Mgr..................................... Janet Madray
Ed. ....Katrina Elsken
Sports Ed........................... Charles Murphy
Prodn. Mgr., Pressroom.................. Ginny Guy
Mechanical Specifications: Type page 11 5/8 x 21 1/2; E - 6 cols, 1 5/8, between; A - 6 cols, 1 5/8, between; C - 9 cols, 1 1/5, between.
Delivery Method: Mail, Newsstand, Carrier, Racks

THE CLEWISTON NEWS (THUR)

107 SW 17th St, Ste D, Okeechobee, FL, 34974-6110, Okeechobee, USA; gen tel (863) 763-3134; gen fax (863) 983-7537; disp adv e-mail adsales@newszap.com; class adv e-mail classads@newszap.com; web site theclewistonnews.com
Circulation: 3,700pd,; Sworn/Estimate/Non-Audited
Advertising rate: (Modular Rates)
Established: 1920
Group: Independent Newsmedia Inc. Usa
Independent Newspapers, Inc. (Florida)
Mechanical Specifications: Type page 13 x 21 1/2; E - 6 cols, 2, 1/6 between; A - 6 cols, 2, 1/6 between; C - 9 cols, 1 2/5, 1/12 between.
Delivery Method: Mail, Racks
Areas Served: Hendry County

ORLANDO

ORLANDO BUSINESS JOURNAL (WED)

255 S Orange Ave, Ste 700, Orlando, FL, 32801-5007, Orange, USA; gen tel (407) 649-8470; adv tel (407) 241-2897; ed tel (407) 241-2889; gen fax (407) 420-1625; adv fax (407) 420-1625; ed fax (407) 420-1625; disp adv e-mail rbobroff@bizjournals.com; class adv e-mail ekoshel@bizjournals.com; ed e-mail cbarth@bizjournals.com; web site www.bizjournals.com/orlando 150,490(visitors)
Circulation: 9,496pd,; Sworn/Estimate/Non-Audited
Advertising rate: Open inch rate $1,368 (1/8P); $2,249 (1/4P); $4,016 (1/2P)
Established: 1984
Digital Platform - Mobile: Apple, Android, Windows, Blackberry
Digital Platform - Tablet: Apple iOS, Android, Windows 7, Blackberry Tablet OS
Ed. ....Cindy Barth
Publisher.................................. Robert Bobroff
Mechanical Specifications: Type page 11 x 14; cols 2.375
Delivery Method: Mail, Newsstand, Racks
Areas Served: Orange County

WINTER PARK-MAITLAND OBSERVER (THUR)

1500 Park Center Dr, Orlando, FL, 32835-5705, Orange, USA; gen tel (407) 563-7000; adv tel (407) 376-2434; ed tel (407) 563-7023; gen fax (407) 563-7099; disp adv e-mail LStern@turnstilemediagroup.com; class adv e-mail tcraft@turnstilemediagroup.com; ed e-mail ibabcock@turnstilemediagroup.com; web site www.wpmobserver.com - 15,000(views)
Circulation: 5,300pd,; Sworn/Estimate/Non-Audited
Advertising rate: Open inch rate $12.00
Established: 1989
Group: Turnstile Media Group
Digital Platform - Mobile: Apple, Android, Windows
Pub..Tracy Craft
Mng Ed ....Isaac Babcock
Advt .... Linda Stern
Mechanical Specifications: Type page: 10.25x16, E - 5 cols , 1.91", 0.18 betweenEquipment & Software: Hardware — APP/Mac; Software — InDesign CS 5
Delivery Method: Mail, Newsstand, Racks
Areas Served: 32789, 32790, 32792, 32793, 32751, 32794, 32814,
Winter Park, Maitland, Baldwin Park, Goldenrod

PALM BEACH GARDENS

PALM BEACH GARDENS FLORIDA WEEKLY (THUR)

11380 Prosperity Farms Rd, Ste 103, Palm Beach Gardens, FL, 33410-3450, Palm Beach, USA; gen tel (561) 904-6470; gen fax (561) 904-6456; disp adv e-mail advertise@floridaweekly.com; class adv e-mail advertise@floridaweekly.com; ed e-mail news@floridaweekly.com; web site www.floridaweekly.com
Circulation: 35,646pd,; CAC
Advertising rate: 1/8 P $250 1/4 P $625 1/2 P $940 Full $2500
President and Group PublisherJ. Pason Gaddis
VP and Exec. Ed............................Jeffrey Cull
VP and Creative Dir. .... Jim Dickerson
Delivery Method: Mail, Newsstand

PALM COAST

PALM COAST OBSERVER (THUR)

1 Florida Park Dr N, Ste 103, Palm Coast, FL, 32137-3843, Flagler, USA; gen tel (386) 447-9723; gen fax (386) 447-9963; disp adv e-mail jaclyn@palmcoastobserver.com; class adv e-mail randi@palmcoastobserver.com; ed e-mail bmcmillan@palmcoastobserver.com; web site www.palmcoastobserver.com - 150,000(views) 75,000(visitors)
Circulation: 11pd, 26,787fr; VAC
Advertising rate: Open inch rate $25.92
Established: 2010
Group: Palm Coast Observer, LLCEditions: (3) Palm Coast Observer, Ormond Beach Observer, Palm Coast Observer Weekender
Digital Platform - Mobile: Apple, Android, Windows
Digital Platform - Tablet: Apple iOS, Android, Windows 7, Kindle, Kindle Fire
Pub. John Walsh
Managing Ed. Brian McMillan
Ad. Manager Jaci Beckett
Mechanical Specifications: Type page 10.375 x 16; 4 cols, 2.45, 0.19 between
Delivery Method: Newsstand, Carrier, Racks
Areas Served: Hammock Dunes, Hammock Beach, Palm Harbor, Grand Haven, Indian Trails, Pine Lakes, Cypress Knoll, Sugar Mill Plantation, Flagler Beach, Bunnell

PANAMA CITY

BAY COUNTY BULLET (FRI)

1714 W 23rd St Ste G, Suite G, Panama City, FL, 32405-2924, Bay, USA; gen tel (850) 640-0855; gen fax (850) 391-6648; disp adv e-mail ads@baybullet.com; class adv e-mail classifieds@baybullet.com; ed e-mail news@baybullet.com; web site www.baybullet.com
Circulation: 3,300pd, 2,700fr; Sworn/Estimate/Non-Audited
Advertising rate: (Modular Rates) 1/16 page 2.26x2.91 - $50 1x
Established: 2009
Editor Phil Lucas
Pub. Linda Lucas
Mechanical Specifications: Type page 9.54 x 12.147
Delivery Method: Mail, Newsstand, Carrier, Racks
Areas Served: Bay County, Callaway, Lynn Haven, Mexico Beach, Panama City, Panama City Beach, Parker, Springfield, Southport, West Bay

PENSACOLA

ESCAMBIA SUN PRESS (THUR)

605 S Old Corry Field Rd, Pensacola, FL, 32507-2129, Escambia, USA; gen tel (850) 456-3121; adv tel (850) 456-3121; ed tel Same; gen fax (850) 456-0103; adv fax (850) 456-0103; ed fax Same; disp adv e-mail info@escambiasunpress.com; class adv e-mail legals@escambiasunpress.com; ed e-mail info@escambiasunpress.com; web site www.escambiasunpress.com
Circulation: 1,600pd,; Sworn/Estimate/Non-Audited
Advertising rate: Open inch rate $11.05
Established: 1948
Owner/Publisher Michael J. Driver
Mng. Ed. Denise Turner
Prodn. Mgr. Phil Driver
Mechanical Specifications: Type page 15.75 x 21; 9 cols, 1.75
Delivery Method: Mail, Racks

PERRY

TACO TIMES (WED)

123 S Jefferson St, Perry, FL, 32347-3232, Taylor, USA; gen tel (850) 584-5513; gen fax (850) 838-1566; disp adv e-mail ads@perrynewspapers.com; class adv e-mail classifieds@perrynewspapers.com; ed e-mail newsdesk@perrynewspapers.com; web site www.perrynewspapers.com
Circulation: 5,346pd,; Sworn/Estimate/Non-Audited
Advertising rate: Open inch rate $8.95
Established: 1961
Pub. Donald D. Lincoln
Adv. Mgr. Carol Lynn Dubose
Circ. Mgr. Debbie Carlton
Mng. Ed. Susan H. Lincoln
Mechanical Specifications: Type page 10.1.25 x 21.5; 6 cols, 1.56, 0.15 between

PLANT CITY

PLANT CITY OBSERVER (FRI)

1507 S Alexander St Ste 103, #103, Plant City, FL, 33563-8413, Hillsborough, USA; gen tel (813) 704-6850; adv tel (813) 704-6850; ed tel (813) 704-6850; gen fax (941) 362-4808; disp adv e-mail vprostko@PlantCityObserver.com; class adv e-mail llancaster@PlantCityObserver.com; ed e-mail meng@PlantCityObserver.com; web site www.PlantCityObserver.com
Circulation: 0pd, 13,246fr; VAC
Advertising rate: Open inch rate $20.97
Group: Plant City Media LLC
Digital Platform - Mobile: Apple, Android, Windows, Blackberry
Digital Platform - Tablet: Apple iOS, Android, Windows 7, Blackberry Tablet OS, Kindle, Nook, Kindle Fire
Mng. Ed./Gen. Mgr. Michael Eng
Asst. Ed. Jess Eng
Adv. Mgr. Veronica Prostko
Pub. Matthew G. Walsh
Adv. Dir. Jill Raleigh
Mechanical Specifications: Type page 10 13/16 x 15; E - 5 cols, 2, 1/6 between; A - 5 cols, 2, 1/6 between; C - 8 cols, 1 1/4, 1/6 between.
Delivery Method: Mail, Newsstand, Racks
Areas Served: 33563, 33565, 33566, 33567, 33527

POMPANO BEACH

HI-RISER - BROWARD (THUR)

1701 Green Rd, Pompano Beach, FL, 33064-1074, Broward, USA; gen tel (954) 356-4000; adv tel (954) 574-5373; ed tel (954) 563-3311; gen fax (954) 429-1207; disp adv e-mail tadams@tribune.com; ed e-mail jzizzo@tribune.com; web site www.forumpubs.comm
Circulation: 16,000fr; CVC
Advertising rate: 2x2 $77.00; 2x3.5 $152.00
Group: Sun-Sentinel Co.
Pres./Pub. Tom Adams
VP/Exec. Ed. Pam Doto
Managing Ed. Judith Zizzo
Circ. Mgr. Mark Ward
Mechanical Specifications: Type page 10 13/16 x 13; A - 5 cols, 2 1/16, between.
Delivery Method: Mail, Racks
Areas Served: 33301, 33304, 33305, 33306, 33308, 33334, 33062

THE SENTRY (THUR)

2500 SE 5th Ct, Pompano Beach, FL, 33062-6108, Broward, USA; gen tel (954) 532-2000; gen fax (954) 532-2002; disp adv e-mail advertise@flsentry.com; ed e-mail editor@flsentry.com; web site www.flsentry.com
Circulation: 5,000pd,; Sworn/Estimate/Non-Audited
Advertising rate: Open inch rate $17.95
Established: 1980
Pub. Karen M. Foley
Ed. Ross Shulmister
Reporter J.P. Bender
Prodn. Mgr. Chas Rogers
Mechanical Specifications: Type page 13 x 21 1/2; A - 6 cols, 2 7/50, 1/6 between; C - 10 cols, 1 3/10, between.Equipment & Software: Hardware — PC; Software — Adobe/PageMaker 6.5.
Areas Served: Broward County

PONTE VEDRA BEACH

PONTE VEDRA RECORDER (FRI)

1102 A1A N, Ste 108, Ponte Vedra Beach, FL, 32082-4098, Saint Johns, USA; gen tel (904) 285-8831; adv tel (904) 686-3938; ed tel (904) 285-8831; disp adv e-mail susan@opcfla.com; ed e-mail Susan@opcfla.com; web site www.pontevedrarecorder.com
Circulation: 1,814pd, 8,000fr; CVC
Advertising rate: Open inch rate $26.00
Established: 1969
Sr. Acct. Exec. Ed Johnson
Publisher Susan Griffin
Circ. Mgr. Rob Conwell
Ed. Kelly Hould
Mechanical Specifications: Type page 9 3/4 x 16; E - 4 cols, 2 5/16, between; A - 4 cols, between; C - 6 cols, 1 1/2, between.Equipment & Software: Hardware — APP/Mac; Software — QPS/QuarkXPress.
Delivery Method: Mail, Newsstand, Racks
Areas Served: St Johns Duval

PORT SAINT JOE

THE STAR (THUR)

135 W Highway 98, Port Saint Joe, FL, 32456-1871, Gulf, USA; gen tel (850) 227-1278; adv tel (850) 227-7847; ed tel (850) 227-7827; gen fax (850) 227-7212; disp adv e-mail kfortune@starfl.com; class adv e-mail starads@starfl.com; ed e-mail tcroft@starfl.com; web site www.starfl.com
Circulation: 2,600fr; Sworn/Estimate/Non-Audited
Advertising rate: Open inch rate $7.90
Group: Halifax Media
Ed. Tim Croft
Ad. Rep. Kari Fortune-Equipment & Software: Hardware — APP/Power Mac 7100, APP/Power Mac 7200, APP/Power Mac 8100, Imagesetter Lino 190; Presses — G/Community; Software — QPS/QuarkXPress 4.0, Adobe/Photoshop 4.0.

PUNTA GORDA

PUNTA GORDA/PORT CHARLOTTE FLORIDA WEEKLY (THUR)

1205 Elizabeth St, Ste G, Punta Gorda, FL, 33950-6054, Charlotte, USA; gen tel (941) 621-3422; gen fax (941) 621-3423; disp adv e-mail advertise@floridaweekly.com; class adv e-mail advertise@floridaweekly.com; ed e-mail news@floridaweekly.com; web site www.floridaweekly.com
Circulation: 35,646pd,; CAC
Advertising rate: 1/8 P $250 1/4 P $625 1/2 P $940 Full $2500
Group: Florida Media Group LLC
VP and Exec. Ed. Jeffrey Cull
Pres./Grp. Pub. J. Pason Gaddis
Pub. Angela Schivinski
Nat'l Adv. Mgr. Shelley Hobbs
Classifieds Mgr. Kelli Carico
Creative Dir. Jim Dickerson
Delivery Method: Mail, Newsstand

QUINCY

GADSDEN COUNTY TIMES (THUR)

112 E Washington St, Quincy, FL, 32351-2415, Gadsden, USA; gen tel (904) 627-7649; gen fax (850) 627-7191; disp adv e-mail poconnell@gadcotimes.com; class adv e-mail classifieds@chronicle.com; ed e-mail editor@gadcotimes.com; web site www.gadcotimes.com
Circulation: 3,500pd, 50fr; Sworn/Estimate/Non-Audited
Advertising rate: Open inch rate $13.50
Established: 1901
Group: Landmark Community Newspapers, LLC
Mng. Ed. Cheri Harris
Office Manager Mary Williams
Ad sales rep. Penny O'Connell
Reporter Erin Hill
Mechanical Specifications: Type page 10.389 x 21; A - 6 cols, 1.627, .125 between; C - 8 cols, 1.152, 0.169 between
Delivery Method: Mail, Racks
Areas Served: Gadsden County, Florida

RUSKIN

OBSERVER NEWS (THUR)

210 Woodland Estates Ave, Ruskin, FL, 33570-4591, Hillsborough, USA; gen tel (813) 645-3111; adv tel (813) 645-3111 ext 213; ed tel (813) 645-3111 ext 210; gen fax (813) 645-4118; adv fax (813) 645-4118; ed fax (813) 645-4118; disp adv e-mail vilma@observernews.net; class adv e-mail classified@observernews.net; ed e-mail editor@observernews.net; web site observernews.net
Circulation: 0pd, 45,569fr; CVC
Advertising rate: Open inch rate $24.50
Established: 1958
Group: M&M Printing Co. Inc.Editions: (3) Observer News, SCC Observer, The Current
Pub./Ed. Brenda Knowles
Sales Mgr. Vilma Stillwell
Adv. Mgr. Nan Kirk
Circ. Mgr. Beverly Kay
Pub. Mgr Wes Mullins
Prod. Mgr. Chere Simmons
Mechanical Specifications: Type page 10.25 x 15.8; 5 cols, 1.875, 0.25 between
Delivery Method: Carrier, Racks
Areas Served: 33572, 33503, 33534, 33586, 33570, 33569, 33568-79

SAINT PETERSBURG

SOUTH TAMPA NEWS & TRIBUNE (WED)

PO Box 31101, Saint Petersburg, FL, 33731-1107, USA; gen tel (813) 259-7711; adv tel (813) 259-7455; adv fax (813) 259-7903; disp adv e-mail adsolutions@tampatrib.com; web site www.tbo.com/south-tampa
Circulation: 18,680pd, 26,334fr; CVC
Advertising rate: Open inch rate $37.80
Group: Tampa Media Group
Pub. Carla Floyd
Adv. Mgr. Dean Azevedo
Circ. Dir. David Kirkman
Mng. Ed. Russell Holecek
Prodn. Mgr. Floyd Mulford
Mechanical Specifications: Type page 10 13/16 x 15; E - 5 cols, 2 1/16, between; A - 5 cols, 2 1/16, between; C - 8 cols, 1, between.
Delivery Method: Mail
Areas Served: 33602, 33603, 33604, 33605, 33606, 33607, 33608, 33609, 33610, 33611, 33616, 33621, 33629

SANFORD

SANFORD HERALD (WED, SUN)

217 E 1st St, Sanford, FL, 32771-1376, Seminole, USA; gen tel (407) 322-2611; gen fax (407) 323-9408; disp adv e-mail rlavender@mysanfordherald.com; class adv e-mail WKourpanidis@MySanfordHerald.com; ed e-mail rdelinski@mysanfordherald.com; web site www.mysanfordherald.com
Circulation: 6,500pd,; Sworn/Estimate/Non-Audited
Advertising rate: Open inch rate $7.25 (Wed); $8.00 (Sun)
Established: 1908
Group: North Carolina Press Service, Inc.
Pub./Adv. Dir. Roxzie Lavender
Ed. Rachel Delinski
Circ. Mgr. Wanda Kourpanidis
Mechanical Specifications: Type page 13 x 21 1/2; E - 6 cols, 2 1/16, 1/8 between; A - 6 cols, 2 1/16, 1/8 between; C - 8 cols, 1 1/2, 1/8 between.Equipment & Software: Hardware — COM, APP/Mac; Presses — 8-G/Community; Software — QPS/QuarkXPress.
Delivery Method: Mail

Areas Served: 32771, 32772, 32773, 32750, 32779, 32746, 32765

SANIBEL

CAPTIVA CURRENT (FRI)

695 Tarpon Bay Rd Unit 13, #13, Sanibel, FL, 33957-3135, Lee, USA; gen tel (239) 472-1587; gen fax (239) 472-8398; disp adv e-mail dpapoi@breezenewspapers.com; ed e-mail mcassidy@breezenewspapers.com; web site www.captivasanibel.com
Circulation: 142pd, 466fr; Sworn/Estimate/ Non-Audited
Advertising rate: Open inch rate $7.22
Established: 1990
Group: Ogden Newspapers Inc.
Ad. Sales .... Danielle Papoi
Pub... Scott Blonde
Editor .... Mckenzie Cassidy
Mechanical Specifications: Type page 10 5/16 x 16; E - 6 cols, 1 9/16, between; A - 6 cols, 1 9/16, between; C - 6 cols, 1 9/16, between. Equipment & Software: Hardware — APP/ Mac; Software — Write Now 5.0, QPS/ QuarkXPress 3.32, Multi-Ad 4.01, Adobe/ PageMaker 5.0, Adobe/Photoshop 4.0.

ISLAND REPORTER (FRI)

2340 Periwinkle Way, Ste K1, Sanibel, FL, 33957-3220, Lee, USA; gen tel (239) 472-1587; adv tel (239) 472-1587; ed tel (239) 472-1587; gen fax (239) 472-8398; adv fax (239) 472-8398; ed fax (239) 472-8398; disp adv e-mail dpapoi@breezenewspapers.com; class adv e-mail dpapoi@breezenewspapers.com; ed e-mail jlinette@breezenewspapers.com; web site www.captivasanibel.com
Circulation: 789pd, 4,752fr; Sworn/Estimate/ Non-Audited
Advertising rate: Open inch rate $42.50
Established: 1973
Group: Ogden Newspapers Inc.
Digital Platform - Mobile: Apple, Android
Digital Platform - Tablet: Apple iOS, Android
Pub... Scott Blonde
Ed. .... Jim Linette
Adv. Sales .... Danielle Papoi
Betsy Judge
Mechanical Specifications: Type page 9 3/4 x 12 5/8; E - 4 cols, between; A - 6 cols, between; C - 6 cols, between.
Delivery Method: Mail, Racks
Areas Served: Lee County

SANTA ROSA BEACH

THE WALTON SUN (SAT)

5597 US Highway 98 W, Ste 204, Santa Rosa Beach, FL, 32459-3283, Walton, USA; gen tel (850) 267-4555; adv tel (850) 654-8448; ed tel (850) 654-8440; gen fax (850) 267-0929; disp adv e-mail agaffka@nwfdailynews.com; ed e-mail whatfield@waltonsun.com; web site www.waltonsun.com
Circulation: 12,000fr; Sworn/Estimate/Non-Audited
Advertising rate: Open inch rate $10.50
Group: Halifax Media
Adv. Dir...................................... Donna Talla
Managing Ed................................ Matt Algarin
Mechanical Specifications: Type page 9 2/3 x 16; E - 5 cols, 1 13/16, between; A - 5 cols, 1 13/16, between; C - 7 cols, 1 3/8, between.

SARASOTA

BUSINESS OBSERVER (FRI)

1970 Main St, Fl 3, Sarasota, FL, 34236-5923, Sarasota, USA; gen tel (941)362-4848; adv tel (941) 726-6145; ed tel (941) 362-4848 x303; gen fax (941) 9362-4808; disp adv e-mail dschaefer@BusinessObserverFL.com; ed e-mail mgordon@BusinessObserverFL.com; web site www.businessobserverfl.com
Circulation: 1,515pd, 5,139fr; VAC
Advertising rate: 1/8 Pg $280.00; 1/4 Pg $515.00; 1/2 Pg $992.00
Established: 1997
Group: Observer Media Group Inc.
Digital Platform - Mobile: Apple
CEO/Pub./Ed. .... Matthew G. Walsh
Assoc. Pub., Adv..................... Diane Schaefer
Ed. .... Mark Gordon
Dir. Sales/Mktg......................... Anne Shumate
Exec. Ed....................................... Kat Hughes
Mechanical Specifications: 10.375" x 16"
Delivery Method: Mail, Newsstand, Carrier
Areas Served: Collier, Hillsborough, Lee, Manatee, Pasco, Pinellas, Sarasota, Polk, Charlotte

BUSINESS OBSERVER-HILLSBOROUGH-PASCO (FRI)

1970 Main St, Ste 400, Sarasota, FL, 34236-5921, Sarasota, USA; gen tel (941) 362-4848; adv tel (941) 726-6145; ed tel (941) 362-4848; gen fax (941) 362-4808; adv fax (941) 362-4808; ed fax (941) 362-4808; disp adv e-mail dschaefer@BusinessObserverFL.com; class adv e-mail kboothroyd@BusinessObserverFL.com; ed e-mail mwalsh@BusinessObserverFL.com; web site www.businessobserverfl.com
Circulation: 403pd, 1,112fr; VAC
Advertising rate: Modular Rate $288 (1/8P); $530 (1/4P); $1021 (1/2P)
Established: 1997
Group: Observer Media Group Inc.
Digital Platform - Mobile: Apple, Android, Windows, Blackberry
Digital Platform - Tablet: Apple iOS, Android, Windows 7, Blackberry Tablet OS
Publisher............................ Matthew G. Walsh
Assoc. Pub./Adv. Dir................ Diane Schaefer
Mng. Ed.. Kat Hughes
Mechanical Specifications: 10.375" x 16"
Delivery Method: Mail, Newsstand, Racks
Areas Served: Hillsborough County, Pasco County

BUSINESS OBSERVER-LEE (FRI)

1970 Main St, Fl 3, Sarasota, FL, 34236-5923, Sarasota, USA; gen tel (941) 906-9386; adv tel (941) 726-6145; ed tel (239) 275-2230; gen fax (239) 936-1001; adv fax (239) 936-1001; ed fax (239) 936-1001; disp adv e-mail dschaefer@BusinessObserverFL.com; class adv e-mail kboothroyd@BusinessObserverFL.com; ed e-mail gruss@BusinessObserverFL.com; web site www.businessobserverfl.com
Circulation: 202pd, 590fr; VAC
Advertising rate: Modular Rate $288 (1/8P); $530 (1/4P); $1021 (1/2P)
Established: 1997
Group: Observer Media Group Inc.
Digital Platform - Mobile: Apple, Android, Windows, Blackberry
Digital Platform - Tablet: Apple iOS, Android, Windows 7, Blackberry Tablet OS
Publisher......................... Matthew G. Walsh
Assoc. Pub./Adv. Dir................ Diane Schaefer
Ed. .... Jean Gruss
Mechanical Specifications: 10.375" x 16"
Delivery Method: Mail, Newsstand, Racks
Areas Served: Lee County

EAST COUNTY OBSERVER (THUR)

1970 Main St, Ste 300, Sarasota, FL, 34236-5921, Sarasota, USA; gen tel (941) 366-3468; adv tel (941) 366-3468; ed tel (941) 366-3468; gen fax (394) 362-4808; disp adv e-mail mwalsh@yourobserver.com; class adv e-mail mwalsh@yourobserver.com; ed e-mail khughes@yourobserver.com; web site www.yourobserver.com
Circulation: 3pd, 22,250fr; VAC
Advertising rate: Open inch rate $20.97
Established: 1998
Group: Observer Media Group Inc.
Adv. Dir.. Jill Raleigh
Publisher...................................... Emily Walsh
Mechanical Specifications: 6 col x 16"
Delivery Method: Newsstand, Carrier, Racks
Areas Served: 34201, 34202, 34203, 34205, 34208, 34211, 34212, 34219, 34222, 34240, 34242, 34243

LONGBOAT OBSERVER (THUR)

1970 Main St, Ste 300, Sarasota, FL, 34236-5921, Sarasota, USA; gen tel (941) 366-3468; adv tel (941) 366-3468; ed tel (941) 366-3468; disp adv e-mail jraleigh@yourobserver.com; class adv e-mail mwalsh@yourobserver.com; ed e-mail khughes@yourobserver.com; web site www.yourobserver.com
Circulation: 271pd, 10,409fr; VAC
Advertising rate: Open inch rate $20.97
Established: 1978
Group: Observer Media Group Inc.
Ad. Dir. .... Jill Raleigh
Publisher...................................... Emily Walsh
Mechanical Specifications: 6 col x 16"Equipment & Software: Hardware — APP/Mac; Software — Microsoft/Word, QPS/QuarkXPress, Baseview/EditPro.
Delivery Method: Mail, Newsstand, Carrier, Racks
Areas Served: 34228, 34236, 34216, 34217

SARASOTA OBSERVER (THUR)

1970 Main St, Ste 300, Sarasota, FL, 34236-5921, Sarasota, USA; gen tel (941) 366-3468; adv tel (941) 366-3468; ed tel (941) 366-3468; gen fax (941) 362-4808; disp adv e-mail mwalsh@yourobserver.com; class adv e-mail mwalsh@yourobserver.com; ed e-mail khughes@yourobserver.com; web site www.yourobserver.com
Circulation: 26pd, 16,743fr; VAC
Advertising rate: Open inch rate $20.97
Established: 2004
Group: Observer Media Group Inc.
Publisher...................................... Emily Walsh
Mechanical Specifications: 6 col x 16"
Delivery Method: Newsstand, Carrier, Racks
Areas Served: 34228, 34229, 34231, 34234, 34236, 34237, 34238, 34239, 34242

SIESTA KEY OBSERVER (THUR)

1970 Main St, Ste 300, Sarasota, FL, 34236-5921, Sarasota, USA; gen tel (941) 366-3468; gen fax (941) 362-4808; disp adv e-mail advertise@yourobserver.com; ed e-mail khughes@yourobserver.com; web site www.yourobserver.com
Circulation: 5,109fr; VAC
Advertising rate: Open inch rate $20.36
Established: 1972
Group: Observer Media Group Inc.
Adv. Dir.. Jill Raleigh
Publisher...................................... Emily Walsh
Mechanical Specifications: 6 col x 16"
Delivery Method: Newsstand, Carrier, Racks
Areas Served: 34242, 34236

SEMINOLE

BEACH BEACON (THUR)

9911 Seminole Blvd, Seminole, FL, 33772-2536, Pinellas, USA; gen tel (727) 397-5563; gen fax (727) 397-5900; disp adv e-mail dautrey@tbnweekly.com; class adv e-mail jrey@tbnweekly.com; ed e-mail bmcclure@tbnweekly.com; web site www.tbnweekly.com 45(visitors)
Circulation: 14,640fr; VAC
Advertising rate: Open inch rate $10.00 - $17.00
Established: 1980
Digital Platform - Mobile: Apple, Windows
Pub./Pres....................................... Dan Autrey
Adv. Mgr.. Jay Rey
Circ. Mgr .... Lee Shiflett
Prod. Mgr...................................... Dave Brown
Mechanical Specifications: 6 col. (11.5") x 21"Equipment & Software: Hardware — Mac; Presses — web offset; Software — Quark Express
Delivery Method: Newsstand, Carrier, Racks
Areas Served: 33706, 33707, 33708, 33715

BELLEAIR BEE (THUR)

9911 Seminole Blvd, Seminole, FL, 33772-2536, Pinellas, USA; gen tel (727) 397-5563; gen fax (727) 397-5900; disp adv e-mail dautrey@tbnweekly.com; class adv e-mail jrey@tbnweekly.com; ed e-mail tgermond@tbnweekly.com; web site www.tbnweekly.com
Circulation: 12,225fr; VAC
Advertising rate: Open inch rate $17.00
Established: 1975
Group: Tampa Bay Newspapers, Inc.
Digital Platform - Mobile: Apple, Windows
Pub./Pres....................................... Dan Autrey
Adv. Mgr.. Jay Rey
Circ. Mgr .... Lee Shiflett
Prod. Mgr...................................... Dave Brown
Mechanical Specifications: 6 col. (11.5") x 21"Equipment & Software: Hardware — APP/ Mac; Software — QPS/QuarkXPress, Adobe/ Illustrator, Adobe/Photoshop
Delivery Method: Newsstand, Carrier, Racks
Areas Served: 33756, 33767, 33770, 33785, 33786

CLEARWATER BEACON (FRI)

9911 Seminole Blvd, Seminole, FL, 33772-2536, Pinellas, USA; gen tel (727) 397-5563; adv tel (727) 397-5563; ed tel (727) 397-5563; gen fax 727-397-5900; disp adv e-mail dautrey@tbnweekly.com; class adv e-mail jrey@tbnweekly.com; ed e-mail lmosby@tbnweekly.com; web site tbnweekly.com/pubs/clearwater_beacon 45,000(visitors)
Circulation: 25,325fr; VAC
Advertising rate: $17.00
Established: 1950
Group: Tampa Bay Newspapers, Inc.
Digital Platform - Mobile: Apple, Windows
Pub./Pres....................................... Dan Autrey
Adv. Mgr.. Jay Rey
Circ. Mgr .... Lee Shiflett
Prod. Mgr...................................... Dave Brown
Ed. .... Logan Mosby
Mechanical Specifications: 6 col. (11.5") x 21"Equipment & Software: Hardware — Mac; Presses — Web Offset; Software — Quark Express
Delivery Method: Newsstand, Carrier, Racks
Areas Served: 33755, 33756, 33759, 33761, 33763, 33764, 33765, 34695

DUNEDIN BEACON (MTHLY)

9911 Seminole Blvd, Seminole, FL, 33772-2536, Pinellas, USA; gen tel (727) 397-5563; adv tel 7273975563; ed tel 7273975563; gen fax (727) 397-5900; disp adv e-mail dautrey@tbnweekly.com; class adv e-mail jrey@tbnweekly.com; ed e-mail tgermond@tbnweekly.com; web site www.tbnweekly.com 45,000(visitors)
Circulation: 19,138fr; CVC
Advertising rate: Open inch rate $10.50 - $12.50
Established: 2009
Group: Tampa Bay Newspapers, Inc.
Digital Platform - Mobile: Apple
President/Pub .... Dan Autrey
Adv. Mgr.. Jay Rey
Circ. Mgr .... Lee Shiflett
Prod. Mgr...................................... Dave Brown
Mechanical Specifications: 10.5" x 11" (6 col.) Equipment & Software: Hardware — Mac; Presses — Web Offset
Delivery Method: Newsstand, Carrier, Racks
Areas Served: 33755, 34683, 34698

LARGO LEADER (THUR)

9911 Seminole Blvd, Seminole, FL, 33772-2536, Pinellas, USA; gen tel (727) 397-5563; gen fax (727) 397-5900; disp adv e-mail dautrey@tbnweekly.com; class adv e-mail jrey@tbnweekly.com; ed e-mail cgeorge@tbnweekly.com; web site www.tbnweekly.com 45,000(visitors)
Circulation: 25,525fr; VAC
Advertising rate: Open inch rate $17.00
Established: 1977
Group: Tampa Bay Newspapers, Inc.
Digital Platform - Mobile: Apple, Windows
Digital Platform - Tablet: Windows 7
Pub./Pres....................................... Dan Autrey
Adv. Mgr.. Jay Rey
Circ. Mgr .... Lee Shiflett
Prod. Mgr...................................... Dave Brown
Mechanical Specifications: 6 col. (11.5") x 21"Equipment & Software: Hardware — Mac; Presses — web offset; Software — QPS/ QuarkXpress
Delivery Method: Newsstand, Carrier, Racks
Areas Served: 33756, 33760, 33764, 33770, 33771, 33773, 33774, 33778

PALM HARBOR BEACON (MTHLY)
9911 Seminole Blvd, Seminole, FL, 33772-2536, Pinellas, USA; gen tel (727) 397-5563; gen fax (727) 397-5900; disp adv e-mail jrey@tbnweekly.com; class adv e-mail jrey@tbnweekly.com; ed e-mail kwilliams@tbnweekly.com; web site www.tbnweekly.com/ 45,000(visitors)
Circulation: 24,384fr; CVC
Advertising rate: Open inch rate $10.50 - $12.50
Established: 2011
Group: Tampa Bay Newspapers, Inc.
Digital Platform - Mobile: Apple, Windows
President/Pub.......Dan Autrey
Adv. Mgr.......Jay Rey
Circ. Mgr.......Lee Shiflett
Prod. Mgr.......Dave Brown
Mechanical Specifications: 10.5" x 11" (6 column) Equipment & Software: Hardware — Mac; Presses — Web Offset
Delivery Method: Newsstand, Carrier, Racks
Areas Served: 34677, 34683, 33684, 34685

PINELLAS PARK BEACON (MTHLY)
9911 Seminole Blvd, Seminole, FL, 33772-2536, Pinellas, USA; gen tel (727) 397-5563; adv tel (727) 397-5563; ed tel (727) 397-5563; gen fax (727) 397-5900; disp adv e-mail dautrey@tbnweekly.com; class adv e-mail jrey@tbnweekly.com; ed e-mail tgermond@tbnweekly.com; web site www.tbnweekly.com 45,000(visitors)
Circulation: 19,375fr; CVC
Advertising rate: Open inch rate $10.50 - $12.50
Established: 2005
Group: Tampa Bay Newspapers, Inc.
Digital Platform - Mobile: Apple, Windows
Pub./Pres.......Dan Autrey
Ed.......Tiffany Razzano
Ad. Sales Dir.......Jay Rey
Circulation.......Lee Shiflett
Prod. Mgr.......Dave Brown
Mechanical Specifications: 6 col. (10.25") x 11"Equipment & Software: Hardware — Mac; Presses — web offset; Software — Quark Express
Delivery Method: Newsstand, Carrier, Racks
Areas Served: 33702, 33709, 33714, 33762, 33773, 33781, 33782

SEMINOLE BEACON (THUR)
9911 Seminole Blvd, Seminole, FL, 33772-2536, Pinellas, USA; gen tel (727) 397-5563; adv tel (727) 397-5563; ed tel (727) 397-5563; gen fax (727) 397-5900; disp adv e-mail dautrey@tbnweekly.com; class adv e-mail jrey@tbnweekly.com; ed e-mail tgermond@tbnweekly.com; web site www.tbnweekly.com 45,000(visitors)
Circulation: 27,875fr; VAC
Advertising rate: Open inch rate $17.00
Established: 1977
Group: Tampa Bay Newspapers, Inc.
Digital Platform - Mobile: Apple, Windows
Pres./Pub.......Dan Autrey
Ad Sales Dir.......Jay Rey
Ed.......Tiffany Razzano
Circ. Mgr.......Lee Shiflett
Prod. Mgr.......Dave Brown
Mechanical Specifications: 6 col. (11.5") x 21"Equipment & Software: Hardware — Mac; Presses — web offset; Software — Quark Express
Delivery Method: Newsstand, Carrier, Racks
Areas Served: 33708, 33772, 33773, 33774, 33776, 33777, 33778

TARPON SPRINGS BEACON (WED)
9911 Seminole Blvd, Seminole, FL, 33772-2536, Seminole, USA; gen tel (727) 397-5563; adv tel (727) 397-5563; ed tel (727) 397-5563; gen fax (727) 397-5900; disp adv e-mail dautrey@tbnweekly.com; class adv e-mail jrey@tbnweekly.com; ed e-mail kwilliams@tbnweekly.com; web site www.tbnweekly.com
Circulation: 24,000fr; Sworn/Estimate/Non-Audited
Advertising rate: Open inch rate $10.50 - $12.50
Pub. Mgr.......Dan Autrey
Adv. Mgr.......Jay Rey
Circ. Mgr.......Lee Shiflett
Prod. Mgr.......Dave Brown
Delivery Method: Newsstand, Carrier, Racks
Areas Served: 34683, 34684, 34685, 34688, 34689

SOUTH MIAMI

KENDALL GAZETTE (TUES)
6796 SW 62nd Ave, South Miami, FL, 33143-3306, Miami-Dade, USA; gen tel (305) 669-7355; gen fax (305) 662-6980; disp adv e-mail sales@communitynewspapers.com; web site communitynewspapers.com/kendall-gazett
Circulation: 10,000fr; Sworn/Estimate/Non-Audited
Advertising rate: Open inch rate $22.00
Group: Miller Publishing
Co-Pub.......Grant Miller
Co-Pub.......Michael Miller
Editor.......Dan Palmer
Sales.......Susan Miller

PALMETTO BAY NEWS (TUES)
6796 SW 62nd Ave, South Miami, FL, 33143-3306, Miami-Dade, USA; gen tel (305) 669-7355; gen fax (305) 662-6980; disp adv e-mail sales@communitynewspapers.com; web site www.communitynewspapers.com
Circulation: 5,000fr; Sworn/Estimate/Non-Audited
Advertising rate: Open inch rate $26.00
Established: 1958
Group: Miller Publishing
Co-Pub.......Grant Miller
Co-Pub.......Michael Miller
Sales.......Susan Miller
Editor.......Dan Palmer

SOUTH MIAMI NEWS (TUES)
6796 SW 62nd Ave, South Miami, FL, 33143-3306, Miami-Dade, USA; gen tel (305) 667-7481; gen fax (305) 662-6980; disp adv e-mail cneditor@gate.net; ed e-mail sales@communitynewspapers.com; web site www.communitynewspapers.com
Circulation: 18,000fr; Sworn/Estimate/Non-Audited
Advertising rate: Open inch rate $35.00
Group: Miller Publishing
Co-Pub.......Grant Miller
Editor.......Dan Palmer
Co-Pub.......Michael Miller
Sales.......Susan Miller

SOUTH PASADENA

THE ISLAND REPORTER (WED, MTHLY)
1331 Sea Gull Dr S, South Pasadena, FL, 33707-3833, Pinellas, USA; gen tel (727) 631-4730; adv tel (727) 631-4730; ed tel (727) 631-4730; gen fax (727) 864-6434; adv fax (727) 864-6434; ed fax (727) 864-6434; disp adv e-mail info@theislandreporter.com; class adv e-mail info@theislandreporter.com; ed e-mail sloane@theislandreporter.com; web site www.theislandreporter.com
Circulation: 30,175fr; CVC
Advertising rate: Open inch rate $40.00
Established: 2003
Digital Platform - Mobile: Apple, Android
Digital Platform - Tablet: Apple iOS, Android
Pub./Ed.......Betsy Judge
Ed.......Sloane Golden
Delivery Method: Mail, Racks
Areas Served: Tampa, St. Petersburg, Clearwarer

STARKE

BRADFORD COUNTY TELEGRAPH (THUR)
135 W Call St, Starke, FL, 32091-3210, Bradford, USA; gen tel (904) 964-6305; adv tel (904) 964-6305; gen fax (904) 964-8628; disp adv e-mail darlene@bctelegraph.com; class adv e-mail classads@bctelegraph.com; ed e-mail editor@bctelegraph.com; web site www.bctelegraph.com
Circulation: 5,825pd, 1,000fr; Sworn/Estimate/Non-Audited
Advertising rate: Open inch rate $7.40
Established: 1879
Pub.......John Miller
Ed.......Mark Crawford
Mechanical Specifications: Type Page 11 x 21; SAU - 6 cols, 1.83" C - 9 cols, 1.181"
Areas Served: 32042, 32044, 32054, 32058, 32083, 32091, 32160, 32622, 32656, 32666, 32698

UNION COUNTY TIMES (THUR)
131 W Call St, Starke, FL, 32091-3210, Bradford, USA; gen tel (904) 964-6305; adv tel (904) 964-6305; gen fax (904) 964-8628; disp adv e-mail kmiller@bctelegraph.com; class adv e-mail classads@bctelegraph.com; ed e-mail editor@bctelegraph.com; web site www.starkejournal.com
Circulation: 1,000pd, 1,750fr; Sworn/Estimate/Non-Audited
Advertising rate: Open inch rate $6.20
Established: 1912
Ed.......Mark Crawford
Mng. Ed.......John Miller
Mechanical Specifications: Type Page 11 x 21; SAU - 6 cols, 1.83" C - 9 cols, 1.181"
Areas Served: 32042, 32044, 32054, 32058, 32083, 32091, 32160, 32622, 32656, 32666, 32698

STUART

JUPITER COURIER (WED, SUN)
1939 SE Federal Hwy, Stuart, FL, 34994-3915, Martin, USA; gen tel (772) 287-1550; adv tel (772) 221-4255; ed tel (561) 745-3311; disp adv e-mail jess.mcallister@scripps.com; class adv e-mail classified@stuartnews.com; ed e-mail feedback@tcpalm.com; web site www.tcpalm.com
Circulation: 8,500pd, 8,500fr; Sworn/Estimate/Non-Audited
Advertising rate: 1/16 Pg $72.25; 1/8 Pg $140.25; 1/4 Pg $255.00
Established: 1957
Group: E. W. Scripps Co.
Ed.......Mark Tomasik
Pres./Pub.......Bob Brunjes
Christine Stonecipher
Gen. Mgr.......Suzanne Antonich
Managing Ed.......Adam Neal

TAMPA

BRANDON NEWS & TRIBUNE (WED)
202 S Parker St, Tampa, FL, 33606-2379, Hillsborough, USA; gen tel (813) 259-7711; adv tel (813) 259-7455; adv fax (813) 259-7903; disp adv e-mail adsolutions@tampatrib.com; web site www.tbo.com/brandon
Circulation: 16,682pd, 41,318fr; Sworn/Estimate/Non-Audited
Advertising rate: Open inch rate $27.30
Established: 1956
Group: Tampa Media Group
Pub.......Carla Floyd
Adv. Mgr.......Annette Demask
Ed.......Susan Anastasia
Mng. Ed.......Russell Holecek
Mechanical Specifications: Type page 10 1/4 x 15; E - 5 cols, 2 1/16, between; A - 5 cols, 2 1/16, between; C - 8 cols, 1 5/12, between.
Delivery Method: Mail
Areas Served: 33510, 33511, 33547, 33578, 33584, 33594, 33596, 33610, 33619

CARROLLWOOD NEWS & TRIBUNE (WED)
202 S Parker St, Tampa, FL, 33606-2379, Hillsborough, USA; gen tel (813) 259-7711; adv tel (813) 259-7455; adv fax (813) 259-7903; disp adv e-mail adsolutions@tampatrib.com; web site www.tbo.com/carrollwood
Circulation: 12,851pd, 35,800fr; Sworn/Estimate/Non-Audited
Advertising rate: Open inch rate $28.35
Group: Tampa Media Group
Pub.......Denise Palmer
Ed.......Russell Holecek
Mechanical Specifications: Type page 10 1/4 x 15; E - 5 cols, 2 1/16, between; A - 5 cols, 2 1/16, between; C - 8 cols, 1 5/12, between.
Delivery Method: Mail
Areas Served: 33548, 33549, 33558, 33612, 33613, 33618, 33624

CREATIVE LOAFING TAMPA BAY (THUR)
1911 N 13th St Ste W200, Ste W200, Tampa, FL, 33605-3652, Hillsborough, USA; gen tel (813) 739-4800; adv tel (813) 739-4843; gen fax (813) 739-4801; disp adv e-mail kelly.moroni@creativeloafing.com; ed e-mail joe.bardi@creativeloafing.com; web site www.cltampa.com
Circulation: 0pd, 33,976fr; VAC
Advertising rate: 1/4 Pg $956.00; 1/2 Pg $1838.00; Jr Pg $2868.00; Full $3419.00
Established: 1988
Group: Womack Newspapers, inc
Pub.......James Howard
Editor-in-Chief.......David Warner
Managing Ed.......Joe Bardi
Adv. Dir.......Chris Madalena
Ad. Sales.......Kelly Moroni

PLANT CITY COURIER & TRIBUNE (WED)
202 S Parker St, Tampa, FL, 33606-2379, Hillsborough, USA; gen tel (813) 259-7711; adv tel (813) 259-7455; ed tel (813) 259-7711; gen fax (813) 259-7903; adv fax (813) 259-7903; ed fax (813) 259-7903; disp adv e-mail adsolutions@tampatrib.com; class adv e-mail adsolutions@tampatrib.com; ed e-mail dnicholson@tampatrib.com; web site www.tbo.com/plant-city
Circulation: 6,621pd, 2,336fr; Sworn/Estimate/Non-Audited
Advertising rate: Open inch rate $13.00
Group: Tampa Media Group
Mng. Ed.......David Nicholson
Pub.......Brian Burns
Dir, Nat'l Sales.......Joe Gess
Mechanical Specifications: Type page 10 13/16 x 15; E - 5 cols, 2, 1/6 between; A - 5 cols, 2, 1/6 between; C - 8 cols, 1 1/4, 1/6 between.
Delivery Method: Mail
Areas Served: 33527, 33563, 33565, 33566, 33567

SOUTH SHORE NEWS (WED)
202 S Parker St, Tampa, FL, 33606-2379, USA; gen tel (813) 259-7711; adv tel (813) 259-7455; adv fax (813) 259-7903; disp adv e-mail adsolutions@tampatrib.com; web site www.tbo.com/south-shore
Circulation: 7,698pd, 21,997fr; CVC
Advertising rate: Open inch rate $22.05
Group: Tampa Media Group
Clerk.......Kathy Vance
Reporter.......Lois Kindle
Ed.......Jack Cormier
Adv.......Melissa Poage
Mechanical Specifications: Type page 11 1/2 x 15; E - 5 cols, 1 3/4, between; A - 5 cols, 1 3/4, between; C - 9 cols, 1 1/16, between.
Delivery Method: Mail
Areas Served: 33534, 33569, 33570, 33572, 33573, 33578, 33579 33598

THE FREE PRESS (SAT)
1010 W Cass St, Tampa, FL, 33606-1307, Hillsborough, USA; gen tel (813) 254-5888; gen fax (813) 902-6599; disp adv e-mail contact@4freepress.com; ed e-mail contact@4freepress.com; web site www.4freepress.com
Circulation: 507pd,; Sworn/Estimate/Non-Audited
Advertising rate: Open inch rate $3.50
Established: 1911
Ed.......Cheryl Marshalsea
Pub.......Paul Clarion
Adv. Dir.......Tommy Todd
Sales Consultant.......Tammy Collins
Areas Served: Hillsborough County

TAVERNIER

FLORIDA KEYS FREE PRESS (WED)

91731 Overseas Hwy, Tavernier, FL, 33070-2649, Monroe, USA; gen tel (305) 853-7277; gen fax (305) 853-0556; disp adv e-mail sales@keysnews.com; class adv e-mail marnold@keysnews.com; ed e-mail freepress@keysnews.com; web site www.keysnews.com
Circulation: 210pd, 14,000fr; Sworn/Estimate/Non-Audited
Advertising rate: Open inch rate $16.50
Group: Cooke Communications Florida, LLC
Pub. .... Paul Clarin
Managing Ed. .... Dan Campbell
Dir, Adv. .... Melanie Arnold
Sales Consultant .... Tammy Collins
Areas Served: Key Largo, Islamorada, Marathon, Big Pine Key

THE REPORTER (FRI)

171 Hood Ave, Ste 22, Tavernier, FL, 33070-2645, Monroe, USA; gen tel (305) 852-3216; ed tel (305) 440-3204; disp adv e-mail jdarden@keysreporter.com; class adv e-mail jpulis@keynoter.com; ed e-mail dgoodhue@keysreporter.com; web site www.flkeysnews.com
Circulation: 7,094pd, 500fr; Sworn/Estimate/Non-Audited
Advertising rate: Open inch rate $13.90
Established: 1973
Group: The McClatchy Company
Circ. Mgr. .... Carter Townshend
Ed. .... David Goodhue
Pub. .... Richard Tamborrino
Class/Web Mgr. .... Joanne Pulis
Delivery Method: Mail, Newsstand, Carrier, Racks
Areas Served: Monroe County, Miami-Dade County

TRENTON

GILCHRIST COUNTY JOURNAL (THUR)

207 N Main St, Trenton, FL, 32693-3439, Gilchrist, USA; gen tel (352) 463-7135; gen fax (352) 463-7393; disp adv e-mail gcjads@bellsouth.net; ed e-mail gilchristjournal@bellsouth.net; web site www.gilchristcounty-journal.net
Circulation: 4,000pd,; Sworn/Estimate/Non-Audited
Advertising rate: Open inch rate $4.00
Ed. .... John Ayers
Adv. .... Chris Rogers
Mechanical Specifications: Type page 13 x 21; 6 cols, 2", 0.25 between

UMATILLA

NORTH LAKE OUTPOST (THUR)

PO Box 1099, Umatilla, FL, 32784-1099, Lake, USA; gen tel (352) 669-2430; gen fax (352) 669-4644; disp adv e-mail northlake-outpost@aol.com; web site www.thenorth-lakeoutpost.com
Circulation: 3,000pd,; USPS
Advertising rate: Open inch rate $3.15
Established: 1979
Publisher .... Holly Newby
Mechanical Specifications: one column = 9.5 picas
Delivery Method: Mail, Racks
Areas Served: Lake County, Florida

VENICE

VENICE GONDOLIER SUN (WED, SUN)

200 E Venice Ave, Fl 1, Venice, FL, 34285-1998, Sarasota, USA; gen tel (941) 207-1000; gen fax (941) 484-8460; ed fax (941) 484-8460; disp adv e-mail majoraccts@sun-herald.com; class adv e-mail classified@sun-herald.com; ed e-mail feedback@sun-herald.com; web site www.venicegondolier.com
Circulation: 14,000pd, 13,000fr; AAM
Advertising rate: Open inch rate $26.60
Established: 1946
Group: Sun Coast Media Group Inc
Ed. .... Ron Dupont
News Ed. .... Greg Giles
Kim Cool
Mechanical Specifications: Type page 6 x 21; E - 6 cols, 2 1/16, between; A - 6 cols, 2 1/16, Classy-6Cols Equipment & Software: Hardware — APP/Mac; Presses — HI/V-15A, G/Urbanite; Software — QPS/QuarkXPress 5.0, Brainworks, Multi-Ad/Creator II 6.2.
Delivery Method: Mail, Newsstand, Carrier, Racks
Areas Served: 34285,34293,34292,34275,34229

WAUCHULA

THE HERALD-ADVOCATE (THUR)

115 S 7th Ave, Wauchula, FL, 33873-2801, Hardee, USA; gen tel (863) 773-3255; gen fax (863) 773-0657; disp adv e-mail publisher@theheraldadvocate.com; web site www.theheraldadvocate.com
Circulation: 4,750pd, 50fr; Sworn/Estimate/Non-Audited
Advertising rate: Open inch rate $4.60
Established: 1955
Circ. Mgr. .... Jeanne Kelly
Ed. & Pub. .... Jim Kelly
Mng. Ed. .... Cynthia Krahl
News/Sports Ed. .... Joan Seaman
Mechanical Specifications: Type page 11 x 21.5; 6 cols, 1.75, 0.1 between
Equipment & Software: Hardware — APP/Mac; Presses — G/Community.
Areas Served: 33873, 33890, 33834, 33865

WELLINGTON

THE TOWN CRIER (THUR)

12794 Forest Hill Blvd, Ste 31, Wellington, FL, 33414-4758, Palm Beach, USA; gen tel (561) 793-7606; gen fax (561) 793-6090; disp adv e-mail news@gotowncrier.com; ed e-mail news@gotowncrier.com; web site www.gotowncrier.com
Circulation: 25,000fr; Sworn/Estimate/Non-Audited
Advertising rate: Open inch rate $11.75
Established: 1980
Group: Newspaper Publishers LLCEditions: (2) 2 total; Royal Palm Beach (10,000); Wellington (10,000);
Pub./Adv. Mgr. .... Barry S. Manning
Assoc. Pub. .... Jody Gorran
Gen. Mgr. .... Dawn Rivera
Ed. .... Joshua I. Manning
Mng. Ed. .... Ron Bukley
News Ed. .... Mark Lioi
Arts/Prodn. Mgr. .... Stephanie Rodriguez
Mechanical Specifications: Type page 9 1/2 x 16; E - 5 cols, 1 3/4, 1/4 between; A - 5 cols, 1 3/4, 1/4 between; C - 5 cols, 1 3/4, 1/4 between.Equipment & Software: Hardware — PC; Software — Adobe/PageMaker, Archetype/Corel Draw.
Delivery Method: Mail, Newsstand, Racks
Areas Served: Wellington, Royal Palm Beach, Loxahatchee, Acreage

WILLISTON

WILLISTON PIONEER SUN NEWS (THUR)

607 SW 1st Ave, Williston, FL, 32696-2515, Levy, USA; gen tel (352) 528-3343; ed tel (352) 528-3343; disp adv e-mail Chad.Thompson@chieflandcitizen.com; class adv e-mail classified@chieflandcitizen.com; ed e-mail editor@willistonpioneer.com; web site www.willistonpioneer.com
Circulation: 1,500pd,; Sworn/Estimate/Non-Audited
Advertising rate: Open inch rate $8.75
Established: 1879
Group: Landmark Community Newspapers, LLC
Landmark Communications, Inc.
Ed. .... Carolyn Ten Broeck
Sales Representative .... Chad Thompson
Mechanical Specifications: Type page 9.888 x 21.25; 6 cols, 1.639
Equipment & Software: Hardware — MAC OS 10; Software — Adobe Creative Suite, Quark, InDesign
Delivery Method: Mail, Newsstand, Racks
Areas Served: 32696, 32668, 32626, 32618

WINTER GARDEN

THE WEST ORANGE TIMES & OBSERVER (THUR)

720 S Dillard St, Winter Garden, FL, 34787-3908, Orange, USA; gen tel (407) 656-2121; adv tel (407) 656-2121; ed tel (407) 656-2121; gen fax (407) 656-6075; disp adv e-mail advertising@orangeobserver.com; class adv e-mail classifieds@orangeobserver.com; ed e-mail news@orangeobserver.com; web site www.orangeobserver.com
Circulation: 22,000pd,; Sworn/Estimate/Non-Audited
Advertising rate: Open inch rate $14.00
Established: 1905
Group: Observer Media Group
Pub. .... Dawn Willis
Circ. Mgr. .... Andrew Bailey
Amy Rhode
Delivery Method: Mail, Racks
Areas Served: Winter Garden, Ocoee, Oakland, Clermont
Horizon West

WINTER HAVEN

THE POLK COUNTY NEWS AND DEMOCRAT (WED, MTHLY, OTHER)

99 3rd St NW, Winter Haven, FL, 33881-4609, Polk, USA; gen tel (863) 533-4183; gen fax (863) 533-0402; disp adv e-mail kedwards@scmginc.com; class adv e-mail aswain@scmginc.com; ed e-mail jroslow@scmginc.com; web site www.polkcountydemocrat.com
Circulation: 2,500pd, 18,000fr; Sworn/Estimate/Non-Audited
Established: 1931
Group: Sun Coast Media Group Inc
Digital Platform - Mobile: Apple, Android, Windows
Digital Platform - Tablet: Apple iOS, Android, Windows 7, Kindle Fire
Pub. .... Chris Sexson
Ed. .... Jeff Roslow
Adv. Dir. .... Kim Edwards
Mechanical Specifications: Type page 15 1/8 x 21; E - 7 cols, 2 1/16, 1/8 between; A - 7 cols, 2 1/16, 1/8 between; C - 9 cols, 1 1/2, 1/8 between.Equipment & Software: Hardware — APP/Macs; Presses — 4-G/Community; Software — Adobe/PageMaker 5.0, Adobe/Photoshop 5.5, QPS/QuarkXPress 3.2, QPS/QuarkXPress 4.0, Baseview/NewsEdit Pro, Adobe/Acrobat 4.0.
Delivery Method: Mail, Newsstand, Carrier, Racks
Areas Served: Winter haven, Lake Wales, Bartow, Davenport, Lakeland, Haines City, Polk County

ZEPHYRHILLS

ZEPHYRHILLS NEWS (THUR)

38333 5th Ave, Zephyrhills, FL, 33542-4978, Pasco, USA; gen tel (813) 782-1558; gen fax (813) 788-7987; disp adv e-mail znewstleblanc@verizon.net; ed e-mail readznews@aol.com; web site www.zephyrhillsnewsonline.com
Circulation: 3,539pd, 469fr; CVC
Advertising rate: 1/8 Pg $135.50; 1/4 Pg $250.00; 1/2 Pg $400.00
Established: 1911
Pub. .... Danny Linville
Pub. .... Jan Linville
Bus. Mgr. .... Linda Wood
Adv. Sales Mgr. .... Theresa LeBlanc
Circ. Mgr. .... Randall Epting
Circ. Mgr .... Katherine Bowman
Mechanical Specifications: Type page 11.25" x 21"; 6 colsEquipment & Software: Hardware — APP/Macs.
Delivery Method: Mail, Carrier, Racks

GEORGIA

ADAIRSVILLE

THE NORTH BARTOW NEWS (TUES)

5943 Joe Frank Harris Pkwy NW, Ste D, Adairsville, GA, 30103-2451, Bartow, USA; gen tel (770) 773-3754; gen fax (770) 773-3757; disp adv e-mail northbartownews@yahoo.com; class adv e-mail northbartownews@yahoo.com; web site No Website
Circulation: 293pd, 7,000fr; Sworn/Estimate/Non-Audited
Advertising rate: Open inch rate $6.80
Pub. .... Alan Davis
Adv. Sales .... Eric Pass
Classifieds Adv. Mgr. .... Janice Reed
Mechanical Specifications: Type page 13 x 21 1/2; E - 6 cols, 2 1/4, between; A - 6 cols, 2 1/4, between; C - 6 cols, 2 1/4, between. Equipment & Software: Hardware — APP/Mac; Presses — WPC/Web Leader; Software — Baseview/Class Act.
Delivery Method: Mail, Newsstand, Carrier, Racks
Areas Served: 30103, 30145

ALBANY

THE ALBANY HERALD (WED, SUN)

126 N Washington St, Albany, GA, 31701-2552, Dougherty, USA; gen tel (229) 888-9300; adv tel (229) 888-9398; ed tel (229) 888-9344; gen fax (229) 438-3200; adv fax (229) 888-9394; ed fax (229) 888-9357; disp adv e-mail class@albanyherald.com; class adv e-mail class@albanyherald.com; ed e-mail letters@albanyherald.com; web site www.albanyherald.com
Circulation: 0pd, 7,972fr; CVC
Advertising rate: $51.82
Established: 1892
Group: Southern Community Newspapers, Inc.
Digital Platform - Mobile: Blackberry
Digital Platform - Tablet: Other
Adv. Accts. Rep., Nat'l/Major .... Phil Cody
Editor .... Jim Hendricks
Managing Editor .... Danny Carter
Metro Editor .... Carlton Fletcher
Sports Editor .... Danny Aller
Director of Operations .... Lynn Ridder
Prodn. Supvr., Composing .... Don Kimsey
Prodn. Supvr., Mailroom .... Charles Holsey
Director of Sales and Marketing .... Scott Brooks
IT Director .... Bill Strickland
Circ. Mgr. .... Kim Purrier
President/Publisher .... Michael Gebhart
Adv. Mgr. .... Bob McCray
Circulation Manager .... Thom Bell
Mechanical Specifications: Type page 11x 21 1/2; E - 6 cols, 1 7/8, 1/6 between; A - 6 cols, 1 7/8, 1/6 between; Equipment & Software: Hardware — Kodak Model TST plate printer, (2) Dell PowerEdge T310 servers; Software — Prinergy Evo (for Kodak CTP)
Delivery Method: Mail, Newsstand, Carrier, Racks
Areas Served: 31701,31707,31709,31710,31719,31721,31010,31015,31714,31714,31716,31719,31730,31744,31763,31765,31768,31779,31780,31781,31784,31787,31789,31791,31793,31794,31795,31796,31832,39813,39817,39819,39823,39826,39834,39837,39840,39841,39842,39845,39846,39851,39859,39862,39870,39877,39886

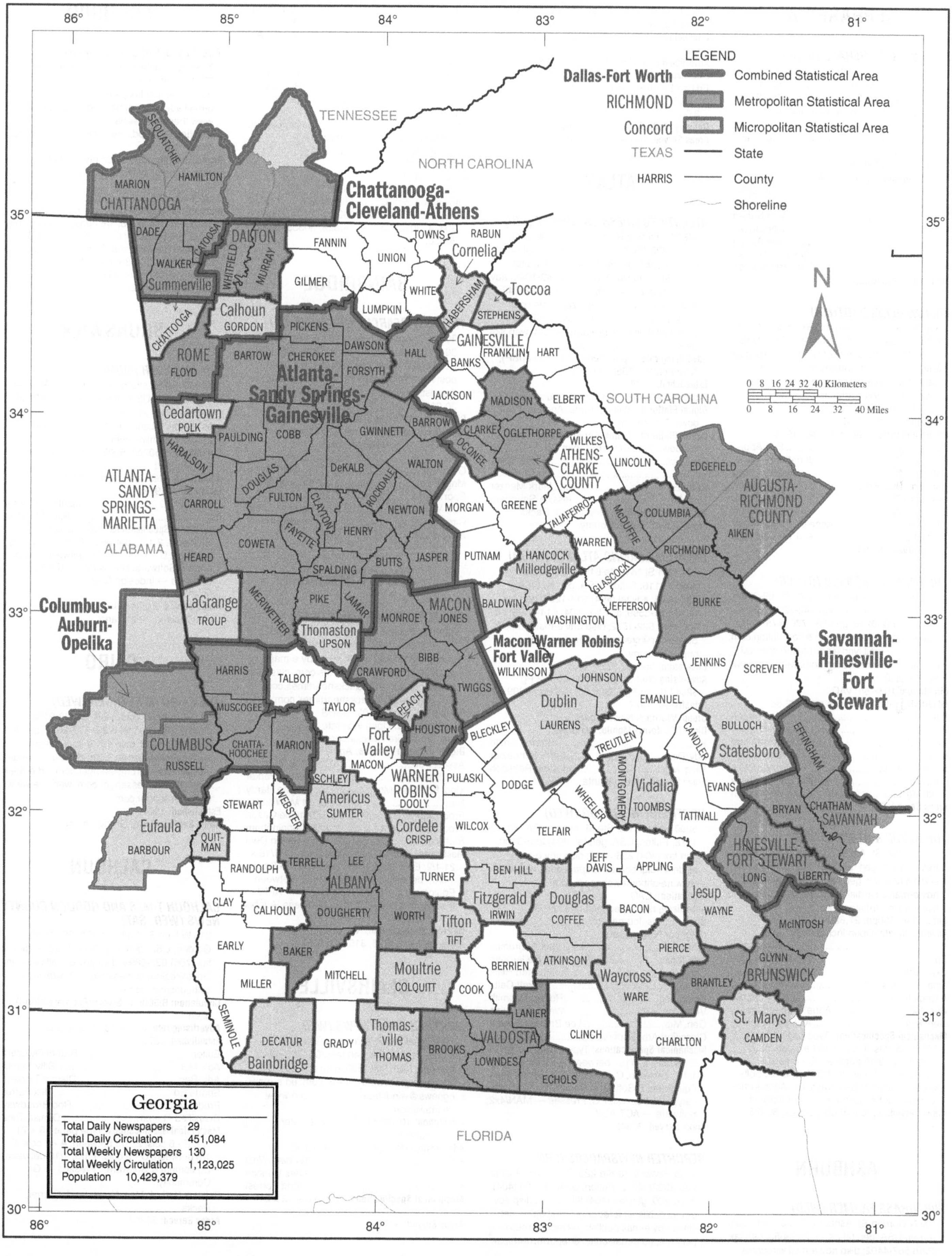

Georgia

Total Daily Newspapers	29
Total Daily Circulation	451,084
Total Weekly Newspapers	130
Total Weekly Circulation	1,123,025
Population	10,429,379

ALPHARETTA

JOHN'S CREEK HERALD (OTHER)
319 N Main St, Alpharetta, GA, 30009-2321, Fulton, USA; gen tel (770)442-3278; adv tel (770) 442-3278; gen fax (770)475-1216; disp adv e-mail advertising@northfulton.com; class adv e-mail lynn@northfulton.com; ed e-mail hhurd@northfulton.com; web site www.NorthFulton.com
Circulation: 19,975fr; CVC
Advertising rate: Open inch rate $22.66
Pub.. Ray Appen
Exec. Ed./ Ed. ....Hatcher Hurd
Mng. Ed./ Bus. Ed. .... Aldo Nahed
Associate Pub.............................. Kelly Brooks
Gen. Mgr. .... Hans Appen
Circ. Mgr................................. Georgie Tiernan
Prod. Mgr.............................. A. J. McNaughton
Areas Served: 30022, 30097

MILTON HERALD (OTHER)
319 N Main St, Alpharetta, GA, 30009-2321, Fulton, USA; gen tel (770) 442-3278; adv tel (770) 442-3278; gen fax (770)475-1216; disp adv e-mail advertising@northfulton.com; class adv e-mail lynn@northfulton.com; ed e-mail jcopsey@northfulton.com; web site www.NorthFulton.com
Circulation: 9,308fr; VAC
Advertising rate: Open inch rate $18.00
Pub.. Ray Appen
Ed. ....Jonathan Copsey
Exec. Ed.......................................Hatcher Hurd
Mng. Ed./ Bus. Ed. .... Aldo Nahed
Associate Pub.............................. Kelly Brooks
Sr. Acct. Exec......................... Wendy Goddard
Circ. Mgr......................... Anne O'Shaughnessy
Prod. Mgr.............................. A. J. McNaughton
Areas Served: 30004

THE FORSYTH HERALD (OTHER)
319 N Main St, Alpharetta, GA, 30009-2321, Fulton, USA; gen tel (770) 442-3278; adv tel (770) 442-3278; gen fax (770) 475-1216; disp adv e-mail advertising@northfulton.com; class adv e-mail lynn@northfulton.com; ed e-mail Aldo@northfulton.com; web site www.NorthFulton.com
Circulation: 16,975fr; VAC
Advertising rate: Open inch rate $22.66
Pub.. Ray Appen
Ed. ....Jonathan Copsey
Exec. Ed.......................................Hatcher Hurd
Mng. Ed./ Bus. Ed. .... Aldo Nahed
Associate Pub.............................. Kelly Brooks
Circ. Mgr......................... Anne O'Shaughnessy
Prod. Mgr.............................. A. J. McNaughton
Areas Served: 30040, 30041

THE REVUE & NEWS (OTHER)
319 N Main St, Alpharetta, GA, 30009-2321, Fulton, USA; gen tel (770) 442-3278; adv tel (770) 442-3278; gen fax (770) 475-1216; disp adv e-mail advertising@northfulton.com; web site www.northfulton.com
Circulation: 350pd, 27,625fr; CVC
Advertising rate: Open inch rate $27.66
Pub.. Ray Appen
Ed. ....Jonathan Copsey
Exec. Ed.......................................Hatcher Hurd
Mng. Ed./ Bus. Ed. .... Aldo Nahed
Associate Pub.............................. Kelly Brooks
Circ. Mgr......................... Anne O'Shaughnessy
Gen. Mgr.............................. A. J. McNaughton
Mechanical Specifications: Type page 10 x 12 3/8; E - 5 cols, 1 7/8, 9/16 between; A - 5 cols, 1 7/8, 9/16 between; C - 8 cols, 1 1/8, 1/8 between.Equipment & Software: ; Software — QPS/QuarkXPress 4.1, Adobe/Photoshop, Adobe/Illustrator, Adobe/Acrobat.
Areas Served: 30009, 30005, 30022, 30075, 30076

ASHBURN

WIREGRASS FARMER (WED)
109 N Gordon St, Ashburn, GA, 31714-5208, Turner, USA; gen tel (229) 567-3655; gen fax (229) 567-4402; disp adv e-mail wiregrassfarmer@yahoo.com; web site www.thewiregrassfarmer.com
Circulation: 2,000pd, 100fr; Sworn/Estimate/Non-Audited
Advertising rate: Open inch rate $7.25
Established: 1902
Ed.Ben BakerEquipment & Software: Hardware — APP/Mac; Software — QPS/QuarkXPress 3.0.
Delivery Method: Mail, Newsstand, Racks
Areas Served: Turner County GA

ATLANTA

ATLANTA BUSINESS CHRONICLE (FRI)
3384 Peachtree Rd NE, Ste 900, Atlanta, GA, 30326-2828, Fulton, USA; gen tel (404) 249-1000; adv tel (404) 249-1069; ed tel (404) 249-1039; gen fax (404) 249-1048; adv fax (404) 249-1048; ed fax (404) 249-1048; disp adv e-mail eboyle@bizjournals.com; class adv e-mail ebaker@bizjournals.com; ed e-mail dallison@bizjournals.com; web site www.bizjournals.com/atlanta
Advertising rate: Open inch rate $2209 (1/8P); $3789 (1/4P); $5885 (1/2P)
Established: 1978
Group: American City Business Journals
Digital Platform - Mobile: Apple, Android, Windows, Blackberry
Digital Platform - Tablet: Apple iOS, Android, Windows 7, Blackberry Tablet OS
Pub.. Ed Baker
Ed. .... David Allison
Exec. Ed....................................... Mark Meltzer
Mng. Ed................................Jessica Saunders
Delivery Method: Mail, Newsstand, Racks
Areas Served: Fulton County

CREATIVE LOAFING ATLANTA (THUR)
231 18th St NW, Ste 8150, Atlanta, GA, 30363-1116, Fulton, USA; gen tel (404) 688-5623; adv tel (404) 614-1267; gen fax (404) 614-3599; adv fax (404) 614-3599; ed fax (404) 522-1532; disp adv e-mail Kerry.Schneider@creativeloafing.com; web site http://clatl.com/
Circulation: 0pd, 52,377fr; VAC
Advertising rate: 1/4 Pg $1181.00; 1/2 Pg $2547.00; Jr Pg $3306.00; Full Pg $4899.00
Established: 1972
Group: Womack Newspapers, inc
Digital Platform - Mobile: Windows
Pub...Sharry Smith
Adv. Dir.................................. Kerry Schneider
Mktg. Mgr....................... Leigh Anne Rehkoph
Areas Served: Metro Atlanta

NORTHSIDE NEIGHBOR (WED)
5290 Roswell Rd, Ste M, Atlanta, GA, 30342-1978, Fulton, USA; gen tel (404) 256-3100; gen fax (404) 256-3292; disp adv e-mail nside@neighbornewspapers.com; web site www.neighbornewspapers.com
Circulation:; CAC
Advertising rate: Open inch rate $50.35
Group: Times-Journal, Inc.
Neighbor Newspapers
Pub... Otis A. Brumby
Adv. Mgr........................ Stephanie DeJarnette
Circ. Mgr...Matt Heck
Ed. .... Everett Catts
Prodn. Mgr. .... Robert Nesmith
VP, Sales/Mktg........................ Wade Stephens
Gen. Mgr. .... Lee Brumby Garrett
Classified Adv. Supervisor............. Alice Davis
Mechanical Specifications: Type page 13 x 21; E - 6 cols, 2 1/16, between; A - 6 cols, 2 1/16, between; C - 10 cols, 1 3/16, between. Equipment & Software: Hardware — 4-Compaq/5500R Server, PC; Presses — MAN/4x2; Software — ACT/ADV.
Areas Served: 30342

REPORTER NEWSPAPERS (FRI)
6065 Roswell Rd Ste 225, Suite 225, Atlanta, GA, 30328-4012, Fulton, USA; gen tel (404) 917-2200; gen fax (404) 917-2201; disp adv e-mail publisher@reporternewspapers.net; class adv e-mail publisher@reporternewspapers.net; ed e-mail editor@reporternewspapers.net; web site www.reporternewspapers.net - 75,000(views) 45,000(visitors)
Circulation: 100,000fr; Sworn/Estimate/Non-Audited
Established: 2006
Group: Springs Publishing LLCEditions: (4) Brookhaven Reporter; Buckhead Reporter; Dunwoody Reporter; Sandy Springs Reporter
Fouder & Publisher..................... Steve Levene
Delivery Method: Carrier, Racks
Areas Served: Sandy Springs, GA
Dunwoody, GA
Brookhaven, GA
Buckhead/City of Atlanta, GA
Intown/Midtown, City of Atlanta, GA
30305, 30306, 30307, 30308, 30309, 30319, 30324, 30327, 30328, 30329, 30338, 30342, 30350.

BAINBRIDGE

THE POST-SEARCHLIGHT (WED, SAT)
301 N Crawford St, Bainbridge, GA, 39817-3612, Decatur, USA; gen tel (229) 246-2827; gen fax (229) 246-7665; disp adv e-mail postsearch@e-postprint.com; web site www.thepostsearchlight.com - 145,000(views) 30,000(visitors)
Circulation: 7,167pd, 242fr; CVC
Advertising rate: Open inch rate $13.30
Group: Boone Newspapers, Inc.
Pub..Jeff Findley
Gen. Mgr. ....Mark Pope
Mng. Ed...................................Ashley Johnson
Sports Ed.. Joe Crine
Adv. Mgr. .... Sammy Griffin
Circ. Mgr.......................................Isaac Manuel
Areas Served: 39817

BLACKSHEAR

THE BLACKSHEAR TIMES (WED)
121 SW Central Ave, Blackshear, GA, 31516-2259, Pierce, USA; gen tel (912) 449-6693; gen fax (912) 449-1719; disp adv e-mail pparker@theblacksheartimes.com; class adv e-mail pparker@theblacksheartimes.com; web site www.theblacksheartimes.com
Circulation: 3,650pd, 0fr; USPS
Advertising rate: Open inch rate $6.65
Group: SouthFire Newspapers
Digital Platform - Mobile: Apple
Assoc. Pub.......................... Cheryl S. Williams
Adv./Sales Mgr............................ Paige Parker
Mng. Ed./ Gen. Mgr.................... Wayne Hardy
Ed. .... Robert M. Williams
Prodn. Mgr. .... Tammie Cason
Production Layout................ Julie Cunningham
Staff Writer.....................................Jason Deal
Mechanical Specifications: Type page 11 1/16 x 21 1/2; E - 6 cols, 1 5/6, between; A - 6 cols, 1 5/6, between; C - 6 cols, 1 5/6, between. Equipment & Software: Hardware — APP/Mac; Software — QPS/QuarkXPress, Adobe/Photoshop.
Delivery Method: Mail, Newsstand
Areas Served: 31516, 31518, 31557

BLAIRSVILLE

NORTH GEORGIA NEWS (WED)
266 Cleveland St, Blairsville, GA, 30512-8537, Union, USA; gen tel (706) 745-6343; gen fax (706) 745-1830; disp adv e-mail northgeorgianews@hotmail.com; ed e-mail ngnews@windstream.net; web site www.nganews.com
Circulation: 10,400pd,; Sworn/Estimate/Non-Audited
Advertising rate: Open inch rate $8.50
Pub..Kenneth West
Ed. .... Charles Duncan
Staff Writer................................... Todd Forrest
Mechanical Specifications: Type page 13 x 21 1/2.
Areas Served: 30514

BLUE RIDGE

THE NEWS-OBSERVER (WED)
5748 Appalachian Hwy, Blue Ridge, GA, 30513-4240, Fannin, USA; gen tel (706) 632-2019; gen fax (706) 632-2577; disp adv e-mail ads@thenewsobserver.com; web site www.thenewsobserver.com
Circulation: 2,372pd,; Sworn/Estimate/Non-Audited
Advertising rate: Open inch rate $13.65
Group: Community Newspapers, Inc.
Pub.. Glenn Harbison
Corp. Mktg. Dir. .... Joel Jenkins
Mechanical Specifications: Type page 13 x 21 1/2; E - 6 cols, 2 1/8, 1/6 between; A - 6 cols, 2 1/8, 1/6 between; C - 6 cols, 2 1/8, 1/6 between.Equipment & Software: Hardware — APP/Mac LC 580, APP/Mac; Software — QPS/QuarkXPress 3.31.
Areas Served: 31092

BRUNSWICK

THE ISLANDER (MON)
1604B Newcastle St, Brunswick, GA, 31520-6729, Glynn, USA; gen tel (912) 265-9654; gen fax (912) 265-3699; disp adv e-mail ssislander@bellsouth.net; web site www.theislanderonline.com
Circulation: 3,500pd, 500fr; Sworn/Estimate/Non-Audited
Advertising rate: Open inch rate $7.75
Established: 1972
Pub...Matthew Permar
Ed. ....Pam Shierling
Mechanical Specifications: Type page 10 x 13; E - 4 cols, 2 1/3, between; A - 4 cols, 2 1/3, between; C - 5 cols, 1 2/3, between.Equipment & Software: Hardware — APP/Mac; Software — Indesign CS2
Delivery Method: Mail
Areas Served: Brunswick, St. Simons Island, Jekyll Island, Sea Island

CAIRO

THE CAIRO MESSENGER (WED)
31 1st Ave NE, Cairo, GA, 39828-2102, Grady, USA; gen tel (229) 377-2032; gen fax (229) 377-4640; disp adv e-mail advertising@cairomessenger.com; class adv e-mail classifieds@cairomessenger.com; ed e-mail lnews@cairomessenger.com; web site www.cairomessenger.com
Established: 1904
Areas Served: Cairo, Grady, Thomas

CALHOUN

CALHOUN TIMES AND GORDON COUNTY NEWS (WED, SAT)
215 W Line St, Calhoun, GA, 30701-1815, Gordon, USA; gen tel (706) 629-2231; gen fax (706) 625-0899; disp adv e-mail calhountimes@calhountimes.com; web site www.calhountimes.com
Circulation: 8,500pd,; Sworn/Estimate/Non-Audited
Advertising rate: Open inch rate $13.72
Established: 1870
Editor.......................................Brandi Owczarz
Adv. Mgr. .... Billy Steele
Adv. Rep.................................. Dianne Tippens
Sports Ed....................................... Alex Farrer
Prodn. Mgr. .... Rob Broadway
Classified / Legal......................... Danika Trice
Mechanical Specifications: Type page 13 x 21 1/4; E - 6 cols, 2, 1/6 between; A - 6 cols, 2, 1/6 between; C - 9 cols, 1 1/3, 1/10 between. Equipment & Software: ; Presses — G/Community.
Delivery Method: Mail, Newsstand, Carrier, Racks
Areas Served: 30701

CAMILLA

CAMILLA ENTERPRISE (WED)

13 S Scott St, Camilla, GA, 31730-1705, Mitchell, USA; gen tel (229) 336-5265; gen fax (229) 336-8476; disp adv e-mail camillaenterprise@camillaga.net; web site No Website
Circulation: 3,300pd,; Sworn/Estimate/Non-Audited
Advertising rate: Open inch rate $8.00
Group: Trib Publications
Pub. .... Darrin Wilson
Circ. Dir. .... Sandra Williams
Mechanical Specifications: Type page 12 1/4 x 21 1/2; E - 6 cols, 1 15/16, 1/6 between; A - 6 cols, 1 15/16, 1/6 between; C - 6 cols, 1 15/16, 1/6 between.Equipment & Software: Hardware — 12-APP/Mac; Presses — G/Community; Software — QPS/QuarkXPress.
Areas Served: 31730

THE PELHAM JOURNAL (WED)

13 S Scott St, Camilla, GA, 31730-1705, Mitchell, USA; gen tel (229) 336-5265; gen fax (229) 336-8476; disp adv e-mail camillaenterprise@camillaga.net; web site No Website
Circulation: 1,800pd, 10fr; Sworn/Estimate/Non-Audited
Advertising rate: Open inch rate $6.85
Group: Trib Publications
Pub. .... Darrin Wilson
Nat'l Adv. Mgr./Adv. Dir. .... Roger Davis
Circ. Dir. .... Sandra Williams
Areas Served: 31730

CANTON

CHEROKEE LEDGER-NEWS (WED)

521 E Main St, Canton, GA, 30114-2805, Cherokee, USA; gen tel (770) 479-1441; gen fax (770) 422-9533; disp adv e-mail wstephens@mdjonline.com; class adv e-mail wstephens@mdjonline.com; ed e-mail rjohnston@cherokeetribune.com; web site www.cherokeetribune.com
Circulation: 10,000fr; CAC
Advertising rate: Open inch rate $57.75
Group: Neighbor Newspapers, Inc.
Pub. .... Otis Brumby
Ed. .... Rebecca Johnston
Gen. Mgr. .... Lee Brumby Garrett
VP, Sales .... Wade Stephens
Delivery Method: Mail

CARROLLTON

BOWDON BULLETIN (WED)

901 Hays Mill Rd, Carrollton, GA, 30117-9576, Haralson, USA; gen tel (770) 834-6631; gen fax (770) 830-9425; disp adv e-mail melissa@times-georgian.com; web site www.times-georgian.com
Circulation: 1,800pd, 1,200fr; Sworn/Estimate/Non-Audited
Advertising rate: Open inch rate $20.00
Pub. .... Leonard Woolsey
Areas Served: 30112, 30116, 30117, 30118, 30119

WEST GEORGIA WEEKLY (WED)

901 Hays Mill Rd, Carrollton, GA, 30117-9576, Carroll, USA; gen tel (770) 834-6631; gen fax (770) 834-9991; disp adv e-mail melissa@times-georgian.com; class adv e-mail melissa@times-georgian.com; ed e-mail bbrowning@times-georgian.com; web site www.times-georgian.com - 239,329(views) 135,195(visitors)
Circulation: 16,000fr; Sworn/Estimate/Non-Audited
Advertising rate: Open inch rate $20.00
Group: Paxton Media Group, LLC
Sports Editor .... Corey Cusick
Delivery Method: Carrier
Areas Served: 30112, 30116, 30117, 30118, 30119

STARNEWS (SUN, MTHLY)

318 Newnan Rd, Carrollton, GA, 30117-3418, Carroll, USA; gen tel (770) 214-9900; gen fax (770) 214-9600; disp adv e-mail suehorn.starnews@gmail.com; class adv e-mail suehorn.starnews@gmail.com; ed e-mail suehorn.starnews@gmail.com; web site www.starnewsga.com - 227,000(views)
Circulation: 5,200pd, 4,800fr; Sworn/Estimate/Non-Audited
Advertising rate: Modular tabloid pricing
Established: 1995
Ed./Pub. .... Sue M. Horn Chappell
Mechanical Specifications: quarter pg. ADs 4.7"x6.5"
half pg. ADs 4.7"x12.25"
full pg. ADs 9.5"x12.25"Equipment & Software: Hardware — APP/Mac.
Delivery Method: Mail, Newsstand, Carrier, Racks
Areas Served: West Georgia area plus subscribers in other 26 states

TALLAPOOSA JOURNAL (THUR)

901 Hays Mill Rd, Carrollton, GA, 30117-9576, Haralson, USA; gen tel (770) 834-6631; adv tel (770) 834-6631 ext. 225; ed tel (770) 834-6631; gen fax (770) 834-9991; adv fax (770) 834-9991; ed fax (770) 834-9991; disp adv e-mail melissa@times-georgian.com; class adv e-mail publisher@times-georgian.com; ed e-mail bbrowning@times-georgian.com; web site www.times-georgian.com/tallapoosa-journal
Advertising rate: Open inch rate $5.75
Digital Platform - Mobile: Apple, Android, Windows, Blackberry
Digital Platform - Tablet: Apple iOS, Android, Windows 7, Blackberry Tablet OS
Pub. .... Leonard Woolsey
Mng. Ed. .... Bruce Browning
Adv. Dir. .... Melissa Wilson
Delivery Method: Mail, Newsstand, Racks
Areas Served: 30117

THE HARALSON COUNTY GATEWAY BEACON (THUR)

901 Hays Mill Rd, Ste A, Carrollton, GA, 30117-9576, Carroll, USA; gen tel (770) 537-2434; adv tel (770) 834-6631 x 225; gen fax (770) 537-8816; disp adv e-mail melissa@times-georgian.com; web site www.times-georgian.com
Circulation: 770pd,; Sworn/Estimate/Non-Audited
Advertising rate: Open inch rate $4.00
Office Mgr. .... Francis Pollard
Ed. .... Amy Lavender
Delivery Method: Mail, Newsstand, Racks
Areas Served: Haralson County, GA

THE VILLA RICAN (THUR)

901 Hays Mill Rd, Carrollton, GA, 30117-9576, Carroll, USA; gen tel (770) 834-6631; gen fax (770) 834-9991; disp adv e-mail melissa@times-georgian.com; class adv e-mail melissa@times-georgian.com; ed e-mail ken@times-georgian.com; web site www.times-georgian.com/villa-rican/ - 239,329(views) 135,195(visitors)
Circulation: 8,200fr; Sworn/Estimate/Non-Audited
Advertising rate: Open inch rate $20.00
Group: Paxton Media Group, LLC
Ed. .... Ken Denney
Delivery Method: Carrier, Racks
Areas Served: Villa Rica, GA

CEDARTOWN

THE POLK COUNTY STANDARD JOURNAL (WED)

213 Main St, Cedartown, GA, 30125-3048, Polk, USA; gen tel (770) 748-1520; gen fax (770) 748-1524; disp adv e-mail tbritt@npco.com; ed e-mail kmyrick@npco.com; web site www.polkstandardjournal.com
Circulation: 3,679pd,; Sworn/Estimate/Non-Audited
Advertising rate: Open inch rate $14.02
Established: 1869
Ed./Pub. .... Kevin Myrick
Delivery Method: Mail, Carrier, Racks
Areas Served: 30125

CHATSWORTH

CHATSWORTH TIMES (WED)

224 N 3rd Ave, Chatsworth, GA, 30705-2536, Murray, USA; gen tel (706) 695-4646; gen fax (706) 695-7181; disp adv e-mail news@chatsworthtimes.com; web site www.chatsworthtimes.com
Circulation: 6,000pd,; Sworn/Estimate/Non-Audited
Advertising rate: Open inch rate $5.75
Group: Cleveland Newspapers, Inc.
Ed./ Gen. Mgr. .... Lorri Harrison
Adv. Director .... Pat Oxford
Classifieds & Legals .... Cari Sluder
Mechanical Specifications: Type page 13 x 21 1/2; E - 6 cols, 2 1/16, 1/8 between; A - 6 cols, 2 1/16, 1/8 between; C - 6 cols, 2 1/16, 1/8 between.Equipment & Software: Hardware — APP/Mac; Software — QPS/QuarkXPress.
Areas Served: 30705

CLAXTON

CLAXTON ENTERPRISE (WED)

24 S Newton St, Claxton, GA, 30417-2044, Evans, USA; gen tel (912) 739-2132; gen fax (912) 739-2140; disp adv e-mail news@claxtonenterprise.com; class adv e-mail advertising@claxtonenterprise.com; ed e-mail editor@claxtonenterprise.com; web site www.claxtonenterprise.com
Circulation: 4,200pd, 50fr; Sworn/Estimate/Non-Audited
Advertising rate: Open inch rate $5.50
Pub. .... Mitchell E. Peace
Pub. .... Pamela A. Peace
Vice Pres., Opns./Adv. .... Paula McNeely
Ed. .... Sarah Tarr
Mechanical Specifications: Type page 13 x 21; E - 6 cols, 2, 1/6 between; A - 6 cols, 2, 1/6 between; C - 6 cols, 2, 1/6 between.Equipment & Software: Hardware — APP/Macs OS X (V10.5.8), HP Flatbed Scanners, Xante/PlateMaker; Software — QPS/QuarkXPress 7(V7.31), Adobe Packages, Creative Suite
Delivery Method: Mail, Racks
Areas Served: 30417, 30429, 30414

CLAYTON

THE CLAYTON TRIBUNE (THUR)

120 N Main St, Clayton, GA, 30525-4266, Rabun, USA; gen tel (706) 782-3312; adv tel (706) 782-3312; ed tel (706) 782-3312; gen fax (706) 782-4230; adv fax (706) 782-4230; ed fax (706) 782-4230; disp adv e-mail thetribune@theclaytontribune.com; class adv e-mail circulation@TheClaytonTribune.com; ed e-mail thetribune@theclaytontribune.com; web site www.theclaytontribune.com
Circulation: 8,000pd,; Sworn/Estimate/Non-Audited
Advertising rate: Open inch rate $15.50
Established: 1897
Group: Community Newspapers, Inc.
Pub. .... Michael Leonard
Ed. .... Blake Spurney
Adv. Sales .... Cyndy Brogdon
Areas Served: 30525

CLEVELAND

WHITE COUNTY NEWS (THUR)

13 E Jarrard St, Cleveland, GA, 30528-1228, White, USA; gen tel (706) 865-4718; adv tel (706) 865-4718; ed tel (706) 865-4718; gen fax (706) 865-3048; adv fax (706) 865-4718; ed fax (706) 865-4718; disp adv e-mail publisher@whitecountynews.net; class adv e-mail publisher@whitecountynews.net; ed e-mail publisher@whitecountynews.net; web site www.whitecountynews.net
Circulation: 5,000pd,; Sworn/Estimate/Non-Audited
Advertising rate: Open inch rate $14.20
Established: 1968
Group: Community Newspapers, Inc.
White County News
Digital Platform - Mobile: Blackberry
Ed./Pub. .... Billy Chism
Delivery Method: Mail, Racks
Areas Served: 30528, 30545, 30571, 30501-07, 30527, 30533, 30523. 30531. 30535

COLQUITT

MILLER COUNTY LIBERAL (WED)

PO Box 37, 157 E Main St, Colquitt, GA, 39837-0037, Miller, USA; gen tel (229) 758-5549; gen fax (229) 758-5540; disp adv e-mail millercountyliberal@gmail.com; ed e-mail terrytoole@mac.com; web site www.millercountyliberal.com
Circulation: 3,000pd,; Sworn/Estimate/Non-Audited
Advertising rate: Open inch rate $5.00
Established: 1897
Digital Platform - Mobile: Apple
Digital Platform - Tablet: Apple iOS, Blackberry Tablet OS
Gen. Mgr. .... Betty Jo Toole
Ed./Pub. .... Terry Toole
Adv./Circ. Mgr. .... Wanda GriffinEquipment & Software: Hardware — APP/Mac; Software — Adobe/InDesign 5.0, Multi-Ad/Creator 4.0, QPS/QuarkXPress 3.2., PhotoShop 5.0
Delivery Method: Mail, Newsstand, Carrier, Racks
Areas Served: 39837

CONYERS

THE NEWTON CITIZEN (WED, FRI, SAT)

969 S Main St NE, Conyers, GA, 30012-4501, Newton, USA; gen tel (770) 483-7108; adv fax (770) 761-4048; ed fax (770) 787-8603; disp adv e-mail Advertising@rockdalecitizen.com; class adv e-mail Advertising@rockdalecitizen.com; ed e-mail news@newtoncitizen.com; web site www.newton-citizen.com
Circulation: 1,863pd, 246fr; CVC
Advertising rate: Open inch rate $29.62
Group: Triple Crown Media
Adv. Dir. .... Brenda Bennett
Circ. Dir. .... Thom Bell
Ed. .... Alice Queen
Areas Served: ATLANTA, GA MSA

THE ROCKDALE CITIZEN (WED, FRI, SAT)

969 S Main St NE, Conyers, GA, 30012-4501, Rockdale, USA; gen tel (770) 483-7108; adv tel (770) 483-7108; ed tel (770) 483-7108; adv fax (770) 761-4048; ed fax (770) 483-5797; disp adv e-mail alice.queen@rockdalecitizen.com; class adv e-mail brenda.bennett@rockdalecitizen.com; ed e-mail news@rockdalecitizen.com; web site www.rockdalecitizen.com
Circulation: 4,267pd, 452fr; CVC
Advertising rate: Open inch rate $22.78
Established: 1953
Group: Southern Community Newspapers, Inc.
Ed. .... Alice Queen
Adv. Dir. .... Brenda Bennett
Retail Adv. Rep. .... Rachel Hayes
Circ. Dir. .... Thom Bell
Mng. Ed. .... Jay Jones
Features Ed. .... Karen Rohr
Sports Ed. .... Manny Fils
Pub. .... J.K. Murphy
Mechanical Specifications: Type page 12 x 21 1/2; E - 6 cols, 1 7/8, 1/8 between; A - 6 cols, 1 7/8, 1/8 between; C - 10 cols, 1/8 between.
Areas Served: ATLANTA, GA MSA

CORDELE

CORDELE DISPATCH (WED, SAT)

401 E 16th Ave, Ste F, Cordele, GA, 31015-1669, Crisp, USA; gen tel (229) 273-2277; adv tel (229) 273-2277; gen fax (229) 273-7239; disp adv e-mail chris.lewis@cordele-dispatch.com; web site www.cordeledispatch.com

Circulation: 4,590pd,; Sworn/Estimate/Non-Audited
Advertising rate: Open inch rate $21.50
Established: 1908
Group: Boone Newspapers, Inc.
Gen. Mngr./Adv. Mngr.................... Chris Lewis
Exec. Ed..Beth Alston
Sports Ed...............................Harvey Simpson
Prodn. Compositor...........................Betty Ruis
Prodn. Compositor.................Cathy Strickland
Circ. Dir............................. Rachel Wainwright
Copy Ed..Peggy King
Adv. Mngr.................................. Laura Rogers
Mechanical Specifications: Type page 13 x 21 1/2; E - 6 cols, 2 1/16, 1/8 between; A - 6 cols, 2 1/16, 1/8 between; C - 9 cols, 1 3/8, 1/16 between.

CORNELIA

THE NORTHEAST GEORGIAN (WED, FRI)

2440 Old Athens Hwy, Cornelia, GA, 30531-5364, Habersham, USA; gen tel (706) 778-4215; gen fax (706) 778-4114; disp adv e-mail news@thenortheastgeorgian.com; class adv e-mail advertising@thenortheast-georgian.com; web site www.thenortheast-georgian.com

Circulation: 9,000pd, 50fr; Sworn/Estimate/Non-Audited
Advertising rate: Open inch rate $18.75
Established: 1892
Group: Community Newspapers, Inc.
Reg. Pub.................................. Alan NeSmith
Regl. Bus. Mgr.........................Mark VanTassel
Ed. .... Lane Gresham
Prodn. Mgr. .... April Compton
Corp. Mktg. Dir. ....Joel JenkinsEquipment & Software: Hardware — 7-APP/Mac; Software — Adobe/PageMaker 6.1.
Areas Served: 30531

COVINGTON

THE COVINGTON NEWS (SUN)

1166 Usher St NW, Covington, GA, 30014-2451, Newton, USA; gen tel (770) 787-6397; gen fax (770) 786-6451; disp adv e-mail cbwarren@covnews.com; class adv e-mail cbwarren@covnews.com; ed e-mail bfazio@covnews.com; web site www.covnews.com

Circulation: 5,500pd, 19fr; USPS
Advertising rate: Open inch rate $8.15
Established: 1865
Group: Morris Multimedia, Inc.
Circ. Mgr...............................Amanda Ellington
Adv. Mgr................................. Cynthia Warren
Digital Mgr.................................. Jason Cosby
Ed. .... Brian Fazio
Mechanical Specifications: Type page 12 1/2 x 21 1/2; E - 6 cols, 2 1/24, 1/6 between; A - 6 cols, 2 1/4, 1/6 between; C - 9 cols, 1 7/24, 1/6 between.Equipment & Software: Hardware — APP/Macs; Software — QPS/QuarkXPress 3.3, Adobe/Photoshop, Dewar Sys 7.1.
Delivery Method: Newsstand, Carrier, Racks
Areas Served: Covington, GA / Newton County, GA, 30016,30054,30014,30025,30055,30056

THE COVINGTON NEWS (TUES)

1166 Usher St NW, Covington, GA, 30014-2451, Newton, USA; gen tel (770) 787-6397; gen fax (770) 786-6451; disp adv e-mail circulation@covnews.com; web site www.covnews.com

Circulation: 43,500fr; Sworn/Estimate/Non-Audited
Advertising rate: Open inch rate $7.50
Pub...................................... Charles H. Morris
Circ. Mgr... Bill Herbert
Mechanical Specifications: Type page 6 x 16; A - 6 cols, 1 1/2, between; C - 6 cols, 1 1/2, between.Equipment & Software: Hardware — APP/Mac G4; Software — QPS/QuarkXPress 4.0, Adobe/Photoshop, Baseview.
Areas Served: 30014, 30016, 30025, 30054, 30055, 30262, 30070, 30012, 30013, 30094

CUMMING

FORSYTH COUNTY NEWS (WED, FRI, SUN)

302 Veterans Memorial Blvd, Cumming, GA, 30040-2644, Forsyth, USA; gen tel (770) 887-3126; adv tel (770) 887-3126; ed tel (770) 887-3126; gen fax (770) 889-6017; adv fax (770) 744 9779; disp adv e-mail adv@forsythnews.com; class adv e-mail rgarmon@forsythnews.com; ed e-mail editor@forsythnews.com; web site www.forsythnews.com - 500,000(views) 90,000(visitors)

Circulation: 12,500pd,; Sworn/Estimate/Non-Audited
Advertising rate: Open inch rate $16.45
Established: 1908
Group: Swartz Media, LLC
Pub.. Vince Johnson
Adv. Dir.................................... Ryan Garmon
Ed. ....Kayla Robins
Circ. Mgr......................................Lisa Salinas
Adv, Account Exec......................Cheri Bullard
Adv. Acct Exec.......................... Connor Kelly
Adv. Acct. Exec..................... Allison Althauser
Online Ed..Jim Dean
Classified Adv....................... Shana Patterson
Production Mgr............................. Tracie Pike
Delivery Method: Carrier, Racks
Areas Served: 30040, 30041, 30028, 30534, 30506, 30024, 30097, 30004, 30005, 30107

DAHLONEGA

THE DAHLONEGA NUGGET (WED)

1074 Morrison Moore Pkwy W, Dahlonega, GA, 30533-1425, Lumpkin, USA; gen tel (706) 864-3613; adv tel (706) 864-3613; gen fax (706) 864-4360; disp adv e-mail nugclass@windstream.net; ed e-mail tellerbee@dahloneganugget.com; web site thedahloneganugget.com

Circulation: 5,025pd, 25fr; Sworn/Estimate/Non-Audited
Advertising rate: Open inch rate $13.80
Group: Community Newspapers, Inc.
Ed. .... Terrie Ellerbee
Pub... Matt Aiken
Corp. Mktg. Dir. ....Joel JenkinsEquipment & Software: ; Software — Microsoft/Works 3.0, Adobe/PageMaker 5.0.
Areas Served: 30533

DALLAS

DALLAS NEW ERA (THUR)

121 W Spring St, Dallas, GA, 30132-4138, Paulding, USA; gen tel (770) 445-3379; gen fax (770) 445-5726; disp adv e-mail newerapr@bellsouth.net; ed e-mail newerapr@bellsouth.net; web site thedallasnewera.com

Circulation: 6,500pd,; Sworn/Estimate/Non-Audited
Advertising rate: Open inch rate $4.00
Pub... W.T. Parker
Circ. Mgr.. Joe Parker
Areas Served: 30312

DAWSON

THE DAWSON NEWS (WED, THUR)

139 W Lee St, Dawson, GA, 39842-1624, Terrell, USA; gen tel (229) 995-2175; gen fax (229) 995-2176; disp adv e-mail news@thedawsonnews.com; class adv e-mail news@thedawsonnews.com; ed e-mail news@thedawsonnews.com

Circulation: 2,500pd, 5,022fr; Sworn/Estimate/Non-Audited
Advertising rate: Open inch rate $6.75
Established: 1866
Secretary, Bookkeeper ....Janice French
Ed, Pub & Owner..................Tommy Rountree
Mechanical Specifications: Type page 11.625 x 21.5; E - 6 cols, 1 5/6, 1/8 between; A - 6 cols, 1 5/6, 1/8 between; C - 6 cols, 1 5/6, 1/8 between.Equipment & Software: Hardware — PC; Software — QPS/QuarkXPress 3.32.
Delivery Method: Mail
Areas Served: 39842

DAWSONVILLE

DAWSON COUNTY NEWS (WED)

30 SHOAL CREEK RD, Dawsonville, GA, 30534, Dawson, USA; gen tel (706) 265-3384; gen fax (706) 265-3276; disp adv e-mail JLyness@dawsonnews.com; class adv e-mail jlyness@dawsonnews.com; ed e-mail editor@dawsonnews.com; web site www.dawsonnews.com

Circulation: 4,024pd, 8fr; Sworn/Estimate/Non-Audited
Advertising rate: Open inch rate $7.00
Group: Morris Multimedia, Inc.
Swartz Media, LLC
Pub./Mktg. Dir.................................... John Hall
Adv. Dir................................... Jennifer Lyness
Ed. .... Stephanie Griffin
Circ. Dir. .... Lisa Salinas
Gen. Mgr. ....Stephanie WoodyEquipment & Software: Hardware — APP/Mac; Software — QPS/QuarkXPress, Adobe/Photoshop.
Areas Served: 30534

DECATUR

CROSSROADSNEWS (SAT)

2346 Candler Rd, Decatur, GA, 30032-6406, Dekalb, USA; gen tel (404) 284-1888; gen fax (404) 284-5007; disp adv e-mail editor@crossroadsnews.com; class adv e-mail advertising@crossroadsnews.com; ed e-mail editor@crossroadsnews.com; web site http://www.crossroadsnews.com

Circulation: 11pd, 27,908fr; VAC
Advertising rate: Open inch rate $40.00
Established: 1995
Digital Platform - Mobile: Apple, Android, Windows, Blackberry
Digital Platform - Tablet: Apple iOS, Android, Windows 7, Blackberry Tablet OS, Kindle, Nook, Kindle Fire
Prod. Mgr.................................... Curtis Parker
Ed./Pub. .... Jennifer Parker
Adv. Mgr....................................... Kathy Warner
Circ. Mgr .... Jami French-Parker
Mechanical Specifications: 10.5 inches wide x 16 inches deep [4-column grid]
Delivery Method: Carrier, Racks
Areas Served: 30030; 30032; 30033; 30034; 30035; 30038; 30058; 30079; 30083; 30087; 30084; 30088; 30002; 30021; 30316; 30317;

DONALSONVILLE

DONALSONVILLE NEWS (THUR)

216 Cherry St, Donalsonville, GA, 39845-1616, Seminole, USA; gen tel (229) 524-2343; gen fax (229) 524-2343; disp adv e-mail scott@donalsonvillenews.com; class adv e-mail classifieds@donalsonvillenews.com; web site www.donalsonvillenews.com

Circulation: 3,500pd,; Sworn/Estimate/Non-Audited
Advertising rate: Open inch rate $4.00
Circ. Mgr.. Janet Hill
Ed. .... Waldo L. McLeod
Areas Served: 39845

DOUGLAS

THE DOUGLAS ENTERPRISE (WED, SUN)

1823 Peterson Ave S, Douglas, GA, 31535-4013, Douglas, USA; gen tel (912) 384-2323; gen fax (912) 383-0218; disp adv e-mail frontdesk@douglasenterprise.net; class adv e-mail adsales@douglasenterprise.net; ed e-mail articles@douglasenterprise.net; web site www.douglasenterprise.net

Circulation: 8,000pd, 5fr; Sworn/Estimate/Non-Audited
Advertising rate: Open inch rate $6.00
Established: 1888
Pub./Ed. .... Tracy Mayo
Adv. Mgr./Sales Rep.................. Cathy Threatt
Circ. Mgr.. Ken Wilson
Mechanical Specifications: Type page 11.5 x 21; E - 6 cols, 2 1/16, 1/16 between; A - 6 cols, 2 1/16, 1/16 between; C - 8 cols, 1 7/12, 1/16 between.Equipment & Software: Hardware — APP/Mac; Presses — 8-WPC/Web Leader; Software — Multi-Ad, QPS/QuarkXPress.
Areas Served: 31533

DOUGLASVILLE

DOUGLAS COUNTY SENTINEL (WED, FRI, SUN)

8501 Bowden St, Douglasville, GA, 30134-1705, Douglas, USA; gen tel (770) 942-6571; adv tel (770) 942-6571; ed tel (770) 942-6571; gen fax (770) 949-7556; adv fax (770) 949-7556; ed fax (770) 949-7556; disp adv e-mail melissa@times-georgian.com; class adv e-mail classifieds@douglascountysentinel.com; ed e-mail news@douglascountysentinel.com; web site www.douglascountysentinel.com - 133,656(views) 94,075(visitors)

Circulation: 1,608pd, 1,013fr; USPS
Advertising rate: Open inch rate $20.00
Established: 1902
Group: Paxton Media Group, LLC
Mng. Ed.. Ron Daniel
Systems Mgr................................ Ricky Stilley
Adv. Dir.................................... Melissa Wilson
Pub..Marvin Enderle
Cir. Mgr.. Mark Golding
Sports Ed...............................Derrick Mahone
Mechanical Specifications: Type page 10 x 21; E - 6 cols, 1 9/16, 1/8 between; A - 6 cols, 1 9/16, 1/8 between; C - 6 cols, 1 9/16, 1/8 between.
Delivery Method: Mail, Newsstand, Carrier, Racks
Areas Served: Douglas County, GA

DUBLIN

THE WHEELER COUNTY EAGLE (WED)

115 S Jefferson St, Dublin, GA, 31021-5146, Treutlen, USA; gen tel (478) 272-5522 ext. 223; gen fax (912) 529-5399; disp adv e-mail wheelercountyeagle@gmail.com; web site www.wheelercountyeagle.com

Circulation: 1,150pd,; Sworn/Estimate/Non-Audited
Advertising rate: Open inch rate $7.00
Established: 1921
Pub.. Griffin Lovett
CEO... Dubose Porter
Mechanical Specifications: Type page 13 x 21 1/2; E - 6 cols, 2, 3/16 between; A - 6 cols, 2, 3/16 between; C - 6 cols, 2, 3/16 between. Equipment & Software: Hardware — APP/Mac; Software — QPS/QuarkXPress.
Areas Served: 30457

DUNWOODY

DUNWOODY CRIER (WED)

5064 Nandina Ln, Ste C, Dunwoody, GA, 30338-4115, DeKalb, USA; gen tel (770) 451-4147; gen fax (770) 451-4223; disp adv e-mail jhart@criernewspapers.com; class adv e-mail dstevens@criernewspapers.com;

ed e-mail thecrier@mindspring.com; web site www.thecrier.net
Circulation: 15,564fr; CAC
Advertising rate: Open inch rate $31.76
Established: 1976
Group: Crier Newspapers LLC
Nat'l/Retail Adv. Dir. .... Jim Hart
Ed. .... Dick Williams
Classified Adv. Mgr. .... Donna Stevens
Prod. Mgr. .... Kenyatta Tallafero
Mechanical Specifications: Type page 10 1/4 x 14.Equipment & Software: Hardware — PC; Software — QPS/QuarkXPress.
Delivery Method: Carrier, Racks
Areas Served: 30338

ELBERTON

THE ELBERTON STAR (WED)

25 N Public Sq, Elberton, GA, 30635-2416, Elbert, USA; gen tel (706) 283-8500; gen fax (706) 283-9700; disp adv e-mail starexaminer@elberton.com; web site www.elberton.com
Circulation: 5,650pd, 159fr; Sworn/Estimate/Non-Audited
Advertising rate: Open inch rate $11.50
Group: Community Newspapers, Inc.
Pub. .... Gary Jones
Office Mgr. .... Kerri Pruitt
Corp. Mktg. Dir. .... Joel Jenkins
Staff writer .... Shana Toney
Mechanical Specifications: Type page 13 x 21 1/4; E - 6 cols, 2, 1/6 between; A - 6 cols, 2, 1/6 between; C - 6 cols, 2, 1/6 between. Equipment & Software: Hardware — IBM, APP/Mac; Software — Adobe/PageMaker 4.0.
Delivery Method: Mail, Newsstand, Racks
Areas Served: 30635, 30624, 30634

ELLIJAY

TIMES-COURIER (WED)

47 River St, Ellijay, GA, 30540-3174, Gilmer, USA; gen tel (706) 635-4313; adv tel (706) 635-7002; ed tel (706) 635-7002; gen fax (706) 635-7006; adv fax (706) 635-7006; ed fax (706) 635-7006; disp adv e-mail adsales@timescourier.com; class adv e-mail Fcclassifieds@timescourier.com; ed e-mail editor@timescourier.com; web site www.timescourier.com - 39,000(views) 5,780(visitors)
Circulation: 6,600pd, 60fr; Sworn/Estimate/Non-Audited
Advertising rate: Open inch rate $7.75
Established: 1875Editions: (52) Times-Courier Pub. Co.
Digital Platform - Mobile: Apple
Digital Platform - Tablet: Apple iOS
Adv. Mgr. .... Shana Parks
Circ./Office Mgr. .... Rhesa Chastain
News Ed. .... Mark Millican
Sports Ed. .... Robbie Bills
Staff Writer .... Ryan Rees
Prod. Mgr. .... Keli Fredrickson
Adv. Sales .... Kathy Aker
Publisher .... Andy Hurst
Mechanical Specifications: Type page 12 x 21; E - 6 cols, 2 1/8, 1/8 between; A - 6 cols, 2 1/8, 1/8 between; C - 6 cols, 2 1/8, 1/8 between. Equipment & Software: Hardware — APP/Mac G4; Software — QPS/QuarkXPress, Baseview/NewsEdit, Microsoft/Windows, Baseview/Class Manager, Adobe/Photoshop, Multi-Ad/Creator.
Delivery Method: Mail, Newsstand, Racks
Areas Served: 30540, 30539

EVANS

THE COLUMBIA COUNTY NEWS-TIMES (WED, SUN)

604 Government Center Way, Ste A, Evans, GA, 30809-7606, Columbia, USA; gen tel (706) 868-1222; adv tel (706) 868-1222; gen fax (706) 823-6062; disp adv e-mail cnt@newstimesonline.com; web site www.newstimes.augusta.com/
Circulation: 18,500pd,; Sworn/Estimate/Non-Audited
Advertising rate: Open inch rate $7.25
Established: 1881
Office Mgr. .... Suzanne Liverett
Visual Journalist .... Jim Blaylock
Staff Writer .... Valerie Rowell
Sports Writer .... Scott RouchEquipment & Software: Hardware — 4-Motorola/Star Max, APP/Mac, HP/Printer, Umax/Scanner; Software — Microsoft/Word, QPS/QuarkXPress, Adobe/Photoshop, Macromedia/Freehand.
Delivery Method: Mail, Newsstand, Carrier, Racks
Areas Served: 30809, 30907, 30814, 30813, 30802

FAYETTEVILLE

THE CITIZEN (WED, THUR)

310 Glynn St N, Ste B, Fayetteville, GA, 30214-1105, Fayette, USA; gen tel (770) 719-1880; ed e-mail Editor@thecitizen.com; web site www.thecitizen.com
Circulation: 23,468fr; CAC
Advertising rate: 1/4 Pg $23.00; 1/2 Pg $21.00; Full $15.00
Established: 1993
Group: Fayette Publishing
Pub. .... Cal Beverly
Adv. Sales Dir. .... Joyce Beverly
Major Accts. Mgr. .... Diann Cupertino
Delivery Method: Newsstand, Carrier, Racks
Areas Served: 30214, 30215, 30269, 30276, 30277, 30290

FITZGERALD

THE HERALD-LEADER (WED)

202 E Central Ave, Fitzgerald, GA, 31750-2503, Ben Hill, USA; gen tel (229) 423-9331; gen fax (229) 423-6533; disp adv e-mail hlnews@alltell.net; class adv e-mail andersonherald@gmail.com; web site www.herald-leader.net
Circulation: 5,300pd,; Sworn/Estimate/Non-Audited
Advertising rate: Open inch rate $6.00
Established: 1916
Adv. Mgr. .... Becky Anderson
Ed. .... Tim Anderson
Areas Served: 31750

FOLKSTON

CHARLTON COUNTY HERALD (WED)

3781 Main St, Ste A, Folkston, GA, 31537-7572, Charlton, USA; gen tel (912) 496-3585; gen fax (912) 496-4585; disp adv e-mail ads@charltonherald.com; class adv e-mail mail@charltonherald.com; ed e-mail editor@charltonherald.com; web site www.charltoncountyherald.com
Circulation: 3,000pd, 100fr; Sworn/Estimate/Non-Audited
Advertising rate: Open inch rate $5.50
Established: 1898
Group: Gardner Newspapers
Advertising .... Marla Ogletree
Ed. .... Matt Gardner
Mechanical Specifications: Type page 13 x 21; E - 6 cols, 2, 1/8 between; A - 6 cols, 2, 1/8 between; C - 6 cols, 2, 1/8 between.
Delivery Method: Mail, Racks
Areas Served: 31537

FOREST PARK

HENRY NEIGHBOR (THUR)

5442 Frontage Rd Ste 130, Suite 130, Forest Park, GA, 30297-2538, Clayton, USA; gen tel (404) 363-8484; gen fax (404) 363-0212; disp adv e-mail smetro@neighbornewspapers.com; web site mdjonline.com/neighbor_newspapers
Circulation: 2pd, 32,464fr; CAC
Advertising rate: Open inch rate $29.80
Group: Times-Journal, Inc.
Neighbor Newspapers
Pub. .... Otis A. Brumby
Adv. Mgr. .... Nat Long
Circ. Dir. .... Russell H. Powell
Ed. .... Nicole Hollimon
Ed. .... Mary Cosgrove
Ed. .... Bill Baldowski
Mechanical Specifications: Type page 13 x 21; E - 6 cols, 2 1/16, between; A - 6 cols, 2 1/16, between; C - 10 cols, 1 3/16, between.
Areas Served: 30274, 30238, 30296, 30297, 30236, 30260, 30273

SOUTH FULTON NEIGHBOR (WED)

5442 Frontage Rd, Ste 130, Forest Park, GA, 30297-2538, Clayton, USA; gen tel (404) 363-8484; gen fax (404) 363-0212; disp adv e-mail nlong@neighbornewspapers.com; class adv e-mail adavis@mdjonline.com; web site mdjonline.com/neighbor_newspapers
Circulation: 3pd, 24,200fr; CAC
Advertising rate: Open inch rate $30.60
Group: Times-Journal, Inc.
Gen. Mgr. .... Otis A. Brumby
Ed. .... Mary Cosgrove
Ed. .... Bill Baldowski
VP, Sales/Mktg. .... Wade Stephens
Mechanical Specifications: Type page 13 x 21; E - 6 cols, 2 1/16, between; A - 6 cols, 2 1/16, between; C - 10 cols, 1 3/16, between.
Areas Served: 30274, 30238, 30296, 30297, 30236, 30260, 30273

GAINESVILLE

LANIER LIFE (WED)

345 Green St NW, Gainesville, GA, 30501-3370, Hall, USA; gen tel (770) 532-1234; gen fax (770) 535-2859; web site http://www.gainesvilletimes.com/
Group: Morris Multimedia, Inc.

GRAY

THE JONES COUNTY NEWS (THUR)

102 Stewart Ave, Gray, GA, 31032-5219, Jones, USA; gen tel (478) 986-3929; adv tel (478) 986-3929; gen fax (478) 986-1935; disp adv e-mail articles@jcnews.com; class adv e-mail legals@jcnews.com; ed e-mail mynews@jcnews.com; web site www.jcnews.com
Circulation: 4,300pd,; Sworn/Estimate/Non-Audited
Advertising rate: Open inch rate $6.50
Established: 1895
Ed. .... Debbie Lurie-Smith
Pub. .... Joshua Lurie
Office Mgr. .... Jennifer Gibson
Adv. Rep. .... Karen Hunsinger
Adv. Rep. .... Kelli Martin
Mechanical Specifications: Type page 13 x 21 1/2; E - 6 cols, 2, 1/6 between; A - 6 cols, 2, 1/6 between; C - 6 cols, 2, 1/6 between. Equipment & Software: Hardware — APP/Macs, PCs; Software — Adobe/PageMaker 7.0, Adobe/Photoshop 7.0, Multi-Ad/Creator 6.5, Adobe/Acrobat 5.0, Adobe/InDesign 2.0.
Areas Served: 31032, 31033, 31031, 31846, 31211, 31217, 31038

GREENSBORO

ADVOCATE DEMOCRAT (THUR)

107 N Main St, Greensboro, GA, 30642-1143, Greene, USA; gen tel (706) 453-7988; gen fax (706) 453-2311; ed e-mail editor@heraldjournal.net; web site No Website
Circulation: 900pd,; Sworn/Estimate/Non-Audited
Advertising rate: Open inch rate $5.00
Adv. Mgr. .... Beth Lyons
Ed. .... Carey Williams
Mechanical Specifications: Type page 13 x 21 1/4.
Areas Served: 30631

HAMILTON

THE HARRIS COUNTY JOURNAL (THUR)

112 S College St, Hamilton, GA, 31811-5330, Harris, USA; gen tel (706) 846-3188; gen fax (706) 846-2206; disp adv e-mail harriscountyjournal@charterinternet.com; starmercurynews@charterinternet.com; web site No Website
Circulation: 4,400pd,; Sworn/Estimate/Non-Audited
Advertising rate: Open inch rate $5.80
Group: Star-Mercury Publishing Co.
Pub. .... John Kuykendall
Adv. Mgr. .... Laurie Lewis
Assoc. Ed. .... Michael C. Snider
Mechanical Specifications: Type page 13 x 21 1/2; E - 6 cols, 2, 1/8 between; A - 6 cols, 2, 1/8 between; C - 6 cols, 2, 1/8 between. Equipment & Software: Hardware — IBM/PC; Presses — 6-KP/News King; Software — Microsoft/Office 1997.
Areas Served: 31811

HARTWELL

THE HARTWELL SUN (THUR)

8 Benson St, Hartwell, GA, 30643-1990, Hart, USA; gen tel (706) 376-8025; gen fax (706) 376-3016; disp adv e-mail hartwellson@hartcom.net; web site www.thehartwellsun.com
Circulation: 6,771pd,; Sworn/Estimate/Non-Audited
Advertising rate: Open inch rate $12.00
Established: 1874
Group: Community Newspapers, Inc.
Pub. .... Robert Rider
Gen. Mgr. .... Peggy Vickery
Ed. .... Mark Hynds
Corp. Mktg. Dir. .... Joel Jenkins
Mechanical Specifications: Type page 11.625 x 21 1/2; 1 column 1.833, 2 column 3.79, 3 column 5.75, 4 column7.708, 5 column 9.667. Equipment & Software: Hardware — Adobe/Page Maker; Presses — G.
Delivery Method: Mail
Areas Served: 30643

HAWKINSVILLE

HAWKINSVILLE DISPATCH AND NEWS (WED)

122 Commerce St, Hawkinsville, GA, 31036-8418, Pulaski, USA; gen tel (478) 783-1291; gen fax (478) 783-1293; disp adv e-mail dn@comsouth.net; web site No Wesbsite
Circulation: 3,000pd,; Sworn/Estimate/Non-Audited
Advertising rate: Open inch rate $5.00
Ed. .... Chuck C. Southerland
Areas Served: 31036

HAZLEHURST

JEFF DAVIS LEDGER (WED)

12 Latimer St, Hazlehurst, GA, 31539-6110, Jeff Davis, USA; gen tel (912) 375-4225; gen fax (912) 375-3704; disp adv e-mail news@jdledger.com; web site www.jdledger.com
Circulation: 3,850pd,; Sworn/Estimate/Non-Audited
Advertising rate: Open inch rate $5.50
Adv. Mgr. .... Kay Purser
Circ. Mgr. .... Kelli Craft
Ed. .... Thomas H. Purser
Prodn. Mgr.Anna PurserEquipment & Software: Hardware — APP/Mac; Software — Adobe/PageMaker 7.0.
Areas Served: 31036

HIAWASSEE

TOWNS COUNTY HERALD (WED)
446 N MAIN ST, Hiawassee, GA, 30546, Towns, USA; gen tel (706) 896-4454; gen fax (706) 896-1745; disp adv e-mail tcherald@windstream.net; web site townscountyherald.net
Circulation: 4,200pd,; Sworn/Estimate/Non-Audited
Advertising rate: Open inch rate $8.00
Pub.....Kenneth West
Adv. Mgr.....Tracie Woodstrom
Areas Served: 30546

HINESVILLE

THE COASTAL COURIER (WED, SUN)
125 S Main St, Hinesville, GA, 31313-3217, Liberty and Long, USA; gen tel (912) 876-0156; gen fax (912) 368-6329; disp adv e-mail vphillips@coastalcourier.com; ed e-mail editor@coastalcourier.com; web site www.coastalcourier.com
Circulation: 5,000pd, 192fr; Sworn/Estimate/Non-Audited
Advertising rate: Open inch rate $10.75
Group: Morris Multimedia, Inc.
Pub.....Marshall Griffin
Gen. Mgr.....Kathryn Fox
Circ. Mgr.....Johnny Brown
Prodn. Mgr.....Leslie Miller
Web Ed.....Pat Watkins
???? ????
Digital Sales Manager.....Susan Nelson
Mechanical Specifications: Type page 13 x 21 1/2; E - 6 cols, 2 1/16, 1/6 between; A - 6 cols, 2 1/16, 1/6 between; C - 9 cols, 1 5/16, 1/6 between.
Delivery Method: Mail, Newsstand, Carrier, Racks
Areas Served: 31313, 31310, 31314, 31315, 31301, 31333, 31309, 31320, 31323, 31316

HIRAM

BARTOW NEIGHBOR (WED)
4471 Jimmy Lee Smith Pkwy, Ste 200, Hiram, GA, 30141-2725, Paulding, USA; gen tel (770) 445-9401; gen fax (770) 445-0565; disp adv e-mail bartow@neighbornewspapers.com; web site mdjonline.com/neighbor_newspapers
Circulation: 10,975fr; CAC
Advertising rate: Open inch rate $26.20
Group: Times-Journal, Inc.
Neighbor Newspapers
Pub.....Otis A. Brumby
Adv. Mgr.....Carol Johnson
Ed.....Monica Burge
Mng. Ed.....Brian Clark
VP, Sales/Mktg.....Wade Stephens
Mechanical Specifications: Type page 13 x 21; E - 6 cols, 2 1/16, between; A - 6 cols, 2 1/16, between; C - 10 cols, 1 3/16, between.
Areas Served: 30141

THE DOUGLAS NEIGHBOR (WED)
4471 Jimmy Lee Smith Pkwy, Ste C, Hiram, GA, 30141-2727, Cobb, USA; gen tel (770) 445-9401; gen fax (770) 942-4348; disp adv e-mail douglas@neighbornewspapers.com; web site mdjonline.com/neighbor_newspapers
Circulation: 1pd, 21,825fr; CAC
Advertising rate: Open inch rate $34.45
Group: Times-Journal, Inc.
Neighbor Newspapers
Pub.....Otis A. Brumby
Ed.....Tom Spigolon
Ed.....Monica Burge
Mechanical Specifications: Type page 13 x 21; E - 6 cols, 2 1/16, between; A - 6 cols, 2 1/16, between; C - 10 cols, 1 3/16, between. Equipment & Software: Hardware — 4-Compaq/5500R; Presses — MAN/4x2; Software — ACT/ADV.
Areas Served: 30141

HOMERVILLE

CLINCH COUNTY NEWS (WED)
113 E Dame Ave, Homerville, GA, 31634-2456, Clinch, USA; gen tel (912) 487-5337; gen fax (912) 487-3227; ed e-mail clinnews@windstream.net; web site www.theclinchcountynews.com
Circulation: 1,800pd, 70fr; Sworn/Estimate/Non-Audited
Advertising rate: Open inch rate $5.50
Bus. Mgr.....Carolyn Burtchaell
Adv. Rep.....Casey Gray
Ed./Pub.....Len Robbins
Prodn. Mgr.....Bonnie Whitley
Advertising Sales Rep.....Cari Fortner
Delivery Method: Mail, Newsstand
Areas Served: 31634

JACKSON

JACKSON PROGRESS-ARGUS (WED)
129 S Mulberry St, Jackson, GA, 30233-2056, Butts, USA; gen tel (770) 775-3107; adv tel (770) 775-3107 x 105; gen fax (770) 775-3855; disp adv e-mail hpope@myjpa.com; web site www.jacksonprogress-argus.com
Circulation: 4,600pd,; Sworn/Estimate/Non-Audited
Advertising rate: Open inch rate $10.50
Established: 1873
Group: Triple Crown Media
Gen. Sales Mgr.....Bonnie Pratt
Ed.....Michael Davis
Mechanical Specifications: Type page 13 x 21 1/2; E - 6 cols, 2, between; A - 6 cols, 2, between; C - 6 cols, 2, between.Equipment & Software: Hardware — APP/Mac; Presses — KP/Color King.
Areas Served: 30223

JEFFERSON

THE BANKS COUNTY NEWS (WED)
33 Lee St, Jefferson, GA, 30549-1345, Jackson, USA; gen tel (706) 367-5233; gen fax (706) 367-8056; disp adv e-mail news@mainstreetnews.com; web site www.mainstreetnews.com
Circulation: 3,400pd, 90fr; Sworn/Estimate/Non-Audited
Advertising rate: Open inch rate $5.00
Established: 1968
Co-Pub./Adv. Mgr.....Scott Buffington
Circ. Mgr.....Debbie Castellaw
Ed.....Angela Gary
Printing Mgr.....Thomas Toles
Co-Pub.....Mike Buffington
Mechanical Specifications: Type page 13 x 21 1/2; E - 6 cols, 2, 1/6 between; A - 6 cols, 2, 1/6 between; C - 6 cols, 2, 1/6 between. Equipment & Software: Hardware — APP/Mac; Presses — 12-G; Software — QPS/QuarkXPress 3.38, Multi-Ad/Creator 4.0, Adobe/Photoshop 4.0.
Areas Served: 30549

THE COMMERCE NEWS (WED)
33 Lee St, Jefferson, GA, 30549-1345, Jackson, USA; gen tel (706) 367-5233; gen fax (706) 367-8056; disp adv e-mail news@mainstreetnews.com; web site commerce-newstoday.com
Circulation: 3,100pd,; Sworn/Estimate/Non-Audited
Advertising rate: Open inch rate $4.75
Established: 1875
Co. Pub.....Mike N. Buffington
Co-Pub./Adv. Mgr.....Scott Buffington
Classified/Billing Mgr.....Debbie Castellaw
Ed.....Mark Beardsley
Mechanical Specifications: Type page 13 x 21 1/2; E - 6 cols, 2, 1/6 between; A - 6 cols, 2, 1/6 between; C - 6 cols, 2, 1/6 between. Equipment & Software: Hardware — APP/Mac; Presses — 12-G/Community.
Areas Served: 30549

THE JACKSON HERALD (WED)
33 Lee St, Jefferson, GA, 30549-1345, Jackson, USA; gen tel (706) 367-5233; gen fax (706) 367-8056; disp adv e-mail ads@mainstreetnews.com; class adv e-mail ads@mainstreetnews.com; web site jacksonheraldtoday.com
Circulation: 9,500pd, 210fr; Sworn/Estimate/Non-Audited
Advertising rate: Open inch rate $7.50
Co-Pub.....Scott Buffington
Bus./Printing Mgr.....Thomas Toles
Circ. Mgr.....Debbie Castellaw
Co-Pub.....Mike Buffington
Prodn. Mgr.....Vickie Thomas
Mechanical Specifications: Type page 13 x 21 1/2; E - 6 cols, 2, 1/6 between; A - 6 cols, 2, 1/6 between; C - 6 cols, 2, 1/6 between. Equipment & Software: Hardware — APP/Macs, APP/Mac Laserprinters; Presses — 12-G/Community.
Areas Served: 30549

THE MADISON COUNTY JOURNAL (WED)
33 Lee St, Jefferson, GA, 30549-1345, Jackson, USA; gen tel (706) 367-5233; gen fax (706) 367-8056; disp adv e-mail ads@mainstreetnews.com; class adv e-mail ads@mainstreetnews.com; ed e-mail news@mainstreetnews.com; web site madisonjournaltoday.com
Circulation: 3,900pd, 210fr; Sworn/Estimate/Non-Audited
Advertising rate: Open inch rate $5.15
Established: 1997
Bus./Printing Mgr.....Thomas Toles
Co-Pub./Adv. Mgr.....Scott Buffington
Circ. Mgr.....Debbie Castellaw
Ed.....Zach Mitcham
Prodn. Mgr.....Ginger Chappell
Frank Gillispie
Co-Pub.....Mike Buffington
Mechanical Specifications: Type page 13 x 21 1/2; E - 6 cols, 2, 1/6 between; A - 6 cols, 2, 1/6 between; C - 6 cols, 2, 1/6 between. Equipment & Software: Hardware — APP/Mac; Presses — 12-G/Community.
Areas Served: 30549

JESUP

THE PRESS-SENTINEL (WED, SAT)
252 W Walnut St, Jesup, GA, 31545-1331, Wayne, USA; gen tel (912) 427-3757; gen fax (912) 427-4092; disp adv e-mail thepsadvertising@bellsouth.net; class adv e-mail thepresslegals@bellsouth.net; ed e-mail drewd01@bellsouth.net; web site www.thepress-sentinel.com
Circulation: 7,000pd,; Sworn/Estimate/Non-Audited
Advertising rate: Open inch rate $10.24
Established: 1865
Group: Press-Sentinel Newspapers Inc.
Pub.....Eric Denty
Circ. Mgr.....Bob Whitley
Ed.....Drew Davis
Prodn. Mgr.....Sheila Hires
Press Mgr.....Danny Strickland
Bus. Mgr.....Lynn Rice
Adv. Mgr.....Mallard MelisaEquipment & Software: Hardware — MacIntosh; Presses — Web offset; Software — Multiple
Delivery Method: Mail, Racks
Areas Served: Wayne County

LA FAYETTE

WALKER COUNTY MESSENGER (WED, FRI)
102 N Main St, La Fayette, GA, 30728-2418, Walker, USA; gen tel (706) 638-1859; gen fax (706) 638-7045; disp adv e-mail walkercountymessenger@walkermessenger.com; web site www.walkermessenger.com
Circulation: 4,700pd, 50fr; Sworn/Estimate/Non-Audited
Advertising rate: Open inch rate $12.17
Group: Rome News-Tribune
Pub.....Don Stilwell
Adv. Mgr.....Angie Clark
Ed.....Becky McDaniel
VP, Ops.....Brenda Burger
Rgl. Adv. Mgr.....William Steele
Adv. Mgr.....Donna Hixon
Mechanical Specifications: Type page 13 x 21 1/4; E - 6 cols, 2 1/16, 1/8 between; A - 6 cols, 2 1/16, 1/8 between; C - 9 cols, 1 3/8, 1/12 between.
Areas Served: 30728

LAGRANGE

THE THOMASTON TIMES (MON, WED, FRI)
PO Box 929, Lagrange, GA, 30241-0117, Troup, USA; gen tel (706) 647-5414; gen fax (706) 647-2833; disp adv e-mail tdean@heartlandpublications.com; class adv e-mail lknight@civitasmedia.com; web site www.thomastontimes.com
Circulation: 4,000pd,; Sworn/Estimate/Non-Audited
Advertising rate: Open inch rate $9.50
Established: 1869
Group: Civitas Media, LLC-OOB
Gen. Mgr.....Rolent Foiles
Adv. Sales Rep.....Tammy K. Dean
Classified Adv. Mgr.....Linda Knight
Mng. Ed.....Tammy Jarrett
Adv. Dir.....Lucy Chaney
Publisher.....Rick Thomason
Areas Served: 30286

LAKELAND

LANIER COUNTY NEWS (WED)
335 W Church St, Lakeland, GA, 31635-1115, Lanier, USA; gen tel (229) 896-2233; gen fax (229) 896-7237; web site http://www.laniercountynewsonline.com/
Circulation: 1,100pd,; Sworn/Estimate/Non-Audited
Advertising rate: Open inch rate $5.50
Circ. Mgr.....Diana Cooper
Ed.....Ann Knight
Areas Served: 31635

LAVONIA

FRANKLIN COUNTY CITIZEN LEADER (THUR)
12150 Augusta Rd, Lavonia, GA, 30553-1208, Franklin, USA; gen tel (706) 356-8557; adv tel (864) 457-3337; ed tel (864) 457-3337; gen fax (706) 356-2008; adv fax (864) 457-5231; ed fax (864) 457-5231; disp adv e-mail jdean@franklincountycitizen.com; class adv e-mail jphillips@franklincountycitizen.com; ed e-mail fcc@franklincountycitizen.com; web site www.franklincountycitizen.com
Circulation: 4,000pd, 150fr; Sworn/Estimate/Non-Audited
Advertising rate: Open inch rate $12.00
Established: 1955
Group: Community Newspapers Inc.
Pub.....Shane Scoggins
Office Mgr.....Jennifer Phillips
Adv. Rep.....Jan DeanEquipment & Software: Hardware — APP/Macs, PC
Delivery Method: Mail, Racks
Areas Served: 30553

THE NEWS LEADER (THUR)
12150 Augusta Rd, Lavonia, GA, 30553-1208, Franklin, USA; gen tel (706) 356-8557; gen fax (706) 356-2008; disp adv e-mail fccitizen@windstream.net; web site www.franklincountycitizen.com
Circulation: 1,950pd,; Sworn/Estimate/Non-Audited
Advertising rate: Open inch rate $11.35
Group: Community Newspapers, Inc.
Pub.....Shane Scoggins
Ed.....Denise Matthews
Areas Served: 30553

LAWRENCEVILLE

GWINNETT DAILY POST (WED, FRI, SUN)

725 Old Norcross Rd, Lawrenceville, GA, 30046-4317, Gwinnett, USA; gen tel (770) 963-9205; adv tel (770) 963-9205; ed tel (770) 339-5850; gen fax (770) 277-5271; adv fax (770) 338-7350; ed fax (770) 339-8081; disp adv e-mail news@gwinnettdailypost.com; class adv e-mail advertising@gwinnettdailypost.com; ed e-mail letters@gwinnettdailypost.com; web site www.gwinnettdailypost.com
Circulation: 335pd, 49fr; CVC
Advertising rate: $83.67
Established: 1970
Group: Southern Community Newspapers, Inc.
Digital Platform - Mobile: Apple, Android, Windows
Vice President/Content
SCNI newspapers.......................... J.K. Murphy
Adv. Mgr., Major Accts. .... Bob McCray
Vice President/Circulation
Southern Community Newspapers, Inc...Thom Bell
Ed. .... Todd Cline
Copy Desk Chief.................. Nate McCullough
Graphics Ed.............................. Nicole Puckett
Sports Ed.................................. Will Hammock
Production Director........................Lynn Ridder
General Sales Manger...................... Jo Pearse
Adv. Mgr., Legal Notices ....Cindy Carter
Controller.. Tina Pethel
Publisher..................................... Mike Gebhart
Mechanical Specifications: Type page 11.83 x 21.5 - 6 cols
Delivery Method: Mail, Carrier, Racks
Areas Served: 30024 30044 30045 30046 30096 30097 30011 30019 30517 30542 30548 30620 30656 30666 30680 30043 30518 30519 30017 30039 30047 30052 30071 30078 30087 30092

LINCOLNTON

THE LINCOLN JOURNAL (THUR)

157 N Peachtree St, Lincolnton, GA, 30817-5884, Lincoln, USA; gen tel (706) 359-3229; gen fax (706) 359-2884; disp adv e-mail journal@nu-z.net; web site www.lincolnjournalonline.com
Circulation: 2,850pd,; Sworn/Estimate/Non-Audited
Advertising rate: Open inch rate $4.00
Mng. Ed... Teri Eno
Office Mgr. .... Anne Price
Ed./Pub.................................. Sparky Newsome
News Ed. .... Jacquelyn Johnson
Areas Served: 30817

MADISON

MORGAN COUNTY CITIZEN (THUR)

259 N Second St, Madison, GA, 30650-1317, Morgan, USA; gen tel (706) 342-7440; gen fax (706) 342-2140; disp adv e-mail citizen@morgancountycitizen.com; web site www.morgancountycitizen.com
Circulation: 5,000pd,; Sworn/Estimate/Non-Audited
Advertising rate: Open inch rate $6.40
Bus. Mgr................................. Sherry Stevens
Adv./Circ. Mgr.......................... Artrose Cooper
Mng. Ed.................................. Kathryn Purcell
Sports Ed.......................................Chris Muthig Equipment & Software: Hardware — APP/Power Mac; Software — QPS/QuarkXPress, Adobe/Photoshop, Microsoft/Word.
Areas Served: 30650

MANCHESTER

HOGANSVILLE HOME NEWS (FRI)

PO Box 426, Manchester, GA, 31816-0426, Meriwether, USA; gen tel (706) 846-3188; gen fax (706) 846-2206; disp adv e-mail starmarcurynews@charterinternet.com; web site www.smalltownpapers.com/newspapers/newspaper.php?id=175
Circulation: 4,300pd,; Sworn/Estimate/Non-Audited
Advertising rate: Open inch rate $5.30
Group: Star-Mercury Publishing Co.
Ed. ....John Kuykendall
Areas Served: 30222, 30293

MERIWETHER VINDICATOR (FRI)

3051 Roosevelt Hwy, Manchester, GA, 31816-6406, Meriwether, USA; gen tel (706) 846-3188; gen fax (706) 846-2206; disp adv e-mail starmercurynews@charterinternet.com; web site No Website
Circulation: 2,700pd,; Sworn/Estimate/Non-Audited
Advertising rate: Open inch rate $5.20
Group: Star-Mercury Publishing Co.
Pub..John Kuykendall
Ed. .... Rob Richardson
Mechanical Specifications: Type page 11 3/8 x 21 1/2; E - 6 cols, 1 3/4, 1/8 between; A - 6 cols, 1 3/4, 1/8 between; C - 6 cols, 1 3/4, 1/8 between.Equipment & Software: Hardware — APP/Mac; Presses — 6-KP/News King.
Areas Served: 30222, 30293

TALBOTTON NEW ERA (FRI)

3051 Roosevelt Hwy, Manchester, GA, 31816-6406, Meriwether, USA; gen tel (706) 846-3188; gen fax (706) 846-2206; disp adv e-mail starmercurynews@charterinternet.com; web site No Website
Circulation: 1,000pd,; Sworn/Estimate/Non-Audited
Advertising rate: Open inch rate $4.80
Group: Trib Publications
Pub..John Kuykendall
Ed .... Vann Chapman
Mechanical Specifications: Type page 13 x 21 1/2; E - 6 cols, 2, 1/8 between; A - 6 cols, 2, 1/8 between; C - 6 cols, 2, 1/8 between. Equipment & Software: ; Presses — 6-KP/News King.
Areas Served: 30222, 30293

MARIETTA

EAST COBB NEIGHBOR (THUR)

580 S Fairground St SE, Marietta, GA, 30060-2751, Cobb, USA; gen tel (770) 428-9411; gen fax (770) 422-9533; disp adv e-mail mdjnews@mdjonline.com; ed e-mail jkirby@mdjonline.com; web site mdjonline.com/neighbor_newspapers
Circulation: 32,464fr; CAC
Advertising rate: Open inch rate $42.30
Group: Times-Journal, Inc.
Pub...Otis A. Brumby
Gen. Mgr..Lee Garrett
Mng. Ed.. Billy Mitchell
VP of Sales & Marketing............ Wade Stephens
Mechanical Specifications: Type page 13 x 21; E - 6 cols, 2 1/16, between; A - 6 cols, 2 1/16, between; C - 10 cols, 1 3/16, between.
Areas Served: 30060

NORTH COBB NEIGHBOR (THUR)

580 S Fairground St SE, Marietta, GA, 30060-2751, Cobb, USA; gen tel (770) 428-9411; disp adv e-mail bopitz@neighbornewspapers.com; class adv e-mail adavis@mdjonline.com; ed e-mail bclark@neighbornewspapers.com; web site www.neighbornewspapers.com
Circulation: 1pd, 23,201fr; CAC
Advertising rate: Open inch rate $30.60
Established: 1968
Group: Neighbor Newspapers, Inc.
Mng. Ed.. Brian Clark
VP, Sales/Mktg.......................... Wade Stephens
Gen. Mgr. .... Lee Brumby Garrett
Adv. Mgr..Becky Opitz
Pub./CEO.................................. Otis A. Brumby

PAULDING NEIGHBOR (THUR)

580 S Fairground St SE, Marietta, GA, 30060-2751, Cobb, USA; gen tel (678) 831-3566; adv tel (770) 428-9411; gen fax (770) 445-0565; disp adv e-mail Neighbors@mdjonline.com ; web site www.neighbornewspapers.com
Circulation: 2pd, 11,979fr; CAC
Group: Times-Journal, Inc.
Neighbor Newspapers
Pub.. Otis A. Brumby
Mktg. Dir............................... Furman Gardner
Circ. Mgr............................... Russell H. Powell
Prodn. Mgr. ....Jeff Buice
VP, Sales/Mktg....................... Wade Stephens
Gen. Mgr. .... Lee Brumby Garrett
Mechanical Specifications: Type page 11 1/16 x 21; E - 6 cols, 1 5/6, 1/16 between; A - 6 cols, 1 5/6, 1/16 between; C - 10 cols, 1/16, between.Equipment & Software: Hardware — 4-Compaq/5500R Server; Presses — MAN/4X2; Software — ACT/ADV.
Areas Served: 30132, 30157, 30141

SOUTH COBB NEIGHBOR (THUR)

580 S Fairground St SE, Marietta, GA, 30060-2751, Cobb, USA; gen tel (770) 428-9411; gen fax (770) 422-9533; disp adv e-mail lgarrett@mdjonline; class adv e-mail adavis@mdjonline.com; ed e-mail jkirby@mdjonline.com; web site www.mdjonline.com
Circulation: 18,737pd,; CAC
Advertising rate: Open inch rate $31.00
Group: Times-Journal, Inc.
Pub. .... Otis Brumby
Gen. Mgr...Lee Garrett
Mng. Ed.. Billy Mitchell
VP, Sales/Mktg....................... Wade Stephens
Mechanical Specifications: Type page 13 x 21; E - 6 cols, 2 1/16, between; A - 6 cols, 2 1/16, between; C - 10 cols, 1 3/16, between.
Areas Served: 30060

MC RAE

THE TELFAIR ENTERPRISE (WED)

31 W Oak St, Mc Rae, GA, 31055-4333, Telfair, USA; gen tel (229) 868-6015; gen fax (229) 868-5486; disp adv e-mail telfairenterprise@windstream.net; web site www.thetelfairenterprise.com
Circulation: 3,200pd, 55fr; Sworn/Estimate/Non-Audited
Advertising rate: Open inch rate $6.40
Group: Community Newspapers, Inc.
Pub.. Eric Denty
Pres. .... Robert M. Williams
Gen. Mgr. ....Donna J. Bell
Pub.. W.H. NeSmith
Ed. .... Don Richardson
Corp. Mktg. Dir. .... Joel Jenkins
Mechanical Specifications: Type page 13 x 21; E - 6 cols, 2, 1/6 between; A - 6 cols, 2, 1/6 between; C - 6 cols, 2, 1/6 between.
Areas Served: 31055

MCDONOUGH

HENRY DAILY HERALD (WED, FRI, SAT)

38 Sloan St, McDonough, GA, 30253-3102, Henry, USA; gen tel (770) 957-9161; adv tel (770) 478-5753 ext. 277; ed tel (770) 957-9161 ext. 228; gen fax (770) 954-0282; disp adv e-mail ladams@henryherald.com; class adv e-mail rshirey@news-daily.com; web site http://www.henryherald.com
Circulation: 2,493pd, 11fr; CAC
Advertising rate: Open inch rate $13.00
Group: Southern Community Newspapers, Inc.
Editor .... Kathy Jefcoats
Pub.. Bonnie Pratt
Classifieds Adv. Mgr......................... Rita Camp
Areas Served: 30253

METTER

THE METTER ADVERTISER (WED)

15 S Rountree St, Metter, GA, 30439-4416, Candler, USA; gen tel (912) 685-6566; gen fax (912) 685-4901; disp adv e-mail ads@metteradvertiser.com; class adv e-mail ads@metteradvertiser.com; web site www.metteradvertiser.com
Circulation: 3,200pd,; Sworn/Estimate/Non-Audited
Advertising rate: Open inch rate $6.25
Established: 1912
Jerri Goodman
Carvy SnellEd.s
Mechanical Specifications: Type page 13 x 21 1/2; E - 6 cols, 2, 1/8 between; A - 6 cols, 2, 1/8 between; C - 6 cols, 2, 1/8 between. Equipment & Software: Hardware — 6-APP/Mac G3, APP/Mac G4; Software — Adobe/PageMaker 6.5, Multi-Ad/Creator 4.0.
Areas Served: 30439

MILLEDGEVILLE

LAKE OCONEE BREEZE (THUR)

165 Garrett Way NW, Milledgeville, GA, 31061-2318, Baldwin, USA; gen tel (478) 453-1432; adv tel (478) 453-1436; disp adv e-mail kmertz@unionrecorder.com; class adv e-mail cgiles@unionrecorder.com; web site lakeoconeebreeze.net
Circulation: 6,200pd,; Sworn/Estimate/Non-Audited
Advertising rate: 1/4 P $122.70 1/2 P $225.40 Full $415.00
Pub..Keith Barlow
Ed. ....Natalie Davis
Adv. Director .... Erin Simmons
Areas Served: 31061

MONROE

THE WALTON TRIBUNE (WED, SUN)

121 S Broad St, Monroe, GA, 30655-2153, Walton, USA; gen tel (770) 267-8371; adv tel (770) 267-4428; ed tel (770) 267-2492; gen fax (770) 267-7780; adv fax (770) 267-7780; ed fax (770 267-7780; disp adv e-mail david.clemons@waltontribune.com; class adv e-mail classified@waltontribune.com; ed e-mail news@waltontribune.com; web site www.waltontribune.com
Circulation: 2,959pd, 396fr; CAC
Advertising rate: Open inch rate $10.00
Established: 1900
Composing Mgr............................. Sheila Tiller
Asst. Circ. Mgr.......................Cynethia Brown
Business Office Mgr......................Kim Powers
Pub./Ed.................................. Patrick Graham
Adv. Mgr. .... Peggy Wheldon
Classified Adv. Mgr.........................Deana Hale
Managing Ed...........................David Clemons
Mechanical Specifications: Type page 11 5/8 x 21; E - 6 cols, 1 13/16, between; A - 6 cols, 1 13/16, between; C - 8 cols, 1 5/16, between. Equipment & Software: Hardware — APP/Mac; Software — QPS/QuarkXPress, Multi-Ad.
Delivery Method: Mail, Newsstand, Carrier, Racks
Areas Served: 30655, 30656, 30052, 30025, 30641, 30018, 30054

MONTICELLO

THE MONTICELLO NEWS (THUR)

247 W Washington St, Monticello, GA, 31064-1241, Jasper, USA; gen tel (706) 468-6511; gen fax (706) 468-6576; disp adv e-mail advertising@themonticellonews.com; class adv e-mail info@themonticellonews.com; ed e-mail editor@themonticellonews.com; web site www.themonticellonews.com
Circulation: 2,600pd,; Sworn/Estimate/Non-Audited
Advertising rate: Open inch rate $5.60
Established: 1881
Adv. Mgr..................................... Jenny Murphy
Ed. ....Kathy Mudd
Legal, Class Mgr
Victoria Lawrence
Sports Ed
Susan Jacobs
Circu Mgr
Hannah Pope

Mechanical Specifications: Type page 13 x 21; E - 6 cols, 2 1/16, 1/8 between; A - 6 cols, 2 1/16, 1/8 between; C - 6 cols, 2 1/16, 1/8 between.Equipment & Software: Hardware — PC; Software — Adobe/PageMaker 5.0, Microsoft/Publisher.
Delivery Method: Mail, Newsstand, Racks
Areas Served: 31064, 31085, 31038, 30055, 30056

NAHUNTA

THE BRANTLEY ENTERPRISE (WED)

84 Satilla Ave, Nahunta, GA, 31553-5347, Brantley, USA; gen tel (912) 462-6776; gen fax (912) 342-4922; disp adv e-mail news@brantleyenterprise.com; class adv e-mail ads@brantleyenterprise.com; ed e-mail editor@brantleyenterprise.com; web site www.brantleyenterprise.com
Circulation: 2,000pd,; Sworn/Estimate/Non-Audited
Advertising rate: Open inch rate $4.00
Established: 1920
Digital Platform - Mobile: Apple, Android, Blackberry
Digital Platform - Tablet: Apple iOS, Android, Blackberry Tablet OS, Kindle Fire
Publisher....Ken Buchanan
Managing editor....Lori Buchanan
Editor....Chris Buchanan
Mechanical Specifications: 10.25 inches by 21.5 inchesEquipment & Software: Hardware — Apple; Software — Adobe
Delivery Method: Mail, Newsstand
Areas Served: 31553

NASHVILLE

THE BERRIEN PRESS (WED)

200 E McPherson Ave, Nashville, GA, 31639-2250, Berrien, USA; gen tel (229) 686-3523; gen fax (229) 686-7771; disp adv e-mail theberrienpress@windstream.net; ed e-mail localnews@windstream.net; web site www.theberrienpress.com
Circulation: 4,200pd, 50fr; Sworn/Estimate/Non-Audited
Advertising rate: Open inch rate $4.50
Gen. Mgr....Jonna Exum
Ed....Donald F. Boyd
Mechanical Specifications: Type page 13 x 21; E - 6 cols, 2 1/8, between; A - 6 cols, 2 1/8, between; C - 6 cols, 2 1/8, between.Equipment & Software: Hardware — PCs; Presses — G; Software — Microsoft/Word, Arts & Letters Editor.
Areas Served: 31639

OCILLA

THE OCILLA STAR (WED)

102 E 4th St, Ocilla, GA, 31774-1541, Irwin, USA; gen tel (229) 468-5433; gen fax (229) 468-5045; disp adv e-mail ocillastar@windstream.net; web site www.theocillastar.com
Circulation: 2,000pd,; Sworn/Estimate/Non-Audited
Advertising rate: Open inch rate $5.50
Pres....Bob Tribble
Pub....Ann Knight
Adv. Mgr....Beverly Bradford
Ed....Diane Pless
Areas Served: 31774

PERRY

THE HOUSTON HOME JOURNAL (WED, SAT)

1210 Washington St, Perry, GA, 31069-2556, Houston, USA; gen tel (478) 987-1823; adv tel (478) 987-1823; gen fax (478) 988-9193; adv fax (478) 988-9193; disp adv e-mail cadams@sunmulti.com; class adv e-mail diannee@sunmulti.com; ed e-mail kriner@sunmulti.com; web site hhjonline.com
Circulation: 13,000pd,; Sworn/Estimate/Non-Audited
Advertising rate: Open inch rate $13.50
Established: 1870
Group: Sun Multimedia Inc.
Pub....Daniel F. Evans
Prodn. Mgr., Mailroom....Jimmy Townsend
Prodn. Mgr., Opns....Billy Townsend
Managing Ed....Krystal Riner
VP, Major Accts. Rep....Cheri Adams
Classified Adv. Mgr....Betty Stubs
d.Don Moncrief
Mechanical Specifications: Type page 11 5/8 x 21; E - 6 cols, 5/6, between; A - 6 cols, 1 5/6, between; C - 8 cols, 1 5/16, between. Equipment & Software: ; Presses — 8-G/Community.
Delivery Method: Mail
Areas Served: 31069, 31047, 31088, 31093, 31005

QUITMAN

QUITMAN FREE PRESS (WED)

112 N Lee St, Quitman, GA, 31643-2124, Brooks, USA; gen tel (229) 263-4615; ed tel 263-4615; gen fax (229) 263-5282; disp adv e-mail quitmanpress@windstream.net; class adv e-mail adelnewstribune@windstream.com; web site thequitmanfreepress.com
Circulation: 3,400pd, 60fr; Sworn/Estimate/Non-Audited
Advertising rate: Open inch rate $6.60
Established: 1876
Group: Cook Publishing Co.
Editor....Bonnell Holmes
Delivery Method: Mail
Areas Served: 31643

REIDSVILLE

THE JOURNAL SENTINEL (THUR)

114B N Main St, Reidsville, GA, 30453-4800, Tattnall, USA; gen tel (912) 557-6761; gen fax (912) 557-4132; disp adv e-mail mail@tattnalljournal.com; web site www.tattnalljs.com
Circulation: 6,000pd,; Sworn/Estimate/Non-Audited
Advertising rate: Open inch rate $5.50
Established: 1879
Pub....Russell J. Rhoden
Circ. Mgr....Lillian Durrence
Ed....Allison CobbEquipment & Software: Hardware — APP/Mac 8500, APP/Mac 7600; Software — QPS/QuarkXPress 3.3, Adobe/Photoshop 3.0.
Areas Served: 30453
30427
30420
30421

RICHLAND

STEWART-WEBSTER JOURNAL (THUR)

106 Broad St, Richland, GA, 31825-6106, Stewart, USA; gen tel (229) 887-3674; gen fax (229) 887-2800; disp adv e-mail swjpc@bellsouth.net; web site www.swjpc.com
Circulation: 4,654pd, 20fr; Sworn/Estimate/Non-Audited
Advertising rate: Open inch rate $ 6.00
Adv. Mgr....Ron T. Provencher
Mng. Ed....Linda Provencher
Mng. Ed....Ron Provencher
Mechanical Specifications: Type page 13 x 21 1/2; E - 6 cols, 2 1/16, 1/6 between; A - 6 cols, 2 1/16, 1/6 between; C - 6 cols, 2 1/16, 1/6 between.Equipment & Software: Hardware — PC; Software — Adobe/PageMaker, QPS/QuarkXPress 4.0.
Delivery Method: Mail, Newsstand, Carrier, Racks
Areas Served: 31825

RICHMOND HILL

BRYAN COUNTY NEWS (WED, THUR, SAT)

10221 Ford Ave, Ste 3, Richmond Hill, GA, 31324-0259, Bryan, USA; gen tel (912) 756-2668; gen fax (912) 756-5907; disp adv e-mail sales@bryancountynews.com; ed e-mail hbarnidge@bryancountynews.net; web site www.bryancountynews.net
Circulation: 3,000pd, 1,000fr; Sworn/Estimate/Non-Audited
Advertising rate: Open inch rate $8.50
Group: Morris Multimedia, Inc.
Pub....Marshall Griffin
Ed....Hollie Barnidge
Delivery Method: Mail, Racks
Areas Served: 31324

RINCON

EFFINGHAM HERALD (WED)

586 S Columbia Ave, Ste 13, Rincon, GA, 31326-4174, Effingham, USA; gen tel (912) 826-5012; gen fax (912) 826-0381; disp adv e-mail dneidlinger@effinghamherald.net; class adv e-mail classifieds@effinghamherald.net; ed e-mail news@effinghamherald.net; web site www.effinghamherald.net
Circulation: 2,323pd, 76fr; AAM
Advertising rate: Open inch rate $7.10
Established: 1908
Pub....Karen Tanksley
Adv. Acct. Exec....Debbie Neidlinger
Mng. Ed....Patrick Donahue
Office Mgr....Karen Stephens
Mechanical Specifications: Type page 10.5 x 21; E - 6 cols, 1 13/16, 1/6 between; A & C- 6 cols, 1 13/16, 1/6 between.Equipment & Software: ; Software — QPS/QuarkXPress 4.0.
Delivery Method: Mail, Racks
Areas Served: 31312, 31326, 31329

RINGGOLD

CATOOSA COUNTY NEWS (WED)

7513 Nashville St, Ringgold, GA, 30736-2357, Catoosa, USA; gen tel (706) 935-2621; gen fax (706) 965-5934; disp adv e-mail catoosacountynews@catoosanews.com; web site catoosawalkernews.com
Circulation: 4,261pd,; Sworn/Estimate/Non-Audited
Advertising rate: Open inch rate $12.04
Group: Rome News-Tribune
Pub....Don Stillwell
Adv. Mgr....Karen Keys
Adv. Rep....Kathy Bruce
Sports Ed....Misty Martin
VP, Ops....Brenda Burger
Rgl. Adv. Mgr....William Steele
Mechanical Specifications: Type page 13 x 21 1/4; E - 6 cols, 2, 1/4 between; A - 6 cols, 2, 1/4 between; C - 9 cols, 1 3/8, 1/8 between.
Areas Served: 30736

ROBERTA

THE GEORGIA POST (THUR)

58 S Dugger Ave, Roberta, GA, 31078-4807, Crawford, USA; gen tel (478) 836-3195; gen fax (478) 836-9634; disp adv e-mail gapost@pstel.net; web site thegeorgiapost.com
Circulation: 3,000pd, 25fr; USPS
Advertising rate: Open inch rate $10.00
Established: 1921
Publisher....Victoria Simmons
Advertising/News reporter....Kristi Watkins
Assistant to the Publisher/Legals....Linda Reynolds
Mechanical Specifications: 6 cox. x 21.5"Equipment & Software: ; Software — CS 3
Delivery Method: Mail, Newsstand, Racks
Areas Served: 31078, 31052, 31008, 31030, 31050, 31016, 31066

ROSWELL

ALPHARETTA NEIGHBOR (WED)

10930 Crabapple Rd, Ste 9, Roswell, GA, 30075-5812, Cobb, USA; gen tel (770) 993-7400; adv tel 7704289411x 501; gen fax (770) 518-6062; class adv e-mail adavis@mdjonline.com; ed e-mail nfulton@neighbornewspapers.com; web site www.neighbornewspapers.com
Circulation: 3pd, 11,800fr; CAC
Advertising rate: Open inch rate $57.75
Established: 1968
Group: Neighbor Newspapers
Neighbor Newspapers, Inc.
Ed....Rachel Kellogg
Mng. Ed....Brian Clark
Gen. Mgr....Lee Brumby Garrett
VP, Sales/Mktg....Wade Stephens
Delivery Method: Mail

DEKALB NEIGHBOR (WED)

10930 Crabapple Rd, Ste 9, Roswell, GA, 30075-5812, Roswell, USA; gen tel (770) 454-9388; gen fax (770) 454-9131; disp adv e-mail dweaver@neighbornewspapers.com; class adv e-mail adavis@mdjonline.com; ed e-mail otis@mdjonline.com; web site mdjonline.com/neighbor_newspapers/dekalb/
Circulation: 7pd, 15,552fr; CAC
Advertising rate: Open inch rate $57.75
Group: Neighbor Newspapers
Times-Journal, Inc.
Pub....Otis A. Brumby
Mng. Ed....Mark Maguire
Gen. Mgr....Lee Brumby Garrett
VP, Sales/Mktg....Wade Stephens

MILTON NEIGHBOR (WED)

10930 Crabapple Rd, Ste 9, Roswell, GA, 30075-5812, Fulton, USA; gen tel (770) 993-7400; gen fax (770) 518-6062; disp adv e-mail lgarrett@mdjonline; class adv e-mail adavis@mdjonline.com; ed e-mail nfulton@neighbornewspapers.com; web site www.neighbornewspapers.com
Circulation: 44pd, 11,986fr; CAC
Advertising rate: Open inch rate $57.75
Established: 1968
Group: Neighbor Newspapers
Neighbor Newspapers, Inc.
Ed....Rachel Kellogg
Gen. Mgr....Lee Brumby Garrett
VP, Sales/Mktg....Wade Stephens
Delivery Method: Mail

ROSWELL NEIGHBOR (WED)

10930 Crabapple Rd, Ste 9, Roswell, GA, 30075-5812, Fulton, USA; gen tel (770) 993-7400; gen fax (770) 518-6062; disp adv e-mail lgarrett@mdjonline; class adv e-mail adavis@mdjonline.com; ed e-mail nfulton@neighbornewspapers.com; web site www.neighbornewspapers.com
Circulation: 19,553pd,; CAC
Advertising rate: Open inch rate $57.75
Established: 1968
Group: Neighbor Newspapers
Neighbor Newspapers, Inc.
Ed....Rachel Kellogg
VP, Sales/Mktg....Wade Stephens
Gen. Mgr....Lee Brumby Garrett

SAINT MARYS

TRIBUNE & GEORGIAN (THUR)

206 Osborne St, Saint Marys, GA, 31558-8400, Camden, USA; gen tel (912) 882-4927; gen fax (912) 882-6519; disp adv e-mail marketing@tribune-georgian.com; class adv e-mail classifieds@tribune-georgian.com; ed e-mail editor1@tds.net; web site www.tribune-georgian.com
Circulation: 6,437pd, 228fr; Sworn/Estimate/Non-Audited
Advertising rate: Open inch rate $12.77
Established: 1894
Group: Community Newspapers, Inc.
Pub....Jill Helton

Ed. ....Emily Heglund
Prodn. Mgr. ....Denese Proctor
Mrkt. Director ....Brad Spaulding
Circ. Director..............................Barbara Boyd
Corp. Mktg. Dir. ....Joel JenkinsEquipment & Software: Hardware — APP/Mac G3; Software — QPS/QuarkXPress 4.0.
Areas Served: 31558

SANDERSVILLE

THE SANDERSVILLE PROGRESS (WED)

118 E Haynes St, Sandersville, GA, 31082-2108, Washington, USA; gen tel (478) 552-3161; gen fax (478) 552-5177; disp adv e-mail sprogress@att.net; web site No Website
Circulation: 4,900pd, 6,700fr; Sworn/Estimate/Non-Audited
Advertising rate: Open inch rate $5.65
Group: Trib Publications
Pub...Robert E. Tribble
Circ. Mgr.......................................Teresa Hinds
Areas Served: 31082

SANDY SPRINGS

NORTHSIDE/SANDY SPRINGS/VININGS/ BROOKHAVEN NEIGHBOR (WED)

5290 Roswell Rd, Ste M, Sandy Springs, GA, 30342-1978, Fulton, USA; gen tel (404) 256-3100; gen fax (404) 256-3292; disp adv e-mail sdjarnette@neighbornewspapers.com; web site www.northside-neighbor.com
Circulation: 27pd, 27,440fr; CAC
Advertising rate: Open inch rate $50.35
Group: Times-Journal, Inc.
Digital Platform - Mobile: Apple, Android, Windows, Blackberry
Digital Platform - Tablet: Apple iOS, Android, Windows 7, Blackberry Tablet OS, Kindle, Kindle Fire
Pub...Otis A. Brumby III
Gen. Mgr...Lee Garrett
Mechanical Specifications: Type page 13 x 21; E - 6 cols, 1.5, between; A - 6 cols, 2 1/16, between; C - 10 cols, 1 3/16, between. Equipment & Software: Hardware — 4-Compaq/5500R Server; Presses — MAN/4x2; Software — ACT/ADV.
Areas Served: 30342

SOPERTON

SOPERTON NEWS (WED)

4075 W Main St, Soperton, GA, 30457-2325, Treutlen, USA; gen tel (912) 529-6624; gen fax (912) 529-5399; disp adv e-mail sopertonnews@nlamerica.com
Circulation: 2,050pd, 44fr; Sworn/Estimate/Non-Audited
Advertising rate: Open inch rate $7.00
Pub...Griffin Lodett
Adv. Mgr.....................................Marilyn Knapp
Circ. Mgr..............................Barney Willamson
Exec. Ed.......................................Dubose Porter
Mechanical Specifications: Type page 13 x 21; E - 6 cols, 2, 3/16 between; A - 6 cols, 2, 3/16 between; C - 6 cols, 2, 1/8 between.Equipment & Software: Hardware — APP/Mac; Software — QPS/QuarkXPress.
Areas Served: 30457

THE MONTGOMERY MONITOR (WED)

Second & Main Sts., Soperton, GA, 30457, Treutlen, USA; gen tel (912) 529-6624; gen fax (912) 529-5399; disp adv e-mail monitor@nlamerica.com
Circulation: 1,950pd,; Sworn/Estimate/Non-Audited
Advertising rate: Open inch rate $7.00
Pub...Griffin Lovett
Exec. Ed...................................DuBose Porter
Mng. Ed.................................Jason Halcombe
Mechanical Specifications: Type page 13 x 21 1/2; E - 6 cols, 2, 3/16 between; A - 6 cols, 2, 3/16 between; C - 6 cols, 2, 3/16 between. Equipment & Software: Hardware — APP/Mac; Software — QPS/QuarkXPress.
Areas Served: 30457

SPARTA

SPARTA ISHMAELITE (THUR)

12671 Broad St, Sparta, GA, 31087-1732, Hancock, USA; gen tel (706) 444-5330; gen fax (706) 444-9063; disp adv e-mail spartish@bellsouth.net; web site No Website
Circulation: 2,210pd, 80fr; Sworn/Estimate/Non-Audited
Advertising rate: Open inch rate $5.75
Established: 1878
Office Mgr. ....Lynda Reynolds
Ed. ....Chuck Reynolds
Mechanical Specifications: Type page 13 1/2 x 21; E - 8 cols, 1 1/2, between; A - 8 cols, 1 1/2, between; C - 8 cols, 1 1/2, between. Equipment & Software: Hardware — 3-PC; Software — WordPerfect, Express Publisher.
Areas Served: 31087

SUMMERVILLE

THE SUMMERVILLE NEWS (THUR)

20 Wildlife Lake Rd, Summerville, GA, 30747-5300, Chattooga, USA; gen tel (706) 857-2494; adv tel (706) 857-2494; ed tel (706) 857-2494; gen fax (706) 857-2393; adv fax (706) 857-2393; ed fax (706) 857-2393; disp adv e-mail thesummervillenews@gmail.com; class adv e-mail sumnews@aol.com; ed e-mail sumnews@aol.com; web site www.thesummervillenews.com/
Circulation: 7,000pd, 75fr; Sworn/Estimate/Non-Audited
Advertising rate: Open inch rate $3.25
Established: 1886
Ed. ....Winston Eugene Espy
Delivery Method: Mail, Newsstand, Racks
Areas Served: 30747 30728 30730 30731

SWAINSBORO

THE FOREST-BLADE (WED)

416 W Moring St, Swainsboro, GA, 30401-3177, Emanuel, USA; gen tel (478) 237-9971; gen fax (478) 237-9451; disp adv e-mail advertising@forest-blade.com; class adv e-mail classifieds@forest-blade.com; ed e-mail news@foreset-blade.com; web site emanuelcountylive.com
Circulation: 4,200pd,; Sworn/Estimate/Non-Audited
Advertising rate: Open inch rate $7.50
Established: 1861
Group: Smith Newspapers
Gen. Mgr. ....Madelyne Meeks
Mechanical Specifications: Type page 13 x 21; E - 6 cols, 2, between; A - 6 cols, 2, between; C - 6 cols, 2, between.Equipment & Software: Hardware — APP/Mac; Presses — G/Community; Software — Baseview.
Delivery Method: Mail, Newsstand, Racks
Areas Served: 30401
30471
30448
30464
30447

SYLVESTER

THE SYLVESTER LOCAL NEWS (WED)

103 E Kelly St, Sylvester, GA, 31791-2159, Worth, USA; gen tel (229) 776-3991; gen fax (229) 776-4607; disp adv e-mail info@thesylvesterlocal.com; web site www.thesylvesterlocal.com
Circulation: 3,800pd, 20fr; Sworn/Estimate/Non-Audited
Advertising rate: Open inch rate $5.00
Established: 1884
Ed. ....Leigh Ford
Areas Served: 31791

THOMSON

THE MCDUFFIE MIRROR (THUR)

108 Railroad St, Thomson, GA, 30824-2733, McDuffie, USA; gen tel (706) 597-0335; gen fax (706) 843-9295; disp adv e-mail news@mcduffiemirror.com; web site www.mcduffiemirror.com
Circulation: 3,700pd,; Sworn/Estimate/Non-Audited
Advertising rate: Open inch rate $7.50
Ed. ....Todd Rainwater
Areas Served: 30824

THE MCDUFFIE PROGRESS (WED, SUN)

101 Church St, Thomson, GA, 30824-2613, McDuffie, USA; gen tel (706) 595-1601; gen fax (706) 597-8974; disp adv e-mail art@mcduffieprogress.com; web site www.mcduffieprogress.com
Circulation: 5,600pd, 128fr; Sworn/Estimate/Non-Audited
Advertising rate: Open inch rate $6.75
Group: Lancaster Management, Inc.
Pub./Ed.....................................Wayne Parham
Office Mgr./Circ. Mgr. ....Dianne Bond
Mechanical Specifications: Type page 13 x 21 1/2; E - 6 cols, 2 1/16, between; A - 6 cols, 2 1/16, between; C - 9 cols, between.Equipment & Software: Hardware — APP/Mac; Presses — 10-KP/King News; Software — QPS/QuarkXPress.
Areas Served: 30824

TOCCOA

THE TOCCOA RECORD (THUR)

151 W Doyle St, Toccoa, GA, 30577-1788, Stephens, USA; gen tel (706) 886-9476; gen fax (706) 886-2161; adv fax (706) 886-1166; disp adv e-mail toccoarecord@windstream.net; web site www.thetoccoarecord.com
Circulation: 7,200pd,; Sworn/Estimate/Non-Audited
Advertising rate: Open inch rate $12.10
Group: Community Newspapers, Inc.
Pub...Tom Law
Adv. Rep...Ty Dooley
Adv. Rep.....................................Sue Fletcher
News Ed...................................Jessica Waters
Corp. Mktg. Dir. ....Joel Jenkins
Areas Served: 30577

VIDALIA

THE ADVANCE (WED)

205 E 1st St, Vidalia, GA, 30474-4717, Toombs, USA; gen tel (912) 537-3131; adv tel (912) 537-3131; gen fax (912) 537-4899; disp adv e-mail theadvance@bellsouth.net
Circulation: 7,000pd, 23,000fr; Sworn/Estimate/Non-Audited
Advertising rate: Open inch rate $6.25
Group: Advance Publications, Inc.
Gen. Mgr. ....William F. Ledford
Adv. Mgr...Daniel Ford
Circ. Mgr...Gail Cauley
Areas Served: 30474

WASHINGTON

THE NEWS-REPORTER (THUR)

116 W Robert Toombs Ave, Washington, GA, 30673-1664, Wilkes, USA; gen tel (706) 678-2636; gen fax (706) 678-3857; disp adv e-mail mary@wilkespublishing.com; class adv e-mail online@wilkespublishing.com; ed e-mail editor@news-reporter.com; web site www.news-reporter.com
Circulation: 3,200pd, 175fr; Sworn/Estimate/Non-Audited
Advertising rate: Open inch rate $6.00
Established: 1967
Circ. Mgr..Teri Eno
Ed./Pub. ....Sparky Newsome
Mng. Ed......................................Mary Newsome
Mechanical Specifications: Type page 13 x 21 1/2; E - 6 cols, 2, 1/8 between; A - 6 cols, 2, 1/8 between; C - 6 cols, 2, 1/8 between.
Delivery Method: Mail, Newsstand, Racks
Areas Served: 30673, 30668,30660,30817,30824,30636,etc

WATKINSVILLE

OCONEE ENTERPRISE (THUR)

26 S Barnett Shoals Rd, Watkinsville, GA, 30677-2500, Oconee, USA; gen tel (706) 769-5175; gen fax (706) 769-8532; disp adv e-mail oconeeenterprise@mindspring.com; web site www.oconeeenterprise.com
Circulation: 4,000pd,; Sworn/Estimate/Non-Audited
Advertising rate: Open inch rate $9.75
Pub...Vinnie Williams
Adv. Rep.....................................Tracy Harmon
Ed. ....Blake Giles
Sports Ed......................................Derek Wiley
Gen. Mgr./Adv. Director..........Maridee Williams
Mechanical Specifications: Type page 13 x 21; E - 6 cols, 2 1/16, 1/8 between; A - 6 cols, 2 1/16, 1/8 between; C - 6 cols, 2 1/16, 1/8 between.Equipment & Software: Hardware — APP/Mac; Software — Microsoft/Word, QPS/QuarkXPress, Adobe/PageMaker.
Areas Served: 30677

WAYNESBORO

THE TRUE CITIZEN (WED)

629 Shadrack St, Waynesboro, GA, 30830-1451, Burke, USA; gen tel (706) 554-2111; disp adv e-mail rchalker@bellsouth.net; class adv e-mail tclegals@gmail.com; ed e-mail rchalker@bellsouth.net; web site www.thetruecitizen.com
Circulation: 4,200pd,; Sworn/Estimate/Non-Audited
Advertising rate: Open inch rate $7.35
Established: 1882
Ed./Pub......................................Roy F. Chalker
Assoc. Ed.................................Elizabeth Billips
Class. & Legals........................Marianne Smith
Staff Reporter........................Ann Marie Kyzer
Jill Dumars
Martha Chalker
Gen. Mgr.......................................Lisa Chance
Mechanical Specifications: Type page 13 x 21 1/2; E - 6 cols, 2 1/12, 1/4 between; A - 6 cols, 2 1/12, 1/4 between; C - 7 cols, 1 1/12, 1/4 between.Equipment & Software: Hardware — PC; Presses — G/Community; Software — Adobe/PageMaker 6.0, WordPerfect 5.1.
Delivery Method: Mail, Racks
Areas Served: 30830. 30456. 30426, 30441

WRIGHTSVILLE

THE WRIGHTSVILLE HEADLIGHT (THUR)

2527 E Elm St, Wrightsville, GA, 31096-2003, Johnson, USA; gen tel (478) 864-3528; gen fax (478) 864-2166; disp adv e-mail wheadlight@bellsouth.net
Circulation: 1,000pd,; Sworn/Estimate/Non-Audited
Advertising rate: Open inch rate $5.50
Established: 1880
Group: Trib Publications
Pres. ....Robert E. Tribble
Pub...Theresa Hines
Ed. ....Sandra Saunders
Mechanical Specifications: Type page 13 x 21 1/2; E - 5 cols, 2 1/4, 1/4 between; A - 6 cols, 2, 1/4 between; C - 6 cols, 2, 1/4 between. Equipment & Software: ; Software — Page Maker.
Areas Served: 31096, 31049, 31002

ZEBULON

PIKE COUNTY JOURNAL AND REPORTER

(WED)
1 Courthouse Square, Zebulon, GA, 30295, Pike, USA; gen tel (770) 567-3446; gen fax (770) 567-8814; disp adv e-mail design-steam@barnesville.com; web site www.pikecountygeorgia.com
Circulation: 3,000pd,; Sworn/Estimate/Non-Audited
Advertising rate: Open inch rate $5.31
Pub....Walter Geiger
Ed./Rep....Rachel McDaniel
Office Mgr....Jennifer Taylor
Adv....Cathy Slegl
Areas Served: 30295

HAWAII

HONOLULU

KAUAI MIDWEEK (WED)
500 Ala Moana Blvd, Ste 7-500, Honolulu, HI, 96813-4930, Kauai, USA; gen tel (808) 529-4700; gen fax (808) 585-6324; adv fax (808) 529-4898; disp adv e-mail displayads@thegardenisland.com; class adv e-mail tgi-classifieds@thegardenisland.com; ed e-mail rnagasawa@midweek.com; web site www.midweekkauai.com
Circulation: 23,426fr; AAM
Advertising rate: $31 pci (rate does not include Hawaii General Excise tax)
Established: 2010
Group: Oahu Publications Inc.
Digital Platform - Mobile: Apple, Android, Windows
Digital Platform - Tablet: Apple iOS, Android, Windows 7, Blackberry Tablet OS
Pres....Dennis Francis
Chief Revenue Officer....Dave Kennedy
VP Regional Sales....Jay Higa
Executive Editor....Bill Mossman
Art Director....Gina Lambert
Mechanical Specifications: Type page 11 x 21; E - 6 cols, 1 - 1/2", 1/8 between; A - 6 cols, 1 - 1/2, 1/8 between; C - 10 cols, 7/8", 3/32"between; tab page size 9.7"w x 10" depth, DT is 20"w x 10"depth.Equipment & Software: Hardware — Offset Presses; Black + 3 ROP Colors; Inserts Accepted (min size 3x4", max 10.5x11") - Preprints, Post-it Notes; 70,000 CPM; Page Cutoff 21".; Presses — 6 Towers Man Roland Regioman 2004; Software — PECOM
Delivery Method: Carrier
Areas Served: Kauai County

MIDWEEK OAHU (WED)
500 Ala Moana Blvd, Ste 7-500, Honolulu, HI, 96813-4930, Honolulu, USA; gen tel (808) 529-4700; gen fax (808) 585-6324; adv fax (808) 529-4898; disp adv e-mail displayads@staradvertiser.com; class adv e-mail classifieds@staradvertiser.com; ed e-mail rnagasawa@midweek.com; web site www.midweek.com
Circulation: 267,859fr; AAM
Advertising rate: $275 pci (rate does not include Hawaii General Excise tax of 4.712%)
Established: 1984
Group: Oahu Publications Inc.
Digital Platform - Mobile: Apple, Android, Windows
Digital Platform - Tablet: Apple iOS, Android, Windows 7, Blackberry Tablet OS, Kindle
Pres....Dennis Francis
Pub....Ron Nagasawa
Chief Revenue Officer....Dave Kennedy
VP/Advertising....Patrick Klein
VP/Bus. Development & Regional Sales....Jay Higa
Executive Editor....Bill Mossman
Mechanical Specifications: Type page 11 x 21;
1/8 pg 4.787" x 2.5"
1/4 pg 4.787 x 5"
1/2 pg horizontal 9.7" x 5"
1/2 pg vertical 4.787" x 10"
full pg 9.7" x 10"
front pg banner 9.7" x 2"
double truck 20" x 10"Equipment & Software: Hardware — Offset Presses; Black + 3 ROP Colors; Inserts Accepted (min size 3x4", max 10.5x11") - Preprints, Post-it Notes; 70,000 CPM; Page Cutoff 21".; Presses — 6 Towers Man Roland Regioman 2004; Software — PECOM
Delivery Method: Mail
Areas Served: Honolulu County

PACIFIC BUSINESS NEWS (FRI)
737 Bishop St, Ste 1590, Honolulu, HI, 96813-3205, Honolulu, USA; gen tel (808) 955-8100; adv tel (808) 955-8053; ed tel (808) 955-8041; gen fax (808) 955-8078; adv fax (808) 955-8051; disp adv e-mail mstofle@bizjournals.com; ed e-mail pacific@bizjournals.com; web site www.bizjournals.com/pacific/ - 510,000(views) 185,000(visitors)
Circulation: 12,290fr; Sworn/Estimate/Non-Audited
Advertising rate: Modular Rate: 1/8 Page, Open $1,205
Established: 1963
Pub....Bob Charlet
Mgn. Ed....Janis Magin
Adv. Mgr....Michelle Stofle
Areas Served: Hawaii

STREET PULSE (FRI)
500 Ala Moana Blvd, Ste 7-500, Honolulu, HI, 96813-4930, Honolulu, USA; gen tel (808) 529-4700; gen fax (808) 585-4898; disp adv e-mail displayads@staradvertiser.com; class adv e-mail classifieds@staradvertiser.com; web site http://www.honolulustreetpulse.com/
Circulation: 47,068fr; AAM
Advertising rate: $25.50 pci
Established: 2012
Group: Oahu Publications Inc.
Pres....Dennis Francis
Pub....Ron Nagasawa
VP/Advertising....Patrick Klein
Dir. of Advertising....Darin Nakakura
VP/Digital Media....Troy Fujimoto
Chief Revenue Officer....Dave Kennedy
Delivery Method: Racks
Areas Served: Honolulu

KAMUELA

NORTH HAWAII NEWS (WED)
65-1279 Kawaihae Rd, Ste 216, Kamuela, HI, 96743-8444, Hawaii, USA; gen tel (808) 930-8675; adv tel (808) 329-9311; ed tel (808) 930-8675; gen fax (808) 885-0601; adv fax (808) 329-3659; ed fax (808) 885-0601; class adv e-mail johnson@northhawaiinews.net; ed e-mail editor@northhawaiinews.com; web site www.northhawaiinews.com 3,500(visitors)
Circulation: 1,798pd,; AAM
Advertising rate: Open inch rate $9.00
Established: 2000
Group: Oahu Publications Inc.
Adv. Mgr. / Pub....Tracey Fosso
Circ. Mgr....John Shackelford
Mgn. Ed....Lisa Dahm
Delivery Method: Mail
Areas Served: Hawaii County

KAUNAKAKAI

THE MOLOKAI DISPATCH (WED)
2 Kamoi St., Ste. 5, Kaunakakai, HI, 96748, Maui, USA; gen tel (808) 552-2781; adv tel (808) 552-2781; ed tel (808) 552-2781; gen fax (808) 552-2334; disp adv e-mail sales@themolokaidispatch.com; ed e-mail editor@themolokaidispatch.com; web site www.themolokaidispatch.com - 16,000(views)
Circulation: 300pd, 3,500fr; Sworn/Estimate/Non-Audited
Advertising rate: modular
Established: 1985
Ed. in Chief....Catherine Cluett Pactol
Mechanical Specifications: Type page 10 1/4 x 14 3/4; E - 4 cols, 2 3/8, 1/4 between; A - 4 cols, 2 3/8, 1/4 between; C - 4 cols, 2 3/8, 1/4 between.Equipment & Software: Hardware — APP/Mac; Software — QPS/QuarkXPress 3.3.
Delivery Method: Mail, Newsstand, Racks
Areas Served: Molokai

WAILUKU

THE MAUI BULLETIN (THUR)
100 Mahalani St, Wailuku, HI, 96793-2529, Maui, USA; gen tel (808) 249-6868; gen fax (808) 249-6870; web site http://www.mauibulletin.com/
Group: Ogden Newspapers Inc.

IDAHO

ABERDEEN

ABERDEEN TIMES (WED)
PO Box 856, 31 S. Main, Aberdeen, ID, 83210-0856, Bingham, USA; gen tel (208) 397-4440 ; gen fax (208) 397-4440 ; disp adv e-mail times1@dcdi.net ; class adv e-mail times1@dcdi.net; ed e-mail times1@dcdi.net; web site www.press-times.com
Circulation: 900pd, 30fr; Sworn/Estimate/Non-Audited
Advertising rate: $7.80
Established: 1912
Group: Crompton Publishing Inc.
Editor....Vicki Gamble
Mechanical Specifications: Seven columns: 11 picas wide (approximately 1 3/4 ")
Classidied: eight columns, 9 picas wide (1 1/2")
Page height: 21.5 inches
Delivery Method: Mail, Newsstand
Areas Served: City of Aberdeen

AMERICAN FALLS

POWER COUNTY PRESS (WED)
174 Idaho St, American Falls, ID, 83211-1234, Power, USA; gen tel (208) 226-5294; gen fax (208) 226-5295; disp adv e-mail press5@press-times.com; class adv e-mail press5@press-times.com; ed e-mail press1@press-times.com; web site www.press-times.com
Circulation: 1,600pd,; Sworn/Estimate/Non-Audited
Advertising rate: Open inch rate $7.20
Established: 1902
Group: Crompton Publishing Inc.
Adv. Mgr....Debbie Crompton
Pub....Brett Crompton
Staff Writer....Daniel Moore
Mechanical Specifications: Type page 13 1/2 x 21 1/2; E - 7 cols, 1 5/6, 1/6 between; A - 7 cols, 1 5/6, 1/6 between; C - 8 cols, 1 1/2, 1/6 between.
Delivery Method: Mail, Newsstand

ARCO

ARCO ADVERTISER (THUR)
146 S Front St, Arco, ID, 83213, Butte, USA; gen tel (208) 527-3038; gen fax (208) 527-8210; disp adv e-mail arcoadv@aol.com; class adv e-mail arcoadv@aol.com; ed e-mail arcoadv@aol.com
Circulation: 1,500pd, 55fr; Sworn/Estimate/Non-Audited
Advertising rate: Open inch rate $5.50
Established: 1909
Adv. Mgr....Thomas D. Cammack
Gen. Mgr....Charles L. Cammack
Office Mgr....Lani Brewer
Dartell Beard
Mechanical Specifications: Type page 13 x 21 1/2; E - 6 cols, 2, 1/6 between; A - 6 cols, 2, 1/6 between; C - 7 cols, 1 3/4, 1/6 between. Equipment & Software: Hardware — 5-PC; Presses — Gemco; Software — Adobe/PageMaker 6.5.
Delivery Method: Mail, Newsstand
Areas Served: 83213, 83251, 83255, 83244

BOISE

IDAHO BUSINESS REVIEW (MON)
855 W Broad St Ste 103, Suite 103, Boise, ID, 83702-7158, Ada, USA; gen tel (208) 336-3768; adv tel (208) 639-3512; gen fax (208) 336-5534; disp adv e-mail advertising@idahobusinessreview.com; ed e-mail news@idahobusinessreview.com; web site idahobusinessreview.com
Circulation: 2,600pd, 75fr; USPS
Advertising rate: (Modular Rates) Full Page: $19.99, Half Page $9.99, Quarter Page $4.79
Digital Platform - Mobile: Apple, Android, Windows, Other
Digital Platform - Tablet: Apple iOS
Assoc. Pub....Cindy Safa
Ed....Anne Allen
Admin Asst....Laura Butler
Acct. Exec....Corey Wong
Acct. Exec....Rocky Cook
Delivery Method: Mail

BONNERS FERRY

BONNERS FERRY HERALD (THUR)
7183 Main St, Bonners Ferry, ID, 83805-8729, Boundary, USA; gen tel (208) 267-5521; gen fax (208) 267-5523; disp adv e-mail jvanetten@bonnersferryherald.com; web site www.bonnersferryherald.com - 5,000(views)
Circulation: 3,200pd, 200fr; Sworn/Estimate/Non-Audited
Advertising rate: Open inch rate $10.73
Established: 1891
Group: Hagadone Corporation
Adv. Rep....Julie Richardson
Office Mgr....Linda Johnson
Ed....Star Silva
Delivery Method: Mail, Newsstand, Racks

BUHL

BUHL HERALD (WED)
PO Box 312, Buhl, ID, 83316-0312, Twin Falls, USA; gen tel (208) 543-4335; gen fax (208) 543-6834; disp adv e-mail buhlherald@cableone.net
Circulation: 2,200pd,; Sworn/Estimate/Non-Audited
Advertising rate: Open inch rate $5.00
Ed....Sandra Wisecaver
Mechanical Specifications: Type page 13 3/5 x 21 1/2; E - 6 cols, 2 1/6, 1/6 between; A - 6 cols, 2 1/6, 1/6 between; C - 7 cols, 2 1/6, 1/6 between.Equipment & Software: ; Software — Adobe/PageMaker 6.5.
Delivery Method: Mail, Newsstand, Racks

CAMBRIDGE

THE UPPER COUNTRY NEWS-REPORTER (THUR)
155 N Superior St, Cambridge, ID, 83610-2001, Washington, USA; gen tel (208) 257-3515; gen fax (208) 257-3540; disp adv e-mail buhlherald@cableone.net; web site facebook.com/theucnr
Circulation: 900pd,; Sworn/Estimate/Non-Audited
Advertising rate: Open inch rate $3.50
Established: 1889
Ed....Norman Dopf
Delivery Method: Mail, Newsstand, Racks

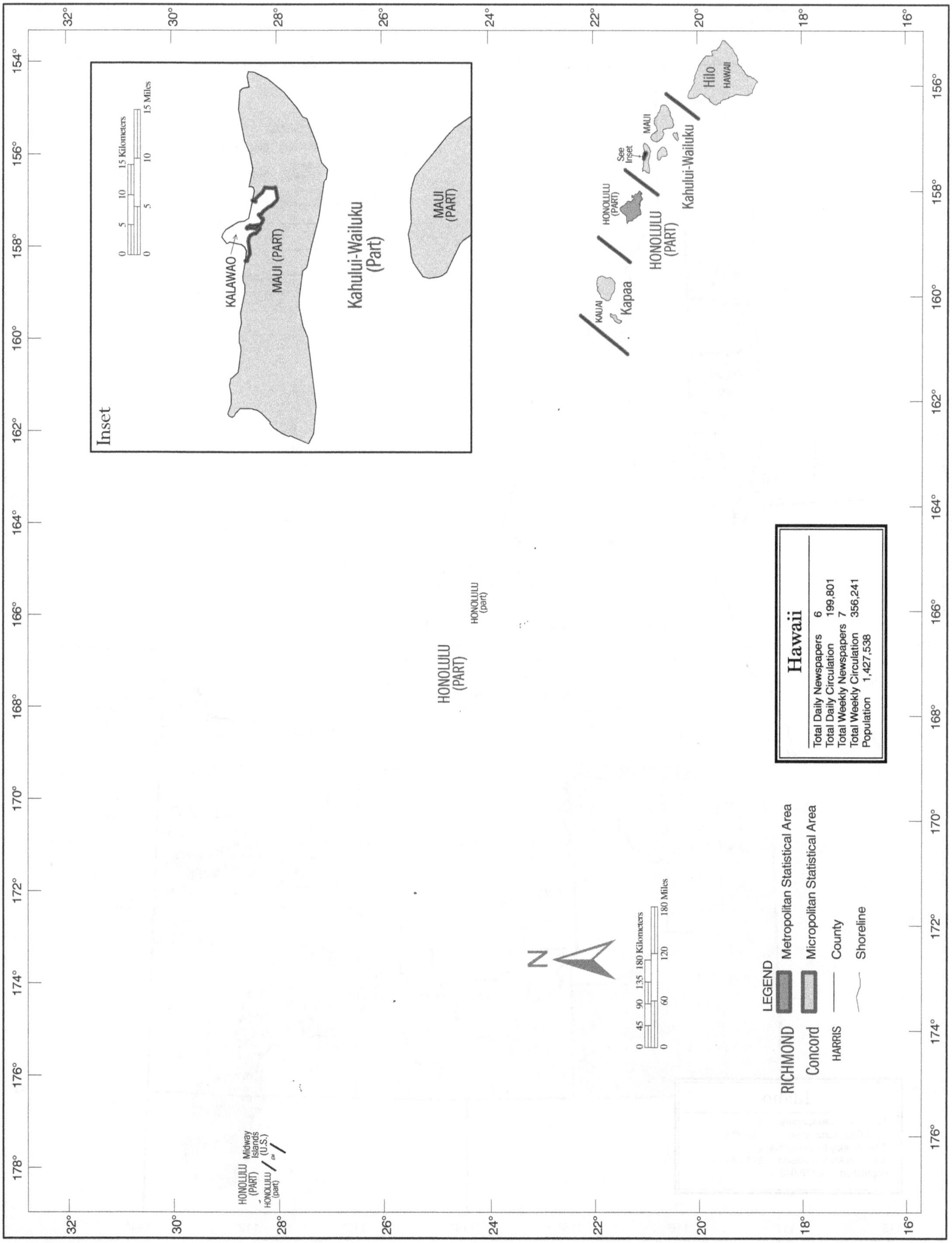
Inset
15 Kilometers
15 Miles
KALAWAO
MAUI (PART)
Kahului-Wailuku (Part)
MAUI (PART)
Hilo
HAWAII
MAUI
See Inset
Kahului-Wailuku
HONOLULU (PART)
HONOLULU (PART)
KAUAI
Kapaa
HONOLULU (part)
HONOLULU (PART)
Midway Islands (U.S.)
HONOLULU (PART)
HONOLULU (part)
Hawaii
Total Daily Newspapers 6
Total Daily Circulation 199,801
Total Weekly Newspapers 7
Total Weekly Circulation 356,241
Population 1,427,538
LEGEND
RICHMOND Metropolitan Statistical Area
Concord Micropolitan Statistical Area
HARRIS County
Shoreline
180 Kilometers
180 Miles
N

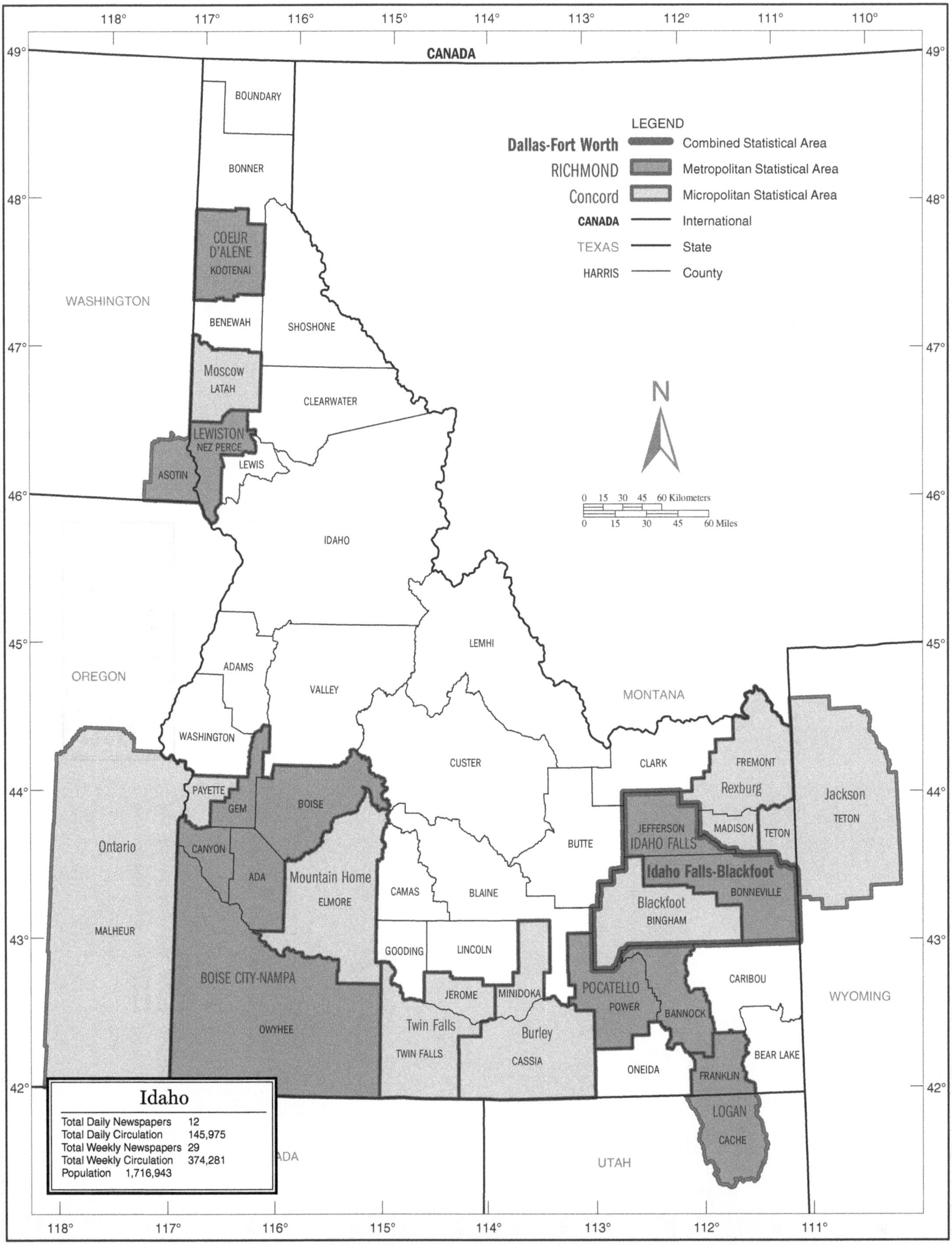
CANADA
WASHINGTON
OREGON
MONTANA
WYOMING
UTAH
LEGEND
Dallas-Fort Worth Combined Statistical Area
RICHMOND Metropolitan Statistical Area
Concord Micropolitan Statistical Area
CANADA International
TEXAS State
HARRIS County
N
0 15 30 45 60 Kilometers
0 15 30 45 60 Miles
BOUNDARY
BONNER
COEUR D'ALENE
KOOTENAI
BENEWAH
SHOSHONE
Moscow
LATAH
CLEARWATER
LEWISTON
NEZ PERCE
ASOTIN
LEWIS
IDAHO
LEMHI
ADAMS
VALLEY
WASHINGTON
CUSTER
CLARK
FREMONT
Rexburg
Jackson
TETON
PAYETTE
GEM
BOISE
JEFFERSON
IDAHO FALLS
MADISON
TETON
Ontario
CANYON
BUTTE
Idaho Falls-Blackfoot
ADA
Mountain Home
CAMAS
BLAINE
BONNEVILLE
ELMORE
Blackfoot
BINGHAM
MALHEUR
GOODING
LINCOLN
BOISE CITY-NAMPA
JEROME
MINIDOKA
POCATELLO
POWER
CARIBOU
BANNOCK
Twin Falls
Burley
OWYHEE
TWIN FALLS
CASSIA
BEAR LAKE
ONEIDA
FRANKLIN
LOGAN
CACHE
Idaho
Total Daily Newspapers 12
Total Daily Circulation 145,975
Total Weekly Newspapers 29
Total Weekly Circulation 374,281
Population 1,716,943

CHALLIS

THE CHALLIS MESSENGER (THUR)

310 E Main Ave, Challis, ID, 83226, Custer, USA; gen tel (208) 879-4445; gen fax (208) 879-5276; disp adv e-mail ameans@challismessenger.com; class adv e-mail ameans@challismessenger.com; ed e-mail ameans@challismessenger.com; web site www.challismessenger.com
Circulation: 1,600pd, 200fr
Advertising rate: $4.85
Established: 1881
Group: Adams Publishing Group, LLC
Office manager....................Veronica Weisbeck
Reporter/photographer.................Todd Adams
Delivery Method: Mail, Newsstand, Racks
Areas Served: 83226

COTTONWOOD

COTTONWOOD CHRONICLE (THUR)

503 King St, Cottonwood, ID, 83522-5263, Idaho, USA; gen tel (208) 962-3851; gen fax (208) 962-7131; ed e-mail editor@cottonwoodchronicle.com; web site www.cottonwoodchronicle.com
Circulation: 583pd, 10fr; Sworn/Estimate/Non-Audited
Advertising rate: Open inch rate $7.00
Established: 1893
Pub..Greg A. Wherry
Mechanical Specifications: 5 column page. Page size 10.25" wide by 13" tall.
Delivery Method: Mail
Areas Served: 83522, 83526, 83533

COUNCIL

THE ADAMS COUNTY RECORD (WED)

108 ILLINOIS AVE, , Council, ID, 83612, Adams, USA; gen tel (208) 253-6961; gen fax (208) 253-6801; disp adv e-mail record@ctcweb.net; class adv e-mail advertising@theadamscountyrecord.com; ed e-mail editor@theadamscountyrecord.com; web site www.theadamscountyrecord.com
Circulation: 1,500pd, 75fr; Sworn/Estimate/Non-Audited
Advertising rate: Open inch rate $5.48
Established: 1908
Pub.. Lyle Sall
Editor ....Dale Fisk
Advertising.............................Chelsea Coon
Layout and Production
Legal Advertising...................Jennifer Rininger
Mechanical Specifications: Type page 13 x 21; E - 6 cols, 2 1/6, 1/6 between; A - 7 cols, 1 5/6, 1/6 between; C - 8 cols, 1 7/12, 1/6 between. Equipment & Software: Hardware — APP/Macs, HP/LaserPrinter, HP/Scanner, Epson/Printer; Software — Adobe/Photoshop, Claris/Works, Quickbooks, QPS/QuarkXPress, Printshop/Deluxe, Global/Fax, Eudora.
Delivery Method: Mail, Newsstand, Carrier
Areas Served: 83612, 83654, 83638, 83610, 83632

DRIGGS

TETON VALLEY NEWS (THUR)

75 N Main St, Driggs, ID, 83422-5141, Teton, USA; gen tel (208) 354-8101; gen fax (208) 354-8621; disp adv e-mail publisher@tetonvalley.net; ed e-mail editor@tetonvalleynews.net; web site www.tetonvalleynews.net
Circulation: 2,300pd, 50fr; Sworn/Estimate/Non-Audited
Advertising rate: Open inch rate $11.00
Established: 1909
Group: Adams Publishing Group, LLC
Digital Platform - Mobile: Apple, Android, Windows, Blackberry
Digital Platform - Tablet: Apple iOS, Android, Windows 7, Blackberry Tablet OS, Kindle, Nook, Kindle Fire, Other
Adv. Mgr.......................................Meg Heinen
Pub..Andy Pennington
Mng. Ed..... Scott StuntzEquipment & Software: Hardware — 7-APP/Mac; Software — Adobe/PageMaker 5.02, QPS/QuarkXPress 4.1, Microsoft/Word, Fox Base, Claris/FileMaker Pro.
Delivery Method: Mail, Racks
Areas Served: 83422, 83455, 83452, 83013

EMMETT

MESSENGER-INDEX (WED, SUN)

120 N Washington Ave, Emmett, ID, 83617-2973, Gem, USA; gen tel (208) 365-6066; adv tel (208) 365-6066 ext. 11; ed tel (208) 365-6066 ext. 17; gen fax (208) 365-6068; disp adv e-mail thyder@messenger-index.com ; ed e-mail newsroom@messenger-index.com; web site messenger-index.com
Circulation: 1,660pd, 50fr; CAC
Advertising rate: Open inch rate $10.67
Established: 1893
Group: Pioneer Newspapers Inc
Digital Platform - Mobile: Apple, Android
Gen. Mgr. ....Diana Baird
Adv. Assoc............................Renee McMahon
Delivery Method: Mail, Newsstand, Carrier

GRANGEVILLE

IDAHO COUNTY FREE PRESS (WED)

900 W Main St, Grangeville, ID, 83530-5192, Idaho, USA; gen tel (208) 983-1200; adv tel (208) 983-1200; ed tel (208) 983-1200; gen fax (208) 983-1336; adv fax (208) 983-1336; ed fax (208) 983-1336; disp adv e-mail freepressads@idahocountyfreepress.com; class adv e-mail wkunkel@idahocountyfreepress.com; ed e-mail freepressnews@idahocountyfreepress.com; web site www.idahocountyfreepress.com
Circulation: 3,600pd, 68fr; Sworn/Estimate/Non-Audited
Advertising rate: Open inch rate $8.70
Established: 1886
Group: Eagle Newspapers, Inc.
Circ. Mgr..Linda Mort
Pub..Sarah Clement
Adv. Rep.......................................Lisa Adkison
Ed. .... David RauziEquipment & Software: ; Software — Microsoft/Windows, QPS/QuarkXPress.
Delivery Method: Mail, Newsstand, Racks
Areas Served: 83520

HOMEDALE

THE OWYHEE AVALANCHE (WED)

20 E IDAHO AVE, Homedale, ID, 83628, Owyhee, USA; gen tel (208) 337-4681; adv tel (208) 337-4866; ed tel (208) 337-4866; gen fax (208) 337-4867; adv fax (208) 337-4866; ed fax (208) 337-4866; disp adv e-mail rob@owyhee.com; class adv e-mail jennifer@owyheeavalanche.com; ed e-mail jon@owyheeavalanche.com; web site www.owyheepublishing.com
Circulation: 1,800pd, 34fr; Sworn/Estimate/Non-Audited
Advertising rate: Open inch rate $6.00
Established: 1865
Owner..Joe E. Aman
Mng. Ed.. Jon P. Brown
Composition................................Robert Aman
Delivery Method: Mail
Areas Served: 83628

IDAHO CITY

IDAHO WORLD (WED)

PO Box 220, Idaho City, ID, 83631-0220, Boise, USA; gen tel (208) 429-1606; gen fax (208) 445-2110; disp adv e-mail editor@idahoworld.com; web site www.idahoworld.com
Circulation: 1,300pd,; Sworn/Estimate/Non-Audited
Advertising rate: Open inch rate $5.00
Adv. Mgr.. Wayne Hart
Ed. .... Erin Sturbaum

KAMIAH

THE CLEARWATER PROGRESS (THUR)

417 Main St, Kamiah, ID, 83536-9700, Lewis, USA; gen tel (208) 935-0838; gen fax (208) 935-0973; disp adv e-mail progress@clearwaterprogress.com; class adv e-mail sales.theprogress@gmail.com; web site www.clearwaterprogress.com
Circulation: 400pd, 3,700fr; Sworn/Estimate/Non-Audited
Advertising rate: Open inch rate $7.95
Established: 1905
Pub./Owner..................................John Bennett
Pub./Owner............................... Susan Bennett
Ed. ....Ben Jorgensen
Adv. Mgr......................................Angela Berger
Mechanical Specifications: 9.5x17
Delivery Method: Mail, Newsstand

KETCHUM

IDAHO MOUNTAIN EXPRESS (WED, FRI)

591 N 1st Ave, Ketchum, ID, 83340, Blaine, USA; gen tel (208) 726-8060; gen fax (208) 726-2329 ; disp adv e-mail advertising@mtexpress.com; class adv e-mail classifieds@mtexpress.com; ed e-mail news@mtexpress.com; web site www.mtexpress.com
Circulation: 11pd, 28,394fr; CVC
Advertising rate: Open inch rate $18.60
Group: Express Publishing, Inc.
Pub...Pam Morris
Production Mgr..........................Tony Barriatua
Adv. Dir..John Ferry
Adv. Rep.................................... Sara Adamiec
Delivery Method: Mail, Newsstand, Racks

KUNA

KUNA MELBA NEWS (WED)

326 Avenue D, Kuna, ID, 83634, Ada, USA; gen tel (208) 922-3008; gen fax (208) 922-3009; disp adv e-mail kunamelbanews@aol.com; web site www.kunamelba.com - 4,000(views)
Circulation: 2,200pd,; Sworn/Estimate/Non-Audited
Advertising rate: Open inch rate $9.50
Established: 1983
Group: Adams Publishing Group, LLC
Pub... Cliff Wright
Ed. .... Mark Barnes
Gen Mgr.. Karri Keller
Delivery Method: Mail, Newsstand, Racks

MALAD CITY

IDAHO ENTERPRISE (THUR)

100 E 90 S, Malad City, ID, 83252-1314, Oneida, USA; gen tel (208) 766-4773; gen fax (208) 766-4774; disp adv e-mail newsdesk@atcnet.net; web site www.idahoenterprise.com
Circulation: 1,300pd,; Sworn/Estimate/Non-Audited
Advertising rate: Open inch rate $8.42
Established: 1879
Ed./Pub. ....Kristine Smith
Office Mgr. .... Helen Ravsten
Adv. Exec.................................... Sherrie Wise
Delivery Method: Mail, Newsstand, Racks

MCCALL

THE STAR-NEWS (THUR)

1000 N 1st St, McCall, ID, 83638-3848, Valley, USA; gen tel (208) 634-2123; adv tel (208) 634-2123; ed tel (208) 634-2123; disp adv e-mail tomigrote@gmail.com; class adv e-mail starclass@frontier.com; ed e-mail starnews@frontier.com; web site www.mccallstarnews.com
Circulation: 4,000pd, 20fr; Sworn/Estimate/Non-Audited
Advertising rate: Open inch rate $10.50
Established: 1915
Ed./Pub. .... Tom Grote
Mechanical Specifications: Image Area: 10.0 inches wide by 19.75 inches deep.Equipment & Software: Hardware — iMacs; Presses — Print Off-Site in Lewiston Idaho; Software — InDesign, PhotoShop, Acrobat, Firefox, Eudora, Excel.
Delivery Method: Mail, Newsstand, Racks
Areas Served: 83638, 83654, 83615, 83611

MONTPELIER

THE NEWS-EXAMINER (WED)

847 Washington St, Montpelier, ID, 83254-1455, Bear Lake, USA; gen tel (208) 847-0552; gen fax (208) 847-0553; disp adv e-mail newseditor@news-examiner.net; class adv e-mail adsales@news-examiner.net; ed e-mail newseditor@news-examiner.net; web site www.news-examiner.net
Circulation: 1,400pd, 30fr; Sworn/Estimate/Non-Audited
Advertising rate: Open inch rate $8.55
Established: 1895
Group: Pioneer Newspapers Inc
Ed./ Gen. Mgr..........................Michelle Higley
Mechanical Specifications: Type page 9.88 x 20.5; 6 cols, 1.55, .111 gutter; Equipment & Software: Hardware — APP/Mac; Software — InDesign CS2 to CS4
Delivery Method: Mail, Racks

MOSCOW

NORTHWEST MARKET (TUES)

220 E 5th St, Rm 205, Moscow, ID, 83843-2981, Latah, USA; gen tel (208) 882-5561; gen fax (208) 883-8205; ed e-mail editor@dnews.com; web site www.dnews.com
Circulation: 10,500fr; Sworn/Estimate/Non-Audited
Advertising rate: Open inch rate $12.00
Established: 1911
Group: TPC Holdings Inc.
Pub.. Nathan Alford
Gen. Mgr. .... Fred Board
Adv. Dir..Angela Kay
Circ. Dir. .... Mark Bryan
Mechanical Specifications: Type page 13 x 21 1/2; E - 6 cols, 2 1/6, between; A - 6 cols, 2 1/6, between; C - 9 cols, 1 5/16, between. Equipment & Software: Hardware — APP/Mac; Presses — HI/V-25; Software — QPS/QuarkXPress.
Delivery Method: Mail
Areas Served: 99263, 83843

MOUNTAIN HOME

MOUNTAIN HOME NEWS (WED)

195 S 3rd E, Mountain Home, ID, 83647-3020, Elmore, USA; gen tel (208) 587-3331; gen fax (208) 587-9205; disp adv e-mail bfincher@mountaintainhomenews.com; class adv e-mail advertising@mountainhomenews.com; ed e-mail borban@mountainhomenews.com; web site www.mountainhomenews.com
Circulation: 2,800pd,; Sworn/Estimate/Non-Audited
Advertising rate: Open inch rate $10.55
Established: 1888
Ed .... Brian Orban
Bus Mgr ....Cristena Ford
Mechanical Specifications: Type page 13 1/4 x 21 1/2; E - 6 cols, 2 1/16, 1/6 between; A - 6 cols, 2 1/16, 1/6 between; C - 6 cols, 2 1/16, 1/6 between.Equipment & Software: Hardware — APP/Mac, PC; Presses — 5-G; Software — Indesign CS3Or

Delivery Method: Mail, Newsstand, Racks
Areas Served: 83647

OROFINO

CLEARWATER TRIBUNE (THUR)

161 Main St, Orofino, ID, 83544, Clearwater, USA; gen tel (208) 476-4571; gen fax (208) 476-0765; disp adv e-mail cleartrib@cbridge.net; web site www.clearwatertribune.com
Circulation: 14pd, 5,061fr; CVC
Advertising rate: Open inch rate $5.55
Established: 1912
Pub..... Marcie StantonEquipment & Software: ; Software — Adobe/PageMaker 6.5.
Delivery Method: Mail, Newsstand, Racks

PAYETTE

INDEPENDENT-ENTERPRISE (WED)

124 S Main St, Payette, ID, 83661-2851, Payette, USA; gen tel (208) 642-3357; gen fax (208) 642-3560; disp adv e-mail andys@argusobserver.com; class adv e-mail lisap@argusobserver.com; ed e-mail editor@argusobserver.com; web site www.argusobserver.com/independent - 260,000(views) 75,000(visitors)
Circulation: 1,245pd, 16fr; VAC
Advertising rate: Open inch rate $5.20
Established: 1891
Group: Wick Communications
Digital Platform - Mobile: Apple, Android, Windows, Blackberry
Digital Platform - Tablet: Apple iOS, Android, Windows 7, Blackberry Tablet OS, Kindle, Kindle Fire
Pub...John Dillon
Ed. .... Scott McIntosh
Adv. Mgr., Retail......................Andy Shimojima
Prodn. Mgr. .... Wade Cordes
Bus Mgr... Dee Lee
Mechanical Specifications: Type page 13 x 21 1/2; E - 6 cols, 2 1/16, 1/8 between; A - 6 cols, 2 1/16, 1/8 between; C - 9 cols, 1 1/4, 1/8 between.
Delivery Method: Mail, Newsstand, Carrier, Racks
Areas Served: Payette County

PRESTON

PRESTON CITIZEN (WED)

1250 Industrial Park Rd, Preston, ID, 83263-5686, Franklin, USA; gen tel (208) 852-0155; gen fax (208) 852-0158; disp adv e-mail addesign@prestoncitizen.com; class adv e-mail jjanke@prestoncitizen.com; ed e-mail editor@prestoncitizen.com; web site www.prestoncitizen.com
Circulation: 3,000pd, 130fr; USPS
Advertising rate: Open inch rate $9.50
Established: 1890
Group: Adams Publishing Group, LLC
Digital Platform - Mobile: Apple, Android
Digital Platform - Tablet: Apple iOS, Android, Blackberry Tablet OS
Adv. Mgr. .... Stacey Comeau
Circ. Mgr............................. Rhonda Gregorson
Gen. Mgr. .... Travis Hansen
Ed. ....Necia Seamons
Mechanical Specifications: Type page 9.88 x 20 1/2; E - 6 cols.Equipment & Software: Hardware — APP/Macs; Presses — 5-WPC/Web Leader; Software — Adobe/Photoshop, Word Perfect, Scroll, QPS/QuarkXPress. Indesign, Word
Delivery Method: Mail, Newsstand
Areas Served: 83263, 83237, 83228, 83232, 83286

SAINT MARIES

SAINT MARIES GAZETTE-RECORD (WED)

610 Main Ave, Saint Maries, ID, 83861-1838, Benewah, USA; gen tel (208) 245-4538; gen fax (208) 245-4011; disp adv e-mail dan@smgazette.com; web site www.gazetterecord.com
Circulation: 3,500pd,; Sworn/Estimate/Non-Audited
Advertising rate: Open inch rate $7.45
Established: 1906
Digital Platform - Mobile: Apple, Android, Windows, Blackberry
Digital Platform - Tablet: Apple iOS, Android, Windows 7, Blackberry Tablet OS, Kindle Fire
Pub....................................Daniel H. Hammes
Delivery Method: Mail, Racks

SANDPOINT

PRIEST RIVER TIMES (WED)

310 Church St, Sandpoint, ID, 83864-1345, Bonner, USA; gen tel (208) 448-2431; gen fax (208) 448-2938; disp adv e-mail prtimesadvertising@priestrivertimes.com; ed e-mail tivie@priestrivertimes.com; web site www.priestrivertimes.com - 4,000(views) 20,000(visitors)
Circulation: 1,427pd, 9,000fr; Sworn/Estimate/Non-Audited
Advertising rate: Open inch rate $9.60
Established: 1914
Group: Hagadone Corporation
Digital Platform - Mobile: Apple
Digital Platform - Tablet: Apple iOS
Adv. Specialist ....Robin Herrin
Ed. ....Kieth Kinnaird
Pub...Jim McKiernan
Mechanical Specifications: Type page 12 1/2 x 21 1/2; E - 6 cols, 1 7/8, between; A - 6 cols, 1 7/8, between; C - 9 cols, between.
Delivery Method: Mail, Newsstand, Racks
Areas Served: 83856, 83822, 83848, 83821, 83841, 83804, 99156

WEISER

WEISER SIGNAL AMERICAN (WED)

18 E Idaho St, Weiser, ID, 83672-2530, Washington, USA; gen tel (208) 549-1717; gen fax (208) 549-1718; disp adv e-mail ads@signalamerican.org; class adv e-mail ads@signalamerican.org; ed e-mail news@signalamerican.org; web site www.signalamerican.org
Circulation: 2,200pd,; Sworn/Estimate/Non-Audited
Advertising rate: 1/16 Pg $90.00; 1/8 Pg $187.00; 1/4 Pg $375.00
Established: 1882
Gen. Mgr. .... Sarah Imada
Adv. Dir............................Stephanie McDaniel
Ed. .... Steve Lyon
Mechanical Specifications: Type page 10 x 21; E - 6 cols, 2 1/16, 1/3 between; A - 6 cols, 2 1/16, 1/3 between; C - 9 cols, 1 1/2, 1/6 between.
Delivery Method: Mail, Newsstand, Carrier, Racks
Areas Served: 83672, 83645, 83610

ILLINOIS

ALBION

THE NAVIGATOR (WED, FRI)

19 W Main St, Albion, IL, 62806-1006, Edwards, USA; gen tel (618) 445-2355; gen fax (618) 445-3459; disp adv e-mail stevesads@nwcable.net; class adv e-mail gatorbills@nwcable.net; ed e-mail gatoreditor@nwcable.net; web site http://www.navigatorjournal.com/
Circulation: 3,400pd, 12,500fr; Sworn/Estimate/Non-Audited
Advertising rate: Open inch rate $6.75
Established: 1995
Group: S&R Media, LLC
Pub.. Patrick Seil
Adv. Mgr. ....Steve Hartsock
Editor .... T.J. Hug
Delivery Method: Mail, Newsstand, Racks
Areas Served: 62806, 62844, 62821, 62863, 62821, 62476

THE PRAIRIE POST (FRI)

19 W Main St, Albion, IL, 62806-1006, Edwards, USA; gen tel (618) 445-2355; gen fax (618) 445-3459; disp adv e-mail gatoreditor@nwcable.net; web site navigatorjournal.com/prairie_post
Circulation: 13,100fr; Sworn/Estimate/Non-Audited
Advertising rate: Open inch rate $8.85
Group: S & R Media
Pub.. Patrick Seil
Adv. Mgr. ....Steve Hartsock
Ed. .... Tj Hug
Delivery Method: Mail

ALEDO

THE TIMES RECORD (WED)

219 S College Ave, Aledo, IL, 61231-1734, Mercer, USA; gen tel (309) 582-5112; gen fax (309) 582-5319; disp adv e-mail rblackford@aledotimesrecord.com; ed e-mail editorial@mchsi.com; web site www.aledotimesrecord.com
Circulation: 3,300pd, 7,387fr; Sworn/Estimate/Non-Audited
Advertising rate: Open inch rate $9.70
Group: GateHouse Media, Inc.
Pub.. Dee Evans
Adv. Dir....................................... Teresa Welch
Mechanical Specifications: Type page 11 1/2 x 21 1/2; E - 6 cols, 1/6 between; A - 6 cols, 1/6 between; C - 8 cols, between.Equipment & Software: Hardware — APP/Macs; Software — QPS/QuarkXPress 3.32, Adobe/Photoshop.
Delivery Method: Mail, Newsstand, Carrier

ALTAMONT

ST. ELMO BANNER (TUES)

7 Do It Dr, Altamont, IL, 62411-1135, Fayette, USA; gen tel (618) 829-3246; gen fax (618) 483-5177; disp adv e-mail altnewsban@frontiernet.net; web site www.altnewsban.com
Circulation: 1,000pd, 1,000fr; Sworn/Estimate/Non-Audited
Advertising rate: Open inch rate $7.95
Established: 1880
Ed. ....Clyde Barr
Delivery Method: Mail, Newsstand, Racks
Areas Served: 62458

THE ALTAMONT NEWS (TUES)

7 Do It Dr, Altamont, IL, 62411-1135, Effingham, USA; gen tel (618) 483-6176; gen fax (618) 483-5177; disp adv e-mail altnewsban@frontiernet.net; web site www.altnewsban.com
Circulation: 900pd,; Sworn/Estimate/Non-Audited
Advertising rate: Open inch rate $7.95
Established: 1881
Group: The Miami Herald Publishing Co.
Owner..Greg Hoskins
Pub................................. Barbara Gathe-Barr
Ed. ....Clyde Barr
Delivery Method: Mail, Newsstand, Racks

ALTON

ADVANTAGE NEWS - EDWARDSVILLE (THUR)

235 - A E Alton Square Mall Dr, Alton, IL, 62002, Madison, USA; gen tel (618) 463-0612 ; gen fax (618) 463-0733; ed fax (1888) 532-4111; disp adv e-mail contactus@todaysadvantage.com; class adv e-mail contactus@todaysadvantage.com; ed e-mail news@todaysadvantage.com; web site advantagenews.com
Circulation: 38,098fr; VAC
Advertising rate: $18.25
Established: 1986
Digital Platform - Mobile: Apple, Android, Windows
Digital Platform - Tablet: Apple iOS, Android, Windows 7, Blackberry Tablet OS, Kindle, Nook, Kindle Fire
President .... Sharon McRoy
Mechanical Specifications: 5 col. x 15 inchesEquipment & Software: Hardware — Macintosh; Software — Adobe Creatiave Suite
Delivery Method: Mail
Areas Served: 62025, 62034, 62062, 62294

AMBOY

THE AMBOY NEWS (WED)

PO Box 162, Amboy, IL, 61310-0162, Lee, USA; gen tel (815) 857-2311; gen fax (815) 857-2517; disp adv e-mail amboyedit@amboynews.com; web site www.amboynews.com
Circulation: 1,600pd, 30fr; Sworn/Estimate/Non-Audited
Advertising rate: Open inch rate $12.20
Group: News Media Corp.
Gen. Mgr./ Adv. Dir. ....Tonja Greenfield
Ed. ....Bonnie Morris
Circ. Mgr...Mary Mays
Mechanical Specifications: Type page 10 inches x 21 inches broadsheetEquipment & Software: Hardware — iMac; Software — Adobe/PageMaker 6.5, Quickbooks 4.0.
Delivery Method: Mail, Newsstand
Areas Served: 61310, 61367

ANNA

MONDAY'S PUB (MON)

112 Lafayette St, Anna, IL, 62906-1544, Union, USA; gen tel (618) 833-2158; gen fax (618) 833-5813; disp adv e-mail news@annanews.com; class adv e-mail news@annanews.com; ed e-mail news@annanews.com; web site www.annanews.com
Circulation: 13,000fr; Sworn/Estimate/Non-Audited
Advertising rate: Open inch rate $14.00
Established: 1979
Pub...Jerry L. Reppert
Gen. Mgr. .... James West
Circ. Mgr.................................Dianne Reppert
Ed. ....Geoffrey Skinner
Ed. .... Barbara Wilson
Mechanical Specifications: Type page 13 1/4 x 22 1/2; E - 6 cols, 2 1/16, between; A - 6 cols, 2 1/16, between; C - 9 cols, 1 1/2, between. Equipment & Software: Hardware — APP/Mac; Presses — G/Community.
Delivery Method: Mail
Areas Served: 62906

THE GAZETTE-DEMOCRAT (THUR)

112 Lafayette St, Anna, IL, 62906-1544, Union, USA; gen tel (618) 833-2158; gen fax (618) 833-5813; disp adv e-mail news@annanews.com; web site www.annanews.com
Circulation: 2,696pd,; Sworn/Estimate/Non-Audited
Advertising rate: Open inch rate $17.64
Established: 1849
Pub...Jerry L. Reppert
Adv. Mgr. .... James West
Circ. Mgr.................................Dianne Reppert
Ed. ....Geoffrey Skinner
Mechanical Specifications: Type page 13 1/4 x 21 1/2; E - 6 cols, 2 1/16, between; A - 6 cols, 2 1/16, between; C - 9 cols, 1 1/2, between. Equipment & Software: Hardware — APP/Mac; Presses — G/Community.
Delivery Method: Mail, Newsstand

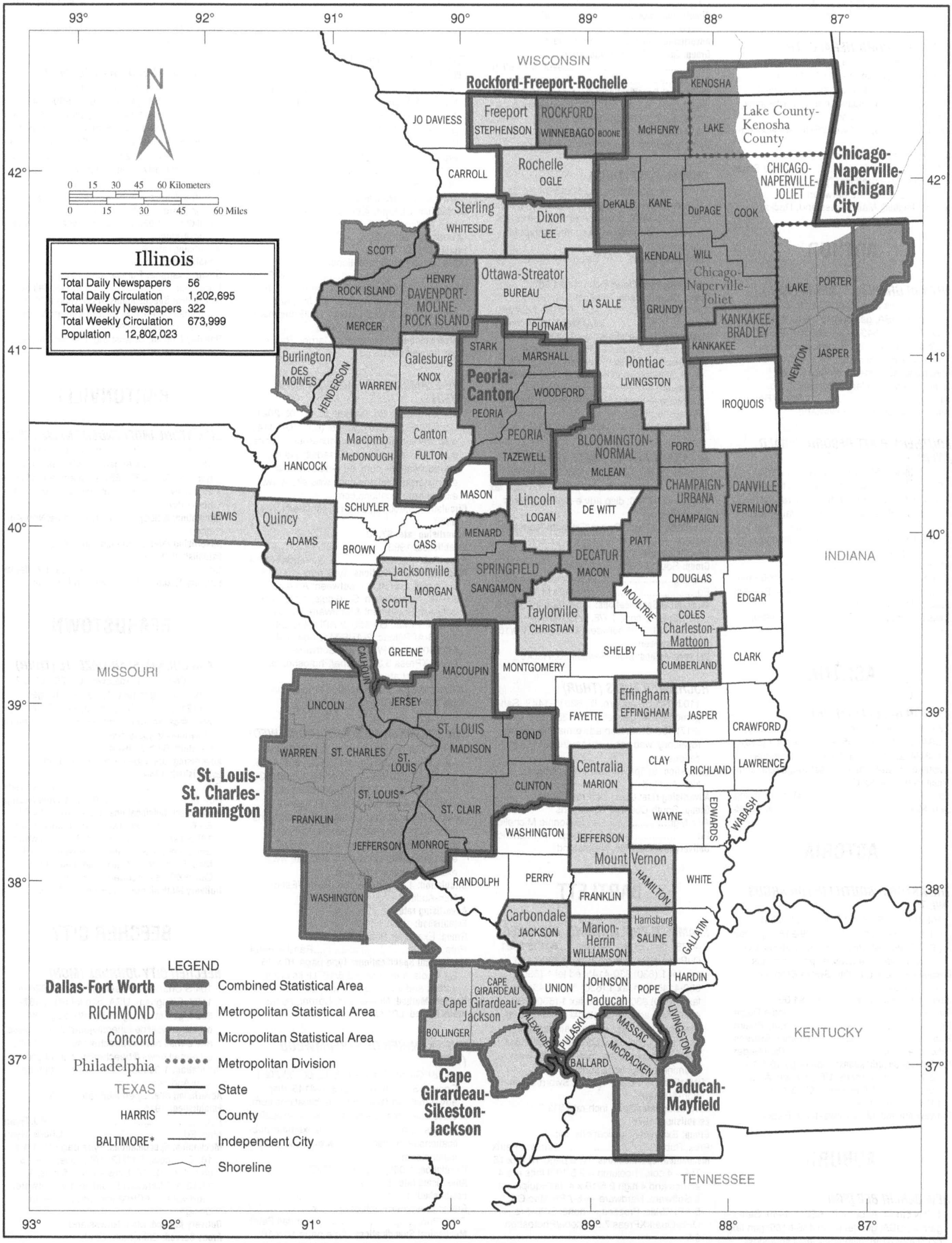
Illinois
Total Daily Newspapers 56
Total Daily Circulation 1,202,695
Total Weekly Newspapers 322
Total Weekly Circulation 673,999
Population 12,802,023
LEGEND
Dallas-Fort Worth Combined Statistical Area
RICHMOND Metropolitan Statistical Area
Concord Micropolitan Statistical Area
Philadelphia Metropolitan Division
TEXAS State
HARRIS County
BALTIMORE* Independent City
Shoreline
0 15 30 45 60 Kilometers
0 15 30 45 60 Miles
WISCONSIN
MISSOURI
INDIANA
KENTUCKY
TENNESSEE
Rockford-Freeport-Rochelle
Chicago-Naperville-Michigan City
Lake County-Kenosha County
CHICAGO-NAPERVILLE-JOLIET
Chicago-Naperville-Joliet
Peoria-Canton
Bloomington-Normal
Champaign-Urbana
Danville
Springfield
Decatur
St. Louis-St. Charles-Farmington
Cape Girardeau-Sikeston-Jackson
Paducah-Mayfield
Freeport
Rockford
Rochelle
Sterling
Dixon
Ottawa-Streator
Davenport-Moline-Rock Island
Burlington
Galesburg
Pontiac
Kankakee-Bradley
Macomb
Canton
Lincoln
Quincy
Jacksonville
Taylorville
Charleston-Mattoon
Effingham
St. Louis
Centralia
Mount Vernon
Carbondale
Marion-Herrin
Harrisburg
Cape Girardeau-Jackson
Paducah
JO DAVIESS
STEPHENSON
WINNEBAGO
BOONE
McHENRY
LAKE
KENOSHA
CARROLL
OGLE
DeKALB
KANE
DuPAGE
COOK
WHITESIDE
LEE
SCOTT
KENDALL
WILL
HENRY
BUREAU
LA SALLE
GRUNDY
ROCK ISLAND
MERCER
PUTNAM
KANKAKEE
PORTER
NEWTON
JASPER
DES MOINES
HENDERSON
WARREN
KNOX
STARK
MARSHALL
LIVINGSTON
WOODFORD
PEORIA
IROQUOIS
HANCOCK
McDONOUGH
FULTON
TAZEWELL
McLEAN
FORD
SCHUYLER
MASON
LOGAN
DE WITT
CHAMPAIGN
VERMILION
LEWIS
ADAMS
BROWN
CASS
MENARD
PIATT
MACON
SANGAMON
MORGAN
PIKE
DOUGLAS
EDGAR
MOULTRIE
COLES
CHRISTIAN
SHELBY
GREENE
CALHOUN
MACOUPIN
MONTGOMERY
CUMBERLAND
CLARK
LINCOLN
JERSEY
FAYETTE
EFFINGHAM
CRAWFORD
MADISON
BOND
WARREN
ST. CHARLES
ST. LOUIS
CLAY
RICHLAND
LAWRENCE
MARION
CLINTON
ST. LOUIS*
FRANKLIN
ST. CLAIR
EDWARDS
WABASH
WAYNE
WASHINGTON
JEFFERSON
MONROE
HAMILTON
WHITE
RANDOLPH
PERRY
JACKSON
WILLIAMSON
SALINE
GALLATIN
UNION
JOHNSON
POPE
HARDIN
BOLLINGER
CAPE GIRARDEAU
ALEXANDER
PULASKI
MASSAC
LIVINGSTON
BALLARD
McCRACKEN
93° 92° 91° 90° 89° 88° 87°
42° 41° 40° 39° 38° 37°

ARCOLA

ARCOLA RECORD-HERALD (THUR)

118 E Main St, Arcola, IL, 61910-1435, Douglas, USA; gen tel (217) 268-4950; gen fax (217) 268-4938; disp adv e-mail slackpub@consolidated.net; web site www.arcolarecordherald.com
Circulation: 2,200pd,; Sworn/Estimate/Non-Audited
Advertising rate: Open inch rate $4.80
Pub., Ed. .... Chris Slack
Mechanical Specifications: Type page 15 x 21; E - 8 cols, 1 3/4, 1/6 between.
Delivery Method: Mail, Newsstand, Racks

ARTHUR

ARTHUR GRAPHIC CLARION (WED)

113 E Illinois St, Arthur, IL, 61911-1331, Douglas, USA; gen tel (217) 543-2151; gen fax (217) 543-2152; disp adv e-mail info@thearthurgraphic.com; web site www.thearthurgraphic.com
Advertising rate: Open inch rate $4.85
Group: The Miami Herald Publishing Co.
Ed. .... Roger Borham
Delivery Method: Mail, Newsstand

SOUTHERN PIATT RECORD HERALD (WED)

113 E Illinois St, Arthur, IL, 61911-1331, Piatt, USA; gen tel (217) 543-2151; gen fax (217) 543-2152; disp adv e-mail recorderherald@consolidated.net; web site facebook.com/SouthernPiattRecordHerald
Circulation: 1,772pd, 8fr; Sworn/Estimate/Non-Audited
Advertising rate: Open inch rate $4.85
Gen. Mgr./Adv. Mgr. .... Stephanie Wierman
Ed. .... Roger Borham
Delivery Method: Mail, Newsstand
Areas Served: 61913, 61818, 61813, 61929, 61856

ASHTON

ASHTON GAZETTE (THUR)

813 Main St, Ashton, IL, 61006-9258, Lee, USA; gen tel (815) 453-2551; gen fax (815) 453-2422; ed e-mail monetta@ashtongazette.com; web site www.ashtongazette.com
Group: News Media Corp.
Ed. .... Monetta Young
Gen. Mgr. .... Mike Feltes

ASTORIA

THE ASTORIA SOUTH FULTON ARGUS (WED)

100 N Pearl St, Astoria, IL, 61501-9545, Fulton, USA; gen tel (309) 329-2151; gen fax (309) 329-2344; disp adv e-mail argus@kkspc.com; web site www.kkspc.com/argus
Circulation: 2,000pd, 62fr; Sworn/Estimate/Non-Audited
Advertising rate: Open inch rate $4.00
Circ. Mgr. .... Jodie Ragle
Ed. .... Judy Beaird
Pub. .... Thomas Stevens
Adv. Sales Rep. .... Paul Sager
Mechanical Specifications: Type page 10 1/4 x 16; E - 5 cols, 1 14/15, 1/6 between; A - 5 cols, 1 14/15, 1/6 between; C - 5 cols, 1 14/15, 1/6 between.
Delivery Method: Mail, Newsstand, Racks

AUBURN

NEW BERLIN BEE (FRI)

110 N 5th St, Auburn, IL, 62615-1449, Sangamon, USA; gen tel (217) 438-6155; gen fax (217) 438-6156; disp adv e-mail southco@royell.org; web site No Website
Circulation: 650pd,; Sworn/Estimate/Non-Audited
Advertising rate: Open inch rate $3.75
Group: South County Publications
Pub. .... Joseph Michelich
Adv. Mgr. .... Connie Michelich
Mechanical Specifications: Type page 10 3/16 x 15 1/2; E - 5 cols, 1 7/8, 3/16 between; A - 5 cols, 1 7/8, 3/16 between; C - 6 cols, 1 9/16, 3/16 between.
Delivery Method: Mail, Newsstand, Racks

PAWNEE POST (THUR)

110 N 5th St, Auburn, IL, 62615-1449, Sangamon, USA; gen tel (217) 438-6155; gen fax (217) 438-6156; disp adv e-mail southco@royell.org; web site www.southcountypublications.net
Circulation: 600pd, 10fr; Sworn/Estimate/Non-Audited
Advertising rate: Open inch rate $4.00
Group: South County Publications
Adv. Mgr. .... Connie Michelich
Ed. .... Joseph M. Michelich
Mechanical Specifications: Type page 10 3/16 x 15 1/2; E - 5 cols, 1 7/8, 3/16 between; A - 5 cols, 1 7/8, 3/16 between; C - 6 cols, 1 9/16, 3/16 between.Equipment & Software: Hardware — APP/Mac; Presses — KP; Software — Adobe/PageMaker 6.5, Adobe/Photoshop 6.0.
Delivery Method: Mail, Newsstand, Racks

PLEASANT PLAINS PRESS (FRI)

110 N 5th St, Auburn, IL, 62615-1449, Sangamon, USA; gen tel (217) 438-6155; gen fax (217) 438-6156; disp adv e-mail southco@royell.org
Circulation: 475pd,; Sworn/Estimate/Non-Audited
Advertising rate: Open inch rate $3.75
Group: South County Publications
Adv. Mgr. .... Connie Michelich
Ed. .... Joseph M. Michelich
Mechanical Specifications: Type page 10 3/16 x 15 1/2; E - 5 cols, 1 7/8, 3/16 between; A - 5 cols, 1 7/8, 3/16 between; C - 6 cols, 1 9/16, 3/16 between.
Delivery Method: Mail, Newsstand, Racks

ROCHESTER TIMES (THUR)

110 N 5th St, Auburn, IL, 62615-1449, Sangamon, USA; gen tel (217) 438-6155; gen fax (217) 438-6156; disp adv e-mail southco@royell.org; web site www.southcountypublications.net
Circulation: 875pd, 3fr; Sworn/Estimate/Non-Audited
Advertising rate: Open inch rate $4.00
Group: South County Publications
Adv. Mgr. .... Connie Michelich
Ed. .... Joseph M. Michelich
Delivery Method: Mail, Newsstand

BARTLETT

EXAMINER PUBLICATIONS, INC. (WED)

4N781 Gerber Rd, Bartlett, IL, 60103-2021, DuPage, USA; gen tel 1 (630) 830-4145; adv tel 1 (630) 830-4145; ed tel 1 (630) 830-4145; gen fax 1 (630) 830-4145; adv fax 1 (630) 830-4145; ed fax 1 (630) 830-4145; disp adv e-mail staff@examinerpublications.com; class adv e-mail classads@examinerpublications.com; ed e-mail ads@examinerpublications.com; web site www.examinerpublications.com
Circulation: 33,447pd, 4,353fr; Sworn/Estimate/Non-Audited
Advertising rate: Open inch rate $12.75
Established: 1976
Group: Examiner Publications, Inc.
Pres, Pub. .... Randall Petrik
Mechanical Specifications: Type page 10 W x 16 T; E - 4 cols, 1 column = 2 5/16" Units are 4 across and 4 high 2 5/16 x 4" tallEquipment & Software: Hardware — 6-APP/Mac G4, 5-APP/iMac; Presses — none; Software — QPS/QuarkXPress 7.5, Adobe/Photoshop 5.5.
Delivery Method: Newsstand, Carrier, Racks
Areas Served: 60103, 60184, 60188/89, 60133, 60177, 60107

THE EXAMINER OF CAROL STREAM (WED)

4N781 Gerber Rd, Bartlett, IL, 60103-2021, Kane, USA; gen tel 1 (630) 830-4145; adv tel 1 (630) 830-4145; ed tel 1 (630) 830-4145; gen fax 1 (630) 830-4145; adv fax 1 (630) 830-4145; disp adv e-mail staff@examinerpublications.com; class adv e-mail classads@examinerpublications.com; ed e-mail news@examinerpublications.com; web site www.examinerpublications.com
Circulation: 1,672pd, 4,892fr; Sworn/Estimate/Non-Audited
Advertising rate: $10.75
Established: 2005
Group: Examiner Publications, Inc.
Pres./Pub. .... Randall Petrik
Mechanical Specifications: Type page 10 x 16; E - 4 cols, 1 column = 2 5/16" Units are 4 across and 4 high 2 5/16 x 4" tallEquipment & Software: ; Presses — none
Delivery Method: Newsstand, Carrier, Racks
Areas Served: 60188/89

THE EXAMINER OF HANOVER PARK (WED)

4N781 Gerber Rd, Bartlett, IL, 60103-2021, Cook/DuPage, USA; gen tel (630) 830-4145; disp adv e-mail staff@examinerpublications.com; class adv e-mail classads@examinerpublications.com; ed e-mail news@examinerpublications.com; web site www.examinerpublications.com
Circulation: 5,500pd,; Sworn/Estimate/Non-Audited
Advertising rate: $7.00
Established: 1993
Pres. Pub. .... Randall Petrik
Mechanical Specifications: Type page 10 x 16; E - 4 cols, 2 5/16, 1/4 between; A - 4 cols, 2 5/16, 1/4 between; C - 6 cols, 1 1/2, 3/16 between.Equipment & Software: Hardware — 2-APP/Mac G4-450, 2-APP/Mac G4-400, 3-APP/iMac, 2-APP/Mac 604, 2-APP/Mac 603, 5-APP/Mac IIci; Software — QPS/QuarkXPress 3.32, Adobe/Photoshop 5.5, Adobe/Illustrator 8.
Delivery Method: Newsstand, Carrier, Racks
Areas Served: 60133

THE EXAMINER OF SOUTH ELGIN (WED)

4N781 Gerber Rd, Bartlett, IL, 60103-2021, Kane/Cook, USA; gen tel 1 (630) 830-4145; adv tel 1 (630) 830-4145; ed tel 1 (630) 830-4145; gen fax 1 (630) 830-4145; adv fax 1 (630) 830-4145; ed fax 1 (630) 830-4145; disp adv e-mail staff@examinerpublications.com; class adv e-mail classads@examinerpublications.com; ed e-mail news@examinerpublications.com; web site www.examinerpublications.com
Circulation: 4,950pd, 2,050fr; Sworn/Estimate/Non-Audited
Advertising rate: 12.75
Established: 1992
Group: Examiner Publications, Inc.
Pres./Pub. .... Randall Petrik
Mechanical Specifications: Type page 10 x 16; E - 4 cols, 1 column = 2 5/16" Units are 4 across and 4 high 2 5/16 x 4" tall
Delivery Method: Newsstand, Carrier, Racks
Areas Served: 60177

THE EXAMINER OF STREAMWOOD (WED)

4N781 Gerber Rd, Bartlett, IL, 60103-2021, Cook, USA; gen tel (630) 830-4145; disp adv e-mail staff@examinerpublications.com; class adv e-mail classads@examinerpublications.com; ed e-mail news@examinerpublications.com; web site www.examinerpublications.com
Circulation: 1,030pd, 5,682fr; CVC
Advertising rate: $10.75
Established: 1997
Group: Examiner Publications, Inc.
Pres./Pub. .... Randall Petrik
Mechanical Specifications: Type page 10 x 16; E - 4 cols, 1 column = 2 5/16" Units are 4 across and 4 high 2 5/16 x 4" tallEquipment & Software: ; Presses — none
Delivery Method: Newsstand, Carrier, Racks
Areas Served: 60107

THE EXAMINER OF WAYNE (WED)

4N781 Gerber Rd, Bartlett, IL, 60103-2021, DuPage, USA; gen tel 1 (630) 830-4145; adv tel 1 (630) 830-4145; ed tel 1 (630) 830-4145; gen fax 1 (630) 830-4145; adv fax 1 (630) 830-4145; ed fax 1 (630) 830-4145; disp adv e-mail staff@examinerpublications.com; class adv e-mail classads@examinerpublications.com; ed e-mail news@examinerpublications.com; web site http://www.examinerpublications.com
Circulation: 1,593pd, 4,864fr; Sworn/Estimate/Non-Audited
Advertising rate: $8
Established: 1978
Group: Examiner Publications, Inc.
Pres./Pub. .... Randall Petrik
Mechanical Specifications: 4 col wide (10") 4 units tall (4" each = 16")Equipment & Software: ; Presses — None
Delivery Method: Newsstand, Carrier, Racks
Areas Served: 60188, 60189

BARTONVILLE

LIMESTONE INDEPENDENT NEWS (WED)

114 Roosevelt St, Bartonville, IL, 61607-1910, Peoria, USA; gen tel (309) 697-1851; gen fax (309) 697-1851; disp adv e-mail limestonenews@yahoo.com; web site facebook.com/LIN715
Circulation: 2,300pd,; Sworn/Estimate/Non-Audited
Advertising rate: Open inch rate $7.00
Established: 1967
Ed. .... Barbara Widener
Delivery Method: Mail, Newsstand, Racks

BEARDSTOWN

CASS COUNTY STAR-GAZETTE (THUR)

1210 Wall St, Beardstown, IL, 62618-2327, Cass, USA; gen tel (217) 323-1010; gen fax (217) 323-1644; disp adv e-mail stargazette@casscomm.com; web site www.beardstownnewspapers.com
Circulation: 640pd,; AAM
Advertising rate: Open inch rate $14.50
Established: 1844
Pub. .... Jamila Khalil
Adv. Mgr. .... Patricia Wellenkamp
Mechanical Specifications: Type page 13 x 21; E - 6 cols, 2, 1/8 between; A - 8 cols, 1 1/2, 1/8 between; C - 8 cols, 1 1/2, 1/8 between. Equipment & Software: Hardware — APP/Mac; Software — Claris/FileMaker, QPS/QuarkXPress, Adobe/Photoshop.
Delivery Method: Mail, Newsstand, Racks

BEECHER CITY

BEECHER CITY JOURNAL (MON)

104 S Charles St, Beecher City, IL, 62414-1137, Effingham, USA; gen tel (618) 487-5634; gen fax (618) 487-5180; disp adv e-mail news@beechercityjournal.com; class adv e-mail news@beechercityjournal.com; ed e-mail news@beechercityjournal.com
Circulation: 1,300pd, 128fr; Sworn/Estimate/Non-Audited
Advertising rate: Open inch rate $4.75
Established: 1915
Pub. .... P.J. Ryan
Mng. Ed. .... Cherie Ryan
Mechanical Specifications: Type page 10 1/4 x 16; E - 5 cols, 1 11/12, 1/6 between; A - 5 cols, 1 11/12, 1/6 between; C - 5 cols, 1 11/12, 1/6 between.Equipment & Software: Hardware — APP/Macs; Software — InDesign
Delivery Method: Mail, Newsstand
Areas Served: Effingham, Shel-

by, Fayette Counties.... 62414, 62461,62422,62463,62465,62431, 62411,62401

BELLEVILLE

O'FALLON PROGRESS (THUR)

120 S Illinois St, Belleville, IL, 62220-2130, Saint Clair, USA; gen tel (618) 239-2688; gen fax (618) 234-1504; disp adv e-mail ofprogress@bnd.com; ed e-mail ghillyer@bnd.com; web site bnd.com/news/local/community/ofallon-progress
Circulation: 7,000pd, 12,000fr; Sworn/Estimate/Non-Audited
Advertising rate: Open inch rate $15.96
Established: 1895
Group: The McClatchy CompanyEditions: (2) 2 total; Fairview Heights (400); O'Fallon (3600);
Sports Ed.................................Todd Eschman
VP Adv.....................................Melissa Mason
Pres./Pub..Jay Tebbe
Ed. ....Curt Libbra
Mechanical Specifications: Type page 13 x 21 1/2; E - 6 cols, 2 1/30, 1/6 between; A - 6 cols, 2 1/30, 1/6 between; C - 9 cols, 1 1/3, between.Equipment & Software: Hardware — APP/Mac; Presses — G/Urbanite, G/Community; Software — QPS/QuarkXPress, Baseview/EditPro.
Delivery Method: Carrier
Areas Served: 62269

BELVIDERE

BOONE COUNTY JOURNAL (FRI)

419 S State St Ste A, Suite A, Belvidere, IL, 61008-3750, Boone, USA; gen tel (815) 544-4430; gen fax (815) 544-4330; disp adv e-mail info@boonecountyjournal.com; web site www.boonecountyjournal.com
Circulation: 10,000fr; Sworn/Estimate/Non-Audited
Advertising rate: Open inch rate $13.00
Established: 1996
Owner/Pub. ....David Larson
Ed. ....James Middleton
Delivery Method: Mail, Newsstand, Racks
Areas Served: Boone County, McHenry, DeKalb

THE BELVIDERE DAILY REPUBLICAN (WED, SUN)

130 S State St, Ste 101, Belvidere, IL, 61008-3772, Boone, USA; gen tel (815) 547-0084; adv tel (815) 547-0084; ed tel (815) 547-0084; gen fax (815) 547-3045; disp adv e-mail bdrads@rvpublishing.com; class adv e-mail mjane@rvpublishing.com; ed e-mail bdrnews@rvpublishing.com; web site www.belvideredailyrepublican.net
Circulation: 3,175pd, 4,275fr; Sworn/Estimate/Non-Audited
Advertising rate: Open inch rate
Established: 1894
Group: Rock Valley Publishing LLC
Pub..Pete Cruger
Gen. Mgr. ....Randy Johnson
Adv. Sales................................Debbie Werner
Circ. Mgr..Lindy Sweet
Mng. Ed.....................Melanie Bradley Marshall
Prodn. Mgr. ....Linda Lano
Ed. ....Tricia Goecks
Mechanical Specifications: Type page 10 1/4 x 13; E - 5 cols, 2 1/14, 1/12 between; A - 5 cols, 2 1/14, 1/12 between; C - 8 cols, 1 2/5, 1/12 between.Equipment & Software: Hardware — APP/Mac; Presses — 8-G/Community; Software — QPS/QuarkXPress, Baseview/NewsEdit
Delivery Method: Mail, Newsstand, Racks
Areas Served: Belvidere and Boone Counties

BENTON

THE PROGRESS (THUR)

PO Box 877, Benton, IL, 62812-0877, Franklin, USA; gen tel (618) 724-9423; gen fax (618) 435-2413; disp adv e-mail progress@clearwave.com; web site No Website
Circulation: 1,000pd,; Sworn/Estimate/Non-Audited
Advertising rate: Open inch rate $5.60
Established: 1905
Group: GateHouse Media, Inc.
Circ. Mgr....................................... Sam Waters
Regional Publisher .... Kevin Haezebroeck
Delivery Method: Mail, Newsstand, Racks

BLUE MOUND

BLUE MOUND LEADER (THUR)

205 W Niles St, Blue Mound, IL, 62513, Macon, USA; gen tel (217) 692-2323; gen fax (217) 692-2323; disp adv e-mail bmleader1@yahoo.com; web site bluemoundleader.com
Circulation: 850pd, 25fr; Sworn/Estimate/Non-Audited
Advertising rate: Open inch rate $5.50
Established: 1886
Pub./Ed...................................Cynthia L. Ervin
Mechanical Specifications: Type page 9 7/8 x 15.Equipment & Software: Hardware — APP/Mac; Software — InDesign
Delivery Method: Mail, Newsstand, Racks
Areas Served: 62513, 62521, 62526, 62544, 62568, 62522

BOURBONNAIS

THE HERALD/COUNTRY MARKET (TUES)

500 Brown Blvd, Bourbonnais, IL, 60914-2328, Kankakee, USA; gen tel (815) 933-1131; gen fax (815) 933-3785; disp adv e-mail sales@bbherald.com; ed e-mail news@bbherald.com; web site www.bbherald.com
Circulation: 3,000pd, 39,000fr; Sworn/Estimate/Non-Audited
Advertising rate: Open inch rate $16.50
Established: 1975
Gen. Mgr...................................Jon Olszewski
Ed. ....Toby Olszewski
Adv. Sales...................................Nancy Cross
Mechanical Specifications: Type page 10 x 16; E - 5 cols, 1 7/8, 1/6 between.Equipment & Software: Hardware — APP/Macs.
Delivery Method: Mail, Newsstand, Racks
Areas Served: 6-914, 60915, 60950, 60910, 60401, 60940, 60941, 60901, 60442, 60954, 60449, 60468, 60964, 60481

BREESE

THE BREESE JOURNAL (THUR)

8060 Old US Highway 50, Breese, IL, 62230-3924, Clinton, USA; gen tel (618) 526-7211; gen fax (618) 526-2590; disp adv e-mail sales@breesepub.com; web site www.breesepub.com
Circulation: 5,058pd, 85fr; Sworn/Estimate/Non-Audited
Advertising rate: Open inch rate $8.12
Established: 1921
Pub..Dave Mahlandt
Ed. ....Vickie Albers
Kelly Ross
Mechanical Specifications: Type page 15 1/2 x 21 1/2; E - 7 cols, 2 1/12, 1/6 between; A - 7 cols, 2 1/12, 1/6 between; C - 9 cols, 1 2/3, 1/6 between.
Delivery Method: Mail, Newsstand, Racks
Areas Served: Clinton County

BRIGHTON

SOUTHWESTERN JOURNAL (THUR)

150 N Washington, Brighton, IL, 62102, Jersey, USA; gen tel (618)372-8451; gen fax (618)372-4925; disp adv e-mail swjnews@sbcglobal.net; web site facebook.com/Southwestern-Journal-News-101665105809
Circulation: 1,150pd,; Sworn/Estimate/Non-Audited
Advertising rate: Open inch rate $4.00
Established: 1971
Editor ....LuAnne Woody
Pub..John M. Galer
Delivery Method: Mail, Newsstand, Racks

BUNKER HILL

GAZETTE-NEWS (THUR)

150 S Washington St, Bunker Hill, IL, 62014-1316, Macoupin, USA; gen tel (618) 585-4411; gen fax (618) 585-3354; disp adv e-mail gazette8@frontiernet.net; web site www.bunkerhillpublications.com
Circulation: 1,650pd,; Sworn/Estimate/Non-Audited
Advertising rate: Open inch rate $4.00
Established: 1866
Pub..John M. Galer
Prodn. Mgr. .... Laura Dabbs
Mechanical Specifications: Type page 10 3/4 x 16 1/2; E - 5 cols, 2 1/16, between; A - 5 cols, 2 1/16, between; C - 5 cols, 2 1/16, between. Equipment & Software: Hardware — APP/Mac; Software — Microsoft/Word.
Delivery Method: Mail, Newsstand, Racks
Areas Served: 62014, 62088, 62033

BUSHNELL

MCDONOUGH-DEMOCRAT (MON)

358 E Main St, Bushnell, IL, 61422-1338, McDonough, USA; gen tel (309) 772-2129; gen fax (309) 772-3994; disp adv e-mail info@themcdonoughdemocrat.com; web site www.themcdonoughdemocrat.com
Circulation: 1,400pd,; Sworn/Estimate/Non-Audited
Advertising rate: Open inch rate $4.50
Established: 1884
Ed. ....David S. Norton
Mechanical Specifications: Type page 16 1/2 x 21.
Delivery Method: Mail, Newsstand, Racks

BYRON

THE TEMPO (THUR)

418 W Blackhawk Dr, # LL3, Byron, IL, 61010-8634, USA; gen tel (815) 234-4821; gen fax (815) 234-4809; disp adv e-mail rmarshall@rvpublishing.com; web site www.rvpublishing.com
Gen. Mgr. ....Randy Johnson
Ed. ....Doug Schroder
Adv. Mgr................................Rhonda Marshall

CAIRO

THE CAIRO CITIZEN (THUR)

231 16th St, Cairo, IL, 62914-1904, Alexander, USA; gen tel (618) 734-4242; gen fax (618) 734-4244; disp adv e-mail thecairocitizen@gmail.com; web site www.cairocitizen.com
Circulation: 3,500pd,; Sworn/Estimate/Non-Audited
Advertising rate: Open inch rate $10.64
Pub..Jerry L. Reppert
Gen. Mgr. ....Scarlett Tarpley
Circ. Mgr..................................Dianne Reppert
Ed. ....George Lamboley
Mechanical Specifications: Type page 13 1/4 x 21 1/2; E - 6 cols, 2 1/8, between; A - 6 cols, 2 1/8, between; C - 9 cols, 1 1/4, between. Equipment & Software: Hardware — APP/Mac; Presses — G/Community.
Delivery Method: Mail, Newsstand, Racks

CAMBRIDGE

CAMBRIDGE CHRONICLE IN ILLINOIS (FRI)

119 W Exchange St, Cambridge, IL, 61238-1158, Henry, USA; gen tel (309) 944-2119; gen fax (309) 944-5615; disp adv e-mail ewalker@geneseorepublic.com; class adv e-mail kclementz@geneseorepublic.com; web site www.cambridgechron.com
Circulation: 1,050pd,; Sworn/Estimate/Non-Audited
Advertising rate: Open inch rate $8.95
Established: 1858
Group: GateHouse Media, Inc.
Digital Platform - Mobile: Apple, Android
Digital Platform - Tablet: Apple iOS, Android
Pub... Dee Evans
Circ. Mgr.................................... Marnie Eggan
Mng. Ed...Mindy Carls
Delivery Method: Mail, Newsstand, Racks
Areas Served: 61238, 61233, 61274, 61262, 61419

CAMP POINT

CAMP POINT JOURNAL (WED)

202 E State St, Camp Point, IL, 62320-1114, Adams, USA; gen tel (217) 593-6515; gen fax (217) 593-7720; disp adv e-mail lisa@elliott-publishing.com; ed e-mail gina@elliott-publishing.com; web site elliott-publishing.com
Circulation: 970pd,; Sworn/Estimate/Non-Audited
Advertising rate: Open inch rate $3.50
Established: 1873
Group: Elliott Publishing, Inc.
Pres. ....James W. Elliott
Gen. Mgr. .... Marcia Elliott
Bookkeeping...............................Gina Maddox
Advertising.....................................Newell Lisa
Mechanical Specifications: Type page 10 1/4 x 16; E - 5 cols, 1 15/16, 1/6 between; A - 5 cols, 1 15/16, 1/6 between; C - 5 cols, 1 15/16, 1/6 between.
Delivery Method: Mail, Newsstand, Racks
Areas Served: 62320, 62324, 62325, 62339, 62346

GOLDEN-CLAYTON NEW ERA (WED)

202 E State St, Camp Point, IL, 62320-1114, Adams, USA; gen tel (217) 593-6515; gen fax (217) 593-7720; disp adv e-mail lisa@elliott-publishing.com; ed e-mail gina@elliott-publishing.com; web site www.elliott-publishing.com
Circulation: 600pd,; Sworn/Estimate/Non-Audited
Advertising rate: Open inch rate $3.50
Established: 1876
Group: Elliott Publishing, Inc.
Pub...James W. Elliott
Ed. .... Marcia Elliott
Receptionist................................Gina Maddox
Graphics ....Lisa Newell
Delivery Method: Mail, Newsstand, Racks
Areas Served: Golden, Clayton area in Adams County

MENDON DISPATCH-TIMES (WED)

202 E State St, Camp Point, IL, 62320-1114, Adams, USA; gen tel (217) 593-6515; gen fax (217) 593-7720; disp adv e-mail lisa@elliott-publishing.com; ed e-mail gina@elliott-publishing.com; web site elliott-publishing.com
Circulation: 845pd,; Sworn/Estimate/Non-Audited
Advertising rate: Open inch rate $3.50
Established: 1871
Group: Elliott Publishing, Inc.
Pub...Jim Elliott
Ed. .... Marcia Elliott
Receptionist................................Gina Maddox
Graphics ....Lisa Newell
Delivery Method: Mail, Newsstand, Racks
Areas Served: Mendon, Ursa, Loraine area in Adams County

CANTON

FULTON DEMOCRAT (WED)

31 S Main St, Canton, IL, 61520-2605, Ful-

ton, USA; gen tel (309) 647-9501; gen fax (309) 543-6844; disp adv e-mail fultondemocrat@att.net; web site www.fultondemocrat.com
Circulation: 3,000pd, 4,000fr; USPS
Advertising rate: Open inch rate $9.50
Established: 1855
Group: Martin Publishing Company
Pub.. Robert L. Martin
Mechanical Specifications: Page 11.75 x 21.5
1 col - 1.834
2 col - 3.817
3 col - 5.8Equipment & Software: ; Presses — Sheet fed -Heidelberg
Web press- Goss; Software — QuarkXpress, InDesign
Delivery Method: Mail, Newsstand, Racks
Areas Served: 61542, 61543, 61519, 61427,615 63,61524,61520,61501,61441,62624, 61531, 61553, 61482, 61484

CARBONDALE

CARBONDALE TIMES (WED)
701 W Main St, Carbondale, IL, 62901-2643, Jackson, USA; gen tel (618) 549-4084; adv tel (618) 549-2799; ed tel (618) 457-4084; gen fax (618) 549-3664; adv fax (618) 549-3664; ed fax (618) 549-3664; disp adv e-mail thomaspublishing@earthlink.net; class adv e-mail thomaspublishing@earthlink.net; ed e-mail ctimes@midwest.net; web site www.carbondaletimes.com
Circulation: 9,000fr; Sworn/Estimate/Non-Audited
Advertising rate: Open inch rate $15.00
Established: 1997
Group: Paddock Publications
Pub....................................... Jason C. Thomas
Adv. Mgr.................................. Debbie Thomas
Ed. .... Dustin Duncan
Delivery Method: Mail, Racks
Areas Served: 62901, 62902, 62966, 62918

CARLINVILLE

COAL COUNTRY TIMES (FRI)
125 E Main St, Carlinville, IL, 62626-1726, Macoupin, USA; gen tel (217) 854-2534; gen fax (217) 854-2535; disp adv e-mail mcednews@campbellpublications.net; web site www.enquirerdemocrat.com
Circulation: 4,100pd,; Sworn/Estimate/Non-Audited
Advertising rate: Open inch rate $5.00
Pub.. Julie Boren
Delivery Method: Mail, Newsstand

MACOUPIN COUNTY ENQUIRER DEMOCRAT (THUR)
125 E Main St, Carlinville, IL, 62626-1726, Macoupin, USA; gen tel (217) 854-2534; gen fax (217) 854-2535; disp adv e-mail mcednews@campbellpublications.net; web site www.enquirerdemocrat.com
Circulation: 4,800pd, 200fr; Sworn/Estimate/Non-Audited
Advertising rate: Open inch rate $6.50
Established: 1852
Pub.. Julie Boren
Daniel Winningham
Ed. Dept.
Eric Becker
Delivery Method: Mail, Newsstand
Areas Served: 62626-0200

CARROLLTON

GREENE PRAIRIE PRESS (WED)
516 N Main St, Carrollton, IL, 62016-1027, Greene, USA; gen tel (217) 942-9100; adv tel (618) 498-1234; gen fax (630) 206-0320; disp adv e-mail jkallal@campbellpublications.net; class adv e-mail jkallal@campbellpublications.net; ed e-mail gppnews@campbellpublications.net; web site www.greenprairiepress.com
Circulation: 2,200pd, 10fr; Sworn/Estimate/Non-Audited
Advertising rate: Open inch rate $11.95
Established: 1846
Group: Campbell Publishing Co., Inc.
Pub.. Julie Boren
regional editor............................ Robert Lyons
Mechanical Specifications: Type page 13 x 21 1/2; E - 6 cols, 2 1/16, between; A - 6 cols, 2 1/16, between; C - 9 cols, 1 5/16, between.
Delivery Method: Mail, Newsstand, Racks
Areas Served: Greene County, IL

CARTHAGE

HANCOCK COUNTY JOURNAL-PILOT (WED)
31 N Washington St, Carthage, IL, 62321-1450, Hancock, USA; gen tel (217) 357-2149; gen fax (217) 357-2177; disp adv e-mail advertising@journalpilot.com; class adv e-mail classified@journalpilot.com; ed e-mail editor@journalpilot.com; web site www.journalpilot.com
Group: Community Media Group
Sports Ed.................................... Ethan Lillard
Ed. .... Emma VanArsdale
Adv. Dir.. Andria Miller
Clas. Adv./Circ........................... Bobbi Cleesen
Delivery Method: Mail

CHATHAM

CHATHAM CLARION (THUR)
PO Box 254, 318 North Main, Suite B, Chatham, IL, 62629-0254, Sangamon, USA; gen tel (217) 483-2614; adv tel (217) 438-6155; gen fax (217) 483-3988; adv fax (217) 438-6156; disp adv e-mail chathamclarion@royell.org; class adv e-mail southco@royell.org; ed e-mail chathamclarion@royell.org; web site www.southcountypublications.net
Circulation: 1,800pd,; Sworn/Estimate/Non-Audited
Advertising rate: Open inch rate $4.00
Established: 1963
Group: South County Publications
Ed.. Joe Pritchett
Adv. Mgr................................ Connie Michelich
Ed.. Joe Pritchett
Mechanical Specifications: Type page 10 3/16 x 15 1/2; E - 5 cols, 1 7/8, between; A - 5 cols, 1 7/8, between; C - 6 cols, 1 9/16, between. Equipment & Software: Hardware — APP/Mac; Presses — KP; Software — Adobe/PageMaker 4.2.
Delivery Method: Mail, Newsstand

CHICAGO

ARLINGTON HEIGHTS POST (THUR)
435 N Michigan Ave, Chicago, IL, 60611-4066, Cook, USA; gen tel (866) 399-0537; adv tel (866) 399-0537; ed tel (312) 222-3429; gen fax (312) 222-2598; ed fax (312) 222-2598; disp adv e-mail jmcdermott@tribpub.com; class adv e-mail jmcdermott@tribpub.com; ed e-mail pjurik@chicagotribune.com; web site chicagotribune.com/suburbs/arlington-heights
Circulation: 2,032pd, 11fr; Sworn/Estimate/Non-Audited
Advertising rate: Open inch rate $20.57
Established: 1912
Display Adv. Mgr............................ Ed Rooney
Regl./Nat'l Adv. Mgr...................... Steve Walzer
Circ. Dir.................................... David Perham
Bureau Chief...................... Kathy Catrambone
Ed. .... Robert Loerzel
Mechanical Specifications: Type page 10 x 13; E - 5 cols, 1 7/8, 1 7/8 between; A - 5 cols, 1 7/8, 1 7/8 between; C - 8 cols, 1 13/16, 1 13/16 between.Equipment & Software: ; Software — QPS/QuarkXPress 5.01, Multi-Ad/Creator 4.03, Adobe/Photoshop 6.01, Adobe/Illustrator 9.02.
Areas Served: 60192, 60193, 60194, 60195, 60196

BRIDGEPORT NEWS (WED)
3506 S Halsted St, Ste 1, Chicago, IL, 60609-1605, Cook, USA; gen tel (773) 927-0025; gen fax (773) 337-6995; disp adv e-mail jrbridgeportnews@aol.com; web site www.bridgeportnews.net
Circulation: 25,300fr; Sworn/Estimate/Non-Audited
Advertising rate: Open Local Inch Rate $11.00
Established: 1939
Pub....................................... Joseph Feldman
Ed/Mgr.............................. Janice Racinowski
Delivery Method: Newsstand, Carrier, Racks
Areas Served: 60608, 60609, 60616, 60632

BRIGHTON PARK - MCKINLEY PARK LIFE (THUR)
2949 W Pope John Paul II Dr, Chicago, IL, 60632-2554, Cook, USA; gen tel (773) 523-3663; gen fax (773) 523-3983; disp adv e-mail brightonparklife@aol.com; web site www.brightonparklife.com
Circulation: 21,000fr; Sworn/Estimate/Non-Audited
Advertising rate: Open inch rate $10.00
Established: 1932
Circ. Mgr................................ Albert H. Silinski
Ed. .... Donna Rooney
Delivery Method: Carrier
Areas Served: 60609, 60632, 60638

BUFFALO GROVE COUNTRYSIDE (THUR)
435 N Michigan Ave, Chicago, IL, 60611-4066, Cook, USA; gen tel (847) 486-7462; ed tel (312) 321-2307; gen fax (847) 486-7434; disp adv e-mail advertisinginfo@suntimes.com; class adv e-mail classifieds@stmedianetwork.com; ed e-mail cberman@pioneerlocal.com; web site buffalogrove.chicagotribune.com
Circulation: 778pd,; AAM
Advertising rate: 1/4 P $360, 1/2 P $830, Full $1300
Established: 1912
Group: Tronc, Inc.
Circ. Dir.................................... David Perham
Bureau Chief...................... Kathy Catrambone
Production Ed......................... Mary Hendricks
Pub./Ed.-in-Chief....................... R. Bruce Dold
Ed. .... Phil Jurik
VP of Adv................................ Jill McDermott
Gen. Mgr. of Suburban Weeklies Maggie Wartik
Mng. Ed....................................... Peter Kendall
Mechanical Specifications: Type page 10 x 13; E - 5 cols, 1 7/8, 1 7/8 between; A - 5 cols, 1 7/8, 1 7/8 between; C - 8 cols, 1 13/16, 1 13/16 between.Equipment & Software: ; Software — QPS/QuarkXPress 5.01, Multi-Ad/Creator 4.03, Adobe/Photoshop 6.01, Adobe/Illustrator 9.02.
Delivery Method: Mail, Newsstand, Racks
Areas Served: 60089, 60047

CHICAGO'S NORTHWEST SIDE PRESS (WED)
4937 N Milwaukee Ave, Chicago, IL, 60630-2114, Cook, USA; gen tel (773) 286-6100; gen fax (773) 286-8151; disp adv e-mail nadignewspapers@aol.com; class adv e-mail nadignewspapers@aol.com; ed e-mail nadignewspapers@aol.com; web site www.nadignewspapers.com
Circulation: 30,000fr; Sworn/Estimate/Non-Audited
Advertising rate: Open inch rate $23.50
Established: 1940
Digital Platform - Mobile: Apple, Android, Windows, Blackberry
Digital Platform - Tablet: Apple iOS, Android, Windows 7, Blackberry Tablet OS
Pub.. Brian Nadig
Pub.. Glenn Nadig
Ed. .... Randy Erickson
Mechanical Specifications: Type page 13 3/4 x 21 1/2; E - 8 cols, between; A - 8 cols, between; C - 8 cols, between.
Delivery Method: Mail, Newsstand, Carrier, Racks

CROWN POINT STAR (THUR)
435 N Michigan Ave, Chicago, IL, 60611-4066, Cook, USA; gen tel (866) 399-0537; adv tel (866) 399-0537; ed tel (312) 222-3429; gen fax (312) 222-2598; adv fax (312) 222-3232; ed fax (312) 222-2598; disp adv e-mail jmcdermott@tribpub.com; class adv e-mail jmcdermott@tribpub.com; ed e-mail pjurik@chicagotribune.com; web site chicagotribune.com/suburbs/post-tribune/crown-point
Circulation: 290pd,; AAM
Advertising rate: Open inch rate $11.00
Established: 1871
Group: Tronc, Inc.
Tronc, Inc.
Adv. Consultant............................ Sue Medved
Gen. Mgr. of Suburban Weeklies Maggie Wartik
Pub./Ed.-in-Chief....................... R. Bruce Dold
Mng. Ed....................................... Peter Kendall
Ed. .... Phil Jurik
VP of Adv................................ Jill McDermott
Mechanical Specifications: Type page 11 x 13; E - 6 cols, 2 1/16, between; A - 6 cols, 2 1/16, between; C - 7 cols, between.

DEERFIELD REVIEW (THUR)
435 N Michigan Ave, Chicago, IL, 60611-4066, Cook, USA; gen tel (866) 399-0537; adv tel (866) 399-0537; ed tel (312) 222-3429; gen fax (312) 222-2598; ed fax (312) 222-2598; disp adv e-mail jmcdermott@tribpub.com; class adv e-mail jmcdermott@tribpub.com; ed e-mail pjurik@chicagotribune.com; web site chicagotribune.com/suburbs/deerfield
Circulation: 898pd,; AAM
Advertising rate: 1/8 Pg $220.00; 1/6 Pg $240.00; 1/4 Pg $360.00
Established: 1912
Group: Tronc, Inc.
Gen. Mgr. of Suburban Weeklies Maggie Wartik
Pub./Ed.-in-Chief....................... R. Bruce Dold
Mng. Ed....................................... Peter Kendall
Ed. .... Phil Jurik
Mechanical Specifications: Type page 10 x 13; E - 5 cols, 1 7/8, 1 7/8 between; A - 5 cols, 1 7/8, 1 7/8 between; C - 8 cols, 1 13/16, 1 13/16 between.Equipment & Software: ; Software — QPS/QuarkXPress 5.01, Multi-Ad/Creator 4.03, Adobe/Photoshop 6.01, Adobe/Illustrator 9.02.
Delivery Method: Mail, Newsstand, Racks
Areas Served: 60015

ELMWOOD PARK LEAVES (THUR)
435 N Michigan Ave, Chicago, IL, 60611-4066, Cook, USA; gen tel (312) 321-2028; ed tel (312) 321-2864; gen fax (847) 486-7454; disp adv e-mail advertisinginfo@suntimes.com; class adv e-mail classifieds@stmedianetwork.com; web site chicagotribune.com/suburbs/elmwood-park
Circulation: 758pd,; AAM
Advertising rate: 1/8 Pg $220.00; 1/6 Pg $240.00; 1/4 Pg $360.00
Established: 1912
Group: Tronc, Inc.
North.. Jill McDemott
Pub./Ed.-in-Chief....................... R. Bruce Dold
Mng. Ed....................................... Peter Kendall
VP of Adv................................ Jill McDermott
Ed. .... Phil Jurik
Gen. Mgr. of Suburban Weeklies Maggie Wartik
Mechanical Specifications: Type page 10 x 13; E - 5 cols, 1 7/8, 1 7/8 between; A - 5 cols, 1 7/8, 1 7/8 between; C - 8 cols, 1 13/16, 1 13/16 between.Equipment & Software: ; Software — QPS/QuarkXPress 5.01, Multi-Ad/Creator 4.03, Adobe/Photoshop 6.01, Adobe/Illustrator 9.02.
Delivery Method: Mail, Newsstand, Racks
Areas Served: 60707

EVANSTON REVIEW (THUR)
435 N Michigan Ave, Chicago, IL, 60611-4066, Cook, USA; gen tel (847) 486-9200; adv tel (847) 486-7300; ed tel (312) 321-2678; ed fax (847) 486-7451; disp adv e-mail advertisinginfo@suntimes.com; class adv e-mail classifieds@stmedianetwork.com; web site chicagotribune.com/suburbs/evanston
Circulation: 1,500pd,; AAM
Advertising rate: 1/4 P $360, 1/2 P $830, Full $1300
Established: 1912
Group: Tronc, Inc.
Gen. Mgr. of Suburban Weeklies Maggie Wartik

Pub./Ed.-in-Chief ....R. Bruce Dold
Mng. Ed.......................................Peter Kendall
Ed. ....Phil Jurik
VP of Adv..................................Jill McDermott
Mechanical Specifications: Type page 10 x 13; E - 5 cols, 1 7/8, 1 7/8 between; A - 5 cols, 1 7/8, 1 7/8 between; C - 8 cols, 1 13/16, 1 13/16 between.Equipment & Software: ; Software — QPS/QuarkXPress 5.01, Multi-Ad/ Creator 4.03, Adobe/Photoshop 6.01, Adobe/ Illustrator 9.02.
Delivery Method: Mail, Newsstand, Racks
Areas Served: 60201, 60202, 60203, 60204

FOREST LEAVES (THUR)

435 N Michigan Ave, Chicago, IL, 60611-4066, Cook, USA; gen tel (312) 321-2034; gen fax (312) 321-9310; disp adv e-mail display@pioneerlocal.com; class adv e-mail classifieds@pioneerlocal.com; web site chicagotribune.com/suburbs/river-forest
Circulation: 384pd,; AAM
Advertising rate: 1/4 P $360, 1/2 P $830, Full $1300
Group: Tronc, Inc.
Gen. Mgr. of Suburban Weeklies Maggie Wartik
Mng. Ed.......................................Peter Kendall
Pub...R. Bruce Dold
Ed. ....Phil Jurik
VP of Adv..................................Jill McDermott
Mechanical Specifications: Type page 10 x 13; E - 5 cols, 1 7/8, 1 7/8 between; A - 5 cols, 1 7/8, 1 7/8 between; C - 8 cols, 1 13/16, 1 13/16 between.Equipment & Software: ; Software — QPS/QuarkXPress 5.01, Multi-Ad/ Creator 4.03, Adobe/Photoshop 6.01, Adobe/ Illustrator 9.02.
Delivery Method: Mail, Newsstand, Racks
Areas Served: 60305

FRANKLIN PARK HERALD-JOURNAL (THUR)

435 N Michigan Ave, Chicago, IL, 60611-4066, Cook, USA; gen tel (866) 399-0537; adv tel (866) 399-0537; ed tel (312) 222-3429; gen fax (312) 222-2598; ed fax (312) 222-2598; disp adv e-mail jmcdermott@tribpub.com; class adv e-mail jmcdermott@tribpub.com; ed e-mail pjurik@chicagotribune.com; web site chicagotribune.com/suburbs/franklin-park
Circulation: 514pd,; AAM
Advertising rate: 1/8 Pg $220.00; 1/6 Pg $240.00; 1/4 Pg $360.00
Established: 1912
Group: Tronc, Inc.
Ed. ....Phil Jurik
Mng. Ed.......................................Peter Kendall
Pub./Ed.-in-Chief ....R. Bruce Dold
Gen. Mgr. of Suburban Weeklies Maggie Wartik
VP of Adv..................................Jill McDermott
Mechanical Specifications: Type page 10 x 13; E - 5 cols, 1 7/8, 1 7/8 between; A - 5 cols, 1 7/8, 1 7/8 between; C - 8 cols, 1 13/16, 1 13/16 between.Equipment & Software: ; Software — QPS/QuarkXPress 5.01, Multi-Ad/ Creator 4.03, Adobe/Photoshop 6.01, Adobe/ Illustrator 9.02.
Delivery Method: Mail, Newsstand, Racks
Areas Served: 60131

GLENCOE NEWS (THUR)

435 N Michigan Ave, Chicago, IL, 60611-4066, Cook, USA; gen tel (866) 399-0537; adv tel (866) 399-0537; ed tel (312) 222-3429; gen fax (312) 222-2598; ed fax (312) 222-2598; disp adv e-mail jmcdermott@tribpub.com; class adv e-mail jmcdermott@tribpub.com; ed e-mail pjurik@chicagotribune.com; web site chicagotribune.com/suburbs/glencoe
Circulation: 439pd,; AAM
Advertising rate: 1/4 P $360, 1/2 P $830, Full $1300
Group: Tronc, Inc.
Mng. Ed.......................................Mike Bivona
Pub./Ed.-in-Chief ....R. Bruce Dold
Ed. ....Phil Jurik
Gen. Mgr. of Suburban Weeklies Maggie Wartik
Mng. Ed.......................................Peter Kendall
VP of Adv..................................Jill McDermott
Mechanical Specifications: Type page 10 x 13; E - 5 cols, 1 7/8, 1 7/8 between; A - 5 cols, 1 7/8, 1 7/8 between; C - 8 cols, 1 13/16, 1 13/16 between.Equipment & Software: ; Software — QPS/QuarkXPress 5.01, Multi-Ad/ Creator 4.03, Adobe/Photoshop 6.01, Adobe/ Illustrator 9.02.
Delivery Method: Mail, Newsstand, Racks
Areas Served: 60022

GLENVIEW ANNOUNCEMENTS (THUR)

435 N Michigan Ave, Chicago, IL, 60611-4066, Cook, USA; gen tel (866) 399-0537; adv tel (866) 399-0537; ed tel (312) 222-3429; gen fax (312) 222-2598; ed fax (312) 222-2598; disp adv e-mail jmcdermott@tribpub.com; class adv e-mail jmcdermott@tribpub.com; ed e-mail pjurik@chicagotribune.com; web site chicagotribune.com/suburbs/glenview
Circulation: 1,171pd,; AAM
Advertising rate: 1/4 P $360, 1/2 P $830, Full $1300
Established: 1912
Group: Tronc, Inc.
Ed. ....Cathy Backer
Pub./Ed.-in-Chief ....R. Bruce Dold
Ed. ....Phil Jurik
Gen. Mgr. of Suburban Weeklies Maggie Wartik
Mng. Ed.......................................Peter Kendall
VP of Adv..................................Jill McDermott
Mechanical Specifications: Type page 10 x 13; E - 5 cols, 1 7/8, 1 7/8 between; A - 8 cols, 1 7/8, 1 7/8 between; C - 8 cols, 1 13/16, 1 13/16 between.Equipment & Software: ; Software — QPS/QuarkXPress 5.01, Multi-Ad/ Creator 4.03, Adobe/Photoshop 6.01, Adobe/ Illustrator 9.02.
Delivery Method: Mail, Newsstand, Racks
Areas Served: 60025, 60029

HIGHLAND PARK NEWS (THUR)

435 N Michigan Ave, Chicago, IL, 60611-4066, Cook, USA; gen tel (847) 486-9200; ed tel (312) 321-2328; disp adv e-mail advertisinginfo@suntimes.com; class adv e-mail classifieds@stmedianetwork.com; web site www.pioneerlocal.com
Circulation: 1,213pd,; AAM
Advertising rate: 1/4 P $360, 1/2 P $830, Full $1300
Established: 1912
Group: Tronc, Inc.
Pub./Ed.-in-Chief ....R. Bruce Dold
Ed. ....Phil Jurik
Gen. Mgr. of Suburban Weeklies Maggie Wartik
Mng. Ed.......................................Peter Kendall
VP of Adv..................................Jill McDermott
Delivery Method: Mail, Newsstand, Racks

HYDE PARK HERALD (WED)

1525 E 53rd St, Ste 920, Chicago, IL, 60615-4530, Cook, USA; gen tel (773) 643-8533; gen fax (773) 643-8542; disp adv e-mail display@hpherald.com; class adv e-mail classifi@hpherald.com; ed e-mail editor@hpherald.com; web site www.hpherald.com
Circulation: 5,400pd, 195fr; Sworn/Estimate/ Non-Audited
Advertising rate: Open inch rate $50.67
Established: 1882
Group: Herald Newspapers, Inc.Editions: Hyde Park Herald
Digital Platform - Mobile: Apple, Android, Windows, Blackberry
Digital Platform - Tablet: Apple iOS, Android, Windows 7, Blackberry Tablet OS, Kindle, Nook, Kindle Fire
Pub...Bruce Sagan
VP/Gen. Mgr. ....Susan J. Walker
Adv. Mgr. ....Carol Cichocki
Ed. ....Gabriel Piemonte
Bus. Mgr.....................................Mary Petrassi
Mechanical Specifications: Type page 10 1/4 x 12 3/4; E - 4 cols, between; A - 6 cols, 1 9/16, between; C - 8 cols, 1 1/8, between. Equipment & Software: Hardware — APP/ Macs, PCs; Software — Adobe/PageMaker, Adobe/Photoshop, Microsoft/Word, Microsoft/ Windows, Synaptic, QPS/QuarkXPress.
Delivery Method: Mail, Newsstand, Carrier
Areas Served: 60615
60637
60653
60649

LAKE FORESTER (THUR)

435 N Michigan Ave, Chicago, IL, 60611-4066, Cook, USA; gen tel (847) 599-6900; ed tel (312) 321-2328; gen fax (847) 486-7454; disp adv e-mail advertisinginfo@suntimes.com; class adv e-mail classifieds@stmedianetwork.com; web site www.pioneerlocal.com
Circulation: 1,466pd,; AAM
Advertising rate: 1/4 P $360, 1/2 P $830, Full $1300
Established: 1912
Group: Tronc, Inc.
Pub./Ed.-in-Chief ....R. Bruce Dold
Ed. ....Phil Jurik
Gen. Mgr. of Suburban Weeklies Maggie Wartik
Mng. Ed.......................................Peter Kendall
VP of Adv..................................Jill McDermott
Mechanical Specifications: Type page 10 x 13; E - 5 cols, 1 7/8, 1 7/8 between; A - 5 cols, 1 7/8, 1 7/8 between; C - 8 cols, 1 13/16, 1 13/16 between.Equipment & Software: ; Software — Adobe/Photoshop 6.01, QPS/ QuarkXPress 5.01, Multi-Ad Creator 4.03, Adobe/Illustrator 9.02.
Delivery Method: Mail, Newsstand, Racks
Areas Served: 60044, 60045

LAKE ZURICH COURIER (THUR)

435 N Michigan Ave, Chicago, IL, 60611-4066, Cook, USA; gen tel (866) 399-0537; adv tel (866) 399-0537; ed tel (312) 222-3429; gen fax (312) 222-2598; ed fax (312) 222-2598; disp adv e-mail jmcdermott@tribpub.com; class adv e-mail jmcdermott@tribpub.com; ed e-mail pjurik@chicagotribune.com; web site chicagotribune.com/suburbs/lake-zurich
Circulation: 644pd,; AAM
Advertising rate: 1/4 P $360, 1/2 P $830, Full $1300
Established: 1912
Group: Tronc, Inc.
Pub./Ed.-in-Chief ....R. Bruce Dold
Ed. ....Phil Jurik
Gen. Mgr. of Suburban Weeklies Maggie Wartik
Mng. Ed.......................................Peter Kendall
VP of Adv..................................Jill McDermott
Mechanical Specifications: Type page 10 x 13; E - 5 cols, 1 7/8, 1 7/8 between; A - 5 cols, 1 7/8, 1 7/8 between; C - 8 cols, 1 13/16, 1 13/16 between.Equipment & Software: ; Software — QPS/QuarkXPress 5.01, Multi-Ad/ Creator 4.03, Adobe/Photoshop 6.01, Adobe/ Illustrator 9.02.
Delivery Method: Mail, Newsstand, Racks
Areas Served: 60047

LIBERTYVILLE REVIEW (THUR)

435 N Michigan Ave, Chicago, IL, 60611-4066, Cook, USA; gen tel (866) 399-0537; adv tel (866) 399-0537; ed tel (312) 222-3429; gen fax (312) 222-2598; ed fax (312) 222-2598; disp adv e-mail jmcdermott@tribpub.com; class adv e-mail jmcdermott@tribpub.com; ed e-mail pjurik@chicagotribune.com; web site chicagotribune.com/suburbs/libertyville
Circulation: 806pd,; AAM
Advertising rate: 1/4 P $360, 1/2 P $830, Full $1300
Established: 1912
Group: Tronc, Inc.
Pub./Ed.-in-Chief ....R. Bruce Dold
Ed. ....Phil Jurik
Gen. Mgr. of Suburban Weeklies Maggie Wartik
Mng. Ed.......................................Peter Kendall
VP of Adv..................................Jill McDermott
Mechanical Specifications: Type page 10 x 13; E - 5 cols, 1 7/8, 1 7/8 between; A - 5 cols, 1 7/8, 1 7/8 between; C - 8 cols, 1 3/16, 1 3/16 between.Equipment & Software: ; Software — QPS/QuarkXPress 5.01, Multi-Ad/ Creator 4.03, Adobe/Photoshop 6.01, Adobe/ Illustrator 9.02.
Delivery Method: Mail, Newsstand, Racks

LINCOLNSHIRE REVIEW (THUR)

435 N Michigan Ave, Chicago, IL, 60611-4066, Cook, USA; gen tel (847) 329-2000; ed tel (312) 321-2324; disp adv e-mail advertisinginfo@suntimes.com; class adv e-mail classifieds@stmedianetwork.com; web site www.pioneerlocal.com
Circulation: 210pd,; AAM
Advertising rate: 1/4 P $360, 1/2 P $830, Full $1300
Established: 1912
Group: Tronc, Inc.
VP of Adv..................................Jill McDermott
Pub./Ed.-in-Chief ....R. Bruce Dold
Ed. ....Phil Jurik
Gen. Mgr. of Suburban Weeklies Maggie Wartik
Mng. Ed.......................................Peter Kendall
Delivery Method: Mail, Newsstand, Racks

LINCOLNWOOD REVIEW (THUR)

435 N Michigan Ave, Chicago, IL, 60611-4066, Cook, USA; gen tel (847) 486-9200; ed tel (312) 321-3277; gen fax (847) 696-3229; disp adv e-mail advertisinginfo@suntimes.com; class adv e-mail classifieds@stmedianetwork.com; web site www.pioneerlocal.com
Circulation: 290pd,; AAM
Advertising rate: 1/4 P $360, 1/2 P $830, Full $1300
Established: 1912
Group: Tronc, Inc.
Pub./Ed.-in-Chief ....R. Bruce Dold
Ed. ....Phil Jurik
Gen. Mgr. of Suburban Weeklies Maggie Wartik
Mng. Ed.......................................Peter Kendall
VP of Adv..................................Jill McDermott
Mechanical Specifications: Type page 10 x 13; E - 5 cols, 1 7/8, 1 7/8 between; A - 5 cols, 1 7/8, 1 7/8 between; C - 8 cols, 1 13/16, 1 13/16 between.Equipment & Software: ; Software — QPS/QuarkXPress 5.01, Multi-Ad/ Creator 4.03, Adobe/Photoshop 6.01, Adobe/ Illustrator 9.02.
Delivery Method: Mail, Newsstand, Racks
Areas Served: 60645, 60646, 60712

MORTON GROVE CHAMPION (THUR)

435 N Michigan Ave, Chicago, IL, 60611-4066, Cook, USA; gen tel (866) 399-0537; adv tel (866) 399-0537; ed tel (312) 222-3429; gen fax (312) 222-2598; ed fax (312) 222-2598; disp adv e-mail jmcdermott@tribpub.com; class adv e-mail jmcdermott@tribpub.com; ed e-mail pjurik@chicagotribune.com; web site chicagotribune.com/suburbs/morton-grove
Circulation: 569pd,; AAM
Advertising rate: 1/4 P $360, 1/2 P $830, Full $1300
Established: 1912
Group: Tronc, Inc.
Vice Pres., Adv..............................Susan Karol
Regl./Nat'l Adv. Mgr......................Steve Walzer
Mgr., Niche Publications..............Kyle Leonard
Circ. Dir......................................David Perham
Exec. Ed...................................John Ambrosia
Bureau Chief................................Randy Blaser
Ed. ....Dan Obermaier
Ed. ....Gary Taylor
Mng. Ed......................................Mike Martinez
Pub./Ed.-in-Chief ....R. Bruce Dold
Ed. ....Phil Jurik
Gen. Mgr. of Suburban Weeklies Maggie Wartik
Mng. Ed.......................................Peter Kendall
VP of Adv..................................Jill McDermott
Mechanical Specifications: Type page 10 x 13; E - 5 cols, 1 7/8, 1 7/8 between; A - 5 cols, 1 7/8, 1 7/8 between; C - 8 cols, 1 13/16, 1 13/16 between.Equipment & Software: ; Software — QPS/QuarkXPress 5.01, Multi-Ad/ Creator 4.03, Adobe/Photoshop 6.01, Adobe/ Illustrator 9.02.
Delivery Method: Mail, Newsstand, Racks
Areas Served: 60053

MUNDELEIN REVIEW (THUR)

435 N Michigan Ave, Chicago, IL, 60611-4066, Cook, USA; gen tel (866) 399-0537; adv tel (866) 399-0537; ed tel (312) 222-3429; gen fax (312) 222-2598; ed fax (312) 222-2598; disp adv e-mail jmcdermott@tribpub.com; class adv e-mail jmcdermott@tribpub.com; ed e-mail pjurik@chicagotribune.com; web site chicagotribune.com/suburbs/mundelein
Circulation: 437pd,; AAM
Advertising rate: 1/4 P $360, 1/2 P $830, Full $1300
Established: 1912
Group: Tronc, Inc.
Pub./Ed.-in-Chief ....R. Bruce Dold

Ed. .... Phil Jurik
Gen. Mgr. of Suburban Weeklies Maggie Wartik
Mng. Ed....................................... Peter Kendall
VP of Adv.................................. Jill McDermott
Mechanical Specifications: Type page 10 x 13; E - 5 cols, 1 7/8, 1 7/8 between; A - 5 cols, 1 7/8, 1 7/8 between; C - 8 cols, 1 7/8, 1 13/16 between.Equipment & Software: ; Software — QPS/QuarkXPress 5.01, Multi-Ad/Creator 4.03, Adobe/Photoshop 6.01, Adobe/Illustrator 9.02.
Delivery Method: Mail, Newsstand, Racks
Areas Served: 60060

NEWS-STAR (WED)

6221 N Clark St, Chicago, IL, 60660-1207, Cook, USA; gen tel (773) 465-9700; gen fax (773) 465-9800; disp adv e-mail insidepublicationschicago@gmail.com; class adv e-mail inside1958@gmail.com; web site www.insideonline.com
Circulation: 318pd, 19,000fr; Sworn/Estimate/Non-Audited
Advertising rate: $25.00
Established: 1906Editions: (52) News-Star, Inside-Booster & Skyline
Digital Platform - Tablet: Apple iOS, Android, Windows 7, Kindle, Nook, Kindle Fire
Pub.. Ron Roenigk
Mechanical Specifications: 10.25" x 15.75" / 5 Columns Equipment & Software: Hardware — iMac; Presses — none; Software — CS4
Delivery Method: Mail, Newsstand, Carrier, Racks
Areas Served: 60610, 60611, 60602, 60613 60614, 60618, 60657, 60645, 60626, 60659, 60660, 60625, 60640

NILES HERALD-SPECTATOR (THUR)

435 N Michigan Ave, Chicago, IL, 60611-4066, Cook, USA; gen tel (847) 696-3133; adv tel (847) 486-7300; ed tel (312) 321-2864; gen fax (847) 696-3229; disp adv e-mail advertisinginfo@suntimes.com; class adv e-mail classifieds@stmedianetwork.com; ed e-mail bmeyerson@pioneerlocal.com; web site www.pioneerlocal.com
Circulation: 393pd,; AAM
Advertising rate: 1/4 P $360, 1/2 P $830, Full $1300
Established: 1912
Group: Tronc, Inc.
Regl./Nat'l Adv. Mgr..................... Steve Walzer
Exec. Ed.................................. John Ambrosia
Bureau Chief.................................... Tom Ganz
Ed. .... Rich Behren
Ed. .... Anne Lunde
Ed. .... Lloyd Weston
Pub./Ed.-in-Chief .... R. Bruce Dold
Ed. .... Phil Jurik
Gen. Mgr. of Suburban Weeklies Maggie Wartik
Mng. Ed....................................... Peter Kendall
VP of Adv.................................. Jill McDermott
Mechanical Specifications: Type page 10 x 13; E - 5 cols, 1 7/8, 1 7/8 between; A - 5 cols, 1 7/8, 1 7/8 between; C - 8 cols, 1 13/16, 1 13/16 between.Equipment & Software: ; Software — QPS/QuarkXPress 5.01, Multi-Ad/Creator 4.03, Adobe/Photoshop 6.01, Adobe/Illustrator 9.02.
Delivery Method: Mail, Newsstand, Racks
Areas Served: 60714

NORRIDGE-HARWOOD HEIGHTS NEWS (THUR)

435 N Michigan Ave, Chicago, IL, 60611-4066, Cook, USA; gen tel (866) 399-0537; adv tel (866) 399-0537; ed tel (312) 222-3429; gen fax (312) 222-2598; ed fax (312) 222-2598; disp adv e-mail jmcdermott@tribpub.com; class adv e-mail jmcdermott@tribpub.com; ed e-mail pjurik@chicagotribune.com; web site chicagotribune.com/suburbs/norridge
Circulation: 866pd,; AAM
Advertising rate: 1/4 P $360, 1/2 P $830, Full $1300
Established: 1984
Group: Tronc, Inc.
Pub./Ed.-in-Chief .... R. Bruce Dold
Ed. .... Phil Jurik
Gen. Mgr. of Suburban Weeklies Maggie Wartik
Mng. Ed....................................... Peter Kendall
VP of Adv.................................. Jill McDermott
Mechanical Specifications: Type page 10 x 13; E - 5 cols, 1 7/8, 1 7/8 between; A - 5 cols, 1 1/8, 1 1/8 between; C - 8 cols, 1 13/16, 1 13/16 between.Equipment & Software: ; Software — QPS/QuarkXPress 5.01, Multi-Ad/Creator 4.03, Adobe/Photoshop 6.01, Adobe/Illustrator 9.02.
Delivery Method: Mail, Newsstand, Racks
Areas Served: 60656, 60634, 60706

NORTHBROOK STAR (THUR)

435 N Michigan Ave, Chicago, IL, 60611-4066, Cook, USA; gen tel (866) 399-0537; adv tel (866) 399-0537; ed tel (312) 222-3429; gen fax (312) 222-2598; ed fax (312) 222-2598; disp adv e-mail jmcdermott@tribpub.com; class adv e-mail jmcdermott@tribpub.com; ed e-mail pjurik@chicagotribune.com; web site chicagotribune.com/suburbs/northbrook
Circulation: 1,238pd,; AAM
Advertising rate: 1/4 P $360, 1/2 P $830, Full $1300
Established: 1912
Group: Tronc, Inc.
Regl./Nat'l Adv. Mgr..................... Steve Walzer
Pub./Ed.-in-Chief .... R. Bruce Dold
Ed. .... Phil Jurik
Gen. Mgr. of Suburban Weeklies Maggie Wartik
Mng. Ed....................................... Peter Kendall
VP of Adv.................................. Jill McDermott
Mechanical Specifications: Type page 10 x 13; E - 5 cols, 1 7/8, between; A - 5 cols, 1 7/8, between; C - 8 cols, 1 13/16, between. Equipment & Software: ; Software — QPS/QuarkXPress 5.01, Multi-Ad/Creator 4.03, Adobe/Photoshop 6.01, Adobe/Illustrator 9.02.
Delivery Method: Mail, Newsstand, Racks
Areas Served: 60062

OAK LEAVES (THUR)

435 N Michigan Ave, Chicago, IL, 60611-4066, Cook, USA; gen tel (866) 399-0537; adv tel (866) 399-0537; ed tel (312) 222-3429; gen fax (312) 222-2598; ed fax (312) 222-2598; disp adv e-mail jmcdermott@tribpub.com; class adv e-mail jmcdermott@tribpub.com; ed e-mail pjurik@chicagotribune.com; web site chicagotribune.com/suburbs/oak-park
Circulation: 893pd,; AAM
Advertising rate: 1/8 Pg $220.00; 1/6 Pg $240.00; 1/4 Pg $360.00
Established: 1912
Group: Tronc, Inc.
Pub./Ed.-in-Chief .... R. Bruce Dold
Ed. .... Phil Jurik
Gen. Mgr. of Suburban Weeklies Maggie Wartik
Mng. Ed....................................... Peter Kendall
VP of Adv.................................. Jill McDermott
Mechanical Specifications: Type page 10 x 13; E - 5 cols, 1 7/8, 1 7/8 between; A - 5 cols, 1 7/8, 1 7/8 between; C - 8 cols, 1 13/16, 1 13/16 between.Equipment & Software: ; Software — QPS/QuarkXPress 5.01, Multi-Ad/Creator 4.03, Adobe/Photoshop 6.01, Adobe/Illustrator 9.02.
Delivery Method: Mail, Newsstand, Racks
Areas Served: 60301, 60302, 60303, 60304

PARK RIDGE HERALD ADVOCATE (THUR)

435 N Michigan Ave, Chicago, IL, 60611-4066, Cook, USA; gen tel (866) 399-0537; adv tel (866) 399-0537; ed tel (312) 222-3429; gen fax (312) 222-2598; ed fax (312) 222-2598; disp adv e-mail jmcdermott@tribpub.com; class adv e-mail jmcdermott@tribpub.com; ed e-mail pjurik@chicagotribune.com; web site chicagotribune.com/suburbs/park-ridge
Circulation: 1,909pd,; AAM
Advertising rate: 1/4 P $360, 1/2 P $830, Full $1300
Established: 1912
Group: Tronc, Inc.
Gen. Mgr. of Suburban Weeklies Maggie Wartik
Pub./Ed.-in-Chief .... R. Bruce Dold
VP of Adv.................................. Jill McDermott
Ed. .... Phil Jurik
Mng. Ed....................................... Peter Kendall
Mechanical Specifications: Type page 10 x 13; E - 5 cols, 1 7/8, 1 7/8 between; A - 5 cols, 1 7/8, 1 7/8 between; C - 8 cols, 1 13/16, 1 13/16 between.Equipment & Software: ; Software — QPS/QuarkXPress 5.01, Multi-Ad/Creator 4.03, Adobe/Photoshop 6.01, Adobe/Illustrator 9.02.
Delivery Method: Mail, Newsstand, Racks
Areas Served: 60068

REDEYE (THUR)

435 N Michigan Ave, Chicago, IL, 60611-4066, Cook, USA; gen tel (312) 222-4970; disp adv e-mail advertisingredeye@tribpub.com; ed e-mail redeye@tribune.com; web site redeyechicago.com
Adv.. Jenny McCabe
Sports Ed....................................... Chris Sosa
Exec. Ed........................... Elise De Los Santos
Digital Ed. .... Michelle Lopes
Dsgn. Dir. .... Aly Morris

REPORTER JOURNAL (SAT)

4937 N Milwaukee Ave, Chicago, IL, 60630-2114, Cook, USA; gen tel (773) 286-6100; gen fax (773) 286-8151; disp adv e-mail nadignewpapers@aol.com; class adv e-mail ads@nadignewspapers.com; web site www.nadignewspapers.com
Circulation: 3,000pd, 10,000fr; Sworn/Estimate/Non-Audited
Advertising rate: Open inch rate $21.50
Established: 1965
Digital Platform - Mobile: Apple, Android, Windows, Blackberry
Digital Platform - Tablet: Apple iOS, Android, Windows 7, Blackberry Tablet OS
Pub... Brian Nadig
Pub... Glenn Nadig
Ed. .... Randy Erickson
Circ. .... Joe Czech
Mechanical Specifications: Type page 10 x 16; E - 6 cols, between; A - 6 cols, between; C - 6 cols, between.
Delivery Method: Carrier

SKOKIE REVIEW (THUR)

435 N Michigan Ave, Chicago, IL, 60611-4066, Cook, USA; gen tel (866) 399-0537; adv tel (866) 399-0537; ed tel (312) 222-3429; gen fax (312) 222-2598; ed fax (312) 222-2598; disp adv e-mail jmcdermott@tribpub.com; class adv e-mail jmcdermott@tribpub.com; ed e-mail pjurik@chicagotribune.com; web site chicagotribune.com/suburbs/skokie
Circulation: 1,167pd, 5fr; AAM
Advertising rate: 1/4 P $360, 1/2 P $830, Full $1300
Established: 1912
Group: Tronc, Inc.
Ed. .... Phil Jurik
Gen. Mgr. of Suburban Weeklies Maggie Wartik
Pub./Ed.-in-Chief .... R. Bruce Dold
VP of Adv.................................. Jill McDermott
Mng. Ed....................................... Peter Kendall
Mechanical Specifications: Type page 10 x 13; E - 5 cols, 1 7/8, 1 7/8 between; A - 5 cols, 1 7/8, 1 7/8 between; C - 8 cols, 1 13/16, 1 13/16 between.Equipment & Software: ; Software — QPS/QuarkXPress 5.01, Multi-Ad/Creator 4.03, Adobe/Photoshop 6.01, Adobe/Illustrator 9.02.
Delivery Method: Mail, Newsstand, Racks
Areas Served: 60076, 60077

THE DOINGS WEEKLY - BURR RIDGE (THUR)

435 N Michigan Ave, Chicago, IL, 60611-4066, Cook, USA; gen tel (866) 399-0537; adv tel (866) 399-0537; ed tel (312) 222-3429; gen fax (312) 222-2598; ed fax (312) 222-2598; disp adv e-mail jmcdermott@tribpub.com; web site chicagotribune.com/suburbs/burr-ridge
Established: 1912
Ed. .... Phil Jurik
Mng. Ed....................................... Peter Kendall
Gen. Mgr. of Suburban Weeklies Maggie Wartik
Pub./Ed.-in-Chief .... R. Bruce Dold
VP of Adv.................................. Jill McDermott
Mechanical Specifications: Type page 10 x 13; E - 5 cols, 1 7/8, 1 7/8 between; A - 5 cols, 1 7/8, 1 7/8 between; C - 8 cols, 1 13/16, 1 13/16 between.Equipment & Software: ; Software — QPS/QuarkXPress 5.01, Multi-Ad/Creator 4.03, Adobe/Photoshop 6.01, Adobe/Illustrator 9.02.
Delivery Method: Mail, Newsstand, Racks

THE DOINGS - CLARENDON HILLS (THUR)

435 N Michigan Ave, Chicago, IL, 60611-4066, Cook, USA; gen tel (866) 399-0537; adv tel (866) 399-0537; ed tel (312) 222-3429; gen fax (312) 222-2598; ed fax (312) 222-2598; disp adv e-mail jmcdermott@tribpub.com; web site chicagotribune.com/suburbs/clarendon-hills
Established: 1912
Ed. .... Phil Jurik
Mng. Ed....................................... Peter Kendall
Gen. Mgr. of Suburban Weeklies Maggie Wartik
Pub./Ed.-in-Chief .... R. Bruce Dold
VP of Adv.................................. Jill McDermott
Delivery Method: Mail, Newsstand, Racks

THE DOINGS - HINSDALE (THUR)

435 N Michigan Ave, Chicago, IL, 60611-4066, Cook, USA; gen tel (866) 399-0537; adv tel (866) 399-0537; ed tel (312) 222-3429; gen fax (312) 222-2598; ed fax (312) 222-2598; disp adv e-mail jmcdermott@tribpub.com; web site chicagotribune.com/suburbs/hinsdale
Established: 1912
Ed. .... Phil Jurik
Mng. Ed....................................... Peter Kendall
Gen. Mgr. of Suburban Weeklies Maggie Wartik
Pub./Ed.-in-Chief .... R. Bruce Dold
VP of Adv.................................. Jill McDermott
Delivery Method: Mail, Newsstand, Racks

THE DOINGS - LA GRANGE (THUR)

435 N Michigan Ave, Chicago, IL, 60611-4066, Cook, USA; gen tel (866) 399-0537; adv tel (866) 399-0537; ed tel (312) 222-3429; gen fax (312) 222-2598; ed fax (312) 222-2598; disp adv e-mail jmcdermott@tribpub.com; web site chicagotribune.com/suburbs/la-grange
Established: 1912
Ed. .... Phil Jurik
Mng. Ed....................................... Peter Kendall
Gen. Mgr. of Suburban Weeklies Maggie Wartik
Pub./Ed.-in-Chief .... R. Bruce Dold
VP of Adv.................................. Jill McDermott
Delivery Method: Mail, Newsstand, Racks

THE DOINGS - OAK BROOK AND ELMHURST (THUR)

435 N Michigan Ave, Chicago, IL, 60611-4066, Cook, USA; gen tel (866) 399-0537; adv tel (866) 399-0537; ed tel (312) 222-3429; gen fax (312) 222-2598; ed fax (312) 222-2598; disp adv e-mail jmcdermott@tribpub.com; web site chicagotribune.com/suburbs/oak-brook
Established: 1912
Ed. .... Phil Jurik
Mng. Ed....................................... Peter Kendall
Gen. Mgr. of Suburban Weeklies Maggie Wartik
Pub./Ed.-in-Chief .... R. Bruce Dold
VP of Adv.................................. Jill McDermott
Delivery Method: Mail, Newsstand, Racks

THE DOINGS - WESTERN SPRINGS (THUR)

435 N Michigan Ave, Chicago, IL, 60611-4066, Cook, USA; gen tel (866) 399-0537; adv tel (866) 399-0537; ed tel (312) 222-3429; gen fax (312) 222-2598; ed fax (312) 222-2598; disp adv e-mail jmcdermott@tribpub.com; web site chicagotribune.com/suburbs/western-springs
Established: 1912
Ed. .... Phil Jurik
Mng. Ed....................................... Peter Kendall
Gen. Mgr. of Suburban Weeklies Maggie Wartik
Pub./Ed.-in-Chief .... R. Bruce Dold
VP of Adv.................................. Jill McDermott
Delivery Method: Mail, Newsstand, Racks

THE NAPERVILLE SUN (WED, FRI, SUN)

435 N Michigan Ave, Fl 10, Chicago, IL, 60611-7556, Cook, USA; gen tel (866) 399-0537; adv tel (866) 399-0537; ed tel (312)

222-3429; gen fax (312) 222-2598; ed fax (312) 222-2598; disp adv e-mail jmcdermott@tribpub.com; web site chicagotribune.com/suburbs/naperville-sun
Circulation: 3,886pd,; AAM
Advertising rate: 1/8 Pg $590.00; 1/6 Pg $710.00; 1/4 Pg $950.00
Established: 1935
Group: Tronc, Inc.
Digital Platform - Mobile: Apple, Android
Digital Platform - Tablet: Apple iOS, Android
VP of Adv. .... Jill McDermott
Ed. .... Phil Jurik
Pub./Ed.-in-Chief .... R. Bruce Dold
Gen. Mgr. of Suburban Weeklies Maggie Wartik
Mng. Ed. .... Peter Kendall
Mechanical Specifications: Type page 11 x 13; E - 5 cols, 2 1/16, between; A - 5 cols, 2 1/16, between; C - 8 cols, 1 3/16, between.
Delivery Method: Newsstand, Carrier, Racks
Areas Served: Will, Kane, DuPage, and Kendall

VERNON HILLS REVIEW (THUR)
435 N Michigan Ave, Chicago, IL, 60611-4066, Cook, USA; gen tel (847) 317-0500; ed tel (312) 321-2328; disp adv e-mail advertisinginfo@suntimes.com; class adv e-mail classifieds@stmedianetwork.com; web site www.pioneerlocal.com
Circulation: 363pd,; AAM
Advertising rate: 1/4 P $360, 1/2 P $830, Full $1300
Established: 1912
Group: Tronc, Inc.
VP of Adv. .... Jill McDermott
Ed. .... Phil Jurik
Pub./Ed.-in-Chief .... R. Bruce Dold
Mng. Ed. .... Peter Kendall
Gen. Mgr. of Suburban Weeklies Maggie Wartik
Delivery Method: Mail, Newsstand, Racks

WILMETTE LIFE (THUR)
435 N Michigan Ave, Chicago, IL, 60611-4066, Cook, USA; gen tel (866) 399-0537; adv tel (866) 399-0537; ed tel (312) 222-3429; gen fax (312) 222-2598; ed fax (312) 222-2598; disp adv e-mail jmcdermott@tribpub.com; class adv e-mail jmcdermott@tribpub.com; ed e-mail pjurik@chicagotribune.com; web site chicagotribune.com/suburbs/wilmette
Circulation: 895pd,; AAM
Advertising rate: 1/4 P $360, 1/2 P $830, Full $1300
Group: Tronc, Inc.
Ed. in Chief .... Jeff Wisser
Sr. Ed. .... Carol Goddard
Sr. Ed. .... Randy Blaser
Mng. Ed. .... Cathy Backer
Ed. .... Phil Jurik
Pub./Ed.-in-Chief .... R. Bruce Dold
Mng. Ed. .... Peter Kendall
VP of Adv. .... Jill McDermott
Gen. Mgr. of Suburban Weeklies Maggie Wartik
Mechanical Specifications: Type page 10 x 13; E - 5 cols, 1 7/8, 1 7/8 between; A - 5 cols, 1 7/8, 1 7/8 between; C - 8 cols, 1 13/16, 1 13/16 between.Equipment & Software: ; Software — QPS/QuarkXPress 5.01, Multi-Ad/Creator 4.03, Adobe/Photoshop 6.01, Adobe/Illustrator 9.02.
Delivery Method: Mail, Newsstand, Racks
Areas Served: 60091, 60043

WINNETKA TALK (THUR)
435 N Michigan Ave, Chicago, IL, 60611-4066, Cook, USA; gen tel (866) 399-0537; adv tel (866) 399-0537; ed tel (312) 222-3429; gen fax (312) 222-2598; ed fax (312) 222-2598; disp adv e-mail jmcdermott@tribpub.com; class adv e-mail jmcdermott@tribpub.com; ed e-mail pjurik@chicagotribune.com; web site chicagotribune.com/suburbs/winnetka
Circulation: 858pd,; AAM
Advertising rate: 1/4 P $360, 1/2 P $830, Full $1300
Established: 1912
Group: Tronc, Inc.
Adv. Dir. .... Peggy Cunniff
Exec. Ed. .... Paul Sassone
Ed. in Chief .... Jeff Wisser
Ed. .... Phil Jurik
Pub./Ed.-in-Chief .... R. Bruce Dold
Mng. Ed. .... Peter Kendall
VP of Adv. .... Jill McDermott
Gen. Mgr. of Suburban Weeklies Maggie Wartik
Mechanical Specifications: Type page 10 x 13; E - 5 cols, 1 7/8, 1 7/8 between; A - 5 cols, 1 7/8, 1 7/8 between; C - 8 cols, 1 13/16, 1 13/16 between.Equipment & Software: ; Software — QPS/QuarkXPress 5.01, Multi-Ad/Creator 4.03, Adobe/Photoshop 6.01, Adobe/Illustrator 9.02.
Delivery Method: Mail, Newsstand, Racks
Areas Served: 60093

CHRISMAN

CHRISMAN LEADER (THUR)
118 E Jefferson Ave, Chrisman, IL, 61924-1109, Edgar, USA; gen tel (217) 269-2811; gen fax (217) 269-3611; disp adv e-mail chrismanleader@insightbb.com; web site facebook.com/thechrismanleader
Circulation: 1,000pd,; Sworn/Estimate/Non-Audited
Advertising rate: Open inch rate $4.50
Owner .... Louis Albert
Pub. .... Sherri Mullenax
Delivery Method: Mail

CISSNA PARK

CISSNA PARK NEWS (THUR)
119 W Garfield Ave, Cissna Park, IL, 60924-6125, Iroquis, USA; gen tel (815) 457-2245; gen fax (815) 457-3245; disp adv e-mail rickbaier@yahoo.com; web site No Website
Advertising rate: Open inch rate $3.50
Established: 1958
Pub. .... Rick A. Baier
Delivery Method: Mail, Newsstand, Racks

RANKIN INDEPENDENT (THUR)
119 W Garfield Ave, Cissna Park, IL, 60924-6125, Iroquis, USA; gen tel (815) 457-2245; gen fax (815) 457-3245; disp adv e-mail rickbaier@yahoo.com
Circulation: 1,858pd,; Sworn/Estimate/Non-Audited
Advertising rate: Open inch rate $3.50
Established: 1958
Pub. .... Rick A. Baier
Ed. .... Steve Scott
Mechanical Specifications: Type page 10 1/4 x 16; E - 5 cols, 1 11/12, 1/6 between; A - 5 cols, 1 11/12, 1/6 between; C - 5 cols, 1 11/12, 1/6 between.Equipment & Software: Hardware — APP/Mac; Software — QPS/QuarkXPress 4.0.
Delivery Method: Mail, Newsstand, Racks

CLIFTON

THE ADVOCATE (THUR)
330 N 4th St, Clifton, IL, 60927-7232, Iroquois, USA; gen tel (815) 694-2122; gen fax (815) 694-2649; disp adv e-mail advocate@dloque.net; web site www.cliftonadvocate.com
Circulation: 1,441pd,; Sworn/Estimate/Non-Audited
Advertising rate: Open inch rate $4.00
Established: 1893
Ed. .... Therese Simoneau
Delivery Method: Mail, Newsstand

CLINTON

CLINTON JOURNAL (TUES, FRI, SAT)
111 S Monroe St, Clinton, IL, 61727-2057, DeWitt, USA; gen tel (217) 935-3171; gen fax (217) 935-6086; disp adv e-mail kpyne@theclintonjournal.com; class adv e-mail kpyne@theclintonjournal.com; ed e-mail gwoods@theclintonjournal.com; web site www.theclintonjournal.com
Circulation: 1,800pd, 6,600fr; Sworn/Estimate/Non-Audited
Advertising rate: Open inch rate $19.25
Group: News Media Corp.
Classified Adv. Mgr. .... Diane Robertson
Gen. Mgr./Ed. .... Gordon Woods
Katy O'Grady-Pyne
Sales Rep. .... Susan Munoz
Mechanical Specifications: Type page 11 1/2 x 21 1/2; E - 8 cols, 1 3/4, 1/8 between; A - 8 cols, 1 3/4, 1/8 between; C - 8 cols, 1 3/4, 1/8 between.
Delivery Method: Mail, Newsstand, Carrier, Racks
Areas Served: Clinton/DeLand/DeWitt/Farmer City/Kenney/Lane/Maroa/Wapella/Waynesville/Weldon

COAL CITY

THE COAL CITY COURANT (WED)
271 S Broadway St, Coal City, IL, 60416-1534, Grundy, USA; gen tel (815) 634-0315; adv tel (815) 476-7966 ext. 209; gen fax (815) 634-0317; adv fax (815) 476-7002; disp adv e-mail fpnads@cbcast.com; class adv e-mail fpnads@cbcast.com; web site www.freepressnewspapers.com
Circulation: 2,125pd, 30fr; Sworn/Estimate/Non-Audited
Advertising rate: Open inch rate $10.35
Established: 1976
Group: Free Press Newspapers
Digital Platform - Mobile: Apple, Android
Digital Platform - Tablet: Other
Pub. .... Eric Fisher
Ed. .... Ann Gill
Mechanical Specifications: Type page 11.12 x 20.5; E - 6 cols, 1.75, 1/6 between; A - 6 cols, 1 5/6, 1/6 between; C - 8 cols, 1 1/3, 1/6 between.Equipment & Software: Hardware — APP/Mac; Presses — none; Software — QPS/QuarkXPress.
Delivery Method: Mail, Newsstand
Areas Served: 60416, 60481, 60407, 60424, 60444

COLLINSVILLE

ILLINOIS SUBURBAN JOURNALS (WED, SUN)
2 Eastport Executive Dr, Collinsville, IL, 62234, Madison, USA; gen tel (618) 344-0264; gen fax (618) 344-3611; disp adv e-mail metroeastnews@yourjournal.com; web site stltoday.com/suburban-journals/illinois
Circulation: 40,335fr; Sworn/Estimate/Non-Audited
Advertising rate: Open inch rate $41.58
Established: 1922
Group: Lee Enterprises, Inc.
Ed. .... Greg Uptain
Promotions Dir./Niche Pub... Mary Ann Wagner
Mechanical Specifications: Type page 12 1/2 x 22 3/4; E - 6 cols, 1 7/8, 1/8 between; A - 6 cols, 1 7/8, 1/8 between; C - 10 cols, 1 1/4, 1/3 between.Equipment & Software: Hardware — IBM, APP/Mac; Software — QPS/QuarkXPress, Multi-Ad, Adobe/PageMaker.
Delivery Method: Mail, Newsstand, Racks

ST. CHARLES COUNTY SUBURBAN JOURNALS (WED, SUN)
2 Eastport Executive Dr, Collinsville, IL, 62234, Madison, USA; gen tel (618) 344-0264; gen fax (618) 344-3831; disp adv e-mail goodnews@yourjournal.com; web site www.yourjournal.com
Circulation: 19,800fr; Sworn/Estimate/Non-Audited
Advertising rate: Open inch rate $9.13
Promotions Dir./Niche Pub... Mary Ann Wagner
Ed. .... Greg UptainEquipment & Software: Hardware — SII/SYS 55, APP/Mac Network; Presses — 30-G/Urbanite, 2-G/Urbanite (3-color units).

DANVILLE

INDEPENDENT NEWS (WED)
2202 Kickapoo Dr, Danville, IL, 61832-5379, Vermilion, USA; gen tel (217) 443-8484; gen fax (217) 443-8490; disp adv e-mail indnews@news-gazette.com; class adv e-mail indnews@news-gazette.com; ed e-mail indnews@news-gazette.com; web site www.the-independent-news.com
Circulation: 330pd,; AAM
Advertising rate: Open inch rate $10.50
Established: 1975
Group: News Gazette Community News
The News-GazetteEditions: (52) The Independent News
Pub. .... John Foreman
Gen. Mgr. .... Tim Evans
Editor/office manager .... Vicki Delhaye
Mechanical Specifications: Full page is 11.75" wide by 21.5" tall, one column is 1.819" wide-Equipment & Software: Hardware — Mac; Presses — 9 unit King; Software — InDesign, Photoshop, Quark XPress
Delivery Method: Mail, Racks
Areas Served: 61832, 61883, 61833, 61846, 61844, 61870, 61850, 61876, 61841, 61810, 61817, 61844, 61841, 61924, 61870

DECATUR

DECATUR TRIBUNE (WED)
132 S Water St, Ste 424, Decatur, IL, 62523-6043, Macon, USA; gen tel (217) 422-9702; gen fax (217) 422-7320; disp adv e-mail decaturtribune@aol.com; class adv e-mail decaturtribune@aol.com; ed e-mail decaturtribune@aol.com; web site www.decaturtribune.com
Circulation: 7,000pd, 0fr; Sworn/Estimate/Non-Audited
Advertising rate: Open inch rate $7.00
Established: 1968
Ed./Pub. .... Paul Osborne
Delivery Method: Mail, Newsstand
Areas Served: Decatur and Macon County 62521, 62522, 62523, 62525

DEKALB

THE MIDWEEK (WED)
1586 Barber Greene Rd, Dekalb, IL, 60115-7900, DeKalb, USA; gen tel (815) 756-4841; gen fax (815) 758-5059; ed e-mail readit@midweeknews.com; web site www.midweek-news.com
Advertising rate: Open inch rate $18.75
Ed. .... Dana Herra
Delivery Method: Mail

VALLEY LIFE (TUES)
1586 Barber Greene Rd, Dekalb, IL, 60115-7900, DeKalb, USA; gen tel (815) 756-4841; gen fax (815) 758-5059; disp adv e-mail vfpads@vfpnews.com; class adv e-mail vfpads@vfpnews.com; ed e-mail vfpnews@vfpnews.com; web site www.valleylifepress.com
Circulation: 15,000fr; Sworn/Estimate/Non-Audited
Advertising rate: Open inch rate $18.75
Group: Shaw Media
Adv. Sales .... Rob Dancey
Ed. .... Debbie Behrends
Delivery Method: Mail
Areas Served: 60531, 60536, 60537, 60541, 60551,60545, 60548, 60549, 60552

DES PLAINES

ARLINGTON HEIGHTS/BUFFALO GROVE/ROLLING MEADOWS/WHEELING JOURNAL (THUR)
622 Graceland Ave, Des Plaines, IL, 60016-4519, Cook, USA; gen tel (847) 299-5511; gen fax (847) 298-8549; disp adv e-mail

journalads@journal-topics.info; ed e-mail journalnews@journal-topics.info; web site journal-topics.com
Advertising rate: Open inch rate $28.62
Managing Ed................................Rick Wessell
Mktg. Mgr. ....Robert Wessell
Ed./Pub....................................Todd Wessell
Delivery Method: Mail

DES PLAINES JOURNAL (WED, FRI)
622 Graceland Ave, Des Plaines, IL, 60016-4519, Cook, USA; gen tel (847) 299-5511; gen fax (847) 298-8549; disp adv e-mail journalnews@mail.com; web site journal-topics.com/news/des_plaines
Advertising rate: Open inch rate $30.12
Established: 1930
Managing Ed. ....Todd Wessell
Adv. Dir...Rick Wessell
Classified Mgr. ....Robert Wessell
Delivery Method: Mail

ELK GROVE JOURNAL (THUR)
622 Graceland Ave, Des Plaines, IL, 60016-4519, Cook, USA; gen tel (847) 299-5511; gen fax (847) 298-8549; disp adv e-mail journalnews@mail.com; web site journal-topics.com/news/des_plaines
Advertising rate: Open inch rate $28.52
Classified Mgr. ....Robert Wessell
Managing Ed...............................Todd Wessell
Adv. Dir...Rick Wessell
Delivery Method: Mail

GLENVIEW JOURNAL (THUR, BI-MTHLY)
622 Graceland Ave, Des Plaines, IL, 60016-4519, Cook, USA; gen tel (847) 299-5511; gen fax (847) 298-8549; disp adv e-mail journalnews@mail.com; web site journal-topics.com/news/glenview
Advertising rate: Open inch rate $30.03
Adv. Dir...Rick Wessell
Classified Mgr. ....Robert Wessell
Managing Ed...............................Todd Wessell
Delivery Method: Mail

MOUNT PROSPECT JOURNAL (WED, FRI)
622 Graceland Ave, Des Plaines, IL, 60016-4519, Cook, USA; gen tel (847) 299-5511; gen fax (847) 298-8549; disp adv e-mail journalnews@mail.com; web site journal-topics.com/news/mt_prospect
Circulation: 22,000pd, 68,996fr; Sworn/Estimate/Non-Audited
Advertising rate: Open inch rate $33.42
Classified Mgr. ....Robert Wessell
Managing Ed...............................Todd Wessell
Adv. Dir...Rick Wessell
Delivery Method: Mail

NILES JOURNAL (WED)
622 Graceland Ave, Des Plaines, IL, 60016-4519, Cook, USA; gen tel (847) 299-5511; gen fax (847) 298-8549; disp adv e-mail journalads@journal-topics.info; ed e-mail journalnews@journal-topics.info; web site journal-topics.com/news/niles
Advertising rate: Open inch rate $30.03
Classified Mgr. ....Robert Wessell
Adv. Dir...Rick Wessell
Managing Ed...............................Todd Wessell
Delivery Method: Mail

PALATINE JOURNAL (THUR)
622 Graceland Ave, Des Plaines, IL, 60016-4519, Cook, USA; gen tel (847) 299-5511; gen fax (847) 298-8549; disp adv e-mail journalnews@mail.com; web site journal-topics.com/news/palatine
Advertising rate: Open inch rate $28.52
Adv. Dir...Rick Wessell
Managing Ed...............................Todd Wessell
Classified Mgr. ....Robert Wessell
Delivery Method: Mail, Newsstand

PARK RIDGE JOURNAL (WED)
622 Graceland Ave, Des Plaines, IL, 60016-4519, Cook, USA; gen tel (847) 299-5511; gen fax (847) 298-8549; disp adv e-mail journalnews@mail.com; web site journal-topics.com/news/park_ridge
Advertising rate: Open inch rate $30.03
Adv. Dir...Rick Wessell
Managing Ed...............................Todd Wessell
Classified Mgr. ....Robert Wessell
Delivery Method: Mail

PROSPECT HEIGHTS JOURNAL (WED, FRI)
622 Graceland Ave, Des Plaines, IL, 60016-4519, Cook, USA; gen tel (847) 299-5511; gen fax (847) 298-8549; disp adv e-mail journalnews@mail.com; web site journal-topics.com/news/prospect_hts
Advertising rate: Open inch rate $30.12
Adv. Dir...Rick Wessell
Managing Ed...............................Todd Wessell
Classified Mgr. ....Robert Wessell
Delivery Method: Mail

ROSEMONT JOURNAL (WED)
622 Graceland Ave, Des Plaines, IL, 60016-4519, Cook, USA; gen tel (847) 299-5511; gen fax (847) 298-8549; disp adv e-mail journalads@mail.com; class adv e-mail journalads@mail.com; web site www.journal-topics.com
Advertising rate: Open inch rate $30.03
Classified Mgr. ....Robert Wessell
Managing Ed...............................Todd Wessell
Adv. Dir...Rick Wessell
Delivery Method: Mail

DIXON

FORRESTON JOURNAL (THUR)
113 S Peoria Ave, Dixon, IL, 61021-2905, Lee, USA; gen tel (815) 732-6166; adv tel (815) 625-3600, Ext. 5613; ed tel (815) 732-6166; gen fax (815) 732-4238; disp adv e-mail leisenberg@oglecountynews.com; class adv e-mail classifieds@svnmail.com; advertising@svnmail.com; ed e-mail vwells@oglecountynews.com; web site www.oglecountynews.com
Circulation: 967pd, 24fr; Sworn/Estimate/Non-Audited
Advertising rate: Open inch rate $8.76
Group: Shaw Media
Gen. Mgr. ....Earleen Hinton
HR ....Kris Boggs
Pub...Trevis Mayfield
Adv. Dir...................................Jennifer Baratta
Ed. ....Vinde Wells
Reporter ....Chris Johnson
Delivery Method: Mail, Newsstand, Racks

MT. MORRIS TIMES (THUR)
113 S Peoria Ave, Dixon, IL, 61021-2905, Lee, USA; gen tel (815) 732-6166; adv tel (815) 625-3600, Ext. 5614; gen fax (815) 732-4238; disp adv e-mail leisenberg@oglecountynews.com; web site www.oglecountynews.com
Circulation: 878pd,; Sworn/Estimate/Non-Audited
Advertising rate: Open inch rate $8.76
Group: Shaw Media
Gen. Mgr ....Earleen Hinton
Ed. ....Vinde Wells
Mechanical Specifications: Type page 13 x 21 1/2; E - 6 cols, 2 1/16, between; A - 6 cols, 2 1/16, between; C - 8 cols, 1 7/16, between. Equipment & Software: Hardware — APP/Mac; Software — Multi-Ad/Creator, Microsoft/Word, Microsoft/Excel.
Delivery Method: Mail, Newsstand, Racks

OREGON REPUBLICAN REPORTER (THUR)
113 S Peoria Ave, Dixon, IL, 61021-2905, Lee, USA; gen tel (815) 732-6166; adv tel (815) 625-3600, Ext. 5615; gen fax (815) 732-4238; disp adv e-mail leisenberg@oglecountynews.com; web site www.oglecountynews.com
Circulation: 1,495pd,; Sworn/Estimate/Non-Audited
Advertising rate: Open inch rate $8.76
Established: 1851
Group: Shaw Media
Gen. Mgr. ....Earleen Hinton
Ed. ....Vinde Wells
Mechanical Specifications: Type page 13 x 21 1/2; E - 6 cols, 2 1/16, between; A - 6 cols, 2 1/16, between; C - 8 cols, 1 7/16, between. Equipment & Software: Hardware — APP/Mac; Software — Multi-Ad/Creator, Microsoft/Word, Microsoft/Excel.
Delivery Method: Mail, Newsstand, Racks

TRI-COUNTY PRESS (THUR)
113 S Peoria Ave, Dixon, IL, 61021-2905, Lee, USA; gen tel (815) 732-6166 ext. 5901; gen fax (815) 732-4238; disp adv e-mail leisenberg@oglecountynews.com; ed e-mail vwells@oglecountynews.com; web site www.oglecountynews.com
Circulation: 1,200pd,; Sworn/Estimate/Non-Audited
Advertising rate: Open inch rate $8.76
Group: Shaw Media
Gen. Mgr. ....Earleen Hinton
Ed. ....Vinde Wells
Adv. Sales Mgr. ....Luke Eisenberg
Delivery Method: Mail, Newsstand, Racks

DOWNERS GROVE

ADDISON SUBURBAN LIFE (WED, THUR, FRI)
1101 31st St, Ste 260, Downers Grove, IL, 60515-5585, DuPage, USA; gen tel (630) 368-1100; adv tel (630) 427-6213; ed tel (630) 427-6250; gen fax (630) 969-0228; disp adv e-mail nshannon@shawmedia.com; class adv e-mail sbissell@shawmedia.com; ed e-mail dgood@shawmedia.com; web site www.mysuburbanlife.com
Circulation: 193pd, 0fr; CAC
Advertising rate: 1/8 Pg $536.00; 1/4 Pg $956.00; 1/2 Pg $1530.00; Full Pg $2550.00
Group: Shaw Media
Marketing Dir............................Katie Sherman
Major/Nat'l Accts./Grp. Sales Dir.........Maureen Ringness
Gen. Mgr. ....Ryan Wells
Adv. Dir.......................................Laura Burke
Delivery Method: Mail, Newsstand, Racks
Areas Served: Dupage

BENSENVILLE PRESS (FRI)
1101 31st St, Ste 100, Downers Grove, IL, 60515-5581, Dupage, USA; gen tel (630) 368-1100; ed tel (630) 368-1144; gen fax (630) 969-0228; disp adv e-mail celebrations@mysuburbanlife.com; ed e-mail letters@mysuburbanlife.com; web site www.mysuburbanlife.com
Circulation: 296pd, 0fr; CAC
Advertising rate: 1/8 Pg $536.00; 1/4 Pg $956.00; 1/2 Pg $1530.00; Full Pg $2550.00
Class Advt Mgr ....Brad Hanahan
Ed ....Dave Lemery
Mechanical Specifications: Type page 12 3/4 x 21 1/2.

BERWYN SUBURBAN LIFE (WED)
1101 31st St, Ste 260, Downers Grove, IL, 60515-5585, DuPage, USA; gen tel (630) 368-1100; adv tel (630) 427-6213; ed tel (630) 427-6254; gen fax (630) 969-0228; disp adv e-mail nshannon@shawmedia.com; class adv e-mail sbissell@shawmedia.com; ed e-mail mhendrickson@shawmedia.com; web site www.mysuburbanlife.com
Circulation: 1,814pd, 63fr; CAC
Advertising rate: 1/8 Pg $378.00; 1/4 Pg $675.0; 1/2 Pg $1080.00; Full Pg $1800.00
Group: Shaw Media
Pub..J. Tom Shaw
Marketing Dir............................Katie Sherman
Major/Nat'l Accts./Grp. Sales Dir.........Maureen Ringness
Ryan Wells
Delivery Method: Mail, Newsstand, Racks

BOLINGBROOK SUBURBAN LIFE (WED)
1101 31st St, Ste 260, Downers Grove, IL, 60515-5585, DuPage, USA; gen tel (630) 368-1100; adv tel (630) 427-6213; ed tel (630) 427-6252; gen fax (630) 969-0228; adv fax (630) 969-0228; ed fax (630) 969-0228; disp adv e-mail nshannon@shawmedia.com; class adv e-mail sbissell@shawmedia.com; ed e-mail rterrell@shawmedia.com; web site www.mysuburbanlife.com
Circulation: 5,256pd,; Sworn/Estimate/Non-Audited
Advertising rate: 1/8 Pg $956.00; 1/4 Pg $1706.00; 1/2 Pg $2730.00; Full Pg $4550.00
Digital Platform - Mobile: Apple, Android, Blackberry
Digital Platform - Tablet: Apple iOS, Android, Blackberry Tablet OS
Pub..J. Tom Shaw
Marketing Dir............................Katie Sherman
Major/Nat'l Accts./Grp. Sales Dir.........Maureen Ringness
Ryan Wells
Delivery Method: Mail, Newsstand, Racks
Areas Served: DuPage County

CAROL STREAM SUBURBAN LIFE (FRI)
1101 31st St Ste 100, Suite 100, Downers Grove, IL, 60515-5581, Dupage, USA; gen tel (630) 368-1100; adv tel (630) 427-6213; ed tel (630) 427-6248; gen fax (630) 969-0228; ed fax (630) 969-0228; disp adv e-mail bkorbel@shawmedia.com; class adv e-mail bhanahan@shawmedia.com; ed e-mail aschier@shawmedia.com; web site www.mysuburbanlife.com
Circulation: 203pd, 154fr; CAC
Advertising rate: 1/8 Pg $378.00; 1/4 Pg $675.0; 1/2 Pg $1080.00; Full Pg $1800.00
Group: Shaw Media
Pub ....J. Tom Shaw
Marketing Dir ....Katie Sherman
Ed. ....Anna Schier
Major/Nat'l Accts./Grp. Sales Dir.........Maureen Ringness
Ryan Wells
Mechanical Specifications: Type page 10 1/8 x 12 1/4; E - 5 cols, 1 9/10, between; A - 5 cols, 1 9/10, between.Equipment & Software: ; Presses — 22-G/Urbanite, 10-G/Suburban.
Delivery Method: Mail, Newsstand, Racks

DOWNERS GROVE SUBURBAN LIFE (WED)
1101 31st St, Ste 260, Downers Grove, IL, 60515-5585, DuPage, USA; gen tel (630) 368-1100; adv tel (630) 427-6213; ed tel (630) 427-6252; gen fax (630) 969-0228; ed fax (630) 969-0228; disp adv e-mail nshannon@shawmedia.com; class adv e-mail sbissell@shawmedia.com; ed e-mail rterrell@shawmedia.com; web site www.mysuburbanlife.com
Circulation: 1,183pd, 11,461fr; CAC
Advertising rate: 1/8 Pg $672.00; 1/4 Pg $1200.00; 1/2 Pg $1920.00; Full Pg $3200.00
Established: 1883
Group: Shaw Media
Pub..J. Tom Shaw
Marketing Dir............................Katie Sherman
Ed. ....Ryan Terrell
Major/Nat'l Accts./Grp. Sales Dir.........Maureen Ringness
Ryan Wells
Mechanical Specifications: Type page 10 1/8 x 12 1/4; E - 4 cols, between; A - 4 cols, between; C - 8 cols, between.Equipment & Software: Hardware — APP/Mac; Presses — G/Suburban; Software — QPS/QuarkXPress 3.1.
Delivery Method: Mail, Newsstand, Racks

ELMHURST SUBURBAN LIFE (WED, THUR, FRI)
2001 Butterfield Rd, Ste 105, Downers Grove, IL, 60515-5479, DuPage, USA; gen tel (630) 368-1100; adv tel (630) 427-6213; ed tel (630) 427-6270; gen fax (630) 969-0228; ed fax (630) 969-0228; disp adv e-mail bkorbel@shawmedia.com; class adv e-mail bhanahan@shawmedia.com; ed e-mail dgood@shawmedia.com; web site www.mysuburbanlife.com
Circulation: 586pd, 73fr; CAC
Advertising rate: 1/8 Pg $536.00; 1/4 Pg $956.00; 1/2 Pg $1530.00; Full Pg $2550.00
Group: Shaw Media

Pub...J. Tom Shaw
Marketing Dir............................Katie Sherman
Ed. ....David Good
Major/Nat'l Accts./Grp. Sales Dir.........Maureen Ringness
Ryan Wells
Mechanical Specifications: Type page 10 1/8 x 12 1/4; E - 4 cols, between; A - 4 cols, between; C - 8 cols, between.
Delivery Method: Mail, Newsstand, Racks

GLEN ELLYN SUBURBAN LIFE (THUR)

1101 31st St, Ste 260, Downers Grove, IL, 60515-5585, Dupage, USA; gen tel (630) 368-1100; adv tel (630) 427-6213; ed tel (630) 427-6248; gen fax (630) 969-0228; disp adv e-mail nshannon@shawmedia.com; class adv e-mail sbissell@shawmedia.com; ed e-mail aschier@shawmedia.com; web site www.mysuburbanlife.com
Circulation: 326pd, 51fr; CAC
Advertising rate: 1/8 Pg $1008.00; 1/4 Pg $1800.00; 1/2 Pg $2880.00; Full Pg $4800.00
Group: Shaw Media
Pub...J. Tom Shaw
Marketing Dir............................Katie Sherman
Ed. ....David Lemery
Ryan Wells
Delivery Method: Mail, Newsstand, Racks

HINSDALE SUBURBAN LIFE (FRI)

1101 31st St, Ste 260, Downers Grove, IL, 60515-5585, Dupage, USA; gen tel (630) 368-1100; adv tel (630) 427-6213; ed tel (630) 427-6270; gen fax (630) 969-0228; ed fax (630) 969-0228; disp adv e-mail nshannon@shawmedia.com; class adv e-mail sbissell@shawmedia.com; ed e-mail dgood@shawmedia.com; web site www.mysuburbanlife.com
Circulation: 873pd, 1,818fr; CAC
Advertising rate: 1/8 Pg $788.00; 1/4 Pg $1406.00; 1/2 Pg $2250.00; Full Pg $3750.00
Established: 1926
Group: Shaw Media
Pub...J. Tom Shaw
Marketing Dir............................Katie Sherman
Ed. ....David Good
Major/Nat'l Accts./Grp. Sales Dir.........Maureen Ringness
Ryan Wells
Mechanical Specifications: Type page 10 3/4 x 14; E - 6 cols, 2, between; A - 6 cols, 2, between; C - 9 cols, 1 5/16, between.Equipment & Software: Hardware — APP/Mac, AU, IBM; Presses — 22-G/Urbanite, 10-G/Urbanite; Software — Dewar.
Delivery Method: Mail, Newsstand, Racks
Areas Served: 60525, 60523, 60513, 60521, 60546, 60480, 60480, 60521, 60514, 60561, 60546, 60154, 60558

LAGRANGE SUBURBAN LIFE (WED)

2001 Butterfield Rd, Ste 105, Downers Grove, IL, 60515-5479, DuPage, USA; gen tel (630) 368-1100; adv tel (630) 427-6213; ed tel (630) 427-6254; gen fax (630) 969-0228; ed fax (630) 969-0228; disp adv e-mail bkorbel@shawmedia.com; class adv e-mail bhanahan@shawmedia.com; ed e-mail mhendrickson@shawmedia.com; web site www.mysuburbanlife.com
Circulation: 471pd, 23fr; AAM
Advertising rate: 1/8 Pg $536.00; 1/4 Pg $956.00; 1/2 Pg $1530.00; Full Pg $2550.00
Group: Shaw Media
Pub...J. Tom Shaw
Ed. ....Matthew Hendrickson
Major/Nat'l Accts./Grp. Sales Dir.........Maureen Ringness
Ryan Wells
Mechanical Specifications: Type page 10 1/2 x 16.
Delivery Method: Mail, Newsstand, Racks

LEMONT SUBURBAN LIFE (FRI)

1101 31st St, Ste 260, Downers Grove, IL, 60515-5585, Dupage, USA; gen tel (630) 368-1100; adv tel (630) 427-6213; ed tel (630) 427-6248; gen fax (630) 969-0228; disp adv e-mail nshannon@shawmedia.com; class adv e-mail sbissell@shawmedia.com; ed e-mail aschier@shawmedia.com; web site www.mysuburbanlife.com
Circulation: 1,002pd, 1,766fr; CAC
Advertising rate: /8 Pg $882.00; 1/4 Pg $1575.00; 1/2 Pg $2520.00; Full Pg $4550.00
Group: Shaw Media
Pub...J. Tom Shaw
Marketing Dir............................Katie Sherman
Anna Schier
Major/Nat'l Accts./Grp. Sales Dir.........Maureen Ringness
Ryan Wells
Delivery Method: Mail, Newsstand, Racks

LISLE SUBURBAN LIFE (WED)

1101 31st St, Ste 260, Downers Grove, IL, 60515-5585, DuPage, USA; gen tel (630) 368-1100; adv tel (630) 427-6213; ed tel (630) 427-6252; gen fax (630) 969-0228; disp adv e-mail nshannon@shawmedia.com; class adv e-mail sbissell@shawmedia.com; ed e-mail rterrell@shawmedia.com; web site www.mysuburbanlife.com
Circulation: 72pd, 3,411fr; CAC
Advertising rate: 1/8 Pg $945.00; 1/4 Pg $1856.00; 1/2 Pg $2970.00; Full Pg $4950.00
Pub...J. Tom Shaw
Marketing Dir............................Katie Sherman
Ed. ....Ryan Terrell
Major/Nat'l Accts./Grp. Sales Dir.........Maureen Ringness
Ryan Wells
Mechanical Specifications: Type page 10 1/8 x 12 1/4; E - 4 cols, between; A - 4 cols, between; C - 8 cols, between.Equipment & Software: Hardware — APP/Mac; Presses — G/Suburban; Software — QPS/QuarkXPress 3.1.
Delivery Method: Mail, Newsstand, Racks

LOMBARD SUBURBAN LIFE (FRI)

1101 31st St, Ste 260, Downers Grove, IL, 60515-5585, Dupage, USA; gen tel (630) 368-1100; adv tel (630) 427-6213; ed tel (630) 427-6270; gen fax (630) 969-0228; disp adv e-mail nshannon@shawmedia.com; class adv e-mail sbissell@shawmedia.com; ed e-mail dgood@shawmedia.com; web site www.mysuburbanlife.com
Circulation: 7,703pd, 450fr; CAC
Advertising rate: 1/8 Pg $536.00; 1/4 Pg $956.00; 1/2 Pg $1530.00; Full Pg $2550.00
Group: Shaw Media
Pub...J. Tom Shaw
Marketing Dir............................Katie Sherman
Ed. ....David Good
Major/Nat'l Accts./Grp. Sales Dir.........Maureen Ringness
Ryan Wells
Mechanical Specifications: Type page 10 1/8 x 12 1/4.Equipment & Software: Hardware — APP/MAC, IBM, AU, APP/Mac; Presses — G; Software — QPS.
Delivery Method: Mail, Newsstand, Racks
Areas Served: 60148

RIVERSIDE & BROOKFIELD SUBURBAN LIFE (WED)

2001 Butterfield Rd, Ste 105, Downers Grove, IL, 60515-5479, Cook, USA; gen tel (630) 368-1100; adv tel (630) 427-6213; ed tel (630) 427-6254; gen fax (630) 969-0228; ed fax (630) 969-0228; disp adv e-mail bkorbel@shawmedia.com; class adv e-mail bhanahan@shawmedia.com; ed e-mail mhendrickson@shawmedia.com; web site www.mysuburbanlife.com
Circulation: 1,432pd, 2,871fr; CAC
Advertising rate: 1/8 Pg $536.00; 1/4 Pg $956.00; 1/2 Pg $1530.00; Full Pg $2550.00
Digital Platform - Mobile: Apple, Android
Digital Platform - Tablet: Apple iOS
Pub...J. Tom Shaw
Marketing Dir............................Katie Sherman
Ed. ....Matthew Hendrickson
Major/Nat'l Accts./Grp. Sales Dir.........Maureen Ringness
Ryan Wells
Mechanical Specifications: Type page 10 1/8 x 10 3/4; E - 4 cols, between; A - 4 cols, between; C - 8 cols, between.Equipment & Software: Hardware — APP/Mac, IBM; Presses — 22-G/Urbanite, 10-G/Suburban.
Delivery Method: Mail, Newsstand, Racks
Areas Served: 60534, 60513, 60546,

ROSELLE ITASCA PRESS (FRI)

1101 31st St, Ste 100, Downers Grove, IL, 60515-5581, Dupage, USA; gen tel (630) 368-1100; gen fax (630) 368-1188; ed e-mail cbrokamp@mysuburbanlife.com; web site www.mysuburbanlife.com
Circulation: 741pd, 18fr; VAC
Advertising rate: 1/8 Pg $945.00; 1/4 Pg $1856.00; 1/2 Pg $2970.00; Full Pg $4950.00
Group: GateHouse Media, Inc.
Local Sales Mgr...............................Bill Korbel
Class Advt Mgr.........................Brad Hanahan
Ed ....Dave Lemery
Mechanical Specifications: Type page 10 1/2 x 16.
Delivery Method: Mail

VILLA PARK SUBURBAN LIFE (FRI)

1101 31st St, Ste 260, Downers Grove, IL, 60515-5585, Dupage, USA; gen tel (630) 368-1100; adv tel (630) 427-6213; ed tel (630) 427-6270; gen fax (630) 969-0228; ed fax (630) 969-0228; disp adv e-mail nshannon@shawmedia.com; class adv e-mail sbissell@shawmedia.com; ed e-mail dgood@shawmedia.com; web site www.mysuburbanlife.com
Circulation: 366pd,; CAC
Advertising rate: 1/8 Pg $536.00; 1/4 Pg $956.00; 1/2 Pg $1530.00; Full Pg $2550.00
Group: Shaw Media
Pub...J. Tom Shaw
Marketing Dir............................Katie Sherman
Ed. ....David Good
Major/Nat'l Accts./Grp. Sales Dir.........Maureen Ringness
Ryan Wells
Delivery Method: Mail, Newsstand, Racks

WEST CHICAGO SUBURBAN LIFE (THUR)

1101 31st St Ste 100, Suite 100, Downers Grove, IL, 60515-5581, Dupage, USA; gen tel (630) 368-1100; adv tel (630) 427-6213; ed tel (630) 427-6248; gen fax (630) 969-0228; ed fax (630) 969-0228; disp adv e-mail bkorbel@shawmedia.com; class adv e-mail bhanahan@shawmedia.com; ed e-mail aschier@shawmedia.com; web site www.mysuburbanlife.com
Circulation: 583pd, 50fr; CAC
Advertising rate: 1/8 Pg $1008.00; 1/4 Pg $1800.00; 1/2 Pg $2880.00; Full Pg $4800.00
Group: Shaw Media
Pub...J. Tom Shaw
Marketing Dir............................Katie Sherman
Ed. ....Anna Schier
Major/Nat'l Accts./Grp. Sales Dir.........Maureen Ringness
Ryan Wells
Mechanical Specifications: Type page 9 13/16 x 14 3/8; E - 4 cols, between; A - 4 cols, between; C - 8 cols, between.Equipment & Software: Hardware — APP/Mac; Presses — G/Community; Software — QPS.
Delivery Method: Mail, Newsstand, Racks

WESTMONT SUBURBAN LIFE (WED)

1101 31st St, Ste 260, Downers Grove, IL, 60515-5585, DuPage, USA; gen tel (630) 368-1100; adv tel (630) 427-6213; ed tel (630) 427-6252; gen fax (630) 969-0228; disp adv e-mail nshannon@shawmedia.com; class adv e-mail sbissell@shawmedia.com; ed e-mail rterrell@shawmedia.com; web site www.mysuburbanlife.com
Circulation: 7,703pd, 450fr; CAC
Advertising rate: 1/8 Pg $672.00; 1/4 Pg $1200.00; 1/2 Pg $1920.00; Full Pg $3200.00
Group: Shaw Media
Pub...J. Tom Shaw
Marketing Dir............................Katie Sherman
Ed. ....Ryan Terrell
Major/Nat'l Accts./Grp. Sales Dir.........Maureen Ringness
Ryan Wells
Mechanical Specifications: Type page 10 x 16; E - 5 cols, 1 7/8, between; A - 5 cols, 1 7/8, between; C - 8 cols, 1 1/8, between.Equipment & Software: Hardware — APP/Mac; Presses — G/Suburban; Software — QPS/QuarkXPress 3.1.
Delivery Method: Mail, Newsstand, Racks

WHEATON SUBURBAN LIFE (THUR)

1101 31st St, Ste 260, Downers Grove, IL, 60515-5585, Dupage, USA; gen tel (630) 368-1100; adv tel (630) 427-6213; ed tel (630) 427-6248; gen fax (630) 969-0228; disp adv e-mail nshannon@shawmedia.com; class adv e-mail sbissell@shawmedia.com; ed e-mail aschier@shawmedia.com; web site www.mysuburbanlife.com
Circulation: 152pd, 8,279fr; CAC
Advertising rate: 1/8 Pg $1008.00; 1/4 Pg $1800.00; 1/2 Pg $2880.00; Full Pg $4800.00
Group: Shaw Media
Pub...J. Tom Shaw
Marketing Dir............................Katie Sherman
Ed. ....Anna Schier
Major/Nat'l Accts./Grp. Sales Dir.........Maureen Ringness
Ryan Wells
Delivery Method: Mail, Newsstand, Racks

WOODRIDGE SUBURBAN LIFE (WED)

1101 31st St, Ste 260, Downers Grove, IL, 60515-5585, DuPage, USA; gen tel (630) 368-1100; adv tel (630) 427-6213; ed tel (630) 427-6252; gen fax (630) 969-0228; disp adv e-mail nshannon@shawmedia.com; class adv e-mail sbissell@shawmedia.com; ed e-mail rterrell@shawmedia.com; web site www.mysuburbanlife.com
Circulation: 503pd, 5,544fr; CAC
Advertising rate: 1/8 Pg $956.00; 1/4 Pg $1706.00; 1/2 Pg $2730.00; Full Pg $4550.00
Group: Shaw Media
Pub...J. Tom Shaw
Marketing Dir............................Katie Sherman
Ed. ....Ryan Terrell
Major/Nat'l Accts./Grp. Sales Dir.........Maureen Ringness
Ryan Wells
Mechanical Specifications: Type page 10 1/8 x 12 1/4; E - 4 cols, between; A - 4 cols, between; C - 8 cols, between.Equipment & Software: Hardware — APP/Mac; Presses — G/Suburban; Software — QPS/QuarkXPress.
Delivery Method: Mail, Newsstand, Racks
Areas Served: 60516

DU QUOIN

ASHLEY NEWS (THUR)

9 N Division St, Du Quoin, IL, 62832-1405, Perry, USA; gen tel (618) 542-2133; gen fax (618) 542-2726; disp adv e-mail dqnews@verizon.net; web site www.duquoin.com
Circulation: 85pd, 10fr; Sworn/Estimate/Non-Audited
Advertising rate: Open inch rate $9.75
Established: 1895
Group: GateHouse Media, Inc.
Adv. Mgr..Craig Smith
Mng. Ed..................................John Croessman
Delivery Method: Mail

RANDOLPH COUNTY HERALD TRIBUNE (WED)

PO Box 184, Du Quoin, IL, 62832-0184, Randolph, USA; gen tel (616) 826-2385; gen fax (618) 826-5181; disp adv e-mail eraby@randolphcountyheraldtribune.com; class adv e-mail srahn@randolphcountyheraldtribune.com; ed e-mail editor@randolphcountyheraldtribune.com; web site www.randolphcountyheraldtribune.com
Circulation: 1,100pd, 0fr; USPS
Advertising rate: Open inch rate $8.50
Established: 1862
Group: Paddock Publications
Office Mgr. ....Sherri Rahn
Multi-Media Sales.............................Eric Raby
Ed. ....Pete Spitler
Delivery Method: Mail, Newsstand, Racks
Areas Served: Randolph County

STEELEVILLE LEDGER (WED)

PO Box 184, Du Quoin, IL, 62832-0184, Randolph, USA; gen tel (618) 826-2385; gen fax (618) 826-5181; disp adv e-mail eraby@randolphcountyheraldtribune.com; class adv e-mail srahn@randolphcountyheraldtribune.com; ed e-mail editor@randolphcounty-

heraldtribune.com; web site facebook.com/SteelevilleLedger
Circulation: 85pd, 0fr; USPS
Advertising rate: Open inch rate $8.50
Established: 1893
Group: Paddock Publications
Office Mgr. .... Sherri Rahn
Ed. .... Pete Spitler
Delivery Method: Mail, Newsstand, Racks
Areas Served: Randolph County

EDINBURG

THE HERALD-STAR (THUR)

103 S Eaton St, Edinburg, IL, 62531-9700, Christian, USA; gen tel (217) 623-5523; gen fax (217) 623-5523; disp adv e-mail herald-star@consolidated.net; ed e-mail herald-star@consolidated.net; web site No Website
Circulation: 610pd, 34fr; Sworn/Estimate/Non-Audited
Advertising rate: Open inch rate $3.12
Established: 1882
Pub.Elizabeth ConowayEquipment & Software: ; Presses — G.
Delivery Method: Mail

EFFINGHAM

REGISTER-NEWS (TUES, THUR, SAT)

PO Box 370, Effingham, IL, 62401-0370, Jefferson, USA; gen tel (618) 242-0113; gen fax (618) 242-8286; ed fax (618) 242-2797; disp adv e-mail sheonna.hill@register-news.com; class adv e-mail sheonna.hill@register-news.com; ed e-mail rick.hayes@register-news.com; web site www.register-news.com
Circulation: 10,260pd,; Sworn/Estimate/Non-Audited
Advertising rate: Open inch rate $13.86
Established: 1871
Group: Community Newspaper Holdings, Inc.
Adv. Mgr. .... Alana Parker
Mng. Ed. .... Tesa Glass
Pub. .... Darrell Lewis
Mechanical Specifications: Type page 13 x 21 1/2; E - 6 cols, 2 1/16, 1/8 between; A - 6 cols, 2 1/16, 1/8 between; C - 9 cols, 1 3/8, 1/16 between.
Areas Served: Mt. Vernon (IL)

EUREKA

THE WOODFORD COUNTY JOURNAL (THUR)

1926 S Main St, Eureka, IL, 61530-1666, Woodford, USA; gen tel (309) 467-3314; adv tel (309) 467-3314 Ext. 203; ed tel (309) 467-3314 Ext. 211; gen fax (309) 467-4563; disp adv e-mail hbowman@pantagraph.com; class adv e-mail hhowman@panteetpm ; ed e-mail cwolfe@pantagraph.com; web site www.woodcojo.com
Circulation: 1,224pd,; AAM
Advertising rate: Open inch rate $11.00
Established: 1867
Digital Platform - Mobile: Apple
Pub. .... Barry Winterland
Gen. Mgr. .... Mark Barra
Ed. .... Cheryl Wolfe
Mechanical Specifications: Type page 11 5/8 x 21; E - 6 cols, 1 3/4, 3/16 between; A - 6 cols, 2 1/8, 3/16 between; C - 9 cols, 1 3/16, 1/8 between.Equipment & Software: Hardware — APP/Power Mac
Dell; Software — Photoshop
Indesign
Delivery Method: Mail, Newsstand, Racks
Areas Served: 61530

FAIRFIELD

WAYNE COUNTY PRESS (MON, THUR)

213 E Main St, Fairfield, IL, 62837-2028, Wayne, USA; gen tel (618) 842-2662; adv tel (618) 842-2662; ed tel (618) 842-2662; gen fax (618) 842-7912; disp adv e-mail news@waycopress.com; class adv e-mail classifieds@waycopress.com; ed e-mail news@waycopress.com; web site www.waycopress.com
Circulation: 5,525pd, 50fr; Sworn/Estimate/Non-Audited
Advertising rate: Open inch rate $11.48
Established: 1866
Adv. Mgr. .... Carol Tannahill
Pub./Gen. Mgr. .... Thomas Mathews
Mechanical Specifications: Type page 13 7/8 x 21; E - 6 cols, 2 1/6, between; A - 6 cols, 2 1/6, between; C - 9 cols, 1 5/12, between. Equipment & Software: Hardware — APP/Power Macs; Presses — KP/Color King, KP/News King; Software — WordPerfect, QPS/QuarkXPress 3.3. Microsoft - InDesign
Delivery Method: Mail, Newsstand, Carrier, Racks

FARINA

FARINA NEWS (THUR)

109 N Walnut St, Farina, IL, 62838-1326, Fayette, USA; gen tel (618) 245-6216; gen fax (618) 245-6216; disp adv e-mail farinanews@yahoo.com
Circulation: 850pd,; Sworn/Estimate/Non-Audited
Advertising rate: Open inch rate $3.50
Established: 1882
Ed./Pub. .... Sara Hunley
Delivery Method: Mail, Newsstand, Racks

FLORA

THE CLAY COUNTY ADVOCATE-PRESS (TUES, THUR)

105 W North Ave, Flora, IL, 62839-1613, Clay, USA; gen tel (618) 662-2108; adv tel (618) 662-2108; ed tel (618) 662-2108; gen fax (618) 662-2939; adv fax (618) 662-2939; ed fax (618) 662-2939; disp adv e-mail admanager@advocatepress.com; class adv e-mail classifieds@advocatepress.com; ed e-mail rmcgrew@olneydailymail.com; web site www.advocatepress.com
Circulation: 3,166pd,; Sworn/Estimate/Non-Audited
Advertising rate: Open inch rate $8.20
Established: 1886
Group: GateHouse Media, Inc.
Circ. Mgr. .... Jennifer Lewis
News Ed. .... Mary Ann Maxwell
Sports Ed. .... Chip Barche
Pub./Adv. Mgr. .... Bob Hiemenz
Mechanical Specifications: Type page 13 3/4 x 21; E - 6 cols, 2 1/16, 1/8 between; A - 6 cols, 2 1/16, 1/8 between; C - 6 cols, 2 1/16, 1/8 between.
Delivery Method: Mail, Newsstand, Carrier, Racks
Areas Served: Clay County (IL)

FREEBURG

THE FREEBURG TRIBUNE (THUR)

820 S State St, Freeburg, IL, 62243-1548, Saint Clair, USA; gen tel (618) 539-3320; gen fax (618) 539-3346; disp adv e-mail newsroom@freeburgtribune.com; class adv e-mail Tom@freeburgtribune.com; ed e-mail newsroom@freeburgtribune.com; web site www.freeburgtribune.com
Circulation: 3,000pd,; Sworn/Estimate/Non-Audited
Advertising rate: Open inch rate $8.00
Established: 1897
Group: Freeburg Printing and Publishing, Inc.
Pub. .... Harold G. Carpenter
Gen. Mgr. .... Thomas Carpenter
News Ed. .... Judy Carpenter
Vice President .... Hal Carpenter
Mechanical Specifications: Type page 13 1/2 x 21 1/2; E - 6 cols, between; A - 6 cols, between; C - 9 cols, between.
Delivery Method: Mail, Newsstand, Racks
Areas Served: 62243, 62285, 62258, 62221, 62223, 62264, 62278, 62284

FULTON

FULTON JOURNAL (WED)

1009 4th St, Frnt Main, Fulton, IL, 61252-1791, Fulton, USA; gen tel (815) 589-2424; gen fax (815) 589-2714; disp adv e-mail journal@whitesidesentinel.com
Advertising rate: Open inch rate $8.00
Established: 1854
Group: WNS Publications Inc.
Pub. .... Sue Patten
Delivery Method: Mail, Newsstand, Racks

GALESBURG

ARGUS-SENTINEL (THUR)

140 S Prairie St, Galesburg, IL, 61401-4605, Knox, USA; gen tel (309) 462-5758; gen fax (309) 462-3221; disp adv e-mail argus@abingdon.net; web site facebook.com/abingdonargussentinel
Circulation: 1,134pd, 7fr; Sworn/Estimate/Non-Audited
Advertising rate: Open inch rate $5.00
Established: 1867
Group: GateHouse Media, Inc.
Pub. .... Lynne Campbell
Adv. Mgr. .... Jane Hasley
Adv. Mgr. .... Lisa Tast
Ed. .... Deb Fowlks
Ed. .... Deb RobinsonEquipment & Software: Hardware — APP/iMac, APP/Super Mac, APP/Mac 4000; Software — QPS/QuarkXPress 4.4.
Delivery Method: Mail, Newsstand, Racks
Areas Served: 61410

ROSEVILLE INDEPENDENT (THUR)

140 S Prairie St, Galesburg, IL, 61401-4605, Knox, USA; gen tel (309) 255-7581; gen fax (309) 833-2346; disp adv e-mail eaglepub@macomb.com; ed e-mail eaglepub@macomb.com; web site www.eaglepublications.com
Circulation: 605pd, 3fr; Sworn/Estimate/Non-Audited
Advertising rate: Open inch rate $2.30
Group: GateHouse Media, Inc.
Ed. .... Phil Gerding
Mechanical Specifications: Type page 10 1/4 x 16; E - 6 cols, 1 7/12, between; A - 6 cols, 1 7/12, between; C - 6 cols, 1 7/12, between.
Delivery Method: Mail

GALVA

GALVA NEWS (THUR)

348 Front St, Galva, IL, 61434-1365, Henry, USA; gen tel (309) 932-2103; gen fax (309) 932-3282; ed e-mail dboock@galvanews.com; web site www.galvanews.com
Circulation: 1,200pd,; Sworn/Estimate/Non-Audited
Advertising rate: Open inch rate $4.50
Pub. .... David Adams
Ed. .... Mike Landis
Adv. Mgr. .... Lisa Leemans
Delivery Method: Mail

GENESEO

GENESEO REPUBLIC (FRI)

108 W 1st St, Geneseo, IL, 61254-1342, Henry, USA; gen tel (309) 944-2119; gen fax (309) 944-5615; ed e-mail editor@geneseorepublic.com; web site www.geneseorepublic.com
Circulation: 4,800pd,; Sworn/Estimate/Non-Audited
Advertising rate: Open inch rate $9.50
Group: GateHouse Media, Inc.
Gen. Mgr. .... Dee Evans
Circ. Mgr. .... Marnie Eggen
Ed. .... Lisa Depies
Pub. .... David Adams
Mechanical Specifications: Type page 13 x 21 1/2.
Delivery Method: Mail, Newsstand, Racks

GILMAN

THE GILMAN STAR (WED)

203 N Central St, Gilman, IL, 60938-1218, USA; gen tel (815) 265-7332; gen fax (815) 265-7880; disp adv e-mail gstar7332@yahoo.com; web site www.thegilmanstar.com
Circulation: 2,200pd,; Sworn/Estimate/Non-Audited
Advertising rate: Open inch rate $5.25
Ed. .... John T. Elliott
Prodn. Mgr. .... Kent Johnson
Delivery Method: Mail, Newsstand, Racks

GIRARD

THE GIRARD GAZETTE (WED)

174 W Center St, Girard, IL, 62640-1222, Macoupin, USA; gen tel (217) 627-2115; gen fax (217) 965-4512; disp adv e-mail nj331@royell.net
Circulation: 1,290pd, 1,320fr; Sworn/Estimate/Non-Audited
Advertising rate: Open inch rate $8.00
Established: 1879
Group: Paddock Publications
Adv. Mgr. .... Nathan Jones
Ed. .... Norris E. Jones
Prodn. Mgr. .... Martin Jones
Mechanical Specifications: Type page 15 1/2 x 21 1/2; E - 7 cols, 2 7/16, 1/8 between; A - 7 cols, 2 7/16, 1/8 between; C - 5 cols, 1 7/8, 1/8 between.Equipment & Software: Hardware — APP/Mac G3; Presses — 9-KP; Software — Adobe/PageMaker 6.5.
Delivery Method: Mail, Newsstand, Racks

GLENVIEW

BARRINGTON COURIER-REVIEW (THUR)

3701 W Lake Ave, Glenview, IL, 60026-1216, Cook, USA; gen tel (847) 486-7300; adv tel (866) 399-0537; ed tel (312) 321-2307; gen fax (312) 222-2598; ed fax (312) 222-2598; disp adv e-mail display@pioneerlocal.com; class adv e-mail classifieds@stmedianetwork.com; ed e-mail pjurik@chicagotribune.com; web site www.pioneerlocal.com
Circulation: 939pd,; AAM
Advertising rate: 1/8 Pg $220.00; 1/6 Pg $240.00; 1/4 Pg $360.00
Established: 1889
Group: Tronc, Inc.
Ed. .... Phil Jurik
Pub./Ed.-in-Chief .... R. Bruce Dold
Mng. Ed. .... Peter Kendall
VP of Adv. .... Jill McDermott
Gen. Mgr. of Suburban WeekliesMaggie Wartik
Mechanical Specifications: Type page 10 x 13; E - 5 cols, 1 7/8, 1 7/8 between; A - 5 cols, 1 7/8, 1 7/8 between; C - 8 cols, 1 13/16, 1 13/16 between.Equipment & Software: ; Software — QPS/QuarkXPress 5.01, Multi-Ad/Creator 4.03, Adobe/Photoshop 6.01, Adobe/Illustrator 9.02.
Delivery Method: Mail, Newsstand, Racks
Areas Served: 60010

GODFREY

ADVANTAGE NEWS (THUR, FRI)

1000 W Homer Adams Pkwy, Godfrey, IL, 62035, Madison, USA; gen tel (618) 463-0612; gen fax (618) 463-0733; ed fax (800) 532-4441; disp adv e-mail ericmcroy@advantagenews.com; class adv e-mail leighanmcroy@advantagenews.com; ed e-mail fredpollard@advantagenews.com; web site www.advantagenews.com - 124,061(views)

29,605(visitors)
Circulation: 77,000fr; Sworn/Estimate/Non-Audited
Advertising rate: Modular size - call
Established: 1986
Group: Rex Encore
Digital Platform - Mobile: Apple, Android, Windows
Digital Platform - Tablet: Apple iOS, Android, Windows 7, Blackberry Tablet OS, Kindle, Nook, Kindle Fire
VP, Rex Encore....Eric McRoy
Mechanical Specifications: Modular size - call Equipment & Software: Hardware — Macintoch; Software — Adobe Creative Suite
Delivery Method: Mail
Areas Served: 62002, 62010, 62018, 62021, 62024, 62035, 62048, 62067, 62084, 62087, 62095

ADVANTAGE NEWS - GRANITE CITY (FRI)
1000 W Homer Adams Pkwy, Godfrey, IL, 62035, Madison, USA; gen tel (618) 462-0612; gen fax (618) 463-0733; ed fax (800) 532-4441; disp adv e-mail johnnyaguirre@advantagenews.com; class adv e-mail contactus@todaysadvantage.com; ed e-mail fredpollard@advantagenews.com; web site www.advantagenews.com
Circulation: 18,631fr; VAC
Advertising rate: Modular size - call
Established: 1986
Group: Rex Encore
Digital Platform - Mobile: Apple, Android, Windows
Digital Platform - Tablet: Apple iOS, Android, Windows 7, Blackberry Tablet OS, Kindle, Nook, Kindle Fire
VP....Eric McRoy
Mechanical Specifications: 5 col. x 15 inchesEquipment & Software: Hardware — Mcintosh; Software — Adobe Creative Suite
Delivery Method: Mail
Areas Served: 62040

GOLCONDA

HERALD-ENTERPRISE (WED)
211 E Main St, Golconda, IL, 62938, Pope, USA; gen tel (618) 683-3531; gen fax (618) 683-3831
Circulation: 1,400pd,; Sworn/Estimate/Non-Audited
Advertising rate: Open inch rate $7.10
Established: 1858Editions: (50)
Ed....Sandra Cowsert
Delivery Method: Mail

GOREVILLE

GOREVILLE GAZETTE (WED)
205 S BROADWAY, Goreville, IL, 62939, Johnson, USA; gen tel (618) 995-9445; gen fax (618) 658-4322; disp adv e-mail gorevillegazette@frontier.com; web site www.gorevillegazette.com
Circulation: 800pd,; Sworn/Estimate/Non-Audited
Advertising rate: Open inch rate $4.26
Established: 1977
Pub....Lonnie Hinton
Ed....Sandra Lively
Delivery Method: Mail, Newsstand, Racks
Areas Served: Johnson, Williamson

GRAYSLAKE

LAKE COUNTY JOURNAL (THUR)
PO Box 343, Grayslake, IL, 60030-0343, Lake, USA; gen tel (847) 223-8161; gen fax (847) 543-1139; disp adv e-mail circulation@nwnewsgroup.com; web site www.lakecountyjournals.com
Circulation: 8,000fr; Sworn/Estimate/Non-Audited
Advertising rate: 1/4 P $99, 1/2 P $159, Full $299
Established: 1956
Group: Shaw Media
Exec. Vice Pres./Gen. Mgr....John Rung
Sr. Reporter....Cassandra Dowell
Reporter....Yadira Sanchez Olson
Mechanical Specifications: Type page 10 1/4 x 16; E - 5 cols, 1 5/6, 1/4 between; A - 5 cols, 1 5/6, 1/4 between; C - 7 cols, 1 1/3, 1/6 between.Equipment & Software: Hardware — 40-APP/Mac, 3-Flatbed Scanners, 2-Negative Scanners, 2-Printer/1200 dpi, 4-Printer/600 dpi; Presses — G/Urbanite; Software — InDesign CS2,
Delivery Method: Racks
Areas Served: 60030, 60002, 60060, 60061, 60046, 60031, 60084, 60020

HARDIN

CALHOUN NEWS-HERALD (WED)
310 S County Rd, Hardin, IL, 62047-4414, Calhoun, USA; gen tel (618) 576-2345; adv tel (618) 498-1234; gen fax (630) 206-0320; disp adv e-mail jkallal@campbellpublications.net; class adv e-mail jkallal@campbellpublications.net; ed e-mail cnhnews@campbellpublications.net; web site calhounnewsherald.com
Circulation: 2,000pd, 50fr; Sworn/Estimate/Non-Audited
Advertising rate: Open inch rate $11.95
Established: 1872
Group: Campbell Publishing Co., Inc.
Pub....Julie Boren
regional editori....Robert Lyons
Mechanical Specifications: Type page 13 x 21 1/2; E - 6 cols, 2 1/16, 1/6 between; A - 6 cols, 2 1/16, 1/6 between; C - 9 cols, 1 5/16, 1/6 between.
Delivery Method: Mail, Newsstand, Racks
Areas Served: 62047

HAVANA

MASON COUNTY DEMOCRAT (WED)
219 W Market St, Havana, IL, 62644-1145, Mason, USA; gen tel (309) 543-3311; gen fax (309) 543-6844; disp adv e-mail mcdemo@havanaprint.com; web site www.masoncountydemocrat.com
Circulation: 3,900pd, 2,400fr; Sworn/Estimate/Non-Audited
Advertising rate: Open inch rate $9.80
Established: 1849
Pub....Robert L. Martin
Circ. Mgr....Dan Pitcher
Vice-Chmn....Wendy Martin
Mechanical Specifications: 11.75 x 21.5
Delivery Method: Mail, Racks
Areas Served: 62644,62617, 61567, 62627, 62655, 61532, 62633, 62673, 61546, 62664, 62682,

HENRY

HENRY NEWS REPUBLICAN (WED)
709 3rd St, Henry, IL, 61537-1446, Henry, USA; gen tel (309) 364-3250; gen fax (309) 364-3858; disp adv e-mail henrynews@frontier.com
Circulation: 2,000pd,; Sworn/Estimate/Non-Audited
Advertising rate: Open inch rate $4.50
Ed....Amy Ziegler
Delivery Method: Mail, Newsstand, Racks

WENONA INDEX (THUR)
709 3rd St, Henry, IL, 61537-1446, Marshall, USA; gen tel (309) 364-3250; gen fax (309) 364-3858
Circulation: 711pd,; Sworn/Estimate/Non-Audited
Advertising rate: Open inch rate $4.50Sheila Healy
Delivery Method: Mail, Newsstand, Racks

HERSCHER

HERSCHER PILOT (THUR)
100 S Main St, Herscher, IL, 60941-9522, Kankakee, USA; gen tel (815) 426-2132; adv tel (815) 426-2132; ed tel (815) 426-2132; gen fax (815) 426-2132; adv fax (815) 426-2132; ed fax (815) 426-2132; disp adv e-mail editor@herscherpilot.com; class adv e-mail editor@herscherpilot.com; ed e-mail editor@herscherpilot.com; web site www.herscherpilot.com
Circulation: 1,200pd,; Sworn/Estimate/Non-Audited
Advertising rate: Open inch rate $4.50
Established: 1976
Digital Platform - Mobile: Apple, Android
Digital Platform - Tablet: Apple iOS, Android
Delivery Method: Mail, Newsstand
Areas Served: 60901, 60913, 60961, 60919, 60917, 60922, 60927, 60941, 60911

HIGHLAND

HIGHLAND NEWS LEADER (THUR)
1 Woodcrest Professional Park, Highland, IL, 62249-1254, Madison, USA; gen tel (618) 654-2366; gen fax (618) 654-1181; disp adv e-mail gbentlage@bnd.com; ed e-mail hnlnews@bnd.com; web site www.highlandnl.com
Circulation: 15,000pd,; Sworn/Estimate/Non-Audited
Advertising rate: Open inch rate $10.88
Established: 1861
Adv. Mgr....Gay Bentlage
News Editor....Curt Libbra
Delivery Method: Mail, Newsstand, Racks

HILLSBORO

MACOUPIN COUNTY JOURNAL (MON)
431 S Main St, Hillsboro, IL, 62049-1433, Montgomery, USA; gen tel (217) 532-3933; gen fax (217) 532-3632; disp adv e-mail advertisejn@consolidated.net; class adv e-mail advertisejn@consolidated.net; web site www.thejournal-news.net
Circulation: 13,200fr; Sworn/Estimate/Non-Audited
Advertising rate: Open inch rate $4.25
Established: 1852
Ed./Gen. Mgr....John Galer
Classifieds Mgr....Cheri Ozee
Mechanical Specifications: Type page 13 x 21 1/2; E - 9 cols, 1 3/10, 1/6 between; A - 9 cols, 1 3/10, 1/6 between; C - 9 cols, 1 3/10, 1/6 between.Equipment & Software: Hardware — APP/Mac; Software — Adobe/PageMaker, QPS/QuarkXPress, Adobe/Photoshop, Adobe/Illustrator.
Delivery Method: Mail, Racks

THE JOURNAL-NEWS (MON, THUR)
431 S Main St, Hillsboro, IL, 62049-1433, Montgomery, USA; gen tel (217) 532-3933; gen fax (217) 532-3632; disp adv e-mail thejournal-news@consolidated.net; class adv e-mail advertisejn@consolidated.net; web site www.thejournal-news.net
Circulation: 6,450pd, 129fr; USPS
Advertising rate: Open inch rate $6.50
Established: 1852
Group: Hillsboro Journal, Inc.
Digital Platform - Mobile: Blackberry
Digital Platform - Tablet: Other
Pub....Mike Plunkett
Mechanical Specifications: Type page 13 x 21 1/2; E - 6 cols, 2, 1/6 between; A - 6 cols, 2, 1/6 between; C - 9 cols, 1 1/3, 1/6 between. Equipment & Software: Hardware — APP/Mac; Software — Adobe/PageMaker, Adobe/Photoshop, Adobe/Illustrator, QPS/QuarkXPress.
Delivery Method: Mail, Racks

HOOPESTON

THE CHRONICLE (WED)
308 E Main St, Hoopeston, IL, 60942-1505, Vermilion, USA; gen tel (217) 283-5111; gen fax (217) 283-5846; disp adv e-mail chronoffice@verizon.net; web site www.thehoopestonchronicle.com
Circulation: 1,100pd,; Sworn/Estimate/Non-Audited
Advertising rate: Open inch rate $10.10
Group: Community Media Group
Advertising Executive....Misty Courtney
Mechanical Specifications: Type page 10 1/2 x 14; A - 6 cols, 1 1/2, between.Equipment & Software: Hardware — APP/Mac; Presses — KP/News King; Software — QPS/QuarkXPress, Adobe/Photoshop, Multi-Ad Creator.

THE HOOPESTON CHRONICLE (WED)
308 E Main St, Hoopeston, IL, 60942-1505, USA; gen tel (217) 283-5111; gen fax (217) 283-5846; class adv e-mail chronoffice@frontier.com; web site http://www.newsbug.info/hoopeston_chronicle
Group: Community Media Group
Circ....Cyndi Grace

ILLIOPOLIS

THE SENTINEL (THUR)
311 W Matilda St, Illiopolis, IL, 62539-3605, Sangamon, USA; gen tel (217) 486-6496; disp adv e-mail thesentinel@comcast.net; web site http://www.illiopolis.com/pages/members/illiopolis_sentinel.htm
Circulation: 1,000pd,; Sworn/Estimate/Non-Audited
Advertising rate: Open inch rate $3.00
Ed./Pub....Cindy Wilson
Mechanical Specifications: Type page 10 x 14 1/2; E - 5 cols, between; A - 5 cols, between; C - 5 cols, between.
Delivery Method: Mail, Racks
Areas Served: Illiopolis, Niantic, & Harristown

JERSEYVILLE

JESEY COUNTY JOURNAL (WED)
832 S State St, Jerseyville, IL, 62052-2343, Jersey County, USA; gen tel (618) 498-1234; adv tel 618-498-1234; gen fax (630) 206-0320; web site www.jerseycountyjournal.com
Circulation: 10,600fr; Sworn/Estimate/Non-Audited
Advertising rate: $11.95
Established: 2003
Group: Campbell Publishing Co., Inc.
Pub....Julie Boren
regional editor....Robert Lyons
Delivery Method: Mail, Newsstand, Racks
Areas Served: Jersey County, Illinois

JOLIET

FARMERS WEEKLY REVIEW (THUR)
100 Manhattan Rd Ste 2, Suite 2, Joliet, IL, 60433-2764, Will, USA; gen tel (815) 727-4811; adv tel (815) 727-4811; ed tel (815) 727-4811; gen fax (815) 727-5570; adv fax (815) 727-5570; ed fax (815) 727-5570; disp adv e-mail debbie@willcfb.com; class adv e-mail debbie@willcfb.com; ed e-mail farmersweekly@sbcglobal.net; web site facebook.com/farmersweekly1921
Circulation: 12,900pd, 50fr; Sworn/Estimate/Non-Audited
Advertising rate: Open inch rate $11.25
Established: 1921
Adv. Mgr....Debbie Werner
Pub....Michael J. Cleary
Ed....Nick Reiher
Mechanical Specifications: Type page 10 x 16; E - 5 cols, 2, between; A - 5 cols, 2, between; C - 5 cols, 2, between.
Delivery Method: Mail, Newsstand, Racks

Areas Served: Will County primarily

THE TIMES WEEKLY (THUR, OTHER)

254 E Cass St, Joliet, IL, 60432-2813, Will, Cook, USA; gen tel (815) 723-0325; adv tel (815) 723-0325 ext. 303; gen fax (815) 723-0326; disp adv e-mail ads@thetimesweekly.com; class adv e-mail ads@thetimesweekly.com; ed e-mail editor@thetimesweekly.com; web site thetimesweekly.com
Circulation: 25,000fr; CVC
Advertising rate: Open inch rate $38.00
Established: 1986
Group: M.I.A. Media Group
Pres./Pub. ....Jayme Cain
Delivery Method: Mail, Racks
Areas Served: Will and Cook Counties

LACON

LACON HOME JOURNAL (TUES)

204 S Washington St, Lacon, IL, 61540-1498, USA, USA; gen tel (309) 246-2865; gen fax (309) 246-3214; disp adv e-mail sonbtp@aol.com; web site laconhomejournal.com
Circulation: 1,800pd,; Sworn/Estimate/Non-Audited
Advertising rate: $5.00
Established: 1847
Ed. ....William H. Sondag
Mechanical Specifications: Type page 16 x 16; E - 5 cols, 1 5/6, 1/12 between; A - 5 cols, 1 5/6, 1/12 between; C - 5 cols, 1 5/6, 1/12 between.Equipment & Software: Hardware — PCs; Presses — ABD; Software — Adobe/PageMaker.
Delivery Method: Mail, Newsstand
Areas Served: 61540 - 61369 - 61375 - 61545

LAWRENCEVILLE

LAWRENCE COUNTY NEWS (THUR)

1209 State St, Lawrenceville, IL, 62439-2332, Lawrence, USA; gen tel (618) 943-2331; adv tel (618) 943-2331; ed tel (618) 943-2331; gen fax (618) 943-3976; adv fax (618) 943-3976; ed fax (618) 943-3976; disp adv e-mail syoung@lawdailyrecord.com; class adv e-mail lkocher@lawdailyrecord.com; ed e-mail mvandorn@lawdailyrecord.com; web site www.lawdailyrecord.com
Circulation: 300pd,; Sworn/Estimate/Non-Audited
Advertising rate: Open inch rate $9.00
Group: Lewis Newspapers
Digital Platform - Mobile: Apple, Android
Digital Platform - Tablet: Apple iOS, Android
Ed. ....Michael Van Dorn
Gen. Mgr. ....Beverly Johnson
Prodn. Mgr. ....Bev Johnson
Delivery Method: Mail, Newsstand
Areas Served: Lawrence County

LENA

NORTHWESTERN ILLINOIS FARMER (WED)

119 W Railroad St, Lena, IL, 61048-9038, Stephenson, USA; gen tel (815) 369-2811; gen fax (815) 369-2816; disp adv e-mail news@nwilfarmer.com
Circulation: 2,090pd,; Sworn/Estimate/Non-Audited
Advertising rate: Open inch rate $8.00
Established: 1867
Ed. ....Norman Templin
Mechanical Specifications: Type page 10 x 15; E - 5 cols, 1 11/12, 1/12 between; A - 5 cols, 1 11/12, 1/12 between; C - 5 cols, 1 11/12, 1/12 between.
Delivery Method: Mail, Newsstand, Racks

LIBERTY

THE LIBERTY BEE-TIMES (WED)

103 E Hannibal St, Liberty, IL, 62347-1055, Adams, USA; gen tel (217) 645 -3033; gen fax (217) 645 -3083; disp adv e-mail libertyb@adams.net; web site www.elliott-publishing.com
Circulation: 3,600pd,; Sworn/Estimate/Non-Audited
Advertising rate: Open inch rate $3.25
Group: Elliott Publishing, Inc.
Pub. ....James W. Elliott
Ed. ....Marcia Elliott
Mechanical Specifications: Type page 10 1/4 x 16; E - 5 cols, 1 15/16, 1/4 between; A - 5 cols, 1 15/16, 1/4 between; C - 5 cols, 1 15/16, 1/4 between.Equipment & Software: Hardware — IBM; Software — Adobe/PageMaker 7.0, Adobe/Photoshop 6.0.
Delivery Method: Mail, Newsstand

LOMBARD

LOMBARDIAN (WED)

929 S Main St, Ste 102, Lombard, IL, 60148-3325, DuPage, USA; gen tel (630) 627-7010; gen fax (630) 627-7027; disp adv e-mail lombardian@sbcglobal.net; web site www.lombardian.info
Circulation: 11,000pd,; Sworn/Estimate/Non-Audited
Advertising rate: Open inch rate $9.50
Established: 1959
Co-Pub. ....Scott D. MacKay
Adv. Mgr. ....Marguerite Micken
Ed./Pub. ....Bonnie MacKay
Mechanical Specifications: Type page 9 3/4 x 16; E - 5 cols, 1 5/8, between; A - 5 cols, 1 5/8, between; C - 6 cols, 1 3/4, between.
Delivery Method: Mail, Newsstand, Carrier

VILLA PARK REVIEW (WED)

929 S Main St, Ste 102, Lombard, IL, 60148-3325, DuPage, USA; gen tel (630) 627-7010; gen fax (630) 627-7027; disp adv e-mail lombardian@sbcglobal.net; web site www.lombardian.info
Circulation: 9,000pd,; Sworn/Estimate/Non-Audited
Advertising rate: Open inch rate $9.50
Established: 1959
Ed./Pub. ....Bonnie MacKay
Mechanical Specifications: Type page 9 3/4 x 16; E - 5 cols, 1 5/8, between; A - 5 cols, 1 5/8, between; C - 6 cols, 1 3/4, between.
Delivery Method: Mail, Newsstand, Carrier

LOUISVILLE

CLAY COUNTY REPUBLICAN (WED)

126 Church St, Louisville, IL, 62858, Clay, USA; gen tel (618) 665-3135; gen fax (618) 665-3135; disp adv e-mail ccrnews@wabash.net; class adv e-mail ccrnews@wabash.net; ed e-mail ccrnews@wabash.net; web site No Website
Circulation: 2,200pd, 95fr; Sworn/Estimate/Non-Audited
Advertising rate: Open inch rate $4.00
Ed. ....Lindell Smith
Delivery Method: Mail

MORRIS

MORRIS HERALD-NEWS (THUR)

909 Liberty St., MORRIS, IL, 60450, Grundy, USA; gen tel 815-280-4100; adv tel (815) 280-4101; ed tel 815-280-4100; gen fax (815) 729-2019; adv fax (815) 729-2019; disp adv e-mail ads@morrisdailyherald.com; ed e-mail news@morrisdailyherald.com; web site morrisherald-news.com
Circulation:; AAM
Established: 1880
Group: Shaw MediaSteve Vanisko
Jon Styf
Denise Pankey
Delivery Method: Mail
Areas Served: Grundy County

MACHESNEY PARK

POST JOURNAL (THUR)

11512 N 2nd St, Machesney Park, IL, 61115-1101, Winnebago, USA; gen tel (815) 877-4044; gen fax (815) 654-4857; disp adv e-mail mbayer@rvpublishing.com; class adv e-mail mbayer@rvpublishing.com; ed e-mail mbradley@rvpublishing.com; web site rvpnews.com
Circulation: 845fr; Sworn/Estimate/Non-Audited
Advertising rate: Open inch rate $16.50
Established: 1968
Group: Rock Valley Publishing LLCEditions: (1) 1 total; Rockford Journal;
Adv. Mgr. ....Maxine Bayer
Circ. Mgr. ....Linda Sweet
Ed. ....Melanie Bradley
Prodn. Mgr. ....Linda Lano
Mechanical Specifications: Type page 10 1/4 x 16; E - 4 cols, between; A - 4 cols, between; C - 6 cols, between.Equipment & Software: Hardware — APP/Mac.
Delivery Method: Mail, Newsstand, Carrier, Racks
Areas Served: Rockton, Roscoe, South Beloit

THE ELMHURST INDEPENDENT (THUR)

11512 N 2nd St, Machesney Park, IL, 61115-1101, Winnebago, USA; web site www.rvpublishing.com
Circulation: 7pd, 7,138fr; VAC
Advertising rate: Open inch rate $7.00Randy Johnson

THE HERALD (THUR)

11512 N 2nd St, Machesney Park, IL, 61115-1101, Winnebago, USA; gen tel (815) 654-4850; gen fax (815) 654-4857; disp adv e-mail heraldads@rvpublishing.com; class adv e-mail heraldads@rvpublishing.com; ed e-mail mbradley@rvpublishing.com; web site www.rvpublishing.com
Circulation: 2,942pd, 6,015fr; Sworn/Estimate/Non-Audited
Advertising rate: Open inch rate $9.65
Group: Rock Valley Publishing LLC
Gen. Mgr. ....Randall Johnson
Ed. ....Melanie Bradley
Mechanical Specifications: Type page 10 1/8 x 16; E - 4 cols, between; A - 4 cols, between; C - 6 cols, between.Equipment & Software: Hardware — APP/Mac; Presses — G/Community.
Delivery Method: Mail, Newsstand, Carrier, Racks
Areas Served: Rockton, Roscoe, South Beloit

MACOMB

MCDONOUGH COUNTY VOICE (MON, WED, FRI)

26 W Side Sq, Macomb, IL, 61455-2219, McDonough, USA; gen tel (309) 837-4428; gen fax (309) 833-2346; disp adv e-mail eaglepub@macomb.com; ed e-mail eaglepub@macomb.com; web site www.mcdonoughvoice.com
Circulation: 2,047pd, 26fr; Sworn/Estimate/Non-Audited
Advertising rate: Open inch rate $5.00
Established: 1999
Group: GateHouse Media, Inc.
Pub. ....Donna Moore
Mechanical Specifications: Type page 6 1/3 x 16; E - 6 cols, 1 1/3, between; A - 6 cols, 1 1/3, between; C - 6 cols, 1 1/3, between.Equipment & Software: Hardware — 4-APP/Power Mac, 4-APP/Mac G3, HP/LaserWriter 5000; Software — Adobe/Photoshop 7.0, QPS/QuarkXPress 6.0.
Delivery Method: Mail
Areas Served: 61455, 61411, 61416, 61420, 62326, 62374, 61438, 61440, 61475

MAHOMET

MAHOMET CITIZEN (WED)

303 E Main St, Ste D, Mahomet, IL, 61853-7448, Champaign, USA; gen tel (217) 586-2512; adv tel (217) 586-2512; ed tel (217) 586-2512; gen fax (217) 586-4821; disp adv e-mail mcitizen@news-gazette.com; class adv e-mail jneidel@news-gazette.com; ed e-mail abenner@news-gazette.com; web site www.mcitizen.com
Circulation: 1,497pd,; AAM
Advertising rate: Open inch rate $9.25
Established: 1853
Group: The News-Gazette
News Gazette Community NewsEditions: (52) Mahomet Citizen
Pub. ....John Foreman
Ed. ....Amelia Benner
Adv. Dir. ....Tom Zalabak
Mechanical Specifications: Type page 11.75 x 21 1/2; E - 6 cols, 1.819", 1/8 between; A - 6 cols, 11.75", 1/8 betweenEquipment & Software: Hardware — APP/Macs; Presses — 9 unit King; Software — Adobe/Photoshop, InDesign, Word
Delivery Method: Mail, Newsstand, Racks
Areas Served: 61853, 61875

MARSHALL

CASEY WESTFIELD REPORTER (TUES, FRI, SAT)

610 Archer Ave, Marshall, IL, 62441-1268, Clark, USA; gen tel (217) 826-3600; adv tel (217) 932-5211; ed tel (217) 826-5487; gen fax (217) 826-3700; adv fax (217) 826-3700; ed fax (217) 826-3700; disp adv e-mail stromnewspapers@gmail.com; class adv e-mail strohmnews@joink.com; ed e-mail stromnewspapers@gmail.com; web site www.strohmnews.com
Circulation: 1,900pd, 7,416fr; Sworn/Estimate/Non-Audited
Advertising rate: Open inch rate $6.75
Established: 1996
Gary Strohm
Melody StrohmPub.s
Delivery Method: Mail, Newsstand, Racks
Areas Served: 62441, 62442, 62477, 62478, 62428, 62474, 62428, 62420, 62481, 47885, 47863, 47876

MARSHALL ADVOCATE (TUES, FRI, SAT)

610 Archer Ave, Marshall, IL, 62441-1268, Clark, USA; gen tel (217) 826-3600; adv tel (217) 932-5211; ed tel (217) 826-5487; gen fax (217) 826-3700; adv fax (217) 826-3700; ed fax (217) 826-3700; disp adv e-mail stromnewspapers@gmail.com; class adv e-mail strohmnews@joink.com; ed e-mail stromnewspapers@gmail.com; web site www.strohmnews.com
Circulation: 1,900pd, 7,416fr; Sworn/Estimate/Non-Audited
Advertising rate: Open inch rate $6.75
Established: 1996
Gary Strohm
Melody StrohmPub.s
Delivery Method: Mail, Newsstand, Racks
Areas Served: 62441, 62442, 62477, 62478, 62428, 62474, 62428, 62420, 62481, 47885, 47863, 47876

WEST VIGO TIMES (TUES, FRI, SAT)

610 Archer Ave, Marshall, IL, 62441-1268, Clark, USA; gen tel (217) 826-3600; adv tel (217) 932-5211; ed tel (217) 826-5487; gen fax (217) 826-3700; adv fax (217) 826-3700; ed fax (217) 826-3700; disp adv e-mail stromnewspapers@gmail.com; class adv e-mail strohmnews@joink.com; ed e-mail stromnewspapers@gmail.com; web site www.strohmnews.com
Circulation: 1,900pd, 7,416fr; Sworn/Estimate/Non-Audited
Advertising rate: Open inch rate $6.75
Established: 1996
Gary Strohm
Melody StrohmPub.s

Delivery Method: Mail, Newsstand, Racks
Areas Served: 62441, 62442, 62477, 62478, 62428, 62474, 62428, 62420, 62481, 47885, 47863, 47876

MASCOUTAH

CLINTON COUNTY NEWS (THUR)

314 E Church St, Ste 1, Mascoutah, IL, 62258-2100, Saint Clair, USA; gen tel (618) 566-8282; gen fax (618) 566-8283; disp adv e-mail ccn@cbnstl.com; web site www.heraldpubs.com
Circulation: 1,131pd,; Sworn/Estimate/Non-Audited
Advertising rate: Open inch rate $6.10
Pub. .... Greg Hoskins
Ed. .... Tam Rensing
Delivery Method: Mail, Newsstand, Racks

FAIRVIEW HEIGHTS TRIBUNE (THUR)

314 E Church St, Mascoutah, IL, 62258-2100, Saint Clair, USA; gen tel (618) 566-8282; gen fax (618) 566-8282; disp adv e-mail adv@heraldpubs.com; ed e-mail tribune@heraldpubs.com; web site www.heraldpubs.com
Circulation: 1,250pd,; Sworn/Estimate/Non-Audited
Advertising rate: Open inch rate $7.79
Pub. .... Greg Hoskins
Mechanical Specifications: Type page 13 x 21; E - 6 cols, 2 1/4, between; C - 8 cols, between.
Delivery Method: Mail, Newsstand, Racks

SCOTT AFB FLIER (THUR)

314 E Church St, Mascoutah, IL, 62258-2100, Saint Clair, USA; gen tel (618)566-8282; gen fax (618)566-8283; disp adv e-mail adv@heraldpubs.com; ed e-mail mascherald@heraldpubs.com; web site www.heraldpubs.com
Advertising rate: Open inch rate $7.79Greg Hoskins
Delivery Method: Mail, Newsstand, Racks

THE MASCOUTAH HERALD (THUR)

314 E Church St, Ste 1, Mascoutah, IL, 62258-2100, Saint Clair, USA; gen tel (618) 566-8282; gen fax (618) 566-8282; disp adv e-mail adv@heraldpubs.com; ed e-mail mascherald@heraldpubs.com; web site www.heraldpubs.com
Circulation: 2,400pd,; Sworn/Estimate/Non-Audited
Advertising rate: Open inch rate $7.79
Pub. .... Greg Hoskins
Delivery Method: Mail, Newsstand, Racks

MASON CITY

MASON CITY BANNER TIMES (TUES)

126 N Tonica St, Mason City, IL, 62664-1115, Mason, USA; gen tel (217) 482-3276; gen fax (217) 482-3277; disp adv e-mail btpublications@frontiernet.net; class adv e-mail btpublications@frontiernet.net; ed e-mail btpublications@frontiernet.net
Circulation: 2,100pd,; Sworn/Estimate/Non-Audited
Advertising rate: Open inch rate $6.00
Pub. .... Mark Rickard
Ed. .... Lois Rickard
Delivery Method: Mail

MC LEANSBORO

THE TIMES-LEADER (THUR)

200 S Washington St, Mc Leansboro, IL, 62859-1139, Hamilton, USA; gen tel (618)643-2387; gen fax (618) 643-3426; disp adv e-mail brenda.tarlton@mcleansborotimesleader.com; class adv e-mail brenda.tarlton@mcleansborotimesleader.com; ed e-mail yournews@mcleansborotimesleader.com; web site www.mcleansborotimesleader.com
Circulation: 3,021pd, 13fr; Sworn/Estimate/Non-Audited
Advertising rate: Open inch rate $7.00
Ed. .... Paul Lorenz
Adv .... Brenda Tarlton
Pub. .... Darrell Lewis
Delivery Method: Mail

MENDOTA

FARMER'S REPORT (WED, MTHLY)

703 Illinois Ave, Mendota, IL, 61342-1637, LaSalle, USA; gen tel (815) 39-9396; gen fax (815) 539-7862; disp adv e-mail kmeaker@mendotareporter.com; class adv e-mail acaylor@mendotareporter.com; ed e-mail bmorris@mendotareporter.com; web site www.mendotareporter.com
Circulation: 2,100pd, 8,000fr; Sworn/Estimate/Non-Audited
Advertising rate: Open inch rate $8.75
Group: News Media Corporation
Ed. .... Jennifer Sommer
Delivery Method: Mail, Newsstand, Racks

MENDOTA REPORTER (MON, WED)

703 Illinois Ave, Mendota, IL, 61342-1637, La Salle, USA; gen tel (815) 539-9396; adv tel (815) 539-9396; gen fax (815) 539-7862; adv fax (815) 539-7862; disp adv e-mail editor@mendotareporter.com; class adv e-mail mark@mendotareporter.com; ed e-mail editor@mendotareporter.com; web site www.mendotareporter.com
Circulation: 4,000pd, 8,000fr; Sworn/Estimate/Non-Audited
Advertising rate: Open inch rate $15.90
Established: 1878
Group: News Media Corp.
Pub. .... Kip Cheek
Gen. Mgr. .... Mark Elston
Ed. .... Bonnie Morris
Mechanical Specifications: Type page 13 x 21 1/2; E - 6 cols, 2, 1/6 between; A - 6 cols, 2, 1/6 between; C - 9 cols, 1 1/3, 1/6 between. Equipment & Software: Hardware — APP/Mac; Software — Multi-Ad/Creator.
Delivery Method: Mail, Racks

METROPOLIS

METROPOLIS PLANET (THUR)

111 E 5th St, Metropolis, IL, 62960-2108, Massac, USA; gen tel (618) 524-2141; gen fax (618) 524-4727; disp adv e-mail ads@metropolisplanet.com; class adv e-mail classifieds@metropolisplanet.com; ed e-mail news@metropolisplanet.com; web site www.metropolisplanet.com
Circulation: 4,100pd, 11,850fr; Sworn/Estimate/Non-Audited
Advertising rate: Open inch rate $9.13
Established: 1865
Group: Paxton Media Group, LLC
Digital Platform - Tablet: Apple iOS, Windows 7, Kindle, Nook, Kindle Fire
Gen. Mgr. .... Areia Hathcock
News Ed. .... Linda Kennedy
Mechanical Specifications: Type page 13 x 19.71; E - 6 cols, 1 5/6, 1/6 between; A - 6 cols, 1 5/6, 1/6 between; C - 9 cols, 1 1/6, 1/6 between.Equipment & Software: Hardware — APP/Mac; Software — Baseview.
Delivery Method: Mail, Newsstand

MIDLOTHIAN

BEVERLY NEWS (THUR)

3840 147th St, Midlothian, IL, 60445-3452, Cook, USA; gen tel (708) 388-2425; gen fax (708) 385-7811; disp adv e-mail spressnews@aol.com
Circulation: 4,080pd,; Sworn/Estimate/Non-Audited
Advertising rate: Open inch rate $10.64
Established: 1948
Group: Southwest Messenger Press, Inc.
Pub./Co-owners .... Luicinda Lysen
Ed./Co-Owners .... Linnea Lysen-Gavin
Delivery Method: Mail, Newsstand, Racks

BRIDGEVIEW INDEPENDENT (WED)

3840 147th St, Midlothian, IL, 60445-3452, Cook, USA; gen tel (708) 388-2425; gen fax (708) 385-7811; disp adv e-mail spressnews@aol.com; class adv e-mail spressnews@aol.com; ed e-mail spressnews@aol.com; web site www.southwestmessenger-press.com
Circulation: 4,500pd, 500fr; Sworn/Estimate/Non-Audited
Advertising rate: Open inch rate $9.24
Group: Southwest Messenger Press, Inc.
Adv. Mgr. .... Carol Beymer
Ed. .... Margaret D. Lysen
Delivery Method: Mail

BURBANK-STICKNEY INDEPENDENT (THUR)

3840 147th St, Midlothian, IL, 60445-3452, Cook, USA; gen tel (708) 388-2425; gen fax (708) 385-7811; ed e-mail spressnews@aol.com; web site www.southwestmessenger-press.com
Circulation: 6,110pd,; Sworn/Estimate/Non-Audited
Advertising rate: Open inch rate $9.24
Group: Southwest Messenger Press, Inc.
Pub. .... Margaret Lysen
Ed. .... Lucinda Lysen
Delivery Method: Mail

BURBANK-STICKNEY INDEPENDENT - SCOTTSDALE EDITION (THUR)

3840 147th St, Midlothian, IL, 60445-3452, Cook, USA; gen tel (708) 388-2425; gen fax (708) 385-7811; disp adv e-mail info@southwestmessengerpress.com; class adv e-mail info@southwestmessengerpress.com; ed e-mail info@southwestmessengerpress.com; web site www.southwestmessenger-press.com
Circulation: 5,975pd,; Sworn/Estimate/Non-Audited
Advertising rate: Open inch rate $10.64
Group: Southwest Messenger Press, Inc.
Pub. .... Margaret Lysen
Delivery Method: Mail

CHICAGO RIDGE CITIZEN (THUR)

3840 147th St, Midlothian, IL, 60445-3452, Cook, USA; gen tel (708) 388-2425; gen fax (708) 385-7811; disp adv e-mail info@southwestmessengerpress.com; class adv e-mail info@southwestmessengerpress.com; ed e-mail info@southwestmessengerpress.com; web site www.southwestmessenger-press.com
Circulation: 2,915pd, 600fr; Sworn/Estimate/Non-Audited
Advertising rate: Open inch rate $10.64
Group: Southwest Messenger Press, Inc.
Pub. .... Margaret Lysen
Ed. .... Lori Taylor

EVERGREEN PARK COURIER (THUR)

3840 147th St, Midlothian, IL, 60445-3452, Cook, USA; gen tel (708) 388-2425; gen fax (708) 385-7811; disp adv e-mail info@southwestmessengerpress.com; web site www.southwestmessengerpress.com
Circulation: 8,729pd, 800fr; Sworn/Estimate/Non-Audited
Advertising rate: Open inch rate $10.64
Group: Southwest Messenger Press, Inc.
Pub. .... Margaret Lysen
Delivery Method: Mail

HICKORY HILLS CITIZEN (THUR)

3840 147th St, Midlothian, IL, 60445-3452, Cook, USA; gen tel (708) 388-2425; gen fax (708) 385-7811; disp adv e-mail spressnews@aol.com; class adv e-mail spressnews@aol.com; ed e-mail spressnews@aol.com
Circulation: 3,530pd, 400fr; Sworn/Estimate/Non-Audited
Advertising rate: Open inch rate $10.64
Group: Southwest Messenger Press, Inc.
Pub. .... Margaret Lysen
Adv. Mgr. .... Carol Beymer
Ed. .... Lori Taylor
Delivery Method: Mail

MIDLOTHIAN-BREMEN MESSENGER (THUR)

3840 147th St, Midlothian, IL, 60445-3452, Cook, USA; gen tel (708) 388-2425; gen fax (708) 385-7811; disp adv e-mail info@southwestmessengerpress.com; class adv e-mail info@southwestmessengerpress.com; ed e-mail info@southwestmessengerpress.com; web site www.southwestmessenger-press.com
Circulation: 10,200pd, 1,106fr; Sworn/Estimate/Non-Audited
Advertising rate: Open inch rate $10.64
Established: 1930
Group: Southwest Messenger Press, Inc.
Pub. .... Linnea Gavin
Delivery Method: Mail

MOUNT GREENWOOD EXPRESS (THUR)

3840 147th St, Midlothian, IL, 60445-3452, Cook, USA; gen tel (708) 388-2425; gen fax (708) 385-7811; disp adv e-mail info@southwestmessengerpress.com; class adv e-mail info@southwestmessengerpress.com; ed e-mail info@southwestmessengerpress.com; web site www.southwestmessenger-press.com
Circulation: 8,729pd, 800fr; Sworn/Estimate/Non-Audited
Advertising rate: Open inch rate $10.64
Group: Southwest Messenger Press, Inc.
Pub. .... Margaret Lysen
Delivery Method: Mail

MOUNT GREENWOOD EXPRESS - ALSIP EDITION (THUR)

3840 147th St, Midlothian, IL, 60445-3452, Cook, USA; gen tel (708) 388-2425; gen fax (708) 385-7811; disp adv e-mail info@southwestmessengerpress.com; class adv e-mail info@southwestmessengerpress.com; ed e-mail info@southwestmessengerpress.com; web site www.southwestmessenger-press.com
Circulation: 8,729pd, 800fr; Sworn/Estimate/Non-Audited
Advertising rate: Open inch rate $10.64
Group: Southwest Messenger Press, Inc.
Pub. .... Margaret Lysen
Delivery Method: Mail

OAK LAWN INDEPENDENT (THUR)

3840 147th St, Midlothian, IL, 60445-3452, Cook, USA; gen tel (708) 388-2425; gen fax (708) 385-7811; disp adv e-mail spressnews@aol.com; class adv e-mail spressnews@aol.com; ed e-mail spressnews@aol.com; web site www.southwestmessenger-press.com
Circulation: 76,000pd, 700fr; Sworn/Estimate/Non-Audited
Advertising rate: Open inch rate $10.64
Group: Southwest Messenger Press, Inc.
Pub. .... Margaret Lysen
Delivery Method: Mail

ORLAND TOWNSHIP MESSENGER (THUR)

3840 147th St, Midlothian, IL, 60445-3452, Cook, USA; gen tel (708) 388-2425; gen fax (708) 385-7811; disp adv e-mail spressnews@aol.com; class adv e-mail spressnews@aol.com; ed e-mail spressnews@aol.com; web site www.southwestmessenger-press.com
Circulation: 3,788pd,; Sworn/Estimate/Non-Audited
Advertising rate: Open inch rate $10.64
Group: Southwest Messenger Press, Inc.
Pub. .... Margaret D. Lysen
Delivery Method: Mail

PALOS CITIZEN (THUR)

3840 147th St, Midlothian, IL, 60445-3452,

Cook, USA; gen tel (708) 388-2425; gen fax (708) 385-7811; disp adv e-mail info@southwestmessengerpress.com; class adv e-mail info@southwestmessengerpress.com; ed e-mail info@southwestmessengerpress.com; web site www.southwestmessengerpress.com
Circulation: 4,600pd, 450fr; Sworn/Estimate/Non-Audited
Advertising rate: Open inch rate $10.64
Group: Southwest Messenger Press, Inc.
Pub. .... Margaret Lysen
Ed. .... Lori Taylor
Delivery Method: Mail
Areas Served: 60464

WORTH CITIZEN (THUR)
3840 147th St, Midlothian, IL, 60445-3452, Cook, USA; gen tel (708) 388-2425; gen fax (708) 385-7811; disp adv e-mail info@southwestmessengerpress.com; web site www.southwestmessengerpress.com
Circulation: 8,729pd, 800fr; Sworn/Estimate/Non-Audited
Advertising rate: Open inch rate $10.64
Group: Southwest Messenger Press, Inc.
Pub. .... Margaret Lysen
Delivery Method: Mail

MILFORD

MILFORD HERALD-NEWS (WED)
18 S Axtel Ave, Milford, IL, 60953-1271, Iroquis, USA; gen tel (815) 889-9930; gen fax (815) 889-9930; disp adv e-mail milfordnews@netoptioninc.com; web site No Website
Circulation: 750pd,; Sworn/Estimate/Non-Audited
Advertising rate: Open inch rate $4.00
Established: 1928
Adv. Mgr. .... Joy Claire
Mechanical Specifications: Type page 14 x 20; E - 7 cols, 1 3/4, 1/8 between; A - 7 cols, 1 3/4, 1/8 between; C - 7 cols, 1 3/4, 1/8 between. Equipment & Software: ; Software — Adobe/PageMaker 5.0.
Delivery Method: Mail

MINIER

OLYMPIA REVIEW (TUES)
102 S Main Ave, Minier, IL, 61759-7523, Tazewell, USA; gen tel (309) 392-2414; gen fax (309) 392-2169
Circulation: 4,498fr; Sworn/Estimate/Non-Audited
Advertising rate: Open inch rate $6.00
Pub. .... Mark Rickard

MOMENCE

THE MOMENCE PROGRESS REPORTER (WED)
110 W River St, Momence, IL, 60954-1516, Kankakee, USA; gen tel (815) 472-2000; gen fax (815) 472-3877; disp adv e-mail m.reporter@mchsi.com; web site momenceprogressreporter.com
Circulation: 900pd,; Sworn/Estimate/Non-Audited
Advertising rate: Open inch rate $3.50
Established: 1903
Pub. .... H. Gene Lincoln
Display Adv. .... Anita Allison
Ed. .... Sue Lincoln
Delivery Method: Mail, Newsstand, Racks
Areas Served: Momence/Kankakee/60954

MONTICELLO

PIATT COUNTY JOURNAL-REPUBLICAN (WED)
118 E Washington St, Monticello, IL, 61856-1641, Piatt, USA; gen tel (217) 762-2511; gen fax (217) 762-8591; disp adv e-mail jrads@news-gazette.com; class adv e-mail journal@journal-republican.com; ed e-mail journal@journal-republican.com; web site www.journal-republican.com
Circulation: 2,672pd,; AAM
Advertising rate: Open inch rate $10.50
Established: 1874
Group: The News-Gazette
News Gazette Community NewsEditions: (52)
Vice Pres./Gen. Mgr. .... Tim Evans
Pub. .... John Foreman
Circ. Mgr. .... Melinda Carpenter
Editor .... Steve Hoffman
Adv. Dir. .... Tom Zalabak
Mechanical Specifications: Type page 9 13/16 x 12; E - 5 cols, 1 13/16, 3/16 between; A - 5 cols, 1 5/16, 3/16 between; C - 7 cols, 1 1/4, 3/16 between.Equipment & Software: Hardware — APP/Mac; Presses — 9-KP/News King; Software — QPS/QuarkXPress.
Delivery Method: Mail, Newsstand, Racks
Areas Served: 61856, 61813, 61818, 61830, 61884, 61839, 61854

MORRIS

HERALD LIFE (THUR)
909 Liberty St, Morris, IL, 60450-1594, Grundy, USA; adv tel (815) 280-4100; adv fax (815) 729-2019; disp adv e-mail ads@morrisdailyherald.com
Circulation: 100fr; Sworn/Estimate/Non-Audited
Group: Shaw Media
Ed. .... Jon Styf
Gen. Mgr. .... Steve Vanisko
Adv. Mgr. .... Denise Pankey
Delivery Method: Mail
Areas Served: Will/Grundy Counties

MORRISON

WHITESIDE NEWS SENTINEL (TUES)
100 E Main St, Morrison, IL, 61270-2694, Whiteside, USA; gen tel (815) 772-7244; adv tel (815) 772-7244; ed tel (815) 772-7244; gen fax (815) 772-4105; adv fax (815) 772-4105; ed fax (815) 772-7244; disp adv e-mail wnssentinel@gmail.com; class adv e-mail wnssentinel@gmail.com; ed e-mail wnssentinel@gmail.com
Circulation: 2,557pd, 28fr; Sworn/Estimate/Non-Audited
Advertising rate: Open inch rate $10.25
Established: 1857
Group: WNS Publications Inc.
Pub./Adv. Mgr. .... Sue Patten
Editor .... Jerry Lindsey
Owner/Mng. Ed. .... Anthony M. Komlanc
Prodn. Mgr. .... Nancy Rutledge
Mechanical Specifications: Type page 13 1/2 x 21; E - 7 cols, 1 3/4, 3/16 between; A - 7 cols, 1 3/4, 3/16 between; C - 10 cols, 1 1/4, 1/4 between.Equipment & Software: Hardware — APP/Mac; Software — QPS/QuarkXPress, Adobe/Photoshop.
Delivery Method: Mail, Newsstand, Racks
Areas Served: 61270, 61252, 61261

MORRISONVILLE

MORRISONVILLE TIMES (WED)
509 Carlin St, Morrisonville, IL, 62546, USA; gen tel (217) 526-3323; gen fax (217) 526-3323
Circulation: 1,000pd, 50fr
Advertising rate: Open inch rate $2.45
Ed. .... Tom Latonis

MOUNT CARROLL

CARROLL COUNTY MIRROR-DEMOCRAT (THUR)
308 N Main St, Mount Carroll, IL, 61053-1024, Carroll, USA; gen tel (815) 244-2411; adv tel (815) 244-2411; ed tel (815) 244-2411; gen fax (815) 244-2965; adv fax (815) 244-2965; ed fax (815) 244-2965; disp adv e-mail mirrordem@grics.net; class adv e-mail mirrordem@grics.net; ed e-mail mirrordem@grics.net; web site mirrordemocrat.com
Circulation: 4,000pd, 8,000fr; Sworn/Estimate/Non-Audited
Advertising rate: Open inch rate $12.00
Established: 1860
Group: Mirror-Democrat Co.
Northwestern Illinois Dispatch
Savanna Times-Journal
Digital Platform - Mobile: Apple
Digital Platform - Tablet: Apple iOS
Ed./Pub./Owner .... Robert (Bob) Watson
Office/Circ. Mgr. .... Mary Maszk
Times-Journal Office Mgr./Adv. Rep. .... Pam Villalobos
Reporter/Adv. Rep. .... Angie Field
Graphic Designer .... Janice Smith
Mechanical Specifications: 10.25" wide x 15.75" long full page
Delivery Method: Mail, Newsstand
Areas Served: 61053, 61074, 61014, 61046, 61051, 61078, 61285, 61041, 52070

MOUNT OLIVE

MOUNT OLIVE HERALD (THUR)
102 E Main St, Mount Olive, IL, 62069-1702, Macoupin, USA; gen tel (217) 999-3941; gen fax (217) 999-5105; disp adv e-mail moherald1880@yahoo.com; web site No Website
Circulation: 1,550pd,; Sworn/Estimate/Non-Audited
Advertising rate: Open inch rate $3.50
Pub. .... John M. Galer
Ed. .... Linda Hasquin
Delivery Method: Mail

MOUNT ZION

THE MT. ZION REGION NEWS (WED)
433 N State Route 121, Mount Zion, IL, 62549-1514, Macon, USA; gen tel (217) 864-4212; gen fax (217) 864-4711; disp adv e-mail mtzionregionnews@comcast.net
Circulation: 1,784pd, 150fr; Sworn/Estimate/Non-Audited
Advertising rate: Open inch rate $4.85
Established: 1959
Group: The Miami Herald Publishing Co.
Pub. .... Greg HoskinsEquipment & Software: Hardware — APP/Mac; Software — Adobe/PageMaker 6.0.
Delivery Method: Mail, Newsstand, Racks

MT STERLING

BROWN COUNTY DEMOCRAT MESSAGE (WED)
123 W MAIN ST, Mt Sterling, IL, 62353-1223, Brown County, USA; gen tel (217) 773-3371; gen fax (217) 773-3369; disp adv e-mail thedmads@yahoo.com; class adv e-mail thedmads@yahoo.com; ed e-mail thedmnews@yahoo.com
Circulation: 2,200pd,; Sworn/Estimate/Non-Audited
Advertising rate: Open inch rate $5.50
Established: 1871
Group: Coulson Publications
Publisher .... Robin Oitker
Delivery Method: Mail, Newsstand, Racks
Areas Served: Brown County, IL

NASHVILLE

THE NASHVILLE NEWS (WED)
211 W Saint Louis St, Nashville, IL, 62263-1161, Washington, USA; gen tel (618) 327-3411; gen fax (618) 327-3299; disp adv e-mail news@nashnews.net; ed e-mail news@nashnews.net; web site www.nashnews.com
Circulation: 5,300pd,; Sworn/Estimate/Non-Audited
Advertising rate: Open inch rate $7.50
Established: 1933
Pub. .... Pam Smith
Ed. .... Alex Haglund
Mechanical Specifications: Type page 11 7/8 x 21 1/2; E - 6 cols, 1 13/16, 1/8 between; A - 6 cols, 1 13/16, 1/8 between; C - 7 cols, 1 1/2, 1/8 between.Equipment & Software: Hardware — APP/Mac; Software — Adobe/PageMaker 5.0.
Delivery Method: Mail

NEWMAN

THE NEWMAN INDEPENDENT (THUR)
207 W Yates St, Newman, IL, 61942-9444, Douglas, USA; gen tel (217) 837-2414; gen fax (217) 837-2071; disp adv e-mail news1@tni-news.com; web site www.newman.net
Circulation: 480pd, 20fr; Sworn/Estimate/Non-Audited
Advertising rate: Open inch rate $3.50
Established: 1874
Owner, publisher .... Cathy Hales
Adv. Mgr. .... Dana Hales
Delivery Method: Mail, Newsstand, Racks
Areas Served: city/multi-county

NEWTON

NEWTON PRESS-MENTOR (MON, THUR)
700 W Washington St, Newton, IL, 62448-1129, Jasper, USA; gen tel (618) 783-2324; adv tel (618) 393-2931; gen fax (618) 783-2325; adv fax (618) 392-2953; disp adv e-mail cslunaker@olneydailymail.com; class adv e-mail abrian@olneydailymail.coom; ed e-mail vking@pressmentor.com; web site www.pressmentor.com
Circulation: 2,500pd, 6,150fr; Sworn/Estimate/Non-Audited
Advertising rate: Open inch rate $6.26 (Mon), $7.51 (Thurs)
Established: 1860
Group: GateHouse Media, Inc.
Mng. Ed. .... Vanette King
Publisher .... Kerry Kocher
Delivery Method: Mail, Newsstand, Racks

TEUTOPOLIS PRESS-DIETERICH SPECIAL GAZETTE (WED)
PO Box 151, Newton, IL, 62448-0151, Effingham, USA; gen tel (217) 857-3116; gen fax (217) 857-3623; disp adv e-mail tpress@frontiernet.net; ed e-mail rmcgrew@olneydailymail.com; web site www.teutopolispress.com
Circulation: 1,100pd,; Sworn/Estimate/Non-Audited
Advertising rate: Open inch rate $6.25
Established: 1898
Pub. .... Ray McGrew
Mechanical Specifications: Type page 11 3/8 x 14; E - 6 cols, 1 9/16, 1/6 between; A - 6 cols, 1 9/16, 1/6 between; C - 6 cols, 1 9/16, 1/6 between.Equipment & Software: Hardware — APP/Macs; Presses — G/Community.
Delivery Method: Mail

NOKOMIS

FREE PRESS-PROGRESS (WED)
112 W State St, Nokomis, IL, 62075-1657, Montgomery, USA; gen tel (217) 563-2115; gen fax (217) 563-7464; disp adv e-mail freepress@consolidated.net; web site nokomisonline.com
Circulation: 2,150pd, 1,900fr; Sworn/Estimate/Non-Audited
Advertising rate: Open inch rate $5.35
Pub. .... Thomas J. Phillips
Ed. .... Tom Latonis
Editor .... John BrouxEquipment & Software: Hardware — APP/Mac; Software — Adobe/PageMaker.

Delivery Method: Mail, Newsstand, Carrier, Racks

NORTHBROOK

THE GLENCOE ANCHOR (THUR)
60 Revere Dr Ste 888, Suite 888, Northbrook, IL, 60062-1580, Cook, USA; gen tel (847) 272-4565; gen fax (847) 272-4648; disp adv e-mail a.nicks@22ndcenturymedia.com; class adv e-mail j.nemec@22ndcenturymedia.com; ed e-mail jacqueline@winnetkacurrent.com; web site glencoeanchor.com
Circulation: 2,963fr; AAM
Adv. Dir. .... Andrew Nicks
Nat. Sales Dir. .... Renee Burker
Circ. Dir. .... Michael Ksycki
Mng. Ed. .... Eric DeGrechie
Pub. .... Joe Caughlin
Delivery Method: Mail

THE GLENVIEW LANTERN (THUR)
60 Revere Dr, Ste 888, Northbrook, IL, 60062-1580, Cook, USA; gen tel (847) 272-4565; gen fax (847) 272-4648; disp adv e-mail m.vinci@22ndcenturymedia.com; class adv e-mail e.fritz@glenviewlantern.com; ed e-mail alex@glenviewlantern.com; web site www.22ndcenturymedia.com
Circulation: 15,709pd,; CAC
Advertising rate: Open inch rate $45.16
Established: 2011
Nat'l Sales Dir. .... Mike Vinci
Adv. Dir. .... Andrew Nicks
Circ. Mgr. .... Hillary Carroll
Delivery Method: Mail

THE HIGHLAND PARK LANDMARK (THUR)
60 Revere Dr Ste 888, Suite 888, Northbrook, IL, 60062-1580, Cook, USA; gen tel (847) 272-4565; gen fax (847) 272-4648; disp adv e-mail a.nicks@22ndcenturymedia.com; class adv e-mail j.nemec@22ndcenturymedia.com; ed e-mail jacqueline@winnetkacurrent.com; web site hplandmark.com
Circulation: 9,974fr; CAC
Adv. Dir. .... Andrew Nicks
Nat. Sales Dir. .... Renee Burker
Circ. Dir. .... Michael Ksycki
Mng. Ed. .... Eric DeGrechie
Pub. .... Joe Caughlin
Delivery Method: Mail

THE LAKE FOREST LEADER (THUR)
60 Revere Dr Ste 888, Suite 888, Northbrook, IL, 60062-1580, Cook, USA; gen tel (847) 272-4565; gen fax (847) 272-4648; disp adv e-mail a.nicks@22ndcenturymedia.com; class adv e-mail j.nemec@22ndcenturymedia.com; ed e-mail jacqueline@winnetkacurrent.com; web site lakeforestleader.com
Circulation: 9,904pd, 0fr; CAC
Adv. Dir. .... Andrew Nicks
Nat. Sales Dir. .... Renee Burker
Circ. Dir. .... Michael Ksycki
Mng. Ed. .... Eric DeGrechie
Pub. .... Joe Caughlin
Delivery Method: Mail

THE NORTHBROOK TOWER (THUR)
60 Revere Dr, Ste 888, Northbrook, IL, 60062-1580, Cook, USA; gen tel (847) 272-4565; gen fax (847) 272-4648; disp adv e-mail m.vinci@22ndcenturymedia.com; class adv e-mail m.vinci@22ndcenturymedia.com; ed e-mail dayna@northbrooktower.com; web site www.22ndcenturymedia.com
Circulation: 14,305pd,; CAC
Advertising rate: Open inch rate $42.44
Established: 2011
Adv. Dir./Nat'l Adv. Mgr. .... Mike Vinci
Delivery Method: Mail

THE WILMETTE BEACON (WED)
60 Revere Dr, Ste 888, Northbrook, IL, 60062-1580, Cook, USA; gen tel (847) 272-4565; gen fax (847) 272-4648; disp adv e-mail m.vinci@22ndcenturymedia.com; class adv e-mail m.vinci@22ndcenturymedia.com; ed e-mail joe@wilmettebeacon.com; web site www.22ndcenturymedia.com
Circulation: 9,774pd,; CAC
Advertising rate: Open inch rate $26.90
Established: 2010
Nat'l Sales Dir. .... Mike Vinci
Adv. Dir. .... Andrew Nicks
Circ. Mgr. .... Hillary Carroll
Delivery Method: Mail

THE WINNETKA CURRENT (WED)
60 Revere Dr, Ste 888, Northbrook, IL, 60062-1580, Cook, USA; gen tel (847) 272-4565; gen fax (847) 272-4648; disp adv e-mail john@winnetkacurrent.com; class adv e-mail john@winnetkacurrent.com; ed e-mail april@winnetkacurrent.com; web site www.22ndcenturymedia.com
Circulation: 6,404pd,; CAC
Advertising rate: Open inch rate $25.45
Established: 2010
Adv. Dir. .... Andrew Nicks
Nat. Sales Dir. .... Renee Burker
Circ. Dir. .... Michael Ksycki
Delivery Method: Mail

OAK PARK

AUSTIN WEEKLY NEWS (THUR)
141 S Oak Park Ave, Ste 1, Oak Park, IL, 60302-2972, Cook, USA; gen tel (773) 626-6332; gen fax (708) 524-0447; disp adv e-mail dawn@austinweeklynews.com; class adv e-mail classifieds@austinweeklynews.com; ed e-mail circulation@wjinc.com; web site www.austinweeklynews.com
Circulation: 12,000fr; Sworn/Estimate/Non-Audited
Advertising rate: Full page: $1462, 3/4 Page: $1204, Half Page: $803, Quarter Page $442
Pub. .... Dan Haley
Ed. .... Terry Dean
Delivery Method: Mail, Newsstand

FOREST PARK REVIEW (WED)
141 S Oak Park Ave, Ste 3, Oak Park, IL, 60302-2900, Cook, USA; gen tel (708) 366-0600; gen fax (708) 524-0447; disp adv e-mail dawn@forestparkreview.com; class adv e-mail classifieds@forestparkreview.com; ed e-mail circulation@wjinc.com; web site www.forestparkreview.com - 70,734(views) 18,273(visitors)
Circulation: 2,400pd, 400fr; Sworn/Estimate/Non-Audited
Advertising rate: (Modular Rates) Full Page: $571, 3/4 page: $442, Half Page: $297, Quarter Page: $154
Established: 1886
Digital Platform - Mobile: Apple, Android, Windows, Blackberry
Digital Platform - Tablet: Apple iOS, Android, Windows 7, Blackberry Tablet OS, Kindle, Nook, Kindle Fire
Pub. .... Dan HaleyEquipment & Software: Hardware — PC; Software — QPS/QuarkXPress 3.32.
Delivery Method: Mail, Newsstand, Racks
Areas Served: Forest Park, IL

LANDMARK (WED)
141 S Oak Park Ave, Ste 1, Oak Park, IL, 60302-2972, Cook, USA; gen tel (708) 524-8300; gen fax (708) 524-0447; web site www.rblandmark.com
Circulation: 2,500pd, 1,100fr; Sworn/Estimate/Non-Audited
Advertising rate: (Modular Rates) Full Page: $656, 3/4 Page: $509, Half Page: $342, Quarter Page: $176
Group: Wednesday Journal, Inc.
Advertising Manager .... Dawn Ferencak
Ed. .... Bob Uphues
Delivery Method: Mail, Newsstand, Racks
Areas Served: Riverside, North Riverside, Brookfield

WEDNESDAY JOURNAL OF OAK PARK & RIVER FOREST (WED)
141 S Oak Park Ave, Ste 1, Oak Park, IL, 60302-2972, Cook, USA; gen tel (708) 524-8300; gen fax (708) 524-0447; disp adv e-mail dawn@oakpark.com; class adv e-mail maryellen@oakpark.com; ed e-mail dhaley@wjinc.com; web site www.oakpark.com - 300,000(views) 18,000(visitors)
Circulation: 5,450pd, 1,400fr; USPS
Advertising rate: (Modular Rates) Full Page-$1,819, Half Page- $923, Quarter Page-$463, 3/4 page $1,393
Established: 1980
Digital Platform - Mobile: Apple, Android, Windows
Digital Platform - Tablet: Apple iOS, Android
Pub. .... Dan Haley
Prodn. Mgr. .... Andy Mead
Mechanical Specifications: Type page 10 1/4 x 12 3/8; E - 4 cols, 2 3/8, between; A - 4 cols, 2 3/8, between; C - 7 cols, 1 1/2, between. Equipment & Software: Hardware — Apple; Software — InDesign
Delivery Method: Mail, Newsstand, Racks
Areas Served: 60301, 60302, 60304, 60305

OKAWVILLE

THE OKAWVILLE TIMES (WED)
109 E Walnut St, P.O. Box 68, Okawville, IL, 62271-1883, Washington, USA; gen tel (618) 243-5563; adv tel (618) 243-5563; gen fax (618) 243-5563; adv fax (618) 243-5563; disp adv e-mail press1@okawvilletimes.com; class adv e-mail press1@okawvilletimes.com; ed e-mail press1@okawvilletimes.com; web site www.okawvilletimes.com
Circulation: 2,550pd,; Sworn/Estimate/Non-Audited
Advertising rate: Open inch rate $8.50
Established: 1893
Digital Platform - Mobile: Apple, Windows
Digital Platform - Tablet: Apple iOS, Windows 7
Pub. .... Gary W. Stricker
Ed. .... Travis Volz
Delivery Method: Mail, Newsstand, Racks
Areas Served: 62271

OQUAWKA

OQUAWKA CURRENT (WED)
PO Box 606, Oquawka, IL, 61469-0606, Henderson, USA; gen tel (309) 867-2515; gen fax (309) 867-6215
Advertising rate: Open inch rate $10.90
Group: GateHouse Media, Inc.
Adv. Dir. .... sheena miller
Production Mgr. .... John Bowens
Delivery Method: Mail, Newsstand, Racks

OREGON

OGLE COUNTY LIFE (FRI)
311 E Washington St, Oregon, IL, 61061-9564, Ogle, USA; gen tel (815) 732-2156; gen fax (815) 732-6154 ; disp adv e-mail leisenberg@oglecountynews.com; web site www.oglecountylife.com
Group: News Media Corp.
Ed. .... Vinde Wells
Gen. Mgr. .... Earleen Hinton
Adv. Mgr. .... Luke Eisenberg

ORION

ORION GAZETTE (FRI)
1018 4th St, Orion, IL, 61273-7731, Henry, USA; gen tel (309) 526-8085; ed e-mail mcarls@oriongazette.com; web site www.oriongazette.com
Advertising rate: $5.50 per colum inch
Established: 1992
Pub. .... Dee Evans
Ed. .... Mindy Carls

ORLAND PARK

THE FRANKFORT STATION (THUR)
11516 183rd Pl, Unit Swofccondo # 3, Orland Park, IL, 60467-9455, Will, USA; gen tel (708) 326-9170; gen fax (708) 326-9179; disp adv e-mail m.vinci@22ndcenturymedia.com; class adv e-mail m.vinci@22ndcenturymedia.com; ed e-mail jon@frankfortstation.com; web site www.22ndcenturymedia.com
Circulation: 9,608pd,; CAC
Advertising rate: Open inch rate $18.13
Established: 2005
Sales Dir. .... Mike Vinci
Classified Adv. Mgr. .... Andrew Nicks
Circ. Mgr. .... Hillary Carroll
Delivery Method: Mail

THE HOMER HORIZON (THUR)
11516 183rd Pl, Unit Swofccondo # 3, Orland Park, IL, 60467-9455, Will, USA; gen tel (708) 326-9170; gen fax (708) 326-9179; disp adv e-mail b.bond@homerhorizon.com; class adv e-mail b.bond@homerhorizon.com; ed e-mail bill@homerhorizon.com; web site http://www.homerhorizon.com/
Circulation: 7,981pd,; CAC
Advertising rate: Open inch rate $16.38
Established: 2005
Circ. Mgr. .... Hillary Carroll
Classified Adv. Mgr. .... Andrew Nicks
Sales Dir. .... Mike Vinci
Delivery Method: Mail

THE LOCKPORT LEGEND (THUR)
11516 183rd Pl, Unit Swofccondo # 3, Orland Park, IL, 60467-9455, Will, USA; gen tel (708) 326-9170; gen fax (708) 326-9179; disp adv e-mail m.vinci@22ndcenturymedia.com; class adv e-mail m.vinci@22ndcenturymedia.com; ed e-mail h.carroll@22ndcenturymedia.com; web site www.22ndcenturymedia.com
Circulation: 10,038pd,; CAC
Advertising rate: Open inch rate $18.13
Established: 2010
Sales Dir. .... Mike Vinci
Classified Adv. Mgr. .... Andrew Nicks
Circ. Mgr. .... Hillary Carroll
Delivery Method: Mail

THE MOKENA MESSENGER (THUR)
11516 183rd Pl, Unit Swofccondo # 3, Orland Park, IL, 60467-9455, Will, USA; gen tel (708) 326-9170; gen fax (708) 326-9179; disp adv e-mail m.vinci@22ndcenturymedia.com; class adv e-mail m.vinci@22ndcenturymedia.com; ed e-mail will@mokenamessenger.com; web site www.22ndcenturymedia.com
Circulation: 8,348pd,; CAC
Advertising rate: Open inch rate $16.48
Established: 2007
Circ. Mgr. .... Hillary Carroll
Classified Adv. Mgr. .... Andrew Nicks
Sales Dir. .... Mike Vinci
Delivery Method: Mail

THE NEW LENOX PATRIOT (THUR)
11516 183rd Pl, Unit Swofccondo # 3, Orland Park, IL, 60467-9455, Will, USA; gen tel (708) 326-9170; gen fax (708) 326-9179; disp adv e-mail m.vinci@22ndcenturymedia.com; class adv e-mail m.vinci@22ndcenturymedia.com; ed e-mail sean@newlenoxpatriot.com; web site http://www.newlenoxpatriot.com/
Circulation: 10,688pd,; CAC
Advertising rate: Open inch rate $20.00
Established: 2007
Sales Dir. .... Mike Vinci
Classified Adv. Mgr. .... Andrew Nicks
Circ. Mgr. .... Hillary Carroll
Delivery Method: Mail

THE ORLAND PARK PRAIRIE (THUR)
11516 183rd Pl, Unit Swofccondo # 3, Orland Park, IL, 60467-9455, Will, USA; gen tel (708) 326-9170; gen fax (708) 326-9179; disp adv e-mail m.vinci@22ndcenturymedia.com; class adv e-mail m.vinci@22ndcenturymedia.com; ed e-mail heather@opprairie.com; web site www.22ndcenturymedia.com

Circulation: 22,580pd,; CAC
Advertising rate: Open inch rate $28.24
Established: 2006
Circ. Mgr..................................... Hillary Carroll
Classified Adv. Mgr..................... Andrew Nicks
Sales Dir. .... Mike Vinci
Delivery Method: Mail

THE TINLEY JUNCTION (THUR)
11516 183rd Pl, Unit Swofccondo # 3, Orland Park, IL, 60467-9455, Will, USA; gen tel (708) 326-9170; gen fax (708) 326-9179; disp adv e-mail m.vinci@22ndcenturymedia.com; class adv e-mail m.vinci@22ndcenturymedia.com; ed e-mail michael@tinleyjunction.com; web site www.22ndcenturymedia.com
Circulation: 19,139pd,; CAC
Advertising rate: Open inch rate $25.89
Established: 2008
Sales Dir. .... Mike Vinci
Classified Adv. Mgr..................... Andrew Nicks
Circ. Mgr..................................... Hillary Carroll
Delivery Method: Mail

PALMYRA

NORTHWESTERN NEWS (WED)
PO Box 157, Palmyra, IL, 62674-0157, Macoupin, USA; gen tel (217) 436-2424; gen fax (217) 965-4512; disp adv e-mail ads@gnnews.net; ed e-mail editor@gnnews.net; web site gnnews.net
Circulation: 1,100pd,; Sworn/Estimate/Non-Audited
Advertising rate: Open inch rate $8.00
Established: 1969
Group: Paddock Publications
Adv. Mgr................................. Nathan E. Jones
Circ. Mgr............................ Julie Westerhausen
Mechanical Specifications: Type page 5 cols, 1 7/8, 1/8 between.Equipment & Software: Hardware — 11-APP/IMAC; Presses — 5-KP; Software — Adobe/IN DESIGN CS3
Delivery Method: Mail, Newsstand
Areas Served: 62674

PALOS HEIGHTS

THE REGIONAL NEWS (THUR)
12243 S Harlem Ave, Palos Heights, IL, 60463-1431, Cook, USA; gen tel (708) 448-4000; gen fax (708) 448-4012; disp adv e-mail theregional@comcast.net; web site www.theregionalnews.com
Circulation: 4,000pd, 95fr; Sworn/Estimate/Non-Audited
Advertising rate: Open inch rate $19.59
Established: 1941
Group: Regional Publishing
Digital Platform - Tablet: Apple iOS, Android
Pub... Amy Richards
Ed. .... Anthony Caciopo
Mechanical Specifications: Type page 13 1/2 x 21 1/4; E - 6 cols, 2 1/4, 5/16 between; A - 6 cols, 2 1/4, 5/16 between; C - 6 cols, 2 1/4, 5/16 between.Equipment & Software: Hardware — 24-IBM; Presses — 5-G/Community; Software — Microsoft/Windows XP.
Delivery Method: Mail, Newsstand, Racks
Areas Served: 60463, 60462, 60464

THE REPORTER (THUR)
12243 S Harlem Ave, Palos Heights, IL, 60463-1431, Cook, USA; gen tel (708) 448-6161; gen fax (708) 448-4012; disp adv e-mail thereporteronline@comcast.net; web site www.thereporteronline.net
Circulation: 4,000pd,; Sworn/Estimate/Non-Audited
Advertising rate: Open inch rate $19.59
Established: 1960
Group: Regional Publishing
Pub... Amy Richards
Ed. .... Joe Boyle
Mechanical Specifications: Type page 13 1/2 x 21 1/4; E - 6 cols, 2 1/4, 3/16 between; A - 6 cols, 2 1/4, 3/16 between; C - 6 cols, 2 1/4, 3/16 between.Equipment & Software: Hardware — IBM; Presses — G/Community; Software — Microsoft/Windows 98, Microsoft/Word.
Delivery Method: Mail, Newsstand, Racks
Areas Served: 60482, 60415, 60465, 60457, 60453, 60805

PANA

PANA NEWS-PALLADIUM (MON, THUR)
205 S Locust St, Pana, IL, 62557-1605, Christian, USA; gen tel (217) 562-2113; gen fax (217) 562-3729; disp adv e-mail pananews@consolidated.net; web site www.pananewsonline.net
Circulation: 3,500pd, 152fr; Sworn/Estimate/Non-Audited
Advertising rate: Open inch rate $4.25
Established: 1864
Group: Nokomis Free Press-Progress
Morrisonville Times
Assumption Golden Prairie News
Pub...................................... Thomas J. Phillips
Ed. .... Thomas R. Latonis
Mechanical Specifications: Type page 16 1/4 x 27; E - 8 cols, 1 3/4, between; A - 8 cols, 1 3/4, between; C - 8 cols, 1 3/4, between. Equipment & Software: Hardware — APP/Mac; Presses — 3-G/Community.; Software — In Design; Creator
Delivery Method: Mail, Newsstand, Racks
Areas Served: 62557; 62080; 62571; 62510; 62422; 62431; 62553; 62555; 62080; 62565; 62568

PARIS

THE PRAIRIE PRESS (SAT)
101 N Central Ave, Paris, IL, 61944-1704, Edgar, USA; gen tel (217) 921-3216; gen fax (217) 921-3309; disp adv e-mail nzeman@prairiepress.net; web site www.prairiepress.net
Circulation:; AAM
Established: 1848
Pub./Pres.................................... Taylor Smith
Ed./VP .... Nancy Zeman
School Ed. .... Gary Henry

PAXTON

FORD COUNTY RECORD (WED)
208 N Market St, Paxton, IL, 60957-1124, Ford County, USA; gen tel (217) 379-2356; ed tel (217) 722-1042 or (217) 379-2356; gen fax (217) 379-3104; disp adv e-mail sschunke@news-gazette.com; class adv e-mail pkillion@news-gazette.com; ed e-mail wbrumleve@fordcountyrecord.com; web site www.fordcountyrecord.com
Circulation: 2,490pd,; AAM
Advertising rate: Open inch rate $7.50
Established: 1865
Group: The News-Gazette
News Gazette Community News
Editor .... William Brumleve
Pub.. John Foreman
Adv. Dir...................................... Tom Zalabak
Mechanical Specifications: Type page 13 x 21; E - 6 cols, 2 1/16, between.
Delivery Method: Mail, Newsstand, Racks
Areas Served: 60968, 60959, 60957, 60936, 60962, 60933, 60952, 61773, 61843, 60949, 60960

PECATONICA

THE GAZETTE (TUES)
111 W 4th St, Pecatonica, IL, 61063-7712, Winnebago, USA; gen tel (815) 239-1028; gen fax (815) 239-9198; disp adv e-mail rmarshall@rvpublishing.com; web site www.rvpublishing.com
Circulation: 2,341pd, 5,020fr; Sworn/Estimate/Non-Audited
Advertising rate: Open inch rate $7.75
Pub.. Pete Crugar
Gen. Mgr.............................. Randall Johnson
Adv. Mgr.............................. Rhonda Marshall
Circ. Mgr....................................... Lindy Sweet
Mng. Ed..................................... Charlie Plumb
Mechanical Specifications: Type page 10 1/8 x 16; E - 5 cols, 2 1/16, between; A - 5 cols, 2 1/16, between; C - 6 cols, between. Equipment & Software: ; Presses — WPC/Web Leader.
Delivery Method: Mail

PEKIN

MORTON TIMES-NEWS (WED)
306 Court St, Pekin, IL, 61554-3104, Peoria, USA; gen tel (309) 346-1111; adv tel (309) 346-1111; ed tel (309) 346-1111; adv fax (309) 686-3122; disp adv e-mail mmehl@timestoday.com; class adv e-mail mmehl@timestoday.com; ed e-mail TCnews@timestoday.com; web site mortontimesnews.com
Circulation: 28,210fr
Group: GateHouse Media, Inc.
Sales Mgr .... Mike Mehl
Executive Ed......................... Jeanette Kendall
Areas Served: 61554, 61611, 61550, 61571

WASHINGTON TIMES REPORTER (WED)
306 Court St, Pekin, IL, 61554-3104, Tazewell, USA; gen tel (309) 346-1111 ext. 660; adv tel (309) 686-3106; ed tel (309) 686-3054; gen fax (309) 346-1446; adv fax (309) 346-9815; ed fax (309) 346-1446; disp adv e-mail mmehl@timestoday.com; class adv e-mail lscott@pekintimes.com; ed e-mail wtr@timestoday.com; web site washingtontimesreporter.com
Circulation: 171pd, 9,488fr; Sworn/Estimate/Non-Audited
Advertising rate: Open inch rate $14.00
Established: 1840
Group: GateHouse Media, Inc.
Exec. Ed................................ Jeanette Kendall
Office Mgr. .... Donna Reaska
Gen. Sales Mgr.................. Linda Smith Brown
Pub.. Ken Mauser
Mechanical Specifications: Type page 11 5/6 x 21 1/2; E - 6 cols, 1 5/6, 1/6 between; A - 6 cols, 1 5/6, 1/6 between; C - 9 cols, 1 1/6, 1/6 between.Equipment & Software: Hardware — APP/Mac; Software — QPS/QuarkXPress 4.0, Adobe/Photoshop 5.0, Adobe/Illustrator 8.0.
Delivery Method: Newsstand, Carrier, Racks
Areas Served: 61571

WOODFORD TIMES (WED)
PO Box 430, Pekin, IL, 61555-0430, Peoria, USA; gen tel (309) 692-6600; adv tel (309) 686-3106; ed tel (309) 692-6600; gen fax (309) 686-3101; adv fax (309) 686-3122; ed fax (309) 686-3101; disp adv e-mail mmehl@timestoday.com; class adv e-mail amakowski@timestoday.com; ed e-mail wt@timestoday.com; web site www.WoodfordTimes.com
Circulation: 4,819fr; Sworn/Estimate/Non-Audited
Advertising rate: Open inch rate $14.00
Established: 2010
Group: GateHouse Media, Inc.
Exec. Ed................................ Jeanette Kendall
Pub.. Ken Mauser
Gen. Sales Mgr.................. Linda Smith Brown
Office Mgr. .... Donna Reaska
Delivery Method: Newsstand, Carrier, Racks

PEORIA

CHILLICOTHE TIMES-BULLETIN (WED)
1 News Plz, Peoria, IL, 61643-0001, Peoria, USA; gen tel (309) 692-6600; adv tel (309) 686-3106; ed tel (309) 686-3016; gen fax (309) 686-3101; adv fax (309) 686-3122; ed fax (309) 686-3101; disp adv e-mail mgillespie@timestoday.com; class adv e-mail lsmithbrown@timestoday.com; ed e-mail ctb@timestoday.com; web site www.chillicothetimesbulletin.com
Circulation: 3,220fr; Sworn/Estimate/Non-Audited
Advertising rate: Open inch rate $73.50
Established: 1883
Group: GateHouse Media, Inc.Jeanette Kendall
Delivery Method: Newsstand, Carrier, Racks
Areas Served: 61523

EAST PEORIA TIMES-COURIER (WED)
1 News Plz, Peoria, IL, 61643-0001, Tazewell County, USA; gen tel (309) 692-6600; ed fax (309) 691-7857; disp adv e-mail eptc@timestoday.com; web site www.eastpeoriatimescourier.com
Circulation: 1,872pd,; Sworn/Estimate/Non-Audited
Advertising rate: Open inch rate $18.90
Established: 1927
Group: GateHouse Media, Inc.
Ed. .... Jeanette Kendall
Mechanical Specifications: Type page 12 1/2 x 21; E - 6 cols, 2, between; A - 6 cols, 2, between; C - 6 cols, 2, between.Equipment & Software: Hardware — APP/Mac; Software — QPS/QuarkXPress 4.04, Adobe/Illustrator 8.0, Adobe/Photoshop 5.0.
Delivery Method: Newsstand, Carrier, Racks
Areas Served: 61611

PEOTONE

THE VEDETTE (THUR)
120 W North St, Peotone, IL, 60468-9226, Will, USA; gen tel (708) 258-3473; gen fax (708) 258-6295; disp adv e-mail newsdesk@cornerstone-media.net; class adv e-mail wendy.massat@clrdigitalsolutions.com; ed e-mail info@russell-publications.com; web site www.russell-publications.com
Circulation: 2,700pd, 98fr; Sworn/Estimate/Non-Audited
Advertising rate: Open inch rate $7.25
Established: 1942
Group: Cornerstone Media
Russell Publications, Inc.
Adv. Mgr...................................... Nancy Cross
Circ. Mgr.................................. Cindy O'Connell
Ed. .... Christopher Russell
Delivery Method: Mail, Newsstand, Racks
Areas Served: Eastern Will County, Northern Kankakee

PERCY

COUNTY JOURNAL (THUR)
1101 E Pine St, Percy, IL, 62272-1333, Randolph, USA; gen tel (618) 497-8272; adv tel (618) 497-8273; ed tel (618) 497-8273; gen fax (618) 497-2607; adv fax (618) 497-8273; ed fax (618) 497-8273; disp adv e-mail cjournal@egyptian.net; class adv e-mail cjournal@egyptian.net; ed e-mail cjournal@egyptian.net; web site countyjournal.org
Circulation: 7,400pd, 75fr; USPS
Advertising rate: Open inch rate $9.50
Established: 1980
Group: Willis Publishing
Digital Platform - Mobile: Apple
Digital Platform - Tablet: Apple iOS
Adv. Mgr................................. John Falkenhein
Co-Pub.. Larry Willis
Sarah Gordon
Co-Pub./Adv. Mgr............................. Gerald Willis
Co-Owner .... Kristin Anderson
Mechanical Specifications: Type page 10 x 21; E - 6 cols, 9 picas, 1/8 inch between; A - 6 cols, 9 picas, 1/8 inch between; C - 7 cols, 9 picas, 1/8 between.Equipment & Software: Hardware — iMac G5
Delivery Method: Mail, Newsstand
Areas Served: Randolph, Perry, Jackson counties in Illinois

PETERSBURG

MENARD COUNTY REVIEW (FRI)
235 E Sangamon Ave, Petersburg, IL, 62675-1245, Menard, USA; gen tel (217) 632-2236; gen fax (217) 632-2237; disp adv e-mail

observer@casscomm.com; class adv e-mail observer@casscomm.com; ed e-mail observer@casscomm.com
Circulation: 1,500pd, 12fr; Sworn/Estimate/Non-Audited
Advertising rate: Open inch rate $3.25
Established: 1971
Pub. .... Jane Cutright
Mechanical Specifications: Type page 10 x 16; E - 5 cols, 1 11/12, 1/6 between; A - 5 cols, 1 11/12, 1/6 between; C - 6 cols, 1 2/3, 1/6 between.Equipment & Software: Hardware — PC; Software — Adobe/PageMaker 6.5.
Delivery Method: Mail
Areas Served: 62642, 62613, 62625

THE PETERSBURG OBSERVER (THUR)
235 E Sangamon Ave, Petersburg, IL, 62675-1245, Menard, USA; gen tel (217) 632-2236; gen fax (217) 632-2237; disp adv e-mail observer@casscomm.com
Circulation: 3,000pd, 39fr; Sworn/Estimate/Non-Audited
Advertising rate: Open inch rate $3.50
Established: 1874
Ed. .... Jane Cutright
Curtis Davis
Jason Cutright
Denise Boeker
Norman Wiseman
Mechanical Specifications: Type page 16 3/8 x 21; E - 8 cols, 1 11/12, 1/6 between; A - 8 cols, 1 11/12, 1/6 between; C - 9 cols, 1 2/3, 1/6 between.Equipment & Software: Hardware — PC; Presses — KP/News King; Software — Adobe/PageMaker 6.5.
Delivery Method: Mail
Areas Served: 62675, 62673, 62688, 62672, 62613, 62625

PITTSFIELD

PIKE COUNTY EXPRESS (WED)
129 N Madison St, Pittsfield, IL, 62363-1405, Pike, USA; gen tel (217) 285-5415; gen fax (217) 285-9564; disp adv e-mail pikecountyexpressnews@yahoo.com
Circulation: 4,600pd,; Sworn/Estimate/Non-Audited
Advertising rate: Open inch rate $6.50
Group: Coulson Publications
Publisher/Owner .... Robin Oitker
Delivery Method: Mail, Newsstand, Carrier, Racks
Areas Served: Pike County

THE WEEKLY MESSENGER (WED)
115 W Jefferson St, Pittsfield, IL, 62363-1424, Pike, USA; gen tel (217) 285-2345; gen fax (630) 206-0320; disp adv e-mail nliehr@campbellpublications.net; class adv e-mail ppnews@campbellpublications.net; ed e-mail ppnews@campbellpublications.net
Circulation: 600pd,; Sworn/Estimate/Non-Audited
Advertising rate: Open inch rate $11.95
Established: 1912
Group: Campbell Publishing Co., Inc.
Digital Platform - Mobile: Apple, Android
Digital Platform - Tablet: Apple iOS, Android
Pub./Ed. .... Julie Boren
Gen. Mgr./Adv. Dir. .... Nichole Liehr
Mechanical Specifications: Type page 13 x 21 1/2; E - 6 cols, 2 1/16, 1/6 between; A - 6 cols, 2 1/16, 1/6 between; C - 9 cols, 1 5/16, 1/6 between.
Delivery Method: Mail, Newsstand, Racks
Areas Served: Pike County

PLAINFIELD

THE BUGLE (WED, THUR)
23856 W Andrew Rd, Ste 104, Plainfield, IL, 60585-8771, Will, USA; gen tel (815) 436-2431; adv tel (815) 436-2431 ext. 103; ed tel (815) 436-2431 ext.118; gen fax (815) 436-2592; disp adv e-mail advertising@verdenews.com; class adv e-mail advertising@verdenews.com; ed e-mail nreiher@buglenewspapers.com; web site www.buglenewspapers.com
Circulation: 500pd, 10,000fr; Sworn/Estimate/Non-Audited
Advertising rate: Open inch rate $16.80
Established: 1957
Group: Voyager Media Publications
Gen. Mgr./VP Adv./Mktg .... Michael James
Classified Adv. Mgr. .... Linda Martin
Delivery Method: Mail, Racks
Areas Served: 60714, 60053, 60068, 60446

THE ENTERPRISE (THUR)
23856 W Andrew Rd, Plainfield, IL, 60585-8770, Will, USA; gen tel (815) 436-2431; adv tel (815) 436-2431 ext. 103; ed tel (815) 436-2431 ext.118; gen fax (815) 436-2592; disp adv e-mail mjames@voyagermedia-online.com; class adv e-mail mjames@voyagermediaonline.com; ed e-mail nreiher@buglenewspapers.com; web site www.budlenewspapers.com
Circulation: 7,100pd, 32,600fr; Sworn/Estimate/Non-Audited
Advertising rate: Open inch rate $11.03
Established: 1887
Group: Voyager Media Publications
VP, Adv./Mktg. .... Michael James
Mechanical Specifications: Type page 10 x 16; E - 5 cols, between; A - 5 cols, between; C - 5 cols, between.Equipment & Software: Hardware — APP/Mac; Software — QPS/QuarkXPress 4.1.
Delivery Method: Mail
Areas Served: MANY

PORT BYRON

THE REVIEW (WED)
1100 N High St, Port Byron, IL, 61275-9031, Whiteside, USA; gen tel (815) 772-7244; gen fax (309) 659-7751; disp adv e-mail review@whitesitesentinel.com
Circulation: 1,803pd, 14fr; Sworn/Estimate/Non-Audited
Advertising rate: Open inch rate $9.50
Established: 1857
Group: Shaw Media
Pub. Owner .... Anthony M. Komlanc
Adv. Mgr. .... Beth Armstrong
Ed. .... Judy James
Delivery Method: Mail, Newsstand
Areas Served: 61250, 61257, 61254

PRINCETON

BUREAU COUNTY REPUBLICAN (WED, THUR, SAT)
800 Ace Rd, Princeton, IL, 61356-2049, Bureau, USA; gen tel (815) 875-4461; gen fax (815) 875-1235; disp adv e-mail advertising@bcrnews.com; class adv e-mail classified@bcrnews.com; ed e-mail news@bcrnews.com; web site www.bcrnews.com
Advertising rate: Open inch rate $10.60
Established: 1847
Group: Shaw Media
Pub./Gen. Mgr. .... Sam R. Fisher
Adv. Mgr. .... Sandy Pistole
Ed. .... Terri Simon
Circ. Mgr. .... Abbie Clark
Mechanical Specifications: Type page 13 x 21 1/2; E - 6 cols, 2, 1/4 between; A - 6 cols, 2, 1/4 between; C - 9 cols, 1 1/4, 1/4 between. Equipment & Software: Hardware — Mac Clone; Presses — G/Community; Software — QPS/QuarkXPress 4.0, Baseview/NewsEdit Pro, Adobe/Illustrator 7.0, Adobe/Photoshop 5.0, Microsoft/Excel, Microsoft/Word 5.0.
Delivery Method: Mail

TONICA NEWS (FRI)
800 Ace Rd, Princeton, IL, 61356-9201, Bureau, USA; gen tel (815) 875-4461; gen fax (815) 875-1235; disp adv e-mail advertising@tonicanews.com; class adv e-mail cwagner@bcrnews.com; ed e-mail news@tonicanews.com; web site www.tonicanews.com
Circulation: 585pd, 50fr; USPS
Advertising rate: Open inch rate $3.75
Group: Shaw Media
Pub. .... Sam R. Fisher
Ed. .... Terri Simon
Adv. Sales .... Ashley Oliver
Mechanical Specifications: Type page 10 1/4 x 16.
Delivery Method: Mail
Areas Served: LaSalle County

PROPHETSTOWN

PROPHETSTOWN ECHO (TUES)
342 Washington St, Prophetstown, IL, 61277-1115, Whiteside, USA; gen tel (815) 772-7244; gen fax (815) 537-2658; disp adv e-mail echo@whitesidesentinel.com; web site www.facebook.com/TheProphetstownEcho/
Circulation: 1,975pd, 113fr; Sworn/Estimate/Non-Audited
Advertising rate: Open inch rate $7.50
Group: WNS Publications Inc.
Owner/Ed. .... Tony Komlanc
Circ. Mgr. .... Marilyn Vegter
Sue Patten
Delivery Method: Mail, Newsstand, Racks

RAMSEY

RAMSEY NEWS-JOURNAL (THUR)
217 S Superior St, Ramsey, IL, 62080-2095, Fayette, USA; gen tel (618) 423-2411; gen fax (618) 423-2514; disp adv e-mail newsj2@frontiernet.net; class adv e-mail newsj2@frontiernet.net; ed e-mail newsj2@frontiernet.net; web site www.facebook.com/pages/Ramsey-News-Journal/414345475416836
Circulation: 1,770pd, 74fr; Sworn/Estimate/Non-Audited
Advertising rate: Open inch rate $6.00
Established: 1886
Ed. .... Robert (B.J.) Mueller
Mechanical Specifications: Type page 10 1/4 x 16; E - 5 cols, 1 7/8, 1/6 between; A - 5 cols, 1 7/8, 1/6 between; C - 5 cols, 1 7/8, 1/6 between.Equipment & Software: Hardware — APP/Mac Power Mac; Software — Adobe/PageMaker 6.0.
Delivery Method: Mail

RANTOUL

RANTOUL PRESS (WED)
216 E Sangamon Ave, Ste A, Rantoul, IL, 61866-3300, Champaign, USA; gen tel (217) 892-9613; adv tel (217) 892-9613; ed tel (217) 892-9613; gen fax (217) 892-9451; disp adv e-mail tevans@news-gazette.com; class adv e-mail kturner@news-gazette.com; ed e-mail news@rantoulpress.com; web site www.rantoulpress.com
Circulation: 400pd,; AAM
Advertising rate: Open inch rate $16.25
Established: 1875
Group: The News-Gazette
News Gazette Community NewsEditions: (52) Rantoul Press
Pub. .... John Foreman
Gen. Mgr. .... Tim Evans
Circ. Mgr. .... Melinda Carpenter
Ed. in Chief .... Dave Hinton
Prod. Mgr. .... Bob Sheldon
Adv. Dir. .... Tom Zalabak
Mechanical Specifications: Type page 9 13/16 x 12; E - 5 cols, 1 13/16, 3/16 between; A - 5 cols, 1 3/16, 3/16 between; C - 7 cols, 1 1/4, 1/8 between.Equipment & Software: Hardware — APP/Mac; Presses — KP/News King; Software — QPS/QuarkXPress, InDesign.
Delivery Method: Mail, Newsstand, Carrier, Racks
Areas Served: 61866, 61847, 61843, 61812, 60949

RAYMOND

THE PANHANDLE PRESS (WED)
PO Box 15, Raymond, IL, 62560-0015, Montgomery, USA; gen tel (217) 227-4425; gen fax (217) 965-4512; disp adv e-mail nj1655@aol.com; web site gnnews.net/index.php
Circulation: 951pd, 30fr; Sworn/Estimate/Non-Audited
Advertising rate: Open inch rate $4.50
Established: 1964
Group: Paddock Publications
Adv. Mgr. .... Nathan Jones
Mechanical Specifications: Type page 15 3/16 x 21 1/2; E - 7 cols, 2 1/16, between; A - 7 cols, 2 1/16, between; C - 5 cols, 1 7/8, between.Equipment & Software: Hardware — APP/Mac IIsi, APP/Power Mac G3; Presses — KP; Software — Adobe/PageMaker 4.2.
Delivery Method: Mail, Newsstand

RED BUD

NORTH COUNTY NEWS (THUR)
124 S Main St, Red Bud, IL, 62278-1103, Randolph, USA; gen tel (618) 282-3803; gen fax (618) 282-6134; disp adv e-mail incnews@htc.net; class adv e-mail nccomp@htc.net; ed e-mail ncnews@htc.net; web site http://www.northcountynews.org/
Circulation: 4,000pd,; Sworn/Estimate/Non-Audited
Advertising rate: Open inch rate $7.25
Established: 1959
Publisher .... Victor L. Mohr
Advertising Manager .... Jesse Heidel
Circ. Mgr./Asst. Ed. .... Jana Kueker
Managing Ed. .... Mary Koester
Classifieds/Composition .... Joel Heidel
Delivery Method: Mail, Newsstand
Areas Served: Randolph County, IL
Particularly the communities of Red Bud, Evansville, Prairie du Rocher and Baldwin

RIVERTON

RIVERTON REGISTER (THUR)
715 N 7th St, Riverton, IL, 62561-1019, Sangamon, USA; gen tel (217) 629-9221; gen fax (217) 629-9223; disp adv e-mail southcountypub@att.net; web site www.southcounty-publications.net
Circulation: 650pd,; Sworn/Estimate/Non-Audited
Advertising rate: Open inch rate $3.50
Group: South County Publications
Ed .... Byron Painter
Delivery Method: Mail, Newsstand
Areas Served: Riverton, Spaulding, Springfield

TRI-CITY REGISTER (THUR)
715 N 7th St, Riverton, IL, 62561-1019, Sangamon, USA; gen tel (217) 629-9221; gen fax (217) 629-9223; disp adv e-mail southcountypub@att.net; web site www.southcounty-publications.net
Circulation: 400pd,; Sworn/Estimate/Non-Audited
Advertising rate: Open inch rate $3.50
Group: South County Publications
Ed .... Byron Painter
Mechanical Specifications: Type page 10 3/16 x 15 1/2; E - 5 cols, 1 7/8, 3/16 between; A - 5 cols, 1 7/8, 3/16 between; C - 6 cols, 1 9/16, 3/16 between.
Delivery Method: Mail, Newsstand
Areas Served: Buffalo, Dawson, Mechanicsburg

WILLIAMSVILLE-SHERMAN SUN TIMES (THUR)
715 N 7th St, Riverton, IL, 62561-1019, Sangamon, USA; gen tel (217) 629-9221; gen fax (217) 629-9223; disp adv e-mail southcountypub@att.net; web site www.southcounty-publications.net
Circulation: 700pd,; Sworn/Estimate/Non-Audited
Advertising rate: Open inch rate $3.50

Group: South County Publications
Editor .... Byron Painter
Mechanical Specifications: Type page 10 3/16 x 15 1/2; E - 5 cols, 1 7/8, 3/16 between; A - 5 cols, 1 7/8, 3/16 between; C - 6 cols, 1 9/16, 3/16 between.
Delivery Method: Mail, Newsstand
Areas Served: Williamsville, Sherman, Springfield

ROANOKE

WOODFORD COUNTY JOURNAL ROANOKE-MINONK EDITION (THUR)

105 E Broad St, Roanoke, IL, 61561-7547, Woodford, USA; gen tel (309) 923-5841; adv tel (309) 467-3314 Ext 202; ed tel (309) 467-3314 Ext 211; gen fax (309) 467-4563; disp adv e-mail mbarra@mtco.com; class adv e-mail wendiwcj@mtco.com; ed e-mail cwolfe@mtco.com; web site www.pantagraph.com
Circulation: 893pd,; AAM
Advertising rate: Open inch rate $10.00
Established: 1936
Ed. .... Mark Pickering
Mechanical Specifications: Type page 11 9/16 x 21 1/2; E - 6 cols, 1 13/16, 1/8 between; A - 6 cols, 1 13/16, 1/8 between; C - 9 cols, 1 3/8, 1/16 between.Equipment & Software: Hardware — APP/Macs
Dell; Software — Photoshop
Indesign
Delivery Method: Mail, Newsstand, Racks
Areas Served: 61561

ROBINSON

THE ROBINSON CONSTITUTION (THUR)

302 S Cross St, Robinson, IL, 62454-2137, Crawford, USA; gen tel (618) 544-2101; adv tel (618) 544-2101; ed tel (618) 544-2101; gen fax (618) 544-9533; adv fax (618) 544-9533; ed fax (618) 544-9533; disp adv e-mail wpiper@robdailynews.com; class adv e-mail classifieds@robdailynews.com; ed e-mail gbilbrey@robdailynews.com; web site www.robdailynews.com
Circulation: 176pd,; Sworn/Estimate/Non-Audited
Advertising rate: Open inch rate $8.50
Established: 1865
Group: Lewis Newspapers
Nat'l Adv. Mgr. .... Winnie Piper
Ed. .... Greg Bilbrey
Delivery Method: Mail, Newsstand
Areas Served: Robinson

ROCHELLE

THE ROCHELLE NEWS LEADER (TUES, THUR, SUN)

211 E Il Route 38, Rochelle, IL, 61068-2303, Ogle, USA; gen tel (815) 562-4171; ed tel (815) 561-2151; gen fax (815) 562-2161; disp adv e-mail kprice@rochellenews-leader.com; ed e-mail jsimmons@rochellenews-leader.com; web site www.rochellenews-leader.com
Circulation: 5,500pd, 585fr; Sworn/Estimate/Non-Audited
Advertising rate: Open inch rate $20.45
Group: News Media Corp.
Pub. .... John Shank
Adv. Mgr. .... Kelly Price
Circ. .... Wanda Brimhall
Managing Ed. .... Jennifer Simmons
Sports Editor .... Russell Hodges
Delivery Method: Mail, Newsstand, Carrier, Racks
Areas Served: 61068

ROCKFORD

THE ROCK RIVER TIMES (WED)

128 N Church St, Rockford, IL, 61101-1002, Winnebago County, USA; gen tel (815) 964-9767; adv tel (815) 964-9767; ed tel (815) 964-9767; gen fax (815) 964-9825; adv fax (815) 964-9825; ed fax (815) 964-9825; disp adv e-mail contact@rockrivertimes.com; class adv e-mail contact@rockrivertimes.com; ed e-mail contact@rockrivertimes.com; web site www.rockrivertimes.com
Circulation: 36pd, 21,954fr; CVC
Advertising rate: 1/8 Pg $120; 1/4 $230.00; Full $705
Established: 1987
Digital Platform - Mobile: Windows
Digital Platform - Tablet: Windows 7
Pub./Ed./Adv. .... Frank Schier
Managing Ed. .... Shane Nicholson
Mechanical Specifications: 10x15 inches full page image area, with six columns at 1 1/2 inches each.
Artwork file requirements, to be published in The Rock River Times:
pdf saved to Acrobat 3.0
Photoshop pdf 300 dpi or higher
eps saved to Illustrator 10
tif 300 dpi or higher
jpeg 300 dpi or higher
black only, not a CMYK combo
do not lock your file!
Delivery Method: Mail, Newsstand, Racks
Areas Served: Winnebago, Stephenson, Boone, Ogle and DeKalb counties in Illinois. Rock County in Wisconsin. Cities: Beloit, Wisconsin AND Belvidere, Byron, Cherry Valley, DeKalb, Durand, Freeport, Loves Park, New Milford, Oregon, Pecatonica, Polo, Rockford, Rockton, Roscoe, South Beloit, Machesney Park, Stillman Valley and Winnebago, Illinois. Zip Codes: 53511, 60115, 61008, 61010, 61016, 61019, 61020, 61024, 61032, 61039, 61047, 61048, 61054, 61061, 61063, 61064, 61067, 61072, 61073, 61077, 61079, 61080, 61084, 61088, 61101, 61102, 61103, 61104, 61107, 61108, 61109, 611010, 61111, 61112, 61114 and 61115.

RUSHVILLE

THE RUSHVILLE TIMES (WED)

110 E Lafayette St, Rushville, IL, 62681-1412, Schuyler, USA; gen tel (217) 322-3321; gen fax (217) 322-2770; ed e-mail editor@rushvilletimes.com
Circulation: 3,612pd, 88fr; Sworn/Estimate/Non-Audited
Advertising rate: Open inch rate $7.45
Established: 1848
Adv. Mgr. .... Teresa Haines
Ed./Owner .... Alan Icenogle
Mechanical Specifications: Type page 16 1/2 x 21; E - 8 cols, 2, 1/6 between; A - 8 cols, 2, 1/6 between; C - 8 cols, 2, 1/6 between.
Delivery Method: Mail, Newsstand, Racks

SAINT CHARLES

KANE COUNTY CHRONICLE (THUR)

333 N Randall Rd, Ste 11, Saint Charles, IL, 60174-1500, Kane, USA; gen tel (630) 232-9222; adv tel (630) 845-5228; ed tel (630) 845-5355; gen fax (630) 444-1645; adv fax (630) 444-1645; ed fax (630) 444-1641; disp adv e-mail advertising@kcchronicle.com; class adv e-mail advertising@kcchronicle.com; ed e-mail editorial@kcchronicle.com; web site www.kcchronicle.com
Circulation: 2,022pd, 732fr; AAM
Advertising rate: Open inch rate $31.57
Established: 1881
Group: Shaw Media
Pub. .... Don Bricker
Ed. .... Kathy Greser
Adv. Dir., Classified .... Shelly Bissell
Mktg. Coord. .... Leslie Shambo
Circ. Mgr., Distr./Sales .... Kara Hansen
Sports Ed. .... Jay Schwab
Prodn. Dir. .... Kevin Elder
Prodn. Mgr., Mailroom .... Clem Garcia
Prodn. Mgr., Pressroom .... Ted Robinson
Group Sales Dir. .... Maureen Ringness
Major Sales Coord. .... Rebecca Dienhart
Mechanical Specifications: Type page 13 x 21; E - 6 cols, 2 1/16, 1/6 between; A - 6 cols, 2 1/16, 1/6 between; C - 9 cols, 1 5/16, 1/6 between.
Areas Served: St. Charles, Geneva, Batavia & Kane Counties

SAINT JOSEPH

THE LEADER (WED)

429 W WARREN ST, Saint Joseph, IL, 61873, Champaign, USA; gen tel (217) 469-0045; adv tel (217) 351-5252; ed tel (217) 469-0045; gen fax (217) 469-0089; disp adv e-mail nmaberry@news-gazette.com; class adv e-mail mstenzel@news-gazette.com; ed e-mail nmaberry@news-gazette.com; web site www.leaderlandnews.com
Circulation: 942pd,; AAM
Advertising rate: Open inch rate $7.50
Established: 1977
Group: The News-Gazette
News Gazette Community NewsEditions: (52) The Leader
Pub. .... John Foreman
Ed. .... Nora Maberry
Mechanical Specifications: Broadsheet - Full page is 11.75" wide x 21.5 inches tall, Each column 1.819" wideEquipment & Software: Hardware — Mac; Presses — King 9 units; Software — InDesign
Delivery Method: Mail, Newsstand, Racks
Areas Served: 61873, 61849, 61859, 61871, 61816, 61810, 61844

SAVANNA

SAVANNA TIMES-JOURNAL (THUR)

315 Main St, Savanna, IL, 61074-1629, Carroll, USA; gen tel (815) 273-2277; gen fax (815) 273-2715; disp adv e-mail savtj@grics.net; web site www.savannatimes-journal.com
Circulation: 2,050pd, 10fr; Sworn/Estimate/Non-Audited
Advertising rate: Open inch rate $11.00
Adv. Mgr. .... Pam Villalobos
Ed./Pub. .... Robert W. Watson
Delivery Method: Mail, Newsstand, Racks

SHAWNEETOWN

GALLATIN DEMOCRAT (WED)

288 N LINCOLN BLVD E, Shawneetown, IL, 62984, Gallatin, USA; gen tel (618) 269-3147; gen fax (618) 269-3147; disp adv e-mail gallatin@yourclearwave.com; web site www.facebook.com/pages/The-Gallatin-Democrat/152210741460695
Circulation: 1,150pd,; Sworn/Estimate/Non-Audited
Advertising rate: Open inch rate $5.00
Established: 1888
Group: GateHouse Media, Inc.
Ed. .... George Wilson
Ed. .... Brian DeNeal
Pub. .... David Adams
Delivery Method: Mail
Areas Served: Gallaton

SHELBYVILLE

DAILY UNION (TUES, THUR, SAT)

100 W Main St, Shelbyville, IL, 62565-1652, Shelby, USA; gen tel (217) 774-2161; adv tel (217) 774-2161; ed tel (217) 774-2161; gen fax (217) 774-5732; adv fax (217) 774-5732; ed fax (217) 774-5732; disp adv e-mail publisher@shelbyvilledailyunion.com; class adv e-mail deanna.sickles@shelbyvilledailyunion.com; ed e-mail news@shelbyvilledailyunion.com; web site www.shelbyvilledailyunion.com
Circulation: 4,156pd,; Sworn/Estimate/Non-Audited
Advertising rate: Open inch rate $6.65
Established: 1863
Group: Community Newspaper Holdings, Inc.
Circ. Mgr./Off. Mgr. .... Ryan Beitz
Sports Ed. .... John Curtis
Adv. Mgr. .... Deanna Sickles
Pub. .... Darrell Lewis
Ed. .... Jeff Long
Mechanical Specifications: Type page 15 1/2 x 21 1/2; E - 6 cols, 2 1/14, 1/8 between; A - 6 cols, 2 1/14, 1/8 between; C - 6 cols, 2 1/14, 1/8 between.
Delivery Method: Mail, Newsstand, Racks
Areas Served: Shelby County

ST CHARLES

BATAVIA CHRONICLE (THUR)

333 N Randall Rd, Ste 2, St Charles, IL, 60174-1500, Kane, USA; gen tel (630) 232-9222; adv tel (630) 513-2737; gen fax (630) 444-1641; disp adv e-mail lsiebolds@shawmedia.com; class adv e-mail lsiebolds@shawmedia.com; ed e-mail kgresey@shawmedia.com; web site www.kcchronicle.com
Circulation: 1,532pd, 220fr; CAC
Advertising rate: 1/32 Pg $90.00; 1/16 Pg $140.00; 1/8 Pg $240.00
Group: Shaw Media
Digital Platform - Mobile: Apple, Android, Windows
Digital Platform - Tablet: Apple iOS, Android, Windows 7, Blackberry Tablet OS, Kindle, Nook, Kindle Fire
Pub. .... Don Bricker
Group Sales Dir/Major Nat'l Accts ...... Maureen Ringness
Ed. .... Kathy Balcazar
Mechanical Specifications: Type page 10 1/8 x 12 1/4; E - 4 cols, between; A - 4 cols, between; C - 8 cols, between.Equipment & Software: Hardware — APP/Mac; Presses — G/Community.
Delivery Method: Mail, Newsstand, Carrier, Racks
Areas Served: 60510

GENEVA CHRONICLE (THUR)

333 N Randall Rd, Ste 2, St Charles, IL, 60174-1500, Kane, USA; gen tel (630)232-9222; gen fax (630) 444-1641; disp adv e-mail lsiebolds@shawmedia.com; class adv e-mail lsiebolds@shawmedia.com; ed e-mail kgresey@shawmedia.com; web site www.kcchronicle.com
Circulation: 271pd, 8,465fr; CAC
Advertising rate: 1/32 Pg $90.00; 1/16 Pg $140.00; 1/8 Pg $240.00
Group: Shaw MediaKathy Gresey
Group Sales Dir/Major Nat'l Accts ...... Maureen Ringness
Sports Ed. .... Jason Rossi
Mechanical Specifications: Type page 10 1/8 x 12 1/4; E - 5 cols, 1 7/8, between; A - 5 cols, 1 7/8, between.Equipment & Software: Hardware — APP/Mac; Presses — 22-G/Urbanite, 10-G/Suburban.
Delivery Method: Mail, Newsstand, Carrier, Racks

ST. CHARLES CHRONICLE (THUR)

333 N Randall Rd, Ste 2, St Charles, IL, 60174-1500, Kane, USA; gen tel (630) 232-9222; gen fax (630) 444-1641; disp adv e-mail lsiebolds@shawmedia.com; class adv e-mail lsiebolds@shawmedia.com; ed e-mail kgresey@shawmedia.com; web site www.kcchronicle.com
Circulation: 311pd, 11,906fr; CAC
Advertising rate: 1/32 Pg $90.00; 1/16 Pg $140.00; 1/8 Pg $240.00
Group: Shaw Media
Group Classified Dir. .... Brad Hanahan
Ed. .... Kathy Balcazar
Mechanical Specifications: Type page 10 3/4 x 14; E - 5 cols, 2, 1/6 between; A - 5 cols, 2, 1/6 between; C - 6 cols, 1, 1/6 between. Equipment & Software: Hardware — APP/Mac; Presses — 22-G/Urbanite, 10-G/Suburban.
Delivery Method: Mail, Newsstand, Carrier, Racks
Areas Served: 60510, 60134, 60134, 60185, 60184, 60175

THE ELBURN HERALD (THUR)
333 N Randall Rd Ste 111, Suite 1, St Charles, IL, 60174-1500, Kane, USA; gen tel (630) 365-6446; gen fax (630) 365-2251; disp adv e-mail ads@elburnherald.com; class adv e-mail ads@elburnherald.com; ed e-mail info@elburnherald.com; web site www.elburnherald.com
Circulation: 1,390pd, 25fr; AAM
Advertising rate: Open inch rate $11.00
Established: 1908
Group: Kaneland Publications, Inc.
Adv. Mgr. .... Leslie Flint
Ed. .... Ryan Wells
Mechanical Specifications: Type page 10 x 16; E - 4 cols, 2 1/2, 3/16 between; A - 4 cols, 2 1/2, 3/16 between; C - 4 cols, 2 1/2, 3/16 between.Equipment & Software: Hardware — APP/Mac; Software — QPS/QuarkXPress.
Delivery Method: Mail

STAUNTON

STAUNTON STAR-TIMES (WED)
108 W Main St, Staunton, IL, 62088-1453, Macoupin, USA; gen tel (618) 635-2000; gen fax (618) 635-5281; disp adv e-mail startime@madisontelco.com; class adv e-mail startime@madisontelco.com; ed e-mail startime@madisontelco.com; web site www.stauntonstartimes.com
Circulation: 3,730pd, 240fr; Sworn/Estimate/Non-Audited
Advertising rate: Open inch rate $8.00
Established: 1878
Pub. .... Walter F. Haase
Mechanical Specifications: Type page 13 x 21; E - 6 cols, 2, 1/6 between; A - 6 cols, 2, 1/6 between.Equipment & Software: Hardware — 2-APP/Mac; Software — Adobe/PageMaker, Adobe/Photoshop.
Delivery Method: Mail, Racks

STRONGHURST

THE HANCOCK-HENDERSON QUILL (WED)
102 N Broadway St, Stronghurst, IL, 61480-5023, Henderson, USA; gen tel (309) 924-1871; gen fax (309) 924-1212; disp adv e-mail quill@hcil.net; web site www.quill-newspaper.com
Circulation: 1,689pd, 50fr; Sworn/Estimate/Non-Audited
Advertising rate: Open inch rate $4.60
Established: 1926
Adv. Mgr. .... Dessa L. Rodeffer
Ed. .... Shirley Linder
Mechanical Specifications: Type page 10 1/2 x 16 1/2; E - 6 cols, 1 5/8, between; A - 6 cols, 1 5/8, between; C - 7 cols, 1 3/8, between. Equipment & Software: Hardware — APP/Mac 7200-120, APP/Mac LC, APP/Mac SE 30; Software — Adobe/PageMaker 6.0.
Delivery Method: Mail

SULLIVAN

NEWS-PROGRESS (WED)
100 W Monroe St, Sullivan, IL, 61951-1400, Moultrie, USA; gen tel (217) 728-7381; gen fax (217) 728-2020; disp adv e-mail ads@newsprogress.com; class adv e-mail class@newsprogress.com; ed e-mail newspro@newsprogress.com; web site www.newsprogress.com
Circulation: 3,720pd, 15fr; Sworn/Estimate/Non-Audited
Advertising rate: Open inch rate $5.65
Established: 1857
Pub. .... Robert R. Best
Adv. Mgr. .... Barry Morgan
Class. Mgr. .... Carolyn Collier
Ed. .... Keith Stewart
Mechanical Specifications: Type page 13 x 21; E - 6 cols, 2, 1/3 between; A - 6 cols, 2, 1/3 between; C - 9 cols, 1 1/2, 1/4 between.
Delivery Method: Mail

SUMMIT

SOUTHWEST NEWS-HERALD (THUR)
7676 W 63rd St, Summit, IL, 60501-1812, Cook, USA; gen tel (708) 496-0265; gen fax (708) 496-3019; disp adv e-mail vonpub@aol.com; web site www.swnewsherald.com
Circulation: 9,300pd,; Sworn/Estimate/Non-Audited
Advertising rate: 1/8 Pg $150.00; 1/4 Pg $270.00; 1/2 Pg $365.00
Established: 1924
Group: Southwest Communiy Newspapers
Pub. .... James Vondrak
Gen. Mgr. .... Bob Gusanders
Circ. Mgr. .... Dave Anderson
Ed. .... Tim Hadac
Display Adv. Dir. .... Renee Lawrence
Delivery Method: Mail, Newsstand, Racks

SOUTHWEST SUBURBAN NEWS-HERALD (FRI)
7676 W 63rd St, Summit, IL, 60501-1812, Cook, USA; gen tel (708) 496-0265; gen fax (708) 496-3019; disp adv e-mail vonpub@aol.com; web site www.swnewsherald.com
Advertising rate: Open inch rate $20.45
Established: 1924
Pub. .... James Vondrak
Gen. Mgr. .... Bob Gusanders
Circ. Mgr. .... John Briggs
Ed. .... Tim Hadac
Delivery Method: Mail, Newsstand, Racks

SUMNER

THE SUMNER PRESS (THUR)
216 S Christy Ave, Sumner, IL, 62466-1142, Lawrence, USA; gen tel (618) 936-2212; gen fax (618) 936-2858; disp adv e-mail sumpress@frontier.com; ed e-mail sumpress@frontier.com; web site www.sumnerpress.com
Circulation: 850pd,; Sworn/Estimate/Non-Audited
Advertising rate: Open inch rate $4.00
Established: 1876
Office manager .... Tasha Legg
Advertising/Graphics Designer .... Cristy Wilson
Mechanical Specifications: Type page 13 x 21; E - 8 cols, 1 1/2, 1/8 between; A - 8 cols, 1 1/2, 1/8 between; C - 8 cols, 1 1/2, 1/8 between.Equipment & Software: Hardware — PCs, HP/LaserJet, IBM/PC, Compaq/PC; Software — XYQUEST/XyWrite, Archetype/Corel Draw.
Delivery Method: Mail

THOMSON

CARROLL COUNTY REVIEW (WED)
809 W Main St, Thomson, IL, 61285-7776, Carroll, USA; gen tel (815) 259-2131; gen fax (815) 259-3226; web site www.gocarroll-county.com
Circulation: 2,066pd, 130fr; Sworn/Estimate/Non-Audited
Advertising rate: Open inch rate $8.00
Established: 1863
Digital Platform - Mobile: Apple
Pub. .... Jonathan K. Whitney
Mechanical Specifications: Type page 10 1/4 x 15 1/4; E - 5 cols, 1 11/12, 1/6 between; A - 5 cols, 1 11/12, 1/6 between; C - 6 cols, between.Equipment & Software: Hardware — APP/Power Mac; Software — QPS/QuarkXPress.
Delivery Method: Mail, Newsstand, Racks
Areas Served: 61285, 61074, 61053, 61014, 61078, 61046, 61051

TISKILWA

BUREAU VALLEY CHIEF (THUR)
108 W Main St, Tiskilwa, IL, 61368-9652, Bureau, USA; gen tel (815) 646-4731; gen fax (815) 646-4376; disp adv e-mail bvchief@comcast.net
Circulation: 1,100pd, 200fr; USPS
Advertising rate: Open inch rate $4.41
Established: 1875
Digital Platform - Mobile: Apple
Digital Platform - Tablet: Other
Adv. Mgr. .... John Murphy
Ed. .... Ginger Murphy
Mechanical Specifications: Type page 11 x 16; E - 5 cols, 10 1/2, 3/8 between; A - 5 cols, 10 1/2, 3/8 between; C - 5 cols, 10 1/2, 3/8 between.Equipment & Software: Hardware — APP/Mac; Software — QPS/QuarkXPress.
Delivery Method: Mail
Areas Served: County

TOLEDO

TOLEDO DEMOCRAT (THUR)
116 Courthouse Sq, Toledo, IL, 62468-1052, Cumberland, USA; gen tel (217) 849-2000; gen fax (217) 849-3237; disp adv e-mail td-news@cell1net.net; web site www.facebook.com/Toledo-Democrat-134064103434272/
Circulation: 1,900pd,; Sworn/Estimate/Non-Audited
Advertising rate: Open inch rate $4.00
Established: 1857Editions: (52) Toledo Democrat
Ed. .... Billie Chambers
Mechanical Specifications: Type page 2 1/4 x 21.
Delivery Method: Mail, Racks
Areas Served: Cumberland County

TRENTON

THE TRENTON SUN (WED)
15 W Broadway, Trenton, IL, 62293-1303, The Trenton Sun, USA; gen tel (618) 224-9422; gen fax (618) 224-2646; disp adv e-mail mike@trentonsun.net; web site www.trentonsun.net
Circulation: 1,700pd,; Sworn/Estimate/Non-Audited
Advertising rate: Open inch rate $7.00
Established: 1880
Ed./Pub. .... Michael Conley
Delivery Method: Mail, Newsstand, Racks

TROY

TROY TIMES-TRIBUNE (THUR)
201 E Market St, Stop 6, Troy, IL, 62294-1518, Madison, USA; gen tel (618) 667-3111; gen fax (618) 667-3128; disp adv e-mail troy.il.news@gmail.com; class adv e-mail TroyNews@aol.com; ed e-mail editor.times.tribune@gmail.com; web site www.troytimestribune.blogspot.com
Circulation: 3,500pd,; Sworn/Estimate/Non-Audited
Advertising rate: Open inch rate $6.60
Adv. Mgr. .... Paul Ping
Ed. .... Steve Rensberry
Sports Reporter .... Jerry Campbell
Reporter .... Norma Mendoza
Reporter .... Lexi Keller
Reporter .... Mae Grapperhaus
Delivery Method: Mail

VANDALIA

THE LEADER-UNION (THUR)
229 S 5th St, Vandalia, IL, 62471-2703, Fayette, USA; gen tel (618) 283-3374; gen fax (618) 283-0977; disp adv e-mail sales@leaderunion.com; class adv e-mail classifieds@leaderunion.com; ed e-mail rbauer@leaderunion.com; web site www.leaderunion.com
Circulation: 4,000pd,; Sworn/Estimate/Non-Audited
Advertising rate: Open inch rate $11.24
Established: 1864
Group: Landmark Community Newspapers, LLC
Office Mgr. .... Lovetta Lockart
Class Adv. mgr. .... Susie Pontious
Mechanical Specifications: Type page 13 x 21 1/2; E - 6 cols, 2, 1/6 between; A - 6 cols, 2, 1/6 between; C - 8 cols, 1 1/2, 1/6 between. Equipment & Software: Hardware — APP/Mac; Presses — G/Community; Software — Microsoft/Word, Multi-Ad/Creator/InDesign.
Delivery Method: Mail, Newsstand, Racks
Areas Served: 62471, 62458, 62418, 62080, 62262, 62880 and 62885

VIENNA

THE VIENNA TIMES (THUR)
305 E Main St, Vienna, IL, 62995-1823, Johnson, USA; gen tel (618) 658-4321; gen fax (618) 658-4322; disp adv e-mail viennatimes@frontier.com; class adv e-mail viennatimes@frontier.com; ed e-mail viennatimes@frontier.com; web site www.theviennatimes.com
Circulation: 2,424pd, 57fr; Sworn/Estimate/Non-Audited
Advertising rate: Open inch rate $4.00
Established: 1879
Ed. .... Lonnie Hinton
Delivery Method: Mail

VILLA GROVE

SOUTHERN CHAMPAIGN CO. TODAY (WED)
5 S Main St, Villa Grove, IL, 61956-1522, Douglas, USA; gen tel (217) 832-4201; gen fax (217) 832-4001; disp adv e-mail scctoday@mediacombb.net; web site www.facebook.com/pages/Southern-Champaign-County-Today/401543786583214?rf=162292340455904
Circulation: 2,685fr; Sworn/Estimate/Non-Audited
Advertising rate: Open inch rate $4.50
Established: 1971
Ed. .... John Broux
Jamie Morse
Delivery Method: Mail, Newsstand

VILLA GROVE NEWS (THUR)
57 S Main St, Villa Grove, IL, 61956-1522, Douglas, USA; gen tel (217) 832-4201; gen fax (217) 832-4001; disp adv e-mail vgads@mediacombb.net; class adv e-mail vgnews@mchsi.com; ed e-mail vgnews@mchsi.com; web site www.facebook.com/TheVillaGrove-News/?ref=page_internal
Circulation: 1,200pd,; Sworn/Estimate/Non-Audited
Advertising rate: Open inch rate $4.50
Group: The Miami Herald Publishing Co.
Gen. Mgr./Ed. .... John Broux
Advertising Representative .... Jamie Morse
Editor ..... Nathan ThompsonEquipment & Software: Hardware — APP/Mac; Presses — G/Community; Software — QPS/QuarkXPress.
Delivery Method: Mail, Racks

VIRDEN

VIRDEN RECORDER (WED)
169 E. Dean St., Virden, IL, 62690, Macoupin, USA; gen tel (217) 965-3355; gen fax (217) 965-4512; disp adv e-mail ads@gnnews.net; ed e-mail editor@gnnews.net; web site www.gnnews.net
Circulation: 6,100pd, 30fr; Sworn/Estimate/Non-Audited
Advertising rate: Open inch rate $8.00
Established: 1916
Group: Paddock Publications
Adv. Mgr. .... Nathan Jones
Circ. Mgr. .... Julie Westerhausen
Mechanical Specifications: 5 cols, 1 7/8, 1/8 between.Equipment & Software: Hardware — APPLE/IMAC; Presses — 5-KP/News King; Software — Adobe/In Design CS3
Delivery Method: Mail, Newsstand

WASHINGTON

COURIER (WED)
100 Ford Ln, Washington, IL, 61571-2668, Tazewell County, USA; gen tel (309) 444-3139; gen fax (309) 444-8505; disp adv e-mail joi67@mtco.com; web site www.courierpaper.com
Circulation: 20,000fr; Sworn/Estimate/Non-Audited
Advertising rate: Open inch rate $20.53
Established: 1973Editions: (3) 3 total - Morton Courier (8,900); Washington Courier (7,800); Woodford Courier (6,000);
Pub....Roger Hagel
Ed. ....Joi DeArmond
Mechanical Specifications: Type page 10 1/4 x 15; E - 5 cols, 1 11/12, 1/6 between; A - 5 cols, 1 11/12, 1/6 between; C - 6 cols, 1 2/3, between.
Delivery Method: Mail, Carrier, Racks
Areas Served: 61571, 61548, 61550, 61530, 61742, 61568, 61733

WOODFORD COURIER (WED)
100 Ford Ln, Washington, IL, 61571-2668, Washington, USA; gen tel (309) 444-3139; ed tel (309)444-3139, x12; gen fax (309) 444-8505; disp adv e-mail bookkper@courierpapers.com; class adv e-mail bookkper@courierpapers.com; ed e-mail Joi67@courierpapers.com; web site www.courierpapers.com
Circulation: 4,600fr; Sworn/Estimate/Non-Audited
Advertising rate: Open inch rate $10.11
Group: Courier Newspapers
Pub....Roger Hagel
Ed. ....Joi DeArmond
Delivery Method: Mail

WAVERLY

WAVERLY JOURNAL (FRI)
130 S Pearl St, Waverly, IL, 62692-1166, Morgan, USA; gen tel (217) 435-9221; gen fax (217) 435-4511; disp adv e-mail journaltrib@mchsi.com; ed e-mail journaltrib@mchsi.com; web site www.facebook.com/pages/Waverly-Journal/169529479729692
Circulation: 1,350pd, 20fr; Sworn/Estimate/Non-Audited
Advertising rate: Open inch rate $4.75
Pub....Nancy P. Copelin
Ed. ....Julie A. SpringerEquipment & Software: Hardware — APP/Mac, Packard Bell; Software — QPS/QuarkXPress.
Delivery Method: Mail

WINCHESTER

SCOTT COUNTY TIMES (WED)
4 S Hill St, Winchester, IL, 62694-1212, Scott, USA; gen tel (217) 742-3313; adv tel (217) 285-2345; ed tel (217) 285-2345; gen fax (630) 206-0320; disp adv e-mail nliehr@campellpublications.net; class adv e-mail ppnews@campbellpublications.net; ed e-mail ppnews@campbellpublications.net; web site scottcountytimes.com
Circulation: 800pd, 20fr; Sworn/Estimate/Non-Audited
Advertising rate: Open inch rate $11.95
Established: 1865
Group: Campbell Publishing Co., Inc.
Pub....Julie Boren
Mechanical Specifications: Type page 13 x 21 1/2; E - 6 cols, 2 1/16, 1/6 between; A - 6 cols, 2 1/16, 1/6 between; C - 9 cols, 1 5/16, 1/6 between.
Delivery Method: Mail, Newsstand, Racks
Areas Served: Scott County, IL

WORDEN

MADISON COUNTY CHRONICLE (THUR)
125 E Wall St, Apt 9, Worden, IL, 62097-1331, Madison, USA; gen tel (618) 459-3655; adv tel (618) 459-3655; ed tel (618) 459-3655; gen fax (618) 459-3655; adv fax (618) 459-3655; ed fax (618) 459-3655; disp adv e-mail chronicl@madisontelco.com
Circulation: 650pd,; Sworn/Estimate/Non-Audited
Advertising rate: Open inch rate $4.00
Established: 1976
Pub....John M. Galer
Prodn. Mgr. ....Vera Eckhardt
Delivery Method: Mail, Newsstand, Racks

YORKVILLE

KENDALL COUNTY RECORD, OSWEGO LEDGER, SANDWICH RECORD, PLANO RECORD (THUR)
109 W Veterans Pkwy, Yorkville, IL, 60560-1905, Kendall, USA; gen tel (630) 553-7034; gen fax (630) 553-7085; class adv e-mail ads@kendallcountynow.com; ed e-mail news@kendallcountynow.com; web site www.kendallcountynow.com
Circulation: 5,997pd, 444fr; Sworn/Estimate/Non-Audited
Advertising rate: Open inch rate $5.15
Established: 1864
Sports Ed....Joshua Welge
Delivery Method: Mail, Newsstand
Areas Served: 60560

LEDGER-SENTINEL (THUR)
109 W Veterans Pkwy, Yorkville, IL, 60560-1905, Kendall, USA; gen tel (630) 553-7034; ed tel (630) 554-8573; gen fax (630) 553-7085; disp adv e-mail adsales@kendallcountynow.com; ed e-mail news@kendallcountynow.com; web site www.kendallcountynow.com
Circulation: 7,900pd, 23fr; Sworn/Estimate/Non-Audited
Advertising rate: Open inch rate $5.00
Pub....Jeffrey A. Farren
Adv. Mgr. ....Kristin Hawkins
Mng. Ed....John Etheridge
Mechanical Specifications: Type page 10 x 16; A - 6 cols, 1 1/2, between; C - 6 cols, 1 1/2, between.
Delivery Method: Mail

PLANO RECORD (THUR)
109 W Veterans Pkwy, Yorkville, IL, 60560-1905, Kendall, USA; gen tel (630) 553-7034; gen fax (630) 553-7085; disp adv e-mail news@kendallcountyrecord.com; class adv e-mail ads@kendallcountyrecord.com
Circulation: 1,395pd, 298fr; Sworn/Estimate/Non-Audited
Advertising rate: Open inch rate $4.81
Established: 1974
Pub....Jeffery A. Farren
Delivery Method: Mail, Newsstand
Areas Served: 60545

SANDWICH RECORD (WED)
222 S Bridge St, Yorkville, IL, 60560-1502, DeKalb, USA; gen tel (630) 553-7034; gen fax (630) 553-7085; disp adv e-mail news@kendallcountyrecord.com; class adv e-mail ads@kendallcountyrecord.com
Circulation: 5,482fr; Sworn/Estimate/Non-Audited
Advertising rate: Open inch rate $5.40
Established: 1985
Digital Platform - Mobile: Apple
Digital Platform - Tablet: Apple iOS
Pub....Jeff Farren
Adv. Mgr. ....Kristen Hawkins
Delivery Method: Mail, Newsstand
Areas Served: 60548

ZION

ZION BENTON NEWS (THUR)
2711 Sheridan Rd Ste 202, Ste. 202, Zion, IL, 60099-2650, Lake, USA; gen tel (847) 746-9000; gen fax (847) 746-9150; disp adv e-mail mpobiecke@kenoshanews.com; class adv e-mail zion@kenoshanews.com; ed e-mail mona@zion-bentonnews.com; web site zion-bentonnews.com
Circulation: 22,000fr; Sworn/Estimate/Non-Audited
Advertising rate: Open inch rate $6.75
Group: United Communications Corporation
Pub....Frank M. Misureli
Ed. ....Mona Shannon
Delivery Method: Carrier, Racks
Areas Served: 60096, 60099, 60087, 60085, 60083, 53178, 60031

INDIANA

ALBION

ALBION NEW ERA (WED)
407 S Orange St, Albion, IN, 46701-1132, Noble, USA; gen tel (260) 636-2727; adv tel (260) 347-0400 Ext. 1002; ed tel (260) 347-0400 Ext. 2546; gen fax (260) 636-2042; disp adv e-mail jlecount@app-printing.com; class adv e-mail kanderson@kpcmedia.com; ed e-mail dkurtz@kpcmedia.com; web site kpcnews.com/news/latest/new_era/
Circulation: 2,250pd,; Sworn/Estimate/Non-Audited
Advertising rate: Open inch rate $5.50
Established: 1876
Group: All Printing & Publishing, Inc
Pub....Robert L. Allman
Adv. Mgr. ....Lisa Smith
Legal Adv. Clerk....Lanette McGuire
Exec. Ed....Dave Kurtz
Mechanical Specifications: Type page 10 1/2 x 15 1/2; E - 6 cols, 1 1/2, 3/16 between; A - 6 cols, 1 1/2, 3/16 between; C - 6 cols, 1 1/2, 3/16 between.
Delivery Method: Mail, Newsstand, Racks

ATTICA

FOUNTAIN COUNTY NEIGHBOR (TUES)
113 S Perry St, Attica, IN, 47918-1349, Fountain, USA; gen tel (765) 762-2411; gen fax (765) 762-1547; disp adv e-mail atticasales@sbcglobal.net; class adv e-mail atticasales@sbcglobal.net; ed e-mail atticaeditor@sbcglobal.net; web site www.fountaincountyneighbor.com
Circulation: 1,803pd,; Sworn/Estimate/Non-Audited
Advertising rate: Open inch rate $13.90
Group: Community Media Group
Gen. Mgr. ....Greg Willhite
Office Mgr. ....Roberta Hembree
Ed....Gretchen Stone
Mechanical Specifications: Type page 11 1/2 x 21; E - 6 cols, 1 9/16, between; A - 6 cols, 1 9/16, between; C - 6 cols, 1 9/16, between. Equipment & Software: Hardware — APP/Mac; Presses — KP; Software — Multi-Ad 3.7, QPS/QuarkXPress 4.0.
Delivery Method: Mail, Newsstand, Racks
Areas Served: 47918

THE REVIEW REPUBLICAN (THUR)
113 S Perry St, Attica, IN, 47918-1349, Fountain, USA; gen tel (765) 762-3322; adv tel (765) 762-3322; ed tel (765) 762-3322; gen fax (765) 762-1547; adv fax (765) 762-1547; ed fax (765) 762-1547; disp adv e-mail atticasales@sbcglobal.net; class adv e-mail fcbhembree@sbcglobal.net; ed e-mail revrep@sbcglobal.net; web site www.newsbug.info/williamsport_review_republican
Advertising rate: Open inch rate $11.20
Established: 1914
Group: Kankakee Valley Publishing
Digital Platform - Mobile: Apple, Android, Windows, Blackberry
Digital Platform - Tablet: Apple iOS, Android, Windows 7, Blackberry Tablet OS, Kindle
Acct. Exec. ....Greg Willhite
Ed. ....Gretchen Stone
Circ. ....Cyndi Grace
Delivery Method: Mail, Newsstand, Racks
Areas Served: Warren County

AUBURN

THE BUTLER BULLETIN (TUES)
118 W 9th St, Auburn, IN, 46706-2225, DeKalb, USA; gen tel (260) 868-5501; adv tel (260) 925-2611 x 2547; gen fax (260) 925-2625; adv fax (260) 925-2625; ed fax (260) 925-2625; disp adv e-mail ldonley@kpcmedia.com; class adv e-mail ldonley@kpcmedia.com; web site www.kpcnews.com
Circulation: 1,547pd, 26fr; Sworn/Estimate/Non-Audited
Advertising rate: Open inch rate $9.94
Established: 1976
Group: KPC Media Group, Inc.
Pres./CEO ....Terry Housholder
Delivery Method: Mail, Newsstand, Racks

THE GARRETT CLIPPER (MON, THUR)
118 W 9th St, Auburn, IN, 46706-2225, De Kalb, USA; gen tel (260) 925-2611 x 45; adv tel (260) 347-0400 Ext. 1002; ed tel (260) 925-2611 Ext. 2545; adv fax (260) 925-2625; disp adv e-mail garrettclipper@kpcnews.net; class adv e-mail garrettclipper@kpcnews.net; ed e-mail garrettclipper@kpcnews.net; web site kpcnews.com
Circulation: 850pd,; Sworn/Estimate/Non-Audited
Advertising rate: Open inch rate $7.29
Established: 1885
Group: KPC Media Group, Inc.
Pres./Pub. ....Terry Housholder
Ed. ....Sue Carpenter
Adv. Dir....Joy Newman
Mechanical Specifications: Type page 13 x 21 1/2; E - 6 cols, 2 1/16, 1/12 between; A - 6 cols, 4 3/16, 1/12 between; C - 6 cols, 6 1/16, 1/12 between.Equipment & Software: Hardware — APP/Power Mac 8500/180; Software — Microsoft/Word 6.0, Baseview/NewsEdit 3.1, QPS/QuarkXPress 4.0, Adobe/Photoshop 4.0.1, Picture Viewer 3.0, Simple Text 1.4.
Delivery Method: Mail, Newsstand, Carrier, Racks

AVON

HENDRICKS COUNTY FLYER (WED, SAT)
8109 Kingston St, Ste 500, Avon, IN, 46123-8211, Hendricks, USA; gen tel (317) 272-5800; adv tel (317) 272-5800 ext. 126; ed tel (317) 272-5800 ext. 134; gen fax (317) 272-5887; adv fax (317) 272-5887; ed fax (317) 272-5887; disp adv e-mail david.johnson@flyergroup.com; class adv e-mail ashley.gauger@flyergroup.com; ed e-mail kathy.linton@flyergroup.com; web site www.flyergroup.com
Circulation: 2,750pd, 28,800fr; Sworn/Estimate/Non-Audited
Advertising rate: Open inch rate $26.00
Established: 1994
Group: Community Newspaper Holdings, Inc.
Pub....Harold Allen
Bus. Mgr....Cathy Wilson
Ed. ....Kathy Linton
Prodn. Dir....Terry Ballard
Adv. Mgr....Jared Selch
Mechanical Specifications: Type page 11 x 21 1/2; E - 6 cols, 1 5/6, 3/8 between; A - 6 cols, 1 5/6, 3/8 between; C - 6 cols, 1 5/6, 3/8 between.Equipment & Software: Hardware — Dell/PC; Software — Atex, PBS, QPS/QuarkXPress 4.0.
Delivery Method: Mail, Newsstand, Carrier,

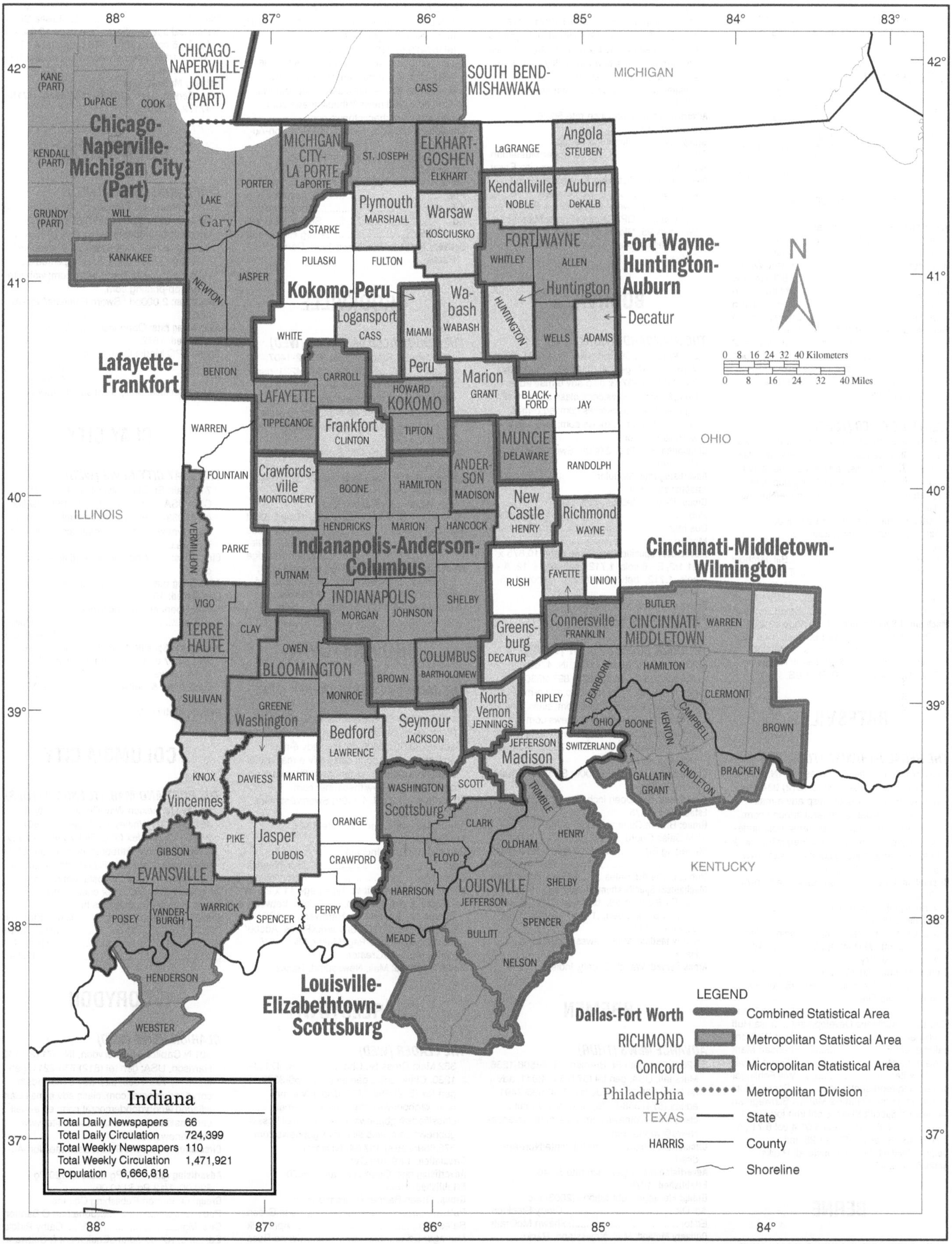
Indiana
Total Daily Newspapers 66
Total Daily Circulation 724,399
Total Weekly Newspapers 110
Total Weekly Circulation 1,471,921
Population 6,666,818
LEGEND
Dallas-Fort Worth Combined Statistical Area
RICHMOND Metropolitan Statistical Area
Concord Micropolitan Statistical Area
Philadelphia Metropolitan Division
TEXAS State
HARRIS County
Shoreline
0 8 16 24 32 40 Kilometers
0 8 16 24 32 40 Miles
N
88°
87°
86°
85°
84°
83°
42°
41°
40°
39°
38°
37°
MICHIGAN
ILLINOIS
OHIO
KENTUCKY
Chicago-Naperville-Michigan City (Part)
CHICAGO-NAPERVILLE-JOLIET (PART)
KANE (PART)
DuPAGE
COOK
KENDALL (PART)
GRUNDY (PART)
WILL
KANKAKEE
SOUTH BEND-MISHAWAKA
CASS
MICHIGAN CITY-LA PORTE
LaPORTE
ST. JOSEPH
ELKHART-GOSHEN
ELKHART
LaGRANGE
Angola
STEUBEN
LAKE
Gary
PORTER
Plymouth
MARSHALL
Warsaw
KOSCIUSKO
Kendallville
NOBLE
Auburn
DeKALB
STARKE
FORT WAYNE
WHITLEY
ALLEN
Fort Wayne-Huntington-Auburn
PULASKI
FULTON
NEWTON
JASPER
Kokomo-Peru
Loganspourt
CASS
MIAMI
Wa-bash
WABASH
HUNTINGTON
Huntington
WELLS
ADAMS
Decatur
WHITE
Lafayette-Frankfort
BENTON
CARROLL
Peru
Marion
GRANT
BLACK-FORD
JAY
LAFAYETTE
TIPPECANOE
HOWARD
KOKOMO
Frankfort
CLINTON
TIPTON
WARREN
MUNCIE
DELAWARE
RANDOLPH
FOUNTAIN
Crawfords-ville
MONTGOMERY
BOONE
HAMILTON
ANDER-SON
MADISON
New Castle
HENRY
Richmond
WAYNE
VERMILLION
PARKE
HENDRICKS
MARION
HANCOCK
Indianapolis-Anderson-Columbus
Cincinnati-Middletown-Wilmington
PUTNAM
INDIANAPOLIS
MORGAN
JOHNSON
SHELBY
RUSH
FAYETTE
UNION
VIGO
TERRE HAUTE
CLAY
OWEN
BUTLER
Connersville
FRANKLIN
CINCINNATI-MIDDLETOWN
WARREN
Greens-burg
DECATUR
COLUMBUS
BARTHOLOMEW
SULLIVAN
BLOOMINGTON
MONROE
BROWN
GREENE
Washington
DEARBORN
HAMILTON
CLERMONT
RIPLEY
North Vernon
JENNINGS
OHIO
BOONE
KENTON
CAMPBELL
BROWN
Seymour
JACKSON
Bedford
LAWRENCE
JEFFERSON
Madison
SWITZERLAND
KNOX
DAVIESS
MARTIN
GALLATIN
GRANT
PENDLETON
BRACKEN
WASHINGTON
SCOTT
TRIMBLE
Vincennes
Scottsburg
ORANGE
CLARK
HENRY
OLDHAM
PIKE
Jasper
DUBOIS
GIBSON
FLOYD
CRAWFORD
EVANSVILLE
HARRISON
LOUISVILLE
JEFFERSON
SHELBY
POSEY
VANDER-BURGH
WARRICK
SPENCER
PERRY
SPENCER
MEADE
BULLITT
NELSON
HENDERSON
Louisville-Elizabethtown-Scottsburg
WEBSTER

Racks
Areas Served: 46103, 46112, 46118, 46121, 46122, 46123, 46149, 46167, 46168, 46214, 46231, 46234, 46241

THE WEEKEND FLYER (WED, SAT)
8109 Kingston St, Ste 500, Avon, IN, 46123-8211, Hendricks, USA; gen tel (317) 272-5800; adv tel (317) 272-5800 ext. 126; ed tel (317) 272-5800 ext. 134; gen fax (317) 272-5887; adv fax (317) 272-5887; ed fax (317) 272-5887; disp adv e-mail flyer@flyergroup.com; ed e-mail Kathy.Linton@flyergroup.com; web site www.flyergroup.com
Circulation: 16,000fr; Sworn/Estimate/Non-Audited
Advertising rate: Open inch rate $7.25
Group: Community Newspaper Holdings, Inc.
Pub. .... Harold Allen
Bus. Mgr. .... Cathy Wilson
Adv. Dir. .... Bill Jarchow
Ed. .... Kathy Linton
Prodn. Dir. .... Terry Ballard
Adv. Dir. .... David Johnson
Mechanical Specifications: Type page 13 x 21 1/2; E - 6 cols, 2 1/16, between; A - 6 cols, 2 1/16, between; C - 10 cols, 1 3/16, between. Equipment & Software: Hardware — APP/Mac; Software — Graphix/Adtaker, Baseview/Managing Editor.

WESTSIDE FLYER (TUES)
8109 Kingston St, Ste 500, Avon, IN, 46123-8211, USA; gen tel (317) 272-5800; gen fax (317) 272-5887; disp adv e-mail flyer@flyergroup.com; web site www.flyergroup.com
Circulation: 15,000fr; Sworn/Estimate/Non-Audited
Advertising rate: Open inch rate $26.00
Group: Community Newspaper Co.
Pub. .... Herald Allan
Adv.Dir. .... Bill Jarchow
Circ. Mgr. .... Tina Williams
Mng. Ed. .... Kathy Linton
Prodn. Mgr. .... Hary Ballard
Adv. Dir. .... David Johnson
Mechanical Specifications: Type page 13 x 21 1/2; E - 6 cols, 1 5/6, 3/8 between; A - 6 cols, 1 5/6, 3/8 between; C - 6 cols, 1 5/6, 3/8 between.Equipment & Software: Hardware — Dell/PC; Software — ATEX, PBS.

BATESVILLE

THE HERALD-TRIBUNE (TUES, FRI)
475 N Huntersville Rd, Batesville, IN, 47006-9205, Franklin, USA; gen tel (812) 934-4343; gen fax (812) 934-6406; disp adv e-mail bonnie.motz@batesvilleheraldtribune.com; class adv e-mail tawnya.birden@indianamediagroup.com; ed e-mail TheHeraldTribune@batesvilleheraldtribune.com; web site www.batesvilleheraldtribune.com
Circulation: 2,000pd,; Sworn/Estimate/Non-Audited
Advertising rate: Open inch rate $14.90
Established: 1891
Group: Community Newspaper Holdings, Inc.
Digital Platform - Mobile: Apple, Android, Windows, Blackberry
Digital Platform - Tablet: Apple iOS, Android, Windows 7, Blackberry Tablet OS, Kindle, Nook, Kindle Fire
Mng Ed. .... Debbie Blank
Reg Dir of Audience Development .... Lisa Huff
publisher .... Laura Welborn
sales director .... Sheridan Mark
assistant editor .... Diane Raver
sports writer .... Will Fehlinger
advertising representative .... Bonnie Motz
advertising representative Marilyn Schwegman
Mechanical Specifications: 6 column format - 1 col 1.6"; 2 col 3.31"; 3 col 5.0"; 4 col 6.71"; 5 col 8.43"; 6 col 10.15" - 21.25" tall
Delivery Method: Mail, Newsstand, Racks
Areas Served: 47006

BERNE

BERNE TRI WEEKLY NEWS (MON, WED, FRI)
153 S Jefferson St, Berne, IN, 46711-2157, Adams, USA; gen tel (260) 589-2101; gen fax (260) 589-8614; adv fax (260) 589-8614; disp adv e-mail news@bernetriweekly.com; web site www.bernetriweekly.com
Circulation: 2,000pd,; Sworn/Estimate/Non-Audited
Advertising rate: Open inch rate $6.20
Established: 1896
Group: Dynamic Resource Group
Pub. .... Roger Muselman
Adv. Mgr. .... Jessica Elvey
Mechanical Specifications: Type page 12 3/4 x 20 1/2; E - 6 cols, 2, 1/6 between; A - 6 cols, 2, 1/6 between.Equipment & Software: ; Software — QPS/QuarkXPress, Microsoft/Windows 95, Microsoft/Word.
Delivery Method: Mail, Newsstand, Carrier, Racks

BOONVILLE

THE STANDARD (THUR)
204 W Locust St, Boonville, IN, 47601-1522, Warrick, USA; gen tel (812) 897-2330; adv fax (812) 897-3703; disp adv e-mail advertising@warricknews.com; class adv e-mail classifieds@warricknews.com; ed e-mail newsroom@warricknews.com; web site www.warricknews.com
Circulation: 4,000pd, 2,000fr; Sworn/Estimate/Non-Audited
Advertising rate: Modular
Established: 1874
Group: Paxton Media Group, LLC
Pub. .... Gary Neal
Bus Mgr .... Debi Neal
Mgr Ed .... Emily May
Mechanical Specifications: Type page 10.875 x 21 1/2; E - 6 cols, 1.712, between - .12; A - 6 cols, 1.712, between -0.12; C - 8 cols,1.25, between - .12.
Delivery Method: Mail, Racks
Areas Served: Warrick County

WARRICK COUNTY TODAY (THUR)
204 W Locust St, Boonville, IN, 47601-1522, Warrick, USA; gen tel (812) 897-2330; gen fax (812) 897-3703; disp adv e-mail advertising@warricknews.com; class adv e-mail advertising@warricknews.com; ed e-mail newsroom@warricknews.com; web site www.warricknews.com - 700,000(views) 157,000(visitors)
Circulation: 4,000pd, 12,000fr; Sworn/Estimate/Non-Audited
Advertising rate: Open inch rate $19.70
Established: 1875
Group: Brehm Communications, Inc.
TSM Sales Coord. .... Debi Neal
Managing Ed. .... Emily May
Adv. .... Karen Hullett
Publications Ad. Sales .... Lavinia Brookshire
Mechanical Specifications: Type page 10 x 21 1/2; E - 6 cols, 1.56, between, .111; A - 6 cols, 1.56, between, .111; C - 6 cols, 1.56, between, .111.
Delivery Method: Mail, Newsstand, Carrier, Racks
Areas Served: Warick County, Indiana

BREMEN

ADVANCE NEWS (THUR)
126 E Plymouth St, Bremen, IN, 46506-1236, Marshall, USA; gen tel (574) 546-2941; adv tel (574) 936-3101; adv fax (574) 936-7491; ed fax (574) 546-5170; class adv e-mail class@thepilotnews.com; ed e-mail Advance-News@yahoo.com
Circulation: 918pd,; Sworn/Estimate/Non-Audited
Advertising rate: Open inch rate $5.40
Established: 1879
Group: Heritage Publications (2003) Inc.
Ad. Dir. .... Cindy Stockton
Editor .... Shawn McGrath
Delivery Method: Mail, Newsstand, Racks
Areas Served: Elkhart County

THE BREMEN ENQUIRER (THUR)
126 E Plymouth St, Bremen, IN, 46506-1236, Marshall, USA; gen tel (574) 546-2941; adv tel (574) 936-3101; ed tel (574) 546-2941; gen fax (574) 546-5170; adv fax (574) 936-7491; disp adv e-mail ads@thepilotnews.com; class adv e-mail class@thepilotnews.com; ed e-mail news@thepilotnews.com; web site www.thepilotnews.com
Circulation: 1,250pd,; Sworn/Estimate/Non-Audited
Advertising rate: Open inch rate $5.72
Established: 1885
Group: Heritage Publications (2003) Inc.
Pub. .... Cindy Stockton
Adv. Mgr. .... Cindy Stockton
Ed. .... Shawn McGrath
Prodn. Mgr. .... Greg Hildebrand
Delivery Method: Mail, Newsstand, Carrier, Racks

BROOKVILLE

THE BROOKVILLE AMERICAN (WED)
531 Main St, Brookville, IN, 47012-1407, Franklin, USA; gen tel (765) 647-4221; gen fax (765) 647-4811; disp adv e-mail info@whitewaterpub.com; class adv e-mail info@whitewaterpub.com; ed e-mail info@whitewaterpub.com; web site www.whitewaterpub.com
Circulation: 5,000pd, 62fr; Sworn/Estimate/Non-Audited
Advertising rate: Open inch rate $7.00
Established: 1838
Group: Whitewater Publications
Pub. .... Gary L. Wolf
Adv. Mgr. .... Mary Ross
Circ. Mgr. .... Donna Schuler
Ed. .... John Estridge
Mechanical Specifications: Type page 13 x 21; E - 6 cols, 2, 1/4 between; A - 6 cols, 2, 1/4 between; C - 8 cols, 1 1/2, 1/8 between.
Delivery Method: Mail, Newsstand, Racks

BROWNSTOWN

THE JACKSON COUNTY BANNER (TUES, THUR)
116 E Cross St, Brownstown, IN, 47220-2011, Jackson, USA; gen tel (812) 358-2111; adv fax (812) 358-5606; disp adv e-mail ads@thebanner.com; class adv e-mail ads@thebanner.com; ed e-mail news@thebanner.com; web site www.thebanner.com
Circulation: 1,730pd, 4,140fr; Sworn/Estimate/Non-Audited
Advertising rate: Open inch rate $9.75
Established: 1869
Group: AIM Media Indiana
Ed .... Nick Hedrick
Office Mgr. .... Aaron Wright
Mechanical Specifications: Type page 11 x 21; E - 6 cols, 2, 1/6 between; C - 6 cols, between. Equipment & Software: Hardware — APP/Mac; Software — QPS/QuarkXPress, Adobe/Photoshop, Adobe/PageMaker, Microsoft/Word, Multi-Ad/Creator.
Delivery Method: Mail, Newsstand, Racks

CHARLESTOWN

THE LEADER (WED)
382 Main Cross St, Charlestown, IN, 47111-1230, Clark, USA; gen tel (812) 256-3377; gen fax (812) 256-3377; disp adv e-mail sales@gbpnews.com; class adv e-mail classifieds@gbpnews.com; ed e-mail jross@gbpnews.com; web site www.gbpnews.com - 378,669(views) 137,646(visitors)
Circulation: 14,964fr; CVC
Advertising rate: Open inch rate $35.70
Established: 1933
Group: Green Banner Publications, Inc.
Pub. .... Joe Green
Sales Mgr. .... April Falk
Manager Ed. .... Janna Ross
Prodn. Mgr. .... Heather Marlman
Circ. Mgr. .... Harry Sanford
Dist. Mgr. .... Leslie Gertin
Mechanical Specifications: Type page 10 1/2 x 16; E - 5 cols, 2 1/16, 3/16 between; A - 5 cols, 2 1/16, 3/16 between; C - 5 cols, 2 1/16, 3/16 between.
Delivery Method: Mail
Areas Served: 4711 47163 47162 47141 47153 47172 47147

CHURUBUSCO

CHURUBUSCO NEWS (WED)
123 N Main St, Churubusco, IN, 46723-1708, Whitley, USA; gen tel (260) 693-3949; gen fax (260) 693-6545; adv fax (260) 693-6545; disp adv e-mail chnews@app-printing.com; class adv e-mail classifieds@kpcmedia.com; ed e-mail nminier@kpcmedia.com; web site www.app-printing.com
Circulation: 2,000pd,; Sworn/Estimate/Non-Audited
Advertising rate: Open inch rate $34.30
Established: 1872
Group: KPC Media Group, Inc.
Adv. Dir. .... Lynche Donley
Pub. .... Robert Allman
Delivery Method: Mail, Newsstand, Racks

CLAY CITY

THE CLAY CITY NEWS (WED)
717 Main St, Clay City, IN, 47841-1331, Clay, USA; gen tel (812) 939-2163; adv fax (812) 939-2286; disp adv e-mail ccnews@claycitynews.com; ed e-mail ccnews@claycitynews.com
Circulation: 1,800pd,; Sworn/Estimate/Non-Audited
Advertising rate: Open inch rate $4.00
Established: 1912
Group: Spencer Evening World
Adv. Mgr. .... Kim Howell
Mng. Ed. .... Travis Curoi
Mechanical Specifications: Type page 15 5/6 x 21; E - 7 cols, 2, 1/8 between; A - 7 cols, 2, 1/8 between; C - 7 cols, 2, 1/8 between. Equipment & Software: Hardware — APP/Mac.
Delivery Method: Mail

COLUMBIA CITY

THE POST AND MAIL (TUESDAY) (TUES)
927 W Connexion Way, Columbia City, IN, 46725-1031, Whitley, USA; gen tel (260) 244-5153; gen fax (260) 244-7598; disp adv e-mail publisher@thepostandmail.com; class adv e-mail postandmailclassifieds@earthlink.net; web site www.thepostandmail.com
Advertising rate: $9.20 per column inch
Group: Horizon Publications Inc.
Publisher/Advertising Mgr. .... Cindy Stockton
Pub. .... Rick Kreps
Ed. .... Nicole Ott
Circu. .... Sally Ballard

CORYDON

CLARION NEWS (WED)
301 N Capitol Ave, Corydon, IN, 47112-1140, Harrison, USA; gen tel (812) 738-2211; gen fax (812) 738-1909; disp adv e-mail ads@corydondemocrat.com; class adv e-mail clasifiedad@corydondemocrat.com; ed e-mail cadams@clarionnews.net; web site www.clarionnews.net
Circulation: 16,600fr; Sworn/Estimate/Non-Audited
Advertising rate: 1/30 Pg $65.00; 1/20 Pg $90.00; 1/12 Pg $140.00
Group: O'Bannon Publishing Co., Inc.
Pub. .... Jonathan O'Bannon
Circ. Mgr. .... Cathy Riddle
Ed. .... Chris AdamsEquipment & Software:

Hardware — APP/Mac; Presses — 4-G/Community; Software — QPS/QuarkXPress 5.1, Adobe/Photoshop 7.0, Freehand 8.0.
Delivery Method: Mail
Areas Served: Crawford, Floyd, Harrison, Washington and Dubois counties

THE CORYDON DEMOCRAT (WED)
301 N Capitol Ave, Corydon, IN, 47112-1151, Harrison, USA; gen tel (812) 738-2211; adv fax (812) 738-1909; disp adv e-mail ads@corydondemocrat.com; class adv e-mail ads@corydondemocrat.com; ed e-mail ctimberlake@corydondemocrat.com; web site www.corydondemocrat.com
Circulation: 6,800pd, 17,600fr; Sworn/Estimate/Non-Audited
Advertising rate: 1/30 Pg $65.00; 1/20 Pg $90.00; 1/12 Pg $140.00
Established: 1856
Group: O'Bannon Publishing Co., Inc.
Pres./Pub. .... Jonathan O'Bannon
Adv. Mgr. .... Jan Crosby
Ed. .... Jo Ann Saylor
Soni O'Bannon
Mechanical Specifications: Type page 13 x 21 1/4; E - 6 cols, between; A - 6 cols, between; C - 8 cols, between.Equipment & Software: Hardware — APP/Mac; Software — Adobe/Photoshop 7.0, QPS/QuarkXPress 5.1., InDesign
Delivery Method: Mail, Newsstand, Carrier, Racks
Areas Served: Harrison County, Crawford County

CROTHERSVILLE

CROTHERSVILLE TIMES (WED)
510 Moore St, Ste 100, Crothersville, IN, 47229-1622, Jackson, USA; gen tel (812) 793-2188; adv tel (812) 793-2188; ed tel (812) 793-2188; gen fax (812) 793-2188; adv fax (812) 793-2188; ed fax (812) 793-2188; disp adv e-mail ctimes@crothersville.net; class adv e-mail ctimes@crothersville.net; ed e-mail ctimes@crothersville.net; web site www.crothersvilletimes.com
Circulation: 1,300pd, 28fr; Sworn/Estimate/Non-Audited
Advertising rate: Open inch rate $4.50
Established: 1980
Digital Platform - Mobile: Android
Ed. .... Curt Kovener
Mechanical Specifications: Type page 10 1/4 x 12.5; E - 6 cols, 1 5/8, 1/6 between; A - 6 cols, 1 5/8, 1/6 between; C - 6 cols, 1 5/8, 1/6 between.Equipment & Software: Hardware — APP/Mac Performa 6360; Software — Adobe/PageMaker 5.0, Adobe/Photoshop 3.0.
Delivery Method: Mail, Racks
Areas Served: Jackson, Scott

DALE

SPENCER COUNTY LEADER (THUR)
208 E Medcalf St, Dale, IN, 47523-9040, Spencer, USA; gen tel (812) 367-2041; adv fax (812) 367-2371; disp adv e-mail ferdnews@psci.net; web site www.ferdinandnews.com
Circulation: 2,100pd,; Sworn/Estimate/Non-Audited
Advertising rate: Open inch rate $5.75
Established: 1960
Group: Dubois Spencer Counties Pubishing Co., Inc.
Co-Pub .... Richard Tretter
Ed. .... Kathy Tretter
Mng. Ed .... Cheryl Hurst
Sports Ed .... Brian Bohne
Mechanical Specifications: Type page 13 x 21 1/2; E - 6 cols, 2, 1/4 between.Equipment & Software: Hardware — APP/Mac; Software — Adobe/PageMaker.
Delivery Method: Mail, Newsstand, Racks

DANVILLE

THE REPUBLICAN (THUR)
6 E Main St, Danville, IN, 46122-1818, Hendricks, USA; gen tel (317) 745-2777; adv fax (317) 745-2777; disp adv e-mail therepublican@sbcglobal.net; class adv e-mail therepublican@sbcglobal.net; ed e-mail therepublican@sbcglobal.net
Circulation: 1,600pd,; Sworn/Estimate/Non-Audited
Advertising rate: Open inch rate $7.00
Established: 1847
Group: Hendricks County Republican, Inc.
Editor .... Betty Bartley
Mechanical Specifications: Type page 11 1/4 x 21; E - 6 cols, 1 3/4, 1/8 between.
Delivery Method: Mail
Areas Served: 46122, 46123, 46112, 46121, 46168, 46180, 46180, 46167, 46165, 46118

DEMOTTE

KANKAKEE VALLEY POST-NEWS (THUR)
827 S Halleck St, Demotte, IN, 46310-8342, Jasper, USA; gen tel (219) 987-5111; gen fax (219) 987-5119; ed fax (219) 987-5119; disp adv e-mail adsales@kvpost.net; class adv e-mail Classifieds@kvpost.net; ed e-mail editor@kvpost.net; web site www.kvonline.info
Circulation: 2,800pd, 19,000fr; Sworn/Estimate/Non-Audited
Advertising rate: Open inch rate $11.50
Established: 1932
Group: Community Media Group
Kankakee Valley Publishing
Gen. Mgr. .... Greg Perrotto
Ed. .... Cheri Shelhart
Circ. .... Cyndi Grace
Delivery Method: Mail, Newsstand, Racks

DUNKIRK

DUNKIRK NEWS AND SUN (WED)
209 S Main St, Dunkirk, IN, 47336-1243, Jay, USA; gen tel (765) 768-6022; gen fax (260) 726-8143; adv fax (260) 726-8143; disp adv e-mail cr.ads@comcast.net
Circulation: 1,000pd, 12fr; Sworn/Estimate/Non-Audited
Advertising rate: Open inch rate $3.00
Established: 1952
Group: Graphic Printing Co., Inc.
Pub .... John C. Ronald
Mechanical Specifications: Type page 14 x 22; E - 6 cols, 2, between; A - 6 cols, 2, between; C - 8 cols, between.Equipment & Software: ; Presses — G.
Delivery Method: Mail, Newsstand
Areas Served: 47336

ELLETTSVILLE

THE ELLETTSVILLE JOURNAL (WED)
211 N Sale St, Ellettsville, IN, 47429-1423, Monroe, USA; gen tel (812) 876-2254; adv fax (812) 876-2853; disp adv e-mail journal@bluemarble.net; ed e-mail journal@bluemarble.net
Circulation: 1,500pd,
Advertising rate: Open inch rate $6.00
Established: 1939
Group: Spencer Evening World
Editor .... Travis Curry
Delivery Method: Mail, Newsstand, Racks

ELWOOD

ALEXANDRIA TIMES-TRIBUNE (WED)
317 S Anderson St, Elwood, IN, 46036-2018, Madison, USA; gen tel (765) 724-4469; gen fax 765-552-3358; disp adv e-mail alextribune@elwoodpublishing.com; class adv e-mail alextribune@elwoodpublishing.com; web site www.elwoodpublishing.com
Circulation: 1,200pd,; Sworn/Estimate/Non-Audited
Advertising rate: Open inch rate $7.75
Established: 1885
Group: Elwood Publishing Co., Inc.
Pub .... Robert Nash
Adv. Director .... Cindy Tyner
Managing Ed .... Jenny Corbett
Prodn. Mgr. .... Randy Bayne
Mechanical Specifications: Type page 10 x 21 1/2; E - 6 cols, 1 5/6, between; A - 6 cols, 1 5/6, between; C - 6 cols, 1 5/6, between. Equipment & Software: ; Software — QPS/QuarkXPress 4.1.
Delivery Method: Mail
Areas Served: 46001,46070,46063

FERDINAND

FERDINAND NEWS (WED)
PO Box 38, 113 W 6th St, Ferdinand, IN, 47532-0038, Dubois, USA; gen tel (812) 367-2041; gen fax (812) 367-2371; disp adv e-mail ferdnews@psci.net; class adv e-mail ads@psci.net; ed e-mail ferdnews@psci.net; web site http://www.ferdinandnews.com/v2/content.aspx?IsHome=1&MemberID=1995&ID=24232
Circulation: 2,500pd,; USPS
Advertising rate: Open inch rate $6.50
Established: 1906
Group: Dubois Spencer Counties Pubishing Co., Inc.
Ed. .... Kathy Tretter
Sports Ed .... Brian Bohne
writer .... Casey Uebelhor
writer .... Lisa Hoppenjans
Advertising manager .... Linda Simpson
Office manager .... Stacy Brown
graphics .... Debbie Powell
Mechanical Specifications: Type page 13 x 21 1/2; E - 3 cols, 4 1/4, 1/4 between; A - 6 cols, 2, 1/4 between; C - 6 cols, 2, 1/4 between. Equipment & Software: Hardware — APP/Mac; Software — Adobe/PageMaker.
Delivery Method: Mail, Newsstand, Racks
Areas Served: Dubois County
Portions of Spencer and Perry counties

FLORA

CARROLL COUNTY COMET (WED)
14 E Main St, Flora, IN, 46929-1351, Carroll, USA; gen tel (574) 967-4135; gen fax (574) 967-3384; disp adv e-mail comet@carrollcountycomet.com; class adv e-mail comet@carrollcountycomet.com; ed e-mail editor@carrollcountycomet.com; web site www.carrollcountycomet.com
Circulation: 3,700pd, 34fr; USPS
Advertising rate: Open inch rate $9.00
Established: 1974
Group: Carroll Papers, Inc.
Digital Platform - Mobile: Apple, Android, Windows
Adv. Mgr. .... Joe Moss
Co-Publisher .... Susan Scholl
Mechanical Specifications: 10.389 wide by 21.5 deep
Delivery Method: Mail, Newsstand, Racks
Areas Served: Carroll County Indiana

FORT BRANCH

SOUTH GIBSON STAR TIMES (TUES)
203 S McCreary St, Fort Branch, IN, 47648-1317, Gibson, USA; gen tel (812) 753-3553; gen fax (812) 753-4251; adv fax (812) 753-4251; disp adv e-mail ads@sgstartimes.com; class adv e-mail classifieds@sgstartimes.com; ed e-mail editor@sgstartimes.com; web site www.sgstartimes.com
Circulation: 4,952pd, 21fr; Sworn/Estimate/Non-Audited
Advertising rate: Open inch rate $6.35
Established: 1955
Group: Pike Publishing
Pres./Pub. .... Frank Heuring
Adv. Mgr. .... John Heuring
Circ. Mgr. .... Rachael Heuring
Ed. .... Andrea Preston
Mechanical Specifications: Type page 9 3/4 x 16; E - 6 cols, 1 1/2, 1/8 between; A - 6 cols, 1 1/2, 1/8 between; C - 6 cols, 1 1/2, 1/8 between.Equipment & Software: Hardware — APP/Mac.
Delivery Method: Mail
Areas Served: Haubstadt, Fort Branch and Owensville

FORT WAYNE

GREATER FORT WAYNE BUSINESS WEEKLY (FRI)
3306 Independence Dr, Fort Wayne, IN, 46808-4510, Allen, USA; gen tel (260) 426-2640; ed tel (260) 426-2640 Ext. 3311; ed e-mail lcardenas@kpcmedia.com; web site http://www.fwbusiness.com/
Circulation:; Sworn/Estimate/Non-Audited
Established: 2005
Group: KPC Media Group, Inc.
Pres. .... Terry Householder
Editor .... Lucretia Cardenas
Delivery Method: Mail

FOWLER

THE BENTON REVIEW (WED)
205 E 5th St, Fowler, IN, 47944-1445, Benton, USA; gen tel (765) 884-1902; adv tel 765-884-1902; ed tel 765-884-1902; gen fax 765-813-0700; adv fax (765) 884-8110; ed fax 765-813-0700; disp adv e-mail bentonreviewads@gmail.com; class adv e-mail bentonreviewads#gmail.com; ed e-mail bentonreview@sbcglobal.net
Circulation: 3,000pd, 76fr; Sworn/Estimate/Non-Audited
Advertising rate: Open inch rate $8.00
Established: 1875
Group: Hoosier Media Group, LLC
Pub .... Don Hurd
Mechanical Specifications: Type page 13 x 21; E - 6 cols, 2 1/12, 1/6 between; A - 6 cols, 2 1/12, 1/6 between; C - 6 cols, 2 1/12, 1/6 between.Equipment & Software: Hardware — APP/Mac; Software — Adobe/PageMaker 5.0, Adobe/Photoshop 3.0, Macromedia/Freehand.
Delivery Method: Mail, Newsstand, Racks
Areas Served: Benton County

FRENCH LICK

SPRINGS VALLEY HERALD (TUES)
8481 W College St, French Lick, IN, 47432-1069, Orange, USA; gen tel (812) 723-2592; adv fax (812) 723-2592; disp adv e-mail peg@ocpnews.com; class adv e-mail peg@ocpnews.com; ed e-mail art@ocpnews.com; web site www.springsvalleyherald.com
Circulation: 2,200pd,; Sworn/Estimate/Non-Audited
Advertising rate: Open inch rate $4.45
Established: 1903
Group: Orange County Publishing, Inc.
Adv. Mgr. .... Peggy Manship
Ed. .... Arthur Hampton
Mechanical Specifications: Type page 10 x 21; E - 6 cols, 2, between; A - 6 cols, 2, between; C - 6 cols, 2, between.Equipment & Software: Hardware — Macs; Software — indesign photoshop
Delivery Method: Mail, Newsstand
Areas Served: 47469, 47432

GAS CITY

OAK HILL TIMES (THUR)
407 E Main St, Gas City, IN, 46933-1532, Grant, USA; gen tel (765) 674-0070; adv tel (270) 442-7389; ed tel (765) 583-0368;

gen fax (765) 674-3496; adv fax (270) 442-5220; ed fax (765) 674-3496; disp adv e-mail kpicphelps@gmail.com; class adv e-mail kpirebekah@gmail.com; ed e-mail kpilay-out@gmail.com
Circulation: 3,130pd, 5,000fr; Sworn/Estimate/Non-Audited
Advertising rate: Open inch rate $16.00
Established: 1902
Group: Kentucky Publishing, Inc.
Digital Platform - Mobile: Apple
Delivery Method: Mail, Newsstand, Carrier, Racks
Areas Served: Sweetser, Swayzee, Greentown, Amboy, Converse, Wabash (Grant, Howard, Wabash & Miami counties)

TWIN CITY JOURNAL-REPORTER (THUR)

787 E Main St, Gas City, IN, 46933-1545, Grant, USA; gen tel (765) 674-0070; gen fax (765) 674-3496; adv fax (765) 674-0071; ed e-mail editor1@indy.rr.com
Circulation: 3,000pd, 27fr; Sworn/Estimate/Non-Audited
Advertising rate: Open inch rate $8.00
Established: 1888
Group: Kentucky Publishing, Inc.
Pub....Greg LeNeave
Mgr....Jan Webster
Ed....Patricia Radiger
Mechanical Specifications: Type page 13 x 21 1/2; E - 6 cols, 2, 1/6 between; A - 6 cols, 2, 1/6 between; C - 6 cols, 2, 1/6 between.
Delivery Method: Mail

GREENFIELD

NEW PALESTINE PRESS (THUR)

22 W New Rd, Greenfield, IN, 46140-1090, Hancock, USA; gen tel (317) 467-6000; adv tel (317) 467-6001; ed tel (317) 467-6022; gen fax (317) 467-6017; adv fax (317) 467-6009; ed fax (317) 467-6017; disp adv e-mail advert@newpalestinepress.com; class adv e-mail class@newpalestinepress.com; ed e-mail news@newpalestinepress.com; web site www.greenfieldreporter.com
Circulation: 2,500pd,; Sworn/Estimate/Non-Audited
Advertising rate: Open inch rate $7.00
Pub....Chuck Wells
Community Ed....Scott Slade
Adv. Dir....John SengerEquipment & Software: Hardware — Adobe/Pagemaker, Microsoft/Word.
Delivery Method: Mail, Carrier

GREENSBURG

THE GREENSBURG TIMES (FRI)

135 S Franklin St, Greensburg, IN, 47240-2023, Decatur, USA; gen tel (812) 663-3111; adv tel (812) 663-3111 x7034; ed tel (812) 663-3111 x7010; gen fax (812) 663-2985; disp adv e-mail natalie.acra@greensburgdailynews.com; ed e-mail news@greensburgdailynews.com; web site http://www.greensburgdailynews.com
Circulation: 692pd, 3fr; Sworn/Estimate/Non-Audited
Advertising rate: Open inch rate $3.50
Established: 1894
Group: Community Newspaper Holdings, Inc.
Reg. Pub....Laura Welborn
Managing Ed....Melissa Conrad
News Ed....Brent Brown
Adv. Mgr....Natalie Acra
Sports Ed....Eric Wohlford
Mechanical Specifications: Type page 13 x 21 1/2; E - 6 cols, 2 1/4, between; A - 6 cols, 2 1/4, between; C - 8 cols, 1 1/2, between. Equipment & Software: Hardware — APP/Mac; Presses — G/Community; Software — QPS/QuarkXPress, Adobe/Photoshop.
Delivery Method: Mail, Racks

GREENWOOD

GREENWOOD AND SOUTHSIDE CHALLENGER (WED)

400 E Main St, Greenwood, IN, 46143-1362, Johnson, USA; gen tel (317) 888-3376; adv tel (317) 888-3376; ed tel (317) 888-3376; gen fax (317) 888-3377; adv fax (317) 888-3377; ed fax (317) 888-3377; disp adv e-mail sgoldsby@hspa.com; class adv e-mail sgoldsby@hspa.com; ed e-mail news@hspa.com; web site www.facebook.com/GreenwoodSouthsideChallengerNewspapers/
Circulation: 5,813pd, 2,000fr; Sworn/Estimate/Non-Audited
Advertising rate: Open inch rate $161.64
Established: 1972
Group: Greenwood Newspapers, Inc.
Digital Platform - Mobile: Apple, Android, Windows
Digital Platform - Tablet: Apple iOS, Android, Windows 7, Blackberry Tablet OS, Kindle, Nook, Kindle Fire
Pub./Ed....Doug L. Chambers
Exec. Dir....Steve Key
Nat'l Adv. Mgr./Classifieds Adv. Mgr....Shawn Goldsby
Mktg. Mgr/Adv. Dir....Pamela Lego
Mechanical Specifications: Type page 10.125 x 21.5; E - 6 cols, 1.583 with 0.1between; A - 6 cols, 1.583 with 0.1between; C - 9 cols, 1, 0.1 between.Equipment & Software: Hardware — 8-PC, 7-HP; Software — Adobe/PageMaker 7.0, Caere/OmniPage Pro 9.0, Quickbooks, Adobe Creative Suite 5.
Delivery Method: Mail, Newsstand, Racks
Areas Served: 46142, 46143, 46217, 46227, 46237, 46131, 46184, 46106

THE FRANKLIN CHALLENGER (THUR)

400 E Main St, Greenwood, IN, 46143-1362, Johnson, USA; gen tel (317) 888-3376; adv tel (317) 888-3376; ed tel (317) 888-3376; gen fax (317) 888-3377; adv fax (317) 888-3377; ed fax (317) 888-3377; disp adv e-mail sgoldsby@hspa.com; class adv e-mail sgoldsby@hspa.com; ed e-mail news@hspa.com; web site www.challengernewspapers.com
Circulation: 3,819pd, 1,500fr; Sworn/Estimate/Non-Audited
Advertising rate: Open inch rate $161.64
Established: 1984
Group: Greenwood Newspapers, Inc.
Digital Platform - Mobile: Apple, Android, Windows
Digital Platform - Tablet: Android, Windows 7, Blackberry Tablet OS, Kindle, Nook, Kindle Fire
Ed./Pub....Doug L. Chambers
Mktg. Mgr./Adv. Dir....Pamela Lego
Nat'l Adv. Mgr./Classifieds Adv. Mgr....Shawn Goldsby
Exec. Dir....Steve Key
Mechanical Specifications: Type page 10.125 x 21.5; E - 6 cols, 1.583 with 0.1 between; A -6 cols, 1.583 with 0.1 between; C - 9 cols, 1, 0.1 between.Equipment & Software: Hardware — 8-IBM, 7-HP; Software — Adobe/PageMaker 7.0, Caere/OmniPage Pro 9.0, Quickbooks, Adobe Creative Suite 5.
Delivery Method: Mail, Newsstand, Racks
Areas Served: 46131, 46184, 46106

HUNTERTOWN

NORTHWEST NEWS (WED)

15605 Lima Rd, Huntertown, IN, 46748-9372, Allen, USA; gen tel (260) 637-9003; adv fax (260) 637-8598; disp adv e-mail nweditor@app-printing.com; web site www.thenorthwestnews.com
Circulation: 1,500pd,; Sworn/Estimate/Non-Audited
Advertising rate: Open inch rate $5.50
Established: 1997
Group: All Printing & Publishing, Inc
Pub....Robert L. Allman
Exec. Ed....Dave Kurtz
Pres./Pub....Terry Householder
Delivery Method: Mail

HUNTINGBURG

THE HUNTINGBURG PRESS (WED)

327 E 4th St, Fl 2, Huntingburg, IN, 47542-1337, Dubois, USA; gen tel (812) 683-5899; adv fax (812) 683-5897; disp adv e-mail kpirebekah@gmail.com; class adv e-mail kpirebekah@gmail.com; ed e-mail kpiads@ky-news.com
Circulation: 1,100pd, 8,900fr; Sworn/Estimate/Non-Audited
Advertising rate: Open inch rate $10.00
Established: 1905
Group: Kentucky Publishing, Inc.
Digital Platform - Mobile: Apple
Digital Platform - Tablet: Apple iOS
Publisher....Greg LeNeave
Advertising Account Executive Rebekah Tatum
Mechanical Specifications: 1 COLUMN IS 1.625" WIDE
FULL PAGE IS 10.625" WIDE X 19.75" TALL
Delivery Method: Mail, Newsstand, Carrier, Racks

INDIANAPOLIS

FRANKLIN TOWNSHIP INFORMER (WED)

8822 Southeastern Ave, Indianapolis, IN, 46239-1341, Marion, USA; gen tel (317) 862-1774; adv fax (317) 862-1775; disp adv e-mail ftinformer@sbcglobal.net; class adv e-mail ftinformer-adsales@sbcglobal.net; web site http://www.ftcivicleague.org/informer/
Circulation: 1,500pd, 0fr; Sworn/Estimate/Non-Audited
Advertising rate: Open inch rate $6.00
Established: 1971
Group: Franklin Township Civic League, Inc.
Editor....Kasie Foster
Delivery Method: Mail
Areas Served: Southeast Marion County

INDIANAPOLIS BUSINESS JOURNAL (MON)

41 E Washington St, Ste 200, Indianapolis, IN, 46204-3517, Marion, USA; gen tel (317) 634-6200; adv tel (317) 472-5321; ed tel (317) 472-5378; gen fax (317) 263-5400; adv fax (317) 472-5321; disp adv e-mail lbradley@ibj.com; ed e-mail gandrews@ibj.com; web site www.ibj.com - 800,000(views) 215,000(visitors)
Circulation: 10,637pd, 494fr; AAM
Advertising rate: 1/4 P $3091, 1/2 P $5396, Full $7732
Established: 1980
Group: IBJ Media Corporation
Digital Platform - Mobile: Apple, Android, Windows, Blackberry
Digital Platform - Tablet: Apple iOS, Android, Windows 7
Pub....Greg Morris
Ed....Greg Andrews
Adv. Dir....Lisa Bradley
Prod. Dir....Patricia Keiffner
Circ. Mgr....Bill Wright
Managing Ed....Lesley Weidenbener
Delivery Method: Mail
Areas Served: Central Indiana

SOUTHSIDE TIMES (THUR)

7670 US 31 S, Indianapolis, IN, 46227-8547, Marion, USA; gen tel (317) 300-8782; gen fax (317) 300-8786; disp adv e-mail Rickm@ss-Times.com; ed e-mail news@ss-times.com; web site www.ss-times.com
Circulation: 17,500fr; Sworn/Estimate/Non-Audited
Advertising rate: Open inch rate $15.30
Established: 1928
Group: Times-Leader Publications, LLC
The Southside Times....Rick Myers
Ed....Nicole Davis
Sales Rep....Steve Laughlin
Mechanical Specifications: Type page 10.75 x 21; E - 6 cols, 1 13/16, 1/2 between; A - 6 cols, 1 13/16, 1/2 between; C - 9 cols, 1 13/16, 1/2 between.
Delivery Method: Mail, Newsstand, Carrier, Racks
Areas Served: 46107, 46142, 46143, 46227, 46239, 46203, 46217, 46225, 46237

SOUTHSIDER VOICE (WED)

6025 Madison Ave, Ste B, Indianapolis, IN, 46227-4722, Marion, USA; gen tel (317) 781-0023; gen fax (317) 781-0253; disp adv e-mail kelly.sawyers@southsidervoice.com; class adv e-mail ads@southsidervoice.com; ed e-mail news@southsidervoice.com; web site www.southsidervoice.com
Circulation: 24,811fr; CVC
Advertising rate: Open inch rate $11.00
Established: 1939
Pub./Owner....Kelly Sawyers
Ed./Owner....Denise Summers
Mechanical Specifications: Broadsheet: Retail column width 1.68" - 6 cols.
Classified Display column width 1.23" - 8 cols. Equipment & Software: Hardware — APP/PCs; Software — Adobe/PageMaker, Caere/Omni.
Delivery Method: Mail, Newsstand, Carrier, Racks
Areas Served: 46107, 46142, 46203
Southside of Indianapolis, Indiana
46217, 46225, 46227, 46237, 46239, 46184

THE INDIANAPOLIS RECORDER (FRI)

2901 N Tacoma Ave, Indianapolis, IN, 46218-2737, Marion, USA; gen tel (317) 924-5143; gen fax (317) 921-6653; adv fax (317) 921-6653; ed fax (317) 921-5148; disp adv e-mail michaelf@indyrecorder.com; class adv e-mail michaelf@indyrecorder.com; ed e-mail newsroom@indyrecorder.com; web site www.indianapolisrecorder.com
Circulation: 4,729pd, 395fr; CVC
Advertising rate: Open inch rate $21.95
Established: 1895
Group: Recorder Media Group
Pub....William Mays
Gen. Mgr....Shannon Williams
Newsroom Mgr....Victoria Davis
Delivery Method: Mail

WEST SIDE COMMUNITY NEWS & WEST INDIANAPOLIS COMMUNITY NEWS (WED)

608 S Vine St, Indianapolis, IN, 46241-0800, USA; gen tel (317) 241-7363; gen fax (317) 240-6397; disp adv e-mail commnews@communitypapers.net
Circulation: 25,000fr; Sworn/Estimate/Non-Audited
Advertising rate: Open inch rate $19.00
Established: 1965
Group: Community Papers, Inc.
Pub./Gen. Mgr./Adv. Mgr....Jackie F. Deppe
Mechanical Specifications: Type page 11 3/4 x 21; E - 6 cols, 1 5/6, 1/6 between; A - 6 cols, 1 5/6, 1/6 between; C - 9 cols, 1 1/16, 1/6 between.Equipment & Software: Hardware — IBM, APP/Mac; Software — Adobe/PageMaker, QPS/QuarkXPress, XYQUEST/XyWrite.
Delivery Method: Carrier, Racks
Areas Served: 46214, 46221, 46222, 46224, 46234, 46241

KENDALLVILLE

THE ADVANCE LEADER (THUR)

102 N Main St, Kendallville, IN, 46755-1714, Noble, USA; gen tel (260) 302-1346; adv tel (260) 347-0400 Ext. 1002; gen fax (260) 347-2693; adv fax (260) 347-7282; disp adv e-mail info@kpcmedia.com; class adv e-mail classified@kpcmedia.com; ed e-mail leader@kpcmedia.com; web site www.kpcnews.com/latest/advanceleader
Circulation: 592pd,; Sworn/Estimate/Non-Audited
Advertising rate: Open inch rate $9.94
Established: 1880
Group: KPC Media Group, Inc.
Pub....Terry Housholder
Ed....Bob Buttgen
Circ. Dir....Bruce Hakala
Adv. Dir....Joy NewmanEquipment & Software:

Hardware — APP/Power Mac; Software — QPS/QuarkXPress 4.0, Baseview/NewsEdit 3.1.
Delivery Method: Mail, Newsstand, Carrier, Racks

KENTLAND

BROOK REPORTER (WED)
305 E Graham St, Kentland, IN, 47951-1235, Jasper, USA; gen tel (219) 474-5532; adv fax (219) 866-3775; disp adv e-mail daily@renssrep.com; web site www.facebook.com/NewtonCountyNewspapers/?ref=page_internal
Advertising rate: Open inch rate $9.25
Established: 1895
Group: Kankakee Valley Publishing
Mng. Ed .... Cindy Brandenburg
Adv .... Connie Nimz
Office Admin .... Betty Long
Delivery Method: Mail

MOROCCO COURIER (WED)
305 E Graham St, Kentland, IN, 47951-1235, Newton, USA; gen tel (219) 474-5532; gen fax (219) 866-3775; adv fax (219) 866-3775; disp adv e-mail daily@rensselaerrepublican.com; class adv e-mail daily@rensselaerrepublican.com; ed e-mail daily@rensselaerrepublican.com; web site newsbug.info/rensselaer_republican
Circulation: 450pd, 10fr; Sworn/Estimate/Non-Audited
Advertising rate: Open inch rate $9.25
Established: 1877
Group: Kankakee Valley Publishing
Pub .... Carla Waters
Cindy Brandenburg
Connie Nimz
Betty Long
Delivery Method: Mail

THE NEWTON COUNTY ENTERPRISE (WED)
305 E Graham St, Kentland, IN, 47951-1235, Newton, USA; gen tel (219) 474-5532; gen fax (219) 474-5354; disp adv e-mail nceeditor@centurylink.net; class adv e-mail ncesales@centurylink.net; ed e-mail nceeditor@centurylink.net; web site newsbug.info; www.newtoncountyenterprise.com
Circulation: 1,600pd,; Sworn/Estimate/Non-Audited
Advertising rate: Open inch rate $9.00
Group: Community Media Group
Adv. Mgr. .... Connie Nimz
Classifieds/Legal Notice .... Betty Long
Mng. Ed.. Carla Waters
Staff Reporter .... Cindy Brandenburg
Pub.. Bette Schmid
Adv. Sales Rep.................... Charlotte Sparks
Mechanical Specifications: Type page 10 1/2 x 14; E - 6 cols, 1 9/16, between; A - 6 cols, 1 9/16, between; C - 6 cols, 1 9/16, between. Equipment & Software: ; Presses — KP.
Delivery Method: Mail, Newsstand, Carrier, Racks

KNIGHTSTOWN

KNIGHTSTOWN BANNER (WED)
24 N Washington St, Knightstown, IN, 46148-1275, Henry, USA; gen tel (765) 345-2292; gen fax (765) 345-2113; disp adv e-mail thebanner@embarqmail.com; class adv e-mail thebanner@embarqmail.com; ed e-mail thebanner@embarqmail.com; web site www.thebanneronline.com
Circulation: 1,400pd, 15fr; Sworn/Estimate/Non-Audited
Advertising rate: Open inch rate $6
Established: 1867
General Manager.............................. Stacy Cox
Ed.. Eric M. Cox
Mechanical Specifications: Type page 10 1/4 x 16; E - 5 cols, 1 11/12, 1/6 between; A - 5 cols, 1 11/12, 1/6 between; C - 5 cols, 1 11/12, 1/6 between.Equipment & Software: Hardware — Gateway, Ricoh/AFLCIO, APP/Mac 2700 Printer; Presses — Web Offset; Software — Microsoft/Word 97, QPS/QuarkXPress 5.0, Adobe/Acrobat 5.0.
Delivery Method: Mail, Newsstand
Areas Served: 46148, 47384, 47351, 46115, 47385

KOKOMO

KOKOMO HERALD (THUR)
207 N Buckeye St, Kokomo, IN, 46901-4521, Howard, USA; gen tel (765) 452-5942; gen fax (765) 452-3037; disp adv e-mail scrouch@kokomoherald.com; web site www.kokomoherald.com
Circulation:; Sworn/Estimate/Non-Audited
Advertising rate: Open inch rate $10.00
Established: 1971
Delivery Method: Mail, Newsstand

LAGRANGE

LAGRANGE NEWS (FRI)
PO Box 148, Lagrange, IN, 46761-0148, Lagrange, USA; gen tel (260) 463-2166; adv fax (260) 463-2734; ed fax (260) 463-2734; disp adv e-mail advertising@lagrangepublishing.com; class adv e-mail advertising@lagrangepublishing.com; ed e-mail editor@lagrangepublishing.com; web site www.lagrangepublishing.com
Circulation: 5,200pd,; Sworn/Estimate/Non-Audited
Advertising rate: Open inch rate $9.90
Established: 1861
Group: LaGrange Publishing, Co.
Pub.. William Connelly
Adv. Mgr.. Scott Faust
Guy Thompson
Mechanical Specifications: Type page 7 x 21 1/2; E - 7 cols, 2 1/12, 6/7 between; A - 7 cols, 2 1/12, 6/7 between; C - 9 cols, 1 7/12, 1/6 between.Equipment & Software: Hardware — PC; Presses — KP/News King; Software — Microsoft/Windows 98, WordPerfect, Adobe/PageMaker.
Delivery Method: Mail, Racks
Areas Served: 46761-46795-46746-46565-46571

LAGRANGE STANDARD (MON)
PO Box 148, Lagrange, IN, 46761-0148, Lagrange, USA; gen tel (260) 463-2166; gen fax (260) 463-2734; adv fax (260) 463-2734; ed fax (260) 463-2734; disp adv e-mail advertising@lagrangepublishing.com; class adv e-mail advertising@lagrangepublishing.com; ed e-mail editor@lagrangepublishing.com; web site www.lagrangepublishing.com
Circulation: 5,200pd,; Sworn/Estimate/Non-Audited
Advertising rate: Open inch rate $9.90
Established: 1856
Group: LaGrange Publishing, Co.
Pub.. William Connelly
Adv. Mgr.. Scott Faust
editor.. Guy Thompson
Mechanical Specifications: Type page 7 x 21 1/2; E - 7 cols, 2 1/12, 6/7 between; A - 7 cols, 2 1/12, 6/7 between; C - 9 cols, 1 7/12, 1/6 between.Equipment & Software: Hardware — PC; Presses — KP/News King; Software — Microsoft/Windows 7, WordPerfect, Adobe/PageMaker.
Delivery Method: Mail, Newsstand, Racks
Areas Served: 46761-46746-46795-46565-46571

LAWRENCEBURG

HARRISON PRESS (WED)
126 W High St, Lawrenceburg, IN, 47025-1908, Hamilton, USA; gen tel (812) 537-0063; adv tel 812-537-0063; ed tel 812-537-0063; gen fax 812-537-5576; adv fax 812-537-5576; ed fax 812-537-5576; disp adv e-mail afritch@registerpublications.com; class adv e-mail customerservice@registerpublications.com; ed e-mail jawad@registerpublications.com; web site www.the-harrison-press.com
Circulation: 4,000pd, 110fr; Sworn/Estimate/Non-Audited
Advertising rate: Open inch rate $12.90
Established: 1928
Group: Delphos Herald Newspapers of Indiana, Inc.
Digital Platform - Mobile: Apple, Android
Digital Platform - Tablet: Apple iOS, Android
Ed. .... Joe Awad
Gen. Mgr. .... April Fritch
Mechanical Specifications: 10.582"x21.0"Equipment & Software: Hardware — Macs; Software — Baseview, Adobe/PageMaker, Adobe/Photoshop, QPS/QuarkXPress.
Delivery Method: Mail, Newsstand, Racks
Areas Served: Hamilton County

THE DEARBORN COUNTY REGISTER (THUR)
126 W High St, Lawrenceburg, IN, 47025-1908, Dearborn, USA; gen tel (812) 537-0063; ed tel (513) 537-0063; gen fax (812) 537-5576; adv fax (812) 537-5576; disp adv e-mail bthies@registerpublications.com; class adv e-mail afritch@registerpublications.com; ed e-mail newsroom@registerpublications.com; web site www.thedcregister.com
Circulation: 6,000pd,; Sworn/Estimate/Non-Audited
Advertising rate: Open inch rate $26.00
Established: 1841
Group: Delphos Herald, Inc.
Register Publications
Adv. Rep. .... Chip Munich
Managing Ed. .... Joe Awad
Gen. Mgr. .... April Fitch
Mechanical Specifications: Type page 14 1/2 x 21; E - 6 cols, 2 3/16, between; A - 6 cols, 2 3/16, between; C - 8 cols, 1 9/16, between.

THE JOURNAL-PRESS (TUES)
126 W High St, Lawrenceburg, IN, 47025-1908, Dearborn, USA; gen tel (812) 537-0063; ed fax (812) 537-5576; disp adv e-mail afritch@registerpublications.com; class adv e-mail afritch@registerpublications.com; ed e-mail erussell@registerpublications.com; web site www.thejournal-press.com
Circulation: 6,300pd,; Sworn/Estimate/Non-Audited
Advertising rate: Open inch rate $26.00
Established: 1975
Group: Register Publications
News Ed. .... Erika Schmidt Russell
Pub.. Tom Brooker
Adv. Dir.. Loretta Day
Mechanical Specifications: Type page 11 1/2 x 21; E - 6 cols, 2 3/16, between; A - 6 cols, 2 3/16, between; C - 8 cols, 1 9/16, between.
Delivery Method: Mail

LOOGOOTEE

THE LOOGOOTEE TRIBUNE (THUR)
514 N John F Kennedy Ave, Loogootee, IN, 47553-1102, Martin, USA; gen tel (812) 295-2500; adv tel (812) 295-2500; ed tel (812) 295-2500; gen fax (812) 295-5221; adv fax (812) 295-5221; ed fax (812) 295-5221; disp adv e-mail advertising@loogooteetribune.com; class adv e-mail advertising@loogooteetribune.com; ed e-mail news@loogooteetribune.com; web site www.loogooteetribune.com
Advertising rate: Open inch rate $3.99
Established: 1873
Group: Hembree Communications
Digital Platform - Mobile: Apple, Android
Digital Platform - Tablet: Apple iOS, Android
Pub./Ed. .... Larry Hembree
Delivery Method: Mail, Newsstand
Areas Served: 47553, 47554

LOWELL

CEDAR LAKE JOURNAL (TUES)
116 Clark St, Lowell, IN, 46356-1702, LaSalle, USA; gen tel (219) 696-7711; gen fax (219) 696-7713; disp adv e-mail pilcherpubco@comcast.net
Circulation: 1,500pd,; Sworn/Estimate/Non-Audited
Advertising rate: Open inch rate $9.00
Pub................................ Mary Jeanette Pilcher
Adv. Mgr. .... Gary A. Pilcher
Ed. .... Connie Schrombeck
Prodn. Mgr. .... Matt Pilcher
Mechanical Specifications: Type page 15 1/8 x 21; E - 8 cols, 1 3/4, 1/4 between; A - 8 cols, 1 3/4, 1/4 between; C - 8 cols, 1 3/4, 1/4 between.
Areas Served: 46307

LOWELL TRIBUNE (TUES)
PO Box 191, Lowell, IN, 46356-0191, Lake, USA; gen tel (219) 696-7711; gen fax (219) 696-7713; disp adv e-mail pilcherpubco@comcast.net; class adv e-mail pilcherpubco@comcast.net; ed e-mail tribune@pilcherpublishing.com; web site www.thelowelltribune.com
Circulation: 4,650pd,; Sworn/Estimate/Non-Audited
Advertising rate: Open inch rate $8.55
Pub.. Matt Pilcher
Adv. Mgr. .... Gary A. Pilcher
Ed. .... Connie Schrombeck
Prodn. Mgr. .... Craig Pilcher
Mechanical Specifications: Type page 15 1/8 x 21; E - 8 cols, 1 3/4, 1/4 between; A - 8 cols, 1 3/4, 1/4 between; C - 8 cols, 1 3/4, 1/4 between.Equipment & Software: ; Presses — 4-G; Software — QPS/QuarkXPress 3.2.
Delivery Method: Mail

MARTINSVILLE

THE MOORESVILLE-DECATUR TIMES (WED, SAT)
60 S Jefferson St, Martinsville, IN, 46151-1968, Morgan, USA; gen tel (317) 831-0280; adv tel (812) 331-4291; ed tel (765) 342-3311 ext. 4412; gen fax (317) 831-7068; adv fax (317) 831-7068; disp adv e-mail cgiddens@heraldt.com; class adv e-mail cgiddens@heraldt.com; ed e-mail bculp@reporter-times.com; web site www.reporter-times.com/mdt/
Circulation: 5,700pd,; Sworn/Estimate/Non-Audited
Advertising rate: Open inch rate $14.89
Established: 1879
Group: Schurz Communications Inc
Adv. Mgr. .... Chad Giddens
Circ. Mgr.. Tim Smith
Adv. Dir.. Laurie Ragle
Managing Ed......................... Alexis Fitzpatrick
Pub... Cory Bollinger
Mechanical Specifications: Type page 14 1/4 x 21 1/2; E - 6 cols, 2 1/4, 3/16 between; A - 6 cols, 2 1/4, 3/16 between; C - 9 cols, 1 3/8, 1/8 between.Equipment & Software: Hardware — APP/Mac; Presses — G/Community.
Delivery Method: Carrier

MIDDLEBURY

THE MIDDLEBURY INDEPENDENT (WED)
PO Box 68, Middlebury, IN, 46540-0068, Elkhart, USA; gen tel (574) 825-9112; gen fax (260) 463-2734; adv fax (260) 463-2734; ed fax (260) 463-2734; disp adv e-mail lagpubco@kuntrynet.com; class adv e-mail advertising@lagrangepublishing.com; ed e-mail editor@lagrangepublishing.com; web site www.lagrangepublishing.com
Circulation: 890pd, 44fr; Sworn/Estimate/Non-Audited
Advertising rate: Open inch rate $4.00
Established: 1946
Group: LaGrange Publishing, Co.
Pub... Bill Connelly

Adv. Mgr. .... Scott Faust
Guy ThompsonEquipment & Software: Hardware — PC; Presses — KP/News King; Software — Microsoft/Windows, WordPerfect, Adobe/PageMaker.
Delivery Method: Mail, Newsstand, Racks
Areas Served: 46540

MIDDLETOWN

THE MIDDLETOWN NEWS (THUR)
106 N 5th St, Middletown, IN, 47356-1439, Henry, USA; gen tel (765) 354-2221; gen fax (765) 354-2221; disp adv e-mail sue@themiddletownnews.com; class adv e-mail sue@themiddletownnews.com; ed e-mail frontpage@themiddletownnews.com; web site www.themiddletownnews.com
Circulation: 2,000pd,; Sworn/Estimate/Non-Audited
Advertising rate: Open inch rate $4.60
Established: 1885
Co-Pub. .... Joey Cooper
Co-Pub. .... Drew Cooper
Design Ed. .... Michael Cooper
Office Mgr./Copy Ed. .... Sue Cooper
Mechanical Specifications: Type page 10 x 14; E - 5 cols, 2, between.Equipment & Software: Hardware — APP/Mac; Software — Adobe/PageMaker.
Delivery Method: Mail

MILFORD

THE MAIL-JOURNAL (WED)
206 S Main St, 206 S Main Street, Milford, IN, 46542-3004, Kosciusko, USA; gen tel (574) 658-4111; gen fax (574) 658-4701; adv fax (800) 886-3796; disp adv e-mail kschumm@the-papers.com; class adv e-mail kschumm@the-papers.com; ed e-mail jseely@the-papers.com; web site www.the-papers.com
Circulation: 3,000pd,; Sworn/Estimate/Non-Audited
Advertising rate: Open inch rate $7.05
Established: 1888
Group: The Papers Incorporated
Pub. .... Ron Baumgartner
Dir., Mktg. .... Kip Schumm
Ed. .... Jeri Seely
Mechanical Specifications: Type page 13 13/16 x 21 1/2; E - 7 cols, 1 13/16, between; A - 7 cols, 1 13/16, between.
Delivery Method: Mail, Newsstand
Areas Served: Serving the communities of Syracuse, Lake Wawasee, Milford, North Webster, Cromwell and Leesburg.

THE PAPER - KOSCIUSKO EDITION (WED)
PO Box 188, 206 S. Main Street, Milford, IN, 46542-0188, Kosciusko, USA; gen tel (574) 658-4111; adv tel (574) 658-4111; ed tel (574) 658-4111; gen fax (800) 886-3796; adv fax (574) 658-3796; ed fax (800) 886-3796; disp adv e-mail kschumm@the-papers.com; class adv e-mail kschumm@the-papers.com; ed e-mail jseely@the-papers.com; web site www.the-papers.com
Circulation: 20,085fr; CVC
Advertising rate: Open inch rate $6.70 - $11.50
Established: 1971
Group: The Papers IncorporatedEditions: (2) Elkhart County; Kosciusko County
Digital Platform - Mobile: Apple
Digital Platform - Tablet: Apple iOS
Pub. .... Ron Baumgartner
Adv. Mgr. .... Kip Schumm
Circ. Mgr. .... Elaine Pearson
Prod. Mgr. .... Todd Clark
Ed. in Chief .... Jeri Seely
Ed. .... Rebecca Whitesel
Business Manager .... Collette Knepp
Associate Editor .... Phoebe Muthart
Associate Editor .... Tim Ashley
Warsaw Office Manager .... Amii Bischof
Syracuse Office Manager ..... Kristine Marshall
Advertising Representative .... Carl Lauster
Advertising Representative ..... Cindy Hathaway
Advertising Representative ...... Susan Littlefield
Advertising Representative .... Toni Ryan
Commercial Printing Sales Rep ..... Barb Walter
Commercial Printing Sales Rep .... Bruce Bultemeier
Circulation .... Jerry Straka
Mechanical Specifications: Type page 9 3/4 x 15 3/4.Equipment & Software: Hardware — APP/Mac; Presses — 16 unit Goss Community
16 unit Manroland Cromoman; Software — DTI, QPS/QuarkXPress, Adobe/PageMaker.
Delivery Method: Newsstand, Carrier
Areas Served: 46510, 46732, 46524, 46538 46539, 46542, 46550, 46962, 46555, 46562 46982, 46567, 46580, 46582, 46590

MONROEVILLE

THE MONROEVILLE NEWS (WED)
115 E South St, Monroeville, IN, 46773-1012, Allen, USA; gen tel (260) 623-3316; adv fax (260) 623-3966; ed e-mail loisternet@yahoo.com; web site monroevillein.com/community-services/newspaper/
Circulation: 1,220pd,; Sworn/Estimate/Non-Audited
Advertising rate: Open inch rate $7.60
Established: 1950
Group: Horizon Publications Inc.
Pub. .... Ron Storey
Adv. Consultant .... Phil Morgan
Ed. .... Lois Ternet
Mechanical Specifications: Type page 11 5/8 x 21 1/4; E - 6 cols, 1 3/4, between.
Delivery Method: Mail

MONTICELLO

NEWS & REVIEW (WED)
202 Rickey Rd, Monticello, IN, 47960-1539, White, USA; gen tel 765-884-1902; adv tel (765)884-1902; ed tel (765)884-1902; gen fax 765-813-0700; adv fax 765-813-0700; ed fax (765) 813-0700; disp adv e-mail bentonreviewads@gmail.com; class adv e-mail bentonreviewads@gmail.com; ed e-mail bentonreviewads@gmail.com; web site www.smalltownpapers.com
Circulation: 1,300pd, 200fr; Sworn/Estimate/Non-Audited
Advertising rate: Open inch rate $5.00
Established: 1887
Group: Hoosier Media Group LLC
Pub. .... Don Hurd
Delivery Method: Mail, Newsstand, Racks
Areas Served: White County

MOUNT VERNON

MOUNT VERNON DEMOCRAT (WED)
132 E 2nd St, Ste B, Mount Vernon, IN, 47620-1805, Posey, USA; gen tel (812) 838-4811; adv fax (812) 838-3696; disp adv e-mail mvdemocrat_ads@insightbb.com; class adv e-mail advertising@mvdemocrat.com; ed e-mail editor@mvdemocrat.com; web site www.mvdemocrat.com
Circulation: 1,500pd, 6,100fr; Sworn/Estimate/Non-Audited
Advertising rate: 1/12 Pg $99.00; 1/8Pg $139.00; 1/4 Pg $239.00
Established: 1867
Group: Landmark Community Newspapers, LLC
Sales Rep .... Sondra Reich
Adv. Sales .... Alicia Bell
Ed. .... Mike Webster
Mechanical Specifications: Type page 13 x 21 1/2.Equipment & Software: Hardware — APP/Mac; Presses — WPC; Software — QPS/QuarkXPress 3.32.
Delivery Method: Mail, Newsstand, Racks

NASHVILLE

BROWN COUNTY DEMOCRAT (WED)
147 E Main St, Nashville, IN, 47448-7008, Brown, USA; gen tel (812) 988-2221; adv fax (812) 988-6502; ed fax (812) 988-6502; disp adv e-mail ads@democrat.com; class adv e-mail ads@democrat.com; ed e-mail newsroom@bcdemocrat.com; web site www.bcdemocrat.com
Circulation: 3,800pd, 42fr; Sworn/Estimate/Non-Audited
Advertising rate: Open inch rate $7.45
Established: 1870
Group: AIM Media Indiana
Gen. Mgr. .... Steve Marshall
Adv. Mgr. .... Keith L. Fleener
Ed. .... Sara Clifford
Delivery Method: Mail, Newsstand, Racks

NEW HARMONY

THE POSEY COUNTY NEWS (TUES)
641 3rd St, New Harmony, IN, 47631-9800, Posey, USA; gen tel (812) 682-3950; adv tel (812) 459-4206; gen fax (812) 682-3944; adv fax (812) 682-3944; disp adv e-mail ads@poseycountynews.com; class adv e-mail news1@poseycountynews.com; ed e-mail news1@poseycountynews.com; web site www.poseycountynews.com
Circulation: 4,500pd,; Sworn/Estimate/Non-Audited
Advertising rate: Open inch rate $6.50
Established: 1955
Owner/Pub. .... David Pearce
Delivery Method: Mail

NORTH VERNON

THE NORTH VERNON SUN (TUES)
528 E O and M Ave, North Vernon, IN, 47265-1217, Jennings, USA; gen tel (812) 346-3973; adv fax (812) 346-8368; disp adv e-mail advertising@northvernon.com; class adv e-mail classifiedspds@northvernon.com; ed e-mail bmayer@northvernon.com; web site www.plaindealer-sun.com
Circulation: 5,000pd, 52fr; Sworn/Estimate/Non-Audited
Advertising rate: Open inch rate $8.24
Established: 1872
Group: North Vernon Plain Dealer & Sun, Inc.
Ed. .... Bryce Mayer
Sports Ed. .... Sharon Hamilton
Pub .... Barbara King
advertisingn rep .... Sue Ross
???? ????
Adv .... Billie Taylor
Mechanical Specifications: Type page 13 x 21 1/2; A - 6 cols, 2 1/16, 1/8 between; C - 7 cols, 1 3/4, 1/8 between.Equipment & Software: Hardware — APP/Macs; Presses — G/Community; Software — QPS/QuarkXPress 6.5.
Delivery Method: Mail, Newsstand
Areas Served: North Vernon/Jennings/47265

ODON

THE ODON JOURNAL (WED)
102 W Main St, Odon, IN, 47562-1306, Daviess, USA; gen tel (812) 636-7350; adv fax (812) 636-7359; disp adv e-mail journal@rtccom.net; ed e-mail journal@rtccom.net; web site www.facebook.com/The-Odon-Journal-110477855656975/
Circulation: 2,990pd,; Sworn/Estimate/Non-Audited
Advertising rate: Open inch rate $4.50
Established: 1873
Group: Myers Enterprises, Inc.
Adv. Mgr. .... Sue Myers
Ed. .... John L. Myers
Delivery Method: Mail

ORLEANS

THE PROGRESS EXAMINER (WED)
233 S 2nd St, Orleans, IN, 47452-1601, Orange, USA; gen tel (812) 865-3242; adv fax (812) 865-3242; disp adv e-mail penews@blueriver.net; class adv e-mail lmac1@blueriver.net; web site N/A
Circulation: 1,684pd, 44fr; Sworn/Estimate/Non-Audited
Advertising rate: Open inch rate $4.75
Established: 1879
Adv. Mgr. .... Neva Stroud
Ed. .... John F. Noblitt
Pub./Asst. Ed. .... Gretchen Nelson
Mechanical Specifications: Type page 13 x 21; E - 6 cols, 2, 1/6 between; A - 6 cols, 2, 1/6 between; C - 6 cols, 2, 1/6 between.Equipment & Software: Hardware — APP/Mac; Software — Adobe Indesign, Photoshop, Acrobat, Microsoft/Word.
Delivery Method: Mail, Newsstand
Areas Served: 47452, 47454, 47432, 47469, 47446

OSSIAN

THE OSSIAN JOURNAL (THUR)
1002 Dehner Dr, Ossian, IN, 46777-9787, Wells, USA; gen tel (260) 622-4108; adv fax (260) 622-6439; disp adv e-mail ossianj@adamswells.com; ed e-mail ossianj@adamswells.com; web site www.sunrisernews.com
Circulation: 500pd, 10fr; Sworn/Estimate/Non-Audited
Advertising rate: Open inch rate $5.20
Established: 1912
Group: News-Banner Publications, Inc.
Adv. Dir .... Jean Bordner
Ed. .... Mark Miller
Mechanical Specifications: Type page 12 3/4 x 21 1/2; E - 6 cols, 2, 1/6 between; A - 6 cols, 2, 1/6 between; C - 6 cols, between.
Delivery Method: Mail

PAOLI

PAOLI NEWS-REPUBLICAN (THUR)
131 S Court St, Paoli, IN, 47454-1323, Orange, USA; gen tel (812) 723-2572; gen fax (812) 723-2592; disp adv e-mail ocpinc@ocpnews.com; class adv e-mail ocpinc@ocpnews.com; ed e-mail ocpinc@ocpnews.com; web site www.paolinews.com
Circulation: 2,800pd,; Sworn/Estimate/Non-Audited
Advertising rate: Open inch rate $4.45
Established: 1875
Group: Orange County Publishing, Inc.
Pub. .... Arthur Hampton
Adv. Mgr. .... Peggy Manship
Ed. .... Dennis Eller
Ed. .... Dennis Ellis
Mechanical Specifications: Type page9.889 x 21; E - 6 cols, 2, 1/6 between; A - 6 cols, 2, 1/6 between; C - 6 cols, 2, 1/6 between.Equipment & Software: Hardware — APP/Macs; Software — QPS/QuarkXPress, Multi-Ad.
Delivery Method: Mail, Newsstand
Areas Served: 47454

PEKIN

THE BANNER-GAZETTE (WED)
490 E State Road 60, Pekin, IN, 47165-7928, Washington, USA; gen tel (812) 967-3176; gen fax (812) 967-3194; disp adv e-mail sales@gbpnews.com; class adv e-mail classifieds@gbpnews.com; ed e-mail gbrowning@gbpnews.com; web site www.gbpnews.com
Circulation: 0pd, 18,021fr; CVC
Advertising rate: Open inch rate $35.70
Group: Green Banner Publications, Inc.
Pub. .... Joe Green
Adv. Mgr. .... April Falk

Circ. Mgr....................................Leslie Gertin
Ed...George Browning
Prodn. Mgr. ....Heather Marlman
Circ. Mgr....................................Harry Sanford
Mechanical Specifications: Type page 10 1/2 x 2 1/16; E - 5 cols, 2 1/16, 3/16 between; A - 5 cols, 2 1/16, 3/16 between; C - 5 cols, 2 1/16, 3/16 between.
Delivery Method: Carrier
Areas Served: 47119 47150 47122 47124 47136 47164 47106 47165 47165

PENDLETON

PENDLETON TIMES-POST (WED)

126 W State St, Pendleton, IN, 46064-1034, Madison, USA; gen tel (765) 778-2324; adv tel (765) 778-2324; ed tel (765) 778-2324; gen fax (765) 778-7152; adv fax (765) 778-7152; ed fax (765) 778-7152; disp adv e-mail mjones@ptlpnews.com; class adv e-mail mjones@ptlpnews.com; ed e-mail sslade@ptlpnews.com; web site www.pendletontime-spost.com
Circulation: 2,400pd,; Sworn/Estimate/Non-Audited
Advertising rate: Open inch rate $5.00
Established: 1897
Group: AIM Media Indiana
Digital Platform - Mobile: Apple, Android, Blackberry
Digital Platform - Tablet: Apple iOS, Android, Blackberry Tablet OS
Pub..Chuck Wells
Ed...Scott Slade
Ad. Director................................John Senger
Delivery Method: Mail, Newsstand, Racks
Areas Served: Pendleton

PETERSBURG

THE PRESS-DISPATCH (WED)

820 E Poplar St, PO Box 68, Petersburg, IN, 47567-1258, Pike, USA; gen tel (574) 936-3101; adv tel (800) 933-0356; gen fax (574) 936-3844; disp adv e-mail ads@pressdispatch.net; class adv e-mail classifieds@pressdispatch.net; ed e-mail news@pressdispatch.net; web site http://www.press-dispatch.net
Circulation: 5,000pd,; USPS
Advertising rate: Open inch rate $6.35
Established: 1898
Group: Pike Publishing
Pres./Pub. ....Frank Heuring
Adv. Mgr. ....John Heuring
Managing Ed. ....Greg Hildebrand
Acct. Mgr. ....Michele Louderback
Mechanical Specifications: Page - 9.75" x 21"Equipment & Software: Hardware — APP/Macs; Software — Adobe CS 4
Delivery Method: Mail, Newsstand, Racks
Areas Served: Pike County, Indiana

PLYMOUTH

BOURBON NEWS-MIRROR (THUR)

214 N Michigan St, Plymouth, IN, 46563-2135, Marshall, USA; gen tel (574) 936-3101; adv fax (574) 936-7491; ed fax (574) 342-8002; disp adv e-mail ads@thepilotnews.com; web site www.thepilotnews.com
Circulation: 911pd,; Sworn/Estimate/Non-Audited
Advertising rate: Open inch rate $4.00
Established: 1870
Group: Heritage Publications (2003) Inc.
Adv. Mgr..................Cindy StocktonEquipment & Software: Hardware — APP/Mac; Software — QPS/QuarkXPress.
Delivery Method: Mail, Newsstand, Carrier, Racks

THE CULVER CITIZEN (FRI)

214 N Michigan St, Plymouth, IN, 46563-2135, Marshall, USA; gen tel (574) 936-3101; adv tel (800) 933-0356; ed tel (574) 216-0075; gen fax (574) 936-3844; adv fax (574) 936-7491; disp adv e-mail culvercitizen@gmail.com; class adv e-mail ads@thepilotnews.com ; ed e-mail news@thepilotnews.com; web site www.thepilotnews.com
Circulation: 900pd,; Sworn/Estimate/Non-Audited
Advertising rate: Open inch rate $4.70
Established: 1894
Group: Heritage Publications (2003) Inc.
Adv. Mgr..................................Cindy Stockton
Circ. Mgr..................................James Radican
Prodn. Mgr. ....Greg Hildebrand
Ed. ....Lois Tomaszewski
Ed. ....Jeff Kenney
Mechanical Specifications: Type page 13 x 21 1/2; E - 6 cols, 2 1/16, 1/8 between; A - 6 cols, 2 1/16, 1/8 between; C - 7 cols, 1 5/8, 1/8 between.Equipment & Software: Hardware — APP/Mac; Software — QPS/QuarkXPress, Multi-Ad/Creator.
Delivery Method: Mail, Newsstand, Carrier, Racks

THE LEADER (THUR)

214 N Michigan St, Plymouth, IN, 46563-2135, Marshall, USA; gen tel (574) 772-2101; adv tel (800) 933-0356; gen fax (574) 936-7491 ; adv fax (574) 772-7041; disp adv e-mail theleader@nitline.net; class adv e-mail class@thepilotnews.com; web site www.thepilotnews.com - 378,669(views) 137,646(visitors)
Circulation: 3,600pd,; Sworn/Estimate/Non-Audited
Advertising rate: Open inch rate $6.05
Established: 1868
Group: Heritage Publications (2003) Inc.
Adv. Mgr..................Cindy StocktonEquipment & Software: Hardware — APP/Mac; Software — QPS/QuarkXPress.
Delivery Method: Mail, Newsstand, Carrier, Racks

PRINCETON

OAKLAND CITY JOURNAL (THUR)

100 N Gibson St, Princeton, IN, 47670-1855, Gibson, USA; gen tel (812) 385-2525; gen fax (812) 386-6199; disp adv e-mail jeff@pdclarion.com; class adv e-mail classifieds@pdclarion.com; ed e-mail news@pdclarion.com; web site www.tristate-media.com
Circulation: 400pd, 0fr; Sworn/Estimate/Non-Audited
Advertising rate: Open inch rate $6.00
Established: 1899
Group: Brehm Communications, Inc.
Princeton Publishing Co., Inc.
Editor ....Andrea Howe
Pub./CEO..............................Jeff Schumacher
Mechanical Specifications: Type page 10 x 21; 6 cols; (1) 1 5/6"Equipment & Software: Hardware — APP/Mac; Presses — 6-G/Community.
Delivery Method: Mail

RENSSELAER

REMINGTON PRESS (WED)

117 N Van Rensselaer St, Rensselaer, IN, 47978-2651, Jasper, USA; gen tel (219) 866-5111; adv fax (219) 866-3775; ed e-mail editor@rensselaerrepublican.com; web site www.facebook.com/pg/Remington-Press-157454220974964/about/
Circulation: 425pd,; Sworn/Estimate/Non-Audited
Advertising rate: Open inch rate $3.00
Established: 1873
Group: Kankakee Valley Publishing
Sports Ed..............................Harley Tomlinson
Prodn. Mgr. ....Misty Longstreth
Delivery Method: Mail

RISING SUN

THE OHIO COUNTY NEWS/RISING SUN RECORDER (THUR)

235 Main St, Rising Sun, IN, 47040-1224, Ohio, USA; gen tel (812) 438-2011; adv tel (812) 537-0063; gen fax (812) 438-3228; adv fax (812)537-5576; disp adv e-mail afritch@registerpublications.com; ed e-mail risingsun@registerpublications.com; web site http://www.theohiocountynews.com/
Circulation: 1,700pd,; Sworn/Estimate/Non-Audited
Advertising rate: Open inch rate $26.00
Established: 1833
Group: Delphos Herald, Inc.
Register Publications
Delivery Method: Mail, Newsstand
Areas Served: Ohio County

ROCKPORT

SPENCER COUNTY JOURNAL-DEMOCRAT (THUR)

541 Main St, Rockport, IN, 47635-1429, Spencer, USA; gen tel (812) 649-9196; gen fax (812) 649-9197; ed e-mail news@spencercountyjournal.com; web site www.spencercountyjournal.com
Circulation: 5,700pd,; Sworn/Estimate/Non-Audited
Advertising rate: Open inch rate $10.85
Established: 1855
Group: Landmark Communications, Inc.
Landmark Community Newspapers, LLC
Pub ....Dave Eldridge
Rgl. Adv. Mgr. ....Cindy Dauby
Ed. ....Vince Leucke
Adv. Consultant........................Melissa Strawn
Classified Adv. Mgr...................Jennifer Heady
Delivery Method: Mail, Newsstand

ROCKVILLE

PARKE COUNTY SENTINEL (WED)

125 W High St, Rockville, IN, 47872-1735, Parke, USA; gen tel (765) 569-2033; gen fax (765) 569-1424; adv fax (765) 569-1424; disp adv e-mail knelson@parkecountysentinel.com; ed e-mail Lbemis@parkecountysentinel.com; web site parkecountysentinel.com
Circulation: 3,500pd, 49fr; Sworn/Estimate/Non-Audited
Advertising rate: Open inch rate $3.50
Established: 1977
Group: Torch Newspapers, Inc.
Pub...Mary Harney
Ed. ....Larry Bemis
Circ. Mgr...............................Christina Valdes
Business/News Coordinator .... Lisa WoodEquipment & Software: ; Software — Lantastic Network.
Delivery Method: Mail

ROYAL CENTER

ROYAL CENTER RECORD (THUR)

102 S Chicago St, Royal Center, IN, 46978-9997, Cass, USA; gen tel (574) 643-3165; gen fax (574) 643-9440; disp adv e-mail rcrecord@mac.com; web site rcr.stparchive.com
Circulation: 802pd, 50fr; Sworn/Estimate/Non-Audited
Advertising rate: Open inch rate $3.25
Established: 1890
Ed. ....Jeffrey C. Funk
Mechanical Specifications: Type page 11 1/2 x 14.

RUSHVILLE

RUSHVILLE REPUBLICAN (TUES, FRI)

315 N Main St, Rushville, IN, 46173-1635, Rush, USA; gen tel (765) 932-2222; adv tel (765) 932-2222; ed tel (765) 932-2222; gen fax (765) 932-4358; adv fax (765) 932-4358; ed fax (765) 932-4358; disp adv e-mail marilyn.land@rushvillerepublican.com; class adv e-mail marilyn.land@rushvillerepublican.com; ed e-mail aaron.kirchoff@rushvillerepublican.com; web site www.rushvillerepublican.com - 548,000(views) 111,700(visitors)
Circulation: 3,682pd,; Sworn/Estimate/Non-Audited
Advertising rate: Open inch rate $14.45 (Retail); $16.45 (Classified)
Established: 1840
Group: McNaughton Newspapers
Community Newspaper Holdings, Inc.
Digital Platform - Mobile: Apple, Android
Digital Platform - Tablet: Apple iOS, Android
Managing Ed..............................Aaron Kirchoff
Shelley Barton
Rgl. Controller............................Lisa Spangler
Rgl. Pub. ....Laura Welborn
Denver E. Sullivan
Rgl. Adv. Dir. ....Keith Wells
Regl. Circ. Mgr. ....Lisa Huff
Graphic Arts Dir. ....Susan Peters
Adv. Mgr......................................Marilyn Land
Mechanical Specifications: Type page 13 x 21 1/2; E - 6 cols, 2 1/16, 1/8 between; A - 6 cols, 2 1/16, 1/8 between; C - 8 cols, 1 17/32, 1/8 between.
Delivery Method: Mail, Newsstand, Carrier, Racks
Areas Served: Rush County

SALEM

THE SALEM DEMOCRAT (THUR)

117 E Walnut St, Salem, IN, 47167-2044, Washington, USA; gen tel (812) 883-3281; adv tel (812) 883-3281; ed tel (812) 883-3281; gen fax (812) 883-4446; adv fax (812) 883-4446; ed fax (812) 883-4446; disp adv e-mail am@salemleader.com; class adv e-mail am@salemleader.com; ed e-mail stephanie@salemleader.com; web site www.salemleader.com
Circulation: 6,000pd,; USPS
Advertising rate: Open inch rate $16.25
Established: 1827
Group: Leader Publishing Co.
Digital Platform - Mobile: Apple
Senior Editor........................Stephanie Ferriell
Sales and Marketing Mgr..............Debbi Hayes
Publisher..............................Nancy Grossman
Gen. Mgr. ....Rhonda Smith
Production Manager...................Dennis Miller
Delivery Method: Mail, Newsstand
Areas Served: Washington, Jackson, Orange, Scott, Clark counties, Indiana

THE SALEM LEADER (TUES)

117 E Walnut St, Salem, IN, 47167-2044, Washington, USA; gen tel (812) 883-3281; gen fax (812) 883-4446; disp adv e-mail am@salemleader.com; class adv e-mail am@salemleader.com; ed e-mail stephanie@salemleader.com; web site www.salemleader.com
Circulation: 5,800pd, 324fr; Sworn/Estimate/Non-Audited
Advertising rate: Open inch rate $7.25
Established: 1878
Group: Leader Publishing Co.
Gen. Mgr. ....Nancy Grossman
Adv. Mgr.....................................Debbie Hayes
Ed. ....Stephanie Taylor
Prodn. Mgr. ....Dennis Miller
Delivery Method: Mail, Newsstand

THE WASHINGTON COUNTY EDITION (WED)

105 E Walnut St, Salem, IN, 47167-2044, Washington, USA; gen tel (812) 883-5555; gen fax (812) 967-3194; disp adv e-mail sales@gbpnews.com; class adv e-mail april@gbpnews.com; ed e-mail gbrowning@gbpnews.com; web site www.gbpnews.com - 378,669(views) 137,646(visitors)
Circulation: 11,338fr; VAC
Advertising rate: Open inch rate $35.70
Established: 1933
Group: Green Banner Publications, Inc.
Pub...Joe Green
Adv. Mgr. ....April Falk
Circ. Mgr.....................................Leslie Gertin
Circ. Mgr....................................Harry Sanford

Prodn. Mgr. .... Heather Marlman
Mechanical Specifications: Type page 10 1/2 x 16; E - 5 cols, 2 1/16, 3/16 between; A - 5 cols, 2 1/16, 3/16 between; C - 5 cols, 2 1/16, 3/16 between.
Delivery Method: Carrier
Areas Served: 417167 47125 47120 47281 47108 47164

YOUR ADVANTAGE (THUR)

117 E Walnut St, Salem, IN, 47167-2044, Washington, USA; gen tel (812) 883-3281; gen fax (812) 883-4446; class adv e-mail office@salemleader.com
Circulation: 12,400fr; Sworn/Estimate/Non-Audited
Advertising rate: Open inch rate $7.25
Pub. .... Nancy Grossman
Adv. Mgr. .... Debbie Hayes
Ed. .... Stephanie Serriell
Prodn. Mgr. .... Dennis Miller
Mechanical Specifications: Type page 13 3/4 x 22 3/4; E - 6 cols, 2 1/32, between; A - 6 cols, 2 1/32, between; C - 7 cols, 1 3/4, between. Equipment & Software: Hardware — APP/Mac; Presses — KP/News King; Software — Baseview/Class Act, Adobe/Photoshop, QPS/QuarkXPress.
Areas Served: 47167

SCOTTSBURG

THE GIVEAWAY (WED)

PO Box 159, Scottsburg, IN, 47170-0159, Scott, USA; gen tel (812) 752-3171; gen fax (812) 967-3194; disp adv e-mail sales@gbpnews.com; class adv e-mail april@gbpnews.com; ed e-mail mamos@gbpnews.com; web site www.gbpnews.com - 378,669(views) 137,646(visitors)
Circulation: 17,970fr; VAC
Advertising rate: Open inch rate $11.15
Established: 1933
Group: Green Banner Publications, Inc.
Publisher .... Joe Green
Adv. Mgr .... April Falk
Distribution Manager .... Lesile Gertin
Editor .... Marcus Amos
Circ. Mgr. .... Harry Sanford
Production Manager .... Heather Marlman
Acct. Exec. .... Judy Lizenby
Mechanical Specifications: Type page 10 1/2 x 16; E - 5 cols, 2 1/6, 3/16 between; A - 5 cols, 2 1/16, 3/16 between; C - 5 cols, 2 1/16, 3/16 between.
Delivery Method: Carrier
Areas Served: 47170 47102 47138 47147 47229 47274 47126 47230

THE SCOTT CO. JOURNAL & CHRONICLE (SAT)

183 E McClain Ave, Scottsburg, IN, 47170-1845, Scott, USA; gen tel (812) 752-3171; adv fax (812) 752-6486; disp adv e-mail sales@gbpnews.com; class adv e-mail sales@gbpnews.com; ed e-mail mamos@gbpnews.com; web site www.gbpnews.com
Circulation: 4,794pd,; Sworn/Estimate/Non-Audited
Advertising rate: Open inch rate $6.50
Established: 1899
Ed. .... Marcus Amos
Adv. Mgr. .... April Falk
Delivery Method: Mail, Racks
Areas Served: 47170 47102 47138 47147

SHOALS

THE SHOALS NEWS (WED)

311 High St, Shoals, IN, 47581-5502, Martin, USA; gen tel (812) 247-2828; adv fax (812) 247-2243; disp adv e-mail steve@theshoalsnews.com; class adv e-mail steve@theshoalsnews.com; ed e-mail steve@theshoalsnews.com; web site www.theshoalsnews.com
Circulation: 2,750pd, 39fr; Sworn/Estimate/Non-Audited
Advertising rate: Open inch rate $3.25
Established: 1888
Editor and Publisher .... Stephen A. Deckard
Mechanical Specifications: 6 col. 11p3Equipment & Software: Hardware — APP/Mac; Software — QPS/QuarkXPress.
Delivery Method: Mail, Newsstand
Areas Served: 47581 47553

SOUTH BEND

TRI-COUNTY NEWS (FRI)

748 S 28th St, South Bend, IN, 46615-2222, St Joseph, USA; gen tel (574) 232-8590; gen fax (574) 232-8592; disp adv e-mail admin@tricountynewsinc.com; class adv e-mail admin@tricountynewsinc.com; ed e-mail admin@tricountynewsinc.com; web site www.tricountynewsinc.com/
Circulation: 1,000pd,; Sworn/Estimate/Non-Audited
Advertising rate: Open inch rate $4.00
Gen. Mgr. .... Lisa J. Andrysiak
Ed. .... Cherie Jolly
Mechanical Specifications: Type page 10 1/4 x 16.
Delivery Method: Mail
Areas Served: St. Joseph, Marshall and Elkhart County

TELL CITY

PERRY COUNTY NEWS (MON, THUR)

9266 Hidden Acres Rd, Tell City, IN, 47586-8879, Perry, USA; gen tel (812) 547-3424; adv fax (812) 547-2847; disp adv e-mail publisher@perrycountynews.com; web site www.perrycountynews.com
Circulation: 6,792pd,; USPS
Advertising rate: Open inch rate $12.70
Established: 1891
Group: Landmark Community Newspapers, LLC
Pub. .... Dave Eldridge
Adv. Mgr. .... Cindy Dauby
Circ. Mgr. .... Joyce Dauby
Ed. .... Vince Leucke
Sports Ed. .... Larry Goffinet
Production Manager .... Gary Smith
Adv. Sales Rep. .... Sara Sommer
Classified Adv. Mgr. .... Corliss Krueger
Editorial Department .... Trina Severson
Mechanical Specifications: Type page 10.38 x 21Equipment & Software: Hardware — Apple; Presses — 8-G/Community; w/4-4c; Software — Baseview/News Edit Pro, QPS/QuarkXPress., adobe cs
Delivery Method: Mail, Newsstand, Racks
Areas Served: 47586, 47520, 47551, 42514, 47525, 57574, 47576, 47588, 47515, 47550, 47531, 47536, 42348, 42351

TIPTON

LEADER-TRIBUNE REVIEW EAST (WED)

116 S Main St, Ste A, Tipton, IN, 46072-1864, Tipton, USA; gen tel (765) 675-2115; adv tel (765) 675-2115; ed tel (765) 675-2115; gen fax (765) 675-4147; adv fax (765) 675-4147; ed fax (765) 675-4147; disp adv e-mail tiptonads@elwoodpublishing.com; class adv e-mail tiptonads@elwoodpublishing.com; ed e-mail tiptoneditor@elwoodpublishing.com; web site www.elwoodpublishing.com
Circulation: 5,400pd, 5,298fr; Sworn/Estimate/Non-Audited
Advertising rate: Open inch rate $6.50; Special Call-Leader: Open inch rate $7.40
Group: Elwood Publishing Co., Inc.
Ray Barnes Newspapers, Inc.
Digital Platform - Mobile: Apple, Android
Digital Platform - Tablet: Apple iOS, Android
Pres. .... Jack Barnes
Pub. .... Robert Nash
Mng. Ed. .... Jackie Henry
Adv. Mgr. .... Scott Blaylock
Circ. Mgr. .... Tammy Boyer
Mechanical Specifications: Type page 13 x 21 1/2; E - 6 cols, 2 1/16, 1/8 between; A - 6 cols, 2 1/16, 1/8 between; C - 8 cols, 1 1/2, 1/8 between.
Delivery Method: Mail, Newsstand, Carrier, Racks
Areas Served: 46072,46076,46049,46036, 46049

LEADER-TRIBUNE REVIEW WEST (WED)

116 S Main St, Ste A, Tipton, IN, 46072-1864, Tipton, USA; gen tel (765) 675-2115; adv tel (765) 675-2115; ed tel (765) 675-2115; gen fax (765) 675-4147; adv fax (765) 675-4147; ed fax (765) 675-4147; disp adv e-mail tiptonads@elwoodpublishing.com; class adv e-mail tiptonads@elwoodpublishing.com; ed e-mail tiptoneditor@elwoodpublishing.com; web site www.elwoodpublishing.com
Circulation: 5,400pd, 5,298fr; Sworn/Estimate/Non-Audited
Advertising rate: Open inch rate $6.50; Special Call-Leader: Open inch rate $7.40
Group: Elwood Publishing Co., Inc.
Ray Barnes Newspapers, Inc.
Digital Platform - Mobile: Apple, Android
Digital Platform - Tablet: Apple iOS, Android
Pres. .... Jack Barnes
Pub. .... Robert Nash
Mng. Ed. .... Jackie Henry
Adv. Mgr. .... Scott Blaylock
Circ. Mgr. .... Tammy Boyer
Mechanical Specifications: Type page 13 x 21 1/2; E - 6 cols, 2 1/16, 1/8 between; A - 6 cols, 2 1/16, 1/8 between; C - 8 cols, 1 1/2, 1/8 between.
Delivery Method: Mail, Newsstand, Carrier, Racks
Areas Served: 46072,46076,46049,46036, 46049

VERSAILLES

OSGOOD JOURNAL (TUES)

115 S Washington St, Versailles, IN, 47042-8016, Ripley, USA; gen tel (812) 689-6364; adv fax (812) 689-6508; disp adv e-mail lchandler@ripleynews.com; class adv e-mail publication@ripleynews.com; ed e-mail publication@ripleynews.com; web site www.ripleynews.com
Circulation: 5,200pd, 48fr; Sworn/Estimate/Non-Audited
Advertising rate: Open inch rate $7.50
Established: 1865
Group: Ripley Publishing
Pub./Adv. Mgr. .... Linda Chandler
Officer Mgr. .... Cindy Roberts
Ed. .... Wanda Burnett
Mechanical Specifications: Type page 14 x 21; E - 6 cols, 2, 1/3 between; A - 6 cols, 2, 1/3 between; C - 8 cols, 1 1/2, 1/3 between. Equipment & Software: Hardware — APP/Mac; Presses — 4-KP; Software — Microsoft/Word, Adobe/PageMaker, Adobe/Illustrator 88.
Delivery Method: Mail
Areas Served: Osgood, Versailles, Milan, Sunman, Batesville,
Holton, Cross Plains, Friendship and Napoleon

VERSAILLES REPUBLICAN (THUR)

115 S Washington St, Versailles, IN, 47042-8016, Ripley, USA; gen tel (812) 689-6364; gen fax (812) 689-6508; disp adv e-mail publication@ripleynews.com; class adv e-mail publication@ripleynews.com; ed e-mail lchandler@ripleynews.com; web site www.ripleynews.com
Circulation: 5,200pd, 48fr; Sworn/Estimate/Non-Audited
Advertising rate: Open inch rate $7.00
Established: 1865
Group: Ripley Publishing
Pub. .... Linda Chandler
Office Mgr. .... Cindy Roberts
Ed. .... Mary Mattingly
Mechanical Specifications: Type page 14 x 21; E - 6 cols, 2, 1/3 between; A - 6 cols, 2, 1/3 between; C - 8 cols, 1 1/2, 1/3 between. Equipment & Software: Hardware — APP/Mac; Presses — 4-KP; Software — Microsoft/Word, Adobe/Illustrator 88, Adobe/PageMaker.
Delivery Method: Mail
Areas Served: Osgood, Versailles, Milan, Sunman, Batesville, Holton, Cross Plains, Friendship and Napoleon

VEVAY

THE SWITZERLAND DEMOCRAT (THUR)

111 W Market St, Vevay, IN, 47043-1159, Switzerland, USA; gen tel (812) 427-2311; adv fax (812) 427-2793; disp adv e-mail vevaynews@gmail.com; class adv e-mail vevaynews@gmail.com; ed e-mail vevaynews@gmail.com; web site www.vevaynewspapers.com
Circulation: 600pd,; Sworn/Estimate/Non-Audited
Advertising rate: Open inch rate $5.30
Established: 1839
Group: Vevay Newspapers, Inc.
Adv. Mgr. .... Eerin Williams
Circ. Mgr. .... Ginny Leap
Pub. .... Patrick Lanman
Mechanical Specifications: Type page 13 x 21 1/2; E - 6 cols, 2 1/16, 1/8 between; A - 6 cols, 2 1/16, 1/8 between; C - 8 cols, 1 1/2, 1/8 between.
Delivery Method: Mail, Newsstand, Racks

VEVAY REVEILLE-ENTERPRISE (THUR)

111 W Market St, Vevay, IN, 47043-1159, Switzerland, USA; gen tel (812) 427-2311; adv fax (812) 427-2793; disp adv e-mail news@vevaynewspapers.com; web site www.vevaynewspapers.com
Circulation: 3,000pd,; Sworn/Estimate/Non-Audited
Advertising rate: Open inch rate $5.30
Established: 1816
Group: Vevay Newspapers, Inc.
Ad. Director .... Erin Williams
Circ. Mgr. .... Ginny Leap
Pub .... Patrick Lanman
Mechanical Specifications: Type page 13 x 21 1/2; E - 6 cols, 2 1/16, 1/8 between; A - 6 cols, 2 1/16, 1/8 between; C - 8 cols, 1 1/2, 1/8 between.
Delivery Method: Mail, Newsstand, Racks

WABASH

THE NEWS-JOURNAL (WED)

606 N State Road 13, Wabash, IN, 46992-7735, Wabash, USA; gen tel (260) 982-6383; adv fax (260) 982-8233; disp adv e-mail mreese@thepaperofwabash.com; web site www.nmpaper.com
Circulation: 2,000pd,; Sworn/Estimate/Non-Audited
Advertising rate: Open inch rate $4.65
Established: 1865
Group: The Paper of Wabash Co. Inc.
Pub. .... Mike Rees
Office Mgr. .... Mike McLaughlin
Adv. Mgr. .... Carrie Vineyard
Ed. .... Eric Christiansen
Mechanical Specifications: Type page 10 3/8 x 15 1/2; E - 5 cols, 1 15/16, 1/8 between; A - 5 cols, 1 15/16, 1/8 between; C - 5 cols, 1 15/16, 1/8 between.Equipment & Software: Hardware — APP/Mac; Software — Adobe/PageMaker.
Delivery Method: Mail

WESTVILLE

THE REGIONAL NEWS (THUR)

PO Box 828, Westville, IN, 46391-0828, La Porte, USA; gen tel (219) 785-2234; adv fax (219) 785-2442; web site www.facebook.com/pg/TheRegionalNews46/about/?ref=page_internal
Circulation: 525pd, 50fr; Sworn/Estimate/Non-Audited
Advertising rate: Open inch rate $4.75
Established: 1922
Group: Paw Prints Publishing

Ed. .... Galen ArmstrongEquipment & Software: Hardware — APP/Macs; Software — QPS/QuarkXPress.

WINAMAC

THE PULASKI COUNTY JOURNAL (WED)

114 W Main St, Winamac, IN, 46996-1208, Pulaski, USA; gen tel (574) 946-6628; gen fax (574) 946-7471; adv fax (574) 946-7471; disp adv e-mail ads@pulaskijournal.com; class adv e-mail ads@pulaskijournal.com; ed e-mail news@pulaskijournal.com; web site www.pulaskijournal.com
Circulation: 3,000pd,; Sworn/Estimate/Non-Audited
Advertising rate: Open inch rate $6.00
Established: 1859
Group: Winamac Publishers, LLC
Pub./Exec. Ed. ....John Haley
Adv. Rep...Chris Ford
Creative Dir..............................Kari Beth Stout
Mechanical Specifications: Type page 10 1/4 x 15 3/4; E - 6 cols, 1 9/16, 1/8 between; A - 6 cols, 1 9/16, 1/8 between; C - 6 cols, 1/8 between.Equipment & Software: Hardware — APP/Mac; Presses — ABD/375; Software — Adobe/PageMaker 5.0.
Delivery Method: Mail, Newsstand
Areas Served: 46996, 46960, 47957, 46534, 46985, 46939, 47946, 46978

ZIONSVILLE

ZIONSVILLE TIMES SENTINEL (WED)

250 S Elm St, Zionsville, IN, 46077-1601, Boone, USA; gen tel (317) 873-6397; adv fax (317) 873-6259; disp adv e-mail rick.whiteman@timessentinel.com; class adv e-mail rick.whiteman@timessentinel.com; ed e-mail news@timessentinel.com; web site www.timessentinel.com
Circulation: 4,300pd,; Sworn/Estimate/Non-Audited
Advertising rate: Open inch rate $9.10
Established: 1860
Group: Community Newspaper Holdings, Inc.
Sales Mgr ....Rick Whiteman
Mechanical Specifications: Type page 12 1/2 x 21; E - 6 cols, 1 4/5, 1/8 between; A - 6 cols, 1 4/5, 1/8 between; C - 6 cols, 1 4/5, 1/8 between.Equipment & Software: Hardware — APP/Mac G3; Software — QPS/QuarkXPress, Adobe/PageMaker, Adobe/Photoshop, Macromedia/Freehand, Adobe/Illustrator, Adobe/Acrobat Exchange.
Delivery Method: Mail, Newsstand, Racks

IOWA

ACKLEY

ACKLEY WORLD JOURNAL (WED)

736 Main St, Ackley, IA, 50601-1538, Hardin, USA; gen tel (641) 847-2592; adv tel (641) 847-2592; ed tel (641) 847-2592; gen fax (641) 847-3010; adv fax (641) 847-3010; ed fax (641) 847-3010; disp adv e-mail ackleywj@iafalls.com; class adv e-mail circulation@iafalls.com; ed e-mail news@iafalls.com; web site www.ackleyworldjournal.com
Advertising rate: Open inch rate $11.00
Group: United Daily News Group
Digital Platform - Mobile: Apple, Android, Windows, Blackberry
Digital Platform - Tablet: Apple iOS, Android, Windows 7, Blackberry Tablet OS
Ed. ....Becky Schipper
Adv. Mgr................................Tony Baranowski
Delivery Method: Mail, Newsstand, Carrier
Areas Served: Ackley and Hardin

ADAIR

ADAIR NEWS (THUR)

403 Audubon St, Adair, IA, 50002-7708, Adair, USA; gen tel (641) 742-3241; adv tel (641) 742-3241; ed tel (641) 742-3241; gen fax (641) 742-3489; adv fax (641) 742-3489; ed fax (641) 742-3489; disp adv e-mail adairnews@iowatelecom.net; class adv e-mail adairnews@iowatelecom.net; ed e-mail adairnews@iowatelecom.net
Advertising rate: Open inch rate $5.50
Established: 1881
Pub./Ed. ....William Littler
Delivery Method: Mail, Newsstand
Areas Served: Adair County

AFTON

AFTON STAR-ENTERPRISE (THUR)

274 N Douglas St, Afton, IA, 50830-7723, Union, USA; gen tel (641) 347-8721; gen fax (641) 347-8721; disp adv e-mail aftonstar@iowatelecom.net; web site No Website
Circulation: 1,125pd, 25fr; Sworn/Estimate/Non-Audited
Advertising rate: Open inch rate $3.50
Pub..Wayne Hill
Mechanical Specifications: Type page 10-1/2 x 21; 6 col. 1/6 between;
Delivery Method: Mail, Racks

AKRON

AKRON HOMETOWNER (WED)

110 Reed St, Akron, IA, 51001-7739, Plymouth, USA; gen tel (712) 568-2208; gen fax (712) 568-2271; disp adv e-mail akronht@hickorytech.net; web site www.akronhometowner.com
Circulation: 1,400pd,; Sworn/Estimate/Non-Audited
Advertising rate: $8.50
Established: 2001
Group: The Akron Hometowner, Inc.
Ed. ....Julie Ann Madden
Advertising..Joe Hook
Mechanical Specifications: Tab size - 16" long by 10.25" wideEquipment & Software: ; Software — InDesign
Photoshop
Illustrator
Delivery Method: Mail, Racks
Areas Served: Akron, Plymouth County 51001, 51023, 51062, 57025,

ALBIA

ALBIA UNION-REPUBLICAN (THUR)

109 Benton Ave E, Albia, IA, 52531-2034, Monroe, USA; gen tel (641) 932-7121; gen fax (641) 932-2822; disp adv e-mail dave@albianews.com; web site www.albianews.com
Circulation: 3,500pd, 3,000fr; Sworn/Estimate/Non-Audited
Advertising rate: Open inch rate $9.20
Established: 1862
Group: Lancaster Management, Inc.
Adv. Mgr...................................Carol Ann Faber
Ed. ....David A. Paxton

MONROE COUNTY NEWS (TUES)

109 Benton Ave E, Albia, IA, 52531-2034, Monroe, USA; gen tel (641) 932-7121; gen fax (641) 932-2822; disp adv e-mail brian@albianews.com; web site www.albianews.com
Circulation: 2,850pd, 900fr; Sworn/Estimate/Non-Audited
Advertising rate: Open inch rate $9.20
Group: Lancaster Management, Inc.
Ed. ....David A. Paxton
Delivery Method: Mail, Newsstand, Carrier, Racks

ALGONA

ALGONA UPPER DES MOINES (THUR)

14 E Nebraska St, Algona, IA, 50511-2630, Kossuth, USA; gen tel (515) 295-3535; gen fax (515) 295-7217; disp adv e-mail ads@algona.com; class adv e-mail ads@algona.com; ed e-mail news@algona.com; web site www.algona.com
Circulation: 3,500pd,; Sworn/Estimate/Non-Audited
Advertising rate: Open inch rate $10.25
Established: 1866
Pub...David Shabaz
Mechanical Specifications: Type page 11 1/2 x 21 1/2; E - 6 cols, 1.812 between; A - 6 cols, 1.812, between; C - 6 cols, 1.812, between.
Delivery Method: Mail, Newsstand, Racks

ALLISON

BUTLER COUNTY TRIBUNE JOURNAL (THUR)

422 N Main St, Allison, IA, 50602-7710, Butler, USA; gen tel (319) 267-2731 ; gen fax (319) 267-2731; disp adv e-mail tribunejournal@netins.net; web site www.butlercountytribune.com
Circulation: 1,600pd,; Sworn/Estimate/Non-Audited
Advertising rate: Open inch rate $6.15
Ed. ....Brad Hicks
Areas Served: 50602

AMES

NEVADA JOURNAL (THUR)

317 5th St, Ames, IA, 50010-6101, Story, USA; gen tel (515) 382-2161; gen fax (515) 382-4299; disp adv e-mail results@nevadaiowajournal.com; web site www.nevadaiowajournal.com
Advertising rate: Open inch rate $7.00
Multi. Sales exec..................Jayme Ollendieck

THE STORY CITY HERALD (WED)

PO Box 380, Ames, IA, 50010-0380, Story, USA; gen tel (515) 733-4318; gen fax (515) 733-4319; disp adv e-mail scherald@storycity.com; web site www.storycityherald.com
Circulation: 1,963pd,; Sworn/Estimate/Non-Audited
Advertising rate: Open inch rate $7.00
Established: 1881
Group: Ames Tribune
Ed. ....Todd Thorson
Adv. Dir..John Greving
Mechanical Specifications: Type page 11 3/4 x 21 1/2; E - 6 cols, 1 7/8, 3/8 between; A - 6 cols, 1 7/8, 3/8 between; C - 6 cols, 1 7/8, 3/8 between.
Delivery Method: Mail

THE TRI-COUNTY TIMES (THUR)

317 5th St, Ste B, Ames, IA, 50010-6101, Story, USA; gen tel (515) 232-2160; gen fax (515) 382-4299; disp adv e-mail results@tricountytimes.com; web site www.tricountytimes.com
Circulation: 2,500pd,; Sworn/Estimate/Non-Audited
Advertising rate: Open inch rate $7.00
Group: Iowa Newspapers, Inc.
Gen. Mgr...................................Marlys Barker
Adv. Mgr.......................................John Greving
Multi. Sales Exec..................Jayme Ollendieck

ANAMOSA

ANAMOSA PUBLICATIONS (THUR)

PO Box 108, P.O. Box 108, Anamosa, IA, 52205-0108, Jones, USA; gen tel (319) 462-3511; adv tel (319) 462-3511; ed tel (319) 462-3511; gen fax (319) 462-4540; adv fax (319) 462-4540; ed fax (319) 462-3511; disp adv e-mail admin@journal-eureka.com; class adv e-mail admin@journal-eureka.com; ed e-mail News@journal-eureka.com; web site www.Journal-Eureka.com
Circulation: 2,500pd, 11,223fr; Sworn/Estimate/Non-Audited
Advertising rate: Open inch rate $11.70
Established: 1856
Group: Anamosa Publications
Pub ....W. James Johnson
Mechanical Specifications: Six-column tabloid 10 x 21 inches
Delivery Method: Mail, Newsstand
Areas Served: 52205, 52212, 52214, 52252, 52305, 52306, 52310, 52312, 52320, 52321, 52323, 52219, 52336, 52362

ANITA

ANITA TRIBUNE (THUR)

850 Main, Anita, IA, 50020, Cass, USA; gen tel (712) 762-4188; gen fax (712) 762-4189; disp adv e-mail gandrews@midlands.net; web site https://www.facebook.com/pages/The-Anita-Tribune/232703986773881
Circulation: 1,100pd,; Sworn/Estimate/Non-Audited
Advertising rate: Open inchr ate $6.50
Established: 1883
Digital Platform - Mobile: Android
Pub./Gen. Mgr./Adv. Mgr. .... Gene Andrews
Ed. ....Dana Larsen
Prod. Mgr. ....Deanna Andrews
Mechanical Specifications: 6 columns x 21 1/2 broadsheet
Delivery Method: Mail, Newsstand, Racks
Areas Served: 50020, 50843, 50853, 50274, 50022

ANTHON

ANTHON SIOUX VALLEY NEWS (WED)

PO Box 299, Anthon, IA, 51004-0299, Woodbury, USA; gen tel (712) 373-5571; gen fax (712) 373-5389; disp adv e-mail siouxvalleynews@ruralwaves.us
Advertising rate: Local pci $5.10

ARMSTRONG

ARMSTRONG JOURNAL (WED)

529 6th St, Armstrong, IA, 50514-7711, Emmet, USA; gen tel (712) 868-3460; adv tel (712) 868-3460; ed tel (712) 868-3460; gen fax (712) 864-3028; adv fax (712) 868-3460; ed fax (712) 868-3460; disp adv e-mail ads@armstrongjournal.com; class adv e-mail clint@armstrongjournal.com; ed e-mail clint@armstrongjournal.com; web site statelinepubs.com
Circulation: 850pd,; Sworn/Estimate/Non-Audited
Advertising rate: Open inch rate $6.87
Group: Stateline Publications
Publisher..............................Kristin Grabinoski
Editor ....Dorothy Cronk
Office Manager..........................Clinton Davis
Delivery Method: Mail, Racks
Areas Served: Emmet, Kossuth, Palo Alto counties

RINGSTED DISPATCH (WED)

520 6th St, Armstrong, IA, 50514-7711, Emmet, USA; gen tel (712) 868-3460; adv tel (712) 868-3460; ed tel (712) 868-3460; gen fax (712) 868-3028; adv fax (712) 868-3460; ed fax (712) 868-3460; disp adv e-mail ads@armstrongjournal.com; class adv e-mail clint@armstrongjournal.com; ed e-mail clint@armstrongjournal.com; web site statelinepubs.com
Circulation: 400pd,; Sworn/Estimate/Non-Audited
Advertising rate: Open inch rate $6.87
Group: Stateline Publications
Publisher.................................. Kris Grabinoski
Office Manager..........................Clinton Davis

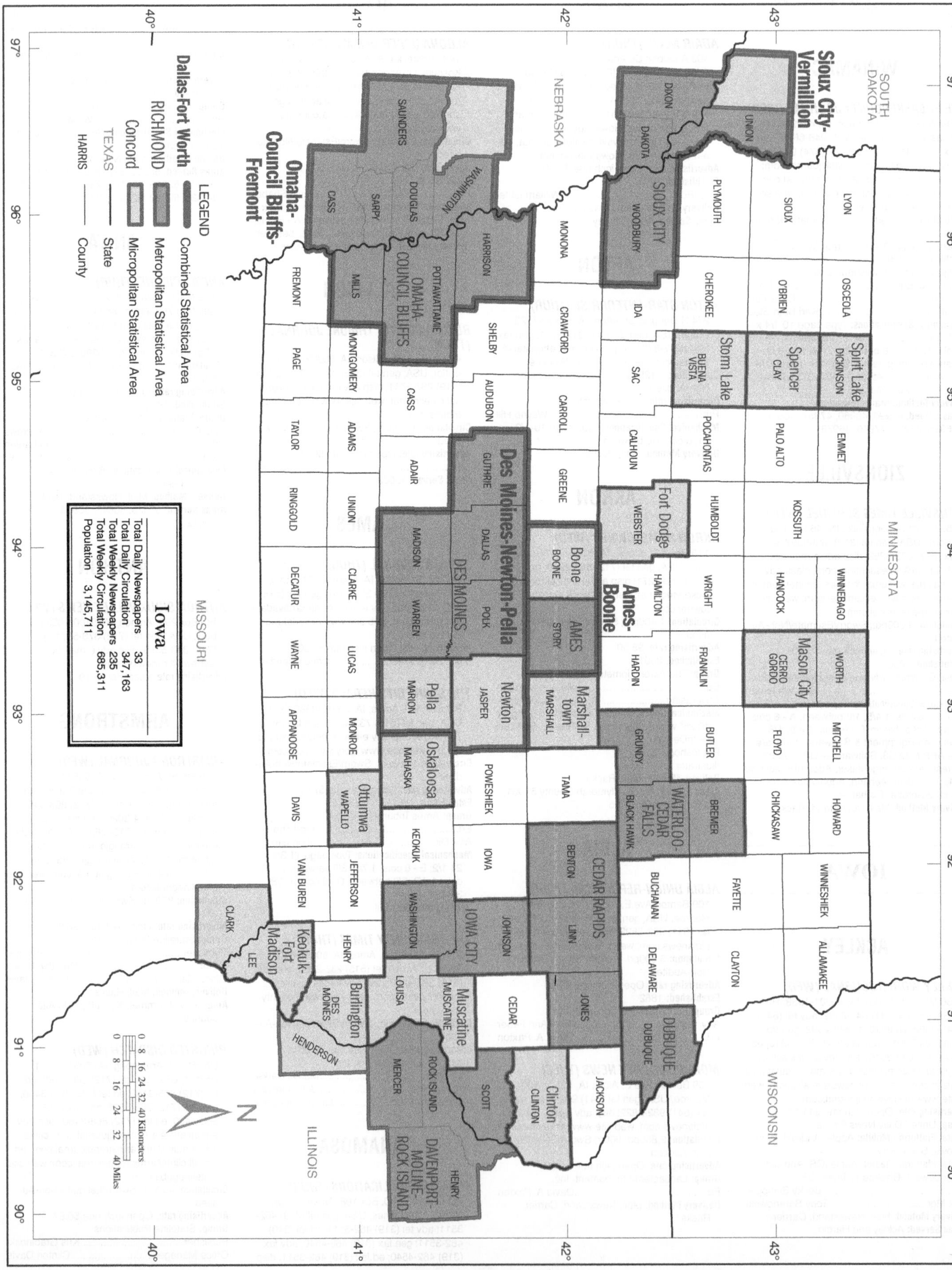
Iowa
Total Daily Newspapers 33
Total Daily Circulation 347,163
Total Weekly Newspapers 235
Total Weekly Circulation 685,311
Population 3,145,711
LEGEND
Dallas-Fort Worth Combined Statistical Area
RICHMOND Metropolitan Statistical Area
Concord Micropolitan Statistical Area
TEXAS State
HARRIS County
Sioux City-Vermillion
Omaha-Council Bluffs-Fremont
Des Moines-Newton-Pella
Ames-Boone
DES MOINES
OMAHA-COUNCIL BLUFFS
SIOUX CITY
WATERLOO-CEDAR FALLS
CEDAR RAPIDS
IOWA CITY
DUBUQUE
DAVENPORT-MOLINE-ROCK ISLAND
Spirit Lake
Spencer
Storm Lake
Fort Dodge
Boone
AMES
Mason City
Marshalltown
Newton
Pella
Oskaloosa
Ottumwa
Muscatine
Burlington
Keokuk-Fort Madison
Clinton
SOUTH DAKOTA
MINNESOTA
WISCONSIN
ILLINOIS
MISSOURI
NEBRASKA

Delivery Method: Mail, Racks
Areas Served: Emmet, Kossuth, Palo Alto counties

AUDUBON

AUDUBON COUNTY ADVOCATE JOURNAL (FRI)

517 Leroy St, Audubon, IA, 50025-1206, Audubon, USA; gen tel (712) 563-2741; ed tel (712) 563-2741; gen fax (712) 563-2740; ed fax (712) 563-2740; disp adv e-mail jeannem@auduboncountynews.com; class adv e-mail dianab@auduboncountynews.com; ed e-mail news@auduboncountynews.com; web site www.auduboncountynews.com
Circulation: 2,100pd, 7,000fr; Sworn/Estimate/Non-Audited
Advertising rate: Open inch rate $7.05
Established: 1879
Group: Community Media Group
Composition....................................Diana Ballou
News Reporter....... Jill ChristensenEquipment & Software: ; Software — Adobe/Pagemaker 7.0.
Delivery Method: Mail, Newsstand, Racks
Areas Served: Audubon 50025; Exira 50076

AURELIA

AURELIA STAR (WED)

PO Box 248, Aurelia, IA, 51005-0248, Cherokee, USA; gen tel (712) 229-5492; disp adv e-mail aurstar@gmail.com; web site aureliastar.webs.com
Circulation: 380pd, 20fr
Advertising rate: $4.75
Owner/Ed.Marci BrownEquipment & Software: ; Software — Quark Express 9
Delivery Method: Mail, Racks
Areas Served: Aurelia, IA 51005
Alta, IA 51002
Cherokee, IA 51012

AVOCA

THE AVOCA JOURNAL-HERALD (THUR)

164 S Elm St, Avoca, IA, 51521-4003, Pottawattamie, USA; gen tel (712) 343-2154; gen fax (712) 343-2262; disp adv e-mail avocajh@iowatelecom.net; web site No Website
Circulation: 1,600pd,; Sworn/Estimate/Non-Audited
Advertising rate: Open inch rate $4.00
Pub..Donald L. Nielson
Ed. .... Rich PriceEquipment & Software: Hardware — APP/Mac; Presses — ABD/360; Software — Adobe/PageMaker, Microsoft.
Delivery Method: Mail, Newsstand, Racks

BANCROFT

THE BANCROFT REGISTER (WED)

101 N Portland St, Bancroft, IA, 50517-8012, Kossuth, USA; gen tel (515) 885-2531; adv tel (712) 868-3460; ed tel (712) 868-3460; gen fax (515) 885-2771; adv fax (712) 868-3460; ed fax (712) 868-3460; disp adv e-mail krisg@armstrongjournal.com; class adv e-mail clint@armstrongjournal.com; ed e-mail bancroftregister@yahoo.com; web site statelinepubs.com
Circulation: 800pd,; Sworn/Estimate/Non-Audited
Advertising rate: Open inch rate $6.87
Group: Stateline Publications
Publisher...............................Kristin Grabinoski
Editor ....Kim Meyer
Delivery Method: Mail, Racks
Areas Served: Kossuth, Emmet, Palo Alto counties

BEDFORD

THE BEDFORD TIMES-PRESS (WED)

404 Main St, Bedford, IA, 50833-1357, Taylor, USA; gen tel (712) 523-2525; disp adv e-mail btimespress@gmail.com; web site www.bedfordtimespress.com
Circulation: 1,700pd,; Sworn/Estimate/Non-Audited
Advertising rate: Open inch rate $5.00
Digital Platform - Mobile: Apple, Android
Digital Platform - Tablet: Apple iOS, Android
Pub... Colleen Larimer
Delivery Method: Mail, Newsstand, Racks

BELLE PLAINE

STAR PRESS UNION (WED)

832 12th St, Belle Plaine, IA, 52208-1761, Benton, USA; gen tel (319) 444-2520; gen fax (319) 444-2522; disp adv e-mail bpunions@netins.net; web site yourweeklypaper.com
Circulation: 1,348pd,; Sworn/Estimate/Non-Audited
Advertising rate: Open inch rate $8.00
Group: Gannett
Pub...Jim Magdefrau
Mechanical Specifications: Type page 10 1/4 x 14; E - 9 cols, 1 1/2, 1/6 between; A - 9 cols, 1 1/2, 1/6 between; C - 9 cols, 1 1/2, 1/6 between.Equipment & Software: Hardware — APP/Mac; Presses — 8-KP; Software — Adobe/InDesign 2.0, Adobe/Acrobat 5.0.
Delivery Method: Mail, Newsstand, Racks

BELLEVUE

BELLEVUE HERALD-LEADER (THUR)

118 S 2nd St, Bellevue, IA, 52031-1318, Jackson, USA; gen tel (563) 872-4159; gen fax (563) 872-4298; disp adv e-mail bhleader@bellevueheraldleader.com; web site www.bellevueheraldleader.com
Circulation: 2,770pd, 12fr; Sworn/Estimate/Non-Audited
Advertising rate: Open inch rate $7.05
Established: 1871
Circ. Mgr..Judy Reed
Ed. .... David Namanny
Mechanical Specifications: Type page 10 1/2 x 16; E - 4 cols, between; A - 6 cols, 1 5/8, between; C - 6 cols, 1 5/8, between.
Delivery Method: Mail, Newsstand, Racks

BELMOND

THE BELMOND INDEPENDENT (THUR)

215 E Main St, Belmond, IA, 50421-1122, Wright, USA; gen tel (641) 444-3333; gen fax (641) 444-7777; disp adv e-mail belmondnews@frontiernet.net; web site www.belmondnews.com
Circulation: 1,500pd, 5fr; Sworn/Estimate/Non-Audited
Advertising rate: Open inch rate $7.00
Established: 1885
Dirk J. Vanderlinden
Lee H. VanderlindenPub.s
Mechanical Specifications: Type page 13 wide x 21 tall; 6 columns, 12 picas per col. with one pica gutter.Equipment & Software: Hardware — APP/Mac; Software — QPS/QuarkXPress 8.1
Delivery Method: Mail, Newsstand
Areas Served: 50421, 50420, 50439, 50449, 50470, 50071, 50457, 50447, 50525

BLOOMFIELD

BLOOMFIELD DEMOCRAT (WED)

207 S Madison St, Bloomfield, IA, 52537-1622, Davis, USA; gen tel (641) 664-2334; gen fax (641) 664-2316; disp adv e-mail ads@bdemo.com; class adv e-mail ads@bdemo.com; ed e-mail bdemo@netins.net; web site www.bdemo.com - 26,000(views) 19,000(visitors)
Circulation: 1,661pd,; Sworn/Estimate/Non-Audited
Advertising rate: $9.50
Established: 1869Editions: (1)
Digital Platform - Mobile: Apple
Digital Platform - Tablet: Apple iOS
Pub ....Karen Spurgeon
Mechanical Specifications: PDF or similar
Delivery Method: Mail
Areas Served: Bloomfield
Davis County

BOONE

BOONE NEWS-REPUBLICAN (TUES, THUR, SAT)

2136 Mamie Eisenhower Ave, Boone, IA, 50036-4437, Boone, USA; gen tel (515) 432-6694; gen fax (515) 432-7811; ed e-mail wsager@newsrepublican.com; web site www.newsrepublican.com 31,173(visitors)
Circulation: 1,399pd, 0fr; VAC
Established: 1888
Digital Platform - Mobile: Apple, Android
Digital Platform - Tablet: Apple iOS, Android
Circ. Mgr.................................. Sandi Hilsabeck
Ed. .... Jason Brooks
Sales Mgr..Mary Scott
Mechanical Specifications: Type page 13 x 21 1/2; E - 6 cols, 2 1/16, 1/8 between; A - 6 cols, 2 1/16, 1/8 between; C - 9 cols, 1 1/3, 1/8 between.
Delivery Method: Mail, Newsstand, Carrier, Racks

BUFFALO CENTER

BUFFALO CENTER TRIBUNE (TUES)

124 N Main St, Buffalo Center, IA, 50424-7752, Winnebago, USA; gen tel (641) 562-2606; gen fax (641) 562-2636; disp adv e-mail bctrib@wctatel.net; web site www.buffalocentertribune.com - 2,000(views) 700(visitors)
Circulation: 1,595pd,; Sworn/Estimate/Non-Audited
Advertising rate: Open inch rate $4.75
Pub...Lanita Kardoes
Delivery Method: Mail, Newsstand, Racks

CALMAR

CALMAR COURIER (TUES)

PO Box 507, Calmar, IA, 52132-0507, Winneshiek, USA; gen tel (563) 562-3488; gen fax (563) 562-3486; disp adv e-mail calmarcourier@hotmail.com; web site www.calmarcourier.com
Circulation: 1,800pd,; Sworn/Estimate/Non-Audited
Advertising rate: Open inch rate $6.00
Established: 2005
Pub... Tina Hageman
Delivery Method: Mail

CARLISLE

THE CARLISLE CITIZEN (THUR)

210 S 1st St, Carlisle, IA, 50047-7601, Warren, USA; gen tel (515) 989-0525; gen fax (515) 989-0743; disp adv e-mail news@carlislecitizen.com; class adv e-mail news@carlislecitizen.com; ed e-mail news@carlislecitizen.com; web site No Website
Circulation: 1,600pd,; Sworn/Estimate/Non-Audited
Advertising rate: Open inch rate $4.25
Established: 1926
Pub...Steven Klein
Ed. .... Sara Davis
Delivery Method: Mail, Racks

CASCADE

CASCADE PIONEER (WED)

PO Box 9, Cascade, IA, 52033-0009, Dubuque, USA; gen tel (563) 852-3217; adv tel (563) 852-3217; ed tel (563) 852-3217; gen fax (563) 852-7188; disp adv e-mail cascadesales@wcinet.com; class adv e-mail cascadesales@wcinet.com; ed e-mail cascadeeditor@wcinet.com; web site www.cpioneer.com
Circulation: 1,875pd,; Sworn/Estimate/Non-Audited
Advertising rate: Open per col. inch rate $9.00
Established: 1876
Group: Woodward Communications, Inc.
Digital Platform - Mobile: Apple, Android
Digital Platform - Tablet: Apple iOS, Android
Publisher.........................Mary Ungs-Sogaard
Reporter/Photo.......................Theresa Collins
Delivery Method: Mail, Newsstand
Areas Served: 52033, 52032 , 52046, 52068, 52045

CENTRAL CITY

LINN NEWS-LETTER (TUES)

38 4th St N, Central City, IA, 52214-7700, Linn, USA; gen tel (319) 438-1313; adv tel (319) 438-1313; ed tel (319) 438-1313; gen fax (319) 438-1838; adv fax (319) 438-1838; ed fax (319) 438-1838; disp adv e-mail linnnewsletter@iowatelecom.net; class adv e-mail linnnewsletter@iowatelecom.net; ed e-mail linnnewsletter@iowatelecom.net; web site www.linncolettershoppr.com
Advertising rate: Open inch rate $4.50
Established: 1888
Ed. ....Rae Ann Holub
Delivery Method: Mail, Newsstand
Areas Served: Linn County

CHARITON

CHARITON HERALD-PATRIOT (THUR)

815 Braden Ave, Chariton, IA, 50049-1742, Lucas, USA; gen tel (641) 774-2137; gen fax (641) 774-2139; disp adv e-mail charnews@charitonleader.com; web site www.charitonleader.com
Circulation: 3,100pd, 19fr; Sworn/Estimate/Non-Audited
Advertising rate: Open inch rate $8.25
Established: 1857
Group: Lancaster Management, Inc.
Pub...David A. Paxton
Adv. Mgr.......................................Susan Smith
Delivery Method: Mail, Newsstand, Carrier

THE CHARITON LEADER (TUES, THUR)

815 Braden Ave, Chariton, IA, 50049-1742, Lucas, USA; gen tel (641) 774-2137; gen fax (641) 774-2139; disp adv e-mail charnews@charitonleader.com; web site www.charitonleader.com
Circulation: 2,500pd,; Sworn/Estimate/Non-Audited
Advertising rate: Open inch rate $8.25
Group: Lancaster Management, Inc.
Sales Rep. ....Susan Smith
Pub...David A. Paxton
Delivery Method: Newsstand, Carrier, Racks

CHEROKEE

CHEROKEE CHRONICLE TIMES (MON, WED, FRI)

111 S 2nd St, Cherokee, IA, 51012-1839, Cherokee, USA; gen tel (712) 225-5111; adv tel (712) 225-5111; ed tel (712) 225-5111; gen fax (712) 225-2910; adv fax (712) 225-2910; ed fax (712) 225-2910; disp adv e-mail ads@ctimes.biz; class adv e-mail troyv@ctimes.biz; ed e-mail pauls@ctimes.biz; web site www.chronicletimes.com - 85,000(views)

15,000(visitors)
Circulation: 2,389pd,; Sworn/Estimate/Non-Audited
Advertising rate: Open inch rate $11.75
Established: 1870
Group: Rust Communications
Digital Platform - Mobile: Apple, Android
Digital Platform - Tablet: Apple iOS, Android
Assc. Pub. & Ed. In Chief................Paul Struck
Assc. Pub./Adv. Mgr. ....Troy Valentine
Ad. ....Rhonda Fassler
Ad. ....Chris Reed
Circ. ....Diana Otto
Staff Writer...................................Ken Ross
Staff Writer...................................Dan Whitney
Mechanical Specifications: Type page 13 x 21 1/2; E - 6 cols, 2 1/16, 1/8 between; A - 6 cols, 2 1/16, 1/8 between; C - 6 cols, 2 1/16, 1/8 between.
Delivery Method: Mail, Carrier

CLARINDA

THE CLARINDA HERALD-JOURNAL (THUR)

114 W Main St, Ste B, Clarinda, IA, 51632-2127, Page, USA; gen tel (712) 542-2181; gen fax (712) 542-5424; disp adv e-mail news@clarindaherald.com; class adv e-mail ads@clarindaherald.com; web site www.clarindaherald.com
Circulation: 2,250pd, 75fr; Sworn/Estimate/Non-Audited
Advertising rate: Open inch rate $8.95
Established: 1859
Group: BH Media Group
Circ. Mgr...................................Marilyn Jones
Ed. ....Kent Dinnebier
publisher...................................John Van Nostrand
graphic design ....Laurie Urich
Delivery Method: Mail, Newsstand, Racks
Areas Served: 51632

CLARION

CLARION WRIGHT COUNTY MONITOR (THUR)

107 2nd Ave NE, Clarion, IA, 50525-1430, Wright, USA; gen tel (515) 532-2871; gen fax (515) 532-2872; disp adv e-mail cmonitor@mchsi.com; web site www.clarionnewsonline.com
Advertising rate: Open inch rate $6.10

CLARKSVILLE

THE CLARKSVILLE STAR (THUR)

422 N Main St, Clarksville, IA, 50619, Butler, USA; gen tel (319) 278-4641; gen fax (319) 278-4641; disp adv e-mail clarksvillestar@butler-bremer.com; web site www.theclarksvillestar.com
Circulation: 1,058pd, 31fr; Sworn/Estimate/Non-Audited
Advertising rate: Open inch rate $4.75
Established: 1865
Ed. ....Pat Racette
Delivery Method: Mail, Newsstand, Racks

CLEAR LAKE

CLEAR LAKE MIRROR REPORTER (WED)

12 N 4th St, Clear Lake, IA, 50428-1815, Cerro Gordo, USA; gen tel (641) 357-2131; gen fax (641) 357-2133; disp adv e-mail office@clreporter.com; web site www.clreporter.com
Circulation: 2,500pd, 45fr; Sworn/Estimate/Non-Audited
Advertising rate: Open inch rate $8.35
Established: 1869
Pub...................................Michael J. Finnegan
Ed. ....Marianne Morf
Mechanical Specifications: Type page 14 x 21; E - 6 cols, 2 1/4, 1/18 between; A - 6 cols, 2 1/4, 1/18 between; C - 6 cols, 2 1/4, 1/18 between.Equipment & Software: Hardware — APP/Mac; Software — Adobe/PageMaker, Adobe/Photoshop, Claris/FileMaker, Adobe/Typestyler.
Delivery Method: Mail
Areas Served: 50428, 50482

COLFAX

JASPER COUNTY TRIBUNE (THUR)

1 W Howard St, Colfax, IA, 50054-1213, Jasper, USA; gen tel (515) 674-3591 ; adv tel (515) 674-3591 ; ed tel (515) 674-3591 ; gen fax (515) 674-3591 ; adv fax (515) 674-3591 ; ed fax (515) 674-3591 ; disp adv e-mail ads@jaspercountytribune.com; class adv e-mail ads@jaspercountytribune.com; ed e-mail news@jaspercountytribune.com; web site Jasper County Tribune
Circulation: 860pd, 0fr; Sworn/Estimate/Non-Audited
Advertising rate: Open inch rate $5.65
Established: 1895
Group: Shaw Media
Editor...................................Mike Mendenhall
Reporter ....Alex Olp
Delivery Method: Mail, Newsstand
Areas Served: Jasper County

COLUMBUS JUNCTION

COLUMBUS GAZETTE (WED)

209 Main St, Columbus Junction, IA, 52738-1136, Louisa, USA; gen tel (319) 728-2413; gen fax (319) 728-3272; disp adv e-mail cjgaz@windstream.net; web site www.thecolumbusgazette.com
Circulation: 1,370pd,; Sworn/Estimate/Non-Audited
Advertising rate: Open inch rate $5.50
Established: 1886
Pub...................................Donna Carpenter
Circ. Mgr...................................Carmen Lawrence
Ed. ....John M. Carpenter
Sports Ed...................................Tammy K. Virzi
Prodn. Mgr. ....Katie Martin
Mechanical Specifications: Type page 13 x 21 1/2; E - 6 cols, 2, 1/3 between; A - 6 cols, 2, 1/3 between; C - 8 cols, 1 1/2, 1/3 between. Equipment & Software: Hardware — APP/Mac; Software — Microsoft/Word 5.0, Aldus/PageMaker 5.0, QPS/QuarkXPress.
Delivery Method: Mail, Newsstand, Racks

COON RAPIDS

COON RAPIDS ENTERPRISE (THUR)

504 Main St, Coon Rapids, IA, 50058-1612, Carroll, USA; gen tel (712) 999-6397; gen fax (712) 999-2821; disp adv e-mail coonrapidsenterprise@crmu.net; web site www.coonrapidsenterprise.com
Circulation: 1,700pd,; Sworn/Estimate/Non-Audited
Advertising rate: Open inch rate $4.00
Established: 1881
Editor ....Charles Nixon
Delivery Method: Mail, Newsstand, Racks
Areas Served: All

CORNING

ADAMS COUNTY FREE PRESS (THUR)

618 Davis Ave, Corning, IA, 50841-1623, Adams, USA; gen tel (641)322-3161; adv tel (641) 322-4126; ed tel (641) 322-4126; gen fax (641) 322-3461; disp adv e-mail advertising@acfreepress.com; class adv e-mail advertising@acfreepress.com; ed e-mail editor@acfreepress.com; web site www.acfreepress.com
Circulation: 2,000pd,; Sworn/Estimate/Non-Audited
Advertising rate: Open inch rate $5.05
Established: 1882
Publisher...................................Don Groves
Mechanical Specifications: Type page 13 x 21 1/2; E - 6 cols, 2 1/8, 1/6 between; A - 6 cols, 2 1/8, 1/6 between; C - 6 cols, 2 1/8, 1/6 between.Equipment & Software: Hardware — APP/Mac; Software — Microsoft/Word, Claris/FileMaker Pro, Abbott Systems/Ready, Set, Go, Adobe/Photoshop.
Delivery Method: Mail
Areas Served: Adams County

CORYDON

CORYDON TIMES REPUBLICAN (TUES)

PO Box 258, 204 S. Franklin St., Corydon, IA, 50060-0258, Wayne, USA; gen tel (641) 872-1234; disp adv e-mail rbennett@corydontimes.com; class adv e-mail rbennett@corydontimes.com; ed e-mail rbennett@corydontimes.com; web site www.corydontimes.com
Circulation: 2,000pd,; Sworn/Estimate/Non-Audited
Advertising rate: Open inch rate $8.00
Established: 1865
Pub ....Rhonda BennettEquipment & Software: ; Software — Adobe/PageMaker, Microsoft/Word.
Delivery Method: Mail, Newsstand
Areas Served: 50060, 50008, 50123, 52544, 52590, 50047

THE HUMESTON NEWS ERA (TUES)

204 S Franklin St, Corydon, IA, 50060-1520, Wayne, USA; gen tel (641) 872-1234; disp adv e-mail rbennett@corydontimes.com; class adv e-mail rbennett@corydontimes.com; ed e-mail rbennett@corydontimes.com; web site www.corydontimes.com/
Circulation: 500pd,; Sworn/Estimate/Non-Audited
Advertising rate: Open inch rate $4.00
Group: Lancaster Management, Inc.
Digital Platform - Mobile: Apple
Pub ....Rhonda Bennett
Mechanical Specifications: Type page 10 3/16 x 12 3/16; A - 5 cols, 1 13/16, 3/16 between; C - 1 cols, 1 13/16, 3/16 between.Equipment & Software: Hardware — 6-APP/Mac; Software — Microsoft/Word.
Delivery Method: Mail, Newsstand, Racks
Areas Served: 50123, 50060, 50147, 50049, 50008

CRESCO

CRESCO TIMES-PLAIN DEALER (WED)

214 N Elm St, Cresco, IA, 52136-1522, Howard, USA; gen tel (563) 547-3601; gen fax (553) 547-4602; disp adv e-mail ads1@crescotimes.com; class adv e-mail ads1@crescotimes.com; ed e-mail tpdeditor@crescotimes.com; web site www.crescotimes.com
Circulation: 2,500pd, 6,000fr; Sworn/Estimate/Non-Audited
Advertising rate: $8.60
Established: 1855
Group: Evans Printing & Publishing, Inc.Editions: (147) 52 times a year
Sports EditorNate TroyEquipment & Software: ; Software — Quark, Photoshop,
Delivery Method: Mail, Newsstand
Areas Served: 52136, 52155, 50628, 52163, 50466, 52155, 52136, 50628

DAVENPORT

BETTENDORF NEWS (THUR)

500 E 3rd St, Davenport, IA, 52801-1708, Scott, USA; gen tel (563) 383-2200; ed tel (563) 383-2396; gen fax (563) 383-2370; ed fax (563) 383-2370; disp adv e-mail bettnews@qctimes.com; ed e-mail newsroom@qctimes.com; web site www.qctimes.com/bettnews
Circulation: 9,700pd, 2,453fr; Sworn/Estimate/Non-Audited
Advertising rate: 1/4 Pg $283.50; 1/2 Pg $567.00; Full Pg $1134.00
Established: 1927
Group: Lee Enterprises, Inc.
Digital Platform - Mobile: Apple, Android, Windows, Blackberry
Digital Platform - Tablet: Apple iOS, Android, Windows 7, Blackberry Tablet OS, Kindle Fire
Pub...................................Greg Veon
Adv. Mgr. ....Ann Boyd
Event Mgr...................................Glenda Verdick
Ed. ....Janet Hill
Classified Adv. Dir...................................Brett Riley
Delivery Method: Mail, Newsstand, Carrier, Racks
Areas Served: 52722, 52753, 52767

DAYTON

DAYTON REVIEW (WED)

25 S Main St, Dayton, IA, 50530-7698, Webster, USA; gen tel (515) 547-2811; gen fax (515) 547-2337; disp adv e-mail daytonreview@lvcta.com
Circulation: 1,100pd, 20fr; Sworn/Estimate/Non-Audited
Advertising rate: Open inch rate $7.00
Established: 1877
Pub...................................Glenn Schreiber
Mechanical Specifications: Type page 9 3/4 x 16; E - 3 cols, 3, 1/3 between; A - 6 cols, 1 7/12, 1/16 between; C - 6 cols, 1 7/12, 1/16 between.Equipment & Software: Hardware — APP/Mac Classic; Software — Adobe Indesign, Photoshop/Open Office
Delivery Method: Mail, Newsstand, Racks

DE WITT

THE OBSERVER (WED, SAT)

512 7th St, De Witt, IA, 52742-1610, Clinton, USA; gen tel (563) 659-3121; gen fax (563) 659-3778; disp adv e-mail obsgm@iowatelecom.net; class adv e-mail obsgm@iowatelecom.net; ed e-mail observer@iowatelecom.net; web site www.dewittobserver.com
Circulation: 4,174pd,; Sworn/Estimate/Non-Audited
Advertising rate: Open inch rate $13.25
Established: 1865
Adv. Mgr. ....Jean Bormann
Gen. Mgr. ....Mary Rueter
Prodn. Mgr. ....Rhonda Richards
News editor...................................Linda Watson
Mechanical Specifications: Type page 10 1/2 x 16; E - 4 cols, 2 1/2, 1/6 between; A - 4 cols, 2 1/2, 1/6 between; C - 6 cols, 1 5/8, 1/6 between.Equipment & Software: Hardware — APP/Mac; Presses — G/Community; Software — Microsoft/Word, QPS/QuarkXPress, Multi-Ad/Creator.
Delivery Method: Mail
Areas Served: 52742, 52751, 52729, 52774, 52757,52731, 52750, 52777

DECORAH

DECORAH PUBLIC OPINION (TUES, THUR)

107 E Water St, Decorah, IA, 52101-1801, Winneshiek, USA; gen tel (563) 382-4221; gen fax (563) 382-5949; disp adv e-mail news@decorahnewspapers.com; class adv e-mail ude@decorahnewspapers.com; ed e-mail fromm@decorahnewspapers.com; web site www.decorahnewspapers.com
Circulation: 5,200pd, 80fr; Sworn/Estimate/Non-Audited
Advertising rate: Open inch rate $7.25
Established: 1898
Adv. Mgr...................................Julie Ude
Ed. ....Richard M. Fromm
Production manager...................................Stephanie Langreck
Bookkeeper ....Amy Usgaard
Mechanical Specifications: Type page 13 1/2 x 23; E - 6 cols, 2, 1/6 between.Equipment & Software: Hardware — APP/Mac G3s; Soft-

ware — Microsoft/Word, Multi-Ad/Creator, QPS/QuarkXPress.
Delivery Method: Mail

THE DECORAH JOURNAL (THUR)

107 E Water St, Decorah, IA, 52101-1801, Winneshiek, USA; gen tel (563) 382-4221; gen fax (563) 382-5949; disp adv e-mail fromm@decorahnewspapers.com; web site www.decorahnewspapers.com
Circulation: 5,185pd, 16,000fr; Sworn/Estimate/Non-Audited
Advertising rate: Open inch rate $7.25
Established: 1895
Circ. Mgr. .... Joanne Stevenson
Mng. Ed. .... Richard M. Fromm
Prodn. Mgr. .... Destiny Langreck
Mechanical Specifications: Type page 13 1/2 x 23; E - 6 cols, 2, 1/6 between; A - 6 cols, 2, between; C - 6 cols, 2, between.Equipment & Software: Hardware — APP/Mac, IBM, APP/Mac G3s; Software — Multi-Ad/Creator, QPS/QuarkXPress, Newsset, Word.
Delivery Method: Mail, Newsstand, Racks

DENVER

DENVER FORUM (WED)

PO Box 509, Denver, IA, 50622-0509, Bremer, USA; gen tel (319) 984-6179; gen fax (319) 827-1125; disp adv e-mail ads@denveriaforum.com; class adv e-mail ads@denveriaforum.com; ed e-mail news@denveriaforum.com; web site www.denveriaforum.com - 15,917(views) 1,219(visitors)
Circulation: 600pd,; Sworn/Estimate/Non-Audited
Advertising rate: Open inch rate $5.55
Established: 1976
Group: Horizon Publishing Company
Publisher .... Kim Adams
Mechanical Specifications: TabloidEquipment & Software: Hardware — Mac; Software — Adobe InDesign CS6
Delivery Method: Mail, Newsstand
Areas Served: 50622

DES MOINES

ALTOONA HERALD-INDEX (WED)

400 Locust St, Ste 500, Des Moines, IA, 50309-2355, Polk, USA; gen tel (515) 699-7000; gen fax (515) 699-7098; disp adv e-mail adwilson@dmreg.com; web site www.altoonaherald.com
Advertising rate: (Modular Rates) Full Page- $840, Half Page- $540, Quarter Page- $270, Eighth Page- $160, Sixteenth Page- $85
Delivery Method: Carrier
Areas Served: Altoona, Bondurant, Mitcheville, Pleasant Hill, Runnells

ANKENY REGISTER & PRESS CITIZEN (TUES, FRI)

400 Locust St, Ste 500, Des Moines, IA, 50309-2355, Polk, USA; gen tel (515) 284-8000; adv tel (515) 238-2334; ed tel (515) 284-8256; gen fax (515) 284-8420; adv fax (515) 284-8420; disp adv e-mail jhanson@dmreg.com; class adv e-mail sucruz@desmoine.gannett.com; ed e-mail mlagesch@dmreg.com; web site desmoinesregister.com/communities/ankeny
Circulation: 24,000fr; Sworn/Estimate/Non-Audited
Advertising rate: ask for details
Established: 1953
Group: Gannett
Digital Platform - Mobile: Apple, Android, Windows, Blackberry
Digital Platform - Tablet: Apple iOS, Android, Windows 7, Blackberry Tablet OS, Kindle, Nook, Kindle Fire
Jolene Hanson
Jody SavageAccount Executives
Mechanical Specifications: standard advertising unitsEquipment & Software: Hardware — APP/Mac Centris 660AV; Software — Multi-Ad/Creator 3.7.
Delivery Method: Carrier
Areas Served: 50021, 50023

DES MOINES BUSINESS RECORD (FRI)

100 4th St, Des Moines, IA, 50309-4742, Polk, USA; gen tel (515) 288-3336; gen fax (515) 288-0309; disp adv e-mail advertising@bpcdm.com; ed e-mail newsroom@bpcdm.com; web site www.businessrecord.com
Circulation: 2,857pd, 2,765fr; VAC
Advertising rate: (Modular Rates) Full Page: $2,815 , Half Page $1770, Quarter Page $1100. (additional $395 with color)
Established: 1983
Group: Business Publications Corporation Inc.
Pub. .... Janette Larkin
Delivery Method: Mail
Areas Served: 503, 502, 500, 501

DOON

DOON PRESS (THUR)

209 Hubbard Ave, Doon, IA, 51235-7716, Lyon, USA; gen tel (712) 726-3313; gen fax (712) 726-3134; disp adv e-mail pressgal@hickorytech.net; web site No Website
Circulation: 2,600pd,; Sworn/Estimate/Non-Audited
Advertising rate: Open inch rate $4.00
Established: 1872
Circ. Mgr. .... Cheri Groeneweg
Co-Ed. .... Bridget Vander Tuin
Delivery Method: Mail, Newsstand, Racks

DUNLAP

DUNLAP REPORTER (THUR)

114 Iowa Ave, Dunlap, IA, 51529-1047, Harrison, USA; gen tel (712) 643-5380; gen fax (712) 643-2173; disp adv e-mail reporter@iowatelecom.net; class adv e-mail dianne@iowatelecom.net; web site dunlapiowa.com
Circulation: 560pd, 10fr; Sworn/Estimate/Non-Audited
Advertising rate: Open inch rate $5.25
Established: 1870
Owner, Publisher/Editor .... Dianne Walker
Office Mngr. .... Mary Crilly
Page design, billing .... Bonnie McCullough
Mechanical Specifications: Type page 15 x 21 1/2; E - 8 cols, 1 3/4, 1/6 between; A - 8 cols, 1 3/4, 1/6 between; C - 8 cols, 1 3/4, 1/6 between.
Delivery Method: Mail, Newsstand, Racks
Areas Served: 51529 & 51530

DYERSVILLE

DYERSVILLE COMMERCIAL (WED)

223 1st Ave E, Dyersville, IA, 52040-1202, Dubuque, USA; gen tel (563) 875-7131; adv tel (563) 875-7131; ed tel (563) 875-7131; gen fax (563) 875-2279; adv fax (563) 875-2279; ed fax (563) 875-2279; disp adv e-mail mungs-sogaard@wcinet.com; class adv e-mail mungs-sogaard@wcinet.com; ed e-mail mungs-sogaard@wcinet.com; web site www.dyersvillecommercial.com
Circulation: 3,950pd,; USPS
Advertising rate: Open inch rate $9.75
Established: 1873
Group: Woodward Communications, Inc.
Publisher .... Mary Ungs-Sogaard
Managing Editor .... Beth Lutgen
Mechanical Specifications: Type page 13 x 21 1/2; E - 6 cols, 2 1/32, 1/8 between; A - 6 cols, 2 1/32, 1/8 between; C - 6 cols, 2 1/32, 1/8 between.Equipment & Software: Hardware — APP/Mac G3, APP/Mac G4; Presses — G; Software — QPS/QuarkXPress.
Delivery Method: Mail, Carrier
Areas Served: Dyersville and Dubuque/Delaware Counties

DYSART

THE DYSART REPORTER (THUR)

317 Main St, Dysart, IA, 52224, Tama, USA; gen tel (319) 476-3550; gen fax (319) 476-2813; ed e-mail editor@dysartreporter.com; web site www.dysartreporter.com
Circulation: 800pd, 10fr; Sworn/Estimate/Non-Audited
Advertising rate: Open inch rate $3.74
Group: Ogden Newspapers Inc.
Pub. .... Mike Schlesinger
Adv. Mgr. .... Kelly Jantzen
Mechanical Specifications: Type page 13 1/2 x 21; E - 6 cols, 2, 1/4 between; A - 6 cols, 2, 1/4 between; C - 6 cols, 2, 1/4 between. Equipment & Software: Hardware — APP/Mac; Software — QPS/QuarkXPress 3.31.

EAGLE GROVE

EAGLE GROVE EAGLE (THUR)

314 W Broadway St, Eagle Grove, IA, 50533-1712, Wright, USA; gen tel (515) 448-4745; gen fax (515) 448-3182; disp adv e-mail egeagle@goldfieldaccess.net; web site www.theeaglegroveeagle.com
Circulation: 2,317pd,; Sworn/Estimate/Non-Audited
Advertising rate: Open inch rate $8.00
Adv. Mgr. .... Leigh Banwell
Ed. .... Kim Demory
Mechanical Specifications: Type page 14 x 21; E - 6 cols, 2 1/8, 1/6 between; A - 6 cols, 2 1/8, 1/6 between; C - 6 cols, 2 1/8, 1/6 between. Equipment & Software: Hardware — APP/Mac; Software — Microsoft/Word, QPS/QuarkXPress, Adobe/PageMaker.
Delivery Method: Mail, Newsstand

EDGEWOOD

EDGEWOOD REMINDER (TUES)

PO Box 458, 109 North Washington St., Edgewood, IA, 52042-0458, Clayton, Delaware, USA; gen tel (563) 928-6876; disp adv e-mail edgewood.reminder@yahoo.com; class adv e-mail edgewood.reminder@yahoo.com; ed e-mail edgewood.reminder@yahoo.com; web site No Website
Circulation: 1,100pd, 17fr; USPS
Advertising rate: Open inch rate $4.50
Owner/Ed. .... Julie Miller
Delivery Method: Mail, Newsstand
Areas Served: 52042 plus more

ELDORA

ELDORA NEWSPAPERS (TUES, FRI)

1513 Edgington Ave, Eldora, IA, 50627-1623, Hardin, USA; gen tel (641) 939-5051; gen fax (641) 939-5541; disp adv e-mail ads@eldoranewspaper.com; ed e-mail news@eldoranewspaper.com; web site eldoranewspapers.com
Circulation: 1,750pd,; Sworn/Estimate/Non-Audited
Advertising rate: Open inch rate $7.50
Established: 1860
Adv. Mgr. .... Pam Warren
Ed. .... Rick Patrie
Scott Bierle
Adv. Mgr. .... Betty Gotto
Delivery Method: Mail, Newsstand, Racks

HARDIN COUNTY INDEX (TUES, FRI)

1513 Edgington Ave, Eldora, IA, 50627-1623, Hardin, USA; gen tel (641) 939-5051; gen fax (641) 939-5541; disp adv e-mail ads@eldoranewspaper.com; ed e-mail news@eldoranewspaper.com; web site www.eldoranewspapers.com
Circulation: 1,500pd,; Sworn/Estimate/Non-Audited
Advertising rate: $6.50
Established: 1865
Group: Washington Advertising Company,LLC
Pub. .... Clint Poock
Gen Mgr. .... Scott Bierle
Ed. .... Rick Patrie
Adv. Mgr. .... Betty Gotto
Delivery Method: Mail
Areas Served: 50627

ELDRIDGE

THE NORTH SCOTT PRESS (WED)

214 N 2nd St, Eldridge, IA, 52748-1271, Scott, USA; gen tel (563) 285-8111; gen fax (563) 285-8114; disp adv e-mail adsales@northscottpress.com; class adv e-mail adsales@northscottpress.com; ed e-mail btubbs@northscottpress.com; web site www.northscottpress.com
Circulation: 5,000pd,; Sworn/Estimate/Non-Audited
Advertising rate: Open inch rate $14.00
Established: 1968
Digital Platform - Mobile: Apple
Pub. .... William F. Tubbs
Adv. Mgr. .... Jeff Martens
Ed. .... Scott Campbell
co-publisher .... Linda Tubbs
Assist. Ed. .... Mark Ridolfi
Mechanical Specifications: Type page 10.2 x 16; E - 4 cols, 2.5, 1/6 between; A - 4 cols, 2.5, 1/6 between; C - 6 cols, 1.67, 1/6 between. Equipment & Software: Hardware — Mac; Software — Microsoft/Word, Adobe Indesign.
Delivery Method: Mail, Newsstand, Racks
Areas Served: Scott County, Iowa

ELKADER

THE CLAYTON COUNTY REGISTER (WED)

205 S Main St, Elkader, IA, 52043-9078, Clayton, USA; gen tel (563) 245-1311; gen fax (563) 245-1312; disp adv e-mail ccrads@alpinecom.net; class adv e-mail ccrads@alpinecom.net; ed e-mail ccrnews@alpinecom.net; web site www.claytoncountyregister.com
Circulation: 1,200pd, 21,000fr; Sworn/Estimate/Non-Audited
Advertising rate: Open inch rate $9.85
Established: 1878
Group: Clayton County Register
Pub. .... Gary Howe
Ed. .... Pam Reinig
Bus. Mgr. .... Dana Richard
Mechanical Specifications: Type page 12 1/2 x 21 1/2; E - 7 cols, 1 1/2, 1/6 between; A - 7 cols, 1 1/2, 1/6 between; C - 7 cols, 1 1/2, 1/6 between.Equipment & Software: Hardware — APP/Mac; Software — Adobe/PageMaker 7.0, Adobe/Typestyler 2.0, Adobe/Illustrator 6.0, Adobe/Photoshop 5.0.
Delivery Method: Mail, Newsstand, Racks
Areas Served: Clayton County, IA and Southwest Wisconsin

EMMETSBURG

REPORTER-DEMOCRAT (THUR)

1901 Main St, Emmetsburg, IA, 50536-2440, Palo Alto, USA; gen tel (712) 852-2323; gen fax (712) 852-3184; disp adv e-mail advertising@emmetsburgnews.com; class adv e-mail advertising@emmetsburgnews.com; web site www.emmetsburgnews.com
Circulation: 2,700pd,; Sworn/Estimate/Non-Audited
Advertising rate: Open inch rate $11.95
Group: Ogden Newspapers Inc.
Pub./Adv. Mgr. .... Dan McCain
Ed. .... Jane Whitmore
Circ. .... Linda Hill
Mechanical Specifications: Type page 11 1/2 x 21 1/2; E - 6 cols, 1 7/8, 1/12 between; A - 6 cols, 1 7/8, 1/12 between; C - 6 cols, 1 7/8, 1/12 between.Equipment & Software: Hardware — APP/Mac; Presses — HI/V-15A, ABD/360; Software — QPS/QuarkXPress 4.0, Adobe/Photoshop 3.0.
Delivery Method: Mail, Newsstand, Racks

THE DEMOCRAT (THUR)
1122 Broadway St, Ste B, Emmetsburg, IA, 50536-1767, Palo Alto, USA; gen tel (712) 852-2323; gen fax (712) 852-3184; disp adv e-mail advertising@emmetsburgnews.com; class adv e-mail advertising@emmetsburgnews.com; ed e-mail jwhitmore@emmetsburgnews.com; web site www.emmetsburgnews.com
Advertising rate: Open inch rate $11.95
Established: 1882
Adv. Mgr....................................... Dan McCain
Pub..Jane Whitmore
Circ. Mgr.. Linda Hill
Delivery Method: Mail, Newsstand, Racks

THE EMMETSBURG REPORTER (TUES)
1122 Broadway St, Stuite B, Emmetsburg, IA, 50536-1767, Palo Alto, USA; gen tel (712) 852-2323; gen fax (712) 852-3184; disp adv e-mail mdune@emmetsburgnews.com; class adv e-mail lhill@emmetsburgnews.com; ed e-mail jwhitmore@emmetsburgnews.com; web site www.emmetsburgnews.com
Circulation: 2,400pd,; Sworn/Estimate/Non-Audited
Advertising rate: Open inch rate $11.95
Established: 1876
Group: Ogden Newspapers Inc.
Pub./Gen. Mgr............................. Dan McCain
Ed. ....Jane Whitmore
Circ. Mgr.. Linda Hill
Mechanical Specifications: Type page 11 1/2 x 21 1/2; E - 6 cols, 1 7/8, 1/12 between; A - 6 cols, 1 7/8, 1/12 between; C - 6 cols, 1 7/8, 1/12 between.Equipment & Software: Hardware — APP/Mac; Presses — HI/V-15A, ABD/360; Software — QPS/QuarkXPress 4.0, Adobe/Photoshop 3.0.
Delivery Method: Mail, Newsstand, Racks

ESTHERVILLE

ESTHERVILLE NEWS (SAT)
10 N 7th St, Estherville, IA, 51334-2232, Emmet, USA; gen tel (712) 362-2622; adv tel (712) 362-2622; ed tel (712) 362-2622; gen fax (712) 362-2624; adv fax (712) 362-2624; ed fax (712) 362-2624; disp adv e-mail disaackson@esthervillenews.net; class adv e-mail disaackson@esthervillenews.net; ed e-mail dswartz@esthervillenews.net; web site www.esthervilledailynews.com - 22,870(views) 7,623(visitors)
Circulation: 2,282pd,; Sworn/Estimate/Non-Audited
Advertising rate: Open inch rate $10.76
Group: Ogden Newspapers Inc.
Digital Platform - Mobile: Apple, Android
Digital Platform - Tablet: Apple iOS, Android
Pub./Classified Adv. Mgr./Business Mgr.... Glen Caron
Sports Ed.................................... David Swartz
Adv. Dir...................................... Dar Isaackson
Bus. Mgr.................................. Tessa Peterson
Mechanical Specifications: Type page 13 x 21 1/2; E - 6 cols, 2 1/16, 1/8 between; A - 6 cols, 2 1/16, 1/8 between; C - 6 cols, 2, 1/16 between.
Delivery Method: Mail, Carrier
Areas Served: Estherville, Emmet County and North Central Iowa

FAIRFIELD

FAIRFIELD TOWN CRIER (TUES)
112 E Broadway Ave, Fairfield, IA, 52556-3202, Jefferson, USA; gen tel (641) 472-4129; gen fax (641) 472-1916; disp adv e-mail adv@fledger.com; class adv e-mail classifieds@fledger.com; ed e-mail news@fledger.com; web site goldentrianglenewspapers.com
Circulation: 10,499fr; CVC
Advertising rate: Open inch rate $10.70
Established: 1980
Group: Inland Newspaper Machinery LLC
Circ. Mgr.. Kim Stout
Pub .... Amy Sparby
Advt Mgr ....Sherry Jipp
Delivery Method: Newsstand, Carrier, Racks
Areas Served: 52556

FARMINGTON

VAN BUREN COUNTY REGISTER (THUR)
102 Elm St, Farmington, IA, 52626-9537, Van Buren, USA; gen tel (319) 878-4111; gen fax (319) 293-3198; disp adv e-mail vbregister@netins.net
Circulation: 1,786pd,; Sworn/Estimate/Non-Audited
Advertising rate: Open inch rate $5.30
Group: Louisa Publishing Co. Ltd.
Gen. Mgr. .... Donna Muir
Ed. .... Russell Ebert
Mechanical Specifications: Type page 13 1/4 x 21; E - 7 cols, 1 3/4, 1/6 between; A - 7 cols, 1 3/4, 1/6 between; C - 7 cols, 1 3/4, 1/6 between.Equipment & Software: Hardware — APP/Mac; Software — Abbott Systems/Ready, Set, Go, Adobe/PageMaker, QPS/QuarkXPress.
Delivery Method: Mail, Newsstand, Racks

FONTANELLE

THE FONTANELLE OBSERVER (WED)
313 Fifth St., Fontanelle, IA, 50846, Adair, USA; gen tel (641) 745-3161; gen fax (641) 743-6378; disp adv e-mail observer1@iowatelecom.net; web site facebook.com/Fontanelle-Observer-345179189144
Circulation: 855pd, 0fr; Sworn/Estimate/Non-Audited
Advertising rate: Open inch rate $4.50
Established: 1863
Ed. .... Paula Jameson
Rptr........................... Caitlin WareEquipment & Software: Hardware — APP/Mac Desktop Publishing; Software — Adobe/PageMaker, Claris/MacWrite.
Delivery Method: Mail, Newsstand, Racks

FOREST CITY

BRITT NEWS-TRIBUNE (WED)
105 S Clark St, Forest City, IA, 50436-1710, Hancock, USA; gen tel (641) 585-2112; gen fax (641) 585-4442; disp adv e-mail news@brittnewstribune.com; web site www.brittnewstribune.com
Advertising rate: $5.70
Digital Platform - Mobile: Apple, Android
Digital Platform - Tablet: Apple iOS, Android
Delivery Method: Mail, Newsstand, Racks

FOREST CITY SUMMIT (WED)
105 S Clark St, Forest City, IA, 50436-1710, Winnebago, USA; gen tel (641) 585-2112; gen fax (641) 585-4442; disp adv e-mail news@forestcitysummit.com; web site www.northiowanews.com
Advertising rate: Open inch rate $7.00
Group: Lee Enterprises, Inc.
Delivery Method: Mail, Newsstand, Racks

GARNER

THE LEADER (WED)
365 State St, Garner, IA, 50438-1236, Hancock, USA; gen tel (641) 923-2684; gen fax (641) 923-2685; disp adv e-mail gleader@qwestoffice.net; web site www.theleaderonline.net
Circulation: 2,500pd, 40fr; Sworn/Estimate/Non-Audited
Advertising rate: Open inch rate $8.65
Group: Mid-America Publishing
Digital Platform - Mobile: Apple, Android
Digital Platform - Tablet: Apple iOS, Android
President/CEO/Publisher............ Ryan Harvey
Office and Production Manager. Ana Olsthoorn
News Editor .... Rebecca Peter
Delivery Method: Mail, Newsstand
Areas Served: Hancock County, Garner, Britt, Ventura, Corwith, Klemme

GEORGE

LYON COUNTY NEWS (THUR)
113 E Michigan Ave, George, IA, 51237-7751, Lyon, USA; gen tel (712) 475-3351; gen fax (712) 475-3353; disp adv e-mail lyonconews@mtcnet.net; class adv e-mail lyonconewsck@mtcnet.net; ed e-mail lyonconewsck@mtcnet.net
Circulation: 750pd, 80fr; Sworn/Estimate/Non-Audited
Advertising rate: Open inch rate $4.10K
Established: 1906
Circ. Mgr.. Milli Krull
Ed. .... Cheryl Koerselman
Ad Sales/Graphic Artist .... Leann Kruger
Mechanical Specifications: Type page 15 x 21 1/2; E - 7 cols, 2, 1/6 between; A - 7 cols, 2, 1/6 between; C - 7 cols, 2, 1/6 between.
Delivery Method: Mail
Areas Served: 51237

GLADBROOK

NORTHERN-SUN PRINT (FRI)
423 2nd St, Gladbrook, IA, 50635-7720, Tama, USA; gen tel (641) 473-2102; gen fax (641) 473-1004; disp adv e-mail editor@northernsunprint.com; ed e-mail editor@northernsunprint.com; web site www.northernsunprint.com
Circulation: 1,100pd,; Sworn/Estimate/Non-Audited
Advertising rate: Open inch rate $6.94
Group: Ogden Newspapers Inc.
Ed. .... Betty Dahms
Mechanical Specifications: Type page 10 1/4 x 14 1/2; E - 5 cols, 1 11/12, 1/6 between; A - 5 cols, 1 11/12, 1/6 between; C - 5 cols, 1 11/12, 1/6 between.Equipment & Software: Hardware — APP/Mac; Software — Microsoft/Word 5.1, QPS/QuarkXPress 3.01.
Delivery Method: Mail, Newsstand

GLENWOOD

OPINION-TRIBUNE (WED)
116 S Walnut St, Glenwood, IA, 51534-1665, Mills, USA; gen tel (712) 527-3191; gen fax (712) 527-3193; disp adv e-mail news@opinion-tribune.com; web site www.opinion-tribune.com
Circulation: 3,900pd, 6,000fr; Sworn/Estimate/Non-Audited
Advertising rate: Open inch rate $8.25
Established: 1864
Group: Landmark Communications, Inc. Landmark Community Newspapers, LLC
Ed. ....Joe Foreman
Pub.. Greg Orear
Adv. Sales...............................Melissa Lorang
Circ. Mgr./Classifieds ....Karen Herzberg
Mechanical Specifications: Type page 13 x 21; E - 6 cols, 1 7/8, between; A - 6 cols, 1 7/8, between; C - 8 cols, 1 3/8, between. Equipment & Software: Hardware — APP/Mac; Software — QPS/QuarkXPress, Multi-Ad/Creator.
Delivery Method: Mail, Newsstand, Racks
Areas Served: 51534, 51561, 51554, 51571, 51551, 51540, 51653, 51654, 51648, 51649, 51652

GLIDDEN

THE GLIDDEN GRAPHIC (WED, THUR)
122 Idaho St., Glidden, IA, 51443, Carroll, USA; gen tel (712) 790-6999; disp adv e-mail news@gliddengraphic.com; web site facebook.com/pages/Glidden-Graphic/155359484478487
Circulation: 600pd,; Sworn/Estimate/Non-Audited
Advertising rate: Open inch rate $4.40
Established: 1889
Pub... Bill Brown
Delivery Method: Mail, Newsstand, Racks

GOWRIE

GOWRIE NEWS (WED)
1108 Market St, Gowrie, IA, 50543-7714, Webster, USA; gen tel (515) 352-3325; gen fax (515) 352-3309; disp adv e-mail gnews@wccta.net; web site daytongowrienews.com
Advertising rate: $6.00 per column inch
Digital Platform - Mobile: Other
Delivery Method: Mail, Racks
Areas Served: Webster,Calhoun,Greene,Boone

GRAETTINGER

THE GRAETTINGER TIMES (WED)
104 W ROBINS ST, Graettinger, IA, 51342, Palo Alto, USA; gen tel (712) 859-3780; gen fax (712) 859-3039; disp adv e-mail grtimes@netins.net; web site facebook.com/The-Graettinger-Times-183153428799597
Circulation: 1,300pd,; Sworn/Estimate/Non-Audited
Advertising rate: Open inch rate $5.50, special rates for multiple runs
Established: 1847
Digital Platform - Mobile: Apple
Pub.. Penny Tonderum
Mechanical Specifications: Type page 10 x 15; E - 5 cols, 2, 3/20 between; A - 5 cols, 2, 3/20 between; C - 5 cols, 2, 3/20 between.Equipment & Software: Hardware — APP/Mac; Software — Microsoft/Word 5.1.
Delivery Method: Mail
Areas Served: Palo Alto city & county, 51342, 50536, 51358, 51333

GREENE

GREENE RECORDER (WED)
PO Box 370, Greene, IA, 50636-0370, Greene, USA; gen tel (641) 816-4525; gen fax (641) 816-4765; disp adv e-mail news@greenerecorder.com; web site www.greenerecorder.com
Circulation: 1,250pd, 20fr; Sworn/Estimate/Non-Audited
Advertising rate: Open inch rate $3.50
Established: 1901
Pub... Ross Hawker
Ed. .... Fred J. Hawker
Ed. ..... Sylvia J. HawkerEquipment & Software: Hardware — 4-APP/Mac; Software — QPS/QuarkXPress 3.0, Adobe/Photoshop 3.1.
Delivery Method: Mail, Newsstand, Racks

GREENFIELD

ADAIR COUNTY FREE PRESS (WED)
141 Public Sq, Greenfield, IA, 50849-1266, Adair, USA; gen tel (641) 743-6121; gen fax (641) 743-6378; disp adv e-mail ads@adairpress.com; class adv e-mail d.mitchell@adairpress.com; ed e-mail editor@adairpress.com
Circulation: 2,000pd,; Sworn/Estimate/Non-Audited
Advertising rate: Open inch rate $8.00
Group: Herald Publishing Company
Circ. Mgr..................................... Denna Mitchell
editor....................................... Tammy Pearson
Hesper Christensen
Sports E................................. Steve Thompson
Melissa Brewer
Sandy McCurdy
Mechanical Specifications: Type page 15 x 20 3/4; E - 7 cols, 2, between; A - 7 cols, 2, between; C - 7 cols, 2, between.Equipment & Software: Hardware — APP/Mac; Software — Microsoft/Word
Indesign

Delivery Method: Mail
Areas Served: 50849

GRINNELL

GRINNELL HERALD-REGISTER (MON, THUR)

813 5th Ave, Grinnell, IA, 50112-1653, Poweshiek, USA; gen tel (641) 236-3113; adv tel (641) 236-3113; ed tel (641) 236-3113; gen fax (641) 236-5135; adv fax (641) 236-5135; ed fax (641) 236-5135; disp adv e-mail ghr@iowatelecom.net; class adv e-mail ghr@iowatelecom.net; ed e-mail ghr@iowatelecom.net
Advertising rate: Open inch rate $7.92
Established: 1936
Pub.......Dorothy Pinder
Ed.......Martha Pinder
News Ed.......Peggy Pinder-Elliot
Adv. Mgr.......John DeGrado
Adv. Sales Rep.......Betty Broders
Delivery Method: Mail, Newsstand, Carrier, Racks
Areas Served: 50112

POWESHIEK COUNTY CHRONICLE-REPUBLICAN (WED)

925 Broad St, Grinnell, IA, 50112-2047, Poweshiek, USA; gen tel (641) 522-7155; gen fax (641) 236-0625; disp adv e-mail powcr@dmreg.com
Group: Gannett

GRISWOLD

GRISWOLD AMERICAN (WED)

519 MAIN ST, Griswold, IA, 51535, Cass, USA; gen tel (712) 778-4337; gen fax (712) 778-4350; disp adv e-mail grisamer@netins.net
Circulation: 900pd, 30fr; Sworn/Estimate/Non-Audited
Advertising rate: Open inch rate $4.50
Established: 1880
Digital Platform - Mobile: Apple
Owner/Ed./Pub.......Donna Forsyth
Delivery Method: Mail, Racks

GRUNDY CENTER

GRUNDY CENTER REGISTER (THUR)

601 G Ave, Grundy Center, IA, 50638-1549, Grundy, USA; gen tel (319) 824-6958; gen fax (319) 824-6288; disp adv e-mail registerads@gcmuni.net; ed e-mail editor@gcmuni.net; web site www.thegrundyregister.com
Advertising rate: $7.10
Sports Ed.......Mitchell Krmpotich
Delivery Method: Mail, Newsstand, Racks

GUTHRIE CENTER

GUTHRIE CENTER TIMES (WED)

205 State St, Guthrie Center, IA, 50115-1370, Guthrie, USA; gen tel (641) 332-2380; gen fax (641) 332-2382; ed e-mail gctimes@netins.net; web site guthriecountynewspapers.com
Circulation: 1,350pd, 17fr; Sworn/Estimate/Non-Audited
Advertising rate: Open inch rate $4.50
Adv. Mgr.......Beth Stanley
Circ. Mgr.......Beth Rogers
Ed.......Scott P. Gonzales
Reporter.......Caitlin Ware
Mechanical Specifications: Type page 15 1/4 x 21 1/2; E - 8 cols, 1 3/4, 1/6 between; A - 8 cols, 1 3/4, 1/6 between; C - 8 cols, 1 3/4, 1/6 between.Equipment & Software: ; Presses — G/Community.
Delivery Method: Mail, Newsstand, Racks

GUTTENBERG

GUTTENBERG PRESS (WED)

10 Schiller St, Guttenberg, IA, 52052-9057, Clayton, USA; gen tel (563) 252-2421; gen fax (563) 252-1275; disp adv e-mail gbpress@alpinecom.net; web site www.guttenbergpress.com
Circulation: 2,600pd,; Sworn/Estimate/Non-Audited
Advertising rate: Open inch rate $8.40
Established: 1896
Group: Clayton County Register
Pub.......Gary Howe
Circ. Mgr.......Jane Thein
Mechanical Specifications: Type page 10 1/2 x 16; E - 4 cols, 2 1/2, 1/6 between; A - 4 cols, 2 1/2, 1/6 between; C - 5 cols, 1 11/12, 1/6 between.Equipment & Software: Hardware — APP/Mac; Presses — G/Community; Software — Adobe/PageMaker 6.5.
Delivery Method: Mail, Newsstand, Racks

HAMBURG

HAMBURG REPORTER (THUR)

1009 Main St, Hamburg, IA, 51640-1231, Fremont, USA; gen tel (712) 382-1234; gen fax (712) 382-1222; disp adv e-mail hamburgreporter@qwestoffice.net; class adv e-mail classad@ncnewspress.com; web site www.hamburgreporter.com
Circulation: 1,100pd,; Sworn/Estimate/Non-Audited
Advertising rate: Open inch rate $6.58
Group: GateHouse Media, Inc.
Ed./Adv. Dir.......Tammy Schumacher
Classified Sales.......Roxanne Schutz
Delivery Method: Mail, Racks
Areas Served: 51640

HAMPTON

HAMPTON CHRONICLE (WED)

9 2nd St NW, Hampton, IA, 50441-1903, Franklin, USA; gen tel (641) 456-2585; gen fax (641) 456-2587; disp adv e-mail chroniclenews@iowaconnect.com; web site www.hamptonchronicle.com
Advertising rate: Open inch rate $7.10

HARLAN

NEWS-ADVERTISER (FRI)

1114 7th St, P O Box 721, Harlan, IA, 51537-1338, Shelby, USA; gen tel (712) 755-3111; gen fax (712) 755-3324; disp adv e-mail news2@harlanonline.com; web site www.harlanonline.com
Circulation: 4,000pd, 43,000fr; Sworn/Estimate/Non-Audited
Advertising rate: Open inch rate $8.75
Established: 1870
Group: Tribune Newspapers Inc
Digital Platform - Mobile: Apple, Android
Digital Platform - Tablet: Apple iOS, Android, Blackberry Tablet OS, Kindle, Nook, Kindle Fire
Co-Pub.......Alan Mores
Co-Pub.......Steven Mores
Adv. Mgr./Mktg. Dir.......Mike Kolbe
Ed.......Bob Bjoin
Mechanical Specifications: Type page 14 3/4 x 21 1/2;
E - 6 cols,
2 inch, 1/6 inch between;
Equipment & Software: Hardware — Mac; Presses — Goss Community; Software — Adobe Indesign
Adobe Photoshop
Neo Office
Interlink
Delivery Method: Mail
Areas Served: 51527 — Defiance
51530 — Earling
51531 — Elk Horn
51537 — Harlan
51446 — Irwin
51447 — Kirkman
51562 — Panama
51565 — Portsmouth
51570 — Shelby
51574 — Tennant
51578 — Westphalia

HARTLEY

HARTLEY SENTINEL-NEWS (THUR)

71 1st St SE, Hartley, IA, 51346-1403, Obrien, USA; gen tel (712) 834-2388; gen fax (712) 928-2223; disp adv e-mail sentinel@tcaexpress.net
Circulation: 1,800pd, 32fr; Sworn/Estimate/Non-Audited
Advertising rate: Open inch rate $4.58
Ed.......Nick Pedley
Sports Ed.......Mike Peterson
Pub. Adv. Mgr.......Kaity Harms
Mechanical Specifications: Type page 15 x 21 1/2; E - 7 cols, 2 1/16, 1/8 between; A - 7 cols, 2 1/16, 1/8 between; C - 9 cols, 1 1/2, 1/8 between.

HAWARDEN

HAWARDEN INDEPENDENT/IRETON EXAMINER (THUR)

926 Avenue F, Hawarden, IA, 51023-2275, Sioux, USA; gen tel (712) 551-1051; gen fax (712) 551-1057; disp adv e-mail independent@longlines.com; web site independentexaminer.net
Circulation: 1,256pd, 21fr; Sworn/Estimate/Non-Audited
Advertising rate: Open inch rate $7.50
Established: 1878Editions: (1)
Digital Platform - Mobile: Apple
Publisher.......Bruce Odson
General Manager.......Mylan Schroeder
Office Manager.......Pam Banta
Reporter/Photographer.......Kim Fickett
Reporter/Photographer.......Nicole HooglandEquipment & Software: Hardware — Apple computers; Software — CS 5.5
Delivery Method: Mail, Newsstand
Areas Served: 51023, 51027, 51001, 57001, 57004, 51062, 57025

HOPKINTON

DELAWARE COUNTY LEADER (TUES)

101 1st St SE, Hopkinton, IA, 52237-7765, Delaware, USA; gen tel (563) 926-2626; gen fax (563) 926-2045; disp adv e-mail hopleader@yahoo.com
Circulation: 1,420pd,; Sworn/Estimate/Non-Audited
Advertising rate: Open inch rate $5.25
Pub.......Mary Helle
Adv. Mgr.......Cathy Smith
Ed.......Cathy Harris
Areas Served: 52223

HOSPERS

SIOUXLAND PRESS (WED)

207 Main St, Hospers, IA, 51238-7725, Sioux, USA; gen tel (712) 752-8401; gen fax (712) 752-8405; disp adv e-mail slpress@nethtc.net
Circulation: 1,800pd, 50fr; Sworn/Estimate/Non-Audited
Advertising rate: Open inch rate $3.50
Established: 1970
Harlan Rouse
Katie RouseEd.s
Delivery Method: Mail, Newsstand, Racks

HUDSON

HUDSON HERALD (THUR)

411 Jefferson St, Hudson, IA, 50643-9719, Black Hawk, USA; gen tel (319) 988-3855; gen fax (319) 988-3855; disp adv e-mail hudherald@gmail.com; class adv e-mail hudherald@gmail.com; ed e-mail hudherald@gmail.com; web site http://www.hudherald.com/
Circulation: 900pd, 25fr; Sworn/Estimate/Non-Audited
Advertising rate: Open inch rate $6.00
Established: 1911
Ed, Pub.......Bonniesue Joy
Mechanical Specifications: Type page 11x22; E - 5 cols, 1.89, 1/8 gutter; A - 5 cols, 1.89, 1/8 gutter; C - 5 cols, 1.89
Delivery Method: Mail, Newsstand
Areas Served: 50613, 50643, 50701, 50702

HULL

SIOUX COUNTY INDEX-REPORTER (WED)

1013 1st St, Hull, IA, 51239-7718, Sioux, USA; gen tel (712) 439-1075; gen fax (712) 439-2001; disp adv e-mail jvisser@ncppub.com; web site ncppub.com/pages/?cat=58
Circulation: 1,221pd, 25fr; Sworn/Estimate/Non-Audited
Advertising rate: Open inch rate $6.15
Adv. Mgr.......Lois Keuhl
Gen. Mgr.......James Hensley
Circ. Mgr.......Robbie Kooistra
Writer.......Joseph Stearns
Mechanical Specifications: Type page 10 5/8 x 15; E - 5 cols, 2, 1/6 between; A - 5 cols, 2, 1/6 between; C - 5 cols, 2, 1/6 between. Equipment & Software: Hardware — APP/Mac; Software — QPS/QuarkXPress 3.3.

HUMBOLDT

HUMBOLDT INDEPENDENT (THUR)

512 Sumner Ave, Humboldt, IA, 50548-1759, Humboldt, USA; gen tel (515) 332-2514; gen fax (515) 332-1505; disp adv e-mail independent@humboldtnews.com; web site www.humboldtnews.com
Circulation: 3,623pd, 197fr; Sworn/Estimate/Non-Audited
Advertising rate: Open inch rate $11.50
Established: 1985
Pub./Gen. Mgr.......James Gargano
Ed.......Jeffrey Gargano
Mechanical Specifications: Type page 11 3/4 x 21; E - 6 cols, 1 7/8, 1/8 between; A - 6 cols, 1 7/8, 1/8 between; C - 6 cols, 1 7/8, 1/8 between.Equipment & Software: Hardware — APP/Mac; Software — Adobe/PageMaker.
Delivery Method: Mail, Newsstand, Racks

IDA GROVE

IDA COUNTY COURIER (WED)

214 Main St, Ida Grove, IA, 51445-1311, Ida, USA; gen tel (712) 364-3131; gen fax (712) 364-3010; disp adv e-mail idacourier@frontiernet.net; class adv e-mail idacourier@frontiernet.net; ed e-mail editor@idacountycourier.com; web site www.idacountycourier.com
Circulation: 2,099pd, 120fr
Advertising rate: Open inch rate $7.40
Established: 1975
Digital Platform - Mobile: Apple, Android
Digital Platform - Tablet: Apple iOS, Android
Pub.......Roger D. Rector
Circ. Mgr.......Peg Peters
Ed.......Beth Wolterman
Business Mgr.......Amy Forbes
Sports Ed.......Mike Thornhill
Reporter.......Deb Loger
Mechanical Specifications: Type page 11 1/2 x 21; E - 6 cols, 1 13/16, 1/8 between; A - 6 cols, 1 13/16, 1/8 between; C - 6 cols, 1 13/16, 1/8 between.Equipment & Software: Hardware — 2-APP/Mac; Software — Adobe/

InDesign CS3
Delivery Method: Mail
Areas Served: 51445, 51006, 51025, 51020, 51431, 51458

INDEPENDENCE

INDEPENDENCE BULLETIN JOURNAL (WED, SAT)
900 5th Ave NE, Ste A, Independence, IA, 50644-1464, Buchanan, USA; gen tel (319) 334-2557; gen fax (319) 334-6752; disp adv e-mail editor@bulletinjournal.com; web site www.bulletinjournal.com
Advertising rate: $11.04
Group: Community Media Group
Delivery Method: Mail

INDIANOLA

RECORD-HERALD AND INDIANOLA TRIBUNE (WED)
112 N Howard St, Indianola, IA, 50125-2510, Warren, USA; gen tel (515) 961-2511; gen fax (515) 961-4833; disp adv e-mail adun-can@dmreg.com; web site www.indianolarecordherald.com
Circulation: 7,480pd,; Sworn/Estimate/Non-Audited
Advertising rate: Open inch rate $9.25
Established: 1856
Group: Gannett
Pub.. Amy Duncan
Sr. Acct. Exec.............................Cindy Nelson
Ed. ....Adam Wilson
Admin./Circ. Mgr. ....Jenna Sergeant
Mechanical Specifications: Type page 12 7/8 x 21; E - 6 cols, 2, 1/8 between; A - 6 cols, 2, 1/8 between; C - 10 cols, between.Equipment & Software: Hardware — APP/Macs; Presses — HI/V-15A; Software — QPS/QuarkXPress, Microsoft/Word.
Delivery Method: Mail, Newsstand, Carrier, Racks

INWOOD

WEST LYON HERALD (WED)
211 S Main St, Inwood, IA, 51240-7807, Lyon, USA; gen tel (712) 753-2258; gen fax (712) 753-4864; disp adv e-mail herald@lyon-siouxpress.com; class adv e-mail ads@ncppub.com; web site ncppub.com/pages/?-cat=23
Circulation: 1,400pd,; Sworn/Estimate/Non-Audited
Advertising rate: Open inch rate $6.00
Established: 1890
Group: New Century Press
CEO... Jim Hensley
Adv. Mgr.. Lois Kuehl
Associate Ed...........................Verdena Kelley
Rachel Gutting
Mechanical Specifications: Type page 10 5/8 x 15; E - 5 cols, 2, 1/6 between; A - 5 cols, 2, 1/6 between; C - 5 cols, 2, 1/6 between. Equipment & Software: Hardware — APP/Mac; Software — QPS/QuarkXPress.
Delivery Method: Mail, Newsstand, Racks

IOWA FALLS

IOWA FALLS IOWA FARM BUREAU SPOKESMAN (WED)
406 Stevens St, Iowa Falls, IA, 50126-2214, Hardin, USA; gen tel (641) 648-2521; gen fax (641) 648-4606; disp adv e-mail spokesman406@gmail.com; web site www.iowafarmbureau.com
Advertising rate: Open inch rate $100
Delivery Method: Mail

JEFFERSON

THE BEE (TUES)
200 N Wilson Ave, Jefferson, IA, 50129-1923, Jefferson, USA; gen tel (515) 386-4161; gen fax (515) 386-4162; disp adv e-mail news@beeherald.com; web site beeherald.com
Circulation: 7,500fr; Sworn/Estimate/Non-Audited
Advertising rate: Open inch rate $7.25
Adv. Mgr.......................................Deb Geisler
Ed. ....Frederick G. Morain
Mechanical Specifications: 10" x 21 - 6 Col, 2 1/4, 3/16 betweenEquipment & Software: Hardware — APP/Mac SE, APP/Mac Classic; Software — Microsoft/Word 4.0, Abbott Systems/Ready, Set, Go 4.5.
Delivery Method: Mail, Newsstand, Racks

THE JEFFERSON HERALD (THUR)
200 N Wilson Ave, Jefferson, IA, 50129-1923, Greene, USA; gen tel (515) 386-4161; gen fax (515) 386-4162; disp adv e-mail news@beeherald.com; web site beeherald.com
Circulation: 2,294pd,; Sworn/Estimate/Non-Audited
Advertising rate: Open inch rate $5.50
Adv. Mgr.......................................Deb Geisler
Mechanical Specifications: Type page 15 3/4 x 21; E - 7 cols, 2 1/12, 1 1/24 between; A - 7 cols, 2 1/12, 1 1/24 between; C - 7 cols, 2 1/12, between.Equipment & Software: Hardware — APP/Mac SE, APP/Mac Classic, APP/Mac LC III; Software — Abbott Systems/Ready, Set, Go 4.5, Microsoft/Word 4.0.
Delivery Method: Mail, Newsstand, Racks

JESUP

JESUP CITIZEN HERALD (WED)
930 6th St, Jesup, IA, 50648-1177, Buchanan, USA; gen tel (319) 827-1128; gen fax (319) 827-1125; disp adv e-mail ads@jesupcitizenherald.com; class adv e-mail ads@jesupcitizenherald.com; ed e-mail editor@jesupcitizenherald.com; web site www.jesupcitizenherald.com - 92,500(views) 2,667(visitors)
Circulation: 1,020pd,; Sworn/Estimate/Non-Audited
Advertising rate: Open inch rate $6.95
Established: 1899
Group: Horizon Publishing Company
Pub................................. Kim Edward Adams
Editor.................................. Nancy Steinbron
Mechanical Specifications: Type page 13 3/4 x 21 1/2; E - 6 cols, 2 1/10, 1/10 between; A - 6 cols, 2 1/10, 1/10 between; C - 6 cols, 2 1/10, 1/10 between.Equipment & Software: Hardware — APP/Mac; Software — Adobe/Indesign CS6.
Delivery Method: Mail, Newsstand
Areas Served: 50648

JEWELL

SOUTH HAMILTON RECORD-NEWS (WED)
602 Main St, Jewell, IA, 50130-2012, Hamilton, USA; gen tel (515) 827-5931; gen fax (515) 827-5760; disp adv e-mail shrecnew@netins.net; web site www.iowanewspapersonline.com
Circulation: 933pd, 17fr; Sworn/Estimate/Non-Audited
Advertising rate: Open inch rate $3.50
Ed. .... Kenneth Scott Ervin

KALONA

SLECHTA COMMUNICATIONS, INC. (MON)
419 B Ave, Kalona, IA, 52247-7719, Washington, USA
Group: Anamosa Publications

THE KALONA NEWS (THUR)
419 B Ave, Kalona, IA, 52247-7719, Washington, USA; gen tel (319) 656-2273; gen fax (319) 656-2299; disp adv e-mail adsales@kalonanews.com; class adv e-mail classifieds@kctc.net; ed e-mail news@kalonanews.com; web site www.kalonanews.com
Circulation: 2,360pd,; Sworn/Estimate/Non-Audited
Advertising rate: Open inch rate $8.50
Established: 1891
Group: Anamosa Publications
Slechta Communications, Inc.
Digital Platform - Mobile: Apple
Digital Platform - Tablet: Apple iOS
News Editor .... Dan Ehl
Delivery Method: Mail, Newsstand
Areas Served: Kalona, Washington and Johnson Counties in Iowa

KEOTA

KEOTA EAGLE (WED)
310 E Broadway Ave, Keota, IA, 52248-9402, Keokuk, USA; gen tel (641) 636-2309; gen fax (641) 636-2309; disp adv e-mail keotaeagle@cloudburst9.net; web site www.keotaeagle.com
Advertising rate: Open inch rate $7.30
Established: 1875
Group: Mid-America Publishing
News Ed. .... Amie Van Patten
Delivery Method: Mail, Newsstand

KINGSLEY

KINGSLEY NEWS-TIMES (WED)
120 Main St, Kingsley, IA, 51028-7725, Plymouth, USA; gen tel (712) 378-2770; gen fax (712) 378-2274; disp adv e-mail knewest@evertek.net
Circulation: 1,000pd,; Sworn/Estimate/Non-Audited
Advertising rate: Open inch rate $5.10
Pub... Randy List
Ed. .... Earl Horlyk
Delivery Method: Mail

KNOXVILLE

THE KNOXVILLE JOURNAL-EXPRESS (THUR)
122 E Robinson St, Knoxville, IA, 50138-2329, Marion, USA; gen tel (641) 842-2155; gen fax (641) 842-2929; class adv e-mail classified@journalexpress.net; ed e-mail editor@journalexpress.net; web site www.journalexpress.net
Circulation: 1,800pd,; Sworn/Estimate/Non-Audited
Advertising rate: Open inch rate $8.20
Established: 1855
Group: Community Newspaper Holdings, Inc.
Raycom Media
Publisher..............................Rebecca Maxwell
Mechanical Specifications: Type page 13 x 21 1/2; E - 6 cols, 2 1/8, 1/8 between; A - 6 cols, 2 1/8, 1/8 between; C - 6 cols, 2 1/8, 1/8 between.Equipment & Software: Hardware — APP/Mac.
Delivery Method: Mail, Newsstand, Racks

LA PORTE CITY

THE PROGRESS-REVIEW (WED)
213 Main St, La Porte City, IA, 50651-1235, Black Hawk, USA; gen tel (319) 342-2429; gen fax (319) 342-2433; disp adv e-mail news@theprogressreview.co; web site www.theprogressreview.com
Circulation: 1,360pd,; Sworn/Estimate/Non-Audited
Advertising rate: Open inch rate $4.95
Established: 1865
Pub./Ed. .... Mike Whittlesey
Delivery Method: Mail, Newsstand, Racks

LAKE CITY

THE LAKE CITY GRAPHIC-ADVOCATE (WED)
121 N Center St, Lake City, IA, 51449-1701, Calhoun, USA; gen tel (712) 464-3188; gen fax (712) 464-3380; disp adv e-mail lcgraphic@iowatelecom.net; web site www.thegraphic-advocate.com
Circulation: 1,150pd,; Sworn/Estimate/Non-Audited
Advertising rate: Open inch rate $5.75
Group: Mid-America Publishing
Pub... Ken Ross
Delivery Method: Mail, Newsstand, Racks

LAKE MILLS

LAKE MILLS GRAPHIC (WED)
204 N Mill St, Lake Mills, IA, 50450-1316, Winnebago, USA; gen tel (641) 592-4222; gen fax (641) 592-6397; disp adv e-mail graphic@wctatel.net; web site www.lmgraphic.com
Circulation: 1,650pd, 0fr; Sworn/Estimate/Non-Audited
Advertising rate: Open inch rate $6.75
Established: 1872
Pub..Terry Gasper
Circ. Mgr.....................................Sheri Gasper
Delivery Method: Mail, Newsstand, Racks

LAMONI

LAMONI CHRONICLE (THUR)
120 N Linden St, Lamoni, IA, 50140-1046, Decatur, USA; gen tel (641) 784-6397; gen fax (641) 784-7669; disp adv e-mail new-news@grm.net
Circulation:; Sworn/Estimate/Non-Audited
Advertising rate: $5.00
Established: 1891
Business Manager....................Michelle Morris
Delivery Method: Mail, Newsstand, Racks

LAMONT

LAMONT LEADER (THUR)
621 Bush St, Lamont, IA, 50650-9041, Buchanan, USA; gen tel (563) 924-2361; gen fax (563) 924-2159; disp adv e-mail lamont-leader@iowatelecom.net
Circulation: 700pd,; Sworn/Estimate/Non-Audited
Advertising rate: Open inch rate $2.75
Ed. .... Steven C. Sanders

LE MARS

REMSEN BELL-ENTERPRISE (THUR)
41 1st Ave NE, Le Mars, IA, 51031-3535, Plymouth, USA; gen tel (712) 786-1196; gen fax (712) 786-1257; disp adv e-mail remsenbell@midlands.net; class adv e-mail systems@semissourian.com; ed e-mail systems@semissourian.com; web site No Website
Circulation: 1,100pd, 4fr; Sworn/Estimate/Non-Audited
Advertising rate: Open inch rate $3.50
Established: 1887
Group: Rust Communications
Office Mgr. ....Megan Sabin
Pub..Randy List
Sr Gen. Mgr.................................... Monte Jost
Mechanical Specifications: Type page 12 7/8 x 21; E - 6 cols, 2, 1/6 between; A - 6 cols, 2, 1/6 between; C - 6 cols, 2, 1/6 between. Equipment & Software: Hardware — 2-Gateway/GPS 166; Software — Microsoft/Windows, Microsoft/Office 97, Microsoft/

Publisher 97.
Delivery Method: Mail, Newsstand

LENOX

LENOX TIME TABLE (WED)

101 E Temple St, # 12, Lenox, IA, 50851-1210, Taylor, Adams, USA; gen tel (641) 333-2810; disp adv e-mail timetable@lenoxia.com; web site No Website
Circulation: 975pd,; Sworn/Estimate/Non-Audited
Advertising rate: Open inch rate $5.00
Established: 1874
Ed. .... Randy Larimer
Delivery Method: Mail, Newsstand, Racks

LEON

THE LEON JOURNAL-REPORTER (WED)

110 N Main St, Ste B, Leon, IA, 50144-1890, Decatur, USA; gen tel (641) 446-4151; gen fax (641) 446-7645; disp adv e-mail jrnews@grm.net
Circulation: 2,100pd, 24fr; Sworn/Estimate/Non-Audited
Advertising rate: Open inch rate $3.75
Established: 1865
Pub .... Corey R. Lindsey
Mechanical Specifications: Type page 15 3/4 x 21; E - 8 cols, 1 3/4, 1/4 between; A - 8 cols, 1 3/4, 1/4 between.Equipment & Software: ; Software — WordPerfect.
Delivery Method: Mail, Racks
Areas Served: 50144, 50140, 50065, 50108, 50067, 50103, 50264, 50262

LITTLE ROCK

LITTLE ROCK FREE LANCE (TUES)

PO Box 185, Little Rock, IA, 51243-0185, Lyon, USA; gen tel (712) 479-2270; disp adv e-mail vksc@mtcnet.net
Circulation: 810pd,; Sworn/Estimate/Non-Audited
Advertising rate: Open inch rate $1.99
Established: 1978
Pub .... Virginia Klaassen
Delivery Method: Mail

LOGAN

THE LOGAN HERALD-OBSERVER (WED)

107 N 4th Ave, Ste 3, Logan, IA, 51546-1365, Harrison, USA; gen tel (712) 644-2705; gen fax (712) 644-2788; disp adv e-mail news@heraldobserver.com; web site www.loganwoodbine.com
Circulation: 1,400pd,; Sworn/Estimate/Non-Audited
Advertising rate: Open inch rate $6.75
Ed. .... Mary Darling
Mechanical Specifications: Type page 15 x 21 1/2; E - 6 cols, 2 1/3, 1/6 between; A - 6 cols, 2 1/3, 1/6 between; C - 9 cols, 1 7/12, 1/6 between.Equipment & Software: Hardware — APP/Mac; Software — Microsoft.

LONE TREE

REPORTER (THUR)

PO Box 13, Lone Tree, IA, 52755-0013, Johnson, USA; gen tel (319) 629-5207; gen fax (319) 629-4203; disp adv e-mail ltnews@iowatelecom.net; web site www.thelonetreereporter.com
Circulation: 775pd,; Sworn/Estimate/Non-Audited
Advertising rate: Open inch rate $8.50
Established: 1897
Pub .... Ronald C. Slechta
Circ. Mgr.Helen SlechtaEquipment & Software: Hardware — APP/Mac Quadra 650; Software — QPS/QuarkXPress 3.32, Microsoft/Word 6.0.1.
Delivery Method: Mail, Newsstand, Racks

MADRID

MADRID REGISTER-NEWS (THUR)

102 S Main St, Madrid, IA, 50156-1232, Boone, USA; gen tel (515) 795-2730; gen fax (515) 795-2012; disp adv e-mail wilcoxprinting@mchsi.com
Circulation: 1,250pd,; Sworn/Estimate/Non-Audited
Advertising rate: Open inch rate $5.00
Established: 1881
Pub .... Dennis W. Wilcox
Circ. Mgr. .... Jennifer Williams
Ed. .... Carol Wilcox
Delivery Method: Mail, Newsstand

MALVERN

FREMONT-MILLS BEACON-ENTERPRISE (THUR)

PO Box 129, Malvern, IA, 51551-0129, Mills, USA; gen tel (712) 624-8512; gen fax (712) 624-9250; disp adv e-mail leaderbeacon@qwestoffice.net; web site No Website
Circulation: 800pd,; Sworn/Estimate/Non-Audited
Advertising rate: Open inch rate $4.25
Adv. Mgr. .... Margaret Waugh
Ed. .... Karol Siekman

THE MALVERN LEADER (THUR)

PO Box 129, Malvern, IA, 51551-0129, Mills, USA; gen tel (712) 624-8512; gen fax (712) 624-9250; disp adv e-mail leaderbeacon@qwestoffice.net; web site No Website
Circulation: 800pd,; Sworn/Estimate/Non-Audited
Advertising rate: Open inch rate $4.25
Adv. Mgr. .... Margaret Waugh
Ed. .... Karol Siekman

MANCHESTER

THE MANCHESTER PRESS (TUES)

109 E Delaware St, Manchester, IA, 52057-2208, Delaware, USA; gen tel (563) 927-2020; gen fax (563) 927-4945; disp adv e-mail manpress@mchsi.com; web site www.manchesterpress.com
Circulation: 4,800pd,; Sworn/Estimate/Non-Audited
Advertising rate: Open inch rate $9.20
Gen. Mgr./Adv. Mgr. .... Lori Schultetrenkamp
Adv. Sales .... Jennifer Klostermann
Delivery Method: Mail, Newsstand, Racks

MANILLA

MANILLA TIMES (THUR)

448 Main St, Manilla, IA, 51454-7708, Crawford, USA; gen tel (712) 654-2911; gen fax (712) 654-2910; disp adv e-mail manillatimesads@fmctc.com; ed e-mail manillatimes@fmctc.com
Circulation: 782pd, 18fr; Sworn/Estimate/Non-Audited
Advertising rate: Open inch rate $4.25
Established: 1899
Office Mgr .... Joleen Sievertsen
Graphic Des, Tech Supp .... Michele Ertz
Adv Mgr .... Kay Rutherford
Delivery Method: Mail, Newsstand

MANNING

MANNING MONITOR (THUR)

411 Main St, Manning, IA, 51455-1032, Carroll, USA; gen tel (712) 653-3854; gen fax (712) 653-9430; disp adv e-mail manningmonitor@iowatelecom.net; web site No Website
Circulation: 1,550pd,; Sworn/Estimate/Non-Audited
Advertising rate: Open inch rate $5.00
Established: 1893
Ed. .... Ronald A. Colling
Mechanical Specifications: Type page 12 1/2 x 21 1/2; E - 7 cols, 2 1/12, 1/6 between; A - 7 cols, 2 1/12, 1/6 between.Equipment & Software: Hardware — Gateway/2000; Presses — ATF/Chief 17, ABD.
Delivery Method: Mail, Newsstand, Racks

MANSON

JOURNAL HERALD (WED)

931 Main St, Manson, IA, 50563-5135, Calhoun, USA; gen tel (712) 469-3381; gen fax (712) 469-2648; disp adv e-mail journal@journalherald.com; class adv e-mail journal@journalherald.com; ed e-mail journal@journalherald.com; web site www.journalherald.com
Circulation: 1,300pd,; Sworn/Estimate/Non-Audited
Advertising rate: Open inch rate $6.00
Established: 1910
Pub .... Gary D. Dudley
Ed. .... Ron Sturgis
Mechanical Specifications: Type page 15 3/4 x 21; E - 8 cols, 1 5/6, 1/6 between; A - 8 cols, 1 5/6, 1/6 between; C - 8 cols, 1 5/6, 1/6 between.Equipment & Software: Hardware — APP/Mac.
Delivery Method: Mail, Newsstand
Areas Served: Calhoun, Southern Pocahontas, and Western Webster County

MAPLETON

MAPLETON PRESS (THUR)

502 Main St, Mapleton, IA, 51034-1215, Monona, USA; gen tel (712) 881-1101; gen fax (712) 881-1330; disp adv e-mail ads@mapletonpress.com; class adv e-mail ads@mapletonpress.com; ed e-mail news@mapletonpress.com; web site www.mapletonpress.com
Circulation: 1,300pd,; USPS
Advertising rate: $9.25 net
Established: 1874
Group: Enterprise Publishing Co.
Publisher .... Brad Swenson
Mechanical Specifications: 1 column = 1.833"
2 columns = 3.792"
3 columns = 5.75"
4 columns = 7.708"
5 columns = 9.667"
6 columns = 11.625"
Page height = 21.5"
Delivery Method: Mail, Newsstand
Areas Served: 51034, 51004, 51010, 51439, 51019, 51044, 51460, 51051, 51461, 51056, 51572, 51060

MAQUOKETA

MAQUOKETA SENTINEL-PRESS (WED, SAT)

108 W Quarry St, Maquoketa, IA, 52060-2244, Clinton, Jackson, USA; gen tel (563) 652-2441; gen fax (563) 652-6094; disp adv e-mail mspress@mspress.net; web site www.maqnews.com
Circulation: 5,050pd,; Sworn/Estimate/Non-Audited
Advertising rate: Open inch rate $10.00
Adv. Mgr. .... Rosie Morehead
Ed. .... Douglas D. Melvold
Delivery Method: Mail, Newsstand

MARENGO

MARENGO PIONEER-REPUBLICAN (THUR)

1152 Marengo Ave, Marengo, IA, 52301-1523, Iowa, USA; gen tel (319) 642-5506; gen fax (319) 642-5509; disp adv e-mail publish@netins.net; web site www.yourweeklypaper.com
Circulation: 2,542pd,; Sworn/Estimate/Non-Audited
Advertising rate: Open inch rate $10.30
Group: Gannett
Pub .... Martin Bunge
Adv. Sales Mgr. .... Paul Thompson
Mechanical Specifications: Type page 14 1/4 x 21; E - 6 cols, 2 1/16, 1/8 between; A - 6 cols, 2 1/16, 1/8 between; C - 6 cols, 2 1/16, 1/8 between.Equipment & Software: Hardware — APP/Mac 9600-233; Presses — 8-KP/News King 2000; Software — Adobe/PageMaker 6.0, Microsoft/Word 5.0.
Delivery Method: Mail, Newsstand, Racks

MC GREGOR

NORTH IOWA TIMES (WED)

220 Main St, Mc Gregor, IA, 52157-8718, Clayton, USA; gen tel (563) 873-2210; gen fax (608) 326-2443; disp adv e-mail howeads@mhtc.net; ed e-mail niteditor@mhtc.net; web site www.northiowatimes.com
Circulation: 750pd, 20,000fr; USPS
Advertising rate: Open inch rate $8.40
Established: 1856
Group: Courier Press
Digital Platform - Mobile: Apple
Publisher .... Gary Howe
Editor .... Audrey Posten
Mechanical Specifications: Type page 10 x 15 1/2; E - 5 cols, 1 11/12, 1/6 between; A - 5 cols, 1 11/12, 1/6 between; C - 5 cols, 1 11/12, 1/6 between.Equipment & Software: Hardware — APP/Mac, PC; Presses — G/Community; Software — APP/Mac CS 5.5
Delivery Method: Mail, Newsstand
Areas Served: 52157

MEDIAPOLIS

MEDIAPOLIS NEWS (THUR)

616 Main St, Mediapolis, IA, 52637-7731, Des Moines, USA; gen tel (319) 394-3174; gen fax (319) 394-3134; disp adv e-mail meponews@mepotelco.net; class adv e-mail meponews@mepotelco.net; web site www.mediapolisnews.com
Circulation: 1,000pd, 600fr; Sworn/Estimate/Non-Audited
Advertising rate: $6.00
Established: 1874
Delivery Method: Mail, Racks
Areas Served: 52637, 52650, 52623, 52601, 52655, 52660, 52640, 52646, 52653, 52644, 52645, 52641, 52440, 50092

MISSOURI VALLEY

MISSOURI VALLEY TIMES-NEWS (WED, FRI)

501 E Erie St, Missouri Valley, IA, 51555-1646, Harrison, USA; gen tel (712) 642-2791; gen fax (712) 642-2595; disp adv e-mail advertising@missourivalleytimes.com; class adv e-mail classifieds@missourivalleytimes.com; ed e-mail news@missourivalleytimes.com; web site www.missourivalleytimes.com
Circulation: 1,900pd,; USPS
Advertising rate: Open inch rate $10.00 net
Established: 1868
Group: Enterprise Publishing Co.
President .... Mark Rhoades
Publisher .... Brad Swenson
Mechanical Specifications: Type page 11.625" x 21.5"; E - 6 cols, 2, 1/8 between; A - 6 cols, 2, 1/8 between; C - 6 cols, 2, 1/8 between.
Delivery Method: Mail, Newsstand
Areas Served: 51555, 51542, 51546, 51550, 51545, 51556, 51557, 51564, 51579, 51529

MONROE

MONROE LEGACY (THUR)
213 W Mills St, Monroe, IA, 50170-7920, Jasper, USA; gen tel (641) 259-2708; disp adv e-mail mmml@iowatelecom.net; web site www.monroelegacy.com
Advertising rate: Open inch rate $3.00
Established: 1873
Delivery Method: Mail, Newsstand, Racks

MONTICELLO

THE MONTICELLO EXPRESS (WED)
111 E Grand St, Monticello, IA, 52310-1688, Jones, USA; gen tel (319) 465-3555; gen fax (319) 465-4611; disp adv e-mail advertising@monicelloexpress.com; web site www.monticelloexpress.com
Circulation: 3,450pd,; Sworn/Estimate/Non-Audited
Advertising rate: Open inch rate $9.70
Established: 1865
Co-Pub....................................Dan Goodyear
Co-Pub....................................Mark Spensley
Ed....................................Kim Brooks
Graph. Dsgn....................................Abby Manternach
Mechanical Specifications: Type page 10 1/4 x 16; E - 6 cols, 1 7/12, 1/6 between; A - 6 cols, 1 7/12, 1/6 between; C - 6 cols, 1 7/12, 1/6 between.Equipment & Software: Hardware — APP/Macs; Software — Adobe/PageMaker 6.0, Multi-Ad/Creator, Adobe/Photoshop, Adobe/Illustrator, Microsoft/Word, QPS/QuarkXPress.
Delivery Method: Mail, Newsstand, Racks
Areas Served: 52321, 52331, 52033, 52205, 52212, 52219, 52237, 52252, 52310

MORNING SUN

MORNING SUN NEWS-HERALD (THUR)
11 Division St, # 8, Morning Sun, IA, 52640-7616, Louisa, USA; gen tel (319) 868-7509; gen fax (319) 868-7509; disp adv e-mail lpc@louisacomm.net
Advertising rate: $5.30
Established: 1881
Delivery Method: Mail, Newsstand, Racks

MOUNT AYR

MOUNT AYR RECORD-NEWS (THUR)
122 W Madison St, Mount Ayr, IA, 50854-1630, Ringgold, USA; gen tel (641) 464-2440; gen fax (641) 464-2229; disp adv e-mail staff@mtayrnews.com; web site mtayrnews.com
Circulation: 2,221pd, 69fr; Sworn/Estimate/Non-Audited
Advertising rate: Open inch rate $5.90
Established: 1865
Group: Paragon Publications
Prodn. Mgr....................................LuAnn Jackson
Ed & Pub....................................Tom Hawley
News Ed....................................Darrell Dodge
Office Mgr....................................Lora Stull
Reporter....................................Chanse Hall
Proofreader....................................Sue Carson
Mechanical Specifications: Type page 11.5 x 21; E -6 cols, 1 5/8, 1/6 between; A - 6 cols, 1 5/8, 1/6 between; C - 6 cols, 1 5/8, 1/6 between.Equipment & Software: Hardware — APP/Mac, APP/Power Mac; Presses — HI; Software — Adobe/PageMaker 6.0, Adobe/Photoshop, Claris/Works, Microsoft/Word.
Delivery Method: Mail, Racks
Areas Served: Ringgold County, Iowa

MOUNT VERNON

MOUNT VERNON-LISBON SUN (THUR)
108 1st St SW, Mount Vernon, IA, 52314-4706, Linn, USA; gen tel (319) 895-6216; gen fax (319) 895-6217; disp adv e-mail advertising@mtvernonlisbonsun.com; ed e-mail news@mtvernonlisbonsun.com; web site www.mvlsun.com
Circulation: 2,500pd, 3,000fr; Sworn/Estimate/Non-Audited
Advertising rate: Open inch rate $7.25
Established: 1869
Group: Woodward Communications Inc
Adv. Mgr....................................Richard Eskelsen
Pub....................................Jake Krob
Ed....................................Margaret Stevens
Nathan Countryman
Mechanical Specifications: Type page 11 x 21 1/2; E - 6 cols, 1.5, 1/6 between; A - 6 cols, 1.5, 1/6 between; C - 6 cols, 1 1/2, 1/6 between.Equipment & Software: Hardware — APP/Mac, 1-PC, 6-APP/Mac; Software — Microsoft/Word, QPS/QuarkXPress 4.1, Appleworks 5, 2-Multi-Ad/Creator 1.5.
Delivery Method: Mail, Newsstand
Areas Served: 52314, 52253, 52306, 52305, 52403

MOVILLE

THE RECORD (THUR)
238 Main St, # 546, Moville, IA, 51039-7713, Woodbury, USA; gen tel (844) 873-3141; gen fax (712) 873-3142; disp adv e-mail record@wiatel.net; class adv e-mail record@wiatel.net; ed e-mail blake@wiatel.net; web site www.movillerecord.com - 4,000(views) 2,400(visitors)
Circulation: 2,500pd, 15fr; Sworn/Estimate/Non-Audited
Advertising rate: Open Inch Rate: $10/column inch
Established: 1943
Group: Baker Newspapers, Inc.
Pres....................................Kent A. Baker
Pub & Ed....................................Blake Stubbs
Produc Mgr....................................Bedford Robinson
Office/Circu/Bus Mgr....................................Lisa Fouts
Composition Mgr....................................Brian Johnson
Kingsley Office Mgr....................................Pam Clark
Sioux Valley News Mgr....................................Karen Newman
Mechanical Specifications: Type page 11 5/8 x 21 1/2; E - 6 cols, 1 5/6, 1/6 between; A - 6 cols, 1 5/6, 1/6 between; C - 6 cols, 1 5/6, 1/6 between.Equipment & Software: Hardware — IBM, APP/Mac; Software — QPS/QuarkXPress.
Delivery Method: Mail, Newsstand
Areas Served: Moville, Iowa - 51039; Lawton, Iowa - 51030; Kingsley, Iowa - 51028; Correctionville, Iowa - 51016; Anthon, Iowa - 51004; Bronson, Iowa - 51007; Pierson, Iowa - 51048; Hornick, Iowa - 51026; Cushing, Iowa - 51018; Washta, Iowa - 51061; Quimby, Iowa - 51049; Oto, Iowa - 51044 Woodbury County, Iowa; Plymouth County, Iowa Cherokee County, Iowa

MUSCATINE

THE MUSCATINE POST (TUES)
301 E 3rd St, Muscatine, IA, 52761-4116, Muscatine, USA; gen tel (563) 263-2169; gen fax (563) 263-7240; web site www.muscatinejournal.com
Circulation: 1pd, 14,913fr; Sworn/Estimate/Non-Audited
Advertising rate: Open inch rate $17.33
Pub....................................Lynn Schultz
Circ. Mgr....................................Tom McCoy

NEOLA

NEOLA GAZETTE (THUR)
107 4th St, Neola, IA, 51559-3126, Pottawattamie, USA; gen tel (712) 485-2276; gen fax (712) 485-2277; disp adv e-mail neolagazette@fbx.com
Advertising rate: Open inch rate $5.00

NEW HAMPTON

NASHUA REPORTER (THUR)
10 N Chestnut Ave, New Hampton, IA, 50659-1349, Chickasaw, USA; gen tel (641) 394-2111; gen fax (641) 394-2113; disp adv e-mail nashuareporter@gmail.com; web site www.nashuareporter.com
Advertising rate: Open inch rate $4.00
Group: Hallmark Integrated Media, Inc.
Delivery Method: Mail, Newsstand, Racks

NEW HAMPTON TRIBUNE (TUES, FRI)
10 N Chestnut Ave, New Hampton, IA, 50659-1349, Chickasaw, USA; gen tel (641) 394-2111; gen fax (641) 394-2113; disp adv e-mail tribune@nhtrib.com
Circulation: 2,600pd,; Sworn/Estimate/Non-Audited
Advertising rate: Open inch rate $10.35
Digital Platform - Mobile: Apple
Digital Platform - Tablet: Apple iOS
Pub....................................Dave Stanley
Mechanical Specifications: Type page 15 1/8 x 21 1/2; E - 6 cols, 2 5/16, between; A - 9 cols, 1 9/16, between; C - 9 cols, 1 9/16, between.Equipment & Software: Hardware — APP/Mac.
Delivery Method: Mail, Newsstand, Racks
Areas Served: Chickasaw County

NEW LONDON

NEW LONDON JOURNAL (THUR)
138 W Main St, New London, IA, 52645-1334, Henry, USA; gen tel (319) 367-2366; gen fax (319) 367-2366; disp adv e-mail lpc@louisacomm.net
Circulation: 1,200pd,; Sworn/Estimate/Non-Audited
Advertising rate: Open inch rate $5.40
Group: Louisa Publishing Co. Ltd.
Pub....................................Michael A. Hodges
Ed........Evelyn GarmoeEquipment & Software: Hardware — APP/Mac; Software — Adobe/PageMaker, Claris/MacWrite, Microsoft/Word.
Delivery Method: Mail, Newsstand, Racks

NORTH LIBERTY

NORTH LIBERTY LEADER (WED)
10 W Cherry St, North Liberty, IA, 52317-8822, Johnson, USA; gen tel (319) 624-2233; gen fax (319) 624-1356; disp adv e-mail hybrid@southslope.net; web site www.northlibertyleader.com
Circulation: 1,100pd,; Sworn/Estimate/Non-Audited
Advertising rate: Open inch rate $4.50
Pub....................................Doug Lindner
Delivery Method: Mail, Newsstand, Racks

NORTHWOOD

MANLY JUNCTION SIGNAL (THUR)
801 Central Ave, Northwood, IA, 50459-1519, Worth, USA; gen tel (641) 324-1051; gen fax (641) 324-2432; disp adv e-mail anchor@northwoodanchor.net; web site www.northanchor.com
Circulation:; Sworn/Estimate/Non-Audited
Advertising rate: Open inch rate $4.50
Pub....................................Jane Podgorniak
Adv. Mgr....................................Jennifer Moe
Delivery Method: Mail, Newsstand

NORA SPRINGS ROCKFORD REGISTER (THUR)
PO Box 107, Northwood, IA, 50459-0107, Worth, USA; gen tel (641) 324-1051; gen fax (641) 324-2432; disp adv e-mail jane@northwoodanchor.net
Circulation:; Sworn/Estimate/Non-Audited
Advertising rate: Open inch rate $4.50
Publisher....................................Jane Podgorniak
Sales....................................Jennifer Moe
Julie Salisbury
Delivery Method: Mail, Newsstand, Racks

NORTHWOOD ANCHOR (WED)
801 Central Ave, Northwood, IA, 50459-1519, Worth, USA; gen tel (641) 324-1051; gen fax (641) 324-2432; disp adv e-mail anchor@northwoodanchor.net; web site www.northwoodanchor.com
Advertising rate: Open inch rate $6.30Jane Podgorniak
Delivery Method: Mail, Newsstand, Racks

NORWALK

NORTH WARREN TOWN AND COUNTY NEWS (THUR)
PO Box 325, Norwalk, IA, 50211-0325, Warren, USA; gen tel (515) 989-3251
Circulation: 1,722pd,; Sworn/Estimate/Non-Audited
Advertising rate: Open inch rate $4.25
Pub....................................Steven Klein

OAKLAND

OAKLAND HERALD (WED)
146 MAIN ST, Oakland, IA, 51560, Pottawattamie, USA; gen tel (888) 343-2154; disp adv e-mail avocajh@iowatelecom.net
Advertising rate: Open inch rate $4.00
Editor....................................Rich Price
Delivery Method: Mail, Newsstand, Racks

OCHEYEDAN

THE OCHEYEDAN PRESS-MELVIN NEWS (WED)
859 Main St, Ocheyedan, IA, 51354-7726, Osceola, USA; gen tel (712) 758-3140; gen fax (712) 758-3186; disp adv e-mail pressinc@nethtc.net
Circulation: 1,000pd, 17fr; Sworn/Estimate/Non-Audited
Advertising rate: Open inch rate $5.45
Gen. Mgr....................................Arlyn Pedley
Ed....................................Jan Reiste Pedley
Delivery Method: Mail
Areas Served: Osceola County and surrounding area

ODEBOLT

THE CHRONICLE (THUR)
216 S Main St, Odebolt, IA, 51458-7605, Sac, USA; gen tel (712) 668-2253; gen fax (712) 668-4364; disp adv e-mail paper@netins.net; web site No Website
Circulation: 1,500pd,; Sworn/Estimate/Non-Audited
Advertising rate: Open inch rate $4.25Editions: (2) 2 total ½ The Chronicle-Odebolt Early Edition; The Chronicle-Wall Lake Edition (650);
Pub....................................Jerry Wiseman
Ed....................................Mary Linda Mack
Ed....................................Mary Linda Mack
Mechanical Specifications: Type page 10 x 15.

OGDEN

OGDEN REPORTER (TUES, WED)
222 W Walnut St, 222 West Walnut St., Ogden, IA, 50212-2004, Boone, USA; gen tel (515) 275-4101; adv tel (515) 275-2101; gen fax (515) 275-2678; adv fax (515) 275-2678; disp adv e-mail alban@netins.net; class adv e-mail sharonalban@gmail.com; ed e-mail alban@netins.net; web site www.ogdenreporter.com
Circulation: 1,850pd,; Sworn/Estimate/Non-Au-

dited
Advertising rate: Open inch rate $6.50
Established: 1884
Digital Platform - Mobile: Apple
Digital Platform - Tablet: Apple iOS
Pub....Sharon Alban
Delivery Method: Mail, Newsstand, Racks
Areas Served:
50212,50309,50036,50140,50040, etc. in Iowa

ONAWA

ONAWA DEMOCRAT (WED)
720 Iowa Ave, Onawa, IA, 51040-1628, Monona, USA; gen tel (712) 423-2411; gen fax (712) 423-2411; disp adv e-mail democrat@longlines.com
Advertising rate: Open inch rate $6.00
Delivery Method: Mail, Newsstand, Racks

ORANGE CITY

SIOUX COUNTY CAPITAL-DEMOCRAT (WED)
113 Central Ave SE, Orange City, IA, 51041-1738, Sioux, USA; gen tel (712) 737-4266; gen fax (712) 737-3896; disp adv e-mail pluimpub@orangecitycomm.net; class adv e-mail pluimpub@orangecitycomm.net; ed e-mail pluimpub@orangecitycomm.net; web site www.siouxcountynews.com
Circulation: 1,800pd, 25fr; Sworn/Estimate/Non-Audited
Advertising rate: Open inch rate $7.25
Established: 1882
Pub....Dale H. Pluim
Gen. Mgr....Bob Hulstein
Adv. Mgr....Dennis Den Hartog
Ed....Doug Calsbeek
Delivery Method: Mail
Areas Served: 51003, 51022, 51238. 51036, 51041

OSAGE

MITCHELL COUNTY PRESS-NEWS (WED)
112 N 6th St, Osage, IA, 50461-1202, Mitchell County, USA; gen tel (641) 732-3721; gen fax (641) 732-5689; disp adv e-mail editor@mcpress.com; class adv e-mail ads@mcpress.com; ed e-mail editor@mcpress.com; web site www.mcpress.com
Circulation: 6,900pd,; Sworn/Estimate/Non-Audited
Advertising rate: Open inch rate $7.50
Group: Lee Enterprises, Inc.
Digital Platform - Tablet: Apple iOS
Mng. Ed....David Namanny
Pub./Gen. Mgr....Howard Query
Adv. Mgr....Greg Wilderman
Mechanical Specifications: Type page 13 x 21 1/2; E - 6 cols, 2, 1/6 between; A - 6 cols, 2, 1/6 between; C - 6 cols, 2, 1/6 between. Equipment & Software: Hardware — APP/Mac; Presses — KP; Software — Adobe/PageMaker, QPS/QuarkXPress.
Delivery Method: Mail, Newsstand, Racks
Areas Served: 50461

OSCEOLA

OSCEOLA SENTINEL-TRIBUNE (THUR)
111 E Washington St, Osceola, IA, 50213-1244, Clarke, USA; gen tel (641) 342-2131; gen fax (641) 342-2060; disp adv e-mail ccpnews@osceolaiowa.com; ed e-mail ccpeditor@osceolaiowa.com; web site www.osceolaiowa.com
Circulation: 3,200pd, 11,000fr; CVC
Advertising rate: Open inch rate $5.50
Group: Shaw Media
Pub....Rich Paulsen
Mng., Ed....Scott Vicker
Mechanical Specifications: Type page 11 x 21 1/2; E - 7 cols, 9 1/9, between; A - 7 cols, 9 1/9, between; C - 8 cols, 9 1/9, between. Equipment & Software: Hardware — 10-APP/Mac, 2-IBM; Presses — 4-G/Community, Risco/11x17, ABD/11x17; Software — QPS/QuarkXPress, Adobe/Photoshop, Adobe/Illustrator, Microsoft/Word.
Delivery Method: Mail, Newsstand
Areas Served: Clarke County

PANORA

GUTHRIE COUNTY VEDETTE (THUR)
111 E Main St, Panora, IA, 50216-1155, Guthrie, USA; gen tel (641) 755-2115; gen fax (641) 755-2425; disp adv e-mail gc-times@netins.net
Circulation: 1,200pd,; Sworn/Estimate/Non-Audited
Advertising rate: Open inch rate $3.00
Gen. Mgr....Gordon Castile
Ed....Scott P. Gonzales
Rptr....Caitlin Ware
Delivery Method: Mail, Newsstand, Racks

PARKERSBURG

PARKERSBURG ECLIPSE-NEWS-REVIEW (WED)
503 Coates St, Parkersburg, IA, 50665-7733, Butler, USA; gen tel (319) 346-1461; gen fax (319) 346-1461; disp adv e-mail butlersales.map@gmail.com
Circulation: 1,500pd, 16fr; Sworn/Estimate/Non-Audited
Advertising rate: Open inch rate $5.50
Group: Mid-America Publishing
Mgr Ed....John Jensen
Office Mgr/Designer....Danielle Potkonak
Reg Sports Ed....Ian Murphy
Mechanical Specifications: Type page 14 1/2 x 21 1/2; E - 8 cols, 1 3/4, 1/12 between; A - 8 cols, 1 3/4, 1/12 between; C - 8 cols, 1 3/4, 1/12 between.Equipment & Software: Hardware — Gateway, Dell; Software — Aldus/PageMaker 6.0, Microsoft/Word.
Delivery Method: Mail, Newsstand, Racks

PELLA

PELLA CHRONICLE (THUR)
812 Main St, Pella, IA, 50219-1522, Marion, USA; gen tel (641) 628-3882; gen fax (641) 628-3905; disp adv e-mail thechronicle@iowatelecom.net; chroniclenews@iowatelecom.net; class adv e-mail chronicleads@iowatelecom.net; ed e-mail chroniclenews@iowatelecom.net; web site www.pellachronicle.com - 15,000(views) 7,000(visitors)
Circulation: 2,000pd,; Sworn/Estimate/Non-Audited
Advertising rate: Open inch rate $8.20
Established: 1866
Group: Community Newspaper Holdings, Inc.
Pub....Maureen Miller
Ed....Clint Brown
Delivery Method: Mail, Newsstand, Racks

PERRY

PERRY CHIEF (FRI)
1316 2nd St, Ste B, Perry, IA, 50220-1549, Dallas, USA; gen tel (515) 465-4666; gen fax (515) 465-3087; disp adv e-mail publisher@theperrychief.com; class adv e-mail ads@theperrychief.com; ed e-mail news@theperrychief.com; web site www.theperrychief.com
Circulation: 1,900pd, 14,500fr; Sworn/Estimate/Non-Audited
Advertising rate: Open inch rate $11.00
Established: 1874
Group: GateHouse Media, Inc.
Publisher....Patricia Snyder
Adv. Mgr....Linda Schumacher
Prodn. Mgr....Don Thomas
Gen. Mgr....Lori Lott
Adv. Sales Rep....Dana Fink
Columnist / Reporter....Melissa Todelo
Mechanical Specifications: Type page 13 1/4 x 21; E - 6 cols, 2, 1/6 between; A - 6 cols, 2, 1/6 between; C - 6 cols, 2, 1/6 between. Equipment & Software: Hardware — APP/Mac; Presses — G/Community; Software — Multi-Ad/Creator, QPS/QuarkXPress, Adobe/Photoshop.
Delivery Method: Mail, Newsstand, Racks

PLEASANTVILLE

MARION COUNTY NEWS (THUR)
901 N Highway 5, Pleasantville, IA, 50225-7532, Marion, USA; gen tel (515) 848-5614; gen fax (515) 848-5614; disp adv e-mail dab@dwx.com
Circulation: 1,300pd,; Sworn/Estimate/Non-Audited
Advertising rate: Open inch rate $3.50
Established: 1880
Pub....Steven Klein
Ed....Deannn Borgerson
Delivery Method: Mail, Newsstand, Racks

POCAHONTAS

LAURENS SUN (WED)
218 N Main St, Pocahontas, IA, 50574-1605, Pocahontas, USA; gen tel (712) 335-3553; adv tel (712) 335-3553; ed tel (712) 335-3553; gen fax (712) 335-3856; adv fax (712) 335-3856; ed fax (712) 335-3856; disp adv e-mail ads@laurenssun.com; class adv e-mail ads@laurenssun.com; ed e-mail publisher@laurenssun.com
Circulation: 500pd,; Sworn/Estimate/Non-Audited
Advertising rate: Open inch rate $7.17
Owner/Pub./Ed....Chris Vrba
Delivery Method: Mail, Newsstand, Racks
Areas Served: 50554, 50565

POCAHONTAS RECORD-DEMOCRAT (WED)
218 N Main St, Ste 1, Pocahontas, IA, 50574-1612, Pocahontas, USA; gen tel (712) 335-3553; adv tel (712) 335-3553; ed tel (712) 335-3553; gen fax (712) 335-3856; adv fax (712) 335-3856; ed fax (712) 335-3856; disp adv e-mail ads@pokyrd.com; class adv e-mail ads@pokyrd.com; ed e-mail publisher@pokyrd.com
Circulation: 1,800pd, 44fr; Sworn/Estimate/Non-Audited
Advertising rate: Open inch rate $7.17
Adv. Mgr....Marcia Hamp
Classified Mgr....Mary Phillips
Owner/Pub./Ed....Chris Vrba
Staff writer....Jamie Whitney
Mechanical Specifications: Type page 27 x 21 1/2; E - 7 cols, 2, between; A - 7 cols, 2, between.Equipment & Software: Hardware — APP/Power Macs; Software — Adobe/PageMaker, Microsoft/Word, Adobe/Illustrator.
Delivery Method: Mail, Newsstand, Racks
Areas Served: 50510, 50515, 50527, 50540, 50541, 50546, 50554, 50562, 50563, 50565, 50568, 50571, 50574, 50575, 50576, 50581, 50593, 51366

POSTVILLE

POSTVILLE HERALD (WED)
101 N Lawler St, Postville, IA, 52162-7799, Allamakee, USA; gen tel (563) 864-3333; gen fax (563) 864-3400; disp adv e-mail ads@postvilleherald.com; class adv e-mail ads@postvilleherald.com; ed e-mail news@postvilleherald.com
Circulation: 1,107pd, 0fr; USPS
Advertising rate: $6.50
Established: 1892
Pub....Jason Meyer
Ed....Sharon Drahn
Circ. Mgr....Nadine Brock
Adv. Mgr....R. Craig White
Mechanical Specifications: 27" Broadsheet, 23" Total Depth
Each Page is 12.5" Wide, 21.5" Deep
7 Columns per Page
Columns 1.625"; Gutter 0.1875"
Delivery Method: Mail, Newsstand
Areas Served: 52047, 52101, 52133, 52135, 52141, 52156, 52157, 52158, 52159, 52161, 52162, 52170, 52172

PRAIRIE CITY

PRAIRIE CITY NEWS (THUR)
104 E 5th St, Prairie City, IA, 50228-7765, Jasper, USA; gen tel (515) 994-2349; disp adv e-mail prairiecitynews@aol.com
Advertising rate: Open inch rate $4.50
Established: 1874
Delivery Method: Mail, Newsstand, Racks

PRESTON

PRESTON TIMES (WED)
4 N Stephens St, Preston, IA, 52069-7742, Jackson, USA; gen tel (563) 689-3841; gen fax (563) 689-3842; web site prestontimesonline.com
Circulation: 1,000pd, 25fr; Sworn/Estimate/Non-Audited
Advertising rate: Open inch rate $3.50
Pub....Terry Mertens
Ed....John Mertens
Delivery Method: Mail, Newsstand, Racks

RED OAK

RED OAK EXPRESS (TUES)
20012 Commerce Dr, Red Oak, IA, 51566, Montgomery, USA; gen tel (712) 623-2566; gen fax (712) 623-2568; disp adv e-mail advertising@redoakexpress.com; ed e-mail news@redoakexpress.com; web site www.redoakexpress.com
Circulation: 3,500pd,; Sworn/Estimate/Non-Audited
Advertising rate: Open inch rate $11.73
Established: 1868
Group: Landmark Communications, Inc.
Landmark Community Newspapers, LLC
Adv. Sales....Sharon Wiese
Gen. Mgr./Ed....Greg Orear
Office Mgr./Bookkeeper....Liz Felos
Reporter....Nick Johansen
Pub. & Ed....Brad Hicks
Mechanical Specifications: Type page 11 5/8 x 21 1/2; E - 6 cols, 1 5/6, between; A - 6 cols, 1 5/6, between; C - 8 cols, 8 1/6, between. Equipment & Software: Hardware — APP/Mac; Presses — G/Community; Software — QPS/QuarkXPress 6.1.
Delivery Method: Mail, Newsstand, Racks

REINBECK

REINBECK COURIER (THUR)
107 Broad St, Reinbeck, IA, 50669-1013, Grundy, USA; gen tel (319) 345-2031; gen fax (319) 345-6767; ed e-mail editor@reinbeckcourier.com; web site www.reinbeckcourier.com
Circulation: 1,112pd,; Sworn/Estimate/Non-Audited
Advertising rate: Open inch rate $7.35
Group: Ogden Newspapers Inc.
Pub....Mike Schlesinger
Adv. Mgr....Molly Dahms
Mechanical Specifications: Type page 11 3/4 x 21 1/2; E - 6 cols, 1 7/8, 1/8 between; A - 6 cols, 1 7/8, 1/8 between; C - 6 cols, 1 7/8, 1/8 between.Equipment & Software: Hardware — G-5; Software — Quark
Delivery Method: Mail, Newsstand, Racks
Areas Served: 50669

RICEVILLE

RICEVILLE RECORDER (THUR)
111 E 2nd St, Riceville, IA, 50466-7717, Howard, USA; gen tel (641) 985-2142; gen fax (641) 985-4185; disp adv e-mail recorder@myomnitel.com; web site facebook.com/RicevilleRecorder
Circulation: 1,350pd,; Sworn/Estimate/Non-Audited
Advertising rate: Open inch rate $4.25
Established: 1886
Pub....Daniel Evans
Ed....Casander Leff
Mechanical Specifications: Type page 13 x 21 1/2; E - 6 cols, 2, 1/6 between; A - 6 cols, 2, 1/6 between; C - 6 cols, 2, 1/6 between.
Delivery Method: Mail, Newsstand, Racks

RICHLAND

THE CLARION-PLAINSMAN (THUR)
107 S Richland St, Richland, IA, 52585-9226, Keokuk, USA; gen tel (319) 456-6641; gen fax (319) 456-6641; disp adv e-mail lpc@louisacomm.net
Advertising rate: $5.40
Established: 1881
Delivery Method: Mail, Newsstand, Racks

ROCK RAPIDS

LYON COUNTY REPORTER (WED)
310 1st Ave, Rock Rapids, IA, 51246-1595, Lyon, USA; gen tel (712) 472-2525; adv tel (712) 472-2525; ed tel (712) 472-2525; gen fax (712) 472-3414; adv fax (712) 472-3414; ed fax (712) 472-3414; disp adv e-mail lmiller@ncppub.com; class adv e-mail lkuehl@ncppub.com; ed e-mail jjensen@ncppub.com; web site www.lyoncountyreporter.com
Circulation: 1,200pd,; Sworn/Estimate/Non-Audited
Advertising rate: Open inch rate $7.40
Group: New Century Press
Digital Platform - Mobile: Apple, Android, Windows, Blackberry
Digital Platform - Tablet: Apple iOS, Android, Windows 7, Blackberry Tablet OS, Kindle, Nook, Kindle Fire
Pub./COO....Jim Hensley
Ed....Jessica Jensen
Gen. Mgr....Lisa Miller
Mechanical Specifications: Type page 11 5/8 x 21 1/2; E - 6 cols, 1 13/16, 1/6 between; A - 6 cols, 1 13/16, 1/6 between; C - 6 cols, 1 13/16, 1/6 between.Equipment & Software: ; Software — QPS/QuarkXPress 4.0.
Delivery Method: Mail, Newsstand
Areas Served: 51246

ROCK VALLEY

ROCK VALLEY BEE (TUES)
1442 Main St, Rock Valley, IA, 51247-1224, Sioux, USA; gen tel (712) 476-2795; gen fax (712) 476-2796; disp adv e-mail rvbee@mtcnet.net
Circulation: 1,400pd, 4,500fr; Sworn/Estimate/Non-Audited
Advertising rate: Open inch rate $7.80
Pub....Chris Godfredsen
Delivery Method: Mail, Newsstand, Racks
Areas Served: 51247

ROCKWELL

ROCKWELL PIONEER ENTERPRISE (THUR)
304 Main St E, Rockwell, IA, 50469-7755, Cerro Gordo, USA; gen tel (641) 822-3193; gen fax (641) 822-3193; disp adv e-mail pioneerenterprise@qwestoffice.net; web site www.pioneerenterprise.com
Advertising rate: Open inch rate $4.75

ROCKWELL CITY

THE GRAPHIC ADVOCATE (WED)
505 4th St, Rockwell City, IA, 50579-1901, Calhoun, USA; gen tel (712) 297-7544; adv tel (712) 464-3188; gen fax (712) 297-7544; disp adv e-mail lcgraphic@iowatelecom.net; ed e-mail gaeditor@iowatelecom.net; web site http://thegraphic-advocate.com/index1.htm
Circulation: 700pd,; Sworn/Estimate/Non-Audited
Advertising rate: Open inch rate $5.25
Established: 1889
Adv. Mgr....Teresa Snyder
Ed....Ken Ross
Delivery Method: Mail, Newsstand, Racks

SAC CITY

THE SAC SUN (TUES)
406 Williams St, Sac City, IA, 50583-1739, Sac, USA; gen tel (712) 662-7161; adv tel (712) 662-7161; ed tel (712) 662-7161; gen fax (712) 662-4198; adv fax (712) 662-4198; ed fax (712) 662-4198; disp adv e-mail sacsuneditor@frontiernet.net; class adv e-mail sacsun1@frontiernet.net; ed e-mail sacsuneditor@frontiernet.net
Circulation: 1,400pd, 85fr; Sworn/Estimate/Non-Audited
Advertising rate: Open inch rate $8.60
Established: 1871
Group: Sac County Newspapers
Ed./Gen. Mgr....Dale P. Wegner
Adv./Graphic Design....Brenda Fiscus
Office Mgr/Billing....Bridget Harms
Advt Sales....Galen Grote
Mechanical Specifications: 15" x 21.5"Equipment & Software: Hardware — IMac; Software — Adobe Creative Suite 5.5
Delivery Method: Mail, Newsstand
Areas Served: 50568, 51450, 50561, 51458, 50567, 50583, 50535, 50551, 51433, 51437

SAINT ANSGAR

ST. ANSGAR ENTERPRISE JOURNAL (SAT)
204 E 4th St, Saint Ansgar, IA, 50472-9606, Mitchell, USA; gen tel (641) 713-4541; gen fax (641) 713-2399; disp adv e-mail staej@iowatelecom.net; web site www.staej.com
Circulation: 1,300pd,; Sworn/Estimate/Non-Audited
Advertising rate: Open inch rate $4.75
Gen. Mgr....Deb Stickney
Ed....Chuck Peterson
Mechanical Specifications: Type page 15 x ; E - 6 cols, 2, 1/8 between; A - 6 cols, 2, 1/8 between.Equipment & Software: Hardware — APP/Power Mac 7300/180; Software — QPS/QuarkXPress.

SANBORN

SANBORN PIONEER (THUR)
121 Main St, Sanborn, IA, 51248-7727, Obrien, USA; gen tel (712) 729-3201; gen fax (712) 729-3202; disp adv e-mail spioneer@tcaexpress.net
Advertising rate: Open inch rate $3.90
Established: 1871
Pub./Ed....scott Chrisman
Delivery Method: Mail, Newsstand, Racks

SCHALLER

SCHALLER HERALD (WED)
203 S Main St, Schaller, IA, 51053-7732, Sac, USA; gen tel (712) 275-4229; gen fax (712) 275-4289; disp adv e-mail herald@schallertel.net; web site facebook.com/Schallerherald
Circulation: 900pd,; Sworn/Estimate/Non-Audited
Advertising rate: Open inch rate $3.36
Ed....Betty Bailey
Delivery Method: Mail, Newsstand, Racks

SCRANTON

SCRANTON JOURNAL (WED)
PO Box 187, Scranton, IA, 51462-0187, Greene, USA; gen tel (712) 651-2321; gen fax (712) 651-2599; disp adv e-mail ciapub@netins.net
Circulation: 832pd,; Sworn/Estimate/Non-Audited
Advertising rate: Open inch rate $4.50
Established: 1880
Ed....Luann Waldo
Delivery Method: Mail

SERGEANT BLUFF

THE SERGEANT BLUFF ADVOCATE (THUR)
204 1st St, Ste A2, Sergeant Bluff, IA, 51054-8589, Woodbury, USA; gen tel (712) 943-2583; adv tel (712) 943-2583; gen fax (712) 943-4606; adv fax (712) 943-4606; disp adv e-mail advocate@longlines.com; class adv e-mail advocate@longlines.com; ed e-mail advocate@longlines.com; web site N/A
Circulation: 1,100pd, 50fr; Sworn/Estimate/Non-Audited
Advertising rate: Open inch rate $5.50
Established: 1970
Group: Domino Publishers, Inc.
Digital Platform - Mobile: Windows, Other
Digital Platform - Tablet: Other
Pblr/Editor....Wayne Dominowski
Mechanical Specifications: Request
Delivery Method: Mail, Newsstand
Areas Served: 51054

SEYMOUR

THE SEYMOUR HERALD (WED)
206 N 4th St, Seymour, IA, 52590-1310, Wayne, USA; gen tel (641) 898-7554; gen fax (641) 898-7554; disp adv e-mail seymourherald@iowatelecom.net; web site No Website
Circulation: 1,500pd,; Sworn/Estimate/Non-Audited
Advertising rate: Open inch rate $4.00
Established: 1884
Karen Young
Vicky DeckerEd.s
Delivery Method: Mail, Newsstand, Racks

SHEFFIELD

SHEFFIELD PRESS (THUR)
305 Gilman St, Sheffield, IA, 50475-5007, Franklin, USA; gen tel (641) 892-4636; disp adv e-mail jzpress@frontiernet.net; web site www.thesheffieldpress.com
Advertising rate: Open inch rate $4.75

SHELDON

N'WEST IOWA REVIEW (SAT)
227 9th St, Sheldon, IA, 51201-1419, Obrien, USA; gen tel (712) 324-5347; gen fax (712) 324-2345; disp adv e-mail editor@iowainformation.com; class adv e-mail ads@iowainformation.com ; ed e-mail editor@iowainformation.com; web site nwestiowa.com
Circulation: 6,647pd,; Sworn/Estimate/Non-Audited
Advertising rate: Open inch rate $7.91
Established: 1972
Group: Iowa Information, Inc.
Pub....Peter W. Wagner
Gen. Mgr....Jeff Wagner
Ed....Jeff Grant
Prodn. Mgr....Connie Wagner
Mechanical Specifications: Type page 13 x 21 1/2; E - 6 cols, 1 5/6, 1/6 between; A - 6 cols, 1 5/6, 1/6 between; C - 6 cols, 1 5/6, 1/6 between.Equipment & Software: Hardware — APP/Macs, AG/Imagesetter; Presses — 7-HI/V-25; Software — QPS/QuarkXPress, Adobe/Photoshop.
Delivery Method: Mail, Newsstand, Carrier, Racks
Areas Served: 512

SHELDON MAIL-SUN (WED)
227 9th St, Sheldon, IA, 51201-1419, O'Brien, Sioux, USA; gen tel (712) 324-5347; gen fax (712) 324-2345; disp adv e-mail drust@iowainformation.com; web site www.nwestiowa.com
Circulation: 2,220pd, 13fr; Sworn/Estimate/Non-Audited
Advertising rate: Open inch rate $7.00
Established: 1862
Pub....Peter W. Wagner
Gen. Mgr....Jeff Wagner
Ed....Derrick Vander Waal
Prodn. Mgr....Dawn Cermak
Mechanical Specifications: Type page 13 x 21 1/2; E - 6 cols, 1 5/6, 1/6 between; A - 6 cols, 1 5/16, 1/6 between; C - 6 cols, 1 5/6, 1/6 between.Equipment & Software: Hardware — APP/Mac, AG/Imagesetter; Presses — 7-HI/V-25; Software — QPS/QuarkXPress, Adobe/Photoshop.
Delivery Method: Mail, Newsstand, Racks
Areas Served: 51201

SHENANDOAH

ESSEX INDEPENDENT (THUR)
PO Box 369, Shenandoah, IA, 51601-0369, Page, USA; gen tel (712) 246-3097; gen fax (712) 246-3099; disp adv e-mail editorial@valleynewstoday.com; web site http://www.valleynewstoday.com/essex_independent/
Circulation: 300pd, 7fr; Sworn/Estimate/Non-Audited
Advertising rate: Open inch rate $5.75
Established: 1953
Ed....Tess Gruber-Nelson
Publisher....Kate Thompson
Mechanical Specifications: Type page 13 x 21; E - 6 cols, 1 5/6, 1/6 between; A - 6 cols, 1 5/6, 1/6 between; C - 6 cols, 1 5/6, 1/6 between.
Delivery Method: Mail, Newsstand

VALLEY NEWS TODAY (MON, WED, SAT)
617 W Sheridan Ave, Shenandoah, IA, 51601-1707, Page, USA; gen tel (712) 246-3097; adv tel (712) 246-3097 ext. 111; ed tel (712) 246-3097 ext. 105; gen fax (712) 246-3099; adv fax (712) 246-3099; ed fax (712) 246-3099; disp adv e-mail ads@valleynewstoday.com; class adv e-mail ads@valleynewstoday.com; ed e-mail editorial@valleynewstoday.com; web site www.valleynewstoday.com - 35,000(views) 5,259(visitors)
Circulation: 2,300pd, 23,000fr; CVC
Advertising rate: Open inch rate $8.95 (Paid publications); $17.45 (TMC)
Established: 1882
Group: BH Media Group
Digital Platform - Mobile: Apple, Android
Digital Platform - Tablet: Apple iOS, Android
Pub....Kate Thompson
Ed....Tess Gruber Nelson
Acct. Exec....Erica Matya
Sports Ed....Jason Glenn
Mechanical Specifications: Type page 11 x 21 1/2; E - 6 cols, 2, 1/6 between; A - 6 cols, 2, 1/6 between; C - 6 cols, 2, 1/6 between.
Delivery Method: Mail, Newsstand, Carrier, Racks
Areas Served: 51601, 51652, 51638

SIBLEY

OSCEOLA COUNTY GAZETTE-TRIBUNE (WED)
201 9th St, Ste 1, Sibley, IA, 51249-1846, Osceola, USA; gen tel (712) 754-2551; gen fax (712) 754-2552; disp adv e-mail gtnews@nethtc.net; web site No Website
Circulation: 1,500pd, 4,800fr; Sworn/Estimate/Non-Audited
Advertising rate: Open inch rate $7.70
Established: 1872
Pub....................................Chris Godfredsen
Mechanical Specifications: Type page 15 x 21 1/2; E - 7 cols, 3/8 between; A - 7 cols, 3/8 between; C - 7 cols, 3/8 between.Equipment & Software: Hardware — APP/Mac; Software — Adobe/Photoshop 4.0, Adobe/PageMaker 6.0, Adobe/InDesign 1.5.
Delivery Method: Mail, Newsstand, Racks

SIDNEY

SIDNEY ARGUS-HERALD (THUR)
614 Main St, PO Box 190, Sidney, IA, 51652-2053, Fremont, USA; gen tel (712) 370-1275; adv tel (712) 374-2241; ed tel (712) 374-2251; gen fax (712)374-2251; adv fax 712 374-2251; ed fax (712) 374-2251; disp adv e-mail news@argusherald.com; class adv e-mail news@argusherald.com; ed e-mail news@argusherald.com; web site N.A.
Circulation: 700pd,; Sworn/Estimate/Non-Audited
Advertising rate: Open inch rate $7.00
Established: 1927
Owner..........................Ellen West Longman
Managing Editor..............Tess Gruber Nelson
Mechanical Specifications: Type page Mechanicals, 9.75" (58 picas) x 21" (126.5 picas); E - 6 cols, 1 7/8, 1/8 between; A - 6 cols, 1 7/8, 1/8 between; C - 6 cols, 1 7/8, 1/8 between.
Delivery Method: Mail, Racks
Areas Served: 51639, 51640, 51641, 51642, 51643, 51644, 51645, 51646, 51647, 51648, 51649, 51650, 51651, 51652, 51653, 51654, 51655, 51656, 51657, 51658, 51659

SIGOURNEY

THE NEWS-REVIEW (WED)
114 E Washington St, Sigourney, IA, 52591-1495, Keokuk, USA; gen tel (641) 622-3110; gen fax (641) 622-2766; disp adv e-mail signred@lisco.com; web site www.sigourneynewsreview.com
Circulation: 2,500pd,; Sworn/Estimate/Non-Audited
Advertising rate: Open inch rate $7.70
Established: 1860
Digital Platform - Mobile: Apple, Android, Windows, Blackberry
Digital Platform - Tablet: Apple iOS, Android, Windows 7, Blackberry Tablet OS, Kindle, Nook, Kindle Fire
Pub..Ken Chaney
Ed...Robin Handy
News Ed...............................Amie Van Patten
Mechanical Specifications: Type page 13 1/4 x 21; E - 7 cols, 1 11/12, between; A - 7 cols, 1 11/12, between; C - 7 cols, 1 11/12, between.Equipment & Software: Hardware — APP/Mac, APP/Mac G4; Software — QPS/QuarkXPress, Adobe/Photoshop.
Delivery Method: Mail, Newsstand, Racks
Areas Served: 52591, 52248, 52576, 52585

SOLON

THE SOLON ECONOMIST (WED)
102 N Market St, Solon, IA, 52333-7702, Johnson, USA; gen tel (319) 624-2233; gen fax (319) 624-1356; disp adv e-mail hybrid@southslope.net; web site www.soloneconomist.com
Circulation: 1,270pd,; Sworn/Estimate/Non-Audited
Advertising rate: Open inch rate $4.50
Pub...Doug Linder
Delivery Method: Mail, Newsstand, Racks

SPIRIT LAKE

DICKINSON COUNTY NEWS (WED, SAT)
3000 18th St, Ste 400, Spirit Lake, IA, 51360-7471, Dickinson, USA; gen tel (712) 336-1211; gen fax (712) 336-1219; disp adv e-mail dcn@dickinsoncountynews.com; web site www.dickinsoncountynews.com - 46,000(views) 15,000(visitors)
Circulation: 3,500pd,; Sworn/Estimate/Non-Audited
Advertising rate: Open inch rate $7.28
Group: Rust Communications
Editor...Russ Mitchell
Mechanical Specifications: Type page 13 x 21 1/2; E - 6 cols, 2 1/8, 1/8 between; A - 6 cols, 2 1/8, 1/8 between; C - 6 cols, 2 1/8, 1/8 between.
Delivery Method: Mail, Newsstand, Racks

STACYVILLE

THE MONITOR REVIEW (THUR)
117 S Broad St, Stacyville, IA, 50476-5041, Mitchell, USA; gen tel (641) 710-2119; gen fax (641) 710-3119; disp adv e-mail themonitorreview@gmail.com; web site facebook.com/TheMonitorReviewNewspaper
Circulation: 1,400pd, 19fr; Sworn/Estimate/Non-Audited
Advertising rate: Open inch rate $3.50
Ed...Robert Adams

STATE CENTER

STATE CENTER MID IOWA ENTERPRISE (THUR)
201 Main St W, # 634, State Center, IA, 50247-7770, Marshall, USA; gen tel (641) 483-2120; ed tel (641) 483-2120; disp adv e-mail midiaenterprise@partnercom.net; web site www.midiaenterprise.com
Circulation: 1,000pd,; Sworn/Estimate/Non-Audited
Advertising rate: $6.00Editions: (1) Mid Iowa Enterprise
Pub..Christine Davis
Ed..Jamie Burdorf
Delivery Method: Mail, Newsstand
Areas Served: Marshall County, Story County

STORM LAKE

PILOT TRIBUNE (TUES, THUR, SAT)
527 Cayuga St, Storm Lake, IA, 50588-2319, Buena Vista, USA; gen tel (712) 732-3130; gen fax (712) 732-3152; disp adv e-mail sledt@ncn.net; web site www.stormlakepilottribune.com
Circulation: 3,085pd,; CVC
Advertising rate: Open inch rate $10.80
Group: Rust Communications
Mng. Ed.....................................Dana Larsen
Prodn. Mgr.................................Tim Marlow
Pub.......................................Paula Buerger
Mechanical Specifications: Type page 13 x 21 1/2; E - 6 cols, 2, 3/16 between; A - 8 cols, 1 1/2, 3/16 between; C - 8 cols, 1 1/2, 3/16 between.Equipment & Software: Hardware — APP/Mac; Software — Baseview, QPS, Multi-Ad/Creator, Caere/OmniPage.

THE STORM LAKE TIMES (WED, FRI)
220 W Railroad St, Storm Lake, IA, 50588-2464, Buena Vista, USA; gen tel (712) 732-4991; gen fax (712) 732-4331; disp adv e-mail sales@stormlake.com; class adv e-mail sales@stormlake.com; ed e-mail times@stormlake.com; web site www.stormlake.com
Circulation: 2,900pd,; USPS
Advertising rate: Open inch rate $6.95
Established: 1990
Digital Platform - Mobile: Apple, Android
Digital Platform - Tablet: Apple iOS, Android
Publisher......................................John Cullen
Editor..Art Cullen
Advertising Manager...................Jeff DeHaan
Circulation Manager...............Rob McCartney
Mechanical Specifications: Type page 11 1/2 x 21; E - 6 cols, 1 5/6, 1/6 between; A - 6 cols, 1 5/6, 1/6 between; C - 6 cols, 1 5/6, 1/6 between.Equipment & Software: Hardware — Mac; Presses — 6-HI/V-15A; Software — QPS/QuarkXPress 9.3.
Delivery Method: Mail, Newsstand, Racks
Areas Served: 50588, 51002, 50576, 50568, 51005, 50535, 50583, 50585

STRATFORD

STRATFORD COURIER (WED)
820 Shakespeare Ave, Stratford, IA, 50249-7771, Hamilton, USA; gen tel (515) 838-2494; gen fax (515) 838-2958; disp adv e-mail shrecnew@netins.net; web site No Website
Circulation: 700pd,; Sworn/Estimate/Non-Audited
Advertising rate: Open inch rate $3.25
Ed...Scott Ervin
Mechanical Specifications: Type page 13 x 21 1/2.Equipment & Software: Hardware — APP/Mac; Software — Claris/MacWrite.

STRAWBERRY POINT

STRAWBERRY PT. PRESS JOURNAL (WED)
107 W Mission St, Strawberry Point, IA, 52076-4400, Clayton, USA; gen tel (563) 933-4370; gen fax (563) 933-4370; disp adv e-mail pressj@iowatelecom.net; web site No Website
Circulation: 1,600pd,; Sworn/Estimate/Non-Audited
Advertising rate: Open inch rate $5.00
Pub.......................................Harry L. Nolda
Kay Behrens
Delivery Method: Mail

STUART

STUART HERALD (THUR)
119 NW 2nd St, Stuart, IA, 50250-7704, Guthrie, USA; gen tel (515) 523-1010; gen fax (515) 523-2825; disp adv e-mail ads@thestuartherald.com; class adv e-mail ads@thestuartherlad.com; ed e-mail news@thestuartherald.com; web site https://www.facebook.com/pages/The-Stuart-Herald-Newspaper-and-Four-County-Bulletin/182134119688
Circulation: 1,100pd, 200fr; Sworn/Estimate/Non-Audited
Advertising rate: Open inch rate $7.75
Established: 1871
Delivery Method: Mail, Newsstand, Racks

SULLY

SULLY HOMETOWN PRESS (THUR)
301 7th Ave, Ste 101, Sully, IA, 50251-1098, Jasper, USA; gen tel (641) 594-3200; adv tel (641) 594-3200; ed tel (641) 594-3200; gen fax (641) 594-3243; adv fax (641) 594-3243; ed fax (641) 594-3243; disp adv e-mail press@netins.net; class adv e-mail press@netins.net; ed e-mail press@netins.net
Circulation: 1,160pd,; USPS
Advertising rate: 5.00
Established: 2009
Group: Co-Line
Editor...........................Margaret VanderWeert
Mechanical Specifications: 16" Tabloid, five 2" columns
Delivery Method: Mail, Newsstand, Racks
Areas Served: 50251, 50153, 50242, 50232, 50112, 50208, 50137, 50135,

SUMNER

SUMNER GAZETTE (THUR)
106 E 1st St, Sumner, IA, 50674-1430, Bremer, USA; gen tel (563) 578-3351; gen fax (563) 578-3352; disp adv e-mail sgazette@mchsi.com; web site facebook.com/Sumner-Gazette-140544807621
Circulation: 1,700pd,; Sworn/Estimate/Non-Audited
Advertising rate: Open inch rate $7.00
Established: 1881
Group: Vanguard Publishing Co., LLC
CO-Pub./Ed...............................Doug Daniels
Circ. Mgr.......................................Mary Pries
Mechanical Specifications: Type page 13 x 21 1/2; E - 6 cols, 2 1/6, 1/6 between; A - 6 cols, 2 1/6, 1/6 between; C - 6 cols, 2 1/6, 1/6 between.
Delivery Method: Mail, Newsstand
Areas Served: 50674

TABOR

TABOR BEACON-ENTERPRISE (THUR)
704 Main St, Tabor, IA, 51653-2067, Fremont, USA; gen tel (712) 629-2255; gen fax (712) 624-9250; disp adv e-mail leaderbeacon@qwestoffice.net
Circulation: 1,000pd,; Sworn/Estimate/Non-Audited
Advertising rate: Open inch rate $4.00
Ed...Karol Siekman

TAMA

THE TAMA NEWS-HERALD (FRI)
220 W 3rd St, Tama, IA, 52339-2308, Tama, USA; gen tel (641) 484-2841; gen fax (641) 484-5705; disp adv e-mail nsund@tamatoledonews.com; class adv e-mail nsund@tamatoledonews.com; ed e-mail jspeer@tamatoledonews.com; web site www.tamatoledonews.com
Circulation: 2,650pd,; Sworn/Estimate/Non-Audited
Advertising rate: Open inch rate $14.03
Established: 1925
Group: Ogden Newspapers Inc.
Pub.............................D. Michael Schlesinger
Gen. Mgr....................................Nancy Sund
Ed...John Speer
Mechanical Specifications: Type page 9 13/16 x 12 1/2; E - 6 cols, 1 7/8, 1 1/2 between; A - 6 cols, 1 7/8, between; C - 6 cols, 1 7/8, between.Equipment & Software: Hardware — 3-APP/Power Mac 6100, 3-APP/Mac Centris 650; Software — QPS/QuarkXPress 3.3, Multi-Ad/Creator.
Delivery Method: Mail, Newsstand

TOLEDO CHRONICLE (TUES)
220 W 3rd St, Tama, IA, 52339-2308, Tama, USA; gen tel (641) 484-2841; gen fax (641) 484-5705; disp adv e-mail nsund@tamatoledonews.com; class adv e-mail nsund@tamatoledonews.com; ed e-mail jspeer@tamatoledonews.com; web site www.tamatoledonews.com
Circulation: 2,650pd,; Sworn/Estimate/Non-Audited
Advertising rate: Open inch rate $10.15
Established: 1853
Group: Ogden Newspapers Inc.
Pub.............................D. Michael Schlesinger
Adv. Mgr....................................Nancy Sund
Ed...John Speer
Mechanical Specifications: Type page 9 13/16 x 12 1/2; E - 6 cols, 1 13/16, 1 1/2 between; A - 6 cols, 1 13/16, between; C - 6 cols, 1 13/16, between.Equipment & Software: Hardware — 3-APP/Power Mac 6100, 3-APP/Mac Centris 650; Software — QPS/QuarkXPress 3.31, Multi-Ad/Creator.

Delivery Method: Mail, Newsstand

THOMPSON

THE THOMPSON COURIER (THUR)

PO Box 318, Thompson, IA, 50478-0318, Winnebago, USA; gen tel (641) 584-2770; disp adv e-mail thompsoncourier.rakeregister@gmail.com; web site www.thompsoncourier.info
Circulation: 600pd,; Sworn/Estimate/Non-Audited
Advertising rate: Open inch rate $8.00
Editor .... Gretchen Daniels
Delivery Method: Mail
Areas Served: Winnebago County, Iowa, USA

TIPTON

LOWDEN SUN-NEWS AND ADVERTISER (THUR)

124 W 5th St, Tipton, IA, 52772-1728, Cedar, USA; gen tel (563) 886-2131; gen fax (563) 886-6466; disp adv e-mail tcadvertising@yahoo.com
Advertising rate: Open inch rate $6.60

TIPTON CONSERVATIVE AND ADVERTISER (WED)

124 W 5th St, Tipton, IA, 52772-1728, Cedar, USA; gen tel (563) 886-2131; gen fax (563) 886-6466; disp adv e-mail StuartC108@aol.com; web site www.tiptonconservative.com
Circulation: 4,582pd, 10fr; Sworn/Estimate/Non-Audited
Advertising rate: Open inch rate $8.30
Established: 1853
Adv. Mgr. .... Pat Kroemer
Circ. Mgr. .... Darla Walling
Ed. .... Stuart Clark
Mechanical Specifications: Type page 15 7/8 x 21; E - 9 cols, 1 2/3, 1/12 between; A - 9 cols, 1 2/3, 1/12 between; C - 9 cols, 1 2/3, 1/12 between.Equipment & Software: Hardware — APP/Mac; Software — Microsoft/Word.

TITONKA

TITONKA TOPIC (WED)

162 Main St N, Titonka, IA, 50480-7724, Kossuth, USA; gen tel (515) 928-2723; gen fax (515) 928-2506; adv fax (515) 928-2506; disp adv e-mail titonkatopic@netins.net; class adv e-mail titonkatopic@netins.net
Circulation: 550pd, 10fr; Sworn/Estimate/Non-Audited
Advertising rate: Open inch rate $4.00
Established: 1898
Ed. .... Mary Ullmann
Mechanical Specifications: Type page 12 1/2 x 20 1/2.Equipment & Software: Hardware — APP/Mac G4; Software — Adobe/PageMaker 7.0.
Delivery Method: Mail, Racks
Areas Served: 50480

TRAER

THE TRAER STAR-CLIPPER (THUR)

625 2nd St, Traer, IA, 50675-1230, Tama, USA; gen tel (319) 478-2323; gen fax (319) 478-2818; disp adv e-mail editor@traerstarclipper.com; web site www.traerstarclipper.com
Circulation: 2,500pd,; Sworn/Estimate/Non-Audited
Advertising rate: Open inch rate $7.59
Group: Ogden Newspapers Inc.
Pub. .... Mike Schlesinger

VILLISCA

VILLISCA REVIEW (THUR)

201 S 5th Ave, Villisca, IA, 50864-1132, Montgomery, USA; gen tel (712) 826-2142; gen fax (712) 826-8888; disp adv e-mail newspapr@netins.net; wordchick@villiscareview.com; class adv e-mail adchick@villiscareview.com; web site facebook.com/Villisca-Review-Stanton-Viking-1703231826555199
Circulation: 1,300pd,; Sworn/Estimate/Non-Audited
Advertising rate: Open inch rate $4.80
Established: 1871
Pub./GM .... Peggy Vermillion
Ed. .... Anne Harter

VINTON

BARR'S POST CARD NEWS (MON, TUES)

108 E 5th St, Vinton, IA, 52349-1759, Benton, USA; gen tel (319) 472-4713; gen fax (319) 472-3117; web site http://www.barrspcn.com
Group: Community Media Group
Circ. Mgr. .... Shelly Haefner

WAPELLO

WAPELLO REPUBLICAN (THUR)

301 Highway 61 N, Wapello, IA, 52653-1242, Louisa, USA; gen tel (319) 523-4631; gen fax (319) 523-8167; disp adv e-mail lpc@louisacomm.net; web site www.facebook.com/The-Wapello-Republican-378443352532
Circulation: 2,300pd, 6fr; Sworn/Estimate/Non-Audited
Advertising rate: Open inch rate $5.95
Established: 1851
Group: Louisa Publishing Co. Ltd.
Gen. Mgr., Editor, Pub. .... Michael A. Hodges
Delivery Method: Mail, Newsstand, Racks

WAUKON

THE STANDARD (WED)

15 1st St NW, Waukon, IA, 52172-1659, Allamakee, USA; gen tel (563) 568-3431; gen fax (563) 568-4242; disp adv e-mail ads@waukonstandard.com; class adv e-mail adsales@waukonstandard.com; ed e-mail news@waukonstandard.com; web site www.waukonstandard.com - 41,175(views) 31,603(visitors)
Circulation: 2,900pd,; Sworn/Estimate/Non-Audited
Advertising rate: Open inch rate $8.55
Established: 1858
Bookkeeper .... Robin Johnson
Mechanical Specifications: 12.5" x 21.5"
Delivery Method: Mail, Racks
Areas Served: 52172 52170 52160 52151 52146 52156 52162 52140

WAVERLY

BREMER COUNTY INDEPENDENT (TUES)

311 W Bremer Ave, Waverly, IA, 50677-3144, Bremer, USA; gen tel (319) 352-3334; adv tel (319) 352-3334; ed tel (319) 352-3334; gen fax (319) 352-5135; adv fax (319) 352-5135; ed fax (319) 352-5135; disp adv e-mail ads@oelweindailyregister.com; class adv e-mail classifieds@oelweindailyregister.com; ed e-mail news@waverlynewspapers.com; web site www.waverlynewspapers.com
Advertising rate: Open inch rate $8.60
Established: 1858
Group: Community Media Group
Digital Platform - Mobile: Apple
Digital Platform - Tablet: Apple iOS
Pub. .... Deb Weigel
Anelia Dimitrova
Delivery Method: Mail, Newsstand, Carrier, Racks
Areas Served: Bremer County

WELLMAN

RIVERSIDE CURRENT (THUR)

230 8th Ave, Wellman, IA, 52356-4707, Washington, USA; gen tel (319) 648-2542; gen fax (319) 646-5904; disp adv e-mail riversidcurrent@netins.net; web site www.theriversidecurrent.com
Circulation: 841pd, 7fr; Sworn/Estimate/Non-Audited
Advertising rate: Open inch rate $6.00
Group: Anamosa Publications
Delivery Method: Mail, Newsstand, Racks

WELLMAN ADVANCE (THUR)

230 8th Ave, Wellman, IA, 52356-4707, Washington, USA; gen tel (319) 646-2712; gen fax (319) 646-5904; disp adv e-mail wellnews@netins.net; web site www.wellmanadvance.com
Circulation: 1,227pd, 16fr; Sworn/Estimate/Non-Audited
Advertising rate: Open inch rate $6.50
Established: 1898
Group: Anamosa Publications
Pub .... Ranee Fladung
Delivery Method: Mail, Newsstand, Racks

WEST BRANCH

WEST BRANCH TIMES (THUR)

124 W Main St, West Branch, IA, 52358-9636, Cedar, USA; gen tel (319) 643-2131; gen fax (319) 643-5853; disp adv e-mail wbtimes@lcom.net; info@westbranchtimes.com; web site www.westbranchtimes.com
Circulation: 1,153pd,; Sworn/Estimate/Non-Audited
Advertising rate: Open inch rate $7.25
Established: 1875
Group: West Branch Communications
Digital Platform - Mobile: Apple, Android
Digital Platform - Tablet: Apple iOS, Android
Pub. .... Jake Krob
Pub. .... Stuart Clark
Editor .... Gregory Norfleet
Adv. Mgr. .... Tom BurgerEquipment & Software: Hardware — APP/Mac; Software — Adobe/Photoshop 5.0, QPS/QuarkXPress 4.1.
Delivery Method: Mail, Newsstand, Racks
Areas Served: 52358

WEST BURLINGTON

DES MOINES COUNTY NEWS (THUR)

204 Broadway St, West Burlington, IA, 52655-1243, Des Moines, USA; gen tel (319) 752-8328; gen fax (319) 752-8328; disp adv e-mail lpc@louisacomm.net; web site No Website
Circulation: 1,900pd, 15fr; Sworn/Estimate/Non-Audited
Advertising rate: Open inch rate $5.40
Group: Louisa Publishing Co. Ltd.
Pub. Michael A. HodgesEquipment & Software: Hardware — APP/Mac.
Delivery Method: Mail, Newsstand, Racks

WEST LIBERTY

WEST LIBERTY INDEX (THUR)

219 N Calhoun St, West Liberty, IA, 52776-1537, Muscatine, USA; gen tel (319) 627-2814; gen fax (319) 627-2110; disp adv e-mail index@Lcom.net; web site www.westlibertyindex.com
Advertising rate: Open inch rate $6.00
GM/Adv. Mgr. .... Tom Burger
Circ. .... John Hawkins
Pub. .... Jake Krob
Pub. .... Stuart Clark

WEST UNION

FAYETTE COUNTY UNION (WED)

119 S Vine St, West Union, IA, 52175-1354, Fayette, USA; gen tel (563) 422-3888; gen fax (563) 422-3488; disp adv e-mail lanews@thefayettecountyunion.com; web site www.westunionfayettecountyunion.com
Circulation: 2,600pd, 4,400fr; Sworn/Estimate/Non-Audited
Advertising rate: 9.00
Established: 1866
Group: Community Media GroupEditions: The Fayette County Union/West Union Area Shopper
Digital Platform - Mobile: Apple, Android
Digital Platform - Tablet: Apple iOS, Android
Pub. .... LeAnn Larson
Vice President .... Jerry Blue
Graphic Design Supervisor .... Steve Murray
Delivery Method: Mail, Newsstand, Racks

FAYETTE LEADER (WED)

119 S Vine St, West Union, IA, 52175-1354, Fayette, USA; gen tel (563) 422-5410; gen fax (563) 422-3488; disp adv e-mail shermen@fayettepublishing.com; class adv e-mail shermen@fayettepublishing.com; ed e-mail zkriener@fayettepublishing.com; web site www.fayettepublishing.com
Circulation: 812pd,; Sworn/Estimate/Non-Audited
Advertising rate: 6.50
Group: Community Media Group
Pub. .... LeAnn Larson
Adv. Exec. .... Steph Hermen
News Writer / Sports Writer .... Zak Kriener
Delivery Method: Mail, Racks
Areas Served: Fayette/Wadena/Hawkeye/Maynard/Westgate
Fayette County

OSSIAN BEE (WED)

119 S Vine St, West Union, IA, 52175-1354, Winneshiek, USA; gen tel (563) 422-5410; gen fax (563) 422-3488; disp adv e-mail thebee@alpinecom.net; web site www.newspapersoffayettecounty.com
Circulation: 812pd,; Sworn/Estimate/Non-Audited
Advertising rate: Open inch rate $4.50
Established: 1889
Group: Community Media Group
Pub. .... LeAnn Larson
Adv. Dir. .... Steph Hermen
News Writer / Sports Writer .... Zak Kriener
Mechanical Specifications: Type page 15 x 21; E - 6 cols, 2 1/3, 1/4 between; A - 6 cols, 2 1/3, 1/4 between; C - 6 cols, 2 1/3, 1/4 between. Equipment & Software: Hardware — 3-APP/Mac SI, 1-APP/Mac; Software — Microsoft/Word, Adobe/PageMaker.
Areas Served: Ossian/Calmar/Castalia/Ft.Atkinson/Festina

THE ELGIN ECHO (WED)

119 S Vine St, West Union, IA, 52175-1354, Fayette, USA; gen tel (563) 422-5410; gen fax (563) 422-3488; disp adv e-mail shermen@fayettepublishing.com; class adv e-mail areiling@fayettepublishing.com; ed e-mail zkriener@fayettepublishing.com; web site www.fayettecountynewspapers.com
Circulation: 875pd,; Sworn/Estimate/Non-Audited
Advertising rate: Open inch rate $5.75
Established: 1886
Group: Community Media Group
Digital Platform - Mobile: Apple
Digital Platform - Tablet: Apple iOS
Pub. .... LeAnn Larson
Acc. Exec. .... Steph Hermen
Prodn. Sup. .... Amanda Reiling
News Writer / Sports Writer .... Zak Kriener
Graphic Designer .... Danielle Luchsinger
Delivery Method: Mail, Newsstand
Areas Served: Clermont/Elgin/Wadena
Faytte & Clayton Counties

WESTSIDE

WESTSIDE OBSERVER (THUR)
324 1st St, Westside, IA, 51467, Crawford, USA; gen tel (712) 663-4362; gen fax (712) 663-4363; disp adv e-mail observer@win-4-u.net; web site www.westsideobserveronline.com
Circulation: 1,140pd, 35fr; USPS
Advertising rate: Open inch rate $4.00
Group: Kock Publishing Inc.
Ed./Pub. .... Janine Kock
Office Mgr. .... Doreen Jons
Office Asst. .... Jessica Berger
Delivery Method: Mail, Newsstand

WHITTEMORE

WHITTEMORE INDEPENDENT (THUR)
419 Broad St, Whittemore, IA, 50598-8512, Kossuth, USA; gen tel (515)884-2648; gen fax (515)884-2648; disp adv e-mail wjournal@ncn.net; web site No website
Circulation: 235pd,; Sworn/Estimate/Non-Audited
Advertising rate: Open inch rate $6.25
Established: 1988
Digital Platform - Mobile: Apple
Digital Platform - Tablet: Apple iOS
Pub. .... Karen Schwartzkopf
Delivery Method: Mail, Newsstand
Areas Served: 50598

WILLIAMSBURG

JOURNAL TRIBUNE (THUR)
208 W State St, Williamsburg, IA, 52361-4708, Iowa, USA; gen tel (319) 668-1240; gen fax (319) 668-9112; disp adv e-mail cvonahse@dmreg.com; web site www.yourweeklypaper.com
Advertising rate: Open inch rate $8.00
Established: 1901
Group: Gannett
Pub. .... Diane Goodlow
Delivery Method: Mail, Newsstand, Racks

WILTON

WILTON-DURANT ADVOCATE NEWS (THUR)
410 Cedar St, Wilton, IA, 52778-9495, Muscatine, USA; gen tel (563) 732-2029; adv tel (563) 732-2029; ed tel (563) 732-2029; gen fax (563) 732-3144; adv fax (563) 732-3144; ed fax (563) 732-3144; disp adv e-mail anads@netwtc.net; class adv e-mail adnews@netwtc.net; ed e-mail dsawvell@netwtc.net; web site Wilton-Durant Advocate News
Advertising rate: Open inch rate $11
Mng. Ed. .... Derek Sawvell
Adv. Mgr. .... Bill Tubs
Delivery Method: Mail, Newsstand
Areas Served: 52778

WINFIELD

WINFIELD BEACON / WAYLAND NEWS (THUR)
107 E Elm St, Winfield, IA, 52659-9780, Henry, USA; gen tel (319) 257-6813; gen fax (319) 257-6902; disp adv e-mail newspapers2@iowatelecom.net; web site No Website
Advertising rate: Open inch rate $3.25
Pub. .... Cathy Lauderdale

WINTERSET

WINTERSET MADISONIAN (WED)
215 N 1st Ave, Winterset, IA, 50273-1506, Madison, USA; gen tel (515) 462-2101; gen fax (515) 462-2102; disp adv e-mail madisonianads@i-rule.net; ed e-mail vpolk@i-rule.net; web site www.wintersetmadisonian.com
Circulation: 3,580pd,; Sworn/Estimate/Non-Audited
Advertising rate: Open inch rate $5.30
Established: 1856
Ed. .... Dave Braga
Pub. .... Ted C. Gorman
Prodn. Mgr. .... Vickie Polk
Mechanical Specifications: Type page 14 x 21 1/2; E - 6 cols, 2, 1/3 between; A - 6 cols, 2, 1/3 between; C - 6 cols, 2, 1/3 between. Equipment & Software: Hardware — APP/Power Mac G3; Software — QPS/QuarkXPress, Microsoft/Word, Adobe/Acrobat, Adobe/Photoshop.

WINTHROP

WINTHROP NEWS (THUR)
225 W Madison St, Winthrop, IA, 50682-7705, Buchanan, USA; gen tel (319) 935-3027; gen fax (319) 935-3082; disp adv e-mail news@thewinthropnews.com; web site www.thewinthropnews.com
Circulation: 3,800pd,; Sworn/Estimate/Non-Audited
Advertising rate: Open inch rate $6.33
Established: 1892
Adv. Mgr. .... Steven Smith
Ed. .... Mary Beth Smith
Mechanical Specifications: Type page 10 1/4 x 14; E - 6 cols, 1 1/2, between.Equipment & Software: Hardware — PCs; Software — Microsoft/Windows 98.
Delivery Method: Mail, Newsstand, Racks

WOODBINE

THE WOODBINE TWINER (WED)
503 Walker St, Woodbine, IA, 51579-1267, Harrison, USA; gen tel (712) 647-2821; gen fax (712) 647-3081; disp adv e-mail ads@woodbinetwiner.com; web site www.woodbinetwiner.com
Circulation: 1,200pd,; Sworn/Estimate/Non-Audited
Advertising rate: Open inch rate $6.75
Established: 1878Daryn Morris
Adv. Rep. .... Kylie Bertelson
Prodn. Sup. .... Mary Lou Noneman
Mechanical Specifications: Type page 13 x 21 1/2; E - 6 cols, 1 3/4, 1/6 between; A - 6 cols, 1 3/4, between; C - 7 cols, 1 1/2, between.
Delivery Method: Mail, Newsstand, Racks
Areas Served: 51579, 51546, 51555, 51529, 51557, 51563, 51564, 51556, 51550

WYOMING

WYOMING MIDLAND TIMES (FRI)
301 W Webster St, Wyoming, IA, 52362-7424, Jones, USA; gen tel (563) 488-2281; disp adv e-mail midtimes@netins.net; web site No Website
Circulation: 1,000pd,; Sworn/Estimate/Non-Audited
Advertising rate: Open inch rate $3.50
Pub. .... Shirley Jones
Delivery Method: Mail, Newsstand

KANSAS

ALMA

THE WABAUNSEE COUNTY SIGNAL-ENTERPRISE (THUR)
323 Missouri Ave, Alma, KS, 66401-9810, Wabaunsee, USA; gen tel (785) 765-3327; disp adv e-mail signal@embarqmail.com; ed e-mail signal@embarqmail.com; web site www.signal-enterprise.com
Circulation: 1,300pd, 12fr; Sworn/Estimate/Non-Audited
Advertising rate: Open inch rate $4.50
Established: 1884
Owner / Publisher / Editor .... Lori Daniel
Mechanical Specifications: Type page 10 x 16; E - 5 cols, 2, between; A - 5 cols, 2, between; C - 5 cols, 2, between.Equipment & Software: Hardware — APP/Mac.
Delivery Method: Mail, Racks

ANDALE

THE CLARION (THUR)
314 N Main St, Andale, KS, 67001-9700, Sedgwick, USA; gen tel (316) 445-2444; adv tel (316) 712-2125; ed tel (316) 712-2125; gen fax (316) 445-2446; disp adv e-mail marketingdesk@clarionpaper.com ; class adv e-mail joey@kspublishingventures.com; ed e-mail editor@clarionpaper.com; web site www.clarionpaper.com
Circulation: 1,500pd,; USPS
Advertising rate: Open inch rate $6.50
Group: Kansas Publishing VenturesEditions: (52)
Pub & Owner .... Joey Young
Mng Ed .... Lindsey Young
Mechanical Specifications: Type page 10 1/4 x 16; E - 4 cols, 2 3/8, 1/6 between; A - 4 cols, 2 3/8, 1/6 between; C - 4 cols, 2 3/8, 1/6 between.Equipment & Software: Hardware — Laptops - cameras
Delivery Method: Mail, Newsstand, Racks
Areas Served: 67001
67543
67101
67030
67108

ANTHONY

ANTHONY REPUBLICAN (WED)
121 E Main St, PO Box 31, Anthony, KS, 67003-2720, Harper, USA; gen tel (620) 842-5129; gen fax (620) 842-5115; disp adv e-mail anthonyrepublican@att.net; class adv e-mail anthonyrepublican@att.net; ed e-mail anthonyrepublican@att.net; web site www.anthonyrepublicannews.com
Circulation: 1,900pd,; Sworn/Estimate/Non-Audited
Advertising rate: Open inch rate $4.70
Established: 1878
Pub .... Larry Dunn
Editor .... Ross Downing
Mechanical Specifications: Type page 15 x 21 1/2; E - 7 cols, 2, between; A - 7 cols, 2, between; C - 7 cols, 1 2/3, between.Equipment & Software: Hardware — Mk, APP/Mac 610, Microtek/Scanner; Presses — 3-KP/News King.
Delivery Method: Mail, Racks
Areas Served: 67003, 67009, 67058, 73758, 73771

ATCHISON

ATCHISON GLOBE (WED, SAT)
308 Commercial St, Atchison, KS, 66002-2519, Atchison, USA; gen tel (913) 367-0583; adv tel (913) 367-0583 ext. 20406; ed tel (913) 367-0583 ext. 20411; gen fax (913) 367-7531; adv fax (913) 367-7531; ed fax (913) 367-7531; disp adv e-mail christym@npgco.com; class adv e-mail christym@npgco.com; ed e-mail joewarren@npgco.com; web site www.atchisondailyglobenow.com
Circulation: 3,293pd,; Sworn/Estimate/Non-Audited
Advertising rate: Open inch rate $11.23 (Local); $14.21 (National)
Established: 1877
Group: News-Press & Gazette Co.
Digital Platform - Mobile: Apple, Android
Digital Platform - Tablet: Apple iOS, Android
Pub./Ed. .... Joe Warren
Bus. Mgr./Circ. .... Marilyn Andre
Adv. Mgr. .... Christy McKibben
Adv. Rep. .... Jim Ervin
News Ed. .... Logan Jackson
Sports Ed. .... Adam Gardner
Lady A Ed. .... Joey May
Mechanical Specifications: Type page 13 x 21 1/2; E - 6 cols, 2 1/16, 1/8 between; A - 6 cols, 2 1/16, 1/8 between; C - 8 cols, 1 1/2, 1/8 between.
Delivery Method: Mail, Newsstand, Carrier
Areas Served: Atchison, Bean, Lake, Cummings, Effingham, Everest, Horton, Lancaster, Muscotah, Nortonville, Rushville, Sugar Lake, and Winchester

ATTICA

ATTICA INDEPENDENT (THUR)
422 N Logan St, Attica, KS, 67009-9224, Harper, USA; gen tel (620) 254-7660; web site www.facebook.com/pages/Attica-Independent/152138318133485
Advertising rate: $3.00 per column inch
Ed./Pub. .... Ray Howell

AUGUSTA

ANDOVER AMERICAN (WED)
204 E 5th Ave, Augusta, KS, 67010-1012, Butler, USA; gen tel (316) 775-2218; adv tel (316) 321-1120; gen fax (316) 775-3220; disp adv e-mail awickwire@eldoradotimes.com; class adv e-mail sbrown@butlercountytimesgazette.com; ed e-mail kbush@andoveramerican.com; web site www.andoveramerican.com
Advertising rate: Open inch rate $9.00
Established: 2011
Group: GateHouse Media, Inc.
Managing Ed. .... Julie Clements
Delivery Method: Carrier

THE BUTLER COUNTY TIMES-GAZETTE (TUES, THUR, SAT)
204 E 5th Ave, Augusta, KS, 67010-1012, Butler, USA; gen tel (316) 321-1120; adv tel (316) 321-1120; ed tel (316) 321-1120; gen fax (316) 775-3220; adv fax (316) 775-3220; ed fax (316) 321-7722; disp adv e-mail awickwire@butlercountytimesgazette.com; class adv e-mail awickwire@butlercountytimesgazette.com; ed e-mail jclements@butlercountytimesgazette.com; web site http://www.butlercountytimesgazette.com
Circulation: 2,247pd,; Sworn/Estimate/Non-Audited
Advertising rate: Open inch rate $12.00
Established: 1902
Group: New Media Investment Group
Digital Platform - Mobile: Apple, Android
Digital Platform - Tablet: Apple iOS, Android
Pub. .... Cristina Janney
Business Mgr. .... Michelle Griffith
Managing Ed. .... Julie Clements
Augusta City Ed. .... Belinda Larsen
Sports Ed. .... Jeremy Costello
Adv. Coord. .... April Wickwire
Adv. Exec. .... Amy Motter
Adv. Exec. .... Jennifer Wilson
Classifieds Adv. .... Kim Lucas
Legal Adv. .... Rhonda Zinn
Circ. Mgr. .... Lori Sibley
El Dorado City Ed. .... Levi Yager

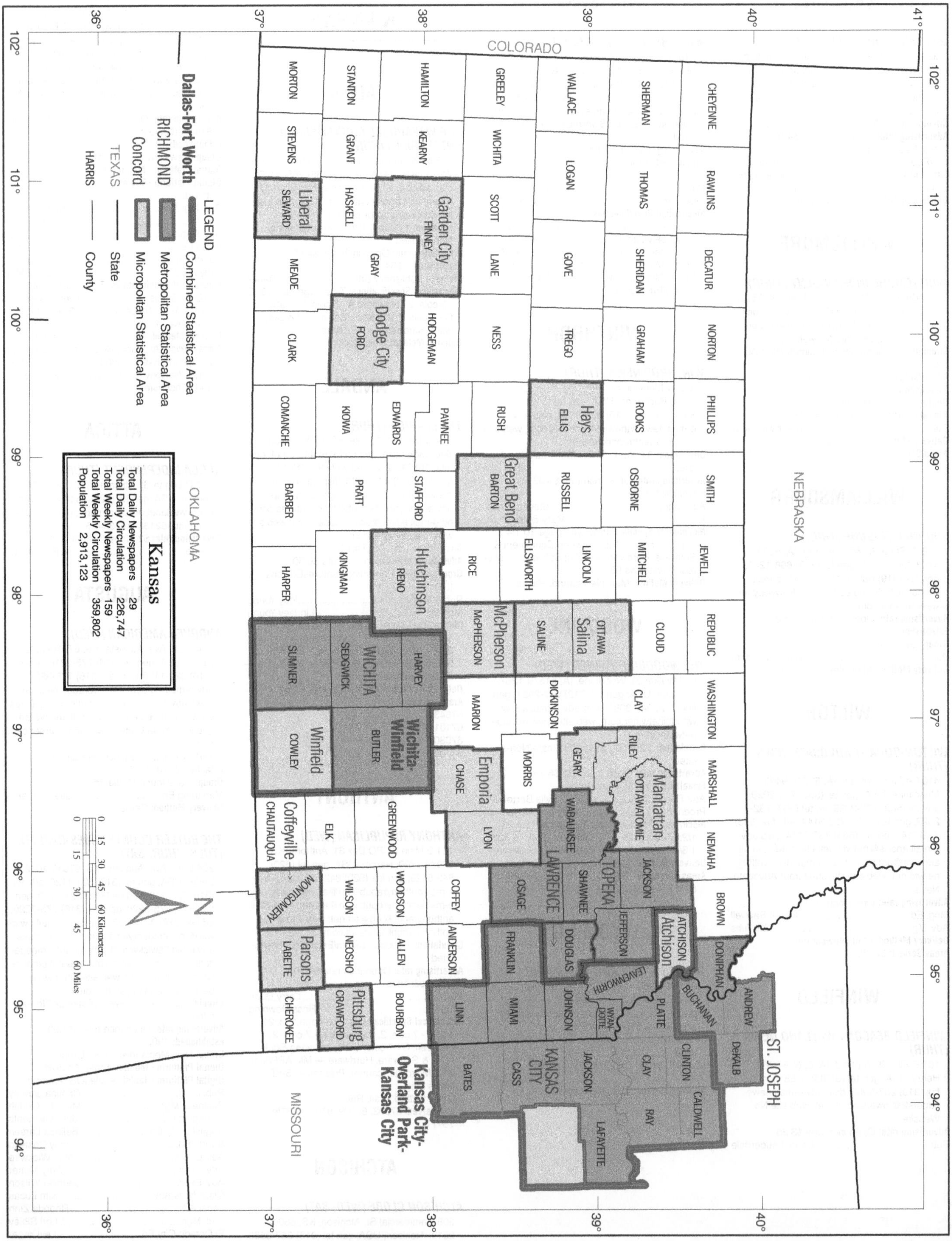
COLORADO
NEBRASKA
OKLAHOMA
MISSOURI
LEGEND
Dallas-Fort Worth Combined Statistical Area
RICHMOND Metropolitan Statistical Area
Concord Micropolitan Statistical Area
TEXAS State
HARRIS County
Kansas
Total Daily Newspapers 29
Total Daily Circulation 226,747
Total Weekly Newspapers 159
Total Weekly Circulation 359,802
Population 2,913,123
0 15 30 45 60 Kilometers
0 15 30 45 60 Miles
N
Wichita-Winfield
WICHITA
Winfield
Kansas City-Overland Park-Kansas City
KANSAS CITY
ST. JOSEPH
TOPEKA
LAWRENCE
Manhattan
Atchison
Emporia
Salina
McPherson
Hutchinson
Great Bend
Hays
Dodge City
Garden City
Liberal
Coffeyville
Parsons
Pittsburg

Mechanical Specifications: Type page 13 x 21; E - 6 cols, 2 3/4, 1/8 between; A - 6 cols, 2 3/4, 1/8 between; C - 6 cols, 2 3/4, 1/8 between.
Delivery Method: Mail, Newsstand, Carrier
Areas Served: Leon, Towanda, Potwin, Whitewater, Benton, Augusta, Andover, Douglas, Leon, Towanda, and Rose Hill

BALDWIN CITY

THE BALDWIN CITY SIGNAL (THUR)
703 High St, Baldwin City, KS, 66006-3015, Douglas, USA; gen tel (785) 594-7080; adv tel (800) 578-8748; ed tel (785) 760-6841; gen fax (785) 843-1922; disp adv e-mail ads@baldwincity.com; ed e-mail editor@baldwincity.com; web site signal.baldwincity.com
Advertising rate: 1/4 P $182, 1/2 P $353
Pub .... John Taylor
Ed. .... Elvyn J. Jones
Delivery Method: Mail

BASEHOR

KANSAS CITY RECORD (THUR)
14690 Parallel Rd, Basehor, KS, 66007-3007, Leavenworth, USA; gen tel (913) 362-1988; disp adv e-mail jon@recordnews.com; ed e-mail news@recordnews.com
Circulation:; USPS
Advertising rate: Open inch rate $12.50
Established: 1888
Pub .... Jon Males
Delivery Method: Mail, Racks

BELLE PLAINE

THE BELLE PLAINE NEWS (THUR)
217 W 5th Ave, P.O. Box 128, Belle Plaine, KS, 67013-9117, Sumner, USA; gen tel (620) 488-2234; disp adv e-mail newsbelleplaine@gmail.com; class adv e-mail newsbelleplaine@gmail.com; ed e-mail newsbelleplaine@gmail.com
Circulation: 500pd, 48fr; Sworn/Estimate/Non-Audited
Advertising rate: Open inch rate $10.00
Group: Main Street Publishing LLC
Publisher .... Bill Rhiley
Mechanical Specifications: Type page 11.5 x 21.5; E - 6 cols, 2, between; A - 5 cols, 2, between; C - 6 cols, 2, between.Equipment & Software: Hardware — Umax, 3-APP/Mac, APP/Mac G4; Software — Adobe/PageMaker 6.0, QPS/QuarkXPress 3.31, Adobe/Photoshop 3.0, Macromedia/Freehand 7.0.
Delivery Method: Mail, Newsstand
Areas Served: Sumner County

THE BELLE PLAINE NEWS & THE OXFORD REGISTER (THUR)
217 W 5th Ave, Belle Plaine, KS, 67013-9117, Sumner, USA; gen tel (620) 488-2234; disp adv e-mail newsbelleplaine@gmail.com; class adv e-mail newsbelleplaine@gmail.com; ed e-mail newsbelleplaine@gmail.com
Circulation: 500pd, 24fr; Sworn/Estimate/Non-Audited
Advertising rate: Open inch rate $10.00
Established: 1879
Group: Main Street Publishing LLC
Publisher .... Bill Rhiley
Mechanical Specifications: Type page 11.5 x 21.5; E - 6 cols, 1 7/8, 1/6 between; A - 5 cols, 1 7/8, 1/6 between; C - 6 cols, 1 7/8, 1/6 between.Equipment & Software: Hardware — Umax, 3-APP/Mac, APP/Mac G4; Software — Adobe/PageMaker 6.0, QPS/QuarkXPress 5.0, Adobe/Photoshop 6, Macromedia/Freehand 7.0.
Delivery Method: Mail, Newsstand
Areas Served: Sumner County

BELLEVILLE

THE BELLEVILLE TELESCOPE (WED)
1805 N St, Belleville, KS, 66935-2247, Republic, USA; gen tel (785) 527-2244; gen fax (785) 527-2225; disp adv e-mail susanism2@yahoo.com; class adv e-mail susanism2@yahoo.com; ed e-mail dhadachek@gmail.com; web site thebellevilletelescope.com
Circulation: 3,500pd,; Sworn/Estimate/Non-Audited
Advertising rate: Open inch rate $6.75
Pub .... Fred Arnold
Ed. .... Deb Hadachek
Adv Dir .... Susan Bartels
Mechanical Specifications: Type page 16 x 23; E - 6 cols, between.
Delivery Method: Mail

BELOIT

BELOIT CALL (MON, WED, FRI)
119 E Main St, Beloit, KS, 67420-3234, Mitchell, USA; gen tel (785) 738-3537; gen fax (785) 738-6442; disp adv e-mail beloitcall@nckcn.com; class adv e-mail beloitcall@nckcn.com; ed e-mail beloitcall@nckcn.com; web site www.beloitcall.com
Circulation:; Sworn/Estimate/Non-Audited
Advertising rate: Open inch rate $6.10
Pub .... Brad Lowell
Ed. .... Sharon Hesket Sahlfeld
Delivery Method: Mail, Carrier, Racks

BLUE RAPIDS

BLUE RAPIDS FREE PRESS (THUR)
203 W 5th St, Blue Rapids, KS, 66411-1201, Marshall, USA; gen tel (785) 363-7779; disp adv e-mail brfreepress@kansas.net; ed e-mail brfreepress@kansas.net; web site www.bluerapidsfreepress.com
Advertising rate: Open inch rate $3.00
Established: 2009
Editor/Publisher/Ad Director .... Jon Brake
Delivery Method: Newsstand, Racks

MANHATTAN FREE PRESS (THUR)
409 E 7th St, Blue Rapids, KS, 66411-1559, Marshall, USA; gen tel (785) 537-8953; adv tel (785) 556-1694; disp adv e-mail freepress@kansas.net; web site www.manhattanfreepress.com
Circulation:; Sworn/Estimate/Non-Audited
Advertising rate: Open inch rate $4.00
Established: 1991
Jon Brake
Linda BrakeCo-Pubs
Delivery Method: Newsstand, Racks
Areas Served: Manhattan, Kansas

BURLINGTON

COFFEY COUNTY REPUBLICAN (TUES, FRI)
324 Hudson St, Burlington, KS, 66839-1327, Coffey, USA; gen tel (620) 364-5325; gen fax (620) 364-2607; disp adv e-mail repubads1@gmail.com; class adv e-mail repubclass@gmail.com; ed e-mail ccrepub@gmail.com; web site www.coffeycountyonline.com
Circulation: 3,000pd,; Sworn/Estimate/Non-Audited
Advertising rate: Open inch rate $8.05
Established: 1856
Pub .... Chris Faimon
Adv. Mgr. .... Jeff Birkatad
Circ. Mgr. .... Kathy Payne
Ed. .... Mark Petterson
Mechanical Specifications: Type page 13 x 21; E - 6 cols, 2 1/12, 1/8 between; A - 6 cols, 2 1/12, 1/8 between; C - 6 cols, 2 1/12, 1/8 between.Equipment & Software: ; Software — Microsoft/Windows 3.1, QPS/QuarkXPress 3.0, Archetype/Corel Draw 6.0.
Delivery Method: Mail

CALDWELL

CALDWELL MESSENGER (WED)
111 S Main St, Caldwell, KS, 67022-1607, Sumner, USA; gen tel (620) 845-2320; gen fax (620) 845-6461; disp adv e-mail messenger@kanokla.net; ed e-mail messenger@kanokla.net; web site www.facebook.com/pages/Caldwell-Messenger/152565398090263
Circulation: 1,350pd,; Sworn/Estimate/Non-Audited
Advertising rate: Open inch rate $3.45
Ed. .... Pat Weber
Delivery Method: Mail

CANEY

MONTGOMERY COUNTY CHRONICLE (THUR)
202 W 4th Ave, Caney, KS, 67333-1462, Montgomery, USA; gen tel (620) 879-2156; gen fax (620) 879-2855; disp adv e-mail adv@taylornews.org; class adv e-mail adv@taylornews.org; ed e-mail chronicle@taylornews.org; web site www.taylornews.org
Advertising rate: Open inch rate $5.50
Group: Taylor NewspapersRudy Taylor
Kathy Taylor
Ed .... Andy Taylor
Delivery Method: Mail, Newsstand, Racks

CHAPMAN

CHAPMAN & ENTERPRISE NEWS-TIMES (THUR)
437 N Marshall St, Chapman, KS, 67431, Dickinson, USA; gen tel (785) 922-6450; gen fax (785) 922-6027; disp adv e-mail chapmannewstimes@gmail.com; web site www.chapmannewstimes.com
Advertising rate: $5.00 per column inchJohn Baetz

CHENEY

TIMES SENTINEL (THUR)
125 N Main St, Cheney, KS, 67025-8844, Sedgwick, USA; gen tel (316) 540-3111; gen fax (316) 540-3283; disp adv e-mail prhodes@tsnews.com; ed e-mail news@tsnews.com; web site www.tsnews.com
Circulation: 3,000pd,; Sworn/Estimate/Non-Audited
Advertising rate: Open inch rate $7.50
Established: 1894
Ed. .... Paul Rhodes
Prodn. Mgr. .... Travis Mounts
Mechanical Specifications: Type page 10 1/4 x 16; E - 5 cols, 10 1/4, 1/6 between; A - 5 cols, 10 1/4, 1/6 between; C - 5 cols, 10 1/4, 1/6 between.Equipment & Software: Hardware — 6-Apple/G3; Software — Microsoft/Word 8.0, Adobe/Pagemaker 6.5, Adobe/Photoshop 5.0.
Delivery Method: Mail

CHERRYVALE

CHERRYVALE CHRONICLE (THUR)
115 N Labette St, Cherryvale, KS, 67335, Montgomery, USA; gen tel (620) 336-2100; gen fax (620) 336-2101; disp adv e-mail chroniclenews@cox.net; web site www.taylornews.org
Circulation: 3,100pd,; Sworn/Estimate/Non-Audited
Advertising rate: Open inch rate $5.50
Pub .... Rudy M. Taylor
Adv. Mgr. .... Amy Taylor
Mng. Ed. .... Kathy Taylor
Mechanical Specifications: Type page 10 x 16; E - 5 cols, 1 7/8, 1/6 between; A - 5 cols, 1 7/8, 1/6 between; C - 5 cols, 1 7/8, 1/6 between.
Equipment & Software: Hardware — APP/Mac; Software — Adobe/PageMaker, Multi-Ad/Creator.

CIMARRON

BUCKLIN BANNER (WED)
PO Box 528, 101 N Main, Cimarron, KS, 67835-0528, Ford, USA; gen tel (620) 826-3311; ed tel 800-658-3755; gen fax (620) 855-2489; disp adv e-mail bucklinbanner@ucom.net; class adv e-mail bucklinbanner@ucom.net; ed e-mail bucklinbanner@ucom.net
Circulation: 200pd,; Sworn/Estimate/Non-Audited
Advertising rate: Open inch rate $3.75
Established: 1901
Group: Golden Plains Publishing
Digital Platform - Mobile: Apple
Digital Platform - Tablet: Apple iOS
Editor .... Kacie Dirks
Delivery Method: Mail
Areas Served: Ford County
zip codes: 67834, 67842, 67801

JACKSONIAN (WED)
101 S Main St, Cimarron, KS, 67835-8856, Gray, USA; gen tel (620) 855-3902; gen fax (620) 855-2489; disp adv e-mail jacksoniannews@me.com; ed e-mail jacksoniannews@me.com
Circulation: 905pd,; Sworn/Estimate/Non-Audited
Advertising rate: Open inch rate $4.75
Group: Golden Plains Publishing
Pub .... Mark Anderson
Ed. .... Kirk Anderson
Delivery Method: Mail

CLYDE

CLYDE REPUBLICAN (THUR)
305 Washington St, Clyde, KS, 66938-9664, Cloud, USA; gen tel (785) 446-2201; gen fax (785) 446-2201; disp adv e-mail clyderepublican@hotmail.com; web site www.facebook.com/TheClydeRepublican/
Circulation: 1,000pd,; Sworn/Estimate/Non-Audited
Advertising rate: Open inch rate $4.75
Ed. .... Margene Cash
Co-Owner/Pub. .... Matthew Jorgenson
Co-Owner .... Crystal Jorgenson
Mechanical Specifications: Type page 13 x 21.
Delivery Method: Mail

COFFEYVILLE

COFFEYVILLE JOURNAL (MON, WED, FRI)
302 W 8th St, Coffeyville, KS, 67337-5829, Montgomery, USA; gen tel (620) 251-3300; adv tel (620) 251-3300; gen fax (620) 251-1905; adv fax (620) 251-1905; disp adv e-mail advertising@cj.kscoxmail.com; class adv e-mail classifieds@cj.kscoxmail.com; ed e-mail gcraven@cj.kscoxmail.com; web site www.facebook.com/TheCoffeyvilleJournal/?ref=page_internal
Circulation: 4,103pd, 10,000fr; Sworn/Estimate/Non-Audited
Advertising rate: Open inch rate $9.67
Established: 1875
Group: Kansas Press Association
Owner/Pub. .... Darrell Sumner
Scott Wood
Adv. Dir. .... Bill Noel
Classified Adv. .... Hayley Henderson
Sr. Ed. .... Deanna Evans
Mechanical Specifications: Type page 13 x 21 1/2; E - 6 cols, 2 1/16, 1/8 between; A - 6 cols, 2 1/16, 1/8 between; C - 9 cols, 1 3/8, 1/8 between.Equipment & Software: Hardware — APP/Mac SE 30, APP/Mac SE, APP/Mac Performa 466; Presses — 6-HI/V-22; Software — Baseview/NewsEdit, Abbott Sys-

tems/Ready, Set, Go, QPS/QuarkXPress 3.3.
Delivery Method: Mail
Areas Served: 67337

COLDWATER

THE WESTERN STAR (THUR)

113 S Central St, Coldwater, KS, 67029-2943, Comanche, USA; gen tel (620) 582-2101; adv tel (620) 582-2101; ed tel (620) 582-2101; disp adv e-mail weststar@gmaxx.us; class adv e-mail weststar@gmaxx.us; ed e-mail weststar@gmaxx.us
Circulation: 750pd, 30fr; Sworn/Estimate/Non-Audited
Advertising rate: Open inch rate $3.50
Established: 1884
Ed./Pub. .... Dennies Andersen
Mechanical Specifications: 5 column tabloid 14.5 inches by 7.75 inchesEquipment & Software: Hardware — PC; Software — Adobe/PageMaker 5.0
Delivery Method: Mail
Areas Served: 67029, 67127, 67155

COLUMBUS

CHEROKEE COUNTY NEWS-ADVOCATE (TUES, FRI)

217 S Kansas Ave, Columbus, KS, 66725-1718, Cherokee, USA; gen tel (620) 429-2773; adv tel (620) 429-2773; ed tel (620) 429-2773; gen fax (620) 429-3223; adv fax (620) 429-3223; ed fax (620) 429-3223; disp adv e-mail advertising@sekvoice.com; class adv e-mail classifieds@sekvoice.com; ed e-mail news@sekvoice.com; web site www.sekvoice.com
Circulation: 3,300pd,; Sworn/Estimate/Non-Audited
Advertising rate: Open inch rate $5.50
Established: 1882
Group: GateHouse Media, Inc.
Pub. .... Chris Zimmerman
Ed. .... Pat Richardson
Pub. .... Cheryl Franklin
Digital Dir. .... Morgan Downs
Delivery Method: Racks

COLUMBUS NEWS REPORT (MON, WED, FRI)

105 S Pennsylvania Ave, Columbus, KS, 66725-1710, Cherokee, USA; gen tel (620) 429-4684; gen fax (620) 429-4694; disp adv e-mail newsreport@columbus-ks.com; ed e-mail newsreport@columbus-ks.com; web site columbusnews-report.com
Circulation: 1,191pd,; USPS
Advertising rate: Open inch rate $5.00
Established: 2010
Editor & Publisher ....
Larry HiattEquipment & Software: Hardware — Macintosh; Software — Adobe CS5
Delivery Method: Mail
Areas Served: 66725, 66728,66773,66781, 66782,

CONWAY SPRINGS

NORWICH NEWS (TUES)

215 S 8th St, Conway Springs, KS, 67031-8817, Kingman, USA; gen tel (620) 456-2232; gen fax (620) 456-2432; disp adv e-mail ajprinting@havilandtelco.com; ed e-mail ajprinting@havilandtelco.com
Advertising rate: Open inch rate $4.00
Pub/Ed .... A.J. Bozarth
Delivery Method: Mail

THE SOUTH HAVEN NEW ERA (TUES)

215 S 8th St, Conway Springs, KS, 67031-8817, Sumner, USA; gen tel (620) 456-2232; gen fax (620) 456-2432; disp adv e-mail ajprinting@havilandtelco.com; web site www.facebook.com/pages/South-Haven-New-Era/154024557969923
Circulation: 330pd, 35fr; Sworn/Estimate/Non-Audited
Advertising rate: Open inch rate $3.50
Ed. .... A.J. Bozarth
Mechanical Specifications: Type page 11 x 17; E - 5 cols, 1 5/6, 1/6 between; A - 5 cols, 1 5/6, 1/6 between.
Delivery Method: Mail

COTTONWOOD FALLS

CHASE COUNTY LEADER-NEWS (THUR)

PO Box K, 306 Broadway St, Cottonwood Falls, KS, 66845-0436, Chase, USA; gen tel (620) 273-6391; adv tel (620) 273-6391; ed tel (620) 273-6391; gen fax (620) 273-8674; adv fax (620) 273-8674; ed fax (620) 273-8674; disp adv e-mail ccleadernews@gmail.com; class adv e-mail ccleadernews@gmail.com; ed e-mail ccleadernews@gmail.com; web site www.facebook.com/chasecountyleadernews/?ref=page_internal
Circulation: 1,200pd, 15fr; Sworn/Estimate/Non-Audited
Advertising rate: Open inch rate $5.00
Established: 1871
Prodn. Mgr. .... Jerry Schwilling
advertising, business manager... Cheri Hopson
Bus. Mgr. .... Marion Weaver
Mechanical Specifications: Type page 13 x 21.Equipment & Software: Hardware — APP/Mac; Software — QPS/QuarkXPress.
Delivery Method: Mail
Areas Served: 66845

COURTLAND

COURTLAND JOURNAL (THUR)

420 Main St, Courtland, KS, 66939-9712, Republic, USA; gen tel (785) 374-4428; gen fax (785) 374-4209; disp adv e-mail cjournal@courtland.net; ed e-mail cjournal@courtland.net; web site www.facebook.com/CourtlandJournal/
Circulation: 700pd, 20fr; Sworn/Estimate/Non-Audited
Advertising rate: Open inch rate $2.50
Established: 1903
Ed. .... Colleen Mainquist
Delivery Method: Mail

CUNNINGHAM

CUNNINGHAM COURIER (THUR)

209 E 1st St, Cunningham, KS, 67035-8824, Kingman, USA; gen tel (620) 298-2659; gen fax (620) 298-4047; disp adv e-mail ckclipper@juno.com; ed e-mail cunninghamcourier@gmail.com; web site www.cunninghamks.com
Advertising rate: Open inch rate $4.50
Pub. .... David Steffen
Ed. .... Kerri Steffen
Delivery Method: Mail

DERBY

DERBY INFORMER (WED)

219 E Madison Ave, Derby, KS, 67037-1711, USA; gen tel (316) 788-4006; gen fax (316) 788-4573; disp adv e-mail mail@derbyinformer.com; web site www.derbyinformer.com - 85,000(views) 11,000(visitors)
Circulation: 2,789pd,; Sworn/Estimate/Non-Audited
Advertising rate: 12.25
Established: 1998
Digital Platform - Mobile: Apple, Android, Windows, Blackberry
Digital Platform - Tablet: Apple iOS, Android, Windows 7, Blackberry Tablet OS
Publisher/Owner .... Jeff Cott
Mechanical Specifications: Call
Delivery Method: Mail, Newsstand, Racks
Areas Served: South Sedgwick, North Sumner and western Butler Counties.

DIGHTON

THE DIGHTON HERALD (WED)

113 E Long St, Dighton, KS, 67839, Lane, USA; gen tel (620) 397-5347; disp adv e-mail dherald@st-tel.net; ed e-mail dherald@st-tel.net
Circulation: 1,000pd,; Sworn/Estimate/Non-Audited
Advertising rate: Open inch rate $3.50
Established: 1885
Pub. .... Jerry Anderson
Ed. .... Mary Hartman
Mechanical Specifications: Type page 10.25 x 21; E - 6 cols, 1 3/16, 1/6 between; A - 6 cols, 1 3/16, 1/6 between; C - 6 cols, 1 3/16, 1/6 between.Equipment & Software: Hardware — APP/Mac
Delivery Method: Mail, Racks

DODGE CITY

HIGH PLAINS JOURNAL (MON)

1500 E Wyatt Earp Blvd, Dodge City, KS, 67801-7001, Ford, USA; gen tel (620) 227-7171; adv tel (620) 227-1847; ed tel (620) 227-1806; gen fax (620) 227-7173; disp adv e-mail art@hpj.com; class adv e-mail ads@hpj.com; ed e-mail journal@hpj.com; web site www.hpj.com
Circulation: 44,232pd, 0fr; Sworn/Estimate/Non-Audited
Advertising rate: Open inch rate $106 (Classifieds)
Established: 1949
Digital Platform - Tablet: Apple iOS, Kindle, Nook
Ed .... Holly Martin
Delivery Method: Mail

DOWNS

DOWNS NEWS AND TIMES (THUR)

717 Railroad St, Downs, KS, 67437-1633, Osborne, USA; gen tel (785) 454-3514; gen fax (785) 454-3866; disp adv e-mail downsnews@ruraltel.net; web site www.mainstreetmedia.us
Circulation: 1,155pd,; Sworn/Estimate/Non-Audited
Advertising rate: Open inch rate $3.35
Group: Main Street Media, Inc.
Pub. .... Jack Krier
Pub. .... Kathy Krier
Ed. .... LaRhea ColeEquipment & Software: Hardware — Austin; Software — Pro Write, Microsoft, Corel/Ventura.
Delivery Method: Mail

EFFINGHAM

NEWSLEAF (TUES)

417 MAIN ST, Effingham, KS, 66023, Atchison, USA; gen tel (913) 833-4180; gen fax (267) 295-8020; disp adv e-mail cap@thenewsleaf.com; web site www.thenewsleaf.com
Advertising rate: Open inch rate $5.00
Pub .... Steve Caplinger
Delivery Method: Mail

ELLINWOOD

ELLINWOOD LEADER (FRI)

105 N Main St, Ellinwood, KS, 67526-1639, Barton, USA; gen tel (620) 564-3116; gen fax (620) 564-2550; disp adv e-mail dsettle@ldn.kscoxmail.com; ed e-mail theellinwoodleadernews@yahoo.com; web site http://www.midksnews.com
Circulation: 1,053pd, 613fr; Sworn/Estimate/Non-Audited
Advertising rate: Open inch rate $3.50
Established: 1894
Group: Hi Neighbor Newspapers
Pub. .... John M. Settle
Circ. Mgr. .... Dennis Martin
Mechanical Specifications: Type page 13 x 21; E - 4 cols, 1/2 between; C - 6 cols, 2, 1/8 between.
Delivery Method: Mail

ELLIS

THE ELLIS REVIEW (THUR)

822 Washington St, Ellis, KS, 67637-2221, Ellis, USA; gen tel (785) 726-4583; gen fax (785) 726-3821; disp adv e-mail review@gbta.net; web site www.mainstreetmedia.us
Circulation: 1,130pd, 32fr; Sworn/Estimate/Non-Audited
Advertising rate: Open inch rate $4.00
Group: Main Street Media, Inc.
Pub. .... Jack Krier
Ed. .... Nickole Byers
Mechanical Specifications: Type page 11 2/3 x 21 1/2; E - 6 cols, 1 3/4, 1/8 between; A - 6 cols, 1 3/4, 1/8 between; C - 6 cols, 1 3/4, 1/8 between.Equipment & Software: Hardware — APP/Mac IIsi, APP/Mac Classic, APP/Mac LaserWriter II; Software — Adobe/PageMaker 5.0, Microsoft/Word 4.0.
Delivery Method: Mail

ELLSWORTH

THE ELLSWORTH COUNTY INDEPENDENT-REPORTER (THUR)

304 N Douglas Ave, Ellsworth, KS, 67439-3218, Ellsworth, USA; gen tel (785) 472-5085; adv tel (785) 472-5085; gen fax (785) 472-5087; disp adv e-mail eciads@eaglecom.net; class adv e-mail eciads@eaglecom.net ; ed e-mail indy@eaglecom.net; web site www.indyrepnews.com
Circulation: 2,700pd, 45fr; Sworn/Estimate/Non-Audited
Advertising rate: Open inch rate $5.50
Established: 1999
Group: Morris Multimedia, Inc.
Pub/Ed .... Linda Mowery-Denning
Bus. Mgr. .... Juanita Kepka
Delivery Method: Mail, Newsstand, Racks
Areas Served: Ellsworth County, Ks. and nearby areas

ERIE

ERIE RECORD (THUR)

213 S Main St, Erie, KS, 66733-1334, Neosho, USA; gen tel (620) 244-3371; gen fax (620) 244-3371; ed e-mail news@erierecord.com; web site www.facebook.com/pages/The-Erie-Record/100524630008815
Advertising rate: Open inch rate $5.00
Pub. .... Eddi Hibbs
Delivery Method: Mail

EUREKA

THE EUREKA HERALD (WED)

822 E River St, Ste 100, Eureka, KS, 67045-2132, Greenworth, USA; gen tel (620) 583-5721; gen fax (620) 583-5922; disp adv e-mail news@eurekaherald.com; ed e-mail news@eurekaherald.com; web site www.eurekaherald.com
Circulation: 2,300pd, 40fr; Sworn/Estimate/Non-Audited
Advertising rate: Open inch rate $6.00
Established: 1868
Pub .... Rachel Clasen
Ed .... Robin Wunderlich
Delivery Method: Mail

FRANKFORT

FRANKFORT AREA NEWS (THUR)

116 E 2nd St, Frankfort, KS, 66427-1403, Marshall, USA; gen tel (785) 292-4726; disp adv e-mail fan@bluevalley.net; class adv e-mail fan@bluevalley.net; ed e-mail fan@bluevalley.net; web site www.frankfortareanews.com
Circulation: 700pd,; USPS
Advertising rate: Open inch rate $6.00
Established: 1991
Ed. ....Connie MusilEquipment & Software: ; Presses — None; Software — Adobe CS3
Delivery Method: Mail, Racks
Areas Served: Marshall County, KS

FREDONIA

WILSON COUNTY CITIZEN (MON, THUR)

406 N 7th St, Fredonia, KS, 66736-1315, Wilson, USA; gen tel (620) 378-4415; gen fax (620) 378-4688; disp adv e-mail news@wilsoncountycitizen.com; ed e-mail news@wilsoncountycitizen.com; web site www.wilsoncountycitizen.com
Circulation: 3,000pd, 69fr; Sworn/Estimate/Non-Audited
Advertising rate: Open inch rate $5.25
Established: 1870
Adv. Mgr. .... Meredith Odell
Ed. .... Joseph Relph
Ed. .... Rita Relph
Mng. Ed. .... Mina S. DeBerry
Photography/IT .... Ross Relph
Delivery Method: Mail

GALENA

GALENA SENTINEL-TIMES (WED)

511 S Main St, Galena, KS, 66739-1292, Cherokee, USA; gen tel (620) 783-5034; gen fax (620) 783-1388; ed e-mail gstimes@kans.com; web site www.sentineltimes.com
Advertising rate: Open inch rate $5.50
Established: 1880
Pub .... David Nelson
Delivery Method: Mail

GARDNER

SPRING HILL NEW ERA (WED)

936 E Santa Fe St, Gardner, KS, 66030-1549, Johnson, USA; gen tel (913) 856-7615; gen fax (913) 856-6707; disp adv e-mail submissions@gardnernews.com; web site www.gardnernews.com
Circulation: 2,000pd, 10fr; Sworn/Estimate/Non-Audited
Advertising rate: Open inch rate $14.00
Pub. .... Rhonda Humble
Adv. Mgr. .... David Highfill
Circ. Mgr. .... Michelle Whitaker
Ed. .... Mark Taylor

GARNETT

ANDERSON COUNTY ADVOCATE (FRI)

117 E 4th Ave, Garnett, KS, 66032-1502, Anderson, USA; gen tel (785) 448-7000; gen fax (785) 448-9800; disp adv e-mail garnettadvocate@yahoo.com; ed e-mail news@andersoncountynewsline.com; web site http://andersoncountynewsline.com/
Advertising rate: Open inch rate $6.00Vern Brown
Delivery Method: Newsstand, Racks

ANDERSON COUNTY REVIEW (TUES)

112 W 6th Ave, Garnett, KS, 66032-1402, Anderson, USA; gen tel (785) 448-3121; gen fax (785) 448-6253; disp adv e-mail Review@garnett-ks.com; ed e-mail Review@garnett-ks.com; web site http://www.garnett-ks.com/
Circulation: 2,318pd, 44fr; Sworn/Estimate/Non-Audited
Advertising rate: Open inch rate $8.00
Established: 1865
Publisher .... Dane Hicks
Delivery Method: Mail, Racks
Areas Served: Anderson County, Kansas, and surrounding communities

GLASCO

THE DELPHOS REPUBLICAN (THUR)

404 E Elm St, Glasco, KS, 67445-9370, Cloud, USA; gen tel (785) 568-2373; gen fax (785) 899-6186; disp adv e-mail sunrepublican@twinvalley.net; web site www.facebook.com/pages/Glasco-Sun-Delphos-Republican/143383312361771
Circulation: 400pd,; Sworn/Estimate/Non-Audited
Advertising rate: Open inch rate $4.00
Ed. .... Kevin Bottrell
Delivery Method: Mail, Racks

GOODLAND

GOODLAND STAR-NEWS (TUES, FRI)

1205 Main Ave, Goodland, KS, 67735-2946, Sherman, USA; gen tel (785) 899-2338; gen fax (785) 899-6186; disp adv e-mail kbentley@nwkansas.com; ed e-mail star.news@nwkansas.com; web site www.nwkansas.com
Circulation: 2,004pd,; Sworn/Estimate/Non-Audited
Advertising rate: Open inch rate $7.95
Established: 1993
Group: Haynes Publishing Co.
Society Ed./composition .... Pat Schiefen
ad designer/traffic manager..... Jessica Corbin
president .... Steve Haynes
Circ. Mgr./office manager............. Sheila Smith
Ed .... Kevin Bottrell
Mechanical Specifications: Type page 12 x 21 1/2; E - 6 cols, 2, 1/8 between; A - 6 cols, 2, 1/8 between; C - 6 cols, 2, 1/8 between. Equipment & Software: Hardware — APP/Mac; Presses — 6-HI/V-15A; Software — Adobe inDesign, neoOffice, PhotoShop
Delivery Method: Mail, Newsstand, Carrier, Racks
Areas Served: 67700-99

HALSTEAD

HARVEY COUNTY INDEPENDENT (THUR)

220 Main St, Halstead, KS, 67056-1913, Harvey, USA; gen tel (316) 835-2235; gen fax (316) 835-3357; disp adv e-mail ads@hcindependent.com; ed e-mail karen@hcindependent.com; web site www.hcindependent.com
Advertising rate: Open inch rate $6.25
Established: 1881
Ed .... Karen Jacobs
Delivery Method: Mail

HARPER

HARPER ADVOCATE (WED)

907 Central St, # 36, Harper, KS, 67058-1112, Harper, USA; gen tel (620) 896-7311; disp adv e-mail harperadvocate@sbcglobal.net; class adv e-mail same as above; ed e-mail harperadvocate@sbcglobal.net; web site NA
Circulation: 1,200pd,; USPS
Advertising rate: Open inch rate $6.50
Established: 1882
Pub. .... Ken Leu
Mechanical Specifications: 8 col (1.75") x 21"
Delivery Method: Mail, Newsstand
Areas Served: 67058

HAVEN

RURAL MESSENGER (TUES)

115 S Kansas St, Haven, KS, 67543-9261, Harvey, USA; gen tel (620) 465-4636; adv tel (620) 465-4636; ed tel (620) 465-4636; gen fax (620) 465-2309; adv fax (620) 465-2309; ed fax (620) 465-2309; disp adv e-mail malfers@ruralmessenger.com; ed e-mail malfers@ruralmessenger.com; web site www.RuralMessenger.com - 36,000(views) 18,000(visitors)
Circulation: 18,000fr; Sworn/Estimate/Non-Audited
Established: 2004Editions: (1)
Pub .... Mike Alfers

HAYSVILLE

HAYSVILLE SUN-TIMES (THUR)

325 N Main St, Haysville, KS, 67060-1159, Sedgwick, USA; gen tel (316) 524-6868; adv tel (316) 540-3111; ed tel (316) 540-0500; gen fax (316) 522-8668; disp adv e-mail graphicsdept@tsnews.com; class adv e-mail classifieds@tsnews.com; ed e-mail haysvillesuntimes@yahoo.com; web site www.tsnews.com
Circulation: 1,100pd,; Sworn/Estimate/Non-Audited
Advertising rate: Open inch rate $7.00
Group: Times-Sentinel Newspapers LLC
Pub .... Travis Mounts
Delivery Method: Mail, Newsstand, Racks
Areas Served: Haysville, Sedgwick County, KS

HERINGTON

THE HERINGTON TIMES (THUR)

106 N Broadway, Herington, KS, 67449-2225, Dickinson, USA; gen tel (785) 366-6186; gen fax 316-445-2446; disp adv e-mail ads@heringtontimes.com; class adv e-mail ads@heringtontimes.com; ed e-mail editor@heringtontimes.com; web site www.facebook.com/theheringtontimes/
Circulation: 800pd, 50fr; Sworn/Estimate/Non-Audited
Advertising rate: Open inch rate $7.75
Established: 1889
Group: Kansas Publishing Ventures
Office Manager..........Kristi LovettEquipment & Software: Hardware — APP/Mac, APP/Mac Performa; Software — Quark XPress 6.5; TextEdit 1.4; Safari 4.1.3
Delivery Method: Mail, Racks
Areas Served: 67410, 67449, 66838, 67451, 66858, 66859, 67475, 67483, 67492, 67872

HESSTON

HESSTON RECORD (THUR)

PO Box 340, Hesston, KS, 67062-0340, Harvey, USA; gen tel (620) 327-4831; gen fax (620) 327-4830; disp adv e-mail ads@hesstonrecord.com; ed e-mail jackie@hesstonrecord.com; web site www.hesstonrecord.com
Circulation: 1,074pd, 130fr; Sworn/Estimate/Non-Audited
Advertising rate: Open inch rate $7.00
Pub. .... Robb Reeves
Ed. .... Jackie Nelson
Blake Spurney
Delivery Method: Mail

THE LEDGER (THUR)

105 N Main St, Hesston, KS, 67062-9143, Harvey, USA; gen tel (620) 327-4831; adv tel (863) 802-7400; ed tel (863) 802-7504; gen fax (620) 345-2170; disp adv e-mail ledg@mtelco.net; class adv e-mail classifieds@theledger.com; ed e-mail lenore.devore@theledger.com; web site www.ledgernewspaper.com
Circulation: 1,300pd,; Sworn/Estimate/Non-Audited
Advertising rate: Open inch rate $5.35
Ed. .... Lenore Devore
Mechanical Specifications: Type page 10 1/2 x 16; E - 5 cols, 2, 1/4 between; A - 5 cols, 2, 1/4 between; C - 5 cols, 2, 1/4 between. Equipment & Software: ; Software — Adobe/PageMaker 5.0.
Areas Served: 67107, 67546

HIAWATHA

HIAWATHA WORLD (TUES, FRI)

607 Utah St, Hiawatha, KS, 66434-2319, Brown, USA; gen tel (785) 742-2111; gen fax (785) 742-2276; disp adv e-mail christym@npgco.com; class adv e-mail world@npgco.com; ed e-mail joewarren@npgco.com; web site www.hiawathaworldonline.com
Circulation: 2,300pd,; Sworn/Estimate/Non-Audited
Advertising rate: Open inch rate $7.50
Established: 1908
Group: News-Press & Gazette Co.
Pub/Ed .... Joe Warren
Adv. Mgr. .... Sarah Davies
Managing Ed .... Joey May
Mechanical Specifications: Type page 13 x 21; E - 6 cols, 2 1/16, 1/8 between; A - 6 cols, 2 1/16, 1/8 between; C - 6 cols, 2 1/16, 1/8 between.Equipment & Software: Hardware — APP/Mac; Presses — 4-HI/Cottrell V-15A; Software — Adobe/PageMaker.
Delivery Method: Mail

HILL CITY

THE HILL CITY TIMES (WED)

110 N Pomeroy Ave, Hill City, KS, 67642-1870, Graham, USA; gen tel (785) 421-5700; gen fax (785) 421-5712; disp adv e-mail times@ruraltel.net; ed e-mail times@ruraltel.net
Circulation: 1,800pd, 10fr; Sworn/Estimate/Non-Audited
Advertising rate: Open inch rate $2.80
Digital Platform - Mobile: Windows
Ed. .... James Logback
Associate Editor .... Diane Boyd
Associate Editor .... SUZIE MCDOWELL
Mechanical Specifications: Type page 11 3/4 x 21 1/2; E - 6 cols, 1 13/16, 3/16 between; A - 6 cols, 1 13/16, 3/16 between; C - 6 cols, 1 13/16, 3/16 between.Equipment & Software: Hardware — Gateway/2000 S-90, Gateway/2000; Software — Microsoft/Windows 98.
Delivery Method: Mail, Racks
Areas Served: 67642, 67625, 67650, 67740, 67672, 67669, 67646, 67645, 67654, 67632, etc.

HILLSBORO

HILLSBORO FREE PRESS (WED)

116 S Main St, Hillsboro, KS, 67063-1526, Marion, USA; gen tel (620) 947-5702; adv tel (620) 947-5702; ed tel (620) 947-5702; gen fax (620) 947-5940; adv fax (620) 947-5940; ed fax (620) 947-5940; disp adv e-mail natalie@hillsborofreepress.com; class adv e-mail nicole@hillsborofreepress.com; ed e-mail don@hillsborofreepress.com; web site www.hillsborofreepress.com - 26,544(views) 5,078(visitors)
Circulation: 120pd, 7,140fr; CVC
Advertising rate: Open inch rate $11.25
Established: 1998
Group: Kansas Publishing Ventures
Digital Platform - Mobile: Apple, Android, Windows, Blackberry
Digital Platform - Tablet: Apple iOS, Android, Windows 7, Blackberry Tablet OS, Kindle, Nook, Kindle Fire
Pub. .... Joel Klaassen
Ed. .... Don Ratzlaff
Adv. Mgr. .... Natalie Hoffman
Circ. Mgr. .... Nicole Suderman

Prod. Mgr. .... Kevin Hower
Pub. .... Joey Young
Mechanical Specifications: 6 col x 21Equipment & Software: Hardware — Mac; Software — Quark
CS5
FotoFusion
Delivery Method: Mail, Carrier, Racks
Areas Served: Hillsboro, Marion, Peabody, Florence, Burns, Goessel, Lost Springs, Lincolnville, Ramona, Tampa, Durham, Lehigh, Canton, Burdick, and Cedar Point

HILLSBORO STAR-JOURNAL (WED)

110 N Main St, Hillsboro, KS, 67063-1139, Marion, USA; gen tel (620) 947-3975; gen fax (620) 382-2262; disp adv e-mail advertising@starj.com; class adv e-mail advertising@starj.com; ed e-mail news@starj.com; web site http://starj.com/
Circulation: 1,200pd, 100fr; Sworn/Estimate/Non-Audited
Advertising rate: Open inch rate $7.50
Established: 1908
Group: Hoch Publishing Co. Inc.Editions: (1)
Advertising sales representative.. Debra Steele
Business and circulation managerJean Stuchlik
President and publisher.................. Eric Meyer
Production director ....Melvin Honeyfield
News editor.............................. Adam Stewart
Reporter .... Ben Kleine
Reporter .... David Colburn
Reporter .... Jennifer Stultz
Reporter .... Rowena Plett
Accounting coordinator............ Tena Lundgren
Mechanical Specifications: 10.125x21 inch usable pageEquipment & Software: Hardware — 10 PC; Software — Adobe Creative Suite, Interlink, Quickbooks
Delivery Method: Mail, Newsstand, Racks
Areas Served: 67063, 67438, 67073, 67053

HOLTON

THE HOLTON RECORDER (MON, WED)

109 W 4th St, Holton, KS, 66436-1701, Jackson, USA; gen tel (785) 364-3141; gen fax (785) 364-3422; disp adv e-mail holtonrecorder@embarqmail.com; ed e-mail holtonrecorder@embarqmail.com; web site www.holtonrecorder.net
Circulation: 4,200pd, 2,700fr; USPS
Advertising rate: Open inch rate $8.20
Established: 1867
Co-Owner .... Connie Powls
Ed. .... David M. Powls
Prodn. Mgr. .... Allen Bowser
Mechanical Specifications: call for detailsEquipment & Software: Hardware — APP/Mac.
Delivery Method: Mail, Newsstand, Racks
Areas Served: stated above

HORTON

HORTON HEADLIGHT (THUR)

133 W 8th St, PO Box 269, Horton, KS, 66439-1601, Brown, USA; gen tel (785) 486-2512; gen fax (785) 486-2512; disp adv e-mail headlight@carsoncomm.com; ed e-mail headlight@carsoncomm.com; web site NA
Circulation: 1,300pd,; Sworn/Estimate/Non-Audited
Advertising rate: Open inch rate $6.50
Pub. .... Dana Foley
Mng. Ed. .... Linda Messer
Ed. .... Susan Higley
Prodn. Mgr. .... Dave Christensen
Mechanical Specifications: Type page 14 x 21.
Delivery Method: Mail, Racks

HOXIE

THE SHERIDAN SENTINEL (THUR)

716 Main St, Hoxie, KS, 67740-8800, Sheridan, USA; gen tel (785) 675-3321; adv tel (785) 657-7417; disp adv e-mail thesheridansentinel@gmail.com; ed e-mail thesheridansentinel@gmail.com; web site https://www.sheridansentinel.com/ - 100(views)
Circulation: 800pd, 50fr; Sworn/Estimate/Non-Audited
Advertising rate: Open inch rate $3.00
Established: June 29, 2016
Group: Sheridan Sentinel, LLC
Owner/Ed/Pub .... Viktorija Briggs
Delivery Method: Mail, Newsstand, Racks
Areas Served: Sheridan County

HUGOTON

THE HUGOTON HERMES (THUR)

522 S Main St, Hugoton, KS, 67951-2428, Stevens, USA; gen tel (620) 544-4321; gen fax (620) 544-7321; disp adv e-mail hermes10@pld.com; class adv e-mail hermes10@pld.com; ed e-mail hermesro@pld.com; web site www.hugotonhermesnew.com
Circulation: 2,300pd,; Sworn/Estimate/Non-Audited
Advertising rate: Open inch rate $5.00
Established: 1887
RoGlenda Coulter
Kay McDaniels
Ruthie WingetCo-Owners
Mechanical Specifications: Type page 12 3/4 x 20; E - 6 cols, 2, 1/6 between; A - 6 cols, 2, 1/6 between; C - 6 cols, 2, 1/6 between. Equipment & Software: Hardware — APP/Mac; Software — Adobe/PageMaker, QPS/QuarkXPress 4.0.
Delivery Method: Mail
Areas Served: 67951

JETMORE

JETMORE REPUBLICAN (WED)

415 Main, Jetmore, KS, 67854, Hodgeman, USA; gen tel (620) 357-8316; disp adv e-mail jetrepub@fairpoint.net; ed e-mail jetrepub@fairpoint.net; web site www.facebook.com/pages/Jetmore-Republican/128074637238247
Advertising rate: Open inch rate $4.00
Pub. .... Mark Anderson
Ed. .... Mike Thornburg
Delivery Method: Mail

KANSAS CITY

WYANDOTTE COUNTY BUSINESS NEWS (MON)

PO Box 13235, Kansas City, KS, 66113-0235, Wyandotte, USA; gen tel (913) 422-8232; disp adv e-mail notices@wyandottecountylegalnews.com; class adv e-mail notices@wyandottecountylegalnews.com; ed e-mail notices@wyandottecountylegalnews.com; web site www.wybiznews.com
Ed .... Emily Campbell
Delivery Method: Mail, Racks

WYANDOTTE DAILY NEWS WEEKLY PRINT EDITION (THUR)

2 S 14th St, Ste 100, Kansas City, KS, 66102-5041, Wyandotte, USA; gen tel (913) 788-5565; gen fax (816) 979-1122; disp adv e-mail ads@wyandottedailynews.com ; class adv e-mail ads@WyandottePublishing.com; ed e-mail news@WyandottePublishing.com; web site http://wyandottedaily.com
Circulation: 1,500pd, 10,000fr
Advertising rate: Open inch rate $20.00
Established: 1968
Group: TrulyLocal Media
Pub. .... Richard Ward
Ed. .... Mary Rupert
Exec. Asst .... Lexie Cocker
Delivery Method: Mail, Newsstand, Carrier, Racks
Areas Served: Kansas City (Wyandotte County) Kansas

WYANDOTTE ECHO (THUR)

450 N 17th St, Kansas City, KS, 66102-4202, Wyandotte, USA; gen tel (913) 342-2444; adv tel (913) 342-2444; ed tel (913) 342-2444; gen fax (913) 362-8406; adv fax (913) 362-8406; ed fax (913) 362-8406; disp adv e-mail mjpkck@aol.com; class adv e-mail mjpkck@aol.com; ed e-mail mjpkck@aol.com; web site www.wyandotteecho.com
Advertising rate: Open inch rate $10.00
Pub. .... Roberta Peterson
Delivery Method: Mail
Areas Served: 66102, 66110

KINGMAN

KINGMAN LEADER-COURIER (THUR)

140 N Main St, Kingman, KS, 67068-1301, Kingman, USA; gen tel (620) 532-3151; gen fax (620) 532-3152; disp adv e-mail advertise@kcnonline.com; class adv e-mail iarensdorf@kcnonline.com; ed e-mail jjump@kcnonline.com; web site www.kcnonline.com
Circulation: 2,400pd, 50fr; Sworn/Estimate/Non-Audited
Advertising rate: Open inch rate $6.75
Established: 1878
Pub. .... Jason Jump
Sub. .... Irene Arensdorf
Bus. Mgr. .... Stephanie Jump
Education and Sports Ed. .... Bob Morris
Delivery Method: Mail, Newsstand
Areas Served: Kingman County, Sedgwick County, Reno County, Harper County, Pratt County

KINSLEY

EDWARDS COUNTY SENTINEL (WED)

221 E 6th St, Kinsley, KS, 67547-1109, Edwards, USA; gen tel (620) 659-2080; gen fax (620) 855-2489; disp adv e-mail edcsentinel@hotmail.com
Circulation: 1,200pd,; Sworn/Estimate/Non-Audited
Advertising rate: Open inch rate $4.00
Group: Golden Plains Publishing
Pub .... Mark Anderson
Editor .... Faith BroKar
Delivery Method: Mail
Areas Served: Edwards County (Kinsley, Lewis, Offerle)

KIOWA

THE KIOWA NEWS (WED)

614 Main St, Kiowa, KS, 67070-1414, Kiowa, USA; gen tel (620) 825-4229; gen fax (620) 825-4229; disp adv e-mail kionews@sctelcom.net; ed e-mail kionews@sctelcom.net; web site www.kiowanews.com
Circulation: 1,250pd, 34fr; Sworn/Estimate/Non-Audited
Advertising rate: Open inch rate $5.40
Established: 1893
Ed. .... Rex Zimmerman
Delivery Method: Mail

LA CROSSE

RUSH COUNTY NEWS (THUR)

112 W 8th St, La Crosse, KS, 67548-9603, Rush, USA; gen tel (785) 222-2555; gen fax (785) 222-2557; disp adv e-mail rcn@gbta.net; ed e-mail rcn@gbta.net; web site www.facebook.com/pages/Rush-County-News/153454468030266
Advertising rate: Open inch rate $4.50
Established: 1941
Pub .... Mary Engel
Ed .... Tim Engel
Delivery Method: Mail

LAKIN

THE LAKIN INDEPENDENT (THUR)

118 N Main St, Lakin, KS, 67860-9474, Kearny, USA; gen tel (620) 355-6162; adv tel 620-355-6162; ed tel 620-355-6162; gen fax (620) 355-6300; adv fax 620-355-6162; ed fax 620-355-6162; disp adv e-mail indpndt@pld.com; class adv e-mail indpndt@pld.com; ed e-mail indpndt@pld.com
Circulation: 1,450pd,; Sworn/Estimate/Non-Audited
Advertising rate: Open inch rate $5.25
Established: 1885
Ed. .... Kathy McVey
Delivery Method: Mail, Racks

LARNED

THE TILLER & TOILER (TUES, FRI)

115 W 5th St, Larned, KS, 67550-9983, Pawnee, USA; gen tel (620) 285-3111; gen fax (620) 285-6062; disp adv e-mail tiller@star.kscoxmail.com; ed e-mail tiller@star.kscoxmail.com; web site www.midksnews.com
Circulation: 1,434pd,; Sworn/Estimate/Non-Audited
Advertising rate: Open inch rate $5.86
Group: Hi Neighbor Newspapers
Pres. .... Marshall Settle
Pub. .... John M. Settle
Adv. Rep. .... Bryan Martin
Adv. Rep. .... Paula Settle
Circ. Mgr. .... Shirley Strassburg
Sports Ed. .... Mark Zwink
Online Mgr. .... Lisa Springer
Prodn. Mgr., Pressroom .... Bob Crawford
Adv. Mgr. .... David Settle
Managing Ed. .... Mike Gilmore
Mechanical Specifications: Type page 12 7/8 x 21 1/2; E - 6 cols, 2 1/16, 1/8 between; A - 6 cols, 2 1/16, 1/8 between; C - 6 cols, 2 1/16, 1/8 between.
Delivery Method: Mail

LEOTI

THE LEOTI STANDARD (WED)

114 S 4th St, Leoti, KS, 67861-7032, Wichita, USA; gen tel (620) 375-2631; disp adv e-mail standard@fairpoint.net
Circulation: 1,000pd, 30fr; Sworn/Estimate/Non-Audited
Advertising rate: Open inch rate $4.00
Group: Golden Plains Publishing
Digital Platform - Mobile: Apple
Pub. .... Mark Anderson
Editor .... Shonda Taylor
Delivery Method: Mail, Newsstand
Areas Served: 67861

LIBERAL

LOS TIEMPOS (THUR)

16 S Kansas Ave, Liberal, KS, 67901-3732, Seward, USA; gen tel (620) 624-2541; gen fax (620) 624-0735; disp adv e-mail ads@swdtimes.com; web site www.facebook.com/pages/Los-Tiempos/174782409548429
Circulation: 8,500fr; Sworn/Estimate/Non-Audited
Advertising rate: Open inch rate $5.00
Pub. .... Larry Reynolds
Bus. Mgr. .... Tammy Garth
Mng. Ed. .... James Gutzmer

LINCOLN

LINCOLN SENTINEL-REPUBLICAN (THUR)

141 W Lincoln Ave, Lincoln, KS, 67455-1917, Lincoln, USA; gen tel (785) 524-4200; gen fax (785) 524-4242; disp adv e-mail lincolnksads@gmail.com; ed e-mail johnbaetz@

gmail.com; web site www.lincolnsentinel.com
Circulation: 1,750pd, 1,750fr; Sworn/Estimate/Non-Audited
Advertising rate: Open inch rate $5.00
Co-Owner .... Bree McReynolds Baetz
Co-Pub....... John BaetzEquipment & Software: Hardware — APP/Mac; Software — Multi-Ad/Creator 6.5.
Delivery Method: Mail, Racks

LINDSBORG

THE LINDSBORG NEWS-RECORD (THUR)

114 S Main St, Lindsborg, KS, 67456-2418, McPherson, USA; gen tel (785) 227-3348; gen fax (785) 227-3740; disp adv e-mail kathy@lnr.kscoxmail.com; class adv e-mail cindy@lnr.kscoxmail.com; ed e-mail dori@lindsborgnewsrecord.com; web site mainstreetmedia.us
Circulation: 2,899pd,; Sworn/Estimate/Non-Audited
Advertising rate: Open inch rate $8.50
Established: 1881
Group: Main Street Media, Inc.
General Mgr. .... Cindy Opat
Prodn. Mgr. .... Dan Carr
Editor/Publisher .... Jack Krier
Delivery Method: Mail, Carrier, Racks

LINN

LINN-PALMER RECORD (THUR)

405 2nd St, Linn, KS, 66953-9562, Washington, USA; gen tel (785) 348-5581; gen fax (785) 348-5549; disp adv e-mail lpr@bluevalley.net; ed e-mail editor@bluevalley.net
Circulation: 700pd, 13fr; Sworn/Estimate/Non-Audited
Advertising rate: Open inch rate $5.00
Established: 1891
Linn Ed .... Lorene Rieth
Delivery Method: Mail, Racks
Areas Served: Southern Washington County, Kansas

LITTLE RIVER

MONITOR-JOURNAL (WED)

270 Main St, Little River, KS, 67457-9072, Rice, USA; gen tel (620) 897-6234; gen fax (620) 897-6287; disp adv e-mail themonitor@lrmutual.com; class adv e-mail themonitor@lrmutual.com; ed e-mail themonitor@lrmutual.com
Circulation: 400pd,; Sworn/Estimate/Non-Audited
Advertising rate: $3.80
Established: 1886
Digital Platform - Mobile: Apple
Denice Dater
Greg DaterCo-Pubs
Mechanical Specifications: col. width 1.551
6 columns
Delivery Method: Mail
Areas Served: Little River, Windom, Marquette, Lyons, McPherson, Inman, Hutchinson

LOGAN

THE LOGAN REPUBLICAN (THUR)

101 E Main St, Logan, KS, 67646-5169, Phillips, USA; gen tel (785) 689-4339; gen fax (785) 689-4338; disp adv e-mail loganrep@ruraltel.net; web site www.facebook.com/pages/Logan-Republican/151744111503720
Circulation: 1,000pd,; Sworn/Estimate/Non-Audited
Advertising rate: Open inch rate $3.00
Ed. ....John Sullivan
Delivery Method: Mail

LUCAS

LUCAS-SYLVAN NEWS (THUR)

203 S Main St, Lucas, KS, 67648-9718, Russell, USA; gen tel (785) 525-6355; gen fax (785) 525-6356; disp adv e-mail lusynews@gmail.com; web site http://www.lucas-sylvan-news.com/
Circulation: 675pd,; Sworn/Estimate/Non-Audited
Advertising rate: Open inch rate $4.80
Established: 1899
Ed. .... LaRee Bretz
Owner/Publisher .... Rita Sharp
Delivery Method: Mail

LYONS

THE LYONS NEWS (TUES, FRI)

210 W Commercial St, Lyons, KS, 67554-2716, Rice, USA; gen tel (620) 257-2368; gen fax (620) 257-2369; disp adv e-mail advertising@ldn.kscoxmail.com; class adv e-mail advertising@ldn.kscoxmail.com; ed e-mail admin@ldn.kscoxmail.com; web site http://www.midksnews.com
Circulation: 2,321pd,; Sworn/Estimate/Non-Audited
Advertising rate: Open inch rate $5.86
Established: 1906
Group: Star Communications
Ed. .... David Settle
Office Mgr./Adv. Mgr. .... Anita Settle
Pub. .... John M. Settle
Office Asst. .... Jennifer Renollet
Distribution .... Debbie Peters
Office Asst, ... Darla Graf
Distribution .... Silver Ingram
Reporter .... Ryan Carlson
Sports Reporter .... Mike Courson
Mechanical Specifications: Type page 13 x 21; E - 6 cols, 2, 1/8 between; A - 6 cols, 2, 1/8 between; C - 6 cols, 2, 1/8 between.Equipment & Software: Hardware — APP/Mac; Presses — 3-HI/15A; Software — Aldus/PageMaker.
Delivery Method: Mail, Newsstand, Carrier

MADISON

THE MADISON NEWS (WED)

225 W Main St, # 12, Madison, KS, 66860-9569, Greenwood, USA; gen tel (620) 437-2433; gen fax (620) 437-2433; disp adv e-mail madnews@madtel.net; ed e-mail madnews@madtel.net; web site www.facebook.com/The-Madison-News-253840751628/
Circulation: 850pd, 15fr; Sworn/Estimate/Non-Audited
Advertising rate: Open inch rate $4.50
Editor and Publisher .... Tammy Seimears
Gen. Mgr. .... Patsy Murphy
Mechanical Specifications: Type page 12 x ; E - 6 cols, between; A - 6 cols, between. Equipment & Software: Hardware — Gateway/2000; Software — Microsoft/Word.
Delivery Method: Mail

MANHATTAN

GRASS & GRAIN (TUES)

1531 Yuma St, Manhattan, KS, 66502-4228, Riley, USA; gen tel (785) 539-7558; gen fax (785) 539-2679; disp adv e-mail agpress2@agpress.com; ed e-mail gandgeditor@agpress.com; web site www.grassandgrain.com
Circulation: 14,000pd,; Sworn/Estimate/Non-Audited
Advertising rate: Open inch rate $9.50
Established: 1953
Ed. .... Donna Sullivan
Delivery Method: Mail

MANKATO

JEWELL COUNTY RECORD (THUR)

111 E Main St, Mankato, KS, 66956-2214, Jewell, USA; gen tel (785) 378-3191; gen fax (785) 378-3782; disp adv e-mail bblauvelt@windstream.net; ed e-mail jcr@nckcn.com; web site www.superiorne.com
Circulation: 700pd,; Sworn/Estimate/Non-Audited
Advertising rate: Open inch rate $4.00
Established: 1970
Group: Superior Publishing Company
Pub. .... Bill Blauvelt
Office Manager .... Joanne Freeman
Mechanical Specifications: Type page 15 x 21; E - 7 cols, 2, 1/6 between; A - 7 cols, 2, 1/6 between; C - 7 cols, 2, 1/6 between.Equipment & Software: Hardware — APP/Mac; Presses — 3-G/Community; Software — Adobe/PageMaker 6.5.
Delivery Method: Mail, Newsstand
Areas Served: Jewell County Kansas

MARION

MARION COUNTY RECORD (WED)

117 S 3rd St, Marion, KS, 66861-1621, Marion, USA; gen tel (620) 382-2165; gen fax (620) 382-2262; disp adv e-mail advertising@marionrecord.com; class adv e-mail classified@marionrecord.com ; ed e-mail news@marionrecord.com; web site http://marionrecord.com/ - 297,000(views) 17,300(visitors)
Circulation: 2,700pd, 100fr; USPS
Advertising rate: Open inch rate $7.50
Established: 1869
Group: Hoch Publishing Co. Inc.Editions: (1)
Columnist .... Pat Wick
Mechanical Specifications: Page size 10.125 x 21 inchesEquipment & Software: Hardware — 10-PC; Software — Adobe Creative Suite
Delivery Method: Mail, Newsstand, Racks
Areas Served: 66861, 66858, 66859, 67475, 67483, 66851

MARQUETTE

THE MARQUETTE TRIBUNE (WED)

112 N Washington St, Marquette, KS, 67464-4010, McPherson, USA; gen tel (785) 546-2266; gen fax (785) 546-2266; disp adv e-mail marquettetribune@eagalecom.net; ed e-mail marquettetribune@eagalecom.net
Circulation: 600pd,; Sworn/Estimate/Non-Audited
Advertising rate: Open inch rate $4.47
Group: Morris Multimedia, Inc.
Ed. .... Dori Weber
Mechanical Specifications: Type page 12 x 21.
Delivery Method: Mail

MARYSVILLE

MARYSVILLE ADVOCATE (THUR)

107 S 9th St, Marysville, KS, 66508-1825, Marshall, USA; gen tel (785) 562-2317; adv tel (785) 562-2317; ed tel (785) 562-2317; gen fax (785) 562-5589; adv fax (785) 562-5589; ed fax (785) 562-5589; disp adv e-mail wkruse@marysvilleonline.net; class adv e-mail mkeller@marysvilleonline.net; ed e-mail skessinger@marysvilleonline.net; web site www.marysvilleonline.net
Circulation: 3,600pd, 100fr; Sworn/Estimate/Non-Audited
Advertising rate: Open inch rate $7
Established: 1885
Group: Advocate Publishing Co.
Digital Platform - Mobile: Apple, Android, Windows, Blackberry
Digital Platform - Tablet: Apple iOS, Android, Windows 7, Blackberry Tablet OS, Kindle, Kindle Fire
Editor emeritus .... Sharon Kessinger
Editor, publisher, owner .... Sarah Kessinger
News editor .... Sally Gray
Sports writer .... Julie Perry
Ad sales .... Mandy Keller
Reporter .... Paul Kessinger
Advertising director .... Wayne Kruse
Circulation manager, business office..... Angela Schmale
Obituary writer, public notices ..... Kelsey Smith
reporter .... JoAnn Shum
Mechanical Specifications: Type page 6 x 21.Equipment & Software: Hardware — APP/Mac; Software — Creative Suite
Delivery Method: Mail, Newsstand, Racks
Areas Served: 66403, 66406, 66411, 66412, 66427, 66438, 66503, 66518, 66541, 66544, 66548, 66933, 66937, 66943, 66944, 66945, 66946, 66953, 66955, 66968, 66962

MEADE

MEADE COUNTY NEWS (WED)

105 S Fowler St, Meade, KS, 67864-6404, Meade, USA; gen tel (620) 873-2118; gen fax (620) 873-5456; disp adv e-mail mcnews@mcnewsonline.com; ed e-mail mcnews@mcnewsonline.com; web site www.mcnewsonline.com
Circulation: 1,300pd,; Sworn/Estimate/Non-Audited
Advertising rate: Open inch rate $4.75
Established: 1885
Ed. .... Denise Kuhns
Delivery Method: Mail

MEDICINE LODGE

THE GYP HILL PREMIERE (MON)

108 N Main St, Medicine Lodge, KS, 67104-1317, Barber, USA; gen tel (620) 886-5654; gen fax (620) 886-5617; disp adv e-mail rnoland@cyberlodg.com; class adv e-mail rnoland@cyberlodg.com; ed e-mail doris@medicinelodge.com; web site www.gyphillpremiere.com
Circulation: 1,200pd,; Sworn/Estimate/Non-Audited
Advertising rate: Open inch rate $4.00
Pub. .... Kevin J. Noland
Adv. Mgr. .... Ronda D. Noland
Ed. .... Doris Sorg
Delivery Method: Mail

MILTONVALE

MILTONVALE RECORD (THUR)

10 W Spruce Ave, PO Box 278, Miltonvale, KS, 67466-5026, Cloud, USA; gen tel (785) 427-2680; gen fax none; disp adv e-mail miltonvalerecord@twinvalley.net; class adv e-mail same; ed e-mail miltonvalerecord@twinvalley.net; web site none
Circulation: 397pd, 8fr; Sworn/Estimate/Non-Audited
Advertising rate: Open inch rate $3.00
Established: 1898
Group: Concordia Blade-Empire
Circulation Direction .... Barbara Mikels
Reporter, photographer .... Sarah Lacy
Mechanical Specifications: Type page 14 x 21.Equipment & Software: Hardware — IBM, HP; Presses — HI/Vanguard; Software — Pro Write, Archetype/Corel Draw, Ventura.
Delivery Method: Mail
Areas Served: Miltonvale, Cloud County, Kansas 67466

MINNEAPOLIS

MINNEAPOLIS MESSENGER (THUR)

108 N Concord St, Minneapolis, KS, 67467-2320, Ottawa, USA; gen tel (785) 392-2129; gen fax (785) 392-2026; disp adv e-mail submit@mymessengerks.com; ed e-mail submit@mymessengerks.com; web site

www.facebook.com/pg/MyMessengerKS/about/?ref=page_internal
Circulation: 2,300pd, 33fr; Sworn/Estimate/Non-Audited
Advertising rate: Open inch rate $3.75
Jason Parks
Erik ShupePub/Eds
Mechanical Specifications: Type page 13 x 21; E - 6 cols, 2 1/16, 1/6 between; A - 6 cols, 2 1/16, 1/6 between; C - 6 cols, 2 1/16, 1/6 between.
Delivery Method: Mail

MINNEOLA

CLARK COUNTY GAZETTE (WED)

119 S Main, Minneola, KS, 67865, Clark, USA; gen tel (620) 885-5040; gen fax (620) 873-5456; disp adv e-mail gazette@clarkcountygazette.com; ed e-mail gazette@clarkcountygazette.com; web site www.clarkcountygazette.com
Advertising rate: Open inch rate $3.25
Editor & Publisher....................... Denise Kuhns
Delivery Method: Mail

MONTEZUMA

MONTEZUMA PRESS (THUR)

208 S Aztec St, Montezuma, KS, 67867-8870, Gray, USA; gen tel (620) 846-2312; gen fax (620) 846-2312; disp adv e-mail montepress@ucom.net; ed e-mail montepress@ucom.net; web site www.montezumapublishing.com/
Advertising rate: Open inch rate $3.20
Pub.. Rudolph Loewen
Ed... Jeanne Loewen
Delivery Method: Mail

MOUNDRIDGE

LEDGER (MOUNDRIDGE) (THUR)

107 S Christian Ave, Moundridge, KS, 67107-9000, McPherson, USA; gen tel (620) 345-6353; gen fax (620) 345-2170; disp adv e-mail ads@hesstonrecord.com; ed e-mail ledge@mtelco.net; web site www.ledger-newspaper.net
Advertising rate: Open inch rate $5.75
Ed.. Randy Frogg
Delivery Method: Mail

MULLINVILLE

MERCHANT'S DIRECTORY (WED)

318 E Kingman, Mullinville, KS, 67109-7116, Kiowa, USA; gen tel (620) 548-2678; gen fax (620) 548-2638; disp adv e-mail merchantsdirectory@yahoo.com; web site www.facebook.com/merchantsdirectory/?ref=page_internal
Circulation: 390pd, 10fr; Sworn/Estimate/Non-Audited
Advertising rate: Open inch rate $2.50
Established: 1969
Digital Platform - Mobile: Blackberry
Ed.. Paul Kendall
Mechanical Specifications: Type page 8 1/2 x 11; E - 3 cols, 2 1/3, 1/4 between; A - 3 cols, 2 1/3, 1/4 between; C - 3 cols, 2 1/3, 1/4 between.Equipment & Software: Hardware — Acer; Software — Microsoft/Windows.
Delivery Method: Mail, Racks
Areas Served: Mullinville, Kiowa County, Ford County, Pratt County

NATOMA

NATOMA LURAY INDEPENDENT (WED, FRI)

120 N Main St, Natoma, KS, 67651-9731, Osbourne, USA; gen tel (785) 885-4582; gen fax (785) 885-4582; disp adv e-mail natomanews@ruraltel.net; web site www.mainstreetmedia.us
Circulation: 6,000pd, 54fr; Sworn/Estimate/Non-Audited
Advertising rate: Open inch rate $6.00
Group: Main Street Media, Inc.
Pub... Jack Krier
Ed. .... Della Richmond
Mechanical Specifications: Type page 13 x 21 1/4; E - 6 cols, 2 1/12, between; A - 6 cols, 2 1/12, between; C - 6 cols, 2 1/12, between.

NEODESHA

NEODESHA DERRICK (THUR)

502 Main St, Neodesha, KS, 66757-1739, Wilson, USA; gen tel (620) 325-3000; gen fax (620) 325-2880; disp adv e-mail thederrick@cableone.net; web site http://www.shopthederrick.com
Circulation: 1,800pd, 99fr; USPS
Advertising rate: Open inch rate $4.00
Adv. Mgr................................ Dee Anne Tigner
Ed. .... Jo Anne Hartley Harper
Delivery Method: Mail
Areas Served: County

NESS CITY

NESS COUNTY NEWS (THUR)

110 S Kansas Ave, Ness City, KS, 67560-1814, Ness, USA; gen tel (785) 798-2213; gen fax (785) 798-2214; disp adv e-mail nessnews@gbta.net; web site www.facebook.com/pages/Ness-County-News/147247601986003
Circulation: 2,200pd, 48fr; Sworn/Estimate/Non-Audited
Advertising rate: Open inch rate $2.80
Ed. ....Jerry ClarkeEquipment & Software: Hardware — Gateway; Software — Adobe/PageMaker.
Delivery Method: Mail

NORTON

THE NORTON TELEGRAM (TUES, FRI)

215 S Kansas Ave, Norton, KS, 67654-2131, Norton, USA; gen tel (785) 877-3361; gen fax (785) 877-3732; disp adv e-mail dpaxton@nwkansas.com; ed e-mail nortontelegram@nwkansas.com; web site www.nwkansas.com
Circulation: 2,704pd,; Sworn/Estimate/Non-Audited
Advertising rate: Open inch rate $5.65
Group: Haynes Publishing Co.
Co-Owner................................ Steven Haynes
Co-Owner............................... Cynthia Haynes
Circ. Mgr................................ Sherry Hickman
Society/Women's Ed...................... Harriett Gill
Mechanical Specifications: Type page 13 3/4 x 22 3/4; E - 6 cols, 2 1/16, 3/16 between; A - 6 cols, 2 1/16, 3/16 between; C - 6 cols, 2 1/16, 3/16 between.Equipment & Software: Hardware — APP/Mac SE-40M, Hyundai/Super 386SE-40M; Software — IBM/Prof Write, IBM/Arts & Letters.
Delivery Method: Mail

OAKLEY

THE OAKLEY GRAPHIC (WED)

118 Center Ave, Oakley, KS, 67748-1712, Logan County, USA; gen tel (785) 672-3228; disp adv e-mail graphic@st-tel.net; ed e-mail graphic@st-tel.net; web site www.facebook.com/pages/The-Oakley-Graphic/134987739878462
Circulation: 1,200pd,; Sworn/Estimate/Non-Audited
Advertising rate: Open inch rate $4.50
Group: Golden Plains Publishing
Pub..................................... Mark Anderson
Barbara Glover
Delivery Method: Mail

OBERLIN

OBERLIN HERALD, THE (WED)

170 S Penn Ave, Oberlin, KS, 67749-2243, Decatur, USA; gen tel (785) 475-2206; gen fax (785) 475-2800; disp adv e-mail oberlin.ads@nwkansas.com; class adv e-mail oberlin.ads@nwkansas.com; ed e-mail oberlin.editor@nwkansas.com; web site www.nwkansas.com
Circulation: 1,724pd, 91fr; Sworn/Estimate/Non-Audited
Advertising rate: Open inch rate $7.30
Established: 1879
Group: Haynes Publishing Co.
Ed. .... Steve Haynes
Gen. Mng................................. Kimberly Davis
Mechanical Specifications: Type page 13 x 21 1/2; E - 6 cols, 2 1/16, 1/8 between; A - 6 cols, 2 1/16, 1/8 between; C - 6 cols, 2 1/16, 1/8 between.Equipment & Software: Hardware — 10-APP/Mac; Software — Adobe/PageMaker 6.5, Adobe/Photoshop.
Delivery Method: Mail, Newsstand, Carrier, Racks
Areas Served: 677

OLATHE

LEGAL RECORD (TUES)

1701 E Cedar St, Ste 111, Olathe, KS, 66062-1775, Johnson, USA; gen tel (913) 780-5790; gen fax (913) 780-5747; disp adv e-mail dvalenti@thelegalrecord.net; class adv e-mail dvalenti@thelegalrecord.net; ed e-mail dvalenti@thelegalrecord.net; web site www.thelegalrecord.net
Advertising rate: 1/4 P $100, 1/2 P $100, Full $200
Pub.. John Lewis
Ed. .... Emily Campbell
Delivery Method: Mail

ONAGA

ONAGA HERALD (THUR)

302 Leonard St, Onaga, KS, 66521-9484, Pottawatomie, USA; gen tel (785) 889-4681; disp adv e-mail oherald@bluevalley.net; ed e-mail oherald@bluevalley.net; web site www.facebook.com/pages/The-Onaga-Herald/105298976204089
Advertising rate: Open inch rate $4.50
Pub.. Joe Harder
Delivery Method: Mail

OSAGE CITY

THE OSAGE COUNTY HERALD-CHRONICLE (THUR)

527 Market St, Osage City, KS, 66523-1157, Osage, USA; gen tel (785) 528-3511; gen fax (785) 528-4811; disp adv e-mail ochcads@gmail.com; class adv e-mail ochcads@gmail.com; ed e-mail ochcnews@gmail.com; web site www.ocherald-chronicle.com
Circulation: 4,000pd,; Sworn/Estimate/Non-Audited
Advertising rate: Open inch rate $7.65
Established: 1869
Pub..................................... Catherine Faimon
Mechanical Specifications: Type page 13 3/4 x 21 1/2; E - 6 cols, 2 1/12, between; A - 6 cols, 2 1/12, between.Equipment & Software: Hardware — APP/Power Macs, APP/Mac Quadra; Software — Microsoft/Word 5.0, QPS/QuarkXPress, Adobe/PageMaker, Multi-Ad.
Delivery Method: Mail, Newsstand, Racks

OSBORNE

OSBORNE COUNTY FARMER (THUR)

210 W Main St, Osborne, KS, 67473-2405, Osborne, USA; gen tel (785) 346-5424; gen fax (785) 346-5400; disp adv e-mail ospubco@ruraltel.net; web site www.mainstreetmedia.us
Circulation: 2,500pd, 100fr; Sworn/Estimate/Non-Audited
Advertising rate: Open inch rate $4.50
Established: 1872
Group: Main Street Media, Inc.
Pub... Jack Krier
Ed. .... Stephanie Baxa
Mechanical Specifications: Type page 12 3/4 x 21 1/2; E - 6 cols, 2, 1/8 between; A - 6 cols, 2, 1/8 between; C - 6 cols, 2, 1/8 between. Equipment & Software: Hardware — APP/Mac; Presses — KP; Software — Creator II, Adobe/PageMaker.
Delivery Method: Mail

OSKALOOSA

OSKALOOSA INDEPENDENT (THUR)

607 Delaware St, Oskaloosa, KS, 66066-5431, Jefferson, USA; gen tel (785) 863-2520; gen fax (785) 863-2730; disp adv e-mail independent@centurylink.net; class adv e-mail independent@centurylink.net; ed e-mail independent@centurylink.net; web site www.jeffcountynews.com
Circulation: 1,530pd, 29fr; Sworn/Estimate/Non-Audited
Advertising rate: Open inch rate $5.50
Established: 1860
Group: Davis Publications Inc.
Digital Platform - Mobile: Windows
Pub.. Clarke Davis
Prodn. Mgr. .... Corey Davis
Ed. .... Rick NicholsEquipment & Software: ; Presses — Goss Web; Software — Indesign
Delivery Method: Mail, Newsstand
Areas Served: Jefferson County, KS

OSWEGO

LABETTE AVENUE (WED)

711 4th St, Oswego, KS, 67356-1601, Labette, USA; gen tel (620) 795-2550; adv tel (800) 592-7606; gen fax (620) 795-4712; disp adv e-mail adv@taylornews.org; class adv e-mail adv@taylornews.org; ed e-mail labetteavenue@taylornews.org; web site www.taylornews.org
Circulation: 1,865pd, 24fr; Sworn/Estimate/Non-Audited
Advertising rate: Open inch rate $5.50
Established: 1879
Group: Taylor Newspapers
Digital Platform - Tablet: Apple iOS, Android, Kindle Fire, Other
Co-Pub.. Rudy Taylor
Co-Pub.. Kathy Taylor
Adv. Dir.. Emalee Mikel
Ed. .... Rena Russell
Mechanical Specifications: 10.5 x 21
Delivery Method: Mail, Newsstand, Racks
Areas Served: Southern Labette County - Kansas

OTTAWA

THE OTTAWA HERALD (TUES, THUR, SAT)

214 S Hickory St, Ottawa, KS, 66067-2392, Franklin, USA; gen tel (785) 242-4700; gen fax (785) 242-9420; disp adv e-mail ads@ottawaherald.com; class adv e-mail classifieds@ottawaherald.com; ed e-mail news@ottawaherald.com; web site www.ottawaherald.com
Circulation: 4,100pd, 700fr; Sworn/Estimate/Non-Audited
Advertising rate: Open inch rate $9.64 net
Established: 1869
Group: GateHouse Media, Inc.
Digital Platform - Mobile: Apple, Android, Windows, Blackberry, Other
Digital Platform - Tablet: Apple iOS, Android, Windows 7, Blackberry Tablet OS, Kindle,

Nook, Kindle Fire, Other
Ed./Pub. ....Tommy Felts
Sr. Writer ....Greg Mast
Data Processing Mgr. ....Kathy Miller
Adv. Dir. ....Laurie Blanco
Graphic Design Coordinator ....Sheila Holle
Circ. coordinator ....Marilyn Stevenson
Mng. Ed. ....Doug Carder
Reader Engagement Ed. ....Jodie Garcia
Sports Reporter ....Clint Dick
Staff Writer ....Kate Shelton
Mechanical Specifications: Type page 12 13/16 x 21 1/2; E - 6 cols, 2, 3/16 between; A - 6 cols, 2, 3/16 between; C - 6 cols, 1 15/16, 3/16 between.
Delivery Method: Mail, Newsstand, Racks
Areas Served: 66006, 66033, 66042, 66044, 66067, 660632, 66076, 66078, 66079, 66080, 66092, 66095, 66510

PAOLA

THE MIAMI COUNTY REPUBLIC (WED)

121 S Pearl St, Paola, KS, 66071-1754, Miami, USA; gen tel (913) 294-2311; gen fax (913) 294-5318; disp adv e-mail republic@miconew.com; class adv e-mail classifieds@miconews.com; ed e-mail republic@miconew.com; web site www.republic-online.com
Circulation: 5,140pd, 10fr; Sworn/Estimate/Non-Audited
Advertising rate: Open inch rate $12.00
Established: 1866
Group: News-Press & Gazette Co.
Group Pub. ....Sandy Nelson
Ed. ....Brian McMauley
Adv. Mgr. ....Teresa Morrow
Mechanical Specifications: Type page 11 5/8 x 21; E - 6 cols, 1 5/6, 1/8 between; A - 6 cols, 1 5/6, 1/8 between; C - 6 cols, 1 5/6, 1/8 between.Equipment & Software: Hardware — APP/Mac; Software — QPS/QuarkXPress.
Delivery Method: Mail, Racks
Areas Served: Miami County

PARSONS

FARM TALK (WED)

1801 S US Highway 59, Parsons, KS, 67357-4958, Labette, USA; gen tel (800) 356-8255; gen fax (620) 421-9473; disp adv e-mail farmtalk@terraworld.net; class adv e-mail farmtalk@terraworld.net; ed e-mail farmtalk@terraworld.net; web site www.farmtalknewspaper.com
Advertising rate: Open inch rate $9.00
Established: 1974
Co-Pub./Adv. Mgr. ....Lance Markley
Delivery Method: Mail

PEABODY

PEABODY GAZETTE-BULLETIN (WED)

113 N Walnut St, Peabody, KS, 66866-1059, Marion, USA; gen tel (620) 382-2165; gen fax (620) 983-2700; disp adv e-mail advertising@peabodykansas.com; class adv e-mail classified@peabodykansas.com; ed e-mail news@peabodykansas.com; web site www.peabodykansas.com
Circulation: 1,400pd, 9fr; Sworn/Estimate/Non-Audited
Advertising rate: Open inch rate $7.50
Group: Hoch Publishing Co. Inc.
Adv. Mgr. ....Debra Steele
Circ. Mgr. ....Jean Stuchlik
Ed. ....Susan Marshall
Delivery Method: Mail, Newsstand, Racks

PHILLIPSBURG

ADVOCATE OF PHILLIPS COUNTY (THUR)

265 F St, Phillipsburg, KS, 67661-1918, Phillips, USA; gen tel (785) 543-2349; gen fax (785) 543-2364; ed e-mail theadvocate@ruraltel.net; web site www.facebook.com/pages/The-Advocate-of-Phillips-County/143662349001002
Circulation:; Sworn/Estimate/Non-Audited
Advertising rate: Open inch rate $4.25
Pub ....Ron Lower
Pub ....Lee Lower
Ed ....Kathy Merklein
Delivery Method: Mail, Newsstand, Racks

PHILLIPS COUNTY REVIEW (WED)

683 3rd St, Phillipsburg, KS, 67661-2138, Phillips, USA; gen tel (785) 543-5242; gen fax (785) 543-5243; disp adv e-mail pcreview@ruraltel.net; ed e-mail news@phillipscountyreview.com; web site www.phillipscountyreview.com
Circulation: 2,000pd,; Sworn/Estimate/Non-Audited
Advertising rate: Open inch rate $8.58
Established: 1869
Group: Main Street Media, Inc.
Ed. ....Kirby Ross
Page Design ....Irene Allen
Mechanical Specifications: Type page 13 x 21; E - 6 cols, 1 13/16, 1/6 between; A - 6 cols, 1 13/16, 1/6 between; C - 6 cols, 1 13/16, 1/6 between.Equipment & Software: Hardware — APP/Mac; Software — Adobe/PageMaker 6.5, Adobe/Photoshop 5.0, Microsoft Word.
Delivery Method: Mail

PLAINVILLE

PLAINVILLE TIMES (THUR)

PO Box 40, 400 W Mill St, Plainville, KS, 67663-0040, Rooks, USA; gen tel (785) 434-4525; gen fax (785) 434-2527; disp adv e-mail pvtimes@ruraltel.net; web site www.mainstreetmedia.us
Circulation: 2,400pd, 40fr; Sworn/Estimate/Non-Audited
Advertising rate: Open inch rate $4.75
Group: Main Street Media, Inc.
Pub. ....Frank Mercer
Adv. Mgr.
Office Mgr ....Janice Bendick
Ed. ....Candace Rachel
Delivery Method: Mail, Newsstand

PLEASANTON

THE LINN COUNTY NEWS (WED)

808 Main St, Pleasanton, KS, 66075-4077, Linn, USA; gen tel (913) 352-6235; gen fax (913) 352-6607; disp adv e-mail raquel@linncountynews.net; class adv e-mail lisa@linncountynews.net; ed e-mail story@linncountynews.net; web site www.linncountynews.net
Circulation: 2,600pd,; Sworn/Estimate/Non-Audited
Advertising rate: Open inch rate $5.95
Pub/Ed ....Jacquelyn I. Taylor
Circ. Mgr. ....Lisa Fort
Reporter ....Deb Cougill
Delivery Method: Mail

PRATT

KIOWA COUNTY SIGNAL (WED)

320 S Main St, Pratt, KS, 67124-2706, Kiowa, USA; gen tel (620) 723-2115; adv tel (620) 672-5511; ed tel (620) 672-5511; gen fax (620) 723-1031; disp adv e-mail cnemec@pratttribune.com; ed e-mail jguy@kiowacountysignal.com; web site www.kiowacountysignal.com
Circulation: 900fr; Sworn/Estimate/Non-Audited
Advertising rate: Open inch rate $5.00
Established: 1886
Group: GateHouse Media, Inc.
Ed. ....Jeff Guy
Pub. ....Conrad Easterday
Delivery Method: Mail

THE PRATT TRIBUNE (TUES, THUR, SAT)

320 S Main St, Pratt, KS, 67124-2706, Pratt, USA; gen tel (620) 672-5511; adv tel (620) 672-5511; ed tel (620) 672-5511; gen fax (620) 672-5514; adv fax (620) 672-5514; ed fax (620) 672-5514; disp adv e-mail editor@pratttribune.com; class adv e-mail bcain@pratttribune.com; ed e-mail editor@pratttribune.com; web site www.pratttribune.com
Circulation: 2,000pd,; Sworn/Estimate/Non-Audited
Advertising rate: Open inch rate $11.19
Established: 1917
Group: New Media Investment Group
Digital Platform - Mobile: Apple, Android
Digital Platform - Tablet: Apple iOS, Android, Windows 7
Pub. ....Randy Mitchell
Gen. Mgr. ....Conrad Easterday
Business Mgr. ....Michelle Griffith
Mechanical Specifications: Type page 13 3/4 x 21 1/2; E - 6 cols, 2 1/16, 1/8 between; A - 6 cols, 2 1/16, 1/8 between; C - 8 cols, 2 1/16, 1/8 between.
Delivery Method: Mail, Newsstand, Carrier
Areas Served: Pratt County

PRETTY PRAIRIE

NINNESCAH VALLEY NEWS (FRI)

201 S Maple St, Pretty Prairie, KS, 67570-8619, Reno, USA; gen tel (620) 459-6322; adv tel (620) 459-6322; ed tel (620) 459-6322; gen fax (620) 459-6729; adv fax (620) 459-6729; ed fax (620) 459-6729; disp adv e-mail nvn@embarqmail.com; class adv e-mail nvn@embarqmail.com; ed e-mail nvn@embarqmail.com; web site www.facebook.com/pages/Ninnescah-Valley-News/142191375827044
Advertising rate: Open inch rate $2.85
Pub.
Nancy Stucky
Delivery Method: Mail
Areas Served: 67570

PROTECTION

PROTECTION PRESS (THUR)

301 N Broadway Ave, Protection, KS, 67127, Comanche, USA; gen tel (620) 622-4288; gen fax (620) 622-4370; disp adv e-mail propress@unitedwireless.com; class adv e-mail ProPress@unitedwireless.com; ed e-mail propress@unitedwireless.com
Circulation: 770pd, 14fr
Advertising rate: Open inch rate $3.50
Established: 1986
Ed. ....Susan Edmonston
Delivery Method: Mail

QUINTER

GOVE COUNTY ADVOCATE (WED)

304 Main St, Quinter, KS, 67752-9526, Gove, USA; gen tel (785) 754-3651; gen fax (785) 754-3878; disp adv e-mail advocate@ruraltel.net; web site www.facebook.com/pages/Gove-County-Advocate/124124657634832
Circulation: 1,800pd, 100fr; Sworn/Estimate/Non-Audited
Advertising rate: Open inch rate $3.50
Pub. ....Roxane K. Broeckelman
Ed. ....Tom W. Broeckelman
Delivery Method: Mail

RILEY

RILEY COUNTIAN (WED)

207 S Broadway St, Riley, KS, 66531-9559, Riley, USA; gen tel (785) 485-2290; gen fax (785) 485-2290; disp adv e-mail countian@twinvalley.net; web site www.facebook.com/pg/The-Riley-Countian-155651394453413/about/?ref=page_internal
Circulation: 1,200pd,; Sworn/Estimate/Non-Audited
Advertising rate: Open inch rate $3.50
Editor/Publisher ....Donna Sullivan
Office Manager ....June Campbell
Delivery Method: Mail, Racks

RUSSELL

THE RUSSELL COUNTY NEWS (WED, FRI)

958 E WICHITA AVE, Russell, KS, 67665, Russell, USA; gen tel (785) 483-2116; gen fax (785) 483-4012; disp adv e-mail russell@mainstreetmedia.us; web site www.mainstreetmedia.us
Circulation: 2,300pd,; Sworn/Estimate/Non-Audited
Advertising rate: Open inch rate $6.72
Group: Main Street Media, Inc.
Pub. ....Chuck Krier
Gen. Mgr. ....Ruth Newman
Adv. Mgr. ....Pam Soetaert
Cir. Mgr. ....Richelle Twenter
Ed. ....Justin Ashlaw
Mechanical Specifications: Type page 15 1/4 x 21 1/2; E - 8 cols, 1 5/6, 1/8 between; A - 8 cols, 1 5/6, 1/8 between; C - 8 cols, 1 5/6, 1/8 between.Equipment & Software: Hardware — 1-COM/7200, 3-COM/Comp II.
Delivery Method: Mail

SABETHA

THE SABETHA HERALD (WED)

1024 Main St, Sabetha, KS, 66534-1831, Nemaha, USA; gen tel (785) 284-3300; gen fax (785) 284-2320; disp adv e-mail advertising@sabethaherald.com.; class adv e-mail advertising@sabethaherald.com.; ed e-mail sabethaherald@sabethaherald.com; web site www.sabethaherald.com
Circulation: 2,542pd, 50fr; Sworn/Estimate/Non-Audited
Advertising rate: Open inch rate $5.00
Established: 1884
Pub. ....Tim Kellenburger
Mechanical Specifications: Type page 13 x 21; E - 6 cols, 2, 1/6 between; A - 6 cols, 2, 1/6 between; C - 6 cols, 2, 1/6 between.Equipment & Software: Hardware — APP/Mac; Software — Microsoft/Word, Adobe/PageMaker.
Delivery Method: Mail

SAINT FRANCIS

BIRD CITY TIMES (THUR)

PO Box 1050, Saint Francis, KS, 67756-1050, Cheyenne, USA; gen tel (785) 332-3162; gen fax (785) 332-3001; disp adv e-mail tburr@nwkansas.com; ed e-mail normamartinez@wildblue.net; web site www.nwkansas.com
Circulation: 565pd, 3fr; Sworn/Estimate/Non-Audited
Advertising rate: Open inch rate $5.25
Group: Haynes Publishing Co.
Ed. ....Norma Martinez
Mechanical Specifications: Type page 13 x 21 1/2; E - 6 cols, 2 1/16, 1/8 between; A - 6 cols, 2 1/16, 1/8 between; C - 6 cols, 2 1/16, 1/8 between.Equipment & Software: Hardware — APP/Mac; Software — Adobe/PageMaker, Adobe/Photoshop.
Delivery Method: Mail

ST. FRANCIS HERALD (THUR)

310 W Washington St, Saint Francis, KS, 67756-9606, Cheyenne, USA; gen tel (785) 332-3162; gen fax (785) 332-3001; disp adv e-mail sf.herald@nwkansas.com; web site www.nwkansas.com
Circulation: 1,288pd, 4fr; USPS
Advertising rate: Open inch rate $6.30
Established: 1912
Group: Haynes Publishing Co.
Publisher ....Karen Krien
Circ. Mgr. ....Leslie McCormick
Mechanical Specifications: Type page 13 x 21

1/2; E - 6 cols, 2 1/16, 1/8 between; A - 6 cols, 2 1/16, 1/8 between; C - 6 cols, 2 1/16, 1/8 between.Equipment & Software: Hardware — APP/Mac; Software — Adobe/PageMaker 6.5, Adobe/Photoshop.
Delivery Method: Mail, Newsstand
Areas Served: 67756

SAINT JOHN

ST. JOHN NEWS (WED)
112 E 3rd Ave, Saint John, KS, 67576-2032, Stafford, USA; gen tel (620) 549-3201; adv tel (620) 672-5511; gen fax (620) 549-3829; adv fax (620) 672-5514; disp adv e-mail ksmith@pratttribune.com; ed e-mail tspradley@sjnewsonline.com; web site www.sjnewsonline.com
Circulation: 700pd, 14fr; Sworn/Estimate/Non-Audited
Advertising rate: Open inch rate $7
Established: 1878
Group: GateHouse Media, Inc.
Mechanical Specifications: Type page 13 x 21 1/2; E - 6 cols, 2 1/16, 1/8 between; A - 6 cols, 2 1/16, 1/8 between; C - 6 cols, 2 1/16, 1/8 between.
Delivery Method: Mail, Newsstand, Racks
Areas Served: Stafford County

SAINT MARYS

ST. MARYS STAR (TUES)
117 S 6th St, Saint Marys, KS, 66536-1606, Pottawatomie, USA; gen tel (785) 437-2935; gen fax (785) 437-2935; disp adv e-mail star@oct.net; ed e-mail star@oct.net; web site www.thesmstar.com
Circulation: 1,850pd,; Sworn/Estimate/Non-Audited
Advertising rate: Open inch rate $6.00
Established: 1884
Group: The White Corporation
Adv. Mgr. .... Lori Hickey
Pub./Gen. Mgr. .... Steven Tetlow
Mechanical Specifications: 6 column; 21 Inches Long Equipment & Software: Hardware — APP/iMac; Software — Adobe/PageMaker 7.0, Adobe/Typestyler 3.0.
Delivery Method: Mail, Racks
Areas Served: 66536, 66533, 66539, 66418, 66422, 66501, 66526

SEDAN

PRAIRIE STAR (WED)
226 E Main St, Sedan, KS, 67361-1629, Chautauqua, USA; gen tel (620) 725-3176; gen fax (620) 725-3272; disp adv e-mail adv@taylornews.org; class adv e-mail adv@taylornews.org; ed e-mail taylornews@taylornews.org; web site www.taylornews.org
Circulation: 1,325pd, 25fr; Sworn/Estimate/Non-Audited
Advertising rate: Open inch rate $5.50
Established: 1870
Mng. Ed .... Rudy Taylor
Kathy Taylor
Ed .... Jenny Diveley
Julie Beckley
Mechanical Specifications: Type page 13 x 21; E - 6 cols, 2, between; A - 6 cols, 2, between; C - 6 cols, 2, between.
Delivery Method: Mail, Newsstand, Racks

SENECA

THE COURIER-TRIBUNE (WED)
512 Main St, Seneca, KS, 66538-1928, Nemaha, USA; gen tel (785) 336-2175; gen fax (785) 336-3475; disp adv e-mail ctseneca@nvcs.com; ed e-mail ctseneca@nvcs.com; web site www.couriertribuneonline.com
Circulation: 3,100pd, 1,800fr; Sworn/Estimate/Non-Audited
Advertising rate: Open inch rate $5.00
Established: 1863
Pub .... Dan Diehl
Mng. Ed .... Matt Diehl
Ad Director .... Kylee Luckeroth
Mechanical Specifications: 6 column 25" broadsheet
Delivery Method: Mail, Carrier, Racks
Areas Served: Nemaha and surrounding counties

SHAWNEE

SHAWNEE DISPATCH (WED)
6301 Pflumm Rd, Ste 102, Shawnee, KS, 66216-2497, Johnson, USA; gen tel (913) 962-3000; adv tel (913) 962-3000; gen fax (913) 962-3004; disp adv e-mail scantrell@ljworld.com; class adv e-mail smilgram@ljworld.com; ed e-mail jkendall@shawneedispatch.com; web site www.shawneedispatch.com
Circulation: 20,108fr; VAC
Advertising rate: Open inch rate $30.03
Established: 2003
Group: Lawrence Journal-World
Ed .... Jason Kendall
Pub .... Scott Stanford
Mike Countryman
Circulation Manager .... Ed Ciambrone
Advertising Manager .... Kathleen Johnson
Delivery Method: Mail, Carrier, Racks

SPEARVILLE

SPEARVILLE NEWS (THUR)
400 N Main St, Spearville, KS, 67876-9501, Ford, USA; gen tel (620) 385-2200; gen fax (620) 385-2610; disp adv e-mail spnews@ucom.net; class adv e-mail spnews@ucom.net; ed e-mail spnews@ucom.net; web site www.facebook.com/pages/Spearville-News-Inc/161631100525188
Circulation: 575pd, 20fr; USPS
Advertising rate: Open inch rate $2.80
Established: 1899
Pub .... Bruce Vierthaler
Ed. .... Cynthia Vierthaler
Mechanical Specifications: Type page 11 1/2 x 17 1/2; E - 5 cols, 2, 1/6 between; A - 5 cols, 2, 1/6 between; C - 5 cols, 2, 1/6 between. Equipment & Software: ; Presses — 3-KP.
Delivery Method: Mail, Newsstand

STAFFORD

THE STAFFORD COURIER (WED)
114 E Broadway St, Stafford, KS, 67578-1803, Stafford, USA; gen tel (620) 234-5241; gen fax (620) 234-5242; disp adv e-mail staffordcourier@sbcglobal.net; ed e-mail staffordcourier@sbcglobal.net; web site www.facebook.com/pages/Courier-Office/123680691012380
Circulation: 1,000pd,; Sworn/Estimate/Non-Audited
Advertising rate: Open inch rate $4.85
Established: 1903
Pub .... David Green
Ed. .... Karen Kalmer
Delivery Method: Mail

STERLING

STERLING BULLETIN (THUR)
107 N Broadway Ave, Sterling, KS, 67579-2130, Rice, USA; gen tel (620) 278-2114; gen fax (620) 278-2330; disp adv e-mail ads@sterlingbulletin.com; class adv e-mail ads@sterlingbulletin.com; ed e-mail news@sterlingbulletin.com; web site www.sterlingbulletin.com
Circulation: 1,100pd, 47fr; Sworn/Estimate/Non-Audited
Advertising rate: Open inch rate $5.25
Established: 1876
Pub .... Ben Marshall
Ed. .... Betty Childs
Mechanical Specifications: Type page 13 x 21; E - 6 cols, 2, 1/8 between; A - 6 cols, 2, 1/8 between; C - 6 cols, 2, 1/8 between.Equipment & Software: Hardware — APP/Mac; Software — Adobe/PageMaker 6.5, Adobe/Photoshop.
Delivery Method: Mail
Areas Served: many

STOCKTON

STOCKTON SENTINEL (THUR)
414 Main St, Stockton, KS, 67669-1930, Rooks, USA; gen tel (785) 425-6354; gen fax (785) 425-7292; disp adv e-mail stkpaper@ruraltel.net; ed e-mail stkpaper@ruraltel.net; web site www.stocktonsentinel.com
Circulation: 1,851pd,; Sworn/Estimate/Non-Audited
Advertising rate: Open inch rate $4.50
Established: 1989
Pub .... Bob Hamilton
News Ed .... Deb Dix
Editorial Writer .... Virginia Laska
Delivery Method: Mail

SUBLETTE

THE HASKELL COUNTY MONITOR-CHIEF (WED)
114 S. Inman St., Sublette, KS, 67877, Haskell, USA; gen tel (620) 675-2204; gen fax (620) 675-2204; disp adv e-mail monitorchief27@att.net; ed e-mail monitorchief27@att.net
Circulation: 800pd,; Sworn/Estimate/Non-Audited
Advertising rate: Open inch rate $3.75
Established: 1891
Group: Golden Plains Publishing
Pub .... Mark Anderson
Mechanical Specifications: Type page 14 x 21; E - 6 cols, 2, 1/8 between; A - 6 cols, 2, 1/8 between.
Delivery Method: Mail
Areas Served: 67877, 67870, 67837

SYRACUSE

THE SYRACUSE JOURNAL (WED)
21 N Main St, Syracuse, KS, 67878-7881, Hamilton, USA; gen tel (620) 384-5640; gen fax (620) 384-5228; disp adv e-mail editor@thesyracusejournal.com; class adv e-mail editor@thesyracusejournal.com; ed e-mail editor@thesyracusejournal.com; web site www.thesyracusejournal.com
Circulation: 650pd, 17fr; Sworn/Estimate/Non-Audited
Advertising rate: Open inch rate $4.75
Established: 1885
Digital Platform - Mobile: Apple, Windows
Owner/Ed .... Marcus AshlockEquipment & Software: Hardware — Dell, Samsung, Xerox, ; Software — Microsoft/Windows 7, Adobe InDesign,
Delivery Method: Mail, Racks
Areas Served: Syracuse/Hamilton County/67878

TONGANOXIE

THE MIRROR (WED)
520 E 4th St, Tonganoxie, KS, 66086-8920, Leavenworth, USA; gen tel (913) 845-2222; gen fax (913) 845-9451; disp adv e-mail mgriffin@theworldco.info; class adv e-mail weeklyclassifieds@ljworld.com; ed e-mail slinenberger@theworldco.info; web site www.tonganoxiemirror.com
Circulation: 2,256pd, 299fr; Sworn/Estimate/Non-Audited
Advertising rate: Open inch rate $6.75
Established: 1882
News Ed .... Shawn Linenberger
Mechanical Specifications: Type page 11 3/4 x 20 7/8; E - 6 cols, 1 1/6, 1/5 between; A - 6 cols, 1 1/6, 1/5 between; C - 9 cols, 1 1/4, 1/5 between.Equipment & Software: ; Software — QPS/QuarkXPress 4.0.
Delivery Method: Mail
Areas Served: 66086, 66007, 66043, 66048

TOPEKA

TOPEKA METRO NEWS (MON)
800 SW Jackson St, Ste 1118, Topeka, KS, 66612-1244, Shawnee, USA; gen tel (785) 232-8600; disp adv e-mail legal@topekametronews.com; ed e-mail legal@topekametronews.com; web site www.topekametro.com
Advertising rate: 1/8 P $50 1/4 P $100 1/2 P $150 Full $200
Delivery Method: Mail, Racks

TRIBUNE

GREELEY COUNTY REPUBLICAN (WED)
507 Broadway Ave, Tribune, KS, 67879-7702, Greeley, USA; gen tel (620) 376-4264; gen fax (620) 376-2433; disp adv e-mail newspaper@sunflowertelco.com; web site http://www.gcrnews.com/
Circulation: 900pd, 14fr; Sworn/Estimate/Non-Audited
Advertising rate: Open inch rate $4.70
Dan M. Epp
Jan EppEd.sEquipment & Software: Hardware — APP/Mac; Software — Microsoft/Word, Adobe/Photoshop 5.0, Adobe/Illustrator, Adobe/PageMaker.
Delivery Method: Mail

TURON

THE RECORD (THUR)
107 S Burns St, Turon, KS, 67583-9513, Reno, USA; gen tel (620) 497-6448; disp adv e-mail record@sctelcom.net; ed e-mail record@sctelcom.net; web site www.facebook.com/pages/Record/133088910068883
Circulation: 550pd, 26fr; Sworn/Estimate/Non-Audited
Advertising rate: Open inch rate $2.50
Pub .... Stephen Green
Delivery Method: Mail

ULYSSES

THE ULYSSES NEWS (THUR)
218 N Main St, Ulysses, KS, 67880-2129, Grant, USA; gen tel (620) 356-1201; gen fax (620) 356-4610; disp adv e-mail ulynews3@pld.com ; ed e-mail ulynews@pld.com; web site www.ulyssesnewsonline.com
Circulation: 2,200pd, 16fr; Sworn/Estimate/Non-Audited
Advertising rate: Open inch rate $5.50 (local); $7.07 (national)
Group: Southwest Kansas Publications Inc.
Adv. Mgr. .... Shayla Hernandez-Jaquez
Delivery Method: Mail, Newsstand

VALLEY CENTER

ARK VALLEY NEWS (THUR)
210 W Main St, Valley Center, KS, 67147-2216, Sedgwick, USA; gen tel (316) 755-0821; gen fax (316) 755-0644; disp adv e-mail ads@arkvalleynews.com; ed e-mail news@arkvalleynews.com; web site www.arkvalleynews.com
Circulation: 3,000pd, 93fr; Sworn/Estimate/Non-Audited
Advertising rate: Open inch rate $7.25
Pub .... Chris Strunk
Mechanical Specifications: Type page 10 1/2 x

16; E - 4 cols, 2 5/12, 1/6 between; A - 4 cols, 2 5/12, 1/6 between; C - 4 cols, 2 5/12, 1/6 between.Equipment & Software: Hardware — APP/Mac 6.0; Software — Microsoft/Word 6.0, QPS/QuarkXPress 3.31.
Delivery Method: Mail

VALLEY FALLS

VALLEY FALLS VINDICATOR (THUR)

416 Broadway St, Valley Falls, KS, 66088-1304, Jefferson, USA; gen tel (785) 945-3257; gen fax (785) 945-3444; disp adv e-mail vindicator@embarqmail.com; web site www.jeffcountynews.com
Circulation: 1,900pd,; Sworn/Estimate/Non-Audited
Advertising rate: Open inch rate $5.50
Established: 1890
Group: Davis Publications Inc.
Digital Platform - Mobile: Windows
Pub/Ed....Clarke Davis
Mgr....Corey Davis
Society Ed....Marveta Davis
Mechanical Specifications: Type page 15 1/2 x 21; E - 7 cols, 2 1/12, 1/6 between; A - 7 cols, 2 1/12, 1/6 between.Equipment & Software: Hardware — PC; Presses — G; Software — Adobe/InDesign
Delivery Method: Mail, Newsstand
Areas Served: Jefferson County, KS

WAKEENEY

WESTERN KANSAS WORLD (THUR)

205 N Main St, Wakeeney, KS, 67672-2104, Trego, USA; gen tel (785) 743-2155; gen fax (785) 743-5340; disp adv e-mail westernkansasworld@yahoo.com; ed e-mail westernkansasworld@yahoo.com; web site www.facebook.com/pages/Western-Kansas-World-World-Print/146562978706908
Circulation: 1,700pd, 400fr; Sworn/Estimate/Non-Audited
Advertising rate: Open inch rate $3.50
Office Mgr....Megan Mowery
Ed....Jerry Millard
Mng. Ed....Cathy Millard
Mechanical Specifications: Type page 13 1/8 x 21; E - 6 cols, 1 3/4, between; A - 6 cols, 1 3/4, between; C - 8 cols, 1 3/8, between. Equipment & Software: Hardware — APP/Mac; Software — Adobe/Photoshop 5.0, Microsoft/Word 6.0, Adobe/PageMaker 6.0.
Delivery Method: Mail

WAMEGO

THE WAMEGO TIMES (THUR)

407 Lincoln Ave, Wamego, KS, 66547-1631, Pottawatomie, USA; gen tel (785) 456-2602; gen fax (785) 456-8484; disp adv e-mail advertising@wamegonews.com; class adv e-mail advertising@wamegonews.com; ed e-mail office@wamegonews.com; web site www.wamegotimes.com
Circulation: 950pd,; Sworn/Estimate/Non-Audited
Advertising rate: Open inch rate $5
Established: 1889
Group: Willgratten Publications LLC
Digital Platform - Mobile: Apple, Android, Windows
Michelle Wilken
Shannon FritzCo-Managing Editors
Delivery Method: Mail

WAMEGO SMOKE SIGNAL (WED)

407 Lincoln Ave, Wamego, KS, 66547-1631, Pottawatomie, USA; gen tel (785) 456-2602; gen fax (785) 456-8484; disp adv e-mail smokesig@wamego.net; ed e-mail smokesig@wamego.net; web site http://thewamegosmokesignal.com
Circulation: 9,823fr; Sworn/Estimate/Non-Audited
Advertising rate: Open inch rate $6.50

Group: The White Corporation
Ed....Beth Howell Day
Pub....Tim Hobbs
Delivery Method: Mail

WASHINGTON

WASHINGTON COUNTY NEWS (THUR)

323 C St, Washington, KS, 66968-1908, Washington, USA; gen tel (785) 325-2219; gen fax (785) 325-3255; disp adv e-mail editor@bluevalley.net; class adv e-mail type@bluevalley.net; ed e-mail editor@bluevalley.net; web site www.backroadsnews.com
Circulation: 2,300pd, 10fr; Sworn/Estimate/Non-Audited
Advertising rate: Open inch rate $7.50
Established: 1869
Circ. Mgr....Judy Wiechman
Ed.........Dan ThalmannEquipment & Software: Hardware — 7-APP/Mac; Software — QPS/QuarkXPress 3.2, WordPerfect 3.5.
Delivery Method: Mail, Racks
Areas Served: Washington County

WATERVILLE

TELEGRAPH (SAT)

113 Commercial St, Waterville, KS, 66548, Marshall, USA; gen tel (785) 363-2061; gen fax (785) 363-2075; disp adv e-mail telegraph@bluevalley.net; web site www.facebook.com/pages/The-Telegraph/146721058690272
Circulation: 750pd, 5fr; Sworn/Estimate/Non-Audited
Advertising rate: Open inch rate $4.25
Ed.......Donald H. KingEquipment & Software: Hardware — APP/Mac G3.

WATHENA

THE KANSAS CHIEF (THUR)

317 E Saint Joseph St, Wathena, KS, 66090-1204, Doniphan, USA; gen tel (785) 989-4415; gen fax (785) 989-4416; disp adv e-mail Kschief@carsoncomm.com; web site NA
Circulation: 2,050pd, 25fr; USPS
Advertising rate: Open inch rate $6.50
Established: 1857
Circ. Mgr....Lori Vertin
Ed....Dana Foley
Mechanical Specifications: Type page 14 x 21.
Delivery Method: Mail, Racks
Areas Served: Doniphan County

WELLINGTON

WELLINGTON DAILY NEWS (WED)

113 W Harvey Ave, Wellington, KS, 67152-3840, Sumner, USA; gen tel (620) 326-3326; adv tel (620) 326-3326; ed tel (620) 326-3326; disp adv e-mail jjordan@wellingtondailynews.com; class adv e-mail jkenemer@wellingtondailynews.com; ed e-mail jjordan@wellingtondailynews.com; web site www.wellingtondailynews.com
Circulation: 2,000pd,; Sworn/Estimate/Non-Audited
Advertising rate: Open inch rate $12.00
Established: 1901
Group: GateHouse Media, Inc.
Digital Platform - Mobile: Apple, Android
Digital Platform - Tablet: Apple iOS, Android, Windows 7
Pub....Cristina Janney
Classifieds....Jackie Fullerton
Circ. Mgr....Jamie Seger
Business Office....Michelle Griffith
Mechanical Specifications: Type page 11 x 10.5, E - 6 cols, 2, 1/8 between; A - 6 cols, 2, 1/8 between; C - 6 cols, 2, 1/8 between.
Delivery Method: Mail, Racks
Areas Served: 67152

WHITE CITY

THE PRAIRIE POST (THUR)

108 W MacKenzie St, White City, KS, 66872-9797, Morris, USA; gen tel (785) 349-5516; gen fax (785) 349-5516; disp adv e-mail ppost@tctelco.net; class adv e-mail ppost@tctelco.net; ed e-mail ppost@tctelco.net
Circulation: 750pd, 15fr; Sworn/Estimate/Non-Audited
Advertising rate: Open inch rate $4.00
Established: 1993
Adv. Mgr....Gloria Smith
Ed....Joann Kahnt
Mechanical Specifications: Type page 10.5 x 21; E - 5 cols, 2 , 1/6 between; A - 5 cols, 2, 1/6 between; C - 5 cols, 2 , 1/6 between.Equipment & Software: Hardware — HP Gateway; Software — Microsoft/Windows 98 3.0, Adobe/PageMaker 5.0, Adobe/Photoshop.
Delivery Method: Mail, Newsstand
Areas Served: 66834, 66846, 66872, 66849

WICHITA

WICHITA BUSINESS JOURNAL (FRI)

121 N Mead St, Ste 100, Wichita, KS, 67202-2784, Sedgwick, USA; gen tel (316) 267-6406; gen fax (316) 267-8570; disp adv e-mail arobuck@bizjournals.com; class adv e-mail arobuck@bizjournals.com; ed e-mail broy@bizjournals.com; web site www.wichitabusinessjournal.com
Advertising rate: 1/4 P $2500, 1/2 P $3900, Full $6000
Established: 1986
Pub....John Ek
Ed....Bill Roy
Adv....Angela Robuck
Delivery Method: Mail

WINCHESTER

FAIRVIEW ENTERPRISE (WED, BI-MTHLY)

15975 126th St, Winchester, KS, 66097-4128, Jefferson, USA; gen tel (913) 774-4430; adv tel (913) 620-7726; ed tel (913) 774-4430; disp adv e-mail dflambertson@gmail.com; class adv e-mail thefairviewenterprise@gmail.com; ed e-mail dflambertson@gmail.com
Circulation: 300pd, 25fr; Sworn/Estimate/Non-Audited
Advertising rate: $4.00 per column inch
Established: 1888
Digital Platform - Mobile: Windows
Delivery Method: Mail

WINFIELD

CEDAR VALE LOOKOUT (THUR)

PO Box 543, Winfield, KS, 67156-0543, Cowley, USA; gen tel (620) 221-1050; gen fax (620) 221-1101; web site www.topix.com/city/cedar-vale-ks
Advertising rate: Open inch rate $7.94
Group: Winfield Publishing Co., Inc.
Publisher....Lloyd Craig
Delivery Method: Mail
Areas Served: 67156 67024

YATES CENTER

YATES CENTER NEWS (THUR)

113 S Main St, P.O. Box 285, Yates Center, KS, 66783-1425, Woodson, USA; gen tel (620) 625-2181; gen fax (620) 625-2081; disp adv e-mail ycn@sekansas.com; ed e-mail ycn@sekansas.com
Circulation: 1,500pd, 40fr; Sworn/Estimate/Non-Audited
Advertising rate: Open inch rate $6.00

Ed....Stewart Braden
Delivery Method: Mail, Newsstand, Racks
Areas Served: County

KENTUCKY

ALBANY

CLINTON COUNTY NEWS (THUR)

116 N Washington St, Albany, KY, 42602-1302, Clinton, USA; gen tel (606) 387-5144; gen fax (606) 387-7949; disp adv e-mail gpcompany@kih.net; web site www.clinton-news.net
Circulation: 3,100pd,; Sworn/Estimate/Non-Audited
Advertising rate: Open inch rate $3.50
Established: 1949
Pub/Ed....Al Gibson
Office Mng....Janie Gibson
News, Advt....Brett Gibson
Advt....Amanda Sharpe
Delivery Method: Mail, Newsstand
Areas Served: Clinton, Cumberland, Russell, Wayne and Pickett Counties

BARBOURVILLE

THE MOUNTAIN ADVOCATE (THUR)

214 Knox St, Barbourville, KY, 40906-1428, Knox, USA; gen tel (606) 546-9225; gen fax (606) 546-3175; ed fax (606) 546-2830; disp adv e-mail advertising@mountainadvocate.com; class adv e-mail advertising@mountainadvocate.com; ed e-mail editor@mountainadvocate.com; web site www.mountainadvocate.com
Circulation: 4,500pd, 25fr; Sworn/Estimate/Non-Audited
Advertising rate: Open inch rate $9.96
Digital Platform - Mobile: Apple, Android
Pub....Jay Nolan
Advr Mgr....Maria Swafford
Delivery Method: Mail
Areas Served: Knox County KY, to include cities of Corbin and Barbourville

BARDSTOWN

KENTUCKY STANDARD (WED, FRI, SUN)

110 W Stephen Foster Ave, Bardstown, KY, 40004-1416, Nelson, USA; gen tel (502) 348-9003; gen fax (502) 348-1971; disp adv e-mail jsizemore@kystandard.com; class adv e-mail classifieds@kystandard.com ; ed e-mail news@kystandard.com; web site www.kystandard.com
Circulation: 7,536pd,; USPS
Advertising rate: Open inch rate $16.67/modular rates are available
Established: 1900
Group: Landmark Community Newspapers, LLC
Pub....Jamie Sizemore
Ed....Forrest Berkshire
Class Advt Mgr....Alice Burgen
Bus Office Mgr....Toni Heady
Circulation Manager....Arlie Hash
Delivery Method: Mail, Newsstand, Carrier, Racks
Areas Served: Bardstown/Nelson County 40004, 40013,40020,40048,40008,40012,40051,40052,40107

BEATTYVILLE

BEATTYVILLE ENTERPRISE (THUR)

203 Main St, Beattyville, KY, 41311-7491, Lee, USA; gen tel (606) 464-2444; gen fax (606) 464-8858; disp adv e-mail beattyill@bellsouth.net; web site www.beattyvilleenter-

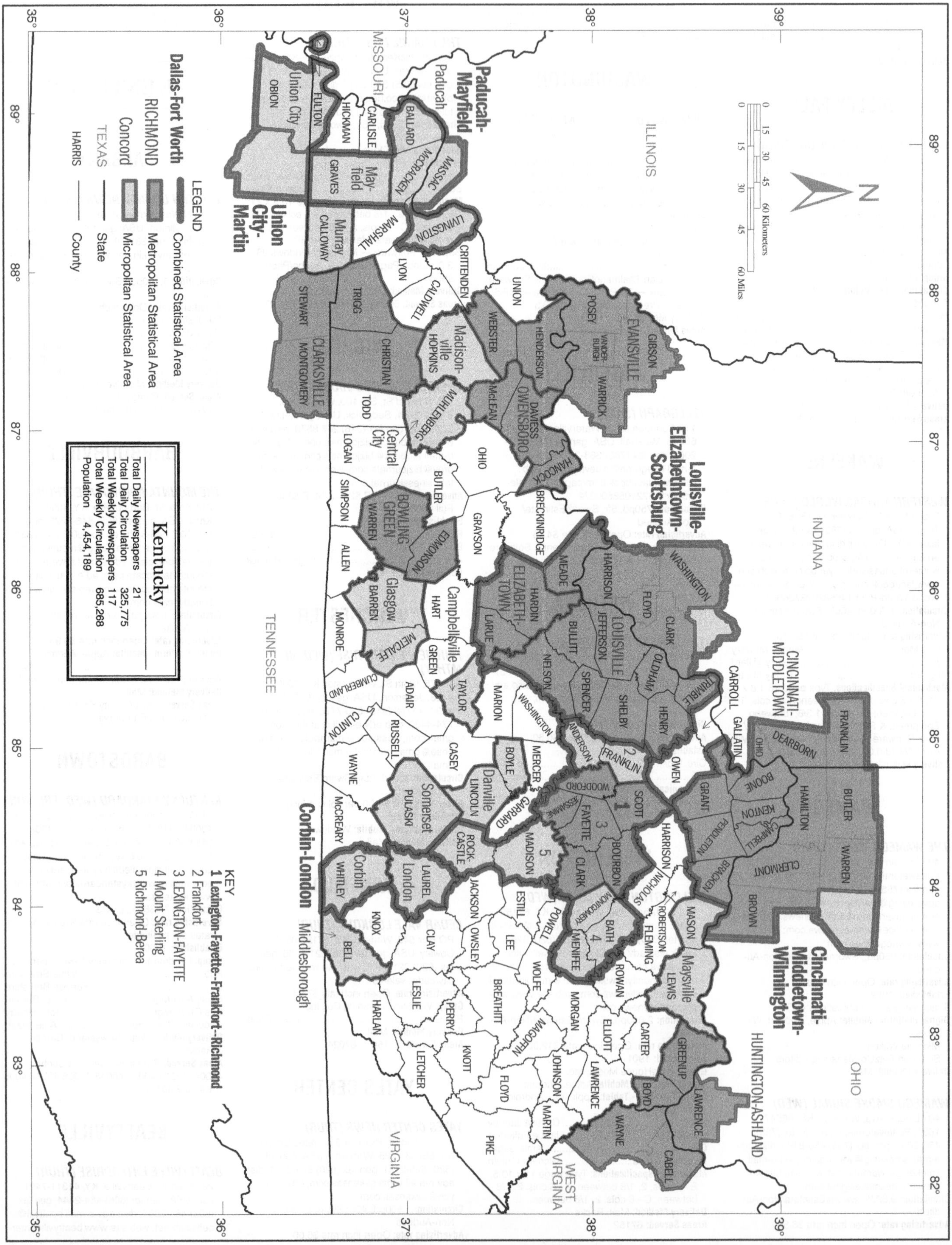
Kentucky
Total Daily Newspapers 21
Total Daily Circulation 325,775
Total Weekly Newspapers 117
Total Weekly Circulation 685,268
Population 4,454,189
LEGEND
Dallas-Fort Worth Combined Statistical Area
RICHMOND Metropolitan Statistical Area
Concord Micropolitan Statistical Area
TEXAS State
HARRIS County
KEY
1 Lexington-Fayette--Frankfort--Richmond
2 Frankfort
3 LEXINGTON-FAYETTE
4 Mount Sterling
5 Richmond-Berea
Paducah-Mayfield
Union City-Martin
Louisville-Elizabethtown-Scottsburg
Cincinnati-Middletown-Wilmington
Corbin-London
CINCINNATI-MIDDLETOWN
HUNTINGTON-ASHLAND
EVANSVILLE
OWENSBORO
CLARKSVILLE
BOWLING GREEN
ELIZABETHTOWN
LOUISVILLE
Paducah
Mayfield
Murray
Union City
Madisonville
Central City
Glasgow
Campbellsville
Danville
Somerset
Corbin
London
Middlesborough
Maysville
ILLINOIS
INDIANA
OHIO
MISSOURI
TENNESSEE
VIRGINIA
WEST VIRGINIA
0 15 30 45 60 Kilometers
0 15 30 45 60 Miles
N

prise.com/
Circulation: 4,000pd,; Sworn/Estimate/Non-Audited
Advertising rate: Open inch rate $5.00
Established: 1883
Pub....Glenn Gray
Adv. Dir....Cheryle Walton
Ed. ...... Edmund ShelbyEquipment & Software: Hardware — APP/Mac; Software — Aldus/PageMaker 4.0.
Areas Served: 28904

BEDFORD

TRIMBLE BANNER (THUR)

127 Highway 42 E, Bedford, KY, 40006-7621, Trimble, USA; gen tel (502) 255-3205; gen fax (502) 732-4261; disp adv e-mail dgarrett@mytrimblenews.com; ed e-mail lgillock@mytrimblenews.com; web site www.mytrimblenews.com
Circulation: 1,325pd, 5fr; Sworn/Estimate/Non-Audited
Advertising rate: Open inch rate $6.06
Established: 1879
Group: Landmark Community Newspapers, LLC
Landmark Communications, Inc.
Pub....Jeff Moore
Circ. Mgr....Carla Kidwell
Adv. Sales Consult....Deborah Garrett
Ed. ....Lorrie Gillock
Mechanical Specifications: Type page 10.38 x 21 1/2.
Delivery Method: Mail
Areas Served: 40006, 40045, 40011, 40070, 40055

BENTON

MARSHALL COUNTY TRIBUNE COURIER (WED)

86B Commerce Blvd, Benton, KY, 42025-1110, Marshall, USA; gen tel (270) 527-3162; gen fax (270) 527-4567; disp adv e-mail emcgill@tribunecourier.com; ed e-mail editor@tribunecourier.com; web site www.tribunecourier.com
Circulation: 5,000pd,; Sworn/Estimate/Non-Audited
Advertising rate: Open inch rate $7.20
Established: 1972
Gen. Mgr....Venita Fritz
Office Mgr....Emiley McGill
Adv. Mgr....Selena Ward
Circ. Mgr....Hilda Norwood
News Ed. ....Chris Wilcox
Sports Ed....David Green
Mechanical Specifications: Type page 11 5/8 x 21 1/4; E - 6 cols, 1 5/6, 1/8 between; A - 6 cols, 1 5/6, 1/8 between; C - 9 cols, 1 1/6, 1/6 between.Equipment & Software: Hardware — APP/Mac; Software — QPS/QuarkXPress, Multi-Ad/Creator, Adobe/PageMaker.
Delivery Method: Mail

BEREA

THE BEREA CITIZEN (THUR)

711 Chestnut St, Ste 2, Berea, KY, 40403-1916, Madison, USA; gen tel (859) 986-0959; gen fax (859) 986-0960; disp adv e-mail bereacitizen@windstream.net; ed e-mail www.bereacitizen@windstream.net; web site citizen.nolangroupmedia.com
Circulation: 4,000pd,; Sworn/Estimate/Non-Audited
Advertising rate: Open inch rate $6.50
Pub....Teresa Scenters
Ed. ....Beth Myers
Mechanical Specifications: Type page 13 x 21 1/2; E - 6 cols, 2 1/8, 3/20 between; A - 6 cols, 2 1/8, 3/20 between; C - 6 cols, 2 1/8, 3/20 between.Equipment & Software: Hardware — APP/Mac; Software — adobe creative suite 5.5
Delivery Method: Mail, Racks

BRANDENBURG

THE MEADE COUNTY MESSENGER (THUR)

138 Broadway St, Ste A, Brandenburg, KY, 40108-1272, Meade, USA; gen tel (270) 422-2155; gen fax (270) 422-2110; disp adv e-mail mcmsales@bbtel.com; class adv e-mail typesetter@bbtel.com; ed e-mail messenger@bbtel.com; web site www.meadecountymessenger.com
Circulation: 5,460pd, 142fr; Sworn/Estimate/Non-Audited
Advertising rate: Open inch rate $9.50
Established: 1882
Pub....Rena Singleton
Ed ....Jim Mansfield
Mechanical Specifications: Type page 13 x 25; E - 6 cols, 2, between; A - 6 cols, 2, between; C - 8 cols, 1 1/2, between.Equipment & Software: Hardware — PCs; Software — Adobe/PageMaker 6.5.
Delivery Method: Mail, Newsstand, Racks

BROOKSVILLE

THE BRACKEN COUNTY NEWS (THUR)

216 Frankfort St, Brooksville, KY, 41004-8306, Bracken, USA; gen tel (606) 735-2198; gen fax (606) 735-2199; disp adv e-mail bcnews@ekns.net; ed e-mail bcnews@ekns.net; web site www.thebrackencountynews.com
Circulation: 3,000pd, 114fr; Sworn/Estimate/Non-Audited
Advertising rate: Open inch rate $4.00
Established: 1927
Pub....Kathy Bay
Circ. Mgr....Amy Meyer
Ed. ....Lynn Darnell
Mechanical Specifications: Type page 11 5/8 x 21; E - 6 cols, 1/4 between; A - 6 cols, 5/6, 1/4 between; C - 6 cols, 1/4 between.Equipment & Software: Hardware — PC, APP/Mac; Software — InDesign CS2.
Delivery Method: Mail, Newsstand
Areas Served: 41004, 41002, 41043, 41044

BROWNSVILLE

EDMONSON NEWS (TUES)

101 S Main St, Brownsville, KY, 42210-7233, Edmonson, USA; gen tel (270) 597-3115; gen fax (270) 597-3115; disp adv e-mail ednews@winstream.net; class adv e-mail ednews@winstream.net; ed e-mail ednews@winstream.net; web site www.edmonson-voice.com/-news
Circulation: 4,200pd,; Sworn/Estimate/Non-Audited
Advertising rate: Open inch rate $7.00
Group: Jobe Publishing
Delivery Method: Mail

BURKESVILLE

CUMBERLAND COUNTY NEWS (WED)

412 Courthouse Sq., Burkesville, KY, 42717, Cumberland, USA; gen tel (270) 864-3891; gen fax (270) 864-3497; disp adv e-mail ccn@mchsi.com; ed e-mail ccn@burkesville.com; web site cumberlandcountynewspaper.com
Circulation: 2,900pd,; Sworn/Estimate/Non-Audited
Advertising rate: Open inch rate $4.85
Pub....Patsy Judd
Ed. ....Cyndi Pritchett
Design and Layout....Billy Guffey
Typesetter....Paula Gunderman
Advertising Manager....Kimberly Johnson
Mechanical Specifications: Type page 13 x 21; E - 6 cols, 2 1/25, 1/6 between; A - 6 cols, 2 1/25, 1/6 between; C - 6 cols, 2 1/25, 1/6 between.Equipment & Software: Hardware — APP/Mac; Software — Adobe/PageMaker.
Delivery Method: Mail

CADIZ

THE CADIZ RECORD (WED)

58 Nunn Blvd, Cadiz, KY, 42211-7968, Trigg, USA; gen tel (270) 522-6605; gen fax (270) 522-3001; disp adv e-mail ads@cadizrecord.com; class adv e-mail chazelmyer@cadizrecord.com; ed e-mail news@cadizrecord.com; web site www.cadizrecord.com
Circulation: 4,800pd, 97fr; Sworn/Estimate/Non-Audited
Advertising rate: Open inch rate $6.95
Gen. Mgr....Mary Beth Carlock
Adv. Exec. ....Connie Puglisi
Adv. Mgr....Cynthia Mitchell
Exec. Ed....Justin McGill
Prodn. Mgr. ....Jennifer Wallace
Mechanical Specifications: Type page 13 x 21 1/2; E - 6 cols, 1 5/6, between; A - 6 cols, 3, between; C - 9 cols, 1 1/6, between.Equipment & Software: Hardware — APP/Mac; Presses — WPC/Web Leader; Software — QPS/QuarkXPress 4.1, Multi-Ad/Creator.
Delivery Method: Mail
Areas Served: 42211

CALHOUN

MCLEAN COUNTY NEWS (THUR)

165 E 2nd St, Calhoun, KY, 42327-2205, McLean, USA; gen tel (270) 273-3287; adv tel (270) 691-7285; ed tel (270) 691-7296; gen fax (270) 273-3544; disp adv e-mail news@mcleannews.com; ed e-mail news@mcleannews.com; web site www.messenger-inquirer.com
Circulation: 3,000pd, 350fr; Sworn/Estimate/Non-Audited
Advertising rate: Open inch rate $6.00
Established: 1884
Pub....Bob Morris
Adv. Mgr....Faye Murry
Editor ....Austin Ramsey
Delivery Method: Mail, Racks
Areas Served: 42322, 42327, 42350, 42352, 42371, 42372

CALVERT CITY

THE LAKE NEWS (THUR)

153 E 5th Ave, Calvert City, KY, 42029-9998, Marshall, USA; gen tel (270) 395-5858; gen fax (270) 395-5858; disp adv e-mail news@thelakenews.com; class adv e-mail news@thelakenews.com; ed e-mail news@thelakenews.com ; web site www.thelakenews.com
Advertising rate: Open inch rate $8.66
Established: 1984
Ed./Pub....Loyd Ford
Delivery Method: Mail, Newsstand, Racks

CAMPBELLSVILLE

CENTRAL KENTUCKY NEWS-JOURNAL (MON, THUR)

200 Albion Way, Campbellsville, KY, 42718-1565, Taylor, USA; gen tel (270) 465-8111; gen fax (270) 465-2500; disp adv e-mail cmagers@cknj.com; class adv e-mail cmagers@cknj.com; ed e-mail publisher@cknj.com; web site www.cknj.com
Circulation: 7,600pd, 12,000fr; Sworn/Estimate/Non-Audited
Advertising rate: Open inch rate $13.48
Established: 1910
Group: Landmark Communications, Inc.
Landmark Community Newspapers, LLC
Ed. ....Rebecca Cassell
Pub/Ed....Jeff Moreland
Prodn. Mgr. ....Suzanne Houk
Adv. Mgr....Cheryl Magers
Circulation Sales RepresentativeAndrea Yates
Pub....Richard Robards
Ad. Sales Rep....Melissa Netherland
Mechanical Specifications: Type page 13 x 21 1/2; E - 6 cols, 2, 5/16 between; A - 6 cols, 2, 5/16 between; C - 8 cols, 1 1/2, 1/48 between.Equipment & Software: Hardware — 12-APP/Mac; Presses — G; Software — QPS/QuarkXPress, Adobe/Photoshop, Microsoft/Word, Multi-Ad/Creator.
Delivery Method: Mail
Areas Served: Campbellsville and Taylor County

CARROLLTON

CARROLLTON NEWS-DEMOCRAT (WED)

122 6th St, Carrollton, KY, 41008-1009, Carroll, USA; gen tel (502) 732-4261; gen fax (502) 732-0453; disp adv e-mail dgarrett@mycarrollnews.com; ed e-mail jwright@mycarrollnews.com; web site www.mycarrollnews.com
Circulation: 2,841pd, 17fr; Sworn/Estimate/Non-Audited
Advertising rate: Open inch rate $9.18
Established: 1868
Group: Landmark Community Newspapers, LLC
Main Street Media, Inc.
Landmark Communications, Inc.
Circ. Mgr....Carla Kidwell
Pub./Ed....Jeff Moore
News Ed. ....Kristin Sherrard
Adv. Consultant....Deborah Garrett
Phyllis McLaughlin
Mechanical Specifications: Type page 10.38 x 21 1/2; E - 6 cols, 2, 1/8 between; A - 6 cols, 2, 1/8 between; C - 8 cols, 1 1/2, 1/8 between. Equipment & Software: ; Software — QPS/QuarkXPress 4.11, Adobe/Photoshop 6.0, Adobe/Acrobat 5.0, Microsoft/Word 2001.
Delivery Method: Mail
Areas Served: 41008, 41098, 41045, 40045

CENTRAL CITY

CENTRAL CITY LEADER NEWS (TUES)

1730 W EVERLY BROTHERS BLVD, Central City, KY, 42330, Muhlenberg, USA; gen tel (270) 754-3000; gen fax (270) 754-9484; disp adv e-mail advp@ky-leadernews.com; class adv e-mail typist@ky-leadernews.com; ed e-mail editor@ky-leadernews.com; web site www.ky-leadernews.com
Circulation:; Sworn/Estimate/Non-Audited
Advertising rate: Open inch rate $6.00
Sales....Jenny Earle
Gen Mgr....Jowanna Bandy
Delivery Method: Mail, Newsstand, Racks

THE TIMES-ARGUS (WED)

202 W Broad St, Central City, KY, 42330-1540, Muhlenberg, USA; gen tel (270) 754-2331; gen fax (270) 754-1805; disp adv e-mail timesargus@bellsouth.net; web site www.timesargus.com
Circulation: 2,600pd,; Sworn/Estimate/Non-Audited
Advertising rate: Open inch rate $4.00
Established: 1906
Adv. Mgr....Debbie Harris
President ....Mark Stone
Mng. Ed....Richard Deavers
Mechanical Specifications: Type page 13 x 21; E - 6 cols, 2, 1/6 between; A - 6 cols, 2, 1/6 between; C - 6 cols, 2, 1/6 between.Equipment & Software: Hardware — APP/Mac.
Delivery Method: Mail

CLAY CITY

THE CLAY CITY TIMES (THUR)

4477 Main St, Clay City, KY, 40380, Powell, USA; gen tel (606) 663-5540; gen fax (606) 663-6397; disp adv e-mail cctimesnews@bellsouth.net; class adv e-mail cctads@windstream.net; web site claycity-times.com
Circulation: 3,200pd,; USPS
Advertising rate: Open inch rate $ 4.95
Established: 1899
Publisher....Teresa Hatfield-Barger

Delivery Method: Mail, Newsstand
Areas Served: 40380, 40312

CLINTON

THE HICKMAN COUNTY GAZETTE (WED)

308 S Washington St, Ste 101, Clinton, KY, 42031-1340, Clinton, USA; gen tel (270) 653-3381; gen fax (270) 653-3322; disp adv e-mail gazette3322@bellsouth.net; web site magicvalleypublishing.com
Circulation: 2,000pd, 25fr; Sworn/Estimate/Non-Audited
Advertising rate: Open inch rate $5.10
Established: 1843
Pub....................................Dennis Richardson
Adv. Mgr......................................Nancy Evans
Ed. ....Gaye Bencini
Mechanical Specifications: Type page 11 5/8 x 21; E - 6 cols, 1 5/6, 1/8 between; A - 6 cols, 1 5/6, 1/8 between; C - 6 cols, 1 5/6, 1/8 between.

THE HICKMAN COUNTY TIMES (TUES)

104 S Jefferson St, Clinton, KY, 42031-1318, Clinton, USA; gen tel (270) 653-4040; disp adv e-mail tommy@thehctimes.com ; ed e-mail tommy@thehctimes.com; web site www.risnerweb.com
Advertising rate: Open inch rate $5.00
Established: 2011
Gaye Bencini
Tommy KimbroCo-Owners
Delivery Method: Mail, Racks

COLUMBIA

ADAIR COUNTY COMMUNITY VOICE (THUR)

316 Public Sq, Columbia, KY, 42728-1456, Adair, USA; gen tel (270) 384-9454; gen fax (270) 384-9343; disp adv e-mail snburton@duo-county.com; class adv e-mail voiceads@duo-county.com; ed e-mail newsroom@adairvoice.com; web site www.adairvoice.com
Circulation: 3,200pd,; Sworn/Estimate/Non-Audited
Advertising rate: Open inch rate $5.31
Established: 1989
Gen. Mgr.................................Mindy Yarberry
Pub./Ed....................................Sharon Burton
Delivery Method: Mail, Newsstand, Racks
Areas Served: 42728

ADAIR PROGRESS (THUR)

98 Grant Ln, Columbia, KY, 42728-2233, Adair, USA; gen tel (270) 384-6471; gen fax (270) 384-6474; disp adv e-mail advertising@adairprogress.com; class adv e-mail advertising@adairprogress.com; ed e-mail editorial@adairprogress.com; web site www.adairprogress.com
Circulation: 4,900pd,; Sworn/Estimate/Non-Audited
Advertising rate: Open inch rate $6.37
Established: 1987
Pub...Donna Hancock
Circ. Mgr....................................Melanie Ollery
Ed. ....Zachery Oakes
Asst Ed ....Ann Melton
Prodn. Mgr. ....Jeremy Birdwell
Advt ....April Burton
Mechanical Specifications: Type page 13 x 21; E - 6 cols, 1/4 between; A - 6 cols, 1/4 between; C - 6 cols, 1/4 between.
Delivery Method: Mail

CORBIN

NEWS JOURNAL (MON, THUR)

215 N Main St, Corbin, KY, 40701-1451, Whitley, USA; gen tel (606) 528-9767; gen fax (606) 528-9779; disp adv e-mail advertising@corbinnewsjournal.com; class adv e-mail advertising@corbinnewsjournal.com; ed e-mail destep@corbinnewsjournal.com; web site thenewsjournal.net
Circulation: 7,774pd,; Sworn/Estimate/Non-Audited
Advertising rate: Open inch rate $13.48
Established: 1908
Group: Forcht Group
Digital Platform - Mobile: Blackberry
Digital Platform - Tablet: Other
Production Mgr.......................Linda Carpenter
Adv. Mgr.................................Melissa Hudsonc
Circ. Mgr................................Jennifer Benfield
Publisher..Don Estep
Managing Ed............................Trent Knuckles
Sports Ed....................................Jim McAlister
Ed. ....Mark White
Adv. Sales Rep...................Melissa Netherland
Mechanical Specifications: Type page 11.25 x 21 1/2; 1 col-1.75, 2 col.- 3.56, 3 col. 5.5- 4 col. 7.45, 5 col.- 9.35, 6 col.- 11.25Equipment & Software: Hardware — APP/Mac; Presses — G/Community; Software — In-Design.
Delivery Method: Mail, Racks
Areas Served: 40701, 40702, 40769

CROMONA

THE LETCHER COUNTY COMMUNITY PRESS (WED)

73 Community Dr, Cromona, KY, 41810-9000, Letcher, USA; gen tel (606) 855-4541; adv tel (606) 855-4541; ed tel (606) 855-4542; gen fax (606) 855-9290; disp adv e-mail Paul@superiorprinting.org; class adv e-mail Tina@superiorprinting.org; ed e-mail Paul@superiorprinting.org; web site http://lch.stparchive.com
Circulation: 2,000pd, 20fr; Sworn/Estimate/Non-Audited
Advertising rate: Open inch rate $6.00
Established: 1959
Adv. Mgr................................Bobbie Whitaker
Ed. ....Charles W. Whitaker
Mng. Ed.............................William M. Whitaker
Delivery Method: Mail

CUMBERLAND

THE TRI-CITY NEWS (WED)

805 E Main St, Cumberland, KY, 40823-1711, Cumberland, USA; gen tel (606) 589-2588; gen fax (606) 589-2589; disp adv e-mail tricitynewsky@gmail.com; class adv e-mail tricitynewsky@gmail.com; ed e-mail tricitynews@yahoo.com; web site www.facebook.com/pg/tcnky/about/?ref=page_internal
Circulation: 2,500pd, 39fr; Sworn/Estimate/Non-Audited
Advertising rate: Open inch rate $4.50
Established: 1929
Adv. Mgr.................................Lindsay Collier
Publishing Ed................................Rachel Ison
Ed. ....Paul J. Wilder
Delivery Method: Mail, Newsstand

CYNTHIANA

CYNTHIANA DEMOCRAT (THUR)

302 Webster Ave, Cynthiana, KY, 41031-1647, Harrison, USA; gen tel (859) 234-1035; gen fax (859) 234-8096; disp adv e-mail ads@cynthianademocrat.com; ed e-mail bbarnes@cynthianademocrat.com; web site www.cynthianademocrat.com
Circulation: 5,500pd,; Sworn/Estimate/Non-Audited
Advertising rate: Open inch rate $9.87
Group: Landmark Communications, Inc.
Landmark Community Newspapers, LLC
Gen. Mgr.................................Patricia Jenkins
Ed. ....Becky Barnes
Josh Guthrie
Mechanical Specifications: Type page 11 5/8 x 21 1/2; E - 6 cols, 1 5/6, between; A - 6 cols, 1 5/6, between; C - 6 cols, 1 5/6, between. Equipment & Software: Hardware — APP/Mac; Presses — G/Community; Software — QPS/QuarkXPress 3.3, Adobe/Photoshop 5.5.
Delivery Method: Mail, Newsstand, Racks

DAWSON SPRINGS

THE DAWSON SPRINGS PROGRESS (WED)

131 S Main St, Dawson Springs, KY, 42408-1745, Hopkins, USA; gen tel (270) 797-3271; gen fax (270) 797-3273; disp adv e-mail progress@vci.net; ed e-mail progress@vci.net; web site www.dawsonspringsprogress.com
Circulation: 1,800pd, 35fr; Sworn/Estimate/Non-Audited
Advertising rate: Open inch rate $4.30
Established: 1919
Managing editor...................Melissa Larimore
editorial assistant.....................Lucas Johnson
Mechanical Specifications: Type page 13 x 21; E - 6 cols, 2, 1/6 between; A - 6 cols, 2, 1/6 between; C - 8 cols, 1 5/12, 1/6 between. Equipment & Software: Hardware — APP/Mac; Software — QPS/QuarkXPress.
Delivery Method: Mail

EDDYVILLE

THE HERALD-LEDGER (WED)

143 W Main St, Eddyville, KY, 42038-7762, Lyon, USA; gen tel (270) 388-2269; gen fax (270) 388-5540; disp adv e-mail sales@heraldledger.com; class adv e-mail sales@heraldledger.com; ed e-mail news@heraldledger.com; web site www.heraldledger.com
Circulation: 2,000pd,; Sworn/Estimate/Non-Audited
Advertising rate: Open inch rate $4.75
Established: 1901
Pub...Rae Wagoner
Office Mgr....................................Becky Fields
Ed. ....Jody Norwood
Delivery Method: Mail, Newsstand, Racks
Areas Served: Lyon and Caldwell Counties

EDMONTON

THE EDMONTON HERALD-NEWS (WED)

116 S MAIN ST, Edmonton, KY, 42129, Metcalfe, USA; gen tel (270) 432-3291; adv tel (270) 590-6625; gen fax (270) 432-4414; disp adv e-mail heraldnews@jpinews.com; web site www.jpinews.com
Circulation: 2,500pd,; USPS
Advertising rate: Open inch rate $7.25
Established: 1894
Group: Jobe Publishing Inc.
Pub./Owner.................................Jeffrey Jobe
Mechanical Specifications: Type page 13 x 21; E - 6 cols, 2 1/8, 1/8 between; A - 6 cols, 2 1/8, 1/8 between; C - 6 cols, 2 1/8, 1/8 between. Equipment & Software: Hardware — APP/Mac; Software — Adobe/PageMaker 6.5, Adobe/Photoshop.
Delivery Method: Mail, Newsstand, Racks
Areas Served: 42129, 42166, 42154, 42214, 42124, 42169, 42141

ELKTON

TODD COUNTY STANDARD (WED)

41 Public Sq, Elkton, KY, 42220-8822, Todd, USA; gen tel (270) 265-2439; gen fax (270) 265-2571; disp adv e-mail tcstandard@kypress.com; ed e-mail tcstandard@kypress.com; web site http://www.toddcountynews.blogspot.com
Circulation: 2,500pd,; Sworn/Estimate/Non-Audited
Advertising rate: Open inch rate $6.00
Established: 1893
Ed. ....Ryan Craig
Mechanical Specifications: Type page 13 x 21; E - 6 cols, 2, 1/4 between; A - 6 cols, 2, 1/4 between; C - 6 cols, 2, 1/4 between.Equipment & Software: Hardware — APP/Mac; Presses — 5-KP/News King, 8-KP/Color King; Software — QPS/QuarkXPress 5.0, Multi-Ad/Creator 2, Adobe/Photoshop 7.0, Adobe/InDesign 2.0.
Delivery Method: Mail, Newsstand, Racks

EMINENCE

HENRY COUNTY LOCAL (WED)

18 S Penn Ave, Eminence, KY, 40019-1036, Henry, USA; gen tel (502) 845-2858; gen fax (502) 845-2921; disp adv e-mail advertising@hclocal.com; class adv e-mail advertising@hclocal.com; ed e-mail news@hclocal.com; web site www.hclocal.com
Circulation: 4,500pd,; Sworn/Estimate/Non-Audited
Advertising rate: Open inch rate $10.88
Group: Landmark Community Newspapers, LLC
Pub...........................Jonna Spelbring Priester
Reporter ....Brad Bowman
Adv Sales ....Barbara Didier
Office Mgr ....Phyllis Banta
Circ Mgr ....Tawnja Morris
Delivery Method: Mail

FALMOUTH

FALMOUTH OUTLOOK (TUES)

210 Main St, Falmouth, KY, 41040-1265, Pendleton County, USA; gen tel (859) 654-3332; gen fax (859) 654-4365; disp adv e-mail ads@falmouthoutlook.com; class adv e-mail classifieds@falmouthoutlook.com; ed e-mail news@falmouthoutlook.com; web site www.falmouthoutlook.com
Circulation: 2,244pd, 5,200fr; Sworn/Estimate/Non-Audited
Advertising rate: $15.95
Established: 1907
Group: Delphos Herald, Inc.Editions: (108) The Falmouth Outlook
News Ed ....Jackie Vaughn
Pub ....Neil Belcher
Graphics Coord ....Jessie Beckett
Mechanical Specifications: 1 col. 1.56
2 col. 3.22
3 col. 4.89
4 col. 6.56
5 col. 8.22
6 col. 9.89
Delivery Method: Mail, Newsstand, Racks
Areas Served: 41040, 41006, 41043, 41007, 41001

FORT KNOX

THE GOLD STANDARD (THUR)

PO Box 1000, 125 Sixth Ave. Bldg 1110, 2nd Floor, Wing B, Fort Knox, KY, 40121-1000, Hardin, USA; gen tel (502) 624-1095; ed tel (502) 624-1095; gen fax (502) 624-2096; disp adv e-mail melissalove@thenewsenterprise.com; ed e-mail bsheroan@thenewsenterprise.com; web site www.fkgoldstandard.com
Advertising rate: Open inch rate $20.75
Pub...Chris Ordway
Ed. ....Ben Sheroan
Larry Jobe
Delivery Method: Mail

FORT MITCHELL

BOONE COMMUNITY RECORDER (THUR)

226 Grandview Dr, Fort Mitchell, KY, 41017-2702, Kenton, USA; gen tel (859) 578-5501; gen fax (859) 578-5515; disp adv e-mail ndaly@communitypress.com; class adv e-mail llawrence@enquirer.com; ed e-mail kynews@communitypress.com; web site www.communitypress.com
Circulation: 15pd, 5,907fr; CAC
Advertising rate: Open inch rate $7.00
Established: 2001
Group: Gannett
Circ. Mgr...........................Sharon Schachleiter

Sr. Ed. ....Nancy Daly
Delivery Method: Mail
Areas Served: 41048, 41005

CAMPBELL COUNTY RECORDER (THUR)

226 Grandview Dr, Fort Mitchell, KY, 41017-2702, Kenton, USA; gen tel (859) 283-0404; gen fax (859) 283-7285; disp adv e-mail kynews@communitypress.com; web site www.communitypress.com
Circulation: 1,747pd, 7,898fr; CAC
Advertising rate: Open inch rate $10.68
Established: 2001
Group: Gannett
Adv. Mgr............................... Debbie Maggard
Circ. Mgr..........................Sharon Schachleiter
Sr. Ed. ....Nancy Daly
Delivery Method: Mail

FLORENCE RECORDER (THUR)

226 Grandview Dr, Fort Mitchell, KY, 41017-2702, Kenton, USA; gen tel (859) 578-5501; gen fax (859) 578-5515; disp adv e-mail kynews@communitypress.com; web site www.communitypress.com
Circulation: 1,398pd, 13,304fr; CAC
Advertising rate: Open inch rate $9.96
Established: 2001
Group: Gannett
Circ. Mgr..........................Sharon Schachleiter
Sr. Ed. ....Nancy Daly
Delivery Method: Mail

FORT THOMAS RECORDER (THUR)

226 Grandview Dr, Fort Mitchell, KY, 41017-2702, Kenton, USA; gen tel (859) 283-0404; gen fax (859) 283-7285; disp adv e-mail kynews@communitypress.com; web site www.communitypress.com
Circulation: 1,024pd, 4,294fr; CAC
Advertising rate: Open inch rate $10.68
Established: 2001
Group: Gannett
Adv. Mgr............................... Debbie Maggard
Circ. Mgr..........................Sharon Schachleiter
Sr. Ed. ....Nancy Daly
Delivery Method: Mail

SOUTH KENTON RECORDER (THUR)

226 Grandview Dr, Fort Mitchell, KY, 41017-2702, Kenton, USA; gen tel (859) 283-0404; adv tel (513) 768-8338; ed tel (859) 283-0404; gen fax (859) 283-7285; disp adv e-mail kynews@communitypress.com; class adv e-mail llawrence@enquirer.com; ed e-mail kynews@communitypress.com; web site www.communitypress.com
Circulation: 911pd, 13,423fr; CAC
Advertising rate: Open inch rate $9.00
Established: 2011
Group: Gannett
Circ. Mgr..........................Sharon Schachleiter
Sr. Ed. ....Nancy Daly
Mechanical Specifications: Type page 13 x 21 1/2; E - 6 cols, 2, 1/8 between; A - 6 cols, 2, 1/8 between; C - 10 cols, 1 1/4, 1/8 between. Equipment & Software: Hardware — APP/Mac; Presses — HI; Software — Multi-Ad, Adobe/Photoshop, QPS/QuarkXPress.
Delivery Method: Mail
Areas Served: 41051, 41015

THE ERLANGER RECORDER (THUR)

226 Grandview Dr, Fort Mitchell, KY, 41017-2702, Kenton, USA; gen tel (859) 283-0404; gen fax (859) 283-7285; disp adv e-mail kynews@communitypress.com; web site www.communitypress.com
Circulation: 130pd, 7,201fr; CAC
Advertising rate: Open inch rate $6.00
Established: 2001
Group: Gannett
Adv. Mgr............................... Debbie Maggard
Circ. Mgr..........................Sharon Schachleiter
Sr. Ed. ....Nancy Daly
Delivery Method: Mail

UNION RECORDER (THUR)

226 Grandview Dr, Fort Mitchell, KY, 41017-2702, Kenton, USA; gen tel (859) 578-5501; gen fax (859) 578-5515; disp adv e-mail kynews@communitypress.com; web site www.communitypress.com
Advertising rate: 1/4 P $351, 1/2 P $649, Full $1144
Established: 2001
Circ. Mgr ....Sharon Schachleiter
Sr. Ed ....Nancy Daly
Delivery Method: Mail

FRANKFORT

KENTUCKY MONTHLY (MTHLY)

100 Consumer Ln, Frankfort, KY, 40601-8489, Franklin, USA; gen tel (502) 227-0053; gen fax (502) 227-5009; disp adv e-mail ads@kentuckymonthly.com; class adv e-mail julie@kentuckymonthly.com; ed e-mail steve@kentuckymonthly.com; web site www.kentuckymonthly.com
Circulation: 35,000pd, 5,000fr; USPS
Advertising rate: 1/3 P $1260, 2/3 P $2520, Full $3610
Established: 1998
Group: Vested Interest Publication
Pub/Ed..Stephen Vest
Executive Editor............................ Ranft Patty
Assistant Editor............. Deborah Kohl Kremer
Delivery Method: Mail, Newsstand

FRANKLIN

FRANKLIN FAVORITE (THUR)

103 N High St, Franklin, KY, 42134-1801, Simpson, USA; gen tel (270) 586-4481; gen fax (270) 586-6031; disp adv e-mail ffads@franklinfavorite.com; class adv e-mail dshelton@franklinfavorite.com; ed e-mail cportmann@franklinfavorite.com; web site www.franklinfavorite.com
Circulation: 4,000pd,; Sworn/Estimate/Non-Audited
Advertising rate: Open inch rate $8.00
Established: 1859
Gen. Mgr. ....Jamie S. Johnson
Mechanical Specifications: Type page 13 1/2 x 21 1/2; E - 6 cols, 1 5/8, 1/6 between; A - 6 cols, 1 5/8, 1/6 between; C - 8 cols, 1 1/4, 1/8 between.Equipment & Software: Hardware — APP/Mac; Presses — 8-WPC/Web Leader quad color; Software — Adobe/Photoshop, Multi-Ad/Creator, QPS/QuarkXPress, Adobe/Acrobat.
Delivery Method: Mail, Newsstand, Racks
Areas Served: 42134, 42135

FULTON

FULTON LEADER (WED)

304 E State Line St, Fulton, KY, 42041-1600, Fulton, USA; gen tel (270) 472-1121; gen fax (270) 472-1129; disp adv e-mail fultonleader@bellsouth.net; web site www.fultonleader.com
Circulation: 2,261pd, 31fr; Sworn/Estimate/Non-Audited
Advertising rate: Open inch rate $7.00
Established: 1898
Group: Magic Valley Publishing Co., Inc
Pub.....................................Dennis Richardson
Adv. Mgr................................ Benita Gammon
Mechanical Specifications: Type page 11 5/8 x 21; E - 6 cols, 1 5/6, 1/8 between; A - 6 cols, 1 5/6, 1/8 between; C - 8 cols, 1 1/3, 1/6 between.Equipment & Software: Hardware — APP; Software — QPS/QuarkXPress 5.0.

DELIVERY METHOD: MAIL, NEWSSTAND GEORGETOWN

GEORGETOWN NEWS-GRAPHIC (TUES, THUR, SAT)

1481 Cherry Blossom Way, Georgetown, KY, 40324-8953, Scott, USA; gen tel (502) 863-1111; gen fax (502) 863-6296; disp adv e-mail mscogin@news-graphic.com; class adv e-mail classifieds@news-graphic.com; ed e-mail news@news-graphic.com; web site www.news-graphic.com
Circulation: 5,780pd, 622fr; Sworn/Estimate/Non-Audited
Advertising rate: Open inch rate $11.25
Established: 1867
Group: Lancaster Management, Inc.
Pres./Pub. .... Mike Scogin
Ed. .. Jerry BoggsEquipment & Software: Hardware — APP/Power Macs; Presses — 16-G/Community, KR/Labeller; Software — QPS/QuarkXPress, Adobe/Photoshop, Baseview/Class.
Delivery Method: Mail, Newsstand, Racks
Areas Served: Georgetown, Sadieville, Stamping Ground

GRAYSON

GRAYSON JOURNAL-ENQUIRER (WED)

211 S Carol Malone Blvd, Grayson, KY, 41143-1355, Carter, USA; gen tel (606) 474-5101; gen fax (606) 474-0013; disp adv e-mail dduncan@journal-times.com ; class adv e-mail dduncan@journal-times.com ; ed e-mail tpreston@journal-times.com; web site www.journal-times.com
Circulation: 2,700pd, 100fr; Sworn/Estimate/Non-Audited
Advertising rate: Open inch rate $7.25
Established: 1916
Group: Community Newspaper Holdings, Inc.
Adv. Dir..Dan Duncan
Publisher and Editor ....Keith Kappes
Mechanical Specifications: Type page 9.889 x 21; 6 cols, .111 between
Delivery Method: Mail, Newsstand, Racks
Areas Served: 41128, 41164, 41332, 41142, 41143, 41146, 41181

GREENSBURG

GREENSBURG RECORD-HERALD (WED)

102 W Court St, Greensburg, KY, 42743-1564, Green, USA; gen tel (270) 932-4381; gen fax (270) 932-4441; disp adv e-mail advertising@record-herald.com; class adv e-mail advertising@record-herald.com; ed e-mail news2@record-herald.com; web site www.record-herald.com
Circulation: 3,500pd, 3,300fr; Sworn/Estimate/Non-Audited
Advertising rate: Open inch rate $11.14
Established: 1895
Office Mgr. ....Anne Gorin
Adv. Mgr. ....Walter C. Gorin
Circ. Mgr.................................. Barbara Harris
Ed. ....Tom Mills
Delivery Method: Mail, Newsstand
Areas Served: 42743, 42782, 42757, 42718, 42719, 42764

GREENUP

GREENUP COUNTY NEWS-TIMES (THUR)

203 Harrison St, Greenup, KY, 41144-1012, Greenup, USA; gen tel (606) 473-9851; gen fax (606) 473-7591; disp adv e-mail tlindley@cnhi.com; web site www.greenupbeacon.com
Circulation: 3,600pd,; Sworn/Estimate/Non-Audited
Advertising rate: Open inch rate $6.45
Group: Community Newspaper Holdings, Inc.
Adv. Mgr. .... Nikki Clay
Circ. Mgr.....................................Stefanie Scott
Ed. ....Cathie Shaffer
Delivery Method: Mail, Newsstand

HARRODSBURG

THE HARRODSBURG HERALD (THUR)

101 W Broadway St, Harrodsburg, KY, 40330-1527, Mercer, USA; gen tel (859) 734-2726; gen fax (859) 734-0737; disp adv e-mail advertising@harrodsburgherald.com; class adv e-mail classifieds@harrodsburgherald.com; ed e-mail newssroom@harrodsburgherald.com; web site www.harrodsburgherald.com
Circulation: 3,326pd,; AAM
Advertising rate: Open inch rate $10.00
Established: 1884
Adv. Mgr. .... Cathy Caton
Circ. Mgr......................................Barbara Yeast
Owner/Gen. Mgr .... April Ellis
Mechanical Specifications: Type page 11 1/2 x 21 1/2; E - 6 cols, 1 3/4, 1/4 between; A - 6 cols, 1 3/4, 1/4 between; C - 8 cols, 1 1/4, 1/4 between.Equipment & Software: Hardware — APP/Mac; Presses — G/Community; Software — Multi-Ad 4.0.1, QPS/QuarkXPress 4.1.
Delivery Method: Mail

HARTFORD

THE OHIO COUNTY TIMES (THUR)

314 S Main St, Hartford, KY, 42347-1129, Ohio, USA; gen tel (270) 298-7100; gen fax (270) 298-9572; disp adv e-mail ads@octimesnews.com; web site www.octimesnews.com
Circulation: 6,700pd, 75fr; Sworn/Estimate/Non-Audited
Advertising rate: Open inch rate $6.00
Group: Delphos Herald, Inc.
Pub... Andy Anderson
Ed. .... Seth Dukes
Community Ed. ....Georgina Dockery
Delivery Method: Mail, Newsstand, Racks

HAWESVILLE

THE HANCOCK CLARION (THUR)

230 Main St, Hawesville, KY, 42348-2626, Hancock, USA; gen tel (270) 927-6945; adv tel (270) 927-6945; gen fax (270) 927-6947; disp adv e-mail hancockclarion@bellsouth.net; class adv e-mail hancockclarion@bellsouth.net; ed e-mail hancockclarion@bellsouth.net; web site www.hancockclarion.com
Circulation: 3,683pd,; Sworn/Estimate/Non-Audited
Advertising rate: Open inch rate $6.50
Established: 1893
Ed. .... Donn K. Wimmer
Mng. Ed.....................................Steve Wimmer
News Ed. ....Ralph Dickerson
Adv Mgr .... Dave Taylor
Mechanical Specifications: Type page 11 5/8 x 21; E - 6 cols, 1 7/8, 1/6 between; A - 6 cols, 1 7/8, 1/6 between; C - 6 cols, 1 7/8, 1/6 between.Equipment & Software: Hardware — APP/Mac; Software — Adobe/PageMaker 6.0, Adobe/PageMaker 6.5, Adobe/Photoshop 3.0.
Delivery Method: Mail

HAZARD

THE HAZARD HERALD (WED)

439 High St, Hazard, KY, 41701-1701, Perry, USA; gen tel (606) 436-5771; adv tel (606) 436-5771; gen fax (606) 436-3140; disp adv e-mail hazardherald@windstream.net; class adv e-mail jjones@civitasmedia.com; web site www.hazard-herald.com
Circulation: 6,775pd,; Sworn/Estimate/Non-Audited
Advertising rate: Open inch rate $9.25
Established: 1911
Group: Lancaster Management, Inc.
Pub.. Joshua Byers
Circ. Mgr..Jenny Jones
Ed. .... Chris Ritchie
Mechanical Specifications: Type page 13 x 21 1/2; E - 6 cols, 2 1/12, 5/8 between; A - 6 cols, 2 1/12, between; C - 6 cols, 2 1/12, between.Equipment & Software: ; Software — QPS/QuarkXPress 4.3, Adobe/Photoshop.
Delivery Method: Mail

HINDMAN

TROUBLESOME CREEK TIMES (THUR)
27 Main St E, Ste 1, Hindman, KY, 41822-9998, Knott, USA; gen tel (606) 785-5134; adv tel (606) 785-5134; ed tel (606) 785-5134; gen fax (606) 785-5134; adv fax (606) 785-5134; ed fax (606) 785-5134; disp adv e-mail shall@troublesomecreektimes.com; class adv e-mail shall@troublesomecreektimes.com; ed e-mail shall@troublesomecreektimes.com; web site www.troublesomecreektimes.com
Circulation: 4,000pd, 250fr; Sworn/Estimate/Non-Audited
Advertising rate: Open inch rate $7.50
Established: 1980
Group: Knott County Publishing Co., Inc.Editions: (51) Troublesome Creek Times
Co-Pub. .... Sharon Kay Hall
Co- Publisher/ Exec. Editor. Karen Jones Cody
Asst. Gen. Mgr./Photographer . Jordan Thomas Hall
Advertising Sales................Tommy Curtis Hall
Classifieds/Production......................Tim Cody
Mechanical Specifications: Type page 10 x 21 1/2; E - 6 cols, 1.53, 1/6 between; A - 6 cols, 1.53, 1/6 between; C - 6 cols, 1.53, 1/6 between.Equipment & Software: Hardware — 3-APP/Mac G3, 3-APP/Power Mac, 2-APP/iMAC; Software — Adobe/PageMaker 6.5, Adobe/Photoshop 5.0.
Delivery Method: Mail, Newsstand, Carrier, Racks
Areas Served: Knott County and surrounding area

HODGENVILLE

LARUE COUNTY HERALD NEWS (WED)
40 Shawnee Dr, Hodgenville, KY, 42748-1639, LaRue, USA; gen tel (270) 358-3118; gen fax (270) 358-4852; disp adv e-mail publisher@laruecountyherald.com; class adv e-mail publisher@laruecountyherald.com; ed e-mail editor@laruecountyherald.com; web site www.laruecountyherald.com
Circulation: 2,842pd, 3,900fr; Sworn/Estimate/Non-Audited
Advertising rate: Open inch rate $9.27
Established: 1885
Group: Landmark Community Newspapers, LLC Landmark Communications, Inc.
Pub ....Allison Shepherd
Ed ....Doug Ponder
Mechanical Specifications: Type page 13 x 21 1/2; E - 6 cols, 2, 1/6 between; A - 6 cols, 2, 1/6 between; C - 8 cols, 1 1/2, 1/6 between.
Delivery Method: Mail, Newsstand, Carrier, Racks
Areas Served: 42748, 42757, 42716, 42784, 42776, 42764

HOPKINSVILLE

EAGLE POST (WED)
1618 E 9th St, Hopkinsville, KY, 42240-4430, Christian, USA; gen tel (270) 887-3241; adv tel (270) 887-3274; ed tel (270) 887-3295; gen fax (270) 439-5142; disp adv e-mail trodgers@kentuckynewera.com; class adv e-mail sellis@kentuckynewera.com; ed e-mail dsnow@theeaglepost.us; web site www.theeaglepost.us
Circulation: 5,490pd, 12,000fr; Sworn/Estimate/Non-Audited
Advertising rate: Open inch rate $7.75
Established: 2008
Group: Kentucky New EraEditions: (52)
Ed. ....David Snow
Delivery Method: Mail, Carrier, Racks
Areas Served: Oak Grove/Pembroke, KY; Fort Campbell, KY

HORSE CAVE

HART COUNTY NEWS HERALD (THUR)
570 S Dixie St, Horse Cave, KY, 42749-1253, Hart, USA; gen tel (270) 786-2676; gen fax (270) 786-4470; disp adv e-mail print@jpinews.com; class adv e-mail print@jpinews.com; ed e-mail print@jpinews.com; web site www.jpinews.com
Circulation: 8,000pd, 4,000fr; USPS
Advertising rate: Open inch rate $7.25
CEO..Jeff S. Jobe
Ed. ....Jerry Matera
Mechanical Specifications: Type page 12 7/8 x 21 1/2; E - 8 cols, 1 1/2, 1/6 between; A - 8 cols, 1 1/2, 1/6 between; C - 8 cols, 1 1/2, 1/6 between.
Delivery Method: Mail, Newsstand, Racks
Areas Served: 42765; 42749; 42722; 42713

HYDEN

THE LESLIE COUNTY NEWS (THUR)
22009 Main St, Hyden, KY, 41749-8568, Leslie, USA; gen tel (606) 672-2841; gen fax (606) 672-7409; disp adv e-mail rebab@tds.net; web site www.facebook.com/pages/Leslie-County-News/141938412518523
Circulation: 3,500pd, 25fr; Sworn/Estimate/Non-Audited
Advertising rate: Open inch rate $5.25
Pub...Vernon Baker
Circ. Mgr...Jan Estep
Mechanical Specifications: Type page 8 x 21.

THOUSANDSTICKS NEWS (TUES)
22009 Main St, Hyden, KY, 41749-8568, Leslie, USA; gen tel (606) 672-3399; gen fax (606) 672-7409; web site www.facebook.com/pages/Thousandsticks-News/168339959850253
Circulation: 3,800pd, 28fr; Sworn/Estimate/Non-Audited
Advertising rate: Open inch rate $5.25
Pub...Vernon Baker
Ed. ....Reba Baker
Mechanical Specifications: Type page 8 x 21 1/2.

INEZ

THE MOUNTAIN CITIZEN (WED)
20 W MAIN ST, Inez, KY, 41224, Martin, USA; gen tel (606) 298-7570; gen fax (606) 298-3711; disp adv e-mail mountaincitizen@bellsouth.net; ed e-mail mountaincitizen@bellsouth.net
Circulation: 6,000pd, 100fr; Sworn/Estimate/Non-Audited
Advertising rate: Open inch rate $5.25
Established: 1975
Pub..Roger Smith
Adv. Mgr.......................................Diane Smith
Circ. Mgr......................................Becky Smith
Ed. ....Gary Ball
Mechanical Specifications: Type page 13 x 21 1/2; E - 6 cols, 2, between; A - 6 cols, 2, between; C - 6 cols, 2, between.
Delivery Method: Mail

IRVINE

CITIZEN VOICE & TIMES (THUR)
108 S Court St, PO Box 660, Irvine, KY, 40336-1079, Estill, USA; gen tel (606) 723-5161; gen fax (606) 723-5509; disp adv e-mail cvtnews@windstream.net; class adv e-mail cvtads@windstream.net; ed e-mail lisa@hatfieldnewspapers.com; web site www.cvt-news.com
Circulation: 3,600pd,; USPS
Advertising rate: Open inch rate $4.95
Established: 1973
Adv. Mgr...................... Teresa Hatfield-Barger
Ad Composition
Classified................................ Megan Parker
Editor..Lisa Bicknell
Delivery Method: Mail, Newsstand
Areas Served: 40336, 40472, 40475

JACKSON

JACKSON TIMES-VOICE (THUR)
1001 College Ave, Ste 1, Jackson, KY, 41339-1036, Breathitt, USA; gen tel (606) 666-2451; gen fax (606) 666-5706; disp adv e-mail info@jacksontimesky.com; ed e-mail info@jacksontimesky.com; web site http://www.jacksontimesvoice.com
Circulation: 4,000pd,; Sworn/Estimate/Non-Audited
Advertising rate: Open inch rate $7.00
Established: 1893
Gen. Mgr. .... James David Fugate
Ed. .... Betty Hardin
Mechanical Specifications: Type page 6 x 21; E - 6 cols, between; A - 6 cols, between.
Delivery Method: Mail, Newsstand

LA GRANGE

OLDHAM ERA (THUR)
202 S 1st Ave, Ste 1, La Grange, KY, 40031-2208, Oldham, USA; gen tel (502) 222-7183; gen fax (502) 222-7194; disp adv e-mail barbara@oldhamera.com; class adv e-mail barbara@oldhamera.com; ed e-mail editor@oldhamera.com; web site www.oldhamera.com
Circulation: 3,200pd,; Sworn/Estimate/Non-Audited
Advertising rate: 12.00 pci + $13 for online
Established: 1876
Group: Landmark Community Newspapers, LLC Landmark Communications, Inc.
Digital Platform - Mobile: Apple
Graphic Designer.....................Talon Hampton
Advertising Representative....Barbara Duncan
Circulation manager ....Tawnja Morris
Sports Ed.......................................Sam Draut
Amanda Manning
Reporter ....Glenn Jennings
Pub...................................... Jane Ashley Pace
Mechanical Specifications: Type page 12 15/16 x 29 1/2; E - 6 cols, 2, 1/6 between; A - 6 cols, 2, 1/6 between; C - 6 cols, 2, 1/6 between. Equipment & Software: ; Software — QPS/QuarkXPress, Multi-Ad/Creator 3.7.
Delivery Method: Mail, Newsstand
Areas Served: Oldham County

LANCASTER

GARRARD CENTRAL RECORD (THUR)
106 Richmond St, Lancaster, KY, 40444-1158, Garrard, USA; gen tel (859) 792-2831; gen fax (859) 792-3448; disp adv e-mail ads@garrardcentralrecord.com; class adv e-mail ads@garrardcentralrecord.com; ed e-mail news@garrardcentralrecord.com; web site www.garrardcentralrecord.com
Circulation: 3,993pd, 95fr; Sworn/Estimate/Non-Audited
Advertising rate: Open inch rate $6.50
Established: 1889
Pub...Jim Cox
Exec. Sec./Adv. Mgr. ....Oneida Black
Mng. Ed..Pattie Cox
Sports Ed.................................... Danny Elam
Melanie Arnold
Ted Cox
Graphic artist .... Pam Fathergill
Mechanical Specifications: Type page 13 x 21; E - 6 cols, 2 1/12, 1/8 between; A - 6 cols, 2 1/12, 1/8 between; C - 8 cols, 1 3/8, 1/8 between.Equipment & Software: Hardware — 6-APP/Mac; Software — QPS/InDesign, Adobe/Photoshop.
Delivery Method: Mail, Newsstand, Racks
Areas Served: 40444, 40461, 40440

LAWRENCEBURG

THE ANDERSON NEWS (WED)
PO Box 410, Lawrenceburg, KY, 40342-0410, Anderson, USA; gen tel (502) 839-6906; gen fax (502) 839-3118; disp adv e-mail advertising@theandersonnews.com; class adv e-mail classifieds@theandersonnews.com; ed e-mail news@theandersonnews.com; web site www.theandersonnews.com - 50,000(views)
Circulation: 5,200pd,; Sworn/Estimate/Non-Audited
Advertising rate: Open inch rate $12.62
Established: 1877
Group: Landmark Communications, Inc. Landmark Community Newspapers, LLCEditions: (52)
Ed./Pub. .... Ben Carlson
Adv. Mgr.......................................Bud Garrison
Adv. Sales Rep........................... Claudia Kuhn
Classified Adv. Mgr...................Shirley Morgan
Mechanical Specifications: Call for details
Delivery Method: Mail, Racks
Areas Served: 40342

LEBANON

LEBANON ENTERPRISE (WED)
119 S Proctor Knott Ave, Lebanon, KY, 40033-1259, Marion, USA; gen tel (270) 692-6026; adv tel (270) 692-6026; gen fax (270) 692-2118; disp adv e-mail enugent@lebanonenterprise.com; ed e-mail editor@lebanonenterprise.com; web site www.lebanonenterprise.com
Circulation: 5,806pd,; Sworn/Estimate/Non-Audited
Advertising rate: Open inch rate $11.53
Group: Landmark Communications, Inc. Landmark Community Newspapers, LLC
Gen. Mgr. .... Stevie Lowery
Ed. .... Steve Lowery
Other...Stephen Lega
Areas Served: 40033

LEITCHFIELD

GRAYSON COUNTY NEWS-GAZETTE (WED, SAT)
PO Box 305, Leitchfield, KY, 42755-0305, Grayson, USA; gen tel (270) 259-9622; adv tel (270) 259-9622, ext. 2012; gen fax (270) 259-5537; disp adv e-mail tarmstrong@civitasmedia.com; class adv e-mail bethdennis@civitasmedia.com; ed e-mail bwise@civitasmedia.com; web site www.gcnewsgazette.com - 79,000(views) 15,000(visitors)
Circulation: 3,000pd,; Sworn/Estimate/Non-Audited
Advertising rate: Open inch rate $8.75
Established: 1890
Group: Paxton Media Group, LLC
Pub.. Chip Turner
Gen Mgr/Ad Mgr............... Theresa Armstrong
Delivery Method: Mail

THE RECORD (THUR)
209C White Oak Rd, Leitchfield, KY, 42754-5816, Grayson, USA; gen tel (270) 259-6061; gen fax (270) 230-8405; disp adv e-mail gm@graysonrecord.com; class adv e-mail circulation@graysonrecord.com; ed e-mail news@graysonrecord.com; web site www.graysonrecord.com
Circulation: 3,167pd, 6fr; USPS
Advertising rate: Open inch rate $12, modular rates available upon request
Established: 1980
Group: Landmark Community Newspapers Inc.
General Manager/Editor.........Rebecca Morris
Advertising representative......... Nancy Farmer
Circulation/office manager.......... Alicia Carter
Advertising representative...... Michaela Priddy
Delivery Method: Mail, Racks
Areas Served: Grayson County, KY. Portions of Edmonson County, KY, Hardin County, KY, and Breckinridge County, KY

LIBERTY

CASEY COUNTY NEWS (WED)
720 Campbellsville St, Liberty, KY, 42539-3106, Casey, USA; gen tel (606) 787-7171; gen fax (606) 787-8306; disp adv e-mail bemerson@caseynews.net; class adv e-mail bemerson@caseynews.net; ed e-mail lrowell@caseynews.net; web site www.caseynews.net
Circulation: 6,000pd, 14fr; Sworn/Estimate/Non-Audited
Advertising rate: Open inch rate $9.11
Group: Landmark Communications, Inc. Landmark Community Newspapers, LLC
Adv. Mgr. .... Britney Emerson
Ed. .... Donna Carman
Delivery Method: Mail, Racks
Areas Served: 42539

LONDON

THE SENTINEL-ECHO (MON, WED, FRI)
123 W 5th St, London, KY, 40741-1837, Laurel, USA; gen tel (606) 878-7400; gen fax (606) 878-7404; adv fax (606) 864-1327; disp adv e-mail kjones@sentinel-echo.com; class adv e-mail classifieds@sentinel-echo.com; ed e-mail editor@sentinel-echo.com; web site www.sentinel-echo.com
Circulation: 9,800pd, 10,000fr; Sworn/Estimate/Non-Audited
Advertising rate: Open inch rate $9.18
Established: 1873
Group: Community Newspaper Holdings, Inc.
Pub. .... Willie Sawyers
Adv. Mgr. .... Kathy Jones
Circ. Mgr. .... Earletta Sparkman
Sports Ed. .... Denis House
Prodn. Mgr. .... Shari Serier
Mechanical Specifications: Type page 11 5/8 x 21 1/2; E - 6 cols, 1 13/16, 1/8 between; A - 6 cols, 1 13/16, 1/8 between; C - 9 cols, 1 1/8, 1/16 between.Equipment & Software: Hardware — APP/Power Mac; Presses — G/Community; Software — QPS/QuarkXPress 3.3.
Delivery Method: Mail

LOUISA

THE BIG SANDY NEWS (WED)
PO Box 766, Louisa, KY, 41230-0766, Johnson, USA; gen tel (606) 638-4581; gen fax (606) 638-9949; disp adv e-mail bcrum@bigsandynews.com; class adv e-mail classifieds@bigsandynews.com; ed e-mail info@bigsandynews.com; web site www.bigsandynews.com
Circulation: 12,000pd,; Sworn/Estimate/Non-Audited
Advertising rate: Open inch rate $10.00
Established: 1885
Adv. Mgr. .... Becky Crum
Circ. Mgr. .... Doug McDavid
Mng. Ed. .... Tony Fyffe
Mechanical Specifications: Type page 11 1/2 x 21 1/4; E - 6 cols, 1 13/16, between; A - 6 cols, 1 13/16, between; C - 10 cols, 1 1/16, between.Equipment & Software: ; Software — QPS/QuarkXPress 4.1, Adobe/Photoshop 7.0.
Delivery Method: Mail

THE TRI-RIVERS ADVERTISER (SAT)
Lousia 41230, Louisa, KY, 41230, Lawrence, USA; gen tel (606) 638-4581; gen fax (606) 638-9949; disp adv e-mail bcrum@bigsandynews.com; class adv e-mail classifieds@bigsandynews.com; ed e-mail info@bigsandynews.com; web site www.bigsandynews.com
Circulation: 25,000fr; Sworn/Estimate/Non-Audited
Advertising rate: Open inch rate $8.00
Pub. .... Marjie Hale
Adv. Mgr. .... Randy Hale
Ed. .... Tony Fyffe
Mechanical Specifications: Type page 10 1/4 x 13; A - 8 cols, 1 1/6, 1/6 between; C - 8 cols, 1 1/6, 1/6 between.Equipment & Software: Hardware — APP/Power Mac 620.
Delivery Method: Mail

LOUISVILLE

LOUISVILLE BUSINESS FIRST (FRI)
462 S 4th St, Ste 450, Louisville, KY, 40202-4403, Jefferson, USA; gen tel (502) 583-1731; adv tel (502) 498-1946; ed tel (502) 498-1958; disp adv e-mail gtyler@bizjournals.com; class adv e-mail gtyler@bizjournals.com; ed e-mail ctimmons@bizjournals.com; web site www.bizjournals.com/louisville
Advertising rate: 1/4 P $2725, 1/2 P $4650, Full $6250
Established: 1984
Ed. .... Carol Brandon Timmons
Mng. Ed. .... Carolyn Greer
Adv. Dir. .... Gary Tyler
Delivery Method: Mail

THE VOICE-TRIBUNE (THUR)
735 E Main St, Louisville, KY, 40202-1005, Jefferson, USA; gen tel (502) 897-8900; gen fax (502) 897-8915; disp adv e-mail advertising@voice-tribune.com; class adv e-mail advertising@voice-tribune.com; ed e-mail circ@voice-tribune.com; web site www.voice-tribune.com
Circulation: 11,587pd, 1,850fr; Sworn/Estimate/Non-Audited
Advertising rate: 1/16 Pg $225.00; 1/8 Pg $435.00; 1/4 Pg $850.00
Established: 1987
Pub. .... Tracy Blue
Ed. .... Angie Fenton
Delivery Method: Mail, Racks

MANCHESTER

THE MANCHESTER ENTERPRISE (THUR)
103 3rd St, Manchester, KY, 40962-1119, Clay, USA; gen tel (606) 598-2319; gen fax (606) 598-2330; class adv e-mail cblair@themanchesterenterprise.com; web site www.themanchesterenterprise.com
Circulation: 6,500pd,; Sworn/Estimate/Non-Audited
Advertising rate: Open inch rate $6.00
Pub. .... Glenn Gray
Adv Mgr .... Rodney Miller

MARION

THE CRITTENDEN PRESS (THUR)
125 E Bellville St, Marion, KY, 42064-1409, Crittenden, USA; gen tel (270) 965-3191; gen fax (270) 965-2516; disp adv e-mail advertising@the-press.com; class adv e-mail information@the-press.com; ed e-mail thepress@the-press.com; web site www.the-press.com
Circulation: 3,800pd, 64fr; Sworn/Estimate/Non-Audited
Advertising rate: Open inch rate $5.35
Pub. .... Chris Evans
Adv. Mgr. .... Allison Mick-Evans
Mng. Ed .... Daryl Tabor
Mechanical Specifications: Type page 13 1/4 x 21 1/2; E - 6 cols, 2, 1/6 between; A - 6 cols, 2, 1/6 between; C - 8 cols, 1 1/2, 1/6 between. Equipment & Software: Hardware — APP/Mac; Presses — G/Community; Software — QPS/QuarkXPress, Adobe/Photoshop, Abbott Systems/Ready, Set, Go.
Delivery Method: Mail

MAYFIELD

THE MAYFIELD MESSENGER (WED, FRI, SUN)
111 S 7th St, Mayfield, KY, 42066-2341, Graves, USA; gen tel (270) 247-5223; adv tel (270) 247-5223; ed tel (270) 247-1516; gen fax (270) 247-6336; adv fax (270) 247-6336; ed fax (270) 247-6336; disp adv e-mail sbseay@mayfield-messenger.com; class adv e-mail mellen@mayfield-messenger.com; ed e-mail news@mayfield-messenger.com; web site http://www.mayfield-messenger.com/
Circulation: 2,000pd,; Sworn/Estimate/Non-Audited
Established: 1900
Group: Paxton Media Group, LLC
Ed. .... Tom Berry
Delivery Method: Mail, Carrier, Racks
Areas Served: Graves county & surrounding area

MC KEE

JACKSON COUNTY SUN (THUR)
101 Main St, Mc Kee, KY, 40447, Jackson, USA; gen tel (606) 287-7197; gen fax (606) 287-7196; disp adv e-mail jcsun@prtcnet.org; ed e-mail tammy@thejacksoncountysun.com; web site www.thejacksoncountysun.com
Circulation: 4,050pd,; Sworn/Estimate/Non-Audited
Advertising rate: Open inch rate $4.00
Established: 1926
Pub. .... Glenn Gray
Adv. Mgr. .... Tammy Spurlock
Mechanical Specifications: Type page 13 x 21 1/2; E - 6 cols, between; A - 6 cols, between; C - 6 cols, between.Equipment & Software: Hardware — APP/Mac; Software — Adobe/PageMaker 4.0.
Delivery Method: Mail

MONTICELLO

THE WAYNE COUNTY OUTLOOK (WED)
45 E Columbia Ave, Monticello, KY, 42633-1293, Wayne, USA; gen tel (606) 348-3338; gen fax (606) 348-8848; disp adv e-mail advertising@wcoutlook.com; class adv e-mail wcoclass@windstream.net; ed e-mail news@wcoutlook.com; web site www.wcoutlook.com
Circulation: 5,800pd,; Sworn/Estimate/Non-Audited
Advertising rate: Open inch rate $6.00
Group: Community Newspaper Holdings, Inc.
Digital Platform - Mobile: Apple
Adv. Mgr. .... Melinda Jones
News Ed. .... Melodie Phelps
Delivery Method: Mail

MOREHEAD

MENIFEE COUNTY NEWS (WED)
722 W 1st St, Morehead, KY, 40351-1404, Rowan, USA; gen tel (606) 784-4116; gen fax (606) 784-7337; web site www.facebook.com/Menifee-County-News-Outlook-190065967691341/
Circulation: 500pd,; Sworn/Estimate/Non-Audited
Advertising rate: Open inch rate $7.15
Adv. Mgr. .... Brad Toy
Mng. Ed. .... Stephanie Ockerman

THE MOREHEAD NEWS (TUES, FRI)
710 W 1st St, Morehead, KY, 40351-1436, Rowan, USA; gen tel (606) 784-4116; gen fax (606) 784-7337; disp adv e-mail dduncan@themoreheadnews.com; class adv e-mail dduncan@themoreheadnews.com; ed e-mail sockerman@themoreheadnews.com; web site www.themoreheadnews.com
Circulation: 4,200pd, 100fr; Sworn/Estimate/Non-Audited
Advertising rate: Open inch rate $8.00
Established: 1883
Group: Community Newspaper Holdings, Inc.
Adv. Dir. .... Dan Duncan
Ed. .... Stephanie Ockermann
Pub. .... Eddie Blakeley
Delivery Method: Mail, Newsstand, Racks
Areas Served: 40313, 40317, 40319, 40351

MORGANFIELD

UNION COUNTY ADVOCATE (WED)
214 W Main St, Morganfield, KY, 42437-1479, Union, USA; gen tel (270) 389-1833; adv tel (270) 389-1833; gen fax (270) 389-3926; adv fax (270) 389-3926; disp adv e-mail ads@ucadvocate.com; class adv e-mail ads@ucadvocate.com; ed e-mail news@ucadvocate.com; web site www.ucadvocate.com
Circulation: 5,000pd, 11fr; Sworn/Estimate/Non-Audited
Advertising rate: Open inch rate $8.98
Established: 1885
Pub. .... Jack Pate
Ed .... Paula Smith
Adv. Mgr. .... Lisa Turner
Gen. Mgr. .... Barbara Starkey
Mechanical Specifications: Type page 13 x 21 1/2; E - 6 cols, between; A - 6 cols, between; C - 8 cols, between.
Delivery Method: Mail

MORGANTOWN

THE BUTLER COUNTY BANNER-REPUBLICAN (WED)
PO Box 219, 120 E. Ohio St., Morgantown, KY, 42261-0219, Butler, USA; gen tel (270) 526-4151; adv tel (270) 590-6625; ed tel (270) 999-3268; gen fax (270) 526-3111; ed fax (270) 526-3111; disp adv e-mail banner@jpinews.com; class adv e-mail banner@jpinews.com; ed e-mail joshgivens@jpinews.com; web site www,jpinews.com
Circulation: 5,900pd, 6,100fr; USPS
Advertising rate: Open inch rate $5.70
Established: 1864
Group: Jobe Publishing Inc.
Pub./Pres. .... Jeffrey Jobe
Editor .... C. Josh Givens
Mechanical Specifications: Type page 13 x 21; E - 6 cols, 2, 1/4 between; C - 6 cols, 2, 1/4 between.Equipment & Software: Hardware — APP/Mac.
Delivery Method: Mail, Newsstand, Racks
Areas Served: 42261

MOUNT STERLING

MT. STERLING ADVOCATE (THUR)
219 Midland Trl, Mount Sterling, KY, 40353-9070, Montgomery, USA; gen tel (859) 498-2222; gen fax (859) 498-2228; disp adv e-mail advertising@msadvocate.com; class adv e-mail classified@msadvocate.com; ed e-mail news@msadvocate.com; web site www.msadvocate.com
Circulation: 7,500pd, 38fr; Sworn/Estimate/Non-Audited
Advertising rate: Open inch rate $5.86
Established: 1890
Pub. .... Matt Hall
Adv. Mgr. .... Sharon Manning
Ed. .... Jamie Vinson
Staff Writer .... Tom MarshallEquipment & Software: Hardware — APP/Mac; Presses — G; Software — Adobe/PageMaker 6.5, QPS/QuarkXPress 4.0.
Delivery Method: Mail

NICHOLASVILLE

THE JESSAMINE JOURNAL (THUR)
507 N Main St, Nicholasville, KY, 40356-1156, Jessamine, USA; gen tel (859) 885-5381; gen fax (859) 887-2966; disp adv e-mail joe.hall@jessaminejournal.com; class adv e-mail finditky@jessaminejournal.com; ed e-mail brittany.fuller@jessaminejournal.com; web site www.jessamineonline.com
Circulation: 3,500pd,; USPS
Advertising rate: Open inch rate $12.50
Established: 1873
Group: Boone Newspapers, Inc.

Ed. .... Brittany Fuller
Pres./Pub. .... Michael Caldwell
Mechanical Specifications: Type page 11 5/8 x 21; E - 6 cols, 1 5/6, 3/16 between; A - 6 cols, 1 5/6, 3/16 between; C - 6 cols, 1 5/6, 3/16 between.Equipment & Software: Hardware — APP/Macs; Software — QPS/QuarkXPress, APP/Works, Baseview/News Edit Pro, Adobe/Photoshop.
Delivery Method: Mail
Areas Served: 40356, 40340, 40390, 40339

OLIVE HILL

OLIVE HILL TIMES (WED)

187 RAILROAD ST, Olive Hill, KY, 41164, Carter, USA; gen tel (606) 286-4201; gen fax (606) 286-0120; disp adv e-mail dduncan@journal-times.com; class adv e-mail dduncan@journal-times.com; ed e-mail tpreston@themoreheadnews.com; web site www.journal-times.com
Circulation: 1,800pd, 100fr; Sworn/Estimate/Non-Audited
Advertising rate: Open inch rate $7.25
Established: 1935
Group: Community Newspaper Holdings, Inc.
Adv. Mgr. .... Dan Duncan
Publisher and Editor .... Keith Kappes
Delivery Method: Mail, Newsstand, Racks
Areas Served: 41128, 41164, 41142, 41173

OWENTON

OWENTON NEWS-HERALD (WED)

152 W Bryan St, Ste 1, Owenton, KY, 40359-1440, Owen, USA; gen tel (502) 484-3431; gen fax (502) 484-3221; ed e-mail jwhitlockr@owentonnewsherald.com; web site www.owentonnewsherald.com
Circulation: 4,129pd,; Sworn/Estimate/Non-Audited
Advertising rate: Open inch rate $9.40
Established: 1868
Group: Landmark Communications, Inc.
Landmark Community Newspapers, LLC
Circ. Mgr. .... Sherry Lyons
News Ed. .... John Whitlock
Pub./Ed./Gen. Mgr. .... Patti Clark
Adv. Sales Rep. .... Scott Hubbard
Mechanical Specifications: Type page 13 x 21 1/2; E - 6 cols, 2, 1/6 between; A - 6 cols, 2, 1/6 between; C - 8 cols, 1 1/2, 1/12 between. Equipment & Software: Hardware — APP/Mac; Software — Indesign
Delivery Method: Mail
Areas Served: 4061, 40701

OWINGSVILLE

BATH COUNTY BULLETIN (FRI)

28 N Court St, Owingsville, KY, 40360, Bath, USA; gen tel (606) 674-2260; adv tel (606) 674-2260; ed tel (606) 674-2260; gen fax (606) 674-2260; adv fax (606) 674-2260; ed fax (606) 674-2260; disp adv e-mail bathcountynews@gmail.com; class adv e-mail bathcountynews@gmail.com; ed e-mail bathcountynews@gmail.com; web site www.facebook.com/Bath-County-Bulletin-208017657623/
Advertising rate: Open inch rate $5.70
Established: 2009
Digital Platform - Mobile: Apple, Android
Digital Platform - Tablet: Apple iOS, Android
Pub./Ed. .... Chris Bailey
Delivery Method: Mail, Newsstand
Areas Served: Bath County

PADUCAH

THE ADVANCE YEOMAN (WED)

1540 McCracken Blvd, Paducah, KY, 42001-9192, Ballard, USA; gen tel (270) 519-3395; gen fax (270) 442-5220; disp adv e-mail larrah@ky-news.com; class adv e-mail larrah@ky-news.com; ed e-mail advanceyeoman@gmail.com; web site http://www.ky-news.com/
Circulation: 4,300pd, 45fr; Sworn/Estimate/Non-Audited
Advertising rate: Open inch rate $11.00
Established: 1889
Pub. .... Greg Leneave
Adv. Mgr. .... Larrah Workman
Ed. .... Bobby Mayberry
Prodn. Mgr. .... Gregory Vaught
Delivery Method: Mail

THE CARLISLE COUNTY NEWS (THUR)

1540 McCracken Blvd, Paducah, KY, 42001-9192, McCracken, USA; gen tel (270) 628-5490; gen fax (270) 442-5220; disp adv e-mail ccn1@galaxycable.net; web site www.ky-news.com
Circulation: 1,625pd, 77fr; Sworn/Estimate/Non-Audited
Advertising rate: Open inch rate $11.00
Established: 1894
Digital Platform - Mobile: Apple
Pub. .... Greg Leneave
Ed.
Lilly Morefield
Staff Writer .... Kate Prince
AD SALES .... STEPHANIE DAWSON
Delivery Method: Mail, Newsstand, Carrier, Racks
Areas Served: Carlisle / Hickman / Fulton NW Tennessee

PAINTSVILLE

THE PAINTSVILLE HERALD (WED, FRI)

978 Broadway St, Paintsville, KY, 41240-1346, Johnson, USA; gen tel (606) 789-5315; gen fax (606) 789-9717; disp adv e-mail ads@paintsvilleherald.com; class adv e-mail classifieds@paintsvilleherald.com; ed e-mail news@paintsvilleherald.com; web site www.paintsvilleherald.com
Circulation: 5,200pd,; Sworn/Estimate/Non-Audited
Advertising rate: Open inch rate $7.50
Established: 1901
Group: Lancaster Management, Inc.
Pub. .... Paula Halm
Mechanical Specifications: Type page 12 1/2 x 21 1/2; E - 6 cols, 2, 1/2 between; A - 6 cols, 2, 1/2 between; C - 8 cols, 1 1/2, 1/3 between.Equipment & Software: Hardware — Performa 63.20; Software — QPS/QuarkXPress 3.3.
Delivery Method: Mail, Newsstand, Carrier, Racks
Areas Served: 41240

PARIS

BOURBON COUNTY CITIZEN (WED)

123 W 8th St, Paris, KY, 40361-1343, Bourbon, USA; gen tel (859) 987-1870; gen fax (859) 987-3729; disp adv e-mail citadinc@bellsouth.net; ed e-mail citadinc@bellsouth.net; web site www.facebook.com/thebourboncountycitizenadvertiser/
Circulation: 3,000pd,; Sworn/Estimate/Non-Audited
Advertising rate: Open inch rate $6.65
Established: 1984
Adv. Mgr. .... Beverly Brannon
Ed. .... Jimmy Brannon
Mng. Ed. .... Genevieve Brannon
Prodn. Mgr. .... Rebecca Brannon Lawyer
Mechanical Specifications: Type page 13 x 21.Equipment & Software: ; Software — Multi-Ad/Creator, Microsoft/Word.
Delivery Method: Mail

PIKEVILLE

THE APPALACHIAN NEWS-EXPRESS (WED, FRI, SAT)

129 Caroline Ave, Pikeville, KY, 41501-1101, Pike, USA; gen tel (606) 437-4054; gen fax (606) 437-4246; disp adv e-mail mkeller@news-expressky.com; class adv e-mail mkeller@news-expressky.com; ed e-mail editor@news-expressky.com; web site www.news-expressky.com
Circulation: 11,000pd,; Sworn/Estimate/Non-Audited
Advertising rate: Open inch rate $9.40
Group: Lancaster Management, Inc.
Pub. .... Jeff Vanderbeck
Circ. Mgr .... Lisa Moore
Ed. .... Russ Cassady
Adv. Dir .... Melissa Keller
Mechanical Specifications: Type page 12 x 21 1/2; E - 6 cols, 1 5/6, 1/4 between; A - 6 cols, 1 5/6, 1/4 between; C - 9 cols, 1 1/6, 1/4 between.
Delivery Method: Mail

PINEVILLE

PINEVILLE SUN (THUR)

PO Box 250, Pineville, KY, 40977-0250, Bell, USA; gen tel (606) 337-2333; gen fax (606) 337-2360; disp adv e-mail news@pinevillesun.net; web site www.facebook.com/pages/The-Pineville-Sun-Cumberland-Courier/129776610402283
Circulation: 3,500pd, 41fr; Sworn/Estimate/Non-Audited
Advertising rate: Open inch rate $7.10
Adv. Dir. .... Rhonda Droughton
Ed. .... Gary Ferguson
Ed. .... Sam Gambrell

PRESTONSBURG

FLOYD COUNTY TIMES (WED, FRI)

263 S Central Ave, Prestonsburg, KY, 41653-1958, Floyd, USA; gen tel (606) 886-8506; gen fax (606) 886-3603; disp adv e-mail fctadvertising@floydcountytimes.com; class adv e-mail fctclassifieds@floydcountytimes.com; ed e-mail news@floydcountytimes.com; web site www.floydcountytimes.com
Circulation: 8,200pd, 110fr; Sworn/Estimate/Non-Audited
Advertising rate: Open inch rate $7.25
Established: 1927
Group: Lancaster Management, Inc.
Pub. .... Joshua Byers
Adv Mgr .... Jamie Vaenhoose
Mng. Ed. .... Ralph B. Davis
Sports Ed. .... Steve LeMaster
Mechanical Specifications: Type page 11 3/4 x 21 1/4; E - 6 cols, 1 5/6, 1/6 between; A - 6 cols, 1 5/6, 1/6 between; C - 8 cols, 1 1/3, 1/6 between.Equipment & Software: Hardware — APP/Mac G4 400 MHZ; Software — Adobe/Acrobat 4.1, QPS/QuarkXPress 3.32, Adobe/Photoshop 6.0.

PRINCETON

TIMES LEADER (WED, SAT)

607 W Washington St, Princeton, KY, 42445-1941, Caldwell, USA; gen tel (270) 365-5588; gen fax (270) 365-7299; disp adv e-mail advertising@timesleader.net; class adv e-mail classifieds@timesleader.net; ed e-mail newsroom@timesleader.net; web site www.timesleader.net
Circulation: 5,490pd, 45fr; Sworn/Estimate/Non-Audited
Advertising rate: Open inch rate $6.00
Established: 1871
Group: Kentucky New EraEditions: (104)
Prodn. Mgr. .... Willie McGregor
Ad Rep/Graphic Designer .... Sherry McGregor
Sports Ed. .... Todd Griffin
Editor & General Manager .... Jared Nelson
Business Manager .... Debbie Frisch
Lifestyles/Features .... Stacey Menser
Circulation/Advertising .... Kayla Stevenson
Printing Rep. .... Roberta Thompson
Photo tech/Online content .... Shelia Brennan
Mechanical Specifications: Type page 13 x 21 1/2; E - 6 cols, 2, 1/6 between; A - 6 cols, 2, 1/6 between; C - 9 cols, 1 3/10, 1/6 between. Equipment & Software: Hardware — APP/Mac G4, APP/iMac, APP/Mac Quadra, APP/Power Mac, APP/Mac G3; Presses — 2-Hamada, 2-Multi, 1-SLN, 1-HI; Software — Adobe CS3, CS5
Delivery Method: Mail, Newsstand, Racks
Areas Served: 42445, 42411, 42038, 42055, 42408

PROVIDENCE

THE JOURNAL ENTERPRISE (THUR)

114 N Broadway St, Providence, KY, 42450-1220, Webster, USA; gen tel (270) 667-2068; gen fax (270) 667-9160; disp adv e-mail chust@journalenterprise.com; ed e-mail matt@journalenterprise.com; web site www.journalenterprise.com
Circulation: 4,500pd,; Sworn/Estimate/Non-Audited
Advertising rate: Open inch rate $6.10
Established: 1905
News Ed. .... Matt Hughes
Ed .... Charles Hust
Mechanical Specifications: Type page 13 x 21 1/2; E - 6 cols, 2, between; A - 6 cols, 2, between; C - 6 cols, 2, between.Equipment & Software: Hardware — APP/Power Mac 8100; Software — QPS/QuarkXPress 3.3, Multi-Ad, Adobe/Typestyler 2.0, Adobe/Photoshop 3.0.
Delivery Method: Mail

RICHMOND

THE MADISON COUNTY ADVERTISER (WED)

380 Big Hill Ave, Richmond, KY, 40475-2012, Madison, USA; gen tel (859) 623-1669; adv tel (859) 624-6685; ed tel (859) 624-6690; gen fax (859) 623-2337; disp adv e-mail tmerlon@richmondregister.com; class adv e-mail pbowlin@richmondregister.com; ed e-mail editor@richmondregister.com; web site www.richmondregister.com
Circulation: 28,000fr; USPS
Advertising rate: Open inch rate $13
Group: CNHI, LLCJonathan Greene
Dave Eldridge
Tim Merlin
Mechanical Specifications: Type page 13 x 21; E - 6 cols, between; A - 6 cols, between; C - 9 cols, between.
Delivery Method: Mail, Racks
Areas Served: 40475, 40403, 40385, 40405

RUSSELL SPRINGS

THE RUSSELL COUNTY NEWS-REGISTER (SAT)

120 Wilson St, Russell Springs, KY, 42642-4315, Russell, USA; gen tel (270) 866-3191; gen fax (270) 866-3198; disp adv e-mail advertising@russellcountynewspapers.com; class adv e-mail advertising@russellcountynewspapers.com; ed e-mail news@russellcountynewspapers.com; web site www.russellcountynewspapers.com
Circulation: 10,000fr; Sworn/Estimate/Non-Audited
Advertising rate: Open inch rate $5.75
Adv. Mgr. .... Stephanie Smith
Ed .... Derek Aaron
Office Mgr .... Michelle Maldonado
Mechanical Specifications: Type page 13 x 21; E - 6 cols, 2 1/16, 1/8 between; A - 6 cols, 2 1/16, 1/8 between; C - 6 cols, 2 1/16, 1/8 between.Equipment & Software: Hardware — APP/Power Macs; Presses — 3-KP; Software — Adobe/PageMaker 6.0.

THE TIMES JOURNAL (THUR, SAT)

120 Wilson St, Russell Springs, KY, 42642-4315, Russell, USA; gen tel (270) 866-3191; gen fax (270) 866-3198; disp adv e-mail advertising@russellcountynewspapers.com;

class adv e-mail advertising@russellcountynewspapers.com; ed e-mail news@russellcountynewspapers.com; web site www.russellcounty.net
Circulation: 5,000pd, 235fr; Sworn/Estimate/Non-Audited
Advertising rate: Open inch rate $5.75
Established: 1949
Pub....David Davenport
Bus. Mgr....Kim Haydon
Adv. Mgr....Stephanie Smith
Mng. Ed....Greg Wells
News/Sports Ed....Derek Aaron
Prodn. Mgr....Renee Daffron
Mechanical Specifications: Type page 13 x 21; E - 6 cols, 2 1/16, 1/8 between; A - 6 cols, 2 1/16, 1/8 between; C - 6 cols, 2 1/16, 1/8 between.Equipment & Software: Hardware — APP/Power Macs; Presses — 3-KP/News King; Software — Adobe/PageMaker 6.0.
Delivery Method: Mail

RUSSELLVILLE

THE NEWS DEMOCRAT & LEADER (TUES, FRI)
250 N Main St, Russellville, KY, 42276-1841, Logan, USA; gen tel (270) 726-8394; gen fax (270) 726-8396; ed e-mail edit-ndl@bellsouth.net; web site www.newsdemocrat-leader.com
Circulation: 6,000pd,; Sworn/Estimate/Non-Audited
Advertising rate: Open inch rate $6.75
Group: Civitas Media, LLC-OOB
Adv. Mgr....Lola Nash
Adv. Sales Rep....Heather Justice
Ed....O.J. Stapleton
Mng. Ed....Chris Cooper
Mechanical Specifications: Type page 13 x 21 1/2; E - 6 cols, 2, 1/4 between; A - 6 cols, 2, 1/4 between; C - 8 cols, between.Equipment & Software: ; Presses — G/Community.
Delivery Method: Mail

SALYERSVILLE

SALYERSVILLE INDEPENDENT (THUR)
900 Parkway Dr, Salyersville, KY, 41465-9251, Magoffin, USA; gen tel (606) 349-2915; gen fax (888) 704-6789; disp adv e-mail vanessa@salyersvilleindependent.com; class adv e-mail jo@salyersvilleindependent.com; web site www.salyersvilleindependent.com
Advertising rate: Open inch rate $7.00
Established: 1821
Pub....David Prater
Delivery Method: Mail

SCOTTSVILLE

THE CITIZEN-TIMES (THUR)
611 E Main St, Scottsville, KY, 42164-1628, Allen, USA; gen tel (270) 237-3441; gen fax (270) 237-4943; disp adv e-mail ctines@nctc.com; ed e-mail ctimes@nctc.com; web site www.thecitizen-times.com
Circulation: 6,000pd, 212fr; Sworn/Estimate/Non-Audited
Advertising rate: Open inch rate $6.70
Established: 1918
Pub....Robert Burns Pitchford
Adv. Mgr....Jeannetta Stinson
Ed....Matthew James Pedigo
Mechanical Specifications: Type page 11.5 x 21; E - 6 cols, 1/8 between; Equipment & Software: Hardware — 8 Power Mac G5... ; Software — Adobe CS3.
Delivery Method: Mail

SHELBYVILLE

THE SENTINEL-NEWS (WED, FRI)
703 Taylorsville Rd, Shelbyville, KY, 40065-9125, Shelby, USA; gen tel (502) 633-4987; gen fax (502) 633-2618; disp adv e-mail dbarry@sentinelnews.com; class adv e-mail dbarry@sentinelnews.com; ed e-mail sdoyle@sentinelnews.com; web site www.sentinelnews.com
Circulation: 7,500pd, 18,000fr; Sworn/Estimate/Non-Audited
Advertising rate: Open inch rate $15.15
Established: 1866
Group: Landmark Community Newspapers, LLC Landmark Communications, Inc.
Pub....Kerry Jonson
Adv. Mgr....Dan Barry
Bookkeeper....Diana Olson
Ed....Todd Martin
Mechanical Specifications: Type page 11 5/8 x 21 1/2; E - 6 cols, 1 7/8, 1/8 between; A - 6 cols, 1 7/8, 1/8 between; C - 8 cols, 1 1/3, between.Equipment & Software: Hardware — APP/Mac; Presses — G/Community; Software — QPS/QuarkXPress, Microsoft/Word, Multi-Ad/Creator.
Delivery Method: Mail

SHEPHERDSVILLE

PIONEER NEWS (MON, WED)
455 N Buckman St, Shepherdsville, KY, 40165-5902, Bullitt, USA; gen tel (502) 543-2288; gen fax (502) 955-9704; disp adv e-mail editor@pioneernews.net; class adv e-mail editor@pioneernews.net; ed e-mail editor@pioneernews.net; web site www.pioneernews.net
Circulation: 5,300pd,; Sworn/Estimate/Non-Audited
Established: 1882
Group: Landmark Communications, Inc. Landmark Community Newspapers, LLC
Sports Ed....Mike Farner
Pub....Thomas J. Barr
Laura Felts
Mechanical Specifications: Type page 13 x 21 1/2; E - 6 cols, 2 1/16, between; A - 6 cols, 2 1/16, between; C - 8 cols, 1 1/2, between. Equipment & Software: Hardware — APP/Mac; Presses — KP/News King; Software — Microsoft/Word.
Delivery Method: Mail, Newsstand, Racks
Areas Served: Bullitt County

SMITHLAND

LIVINGSTON LEDGER (THUR)
130 E Adair St, Smithland, KY, 42081-9998, Livingston, USA; gen tel (270) 442-7389; disp adv e-mail kpiads@ky-news.com; web site www.ky-news.com
Circulation: 3,400pd, 30fr; Sworn/Estimate/Non-Audited
Group: Kentucky Publishing, Inc.
Digital Platform - Mobile: Apple
Digital Platform - Tablet: Apple iOS
Pub....Greg Leneave
Ed....Pat Thomann
Delivery Method: Mail, Racks
Areas Served: BURNA, GRAND RIVERS, LAKE CITY, LEDBETTER, SMITHLAND, SALEM, TILINE (LIVINGSTON CO.)
MARION (CRITTENDEN CO.), PRINCETON, FREDONIA (CALDWELL CO.)

SPRINGFIELD

SPRINGFIELD SUN (WED)
108 Progress Ave, Springfield, KY, 40069-1400, Washington, USA; gen tel (859) 336-3716; gen fax (859) 336-7718; disp adv e-mail shorty@thespringfieldsun.com; class adv e-mail shorty@thespringfieldsun.com; ed e-mail bmattingly@thespringfieldsun.com; web site www.thespringfieldsun.com
Circulation: 3,500pd,; Sworn/Estimate/Non-Audited
Advertising rate: Open inch rate $11.47
Group: Landmark Community Newspapers, LLC
Circ. Mgr./Bookkeeper....Renee Webb
Gen. Mgr./Adv. Mgr....Shorty Lassitter
Ed....Geoff Hamill
Sports and news reporter...Brandon Mattingly
News clerk....Lula Mae Adams
Mechanical Specifications: Type page 9.89 x 21 1/2;
Delivery Method: Mail, Newsstand, Racks
Areas Served: 40069, 40078, 40040, 40061

STANFORD

THE INTERIOR JOURNAL (THUR)
301 W Main St, Stanford, KY, 40484-1215, Lincoln, USA; gen tel (606) 365-2104; adv tel (859) 469-6429; gen fax (606) 365-2105; disp adv e-mail Larry.hensley@theinteriorjournal.com; class adv e-mail Carrie.shields@theinteriorjournal.com; ed e-mail Abigail.whitehouse@theinteriorjournal.com; web site www.theinteriorjournal.com
Circulation: 2,400pd,; USPS
Advertising rate: Open inch rate $9.00
Established: 1860
Group: Boone Newspapers, Inc.Bonnie Kolasa
Pub....Larry Hensley
Editor....Abigail Whitehouse
Sports Editor....Nancy Leedy
Mechanical Specifications: Type page 13 x 21 1/2; E - 6 cols, 2 1/16, 1/6 between; A - 6 cols, 2, 1/6 between; C - 8 cols, 1 1/2, 1/6 between.Equipment & Software: Hardware — APP/Mac; Software — QPS/QuarkXPress 3.2, Adobe/Photoshop 3.0, Adobe/PageMaker.
Delivery Method: Mail, Newsstand, Racks
Areas Served: 40484, 40419, 40437, 40442, 40442, 40448, 40489

TAYLORSVILLE

SPENCER MAGNET (WED)
100 W Main St, Taylorsville, KY, 40071-8624, Spencer, USA; gen tel (502) 477-2239; adv tel (502) 477-2239 ext 25; ed tel 5024772239 ext 24; gen fax (502) 477-2110; disp adv e-mail lmason@spencermagnet.com; class adv e-mail lmason@spencermagnet.com; ed e-mail lmason@spencermagnet.com; web site www.spencermagnet.com
Circulation: 3,600pd,; AAM
Advertising rate: $8.40
Established: 1867
Group: Landmark Community Newspapers, LLC Landmark Communications, Inc.Editions: (52)
Digital Platform - Mobile: Apple, Android, Windows, Blackberry
Digital Platform - Tablet: Apple iOS, Android, Windows 7, Blackberry Tablet OS, Kindle, Kindle Fire
graphics designer....Jeff Sopland
Publisher....Lynette Mason
Circulation Manager....Susan Collins
Editor....John Shindlebower
Delivery Method: Mail, Newsstand, Racks
Areas Served: 40071, 40023, 40008, 40065, 40064, and more

TOMPKINSVILLE

THE MONROE COUNTY CITIZEN (THUR)
201 N Main St, Ste A, Tompkinsville, KY, 42167-1685, Monroe, USA; gen tel (270) 487-8666; adv tel (270) 590-6625; gen fax (270) 786-4470; disp adv e-mail citizen@jpinews.com; class adv e-mail citizen@jpinews.com; ed e-mail jobe@jobeinc.com; web site www.jobeforkentucky.com
Circulation: 1,026pd, 4,874fr; Sworn/Estimate/Non-Audited
Advertising rate: Open inch rate $7.18
Group: Jobe Publishing Inc.
Pub....Jeff Jobe
Mechanical Specifications: Type page 14 x 22 3/8; E - 8 cols, 1 1/2, 1/8 between; A - 8 cols, 1 1/2, 1/8 between; C - 8 cols, 1 1/2, 1/8 between.
Delivery Method: Mail, Newsstand, Racks
Areas Served: 42167;42157;42151;42140

TOMPKINSVILLE NEWS (THUR)
105 N Main St, Tompkinsville, KY, 42167-1507, Monroe, USA; gen tel (270) 487-5576; adv tel (270) 487-5576; ed tel (270) 487-5576; gen fax (270) 487-8839; adv fax (270) 487-8839; ed fax (270) 487-8839; disp adv e-mail admanager@tompkinsvillenews.com; class adv e-mail classifieds@tompkinsvillenews.com; ed e-mail tvillenews@tompkinsvillenews.com; web site www.tompkinsvillenews.com
Circulation: 3,594pd, 488fr; Sworn/Estimate/Non-Audited
Advertising rate: Open inch rate $6.71
Established: 1903
Group: Monroe County Press, Inc.
Digital Platform - Mobile: Apple
Digital Platform - Tablet: Apple iOS
Publisher....Blanche B. Trimble
Gen. Mgr....Mark Elam
Ed....Ronda Elam
Graphics....Ledeana Creech
Advertising....Kristin Turner
Circulation mgr....Brenda Bradstreet
Office Mgr., Bookkeeping....Carolyn Jordan
Mechanical Specifications: Type page 12 3/4 x 21; E - 6 cols, 2 1/16, 1/6 between; A - 6 cols, 2 1/16, 1/6 between; C - 6 cols, 2 1/16, 1/6 between.Equipment & Software: ; Presses — Heidelberg/KORD, 2-Davidson/500s,
Delivery Method: Mail, Newsstand, Racks
Areas Served: 42167, 42140, 42133, 42151, 42157, 42166, 37150, 38575

VANCEBURG

LEWIS COUNTY HERALD (TUES)
187 Main St, Vanceburg, KY, 41179-1031, Lewis, USA; gen tel (606) 796-6182; gen fax (606) 796-3110; disp adv e-mail heraldadvertising@yahoo.com; class adv e-mail heraldadvertising@yahoo.com; ed e-mail dkb.lch@gmail.com; web site www.lewiscountyherald.com
Circulation: 4,400pd,; Sworn/Estimate/Non-Audited
Advertising rate: Open inch rate $3.00
Mng. Ed....Patricia Bloomfield
Sports Ed....Gary Kidwell
Delivery Method: Mail

VERSAILLES

WOODFORD SUN (THUR)
PO Box 29, Versailles, KY, 40383-0029, Woodford, USA; gen tel (859) 873-4131; gen fax (859) 873-0300; disp adv e-mail news@woodfordsun.com; web site www.woodfordsun.com
Established: 1869
Delivery Method: Mail, Racks

WARSAW

THE GALLATIN COUNTY NEWS (WED)
211 3rd St, Warsaw, KY, 41095-2002, Gallatin, USA; gen tel (859) 567-5051; gen fax (859) 567-6397; disp adv e-mail galnews@zoomtown.com; ed e-mail galnews@zoomtown.com; web site www.thegallatincountynews.com
Circulation: 2,400pd, 37fr; Sworn/Estimate/Non-Audited
Advertising rate: Open inch rate $5.68
Established: 1880
Digital Platform - Mobile: Apple
Pub....Denny K. Warnick
Adv. Mgr....Clay Warnick
Mng. Ed....Kelly Warnick
Prodn. Mgr.Terry Combs-CaldwellEquipment & Software: Hardware — APP/Mac.
Delivery Method: Mail, Newsstand
Areas Served: Warsaw, Gallatin, Carroll, Owen, Grant, Pendleton, Campbell, Kenton, Boone

WEST LIBERTY

ELLIOTT COUNTY NEWS (FRI)
142 Prestonsburg St, West Liberty, KY, 41472-1028, Morgan, USA; gen tel (606) 743-3551; gen fax (606) 743-3565; disp adv e-mail courier@mrtc.com; class adv e-mail courier@mrtc.com
Circulation: 1,800pd,; Sworn/Estimate/Non-Audited
Advertising rate: Open inch rate $3.90
Ed. .... Flora Whitley
Delivery Method: Mail, Newsstand
Areas Served: Sandy Hook KY

WHITESBURG

THE MOUNTAIN EAGLE (WED)
41 N Webb St, Whitesburg, KY, 41858-7324, Letcher, USA; gen tel (606) 633-2252; gen fax (606) 633-2843; disp adv e-mail mtneagle@bellsouth.net; ed e-mail mtneagle@bellsouth.net; web site www.themountain-eagle.com
Circulation: 4,748pd, 92fr; AAM
Advertising rate: Open inch rate $8.25
Established: 1907
Pub...Thomas Gish
Adv. Mgr.....................................Freddy Oakes
Ed. .... Benjamin T. Gish
Mechanical Specifications: Type page 13 x 21; E - 6 cols, 2 1/16, 1/8 between.Equipment & Software: Hardware — APP/Mac; Software — Microsoft/Word, Adobe/PageMaker, Adobe/Photoshop, Dewar/Sys 7.5.
Delivery Method: Mail

WHITLEY CITY

THE MCCREARY COUNTY VOICE (THUR)
57 Oaks Ln, Whitley City, KY, 42653-6173, McCreary, USA; gen tel (606) 376-5500; gen fax (606) 376-8609; disp adv e-mail susie@tmcvoice.com; class adv e-mail susie@tmcvoice.com; ed e-mail editor@tmcvoice.com; web site www.themccrearyvoice.com
Circulation:; Sworn/Estimate/Non-Audited
Advertising rate: Open inch rate $5.75
Established: 2000
Ed. ....Greg Bird
Delivery Method: Mail, Newsstand, Racks
Areas Served: McCreary County

WILLIAMSTOWN

GRANT COUNTY NEWS AND EXPRESS (MON)
1406 N Main St, Ste 2, Williamstown, KY, 41097-8500, Grant, USA; gen tel (859) 824-3343; gen fax (859) 824-5888; disp adv e-mail grantads@grantky.com; class adv e-mail kstone@grantky.com; ed e-mail gceditorial@grantky.com; web site www.grantky.com
Circulation: 5,000pd, 12,900fr; USPS
Advertising rate: Open inch rate $11.27
Established: 1906
Group: Landmark Communications, Inc.
Landmark Community Newspapers, LLC
Pub.. Ken Stone
Ed. .... Jamie Baker-Nantz
Adv. Asst.....................................Janet McKee
Publisher.. Ken Stone
Classified, Circulation Manager.... Anita Appler
Assistant Sales to Mr. Stone.......... May Evans
Mechanical Specifications: Full Page = 9.89" x 21.5" (6 col.)
Classified Full page = 8 col.
1 col. ROP = 1.56"
1 col. Class. = 1.14"
Delivery Method: Mail
Areas Served: 41097, 41045, 41035, 41030, 41010, 41052, 41033, 41040

LOUISIANA

ALEXANDRIA

CENLA FOCUS MAGAZINE (WED, MTHLY)
3911 Parliament Dr, Alexandria, LA, 71303-3016, Rapides, USA; gen tel (318) 442-8277; gen fax (318) 484-3745; disp adv e-mail contact@cenlafocus.com; web site www.cenlafocus.com
Advertising rate: 1/4 P $580, 1/2 P $800, Full $1200
Established: 1997
Pub. .... Willie Harp
Delivery Method: Newsstand, Racks

AMITE

AMITE TANGI-DIGEST (WED)
120 NE Central Ave, Amite, LA, 70422-2547, Tangipahoa, USA; gen tel (985) 748-7156; gen fax (985) 748-7104; disp adv e-mail suzanne.lee@tangilena.com; class adv e-mail classifieds@tangilena.com; ed e-mail carol.brooke@tangilena.com; web site www.tangilena.com
Circulation: 1,500pd, 19,866fr; Sworn/Estimate/Non-Audited
Advertising rate: Open inch rate $5.50
Established: 1868
Circ. Mgr....................................... Marcia Sims
Business Mgr. ....Jennifer Decota
Mechanical Specifications: Type page 13 x 21 1/2; E - 6 cols, 1/6 between; A - 6 cols, 1/6 between; C - 9 cols, 1/6 between.
Delivery Method: Mail, Newsstand, Carrier, Racks
Areas Served: Amite, Tangipahoa, 70422

ARABI

THE ST. BERNARD VOICE (FRI)
234 Mehle St, Arabi, LA, 70032-1054, Saint Bernard, USA; gen tel (504) 279-7488; gen fax (504) 309-5532; disp adv e-mail ads@thestbernardvoice.com; class adv e-mail ads@thestbernardvoice.com; ed e-mail copy@thestbernardvoice.com; web site www.thestbernardvoice.com
Circulation: 3,150pd,; Sworn/Estimate/Non-Audited
Advertising rate: $4.50 per column inch black/white, $9.00 per column inch color
Established: 1890
Graphic Designer .... Brandi Rollo
Publisher...................................... Norris Babin
Reporter .... Amber Prattini
Mechanical Specifications: 11.25 inches wide x 21.5 inches deep
six columns
1 column = 1.7361 inches
1 gutter= 0.1667 inches
Delivery Method: Mail, Newsstand, Racks
Areas Served: St. Bernard Parish
70032 Arabi
70043 Chalmette
70044 Chalmette
70075 Cypress Gardens
70085 Delacroix
70075 Francis Place
70092 Hi Land
70085 Hopedale
70085 Kenilworth
70075 Meraux
70085 Poydras
70085 Reggio
70085 Saint Bernard
70075 Saint Bernard Grove
70085 Shell Beach
70085 Toca
70085 Verret
70092 Violet

ARCADIA

BIENVILLE DEMOCRAT (THUR)
1952 N Railroad Ave, Arcadia, LA, 71001-3422, Bienville, USA; gen tel (318) 263-2922; gen fax (318) 263-8897; disp adv e-mail news@bienvilledemocrat.com; web site www.facebook.com/pages/The-Bienville-Democrat/148805565147072
Circulation: 1,903pd,; Sworn/Estimate/Non-Audited
Advertising rate: Open inch rate $5.85
Group: Natchitoches Times Newspapers
Ed./Adv. Mgr............................. Priscilla Smith
Pub.. Wayne R. Dring
Mechanical Specifications: Type page 13 x 21; E - 6 cols, between.

BASILE

THE BASILE WEEKLY (THUR)
3014 Stagg Ave, Basile, LA, 70515-5578, Evangeline, USA; gen tel (337) 432-6807; gen fax (337) 432-6822; disp adv e-mail thebasileweekly@hotmail.com; class adv e-mail thebasileweeklyads@yahoo.com; ed e-mail thebasileweekly@hotmail.com; web site www.facebook.com/thebasileweekly/
Circulation: 800pd,; Sworn/Estimate/Non-Audited
Advertising rate: Open inch rate $4.00
Established: 1964
Group: LSN Publishing Company LLC
La. State Newspapers
Adv. Mgr.................................Rachel Fontenot
Ed. .... Darrel B. LeJeune
Mechanical Specifications: Type page 12 1/4 x 21 1/2; E - 6 cols, 2, 1/2 between; A - 6 cols, 2, 1/2 between; C - 6 cols, 2, 1/2 between.
Delivery Method: Mail

BATON ROUGE

COUNTRY ROADS MAGAZINE (WED, MTHLY)
758 Saint Charles St, Baton Rouge, LA, 70802-6446, East Baton Rouge, USA; gen tel (225) 343-3714; gen fax (815) 550-2272; disp adv e-mail sales@countryroadsmag.com; class adv e-mail rikki@countryroadsmag.com; ed e-mail dorcas@countryroadsmag.com; web site www.countryroadsmagazine.com
Advertising rate: 1/4 P $655, 1/2 P $1155, Full $1810
Established: 1983
Associate Pub. ....Ashley Fox-Smith
Delivery Method: Mail, Newsstand, Racks
Areas Served: East Baton Rogue, West Baton Rogue, Ascension, Livingston, West Feliciana, East Feliciana, Pointe Coupee, Iberville, St. Helena, Assumption, St. James

LOUISIANA FOOTBALL MAGAZINE (MON)
PO Box 86638, Baton Rouge, LA, 70879-6638, East Baton Rouge, USA; gen tel (225) 262-7667; web site www.lafootballmagazine.com
Established: 1996

THE ZACHARY PLAINSMAN-NEWS (WED)
PO Box 588, Baton Rouge, LA, 70821-0588, East Baton Rouge, USA; gen tel (225) 654-6841; gen fax (225) 654-8271; disp adv e-mail wendy.pate@zacharytoday.com; class adv e-mail cindy.munn@zacharytoday.com; ed e-mail stacy.gill@zacharytoday.com; web site http://www.zacharytoday.com
Circulation: 2,000pd,; Sworn/Estimate/Non-Audited
Advertising rate: Open inch rate $6.93
Established: 1953
Ed. .... Stacy Gill
Pub .... Gary Miller
Sales Mgr .... Wendy Pate
Classified Mgr........... Cindy MunnEquipment & Software: Hardware — APP/Mac PC Network Server; Software — QPS, Adobe/Photoshop.
Delivery Method: Mail, Racks
Areas Served: 70791

BELLE CHASSE

PLAQUEMINES GAZETTE (TUES)
7962 Highway 23, Belle Chasse, LA, 70037-2432, Plaquemines, USA; gen tel (504) 392-1619; gen fax (504) 392-7526; disp adv e-mail ads@plaqueminesgazette.com; class adv e-mail ads@plaqueminesgazette.com; ed e-mail copy@plaqueminesgazette.com; web site www.plaqueminesgazette.com
Circulation: 2,846pd, 26fr; USPS
Advertising rate: $4.50 per column inch black/white, $9.00 per column inch color
Established: 1928
Circ. Mgr....................................... Norris Babin
Ed. .... Dale Benoit
Graphic Designer, Layout Artist.... Brandi Rollo
Mechanical Specifications: Type page 11.25 x 21.5
6 columns
Column = 1.7361 in
Gutter = 0.1667 inEquipment & Software: Hardware — APP/Mac; Presses — G/Community; Software — QPS/QuarkXPress 3.1.
Delivery Method: Mail, Newsstand, Racks
Areas Served: Plaquemines Parish, Louisiana
Zip codes include:
70037 Belle Chasse
70038 Boothville
70040 Belair
70040 Braithwaite
70040 Davant
70040 Carlisle
70041 Buras
70041 Ostrica
70041 Triumph
70041 Pilottown
70050 Empire
70081 Buras
70081 Pilottown
70082 Bohemia
70082 Pointe A la Hache
70082 Point a la Hache
70082 Davant
70083 Home Place
70083 Ironton
70083 Myrtle Grove
70083 Port Sulphur
70083 Potash
70083 West Pointe A la Hache
70091 Burrwood
70091 Port Eads
70091 Venice
70091 South Pass
70093 Belle Chasse

BERNICE

THE BERNICE BANNER (THUR)
227 Boyette Rd, Bernice, LA, 71222-5327, Union, USA; gen tel (318) 285-7424; adv tel (318) 285-7424; ed tel (318) 285-7424; gen fax (318) 285-7420; adv fax (318) 285-7420; ed fax (318) 285-7420; disp adv e-mail bernicebanner@oeccwildblue.com; class adv e-mail bernicebanner@oeccwildblue.com; ed e-mail bernicebanner@oeccwildblue.com; web site bernicebanner.weebly.com
Advertising rate: Open inch rate $4.50
Established: 1995
Pub./Ed. .... Jessie Kelley Boyett
Delivery Method: Mail, Newsstand
Areas Served: 71222

BOGALUSA

BOGALUSA DAILY NEWS (WED, FRI, SAT)
525 Avenue V, Bogalusa, LA, 70427-4493, USA; gen tel (985) 732-2565; gen fax (985) 732-4036; web site www.bogalusadailynews.com
Circulation: 5,195pd,; Sworn/Estimate/Non-Audited

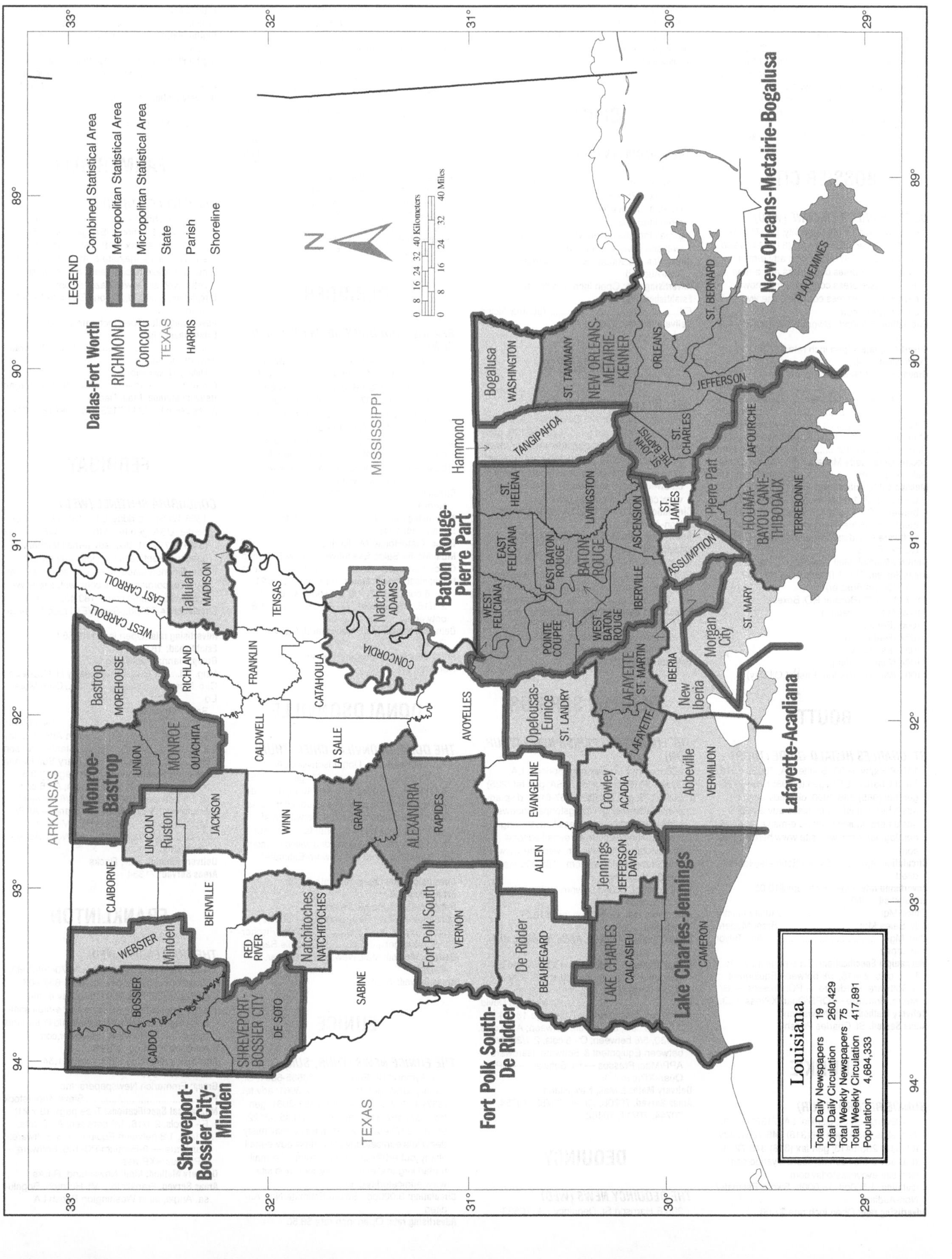
LEGEND
Dallas-Fort Worth Combined Statistical Area
RICHMOND Metropolitan Statistical Area
Concord Micropolitan Statistical Area
TEXAS State
HARRIS Parish
Shoreline
0 8 16 24 32 40 Kilometers
0 8 16 24 32 40 Miles
Louisiana
Total Daily Newspapers 19
Total Daily Circulation 260,429
Total Weekly Newspapers 75
Total Weekly Circulation 417,891
Population 4,684,333
ARKANSAS
MISSISSIPPI
TEXAS
Shreveport-Bossier City-Minden
Monroe-Bastrop
Fort Polk South-De Ridder
Baton Rouge-Pierre Part
Lake Charles-Jennings
Lafayette-Acadiana
New Orleans-Metairie-Bogalusa
Hammond
CADDO
BOSSIER
SHREVEPORT-BOSSIER CITY
DE SOTO
WEBSTER
Minden
CLAIBORNE
BIENVILLE
RED RIVER
LINCOLN
Ruston
JACKSON
UNION
MONROE
OUACHITA
Bastrop
MOREHOUSE
WEST CARROLL
EAST CARROLL
RICHLAND
Tallulah
MADISON
FRANKLIN
TENSAS
CALDWELL
WINN
LA SALLE
CATAHOULA
Natchez
ADAMS
CONCORDIA
GRANT
ALEXANDRIA
RAPIDES
AVOYELLES
Natchitoches
NATCHITOCHES
SABINE
Fort Polk South
VERNON
De Ridder
BEAUREGARD
ALLEN
EVANGELINE
Opelousas-Eunice
ST. LANDRY
Jennings
JEFFERSON DAVIS
LAKE CHARLES
CALCASIEU
CAMERON
Crowley
ACADIA
LAFAYETTE
Abbeville
VERMILION
ST. MARTIN
IBERIA
New Iberia
Morgan City
ST. MARY
WEST FELICIANA
EAST FELICIANA
POINTE COUPEE
WEST BATON ROUGE
EAST BATON ROUGE
BATON ROUGE
IBERVILLE
ST. HELENA
LIVINGSTON
ASCENSION
ASSUMPTION
ST. JAMES
Pierre Part
HOUMA-BAYOU CANE-THIBODAUX
TERREBONNE
LAFOURCHE
ST. JOHN THE BAPTIST
ST. CHARLES
TANGIPAHOA
Bogalusa
WASHINGTON
ST. TAMMANY
NEW ORLEANS-METAIRIE-KENNER
ORLEANS
JEFFERSON
ST. BERNARD
PLAQUEMINES
33°
32°
31°
30°
29°
89°
90°
91°
92°
93°
94°

Advertising rate: Open inch rate $16
Established: 1927
Group: Boone Newspapers, Inc.
Adv. Dir. .... Carol Case
Business Office Mgr. .... Mildred Newman
Publisher and Editor .... Justin Schuver
Mechanical Specifications: Type page 13 x 21 1/2; E - 6 cols, 2, 1/6 between; A - 6 cols, 2, 1/6 between; C - 9 cols, between.
Delivery Method: Mail
Areas Served: Washington Parish, Louisiana

BOSSIER CITY

BOSSIER PRESS-TRIBUNE (WED)

6346 Venecia Dr, Bossier City, LA, 71111-7454, Bossier, USA; gen tel (318) 747-7900; gen fax (318) 747-5298; disp adv e-mail ads@bossierpress.com; class adv e-mail ads@bossierpress.com; ed e-mail newsroom@bossierpress.com; web site www.bossierpress.com
Circulation: 5,000pd,; Sworn/Estimate/Non-Audited
Advertising rate: Open inch rate $12.00
Established: 1927
Group: Specht Newspapers, Inc.
Pub .... Randy Brown
Vice President & Publisher .... David A. Specht
Mng. Ed. .... Sean Green
Sports Ed. .... Hedges Russell
Managing Editor .... Amanda Simmons
Composing Director .... Kathleen Weir
Legals/Classifieds Manager .... Jamie Green
Sales Manager .... Dianna Smathers
Mechanical Specifications: Type page 10.5 x 21; E - 6 cols, 2, 1/6 between; A - 6 cols, 1.6, 1/6 between; C - 9 cols, 1, 1/6 between.Equipment & Software: Hardware — APP/Mac; Software — Adobe/Photoshop CS2, QPS/QuarkXPress 7.
Delivery Method: Mail, Newsstand, Racks
Areas Served: 71111 (North Bossier)
71112 (South Bossier)
71171&71172 (Bossier P.O. Boxes)
710 & 711 (Shreveport)
71006 (Benton)
71037 (Haughton)
71051 (Elm Grove)
71064 (Plain Dealing)
71061 (West of Benton, East of Oil City)

BOUTTE

ST. CHARLES HERALD-GUIDE (THUR)

14236 Highway 90, Boutte, LA, 70039-3516, Saint Charles, USA; gen tel (985) 758-2795; gen fax (985) 758-7000; disp adv e-mail ads@heraldguide.com; class adv e-mail ads@heraldguide.com; ed e-mail editorial@heraldguide.com; web site www.heraldguide.com
Circulation: 4,600pd,; Sworn/Estimate/Non-Audited
Advertising rate: Open inch rate $10.05
Established: 1993
Office Mgr. .... Jaunita Guidry
Adv. Sales Mgr. .... Brent Madere
Circ. Mgr. .... Ann Talyor
Joe Lopez
Mechanical Specifications: Type page 13 x 21; E - 6 cols, 2 1/16, 1/8 between.Equipment & Software: Hardware — PC; Presses — G/Metro; Software — QPS/QuarkXPress 4.03.
Delivery Method: Mail, Newsstand
Areas Served: St. Charles Parish

BUNKIE

BUNKIE RECORD (THUR)

637 Evergreen St, Bunkie, LA, 71322-3903, Avoyelles, USA; gen tel (318) 346-7251; adv tel (318) 253-5413; gen fax (318) 346-7253; disp adv e-mail bunkierecord@yahoo.com; web site avoyellestoday.com
Circulation: 1,500pd, 18,000fr; Sworn/Estimate/Non-Audited
Advertising rate: Open inch rate $7.06
Established: 1888
Group: LSN Publishing Company LLC
Gen. Mgr. .... Penny St. Romain
Delivery Method: Mail, Newsstand, Racks
Areas Served: 71322, 71351, 71333, 71341, 71327, 71355, 71367, 70586, 71325

CLINTON

THE WATCHMAN (WED)

11317B CHURCH ST, Clinton, LA, 70722, East Feliciana, USA; gen tel (225) 683-5196; gen fax (225) 683-4276; disp adv e-mail tabatha.alcina@felicianatoday.com; class adv e-mail tabatha.alcina@felicianatoday.com; ed e-mail tabatha.alcina@felicianatoday.com; web site www.felicianatoday.com
Circulation: 18,900pd,; Sworn/Estimate/Non-Audited
Advertising rate: Open inch rate $6.10
Established: 1878
Ed .... Tabatha Alcina
Delivery Method: Mail

COLUMBIA

CALDWELL WATCHMAN (WED)

241 Martin Luther St., Columbia, LA, 71418, Caldwell, USA; gen tel (318) 649-7136; gen fax (318) 649-7776; disp adv e-mail caldwellwatchman@bellsouth.net; class adv e-mail caldwellwatchman@bellsouth.net; ed e-mail caldwellwatchman@bellsouth.net; web site www.caldwellwatchman.com
Circulation: 1,200pd, 40fr; Sworn/Estimate/Non-Audited
Advertising rate: Open inch rate $4.75
Established: 1885
Group: LSN Publishing Company LLC
Pub. .... Paul Stanton
Adv. Mgr. .... Becky Stapleton
Ed. .... Melissa Nagler
Mechanical Specifications: Type page 13 x 21; E - 6 cols, 2 1/5, 1/6 between; A - 6 cols, 2 1/5, 1/6 between; C - 6 cols, 2 1/5, 1/6 between. Equipment & Software: Hardware — PC.
Delivery Method: Mail

DENHAM SPRINGS

THE LIVINGSTON PARISH NEWS (THUR, SUN)

688 Hatchell Ln, Denham Springs, LA, 70726-3015, Livingston, USA; gen tel (225) 665-5176; gen fax (225) 667-0167; disp adv e-mail advertising@livingstonparishnews.com; class adv e-mail classifieds@livingstonparishnews.com; ed e-mail editor@livingstonparishnews.com; web site www.livingstonparishnews.com - 185,000(views) 125,000(visitors)
Circulation: 30,000pd,; Sworn/Estimate/Non-Audited
Advertising rate: Open inch rate $16.27
Established: 1898
Digital Platform - Mobile: Apple, Android, Windows, Blackberry
Digital Platform - Tablet: Apple iOS, Android, Windows 7, Blackberry Tablet OS, Kindle, Nook, Kindle Fire
Pub. .... McHugh David
Mechanical Specifications: Type page 13 3/4 x 21; E - 6 cols, 2 1/30, 5/6 between; A - 6 cols, 2 1/30, 5/6 between; C - 6 cols, 2 1/30, 5/6 between.Equipment & Software: Hardware — APP/Mac; Presses — HI; Software — QPS/QuarkXPress 4.0.
Delivery Method: Mail, Newsstand
Areas Served: 70706, 70726, 70785, 70754, 70744, 70711, 70462

DEQUINCY

THE DEQUINCY NEWS (WED)

203 E Harrison St, Dequincy, LA, 70633-3545, Calcasieu, USA; gen tel (337) 786-8004; gen fax (337) 786-8131; disp adv e-mail dequincynews@centurytel.net; class adv e-mail classifieds@centurytel.net; ed e-mail dequincynews@centurytel.net; web site www.dequincynews.com - 5,000(views)
Circulation: 3,600pd,; Sworn/Estimate/Non-Audited
Advertising rate: Open inch rate $6.50
Established: 1923
Pub. .... Joy Wise
Adv. Mgr. .... Jeffrey DeViney
Ed. .... Jerry Wise
Mechanical Specifications: Type page 11 1/2 x 21; E - 6 cols, 1 3/4, 1/8 between; A - 6 cols, 1 3/4, 1/8 between; C - 6 cols, 1 3/4, 1/8 between.Equipment & Software: Hardware — PCs, APP/Macs.
Delivery Method: Mail, Racks
Areas Served: 70633, 70652, 70661

DERIDDER

BEAUREGARD DAILY NEWS (WED, FRI, SUN)

903 W 1st St, Deridder, LA, 70634-3701, Beauregard, USA; gen tel (337) 462-0616; adv tel (337) 462-0616; ed tel (337) 462-0616; gen fax (337) 463-5347; adv fax (337) 463-5347; ed fax (337) 463-5347; disp adv e-mail classifieds@beauregarddailynews.net; class adv e-mail classifieds@beauregarddailynews.net; ed e-mail rsteffan@beauregarddailynews.net; web site www.beauregarddailynews.net
Circulation: 2,800pd, 5,500fr; Sworn/Estimate/Non-Audited
Advertising rate: Open inch rate $13.46
Established: 1945
Group: GateHouse Media, Inc.
Multi Media Sales Executive .... Cindy Sherman
Office Manager .... Larissa Williams
Mechanical Specifications: Type page 13 x 21; E - 6 cols, 2 1/16, 1/8 between; A - 6 cols, 2 1/16, 1/8 between; C - 8 cols, 1 7/16, 1/8 between.
Delivery Method: Mail, Newsstand, Carrier, Racks
Areas Served: Beauregard Parish, Deridder, LA

DONALDSONVILLE

THE DONALDSONVILLE CHIEF (THUR)

120 Railroad Ave, Donaldsonville, LA, 70346-2520, Ascension, USA; gen tel (225) 473-3101; gen fax (225) 473-4060; disp adv e-mail cbarrett@gatehousemedia.com; class adv e-mail jsagona@donaldsonvillechief.com; ed e-mail news@donaldsonvillechief.com; web site www.donaldsonvillechief.com
Circulation: 1,000pd, 50fr; Sworn/Estimate/Non-Audited
Advertising rate: Open inch rate $7.02
Established: 1871
Group: GateHouse Media, Inc.
Multi Media Sales Representative Bob Prejean
Editor .... Greg Fischer
Office manager .... Julie Sagona
Delivery Method: Mail, Newsstand, Carrier, Racks
Areas Served: 70346

EUNICE

THE EUNICE NEWS (THUR, SUN)

456 Aymond St, Eunice, LA, 70535-6601, St. Landry, USA; gen tel (337) 457-3061; adv tel (337) 457-3061; ed tel (337) 457-3061; gen fax (337) 457-3122; adv fax (337) 457-3122; ed fax (337) 457-3122; disp adv e-mail misty.deaville@eunicetoday.com; class adv e-mail tiffany.joubert@eunicetoday.com; ed e-mail harlan.kirgan@eunicetoday.com; web site www.eunicetoday.com
Circulation: 3,000pd,; Sworn/Estimate/Non-Audited
Advertising rate: Open inch rate $8.50
Established: 1903
Group: LSN Publishing Company LLC
Digital Platform - Mobile: Apple, Android, Windows, Blackberry
Digital Platform - Tablet: Apple iOS, Android, Windows 7, Blackberry Tablet OS, Kindle
COO/Pub. .... Darrell Guillory
Delivery Method: Mail, Newsstand, Carrier, Racks
Areas Served: 70535

FARMERVILLE

THE GAZETTE (THUR)

104 N Washington St, Farmerville, LA, 71241-2916, Union, USA; gen tel (318) 368-9732; gen fax (318) 368-7331; disp adv e-mail hillary@fgazette.com; class adv e-mail nicole@fgazette.com; ed e-mail news@fgazette.com; web site www.fgazette.com
Circulation: 3,300pd,; Sworn/Estimate/Non-Audited
Advertising rate: Open inch rate $6.00
Established: 1886
Editor .... Mark Rainwater
Advertising sales
Hillary Newcomb
Circulation manager .... Nicole Morgan
Delivery Method: Mail, Racks
Areas Served: 71241/71234/71270/71222/712 607/71280

FERRIDAY

CONCORDIA SENTINEL (WED)

1308 1st St, Ferriday, LA, 71334-2847, Concordia, USA; gen tel (318) 757-3646; gen fax (318) 757-3001; disp adv e-mail leighann@concordiasentinel.com; class adv e-mail cora@concordiasentinel.com; ed e-mail stanley@concordiasentinel.com; web site www.concordiasentinel.com - 189,432(views)
Circulation: 4,700pd,; Sworn/Estimate/Non-Audited
Advertising rate: Open inch rate $6.50
Established: 1876
Group: Hanna Publishing Co.
Mng. Ed. .... Lesley H. Capdepon
Circ. Mgr. .... Cora Morace
Ed
Sam Hanna Jr.
Sport Ed .... Joey Martin
Advertising .... Leigh Ann Delaney
Ed. .... Stanley Nelson
Pub. .... Mary Sue Hanna
Mechanical Specifications: Type page 13 3/8 x 21; E - 6 cols, 2, 1/6 between; A - 6 cols, 2, 1/6 between; C - 6 cols, 2, 1/6 between. Equipment & Software: Hardware — APP/Mac; Software — Adobe/PageMaker 6.0, QPS/QuarkXPress, Microsoft/Word, Adobe/Photoshop.
Delivery Method: Mail, Racks
Areas Served: 71334

FRANKLINTON

THE ERA-LEADER (WED)

1137 Main St, Franklinton, LA, 70438-2083, Washington, USA; gen tel (985) 839-9077; gen fax (985) 839-9096; disp adv e-mail info@era-leader.com; class adv e-mail sheila@era-leader.com; ed e-mail info@era-leader.com; web site www.era-leader.com
Circulation: 4,088pd,; USPS
Advertising rate: Open inch rate $11.54
Established: 1910
Group: Emmerich Newspapers, Inc.
Pub. .... Steve Kuperstock
Mechanical Specifications: Type page 13 x 21; E - 6 cols, 2 1/16, 1/8 between; A - 6 cols, 2 1/16, 1/8 between.Equipment & Software: Hardware — 8-Pentium/PC-166; Software — QPS/QuarkXPress.
Delivery Method: Mail, Newsstand, Racks
Areas Served: Franklinton, Mt. Hermon, Bogalusa, Angie, all of Washington Parish LA

GONZALES

GONZALES WEEKLY CITIZEN (THUR)

231 W Cornerview St, Gonzales, LA, 70737-2841, Ascension, USA; gen tel (225) 644-6397; adv tel (225) 644-6397; ed tel (225) 644-6397; gen fax (225) 644-2069; disp adv e-mail cbarrett@gatehousemedia.com; class adv e-mail bgautreau@weeklycitizen.com; ed e-mail editor@weeklycitizen.com; web site www.weeklycitizen.com

Circulation: 2,500pd, 250fr; Sworn/Estimate/Non-Audited

Advertising rate: Open inch rate $9.20

Established: 1998

Group: GateHouse Media, Inc.

Circ. Mgr............................ Marie Schexnaydre
Classified Adv. Mgr............... Brenda Gautreau
General Manager/Bookkeeper ....Stephanie Schexnaydre
Advertising Manager..................Crystal Barrett

Mechanical Specifications: Type page 11 5/8 x 21; E - 6 cols, 2 1/16, between; A - 6 cols, 2 1/16, between; C - 6 cols, 2 1/16, between. Equipment & Software: Hardware — IBM; Presses — HI/Cotrell V-15A; Software — Adobe/PageMaker 6.5, Adobe/Photoshop 4.0, Adobe/Illustrator 7.0, Macromedia/Freehand, Microsoft/Windows 95.

Delivery Method: Mail, Newsstand, Carrier, Racks

Areas Served: 70737, 70769, 70734, 70778, 70728, 70725, 70718, 70726, 70449

GREENSBURG

ST. HELENA ECHO (WED)

Corner of Main and Lafette, Greensburg, LA, 70441, St. Helena, USA; gen tel (225) 222-4541; gen fax (225) 222-4542; disp adv e-mail echo@tangilena.com; class adv e-mail echo@tangilena.com; ed e-mail echo@tangilena.com; web site www.facebook.com/St-Helena-Echo-305375052815206/?ref=page_internal

Circulation: 1,150pd, 4,438fr; Sworn/Estimate/Non-Audited

Advertising rate: Open inch rate $13.00

Established: 1857

Circ. Mgr....................................... Marcia Sims
Pub .... Gary Miller
Ed .... Stephanie Warren

Mechanical Specifications: Type page 13 x 21; E - 6 cols, between; A - 6 cols, between; C - 9 cols, between.

Delivery Method: Mail

GREENWELL SPRINGS

CENTRAL CITY NEWS (THUR)

PO Box 1, Greenwell Springs, LA, 7073-90001, East Baton Rouge, USA; gen tel (225) 261-5055; gen fax Fax (225) 261-5022; disp adv e-mail centralcitynews@hotmail.com; web site www.centralcitynews.us

Advertising rate: Full Page 12x- $900; 3/4 page 12x-$825; 1/2 page 12x- $500; 1/8 page 12x- $175

GUEYDAN

GUEYDAN JOURNAL (THUR)

311 Main St, Gueydan, LA, 70542-3631, Vermilion, USA; gen tel (337) 536-6016; gen fax (337) 536-9997; disp adv e-mail angie.longon@vermiliontoday.com; class adv e-mail angie.longon@vermiliontoday.com; ed e-mail judy.leblanc@vermiliontoday.com; web site www.gueydantoday.com

Circulation: 1,200pd, 15fr; Sworn/Estimate/Non-Audited

Advertising rate: Open inch rate $6.05

Group: LSN Publishing Company LLC

Adv. Mgr. ....Angie Longon

Mechanical Specifications: Type page 13 x 21 1/2.

Delivery Method: Mail

HOMER

HOMER GUARDIAN-JOURNAL (THUR)

620 N Main St, Homer, LA, 71040-3847, Claiborne, USA; gen tel (318) 927-3541; gen fax (318) 927-3542; disp adv e-mail Guardian-Journal@ClaiborneOne.com; ed e-mail Guardian-Journal@ClaiborneOne.com; web site www.claiborneone.org

Circulation: 3,200pd,; Sworn/Estimate/Non-Audited

Advertising rate: Open inch rate $6.50

Ed ....Michelle Bates
Co-Owner ....Kathryn H. Hightower
Pub.................................. Geraldine Hightower

Mechanical Specifications: Type page 13 x 21; E - 6 cols, 2 1/16, between; A - 6 cols, 2 1/16, between; C - 8 cols, 1 1/2, between.

Delivery Method: Mail

THE HAYNESVILLE NEWS (TUES, THUR)

604 N Main St, Homer, LA, 71040-3806, Claiborne, USA; gen tel (318) 927-3721; disp adv e-mail THN@ClaiborneOne.org; class adv e-mail THN@ClaiborneOne.org; ed e-mail THN@ClaiborneOne.org; web site http://www.claiborneone.org/thn/

Circulation: 1,200pd, 8,233fr; Sworn/Estimate/Non-Audited

Advertising rate: Open inch rate $5.15

Established: 1924

Ed. .... Jackie Roberts

Delivery Method: Mail

HOUMA

POINT OF VUE (THUR, MTHLY)

6160 W Park Ave, Houma, LA, 70364-1700, Terrebonne, USA; gen tel (985) 868-7515; gen fax (985) 873-9009; disp adv e-mail sales@rushing-media.com; class adv e-mail sales@rushing-media.com; ed e-mail editor@rushing-media.com; web site www.povhouma.com

Advertising rate: 1/4 Pg $559.00; 1/2 Pg $973.00; Full Pg $1799.00

Established: 2007

Pub... Brian Rushing
Ed. .... Terry Trahan Jr.
Creative Dir..............................Gavin Stevens

Delivery Method: Mail, Newsstand

Areas Served: 70360-70364, 70301-70310

TRI-PARISH TIMES & BUSINESS NEWS (WED)

4924 Highway 311, Houma, LA, 70360-2873, Terrebonne, USA; gen tel (985) 876-3008; adv tel (985) 876-3008; ed tel (985) 876-3008; gen fax (985) 876-0950; adv fax (985) 876-0950; ed fax (985) 876-0950; disp adv e-mail sales@tri-parishtimes.com; class adv e-mail sales@tri-parishtimes.com; ed e-mail editor@tri-parishtimes.com; web site www.tri-parishtimes.com

Circulation: 5,076pd, 943fr; CVC

Advertising rate: Open inch rate $875.00

Established: 1997

Digital Platform - Mobile: Apple, Android, Windows, Blackberry

Digital Platform - Tablet: Apple iOS, Android, Windows 7, Blackberry Tablet OS

Exec. Ed................................. Shell Armstrong
Adv. Dir ....Brad Thibodaux
Pub .... Darrin Guidry

Delivery Method: Mail, Racks

Areas Served: 70360-70364

JENA

THE JENA-TIMES/OLLA-TULLOS-URANIA SIGNAL (WED)

1509 N 3RD ST, Jena, LA, 71342, LaSalle, USA; gen tel (318) 992-4121; gen fax (318) 992-2287; disp adv e-mail sales@thejenatimes.net; class adv e-mail classifieds@thejenatimes.net; ed e-mail editor@thejenatimes.net; web site www.thejenatimes.net

Circulation: 4,000pd,; Sworn/Estimate/Non-Audited

Advertising rate: Open inch rate $6.00

Established: 1905

Pub., Ed.................................. Sammy Franklin
Business Mgr. .... Ashley Keene
Classifieds/subscriptions ....Kristie Taylor
Shop Foreman.......................... Sherry Steele
Advertising Sales...................... Libby Warwick
Reporter/Photographer..............Morgan Smith
Writer/photographer...................Craig Franklin

Mechanical Specifications: Type page 13 x 21; E - 6 cols, 2, 1/6 between; A - 6 cols, 2, 1/6 between; C - 8 cols, 1 1/2, 1/6 between.

Delivery Method: Mail, Newsstand

Areas Served: 71342, 71465, 71479, 71480, 71371

JONESBORO

THE JACKSON INDEPENDENT (THUR)

624 Hudson Ave, Jonesboro, LA, 71251-3851, Jackson, USA; gen tel (318) 259-2551; gen fax (318) 259-8537; disp adv e-mail graphics@thejacksonindependent.com; class adv e-mail accounting@thejacksonindependent.com; ed e-mail news@thejacksonindependent.com

Circulation: 3,400pd, 3,000fr; Sworn/Estimate/Non-Audited

Advertising rate: Open inch rate $6.57

Ed. .... Chris Smith

Mechanical Specifications: Type page 13 x 21; E - 6 cols, 2 1/16, 1/6 between; A - 6 cols, 2 1/16, 1/6 between; C - 6 cols, 2 1/16, 1/6 between.Equipment & Software: Hardware — PC; Software — QPS/QuarkXPress 4.0.

Delivery Method: Mail

Areas Served: 71226
71238
71251
71268
71247

JONESVILLE

CATAHOULA NEWS BOOSTER (WED)

103 Third St, Jonesville, LA, 71343-2339, Catahoula, USA; gen tel (318) 339-7242; gen fax (318) 339-7243; disp adv e-mail catahoulaads@bellsouth.net; class adv e-mail catahoulaads@bellsouth.net; ed e-mail newsbooster@bellsouth.net; web site www.thenewsbooster.com

Circulation: 3,200pd, 10fr; Sworn/Estimate/Non-Audited

Advertising rate: Open inch rate $5.00

Established: 1853

Adv. Mgr. ....Maranda Clifton
Ed. .... Will Clifton

Mechanical Specifications: Type page 13 1/4 x 21; E - 6 cols, 2, between; A - 6 cols, 2, between; C - 6 cols, 2, between.

Delivery Method: Mail

KAPLAN

THE KAPLAN HERALD (WED)

219 N Cushing Ave, Kaplan, LA, 70548-4119, Vermilion, USA; gen tel (337) 643-8002; gen fax (337) 643-1382; disp adv e-mail ejbheart@hotmail.com; class adv e-mail ejbheart@hotmail.com; ed e-mail judy.mire@vermiliontoday.com; web site www.kaplantoday.com

Circulation: 2,000pd,; Sworn/Estimate/Non-Audited

Advertising rate: Open inch rate $5.10

Group: LSN Publishing Company LLC

Pub... Kathy Cormier
Adv. Mgr. .... June Breaux
Ed. .... Judy Mire

Delivery Method: Mail

KENTWOOD

THE KENTWOOD NEWS-LEDGER (WED)

234 Avenue F, Kentwood, LA, 70444-2522, Tangipahoa, USA; gen tel (985) 229-8607; gen fax (985) 229-8698; disp adv e-mail editor.newsledger@tangilena.com; ed e-mail editor.newsledger@tangilena.com; web site http://www.tangilena.com

Circulation: 1,525pd,; Sworn/Estimate/Non-Audited

Advertising rate: Open inch rate $5.25

Established: 1934

Ed. .... Joy Lofton
Acct. Exec. .... Karen Walker
Ed. .... Cathy Chapman

Mechanical Specifications: Type page 13 x 21 1/2; E - 6 cols, 2, between; A - 6 cols, 2, between.

Delivery Method: Mail

KINDER

KINDER COURIER NEWS (THUR)

1024 3rd Ave, Kinder, LA, 70648-3413, Allen, USA; gen tel (337) 738-5642; gen fax (337) 738-5630; disp adv e-mail kindernews@yahoo.com; class adv e-mail kindernews@yahoo.com; ed e-mail kindernews@centurytel.net; web site www.kindernow.com

Circulation: 880pd,; Sworn/Estimate/Non-Audited

Advertising rate: Open inch rate $6.82

Established: 1979

Group: LSN Publishing Company LLC

Pub... David Ortego
Office Mgr. .... Rebekah Ogea
Adv. Mgr. .... Marcus Norris
Circ. Mgr.................................. Jennifer Allsion
Mng. Ed..................................... Mark Leibson

Mechanical Specifications: Type page 11 3/5 x 21 1/2; E - 6 cols, 1 4/5, 1/8 between; A - 6 cols, 1 4/5, 1/8 between; C - 9 cols, 1 1/5, 1/8 between.Equipment & Software: Hardware — APP/Power Mac, APP/Power Mac; Software — QPS/QuarkXPress 4.1, Adobe/Photoshop.

Delivery Method: Mail, Newsstand

Areas Served: Kinder 70648
Oberlin 70655
Reeves 70658

LA PLACE

L'OBSERVATEUR (WED, THUR, SAT)

116 Newspaper Dr, La Place, LA, 70068-4509, St. John the Baptist, USA; gen tel (985) 652-9545; gen fax (985) 652-1633; disp adv e-mail lobpress@bellsouth.net; class adv e-mail lobpress@bellsouth.net; ed e-mail lobnews@bellsouth.net; web site www.lobservateur.com

Circulation: 5,000pd,; Sworn/Estimate/Non-Audited

Advertising rate: Open inch rate $10.50

Group: Boone Newspapers, Inc.
Carpenter Newsmedia

Gen. Mgr/Mng. Ed........................David Vitrano
Circ. Mgr .... Rhett Triche

Delivery Method: Mail, Carrier

LAKE PROVIDENCE

BANNER-DEMOCRAT (THUR)

313 Lake St, Lake Providence, LA, 71254-2629, East Carroll, USA; gen tel (318) 559-2750; gen fax (318) 559-2750; disp adv e-mail bannerdemocrat@bellsouth.net; ed e-mail bannerdemocrat@bellsouth.net; web site www.facebook.com/The-Banner-Democrat-127683417309400/

Circulation: 1,825pd, 42fr; Sworn/Estimate/Non-Audited

Advertising rate: Open inch rate $4.37

Established: 1887

Adv. Mgr. .... Judy Whitaker
Reporter .... Billy Coleman

Adv, Mgr.................................... Judy Whitaker
Circ. Mgr............................. Jimmy Neighbours
Managing Editor ....Lynn Bearden
Mechanical Specifications: Type page 11 x 21; E - 6 cols, 2, 1/6 between; A - 6 cols, 2, 1/6 between; C - 6 cols, 2, 1/6 between. Equipment & Software: Hardware — APP/Mac; Presses — Ryobi; Software — QPS/QuarkXPress 3.32.
Delivery Method: Mail, Racks
Areas Served: 712 prefixes, other states

LAROSE

LAFOURCHE GAZETTE (WED, SUN)

12958 E MAIN ST, Larose, LA, 70373, Lafourche, USA; gen tel (985) 693-7229; gen fax (985) 693-8282; disp adv e-mail ads@tlgnewspaper.com; class adv e-mail news@tlgnewspaper.com; ed e-mail news@tlgnewspaper.com; web site www.tlgnewspaper.com - 33,000(views) 4,800(visitors)
Circulation: 15,325fr; VAC
Advertising rate: Open inch rate $16.30
Established: 1965
Digital Platform - Mobile: Apple
Ed./Adv. Mgr.............................. Vicki Chaisson
Publisher..................................Addy Legendre
Mechanical Specifications: Type page 11 x 22; E - 6 cols, 1.73, between; A - 6 cols, 1.73, between; C - 9 cols, 1.11, between.Equipment & Software: Hardware — APP/Mac, APP/Mac SE 30, APP/Mac Performa 6200-CD, APP/Power Mac 4400-200; Software — QPS/QuarkXPress.
Delivery Method: Carrier
Areas Served: 70373, 70394, 70375, 70374, 70345, 70354, 70357, 70358

LEESVILLE

THE LEESVILLE DAILY LEADER (WED, FRI, SUN)

206 E Texas St, Leesville, LA, 71446-4056, Vernon, USA; gen tel (337) 239-3444; adv tel (337) 239-3444; ed tel (337) 239-3444; gen fax (337) 238-1152; adv fax (337) 238-1152; ed fax (337) 238-1152; disp adv e-mail advertising@leesvilledailyleader.com; class adv e-mail advertising@leesvilledailyleader.com; ed e-mail news@leesvilledailyleader.com; web site www.leesvilledailyleader.com
Circulation: 2,800pd, 5,000fr; Sworn/Estimate/Non-Audited
Advertising rate: 10.00
Established: 1898
Group: GateHouse Media, Inc.
Office Manager....................... Larissa Williams
Editor .... Rachel Steffan
Mechanical Specifications: Type page 12 1/2 x 21; E - 6 cols, 2 1/16, 1/8 between; A - 6 cols, 2 1/16, 1/8 between; C - 8 cols, 1 1/2, 1/8 between.
Delivery Method: Mail, Newsstand, Carrier, Racks
Areas Served: Vernon Parish Louisiana

MANSFIELD

THE ENTERPRISE & INTERSTATE PROGRESS (THUR)

202 Adams St, Mansfield, LA, 71052-2430, De Soto, USA; gen tel (318) 872-4120; gen fax (318) 872-6038; disp adv e-mail enterprise@wnonline.net; ed e-mail enterprise@wnonline.net; web site ent.stparchive.com
Circulation: 4,000pd,; Sworn/Estimate/Non-Audited
Advertising rate: Open inch rate $6.00
Established: 1889
Group: Natchitoches Times Newspapers
Pub.. Lovan Thomas
Gen. Mgr......................................Bennie Hall
Ed. .... Cindy Williams
Mechanical Specifications: Type page 13 x 21; E - 6 cols, 2 1/16, 1/8 between; A - 6 cols, 2 1/16, 1/8 between; C - 8 cols, 1 8/2, 1/8 between.
Delivery Method: Mail, Newsstand
Areas Served: 71052, 71419, 71030, 71032, 71063, 71049, 71078, 71046

MANY

THE SABINE INDEX (WED)

875 San Antonio Ave, Many, LA, 71449-3140, Sabine, USA; gen tel (318) 256-3495; gen fax (318) 256-9151; disp adv e-mail sales@sabineindex.net ; class adv e-mail classifieds@sabineindex.net ; ed e-mail news@sabineindex.net ; web site www.thesabineindex.com
Circulation: 6,130pd, 25fr; Sworn/Estimate/Non-Audited
Advertising rate: Open inch rate $9.45
Established: 1879
Pub.. Robert Gentry
Daniel Jones
Mechanical Specifications: Type page 13 x ; E - 6 cols, 2, between; A - 6 cols, 2, between; C - 6 cols, 2, between.
Delivery Method: Mail

MARKSVILLE

AVOYELLES JOURNAL (WED, SUN)

105 N Main St, Marksville, LA, 71351-2405, Avoyelles, USA; gen tel (318) 253-5413; gen fax (318) 253-7223; disp adv e-mail ads@avoyelles.com; class adv e-mail ads@avoyelles.com; web site www.avoyelles.com
Circulation: 16,000fr; Sworn/Estimate/Non-Audited
Advertising rate: Open inch rate $12.90
Established: 1978
Group: LSN Publishing Company LLC
Circ. Mgr.. Kathy Lipe
Pub./Ed.................................... Randy DeCuir
Adv. Mgr.. Amy Ducote
Delivery Method: Mail

THE MARKSVILLE WEEKLY NEWS (THUR)

PO Box 36, Marksville, LA, 71351-0036, Avoyelles, USA; gen tel (318) 253-5413; gen fax (318) 253-7223; disp adv e-mail ads@avoyelles.com; ed e-mail avoyellesjournal@yahoo.com; web site www.avoyelles.com
Circulation: 3,500pd,; Sworn/Estimate/Non-Audited
Advertising rate: Open inch rate $7.06
Group: LSN Publishing Company LLC
Pub.. Randy DeCuir
Delivery Method: Mail

METAIRIE

NEW ORLEANS CITY BUSINESS (MON)

3445 N Causeway Blvd, Ste 901, Metairie, LA, 70002-3768, Jefferson, USA; gen tel (504) 834-9292; disp adv e-mail mail@nopg.com; web site www.neworleanscitybusiness.com
Circulation: 3,311pd, 2,380fr; VAC
Advertising rate: 1/8 Pg $960.00; 1/9 Pg $1220.00; 1/4 Pg $1665.00
Ed. ....Greg LaRose
Pub.....................................Mark Singletary
Sales Mgr...................................Lisa Blossman
Production Mgr...........................Julie Bernard

NATCHITOCHES

NATCHITOCHES TIMES (THUR, SAT)

904 South Dr, Natchitoches, LA, 71457-3053, Natchitoches, USA; gen tel (318) 352-3618; adv tel (318) 352-3618; ed tel (318) 352-3618; gen fax (318) 352-7842; adv fax (318) 352-7842; ed fax (318) 352-7842; disp adv e-mail news@natchitochestimes.com; class adv e-mail advertising@natchitochestimes.com; ed e-mail reporter@natchitochestimes.com; web site www.natchitochestimes.com
Circulation: 4,805pd,; Sworn/Estimate/Non-Audited
Advertising rate: Open inch rate $11.64
Established: 1903
Digital Platform - Mobile: Apple
Pres./Pub.................................. Lovan Thomas
Mgr., Mktg./Promo....................... Steve Clowell
Circ. Mgr...................................... Jerry Hooper
Ed. .... Carolyn Roy
Prodn. Mgr. .... Ernie Davis
Systems Mgr...................................Dennis Doll
Mechanical Specifications: Type page 13 x 21; A - 6 cols, 2, between.
Delivery Method: Mail, Racks
Areas Served: 71457

NEW ORLEANS

THE TIMES-PICAYUNE (WED, FRI, SUN)

365 Canal St, Ste 3100, New Orleans, LA, 70130-6509, Orleans, USA; gen tel (800) 925-0000; adv tel (504) 826-3075; ed tel (504) 826-3300; gen fax (504) 826-3636; adv fax (504) 826-3800; ed fax (504) 826-3007; disp adv e-mail ads@timespicayune.com; class adv e-mail ads@timespicayune.com; ed e-mail editor@timespicayune.com; web site www.nola.com
Advertising rate: Open inch rate $186.20 (Wed/Fri); $190.65 (Sun)
Established: 1837
Group: Advance Publications, Inc.
Vice Pres., Adv .... Kelly Rose
Ed. .... Jim Amoss
Pub.. Ricky Mathews
Vice Pres./Bus. Mgr.................... David Francis
VP Digital Solutions........................ Mark Rose
Asst. Adv. Dir.
Brad Breuhl
Mechanical Specifications: Type page 11 5/8 x 21; E - 6 cols, 1 3/4, 1/8 between; A - 6 cols, 1 3/4, 1/8 between; C - 10 cols, 1 1/16, 1/16 between.

NEW ROADS

THE POINTE COUPEE BANNER (THUR)

123 Saint Mary St, New Roads, LA, 70760-3529, Pointe Coupee, USA; gen tel (225) 638-7155; gen fax (225) 638-8442; disp adv e-mail ThePCBanner@yahoo.com; class adv e-mail ThePCBanner@yahoo.com; ed e-mail ThePCBanner@yahoo.com; web site pointecoupeereporter.com
Circulation: 5,000pd,; Sworn/Estimate/Non-Audited
Advertising rate: Open inch rate $7.00
Established: 1880
Pub... Mary LaCour
Pub.. Brent Roy
Ed. .... Tommy Comeaux
Delivery Method: Mail

OAK GROVE

THE WEST CARROLL GAZETTE (WED)

512 S Constitution Ave, Oak Grove, LA, 71263-2514, West Carroll, USA; gen tel (318) 428-3207; gen fax (318) 428-2747; disp adv e-mail wcarrollgazette@bellsouth.net; class adv e-mail wcarrollgazette@bellsouth.net; ed e-mail wcarrollgazette@bellsouth.net; web site http://www.westcarrollgazette.com
Circulation: 2,000pd, 100fr; Sworn/Estimate/Non-Audited
Advertising rate: Open inch rate $10.75
Established: 1910
Group: LSN Publishing Company LLC
Pub./Gen. Mgr.............................. Mary Terry
Office Mgr. .... Melba West
Adv. Mgr. .... Renee Graham
Ed. .... Johney S. Turner
Lifestyle Ed.......................... Jessica Townsend
Mechanical Specifications: Type page 13 x 21; E - 4 cols, 3 1/8, between; A - 6 cols, 2, between; C - 9 cols, 1 5/16, between.
Delivery Method: Mail

OAKDALE

THE OAKDALE JOURNAL (THUR)

231 E 6th Ave, Oakdale, LA, 71463-2617, Allen, USA; gen tel (318) 335-0635; gen fax (318) 335-0431; disp adv e-mail oakdalejournal@bellsouth.net; class adv e-mail oakdalejournal@bellsouth.net; ed e-mail oakdalejournal@bellsouth.net; web site www.facebook.com/pages/Oakdale-Journal/143123332400740
Circulation: 1,700pd, 12,939fr; Sworn/Estimate/Non-Audited
Advertising rate: Open inch rate $6.30
Established: 1913
Group: LSN Publishing Company LLC
Pub... David Ortego
Adv. Mgr...................................... Peggy Byrd
Circ. Mgr.................................. Jennifer Allison
Ed. .... Barbara Doyle
Delivery Method: Mail

PLAQUEMINE

POST SOUTH (THUR)

58650 Belleview Rd, Plaquemine, LA, 70764-3915, Iberville, USA; gen tel (225) 687-3288; adv tel (225) 644-6397 ; gen fax (225) 687-1814; disp adv e-mail cbarrett@gatehousemedia.com; class adv e-mail cbarrett@gatehousemedia.com; ed e-mail ppasqua@postsouth.com ; web site www.postsouth.com
Circulation: 5,500pd, 12fr; Sworn/Estimate/Non-Audited
Advertising rate: Open inch rate $6.50
Established: 1957
Group: GateHouse Media, Inc.
Adv. Mgr. .... Crystal Barrett
Classified Adv. .... Terri Dupree
Circ. Mgr.. Ferol Rome
Mechanical Specifications: Type page 11 5/8 x 21; E - 6 cols, 1 5/6, 3/16 between; A - 6 cols, 1 5/6, 3/16 between; C - 6 cols, 1 5/6, 3/16 between.Equipment & Software: Hardware — APP/Mac; Presses — HI/V-15A; Software — Adobe/PageMaker, Adobe/Photoshop, Macromedia/Freehand, Microsoft/Word, QPS/QuarkXPress.
Delivery Method: Mail

PONCHATOULA

THE DRUM (THUR, MTHLY)

17253 Lavigne Rd, Ponchatoula, LA, 70454-2485, Tangipahoa, USA; gen tel (225) 927-3717; disp adv e-mail news@thedrumnews.com; class adv e-mail news@thedrumnews.com; ed e-mail news@thedrumnews.com; web site thedrumnewspaper.info
Circulation: 2,000fr; Sworn/Estimate/Non-Audited
Advertising rate: Open inch rate $14.00
Established: 1985
Ed. .... Eddie Ponds
Delivery Method: Mail

THE PONCHATOULA TIMES (THUR)

PO Box 743, 170 N 7th Street, Ponchatoula, LA, 70454-0743, Tangipahoa, USA; gen tel (985) 386-2877; gen fax (985) 386-0458; disp adv e-mail ads@ponchatoula.com; ptimes@ponchatoula.com; class adv e-mail ads@ponchatoula.com; ed e-mail editor@ponchatoula.com; web site www.ponchatoula.com/ptimes
Circulation: 9,047pd, 3,500fr; Sworn/Estimate/Non-Audited
Advertising rate: Open inch rate $6.49
Established: 1981
Digital Platform - Mobile: Windows
Pub./Ed............................. Bryan T. McMahon
Mechanical Specifications: Type page 13 x 21 1/2.Equipment & Software: Hardware — IBM; Software — Corel.
Delivery Method: Mail, Newsstand, Racks
Areas Served: Tangipahoa Parish, Livingston Parish, St. Tammany Parish

PORT ALLEN

RIVERSIDE READER (WED)
570 N Jefferson Ave, Ste A, Port Allen, LA, 70767-2412, West Baton Rouge, USA; gen tel (225) 336-0749; gen fax (225) 336-4157; disp adv e-mail Advertising@riversidereader.com; web site www.riversidereader.com
Advertising rate: Open inch rate $15.00
Pub....John Michael Lockhart
Adv. Sales....Rachel Thornhill
Circ. Mgr....Josh Ledet

WEST SIDE JOURNAL (THUR)
668 N Jefferson Ave, Port Allen, LA, 70767-2414, West Baton Rouge, USA; gen tel (225) 343-2540; gen fax (225) 344-0923; disp adv e-mail advertising@thewestsidejournal.com; class adv e-mail advertising@thewestsidejournal.com; ed e-mail editor@thewestsidejournal.com; web site www.thewestsidejournal.com
Circulation: 2,473pd,; Sworn/Estimate/Non-Audited
Advertising rate: Open inch rate $7.75
Established: 1937
Pub....Darrell Guilbeau
Ed....Aaron Williams
Graphic Artist....Cole WilliamsEquipment & Software: Hardware — APP/Mac; Software — QPS/QuarkXPress 4.1.
Delivery Method: Mail
Areas Served: 70767, 70719, 70710, 70729

RAYNE

THE RAYNE-ACADIAN TRIBUNE (THUR)
108 N Adams Ave, Rayne, LA, 70578-5918, Acadia, USA; gen tel (337) 334-3186; gen fax (337) 334-8474; disp adv e-mail admin@raynetoday.com; class adv e-mail admin@raynetoday.com; ed e-mail admin@raynetoday.com; web site www.raynetoday.com
Circulation: 4,105pd, 8,400fr; Sworn/Estimate/Non-Audited
Advertising rate: Open inch rate $10.56
Established: 1904
Group: LSN Publishing Company LLC
Adv. Rep....Josie Henry
Mechanical Specifications: Type page 11 3/5 x 21 1/2; E - 6 cols, 1 4/5, between; A - 6 cols, 2 1/16, between; C - 9 cols, 2 1/16, between.Equipment & Software: Hardware — APP/Mac.
Delivery Method: Mail, Newsstand, Carrier
Areas Served: 70578, 70516, 70525, 70526, 70527, 70529

RAYVILLE

RICHLAND BEACON-NEWS (THUR)
603 Louisa St, Rayville, LA, 71269-2112, Richland, USA; gen tel (318) 728-6467; gen fax (318) 728-5991; disp adv e-mail maryterry@bellsouth.net; web site www.richlandtoday.com
Circulation: 3,000pd, 10,000fr; Sworn/Estimate/Non-Audited
Advertising rate: Open inch rate $7.25
Established: 1868
Group: LSN Publishing Company LLC
Pub....Mary Terry
Mng. Ed....Darryl Riser
Mechanical Specifications: Type page 13 x 21; E - 6 cols, 2 1/16, 1/6 between; A - 6 cols, 2 1/16, 1/6 between; C - 9 cols, 1 1/4, 1/6 between.

THE DELHI DISPATCH (THUR)
603 Louisa St, Rayville, LA, 71269-2112, Richland, USA; gen tel (318) 878-2444; gen fax (318) 728-5991; disp adv e-mail maryterry@bellsouth.net
Circulation: 1,000pd, 39fr; Sworn/Estimate/Non-Audited
Advertising rate: Open inch rate $5.75
Group: LSN Publishing Company LLC
Pub....Mary Terry
Ed....Darryl Riser
Mechanical Specifications: Type page 13 x 21; E - 6 cols, 2 1/6, 1/6 between; A - 6 cols, 2 1/6, 1/6 between; C - 9 cols, 1 1/4, 1/6 between.

SAINT FRANCISVILLE

ST. FRANCISVILLE DEMOCRAT (THUR)
4749 Johnson St, Saint Francisville, LA, 70775-4330, West Feliciana, USA; gen tel (225) 635-3366; gen fax (225) 635-3398; disp adv e-mail sfdemocrat@bellsouth.net; web site www.facebook.com/pg/SFDemocrat/about/?ref=page_internal
Circulation: 2,000pd,; Sworn/Estimate/Non-Audited
Advertising rate: Open inch rate $6.10
Pub....Randall Newsom

SAINT MARTINVILLE

TECHE NEWS (WED)
214 N Main St, Saint Martinville, LA, 70582-4028, St. Martin, USA; gen tel (337) 394-6232; gen fax (337) 394-7511; disp adv e-mail advertise@techetoday.com; class adv e-mail cynthia.dore@techetoday.com; ed e-mail sally.angelle@techetoday.com; web site www.techetoday.com
Advertising rate: Open inch rate $7.30(B&W), $9.30(Color)
Established: 1886
Group: LSN Publishing Company LLCKen Grissom
Henri Bienvenu
Delivery Method: Mail

SHREVEPORT

THE FORUM (WED)
1158 Texas Ave, Shreveport, LA, 71101-3343, Caddo, USA; gen tel (318) 222-409; disp adv e-mail angela@theforumnews.com; class adv e-mail angela@theforumnews.com; ed e-mail editor@theforumnews.com; web site www.theforumnews.com
Circulation: 43pd, 22,755fr; CVC
Advertising rate: 1/16 Pg $224.00; 1/8 Pg $380.00; 1/4 Pg $727.00
Established: 1988
Group: Forum Communications Co.
Pub....Jay Covington
Adv. Mgr/Gen. Mgr....Fayline Bass
Circ. Mgr....Chris Welch
Prod. Mgr....Jill French
Sales Mgr....Angela Haacker

SPRINGHILL

SPRINGHILL PRESS & NEWS-JOURNAL (THUR)
403 Butler St, Springhill, LA, 71075-2735, Webster, USA; gen tel (318) 539-3511; gen fax (318) 539-3512; disp adv e-mail nittimes@wnonline.net; web site www.facebook.com/pages/Springhill-Press-News-Journal/115652755161535
Circulation: 4,000pd, 9,100fr; Sworn/Estimate/Non-Audited
Advertising rate: Open inch rate $5.35
Established: 1937
Group: Natchitoches Times Newspapers
Ed....Vicky Darst
Mechanical Specifications: Type page 13 x 21.Equipment & Software: Hardware — APP/Mac.
Delivery Method: Mail

SULPHUR

SOUTHWEST DAILY NEWS (WED, FRI, SUN)
120 S Huntington St, Sulphur, LA, 70663-3332, Calcasieu, USA; gen tel (337) 527-7075; adv tel (337) 527-7075; ed tel (337) 527-7075; gen fax (337) 528-9557; adv fax (337) 528-9557; ed fax (337) 528-9557; disp adv e-mail sdneditorial@yahoo.com; class adv e-mail swtdaily@yahoo.com; ed e-mail sdneditorial@yahoo.com; web site www.sulphurdailynews.com
Circulation: 4,631pd,; Sworn/Estimate/Non-Audited
Advertising rate: Open inch rate $10.50
Established: 1930
Group: Shearman Corporation
Rgl. Pub....Suzanne Peveto-Nelson
Newsroom Mgr....Marilyn Monroe
Sports Ed....Rodrick Anderson
Rgl. Exec. Ed....Brian Trahan
Adv. Dir....Andy Jacobson
Multimedia Acct. Specialist....Joan Stevens
Multimedia Acct. Specialist....Bernadine Consundado
Mechanical Specifications: Type page 13 x 21; E - 6 cols, 2 1/16, 1/8 between; A - 6 cols, 2 1/16, 1/8 between; C - 8 cols, 1 1/2, 1/8 between.
Delivery Method: Mail, Newsstand, Carrier, Racks
Areas Served: Calcasieu Parish

VINTON NEWS (THUR)
716 E Napoleon St, Sulphur, LA, 70663-3402, Calcasieu, USA; gen tel (337) 527-7075; gen fax (337) 528-3044; disp adv e-mail sdneditorial@yahoo.com; web site www.sulphurdailynews.com
Circulation: 4,200pd, 11,800fr; Sworn/Estimate/Non-Audited
Advertising rate: Open inch rate $13.97
Group: Shearman Corporation
Pub....Suzanne Peveto-Nelson
Mechanical Specifications: Type page 13 x 21; E - 6 cols, 2 1/12, between; A - 6 cols, 2 1/12, between; C - 8 cols, 1 1/2, between.

TALLULAH

MADISON JOURNAL (THUR)
300 S Chestnut St, Tallulah, LA, 71282-4206, Madison, USA; gen tel (318) 574-1404; gen fax (318) 574-4219; disp adv e-mail publisher@madisonjournal.com
Circulation: 2,000pd,; Sworn/Estimate/Non-Audited
Advertising rate: Open inch rate $8.00
Group: Emmerich Newspapers, Inc.

VACHERIE

THE ENTERPRISE (WED)
2677 HIGHWAY 20, Vacherie, LA, 70090, USA; gen tel (225) 265-2120; gen fax (225) 265-2133; disp adv e-mail karenenterprise@bellsouth.net; web site http://www.vacherie-news.com
Circulation: 1,800pd,; Sworn/Estimate/Non-Audited
Advertising rate: Open inch rate $6.55
Pub....Wilbur Reynaud
Ed....David Reynaud

VILLE PLATTE

THE MAMOU ACADIAN PRESS (TUES)
PO Box 220, Ville Platte, LA, 70586-0220, Evangeline, USA; gen tel (337) 363-2103; adv tel (337) 363-2103; ed tel (337) 363-2103; gen fax (337) 363-2841; adv fax (337) 363-2841; ed fax (337) 363-2841; disp adv e-mail kathy.gazette@yahoo.com; class adv e-mail classifieds.vp@centurytel.net; ed e-mail vpgaz@centurytel.net; web site evangelinetoday.com
Circulation: 3,000fr; Sworn/Estimate/Non-Audited
Advertising rate: Open inch rate $5.47
Group: LSN Publishing Company LLC
Digital Platform - Mobile: Apple
Digital Platform - Tablet: Other
Pub....David L. Ortego
Adv. Mgr....Kathy Longino
Circ. Mgr....Jennifer Allison
Ed....Mike Bordelon
Mechanical Specifications: Type page 13 x 21 1/2; E - 6 cols, between; A - 6 cols, between; C - 9 cols, between.
Delivery Method: Mail
Areas Served: 70554

VILLE PLATTE GAZETTE (THUR, SUN)
145 Court St, Ville Platte, LA, 70586-4409, Evangeline, USA; gen tel (337) 363-3939; adv tel (337) 363-3939; ed tel (337) 363-3939; gen fax (337) 363-2841; adv fax (337) 363-2841; ed fax (337) 363-2841; disp adv e-mail ads2.vp@centurytel.net or kathy.gazette@yahoo.com; class adv e-mail classifieds.vp@centurytel.net; ed e-mail vpgaz@centurytel.net; web site evangelinetoday.com
Circulation: 3,000pd,; Sworn/Estimate/Non-Audited
Advertising rate: Open inch rate $8.20
Established: 1913
Group: LSN Publishing Company LLC
Digital Platform - Mobile: Apple
Digital Platform - Tablet: Other
Pub....Ortego David
Longino Kathy
Editor....Michael Bordelon
Mechanical Specifications: Type page 12 1/2 x 22; E - 6 cols, 1 4/5, 1/6 between; A - 6 cols, 1 4/5, 1/6 between; C - 9 cols, 1 3/16, between.Equipment & Software: Hardware — APP/Mac; Software — Adobe/Photoshop 6.0, Adobe/Acrobat 4.0, Flight Check.
Delivery Method: Mail, Carrier, Racks
Areas Served: 70586,

VIVIAN

CADDO CITIZEN (THUR)
203 S Spruce St, Vivian, LA, 71082-2841, Caddo, USA; gen tel (318) 375-3294; gen fax (318) 375-3380; disp adv e-mail caddocitizen@centurytel.net; web site www.facebook.com/The-Caddo-Citizen-425796657560617/?ref=page_internal
Circulation: 1,350pd,; Sworn/Estimate/Non-Audited
Advertising rate: Open inch rate $6.13
Pub....Mary Haddox

WELSH

THE WELSH CITIZEN (TUES)
119 S Elms St, Welsh, LA, 70591-4211, Jefferson, USA; gen tel (337) 734-2891; gen fax (337) 734-4457; disp adv e-mail welsh-citizen@centurytel.net; web site http://www.jeffdavistoday.com/
Circulation: 1,000pd,; Sworn/Estimate/Non-Audited
Advertising rate: Open inch rate $6.05
Established: 1958
Ed....Bengt Lindell

WEST MONROE

THE OUACHITA CITIZEN (THUR)
4423 Cypress St, West Monroe, LA, 71291-7405, Ouachita, USA; gen tel (318) 322-3161; gen fax (318) 325-2285; disp adv e-mail news@ouachitacitizen.com; ed e-mail News@ouachitacitizen.com ; web site www.hannapub.com/ouachitacitizen
Circulation: 5,200pd,; Sworn/Estimate/Non-Audited
Advertising rate: Open inch rate $5.50
Established: 1924
Publisher....Sam Hanna
Ed....Scott Rogers
Mechanical Specifications: 10x21.5 image size on 6 columns with standard gutter. Equipment & Software: Hardware — APP/Mac; Presses — 5-KP; Software — QPS/QuarkX-

Press 3.32.
Delivery Method: Mail

WINNFIELD

WINN PARISH ENTERPRISE-NEWS AMERICAN (WED)

500 E Main St, Winnfield, LA, 71483-4301, Winn, USA; gen tel (318) 628-2712; gen fax (318) 628-6196; disp adv e-mail advertising@winnparishenterprise.com; class adv e-mail classifieds@winnparishenterprise.com; ed e-mail news@winnparishenterprise.com; web site www.winnparishenterprise.com
Circulation: 3,995pd, 75fr; Sworn/Estimate/Non-Audited
Advertising rate: Open inch rate $5.36
Established: 1924
Group: Natchitoches Times Newspapers
Adv. Mgr. .... Nanie Young
Circ. Mgr. .... Verlene Henderson
Ed. .... Crystal Evans
Mechanical Specifications: Type page 13 x 21; E - 6 cols, 2, 1/4 between; A - 6 cols, 2, between; C - 8 cols, 1 1/2, between.Equipment & Software: Hardware — APP/Mac; Presses — KP/News King; Software — Adobe/Photoshop, Microsoft/Office 98, Multi-Ad 4.0.
Delivery Method: Mail
Areas Served: 71483, 71440, 71422, 71454, 71031

WINNSBORO

THE FRANKLIN SUN (WED)

514 Prairie St, Winnsboro, LA, 71295-2737, Franklin, USA; gen tel (318) 435-4521; gen fax (318) 435-9220; disp adv e-mail Monica@franklinsun.com; class adv e-mail wanda@franklinsun.com; ed e-mail Samhannajr@samhannajr.com; web site www.franklinsun.com - 135,862(views)
Circulation: 6,200pd,; USPS
Advertising rate: Open inch rate $5.50
Established: 1856
Group: Hanna Publishing Co.
Circ. Mgr. .... Nicki Vines
Photographer
Monica Huff
Sports Ed./Gen. Ed. .... Matt Reynolds
Community Ed.
General News .... Marcy Thompson
Public Notice/Class. .... Wanda Berry
Gen Mgr. .... Lesley Capdepon
Ed .... Sam Hanna Jr.
Advertising .... Patricia Caldwell
Mechanical Specifications: Type page 13 x 21; E - 2 cols, 4 1/4, 1/8 between; A - 6 cols, 1/8 between; C - 6 cols, 1/8 between.Equipment & Software: Hardware — APP/Mac; Software — Adobe/PageMaker 6.5, QPS/QuarkXPress 4.0.
Delivery Method: Mail, Racks
Areas Served: 71295

MAINE

BANGOR

THE WEEKLY (THUR)

491 Main St, Bangor, ME, 04401-6296, Penobscot, USA; gen tel (207) 990-8000; adv tel (207) 990-8000; ed tel (207) 990-8175; gen fax (207) 990-8041; adv fax (207) 990-8041; ed fax (207) 990-8041; disp adv e-mail advertising@bangordailynews.net; class adv e-mail tmcleod@bangordailynews.com; ed e-mail syoung@bangordailynews.com; web site www.bangordailynews.com/weekly
Circulation: 24,775pd,; Sworn/Estimate/Non-Audited
Advertising rate: Open inch rate $52.01
Pub. .... Richard J. Warren
Vice Pres. .... Robert W. Stairs
Controller .... Timothy Reynolds
Adv. Dir. .... Mike Kearney
Circ. Dir. .... Jim Hayes
Exec. Ed. .... A. Mark Woodward
Mng. Ed. .... Michael J. Dowd
Sports Ed. .... Joseph McLaughlin
Prodn. Mgr. .... Charles Villard
Mechanical Specifications: Type page 11 5/8 x 20 3/4; E - 6 cols, 1 5/6, 1/8 between; A - 6 cols, 1 5/6, 1/8 between; C - 9 cols, 1 7/8, 1/8 between.

BAR HARBOR

MOUNT DESERT ISLANDER (THUR)

310 Main St, Bar Harbor, ME, 04609-1638, Hancock, USA; gen tel (207) 288-0556; adv tel (207) 288-0556; ed tel (207) 288-0556; gen fax (207) 288-0559; adv fax (207) 288-0559; ed fax (207) 288-0559; disp adv e-mail jclark@ellsworthamerican.com; class adv e-mail jclark@ellsworthamerican.com; ed e-mail news@mdislander.com; web site www.mdislander.com
Circulation: 4,369pd, 65fr; Sworn/Estimate/Non-Audited
Advertising rate: Rates vary
Established: 1851
Digital Platform - Mobile: Apple, Android
Digital Platform - Tablet: Apple iOS, Android
Pub. .... Alan L. Baker
Delivery Method: Mail, Newsstand, Carrier, Racks
Areas Served: Bar Harbor

BATH

COASTAL JOURNAL (THUR)

97 Commercial St, Bath, ME, 04530-2563, Sagadahoc, USA; gen tel (207) 443-6241; adv tel (207) 443-6241; gen fax (207) 443-5605; adv fax (207) 443-5605; disp adv e-mail ads@coastaljournal.com; class adv e-mail ads@coastaljournal.com; ed e-mail editor@coastaljournal.com; web site www.coastaljournal.com
Circulation: 19,200fr; Sworn/Estimate/Non-Audited
Advertising rate: Open inch rate $16.00
Established: 1966
Ed./Pub. .... Bruce Hardina
Asst. Ed. .... Rachel Shelley
Adv. Rep, greater Brunswick Kathy McDonough
Adv. Rep., greater Bath .... Annie Merry
Mechanical Specifications: Type page 10 7/12 x 12 7/12; E - 5 cols, 2 1/12, 1/12 between; A - 5 cols, 2 1/12, 1/12 between; C - 7 cols, 2 1/3, 1/12 between.Equipment & Software: Hardware — APP/Mac; Software — QPS/QuarkXPress 4.10, Adobe/PageMaker 6.5.
Delivery Method: Newsstand, Racks
Areas Served: Freeport to Camden

BELFAST

THE REPUBLICAN JOURNAL (THUR)

161 High St, Belfast, ME, 04915-6548, Waldo, USA; gen tel (207) 338-3333; adv tel (207) 338-3333; gen fax (207) 338-5498; adv fax (207) 338-5498; disp adv e-mail sales@courierpublicationsllc.com; class adv e-mail sales@courierpublicationsllc.com; ed e-mail news@villagesoup.com; web site www.villagesoup.com
Circulation: 8,000pd, 162fr; Sworn/Estimate/Non-Audited
Advertising rate: Open inch rate $8.80
Established: 1829
Group: Courier Publications, LLC
Crescent Publishing Company LLC
Village Netmedia, Inc.
Digital Platform - Mobile: Apple, Android
Pres./Pub. .... Reade Brower
Sales Dir. .... Dave Libby
Oper. Mgr. .... Bryan Gess
Ed. .... Daniel Dunkle
Mechanical Specifications: Type page 13 x 21; A - 6 cols, 1.778, 1/8 between; C - 9 cols, 1.167, 1/8 between.
Delivery Method: Mail, Newsstand, Carrier, Racks
Areas Served: Waldo County

BETHEL

THE BETHEL CITIZEN (THUR)

19 Main St, Bethel, ME, 04217-4014, Oxford, USA; gen tel (207) 824-2444; adv tel (207) 824-2444; gen fax (207) 824-2426; adv fax (207) 824-2426; disp adv e-mail ads@bethelcitizen.com; class adv e-mail ads@bethelcitizen.com; ed e-mail news@bethelcitizen.com; web site www.bethelcitizen.com
Circulation: 3,600pd,; Sworn/Estimate/Non-Audited
Advertising rate: Open inch rate $5.70
Established: 1895
Group: Sun Media Group
Pub. .... Edward M. Snook
Ed. .... Allison Aloisio
Prodn. Mgr. .... Nancy Forest
Mechanical Specifications: Type page 11 5/8 x 21; E - 6 cols, 1 5/6, between; A - 6 cols, 1 5/6, between; C - 6 cols, 1 5/6, between. Equipment & Software: Hardware — IBM; Software — QPS/QuarkXPress.
Delivery Method: Mail, Newsstand, Carrier, Racks
Areas Served: Bethel & Neighboring communities

BIDDEFORD

BIDDEFORD COURIER (THUR)

180 Main St, Biddeford, ME, 04005-2410, York, USA; gen tel (207) 282-4337; adv tel (207) 282-4337; gen fax (207) 282-4339; adv fax (207) 282-4339; disp adv e-mail ads@mainelymediallc.com; class adv e-mail sacoads@inthecourier.com; ed e-mail editor@inthecourier.com; web site www.mainelymediallc.com
Circulation: 22,500fr; Sworn/Estimate/Non-Audited
Advertising rate: Open inch rate $11.80
Group: Mainely Media, LLC
Digital Platform - Mobile: Apple, Android
Digital Platform - Tablet: Apple iOS, Android
Mng. Ed. .... Molly Lovell
Adv. Mgr./Gen. Mgr. .... David Clark
Bus. Mgr. .... Sandy Porrazo
Ed. .... Steve Betts
Mechanical Specifications: Type page 10 1/6 x 16; E - 6 cols, 1 9/16, 1/6 between; A - 6 cols, 1 9/16, 1/6 between; C - 7 cols, 1 7/16, 1/6 between.Equipment & Software: Hardware — APP/Macs; Software — Microsoft/Word, Adobe/PageMaker.
Delivery Method: Mail, Newsstand
Areas Served: Biddeford, Saco, and Old Orchard Beach

KENNEBUNK POST (FRI)

180 Main St, Biddeford, ME, 04005-2410, York, USA; gen tel (207) 282-4337; adv tel (207) 282-4337; ed tel (207) 282-4337; gen fax (207) 282-4339; adv fax (207) 282-4339; ed fax (207) 282-4339; disp adv e-mail ads@kennebunkpost.com; class adv e-mail ads@kennebunkpost.com; ed e-mail editor@kennebunkpost.com; web site www.mainelymediallc.com
Advertising rate: Open inch rate $9.40
Group: Mainely Media, LLC
Digital Platform - Mobile: Apple, Android
Digital Platform - Tablet: Apple iOS, Android
Gen. Mgr./Adv. Mgr. .... David Clark
Ed. .... Dan King
Delivery Method: Mail, Newsstand
Areas Served: Kennebunk, Kennebunkport, and Arundel

MAKING IT AT HOME (THUR)

180 Main St, Biddeford, ME, 04005-2410, York, USA; gen tel (207) 282-4337 ; adv tel (207) 282-4337 ext. 214 ; ed tel (207) 282-4337 ; gen fax (207) 282-4339 ; adv fax (207) 282-4339 ; ed fax (207) 282-4339 ; disp adv e-mail ads@mainelymediallc.com; class adv e-mail ads@mainelymediallc.com; ed e-mail editor@scarboroughleader.com; web site www.mainelymediallc.com
Advertising rate: Open inch rate $8.55
Group: Mainely Media, LLC
Digital Platform - Mobile: Apple, Android
Digital Platform - Tablet: Apple iOS, Android
Gen. Mgr./Adv. Mgr. .... David Clark
Bus. Mgr. .... Sandy Porrazzo
Mng. Ed. .... Molly Lovell
Ed. .... Dan King
Delivery Method: Mail, Newsstand
Areas Served: Wells, Ogunquit, and Moody

REGISTER GAZETTE (THUR)

180 Main St, Biddeford, ME, 04005-2410, York, USA; gen tel (207) 282-4337 ; adv tel (207) 282-4337 ext. 214 ; ed tel (207) 282-4337 ; gen fax (207) 282-4339 ; adv fax (207) 282-4339 ; ed fax (207) 282-4339 ; disp adv e-mail ads@intheregister.com; class adv e-mail ads@mainelymediallc.com; ed e-mail editor@scarboroughleader.com; web site www.mainelymediallc.com
Advertising rate: Open inch rate $9.65
Group: Mainely Media, LLC
Digital Platform - Mobile: Apple, Android
Digital Platform - Tablet: Apple iOS, Android
Gen. Mgr./Adv. Mgr. .... David Clark
Bus. Mgr. .... Sandy Porrazzo
Mng. Ed. .... Molly Lovell
Ed. .... Dan King
Delivery Method: Mail, Newsstand
Areas Served: York County

SOUTH PORTLAND-CAPE/ELIZABETH SENTRY (FRI)

180 Main St, Biddeford, ME, 04005-2410, York, USA; gen tel (207) 282-4337; adv tel (207) 282-4337; ed tel (207) 282-4337; gen fax (207) 282-4339; adv fax (207) 282-4339; ed fax (207) 282-4339; disp adv e-mail ads@mainelymediallc.com; class adv e-mail ads@mainelymediallc.com; ed e-mail editor@scarboroughleader.com; web site www.mainelymediallc.com
Advertising rate: Open inch rate $12.30
Group: Mainely Media, LLC
Digital Platform - Mobile: Apple, Android
Digital Platform - Tablet: Apple iOS, Android
Adv. Mgr./Gen. Mgr .... David Clark
Mng. Ed. .... Molly Lovell
Delivery Method: Mail, Newsstand
Areas Served: South Portland and Cape Elizabeth

BLUE HILL

CASTINE PATRIOT (THUR)

13 Main St, Blue Hill, ME, 04614-5985, Hancock, USA; gen tel (207) 374-2341; adv tel (207) 374-2341; ed tel (207) 374-2341; gen fax (207) 374-2343; adv fax (207)374-2343; ed fax (207) 374-2343; disp adv e-mail ads@pbp.me; class adv e-mail classifieds@pbp.me; ed e-mail news@pbp.me; web site www.penobscotbaypress.com
Circulation: 600pd, 50fr; Sworn/Estimate/Non-Audited
Advertising rate: Open inch rate $15.00
Established: 1980
Group: Penobscot Bay Press, Inc.
Pub & Owner .... R. Nathaniel W. Barrows
Circulation Mgr .... Cathy Marshall
Mng. Ed. .... Faith DeAmbrose
Sales Rep. .... Heather Oliver
Classifieds & Coming Events Manager .. Tegan McGuire
Financial Manager .... Debra Larrabee
Delivery Method: Mail, Newsstand, Carrier, Racks
Areas Served: Castine, ME and Penobscot, ME

THE WEEKLY PACKET (THUR)

13 Main St, Blue Hill, ME, 04614-5985, Hancock, USA; gen tel (207) 374-2341; adv tel (207) 374-2341; ed tel (207) 374-2341; gen

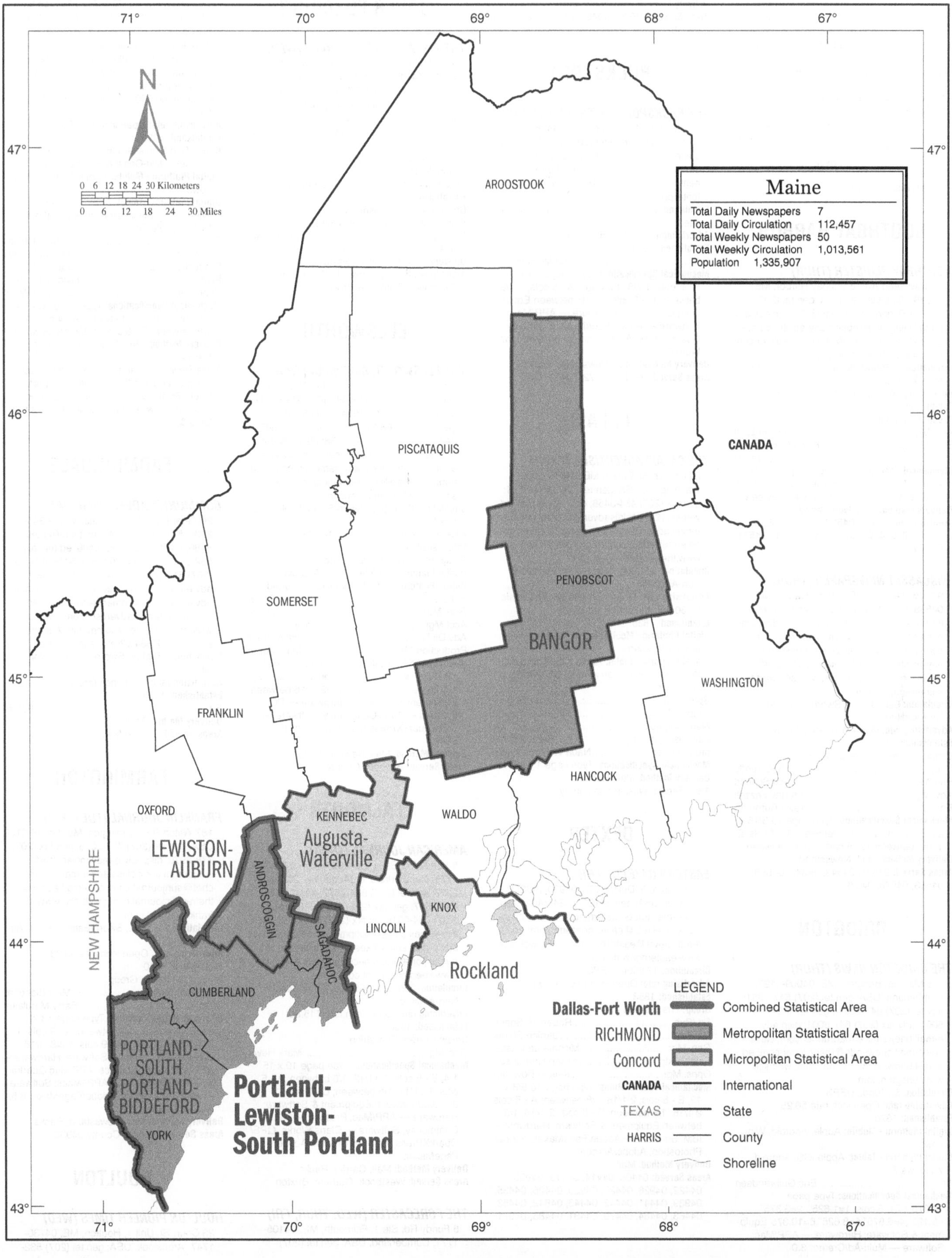

Maine
Total Daily Newspapers 7
Total Daily Circulation 112,457
Total Weekly Newspapers 50
Total Weekly Circulation 1,013,561
Population 1,335,907
AROOSTOOK
PISCATAQUIS
CANADA
PENOBSCOT
SOMERSET
BANGOR
WASHINGTON
FRANKLIN
HANCOCK
OXFORD
KENNEBEC
WALDO
Augusta-Waterville
LEWISTON-AUBURN
ANDROSCOGGIN
NEW HAMPSHIRE
KNOX
SAGADAHOC
LINCOLN
Rockland
CUMBERLAND
PORTLAND-SOUTH PORTLAND-BIDDEFORD
YORK
Portland-Lewiston-South Portland
LEGEND
Dallas-Fort Worth Combined Statistical Area
RICHMOND Metropolitan Statistical Area
Concord Micropolitan Statistical Area
CANADA International
TEXAS State
HARRIS County
Shoreline
0 6 12 18 24 30 Kilometers
0 6 12 18 24 30 Miles
N
71° 70° 69° 68° 67°
47° 46° 45° 44° 43°

fax (207) 374-2343; adv fax (207) 374-2343; ed fax (207) 374-2343; disp adv e-mail ads@pbp.me; class adv e-mail classifieds@pbp.me; ed e-mail news@pbp.me; web site www.weeklypacket.com
Circulation: 1,610pd, 22fr; Sworn/Estimate/Non-Audited
Advertising rate: Open inch rate $15
Established: 1960
Ed. .... R. Nathaniel W. Barrows
Circ. Mgr.................................... Cathy Marshall
Managing Editor .... Faith DeAmbrose
Delivery Method: Mail, Newsstand, Carrier, Racks
Areas Served: Blue Hill

BOOTHBAY HARBOR

BOOTHBAY REGISTER (THUR)

97 Townsend Ave, Boothbay Harbor, ME, 04538-1843, Lincoln, USA; gen tel (207) 633-4620; gen fax (207) 633-7123; class adv e-mail classifieds@boothbayregister.com; ed e-mail kevinburnham@boothbayregister.com; web site boothbayregister.com
Circulation: 3,555pd, 300fr; Sworn/Estimate/Non-Audited
Advertising rate: Open inch rate $11.25
Established: 1876
Group: Maine-OK Enterprises, Inc.
Adv. Mgr...................................... Kathy Frizzell
Editor .... Kevin G. Burnham
Pub.. A.R. Tandy
Mechanical Specifications: Type page 15 3/16 x 21; E - 7 cols, 2 1/16, between; A - 7 cols, 2 1/16, between; C - 8 cols, 1 3/4, between.
Delivery Method: Mail, Newsstand
Areas Served: 04535, 04537, 04538, 04543, 04342, 04544, 04556, 04553, 04576, 04571, 04575

WISCASSET NEWSPAPER (THUR)

97 Townsend Ave, Boothbay Harbor, ME, 04538-1843, Lincoln, USA; gen tel (207) 633-4620; gen fax (207) 633-7123; disp adv e-mail newsdesk@wiscassetnewspaper.com; class adv e-mail classifieds@boothbayregister.com; ed e-mail newsdesk@wiscassetnewspaper.com; web site wiscassetnewspaper.com
Circulation: 690pd, 23fr; Sworn/Estimate/Non-Audited
Advertising rate: Open inch rate $11.25
Established: 1970
Group: Maine-OK Enterprises, Inc.
Pub.. A.R. Tandy
Bus. Mgr.. Pat Schmid
Adv. Mgr...................................... Kathy Frizzell
Ed. .... Kevin Burnham
Mechanical Specifications: Type page 15 3/16 x 21; E - 7 cols, 2 1/16, between; A - 7 cols, 2 1/16, between; C - 8 cols, 1 3/4, between.
Delivery Method: Mail, Newsstand
Areas Served: 04535, 04543, 04342, 04556, 04553, 04578, 04579

BRIDGTON

THE BRIDGTON NEWS (THUR)

118 Main St, Bridgton, ME, 04009-1127, Cumberland, USA; gen tel (207) 647-2851; adv tel (207) 647-2851 ; gen fax (207) 647-5001; adv fax (207) 647-5001; disp adv e-mail bnewsads@roadrunner.com; class adv e-mail bnewsads@roadrunner.com; ed e-mail bnews@roadrunner.com; web site www.bridgton.com
Circulation: 5,500pd,; USPS
Advertising rate: Open inch rate $6.25
Established: 1870
Digital Platform - Mobile: Apple, Android, Windows
Digital Platform - Tablet: Apple iOS, Android, Windows 7
Adv. .... Eric Gulbrandsen
Mechanical Specifications: Type page 10.375 x 21; 6 cols, 1=1.625", 2=3.375", =5.125",4=6.875",5=8.625",6=10.375"Equipment & Software: Hardware — APP/Mac; Software — Multi-Ad/Creator 3.0.
Delivery Method: Mail, Newsstand
Areas Served: 04009 04040 04015 04022 04037 04055

BUCKSPORT

THE BUCKSPORT ENTERPRISE (THUR)

105 Main St, Bucksport, ME, 04416-4028, Hancock, USA; gen tel (207) 469-6722; disp adv e-mail theenterpr@aol.com; class adv e-mail theenterpr@aol.com; ed e-mail theenterpr@aol.com; web site www.bucksporttenterprise.com
Circulation: 2,300pd,; Sworn/Estimate/Non-Audited
Advertising rate: Open inch rate $7
Established: 1991
Ed. .... Donald M. Houghton
Mechanical Specifications: Type page 10 x 15; E - 5 cols, 1 7/8, between; A - 5 cols, 1 7/8, between; C - 5 cols, 1 7/8, between.Equipment & Software: Hardware — APP/Mac; Software — Adobe/PageMaker 6.5, QPS/QuarkXPress, Adobe/Photoshop, Microsoft/Word 6.
Delivery Method: Mail, Newsstand, Racks
Areas Served: 04416, 04472, 04431, 04981

CALAIS

THE CALAIS ADVERTISER (THUR)

23 Church St, Calais, ME, 04619-1639, Washington, USA; gen tel (207) 454-3561; gen fax (207) 454-3458; disp adv e-mail advertising@thecalaisadvertiser.com; class adv e-mail advertising@thecalaisadvertiser.com; ed e-mail editorcalais@gmail.com; web site www.thecalaisadvertiser.com
Circulation: 3,200pd, 15fr; Sworn/Estimate/Non-Audited
Advertising rate: Open inch rate $6.30. Legals $6.30 pdf; National Rate $7.25
Established: 1836
Digital Platform - Mobile: Apple, Android, Windows, Blackberry
Digital Platform - Tablet: Apple iOS, Android, Windows 7, Blackberry Tablet OS, Kindle, Nook, Kindle Fire
Sports Ed. .... John Rogers
Graphic Designer.................... Cheryl Stabinski
Managing editor........................... Lura Jackson
advertising manager.................... Beth McCray
proof reader..................... Nada Williams-White
Mechanical Specifications: Type page 11 x 17.
Delivery Method: Mail, Racks
Areas Served: Washington county

DEXTER

EASTERN GAZETTE (FRI)

97 Church St, Dexter, ME, 04930-1332, Penobscot, USA; gen tel (207) 924-7402; disp adv e-mail ads@easterngazette.com; class adv e-mail ads@easterngazette.com; ed e-mail news@easterngazette.com; web site www.easterngazette.com
Circulation: 17,000fr; USPS
Advertising rate: Open inch rate $15.00
Established: 1853
Group: The Gazette Inc.
Ed./Pub. .... Robert H. Shank
Co-Pub.. Janice Shank
Gen. Mgr. .... Michele Lancaster
Sales/Mktg.......................... Joanne Henderson
Opns. Mgr. .... Kelsee Bowman
Mechanical Specifications: Type page 10 5/8 x 15; E - 5 cols, 2 1/16, 1/8 between; A - 5 cols, 2 1/16, 1/8 between; C - 5 cols, 2 1/16, 1/8 between.Equipment & Software: Hardware — IBM; Software — Adobe/PageMaker, Adobe/Photoshop, Adobe/Acrobat.
Delivery Method: Mail
Areas Served: 04406, 04414, 04415, 04923, 04422, 04928, 04427, 04930, 04426, 04435, 04939, 04441, 04442, 04443, 04942, 04453, 04463, 04464, 04479, 04481, 04485, 04971

DOVER FOXCROFT

THE PISCATAQUIS OBSERVER (WED)

12 E Main St, Ste A, Dover Foxcroft, ME, 04426-1414, Piscataquis, USA; gen tel (207) 564-8355; gen fax (207) 564-7056; disp adv e-mail observersales@bangordailynews.com; class adv e-mail observersales@bangordailynews.com; ed e-mail observer@bangordailynews.com; web site www.observer-me.com
Circulation: 2,000pd, 10fr; Sworn/Estimate/Non-Audited
Advertising rate: Open inch rate $15.50
Established: 1838
Group: Bangor Publishing Company
Digital Platform - Tablet: Windows 7
Manager .... Mike Dowd
Sales.. Keri Foster
Delivery Method: Mail, Newsstand, Racks
Areas Served: Dover-Foxcroft, Dexter, Milo, Greenville, Guilford & Brownville

ELLSWORTH

THE ELLSWORTH AMERICAN (THUR)

30 Water St, Ellsworth, ME, 04605-2033, Hancock, USA; gen tel (207)667-2576; adv tel (207) 667-2576; ed tel (207) 667-2576; gen fax (207) 667-7656; adv fax (207) 667-3431; ed fax (207) 667-7656; disp adv e-mail skimball@ellsworthamerican.com; class adv e-mail skimball@ellsworthamerican.com; ed e-mail sfay@ellsworthamerican.com; web site www.ellsworthamerican.com
Circulation: 8,477pd,; Sworn/Estimate/Non-Audited
Advertising rate: Open inch rate $23.00
Established: 1851
Group: Ellsworth American, Inc.
Digital Platform - Mobile: Apple, Android
Digital Platform - Tablet: Apple iOS, Android
Pub... Alan L. Baker
Gen. Mgr. .... Terry Carlisle
Acct Mgr .... Sally Hutchins
Adv Dir... Scott Kimball
Production Manager .... Matt Martin
Mechanical Specifications: Type page 15 x 21 1/4; E - 7 cols, 2, 1/4 between; A - 7 cols, 2, 1/4 between; C - 9 cols, 1 1/2, 3/16 between. Equipment & Software: Hardware — PC; Presses — 10-G/Community; Software — QPS/QuarkXPress 6.0, Novell/Netware, ECR.
Delivery Method: Mail, Newsstand, Carrier
Areas Served: Hancock County

FALMOUTH

AMERICAN JOURNAL (THUR)

5 Fundy Rd, Ste 1, Falmouth, ME, 04105-1771, Cumberland, USA; gen tel (207) 854-2577; adv tel (207) 854-2577; ed tel (207) 854-2577; gen fax (207) 854-0018; adv fax (207) 854-0018; ed fax (207) 854-0018; disp adv e-mail sales@keepmecurrent.com; class adv e-mail sales@keepmecurrent.com; ed e-mail jlord@keepmecurrent.com; web site www.keepmecurrent.com
Circulation: 7,600pd, 556fr; Sworn/Estimate/Non-Audited
Advertising rate: Open inch rate $15.50
Established: 1950
Group: Current Publishing
Circ. Mgr.. Mark Hews
Mechanical Specifications: Type page 10 x 15 1/4; E - 5 cols, 1 11/12, 1/6 between; A - 5 cols, 1 11/12, 1/6 between; C - 7 cols, 1 3/8, 3/32 between.Equipment & Software: Hardware — APP/Mac; Presses — 6-G/Community; Software — Claris/Works, QPS/QuarkXPress, Multi-Ad/Creator, Adobe/PageMaker.
Delivery Method: Mail, Carrier, Racks
Areas Served: Westbook, Gorham, Buxton

THE FORECASTER (WED, THUR, FRI)

5 Fundy Rd, Ste 1, Falmouth, ME, 04105-1771, Cumberland, USA; gen tel (207) 781-3661; adv tel (207) 781-3661; ed tel (207) 781-3661; gen fax (207) 781-2060; adv fax (207) 781-2060; ed fax (207) 781-2060; disp adv e-mail cgardner@theforecaster.net; class adv e-mail jallen@theforecaster.net; ed e-mail editor@theforecaster.net ; web site www.theforecaster.net
Circulation: 60,000fr; Sworn/Estimate/Non-Audited
Advertising rate: Open inch rate $36
Established: 1986
Group: Sun Media GroupEditions: (4) Portland, Northern, Mid-Coast & Southern editions
Digital Platform - Mobile: Apple, Android, Windows
Digital Platform - Tablet: Apple iOS, Android, Windows 7, Blackberry Tablet OS, Kindle, Nook, Kindle Fire
Ed. .... Mo Mehlsak
Sports Ed.................................. Michael Hoffer
Production Mgr...................... Suzanne Piecuch
Pres. .... David W. Costello
Publisher....................................... Karen Wood
Mechanical Specifications: Type page 10 x 14; E - 4 cols, 2 3/8, 1/6 between; A - 4 cols, 2 3/8, 1/6 between; C - 6 cols, 1 3/4, 1/6 between.
Delivery Method: Mail, Newsstand, Carrier, Racks
Areas Served: Portland, Falmouth, Yarmouth, Cumberland, North Yarmouth, Freeport, South Portland, Cape Elizabeth, Scarborough, Brunswick, Bath, Topsham, Harswell, Orr's & Bailey Islands

FARMINGDALE

COMMUNITY ADVERTISER (SAT)

20 Peter Path, Farmingdale, ME, 04344-2930, Kennebec, USA; gen tel (207) 582-8486; adv tel (207) 582-8486; ed tel (207) 582-8486; gen fax (207) 512-5388; adv fax (207) 512-5388; ed fax (207) 512-5388; disp adv e-mail ads@comadvertiser.com; class adv e-mail ads@comadvertiser.com; ed e-mail ads@comadvertiser.com ; web site www.facebook.com/Community-Advertiser-138769906840/?ref=page_internal
Circulation: 15,000fr; Sworn/Estimate/Non-Audited
Advertising rate: Open inch rate $7.50
Established: 1938
Ed. .... Keith E. Peters
Delivery Method: Mail
Areas Served: Central Maine

FARMINGTON

FRANKLIN JOURNAL (TUES, FRI)

187 Wilton Rd, Farmington, ME, 04938-6120, USA; gen tel (207) 778-2075; gen fax (207) 778-6970; disp adv e-mail mblanchet@sunjournal.com; class adv e-mail mblanchet@sunjournal.com; ed e-mail editor@thefranklinjournal.com ; web site www.thefranklinjournal.com
Circulation: 2,500pd,; Sworn/Estimate/Non-Audited
Advertising rate: Open inch rate $9.93
Established: 1840
Group: Sun Media Group
Adv. Acct. Exec. .... Mike Blanchet
Editor .... Barry Matulaitis
Mechanical Specifications: Type page 13 x 21; E - 6 cols, 2, 1/8 between; A - 9 cols, 1 3/8, 1/16 between; C - 9 cols, 1 3/8, 1/16 between.Equipment & Software: Hardware — APP/Mac Color Classics, APP/Mac Quadra 660, APP/Power Mac, APP/iMacs; Software — APP/Appleworks, Adobe/PageMaker 6.5, Adobe/Photoshop 4.0.
Delivery Method: Mail, Newsstand, Racks
Areas Served: Franklin County 04938

HOULTON

HOULTON PIONEER TIMES (WED)

23 Court St, Unit 1, Houlton, ME, 04730-1747, Aroostook, USA; gen tel (207) 532-

2281; gen fax (207) 532-2403; disp adv e-mail hptsales@bangordailynews.com; class adv e-mail pioneertimes@bangordailynews.com; ed e-mail pioneertimes@bangordailynews.com; web site www.thecounty.me
Circulation: 4,188pd, 12fr; Sworn/Estimate/Non-Audited
Advertising rate: Open inch rate $15.50
Established: 1857
Group: Bangor Publishing Company
Digital Platform - Mobile: Windows
Sales Rep. .... David Bates
Editor .... Rick Levasseur
Delivery Method: Mail, Newsstand, Carrier, Racks
Areas Served: 04730, 04747, 04760, 04761, 04763, 04765, 04776, 04780, 04424

KINGFIELD

ORIGINAL IRREGULAR (WED)

239 Main St, # 1, Kingfield, ME, 04947-4233, Franklin, USA; gen tel (207) 265-2773; adv tel (207) 265-2773; ed tel (207) 265-2773; gen fax (207) 265-2775; adv fax (207) 265-2775; ed fax (207) 265-2775; disp adv e-mail irregular.ads@tds.net; class adv e-mail irregular.classifieds@tds.net; ed e-mail theirregular@tds.net; web site www.theirregular.com
Circulation: 3,600pd,; Sworn/Estimate/Non-Audited
Advertising rate: Modular sizes: One sixth page $71; One half page $189; Full page $339
Established: 1968
Digital Platform - Mobile: Apple, Android, Windows, Blackberry
Digital Platform - Tablet: Apple iOS, Android, Windows 7, Blackberry Tablet OS
Pub./Prod. Mgr. .... Heidi Murphy
Ed. .... Robert J. Gray
Ad. Director.......................... Melanie Meldrum
Mechanical Specifications: 1 col = 3.25"; W = modular sizes
Delivery Method: Mail, Newsstand
Areas Served: 04947, 04983, 04982, 04966, 04936, 04970, 04964, 04961,

LINCOLN

LINCOLN NEWS (THUR)

PO Box 35, 78 W Broadway, Lincoln, ME, 04457-0035, Penobscot, USA; gen tel (207) 794-6532; gen fax (207) 794-2004; disp adv e-mail news@lincnews.com; class adv e-mail news@lincnews.com; ed e-mail editor@lincnews.com; web site www.lincnews.com
Circulation: 6,450pd, 19fr; USPS
Advertising rate: Open inch rate $8.00
Established: 1959
Office Mgr. .... Laverne Carll
Gen. Mgr. .... David Whalen
Mechanical Specifications: Type page 10 x 16; E - 5 cols, 1 7/8, 1/4 between; A - 5 cols, 1 7/8, 1/4 between; C - 5 cols, 1 7/8, 1/4 between. Equipment & Software: Hardware — APP/Mac; Presses — G/Suburban; Software — Adobe/PageMaker 6.5.
Delivery Method: Mail, Newsstand
Areas Served: 04417, 04448, 04455, 04459, 04462, 04475, 04495, 04430, 04451, 04457, 04460, 04467, 04493, 04487, 04457, 04460, 04493

LIVERMORE FALLS

LIVERMORE FALLS ADVERTISER (THUR)

59 Main St, Livermore Falls, ME, 04254-1528, Androscoggin, USA; gen tel (207) 897-4321; adv tel (207) 897-4321; ed tel (207) 897-4321; gen fax (207) 897-4322; adv fax (207) 897-4322; ed fax (207) 897-4322; disp adv e-mail Lfanews@myfairpoint.net; class adv e-mail Lfanews@myfairpoint.net; ed e-mail Lfanews@myfairpoint.net; web site lfadvertiser.com
Circulation: 3,000pd,; Sworn/Estimate/Non-Audited
Advertising rate: Open inch rate $7.30
Group: Sun Media Group
Pres. .... James R. Costello
Ed. .... Barry Matulaitis
Mechanical Specifications: Type page 13 x 21; E - 6 cols, 2, 1/8 between; A - 9 cols, 1 3/8, 1/8 between; C - 9 cols, 1 3/8, 1/8 between. Equipment & Software: Hardware — APP/Mac; Software — Adobe/PageMaker 5.0, Adobe/Photoshop 4.0, Claris/MacWrite Pro.
Delivery Method: Mail, Newsstand, Carrier, Racks
Areas Served: Jay, Livermore, and Livermore Falls

MACHIAS

MACHIAS VALLEY NEWS OBSERVER (WED)

41 Broadway, Machias, ME, 04654-1105, Washington County, USA; gen tel (207) 255-6561; adv tel (207) 255-6561; ed tel (207) 255-6561; gen fax (207) 255-4058; adv fax (207) 255-4058; ed fax (207) 255-4058; disp adv e-mail sales@machiasnews.com; class adv e-mail sales@machiasnews.com; ed e-mail editor@machiasnews.com; web site www.machiasnews.com
Circulation: 2,971pd, 70fr; Sworn/Estimate/Non-Audited
Advertising rate: Open inch rate $5.50
Established: 1852
Pub. Emiritus .... Jay B. Hinson
Pub.. Patricia Townsend
Ed./Pub. .... Karen Hinson
Reporter .... Wendy Dyer
Bus. Mgr. .... Mary Bury
Mechanical Specifications: Type page 11 x 17; E - 5 cols, 1 3/4, 1/4 between; A - 5 cols, 1 3/4, 1/4 between; C - 5 cols, 1 3/4, 1/4 between. Equipment & Software: Hardware — APP/Mac Performa, APP/Mac G4; Software — Microsoft/Word 6.0, Adobe/PageMaker 5.0, Adobe/Photoshop 5.0.
Delivery Method: Mail, Newsstand
Areas Served: All over US

MADAWASKA

ST. JOHN VALLEY TIMES (WED)

328 Main St, # 102, Madawaska, ME, 04756-1166, Aroostook, USA; gen tel (207) 728-3336; gen fax (207) 728-3825; disp adv e-mail advertising@sjvalley-times.com; class adv e-mail linda.pelletier@sjvalley-times.com; ed e-mail don.eno@sjvalley-times.com; web site www.sjvalley-times.com
Circulation: 4,415pd,; USPS
Advertising rate: Open inch rate $10.20 (Local); $11.02 (National)
Established: 1957
Group: Cleveland Newspapers, Inc.
Digital Platform - Mobile: Apple, Android
Digital Platform - Tablet: Apple iOS, Android
Pub./Ed. .... Tessie Dubois
Press Mgr. .... Dan Doyon
Print Shop Customer Service Director ... Alison Voisine
General Manager.................... Jessica Blalock
Bookkeeper .... Crystal Berube
News Director .... Don Eno
Reporter .... Monique Labbe
Circulation Director.................. Linda Pelletier
Print Shop Assistant .... Sharon Williams
Mechanical Specifications: Type page 10 x 15; E - 5 cols, 1 9/10, between; A - 5 cols, 1 9/10, between; C - 5 cols, 1 9/10, between. Equipment & Software: Hardware — APP/Mac
Delivery Method: Mail, Newsstand, Carrier, Racks
Areas Served: Aroostook County

NEWCASTLE

THE LINCOLN COUNTY NEWS (THUR)

116 Mills Rd, Newcastle, ME, 04553-3408, Lincoln, USA; gen tel (207) 563-3171; adv tel (207) 563-3171; ed tel (207) 563-3171; gen fax (207) 563-3127; adv fax (207) 563-3127; ed fax (207) 563-3127; disp adv e-mail ads@lcnme.com; ed e-mail info@lcnme.com; web site lcnme.com
Circulation:; Sworn/Estimate/Non-Audited
Advertising rate: Open inch rate $8.75
Established: 1875
Digital Platform - Mobile: Apple, Android, Windows, Blackberry
Digital Platform - Tablet: Apple iOS, Windows 7, Blackberry Tablet OS, Kindle
Publisher.......................... Christopher Roberts
J.W. Oliver
Mechanical Specifications: 2.065 inch columns Page size 7 columns by 21 inchesEquipment & Software: Hardware — COM, IBM; Presses — KP/News King; Software — Adobe/PageMaker, Adobe/Photoshop, In Design QuarkXpress.
Delivery Method: Mail, Newsstand
Areas Served: Lincoln County, Maine

NEWPORT

ROLLING THUNDER EXPRESS (MON)

134A Main St, Newport, ME, 04953-3105, Penobscot, USA; gen tel (207) 876-4957; adv tel (207) 368-2028; ed tel (207) 368-2028; gen fax (207) 368-5513; adv fax (207) 368-5513; ed fax (207) 368-5513; disp adv e-mail info@rollingthunderexpress.com; class adv e-mail info@rollingthunderexpress.com; ed e-mail info@rollingthunderexpress.com; web site www.rollingthunderexpress.com
Circulation: 16,200fr; Sworn/Estimate/Non-Audited
Advertising rate: Open inch rate $6.87
Established: 1985
Pub................................ Sylvia Angel-Currier
Office Mgr. .... Dawn Angel
Circ. Mgr... David Dube
Mng. Ed.................................. Colleen Theriault
Mechanical Specifications: Type page 10 1/4 x 15.Equipment & Software: Hardware — APP/Mac; Software — QPS/QuarkXPress.
Delivery Method: Mail, Newsstand, Carrier, Racks
Areas Served: 04406, 04434, 04435, 04443, 04479, 04488, 04922, 04923, 04928, 04929, 04930, 04932, 04933, 04939, 04943, 04953, 04965, 04967, 04969, 04971

NORWAY

ADVERTISER DEMOCRAT (THUR)

1 Pikes Hl, Norway, ME, 04268-4350, Oxford, USA; gen tel (207) 743-7011; adv tel (207) 743-7011; ed tel (207) 743-7011; gen fax (207) 743-2256; adv fax (207) 743-2256; ed fax (207) 743-2256; disp adv e-mail ads@advertiserdemocrat.com; class adv e-mail ads@advertiserdemocrat.com; ed e-mail newsteam@advertiserdemocrat.com; web site www.advertiserdemocrat.com
Circulation: 4,000pd, 100fr; Sworn/Estimate/Non-Audited
Advertising rate: Open inch rate $8.95
Established: 1826
Group: Sun Media Group
Ed .... A.M. Sheehan
Pub.. Lisa DeSisto
Delivery Method: Mail, Newsstand, Carrier, Racks
Areas Served: 04231, 04051, 04255, 04270, 04268, 04271, 04040, 04220, 04292, 04219, 04289, 04238, 04256, 04274, 04088, 04258

OLD TOWN

PENOBSCOT TIMES (THUR)

282 Main St, Old Town, ME, 04468-1529, Penobscot, USA; gen tel (207) 827-4451; gen fax (207) 827-2280; disp adv e-mail news@thepenobscottimes.com; class adv e-mail news@thepenobscottimes.com; ed e-mail news@thepenobscottimes.com; web site thepenobscottimes.com
Circulation: 4,500pd,; Sworn/Estimate/Non-Audited
Advertising rate: Open inch rate $7.24
Established: 1888
Group: Sun Media Group
Pub.. Lynn Higgins
Ed. .... Greg Fish
Delivery Method: Mail, Newsstand, Carrier, Racks
Areas Served: Penobscot county

PORTLAND

MAINEBIZ (MON)

48 Free St, Ste 109, Portland, ME, 04101-3874, Cumberland, USA; gen tel (207) 761-8379; adv tel (207) 761-8379; ed tel (207) 761-8379; gen fax (207) 761-0732; adv fax (207) 761-0732; ed fax (207) 761-0732; disp adv e-mail leila@mainebiz.biz; class adv e-mail leila@mainebiz.biz; ed e-mail ccoultas@mainebiz.biz; web site www.mainebiz.biz 20,000(visitors)
Circulation: 2,242pd, 7,034fr; Sworn/Estimate/Non-Audited
Advertising rate: 1/6 Pg $1010.00; 1/4 Pg $1190.00; 3/8 Pg $1625.00
Established: 1994
Group: New England Business Media
Pub.. Donna Brassard
Mktg. Mgr. .... Rebekah Roy
Adv. Dir..................................... Leila Musacchio
Delivery Method: Mail, Newsstand
Areas Served: all of Maine

PRESQUE ISLE

AROOSTOOK REPUBLICAN AND NEWS (WED)

PO Box 510, Presque Isle, ME, 04769-0510, Aroostook, USA; gen tel (207) 496-3251; gen fax (207) 492-4351; disp adv e-mail republicansales@bangordailynews.com; class adv e-mail republican@bangordailynews.com; ed e-mail republican@bangordailynews.com; web site www.thecounty.me
Circulation: 2,643pd, 32fr; Sworn/Estimate/Non-Audited
Advertising rate: Open inch rate $15.50
Established: 1880
Group: Bangor Publishing Company
Digital Platform - Mobile: Windows
Editor .... Rick Levasseur
Sales Manager .... Danielle Camping
Delivery Method: Mail, Newsstand, Carrier, Racks
Areas Served: Caribou, Limestone, New Sweden, Stockholm, Fort Fairfield, Washburn, Woodland

PRESQUE ISLE STAR-HERALD (WED)

40 North St, 40 North St, Presque Isle, ME, 04769-2287, Aroostook, USA; gen tel (207) 768-5431; adv tel (207) 768-5431; ed tel (207) 768-5431; gen fax (207) 764-7585; adv fax (207) 764-7585; ed fax (207) 764-7585; disp adv e-mail starheraldsales@nepublish.com; class adv e-mail starheraldsales@nepublish.com; ed e-mail starherald@nepublish.com; web site www.starherald-me.com
Circulation: 7,500pd, 52fr; Sworn/Estimate/Non-Audited
Advertising rate: Open inch rate $14.25
Established: 1871
Managing Ed. .... Mark Putnam
Mechanical Specifications: Type page 13 x 21 1/2; E - 6 cols, 2 1/16, 1/8 between; A - 6 cols, 2 1/16, 1/8 between; C - 9 cols, 2 1/16, 1/8 between.
Delivery Method: Mail, Carrier, Racks
Areas Served: 04769, 04740, 04757, 04758, 04732

ROCKLAND

FREE PRESS (THUR)

8 N Main St, Ste 101, Rockland, ME, 04841-3154, Knox, USA; gen tel (207) 596-0055; adv tel (207) 596-0055; ed tel (207) 596-

0055; gen fax (207) 596-6698; adv fax (207) 596-6698; ed fax (207) 596-6698; disp adv e-mail admanager@freepressonline.com; class adv e-mail admanager@freepressonline.com; ed e-mail editor@freepressonline.com; web site www.freepressonline.com
Circulation: 12,500fr; Sworn/Estimate/Non-Audited
Advertising rate: Open inch rate $11.00
Established: 1985
Adv. Mgr. .... Steve Davis
Sr. Sales Rep. .... Glenn Billington
Pub. .... Alice McFadden
Ed. .... Patty Poe
Prodn. Mgr. .... Wendell Greer
Mechanical Specifications: Type page 10 1/8 x 15.Equipment & Software: Hardware — APP/Mac; Software — QPS/QuarkXPress.
Delivery Method: Mail, Newsstand, Carrier, Racks
Areas Served: 04538, 04543, 04547, 04553, 04555, 04563, 04572, 04574, 04578, 04841, 04843, 04849, 04854, 04855, 04856, 04858, 04859, 04860, 04861, 04862, 04864, 04915, 04974

THE CAMDEN HERALD (WED)
91 Camden St, Ste 403, Rockland, ME, 04841-2421, Knox, USA; gen tel (207) 236-8511; gen fax (207) 236-2816; disp adv e-mail sales@courierpublicationsllc.com; class adv e-mail sales@courierpublicationsllc.com; ed e-mail news@courierpublicationsllc.com; web site knox.villagesoup.com
Circulation: 8,438pd, 1,407fr; Sworn/Estimate/Non-Audited
Advertising rate: Open inch rate $9.75
Established: 1869
Group: Courier Publications, LLC
Digital Platform - Mobile: Apple, Android
Owner .... Reade Brower
Operations Dir. .... Bryan Gess
Ed. .... Stephanie Grinnell
Prodn. Mgr. .... Christine Dunkle
Mechanical Specifications: Type page 13 x 21; A - 6 cols, 2 1/16, 1/8 between; C - 9 cols, 1 5/16, 1/8 between.Equipment & Software: Hardware — APP/Macs; Software — Adobe/PageMaker, WordPerfect, QPS/QuarkXPress.
Delivery Method: Mail, Newsstand, Racks
Areas Served: Knox County

RUMFORD

RUMFORD FALLS TIMES (WED)
69 Congress St, Rumford, ME, 04276-2015, Oxford, USA; gen tel (207) 364-7893; adv tel (207) 364-7893; ed tel (207) 364-7893; gen fax (207) 369-0170; adv fax (207) 369-0170; ed fax (207) 369-0170; disp adv e-mail spenney@sunjournal.com; class adv e-mail spenney@sunjournal.com; ed e-mail editor@rumfordfallstimes.com; web site www.rumfordfallstimes.com
Circulation: 4,000pd, 26fr; Sworn/Estimate/Non-Audited
Advertising rate: Open inch rate $8.95
Established: 1883
Group: MaineToday Media
Mng. Ed. .... Bruce Farrin
Delivery Method: Mail, Newsstand, Carrier, Racks
Areas Served: Rumford (ME) & Neighboring Communities

SANFORD

SANFORD NEWS (THUR)
835 Main St, Sanford, ME, 04073-3522, York, USA; gen tel (207) 324-5986; adv tel (207) 324-5986; ed tel (207) 324-5986; gen fax (207) 490-1431; adv fax (207) 490-1431; ed fax (207) 490-1431; disp adv e-mail news@sanfordnews.com; class adv e-mail news@sanfordnews.com; ed e-mail news@sanfordnews.com; web site www.sanfordnews.com
Circulation: 5,970pd,; Sworn/Estimate/Non-Audited
Advertising rate: Open inch rate $10.60
Established: 1980
Pub. .... Robert H. Foster
Ed. .... Shawn Sullivan
Adv. Mgr. .... Chris Olio
Circ. Mgr. .... Jerry Perkins
CEO .... Rich Conner
VP, Adv. .... Michelle Lester
Mechanical Specifications: Type page 10 15/16 x 21 1/2; E - 6 cols, 1 5/6, between; A - 6 cols, 1 5/6, between; C - 9 cols, 1 3/16, between. Equipment & Software: Hardware — Intel/Pentium; Software — QPS/QuarkXPress.
Delivery Method: Mail
Areas Served: York County

SOUTH CHINA

TOWN LINE (THUR)
PO Box 89, South China, ME, 04358-0089, Kennebec, USA; gen tel (207) 445-2234; adv tel (207) 445-2234; ed tel (207) 445-2234; gen fax (207) 445-2265; adv fax (207) 445-2265; ed fax (207) 445-2265; disp adv e-mail townline@fairpoint.net ; class adv e-mail townline@fairpoint.net ; ed e-mail townline@fairpoint.net ; web site townline.org
Advertising rate: Open inch rate $12.50
Established: 1989
Mng. Ed. .... Roland Hallee
Circulation Director .... Claire Breton
Delivery Method: Newsstand, Racks
Areas Served: Central Maine & Somerset County

STONINGTON

ISLAND AD-VANTAGES (THUR)
69 Main St, Stonington, ME, 4681, Hancock, USA; gen tel (207) 367-2200; adv tel (207) 367-2200; ed tel (207) 367-2200; gen fax (207) 367-6397; adv fax (207) 367-6397; ed fax (207) 367-6397; disp adv e-mail ads@pbp.me; class adv e-mail classifieds@pbp.me; ed e-mail news@pbp.me; web site www.islandadvantages.com
Circulation: 1,684pd, 29fr; Sworn/Estimate/Non-Audited
Advertising rate: Open inch rate $15
Established: 1882
Ed. .... R. Nathaniel W. Barrows
Managing Ed. .... Faith DeAmbrose
Circ. Mgr. .... Cathy Marshall
Mechanical Specifications: Type page 10 3/8 x 15; E - 5 cols, 2, 1/8 between; A - 4 cols, 2 1/2, 1/8 between; C - 5 cols, 2, 2 between.
Delivery Method: Mail, Newsstand, Carrier
Areas Served: Stonington

WELLS

WEEKLY SENTINEL (FRI)
952 Post Rd, Unit 10, Wells, ME, 04090-4142, York, USA; gen tel (207) 646-8448; gen fax (207) 646-8477; disp adv e-mail ads@theweeklysentinel.com; ed e-mail editor@theweeklysentinel.com; web site www.theweeklysentinel.com
Circulation: 39,592fr; USPS
Advertising rate: $12.00 pci
Established: 2005
Operations Mgr. .... Dan Brennan
Acct. Mgr. .... David Kennedy
Mechanical Specifications: page measurement—5 cols (10 inches) x 14.5 inches in depth
Delivery Method: Mail, Racks
Areas Served: All of York County excluding Biddeford and Saco

WESTBROOK

REPORTER (FRI)
840 Main St, Westbrook, ME, 04092-2847, Cumberland, USA; gen tel (207) 854-2577; adv tel (207) 854-2577; ed tel (207) 854-2577; gen fax (207) 854-0018; adv fax (207) 854-0018; ed fax (207) 854-0018; disp adv e-mail sales@keepmecurrent.com; class adv e-mail sales@keepmecurrent.com; ed e-mail info@keepmecurrent.com; web site www.keepmecurrent.com
Advertising rate: Open inch rate $10.00
Established: 2001
Group: Current Publishing
Pres./Pub. .... Lee Hews
Exec. Ed. .... Jane P. Lord
Advertising/Circulation Director .... Mark Hews
Mng. Ed. .... Ben Bragdon
Delivery Method: Mail, Newsstand, Carrier, Racks
Areas Served: Alfred, Limerick, Lyman, Newfield, Shapleigh, Waterboro

SUN CHRONICLE (THUR)
840 Main St, Westbrook, ME, 04092-2847, Cumberland, USA; gen tel (207) 854-2577; adv tel (207) 854-2577; ed tel (207) 854-2577; gen fax (207) 854-0018; adv fax (207) 854-0018; ed fax (207) 854-0018; disp adv e-mail sales@keepmecurrent.com; class adv e-mail sales@keepmecurrent.com; ed e-mail info@keepmecurrent.com; web site www.keepmecurrent.com
Advertising rate: Open inch rate $13.00
Established: 2001
Group: Current Publishing
Ed. .... Jane P. Lord
Mark Hews
Ben Bragdon
Delivery Method: Mail, Newsstand, Carrier, Racks
Areas Served: Biddeford, Saco & Old Orchard Beach

THE CURRENT (THUR)
840 Main St, Westbrook, ME, 04092-2847, Cumberland, USA; gen tel (207) 854-2577; adv tel (207) 854-2577; ed tel (207) 854-2577; gen fax (207) 854-0018; adv fax (207) 854-0018; ed fax (207) 854-0018; disp adv e-mail sales@keepmecurrent.com; class adv e-mail sales@keepmecurrent.com; ed e-mail info@keepmecurrent.com; web site www.keepmecurrent.com
Advertising rate: Open inch rate $15.50
Established: 2001
Group: Current Publishing
Digital Platform - Mobile: Apple, Android
Ed. .... Jane P. Lord
Ad. Director .... Mark Hews
Delivery Method: Mail, Newsstand, Carrier, Racks
Areas Served: Scarborough, South Portland, Cape Elizabeth

THE LAKES REGION WEEKLY (FRI)
840 Main St, Westbrook, ME, 04092-2847, Cumberland, USA; gen tel (207) 854-2577; adv tel (207) 854-2577; ed tel (207) 854-2577; gen fax (207) 854-0018; adv fax (207) 854-0018; ed fax (207) 854-0018; disp adv e-mail sales@keepmecurrent.com; class adv e-mail sales@keepmecurrent.com; ed e-mail info@keepmecurrent.com ; web site www.keepmecurrent.com
Circulation: 5,800pd,; Sworn/Estimate/Non-Audited
Advertising rate: Open inch rate $19.00
Established: 2001
Group: Current Publishing
Pub. .... Lee Hewes-Casler
Circ. Mgr. .... Mark Hews
Ed. .... Brendan Moran
Exec. Ed. .... Jane P. Lord
Mechanical Specifications: Type page 10 1/2 x 15; E - 5 cols, 1 15/16, 1/6 between; C - 6 cols, between.Equipment & Software: Hardware — APP/Macs; Software — Adobe/PageMaker 7.1, Claris.
Delivery Method: Mail, Newsstand, Carrier, Racks
Areas Served: Windham, Standish, Raymond, Sebago, Naples

TRI-TOWN WEEKLY (WED)
840 Main St, Westbrook, ME, 04092-2847, Cumberland, USA; gen tel (207) 854-2577; adv tel (207) 854-2577; ed tel (207) 854-2577; gen fax (207) 854-0018; adv fax (207) 854-0018; ed fax (207) 854-0018; disp adv e-mail sales@keepmecurrent.com; class adv e-mail sales@keepmecurrent.com; ed e-mail info@keepmecurrent.com; web site www.keepmecurrent.com
Advertising rate: Open inch rate $11.00
Established: 2001
Group: Current Publishing
Digital Platform - Mobile: Apple, Android
Ed. .... Jane P. Lord
Ad. Dir. .... Mark Hews
Delivery Method: Mail, Newsstand, Carrier, Racks
Areas Served: Durham, Pownal, Freeport

WEEKLY OBSERVER (FRI)
840 Main St, Westbrook, ME, 04092-2847, Cumberland, USA; gen tel (207) 854-2577; adv tel (207) 854-2577; ed tel (207) 854-2577; gen fax (207) 854-0018; adv fax (207) 854-0018; ed fax (207) 854-0018; disp adv e-mail sales@keepmecurrent.com; class adv e-mail sales@keepmecurrent.com; ed e-mail info@keepmecurrent.com; web site www.keepmecurrent.com
Advertising rate: Open inch rate $10.00
Established: 2001
Group: Current Publishing
Digital Platform - Mobile: Apple, Android
Ed. .... Jane P. Lord
Ad. Dir. .... Mark Hews
Delivery Method: Mail, Newsstand, Carrier, Racks
Areas Served: Sanford, Springvale, Acton, Lebanon

MARYLAND

ANNAPOLIS

BOWIE BLADE-NEWS (THUR)
2000 Capital Dr, Annapolis, MD, 21401-3155, Anne Arundel, USA; gen tel (410) 268-5000; adv tel (410) 268-5000; gen fax (410) 268-4643; adv fax (410) 280-5974; disp adv e-mail localads@capgaznews.com; class adv e-mail classifieds@capgaznews.com; ed e-mail tips@capgaznews.com; web site www.capitalgazette.com/bowie_bladenews
Circulation: 35,000fr; Sworn/Estimate/Non-Audited
Advertising rate: Open inch rate $37.52
Established: 1900
Group: Landmark Media Enterprises, LLC
Digital Platform - Mobile: Apple, Android
Digital Platform - Tablet: Apple iOS, Android, Kindle
Pub. .... Pat Richardson
Circ. Dir. .... Rob Pryor
Areas Served: Bowie

CROFTON-WEST COUNTY GAZETTE (THUR)
2000 Capital Dr, Annapolis, MD, 21401-3155, Anne Arundel, USA; gen tel (410) 268-5000; adv tel (410) 268-5000; ed tel (410) 280-5959; gen fax (410) 268-4643; adv fax (410) 280-5974; ed fax (410) 280-5953; disp adv e-mail localads@capgaznews.com; class adv e-mail classifieds@capgaznews.com; ed e-mail cwcgazette@capgaznews.com; web site www.capitalgazette.com/crofton_west-county
Advertising rate: Open inch rate $37.52
Established: 1995
Group: Landmark Media Enterprises, LLC
Digital Platform - Mobile: Apple, Android
Digital Platform - Tablet: Apple iOS, Android, Kindle
Pub. .... Pat Richardson
Ed. .... Steve Gunn
Adv. Dir. .... Marty Padden
Areas Served: Crofton, Gambrills, Odenton, Piney Orchard, Seven Oaks

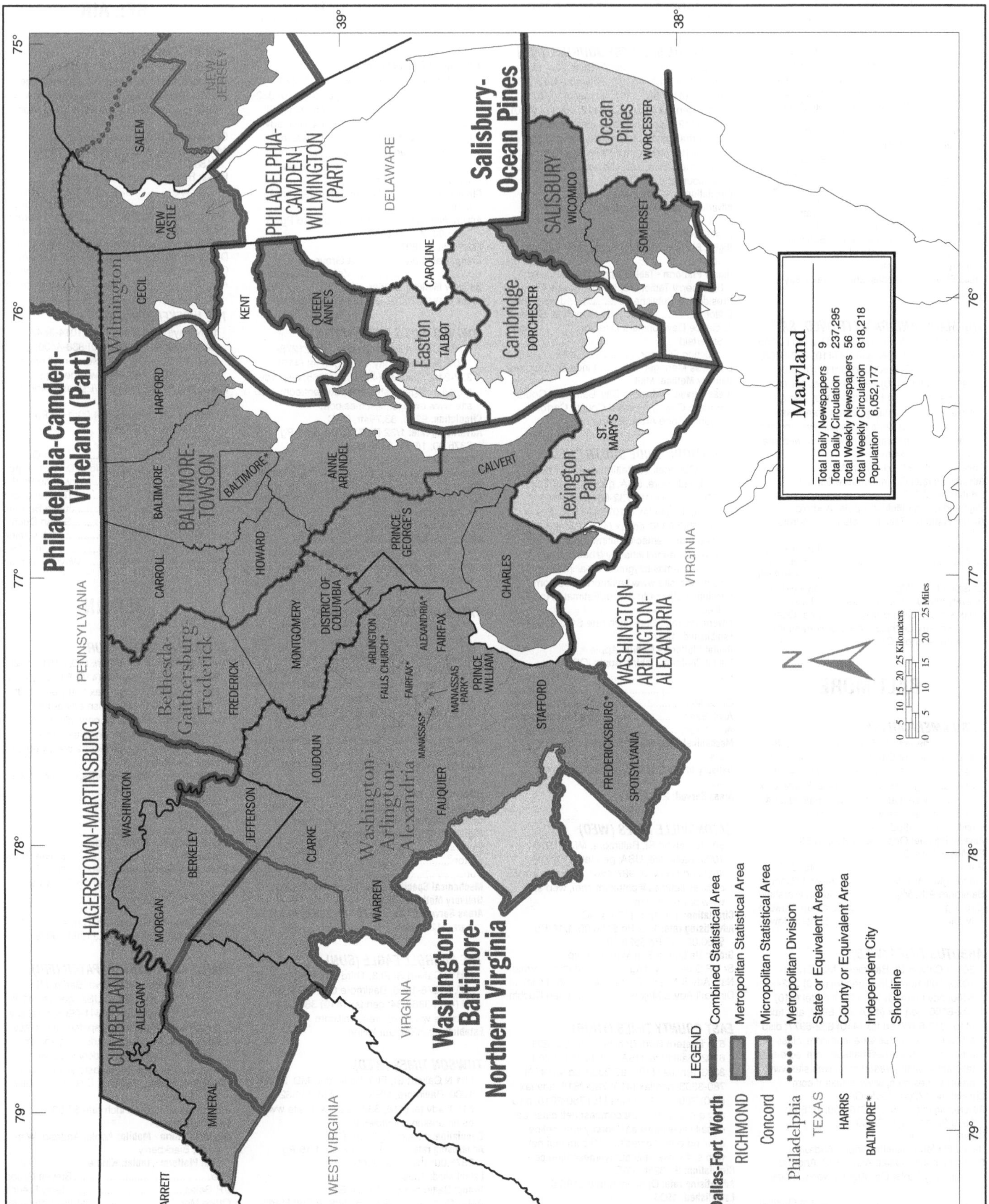
Maryland
Total Daily Newspapers 9
Total Daily Circulation 237,295
Total Weekly Newspapers 56
Total Weekly Circulation 818,218
Population 6,052,177
Philadelphia-Camden-Vineland (Part)
PHILADELPHIA-CAMDEN-WILMINGTON (PART)
Salisbury-Ocean Pines
Washington-Baltimore-Northern Virginia
HAGERSTOWN-MARTINSBURG
WASHINGTON-ARLINGTON-ALEXANDRIA
BALTIMORE-TOWSON
Wilmington
Bethesda-Gaithersburg-Frederick
Washington-Arlington-Alexandria
CUMBERLAND
SALISBURY
Ocean Pines
Easton
Cambridge
Lexington Park
PENNSYLVANIA
NEW JERSEY
DELAWARE
VIRGINIA
WEST VIRGINIA
SALEM
NEW CASTLE
CECIL
KENT
QUEEN ANNE'S
CAROLINE
TALBOT
DORCHESTER
WICOMICO
WORCESTER
SOMERSET
HARFORD
BALTIMORE
BALTIMORE*
ANNE ARUNDEL
CALVERT
ST. MARY'S
CARROLL
HOWARD
PRINCE GEORGE'S
CHARLES
MONTGOMERY
DISTRICT OF COLUMBIA
ARLINGTON
FALLS CHURCH*
ALEXANDRIA*
FAIRFAX
FAIRFAX*
MANASSAS PARK*
MANASSAS*
PRINCE WILLIAM
STAFFORD
FREDERICKSBURG*
SPOTSYLVANIA
FREDERICK
LOUDOUN
FAUQUIER
WASHINGTON
JEFFERSON
BERKELEY
CLARKE
MORGAN
WARREN
ALLEGANY
MINERAL
GARRETT
75°
76°
77°
78°
79°
39°
38°
0 5 10 15 20 25 Kilometers
0 5 10 15 20 25 Miles
N
LEGEND
Dallas-Fort Worth Combined Statistical Area
RICHMOND Metropolitan Statistical Area
Concord Micropolitan Statistical Area
Philadelphia Metropolitan Division
TEXAS State or Equivalent Area
HARRIS County or Equivalent Area
BALTIMORE* Independent City
Shoreline

PASSWORDS (THUR)
1160 Spa Rd, Ste 1A, Annapolis, MD, 21403-1097, Anne Arundel, USA; gen tel (410) 626-9888; gen fax (410) 626-0008; disp adv e-mail ads@bayweekly.com; class adv e-mail ads@bayweekly.com; ed e-mail editor@bayweekly.com; web site www.bayweekly.com
Circulation: 17,000fr; Sworn/Estimate/Non-Audited
Advertising rate: Open inch rate $35.00
Established: 1993Editions: (52)
Ed./Pub. .... Sandra Martin
Gen. Mgr. .... J. Alex Knoll
Mktg. Dir. .... Lisa Edler Knoll
Prod. Mgr. .... Betsy Kehne
Editorial assistant .... Kathy Knotts
Mechanical Specifications: Changed July 2104 to 9.625"W x 12.75"HEquipment & Software: Hardware — Full Apple Shop
Delivery Method: Racks
Areas Served: Annapolis-Chesapeake Bay Region

THE MARYLAND GAZETTE (WED, SAT)
2000 Capital Dr, Annapolis, MD, 21401-3155, Anne Arundel, USA; gen tel (410) 268-5000; adv tel (410) 268-5000; ed tel (410) 280-5959; gen fax (410) 280-5953; adv fax (410) 280-5974; ed fax (410) 280-5953; disp adv e-mail localads@capgaznews.com; class adv e-mail classifieds@capgaznews.com; ed e-mail gazstaff@capgaznews.com; web site www.capitalgazette.com
Circulation: 13,977pd, 919fr; AAM
Advertising rate: Open inch rate $35.79
Established: 1727
Digital Platform - Mobile: Apple, Android
Digital Platform - Tablet: Apple iOS, Android, Kindle
Adv. Dir. .... Marty Padden
Circ. Dir. .... Rob Pryor
Ed. .... Rick Hutzell
Classified Adv. Mgr. .... Carolyn Gooden
Delivery Method: Mail, Newsstand, Racks
Areas Served: Glen Burnie, Pasadena, Odenton, Severn, Linthicum & other communities in Anne Arundel County

BALTIMORE

AFRO AMERICAN (SAT)
2519 N Charles St, Baltimore, MD, 21218-4602, Baltimore City, USA; gen tel (410) 554-8200; adv tel (410) 554-8271; ed tel (410) 554- 8277; gen fax (410) 554-8213; disp adv e-mail lhowze@afro.com; ed e-mail editor@afro.com; web site www.afro.com
Circulation: 5,948pd,; AAM
Advertising rate: Open inch rate $46.56
Established: 1892
Pub. .... John J. Oliver
Washington Adv. Mgr. .... Kevin O'Connor
Baltimore Adv. Mgr. .... Susan Warshaw
Circ. Mgr. .... J. Coleman Balware
Adv. Dir. .... Lenora Howze

ARBUTUS TIMES (WED)
501 N Calvert St, Baltimore, MD, 21278-1000, Baltimore, USA; gen tel (410) 332-6000; adv tel (410) 332-6300; ed tel (410) 332-6000; gen fax (410) 332-6977; adv fax (410) 332-6977; ed fax (410) 332-6977; disp adv e-mail advertise@baltsun.com; class adv e-mail advertise@baltsun.com; ed e-mail talkback@baltimoresun.com; web site www.arbutustimes.com; www.patuxent.com
Circulation: 470pd, 205fr; CAC
Advertising rate: 1/32 Pg $150.00; 1/16 Pg $300.00; 1/8 Pg $525.00
Group: Tronc, Inc.
Digital Platform - Mobile: Apple, Android
Digital Platform - Tablet: Apple iOS, Android, Blackberry Tablet OS, Kindle, Nook, Kindle Fire
Pub. .... Jim Quimby
Mng. Ed. .... Keith Meisel
Sr. VP, Sales/Mktg. .... Judith Berman
Nat'l Adv. Majors/Sales Mgr. .... Matt Cimino
Dir, Nat'l Adv. .... Susan Duchin
Dir., Direct Mktg. .... Jim Alvey
Dir, Classified Adv. .... Wayne Lowman
Areas Served: Arbutus, Baltimore Highlands, Relay, Lansdowne & Halethorpe

BALTIMORE BUSINESS JOURNAL (FRI)
36 S Charles St Ste 2500, Suite 205, Baltimore, MD, 21201-3107, Baltimore City, USA; gen tel (410) 576-1161; adv tel (410) 576-1161; gen fax (410) 752-3112; adv fax (410) 752-3112; disp adv e-mail mdamareck@bizjournals.com; class adv e-mail mdamareck@bizjournals.com; ed e-mail jsullivan@bizjournals.com; web site www.baltimorebusinessjournal.com
Circulation: 9,206pd,; AAM
Advertising rate: Rates vary. Call for current pricing
Established: 1983
Digital Platform - Mobile: Apple, Android, Windows
Digital Platform - Tablet: Apple iOS, Android, Blackberry Tablet OS, Kindle, Kindle Fire
President & Publisher .... John Dinkel
Editor .... Joanna Sullivan
Audience Development Director .... Eileen Silberfeld
Production Director .... Mike Gillispie
Business Manager .... Linda Schummers
Delivery Method: Mail
Areas Served: Baltimore City, Baltimore County, Harford County, Howard County Carroll County, Anne Arundel County

BALTIMORE GUIDE SOUTH (WED)
2935 Odonnell St, Baltimore, MD, 21224-4823, Baltimore, USA; gen tel (410) 732-6600; adv tel (410) 732-6600; ed tel (410) 732-6600; gen fax (410) 732-6336; adv fax (410) 732-6336; ed fax (410) 732-6336; disp adv e-mail lnemec@baltimoreguide.com; class adv e-mail jchaney@baltimoreguide.com; ed e-mail ezygmont@baltimoreguide.com; web site www.baltimoreguide.com
Circulation: 25,000fr; Sworn/Estimate/Non-Audited
Advertising rate: Open inch rate $18.08
Established: 1927
Digital Platform - Mobile: Apple
Digital Platform - Tablet: Apple iOS
Pub. .... Perry Corsetti
Ed. .... Erik Zygmont
Office Mgr. .... Jackie Miller
Acct. Exec .... Lisa Nemec
Acct. Exec. .... Jessica Chaney
Mechanical Specifications: Type page 10 x 13 3/4.
Delivery Method: Mail, Newsstand, Carrier, Racks
Areas Served: 21230

CATONSVILLE TIMES (WED)
501 N Calvert St, Baltimore, MD, 21278-1000, Baltimore, USA; gen tel (410) 788-4500; ed fax (410) 997-4564; disp adv e-mail catonsvilletimes@patuxent.com; web site www.patuxent.com
Circulation: 1,421pd, 175fr; CAC
Advertising rate: 1/32 Pg $150.00; 1/16 Pg $300.00; 1/8 Pg $525.00
Group: Baltimore Sun Media Group
Sr. VP Sales & Mktg. .... Judith Berman
Nat'l Adv & Majors Sales Mgr .... Matt Cimino
Dir Nat'l Adv & Majors .... Susan Duchin

EAST COUNTY TIMES (THUR)
513 Eastern Blvd, Baltimore, MD, 21221-6702, Baltimore, USA; gen tel (410) 780-3303; adv tel (410) 780-3303; ed tel (410) 780-3303; gen fax (410) 780-2616; adv fax (410) 780-2616; ed fax (410) 780-2616; disp adv e-mail ectsales@comcast.net; class adv e-mail classified@eastcountytimesonline.com; ed e-mail ectеditorial@comcast.net; web site www.eastcountytimesonline.com
Circulation: 31,325fr; VAC
Advertising rate: Open inch rate $19.75
Established: 1995
Group: Chatsworth Enterprises, Inc.
Pub./Gen. Mgr. .... George Wilbanks
Adv. Mgr. .... Linda K. Mrok
Opns. Mgr. .... Mike Wilbanks
Ed. .... Allison McAlister
Art. Dir. .... Angie Hess
Delivery Method: Mail, Carrier, Racks
Areas Served: Eastern Baltimore County - 21219, 21220, 21221, 21222, 21224, 21236, 21237, 21128, 21162, 21087

LAUREL LEADER (THUR)
501 N Calvert St, Baltimore, MD, 21278-1000, Baltimore City, USA; gen tel (410) 332-6594; ed tel (410) 332-6594; gen fax (410) 332-6594; ed fax (410) 332-6594; disp adv e-mail jduchman@baltsun.com; class adv e-mail classifieds@baltsun.com; ed e-mail Laurelleadernews@tronc.com; web site www.laurelleader.com
Circulation: 30,512fr; Sworn/Estimate/Non-Audited
Advertising rate: 1/32 Pg $188.00; 1/16 Pg $375.00; 1/8 Pg $656.00
Established: 1897
Group: Baltimore Sun Media Group
Ed. .... Melanie Dzwonchyk
Delivery Method: Carrier
Areas Served: 20707, 20708, 20723, 20724

OWINGS MILLS TIMES (MTHLY)
501 N Calvert St, Baltimore, MD, 21278-1000, Baltimore City, USA; gen tel (410) 337-2400; gen fax (410) 997-0885; disp adv e-mail owingsmillstimes@patuxent.com; web site www.owingsmillstimes.com
Circulation: 92pd, 33,794fr; CAC
Advertising rate: 1/32 Pg $188.00; 1/16 Pg $375.00; 1/8 Pg $656.00
Group: Baltimore Sun Media Group
Adv. Mgr. .... Pat Sweeney
Ed. .... Janice Jewell
Nat'l Adv. & Majors Sales Mgr. .... Matt Cimino
Dir, Nat'l Adv & Majors .... Susan Duchin
Sr VP Sales & Mkting .... Judith Berman
Mechanical Specifications: Type page 10 x 12 1/2; E - 5 cols, 1 5/6, 1/6 between; A - 5 cols, 1 5/6, 1/6 between; C - 8 cols, 1 1/12, 1/12 between.

THE BALTIMORE GUIDE (WED)
2935 Odonnell St, Baltimore, MD, 21224-4823, Baltimore City, USA; gen tel (410) 732-6600; adv tel (410) 732-6616; gen fax (410) 732-6336; adv fax (410) 732-6336; disp adv e-mail lnemec@baltimoreguide.com; class adv e-mail ehoffman@baltimoreguide.com; ed e-mail editor@baltimoreguide.com; web site www.baltimoreguide.com
Circulation: 35,000fr; Sworn/Estimate/Non-Audited
Advertising rate: 1/32 Pg $60.00; 1/16 Pg $100.00; 1/8 Pg $170.00
Established: 1927
Group: Ascend Publishing
Digital Platform - Mobile: Apple, Android
Digital Platform - Tablet: Apple iOS
Pub. .... Perry Corsetti
Editor .... Erik Zygmont
Pub. .... Ed Hoffman
Mechanical Specifications: Type page 9 1/2 x 10
Delivery Method: Carrier
Areas Served: 21231, 21224, 21202 part, 21205 part, 21222 part

THE CARROLL EAGLE (SUN)
501 N Calvert St Fl 3, Third Floor, Baltimore, MD, 21278-1000, Baltimore City, USA; gen tel (410) 386-334; gen fax (410) 386-0340; web site www.explorecarroll.com
Established: 2009Paul Milton

TOWSON TIMES (WED)
501 N Calvert St, Fl 3, Baltimore, MD, 21278-1000, Baltimore, USA; gen tel (410) 332-6100; adv tel (410) 332-6300; web site www.baltimoresun.com/towson
Circulation: 110pd, 13,251fr; CAC
Advertising rate: 1/32 Pg $188.00; 1/16 Pg $375.00; 1/8 Pg $656.00
Established: 1958
Group: Baltimore Sun Media Group
AME, Community News, Baltimore Sun Media Group .... Elizabeth Eck
Areas Served: 21030, 21093, 21204, 21286, 21212, 21239, 21234

BEL AIR

THE RECORD (FRI)
10 N Hays St, Bel Air, MD, 21014-3643, Harford, USA; gen tel (410) 838-4451; gen fax (410) 838-7867; disp adv e-mail news@theaegis.com; web site www.hdgrecordonline.com
Circulation: 1,672pd, 56fr; AAM
Advertising rate: 1/32 Pg $94.00; 1/16 Pg $188.00; 1/8 Pg $328.00
Group: Baltimore Sun Media Group
Pub. .... John D. Worthington
Exec. Ed. .... Ted Hendricks
Sr VP Sales & Mkting .... Judith Berman
Dir, Nat'l Adv & Majors .... Susan Duchin
Nat'l Adv & Majors, Sales Mgr. .... Matt Cimino
Dir, Direct Mktg. .... Jim Alvey
Classified Adv. Dir. .... Wayne Lowman
Adv. Dir .... Daniel Sarko

THE WEEKENDER (FRI)
10 N Hays St, Bel Air, MD, 21014-3643, Harford, USA; gen tel (410) 838-4400; gen fax (410) 638-0357; disp adv e-mail news@theaegis.com; web site www.theaegis.com
Circulation: 87,000fr; Sworn/Estimate/Non-Audited
Advertising rate: 1/32 Pg $94.00; 1/16 Pg $188.00; 1/8 Pg $328.00
Group: Tronc, Inc.
Pres. .... Jim Quimby
Pub. .... John D. Worthington
Adv. Dir. .... Mary Anne Pfeffer
Exec. Ed. .... Ted Hendricks
Sr. VP. Sales/Mktg. .... Judith Berman
Dir. Nat'l Adv. .... Susan Duchin
Nat'l Adv./Sales Mgr, ... Matt Cimino
Dir. Direct Mktg. .... Jim Alvey
Classified Adv. Dir. .... Wayne Lowman

BERLIN

BAYSIDE GAZETTE (THUR)
11 S Main St, # 1A, Berlin, MD, 21811-1426, Worcester, USA; gen tel (410) 641-0039; ed tel (410) 641-0039; gen fax (410) 641-0085; ed fax (410) 641-0085; disp adv e-mail ebrady@baysidegazette.com; class adv e-mail classifieds@oceancitytoday.net; ed e-mail editor@baysidegazette.com; web site www.baysideoc.com
Circulation: 10,000fr; Sworn/Estimate/Non-Audited
Advertising rate: $11.47
Established: 2004
Group: Ocean City Today
Digital Platform - Tablet: Kindle
Pres./Pub. .... Elaine Brady
Mechanical Specifications: page width 9 3/4" page depth 13 1/4"Equipment & Software: ; Software — Quark In-Design
Delivery Method: Newsstand, Carrier
Areas Served: 21811,21842,21893,19975

MARYLAND COAST DISPATCH (FRI)
10012 Old Ocean City Blvd, Berlin, MD, 21811-1145, Worcester, USA; gen tel (410) 641-4561; gen fax (410) 641-0966; disp adv e-mail editor@mdcoastdispatch.com; class adv e-mail classifieds@mdcoastdispatch.com; ed e-mail editor@mdcoastdispatch.com; web site www.mdcoastdispatch.com
Circulation: 500pd, 25,000fr; Sworn/Estimate/Non-Audited
Advertising rate: Open inch rate $7.00
Established: 1984
Digital Platform - Mobile: Apple, Android, Windows, Blackberry
Digital Platform - Tablet: Kindle
Pub. .... Steven Green
VP, Sales .... Terry French
Office Mgr. .... Patricia Lohmeyer
Ed. .... J. Steven Green
News Ed. .... Shawn Soper
Delivery Method: Mail, Newsstand, Carrier, Racks
Areas Served: Ocean City, Salisbury, etc.

OCEAN PINES INDEPENDENT (WED)
11021 Nicholas Ln, Ste 10, Berlin, MD, 21811-3244, Worcester, USA; gen tel (410) 213-9442; gen fax (410) 213-9458; ed e-mail Newshub@DelmarvaNow.com; web site www.oceanpinesindependent.com
Circulation: 8,600fr; Sworn/Estimate/Non-Audited
Advertising rate: Open inch rate $10.20
Group: Gannett
Exec. Ed....................................Michael Kilian
Areas Served: 21842, 21811

BRUNSWICK

THE VALLEY CITIZEN (THUR)
101 W Potomac St, Brunswick, MD, 21716-1114, Frederick, USA; gen tel (301) 834-7722; disp adv e-mail citizen@mip.net; web site www.citizennewspapers.com
Circulation: 2,200pd,; Sworn/Estimate/Non-Audited
Advertising rate: Open inch rate $6.45
Established: 1990
Ed. .... Julie MaynardEquipment & Software: Hardware — APP/Mac
Delivery Method: Mail, Newsstand, Racks
Areas Served: 21769, 21773, 21755, 21714, 21713

CALIFORNIA

THE ENTERPRISE (WED, FRI)
23125 Campton Way, California, MD, 20653, St. Mary's, USA; gen tel (301) 862-2111; gen fax (301) 737-2896; disp adv e-mail adaily@somdnews.com; web site www.somdnews.com
Circulation: 11,260pd,; CAC
Advertising rate: Open inch rate $22.71
Group: Adams Publishing Group, LLC
Pub..Karen Acton
Adv. Dir..Al Dailey
Ed. ....Rick Boyd
Mng. Ed.................................. Donnie Morgan
Circ. Exec..................................... Phyllis Dietz
Mechanical Specifications: Type page 13 x 21; E - 6 cols, 2 1/16, between; A - 6 cols, 2 1/16, between; C - 9 cols, between.

CAMBRIDGE

DORCHESTER BANNER (WED, FRI)
103 Cedar St, Cambridge, MD, 21613-2361, Dorchester, USA; gen tel (410) 228-3131; adv tel (410) 228-3131; ed tel (410) 228-3131; gen fax (410) 228-6547; disp adv e-mail banner@newszap.com; class adv e-mail classads@newszap.com; ed e-mail banner@newszap.com; web site http://www.dorchesterbanner.com/
Circulation: 1,400pd, 848fr; CAC
Advertising rate: 1/8 Pg $279; 1/4 Pg $419; 1/2 Pg $759; Full Pg $1409
Established: 1897
Group: Independent Newsmedia Inc. Usa
Pub..Darel LaPrade
Promotions Manager .... Heather Cregar
Major Accts. Adv. Mgr.........................Tim Gary
Delivery Method: Mail, Newsstand, Carrier, Racks
Areas Served: 21613,21622,21631,21632,21643,21655,21659,21664,21669,21673,21675,21677,21835,21869

THE DORCHESTER STAR (FRI)
511 Poplar St, Cambridge, MD, 21613-1833, Dorchester, USA; gen tel (410) 228-0222; adv tel (410) 228-0222; ed tel (410) 228-0222; gen fax (410) 228-0685; disp adv e-mail news@dorchesterstar.com; web site www.dorchesterstar.com
Circulation: 10,000fr; Sworn/Estimate/Non-Audited
Advertising rate: Open inch rate $10.08
Group: Adams Publishing Group, LLC
VP/Pub..David Fike
Adv. Mgr... Paul Myers
Ed. .... Gail DeanEquipment & Software: Hardware — APP/Mac; Presses — G/Community, G/Urbanite.
Delivery Method: Mail
Areas Served: Dorchester County

CENTREVILLE

QUEEN ANNE'S RECORD OBSERVER (FRI)
114 Broadway, Centreville, MD, 21617-1006, Queen Annes, USA; gen tel (410) 758-1400; adv tel (410) 758-1400; ed tel (410) 758-1400; gen fax (410) 758-1701; disp adv e-mail recordobserver@chespub.com; ed e-mail newsroom@recordobserver.com; web site www.myeasternshoremd.com
Circulation: 5,000pd,; Sworn/Estimate/Non-Audited
Advertising rate: Open inch rate $10.65
Group: Adams Publishing Group, LLC
Pub...David Fike
Adv. Exec..................................Tiffany Hardey
Ed. ....Janice Colvin
Areas Served: Queen Anne's County

CHESTER

THE BAY TIMES (WED)
300 Abruzzi Dr, Ste C, Chester, MD, 21619-2395, Queen Anne's, USA; gen tel (410) 643-7770; gen fax (410) 643-8374; disp adv e-mail baytimes@kibaytimes.com; class adv e-mail classads@chespub.com; ed e-mail baytimes@kibaytimes.com ; web site www.kibaytimes.com
Circulation: 6,000pd, 106fr; Sworn/Estimate/Non-Audited
Advertising rate: Open inch rate $10.08
Established: 1963
Group: Adams Publishing Group, LLC
Digital Platform - Mobile: Apple, Android, Windows, Blackberry
Digital Platform - Tablet: Apple iOS, Android, Windows 7, Blackberry Tablet OS, Kindle, Nook, Kindle Fire, Other
VP/Pub ....David Fike
Ed. .... Angela Price
Advertising Manager.......................Gail Ruppe
Mechanical Specifications: Type page 10 x 12 1/2; E - 6 cols, 2, between; A - 6 cols, 2, between; C - 8 cols, 1, between.
Delivery Method: Mail, Newsstand, Carrier, Racks
Areas Served: 21666, 21619, 21638, 21658, 21617

CHESTERTOWN

KENT COUNTY NEWS (THUR)
217 High St, Chestertown, MD, 21620-1517, Kent, USA; gen tel (410) 778-2011; adv tel (410) 778-2011; ed tel (410) 778-2011; gen fax (410) 778-6522; disp adv e-mail eastonad@chespub.com; class adv e-mail eastonad@chespub.com; ed e-mail editor@thekentcountynews.com; web site www.thekentcountynews.com
Circulation: 7,506pd, 12fr; CAC
Advertising rate: Open inch rate $12.60
Group: Adams Publishing Group, LLC
Pub./Gen. Mgr./Adv. Mgr. .... Mary Burton
VP/Pub..David Fike
Classified Adv. Mgr............. Betty Jean Bryden
Ed. ....Trish McGee
Circ. Exec....................... Kathleen McLaughlin
Mechanical Specifications: Type page 13 x 21; E - 6 cols, 1 7/8, 1/6 between; A - 6 cols, 1 7/8, 1/6 between; C - 9 cols, 1 1/4, between. Equipment & Software: ; Software — QPS/QuarkXPress, Microsoft/Word.
Areas Served: Kent County

COLUMBIA

COLUMBIA FLIER (THUR)
10750 Little Patuxent Pkwy, Columbia, MD, 21044-3106, Howard, USA; gen tel (410) 730-3620; ed fax (410) 997-4564; web site www.explorehoward.com
Circulation: 1,292pd, 26,779fr; CAC
Advertising rate: 1/32 Pg $188.00; 1/16 Pg $375.00; 1/8 Pg $656.00
Group: Baltimore Sun Media Group
Sr. VP Sales & Mkting................Judith Berman
Dir, Nat'l Adv & Majors................Susan Duchin
Nat'l Adv & Majors Sales Mgr........Matt Cimino

HOWARD COUNTY TIMES (THUR)
10750 Little Patuxent Pkwy, Columbia, MD, 21044-3106, Howard, USA; gen tel (410) 730-3620; adv tel (410) 730-3620; ed fax (410) 997-4564; disp adv e-mail mcimino@baltsun.com; class adv e-mail wayne.lowman@baltsun.com; web site www.howardcountytimes.com
Circulation: 4,084pd, 6,111fr; CAC
Advertising rate: 1/32 Pg $188.00; 1/16 Pg $375.00; 1/8 Pg $656.00
Group: Tronc, Inc.
Exec. Dir... Paul Milton
Adv................................... Allison Thompson
Sr VP Sales & Mkting ....Judith Berman
Dir, Nat'l Adv & Majors................Susan Duchin
Nat'l Adv & Majors Sales Mgr........Matt Cimino
Mechanical Specifications: Type page 10 x 12 1/2; E - 5 cols, 1 5/6, 1/6 between; A - 5 cols, 1 5/6, 1/6 between; C - 8 cols, 1 1/12, 1/12 between.

CRISFIELD

CRISFIELD-SOMERSET COUNTY TIMES (WED)
914 W Main St, Crisfield, MD, 21817-1016, Somerset County, USA; gen tel (410) 968-1188; adv tel (410) 968-1189; ed tel (410) 968-1188; gen fax (410) 968-1197; adv fax (410) 968-1197; ed fax (410) 968-1197; disp adv e-mail adsales@newszap.com; class adv e-mail classads@newszap.com; ed e-mail crisfieldnews@newszap.com; web site www.csctimes.com
Circulation: 1,043pd, 50fr; CAC
Advertising rate: 1/16 Pg $86.00; 1/8 Pg $159.00; 1/6 Pg $202.00
Established: 1889
Group: Independent Newsmedia Inc. Usa
Ed./Gen Mgr. ....Richard Crumbaker
Adv. Consultant........................... Karen Riggin
Adv./Promo Coord. .... Heather Cregar
Major Accts. Adv. Mgr........................Tim Gary
Classified Ops. Mgr.....................Diana Sellers
Delivery Method: Mail, Newsstand, Racks
Areas Served: 21817, 21853, 21871

CUMBERLAND

THE GARRETT COUNTY WEEKENDER (THUR)
19 Baltimore St, Cumberland, MD, 21502-3023, Allegany, USA; gen tel (301) 722-4600; adv tel (301) 722-4600; ed tel (301) 722-4600; gen fax (301) 722-2021; adv fax (301) 722-4870; ed fax (301) 722-5270; disp adv e-mail advertising@times-news.com; class adv e-mail classified@times-news.com; ed e-mail weeklies@times-news.com; web site www.times-news.com
Circulation: 18,000fr; Sworn/Estimate/Non-Audited
Advertising rate: Open inch rate $9.31
Group: Community Newspaper Holdings Inc.
Pub..Robin Quillion
Advertising Director ....Craig Springer
Managing Editor ....John Smith
Circulation Manager ....Jeff Clark
Mechanical Specifications: Type page 13 x 21 1/2; E - 6 cols, 2 1/16, 1/8 between; A - 6 cols, 2 1/16, 1/8 between; C - 6 cols, 2 1/16, 1/8 between.Equipment & Software: Hardware — PC; Presses — G/Cosmo; Software — CText/Classified, CText/Editorial.
Delivery Method: Mail
Areas Served: Garrett County, MD

DENTON

THE TIMES RECORD (WED)
212 Market St, Denton, MD, 21629-1037, Denton, Caroline County, USA; gen tel (410) 479-1800; adv tel (410) 479-1800; ed tel (410) 479-1800; gen fax (410) 479-3174; web site www.myeasternshoremd.com
Circulation: 4,200pd,; Sworn/Estimate/Non-Audited
Advertising rate: Open inch rate $10.08
Group: Adams Publishing Group, LLC
Pub... Larry Effingham
Adv. Mgr.................................. Margaret Iovino
Ed. .... John Evans

DUNDALK

THE AVENUE NEWS (THUR)
4 N Center Pl, Dundalk, MD, 21222-4300, Baltimore, USA; gen tel (410) 687-7775; gen fax (410) 687-7881; ed e-mail aveeditorial@chespub.com; web site www.avenuenews.com
Circulation: 55,423fr; CAC
Advertising rate: Open inch rate $23.00
Group: Adams Publishing Group, LLCEditions: (2) 2 total The Essex Avenue (40,000); The Perryhall Avenue (30,000);
Vice. Pres./Pub. ....David Fike
Gen, Mgr.................................. Claudio Nimmo
Adv. Mgr................................ Shiela Malatesta
Reg. Dir., Adv.........................Konrad LaPrade
Dir., Adv. .... Harry Porter
Reg, Dir., Circ. .... Bill Sims
Circ. Mgr..................................Mary Ferguson
Ed. .... Amy Graziano
Adv. Dir..Brian Doane
Mechanical Specifications: Type page 10 1/4 x 14; E - 4 cols, 2 3/8, 1/6 between; A - 6 cols, 1 9/16, 1/6 between; C - 6 cols, 1 9/16, 1/6 between.Equipment & Software: Hardware — APP/Mac, IBM; Presses — G/Community; Software — QPS/QuarkXPress, Baseview/Managing Editor.

THE DUNDALK EAGLE (THUR)
4 N Center Pl, Dundalk, MD, 21222-4300, Baltimore, USA; gen tel (410) 288-6060; adv tel (410) 288-6060; ed tel (410) 288-6060; gen fax (410) 288-6963; adv fax (410) 288-2712; ed fax (410) 288-6963; disp adv e-mail ads@dundalkeagle.net; class adv e-mail classifieds@dundalkeagle.net; ed e-mail editor@dundalkeagle.net; web site www.dundalkeagle.com
Circulation: 18,000pd,; Sworn/Estimate/Non-Audited
Advertising rate: Open inch rate $18.20
Established: 1969
Pub......................................Deborah Cornely
Editor .... Steve Matrazzo
Advertising Director ....Jason O'Neill
Gen. Mgr. .... Paul Rosenberger
Editor ....Jonathan O'Neill
Mechanical Specifications: Type page 10 1/8 x 14; E - 6 cols, 1 7/16, 1/8 between; A - 6 cols, 1 7/16, 1/8 between; C - 6 cols, 1 7/16, 1/8 between.Equipment & Software: Hardware — APP/Mac, APP/Mac G4, APP/Mac iMac; Software — Multi-Ad/Creator, Adobe/InDesign, QPS/QuarkXPress, Adobe/Photoshop, Adobe/Illustrator, Baseview.
Delivery Method: Mail
Areas Served: Greater Dundalk

EASTON

EASTERN SHORE BARGAINEER (FRI)
29088 Airpark Dr, Easton, MD, 21601-7000, Talbot, USA ; gen tel (410) 822-1500; gen fax (410) 770-4019; web site www.stardem.com
Group: Adams Publishing Group, LLC

Ed. .... Josh Griep

ELKTON

CECIL WHIG (MON, WED, FRI)

601 N Bridge St, Elkton, MD, 21921-5307, Cecil, USA; gen tel (410) 398-3311; adv tel (443) 245-5045; ed tel (410) 398-3311; gen fax (410) 398-4044; adv fax (410) 398-4044; ed fax (443) 245-5043; disp adv e-mail mfoglio@chespub.com; class adv e-mail mfoglio@chespub.com; ed e-mail jowens@cecilwhig.com; web site www.cecildaily.com

Circulation: 12,163pd,; Sworn/Estimate/Non-Audited
Advertising rate: Open inch rate $22.90
Established: 1841
Group: Adams Publishing Group, LLC
Digital Platform - Mobile: Apple, Android
Digital Platform - Tablet: Apple iOS, Android, Kindle, Nook, Kindle Fire
Pub... David Fike
News Ed. .... Jake Owens
Features Ed. .... Dara McBride
Sports Ed.................................. Chuck Ristano
Adv. Dir.. Maria Foglio
Delivery Method: Mail, Newsstand, Carrier, Racks
Areas Served: Cecil County

NEWARK POST (FRI)

601 N Bridge St, Elkton, MD, 21921-5307, Cecil, USA; gen tel (302) 737-0724; gen fax (302) 737-9019; web site www.newarkpostonline.com

Circulation: 12,500pd,; Sworn/Estimate/Non-Audited
Advertising rate: Open inch rate $16.80
Gen. Mgr. .... Marty Valania
Adv. Mgr... Ed Hoffman
Circ. Dir.. Bill Sims
Ed. .... Scott Goss
Mechanical Specifications: Type page 10 13/16 x 16; E - 5 cols, 2, 1/6 between; A - 5 cols, 2, 1/6 between; C - 7 cols, 1 3/8, 1/6 between. Equipment & Software: Hardware — APP/Mac; Software — QPS/QuarkXPress 4.0, Adobe/Photoshop 4.0, Multi-Ad 4.2.

GAITHERSBURG

BUSINESS GAZETTE (FRI)

9030 Comprint Ct, Gaithersburg, MD, 20877-1307, Montgomery, USA; gen tel (301) 948-3120; adv tel (301) 670-2500; ed tel (301) 948-3120; gen fax (301) 670-7183; adv fax (301) 670-7183; ed fax (301) 670-7183; disp adv e-mail dwilston@gazette.net; class adv e-mail class@gazette.net; ed e-mail editor@gazette.net; web site www.gazette.net

Circulation: 3,879pd, 942fr; VAC
Advertising rate: Open inch rate $120.67
Established: 1988Editions: (16) Aspen Hill Gazette (8,906); Bethesda Gazette (27,676); Burtonsville Gazette (24,439); Chevy Chase Gazette (8,019); Damascus Gazette (7,491); Gaithersburg Gazette (31,728); Germantown Gazette (22,112); Kensington Gazette (7,311)
Digital Platform - Mobile: Apple, Android, Windows, Blackberry
Digital Platform - Tablet: Apple iOS, Android, Windows 7, Blackberry Tablet OS, Kindle, Nook, Kindle Fire
Vice Pres./Adv. Dir. .... Cliff Chiet
Circ. Dir.. Jean Casey
Sports Ed............................ John Wehmueller
Mechanical Specifications: Type page 10 3/8 x 13; E - 5 cols, between; A - 5 cols, between; C - 8 cols, between.Equipment & Software: Hardware — APP/Mac, PC.
Delivery Method: Mail, Newsstand, Racks
Areas Served: Montgomery County

THE GAZETTE - DAMASCUS / CLARKSBURG (WED)

9030 Comprint Ct, Gaithersburg, MD, 20877-1307, Bethesda, Montgomery County, USA; gen tel (301) 948-3120; adv tel (301) 670-2500; gen fax (301) 670-7183; disp adv e-mail editor@gazette.net; class adv e-mail circulation@gazette.net; classifieds@gazette.net; ed e-mail sports@gazette.net; web site www.gazette.net

Circulation: 7,486fr; VAC
Advertising rate: Open inch rate $34.97
Established: 1988
Group: Post Newsweek Media, LLCEditions: (16) Aspen Hill Gazette (8,906); Bethesda Gazette (27,676); Burtonsville Gazette (24,439); Chevy Chase Gazette (8,019); Damascus Gazette (7,491); Gaithersburg Gazette (31,728); Germantown Gazette (22,112); Kensington Gazette (7,311)
Pub..................................... James Mannarino
Vice Pres., Sales .... Cliff Chiet
Adv. Coord. .... Maria Lampos
Circ. Dir... Jean Casey
Prodn. Mgr. .... Lisa Merhi
Ed. .... Melissa A. Chadwick
Sports Ed............................ John Wehmueller
Corp. Classified Dir. .... Mona Bass
Corp. Adv. Dir.......................... Dennis Wilston
Mechanical Specifications: Type page 10 3/8 x 13; E - 5 cols, between; A - 5 cols, between; C - 8 cols, between.Equipment & Software: Hardware — APP/Mac, PC.
Delivery Method: Mail, Carrier, Racks

THE GAZETTE - POTOMAC / NORTH POTOMAC (WED)

9030 Comprint Ct, Gaithersburg, MD, 20877-1307, Bethesda, Montgomery County, USA; gen tel (301) 948-3120; adv tel (301) 670-2500; gen fax (301) 670-7183; disp adv e-mail editor@gazette.net; class adv e-mail classifieds@gazette.net; ed e-mail editor@gazette.net; web site www.gazette.net

Circulation: 16,463fr; VAC
Advertising rate: Open inch rate $34.97
Established: 1988
Group: Post Newsweek Media, LLCEditions: (16) Aspen Hill Gazette (8,906); Bethesda Gazette (27,676); Burtonsville Gazette (24,439); Chevy Chase Gazette (8,019); Damascus Gazette (7,491); Gaithersburg Gazette (31,728); Germantown Gazette (22,112); Kensington Gazette (7,311)
Pub..................................... James Mannarino
Vice Pres., Sales .... Cliff Chiet
Adv. Coord. .... Maria Lampos
Circ. Dir... Jean Casey
Prodn. Mgr. .... Lisa Merhi
Ed. .... Melissa A. Chadwick
Sports Ed............................ John Wehmueller
Corp. Classified Dir. .... Mona Bass
Corp. Adv. Dir.......................... Dennis Wilston
Mechanical Specifications: Type page 10 3/8 x 13; E - 5 cols, between; A - 5 cols, between; C - 8 cols, between.Equipment & Software: Hardware — APP/Mac, PC.

GREENBELT

GREENBELT NEWS REVIEW (THUR)

15 Crescent Rd, Ste 100, Greenbelt, MD, 20770-0807, Prince Georges, USA; gen tel (301) 474-4131; adv tel (301) 474-4131; ed tel (301) 474-4131; gen fax (301) 474-5880; adv fax (301) 474-5880; ed fax (301) 474-5880; disp adv e-mail newsreview@verizon.net; class adv e-mail newsreview@verizon.net; ed e-mail newsreview@verizon.net; web site www.greenbeltnewsreview.com

Circulation: 80pd, 9,400fr; Sworn/Estimate/Non-Audited
Advertising rate: Open inch rate $12.00
Established: 1937
Pres. .... Eileen Farnham
Vice Pres. .... Thomas X. White
Treasurer .... Judy Bell
Bus. Mgr...................................... Diane Oberg
Sec.. Carol Griffith
Circ. Mgr.................................... Ian Tuckman
Ed. .... Mary Lou Williamson
Asst. Ed............................... Barbara Likowski
News Ed. .... Elaine Skolnik
Mechanical Specifications: Type page 10 x 16; E - 5 cols, 1 11/12, between; A - 5 cols, 1 11/12, between; C - 5 cols, 1 11/12, between.Equipment & Software: ; Software — WordPerfect.

Delivery Method: Carrier
Areas Served: 20770

HANCOCK

THE HANCOCK NEWS (WED)

263 N Pennsylvania Ave, Hancock, MD, 21750-1098, Washington, USA; gen tel (301) 678-6255; gen fax (301) 678-5520; disp adv e-mail ads@morganmessenger.com; class adv e-mail ads@morganmessenger.com; ed e-mail news@hancocknews.us

Circulation: 1,800pd,; Sworn/Estimate/Non-Audited
Advertising rate: Open inch rate $5.00
Established: 1914
Group: The Morgan Messenger
Mgr Ed. .... Sandra Buzzerd
Ed .... Kate Shunney
Mechanical Specifications: Type page 11 3/5 x 21; E - 6 cols, 1 4/5, 1/8 between; A - 6 cols, 1 4/5, 1/8 between.
Delivery Method: Mail, Newsstand
Areas Served: 21750

LAUREL

BOWIE STAR (THUR)

13501 Konterra Dr, Laurel, MD, 20707-6505, Prince Georges, USA; gen tel (240) 473-7500; gen fax (240) 473-7501; disp adv e-mail editor@gazette.net; web site www.gazette.net

Circulation: 22,769fr; VAC
Advertising rate: Open inch rate $39.25David Simon

OCEAN CITY

MARYLAND BEACHCOMBER (FRI)

12417 Ocean Gtwy, Ste 7, Ocean City, MD, 21842-9522, Worcester, USA; gen tel (410) 213-9442; gen fax (410) 213-9459; web site www.marylandbeachcomber.com

Circulation: 22,000fr; Sworn/Estimate/Non-Audited
Advertising rate: Open inch rate $10.85
Established: 1965
Group: Gannett
Pub.. Greg Desset
Ed. .... Kelsey Collins
Mechanical Specifications: Type page 10 3/4 x 13 1/4; E - 5 cols, 1 15/16, 1/6 between; A - 5 cols, 1 15/16, 1/6 between; C - 7 cols, 1 5/16, 1/6 between.Equipment & Software: Hardware — APP/Mac; Software — QPS/QuarkXPress 3.32.

OCEAN CITY TODAY (FRI)

8200 Coastal Hwy, Ocean City, MD, 21842-2834, Worcester, USA; gen tel (410) 723-6397; gen fax (410) 723-6511; disp adv e-mail ebrady@oceancitytoday.net; class adv e-mail sales@oceancitytoday.net; ed e-mail editor@oceancitytoday.net; web site www.oceancitytoday.net

Circulation: 16,500fr; Sworn/Estimate/Non-Audited
Advertising rate: Open inch rate $11.73
Established: 1993
Digital Platform - Mobile: Apple, Android, Blackberry
Digital Platform - Tablet: Apple iOS, Android, Blackberry Tablet OS
Ed./Pub. .... Stewart Dobson
Sales Manager .... Elaine Brady
Managing Editor .... Lisa Capitelli
Phil Jacobs
Mechanical Specifications: Type page 9.5 x 13.25; E - 4 cols, 1/6 between; A - 4 cols, 1/6 between.Equipment & Software: Hardware — APP/Mac, PC; Software — QPS/QuarkXPress 6.5.
Delivery Method: Racks
Areas Served: 21842, 21843, 21811, 21813, 21841, 21862, 21872

PRINCE FREDERICK

THE CALVERT RECORDER (WED, FRI)

134 Main St, Ste 102, Prince Frederick, MD, 20678-6150, Calvert, USA; gen tel (410) 535-1234; adv tel (410) 535-1234; ed tel (410) 535-1234; gen fax (443) 378-3498; adv fax (443) 378-3498; ed fax (443) 378-3498; disp adv e-mail bash@chespub.com; class adv e-mail chesAds@chespub.com; ed e-mail mcady@somdnews.com; web site www.somdnews.com/recorder

Circulation: 10,500pd,; Sworn/Estimate/Non-Audited
Advertising rate: modular ($14)
Established: 1971
Group: Adams Publishing Group, LLC
Digital Platform - Mobile: Apple, Android
Digital Platform - Tablet: Apple iOS, Android
Pub .... Art Crofoot
Delivery Method: Mail, Newsstand, Carrier, Racks
Areas Served: Calvert County, MD

ROCKVILLE

MONTGOMERY COUNTY SENTINEL (THUR)

22 W Jefferson St, Ste 309, Rockville, MD, 20850-4259, Montgomery, USA; gen tel (301) 838-0788; adv tel (301) 306-9500; ed tel (301) 838-0788; gen fax (301) 838-3458; adv fax (301) 306-0134; ed fax (301) 838-3458; disp adv e-mail lonnie@thesentinel.com; class adv e-mail lonnie@thesentinel.com; ed e-mail editor-mc@thesentinel.com; web site www.thesentinel.com

Circulation: 10,000pd,; Sworn/Estimate/Non-Audited
Advertising rate: Open inch rate $14.52
Established: 1855
CEO... Lynn Kapiloff
Ed. .... Brian Karen
Adv. Mgr................................. Lonnie Johnson
Mark Kapiloff
Sharmia Bush
Strategic Information Mgr.......... Pete Hajiantoni
Areas Served: Montgomery County (MD)

SALISBURY

SALISBURY INDEPENDENT (THUR)

PO Box 1385, Salisbury, MD, 21802-1385, Wicomico, USA; gen tel (410) 543-4500; adv tel (410) 543-4500; ed tel (410) 543-4500; disp adv e-mail salisburysales@newszap.com; class adv e-mail classads@newszap.com; ed e-mail SalisburyIndependent@newszap.com; web site salisburyindependent.net

Circulation: 19,195fr; CAC
Advertising rate: Full page = $2,869
Established: 2014
Group: Independent Newsmedia Inc. Usa
Ed./Gen. Mgr. .... Greg Bassett
Publisher.................................. Darel La Prade
Delivery Method: Newsstand, Racks
Areas Served: 21801,21804,21826,21856, 21875, 19940

SOMERSET HERALD (WED)

618 Beam St, Salisbury, MD, 21801-7803, Somerset, USA; gen tel (410) 651-1600; adv tel (410) 749-7171; disp adv e-mail cstubbs@dmg.gannett.com; class adv e-mail pmaher@gannett.com; ed e-mail somersetherald@gannett.com; web site www.delmarvanow.com

Circulation: 4,000pd,; Sworn/Estimate/Non-Audited
Advertising rate: Open inch rate $11.38
Established: 1828
Group: Gannett
Sales Dir. .... Robb Scott
Ed. .... Liz Holland
Executive Editor......................... Michael Kilian
Mechanical Specifications: Type page 12 3/4 x 21 1/2; E - 6 cols, 2, 3/16 between; A - 6 cols, 2,

3/16 between; C - 9 cols, 1 3/8, 1/8 between. Equipment & Software: Hardware — APP/ Mac; Software — QPS/QuarkXPress.
Delivery Method: Racks
Areas Served: Somerset County, Maryland

SEABROOK

THE PRINCE GEORGE'S SENTINEL (WED)

9458 Lanham Severn Rd, Ste 200, Seabrook, MD, 20706-2661, Prince George, USA; gen tel (301) 306-9500; adv tel (301) 306-9500; ed tel (301) 306-9500; gen fax (301) 306-0134; adv fax (301) 306-0134; ed fax (301) 306-0134; disp adv e-mail lonnie@thesentinel.com; class adv e-mail lonnie@thesentinel.com; ed e-mail editor-pg@thesentinel.com; web site www.thesentinel.com
Circulation: 4,000pd, 20,000fr; Sworn/Estimate/Non-Audited
Advertising rate: Open inch rate $34.92
Established: 1932
CEO.......... Lynn Kapiloff
Adv. Dir.......... Lonnie Johnson
Mng. Ed.......... Donna Lechly
Strategic Information Mgr.......... Pete Hajiantoni
Delivery Method: Mail, Newsstand
Areas Served: Prince George's county

TOWSON

JEFFERSONIAN (TUES, THUR)

409 Washington Ave, Towson, MD, 21204-4920, Baltimore, USA; gen tel (410) 337-2400; gen fax (410) 337-2490; disp adv e-mail jtynes@patuxent.com; web site www.thejeffersonian.com
Circulation: 292pd, 187fr; CAC
Advertising rate: 1/64 Pg $75.00; 1/32 Pg $150.00; 1/16 Pg $300.00
Group: Tronc, Inc.
Pub.......... Trish Carroll
Circ. Mgr.......... David Piel
Ed.......... Michael Aaron
Nat'l Adv & Majors, Sales Mgr.......... Matt Cimino
Sr VP Sales & Mkting.......... Judith Berman
Dir, Nat'l Adv & Majors.......... Susan Duchin

UPPER MARLBORO

PRINCE GEORGE'S POST (THUR)

15207 Marlboro Pike, Ste B, Upper Marlboro, MD, 20772-3112, Prince Georges, USA; gen tel (301) 627-0900; adv tel (301) 627-0900; ed tel (301) 627-0900; gen fax (301) 627-8147; adv fax (301) 627-6260; ed fax (301) 627-6260; disp adv e-mail pgpost@gmail.com; class adv e-mail pgpost@gmail.com; ed e-mail pgpost@gmail.com; web site www.pgpost.com
Circulation: 15,000pd,; Sworn/Estimate/Non-Audited
Advertising rate: Open inch rate $21.00
Established: 1932
Ed.......... Michal Frangia
Gen. Mgr./Adv. Mgr. .... Brenda Boice
Managing Ed.......... Lea Greve
Areas Served: Prince George's County

WALDORF

THE ENQUIRER-GAZETTE (THUR)

7 Industrial Park Dr, Waldorf, MD, 20602-2753, Charles, USA; gen tel (301) 627-2833; gen fax (301) 627-2795; disp adv e-mail princegeorges@gazette.net; web site www.somdnews.com
Circulation: 2,475pd,; CAC
Advertising rate: Open inch rate $21.43
Group: Southern Maryland Newspapers
Pub.......... Karen Acton
Ed.......... Vanessa Harrton
Adv. Mgr.......... Christy Bailey
Circ. Dir.......... Ron Notter
Adv. Mgr.......... Kim Minopoli
Mechanical Specifications: Type page 13 x 21; E - 6 cols, 2 1/16, 1/6 between; A - 6 cols, 2 1/16, 1/6 between; C - 9 cols, 1 5/16, 1/12 between.Equipment & Software: Hardware — APP/Mac, PCs; Presses — 8-G/Urbanite, G/Community; Software — QPS/QuarkXPress 3.32, Adobe/Typestyler 2.0, Multi-Ad/Creator 4.02, Adobe/Photoshop 4.0, Adobe/Acrobat Exchange 3.0, Adobe/PageMaker 6.0, Microsoft/Word 6.0.

WESTMINSTER

COMMUNITY TIMES (WED)

201 Railroad Ave, Westminster, MD, 21157-4823, Carroll, USA; gen tel (410) 875-5400; gen fax (410) 857-8749; web site www.carrollcountytimes.com
Circulation: 500pd, 11,500fr; Sworn/Estimate/Non-Audited
Advertising rate: Open inch rate $16.05
Adv. Dir.......... Erin Hahn
Ed.......... Jim Lee
Areas Served: 21157, 21136, 21117, 21071, 21133

THE ADVOCATE OF ELDERSBURG AND SYKESVILLE (WED)

201 Railroad Ave, Westminster, MD, 21157-4823, Eldersburg/Sykesville, Carroll County, USA; gen tel (410) 857-4400; adv tel (410) 857-7888; gen fax (410) 857-8749; disp adv e-mail erin.hahn@carrollcountytimes.com; class adv e-mail erin.hahn@carrollcountytimes.com; web site www.eldersburgadvocate.com
Circulation: 4,160pd, 9,740fr; Sworn/Estimate/Non-Audited
Advertising rate: 8.69
Established: 2004
Pub.......... Pat Richardson
Delivery Method: Carrier
Areas Served: Eldersburg/Sykesville

WHITE PLAINS

THE MARYLAND INDEPENDENT (WED, FRI)

4475 Regency Pl, Ste 301, White Plains, MD, 20695-3077, Charles, USA; gen tel (301) 645-9480; adv tel (301) 645-9480; ed tel (301) 645-9480; gen fax (301) 884-9403; adv fax (301) 884-9403; ed fax (301) 884-9403; disp adv e-mail kminopoli@somdnews.com; class adv e-mail sheadley@somdnews.com; ed e-mail abreck@somdnews.com; web site www.somdnews.com
Circulation: 15,140pd,; CAC
Advertising rate: Open inch rate $25.73
Established: 1872
Group: Adams Publishing Group, LLC
Digital Platform - Mobile: Apple, Android
Digital Platform - Tablet: Apple iOS, Android
Pub.......... Karen Acton
Adv. Dir.......... Kim Minopoli
Circ. Mgr.......... Ron Notter
Ed.......... Angela Breck
Mng. Ed.......... Joel Davis
Prodn. Mgr. .... Ellen Pankake
Circ. Mgr.......... Phyllis Dietz
Mechanical Specifications: Type page 13 x 21; E - 6 cols, 2 1/16, 1/6 between; A - 6 cols, 2 1/16, 1/6 between; C - 9 cols, 1 5/16, 1/12 between.Equipment & Software: Hardware — APP/Mac, PCs; Presses — G/Urbanite, G/Community; Software — Multi-Ad/Creator 4.0.2, QPS/QuarkXPress 3.32, Adobe/Typestyler 2.0, Adobe/Acrobat Exchange 3.0, Adobe/Photoshop 4.0, Adobe/PageMaker 6.0, MS/Word 6.0.
Delivery Method: Mail, Newsstand, Carrier, Racks
Areas Served: Charles county

MASSACHUSETTS

ANDOVER

ANDOVER TOWNSMAN (THUR)

33 Chestnut St, Andover, MA, 01810-3623, Essex, USA; gen tel (978) 475-7000; adv tel (978) 475-7000; ed tel (978) 475-7000; gen fax (978) 470-2819; adv fax (978) 470-2819; ed fax (978) 470-2819; disp adv e-mail Adsales@andovertownsman.com; class adv e-mail Adsales@andovertownsman.com; ed e-mail bkirk@andovertownsman.com; web site www.andovertownsman.com - 64,000(views) 24,000(visitors)
Circulation: 5,000pd, 500fr; Sworn/Estimate/Non-Audited
Advertising rate: Open inch rate $26.16
Established: 1887
Group: Community Newspaper Holdings, Inc.
Reg. Pub.......... Karen Andreas
Adv. Dir.......... Cathy Goss
Ops. Dir.......... James Falzone
Circ. Dir.......... Steve Baskin
Ed.......... Bill Kirk
Mechanical Specifications: Type page 11 5/8 x 21 1/2; E - 6 cols, 1 5/6, 1/8 between; A - 6 cols, 1 5/6, 1/8 between; C - 10 cols, 1 1/16, 1/16 between.Equipment & Software: Hardware — APP/Mac
Delivery Method: Mail, Newsstand
Areas Served: 01845, 01810

BARRE

BARRE GAZETTE (THUR)

5 Exchange St, Barre, MA, 01005-8702, Worcester, USA; gen tel (978) 355-4000; adv tel (978) 355-4000; ed tel (978) 355-4000; gen fax (978) 355-6274; adv fax (978) 355-6274; ed fax (978) 355-6274; disp adv e-mail bbaker@turley.com; class adv e-mail classifieds@turley.com; ed e-mail edowner@turley.com; web site barregazette.turley.com
Circulation: 2,666pd,; Sworn/Estimate/Non-Audited
Advertising rate: Open inch rate $10.75
Established: 1834
Group: Turley Publications, Inc.
Owner.......... Patrick H. Turley
Ed.......... Ellie Downer
Adv. Mgr.......... Beth Baker
Circ. Mgr.......... Charlann Griswold
Exec. Ed.......... Tim Kane
Sports Ed.......... David Forbes
Delivery Method: Mail
Areas Served: Barre, South Barre, north Brookfield, Oakham, Rutland, Hubbardston, Petersham, Wheelwright, Hardwick, New Braintree, Ware

BELCHERTOWN

THE SENTINEL (THUR)

10 S Main St, Belchertown, MA, 01007-8829, Hampshire, USA; gen tel (413) 323-5999; adv tel (413) 323-5999; ed tel (413) 323-5999; gen fax (413) 323-9424; adv fax (413) 323-9424; ed fax (413) 323-9424; disp adv e-mail mmcgarrett@turley.com; class adv e-mail classifieds@turley.com; ed e-mail ahenderson@turley.com; web site www.belchertownsentinelonline.com
Circulation: 10,054fr; Sworn/Estimate/Non-Audited
Advertising rate: Open inch rate $12.75
Established: 1915
Group: Turley Publications, Inc.
Pub.......... Patrick Turley
Ed.......... Aimee Henderson
Gen. Mgr.......... David Anderson
Ad. Director.......... Beth Baker
Circulation Director.......... Charlann Griswold
Mechanical Specifications: Type page 10 x 16; E - 6 cols, 1 1/2, between.
Delivery Method: Mail, Racks
Areas Served: Belchertown, Granby, Amherst, Hadley

BELLINGHAM

BELLINGHAM BULLETIN (THUR, MTHLY)

36 Rakeville Cir, Bellingham, MA, 02019-2132, Norfolk, USA; gen tel (508) 883-3252; adv tel (508) 883-3252; ed tel (508) 883-3252; gen fax (508) 883-3252; adv fax (508) 883-3252; ed fax (508) 883-3252; disp adv e-mail cyndyrogers@charter.net; class adv e-mail cyndyrogers@charter.net; ed e-mail email@BellinghamBulletin.com; web site www.bellinghambulletin.com
Advertising rate: Open inch rate $54
Established: 1994
Adv. Dir.......... Cyndy Rogers
Areas Served: Bellingham (MA)

BOSTON

BOSTON BUSINESS JOURNAL (THUR)

160 Federal St, Fl 12th, Boston, MA, 02110-1700, Suffolk, USA; gen tel (617) 330-1000; adv tel (617) 330-1000; ed tel (617) 330-1000; gen fax (617) 330-1015; adv fax (617) 330-1015; ed fax (617) 330-1015; disp adv e-mail boston@bizjournals.com; class adv e-mail boston@bizjournals.com; ed e-mail newsroom@masshightech.com; web site www.amcity.com/boston
Advertising rate: 1/8 P $2800 1/4 $4500 1/2 P $7100 Full $10000
Established: 1981
Controller.......... Heather Lacey

MASSACHUSETTS LAWYERS WEEKLY (MON)

10 Milk St, Ste 1000, Boston, MA, 02108-4620, Suffolk, USA; gen tel (617) 451-7300; adv tel (617) 451-7300; ed tel (617) 451-7300; disp adv e-mail sziegler@lawyersweekly.com; class adv e-mail sziegler@lawyersweekly.com; ed e-mail hcampagne@lawyersweekly.com.; web site www.masslawyersweekly.com
Circulation:; Sworn/Estimate/Non-Audited
Advertising rate: Call for rates
Established: 1972
Pub.......... Susan Bocamazo
Ed.......... Henriette Campagne
Ad. Dir.......... Charlene Smith
Delivery Method: Mail, Carrier

RHODE ISLAND LAWYERS WEEKLY (MON)

10 Milk St, Ste 1000, Boston, MA, 02108-4620, Suffolk, USA; gen tel (617) 451-7300; adv tel (617) 451-7300; ed tel (617) 451-7300; gen fax (617) 451-7324; adv fax (617) 451-7324; ed fax (617) 451-7324; disp adv e-mail charlene.smith@lawyersweekly.com; class adv e-mail charlene.smith@lawyersweekly.com; ed e-mail henriette.campagne@lawyersweekly.com; web site www.rilawyersweekly.com
Advertising rate: Modular rates: Full $1,575; Half $955; Quarter $535
Ed.......... Henriette Campagne
Ad. Director.......... Charlene Smith
Pub.......... Susan Bocamazo
Delivery Method: Mail, Carrier
Areas Served: Rhode Island

THE BEACON HILL TIMES (TUES)

25 Myrtle St, Boston, MA, 02114-4509, Suffolk, USA; gen tel (617) 523-9490; adv tel (617) 523-9490; ed tel (617) 523-9490; gen fax (617) 523-8668; adv fax (617) 523-8668; ed fax (617) 523-8668; disp adv e-mail tverhoogen@beaconhilltimes.com; class adv e-mail tverhoogen@beaconhilltimes.com; ed e-mail editor@beaconhilltimes.com; web site www.beaconhilltimes.com

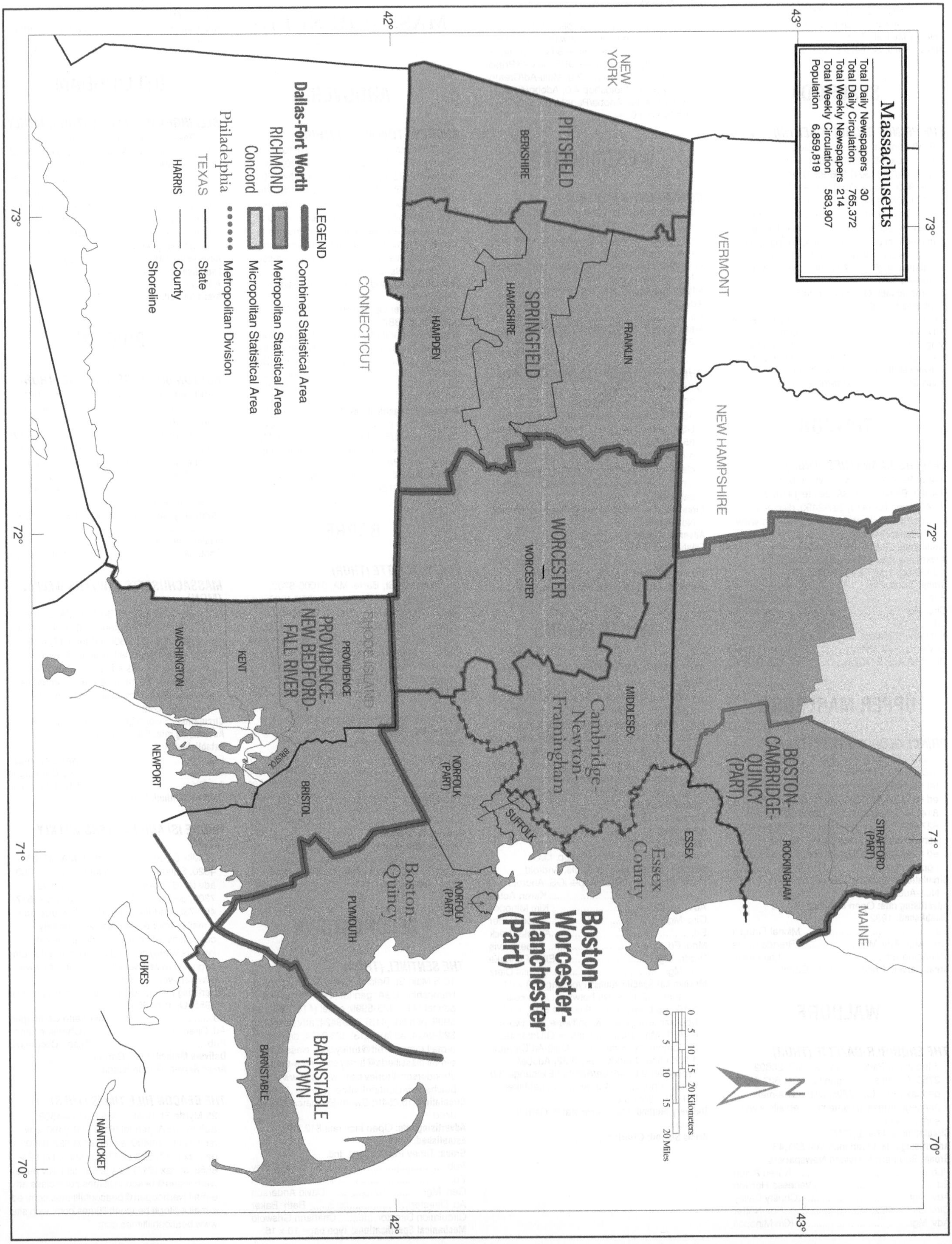
Massachusetts
Total Daily Newspapers 30
Total Daily Circulation 765,372
Total Weekly Newspapers 214
Total Weekly Circulation 583,907
Population 6,859,819
LEGEND
Combined Statistical Area
Metropolitan Statistical Area
Micropolitan Statistical Area
Metropolitan Division
State
County
Shoreline
Dallas-Fort Worth
RICHMOND
Concord
Philadelphia
TEXAS
HARRIS
NEW YORK
VERMONT
NEW HAMPSHIRE
MAINE
CONNECTICUT
RHODE ISLAND
PITTSFIELD
BERKSHIRE
SPRINGFIELD
FRANKLIN
HAMPSHIRE
HAMPDEN
WORCESTER
WORCESTER
MIDDLESEX
Cambridge-Newton-Framingham
BOSTON-CAMBRIDGE-QUINCY (PART)
STRAFFORD (PART)
ROCKINGHAM
ESSEX
Essex County
Boston-Worcester-Manchester (Part)
NORFOLK (PART)
SUFFOLK
NORFOLK (PART)
Boston-Quincy
PLYMOUTH
PROVIDENCE-NEW BEDFORD-FALL RIVER
PROVIDENCE
KENT
WASHINGTON
BRISTOL
BRISTOL
NEWPORT
DUKES
BARNSTABLE TOWN
BARNSTABLE
NANTUCKET
0 5 10 15 20 Kilometers
0 5 10 15 20 Miles
N
42°
43°
73°
72°
71°
70°

Circulation: 10,500fr; Sworn/Estimate/Non-Audited
Advertising rate: Open inch rate $16.00
Established: 1995
Group: Independent Newspaper Group
Ed. & Pub. .... Karen Cord Taylor
Mng. Ed.................................Suzanne Besser
Mechanical Specifications: Type page 10 x 15 3/8; E - 5 cols, 1 7/8, between.Equipment & Software: Hardware — APP/Power Mac; Software — QPS/QuarkXPress, WordPerfect, Microsoft/Word.
Areas Served: 02114, 02116, 02108

BROCKTON

AVON MESSENGER (THUR)

1324 Belmont St Ste 102, Unit 102, Brockton, MA, 02301-4435, Plymouth, USA; gen tel (508) 967-3523; adv tel (781) 837-4591; ed tel (508) 427-4038; gen fax (508) 967-3501; adv fax (508) 967-3501; ed fax (508) 967-3501; disp adv e-mail wmurphy@wickedlocal.com; class adv e-mail rbright@wickedlocal.com; ed e-mail newsroom@enterprisenews.com; web site www.wickedlocal.com/avon
Circulation: 1,022pd,; Sworn/Estimate/Non-Audited
Advertising rate: Open inch rate $10.95
Class. Adv. Mgr. .... Ron Bright
Adv. Dir.. Nick Bolitho
Mechanical Specifications: Type page 10 9/16 x 16; E - 6 cols, between; A - 6 cols, between; C - 7 cols, between.
Areas Served: 2322

THE LAKEVILLE CALL (WED)

1324 Belmont St, Ste 102, Brockton, MA, 02301-4435, Bristol, USA; gen tel (508) 967-3520; adv tel (781) 837-4598; ed tel (508) 967-3520; gen fax (508) 967-3501; adv fax (508) 967-3501; ed fax (508) 967-3501; disp adv e-mail dteehan@wickedlocal.com; class adv e-mail rbright@wickedlocal.com; ed e-mail molivieri@wickedlocal.com; web site lakeville.wickedlocal.com
Advertising rate: Open inch rate $11.50
Group: Community Newspaper Co. - South
Digital Platform - Mobile: Apple, Android, Blackberry
Digital Platform - Tablet: Apple iOS, Android, Blackberry Tablet OS
Ed. .... Alice Coyle
Adv. Dir.. Nick Bolitho
Delivery Method: Mail, Racks
Areas Served: Lakeville

CANTON

CANTON CITIZEN (THUR)

866 Washington St, Canton, MA, 02021-2514, Norfolk, USA; gen tel (781) 821-4418; adv tel (781) 821-4418; ed tel (781) 821-4418; gen fax (781) 821-4419; adv fax (781) 821-4419; ed fax (781) 821-4419; disp adv e-mail ads@thecantoncitizen.com; class adv e-mail ads@thecantoncitizen.com; ed e-mail submissions@thecantoncitizen.com; web site www.thecantoncitizen.com
Circulation: 3,600pd, 20fr; Sworn/Estimate/Non-Audited
Advertising rate: Open inch rate $10.00
Established: 1987
Ed./Pub. .... Beth Erickson
Adv. Mgr. .... Connor Erickson
Assistant Editor............................... Jay Turner
Delivery Method: Mail, Newsstand
Areas Served: 02021

CARLISLE

CARLISLE MOSQUITO (FRI)

662A Bedford Rd, Carlisle, MA, 01741-1859, Middlesex, USA; gen tel (978) 369-8313; adv tel (978) 369-8313; ed tel (978) 369-8313; gen fax (978) 369-3569; adv fax (978) 369-3569; ed fax (978) 369-3569; disp adv e-mail ads@carlislemosquito.org; class adv e-mail ads@carlislemosquito.org; ed e-mail mail@carlislemosquito.org; web site www.carlislemosquito.org
Circulation: 2,100fr; Sworn/Estimate/Non-Audited
Advertising rate: Open inch rate $10.00
Established: 1972
Gen. Mgr. .... Susan Emmons
Adv. Mgr. .... Susan Mills
Features Ed. .... Ann Quenin
News Ed. .... Betsy Fell
Asst. Ed. .... Penny Zezima
Delivery Method: Mail
Areas Served: Carlisle (MA)

CHARLESTOWN

THE CHARLESTOWN PATRIOT-BRIDGE (THUR)

87 Warren St, Charlestown, MA, 02129-3615, Suffolk, USA; gen tel (617) 241-8500; adv tel (617) 241-8500; ed tel (617) 241-8500; gen fax (617) 241-8505; adv fax (617) 241-8505; ed fax (617) 241-8505; disp adv e-mail tverhoogen@charlestownbridge.com; class adv e-mail tverhoogen@charlestownbridge.com; ed e-mail editor@charlestownbridge.com; web site www.charlestownbridge.com
Circulation: 4,500pd,; Sworn/Estimate/Non-Audited
Advertising rate: Open inch rate $14.40
Group: Independent Newspaper Group
Ed./Pub. .... Karen Cord Taylor
Adv. Mgr. .... Therese Herhoogen
Mng. Ed. .... Alexandra Bowers
Mechanical Specifications: Type page 10 1/4 x 16; E - 6 cols, 1 1/2, 1/4 between; A - 6 cols, 1 1/2, 1/4 between; C - 6 cols, 1 1/2, 1/4 between.Equipment & Software: Hardware — APP/Mac Quadra 650, APP/Mac Quadra 610; Software — QPS/QuarkXPress 3.2.
Areas Served: Charlestown

CHATHAM

THE CAPE COD CHRONICLE (THUR)

60 Munson Meeting Way, Ste C, Chatham, MA, 02633-1992, Barnstable, USA; gen tel (508) 945-2220; adv tel (508) 945-2229; ed tel (508) 945-2220; gen fax (508) 945-2579; adv fax (508) 945-2579; ed fax (508) 945-2579; disp adv e-mail debbie@capecodchronicle.com; class adv e-mail debbie@capecodchronicle.com; ed e-mail twood@capecodchronicle.com; web site www.capecodchronicle.com
Circulation: 27,404pd, 721fr; AAM
Advertising rate: Open inch rate $16.60Editions: (2) Chatham (5,100); Harwich (4,000);
Ed. .... Tim Wood
Adv. Mgr. .... Deb DeCosta
Mechanical Specifications: Type page 10 1/4 x 16.
Delivery Method: Mail, Newsstand
Areas Served: Chatham, Harwich, Orleans

CHICOPEE

THE CHICOPEE REGISTER (THUR)

333 Front St, Ste 5, Chicopee, MA, 01013-2798, Hampden, USA; gen tel (413) 592-3599; adv tel (413) 592-3599; ed tel (413) 592-3599; gen fax (413) 592-3568; adv fax (413) 592-3568; ed fax (413) 592-3568; disp adv e-mail bbaker@turley.com; class adv e-mail classifieds@turley.com; ed e-mail kmitchell@turley.com; web site chicopeeregister.turley.com
Circulation: 17,000fr; Sworn/Estimate/Non-Audited
Advertising rate: Open inch rate $11.75
Established: 1970
Group: Turley Publications, Inc.
Ed. .... Kathy Mitchell
Pub. .... Patrick H. Turley
Ad. Director .... Beth Baker
Delivery Method: Racks
Areas Served: Chicopee, Holyoke, South Hadley, West Springfield, East Springfield

THE HOLYOKE SUN (FRI)

333 Front St, Chicopee, MA, 01013-3194, Hampden, USA; gen tel (413) 612-2310; adv tel (413) 612-2310; ed tel (413) 612-2310; gen fax (413) 592-3568; adv fax (413) 592-3568; ed fax (413) 592-3568; disp adv e-mail bbaker@turley.com; class adv e-mail classifieds@turley.com; ed e-mail kwill@turley.com; web site sun.turley.com
Circulation: 10,000fr; Sworn/Estimate/Non-Audited
Advertising rate: Open inch rate $11.75
Established: 1995
Group: Turley Publications, Inc.
Pub. .... Patrick H. Turley
Ed. .... Kristin Will
Ad. Director .... Beth Baker
Delivery Method: Racks
Areas Served: Holyoke, South Hadley, Chicopee

CLINTON

THE BANNER (FRI)

156 Church St, Clinton, MA, 01510-2563, Worcester, USA; gen tel (508) 835-4865; adv tel (508) 835-4865; ed tel (508) 835-4865; gen fax (978) 368-1151; adv fax (978) 368-1151; ed fax (978) 368-1151; disp adv e-mail itemads@telegram.com; class adv e-mail itemads@telegram.com; ed e-mail bannews@yahoo.com; web site www.weeklybanner.com
Circulation: 1,800pd,; Sworn/Estimate/Non-Audited
Advertising rate: Open inch rate $9.35
Established: 1978
Group: Coulter Press
Pub. .... Gary Hutner
Ed. .... Michael Kane
Mng. Ed. .... Jan Gottesman
Prodn. Mgr. .... Patricia Houck
Mechanical Specifications: Type page 9 2/3 x 12; E - 5 cols, 2 1/16, between; A - 5 cols, 2 1/16, between; C - 5 cols, 2 1/16, between.
Delivery Method: Mail, Newsstand
Areas Served: Boylston & West Boylston

THE ITEM (FRI)

156 Church St, Ste 1, Clinton, MA, 01510-2563, Worcester, USA; gen tel (978) 368-0176; adv tel (978) 368-0176; ed tel (978) 368-0176; gen fax (978) 368-1151; adv fax (978) 368-1151; ed fax (978) 368-1151; disp adv e-mail itemads@telegram.com; class adv e-mail itemads@telegram.com; ed e-mail clintonitem@yahoo.com; web site www.clintonitem.com
Circulation: 5,100pd, 100fr; Sworn/Estimate/Non-Audited
Advertising rate: Open inch rate $11.15
Established: 1893
Group: Coulter Press
Pub. .... Gary Hutner
Circ. Mgr. .... Ed Grant
Ed. .... Jan Gottesman
Sports Ed. .... Graham Entwistle
Mechanical Specifications: Type page 9.667X12.75 E - 5 cols
Delivery Method: Mail, Carrier
Areas Served: Clinton, Berlin, Bolton, Lancaster & Sterling

CONCORD

THE BEACON-VILLAGER (THUR)

150 Baker Avenue Ext, Ste 105, Concord, MA, 01742-2198, Middlesex, USA; gen tel (978) 371-5775; adv tel (978) 371-5723; ed tel (978) 371-5736; gen fax (781) 433-6965; adv fax (781) 433-6965; ed fax (781) 433-6965; disp adv e-mail salesteam@wickedlocal.com; class adv e-mail salesteam@wickedlocal.com; ed e-mail kcordeiro@wickedlocal.com; web site acton.wickedlocal.com
Circulation: 796pd,; AAM
Advertising rate: Open inch rate $25.50
Group: GateHouse Media, Inc.
Pub. .... Chuck Goodrich
Ed. in Chief .... Kathy Cordeiro
Sports Ed. .... Steve Tobey
Adv. Dir. .... Nick Bolitho
Areas Served: 01754, 01775

BEDFORD MINUTEMAN (THUR)

150 Baker Avenue Ext, Ste 101, Concord, MA, 01742-2199, Middlesex, USA; gen tel (978) 371-5796; adv tel (978) 371-5723; ed tel (978) 371-5796; gen fax (978) 371-5711; adv fax (978) 371-5712; ed fax (978) 371-5711; disp adv e-mail pcalder@wickedlocal.com; class adv e-mail classifieds@wickedlocal.com; web site http://bedford.wickedlocal.com/
Circulation: 1,132pd,; AAM
Advertising rate: Open inch rate $24.15
Established: 1956
Group: GateHouse Media, Inc.
Digital Platform - Mobile: Apple, Android, Windows, Blackberry
Digital Platform - Tablet: Apple iOS, Android, Windows 7, Blackberry Tablet OS, Kindle, Nook, Kindle Fire
Publisher .... Chuck Goodrich
Delivery Method: Mail

BILLERICA MINUTEMAN (THUR)

150 Baker Avenue Ext, Concord, MA, 01742-2126, Middlesex, USA; gen tel (978) 667-2156; adv tel (978) 667-2156; ed tel (978) 667-2156; gen fax (978) 371-5212; adv fax (978) 371-5212; ed fax (978) 371-5212; disp adv e-mail speters@wickedlocal.com; class adv e-mail rbright@wickedlocal.com; ed e-mail kcordeiro@wickedlocal.com; web site billerica.wickedlocal.com
Circulation: 1,649pd,; AAM
Advertising rate: Open inch rate $21.05
Group: GateHouse Media, Inc.
Digital Platform - Mobile: Apple, Android, Blackberry
Pub. .... Chuck Goodrich
Ed. in Chief .... Kathleen Cordeiro
Sports Ed. .... Doug Hastings
Areas Served: Bellirica (MA)

BURLINGTON UNION (THUR)

150 Baker Avenue Ext, Concord, MA, 01742-2126, Middlesex, USA; gen tel (781) 371-5742; adv tel (978) 739-1364; ed tel (978) 371-5742; disp adv e-mail aninos@wickedlocal.com; class adv e-mail cncclassads@wickedlocal.com; ed e-mail Burlington@wickedlocal.com; web site burlington.wickedlocal.com
Circulation: 1,479pd,; AAM
Established: 1963
Group: GateHouse Media, Inc.
Digital Platform - Mobile: Apple, Android, Blackberry
Pub. .... Chuck Goodrich
Circ. Mgr. .... Linda Vahey
Ed. .... Christine Herter Warren
Sports Ed. .... Doug Hastings
Adv. Dir. .... Nick Bolitho
Delivery Method: Mail, Newsstand
Areas Served: Burlington (MA)

CHELMSFORD INDEPENDENT (THUR)

150 Baker Avenue Ext, Concord, MA, 01742-2126, Middlesex, USA; gen tel (978) 256-7196; adv tel (978) 256-7196; ed tel (978) 256-7196; gen fax (978) 371-5212; adv fax (978) 371-5212; ed fax (978) 371-5212; disp adv e-mail speters@wickedlocal.com; class adv e-mail rbright@wickedlocal.com; ed e-mail chelmsford@wickedlocal.com; web site www.wickedlocal.com/chelmsford
Circulation: 1,490pd,; AAM
Advertising rate: Open inch rate $20.45
Group: GateHouse Media, Inc.
Digital Platform - Mobile: Apple, Android, Blackberry
Pub. .... Chuck Goodrich
Kathleen Cordeiro
Adv. Dir. .... Nick Bolitho
Ed. .... Margaret Smith
Areas Served: Chelmsford (MA)

LINCOLN JOURNAL (THUR)
150 Baker Avenue Ext, Ste 101, Concord, MA, 01742-2199, Middlesex, USA; gen tel (781) 259-8533; adv tel (781) 433-6925; ed tel (978) 371-5742; gen fax (978) 371-5711; adv fax (978) 371-5711; ed fax (978) 371-5711; disp adv e-mail jcutter@wickedlocal.com; class adv e-mail salesteam@wickedlocal.com; ed e-mail kragsdale@wickedlocal.com; web site www.wickedlocal.com/lincoln
Circulation: 525pd, 2fr; AAM
Advertising rate: Open inch rate $21.95
Group: GateHouse Media, Inc.
Digital Platform - Mobile: Apple, Android, Blackberry
Pub....Chuck Goodrich
Ed. in Chief....Kathy Cordeiro
Ed....Kathie Ragsdale
Adv. Dir....Nick Bolitho
Areas Served: Lincoln (MA)

LITTLETON INDEPENDENT (THUR)
150 Baker Avenue Ext, Ste 101, Concord, MA, 01742-2199, Middlesex, USA; gen tel (781) 433-6905; adv tel (781) 433-6905; ed tel (781) 433-6905; gen fax (781) 433-6965; adv fax (781) 433-6965; ed fax (781) 433-6965; disp adv e-mail pcalder@wickedlocal.com; class adv e-mail salesteam@wickedlocal.com; ed e-mail jcrane@wickedlocal.com; web site www.wickedlocal.com/littleton
Circulation: 825pd, 2fr; AAM
Advertising rate: Open inch rate $18.90
Group: Colorado Community Media
GateHouse Media, Inc.
Digital Platform - Mobile: Apple, Android, Blackberry
Pub....Chuck Goodrich
Adv. Mgr., Display....Pamela Calder
Ed. in Chief....Kathy Cordeiro
News Ed....Joyce Pellino Crane
Adv. Dir....Nick Bolitho
Areas Served: Littleton (MA)

TEWKSBURY ADVOCATE (THUR)
150 Baker Avenue Ext, Ste 105, Concord, MA, 01742-2198, Middlesex, USA; gen tel (978) 937-2634; adv tel (978) 371-5706; ed tel (978) 371-5744; gen fax (978) 371-5214; adv fax (978) 371-5214; ed fax (978) 371-5214; disp adv e-mail speters@wickedlocal.com; class adv e-mail rbright@wickedlocal.com; ed e-mail tewksbury@wickedlocal.com; web site www.wickedlocal.com/tewksbury
Circulation: 294pd, 1fr; AAM
Advertising rate: Open inch rate $23.85
Group: GateHouse Media, Inc.
Digital Platform - Mobile: Apple, Android, Blackberry
Pub....Chuck Goodrich
Ed. in Chief....Kathy Cordeiro
Ed....Mac McEntire
Adv. Dir....Nick Bolitho
Areas Served: Tewksbury

THE BOLTON COMMON (FRI)
150 Baker Avenue Ext, Ste 101, Concord, MA, 01742-2199, Middlesex, USA; gen tel (781) 433-6905; adv tel (978) 371-5737; ed tel (978) 371-5759; gen fax (781) 433-6965; disp adv e-mail mmanuppelli@wickedlocal.com; class adv e-mail mmanuppelli@wickedlocal.com; ed e-mail hcamero@wickedlocal.com; web site www.wickedlocal.com/bolton
Circulation: 1,141pd,; Sworn/Estimate/Non-Audited
Advertising rate: Open inch rate $17.30
Established: 1988
Group: GateHouse Media, Inc.
Digital Platform - Mobile: Apple, Android, Blackberry
Pub....Chuck Goodrich
Ed....Holly Camero
Ed. in Chief....Kathleen Cordeiro
Adv. Dir...... Nick BolithoEquipment & Software: Hardware — APP/Mac; Software — QPS/QuarkXPress 4.1, Adobe/Photoshop 6.0.
Areas Served: Bolton

THE CONCORD JOURNAL (THUR)
150 Baker Avenue Ext, Ste 101, Concord, MA, 01742-2199, Middlesex, USA; gen tel (978) 369-2800; adv tel (978) 371-5723; ed tel (978) 371-5742; gen fax (978) 371-5220; adv fax (978) 371-5220; ed fax (978) 371-5220; disp adv e-mail pcalder@wickedlocal.com; class adv e-mail rbright@wickedlocal.com; ed e-mail kragsdale@wickedlocal.com; web site www.wickedlocal.com/concord
Circulation: 3,147pd, 514fr; AAM
Advertising rate: Open inch rate $30.15
Group: GateHouse Media, Inc.
Digital Platform - Mobile: Apple, Android, Blackberry
Pub....Chuck Goodrich
Ed. in Chief....Kathy Cordeiro
Ed....Kathie Ragsdale
Adv. Dir....Nick Bolitho
Areas Served: Concord

THE HARVARD POST (FRI)
150 Baker Avenue Ext, Ste 105, Concord, MA, 01742-2198, Middlesex, USA; gen tel (781) 433-6905; adv tel (978) 371-5737; ed tel (978) 371-5759; gen fax (781) 433-6965; adv fax (781) 433-6965; ed fax (781) 433-6965; disp adv e-mail mmanuppelli@wickedlocal.com ; class adv e-mail salesteam@wickedlocal.com; ed e-mail hcamero@wickedlocal.com; web site www.wickedlocal.com/harvard
Circulation: 83fr; AAM
Advertising rate: Open inch rate $17.30
Established: 1973
Group: GateHouse Media, Inc.
Digital Platform - Mobile: Apple, Android, Blackberry
Pub....Chuck Goodrich
Ed. in Chief....Kathy Cordeiro
Regional Ed.....Holly CameroEquipment & Software: Hardware — APP/Mac; Software — QPS/QuarkXPress 4.1, Adobe/Photoshop 6.0.
Areas Served: 01451, 01467

TIMES & COURIER (THUR)
150 Baker Avenue Ext, Ste 101, Concord, MA, 01742-2199, Middlesex, USA; gen tel (978) 371-5759; adv tel (978) 371-5737; ed tel (978) 371-5740; gen fax (978) 371-5711; disp adv e-mail times-courier@wickedlocal.com; class adv e-mail rbright@wickedlocal.com; ed e-mail times-courier.sports@wickedlocal.com; web site www.wickedlocal.com/clinton
Circulation: 2,809pd,; Sworn/Estimate/Non-Audited
Advertising rate: Open inch rate $16.80
Group: GateHouse Media, Inc.
Digital Platform - Mobile: Apple, Android, Blackberry
Pub....Chuck Goodrich
Ed....Christine Herter Warren
Vice Pres., Adv....Mark Cohen
Ed.-in-Chief....Kathleen Cordeiro
Classified Adv. Mgr....Ron Bright
National Adv. Mgr....Jeff McEvoy
Online Adv. Mgr....Chris Eck
Adv. Dir....Nick Bolitho
Mechanical Specifications: Type page 12 x 12; E - 5 colsEquipment & Software: Hardware — PCs; Software — Publisher 2000, QPS/QuarkXPress 5.0.
Delivery Method: Mail, Newsstand, Racks
Areas Served: 01523, 01510

WESTFORD EAGLE (THUR)
150 Baker Avenue Ext, Ste 101, Concord, MA, 01742-2199, Middlesex, USA; gen tel (978) 371-5729; adv tel (978) 371-5706; ed tel (978) 371-5729; gen fax (978) 371-5711; adv fax (978) 371-5712; ed fax (978) 371-5711; disp adv e-mail speters@wickedlocal.com; class adv e-mail classifieds@wickedlocal.com; ed e-mail westford@wickedlocal.com; web site http://westford.wickedlocal.com/
Circulation: 1,641pd, 134fr; AAM
Advertising rate: Open inch rate $25.50
Group: GateHouse Media, Inc.
Digital Platform - Mobile: Apple, Android, Blackberry
Pub....Chuck Goodrich
Vice Pres., Adv....Mark Cohen
Ed. in Chief....Kathy Cordeiro
Ed....Joyce Crane
Adv. Dir....Nick Bolitho
Areas Served: Westford

WILMINGTON ADVOCATE (THUR)
150 Baker Avenue Ext, Ste 101, Concord, MA, 01742-2199, Middlesex, USA; gen tel (978) 371-5744; adv tel (978) 371-5707; ed tel (978) 371-5744; gen fax (978) 371-5214; adv fax (978) 371-5214; ed fax (978) 371-5214; disp adv e-mail cpineau@wickedlocal.com; class adv e-mail rbright@wickedlocal.com; ed e-mail wilmington@wickedlocal.com; web site www.wickedlocal.com/wilmington
Circulation: 218fr; AAM
Advertising rate: Open inch rate $23.85
Group: GateHouse Media, Inc.
Digital Platform - Mobile: Apple, Android, Blackberry
Pub....Chuck Goodrich
Ed....Mac McEntire
Ed. in Chief....Kathleen Cordeiro
Adv. Dir....Nick Bolitho
Areas Served: Wilmington

WOBURN ADVOCATE (THUR)
150 Baker Ave, Ste 101, Concord, MA, 01742-2117, Middlesex, USA; gen tel (978) 371-5744; adv tel (978) 739-1320; ed tel (978) 371-5744; gen fax (978) 371-5711; adv fax (978) 371-5711; ed fax (978) 371-5711; disp adv e-mail aninos@wickedlocal.com; class adv e-mail classifieds@wickedlocal.com; ed e-mail woburn@wickedlocal.com; web site http://woburn.wickedlocal.com/
Circulation: 3,755fr; AAM
Advertising rate: Open inch rate $25.00
Group: GateHouse Media, Inc.
Digital Platform - Mobile: Apple, Android, Blackberry
Pub....Chuck Goodrich
Ed....Kathleen Cordeiro
Adv. Dir....Nick Bolitho
Areas Served: Woburn

DANVERS

AMESBURY NEWS (FRI)
75 Sylvan St, Ste C105, Danvers, MA, 01923-2765, Essex, USA; gen tel (978) 739-1347; adv tel (978) 739-1350; ed tel (978) 739-8506; gen fax (978) 739-8501; adv fax (978) 739-8501; ed fax (978) 739-8501; disp adv e-mail ameltzer@wickedlocal.com; class adv e-mail pfraney@wickedlocal.com; ed e-mail amesbury@wickedlocal.com; web site www.wickedlocal.com/amesbury
Circulation: 7,767pd, 295fr; AAM
Advertising rate: Open inch rate $17.20
Group: Community Newspaper Co.-North
GateHouse Media, Inc.
Pub....Chuck Goodrich
Ed.-in-Chief....Pete Chianca
Ed....Rosemary Herbert
Vice Pres., Adv....Mark Cohen
Nat'l Adv. Mgr....James McEvoy
Ed....John Lockwood
News Ed....Janet Mackay Smith
Sports Ed....Dom NiCastro
Prodn. Mgr....Pat Coen
Adv. Dir....Nick Bolitho
Areas Served: Amesbury (MA)

BEVERLY CITIZEN (THUR)
75 Sylvan St, Ste C105, Danvers, MA, 01923-2765, Essex, USA; gen tel (978) 927-2777; adv tel (978) 739-1320; ed tel (978) 927-2777; gen fax (978) 739-8501; adv fax (978) 739-1391; ed fax (978) 739-8501; disp adv e-mail mkasper@wickedlocal.com; class adv e-mail classifieds@wickedlocal.com; ed e-mail beverly@wickedlocal.com; web site http://beverly.wickedlocal.com/
Circulation: 1,254pd,; AAM
Advertising rate: Open inch rate $24.80
Established: 1851
Group: Community Newspaper Co.-North
GateHouse Media, Inc.
Pub....Chuck Goodrich
Adv. Dir....Nick Bolitho
Mechanical Specifications: Type page 10 13/16 x 16; E - 5 cols, 2 1/16, between; A - 5 cols, 2 1/16, between; C - 8 cols, 1 7/32, between.
Areas Served: Beverly (MA)

CAPE ANN BEACON (FRI)
75 Sylvan St, Ste C105, Danvers, MA, 01923-2765, Essex, USA; gen tel (978) 739-1300; adv tel (978) 739-1320; ed tel (978) 739-1300; gen fax (978) 739-8501; adv fax (978) 739-1391; ed fax (978) 739-8501; disp adv e-mail mkasper@wickedlocal.com; class adv e-mail classifieds@wickedlocal.com; ed e-mail capeann@wickedlocal.com; web site http://gloucester.wickedlocal.com/
Circulation: 5,500fr; AAM
Advertising rate: Open inch rate $35.00
Group: Community Newspaper Co.-North
Digital Platform - Mobile: Apple, Android, Blackberry
Ed.-in-Chief....Peter Chianca
Managing Ed....Janet Mackay-Smith
Adv. Dir....Nick Bolitho
Areas Served: Gloucester, Rockport, Essex & Manchester-by-the-Sea (MA)

DANVERS HERALD (THUR)
75 Sylvan St, Ste C105, Danvers, MA, 01923-2765, Essex, USA; gen tel (978) 774-0505; adv tel (978) 774-0505; ed tel (978) 774-0505; gen fax (978) 739-8501; adv fax (978) 739-8501; ed fax (978) 739-8501; disp adv e-mail danvers@cnc.com; obits@cnc.com; photoreprints@cnc.com; mypaper@cnc.com; class adv e-mail salesteam@wickedlocal.com; ed e-mail legals@cnc.com; web site www.wickedlocal.com/danvers
Circulation: 1,614pd, 193fr; AAM
Advertising rate: Open inch rate $22.60
Group: Community Newspaper Co.-North
GateHouse Media, Inc.
Pub....Charles Goodrich
Ed....Jeffrey Pope
Ed. in Chief....Pete Chianca
Adv. Dir....Nick Bolitho
Mechanical Specifications: Type page 10 13/16 x 16; E - 5 cols, 2 1/16, between; A - 5 cols, 2 1/16, between; C - 8 cols, 1 7/32, between.

GEORGETOWN RECORD (THUR)
75 Sylvan St, Ste C105, Danvers, MA, 01923-2765, Essex, USA; gen tel (978) 739-8506; adv tel (781) 433-6925; ed tel (978) 739-8506; gen fax (978) 739-8501; adv fax (781) 433-7951; ed fax (781) 433-6965; disp adv e-mail salesteam@wickedlocal.com; class adv e-mail salesteam@wickedlocal.com; ed e-mail georgetown@wickedlocal.com; web site www.wickedlocal.com/georgetown
Circulation: 678pd,; AAM
Advertising rate: Open inch rate $17.85
Group: Community Newspaper Co.-North
GateHouse Media, Inc.
Digital Platform - Mobile: Apple, Android, Blackberry
Pub....Charles Goodrich
Cir. Mgr....Linda Vahey
Ed. in Chief....Pete Chianca
Ed....Tim McCarthy
Adv. Dir....Nick Bolitho
Mechanical Specifications: Type page 10 13/16 x 16; E - 5 cols, 2 1/16, between; A - 5 cols, 2 1/16, between; C - 8 cols, 1 7/32, between.
Areas Served: Georgetown (MA)

HAMILTON-WENHAM CHRONICLE (THUR)
75 Sylvan St, Ste C105, Danvers, MA, 01923-2765, Essex, USA; gen tel (978) 468-1911; adv tel (978) 468-1911; ed tel (978) 468-1911; gen fax (978) 739-8501; adv fax (978) 739-8501; ed fax (978) 739-8501; disp adv e-mail salesteam@wickedlocal.com; class adv e-mail salesteam@wickedlocal.com; ed e-mail hamilton-wenham@wickedlocal.com; web site www.wickedlocal.com/hamilton
Circulation: 1,003pd,; AAM
Advertising rate: Open inch rate $18.65
Group: Community Newspaper Co.-North
GateHouse Media, Inc.
Digital Platform - Mobile: Apple, Android,

Blackberry
Pub..Charles Goodrich
Ed. in Chief .... Pete Chianca
Managing Ed.....................Janet Mackay-Smith
News Ed. ....Jennie Omeig
Adv. Dir..Nick Bolitho
Mechanical Specifications: Type page 10 13/16 x 16; E - 5 cols, 2 1/16, between; A - 5 cols, 2 1/16, between; C - 8 cols, 1 7/32, between.
Areas Served: Hamilton (MA)

IPSWICH CHRONICLE (THUR)

75 Sylvan St, # 105, Danvers, MA, 01923-2763, Essex, USA; gen tel (978) 739-1303; adv tel (978) 739-1303; ed tel (978) 739-1303; gen fax (978) 739-8501; adv fax (978) 739-8501; ed fax (978) 739-8501; disp adv e-mail salesteam@wickedlocal.com; class adv e-mail salesteam@wickedlocal.com; ed e-mail Ipswich@wickedlocal.com; web site www.wickedlocal.com/ipswich
Circulation: 2,233pd, 2fr; AAM
Advertising rate: Open inch rate $22.60
Group: Community Newspaper Co.-North GateHouse Media, Inc.Editions: (1) 1 total; Ipswich Chronicle-Rowley Edition;
Digital Platform - Mobile: Apple, Android, Blackberry
Pub.......................................Charles Goodrich
Ed. ....Wendall Waters
Ed. ....Dan Mac Alpine
Mng. Ed. ....Janet Mackay Smith
Adv. Dir..Nick Bolitho
Mechanical Specifications: Type page 10 13/16 x 16; E - 5 cols, 2 1/16, between; A - 5 cols, 2 1/16, between; C - 8 cols, 1 7/32, between.
Areas Served: Ipswich (MA)

MALDEN OBSERVER (FRI)

75 Sylvan St, # 105, Danvers, MA, 01923-2763, Essex, USA; gen tel (781) 393-1827; adv tel (978) 739-1343; ed tel (781) 393-1827; gen fax (617) 629-3381; adv fax (617) 629-3381; ed fax (617) 629-3381; disp adv e-mail ameltzer@wickedlocal.com; class adv e-mail salesteam@wickedlocal.com; ed e-mail malden@wickedlocal.com; web site www.wickedlocal.com/malden
Circulation: 860pd, 13fr; AAM
Advertising rate: Open inch rate $22.85
Group: Community Newspaper Co.-North GateHouse Media, Inc.
Digital Platform - Mobile: Apple, Android, Blackberry
Pub.......................................Charles Goodrich
Ed. in Chief .... Pete Chianca
Ed. ....Nell Escobar Coakley
Sports Ed......................................Chris Hurley
Adv. Dir..Nick Bolitho
Mechanical Specifications: Type page 10 13/16 x 16; E - 5 cols, 2 1/16, between; A - 5 cols, 2 1/16, between; C - 8 cols, 1 7/32, between.
Areas Served: Malden (MA)

MEDFORD TRANSCRIPT (THUR)

75 Sylvan St, Ste C105, Danvers, MA, 01923-2765, Essex, USA; gen tel (781) 396-1982; adv tel (978) 739-1350; ed tel (781) 396-1982; gen fax (781) 393-1821; adv fax (781) 393-1821; ed fax (781) 393-1821; disp adv e-mail ameltzer@wickedlocal.com; class adv e-mail salesteam@wickedlocal.com; ed e-mail medford@wickedlocal.com; web site www.wickedlocal.com/medford
Circulation: 15,819pd, 1,179fr; AAM
Advertising rate: Open inch rate $25.30
Group: Community Newspaper Co.-North GateHouse Media, Inc.
Digital Platform - Mobile: Apple, Android, Blackberry
Pub.......................................Charles Goodrich
Ed. in Chief .... Pete Chianca
Ed. .... Nell Escobar-Coakley
Sports Ed......................................Chris Hurley
Adv. Dir..Nick Bolitho
Mechanical Specifications: Type page 13 x 21; E - 6 cols, 2 1/16, between; A - 6 cols, 2 1/16, between; C - 10 cols, 1 7/32, between.
Areas Served: Medford

MELROSE FREE PRESS (THUR)

75 Sylvan St Ste C105, 75 Sylvan St Ste C 105, Danvers, MA, 01923-2765, Essex, USA; gen tel (978) 739-1314; adv tel (978) 739-1350; ed tel (978) 739-1314; gen fax (978) 739-8501; adv fax (978) 739-1391; ed fax (978) 739-8501; disp adv e-mail thosker@wickedlocal.com; class adv e-mail classifieds@wickedlocal.com; ed e-mail melrose@wickedlocal.com; web site http://melrose.wickedlocal.com/
Circulation: 2,244pd,; AAM
Advertising rate: Open inch rate $24.40
Established: 1901
Group: Community Newspaper Co.-North GateHouse Media, Inc.
Digital Platform - Mobile: Apple, Android, Blackberry
Pub...Chuck Goodrich
Ed.-in-Chief................................ Pete Chianca
Mng. Ed. ....Nell Escobar Coakley
Adv. Dir..Nick Bolitho
Mechanical Specifications: Type page 13 x 21; E - 6 cols, 2 1/16, between; A - 6 cols, 2 1/16, between; C - 10 cols, 1 7/32, between.
Areas Served: Melrose

NEWBURYPORT CURRENT (FRI)

75 Sylvan St, Ste C105, Danvers, MA, 01923-2765, Essex, USA; gen tel (978) 739-1331; adv tel (978) 739-1350; ed tel (978) 739-1331; gen fax (978) 739-8501; adv fax (978) 739-8501; ed fax (978) 739-8501; disp adv e-mail ameltzer@wickedlocal.com; class adv e-mail salesteam@wickedlocal.com; ed e-mail newburyport@wickedlocal.com; web site www.wickedlocal.com/newburyport
Circulation: 7,428fr; AAM
Advertising rate: Open inch rate $22.85
Group: Community Newspaper Co.-North GateHouse Media, Inc.
Digital Platform - Mobile: Apple, Android, Blackberry
Pub...Chuck Goodrich
Ed. in Chief .... Pete Chianca
Ed. ....John Lockwood
ed.......................................Janet Mackay-Smith
Adv. Dir..Nick Bolitho
Mechanical Specifications: Type page 10 13/16 x 16; E - 5 cols, 2 1/16, between; A - 5 cols, 2 1/16, between; C - 8 cols, 1 7/32, between.
Areas Served: Newbury, Newburyport, Salisbury

NORTH ANDOVER CITIZEN (FRI)

75 Sylvan St, Ste C105, Danvers, MA, 01923-2765, Essex, USA; gen tel (978) 739-1300; adv tel (978) 739-1350; ed tel (978) 739-1320; gen fax (978) 739-8501; adv fax (978) 739-8501; ed fax (978) 739-8501; disp adv e-mail ameltzer@wickedlocal.com; class adv e-mail salesteam@wickedlocal.com; ed e-mail northandover@wickedlocal.com; web site www.wickedlocal.com/northandover
Circulation: 589pd, 0fr; AAM
Advertising rate: Open inch rate $20.65
Group: Community Newspaper Co.-North GateHouse Media, Inc.
Digital Platform - Mobile: Apple, Android, Blackberry
Pub...Chuck Goodrich
Ed. in Chief .... Pete Chianca
Ed. ....Tim McCarthy
Sports Ed..................................Joe McConnel
Adv. Dir..Nick Bolitho
Mechanical Specifications: Type page 10 13/16 x 16; E - 5 cols, 2 1/16, between; A - 5 cols, 2 1/16, between; C - 8 cols, 1 7/32, between.
Areas Served: North Andover

NORTH SHORE SUNDAY (SUN)

75 Sylvan St, Ste C105, Danvers, MA, 01923-2765, Essex, USA; gen tel (978) 739-1347; adv tel (978) 739-1350; ed tel (978) 739-1347; gen fax (978) 739-8501; adv fax (978) 739-8501; ed fax (978) 739-8501; disp adv e-mail ameltzer@wickedlocal.com; class adv e-mail dwinder@wickedlocal.com; ed e-mail northshore@wickedlocal.com; web site www.wickedlocal.com/northofboston
Circulation: 18,168fr; AAM
Advertising rate: Open inch rate $35.25
Group: Community Newspaper Co.-North GateHouse Media, Inc.
Digital Platform - Mobile: Apple, Android, Blackberry
Pub...Chuck Goodrich
Ed. in Chief .... Pete Chianca
Mng. Ed. ....Janet Mackay-Smith
Adv. Dir..Nick Bolitho
Mechanical Specifications: Type page 10 13/16 x 16; E - 5 cols, 2 1/16, between; A - 5 cols, 2 1/16, between; C - 8 cols, 1 7/32, between.
Areas Served: Danvers, Lynn, Peabody, Salem

READING ADVOCATE (WED)

75 Sylvan St, Ste C105, Danvers, MA, 01923-2765, Essex, USA; gen tel (781) 942-2252; adv tel (978) 739-1320; ed tel (781) 942-2252; gen fax (978) 371-5214; adv fax (978) 739-1391; ed fax (978) 371-5214; disp adv e-mail clucas@wickedlocal.com; class adv e-mail classifieds@wickedlocal.com; ed e-mail reading@wickedlocal.com; web site http://reading.wickedlocal.com/
Circulation: 600pd,; AAM
Advertising rate: Open inch rate $25.00
Group: GateHouse Media, Inc.
Digital Platform - Mobile: Apple, Android, Blackberry
Pub...Chuck Goodrich
Ed. in Chief .... Pete Chianca
Ed. ....Steve Ryan
Adv. Dir..Nick Bolitho
Areas Served: Reading

SALEM GAZETTE (FRI)

75 Sylvan St, Ste C105, Danvers, MA, 01923-2765, Essex, USA; gen tel (978) 739-1312; adv tel (978) 739-1350; ed tel (978) 739-1312; gen fax (978) 739-8501; adv fax (978) 739-8501; ed fax (978) 739-8501; disp adv e-mail ameltzer@wickedlocal.com; class adv e-mail salesteam@wickedlocal.com; ed e-mail salem@wickedlocal.com; web site www.wickedlocal.com/salem
Advertising rate: Open inch rate $23.80
Group: Community Newspaper Co.-North GateHouse Media, Inc.
Digital Platform - Mobile: Apple, Android, Blackberry
Ed.-in-Chief................................ Pete Chianca
Managing Ed...................Janet Mackay-Smith
Adv. Dir..Nick Bolitho
Areas Served: Salem

SAUGUS ADVERTISER (THUR)

75 Sylvan St, Ste C, Danvers, MA, 01923-2763, Essex, USA; gen tel (978) 739-1395; adv tel (978) 739-1320; ed tel (978) 739-1395; gen fax (978) 739-8501; adv fax (978) 739-1391; ed fax (978) 739-8501; disp adv e-mail clucas@wickedlocal.com; class adv e-mail classifieds@wickedlocal.com; ed e-mail saugus@wickedlocal.com; web site http://saugus.wickedlocal.com/
Circulation: 1,540pd,; AAM
Advertising rate: Open inch rate $23.45
Group: Community Newspaper Co.-North GateHouse Media, Inc.
Digital Platform - Mobile: Apple, Android, Blackberry
Pub...Chuck Goodrich
Ed. in Chief .... Pete Chianca
Ed. ....Michael Gaffney
Sports Ed.................................Joe McConnell
Mng. Ed. ....Nell Escobar Coakley
Adv. Dir..Nick Bolitho
Mechanical Specifications: Type page 13 x 21; E - 6 cols, 2 1/16, between; A - 6 cols, 2 1/16, between; C - 10 cols, 1 7/32, between.
Areas Served: Saugus

TRI-TOWN TRANSCRIPT (FRI)

75 Sylvan St, Ste C, Danvers, MA, 01923-2763, Essex, USA; gen tel (978) 739-1300; adv tel (978) 739-1350; ed tel (978) 739-1393; gen fax (978) 739-8501; adv fax (978) 739-8501; ed fax (978) 739-8501; disp adv e-mail ameltzer@wickedlocal.com; class adv e-mail salesteam@wickedlocal.com; ed e-mail tritown@wickedlocal.com; web site www.wickedlocal.com/boxford
Circulation: 2,604pd,; AAM
Advertising rate: Open inch rate $21.25
Group: Community Newspaper Co.-North GateHouse Media, Inc.
Digital Platform - Mobile: Apple, Android, Blackberry
Pub. ....Chuck Goodrich
Ed. in Chief .... Pete Chianca
Ed. .... Kathryn O'Brien
Sports Ed.................................Joshua Boyd
Adv. Dir..Nick Bolitho
Mechanical Specifications: Type page 10 13/16 x 16; E - 5 cols, 2 1/16, between; A - 5 cols, 2 1/16, between; C - 8 cols, 1 7/32, between.
Areas Served: Boxford, Middleton, Topsfield

WAKEFIELD OBSERVER (THUR)

75 Sylvan St, Ste C, Danvers, MA, 01923-2763, Essex, USA; gen tel (978) 739-8509; adv tel (978) 739-1350; ed tel (978) 371-5750; gen fax (978) 739-8501; adv fax (978) 739-8501; ed fax (978) 739-8501; disp adv e-mail ameltzer@wickedlocal.com; class adv e-mail salesteam@wickedlocal.com; ed e-mail wakefield@wickedlocal.com; web site www.wickedlocal.com/wakefield
Circulation: 250pd,; AAM
Advertising rate: Open inch rate $17.65
Group: Community Newspaper Co.-North GateHouse Media, Inc.
Digital Platform - Mobile: Apple, Android, Blackberry
Pub...Chuck Goodrich
Ed. in Chief .... Pete Chianca
Ed. ....Steve Ryan
Mng. Ed. ....Nell Escobar Coakley
Adv. Dir..Nick Bolitho
Mechanical Specifications: Type page 10 13/16 x 16; E - 5 cols, 2 1/16, between; A - 5 cols, 2 1/16, between; C - 8 cols, 1 7/32, between.
Areas Served: Wakefield

DEVENS

AYER PUBLIC SPIRIT (WED)

78 Barnum Rd, Devens, MA, 01434-3508, Middlesex, USA; gen tel (978) 772-0777; adv tel (978) 772-0777; ed tel (978) 772-0777; gen fax (978) 772-4012; adv fax (978) 772-4012; ed fax (978) 772-4012; disp adv e-mail Advertising@MediaOneMarketPlace.com; class adv e-mail Advertising@MediaOneMarketPlace.com; ed e-mail editor@nashobapub.com; web site www.ayerpublicspirit.com
Circulation: 114pd,; AAM
Advertising rate: Open inch rate $22.00
Established: 1869
Pub...Mark O'Neil
Ed. ....Jennifer Paluzzi
Delivery Method: Mail, Newsstand, Racks
Areas Served: Ayer

GROTON LANDMARK (FRI)

78 Barnum Rd, Devens, MA, 01434-3508, Middlesex, USA; gen tel (978) 772-0777; adv tel (978) 772-0777; ed tel (978) 772-0777; gen fax (978) 772-4012; adv fax (978) 772-4012; ed fax (978) 772-4012; disp adv e-mail Advertising@MediaOneMarketPlace.com; class adv e-mail Advertising@MediaOneMarketPlace.com; ed e-mail editor@nashobapub.com; web site www.grotonlandmark.com
Circulation: 695pd,; AAM
Advertising rate: Open inch rate $22.00
Established: 1869
Pub...Mark O'Neil
Mng. Ed.. Kate King
Delivery Method: Mail, Newsstand, Racks
Areas Served: 01450, 01827

HARVARD HILLSIDE (FRI)

78 Barnum Rd, Devens, MA, 01434-3508, Middlesex, USA; gen tel (978) 772-0777; adv tel (978) 772-0777; ed tel (978) 772-0777; gen fax (978) 772-4012; adv fax (978) 772-4012; ed fax (978) 772-4012; disp adv e-mail hconry@mediaonene.com; class adv e-mail Advertising@MediaOneMarketPlace.com; ed e-mail editor@nashobapub.com ; web site www.harvardhillside.com
Circulation: 117pd,; AAM
Advertising rate: Open inch rate $22.00
Pub...Mark O'Neil
Mng. Ed.. Kate King
Sports Ed.. Ed Niser
Pub...Larry Hubner
Mechanical Specifications: Type page 12 x 21; E - 6 cols, between; A - 6 cols, between; C - 9

cols, between.
Delivery Method: Mail, Newsstand, Racks
Areas Served: Harvard (MA)

PEPPERELL FREE PRESS (FRI)
78 Barnum Rd, Devens, MA, 01434-3508, Middlesex, USA; gen tel (978) 772-0777; adv tel (978) 772-0777; ed tel (978) 772-0777; gen fax (978) 772-4012; adv fax (978) 772-4012; ed fax (978) 772-4012; disp adv e-mail hconry@mediaonene.com; class adv e-mail Advertising@MediaOneMarketPlace.com; ed e-mail editor@nashobapub.com; web site www.pepperellfreepress.com
Circulation: 1,023pd,; AAM
Advertising rate: Open inch rate $15.45
Established: 1869
Office Coord.......................... Rebecca Pellerin
Circ. Mgr.................................... Mike Sheehan
Mng. Ed.. Kate King
Sports Ed... Ed Niser
Opns. Dir... Bill Walker
Pub... Larry Hubner
Mechanical Specifications: Type page 12 x 21; E - 6 cols, between; A - 6 cols, between; C - 9 cols, between.
Areas Served: Pepperell

SHIRLEY ORACLE (FRI)
78 Barnum Rd, Devens, MA, 01434-3508, Middlesex, USA; gen tel (978) 772-0777; adv tel (978) 772-0777; ed tel (978) 772-0777; gen fax (978) 772-4012; adv fax (978) 772-4012; ed fax (978) 772-4012; disp adv e-mail advertising@mediaonemarketplace.com; class adv e-mail advertising@mediaonemarketplace.com; ed e-mail editor@nashobapub.com; web site www.shirleyoracle.com
Circulation: 278pd,; AAM
Advertising rate: Open inch rate $22.00
Pub.. Mark O'Neil
Office Coord.......................... Rebecca Pellerin
Circ. Mgr.................................... Mike Sheehan
Mng. Ed.. Kate King
Sports Ed... Ed Niser
Opns. Dir... Bill Walker
Mechanical Specifications: Type page 12 x 21; E - 6 cols, between; A - 6 cols, between; C - 9 cols, between.
Delivery Method: Mail, Newsstand, Racks
Areas Served: Shirley

TOWNSEND TIMES (FRI)
78 Barnum Rd, Devens, MA, 01434-3508, Middlesex, USA; gen tel (978) 772-0777; adv tel (978) 772-0777; ed tel (978) 772-0777; gen fax (978) 772-4012; adv fax (978) 772-4012; ed fax (978) 772-4012; disp adv e-mail hconry@MediaOneNE.com; class adv e-mail hconry@MediaOneNE.com; ed e-mail editor@nashobapub.com; web site www.nashobapublishing.com/townsend_times
Circulation: 643pd,; AAM
Advertising rate: Open inch rate $22.00
Pub.. Mark O'Neil
Office Coord.......................... Rebecca Pellerin
Circ. Mgr.................................... Mike Sheehan
Mng. Ed.................................. Kathleen Walsh
Sports Ed................................ Ken Blanchette
Opns. Dir... Bill Walker
Mechanical Specifications: Type page 12 x 21; E - 6 cols, between; A - 6 cols, between; C - 9 cols, between.
Delivery Method: Mail, Newsstand, Racks
Areas Served: 01469, 01474

DORCHESTER

BOSTON HAITIAN REPORTER (MTHLY)
150 Mount Vernon St, Ste 120, Dorchester, MA, 02125-3135, Suffolk, USA; gen tel (617) 436-1222; adv tel (617) 436-1222; ed tel (617) 436-1222; gen fax (617) 825-5516; adv fax (617) 825-5516; ed fax (617) 825-5516; disp adv e-mail addesk@dotnews.com; class adv e-mail addesk@dotnews.com; ed e-mail newseditor@dotnews.com; web site www.bostonhaitian.com
Advertising rate: Open inch rate $13.25
Established: 1983
Group: Boston Neighborhood News, Inc.
Pub.. Edward Forrey
Ed... William Forry
Ad. Director................................ Jack Conboy
Prod. Mgr.............................. Barbara Langis
Delivery Method: Mail

BOSTON IRISH REPORTER (MTHLY)
150 Mount Vernon St, Ste 120, Dorchester, MA, 02125-3135, Suffolk, USA; gen tel (617) 436-1222; adv tel (617) 436-1222; ed tel (617) 436-1222; gen fax (617) 825-5516; adv fax (617) 825-5516; ed fax (617) 825-5516; disp adv e-mail addesk@dotnews.com; class adv e-mail addesk@dotnews.com; ed e-mail newseditor@dotnews.com; web site www.bostonirish.com
Advertising rate: Open inch rate $13.25
Established: 1983
Group: Boston Neighborhood News, Inc.
Pub.. Edward Forrey
Ed... William Forry
Ad. Director................................ Jack Conboy
Prod. Mgr.............................. Barbara Langis
Delivery Method: Mail

MATTAPAN REPORTER (THUR)
150 Mount Vernon St, Ste 120, Dorchester, MA, 02125-3135, Suffolk, USA; gen tel (617) 436-1222; adv tel (617) 436-1222; ed tel (617) 436-1222; gen fax (617) 825-5516; adv fax (617) 825-5516; ed fax (617) 825-5516; disp adv e-mail addesk@dotnews.com; class adv e-mail addesk@dotnews.com; ed e-mail newseditor@dotnews.com; web site www.dotnews.com/mattapan
Advertising rate: Open inch rate $13.25
Established: 1983
Group: Boston Neighborhood News, Inc.
Pub.. Edward Forrey
Ed... William Forry
Ad. Director................................ Jack Conboy
Prod. Mgr.............................. Barbara Langis
Delivery Method: Mail
Areas Served: Mattapan

THE DORCHESTER REPORTER (THUR)
150 Mount Vernon St, Ste 120, Dorchester, MA, 02125-3135, Suffolk, USA; gen tel (617) 436-1222; adv tel (617) 436-1222; ed tel (617) 436-1222; gen fax (617) 825-5516; adv fax (617) 825-5516; ed fax (617) 825-5516; disp adv e-mail addesk@dotnews.com; class adv e-mail addesk@dotnews.com; ed e-mail newseditor@dotnews.com; web site www.dotnews.com
Circulation: 22,000pd,; Sworn/Estimate/Non-Audited
Advertising rate: Open inch rate $13.25
Established: 1983
Pub....................................... Edward W. Forry
Adv. Mgr..................................... Jack Conboy
Mng. Ed.................................... William Forry
Prodn. Mgr.............................. Barbara Langis
Delivery Method: Mail, Newsstand
Areas Served: Dorchester, Mattapan, Roxbury, North Quincy, Milton, South Boston

DUXBURY

DUXBURY CLIPPER (WED)
11 S Station St, Duxbury, MA, 02332-4534, Plymouth, USA; gen tel (781) 934-2811; gen fax (781) 934-5917; disp adv e-mail newsroom@duxburyclipper.com; class adv e-mail ads@duxburyclipper.com; ed e-mail editor@duxburyclipper.com; web site www.duxburyclipper.com
Circulation: 4,500pd,
Advertising rate: Open inch rate $8.85
Established: 1950
Group: Duxbury Clipper
Pub................................... Deborah Anderson
Ed.. Gillian Smith
Office Mgr.......................... Amy McWilliams
Adv. Asst..................................... Robin Nudd
Sports Ed................................ Mike Halloran
Prodn. Mgr.......................... Lindsey Gardner
Areas Served: 02332, 02331

EAST LONGMEADOW

REMINDER METROWEST / CHICOPEE HERALD (FRI)
280 N Main St, East Longmeadow, MA, 01028-1868, Hampden, USA; gen tel (413) 525-3247; adv tel (413) 525-3247; ed tel (413) 525-3247; gen fax (413) 525-5882; adv fax (413) 525-5882; ed fax (413) 525-5882; disp adv e-mail marketing@reminderpublications.com; class adv e-mail marketing@reminderpublications.com; ed e-mail news@reminderpublications.com; web site www.thereminder.com
Circulation: 2pd, 8,926fr; CVC
Advertising rate: Open inch rate $20.00 - 22.25
Established: 1962
Group: Reminder Publications
Pub.............................. Christopher Buendo
Co-Pub.................................. Daniel Buendo
Adv. Mgr.................................. Barbara Perry
Circ. Mgr................................. Holly Mulligan
Editorial Mgr.......................... Michael Dobbs
Prodn. Mgr................................ Beth Thurber
Mechanical Specifications: Type page 10 x 13; E - 5 cols, 2, 1/8 between; A - 5 cols, 2, 1/8 between; C - 5 cols, 2, 1/8 between.Equipment & Software: Hardware — APP/Mac; Software — QPS/QuarkXPress, Adobe/Photoshop.
Delivery Method: Mail, Carrier
Areas Served: Westfield, West Springfield, Southwick, Agawam

SPRINGFIELD REMINDER (FRI)
280 N Main St, East Longmeadow, MA, 01028-1868, Hampden, USA; gen tel (413) 525-3247; adv tel (413) 525-3247; ed tel (413) 525-3247; gen fax (413) 525-5882; adv fax (413) 525-5882; ed fax (413) 525-5882; disp adv e-mail marketing@reminderpublications.com; class adv e-mail marketing@reminderpublications.com; ed e-mail news@reminderpublications.com; web site www.thereminder.com
Circulation: 2pd, 5,931fr; CVC
Advertising rate: Open inch rate $20.00 - 22.25
Established: 1962
Group: Reminder Publications
Pub.............................. Christopher Buendo
Co-Pub.................................. Daniel Buendo
Editorial Mgr.......................... Michael Dobbs
Prodn. Mgr................................ Beth Thurber
Adv. Dir.................................. Doug Fabian
Circ. Mgr...................................... Gail Breton
Adv. Mgr.................................. Barbara Perry
Circ. Mgr................................. Holly Mulligan
Mechanical Specifications: Type page 10 x 13; E - 5 cols, 2, 1/8 between; A - 5 cols, 2, 1/8 between; C - 5 cols, 2, 1/8 between.Equipment & Software: Hardware — APP/Mac; Software — QPS/QuarkXPress, Adobe/Photoshop.
Delivery Method: Mail, Carrier
Areas Served: Springfield

THE HERALD (WED)
280 N Main St, East Longmeadow, MA, 01028-1868, Hampden, USA; gen tel (413) 525-6661; adv tel (413) 525-6661; ed tel (413) 525-6661; gen fax (413) 525-5882; adv fax (413) 525-5882; ed fax (413) 525-5882; disp adv e-mail bperry@reminderpublications.com; class adv e-mail KBarba@ReminderPublications.com; ed e-mail mdobbs@ReminderPublications.com; web site www.thereminder.com
Circulation: 10,000fr; Sworn/Estimate/Non-Audited
Advertising rate: Open inch rate $16.00
Pub......................... Christopher M. Buendo
Adv. Mgr.................................. Barbara Perry
Circ. Mgr.............................. Diane Damarjian
Circ. Mgr................................. Holly Mulligan
Ed...................................... G. Michael Dobbs
Prodn. Mgr................................ Beth Thurber
Mechanical Specifications: Type page 10 1/4 x 16; E - 5 cols, between; A - 5 cols, between; C - 5 cols, between.Equipment & Software: Hardware — APP/Mac; Software — QPS/QuarkXPress.
Delivery Method: Mail, Racks
Areas Served: Holyoke, South Hadley, Chicopee, Granby

THE REMINDER (THUR, FRI)
280 N Main St, Ste 1, East Longmeadow, MA, 01028-1814, Hampden, USA; gen tel (413) 525-3247; adv tel (413) 525-3247; ed tel (413) 525-3247; gen fax (413) 525-5882; adv fax (413) 525-5882; ed fax (413) 525-5882; disp adv e-mail marketing@reminderpublications.com; class adv e-mail marketing@reminderpublications.com; ed e-mail news@reminderpublications.com; web site www.thereminder.com
Circulation: 4pd, 24,971fr; VAC
Advertising rate: Open inch rate $20.00 - 22.25
Established: 1962
Group: Reminder Publications
Pub.............................. Christopher Buendo
Co-Pub.................................. Daniel Buendo
Circ. Mgr................................. Holly Mulligan
Editorial Mgr.......................... Michael Dobbs
Prodn. Mgr................................ Beth Thurber
Mechanical Specifications: Type page 10 x 13; E - 5 cols, 2, 1/8 between; A - 5 cols, 2, 1/8 between; C - 5 cols, 2, 1/8 between.Equipment & Software: Hardware — APP/Mac; Software — QPS/QuarkXPress, Adobe/Photoshop.
Delivery Method: Mail, Carrier
Areas Served: East Longmeadow, Hampden, Longmeadow, Sixteen Acres and Wilbraham

EDGARTOWN

VINEYARD GAZETTE (FRI)
34 S Summer St, Edgartown, MA, 02539-8104, Dukes, USA; gen tel (508) 627-4311; adv tel (508) 627-4311; ed tel (508) 627-4311; gen fax (508) 627-7444; adv fax (508) 627-7444; ed fax (508) 627-7444; disp adv e-mail ads@mvgazette.com; class adv e-mail classifieds@mvgazette.com; ed e-mail news@mvgazette.com; web site vineyardgazette.com
Circulation: 9,000pd, 150fr; Sworn/Estimate/Non-Audited
Advertising rate: Open inch rate $22.90
Established: 1846
Group: Vineyard Gazette LLC
Digital Platform - Mobile: Apple, Android, Blackberry
Digital Platform - Tablet: Apple iOS, Android
Business Mgr............................ Sarah Gifford
Ed.. Julia Wells
Mng. Ed.. Bill Eville
Prodn. Mgr................................ Steve Durkee
Pub....................................... Jane Seagrave
Director of Sales and Marketing..... Skip Finley
Mechanical Specifications: Type page 16 1/4 x 20 3/4; E - 7 cols, 2 1/8, 1/4 between; A - 7 cols, 2 1/8, 1/4 between; C - 7 cols, 2 1/8, 1/4 between.Equipment & Software: Hardware — APP/Mac; Presses — G/Community; Software — Adobe Creative Suite
Delivery Method: Mail, Newsstand, Racks
Areas Served: 02539, 02557, 02535, 02568

EVERETT

EVERETT LEADER HERALD NEWS GAZETTE (THUR)
28 Church St, Everett, MA, 02149-2719, Middlesex, USA; gen tel (617) 387-4570; adv tel (617) 387-4570; ed tel (617) 387-4570; gen fax (617) 387-0409; adv fax (617) 387-0409; ed fax (617) 387-0409; disp adv e-mail everettleader@comcast.net; class adv e-mail everettleader@comcast.net; ed e-mail everettleader@comcast.net; web site www.facebook.com/pages/Everett-Leader-Herald-News-Gazette/155161251187065
Circulation: 15,000fr; Sworn/Estimate/Non-Audited
Advertising rate: Open inch rate $10.00
Established: 1885
Pub................................. Joseph A. Curnane
Mechanical Specifications: Type page 13 5/8 x 21; E - 6 cols, 2, between; A - 6 cols, 2, between; C - 9 cols, 1 5/16, between.
Delivery Method: Carrier
Areas Served: Everett (MA)

FAIRHAVEN

THE ADVOCATE (THUR)
PO Box 711, Fairhaven, MA, 02719-0700, Bristol, USA; gen tel (508) 992-1522; gen fax (508) 961-2245; disp adv e-mail theadvocatenewspaper@yahoo.com; editor@advocatenewsonline.com
Circulation: 1,518pd, 141fr; Sworn/Estimate/Non-Audited
Advertising rate: Open inch rate $19.95
Group: Dow Jones Local Media Group
Pub.................................. Warren A. Hathaway
Gen. Mgr................................ Barry Harrington
Ed...Michael Medeiros

FALMOUTH

THE BOURNE ENTERPRISE (THUR)
50 Depot Ave, Falmouth, MA, 02540-2302, Barnstable, USA; gen tel (508) 548-4700; adv tel (508) 548-4700; ed tel (508) 548-4700; gen fax (508) 540-8407; adv fax (508) 540-8407; ed fax (508) 540-8407; disp adv e-mail ads@capenews.net; class adv e-mail ads@capenews.net; ed e-mail paradise@capenews.net; web site www.capenews.net
Advertising rate: Open inch rate $15.00
Established: 1895
Group: Enterprise
Ed./Pub..Bill Hough
Managing Ed.............................John Paradise
Ad. Director................................Sean Randall
Areas Served: Bourne (MA)

THE FALMOUTH ENTERPRISE (FRI)
50 Depot Ave, Falmouth, MA, 02540-2302, Barnstable, USA; gen tel (508) 548-4700; adv tel (508) 548-4700; ed tel (508) 548-4700; gen fax (508) 540-8407; adv fax (508) 540-8407; ed fax (508) 540-8407; disp adv e-mail ptheall@capenews.net; class adv e-mail ads@capenews.net; ed e-mail bennett@capenews.net; web site www.capenews.net
Circulation: 7,759pd, 66fr; AAM
Advertising rate: Open inch rate $15.00
Established: 1895
Group: Enterprise
Pub./Ed..Bill Hough
Sales Director................................ Patti Theall
Delivery Method: Mail, Newsstand, Carrier, Racks
Areas Served: Falmouth (MA)

THE MASHPEE ENTERPRISE (FRI)
50 Depot Ave, Falmouth, MA, 02540-2302, Barnstable, USA; gen tel (508) 548-4700; adv tel (508) 548-4700; ed tel (508) 548-4700; gen fax (508) 540-8407; adv fax (508) 540-8407; ed fax (508) 540-8407; disp adv e-mail ads@capenews.net; class adv e-mail ads@capenews.net; ed e-mail kehrl@capenews.net; web site www.capenews.net
Advertising rate: Open inch rate $15.00
Established: 1895
Group: Enterprise
Ad. Director................................ Sean Randall
Mng. Ed... Brian Kehrl
Ed...Jim Kinsella
Areas Served: Mashpee (MA)

THE SANDWICH ENTERPRISE (FRI)
50 Depot Ave, Falmouth, MA, 02540-2302, Barnstable, USA; gen tel (508) 548-4700; adv tel (508) 548-4700; ed tel (508) 548-4700; gen fax (508) 540-8407; adv fax (508) 540-8407; ed fax (508) 540-8407; disp adv e-mail ads@capenews.net; class adv e-mail ads@capenews.net; ed e-mail paradise@capenews.net web site www.capenews.net
Advertising rate: Open inch rate $15.00
Established: 1895
Group: Enterprise
Ed./Pub. ....Bill Hough
Ed. ....John Paradise
Ad. Director............................... Sean Randall
Areas Served: Sandwich (MA)

FEEDING HILLS

AGAWAM ADVERTISER NEWS (THUR)
23 Southwick St, Feeding Hills, MA, 01030, Hampden, USA; gen tel (413) 786-7747; adv tel (413) 786-7747; ed tel (413) 786-7747; gen fax (413) 786-8457; adv fax (413) 786-8457; ed fax (413) 786-8457; disp adv e-mail jbaskin@turley.com; class adv e-mail classifieds@turley.com; ed e-mail aan@turley.com; web site www.agawamnewsonline.com
Circulation: 6,500pd,; Sworn/Estimate/Non-Audited
Advertising rate: Open inch rate $10.75
Established: 1965
Group: Turley Publications, Inc.
Pub.. Patrick H. Turley
Adv. Mgr.. Beth Baker
Ed. .... Jennifer Wroblewski
Delivery Method: Mail, Newsstand
Areas Served: Agawam & Feeding Hills

SOUTHWICK SUFFIELD NEWS (FRI)
23 Southwick St, Feeding Hills, MA, 01030-2023, Hampden, USA; gen tel (413) 786-7747; adv tel (413) 786-7747; ed tel (413) 786-7747; gen fax (413) 786-8457; adv fax (413) 786-8457; ed fax (413) 786-8457; disp adv e-mail bbaker@turley.com; class adv e-mail classifieds@turley.com; ed e-mail tkane@turley.com; web site www.southwicknewsonline.com
Circulation: 9,000fr; Sworn/Estimate/Non-Audited
Advertising rate: Open inch rate $10.75
Established: 1967
Group: Turley Publications, Inc.
Ed. ....Tim Kane
Pub.. Patrick H. Turley
Adv. Dir..Nick Bolitho
Delivery Method: Racks
Areas Served: Suffield (CT), Southwick, Westfield (MA)

FOXBORO

THE FOXBORO REPORTER (THUR)
36 Mechanic St, Ste 107, Foxboro, MA, 02035-2073, Norfolk, USA; gen tel (508) 543-4851; adv tel (508) 543-4851; ed tel (508) 543-4851; gen fax (508) 543-4888; adv fax (508) 543-4888; ed fax (508) 543-4888; disp adv e-mail msutherland@thesunchronicle.com; class adv e-mail msutherland@thesunchronicle.com; ed e-mail foxboronews@yahoo.com; web site www.foxbororeporter.com
Circulation: 2,500pd,; Sworn/Estimate/Non-Audited
Advertising rate: Open inch rate $10.22
Group: United Communications Corp
Managing Ed................................Bill Stedman
Office manager.......................... Ruth Jackson
Reporter .... Bera Dunau
Mechanical Specifications: Type page 11 5/8 x 21 1/4; E - 6 cols, 1 7/8, between.
Delivery Method: Mail, Newsstand
Areas Served: Foxborough

FRAMINGHAM

ASHLAND TAB (FRI)
33 New York Ave, Framingham, MA, 01701-8857, Middlesex, USA; gen tel (508) 626-3957; adv tel (508) 626-3984; ed tel (508) 626-3957; gen fax (508) 626-4400; adv fax (508) 626-4400; ed fax (508) 626-4400; disp adv e-mail crobinso@wickedlocal.com; class adv e-mail crobinso@wickedlocal.com; ed e-mail ashland@wickedlocal.com; web site www.wickedlocal.com/ashland
Circulation: 987pd,; Sworn/Estimate/Non-Audited
Advertising rate: Open inch rate $19.75
Group: Community Newspaper Co.-West GateHouse Media, Inc.
Digital Platform - Mobile: Apple, Android, Blackberry
Ed. in Chief...............................Richard Lodge
Sports Ed................................... Art Davidson
Adv. Dir...Nick Bolitho
Areas Served: Ashland (MA)

FRAMINGHAM TAB (FRI)
33 New York Ave, Framingham, MA, 01701-8857, Middlesex, USA; gen tel (508) 626-3800; adv tel (508) 626-3800; ed tel (508) 626-3800; gen fax (508) 626-4400; adv fax (508) 626-4400; ed fax (508) 626-4400; disp adv e-mail salesteam@wickedlocal.com; class adv e-mail salesteam@wickedlocal.com; ed e-mail framingham@wickedlocal.com; web site www.wickedlocal.com/framingham
Circulation: 4,637fr; AAM
Advertising rate: Open inch rate $31.90
Group: Community Newspaper Co.-West GateHouse Media, Inc.
Digital Platform - Mobile: Apple, Android, Blackberry
Ed. in Chief...............................Richard Lodge
Ed...Phil Maddocks
Dir. Corp. Sales.............................Paul Farrell
Areas Served: Framingham (MA)

HOLLISTON TAB (THUR)
33 New York Ave, Framingham, MA, 01701-8857, Middlesex, USA; gen tel (508) 323-3957; adv tel (508) 323-3957; ed tel (508) 323-3957; gen fax (508) 626-4400; adv fax (508) 626-4400; ed fax (508) 626-4400; disp adv e-mail crobinso@wickedlocal.com; class adv e-mail salesteam@wickedlocal.com; ed e-mail joconnell@wickedlocal.com; web site www.wickedlocal.com/holliston
Circulation: 1,343pd,; Sworn/Estimate/Non-Audited
Advertising rate: Open inch rate $15.85
Group: Community Newspaper Co.-West GateHouse Media, Inc.
Digital Platform - Mobile: Apple, Android, Blackberry
Tab Ed....................................... Joe O'Connell
Adv. Dir...Nick Bolitho
Areas Served: Holliston (MA)

HOPKINTON CRIER (FRI)
33 New York Ave, Framingham, MA, 01701-8857, Middlesex, USA; gen tel (508) 626-4412; adv tel (508) 626-4412; ed tel (508) 626-4332; gen fax (508) 626-4400; adv fax (508) 626-4400; ed fax (508) 626-4400; disp adv e-mail salesteam@wickedlocal.com; class adv e-mail salesteam@wickedlocal.com; ed e-mail hopkinton@wickedlocal.com; web site www.wickedlocal.com/hopkinton
Circulation: 240pd,; AAM
Advertising rate: Open inch rate $16.50
Established: 1987
Group: Community Newspaper Co.-West GateHouse Media, Inc.
Digital Platform - Mobile: Apple, Android, Blackberry
Ed. .... Alison McCall
Ed. in Chief...............................Richard Lodge
Elizabeth Banks
Adv. Dir...Nick Bolitho
Delivery Method: Mail, Newsstand, Racks
Areas Served: Hopkinton (MA)

HUDSON SUN (THUR)
33 New York Ave, Framingham, MA, 01701-8857, Middlesex, USA; gen tel (508) 490-7455; adv tel (508) 626-3833; ed tel (508) 626-3926; gen fax (508) 626-4400; adv fax (508) 626-4400; ed fax (508) 626-4400; disp adv e-mail lgreen@wickedlocal.com; ed e-mail hudson@wickedlocal.com; web site www.wickedlocal.com/hudson
Circulation: 2,968pd, 27,387fr; AAM
Advertising rate: Open inch rate $26.50
Group: Community Newspaper Co.-West GateHouse Media, Inc.
Ed. in Chief...............................Richard Lodge
Ed. ....Cathy Buday
Pub... Chuck Goodrich
Adv. Dir......Nick BolithoEquipment & Software: ; Software — CJ.
Delivery Method: Mail

MARLBOROUGH ENTERPRISE (THUR)
33 New York Ave, Framingham, MA, 01701-8857, Middlesex, USA; gen tel (508) 490-7455; adv tel (508) 490-7455; ed tel (508) 490-7455; gen fax (508) 490-7471; disp adv e-mail crobinson@wickedlocal.com; class adv e-mail salesteam@wickedlocal.com; ed e-mail marlborough@wickedlocal.com; web site www.wickedlocal.com/marlborough
Circulation: 1,746pd,; Sworn/Estimate/Non-Audited
Advertising rate: Open inch rate $26.50
Group: Community Newspaper Co.-West GateHouse Media, Inc.
Digital Platform - Mobile: Apple, Android, Blackberry
Ed. in Chief...............................Richard Lodge
Digital Ed. .... Meghan Kelly
Sports Ed. .... Art Davidson
Adv. Dir...Nick Bolitho
Areas Served: Marlborough (MA)

NATICK BULLETIN & TAB (FRI)
33 New York Ave, Framingham, MA, 01701-8857, Middlesex, USA; gen tel (508) 626-4437; adv tel (781) 433-6930; ed tel (866) 746-8603; gen fax (508) 626-4400; adv fax (781) 433-7951; ed fax (508) 626-4400; disp adv e-mail crobinso@wickedlocal.com; class adv e-mail salesteam@wickedlocal.com; ed e-mail natick@wickedlocal.com; web site www.wickedlocal.com/natick
Circulation: 4,696pd,; Sworn/Estimate/Non-Audited
Advertising rate: Open inch rate $23.30
Established: 1986
Group: GateHouse Media, Inc.
Digital Platform - Mobile: Apple, Android, Blackberry
Ed. in Chief...............................Richard Lodge
Adv. Dir...Nick Bolitho
Areas Served: Natick

SHREWSBURY CHRONICLE (THUR)
33 New York Ave, Framingham, MA, 01701-8857, Middlesex, USA; gen tel (508) 490-7454; adv tel (508) 626-3984; ed tel (508) 490-7454; gen fax (508) 490-7471; adv fax (508) 490-7471; ed fax (508) 490-7471; disp adv e-mail crobinso@wickedlocal.com; class adv e-mail salesteam@wickedlocal.com; ed e-mail Shrewsbury@wickedlocal.com; web site www.wickedlocal.com/shrewsbury
Circulation: 269pd, 1,942fr; AAM
Advertising rate: Open inch rate $19.00
Group: Community Newspaper Co.-West GateHouse Media, Inc.
Digital Platform - Mobile: Apple, Android, Blackberry
Ed. ....Glenda Hazard
Ed. in Chief...............................Richard Lodge
Adv. Dir...Nick Bolitho
Delivery Method: Mail, Newsstand
Areas Served: 01545

SUDBURY TOWN CRIER (THUR)
33 New York Ave, Framingham, MA, 01701-8857, Middlesex, USA; gen tel (508) 626-3926; adv tel (508) 626-3913; ed tel (508) 626-3926; gen fax (508) 626-4400; disp adv e-mail subury@wickedlocal.com; ed e-mail sudbury@wickedlocal.com; web site www.wickedlocal.com/sudbury
Circulation: 3,969pd,; Sworn/Estimate/Non-Audited
Advertising rate: Open inch rate $20.65
Group: GateHouse Media, Inc.
President, Group Publisher .... Sean Burke
Ed. in Chief...............................Richard Lodge
Delivery Method: Mail, Newsstand
Areas Served: Sudbury, MA

THE VILLAGER (FRI)
33 New York Ave, Framingham, MA, 01701-8857, Middlesex, USA; gen tel (508) 490-7454; adv tel (508) 626-3984; ed tel (508) 490-7454; gen fax (508) 490-7471; adv fax (508) 490-7471; ed fax (508) 490-7471; disp adv e-mail crobinso@wickedlocal.com; class adv e-mail salesteam@wickedlocal.com; ed e-mail northboro-southboro@wickedlocal.com; web site www.wickedlocal.com/north-

borough
Circulation: 429pd, 4fr; AAM
Advertising rate: Open inch rate $19.30
Group: GateHouse Media, Inc.
Digital Platform - Mobile: Apple, Android, Blackberry
Ed. .... Glenda Hazard
Ed. in Chief .... Richard Lodge
Adv. Dir.....Nick BolithoEquipment & Software: ; Software — CJ.
Areas Served: Northborough, Southborough

THE WESTBOROUGH NEWS (FRI)

33 New York Ave, Framingham, MA, 01701-8857, Middlesex, USA; gen tel (508) 836-3700; adv tel (508) 626-3984; ed tel (508) 626-3871; gen fax (508) 490-7471; adv fax (508) 490-7471; ed fax (508) 490-7471; disp adv e-mail crobinson@wickedlocal.com; class adv e-mail salesteam@wickedlocal.com; ed e-mail westboroevents@wickedlocal.com; web site www.wickedlocal.com/westborough
Circulation: 2,004pd,
Advertising rate: Open inch rate $18.55
Group: Community Newspaper Co.-West GateHouse Media, Inc.
Digital Platform - Mobile: Apple, Android, Blackberry
Ed. in Chief .... Richard Lodge
Adv. Dir.. Nick Bolitho
Areas Served: Westborough

WAYLAND TOWN CRIER (THUR)

33 New York Ave, Framingham, MA, 01701-8857, Middlesex, USA; gen tel (508) 626-4441; adv tel (508) 626-3984; ed tel (508) 626-4441; gen fax (508) 626-4400; adv fax (508) 626-4400; ed fax (508) 626-4400; disp adv e-mail crobinso@wickedlocal.com; class adv e-mail salesteam@wickedlocal.com; ed e-mail wayland@wickedlocal.com; web site www.wickedlocal.com/wayland
Circulation: 2,362pd,; Sworn/Estimate/Non-Audited
Advertising rate: Open inch rate $22.00
Group: GateHouse Media, Inc.
Digital Platform - Mobile: Apple, Android, Blackberry
Pub... Mark Olivieri
Ed. in Chief .... Richard Lodge
Ed. .... Michael Wyner
Adv. Dir.. Nick Bolitho
Areas Served: Wayland

WESTON TOWN CRIER (THUR)

33 New York Ave, Framingham, MA, 01701-8857, Middlesex, USA; gen tel (508) 626-4441; adv tel (508) 626-3984; ed tel (508) 626-4441; gen fax (508) 626-4400; adv fax (508) 626-4400; ed fax (508) 626-4400; disp adv e-mail crobinson@wickedlocal.com; class adv e-mail salesteam@wickedlocal.com; ed e-mail weston@wickedlocal.com; web site www.wickedlocal.com/weston
Circulation: 2,968pd, 27,387fr; AAM
Advertising rate: Open inch rate $22.00
Group: Community Newspaper Co.-West GateHouse Media, Inc.
Digital Platform - Mobile: Apple, Android, Blackberry
VP., Adv....................................... Mark Cohen
Ed. in Chief .... Richard Lodge
News Ed. .... Michael Wyner
Adv. Dir.....Nick BolithoEquipment & Software: ; Software — CJ.
Areas Served: Weston

GREAT BARRINGTON

THE BERKSHIRE RECORD (THUR)

21 Elm St, Great Barrington, MA, 01230-1516, Berkshire, USA; gen tel (413) 528-5380; adv tel (413) 528-5380; ed tel (413) 528-5380; gen fax (413) 528-9449; adv fax (413) 528-9449; ed fax (413) 528-9449; disp adv e-mail berkads@bcn.net; class adv e-mail berkads@bcn.net; ed e-mail berkrec@bcn.net; web site www.berkshirerecord.net
Circulation: 14,000pd,; Sworn/Estimate/Non-Audited
Advertising rate: Open inch rate $14.00
Group: Limestone Communications Inc
Pub.................................. Anthony Prisendorf
Ed. .... Donna Prisendorf
Delivery Method: Mail, Newsstand, Racks
Areas Served: Southern Berkshire County

HANSON

PLYMPTON-HALIFAX EXPRESS (FRI)

PO Box 60, 1000 Main Street, Hanson, MA, 02341-0060, Plymouth, USA; gen tel (781) 293-0420; gen fax (781) 293-0421; disp adv e-mail ads@whphexpress.com; class adv e-mail ads@whphexpress.com; ed e-mail editor@whphexpress.com; web site www.plymptonhalifaxexpress.com
Circulation: 623pd, 83fr; USPS
Advertising rate: 11.50 per column inch
Established: 2014
Group: Anderson Newspapers, Inc., d/b/a Express Newspapers
Pub .... Deborah Anderson
Ed. .... Tracey Seelye
Delivery Method: Mail
Areas Served: Plympton, Halifax, Plymouth County

WHITMAN-HANSON EXPRESS (THUR)

1000 Main St, Hanson, MA, 02341-1560, Plymouth, USA; gen tel (781) 293-0420; gen fax (781) 293-0421; disp adv e-mail ads@whphexpress.com; class adv e-mail ads@whphexpress.com; ed e-mail editor@whphexpress.com; web site www.whitmanhansonexpress.com
Circulation: 1,987pd, 126fr; USPS
Advertising rate: 11.50 per column inch
Established: 2002
Group: Anderson Newspapers, Inc., d/b/a Express Newspapers
Pub .... Deborah Anderson
Ed. .... Tracey Seelye
Delivery Method: Mail, Newsstand
Areas Served: Whitman, Hanson, Plymouth County

HARVARD

THE HARVARD PRESS (FRI)

1 Still River Rd, Fl 3rd, Harvard, MA, 01451-1330, Worcester, USA; gen tel (978) 456-3700; adv tel (978) 456-3700; ed tel (978) 456-3700; gen fax (978) 456-0330; adv fax (978) 456-0330; ed fax (978) 456-0330; disp adv e-mail classifieds@harvardpress.com; class adv e-mail classifieds@harvardpress.com; ed e-mail editor@harvardpress.com; web site www.harvardpress.com - 20,000(views) 5,000(visitors)
Advertising rate: Open inch rate $9.00
Ed. .... Matthew Cook
Delivery Method: Mail, Racks
Areas Served: Harvard (MA)

HINGHAM

COHASSET MARINER (FRI)

73 South St, Hingham, MA, 02043-2421, Plymouth, USA; gen tel (781) 749-0031; adv tel (781) 749-0031; ed tel (781) 749-0031; gen fax (781) 741-2931; adv fax (781) 741-2931; ed fax (781) 741-2931; disp adv e-mail coliver@wickedlocal.com; class adv e-mail toliver@wickedlocal.com; ed e-mail cohasset@wickedlocal.com; web site www.wickedlocal.com/cohasset
Circulation: 1,504pd, 356fr; AAM
Advertising rate: Open inch rate $19.05
Group: Community Newspaper Co. - South GateHouse Media, Inc.
Digital Platform - Mobile: Apple, Android, Blackberry
Pub.. Mark Olivieri
Ed. in Chief .... Gregory Mathis
Ed. .... Mary Ford
Act. Exec. .... Claudia Oliver
Adv. Dir.. Nick Bolitho
Areas Served: Cohasset (MA)

HINGHAM JOURNAL (THUR)

73 South St, Hingham, MA, 02043-2421, Plymouth, USA; gen tel (781) 749-0031; adv tel (781) 749-0031; ed tel (781) 749-0031; gen fax (781) 741-2931; adv fax (781) 741-2931; ed fax (781) 741-2931; disp adv e-mail srussell@wickedlocal.com; class adv e-mail salesteam@wickedlocal.com; ed e-mail mford@wickedlocal.com; web site www.wickedlocal.com/hingham
Circulation: 3,621pd, 1,447fr; AAM
Advertising rate: Open inch rate $19.55
Group: Community Newspaper Co. - South GateHouse Media, Inc.
Digital Platform - Mobile: Apple, Android, Blackberry
Pub.. Mark Olivieri
Natl. Adv. Dir. .... Jeff McEvoy
News Ed. .... Mary Ford
Sports Ed........................... William Wassersug
Adv. Dir.. Nick Bolitho
Areas Served: Hingham (MA)

HOLDEN

THE LANDMARK (THUR)

1105A Main St, Holden, MA, 01520-1219, Worcester, USA; gen tel (508) 829-5981; adv tel (508) 829-5981; ed tel (508) 829-5981; gen fax (508) 749-3165; adv fax (508) 749-3165; ed fax (508) 749-3165; disp adv e-mail sales@holdenlandmark.com; class adv e-mail sales@centralmassclass.com; ed e-mail editor@thelandmark.com; web site www.thelandmark.com
Circulation: 8,909pd, 350fr; Sworn/Estimate/Non-Audited
Advertising rate: Open inch rate $12.75
Established: 1976
Pres. .... Kirk A. Davis
Sales/Gen. Mgr. .... Barbara Brown
Circ. Mgr.. Tom Sidna
Prodn. Mgr. .... Don Cloutier
Mechanical Specifications: Type page 11 x 16; E - 4 cols, 2 3/8, 3/16 between; A - 6 cols, 1 9/16, 3/16 between; C - 6 cols, 1 9/16, 3/16 between.Equipment & Software: Hardware — APP/Mac; Software — Microsoft/Word, QPS/QuarkXPress, Multi-Ad/Creator.
Delivery Method: Mail, Racks
Areas Served: Holden, Paxton, Princeton, Rutland & Sterling

HULL

THE HULL TIMES (THUR)

412 Nantasket Ave, Hull, MA, 02045-2712, Plymouth, USA; gen tel (781) 925-9266; gen fax (781) 925-0336; disp adv e-mail hulltimes@aol.com; class adv e-mail hulltimes@aol.com; ed e-mail hulltimes@aol.com; web site www.hulltimes.com
Circulation: 3,000pd,; Sworn/Estimate/Non-Audited
Advertising rate: Open inch rate $10.00
Established: 1930
Digital Platform - Mobile: Apple
Digital Platform - Tablet: Apple iOS, Android
Ed. .... Susan Ovans
Prodn. Mgr. .... Roger Jackson
Mechanical Specifications: Type page 10 x 15 3/4.
Delivery Method: Mail, Newsstand
Areas Served: 02045 and others

HUNTINGTON

COUNTRY JOURNAL (THUR)

5 Main St, Huntington, MA, 01050-9678, Hampshire, USA; gen tel (413) 667-3211; gen fax (413) 667-3011; disp adv e-mail bbaker@turley.com; class adv e-mail classifieds@turley.com; ed e-mail countryjournal@turley.com; web site www.turley.com/countryjournal.html
Circulation: 3,317fr; Sworn/Estimate/Non-Audited
Advertising rate: Open inch rate $10.75
Established: 1979
Group: Turley Publications, Inc.
Ed. .... Christine Charnosky
Pub.. Patrick H. Turley
Ad. Director..................................... Beth Baker
Mechanical Specifications: Type page 10 1/4 x 16; E - 5 cols, 1 11/12, 1/6 between; A - 5 cols, 1 11/12, 1/6 between; C - 6 cols, 1 7/12, 5/36 between.Equipment & Software: Hardware — PCs.
Delivery Method: Mail, Newsstand
Areas Served: Blandford, Chester, Chesterfield, Cummington, Westhampton, Easthampton, Goshen, Haydenville, Huntington, Northampton, Florence, Plainfield, Russell, Southampton, Westfield, Montgomery, Williamsburg, Worthington, Fittsfield, Becket, Washington, Dalton, Hinsdale, Peru, Middlefield, Otis

HYANNIS

BARNSTABLE PATRIOT (FRI)

4 Ocean Ave, Hyannis, MA, 02601-4419, Barnstable, USA; gen tel (508) 771-1427; adv tel (508) 771-1427; ed tel (508) 771-1427; gen fax (508) 790-3997; adv fax (508) 790-3997; ed fax (508) 790-3997; disp adv e-mail advertising@barnstablepatriot.com; class adv e-mail advertising@barnstablepatriot.com; ed e-mail letters@barnstablepatriot.com; web site www.barnstablepatriot.com - 59,000(views) 29,837(visitors)
Circulation: 4,905pd, 350fr; Sworn/Estimate/Non-Audited
Advertising rate: Open inch rate $14.50
Established: 1830
Group: Dow Jones Local Media Group
Pub....................................... Robert F. Sennott
Bus. Mgr.......................... Barbara J. Hennigan
Adv. Rep................................ Lucinda Harrison
Ed. .... Deborah Stetson
Mechanical Specifications: Type page 11.625 x 21.25; E - 6 cols, 1.83, between.
Delivery Method: Mail, Newsstand
Areas Served: Barnstable

BOURNE COURIER (WED)

319 Main St, Hyannis, MA, 02601-4037, Barnstable, USA; gen tel (508) 888-0000; adv tel (781) 433-6934; ed tel (508) 375-4945; gen fax (508) 375-4903; adv fax (508) 375-4903; ed fax (508) 375-4903; disp adv e-mail salesteam@wickedlocal.com; class adv e-mail salesteam@wickedlocal.com; ed e-mail jbasile@wickedlocal.com; web site www.wickedlocal.com/bourne
Advertising rate: Open inch rate $15.10
Group: Community Newspaper Co. - South
Digital Platform - Mobile: Apple, Android, Blackberry
Pub.. Mark Olivieri
Mng. Ed. .... John Basile
Adv. Dir.. Nick Bolitho
Delivery Method: Mail, Newsstand, Racks
Areas Served: Bourne

THE REGISTER (THUR)

319 Main St, Hyannis, MA, 02601-4037, Barnstable, USA; gen tel (508) 375-4945; adv tel (508) 375-4917; ed tel (508) 375-4945; gen fax (508) 375-4903; adv fax (508) 375-4901; ed fax (508) 375-4903; disp adv e-mail lporter@wickedlocal.com; class adv e-mail lporter@wickedlocal.com; ed e-mail jbasile@wickedlocal.com; web site www.wickedlocal.com/capecod
Circulation: 4,000pd,; Sworn/Estimate/Non-Audited
Advertising rate: Open inch rate $26.30
Established: 1836
Group: GateHouse Media, Inc.
Digital Platform - Mobile: Apple, Android, Blackberry
Managing Ed.................................. John Basile
Delivery Method: Mail, Newsstand
Areas Served: 02664, 02601, 02675, 02638

HYDE PARK

THE BOSTON BULLETIN (THUR)

1 Westinghouse Plz, Ste 26, Hyde Park, MA, 02136-2078, Suffolk, USA; gen tel (617) 361-8400; adv tel (617) 361-8400; ed tel (617) 361-8400; gen fax (617) 361-1933; adv fax (617) 361-1933; ed fax (617) 361-1933; disp adv e-mail info@bulletinnewspapers.com; class adv e-mail info@bulletinnewspapers.com; ed e-mail news@bulletinnewspapers.com; web site www.bulletinnewspapers.com
Circulation: 3,000fr; Sworn/Estimate/Non-Audited
Advertising rate: Open inch rate $31.80
Pub....Paul DiModica
Ed./Co-Pub. ....Dennis Cawley
Adv. Mgr....Susan Yandell
Delivery Method: Mail, Newsstand
Areas Served: Allston-Brighton, Dorchester, Jamaica Plain, North End, South Boston

WEST ROXBURY/ROSINDALE BULLETIN (THUR)

1 Westinghouse Plz, Hyde Park, MA, 02136-2075, Suffolk, USA; gen tel (617) 361-8400; adv tel (617) 361-8400; ed tel (617) 361-8400; gen fax (617) 361-1933; adv fax (617) 361-1933; ed fax (617) 361-1933; disp adv e-mail news@westroxburybulletin.com; news@bulletinnewspapers.com; ed e-mail news@bulletinnewspapers.com; web site www.bulletinnewspapers.com
Circulation: 11,500fr; Sworn/Estimate/Non-Audited
Advertising rate: Open inch rate $17.25
Established: 1992
Digital Platform - Mobile: Windows
Digital Platform - Tablet: Windows 7
Pub....Paul DiModica
Pub....Dennis Cawley
Adv. Mgr....Susan Yandell
Ed. ....Joe Mont
Delivery Method: Mail, Newsstand, Racks
Areas Served: 02132, 02131

LENOX DALE

BERKSHIRE BEACON (THUR)

PO Box 312, Lenox Dale, MA, 01242-0312, Berkshire, USA; gen tel (413) 637-2250; adv tel (413) 637-2250; ed tel (413) 637-2250; gen fax (413) 637-2250; adv fax (413) 637-2250; ed fax (413) 637-2250; disp adv e-mail ads@berkshirebeacon.com ; class adv e-mail ads@berkshirebeacon.com; ed e-mail news@berkshirebeacon.com; web site www.berkshirebeacon.com 26,000(visitors)
Advertising rate: Open inch rate $10
Established: 2011
Digital Platform - Tablet: Kindle, Nook
Ed./Pub. ....George Jordan III
Editorial Assistant....Kameron Spaulding
Copy Ed. ....Catherine Krummy
Graphic Designer ....Susan Robinson
Mechanical Specifications: tab 10.5 by 12.5Equipment & Software: Hardware — n/a; Presses — n/a; Software — n/a
Delivery Method: Newsstand, Racks
Areas Served: Berkshire MA County

LEOMINSTER

LEOMINSTER CHAMPION (FRI)

285 Central St, Ste 202, Leominster, MA, 01453-6144, Worcester, USA; gen tel (978) 534-6006; adv tel (978) 534-6006; gen fax (978) 534-6004; adv fax (978) 534-6004; disp adv e-mail sales@leominsterchamp.com; class adv e-mail sales@centralmassclass.com; ed e-mail editor@leominsterchamp.com; web site www.leominsterchamp.com - 28,136(views) 7,518(visitors)
Circulation: 5,984fr; VAC
Advertising rate: CP
Established: 2006
Group: Holden Landmark Corp
Digital Platform - Mobile: Apple, Android
Digital Platform - Tablet: Apple iOS, Android
Ed. ....David Dore
Pub....Barbara Brown
Adv. Mgr....Tom Signa
Prod. Mgr....Don Cloutier
Mechanical Specifications: Type page 9.5" x 10.75"; 6 cols
Delivery Method: Racks
Areas Served: 01453

LEXINGTON

ARLINGTON ADVOCATE (THUR)

9 Meriam St, Lexington, MA, 02420-5300, Middlesex, USA; gen tel (781) 674-7726; adv tel (978) 371-5717; ed tel (781) 674-7726; gen fax (781) 674-7735; adv fax (978) 371-5712; ed fax (781) 674-7735; disp adv e-mail pgaudette@wickedlocal.com; class adv e-mail classifieds@wickedlocal.com; ed e-mail arlington@wickedlocal.com; web site http://arlington.wickedlocal.com/
Circulation: 2,933pd, 329fr; AAM
Advertising rate: Open inch rate $29.25
Group: GateHouse Media, Inc.
Pub....Chuck Goodrich
Vice Pres., Adv....Mark Cohen
Adv. Mgr. ....Anne Marie Magerman
Adv. Mgr., Display ....Mike Murphy
Ed. ....Eileen Kennedy
Ed. in Chief ....Kathleen Cordiero
Sales Mgr....Mike Bentle
Classified Adv. Mgr....Ron Bright
Mechanical Specifications: Type page 13 x 21 1/2; E - 6 cols, 2, 1/6 between; A - 6 cols, 2, 1/6 between.Equipment & Software: Hardware — HP; Software — Geac, CJ.
Areas Served: Arlington (MA)

BELMONT CITIZEN-HERALD (THUR)

9 Meriam St, Ste 11, Lexington, MA, 02420-5312, Middlesex, USA; gen tel (617) 484-2633; disp adv e-mail salesteam@wickedlocal.com; ed e-mail belmont@wickedlocal.com; web site www.wickedlocal.com/belmont/
Circulation: 2,341pd, 4fr; Sworn/Estimate/Non-Audited
Advertising rate: Open inch rate $26.40
Group: GateHouse Media, Inc.
Digital Platform - Mobile: Apple, Android, Blackberry
Pub....Chuck Goodrich
Adv. Mgr., Classified ....Ron Bright
Ed. ....Joanna Kaselis Tzouvelis
Sports Ed....Doug Hastings
Adv. Mgr....Mike Bentle
Mechanical Specifications: Type page 13 x 21 1/2; E - 6 cols, 2, 1/6 between; A - 6 cols, 2, 1/6 between.Equipment & Software: Hardware — HP.
Areas Served: Belmont (MA)

LEXINGTON MINUTEMAN (THUR)

9 Meriam St, Lexington, MA, 02420-5300, Middlesex, USA; gen tel (781) 674-7725; adv tel (978) 371-5717; ed tel (781) 674-7725; disp adv e-mail pgaudette@wickedlocal.com; ed e-mail lexington@wickedlocal.com; web site lexington.wickedlocal.com
Circulation: 3,944pd, 253fr; AAM
Established: 1870
Group: GateHouse Media, Inc.
Pub....Chuck Goodrich
Circ. Mgr....Jim O'Rourke
Ed. ....Bryan Mahoney
Adv. Dir....Nick Bolitho
Delivery Method: Mail, Newsstand
Areas Served: Lexington, MA

WINCHESTER STAR (THUR)

9 Meriam St, Lexington, MA, 02420-5300, Middlesex, USA; gen tel (781) 674-7740; adv tel (978) 371-5717; ed tel (781) 674-7740; gen fax (781) 674-7735; adv fax (781) 674-7735; ed fax (781) 674-7735; disp adv e-mail jcutter@wickedlocal.com; class adv e-mail rbright@wickedlocal.com; ed e-mail winchester@wickedlocal.com ; web site www.wickedlocal.com/winchester
Circulation: 2,163pd, 239fr; AAM
Advertising rate: Open inch rate $25.45
Group: GateHouse Media, Inc.
Digital Platform - Mobile: Apple, Android, Blackberry
Pub....Chuck Goodrich
Ed. in Chief ....Kathy Cordeiro
Sports Ed....Stephen Toby
Adv. Dir....Nick Bolitho
Areas Served: Winchester

LOWELL

BROADCASTER (FRI)

491 Dutton St, Lowell, MA, 01854-4289, Middlesex, USA; gen tel (978) 970-4700; adv tel (978) 970-4700; ed tel (978) 970-4700; gen fax (978) 970-4723; adv fax (978) 970-4723; ed fax (978) 970-4723; disp adv e-mail jhiggins@MediaOneNE.com; class adv e-mail amendes@MediaOneNE.com; ed e-mail letters@lowellsun.com; web site www.freebroadcaster.com
Circulation: 68,364fr; Sworn/Estimate/Non-Audited
Advertising rate: Open inch rate $18
Pres./Pub. ....Mark O'Neil
Ed. ....John Campanini
Circ. Dir. ....Mike Sheehan
Mechanical Specifications: Type page 21 x 16; E - 7 cols, 1 5/16, 1/4 between; A - 7 cols, 1 5/16, 1/4 between; C - 7 cols, 1 5/16, 1/4 between.Equipment & Software: ; Software — Adobe/PageMaker 4.0, Archetype/Corel Draw 2.0.
Areas Served: Merrimack, Milford, Brookline, Hudson, Amherst, Nashua, Pelham (NH); Lowell, North Chelmsford, Dunstable, Tyngsborough, Westford (MA)

NASHOBA VALLEY VOICE (FRI)

491 Dutton St, Unit 401, Lowell, MA, 01854-4290, Middlesex, USA; gen tel (978) 772-0777; gen fax (978) 772-4012; disp adv e-mail enajeeullah@mediaonene.com; ed e-mail jpaluzzi@nashobavalleyvoice.com; web site www.nashobavalleyvoice.com
Circulation: 3,500pd, 15,000fr; Sworn/Estimate/Non-Audited
Established: 2015
Group: MediaNews Group
Editor....Jennifer Lord Paluzzi
Delivery Method: Mail, Newsstand
Areas Served: Middlesex County

THE DISPATCH NEWS (FRI)

491 Dutton St, Lowell, MA, 01854-4289, Middlesex, USA; gen tel (978) 458-7100; adv tel (978) 458-3311; ed tel (978) 970-4623; gen fax (978) 970-4723; adv fax (978) 970-4723; ed fax (978) 970-4723; disp adv e-mail fsplaine@mediaonene.com; class adv e-mail fsplaine@mediaonene.com; ed e-mail backtalk@lowellsun.com; web site www.thevalleydispatch.com
Circulation: 18,000fr; Sworn/Estimate/Non-Audited
Advertising rate: Open inch rate $12.00
Pres./Pub. ....Mark O'Neil
CEO....Kendall Wallace
Dir., Circ....Mike Sheehan
Circ. Opns. Mgr. ....Gary Wright
Ed. ....James Campanini
Mng. Ed....Kris Pisarik
Mng. Ed....Tom Zuppa
Mechanical Specifications: Type page 10 x 16; E - 6 cols, 1 1/4, 1/4 between; A - 6 cols, 1 1/4, 1/4 between; C - 6 cols, 1 1/4, 1/4 between. Equipment & Software: Hardware — APP/Macs.
Areas Served: 01826, 01879, 03075

MANCHESTER

THE MANCHESTER CRICKET (FRI)

50 Summer St, Manchester, MA, 01944-1518, Essex, USA; gen tel (978) 526-7131; adv tel (978) 526-7131; ed tel (978) 526-7131; gen fax (978) 526-8193; adv fax (978) 526-8193; ed fax (978) 526-8193; disp adv e-mail news@cricketpress.com; info@cricketpress.com; class adv e-mail info@cricketpress.com; ed e-mail news@cricketpress.com; web site www.themanchestercricket.com
Circulation: 2,500pd,; USPS
Advertising rate: Open inch rate $10.00
Established: 1888
Group: The Cricket Press, Inc.
Ed. ....Patricia C. Slade
Mechanical Specifications: Type page 11 x 23; E - 6 cols, 1.625, .082 between; A - 6 cols, 1.625, .083 between; C - 6 cols, 1.65, .083 between.Equipment & Software: Hardware — APP/Mac.
Delivery Method: Mail, Newsstand
Areas Served: Manchester-by-the-Sea

MARBLEHEAD

MARBLEHEAD REPORTER (THUR)

40 South St Ste 102, Suite 102, Marblehead, MA, 01945-3274, Essex, USA; gen tel (781) 639-4800; adv tel (978) 739-1320; ed tel (781) 639-4800; gen fax (781) 639-4801; adv fax (978) 739-1391; ed fax (781) 639-4801; disp adv e-mail rmurphy@wickedlocal.com; class adv e-mail classifieds@wickedlocal.com; ed e-mail marblehead@wickedlocal.com; web site http://marblehead.wickedlocal.com/
Circulation: 3,507pd, 890fr; AAM
Advertising rate: Open inch rate $33.25
Group: Community Newspaper Co.-North GateHouse Media, Inc.
Digital Platform - Mobile: Apple, Android, Blackberry
Pub....Charles Goodrich
Ed. in Chief ....Peter Chianca
Adv. Dir....Nick Bolitho
Arts and More Section Ed....Mary Reines
Mechanical Specifications: Type page 10 13/16 x 16; E - 5 cols, 2 1/16, between; A - 5 cols, 2 1/16, between; C - 8 cols, 1 7/32, between.
Areas Served: Marblehead (MA)

SWAMPSCOTT REPORTER (THUR)

11 State St, Marblehead, MA, 01945-3592, Essex, USA; gen tel (781) 639-4800; adv tel (978) 739-1364; ed tel (781) 639-4806; gen fax (781) 639-4801; adv fax (781) 639-4801; ed fax (781) 639-4801; disp adv e-mail ameltzer@wickedlocal.com; class adv e-mail ksmith@wickedlocal.com; ed e-mail pchianca@wickedlocal.com; web site www.wickedlocal.com/swampscott - 1,154,957(views) 244,866(visitors)
Circulation: 1,173pd, 26fr; AAM
Advertising rate: Open inch rate $32.50
Established: 1850
Group: Community Newspaper Co.-North GateHouse Media, Inc.
Digital Platform - Mobile: Apple, Android, Blackberry
Digital Platform - Tablet: Apple iOS, Android
Pub....Charles Goodrich
Senior Ed....Janet Mackay-Smith
Ed. in Chief ....Pete Chianca
Adv. Dir....Nick Bolitho
Arts and More Section Ed....Mary Reines
Chuck Goodrich
Mechanical Specifications: Type page 10 13/16 x 16; E - 5 cols, 2 1/16, between; A - 5 cols, 2 1/16, between; C - 8 cols, 1 7/32, between.
Delivery Method: Mail, Carrier
Areas Served: Swampscott

MARSHFIELD

ABINGTON MARINER (FRI)

165 Enterprise Dr, Marshfield, MA, 02050-2132, Plymouth, USA; gen tel (781) 837-4500; adv tel (781) 837-4500; ed tel (781) 837-4500; gen fax (781) 837-4540; adv fax (781) 837-4540; ed fax (781) 837-4540; disp adv e-mail salesteam@wickedlocal.com; class adv e-mail salesteam@wickedlocal.com; ed e-mail sjacobson@wickedlocal.com; web site www.wickedlocal.com/abington
Circulation: 859pd,; AAM
Advertising rate: Open inch rate $18.55

Group: GateHouse Media, Inc.
Pub....................Mark Olivieri
Sports Ed....................Paul Harber
Ed. ....Seth Jacobson
Ed. In Chief....................Gregory Mathis
Areas Served: Abington (MA)

DUXBURY REPORTER (FRI)

165 Enterprise Dr, Marshfield, MA, 02050-2132, Plymouth, USA; gen tel (781) 837-4545; adv tel (781) 837-4545; ed tel (781) 837-4545; gen fax (781) 837-4543; adv fax (781) 837-4543; ed fax (781) 837-4543; web site www.wickedlocal.com/duxbury
Circulation: 0pd, 2,725fr; CAC
Advertising rate: Open inch rate $15.20
Established: 1987
Group: Community Newspaper Co. - South GateHouse Media, Inc.
Pub....................Mark Olivieri
Ed. .... David SmithEquipment & Software: ; Presses — WPC/Web Leader.

HALIFAX-PLYMPTON REPORTER (FRI)

165 Enterprise Dr, Marshfield, MA, 02050-2132, Plymouth, USA; gen tel (508) 746-5555; adv tel (508) 746-5555; ed tel (508) 746-5555; gen fax (508) 747-2148; adv fax (508) 747-2148; ed fax (508) 747-2148; disp adv e-mail newsroom@mpgnews.com; web site www.plymptonhalifaxexpress.com
Circulation: 750pd, 1fr; CAC
Advertising rate: Open inch rate $14.05
Established: 1983
Group: Community Newspaper Co. - South GateHouse Media, Inc.
Ed.-in-Chief....................Gregory Mathis
Publisher Mark OlivieriEquipment & Software: ; Presses — WPC/Web Leader.

HANOVER MARINER (WED)

165 Enterprise Dr, Marshfield, MA, 02050-2132, Plymouth, USA; gen tel (781) 837-4560; adv tel (781) 837-4560; ed tel (781) 837-4560; gen fax (781) 837-4540; adv fax (781) 837-4540; ed fax (781) 837-4540; disp adv e-mail hanover@cnc.com; class adv e-mail hanover@cnc.com; ed e-mail hanover@cnc.com; web site www.wickedlocal.com/hanover
Circulation: 1,040pd,; AAM
Advertising rate: Open inch rate $17.45
Established: 1980
Group: Community Newspaper Co. - South GateHouse Media, Inc.
Pub....................Mark Olivieri
Sr. Mng. Ed....................Gregory Mathis
Adv. Dir....................Nick Bolitho

MANSFIELD NEWS (FRI)

165 Enterprise Dr, Marshfield, MA, 02050-2132, Plymouth, USA; gen tel (508) 967-3500; adv tel (508) 967-3500; ed tel (508) 967-3500; gen fax (508) 967-3501; adv fax (508) 967-3501; ed fax (508) 967-3501; disp adv e-mail mansfield@cnc.com; class adv e-mail salesteam@wickedlocal.com; ed e-mail mansfield@cnc.com; web site www.wickedlocal.com
Circulation: 2,237pd,; AAM
Advertising rate: Open inch rate $16.75
Established: 1872
Group: Community Newspaper Co.-West GateHouse Media, Inc.
Digital Platform - Mobile: Apple, Android, Blackberry
Pub....................Mark Olivieri
Adv. Dir....................Nick Bolitho

MARSHFIELD MARINER (WED)

165 Enterprise Dr, Marshfield, MA, 02050-2132, Plymouth, USA; gen tel (781) 837-3500; adv tel (781) 837-3500; ed tel (781) 837-3500; gen fax (781) 837-4540; adv fax (781) 837-4540; ed fax (781) 837-4540; disp adv e-mail marshfield@wickedlocal.com; ed e-mail marshfield@wickedlocal.com; web site www.wickedlocal.com/marshfield
Circulation: 9,452pd, 1,236fr; AAM
Advertising rate: Open inch rate $18.70
Group: Community Newspaper Co. - South GateHouse Media, Inc.
Digital Platform - Mobile: Apple, Android, Blackberry
CEO....................Kirk Davis
Circ. Mgr....................Louise Reid
News Ed. ....Bill Fonda
Prodn. Mgr. ....Shawn Holmes
Pub....................Sean Burke
Adv. Mgr....................Charlie Matheson
Vice Pres., Adv....................Mark Cohen
Mng. Ed....................George Brennan
Mechanical Specifications: Type page 10 3/4 x 16; E - 5 cols, 2, between; A - 5 cols, 2, between.Equipment & Software: ; Presses — WPC/Web Leader.

NORWELL MARINER (THUR)

165 Enterprise Dr, Marshfield, MA, 02050-2132, Plymouth, USA; gen tel (781) 837-3500; adv tel (781) 837-3500; ed tel (781) 837-3500; gen fax (781) 837-4543; adv fax (781) 837-4543; ed fax (781) 837-4543; disp adv e-mail srussell@wickedlocal.com; class adv e-mail salesteam@wickedlocal.com; ed e-mail molivieri@wickedlocal.com; web site www.wickedlocal.com/norwell
Circulation: 1,061pd, 206fr; AAM
Advertising rate: Open inch rate $19.00
Established: 1974
Group: Community Newspaper Co. - South GateHouse Media, Inc.
Digital Platform - Mobile: Apple, Android, Blackberry
Ed. in Chief....................Gregory Mathis
Editor....................Erin Tiernan
Adv. Dir....................Nick Bolitho
Areas Served: Norwell

PEMBROKE MARINER & EXPRESS (FRI)

165 Enterprise Dr, Marshfield, MA, 02050-2132, Plymouth, USA; gen tel (781) 837-4500; gen fax (781) 837-4540; disp adv e-mail pembroke@cnc.com; ed e-mail gmathis@wickedlocal.com; web site www.wickedlocal.com/pembroke
Circulation: 1,275pd,; Sworn/Estimate/Non-Audited
Advertising rate: 15.45
Established: 1983
Group: Community Newspaper Co. - South GateHouse Media, Inc.
Pub....................Mark Olivieri
Adv. Dir....................Nick Bolitho

ROCKLAND STANDARD (THUR)

165 Enterprise Dr, Marshfield, MA, 02050-2132, Plymouth, USA; gen tel (781) 837-3500; adv tel (781) 837-4519; ed tel (781) 837-4560; gen fax (781) 837-4543; adv fax (781) 837-4543; ed fax (781) 837-4543; disp adv e-mail coliver@wickedlocal.com; class adv e-mail salesteam@wickedlocal.com; ed e-mail gmathis@wickedlocal.com; web site www.wickedlocal.com/rockland
Circulation: 1,064fr; AAM
Advertising rate: Open inch rate $10.00
Group: Community Newspaper Co. - South GateHouse Media, Inc.
Digital Platform - Mobile: Apple, Android, Blackberry
Pub....................Mark Olivieri
Ed. ....Seth Jacobson
Ed. in Chief....................Gregory Mathis
Adv. Dir....................Nick Bolitho
Mechanical Specifications: Type page 10 9/16 x 16; E - 6 cols, between; A - 6 cols, between; C - 7 cols, between.Equipment & Software: Hardware — PC; Presses — G/Community with Suburban folders; Software — Adobe/PageMaker 6.5.
Areas Served: Rockland

SCITUATE MARINER (THUR)

165 Enterprise Dr, Marshfield, MA, 02050-2132, Plymouth, USA; gen tel (781) 837-3500; adv tel (781) 837-4519; ed tel (781) 837-4560; gen fax (781) 837-4543; adv fax (781) 837-4543; ed fax (781) 837-4543; disp adv e-mail coliver@wickedlocal.com; class adv e-mail salesteam@wickedlocal.com; ed e-mail gmathis@wickedlocal.com; web site wickedlocal.com/scituate
Circulation: 3,286pd, 203fr; AAM
Advertising rate: Open inch rate $19.00
Group: Community Newspaper Co. - South GateHouse Media, Inc.
Digital Platform - Mobile: Apple, Android, Blackberry
Ed. in Chief....................Gregory Mathis
Adv. Dir....................Nick Bolitho
Areas Served: Scituate

MATTAPOISETT

THE WANDERER (THUR)

55 County Rd, Mattapoisett, MA, 02739-1652, Plymouth, USA; gen tel (508) 758-9055; adv tel (508) 758-9055; ed tel (508) 758-9055; ed fax (508) 758-4845; disp adv e-mail office@wanderer.com; class adv e-mail office@wanderer.com; ed e-mail news@wanderer.com; web site www.wanderer.com
Circulation: 4,700fr; Sworn/Estimate/Non-Audited
Advertising rate: Modular Rates
Established: 1992
Pub....................Paul R. Lopes
Mechanical Specifications: Type page 8 1/2 x 11; E - 2 cols, 4, 1/2 between; A - 2 cols, 4, 1/2 between; C - 3 cols, 2 1/2, 1/2 between. Equipment & Software: Hardware — APP/Mac, PC; Software — Microsoft/Word 5.1, Claris/MacWrite, Adobe/PageMaker 6.0.
Delivery Method: Racks
Areas Served: Marion, Mattapoisett & Rochester

MIDDLEBORO

MIDDLEBORO GAZETTE (THUR)

148 W Grove St, Middleboro, MA, 02346-1457, Plymouth, USA; gen tel (508) 947-1760; gen fax (508) 947-9426; disp adv e-mail news@gazettenewsonline.com; ed e-mail editor@gazettenewsonline.com; web site www.southcoasttoday.com
Circulation: 4,802pd, 184fr; Sworn/Estimate/Non-Audited
Advertising rate: Open inch rate $45.00
Established: 1852
Group: Dow Jones Local Media Group
Adv. Rep....................Mary-Ann Cole
Ed. ....Jane Lopes
Office manager....................April Belanger
Circ. Mgr....................Susan Duff
Delivery Method: Mail, Newsstand

MILFORD

THE COUNTRY GAZETTE (FRI)

197 Main St, Milford, MA, 01757-2635, Worcester, USA; gen tel (508) 634-7500; adv tel (508) 626-3984; ed tel (508) 634-7584; gen fax (508) 634-7568; adv fax (508) 634-7568; ed fax (508) 634-7568; disp adv e-mail crobinson@wickedlocal.com; class adv e-mail salesteam@wickedlocal.com; ed e-mail gazette@wickedlocal.com; web site www.wickedlocal.com/franklin
Circulation: 20,808fr; AAM
Advertising rate: Open inch rate $45.15
Established: 1985
Group: Community Newspaper Co.-West GateHouse Media, Inc.
Digital Platform - Mobile: Apple, Android, Blackberry
Ed. in Chief....................Richard Lodge
Ed. ....Heather McCarron
Adv. Dir....................Nick Bolitho
Areas Served: Bellingham, Foxboro, Franklin, Medway, Millis, Norfolk, Plainville, Wrentham

MILTON

MILTON TIMES (THUR)

3 Boulevard St, Ste 5, Milton, MA, 02186-5400, Norfolk, USA; gen tel (617) 696-7758; adv tel (617) 696-7758; ed tel (617) 696-7758; adv fax (617) 696-3681; disp adv e-mail Ads@miltontimes.com; class adv e-mail ads@miltontimes.com; ed e-mail editor@miltontimes.com; web site www.miltontimes.com
Circulation: 4,600pd,; Sworn/Estimate/Non-Audited
Advertising rate: $19.00
Established: 1995
Digital Platform - Mobile: Apple, Android
Digital Platform - Tablet: Apple iOS, Android, Blackberry Tablet OS, Kindle
Ad. Director....................Nadine Leary
Publisher....................Pat Desmond
circulation manager....................Karen Wilkinson
Editor....................Douglas Scibeck
Mechanical Specifications: Tabloid, 6 col. 1 and 5/8" per column, 16" depth available.Equipment & Software: ; Software — Indesign 5,5, Incopy
Delivery Method: Mail, Newsstand
Areas Served: 02186

NANTUCKET

NANTUCKET TODAY (MTHLY, OTHER)

1 Old South Rd, Nantucket, MA, 02554-2836, Nantucket, USA; gen tel (508) 228-0001; gen fax (508) 325-5089; web site www.nantuckettodayonline.com
Group: Dow Jones Local Media Group
Circ. ....Kevin Stanton

THE INQUIRER AND MIRROR (THUR)

1 Old South Rd, Nantucket, MA, 02554-2836, Nantucket, USA; gen tel (508) 228-0001; adv tel (508) 228-0001; ed tel (508) 228-0001; gen fax (508) 325-5089; adv fax (508) 325-5089; ed fax (508) 325-5089; disp adv e-mail advertising@inkym.com; class adv e-mail classified@inkym.com; ed e-mail newsroom@inkym.com; web site www.ack.net
Circulation: 8,903pd, 162fr; USPS
Advertising rate: Open inch rate $22.16
Established: 1865
Group: Dow Jones Local Media Group
Digital Platform - Mobile: Apple
Digital Platform - Tablet: Apple iOS, Android
Office Mgr....................Lynda St. Peter
Adv. Mgr....................Lora Kebbati
Ed. ....Marianne Stanton
Mng. Ed....................Joshua H. Balling
Prodn. Dir....................Greg Derr
Circulation/Classified Manager...Kevin Stanton
Assistant Editor....................Joshua Balling
Circ. Dir. ....Denese B. Allen
Prodn. Dir....................Sean Kalman
Jason Graziadei
Delivery Method: Mail, Newsstand

NEEDHAM

ALLSTON-BRIGHTON TAB (FRI)

254 2nd Ave, Needham, MA, 02494-2829, Norfolk, USA; gen tel (781) 433-8365; adv tel (781) 433-8204; ed tel (781) 433-8384; gen fax (781) 433-8202; adv fax (781) 433-8202; ed fax (781) 433-8202; disp adv e-mail landler@wickedlocal.com ; class adv e-mail landler@wickedlocal.com; ed e-mail jcohen@wickedlocal.com; web site www.wickedlocal.com/allston
Circulation: 185pd,; AAM
Advertising rate: Open inch rate $21.75
Established: 1996
Group: Community Newspaper Co.-Metro GateHouse Media, Inc.
Pub....................Chuck Goodrich
Ed. in Chief....................Jesse Floyd
Ed....................Julie Cohen
Adv. Dir....................Nick Bolitho
Areas Served: Allston-Brighton

BROOKLINE TAB (THUR)

254 2nd Ave, Needham, MA, 02494-2829, Norfolk, USA; gen tel (781) 433-8334; adv tel (781) 433-6925; ed tel (781) 433-8334; gen fax (781) 433-8202; adv fax (781) 433-8202; ed fax (781) 433-8202; disp adv e-mail cwarren@wickedlocal.com; class adv

e-mail landler@wickedlocal.com ; ed e-mail eclossey@wickedlocal.com; web site www.wickedlocal.com/brookline
Circulation: 9,887fr; AAM
Advertising rate: Open inch rate $41.95
Group: Joseph Jacobs Organization
Community Newspaper Co.-Metro
GateHouse Media, Inc.
Digital Platform - Mobile: Apple, Android, Blackberry
Pub. ....Charles Goodrich
News Ed. ....Erin Clossey
Adv. Dir..Nick Bolitho
Areas Served: Brookline (MA)

DOVER-SHERBORN PRESS (THUR)
254 2nd Ave, Needham, MA, 02494-2829, Norfolk, USA; gen tel (781) 433-8226; adv tel (781) 433-8313; ed tel (781) 433-6925; gen fax (781) 433-8202; adv fax (781) 433-8202; ed fax (781) 433-8202; disp adv e-mail cwarren@wickedlocal.com; class adv e-mail dmaher@wickedlocal.com; ed e-mail wbraverman@wickedlocal.com; web site www.wickedlocal.com/dover
Circulation: 439pd,; AAM
Advertising rate: Open inch rate $20.50
Group: Community Newspaper Co.-Metro
GateHouse Media, Inc.
Pub. ....Chuck Goodrich
Reg. Adv. Dir. ....Cris Warren
Mng. Ed.............................Wayne Braverman
Ed. in Chief ....Jesse Floyd
Adv. Dir..Nick Bolitho
Areas Served: Dover-Sherborn (MA)

MEDFIELD PRESS (FRI)
254 2nd Ave, Ste 1, Needham, MA, 02494-2829, Norfolk, USA; gen tel (781) 433-8356; adv tel (781) 433-8313; ed tel (781) 433-8354; gen fax (781) 433-8375; adv fax (781) 433-8375; ed fax (781) 433-8375; disp adv e-mail cpetrillo@wickedlocal.com; class adv e-mail salesteam@wickedlocal.com; ed e-mail medfield@wickedlocal.com; web site www.wickedlocal.com/medfield
Circulation: 2,968pd, 27,387fr; AAM
Advertising rate: Open inch rate $17.35
Group: Community Newspaper Co.-West
GateHouse Media, Inc.
Pub...Chuck Goodrich
Ed. ....Max Bowen
Adv. Dir..Nick Bolitho
Areas Served: Medfield

NEEDHAM TIMES (WED, THUR, FRI)
254 2nd Ave, Ste 1, Needham, MA, 02494-2829, Norfolk, USA; gen tel (781) 433-6905; adv tel (781) 433-8313; ed tel (781) 433-8366; gen fax (781) 433-8202; adv fax (781) 433-8202; ed fax (781) 433-8202; disp adv e-mail cwarren@wickedlocal.com; class adv e-mail salesteam@wickedlocal.com; ed e-mail vzic@wickedlocal.com ; web site www.wickedlocal.com/needham
Circulation: 9,169pd, 25,687fr; AAM
Advertising rate: Open inch rate $24.90
Established: 1874
Group: Community Newspaper Co.-Metro
GateHouse Media, Inc.
Digital Platform - Mobile: Apple, Android, Blackberry
Pub...Chuck Goodrich
Ed. ....Valentina Zic
Reporter ....Wei-Huan Chen
Adv. Dir. ....Nick Bolitho
Areas Served: Needham

NEWTON TAB (WED)
254 2nd Ave, Ste 1, Needham, MA, 02494-2829, Norfolk, USA; gen tel (781) 433-8200; adv tel (781) 433-8200; ed tel (781) 433-8200; gen fax (781) 433-8202; adv fax (781) 433-8202; ed fax (781) 433-8202; disp adv e-mail cwarren@wickedlocal.com; class adv e-mail salesteam@wickedlocal.com; ed e-mail newton@wickedlocal.com; web site www.wickedlocal.com/newton
Circulation: 24,626fr; AAM
Advertising rate: Open inch rate $48.55
Group: Community Newspaper Co.-Metro
GateHouse Media, Inc.
Digital Platform - Mobile: Apple, Android, Blackberry
Pub. ....Chuck Goodrich
Ed.-in-Chief...............................Richard Lodge
Adv. Dir..Nick Bolitho
Areas Served: Newton

NORWOOD TRANSCRIPT & BULLETIN (FRI)
254 2nd Ave, Needham, MA, 02494-2829, Norfolk, USA; gen tel (781) 433-8322; adv tel (781) 433-8313; ed tel (781) 433-8322; gen fax (781) 433-8375; adv fax (781) 433-8375; ed fax (781) 433-8375; disp adv e-mail ageisinger@wickedlocal.com; class adv e-mail salesteam@wickedlocal.com; ed e-mail psalisbury@wickedlocal.com; web site www.wickedlocal.com/norwood
Circulation: 654pd, 51fr; AAM
Advertising rate: Open inch rate $16.15
Group: Community Newspaper Co.-West
GateHouse Media, Inc.
Digital Platform - Mobile: Apple, Android, Blackberry
Pub...Chuck Goodrich
Ed. ....Phil Salisbury
Adv. Dir..Nick Bolitho
Areas Served: Norwood

ROSLINDALE TRANSCRIPT (THUR)
254 2nd Ave, Needham, MA, 02494-2829, Norfolk, USA; gen tel (781) 433-8366; adv tel (781) 433-8366; ed tel (781) 433-8366; gen fax (781) 433-8202; adv fax (781) 433-8202; ed fax (781) 433-8202; disp adv e-mail cwarren@wickedlocal.com; class adv e-mail cparis@WickedLocal.com; ed e-mail jcohen@wickedlocal.com; web site www.wickedlocal.com/roslindale
Circulation: 218pd,; AAM
Advertising rate: Open inch rate $24.40
Group: Community Newspaper Co.-Metro
Digital Platform - Mobile: Apple, Android, Blackberry
Pub...Chuck Goodrich
Ed. in Chief ....Jesse Floyd
Ed. ....Julie Cohen
Mechanical Specifications: Type page 10 1/4 x 13 5/8; E - 5 cols, 1 11/12, 1/6 between; A - 5 cols, 1 11/12, between; C - 8 cols, 1 1/8, between.Equipment & Software: Hardware — HP; Software — Geac, CJ.
Areas Served: Roslindale

SHARON ADVOCATE (FRI)
254 2nd Ave, Needham, MA, 02494-2829, Norfolk, USA; gen tel (781) 784-1487; adv tel (781) 433-8313; ed tel (781) 433-8325; gen fax (781) 433-8375; adv fax (781) 433-8375; ed fax (781) 433-8375; disp adv e-mail cwarren@wickedlocal.com; class adv e-mail salesteam@wickedlocal.com; ed e-mail wbraverman@wickedlocal.com; web site www.wickedlocal.com/sharon
Circulation: 1,970pd,; AAM
Advertising rate: Open inch rate $19.20
Group: Community Newspaper Co.-West
GateHouse Media, Inc.
Digital Platform - Mobile: Apple, Android, Blackberry
Pub...Chuck Goodrich
Ed. in Chief ....Jesse Floyd
Mng. Ed. ....Wayne Braverman
Adv. Dir..Nick Bolitho
Areas Served: Sharon

THE DEDHAM TRANSCRIPT (WED)
254 2nd Ave, Ste 1, Needham, MA, 02494-2829, Norfolk, USA; gen tel (781) 433-6700; adv tel (781) 433-8222; ed tel (781) 433-6700; adv fax (781) 433-8201; disp adv e-mail jlamp@wickedlocal.com; class adv e-mail classifieds@wickedlocal.com; ed e-mail dedham@wickedlocal.com; web site http://dedham.wickedlocal.com/
Circulation: 454pd,; AAM
Advertising rate: Open inch rate $19.20
Established: 1873
Group: GateHouse Media, Inc.
Digital Platform - Mobile: Apple, Android, Blackberry
Pub. ....Chuck Goodrich
Ed. ....Phil Salisbury
Retail Adv. ....Carlo Petrillo
Reg. Adv. Dir. ....Cris Warren
Delivery Method: Mail, Newsstand, Racks
Areas Served: Dedham

WALTHAM NEWS TRIBUNE (FRI)
254 2nd Ave, Needham, MA, 02494-2829, Norfolk, USA; gen tel (781) 398-8002; adv tel (781) 433-8272; ed tel (781) 398-8002 ; disp adv e-mail newstribune@wickedlocal.com; class adv e-mail salesteam@wickedlocal.com; ed e-mail pcrocetti@wickedlocal.com; web site www.wickedlocal.com/waltham
Circulation: 2,191pd,; AAM
Advertising rate: Open inch rate $19.10
Group: GateHouse Media, Inc.
Digital Platform - Mobile: Apple, Android, Blackberry
Adv. Dir..Nick Bolitho
Areas Served: Waltham

WATERTOWN TAB (FRI)
254 2nd Ave, Needham, MA, 02494-2829, Norfolk, USA; gen tel (781) 433-6700; adv tel (781) 433-8222; ed tel (781) 433-6700; adv fax (781) 433-8201; disp adv e-mail pdoran@wickedlocal.com; class adv e-mail classifieds@wickedlocal.com; ed e-mail watertown@wickedlocal.com; web site http://watertown.wickedlocal.com/
Circulation: 9,169pd, 25,687fr; AAM
Advertising rate: Open inch rate $23.15
Group: Community Newspaper Co.-Metro
GateHouse Media, Inc.
Digital Platform - Mobile: Apple, Android, Blackberry
Pub...Chuck Goodrich
Ed. ....Dana Forsythe
Ed. in Chief ....Jesse Floyd
Adv. Dir..Nick Bolitho
Areas Served: Watertown

WELLESLEY TOWNSMAN (THUR)
254 2nd Ave, Ste 1, Needham, MA, 02494-2829, Norfolk, USA; gen tel (781) 431-2000; adv tel (781) 433-8276; ed tel (781) 431-2003; gen fax (781) 431-2001; adv fax (781) 431-2001; ed fax (781) 431-2001; disp adv e-mail cwarren@wickedlocal.com; class adv e-mail salesteam@wickedlocal.com; ed e-mail wellesley@wickedlocal.com; web site www.wickedlocal.com/wellesley
Circulation: 3,187pd, 122fr; AAM
Advertising rate: Open inch rate $26.35
Group: Community Newspaper Co.-Metro
GateHouse Media, Inc.
Digital Platform - Mobile: Apple, Android, Blackberry
Pub...Chuck Goodrich
Ed.-in-Chief.....................................Jesse Floyd
Ed. ....Cathy Brauner
Sports Ed.......................................Tom Wilcox
Adv. Dir..Nick Bolitho
Mechanical Specifications: Type page 13 x 21 1/2; E - 6 cols, 2, 1/6 between; A - 6 cols, 2, 1/6 between; C - 10 cols, 1 1/8, between. Equipment & Software: Hardware — HP; Software — Geac, CJ.
Areas Served: Wellesley

WEST ROXBURY TRANSCRIPT (THUR)
254 2nd Ave, Ste 1, Needham, MA, 02494-2829, Norfolk, USA; gen tel (781) 433-6700; adv tel (781) 433-6700; ed tel (781) 433-6700; gen fax (781) 433-8202; adv fax (781) 433-8202; ed fax (781) 433-8202; disp adv e-mail cwarren@wickedlocal.com; class adv e-mail cparis@WickedLocal.com; ed e-mail jcohen@wickedlocal.com; web site www.wickedlocal.com/west-roxbury
Circulation: 567pd,; AAM
Advertising rate: Open inch rate $24.40
Group: Community Newspaper Co.-Metro
GateHouse Media, Inc.
Digital Platform - Mobile: Apple, Android, Blackberry
Ed. ....Julie Cohen
Adv. Dir..Nick Bolitho
Mechanical Specifications: Type page 10 1/4 x 13 5/8; E - 5 cols, 1 11/12, 1/6 between; A - 5 cols, 1 11/12, 1/6 between; C - 8 cols, 1 1/8, between.Equipment & Software: Hardware — HP; Software — Geac, CJ.
Areas Served: West Roxbury

WESTWOOD PRESS (FRI)
254 2nd Ave, Ste 1, Needham, MA, 02494-2829, Norfolk, USA; gen tel (781) 433-6700; adv tel (781) 433-8222; ed tel (781) 433-6700; adv fax (781) 433-8201; disp adv e-mail jlamp@wickedlocal.com; class adv e-mail classifieds@wickedlocal.com; ed e-mail westwood@wickedlocal.com; web site http://westwood.wickedlocal.com/
Circulation: 482pd,; AAM
Advertising rate: Open inch rate $17.25
Group: Community Newspaper Co.-West
GateHouse Media, Inc.
Digital Platform - Mobile: Apple, Android, Blackberry
Pub...Chuck Goodrich
Ed. ....Max Bowen
Ed. in Chief ....Jesse Floyd
Adv. Dir..Nick Bolitho
Areas Served: Westwood

NEW BEDFORD

THE CHRONICLE (WED)
25 Elm St, New Bedford, MA, 02740-6228, USA; gen tel (508) 979-4431 ; gen fax (508) 997-7491; disp adv e-mail chronnews@aol.com
Circulation: 3,995pd, 196fr; Sworn/Estimate/Non-Audited
Advertising rate: Open inch rate $19.64
Group: Dow Jones Local Media Group
Gen. Mgr. ....Phil Devitt
Ed. ....Robert Barboza

THE SPECTATOR (WED)
25 Elm St, New Bedford, MA, 02740-6228, USA; gen tel (508) 674-4656; gen fax (508) 677-1210; disp adv e-mail news@hathawaypublishing.com; ed e-mail editor@spectatornewsonline.com; web site www.southcoasttoday.com
Circulation: 4,338pd, 105fr; CAC
Advertising rate: 1x1.75 $14.73; 2x1.75 Pg $29.402x3.50 $58.56; Call for other sizing
Established: 1932
Group: Dow Jones Local Media Group
Adv. Rep..Jerry Reis
Adv. Rep..Gerry Rego
Ed. ....George Austin
Pub./Pres......................................Peter Meyer
nat'l Adv. Mgr..............................Gregory Appel
Adv. Dir..............................Sheila McGlinchey
Classified Adv. Mgr.........................Kerry Silvia
Areas Served: 02725, 02726, 02777

NORTH ADAMS

THE ADVOCATE WEEKLY (THUR)
85 Main St, Ste 2, North Adams, MA, 01247-3489, Berkshire, USA; gen tel (413) 663-3741; adv tel (413) 663-3741; ed tel (413) 663-3741; gen fax (413) 664-7900; adv fax (413) 664-7900; ed fax (413) 664-7900; disp adv e-mail sales@advocateweekly.com; class adv e-mail advertising@mediaonemarketplace.com; ed e-mail news@advocateweekly.com; web site www.advocateweekly.com 10,000(visitors)
Circulation: 13,000fr; Sworn/Estimate/Non-Audited
Advertising rate: Open inch rate $11.85
Established: 1981
Editor ....Erik Sokolowski
Publisher.......................................Peter Lynch
Mechanical Specifications: Type page 9 7/8 x 16; E - 6 cols, 1 1/2, between; A - 6 cols, 1 1/2, between.Equipment & Software: Hardware — APP/Mac; Software — Quark
Delivery Method: Racks
Areas Served: Bennington County

NORTH ANDOVER

THE HAVERHILL GAZETTE (THUR)
100 Turnpike St, North Andover, MA, 01845-5033, Essex, USA; gen tel (978) 946-2000;

adv tel (978) 946-2152; ed tel (978) 946-2215; gen fax (978) 521-6790; adv fax (978) 521-6790; ed fax (978) 521-6790; disp adv e-mail ewholley@eagletribune.com; class adv e-mail ewholley@eagletribune.com; ed e-mail editor@hgazette.com; web site www.hgazette.com
Circulation: 3,590pd, 292fr; Sworn/Estimate/Non-Audited
Advertising rate: Open inch rate $14.66
Established: 1821
Group: Community Newspaper Holdings, Inc.
Pub....................Al Getler
Adv. Dir....................Tim Brady
Circ. Dir....................Steve Milone
Mechanical Specifications: Type page 11 5/8 x 21 1/2; E - 6 cols, 1 5/6, 1/8 between; A - 6 cols, 1 5/6, 1/8 between; C - 10 cols, 1 1/16, 1/16 between.
Delivery Method: Newsstand, Carrier, Racks
Areas Served: 01830, 01832, 01835

NORTH ATTLEBORO

NORTH ATTLEBORO FREE PRESS (WED)
31 N Washington St, Unit 7, North Attleboro, MA, 02760-1650, Bristol, USA; gen tel (508) 699-6755; adv tel (508) 699-6755; ed tel (508) 699-6755; gen fax (508) 699-8545; adv fax (508) 699-8545; ed fax (508) 699-8545; disp adv e-mail ads@nafreepress.com; class adv e-mail ads@nafreepress.com; ed e-mail news@nafreepress.com; web site www.wickedlocal.com/northattleborough
Circulation: 16,993fr; Sworn/Estimate/Non-Audited
Advertising rate: Open inch rate $10.00
Established: 1987
Digital Platform - Mobile: Apple, Android, Blackberry
Ed....................Peter Cox
Pub....................Jim Orourke
Ed....................John Andre
Adv. Dir....................Nick Bolitho
Mechanical Specifications: Type page 10 1/2 x 15 3/4; E - 4 cols, 2 3/8, 1/6 between; A - 4 cols, 2 3/8, 1/6 between; C - 6 cols, 1 5/8, 1/6 between.Equipment & Software: Hardware — 4-PC, 1-Okidata/Dot Matrix Printer.
Areas Served: North Attleborough

NORTHAMPTON

AMHERST BULLETIN (FRI)
115 Conz St, Northampton, MA, 01060-4444, Hampshire, USA; gen tel (413) 584-5000; adv tel (413) 585-5357; ed tel 413-584-5000; gen fax (413) 585-5299; adv fax (413) 549-8181; ed fax (413) 549-8181; disp adv e-mail sales@gazettenet.com; class adv e-mail sales@gazettenet.com; ed e-mail editor@gazettenet.com; web site www.amherstbulletin.com - 1,000,699(views) 191,262(visitors)
Circulation: 108pd, 12,750fr; Sworn/Estimate/Non-Audited
Advertising rate: Open inch rate $18.18
Established: 1786
Group: Newspapers of New England
Exec Editor....................Jeff Good
Pub....................Michael RifanburgEquipment & Software: Hardware — PCs, SII; Presses — G/Urbanite; Software — ACT Editorial.
Delivery Method: Mail, Carrier, Racks
Areas Served: Amherst, Hadley, Belchertown, Sunderland, Deerfield, Leverett, Shutesbury and Pelham

NORWOOD

HYDE PARK BULLETIN (THUR)
661 Washington St, Ste 202, Norwood, MA, 02062-3529, Norfolk, USA; gen tel (617) 361-8400; adv tel (617) 361-8400; ed tel (617) 361-8400; gen fax (617) 361-1933; adv fax (617) 361-1933; ed fax (617) 361-1933; disp adv e-mail news@hydeparkbulletin.com; class adv e-mail bulletingraphics@aol.com; ed e-mail news@hydeparkbulletin.com; web site www.bulletinnewspapers.com; www.hydeparkbulletin.com
Circulation: 5,500fr; Sworn/Estimate/Non-Audited
Advertising rate: Open inch rate $31.80
Established: 1992
Pub....................Paul DiModica
Adv....................Susan Yandell
Delivery Method: Mail, Newsstand, Racks
Areas Served: 02136, 02137

ORLEANS

HARWICH ORACLE (WED)
5 Namskaket Rd, Orleans, MA, 02653-3202, Barnstable, USA; gen tel (508) 247-3255; adv tel (508) 247-3255; ed tel (508) 247-3255; gen fax (508) 247-3203; adv fax (508) 247-3203; ed fax (508) 247-3203; disp adv e-mail harwich@cnc.com; obits@cnc.com; class adv e-mail salesteam@wickedlocal.com; ed e-mail harwich@cnc.com; web site www.wickedlocal.com
Circulation: 1,304pd,; Sworn/Estimate/Non-Audited
Advertising rate: Open inch rate $18.95
Established: 1986
Group: Community Newspaper Co. - South GateHouse Media, Inc.
Ed....................Douglas Karlson
Adv. Dir....................Nick Bolitho

THE CAPE CODDER (FRI)
5 Namskaket Rd, Orleans, MA, 02653-3202, Barnstable, USA; gen tel (508) 247-3255; adv tel (508) 247-3255; ed tel (508) 247-3255; gen fax (508) 247-3203; adv fax (508) 247-3203; ed fax (508) 247-3203; disp adv e-mail codder@cnc.com; class adv e-mail codder@cnc.com; ed e-mail cdumas@cnc.com; web site www.wickedlocal.com
Circulation: 6,304pd,; AAM
Advertising rate: Open inch rate $36.35
Established: 1946
Group: GateHouse Media, Inc.
Digital Platform - Mobile: Apple, Android, Blackberry
Editor....................Carol Dumas
Areas Served: Bellingham, Foxboro, Franklin, Medway, Millis, Norfolk, Plainville, Wrentham

PALMER

THE JOURNAL REGISTER (THUR)
24 Water St, Palmer, MA, 01069-1885, Hampden, USA; gen tel (413) 283-8393; adv tel (413) 283-8393; ed tel (413) 283-8393; gen fax (413) 289-1977; adv fax (413) 289-1977; ed fax (413) 289-1977; disp adv e-mail bbaker@turley.com; class adv e-mail classifieds@turley.com; ed e-mail journalregister@turley.com; web site www.palmerjr.com
Circulation: 5,200pd,; Sworn/Estimate/Non-Audited
Advertising rate: Open inch rate $10.75
Established: 1850
Group: McNaughton Newspapers Turley Publications, Inc.
Ed....................Doug Farmer
Pub....................Patrick H. Turley
Ad. Director....................Beth BakerEquipment & Software: Hardware — APP/Mac; Software — QPS/QuarkXPress 4.0, Adobe/Photoshop, Adobe/Illustrator.
Delivery Method: Mail
Areas Served: Palmer, Monson, Brimfield, Wales, holland, Bondsville, Thorndike, Three Rivers, Fiskdale

THE TANTASQUA TOWN COMMON (THUR)
24 Water St, Palmer, MA, 01069-1885, Hampden, USA; gen tel (413) 283-8393; adv tel (413) 283-8393; ed tel (413) 283-8393; gen fax (413) 289-1977; adv fax (413) 289-1977; ed fax (413) 289-1977; disp adv e-mail jbonsall@turley.com; class adv e-mail classifieds@turley.com; ed e-mail towncommon@turley.com; web site www.thetantasquatowncommon.com
Advertising rate: Open inch rate $10.75
Digital Platform - Mobile: Apple, Android, Windows, Blackberry
Digital Platform - Tablet: Apple iOS, Android, Windows 7, Blackberry Tablet OS
Ed....................Tim Kane
Adv. Rep....................Jeanna Bonsall
Adv. Rep....................Jacqueline Haesaert-Perrot
Delivery Method: Racks
Areas Served: Brimfield, Holland, Sturbridge, and Wales

PEABODY

WEEKLY NEWS (THUR)
10 1st Ave, Peabody, MA, 01960-4914, Essex, USA; gen tel (978) 532-5880; adv tel (978) 532-5880; ed tel (978) 532-5880; gen fax (978) 532-4250; adv fax (978) 532-4250; ed fax (978) 532-4250; disp adv e-mail ads@weeklynews.net; class adv e-mail ads@weeklynews.net; ed e-mail editor@weeklynews.net; web site www.weeklynews.net
Circulation: 19,263fr; CAC
Advertising rate: Open inch rate $20.55Editions: (2) 2 total pound; Weekly News-Lynnfield (4,408); Weekly News-Peabody (14,855);
Pub....................Richard H. Ayer
Ed....................Jeff Shmase
Circ. Mgr....................Jim Downey
Sports Ed....................Matt Roy
Prodn. Mgr....................Jessica Price
Mechanical Specifications: Type page 10 x 15 3/4; E - 5 cols, 2 1/16, 1/8 between; A - 5 cols, 2 1/16, 1/8 between; C - 6 cols, 1 11/16, 5/16 between.Equipment & Software: Hardware — APP/Mac G4, APP/Mac G3; Software — QPS/QuarkXPress 4.1, Adobe/Illustrator 9.0, Adobe/Photoshop 6.0, Adobe/Acrobat 4.0.
Delivery Method: Mail, Newsstand, Racks
Areas Served: Peabody & Lynnfield

PITTSFIELD

THE PITTSFIELD GAZETTE (THUR)
10 Wendell Avenue Ext, Ste 101, Pittsfield, MA, 01201-6284, Berkshire, USA; gen tel (413) 443-2010; gen fax (413) 443-2445; disp adv e-mail info@pittsfieldgazette.com; class adv e-mail info@pittsfieldgazette.com; ed e-mail info@pittsfieldgazette.com; web site www.pittsfieldgazette.com
Circulation: 1,500pd, 0fr; USPS
Advertising rate: Open inch rate $8.00
Established: 1991
Ed....................Jonathan Levine
Mechanical Specifications: Type page 10 1/4 x 16; E - 5 cols, 1 11/12, between; A - 5 cols, 1 11/12, between.Equipment & Software: Hardware — APP/Mac.
Delivery Method: Mail, Newsstand, Racks
Areas Served: 01201, 01202

PLYMOUTH

CARVER REPORTER (FRI)
182 Standish Ave, Plymouth, MA, 02360-4162, Plymouth, USA; gen tel (508) 591-6605; adv tel (508) 591-6605; ed tel (508) 591-6605; gen fax (508) 591-6601; adv fax (508) 591-6601; ed fax (508) 591-6601; disp adv e-mail salesteam@wickedlocal.com; class adv e-mail salesteam@wickedlocal.com; ed e-mail dsmith@wickedlocal.com; web site www.wickedlocal.com/carver
Circulation: 736pd,; CAC
Advertising rate: Open inch rate $14.05
Established: 1980
Group: Community Newspaper Co. - South GateHouse Media, Inc.
Digital Platform - Mobile: Apple, Android, Blackberry
Pub....................Mark Olivieri
Sales Mgr....................Tim Oliver
Reporter....................Bobbi Sistrunk
Sports Ed....................Adam Ellis
Adv. Dir....................Nick Bolitho
Mechanical Specifications: Type page 10 3/4 x 16; E - 5 cols, 2, between; A - 5 cols, 2, between.Equipment & Software: ; Presses — WPC/Web Leader.
Areas Served: Carver (MA)

KINGSTON REPORTER (FRI)
182 Standish Ave, Plymouth, MA, 02360-4162, Plymouth, USA; gen tel (781) 837-4504; adv tel (781) 433-6934; ed tel (508) 591-6605; gen fax (508) 591-6601; adv fax (508) 591-6601; ed fax (508) 591-6601; disp adv e-mail salesteam@wickedlocal.com; class adv e-mail salesteam@wickedlocal.com; ed e-mail scsmith@wickedlocal.com; web site www.wickedlocal.com/kingston
Circulation: 1,118pd, 0fr; AAM
Advertising rate: Open inch rate $16.10
Group: Community Newspaper Co. - South GateHouse Media, Inc.
Digital Platform - Mobile: Apple, Android, Blackberry
Pub....................Mark Olivieri
Ed. in Chief....................Gregory Mathis
Mng. Ed....................Scott Smith
Adv. Dir....................Nick Bolitho
Mechanical Specifications: Type page 10 3/4 x 16; E - 5 cols, 2, between; A - 5 cols, 2, between.Equipment & Software: ; Presses — WPC/Web Leader.
Areas Served: Kingston (MA)

OLD COLONY MEMORIAL (WED, SAT)
182 Standish Ave, Plymouth, MA, 02360-4162, Plymouth, USA; gen tel (508) 591-6615; adv tel (781) 433-6934; ed tel (508) 591-6605; gen fax (508) 591-6601; adv fax (508) 591-6601; ed fax (508) 591-6601; disp adv e-mail salesteam@wickedlocal.com; class adv e-mail salesteam@wickedlocal.com; ed e-mail scsmith@wickedlocal.com; web site www.wickedlocal.com/plymouth
Circulation: 4,852pd, 24fr; AAM
Advertising rate: Open inch rate Mid-week OR weekend $31.20; Mid-week AND weekend $46.80
Group: Community Newspaper Co. - South GateHouse Media, Inc.
Digital Platform - Mobile: Apple, Android, Blackberry
Pub....................Mark Olivieri
Ed. in Chief....................Gregory Mathis
Sports Ed....................David Wolcott
Adv. Dir....................Nick Bolitho
Mechanical Specifications: Type page 13 x 21 1/2; E - 6 cols, 2, between; A - 6 cols, 2, between.Equipment & Software: ; Presses — WPC/Web Leader.
Areas Served: Plymouth

THE SENTINEL (THUR)
182 Standish Ave, Plymouth, MA, 02360-4162, Plymouth, USA; gen tel (508) 591-6605; adv tel (781) 433-6934; ed tel (508) 591-6605; gen fax (508) 591-6601; adv fax (508) 591-6601; ed fax (508) 591-6601; disp adv e-mail toliver@wickedlocal.com; class adv e-mail salesteam@wickedlocal.com; ed e-mail gmathis@wickedlocal.com; web site www.wickedlocal.com/marion
Circulation: 654pd, 4fr; CAC
Advertising rate: Open inch rate $15.10
Established: 1822
Group: GateHouse Media, Inc.
Digital Platform - Mobile: Apple, Android, Blackberry
Pub....................Michael Olivieri
Ed. in Chief....................Gregory Mathis
Ed....................Sarah Glaser
Mechanical Specifications: Type page 10 3/4 x 16; E - 5 cols, 2, between; A - 5 cols, 2, between.Equipment & Software: ; Presses — WPC/Web Leader.
Areas Served: Marion, Mattapoisett, Rochester

WAREHAM COURIER (THUR)
182 Standish Ave, Plymouth, MA, 02360-4162, Plymouth, USA; gen tel (508) 591-6605; adv tel (781) 433-6934; gen fax (508) 591-6601; disp adv e-mail salesteam@wickedlocal.com; ed e-mail wareham@wickedlocal.com; web site www.wickedlocal.

com/wareham
Circulation: 1,067pd, 192fr; AAM
Advertising rate: Open inch rate $17.40
Established: 1964
Group: Community Newspaper Co. - South GateHouse Media, Inc.
Pub....Mark Olivieri
Adv. Dir....Nick Bolitho

PROVINCETOWN

PROVINCETOWN BANNER (THUR)

167 Commercial St, Provincetown, MA, 02657-2144, Barnstable, USA; gen tel (508) 487-7400; gen fax (508) 487-7144; ed e-mail editor@provincetownbanner.com ; web site www.wickedlocal.com/provincetown
Circulation: 3,615pd, 316fr; AAM
Advertising rate: 20.50
Established: 1995
Group: GateHouse Media, Inc.
Ed....Sally Rose
Adv. Dir....Nick Bolitho

QUINCY

THE QUINCY SUN (THUR)

1372 Hancock St, Ste 102, Quincy, MA, 02169-5107, Norfolk, USA; gen tel (617) 471-3100; adv tel (617) 471-3100; ed tel (617) 471-3100; gen fax (617) 472- 3963; adv fax (617) 472- 3963; ed fax (617) 472- 3963; disp adv e-mail quincysunads@verizon.net; class adv e-mail quincysunads@verizon.net; ed e-mail rbosworth@thequincysun.com; web site www.thequincysun.com
Circulation: 7,000pd,; Sworn/Estimate/Non-Audited
Advertising rate: Open inch rate $13.00
Established: 1968
Ed. & Pub....Robert H. Bosworth
Adv. Dir....Michelle Collins
Circ. Mgr....Donna Gray
Asst. Mgr....Dolly Newman
Delivery Method: Mail, Newsstand, Carrier, Racks
Areas Served: Quincy

RANDOLPH

BRAINTREE FORUM (THUR)

15 Pacella Park Dr, Ste 120, Randolph, MA, 02368-1700, Norfolk, USA; gen tel (781) 682-4850; adv tel (781) 682-4850; ed tel (781) 682-4850; gen fax (781) 682-4851; adv fax (781) 682-4851; ed fax (781) 682-4851; disp adv e-mail sgenerous@wickedlocal.com; class adv e-mail toliver@wickedlocal.com; ed e-mail Bfonda@wickedlocal.com; web site www.wickedlocal.com/braintree
Circulation: 1,639pd,; AAM
Advertising rate: Open inch rate $17.25
Group: Community Newspaper Co. - South GateHouse Media, Inc.
Pub....Mark Olivieri
Ed....Bill Fonda
Ed. in Chief....Gregory Mathis
Adv. Dir....Nick Bolitho
Areas Served: Braintree (MA)

HOLBROOK SUN (FRI)

15 Pacella Park Dr, Ste 200, Randolph, MA, 02368-1700, Norfolk, USA; gen tel (781) 682-4850; adv tel (781) 837-4547; ed tel (781) 837-4560; gen fax (781) 682-4851; adv fax (781) 682-4851; ed fax (781) 682-4851; disp adv e-mail salesteam@wickedlocal.com; class adv e-mail toliver@wickedlocal.com; ed e-mail bfonda@wickedlocal.com ; web site www.wickedlocal.com/holbrook - 1,154,957(views) 244,866(visitors)
Circulation: 366pd,; AAM
Advertising rate: Open inch rate $16.65
Established: 1958
Group: Community Newspaper Co. - South GateHouse Media, Inc.
Digital Platform - Mobile: Apple, Android
Digital Platform - Tablet: Apple iOS, Android
Pub....Mark Olivieri
Sports Ed....Paul Harber
Adv. Dir....Nick BolithoEquipment & Software: Hardware — PC; Presses — 8-G/Community; Software — Adobe/PageMaker 6.5.
Delivery Method: Mail, Carrier

RANDOLPH HERALD (WED)

5 Pacella Park Dr, Randolph, MA, 02368-1772, Bristol, USA; gen tel (508) 967-3515; adv tel (781) 837-4591; ed tel (508) 967-3505; gen fax (508) 967-3501; adv fax (508) 967-3501; ed fax (508) 967-3501; disp adv e-mail bmurphy@wickedlocal.com; class adv e-mail rbright@wickedlocal.com; ed e-mail acoyle@wickedlocal.com; web site www.wickedlocal.com/randolph
Circulation: 116pd, 2,556fr; AAM
Advertising rate: Open inch rate $15.60
Established: 1924
Group: Community Newspaper Co. - South GateHouse Media, Inc.
Digital Platform - Mobile: Apple, Android, Blackberry
Pub....Mark Olivieri
Managing Ed....Alice Coyle
Adv. Dir....Nick Bolitho
Mechanical Specifications: Type page 10 9/16 x 16; E - 6 cols, 1 9/16, 1/6 between; A - 6 cols, between; C - 7 cols, between.Equipment & Software: Hardware — PC; Presses — 8-G/Community; Software — Adobe/PageMaker 6.5.
Areas Served: Randolph

WEYMOUTH NEWS (WED)

15 Pacella Park Dr, Ste 120, Randolph, MA, 02368-1700, Norfolk, USA; gen tel (781) 682-4850; adv tel (617) 786-7190; ed tel (781) 837-4560; gen fax (781) 682-4851; adv fax (781) 682-4851; ed fax (781) 682-4851; disp adv e-mail vharrington@wickedlocal.com; class adv e-mail salesteam@wickedlocal.com; ed e-mail bfonda@wickedlocal.com; web site www.wickedlocal.com/weymouth
Circulation: 1,936pd,; AAM
Advertising rate: Open inch rate $20.80
Group: Community Newspaper Co. - South GateHouse Media, Inc.
Digital Platform - Mobile: Apple, Android, Blackberry
Pub....Mark Olivieri
Adv. Mgr., Retail....Timothy Oliver
Ed....Bill Fonda
Ed. in Chief....Gregory Mathis
Adv. Dir....Nick Bolitho
Areas Served: Weymouth

RAYNHAM

BRIDGEWATER INDEPENDENT (WED)

370 Paramount Dr, Ste 3, Raynham, MA, 02767-5419, Bristol, USA; gen tel (508) 967-3520; adv tel (781) 837-4598; ed tel (508) 967-3505; gen fax (508) 967-3501; adv fax (508) 967-3501; ed fax (508) 967-3501; disp adv e-mail dteehan@wickedlocal.com; class adv e-mail rbright@wickedlocal.com; ed e-mail acoyle@wickedlocal.com; web site www.wickedlocal.com/bridgewater
Circulation: 371pd, 1,556fr; CAC
Advertising rate: 15.60
Established: 1875
Group: Community Newspaper Co. - South GateHouse Media, Inc.
Managing Ed....Alice Coyle
Adv. Dir....Nick BolithoEquipment & Software: Hardware — HP; Presses — 8-G/Community; Software — Adobe/PageMaker 6.5.
Areas Served: 02324

CANTON JOURNAL (FRI)

370 Paramount Dr, Ste 3, Raynham, MA, 02767-5419, Bristol, USA; gen tel (508) 967-3515; adv tel (508) 967-3515; ed tel (508) 967-3515; gen fax (508) 967-3501; adv fax (508) 967-3501; ed fax (508) 967-3501; disp adv e-mail canton@cnc.com; class adv e-mail rbright@wickedlocal.com; ed e-mail acoyle@wickedlocal.com; web site www.wickedlocal.com/canton
Circulation: 21,614pd, 280fr; AAM
Advertising rate: Open inch rate $17.05
Established: 1876
Group: Community Newspaper Co.-West GateHouse Media, Inc.
Managing Ed....Alice Coyle
News Ed....Stuart Green
Adv. Dir....Nick Bolitho
Areas Served: Canton (MA)

EASTON JOURNAL (FRI)

370 Paramount Dr, Ste 3, Raynham, MA, 02767-5419, Bristol, USA; gen tel (508) 967-3510; adv tel (508) 967-3510; ed tel (508) 967-3510; gen fax (508) 967-3501; adv fax (508) 967-3501; ed fax (508) 967-3501; disp adv e-mail msutherland@wickedlocal.com; class adv e-mail rbright@wickedlocal.com; ed e-mail acoyle@wickedlocal.com; web site www.wickedlocal.com/easton
Circulation: 350pd,; AAM
Advertising rate: Open inch rate $19.35
Group: Community Newspaper Co.-West GateHouse Media, Inc.
Digital Platform - Mobile: Apple, Android, Blackberry
Pub....Mark Olivieri
Mng. Ed....Alice Coyla
Sports Ed....John Quattrucci
Adv. Dir....Nick Bolitho
Areas Served: Easton (MA)

NORTON MIRROR (FRI)

370 Paramount Dr, Ste 3, Raynham, MA, 02767-5419, Bristol, USA; gen tel (508) 967-3510; adv tel (508) 967-3510; ed tel (508) 967-4593; gen fax (508) 967-3501; adv fax (508) 967-3501; ed fax (508) 967-3501; disp adv e-mail msutherland@wickedlocal.com; class adv e-mail rbright@wickedllocal.com; ed e-mail acoyle@wickedlocal.com; web site www.wickedlocal.com/norton
Circulation: 721pd,; Sworn/Estimate/Non-Audited
Advertising rate: Open inch rate $16.75
Established: 1987
Group: Community Newspaper Co.-West GateHouse Media, Inc.
Digital Platform - Mobile: Apple, Android, Blackberry
Pub....Mark Olivieri
Ed....Alice Coyle
Adv. Dir....Nick BolithoEquipment & Software: Hardware — PC; Presses — G/Community, G/Suburban; Software — Adobe/PageMaker 6.5.
Areas Served: Norton

STOUGHTON JOURNAL (FRI)

370 Paramount Dr, Ste 3, Raynham, MA, 02767-5419, Bristol, USA; gen tel (508) 967-3515; gen fax (508) 967-3501; class adv e-mail salesteam@wickedlocal.com; ed e-mail acoyle@wickedlocal.com; web site www.wickedlocal.com/stoughton
Circulation: 189pd,; AAM
Advertising rate: 16.10
Established: 1989
Group: Community Newspaper Co.-West GateHouse Media, Inc.
Digital Platform - Mobile: Apple, Android, Blackberry
Managing Ed....Alice Coyle
Ed....Stuart Green
Adv. Dir...... Nick BolithoEquipment & Software: ; Presses — 8-G/Community/Suburban; Software — Adobe/PageMaker 6.5.

REVERE

CHELSEA RECORD (THUR)

385 Broadway, Ste 105, Revere, MA, 02151-3049, Suffolk, USA; gen tel (781) 284-2400; adv tel (781) 284-2400; ed tel (781) 284-2400; gen fax (781) 485-1403; adv fax (781) 485-1403; ed fax (781) 485-1403; disp adv e-mail ads.journal@verizon.net; class adv e-mail ads.journal@verizon.net; ed e-mail editor@chelsearecord.com; web site www.chelsearecord.com
Circulation: 4,500pd,; Sworn/Estimate/Non-Audited
Advertising rate: Open inch rate $9.45
Established: 1890
Group: Independent Newspaper Group
Vice Pres./executive editor....Joshua Resnek
Adv. Mgr....Debra DiGregorio
Ed. in Chief....Cary Shuman
Prodn. Mgr....Stephen Quigley
Mechanical Specifications: Type page 13 x 21; E - 6 cols, 2 1/16, 1/8 between; A - 6 cols, 2 1/16, 1/8 between; C - 6 cols, 1 5/16, 1/8 between.Equipment & Software: Hardware — APP/Macs, PC; Software — Multi-Ad, Solomon, Graphix/Adtaker.
Delivery Method: Mail, Newsstand
Areas Served: Chelsea (MA)

EAST BOSTON TIMES (WED, THUR)

385 Broadway, Ste 105, Revere, MA, 02151-3049, Suffolk, USA; gen tel (781) 485-0588; adv tel (781) 485-0588; ed tel (781) 485-0588; gen fax (781) 485-1403; adv fax (781) 485-1403; ed fax (781) 485-1403; disp adv e-mail ads.journal@verizon.net; class adv e-mail ADS.JOURNAL@VERIZON.NET; web site www.eastietimes.com
Circulation: 8,000fr; Sworn/Estimate/Non-Audited
Advertising rate: Open inch rate $27.50
Group: Independent Newspaper Group
Vice Pres....Joshua Resnek
Prodn. Mgr....Stephen Quigley
Mechanical Specifications: Type page 13 x 21 1/2; E - 6 cols, 2 1/16, 1/8 between; A - 6 cols, 2 1/16, 1/8 between; C - 6 cols, 1 5/16, 1/8 between.Equipment & Software: Hardware — APP/Mac, PCs; Presses — G/Community; Software — Multi-Ad, Solomon, Graphix/Adtaker.
Areas Served: East Boston (MA)

EVERETT INDEPENDENT (WED)

385 Broadway, Ste 105, Revere, MA, 02151-3049, Suffolk, USA; gen tel (781) 284-2400; adv tel (781) 284-2400; ed tel (781) 284-2400; gen fax (781) 485-1403; adv fax (781) 485-1403; ed fax (781) 485-1403; disp adv e-mail ads.journal@verizon.net; class adv e-mail ads.journal@verizon.net; ed e-mail editor@everettindependent.com; web site www.everettindependent.com
Circulation: 12,500fr; Sworn/Estimate/Non-Audited
Advertising rate: Open inch rate $10.00
Group: Independent Newspaper Group
Pres....Stephen Quigley
Ed....Joshua Resnek
Areas Served: Everett (MA)

THE BACK BAY SUN (FRI)

385 Broadway, Ste 105, Revere, MA, 02151-3049, Suffolk, USA; gen tel (617) 523-9490; adv tel (617) 523-9490; ed tel (617) 523-9490; gen fax (617) 523-8668; adv fax (617) 523-8668; ed fax (617) 523-8668; disp adv e-mail tverhoogen@backbaysun.com; class adv e-mail tverhoogen@backbaysun.com; ed e-mail editor@backbaysun.com; web site www.backbaysun.com
Advertising rate: Open inch rate $16.00
Group: Independent Newspaper Group
Exec. Ed. & Pub....Karen Cord Taylor
Mng. Dir....Jacqueline Harris
Ad. Director....Therese Verhoogen
Areas Served: Boston

THE LYNN JOURNAL (TUES)

385 Broadway, Ste 105, Revere, MA, 02151-3049, Suffolk, USA; gen tel (781) 284-2400; adv tel (781) 284-2400; ed tel (781) 284-2400; gen fax (781) 485-1403; adv fax (781) 485-1403; ed fax (781) 485-1403; disp adv e-mail ads.journal@verizon.net; class adv e-mail ads.journal@verizon.net; ed e-mail editor@lynnjournal.com ; web site www.lynnjournal.com
Circulation: 10,000fr; Sworn/Estimate/Non-Audited
Advertising rate: Open inch rate $9.95
Established: 1998

Group: Independent Newspaper Group
Adv. Mgr. .... Debra DiGregorio
Ed. .... Stephen Quigley
Delivery Method: Mail, Racks
Areas Served: Lynn (MA)

THE REVERE JOURNAL (WED)

385 Broadway, Ste 105, Revere, MA, 02151-3049, Suffolk, USA; gen tel (781) 485-0588; adv tel (781) 485-0588; ed tel (781) 485-0588; gen fax (781) 485-1403; adv fax (781) 485-1403; ed fax (781) 485-1403; disp adv e-mail tverhoogen@charlestownbridge.com; class adv e-mail tverhoogen@charlestownbridge.com; ed e-mail editor@reverejournal.com; web site www.reverejournal.com
Circulation: 7,500pd,; Sworn/Estimate/Non-Audited
Advertising rate: Open inch rate $11.95
Group: Independent Newspaper Group
Pub. .... Karen Cord Taylor
Circ. Mgr. .... Glenda Harris
Ed. .... David O'Connor
Adv. Dir. .... Debra DiGregorio
Mechanical Specifications: Type page 13 x 21 1/2; E - 6 cols, 2 1/16, 1/8 between; A - 6 cols, 2 1/16, 1/8 between; C - 6 cols, 1 5/16, 1/8 between.Equipment & Software: Hardware — APP/Macs, PC; Software — Multi-Ad, Solomon, Graphix/Adtaker.
Areas Served: Revere

WINTHROP SUN-TRANSCRIPT (THUR)

385 Broadway, Ste 105, Revere, MA, 02151-3049, Suffolk, USA; gen tel (781) 284-2400; gen fax (781) 485-1403; disp adv e-mail ads.journal@verizon.net; web site www.reverejournal.com
Circulation: 4,300pd,; Sworn/Estimate/Non-Audited
Advertising rate: Open inch rate $10.00
Group: Independent Newspaper Group
Pres. .... Stephen Quigley
Mng. Ed. .... Joshua Resnek

ROWLEY

THE TOWN COMMON (WED)

77 Wethersfield St, Rowley, MA, 01969-1713, Essex, USA; gen tel (978) 948-8696; adv tel (978) 948-8696; ed tel (978) 948-8696; gen fax (978) 948-2564; adv fax (978) 948-2564; ed fax (978) 948-2564; disp adv e-mail advertise@thetowncommon.com; class adv e-mail advertise@thetowncommon.com; ed e-mail editor@thetowncommon.com; web site www.thetowncommon.com
Advertising rate: Open inch rate $24.00
Established: 2004
Digital Platform - Mobile: Apple, Android, Windows, Blackberry
Digital Platform - Tablet: Apple iOS, Android, Windows 7, Blackberry Tablet OS, Kindle, Nook, Kindle Fire
Pub./Ed. .... Marc Maravalli
Delivery Method: Newsstand, Racks
Areas Served: North Shore of Massachusetts & Coastal New Hampshire

SHELBURNE FALLS

WEST COUNTY NEWS (THUR)

87 Bridge St, Shelburne Falls, MA, 01370-1102, Franklin, USA; gen tel (413) 625-4660; gen fax (413) 625-4661; disp adv e-mail wc-news@turley.com; web site www.turley.com
Circulation: 21,629fr; Sworn/Estimate/Non-Audited
Advertising rate: Open inch rate $7.00
Established: 1979
Pub. .... Patrick H. Turley
Adv. Mgr. .... Beth Baker
Ed. .... Patrick O'Connor
Mechanical Specifications: Type page 10 1/4 x 16; E - 5 cols, 1 7/8, 1/8 between.Equipment & Software: Hardware — PC, Compaq/2000; Software — Adobe/PageMaker 6.5, Adobe/Illustrator, Adobe/Photoshop, Archetype/Corel Draw.

SOMERVILLE

CAMBRIDGE CHRONICLE & TAB (THUR)

80 Central St, Somerville, MA, 02143-1612, Middlesex, USA; gen tel (617) 629-3387; adv tel (781) 433-8253; ed tel (617) 629-3382; gen fax (617) 629-3381; adv fax (617) 629-3381; ed fax (617) 629-3381; disp adv e-mail cwarren@wickedlocal.com; class adv e-mail esiegal@wickedlocal.com; ed e-mail cambridge@wickedlocal.com; web site www.wickedlocal.com/cambridge
Circulation: 700pd, 5,628fr; AAM
Advertising rate: Open inch rate $39.75
Established: 1846
Group: Community Newspaper Co.-Metro GateHouse Media, Inc.
Digital Platform - Mobile: Apple, Android, Blackberry
Ed. .... Amy Saltzman
Assist. Ed. .... Erin Baldassari
Reg. Adv. Dir. .... Cris Warren
Adv. Dir. .... Nick Bolitho
Areas Served: Cambridge (MA)

SOMERVILLE JOURNAL (WED)

80 Central St, Somerville, MA, 02143-1612, Middlesex, USA; gen tel (617) 625-6300; adv tel (781) 433-8253; ed tel (617) 629-3385; gen fax (617) 629-3381; adv fax (617) 629-3381; ed fax (617) 629-3381; disp adv e-mail esiegal@wickedlocal.com; class adv e-mail salesteam@wickedlocal.com; ed e-mail datkinson@wickedlocal.com; web site www.wickedlocal.com/somerville
Circulation: 1,213pd, 2fr; AAM
Advertising rate: Open inch rate $32.05
Established: 1870
Group: Community Newspaper Co.-Metro GateHouse Media, Inc.
Digital Platform - Mobile: Apple, Android, Blackberry
Pub. .... Chuck Goodrich
Ed. .... Dan Atkinson
Ed. in Chief .... Jesse Floyd
Adv. Dir. .... Nick Bolitho
Areas Served: Somerville

STONEHAM SUN (WED)

20 Holland St, Ste 40, Somerville, MA, 02144-2749, Middlesex, USA; gen tel (978) 739-8509; adv tel (978) 739-1344; ed tel (978) 739-8509; gen fax (781) 393-1821; adv fax (781) 393-1821; ed fax (781) 393-1821; disp adv e-mail ameltzer@wickedlocal.com; class adv e-mail salesteam@wickedlocal.com; ed e-mail stoneham@wickedlocal.com; web site www.wickedlocal.com/stoneham
Circulation: 3,821fr; AAM
Advertising rate: Open inch rate $19.10
Group: Community Newspaper Co.-North GateHouse Media, Inc.
Digital Platform - Mobile: Apple, Android, Blackberry
Pub. .... Chuck Goodrich
Ed. in Chief .... Pete Chianca
Ed. .... Matt Reid
Adv. Dir. .... Nick Bolitho
Mechanical Specifications: Type page 10 13/16 x 16; E - 5 cols, 2 1/16, between; A - 5 cols, 2 1/16, between; C - 8 cols, 1 7/32, between.
Areas Served: Stoneham

THE SOMERVILLE TIMES (WED)

699 Broadway, Somerville, MA, 02144-2223, Middlesex, USA; gen tel (617) 666-4010; adv tel (617) 666-4010; ed tel (617) 666-4010; gen fax (617) 628-0422; adv fax (617) 628-0422; ed fax (617) 628-0422; disp adv e-mail ads@thesomervilletimes.com; class adv e-mail ads@thesomervilletimes.com; ed e-mail jimclark@thesomervilletimes.com; web site www.thesomervillenews.com
Advertising rate: Open inch rate $10.00
Established: 1969
Digital Platform - Mobile: Apple, Android, Blackberry
Digital Platform - Tablet: Apple iOS, Android, Blackberry Tablet OS
Ed. .... Jim Clark
Adv. Dir. .... Bobbie Toner
Delivery Method: Mail, Racks
Areas Served: Somerville

SOUTH GRAFTON

THE GRAFTON VILLAGER (THUR)

90 Milford Rd, South Grafton, MA, 01560-1214, Worcester, USA; gen tel (508) 736-5893; adv tel (508) 839-2838; ed tel (508) 839-2259; gen fax (508) 839-5235; adv fax (508) 839-5235; ed fax (508) 839-5235; disp adv e-mail graftonvillager@gmail.com; class adv e-mail graftonvillager@gmail.com; ed e-mail editor@thegraftonnews.com; web site www.thegraftonvillager.com
Circulation: 4,024pd, 60fr; Sworn/Estimate/Non-Audited
Advertising rate: Open inch rate $6.00
Established: 1958
Graphic Designer .... Wendy Watkins
Editor .... Richard Price
Mechanical Specifications: Type page 10 1/4 x 15 1/2; E - 6 cols, 1 1/2, 1/4 between.Equipment & Software: Hardware — APP/Mac; Software — Adobe/PageMaker 5.0.
Delivery Method: Mail, Carrier, Racks
Areas Served: Grafton

SOUTH HADLEY

TOWN REMINDER (FRI)

136 College St, Ste 2, South Hadley, MA, 01075-1402, Hampshire, USA; gen tel (413) 536-5333; adv tel (413) 536-5333; ed tel (413) 536-5333; gen fax (413) 536-5334; adv fax (413) 536-5334; ed fax (413) 536-5334; disp adv e-mail bbaker@turley.com; class adv e-mail classifieds@turley.com; ed e-mail kwill@turley.com; web site www.townreminderonline.com
Circulation: 12,000fr; Sworn/Estimate/Non-Audited
Advertising rate: Open inch rate $11.75
Established: 1968
Group: Turley Publications, Inc.
Pub. .... Patrick H. Turley
Ed. .... Kristin Will
Ad. Director .... Beth Baker
Delivery Method: Racks
Areas Served: South Hadley, Chicopee, Granby, Holyoke, Ludlow

SOUTHBRIDGE

AUBURN NEWS (WED)

25 Elm St, Southbridge, MA, 01550-2605, Worcester, USA; gen tel (508) 764-4325; adv tel (508) 909-4104; ed tel (508) 909-4130; gen fax (508) 764-8102; adv fax (508) 764-8102; ed fax (508) 764-8102; disp adv e-mail jashton@stonebridgepress.com; class adv e-mail classifieds@stonebridgepress.com; ed e-mail aminor@stonebridgepress.com; web site www.theheartofmassachusetts.com
Circulation: 1,600pd, 8fr; Sworn/Estimate/Non-Audited
Advertising rate: Open inch rate $10.00
Group: Stonebridge Press, Inc.
Pub. .... Frank Chilinski
CFO .... Ron Tremblay
Adv. Mgr. .... Jean Ashton
Ed. .... Adam Minor
Mechanical Specifications: Type page 11 1/2 x 21; E - 6 cols, 1 1/2, 1/4 between; A - 8 cols, 1 5/4, 1/4 between.Equipment & Software: Hardware — APP/Mac; Presses — HI; Software — QPS/QuarkXPress.
Delivery Method: Mail
Areas Served: Auburn (MA)

BLACKSTONE VALLEY TRIBUNE (FRI)

25 Elm St, Southbridge, MA, 01550-2605, Worcester, USA; gen tel (508) 764-4325; adv tel (508) 764-4325; ed tel (508) 764-4325; gen fax (508) 764-8102; adv fax (508) 764-8102; ed fax (508) 764-8102; disp adv e-mail jashton@stonebridgepress.com; class adv e-mail classifieds@stonebridgepress.com; ed e-mail aminor@stonebridgepress.com; web site www.blackstonevalleytribune.com
Circulation: 15,000pd,; Sworn/Estimate/Non-Audited
Advertising rate: Open inch rate $10.00
Established: 1949
Group: Stonebridge Press, Inc.
Publisher .... Frank G. Chilinski
Adv. .... Jean Ashton
Circulation Director .... Kerri Peterson
Ed. .... Adam Minor
Delivery Method: Mail
Areas Served: Douglad, Uxbridge, Northridge (MA)

CHARLTON VILLAGER (FRI)

25 Elm St, Southbridge, MA, 01550-2605, Worcester, USA; gen tel (508) 764-4325; adv tel (508) 909-4104; ed tel (508) 909-4130; gen fax (508) 764-8102; adv fax (508) 764-8102; ed fax (508) 764-8102; disp adv e-mail jashton@stonebridgepress.com; class adv e-mail classifieds@stonebridgepress.com; ed e-mail aminor@stonebridgepress.com; web site www.theheartofmassachusetts.com
Advertising rate: Open inch rate $10.00
Ed. .... Adam Minor
Ad. Director .... Jean Ashton
Delivery Method: Mail
Areas Served: Charlton (MA)

SPENCER NEW LEADER (THUR)

25 Elm St, Southbridge, MA, 01550-2605, Worcester, USA; gen tel (508) 764-4325; adv tel (508) 764-4325; ed tel (508) 764-4325; gen fax (508) 764-8015; adv fax (508) 764-8015; ed fax (508) 764-8015; disp adv e-mail frank@stonebridgepress.com; class adv e-mail classifieds@stonebridgepress.com; ed e-mail aminor@stonebridgepress.com; web site www.spencernewleader.com
Circulation: 17,200fr; Sworn/Estimate/Non-Audited
Advertising rate: Open inch rate $8.00
Group: Stonebridge Press, Inc.
President & Publisher .... Frank Chilinski
Adv. Dir. .... Jean Ashton
Delivery Method: Mail
Areas Served: Brookfield, W/E/N Brookfield, Spencer, Leicester (MA)

STURBRIDGE VILLAGER (FRI)

25 Elm St, Southbridge, MA, 01550-2605, Worcester, USA; gen tel (508) 764-4325; adv tel (508) 909-4104; ed tel (508) 909-4130; gen fax (508) 764-8102; adv fax (508) 764-8102; ed fax (508) 764-8102; disp adv e-mail jashton@stonebridgepress.com; class adv e-mail classifieds@stonebridgepress.com; ed e-mail aminor@stonebridgepress.com; web site www.theheartofmassachusetts.com
Advertising rate: Open inch rate $12.80
Ed. .... Adam Minor
Adv. Dir. .... Sarah Mortensen
Dir. Sales/Mktg. .... Jean Ashton
Delivery Method: Mail
Areas Served: Brimfield, Wales, Holland, Sturbridge (MA)

THE WEBSTER TIMES (FRI)

25 Elm St, Southbridge, MA, 01550-2605, Worcester, USA; gen tel (508) 764-4325; adv tel (508) 909-4104; ed tel (508) 909-4130; gen fax (508) 764-8102; adv fax (508) 764-8102; ed fax (508) 764-8102; disp adv e-mail jashton@stonebridgepress.com; class adv e-mail classifieds@stonebridgepress.com; ed e-mail aminor@stonebridgepress.com; web site www.webstertimes.net
Circulation: 15,200pd, 17,000fr; Sworn/Estimate/Non-Audited
Advertising rate: Open inch rate $10.00
Group: Stonebridge Press, Inc.
President & Publisher .... Frank Chilinski
Adv. Mgr. .... Jean Ashton
Exec. Ed. .... Walter Bird
Ed. .... Adam Minor
Delivery Method: Mail
Areas Served: Oxford, Dudley, Webster (MA)

STONEHAM

THE STONEHAM INDEPENDENT (WED)

200F Main St, Ste 343, Stoneham, MA, 02180-1619, USA, USA; gen tel (781) 438-1660; adv tel (781) 438-1660; ed tel (781) 438-1660; gen fax (781) 438-6762; adv fax (781) 438-6762; ed fax (781) 438-6762; disp adv e-mail news@stonehamindependent.com; class adv e-mail news@stonehamindependent.com; ed e-mail news@stonehamindependent.com; web site www.homenewshere.com
Circulation: 3,000pd,; Sworn/Estimate/Non-Audited
Advertising rate: Open inch rate $12.60
Established: 1870
Group: Woburn Daily Times, Inc.
Pub....................................Peter M. Haggerty
Business Manager................Mark J. Haggerty
Adv. Mgr.......................................Paul Whalen
Prodn. Mgr. ....Jay M. Haggerty
Reporter ....Patrick Blais
Mechanical Specifications: Type page 11 5/8 x 21; E - 6 cols, 1 13/16, between; A - 6 cols, 1 13/16, between; C - 9 cols, 1 1/16, between. Equipment & Software: Hardware — APP/Mac; Presses — G/Community; Software — QPS/QuarkXPress 7.0, Adobe/Acrobat.
Delivery Method: Mail, Newsstand, Racks
Areas Served: 02180

TAUNTON

THE RAYNHAM CALL (WED)

5 Cohannet St, Taunton, MA, 02780-3903, Bristol, USA; gen tel (508) 967-3520; adv tel (508) 967-3520; ed tel (508) 967-3520; gen fax (508) 967-3501; adv fax (508) 967-3501; ed fax (508) 967-3501; class adv e-mail salesteam@wickedlocal.com; ed e-mail acoyle@wickedlocal.com; web site http://www.wickedlocal.com/raynham
Circulation: 181pd, 1,729fr; AAM
Advertising rate: Open inch rate $15.35
Group: Community Newspaper Co. - South
Digital Platform - Mobile: Apple, Android, Blackberry
Ed. ....Alice Coyle
Adv. Dir..Nick Bolitho
Areas Served: Raynham

VINEYARD HAVEN

THE MARTHA'S VINEYARD TIMES (THUR)

30 Beach Rd, Vineyard Haven, MA, 02568-5582, Dukes, USA; gen tel (508) 693-6100; adv tel (508) 693-6100; ed tel (508) 693-6100; gen fax (508) 693-6000; adv fax (508) 693-6000; ed fax (508) 693-6000; disp adv e-mail carrie@mvtimes.com; class adv e-mail class@mvtimes.com; ed e-mail mvt@mvtimes.com ; web site www.mvtimes.com - 2,700,000(views) 860,000(visitors)
Circulation: 250pd, 16,000fr; Sworn/Estimate/Non-Audited
Advertising rate: 2-15 Mod $50.00; 16-60 mod $44.00; 1/2 Pg $1200.00;
Established: 1984
Digital Platform - Mobile: Apple
Digital Platform - Tablet: Apple iOS
Pub.......................................Barbara Oberfest
Pub..Peter Oberfest
Ed. ....Doug Cabral
Adv. Dir...................................Carrie Waltersdorf
Circ. Mgr...Jim Osborn
Production mgr..........................Susan Safford
Classified Adv. Mgr.........................Linda Wood
Areas Served: Martha's Vineyard

WAKEFIELD

NORTH READING TRANSCRIPT (THUR)

26 Albion St, Wakefield, MA, 01880-2803, Middlesex, USA; gen tel (781)245-0080; adv tel (781)245-0080; ed tel (781)245-0080; gen fax (781) 246-0061; adv fax (781) 246-0061; ed fax (781) 246-0061; disp adv e-mail ads@wakefielditem.com; class adv e-mail ads@wakefielditem.com; ed e-mail nrtranscript@rcn.com
Circulation: 4,000pd, 290fr; USPS
Advertising rate: Open inch rate $10.50
Established: 1956
Group: Wakefield Item
Ed. ....Robert Turosz
Adv. Dir...................................Phil Solmonson
Bob Burgess
Mechanical Specifications: Type page 10 13/16 x 16; E - 5 cols, 2 1/16, 1/8 between; A - 5 cols, 2 1/16, 1/8 between; C - 5 cols, 2 1/16, 1/8 between.Equipment & Software: Hardware — APP/Macs; Software — QPS/QuarkXPress, Write Now.
Delivery Method: Mail, Newsstand, Carrier
Areas Served: 1864

THE LYNNFIELD VILLAGER (WED)

26 Albion St, Wakefield, MA, 01880-2803, Middlesex, USA; gen tel (781) 334-6319; adv tel (781) 334-6319; ed tel (781) 334-6319; gen fax (781) 246-0061; adv fax (781) 246-0061; ed fax (781) 246-0061; disp adv e-mail ads@wakefielditem.com; class adv e-mail ads@wakefielditem.com; ed e-mail greatoakadguy@aol.com; web site wp.localheadlinenews.com/?cat=4
Circulation: 1,615pd, 207fr; Sworn/Estimate/Non-Audited
Advertising rate: Open inch rate $9.00
Established: 1973
Group: Great Oak Publications
Pub./Ed. ....Glenn Golbeare
Adv. Dir...................................Phil Solmonson
Ed. ....Robert Burgess
Mechanical Specifications: Type page 10 13/16 x 16; E - 5 cols, 2 1/16, 1/8 between; A - 5 cols, 2 1/16, 1/8 between; C - 5 cols, 2 1/16, 1/8 between.Equipment & Software: Hardware — APP/Macs; Software — QPS/QuarkXPress, Write Now
Delivery Method: Mail, Newsstand, Carrier
Areas Served: 01940

WALPOLE

THE WALPOLE TIMES (THUR)

7 West St, Ste 2, Walpole, MA, 02081-2856, Norfolk, USA; gen tel (508) 668-0243; adv tel (781) 433-8238; ed tel (508) 921-1857; gen fax (508) 668-5174; adv fax (508) 668-5174; disp adv e-mail cpetrillo@wickedlocal.com; class adv e-mail adsales@walpoletimes.com; ed e-mail keith@walpoletimes.com; web site www.wickedlocal.com/walpole
Circulation: 549pd,; Sworn/Estimate/Non-Audited
Advertising rate: Open inch rate $10.75
Group: GateHouse Media, Inc.
Digital Platform - Mobile: Apple, Android, Blackberry
Pub.......................................Chuck Goodrich
Adv. Sales Rep..........................Carlo Petrillo
Ed. ....Keith Fergusen
Ed. in Chief ....Jesse Floyd
Adv. Dir...Nick Bolitho
Mechanical Specifications: Type page 12 7/8 x 21; E - 6 cols, between; A - 6 cols, between; C - 10 cols, between.Equipment & Software: ; Software — Merrimac Publishing/Windows.
Delivery Method: Mail, Newsstand, Racks
Areas Served: Walpole (MA)

WARE

QUABOAG CURRENT (THUR)

80 Main St, Ware, MA, 01082-1318, Hampshire, USA; gen tel (413) 967-3505; adv tel (413) 967-3505; ed tel (413) 967-3505; gen fax (413) 967-6009; adv fax (413) 967-6009; ed fax (413) 967-6009; disp adv e-mail bbaker@turley.com; class adv e-mail classifieds@turley.com; ed e-mail tkane@turley.com; web site www.quaboagcurrent.com
Advertising rate: Open inch rate $12.75
Ed. ....Tim Kane
Ad. Director.................................Beth Baker
Delivery Method: Mail, Racks
Areas Served: Brookfield, Ware, Warren, West Warren, West Brookfield, North Brookfield, East Brookfield, New Braintree

WARE RIVER NEWS (THUR)

80 Main St, Ware, MA, 01082-1318, Hampshire, USA; gen tel (413) 967-3505; adv tel (413) 967-3505; ed tel (413) 967-3505; gen fax (413) 967-6009; adv fax (413) 967-6009; ed fax (413) 967-6009; disp adv e-mail jhaesaert@turley.com; class adv e-mail classifieds@turley.com; ed e-mail tkane@turley.com; web site www.warenewsonline.com
Circulation: 4,429pd,; Sworn/Estimate/Non-Audited
Advertising rate: Open inch rate $10.75
Established: 1887
Group: Turley Publications, Inc.
Pub.......................................Patrick H. Turley
Ed. ....Tim Kane
Dir., Adv. ....Beth Baker
Delivery Method: Mail
Areas Served: Ware, Hardwich, Wheelwright, Gilbertville, West Brookfield, Warren, West Warren, Palmer

WEST SPRINGFIELD

WEST SPRINGFIELD RECORD (THUR)

516 Main St, West Springfield, MA, 01089-3973, Hampden, USA; gen tel (413) 736-1587; adv tel (413) 736-1587; gen fax (413) 739-2477; adv fax (413) 739-2477; disp adv e-mail wsrecord@comcast.net; class adv e-mail wsrecord@comcast.net; ed e-mail wsrecord@comcast.net; web site www.facebook.com/westspringfield.record/?ref=page_internal
Circulation: 5,600pd,; Sworn/Estimate/Non-Audited
Advertising rate: Open inch rate $4.00
Established: 1953
Gen. Mgr. ....Marie Coburn
Ed. ....Tom Coburn
Delivery Method: Mail, Newsstand, Racks
Areas Served: West Springfield

WESTBOROUGH

COMMUNITY ADVOCATE (FRI)

32 South St, Westborough, MA, 01581-1619, Worcester, USA; gen tel (508) 366-5500; adv tel (508) 366-5500; gen fax (508) 366-2812; adv fax (508) 366-2812; disp adv e-mail adguy@communityadvocate.com; class adv e-mail adguy@communityadvocate.com; ed e-mail news@communityadvocate.com; web site www.communityadvocate.com
Circulation: 16,000pd, 5,194fr; Sworn/Estimate/Non-Audited
Advertising rate: $34.00 per column inch
Established: 1974Editions: (2) 2 total; Community Advocate/Marlboro/Hudson (4,800); Community Advocate/Regional (16,500);
Office Mgr. ....Tracy Nickerson
Ed. ....David Bagdon
Mng. Ed....................................Barbara Polan
Mechanical Specifications: Type page 10 x 13; E - 5 cols, 1 5/8, between; A - 5 cols, 1 5/8, between; C - 7 cols, 1 3/16, between.
Areas Served: Westborough, Shrewsbury, Northborough, Southborough, Marlborough & Hudson (MA)

WILBRAHAM

THE REGISTER (WED)

2341 Boston Rd, Ste B200, Wilbraham, MA, 01095-1244, Hampden, USA; gen tel (413) 283-8393; adv tel (413) 283-8393; gen fax (413) 289-1977; adv fax (413) 289-1977; disp adv e-mail twhitney@turley.com; class adv e-mail classifieds@turley.com; ed e-mail pkillough@turley.com; web site register.turley.com
Circulation: 12,500fr; Sworn/Estimate/Non-Audited
Advertising rate: Open inch rate $11.75
Established: 1946
Group: Community Newspaper Co. - South Turley Publications, Inc.
Pub.......................................Patrick H. Turley
Adv. Mgr...Beth Baker
Ed. ....Paula Killough
Delivery Method: Racks
Areas Served: Ludlow, Indian Orchard, Wilbraham

WILBRAHAM-HAMPDEN TIMES (THUR)

2341 Boston Rd Ste B200, Wilbraham Shops, Wilbraham, MA, 01095-1244, Hampden, USA; gen tel (413) 682-0007; adv tel (413) 682-0007; ed tel (413) 682-0007; gen fax (413) 682-0013; adv fax (413) 682-0013; ed fax (413) 682-0007; disp adv e-mail cbennett@turley.com; class adv e-mail jwalker@turley.com; ed e-mail cbennett@turley.com; web site www.wilbrahamtimes.com
Circulation: 9,300fr; Sworn/Estimate/Non-Audited
Advertising rate: Open inch rate $11.50
Established: 2002
Group: Turley Publications, Inc.
Pub.......................................Patrick H. Turley
Adv. Mgr...Beth Baker
Ed. ....Charles Bennett
Advertising Rep. ....Jocelyn Walker
Delivery Method: Mail
Areas Served: 01095, 01036

WINCHENDON

THE WINCHENDON COURIER (FRI)

44 Central St, Winchendon, MA, 01475-1608, Worcester, USA; gen tel (978) 297-0050; gen fax (978) 297-2177; disp adv e-mail ruth@stonebridgepress.news; web site www.winchendoncourier.com
Circulation: 1,500pd, 120fr; Sworn/Estimate/Non-Audited
Advertising rate: Open inch rate $8.00
Established: 1878
Group: Stonebridge Press, Inc.
Pub...Frank Chilinski
Ed./Adv Mgr. ....Ruth DeAmicis
Circ. Mgr.....................................Kerri Peterson
Mechanical Specifications: Type page 11 x 17; E - 6 cols, 1 1/2, 1/6 between; A - 6 cols, 1 1/2, 1/6 between; C - 6 cols, 1 1/2, 1/6 between.
Delivery Method: Mail, Newsstand
Areas Served: Winchendon (MA)

WOBURN

TOWN CRIER (WED)

1 Arrow Dr, Woburn, MA, 01801-2039, Middlesex, USA; gen tel (978) 658-2346 x100; adv tel (978) 658-2346 x100; ed tel (978) 658-2346 x100; gen fax (978) 658-2266; adv fax (978) 658-2266; ed fax (978) 658-2266; disp adv e-mail office@yourtowncrier.com; class adv e-mail bruce@yourtowncrier.com; ed e-mail jayne@yourtowncrier.com; web site www.HomeNewsHere.com
Circulation: 6,000pd, 500fr; Sworn/Estimate/Non-Audited
Advertising rate: Open inch rate $13.50
Established: 1955
Group: Daily Times Chronicle
Pub...Peter Haggarty
Office Mgr. ....Joel Haggerty
Mng. Ed...Stu Neilson
News Editor ....Jayne Miller
Advertising Rep ....Bruce Hilliard
Mechanical Specifications: Type page 11 x 21; E - 6 cols, 2 1/16, between; A - 6 cols, 2 1/16, between; C - 6 cols, 2 1/16, between. Equipment & Software: Hardware — APP/Mac; Software — Quark 7.0
Delivery Method: Mail, Newsstand, Carrier, Racks
Areas Served: 01887, 01876

WORCESTER

MILLBURY-SUTTON CHRONICLE (THUR)
101 Water St, Worcester, MA, 01604-5033, Worcester, USA; gen tel (508) 749-3164; adv tel (508) 749-3164; ed tel (508) 749-3164; gen fax (508) 865-7979; adv fax (508) 865-7979; ed fax (508) 865-7979; disp adv e-mail sales@millburysutton.com; class adv e-mail sales@centralmassclass.com; ed e-mail editor@millburysutton.com; web site www.millburysutton.com
Advertising rate: Open inch rate $6.54
Digital Platform - Mobile: Apple
Digital Platform - Tablet: Apple iOS
Ed. .... Joshua Farnsworth
Ad. Exec.................................... Rebecca White
Delivery Method: Mail, Newsstand
Areas Served: Worcester County

WORCESTER BUSINESS JOURNAL (MON)
172 Shrewsbury St, Ste 2, Worcester, MA, 01604-4636, Worcester, USA; gen tel (508) 755-8004; gen fax (508) 755-8860; disp adv e-mail bleroux@wbjournal.com; ed e-mail Rsaia@wbjournal.com; web site wbjournal.com
Circulation: 929pd, 8,353fr; VAC
Advertising rate: 1/4 P $855 1/2 P $1,315 Full $2,250
Established: 1990
Group: New England Business Media
Ed. .... Rick Saia
Delivery Method: Mail, Newsstand
Areas Served: Worcester County, Massachusetts

YARMOUTH PORT

SANDWICH BROADSIDER (WED)
923 Route 6A, Unit G, Yarmouth Port, MA, 02675-2159, USA; gen tel (508) 375-4947; adv tel (508) 375-4928 ; ed tel (508) 375-4945; gen fax (508) 375-4903; adv fax (508) 375-4903; ed fax (508) 375-4903; class adv e-mail salesteam@wickedlocal.com; ed e-mail jbasile@wickedlocal.com; web site www.wickedlocal.com/sandwich
Circulation: 2,332pd,; Sworn/Estimate/Non-Audited
Advertising rate: 14.25
Established: 2007
Group: Community Newspaper Co. - South GateHouse Media, Inc.
Senior Managing Ed. .... Carol Dumas
Adv. Dir.. Nick Bolitho

THE BULLETIN (THUR)
923 Route 6A, Unit G, Yarmouth Port, MA, 02675-2159, Barnstable, USA; gen tel (508) 888-0000; adv tel (508) 888-0000; ed tel (508) 888-0000; gen fax (508) 375-4903; adv fax (508) 375-4903; ed fax (508) 375-4903; disp adv e-mail salesteam@wickedlocal.com; class adv e-mail salesteam@wickedlocal.com; ed e-mail jbasile@wickedlocal.com; web site www.wickedlocal.com/falmouth
Circulation: 6,525pd,; Sworn/Estimate/Non-Audited
Advertising rate: Open inch rate $20.90
Established: 2007
Group: GateHouse Media, Inc.
Pub.. Mark Olivieri
Ed. .... John Basile
Adv. Dir.. Nick Bolitho
Areas Served: Falmouth, Mashpee (MA)

MICHIGAN

ALBION

ALBION RECORDER (THUR)
125 E Cass St, Albion, MI, 49224-1726, Calhoun, USA; gen tel (517) 629-0041; gen fax (517) 629-5210; disp adv e-mail therecorder@frontiernet.net
Circulation: 1,100pd,; Sworn/Estimate/Non-Audited
Advertising rate: Open inch rate $8.24
Adv. Mgr., Ed.................................. Kathy Palon
Mgr., Adv. Consultant.................. Kara DeChalk
Mechanical Specifications: Type page 13 3/4 x 22; E - 6 cols, 2 1/16, 1/8 between; A - 6 cols, 2 1/16, 1/8 between; C - 6 cols, 2 1/16, 1/8 between.Equipment & Software: Hardware — APP/Mac, APP/Mac Plus, 2-COM/4961, 1-COM/7200, 1-COM/Comp 4; Software — KE/512, QPS/QuarkXPress 3.1.
Delivery Method: Mail, Newsstand
Areas Served: Albion MI, Calhoun County 49224, Concord MI, Jackson County 49237, Springport MI, Jackson County 49284

ALLEGAN

ALLEGAN COUNTY NEWS (THUR)
241 Hubbard St, Allegan, MI, 49010-1320, Allegan, USA; gen tel (269) 673-5534; adv tel (269) 673-5534; ed tel (269) 673-5534; gen fax (269) 673-5535; adv fax (269) 673-5535; ed fax (269) 673-5535; disp adv e-mail accountsrec@allegannews.com; class adv e-mail accountsrec@allegannews.com; ed e-mail editor@allegannews.com; web site www.allegannews.com
Circulation: 3,361pd, 83fr; Sworn/Estimate/Non-Audited
Advertising rate: Open inch rate $11.68
Established: 1858
Group: Kaechele Publications, Inc.
Ed. .... Ryan Lewis
Publisher, owner.......................... Mike Wilcox
Mechanical Specifications: Full page image size 10.5" x 21 1/2"; 6 cols, 1.646", 1/8 between. Equipment & Software: Hardware — APP/Mac; Software — Microsoft/Word 11.5.6, Adobe/Photoshop 11.0.2, QPS/QuarkXPress 9.3.
Delivery Method: Mail, Newsstand
Areas Served: All Allegan County

UNION ENTERPRISE (MON)
231 Trowbridge St, Ste 17, Allegan, MI, 49010-1330, Allegan, USA; gen tel (269) 673-5534; adv tel (269) 673-5534; ed tel (269) 673-5534; gen fax (269) 673-5535; adv fax (269) 673-5535; ed fax (269) 673-5535; disp adv e-mail publisher@allegannews.com; class adv e-mail advertising@allegannews.com; ed e-mail editor@allegannews.com; web site allegannews.com
Circulation: 519pd, 35fr; USPS
Advertising rate: Open inch rate $8.86
Established: 1871
Group: Kaechele Publications, Inc.
Pub.................................... Cheryl A. Kaechele
Ed. .... Ryan Lewis
Mechanical Specifications: Full page image size 10.5" X 16"; 6 cols, 1.646", 1/8 between columnsEquipment & Software: Hardware — APP/Mac; Software — Microsoft/Word 11.5.6, Adobe/Photoshop 11.0.2, QPS/QuarkXPress 9.3
Delivery Method: Mail
Areas Served: 49080, 49078

ANN ARBOR

ANN ARBOR OBSERVER (MTHLY)
2390 Winewood Ave, Ann Arbor, MI, 48103-3841, Washtenaw, USA; gen tel (734) 769-3175; gen fax (734) 769-3375; disp adv e-mail ads@aaobserver.com; class adv e-mail adsales@aaobserver.com; ed e-mail editor@aaobserver.com; web site www.aaobserver.com - 500,000(views)
Circulation: 2,125pd, 28,534fr; CAC
Established: 1976
Creative Director.......... Caron Valentine-Marsh
Delivery Method: Mail
Areas Served: Ann Arbor zip codes and school district

THE ANN ARBOR NEWS (THUR, SUN)
111 N Ashley St, Ste 100, Ann Arbor, MI, 48104-1307, Washtenaw, USA; gen tel (734) 623-2500; adv tel (900) 878-1400; ed tel (734) 623-2500; disp adv e-mail advertise@mlive.com; class adv e-mail advertise@mlive.com; ed e-mail annarbornews@mlive.com; web site www.mlive.com/ann-arbor
Circulation: 20,030pd, 2,407fr; AAM
Advertising rate: Open inch rate $33.39 Daily/$41.54 Sunday
Established: 2009
Group: Advance Publications, Inc.
Digital Platform - Mobile: Apple, Android
Digital Platform - Tablet: Apple iOS, Android
Mktg. Analyst .... Meyer Erin
Mechanical Specifications: Type page 11 5/8 x 22; E - 6 cols, 2 1/16, 1/8 between; A - 6 cols, 2 1/16, 1/8 between; C - 10 cols, 1 1/4, 1/16 between.
Delivery Method: Mail, Newsstand, Carrier, Racks
Areas Served: 48103 through 49287

THE CURRENT (WED)
3003 Washtenaw Ave, Ste 3, Ann Arbor, MI, 48104-5107, Ann Arbor, USA; gen tel (734) 668-4044; gen fax (734) 668-0555; disp adv e-mail a2sales@adamsstreetpublishing.com; class adv e-mail sales@adamsstreetpublishing.com; ed e-mail cjacobs@toledocitypaper.com; web site http://www.ecurrent.com/contact/
Circulation: 1,500pd, 150fr; Sworn/Estimate/Non-Audited
Advertising rate: Open inch rate $3.85
Pub.. Bob Wurzer
Ed. .... Patricia Pollard
Adv. Mgr.................................... Vicki Underhill
Comp. Mgr.Elaine ThomEquipment & Software: ; Software — QPS/QuarkXPress.

ATLANTA

THE MONTMORENCY COUNTY TRIBUNE (WED)
12625 State St., Atlanta, MI, 49709, Montmorency, USA; gen tel (989) 785-4214; gen fax (989) 785-3118; disp adv e-mail office@montmorencytribune.com; class adv e-mail office@montmorencytribune.com; ed e-mail editor@montmorencytribune.com; web site www.montmorencytribune.com
Circulation: 5,200pd,; Sworn/Estimate/Non-Audited
Advertising rate: Open inch rate $6.75
Established: 1886
Ed. .... James Young
Mechanical Specifications: Type page 10 1/4 x 16; E - 6 cols, 1 1/2, 1/6 between; A - 6 cols, 1 1/2, 1/6 between; C - 6 cols, 1 1/2, 1/6 between.Equipment & Software: Hardware — IBM; Presses — G/Community; Software — Adobe/PageMaker 7.0.
Delivery Method: Mail, Newsstand

BAD AXE

HURON COUNTY VIEW (THUR)
592 N Port Crescent St, Bad Axe, MI, 48413-1209, Huron, USA; gen tel (989) 269-9918; gen fax (989) 269-7730; disp adv e-mail info@mihomepaper.com; class adv e-mail sales@mihomepaper.com; ed e-mail jbonke@mihomepaper.com; web site www.huroncountyview.com
Circulation: 18,483fr; Sworn/Estimate/Non-Audited
Advertising rate: Modular format rate equivalent $14.50 pci
Established: 1980
Group: JAMS Media
Digital Platform - Mobile: Apple
Digital Platform - Tablet: Apple iOS
Pub....................................... Jane Vanderpoel
Mechanical Specifications: Tabloid Size: 9.5"X10" in four column formatEquipment & Software: Hardware — APP/Mac; Software — Adobe/PageMaker, QuarkX, InDesign
Delivery Method: Mail
Areas Served: 48413, 48441, 48432, 48445, 48467, 48468, 48470, 48475, 48720, 48725, 48731, 48735, 48754, 48755, 48759, 48767

BALDWIN

LAKE COUNTY STAR (THUR)
851 Michigan Ave, Baldwin, MI, 49304-8140, Lake, USA; gen tel (231) 745-4635; gen fax (231) 745-7733; disp adv e-mail lcstar@pioneergroup.com; class adv e-mail starclass@pioneergroup.com; ed e-mail lcstar@pioneergroup.com ; web site lakecountystar.com
Circulation: 2,976pd,; Sworn/Estimate/Non-Audited
Advertising rate: Open inch rate $13.00
Established: 1873
Group: Pioneer Group
Pub.. John S. Norton
Prod. Mgr. .... Kym Roldan
Mechanical Specifications: Type page 10 x 16; E - 5 cols, 2, between; A - 5 cols, 2, between; C - 5 cols, 2, between.
Delivery Method: Mail
Areas Served: 49304, 49309, 49402, 49623, 49642, 49644, 49656

BAY CITY

THE VALLEY FARMER (THUR)
410 Raymond St, Bay City, MI, 48706-4377, Bay, USA; gen tel (989) 893-6507; gen fax (989) 893-6507; disp adv e-mail dbhebert1@charter.net
Circulation: 600pd, 20fr; USPS
Advertising rate: Open inch rate $4.40
Established: 1929
Digital Platform - Mobile: Windows
Pub.. David Hebert
Mechanical Specifications: Type page 10 1/2 x 15; E - 6 cols, 1 7/12, 1/8 between.
Delivery Method: Mail
Areas Served: eastern central michigan & thumb

BELLEVILLE

BELLEVILLE-AREA INDEPENDENT (THUR)
152 Main St, Ste 9, Belleville, MI, 48111-3911, Wayne, USA; gen tel (734) 699-9020; gen fax (734) 699-8962; disp adv e-mail mail@bellevilleareaindependent.com; web site www.bellevilleareaindependent.com
Circulation: 342pd, 6,600fr; Sworn/Estimate/Non-Audited
Advertising rate: Open inch rate $12
Established: 1995
Digital Platform - Mobile: Blackberry
Adv. Mgr.................................... Robert Mytych
PUB. .... Rosemary K. Otzman
Prodn. Mgr. .... James Otzman
Janet Millard
Mechanical Specifications: Type page 10 x 12 3/4; E - 4 cols, 2 3/8, 3/8 between; A - 4 cols, 2 3/8, 3/8 between; C - 4 cols, 2 3/8, 3/8 between.Equipment & Software: Hardware — APP/Mac; Software — QPS/QuarkXPress 6.0, Adobe/Photoshop 7.0, Adobe/InDesign 2.0, Adobe/Acrobat 6.0, Page Maker 7.0.
Delivery Method: Mail, Racks
Areas Served: 48111

THE BELLEVILLE ENTERPRISE (THUR)
152 Main St Ste 9, Suite 9, Belleville, MI, 48111-3911, Wayne, USA; gen tel (734) 699-9020; gen fax (734) 699-8962; disp adv

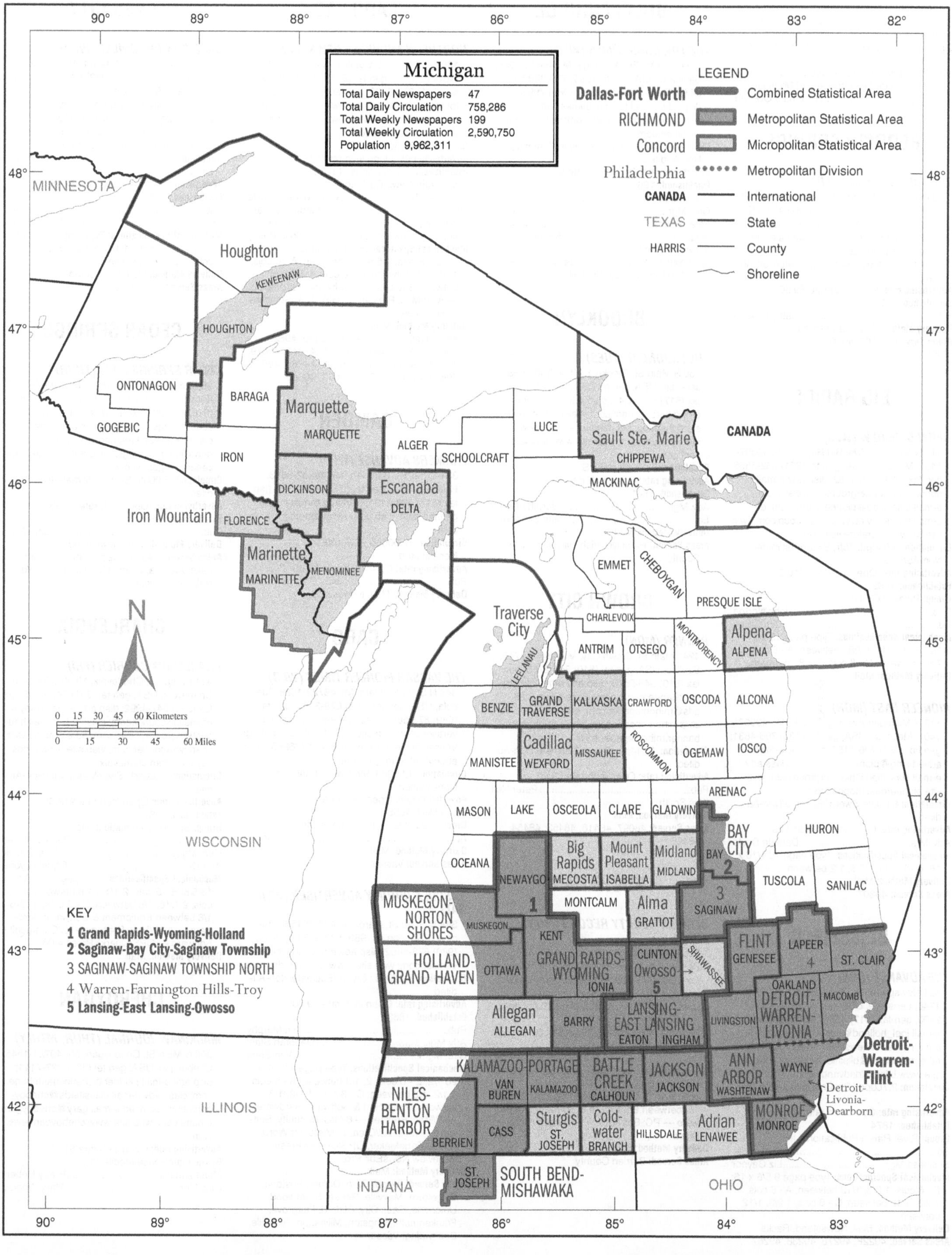
Michigan
Total Daily Newspapers 47
Total Daily Circulation 758,286
Total Weekly Newspapers 199
Total Weekly Circulation 2,590,750
Population 9,962,311
LEGEND
Dallas-Fort Worth Combined Statistical Area
RICHMOND Metropolitan Statistical Area
Concord Micropolitan Statistical Area
Philadelphia Metropolitan Division
CANADA International
TEXAS State
HARRIS County
Shoreline
KEY
1 Grand Rapids-Wyoming-Holland
2 Saginaw-Bay City-Saginaw Township
3 SAGINAW-SAGINAW TOWNSHIP NORTH
4 Warren-Farmington Hills-Troy
5 Lansing-East Lansing-Owosso
0 15 30 45 60 Kilometers
0 15 30 45 60 Miles
N
MINNESOTA
WISCONSIN
ILLINOIS
INDIANA
OHIO
CANADA
Houghton
KEWEENAW
HOUGHTON
ONTONAGON
BARAGA
GOGEBIC
IRON
Marquette
MARQUETTE
ALGER
SCHOOLCRAFT
LUCE
Sault Ste. Marie
CHIPPEWA
MACKINAC
DICKINSON
Escanaba
DELTA
Iron Mountain
FLORENCE
Marinette
MARINETTE
MENOMINEE
EMMET
CHEBOYGAN
PRESQUE ISLE
Traverse City
CHARLEVOIX
ANTRIM
OTSEGO
MONTMORENCY
Alpena
ALPENA
LEELANAU
BENZIE
GRAND TRAVERSE
KALKASKA
CRAWFORD
OSCODA
ALCONA
Cadillac
WEXFORD
MISSAUKEE
MANISTEE
ROSCOMMON
OGEMAW
IOSCO
ARENAC
MASON
LAKE
OSCEOLA
CLARE
GLADWIN
BAY CITY
BAY
HURON
OCEANA
NEWAYGO
Big Rapids
MECOSTA
Mount Pleasant
ISABELLA
Midland
MIDLAND
TUSCOLA
SANILAC
SAGINAW
MUSKEGON-NORTON SHORES
MUSKEGON
MONTCALM
Alma
GRATIOT
KENT
FLINT
GENESEE
LAPEER
ST. CLAIR
HOLLAND-GRAND HAVEN
OTTAWA
GRAND RAPIDS-WYOMING
IONIA
CLINTON
Owosso
SHIAWASSEE
OAKLAND
DETROIT-WARREN-LIVONIA
MACOMB
Allegan
ALLEGAN
BARRY
LANSING-EAST LANSING
EATON
INGHAM
LIVINGSTON
Detroit-Warren-Flint
KALAMAZOO-PORTAGE
VAN BUREN
KALAMAZOO
BATTLE CREEK
CALHOUN
JACKSON
ANN ARBOR
WASHTENAW
WAYNE
Detroit-Livonia-Dearborn
NILES-BENTON HARBOR
BERRIEN
CASS
Sturgis
ST. JOSEPH
Coldwater
BRANCH
HILLSDALE
Adrian
LENAWEE
MONROE
SOUTH BEND-MISHAWAKA
90°
89°
88°
87°
86°
85°
84°
83°
82°
48°
47°
46°
45°
44°
43°
42°

e-mail mail@bellevilleareaindependent.com; ed e-mail rotzman@ameritech.net; web site http://bellevilleareaindependent.com/
Circulation: 1,900pd,; Sworn/Estimate/Non-Audited
Advertising rate: Open inch rate $10.60
Group: Associated Newspapers of Michigan
Ed. .... Rosemary Otzman

BERRIEN SPRINGS

THE JOURNAL ERA (WED)

101 W Ferry St, Berrien Springs, MI, 49103-1154, Berrien, USA; gen tel (269) 473-5421; adv tel (269) 473-1533; gen fax (269) 471-1362; disp adv e-mail thejournalera@yahoo.com; web site thejournalera.com
Circulation: 2,000pd,; Sworn/Estimate/Non-Audited
Advertising rate: Open inch rate $9.50
Established: 1874
Ed. .... Kathy Pullano
Delivery Method: Mail, Newsstand
Areas Served: 49103, 49102, 49022, 49127, 49085, 49111

BIG RAPIDS

HERALD REVIEW (WED)

115 N Michigan Ave, Big Rapids, MI, 49307-1401, Mecosta, USA; gen tel (231) 832-5566; gen fax (231) 796-1152; disp adv e-mail bbriscoe@pioneergroup.com; class adv e-mail classified@pioneergroup.com; ed e-mail heraldreview@pioneergroup.com; web site www.theheraldreview.com
Circulation: 3,500pd, 15fr; Sworn/Estimate/Non-Audited
Advertising rate: Open inch rate $10.00
Established: 1862
Group: Pioneer Group
Pub. .... John Norton
Ed. .... Jim Crees
Mechanical Specifications: Type page 12 x 21 1/2; E - 6 cols, 1 7/8, between; A - 6 cols, 1 7/8, between; C - 6 cols, 1 7/8, between.
Delivery Method: Mail

PIONEER EAST (MON)

115 N Michigan Ave, Big Rapids, MI, 49307-1401, Mecosta, USA; gen tel (231) 796-4831; gen fax (231) 796-1152; disp adv e-mail advertising@pioneergroup.com; class adv e-mail classified@pioneergroup.com; web site pioneereastshopper.com
Circulation: 8,000fr; Sworn/Estimate/Non-Audited
Advertising rate: Open inch rate $13.25
Adv. Mgr. .... Danette Doyle
Mechanical Specifications: Type page 10 1/16 x 16; A - 7 cols, 1 3/8, 1/2 between.
Delivery Method: Mail
Areas Served: 49307

BLISSFIELD

THE ADVANCE (SUN)

121 Newspaper St, Blissfield, MI, 49228-1248, Lenawee, USA; gen tel (517) 486-2400; gen fax (517) 486-4675; disp adv e-mail joel_holland@mlive.com; class adv e-mail advancenewsclassified@mlive.com; ed e-mail news@blissfieldadvance.com; web site www.blissfieldadvance.com
Circulation: 2,700pd,; Sworn/Estimate/Non-Audited
Advertising rate: Open inch rate $74.63
Established: 1874
Group: River Raisin Publications, Inc.
Ed. .... Marcia Loader
Business Mgr. .... Liz Gaynor
Mechanical Specifications: Type page 6 5/6 x 16; E - 6 cols, 1 2/3, 1/12 between; A - 6 cols, 1 2/3, 1/12 between; C - 6 cols, 1 2/3, 1/12 between.
Delivery Method: Mail, Newsstand, Racks
Areas Served: 49228, 49276, 49238, 49267

BRECKENRIDGE

THE TOWNSHIP TIMES (WED)

PO Box 396, Breckenridge, MI, 48615-0396, Saginaw, USA; gen tel (989) 799-3200; adv tel (989) 842-3164; gen fax (989) 799-7085; disp adv e-mail tari@twptimes.com; ed e-mail nicole@twptimes.com; web site www.twptimes.com
Circulation: 4,360pd, 293fr; Sworn/Estimate/Non-Audited
Advertising rate: Open inch rate $8.50
Established: 1964
Pub. .... Ed Belles
Gen. Mgr. .... Lisa Guthrie
Sales Assoc. .... Tari Newvine
Mng. Ed. .... Nicole Wagner
Delivery Method: Mail, Racks
Areas Served: Saginaw, Thomas, James, Richland, Tittabawassee, Kochville

BROOKLYN

THE EXPONENT (TUES)

160 S Main St, Brooklyn, MI, 49230-8588, Jackson, USA; gen tel (517) 592-2122; gen fax (517) 592-3241; disp adv e-mail dorothy@theexponent.com; class adv e-mail sell@theexponent.com; ed e-mail news@theexponent.com; web site www.theexponent.com
Circulation: 5,000pd,; USPS
Advertising rate: Open inch rate $7.25
Established: 1881
Adv. Mgr. .... Dorothy Booth
Ed. .... Matt Schepeler
Delivery Method: Mail
Areas Served: Brooklyn, Irish Hills and Jackson County

BROWN CITY

BANNER (MON)

4241 Main St, Brown City, MI, 48416-7715, Sanilac, USA; gen tel (810) 346-2753; gen fax (810) 346-2579; disp adv e-mail bcbanner@lapeergroup.com; class adv e-mail ads@mihomepaper.com; ed e-mail lettersbcb@mihomepaper.com; web site browncitybanner.mihomepaper.com
Circulation: 1,814pd,; Sworn/Estimate/Non-Audited
Advertising rate: Open inch rate $9.40
Pub. .... Peter Neil
Wes Smith
Delivery Method: Mail
Areas Served: 48097, 48416, 48453, 48454, 48466

BUCHANAN

BERRIEN COUNTY RECORD (MON, THUR)

206 Main St, Buchanan, MI, 49107-1376, Berrien, USA; gen tel (269) 695-3878; gen fax (269) 695-3880; ed e-mail bcrnews@bcrnews.net; web site www.bcrnews.net
Circulation: 2,600pd, 176fr; Sworn/Estimate/Non-Audited
Advertising rate: Open inch rate $5.50
Established: 1865
Pub. .... Dean Henricksen
Mechanical Specifications: Type page 13 x 21 1/2; E - 6 cols, 2 1/16, 1/4 between; A - 6 cols, 2 1/16, 1/4 between; C - 6 cols, 2 1/16, 1/4 between.Equipment & Software: Hardware — PC; Software — Archetype/Corel Draw.
Delivery Method: Mail
Areas Served: Berrien County

CADILLAC

NORTHERN MICHIGAN NEWS (MON)

130 N Mitchell St, Cadillac, MI, 49601-1856, Wexford, USA; gen tel (231) 775-6565; gen fax (231) 775-8790; disp adv e-mail customerservice@cadillacnews.com; class adv e-mail jbailey@cadillacnews.com; web site www.cadillacnews.com
Circulation: 28,500fr; USPS
Advertising rate: Open inch rate $18.25
Established: 1872Editions: (3) 3 total - Northern Michigan News-Cadillac;
Pub./Gen. Mgr. .... Christopher Huckle
Mng. Ed. .... Matthew Seward
Prodn. Mgr. .... Ken Koch
Sales and Marketing Leader .... Josh Bailey
Mechanical Specifications: Type page 11 5/8 x 22; E - 6 cols, 1 5/6, 1/8 between; A - 6 cols, 1 5/6, 1/8 between; C - 6 cols, 1 5/6, 1/8 between.Equipment & Software: Hardware — APP/Mac; Presses — HI/V-15A; Software — Baseview.
Delivery Method: Mail
Areas Served: 49601, 49618, 49620, 49623, 49631, 49632, 49638, 49639, 47642, 49679, 47651, 49655, 49656, 49663, 49665, 49657, 49667, 49668, 49338, 49677, 49688

CAMDEN

FARMERS ADVANCE (WED)

331 E Bell St, Camden, MI, 49232-9613, Hillsdale, USA; gen tel (517) 368-0365; gen fax (517) 368-5131; disp adv e-mail jhite@gannett.com; web site www.farmersadvance.com
Circulation: 12,000pd,; Sworn/Estimate/Non-Audited
Advertising rate: Open inch rate $9.60
Pub. .... Cindy George-Bealer
Delivery Method: Mail, Newsstand

CARO

THE VASSAR PIONEER TIMES (WED)

344 N State St, Caro, MI, 48723-1538, Tuscola, USA; gen tel (989) 678-3181; gen fax (989) 673-5662; disp adv e-mail ads@tcadvertiser.com; web site www.facebook.com/pg/Vassar-Pioneer-Times-106721472696367/about/?ref=page_internal
Circulation: 1,500pd, 9fr; Sworn/Estimate/Non-Audited
Advertising rate: Open inch rate $6.50
Established: 1856
Group: Hearst Communications, Inc.
Adv. .... Tim Murphy
Delivery Method: Mail
Areas Served: Vassar

TUSCOLA COUNTY ADVERTISER (WED, SAT)

344 N State St, Caro, MI, 48723-1538, Tuscola, USA; gen tel (989) 673-3181; gen fax (989) 673-5662; disp adv e-mail ads@tcadvertiser.com; web site www.tuscolatoday.com
Circulation: 8,220pd,; Sworn/Estimate/Non-Audited
Advertising rate: Open inch rate $9.00
Established: 1868
Pub. .... Tim Murphy
Adv Mgr. .... Deborah Stahl
Circ. Mgr. .... Ven Stark
Mechanical Specifications: Type page 11 1/2 x 20 1/2; E - 6 cols, 2, 1/3 between; A - 8 cols, 1 1/2, 1/3 between; C - 8 cols, 1 1/2, 1/3 between.Equipment & Software: Hardware — APP/Mac; Presses — 6-G/Community; Software — Multi-Ad/Creator, Microsoft/Word, Adobe/PageMaker, QPS/QuarkXPress, Baseview NewsEdit Pro.
Delivery Method: Mail
Areas Served: Akron, Caro, Deford, Fostoria, Gagetown, Mayville, Reese, Silverwood, Unionville, Cass City, Clifford, Fairgrove, Frankenmuth, Kingston, Millington, Richville, Sebewaing, Vassar

CASS CITY

CASS CITY CHRONICLE (WED)

6550 Main St, Cass City, MI, 48726-1561, Tuscola, USA; gen tel (989) 872-2010; gen fax (989) 872-3810; disp adv e-mail chronicle@cass-city.net; class adv e-mail sales@cchronicle.net; ed e-mail tom@cchronicle.net; web site www.facebook.com/pg/casscity-chronicle/about/?ref=page_internal
Circulation: 3,600pd,; Sworn/Estimate/Non-Audited
Advertising rate: Open inch rate $4.95
Established: 1899
Pub. .... Clarke Haire
Ed. .... Tom Montgomery
Mechanical Specifications: Type page 13 3/4 x 21 1/4; E - 8 cols, 1 1/2, 1/4 between; C - 8 cols, 1 1/2, 1/4 between.
Delivery Method: Mail, Newsstand
Areas Served: Cass City

CEDAR SPRINGS

CEDAR SPRINGS POST (THUR)

36 E Maple, Cedar Springs, MI, 49319-5143, Kent, USA; gen tel (616) 696-3655; gen fax (616) 696-9010; disp adv e-mail news@cedarspringspost.com; class adv e-mail classifieds@cedarspringspost.com; ed e-mail news@cedarspringspost.com; web site www.cedarspringspost.com
Circulation: 5,000fr; Sworn/Estimate/Non-Audited
Advertising rate: Open inch rate $7.95
Established: 1988
Pub. .... Lois Allen
Delivery Method: Mail, Newsstand
Areas Served: 49319 - Cedar Springs, Sand Lake, Algoma, Solon, Courtland/Oakfield, Nelson, Spencer

CHARLEVOIX

CHARLEVOIX COURIER (FRI)

411 Bridge St, Charlevoix, MI, 49720-1416, Charlevoix, USA; gen tel (231) 547-6558; gen fax (231) 547-4992; disp adv e-mail jfoley@charlevoixcourier.com; class adv e-mail haugust@petoskeynews.com; ed e-mail news@charlevoixcourier.com; web site www.petoskeynews.com/charlevoix
Circulation: 3,500pd,; Sworn/Estimate/Non-Audited
Advertising rate: Open inch rate $13.68
Established: 1883
Group: Schurz Communications Inc
Pub. .... Doug Caldwell
Gen. Mgr. .... Lisa Sladek
Adv. Dir. .... Christy Lyons
Mechanical Specifications: Type page 10 13/16 x 13 5/8; E - 5 cols, 2 1/16, 1/8 between; A - 5 cols, 2 1/16, 1/8 between; C - 5 cols, 2 1/16, 1/8 between.Equipment & Software: Hardware — APP/Mac; Presses — G/Community; Software — QPS/QuarkXPress 4.03.
Delivery Method: Mail

CHEBOYGAN

MACKINAW JOURNAL (THUR, MTHLY)

308 N Main St, Cheboygan, MI, 49721-1545, Cheboygan, USA; gen tel (231) 627-7144; disp adv e-mail nkidder@cheboygantribune.com; class adv e-mail classifieds@cheboygantribune.com; ed e-mail gary@cheboygantribune.com; web site www.cheboygannews.com
Advertising rate: Open inch rate $11.50
Group: GateHouse Media, Inc.
Managing Ed. .... Brady Hebert
Circ. Mgr. .... Mary Whaley

CHESANING

TOWNSHIP VIEW (THUR)

110 S Chapman St, Chesaning, MI, 48616-1221, Saginaw, USA; gen tel (989) 393-4100; gen fax (989) 845-4397; adv fax ; disp adv e-mail jvanderpoel@mihomepaper.com; class adv e-mail jvanderpoel@mihomepaper.com; ed e-mail jvanderpoel@mihomepaper.com; web site http://townshipview.mihomepaper.com/
Circulation: 20,268fr; CVC
Advertising rate: Modular Full Page $685
Established: 2010
Group: View Newspaper Group
Digital Platform - Mobile: Apple, Android, Windows, Blackberry
Digital Platform - Tablet: Apple iOS, Android, Windows 7, Blackberry Tablet OS
Pub./Ed. .... Wes Smith
General Manager .... Jane Vanderpoel
Mechanical Specifications: Type page 9.75" x 10"; 4 cols
Delivery Method: Mail, Racks
Areas Served: 48602, 48603, 48638, 48609

CLARE

THE CLARE COUNTY REVIEW (FRI)

2141 E Ludington Dr, Clare, MI, 48617-8801, Clare, USA; gen tel (989) 386-4414; gen fax (989) 386-2412; disp adv e-mail info@clarecountyreview.com; class adv e-mail info@clarecountyreview.com; ed e-mail info@clarecountyreview.com; web site www.clarecountyreview.com
Circulation: 473pd, 9,557fr; Sworn/Estimate/Non-Audited
Advertising rate: Open inch rate $10.75
Established: 1947
Owner/Pub. .... Patricia Maurer
Mechanical Specifications: Type page 11 1/2 x 21; E - 6 cols, 1 3/4, between; A - 6 cols, 1 3/4, between; C - 8 cols, 1 3/16, between. Equipment & Software: Hardware — 5-IBM; Software — Microsoft/Word, Adobe/Photoshop 5.5, Adobe/Pagemaker, Adobe/Illustrator.
Areas Served: 48617, 48622, 48625, 48878, 48632

CLARKSTON

CLARKSTON NEWS (WED)

5 S Main St, Ste 1, Clarkston, MI, 48346-1597, Oakland, USA; gen tel (248) 625-3370; adv tel (248) 625-3370; ed tel (248) 625-3370; gen fax (248) 625-0706; disp adv e-mail shermanpub@aol.com; ed e-mail clarkstonnews@gmail.com; web site www.clarkstonnews.com
Circulation: 2,910pd, 0fr; Sworn/Estimate/Non-Audited
Advertising rate: Open inch rate $14.64
Established: 1929
Group: Sherman Publications, Inc.
Pub. .... James A. Sherman
Gen. Mgr. .... Don Rush
Ed. .... Phil Custodio
Mechanical Specifications: Type page 10 x 11; E - 8 cols, 3 1/5, 1/5 between; A - 6 cols, 1 8/15, 1/5 between; C - 6 cols, 1 8/15, 1/5 between.Equipment & Software: Hardware — PC; Presses — G/Community; Software — Microsoft/Windows, Adobe/PageMaker 6.5.
Delivery Method: Mail
Areas Served: 48346, 48348, 48350, 48347

CLIMAX

THE CLIMAX CRESCENT (FRI)

150 N Main St, Climax, MI, 49034-9637, Kalamazoo, USA; gen tel (269) 746-4331; disp adv e-mail scribe@ctsmail.net; web site www.theclimaxcrescent.com
Circulation: 1,050pd,; Sworn/Estimate/Non-Audited
Advertising rate: Open inch rate $3.50
Established: 1912
Ed. .... Bruce Rolfe
Delivery Method: Mail, Newsstand

CLINTON

THE CLINTON LOCAL (WED)

108 Tecumseh Rd, Clinton, MI, 49236-9507, Lenawee, USA; gen tel (517) 456-4100; adv tel (517) 456-4100; ed tel (517) 442-8616; gen fax (517) 456-4100; adv fax (517) 456-4100; class adv e-mail localcokelady@comcast.net; web site www.theclintonlocal.com
Circulation: 1,500pd,; USPS
Advertising rate: Open inch rate $3.50
Established: 1884
Group: The Clinton LocalEditions: (78,000)
Digital Platform - Mobile: Apple, Windows
Ed. .... Maryann Habrick
Mechanical Specifications: 10" wide x 16" deep-Equipment & Software: ; Presses — Not printed here
Delivery Method: Mail, Newsstand, Racks
Areas Served: 49236, 49286, 49287, 48158, 49221, numerous out of area by subscription

CLINTON TOWNSHIP

BLUE WATER VOICE (WED)

19176 Hall Rd, Ste 200, Clinton Township, MI, 48038-6914, Macomb, USA; gen tel (586) 716-8100; gen fax (586) 719-8918; disp adv e-mail dawn.emke@voicenews.com; class adv e-mail classified.voice@voicenews.com; ed e-mail editor@voicenews.com ; web site www.voicenews.com
Circulation: 40pd, 9,697fr; Sworn/Estimate/Non-Audited
Advertising rate: Open inch rate $14.35
Established: 1983
Group: Digital First Media
Gen. Mgr. .... Debbie Loggins
Ed. .... Jeff Payne
VP .... Don Wyatt
Mechanical Specifications: Type page 10 x 15; E - 5 cols, 1 15/16, 1/8 between; A - 5 cols, 1 15/16, 1/8 between; C - 6 cols, 1 7/10, 1/8 between.Equipment & Software: Hardware — APP/Mac G4, PC; Presses — G/Community; Software — Adobe/PageMaker.
Delivery Method: Mail, Newsstand, Carrier, Racks
Areas Served: Northern Macomb & Southern St. Clair counties

DOWNRIVER VOICE (WED)

19176 Hall Rd, Ste 200, Clinton Township, MI, 48038-6914, Macomb, USA; gen tel (586) 716-8100; gen fax (586) 716-8918; disp adv e-mail debbie.loggins@voicenews.com; class adv e-mail classified.voice@voicenews.com; ed e-mail editor@voicenews.com; web site www.voicenews.com
Circulation: 9,234fr; Sworn/Estimate/Non-Audited
Advertising rate: Open inch rate $13.12
Established: 1983
Gen. Mgr. .... Debra Loggins
Ed. .... Jeff Payne
Circ. Mgr. .... Rene Allard
Mechanical Specifications: Type page 10 x 15; E - 5 cols, 1 15/16, 1/8 between; A - 5 cols, 1 15/16, 1/8 between; C - 6 cols, 1 7/10, 1/8 between.Equipment & Software: Hardware — APP/Mac G4, PC; Presses — G/Community; Software — Adobe/PageMaker.
Delivery Method: Mail, Newsstand, Carrier, Racks
Areas Served: Northern Macomb & Southern St. Clair Counties

THE ADVISOR & SOURCE (SUN)

19176 Hall Rd, Ste 200, Clinton Township, MI, 48038-6914, Macomb, USA; gen tel (586) 716-8100; adv tel (586) 716-8107 ext.600; gen fax (586) 716-8533; disp adv e-mail ads@advisorsource.com; class adv e-mail nklomp@21st-centurymedia.com; ed e-mail jody.mcveigh@advisorsource.com; web site www.sourcenewspapers.com
Circulation: 115,389fr; CAC
Advertising rate: Open inch rate $39.35Editions: (3) 3 total; The Advisor-Mt. Clemens/Macomb/Clinton; The Advisor-Roseville/Eastpointe/St. Clair Shores; The Advisor - Warren/Center Line;
Ed. .... Lena Khzouz
Mechanical Specifications: Type page 13 x 21 1/2; E - 6 cols, 2 1/16, 1/8 between; A - 6 cols, 2 1/16, 1/8 between; C - 10 cols, 1 7/32, 1/8 between.Equipment & Software: Hardware — APP/Mac; Presses — G/Cosmo; Software — Multi-Ad, QPS/QuarkXPress.

THE ARMADA TIMES (WED)

19176 Hall Rd, Ste 200, Clinton Township, MI, 48038-6914, Macomb, USA; gen tel (586) 716-8100; adv tel (800) 561-2248; gen fax (586) 716-8918; adv fax (586) 716-8533; disp adv e-mail debbie.loggins@voicenews.com; class adv e-mail classified.voice@voicenews.com; ed e-mail editor@voicenews.com; web site www.voicenews.com
Circulation: 59,500fr; Sworn/Estimate/Non-Audited
Advertising rate: Open inch rate $7.95
Established: 1887
Gen. Mgr. .... Debra Loggins
Adv. Asst. .... Anna Eerola
Circ. Mgr. .... Rene Allard
Ed. .... Jeff Payne
Mechanical Specifications: Type page 10 x 15; E - 5 cols, 2, between; A - 5 cols, 2, between; C - 6 cols, 1 7/10, between.
Delivery Method: Mail, Newsstand, Racks
Areas Served: Northern Macomb & Southern St. Clair

THE BAY VOICE (WED)

19176 Hall Rd, Ste 200, Clinton Township, MI, 48038-6914, Macomb, USA; gen tel (586) 716-8100; gen fax (586) 719-8918; disp adv e-mail debbie.loggins@voicenews.com; class adv e-mail classified.voice@voicenews.com; ed e-mail editor@voicenews.com ; web site www.voicenews.com
Circulation: 40pd, 9,697fr; Sworn/Estimate/Non-Audited
Advertising rate: Open inch rate $14.35
Established: 1983
Group: Digital First Media
Gen. Mgr. .... Debbie Loggins
Ed. .... Jeff Payne
Circ. Mgr. .... Rene Allard
Mechanical Specifications: Type page 10 x 15; E - 5 cols, 1 15/16, 1/8 between; A - 5 cols, 1 15/16, 1/8 between; C - 6 cols, 1 7/10, 1/8 between.Equipment & Software: Hardware — APP/Mac G4, PC; Presses — G/Community; Software — Adobe/PageMaker.
Delivery Method: Mail, Newsstand, Carrier, Racks
Areas Served: Northern Macomb & Southern St. Clair counties

THE MACOMB VOICE (WED)

19176 Hall Rd, Ste 200, Clinton Township, MI, 48038-6914, Macomb, USA; gen tel (586) 716-8100; gen fax (586) 716-8918; adv fax (586) 716-8533; disp adv e-mail debbie.loggins@voicenews.com; class adv e-mail classified.voice@voicenews.com; ed e-mail editor@voicenews.com; web site www.voicenews.com
Circulation: 4,000pd,; Sworn/Estimate/Non-Audited
Advertising rate: Open inch rate $8.10
Established: 1983
Group: Digital First Media
Gen. Mgr. .... Debra Loggins
Ed. .... Jeff Payne
Circ. Mgr. .... Rene Allard
Mechanical Specifications: Type page 10 x 15; E - 5 cols, 2, between; A - 5 cols, 2, between; C - 6 cols, 1 7/10, between.
Delivery Method: Mail, Newsstand, Carrier, Racks
Areas Served: Northern Macomb & Southern St. Clair Counties

THE NORTH MACOMB VOICE (WED)

19176 Hall Rd, Ste 200, Clinton Township, MI, 48038-6914, Macomb, USA; gen tel (586) 716-8100; gen fax (586) 716-8918; adv fax (586) 716-8533; disp adv e-mail debbie.loggins@voicenews.com; class adv e-mail classified.voice@voicenews.com; ed e-mail editor@voicenews.com; web site www.voicenews.com
Circulation: 9,636fr; Sworn/Estimate/Non-Audited
Advertising rate: Open inch rate $12.15
Established: 1983
Group: Digital First Media
Ed. .... Jeff Payne
Adv. .... Debbie Loggins
Circ. Mgr. .... Rene Allard
Mechanical Specifications: Type page 10 x 15; E - 5 cols, 2, between; A - 5 cols, 2, between; C - 6 cols, 1 7/10, between.
Delivery Method: Mail, Newsstand, Carrier, Racks
Areas Served: Norther Macomb & Southern St. Clair

THE VOICE (WED)

19176 Hall Rd, Ste 200, Clinton Township, MI, 48038-6914, Macomb, USA; gen tel (586) 716-8100; gen fax (586) 716-8533; disp adv e-mail dawn.emke@voicenews.com; class adv e-mail classified.voice@voicenews.com; ed e-mail editor@voicenews.com; web site voicenews.com
Pub. .... Jeannie Parent
VP .... Teresa Goodrich
Ed. .... Jeff Payne

CLIO

GENESEE COUNTY HERALD, INC. (MON)

G 10098 N Dort Hwy, Clio, MI, 48420, Genesee, USA; gen tel (810) 686-3840; gen fax (810) 686-9181; web site www.myherald.net
Circulation: 22,153fr; Sworn/Estimate/Non-Audited
Advertising rate: Open inch rate $6.60
Pub. .... Mike Harrington
Mechanical Specifications: Type page 10 1/4 x 16; E - 6 cols, between.

COLDWATER

BRONSON JOURNAL (THUR)

15 W Pearl St, Coldwater, MI, 49036-1912, Branch, USA; gen tel (517) 369-5085; gen fax (517) 369-2225; disp adv e-mail editor@thedailyreporter.com; web site www.thebronsonjournal.com
Circulation: 1,000pd,; Sworn/Estimate/Non-Audited
Advertising rate: Open inch rate $4.00
Mng. Ed. .... Amanda VanAuker
Mechanical Specifications: Type page 13 x 21 1/2; E - 6 cols, 2 1/16, 1/6 between; A - 6 cols, 2 1/16, 1/6 between; C - 6 cols, 2 1/16, 1/6 between.Equipment & Software: Hardware — APP/Mac; Software — Adobe/PageMaker 4.2.

REGISTER-TRIBUNE (THUR)

15 W Pearl St, Coldwater, MI, 49036-1912, Branch, USA; gen tel (517) 278-2318; gen fax (517) 278-6041; disp adv e-mail editor@thedailyreporter.com
Circulation: 1,150pd, 125fr; Sworn/Estimate/Non-Audited
Advertising rate: Open inch rate $3.25
Pub. .... David Ferro
Mechanical Specifications: Type page 13 x 21 1/2; E - 6 cols, 2 1/16, 1/6 between; A - 6 cols, 2 1/16, 1/6 between; C - 6 cols, 2 1/16, 1/6 between.Equipment & Software: Hardware — APP/Mac

COLON

COLON EXPRESS (WED)
PO Box 483, 212 East State Street, Colon, MI, 49040-0483, USA; gen tel (269) 432-3488; disp adv e-mail sales@fabmagic.com; class adv e-mail sales@fabmagic.com; ed e-mail sales@fabmagic.com; web site www.thecolonexpress.com
Circulation: 1,111pd, 27fr; Sworn/Estimate/Non-Audited
Advertising rate: Open inch rate $2.75
Established: 2015
Group: FAB Magic Mfg Company
Publisher,editor.............Rick FisherEquipment & Software: Hardware — APP/Power Mac; Software — Adobe/PageMaker.
Delivery Method: Mail
Areas Served: 49040

DAVISON

FLINT TOWNSHIP VIEW (THUR)
220 N Main St, Davison, MI, 48423-1432, Genesee, USA; gen tel (810) 653-3511; adv tel (810) 664-0811; gen fax (810) 667-6309; adv fax (810) 667-6309; disp adv e-mail pclinton@mihomepaper.comc; class adv e-mail pclinton@mihomepaper.com; ed e-mail ggould@mihomepaper.com; web site http://flinttownshipview.mihomepaper.com
Circulation: 8,125fr; VAC
Advertising rate: Modular Full Page $360
Established: 2010
Group: View Newspaepr Group
Digital Platform - Mobile: Apple, Android, Windows, Blackberry
Digital Platform - Tablet: Apple iOS, Android, Windows 7, Blackberry Tablet OS
Pub./Ed. ....Wes Smith
Adv. Mgr... Pete Clinton
Mechanical Specifications: Type page 9.75" x 10"; 4 cols
Delivery Method: Mail
Areas Served: 48532, 48507

GRAND BLANC VIEW (THUR)
220 N Main St, Davison, MI, 48423-1432, Genesee, USA; gen tel (810) 653-3511; ed tel (810) 653-3511 ext. 211; gen fax (810) 667-6309; disp adv e-mail pclinton@mihomepaper.com; class adv e-mail pclinton@mihomepaper.com; ed e-mail ggould@mihomepaper.com; web site http://grandblancview.mihomepaper.com/
Circulation: 27,641fr; CVC
Advertising rate: Modular full page: $966
Established: 2005
Group: View Newspaper Group
Digital Platform - Mobile: Apple, Android, Windows, Blackberry
Digital Platform - Tablet: Apple iOS, Android, Windows 7, Blackberry Tablet OS
Pub./Ed. ....Wes Smith
Adv. Mgr.. Pete Clinton
Circ. Mgr .... Dale Phillips
Owner... Rick Burrough
Mechanical Specifications: Type page 9.75" x 10"; 4 cols
Delivery Method: Mail
Areas Served: 48439, 48438, 48507, 48442

SWARTZ CREEK VIEW (THUR)
220 N Main St, Davison, MI, 48423-1432, Genesee, USA; gen tel (810) 653-3511; adv tel (810) 664-0811; gen fax (810) 667-6309; disp adv e-mail pclinton@mihomepaper.comc; class adv e-mail pclinton@mihomepaper.com; ed e-mail ggould@mihomepaper.com; web site http://swartzcreekview.mihomepaper.com/
Circulation: 9,418fr; CVC
Advertising rate: Modular Full Page $360
Established: 2010
Group: View Newspaper Group
Digital Platform - Mobile: Apple, Android, Windows, Blackberry
Digital Platform - Tablet: Apple iOS, Android, Windows 7, Blackberry Tablet OS
Pub./Ed. ....Wes Smith
Adv. Mgr....................................... Pete Clinton
Mechanical Specifications: Type page 9.75" x 10"; 4 cols
Delivery Method: Mail
Areas Served: 48473

THE DAVISON INDEX (THUR)
220 N Main St, Davison, MI, 48423-1432, Genesee, USA; gen tel (810) 653-3511; adv tel 810-653-3511; ed tel (810) 452-2650; gen fax (810) 653-6309; disp adv e-mail pclinton@mihomepaper.com; class adv e-mail pclinton@mihomepaper.com; ed e-mail ggould@mihomepaper.com; web site http://davisonindex.mihomepaper.com/
Circulation: 14,593fr; VAC
Advertising rate: Modular full page: $626
Established: 1889
Group: View Newspaper Group
Pub..Wes Smith
Ed .... Gary Gould
Adv. Mgr....................................... Pete Clinton
Circ. Mgr .... Dale Phillips
Prod. MgrDonna AshbyEquipment & Software: ; Presses — G/Community.
Delivery Method: Mail
Areas Served: 48423

DEARBORN

DEARBORN TIMES-HERALD (WED)
13730 Michigan Ave, Dearborn, MI, 48126-3520, Wayne, USA; gen tel (313) 584-4000; gen fax (313) 584-1357; disp adv e-mail timesheraldads@yahoo.com; class adv e-mail timesheraldclassifieds@yahoo.com. ; ed e-mail DbnTHerald@aol.com; web site www.downriversundaytimes.com
Circulation: 5,639pd, 847fr; Sworn/Estimate/Non-Audited
Advertising rate: Open inch rate $21.50
Established: 1963
Pub... Michael Bewick
Adv. Mgr...Jonh Manzi
Circ. Mgr...Jon Walton
Mechanical Specifications: Type page 13 x 21 1/2; E - 6 cols, 2 1/4, 1/6 between; A - 6 cols, 2 1/4, 1/6 between; C - 10 cols, 1 1/4, 1/6 between.
Delivery Method: Mail, Newsstand, Carrier
Areas Served: 48124, 48120, 48121, 48122, 48123, 48124, 48125, 48126, 48128, 48127

DECATUR

DECATUR REPUBLICAN (THUR)
121 S Phelps St, Decatur, MI, 49045-1117, Van Buren, USA; gen tel (269) 423-2411; web site www.facebook.com/pages/Decatur-Republican/144973075525863
Circulation: 1,960pd, 49fr; Sworn/Estimate/Non-Audited
Advertising rate: Open inch rate $2.75
Ed. .... David D. Moormann

DETROIT

BIRMINGHAM ECCENTRIC (SUN)
615 W Lafayette Blvd, # 2, Detroit, MI, 48226-3124, Wayne, USA; gen tel (866) 887-2737; adv tel (800) 579-7355; ed tel (313) 222-5397; disp adv e-mail fcibor@hometownlife.com; class adv e-mail cewilson@hometownlife.com; ed e-mail srosiek@hometownlife.com; web site www.hometownlife.com
Circulation: 1,748pd, 4,705fr; CAC
Advertising rate: Open inch rate $33.30
Established: 1869
Group: Gannett
Reporter ....Jay Grossman
Sports Ed. .... Marty Budner
Mechanical Specifications: Type page 11 5/8 x 21 1/4; E - 6 cols, 1 13/16, 1/8 between; A - 6 cols, 1 13/16, 1/16 between; C - 9 cols, 1 3/16, 1/16 between.Equipment & Software: ; Software — QPS/QuarkXPress 4.11, Baseview/News Edit Pro, Future Proof Ad Booking (Miles 33), PBS (Accounts Receivable), Beacon (Miles 33), Future Proof Prodn. Tracking (Miles 33).
Delivery Method: Newsstand, Carrier, Racks
Areas Served: Bermingham

CANTON OBSERVER (THUR, SUN)
615 W Lafayette Blvd, # 2, Detroit, MI, 48226-3124, Wayne, USA; gen tel (866) 887-2737; adv tel (800) 579-7355; ed tel (313) 222-5397; disp adv e-mail fcibor@hometownlife.com; class adv e-mail cewilson@hometownlife.com; ed e-mail srosiek@hometownlife.com; web site www.hometownlife.com
Circulation: 2,232pd, 4,350fr; CAC
Advertising rate: Open inch rate $24.40
Established: 1869
Group: Gannett
Reporter ....Darrell Clem
Mechanical Specifications: Type page 11 5/8 x 21 1/4; E - 6 cols, 1 13/16, 1/8 between; A - 6 cols, 1 13/16, 1/16 between; C - 9 cols, 1 3/16, 1/16 between.Equipment & Software: ; Software — QPS/QuarkXPress 4.11, Baseview/News Edit Pro Ique, Miles 33/Future Proof Ad Booking, PBS (Accounts Receivable), Miles 33/Beacon, Miles 33/Future Proof Production Tracking.
Delivery Method: Newsstand, Carrier, Racks
Areas Served: 48187, 48188

FARMINGTON OBSERVER (THUR, SUN)
615 W Lafayette Blvd, # 2, Detroit, MI, 48226-3124, Wayne, USA; gen tel (866) 887-2737; adv tel (800) 579-7355; gen fax (313) 223-3318; web site www.hometownlife.com
Circulation: 1,700pd, 8fr; CAC
Advertising rate: Open inch rate $21.60
Group: Gannett
Dir. Adv...Jani Hayden
Mechanical Specifications: Type page 11 5/8 x 21 1/4; E - 6 cols, 1 13/16, 1/8 between; A - 6 cols, 1 13/16, 1/16 between; C - 9 cols, 1 3/16, 1/16 between.Equipment & Software: ; Software — QPS/QuarkXPress 4.11, Baseview/News Edit Pro Ique, Miles 33/Future Proof Ad Booking, PBS (Accounts Receivable), Miles 33/Beacon, Miles 33/Future Proof Production Tracking.
Delivery Method: Newsstand, Carrier, Racks
Areas Served: 48331, 48334, 48335, 48336

GARDEN CITY OBSERVER (THUR, SUN)
615 W Lafayette Blvd, # 2, Detroit, MI, 48226-3124, Wayne, USA; gen tel (866) 887-2737; adv tel (800) 579-7355; ed tel (313) 222-5397; ed fax (313) 223-3318; disp adv e-mail fcibor@hometownlife.com; class adv e-mail cewilson@hometownlife.com; ed e-mail srosiek@hometownlife.com; web site www.hometownlife.com
Circulation: 1,000pd, 2fr; CAC
Advertising rate: Open inch rate $23.40
Established: 1869
Group: Gannett
Dir. Adv. ....Jani Hayden
Mechanical Specifications: Type page 11 5/8 x 21 1/4; E - 6 cols, 1 13/16, 1/8 between; A - 6 cols, 1 13/16, 1/16 between; C - 9 cols, 1 3/16, 1/16 between.Equipment & Software: ; Presses — G/Metro; Software — QPS/QuarkXPress 4.11, Baseview/News Edit Pro Ique, Miles 33/Future Proof Ad Booking, PBS (Accounts Receivable), Miles 33/Beacon, Miles 33/Future Proof Production Tracking.
Delivery Method: Mail, Newsstand, Racks
Areas Served: 48135

LAKE ORION ECCENTRIC (THUR, SUN)
615 W Lafayette Blvd, # 2, Detroit, MI, 48226-3124, Wayne, USA; gen tel (866) 887-2737; gen fax (313) 223-3318; disp adv e-mail fcibor@hometownlife.com; web site www.hometownlife.com
Circulation: 382pd, 86,005fr; CAC
Advertising rate: Open inch rate $21.60
Group: Gannett
Mktg./Research Mgr.................Carol McCloud
Circ. Dir. .... Mark Warren
Exec. Ed.....................................Susan Rosiek
IT Mgr...Darren Jasey
Prodn. Mgr. ....Mark Vines
Mechanical Specifications: Type page 11 5/8 x 21 1/4; E - 6 cols, 1 13/16, 1/8 between; A - 6 cols, 1 13/16, 1/16 between; C - 9 cols, 1 3/16, 1/16 between.Equipment & Software: ; Presses — G/Metro; Software — QPS/QuarkXPress 4.11, Baseview/News Edit Pro Ique, Miles 33/Future Proof Ad Booking, PBS (Accounts Receivable), Miles 33/Beacon, Miles 33/Future Proof Production Tracking.
Delivery Method: Newsstand, Carrier, Racks
Areas Served: 48359, 48360, 48362

LIVONIA OBSERVER (THUR, SUN)
615 W Lafayette Blvd, # 2, Detroit, MI, 48226-3124, Wayne, USA; gen tel (866) 887-2737; adv tel (800) 579-7355; ed tel (313) 222-5397; disp adv e-mail fcibor@hometownlife.com; class adv e-mail cewilson@hometownlife.com; ed e-mail srosiek@hometownlife.com; web site www.hometownlife.com
Circulation: 5,477pd, 5,160fr; CAC
Advertising rate: Open inch rate $31.20
Established: 1869
Group: Gannett
Circ. Dir. .... Mark Warren
Executive Editor/Publisher..........Susan Rosiek
Mechanical Specifications: Type page 11 5/8 x 21 1/4; E - 6 cols, 1 13/16, 1/8 between; A - 6 cols, 1 13/16, 1/16 between; C - 9 cols, 1 3/16, 1/16 between.Equipment & Software: ; Software — QPS/QuarkXPress 4.11, Baseview/News Edit Pro Ique, Miles 33/Future Proof Ad Booking, PBS (Accounts Receivable), Miles 33/Beacon, Miles 33/Future Proof Production Tracking.
Delivery Method: Mail, Newsstand, Carrier
Areas Served: 48150, 48152, 48154

MILFORD TIMES (THUR)
615 W Lafayette Blvd, # 2, Detroit, MI, 48226-3124, Wayne, USA; gen tel (866) 887-2737; gen fax (313) 223-3318; disp adv e-mail news@milfordtimes.com; web site www.hometownlife.com
Circulation: 3,137pd, 1,309fr; CAC
Advertising rate: Open inch rate $13.50
Group: Gannett
Exec. Ed./Pub. ....Susan Rosiek
Dir. Adv..Jani Hayden
Delivery Method: Mail

NORTHVILLE RECORD (THUR)
615 W Lafayette Blvd, # 2, Detroit, MI, 48226-3124, Wayne, USA; gen tel (866) 887-2737; adv tel (800) 579-7355; gen fax (313) 223-3318; web site www.hometownlife.com
Circulation: 3,405pd, 1,129fr; CAC
Advertising rate: Open inch rate $17.42
Group: Gannett
Exec. Ed./Pub. ....Susan Rosiek
Dir. Adv. ....Jani Hayden
Delivery Method: Mail

NOVI NEWS (THUR)
615 W Lafayette Blvd, # 2, Detroit, MI, 48226-3124, Wayne, USA; gen tel (866) 887-2737; gen fax (313) 223-3318; disp adv e-mail sunnewslink@freedom.com; web site www.hometownlife.com
Circulation: 2,257pd, 884fr; CAC
Advertising rate: Open inch rate $16.40
Group: Gannett
Gen. Mgr.......................................Grace Perry
Dir. Adv. ....Jani Hayden
Delivery Method: Mail

OBSERVER & ECCENTRIC MEDIA (THUR, SUN)
615 W Lafayette Blvd, # 2, Detroit, MI, 48226-3124, Wayne, USA; gen tel (866) 887-2737; adv tel (800) 579-7355; adv fax (734) 582-8366; ed fax (313) 223-3318; web site www.hometownlife.com
Circulation: 18,846pd, 36,042fr; CAC
Group: Gannett
Dir. Adv. ....Jani Hayden

PLYMOUTH OBSERVER (THUR, SUN)
615 W Lafayette Blvd, # 2, Detroit, MI, 48226-3124, Wayne, USA; gen tel (866)

887-2737; adv tel (800) 579-7355; gen fax (313) 223-3318; disp adv e-mail fcibor@hometownlife.com; class adv e-mail cewilson@hometownlife.com; ed e-mail srosiek@hometownlife.com; web site www.hometownlife.com
Circulation: 2,111pd, 1,827fr; CAC
Advertising rate: $14.35 per column inch
Established: 1869
Group: Gannett
Circ. Dir. .... Mark Warren
Mktg. Mgr. .... Choya Jordan
Adv. Dir. .... Marty Carry
Mechanical Specifications: Type page 11 5/8 x 21 1/4; E - 6 cols, 1 13/16, 1/8 between; A - 6 cols, 1 13/16, 1/16 between; C - 9 cols, 1 3/16, 1/16 between.Equipment & Software: ; Software — QPS/QuarkXPress 4.11, Baseview/News Edit Pro Ique, Miles 33/Future Proof Ad Booking, PBS (Accounts Receivable), Miles 33/Beacon, Miles 33/Future Proof Production Tracking.
Delivery Method: Carrier
Areas Served: 48170

REDFORD OBSERVER (THUR, SUN)
615 W Lafayette Blvd, # 2, Detroit, MI, 48226-3124, Wayne, USA; gen tel (866) 887-2737; adv tel (800) 579-7355; ed tel (313) 222-5397; disp adv e-mail fcibor@hometownlife.com; class adv e-mail cewilson@hometownlife.com; ed e-mail srosiek@hometownlife.com; web site www.hometownlife.com
Circulation: 1,220pd, 6fr; CAC
Advertising rate: Open inch rate $31.20
Established: 1869
Group: Gannett
Executive Editor/Publisher .... Susan Rosiek
Circ. Dir. .... Mark Warren
Dir. Adv. .... Jani Hayden
Mechanical Specifications: Type page 11 5/8 x 21 1/4; E - 6 cols, 1 13/16, 1/8 between; A - 6 cols, 1 13/16, 1/16 between; C - 9 cols, 1 3/16, 1/16 between.Equipment & Software: ; Software — QPS/QuarkXPress 4.11, Baseview/News Edit Pro Ique, Miles 33/Future Proof Ad Booking, PBS (Accounts Receivable), Miles 33/Beacon, Miles 33/Future Proof Production Tracking.
Delivery Method: Mail, Newsstand
Areas Served: 48239, 48240

SOUTH LYON HERALD (THUR)
615 W Lafayette Blvd, # 2, Detroit, MI, 48226-3124, Wayne, USA; gen tel (866) 887-2737; gen fax (313) 223-3318; disp adv e-mail news@southlyonherald.com; web site www.hometownlife.com
Circulation: 3,676pd, 1,151fr; CAC
Advertising rate: Open inch rate $16.00
Group: Gannett
Adv. Mgr. .... Lisa Dranginis
Adv. Dir. .... Jani Hayden
Delivery Method: Mail

SOUTH OAKLAND ECCENTRIC (SUN)
615 W Lafayette Blvd, # 2, Detroit, MI, 48226-3124, Wayne, USA; gen tel (866) 887-2737; adv tel (800) 579-7355; gen fax (313) 223-3318; disp adv e-mail sdobkin@hometownlife.com; class adv e-mail cewilson@hometownlife.com; ed e-mail sarmbruster@hometownlife.com; web site www.hometownlife.com
Circulation: 450pd, 8,658fr; CAC
Group: Gannett
Circ. Dir. .... Mark Warren
Gen. Mgr. .... Peter Neill
Adv. Dir. .... Marty Carry
Adv. Dir. .... Jani Hayden
Mechanical Specifications: Type page 11 5/8 x 21 1/4; E - 6 cols, 1 13/16, 1/8 between; A - 6 cols, 1 13/16, 1/16 between; C - 9 cols, 1 3/16, 1/16 between.Equipment & Software: ; Presses — G/Metro; Software — QPS/QuarkXPress 4.11, Baseview/News Edit Pro Ique, Miles 33/Future Proof Ad Booking, PBS (Accounts Receivable), Miles 33/Beacon, Miles 33/Future Proof Prodn. Tracking.
Delivery Method: Newsstand, Carrier, Racks
Areas Served: 48033, 48034, 48075, 48076, 48067, 48073, 48017, 48072, 48220, 48069

WESTLAND OBSERVER (THUR, SUN)
615 W Lafayette Blvd, # 2, Detroit, MI, 48226-3124, Wayne, USA; gen tel (866) 887-2737; adv tel (800) 579-7355; gen fax (313) 223-3318; web site www.hometownlife.com
Circulation: 27,927pd, 80fr; CAC
Advertising rate: Open inch rate $14.35
Group: Gannett
Circ. Dir. .... Mark Warren
Executive Editor/ Publisher .... Susan Rosiek
Advertising Director .... Grace Perry
Gen. Mgr. .... Peter Neill
Adv. Dir. .... Marty Carry
IT Mgr. .... Rich Jones
Mechanical Specifications: Type page 11 5/8 x 21 1/4; E - 6 cols, 1 13/16, 1/8 between; A - 6 cols, 1 13/16, 1/16 between; C - 9 cols, 1 3/16, 1/16 between.Equipment & Software: ; Software — QPS/QuarkXPress 4.11, Baseview/News Edit Pro Ique, Miles 33/Future Proof Ad Booking, PBS (Accounts Receivable), Miles 33/Beacon, Miles 33/Future Proof Production Tracking.
Delivery Method: Newsstand, Carrier, Racks
Areas Served: 48185, 48186

EAST TAWAS

IOSCO COUNTY NEWS HERALD (WED)
110 W State St, East Tawas, MI, 48730-1229, Losco, USA; gen tel (989) 362-3456; gen fax (989) 362-6601; disp adv e-mail advertising@iosconews.com; ed e-mail editor@iosconews.com; web site www.iosconews.com
Circulation: 4,800pd,; USPS
Advertising rate: Open inch rate $11.45
Group: Community Media Group
Ed. .... Holly Nelson
Mechanical Specifications: Type page 10 x 16 1/2; E - 5 cols, 1 11/12, between; A - 5 cols, 1 11/12, between; C - 6 cols, between. Equipment & Software: ; Software — Archetype/Corel Draw.
Delivery Method: Mail, Racks
Areas Served: Iosco County

FENTON

TRI-COUNTY TIMES (WED, SUN)
256 N Fenway Dr, Fenton, MI, 48430-2699, Genesee, USA; gen tel (810) 629-8282; adv tel (810) 433-6778; gen fax (810) 629-9227; disp adv e-mail tallen@tctimes.com; class adv e-mail hpoyner@tctimes.com; ed e-mail sstone@tctimes.com; web site www.tctimes.com
Circulation: 9,881pd, 19,800fr; Sworn/Estimate/Non-Audited
Established: 1955
Group: Rockman Communications, Inc
Digital Platform - Mobile: Apple, Android, Windows, Blackberry, Other
Digital Platform - Tablet: Apple iOS, Android, Windows 7, Blackberry Tablet OS, Kindle, Nook, Kindle Fire, Other
Bus Mgr .... John Evans
Marketing Director .... Terese Allen
General Manager .... Jennifer Ward
Publisher .... Craig Rockman
Editor .... Sharon Stone
Mechanical Specifications: Type page 10 x 14; A - 4 cols, 2 3/8, 1/4 between; C - 6 cols, 1 1/2, 3/16 between.Equipment & Software: Hardware — PC; Software — Adobe/PageMaker 6.5.
Delivery Method: Mail, Newsstand, Carrier, Racks
Areas Served: 48430, 48442, 48451, 48363, 48439,

FLINT

GRAND BLANC NEWS (SUN)
200 E 1st St, Flint, MI, 48502-1911, Genesee, USA; gen tel (810) 766-6323; gen fax (810) 766-6393; web site www.thecommunitynewspapers.com
Circulation: 14,951pd,; Sworn/Estimate/Non-Audited
Advertising rate: Open inch rate $12.50
Group: Advance Publications, Inc.
Pub. .... Dave Sharp
Adv. Mgr. .... Mary Alexander
Ed. .... Katie Bach

THE BURTON NEWS (SUN)
200 E 1st St, Flint, MI, 48502-1911, Genesee, USA; gen tel (810) 766-6100; gen fax (810) 766-7518; disp adv e-mail theburtonnews@communitynewspapers.com; web site www.burtonsuburbannews.com
Circulation: 15,000pd,; Sworn/Estimate/Non-Audited
Advertising rate: Open inch rate $10.20
Established: 2002
Group: Advance Publications, Inc.
Ed. .... Katie Bach
Mechanical Specifications: Type page 11 1/2 x 21; E - 6 cols, 1 3/16, between; A - 6 cols, 1 3/16, between; C - 10 cols, 1 3/16, between.
Delivery Method: Mail
Areas Served: 48506, 48509, 48519, 48529

THE FENTON PRESS (SUN)
200 E 1st St, Flint, MI, 48502-1911, Genesee, USA; gen tel (810) 766-6100; gen fax (810) 767-7518; disp adv e-mail weeklyjournal@fledjournal.com; web site www.mlive.com
Circulation: 16,486fr; Sworn/Estimate/Non-Audited
Advertising rate: Open inch rate $10.75
Group: Advance Publications, Inc.
Ed. .... Barb Modrack
Mng. Ed. .... Brooke Rausch

THE FLINT TOWNSHIP NEWS (SUN)
540 S Saginaw St, Ste 101, Flint, MI, 48502-1813, Genesee, USA; gen tel (810) 766-6100; gen fax (810) 767-7518; disp adv e-mail editor@flinttownshipnews.com; web site www.mlive.com/flinttownship
Circulation: 7,188fr; Sworn/Estimate/Non-Audited
Advertising rate: Open inch rate $8.40
Group: Advance Publications, Inc.
Ed. .... Katie Bach

THE SWARTZ CREEK NEWS (SUN)
200 E 1st St, Flint, MI, 48502-1911, Genesee, USA; gen tel (810) 766-6100; gen fax (810) 767-7518; disp adv e-mail tcn@thecommunitynewspapers.com; web site www.theswartznews.com
Circulation: 7,455fr; Sworn/Estimate/Non-Audited
Advertising rate: Open inch rate $8.40
Group: Advance Publications, Inc.
Mng. Ed. .... Brooke Rausch

FRANKENMUTH

FRANKENMUTH NEWS (WED)
527 N Franklin St, Ste A, Frankenmuth, MI, 48734-2011, Saginaw, USA; gen tel (989) 652-3246; gen fax (989) 652-2417; disp adv e-mail frankenmuthnews@airadvantage.net; class adv e-mail frankenmuthnews@airadv.net; ed e-mail swenzel@airadv.net; web site www.frankenmuthnews.com
Circulation: 5,000pd,; Sworn/Estimate/Non-Audited
Advertising rate: Open inch rate $6.35
Established: 1906
Pub. .... Steven Grainger
Adv. Mgr. .... Vicky Hayden
Ed. .... Scott Wenzel
Mechanical Specifications: Type page 13 3/4 x 21 1/4; E - 6 cols, 2 1/8, between; A - 6 cols, 2 1/8, between; C - 8 cols, 1 5/8, between. Equipment & Software: Hardware — PC; Presses — ATF/Davidson, HI; Software — Archetype/Corel Draw 5.0, XYQUEST/XyWrite, Ventura.
Delivery Method: Mail, Newsstand

FRANKFORT

THE BENZIE COUNTY RECORD-PATRIOT (WED)
417 Main St, Frankfort, MI, 49635-9142, Benzie, USA; gen tel (231) 352-9659; adv tel (231) 352-9659; ed tel (231) 352-9659; gen fax (231) 352-7874; disp adv e-mail scard@pioneergroup.com; class adv e-mail classrecpat@pioneergroup.com; ed e-mail recpat@pioneergroup.com; web site www.recordpatriot.com
Circulation: 4,500pd,; Sworn/Estimate/Non-Audited
Advertising rate: Open inch rate $34.00
Established: 1888
Group: Pioneer Group
Digital Platform - Tablet: Kindle
Pub. .... John Norton
Mechanical Specifications: Type page 10 3/16 x 16; E - 5 cols, 1 7/8, between; A - 5 cols, 1 7/8, between; C - 5 cols, 1 7/8, between.
Delivery Method: Mail

FREMONT

FREMONT TIMES-INDICATOR (TUES, FRI)
44 W Main St, Fremont, MI, 49412-1176, Newaygo, USA; gen tel (231) 924-4400; gen fax (231) 924-4066; disp adv e-mail tinews@comcast.net; web site www.timesindicator.com
Circulation: 7,500pd,; Sworn/Estimate/Non-Audited
Advertising rate: Open inch rate $9.25
Established: 1878
Ed. .... Richard C. Wheater
Delivery Method: Mail

GAYLORD

GAYLORD HERALD TIMES (WED, SAT)
2058 S Otsego Ave, Gaylord, MI, 49735-9422, Otsego, USA; gen tel (989) 732-1111; gen fax (989) 732-3490; disp adv e-mail editor@gaylordheraldtimes.com; web site www.gaylordheraldtimes.com
Circulation: 7,000pd, 13,000fr; Sworn/Estimate/Non-Audited
Advertising rate: Open inch rate $11
Established: 1875
Group: Schurz Communications Inc
Digital Platform - Mobile: Apple
Digital Platform - Tablet: Apple iOS
Ed. .... Jeremy Speer
Mechanical Specifications: Type page 10 5/8 x 21.
Delivery Method: Mail, Newsstand, Racks
Areas Served: Gaylord, MI

GLADWIN

GLADWIN COUNTY RECORD (WED)
700 E Cedar Ave, Gladwin, MI, 48624-2218, Gladwin, USA; gen tel (989) 426-9411; gen fax (989) 426-2023; disp adv e-mail sdoane@thegladwincountyrecord.com; class adv e-mail dlaidlaw@thegladwincountyrecord.com; ed e-mail npaisley@thegladwincountyrecord.com; web site www.gladwinmi.com
Circulation: 4,200pd, 120fr; Sworn/Estimate/Non-Audited
Advertising rate: Open inch rate $11.66
Established: 1877
Group: Adams Publishing Group, LLC
Office Mgr. .... Dawn Laidlaw
Mechanical Specifications: Type page 11 1/4 x 20; E - 6 cols, 1/6 between; A - 6 cols, 1/6 between; C - 6 cols, 1/6 between.Equipment & Software: Hardware — APP/Mac; Software — Baseview/NewsEdit 2.2, Adobe/Illustrator 6.0, QPS/QuarkXPress 4.2.
Delivery Method: Mail, Newsstand
Areas Served: 48624, 48612

GRAND RAPIDS

MIBIZ (MON)
65 Monroe Center St NW Ste 500, Suite 500, Grand Rapids, MI, 49503-2936, Kent, USA; gen tel (616) 608-6170; adv tel (616) 608-6170; gen fax (616) 608-6182; adv fax (616) 608-6182; disp adv e-mail sales@mibiz.com; class adv e-mail sales@mibiz.com; ed e-mail editor@mibiz.com; web site www.mibiz.com - 200,000(views) 35,000(visitors)
Circulation: 11,345fr; Sworn/Estimate/Non-Audited
Established: 1988
Group: REVUE Holding Company, Inc.
Digital Platform - Mobile: Apple, Android, Windows, Blackberry
Digital Platform - Tablet: Apple iOS, Android, Windows 7, Blackberry Tablet OS, Kindle Fire
Pub .... Brian Edwards
Delivery Method: Mail, Newsstand
Areas Served: Michigan Metro Areas: Grand Rapids, Kalamazoo, Battle Creek, Lansing, Holland, Grand Haven, Muskegon

GRAYLING

CRAWFORD COUNTY AVALANCHE (THUR)
102 E Michigan Ave, Grayling, MI, 49738-1741, Crawford, USA; gen tel (989) 348-6811; gen fax (989) 348-6806; disp adv e-mail avalanche@i2k.net; web site www.crawfordcountyavalanche.com
Circulation: 5,000pd,; Sworn/Estimate/Non-Audited
Advertising rate: Open inch rate $7.00
Established: 1879
Gen. Mgr. .... Linda Golnick
Managing Ed. .... Caleb Casey
Delivery Method: Mail, Newsstand

GROSSE POINTE WOODS

GROSSE POINTE NEWS (THUR)
21316 Mack Ave, Grosse Pointe Woods, MI, 48236-1047, Wayne, USA; gen tel (313) 882-6900; adv tel (313) 882-3500; ed tel (313) 882-0294; gen fax (313) 343-5569; adv fax (313) 882-1585; ed fax (313) 882-1585; disp adv e-mail schambers@grossepointenews.com; class adv e-mail apanski@grossepointenews.com; ed e-mail editor@grossepointenews.com; web site www.grossepointenews.com
Circulation: 12,014pd,; Sworn/Estimate/Non-Audited
Advertising rate: Open inch rate $25.00
Established: 1940
Pub .... Scott Chambers
Mechanical Specifications: Type page 11 5/8 x 21; E - 6 cols, 1 3/4, 3/20 between; A - 6 cols, 1 3/4, 3/20 between; C - 8 cols, 1 3/8, 1/10 between.Equipment & Software: Hardware — APP/Mac; Presses — WPC; Software — QPS/QuarkXPress, Adobe/Photoshop, Adobe/Illustrator, Multi-Ad/Creator.
Delivery Method: Mail
Areas Served: 40236, 48230, 48225

THE CONNECTION (THUR)
21316 Mack Ave, Grosse Pointe Woods, MI, 48236-1047, Wayne, USA; gen tel (313) 882-6900; gen fax (313) 882-1585; disp adv e-mail jminnis@grossepointenews.com; web site www.grossepointenews.com
Circulation: 30,000fr; Sworn/Estimate/Non-Audited
Advertising rate: Open inch rate $24.25
Adv. Mgr. .... Peter Birkner
Circ. Mgr. .... Jill Carlsen
Mechanical Specifications: Type page 11 5/8 x 21; E - 6 cols, 1 4/5, 3/20 between; A - 6 cols, 1 4/5, 3/20 between; C - 8 cols, 1 3/8, 1/10 between.Equipment & Software: Hardware — APP/Mac; Presses — WPC; Software — QPS/QuarkXPress, Adobe/Photoshop, Adobe/Illustrator, Multi-Ad/Creator.

HARBOR SPRINGS

HARBOR LIGHT (WED)
211 E 3rd St, Harbor Springs, MI, 49740-1534, Emmet, USA; gen tel (231) 526-2191; gen fax (231) 526-7634; disp adv e-mail michelle@ncpublish.com; class adv e-mail michelle@ncpublish.com; ed e-mail news@ncpublish.com; web site www.harborlight-news.com
Circulation: 2,000pd, 69fr; Sworn/Estimate/Non-Audited
Advertising rate: Open inch rate $12.75
Established: 1970
Adv. Mgr. .... Michelle Ketterer
Ed. .... Charles O'Neill
News Editor .... Kate Bassett
Mechanical Specifications: Type page 13 x 21; E - 6 cols, between.Equipment & Software: Hardware — PC; Software — Adobe/PageMaker 6.5.
Delivery Method: Mail, Newsstand, Racks
Areas Served: Emmet County

HARRISVILLE

ALCONA COUNTY REVIEW (WED)
111 N Lake St, Harrisville, MI, 48740-9696, Alcona, USA; gen tel (989) 724-6384; adv tel (989) 724-6384; ed tel (989) 724-6384; gen fax (989) 724-6655; adv fax (989) 724-6655; ed fax (989) 724-6655; disp adv e-mail comp@alconareview.com; class adv e-mail subscribe@alconareview.com; ed e-mail editor@alconareview.com; web site www.alconareview.com
Circulation: 3,200pd,; Sworn/Estimate/Non-Audited
Advertising rate: Open inch rate $6.00
Established: 1877
Pub./Ed. .... Cheryl L. Peterson
Prodn. Mgr. .... John Boufford
Office/Circ. Mgr. .... Eileen Roe
Delivery Method: Mail, Newsstand
Areas Served: Alcona County

HART

OCEANA'S HERALD-JOURNAL (THUR)
123 S State St, Hart, MI, 49420-1124, Oceana, USA; gen tel (231) 873-5602; gen fax (231) 873-4775; ed e-mail editor@oceanaheraldjournal.com; web site www.oceanaheraldjournal.com
Circulation: 5,525pd, 15fr; USPS
Advertising rate: Open inch rate $12.15
Group: Community Media Group
Ed. .... Andy Skinner
Pub. .... Ray McGrew
Mechanical Specifications: Type page 14 1/4 x 21; E - 6 cols, 2 1/4, 3/16 between; A - 6 cols, 2 1/4, 3/16 between; C - 8 cols, 1 5/8, 1/8 between.Equipment & Software: Hardware — APP/Mac; Software — QPS/QuarkXPress 4.0, Adobe/Photoshop 3.0.4.
Delivery Method: Mail, Newsstand, Racks
Areas Served: 49420, 49455, 49436, 49446, 49449, 49459, 49431, 49421, 49452, 49437

HASTINGS

MAPLE VALLEY NEWS (SAT)
1351 N M 43 Hwy, Hastings, MI, 49058-8499, Barry, USA; gen tel (269) 945-9554 ext.229; adv tel (269) 945-9554; gen fax (269) 945-5192; adv fax (269) 945-5192; disp adv e-mail ads@j-adgraphics.com; class adv e-mail ads@j-adgraphics.com; ed e-mail news@j-adgraphics.com; web site wwwhastingsreminder
Circulation: 160pd, 4,226fr; Sworn/Estimate/Non-Audited
Advertising rate: Open inch rate $4.94
Established: 1873
Group: J-Ad Graphics
Pub .... Fred Jacobs
Adv. Mgr. .... Scott Ommen
Circulation Mgr .... Bruce Fuller
Mechanical Specifications: Type page 10 1/2 x 16; E - 6 cols, 1 2/3, 1/36 between.Equipment & Software: Hardware — APP/Mac; Presses — Mercury; Software — Baseview, QPS/QuarkXPress.
Delivery Method: Newsstand, Carrier
Areas Served: 49073, 49096, 48813, 48897

REMINDER (SAT)
1351 N M 43 Hwy, Hastings, MI, 49058-8499, Barry, USA; gen tel (269) 945-9554; gen fax (269) 945-5192; disp adv e-mail news@j-adgraphics.com; web site www.hastingsreminder.com
Circulation: 74pd, 27,010fr; VAC
Advertising rate: Open inch rate $11.68
Established: 1945
Group: J-Ad Graphics
Pub./Adv. Mgr. .... Fred Jacobs
Adv. Mgr .... Scott Ommen
Circ. Mgr .... Dennis Rasey
Prod. Mgr .... Tim Sutton
Mechanical Specifications: Type page 10.5" X 16"; 6 colsEquipment & Software: Hardware — APP/Mac, COM, APP/Mac Quadra 500; Presses — HI; Software — Mk, Baseview.
Delivery Method: Racks
Areas Served: 49058

SUN & NEWS (SAT)
1351 N M43 Hwy, Hastings, MI, 49058, Barry, USA; gen tel (269) 945-9554; gen fax (269) 945-5192; class adv e-mail ads@j-adgraphics.com
Circulation: 170pd, 13,025fr; Sworn/Estimate/Non-Audited
Advertising rate: Open inch rate $7.62
Established: 1949
Group: J-Ad Graphics
Pub .... Fred Jacobs
Mechanical Specifications: Type page 10 1/2 x 16; E - 6 cols, 1 5/8, between; A - 6 cols, between; C - 6 cols, between.Equipment & Software: Hardware — APP/Mac; Presses — HI/Mercury; Software — QPS/QuarkXPress.

THE HASTINGS BANNER (THUR)
1351 N M-43 Hwy, Hastings, MI, 49058, Barry, USA; gen tel (269) 945-9554; adv tel (269) 945-9554; gen fax (269) 945-5192; adv fax (269) 945-5522; disp adv e-mail ads@j-adgraphics.com ; class adv e-mail ads@j-adgraphics.com; ed e-mail news@j-adgraphics.com; web site www.hastingsbanner.com
Circulation: 4,998pd, 30,000fr; Sworn/Estimate/Non-Audited
Advertising rate: Open inch rate $6.60
Established: 1856
Group: J-Ad Graphics
Pres./Pub. .... John Jacobs
Circ. Mgr .... Dennis Rasey
Mechanical Specifications: Type page 14 3/4 x 22 3/4; E - 5 cols, 2 1/2, 1/2 between.Equipment & Software: Hardware — APP/Mac; Presses — Mercury; Software — Baseview, QPS/QuarkXPress.
Delivery Method: Mail, Newsstand

HIGHLAND

SPINAL COLUMN NEWSWEEKLY (WED)
PO Box 1426, 1103 South Milford Road, Highland, MI, 48357-1426, Oakland, USA; gen tel (248) 360-7355; adv tel (248) 360-7355 x21; ed tel (248) 360-7355 x12; gen fax (248) 360-5308; adv fax (248) 360-5308; disp adv e-mail bonnieboes@scnmail.com; class adv e-mail lynndonohue@scnmail.com; ed e-mail aliarmstrong@scnmail.com; web site www.spinalcolumnonline.com - 10,700(views) 23,700(visitors)
Circulation: 17,700fr; Sworn/Estimate/Non-Audited
Advertising rate: 1/16 Pg $150; 1/8 Pg $265, 1/4 495; 1/2 Pg. $885; Full $1,495
Established: 1961
Group: Kingsett, LLCEditions: (1) Spinal Column Newsweekly
Digital Platform - Mobile: Apple, Android, Windows, Blackberry
Digital Platform - Tablet: Apple iOS, Android, Windows 7, Blackberry Tablet OS, Kindle, Kindle Fire
Pub. .... Jim Stevenson
Partner .... Phil Catlain
Partner .... Bob Ely
Sales Leader/Asst. pub. .... Cindie Audia
Mechanical Specifications: Spinal Column Newsweekly
IMAGE AREA:
6 columns x 20" or 10" or 60picas
One Columns Wide: 1.51" or 9 picas
Two Columns Wide: 3.20" or 19.3 picas
Three Columns Wide: 4.90" or 19.3 picas
Four Columns Wide: 6.6" or 39.7 picas
Five Columns Wide: 8.3" or 49.9 picas
Six Columns Wide: 10" or 60 picas
Delivery Method: Mail, Newsstand
Areas Served: 48382, 48356, 48357, 48380, 48381, 48383, 48386, 48390, 48393

HOMER

THE HOMER INDEX (WED)
119 W Main St, Homer, MI, 49245-1023, Calhoun, USA; gen tel (517) 568-4646; gen fax (517) 568-4346; disp adv e-mail ads@homerindex.com; class adv e-mail ads@homerindex.com; ed e-mail news@homerindex.com; web site www.homerindex.com
Circulation: 1,150pd, 20fr; Sworn/Estimate/Non-Audited
Advertising rate: Open inch rate $6.00
Established: 1872
Gen. Mgr. .... Sharon Warner
Ed. .... Mike Warner
Mechanical Specifications: Type page 12 15/16 x 21; E - 6 cols, 2, 3/16 between; A - 6 cols, 2, 3/16 between; C - 6 cols, 2, 3/16 between. Equipment & Software: Hardware — APP/Power Mac; Software — QPS/QuarkXPress 3.3.
Delivery Method: Mail, Newsstand
Areas Served: Calhoun, Hillsdale

HOUGHTON LAKE

THE HOUGHTON LAKE RESORTER (THUR)
4049 W Houghton Lake Dr, Houghton Lake, MI, 48629-9208, Roscommon, USA; gen tel (989) 366-5341; gen fax (989) 366-4472; disp adv e-mail news@houghtonlakeresorter.com; class adv e-mail ads@houghtonlakeresorter.com; ed e-mail news@houghtonlakeresorter.com; web site www.houghtonlakeresorter.com
Circulation: 7,800pd, 58fr; Sworn/Estimate/Non-Audited
Advertising rate: Open inch rate $9.00
Established: 1939
Office Mgr. .... Jo Ann Juruzel
Pub./Ed. .... Thomas W. Hamp
Mng. Ed. .... Eric M. Hamp
Prodn. Mgr. .... Bryan Hamp
Mechanical Specifications: Type page 13 1/2 x 21 3/8; E - 6 cols, 2, 1/6 between; A - 6 cols, 2, 1/6 between; C - 6 cols, 2, 1/6 between. Equipment & Software: Hardware — APP/Mac; Presses — KP/Color King; Software — Baseview.
Delivery Method: Mail, Newsstand, Racks
Areas Served: 48629, 48630, 48651, 48653

IMLAY CITY

TRI-CITY TIMES (WED)
594 N Almont Ave, Imlay City, MI, 48444-1000, Lapeer, USA; gen tel (810) 724-2615; gen fax (810) 724-8552; disp adv e-mail rjorgensen@pageone-inc.com; class adv e-mail rjorgensen@pageone-inc.com; ed e-mail cminolli@pageone-inc.com; web site www.tricitytimes-online.com
Circulation: 5,771pd, 1,229fr; USPS
Advertising rate: Open inch rate $7.85
Pub. .... Delores Heim

Delivery Method: Mail, Newsstand
Areas Served: Imlay, Almont, Capac, Dryden

INDIAN RIVER

STRAITSLAND RESORTER (THUR)

3636 S Straits Hwy, Indian River, MI, 49749-5136, Cheboygan, USA; gen tel (231) 238-7362; gen fax (231) 238-1290; disp adv e-mail ads@resorter.com; class adv e-mail ads@resorter.com; ed e-mail editor@resorter.com; web site www.resorter.com
Circulation: 3,200pd, 65fr; Sworn/Estimate/Non-Audited
Advertising rate: Open inch rate $3.85
Established: 1963
Pub. .... Kathy Swanson
Ed. .... Scott Swanson
Mechanical Specifications: Type page 9 9/10 x 16; E - 6 cols, 1 1/2, 1/5 between.
Delivery Method: Mail
Areas Served: Cheboygan County, Indiana River, Burt Lake, Mullett Lake, Afton, Topinabee, Wolverine

IRON RIVER

REPORTER (WED)

801 W Adams St, Iron River, MI, 49935-1218, Iron, USA; gen tel (906) 265-9927; gen fax (906) 265-5755; disp adv e-mail sales@ironcountyreporter.com; class adv e-mail sales@ironcountyreporter.com; ed e-mail news@ironcountyreporter.com; web site www.ironcountyreporter.com
Circulation: 5,000pd,; Sworn/Estimate/Non-Audited
Advertising rate: Open inch rate $6.50
Established: 1885
Ed. .... Jerry DeRoche
Delivery Method: Mail

ITHACA

GRATIOT COUNTY HERALD (THUR)

123 N Main St, Ithaca, MI, 48847-1131, Gratiot, USA; gen tel (989) 875-4151; gen fax (989) 875-3159; disp adv e-mail gcherald@gcherald.com; ed e-mail greg@gcherald.com; web site www.gcherald.com
Circulation: 6,727pd,; Sworn/Estimate/Non-Audited
Advertising rate: Open inch rate $9.50
Ed. .... Greg Nelson
Pub. .... Tom MacDonald
Delivery Method: Mail
Areas Served: 48801, 48806, 48807, 48615, 48830, 48832, 48847, 48856, 48862, 48871, 48874, 48877, 48880, 48889, 48662, 48811, 48818, 48831, 48853, 48637, 48883, 48879, 48888

JACKSON

THE ZONE (SUN)

214 S Jackson St, Jackson, MI, 49201-2267, Jackson, USA; gen tel (517) 787-2300; gen fax (517) 789-1249; web site www.mlive.com/citpat
Circulation: 30,000fr; Sworn/Estimate/Non-Audited
Advertising rate: Open inch rate $7.75
Pub. .... Sandra Petykiewicz
Adv. Mgr. .... Margaret Parshall

JENISON

SOUTH ADVANCE (SUN)

2141 Port Sheldon St, Jenison, MI, 49428-9315, Ottawa, USA; gen tel (616) 669-2700; gen fax (616) 669-1162; disp adv e-mail retailsales@advancenewspapers.com; web site www.advancenewspapers.com
Circulation: 256pd, 14,860fr; CVC
Advertising rate: Open inch rate $16.05
Established: 1965
Group: Advance Publications, Inc.
Pub./Mktg. Dir./Adv. Mgr. .... Joel Holland
Circ. Mgr. .... Terry Alvesteffer
Prodn. Mgr. .... Marilyn Dreisenga
Mechanical Specifications: Type page 10 3/8 x 16; A - 6 cols, 1 5/8, 1/8 between.Equipment & Software: Hardware — APP/Mac; Presses — G; Software — QPS/QuarkXPress 4.0, Adobe/Acrobat.
Areas Served: 49315, 49548, 49509, 49316, 49512

LAKE LEELANAU

THE LEELANAU ENTERPRISE (THUR)

7200 E Duck Lake Rd, Lake Leelanau, MI, 49653-9779, Leelanau, USA; gen tel (231) 256-9827; gen fax (231) 256-7705; disp adv e-mail info@leelanaunews.com; class adv e-mail classifieds@leelanaunews.com; ed e-mail mspencer@leelanaunews.com; web site www.leelanaunews.com
Circulation: 8,100pd, 24fr; Sworn/Estimate/Non-Audited
Advertising rate: Open inch rate $10.35
Established: 1975
Adv. Mgr. .... Debra Campbell
Ed. .... Alan C. Campbell
Mng. Ed. .... Amy Hubbell
Mechanical Specifications: Type page 10 x 16; E - 5 cols, 1 5/6, 1/6 between; A - 5 cols, 1 5/6, 1/6 between; C - 5 cols, 1 5/6, 1/6 between. Equipment & Software: Hardware — APP/Mac; Presses — G/Community.
Delivery Method: Mail, Newsstand

LAKE ORION

THE LAKE ORION REVIEW (WED)

30 N Broadway St, Lake Orion, MI, 48362-3100, Oakland, USA; gen tel (248) 693-8331; adv tel 2486284801 ext20; ed tel (248) 693-8331; gen fax (248) 693-5712; disp adv e-mail lakeorionreview@gmail.com; web site www.lakeorionreview.com
Circulation: 2,500pd, 66fr; USPS
Advertising rate: 1/4 P $172, 1/2 P $332, Full $649
Established: 1881
Group: Sherman Publications, Inc.
Pub. .... Jim Sherman
Asst. Pub. .... Don Rush
Adv. Mgr. .... Eric Lewis
jim newell
Mechanical Specifications: Type page 10 x11; 8, 1/5 between; between.
Delivery Method: Mail, Newsstand
Areas Served: 48359, 48360, 48361, 48362

LANSE

L'ANSE SENTINEL (WED)

202 N Main St, Lanse, MI, 49946-1118, Baraga, USA; gen tel (906) 524-6194; gen fax (906) 524-6197; disp adv e-mail sentinel1886@gmail.com; web site www.lansesentinel.net
Circulation: 2,200pd,; USPS
Advertising rate: Open inch rate $8.80
Established: 1880
Pub. .... Ed Danner
Ed. .... Barry Drue
Production. Mgr. .... Gale Eilola
Reporter .... Nancy Besonen
Reporter .... Melissa Newland
Composition/Photo Editor .... Tammy Golde
Ad Design/Graphic Artist .... Mary Rogala
Mechanical Specifications: Type page 13 x 22; E - 6 cols, 2 1/4, 1/4 between.
Delivery Method: Mail, Newsstand

LANSING

CLINTON COUNTY NEWS (SUN)

120 E Lenawee St, Lansing, MI, 48919-1000, Ingham, USA; gen tel (517) 377-1000; adv tel (517) 377-1082; disp adv e-mail sking@lsj.com; class adv e-mail classifieds@lsj.com; ed e-mail sangel@lsj.com; web site www.lsj.com
Circulation: 12pd, 8,278fr; AAM
Advertising rate: Open inch rate $15.00
Established: 1856
Pub. .... Preston Odette
Pub. .... Brian Priester
Gen. Mgr. .... Tricia Johnson
Adv. Mgr. .... Stacia King
Circ. Mgr .... Mark Conover
Mechanical Specifications: Type page 10 x 10; E - 6 cols, 1 9/16, 3/16 between; A - 6 cols, 1 9/16, 3/16 between; C - 6 cols, 1 9/16, 3/16 between.
Delivery Method: Mail

DELTA WAVERLY COMMUNITY NEWS (SUN)

120 E Lenawee St, Lansing, MI, 48919-1000, Ingham, USA; gen tel (517) 377-1000; adv tel (517) 377-1082; disp adv e-mail sking@lsj.com; class adv e-mail classifieds@lsj.com; ed e-mail sangel@lsj.com; web site www.lsj.com
Circulation: 4,344fr; CVC
Advertising rate: Open inch rate $15.00
Established: 1856
Pub. .... Brian Priester
Adv. Mgr. .... Stacia King
Circ. Mgr .... Mark Conover
Prod. Mgr .... Jack Conaboy
Mechanical Specifications: Type page: 10 x 10; 6 col
Delivery Method: Mail

DEWITT BATH REVIEW (SUN)

120 E Lenawee St, Lansing, MI, 48919-1000, Ingham, USA; gen tel (517) 377-1000; adv tel (517) 377-1082; disp adv e-mail sking@lsj.com; class adv e-mail classifieds@lsj.com; ed e-mail sangel@lsj.com; web site www.lsj.com
Circulation: 5pd, 6,261fr; AAM
Advertising rate: Open inch rate $15.00
Established: 1856
Pub. .... Brian Priester
Adv. Mgr. .... Stacia King
Circ. Mgr .... Mark Conover
Prod. Mgr .... Jack Conaboy
Mechanical Specifications: Type page: 10 x 10; 6 col
Delivery Method: Mail

EATON RAPIDS COMMUNITY NEWS (SUN)

120 E Lenawee St, Lansing, MI, 48919-1000, Ingham, USA; gen tel (517) 377-1000; adv tel (517) 377-1082; disp adv e-mail sking@lsj.com; class adv e-mail classifieds@lsj.com; ed e-mail sangel@lsj.com; web site www.lsj.com
Circulation: 3pd, 4,321fr; AAM
Advertising rate: Open inch rate $15.00
Established: 1856
Pub. .... Brian Priester
Adv. Mgr. .... Stacia King
Circ. Mgr .... Mark Conover
Prod. Mgr .... Jack Conaboy
Mechanical Specifications: Type page: 10 x 10; 6 col
Delivery Method: Mail

GRAND LEDGE INDEPENDENT (SUN)

300 S Washington Sq, Ste 300, Lansing, MI, 48933-2102, Ingham, USA; gen tel (517) 377-1000; adv tel (517) 377-1082; gen fax (517) 627-3497; disp adv e-mail sking@lsj.com; class adv e-mail classifieds@lsj.com; ed e-mail sangel@lsj.com; web site www.lsj.com
Circulation: 6pd, 7,643fr; Sworn/Estimate/Non-Audited
Advertising rate: Open inch rate $15.00
Established: 1856
Pub. .... Brian Priester
Adv. Mgr. .... Stacia King
Circ. Mgr .... Mark Conover
Prod. Mgr .... Jack Conaboy
Mechanical Specifications: Type page 10 x 10; E - 6 cols, 1 9/16, 1/6 between; A - 6 cols, 1 9/16, 1/6 between; C - 6 cols, 1 9/16, 1/6 between.
Delivery Method: Mail

INGHAM COUNTY COMMUNITY NEWS (SUN)

120 E Lenawee St, Lansing, MI, 48919-1000, Ingham, USA; gen tel (517) 377-1000; adv tel (517) 377-1082; disp adv e-mail slucius@gannett.com; class adv e-mail classifieds@lsj.com; ed e-mail sangel@lsj.com; web site www.lsj.com
Circulation: 6,993fr; AAM
Advertising rate: Open inch rate $15.00
Established: 1856
Pub. .... Brian Priester
Adv. Mgr. .... Stacia King
Circ. Mgr .... Mark Conover
Prod. Mgr .... Jack Conaboy
Mechanical Specifications: Type page: 10 x 10; 6 col
Delivery Method: Mail

LANSING CITY COMMUNITY NEWS (SUN)

300 S Washington Sq, Ste 300, Lansing, MI, 48933-2102, Ingham, USA; gen tel (517) 377-1000; adv tel (517) 377-1082; disp adv e-mail sholmes@gannett.com; class adv e-mail classifieds@lsj.com; ed e-mail sangel@lsj.com; web site www.lsj.com
Circulation: 3pd, 27,120fr; Sworn/Estimate/Non-Audited
Advertising rate: Open inch rate $15.00
Established: 1856
Pub. .... Brian Priester
Adv. Mgr. .... Stacia King
Circ. Mgr .... Mark Conover
Prod. Mgr .... Jack Conaboy
Mechanical Specifications: Type page: 10 x 10; 6 col
Delivery Method: Mail

LANSING STATE JOURNAL (SUN)

300 S Washington Sq, Ste 300, Lansing, MI, 48933-2102, Ingham, USA; gen tel (517) 377-1000; adv tel (517) 377-1082; disp adv e-mail sholmes@gannett.com; class adv e-mail classifieds@lsj.com; ed e-mail sangel@lsj.com; web site http://www.lansingstatejournal.com/news/communities-holt/
Circulation: 2pd, 6,259fr; AAM
Advertising rate: Open inch rate $15.00
Established: 1856
Pub. .... Brian Priester
Adv. Mgr. .... Stacia King
Circ. Mgr .... Mark Conover
Prod. Mgr .... Jack Conaboy
Mechanical Specifications: Type page: 10 x 10; 6 col
Delivery Method: Mail

PORTLAND REVIEW & OBSERVER (SUN)

300 S Washington Sq, Lansing, MI, 48933-2100, Ingham, USA; gen tel (517) 377-1000; adv tel (517) 377-1082; disp adv e-mail sholmes@gannett.com; class adv e-mail classifieds@lsj.com; ed e-mail sangel@lsj.com; web site www.lsj.com
Circulation: 4pd, 5,168fr; Sworn/Estimate/Non-Audited
Advertising rate: Open inch rate $15.00
Established: 1856
Group: Gannett
Pub .... Brian Priester
Adv. Mgr. .... Stacia King
Circ. Mgr .... Mark Conover
Prod. Mgr .... Jack Conaboy
Mechanical Specifications: Type page 10 x 10; E - 6 cols, 1 9/16, 1/6 between; A - 6 cols, 1 9/16, 1/6 between; C - 6 cols, 1 9/16, 1/6 between.Equipment & Software: Hardware — APP/Macs; Presses — G; Software — QPS/QuarkXPress, Adobe/Photoshop, Multi-Ad/Creator.
Delivery Method: Mail

LAPEER

LA VIEW (THUR)

1521 Imlay City Rd, Lapeer, MI, 48446-3175, Lapeer, USA; gen tel (810) 664-0811; gen fax (810) 667-6309; disp adv e-mail pclinton@mihomepaper.com; class adv e-mail pclinton@mihomepaper.com; ed e-mail jhogan@mihomepaper.com; web site http://lapeer-areaview.mihomepaper.com/

Circulation: 34,608fr; VAC
Advertising rate: Modular Full Page: $1247
Established: 2003
Group: View Newspaper Group
Digital Platform - Mobile: Apple, Android, Windows, Blackberry
Digital Platform - Tablet: Apple iOS, Android, Windows 7, Blackberry Tablet OS
Pub./Ed. .... Wes Smith
Adv. Mgr. .... Pete Clinton
Circ. Mgr .... Dale Phillips
Prod. Mgr .... Donna Ashby
Mechanical Specifications: Type page 9.75" x 10"; 4 cols
Delivery Method: Mail
Areas Served: 48003, 48412, 48727, 48421, 48428, 48440, 48444, 48446, 48455, 48461, 48464

THE COUNTY PRESS (WED, SUN)

1521 Imlay City Rd, Lapeer, MI, 48446-3195, Lapeer, USA; gen tel (810) 664-0811; gen fax (810) 667-6309; disp adv e-mail info@mihomepaper.com; class adv e-mail sales@mihomepaper.com; ed e-mail editor@mihomepaper.com; web site http://thecounty-press.mihomepaper.com/

Circulation: 7,941pd, 233fr; AAM
Advertising rate: Open inch rate $43.58
Established: 1839
Circ. Mgr .... Theresa Richey
Ed. .... Jeff Hogan
Adv. Dir. .... Wes Smith
Mechanical Specifications: Type page 10 5/8 x 21; A - 6 cols, 1 3/8, 1/6 between; C - 10 cols, 1 3/16, 1/6 between.Equipment & Software: Hardware — APP/Mac; Presses — 13-G/Community, SC/Folder; Software — Baseview/Editorial, Baseview/Classified.
Delivery Method: Mail
Areas Served: 48002, 48003, 48014, 48371, 48412, 48416, 48421, 48428, 48435, 48444, 48446, 48453, 48455, 48461, 48464, 48727, 48744, 48760

LOWELL

LOWELL LEDGER (WED)

105 N Broadway St, Lowell, MI, 49331-1085, Kent, USA; gen tel (616) 897-9261; gen fax (616) 897-4809; disp adv e-mail displayads@lowellbuyersguide.com; class adv e-mail classifieds@lowellbuyersguide.com; ed e-mail ledger@lowerssbuyersguide.com; web site www.lowellbuyersguide.com

Circulation: 4,000pd, 200fr; Sworn/Estimate/Non-Audited
Advertising rate: Open inch rate $5.25
Established: 1893
Circ. Mgr. .... Tammy Janowich
Ed. .... Jon Jacobs
Delivery Method: Mail, Newsstand

MANISTIQUE

PIONEER TRIBUNE (THUR)

212 Walnut St, Manistique, MI, 49854-1445, Schoolcraft, USA; gen tel (906) 341-5200; gen fax (906) 341-5914; disp adv e-mail ads@pioneertribune.com; class adv e-mail ads@pioneertribune.com; ed e-mail editor@pioneertribune.com; web site www.pioneer-tribune.com

Circulation: 3,500pd,; Sworn/Estimate/Non-Audited
Advertising rate: Open inch rate $5.70
Established: 1876
Pub. .... Lisa A. Demers
Mechanical Specifications: Type page 15 x 21 1/2; A - 8 cols, 1 3/4, 1/6 between; C - 9 cols, 1 1/16, 1/6 between.Equipment & Software: Hardware — IBM; Presses — HI/Cottrell; Software — Adobe/PageMaker 7.0, Microsoft/Publisher 98, Microsoft/Publisher 2000, Adobe/Photoshop 6.0, Adobe/Illustrator 8.0.
Delivery Method: Mail, Newsstand, Carrier
Areas Served: Schoolcraft County

MARCELLUS

MARCELLUS NEWS (THUR)

149 E Main St, Marcellus, MI, 49067-5102, Cass, USA; gen tel (269) 646-2101; gen fax (269) 646-2102; ed e-mail editor@marcellus-news.com; web site www.marcellusnews.com

Circulation: 1,600pd,; Sworn/Estimate/Non-Audited
Advertising rate: Open inch rate $2.75
Ed. .... Ramona Moormann

MARION

THE MARION PRESS (WED)

301 E. Mill St., Marion, MI, 49665, Osceola, USA; gen tel (231) 743-2481; gen fax (989) 386-2412; ed e-mail yourmarionpress@gmail.com; web site http://www.marion-press.com

Circulation: 1,941pd, 10fr; Sworn/Estimate/Non-Audited
Advertising rate: Open inch rate $7.00
Publ .... Mike Wilcox

MARSHALL

AD-VISOR AND CHRONICLE (SAT)

514 S Kalamazoo Ave, Marshall, MI, 49068-1719, Calhoun, USA; gen tel (269) 781-5444; gen fax (269) 781-7766; disp adv e-mail theresach@j-adgraphics.com; class adv e-mail kmiller@j-adgraphics.com; ed e-mail jhendler@j-adgraphics.com; web site www.advisor-chronicle.com

Circulation: 220pd, 18,849fr; VAC
Advertising rate: Open inch rate $8.11
Established: 1985
Group: J-Ad Graphics
Owner .... John Jacobs
News Ed. .... John Hendler
Adv. .... Kathy Miller
Circ. Mgr .... Marcia Furu
Prod. Mgr .... Tim Sutton
Mechanical Specifications: Type page 10.5" x 16"; 6 colsEquipment & Software: Hardware — APP/Mac, QMS/PS-810.
Delivery Method: Carrier, Racks
Areas Served: Marshall, Albion, Olivet, Homer, Bellevue & Tekonsha

MAYVILLE

MAYVILLE MONITOR (WED)

6037 Fox St, Mayville, MI, 48744-9004, Tuscola, USA; gen tel (989) 843-6242; adv tel (989) 843-6242; ed tel (989) 843-6242; gen fax (989) 843-6242; disp adv e-mail mayvillemonitor@hotmail.com; class adv e-mail mayvillemonitor@hotmail.com; ed e-mail mayvillemonitor@hotmail.com

Circulation: 600pd,; Sworn/Estimate/Non-Audited
Advertising rate: Open inch rate $4.00
Established: 1884
Editor & Publisher .... Gale Langford
Mechanical Specifications: Type page 10 1/4 x 15; E - 6 cols, 1 7/12, 1/6 between; A - 6 cols, 1 7/12, 1/6 between; C - 6 cols, 1 7/12, 1/6 between.
Delivery Method: Mail, Newsstand
Areas Served: 48744, 48760, 48435

MINDEN CITY

THE MINDEN CITY HERALD (THUR)

1524 Main St, Minden City, MI, 48456-9404, Sanilac, USA; gen tel (989) 864-3630; gen fax (989) 864-5363; ed e-mail mcherald@hbch.com

Circulation: 1,500pd,; Sworn/Estimate/Non-Audited
Advertising rate: Open inch rate $4.50
Ed. .... Paul Engel

MONROE

BEDFORD NOW (SAT)

20 W 1st St, Monroe, MI, 48161-2333, Monroe, USA; gen tel (734) 242-1100; adv tel (734) 240-5712; ed tel (734) 240-5776; gen fax (734) 242-0937; disp adv e-mail trent@monroenews.com; class adv e-mail ebaldock@monroenews.com; web site www.bedfordnow.com

Group: New Media Investment Group
Reporter .... Paula Wethington
Circ. & Classified Mgr. .... David Zewicky
Pub. .... Lonnie Peppler-Moyer
Ops. Mgr. .... Trent Langton
C.F.O. .... Jay Hollon
Adv. Mgr./Retail .... Jeanine Bragg
Areas Served: 48161

MORENCI

STATE LINE OBSERVER (WED)

120 North St, Morenci, MI, 49256-1446, Lenawee, USA; gen tel (517) 458-6811; gen fax (517) 458-6811; ed e-mail editor@statelineobserver.com; web site www.statelineobserver.com

Circulation: 2,321pd,; USPS
Advertising rate: Open inch rate $6.25
Established: 1872
Ed. .... David G. Green
Mechanical Specifications: Type page 10 1/4 x 16; E - 4 cols, 2 1/2, 1/6 between; A - 6 cols, 1 1/2, 1/12 between; C - 6 cols, 1 1/2, 1/12 between.
Delivery Method: Mail, Newsstand
Areas Served: 49247, 49256, 49279, 43533, 43567, 43521, 49288, 49235

MOUNT PLEASANT

NORTHEASTERN SHOPPER SOUTH (SUN)

711 W Pickard St, Ste P, Mount Pleasant, MI, 48858-1587, Isabella, USA; gen tel (989) 362-6111; gen fax (989) 362-7080; ed e-mail afrattura@journalregister.com; web site www.morningstarnewspapers.com

Advertising rate: 1/4 P $150 1/2 P $300 Full $601
Established: 1954Al Frattura
Delivery Method: Mail

MUNISING

THE MUNISING NEWS (WED)

132 E Superior St, Munising, MI, 49862-1122, Alger, USA; gen tel (906) 387-3282; adv tel (906) 387-3282; ed tel (906) 387-3282; gen fax (906) 387-4054; disp adv e-mail munisingnews@jamadots.com; class adv e-mail munisingnews@jamadots.com; ed e-mail munisingnews@jamadots.com; web site www.themunisingnews.com

Circulation: 2,250pd, 5,000fr; Sworn/Estimate/Non-Audited
Advertising rate: Open inch rate $7.00
Established: 1896
Group: Peterson Publishing, Inc
Pub. .... Willie J. Peterson
Mechanical Specifications: Type page 15 x 21 1/2; E - 9 cols, 1 5/8, 1/6 between; A - 9 cols, 1 5/8, 1/6 between; C - 9 cols, 1 5/8, 1/6 between.
Delivery Method: Mail, Newsstand
Areas Served: 49862 49895 49884 49883 49839 49822 49806 49806 49885 49891 49825 49816

NEW BUFFALO

HARBOR COUNTRY NEWS (THUR)

122 N Whittaker St, New Buffalo, MI, 49117-1169, Berrien, USA; gen tel (800) 726-5735; adv tel (219) 874-7211; disp adv e-mail news@harborcountry-news.com; class adv e-mail lsherman@harborcountry-news.com; ed e-mail news@harborcountry-news.com; web site http://www.harborcountry-news.com/

Circulation: 9,200fr; Sworn/Estimate/Non-Audited
Advertising rate: Open inch rate $10.50
Established: 1984
Group: Paxton Media Group, LLC
Adv. Dir. .... Isis Cains
Ed. .... Dave Johnson
Mechanical Specifications: Type page 10 1/4 x 13; E - 5 cols, between; A - 5 cols, between; C - 7 cols, between.
Delivery Method: Mail, Newsstand, Carrier, Racks
Areas Served: 49106,49115, 49116, 49117, 49125, 49128, 49129

NEW BUFFALO TIMES (THUR)

430 S Whittaker St, New Buffalo, MI, 49117-1764, Berrien, USA; gen tel (269) 469-1100; gen fax (269) 469-1754; disp adv e-mail info@newbuffalotimes.com; class adv e-mail advertising@newbuffalotimes.com; ed e-mail editorial@newbuffalotimes.com; web site www.newbuffalotimes.com

Circulation: 5,000pd,; Sworn/Estimate/Non-Audited
Advertising rate: 1/4 P $165, 1/2 P $240, Full $330
Established: 1943
Ed. .... Mary Beth Moriarty
Delivery Method: Mail

NEWBERRY

THE NEWBERRY NEWS (WED)

316 Newberry Ave, Newberry, MI, 49868-1105, Luce, USA; gen tel (906) 293-8401; gen fax (906) 293-8815; disp adv e-mail nbyads@jamadots.com; class adv e-mail nbynews@jamadots.com; ed e-mail nbynews@att.net; web site www.newberry-news.com

Circulation: 3,600pd,; Sworn/Estimate/Non-Audited
Advertising rate: Open inch rate $6.00
Established: 1886
Ed. .... James Diem
Bus. Mgr. .... Caroline Diem
Adv. Mgr. .... Teri Petrie
Mechanical Specifications: Type page 11 5/8 x 21 1/2; E - 6 cols, 1 13/16, 1/8 between; A - 6 cols, 1 13/16, 1/8 between; C - 6 cols, 1 13/16, 1/8 between.
Delivery Method: Mail, Newsstand
Areas Served: 49868, 49853, 49748, 49728, 49820, 49768, 49827, 49883, 49839, 49836, 49793, 49762, 49838, 49760

NILES

CASSOPOLIS VIGILANT (THUR)

217 N 4th St, Niles, MI, 49120-2301, Berrien, USA; gen tel (269) 683-2101; gen fax (269) 683-2175; disp adv e-mail phil.langer@leaderpub.com; class adv e-mail donna.knight@leaderpub.com; ed e-mail ambrosia.neldon@leaderpub.com; web site www.cassopolis-vigilant.com

Circulation: 800pd,; Sworn/Estimate/Non-Audited
Group: Boone Newspapers, Inc.

Community ed................................Scott Novak
Mechanical Specifications: Type page 13 x 21 1/4; E - 8 cols, 1 1/2, between; A - 8 cols, 1 1/2, between; C - 8 cols, 1 1/2, between. Equipment & Software: Hardware — APP/Mac; Presses — KP/Newsking; Software — QPS/QuarkXPress.
Delivery Method: Mail, Newsstand, Racks
Areas Served: Cassopolis, Vigilant

EDWARDSBURG ARGUS (THUR)

217 N 4th St, Niles, MI, 49120-2301, Berrien, USA; gen tel (269) 683-2100; ed tel (269) 687-7713; gen fax (269) 683-2175; disp adv e-mail phil.langer@leaderpub.com; ed e-mail ambrosia.neldon@leaderpub.com; web site www.edwardsburgargus.com
Circulation: 800pd, 21fr; Sworn/Estimate/Non-Audited
Group: Boone Newspapers, Inc.
Community Ed..............................Scott Novak
Mechanical Specifications: Type page 13 x 21 1/4; E - 8 cols, 1 1/2, between; A - 8 cols, 1 1/2, between; C - 8 cols, 1 1/2, between. Equipment & Software: Hardware — APP/Mac, 8-APP/Power Mac; Presses — KP/News King; Software — QPS/QuarkXPress, Microsoft/Word, Adobe/Photoshop.
Delivery Method: Mail, Newsstand, Racks
Areas Served: Edwardsburg, Michigan

ONTONAGON

THE ONTONAGON HERALD (WED)

326 River St, Ontonagon, MI, 49953-1612, Ontonagon, USA; gen tel (906) 884-2826; gen fax (906) 884-2939; ed e-mail maureen@ontonagonherald.com; web site www.ontonagonherald.com
Circulation: 3,700pd, 70fr; Sworn/Estimate/Non-Audited
Advertising rate: Open inch rate $4.95
Established: 1881
Ed.. Maureen Guzek
Mechanical Specifications: Type page 13 1/2 x 21; E - 6 cols, 2 1/16, 1/6 between; A - 6 cols, 2 1/16, 1/6 between; C - 9 cols, 1 1/3, 1/12 between.Equipment & Software: ; Presses — ATF/Chief 17.
Delivery Method: Mail

ORTONVILLE

CITIZEN (SAT)

12 South St, Ortonville, MI, 48462-7717, Oakland, USA; gen tel (248) 627-4332; adv tel (248) 627-4332; ed tel (248) 627-4332; gen fax (248) 627-4408; adv fax (248) 627-4408; disp adv e-mail citads@citnewspaper.com; class adv e-mail citads@citnewspaper.com; ed e-mail citnews@citnewspaper.com; web site www.thecitizenonline.com
Circulation: 11,800fr; Sworn/Estimate/Non-Audited
Advertising rate: 1/4 P $258, 1/2 P $503, Full $1019
Established: 1995
Group: Sherman Publications, Inc.
Digital Platform - Mobile: Windows
Pub...Jim Sherman
Adv. Mgr.....................................Jackie Nowiki
Mechanical Specifications: Type page 10 x 11; E - 6 cols, between.
Delivery Method: Mail
Areas Served: 48438, 48462

OSCODA

OSCODA PRESS (WED)

311 S State St, Oscoda, MI, 48750-1636, Iosco, USA; gen tel (989) 739-2054; gen fax (989) 739-3201; disp adv e-mail comp@iosconews.com; class adv e-mail comp@iosconews.com; ed e-mail editor1@oscodapress.com; web site http://www.iosconews.com/oscoda_press/
Circulation: 3,900pd,; USPS
Advertising rate: Open inch rate $11.45
Established: 1879
Group: Community Media Group
Ed..Holly Nelson
Gen. Mgr...Jim Young
Delivery Method: Mail, Newsstand, Racks
Areas Served: Iosco County

OWOSSO

SUNDAY INDEPENDENT (WED, SUN)

1907 W. M-21, Owosso, MI, 48867, Shiawassee, USA; gen tel (989) 723-1118; gen fax (989) 725-1834; ed e-mail indysales@chartermi.net; web site www.owossoindependent.com
Circulation: 32,035fr; Sworn/Estimate/Non-Audited
Advertising rate: Open inch rate $22.75
Established: 1968
Pub...Michael Flores
Ed.. William Constine
Adv. Mgr.`.......................................Kim Lazar
Mechanical Specifications: Type page 10 x 15; E - 6 cols, 1 1/2, 1/8 between.Equipment & Software: Hardware — APP/Mac; Software — QPS/QuarkXPress 6.0, Adobe/Photoshop 7.0, Adobe/Illustrator 9.0.
Delivery Method: Mail, Carrier

OXFORD

OXFORD LEADER (WED)

666 S Lapeer Rd, Oxford, MI, 48371-5034, Oakland, USA; gen tel (248) 628-4801; adv tel (248) 628-4801 ext.20; ed tel (248) 628-4801; gen fax (248) 628-9750; disp adv e-mail shermanpub@aol.com; web site www.oxfordleader.com
Circulation: 2,300pd, 97fr; USPS
Advertising rate: 1/4 P $172, 1/2 P $332, Full $649
Established: 1889
Group: Sherman Publications, Inc.
Pub....................................James A. Sherman
Asst. Pub ....Don Rush
Adv. Mgr...Eric Lewis
Ed...C.J. Carnacchis
Mechanical Specifications: Type page 10 x 11 A -8 cols, 1 1/8 between.1/8Equipment & Software: Hardware — PC; Presses — G; Software — Adobe/PageMaker 6.5.
Delivery Method: Mail
Areas Served: 48371, 48370, 48367, 48366

PARMA

COUNTY PRESS (WED)

PO Box 279, 11501 Mackie Rd, Parma, MI, 49269-0279, Jackson, USA; gen tel (517) 531-4542; gen fax (517) 531-3576; disp adv e-mail advertising@jxncopress.com; ed e-mail editor@jxncopress.com; web site www.jxncopress.com
Circulation: 1,500pd, 0fr; AAM
Advertising rate: Open inch rate $43.58
Established: 1868
Publ./Bus Mgr. .... Erika Sponsler
Ed./Pub................................... Lucas Sponsler
Mechanical Specifications: Type page 10 x 15; E - 5 cols, 2, between; A - 5 cols, 2, between; C - 5 cols, 2, between.
Delivery Method: Mail, Racks
Areas Served: The western parts of Jackson County, Mich.

PAW PAW

COURIER-LEADER (FRI, SUN)

32280 E Red Arrow Hwy, Paw Paw, MI, 49079-8764, Van Buren, USA; gen tel (269) 657-3072; gen fax (269) 657-5723; disp adv e-mail ads@vineyardpress.biz; class adv e-mail sales@vineyardpress.biz; ed e-mail couriereditorial@vineyardpress.biz; web site www.pawpawcourierleader.com
Circulation: 2,987pd, 16,300fr; USPS
Advertising rate: Open inch rate $8.00
Established: 1844
Digital Platform - Tablet: Kindle
Gen. Mgr. .... Steven A. Racette
Mng. Ed...Robin Griffin
Adv...Ashley Moore
Mechanical Specifications: Type page 13 x 21; E - 6 cols, 2 1/8, 1/8 between; A - 6 cols, 2 1/8, 1/8 between; C - 6 cols, 2 1/8, 1/8 between. Equipment & Software: Hardware — APP/MAC; Software — QPS/QuarkXPress , Adobe/Photoshop , Adobe/Illustrator .
Delivery Method: Mail, Newsstand, Carrier, Racks
Areas Served: 49079, 49064, 49071, 49065, 49055,49026,49045,49009,49067,

PINCKNEY

THE SUN TIMES NEWS (TUES)

9573 Dexter Pinckney Rd, Pinckney, MI, 48169-9667, USA; gen tel (734) 562-2325; gen fax (734) 562-2398; disp adv e-mail Info@thesuntimesnews.com; class adv e-mail Advertising@thesuntimesnews.com; ed e-mail Wendy@thesuntimesnews.com; web site https://thesuntimesnews.com
Circulation: 358pd, 16,561fr; USPS
Advertising rate: Open inch rate $10.00
Established: 1878
Owner/Pub................................ Robert Nester
Mechanical Specifications: Type page 10.75 x 20.5; E - 2 cols, 1 5/8, 1/8 between; A - 6 cols, 1 5/8, 1/8 between; C - 1 cols, 1 5/8, 1/8 between.
Delivery Method: Mail, Newsstand, Racks
Areas Served: 49285, 49259, 48137, 49251, 48169, 49272, 48819, 49240, 48118, 49201, 48130

PLYMOUTH

CANTON EAGLE (THUR)

502 Forest Ave, Plymouth, MI, 48170-1752, Wayne, USA; gen tel (734) 467-1900; gen fax (734) 729-1840; disp adv e-mail ads@journalgroup.com; ed e-mail editor@journalgroup.com; web site www.journalgroup.com
Circulation: 15,000pd,; Sworn/Estimate/Non-Audited
Advertising rate: Open inch rate $43.00
Established: 2002
Group: Associated Newspapers of Michigan
Digital Platform - Mobile: Windows
Pub...Susan Willett
Mechanical Specifications: 11.125" x 20.5 "
Delivery Method: Mail, Newsstand, Carrier, Racks
Areas Served: 48187-48188

NORTHVILLE EAGLE (THUR)

502 Forest Ave, Plymouth, MI, 48170-1752, Wayne, USA; gen tel (734) 467-1900; gen fax (734) 729-1840; disp adv e-mail ads@journalgroup.com; ed e-mail editor@journalgroup.com; web site www.journalgroup.com
Circulation: 4,662pd,; Sworn/Estimate/Non-Audited
Advertising rate: Open inch rate $25
Established: 2002
Group: Associated Newspapers of Michigan
Digital Platform - Mobile: Windows
Pub...Susan Willett
Delivery Method: Mail, Carrier, Racks
Areas Served: 48168 48168

PLYMOUTH EAGLE (THUR)

502 Forest Ave, Plymouth, MI, 48170-1752, Wayne, USA; gen tel (734) 467-1900; gen fax (734) 729-1840; disp adv e-mail ads@journalgroup.com; ed e-mail swillett@journalgroup.com; web site www.journalgroup.com
Circulation: 6,000pd,; Sworn/Estimate/Non-Audited
Advertising rate: Open inch rate $25
Established: 2000
Group: Associated Newspapers of Michigan
Digital Platform - Mobile: Windows
Pub...Susan Willett
Mechanical Specifications: 11.125" x 20.5 "
Delivery Method: Mail, Newsstand, Carrier, Racks
Areas Served: 48170 Plymouth

THE INKSTER LEDGER STAR (THUR)

502 Forest Ave, Plymouth, MI, 48170-1752, Wayne, USA; gen tel (734) 467-1900; gen fax (734) 729-1840; disp adv e-mail ads@journalgroup.com; ed e-mail swillett@journalgroup.com; web site www.journalgroup.com
Circulation: 1,940pd, 1,263fr; Sworn/Estimate/Non-Audited
Advertising rate: Open inch rate $43.00
Established: 1947
Group: Associated Newspapers of Michigan
Digital Platform - Mobile: Windows
Pub...Susan Willett
Mechanical Specifications: 11,125" x 20.5"
Delivery Method: Mail, Carrier
Areas Served: 48141

THE ROMULUS ROMAN (THUR)

502 Forest Ave, Plymouth, MI, 48170-1752, Wayne, USA; gen tel (734) 467-1900; gen fax (734) 729-1840; disp adv e-mail ads@journalgroup.com; ed e-mail swillett@journalgroup.com; web site www.journalgroup.com
Circulation: 1,163pd, 307fr; Sworn/Estimate/Non-Audited
Advertising rate: Open inch rate $25
Established: 1885
Group: Associated Newspapers of MichiganEditions: Eagle Romulus Roman
Digital Platform - Mobile: Windows
Ed./Pub.......................................Susan Willett
Mechanical Specifications: 11.125" x 20.5"
Delivery Method: Mail, Newsstand, Carrier, Racks
Areas Served: 48174

THE WAYNE EAGLE (THUR)

502 Forest Ave, Plymouth, MI, 48170-1752, Wayne, USA; gen tel (734) 467-1900; gen fax (734) 729-1840; disp adv e-mail ads@journalgroup.com; ed e-mail swillett@journalgroup.com; web site www.journalgroup.com
Circulation: 1,253pd, 998fr; Sworn/Estimate/Non-Audited
Advertising rate: Open inch rate $25
Group: Associated Newspapers of Michigan
Digital Platform - Mobile: Windows
Pub...Susan Willett
Mechanical Specifications: 11/125" x 20.5 "
Delivery Method: Mail, Newsstand, Carrier, Racks
Areas Served: City 48184

THE WESTLAND EAGLE (THUR)

502 Forest Ave, Plymouth, MI, 48170-1752, Wayne, USA; gen tel (734) 467-1900; gen fax (734) 729-1840; disp adv e-mail ads@journalgroup.com; ed e-mail swillett@journalgroup.com; web site www.associatednewspapers.net
Circulation: 100pd, 1,300fr; Sworn/Estimate/Non-Audited
Advertising rate: Open inch rate $25
Established: 1885
Group: Associated Newspapers of Michigan
Digital Platform - Mobile: Windows
Pub...Susan Willett
Mechanical Specifications: 11,125" x 20.5 "
Delivery Method: Mail, Newsstand, Carrier, Racks
Areas Served: 48185 48186 Westland

ROCKFORD

ROCKFORD SQUIRE (THUR)

331 Northland Dr NE, Rockford, MI, 49341-1025, Kent, USA; gen tel (616) 866-4465; gen fax (616) 866-3810; disp adv e-mail squiresalesteam@gmail.com; class adv e-mail squiresales@gmail.com; ed e-mail squiremail@aol.com; web site rockfordsquire.com
Circulation: 11,300fr; Sworn/Estimate/Non-Audited
Advertising rate: Open inch rate $8.50
Established: 1871

Owner/Ed. Beth AltenaEquipment & Software: ; Software — Adobe/PageMaker 6.0, APP/Mac AppleWorks.
Delivery Method: Mail
Areas Served: Rockford MI, 49341

ROGERS CITY

PRESQUE ISLE COUNTY ADVANCE (THUR)

104 S Third St, Rogers City, MI, 49779-1710, Presque Isle, USA; gen tel (989) 734-2105; gen fax (989) 734-3053; ed e-mail editor@pi-advance.com; web site www.piadvance.com
Circulation: 3,800pd, 50fr; USPS
Advertising rate: Open inch rate $7.90
Established: 1878
Pub .... Richard W. Lamb
Mechanical Specifications: Type page 10.375 wide by 21 tall. 1.625 inch column, 6 column formatEquipment & Software: Hardware — APP/Mac; Presses — none; Software — Microsoft Word, Adobe Creative Suite, Creator
Delivery Method: Mail, Newsstand
Areas Served: 49779

SAGINAW

SAGINAW PRESS (FRI)

100 S Michigan Ave, Saginaw, MI, 48602-2054, Saginaw, USA; gen tel (989) 793-8070; gen fax (989) 921-7225; ed e-mail editor@thesaginawnews.com
Circulation: 448pd, 6fr; Sworn/Estimate/Non-Audited
Advertising rate: Open inch rate $5.88
Circ. Dir. .... George W. Baxter
Ed .... Jodi Mcfarland
Mechanical Specifications: Type page 13 1/2 x 19 1/2; E - 6 cols, 2 2/3, 1/12 between; A - 6 cols, 2 2/3, 1/12 between; C - 6 cols, 2 2/3, 1/12 between.

SAINT IGNACE

THE ST. IGNACE NEWS (THUR)

359 Reagon St, Saint Ignace, MI, 49781-1134, Mackinac, USA; gen tel (906) 643-9150; gen fax (906) 643-9122; disp adv e-mail ads@SaintIgnaceNews.com; ed e-mail news@SaintIgnaceNews.com; web site www.saintignacenews.com
Circulation: 4,985pd,; Sworn/Estimate/Non-Audited
Advertising rate: Open inch rate $11.00
Established: 1878
Bus. Mgr. .... Mary Maurer
Circ. Mgr. .... Wendy Colegrove
Pub .... Wesley H. Jr. Maurer
Ed. .... Ellen Paquin
Mechanical Specifications: Type page 12 1/2 x 20; E - 6 cols, 1 15/16, 1/8 between; A - 6 cols, 1 15/16, 1/8 between; C - 9 cols, 1 1/4, 1/8 between.Equipment & Software: Hardware — APP/Mac, COM, Gateway; Presses — Ik; Software — QPS/QuarkXPress, WordStar.
Delivery Method: Mail
Areas Served: 49781, 49719, 49745, 49757, 49868, 49774, 49762, 49760

SALINE

YPSILANTI COURIER (THUR)

1 Heritage Dr Ste 100, Saline, MI, 48176, Washtenaw, USA; gen tel (734) 429-7380; gen fax (734) 697-4610; disp adv e-mail westadvertising@heritage.com; class adv e-mail classifieds@heritage.com; ed e-mail editor@ypsilanticourier.com; web site http://www.thenewsherald.com
Circulation: 467pd, 4,503fr; CAC
Advertising rate: Open inch rate $79.75
Ed .... James Pruitt
Mechanical Specifications: Type page 13 x 21; E - 6 cols, 2, 1/6 between; A - 6 cols, 2, 1/6 between; C - 9 cols, 1 1/10, 1/6 between. Equipment & Software: Hardware — IBM; Presses — G/Community; Software — Microsoft/Word 97.
Delivery Method: Mail, Newsstand, Carrier
Areas Served: Belleville, Ypsilanti, Ypsilanti Township, Augusta Township and Superior Township

SANDUSKY

SANILAC COUNTY NEWS (WED)

65 S Elk St, Sandusky, MI, 48471-1337, MI, USA; gen tel (810) 648-4000; adv tel (810) 648-4000; ed tel (810) 648-4000; gen fax (810) 648-4526; adv fax (810) 648-4526; ed fax (810) 648-4526; disp adv e-mail info@mihomepaper.com; class adv e-mail sales@mihomepaper.com; ed e-mail jvanderpoel@mihomepaper.com; web site www.mihomepaper.com
Circulation: 5,674pd, 197fr; CVC
Advertising rate: $14.35 pci
Established: 1971
Group: JAMS Media
Digital Platform - Mobile: Apple, Android
Digital Platform - Tablet: Apple iOS, Android
Pub .... Jane Vanderpoel
Ed. .... Eric Levine
Mechanical Specifications: Type page 11 67/500 x 20; E - 6 cols, 1 1/2, between; A - 6 cols, 1 1/2, between; C - 6 cols, 1 1/2, between. Equipment & Software: Hardware — APP/Macs; Presses — 7-G; Software — Microsoft/Word, Adobe/PageMaker, Adobe/Photoshop.
Delivery Method: Mail, Newsstand, Racks
Areas Served: Sanilac County MI

THE BROWN CITY BANNER (MON)

65 S Elk St, Sandusky, MI, 48471-1337, Sanilac, USA; web site www.mihomepaper.com
Circulation: 676pd, 95fr; CVC
Advertising rate: Open inch rate $9.68
Adv. Mgr .... Pete Clinton
Circ. Mgr .... Dale Phillips
Prod. Mgr .... Donna Ashby

THE JEFFERSONIAN (FRI)

65 S Elk St, Sandusky, MI, 48471-1337, Sanilac, USA; gen tel (810) 648-4000; adv tel (810) 648-4000; ed tel (810) 648-4000; gen fax (810) 648-4526; adv fax (810) 648-4526; ed fax (810) 648-4526; disp adv e-mail jvanderpoel@mihomepaper.com; class adv e-mail jvanderpoel@mihomepaper.com; ed e-mail jvanderpoel@mihomepaper.com; web site www.mihomepaper.com
Circulation: 0pd, 5,688fr; CVC
Advertising rate: Open inch rate $14.35
Established: 1971
Group: JAMS Media
Digital Platform - Mobile: Apple, Android
Digital Platform - Tablet: Apple iOS, Android
Ed. .... Eric Levine
Pub .... Jane Vanderpoel
Mechanical Specifications: Type page 11 67/500 x 20; E - 6 cols, 1 1/2, between; A - 6 cols, 1 1/2, between; C - 6 cols, 1 1/2, between. Equipment & Software: Hardware — APP/Macs; Presses — 7-G; Software — Microsoft/Word, Adobe/PageMaker, Adobe/Photoshop.
Delivery Method: Mail, Racks
Areas Served: Sanilac County, MI

TRI-COUNTY CITIZEN (SUN)

65 S Elk St, Sandusky, MI, 48471-1337, Sanilac, USA; gen tel (989) 845-7403; gen fax (989) 845-4397; disp adv e-mail tccsales@mihomepaper.com; class adv e-mail tccsales@mihomepaper.com; ed e-mail tccnews@mihomepaper.com; web site www.mihomepaper.com
Circulation: 17,844fr; CVC
Advertising rate: Open inch rate $9.45
Established: 1983
Pub .... Robert Grnak
Wes Smith
Adv. Mgr .... Pete Clinton
Circ. Mgr .... Dale Phillips
Prod. Mgr .... Donna Ashby
Mechanical Specifications: Type page: 9.75 x 15.875; 6 col
Delivery Method: Carrier
Areas Served: 48616, 48614, 48655, 48457, 48460, 48433, 48649 48420

TRIBUNE RECORDER LEADER (TUES)

43 S Elk St, Sandusky, MI, 48471-1353, Sanilac, USA; gen tel (810) 648-5282; gen fax (810) 376-4058; ed e-mail recorder@thumb.net; web site http://www.tribunerecorderleader.com/
Circulation: 1,500pd, 10fr; Sworn/Estimate/Non-Audited
Advertising rate: Open inch rate $3.50
Established: 1893
Group: Hearst Communications, Inc.
Ed. .... Douglas Regentin
Mechanical Specifications: Type page 10 x 15; E - 6 cols, 1 1/2, 1/8 between; A - 6 cols, 1 1/2, 1/8 between; C - 6 cols, 1 1/2, 1/8 between. Equipment & Software: Hardware — PC; Software — Microsoft/Word 6.0.

SAUGATUCK

THE COMMERCIAL RECORD (THUR)

3217 Blue Star Hwy, Saugatuck, MI, 49453-9723, Allegan, USA; gen tel (269) 857-2570; gen fax (269) 857-4637; disp adv e-mail commrec@allegannews.com; ed e-mail editorcommrec@allegannews.com; web site www.thecommercialrecord.com
Circulation: 1,020pd, 21fr; USPS
Advertising rate: Open inch rate $7.98
Established: 1869
Group: Kaechele Publications, Inc.
Pub .... Cheryl Kaechele
Office Mgr. .... Connie Ellis
Mechanical Specifications: full page image size 10.5" x 21.5"; 6 cols, 1.646, 1/8 betweenEquipment & Software: Hardware — APP/Mac; Software — Microsoft/Word 11.5.6, Adobe/Photoshop 11.0.2, QPS/QuarkXPress 9.3
Delivery Method: Mail, Newsstand
Areas Served: 49453, 49406

SOUTH HAVEN

SOUTH HAVEN TRIBUNE (SUN)

308 Kalamazoo St, South Haven, MI, 49090-1308, Van Buren, USA; gen tel (269) 637-1104; adv tel (269) 429-2400 ext.405; ed tel (269) 637-1104 ext.14; gen fax (269) 637-8415; disp adv e-mail bcelmer@TheH-P.com; class adv e-mail bcelmer@TheH-P.com; ed e-mail news@southhaventribune.com; web site www.southhaventribune.net
Circulation: 13,665fr; Sworn/Estimate/Non-Audited
Established: 1899
Group: Paxton Media Group, LLC
Pub .... David Holgate
Ed./Gen. Mgr. .... Becky Burkert
Adv. Dir. .... Stacey Ramsey
Circ. Dir. .... Barry Whitman
Mechanical Specifications: Type page 11 5/8 x 22; E - 6 cols, 1 5/6, 1/8 between; A - 6 cols, 1 5/6, 1/8 between; C - 9 cols, 1 13/16, 1/8 between.Equipment & Software: Hardware — Apple computers; Software — Microsoft/Word, APP/Mac Caliber Classified, InDesign, Adobe Photoshop, Adobe Illustrator
Delivery Method: Newsstand, Carrier, Racks
Areas Served: Van Buren County

SOUTHGATE

HERITAGE SUNDAY (WED, SUN)

1 Heritage Dr, Ste 100, Southgate, MI, 48195-3047, Wayne, USA; gen tel (734) 246-0800; gen fax (734) 284-2117; disp adv e-mail westadvertising@heritage.com; class adv e-mail classifieds@heritage.com; ed e-mail editor@heritage.com; web site www.heritage.com
Circulation: 56,387pd, 15,608fr; Sworn/Estimate/Non-Audited
Advertising rate: Open inch rate $63.58
Established: 1879
Ed. .... Karl Ziomek

ILE CAMERA (FRI)

1 Heritage Dr Ste 100, Suite 100, Southgate, MI, 48195-3047, Wayne, USA; gen tel (734) 246-2800; gen fax (734) 282-7942; disp adv e-mail westadvertising@heritage.com; class adv e-mail classifieds@heritage.com; ed e-mail editor@ilecamera.com; web site www.thenewsherald.com/ile_camera
Circulation: 1,686pd, 7fr; CAC
Advertising rate: Modular rates. Call for pricing
Established: 1945
Group: Digital First Media
Ed. .... Lena Khzouz
Delivery Method: Mail, Carrier
Areas Served: Grosse Isle

NEWS-HERALD (WED, FRI, SUN)

1 Heritage Dr, Ste 100, Southgate, MI, 48195-3047, Wayne, USA; gen tel (734) 246-0800; gen fax (734) 284-2117; disp adv e-mail westadvertising@heritage.com; class adv e-mail classifieds@heritage.com; ed e-mail editor@thenewsherald.com; web site www.thenewsherald.com
Circulation: 17,219pd, 33,120fr; CAC
Advertising rate: Open inch rate $41.00
Established: 1986
Group: Digital First Media
Mng. Ed. .... Rick Kessler
Pub. .... Jeannie Parent
Editor .... Jason Alley
Delivery Method: Mail, Carrier
Areas Served: Southeast Wayne County

PRESS & GUIDE (WED, SUN)

1 Heritage Dr, Ste 100, Southgate, MI, 48195-3047, Wayne, USA; gen tel (734) 246-0800; gen fax (734) 284-2117; disp adv e-mail westadvertising@heritage.com; class adv e-mail classifieds@heritage.com; ed e-mail editor@pressandguide.com; web site www.pressandguide.com
Circulation: 3,989pd, 11,558fr; CAC
Advertising rate: Open inch rate $45.90
Established: 1918
Group: Digital First Media
Mktg. Dir. .... Bill Dillingham
Delivery Method: Mail, Carrier
Areas Served: Wayne County

THE CHELSEA STANDARD (THUR)

1 Heritage Dr Ste 100, Suite 100, Southgate, MI, 48195-3047, Wayne, USA; gen tel (734) 475-1371; gen fax (734) 429-3621; disp adv e-mail westadvertising@heritage.com; class adv e-mail classifieds@heritage.com; ed e-mail editor@chelseastandard.com; web site www.chelseastandard.com
Circulation: 1,811pd, 16fr; CAC
Advertising rate: Open inch rate $79.75
Established: 1873
Group: Digital First Media
Heritage Newspapers, Inc.
Ed .... Jason Alley
VP .... Teresa Goodrich
Pub .... Jeannie Parent
Mechanical Specifications: Type page 13 x 21 1/2; E - 6 cols, between.Equipment & Software: Hardware — PC; Software — QPS/QuarkXPress, Microsoft/Word.
Areas Served: Chelsea

THE SALINE REPORTER (THUR)

1 Heritage Dr Ste 100, Suite 100, Southgate, MI, 48195-3047, Wayne, USA; gen tel (734) 429-7380; gen fax (734) 429-3621; disp adv e-mail westadvertising@heritage.com; class adv e-mail classifieds@heritage.com; ed e-mail editor@salinereporter.com; web site www.salinereporter.com
Circulation: 1,835pd, 42fr; CAC
Advertising rate: Open inch rate $79.75
Established: 1883
Ed. .... Michelle Rogers
Delivery Method: Mail, Carrier
Areas Served: Washtenaw County

THE VIEW (THUR)
1 Heritage Dr Ste 100, Suite 100, Southgate, MI, 48195-3047, Wayne, USA; gen tel (734) 429-7380; gen fax (734) 429-3621; disp adv e-mail westadvertising@heritage.com; class adv e-mail classifieds@heritage.com; ed e-mail editor@belleville view.com; web site www.heritage.com/belleville_view
Circulation: 504pd, 296fr; Sworn/Estimate/ Non-Audited
Advertising rate: Open inch rate $79.75
Established: 1994
Group: Digital First Media
Ed. .... Laura Zoochi
Areas Served: Wayne & Washtenaw Counties

SPRINGPORT

SPRINGPORT SIGNAL (THUR)
123 W Main St, Springport, MI, 49284-9501, Jackson, USA; gen tel (517) 857-2500; gen fax (517) 857-2887; ed e-mail springportsignal@springcom.com; web site http://www.springportmi.com/newspaper.htm
Circulation: 1,100pd, 10fr; Sworn/Estimate/ Non-Audited
Advertising rate: Open inch rate $5.00
Ed. .... Dawn Doner

STANDISH

ARENAC COUNTY INDEPENDENT (WED)
1010 W Cedar St, Standish, MI, 48658-9421, Arenac, USA; gen tel (989) 846-4531; gen fax (989) 846-9868; disp adv e-mail sales@arenacindependent.com; class adv e-mail classifieds@arenacindependent.com; ed e-mail news@arenacindependent.com; web site www.arenacindependent.com
Circulation: 6,000pd,; Sworn/Estimate/Non-Audited
Advertising rate: Open inch rate $7.50
Established: 1883
Pub. .... Elizabeth Gorske
Mng. Ed.. Eric Young
Sales.. Carla Reeves
Delivery Method: Mail
Areas Served: Greater Arenac County

TECUMSEH

THE TECUMSEH HERALD (MON, THUR)
110 E Logan St, Tecumseh, MI, 49286-1559, Lenawee, USA; gen tel (517) 423-2174; gen fax (517) 423-6258; disp adv e-mail brian@tecumsehherald.com; class adv e-mail sharonm@tecumsehherald.com; ed e-mail managingeditor@tecumsehherald.com; web site www.tecumsehherald.com
Circulation: 4,000pd,; USPS
Advertising rate: Open inch rate $11.15
Established: 1850
Pub....................................... James C. Lincoln
Ed. .... Mickey Alvarado
Circ. Mgr..................................... Patti Brugger
Adv. Mgr.................................. Brian Callaghan
Mechanical Specifications: Type page 13 x 21; E - 6 cols, 2, 1/6 between; A - 6 cols, 2, 1/6 between; C - 6 cols, 2, 1/6 between. Equipment & Software: Hardware — Apple; Presses — 6-G/Community, 1-G/Universal 4-colon; Software — QPS/QuarkXPress 4.0, Adobe/PageMaker 6.5, Microsoft/Word 98, Adobe/Photoshop 6.0, Adobe/Illustrator, Adobe/InDesign.
Delivery Method: Mail, Newsstand
Areas Served: Tecumseh, Clinton, Britton, Adrian, Irish Hills

TRAVERSE CITY

NORTHERN EXPRESS (MON)
129 1/2 E Front St, Ste 305, Traverse City, MI, 49684-2508, Grand Traverse, USA; gen tel (231) 947-8787; gen fax (231) 947-2425; disp adv e-mail ads@northernexpress.com; ed e-mail info@northernexpress.com; web site northernexpress.com
Circulation: 34,000fr; VAC
Advertising rate: 1/4 P $425, 1/2 P $758, Full $1515
Established: 1992
Group: Express Publications, Inc.
Ed. .... Robert Downes
Delivery Method: Mail, Newsstand
Areas Served: Grand Traverse, Leelanau, Benzie, Kalkaska, Antrim, Wexford, Manistee, Emmet, Charlevoix, Otsego, Cheboygan, Roscommon, Isabella

THE LEADER AND THE KALKASKIAN (WED)
415 Cass St, Ste 2D, Traverse City, MI, 49684-2589, Grand Traverse, USA; gen tel (231) 486-0072; adv tel (231) 620-5707; ed tel (231) 620-5707; gen fax (231) 486-2203; disp adv e-mail plein@michigannewspapers.com; class adv e-mail dlein@michigannewspapers.com; ed e-mail news@grandtraverseinsider.com; web site http://www.themorningsun.com/contact
Circulation: 3,517pd, 25fr; Sworn/Estimate/ Non-Audited
Advertising rate: Open inch rate $6.30
Group: Digital First Media
Morning Star
Ed. .... Dave Lein
Adv. Mgr........ Pam LeinEquipment & Software: Hardware — APP/Mac.
Delivery Method: Mail, Racks

WAKEFIELD

WAKEFIELD NEWS/ BESSEMER PICK & AXE (THUR)
405 Sunday Lake St, Wakefield, MI, 49968-1337, Gogebic, USA; gen tel (906) 224-9561; gen fax (906) 224-9921; ed e-mail news@wnbpa.net
Circulation: 1,700pd, 48fr; USPS
Advertising rate: Open inch rate $4.50
Established: 1925
Ed. .... Andrew Hill
Mechanical Specifications: pdf or .jpg
Delivery Method: Mail, Newsstand

WALKER

CADENCE (SUN)
3102 Walker Ridge Dr NW, Walker, MI, 49544-9125, Kent, USA; gen tel (616) 669-2700; disp adv e-mail Advanceadvertising@mlive.com; class adv e-mail advancenews-classified@mlive.com; ed e-mail advancenewssubmissions@mlive.com; web site www.advancenewspapers.com
Circulation: 48,302fr; Sworn/Estimate/Non-Audited
Advertising rate: Open inch rate $20.50
Established: 1965
Group: Advance Publications, Inc.
Editor .... Sheila McGrath
Mechanical Specifications: Type page 10 3/8 x 16; A - 6 cols, 1 5/8, 1/8 between.Equipment & Software: Hardware — APP/Mac; Presses — G; Software — QPS/QuarkXPress 4.0, Adobe/Acrobat 4.0.
Delivery Method: Carrier
Areas Served: 49506

GRAND VALLEY ADVANCE (SUN)
3102 Walker Ridge Dr NW, Walker, MI, 49544-9125, Kent, USA; gen tel (616) 669-2700; disp adv e-mail Advanceadvertising@mlive.com; class adv e-mail advancenews-classified@mlive.com; ed e-mail advancenewssubmissions@mlive.com; web site www.advancenewspapers.com
Circulation: 37,280fr; Sworn/Estimate/Non-Audited
Advertising rate: Open inch rate $22.50
Group: Advance Publications, Inc.
Editor ...Sheila McGrathEquipment & Software: ; Software — QPS/QuarkXPress 4.0, Adobe/Acrobat 4.0.
Delivery Method: Carrier
Areas Served: 49418, 49426, 49427, 49428, 49401

SOUTHEAST ADVANCE (SUN)
3102 Walker Ridge Dr NW, Walker, MI, 49544-9125, Kent, USA; gen tel (616) 669-2700; disp adv e-mail Advanceadvertising@mlive.com; class adv e-mail advancenews-classified@mlive.com; ed e-mail advancenewssubmissions@mlive.com; web site www.advancenewspapers.com
Circulation: 29,749fr; Sworn/Estimate/Non-Audited
Advertising rate: Open inch rate $16.00
Established: 1965
Group: Advance Publications, Inc.
Editor .... Sheila McGrath
Mechanical Specifications: Type page 10 3/8 x 16.Equipment & Software: Hardware — APP/ Mac; Presses — G.; Software — QPS/ QuarkXPress 4.0, Adobe/Acrobat 4.0.
Delivery Method: Carrier
Areas Served: 49316, 49548, 49512, 49508

NORTHEAST ADVANCE (SUN)
3102 Walker Ridge Dr NW, Walker, MI, 49544-9125, Kent, USA; gen tel (616) 669-2700; disp adv e-mail Advanceadvertising@mlive.com; class adv e-mail advancenews-classified@mlive.com; ed e-mail advancenewssubmissions@mlive.com; web site www.advancenewspapers.com
Circulation: 22,040fr; Sworn/Estimate/Non-Audited
Advertising rate: Open inch rate $15.50
Established: 1965
Group: Advance Publications, Inc.
Editor .... Sheila McGrath
Mechanical Specifications: Type page 10 3/8 x 16; A - 6 cols, 1 5/8, 1/8 between.Equipment & Software: Hardware — APP/Mac; Presses — G; Software — QPS/QuarkXPress 4.0, Adobe/Acrobat 4.0.
Delivery Method: Carrier
Areas Served: 49503, 49505, 49525

NORTHWEST ADVANCE (SUN)
3102 Walker Ridge Dr NW, Walker, MI, 49544-9125, Kent, USA; gen tel (616) 669-2700; disp adv e-mail Advanceadvertising@mlive.com; class adv e-mail advancenews-classified@mlive.com; ed e-mail advancenewssubmissions@mlive.com; web site www.advancenewspapers.com
Circulation: 44,911fr; Sworn/Estimate/Non-Audited
Advertising rate: Open inch rate $17.00
Established: 1965
Group: Advance Publications, Inc.
Editor .... Sheila McGrath
Mechanical Specifications: Type page 10 3/8 x 16; A - 6 cols, 1 5/8, 1/8 between.Equipment & Software: Hardware — APP/Mac; Presses — G; Software — QPS/QuarkXPress 4.0, Adobe/Acrobat 4.0.
Delivery Method: Carrier
Areas Served: 49401, 49460, 49435, 49404, 49403, 49544, 49451, 49464

PENASEE GLOBE (SUN)
3102 Walker Ridge Dr NW, Walker, MI, 49544-9125, Kent, USA; gen tel (616) 669-2700; disp adv e-mail Advanceadvertising@mlive.com; class adv e-mail advancenews-classified@mlive.com; ed e-mail advancenewssubmissions@mlive.com; web site http://www.mlive.com/penaseeglobe/
Circulation: 14,000fr; Sworn/Estimate/Non-Audited
Advertising rate: Open inch rate $15.50
Established: 1884
Group: Advance Publications, Inc.
Editor .... Sheila McGrath
Mechanical Specifications: Type page 10 1/4 x 16; A - 6 cols, 1 1/2, 1/6 between; C - 6 cols, 1 1/2, 1/6 between.Equipment & Software: Hardware — APP/Macs; Software — Adobe/ PageMaker 7.0.
Delivery Method: Carrier
Areas Served: 49314, 49323, 49335, 49344, 49348

SOUTHWEST ADVANCE (SUN)
3102 Walker Ridge Dr NW, Walker, MI, 49544-9125, Kent, USA; gen tel (616) 669-2700; disp adv e-mail Advanceadvertising@mlive.com; class adv e-mail advancenews-classified@mlive.com; ed e-mail advancenewssubmissions@mlive.com; web site www.advancenewspapers.com
Circulation: 28,705fr; Sworn/Estimate/Non-Audited
Advertising rate: Open inch rate $16.25
Established: 1965
Group: Advance Publications, Inc.
Editor .... Sheila McGrath
Mechanical Specifications: Type page 10 3/8 x 16; A - 6 cols, 1 5/8, 1/8 between.Equipment & Software: Hardware — APP/Mac; Presses — G; Software — QPS/QuarkXPress 4.0, Adobe/Acrobat 4.0.
Delivery Method: Carrier
Areas Served: 49548, 49509

WARREN

ADVERTISER TIMES (WED, OTHER)
13650 E 11 Mile Rd, Warren, MI, 48089-1422, USA; gen tel (586) 498-8000; adv tel 586-498-1032; ed tel 586-498-1053; gen fax (586) 498-9631; disp adv e-mail kboz@candgnews.com; ed e-mail dwallace@candgnews.com; web site www.candgnews.com
Circulation: 24,477fr; CVC
Advertising rate: Open inch rate $37.05
Established: 1981
Group: C & G Newspapers
Owner.. Gregg Demers
Adv. Mgr.. Jeff Demers
Mng. Ed... Gilbert Demers
Prodn. Mgr. .... Keith Demers
Adv. Mgr....................................... Elaine Myers
Circ. Mgr .... David Demers
Prod. Mgr...................................... Barry Bernard
Mechanical Specifications: Type page 10 4/5 x 13 1/2; E - 5 cols, 2, 1/6 between; A - 5 cols, 2, 1/6 between; C - 6 cols, 1 1/2, 1/6 between. Equipment & Software: Hardware — APP/ Mac; Software — QPS/QuarkXPress.
Delivery Method: Mail
Areas Served: Wayne County

BIRMINGHAM-BLOOMFIELD EAGLE (WED)
13650 E 11 Mile Rd, Warren, MI, 48089-1422, Macomb, USA; gen tel (586) 498-8000; adv tel (586) 498-1051; ed tel (586) 498-1071; gen fax (586) 498-9631; disp adv e-mail emyers@candgnews.com; class adv e-mail jpadley@candgnews.com; ed e-mail gdemers@candgnews.com; web site www.candgnews.com
Circulation: 33,280fr; CAC
Advertising rate: Open inch rate $35.85
Established: 2003
Group: C & G Newspapers
Adv. Sales Mgr.................................. Jeff Demers
Ed. .... Gregg Demers
Adv. Mgr....................................... Elaine Myers
Circ. Mgr .... David Demers
Prod. Mgr...................................... Barry Bernard
Delivery Method: Mail, Racks
Areas Served: 48009, 48025, 48301, 48302, 49304

FARMINGTON PRESS (WED)
13650 E 11 Mile Rd, Warren, MI, 48089-1422, Macomb, USA; gen tel (586) 498-8000; adv tel (586) 498-1032; ed tel (586) 498-1071; gen fax (586) 498-9631; disp adv e-mail kboz@candgnews.com; class adv e-mail classified@candgnews.com; ed e-mail abates@candgnews.com; web site www.candgnews.com
Circulation: 37,825fr; CVC
Advertising rate: Open inch rate $39.19
Established: 2008
Group: C & G Newspapers
Dir of Sales.. Jeff Demers
Adv. Mgr....................................... Elaine Myers
Circ. Mgr .... David Demers
Prod. Mgr...................................... Barry Bernard
Delivery Method: Mail

Areas Served: 48167, 48331, 48334, 48335, 48336

FRASER-CLINTON CHRONICLE (WED)

13650 E 11 Mile Rd, Warren, MI, 48089-1422, Macomb, USA; gen tel (586) 498-8000; adv tel (586) 498-1032; ed tel (586) 498-1059; gen fax (586) 498-9631; disp adv e-mail kboz@candgnews.com; class adv e-mail classified@candgnews.com; ed e-mail jmalavolti@candgnews.com; web site www.candgnews.com
Circulation: 32,334fr; CAC
Advertising rate: Open inch rate $35.85
Established: 1989
Group: C & G Newspapers
Adv. Mgr. ....Jeff Demers
Circ. Mgr. ....Keith Demers
Mng. Ed. ....Gregg Demers
Prodn. Mgr. ....Barry Bernard
Adv. Mgr ....Elaine Myers
Circ. Mgr ....David Demers
Prod. Mgr ....Barry Bernard
Mechanical Specifications: Type page 9.5 x 11; E - 5 cols, 5/16, 3/16 between; A - 5 cols, 5/16, 3/16 between; C - 5 cols, 1/4, 3/16 between. Equipment & Software: Hardware — APP/Mac; Software — QPS/QuarkXPress.
Delivery Method: Mail
Areas Served: 48026 48035 48036 48038

GROSSE POINTE TIMES (THUR)

13650 E 11 Mile Rd, Warren, MI, 48089-1422, Macomb, USA; gen tel (586) 498-8000; adv tel (586) 279-1113; ed tel (586) 498-1053; gen fax (586) 498-9631; disp adv e-mail emyers@candgnews.com; class adv e-mail classified@candgnews.com; ed e-mail dwallace@candgnews.com; web site www.candgnews.com
Circulation: 18,751fr; AAM
Advertising rate: Open inch rate $29.56
Established: 1982
Group: C & G Newspapers
Adv. Mgr. ....Jeff Demers
Adv. Mgr ....Elaine Myers
Circ. Mgr ....David Demers
Prod. Mgr ....Barry Bernard
Mechanical Specifications: Type page 10 5/16 x 12 5/8; E - 5 cols, 2, 1/6 between; A - 5 cols, 2, 1/6 between; C - 6 cols, 1 1/2, 1/6 between.Equipment & Software: Hardware — APP/Mac; Software — QPS/QuarkXPress.
Delivery Method: Mail, Racks
Areas Served: 48230, 48236

JOURNAL (WED)

13650 E 11 Mile Rd, Warren, MI, 48089-1422, Macomb, USA; gen tel (586) 498-8000; adv tel (586) 498-1032; ed tel (586) 498-1059; gen fax (586) 498-9631; disp adv e-mail kboz@candgnews.com; class adv e-mail classified@candgnews.com; ed e-mail jmalavolti@candgnews.com; web site www.candgnews.com
Circulation: 34,010fr; CVC
Advertising rate: Open inch rate $35.85
Established: 1988
Group: C & G Newspapers
Prodn. Mgr. ....Keith Demers
Pub. ....Jeff Demers
Adv. Mgr ....Elaine Myers
Circ. Mgr ....David Demers
Prod. Mgr ....Barry Bernard
Gregg Demers
Mechanical Specifications: Type page 10 4/5 x 13 1/6; E - 5 cols, 2, 1/6 between; A - 5 cols, 2, 1/6 between; C - 6 cols, 1 1/2, 1/6 between. Equipment & Software: Hardware — APP/Mac; Software — QPS/QuarkXPress.
Delivery Method: Mail
Areas Served: 48035, 48036, 48043, 48045

MACOMB CHRONICLE (THUR)

13650 E 11 Mile Rd, Warren, MI, 48089-1422, Macomb, USA; gen tel (586) 498-8000; adv tel (586) 498-1072; ed tel (586) 498-1059; gen fax (586) 498-9631; disp adv e-mail emyers@candgnews.com; class adv e-mail classified@candgnews.com; ed e-mail jmalavolti@candgnews.com; web site www.candgnews.com
Circulation: 29,266fr; CAC
Advertising rate: Open inch rate $22.87
Established: 1989
Group: C & G Newspapers
Adv. Sales Mgr. ....Jeff Demers
Ed. ....Gregg Demers
Adv. Mgr ....Elaine Myers
Circ. Mgr ....David Demers
Prod. Mgr ....Barry Bernard
Delivery Method: Mail, Racks
Areas Served: 48042, 48044

MADISON-PARK NEWS (WED)

13650 E 11 Mile Rd, Warren, MI, 48089-1422, Macomb, USA; gen tel (586) 498-8000; adv tel (586) 498-1083; ed tel (586) 498-1059; gen fax (586) 498-9631; disp adv e-mail emyers@candgnews.com; class adv e-mail classified@candgnews.com; ed e-mail jmalavolti@candgnews.com; web site www.candgnews.com
Circulation: 19,259fr; CAC
Advertising rate: Open inch rate $25.41
Established: 1982
Group: C & G Newspapers
Adv. Mgr ....Jeff Demers
Circ. Mgr ....David Demers
Adv. Mgr ....Elaine Myers
Prod. Mgr ....Barry Bernard
Mechanical Specifications: Type page 10 5/16 x 12 5/8; E - 5 cols, 2, 1/6 between; A - 5 cols, 2, 1/6 between; C - 6 cols, 1 1/2, 1/6 between.Equipment & Software: Hardware — APP/Mac; Software — QPS/QuarkXPress.
Delivery Method: Mail, Racks
Areas Served: 48030, 48071

ROCHESTER POST (THUR)

13650 E 11 Mile Rd, Warren, MI, 48089-1422, Macomb, USA; gen tel (586) 498-8000; adv tel (586) 498-1032; ed tel (586) 498-1071; gen fax (586) 498-9631; disp adv e-mail kboz@candgnews.com; class adv e-mail classified@candgnews.com; ed e-mail abates@candgnews.com; web site www.candgnews.com
Circulation: 39,306fr; CAC
Advertising rate: Open inch rate $39.19
Established: 2005
Group: C & G Newspapers
Dir of Sales ....Jeff Demers
Ad. Mgr ....Elaine Myers
Circ. Mgr ....David Demers
Prod. Mgr ....Barry Bernard
Mechanical Specifications: Type page 9.5" x 11"; 5 cols
Delivery Method: Mail
Areas Served: 48306, 48307, 48309, 48363

ROYAL OAK REVIEW (WED)

13650 E 11 Mile Rd, Warren, MI, 48089-1422, Macomb, USA; gen tel (586) 498-8000; adv tel (586) 498-1031; ed tel (586) 498-1053; gen fax (586) 498-9631; disp adv e-mail kboz@candgnews.com; class adv e-mail classified@candgnews.com; ed e-mail dwallace@candgnews.com; web site www.candgnews.com
Circulation: 31,937fr; CAC
Advertising rate: Open inch rate $35.85
Established: 2003
Group: C & G Newspapers
Dir of Sales ....Jeff Demers
Adv. Mgr ....Elaine Myers
Circ. Mgr ....David Demers
Prod. Mgr ....Barry Bernard
Delivery Method: Mail
Areas Served: 48017, 48067, 48073

SHELBY-UTICA NEWS (WED)

13650 E 11 Mile Rd, Warren, MI, 48089-1422, Macomb, USA; gen tel (586) 498-8000; adv tel (586) 498-1091; ed tel (586) 498-1053; gen fax (586) 498-9631; disp adv e-mail emyers@candgnews.com; class adv e-mail classified@candgnews.com; ed e-mail dwallace@candgnews.com; web site www.candgnews.com
Circulation: 30,914fr; CAC
Advertising rate: Open inch rate $28.49
Established: 1992
Group: C & G Newspapers
Adv. Mgr ....Elaine Myers
Circ. Mgr ....David Demers
Prod. Mgr ....Barry Bernard
Mechanical Specifications: Type page 10 5/16 x 12 5/8; E - 4 cols, 2 7/16, 3/16 between; A - 4 cols, 2 7/16, 3/16 between; C - 6 cols, 1 9/16, 3/16 between.Equipment & Software: Hardware — APP/Mac; Software — QPS/QuarkXPress.
Delivery Method: Mail
Areas Served: 48315, 48316, 48317

SOUTHFIELD SUN (THUR)

13650 E 11 Mile Rd, Warren, MI, 48089-1422, Macomb, USA; gen tel (586) 498-8000; adv tel (586) 498-1032; ed tel (586) 498-1071; gen fax (586) 498-9631; disp adv e-mail kboz@candgnews.com; class adv e-mail classified@candgnews.com; ed e-mail abates@candgnews.com; web site www.candgnews.com
Circulation: 30,914fr; CAC
Advertising rate: Open inch rate $39.19
Established: 2004
Group: C & G Newspapers
Dir of Sales ....Jeff Demers
Ad. Mgr ....Elaine Myers
Circ. Mgr ....David Demers
Prod. Mgr ....Barry Bernard
Delivery Method: Mail
Areas Served: 48033, 48034, 48075, 48076

ST. CLAIR SHORES SENTINEL (WED)

13650 E 11 Mile Rd, Warren, MI, 48089-1422, Macomb, USA; gen tel (586) 498-8000; adv tel (586) 498-8117; ed tel (586) 498-1059; gen fax (586) 498-9631; disp adv e-mail emyers@candgnews.com; class adv e-mail classified@candgnews.com; ed e-mail jmalavolti@candgnews.com; web site www.candgnews.com
Circulation: 27,068fr; CVC
Advertising rate: Open inch rate $35.85
Established: 1981
Group: C & G Newspapers
Pub. ....Jeff Demers
Adv. Mgr ....Elaine Myers
Circ. Mgr ....David Demers
Prod. Mgr ....Barry Bernard
Mechanical Specifications: Type page 10 5/16 x 12 5/8; E - 5 cols, 2, 1/6 between; A - 5 cols, 2, 1/6 between; C - 6 cols, 1 1/2, 1/6 between.Equipment & Software: Hardware — APP/Mac; Software — QPS/QuarkXPress.
Delivery Method: Mail, Racks
Areas Served: 48080, 48081, 48082

STERLING HEIGHTS SENTRY (WED)

13650 E 11 Mile Rd, Warren, MI, 48089-1422, Macomb, USA; gen tel (586) 498-8000; adv tel (586) 498-1032; ed tel (586) 498-1071; gen fax (586) 498-9631; disp adv e-mail kboz@candgnews.com; class adv e-mail classified@candgnews.com; ed e-mail abates@candgnews.com; web site www.candgnews.com
Circulation: 48,349fr; CAC
Advertising rate: Open inch rate $41.73
Established: 1990
Group: C & G Newspapers
Pub. ....Jeff Demers
Circ. Mgr. ....Keith Demers
Mng. Ed. ....Gregg Demers
Prodn. Mgr. ....Barry Bernard
Adv. Mgr ....Elaine Myers
Circ. Mgr ....David Demers
Mechanical Specifications: Type page 9.5 x 11; E - 5 cols, 2, 1/6 between; A - 5 cols, 2, 1/6 between; C - 6 cols, 1 1/2, 1/6 between. Equipment & Software: Hardware — APP/Mac; Software — QPS/QuarkXPress.
Delivery Method: Mail
Areas Served: 48310, 48312, 48313, 48314

THE EASTSIDER (WED)

13650 E 11 Mile Rd, Warren, MI, 48089-1422, Macomb, USA; gen tel (586) 498-8000; adv tel (586) 498-1088; ed tel (586) 498-1053; gen fax (586) 498-9631; disp adv e-mail emyers@candgnews.com; class adv e-mail classified@candgnews.com; ed e-mail dwallace@candgnews.com; web site www.candgnews.com
Circulation: 30,894fr; AAM
Advertising rate: Open inch rate $35.85
Established: 1982
Group: C & G Newspapers
Pub. ....Jeff Demers
Adv. Mgr ....Elaine Myers
Circ. Mgr ....David Demers
Prod. Mgr ....Barry Bernard
Mechanical Specifications: Type page 10 4/5 x 13 1/6; E - 5 cols, 2, 1/6 between; A - 5 cols, 2, 1/6 between; C - 6 cols, 1 1/2, 1/6 between. Equipment & Software: Hardware — APP/Mac; Software — QPS/QuarkXPress.
Delivery Method: Mail, Racks
Areas Served: 48021, 48066

TROY TIMES (THUR)

13650 E 11 Mile Rd, Warren, MI, 48089-1422, Macomb, USA; gen tel (586) 498-8000; adv tel (586) 498-1087; ed tel (586) 498-1071; gen fax (586) 498-9631; disp adv e-mail emyers@candgnews.com; class adv e-mail classified@candgnews.com; ed e-mail abates@candgnews.com; web site www.candgnews.com
Circulation: 31,432fr; CAC
Advertising rate: Open inch rate $34.78
Established: 1985
Group: C & G Newspapers
Circ. Mgr. ....Jeff Demers
Adv. Mgr ....Elaine Myers
Prod. Mgr ....Barry Bernard
Mechanical Specifications: Type page 10 5/16 x 12 5/8; E - 4 cols, 2 7/16, 3/16 between; A - 4 cols, 2 7/16, 3/16 between; C - 6 cols, 1 9/16, 3/16 between.Equipment & Software: Hardware — APP/Mac; Software — QPS/QuarkXPress.
Delivery Method: Mail, Carrier, Racks
Areas Served: 48083, 48084, 48085, 48098

WARREN WEEKLY (WED)

13650 E 11 Mile Rd, Warren, MI, 48089-1422, Macomb, USA; gen tel (586) 498-8000; adv tel (586) 498-1078; ed tel (586) 498-1059; gen fax (586) 498-9631; disp adv e-mail emyers@candgnews.com; class adv e-mail classified@candgnews.com; ed e-mail jmalavolti@candgnews.com; web site www.candgnews.com
Circulation: 55,285fr; CAC
Advertising rate: Open inch rate $46.15
Established: 1981
Group: C & G Newspapers
Pub. ....Jeff Demers
Prod. Mgr. ....Barry Bernard
Adv. Mgr ....Elaine Myers
Circ. Mgr ....David Demers
Mechanical Specifications: Type page 10 5/16 x 12 5/8; E - 5 cols, 2, 1/6 between; A - 5 cols, 2, 1/6 between; C - 6 cols, 1 1/2, 1/6 between.Equipment & Software: Hardware — APP/Mac; Software — QPS/QuarkXPress.
Delivery Method: Mail, Racks
Areas Served: 48015, 48088, 48089, 48091, 48092, 48093

WEST BLOOMFIELD BEACON (WED)

13650 E 11 Mile Rd, Warren, MI, 48089-1422, Macomb, USA; gen tel (586) 498-8000; adv tel (586) 498-1032; ed tel (586) 498-1071; gen fax (586) 498-9631; disp adv e-mail kboz@candgnews.com; class adv e-mail classified@candgnews.com; ed e-mail abates@candgnews.com; web site www.candgnews.com
Circulation: 27,436fr; CAC
Advertising rate: Open inch rate $34.78
Established: 2004
Group: C & G Newspapers
Pub. ....Jeff Demers
Adv. Mgr ....Elaine Myers
Circ. Mgr ....David Demers
Prod. Mgr ....Barry Bernard
Delivery Method: Mail
Areas Served: 48320, 48322, 48323, 48324

WOODWARD TALK (WED)

13650 E 11 Mile Rd, Warren, MI, 48089-1422, Macomb, USA; gen tel (586) 498-8000; adv tel (586) 498-1032; ed tel (586) 498-1053; gen fax (586) 498-9631; disp adv e-mail kboz@candgnews.com; class adv e-mail classified@candgnews.com; ed e-mail dwallace@candgnews.com; web site www.

candgnews.com
Circulation: 20,019fr; CAC
Advertising rate: Open inch rate $25.41
Established: 2004
Group: C & G Newspapers
Ed. Dir. .... Gregg Demers
Ed. .... David Wallace
Dir of Sales .... Jeff Demers
Adv. Mgr. .... Elaine Myers
Circ. Mgr .... David Demers
Prod. Mgr .... Barry Bernard
Delivery Method: Mail
Areas Served: 48072, 48070, 48220, 48069

WEST BRANCH

OGEMAW COUNTY HERALD (THUR)
215 W Houghton Ave, West Branch, MI, 48661-1219, Ogemaw, USA; gen tel (989) 345-0044; gen fax (989) 345-5609; disp adv e-mail sales2@ogemawherald.com; class adv e-mail classifieds@ogemawherald.com; ed e-mail editor@ogemawherald.com; web site http://www.ogemawherald.com
Circulation: 6,700pd, 76fr; Sworn/Estimate/Non-Audited
Advertising rate: Open inch rate $120.35
Established: 1878
Pub. .... Liz Gorske
Ed. .... Eric Young
Delivery Method: Mail, Newsstand

OGEMAW/OSCODA COUNTY STAR (SUN)
420 W Houghton Ave, West Branch, MI, 48661-1224, Ogemaw, USA; gen tel (989) 345-0510; gen fax (989) 345-3750; disp adv e-mail cturner@michigannewspapers.com; class adv e-mail classifieds@michigannewspapers.com; ed e-mail rmills@michigannewspapers.com; web site http://www.themorningsun.com/about_us/ogemawoscoda/
Circulation: 14,654fr; CVC
Advertising rate: Open inch rate $19.70
Established: 1976
Group: Morning Star Publishing Company
Pub. .... Jeannie Parent
Adv. Mgr. .... Tammy Fisher
Circ. Mgr. .... Christine Fox
Prod. Mgr. .... Ron Martin
Mechanical Specifications: Type page: 9.75 x 16; 6 col

WHITEHALL

WHITE LAKE BEACON (SUN)
432 E Spring St, Whitehall, MI, 49461-1153, Muskegon, USA; gen tel (231) 894-5356; gen fax (231) 894-2174; disp adv e-mail editor@whitelakebeacon.com; class adv e-mail mindy@whitelakebeacon.com; ed e-mail editor@whitelakebeacon.com; web site www.whitelakebeacon.com
Circulation: 4,062pd, 6,375fr; Sworn/Estimate/Non-Audited
Advertising rate: Open inch rate $12.19
Established: 1983
Group: Community Media Group
Ed. .... Greg Means
Mechanical Specifications: Type page 14 1/4 x 21; E - 6 cols, 2 1/4, 1/8 between; A - 6 cols, 2 1/4, 1/8 between; C - 8 cols, 1 5/8, 3/16 between.Equipment & Software: Hardware — APP/Mac
Delivery Method: Mail, Newsstand, Carrier
Areas Served: 49452, 49437, 49461, 49445, 49457

YALE

THE YALE EXPOSITOR (WED)
21 S Main St, Yale, MI, 48097-3317, St. Clair, USA; gen tel (810) 387-2300; adv tel (810) 387-2300; ed tel (810) 387-2300; gen fax (810) 387-9490; disp adv e-mail YaleExpositor@gmail.com; class adv e-mail YaleExpositor@gmail.com; ed e-mail YaleExpositor@gmail.com; web site YaleExpositor.com
Circulation: 2,500pd, 0fr; Sworn/Estimate/Non-Audited
Advertising rate: Open inch rate $8.50
Established: 1882
Ed .... Barbara Stasik
Pub .... James Brown
Delivery Method: Mail, Newsstand
Areas Served: 48097
48006

ZEELAND

ZEELAND RECORD (THUR)
16 S Elm St, Zeeland, MI, 49464-1751, Ottawa, USA; gen tel (616) 772-2131; gen fax (616) 772-9771; disp adv e-mail advertising@zeelandrecord.net; class adv e-mail advertising@zeelandrecord.net; ed e-mail newsrelease@zeelandrecord.net
Circulation: 1,100pd,; Sworn/Estimate/Non-Audited
Advertising rate: Open inch rate $6.00
Established: 1893
Adv. Mgr. .... Kraig Van Koevering
Ed. .... Kurt Van Koevering
Mechanical Specifications: Type page 10 1/2 x 15; E - 5 cols, 2, 1/8 between; A - 5 cols, 2, 1/8 between; C - 5 cols, 2, 1/8 between. Equipment & Software: Hardware — IBM; Software — Adobe/PageMaker 6.5, Adobe/Photoshop 5.0.
Delivery Method: Mail
Areas Served: 49464

MINNESOTA

ADA

NORMAN COUNTY INDEX (TUES)
307 W Main St, Ada, MN, 56510-1251, Norman, USA; gen tel (218) 784-2541; gen fax (218) 784-2551; ed e-mail nci@loretel.net
Circulation: 1,653pd,; Sworn/Estimate/Non-Audited
Advertising rate: Open inch rate $5.00
Established: 1880
Group: Index Printing, Inc.
Digital Platform - Mobile: Apple
Pub. .... Ross Pfund
Mechanical Specifications: Type page 6 x 21; E - 6 cols, 2, 1/6 between; A - 6 cols, 2, 1/6 between; C - 6 cols, 2, 1/6 between.Equipment & Software: Hardware — APP/Mac; Presses — Ryobi; Software — QPS/QuarkXPress.
Delivery Method: Mail, Newsstand
Areas Served: 56510

ADAMS

MONITOR REVIEW (THUR)
318 W Main St, Adams, MN, 55909-9771, Mower, USA; gen tel (507) 582-3542; gen fax (507) 582-3542; disp adv e-mail monitor@omnitelcom.com; ed e-mail themonitorreview@gmail.com
Circulation: 1,127pd, 19fr; Sworn/Estimate/Non-Audited
Advertising rate: Open inch rate $3.50
Ed. .... Robert Adams
Mechanical Specifications: Type page 6 x 21 1/2; E - 6 cols, 2 1/18, 1/6 between; A - 6 cols, 2 1/18, 1/6 between; C - 6 cols, 2 1/18, 1/6 between.Equipment & Software: Hardware — 4-APP/Mac; Software — Adobe/PageMaker 4.2.

ADRIAN

NOBLES COUNTY REVIEW (WED)
108 Maine Ave, Adrian, MN, 56110-1192, Nobles, USA; gen tel (507) 483-2213; gen fax (507) 483-2219; ed e-mail ncreview@frontier.com; web site www.noblescountyreview.net
Circulation: 1,067pd, 1,300fr; Sworn/Estimate/Non-Audited
Advertising rate: Open inch rate $5.50
Group: Johnson Publishing Company
Pub. .... Gerald Johnson
Ed. .... Kathryn A. Burzlaff
Delivery Method: Mail, Newsstand

AITKIN

AITKIN INDEPENDENT AGE (WED)
213 Minnesota Ave N, Aitkin, MN, 56431-1411, Aitkin, USA; gen tel (218) 927-3761; adv tel 218-927-3761; ed tel 218-927-3761; gen fax (218) 927-3763; adv fax 218-927-3763; ed fax 218-927-3763; disp adv e-mail rbouley@aitkinage.com; class adv e-mail subscriptions@aitkinage.com; ed e-mail news@aitkinage.com; web site www.aitkinage.com
Circulation: 3,800pd,; Sworn/Estimate/Non-Audited
Advertising rate: Open inch rate $11.15
Established: 1883
Group: Adams Publishing Group, LLC
Operations Mgr. .... Roxanne Bouley
Ed. .... Brielle BredstenEquipment & Software: Hardware — APP/Mac; Software — QPS/QuarkXPress 3.3, Adobe/PageMaker 6.52, Adobe/Photoshop 5.0.
Delivery Method: Mail, Newsstand
Areas Served: 56431, 55760, 56469, 55787, 55748, 55752

ALBANY

STEARNS-MORRISON ENTERPRISE (TUES)
561 Railroad Ave, Albany, MN, 56307-9804, Stearns, USA; gen tel (320) 845-2700; gen fax (320) 845-4805; disp adv e-mail missy@saukherald.com; class adv e-mail kayla@saukherald.com; ed e-mail liz@albanyenterprise.com; web site www.albanyenterprise.com
Circulation: 1,870pd, 3,150fr; Sworn/Estimate/Non-Audited
Advertising rate: Open inch rate $5.56
Group: Star Publications/Upper Michigan LLC
Co-Pub. .... Peggy Bakken
Co-Pub. .... Bruce Treichler
Ed. .... Michael Kosik

ALEXANDRIA

ECHO-PRESS (WED, FRI)
225 7th Ave E, Alexandria, MN, 56308-1831, Douglas, USA; gen tel (320) 763-3133; adv tel (320) 763-3133; ed tel (320) 763-3133; gen fax (320) 763-3258; adv fax (320) 763-3258; ed fax (320) 763-3258; disp adv e-mail jhanson@echopress.com; class adv e-mail mweller@echopress.com; ed e-mail jbeach@echopress.com; web site www.echopress.com
Circulation: 6,920pd,; VAC
Advertising rate: $16.50
Established: 1891
Group: Forum Communications Co.
Pub. .... Jody Hanson
Circ. Mgr. .... Lynn Mounsdon
Bus. Mgr. .... Diann Drew
News Ed./Opinion Page Ed. .... Al Edenloff
Ed. .... Jeff Beach
Delivery Method: Mail, Newsstand, Carrier
Areas Served: 56308 and 30 mile radius

OSAKIS REVIEW (TUES)
PO Box 5, Alexandria, MN, 56308-0005, Douglas, USA; gen tel (320) 859-2143 ; adv tel (320) 763-1225 ; gen fax (320) 763-3258; disp adv e-mail achaffins@osakisreview.com; ed e-mail news@theosakisreview.com; web site www.theosakisreview.com
Circulation: 1,147pd, 28fr; Sworn/Estimate/Non-Audited
Advertising rate: Open inch rate $5.25
Established: 1890
Group: Forum Communications Co.
Pub. .... Jody Hanson
Mng. Ed. .... Greta Petrich
Circ. Mgr. .... Lynn Mounsdon
Mechanical Specifications: Type page 5 x 16 1/2; E - 4 cols, 2 1/5, 1/60 between; A - 4 cols, 2 1/5, 1/60 between; C - 4 cols, 2 1/5, 1/60 between.Equipment & Software: Hardware — APP/Mac; Software — QPS/QuarkXPress.
Delivery Method: Mail, Carrier

ANNANDALE

ANNANDALE ADVOCATE (WED)
73 Oak Ave S, Annandale, MN, 55302-1205, Wright, USA; gen tel (320) 274-3052; gen fax (320) 274-2301; disp adv e-mail ads@annandaleadvocate.com; ed e-mail news@annandaleadvocate.com; web site www.annandaleadvocate.com
Circulation: 2,515pd,; Sworn/Estimate/Non-Audited
Advertising rate: Open inch rate $6.45
Pub. .... Steven Prinsen
Co-Pub. .... Sharon Schumacher
Ed. .... Paul Downer
Delivery Method: Mail

APPLE VALLEY

DAKOTA COUNTY TRIBUNE (THUR)
15322 Galaxie Ave Ste 219, Suite 219, Apple Valley, MN, 55124-3150, Dakota, USA; gen tel (952) 894-1111; gen fax (952) 846-2010; disp adv e-mail ads.thisweek@ecm-inc.com; class adv e-mail class.thisweek@ecm-inc.com; ed e-mail tad.johnson@ecm-inc.com; web site http://sunthisweek.com/dakota-county-tribune/
Circulation: 19pd, 12,687fr; CAC
Advertising rate: Open inch rate $9.50
Established: 1887
Group: Adams Publishing Group, LLC
Gen Mgr. .... Mike Jetchick
Ed. .... Tad Johnson
Pub. .... Julian AndersenEquipment & Software: Hardware — 11-APP/iMac, 9-APP/Powermac G4, 3-APP/Powermac G3; Software — QPS/QuarkXPress 4.1.1, Adobe/Illustrator 8, Adobe/Photoshop 5.5.

SUN THISWEEK LAKEVILLE (THUR)
15322 Galaxie Ave Ste 219, Suite 219, Apple Valley, MN, 55124-3150, Dakota, USA; gen tel (952) 894-1111; gen fax (952) 846-2010; disp adv e-mail sharon.buechner@ecm-inc.com; ed e-mail tad.johnson@ecm-inc.com; web site www.sunthisweek.com
Circulation: 22pd, 16,807fr; CAC
Advertising rate: Open inch rate $18.00
Established: 1979
Group: Adams Publishing Group, LLC
Mng. Ed. .... Tad Johnson
Ed. .... John GessnerEquipment & Software: Hardware — 11-APP/iMac, 7-APP/Powermac G4, 3-APP/Powermac G3; Software — Adobe CS4 InCopy
Delivery Method: Carrier
Areas Served: 55044

SUN THISWEEK APPLE VALLEY (THUR)
15322 Galaxie Ave Ste 219, Suite 219, Apple Valley, MN, 55124-3150, Dakota, USA; gen tel (952) 894-1111; adv tel (952) 846-2019; gen fax (952) 846-2010; disp adv e-mail ads.thisweek@ecm-inc.com; ed e-mail andrew.miller@ecm-inc.com; web site sunthisweek.com - 100,000(views) 27,000(visitors)
Circulation: 25pd, 11,248fr; CAC
Advertising rate: Open inch rate $14.00
Established: 1979
Group: Adams Publishing Group, LLC
Digital Platform - Mobile: Apple, Android, Windows
Digital Platform - Tablet: Apple iOS, Android,

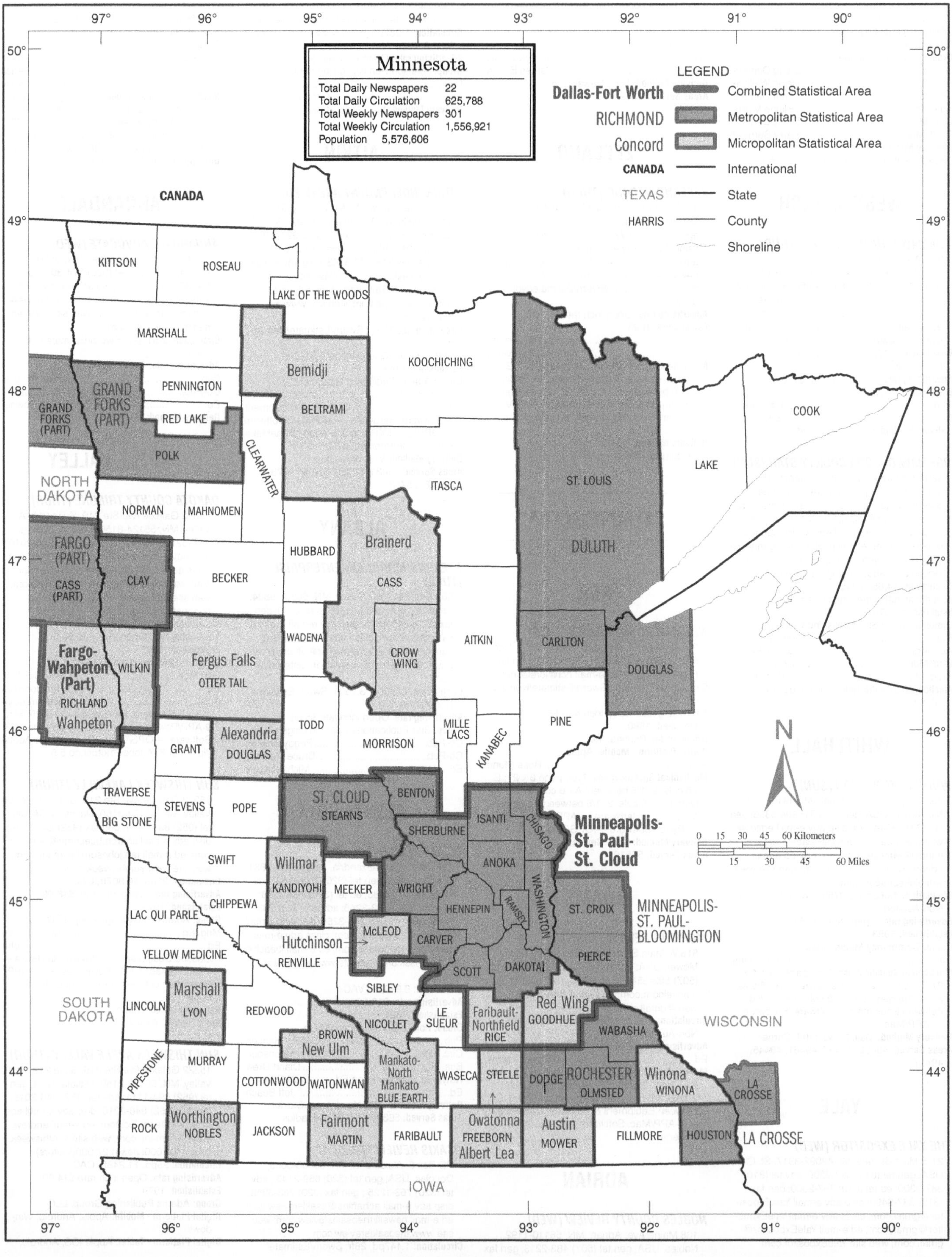
Minnesota
Total Daily Newspapers 22
Total Daily Circulation 625,788
Total Weekly Newspapers 301
Total Weekly Circulation 1,556,921
Population 5,576,606
LEGEND
Dallas-Fort Worth Combined Statistical Area
RICHMOND Metropolitan Statistical Area
Concord Micropolitan Statistical Area
CANADA International
TEXAS State
HARRIS County
Shoreline
CANADA
NORTH DAKOTA
SOUTH DAKOTA
WISCONSIN
IOWA
KITTSON
ROSEAU
LAKE OF THE WOODS
MARSHALL
Bemidji
BELTRAMI
KOOCHICHING
GRAND FORKS (PART)
GRAND FORKS (PART)
PENNINGTON
RED LAKE
POLK
CLEARWATER
NORMAN
MAHNOMEN
ITASCA
ST. LOUIS
DULUTH
LAKE
COOK
FARGO (PART)
CASS (PART)
CLAY
BECKER
HUBBARD
Brainerd
CASS
CROW WING
WADENA
AITKIN
CARLTON
DOUGLAS
Fargo-Wahpeton (Part)
RICHLAND
Wahpeton
WILKIN
Fergus Falls
OTTER TAIL
TODD
MORRISON
MILLE LACS
KANABEC
PINE
Alexandria
DOUGLAS
GRANT
TRAVERSE
STEVENS
POPE
BIG STONE
ST. CLOUD
STEARNS
BENTON
SHERBURNE
ISANTI
CHISAGO
Minneapolis-St. Paul-St. Cloud
SWIFT
Willmar
KANDIYOHI
MEEKER
WRIGHT
ANOKA
WASHINGTON
HENNEPIN
RAMSEY
ST. CROIX
MINNEAPOLIS-ST. PAUL-BLOOMINGTON
CHIPPEWA
LAC QUI PARLE
McLEOD
CARVER
Hutchinson
RENVILLE
YELLOW MEDICINE
SCOTT
DAKOTA
PIERCE
SIBLEY
Marshall
LYON
LINCOLN
REDWOOD
NICOLLET
LE SUEUR
Faribault-Northfield
RICE
Red Wing
GOODHUE
WABASHA
BROWN
New Ulm
PIPESTONE
MURRAY
COTTONWOOD
WATONWAN
Mankato-North Mankato
BLUE EARTH
WASECA
STEELE
DODGE
ROCHESTER
OLMSTED
Winona
WINONA
LA CROSSE
Worthington
NOBLES
ROCK
JACKSON
Fairmont
MARTIN
FARIBAULT
Owatonna
FREEBORN
Albert Lea
Austin
MOWER
FILLMORE
HOUSTON
LA CROSSE
N
0 15 30 45 60 Kilometers
0 15 30 45 60 Miles
97° 96° 95° 94° 93° 92° 91° 90°
50° 49° 48° 47° 46° 45° 44°

Windows 7, Blackberry Tablet OS
Mng. Ed....................................... Tad Johnson
Sales Mgr.................................. Mike Jetchick
Mechanical Specifications: Type page 6 x 21; E - 5 cols, 2, 3/16 between; A - 5 cols, 2, 3/16 between; C - 8 cols, 1 1/8, 1/8 between. Equipment & Software: Hardware — 11-APP/iMac, 9-APP/Power Mac G4, 3-APP/Power Mac G3; Software — QPS/QuarkXPress 4.1.1, 8-Adobe/Illustrator 8, Adobe/Photoshop 9.
Delivery Method: Carrier
Areas Served: 55124

THISWEEK BURNSVILLE-EAGAN SUN (THUR)

15322 Galaxie Ave Ste 219, Suite 219, Apple Valley, MN, 55124-3150, Dakota, USA; gen tel (952) 894-1111; adv tel (952) 846-2000; gen fax (952) 846-2010; disp adv e-mail gina.lee@ecm-inc.com; class adv e-mail judy.johnson@ecm-inc.com; ed e-mail john.gessner@ecm-inc.com; web site www.sunthisweek.com
Circulation: 77pd, 25,733fr; CAC
Advertising rate: Open inch rate $19.00
Established: 1979
Group: Adams Publishing Group, LLC
Digital Platform - Mobile: Apple, Android
Digital Platform - Tablet: Apple iOS, Android, Kindle, Kindle Fire
Ed. .... John Gessner
Adv... Gina Lee
Ed. .... Tad Johnson
Mechanical Specifications: Type page 10 x 15; E - 5 cols, 2, 3/16 between; A - 5 cols, 2, 1/8 between; C - 8 cols, 1 1/8, 1/8 between. Equipment & Software: Hardware — 11-APP/iMac, 9-APP/Power Mac G4, 3-APP/Power-mac G3; Software — Indesign Adobe/Photoshop 5.5, Adobe/Illustrator 8.
Delivery Method: Carrier
Areas Served: 55337, 55306

THISWEEK NEWSPAPERS (SAT)

15322 Galaxie Ave Ste 219, Suite 219, Apple Valley, MN, 55124-3150, Dakota, USA; gen tel (952) 469-2181; gen fax (952) 846-2010; disp adv e-mail mike.jetchick@ecm-inc.com; ed e-mail tad.johnson@ecm-inc.com; web site http://sunthisweek.com/
Circulation: 62,000fr; Sworn/Estimate/Non-Audited
Advertising rate: Open inch rate $39
Established: 1884
Group: New Media Investment Group
Pub....................................... Julian Andereson
Ed. .... Tad Johnson
Ed. .... John Gessner
Mechanical Specifications: Type page 10 1/4 x 15; E - 4 cols, 1 5/12, 1/4 between; A - 4 cols, 1 5/12, 1/6 between; C - 6 cols, 1 7/12, 1/6 between.Equipment & Software: Hardware — 12-APP/Mac; Software — Adobe/PageMaker 6.0, Adobe/Photoshop 3.0, Adobe/Illustrator 5.5.

APPLETON

THE APPLETON PRESS (WED)

241 W Snelling Ave, Appleton, MN, 56208-1396, Swift, USA; gen tel (320) 289-1323; gen fax (320) 289-2702; disp adv e-mail ads@appletonpress.com; ed e-mail editor@appletonpress.com; web site http://www.appletonpress.com/
Circulation: 2,110pd,; Sworn/Estimate/Non-Audited
Advertising rate: Open inch rate $4.25
Adv. Mgr... April Coots
Ed. .... Leslie Ehrenberg

ARLINGTON

ARLINGTON ENTERPRISE (THUR)

402 W Alden St, Arlington, MN, 55307-2214, Sibley, USA; gen tel (507) 964-5547; gen fax (507) 964-2423; disp adv e-mail info@arlingtonMNnews.com; class adv e-mail info@arlingtonmnnews.com; ed e-mail KurtM@arlingtonmnnews.com; web site www.arlingtonMNnews.com
Circulation: 1,040pd, 400fr; Sworn/Estimate/Non-Audited
Advertising rate: Open inch rate $6.62
Established: 1884
Group: McLeod Publishing, Inc.
Ed .... Kurt Menk
Delivery Method: Mail, Newsstand
Areas Served: Arlington and Green Isle

ASKOV

ASKOV AMERICAN (THUR)

6351 Kobmagergade, Askov, MN, 55704-4280, Pine, USA; gen tel (320) 838-3151; gen fax (320) 838-3152; disp adv e-mail askovamerican@scicable.net; class adv e-mail askovamerican@scicable.net; ed e-mail askovamerican@scicable.com; web site www.askovamerican.com
Circulation: 1,786pd,; Sworn/Estimate/Non-Audited
Advertising rate: Open inch rate $5.50
Established: 1914
Editor .... Shawn Jansen
Mechanical Specifications: Type page 6x 21; E - 7 cols, 2, 1/6 between; A - 7 cols, 2, 1/6 between; C - 7 cols, 2, 1/6 between.Equipment & Software: Hardware — APP/Mac Plus, APP/Mac Classic.
Delivery Method: Mail, Newsstand
Areas Served: 55072, 55704, 55783

BAGLEY

FARMERS INDEPENDENT (WED)

102 N Main Ave, Bagley, MN, 56621-8317, Clearwater, USA; gen tel (218) 694-6265; gen fax (218) 694-6015; disp adv e-mail farmpubads@gvtel.com; ed e-mail farmpub@gvtel.com
Circulation: 2,350pd,; Sworn/Estimate/Non-Audited
Advertising rate: Open inch rate $5.80
Established: 1918
Ed.
Tom Burford
Mechanical Specifications: Type page 6 x 21 1/2; E - 6 cols, 1-5/8, 1/8 between; A - 6 cols, 1-5/8, 1/8 between; C - 6 cols, 1-5/8, 1/8 between.Equipment & Software: Hardware — PC's, Windows; Software — Microsoft/Word 6.0, In-Design, Adobe Acrobat, Photoshop Elements
Delivery Method: Mail, Newsstand
Areas Served: 56621, 56676, 56634, 56644

BALATON

BALATON PRESS TRIBUNE (WED)

220 Central Ave S, Balaton, MN, 56115-1032, Lyon, USA; gen tel (507) 734-5421; gen fax (507) 734-5457; disp adv e-mail balatonpublishing@yahoo.com
Circulation: 415pd,; Sworn/Estimate/Non-Audited
Advertising rate: Open inch rate $5.50
Established: 1910
Group: Balaton Press Tribune
Office Manager......................... Connie Skaug
Editor .... Mckenzie Swanson
Accounting.................................. Donna Miller
Mechanical Specifications: Type page 12 3/4 x 21 1/2.Equipment & Software: Hardware — APP/Mac; Software — Claris/FileMaker Pro, MS/Word.
Delivery Method: Mail
Areas Served: Balaton and surrounding communities of Lyon County

BARNESVILLE

BARNESVILLE RECORD REVIEW (MON)

424 Front St S, Barnesville, MN, 56514-3825, Clay, USA; gen tel (218) 354-2606; gen fax (218) 354-2246; disp adv e-mail adsrecordreview@bvillemn.net ; ed e-mail newsrecordreview@bvillemn.net ; web site www.barnesvillerecordreview.net
Circulation: 1,725pd,; Sworn/Estimate/Non-Audited
Advertising rate: Open inch rate $8.00
Established: 1903
Group: Prim Group
Ed. .... Eugene A. Prim
Delivery Method: Mail
Areas Served: Barnesville and surrounding communities of Clay County

BATTLE LAKE

BATTLE LAKE REVIEW (WED)

114 N Lake Ave, Battle Lake, MN, 56515-4049, Otter Tail, USA; gen tel (218) 864-5952; gen fax (218) 864-5212; ed e-mail blreview@arvig.net; web site http://www.battlelakereview.com/
Circulation: 2,026pd,; Sworn/Estimate/Non-Audited
Advertising rate: Open inch rate $6.55
Established: 1884
Ed. .... Jon Tamke
Mechanical Specifications: Type page 6 x 21; E - 7 cols, 2, between; A - 7 cols, 2, between; C - 7 cols, 2, between.Equipment & Software: Hardware — APP/Mac; Software — QPS/QuarkXPress 4.0.

BAUDETTE

THE NORTHERN LIGHT REGION (WED)

212 Main Ave. N, Suite A, Baudette, MN, 56623, Lake of the Woods, USA; gen tel (218) 634-2700; gen fax (218) 634-2777; disp adv e-mail mikeh@wiktel.com; ed e-mail norlight@wiktel.com; web site www.page1publications.com
Circulation: 1,415pd, 38fr; Sworn/Estimate/Non-Audited
Advertising rate: Open inch rate $4.75
Group: Page One Publications
Pub....................................... Julie M. Bergman
Ed. .... Doris Knutson
Mechanical Specifications: Type page 6 x 20.75; E - 6 cols, 2, 1/6 between; A - 6 cols, 2, 1/6 between; C - 6 cols, 2, 1/6 between.Equipment & Software: Hardware — APP/Mac IIsi; Software — QPS/QuarkXPress 3.2.
Delivery Method: Mail

BECKER

SHERBURNE COUNTY CITIZEN (SAT)

14054 Bank St, Becker, MN, 55308-8865, Sherburne, USA; gen tel (763) 261-5880; gen fax (763) 261-5884; disp adv e-mail ads@westsherburnetribune.net; class adv e-mail citizenidonna@sherbtel.net; ed e-mail citizennewspaper@midconetwork.com; web site www.citizennewspaper.com - 58,182(views) 20,818(visitors)
Circulation: 30pd, 11,139fr; CVC
Advertising rate: Open inch rate $10.40
Established: 1994
Group: Meyer Publications
Pub... Gary W. Meyer
Adv. Mgr... Dick Behm
Circ. Mgr .... Roberta Hibbison
Mechanical Specifications: Type page: 12 x 20; 6 col

BELGRADE

THE BELGRADE OBSERVER (WED)

303 Washburn Ave, Belgrade, MN, 56312-4626, Stearns, USA; gen tel (320) 254-8250; gen fax (320) 254-3215; ed e-mail observer@belgradearea.com; web site belgradearea.com
Circulation: 1,075pd,; Sworn/Estimate/Non-Audited
Advertising rate: Open inch rate $3.75
Pub./Ed./Adv. Mgr. .... James Lemmer
Delivery Method: Mail, Newsstand
Areas Served: 56312

BELLE PLAINE

BELLE PLAINE HERALD (WED)

113 E Main St, Belle Plaine, MN, 56011-1821, Scott, USA; gen tel (952) 873-2261; gen fax (952) 873-2262; ed e-mail bpherald@frontiernet.net; web site www.belleplaineherald.com
Circulation: 3,834pd,; Sworn/Estimate/Non-Audited
Advertising rate: Open inch rate $8.00
Established: 1882
Pub.................................. C. Edward Townsend
Delivery Method: Mail

BEMIDJI

THE AMERICAN (FRI)

1320 Neilson Ave SE, Bemidji, MN, 56601-5406, Beltrami, USA; gen tel (218) 333-9200; gen fax (218) 333-9819; disp adv e-mail advertising@bemidjipioneer.com; class adv e-mail advertising@bemidjipioneer.com; ed e-mail bldknews@blackduckamerican.com; web site http://www.bemidjipioneer.com
Circulation: 525pd,; Sworn/Estimate/Non-Audited
Advertising rate: Open inch rate $12.65
Established: 1901
Group: Forum Communications Co.
Digital Platform - Mobile: Apple, Android, Windows
Digital Platform - Tablet: Apple iOS, Android, Windows 7
Pub... Dennis Doeden
Mechanical Specifications: Type page 6 x 21; E - 6 cols, 1 13/16, 3/16 between; A - 6 cols, 1 13/16, 3/16 between; C - 9 cols, 1 3/16, 1/8 between.Equipment & Software: ; Software — QPS/QuarkXPress 3.2.
Delivery Method: Mail, Carrier, Racks
Areas Served: 56630, 56650

BENSON

SWIFT COUNTY MONITOR & NEWS (WED)

101 12th St S, Benson, MN, 56215-1844, Swift, USA; gen tel (320) 843-4111; gen fax (320) 843-3246; disp adv e-mail ads@monitor-news.com; ed e-mail reed@monitor-news.com; web site www.swiftcountymonitor.com
Circulation: 2,299pd,; Sworn/Estimate/Non-Audited
Advertising rate: Open inch rate $6.95
Established: 1886
Group: Swift County Monitor-News
Pub...................................... Reed W. Anfinson
Advertising.................................. Nancy Ridler
Delivery Method: Mail, Carrier

BIG LAKE

CLEARWATER TRIBUNE (SAT)

29 Lake St S, Big Lake, MN, 55309-4588, Sherburne, USA; gen tel (763) 263-3602; adv tel (763) 263-3602; gen fax (763) 263-3602; disp adv e-mail sales.westrib@izoom.net; ed e-mail editor@westsherburnetribune.net; web site www.westsherburnetribune.com - 38,768(views) 17,463(visitors)
Circulation: 24pd, 4,942fr; CVC
Advertising rate: Open inch rate $11.00
Established: 1984
Group: West Sherburne Tribune
Ed. / Pub.................................. Gary W. Meyer
Circ. Mgr...................................... Gail Evans
Mechanical Specifications: Type page: 12 x 20;

6 col
Areas Served: Sherburne County

WEST SHERBURNE TRIBUNE (SAT)
29 Lake St S, Big Lake, MN, 55309-4588, Sherburne, USA; gen tel (763) 263-3602; gen fax (763) 263-8458; disp adv e-mail westrib@sherbtel.net; ed e-mail editor@westsherburnetribune.net; web site www.westsherburnetribune.com - 43,376(views) 17,422(visitors)
Circulation: 35pd, 10,987fr; VAC
Advertising rate: Open inch rate $11.00
Established: 1979
Pub....... Gary W. Meyer
Adv. Mgr....... Dick Behm
Circ. Mgr....... Gail Evans
Prod. Mgr....... Mary Mayer
Mechanical Specifications: Type page: 12 x 21; 6 col

BIRD ISLAND

BIRD ISLAND UNION (WED)
750 ASH AVE, Bird Island, MN, 55310, Renville, USA; gen tel (320) 365-3266; gen fax (320) 365-4506; disp adv e-mail union@willmar.com; ed e-mail newsmir@hcctel.net
Circulation: 325pd,; Sworn/Estimate/Non-Audited
Advertising rate: Open inch rate $5.65
Established: 1936
Pub....... John N. Hubin
Adv. Mgr....... Aaron Hubin
Mechanical Specifications: Type page 15 x 21; E - 6 cols, 2 1/4, 1/4 between; A - 6 cols, 2 1/4, 1/4 between; C - 7 cols, 2, 1/5 between. Equipment & Software: Hardware — APP/Mac; Software — QPS/QuarkXPress 3.3.
Areas Served: 55310,56253

BLOOMING PRAIRIE

PRAIRIE TIMES (TUES)
411 E Main St, Blooming Prairie, MN, 55917-1439, Steele, USA; gen tel (507) 583-4431; gen fax (507) 583-4445; ed e-mail bptimes@frontiernet.net; web site www.bloomingprairieonline.com
Circulation: 1,073pd,; Sworn/Estimate/Non-Audited
Advertising rate: Open inch rate $4.25
Pub....... Rick Bussler
Adv. Mgr....... Joyce Evans
Delivery Method: Mail

BLUE EARTH

FARIBAULT COUNTY REGISTER (MON)
125 N Main St, Blue Earth, MN, 56013-1960, Faribault, USA; gen tel (507) 526-7324; gen fax (507) 526-4080; disp adv e-mail lnauman@faribaultcountyregister.com; class adv e-mail wgieser@faribaultcountyregister.com; ed e-mail chunt@faribaultcountyregister.com; web site www.faribaultcountyregister.com - 45,000(views)
Circulation: 3,000pd,; Sworn/Estimate/Non-Audited
Advertising rate: Open inch rate $10.00
Established: 1868
Group: Ogden Newspapers Inc.
Pub./Gen. Mng....... Lori Nauman
Ed....... Chuck Hunt
Circ. Mng.... Hanna AnnEquipment & Software: Hardware — Mac
Delivery Method: Mail, Newsstand, Carrier, Racks
Areas Served: 56013 56098 56023 56025 56047 56039 56010 56090 56027 56033 56014 56097 56051 56068 50424 50451 50556

BRAINERD

NEWS HOPPER (SAT)
21 Washington St, Brainerd, MN, 56401-3334, Crow Wing, USA; gen tel (218) 772-0300; gen fax (218) 772-0301; ed e-mail hopper@cosbyironton.net; web site www.newshopper.net
Circulation: 17,492fr; VAC
Advertising rate: Open inch rate $12.50
Established: 2000
Group: NewsHopper Publications Inc.
Digital Platform - Mobile: Apple
Digital Platform - Tablet: Apple iOS
Owner....... Laura Heglund
Adv. Mgr....... Eric Heglund
Mechanical Specifications: Type page: 10.15 x 21.25; 6 col
Delivery Method: Mail, Racks

PINEANDLAKES ECHO JOURNAL (THUR)
506 James St, Brainerd, MN, 56401-2942, Crow Wing, USA; gen tel (218) 829-4705; gen fax ; disp adv e-mail ; class adv e-mail ; ed e-mail nancy.vogt@pequotlakesecho.com; web site www.pineandlakes.com - 108,003(views) 20,428(visitors)
Circulation: 3,400pd, 52fr; Sworn/Estimate/Non-Audited
Established: 1935
Pub....... Pete Mohs
Mechanical Specifications: Type page: 10.25 x 14.75; 6 col
Delivery Method: Mail, Racks

BRANDON

WEST DOUGLAS COUNTY RECORD (THUR)
510 Central Ave N, Brandon, MN, 56315-4626, Douglas, USA; gen tel (320) 834-4924; ed e-mail wdrecord@gctel.com
Circulation: 36pd, 1,623fr; VAC
Advertising rate: Open inch rate $7.50
Established: 1979
Cathy Bedore
Dave BedorePub.s
Mechanical Specifications: Type page: 10 x 15; 5 col

BROOTEN

BONANZA VALLEY VOICE (THUR)
131 Central Ave N, Brooten, MN, 56316-4665, Stearns, USA; gen tel (320) 346-2400; gen fax (320) 346-2379; disp adv e-mail bonanzavalvoice@tds.net; class adv e-mail bonanzavalvoice@tds.net; ed e-mail bonanzavalvoice@tds.net; web site http://www.bonanzavalleyvoice.com/
Circulation: 1,450pd,; USPS
Advertising rate: Open inch rate $3.14
Established: 1969
Digital Platform - Mobile: Apple
Ad Design/Layout....... Jennifer Murphey
Delivery Method: Mail, Racks
Areas Served: Swift, Kandiyohi, Pope and Stearns counties.

BROWERVILLE

BROWERVILLE BLADE (THUR)
609 Main St N, Browerville, MN, 56438-5186, Todd, USA; gen tel (320) 594-2911; gen fax (218) 756-2126; disp adv e-mail cindy@inhnews.com; ed e-mail blade@inhnews.com; web site www.bladepublishing.net
Circulation: 1,382pd, 6,500fr; Sworn/Estimate/Non-Audited
Advertising rate: Open inch rate $6.00
Established: 1906
Circ. Mgr....... Peggy Deering
Ed....... Aaron Quirt
Mechanical Specifications: Type page 5 x 15; E - 5 cols, 1 3/4, between.
Delivery Method: Mail
Areas Served: Todd County and surrounding areas in Central Minnesota

BUFFALO

WRIGHT COUNTY JOURNAL-PRESS (THUR)
108 Central Ave, Buffalo, MN, 55313-1521, Wright, USA; gen tel (763) 682-1221; gen fax (763) 682-5458; disp adv e-mail ads@thedummer.com; ed e-mail edd@thedrummer.com; web site www.thedrummer.com
Circulation: 5,230pd,; Sworn/Estimate/Non-Audited
Advertising rate: Open inch rate $6.86
Established: 1887
Ed....... James P. McDonnell
Delivery Method: Mail, Newsstand

BYRON

BYRON REVIEW (TUES)
1011 Tompkins Dr NE, Byron, MN, 55920-3001, Olmsted, USA; gen tel (507) 775-6180; gen fax (507) 374-9327; disp adv e-mail communitynewscorp@kmtel.com; class adv e-mail communitynewscorp@kmtel.com; ed e-mail communitynewscorp@kmtel.com; web site www.communitynewscorp.com
Circulation: 1,200pd,; Sworn/Estimate/Non-Audited
Advertising rate: Open inch rate $8.75
Established: 1958
Group: Community News Corporation
Adv. Mgr....... Larry Dobson
Ed....... Melanie Dobson
Delivery Method: Mail, Newsstand
Areas Served: Western Olmsted County, eastern Dodge County

CALEDONIA

THE CALEDONIA ARGUS (WED)
314 W Lincoln St, Caledonia, MN, 55921-1040, Houston, USA; gen tel (507) 724-3475; gen fax (507) 725-8610; disp adv e-mail amanda.ninneman@ecm-inc.com; ed e-mail dan.mcgonigle@ecm-inc.com; web site www.hometownargus.com
Circulation: 2,094pd, 3,748fr; CAC
Advertising rate: Open inch rate $7.75
Established: 1875
Group: Adams Publishing Group, LLC
Adv. Dir....... Pamela DeMorett
Office Mgr....... Deanna McCabe
Gen. Mgr....... Emily Biakowski
Ed....... Daniel McGonigle
Mechanical Specifications: Type page 12 3/4 x 21 1/2; E - 6 cols, 2, 1/4 between; A - 6 cols, 2, between; C - 6 cols, 2, between.
Delivery Method: Mail, Newsstand

CAMBRIDGE

ISANTI COUNTY NEWS (WED)
234 Main St S, Cambridge, MN, 55008-1611, Isanti, USA; gen tel (763) 689-1981; gen fax (763) 689-4372; disp adv e-mail neil.anderson@ecm-inc.com; ed e-mail editor.countynews@ecm-inc.com; web site www.isanticountynews.com
Circulation: 125pd, 12,948fr; CAC
Advertising rate: Open inch rate $10.30
Established: 1900
Group: Adams Publishing Group, LLC
Rgl Gen. Mgr....... Jeff Andres
Ed....... Rachel Kytonen
Mechanical Specifications: Type page: 10.4 x 21; 6 col
Areas Served: 55006, 55080. 55029, 55008, 55040

ISANTI-CHISAGO COUNTY STAR (THUR)
930 Cleveland St S, Cambridge, MN, 55008-1785, Isanti, USA; gen tel (763) 698-1181; gen fax (763) 698-1185; disp adv e-mail akrist@moraminn.com; class adv e-mail starclass@countystar.com; ed e-mail editor@countystar.com; web site http://isanti-chisagocountystar.com
Circulation: 8,263fr; VAC
Advertising rate: Open inch rate $10.00
Established: 1905
Group: Northstar Media, Inc.
Pub....... Keith Hansen
Adv. Mgr....... Eric Champion
Circ. Mgr....... Scott Kittelson
Ed....... Becky Glander
Prod. Mgr....... Matt Mcolly
Mechanical Specifications: Type page 13 x 21.Equipment & Software: Hardware — APP/Mac; Presses — HI/Cottrell V-15A; Software — QPS/QuarkXPress 4.2.
Delivery Method: Mail
Areas Served: 55008, 55006, 55056, 55040, 55080, 55032, 55069

THE POST REVIEW (WED)
234 Main St S, Cambridge, MN, 55008-1611, Isanti, USA; gen tel (763) 691-6000; gen fax (763) 689-4372; disp adv e-mail helen.rosing@ecm-inc.com ; ed e-mail derrick.knutson@ecm-inc.com ; web site www.ecm-postreview.com
Circulation: 1,259pd, 0fr; CAC
Advertising rate: Open inch rate $9.30
Established: 1875
Group: Adams Publishing Group, LLC
Pub....... Julian Anderson
Adv. Mgr....... Mary Eslinger
Ed....... Mary Helen Swanson
Mechanical Specifications: Type page: 10.4 x 21; 6 col Equipment & Software: Hardware — APP/Mac; Presses — HI; Software — QPS/QuarkXPress.
Delivery Method: Mail

CANBY

CANBY NEWS (WED)
123 1st St E, Canby, MN, 56220-1342, Yellow Medicine, USA; gen tel (507) 223-5303; gen fax (507) 223-5404; disp adv e-mail cnews@frontiernet.net; class adv e-mail ads.cnews@gmail.com; ed e-mail thecanbynews@thecanbynews.com; web site www.frontiernet.net/~cnews/
Circulation: 1,799pd,; Sworn/Estimate/Non-Audited
Advertising rate: Open inch rate $3.70
Established: 1878
Pub....... Richard Gail
Adv. Mgr....... Sara Stokes
Mechanical Specifications: Type page 6 x 21.
Areas Served: Canby, Gary, Taunton, Minneota, Porter

CANNON FALLS

CANNON FALLS BEACON (THUR)
120 4th St S, Cannon Falls, MN, 55009-2433, Goodhue, USA; gen tel (507) 263-3991; gen fax (507) 263-2300; adv fax (507) 263-2319; disp adv e-mail beacon@cannonfalls.com; class adv e-mail dave@cannonfalls.com; ed e-mail dick@cannonfalls.com; web site www.cannonfalls.com
Circulation: 3,900pd,; Sworn/Estimate/Non-Audited
Advertising rate: Open inch rate $6.95
Established: 1876
Pub....... G. Richard Dalton
Ed....... Dick Dalton
Mechanical Specifications: Type page 6 x 21 1/2; E - 6 cols, 2, 1/36 between; A - 6 cols, 2, 1/36 between.Equipment & Software: Hardware — App/Mac; Software — Adobe/PageMaker, QPS/QuarkXPress.

CASS LAKE

THE CASS LAKE TIMES (THUR)
128 2nd St NW, Cass Lake, MN, 56633-3623, Cass, USA; gen tel (218) 335-2290; adv tel (218) 689-7290; gen fax (218) 335-2290; ed e-mail cltimes1@arvig.net; web site

http://www.lakeandpine.com/46691/2205/the-cass-lake-timespdf
Circulation: 1,077pd, 11fr; Sworn/Estimate/Non-Audited
Advertising rate: Open rate $5.50
Adv. Mgr. .... Allan Olson
Ed. .... Tim Bloomquist
Mechanical Specifications: Type page 6 x 21 1/2; E - 6 cols, 1 5/8, 1/6 between; A - 6 cols, 1 5/8, 1/6 between; C - 6 cols, 1 5/8, 1/6 between.
Delivery Method: Mail, Newsstand

CHASKA

CHANHASSEN VILLAGER (THUR)

123 W 2nd St, Chaska, MN, 55318-1907, Carver, USA; gen tel (952) 934-5045; adv tel (952) 345-6477; gen fax (952) 448-3146; disp adv e-mail jhiltunen@swpub.com; class adv e-mail classified@swpub.com; ed e-mail editor@chanvillager.com; web site http://www.swnewsmedia.com/chanhassen_villager/
Circulation: 4,532fr; Sworn/Estimate/Non-Audited
Advertising rate: Open inch rate $11.75
Group: Red Wing Publishing Co.
Ed .... Richard Crawford
Pub./Gen. Mgr. .... Bill Davis
Adv. Dir .... Jen Hiltunen
Delivery Method: Mail

CHASKA HERALD (THUR)

123 W 2nd St, Chaska, MN, 55318-1907, Carver, USA; gen tel (952) 448-2650; adv tel (952) 345-6477; ed tel (952) 345-6574; gen fax (952) 448-3146; disp adv e-mail jhiltunen@swpub.com; class adv e-mail classified@swpub.com; ed e-mail editor@chaskaherald.com; web site http://www.swnewsmedia.com/chaska_herald/
Circulation: 4,532pd, 290fr; Sworn/Estimate/Non-Audited
Advertising rate: Open inch rate $11.75
Established: 1862
Group: Red Wing Publishing Co.
Adv .... Bob Suel
Ed. .... Mark Olson
Mechanical Specifications: Type page 6 x 21 1/2; E - 6 cols, 2, 1/60 between; A - 6 cols, 2, 1/60 between; C - 8 cols, 1 1/2, 1/8 between.
Delivery Method: Mail

CHATFIELD

THE CHATFIELD NEWS (TUES)

220 Main St S, Chatfield, MN, 55923-1225, Fillmore, USA; gen tel (507) 867-3870; gen fax (507) 867-3870; disp adv e-mail info@bluffcountrynews.com; class adv e-mail classifieds@bluffcountrynews.com; ed e-mail chatfieldnews@bluffcountrynews.com; web site http://bluffcountrynews.com/Content/The-Chatfield-News/44
Circulation: 1,413pd,; Sworn/Estimate/Non-Audited
Advertising rate: Open inch rate $6.00
Group: Bluff Country Reader
Bluff Country Newspaper Group
Dave Phillips
Pan BluhmEd.s
Delivery Method: Mail

CHISHOLM

THE CHISHOLM TRIBUNE PRESS (WED)

131 W Lake St, Ste 2, Chisholm, MN, 55719-3748, St. Louis, USA; gen tel (218) 254-4432; gen fax (218) 254-7141; ed e-mail tribune@mx3.com
Circulation: 900pd, 143fr; Sworn/Estimate/Non-Audited
Advertising rate: Open inch rate $5.70
Group: Adams Publishing Group, LLC
Pub. .... Todd Manney
Delivery Method: Mail

CHOKIO

CHOKIO REVIEW (THUR)

121 Main St, Chokio, MN, 56221, Stevens, USA; gen tel (320) 324-2405; gen fax (320) 324-2449; ed e-mail chreview@fedtel.net; web site www.chokioreview.com
Circulation: 744pd, 35fr; Sworn/Estimate/Non-Audited
Advertising rate: Open inch rate $3.50
Established: 1897
Group: Free Scout Press, Inc
Pub. .... Kay Grossman
Ed. .... Nick Ripperger
Mechanical Specifications: Type page 5x 15; A - 5 cols, 2, 1/8 between.Equipment & Software: Hardware — APP/Mac; Presses — Ryobi; Software — QPS/QuarkXPress 3.32.
Delivery Method: Mail

CLARA CITY

THE CLARA CITY HERALD (WED)

34 Center Ave E, Clara City, MN, 56222-1182, Chippewa, USA; gen tel (320) 847-3130; gen fax (320) 847-2630; ed e-mail ccherald@hcinet.net; web site www.claracityherald.com
Circulation: 1,275pd, 40fr; Sworn/Estimate/Non-Audited
Advertising rate: Open inch rate $5.00
Established: 1895
Pub. .... T.J. Almen
Ed .... Josie Oliver
Co-Ed..... Laura ProsserEquipment & Software: Hardware — APP/Macs; Software — Write Now.

CLARISSA

INDEPENDENT NEWS HERALD (TUES)

310 Main St W, Clarissa, MN, 56440-2200, Todd, USA; gen tel (218) 756-2131; gen fax (218) 756-2126; disp adv e-mail cindy@inhnews.com; ed e-mail kathy@inhnews.com; web site www.inhnews.com
Circulation: 2,375pd, 92fr; Sworn/Estimate/Non-Audited
Advertising rate: Open inch rate $7.00
Pub. .... Marlo Benning
Pub. .... Ray Benning
Adv. Mgr. .... Katrina Nauber
Circ. Mgr. .... Danielle Hanson
Mechanical Specifications: Type page 6x 21 1/2; E - 6 cols, 2, between; A - 6 cols, 2, between; C - 6 cols, 2, between.Equipment & Software: Hardware — APP/Mac; Presses — G; Software — QPS/QuarkXPress 3.32.
Delivery Method: Mail

CLINTON

NORTHERN STAR (THUR)

128 Main St, Clinton, MN, 56225-5174, Big Stone, USA; gen tel (320) 325-5152; gen fax (320) 325-5280; ed e-mail northernstar@mchsi.com
Circulation: 1,802pd, 20fr; USPS
Advertising rate: Open inch rate $5.50
Established: 1965
Group: Kaercher Publications
Pub. .... Sue Kaercher
Adv. Mgr. .... Denese Gustafson
Mng. Ed. .... Lois Torgerson
Mechanical Specifications: Type page 6 x 21 1/2; E - 6 cols, 2 1/8, 1/6 between; A - 6 cols, 2 1/8, 1/6 between; C - 6 cols, 2 1/8, 1/6 between.Equipment & Software: ; Presses — 4-G/Community; Software — QPS/QuarkXPress.
Areas Served: 56225, 56240, 56211, 56219, 56236, 56221

COKATO

DASSEL-COKATO ENTERPRISE DISPATCH (FRI)

185 3rd St SW, Cokato, MN, 55321-4595, Wright, USA; gen tel (320) 286-2118; gen fax (320) 286-2119; disp adv e-mail hj@herald-journal.com; class adv e-mail ads@herald-journal.com; ed e-mail news@dasselcokato.com; web site www.dasselcokato.com
Circulation: 2,200pd,; Sworn/Estimate/Non-Audited
Advertising rate: Open inch rate $7.90
Established: 1885
Group: Herald Journal Publishing, Inc.Chris Schultz
Mechanical Specifications: Type page 6x 21 1/2; E - 6 cols, 2, 5/24 between; A - 6 cols, 2, 5/24 between; C - 6 cols, 2, 5/24 between.Equipment & Software: Hardware — APP/Mac; Software — InDesign
Delivery Method: Mail, Newsstand
Areas Served: Darwin, Dassel, Cokato, Howard Lake

COLD SPRING

COLD SPRING RECORD (TUES)

403 Westwind Ct, PO Box 456, Cold Spring, MN, 56320-4560, Stearns, USA; gen tel (320) 685-8621; gen fax (320) 685-8885; disp adv e-mail ads-csrecord@midconetwork.com; ed e-mail csrecord@midconetwork.com; web site www.csrecord.net
Circulation: 3,400pd, 12fr; Sworn/Estimate/Non-Audited
Advertising rate: Open inch rate $5.00
Established: 1899
Digital Platform - Mobile: Apple
Digital Platform - Tablet: Apple iOS
Ed. .... Mike Austreng
Adv. Mgr. .... Jeanie Austreng
Delivery Method: Mail

COMFREY

COMFREY TIMES (THUR)

112 Brown St W, Comfrey, MN, 56019-7701, Brown, USA; gen tel (507) 877-2281; gen fax (507) 877-2251; ed e-mail comfreytimes@frontiernet.net
Circulation: 650pd,; Sworn/Estimate/Non-Audited
Advertising rate: Open inch rate $4.00
Ed. .... Steve Christiansen
Mechanical Specifications: Type page 13 1/2 x 22.

COON RAPIDS

ANOKA COUNTY UNION HERALD (FRI)

4101 Coon Rapids Blvd NW, Coon Rapids, MN, 55433-2525, Anoka, USA; gen tel (763) 421-4444; adv tel (763) 712-3520; ed tel (763) 712-3514; gen fax (763) 421-4315; ed fax (763) 712-3519; disp adv e-mail david.traub@ecm-inc.com; class adv e-mail class@ecm-inc.com; ed e-mail mandy.froemming@ecm-inc.com; web site www.abcnewspapers.com - 204,663(views) 55,607(visitors)
Circulation: 4,404pd, 89fr; CAC
Established: 1865
Group: Adams Publishing Group, LLC
Adv. Dir/Gen. Mgr. .... Tom Murray
Bus. Mgr. .... Jill Donahue
Ed. .... Mandy Froemming
Mechanical Specifications: Type page 10 x 21; E - 6 cols, 1 3/4, 1/8 between; A - 6 cols, 1 3/4, 1/8 between; C - 8 cols, 1 1/2, 1/8 between. Equipment & Software: Hardware — APP/Mac Quadra 800s, APP/Power Macs, APP/Mac G3; Presses — 6-HI/V-25, 14-G, 9-Dauphin; Software — In Design CS.
Delivery Method: Mail, Newsstand, Racks
Areas Served: 55303, 55304, 55433, 55434, 55070, 55432

BLAINE-SPRING LAKE PARK LIFE (FRI)

4101 Coon Rapids Blvd NW, Coon Rapids, MN, 55433-2525, Anoka, USA; gen tel (763) 421-4444; adv tel (763) 421-4444; ed tel (763) 421-4444; gen fax (763) 421-4315; disp adv e-mail david.traub@ecm-inc.com; class adv e-mail david.traub@ecm-inc.com; ed e-mail mandy.froemming@ecm-inc.com; web site www.abcnewspapers.com - 204,000(views) 61,122(visitors)
Circulation: 145pd, 15,756fr; CAC
Advertising rate: Open inch rate $15.50
Established: 1969
Group: Adams Publishing Group, LLC
Adv. Dir/Gen. Mgr. .... Tom Murray
Rgl Adv. Dir. .... Jason Pietraszewski
Mechanical Specifications: Type page 10 x 21; E - 6 cols, 1 3/4, 1/8 between; A - 6 cols, 1 3/4, 1/8 between; C - 8 cols, 1 1/2, 1/8 between. Equipment & Software: Hardware — APP/Mac; Presses — 14-G, 9-Dauphin, 6-HI; Software — InDesign/CS.
Delivery Method: Carrier
Areas Served: 55449, 55434, 55432

COON RAPIDS HERALD (FRI)

4101 Coon Rapids Blvd NW, Coon Rapids, MN, 55433-2525, Anoka, USA; gen tel (763) 421-4444; gen fax (763) 421-4315; disp adv e-mail steve.rajtar@ecm-inc.com; class adv e-mail kjel.nordstrom@ecm-inc.com; ed e-mail mandy.froemming@ecm-inc.com; web site www.abcnewspapers.com - 205,457(views) 44,852(visitors)
Circulation: 2,650pd, 76fr; CVC
Advertising rate: Open inch rate $7.50
Established: 1875
Pub. .... Julian Andersen
Mng. Ed. .... Peter Bodley
Gen. Mgr. .... Tom Murray
Mechanical Specifications: Type page 10 x 21; E - 6 cols, 1 3/4, 1/8 between; A - 6 cols, 1 3/4, 1/8 between; C - 8 cols, 1 1/2, 1/8 between. Equipment & Software: Hardware — APP/Power Macs; Presses — 6-HI/V-25, 14-G, 9-Dauphin; Software — InDesign/CS.
Delivery Method: Mail
Areas Served: 55433, 55448

COTTONWOOD

TRI COUNTY NEWS (WED)

1 Barstad Rd N, Cottonwood, MN, 56229-2269, Lyon, USA; gen tel (507) 423-6239; gen fax (507) 423-6230; ed e-mail tcedit@mvtvwireless.com
Circulation: 842pd,; Sworn/Estimate/Non-Audited
Advertising rate: Open inch rate $4.45
Established: 1989
Pub. .... David Smigelski

CROSBY

CROSBY-IRONTON COURIER (WED)

12 E Main St, Crosby, MN, 56441-1614, Crow Wing, USA; gen tel (218) 546-5029; gen fax (218) 546-8352; ed e-mail courier@crosbyironton.net; web site www.cicourierinc.com
Circulation: 3,341pd,; Sworn/Estimate/Non-Audited
Advertising rate: Open inch rate $7.75
Established: 1911
Pub. .... T.M. Swensen
Gen. Mgr. .... Lori LaBorde
Mechanical Specifications: Type page 10 1/2 x 21 1/4; E - 6 cols, 1 7/8, 1/5 between. Equipment & Software: ; Software — QPS/QuarkXPress 5.0, Adobe/Illustrator 10.0, Adobe/Photoshop 7.0.
Delivery Method: Mail, Newsstand, Racks

CROSSLAKE

NORTHLAND PRESS (TUES)

13833 Riverwood Ln, Ste 2, Crosslake, MN,

56442-2823, Crow Wing, USA; gen tel (218) 692-5842; adv tel (218) 692-5842; ed tel (218) 692-5842; gen fax (218) 792-5844; adv fax (218) 792-5844; ed fax (218) 792-5844; disp adv e-mail news@northlandpress.com; class adv e-mail news@northlandpress.com; ed e-mail news@northlandpress.com; web site www.northlandpress.com
Circulation: 5,218fr; CVC
Advertising rate: Open inch National Rate $16.00 - Local rate $9.90
Established: 2005
Publisher.................................Joanne Boblett
Editor and Advertising Manager....Paul Boblett
Mechanical Specifications: Type page: 11.75 x 20.5; 6 col
Delivery Method: Mail
Areas Served: Breezy Point, Crosslake, Emily, Fifty Lakes, Jenkins, Manhattan Beach, Merrifield,Outing, Pequot Lakes, Pine River and surrounding townships

DAWSON

DAWSON SENTINEL (WED)
674 CHESTNUT ST, Dawson, MN, 56232, Lac Qui Parle, USA; gen tel (320) 769-2497; gen fax (320) 769-2459; ed e-mail dawsonsentinel@frontiernet.net; web site www.dawsonmn.com
Circulation: 1,662pd, 15fr; Sworn/Estimate/Non-Audited
Advertising rate: Open inch rate $5.25
Established: 1884
Pub..Bill Klaimon
Ed. ....Dave Hickey

DEER RIVER

WESTERN ITASCA REVIEW (THUR)
15 1st St NE, Deer River, MN, 56636-8769, Itasca, USA; gen tel (218) 246-8533; gen fax (218) 246-8540; ed e-mail drpub@paulbunyan.net; web site http://www.deerriverreviewmn.com/
Circulation: 1,618pd, 22fr; Sworn/Estimate/Non-Audited
Advertising rate: Open inch rate $3.76
Established: 1896
Pub..Rebecca Passeri
Mechanical Specifications: Type page 6 x 16 1/4; E - 6 cols, 1 5/8, 1/4 between; A - 6 cols, 1 5/8, 1/4 between; C - 6 cols, 1 5/8, 1/4 between.
Areas Served: 56636, 56628, 56657, 56626, 56631, 56637, 56639, 55744, 56680, 56681

DELANO

DELANO HERALD JOURNAL (FRI)
701 Babcock Blvd E, Ste 110, Delano, MN, 55328-4643, Wright, USA; gen tel (763) 972-1028; gen fax (763) 972-1029; disp adv e-mail hj@heraldjournal.com; class adv e-mail ads@heraldjournal.com; ed e-mail delano@heraldjournal.com; web site www.delanoheraldjournal.com
Circulation: 1,925pd,; USPS
Advertising rate: Open inch rate $7.90
Established: 2006
Group: Herald Journal Publishing, Inc.Chris Shultz
Gen. Mgr. .... Dale Kovar
Ed. ....Gabe Licht
Mechanical Specifications: 6 col x 21.5"Equipment & Software: Hardware — Mac; Software — InDesign, Photoshop
Delivery Method: Mail, Newsstand

DETROIT LAKES

DETROIT LAKES TRIBUNE (WED, SUN)
511 Washington Ave, Detroit Lakes, MN, 56501-3007, Becker, USA; gen tel (218) 847-3151; gen fax (218) 847-9409; ed e-mail recordtribune@dlnewspapers.com; web site www.dl-online.com
Circulation: 3,400pd, 59fr; VAC
Advertising rate: Open inch rate $19.50
Established: 1872
Group: Forum Communications Co.
Circ. Mgr.................................Viola Anderson
Publisher.............................Melissa Swenson
Editor ....Paula Quam
Delivery Method: Mail, Carrier
Areas Served: 56501, 56544, 56554, 56511, 56589, 56587, 56569, 56578, 56575

LAKE AREA PRESS (SAT)
511 Washington Ave, Detroit Lakes, MN, 56501-3007, Becker, USA; gen tel (218) 847-3151; adv tel 218-844-1451; ed tel (218) 844-1466; gen fax (218) 847-9409; disp adv e-mail MSWENSON@DLNEWSPAPERS.COM; class adv e-mail lholmer@dlnewspapers.com; ed e-mail pquam@dlnewspapers.com; web site www.dl-online.com
Circulation: 9,958fr; VAC
Advertising rate: Open Inch
Group: Forum Communications Co.
Publisher.............................Melissa Swenson
Delivery Method: Mail, Carrier
Areas Served: 56501

THE DETROIT LAKES TRIBUNE (WED)
511 Washington Ave, Detroit Lakes, MN, 56501-3007, Becker, USA; gen tel (218) 847-3151; gen fax (218) 847-9409; ed e-mail recordtribune@dlnewspapers.com; web site www.dl-online.com
Circulation: 3,584pd, 94fr; VAC
Advertising rate: Open inch rate $7.60
Group: Forum Communications Co.
Pub..................................Dennis Winskowski
Adv. Mgr.......................................Mary Brenk
Circ. Mgr.................................Viola Anderson
Ed. ....Nathan Bowe
Delivery Method: Mail, Carrier

DODGE CENTER

DODGE CENTER STAR-HERALD (WED)
40 W Main St, Dodge Center, MN, 55927-9117, Dodge, USA; gen tel (507) 374-6531; adv tel (507) 633-9327; disp adv e-mail dcstar@kmtel.com; class adv e-mail cncads@kmtel.com; ed e-mail cnceditor@kmtel.com; web site www.communitynewscorp.com
Circulation: 1,774pd, 50fr; USPS
Advertising rate: Open inch rate $9.65
Established: 1869
Digital Platform - Mobile: Apple
Digital Platform - Tablet: Apple iOS
Pub..Larry Dobson
Ed. ....Melanie Dobson
Mechanical Specifications: Type page 6 x 21; E - 6 cols, 1.729inches, .126 inches between.
Delivery Method: Mail, Newsstand
Areas Served: 55918, 55924, 55927, 55940, 55955, 55982, 55985

DULUTH

DULUTH BUDGETEER NEWS (SUN)
424 W 1st St, Duluth, MN, 55802-1596, Saint Louis, USA; gen tel (218) 723-5281; adv tel (218) 590-7592; ed tel (218) 723-5235; gen fax (218) 723-5295; disp adv e-mail web@duluthnews.com; class adv e-mail dwruck@duluthnews.com; ed e-mail budgeteer@duluthbudgeteer.com ; web site www.duluthbudgeteer.com
Circulation: 21,606fr; VAC
Advertising rate: Open inch rate $28.11
Established: 1931
Group: Forum Communications Co.
Pub..Ken Browall
Sales Mgr.......................Kathleen Pennington
Ed.Naomi YaegerEquipment & Software: Hardware — APP/Power Mac; Software — Adobe/Photoshop 5.0, QPS/QuarkXPress 4.0.
Delivery Method: Carrier

DULUTH-ZENITH NEWS (TUES)
PO Box 3280, Duluth, MN, 55803-3280, St. Louis, USA; gen tel (218) 940-3132; disp adv e-mail zenithcityweekly@yahoo.com; web site www.zenithcitynews.com
Circulation: 11,000fr; Sworn/Estimate/Non-Audited
Advertising rate: Modular Rates: 1/9 P $75 1/6 P $95 1/2 P $275 Full $550
Established: 2007
Pub...............................Taylor Martin-Romme
Areas Served: Duluth, Hermantown, Two Harbors, Cloquet, and Superior, Wisconsin

THE PINE JOURNAL (WED)
424 W 1st St, Duluth, MN, 55802-1516, Carlton, USA; gen tel (218) 879-1950; adv tel (218) 590-8392; ed tel (218) 879-1950 ; gen fax (218) 879-2078; disp adv e-mail news@pinejournal.com; class adv e-mail ads@pinejournal.com ; ed e-mail jpeterson@pinejournal.com; web site www.pinejournal.com
Circulation: 4,471pd,; Sworn/Estimate/Non-Audited
Advertising rate: Open inch rate $18.61
Established: 1884
Group: Forum Communications Co.
Pub...Neal Ronquist
Ed ....Jana Peterson
Adv. Dir ....Mike Mazzio
Bus. Mgr......................................Julie Fchulz
Mechanical Specifications: Type page 6x 21; E - 6 cols, 1 5/6, 1/6 between; A - 6 cols, 2, between; C - 6 cols, 1 5/6, 1/6 between.Equipment & Software: Hardware — APP/Power Mac 7600; Software — QPS/QuarkXPress.

EAST GRAND FORKS

THE EXPONENT (WED)
207 2nd Ave NE, East Grand Forks, MN, 56721-2405, Polk, USA; gen tel (218) 773-2808; gen fax (218) 773-9212; disp adv e-mail ads@page1publications.com; ed e-mail exponent@rrv.net; web site www.page1publications.com
Circulation: 1,343pd,; Sworn/Estimate/Non-Audited
Advertising rate: Open inch rate $6.25
Group: Page One Publications
Pub..........................Julie M. Nordine Bergman
Mng. Ed.................................. Rollin Bergman

EDEN PRAIRIE

BLOOMINGTON SUN-CURRENT (THUR)
10917 Valley View Rd, Eden Prairie, MN, 55344-3730, Hennepin, USA; gen tel (952) 392-6800; adv tel (952) 392-6888; ed tel (763) 424-7352; gen fax (952) 392-6802; disp adv e-mail jeremy.bradfield@ecm-inc.com ; class adv e-mail krista.jech@ecm-inc.com ; ed e-mail matthew.hankey@ecm-inc.com; web site http://current.mnsun.com/
Circulation: 391pd, 24,491fr; CAC
Advertising rate: Open inch rate $24.00
Established: 1954
Group: Adams Publishing Group, LLC
Sun Newspapers
Adv. Sales....................................Nancy Etzel
Mng. Ed.........................Joseph Palmersheim
Mechanical Specifications: Type page 4 x 10; E - 4 cols, 2 1/2, 1/4 between; A - 5 cols, 1 5/8, between; C - 8 cols, 1 1/6, 5/24 between. Equipment & Software: Hardware — APP/Mac; Software — QPS/QuarkXPress.
Delivery Method: Carrier
Areas Served: 55439, 55438, 55437, 55431, 55425

COLUMBIA HEIGHTS/FRIDLEY SUN FOCUS (THUR)
10917 Valley View Rd, Eden Prairie, MN, 55344-3730, Hennepin, USA; gen tel (952) 392-6800; adv tel (952) 392-6888; gen fax (763) 424-7388; disp adv e-mail cheri.obannon@ecm-inc.com ; class adv e-mail krista.jech@ecm-inc.com ; ed e-mail matthew.hankey@ecm-inc.com; web site http://focus.mnsun.com
Circulation: 36pd, 14,254fr; CAC
Advertising rate: Open inch rate $18.00
Established: 1968
Group: Adams Publishing Group, LLC
American Community Newspapers LLC
Ed.......................................Kassie Petermann
Gen. Mgr. ....Mark Weber
Mktg. Mgr. ....Krista Jech
Mechanical Specifications: Type page 4 x 10; E - 5 cols, between; A - 5 cols, 1 5/8, between; C - 8 cols, between.Equipment & Software: Hardware — APP/Mac; Software — QPS/QuarkXPress, Adobe/Photoshop.
Delivery Method: Carrier
Areas Served: 55421, 55432

EDEN PRAIRIE NEWS (THUR)
250 Prairie Center Dr Ste 211, Suite 211, Eden Prairie, MN, 55344-7911, Hennepin, USA; gen tel (952) 942-7885; adv tel (952) 345-6477; gen fax (952) 942-7975; disp adv e-mail netzel@swpub.com; class adv e-mail classified@swpub.com; ed e-mail editor@edenprairienews.com; web site www.edenprairienews.com
Circulation: 11,632fr; Sworn/Estimate/Non-Audited
Advertising rate: Open inch rate $18.00
Established: 1976
Group: Red Wing Publishing Co.
Pub...Mark Weber
Circ. Mgr......................................Ruby Mohlin
Ed. ....Karla Wennerstrom
Delivery Method: Mail
Areas Served: city of Eden Prairie

EDEN PRAIRIE SUN-CURRENT (THUR)
10917 Valley View Rd, Eden Prairie, MN, 55344-3730, Hennepin, USA; gen tel (952) 392-6800; adv tel (952) 392-6888; gen fax (763) 424-7388; disp adv e-mail nancy.etzel@ecm-inc.com; class adv e-mail pam.miller@ecm-inc.com; ed e-mail matthew.hankey@ecm-inc.com; web site www.current.mnsun.com
Circulation: 86pd, 14,760fr; CAC
Advertising rate: Open inch rate $17.00
Established: 1954
Group: Adams Publishing Group, LLC
American Community Newspapers LLC
Gen. Mgr. ....Mark Webber
Ed. .... Matthew Hankey
Mktg. Mgr. ....Krista Jech
Delivery Method: Carrier
Areas Served: 55347, 55438

EDINA SUN-CURRENT (THUR)
10917 Valley View Rd, Eden Prairie, MN, 55344-3730, Hennepin, USA; gen tel (952) 392-6800; adv tel (952) 392-6888; gen fax (952) 392-6802; disp adv e-mail lisa.kaczke@ecm-inc.com; class adv e-mail nicole.jorgenson@ecm-inc.com; ed e-mail lisa.kaczke@ecm-inc.com; web site http://current.mnsun.com/
Circulation: 219pd, 15,755fr; CAC
Advertising rate: Open inch rate $18.00
Established: 1954
Group: Adams Publishing Group, LLC
American Community Newspapers LLC
CEO ....Gene Carr
Gen. Mgr. .... Bernie Kelcher
Adv. Mgr...Pam Miller
Dist. Mgr...................................Craig Anderson
Mng. Ed..Peggy Bakken
Mechanical Specifications: Type page 4 x 10; E - 4 cols, 2 1/2, 1/4 between; A - 5 cols, 2, 1/8 between; C - 8 cols, 1 1/6, 5/24 between. Equipment & Software: Hardware — APP/Mac; Software — QPS/QuarkXPress.
Delivery Method: Carrier
Areas Served: 55436, 55424, 55410, 55439, 55435

EXCELSIOR/SHOREWOOD/CHANHASSEN SUN SAILOR (THUR)
10917 Valley View Rd, Eden Prairie, MN, 55344-3730, Hennepin, USA; gen tel (952) 392-6800; adv tel (952) 392-6888; gen fax (952) 392-6802; disp adv e-mail chris.dillmann@ecm-inc.com; class adv e-mail cheri.obannon@ecm-inc.com ; ed e-mail chris.

dillmann@ecm-inc.com; web site http://sailor.mnsun.com/
Circulation: 60pd, 5,963fr; CAC
Advertising rate: Open inch rate $11.00
Established: 1970
Group: Adams Publishing Group, LLC
American Community Newspapers LLC
CEO.......Gene Carr
Pub.......Bob Cole
Adv. Mgr.......Jeremy Bradford
Class. Adv. Mgr.......Pam Miller
Mktg. Mgr.......Krista Jech
Gen Mgr.......Mark Weber
Mng. Ed.......Paul Groessel
Mechanical Specifications: Type page 4 x 10; E - 4 cols, 2 1/2, 1/4 between; A - 5 cols, 1 5/8, 1/4 between; C - 8 cols, 1 1/6, 5/24 between. Equipment & Software: Hardware — APP/Mac; Software — QPS/QuarkXPress.
Delivery Method: Carrier
Areas Served: 55331, 55317

MINNETONKA/DEEPHAVEN/HOPKINS SUN SAILOR (THUR)

10917 Valley View Rd, Eden Prairie, MN, 55344-3730, Hennepin, USA; gen tel (952) 392-6800; adv tel (952) 392-6888; gen fax (952) 392-6802; disp adv e-mail robbie.shoemaker@ecm-inc.com; class adv e-mail robbie.shoemaker@ecm-inc.com; ed e-mail paul.wahl@ecm-inc.com; web site sailor.mnsun.com
Circulation: 88pd, 18,076fr; CAC
Advertising rate: Open inch rate $20.00
Established: 1970
Group: Adams Publishing Group, LLC
Sun Newspapers
Adv. Mgr.......Pam Miller
Mng. Ed.......Peggy Bakken
Prod. Mgr.......Mike Erickson
Mechanical Specifications: Type page 4 x 10; E - 4 cols, 2 1/2, 1/4 between; A - 5 cols, 1 5/8, 1/4 between; C - 8 cols, 1 1/6, 5/24 between. Equipment & Software: Hardware — APP/Mac; Software — QPS/QuarkXPress.
Delivery Method: Carrier
Areas Served: 55345, 55391, 55305, 55343

MOUNDS VIEW/NEW BRIGHTON SUN FOCUS (THUR)

10917 Valley View Rd, Eden Prairie, MN, 55344-3730, Hennepin, USA; gen tel (952) 392-6800; adv tel (952) 392-6888; gen fax (952) 392-6802; disp adv e-mail kassie.petermann@ecm-inc.com; class adv e-mail krista.jech@ecm-inc.com; ed e-mail kassie.petermann@ecm-inc.com; web site http://focus.mnsun.com
Circulation: 12pd, 9,309fr; CAC
Advertising rate: Open inch rate $15.00
Established: 1968
Group: Adams Publishing Group, LLC
Ed.......Peggy Bakken
Prod. Mgr.......Mike Erickson
Gen. Mgr.......Jeff Coolman
Mechanical Specifications: Type page 4 x 10; E - 4 cols, 2 1/2, 1/4 between; A - 5 cols, 1 5/8, between; C - 8 cols, 1 1/6, 5/24 between.
Delivery Method: Carrier
Areas Served: 55112

RICHFIELD SUN-CURRENT (THUR)

10917 Valley View Rd, Eden Prairie, MN, 55344-3730, Hennepin, USA; gen tel (952) 392-6800; adv tel (952) 392-6888; gen fax (952) 392-6802; disp adv e-mail jorgenson-nicole@hotmail.com; class adv e-mail krista.jech@ecm-inc.com; ed e-mail andrew.wig@ecm-inc.com; web site www.current.mnsun.com
Circulation: 163pd, 9,831fr; CAC
Advertising rate: Open inch rate $15.50
Established: 1954
Group: Adams Publishing Group, LLC
Prod. Mgr.......Mike Erickson
Mng. Ed.......Peggy Baken
Mktg. Mgr.......Krista Jech
Mechanical Specifications: Type page 4 x 10; E - 4 cols, 2 1/2, 1/4 between; A - 5 cols, 1 5/8, between; C - 8 cols, 1 1/6, 5/24 between. Equipment & Software: Hardware — APP/Mac; Software — QPS/QuarkXPress.
Delivery Method: Carrier
Areas Served: 55423

ROBBINSDALE/CRYSTAL/NEW HOPE/GOLDEN VALLEY SUN-POST (THUR)

10917 Valley View Rd, Eden Prairie, MN, 55344-3730, Hennepin, USA; gen tel (952) 392-6800; adv tel (952) 392-6888; gen fax (763) 424-7388; disp adv e-mail lance.barker@ecm-inc.com; class adv e-mail krista.jech@ecm-inc.com; ed e-mail joe-bowen@ecm-inc.com; web site www.post.mnsun.com
Circulation: 154pd, 10,255fr; CAC
Advertising rate: Open inch rate $24.00
Established: 1938
Group: Adams Publishing Group, LLC
American Community Newspapers LLC
Pub.......Bob Cole
Circ. Mgr.......Herb Hesse
Class. Adv. Mgr.......Pam Miller
Ed.......Peggy Bakken
Mechanical Specifications: Type page 10 3/8 x 15; E - 4 cols, 2 1/2, 1/4 between; A - 5 cols, 1 5/8, between; C - 8 cols, 1 1/6, 5/24 between.Equipment & Software: Hardware — APP/Mac; Software — QPS/QuarkXPress.
Delivery Method: Carrier
Areas Served: 55422, 55427, 55428, 55429, 55426, 55416

WAYZATA/ORONO/PLYMOUTH/LONG LAKE SUN SAILOR (THUR)

10917 Valley View Rd, Eden Prairie, MN, 55344-3730, Hennepin, USA; gen tel (952) 392-6800; adv tel (952) 392-6888; gen fax (952) 392-6802; disp adv e-mail robbie.shoemaker@ecm-inc.com; class adv e-mail linda.bank@ecm-inc.com; ed e-mail jared.huizenga@ecm-inc.com; web site http://sailor.mnsun.com/
Circulation: 146pd, 18,039fr; CAC
Advertising rate: Open inch rate $23.00
Established: 1970
Group: Adams Publishing Group, LLC
American Community Newspapers LLC
Pub.......Bob Cole
Adv. Dir.......Nathen Bliss
Mng. Ed.......Yvonne Klinnert
Circ. Mgr.......Herb Hesse
Mechanical Specifications: Type page 4 x 10; E - 4 cols, 2 1/2, 1/4 between; A - 5 cols, 1 5/8, 1/4 between; C - 8 cols, 1 1/6, 5/24 between. Equipment & Software: Hardware — APP/Mac; Software — QPS/QuarkXPress.
Delivery Method: Carrier
Areas Served: 55356, 55323, 55361, 55384, 55391, 55392, 55442, 55441, 55446, 55447

EDGERTON

EDGERTON ENTERPRISE (WED)

831 MAIN ST, Edgerton, MN, 56128-1151, Pipestone, USA; gen tel (507) 442-6161; gen fax (507) 631-7542; ed e-mail edgent@iw.net; web site www.edgertonenterprise.com
Circulation: 1,679pd,; Sworn/Estimate/Non-Audited
Advertising rate: Open inch rate $6.50
Established: 1883
Pub.......Jill Fennema
Pub.......Irene Gunnink
Asst. Ed.......Ashley Stoel
Mechanical Specifications: Type page 6 x 21 1/2; E - 7 cols, 2 1/16, 3/16 between; A - 7 cols, 2 1/16, 3/16 between; C - 7 cols, 2 1/16, 3/16 between.Equipment & Software: Hardware — APP/Mac; Software — Write Now 4.0, Multi Ad/Creator 4.0.
Delivery Method: Mail
Areas Served: Edgerton, Chandler, and Leota

ELBOW LAKE

GRANT COUNTY HERALD (WED)

35 Central Ave N, Elbow Lake, MN, 56531-4123, Grant, USA; gen tel (218) 685-5326; adv tel (218) 685-5326; ed tel (218) 685-5326; gen fax (218) 685-5327; adv fax (218) 685-5327; ed fax (218) 685-5327; disp adv e-mail gcanne@runestone.net; class adv e-mail gcdonna@runestone.net; ed e-mail gcnews@runestone.net; web site www.grantherald.com
Circulation: 2,200pd, 35fr; Sworn/Estimate/Non-Audited
Advertising rate: Open inch rate $8.00
Established: 1879
Group: Whitney Rae Publishing
Digital Platform - Mobile: Apple, Android
Digital Platform - Tablet: Apple iOS, Android, Nook
Circ. Mgr.......Penny Pederson
Ed.......Christopher A. Ray
Prodn. Mgr.......Pauline Martinson
Nikki Eystad
Darla Johnson
Designer.......Kara Engquist
Publishers.......Reed/Shelly Anfinson
General Manager.......Anne O'Flynn
Mechanical Specifications: Type page 6 x 21 1/2; E - 6 cols, 2, 1/8 between; A - 6 cols, 2, 1/8 between; C - 6 cols, 2, 1/8 between.Equipment & Software: Hardware — APP/Mac; Software — InDesign ADobe,
Delivery Method: Mail, Newsstand
Areas Served: 56531, 56590, 56311, 56248, 56309, 56339

ELY

THE ELY ECHO (SAT)

15 E Chapman St, Ely, MN, 55731-1227, Saint Louis, USA; gen tel (218) 365-3141; gen fax (218) 365-3142; disp adv e-mail ads@elyecho.com; class adv e-mail ads@elyecho.com; ed e-mail thepub@elyecho.com; web site www.elyecho.com
Circulation: 3,329pd, 32fr; Sworn/Estimate/Non-Audited
Advertising rate: Open inch rate $12.30
Established: 1972
Group: Milestones, Inc.Editions: (52)
Digital Platform - Mobile: Apple, Android, Windows
Digital Platform - Tablet: Apple iOS, Android, Windows 7, Blackberry Tablet OS, Kindle, Nook, Kindle Fire
Pub.......Anne Swenson
Adv. Mgr.......Nick Wognum
Mng. Ed.......Tom Coombe
Advt Dir.......Lisa Vidal-Sainio
Mechanical Specifications: Type page 6 x 19; E - 6 cols, 1.59, 1/6 betweenEquipment & Software: Hardware — 6-APP/Mac, 1-PC; Software — Adobe/InDesignAdobe/Photoshop, Macromedia/Freehand.
Delivery Method: Mail, Newsstand, Racks
Areas Served: 55731, 55706, 55796, 55782, 55790

ERSKINE

THE ERSKINE ECHO (THUR)

309 1st St S, Erskine, MN, 56535-4142, Polk, USA; gen tel (218) 687-3775; gen fax (218) 687-3744; disp adv e-mail echonews@gvtel.com
Circulation: 969pd, 23fr; Sworn/Estimate/Non-Audited
Advertising rate: Open inch rate $4.85
Established: 1899
Ed.......Robert HoleEquipment & Software: Hardware — APP/i Mac OS 10; Presses — Ryobi/2800 CD, ATF; Software — QPS/QuarkXPress 8.0., Adobe Professional,
Delivery Method: Mail
Areas Served: 56535, 56592, 56556, 56736

FAIRFAX

FAIRFAX STANDARD GAZETTE (WED)

102 SE First St., Fairfax, MN, 55332, Renville, USA; gen tel (507) 426-7235; gen fax (507) 426-7264; disp adv e-mail fxstandard-comp@gmail.com; ed e-mail fxstandard-news@gmail.com; web site standard-gazette.com
Circulation: 1,423pd,; Sworn/Estimate/Non-Audited
Advertising rate: Open inch rate $6.45
Established: 2000
Group: D&D Publications LLC
Ed.......Daniel McGonigle
Mechanical Specifications: Type page 6 x 21 1/2; E - 7 cols, 2, 1/4 between; A - 7 cols, 2, 1/4 between; C - 7 cols, 2, 1/4 between.Equipment & Software: Hardware — APP/Mac 7200/120, 2-APP/Mac 8100; Software — Clarise Work 1.02, QPS/QuarkXPress 3.32.

FARMINGTON

THE FARMINGTON INDEPENDENT (THUR)

312 Oak St, Farmington, MN, 55024-1359, Dakota, USA; gen tel (651) 460-6606; gen fax (651) 463-7730; disp adv e-mail editor@farmingtonindependent.com; ed e-mail editor@farmingtonindependent.com; web site www.farmingtonindependent.com
Circulation: 2,500pd,; Sworn/Estimate/Non-Audited
Advertising rate: Open inch rate $6.70
Group: Forum Communications Co.
Gen. Mgr.......Steve Gall
Ed.......Nathan Hansen
Mechanical Specifications: Type page 13 x 21; E - 6 cols, 2, 1/4 between; A - 6 cols, 2, 1/4 between; C - 8 cols, 2, 1/4 between.

THE ROSEMOUNT TOWN PAGES (FRI)

312 Oak St, Farmington, MN, 55024-1359, Dakota, USA; gen tel (651) 460-6606; gen fax (651) 463-7730; disp adv e-mail info@rosemounttownpages.com; ed e-mail editor@rosemounttownpages.com; web site www.rosemounttownpages.com
Circulation: 1,594pd,; Sworn/Estimate/Non-Audited
Advertising rate: Open inch rate $6.50
Group: Forum Communications Co.
Gen. Mgr.......Chad Haellming
Ed.......Nathan Hansen
Mng. Ed.......Jeff Mores
Mechanical Specifications: Type page 6 x 20.
Delivery Method: Mail, Carrier
Areas Served: 55068

FERTILE

THE FERTILE JOURNAL (WED)

214 N MILL ST, Fertile, MN, 56540, Polk, USA; gen tel (218) 945-6120; gen fax (218) 945-6125; ed e-mail fertjou@gvtel.com; web site http://www.fertilejournal.com/mobile/
Circulation: 1,348pd,; Sworn/Estimate/Non-Audited
Advertising rate: Open inch rate $4.35
Established: 1882
Ed.......Rod Thoreson
Pub.......Karie KirschbaumEquipment & Software: Hardware — APP/Mac; Software — QPS/QuarkXPress.

FLOODWOOD

PORTAGE NEWS (TUES)

121 W 7th Ave, Floodwood, MN, 55736-1200, St. Louis, USA; gen tel (218) 476-3210; gen fax (218) 476-3211; disp adv e-mail portage.ads@frontier.com; ed e-mail vpofmg.sec@frontiernet.net; web site http://www.thevoyageurpress.com/portagenews.html
Advertising rate: Open inch rate $5.00
Pub.......John Grones
Gen. Mgr./Adv.......Pat Murphy
Delivery Method: Mail

FOLEY

BENTON COUNTY NEWS (TUES)

220 Broadway Ave N, Foley, MN, 56329-8802, Benton, USA; gen tel (320) 968-7220; adv tel 320.352.6577; ed tel same; gen fax (320) 968-8821; adv fax 320.352.5647; ed fax same; disp adv e-mail missy@saukherald.com; class adv e-mail robin@saukherald.

com; ed e-mail natasha@saukherald.com; web site http://www.bentonconews.com
Circulation: 1,300pd,; USPS
Advertising rate: Open inch rate $7.00
Established: 1932
Group: Star Publications
Sales Mgr....Missy Traeger
Ed....Natasha Barber
Reporter....Mitch Cottew
Delivery Method: Mail, Racks
Areas Served: Foley and surrounding communities of Benton County

FOREST LAKE

FOREST LAKE TIMES (THUR)

146 Lake St N, Ste 125, Forest Lake, MN, 55025-2109, Washington, USA; gen tel (651) 464-4601; gen fax (651) 464-4605; disp adv e-mail clint.riese@ecm-inc.com; class adv e-mail nicholas.hall@ecm-inc.com; ed e-mail ryan.howard@ecm-inc.com; web site www.forestlaketimes.com - 71,380(views) 13,746(visitors)
Circulation: 175pd, 12,901fr; CAC
Advertising rate: Open inch rate $13.60
Established: 1903
Group: Adams Publishing Group, LLC
Gen. Mgr....Jeff Andres
Ed....Cliff Buchan
Adv. Dir....Jerry Gloe
Mechanical Specifications: Type page 10 2/5 x 21; E - 6 cols, 1 3/4, 1/8 between; A - 6 cols, 1 3/4, 1/8 between; C - 8 cols, 1 3/4, 1/12 between.Equipment & Software: Hardware — APP/Mac; Presses — 8-HI; Software — QPS/QuarkXPress, Adobe/Illustrator, Adobe/Photoshop.
Areas Served: 55025, 55092, 55073

FOSSTON

THE THIRTEEN TOWNS (TUES)

118 Johnson Ave N, Fosston, MN, 56542-1328, Polk, USA; gen tel (218) 435-1313; gen fax (218) 435-1309; disp adv e-mail ads13towns@gvtel.com; ed e-mail 13towns@gvtel.com; web site 13Towns.com
Circulation: 1,600pd,; Sworn/Estimate/Non-Audited
Advertising rate: Open inch rate $5.95
Established: 1884
Group: Thirteen Towns of Fosston
Digital Platform - Mobile: Apple, Android, Windows, Blackberry
Digital Platform - Tablet: Apple iOS, Android, Windows 7, Blackberry Tablet OS, Kindle, Nook, Kindle Fire
Pub....Michael Moore
Ed....Ed Lavelle
Delivery Method: Mail, Newsstand, Racks
Areas Served: Polk, Red Lake, Pennington, Clearwater, Beltrami, Mahnomen & Norman Counties

FRAZEE

FRAZEE-VERGAS FORUM (THUR)

112 W Main Ave, Frazee, MN, 56544, Becker, USA; gen tel (218) 334-3566; gen fax (218) 334-3567; disp adv e-mail fforum@loretel.net; web site www.frazeeforum.com
Circulation: 1,750pd, 25fr; Sworn/Estimate/Non-Audited
Advertising rate: Open inch rate $11.50
Established: 1960
Digital Platform - Mobile: Apple, Windows
Digital Platform - Tablet: Apple iOS, Windows 7, Kindle, Kindle Fire
Gen. Mgr....Delair Kaas
Ed....Gale Kaas
Mechanical Specifications: Type page 6 x 21 1/2; E - 6 cols, 2, between; A - 6 cols, 2, between; C - 6 cols, 2, between.Equipment & Software: Hardware — PC; Software — QPS/QuarkXPress 5.0.
Delivery Method: Mail, Newsstand
Areas Served: 56544, 56587, 56593, 56501, 56573

FULDA

FULDA FREE PRESS (WED)

118 N St Paul Ave, Fulda, MN, 56131-4463, Murray, USA; gen tel (507) 425-2303; gen fax (507) 425-2501; disp adv e-mail text@fuldafreepress.net; ed e-mail photo@fuldafreepress.net; web site www.fuldafreepress.net
Circulation: 1,148pd,; Sworn/Estimate/Non-Audited
Advertising rate: Open inch rate $6.50
Established: 1879
Digital Platform - Mobile: Apple
Digital Platform - Tablet: Apple iOS
Ed....Gerald D. Johnson
Delivery Method: Mail
Areas Served: Fulda city, murray

GLENCOE

THE MCLEOD COUNTY CHRONICLE (WED)

716 10th St E, Glencoe, MN, 55336-2212, McLeod, USA; gen tel (320) 864-5518; gen fax (320) 864-5510; disp adv e-mail brendaf@glencoenews.com; class adv e-mail suek@glencoenews.com; ed e-mail bulletinnews@embarqmail.com; web site www.glencoenews.com
Circulation: 3,367pd, 50fr; Sworn/Estimate/Non-Audited
Advertising rate: Open inch rate $7.15
Pub....William Ramige
Adv. Mgr....Sue Colden
Circ. Mgr....Trisha Karels
Ed....Lori Copler
Prod. Mgr....Jessica Belland
Mechanical Specifications: Type page 13 x 21 1/2; E - 6 cols, 2, 1/4 between; A - 6 cols, 2, 1/4 between; C - 6 cols, 2, 1/4 between. Equipment & Software: Hardware — APP/Mac; Software — QPS/QuarkXPress 4.1, Adobe/Illustrator, Adobe/Photoshop, APP/Works.
Delivery Method: Mail

GLENWOOD

POPE COUNTY TRIBUNE (MON)

14 1st Ave SE, Glenwood, MN, 56334-1621, Pope, USA; gen tel (320) 634-4571; gen fax (320) 634-5522; disp adv e-mail design@pctribune.com; class adv e-mail design@pctribune.com; ed e-mail tdouglass@pctribune.com; web site www.pctribune.com - 800,000(views) 40,000(visitors)
Circulation: 3,200pd,; USPS
Advertising rate: Open inch rate $8.70
Established: 1920
Digital Platform - Mobile: Apple
Digital Platform - Tablet: Apple iOS, Kindle
Pub./Ed....Tim Douglass
Mechanical Specifications: Type page 6 x 21 1/2; E - 6 cols, 2 1/4, 1/6 between; A - 6 cols, 2 1/4, 1/6 between; C - 6 cols, 2 1/4, 1/6 between.Equipment & Software: Hardware — Mac; Presses — off site; Software — Mac OS
Delivery Method: Mail, Newsstand, Racks
Areas Served: 56334 56381 5631656215 56308 56323 56327 56343 56349 56385 56267

THE STARBUCK TIMES (TUES)

14 1st Ave SE, Glenwood, MN, 56334-1621, Pope, USA; gen tel (320) 239-2244; gen fax (320) 239-2254; disp adv e-mail ads@pctribune.com; class adv e-mail locals@pctribune.com; ed e-mail news.times@hcinet.net; web site http://www.pctribune.com/starbuck.php
Circulation: 1,320pd,; USPS
Advertising rate: Open inch rate $4.85
Pub....Tim Douglas
Ed....Zach Anderson
Gen. Mgr....Erika Andreas
Mechanical Specifications: Type page 6 x 21 1/2; E - 6 cols, 2 1/4, 1/8 between; A - 6 cols, 2 1/4, 1/8 between; C - 6 cols, 2 1/4, 1/8 between.Equipment & Software: Hardware — APP/Mac; Software — MAC Indesign
Areas Served: 56381 56334 56323 56349 56215 56267 56244

GONVICK

LEADER RECORD (WED)

239 2ND AVE, Gonvick, MN, 56644, Clearwater, USA; gen tel (218) 487-5225; gen fax (218) 487-5251; ed e-mail richards@gvtel.com; web site http://www.tricocanary.com/leader-record
Circulation: 1,535pd,; Sworn/Estimate/Non-Audited
Advertising rate: Open inch rate $4.25
Pub....Richard D. Richards
Ed. . Corrine J. RichardsEquipment & Software: Hardware — PCs; Presses — WPC/Web Leader; Software — Adobe/PageMaker 6.0.

GRAND MARAIS

COOK COUNTY NEWS-HERALD (SAT)

15 1st Ave W, Grand Marais, MN, 55604-3131, Cook, USA; gen tel (218) 387-1025; gen fax (218) 387-9500; disp adv e-mail heraldads@boreal.org; ed e-mail starnews@boreal.org; web site www.cookcountynews-herald.com
Circulation: 4,010pd, 66fr; CVC
Advertising rate: Open inch rate $8.00
Established: 1881
Pub....Deidre Kettunen
Pub....Hal Kettunen
Ed....Rhonda Silence
Adv. Mgr....Mary Fleace
Delivery Method: Mail

GRAND MEADOW

MEADOW AREA SHOPPER (WED)

125 S. Main St., Grand Meadow, MN, 55936, Mower, USA; gen tel (507) 754-5486; adv tel (507) 324-5325; ed tel (507) 754-5486; gen fax (507) 754-5151; adv fax (507) 324-5267; disp adv e-mail evansppc@mediacombb.net; class adv e-mail evansppc@mediacombb.net; ed e-mail evansppc@mediacombb.net
Circulation: 0pd, 2,700fr; Sworn/Estimate/Non-Audited
Advertising rate: Open inch rate $5.50
Established: 1988
Group: Evans Publishing & Printing, Inc.
Pub....Dan Evans
Ed....Marciel Skifter
Delivery Method: Mail
Areas Served: Mower County, MN

GRAND RAPIDS

GRAND RAPIDS HERALD-REVIEW (WED, SUN)

301 NW 1st Ave, Grand Rapids, MN, 55744-2704, Itasca, USA; gen tel (218) 326-6623; gen fax (218) 326-6627; disp adv e-mail grads@grandrapidsheraldreview.net; class adv e-mail beiesland@grandrapidsheraldreview.net; ed e-mail barendt@grandrapidsheraldreview.net; web site www.grandrapidsmn.com
Circulation: 7,883pd,; Sworn/Estimate/Non-Audited
Advertising rate: Open inch rate $14.15
Established: 1894
Group: APG Media
Digital Platform - Mobile: Apple
Digital Platform - Tablet: Apple iOS, Blackberry Tablet OS, Kindle Fire
Ed....Britta Arendt
Pub....Mark Roy
Delivery Method: Mail, Newsstand, Carrier
Areas Served: Itasca

GRANITE FALLS

GRANITE FALLS-CLARKFIELD ADVOCATE-TRIBUNE (THUR)

713 Prentice St, Granite Falls, MN, 56241-1519, Yellow Medicine, USA; gen tel (320) 564-2126; gen fax (320) 564-4293; disp adv e-mail bsommervold@granitefallsnews.com; ed e-mail stedrick@granitefallsnews.com; web site www.granitefallsnews.com
Circulation: 2,108pd,; Sworn/Estimate/Non-Audited
Advertising rate: Open inch rate $7.95
Group: GateHouse Media, Inc.
Pub....David Smiglewski
Gen. Mgr....Mike Dupere
Ed....Scott Tedrick
Adv. Mgr....Bev Sommervold

GREENBUSH

TRIBUNE (WED)

192 Hill St., Greenbush, MN, 56726, Roseau, USA; gen tel (218) 782-2275; gen fax (218) 782-2277; disp adv e-mail tribune@wiktel.com; ed e-mail mavis@wiktel.com; web site www.page1publications.com
Circulation: 986pd,; Sworn/Estimate/Non-Audited
Advertising rate: Open inch rate $4.75
Group: Page One Publications
Pub....Rollin Bergman
Ed....Julie Nordine
Delivery Method: Mail

GRYGLA

THE GRYGLA EAGLE (WED)

127 S MAIN AVE, Grygla, MN, 56727, Marshall, USA; gen tel (218) 294-6220; gen fax (218) 487-5251; disp adv e-mail richards@gvtel.com
Circulation: 700pd,; Sworn/Estimate/Non-Audited
Advertising rate: Open inch rate $2.50
Pub....Richard D. Richards
Ed....Kari Sundberg

HALLOCK

KITTSON COUNTY ENTERPRISE (WED)

118 2nd St NE, Hallock, MN, 56728-4320, Kittson, USA; gen tel (218) 843-2868; disp adv e-mail kce@wiktel.com; class adv e-mail kce@wiktel.com; ed e-mail kce@wiktel.com; web site www.kittsonarea.com
Circulation: 1,200pd,; Sworn/Estimate/Non-Audited
Advertising rate: Open inch rate $6.10
Established: 1881
Mechanical Specifications: Type page 13 x 21.
Delivery Method: Mail
Areas Served: 567, 582

HASTINGS

FARMINGTON ROSEMOUNT INDEPENDENT TOWN PAGES (THUR)

PO Box 277, Hastings, MN, 55033-0277, Dakota, USA; gen tel (651) 460-6606; adv tel (715) 426-1039 ; ed tel (651) 301-7875; gen fax (651) 463-7730 ; ed e-mail editor@farmingtonindependent.com; web site http://www.rosemounttownpages.com
Group: Forum Communications Co.
Pub....Nathan Hansen
Adv. Dir....Steve Engelhart

HASTINGS STAR GAZETTE (THUR)

PO Box 277, Hastings, MN, 55033-0277, Dakota, USA; gen tel (651) 437-6153; adv tel (715) 426-1039; ed tel (651) 319-4501; gen fax (651) 437-5911; ed e-mail news@

hastingsstargazette.com; web site www.hastingsstargazette.com
Circulation: 4,918pd,; Sworn/Estimate/Non-Audited
Advertising rate: Open inch rate $9.99
Group: Forum Communications Co.
Pub....................................Steven R. Messick
Ed.......................................Chad Richardson
Adv. Dir...................................Steve Engelhart
Delivery Method: Mail, Carrier

SOUTH WASHINGTON COUNTY BULLETIN (WED)
217 Ramsey St, Hastings, MN, 55033-1220, Washington, USA; gen tel (651) 319-4280; adv tel (651) 319-4515 ; ed tel (651) 459-7600 ; gen fax (651) 459-9491; ed e-mail editor@swcbulletin.com; web site www.swcbulletin.com
Circulation: 4,529pd,; Sworn/Estimate/Non-Audited
Advertising rate: Open inch rate $14.63
Group: Forum Communications Co.
Pub....................................Steven R. Messick
Gen. Mgr...............................Jeffrey Patterson
Mng. Ed......................................Patricia Drey
Prodn. Mgr.........................Thomas Bonneville
Mechanical Specifications: Type page 6 x 21 1/2; E - 6 cols, 2 1/16, 1/16 between; A - 6 cols, 2 1/16, 1/16 between; C - 8 cols, 1 1/2, 1/16 between.Equipment & Software: Hardware — APP/Mac; Software — QPS/QuarkXPress, Adobe/Photoshop, Adobe/PageMaker, Adobe/Illustrator, Macromedia/Freehand.
Areas Served: 55016, 55055, 55071, 55033

WOODBURY BULLETIN (WED)
PO Box 277, Hastings, MN, 55033-0277, Washington, USA; gen tel (651) 319-4270; gen fax (651) 702-0977; disp adv e-mail sengelhart@woodburybulletin.com; ed e-mail editor@woodburybulletin.com; web site www.woodburybulletin.com
Circulation: 4,892fr; Sworn/Estimate/Non-Audited
Advertising rate: Open inch rate $14.63
Group: Forum Communications Co.
Ed..Hank Long
Adv. Dir ....Steve Engelhart
Jean Marie Brown
Mechanical Specifications: Type page 6 x 21 1/2; E - 6 cols, 2 1/16, 1/16 between; A - 6 cols, 2 1/16, 1/16 between; C - 8 cols, 1 1/2, 1/16 between.Equipment & Software: Hardware — APP/Mac; Software — QPS/QuarkXPress, Adobe/Photoshop, Macromedia/Freehand, Adobe/Illustrator.
Delivery Method: Mail, Carrier

HAWLEY

LAKE PARK JOURNAL (MON)
PO Box 709, Hawley, MN, 56549-0709, Clay, USA; gen tel (218) 238-6872; gen fax (218) 483-4457; disp adv e-mail ads@hawleyherald.net; class adv e-mail frontdesk@hawleyherald.net; ed e-mail marc@hawleyherald.net
Circulation: 1,712pd,; Sworn/Estimate/Non-Audited
Advertising rate: Open inch rate $8.50
Established: 1922
Pub...Eugene Prim
Ed...Marc Ness

THE HAWLEY HERALD (MON)
119 6th St, Hawley, MN, 56549-4121, Clay, USA; gen tel (218) 483-3306; gen fax (218) 483-4457; disp adv e-mail ads@hawleyherald.net; ed e-mail marc@hawleyherald.net; web site www.hawleyherald.net
Circulation: 1,712pd,; Sworn/Estimate/Non-Audited
Advertising rate: Open inch rate $8.50
Established: 1927
Ed...Marc Ness
Delivery Method: Mail

HECTOR

THE NEWS MIRROR (WED)
201 S. Main, Hector, MN, 55342, Renville, USA; gen tel (320) 848-2248; gen fax (320) 848-2249; disp adv e-mail newsmir@hcctel.net
Circulation: 1,495pd,; Sworn/Estimate/Non-Audited
Advertising rate: Open inch rate $7.18 N*M only - $9.28 common section
Established: 1977
Adv. Mgr.......................................Aaron Hubin
Ed...John Hubin
Delivery Method: Mail, Newsstand, Racks
Areas Served: 55342,55314,55385,56228

HENDERSON

HENDERSON INDEPENDENT (WED)
407 Main St, Henderson, MN, 56044-7742, Sibley, USA; gen tel (507) 248-3223; gen fax (507) 248-3611; disp adv e-mail hendersonmnnews@gmail.com; class adv e-mail hendersonmnnews@gmail.com; ed e-mail hendersonind@frontiernet.net; web site https://www.facebook.com/HendersonIndependent/?ref=page_internal
Circulation: 785pd, 85fr; Sworn/Estimate/Non-Audited
Advertising rate: Open inch rate $8.00
Established: 1874
Pub..................................C. Edward Townsend
Mechanical Specifications: Type page 4 x 15; E - 4 cols, 2 1/4, 1/3 between; A - 4 cols, 2 1/4, 1/3 between; C - 6 cols, 1 1/2, 1/6 between. Equipment & Software: Hardware — APP/Macs; Software — Adobe/PageMaker 5.0.
Delivery Method: Mail, Newsstand
Areas Served: 56044

HENDRICKS

THE HENDRICKS PIONEER (WED)
202 S Main St, Hendricks, MN, 56136-1244, Lincoln, USA; gen tel (507) 275-3197; gen fax (507) 275-3108; ed e-mail hendrickspioneer@gmail.com; web site www.thehendrickspioneer.com
Circulation: 748pd,; Sworn/Estimate/Non-Audited
Advertising rate: Open inch rate $5.70
Established: 1900
Co-Pub...Diane Clark
Co-Pub..William Clark
Ed....Robert WolsingtonEquipment & Software: Hardware — PC; Software — Adobe/PageMaker, Adobe/Photoshop, Archetype/Corel Draw.
Delivery Method: Mail

HENNING

CITIZEN'S ADVOCATE (TUES)
412 Douglas Ave, Henning, MN, 56551-4001, Otter Tail, USA; gen tel (218) 548-5585; gen fax (218) 548-5582; disp adv e-mail news@henningadvocate.com; web site www.henningadvocate.com
Circulation: 910pd, 27fr; Sworn/Estimate/Non-Audited
Advertising rate: Open inch rate $7.90
Established: 1891
Group: Henning Publications, LLCChad Koenen Danielle Koenen
Delivery Method: Mail, Newsstand
Areas Served: 56551, 56527, 56588, 56571

HERMAN

HERMAN-HOFFMAN TRIBUNE (THUR)
408 Berlin Ave S, Herman, MN, 56248-1044, Grant, USA; gen tel (320)677-2229; gen fax (320) 677-2229; ed e-mail hcreview@frontiernet.net; web site www.hermanhoffmantribune.com
Circulation: 1,250pd,; Sworn/Estimate/Non-Audited
Advertising rate: Open inch rate $5.25
Established: 1900
Group: Grant County Herald
Pub...Nick Ripperger
Mechanical Specifications: Type page 11 x 20; A - 6 cols, 1.7, 3/16 between.Equipment & Software: Hardware — APP/Mac; Software — QPS/QuarkXPress.
Delivery Method: Mail, Newsstand
Areas Served: 56248, 56274, 56339, 56343, 56311

HERMANTOWN

HERMANTOWN STAR (THUR)
4940 Lightning Dr, Hermantown, MN, 55811-1355, Saint Louis, USA; gen tel (218) 727-0419; gen fax (218) 722-5821; ed e-mail wpetrich@hermantownstar.com; web site www.hermantownstar.com
Circulation: 1,752pd,; Sworn/Estimate/Non-Audited
Advertising rate: Open inch rate $9.35
Pub..Wade Petrich

HERON LAKE

TRI COUNTY NEWS (WED)
PO Box 227, 931 2nd Ave, Heron Lake, MN, 56137-0227, Jackson, USA; gen tel (507) 793-2327; adv tel (507) 793-2327; ed tel (507) 793-2327; gen fax (507) 793-2327; adv fax (507) 793-2327; ed fax (507) 793-2327; disp adv e-mail tcnews@mysmbs.com; class adv e-mail tcnews@mysmbs.com; ed e-mail tcnews@mysmbs.com; web site www.tricountynewsmn.net
Circulation: 797pd,; Sworn/Estimate/Non-Audited
Advertising rate: Open inch rate $6.20
Established: 1885
Pub....................................Gerald D. Johnson
Ed...Carol Schreiber
Mechanical Specifications: Type page 8 x 21 1/2; E - 8 cols, 1 3/4, 1/6 between; A - 8 cols, 1 3/4, 1/6 between; C - 8 cols, 1 3/4, 1/6 between.Equipment & Software: Hardware — APP/Mac; Software — QPS/QuarkXPress 5.0.
Delivery Method: Mail, Newsstand
Areas Served: 56137, 56119, 56167, 56161, 56150

HINCKLEY

HINCKLEY NEWS (THUR)
115 Main St E, Hinckley, MN, 55037-8763, Pine, USA; gen tel (320) 384-6188; gen fax (320) 384-7844; disp adv e-mail hinckleynews@scicable.com; web site hinckleynews.com
Circulation: 1,600pd,; Sworn/Estimate/Non-Audited
Advertising rate: Open inch rate $7.25
Established: 1891
Pub...Tim Franklin
Adv. Mgr...................................Mary Franklin
Steve Klumb
Mechanical Specifications: Type page 6 x 21 1/2; E - 7 cols, 2, 1/4 between; A - 7 cols, 2, 1/4 between; C - 7 cols, 2, 1/4 between.Equipment & Software: Hardware — 1-APP/Power Mac; Software — QPS/QuarkXPress 3.32.
Delivery Method: Mail, Newsstand, Racks
Areas Served: Hinckley/Pine/55037

HOUSTON

THE HOUSTON BANNER (THUR)
205 S Ellsworth St, Houston, MN, 55943-8627, Houston, USA; gen tel (507) 896-2107; gen fax (507) 896-2107; disp adv e-mail banner@acegroup.cc
Circulation: 578pd, 15fr; Sworn/Estimate/Non-Audited
Advertising rate: Open inch rate $5.94
Established: 1999
Ed..Ellyn Baumann
Mechanical Specifications: Type page 4 x 9 3/4; E - 4 cols, 1 4/5, 1/5 between; A - 4 cols, 1 4/5, 1/5 between; C - 4 cols, 1 4/5, 1/5 between.

HUTCHINSON

HUTCHINSON LEADER (TUES, THUR)
170 Shady Ridge Rd NW, Ste 100, Hutchinson, MN, 55350-2490, McLeod, USA; gen tel (320) 587-5000; adv tel (320) 234-4141; ed tel (320) 234-4156; gen fax (320) 587-6104; disp adv e-mail addirector@hutchinsonleader.com; class adv e-mail warden@hutchinsonleader.com; ed e-mail hanneman@hutchinsonleader.com; web site http://www.crowrivermedia.com/hutchinsonleader/
Circulation: 3,986pd, 379fr; CAC
Advertising rate: Open inch rate $9.50
Established: 1880
Group: Red Wing Publishing Co.
Pub...Matt McMillan
Adv. Mgr....................................Tina McMillan
Ed.......................................Doug Hanneman
Adv. Dir..Kevin True
Mechanical Specifications: Type page 6 x 21 1/2; E - 6 cols, 2, between; A - 6 cols, 2, between; C - 6 cols, 2, between.Equipment & Software: Hardware — APP/Mac; Presses — G/Community; Software — Multi-Ad/Creator.
Delivery Method: Mail, Carrier
Areas Served: 55350,56209,55336,55312,55336,55354,55370,55381,55385,55395,56228,55324,55325,55329,56243,55355,55389,55314,55342,55366,55396,55353,56362,55321,55382

INTERNATIONAL FALLS

THE JOURNAL (WED, SAT)
1602 Highway 71, International Falls, MN, 56649-2161, Koochiching, USA; gen tel (218) 285-7411; adv tel (218) 283-3377 ext 225; ed tel (218) 283-3377 ext. 230; gen fax (218) 285-7206; adv fax (218) 285-7206; ed fax (218) 285-7206; disp adv e-mail karley@ifallsjournal.com; class adv e-mail wendy@ifallsjournal.com; ed e-mail laurel@ifallsdaily-journal.com; web site www.ifallsjournal.com
Circulation: 3,109pd,; Sworn/Estimate/Non-Audited
Advertising rate: 1/4 Pg $318.15; 1/2 Pg $636.30; Full $1302.90
Established: 1911
Group: Red Wing Publishing Co.
Digital Platform - Mobile: Apple, Android
Digital Platform - Tablet: Apple iOS, Android
Pub......................................Rob Davenport
Circ. Mgr......................................Dana Hartje
Ed...Laurel Beager
Reporter ....Emily Gedde
Lifestyle Editor..........................Tammie Calder
Sports editor.................................Danny Chen
Mechanical Specifications: Type page 6x 21 1/2; E - 6 cols, 2 1/16, 1/8 between; A - 6 cols, 2 1/16, 1/8 between; C - 8 cols, 1 1/2, 1/8 between.
Delivery Method: Mail, Carrier, Racks
Areas Served: 56649

ISLE

MILLE LACS MESSENGER (WED)
PO Box 26, 280 W. Main St., Isle, MN, 56342-0026, Mille Macs, USA; gen tel (320) 676-3123; gen fax (320) 676-8450; disp adv e-mail phototech@millelacsmessenger.com; class adv e-mail phototech@millelacsmessenger.com; ed e-mail vlamoore@millelacsmessenger.com; web site www.millelacsmessenger.com
Circulation: 3,800pd,; Sworn/Estimate/Non-Au-

dited
Advertising rate: Open inch rate $11.85
Established: 1913
Group: Adams Publishing Group, LLC
Digital Platform - Mobile: Apple
Digital Platform - Tablet: Apple iOS
Adv. .... Monica Weets
Ed. .... Shauna Tetrault
Operations Mgr.
RoxAnne Bouley
Mechanical Specifications: Type page 6 x 14.75; E - 6 cols, 1 5/8, 1/6 between; A - 6 cols, 1 5/8, 1/6 between; C - 7 cols, 1 3/8, 1/6 between.Equipment & Software: Hardware — APP/Mac; Software — QPS/QuarkXPress 9
Delivery Method: Mail, Newsstand

IVANHOE

THE IVANHOE TIMES (THUR)
315 N Norman St, Ivanhoe, MN, 56142-9580, Lincoln, USA; gen tel (507) 694-1246; gen fax (507) 694-1246; ed e-mail luminamin@yahoo.com; web site http://ivanhoetimes-com.webs.com
Circulation: 847pd,; Sworn/Estimate/Non-Audited
Advertising rate: Open inch rate $7.00
Adv./Prod. Mgr. .... Brent Breck
Mng. Ed. .... Ellen Beck
Mechanical Specifications: Type page 6 x 21 1/2; E - 6 cols, 2, 3/16 between; A - 6 cols, 2, 3/16 between; C - 1 cols, 2, 3/16 between.Equipment & Software: Hardware — APP/Mac; Software — Adobe/Photoshop.

JACKSON

JACKSON COUNTY PILOT (THUR)
310 2nd St, Jackson, MN, 56143-1640, Jackson, USA; gen tel (507) 847-3771; gen fax (507) 847-5822; disp adv e-mail info@livewireprinting.com; class adv e-mail eileenc@livewireprinting.com; ed e-mail editor@livewireprinting.com; web site www.jacksoncountypilot.com
Circulation: 1,700pd,; Sworn/Estimate/Non-Audited
Advertising rate: Open inch rate $10.25
Pub. .... Justin Lessman
Ed. .... Ryan Brinks
Adv. Sales Rep. .... Dallas Luhmann
Circ. Mgr. .... Marilyn Knutson
Mechanical Specifications: Type page 8 x 21 1/2; E - 8 cols, 1 1/2, 1/8 between; A - 8 cols, 1 1/2, 1/8 between; C - 8 cols, 1 1/2, 1/8 between.Equipment & Software: Hardware — IBM, PC; Software — Adobe/PageMaker 6.52.
Delivery Method: Mail

JANESVILLE

JANESVILLE ARGUS (THUR)
107 N Main St, Janesville, MN, 56048-9538, Waseca, USA; gen tel (507) 835-3380; gen fax (507) 835-3435; disp adv e-mail kbiehn@wasecacountynews.com; class adv e-mail classifieds@wasecacountynews.com; ed e-mail srook@wasecacountynews.com; web site www.southernminn.com/janesville_argus/
Circulation: 764pd, 2fr; Sworn/Estimate/Non-Audited
Advertising rate: Open inch rate $5.55
Pub. .... Julie Frazier
Ed. .... Suzanne Rook
Mechanical Specifications: Type page 11 5/8 x 21 1/2; E - 6 cols, 1 5/6, between; A - 6 cols, 1 5/6, between; C - 6 cols, 1 5/6, between.
Areas Served: 56048

JORDAN

JORDAN INDEPENDENT (THUR)
109 Rice St S, Jordan, MN, 55352-1513, Scott, USA; gen tel (952) 492-2224; adv tel (952) 345-6477; gen fax (952) 492-2231; disp adv e-mail jhiltunen@swpub.com; class adv e-mail classified@swpub.com; ed e-mail editor@jordannews.com; web site http://www.swnewsmedia.com/jordan_independent/
Circulation: 1,709pd,; Sworn/Estimate/Non-Audited
Advertising rate: Open inch rate $6.50
Group: Red Wing Publishing Co.
Pub. .... Laurie Hartmann
Circ. Mgr. .... Ruby Winings
Ed. .... Mathias Baden
Adv. Mgr. .... Jen Hiltunen
Delivery Method: Mail

KARLSTAD

NORTH STAR NEWS (THUR)
204 Main St S, Karlstad, MN, 56732-4002, Kittson, USA; gen tel (218) 436-2157; gen fax (218) 436-3271; disp adv e-mail norstar@wiktel.com; class adv e-mail nsads@wiktel.com; ed e-mail dan@wiktel.com; web site www.page1publications.com
Circulation: 1,490pd,; Sworn/Estimate/Non-Audited
Advertising rate: Open inch rate $5.25
Established: 1904
Group: Page One Publications
Pub. .... Rollin Bergman
Adv. Mgr. .... Larina Berggren
Ed. .... Julie M. Nordine

KASSON

DODGE COUNTY INDEPENDENT (WED)
121 W Main St, Kasson, MN, 55944-1456, Dodge, USA; gen tel (507) 634-7503; gen fax (507) 634-4446; disp adv e-mail dci@kmtel.com; ed e-mail bptimes@frontiernet.net; web site http://www.bloomingprairieonline.com/dodge-county-independent
Circulation: 1,419pd,; Sworn/Estimate/Non-Audited
Advertising rate: Open inch rate $7.75
Adv. Mgr. .... June Howard
Ed. .... Randy Carlsen
Delivery Method: Mail, Newsstand

KENYON

KENYON LEADER (WED)
638 2nd St, Kenyon, MN, 55946-1334, Goodhue, USA; gen tel (507) 789-6161; adv tel (507) 333-3148; disp adv e-mail nbrandon@faribault.com; class adv e-mail echristensen@southernminndigital.com; ed e-mail editor@thekenyonleader.com; web site http://www.southernminn.com/the_kenyon_leader/
Circulation: 636pd, 2,334fr; Sworn/Estimate/Non-Audited
Advertising rate: Open inch rate $9.95
Established: 1885
Group: Adams Publishing Group, LLC
Digital Platform - Mobile: Apple, Android, Windows, Blackberry
Digital Platform - Tablet: Apple iOS, Android, Windows 7, Blackberry Tablet OS, Kindle, Nook, Kindle Fire
Ed./Pub. .... Terri Lenz
Circ. Mgr. .... Kris Johnson
Mechanical Specifications: Type page 6 x 21 1/2; E - 6 cols, 1 5/16, between; A - 6 cols, 1 5/16, between; C - 6 cols, 1 5/16, between. Equipment & Software: Hardware — 3-APP/Mac; Software — Adobe/InDesign 2.0, Baseview/NewsEdit Pro IQUE 4.0.4b5.
Delivery Method: Mail, Newsstand, Carrier, Racks
Areas Served: 55946, 55983, 55989, 55053

KERKHOVEN

KERKHOVEN BANNER (WED)
1001 Atlantic Ave., Kerkhoven, MN, 56252, Swift, USA; gen tel (320) 264-3071; gen fax (320) 264-3070; disp adv e-mail kbanner@midstate.tds.net; ed e-mail kbanner@tds.net; web site www.kerkhovenbanner.com
Circulation: 1,220pd,; Sworn/Estimate/Non-Audited
Advertising rate: Open inch rate $4.50
Ed. .... Theodore J. Almen
Mechanical Specifications: Type page 6 x 21 1/2; E - 6 cols, 2 1/8, 3/16 between; A - 6 cols, 2 1/8, 3/16 between; C - 6 cols, 2 1/8, 3/16 between.Equipment & Software: Hardware — 1-APP/Mac 7200, 2-APP/Mac LCII; Software — Adobe/Photoshop, QPS/QuarkXPress.

KIESTER

THE COURIER-SENTINEL (THUR)
405 W Center St, Kiester, MN, 56051, Faribault, USA; gen tel (507) 294-3400; gen fax (507) 294-3400; ed e-mail coursent@smig.net
Circulation: 1,393pd,; Sworn/Estimate/Non-Audited
Advertising rate: Open inch rate $5.20
Established: 1900
Adv. Mgr. .... Tamra Aadsen
Pub./Ed. .... Nicole Swanson

KIMBALL

TRI-COUNTY NEWS (THUR)
70 S Main St, Kimball, MN, 55353-1205, Stearns, USA; gen tel (320) 398-5000; gen fax (320) 398-5000; disp adv e-mail ads@tricountynews.MN; class adv e-mail ads@tricountynews.mn; ed e-mail news@tricountynews.mn; web site www.tricountynews.mn - 60,000(views)
Circulation: 1,385pd, 1,000fr; Sworn/Estimate/Non-Audited
Advertising rate: Open inch rate $9.35
Established: 1948Editions: (1) Tri-County News, Eden Valley-Watkins News
Digital Platform - Mobile: Apple, Android
Digital Platform - Tablet: Apple iOS, Android
Owner/Pub./Ed. .... Jean Matua
Office Asst .... Maxine Doran
Mechanical Specifications: Tabloid format: 15" high
5 columns wide = 10.25" (.125" between columns)Equipment & Software: Hardware — APP/Mac; Software — Adobe Creative Suite 6 (InDesign, Photoshop, etc.)
Delivery Method: Mail, Newsstand
Areas Served: 55329, 55353, 55382, 55389

LAFAYETTE

LAFAYETTE NICOLLET LEDGER (THUR)
750 Main Ave, Lafayette, MN, 56054-4401, Nicollet, USA; gen tel (507) 228-8985; gen fax (507) 228-8779; ed e-mail ledger@prairiepublishingmn.com; web site http://www.prairiepublishingmn.com
Circulation: 1,263pd, 11fr; Sworn/Estimate/Non-Audited
Advertising rate: Open inch rate $6.00
Established: 1904
Group: Prairie Publishing, Inc
Pub .... Michael Koob
Delivery Method: Mail

LAKE CITY

THE LAKE CITY GRAPHIC (THUR)
111 S 8th St, Lake City, MN, 55041-1666, Wabasha, USA; gen tel (651) 345-3316; gen fax (651) 345-4200; disp adv e-mail ads@lakecitygraphic.com; ed e-mail andrew@lakecitygraphic.com; web site www.lakecitygraphic.com - 15,000(views) 5,500(visitors)
Circulation: 2,300pd,; Sworn/Estimate/Non-Audited
Advertising rate: Open inch rate $10.20
Established: 1861
Pub. .... Terry Schumacher
Adv. Mgr. .... Dean Schumacher
Editor .... Andrew Eggenberger
Mechanical Specifications: Type page 6 x 21; E - 6 cols, 1.667,
Equipment & Software: Hardware — APP/Mac; Software — InDesign, Adobe/Photoshop.
Delivery Method: Mail, Racks
Areas Served: City of Lake City; Wabasha County; Goodhue County

LAKE CRYSTAL

LAKE CRYSTAL TRIBUNE (WED)
101 W Humphrey St, Lake Crystal, MN, 56055-2035, Blue Earth, USA; gen tel (507) 726-2133; gen fax (507) 726-2265; disp adv e-mail tribune@hickorytech.net
Circulation: 1,150pd, 33fr; Sworn/Estimate/Non-Audited
Advertising rate: Open inch rate $4.50
Established: 1882
Ed. .... Don R. Marben
Office Manager/Subscription/Accouonts Payable .... Mindy Kranz
Areas Served: 56055, 56001, 56037, 56034,

LAKEFIELD

LAKEFIELD STANDARD (THUR)
403 Main St, Lakefield, MN, 56150-1201, Jackson, USA; gen tel (507) 662-5555; gen fax (507) 662-6770; disp adv e-mail info@livewireprinting.com; ed e-mail editor@livewireprinting.com; web site www.lakefieldstandard.com
Circulation: 1,055pd, 41fr; Sworn/Estimate/Non-Audited
Advertising rate: Open inch rate $6.20
Ed. .... Justin Lessman
Delivery Method: Mail

LAMBERTON

LAMBERTON NEWS (WED)
218 S Main St, Lamberton, MN, 56152-1389, Redwood, USA; gen tel (507) 752-7181; gen fax (507) 752-7181; ed e-mail lambnews@centurylink.net
Circulation: 1,700pd, 4fr; Sworn/Estimate/Non-Audited
Advertising rate: Open inch rate $2.50
Established: 1923
Ed. .... J.G. Dietl
Mechanical Specifications: Type page 6 x 21 1/4; E - 6 cols, 2, 1/6 between; A - 6 cols, 2, 1/6 between.Equipment & Software: Hardware — APP/Mac G4; Presses — Davidson/500, Davidson/700; Software — QPS/QuarkXPress 4.0.

LE CENTER

LE SUEUR NEWS-HERALD (WED)
62 E Minnesota St, Le Center, MN, 56057-1502, Le Sueur, USA; gen tel (507) 665-3332; adv tel (507) 931-8574; ed tel (507) 931-8571; gen fax (507) 665-3334; disp adv e-mail news@lesueurnews-herald.com; ed e-mail editor@lesueurnews-herald.com; web site www.lesueurnews-herald.com
Circulation: 864pd, 45fr; CAC
Advertising rate: Open inch rate $14.20
Group: Adams Publishing Group, LLC
Reg Mgr Ed .... Suzanne Rook
Reg Gen Mgr .... Chad Hjellming
Mechanical Specifications: Type page 6 x 21 1/2; E - 6 cols, 1 5/6, between; A - 6 cols, 1 5/6, between; C - 6 cols, 1 5/6, between.Equipment & Software: Hardware — 3-APP/Power-

Mac G4; Software — Baseview/NewsEdit Pro IQUE 4.0.4b5.
Delivery Method: Mail
Areas Served: 56058

THE LE CENTER LEADER (WED)
62 E Minnesota St, Le Center, MN, 56057-1502, La Sueur, USA; gen tel (507) 357-2233; gen fax (507) 357-6656; disp adv e-mail mdaschner@lecenter.com; class adv e-mail bnguyen@owatonna.com; ed e-mail srook@lecenter.com; web site http://www.southernminn.com/le_center_leader/
Circulation: 1,096pd, 1fr; Sworn/Estimate/Non-Audited
Advertising rate: Open inch rate $14.20
Group: Adams Publishing Group, LLC
Adv. Mgr. .... Terri McMillen
Mng. Ed. .... Suzanne Rook
Class. Adv. .... Bonnie Nguyen
Mechanical Specifications: Type page 6 x 21 1/2; E - 6 cols, 1 5/6, between; A - 6 cols, 1 5/6, between; C - 6 cols, 1 5/6, between.Equipment & Software: Hardware — 2-APP/PowerMac G4; Software — Baseview/NewsEdit Pro IQUE 4.0.4b5.
Delivery Method: Mail
Areas Served: 56057, 56017

LINDSTROM

CHISAGO COUNTY PRESS (THUR)
12631 Lake Blvd, Lindstrom, MN, 55045-9344, Chisago, USA; gen tel (651) 257-5115; gen fax (651) 257-5500; ed e-mail chisago@citlink.net; web site www.chisagocountypress.com
Circulation: 3,413pd, 115fr; Sworn/Estimate/Non-Audited
Advertising rate: Open inch rate $7.65
Established: 1898
Pub. .... Matt Silver
Mng. Ed. .... Denise Martin
Prod. Mgr. .... Laure Peterson
Mechanical Specifications: Type page 6 x 21 1/2; E - 6 cols, 2 1/16, 1/6 between; A - 6 cols, 2 1/16, 1/6 between; C - 6 cols, 2 1/16, 1/6 between.Equipment & Software: Hardware — APP/Mac, PC; Software — QPS/QuarkXPress 8.1.
Delivery Method: Mail, Newsstand
Areas Served: 55012, 55013, 55045, 55056, 55079, 55084, 55073, 55076, 55092

LITCHFIELD

INDEPENDENT REVIEW (THUR, SUN)
217 N Sibley Ave, Litchfield, MN, 55355-2140, Meeker, USA; gen tel (320) 693-3266; gen fax (320) 693-9177; disp adv e-mail true@hutchinsonleader.com; class adv e-mail mcmanus@independentreview.net; ed e-mail schacherer@hutchinsonleader.com; web site http://www.crowrivermedia.com/independentreview/
Circulation: 2,659pd, 11fr; CAC
Advertising rate: Open inch rate $8.25
Ed. .... Matt McMillian
Pub. .... Brent Schacherer
Ad. Dir. .... Kevin True
Mechanical Specifications: Type page 6 x 21 1/2; E - 8 cols, 1 3/4, between; A - 8 cols, 1 3/4, between; C - 8 cols, 1 3/4, between.Equipment & Software: Hardware — APP/Mac; Presses — G/Community; Software — QPS/QuarkXPress.

LITTLE FALLS

MORRISON COUNTY RECORD (SUN)
216 1st St SE, Little Falls, MN, 56345-3004, Morrison, USA; gen tel (320) 632-2345; gen fax (320) 632-2348; disp adv e-mail mcr@mcrecord.com; class adv e-mail mcr@mcrecord.com; ed e-mail terry.lehrke@mcrecord.com; web site www.mcrecord.com - 238,641(views) 21,751(visitors)
Circulation: 350pd, 18,114fr; CAC
Advertising rate: Open inch rate $11.07
Established: 1969
Group: Adams Publishing Group, LLC
Digital Platform - Mobile: Apple, Android, Windows, Blackberry
Digital Platform - Tablet: Apple iOS, Android, Windows 7, Blackberry Tablet OS
Bus. Mgr. .... Judy Espino
Circ. Mgr. .... Karen Grittner
News Ed. .... Terry Lehrke
General Manager .... Carmen Meyer
Sales Manager .... Tena Wensman
Mechanical Specifications: ROP Type page 6 col x 21; Col width 9p4 (1.55"); 0p8 gutter between cols. Classified page 7 col x 21; Col width 7p10 (1.30") 0p8 gutter. Equipment & Software: Hardware — 4-APP/Power Mac, APP/Mac G4, APP/Mac G3, APP/iMac, Dell; Software — Synaptic.
Delivery Method: Carrier
Areas Served: 56314, 56317, 56433, 56328, 56338, 56344, 56345, 56466, 56364, 56475, 56347, 56329

LITTLEFORK

THE LITTLEFORK TIMES (THUR)
720 3rd Ave, Littlefork, MN, 56653-2001, Koochiching, USA; gen tel (218) 278-4143; gen fax (218) 278-4147; disp adv e-mail msfair@northwinds.net; ed e-mail littlefork-times@frontiernet.net
Advertising rate: Open inch rate $3.50
Pub .... Stephanie Fairchild

LONG PRAIRIE

THE LONG PRAIRIE LEADER (WED)
21 3rd St S, Long Prairie, MN, 56347-1195, Todd, USA; gen tel (320) 732-2151; gen fax (320) 732-2152; disp adv e-mail advertising@lpleader.com; class adv e-mail info@lpleader.com; ed e-mail news@lpleader.com; web site www.lpleader.com
Circulation: 2,392pd,; Sworn/Estimate/Non-Audited
Advertising rate: Open inch rate $6.90
Established: 1883
Ed./Pub. .... Jason Brown
Bus. Mgr. .... Gary Brown
Adv. .... Susan LubbersEquipment & Software: Hardware — APP/Mac.
Delivery Method: Mail

LONGVILLE

PINE CONE PRESS CITIZEN (TUES)
166 Hardy Ln., STE 100, Longville, MN, 56655, Cass, USA; gen tel (218) 363-2002; gen fax (218) 363-3043; ed e-mail presscit@arvig.net; web site www.pineconepresscitizen.com
Circulation: 250pd, 6,986fr; Sworn/Estimate/Non-Audited
Advertising rate: Open inch rate $8.75
Established: 1984
Ed/Office Mgr. .... Marilyn Ford
Sales Mgr. .... Dave DeLost
Ed. .... Bill DeLostEquipment & Software: Hardware — APP/Mac; Software — InDesign/Photoshop
Delivery Method: Mail, Newsstand
Areas Served: 56484, 56435, 56471, 56452, 56641, 56655, 55748, 56662, 56433, 56672

LONSDALE

LONSDALE AREA NEWS-REVIEW (TUES)
PO Box 352, Lonsdale, MN, 55046-0352, Rice, USA; gen tel (507) 744-2551; adv tel (507) 645-1120; ed tel (507) 744-2551; disp adv e-mail jpetsche@northfieldnews.com; class adv e-mail suzyrook@gmail.com; ed e-mail editor@northfieldnews.com; web site http://www.southernminn.com/lonsdale_area_news_review/
Circulation: 17pd, 2,445fr; CAC
Group: Adams Publishing Group, LLCSuzanne Rook
Reporter .... Misty Schwab

LONSDALE NEWS - REVIEW (TUES)
PO Box 352, 102 5th Ave. NW, Lonsdale, MN, 55046-0352, Rice, USA; gen tel (507) 744-2551; gen fax (507) 645-6005; disp adv e-mail lnickel@lonsdalenewsreview.com; class adv e-mail bnguyen@owatonna.com; ed e-mail lnickel@lonsdalenewsreview.com; web site www.lonsdalenewsreview.com
Circulation: 0pd, 2,555fr; Sworn/Estimate/Non-Audited
Advertising rate: Open inch rate $6.90
Established: 2006
Group: Adams Publishing Group, LLCLori Nickel
Mechanical Specifications: Type page: 10.25 x 21; 6 col
Delivery Method: Carrier
Areas Served: Lonsdale /Rice /55042

LUVERNE

HILLS CRESCENT (THUR)
117 W Main St, Luverne, MN, 56156-1843, Rock, USA; gen tel (507) 283-2333; gen fax (507) 283-2335; disp adv e-mail sales@star-herald.com; ed e-mail hceditor@star-herald.com; web site http://www.star-herald.com/crescent
Circulation: 394pd,; USPS
Advertising rate: Open inch rate $6.34
General manager .... Rick Peterson
Ed. .... Lori Ehde
Gen. Mgr. .... Rick Peterson
Delivery Method: Mail

THE ROCK COUNTY STAR HERALD (THUR)
117 W Main St, Luverne, MN, 56156-1843, Rock, USA; gen tel (507) 283-2333; gen fax (507) 283-2335; disp adv e-mail sales@star-herald.com; ed e-mail editor@star-herald.com; web site www.star-herald.com
Circulation: 2,300pd,; USPS
Advertising rate: Open inch rate $8.85
Established: 1940
Digital Platform - Mobile: Apple
Digital Platform - Tablet: Apple iOS
Gen. Mgr. .... Rick Peterson
Ed. .... Lori Ehde
Ed. .... Glenda McGaffee Equipment & Software: Hardware — APP/Mac; Software — Adobe/PageMaker, Multi-Ad/Creator, Microsoft/Word.
Delivery Method: Mail
Areas Served: Rock County

MADELIA

MADELIA TIMES-MESSENGER (THUR)
112 W Main St, Madelia, MN, 56062-1440, Watonwan, USA; gen tel (507) 642-3636; gen fax (507) 642-3535; ed e-mail tm@prairiepublishingmn.com; web site http://www.prairiepublishingmn.com/
Circulation: 875pd, 16fr; Sworn/Estimate/Non-Audited
Advertising rate: Open inch rate $6.00
Established: 1871
Group: Prairie Publishing, Inc
Pub. .... Michael Koob
Adv. .... Shari Kilmer
Delivery Method: Mail

THE HANSKA HERALD (THUR)
112 W Main St, Madelia, MN, 56062-1440, Watonwan, USA; gen tel (507) 642-3636; gen fax (507) 642-3535; ed e-mail hh@prairiepublishingmn.com; web site www.hanskaherald.com
Circulation: 349pd,; Sworn/Estimate/Non-Audited
Advertising rate: Open inch rate $3.00
Pub. .... David Parker
Ed. .... N. Ross Becken

Mechanical Specifications: Type page 6 x 21; E - 7 cols, 2 1/16, 1/6 between; A - 7 cols, 2 1/16, 1/6 between; C - 11 cols, 2 1/16, 1/6 between.Equipment & Software: Hardware — APP/Mac 950, APP/Mac SE; Software — Caere/OmniPage, Adobe/Photoshop, QPS/QuarkXPress.
Delivery Method: Mail

MADISON

THE WESTERN GUARD (WED)
216 6th Ave, Madison, MN, 56256-1309, Lac qui Parle, USA; gen tel (320) 598-7521; gen fax (320) 598-7523; disp adv e-mail westerng@frontiernet.net
Circulation: 1,691pd, 15fr; Sworn/Estimate/Non-Audited
Advertising rate: Open inch rate $6.75
Pub. .... Adam Conroy

MAHNOMEN

THE MAHNOMEN PIONEER (THUR)
207 North Main Street, Mahnomen, MN, 56557, Mahnomen, USA; gen tel (218) 935-5296; gen fax (218) 935-2555; disp adv e-mail mahpioneer@arvig.net; ed e-mail mahedit@arvig.net; web site www.mahnomen-pioneer.com
Circulation: 1,600pd, 100fr; Sworn/Estimate/Non-Audited
Advertising rate: Open inch rate $3.75
Established: 1905
Digital Platform - Mobile: Windows
Ed. .... Sue Gruman Kraft
Mechanical Specifications: Type page 10.5" x 21"
Delivery Method: Mail, Newsstand
Areas Served: 56557, 56589, 56566, 56545, 56521, 56569, 56592

MAPLE LAKE

MAPLE LAKE MESSENGER (WED)
218 Division St W, Maple Lake, MN, 55358-4576, Wright, USA; gen tel (320) 963-3813; gen fax (320) 963-6114; disp adv e-mail ads@maplelakemessenger.com; class adv e-mail vicki@maplelakemessenger.com; ed e-mail news@maplelakemessenger.com; web site www.maplelakemessenger.com
Circulation: 1,113pd,; Sworn/Estimate/Non-Audited
Advertising rate: Open inch rate $6.05
Adv. Mgr. .... Kayla Erickson
Pub. .... Michele Pawlenty
Mechanical Specifications: Type page 6 x 21 1/2; E - 6 cols, 2, 1/12 between; A - 6 cols, 2, 1/12 between; C - 6 cols, 2, 1/12 between.Equipment & Software: Hardware — APP/Macs; Software — QPS/QuarkXPress.
Delivery Method: Mail

MAPLETON

MAPLE RIVER MESSENGER (THUR)
309 Main St W, Mapleton, MN, 56065-2062, Blue Earth, USA; gen tel (507) 524-3212; gen fax (507) 524-4249; disp adv e-mail mrm@prairiepublishingmn.com; ed e-mail editor@maplerivermessenger.com; web site www.maplerivermessenger.com
Circulation: 1,113pd, 8fr; Sworn/Estimate/Non-Audited
Advertising rate: Open inch rate $6.00
Pub. .... Michael Koob
Ed. .... Kelly Spillman
Delivery Method: Mail

MCGREGOR

THE VOYAGEUR PRESS OF MCGREGOR

(TUES)
15 Country House Ln, McGregor, MN, 55760-1417, Aitkin, USA; gen tel (218) 768-3405; gen fax (218) 768-7046; disp adv e-mail vpofmg@frontiernet.net; ed e-mail port; web site www.thevoyageurpress.com
Circulation: 1,162pd,; Sworn/Estimate/Non-Audited
Advertising rate: Open inch rate $6.00
Established: 2000
Pub...John Grones
Ed/Office Mgr.................................Dora Potts
Circ. Mgr.....................................Lucia Grones
Delivery Method: Mail
Areas Served: McGregor, Palisade, Tamrack, Cromwell, Wright, McGrath, Jacobson

MCINTOSH

MCINTOSH TIMES (WED)
115 Broadway NW, McIntosh, MN, 56556-5777, Polk, USA; gen tel (218) 563-3585; gen fax (218) 487-5251; disp adv e-mail richards@gvtel.com; ed e-mail mcintoshtimes@gmail.com; web site http://www.tricocanary.com/contact
Circulation: 939pd,; Sworn/Estimate/Non-Audited
Advertising rate: Open inch rate $3.75
Established: 1888
Pub...................................Richard D. Richards
Ed. ....Kim Hedlund

MELROSE

MELROSE BEACON (SAT)
408 E Main St, Melrose, MN, 56352-1186, Stearns, USA; gen tel (320) 256-3240; gen fax (320) 256-3363; disp adv e-mail missy@saukherald.com; class adv e-mail kayla@saukherald.com; ed e-mail carol@melrose-beacon.com; web site www.melrosebeacon.com
Circulation: 1,900pd, 2,300fr; Sworn/Estimate/Non-Audited
Advertising rate: Open inch rate $5.56
Ed. ....Carol Moorman
Bus. Mgr...................................Joyce Frericks
Prod. Mgr. ....Pat Turner
Mechanical Specifications: Type page 6 x 21; E - 7 cols, 2, 1/8 between; A - 7 cols, 2, 1/8 between; C - 7 cols, 2, 1/8 between.Equipment & Software: Hardware — APP/Mac; Software — Adobe/PageMaker 6.0, QPS/QuarkXPress 4.0.
Delivery Method: Mail

MIDDLE RIVER

MIDDLE RIVER HONKER (SAT)
655 2nd St N, Middle River, MN, 56737-4136, Marshall, USA; gen tel (218) 222-3501; disp adv e-mail honkernews@wiktel.com; class adv e-mail honkernews@wiktel.com; ed e-mail honkernews@wiktel.com; web site www.thehonker.com
Circulation: 1,100pd, 15fr; USPS
Advertising rate: Open inch rate $6.00
Established: 2006
Pub...Babara Geer
Delivery Method: Mail

MINNEAPOLIS

NORTH NEWS (THUR, MTHLY)
125 W Broadway Ave, Ste 130, Minneapolis, MN, 55411-2245, Hennepin, USA; gen tel (651) 245-2647; adv tel (651) 245-2647; ed tel (651) 245-2647; disp adv e-mail okeefek@puc-mn.org; class adv e-mail okeefek@puc-mn.org; ed e-mail okeefek@puc-mn.org; web site www.facebook.com/mynorthnews
Circulation: 10,000fr; Sworn/Estimate/Non-Audited
Advertising rate: Modular $110-$1100
Established: 1991
Group: Pillsbury United Communities
Digital Platform - Mobile: Apple, Android
Digital Platform - Tablet: Apple iOS, Android
Delivery Method: Racks
Areas Served: North of Interstate Highway 394 and West of the Mississippi River

NORTHEASTER (WED)
2844 Johnson St NE, Minneapolis, MN, 55418-3056, Hennepin, USA; gen tel (612) 788-9003; gen fax (612) 788-3299; disp adv e-mail Margo@MyNortheaster.com; class adv e-mail contact@MyNortheaster.com; ed e-mail contact@mynortheaster.com; web site www.MyNortheaster.com 1,810(visitors)
Circulation: 29pd, 32,195fr; CVC
Advertising rate: Modular $111-$2,186
Established: 1978
Group: Pro Media, Inc
Digital Platform - Mobile: Apple, Android
Digital Platform - Tablet: Apple iOS, Android
Pub.......................................Margo Ashmore
Delivery Method: Carrier
Areas Served: 55413, 55418, 55421,

SOUTHWEST JOURNAL (MON, MTHLY)
1115 Hennepin Ave, Minneapolis, MN, 55403-1705, Hennepin, USA; gen tel (612) 825-9205; adv tel (612) 825-9205; ed tel (612) 825-9205; gen fax (612) 825-0929; adv fax (612) 825-0929; ed fax (612) 825-0929; disp adv e-mail sales@mnpubs.com; class adv e-mail tgahan@swjournal.com; ed e-mail dthomas@swjournal.com; web site www.swjournal.com
Advertising rate: Open inch rate $18.75
Group: Minnesota Premier Publications
Digital Platform - Mobile: Apple, Android, Windows, Blackberry
Digital Platform - Tablet: Apple iOS, Android, Windows 7, Blackberry Tablet OS
Ed. ....Sarah McKenzie
Gen. Mgr. ....Chris Damlo
Pub..Janis Hall
Delivery Method: Mail, Newsstand, Racks
Areas Served: 55405, 55416, 55408, 55410, 55409, 55419

THE BUSINESS JOURNAL (FRI)
333 S 7th St Ste 350, Suite 350, Minneapolis, MN, 55402-2466, Hennepin, USA; gen tel (612) 288-2100; adv tel (612) 288-2134; gen fax (612) 288-2121; disp adv e-mail gsundeen@bizjournals.com; class adv e-mail asullivan@bizjournals.com; ed e-mail ddeyoung@bizjournals.com; web site www.bizjournals.com/twincities
Advertising rate: 1/8 P $2,355 1/4 P$3,610 1/2 P $5,360 Full $8,105
Established: 1983
Pub..Tammy Mencel
Adv. Dir..................................Kathy Robideau
Ed. ....Dirk DeYoung
Delivery Method: Mail

THE DOWNTOWN JOURNAL (MON, BI-MTHLY)
1115 Hennepin Ave, Minneapolis, MN, 55403-1705, Hennepin, USA; gen tel (612) 825-9205; gen fax (612)825-0929; disp adv e-mail sales@mnpubs.com; class adv e-mail tgahan@journalmpls.com; ed e-mail dthomas@journalmpls.com; web site http://www.journalmpls.com/
Circulation: 220pd, 30,000fr; Sworn/Estimate/Non-Audited
Advertising rate: Open inch rate $35.30
Pub..Janis Hall
Adv. Mgr......................................Terry Gahan
Ed. ....Sarah McKenzie
Mechanical Specifications: Type page 6 x 17; E - 4 cols, 2 3/8, between; A - 5 cols, 1 15/16, 3/16 between; C - 6 cols, 1 1/8, between. Equipment & Software: Hardware — APP/Mac, Ethernet/Network; Software — QPS/QuarkXPress 4.0, Adobe/Photoshop 5.0, Adobe/Illustrator 7.0.
Areas Served: 55418, 55413, 55411, 55401, 55405, 55414, 55415, 55402, 55403, 55404, 55405, 55408

MINNEOTA

MINNEOTA MASCOT (WED)
201 N JEFFERSON ST, Minneota, MN, 56264, Lyon, USA; gen tel (507) 872-6492; gen fax (507) 872-6840; disp adv e-mail byron@minneotamascot.com; class adv e-mail same; ed e-mail same; web site www.theminneotamascot.com
Circulation: 1,200pd,; Sworn/Estimate/Non-Audited
Advertising rate: Open inch rate $6.50
Established: 1891
Pub...Byron Higgin
Delivery Method: Mail, Newsstand

MINNESOTA LAKE

MINNESOTA LAKE TRIBUNE (THUR)
227 N Main St, Minnesota Lake, MN, 56068, Faribault, USA; gen tel (507) 462-3321; gen fax (507) 462-3321; ed e-mail mltrib@bevcomm.net
Circulation: 896pd, 25fr; Sworn/Estimate/Non-Audited
Advertising rate: Open inch rate $4.75
Established: 1985
Pub..Donald Kain
Delivery Method: Mail

MONTEVIDEO

MONTEVIDEO AMERICAN-NEWS (THUR)
223 S 1st St, Montevideo, MN, 56265-1412, Chippewa, USA; gen tel (320) 269-2156; gen fax (320) 269-2159; disp adv e-mail mbutzin@montenews.com; class adv e-mail kchristians@montenews.com; ed e-mail bolson@montenews.com; web site www.montenews.com
Circulation: 3,257pd, 41fr; Sworn/Estimate/Non-Audited
Advertising rate: Open inch rate $10.05
Group: GateHouse Media, Inc.
Circ. Mgr.......................................Donna Moe
Ed. ....Bruce Olson
Prod. Mgr. ....Janell Sjurseth
Mechanical Specifications: Type page 6 x 21 1/2; E - 5 cols, 2 1/4, 1/8 between; A - 6 cols, 1 1/2, 1/8 between; C - 7 cols, 1 1/2, 1/8 between.Equipment & Software: Hardware — APP/Mac; Presses — HI/JV15; Software — QPS/QuarkXPress 4.1.
Areas Served: 56265, 56262, 56295, 56232, 56223

MONTGOMERY

MONTGOMERY MESSENGER (THUR)
310 1st St S, Montgomery, MN, 56069-1604, Le Sueur, USA; gen tel (507) 364-8601; adv tel (507) 364-8601; ed tel (507) 364-8601; gen fax (507) 364-8602; disp adv e-mail wade@montgomerymnnews.com; class adv e-mail wade@montgomerymnnews.com; ed e-mail wade@montgomerymnnews.com
Circulation: 1,777pd, 15fr; Sworn/Estimate/Non-Audited
Advertising rate: Open inch rate $8.50
Group: Suel Printing Co.
Pub.......................................E. Charles Wann
Ed. ....Wade Young
Delivery Method: Mail, Newsstand
Areas Served: 56069 Le Sueur County

MONTICELLO

MONTICELLO TIMES (THUR)
540 Walnut St, Monticello, MN, 55362-8663, Wright, USA; gen tel (763) 295-3131; gen fax (763) 295-3080; disp adv e-mail craig.dahlberg@ecm-inc.com; class adv e-mail terri.sweet@ecm-inc.com; ed e-mail tim.hennagir@ecm-inc.com; web site www.monticellotimes.com
Circulation: 1,312pd, 18fr; CAC
Advertising rate: Open inch rate $19.95
Group: Adams Publishing Group, LLC
American Community Newspapers LLC
Pub.......................................Bruce Treichler
Ed. ....Mike Schoemer
Circ. Mgr ....Sylvia Fitzsimmons
Mechanical Specifications: Type page 6 x 21 1/2; E - 6 cols, 2, 1/4 between; A - 6 cols, 2, 1/4 between.Equipment & Software: Hardware — APP/Mac; Software — QPS/QuarkXPress, Adobe/Illustrator, Adobe/Photoshop.
Areas Served: 55362, 55308, 55309, 55320, 55301, 55358, 55313, 55330, 55319, 55376, 55398

MOORHEAD

THE FM EXTRA (THUR)
810 4th Ave S Ste 120, Suite 120, Moorhead, MN, 56560-2800, Clay, USA; gen tel (218) 284-1288; gen fax (218) 284-1289; disp adv e-mail extra@ncppub.com; class adv e-mail Bryantheextrasales@gmail.com; ed e-mail tfinney@ncppub.com; web site www.thefmextra.com
Circulation: 5,635fr; CVC
Advertising rate: Open inch rate $15.00
Established: 2001
Ed ....Tammy Finney
Pub...Lisa Miller
Circ. Mgr ....Tasha Lange
Adv. Sales...............................Shawn Dietrich
Mechanical Specifications: Type page: 10.02 x 10.5; 6 col

MOOSE LAKE

MOOSE LAKE STAR GAZETTE (THUR)
308 Elm Ave, Moose Lake, MN, 55767-7706, Carlton, USA; gen tel (218) 485-4406; gen fax (218) 485-0237; ed e-mail evergreen@mooselakestargazette.com; web site www.mooselakestargazette.com
Circulation: 3,865pd,; Sworn/Estimate/Non-Audited
Advertising rate: Open inch rate $6.00
Pub... Connie BerruungfEquipment & Software: Hardware — APP/Macs; Software — Adobe/PageMaker 6.0.
Delivery Method: Mail

MORA

KANABEC COUNTY TIMES (THUR)
107 Park St S, Mora, MN, 55051-1459, Kanabec, USA; gen tel (320) 679-2661; adv tel (320) 225-5124; ed tel (320) 225-5128; gen fax (320) 679-2663; adv fax (320) 679-2661; ed fax (320) 679-2661; disp adv e-mail akrist@moraminn.com; class adv e-mail frontdesk@moraminn.com; ed e-mail editor@moraminn.com; web site www.moraminn.com
Circulation: 3,000pd,; Sworn/Estimate/Non-Audited
Advertising rate: Open inch rate $5.95
Pub..Wade Weber
Adv. Mgr......................................Annette Krist
Ed. ....Kristen Faurie
Delivery Method: Mail

MORGAN

MORGAN MESSENGER (WED)
510 2ND ST W, Morgan, MN, 56266, Redwood, USA; gen tel (507) 249-3130; gen fax (507) 249-3131; disp adv e-mail fxstandardnews@gmail.com; class adv e-mail fxstandardnews@gmail.com; ed e-mail morganmess@yahoo.com; web site http://www.standard-gazette.com/aboutus.html
Circulation: 968pd, 50fr; Sworn/Estimate/Non-Audited

Advertising rate: Open inch rate $3.50
Ed. ....Daniel McGonigle
Pub...Denise Bonsack
Gen. Mgr. ....Marilyn Brandel
Mechanical Specifications: Type page 6 x 21.
Delivery Method: Mail

MORRIS

MORRIS SUN TRIBUNE (SAT)

607 Pacific Ave, Morris, MN, 56267-1942, Stevens, USA; gen tel (320) 589-2525; gen fax (320) 589-4357; disp adv e-mail sales@morrissuntribune.com; class adv e-mail classifieds@morrissuntribune.com; ed e-mail news@morrissuntribune.com; web site www.morrissuntribune.com - 29,000(views) 4,500(visitors)
Circulation: 2,561pd,; Sworn/Estimate/Non-Audited
Advertising rate: Open inch rate $9.25
Established: 1899
Group: Forum Communications Co.
Digital Platform - Mobile: Apple, Android, Windows, Blackberry
Digital Platform - Tablet: Apple iOS, Android, Windows 7
Pub..Sue Dieter
Ed. ....Kim Ukura
Bus. Mgr.......................................Heidi Roiland
Mechanical Specifications: 6 column x 21"
1 column = 1.66 inches
2 columns = 3.451
3 columns = 5.243
4 columns = 7.035
5 columns = 8.826
6 columns = 10.625 inches
Delivery Method: Mail, Newsstand, Carrier, Racks
Areas Served: 56267, 56207, 56208, 56215, 56221

THE HANCOCK RECORD (THUR)

607 Pacific Ave, Morris, MN, 56267-1942, Stevens, USA; gen tel (320) 392-5527; gen fax (320) 589-4357; disp adv e-mail ads@morrissuntribune.com; class adv e-mail classifieds@morrissuntribune.com; ed e-mail news@hancockrecord.com; web site www.hancockrecord.com
Circulation: 759pd, 15fr; Sworn/Estimate/Non-Audited
Advertising rate: Open inch rate $3.60
Established: 1899
Group: Forum Communications Co.
Pub..Sue Dieter
Ed. ....Katie Erdman
Circ. Dir. ....Christine McKenzie

MOUNTAIN LAKE

MOUNTAIN LAKE/BUTTERFIELD OBSERVER-ADVOCATE (WED)

1025 2nd Ave, Ste 2, Mountain Lake, MN, 56159-1456, Cottonwood, USA; gen tel (507) 427-2725; gen fax (507) 427-2724; disp adv e-mail suef@mtlakenews.com; ed e-mail rahnl@windomnews.com; web site www.mtlakenews.com
Circulation: 1,141pd,; Sworn/Estimate/Non-Audited
Advertising rate: Open inch rate $7.10
Gen. Mgr. ....Trevor Slette
Sales Mgr.............................Sue Frederickson
Ed. ....Kris Langland
Mechanical Specifications: Type page 6 x 21 1/2; E - 6 cols, 2, 1/6 between; A - 6 cols, 2, 1/6 between; C - 6 cols, 2, 1/6 between.Equipment & Software: ; Software — Microsoft/ Word 3.1, Adobe/PageMaker.
Delivery Method: Mail, Carrier

NEW PRAGUE

ELYSIAN ENTERPRISE (THUR)

200 Main St E, New Prague, MN, 56071-2438, Le Sueur, USA; gen tel (507) 267-4323; gen fax (507) 362-4458; disp adv e-mail ads@newpraguetimes.com; class adv e-mail classifieds@newpraguetimes.com; ed e-mail news@newpraguetimes.com; web site http://www.newpraguetimes.com/category/publication/elysian-enterprise
Circulation: 422pd,; Sworn/Estimate/Non-Audited
Advertising rate: Open inch rate $3.75
Pub....................................... E. Charles Wann
Ed. .... Jay Schneider
Adv. Dir... Mark Slavik
Delivery Method: Mail

LAKE REGION LIFE (THUR)

200 Main St E, New Prague, MN, 56071-2438, Le Sueur, USA; gen tel (952) 758-4435; gen fax (952) 758-4135; disp adv e-mail ads@newpraguetimes.com; class adv e-mail classifieds@newpraguetimes.com; ed e-mail news@newpraguetimes.com; web site newpraguetimes.com/category/publication/waterville-lake-region-life
Circulation: 1,425pd, 65fr; Sworn/Estimate/Non-Audited
Advertising rate: Open inch rate $6.50
Established: 1970
Pub..Chuck Wann
Adv. Mgr. ....Lisa Ingebrand
Circ. Mgr...................................Debbie Atherton
Ed. ....Jay Schneider

THE NEW PRAGUE TIMES (THUR)

200 Main St E, New Prague, MN, 56071-2438, Le Sueur, USA; gen tel (952) 758-4435; gen fax (952) 758-4135; disp adv e-mail ads@newpraguetimes.com; class adv e-mail classifieds@newpraguetimes.com; ed e-mail news@newpraguetimes.com; web site www.newpraguetimes.com
Circulation: 3,700pd,; Sworn/Estimate/Non-Audited
Advertising rate: Open inch rate $9.50
Established: 1889
Pub....................................... E. Charles Wann
Adv. Mgr. ....Mark Slavik
Mng. Ed...Chuck Kajer
Delivery Method: Mail

NEW RICHLAND

STAR EAGLE (THUR)

128 Broadway Ave N, New Richland, MN, 56072-2020, Waseca, USA; gen tel (507) 463-8112; gen fax (507) 463-0504; ed e-mail steagle@hickorytech.net; web site www.newrichlandstar.com
Circulation: 2,000pd,; Sworn/Estimate/Non-Audited
Advertising rate: Open inch rate $6.45
Established: 1887
Ed. ....Jim Lutgens
Delivery Method: Mail, Newsstand, Racks
Areas Served: Waseca County, Steele County, Freeborn County

NEW YORK MILLS

NEW YORK MILLS HERALD (THUR)

106 S Boardman Ave, New York Mills, MN, 56567-4101, Otter Tail, USA; gen tel (218) 385-7720; gen fax (218) 548-5582; disp adv e-mail nymdispatch@arvig.net; ed e-mail news@nymdispatch.com; web site http://nymdispatch.com
Circulation: 1,835pd,; Sworn/Estimate/Non-Audited
Advertising rate: Open inch rate $9.60
Group: Forum Communications Co.
Co-Pub..Chad Koenen
Co-Pub...Dani Koenen
Ed. ....Connie Vandermay
Mechanical Specifications: Type page 13 x 21 1/2; E - 6 cols, 2, 1/6 between; A - 6 cols, 2, 1/6 between; C - 9 cols, 1 5/12, 1/6 between. Equipment & Software: Hardware — Intel/ Pentium 1999.

NORTH SAINT PAUL

MAPLEWOOD REVIEW (WED)

2515 7th Ave E, North Saint Paul, MN, 55109-3098, Washington, USA; gen tel (651) 777-8800; adv tel (651) 748-7862; ed tel (651) 748-7820; gen fax (651) 777-8288; disp adv e-mail tfragnito@lillienews.com; class adv e-mail rnisswandt@lillienews.com; ed e-mail mlhagert@lillienews.com; web site http://www.lillienews.com/ramsey-co-maple-wood-review
Circulation: 36pd, 4,554fr; VAC
Advertising rate: Open inch rate $25.20
Group: Lillie Suburban Newspapers
Co-Pub................................Jeffery R. Enright
Co-Pub...Ted H. Lillie
Adv. Mgr. ....Tony Fragnito
Circ. Mgr.......................................Laura Young
Mng. Ed...............................Mary Lee Hagert
Ed. ....Holly Wenzel
Mechanical Specifications: Type page 12 7/8 x 21; E - 6 cols, 1 13/16, between; A - 6 cols, 1 13/16, between; C - 10 cols, 1 13/16, between.

NEW BRIGHTON-MOUNDS VIEW BULLETIN (WED)

2515 7th Ave E, North Saint Paul, MN, 55109-3004, Ramsey, USA; gen tel (651) 777-8800; adv tel (651) 748-7860; ed tel (651) 748-7800; gen fax (651) 777-8288; disp adv e-mail tfragnito@lillienews.com; class adv e-mail sanderson@lillienews.com; ed e-mail mlhagert@lillienews.com; web site http://www.lillienews.com/articles/new-brighton-mounds-view-bulletin-news
Circulation: 230pd, 26,000fr; Sworn/Estimate/Non-Audited
Advertising rate: Open inch rate $30.50
Group: Lillie Suburban Newspapers
Circ. Mgr.......................................Laura Young
Exec. Ed...............................Mary Lee Hagert
Adv. Mgr. ....Tony Fragnito
Mechanical Specifications: Type page 12 7/8 x 21; E - 6 cols, 1 13/16, between; A - 6 cols, 1 13/16, between; C - 10 cols, 1 13/16, between.
Delivery Method: Mail

OAKDALE LAKE ELMO REVIEW (WED)

2515 7th Ave E, North Saint Paul, MN, 55109-3098, Ramsey, USA; gen tel (651) 777-8800; adv tel (651) 748-7863; ed tel (651) 748-7820; gen fax (651) 777-8288; disp adv e-mail tfragnito@lillienews.com; class adv e-mail rnisswandt@lillienews.com; ed e-mail mlhagert@lillienews.com; web site http://www.lillienews.com/oakdale-lake-elmo-review
Circulation: 37pd, 6,710fr; VAC
Advertising rate: Open inch rate $20.40
Established: 1986
Group: Lillie Suburban Newspapers
Co-Pub................................Jeffery R. Enright
Co-Pub...Ted H. Lillie
Adv. Dir..Tony Fragnito
Circ. Mgr.......................................Laura Young
Mng. Ed...............................Mary Lee Hagert
Mechanical Specifications: Type page 10" x 21; Display - 6 cols,, between; Classified - 10 cols, .
Delivery Method: Carrier
Areas Served: 55128, 55042, 55082

RAMSEY COUNTY REVIEW (WED)

2515 7th Ave E, North Saint Paul, MN, 55109-3098, Ramsey, USA; gen tel (651) 777-8800; adv tel (651) 748-7862; ed tel (651) 748-7820; gen fax (651) 777-8288; disp adv e-mail tfragnito@lillienews.com; class adv e-mail rnisswandt@lillienews.com; ed e-mail mlhagert@lillienews.com; web site http://www.lillienews.com/ramsey-co-maple-wood-review
Circulation: 39pd, 2,503fr; VAC
Advertising rate: 26
Established: 1938
Group: Lillie Suburban Newspapers
Circ. Mgr.......................................Laura Young
Exec. Ed...............................Mary Lee Hagert
Adv. Dir..Tony Fragnito
Mechanical Specifications: Type page 6 x 21; Display - 6 cols, Classified - 10 cols.
Delivery Method: Carrier
Areas Served: 55109, 55119

REVIEW PERSPECTIVES (MON)

2515 7th Ave E, North Saint Paul, MN, 55109-3004, Ramsey, USA; gen tel (651) 777-8800; ed tel (651) 748-7820; gen fax (651) 777-8288; disp adv e-mail tfragnito@lillienews.com; class adv e-mail rnisswandt@lillienews.com; ed e-mail mlhagert@lillienews.com; web site http://www.lillienews.com/perspectives
Circulation: 6,613fr; VAC
Advertising rate: Open inch rate $25.50
Group: Lillie Suburban Newspapers
Co-Pub................................Jeffery R. Enright
Co-Pub...Ted H. Lillie
Adv. Dir..Tony Fragnito
Circ. Mgr.......................................Laura Young
Ed. ....Mary Lee Hagert
Mechanical Specifications: Type page 11 1/2 x 20 3/4; E - 6 cols, 1 13/16, 3/16 between; A - 6 cols, 1 13/16, 13/16 between; C - 10 cols, between.
Delivery Method: Mail

ROSEVILLE REVIEW (TUES)

2515 7th Ave E, North Saint Paul, MN, 55109-3098, Ramsey, USA; gen tel (651) 777-8800; adv tel (651) 748-7864; ed tel (651) 748-7820; gen fax (651) 777-8288; disp adv e-mail tfragnito@lillienews.com; class adv e-mail rnisswandt@lillienews.com; ed e-mail mlhagert@lillienews.com; web site http://www.lillienews.com/roseville-little-canada-review
Circulation: 18pd, 12,276fr; VAC
Advertising rate: Open inch rate $24.50
Established: 1938
Group: Lillie Suburban Newspapers
Co-Pub................................Jeffery R. Enright
Co-Pub...Ted H. Lillie
Adv. Dir ....Tony Fragnito
Ed. ....George Fairbank
Mng. Ed...............................Mary Lee Hagert
Mechanical Specifications: Type page 6 x 21; Display - 6 cols, Classified - 10 cols.
Delivery Method: Carrier
Areas Served: 55113, 55117, 55108,

SHOREVIEW ARDEN HILLS BULLETIN (WED)

2515 7th Ave E, North Saint Paul, MN, 55109-3004, Ramsey, USA; gen tel (651) 777-8800; adv tel (651) 748-7860; ed tel (651) 748-7820; gen fax (651) 777-8288; disp adv e-mail tfragnito@lillienews.com; class adv e-mail sanderson@lillienews.com; ed e-mail mlhagert@lillienews.com; web site http://www.lillienews.com/articles/shoreview-arden-hills-bulletin-news
Circulation: 38pd, 19,683fr; VAC
Advertising rate: Open inch rate $38.00
Group: Lillie Suburban Newspapers
Co-Pub.................................Jeffery J. Enright
Co-Pub...Ted H. Lillie
Adv. Dir..Tony Fragnito
Exec. Ed...............................Mary Lee Hagert
Mechanical Specifications: 10" x 21" display spread over 6 columns and classified spread over 10 columns
Delivery Method: Carrier
Areas Served: 55112, 55127, 55126, 55421, 55418

SHOREVIEW BULLETIN (WED)

2515 7th Ave E, North Saint Paul, MN, 55109-3004, Ramsey, USA; gen tel (651) 777-8800; adv tel (651) 748-7860; ed tel (651) 748-7820; gen fax (651) 777-8288; disp adv e-mail tfragnito@lillienews.com; class adv e-mail sanderson@lillienews.com; ed e-mail mlhagert@lillienews.com; web site http://www.lillienews.com/articles/shoreview-arden-hills-bulletin-news
Circulation: 10pd, 6,333fr; VAC
Advertising rate: Open inch rate $9.20
Group: Lillie Suburban Newspapers
Co-Pub................................Jeffery R. Enright
Co-Pub...Ted H. Lillie
Adv. Dir..Tony Fragnito

Circ. Mgr....................................... Laura Young
Mng. Ed.................................Mery Lee Hagert
Mechanical Specifications: Type page 12 7/8 x 21; E - 6 cols, 1 13/16, between; A - 6 cols, 1 13/16, between; C - 10 cols, 1 13/16, between.

SOUTH-WEST REVIEW (MON)

2515 7th Ave E, North Saint Paul, MN, 55109-3004, Ramsey, USA; gen tel (651) 777-8800; adv tel (651) 748-7860; ed tel (651) 748-7820; gen fax (651) 777-8288; disp adv e-mail tfragnito@lillienews.com; class adv e-mail rnisswandt@lillienews.com; ed e-mail mlhagert@lillienews.com; web site http://www.bulletin-news.com/south-west-review
Circulation: 46pd, 10,975fr; VAC
Advertising rate: Open inch rate $29.50
Established: 1938
Group: Lillie Suburban Newspapers
Adv. Dir.. Tony Fragnito
Circ. Mgr....................................... Laura Young
Mng. Ed.................................Mary Lee Hagert
Mechanical Specifications: Type page 10 x 21; E - 6 cols, between; A - 6 cols, between; C - 10 cols, between.
Delivery Method: Carrier
Areas Served: 55150, 55120, 55118, 55077, 55076, 55075

ST. ANTHONY BULLETIN (WED)

2515 7th Ave E, North Saint Paul, MN, 55109-3004, Ramsey, USA; gen tel (651) 777-8800; adv tel (651) 748-7866; ed tel (651) 748-7820; gen fax (651) 633-3846; disp adv e-mail tfragnito@lillienews.com; class adv e-mail sanderson@lillienews.com; ed e-mail mlhagert@lillienews.com; web site http://www.bulletin-news.com/articles/st-anthony-bulletin-news
Circulation: 1pd, 2,046fr; VAC
Advertising rate: Open inch rate $29.40
Group: Lillie Suburban Newspapers
Co-Pub................................ Jeffery R. Enright
Co-Pub...Ted H. Lillie
Adv. Dir.. Tony Fragnito
Ed. .... George Fairbank
Mng. Ed.................................Mary Lee Hagert
Mechanical Specifications: Type page 13 1/2 x 21; E - 6 cols, 1 13/16, 1/4 between; A - 6 cols, 1 13/16, 1/4 between; C - 10 cols, 1 13/16, 1/8 between.Equipment & Software: Hardware — APP/Mac; Software — QPS/QuarkXPress.

NORTH ST PAUL

EAST SIDE REVIEW (MON)

2515 7th Ave E, North St Paul, MN, 55109-3004, Ramsey, USA; gen tel (651) 777-8800; adv tel (651) 748-7860; ed tel (651) 748-7820; gen fax (651) 777-8288; disp adv e-mail tfragnito@lillienews.com; class adv e-mail rnisswandt@lillienews.com; ed e-mail mlhagert@lillienews.com; web site http://www.lillienews.com/east-side-review
Circulation: 20pd, 9,277fr; VAC
Advertising rate: Open inch rate $27.40
Established: 1938
Group: Lillie Suburban Newspapers
Co-Pub................................ Jeffery R. Enright
Co-Pub...Ted H. Lillie
Adv. Dir.. Tony Fragnito
Circ. Mgr....................................... Laura Young
Mng. Ed.................................Mary Lee Hagert
Mechanical Specifications: Type page 6 x 21; Display - 6 cols, Classified - 10 cols.
Delivery Method: Carrier
Areas Served: 55130, 55106, 55119

NEW BRIGHTON BULLETIN (WED)

2515 7th Ave E, North St Paul, MN, 55109-3004, Ramsey, USA; gen tel (651) 777-8800; adv tel (651) 777-7860; ed tel (651) 748-7820; gen fax (651) 777-8288; disp adv e-mail tfragnito@lillienews.com; class adv e-mail sanderson@lillienews.com; ed e-mail mlhagert@lillienews.com; web site http://www.lillienews.com/articles/new-brighton-mounds-view-bulletin-news

Circulation: 12pd, 5,245fr; VAC
Advertising rate: Open inch rate $38.00
Group: Lillie Suburban Newspapers
Co-Pub ....Ted H. Lillie
Co-Pub.. Jeff R. Enright
Adv. Dir....................................... Tony Fragnito
Circ. Mgr....................................... Laura Young
Ed. ....Mary Hagert
Delivery Method: Mail

SOUTH ST. PAUL - SOUTH WEST REVIEW (MON)

2515 7th Ave E, North St Paul, MN, 55109-3004, Ramsey, USA; gen tel (651) 777-8800; adv tel (651) 748-7860; ed tel (651) 748-7820; gen fax (651) 777-8288; disp adv e-mail tfragnito@lillienews.com; class adv e-mail rnisswandt@lillienews.com; ed e-mail mlhagert@lillienews.com; web site http://www.lillienews.com/articles/south-st-paul
Circulation: 21pd, 4,696fr; VAC
Advertising rate: Open inch rate $31.90
Established: 1938
Group: Lillie Suburban Newspapers
Adv. Dir....................................... Tony Fragnito
Ed. ....Mary Hagert
Circ. Mgr....................................... Laura Young
Mechanical Specifications: 10"x21 spread over 6 column for display and 10 column for classified
Delivery Method: Carrier
Areas Served: 55150, 55120, 55118, 55077, 55076, 55075

NORTHFIELD

NORTHFIELD NEWS (WED, SAT)

115 5th St W, Northfield, MN, 55057-2017, Rice, USA; gen tel (507) 645-5615; adv tel (507) 645-1110; ed tel (507) 645-1136; gen fax (507) 645-6005; disp adv e-mail jpetsche@northfieldnews.com; class adv e-mail chjellming@northfieldnews.com; ed e-mail ngerhardt@northfieldnews.com; web site www.northfieldnews.com
Circulation: 2,850pd, 0fr; Sworn/Estimate/Non-Audited
Advertising rate: Open inch rate $17.85
Established: 1876
Group: Adams Publishing Group, LLC
Pub...Sam Gett
Prodn. Mgr. .... Roger Stolley
Pub...Chad Hjellming
Mechanical Specifications: Type page 6 x 21 1/2; E - 6 cols, 1 5/6, between; A - 6 cols, 1 5/6, between; C - 6 cols, 1 5/6, between. Equipment & Software: ; Presses — 16-G/Community; Software — Baseview/NewsEdit Pro IQUE 4.0.4b5, Adobe/InDesign CS 2.0, Baseview/Ad Manager Pro 1.9.1.77.
Delivery Method: Mail
Areas Served: 55057, 55019, 55009, 55031, 55088, 55046, 55046, 55018, 55065

OKLEE

THE OKLEE HERALD (WED)

301 Main St, Oklee, MN, 56742, Red Lake, USA; gen tel (218) 796-5181; gen fax (218) 487-5251; disp adv e-mail richards@gvtel.com
Circulation: 895pd,; Sworn/Estimate/Non-Audited
Advertising rate: Open inch rate $3.30
Pub.................................... Richard D. Richards
Ed. ....Bonita Cote

ORTONVILLE

THE ORTONVILLE INDEPENDENT (TUES)

789 US Highway 75, Ortonville, MN, 56278-4084, Big Stone, USA; gen tel (320) 839-6163; gen fax (320) 839-3761; disp adv e-mail mail@ortonvilleindependent.com; web site www.ortonvilleindependent.com
Circulation: 2,619pd, 100fr; USPS
Advertising rate: Open inch rate $8.00

Established: 1920
Group: Kaercher Publications, Inc.
Suzette Kaercher-Blake
Philip BlakeCo-Pub.s
Mechanical Specifications: Type page 6 x 21 1/2; E - 6 cols, 2 1/8, 1/6 between; A - 6 cols, 2 1/8, 1/6 between; C - 6 cols, 2 1/8, 1/6 between.Equipment & Software: Hardware — APP/Mac; Presses — 4-G/Community; Software — QPS/QuarkXPress.
Delivery Method: Mail, Newsstand
Areas Served: Western Minnesota

OSSEO

BROOKLYN CENTER/BROOKLYN PARK SUN-POST (THUR)

33 2nd St NE, Osseo, MN, 55369-1252, Hennepin, USA; gen tel (952) 392-6800; adv tel (952) 392-6888; ed tel (763) 425-3323; gen fax (763) 424-7388; disp adv e-mail cheri.obannon@ecm-inc.com; class adv e-mail tena.wensman@ecm-inc.com; ed e-mail peggy.bakken@ecm-inc.com; web site http://post.mnsun.com/
Circulation: 62pd, 6,969fr; CAC
Advertising rate: Open inch rate $23.00
Established: 1938
Group: Adams Publishing Group, LLC
Sun Newspapers
Ed. ....Peggy Bakken
Adv. Dir.................................. Cheri O'Bannon
Gen. Mgr.......................................Mark Weber
Mechanical Specifications: Type page 4 x 10; E - 4 cols, 2 1/2, 1/4 between; A - 5 cols, 1 5/8, between; C - 8 cols, 1 1/6, 5/24 between. Equipment & Software: Hardware — APP/Mac; Software — QPS/QuarkXPress.
Delivery Method: Carrier
Areas Served: 55428, 55429, 55430, 55443, 55444, 55445

CHAMPLIN-DAYTON PRESS (THUR)

33 2nd St NE, Osseo, MN, 55369-1252, Hennepin, USA; gen tel (763) 425-3323; gen fax (763) 425-2945; disp adv e-mail jeremy.bradfield@ecm-inc.com ; class adv e-mail mike.specht@ecm-inc.com; ed e-mail peggy.bakken@ecm-inc.com; web site www.pressnews.com
Circulation: 47pd, 6,214fr; CAC
Advertising rate: Open inch rate $7.35
Group: Adams Publishing Group, LLC
American Community Newspapers LLC
Ed. ....Peggy Bakken
Gen. Mgr.......................................Mark Weber
Adv. Dir..................................Jeremy Bradfield
Mechanical Specifications: Type page 6 x 21; E - 7 cols, 2 5/8, 1/8 between; A - 7 cols, 2 5/8, 1/8 between; C - 7 cols, 2 5/8, 1/8 between. Equipment & Software: Hardware — APP/Mac G3, APP/Mac Power Book; Presses — G/Urbanite; Software — QPS/QuarkXPress 4.1, Adobe/Photoshop 5.0.
Areas Served: 55316, 55327

NORTH CROW RIVER NEWS (THUR)

33 2nd St NE, Osseo, MN, 55369-1252, Hennepin, USA; gen tel (763) 425-3323; gen fax (763) 425-2945; disp adv e-mail jeremy.bradfield@ecm-inc.com; class adv e-mail mike.specht@ecm-inc.com; ed e-mail peggy.bakken@ecm-inc.com; web site www.pressnews.com
Circulation: 3,280pd, 6,214fr; CAC
Advertising rate: Open inch rate $8.60
Established: 1963
Group: Adams Publishing Group, LLC
American Community Newspapers LLC
Ed. ....Peggy Bakken
Adv. Dir..................................Jeremy Bradfield
Gen. Mgr.......................................Mark Weber
Mechanical Specifications: Type page 6 x 21; E - 6 cols, 1 5/6, 1/8 between; A - 6 cols, 1 5/6, 1/8 between; C - 9 cols, 1 3/16, 1/8 between. Equipment & Software: Hardware — APP/Mac G3, APP/Power Mac; Presses — G/Urbanite; Software — QPS/QuarkXPress 4.1, Adobe/Photoshop 5.1.
Areas Served: 55301, 55376, 55374

OSSEO-MAPLE GROVE PRESS (THUR)

33 2nd St NE, Osseo, MN, 55369-1252, Hennepin, USA; gen tel (763) 425-3323; adv tel (763) 424-7355; gen fax (763) 425-2945; disp adv e-mail jeremy.bradfield@ecm-inc.com; class adv e-mail mike.specht@ecm-inc.com; ed e-mail peggy.bakken@ecm-inc.com; web site www.pressnews.com
Circulation: 3,280pd, 6,214fr; CAC
Advertising rate: Open inch rate $9.85
Established: 1924
Group: Adams Publishing Group, LLC
American Community Newspapers LLC
Ed. ....Peggy Bakken
Gen. Mgr.......................................Mark Weber
Adv. Dir..................................Jeremy Bradfield
Mechanical Specifications: Type page 6 x 21; E - 6 cols, 1 5/6, 1/8 between; A - 6 cols, 1 5/6, 1/8 between; C - 9 cols, 1 3/16, 1/8 between. Equipment & Software: Hardware — APP/Mac G3, APP/Mac Power Book; Presses — G/Urbanite; Software — QPS/QuarkXPress 4.1, Adobe/Photoshop 5.0.
Delivery Method: Mail
Areas Served: 55313, 55369

ROCKFORD AREA NEWS LEADER (MON)

33 2nd St NE, Osseo, MN, 55369-1252, Hennepin, USA; gen tel (763) 425-3323; gen fax (763) 425-2945; disp adv e-mail jeremy.bradfield@ecm-inc.com; class adv e-mail mike.specht@ecm-inc.com; ed e-mail peggy.bakken@ecm-inc.com; web site www.pressnews.com
Circulation: 780pd, 3,149fr; Sworn/Estimate/Non-Audited
Advertising rate: Open inch rate $7.60
Established: 1963
Group: Press and News Publications
Ed. ....Peggy Bakken
Adv Dir..................................Jeremy Bradfield
Gen. Mgr.......................................Mark Weber
Mechanical Specifications: Type page 6 x 21; E - 6 cols, 1 5/6, 1/8 between; A - 6 cols, 1 5/6, 1/8 between; C - 9 cols, 1 3/16, 1/8 between. Equipment & Software: Hardware — APP/Mac G3, APP/Mac Power Book; Presses — G/Urbanite; Software — QPS/QuarkXPress 4.1, Adobe/Photoshop 5.0.
Areas Served: 55373

SOUTH CROW RIVER NEWS (THUR)

33 2nd St NE, Osseo, MN, 55369-1252, Hennepin, USA; gen tel (763) 425-3323; gen fax (763) 425-2945; disp adv e-mail jeremy.bradfield@ecm-inc.com; class adv e-mail mike.specht@ecm-inc.com; ed e-mail peggy.bakken@ecm-inc.com; web site www.pressnews.com
Circulation: 715pd, 420fr; CAC
Advertising rate: Open inch rate $5.70
Established: 1963
Group: Adams Publishing Group, LLC
Press and News Publications
Ed. ....Peggy Bakken
Gen. Mgr.......................................Mark Weber
Adv. Mgr..................................Jeremy Bradfield
Mechanical Specifications: Type page 11 5/8 x 21; E - 6 cols, 1 5/6, 1/8 between; A - 6 cols, 1 5/6, 1/8 between; C - 9 cols, 1 3/16, 1/8 between.Equipment & Software: Hardware — APP/Mac G3, APP/Power Mac; Presses — G/Urbanite; Software — QPS/QuarkXPress 4.1, Adobe/Photoshop 5.0.

ST. LOUIS PARK SUN SAILOR (THUR)

33 2nd St NE, Osseo, MN, 55369-1252, Hennepin, USA; gen tel (763) 425-3323; gen fax (763) 425-2945; disp adv e-mail cheri.obannon@ecm-inc.com; class adv e-mail robbie.shoemaker@ecm-inc.com; ed e-mail peggy.bakken@ecm-inc.com; web site sailor.mnsun.com
Circulation: 148pd, 10,821fr; CAC
Advertising rate: Open inch rate $15.00
Established: 1970
Group: Adams Publishing Group, LLC
Adv. Dir.................................. Cheri O'Bannon
Gen. Mgr.......................................Mark Weber
Ed. ....Peggy BakkenEquipment & Software: Hardware — APP/Mac; Software — QPS/QuarkXPress.
Delivery Method: Carrier
Areas Served: 55426, 55416

PARK RAPIDS

PARK RAPIDS ENTERPRISE (WED, SAT)
203 Henrietta Ave N, Park Rapids, MN, 56470-2617, Hubbard, USA; gen tel (218) 732-3364; adv tel (218) 237-1816; ed tel (218) 237-1815 ; gen fax (218) 732-8757; disp adv e-mail cparks@parkrapidsenterprise.com; class adv e-mail mharmon@parkrapidsenterprise.com; ed e-mail kcederstrom@parkrapidsenterprise.com; web site www.parkrapidsenterprise.com
Circulation: 3,341pd, 73fr; VAC
Advertising rate: Open inch rate $13.50
Group: Forum Communications Co.
Pub....Rory Palm
Adv. Mgr....Candy Parks
Circ. Mgr....Kathy Dennis
Delivery Method: Mail, Newsstand
Areas Served: 56470

PARKERS PRAIRIE

THE PARKERS PRAIRIE INDEPENDENT, LLC (THUR)
117 N Otter Ave, Parkers Prairie, MN, 56361-4996, Otter Tail, USA; gen tel (218) 338-2741; gen fax (218) 338-2745; ed e-mail ppinews@me.com; web site www.ppindependent.net
Circulation: 1,400pd,; Sworn/Estimate/Non-Audited
Advertising rate: Open inch rate $9.00
Established: 1902
Digital Platform - Mobile: Apple
Digital Platform - Tablet: Apple iOS
Co-Pub/Ed....Jakki Wehking
Pub....Jennifer Marquard
Delivery Method: Mail, Newsstand
Areas Served: 56361, 56354, 56308, 56446

PAYNESVILLE

PAYNESVILLE PRESS (WED)
211 Washburne Ave, Paynesville, MN, 56362-1642, Stearns, USA; gen tel (320) 243-3772; gen fax (320) 243-4492; disp adv e-mail adsales@paynesvillepress.com; class adv e-mail classifieds@paynesvillepress.com; ed e-mail editor@paynesvillepress.com; web site www.paynesvillearea.com
Circulation: 2,142pd, 177fr; Sworn/Estimate/Non-Audited
Advertising rate: Open inch rate $7.15
Established: 1887
Ed....Michael Jacobson
Mechanical Specifications: Type page 6 x 20 3/4; E - 6 cols, 2, 1/8 between; A - 6 cols, 2, 1/8 between; C - 6 cols, 2, 1/8 between.Equipment & Software: Hardware — APP/Macs; Software — QPS/QuarkXPress 4.0.

PELICAN RAPIDS

PELICAN RAPIDS PRESS (WED)
29 W Mill Ave, Pelican Rapids, MN, 56572-4228, Otter Tail, USA; gen tel (218) 863-1421; gen fax (218) 863-1423; disp adv e-mail adsprpress@loretel.net; class adv e-mail joprpress@loretel.net; ed e-mail jeffprpress@loretel.net; web site www.pelicanrapidspress.com
Circulation: 2,470pd,; Sworn/Estimate/Non-Audited
Advertising rate: Open inch rate $8.50
Established: 1897
Pub....Julie Meyer
Adv. Mgr....Jeff Meyer
Mechanical Specifications: Type page 6 x 11; E - 5 cols, 2 3/8, between; A - 6 cols, 2, between; C - 6 cols, 2, between.Equipment & Software: Hardware — 5-APP/Mac, 1-IBM; Software — QPS/QuarkXPress.
Areas Served: 56572, 56579, 56534

PEQUOT LAKES

ECHO JOURNAL (THUR)
4285 W Lake St, Pequot Lakes, MN, 56472-3014, Cass, USA; gen tel (218) 829-4705; adv tel (218) 855-5836 ; ed tel (218) 855-5877 ; web site http://www.pineandlakes.com/
Group: Forum Communications Co.
Adv. Mgr....Susie Alters
Ed....Nancy Vogt
Pub....Pete Mohs

LAKE COUNTRY ECHO (THUR)
4285 W Lake St, Pequot Lakes, MN, 56472-3014, Cass, USA; gen tel (218) 568-8521; gen fax (218) 568-5407; disp adv e-mail news@pequotlakesecho.com; class adv e-mail kathy.bittnerlee@pequotlakesecho.com; ed e-mail nancy.vogt@pequotlakesecho.com; web site www.pineandlakes.com - 106,516(views) 20,572(visitors)
Circulation: 2,820pd, 59fr; CVC
Advertising rate: Open inch rate $7.00
Established: 1972
Pub....Pete Mohs
Ed....Nancy Vogt
Mechanical Specifications: Type page: 10.25 x 14.75; 6 col
Delivery Method: Mail, Racks

PERHAM

ENTERPRISE BULLETIN (THUR)
222 2nd Ave SE, Frnt, Perham, MN, 56573-1706, Otter Tail, USA; gen tel (218) 346-5900; gen fax (218) 346-5901; disp adv e-mail perhameb@eot.com; ed e-mail louish@eot.com; web site www.eotfocus.com
Circulation: 3,200pd, 50fr; Sworn/Estimate/Non-Audited
Advertising rate: Open inch rate $11.72
Established: 1882
Group: Forum Communications Co.
Bus. Mgr....Kathy Bope
Adv. Mgr....Melissa Swenson
Ed....Louis Hoglund
Mechanical Specifications: Type page 13 x 21 1/2; E - 6 cols, 2 1/24, 1/6 between; A - 6 cols, 2 1/24, 1/6 between; C - 9 cols, between.Equipment & Software: Hardware — APP/Mac; Software — QPS/QuarkXPress 4.0.
Delivery Method: Mail, Carrier

PERHAM FOCUS (THUR)
222 2nd Ave SE, Perham, MN, 56573-1707, Otter Tail, USA; gen tel (218) 346-5900; gen fax (218) 346-5901; disp adv e-mail kdobberstein@perhamfocus.com; class adv e-mail jbrown@perhamfocus.com; ed e-mail pquam@perhamfocus.com; web site www.perhamfocus.com
Circulation: 2,100pd,; Sworn/Estimate/Non-Audited
Group: Forum Communications Co.
Adv. Mgr....Kim Dobberstein
Publisher....Jason Miller
Delivery Method: Mail, Newsstand
Areas Served: Perham, MN and East Otter Tail County

PINE CITY

PINE CITY PIONEER (THUR)
405 2nd Ave SE, Pine City, MN, 55063-1504, Pine, USA; gen tel (320) 629-6771; adv tel (320) 225-5124; gen fax (320) 629-6772; disp adv e-mail ads@pinecitymn.com; ed e-mail editor@pinecitymn.com; web site www.pinecitymn.com
Circulation: 2,588pd, 104fr; Sworn/Estimate/Non-Audited
Advertising rate: Open inch rate $7.50
Established: 1895
Pub....Annette Krist
Ed....Mike Gainor
Mechanical Specifications: Type page 6 x 21 1/2; E - 6 cols, 2 1/8, 3/16 between; A - 6 cols, 2 1/8, 3/16 between; C - 9 cols, 1 3/8, 1/16 between.
Delivery Method: Mail

PINE COUNTY COURIER (THUR)
405 2nd Ave SE, Pine City, MN, 55063-1504, Pine, USA; gen tel (320) 245-2368; gen fax (320) 245-2438; disp adv e-mail ads@pinecitymn.com; ed e-mail editor@pinecitymn.com; web site http://www.pinecitymn.com/
Circulation: 1,744pd, 90fr; Sworn/Estimate/Non-Audited
Advertising rate: Open inch rate $6.75
Established: 1894Editions: (52)
Pub....Annette Krist
Ed....Mike Gainor
Mechanical Specifications: 11.625 x 21Equipment & Software: Hardware — APP/Mac Performa 450; Software — QPS/QuarkXPress.
Delivery Method: Mail, Newsstand, Racks
Areas Served: Pine, Kanabec, Aitkin, Carlton

PIPESTONE

PIPESTONE COUNTY STAR (THUR)
115 2nd St NE, Ste 100, Pipestone, MN, 56164-1957, Pipestone, USA; gen tel (507) 825-3333; gen fax (507) 825-2168; disp adv e-mail plorang@pipestonestar.com; class adv e-mail prepress@pipestonestar.com; ed e-mail editor@pipestonestar.com; web site www.pipestonestar.com
Circulation: 2,445pd, 15fr; Sworn/Estimate/Non-Audited
Advertising rate: Open inch rate $13.45
Established: 1879
Publisher....John C. Draper
Adv. Mgr....Paul Lorang
Ed....Debra Fitzgerald
Mechanical Specifications: Type page 6 x 21 1/2; E - 6 cols, 2 1/16, 1/8 between; A - 6 cols, 2 1/16, 1/8 between; C - 6 cols, 2 1/16, 1/8 between.Equipment & Software: Hardware — 10-APP/Macs; Software — Microsoft/Word, Multi-Ad/Creator 4.0, Adobe/PageMaker 6.5.2, QPS/QuarkXPress 4.1.1, Adobe/Photoshop 6.0.
Delivery Method: Mail, Newsstand, Carrier
Areas Served: 56164

PRESTON

FILLMORE COUNTY JOURNAL (MON)
136 Saint Anthony St S, P.O. Box 496, Preston, MN, 55965-1151, Fillmore, USA; gen tel (507) 765-2151; adv tel 5077652151; ed tel 5077652151; gen fax (507) 765-2468; disp adv e-mail jason@fillmorecountyjournal.com; class adv e-mail ads@fillmorecountyjournal.com; ed e-mail news@fillmorecountyjournal.com; web site www.fillmorecountyjournal.com - 24,158(views) 10,663(visitors)
Circulation: 200pd, 13,100fr; CVC
Advertising rate: Open inch rate $15.86
Established: 1985
Group: Sethre Media Group, Inc.
Digital Platform - Mobile: Apple, Android, Windows, Blackberry
Digital Platform - Tablet: Apple iOS, Android, Windows 7, Blackberry Tablet OS, Kindle, Nook, Kindle Fire
Pres & Pub....Jason Sethre
Asst. Ed....Ellen Whalen
Assoc. Pub....Amanda Sethre
Creative Dir....Jana Boyum
Mechanical Specifications: Type page 10 x 15; E - 5 cols, 2, between; A - 5 cols, 2, between; C - 5 cols, 2, between.Equipment & Software: ; Software — Adobe/InDesign CS.
Delivery Method: Mail, Racks
Areas Served: Fillmore County Houston County

FILLMORE COUNTY NEWS LEADER (THUR)
124 Main St SE, Ste 200, Preston, MN, 55965-1202, Fillmore, USA; gen tel (507) 765-2752; gen fax (507) 765-2752; disp adv e-mail ads@bluffcountrynews.com; class adv e-mail classifieds@bluffcountrynews.com; ed e-mail mvanderplas@bluffcountrynews.com; web site www.fillmorecountynewsleader.com
Circulation: 1,412pd,; USPS
Advertising rate: Open inch rate $8.00
Group: Bluffs Country Newspaper Group
Pub....David Phillips
Delivery Method: Mail
Areas Served: 55965, 55935, 55939, 55954, 55949, 55922

OLMSTED COUNTY JOURNAL (WED)
136 Saint Anthony St S, Preston, MN, 55965-1151, Olmsted, USA; gen tel (507) 288-5201; gen fax (507) 288-9560; disp adv e-mail news@olmstedcountyjournal.com; class adv e-mail bob@olmstedcountyjournal.com; ed e-mail jade@olmstedcountyjournal.com
Circulation: 36,986fr; CVC
Advertising rate: Open inch rate $20.22
Established: 2011
Pub....Jason Sethre
Mechanical Specifications: Type page: 10 x 15; 5 col
Delivery Method: Mail, Racks

PRINCETON

MILLE LACS COUNTY TIMES (THUR)
208 N Rum River Dr, Ste 1, Princeton, MN, 55371-1632, Mille Lacs, USA; gen tel (763) 389-1222; gen fax (763) 389-1728; disp adv e-mail brigitte.larson@ecm-inc.com; class adv e-mail becky.southard@ecm-inc.com; ed e-mail jeff.hage@ecm-inc.com; web site www.millelacscountytimes.com
Circulation: 1,559pd,; CAC
Advertising rate: Open inch rate $8.10
Group: Adams Publishing Group, LLC
Gen. Mgr....Jeff Andres
Ed....Jeff Hage
Adv. Dir....Jerry Gloe
Delivery Method: Mail, Newsstand
Areas Served: Milaca, Foreston, Pease, Bock

PRINCETON UNION-EAGLE (THUR)
208 N Rum River Dr, Ste 1, Princeton, MN, 55371-1632, Mille Lacs, USA; gen tel (763) 389-1222; gen fax (763) 389-1728; disp adv e-mail becky.southard@ecm-inc.com ; class adv e-mail brigitte.alday@ecm-inc.com; ed e-mail jeff.hage@ecm-inc.com; web site www.princetonunioneagle.com - 74,319(views) 13,433(visitors)
Circulation: 1,806pd,; CAC
Advertising rate: Open inch rate $8.30
Established: 1876
Group: Adams Publishing Group, LLC
Gen. Mgr....Jeff Andres
Ed....Jeff Hage
Adv. Dir....Jerry Gloe
Mechanical Specifications: Type page 10.3339 x 21; E - 6 cols, 1 11/12, 1/6 between; A - 6 cols, 1 11/12, 1/6 between; C - 8 cols, 1 1/2, 1/12 between.Equipment & Software: Hardware — APP/Mac; Software — QPS/QuarkXPress 4.1.
Areas Served: 55371

PROCTOR

PROCTOR JOURNAL (THUR)
215 5th St, Proctor, MN, 55810-1628, Saint Louis, USA; gen tel (218) 624-3344; gen fax (218) 624-7037; disp adv e-mail journal@proctormn.com; class adv e-mail journal@proctormn.com; ed e-mail journal@proctormn.com; web site www.proctormn.com
Circulation: 1,800pd,; Sworn/Estimate/Non-Audited
Advertising rate: Open inch rate $9.45
Established: 1906
Gen. Mgr....Diane Giuliani
Ed....Jake Benson
Associate Editor....Lauren Anderson
Mechanical Specifications: 15 H x 9.75 w 5 column - 11 pica
Delivery Method: Mail, Newsstand
Areas Served: 55810, 55811, 55720, 55701,

55779, 55770, 55702, 55803, 55733, 55765, 55736, 55798

RED LAKE FALLS

THE GAZETTE (WED)
105 Main Ave S, Red Lake Falls, MN, 56750-4701, Red Lake, USA; gen tel (218) 253-2594; gen fax (218) 253-4114; ed e-mail rlfgaz@gvtel.com; web site http://www.redlakefallsgazette.com/
Circulation: 1,171pd,; Sworn/Estimate/Non-Audited
Advertising rate: Open inch rate $4.90
Circ. Mgr. .... Rod Thoreson
Prod. Mgr. .... Don Johanneck
Pub. .... Karie Kirschbaum
Mechanical Specifications: Type page 6 x 21 1/4; E - 6 cols, 2, 1/6 between; A - 6 cols, 2, 1/6 between; C - 6 cols, 2, 1/6 between.Equipment & Software: Hardware — APP/Mac; Software — QPS/QuarkXPress.

RED WING

REPUBLICAN EAGLE (WED, SAT)
2760 N Service Dr, Red Wing, MN, 55066-1985, Goodhue, USA; gen tel (651) 388-8235; adv tel (651) 301-7855 ; ed tel (651) 301-7870; gen fax (651) 388-3404; disp adv e-mail pfrebault@rivertowns.net; class adv e-mail chjellming@rivertowns.net; ed e-mail letters@republican-eagle.com; web site www.republican-eagle.com - 433,764(views) 48,782(visitors)
Circulation: 5,414pd,; Sworn/Estimate/Non-Audited
Advertising rate: Open inch rate $15.13
Established: 1857
Group: Forum Communications Co.
Digital Platform - Mobile: Apple, Android, Windows, Blackberry
Digital Platform - Tablet: Apple iOS, Android, Windows 7, Blackberry Tablet OS, Kindle, Nook, Kindle Fire
Pub. .... Steve Messick
Gen. Mgr. .... Michael Keuhn
News Ed. .... Anne Jacobson
Adv. Dir. .... Steve Gall
Mechanical Specifications: Type page 6 x 21 1/2; E - 6 cols, 2 1/16, 1/8 between; A - 6 cols, 2 1/16, 1/8 between; C - 8 cols, between.
Delivery Method: Mail, Carrier

REDWOOD FALLS

THE REDWOOD FALLS GAZETTE (MON, THUR)
219 S Washington St, Redwood Falls, MN, 56283-1700, Redwood, USA; gen tel (507) 637-2929; gen fax (507) 637-3175; disp adv e-mail sdahmes@redwoodfallsgazette.com; class adv e-mail sdahmes@redwoodfallsgazette.com; ed e-mail t.krause@redwoodfallsgazette.com; web site www.redwoodfallsgazette.com
Circulation: 1,401pd,; Sworn/Estimate/Non-Audited
Advertising rate: Open inch rate $9.35
Group: GateHouse Media, Inc.
Ed. .... Troy Krause
General Manager .... Duane (Doc) Durheim
Gen Mgr .... Lisa Drafall
Delivery Method: Mail, Newsstand
Areas Served: Redwood county and surrounding counties

RENVILLE

RENVILLE COUNTY REGISTER (THUR)
110 NW Dupont Ave, Renville, MN, 56284, Renville, USA; gen tel (320) 329-3324; adv tel (320) 329-3324; ed tel (320) 523-2032; gen fax (320) 329-3432; adv fax (320) 329-3432; ed fax (320) 523-2033; disp adv e-mail oproduction@rencopub.com; class adv e-mail oclassifieds@rencopub.com; ed e-mail editor@rencopub.com
Circulation: 1,800pd,; Sworn/Estimate/Non-Audited
Advertising rate: Open inch rate $8.20
Established: 1872
Publisher .... Rose Hettig
Circ. Mgr. .... Karen Harrier
Editor .... Luke Stadther
Mechanical Specifications: Type page 14 1/4 x 21 1/2; E - 7 cols, between; A - 7 cols, between.Equipment & Software: Hardware — APP/Power Mac; Software — QPS/QuarkXPress 3.3.
Delivery Method: Mail, Newsstand

ROCHESTER

AGRI NEWS (THUR)
18 1st Ave SE, Rochester, MN, 55904-3722, Olmsted, USA; gen tel (507) 285-7600; adv tel (507) 285-7607; gen fax (507) 281-7436; disp adv e-mail lschell@postbulletin.com; class adv e-mail classifieds@agrinews.com; ed e-mail wilmes@agrinews.com; web site www.agrinews.com
Circulation: 7,740pd, 420fr; CAC
Established: 1975
Circ. Mgr. .... Todd Heroff
Mng. Ed. .... Mychal Wilmes
Adv Mgr. .... Lisa Schell
Delivery Method: Mail, Newsstand

ROSEAU

ROSEAU TIMES-REGION (SAT)
1307 3rd St NE Ste 109, Suite 109, Roseau, MN, 56751-2105, Roseau, USA; gen tel (218) 463-1521; gen fax (218) 463-1530; ed e-mail rtr@mncable.net; web site http://www.roseautimes.com/
Circulation: 3,191pd,; Sworn/Estimate/Non-Audited
Advertising rate: Open inch rate $5.25
Established: 1892
Pub. .... Jodi Driscoll
Mechanical Specifications: Type page 6 x 21 1/2; E - 6 cols, 2, between; A - 6 cols, 2, between; C - 6 cols, 2, between.Equipment & Software: Hardware — APP/Mac; Software — QPS/QuarkXPress 4.0.

RUSHFORD

TRI-COUNTY RECORD (THUR)
300 S Mill St, Ste 1, Rushford, MN, 55971-8824, Fillmore, USA; gen tel (507) 864-7700; adv tel (507) 864-7700; ed tel (507) 864-7700; gen fax (507) 864-2356; disp adv e-mail info@bluffcountrynews.com; class adv e-mail classifieds@bluffcountrynews.com; ed e-mail sbestul@bluffcountrynews.com; web site www.rushford.net
Circulation: 1,063pd, 53fr; USPS
Advertising rate: Open inch rate $8.00
Established: 1915
Group: Bluff Country Newspaper Group
Phillips Publishing, Inc. - Bluff Country Newspaper Group
Publisher .... David Phillips
Mechanical Specifications: Type page 6 x 21 1/2; E - 6 cols, 1/32, 1/6 between; A - 6 cols, 2 3/16, 1/6 between; C - 6 cols, 2 3/16, 1/6 between.Equipment & Software: ; Software — Microsoft/Windows, Adobe/InD, /Corel Draw, Adobe/InDesign.
Delivery Method: Mail, Newsstand
Areas Served: 55971, 55943, 55962, 55949

RUTHTON

BUFFALO RIDGE NEWSPAPERS (WED)
320 Aetna St, Ruthton, MN, 56170-5005, Lincoln, USA; gen tel (507) 658-3919; gen fax (507) 658-3404; ed e-mail brgazette@woodstocktel.net; web site http://photos.buffaloridgenews.com/
Circulation: 740pd,; Sworn/Estimate/Non-Audited
Advertising rate: Open inch rate $4.95
Established: 1873
Pub. .... Chuck HuntEquipment & Software: Hardware — IBM; Software — Adobe/PageMaker, Adobe/Photoshop.
Delivery Method: Mail, Newsstand

SAINT CHARLES

LEWISTON JOURNAL (THUR)
924 Whitewater Ave, Saint Charles, MN, 55972-1131, Winona, USA; gen tel (507) 523-2119; gen fax (507) 932-5537; web site http://www.lewistonjournal.net/
Circulation: 974pd,; Sworn/Estimate/Non-Audited
Advertising rate: Open inch rate $10.40
Group: Stumpf Publishing Co., Inc.
Pub. .... Daniel Y. Stumpf
Ed. .... Carol A. Boynton

ST. CHARLES PRESS (THUR)
924 Whitewater Ave, Saint Charles, MN, 55972-1131, Winona, USA; gen tel (507) 932-3663; gen fax (507) 932-5537; disp adv e-mail scpress@hbcsc.com; ed e-mail dan@rochesterbg.com; web site http://www.gmdmedia.net/st-charles-press
Circulation: 1,475pd,; Sworn/Estimate/Non-Audited
Advertising rate: Open inch rate $11.50
Group: Stumpf Publishing Co., Inc.
Pub. .... Daniel Stumpf
Ed. .... Nathan Cambell

SAINT JAMES

ST JAMES PLAINDEALER (THUR)
604 1st Ave S, Saint James, MN, 56081-1729, Watonwan, USA; gen tel (507) 375-3161; gen fax (507) 375-3221; disp adv e-mail ddurheim@stjamesnews.com; web site www.stjamesnews.com
Circulation: 1,145pd, 40fr; Sworn/Estimate/Non-Audited
Advertising rate: Open inch rate $10.65
Group: GateHouse Media, Inc.
Gen. Mgr./Adv. Mgr. .... Duane (Doc) Durheim
Mechanical Specifications: Type page 6 x 21 1/2. Equipment & Software: Hardware — APP/Mac; Software — QPS/QuarkXPress.
Delivery Method: Mail, Newsstand

TOWN & COUNTRY SHOPPER (MON)
604 1st Ave S, Saint James, MN, 56081-1729, Watonwan, USA; gen tel (507) 375-3161; gen fax (507) 375-3221; disp adv e-mail ddurheim@stjamesnews.com
Circulation: 9,648fr; CVC
Advertising rate: 10.50
Group: GateHouse Media, Inc.
Gen. Mgr. .... Duane (Doc) Durheim
Mechanical Specifications: 10.375 X 15
Delivery Method: Mail, Carrier
Areas Served: Watonwan and surrounding counites

SAINT JOSEPH

SARTELL NEWSLEADER (FRI)
32 1st Ave NW, Saint Joseph, MN, 56374-4524, Stearns, USA; gen tel (320) 363-7741; gen fax (320) 363-4195; disp adv e-mail sales@thenewsleaders.com; class adv e-mail sales@thenewsleaders.com; ed e-mail news@thenewsleaders.com; web site www.thenewsleaders.net - 18,578(views) 9,446(visitors)
Circulation: 8,387fr; VAC
Advertising rate: Open inch rate $19
Established: 1995
Group: Von Meyer Publishing Inc.
CEO/Owner/Publisher .... Janelle Von Pinnon
Production Manager/Designer .... Tara Wiese
Editor .... Dennis Dalman
Assignment Editor .... Carolyn Bertsch
Mechanical Specifications: Type page 10 x 15; E - 5 cols, 2 1/2, 1/6 between; A - 5 cols, 1 7/8, 1/6 between; C - 5 cols, 1 7/8, 1/6 between. Equipment & Software: ; Software — QPS/QuarkXPress 4.0/4.1, Adobe/PhotoShop 6.0, Adobe/Illustrator 9.0.
Delivery Method: Mail, Newsstand
Areas Served: 56377, 56375

ST. JOSEPH NEWSLEADER (FRI)
32 1st Ave NW, Saint Joseph, MN, 56374-4524, Stearns, USA; gen tel (320) 363-7741; gen fax (320) 363-4195; disp adv e-mail sales@thenewsleaders.com; class adv e-mail sales@thenewsleaders.com; ed e-mail news@thenewsleaders.com; web site www.thenewsleaders.net - 18,578(views) 9,446(visitors)
Circulation: 3,663fr; VAC
Advertising rate: Open inch rate $10
Established: 1989
Group: Von Meyer Publishing Inc.
Publisher .... Janelle Von Pinnon
Production Manager/Designer .... Tara Wiese
Editor .... Dennis Dalman
Assignment Editor .... Carolyn Bertsch
Mechanical Specifications: Type page 10 x 15; E - 5 cols, 2 1/2, 1/6 between; A - 5 cols, 1 7/8, 1/6 between; C - 5 cols, 1 7/8, 1/6 between. Equipment & Software: Hardware — 4 IMacs, 1 PC; Software — InDesign CS3, Adobe/PhotoShop 6.0, Adobe/Illustrator 9.0.
Delivery Method: Mail, Newsstand
Areas Served: 56374

SAINT PAUL

ACCESS PRESS (WED, MTHLY)
161 Saint Anthony Ave, Ste 910, Saint Paul, MN, 55103-2454, Ramsey, USA; gen tel (651) 644-2133; adv tel (651) 807-1078; gen fax (651) 644-2136; disp adv e-mail access@accesspress.org; class adv e-mail Michelle@accesspress.org; ed e-mail tim@accesspress.org; web site www.accesspress.org
Circulation: 550pd, 12,000fr; Sworn/Estimate/Non-Audited
Advertising rate: Open inch rate $3.00
Established: 1990
Publisher/Editor .... Tim Benjamin
Delivery Method: Mail
Areas Served: Minneapolis - St. Paul, Duluth, East Grand Forks, Fargo, Hibbing, Mankato, Marshall, St. Cloud, Willmar

BIRD DOG & RETRIEVER NEWS (BI-MTHLY)
563 17th Ave NW, Saint Paul, MN, 55112-6514, Ramsey, USA; gen tel 612-868-9169; disp adv e-mail publisher@Bird-dog-news.com; class adv e-mail publisher@Bird-dog-news.com; ed e-mail publisher@Bird-dog-news.com; web site www.Bdarn.com
Circulation: 10,000pd, 17,000fr; Sworn/Estimate/Non-Audited
Advertising rate: $120
Established: 1992
Pub. .... Dennis Guldan
Delivery Method: Mail
Areas Served: St Paul/ Ramsey/ 55112

THE PARK BUGLE (THUR, MTHLY)
2190 Como Ave, Saint Paul, MN, 55108-1850, Ramsey, USA; gen tel (651) 646-5369; disp adv e-mail bradley.wolfe@parkbugle.org; class adv e-mail classifieds@parkbugle.org; ed e-mail editor@parkbugle.org; web site www.parkbugle.com
Advertising rate: Open inch rate $21.60
Established: 1974
Ed .... Kristal Leebrick
Prod. Mgr. .... Steve Parker
Adv. Mgr. .... Bradley Wolfe
Delivery Method: Carrier
Areas Served: St. Anthony Park, Lauderdale, Falcon Heights, Como Park

VILLAGER (WED)
757 Snelling Ave S, Saint Paul, MN, 55116-2296, Ramsey, USA; gen tel (651) 699-1462; gen fax (651) 699-6501; disp adv e-mail displayads@myvillager.com; class adv e-mail wantads@myvillager.com; ed e-mail news@myvillager.com; web site www.myvillager.com
Circulation: 72pd, 59,727fr; CVC
Advertising rate: 56.18
Established: 1953
Pub .... Michael Mischke
CEO .... John Rauch
Mechanical Specifications: Type page: 10.3334 x 15; 6 col
Delivery Method: Mail, Newsstand, Carrier
Areas Served: 55116 55105 55104 55102 55406 55417 55118 55120

SAINT PETER

ST. PETER HERALD (THUR)
311 S Minnesota Ave, Saint Peter, MN, 56082-2523, Nicollet, USA; gen tel (507) 931-4520; adv tel (507) 931-8564; ed tel (507) 931-8571; gen fax (507) 931-4522; disp adv e-mail kdavies@stpeterherald.com; class adv e-mail gstelten@stpeterherald.com; ed e-mail srook@stpeterherald.com; web site http://www.southernminn.com/st_peter_herald
Circulation: 1,191pd, 200fr; CAC
Advertising rate: Open inch rate $15.50
Group: Adams Publishing Group, LLC
Adv. Mgr. .... Kathleen Davies
Mng. Ed. .... Suzanne Rook
Gen. Mgr. .... Chad Hjellming
Mechanical Specifications: Type page 6 x 21 1/2; E - 6 cols, 1 5/6, between; A - 6 cols, 1 5/6, between; C - 6 cols, 1 5/6, between.Equipment & Software: ; Software — Baseview/NewsEdit Pro IQUE 4.0.4b5, Adobe/InDesign CS 2.0, Baseview/Ad Manager Pro 1.9.1.77.
Delivery Method: Mail
Areas Served: 55082, 56017

SAUK CENTRE

SAUK CENTRE HERALD (TUES)
522 Sinclair Lewis Ave, Sauk Centre, MN, 56378-1246, Stearns, USA; gen tel (320) 352-6577; gen fax (320) 352-5647; disp adv e-mail missy@saukherald.com; class adv e-mail office@saukherald.com; ed e-mail diane@saukherald.com; web site www.saukherald.com
Circulation: 3,276pd,; Sworn/Estimate/Non-Audited
Advertising rate: Open inch rate $15.92
Established: 1868
Bus. Mgr. .... Joyce Frierick
Sales Mgr. .... Missy Traeger
Ed. .... Diane Leukam
Delivery Method: Mail

SAVAGE

PRIOR LAKE AMERICAN (SAT)
12925 Eagle Creek Pkwy, Savage, MN, 55378-1271, Scott, USA; gen tel (952) 447-6669; adv tel (952) 345-6477; ed tel (952) 345-6378; gen fax (952) 447-6671; disp adv e-mail jhiltunen@swpub.com; class adv e-mail classified@swpub.com; ed e-mail editor@plamerican.com; web site http://www.swnewsmedia.com/prior_lake_american
Circulation: 740pd, 8,340fr; Sworn/Estimate/Non-Audited
Advertising rate: Open inch rate $13.30
Established: 1960
Group: Red Wing Publishing Co.
Op. Dir. .... Laurie Hartmann
Ed. .... Lorie Carlson
Gen. Mgr. .... Bill Davis
Delivery Method: Mail

SAVAGE PACER (SAT)
12925 Eagle Creek Pkwy, Savage, MN, 55378-1271, Scott, USA; gen tel (952) 440-1234; adv tel (952) 345-6477; gen fax (952) 445-3335; disp adv e-mail jhiltunen@swpub.com; class adv e-mail classified@swpub.com; ed e-mail editor@savagepacer.com; web site http://www.swnewsmedia.com/savage_pacer/
Circulation: 5,614fr; Sworn/Estimate/Non-Audited
Advertising rate: Open inch rate $11.10
Group: Red Wing Publishing Co.
Op. Dir. .... Laurie Hartmann
Circ. Mgr. .... Ruby Winings
Ed. .... Richard Crawford
Delivery Method: Mail, Newsstand
Areas Served: 55378

SHAKOPEE VALLEY NEWS (THUR)
12925 Eagle Creek Pkwy, Savage, MN, 55378-1271, Scott, USA; gen tel (952) 445-3333; adv tel (952) 345-6470; gen fax (952) 445-3335; disp adv e-mail editor@shakopeenews.com; class adv e-mail classified@swpub.com ; ed e-mail editor@shakopeenews.com; web site www.shakopeenews.com
Circulation: 4,602pd,; Sworn/Estimate/Non-Audited
Advertising rate: Open inch rate $9.65
Group: Red Wing Publishing Co.
Pub. .... Laurie Hartman
Adv. Rep. .... Tess Lee
Ed. .... Pat Minelli
Circulation .... Ruby Winings
Delivery Method: Mail, Newsstand

SCANDIA

MESSENGER (WED)
PO Box 96, Scandia, MN, 55073-0096, Washington, USA; gen tel (651) 433-3845; gen fax (651) 433-3158; disp adv e-mail sales@osceolasun.com; ed e-mail editor@countrymessenger.com; web site www.countrymessenger.com
Circulation: 1,600pd,; Sworn/Estimate/Non-Audited
Advertising rate: Open inch rate $5.88
Established: 1897
Ad. Sales .... Teresa Holmdahl
Circ. Mgr. .... Carrie Larson
Tom Stangl
Mechanical Specifications: Type page 6 x 14 1/2.
Areas Served: 55046, 55073

SEBEKA

THE REVIEW MESSENGER (WED)
112 Minnesota Ave W, Sebeka, MN, 56477-6004, Wadena, USA; gen tel (218) 837-5558; gen fax (218) 837-5560; disp adv e-mail remess@wcta.net; class adv e-mail remess@wcta.net; ed e-mail remess@wcta.net; web site www.lakeandpine.com
Circulation: 2,958pd,; Sworn/Estimate/Non-Audited
Advertising rate: Open inch rate $10.50
Established: 1898
Ed./Pub. .... Timothy M. Bloomquist
Adv. Mgr. .... Bernice Eckenrode
Mechanical Specifications: 6 col (10-5/8") x 21.5"
Delivery Method: Mail, Newsstand
Areas Served: 564-565

SHERBURN

THE MARTIN COUNTY STAR (WED)
30 N MAIN ST, Sherburn, MN, 56171, Martin, USA; gen tel (507) 764-6681; gen fax (507) 764-2756; ed e-mail mcstar@frontiernet.net
Circulation: 900pd,; Sworn/Estimate/Non-Audited
Advertising rate: Open inch rate $6.00
Office Mgr. .... Sheila Yurcek
Ed. .... Al Klein
Delivery Method: Mail, Newsstand
Areas Served: 561 and 560

SLAYTON

MURRAY COUNTY NEWS (WED)
2627 Broadway Ave, Slayton, MN, 56172-1311, Murray, USA; gen tel (507) 836-8929; gen fax (507) 836-6162; web site www.murraycountynews.net
Circulation: 950pd,; Sworn/Estimate/Non-Audited
Advertising rate: Open inch rate $5.75
Pub. .... Gerald D. Johnson
Delivery Method: Mail, Racks
Areas Served: Murray County

SLEEPY EYE

SLEEPY EYE HERALD-DISPATCH (THUR)
119 Main St E, Sleepy Eye, MN, 56085-1352, Brown, USA; gen tel (507) 794-3511; gen fax (507) 794-5031; disp adv e-mail aberg@sleepyeyenews.com; ed e-mail dmoldaschel@sleepyeyenews.com; web site www.sleepyeyenews.com
Circulation: 1,515pd,; Sworn/Estimate/Non-Audited
Advertising rate: Open inch rate $8.95
Established: 1880
Group: GateHouse Media, Inc.
Digital Platform - Mobile: Apple
Digital Platform - Tablet: Apple iOS
GM .... Duane Durheim
Ed. .... Deb Moldaschel
Mechanical Specifications: 6 col x 21.5"
Delivery Method: Mail, Newsstand
Areas Served: city 56085

SPRING GROVE

SPRING GROVE HERALD (WED)
115 W Main St, Spring Grove, MN, 55974-1276, Houston, USA; gen tel (507) 498-3868; gen fax (507) 498-6397; disp adv e-mail sgherald@bluffcountrynews.com; ed e-mail hgray@bluffcountrynews.com; web site www.springgroveherald.com
Circulation: 1,099pd, 15fr; Sworn/Estimate/Non-Audited
Advertising rate: Open inch rate $7.25
Established: 1892
Group: Bluff Country Newspaper Group
Bluffs Country Newspaper Group
Pub. .... Dave Phillips
Ed. .... Heather Gray
Mechanical Specifications: Type page 6 x 21; E - 6 cols, 1.95", 1/8 between; A - 6 cols, 1 5/6, .16" between; C - 6 colsEquipment & Software: Hardware — 4-APP/Mac; Software — CS5 Suite
Delivery Method: Mail
Areas Served: 55974

SPRING VALLEY

SPRING VALLEY TRIBUNE (WED)
112 N Broadway St, Spring Valley, MN, 55975-1224, Fillmore, USA; gen tel (507) 346-7365; gen fax (507) 346-7366; disp adv e-mail svtribune@bluffcountrynews.com; class adv e-mail classifieds@bluffcountrynews.com; ed e-mail svtribune@bluffcountrynews.com; web site www.svtribune.com
Circulation: 1,219pd,; USPS
Advertising rate: Open inch rate $6.50
Established: 1880
Group: Bluff Country Newspaper Group
Bluffs Country Newspaper Group
Pub. .... Dave Phillips
Circ. Mgr. .... Debbie Groth
Adv. .... Sue Bly
Mechanical Specifications: Type page 6 x 21 1/2; E - 6 cols, between; A - 6 cols, between; C - 6 cols, between.Equipment & Software: Hardware — APP/Mac G4; Software — QPS/QuarkXPress 4.0, Adobe/PageMaker 5.0.
Delivery Method: Mail, Racks
Areas Served: 55975, 55990, 55961

SPRINGFIELD

SPRINGFIELD ADVANCE-PRESS (WED)
13 S Marshall Ave, Springfield, MN, 56087-1612, Brown, USA; gen tel (507) 723-4225; gen fax (507) 723-4400; ed e-mail comp.aps@newulmtel.net; web site http://www.springfieldap.com
Circulation: 1,813pd, 39fr; Sworn/Estimate/Non-Audited
Advertising rate: Open inch rate $5.25
Established: 1888
Pub. .... P.C. Hedstrom
Ed. .... Doris M. Weber
Mechanical Specifications: Type page 6 x 21.Equipment & Software: Hardware — APP/Macs.

STAPLES

STAPLES WORLD (THUR)
224 4th St NE, Staples, MN, 56479-2428, Todd, USA; gen tel (218) 894-1112; gen fax (218) 894-3570; disp adv e-mail info@staplesworld.com; class adv e-mail office@staplesworld.com; ed e-mail editor@staplesworld.com; web site www.staplesworld.com
Circulation: 1,800pd,; Sworn/Estimate/Non-Audited
Advertising rate: Open inch rate $9.80
Established: 1890
Group: Devlin Newspapers, Inc.
Gen. Mgr. .... Brenda Halvorson
Adv. Mgr. .... Gary Mueller
Circ. Mgr. .... Kathy Odden
Ed. .... Mark Anderson
Dawn Timbs
graphic designer/photo tech .... Janice Winter
Mechanical Specifications: Type page 6 x 21 1/2; E - 6 cols, 1.6319, 1/6 between; A - 6 cols, 1.6319, 1/6 between; C - 6 cols, 1.6319, 1/6 between.Equipment & Software: Hardware — 27 in. iMac; Software — InDesign, Photo-Shop, Illustrator, Acrobat
Delivery Method: Mail, Newsstand
Areas Served: 56479, 56466, 56473, 56481, 56434, 56443

STEPHEN

MESSENGER BANNER (THUR)
586 Pacific Ave, Stephen, MN, 56757, Marshall, USA; gen tel (218) 478-2210; gen fax (218) 478-2210; ed e-mail messenger@wiktel.com
Circulation: 1,499pd,; Sworn/Estimate/Non-Audited
Advertising rate: Open inch rate $3.00
Established: 1882
Ed. .... Keith SustadEquipment & Software: ; Presses — G.
Delivery Method: Mail

STEWARTVILLE

STEWARTVILLE STAR (TUES)
102 Main St N, Stewartville, MN, 55976-2607, Olmsted, USA; gen tel (507) 533-4271; gen fax (507) 533-4272; disp adv e-mail starads@stewiestar.com; ed e-mail stareditor@stewiestar.com; web site www.thinkstewartville.com
Circulation: 1,575pd, 4,800fr; USPS
Advertising rate: Open inch rate $8.00
Established: 1891
Group: Galaxy Publications LLC
Pub .... Bill Schroeder
Circ. Mgr. .... Sharon Moehnke
Ed. .... Mark Peterson
Mechanical Specifications: Type page 6 x 21; E - 6 cols, 2, 1/6 between; A - 6 cols, 2, 1/6 between; C - 6 cols, 2, 1/6 between. Equipment & Software: Hardware — APP/Mac G3, APP/Power Mac; Software — QPS/QuarkXPress 4.0.
Delivery Method: Mail, Newsstand

Areas Served: Stewartville/Olmsted/55976

STILLWATER

STILLWATER GAZETTE (WED, FRI)

1931 Curve Crest Blvd W, Stillwater, MN, 55082-6063, Washington, USA; gen tel (651) 439-3130; adv tel (651) 796-1116; ed tel (651) 796-1112; gen fax (651) 439-4713; adv fax (651) 439-4713; ed fax (651) 439-4713; disp adv e-mail doug.lacher@ecm-inc.com; class adv e-mail brad.solem@ecm-inc.com; web site www.stillwatergazette.com
Circulation: 1,591pd, 24fr; Sworn/Estimate/Non-Audited
Advertising rate: Open inch rate $12.60
Established: 1870
Group: Adams Publishing Group, LLC
Digital Platform - Mobile: Apple, Android
Digital Platform - Tablet: Apple iOS, Android
Adv. Acct. Exec. .... Doug Lacher
Adv. Acct. Exec. .... Brad Solem
Sports Ed.............................Stuart Groskreutz
Mng Ed ....Jonathan Young
Mechanical Specifications: Type page 6 x 21; E - 6 cols, 2 1/16, 1/8 between; A - 6 cols, 2 1/16, 1/8 between; C - 9 cols, 1 3/8, 1/16 between.
Delivery Method: Mail, Carrier
Areas Served: 55082, 55003, 55042, 55043, 55001, 55047, 54016, 54025

THIEF RIVER FALLS

NORTHERN WATCH (SAT)

324 Main Ave N, Thief River Falls, MN, 56701-1906, Pennington, USA; gen tel (218) 681-4450; gen fax (218) 681-4455; disp adv e-mail sales@trftimes.com; class adv e-mail classified@trftimes.com; ed e-mail dhill@trftimes.com; web site http://www.trftimes.com/northernwatch
Circulation: 22,000fr; Sworn/Estimate/Non-Audited
Advertising rate: Open inch rate $8.00
Established: 1910
Adv. Mgr.....................................Dede Coltam
Circ. Mgr..Sue Phillip
Ed. ....Dave Hill
Mechanical Specifications: Type page 14 x 22 3/4; E - 6 cols, 2, 1/8 between; A - 6 cols, 2, 1/8 between; C - 6 cols, 2, 1/8 between. Equipment & Software: Hardware — APP/Mac; Presses — G/Community; Software — QPS/QuarkXPress 4.01.

THIEF RIVER FALLS TIMES (WED)

324 Main Ave N, Thief River Falls, MN, 56701-1906, Pennington, USA; gen tel (218) 681-4450; gen fax (218) 681-4455; disp adv e-mail sales@trftimes.com; class adv e-mail classified@trftimes.com; ed e-mail dhill@trftimes.com; web site www.trftimes.com
Circulation: 4,997pd, 71fr; Sworn/Estimate/Non-Audited
Advertising rate: Open inch rate $8.25
Established: 1910
Group: MCM Ohio LLC
Ed. ....Dave Hill
Circ. Mgr...Sue Phillpp
Kathy Svidal
Mechanical Specifications: Type page 6 x 21 1/2; E - 6 cols, 2, 1/8 between; A - 6 cols, 2, 1/8 between; C - 6 cols, 2, 1/8 between.Equipment & Software: Hardware — APP/Mac; Presses — G/Community; Software — QPS/QuarkXPress 4.01.
Delivery Method: Mail, Newsstand
Areas Served: 56701, 56764, 56725, 56737, 56760

TOWER

ELY TIMBERJAY (FRI)

414 Main St, Tower, MN, 55790-5105, Saint Louis, USA; gen tel (218) 365-3114; adv tel (218) 753-2950; ed tel (218) 365-3114; gen fax (218) 753-2916; disp adv e-mail editor@timberjay.com; ed e-mail editor@timberjay.com; web site www.timberjay.com
Circulation: 1,208pd,; USPS
Advertising rate: Open inch rate $8.25
Digital Platform - Tablet: Kindle
Pub...............................Marshall Helmberger
Delivery Method: Mail, Newsstand
Areas Served: 55731

TIMBERJAY (FRI)

414 Main St, Tower, MN, 55790-5105, Saint Louis, USA; gen tel (218) 753-2950; gen fax (218) 753-2916; disp adv e-mail editor@timberjay.com; ed e-mail editor@timberjay.com; web site www.timberjay.com
Circulation: 3,430pd, 80fr; USPS
Advertising rate: Open inch rate $8.40
Established: 1989
Pub...............................Marshall Helmberger
Adv. Mgr./Ed...............................Jodi Summit
Circ. Mgr.....................................Mickey White
Keith Vandervort
Delivery Method: Mail, Racks

TRACY

TRACY HEADLIGHT-HERALD (WED)

207 4th St, Tracy, MN, 56175-1221, Lyon, USA; gen tel (507) 629-4300; gen fax (507) 629-4301; disp adv e-mail admanager@headlightherald.com; class adv e-mail kris@headlightherald.com; ed e-mail per@headlightherald.com; web site www.headlightherald.com
Circulation: 1,685pd, 4,600fr; Sworn/Estimate/Non-Audited
Advertising rate: Open inch rate $8.25
Established: 1879
Group: Tracy Publishing Company, Inc
Adv. Mgr. .... Lisa Sell
Pub./Gen. Mgr............................Seth Schmidt
Ed. .... Per Peterson
Delivery Method: Mail, Newsstand, Carrier, Racks
Areas Served: 56175 5612356115 56132

TRUMAN

TRUMAN TRIBUNE (WED)

118 E Ciro St, Truman, MN, 56088-2017, Martin, USA; gen tel (507) 776-2751; gen fax (507) 776-2751; disp adv e-mail neal@thetrumantribune.com; ed e-mail thetrumantribune@gmail.com; web site thetrumantribune.com
Circulation: 821pd, 250fr; Sworn/Estimate/Non-Audited
Advertising rate: Open inch rate $8.50
Established: 1899
Digital Platform - Mobile: Apple, Android, Windows, Blackberry
Digital Platform - Tablet: Apple iOS, Android, Windows 7, Blackberry Tablet OS, Kindle, Nook, Kindle Fire
Pub .... Nicole Meyer
Adv. Mgr......................................Neal Meyer
Delivery Method: Mail, Racks

TWIN VALLEY

TWIN VALLEY TIMES/GARY GRAPHIC (TUES)

101 Main Ave W, Twin Valley, MN, 56584-4039, Norman, USA; gen tel (218) 584-5195; gen fax (218) 584-5196; ed e-mail tvtimes@arvig.net; web site http://www.twinvalleytimes.com/
Circulation: 1,241pd,; Sworn/Estimate/Non-Audited
Advertising rate: Open inch rate $4.35
Mng. Ed..................................... Rod Thoreson
Mechanical Specifications: Type page 6 x 21.Equipment & Software: Hardware — APP/Mac; Software — QPS/QuarkXPress 3.30.

TWO HARBORS

LAKE COUNTY NEWS-CHRONICLE (FRI)

109 Waterfront Dr, Two Harbors, MN, 55616-1525, Lake, USA; gen tel (218) 834-2141; gen fax (218) 834-2144; disp adv e-mail chronicle@lcnewschronicle.com; class adv e-mail class@lcnewschronicle.com; ed e-mail rlubbers@duluthnews.com; web site www.twoharborsmn.com
Circulation: 2,031pd,; Sworn/Estimate/Non-Audited
Advertising rate: Open inch rate $10.10
Established: 1890
Group: Forum Communications Co.
Com. Ed................................Adelle Whitefoot
Pub.. Neal Ronquist
Ed. ....Rick LubbersEquipment & Software: ; Software — QPS/QuarkXPress 4.0.
Delivery Method: Mail, Newsstand, Carrier, Racks
Areas Served: 55616, 55614, 55609, 55601, 55602, 55603, 55607

TYLER

TYLER TRIBUTE (WED)

124 N Tyler St, Tyler, MN, 56178-1160, Lincoln, USA; gen tel (507) 247-5502; gen fax (507) 247-5502; disp adv e-mail tributeadvertising@gmail.com; ed e-mail tributeeditor@gmail.com; web site www.tylertribute.com
Circulation: 1,081pd, 134fr; Sworn/Estimate/Non-Audited
Advertising rate: Open inch rate $5.70
Co-Pub.......................................Diane Clark
Ed. .... Robert Wolfington
Co-Pub./Ed ....Mark Whimes
Mechanical Specifications: Type page 6 x 21 1/2; E - 6 cols, 2, 1/8 between; A - 6 cols, 2, 1/8 between; C - 6 cols, 2, 1/8 between.Equipment & Software: Hardware — PCs; Software — Microsoft/Word 5.0, Microsoft/Publisher.
Delivery Method: Mail

ULEN

CLAY COUNTY UNION (MON)

112 2nd St NE, Ulen, MN, 56585-4200, Clay, USA; gen tel (218) 596-8813; gen fax (218) 483-4457; disp adv e-mail news@claycountyunion.net; ed e-mail marc@hawleyherald.net; web site www.claycountyunion.net
Circulation: 1,226pd,; Sworn/Estimate/Non-Audited
Advertising rate: Open inch rate $8.00
Ed. .... John Kolness
Adv ....Renne Nyestvold
Delivery Method: Mail

VERNDALE

THE VERNDALE SUN (THUR)

121 W Farewell St, Verndale, MN, 56481, Wadena, USA; gen tel (218) 445-6397; gen fax (218) 756-2126; disp adv e-mail cindy@inhnews.com; class adv e-mail verndalesun@inhnews.com; ed e-mail kathy@inhnews.com; web site http://www.inhnews.com/about.html
Circulation: 870pd,; Sworn/Estimate/Non-Audited
Advertising rate: Open inch rate $8.50
Co-Pub.....................................Marlo Benning
Co-Pub.. Ray Benning
Ed. .... Kathy Marquardt
Delivery Method: Mail

WABASSO

WABASSO STANDARD (WED)

1034 Cedar St, Wabasso, MN, 56293-1408, Redwood, USA; gen tel (507) 342-5143; gen fax (507) 342-5144; disp adv e-mail manderson@wabasso-standard.com; ed e-mail jisaackson@wabasso-standard.com
Circulation: 1,200pd,; Sworn/Estimate/Non-Audited
Advertising rate: Open inch rate $3.95
Pub...Pat Schmidt

WACONIA

CARVER COUNTY NEWS (THUR)

8 S Elm St, Waconia, MN, 55387-1412, Carver, USA; gen tel (952) 442-4414; gen fax (952) 442-1272 ; disp adv e-mail rick.brauer@ecm-inc.com; class adv e-mail norma.carstensen@ecm-inc.com; ed e-mail jason.schmucker@ecm-inc.com; web site http://sunpatriot.com/tag/ccn/
Circulation: 44fr; CAC
Advertising rate: Open inch rate $5.70
Established: 1976
Group: Adams Publishing Group, LLC
Adv.. Rick Brauer
Comm. Ed............................... Melissa Priebe
Ed. ....Jason Schmucker

NORWOOD YOUNG AMERICA TIMES (THUR)

8 S Elm St, Waconia, MN, 55387-1412, Carver, USA; gen tel (952) 442-4414; gen fax (952) 442-6815; disp adv e-mail rick.brauer@ecm-inc.com; class adv e-mail norma.carstensen@ecm-inc.com; ed e-mail jason.schmucker@ecm-inc.com; web site http://sunpatriot.com/tag/nya-times/
Circulation: 2,550pd, 41fr; Sworn/Estimate/Non-Audited
Advertising rate: Open inch rate $5.40
Group: Adams Publishing Group, LLC
Digital Platform - Mobile: Apple, Android
Digital Platform - Tablet: Apple iOS, Android
Pres./COO ....Marge Winkelman
Ed. ....Jason Schmucker
Adv. Mgr....................................... Rick Brauer
Delivery Method: Mail
Areas Served: Carver County

THE LAKER (SAT)

8 S Elm St, Waconia, MN, 55387-1412, Carver, USA; gen tel (952) 442-4414; gen fax (952) 442-6815; disp adv e-mail kristi.pexa@ecm-inc.com; class adv e-mail norma.carstensen@ecm-inc.com; ed e-mail jason.schmucker@ecm-inc.com; web site www.lakerpioneer.com/
Circulation: 10pd, 6,499fr; CAC
Advertising rate: Open inch rate $19.50
Group: Adams Publishing Group, LLC
Digital Platform - Mobile: Apple, Android
Digital Platform - Tablet: Apple iOS, Android
Adv. Mgr..Kristi Pexa
Ed. ....Jason Schmucker
Class. Adv. ....Norma Carstensen
Delivery Method: Mail
Areas Served: Carver County

THE PIONEER (SAT)

8 S Elm St, Waconia, MN, 55387-1412, Carver, USA; gen tel (952) 442-4414; gen fax (952) 442-6815; disp adv e-mail kristi.pexa@ecm-inc.com; class adv e-mail norma.carstensen@ecm-inc.com; ed e-mail jason.schmucker@ecm-inc.com; web site www.lakerpioneer.com/
Circulation: 15pd, 11,459fr; CAC
Advertising rate: Open inch rate $19.50
Group: Adams Publishing Group, LLC
Digital Platform - Mobile: Apple, Android
Digital Platform - Tablet: Apple iOS, Android
Adv. Mgr..Kristi Pexa
Class. Adv. ....Norma Carstensen
Ed. ....Jason Schmucker
Delivery Method: Mail
Areas Served: Carver County

THE WACONIA PATRIOT (THUR)

8 S Elm St, Waconia, MN, 55387-1412, Carver, USA; gen tel (952) 442-4414; gen fax (952) 442-6815; disp adv e-mail kristi.pexa@ecm-inc.com; class adv e-mail norma.carstensen@ecm-inc.com; ed e-mail jason.

schmucker@ecm-inc.com; web site www.waconiapatriot.com
Circulation: 4,640pd, 6,528fr; Sworn/Estimate/Non-Audited
Advertising rate: Open inch rate $7.60
Established: 1976
Group: Adams Publishing Group, LLC
Digital Platform - Mobile: Apple, Android
Digital Platform - Tablet: Apple iOS, Android
Pres./COO .... Marge Winkelman
Adv. Mgr. .... Kristi Pexa
Ed. .... Jason Schmucker
Delivery Method: Mail
Areas Served: Carver County

WADENA

INTERCOM (SAT)

314 Jefferson St S, Wadena, MN, 56482-1534, Wadena, USA; gen tel (218) 631-2561; gen fax (218) 631-1621; disp adv e-mail editorial@wadenapj.com; web site www.wadenapj.com
Circulation: 0pd, 9,325fr; VAC
Group: Forum Communications Co.
Ed. .... Steve Schultz

WADENA PIONEER JOURNAL (THUR)

314 Jefferson St S, Wadena, MN, 56482-1534, Wadena, USA; gen tel (218) 631-2561; ed tel (218) 346-5900 x226; gen fax (218) 631-1621; ed e-mail editorial@wadenapj.com; web site www.wadenapj.com
Circulation: 1,860pd, 38fr; VAC
Group: Forum Communications Co.
Ed. .... Paula Quam
Delivery Method: Mail, Carrier, Racks

WALKER

THE PILOT-INDEPENDENT (WED)

408 MINNESOTA AVE, Walker, MN, 56484, Cass, USA; gen tel (218) 547-1000; gen fax (218) 547-3000; disp adv e-mail pilotads@pilotindependent.com; class adv e-mail pilotclassifieds@pilotindependent.com; ed e-mail dmorrill@pilotindependent.com; web site www.walkermn.com
Circulation: 2,200pd,; Sworn/Estimate/Non-Audited
Advertising rate: Open inch rate $7.75
Established: 1900
Ed. .... Dean Morrill
Gen. Mgr. .... Terri Fierstine
Circ. Mgr .... Deb Bitker
Mechanical Specifications: Type page 6 x 21; E - 6 cols, 1 4/5, 1/6 between; A - 6 cols, 1 4/5, 1/6 between; C - 6 cols, 1 4/5, 1/6 between. Equipment & Software: Hardware — APP/Power Mac 8500, APP/Mac G3; Software — QPS/QuarkXPress 4.01.
Delivery Method: Mail, Racks
Areas Served: 56484, 56452, 56435, 56436, 56461

WARREN

WARREN SHEAF (WED)

127 W Johnson Ave, Warren, MN, 56762-1102, Marshall, USA; gen tel (218) 745-5174; gen fax (218) 745-5175; ed e-mail warrensheaf@mncable.net; web site http://www.warrensheaf.net/
Circulation: 1,929pd,; Sworn/Estimate/Non-Audited
Advertising rate: Open inch rate $4.50
Established: 1880
Ed. .... Eric N. Mattson
Mechanical Specifications: Type page 6 x 21; E - 6 cols, 2 1/8, 1/6 between; A - 6 cols, 2 1/8, 1/6 between.Equipment & Software: ; Software — QPS/QuarkXPress 3.1.
Delivery Method: Mail

WARROAD

THE WARROAD PIONEER (TUES)

501 Lake St NE, P.O. Box E, Warroad, MN, 56763-2304, Roseau, USA; gen tel (218) 386-3970; gen fax (218) 386-3120; disp adv e-mail warroadpioneer@gmail.com; class adv e-mail warroadnews@gmail.com; ed e-mail warroadnews@gmail.com; web site www.warroadmnnews.com
Circulation: 1,518pd, 73fr; Sworn/Estimate/Non-Audited
Advertising rate: Open inch rate $6.25
Established: 1902
Group: Advantage Marketing & Promotional Design Inc.
Ed .... Koren Zaiser
Office Mgr. .... Shelley Galle
Delivery Method: Mail, Newsstand
Areas Served: Warroad/ Roseau /56763

WASECA

WASECA COUNTY NEWS (FRI)

213 2nd St NW, Waseca, MN, 56093-2401, Waseca, USA; gen tel (507) 835-3380; gen fax (507) 835-3435; disp adv e-mail kbiehn@wasecacountynews.com; class adv e-mail classifieds@wasecacountynews.com; ed e-mail jfrazier@wasecacountynews.com; web site http://www.southernminn.com/waseca_county_news/
Circulation: 1,907pd, 100fr; CAC
Advertising rate: Open inch rate $15.70
Established: srook@wasecacountynews.com
Group: Adams Publishing Group, LLC
Ed .... Suzanne Rook
Adv. .... Kristie Biehn
Gen. Mgr .... Chad Hjellming
Mechanical Specifications: Type page 6 x 21 1/2; E - 6 cols, 1 5/6, between; A - 6 cols, 1 5/6, between; C - 6 cols, 1 5/6, between.Equipment & Software: ; Presses — G/Community; Software — Baseview/NewsEdit Pro IQUE 4.0.4b5, Adobe/InDesign CS 2.0.
Areas Served: 56093, 56048, 56096, 56072, 56078, 56091

WAYZATA

LAKESHORE WEEKLY NEWS (TUES)

1001 Twelve Oaks Center Dr, Ste 1017, Wayzata, MN, 55391-4310, Hennepin, USA; gen tel (952) 473-0890; gen fax (952) 473-0895; disp adv e-mail jhiltunen@swpub.com; class adv e-mail classified@swpub.com; ed e-mail editor@weeklynews.com; web site http://www.swnewsmedia.com/lakeshore_weekly
Circulation: 11pd, 14,280fr; CAC
Advertising rate: Open inch rate $24.00
Ed .... Richard Crawford
Op. Dir. .... Laurie Hartmann
Adv. Dir. .... Jen Hiltunen

WELLS

WELLS MIRROR (THUR)

40 W Franklin St, Wells, MN, 56097-1927, Faribault, USA; gen tel (507) 553-3131; gen fax (507) 553-3132; disp adv e-mail mirror.shopper@gmail.com; ed e-mail mirror.shopper@gmail.com; web site https://www.facebook.com/Wells-Mirror-Shopper-461335810602923/about/?ref=page_internal
Circulation: 1,396pd, 71fr; Sworn/Estimate/Non-Audited
Advertising rate: Open inch rate $4.00
Sales and Customer Service Representative... Diana Brooks
Staff Writer .... Jacob Winter
Mechanical Specifications: Type page 6 x 21 1/2; E - 6 cols, 2, 3/16 between; A - 6 cols, 2, 3/16 between; C - 6 cols, 2, 3/16 between. Equipment & Software: Hardware — APP/Mac G4; Software — QPS/QuarkXPress, Microsoft/Word.
Delivery Method: Mail, Newsstand

WEST ST PAUL

THE ST. PAUL VOICE, DOWNTOWN ST. PAUL VOICE, SOUTH ST. PAUL VOICE AND LA VOZ LATINA (MTHLY)

1643 Robert St S Ste 60B, Suite 60B, West St Paul, MN, 55118-4582, Dakota, USA; gen tel (651) 457-1177; gen fax (651) 457-1077; disp adv e-mail john@stpaulpublishing.com; ed e-mail tim@stpaulpublishing.com; web site www.stpaulpublishing.com
Circulation: 37,500fr; Sworn/Estimate/Non-Audited
Advertising rate: Open inch rate $22.19
Established: 1966
Group: St. Paul Publishing Co.
Digital Platform - Mobile: Windows
Pub./Ed. .... Tim Spitzack
Adv. Mgr. .... John Ahlstrom
Delivery Method: Carrier, Racks
Areas Served: 55107, 55118, 55120, 55075, 55407, 55408

WESTBROOK

WESTBROOK SENTINEL TRIBUNE (WED)

611 1st Ave, Westbrook, MN, 56183-9500, Cottonwood, USA; gen tel (507) 274-6136; gen fax (507) 274-6137; disp adv e-mail pharms@ncppub.com; ed e-mail sebeling@ncppub.com; web site www.ncppub.com
Circulation: 997pd,; Sworn/Estimate/Non-Audited
Advertising rate: Open inch rate $5.15
Group: New Century Press
Ed .... Jessica Jensen

WHEATON

WHEATON GAZETTE (TUES)

1114 Broadway, Wheaton, MN, 56296-1308, Traverse, USA; gen tel (320) 563-8146; gen fax (320) 563-8147; ed e-mail wgazette@frontiernet.net
Circulation: 1,750pd, 26,643fr; Sworn/Estimate/Non-Audited
Advertising rate: Open inch rate $6.60
Established: 1885
Mng. Ed. .... Michael P. Kremer

WHITE BEAR LAKE

FOREST LAKE LOWDOWN (FRI, BI-MTHLY)

4779 Bloom Ave, White Bear Lake, MN, 55110-2764, Ramsey, USA; gen tel (651) 407-1200; adv tel (651) 407-1208; gen fax (651) 429-1242; disp adv e-mail lowdown3@presspubs.com; class adv e-mail classified@presspubs.com; ed e-mail lowdownnews@presspubs.com; web site http://www.presspubs.com/forest_lake/
Circulation: 58pd, 11,584fr; VAC
Advertising rate: Open inch rate $15.70
Established: 1903
Group: Press Publications, Inc.
Digital Platform - Mobile: Apple, Android
Digital Platform - Tablet: Apple iOS, Android, Kindle, Kindle Fire
Pub. .... Carter Johnson
Circ. Mgr. .... Greg Workman
Mechanical Specifications: Type page 6 x 21; E - 6 cols, 1.57", 1/6 between; A - 6 cols, 1.57", 1/6 between; C - 9 cols, 1.037, 1/12 between.Equipment & Software: Hardware — APP/Mac; Presses — HI; Software — QPS/QuarkXPress, Adobe/Photoshop.
Delivery Method: Mail, Newsstand, Carrier, Racks
Areas Served: 55110, 55115, 55090, 55082

QUAD COMMUNITY PRESS (TUES)

4779 Bloom Ave, White Bear Lake, MN, 55110-2764, Ramsey & Washington, USA; gen tel (365) 407-1200; gen fax (651) 429-1242; disp adv e-mail quadpressrep@presspubs.com; class adv e-mail classified@presspubs.com; ed e-mail quadnews@presspubs.com; web site www.presspubs.com
Circulation: 708pd, 5,987fr; VAC
Advertising rate: Open inch rate $14.60
Established: 1981
Group: Press Publications, Inc.
Pub. .... Eugene D. Johnson
Adv. .... Patti Carlson
Circ. Mgr. .... Amy Johnson
Mechanical Specifications: Type page 11 1/2 x 21; E - 6 cols, 1 13/16, between; A - 6 cols, 1 13/16, between; C - 10 cols, 1 1/4, 1/2 between.Equipment & Software: Hardware — APP/Mac; Presses — HI; Software — QPS/QuarkXPress, Adobe/Photoshop.
Delivery Method: Mail, Carrier
Areas Served: 55014, 55038

THE HUGO CITIZEN (THUR)

4779 Bloom Ave, White Bear Lake, MN, 55110-2764, Ramsey, USA; gen tel (651) 407-1200; gen fax (651) 407-1242; disp adv e-mail wbpressad3@presspubs.com; class adv e-mail classified@presspubs.com; ed e-mail citizen@presspubs.com; web site www.readthecitizen.com
Circulation: 8,262fr; Sworn/Estimate/Non-Audited
Advertising rate: Open inch rate $25.00
Established: 1998
Group: Press Publications, Inc.Editions: (1) The Citizen
Pub .... Carter Johnson
Delivery Method: Mail
Areas Served: 55038, 55110

THE LOWDOWN - FOREST LAKE AREA (FRI)

4779 Bloom Ave, White Bear Lake, MN, 55110-2764, Ramsey, USA; gen tel (651) 407-1200; adv tel (651) 407-1213; ed tel (651) 407-1200; gen fax (651) 429-1242; adv fax (651) 429-1242; ed fax (651) 429-1242; disp adv e-mail lowdown2@presspubs.com; class adv e-mail classified@presspubs.com; ed e-mail lowdownnews@presspubs.com; web site www.presspubs.com
Circulation: 62pd, 2,923fr; VAC
Established: 1996
Group: Press Publications, Inc.
Pub. .... Carter Johnson
Mechanical Specifications: Type page 11 1/2 x 21 1/2; E - 6 cols, 1 13/16, 1/6 between; A - 6 cols, 1 13/16, 1/6 between; C - 10 cols, 1 1/4, 1/12 between.Equipment & Software: Hardware — Mac; Software — CS5
Delivery Method: Mail, Racks
Areas Served: 55025, 55092

THE LOWDOWN - ST. CROIX VALLEY AREA (FRI)

4779 Bloom Ave, White Bear Lake, MN, 55110-2764, Ramsey, USA; gen tel (365) 407-1200; adv tel (651) 407-1213; ed tel (651) 407-1200; gen fax (651) 429-1242; adv fax (651) 429-1242; ed fax (651) 407-1242; disp adv e-mail wbpressad3@presspubs.com; class adv e-mail classified@presspubs.com; ed e-mail whitebearnews@presspubs.com; web site www.presspubs.com
Circulation: 125pd, 2,850fr; VAC
Advertising rate:
Established: 1903
Group: Press Publications, Inc.
Digital Platform - Mobile: Apple, Android
Digital Platform - Tablet: Apple iOS, Android, Kindle, Kindle Fire
Pub .... Carter Johnson
Mechanical Specifications: Type page 6 x 21; E - 6 cols, 1.57", 1/6 between; A - 6 cols, 1.57", 1/6 between; C - 9 cols, 1.037, 1/12 between.Equipment & Software: Hardware — APP/Mac; Presses — HI; Software — QPS/QuarkXPress, Adobe/Photoshop.
Delivery Method: Mail, Newsstand, Carrier, Racks
Areas Served: 55082, 55042, 55047

VADNAIS HEIGHTS PRESS (WED)
4779 Bloom Ave, White Bear Lake, MN, 55110-2764, Ramsey, USA; gen tel (365) 407-1200; adv tel (651) 407-1200; gen fax (651) 429-1242; adv fax (651) 429-1242; ed fax (651) 429-1242; disp adv e-mail wbpressad1@presspubs.com; class adv e-mail classified@presspubs.com; ed e-mail vadnaisheightsnews@presspubs.com; web site www.presspubs.com
Circulation: 226pd, 3,312fr; VAC
Advertising rate: Open inch rate $22.44
Established: 1975
Group: Press Publications, Inc.
Digital Platform - Mobile: Apple, Android, Windows, Blackberry
Digital Platform - Tablet: Apple iOS, Android, Kindle, Kindle Fire
Pub.......... Carter Johnson
Classified Adv. Mgr.......... Jill Twedt
Circulation Manager .... Amy Johnson
Mechanical Specifications: Type page 10 x 21 1/2; E - 6 cols, 1.57", between; A - 6 cols, 1,57", between; C - 10 cols, 1 1/4, 3/4 between.Equipment & Software: Hardware — APP/Mac; Software — QPS/QuarkXPress, Adobe/Photoshop.
Delivery Method: Mail, Newsstand, Carrier
Areas Served: 55127,55110

WHITE BEAR PRESS (WED)
4779 Bloom Ave, White Bear Lake, MN, 55110-2764, Ramsey, USA; gen tel (365) 407-1200; gen fax (651) 429-1242; disp adv e-mail wbpressad1@presspubs.com; class adv e-mail classified@presspubs.com; ed e-mail whitebearnews@presspubs.com; web site www.presspubs.com
Circulation: 2,477pd, 11,370fr; VAC
Advertising rate: Open inch rate $22.00
Established: 1903
Group: Press Publications, Inc.
Digital Platform - Mobile: Apple, Android
Digital Platform - Tablet: Apple iOS, Android, Kindle, Kindle Fire
Pub.......... Carter Johnson
Pres.......... Eugene Johnson
Greg Workman
Patty Steele
Mechanical Specifications: Type page 6 x 21; E - 6 cols, 1.57", 1/6 between; A - 6 cols, 1.57", 1/6 between; C - 9 cols, 1.037, 1/12 between.Equipment & Software: Hardware — APP/Mac; Presses — HI; Software — QPS/QuarkXPress, Adobe/Photoshop.
Delivery Method: Mail, Newsstand, Carrier, Racks
Areas Served: 55110, 55115, 55090, 55082

WINDOM

COTTONWOOD COUNTY CITIZEN (WED)
260 10th St, Windom, MN, 56101-1411, Cottonwood, USA; gen tel (507) 831-3455; gen fax (507) 831-3740; disp adv e-mail jenw@windomnews.com; class adv e-mail terriw@windomnews.com; ed e-mail rahnl@windomnews.com; web site www.windomnews.com
Circulation: 2,579pd, 188fr; Sworn/Estimate/Non-Audited
Advertising rate: Open inch rate $10.70
Established: 1883
Pub.......... Trevor Slette
Ed.......... Rahn Larson
Office Mgr.......... Michelle Riihl
Circ. Mgr.......... Teri Scott
Delivery Method: Mail, Newsstand, Racks
Areas Served: Cottonwood County

WINONA

WINONA POST (WED, SUN)
64 E 2nd St, Winona, MN, 55987-3409, Winona, USA; gen tel (507) 452-1262; gen fax (507) 454-6409; disp adv e-mail farkas@winonapost.com; class adv e-mail class@winonapost.com; ed e-mail winpost@winonapost.com; web site www.winonapost.com - 162,885(views) 12,780(visitors)
Circulation: 75pd, 22,024fr; VAC
Advertising rate: Open inch rate $19.80
Established: 1971
VP/Pub.......... Patrick Marek
Ed.......... Sarah Squires
Adv. Mgr.......... Kim Farkas
Class. Adv.......... Twila Lorenz
Circ. Dir.......... Mary Veraguth
Mechanical Specifications: Type page 11.375 x 21 1/2; E - 6 cols, 2, 1/8 between; A - 6 cols, 2, 1/8 between; C - 8 cols, 1 1/2, 1/16 between.Equipment & Software: Hardware — APP/Macs; Presses — HI/V-15A; Software — Adobe/PageMaker, APP/Mac Write, Claris/Works, Multi-Ad/Creator.
Delivery Method: Carrier
Areas Served: 55987,55988,54610,54612,54622, 54625,54629,54630, 54661, 54756, 55910, 55945, 55952, 55959, 55969, 55971, 55972, 55979, 55981,

WINSTED

HERALD JOURNAL (FRI)
120 6th St N, Winsted, MN, 55395-1024, McLeod, USA; gen tel (320) 485-2535; gen fax (320) 485-2878; disp adv e-mail hj@herald-journal.com; class adv e-mail ads@herald-journal.com; ed e-mail news@heraldjournal.com; web site www.herald-journal.com
Circulation: 3,100pd,; USPS
Advertising rate: Open inch rate $7.90
Group: Herald Journal Publishing, Inc.
Gen. Mgr.......... Dale Kovar
Adv. Mgr.......... Chris Schultz
Mechanical Specifications: Type page 6 x 21 1/2; E - 7 cols, 2, 5/24 between; A - 7 cols, 2, 5/24 between; C - 7 cols, 2, 5/24 between.Equipment & Software: Hardware — APP/Mac; Software — InDesign, Adobe/Photoshop.
Delivery Method: Mail, Newsstand

WINTHROP

THE WINTHROP NEWS (WED)
110 N Carver St, Winthrop, MN, 55396-2800, Sibley, USA; gen tel (507) 647-5357; gen fax (507) 647-5358; disp adv e-mail winnews@means.net; ed e-mail winthropnews@gmail.com
Circulation: 1,148pd,; Sworn/Estimate/Non-Audited
Advertising rate: Open inch rate $6.00
Pub.......... Doug Hanson
Ed.......... Michael Mattison

ZUMBROTA

NEWS-RECORD (WED)
225 S Main St, Zumbrota, MN, 55992-1698, Goodhue, USA; gen tel (507) 732-7617; gen fax (507) 732-7619; ed e-mail news@zumbrota.com; web site www.zumbrota.com
Circulation: 3,550pd,; Sworn/Estimate/Non-Audited
Advertising rate: Open inch rate $7.30
Adv. Mgr.......... Peter K. Grimsrud
Ed.......... Matthew Grimsrud
Delivery Method: Mail

MISSISSIPPI

ACKERMAN

THE CHOCTAW PLAINDEALER (WED)
48 N LOUISVILLE ST, Ackerman, MS, 39735, Choctaw, USA; gen tel (662) 285-6248; gen fax (662) 285-6695; disp adv e-mail ads@websterprogresstimes.com; ed e-mail newsroom@winstoncountyjournal.com; web site www.choctawplaindealer.com
Circulation: 1,200pd, 100fr; Sworn/Estimate/Non-Audited
Advertising rate: Open inch rate $3.50
Group: Emmerich Newspapers, Inc.
Circ. .... Chasatie Fisher
Circ. Mgr.......... Brenda Perry
Ed.......... Joseph McCain
Mechanical Specifications: Type page 13 x 21 1/2.

AMORY

MONROE COUNTY JOURNAL (WED)
115 Main St S, Amory, MS, 38821-3407, Monroe, USA; gen tel (662) 256-5647; gen fax (662) 256-5701; disp adv e-mail advertising@monroecountyjournal.com; class adv e-mail advertising@monroecountyjournal.com; ed e-mail news1@monroecountyjournal.com; web site http://djournal.com/monroe/
Circulation: 7,300pd, 132fr; Sworn/Estimate/Non-Audited
Advertising rate: Open inch rate $5.90
Group: Journal Publishing Company
Ed.......... Chris Wilson
Mechanical Specifications: Type page 13 1/2 x 21 1/2; E - 6 cols, 2 1/4, 1/8 between; A - 6 cols, 2 1/4, 1/8 between; C - 8 cols, 1 7/8, 1/8 between.Equipment & Software: Hardware — APP/Mac, APP/Mac G3, APP/Mac G4, 7200/HP5000N Printer; Software — QPS/QuarkXPress 4.1, Adobe/Photoshop 5.5.

BALDWYN

BALDWYN NEWS (THUR)
102 W Main St, Baldwyn, MS, 38824-1814, Prentiss, USA; gen tel (662) 365-3232; gen fax (662) 365-7989; disp adv e-mail thebaldwynnews@dixie-net.com; ed e-mail thebaldwynnews@dixie-net.com; web site https://www.facebook.com/The-Baldwyn-News-101395283376480/?ref=page_internal
Circulation: 2,500pd, 20fr; Sworn/Estimate/Non-Audited
Advertising rate: Open inch rate $5.50
Mng. Ed.......... Tammy Bullock
Mechanical Specifications: Type page 13 x 21 1/2; E - 6 cols, 2 1/16, 1/6 between; A - 6 cols, 2 1/16, 1/6 between; C - 8 cols, 1 1/2, 1/6 between.Equipment & Software: Hardware — APP/Mac; Software — QPS/QuarkXPress 3.32.

BATESVILLE

THE PANOLIAN (TUES, WED, FRI)
363 Highway 51 N, Batesville, MS, 38606-2311, Panola, USA; gen tel (662) 563-4591; gen fax (662) 563-5610; disp adv e-mail advertising@panolian.com; class adv e-mail classifieds@panolian.com; ed e-mail newsroom@panolian.com; web site www.panolian.com - 9,633(views) 2,519(visitors)
Circulation: 5,650pd, 5,500fr; Sworn/Estimate/Non-Audited
Advertising rate: Open inch rate $8.00
Established: 1882
Pub.......... John Howell
Mng. Ed.......... Rupert Howell
News Ed.......... Rita W. Howell
Sports Ed.......... Myra Bean
Advt Mgr, Graphic Designer ... Margaret Buntin
Mechanical Specifications: Type page 11 1/2 x 21 1/4; E - 6 cols, 1 3/4, 1/6 between; A - 6 cols, 1 3/4, 1/6 between; C - 9 cols, 1 3/16, 1/6 between.Equipment & Software: Hardware — APP/Mac; Software — QPS/QuarkXPress 4.1.
Delivery Method: Mail, Newsstand, Racks
Areas Served: 38606, 38658, 38666, 38620, 38619, 38621

BAY SAINT LOUIS

SEA COAST ECHO (WED, SAT)
124 Court St, Bay Saint Louis, MS, 39520-4516, Hancock, USA; gen tel (228) 467-5473; adv tel (228) 467-5474; gen fax (228) 467-0333; adv fax (228) 467-0333; disp adv e-mail gbelcher@seacoastecho.com; class adv e-mail classifieds@seacoastecho.com; ed e-mail rponder@seacoastecho.com; web site www.seacoastecho.com - 350,000(views) 80,000(visitors)
Circulation: 6,100pd,; Sworn/Estimate/Non-Audited
Advertising rate: Open Inch Rate $23.00
Established: 1892
Group: Lancaster Management, Inc.
Digital Platform - Mobile: Apple
Digital Platform - Tablet: Apple iOS
Pub./Ed.......... James Randy Ponder
News Ed.......... Geoff Belcher
Mechanical Specifications: Type page 10 x 21 1/2; E - 6 cols, 1.7between; A - 6 cols, 2 1/16, between; C - 6 cols, 2 1/16, between. Equipment & Software: ; Presses — KP/News King.
Delivery Method: Mail, Newsstand, Carrier, Racks
Areas Served: Hancock/Harrison

BAY SPRINGS

THE JASPER COUNTY NEWS (WED)
3362 HIGHWAY 15, Bay Springs, MS, 39422-5181, USA; gen tel (601) 764-3104; ed tel (601) 764-9776; gen fax (601) 764-3106; disp adv e-mail bni@teleclipse.net; ed e-mail news@jaspercountynews.net
Circulation: 2,772pd, 110fr; Sworn/Estimate/Non-Audited
Advertising rate: Open inch rate $6.50
Pub.......... Ronnie L. Buckley
Sales Rep.......... Kristie Scott
Circ. Mgr.......... Ellen Paul
Ed.......... Anna King
Prodn. Mgr.......... Missy Clark
Mechanical Specifications: Type page 12 1/2 x 21 1/2.

BELZONI

THE BELZONI BANNER (WED)
115 E Jackson St, Belzoni, MS, 39038-3641, Humphreys, USA; gen tel (662) 247-3373; gen fax (662) 247-3372; disp adv e-mail editor@thebelzonibanner.com; class adv e-mail editor@thebelzonibanner.com; ed e-mail editor@thebelzonibanner.com; web site www.thebelzonibanner.com
Circulation: 1,100pd, 50fr; USPS
Advertising rate: Open inch rate $6.00
Established: 1914
Ed.......... Julian Toney
Mechanical Specifications: Broadsheet-11" x 21.5"Equipment & Software: ; Software — Adobe/InDesign CS5, Adobe/Photoshop CS2, Microsoft/Word.
Delivery Method: Mail, Newsstand, Carrier

BILOXI

BILOXI-D'IBERVILLE PRESS (THUR)
819 Jackson St, Biloxi, MS, 39530-4235, Harrison, USA; gen tel (228) 435-0720; gen fax (228) 436-7737; disp adv e-mail ads@biloxi-diberville-press.com; class adv e-mail legal@biloxi-diberville-press.com; ed e-mail news@biloxi-diberville-press.com; web site www.biloxi-diberville-press.com
Circulation: 4,000pd, 1,000fr; Sworn/Estimate/Non-Audited
Advertising rate: Open inch rate $10.00
Established: 1973
Group: Bay Corporation, Inc.
Production Mgr.......... Vicki Fox
Pub.......... Cindy Picard

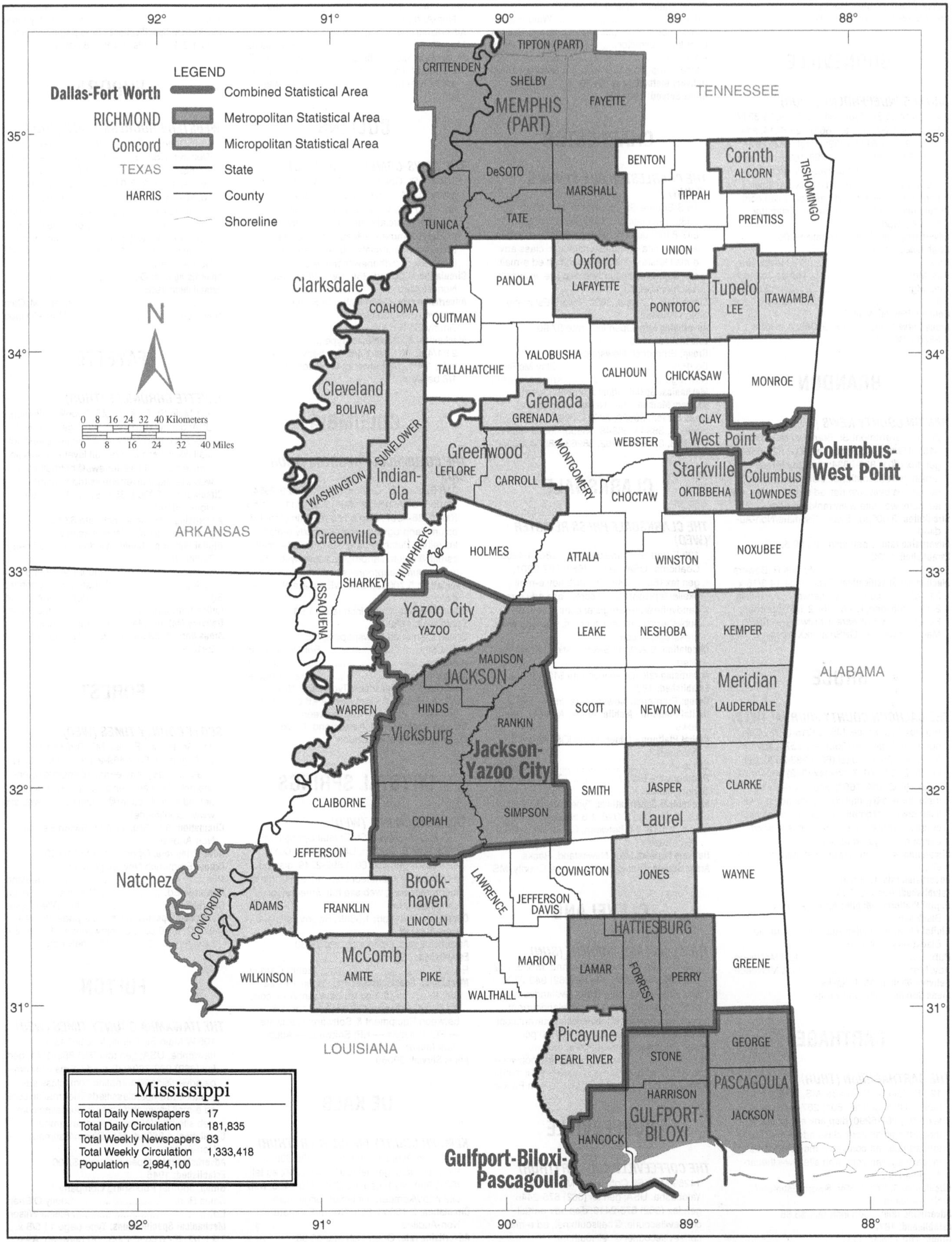
LEGEND
Dallas-Fort Worth Combined Statistical Area
RICHMOND Metropolitan Statistical Area
Concord Micropolitan Statistical Area
TEXAS State
HARRIS County
Shoreline
N
0 8 16 24 32 40 Kilometers
0 8 16 24 32 40 Miles
92°
91°
90°
89°
88°
35°
34°
33°
32°
31°
TENNESSEE
ARKANSAS
ALABAMA
LOUISIANA
TIPTON (PART)
CRITTENDEN
SHELBY
MEMPHIS (PART)
FAYETTE
DeSOTO
MARSHALL
BENTON
TIPPAH
Corinth
ALCORN
TISHOMINGO
TUNICA
TATE
PRENTISS
UNION
Oxford
LAFAYETTE
PANOLA
Clarksdale
COAHOMA
QUITMAN
Tupelo
LEE
ITAWAMBA
PONTOTOC
TALLAHATCHIE
YALOBUSHA
CALHOUN
CHICKASAW
MONROE
Cleveland
BOLIVAR
Grenada
GRENADA
CLAY
West Point
Columbus-West Point
SUNFLOWER
Greenwood
LEFLORE
Indian-ola
WASHINGTON
CARROLL
MONTGOMERY
WEBSTER
Starkville
OKTIBBEHA
Columbus
LOWNDES
CHOCTAW
Greenville
HUMPHREYS
HOLMES
ATTALA
WINSTON
NOXUBEE
SHARKEY
ISSAQUENA
Yazoo City
YAZOO
MADISON
JACKSON
LEAKE
NESHOBA
KEMPER
Meridian
LAUDERDALE
WARREN
HINDS
Vicksburg
RANKIN
SCOTT
NEWTON
Jackson-Yazoo City
SMITH
JASPER
CLARKE
Laurel
CLAIBORNE
COPIAH
SIMPSON
JEFFERSON
COVINGTON
JONES
WAYNE
Natchez
CONCORDIA
ADAMS
FRANKLIN
Brook-haven
LINCOLN
LAWRENCE
JEFFERSON DAVIS
HATTIESBURG
McComb
AMITE
PIKE
WILKINSON
MARION
LAMAR
FORREST
PERRY
GREENE
WALTHALL
Picayune
PEARL RIVER
STONE
GEORGE
HARRISON
GULFPORT-BILOXI
PASCAGOULA
JACKSON
HANCOCK
Gulfport-Biloxi-Pascagoula
Mississippi
Total Daily Newspapers 17
Total Daily Circulation 181,835
Total Weekly Newspapers 83
Total Weekly Circulation 1,333,418
Population 2,984,100

Delivery Method: Mail, Racks
Areas Served: Biloxi D'Iberville/Harrison

BOONEVILLE

BANNER INDEPENDENT (THUR)

208 N Main St, Booneville, MS, 38829-3317, Prentiss, USA; gen tel (662) 728-6214; adv tel (662) 287-6111 x339; ed tel (662) 287-6111 340; gen fax (662) 728-1636; disp adv e-mail admanager@dailycorinthian.com; class adv e-mail classad@dailycorinthian.com; ed e-mail editor@dailycorinthian.com
Circulation: 4,400pd, 35fr; Sworn/Estimate/Non-Audited
Advertising rate: Open inch rate $8.00
Established: 1898
Pub. .... Reese Terry
Adv. Mgr. .... Renee Johnson
Circ. Mgr. .... Chris Enderle
Ed. .... Kenny Goode
Delivery Method: Mail, Racks
Areas Served: 38832, 38829, 38834, 38856, 38865, 38873

BRANDON

RANKIN COUNTY NEWS (WED)

207 E Government St, Brandon, MS, 39042-3151, Rankin, USA; gen tel (601) 825-8333; gen fax (601) 825-8334; disp adv e-mail rankincn@bellsouth.net; class adv e-mail rankincn@bellsouth.net; ed e-mail rankincn@aol.com; web site www.rankincn.com
Circulation: 8,000pd,; Sworn/Estimate/Non-Audited
Advertising rate: Open inch rate $9.50
Established: 1852
Ed. .... Marcus R. Bowers
Mechanical Specifications: Type page 14 3/16 x 21 1/2; E - 6 cols, 2 1/6, between; A - 6 cols, 2 1/6, between; C - 6 cols, 2 1/6, between. Equipment & Software: Hardware — APP/Mac; Software — QPS/QuarkXPress 4.0.

BRUCE

THE CALHOUN COUNTY JOURNAL (WED)

PO Box 278, Bruce, MS, 38915-0278, Calhoun, USA; gen tel (662) 983-2570; adv tel (662) 983-2570; ed tel (662) 983-2570; gen fax (662) 983-7667; adv fax (662) 983-7667; ed fax (662) 983-7667; disp adv e-mail joelmcneece@gmail.com; class adv e-mail lisamcneece@gmail.com; ed e-mail calhouncountyjournal@gmail.com; web site www.calhouncountyjournal.com
Circulation: 4,700pd,; Sworn/Estimate/Non-Audited
Advertising rate: Open inch rate $5.78
Established: August 1953
Digital Platform - Mobile: Apple, Android, Blackberry
Digital Platform - Tablet: Apple iOS, Android, Blackberry Tablet OS
Pub. .... Joel McNeece
Adv. Mgr. .... Lisa McNeece
Delivery Method: Mail, Racks
Areas Served: Calhoun County

CARTHAGE

THE CARTHAGINIAN (THUR)

123 E Main St, Carthage, MS, 39051-4102, Leake, USA; gen tel (601) 267-4501; gen fax (601) 267-5290; disp adv e-mail ads@thecarthaginian.com; class adv e-mail ads@thecarthaginian.com; ed e-mail brendah@thecarthaginian.com; web site www.thecarthaginian.com
Circulation: 5,700pd, 59fr; Sworn/Estimate/Non-Audited
Advertising rate: Open inch rate $8.65
Established: 1872
Group: The 'Ginian, LLC
Digital Platform - Tablet: Apple iOS
Ed./Pub. .... Waid Prather
News-sports .... Jacob Grimes
Circulation Director .... Moore Jimmy
Ad director .... Bobby Latham
Office manager .... Brenda Howell
Delivery Method: Mail, Racks
Areas Served: 39051

CHARLESTON

THE CHARLESTON SUN-SENTINEL (THUR)

16 S Square St, Charleston, MS, 38921-2335, Tallahatchie, USA; gen tel (662) 647-8462; gen fax (662) 647-3830; disp adv e-mail krista@charlestonsun.net; class adv e-mail krista@charlestonsun.net; ed e-mail clay@charlestonsun.net; web site www.tallahatchienews.ms
Circulation: 1,746pd, 100fr; Sworn/Estimate/Non-Audited
Advertising rate: Open inch rate $7.90
Established: 1856
Group: Emmerich Newspapers, Inc.
Ed./Pub. .... Clay McFerrin
Adv. Mgr. .... Krista McFerrin
Mechanical Specifications: Berliner format
Delivery Method: Mail, Newsstand, Racks
Areas Served: 38920, 38921, 38927, 38928, 38940, 38945, 38948, 38950, 38953, 38957, 38958, 38961, 38962, 38963, 38964, 38966

CLARKSDALE

THE CLARKSDALE PRESS REGISTER (WED)

128 E 2nd St, Clarksdale, MS, 38614-4206, Coahoma, USA; gen tel (662) 627-2201; gen fax (662) 624-5125; disp adv e-mail bkeller@pressregister.com; class adv e-mail sandyhite@pressregister.com; ed e-mail publisher@pressregister.com; web site www.pressregister.com
Circulation: 5,200pd,; Sworn/Estimate/Non-Audited
Advertising rate: Open inch rate $12.60
Established: 1826
Group: Emmerich Newspapers, Inc.
Digital Platform - Mobile: Apple, Android, Windows
Digital Platform - Tablet: Apple iOS, Android, Windows 7
Office Mgr. .... Sandy Hite
Photography Ed. .... Troy Catchings
Taylor Mitchell
Mechanical Specifications: Type page 13 x 21 1/2; E - 6 cols, 2 1/16, 1/8 between; A - 6 cols, 2 1/16, 1/8 between; C - 8 cols, 1 1/2, 1/8 between.
Delivery Method: Mail, Newsstand, Racks
Areas Served: Clarksdale/Coahoma County, MS

CLEVELAND

THE CLEVELAND CURRENT (SUN)

125 S Court St, Ste 1, Cleveland, MS, 38732-2635, Bolivar, USA; gen tel (662) 843-2700; disp adv e-mail kristy@theclevelandcurrent.com; ed e-mail pam@theclevelandcurrent.com; web site www.theclevelandcurrent.com
Advertising rate: Open inch rate $7.00 pci
Group: Coopwood Newspapers, Inc
Pub. .... Scott Coopwood
Ads .... Kristy Kitchings
Managing Ed. .... Pam Parker

COFFEEVILLE

THE COFFEEVILLE COURIER (THUR)

14259 Main St, Coffeeville, MS, 38922-2596, Yalobusha, USA; gen tel (662) 675-2446; gen fax (662) 675-2416; disp adv e-mail coffeevillecourier@bellsouth.net; ed e-mail coffeevillecourier@bellsouth.net
Circulation: 2,100pd, 50fr; Sworn/Estimate/Non-Audited
Advertising rate: Open inch rate $3.50
Mng. Ed. .... Sarah H. Williams
Mechanical Specifications: Type page 10 x 13; E - 6 cols, 1 1/2, 1/6 between; A - 6 cols, 1 1/2, 1/6 between; C - 6 cols, 1 1/2, 1/6 between.

COLLINS

THE NEWS-COMMERCIAL (WED)

104 1st St, Collins, MS, 39428-4140, Covington, USA; gen tel (601) 765-8275; gen fax (601) 765-6952; disp adv e-mail thenewscommercial@att.net; class adv e-mail thenewscommercial@att.net; ed e-mail thenewscommercial@att.net; web site www.facebook.com/thenewscommercial
Circulation: 4,200pd, 35fr; Sworn/Estimate/Non-Audited
Advertising rate: Open inch rate $6.00
Analyn Arrington-Goff
Jimmy GoffEd.s
Mechanical Specifications: Type page 11 3/5 x 21 1/4; E -6 cols, 1 4/5, 1/8 between; A - 6 cols, 1 4/5, 1/8 between; C - 6 cols, 1 4/5, 1/8 between.

COLUMBIA

THE COLUMBIAN-PROGRESS (THUR, SAT)

318 Second St, Columbia, MS, 39429-2954, Marion, USA; gen tel (601) 736-2611; gen fax (601) 736-4507; disp adv e-mail kimgingell@columbianprogress.com; class adv e-mail lmizell@columbianprogress.com; ed e-mail csmith@columbianprogress.com; web site www.columbianprogress.com
Circulation: 5,700pd,; Sworn/Estimate/Non-Audited
Advertising rate: Open inch rate 11.50
Established: 1882
Group: Emmerich Newspapers, Inc.
Office Mgr. .... Bonnie Hudson
Adv. Mgr. .... Kim Gingell
Managing Ed. .... Mark Rogers
Mechanical Specifications: Type page 13 x 21 1/2; E - 6 cols, 2, between; A - 6 cols, 2, between; C - 8 cols, 1 1/2, between.
Delivery Method: Mail, Newsstand, Racks
Areas Served: Marion County

CRYSTAL SPRINGS

THE METEOR INC. (WED)

201 E Georgetown St, Crystal Springs, MS, 39059-2516, Copiah, USA; gen tel (601) 892-2581; gen fax (601) 892-2249; disp adv e-mail info@themeteor.com; ed e-mail info@themeteor.com; web site http://themeteor.com/index.html
Circulation: 3,615pd, 1,385fr; Sworn/Estimate/Non-Audited
Advertising rate: Open inch rate $6.30
Established: 1881
Ed. .... Henry Carney
Mechanical Specifications: Type page 15 x 22 3/4; E - 6 cols, 2 1/6, 1/6 between; A - 6 cols, 2 1/6, 1/6 between; C - 6 cols, 2 1/6, 1/6 between. Equipment & Software: Hardware — PC; Presses — KP; Software — Adobe/PageMaker.
Areas Served: 39059

DE KALB

KEMPER COUNTY MESSENGER (THUR)

102 Main Ave, De Kalb, MS, 39328-6381, Kemper, USA; gen tel (601) 743-5760; ed tel (601) 938-2471; gen fax (601) 743-4430; web site http://kempercountymessenger.com/
Circulation: 2,100pd, 85fr; Sworn/Estimate/Non-Audited
Advertising rate: Open inch rate $5.00
Pub. .... Jim Prince
Ed. .... Carver Rayburen
Mechanical Specifications: Type page 11 5/8 x 21 1/2; E - 6 cols, 1 1/8, 1/8 between.

EUPORA

WEBSTER PROGRESS-TIMES (THUR)

58 N Dunn St, Eupora, MS, 39744-2631, Webster, USA; gen tel (662) 773-6241; adv tel (662) 258-7532; ed tel (662) 258-3109; gen fax (662) 258-6474; disp adv e-mail ads@websterprogresstimes.com; class adv e-mail ads@websterprogresstimes.com; ed e-mail news@websterprogresstimes.com; web site www.websterprogresstimes.com
Circulation: 2,500pd, 6,500fr; Sworn/Estimate/Non-Audited
Advertising rate: Open inch rate $6.25
Established: 1968
Pub. .... Joseph McCain
News Ed. .... Russell Hood

FAYETTE

FAYETTE CHRONICLE (THUR)

501 Main St, Fayette, MS, 39069, Jefferson, USA; gen tel (601) 786-3661; gen fax (601) 786-3661; disp adv e-mail fayettenews@hotmail.com; class adv e-mail fayette1866@aol.com; ed e-mail fayettenews@hotmail.com; web site http://fayettenews.tripod.com/
Circulation: 2,500pd, 35fr; Sworn/Estimate/Non-Audited
Advertising rate: Open inch rate $7.00
Digital Platform - Mobile: Blackberry
Digital Platform - Tablet: Windows 7, Blackberry Tablet OS
Adv. Mgr. .... Tenodra M. Shepphard
Circ. Mgr. .... Ashanta A. Shepphard
Ed. .... Charles K. Shepphard
Office Manager .... Joe Turner
Delivery Method: Mail, Newsstand, Racks
Areas Served: 39069-39096-39120-39150-39180-

FOREST

SCOTT COUNTY TIMES (WED)

311 Smith Ave, Forest, MS, 39074-4159, USA; gen tel (601) 469-2561; gen fax (601) 469-2004; disp adv e-mail blatham@sctonline.net; class adv e-mail charrell@sctonline.net; ed e-mail cbaker@sctonline.net; web site www.sctonline.net
Circulation: 5,500pd, 4,000fr; Sworn/Estimate/Non-Audited
Advertising rate: Open inch rate $10.00
Group: Emmerich Newspapers, Inc.
Pub. .... Tim Beeland
Features Ed. .... Courtney Robinson
Sports Ed. .... Chris Allen Baker
Mechanical Specifications: Type page 13 1/4 x 21 1/2; E - 6 cols, 2, between; A - 6 cols, 2, between; C - 8 cols, 1 1/2, between.

FULTON

THE ITAWAMBA COUNTY TIMES (WED)

106 W Main St, Fulton, MS, 38843-1146, Itawamba, USA; gen tel (662) 862-3141; gen fax (662) 862-7804; disp adv e-mail itawamba.advertising@journalinc.com; class adv e-mail itawamba.classifieds@journalinc.com; ed e-mail itawamba.times@journalinc.com; web site http://djournal.com/itawamba/
Circulation: 4,850pd, 45fr; Sworn/Estimate/Non-Audited
Advertising rate: Open inch rate $7.00
Established: 1945
Group: Journal Publishing Company
Sales Rep. .... Shelly O'Brien
Ed. .... Alisha Wilson
Mechanical Specifications: Type page 11 5/8 x 21 1/2; E - 6 cols, 1 2/3, 1/6 between; A - 6

cols, 1 2/3, 1/6 between; C - 9 cols, 1 1/6, 1/6 between.Equipment & Software: Hardware — APP/Mac; Software — QPS/QuarkXPress.
Areas Served: 38843, 38855, 38876, 38847, 38858

GLOSTER

WILK-AMITE RECORD (FRI)

243 E Main St, Gloster, MS, 39638-9009, Amite, USA; gen tel (601) 225-9200; gen fax (601) 225-4531; disp adv e-mail wilkamiterecord@yahoo.com; class adv e-mail wilkamiterecord@yahoo.com; ed e-mail info@wilkamiterecord.com; web site http://www.wilkamiterecord.com/
Circulation: 2,400pd, 10fr; Sworn/Estimate/Non-Audited
Advertising rate: Open inch rate $6.00
Established: 1892
Ed. ....Bettty N. Stevens
Mechanical Specifications: Type page 15 x 21; E - 7 cols, 1 3/4, 1/6 between; A - 7 cols, 1 3/4, 1/6 between; C - 7 cols, 1 3/4, 1/6 between. Equipment & Software: Hardware — APP/Mac; Presses — KP; Software — QPS/QuarkXPress.

GRENADA

GRENADA STAR (TUES, FRI)

50 Corporate Row, Grenada, MS, 38901-2823, Grenada, USA; gen tel (662) 226-4321; gen fax (662) 226-8310; disp adv e-mail Sales1@GrenadaStar.com; class adv e-mail Classifieds@GrenadaStar.com; ed e-mail Editor@GrenadaStar.com; web site www.grenadastar.com
Circulation: 5,776pd,; Sworn/Estimate/Non-Audited
Advertising rate: Open inch rate $10.40
Established: 1854
Digital Platform - Mobile: Apple, Android
Digital Platform - Tablet: Apple iOS, Android
Gen. Mgr. .... Fred Adams
Pub./Ed. .... Joseph B. Lee
Sec./Treasurer .... Brenda R. Lee
Adv. Sales.....................................Anita Turner
Circ. Dir. .... Stephanie Dees
Managing Ed.......................... Nannette Lascer
Sports Ed.............................. Chuck Hathcock
Creative Servs. Mgr. ....Musset McPhail
Mechanical Specifications: Type page 13 x 21 1/2; E - 6 cols, 2 1/16, 1/8 between; A - 6 cols, 2 1/16, 1/8 between; C - 6 cols, 2 1/16, 1/8 between.
Delivery Method: Mail, Carrier
Areas Served: 38901; 38902; 38920; 38925; 38926; 38929; 38940; 38953; 38960; 38961

HATTIESBURG

HATTIESBURG AMERICAN (WED, FRI, SUN)

4200 Mamie St, Ste 200, Hattiesburg, MS, 39402-1729, Forrest, Lamar, USA; gen tel (601) 582-4321; adv tel (601) 582-4321; ed tel (601)584-3070; gen fax (601) 584-3075; adv fax (601)584-3074; ed fax (601) 584-3130; disp adv e-mail tfowler@hattiesburgamerican.com; class adv e-mail tfowler@hattiesburgamerican.com; ed e-mail tfowler@hattiesburgamerican.com; web site www.hattiesburgamerican.com 248,190(visitors)
Circulation: 6,886pd, 106fr; AAM
Advertising rate: Open inch rate $180.35 (Mon-Fri); $180.35 (Sat)
Established: 1897
Group: Gannett
Digital Platform - Mobile: Apple, Android, Windows, Blackberry
Digital Platform - Tablet: Apple iOS, Android, Windows 7, Blackberry Tablet OS, Kindle, Nook, Kindle Fire
News Dir. ....Erin Kosnac
Engagement Ed. .... Lici Beveridge
Mgr., Bus. Systems.................... Sherri McCain
Circ. Mgr. .... deborah Tarwater
Sports Producer .... Ben Sutton
Mechanical Specifications: Type page 13 x 21 1/2; E - 6 cols, 2 1/16, 1/8 between; A - 6 cols, 2 1/16, 1/8 between; C - 9 cols, 1 5/16, 1/8 between.
Delivery Method: Mail, Newsstand, Carrier, Racks
Areas Served: 39401, 39402, 39465, 39455, 39474

THE LAMAR TIMES (THUR)

103 N 40th Ave, Hattiesburg, MS, 39401-6606, Forrest, USA; gen tel (601) 268-2331; gen fax (601) 268-2965; disp adv e-mail kristen@hubcityspokes.com; class adv e-mail missy@hubcityspokes.com; ed e-mail beth@hubcityspokes.com; web site hubcityspokes.com/lamar-times
Circulation: 5,000pd,; Sworn/Estimate/Non-Audited
Advertising rate: Open inch rate $17.00
Group: Hattiesburg Publishing, Inc.
Mng. Ed... Beth Bunch
Adv. Mgr. .... Samantha Mlot
Ed./Pub. .... David Gustafson
Art Dir..Emily Hall
Delivery Method: Mail, Newsstand, Racks
Areas Served: Lamar County, Mississippi including communities of Hattiesburg, Oak Grove, Purvis, Sumrall, and Lumberton.

THE HATTIESBURG POST (THUR)

103 N 40th Ave, Hattiesburg, MS, 39401-6606, Forrest, USA; gen tel (601) 268-2331; gen fax (601) 268-2965; disp adv e-mail kristen@hubcityspokes.com; web site www.hubcityspokes.com
Circulation: 9,000pd,; Sworn/Estimate/Non-Audited
Advertising rate: $17
Established: 2013
Group: Emmerich Newspapers, Inc.
Ed./Pub. .... David Gustafson
Mng Ed. .... Beth Bunch
Adv. Mgr. ....Kristen Brock
Areas Served: Hattiesburg

THE PETAL NEWS (THUR)

103 N 40th Ave, Hattiesburg, MS, 39401-6606, Forrest, USA; gen tel (601) 268-2331; gen fax (601) 268-2965; disp adv e-mail kristen@HubCitySPOKES.com; class adv e-mail missyHubCitySPOKES.com; ed e-mail beth@hubcityspokes.com; web site hubcityspokes.com
Circulation: 3,000pd,; Sworn/Estimate/Non-Audited
Advertising rate: Open inch rate $7.00
Group: Emmerich Newspapers, Inc.
Editor/Publisher .... David Gustafson
Adv. Mgr. ....Kristen Brock
Mng. Ed... Beth Bunch
Delivery Method: Mail, Newsstand, Racks
Areas Served: Petal, Mississippi

HAZLEHURST

COPIAH COUNTY COURIER (WED)

103 S Ragsdale Ave, Hazlehurst, MS, 39083-3037, Copiah, USA; gen tel (601) 894-3141; gen fax (601) 894-3144; disp adv e-mail copiahcc@bellsouth.net; class adv e-mail copiahcc@bellsouth.net; ed e-mail news@copiahcountycourier.com; web site www.copiahcountycourier.com
Circulation: 4,400pd, 1,600fr; Sworn/Estimate/Non-Audited
Advertising rate: Open inch rate $8.25
Established: 1874
Digital Platform - Mobile: Apple, Android, Blackberry
Digital Platform - Tablet: Apple iOS, Android, Windows 7, Blackberry Tablet OS, Kindle, Nook, Kindle Fire
Publisher, Marketing Director, Account Rep Editor, Sports Director ....Joe Coates
Mechanical Specifications: 6 columns, 10.8333 x 21Equipment & Software: Hardware — APP/Mac; Presses — KP/News King; Software — QPS/QuarkXPress.
Delivery Method: Mail, Newsstand, Racks

HERNANDO

DESOTO TIMES-TRIBUNE (TUES, THUR, SAT)

2445 Highway 51 S, Hernando, MS, 38632-1734, DeSoto, USA; gen tel (662) 429-6397; adv tel (662) 429-6397 ext. 227; ed tel (662) 429-6397 ext. 247; gen fax (662) 429-5229; adv fax (662) 429-5229; ed fax (662) 429-5229; disp adv e-mail lyla@dttclick.com; class adv e-mail classifieds@desototimestribune.com; ed e-mail editor@desototimestribune.com; web site www.desototimes.com
Circulation: 7,810pd,; Sworn/Estimate/Non-Audited
Advertising rate: Open inch rate $11.35
Established: 1839
Digital Platform - Mobile: Apple, Android, Windows
Digital Platform - Tablet: Apple iOS, Android, Windows 7
News Ed. ....Terri Smith
Dir. of Marketing & Adv. ....Angie Pittman
Mechanical Specifications: Type page 13 x 21; E - 6 cols, 2 3/100, 1/6 between; A - 6 cols, 2 3/100, 1/6 between; C - 8 cols, 1 1/2, 1/6 between.
Delivery Method: Mail, Carrier, Racks

HOLLY SPRINGS

SOUTH REPORTER (THUR)

157 S Center St, Holly Springs, MS, 38635-3040, Marshall, USA; gen tel (662) 252-4261; gen fax (662) 252-3388; disp adv e-mail southreporter@dixie-net.com; class adv e-mail southreporter@dixie-net.com; ed e-mail southreporter@dixie-net.com; web site www.southreporter.com
Circulation: 5,200pd, 52fr; Sworn/Estimate/Non-Audited
Advertising rate: Open inch rate $5.80
Established: 1865
Ed. .... Barry Burleson
Prodn. Mgr. .... Barbara Taylor
Mechanical Specifications: Type page 13 x 21; E - 6 cols, 2, 1/8 between; A - 6 cols, 2, 1/8 between; C - 8 cols, 1 1/2, 1/8 between. Equipment & Software: Hardware — APP/Mac G3; Software — Adobe/Photoshop, QPS/QuarkXPress 4.0.

HOUSTON

CHICKASAW JOURNAL (WED)

225 E Madison St, Houston, MS, 38851-2320, Chickasaw, USA; gen tel (662) 456-3771; gen fax (662) 456-5202; disp adv e-mail charlotte.wolfe@journalinc.com; ed e-mail news@chickasaw360.com; web site www.chickasawjournal.com
Circulation: 2,000pd, 10,500fr; Sworn/Estimate/Non-Audited
Advertising rate: Open inch rate $8.50
Group: Journal Publishing Company
Pub..Lisa Boyles

INDIANOLA

THE ENTERPRISE-TOCSIN (THUR)

114 Main St, Indianola, MS, 38751-2844, Sunflower, USA; gen tel (662) 887-2222; gen fax (662) 887-2999; disp adv e-mail advertising@enterprise-tocsin.com; ed e-mail news@enterprise-tocsin.com; web site enterprise-tocsin.com
Circulation: 4,000pd, 50fr; Sworn/Estimate/Non-Audited
Advertising rate: Open inch rate $9.15
Established: 1888
Group: Emmerich Newspapers, Inc.
Editor/Publisher .... Charlie Smith
Adv. Mgr. .... Mary Gray
Mechanical Specifications: Type page 10 x 16 1/2; E - 6 cols, between; C - 6 cols, between.Equipment & Software: Hardware — Mac computers; Software — Quark Xpress 9 for page layout
Delivery Method: Mail, Newsstand, Racks
Areas Served: Sunflower County, northern Humphreys County

IUKA

TISHOMINGO COUNTY NEWS (THUR)

PO Box 70, Iuka, MS, 38852-0070, Tishomingo, USA; gen tel (662) 423-2211; gen fax (662) 423-2214; disp adv e-mail tcnews@bellsouth.net; class adv e-mail tcnews@bellsouth.net; ed e-mail tcnews@bellsouth.net; web site www.facebook.com/pages/The-Tishomingo-County-NewsThe-Vidette
Circulation: 6,000pd, 100fr; Sworn/Estimate/Non-Audited
Advertising rate: Open inch rate $4.00
Established: 1877
Pub...John H. Biggs
Ed. ....Charlotte McVay

JACKSON

MISSISSIPPI BUSINESS JOURNAL (FRI)

200 N Congress St Ste 400, Suite 400, Jackson, MS, 39201-1902, Hinds, USA; gen tel (601) 364-1011; adv tel (601) 364-1011; ed tel (601) 364-1018; gen fax (601) 364-1007; ed fax (601) 364-1035; disp adv e-mail tami.jones@msbusiness.com; class adv e-mail tami.jones@msbusiness.com; ed e-mail ross.reily@msbusiness.com; web site msbusiness.com
Circulation: 3,941pd, 174fr; VAC
Established: 1978
Group: Journal Inc.Alan Turner
Editor ....Ross Reily
Associate Publisher........................Tami Jones
Prod Mgr.....................................Tacy Rayburn
Circ. Mng............................... Charins Rhodes
Delivery Method: Mail, Newsstand
Areas Served: State of Mississippi

NORTHSIDE SUN (THUR)

246 Briarwood Dr, Jackson, MS, 39206-3027, Hinds, USA; gen tel (601) 957-1122; adv tel (601) 977-8181; ed tel (601) 957-1123; gen fax (601) 957-1533; disp adv e-mail jennifer@northsidesun.com; class adv e-mail lauren@northsidesun.com; ed e-mail jimmye@northsidesun.com; web site www.northsidesun.com
Circulation: 11,144pd, 548fr; Sworn/Estimate/Non-Audited
Advertising rate: Open inch rate $18.30
Group: Emmerich Newspapers, Inc.
Pub./Adv. Mgr...................... J. Wyatt Emmerich
Ed. ....Jimmye Sweat
Circ. Mgr... Dani Poe

KOSCIUSKO

THE STAR-HERALD (THUR)

207 N Madison St, Kosciusko, MS, 39090-3626, Attala, USA; gen tel (662) 289-2251; adv tel (662) 289-2251 ; ed tel (662) 289-2251; gen fax (662) 289-2254; disp adv e-mail dcasteel@starherald.net; class adv e-mail dcasteel@starherald.net; ed e-mail kfioretti@starherald.net; web site www.starherald.net
Circulation: 4,800pd, 100fr; Sworn/Estimate/Non-Audited
Advertising rate: Open inch rate $9.75
Established: 1866
Group: Emmerich Newspapers, Inc.
Publisher.......................................Karen Fioretti
Mechanical Specifications: 6 Columns; 11" x 21 1/2"
Delivery Method: Mail, Carrier, Racks
Areas Served: Attala & Holmes Counties (MS)

LAUREL

LAUREL LEADER-CALL (TUES, THUR, SAT)

318 N Magnolia St, Laurel, MS, 39440-3932, Jones, USA; gen tel (601) 649-9388; gen fax (601) 649-9390; disp adv e-mail reporter@leader-call.com; class adv e-mail legals@leader-call.com; ed e-mail murph@leader-call.com; web site www.leader-call.com
Circulation: 7,500pd,; Sworn/Estimate/Non-Audited
Advertising rate: Open inch rate $10.00 (National rate $11.77)
Established: 1911
Group: Community Newspaper Holdings, Inc.
Digital Platform - Mobile: Apple, Android, Windows
Digital Platform - Tablet: Apple iOS, Android, Windows 7
Editor....Mark Thornton
Gen. Mgr....Robin Bice
Managing editor....Sean Murphy
Publisher....Jim Cegielski
Mechanical Specifications: Type page 13 x 21 1/2; E - 6 cols, 2 1/16, 1/8 between; A - 6 cols, 2 1/16, 1/8 between; C - 9 cols, 1 3/8, 1/16 between.
Delivery Method: Mail, Newsstand, Racks
Areas Served: 39443, 39440, 39437, 39168, 39422, 39439, 39441, 39442, 39459, 39464, 39477, 39480, 39481

THE LAUREL CHRONICLE (TUES)

130 Leontyne Price Blvd, Laurel, MS, 39440-4428, USA; gen tel (601) 651-2000; adv tel (601) 651-2006; ed tel (601) 651-2010; gen fax (601) 651-2020; disp adv e-mail mrobinson@thechronicle.ms; ed e-mail jniblett@thechronicle.ms
Established: 2012
Group: Emmerich Newspapers, Inc.
Ed./Pub....Jason Niblett
Sports Ed....Dale McKee
Ad Sales....Marquita Robinson
Ad Sales....Julie Whatley
Office Mgr....Sonya James
Circ. Mgr....Lisa Miller
Areas Served: Laurel, Ellisville, and Jones County

LEAKESVILLE

GREENE COUNTY HERALD (THUR)

431 Main St, Leakesville, MS, 39451-6502, Greene, USA; gen tel (601) 394-5070; gen fax (601) 394-4389; disp adv e-mail advertising_gcherald@tds.net; class adv e-mail advertising_gcherald@tds.net; ed e-mail herald@tds.net; web site www.greenecountyheraldonline.com
Circulation: 3,100pd, 52fr; Sworn/Estimate/Non-Audited
Advertising rate: Open inch rate $5.95
Established: 1898
Group: THE TURNER GROUP LLC
Digital Platform - Mobile: Android, Windows
Ed....Russell Turner
Mechanical Specifications: 11.625 x 21
Delivery Method: Mail, Newsstand, Racks
Areas Served: 39451,39452, 39456, 39461, 39362, 39476

LELAND

LELAND PROGRESS (THUR)

119 E 3rd St, Leland, MS, 38756-2705, Washington, USA; gen tel (662) 771-4012; gen fax (662) 580-4068; disp adv e-mail editor@thelelandprogress.com; class adv e-mail editor@thelelandprogress.com; ed e-mail editor@thelelandprogress.com; web site www.thelelandprogress.com
Circulation: 1,000pd, 50fr; Sworn/Estimate/Non-Audited
Advertising rate: $6.00
Established: 1897
Publisher/Editor....Stephanie Patton
Delivery Method: Mail, Newsstand
Areas Served: 38756, 38701, 38702, 38703, 38704, etc

LEXINGTON

HOLMES COUNTY HERALD (THUR)

308 Court Sq, Lexington, MS, 39095-3636, Holmes, USA; gen tel (662) 834-1151; gen fax (662) 834-1074; disp adv e-mail hcherald@gmail.com; web site www.holmescountyherald.com
Circulation: 2,000pd,; Sworn/Estimate/Non-Audited
Advertising rate: Open inch rate $7.50
Established: 1959
General Manager....Julie Ellison
Editor....Matthew Breazeale
Mechanical Specifications: 10.25 x 16 full page
Delivery Method: Mail, Racks

LIBERTY

THE SOUTHERN HERALD (THUR)

260 Main St, Liberty, MS, 39645, Amite, USA; gen tel (601) 657-4818; gen fax (601) 657-4818; disp adv e-mail southernherald@bellsouth.net; class adv e-mail southernherald@bellsouth.net; ed e-mail southernherald@bellsouth.net; web site https://www.facebook.com/The-Southern-Herald-215266298536196/?ref=page_internal
Circulation: 900pd, 25fr; USPS
Advertising rate: Open inch rate $6.00
Established: 1825
Digital Platform - Mobile: Apple, Windows
Digital Platform - Tablet: Apple iOS, Windows 7, Kindle
Ed./owner....Richard H. StrattonEquipment & Software: Hardware — APP/Mac; Software — QPS/QuarkXPress 4.0.
Delivery Method: Mail, Newsstand

LOUISVILLE

WINSTON COUNTY JOURNAL (WED)

233 N Court Ave, Louisville, MS, 39339-2648, Winston, USA; gen tel (662) 773-6241; adv tel (662) 773-6241 x25; ed tel (662) 773-6241 x12; gen fax (662) 773-6242; disp adv e-mail lwhite@winstoncountyjournals.com; class adv e-mail sales@winstoncountyjournal.com; ed e-mail newsroom@winstoncountyjournal.com; web site www.winstoncountyjournal.com
Circulation: 2,703pd, 20fr; Sworn/Estimate/Non-Audited
Advertising rate: Open inch rate $17.25
Group: Emmerich Newspapers, Inc.
Circ. Mgr....Brenda Perry
Ed....Joseph McCain

LUCEDALE

GEORGE COUNTY TIMES (THUR)

5133 Main St, Lucedale, MS, 39452-6523, Jackson, USA; gen tel (601) 947-2967; gen fax (601) 947-6828; disp adv e-mail gctimes@bellsouth.net
Circulation: 6,300pd,; Sworn/Estimate/Non-Audited
Advertising rate: Open inch rate $6.75
Ed....O.G. Sellers

MACON

MACON BEACON (THUR)

2904 Jefferson St, Macon, MS, 39341-2273, Noxubee, USA; gen tel (662) 726-4747; gen fax (662) 726-4742; disp adv e-mail maconbeacon@aol.com; class adv e-mail maconbeacon@aol.com; ed e-mail maconbeacon@aol.com; web site www.facebook.com/MaconBeacon
Circulation: 3,100pd, 40fr; Sworn/Estimate/Non-Audited
Advertising rate: Open inch rate $5.00
Established: 1849
Ed....R. Scott Boyd
Mechanical Specifications: Type page 13 x 21; E - 6 cols, 2, between; A - 6 cols, 2, between; C - 6 cols, 2, between.Equipment & Software: Hardware — IBM/PC.

MAGEE

SIMPSON COUNTY NEWS (THUR)

206 Main Ave N, Magee, MS, 39111-3536, Simpson, USA; gen tel (601) 847-2525; adv tel (601) 849-3434; ed tel (601) 849-3434; gen fax (601) 847-2571; disp adv e-mail nbrown@mageecourier.ms; class adv e-mail mbratcher@countynews.ms; ed e-mail pbrown@mageecourier.ms; web site simpsoncounty.ms
Circulation: 3,750pd, 40fr; Sworn/Estimate/Non-Audited
Advertising rate: Open inch rate $9.00
Group: Emmerich Newspapers, Inc.
Circ. Mgr....Marsha Bratcher
Ed....Pat Brown
Mechanical Specifications: Type page 13 x 21 1/2; E - 6 cols, between; A - 6 cols, between; C - 8 cols, between.Equipment & Software: Hardware — PCs; Presses — KP/News King; Software — QPS/QuarkXPress.

THE MAGEE COURIER (THUR)

PO Box 338, Magee, MS, 39111-0338, Simpson, USA; gen tel (601) 849-3434; gen fax (601) 849-6828; disp adv e-mail nbrown@mageecourier.ms; ed e-mail dminsky@mageecourier.ms; web site simpsoncounty.ms
Circulation: 3,750pd, 125fr; Sworn/Estimate/Non-Audited
Advertising rate: Open inch rate $9.95
Established: 1899
Group: Emmerich Newspapers, Inc.Editions: (52)
Circ. Mgr....Marsha Bratcher
Ed....John Pat Brown
Mechanical Specifications: Type page 10.246x15.5 ; E - 6 cols, 2 1/16, 1/8 between; A - 6 cols, 2 1/16, 1/8 between; C - 7 cols, 2 1/6, 1/8 between.Equipment & Software: Hardware — PC; Presses — none; Software — QPS/QuarkXPress.
Delivery Method: Mail, Racks
Areas Served: 39111, 39114, 39044,39062,39082 and 39149

MAGNOLIA

THE MAGNOLIA GAZETTE (THUR)

280 Magnolia St, Magnolia, MS, 39652-2828, Pike, USA; gen tel (601) 783-2441; gen fax (601) 783-2091; disp adv e-mail magnoliagazette@bellsouth.net; web site www.magnoliagazette.com
Circulation: 1,400pd,; Sworn/Estimate/Non-Audited
Advertising rate: Open inch rate $6.00
Adv. Mgr....Joy Reeves
Ed....Luke Lampton
Mng. Ed....Donna DeLee
Mechanical Specifications: Type page 13 x 21 1/2; E - 6 cols, 2 1/16, 1/8 between; A - 6 cols, 2 1/16, 1/8 between; C - 6 cols, 2 1/16, 1/6 between.

MCCOMB

SOUTHWEST SUN (WED)

113 OLIVER EMMERICH DR, McComb, MS, 39648, Pike, USA; gen tel (601) 684-2421; gen fax (601) 684-0836; disp adv e-mail advertising@enterprise-journal.com; class adv e-mail classifieds@enterprise-journal.com; ed e-mail publisher@enterprise-journal.com; web site www.enterprise-journal.com
Circulation: 8,500fr; Sworn/Estimate/Non-Audited
Advertising rate: Open inch rate $2.00
Group: Emmerich Newspapers, Inc.
Adv. Mgr....Lauren Devereaux
Circ. Mgr....Tammy Britt
Ed....Jack Ryan
Mng. Ed....Matt Williamson
Prodn. Mgr....Keith Hux
Mechanical Specifications: Type page 13 x 21 1/2; E - 6 cols, 2 1/16, 1/6 between; A - 6 cols, 2 1/16, 1/6 between; C - 8 cols, 2 1/16, 1/6 between.

MEADVILLE

FRANKLIN ADVOCATE (WED, THUR)

111 MAIN ST E, Meadville, MS, 39653, Franklin, USA; gen tel (601) 384-2484; gen fax (601) 384-2276; disp adv e-mail advocate@telepak.net; web site http://franklinadvocate.com/
Circulation: 3,200pd, 12fr; Sworn/Estimate/Non-Audited
Advertising rate: Open inch rate $5.00
Established: 1890
Digital Platform - Mobile: Windows
Pub. Emeritus....Mary Lou Webb
Pub./Ed....Heather Jacobs
Ed./Pub....Marsha Webb
Mechanical Specifications: Type page 15 x 21; E - 7 cols, 1 3/4, 1/6 between; A - 7 cols, 1 3/4, 1/6 between; C - 7 cols, 1 3/4, 1/6 between. Equipment & Software: Hardware — APP/Mac; Software — digital computers
Delivery Method: Mail, Newsstand
Areas Served: 39653
39661
39630

MONTICELLO

LAWRENCE COUNTY PRESS (WED)

296 F E Sellers Hwy, Monticello, MS, 39654-9555, Lawrence, USA; gen tel (601) 587-2781; gen fax (601) 587-2794; disp adv e-mail info@lawrencecountypress.com; class adv e-mail info@lawrencecountypress.com; ed e-mail info@lawrencecountypress.com; web site lawrencecountypress.com
Circulation: 2,814pd, 34fr; USPS
Advertising rate: Open inch rate $9.30
Established: 1888
Business Manager....J.J. Carney
Pub./Ed./News Ed./Adv. Mgr....John H. Carney
Graphics Design....Reba Powell
Mechanical Specifications: Type page 10.833 x 21; 6 cols, 1.6667 between
Delivery Method: Mail, Racks
Areas Served: 39654, 39656, 39665, 39663, 39140, 39641

NEW ALBANY

NEW ALBANY GAZETTE (WED, FRI)

PO Box 300, New Albany, MS, 38652-0300, Union, USA; gen tel (662) 534-6321; gen fax (662) 534-6355; disp adv e-mail advertising@newalbanygazette.com; class adv e-mail classifieds@newalbanygazette.com; ed e-mail news@newalbanygazette.com; web site djournal.com/new-albany
Circulation: 4,200pd, 12,000fr; Sworn/Estimate/Non-Audited
Advertising rate: $9.45 inch; $14.15 with shopper
Established: 1889
Group: Journal Inc.
Pub....T. Wayne Mitchell
Managing Ed....David Johnson
Editor....J. Lynn West
Mechanical Specifications: Type page 11 x 20.5; E - 6 cols, 2, 1/6 between; A - 6 cols, 2, 1/6 between; C - 6 cols, 2, 1/6 between.Equipment & Software: Hardware — APP/MacCS3; Software — Adobe InDesign CS3, Adobe/Photoshop CS3.

Delivery Method: Mail, Newsstand, Racks
Areas Served: 38652,38828,38627,38650

OCEAN SPRINGS

OCEAN SPRINGS RECORD (THUR)

807 Holcomb Blvd, Ocean Springs, MS, 39564-3943, Jackson, USA; gen tel (228)207-4709; gen fax (228)207-4678; disp adv e-mail adv@osrecord.com; class adv e-mail adv@osrecord.com; ed e-mail editor@osrecord.com; web site www.osrecord.com
Circulation: 3,500pd, 500fr; Sworn/Estimate/Non-Audited
Advertising rate: Open inch rate $8.00
Established: 1965
Editor....................Gene Coleman
Pub....................Leigh Colman
Mechanical Specifications: Type page 11 1/2 x 21 1/2; E - 6 cols, between; A - 6 cols, between; C - 8 cols, between.Equipment & Software: Hardware — APP/Mac; Software — QPS/QuarkXPress 4.11.

OKOLONA

OKOLONA MESSENGER (WED)

249 W Main St, Okolona, MS, 38860-1498, Chickasaw, USA; gen tel (662) 447-5501; disp adv e-mail okmessenger@bellsouth.net; web site www.facebook.com/pages/Okolona-Messenger
Circulation: 1,300pd, 19fr; Sworn/Estimate/Non-Audited
Advertising rate: Open inch rate $4.00
Ed....................Murry Blankenship
Delivery Method: Mail, Racks
Areas Served: Chickasaw

PASCAGOULA

THE MISSISSIPPI PRESS (WED, FRI, SUN)

909 CONVENT AVE, Pascagoula, MS, 39567, Jackson, USA; gen tel (228) 762-1111; adv tel (228) 762-1111; ed tel (228) 934-1424; gen fax (228) 934-1454; adv fax (228) 934-1454; ed fax (228) 934-1474; disp adv e-mail msnews@themississippipress.com; class adv e-mail pressads@themississippipress.com; ed e-mail msnews@themississippipress.com; web site www.gulflive.com/mississippipress
Circulation: 5,749pd,; AAM
Advertising rate: Open inch rate $33.80
Established: 1964
Group: Advance Publications, Inc.
Digital Platform - Mobile: Apple, Android
Digital Platform - Tablet: Apple iOS, Android
Pub....................Wanda Heary Jacobs
Pub....................Gareth Clary
Adv. Mgr....................Roy May
Features Ed....................Susan Ruddiman
Mechanical Specifications: Type page 11 5/8 x 21 1/2; E - 6 cols, 1 13/16, 1/8 between; A - 6 cols, 1 13/16, 1/8 between; C - 10 cols, 1 1/16, 1/8 between.
Delivery Method: Mail, Carrier

PHILADELPHIA

THE NESHOBA DEMOCRAT (WED)

439 E Beacon St, Philadelphia, MS, 39350-2950, Neshoba, USA; gen tel (601) 656-4000; gen fax (601) 656-6379; disp adv e-mail summerhines@neshobademocrat.com; class adv e-mail advertising@neshobademocrat.com; ed e-mail jprince@neshobademocrat.com; web site www.neshobademocrat.com
Circulation: 8,000pd, 70fr; Sworn/Estimate/Non-Audited
Advertising rate: Open inch rate $10.50
Adv. Dir....................Wayne Ceacey
Circ. Mgr....................Irda Wards
Ed....................Jim Prince
Assoc. Ed....................Carver Rayburn
Mng. Ed....................Debbie Myers
Mechanical Specifications: Type page 14 x 21 1/2.Equipment & Software: Hardware — 5-APP/Mac; Software — QPS/QuarkXPress 3.32, Microsoft/Word 6.0, Adobe/Photoshop 3.0.

PONTOTOC

PONTOTOC PROGRESS (WED)

13 E Jefferson St, Pontotoc, MS, 38863-2807, Pontotoc, USA; gen tel (662) 489-3511; gen fax (662) 489-6714; disp adv e-mail pontotoc.advertising@journainc.com; class adv e-mail pontotoc.advertising@journainc.com; ed e-mail pontotoc.news@journalinc.com; web site http://pontotoc-progress.com/
Circulation: 7,800pd, 221fr; Sworn/Estimate/Non-Audited
Advertising rate: Open inch rate $8.75
Established: 1929
Group: Journal Publishing Company
Mng. Ed....................Brenda Owen

POPLARVILLE

THE POPLARVILLE DEMOCRAT (THUR)

418 S Main St, Poplarville, MS, 39470-2826, Pearl River, USA; gen tel (601) 795-2247; gen fax (601) 795-2232; disp adv e-mail laci.lee@picayuneitem.com; class adv e-mail laura.henley@picayuneitem.com; ed e-mail jeremy.pittari@picayuneitem.com; web site http://www.picayuneitem.com/
Circulation: 2,222pd, 14fr; Sworn/Estimate/Non-Audited
Advertising rate: Open inch rate $12.00
Established: 1976
Group: Community Newspaper Holdings, Inc.
Ed....................Butch Weir
Publisher....................Linda Gilmore
Adv. Mgr....................Julie Bounds
Adv. Dir....................Mary Jim Weems
Mechanical Specifications: Type page 13 x 21 1/2; E - 6 cols, between; A - 6 cols, between; C - 6 cols, between.Equipment & Software: Hardware — APP/Mac; Software — QPS/QuarkXPress 4.0, Baseview/News Edit Pro, Adobe/Photoshop 4.0.
Delivery Method: Mail, Newsstand, Racks
Areas Served: 39470

PORT GIBSON

THE PORT GIBSON REVEILLE (THUR)

708 Market St, Port Gibson, MS, 39150-2332, Claiborne, USA; gen tel (601) 437-5103; gen fax (601) 437-4410; disp adv e-mail reveille@bellsouth.net; class adv e-mail reveille@bellsouth.net
Circulation: 1,600pd, 51fr; Sworn/Estimate/Non-Audited
Advertising rate: Open inch rate $6.00
Adv./Circ. Mgr....................Janice G. Bufkin
Pub./Ed....................Emma F. Crisler
Adv. Manager....................Marjorie Bufkin
Mechanical Specifications: Type page 12 x 21; E - 6 cols, 2 1/24, 1/4 between; A - 6 cols, 2 1/24, 1/4 between; C - 6 cols, 2 1/24, 1/4 between.Equipment & Software: Hardware — APP/Mac; Software — QPS/QuarkXPress 2.12.
Delivery Method: Mail, Racks

PRENTISS

PRENTISS HEADLIGHT (WED)

1020 Third St, Prentiss, MS, 39474-6002, Jefferson Davis, USA; gen tel (601) 792-4221; gen fax (601) 792-4222; disp adv e-mail editor@prentissheadlight.com; class adv e-mail business@prentissheadlight.com; ed e-mail holley.cochran@prentissheadlight.com; web site http://www.dailyleader.com/prentiss
Circulation: 1,568pd, 25fr; Sworn/Estimate/Non-Audited
Advertising rate: Open inch rate $7.83
Established: 1906
Group: Prentiss Publishers, Inc
Ed./Gen. Mgr....................Karen Sanford
Pres./Pub....................Rick Reynolds
Mechanical Specifications: Type page 10.125 x 21 1/2; E - 6 cols, 2 1/16, 1/3 between; A - 6 cols, 2 1/16, 1/3 between.Equipment & Software: ; Software — QPS/QuarkXPress 4.11.
Delivery Method: Mail, Newsstand, Carrier, Racks
Areas Served: 39474, 39421, 39427, 39656, 39663, 39140, 39482

QUITMAN

CLARKE COUNTY TRIBUNE (THUR)

101 Main St, Quitman, MS, 39355-2119, Clarke, USA; gen tel (601) 776-3726; gen fax (601) 776-5793; disp adv e-mail mcranford@clarkecountytrib.com; ed e-mail cbaxley@clarkecountytrib.com; web site http://clarkecountytrib.com/
Circulation: 3,735pd, 50fr; Sworn/Estimate/Non-Audited
Advertising rate: Open inch rate $7.00
Group: Emmerich Newspapers, Inc.
Owner....................Wyatt Emmerich
Adv. Mgr....................Wade Bolen
Ed....................Cindy Baxley
Mechanical Specifications: Type page 10.25 x 16; E - 6 cols, 2, between; A - 6 cols, 2, between.

RALEIGH

SMITH COUNTY REFORMER (WED)

153 MAIN ST, Raleigh, MS, 39153, Smith, USA; gen tel (601) 782-4358; gen fax (601) 782-9081; disp adv e-mail ads@smithcountyreformer.net; class adv e-mail legals@smithcountyreformer.net; ed e-mail ads@smithcountyreformer.net
Circulation: 2,965pd, 720fr; Sworn/Estimate/Non-Audited
Advertising rate: Open inch rate $7.00
Established: 1889
Group: Buckley Newspapers
Gen. Mgr./Marketing....................Brenda Ingram
Delivery Method: Mail, Racks
Areas Served: 39153, 39422, 39168, 39117

RICHTON

THE RICHTON DISPATCH (THUR)

110 Walnut St, Richton, MS, 39476, Perry, USA; gen tel (601) 788-6031; gen fax (601) 788-6031; disp adv e-mail news@therichtondispatch.com; class adv e-mail news@therichtondispatch.com; ed e-mail news@therichtondispatch.com; web site therichtondispatch.com
Circulation: 1,825pd, 8fr; Sworn/Estimate/Non-Audited
Advertising rate: Open inch rate $4.15
Established: 1905
Gen. Mgr....................Dean Wilson
Ed....................Larry A. Wilson
Mechanical Specifications: Type page 13 x 21; E - 6 cols, 2, 1/6 between; A - 6 cols, 2, 1/6 between; C - 6 cols, 2, 1/6 between.Equipment & Software: Hardware — APP/Mac IIcx; Software — QPS/QuarkXPress 3.3.
Delivery Method: Mail, Racks

RIDGELAND

MADISON COUNTY HERALD (TUES, THUR, SAT)

670 Highway 51, Ste B, Ridgeland, MS, 39157-2138, Madison, USA; gen tel (601) 853-8783; adv tel (601) 961-7100; ed tel (601) 961-7163; disp adv e-mail slucius@gannett.com; ed e-mail publisher@clarion-ledger.com; web site www.mcherald.com
Circulation: 3,809pd, 29fr; Sworn/Estimate/Non-Audited
Advertising rate: Open inch rate $22.20
Group: Gannett
Pres./Pub....................Leslie Hurst
Brian Tolley
Nat'l Acct. Coord....................Beverly Bennett
Sales Dir....................Katie Hodges
Adv. Sales Mgr....................Katie Parkman
Mechanical Specifications: Type page 13 x 21; E - 6 cols, 2 1/30, between; A - 6 cols, 2 1/30, between; C - 10 cols, 1 1/6, between.Equipment & Software: ; Presses — G/Metro.

MADISON COUNTY JOURNAL (THUR)

293 Commerce Park Dr, Ridgeland, MS, 39157-2233, Madison, USA; gen tel (601) 853-4222; gen fax (601) 856-9419; disp adv e-mail msimmons@onlinemadison.com; class adv e-mail msimmons@onlinemadison.com; ed e-mail msimmons@onlinemadison.com; web site www.onlinemadison.com
Circulation: 3,600pd,; Sworn/Estimate/Non-Audited
Advertising rate: Open inch rate $9.65
Established: 1982
Group: Prince Newspaper Holdings
Ed....................Jim Prince
Associate Ed/Pub....................Michael Simmons
Mechanical Specifications: Type page 11 x 21 1/2; E - 6 cols, 2 1/16, between; A - 6 cols, 2 1/16, between; C - 8 cols, 2 1/6, between. Equipment & Software: Hardware — APP/Mac; Software — QPS/QuarkXPress.
Delivery Method: Mail, Newsstand, Racks
Areas Served: 39110, 39130, 39157, 39158, 39046, 39071, 39046, Madison, Ridgeland, Canton & Flora

RIPLEY

SOUTHERN ADVOCATE (THUR)

1701 City Ave N, Ripley, MS, 38663-1124, Tippah, USA; gen tel (662) 837-8111; gen fax (662) 837-4504; disp adv e-mail advertising@tippah360.com; class adv e-mail advertising@tippah360.com; ed e-mail news@tippah360.com; web site http://southern-advocate.com
Circulation: 1,600pd,; Sworn/Estimate/Non-Audited
Advertising rate: Open inch rate $3.80
Group: Journal Publishing Company
Pub....................Tim Watson
Mng. Ed....................Gene Ladnier
Mechanical Specifications: Type page 13 x 21; E - 6 cols, 2, 1/6 between; A - 6 cols, 2, 1/6 between; C - 8 cols, 1 7/16, 1/6 between. Equipment & Software: Hardware — APP/Mac si, APP/Mac Performa, APP/Mac Perfecta; Software — Adobe/PageMaker 6.0.

SOUTHERN SENTINEL (WED, SAT)

1701 City Ave N, Ripley, MS, 38663-1124, Tippah, USA; gen tel (662) 837-8111; gen fax (662) 837-4504; disp adv e-mail advertising@tippah360.com; class adv e-mail advertising@tippah360.com; ed e-mail news@tippah360.com; web site http://southern-advocate.com
Circulation: 6,800pd,; Sworn/Estimate/Non-Audited
Advertising rate: Open inch rate $7.05
Established: 1879
Group: Journal Publishing Company
Asst. Pub....................Tina Campbell
Office Mgr....................Jessica Davis
News Ed....................Joyce Brock
Pub....................Tim Watson
Mechanical Specifications: Type page 11 1/2 x 21 1/2; E - 6 cols, 1 13/16, 2/3 between; A - 6 cols, 1 13/16, 2/3 between; C - 9 cols, 1 1/6, 2/3 between.Equipment & Software: Hardware — APP/Mac; Software — QPS/QuarkXPress 4.0, Adobe/Photoshop.
Areas Served: 38663, 38610, 38625, 38629, 38674, 38683

ROLLING FORK

DEER CREEK PILOT (THUR)
145 N First St, Rolling Fork, MS, 39159-2749, Sharkey, USA; gen tel (662) 873-4354; gen fax (662) 873-4355; disp adv e-mail deercreekpilot@bellsouth.net; ed e-mail deercreekpilot@bellsouth.net
Circulation: 1,500pd, 50fr; Sworn/Estimate/Non-Audited
Advertising rate: Open inch rate $5.60
Ed. .... Ray Mosby
Areas Served: Sharkey & Issaquena Counties, Mississippi

SARDIS

THE SOUTHERN REPORTER (THUR)
211 S Pocahontas St, Sardis, MS, 38666-1625, Panola, USA; gen tel (662) 487-1551; gen fax (662) 487-1552; disp adv e-mail southernreporter@bellsouth.net
Circulation: 2,250pd, 343fr; Sworn/Estimate/Non-Audited
Advertising rate: Open inch rate $4.50
Ed. .... David Howell

SENATOBIA

THE DEMOCRAT (TUES)
219 E Main St, Senatobia, MS, 38668-2123, Tate, USA; gen tel (662) 562-4414; gen fax (662) 562-8866; disp adv e-mail strimm@taterecord.com; class adv e-mail classifieds@taterecord.com; ed e-mail pageeditor@taterecord.com; web site http://www.taterecord.com
Circulation: 5,200pd,; Sworn/Estimate/Non-Audited
Advertising rate: Open inch rate $10.30
Pub...Joseph B. Lee
Adv. Mgr.....................................Shirley Trimm
Ed. ....Melissa Turner
Mechanical Specifications: Type page 13 x 21 1/2; E - 6 cols, 1 5/6, 1/6 between; A - 6 cols, 1 5/6, 1/6 between; C - 6 cols, 1 5/6, 1/8 between.Equipment & Software: Hardware — APP/Mac LC II; Software — QPS/QuarkXPress 4.0.

TUNICA

THE TUNICA TIMES (FRI)
986 Magnolia St, Tunica, MS, 38676-9742, Tunica, USA; gen tel (662) 363-1511; gen fax (662) 363-9969; disp adv e-mail ads@tunicatimes.com; class adv e-mail ads@tunicatimes.com; ed e-mail news@tunicatimes.com; web site www.tunicatimes.com
Circulation: 2,400pd,; Sworn/Estimate/Non-Audited
Advertising rate: Open inch rate $5.75
Established: 1904
Publisher.................................Brooks N. Taylor
Managing Editor ....Meg Coker
Mechanical Specifications: Type page 11 1/2 x 20 3/4; E - 6 cols, 1 7/10, 1/8 between; A - 6 cols, 1 7/10, 1/8 between; C - 8 cols, 1 1/3, 1/8 between.Equipment & Software: Hardware — APP/Mac; Software — QPS/QuarkXPress 3.3.
Delivery Method: Mail, Racks
Areas Served: 38676, 38626, 38664

TYLERTOWN

THE TYLERTOWN TIMES (THUR)
727 Beulah Ave, Tylertown, MS, 39667-2709, Walthall, USA; gen tel (601) 876-5111; gen fax (601) 876-5280; disp adv e-mail tylertowntimes@bellsouth.net; class adv e-mail tylertowntimes@bellsouth.net; ed e-mail tylertowntimes@bellsouth.net; web site www.thetylertowntimes.org
Circulation: 3,248pd, 6,729fr; Sworn/Estimate/Non-Audited
Advertising rate: Open inch rate $12.50
Established: 1907
Owner/Ed./Pub...........................Carolyn Dillon
Delivery Method: Mail
Areas Served: Prinarukt 39667

UNION

THE NEWTON COUNTY APPEAL (WED)
105 Main St, Union, MS, 39365-2519, Newton, USA; gen tel (601) 774-9433; adv tel (601) 683-7810; ed tel (601) 774-9433; gen fax (601) 774-8301; disp adv e-mail askinner@newtoncountyappeal.com; class adv e-mail mfarrow@newtoncountyappeal.com; ed e-mail dthompson@newtoncountyappeal.com; web site www.thenewtoncountyappeal.com
Circulation: 3,200pd,; Sworn/Estimate/Non-Audited
Advertising rate: Open inch rate $5.50
Established: 1910
Group: Emmerich Newspapers, Inc.
Managing Editor ....Demetrius Thompson
Publisher.....................................Luke Horton
Adv Director...............................Michael Miller
Sports..Austin Bishop
Areas Served: Newton, Union, Decatur and all of Newton County

WATER VALLEY

NORTH MISSISSIPPI HERALD (THUR)
416 N Main St, Water Valley, MS, 38965-2506, Yalobusha, USA; gen tel (662) 473-1473; ed tel (662) 473-8444; gen fax (662) 473-9133; disp adv e-mail heraldads@bellsouth.net; ed e-mail dhowl@bellsouth.net; web site www.yalnews.com
Circulation: 2,900pd, 102fr; Sworn/Estimate/Non-Audited
Advertising rate: Open inch rate $5.00
Gen. Mgr....................................Betty Shearer
Ed. ....David Howell
Mechanical Specifications: Type page 12 3/4 x 21; E - 6 cols, 2, 1/6 between; A - 6 cols, 2, 1/6 between; C - 8 cols, 1 1/2, 1/6 between. Equipment & Software: Hardware — APP/Macs; Software — QPS/QuarkXPress 3.2.
Delivery Method: Mail, Racks
Areas Served: 38965
38921
38948

WAYNESBORO

THE WAYNE COUNTY NEWS (THUR)
716 South St, Waynesboro, MS, 39367-2727, Wayne, USA; gen tel (601) 735-4341; gen fax (601) 735-1111; disp adv e-mail advertising@thewaynecountynews.com; class adv e-mail legals@thewaynecountynews.com; ed e-mail editor@thewaynecountynews.com; web site www.thewaynecountynews.com
Circulation: 4,000pd, 79fr; Sworn/Estimate/Non-Audited
Advertising rate: Open inch rate $6.30
Established: 1890
Group: Keane Media, Inc.
Bolton Publications
Pub..Paul Keane
Adv...Doris Keane
Circ. ....Anna Dearmon
Delivery Method: Mail

WIGGINS

STONE COUNTY ENTERPRISE (WED)
143 First St S, Wiggins, MS, 39577-2733, Stone, USA; gen tel (601) 928-4802; gen fax (601) 928-2191; disp adv e-mail ads@stonecountyenterprise.com; class adv e-mail classifieds@stonecountyenterprise.com; ed e-mail editor@stonecountyenterprise.com; web site www.stonecountyenterprise.com
Circulation: 3,540pd, 25fr; Sworn/Estimate/Non-Audited
Advertising rate: Open inch rate $8.50
Established: 1916
Group: Lancaster Management, Inc.
Ed./Pub. ....Heather Anderson
Staff Writer...................................Jody O'Hara
Ad Sales ....Charlotte Wippler
Classified Clerk...........................Alexis Nichols
Adv./Sales/Design ....Cheryl Rasbury
Mechanical Specifications: Type page 13 x 21 1/2.Equipment & Software: Hardware — APP/Mac; Software — QPS/QuarkXPress, Adobe/PageMaker.
Delivery Method: Mail, Newsstand, Racks
Areas Served: 39577

WINONA

THE CONSERVATIVE (THUR)
401 Summit St, Rm 108, Winona, MS, 38967-2240, Montgomery, USA; gen tel (662) 283-1131; gen fax (662) 283-5374; disp adv e-mail wandaroche@winonatimes.com; class adv e-mail bookkeeping@winonatimes.com; ed e-mail publisher@winonatimes.com; web site www.winonatimes.com
Circulation: 1,350pd, 14fr; Sworn/Estimate/Non-Audited
Advertising rate: Open inch rate $4.65
Established: 1865
Group: Emmerich Newspapers, Inc.
Ed. .... Amanda Sexton

THE WINONA TIMES (THUR)
401 Summit St, Rm 108, Winona, MS, 38967-2240, Montgomery, USA; gen tel (662) 283-1131; gen fax (662) 283-5374; disp adv e-mail wandaroche@winonatimes.com; class adv e-mail bookkeeping@winonatimes.com; ed e-mail publisher@winonatimes.com; web site www.winonatimes.com
Circulation: 3,650pd, 61fr; Sworn/Estimate/Non-Audited
Advertising rate: Open inch rate $10.00
Established: 1881
Group: Emmerich Newspapers, Inc.
Pub.. Amanda Sexton

WOODVILLE

THE WOODVILLE REPUBLICAN (THUR)
425 Depot St, Woodville, MS, 39669-3597, Wilkinson, USA; gen tel (601) 888-4293; gen fax (601) 888-6156; disp adv e-mail wrepublican@bellsouth.net; class adv e-mail wrepublican@bellsouth.net; ed e-mail wrepublican@bellsouth.net; web site http://www.smalltownpapers.com/newspapers
Circulation: 2,590pd, 50fr; USPS
Advertising rate: Open inch rate $8.47
Established: 1824
Adv. Mgr.....................................Elise R. Lewis
Ed. ....Andrew J. Lewis
Mechanical Specifications: Type page 13 1/4 x 21; E - 8 cols, 1 1/2, 1/6 between; A - 8 cols, 1 1/2, 1/6 between; C - 8 cols, 1 1/2, 1/6 between.Equipment & Software: Hardware — APP/Mac 11cx, APP/Mac Quadra; Software — QPS/QuarkXPress 3.1.
Delivery Method: Mail, Newsstand

YAZOO CITY

THE YAZOO HERALD (WED, SAT)
1025 GRAND AVE, Yazoo City, MS, 39194-2946, Yazoo County, USA; gen tel (662) 746-4911; gen fax (662) 746-4915; disp adv e-mail sharon@yazooherald.net; class adv e-mail sheila@yazooherald.net; ed e-mail jason@yazooherald.net; web site www.yazooherald.net
Circulation: 3,400pd, 3,400fr; Sworn/Estimate/Non-Audited
Advertising rate: Open inch rate $10
Established: 1871
Group: Emmerich Newspapers, Inc.
Ed & Pub ....Jason Patterson
Mng Ed ....Jamie Patterson
Staff Writer.........................Cathryn Cartwright
Mechanical Specifications: Type page 10.25x16; E - 6 cols, 2, 1/6 between; A - 6 cols, 2, 1/6 between; C - 9 cols, 1 1/4, 1/6 between. Equipment & Software: Hardware — PC; Software — QuarkXPress 10, Adobe Photoshop CS5
Delivery Method: Mail, Newsstand, Racks
Areas Served: Yazoo City/Yazoo County

MISSOURI

ALBANY

THE ALBANY LEDGER (WED)
213 W Clay St, Albany, MO, 64402-1603, Gentry, USA; gen tel (660) 726-3998; gen fax (660) 726-3997; disp adv e-mail taradodge@aledger.net; class adv e-mail christy@aledger.net; ed e-mail news@aledger.net; web site www.aledger.net
Circulation: 1,500pd, 45fr; Sworn/Estimate/Non-Audited
Advertising rate: Open inch rate $6
Established: 1868
Ed. ....Don Groves
Ad ....Tara Dodge
Pub./Graphic Artist ....Christy Groves
Delivery Method: Mail, Racks
Areas Served: 64402

ALMA

THE SANTA FE TIMES (THUR)
106 3rd St., Ste 1, Alma, MO, 64001, Lafayette, USA; gen tel (660) 674-2250; gen fax (660) 674-2250; disp adv e-mail safetnews@yahoo.com; web site http://ww2.mainstreetnewsgroup.com/v2/content.aspx?ID=78605&MemberID=2218
Circulation: 800pd, 20fr; Sworn/Estimate/Non-Audited
Advertising rate: Open inch rate $3.80
Group: Main Street Media, Inc.
Main Street Media, Inc.
Pub...Frank Mercer
Mng. Ed ....Klarissa Olvera
Mechanical Specifications: Type page 11 9/16 x 21; E - 6 cols, 1 13/16, 1/8 between; A - 6 cols, 1 13/16, 1/8 between; C - 6 cols, 2 13/16, 1/8 between.
Areas Served: 64001, 64096, 65321, 65339

APPLETON CITY

APPLETON CITY JOURNAL (FRI)
104 E 4th St, Appleton City, MO, 64724-1122, Saint Clair, USA; gen tel (660) 476-5566; gen fax (660) 646-8015; disp adv e-mail sacosagenews@centurytel.net; ed e-mail sacosagenews@centurytel.net
Circulation: 1,200pd, 64fr; Sworn/Estimate/Non-Audited
Advertising rate: Open inch rate $5.00
Group: Main Street Media, Inc.
Ed. ....Mike Crawford

ASH GROVE

ASH GROVE COMMONWEALTH (WED)
100 E Main St, Ash Grove, MO, 65604-9096, Greene, USA; gen tel (417) 363-7025; gen fax (417) 751-3499; ed e-mail agcommonwealth@sbcglobal.net; web site http://www.greenecountycommonwealth.com/
Circulation: 2,000pd, 3,725fr; Sworn/Estimate/

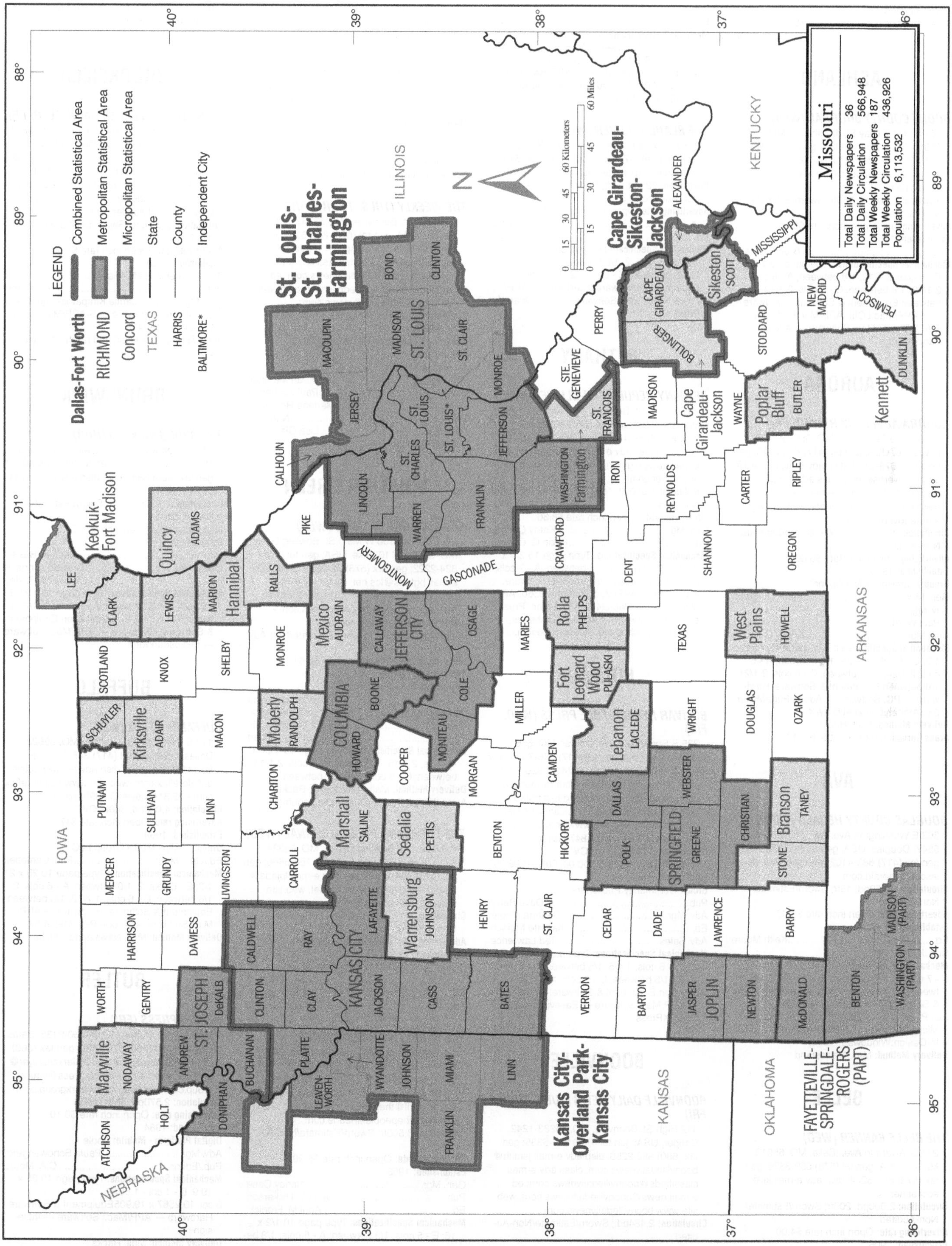
Missouri
Total Daily Newspapers 36
Total Daily Circulation 566,948
Total Weekly Newspapers 187
Total Weekly Circulation 436,926
Population 6,113,532
LEGEND
Dallas-Fort Worth Combined Statistical Area
RICHMOND Metropolitan Statistical Area
Concord Micropolitan Statistical Area
TEXAS State
HARRIS County
BALTIMORE* Independent City
St. Louis-St. Charles-Farmington
Cape Girardeau-Sikeston-Jackson
Kansas City-Overland Park-Kansas City
FAYETTEVILLE-SPRINGDALE-ROGERS (PART)
Keokuk-Fort Madison
Quincy
Hannibal
Mexico
JEFFERSON CITY
COLUMBIA
Moberly
Kirksville
Marshall
Sedalia
Warrensburg
ST. JOSEPH
Maryville
KANSAS CITY
SPRINGFIELD
JOPLIN
Branson
West Plains
Lebanon
Fort Leonard Wood
Rolla
Farmington
Poplar Bluff
Kennett
Sikeston
IOWA
ILLINOIS
KENTUCKY
ARKANSAS
OKLAHOMA
KANSAS
NEBRASKA
0 15 30 45 60 Miles
0 15 30 45 60 Kilometers

Non-Audited
Advertising rate: Open inch rate $6.00
Pub....................Laura Scott

ASHLAND

BOONE COUNTY JOURNAL (WED)

201 S Henry Clay Blvd, Ashland, MO, 65010-9437, Boone, USA; gen tel (573) 657-2334; gen fax (573) 657-2002; disp adv e-mail reporter@bocojo.com; web site www.bocojo.com
Circulation: 2,000pd, 150fr; Sworn/Estimate/Non-Audited
Advertising rate: Open inch rate $6.00
Established: 1969
Pub....................Bruce Wallace
Mechanical Specifications: Type page 13 x 21; E - 6 cols, 2 1/12, 1/8 between; A - 6 cols, 2 1/12, 1/8 between; C - 6 cols, 2 1/12, 1/8 between.Equipment & Software: Hardware — 3-APP/Mac LCIII, APP/Mac Performa, 2-APP/Power Mac; Software — Adobe/PageMaker.

AURORA

AURORA ADVERTISER (WED, FRI)

33 W Olive St, Aurora, MO, 65605-1430, Lawrence, USA; gen tel (417) 678-2115; gen fax (417) 678-2117; disp adv e-mail pward@auroraadvertiser.net; class adv e-mail classifieds@auroraadvertiser.net; ed e-mail news@auroraadvertiser.net; web site www.auroraadvertiser.net
Circulation: 1,100pd, 7,000fr; Sworn/Estimate/Non-Audited
Advertising rate: Open Rate $6.00
Established: 1886
Group: GateHouse Media, Inc.
Gen. Mgr....................Judy Dingman
Adv. Mgr.
Paul Ward
Circ. Mgr....................Krissy Garoutte
Mechanical Specifications: Type page 13 x 21 1/2; E - 6 cols, 2 1/24, 1/6 between; A - 6 cols, 2 1/24, 1/6 between; C - 6 cols, 2 1/24, 1/6 between.Equipment & Software: Hardware — PC; Software — Adobe/PageMaker 6.5, Archetype/Corel Draw 4.0.
Delivery Method: Mail, Racks
Areas Served: 65605, 65705, 65712

AVA

DOUGLAS COUNTY HERALD (THUR)

302 E Washington Ave, Ava, MO, 65608-5547, Douglas, USA; gen tel (417) 683-4181; gen fax (417) 683-4102; web site www.douglascountyherald.com
Circulation: 3,150pd, 15fr; Sworn/Estimate/Non-Audited
Advertising rate: Open inch rate $3.00
Established: 1887
Ed....................Keith Moore
Sue Jones
Mechanical Specifications: Type page 15 x 21; E - 7 cols, 2, 1/6 between; A - 7 cols, 2, 1/6 between; C - 7 cols, 2, 1/6 between.Equipment & Software: Hardware — APP/Mac PC; Presses — 3-G/Community; Software — Microsoft/Word 14.2; Multi-Ad/Creator 8.5; In-Design;Windows 7
Delivery Method: Mail, Newsstand

BELLE

THE BELLE BANNER (WED)

217 S. Alvarado Ave., Belle, MO, 65013, Maries, USA; gen tel (573) 859-3328; gen fax (573) 859-6274; disp adv e-mail kjl@socket.net
Circulation: 2,000pd, 200fr; Sworn/Estimate/Non-Audited
Advertising rate: Open inch rate $4.00
Established: 1906
Pub....................Kurt J. Lewis
Ed....................Ron J. Lewis
Mechanical Specifications: Type page 13 x 21; E - 6 cols, 2, 1/8 between; A - 6 cols, 2, 1/8 between; C - 6 cols, 2, 1/8 between.Equipment & Software: Hardware — APP/Power, APP/Mac G3, APP/iMac, APP/iBook; Software — QPS/QuarkXPress.

THE BLAND COURIER (WED)

217 S. Alvarado Ave., Belle, MO, 65013, USA; gen tel (573) 859-3328; gen fax (573) 859-6274; disp adv e-mail kjl@sockets.net
Circulation: 728pd, 30fr; Sworn/Estimate/Non-Audited
Advertising rate: Open inch rate $4.00
Pub....................Kurt J. Lewis
Ed....................Ron J. Lewis
Mechanical Specifications: Type page 13 x 21 1/2; E - 6 cols, 2, 1/8 between; A - 6 cols, 2, 1/8 between; C - 6 cols, 2, 1/8 between. Equipment & Software: Hardware — APP/Power Mac 7200; Software — QPS/QuarkXPress.

BETHANY

BETHANY REPUBLICAN-CLIPPER (WED)

202 N 16th St, Bethany, MO, 64424-1204, Harrison, USA; gen tel (660) 425-6325; gen fax (660) 425-3441; disp adv e-mail ad1@grm.net; class adv e-mail ad2@grm.net; ed e-mail news@grm.net; web site www.bethanyclipper.com
Circulation: 3,550pd, 10,000fr; Sworn/Estimate/Non-Audited
Advertising rate: Open inch rate $8.36
Circ. Mgr....................Kathy Conger
Ed....................Philip G. Conger
Mechanical Specifications: Type page 15 3/4 x 21; E - 7 cols, 2 1/4, 1/6 between; A - 7 cols, 2 1/4, 1/6 between.Equipment & Software: Hardware — APP/Mac Performa 6360, APP/Mac G3, APP/Mac G4, 2-APP/i-Mac; Presses — HI; Software — Adobe/PageMaker, Adobe/Photoshop 4.0, Adobe/InDesign.

BOLIVAR

BOLIVAR HERALD-FREE PRESS (WED, FRI)

335 S Springfield Ave, Bolivar, MO, 65613-2040, Polk, USA; gen tel (417) 326-7636; adv tel (417) 777-9731; gen fax (417) 326-8701; disp adv e-mail deannam@bolivarmonews.com; class adv e-mail amandao@bolivarmonews.com; ed e-mail jessicam@bolivarmonews.com; web site www.bolivarmonews.com - 93,705(views) 21,847(visitors)
Circulation: 5,061pd, 77fr; CVC
Advertising rate: 1/32 Pg $50.00; Full $1298.00
Established: 1868
Group: Community Publishers, Inc.
Pub....................Dave Berry
Adv. Mgr....................Deanna Moore
Ed....................Charlotte Marsch
Adv. Sales....................Ted Lawrence
Mechanical Specifications: Type page 10.25 x 21; E - 6 cols, 1 4/5, 1/5 between; A - 6 cols, 1 4/5, 1/5 between; C - 7 cols, 1 1/2, 1/5 between.Equipment & Software: Hardware — APP/Mac; Software — Baseview, QPS/QuarkXPress.

BOONVILLE

BOONVILLE DAILY NEWS (TUES, THUR, FRI)

412 High St, Boonville, MO, 65233-1242, Cooper, USA; gen tel (660) 882-5335; gen fax (660) 882-2256; disp adv e-mail jsmith@boonvilledailynews.com; class adv e-mail classifieds@boonvilledailynews.com; ed e-mail news@boonvilledailynews.com; web site www.boonvilledailynews.com
Circulation: 2,484pd,; Sworn/Estimate/Non-Audited
Advertising rate: Open inch rate $9.00
Established: 1919
Group: New Media Investment Group
Bus. Mgr....................Marlene Ridgway
Circ. Mgr....................Kendra Keith
Mult. Sales Consultant....................William Donahue
Mult. Sales Executive....................Billie Vollrath-McCoy
Managing Ed....................Edward Lang
Sports Ed....................Chris Bowie
Mechanical Specifications: Type page 13 x 21; E - 6 cols, 2 1/16, 1/8 between; A - 6 cols, 2 1/16, 1/8 between; C - 6 cols, 2 1/16, 1/8 between.
Delivery Method: Mail, Carrier, Racks

THE WEEKLY (TUES, THUR, FRI)

412 High St, Boonville, MO, 65233-1242, Cooper, USA; gen tel (660) 882-5335; gen fax (660) 882-2256; disp adv e-mail jsmith@boonvilledailynews.com; class adv e-mail classifieds@boonvilledailynews.com; ed e-mail news@boonvilledailynews.com; web site www.boonvilledailynews.com
Circulation: 2,144pd, 11,000fr; Sworn/Estimate/Non-Audited
Advertising rate: Open inch rate $9.00
Established: 1911
Group: GateHouse Media, Inc.
Adv. Mgr....................Deborah Marshall
Gen. Mgr....................Paul Zacharias
Pub....................Marlene Ridgeway
Ed....................Nate Birt
Circ. Mgr....................Lisa Glasscock
Delivery Method: Mail, Carrier

BOWLING GREEN

BOWLING GREEN TIMES (WED)

PO Box 110, 106 W Main St, Bowling Green, MO, 63334-0110, Pike, USA; gen tel (573) 324-2222; gen fax (573) 324-3991; disp adv e-mail bgtads@lcs.net; class adv e-mail bgtads@lcs.net; ed e-mail bgted@lcs.net; web site www.bowlinggreentimes.com - 401,000(views) 8,825(visitors)
Circulation: 3,125pd,; Sworn/Estimate/Non-Audited
Advertising rate: Open inch rate $6.61
Established: 1874
Group: Lakeway Publishers, Inc.
Pub....................Linda Luebrecht
Advertising....................Amy Patterson
Circulation....................Amanda Chamberlain
Editor....................Ethan Colbert
Mechanical Specifications: Type page 13 x 21; E - 6 cols, 2 1/16, between; A - 6 cols, 2 1/16, between; C - 6 cols, 2 1/16, between.
Delivery Method: Mail, Newsstand, Racks
Areas Served: Pike & Surrounding counties

THE LOUISIANA PRESS-JOURNAL (WED)

PO Box 110, Bowling Green, MO, 63334-0110, Pike, USA; gen tel (573) 754-5566; gen fax (573) 754-4749; disp adv e-mail lpjads@lcs.net; ed e-mail lpjed@lcs.net; web site www.louisianapressjournal.com
Circulation: 3,175pd, 21fr; Sworn/Estimate/Non-Audited
Advertising rate: Open inch rate $5.80
Established: 1855
Group: Lakeway Publishers of Missouri
Pub....................Valerie Gilbert
Ed....................Dave Moller
Adv. Mgr....................Neil Darnell

THE PEOPLE'S TRIBUNE (TUES)

17 N Main Cross St, Bowling Green, MO, 63334-1643, Pike, USA; gen tel (573) 324-6111; gen fax (573) 324-2551; disp adv e-mail peoplestribune@sbcglobal.net; ed e-mail april@thepeoplestribune.com; web site www.thepeoplestribune.com
Circulation: 8,500fr; Sworn/Estimate/Non-Audited
Advertising rate: Open inch rate $5.90
Established: 1996
Gen. Mgr....................Nancy Case
Pub....................Jerry L. Hickerson
Ed....................April M. Fronick.
Mechanical Specifications: Type page 10 1/2 x 16; E - 5 cols, 1/8 between; A - 5 cols, 1/8 between; C - 5 cols, 1/8 between.Equipment & Software: Hardware — PC; Software — Adobe/Photoshop 7.0, QPS/QuarkXPress 4.1.

BROOKFIELD

LINN COUNTY LEADER (MON, WED, FRI)

314 N Main St, Brookfield, MO, 64628-1601, Linn, USA; gen tel (660) 258-7237; gen fax (660) 258-7238; disp adv e-mail lmeissen@linncountyleader.com; class adv e-mail tniemeier@linncountyleader.com; ed e-mail dwatson@linncountyleader.com; web site www.linncountyleader.com
Circulation: 3,300pd,; Sworn/Estimate/Non-Audited
Advertising rate: Open inch rate $7.00
Established: 2001
Group: GateHouse Media, Inc.
Pub....................Rod Dixon
Circ. Mgr....................Jamie KirkpatrickEquipment & Software: Hardware — 5-APP/Mac LC III, 2-LaserMaster/4M.
Areas Served: Brookfield and north central Linn County

BRUNSWICK

THE BRUNSWICKER (THUR)

118 E Broadway St, Brunswick, MO, 65236-1232, Chariton, USA; gen tel (660) 548-3171; gen fax (660) 388-6688; disp adv e-mail ps@cvalley.net
Circulation: 1,630pd, 50fr; Sworn/Estimate/Non-Audited
Advertising rate: Open inch rate $3.50
Established: 1847
Pub....................Susan K. Baxley
Office Mgr....................Colleen Johnson
Ed....................Larry M. Baxley
Mechanical Specifications: Type page 13 x 21; E - 6 cols, 2, 1/6 between; A - 6 cols, 2, 1/6 between; C - 6 cols, 2, 1/6 between.Equipment & Software: Hardware — APP/Mac; Software — Microsoft/Word.

BUFFALO

BUFFALO REFLEX (WED)

114 E LINCOLN ST, Buffalo, MO, 65622, Dallas, USA; gen tel (417) 345-2224; gen fax (417) 345-2235; disp adv e-mail paulc@buffaloreflex.com; web site www.buffaloreflex.com - 35,818(views) 8,709(visitors)
Circulation: 4,000pd, 380fr; CVC
Advertising rate: Open inch rate $17
Established: 1869
Group: Phillips Media Group LLC
Ed./Gen. Mngr....................Paul Campbell
Mechanical Specifications: Type page 10.25 x 21 1/2; E - 6 cols, 2, 1/6 between; A - 6 cols, 2, 1/6 between; C - 6 cols, 1 7/12, 1/6 between. Equipment & Software: Hardware — APP/Mac; Software — Adobe/PageMaker 5.0.
Delivery Method: Mail, Newsstand, Racks

BUTLER

NEWS-XPRESS (FRI)

5 N Main St, Butler, MO, 64730-2135, Bates, USA; gen tel (660) 679-6126; gen fax (660) 679-4905; disp adv e-mail butlerxchanger@gmail.com; ed e-mail newsxpress@yourxgroup.com; web site www.yourxgroup.com
Circulation: 2,570pd, 65fr; USPS
Advertising rate: Open inch rate $6.10
Established: 1984
Digital Platform - Mobile: Apple
Adv. Mgr....................Paula Schowengerdt
Pub./Editor....................C.A. Moore
Mechanical Specifications: Type page 10.25 x 19.9; E - 1 col - 1.5672
6 col. 10.2567 x 19.905Equipment & Software: Hardware — APP/Mac.; Software — InDesign
Delivery Method: Mail, Racks

Areas Served: 64730, 64779, 64720, 64723, 64722, 64724

CABOOL

CABOOL ENTERPRISE (THUR)

525 Main St, Cabool, MO, 65689-8104, Texas, USA; gen tel (417) 962-4411; gen fax (417) 962-4455; disp adv e-mail cabent@centurytel.net; class adv e-mail ads@thecaboolenterprise.com; ed e-mail news@thecaboolenterprise.com; web site www.thecaboolenterprise.com

Circulation: 1,369pd, 41fr; Sworn/Estimate/Non-Audited

Advertising rate: Open inch rate $7.90

Established: 1884

Pub..Dala Whittaker

Mechanical Specifications: Type page 13 x 21; E - 6 cols, 2 1/8, between; A - 6 cols, 2 1/8, between; C - 6 cols, 2 1/8, between.

Delivery Method: Mail, Newsstand

Areas Served: 65689, 65711, 65464, 65483, 65789

CALIFORNIA

CALIFORNIA DEMOCRAT (WED)

319 S High St, California, MO, 65018-1807, Moniteau, USA; gen tel (573) 796-2135; gen fax (573) 796-4220; disp adv e-mail denise@californiademocrat.com; class adv e-mail denise@californiademocrat.com; ed e-mail editor@californiandemocrat.com; web site www.californiademocrat.com

Circulation: 2,750pd,; Sworn/Estimate/Non-Audited

Advertising rate: Open inch rate $6.90

Established: 1858

Group: WEHCO Media, Inc.
NAN LLC

Mechanical Specifications: Type page 13 x 21 1/2; E - 6 cols, 2 1/30, 1/6 between; A - 6 cols, 2 1/30, 1/6 between; C - 6 cols, 2 1/30, 1/6 between.Equipment & Software: Hardware — APP/Mac; Software — QPS/QuarkXPress 4.0.

Delivery Method: Mail, Newsstand, Carrier, Racks

Areas Served: 65018

CAMERON

THE CITIZEN OBSERVER (THUR)

403 E Evergreen St, Cameron, MO, 64429-2096, Clinton, USA; gen tel (816) 632-6543; gen fax (816) 632-4508; disp adv e-mail sales@mycameronnews.com; class adv e-mail classifieds@mycameronnews.com; ed e-mail editor@mycameronnews.com; web site www.mycameronnews.com

Circulation: 2,800pd,; Sworn/Estimate/Non-Audited

Advertising rate: Open inch rate $7.50

Prodn. Dir..Jeff King
Pub..Wally Gallian
Office Mgr. .... Debbie Wiedmaier
Ed. ....Annette Bauer

Mechanical Specifications: Type page 13 1/2 x 20 1/2; E - 6 cols, 2 1/6, 1/6 between; A - 8 cols, 1 7/12, 1/6 between; C - 8 cols, 1 7/12, 1/6 between.Equipment & Software: Hardware — APP/Mac; Presses — 4-G/Community; Software — QPS/QuarkXPress 3.3, Adobe/PageMaker 5.0.

Delivery Method: Mail, Racks

Areas Served: DeKalb, Clinton, Daviess, Caldwell Counties

CARTHAGE

THE CARTHAGE PRESS (WED)

800 W Central Ave, Carthage, MO, 64836-1023, Jasper, USA; gen tel (417) 358-2191; adv tel (417) 358-2191; ed tel (417) 358-2422; gen fax (417) 358-7428; adv fax (417) 358-7428; ed fax (417) 358-7428; disp adv e-mail advertising2@carthagepress.com; ed e-mail jhacker@carthagepress.com; web site www.carthagepress.com

Circulation: 1,000pd, 200fr; Sworn/Estimate/Non-Audited

Advertising rate: Open inch rate $10.20

Established: 1884

Group: New Media Investment Group

Digital Platform - Mobile: Apple, Android

Digital Platform - Tablet: Apple iOS, Android

Mng. Ed..John Hacker
Sports Ed............................ Brennan Stebbins
Publisher.............................. Jamie Honeycutt

Mechanical Specifications: Type page 13 x 21 1/2; E - 6 cols, 2 1/16, 1/8 between; A - 6 cols, 2 1/16, 1/8 between; C - 9 cols, 1 5/8, 1/8 between.

Delivery Method: Mail, Racks

CARUTHERSVILLE

THE DEMOCRAT ARGUS (THUR)

1011 Truman Blvd, Caruthersville, MO, 63830-1745, Pemiscot, USA; gen tel (573) 333-4336; gen fax (573) 333-2307; disp adv e-mail news@democratargus.com; ed e-mail news@democratargus.com; web site www.democratargus.com

Circulation: 2,417pd, 30fr; Sworn/Estimate/Non-Audited

Advertising rate: Open inch rate $7.50

Established: 1868

Group: Rust Communications

Pub...David Tennyson
Gen. Mgr. ....Lisa Helfer
Adv. Mgr. ....Lisa Bryant
Circ. Mgr...................................... Ashley Sides
Ed. ....Herbie Smith

Mechanical Specifications: Type page 13 x 21 1/2; E - 6 cols, between; A - 6 cols, between; C - 9 cols, between.Equipment & Software: Hardware — APP/Mac.

CASSVILLE

BARRY COUNTY ADVERTISER (WED)

904 West St, Cassville, MO, 65625-1356, Barry, USA; gen tel (417) 847-4475; gen fax (417) 847-4523; disp adv e-mail sales@4bca.com; class adv e-mail ads@4bca.com; ed e-mail editor@4bca.com; web site www.4bcaonline.com - 70,000(views) 20,000(visitors)

Circulation: 200pd, 13,200fr; USPS

Advertising rate: Open inch rate $5.00

Established: 1966

Digital Platform - Mobile: Apple

Prodn. Mgr. ....Marty Jenkins
Office Manager.................... Rachael Freeman
Editor .... Charlea Estes

Mechanical Specifications: Type page 11 x 17; E - 6 cols, between; A - 6 cols, between; C - 6 cols, between.Equipment & Software: Hardware — HI/Cottrell Model V-15A, 1-USA.

Delivery Method: Mail

Areas Served: Barry County Missouri

CASSVILLE DEMOCRAT (WED)

600 Main St, Cassville, MO, 65625-1420, Barry, USA; gen tel (417) 847-2610; gen fax (417) 847-3092; disp adv e-mail community@monett-times.com; class adv e-mail darlene@caseville-democrat.com; ed e-mail editor@cassville-democrat.com; web site www.cassville-democrat.com

Circulation: 3,000pd,; Sworn/Estimate/Non-Audited

Advertising rate: Open inch rate $5.95

Established: 1871

Group: Rust Communications

Pub...Jacob Brower
Ed. .... Kyle Troutman
Mktg. Dir...Lisa Craft

Delivery Method: Mail, Newsstand, Racks

CENTRALIA

THE CENTRALIA FIRESIDE GUARD (WED)

123 N Allen St, Centralia, MO, 65240-1301, Boone, USA; gen tel (573) 682-2133; gen fax (573) 682-3361; disp adv e-mail cfgmgr@lcs.net; class adv e-mail cfgbkkpr@lcs.net; ed e-mail cfged@lcs.net; web site www.fireside-guard.com

Circulation: 3,700pd,; Sworn/Estimate/Non-Audited

Advertising rate: Open inch rate $6.59

Established: 1868

Group: Lakeway Publishers, Inc.

Pub.. Walt Gilbert
General manager.......................... Jeff Grimes

Delivery Method: Mail, Newsstand, Racks

Areas Served: 65240,65255,65284,65243,65285

CHARLESTON

MISSISSIPPI COUNTY TIMES (TUES)

207 S Main St, Charleston, MO, 63834-1639, Mississippi, USA; gen tel (573) 683-6689; gen fax (573) 683-4291; disp adv e-mail countytimes@sbcglobal.net; ed e-mail countytimes@sbcglobal.net; web site www.misscotimes.com

Advertising rate: Open inch rate $4.50

Ed. .... Richard Scheffer

CHESTERFIELD

NORTH SIDE JOURNAL (WED)

14522 S Outer 40 Rd, Ste 300, Chesterfield, MO, 63017-5755, St. Louis, USA; gen tel (314) 340-8000; adv tel (314) 340-8500; ed tel (314) 340-3139; gen fax (314) 831-4986; disp adv e-mail cmarty@yourjournal.com; ed e-mail mkoenig@post-dispatch.com; web site www.yourjournal.com

Circulation: 31,000fr; Sworn/Estimate/Non-Audited

Advertising rate: Open inch rate $7.80

Pub.. Carolyn Marty
Circ Dir.................................... Dan Crockwell
Circ. Mgr.. Rich Sisak
Promo. Dir........................... Mary Ann Wagner

Mechanical Specifications: Type page 12 x 21 1/2; E - 6 cols, 1 7/8, 1/8 between; A - 6 cols, 1 7/8, 1/8 between; C - 10 cols, 1 1/4, 1/3 between.Equipment & Software: Hardware — SII/Sys 55, APP/Mac Network; Presses — 32-G/Urbanite.

CLARENCE

CLARENCE COURIER (WED)

106 E Maple St, Clarence, MO, 63437-1723, Shelby, USA; gen tel (660) 699-2344; gen fax (660) 699-2194; disp adv e-mail advertising@clarencecourier.com; ed e-mail editor@clarencecourier.com

Circulation: 1,600pd, 118fr; Sworn/Estimate/Non-Audited

Advertising rate: Open inch rate $3.80

Pub., Ed. .... Dennis Williams

CONCORDIA

THE CONCORDIAN (WED)

714 S Main St, Concordia, MO, 64020-9602, Lafayette, USA; gen tel (660) 463-7522; gen fax (660) 463-7942; disp adv e-mail amilligan@marshallnews.com; class adv e-mail concordianclass@centurytel.net; ed e-mail sreed@marshallnews.com; web site www.theconcordianonline.com

Circulation: 2,635pd,; Sworn/Estimate/Non-Audited

Advertising rate: Open inch rate $5.25

Established: 1893

Group: Rust Communications

Pub .... Dave Phillips
Sarah Reed
Staff Writer.............................. Charles Dunlap

Mechanical Specifications: Type page 13 x 21; E - 6 cols, 2, 1/6 between; A - 6 cols, 2, 1/6 between; C - 6 cols, 2, 1/6 between.Equipment & Software: Hardware — APP/Mac

CRANE

CRANE CHRONICLE/STONE COUNTY REPUBLICAN (THUR)

114 Main St, Crane, MO, 65633-7359, Stone, USA; gen tel (417) 723-5248; gen fax (417) 723-8490; disp adv e-mail screditor@centurylink.net; class adv e-mail scrbilling@centurylink.net; ed e-mail screditor@centurylink.net

Circulation: 1,400pd, 10fr; Sworn/Estimate/Non-Audited

Advertising rate: Open inch rate $4.50

Established: 1876

Group: Stone County Publishing, Inc.

Ed ....Isaac Estes-Jones
Legals.. Shana Harter
Reception/Classifieds................ Judy Waisner

Mechanical Specifications: Type page 11 x 17; E - 5 cols, 2, between; A - 5 cols, 2, between; C - 5 cols, 2, between.Equipment & Software: Hardware — APP/Mac; Software — Adobe/PageMaker 4.2.

Delivery Method: Mail

Areas Served: Stone County

CUBA

THE CUBA FREE PRESS (THUR)

501 E Washington St, Cuba, MO, 65453-1834, Crawford, USA; gen tel (573) 885-7460; gen fax (573) 885-3803; disp adv e-mail advertising@threeriverspublishing.com; class adv e-mail smorice@cubafreepress.com; ed e-mail news@cubafreepress.com; web site http://www.threeriverspublishing.com

Circulation: 3,450pd,; USPS

Advertising rate: Open inch rate $5.50

Established: 1960

Group: Three Rivers Publishing, Inc.

Digital Platform - Mobile: Apple, Android, Windows, Blackberry

Digital Platform - Tablet: Apple iOS

Pub... Rob Viehman
Ed... Chris Case
Advertising................................. Sandy Morice

Mechanical Specifications: 21.5 inches tall
1 col - 1.833 inches
2 col - 3.792 inches
3 col - 5.75 inches
4 col - 7.708 inches
5 col - 9.667 inches
6 col - 11.625 inches
Equipment & Software: Hardware — APP/Mac; Software — Adobe/PageMaker 6.5.

Delivery Method: Mail, Newsstand

Areas Served: Cuba and northern Crawford County, MO

DEXTER

THE NORTH-STODDARD COUNTIAN (WED)

133 S Walnut St, Dexter, MO, 63841-2141, Stoddard, USA; gen tel (573) 624-4545; gen fax (573) 624-7449; disp adv e-mail cnoles@dailystatesman.com; web site www.dailystatesman.com/nsc

Circulation: 2,000pd,; Sworn/Estimate/Non-Audited

Advertising rate: Open inch rate $6.35

Established: 1877

Pub... Bud Hunt
Adv. Mgr. .... Betty Watkins
Ed. .... Corey Noles

DIXON

DIXON PILOT NEWSPAPER AND PRINT SHOP (WED)
302 N Locust St, Dixon, MO, 65459-6055, USA; gen tel (573) 759-2127; gen fax (573) 759-6226; disp adv e-mail dixonpilotnews@yahoo.com; news@dixonpilot.com; web site www.dixonpilot.com
Circulation: 2,200pd,; Sworn/Estimate/Non-Audited
Advertising rate: Open inch rate $4.00
Established: 1915
Co Publishers .... Rick Blackburn
Connie Erisman
Delivery Method: Mail, Racks

DONIPHAN

THE PROSPECT-NEWS (WED)
110 Washington St, Doniphan, MO, 63935-1761, Ripley, USA; gen tel (573) 996-2103; gen fax (573) 996-2217; disp adv e-mail pnpaper@windstream.net
Circulation: 3,000pd,; Sworn/Estimate/Non-Audited
Advertising rate: Open inch rate $9.45
Established: 1874
Group: Butler County Publishing
Pub... Don Schrieber
Ed. .... Barbie Rogers
Mechanical Specifications: 1.562 inches per column
Delivery Method: Mail, Carrier, Racks
Areas Served: 63935, 63939, 63942, 63953, 63943

EAST PRAIRIE

EAST PRAIRIE EAGLE & ENTERPRISE-COURIER (TUES)
101 E Main St, East Prairie, MO, 63845-1136, Mississippi, USA; gen tel (573) 683-3351; gen fax (573) 649-9530; disp adv e-mail advertising@enterprisecourier.com; ed e-mail news@enterprisecourier.com; web site www.enterprisecourier.com
Circulation: 2,500pd,; Sworn/Estimate/Non-Audited
Advertising rate: Open inch rate $4
Publisher................................... Carlin Bennett
Editor .... Adam Rhodes
Areas Served: 63845, 63834

EDINA

THE EDINA SENTINEL (WED)
207 N Main St, Edina, MO, 63537-1350, Knox, USA; gen tel (660) 397-2226; gen fax (660) 397-3558; disp adv e-mail edinasentinel@att.net; ed e-mail themedia@centurytel.net; web site www.nemonews.net
Circulation: 1,600pd,; Sworn/Estimate/Non-Audited
Advertising rate: Open inch rate $5.50
Established: 1868
Circ. Mgr... Donna Otte
Ed. .... Mike Scott

EL DORADO SPRINGS

EL DORADO SPRINGS SUN (THUR)
125 N Main St, El Dorado Springs, MO, 64744-1141, Cedar, USA; gen tel (417) 876-3841; gen fax (417) 876-3848; ed e-mail sunnews@socket.net; web site www.eldoradospringsmo.com
Circulation: 3,800pd, 3,580fr; USPS
Advertising rate: Open inch rate $7.00
Established: 1890
Pub.. Kimball S. Long
Ed. .... Kenneth W. Long
Mechanical Specifications: Type page 11 2/3 x 21 1/2; E - 6 cols, 1 5/6, 1/8 between; A - 6 cols, 1 5/6, 1/8 between; C - 6 cols, 1 5/6, 1/8 between.
Delivery Method: Mail, Racks
Areas Served: 64724, 64780, 64783, 64750, 64790, 64767, 64756, 64744, 65785, 64738, 64781, 64776

THE STAR (THUR)
105 S Main St, El Dorado Springs, MO, 64744-1123, Cedar, USA; gen tel (417) 876-2500; gen fax (417) 876-5986; ed e-mail thestar@socket.net
Circulation: 550pd, 5fr; Sworn/Estimate/Non-Audited
Advertising rate: Open inch rate $4.50
Established: 1987
Gen. Mgr. .... Mae McNeece
Ed. .... Patsy Brownlee

ELDON

ELDON ADVERTISER (THUR)
415 S Maple St, Eldon, MO, 65026-1856, Miller, USA; gen tel (573) 392-5658; gen fax (573) 392-7755; disp adv e-mail dfair@vernonpublishing.com; ed e-mail tvernon@vernonpublishing.com; web site http://www.vernonpublishing.com/Advertiser/Main/
Circulation: 4,825pd, 52fr; Sworn/Estimate/Non-Audited
Advertising rate: Open inch rate $5.50
Group: Vernon Publishing
Gen. Mgr. .... Sharene Vernon
Ed. .... Tim Flora
Pub... Trevor Vernon
Mechanical Specifications: Type page 13 x 21; E - 6 cols, 2 1/16, 1/8 between; A - 6 cols, 2 1/16, 1/8 between; C - 7 cols, 1 23/32, 1/8 between.Equipment & Software: Hardware — Metro/Mac; Presses — G/Community; Software — InDesign
Delivery Method: Mail, Newsstand, Racks
Areas Served: 65026, 65011, 65032, 65072, 65074, 65042, 65049, 65065

MILLER COUNTY AUTOGRAM SENTINEL (THUR)
415 S Maple St, Eldon, MO, 65026-1856, Miller, USA; gen tel (573) 392-5658; adv tel (573) 392-5658; gen fax (573) 392-7755; disp adv e-mail autogram-sentinel@vernonpublishing.com; class adv e-mail dfair@vernonpublishing.com; ed e-mail gduffield@vernonpublishing.com; web site http://www.vernonpublishing.com/Autogram-Sentine
Circulation: 1,875pd, 20fr; Sworn/Estimate/Non-Audited
Advertising rate: Open inch rate $3.75
Established: 1883
Group: Vernon Publishing
Pub... Trevor Vernon
Ed. .... Ginny Duffield
Ad Sales .... Debbie Fair
Mechanical Specifications: Type page 13 x 21; E - 6 cols, 2 1/16, 1/8 between; A - 6 cols, 2 1/16, 1/8 between; C - 7 cols, 1 23/32, 1/8 between.Equipment & Software: Hardware — APP/Mac; Presses — G/Community; Software — Adobe/PageMaker 6.5.
Areas Served: 65082, 65075, 65486

ELSBERRY

THE ELSBERRY DEMOCRAT (WED)
106 N 3rd St, Ste A, Elsberry, MO, 63343-1344, Lincoln, USA; gen tel (573) 898-2318; gen fax (573) 898-2173; disp adv e-mail edgenmgr@lcs.net; class adv e-mail edgenmgr@lcs.net; ed e-mail edgenmgr@lcs.net; web site www.elsberrydemocrat.com
Circulation: 1,350pd, 5fr; Sworn/Estimate/Non-Audited
Advertising rate: Open inch rate $3.50
Established: 1901
Group: Lakeway Publishers, Inc.
Pub.. Walter Gilbert
Ed. .... Michael Short
Reporter .... Jordan Lanham

EMINENCE

CURRENT WAVE LLC (WED)
102 PLUM ST, Eminence, MO, 65466, Shannon, USA; gen tel (573) 226-5229; gen fax (573) 226-3335; disp adv e-mail cwave128@gmail.com; ed e-mail cwave128@gmail.com; web site www.shannoncountycurrentwave.com
Circulation: 1,600pd, 24fr; Sworn/Estimate/Non-Audited
Advertising rate: Open inch rate $5.00
Established: 1874
Office Mgr. .... Susie Gates
Ed. .... Roger Dillon
Bookkeeper, Ad design............. julie Anderson
Delivery Method: Mail, Newsstand, Racks
Areas Served: Shannon County

FAIRFAX

THE FAIRFAX FORUM (THUR)
119 E Main St, Fairfax, MO, 64446-9305, Atchison, USA; gen tel (660) 686-2741; adv tel (660) 736-4111; gen fax (660) 686-3442; disp adv e-mail amail.rpt.coop; ed e-mail forum@fairfaxmo.net; web site http://farmer-publishing.com/
Circulation: 800pd, 14fr; Sworn/Estimate/Non-Audited
Advertising rate: Open inch rate $4.00
Established: 1892Lori Shaw
Mechanical Specifications: Type page 12 1/2 x 20 1/2; E - 6 cols, 2 1/8, between; A - 6 cols, 2 1/8, between; C - 6 cols, 2 1/8, between. Equipment & Software: Hardware — HP/286 Limited Data Desk Int'1, APP/Mac.

FARMINGTON

THE FARMINGTON PRESS (WED)
227 E Columbia St, Farmington, MO, 63640-3106, St. Francois, USA; gen tel (573) 756-8927; gen fax (573) 756-9160; disp adv e-mail mnicholson@farmingtonpressonline.com; class adv e-mail mnicholson@farmingtonpressonline.com; ed e-mail srobinson@farmingtonpressonline.com; web site http://dailyjournalonline.com/farmington-press/
Advertising rate: 1/8 P $261 1/4 P $457 1/2 P $757 Full $1,335
Established: 1928
Mng. Ed .... Shawnna Robinson

FAYETTE

FAYETTE ADVERTISER (WED)
203 N Main St, Fayette, MO, 65248-1421, Howard, USA; gen tel (660) 248-2235; gen fax (660) 248-1200; disp adv e-mail advertising@fayettenews.com; class adv e-mail advertising@fayettenews.com; ed e-mail proll@fayettenews.com; web site www.fayettenewspapers.com
Circulation: 1,800pd,; Sworn/Estimate/Non-Audited
Advertising rate: Open inch rate $6.50
Established: 1840
Publisher....................................... Patrick Roll
Office Mgr................................ Linda Vroman
Sports Editor................................ Mike Ursery
Mechanical Specifications: Type page 14 x 22; E - 6 cols, 2 1/16, between; A - 6 cols, 2 1/16, between.Equipment & Software: Hardware — APP/Mac G3; Software — Adobe/PageMaker, Adobe/Photoshop, Claris/Word.
Delivery Method: Mail, Newsstand

THE FAYETTE ADVERTISER (WED, SAT)
203 N Main St, Fayette, MO, 65248-1421, Howard, USA; gen tel (660) 248-2235; gen fax (660) 248-1200; disp adv e-mail advertising@fayettenews.com; class adv e-mail advertising@fayettenews.com; ed e-mail gjackson@fayettenews.com; web site www.fayettenewspapers.com
Circulation: 2,300pd,; Sworn/Estimate/Non-Audited
Advertising rate: Open inch rate $6.10
Established: 1840
Ed. .... James H. Steele
Patrick Roll
Greg Jackson
Linda Vroman
Carol Leech
Mechanical Specifications: Type page 14 x 22; E - 6 cols, 2 1/16, 1/8 between; A - 6 cols, 2 1/16, 1/8 between; C - 6 cols, 2 1/16, 1/8 between.Equipment & Software: Hardware — APP/Mac G3; Software — Adobe/PageMaker 4.1, Claris, Adobe/Photoshop.

FLORISSANT

INDEPENDENT NEWS (THUR)
25 Saint Anthony Ln, Florissant, MO, 63031-6720, Saint Louis, USA; gen tel (314) 831-4645; adv tel (314) 831-4645; ed tel (314) 831-4645; gen fax (314) 831-4566; adv fax (314) 831-4566; ed fax (314) 831-4566; disp adv e-mail independentnws@aol.com; class adv e-mail independentnws@aol.com; ed e-mail independentnws@aol.com; web site www.flovalleynews.com - 50,000(views) 2,500(visitors)
Circulation: 26,925fr; CVC
Advertising rate: Open inch rate $12.50
Established: 1987
Group: Two Rivers Publishing o. Inc.
Digital Platform - Tablet: Kindle Fire
Circ. Mgr.................................. Phil Tankersley
Editor-Publisher....................... Robert Lindsey
Reporter .... Carol Arnett
Sales Mgr.................................... Tom Anselm
Assistant editor- EntertainmentPatricia Lindsey
Copy& Associate Editor....Nichole Richardson
Mechanical Specifications: Type page 10 x 16; E - 5 cols, 2, 3/8 between; A - 5 cols, 2, 3/8 between; C - 8 cols, 1 1/2, 1/8 between. Equipment & Software: Hardware — APP/Mac, HP; Software — Adobe/PageMaker 7.0, 1-Adobe/Photoshop 8.0.
Delivery Method: Carrier, Racks
Areas Served: 63031, 63033, 63034, 63042, 63138

FORT LEONARD WOOD

FORT LEONARD WOOD GUIDON (THUR)
4079 Illinois Ave, Fort Leonard Wood, MO, 65473-9105, Pulaski, USA; gen tel (573) 563-5014; adv tel (417) 837-1904; gen fax (573) 336-5487; disp adv e-mail dgunter@gannett.com; ed e-mail guidoneditor@myguidon.com; web site www.myguidon.com
Advertising rate: Open inch rate $10.40
Ed. .... Mike Bowers
Asst. Ed...................................... Marti Yoshida
Adv.................................... Amanda Thompson
Areas Served: Fort Leonard Wood

FREDERICKTOWN

DEMOCRAT NEWS (WED)
131 S Main St, Fredericktown, MO, 63645-1451, Madison, USA; gen tel (573) 783-3366; gen fax (573) 783-6890; disp adv e-mail dn@democratnewsonline.com; class adv e-mail spogue@democratnewsonline.com; ed e-mail akopitsky@democratnewsonline.com; web site www.dailyjournalonline.com/dn
Circulation: 2,300pd, 300fr; Sworn/Estimate/Non-Audited
Advertising rate: Open inch rate $7.15
Established: 1870
Group: Lee Enterprises, Inc.
Digital Platform - Mobile: Apple, Android
General Manager....................... Alan Kopitsky
Delivery Method: Mail, Newsstand, Carrier, Racks
Areas Served: Fredericktown, Madison County Missouri

GAINESVILLE

OZARK COUNTY TIMES (WED)

504 Third Street, Gainesville, MO, 65655, Ozark, USA; gen tel (417) 679-4641; gen fax (417) 679-3423; disp adv e-mail jenny@ozarkcountytimes.com; class adv e-mail norene@ozarkcountytimes.com; ed e-mail editor@ozarkcountytimes.com; web site www.ozarkcountytimes.com
Circulation: 3,050pd,; Sworn/Estimate/Non-Audited
Advertising rate: Open inch rate $5.35
Established: 1876
Group: Ozark County Media LLC
Digital Platform - Mobile: Apple, Android, Windows, Blackberry
Digital Platform - Tablet: Apple iOS, Android, Windows 7, Blackberry Tablet OS
Pub....................................... Norene Prososki
Adv. Mgr.................................. Jennifer Yarger
Ed...Sue Ann Jones
Online manager/reporter........ Jessi Dreckman
Mechanical Specifications: Type page 13 x 21 1/2; E - 6 cols, 2 1/12, 1/6 between; A - 6 cols, 2 1/12, 1/6 between; C - 6 cols, 2 1/12, 1/6 between.Equipment & Software: Hardware — APP/Mac; Software — InDesign
Delivery Method: Mail, Racks
Areas Served: 65655, 65666, 65676, 65715, 65729, 65733, 65741, 65760, 65761, 65762, 65773, 65784

GALLATIN

GALLATIN NORTH MISSOURIAN (WED)

609B S Main St, Gallatin, MO, 64640-1447, Daviess, USA; gen tel (660) 663-2154; adv tel (660) 663-2154; ed tel (660) 663-2154; gen fax (660) 663-2498; adv fax (660) 663-2498; ed fax (660) 663-2498; disp adv e-mail GPC@GPCink.com; class adv e-mail ads@GPCink.com; ed e-mail news@GPCink.com; web site www.NorthMissourian.com - 2,561(views) 1,888(visitors)
Circulation: 1,700pd,; Sworn/Estimate/Non-Audited
Advertising rate: Open inch rate $5.00
Established: 1864
Digital Platform - Mobile: Apple
Digital Platform - Tablet: Windows 7
Liz Wilkinson
Darryl WilkinsonOwner/Pub.s
Mechanical Specifications: Type page 10" x 16"; E - 5 cols, 1 5/6, 1/6 between; A - 5 cols, 1 5/6, 1/6 between; C - 5 cols, 1 5/6, 1/6 between.Equipment & Software: Hardware — PC; Presses — KP/News King; Software — Archetype/Corel Draw, Ventura.
Delivery Method: Mail, Newsstand, Racks
Areas Served: 64640

GLASGOW

GLASGOW MISSOURIAN (FRI)

109 Market St, Glasgow, MO, 65254-1052, Howard, USA; gen tel (660) 338-2195; gen fax (660) 338-2494; ed e-mail glasgow@mcmsys.com; web site www.mainstreetmedia.us
Circulation: 1,625pd, 22fr; Sworn/Estimate/Non-Audited
Advertising rate: Open inch rate $4.00
Established: 1879
Group: Main Street Media, Inc.
Main Street Media, Inc.
Pub......................................Frank Mercer
Ed....................................... Mike Heying
Mechanical Specifications: Type page 13 x 21 1/2; E - 6 cols, 2 1/16, between; A - 6 cols, 2 1/16, between; C - 6 cols, 2 1/16, between. Equipment & Software: Hardware — APP/Mac 7200, APP/Mac Classic; Software — Claris/MacWrite, Adobe/PageMaker, Adobe/Photoshop Deskscan.

GRANDVIEW

JACKSON COUNTY ADVOCATE (THUR)

1102 Main St Ste A, Suite A, Grandview, MO, 64030-2480, Jackson, USA; gen tel (816) 761-6200; gen fax (816) 761-8215; disp adv e-mail mwilson@jcadvocate.com; class adv e-mail bdavis@jcadvocate.com; ed e-mail mwilson@jcadvocate.com; web site http://jcadvocate.blogspot.com/
Circulation: 6,000pd, 175fr; Sworn/Estimate/Non-Audited
Advertising rate: Open inch rate $9.00
Established: 1953
Editor.. Mary Wilson
Delivery Method: Mail, Newsstand, Racks
Areas Served: 64030, 64147, 64146, 64145, 64137, 64131, 64114, 64134, 64132, 64130, 64129, 64113

GRANT CITY

THE TIMES TRIBUNE (WED)

E 3rd St, Grant City, MO, 64456, Worth, USA; gen tel (660) 564-3603; gen fax (660) 564-3603; disp adv e-mail timestribune@grantcity.net; class adv e-mail timestribune@grantcity.net; ed e-mail timestribune@grantcity.net
Circulation: 1,200pd, 36fr; Sworn/Estimate/Non-Audited
Advertising rate: Open inch rate $4.50
Established: 1929
Ed.. Bridget Gibson

GREENFIELD

THE VEDETTE (THUR)

7 N Main St, Greenfield, MO, 65661-1128, Dade, USA; gen tel (417) 637-2712; gen fax (417) 637-2232; disp adv e-mail greenfieldvedettegraphics@mchsi.com; ed e-mail greenfieldvedettepublisher@mchsi.com; web site www.greenfieldvedette.com
Circulation: 2,403pd,; Sworn/Estimate/Non-Audited
Advertising rate: Open inch rate $5.35
Established: 1866
Group: Lewis Co.Press
Ed...Marlene DeClue
Delivery Method: Mail
Areas Served: 65661

HALE

HALE HORIZONS (WED)

29236 Highway J, Hale, MO, 64643, Carroll, USA; gen tel (660) 565-2555; gen fax (660) 565-2556; ed e-mail halehorizons@cvalley.net; web site https://www.facebook.com/pages/Hale-Horizons/133432296718836
Circulation: 750pd,; Sworn/Estimate/Non-Audited
Advertising rate: Open inch rate $7.00
Established: 1996
Publisher...................................Cynthia Corf
Mechanical Specifications: Type page 9 1/2 x 13; E - 3 cols, 3, 1/4 between; A - 3 cols, 3, 1/4 between; C - 3 cols, between.Equipment & Software: Hardware — Packard Bell.
Delivery Method: Mail, Newsstand

HAMILTON

THE CALDWELL COUNTY NEWS (WED)

101 S Davis St, Hamilton, MO, 64644-1405, Caldwell, USA; gen tel (816) 583-2116; gen fax (816) 583-2118; disp adv e-mail ads@mycaldwellcounty.com; class adv e-mail ads@mycaldwellcounty.com; ed e-mail news@mycaldwellcounty.com; web site www.mycaldwellcounty.com
Circulation: 1,140pd, 72fr; Sworn/Estimate/Non-Audited
Advertising rate: Open inch rate $3.85
Established: 1869
Publisher and editor.................. Anne L. Tezon
Ed.. Debbie Rankin
Owner/Marketing Consultant............Stephanie HunryEquipment & Software: Hardware — 5-APP/Mac; Software — Adobe/PageMaker 6.0.
Delivery Method: Mail, Newsstand, Racks
Areas Served: Caldwell County

THE HAMILTON ADVOCATE (WED)

412 S Davis St, Hamilton, MO, 64644-1432, USA; gen tel (816) 583-2116; gen fax (816) 583-2118; disp adv e-mail news@llpublications.com; web site www.caldwell-countynews.com
Circulation: 1,450pd, 77fr; Sworn/Estimate/Non-Audited
Advertising rate: Open inch rate $4.00
Established: 1869
Pub..Marshall Tezon
Circ. Mgr..Ann Childs
Ed.. Anne L. Tezon
Mechanical Specifications: Type page 10 x 12; E - 4 cols, 2 5/8, 1/4 between; A - 4 cols, 2 5/8, 1/4 between; C - 4 cols, 2 5/8, 1/4 between. Equipment & Software: Hardware — 3-APP/Power Mac 7200; Software — Adobe/PageMaker 6.0, Adobe/Photoshop 3.0.

HANNIBAL

SALT RIVER JOURNAL (WED)

200 N 3rd St, Hannibal, MO, 63401-3504, Marion, USA; gen tel (573) 221-2800; adv tel (573) 248-2711; ed tel (573) 248-2750; gen fax (573) 221-1568; disp adv e-mail jreynolds@gatehousemedia.com; class adv e-mail samara.campen@courierpost.com; ed e-mail eric.dundon@courierpost.com; web site www.hannibal.net
Circulation: 5,383pd, 9,230fr; Sworn/Estimate/Non-Audited
Advertising rate: Open inch rate $6.25
Established: 1838
Circ Mgr................................Jenetta Cranmer
Ed.. Eric Dundon
News Ed.............................. Catherine Ripley
Gen. Mgr............................ Jessica Spurgron
Mechanical Specifications: Type page 11 3/4 x 21 1/2; E - 6 cols, 1 5/6, 1/8 between; A - 6 cols, 1 1/4, 1/8 between; C - 9 cols, 1 5/6, 1/12 between.Equipment & Software: Hardware — APP/G-4, MON/1270 Imagesetter, AGFA/Accu Set 1000; Presses — 9-G/Community; Software — QPS/QuarkXPress 4.1.
Areas Served: 63459, 63353, 63436, 63441, 63462, 63463, 63401

HARRISONVILLE

CASS COUNTY DEMOCRAT-MISSOURIAN (FRI)

301 S Lexington St, Harrisonville, MO, 64701-2446, Cass, USA; gen tel (816) 380-3228; gen fax (816) 380-7650; disp adv e-mail kfeiss@demo-mo.com; class adv e-mail janslinger@demo-mo.com; ed e-mail jbeaudoin@demo-mo.com; web site www.demo-mo.com
Circulation: 5,600pd, 10,000fr; Sworn/Estimate/Non-Audited
Group: The McClatchy Company
General Sales Assistant.................Julie Hicks
Ad Manager................Kristi FeissEquipment & Software: Hardware — IBM, APP/Power Mac; Presses — 10-G; Software — QPS/QuarkXPress, Claris/MacWrite, Multi-Ad/Creator, Dewar/Sys 7.
Delivery Method: Mail

HAZELWOOD

FLORISSANT/BLACK JACK-NORTH COUNTY JOURNAL (WED, SUN)

7751 N Lindbergh Blvd, Hazelwood, MO, 63042-2135, St. Louis, USA; gen tel (314) 972-1111; gen fax (314) 831-7643; ed e-mail cmarty@yourjournal.com; web site suburbanjournals.stltoday.com
Circulation: 35,000fr; Sworn/Estimate/Non-Audited
Advertising rate: Open inch rate $8.50
Promotions Dir.....................Mary Ann Wagner
Adv. Mgr................................ Tammie Sprinkle
Mechanical Specifications: Type page 12 x 21 1/2; E - 6 cols, 1 7/8, 1/8 between; A - 6 cols, 1 7/8, 1/8 between; C - 10 cols, 1 1/4, 1/3 between.Equipment & Software: Hardware — SII/Sys 55, APP/Mac Network; Presses — 32-G/Urbanite.

OVERLAND/ST. ANN JOURNAL-NORTH COUNY JOURNAL (WED)

7751 N Lindbergh Blvd, Hazelwood, MO, 63042-2135, St. Louis, USA; gen tel (314) 972-1111; gen fax (314) 831-7643; ed e-mail cmarty@yourjournal.com; web site suburbanjournals.stltoday.com
Circulation: 22,260fr; Sworn/Estimate/Non-Audited
Advertising rate: Open inch rate $7.45
Pub.. Carolyn Marty
Adv. Mgr............................. Tammy Mortensen
Circ. Mgr...................................Dan Crockwell
Mechanical Specifications: Type page 12 x 21 1/2; E - 6 cols, 1 7/8, 1/8 between; A - 6 cols, 1 7/8, 1/8 between; C - 10 cols, 1 1/4, 1/3 between.Equipment & Software: Hardware — SII/Sys 55, APP/Mac Network; Presses — 32-G/Urbanite.

HERMANN

NEW HAVEN LEADER (WED)

136 E 4th St, Hermann, MO, 65041-1177, Gasconade, USA; gen tel (573) 237-3222; gen fax (573) 237-7222; disp adv e-mail hacmgr@lcs.net; ed e-mail nhleditor@lcs.net; web site www.newhavenleader.com
Circulation: 1,700pd,; Sworn/Estimate/Non-Audited
Advertising rate: Open inch rate $5.50
Established: 1895
Ed..Buck Collier
Delivery Method: Mail

THE HERMANN ADVERTISER-COURIER (WED)

136 E 4th St, Hermann, MO, 65041-1177, Gasconade, USA; gen tel (573) 486-5418; gen fax (573) 486-5524; disp adv e-mail hacmgr@lcs.net; ed e-mail monews@lcs.net; web site www.hermannadvertisercourier.com
Circulation: 3,900pd,; Sworn/Estimate/Non-Audited
Advertising rate: Open inch rate $6.89
Established: 1837
Group: Lakeway Publishers, Inc.
Digital Platform - Mobile: Apple, Android, Windows, Blackberry
Digital Platform - Tablet: Apple iOS, Android, Windows 7, Blackberry Tablet OS, Kindle, Nook, Kindle Fire, Other
Gen. Mgr... Cathi Utley
Mechanical Specifications: Type page 13 x 21 1/2; E - 6 cols, 2 1/8, between; A - 6 cols, 2 1/8, between.Equipment & Software: ; Software — QPS/QuarkXPress 4.1, APP/Mac System 3.
Areas Served: Hermann 65041

HERMITAGE

THE INDEX (WED)

109 W. Polk St., Hermitage, MO, 65668, Hickory, USA; gen tel (417) 745-6404; gen fax (417) 745-2222; disp adv e-mail jfoltz@vernonpublishing.com; ed e-mail tvernon@vernonpublishing.com; web site https://www.vernonpublishing.com/Index/
Circulation: 4,300pd,; Sworn/Estimate/Non-Audited
Advertising rate: Open inch rate $5.00
Established: 1903
Pub..Trevor Vernon

Ed. ....Charles Dryer
Adv..Jamie Foltz
Mechanical Specifications: 6 col x 21.5" 2" columnsEquipment & Software: Hardware — Mac Imacs; Presses — Kingpress 4-unit; Software — Adobe Creative Suite
Delivery Method: Mail, Newsstand
Areas Served: 65668, 65779, 65774, 65732, 65634, 65724, 65767, 65650, 64738, 65674, 65735

HIGGINSVILLE

HIGGINSVILLE ADVANCE (WED)

3002 Highway 13 Blvd, Higginsville, MO, 64037-1870, Lafayette, USA; gen tel (660) 584-3611; gen fax (660) 584-7966; disp adv e-mail bmackie@ctcis.net; class adv e-mail bmackie@ctcis.net; ed e-mail higvladv@ctcis.net; web site http://www.mainstreet-media.us/
Circulation: 1,700pd, 15fr; Sworn/Estimate/Non-Audited
Advertising rate: Open inch rate $6.75
Established: 1876
Group: Main Street Media, Inc
Pub ....Frank Mercer
Delivery Method: Mail, Racks

HOLLISTER

BRANSON TRI-LAKES NEWS (WED, SAT)

200 Industrial Park Dr, Hollister, MO, 65672-5327, Taney, USA; gen tel (417) 334-3161; gen fax (417) 334-1460; disp adv e-mail shane@bransontrilakesnews.com; class adv e-mail classifieds@bransontrilakesnews.com; ed e-mail csain@bransontrilakesnews.com; web site www.bransontrilakesnews.com
Circulation: 9,300pd, 19,000fr; Sworn/Estimate/Non-Audited
Advertising rate: Open inch rate $17.00
Established: 1895
Group: Lancaster Management, Inc.
Bus. Office ....Robert Erickson
Ed. ....Cliff Sain
Advertising Manager..................Shane Walton
Mechanical Specifications: Type page 11 1/2 x 21; E - 6 cols, 1 13/16, 1/8 between; A - 6 cols, 1 13/16, 1/8 between; C - 6 cols, 1 13/16, 1/8 between.
Delivery Method: Mail, Newsstand, Racks
Areas Served: 65672

HOPKINS

THE HOPKINS JOURNAL (THUR)

411 E Barnard St, Hopkins, MO, 64461, Nodaway, USA; gen tel (660) 778-3205; gen fax (660) 778-3205; ed e-mail hopkinsjournal@embarqmail.com
Circulation: 750pd, 100fr; USPS
Advertising rate: Open inch rate $4.00
Established: 1875
Adv. Mgr. ....Steve Thompson
Ed. ....Darla Thompson
Mechanical Specifications: Type page 12 x 21.Equipment & Software: Hardware — IBM; Software — Adobe/PageMaker.
Delivery Method: Mail, Racks
Areas Served: 64461, 64476, 64468, 50833,

HOUSTON

HOUSTON HERALD (THUR)

113 N Grand Ave, Houston, MO, 65483-1223, Texas, USA; gen tel (417) 967-2000; gen fax (417) 967-2096; disp adv e-mail ads@houstonherald.com; class adv e-mail ads@houstonherald.com; ed e-mail news@houstonherald.com; web site www.houstonherald.com - 2,000,000(views) 100,000(visitors)
Circulation: 4,075pd, 6,100fr; USPS
Advertising rate: Open inch rate $8.50
Established: 1878
Digital Platform - Mobile: Apple, Android, Windows
Digital Platform - Tablet: Apple iOS, Android, Windows 7, Kindle, Kindle Fire
Publisher.............................Bradley G. Gentry
Ed. ....Jeff McNiell
Mechanical Specifications: Type page 11.625 x 21; E - 6 cols, 1.83, 1/6 between; A - 6 cols, 1.83, 1/6 between; C - 6 cols, 1.83, 1/6 between.Equipment & Software: Hardware — APP; Presses — G; Software — Adobe InDesign 4Microsoft/Word, FileMaker.
Delivery Method: Mail, Newsstand, Carrier, Racks
Areas Served: 65444, 65689, 65464, 65468, 65479, 65483, 65484, 65542, 65555, 65557, 65564, 65570, 65542, 65560, 65436, 65461, 65462

HUMANSVILLE

HUMANSVILLE STAR-LEADER (FRI)

117 N Ohio St, Humansville, MO, 65674-8734, Polk, USA; gen tel (417) 754-2228; gen fax (417) 646-8015; disp adv e-mail humansvillestarleader@gmail.com; class adv e-mail sacosageads@centurytel.net; ed e-mail sacosagenews@centurytel.net; web site http://www.mainstreetmedia.us/
Circulation: 1,715pd, 10fr; Sworn/Estimate/Non-Audited
Advertising rate: Open inch rate $5.00
Established: 1887
Group: Main Street Media, Inc.
Adv. Mgr. ....Donna White
Ed. ....Michael Crawford
Delivery Method: Mail
Areas Served: Humansville

IRONTON

THE MOUNTAIN ECHO (WED)

110 N Main St, Ironton, MO, 63650-1108, Iron, USA; gen tel (573) 546-3917; adv tel (573) 546-3917; ed tel (573) 546-3917; disp adv e-mail sue@myironcountynews.com; class adv e-mail sue@myironcountynews.com; ed e-mail randy@myironcountynews.com; web site www.myironcountynews.com
Circulation: 1,407pd, 4,976fr; USPS
Advertising rate: Open inch rate $5.50 TMC - $8.75
Established: 1937
Digital Platform - Mobile: Apple, Android
Digital Platform - Tablet: Apple iOS, Android
Off. Mgr/Owner ....Susan Pribble
Ed/Pub/owner.........................Randall Pribble
Mechanical Specifications: Type page 11 5/8 x 21 1/2; E - 6 cols, 1 1/8, 1/6 between; A - 6 cols, 1 1/8, 1/6 between; C - 6 cols, 1 1/8, 1/6 between.Equipment & Software: Hardware — APP/Mac G4; Software — InDesign, Photoshop, Illustrator
Delivery Method: Mail, Newsstand, Racks
Areas Served: 63650, 63663, 63621, 63656, 63623, 63620, 63654, 63625, 63636

JACKSON

CASH-BOOK JOURNAL/THE WEEKENDER (WED, FRI)

210 W Main St, Jackson, MO, 63755-1822, Jackson, USA; gen tel (573) 243-3515; gen fax (573) 243-3517; disp adv e-mail stephanie.watkins@thecash-book.com; class adv e-mail cbjadvleg@socket.net; ed e-mail denise.kinder@thecash-book.com; web site www.thecash-book.com
Circulation: 6,000pd, 4,000fr; Sworn/Estimate/Non-Audited
Advertising rate: Open inch rate $12.00
Established: 1870
Pub...Gina Raffety
Adv. Mgr. ....Jim Salzman
Circ. Mgr.......................................Elaine Hale
Asst. Pub.....................................David Bloom
Prodn. Mgr. ....Greg DullumEquipment & Software: Hardware — 1-APP/Power Mac 7200, 1-APP/Power Mac 7200, 1-APP/Mac Centris 650, 1-APP/Mac Centris 610, 2-APP/Mac, 1-HP/Scarlet 3C, 1-APP/LaserWriter 161600 PS, 1-APP/Macx LaserWriter II; Software — Adobe/Photoshop 2.5.1, Adobe/PageMaker 5.0, Adobe/Illustrat
Areas Served: 63701-63703, 63770, 63739, 63743, 63745, 63747, 63755, 63755, 63752, 63766, 63769, 63779, 63785

JAMESPORT

TRI-COUNTY WEEKLY (THUR)

103 S Broadway, Jamesport, MO, 64648, Daviess, USA; gen tel (660) 684-6515; gen fax (660) 684-6515; ed e-mail nert@grm.net; web site www.jamesporttricountyweekly.com
Circulation: 1,500pd,; Sworn/Estimate/Non-Audited
Advertising rate: Open inch rate $3.75
Ed. ....Natha McAllisterEquipment & Software: Hardware — APP/Mac 7200; Software — Adobe/PageMaker 6.0.
Areas Served: Jamesport, Daviess - Grundy - Livingston

KAHOKA

THE MEDIA (WED)

178 W Main St, Kahoka, MO, 63445-1637, Clark, USA; gen tel (660) 727-3395; gen fax (660) 727-2475; ed e-mail themedia@thecenturytel.net; web site http://nemonews.net/category/kahoka-news/
Circulation: 2,650pd,; Sworn/Estimate/Non-Audited
Advertising rate: Open inch rate $4.75
Established: 1977
Pub...Mike Scott
Ed. ....Sue Scott
Office Manager............................Vicki Gutting
Mechanical Specifications: Type page 13 x 21; E - 6 cols, 2, 1/6 between; A - 6 cols, 1/6 between; C - 8 cols, 1 1/2, 1/6 between.Equipment & Software: Hardware — PC; Software — Microsoft/Windows 95.
Delivery Method: Mail, Newsstand

KANSAS CITY

KANSAS CITY BUSINESS JOURNAL (FRI)

1100 Main St, Ste 2450, Kansas City, MO, 64105-5189, Jackson, USA; gen tel (816) 421-5900; gen fax (816) 472-4010; disp adv e-mail coster@bizjournals.com; class adv e-mail sprosser@bizjournals.com; ed e-mail bkaberline@bizjournals.com; web site www.kansascity.bizjournals.com
Circulation: 10,500pd,; AAM
Advertising rate: Open inch rate $6,050.00 (Full-Page)
Established: 1982
Digital Platform - Mobile: Apple, Android
Digital Platform - Tablet: Apple iOS, Android
Pub..Stacie Prosser
Ed. ....Brian Kaberline
Circ. Dir. ....Kent Barthol
Delivery Method: Mail, Newsstand, Racks
Areas Served: Kansas City

LEE'S SUMMIT JOURNAL (WED, FRI)

PO Box 413068, Kansas City, MO, 64141-3068, Jackson, USA; gen tel (816) 524-2345; adv tel (816) 282-7003; ed tel (816) 282-7001; gen fax (816) 524-5136; disp adv e-mail shernandez@lsjournal.com; class adv e-mail mleonard@lsjournal.com; ed e-mail mmartin@kcstar.com; web site www.lsjournal.com
Circulation: 3,369pd, 2,521fr; VAC
Advertising rate: Open inch rate $17.00
Established: 1881
Group: The McClatchy Company
Ed. ....Maria Martin
Circ. Mgr.....................................John McCall
Adv. Sales Mgr......................Sonja Hernandez
Mechanical Specifications: Type page 13 x 21; E - 6 cols, 2 1/16, 1/8 between; A - 6 cols, 2 1/16, 1/8 between; C - 9 cols, 1 3/4, 1/8 between.Equipment & Software: Hardware — PC; Software — QPS/QuarkXPress 3.1, Adobe/Photoshop 3.0.

THE NORTHEAST NEWS (WED)

5715 Saint John Ave, Kansas City, MO, 64123-1819, Jackson, USA; gen tel (816) 241-0765; gen fax (816) 241-3255; disp adv e-mail northeastnews@socket.net; class adv e-mail dorri@northeastnews.net; ed e-mail mbushnell@northeastnews.net; web site www.northeastnews.net
Circulation: 28pd, 10,000fr; CVC
Advertising rate: Open inch rate $9.00
Established: 1932
Pub./Adv. ....Michael Bushnell
Managing Editor ....Paul Thompson
Creative Director.......................Bryan Stalder
Account Executive.......................Dorri Partain
Delivery Method: Carrier
Areas Served: Jackson County, MO, 64123, 24, 25, 26, 27.

THE OLATHE NEWS (WED, SAT)

1729 Grand Blvd, Kansas City, MO, 64108-1413, Jackson, USA; gen tel (816) 234-4636; adv tel (816) 234-4000; ed tel (816) 234-7738; disp adv e-mail respinoza@theolathenews.com; class adv e-mail jleary@kcstar.com; ed e-mail srosen@kcstar.com; web site www.theolathenews.com
Circulation: 25,000pd,; Sworn/Estimate/Non-Audited
Advertising rate: Open inch rate $149.00 (single insertion rates)
Established: 1960
Group: The McClatchy Company
Digital Platform - Mobile: Apple, Android, Windows
Digital Platform - Tablet: Apple iOS, Android, Windows 7
Ed ....Grace Hobson
Circ ....Ginger House
Adv...Ciani Ron
Class. Mgr..........................Anderson Deborah
Delivery Method: Mail, Newsstand, Carrier
Areas Served: 66061,66062,66030,66083,66018

KEARNEY

THE KEARNEY COURIER (THUR)

102 W Washington St, Kearney, MO, 64060-8630, Clay, USA; gen tel (816) 628-6010; gen fax (816) 628-4422; disp adv e-mail ryan.johnson@kearneycourier.com; class adv e-mail jmaddox@npgco.com; ed e-mail amanda.lubinski@kearneycourier.com; web site www.kearneycourier.com
Circulation: 4,000pd,; Sworn/Estimate/Non-Audited
Advertising rate: Open inch rate $7.98
Pub...Sandy Nelson
Ryan Johnson
Ed. ....Amanda Lubinski

KENNETT

DELTA NEWS CITIZEN (WED)

PO Box 669, Kennett, MO, 63857-0669, Pike, USA; gen tel (573) 276-5148; gen fax (573) 276-3687; disp adv e-mail csummers@ddd-news.com; ed e-mail srouse@stategazette.com; web site http://www.deltanewscitizen.com/
Circulation: 2,500pd,; Sworn/Estimate/Non-Audited
Advertising rate: Open inch rate $11.20
Established: 1997
Group: Rust Communications
Pub...Shelia Rose
Ed. ....Trina Bell
Gen. Mgr. ....Mike Smith

KNOB NOSTER

KNOB NOSTER ITEM (THUR)
111 N Jackson Ave, Knob Noster, MO, 65336-1315, Johnson, USA; gen tel (660) 563-3606; ed e-mail knobnosteritem@sbc-global.net
Circulation: 800pd, 10fr; USPS
Advertising rate: Open inch rate $3.75
Established: 1958
Ed. .... Stan Hall
Areas Served: 65336, 65305, 64093, 65337

LA GRANGE

THE CANTON PRESS-NEWS JOURNAL (THUR)
109 N 4th St, La Grange, MO, 63448-1342, Lewis, USA; gen tel (573) 288-5668; gen fax (573) 288-0000; disp adv e-mail ads@lewispnj.com; ed e-mail rita1@lewispnj.com; web site www.lewispnj.com
Circulation: 3,000pd,; Sworn/Estimate/Non-Audited
Advertising rate: Open inch rate $4.00
Adv. Mgr. .... Jennifer Pegler
Ed. .... Daniel Steinbeck
Mechanical Specifications: Type page 11 3/4 x 21; E - 6 cols, 1 3/4, 1/4 between; A - 6 cols, 1 3/4, 1/4 between; C - 6 cols, 1 3/4, 1/4 between.Equipment & Software: Hardware — APP/Mac; Software — Microsoft/Word 5.0, Adobe/PageMaker 6.0.

LA PLATA

THE HOME PRESS (WED)
115 N. Rubey, La Plata, MO, 63549, Macon, USA; gen tel (660) 332-4431; gen fax (660) 332-7561; disp adv e-mail scoram.home-press@gmail.com; class adv e-mail news.homepress@gmail.com; ed e-mail news.homepress@gmail.com; web site http://www.maconhomepress.com
Circulation:; Sworn/Estimate/Non-Audited
Advertising rate: Open inch rate $5.00
Established: 1876
Digital Platform - Mobile: Apple, Windows
Pub. .... Shon Coram
Delivery Method: Mail
Areas Served: Macon County, Missouri

LAMAR

LAMAR DEMOCRAT (WED, SAT)
100 E 11th St, Lamar, MO, 64759-1943, Barton, USA; gen tel (417) 682-5529; adv tel (417) 682-5529 x11; ed tel (417) 682-5529 x16; gen fax (417) 682-5595; disp adv e-mail melissa@lamardemocrat.com; ed e-mail melodymetzger@lamardemocrat.com; web site www.lamardemocrat.com
Circulation: 3,335pd,; USPS
Advertising rate: Open inch rate $6.80
Established: 1920
Pub. .... Douglas D. Davis
Circ. Mgr. .... Melody Metzger
Ed. .... Rayma B. DavisEquipment & Software: Hardware — APP/Mac.; Software — InDesign, Photoshop
Delivery Method: Mail, Racks
Areas Served: 64759 and multiple others around the country

LAWSON

THE LAWSON REVIEW (WED)
405 N Pennsylvania Ave, Lawson, MO, 64062-9402, Clay and Ray, USA; gen tel (816) 296-3412; gen fax (816) 296-3412; ed e-mail lawsonreview@juno.com; web site https://www.facebook.com/thelawsonreview
Circulation: 2,200pd,; Sworn/Estimate/Non-Audited
Advertising rate: Open inch rate $3.80
Established: 1881
Pub. .... R. Cress Hewitt
Ed. .... David Blyth
Mechanical Specifications: Type page 10 x 16; E - 4 cols, 2 1/4, 1/4 between; A - 4 cols, 2 1/4, 1/4 between; C - 4 cols, 2 1/4, 1/4 between. Equipment & Software: Hardware — APP/Mac; Software — Adobe/PageMaker.

LEES SUMMIT

LEE'S SUMMIT TRIBUNE (SAT)
219 SE Douglas St, Lees Summit, MO, 64063-2328, Jackson, USA; gen tel (816) 524-0061; adv tel (816) 524-0061; ed tel (816) 524-0061; gen fax (816) 600-6102; adv fax (816) 600-6102; ed fax (816) 600-6102; disp adv e-mail editor@lstribune.net; class adv e-mail editor@lstribune.net; ed e-mail Linda@lstribune.net; web site www.lstribune.net - 100,000(views) 44,000(visitors)
Circulation: 3,500pd,; Sworn/Estimate/Non-Audited
Advertising rate: Open inch rate $17.50
Established: 2002
Digital Platform - Mobile: Apple
Digital Platform - Tablet: Apple iOS
Owner/Pub. .... Linda Ahern
Mechanical Specifications: 10.5" wide by 21.5" tall
Delivery Method: Mail, Newsstand, Racks
Areas Served: Lee's Summit, Greenwood, Lake Lotawana, and Lone Jack

LEXINGTON

THE LEXINGTON NEWS (WED, FRI)
1009 Franklin Ave, Lexington, MO, 64067-1333, Lafayette, USA; gen tel (660) 259-2266; gen fax (660) 259-4870; ed e-mail lexingtonnews@mbarkmail.com; web site mainstreetmedia.us
Circulation: 4,000pd, 30fr; Sworn/Estimate/Non-Audited
Advertising rate: Open inch rate $5.00
Established: 1868
Group: Main Street Media, Inc.
Main Street Media
Pub. .... Frank W. Mercer
Bus Mgr. .... Devon Ellis-Miranda
Adv. Mgr. .... Marian Couch
Circ. Mgr. .... Nancy Oles
Ed. .... Joe Parmon
Mechanical Specifications: Type page 13 x 21; A - 6 cols, 2, 1/4 between; C - 6 cols, 2, 1/4 between.
Delivery Method: Mail

LIBERAL

LIBERAL NEWS (THUR)
106 S Main St, Liberal, MO, 64762-9313, Barton, USA; gen tel (417) 843-5315; gen fax (417) 843-5315
Circulation: 700pd, 0fr; Sworn/Estimate/Non-Audited
Advertising rate: Open inch rate $4.00
Established: 1910
Darvin E. Weaver
Ruth Ann WeaverEd.s
Areas Served: Liberal and Barton County

LIBERTY

GLADSTONE DISPATCH (THUR)
104 N Main St, Liberty, MO, 64068-1640, Clay, USA; gen tel (816) 454-9660; gen fax (816) 781-0909; disp adv e-mail quinn.gregg@npgco.com; class adv e-mail rachel.chrisman@npgco.com; ed e-mail amy.neal@npgco.com; web site gladstonedispatch.com
Ed. .... Amy Neal
Pub. .... Sandy Nelson

LIBERTY TRIBUNE (THUR)
104 N Main St, Liberty, MO, 64068-1640, Clay, USA; gen tel (816) 781-4941; adv tel (816) 389-6618; ed tel (816) 389-6630; gen fax (816) 781-0909; disp adv e-mail quinn.gregg@libertytribune.com; class adv e-mail rachel.chrisman@libertytribune.com; ed e-mail amy.neal@libertytribune.com; web site www.libertytribune.com
Circulation: 2,863pd, 8,594fr; Sworn/Estimate/Non-Audited
Advertising rate: Open inch rate $15.25
Established: 1846
Managing Editor .... Amy Neal
Adv. Dir. .... Tracey Mummaw
Pub. .... Sandy Nelson
Circ. Mgr. .... Stephanie Cates
Mechanical Specifications: Type page 13 x 21; E - 6 cols, 2 1/8, between; A - 6 cols, 2 1/8, between; C - 9 cols, 1 3/8, between.
Delivery Method: Mail
Areas Served: Liberty, Clay County

LICKING

THE LICKING NEWS (THUR)
115 S Main St, Licking, MO, 65542, Texas, USA; gen tel (573) 674-2412; gen fax (573) 674-4892; disp adv e-mail news_ads@thelickingnews.com; class adv e-mail donna@thesalemnewsonline.com; ed e-mail angela@thelickingnews.com; web site www.thelickingnews.com
Circulation: 2,421pd,; Sworn/Estimate/Non-Audited
Advertising rate: Open inch rate $4.00
Established: 1893
Pub. .... Donald Dodd
Mng. Ed. .... Angela Barnes

LINN

UNTERRIFIED DEMOCRAT (WED)
300 E Main St, Linn, MO, 65051-9000, Osage, USA; gen tel (573) 897-2109; gen fax (573) 897-0076; disp adv e-mail udna@socket.net; ed e-mail udnews@socket.com
Circulation: 7,100pd,; Sworn/Estimate/Non-Audited
Advertising rate: Open inch rate $4.00
Established: 1866
Ed. .... Jerrilynn S. Voss
Mechanical Specifications: Type page 15 3/4 x 21; E - 6 cols, 2 1/3, between; A - 8 cols, 1 5/6, between; C - 8 cols, 2, 1/6 between. Equipment & Software: Hardware — APP/Mac; Software — Adobe/PageMaker 5.0.
Delivery Method: Mail

MANSFIELD

THE MANSFIELD MIRROR/WRIGHT CO. REPUBLICAN (THUR)
300 E Commercial St, Mansfield, MO, 65704-2502, Wright, USA; gen tel (417) 924-3226; gen fax (417) 924-3227; disp adv e-mail susie@mansfieldmirror.com; ed e-mail larry@mansfieldmirror.com; web site www.mansfieldmirror.com
Circulation: 2,158pd, 17fr; Sworn/Estimate/Non-Audited
Advertising rate: Open inch rate $3.45
Established: 1908
Ed./Pub. .... Larry Dennis
Assist. Pub. .... Suzann Choate
Mechanical Specifications: Type page 13 x 21; E - 6 cols, 2 1/16, 1/8 between; A - 6 cols, 2 1/16, 1/8 between; C - 6 cols, 2 1/16, 1/8 between.Equipment & Software: ; Software — Adobe/PageMaker 6.0.
Delivery Method: Mail, Newsstand

MARBLE HILL

THE BANNER-PRESS (WED)
103 WALNUT ST, Marble Hill, MO, 63764, Bollinger, USA; gen tel (573) 238-2821; gen fax (573) 238-0020; ed e-mail banpress@hotmail.com; web site http://www.thebanner-press.com/
Circulation: 4,200pd,; Sworn/Estimate/Non-Audited
Advertising rate: Open inch rate $6.00
Established: 1881
Group: Rust Communications
Pub. .... Gera LeGrand
Gen. Mgr. .... Linda Redeffer
Delivery Method: Mail, Newsstand, Racks
Areas Served: Marble Hill

MARSHFIELD

THE MARSHFIELD MAIL (WED)
225 N Clay St, Marshfield, MO, 65706-1652, Webster, USA; gen tel (417) 468-2013; gen fax (417) 859-7930; disp adv e-mail debbiec@marshfieldmail.com; class adv e-mail janc@marshfieldmail.com; ed e-mail scottk@marshfieldmail.com; web site www.marshfieldmail.com - 38,832(views) 8,992(visitors)
Circulation: 4,814pd, 99fr; USPS
Advertising rate: Open inch rate $13.50
Established: 1891
Group: Phillips Media Group LLC
Digital Platform - Mobile: Apple, Android
Digital Platform - Tablet: Apple iOS, Android
Adv. Mgr. .... Debbie Chapman
Pub. .... Dave Berry
Gen. Mgr/Ed. .... Scott Kerber
Circ. .... Jim Kennedy
Mechanical Specifications: Type page 10.25 x 21; E - 6 cols, 2 1/6, 1/6 between; A - 6 cols, 2 1/6, 1/6 between; C - 8 cols, 1 1/2, 1/6 between.Equipment & Software: Hardware — APP/Mac; Software — QPS/QuarkXPress, Adobe/Photoshop, Macromedia/Freehand.
Delivery Method: Mail, Newsstand
Areas Served: Marshfield, Webster County

MARYVILLE

NODAWAY NEWS LEADER (THUR)
116 E 3rd St, Maryville, MO, 64468-1640, Nodaway, USA; gen tel (660) 562-4747; gen fax (660) 562-3607; disp adv e-mail ldalton@nodawaynews.com; class adv e-mail ldalton@nodawaynews.com; ed e-mail kwilson@nodawaynews.com; web site www.nodawaynews.com
Circulation: 2,649pd,; Sworn/Estimate/Non-Audited
Advertising rate: Open inch rate $23.60
Established: 1996
Digital Platform - Mobile: Apple, Android
Digital Platform - Tablet: Apple iOS, Android
Pub./Owner. .... Kay Wilson
Adv. Mgr. .... Lisa Dalton
Delivery Method: Mail, Newsstand
Areas Served: Nodaway County

MAYSVILLE

DEKALB COUNTY RECORD-HERALD (THUR)
201 N Polk St, Maysville, MO, 64469-9089, Dekalb, USA; gen tel (816) 449-2121; gen fax (816) 449-2808; web site http://maysville.k12.mo.us/
Circulation: 1,900pd, 73fr; Sworn/Estimate/Non-Audited
Advertising rate: Open inch rate $5.00
Pub. .... Terry Pearl
Ed. .... Chrissy Jestes

MEMPHIS

MEMPHIS DEMOCRAT (WED)
121 S Main St, Memphis, MO, 63555-1423, Scotland, USA; gen tel (660) 465-7016; gen fax (660) 465-2803; disp adv e-mail memdemoc@nemr.net; class adv e-mail chris@memphisdemocrat.com; ed e-mail chris@memphisdemocrat.com; web site www.memphisdemocrat.com
Circulation: 2,780pd,; Sworn/Estimate/Non-Audited
Advertising rate: Open inch rate $4.50
Established: 1872
Ed. .... Chris Feeney

MILAN

THE MILAN STANDARD (THUR)
105 S Market St, Milan, MO, 63556-1329, Sullivan, USA; gen tel (660) 265-4244; gen fax (660) 265-3180; ed e-mail milanstd@nemr.net
Circulation: 3,100pd, 40fr; Sworn/Estimate/Non-Audited
Advertising rate: Open inch rate $6.25
Established: 1877
Adv. Mgr. .... Suzie E. Wilson
Circ. Mgr. .... Phyllis Fleshman
Prod. Mgr. .... Joe Lewis
Charlene Pittman
Bonnie Gormley
Mechanical Specifications: Type page 13 x 21 1/2; E - 6 cols, 2 1/16, 1/6 between; A - 6 cols, 2 1/16, 1/6 between; C - 6 cols, 2 1/16, 1/6 between.Equipment & Software: Hardware — APP/Mac, HP; Presses — G/Community, ABD/9810, Riso/3750 es, Riso/GR 3710, Xerox 7120, Brother; Software — QPS/QuarkXPress, Adobe/Photoshop, Microsoft/Windows 95, Microsoft/Quickbooks Pro.
Delivery Method: Mail, Newsstand

MONTGOMERY CITY

MONTGOMERY STANDARD (WED)
115 W 2nd St, Montgomery City, MO, 63361-1812, Montgomery, USA; gen tel (573) 564-2339; gen fax (573) 564-2313; ed e-mail standard@socket.net
Circulation: 3,200pd, 73fr; Sworn/Estimate/Non-Audited
Advertising rate: Open inch rate $4.00
Established: 1868
Ed. ....John FisherEquipment & Software: Hardware — APP/Mac; Software — Adobe/PageMaker.
Delivery Method: Mail, Racks

MOUND CITY

MOUND CITY NEWS (THUR)
511 State St, Mound City, MO, 64470-1144, Holt, USA; gen tel (660) 442-5423; gen fax (660) 442-5423; ed e-mail moundcitynews@socket.net; web site www.moundcitynews.com
Circulation: 2,600pd,; Sworn/Estimate/Non-Audited
Advertising rate: Open inch rate $6.00
Established: 1879
Ed. .... Adam Johnson
Mechanical Specifications: Type page 13 x 21 1/2; E - 6 cols, 2 1/16, 1/6 between; A - 6 cols, 2 1/16, 1/6 between; C - 7 cols, 1 4/5, 1/6 between.Equipment & Software: Hardware — APP/Mac; Software — Adobe/PageMaker, Microsoft/Word.
Areas Served: 64470, 64437, 64473, 64451, 64455, 64466, 64487

MOUNT VERNON

LAWRENCE COUNTY RECORD (WED)
312 S Hickory St, Mount Vernon, MO, 65712-1450, Lawrence, USA; gen tel (417) 466-2185; gen fax (417) 466-7865; disp adv e-mail marketing@lawrencecountyrecord.com; class adv e-mail classifieds@lawrencecountyrecord.com; ed e-mail thepaper@lawrencecountyrecord.com; web site www.lawrencecountyrecord.com
Circulation: 4,000pd, 7,600fr; Sworn/Estimate/Non-Audited
Advertising rate: Open inch rate $5.70
Established: 1876
Pub./Ed. .... Ryan Squibb
Adv. Mgr. .... Cheryl Reynolds
Mechanical Specifications: Type page 11 5/8 x 21 1/2; E - 6 cols, 1 3/4, 1/6 between; A - 6 cols, 2 1/16, 1/6 between; C - 6 cols, 2 1/16, 1/6 between.Equipment & Software: Hardware — APP/Mac; Software — Adobe/InDesign
Delivery Method: Mail, Newsstand, Carrier, Racks
Areas Served: 65712, 65707, 65756

MOUNTAIN GROVE

MOUNTAIN GROVE NEWS-JOURNAL (WED)
150 E 1st St, Mountain Grove, MO, 65711-1742, Wright, USA; gen tel (417) 926-5148; gen fax (417) 926-6648; disp adv e-mail classifieds@news-journal.net; class adv e-mail classifieds@news-journal.net; ed e-mail doug@news-journal.net; web site www.news-journal.net
Circulation: 3,200pd, 9,850fr; Sworn/Estimate/Non-Audited
Advertising rate: Open inch rate $7.50 (NET)
Established: 1882
Group: Lebanon Publishing Co.
Pub. .... Sandy Anderson
Ed. .... Doug Berger
Mechanical Specifications: Type page 13 x 21; E - 6 cols, 2 1/16, between; A - 6 cols, 2 1/16, between; C - 6 cols, 2 1/16, between. Equipment & Software: Hardware — PC, HP; Presses — HI; Software — Adobe/PageMaker 6.5.
Delivery Method: Mail
Areas Served: 65711, 65608, 65689, 65667, 65704

MOUNTAIN VIEW

MOUNTAIN VIEW STANDARD (WED)
1004 E US Highway 60, Mountain View, MO, 65548-8070, Howell, USA; gen tel (417) 934-2025; gen fax (417) 934-1591; disp adv e-mail standardnews@centurytel.net; class adv e-mail brian@mvstandard.com; ed e-mail tianna@mvstandard.com; web site http://www.mountainviewstandard.com/
Circulation: 7,600pd, 550fr; Sworn/Estimate/Non-Audited
Advertising rate: Open inch rate $3.50
Established: 1906
Ed. .... Tianna Brook
Areas Served: Howell and Shannon County

NEOSHO

NEWTON COUNTY NEWS (WED)
200 S Jefferson St, Neosho, MO, 64850-1753, Newton, USA; gen tel (417) 455-9390; gen fax (417) 472-6311; ed e-mail news@newconews.com; web site www.newtoncountynews.net
Circulation: 2,500pd, 10fr; Sworn/Estimate/Non-Audited
Advertising rate: Open inch rate $7.65
Ed. .... Jennifer Lamp
Pub .... Ronnie Bell
Adv. Mgr. .... Jason Overman

NEVADA

NEVADA HERALD (SAT)
131 S Cedar St, Nevada, MO, 64772-3309, Vernon, USA; gen tel (417) 667-3344; gen fax (417) 667-8384; disp adv e-mail ndmcomposing@gmail.com; class adv e-mail lmcvay@nevadadailymail.com; ed e-mail ndmeditorial@gmail.com; web site www.nevadadailymail.com
Circulation: 5,500pd, 105fr; Sworn/Estimate/Non-Audited
Advertising rate: Open inch rate $9.85
Established: 1883
Pub./Adv. Mgr. .... Lorie Harter
Ed. .... Ralph Pokorny
Prod. Mgr. .... Chris Jones
Circ. Mgr. .... Linda Shankel
Mechanical Specifications: Type page 13 x 21; E - 6 cols, 2 1/16, 1/8 between; A - 6 cols, 2 1/16, 1/8 between; C - 6 cols, 2 1/16, 1/8 between.Equipment & Software: Hardware — APP/Mac; Presses — G/Community; Software — QPS/QuarkXPress 3.3.
Delivery Method: Mail, Newsstand, Racks

NEW LONDON

RALLS COUNTY HERALD-ENTERPRISE (THUR)
404 S Main St, New London, MO, 63459-1326, Ralls, USA; gen tel (573) 985-3420; gen fax (573) 985-5531; ed e-mail danielcrockwell@rallshe.com; web site www.rallscountypaper.com
Circulation: 1,300pd, 0fr; Sworn/Estimate/Non-Audited
Advertising rate: Open inch rate $4.00
Established: 1865
Pub. .... Judith Statler
Ed. .... Gene Statler
Ed. .... Carolyn Trower
Mechanical Specifications: Type page 13 x 21 1/2; E - 6 cols, 2, 1/6 between; A - 6 cols, 2, 1/6 between; C - 6 cols, 2, 1/6 between. Equipment & Software: Hardware — APP/Mac; Software — Adobe/PageMaker 6.5.

NEW MADRID

THE WEEKLY RECORD (FRI)
218 Main St, New Madrid, MO, 63869-1911, New Madrid, USA; gen tel (573) 748-2120; gen fax (573) 748-5435; disp adv e-mail ed@weeklyrecord.net; ed e-mail ed@weeklyrecord.net; web site www.weeklyrecord.net
Circulation: 1,000pd, 60fr; Sworn/Estimate/Non-Audited
Advertising rate: Open inch rate $4.25
Established: 1866
Digital Platform - Mobile: Apple, Windows
Digital Platform - Tablet: Apple iOS
Pub. .... Ed Thomason
Mechanical Specifications: Type page 10 x 21 1/4; E - 6 cols, 3/16 between; A - 6 cols, .125 between; C - 6 cols, .125 between.Equipment & Software: Hardware — Nobilis; Software — Adobe/PageMaker.
Delivery Method: Mail, Newsstand, Racks
Areas Served: 63869, 63862, and surrounding zip codes

NIXA

NIXA NEWS ENTERPRISE (FRI)
123 W Sherman Way, Ste 101, Nixa, MO, 65714-7657, Christian, USA; gen tel (417) 725-3745; gen fax (417) 725-3683; disp adv e-mail paulj@ccheadliner.com; ed e-mail ameliaw@ccheadliner.com; web site http://ccheadliner.com/
Circulation: 2,463pd,; Sworn/Estimate/Non-Audited
Advertising rate: Open inch rate $6.30
Gen. Mgr. .... Chuck Branch
Ed. .... Matt Roberts

NORBORNE

NORBORNE DEMOCRAT-LEADER (THUR)
106 S Pine St, Norborne, MO, 64668-1238, Carroll, USA; gen tel (660) 593-3712; gen fax (660) 593-3712; disp adv e-mail leader@greenhills.net; ed e-mail leader@greenhills.net
Circulation: 1,300pd,; Sworn/Estimate/Non-Audited
Advertising rate: Open inch rate $3.20
Group: Main Street Media, Inc.
Main Street Media, Inc.
Ed. .... Frank Mercer

ODESSA

THE ODESSAN (THUR)
212 W Mason St, Odessa, MO, 64076-1263, Lafayette, USA; gen tel (816) 230-5311; adv tel 816-230-5311; ed tel 816-230-5311; gen fax None; adv fax 816-633-8430; ed fax None; disp adv e-mail spaar@iland.net; class adv e-mail spaar@iland.net; ed e-mail spaar@iland.net; web site www.theodessan.net
Circulation: 4,200pd,; USPS
Advertising rate: Open inch rate $7.25
Established: 1880
Owner .... Betty S. Spaar
Gen. Mgr. .... Renee Spaar
Adv. Mgr. .... John Spaar
Prod. Mgr. .... Joe Spaar
news editor .... Hannah Spaar
Mechanical Specifications: 22 inch webEquipment & Software: Hardware — 7-APP/Mac.
Delivery Method: Mail, Racks
Areas Served: 64076, 64075, 64067, 64011, 64097, 64074, 64037, 64071

OREGON

TIMES OBSERVER (THUR)
119 W Nodaway St, Oregon, MO, 64473, Holt, USA; gen tel (660) 446-3331; gen fax (660) 446-3077; ed e-mail drlogo5@ofmlive.net
Circulation: 2,000pd, 10fr; Sworn/Estimate/Non-Audited
Advertising rate: Open inch rate $5.00
Ed. .... Robert E. Ripley
Delivery Method: Mail, Newsstand

OSCEOLA

ST. CLAIR CO. COURIER (THUR)
285 Pine St, Osceola, MO, 64776-7466, Saint Clair, USA; gen tel (417) 646-2211; gen fax (417) 646-8015; disp adv e-mail sacosageads@centurytel.net; ed e-mail sacosagenews@centurytel.net; web site https://www.facebook.com/St-Clair-County-Courier-150568565081049/about/?ref=page_internal
Circulation: 2,165pd, 24,000fr; Sworn/Estimate/Non-Audited
Advertising rate: Open inch rate $5.00
Group: Main Street Media, Inc.
Reporter .... John Farrell
Pub. .... Michael Crawford
Ad. Sales .... Derek Wood

OWENSVILLE

GASCONADE COUNTY REPUBLICAN (WED)
106 E Washington Ave, Owensville, MO, 65066-1316, Gasconade, USA; gen tel (573) 437-2323; gen fax (573) 437-3033; disp adv e-mail ads@wardpub.com; ed e-mail news@wardpub.com; web site http://www.gasconadecountyrepublican.com/
Circulation: 3,398pd,; Sworn/Estimate/Non-Audited

Advertising rate: Open inch rate $4.85
Established: 1905
Assoc. .... Don Warden
Pub./Adv. Mgr. .... Dennis Warden
Ed. .... Dave Marner
Mechanical Specifications: Type page 13 x 21 1/2; E - 6 cols, 2 1/30, 1/6 between; A - 6 cols, 2 1/30, 1/6 between; C - 6 cols, 2 1/30, 1/6 between.Equipment & Software: Hardware — APP/iMac, APP/Power Mac 7200; Software — Adobe/PageMaker 6.5.

OZARK

CHRISTIAN COUNTY HEADLINER NEWS (WED)

114 N 2nd Ave, Ozark, MO, 65721-8453, Christian, USA; gen tel (417) 581-3541; gen fax (417) 581-3577; disp adv e-mail triciac@ccheadliner.com; class adv e-mail ashleys@ccheadliner.com; ed e-mail ameliaw@ccheadliner.com; web site www.ccheadliner.com - 47,039(views) 13,480(visitors)
Circulation: 3,412pd, 377fr; CVC
Advertising rate: Open inch rate $12.50
Established: 1961
Digital Platform - Mobile: Apple, Android, Blackberry
Digital Platform - Tablet: Apple iOS, Android, Blackberry Tablet OS, Kindle, Kindle Fire
Ed. .... Amelia Wigton
Pub. .... Dave Berry
Gen. Mgr. .... Tricia Chapman
Mechanical Specifications: Type page 10 1/2 x 21; E - 6 cols, 1 4/5, between; A - 6 cols, 1 4/5, between; C - 6 cols, 1 4/5, between. Equipment & Software: ; Software — QPS/QuarkXPress 3.3.
Delivery Method: Mail, Newsstand, Racks

PALMYRA

PALMYRA SPECTATOR (WED)

304 S Main St, Palmyra, MO, 63461-1652, Marion, USA; gen tel (573) 769-3111; gen fax (573) 769-3554; disp adv e-mail advertising@palmyra-spectator.com; class adv e-mail office@palmyra-spectator.com; ed e-mail editorial@palmyra-spectator.com; web site http://www.palmyra-spectator.com/
Circulation: 2,628pd, 75fr; Sworn/Estimate/Non-Audited
Advertising rate: Open inch rate $4.25
Established: 1839
Pub. .... Mark Cheffey

PARIS

MONROE COUNTY APPEAL (THUR)

230 N Main St, Paris, MO, 65275-1329, Monroe, USA; gen tel (314) 574-4401; adv tel (314) 574-4401; ed tel (314) 574-4401; gen fax (660) 327-4847; disp adv e-mail ads@monroecountyappeal.com; class adv e-mail ads@monroecountyappeal.com; ed e-mail news@monroecountyappeal.com; web site www.monroecountyappeal.com
Circulation: 1,000pd, 0fr; Sworn/Estimate/Non-Audited
Advertising rate: Open inch rate $4.50
Established: 1868
Group: Lewis County Press
Pub .... Dan Crockwell
Ad Design .... Margie CrockwellEquipment & Software: Hardware — APP/Mac.
Delivery Method: Mail, Newsstand
Areas Served: Monroe County Missouri

PARK HILLS

FARMINGTON PRESS (WED)

1513 S Saint Joe Dr, Park Hills, MO, 63601-2402, St. Francois, USA; gen tel (573) 431-2010; gen fax (573) 431-7640; adv fax (573) 518-0765; ed e-mail dsmith@dailyjournalonline.com; web site www.pressleader.com
Advertising rate: 1/8 P $188 1/4 P $320 1/2 P $530 Full $934
Ed. .... Doug Smith
Pub. .... Eugene Jackson
Circ. Dir. .... George Easley

PERRYVILLE

THE PERRY COUNTY REPUBLIC-MONITOR (TUES, THUR)

10 W Sainte Marie St, Perryville, MO, 63775-1347, Perry, USA; gen tel (573) 547-4567; adv tel (573) 547-4567; ed tel (573) 547-4567; gen fax (573) 547-1643; disp adv e-mail sales@perryvillenews.com; class adv e-mail republic-monitor@perryvillenews.com; ed e-mail editor@perryvillenews.com; web site www.perryvillenews.com - 50,000(views)
Circulation: 3,800pd,; Sworn/Estimate/Non-Audited
Advertising rate: Open inch rate $9.85
Established: 1889
Group: PTS, Inc.
Pub. .... Beth Durreman
Mechanical Specifications: Type page 11 5/8 x 21; E - 6 cols, 1 7/8, 1/6 between; A - 6 cols, 1 7/8, 1/6 between; C - 9 cols, 1 3/16, 1/6 between.
Delivery Method: Mail, Newsstand, Racks
Areas Served: Perryville, St. Mary, Perry County, Ste. Genevieve County

PIEDMONT

WAYNE COUNTY JOURNAL-BANNER (THUR)

101 W Elm St, Piedmont, MO, 63957-1417, Wayne, USA; gen tel (573) 223-7122; gen fax (573) 223-7871; disp adv e-mail susane@waynecojournalbanner.com; class adv e-mail jhaggett@waynecojournalbanner.com; ed e-mail harold@waynecojounalbanner.com; web site www.waynecojournalbanner.com
Circulation: 3,200pd, 70fr; USPS
Advertising rate: Open inch rate $8.40
Established: 1876
Group: Ellinghouse Publishing Co., Inc.
Pub .... Harold T. Ellinghouse
Ed./Bus. Mgr. .... Brenda Ellinghouse
Adv. Mgr. .... Susan Eaton
Mechanical Specifications: Type page 11.125 x 21.5; E - 6 cols, 1 5/6, 1/8 between; A - 6 cols, 1 5/6, 1/8 between; C - 6 cols, 1 5/6, 1/8 between.Equipment & Software: Hardware — APP/Mac; Presses — KP; Software — Adobe/PageMaker 7.0.
Delivery Method: Mail, Newsstand
Areas Served: Wayne County and adjoining counties

PINEVILLE

MCDONALD COUNTY NEWS-GAZETTE (THUR)

11248 US-71, Pineville, MO, 64856, McDonald, USA; gen tel (417) 223-4675; gen fax (418) 223-4049; ed e-mail thepress@olemac.net
Circulation: 1,431pd,; Sworn/Estimate/Non-Audited
Advertising rate: Open inch rate $4.60
Pub. .... George Pogue
Donnie Parlet
Mng. Ed. .... Rick Peck
Delivery Method: Mail, Newsstand, Racks
Areas Served: 64856, 64861, 64874, 64867, 65730

MCDONALD COUNTY PRESS (WED)

11248 US-71, Pineville, MO, 64856, McDonald, USA; gen tel (417) 223-4675; gen fax (417) 223-4049; ed e-mail thepress@olemac.net; web site http://www.stephensmedia.com/newspapers/missouri/
Circulation: 6,127pd,; Sworn/Estimate/Non-Audited
Advertising rate: Open inch rate $9.00
Group: WEHCO Media, Inc.
Ed. .... Rick Peck
Pub. .... George Pogue
Donnie ParletEquipment & Software: Hardware — APP/Mac, IBM.
Delivery Method: Mail
Areas Served: 64854, 64847

THE ANDERSON GRAPHIC (WED)

11248 US-71, Pineville, MO, 64856, McDonald, USA; gen tel (417) 223-4675; gen fax (417) 223-4049; ed e-mail thepress@olemac.net; web site http://www.stephensmedia.com/newspapers/missouri/
Circulation: 683pd,; Sworn/Estimate/Non-Audited
Advertising rate: Open inch rate $4.05
Adv. Mgr. .... Donnie Parlet
Sports Ed. .... Rick Peck
Pub. .... George Pogue
Delivery Method: Mail
Areas Served: 64831, 64868

THE GOODMAN NEWS-DISPATCH (WED)

11248 US-71, Pineville, MO, 64856, McDonald, USA; gen tel (417) 223-4675; gen fax (417) 223-4049; ed e-mail The Goodman News-Dispatch; web site http://www.stephensmedia.com/newspapers/missouri/
Circulation: 200pd,; Sworn/Estimate/Non-Audited
Advertising rate: Open inch rate $3.75
Ed. .... Rick Peck
Pub. .... George Pogue
Adv. Mgr. .... Donnie Parlet
Delivery Method: Mail
Areas Served: 64843

THE SOUTHWEST CITY REPUBLIC (WED)

11248 US-71, Pineville, MO, 64856, McDonald, USA; gen tel (417) 223-4675; gen fax (417) 223-4049; ed e-mail thepress@olemac.net; web site http://www.stephensmedia.com/newspapers/missouri/
Circulation: 5,500pd,; Sworn/Estimate/Non-Audited
Advertising rate: Open inch rate $7.00
Pub. .... George Pogue
Adv. Mgr. .... Donnie Parlet
Ed. .... Rick Peck
Delivery Method: Mail
Areas Served: 64863

PLATTE CITY

THE LANDMARK (THUR)

252 Main St, Platte City, MO, 64079-8461, Platte, USA; gen tel (816) 858-0363; gen fax (816) 858-2313; disp adv e-mail news@plattecountylandmark.com; class adv e-mail advertising@plattecountylandmark.com; ed e-mail ivan@plattecountylandmark.com; web site www.plattecountylandmark.com
Circulation: 3,600pd, 100fr; Sworn/Estimate/Non-Audited
Advertising rate: Open inch rate $8.00
Established: 1865
Ed. .... Ivan Foley
Mechanical Specifications: Type page 12 5/8 x 21; E - 6 cols, 2, 1/4 between; A - 6 cols, 2, 1/4 between.Equipment & Software: ; Software — Adobe/PageMaker 5.0.
Areas Served: Platte City, Parkville, Kansas City, Riverside, Weston, Barry Road, Platte Woods, Dearborn, Camden Point, Edgerton, Tracy Farley, Waldron, Smithville, Ferrelview, Northmoor, Leavenworth - KS

THE PLATTE COUNTY CITIZEN (WED)

PO Box 888, 812 Third Street, Platte City, MO, 64079-0888, Platte, USA; gen tel (816) 858-5154; gen fax (816) 858-2154; disp adv e-mail advertising@plattecountycitizen.com; class adv e-mail advertising@plattecountycitizen.com; ed e-mail editor@plattecountycitizen.com; web site www.plattecountycitizen.com - 16,800(views) 4,800(visitors)
Circulation: 3,942pd, 8,600fr; Sworn/Estimate/Non-Audited
Advertising rate: Open inch rate $10.00
Established: 1962
Delivery Method: Mail, Racks
Areas Served: Platte County (MO) & Surrounding areas

PLATTSBURG

THE CLINTON COUNTY LEADER (THUR)

102 E Maple St, Plattsburg, MO, 64477-1246, Clinton, USA; gen tel (816) 539-2111; gen fax (816) 539-3530; disp adv e-mail nikki@clintoncountyleader.com; class adv e-mail ads@clintoncountyleader.com; ed e-mail leader@clintoncountyleader.com; web site www.ClintonCountyLeader.com
Circulation: 2,400pd,; Sworn/Estimate/Non-Audited
Advertising rate: Open inch rate $6.42
Established: 1895
Pub .... Steven Tinnen
Gen. Mgr. .... Betty Dickinson
Delivery Method: Mail

PLEASANT HILL

PLEASANT HILL TIMES (WED)

126 S 1st St, Pleasant Hill, MO, 64080-1604, Cass, USA; gen tel (816) 540-3500; gen fax (816) 987-5699; disp adv e-mail cheryl.phtimes@comcast.net; ed e-mail editor.phtimes@comcast.net; web site www.phtimes.net
Advertising rate: Open inch rate $6.75
Established: 1901
Pub./Ed. .... F. Erik Powell
Pub. .... Jan Powell
Mechanical Specifications: The Times: 6 columns by 20.5 inches.
Column widths are: 1 column, 1.611 inches
Delivery Method: Mail, Racks
Areas Served: Pleasant Hill and north-eastern Cass County

PORTAGEVILLE

MISSOURIAN-NEWS (THUR)

413 E Main St, Portageville, MO, 63873-1617, New Madrid, USA; gen tel (573) 379-5355; gen fax (573) 379-5488; disp adv e-mail lcollins@dddnews.com; ed e-mail sseal@dddnews.com; web site http://www.pvmonews.com/
Circulation: 1,700pd,; Sworn/Estimate/Non-Audited
Advertising rate: Open inch rate $6.12
Group: Rust Communications
Pub. .... Bud Hunt
Ed./Gen. Mgr. .... H. Scott Seal
Mechanical Specifications: Type page 11 3/5 x 21 1/2; E - 6 cols, 1 4/5, 1/5 between; A - 6 cols, 1 4/5, 1/5 between; C - 6 cols, 1 4/5, 1/5 between.Equipment & Software: Hardware — APP/Power Mac 7200/90, APP/Mac; Software — Adobe/PageMaker 6.5, Creator, Adobe/Photoshop.
Areas Served: 63873, 63862, 63869

POTOSI

THE INDEPENDENT-JOURNAL (THUR)

119 E High St, Potosi, MO, 63664-1906, Washington, USA; gen tel (573) 438-5141; gen fax (573) 438-4472; ed e-mail ijnews@centurytel.net
Circulation: 4,485pd, 425fr; Sworn/Estimate/Non-Audited
Advertising rate: Open inch rate $6.00
Established: 1872
Digital Platform - Mobile: Apple
Digital Platform - Tablet: Apple iOS
Adv. Mgr. .... Kris Richards
Ed. .... Neil Richards
Mechanical Specifications: Type page 13 x 21; E - 6 cols, 2 1/8, 1/16 between; A - 6 cols, 2 1/16, 1/16 between; C - 6 cols, 2 1/16, 1/8

between.Equipment & Software: Hardware — APP/IN DESIGN; Software — Adobe/ PageMaker.
Delivery Method: Mail, Racks

PRINCETON

PRINCETON POST-TELEGRAPH (THUR)
704 W Main St, Princeton, MO, 64673-1141, Mercer, USA; gen tel (660) 748-3266; gen fax (660) 748-3267; disp adv e-mail posttele@grm.net; ed e-mail posttele@grm.net
Circulation: 1,100pd, 5,200fr; Sworn/Estimate/ Non-Audited
Advertising rate: Open inch rate $4.15
Established: 1873
Pub. .... Ron Kinzler
Ed. .... Preston J. Cole
Delivery Method: Mail, Newsstand
Areas Served: 64673 - 64661 - 64632 - 50147 - 64679 et al

PUXICO

PUXICO PRESS (WED)
141 S E L HAWKS ST, Puxico, MO, 63960, Stoddard, USA; gen tel (573) 222-3243; gen fax (573) 222-6327; ed e-mail puxpress@sbcglobal.net; web site http://www.darnews.com/Daily_American_Republic/Contact_Us.html
Circulation: 1,285pd, 3,021fr; Sworn/Estimate/ Non-Audited
Advertising rate: Open inch rate $6.70
Established: 1884
Group: Rust Communications
Pub. .... Don Schrieber
Ed. .... Sierra John
Mechanical Specifications: Type page 13 x 21; E - 6 cols, 2, between; A - 6 cols, 2, between; C - 6 cols, 2, between.Equipment & Software: Hardware — APP/Mac.

REPUBLIC

THE REPUBLIC MONITOR (WED)
249 US Highway 60 W, Republic, MO, 65738-1432, Greene, USA; gen tel (417) 732-2525; gen fax (417) 732-2980; disp adv e-mail advertising@republicmonews.com; ed e-mail katieb@republicmonews.com; web site http://www.greenecountycommonwealth.com - 12,231(views) 3,769(visitors)
Circulation: 1,845pd, 223fr; CVC
Advertising rate: Open inch rate $13.50
Established: 1894
Group: Community Publishers, Inc.
Digital Platform - Mobile: Apple, Android
Digital Platform - Tablet: Apple iOS, Android
Ed. .... Katie Barton
Dave Berry
Mechanical Specifications: Type page: 10.25 x 21; 6 col Equipment & Software: Hardware — Mac; Presses — Goss
Delivery Method: Mail, Newsstand

RICH HILL

RICH HILL MINING REVIEW (FRI)
602 E Park Ave, Rich Hill, MO, 64779-1224, Bates, USA; gen tel (417) 395-4131; gen fax (417) 646-8015; ed e-mail sacosagenews@centurytel.net
Circulation: 1,000pd, 0fr; Sworn/Estimate/ Non-Audited
Advertising rate: Open inch rate $3.25
Group: Main Street Media, Inc.
Pub. .... Micheal Crawford

RICHMOND

RICHMOND NEWS (TUES, WED, FRI)
204 W North Main St, Richmond, MO, 64085-1610, Ray, USA; gen tel (816) 776-5454; adv tel (816) 776-5454; gen fax (816) 470-6397; adv fax (816) 470-6397; disp adv e-mail marie@richmond-dailynews.com; class adv e-mail ads@richmond-dailynews.com; ed e-mail editor@richmond-dailynews.com; web site www.richmond-dailynews.com
Circulation: 2,050pd, 8,940fr; Sworn/Estimate/ Non-Audited
Advertising rate: Open inch rate $7.00
Established: 1914
Group: Excelsior Springs Publishing
Digital Platform - Mobile: Apple, Android, Windows
Digital Platform - Tablet: Apple iOS, Android, Windows 7
Pub. .... JoEllen Black
Sales Mgr. .... Marie King
Print/Dig Media Consultant .... Tess Harris
Mng. Ed. .... Joy Tipping
Sports Ed. .... Russ Green
Pressman/Prod. Supervisor .... Arron Sander
Mechanical Specifications: Type page 12 1/4 x 21 1/2; E - 4 cols, 2 31/32, 1/8 between; A - 7 cols, 1 5/8, 1/8 between; C - 7 cols, 1 5/8, 1/8 between.
Delivery Method: Mail, Newsstand, Carrier
Areas Served: Ray County

ROCK PORT

ATCHISON COUNTY MAIL (THUR)
300 S Main St, Rock Port, MO, 64482-1534, Atchison, USA; gen tel (660) 744-6245; gen fax (660) 744-2645; ed e-mail amail@rpt.coop; web site http://farmerpublishing.com/weekly-editions/atchison-county-mail/
Circulation: 2,200pd, 30fr; Sworn/Estimate/ Non-Audited
Advertising rate: Open inch rate $6.00
Ed. .... William C. Farmer
Mng. Ed.... Mike FarmerEquipment & Software: Hardware — APP/Mac; Software — Adobe/ PageMaker 6.0.

ROGERSVILLE

SOUTH COUNTY MAIL (WED)
115 E Center St, Rogersville, MO, 65742-9703, Webster, USA; gen tel (417) 753-2800; gen fax (417) 753-2792; disp adv e-mail debbiec@marshfieldmail.com; ed e-mail debbiec@marshfieldmail.com; web site http://marshfieldmail.com/rogersville/
Circulation: 1,200pd, 10fr; Sworn/Estimate/ Non-Audited
Advertising rate: Open inch rate $10.60
Group: Community Publishers, Inc.
Pub .... Dave Berry
Ed./GM .... Scott Kerber

SAINT CHARLES

ST. CHARLES COUNTY JOURNAL (WED, SUN)
330 N Main St, Ste 202, Saint Charles, MO, 63301-2028, St. Charles, USA; gen tel (636)724-1080; gen fax (636) 724-1080; ed e-mail shannon@pulselegal.com; web site http://www.pulselegal.com/
Circulation: 18,600fr; Sworn/Estimate/Non-Audited
Advertising rate: Open inch rate $7.25
Established: 2010
Pub. .... Shannon Grindinger
Mechanical Specifications: Type page 12 x 21 1/2; E - 6 cols, 1 7/8, 1/8 between; A - 6 cols, 1 7/8, 1/8 between; C - 10 cols, 1 1/4, 1/3 between.Equipment & Software: Hardware — SII/Sys 55, APP/Mac Network; Presses — 32-G/Urbanite.
Delivery Method: Mail

SAINT JOSEPH

SAINT JOSEPH TELEGRAPH (THUR)
202 Blake St, Saint Joseph, MO, 64504, Buchanan, USA; gen tel (816) 754-6462; disp adv e-mail info@stjtelegraph.com; ed e-mail news@stjtelegraph.org; web site www.stjtelegraph.org
Circulation: 27pd, 138fr; Sworn/Estimate/ Non-Audited
Advertising rate: Open inch rate $6.00
Established: 1989
Pub./Ed. .... Mike Bozarth
Mechanical Specifications: Type page 9.75 x 12.5; E - 5 cols, 1 5/6, 1/6 between; A - 5 cols, 1 5/6, 1/6 between; C - 5 cols, 1 5/6, 1/6 between.Equipment & Software: Hardware — APP/Mac G3; Software — Adobe/ PageMaker 6.5.
Delivery Method: Mail, Racks
Areas Served: 64501, 64502, 64503, 64504, 64505, 64506, 64507, 64430, 66024

SAINT LOUIS

CHESTERFIELD JOURNAL (WED)
900 N Tucker Blvd, Saint Louis, MO, 63101-1069, St. Louis, USA; gen tel (314) 821-1110; gen fax (314) 821-3408; ed e-mail mshatiro@yourjournal.com; web site http://www.stltoday.com/suburban-journals/
Circulation: 17,000fr; Sworn/Estimate/Non-Audited
Advertising rate: Open inch rate $9.50
Pub. .... Bob Williams
Circ. Mgr. .... Dan Crockwell
Promo. Dir. .... Mary Ann Wagner
Mechanical Specifications: Type page 12 x 21 1/2; E - 6 cols, 1 7/8, 1/8 between; A - 6 cols, 1 7/8, 1/8 between; C - 10 cols, 1 1/4, 1/3 between.Equipment & Software: Hardware — SII/Sys 55, APP/Mac Network; Presses — 32-G/Urbanite.

SOUTH COUNTY TIMES (FRI)
122 W Lockwood Ave, Fl 2, Saint Louis, MO, 63119-2916, Saint Louis, USA; gen tel (314) 968-2699; gen fax (314) 968-2961; disp adv e-mail mchambers@timesnewspapers.com; class adv e-mail classifieds@timesnewspapers.com; ed e-mail corrigan@timesnewspapers.com; newsroom@timesnewspapers.com; web site http://www.timesnewspapers.com
Circulation: 36,975fr; CVC
Advertising rate: 1/32 Pg $56.00; 1/16 Pg $111.00; 1/8 Pg $220.00; 1/4 pg $437; 1/2 pg $872; Full pg $1532
Established: 1947
Group: Webster-Kirkwood Times, Inc.
Pub. .... Dwight Bitikofer
Ed. .... Don Corrigan
Adv. Mgr. .... Mary Chambers
Mng. Ed. .... Kevin Murphy
Circ. Mgr .... Kim Besterfeldt
Prod. Mgr .... Randy Drilingas
circulation manager .... Dustin Bitikofer
Mechanical Specifications: see online rate card and media kit
Delivery Method: Carrier, Racks
Areas Served: 63026, 63123, 63126, 63127, 63128

ST. LOUIS BUSINESS JOURNAL (FRI)
815 Olive St Ste 100, Suite 100, Saint Louis, MO, 63101-1509, Saint Louis City, USA; gen tel (314) 421-6200; adv tel (314) 421-8340; ed tel (314) 421-8324; gen fax (314) 621-5031; disp adv e-mail gwells@bizjournals.com; class adv e-mail mceresia@bizjournals.com; ed e-mail jdwyer@bizjournals.com; web site www.bizjournals.com/stlouis
Advertising rate: Open inch rate $930 (1/16P); $1720 (1/8P); $3270 (1/4P); $6175 (1/2P)
Established: 1980
Digital Platform - Mobile: Apple, Android, Windows, Blackberry
Digital Platform - Tablet: Apple iOS, Android, Windows 7, Blackberry Tablet OS
Pub. .... Ellen Sherberg
Ed. .... Patricia Miller
Adv. Dir. .... Glynelle Wells
Delivery Method: Mail, Newsstand, Racks
Areas Served: St. Louis, St. Charles, and St. Clair

ST. LOUIS/SOUTHERN ILLINOIS LABOR TRIBUNE (THUR)
505 S Ewing Ave, Saint Louis, MO, 63103-2901, Saint Louis City, USA; gen tel (314) 535-9660; adv tel (314) 256-4136; ed tel (314) 535-9660; gen fax (314) 535-9013; adv fax Same; ed fax (314) 535-9013; disp adv e-mail advertising@labortribune.com; class adv e-mail advertising@labortribune.com; ed e-mail news@labortribune.com; web site www.labortribune.com
Circulation: 30,963pd, 2,348fr; USPS
Advertising rate: $52.80
Established: 1937
Group: Tronc, Inc.
Publisher .... Ed Finkelstein
Associate Editor .... Tim Rowden
Gen. Mgr. .... Marvin Naftolin
Mechanical Specifications: Full page: 10 5/16" x 13"
Half page: 5 1/16" 13"
Quarter page: 5 1/16" x 6 1/2"
Eighth page: 3 5/16" x 5"
Delivery Method: Mail
Areas Served: Eastern Missouri & Southern Illinois

WEBSTER-KIRKWOOD TIMES, INC. (FRI)
122 W Lockwood Ave, Fl 2, Saint Louis, MO, 63119-2916, Saint Louis, USA; gen tel (314) 968-2699; gen fax (314) 968-2961; disp adv e-mail mchambers@timesnewspapers.com; class adv e-mail classified@timesnewspapers.com; ed e-mail corrigan@timesnewspapers.com; newsroom@timesnewspapers.com; web site http://www.timesnewspapers.com
Circulation: 40,474fr; CVC
Advertising rate: 1/32 Pg $63.00; 1/16 Pg $125.00; 1/8 Pg $248.00; 1/4 pg $490; 1/2 pg $974; Full pg $1670
Established: 1978
Group: Webster-Kirkwood Times, Inc.
Pub. .... Dwight Bitikofer
Ed. .... Don Corrigan
Mng. Ed. .... Kevin Murphy
Adv. Mgr. .... Mary Chambers
Circ. Mgr .... Kim Besterfeldt
Prod. Mgr .... Randy Drilingas
circulation manager .... Dustin Bitikofer
Mechanical Specifications: Type page 10 x 15 3/4; E - 4 cols, 2 3/8, 1/4 between; A - 4 cols, 2 3/8, 1/4 between; C - 4 cols, 2 3/8, 1/4 between.Equipment & Software: Hardware — APP/Mac; Software — QPS/QuarkXPress 4.0.
Delivery Method: Carrier, Racks
Areas Served: 63119, 63122, 63131

WEST END WORD (FRI)
122 W Lockwood Ave, Saint Louis, MO, 63119-2916, Saint Louis, USA; gen tel (314) 968-2699; gen fax (314) 968-2961; disp adv e-mail advertising@timesnewspapers.com; class adv e-mail classified@timesnewspapers.com; ed e-mail corrigan@timesnewspapers.com; web site http://www.websterkirkwoodtimes.com - 106,485(views) 5,099(visitors)
Circulation: 18,291fr; CVC
Advertising rate: 1/32 Pg $50.00; 1/16 Pg $98.00; 1/8 Pg $194.00
Established: 1972
Group: Webster-Kirkwood Times, Inc.
Digital Platform - Tablet: Apple iOS
Ed. .... Don Corrigan
Mng. Ed. .... Kevin Murphy
Adv. Mgr. .... Mary Chambers
Circ. Mgr .... Kim Besterfeldt
Prod. Mgr .... Randy Drilingas
publisher .... Dwight Bitikofer
circulation manager .... Dustin Bitikofer
Managing Editor .... Fran Mannino
Mechanical Specifications: Type page 10 x 15 3/4; E - 4 cols, 2 3/8, 1/4 between; A - 4 cols, 2 3/8, 1/4 between; C - 4 cols, 2 3/8, 1/4 between.Equipment & Software: Hardware — APP/Mac; Software — QPS/QuarkXPress

4.0.
Delivery Method: Carrier, Racks
Areas Served: 63108, 63112, 63105, 63130; 63117, 63103, 63143

SAINT ROBERT

PULASKI COUNTY MIRROR (WED)
555 Marshall Dr, Saint Robert, MO, 65584-5601, Pulaski, USA; gen tel (573) 336-5359; gen fax (573) 336-7619; disp adv e-mail ldr-lrbarker@lebanondailyrecord.com; class adv e-mail anitav@lebanondailyrecord.com; ed e-mail ssmith@pulaskicountymirror.com; web site www.pulaskicountymirror.com
Circulation: 1,200pd, 10,150fr; Sworn/Estimate/Non-Audited
Advertising rate: Open inch rate $5.50
Ed. .... Steve Smith
Adv. Sales Mgr. .... Rene Barker
Class. Adv. Mgr. .... Anita Hooser
Mechanical Specifications: Type page 12 x 21 1/2.Equipment & Software: Hardware — IBM; Software — Adobe.
Delivery Method: Mail, Racks

SAINTE GENEVIEVE

STE. GENEVIEVE HERALD (WED)
330 Market St, Sainte Genevieve, MO, 63670-1638, Sainte Genevieve, USA; gen tel (573) 883-2222; gen fax (573) 883-2833; disp adv e-mail jgettinger@stegenherald.com; class adv e-mail afox@stegenherald.com; ed e-mail tcarrig@stegenherald.com; web site www.stegenherald.com - 50,000(views) 17,000(visitors)
Circulation: 3,665pd, 76fr; USPS
Advertising rate: Open inch rate $7.00
Established: 1882
Group: Ste. Genevieve Media, LLC Editions: (1) Ste. Genevieve Herald
Digital Platform - Mobile: Apple
Pub./Ed. .... Toby Carrig
Adv. Mgr. .... Jill Gettinger
Circ. Mgr. .... Lindsay Resinger
Mechanical Specifications: Type page 11 x 20.5; E - 6 cols, 1 3/4, 1/8 between; A - 6 cols, 1 3/4, 1/8 between; C - 6 cols, 1 3/4, 1/8 between.Equipment & Software: Hardware — 10-APP/Mac, HP; Software — Adobe InDesign CS4
Delivery Method: Mail, Newsstand
Areas Served: 63627, 63670, 63673

SALEM

THE SALEM NEWS (TUES)
PO Box 798, 500 North Washington Street, Salem, MO, 65560-0798, Dent, USA; gen tel (573) 729-4126; adv tel (573) 729-4126; ed tel (573) 729-4126; gen fax (573) 729-4126; adv fax (573) 729-4126; ed fax (573) 729-4126; disp adv e-mail donald@thesalemnewsonline.com; class adv e-mail donald@thesalemnewsonline.com; ed e-mail donald@thesalemnewsonline.com; web site www.thesalemnewsonline.com
Circulation: 3,800pd, 4,700fr; USPS
Advertising rate: Open inch rate $5.60
Pub. .... Donald Dodd
Adv. Mgr. .... Karen Barred
Mechanical Specifications: Type page 13 x 21 1/2; E - 6 cols, 2 1/8, between; A - 6 cols, 2 1/8, between; C - 6 cols, 2 1/8, between. Equipment & Software: Hardware — APP/Mac; Presses — G/Community; Software — Multi-Ad, Adobe/PageMaker, QPS/QuarkXPress.
Delivery Method: Mail, Newsstand
Areas Served: 65560

SALISBURY

SALISBURY PRESS-SPECTATOR (THUR)
111 S Broadway, Salisbury, MO, 65281-1033, Chariton, USA; gen tel (660) 388-6131; gen fax (660) 388-6688
Circulation: 1,500pd, 0fr; Sworn/Estimate/Non-Audited
Advertising rate: Open inch rate $4.75
Established: 1870
Pub. .... Susan K. Baxley
Gen. Mgr. .... Larry M. Baxley
Ed. .... Lucy Vaughn

SARCOXIE

PIERCE CITY LEADER-JOURNAL (WED)
PO Box 400, Sarcoxie, MO, 64862-0400, Lawrence, USA; gen tel (417) 548-3311; gen fax (417) 548-3312; disp adv e-mail fstop@centurytel.net
Circulation: 950pd, 50fr; Sworn/Estimate/Non-Audited
Advertising rate: Open inch rate $6.60
Established: 1903
Ed. .... Paul E. Donley
Gen Mgr .... Katrina Keys
Delivery Method: Mail, Newsstand, Racks
Areas Served: 65723

THE SARCOXIE RECORD (WED)
101 N 6th St, Sarcoxie, MO, 64862-9453, Jasper, USA; gen tel (417) 548-3311; gen fax (417) 548-3312; adv fax (417) 548-3312; disp adv e-mail fstop@centurytel.net
Circulation: 1,150pd,; Sworn/Estimate/Non-Audited
Advertising rate: Open inch rate $6.60
Established: 1901
Pub. .... Paul E. Donley
Gen Mgr .... Katrina Keys
Delivery Method: Mail, Racks
Areas Served: 64862

SAVANNAH

SAVANNAH REPORTER AND ANDREW COUNTY DEMOCRAT (THUR)
107 W US Highway 71 Ste E, Suite E, Savannah, MO, 64485-2305, Andrew, USA; gen tel (816) 324-3149; gen fax (816) 324-3632; disp adv e-mail adsales@stjoelive.com; ed e-mail editor@stjoelive.com; web site www.thesavannahreporter.com
Circulation: 2,700pd,; Sworn/Estimate/Non-Audited
Advertising rate: Open inch rate $5.55
Established: 1876
Pub. .... Guy Speckman
Ed. .... Leslie Speckman
Ad Sales .... Brandi Abbott
Areas Served: 64485

SENECA

SENECA NEWS-DISPATCH (THUR)
1108 Cherokee Ave, Seneca, MO, 64865-9207, Newton, USA; gen tel (417) 776-2236; gen fax (417) 776-2204; disp adv e-mail newsdis@netins.net; ed e-mail jimmy@thenewsdispatch.net; web site www.senecanewsdispatch.com
Circulation: 1,800pd, 0fr; Sworn/Estimate/Non-Audited
Advertising rate: Open inch rate $4.50
Established: 1882
Ed. .... Diane Friend
Mechanical Specifications: Type page 11 2/3 x 21 1/2; E - 6 cols, 1 5/6, 1/8 between; A - 6 cols, 1 5/6, 1/8 between; C - 6 cols, 1 5/6, 1/8 between.Equipment & Software: Hardware — APP/Mac; Software — QPS/QuarkXPress 4.1, Adobe/Photoshop 6.0.
Areas Served: 64865, 64850, 74370; Neosho & Newton County

SEYMOUR

WEBSTER COUNTY CITIZEN (WED)
221 S Commercial St, Seymour, MO, 65746-8743, Webster, USA; gen tel (417) 935-2257; gen fax (417) 935-2487; disp adv e-mail anna@webstercountycitizen.com; class adv e-mail citizen190@gmail.com; ed e-mail citizen@webstercountycitizen.com; web site www.webstercountycitizen.com
Circulation: 2,005pd, 7fr; Sworn/Estimate/Non-Audited
Advertising rate: Open inch rate $4.50
Established: 1907
Ed. .... Dan Wehmer
Prod. Mgr. .... Beverly Hannum
Gen. Mgr. .... Anna Sturdefant
Mechanical Specifications: Type page 13 x 21; E - 6 cols, 2, 1/6 between; A - 6 cols, 2, 1/6 between; C - 6 cols, 2, 1/6 between.Equipment & Software: Hardware — APP/Mac; Presses — 8-G/Community; Software — Adobe/PageMaker 6.0.

SHELBYVILLE

SHELBY COUNTY HERALD (WED)
109 E Main St, Shelbyville, MO, 63469-1433, Shelby, USA; gen tel (573) 633-2261; gen fax (573) 633-2133; disp adv e-mail news@shelbycountyherald.com; web site www.shelbycountyherald.com
Circulation: 1,500pd, 40fr; Sworn/Estimate/Non-Audited
Advertising rate: Open inch rate $4.00
Group: NEMOnews Media Group, LLC
Ed. .... Martha Jane East
Mechanical Specifications: Type page 13 x 21 1/2; A - 6 cols, between; C - 6 cols, between.Equipment & Software: Hardware — APP/Mac; Software — Abbott Systems/Ready, Set, Go, Adobe/PageMaker, Microsoft/Works.
Delivery Method: Mail, Newsstand
Areas Served: Shelby County Missouri

SLATER

SLATER MAIN STREET NEWS (THUR)
222 Main St, Slater, MO, 65349-1412, Saline, USA; gen tel (660) 529-2249; gen fax (660) 529-2474; disp adv e-mail slaternews@socket.net
Circulation: 1,200pd, 13fr; Sworn/Estimate/Non-Audited
Advertising rate: Open inch rate $5.50
Established: 1886
Adv. Mgr. .... James Stanfield
Ed. .... Jean E. Black
Receptionist .... Suzette Large
Mechanical Specifications: Type page - 6 cols, 1.80, 1/8 between; A - 6 cols, 1.80, 1/8 between; C - 6 cols, 2, 1/8 between.
11.66x21", 6 cols, 1.80SEquipment & Software: ; Software — Microsoft/Works.
Delivery Method: Mail, Newsstand, Racks

SMITHVILLE

THE SMITHVILLE HERALD (WED)
103 E MAIN ST, Smithville, MO, 64089, Clay, USA; gen tel (816) 532-4444; gen fax (816) 532-4918; disp adv e-mail sandy.nelson@npgco.com; class adv e-mail jim.card@smithvilleherald.com; ed e-mail amy.neal@npgco.com; web site www.smithvilleherald.com
Circulation: 2,000pd,; USPS
Advertising rate: Open inch rate $7.98
Established: 1888
Pub. .... Sandy Nelson
Ed. .... Amy Neal
Mechanical Specifications: Type page 10 1/4 x 20; E - 6 cols, 2, 1/6 between; A - 6 cols, 2, 1/6 between; C - 6 cols, 2, 1/6 between. Equipment & Software: Hardware — APP/Mac; Software — Adobe/PageMaker.
Delivery Method: Mail, Newsstand, Racks
Areas Served: 64089, 64492, 64444

SPRINGFIELD

SPRINGFIELD BUSINESS JOURNAL (MON)
313 Park Central W, Springfield, MO, 65806-1244, Greene, USA; gen tel (417) 831-3238; gen fax (417) 831-4901; disp adv e-mail tbrierly@sbj.net; ed e-mail eolson@sbj.net; web site http://sbj.net/
Circulation: 4,306pd, 1,530fr; Sworn/Estimate/Non-Audited
Established: 1980
Ed. .... Eric Olson
Pub. .... Jennifer Jackson
Pres. .... Dianne Elizabeth Osis

STEELE

THE STEELE ENTERPRISE (THUR)
227 W Main St, Steele, MO, 63877-1435, Pemiscot, USA; gen tel (573) 695-3415; gen fax (573) 695-2114; disp adv e-mail steeleenterprise63877@yahoo.com; ed e-mail steelenews@steelemoenterprise.com; web site http://couriernews.net/
Circulation: 2,250pd,; Sworn/Estimate/Non-Audited
Advertising rate: Open inch rate $7.00
Established: 1922
Group: Rust Communications
Pub. .... David Tennyson
Ed. .... Lisa Rhoades
Mechanical Specifications: Type page 11 5/8 x 21; E - 6 cols, 1 4/5, between; A - 6 cols, 1 4/5, between; C - 6 cols, 1 4/5, between. Equipment & Software: Hardware — APP/Power Mac 4400, APP/Mac 4400; Software — QPS/QuarkXPress.
Delivery Method: Mail, Newsstand, Racks

STEELVILLE

STEELVILLE STAR-CRAWFORD MIRROR (WED)
103 W MAIN ST, Steelville, MO, 65565, Crawford, USA; gen tel (573) 775-5454; gen fax (573) 775-2668; disp adv e-mail matt@threeriverspublishing.com; class adv e-mail dforbes@steelvillestar.com; ed e-mail ccase@cubafreepress.com; web site www.steelvillestar.com
Circulation: 3,500pd, 2,250fr; USPS
Advertising rate: Open inch rate $5.50
Established: 1872
Group: Three Rivers Publishing, Inc.
Digital Platform - Mobile: Apple, Android, Windows, Blackberry
Digital Platform - Tablet: Apple iOS
Pub. .... Rob Viehman
Ed. .... Chris Case
Circ. Mgr. .... Janice McMillen
Mechanical Specifications: 1 col - 1.833 inches
2 col - 3.792 inches
3 col - 5.75 inches
4 col - 7.708 inches
5 col - 9.667 inches
6 col - 11.625 inches
Page height - 21.5 inches
Delivery Method: Mail, Newsstand
Areas Served: Steelville, Viburnum and Southern Crawford County, MO

STOCKTON

CEDAR COUNTY REPUBLICAN/ STOCKTON JOURNAL (WED)
26 Public Sq, Stockton, MO, 65785-7617, Cedar, USA; gen tel (417) 276-4211; gen fax (417) 276-5760; disp adv e-mail marilyne@cedarrepublican.com; ed e-mail robertj@cedarrepublican.com; web site www.cedarrepublican.com - 28,186(views) 5,489(visitors)
Circulation: 2,714pd, 267fr; CVC

Advertising rate: Open inch rate $50.00
Established: 1885
Group: Community Publishers, Inc.
Pub....Dave Berry
Adv. Mgr....Marilyn Ellis
Ed....Robert Jackson
Mechanical Specifications: Type page: 10.25 x 21; 6 col

STOVER

MORGAN COUNTY PRESS (WED)

201 S Maple St, Stover, MO, 65078-0822, Morgan, USA; gen tel (573) 378-5441; gen fax (573) 378-4292; ed e-mail news@morgancountypress.com; web site http://morgancountypress.com
Circulation: 1,300pd, 279fr; Sworn/Estimate/Non-Audited
Advertising rate: Open inch rate $3.75
Established: 1911
Ed....R.D Fish
Pub....Bryan Jones
Mechanical Specifications: Type page 10.875 x 21; E - 6 cols, 1.729 in., .1 in. betweenEquipment & Software: Hardware — APP/Mac; Software — Adobe/InDesign.
Delivery Method: Mail, Newsstand, Racks
Areas Served: Stover, Morgan County 65078

SULLIVAN

SULLIVAN INDEPENDENT NEWS (WED)

411 Scottsdale Dr, Sullivan, MO, 63080-1307, Franklin and Crawford County, USA; gen tel (573) 468-6511; adv tel (573) 468-6511; ed tel (573) 468-6511; gen fax (573) 468-4046; adv fax (573) 468-4046; disp adv e-mail nuz4u@fidnet.com; class adv e-mail nuz4u@fidnet.com; ed e-mail nuz4u@fidnet.com; web site www.mysullivannews.com - 1,200(views)
Circulation: 5,960pd, 240fr; Sworn/Estimate/Non-Audited
Advertising rate: Open inch rate $6.00
Established: 1964
Group: New Haven Independent Newspaper - Parent Company is Sullivan Independent Newspaper
Owner Mng. Ed....James Bartle
Adv. Mgr....Mark Hilse
Owner....Jennifer Manion
Office/Bus Mgr
Carmin Ball
Mngr....Chris Hopwood
Delivery Method: Mail, Newsstand, Racks
Areas Served: 63077, 63080, 65441, 65453, 63037, 65535,63056, 65066,63079, 63089

TARKIO

THE TARKIO AVALANCHE (THUR)

521 Main St, Tarkio, MO, 64491-1546, Atchison, USA; gen tel (660) 736-4111; gen fax (660) 736-5700; disp adv e-mail avalanche@rpt.com; ed e-mail amail@rpt.coop; web site http://farmerpublishing.com
Circulation: 2,000pd, 230fr; Sworn/Estimate/Non-Audited
Advertising rate: Open inch rate $4.00
Established: 1884
Pub....Joy L. Johnson
Ed....William W. Johnson
Mechanical Specifications: Type page 13 x 21 1/2; E - 6 cols, 2 1/16, 1/8 between; A - 6 cols, 2 1/16, 1/8 between; C - 6 cols, 2 1/16, 1/8 between.

THAYER

SOUTH MISSOURIAN-NEWS (THUR)

109 Chestnut St, Thayer, MO, 65791-1201, Oregon, USA; gen tel (417) 264-3085; adv tel (870) 895-3207; gen fax (417) 264-3814; ed e-mail news@areawidenews.com; web site http://www.areawidenews.com/
Circulation: 1,500pd, 19,600fr; Sworn/Estimate/Non-Audited
Advertising rate: Open inch rate $6.75
Group: Rust Communications
Pub....Janie Flynn
Mng. Ed....Tammy Curtis
Ed....Richard Irby
Circ. Mgr....Debra Perryman
Mechanical Specifications: Type page 13 x 21; E - 6 cols, 2, 1/6 between; A - 6 cols, 2, 1/6 between; C - 6 cols, 2, 1/6 between.Equipment & Software: Hardware — APP/Mac; Presses — KP; Software — Multi-Ad, QPS/QuarkXPress.

TIPTON

THE TIPTON TIMES (THUR)

113 E Morgan St, Tipton, MO, 65081-8322, Moniteau, USA; gen tel (660) 433-5721; gen fax (660) 433-2222; disp adv e-mail times@vernonpublishing.com; class adv e-mail times@vernonpublishing.com; ed e-mail times@vernonpublishing.com; web site https://www.vernonpublishing.com/Times/News
Circulation: 1,900pd,; Sworn/Estimate/Non-Audited
Advertising rate: Open inch rate 5.00
Established: 1875
Group: Vernon Publishing
Pub....Dane Vernon
Ed....Becky Holloway
Mechanical Specifications: Type page 13 x 21; E - 6 cols, 2 1/16, 1/8 between; A - 6 cols, 2 1/16, 1/8 between; C - 7 cols, 1 23/32, 1/8 between.Equipment & Software: Hardware — APP/Mac; Software — Adobe/Indesign CS2
Delivery Method: Mail, Newsstand, Racks
Areas Served: Tipton, Moniteau

TOWN AND COUNTRY

CITIZEN JOURNAL (WED)

14522 S Outer 40 Rd, Town And Country, MO, 63017-5737, St. Louis, USA; gen tel (314) 821-1110; gen fax (314) 821-3408; disp adv e-mail service@stltoday.com; ed e-mail gbailon@post-dispatch.com; web site suburbanjournals.stltoday.com
Circulation: 15,500fr; Sworn/Estimate/Non-Audited
Advertising rate: Open inch rate $7.50
Established: 1940
Adv. Mgr....Bob Williams
Circ. Mgr....Dan Crockwell
Mng. Ed....Monika Kleban
Mechanical Specifications: Type page 12 x 21 1/2; E - 6 cols, 1 7/8, 1/8 between; A - 6 cols, 1 7/8, 1/8 between; C - 10 cols, 1 1/4, 1/3 between.Equipment & Software: Hardware — SII/Sys 55, APP/Mac Network; Presses — 32-G/Urbanite.

LOUISIANA PRESS JOURNAL (WED)

14522 S Outer 40 Rd, Town And Country, MO, 63017-5737, St. Louis, USA; gen tel (314) 821-1110; gen fax (314) 821-0745; disp adv e-mail service@stltoday.com; ed e-mail gbailon@post-dispatch.com; web site suburbanjournals.stltoday.com
Circulation: 89,722pd, 226,000fr; Sworn/Estimate/Non-Audited
Advertising rate: Open inch rate $17.98
Established: 1922
Group: Lakeway Publishers, Inc.
Pub....Bob Williams
Adv. Dir....Keith Carpenter
Circ. Dir....Dan Crockwell
Mng. Ed....Monika Kleban
Mechanical Specifications: Type page 12 x 21 1/2; E - 6 cols, 1 7/8, 1/8 between; A - 6 cols, 1 7/8, 1/8 between; C - 10 cols, 1 1/4, 1/3 between.Equipment & Software: Hardware — SII/Sys 55, APP/Mac Network; Presses — 33-G/Urbanite.
Areas Served: Madison County, Illinois; St. Charles, Missouri

SOUTHWEST COUNTY JOURNAL (WED, SUN)

14522 S Outer 40 Rd, Town And Country, MO, 63017-5737, St. Louis, USA; gen tel (314) 821-1110; gen fax (314) 821-0843; disp adv e-mail service@stltoday.com; ed e-mail gbailon@post-dispatch.com; web site suburbanjournals.stltoday.com
Circulation: 29,000fr; Sworn/Estimate/Non-Audited
Advertising rate: Open inch rate $14.00
Circ. Dir....Dan Crockwell
Mechanical Specifications: Type page 12 x 21 1/2; E - 6 cols, 1 7/8, 1/8 between; A - 6 cols, 1 7/8, 1/8 between; C - 10 cols, 1 1/4, 1/3 between.Equipment & Software: Hardware — SII/Sys 55, APP/Mac Network; Presses — 32-G/Urbanite.

TROY

THE LINCOLN COUNTY JOURNAL (TUES)

20 Business Park Dr, Troy, MO, 63379-2819, Lincoln, USA; gen tel (636) 528-9550; adv tel (636) 528-9550; ed tel (636) 528-9550; gen fax (636) 528-6694; adv fax (636) 528-6694; ed fax (636) 528-6694; disp adv e-mail lcjpub@lcs.net; class adv e-mail lcjpub@lcs.net; ed e-mail lcjpub@lcs.net; web site www.lincolncountyjournal.com
Circulation: 18,900pd, 18,800fr; Sworn/Estimate/Non-Audited
Advertising rate: Open inch rate $13.87
Established: 1986
Group: Lakeway Publishers, Inc.
Digital Platform - Mobile: Apple, Android, Windows, Blackberry
Digital Platform - Tablet: Apple iOS, Android, Windows 7, Blackberry Tablet OS
Editor....Bob Simmons
Delivery Method: Mail, Carrier, Racks
Areas Served: Lincoln County

TROY FREE PRESS (WED)

20 Business Park Dr, Troy, MO, 63379-2819, Lincoln, USA; gen tel (636) 528-9550; gen fax (636) 528-6694; disp adv e-mail lcjpub@lcs.net; class adv e-mail lcjpub@lcs.net; ed e-mail lcjeditor@lcs.net; web site lincolncountyjournal.com
Circulation: 1,000pd,; Sworn/Estimate/Non-Audited
Advertising rate: Open inch rate $5.68
Group: Lakeway Publishers
Digital Platform - Mobile: Apple, Android
Digital Platform - Tablet: Apple iOS, Windows 7
Ed....Bob Simmons
Delivery Method: Mail, Newsstand, Racks
Areas Served: 63379

UNIONVILLE

UNIONVILLE REPUBLICAN (WED)

111 S 16th St, Unionville, MO, 63565-1624, Putnam, USA; gen tel (660) 947-2222; gen fax (660) 947-2223; disp adv e-mail unionvillerepublican@mac.com; ed e-mail urep@nemr.net; web site www.unionvillerepublicanonline.com
Circulation: 1,700pd, 5,000fr; USPS
Advertising rate: Open inch rate $4.50
Established: 1865
Ed./Pub....Ron Kinzler
Mechanical Specifications: 6 col. SAU
Delivery Method: Mail, Newsstand
Areas Served: 63565

VAN BUREN

THE CURRENT LOCAL (THUR)

504 Ash St, Van Buren, MO, 63965, Carter, USA; gen tel (573) 323-4515; gen fax (573) 323-4515; disp adv e-mail currentlocal@centurytel.net; class adv e-mail currentlocal@centurytel.net; ed e-mail currentlocal@centurytel.net; web site currentlocal@centurytel.net
Circulation: 1,700pd, 0fr; Sworn/Estimate/Non-Audited
Advertising rate: Open inch rate $6.00
Established: 1884
Delivery Method: Mail, Newsstand, Racks
Areas Served: 63965 63937 63936 63941 63943 63901 63638

VANDALIA

THE VANDALIA LEADER (WED)

108 W State St, Vandalia, MO, 63382-1737, Audrain, USA; gen tel (573) 594-2222; gen fax (573) 594-6741; disp adv e-mail tvlads@lcs.net; ed e-mail tvlgenmgr@lcs.net; web site www.vandalialeader.com
Circulation: 2,217pd, 9fr; Sworn/Estimate/Non-Audited
Advertising rate: Open inch rate $4.10
Established: 1874
Group: Lakeway Publishers, Inc.
Gen. Mgr./Ed....Ron Schott
Mechanical Specifications: Type page 12 x 21 1/2; A - 6 cols, 2, 1/8 between; C - 8 cols, 1 7/16, 1/8 between.
Areas Served: 63382, 63345, 63352, 63339

VERSAILLES

THE VERSAILLES LEADER-STATESMAN (THUR)

104 W Jasper St, Versailles, MO, 65084-1020, Morgan, USA; gen tel (573) 378-5441; gen fax (573) 378-4292; disp adv e-mail leader-statesman@vernonpublishing.com; class adv e-mail dbatson@vernonpublishing.com; ed e-mail bjones@vernonpublishing.com; web site http://leader-statesman.com/
Circulation: 4,100pd, 100fr; Sworn/Estimate/Non-Audited
Advertising rate: Open inch rate $4.75
Established: 1878
Group: Vernon Publishing
Pub....Dane Vernon
Ed....Bryan Jones
Mechanical Specifications: Type page 10 1/4 x 21; E - 6 cols, 2 1/8, 1/8 between; A - 6 cols, 2 1/8, 1/8 between; C - 7 cols, 1 3/4, 1/8 between.Equipment & Software: Hardware — APP/Mac; Presses — 4-G/Community; Software — Adobe InDesign CS2 Adobe Photoshop CS2
Delivery Method: Mail, Newsstand, Racks
Areas Served: 65084, 65037, 65011, 65072, 65038, 65042, 65078, 65079

VIENNA

MARIES COUNTY GAZETTE (WED)

218 S MAIN ST, Vienna, MO, 65582, Maries, USA; gen tel (573) 422-3441; gen fax (573) 422-3441; web site https://www.facebook.com/pages/maries-county-gazette/163412607020457
Circulation: 1,500pd,; Sworn/Estimate/Non-Audited
Advertising rate: Open inch rate $3.75
Pub....Kurt Lewis
Ed....Nichoel Snodgrass
Mechanical Specifications: Type page 13 x 21 1/2; E - 6 cols, 2, 1/8 between; A - 6 cols, 2, 1/8 between; C - 6 cols, 2, 1/8 between. Equipment & Software: Hardware — APP/Mac G3, APP/Mac 7200; Software — QPS/QuarkXPress, Microsoft/Windows, Adobe/Photoshop.

WARRENTON

WARREN COUNTY RECORD (THUR)

103 E Booneslick Rd, Warrenton, MO, 63383-2003, Warren, USA; gen tel (636) 456-6397; gen fax (636) 456-6150; disp adv e-mail jtodd@warrencountyrecord.com; class adv e-mail recordclass@warrencountyrecord.com; ed e-mail recordnews@warrencoun-

tyrecord.com; web site www.warrencountyrecord.com
Circulation: 3,555pd,; USPS
Advertising rate: Open inch rate $6.00
Established: 1896
Group: Missourian Publishing Co.
Pub....William L. Miller
Adv. Dir....Jana Todd
Ed. ....Kate Miller
Mechanical Specifications: Type page 12 1/2 x 21 1/2; E - 6 cols, 1 15/16, between; A - 6 cols, 1 15/16, between; C - 6 cols, 1 15/16, between.Equipment & Software: Hardware — APP/Mac; Presses — HI; Software — Adobe/PageMaker 5.0, WordPerfect, QPS/QuarkXPress.
Delivery Method: Mail, Newsstand, Racks
Areas Served: Warren County

WARSAW

BENTON COUNTY ENTERPRISE (THUR)
107 Main St, Warsaw, MO, 65355, Benton, USA; gen tel (660) 438-6312; gen fax (660) 438-3464; disp adv e-mail carrieriemann@bentoncountyenterprise.com; ed e-mail jameswhite@bentoncountyenterprise.com; web site www.bentoncountyenterprise.com
Circulation: 5,700pd, 30fr; Sworn/Estimate/Non-Audited
Advertising rate: Open inch rate $4.00
Pub....James Mahlon White
Asst. Pub....Jane Salley
Prod. Dir....Lisa Firsick

WASHINGTON

WASHINGTON MISSOURIAN (WED, SAT)
14 W Main St, Washington, MO, 63090-2518, Franklin, USA; gen tel (636) 239-7701; adv tel (636) 390-3013; gen fax (636) 239-0915; disp adv e-mail washnews@emissourian.com; class adv e-mail bacott@emissourian.com; ed e-mail billmiller@emissourian.com; web site www.emissourian.com
Circulation: 11,648pd, 1,849fr; AAM
Advertising rate: Open inch rate $11.65
Established: 1937
Group: Missourian Publshing Co.Editions: (3) 3 total; St. Clair Edition (2,683); Union Edition (3,354); Washington Edition (10,682);
Digital Platform - Mobile: Apple, Android, Windows, Blackberry
Digital Platform - Tablet: Apple iOS, Android, Windows 7, Blackberry Tablet OS, Kindle, Nook, Kindle Fire
Ed. ....Bill Miller
Adv. Mgr....Jeanine York
Asst. Mgr Ed....Susan Miller Warden
Asst. Mgr. Editor....Gregg Jones
Mechanical Specifications: Full Page 11.50 x 21.37", 1 col.- 1.812, 2 col. - 3.75", 3 col. - 5.687", 4 col. - 7.625", 5 col. - 9.562" 6 col. - 11.50"Equipment & Software: Hardware — APP/Mac; Presses — G/Urbanite.
Delivery Method: Mail, Carrier, Racks

WEBB CITY

WEBB CITY SENTINEL (WED)
8 S Main St, Webb City, MO, 64870-2326, Jasper, USA; gen tel (417) 673-2421; gen fax (417) 673-5308; disp adv e-mail sales@webbcity.net; class adv e-mail sales@webbcity.net; ed e-mail news@webbcity.net; web site www.webbcity.net
Circulation: 2,000pd, 50fr; Sworn/Estimate/Non-Audited
Advertising rate: Open inch rate $8.41
Established: 1879
Ed. ....Bob Foos
Mechanical Specifications: Type page 11 5/8 x 21 1/2; E - 6 cols, 1 5/6, 1/8 between; A - 6 cols, 1 5/6, 1/8 between; C - 6 cols, 1 5/6, 1/8 between.Equipment & Software: Hardware — APP/Mac; Software — QPS/QuarkXPress 4.0.
Delivery Method: Mail, Carrier, Racks

Areas Served: 64870, 64834, 64835, 64855, 64830

WESTON

WESTON CHRONICLE (WED)
18275 Hwy. 45 N., Weston, MO, 64098, Platte, USA; gen tel (816) 640-2251; adv tel (816) 640-2251; ed tel (816) 640-2251; disp adv e-mail wcnews@embarqmail.com; class adv e-mail wcads@embarqmail.com; ed e-mail wcnews@embarqmail.com; web site www.plattechronicle.com
Circulation: 1,600pd,; Sworn/Estimate/Non-Audited
Advertising rate: Open inch rate $5.10
Established: 1872
Adv. & Sports....Jim McPherson
Ed. & Pub....Beth McPherson
Ad Designer....Bev Knoll
Mechanical Specifications: Type page 12 3/4 x 21; E - 6 cols, 2, 1/8 between; A - 6 cols, 2, 1/8 between; C - 6 cols, 2, 1/8 between. Equipment & Software: Hardware — APP/Mac; Software — Adobe/PageMaker 6.5.
Areas Served: 64098, 64079, 64028, 64440, 64484, 64439

WILLARD

CROSS COUNTRY TIMES (WED)
100 E JACKSON ST, Willard, MO, 65781, Greene, USA; gen tel (417) 685-4328; gen fax (417) 751-3499; ed e-mail editor@crosscountrytimes.com
Circulation: 1,500pd,; Sworn/Estimate/Non-Audited
Advertising rate: Open inch rate $6.00
Established: 1979
Group: Greene County Commonwealth and continuing the Republic Monitor
Mgr....Cimmy Abbott
Ed. ....Laura Scott
Mechanical Specifications: Type page 11 1/2 x 20; E - 6 cols, 2, 1/4 between; A - 6 cols, 2, 1/4 between; C - 6 cols, 2, 1/4 between. Equipment & Software: ; Presses — KP; Software — Adobe/Photoshop.

WINDSOR

THE WINDSOR REVIEW (FRI)
205 S Main St, Windsor, MO, 65360-1869, Henry, USA; gen tel (660) 647-2121; gen fax (660) 647-2122; ed e-mail news@windsornews.net
Circulation: 1,850pd,; Sworn/Estimate/Non-Audited
Advertising rate: Open inch rate $4.00
Established: 1876
Group: Main Street Media, Inc.
Pub....Frank Mercer
Gen. Mgr....Colby Gordon
Mechanical Specifications: Type page 13 x 21.

MONTANA

ANACONDA

ANACONDA LEADER (WED, FRI)
121 Main St, Anaconda, MT, 59711-2251, Deer Lodge, USA; gen tel (406) 563-5283; gen fax (406) 563-5284; disp adv e-mail leadernews@anacondaleader.com; class adv e-mail advertising@anacondaleader.com; ed e-mail leadernews@anacondaleader.com; web site www.facebook.com/pages/Anaconda-Leader/153849391344489
Circulation: 3,816pd, 59fr; Sworn/Estimate/Non-Audited
Advertising rate: Open inch rate $8.35
Established: 1972
Owner....Dean A. Neitz
Ed. ....Kathie Miller
Prodn. Mgr. .... Debbie JohnsEquipment & Software: Hardware — APP/Mac; Presses — HI/Cotrell; Software — Adobe/PageMaker.
Delivery Method: Newsstand, Carrier, Racks
Areas Served: 59711

BAKER

FALLON COUNTY TIMES (FRI)
115 S Main St, Baker, MT, 59313-9013, Fallon, USA; gen tel (406) 778-3344; gen fax (406) 778-3347; disp adv e-mail fctimes@midrivers.com; ed e-mail fctimes@midrivers.com; web site http://www.falloncountyextra.com/
Circulation: 1,200pd, 49fr; Sworn/Estimate/Non-Audited
Advertising rate: Local - $7.10; National - $8.29
Established: 1916
Group: Country Media Inc.
Country Media, Inc
Ed. ....Darlene Hornung
Mktg....Tammy O'Donnell
Delivery Method: Mail, Newsstand

BELGRADE

BELGRADE NEWS (TUES, FRI)
29 W Main St, Belgrade, MT, 59714-3716, Gallatin, USA; gen tel (406) 388-5101; adv tel (406) 388-5101 x10; ed tel (406) 388-5101 x12; gen fax (406) 388-5103; disp adv e-mail ghoffman@belgrade-news.com; class adv e-mail ghoffman@belgrade-news.com; ed e-mail editor@belgrade-news.com; web site www.belgrade-news.com - 55,000(views) 16,000(visitors)
Circulation: 300pd, 4,500fr; Sworn/Estimate/Non-Audited
Advertising rate: Modular
Established: 2004
Group: Adams Publishing Group, LLC
Digital Platform - Mobile: Apple, Android
Digital Platform - Tablet: Apple iOS, Android
Pub....Stephanie Pressly
Ed. ....Michael Tucker
Adv. Dir....George Hoffman
Mechanical Specifications: 1/8 4.75 x 3.9, 1/4 4.75 x 7.9, 1/2 9.667 x 7.9, full 9.667 x 15.75
Delivery Method: Mail, Newsstand, Racks
Areas Served: 59714, 59741, 59715, 59718, 59730, 59752

BIG SANDY

THE MOUNTAINEER (WED)
122 Johannas Ave, Big Sandy, MT, 59520, Chouteau, USA; gen tel (406) 378-2176; adv tel (406) 357-3573; gen fax (406) 378-2176; disp adv e-mail bsmnews@mtintouch.net; ed e-mail bcjnews@itstriangle.com; web site http://www.bigsandymountaineer.com
Circulation: 926pd, 99fr; Sworn/Estimate/Non-Audited
Advertising rate: Open inch rate $4.92
Established: 1911
Mng. Ed....Keith Hanson
Delivery Method: Mail, Newsstand
Areas Served: Chouteau

BIG TIMBER

THE BIG TIMBER PIONEER (THUR)
105 E 2nd Ave, Big Timber, MT, 59011-8800, Sweet Grass, USA; gen tel (406) 932-5298; adv tel (406) 932-5298; gen fax (406) 932-4931; disp adv e-mail ads@bigtimberpioneer.net; ed e-mail editor@bigtimberpioneer.net; web site http://bigtimberpioneer.net/
Circulation: 1,768pd,; Sworn/Estimate/Non-Audited
Advertising rate: Open inch rate $7.00
Established: 1890
Group: Yellowstone Communications
Editor / General Manager....Laura Nelson
Lois Huffman
Delivery Method: Mail, Newsstand, Racks
Areas Served: 59011

BIGFORK

THE BIGFORK EAGLE (WED)
8299 Mt Highway 35, Ste 4, Bigfork, MT, 59911-3574, Flathead, USA; gen tel (406) 837-5131; adv tel (406) 758-4410; ed tel (406) 837-5131; gen fax (406) 837-1132; disp adv e-mail kfritz@dailyinterlake.com; class adv e-mail classifieds@dailyinterlake.com; ed e-mail editor@bigforkeagle.com; web site www.bigforkeagle.com
Circulation: 14,954pd, 403fr; CAC
Advertising rate: Open inch rate $5.52
Prodn. Mgr. & Circulation Director ... Ken Varga
Publisher....Rick Weaver
Editor....Dave Reese
General Manager....Laurie Ramos
Mechanical Specifications: Type page 11 7/10 x 20 3/4; E - 6 cols, 1 4/5, 7/100 between; A - 6 cols, 1 4/5, 7/100 between; C - 6 cols, 1 4/5, 7/100 between.Equipment & Software: Hardware — APP/Mac, APP/Power Mac; Software — Adobe/PageMaker 5.0, QPS/QuarkXPress 4.0, Adobe/Photoshop 5.0, Adobe/Illustrator 8.0.
Delivery Method: Mail, Newsstand, Racks

BILLINGS

BILLINGS TIMES (THUR)
2919 Montana Ave, Billings, MT, 59101-2143, Yellowstone, USA; gen tel (406) 245-4994; gen fax (406) 245-5115; disp adv e-mail mail@billingstimes.net; ed e-mail mail@billingstimes.net; web site http://www.billingstimes.net/
Advertising rate: Open inch rate $10.00
Established: 1891Editions: (1)
Editor & Publisher....Scott Turner
Delivery Method: Mail
Areas Served: Yellowstone County

BOULDER

THE BOULDER MONITOR (WED)
104 W Centennial Ave, Boulder, MT, 59632, Jefferson, USA; gen tel (406) 225-3822; gen fax (406) 225-3821; disp adv e-mail ads1@jeffersoncountycourier.com; web site www.boulder-monitor.com, www.jeffersoncounty-courier.com
Circulation:; Sworn/Estimate/Non-Audited
Pub....David Anderson
Ed. ....Jan AndersonEquipment & Software: ; Software — Adobe/InDesign CS4, Adobe/Acrobat 5.0, Adobe/Photoshop CS4, Adobe/Illustrator CS4.
Delivery Method: Mail, Newsstand, Racks

BROWNING

GLACIER REPORTER (WED)
208 N PIEGAN ST, Browning, MT, 59417, Glacier, USA; gen tel (406) 338-2090; gen fax (406) 338-2410; disp adv e-mail pressads@bresnan.net; ed e-mail cbpress@bresnan.net; web site http://cutbankpioneerpress.com/glacier_reporter/
Circulation: 2,362pd,; Sworn/Estimate/Non-Audited
Advertising rate: Open inch rate $6.25
Pub....Brian Kavanagh
Adv. Sales....Marlene Augare
Editor....John McGill

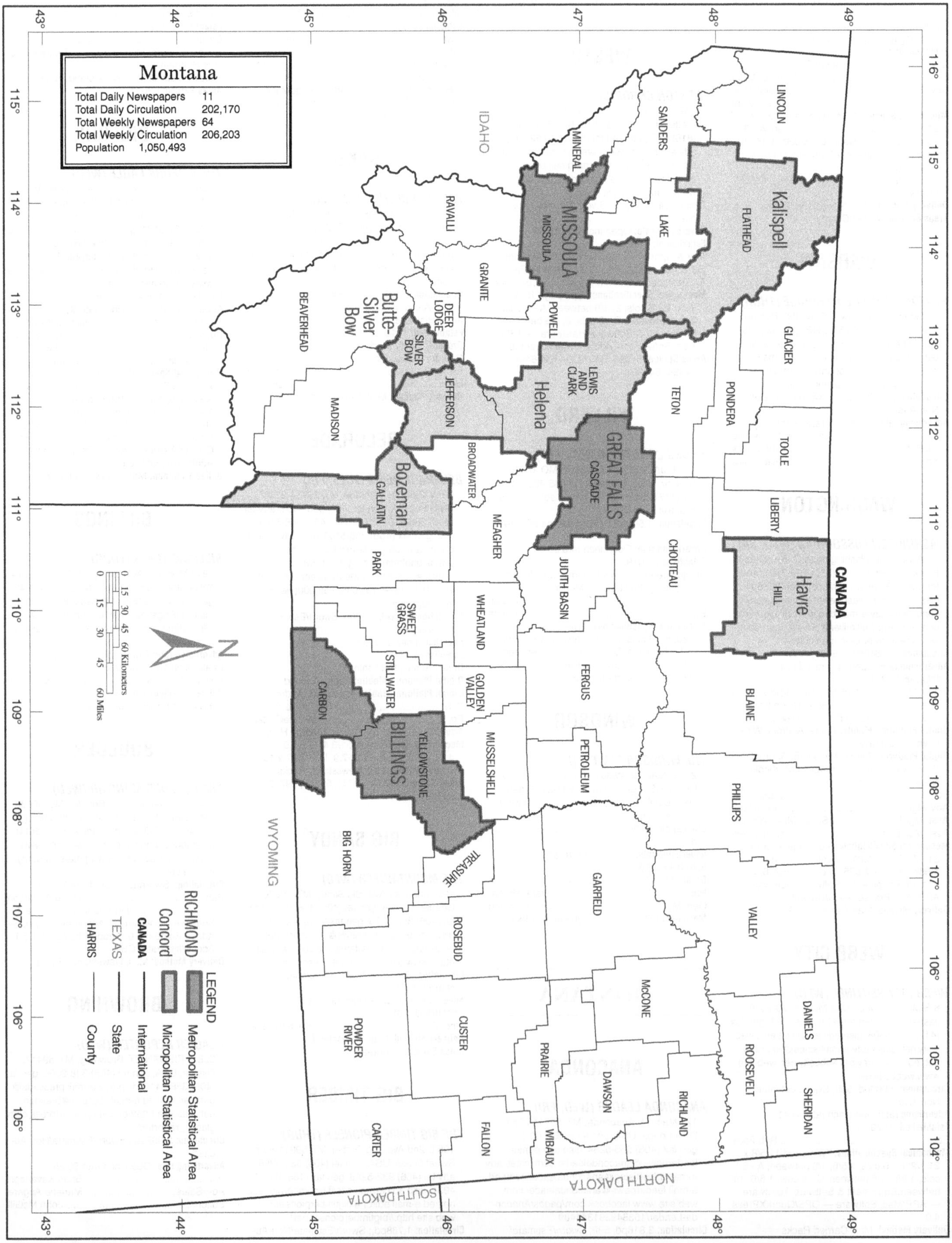
Montana
Total Daily Newspapers 11
Total Daily Circulation 202,170
Total Weekly Newspapers 64
Total Weekly Circulation 206,203
Population 1,050,493
LEGEND
Metropolitan Statistical Area
Micropolitan Statistical Area
International
State
County
RICHMOND
Concord
CANADA
TEXAS
HARRIS
0 15 30 45 60 Kilometers
0 15 30 45 60 Miles
N
IDAHO
WYOMING
SOUTH DAKOTA
NORTH DAKOTA
CANADA
MISSOULA
Kalispell
Butte-Silver Bow
Helena
GREAT FALLS
Bozeman
Havre
BILLINGS
LINCOLN
SANDERS
MINERAL
MISSOULA
LAKE
FLATHEAD
RAVALLI
GRANITE
DEER LODGE
POWELL
BEAVERHEAD
SILVER BOW
JEFFERSON
LEWIS AND CLARK
TETON
PONDERA
GLACIER
TOOLE
MADISON
BROADWATER
CASCADE
GALLATIN
LIBERTY
MEAGHER
CHOUTEAU
HILL
PARK
JUDITH BASIN
SWEET GRASS
WHEATLAND
FERGUS
BLAINE
STILLWATER
GOLDEN VALLEY
CARBON
YELLOWSTONE
MUSSELSHELL
PETROLEUM
PHILLIPS
BIG HORN
TREASURE
GARFIELD
VALLEY
ROSEBUD
McCONE
DANIELS
POWDER RIVER
CUSTER
PRAIRIE
DAWSON
ROOSEVELT
SHERIDAN
RICHLAND
CARTER
FALLON
WIBAUX
43° 44° 45° 46° 47° 48° 49°
116° 115° 114° 113° 112° 111° 110° 109° 108° 107° 106° 105° 104°

BUTTE

THE BUTTE WEEKLY (WED)

PO Box 4898, Butte, MT, 59702-4898, Silver Bow, USA; gen tel (406) 782-3820; adv tel (406) 782-3820; ed tel (406) 782-3820; disp adv e-mail butte.news@butteweekly.com; class adv e-mail butte.news@butteweekly.com; ed e-mail editor@butteweekly.com; web site www.butteweekly.com

Circulation: 5,500fr; Sworn/Estimate/Non-Audited
Advertising rate: Open inch rate $10.10
Established: 1992
Group: Butte Weekly
Publisher/owner....................Linda Anderson
Mechanical Specifications: Type page 10 x 15 3/4; E - 4 cols, 2 5/12, 1/6 between; A - 4 cols, 2 5/12, 1/6 between; C - 4 cols, 2 5/12, 1/6 between.Equipment & Software: Hardware — APP/Mac G4; Software — Adobe/PageMaker 6.5, QPS/QuarkXPress 4.1, Adobe/Photoshop 5.0.
Delivery Method: Racks
Areas Served: Butte, Mt/Silver Bow/59701

CASCADE

CASCADE COURIER (THUR)

338 2nd St N, Cascade, MT, 59421-4801, Cascade, USA; gen tel (406) 468-9231; gen fax (406) 468-3030; disp adv e-mail cascadecourier@mcn.net; ed e-mail cascadecourier@mcn.net; web site http://www.cascademontana.com/courier.htm

Circulation: 560pd, 13fr; Sworn/Estimate/Non-Audited
Advertising rate: Open inch rate $5.00
Established: 1910
Group: Montana Newspaper Advertising Service, Inc.
Ed..Judith Dotson
Pub./Ed..................................Felicia O'Brien
Mechanical Specifications: Type page 10 1/4 x 12 1/2.Equipment & Software: Hardware — APP/Mac.

CHESTER

LIBERTY COUNTY TIMES (WED)

46 1st St E, Chester, MT, 59522, Liberty, USA; gen tel (406) 759-5355; gen fax (406) 759-5261; disp adv e-mail lctimes@itstriangle.com; ed e-mail lctimes@itstriangle.com; web site www.libertycountytimes.net

Circulation: 1,202pd, 17fr; Sworn/Estimate/Non-Audited
Advertising rate: Open inch rate $6.00
Established: 1905
Pub..Paul Overlie
Delivery Method: Mail
Areas Served: West Hill, Liberty, East Toole

CHINOOK

JOURNAL NEWS OPINION (WED)

217 Indiana St, Chinook, MT, 59523-9716, Blaine, USA; gen tel (406) 357-2680; adv tel (406) 357-3573; gen fax (406) 357-3736; disp adv e-mail bcjnews@ttc-cmc.net; ed e-mail bcjnews@itstriangle.com; web site http://www.blainecountyjournal.com/

Circulation: 2,150pd, 48fr; Sworn/Estimate/Non-Audited
Advertising rate: Open inch rate $9.00
Established: 1890
Prodn. Mngr..........................Keith A. Hanson
Ed..Keri Hanson
Delivery Method: Mail, Racks
Areas Served: Blaine

CHOTEAU

CHOTEAU ACANTHA (WED)

216 1st Ave NW, Choteau, MT, 59422-9269, United States, USA; gen tel (406) 466-2403; adv tel (406) 466-2403; ed tel (406) 466-2403; gen fax (406) 466-2403; disp adv e-mail tetonads@3rivers.net; class adv e-mail tetonads@3rivers.net; ed e-mail acantha@3rivers.net; web site www.choteauacantha.com

Circulation: 1,600pd, 20fr; USPS
Advertising rate: Open inch rate $6.60
Established: 1893
Digital Platform - Mobile: Apple
Adv. Mgr.........................Jeffrey O. Martinsen
Ed...................................Melody Martinsen
Mechanical Specifications: type page is 6 col. wide by 21.75 inches deep. ROP col. width is 11.125". Classified page is 7 col. wide. 0p9 picas between each columnEquipment & Software: Hardware — APP/Mac; Software — Adobe/PageMaker 6.5, Adobe/Photoshop 5.0.
Delivery Method: Mail, Newsstand
Areas Served: Choteau, MT 59422
Teton County, MT 59422, 59436, 59433, 59468, 59467, 59419

CIRCLE

THE CIRCLE BANNER (THUR)

219 Main St,, Circle, MT, 59215, McCone, USA; gen tel (406) 974-3409; gen fax (406) 485-2330; disp adv e-mail banner@midrivers.com; web site http://www.circlebanner.com/

Circulation: 1,150pd,; Sworn/Estimate/Non-Audited
Advertising rate: Open inch rate $6.00
Established: 1914
Group: Montana Newspaper Advertising Service, Inc.
Pub...Kathy Boshart
Mng. Ed....................................Ryan Grigg
Delivery Method: Mail

COLUMBIA FALLS

HUNGRY HORSE NEWS (WED)

926 Nucleus Ave, Columbia Falls, MT, 59912, Flathead, USA; gen tel (406) 892-2151; gen fax (406) 892-5600; disp adv e-mail abrowning@hungryhorsenews.com; class adv e-mail ads@hungryhorsenews.com; ed e-mail editor@hungryhorsenews.com; web site www.hungryhorsenews.com

Circulation: 1,998pd, 0fr; CAC
Advertising rate: Open inch rate $15.51
Established: 1947
Group: Hagadone Corporation
Digital Platform - Tablet: Apple iOS, Android, Blackberry Tablet OS
Pub...Rick Weaver
Ed...Chris Peterson
Ad Director..........................Andrea Browning
Mechanical Specifications: Type page 11 7/10 x 20 3/4; E - 6 cols, 1 4/5, 7/50 between; A - 6 cols, 1 4/5, 7/50 between; C - 6 cols, 2, 1/4 between.Equipment & Software: Hardware — APP/Mac G4; Presses — G; Software — QPS/QuarkXPress 4.0, Adobe/Photoshop 5.0, Adobe/Illustrator 8.0.
Delivery Method: Mail, Newsstand, Racks
Areas Served: Columbia Falls, Glacier National Park, Surrounding National Forest

COLUMBUS

THE STILLWATER COUNTY NEWS (THUR)

38 N 4th St, Columbus, MT, 59019-7364, Stillwater, USA; gen tel (406) 322-5212; gen fax (406) 322-5391; disp adv e-mail ads@stillwatercountynews.com; class adv e-mail classifieds@stillwatercountynews.com; ed e-mail editor@stillwatercountynews.com; web site www.stillwatercountynews.com

Circulation: 2,100pd, 5fr; Sworn/Estimate/Non-Audited
Advertising rate: Open inch rate $7.10.
Group: Yellowstone Communications
Pub.....................................Frank Perea II
Adv.....................................Melany Preece
Ed....................................Jillian Shoemaker
Prodn. Mgr..............................Amy Spaulding
Mechanical Specifications: Type page 13 x 21; E - 6 cols, 2, 1/6 between; A - 6 cols, 2, 1/6 between; C - 6 cols, 2, 1/6 between.Equipment & Software: Hardware — APP/Mac G3; Software — Adobe/Illustrator 8.0, Adobe/PageMaker 6.5, Adobe/Photoshop 5.0, QPS/QuarkXPress 4.0, Adobe/Acrobat 4.0.
Delivery Method: Mail, Newsstand, Racks
Areas Served: Stillwater, Columbus, Absarokee, Fishtail, Nye, Park City, Rapelje, Reedpoint

CONRAD

INDEPENDENT OBSERVER (THUR)

7 3rd Ave SE, Conrad, MT, 59425-2039, Pondera, USA; gen tel (406) 271-5561; disp adv e-mail indobserv@3rivers.net; class adv e-mail indobserv@3rivers.net; ed e-mail indobserv@3rivers.net; web site www.independentobserver.com

Circulation: 1,900pd, 60fr; Sworn/Estimate/Non-Audited
Advertising rate: Open inch rate $6.50
Established: 1906
Pub...Patricia Lee
Office Mgr..............................Julie Anderson
Production-Adv. Mgr..................Barb Stratman
Adv. Asst..............................Donna Arvidson
Reporter..................................Allan Diedrich
Mechanical Specifications: 1 column - 1.83"
2 column - 3.79"
3 column - 5.75"
4 column - 7.708"
5 column - 9.66"
6 column - 11.625"
Equipment & Software: Hardware — APP/Mac.; Software — Adobe Creative Suite 6
Delivery Method: Mail, Newsstand, Carrier
Areas Served: 59486, 59416, 59456, 59433, 59432

CULBERTSON

THE SEARCHLIGHT (THUR)

11 Broadway, Culbertson, MT, 59218, Roosevelt, USA; gen tel (406) 787-5821; adv tel (406) 787-5821; ed tel (406) 653-2222; gen fax (406) 787-5271; disp adv e-mail searchlight@nemont.net; web site www.northeastmontananews.com

Circulation: 850pd,; Sworn/Estimate/Non-Audited
Advertising rate: Open inch rate $5.50
Established: 1902
Pub.....................................Darla Shumway
Delivery Method: Mail, Newsstand
Areas Served: roosevelt, sheridan, richland

CUT BANK

CUT BANK PIONEER PRESS (WED)

19 S Central Ave, Cut Bank, MT, 59427-2914, USA; gen tel (406) 873-2201; gen fax (406) 873-2443; disp adv e-mail pressads@bresnan.net; web site www.cutbankpioneerpress.com

Circulation: 1,600pd,; USPS
Advertising rate: Open inch rate $6.00
Pub.....................................Brian Kavanagh
Adv. Mgr...............................Jonna Tafelmeyer
Ed....................................LeAnne Kavanagh
Steven Gall
Samantha RadtkeEquipment & Software: Hardware — APP/Mac; Software — Adobe/PageMaker.
Delivery Method: Mail, Newsstand, Carrier, Racks

THE VALIERIAN (WED)

19 S Central Ave, Cut Bank, MT, 59427-2914, USA; gen tel (406) 279-3440; gen fax (406) 873-2443; disp adv e-mail valierian@bresnan.net; web site www.thevalierian.com

Circulation:; USPS
Advertising rate: $4.00
Delivery Method: Mail, Newsstand

DEER LODGE

SILVER STATE POST (WED)

312 Missouri Ave, Deer Lodge, MT, 59722-1077, Powell, USA; gen tel (406) 846-2424; gen fax (406) 846-2453; disp adv e-mail ads@pburgmail.com; class adv e-mail design@sspmt.com; ed e-mail news@sspmt.com; web site www.sspmt.com/

Circulation: 1,900pd, 2,200fr; Sworn/Estimate/Non-Audited
Advertising rate: Open inch rate $12.00
Established: 1887Editions: (2) Silver State Post, Free Express
Office Mgr...................................Jane Harr
Ed......................................Jared Cooksey
Ad. Design............................Christina Bledsoe
Ad. Sales
Grace Silverstein
Delivery Method: Mail, Newsstand, Racks
Areas Served: 59722, 59731, 59733, 59728

DILLON

DILLON TRIBUNE (WED)

31 S Idaho St, Dillon, MT, 59725-2509, Beaverhead, USA; gen tel (406) 683-2331; adv tel (406) 988-7983; ed tel (406) 988-7986; gen fax (406) 683-2332; disp adv e-mail ads@dillontribune.com; class adv e-mail accounts@dillontribune.com; ed e-mail editor@dillontribune.com; web site www.dillontribune.com

Circulation: 2,700pd, 0fr; Sworn/Estimate/Non-Audited
Advertising rate: Open inch rate $7.85
Established: 1881
Group: Yellowstone Communications
Digital Platform - Tablet: Apple iOS, Android, Windows 7, Kindle Fire
pUB......................................Dick Crockford
Office Mgr...........................Jennifer Engstrom
Advertising Mgr............................Kayla Parker
Managing Ed...................................J.P. Plutt
Dist. Mgr.....................................Debbie Melle
Sports Reporter...........................Jesse Alberi
Graphics Artist.................Cassie Scheidecker
Mechanical Specifications: Column Widths: Display 1.81 inches with 1-pica (1/6 inch) gutter (6 columns per page)
Classified Display 1.35 inches with 9-point gutter (8 columns per page)
Page Size: 11.7 inches wide by 21 inches deep
Unit of Measure: Column inch (1 column wide by one inch deep)
Delivery Method: Mail, Newsstand, Carrier, Racks
Areas Served: 59725, 59710, 59727, 59736, 59739, 59743, 59749, 59751, 59754, 59755, 59761, 59762

EKALAKA

THE EKALAKA EAGLE (FRI)

307 N Main St, Ekalaka, MT, 59324, Carter, USA; gen tel (406) 775-6245; gen fax (719) 623-0209; disp adv e-mail ekeagle@midrivers.com; ed e-mail ekeagle@midrivers.com

Circulation: 1,100pd,; Sworn/Estimate/Non-Audited
Advertising rate: Open inch rate $4.50
Established: 1909
Group: Montana Newspaper Advertising Service, Inc.
Adv. Mgr................................Jeanette Adams
Ed....................................M. Brice Lambert
Delivery Method: Mail
Areas Served: Carter, Falon

ENNIS

THE MADISONIAN (THUR)
65 Mt Highway 287, Ennis, MT, 59729-9117, Madison, USA; gen tel (406) 682-7755; gen fax (406) 682-5013; disp adv e-mail ads@madisoniannews.com; ed e-mail editor@madisoniannews.com; web site www.madisoniannews.com - 16,000(views)
Circulation: 2,300pd,; Sworn/Estimate/Non-Audited
Advertising rate: Open inch rate $6.50
Established: 1873Editions: (2) The Loop
Owner/Adv. Dir. .... Erin Leonard
Owner/Dir., Sales/Mktg. .... Susanne Hill
News Ed. .... Abigail Dennis
Delivery Method: Mail, Newsstand, Carrier, Racks
Areas Served: Madison Valley, Ruby Valley

EUREKA

TOBACCO VALLEY NEWS (WED)
200 Cliff Ave., Eureka, MT, 59917, Lincoln, USA; gen tel (406) 297-2514; gen fax (406) 297-7807; disp adv e-mail robnewman22@gmail.com; class adv e-mail robnewman22@gmail.com; ed e-mail eurekaeditor@tobaccovalleynews.com; web site www.tobaccovalleynews.com
Circulation: 2,101pd, 13fr; Sworn/Estimate/Non-Audited
Advertising rate: Open inch rate $6.20
Established: 1960
Ed. .... Steve Newman
Mng. Ed. .... Robin Newman
Delivery Method: Mail, Newsstand, Carrier
Areas Served: Lincoln County

FAIRFIELD

FAIRFIELD SUN TIMES (THUR)
PO Box 578, 409 Central Ave., Fairfield, MT, 59436-0578, Teton, USA; gen tel (406) 467-2334; gen fax (406) 467-3354; disp adv e-mail suntimes@3rivers.net; class adv e-mail ads@fairfieldsuntimes.com; ed e-mail suntimes@fairfieldsuntimes.com; web site http://www.fairfieldsuntimes.com - 200,000(views) 15,000(visitors)
Circulation: 760pd, 10fr; Sworn/Estimate/Non-Audited
Advertising rate: Open inch rate $6.50
Established: 1912
Group: Sun Times Printing & Publishing, LLC
Digital Platform - Mobile: Apple, Android, Windows, Blackberry
Digital Platform - Tablet: Apple iOS, Android
Ed., Pub., Propr. ....
Darryl FlowersEquipment & Software: Hardware — Apple MAC's (iMACs and MacBook Pro); Synology 8TB NAS Server; Drobo 8TB backup server; Presses — Konica-Minolta; RISO; Software — InDesign CC
QuarkXpress 10
Delivery Method: Mail, Newsstand
Areas Served: All of Teton County, including Choteau, Fairfield, Power, Dutton; northern Lewis & Clark County, including Augusta, Wolf Creek and Lincoln; northern Cascade County, including Vaughn, Sun River, Simms and Fort Shaw.

FORSYTH

HYSHAM ECHO (THUR)
214 N 13th Ave, Forsyth, MT, 59327, Rosebud, USA; gen tel (406) 346-7067; disp adv e-mail cklinker@rangeweb.net
Circulation: 307pd,; Sworn/Estimate/Non-Audited
Advertising rate: Open inch rate $3.50
Established: 1911
Ed. .... Carol Klinker

THE INDEPENDENT PRESS (THUR)
192 N 10th Ave, Forsyth, MT, 59327, Rosebud, USA; gen tel (406) 346-2149; gen fax (406) 346-2140; disp adv e-mail ip-ads@rangeweb.net; class adv e-mail classified@rangeweb.net; ed e-mail ip-news@rangeweb.net; web site www.yellowstonecommunications.com
Circulation: 1,375pd, 23fr; Sworn/Estimate/Non-Audited
Advertising rate: Open inch rate $5.59
Group: Yellowstone Communications
Adv. Mgr. .... Connie Brown
Managing Editor .... Christy Suits
Admin. Assistant/Bookkeeper .... Krista Bartz
Mechanical Specifications: Type page 13 x 21; E - 6 cols, 2 1/16, 1/8 between; A - 6 cols, 2 1/16, 1/8 between; C - 6 cols, 2 1/16, 1/8 between.
Delivery Method: Mail, Newsstand, Racks
Areas Served: Rosebud, Forsyth, Colstrip, Ashland, Lame Deer

FORT BENTON

THE RIVER PRESS (WED)
114 Front St., Fort Benton, MT, 59442, Chouteau, USA; gen tel (406) 622-3311; gen fax (406) 622-5446; disp adv e-mail riverpress@live.com; ed e-mail riverpress@live.com; web site www.riverpressnews.com
Circulation: 2,000pd, 50fr; Sworn/Estimate/Non-Audited
Advertising rate: Open inch rate $5.50
Established: 1880
Adv. Mgr. .... Lindsey Kraus
Ed. .... Tim Burmeister
Mechanical Specifications: Type page 13 x 21 1/2; E - 6 cols, 2, 1/6 between; A - 6 cols, 2, 1/6 between; C - 6 cols, 2, 1/6 between. Equipment & Software: Hardware — 4-APP/Mac; Software — Adobe/PageMaker 6.5.
Delivery Method: Mail, Newsstand, Carrier
Areas Served: Fort Benton

GLASGOW

THE GLASGOW COURIER (WED)
341 3rd Ave S, Glasgow, MT, 59230-2401, Valley, USA; gen tel (406) 228-9301; gen fax (406) 228-2665; disp adv e-mail sales@glasgowcourier.com; ed e-mail courier@glasgowcourier.com; web site www.glasgowcourier.com
Circulation: 2,707pd, 95fr; Sworn/Estimate/Non-Audited
Advertising rate: Open inch rate $7.75
Established: 1913
Group: Stevenson/Hicks Newspapers
Publisher .... Jim Orr
Editor .... Samar Fay
Office manager .... Terry Trang
Production manager .... Stan Sonsteng
Delivery Method: Mail, Newsstand, Carrier
Areas Served: 59230

GLENDIVE

GLENDIVE RANGER-REVIEW (THUR, SUN)
119 W Bell St, Glendive, MT, 59330-1614, Dawson, USA; gen tel (406) 377-3303; gen fax (406) 377-5435; disp adv e-mail rrads@rangerreview.com; class adv e-mail rrads@rangerreview.com; ed e-mail rrnews@rangerreview.com; web site www.rangerreview.com
Circulation: 3,200pd, 20fr; Sworn/Estimate/Non-Audited
Advertising rate: Open inch rate $8.12
Established: 1881
Group: Montana Newspaper Advertising Service, Inc.
Yellowstone CommunicationsEditions: (2) Glendive Ranger-Review, Glendive Farm and Ranch Weekly
Pub. .... Jamie Crisafulli
Adv. Sales .... Pamela Ruth
Mechanical Specifications: Type page 13 x 21 1/2; E - 6 cols, 2 1/15, 1/6 between; A - 6 cols, 2 1/15, 1/6 between; C - 8 cols, 1/6 between.Equipment & Software: Hardware — APP/Mac; Software — QPS/QuarkXPress 4.0.
Delivery Method: Mail, Newsstand, Carrier
Areas Served: Dawson County, Montana

HARDIN

BIG HORN COUNTY NEWS (THUR)
204 N Center Ave, Hardin, MT, 59034-1908, Big Horn, USA; gen tel (406) 665-1008; gen fax (406) 665-1012; disp adv e-mail news@bighorncountynews.com; class adv e-mail classifieds@bighorncountynews.com; ed e-mail news@bighorncountynews.com; web site www.bighorncountynews.com - 24,000(views)
Circulation: 2,200pd, 50fr; Sworn/Estimate/Non-Audited
Advertising rate: Open inch rate $7.25
Established: 1908
Group: Yellowstone CommunicationsEditions: (5,616)
Ed. .... Andrew Turck
Pub. .... Frank Perea
Gen. Mngr. .... Jim Eshleman
Sub/Classifieds .... Barb Eben
Finance .... Janene McKenney
Mechanical Specifications: Type page 11 5/8 x 21; E - 6 cols, 1 5/6, 1/6 between; A - 6 cols, 1 5/6, 1/6 between; C - 6 cols, 1 5/6, 1/6 between.Equipment & Software: Hardware — APP/Mac G3; Software — Adobe/Acrobat 5.0, Adobe/Illustrator 8.0, Adobe/PageMaker 6.5, Adobe/Photoshop 5.0, QPS/QuarkXPress 4.0, Adobe/InDesign 2.0, APP/Appleworks 6.0.
Delivery Method: Mail, Carrier, Racks
Areas Served: Big Horn, Rosebud

HARLOWTON

THE TIMES CLARION (THUR)
111 Central Ave S, Harlowton, MT, 59036-5034, Wheatland, USA; gen tel (406) 632-5633; gen fax (406) 632-5644; disp adv e-mail harlotms@mtintouch.net
Circulation: 1,325pd, 5fr; Sworn/Estimate/Non-Audited
Advertising rate: Open inch rate $4.25
Established: 1917
Adv. Mgr. .... Shelli Randles
Ed. .... Shirley Wagner
Mechanical Specifications: Type page 11 5/8 x 21; E - 6 cols, 1 13/16, 1/6 between; A - 6 cols, 1 13/16, 1/6 between; C - 6 cols, 1 13/16, 1/6 between.Equipment & Software: Hardware — APP/Macs; Software — Microsoft/Word 6.0, Adobe/PageMaker 6.5, Claris/FileMaker Pro, Microsoft/Excel.
Areas Served: 59036, 59085, 59074, 59046, 59453, 59078

HUNTLEY

THE YELLOWSTONE COUNTY NEWS (FRI)
113 Northern Ave, Huntley, MT, 59037-9101, Yellowstone, USA; gen tel (406) 348-2649; adv tel (406) 348-2650; gen fax (406) 348-2302; disp adv e-mail ads@yellowstonecountynews.com; ed e-mail info@yellowstonecountynews.com; web site https://www.facebook.com/pages/Yellowstone-County-News/337310421752
Circulation: 1,900pd,; Sworn/Estimate/Non-Audited
Advertising rate: Open inch rate $6.35
Established: 1976
Adv. Mgr. .... Jeanne Travisono
Ed. .... Rebecca Tescher Robison
Mechanical Specifications: Type page 10 x 16; E - 5 cols, 1 5/6, 5/24 between; C - 6 cols, between.Equipment & Software: Hardware — APP/Power Mac, APP/Mac; Software — Adobe/InDesign CS3, Adobe/Photoshop CS3, Microsoft/Word for Mac.
Delivery Method: Mail, Newsstand, Racks
Areas Served: 59101, 59102, 59105, 59079, 59024, 59037, 59088, 59064

KALISPELL

FLATHEAD BEACON (WED)
17 Main St, Kalispell, MT, 59901-4449, Flathead, USA; gen tel (406) 257-9220; adv tel (406) 407-9547; gen fax (406) 257-9231; disp adv e-mail hunt@flatheadbeacon.com; class adv e-mail hunt@flatheadbeacon.com; ed e-mail hunt@flatheadbeacon.com; web site www.flatheadbeacon.com - 700,000(views) 250,000(visitors)
Circulation: 25,000fr; Sworn/Estimate/Non-Audited
Advertising rate: TOMA - $166; 1/8 - $298; 1/4 - $528; 1/2 - $925; Full - $1584
Established: 2007
Digital Platform - Mobile: Apple, Android, Windows, Blackberry, Other
Digital Platform - Tablet: Apple iOS, Android, Windows 7, Blackberry Tablet OS, Other
Ed .... Kellyn Brown
Adv. Dir. .... Bob Hunt
Delivery Method: Newsstand, Carrier, Racks
Areas Served: Flathead, Lincoln, Lake, Glacier

LAUREL

LAUREL OUTLOOK (WED)
415 E Main St, Laurel, MT, 59044-3120, Yellowstone, USA; gen tel (406) 628-4412; adv tel (406) 628-4412 x102; ed tel (406) 628-4412 x103; gen fax (406) 628-8260; disp adv e-mail ads@laureloutlook.com; class adv e-mail classifieds@laureloutlook.com; ed e-mail publisher@laureloutlook.com; web site www.laureloutlook.com
Circulation: 3,700pd, 100fr; Sworn/Estimate/Non-Audited
Advertising rate: Open inch rate $8.75
Group: Montana Newspaper Advertising Service, Inc.
Yellowstone Communications
Pub. .... Gloria Wester
Adv. Mgr. .... Ronda McCrone
Circ. Mgr. .... Sandy Erickson
Prodn. Mgr. .... Milton Wester
Mechanical Specifications: Type page 13 x 21; E - 6 cols, 2, 1/6 between; A - 6 cols, 2, 1/6 between; C - 6 cols, 2, 1/6 between.Equipment & Software: Hardware — APP/Mac; Presses — 4-G/Suburban; Software — QPS/QuarkXPress 3.2.
Delivery Method: Mail, Newsstand, Carrier, Racks
Areas Served: Laurel, Park, Billings, Columbus, Fromberg, Roberts, Molt

LEWISTOWN

JUDITH BASIN PRESS (THUR)
PO Box 900, Lewistown, MT, 59457-0900, Fergus, USA; gen tel (406) 566-2471; gen fax (406) 566-2312; disp adv e-mail advertising1@lewistownnews.com; ed e-mail pressoffice@itstriangle.com
Circulation: 500pd,; Sworn/Estimate/Non-Audited
Advertising rate: Open inch rate $4.95
Established: 1909
Group: Yellowstone Communications
Pub. .... Jacques Rutten
Editor .... Vicky McCray
Adv. .... Kimberlee Smith
Delivery Method: Mail, Newsstand
Areas Served: 59452, 59479

LEWISTOWN NEWS-ARGUS (WED, SAT)
521 W Main St, Lewistown, MT, 59457-2603, Fergus, USA; gen tel (406) 535-3401; gen fax (406) 535-3405; disp adv e-mail advertising@lewistownnews.com; class adv e-mail classified@lewistownnews.com; ed e-mail

editor@lewistownnews.com; web site www.lewistownnews.com
Circulation: 4,551pd, 108fr; Sworn/Estimate/Non-Audited
Advertising rate: Open inch rate $7.85
Established: 1883
Group: Montana Newspaper Advertising Service, Inc.
Yellowstone Communications
Adv. Mgr. .... Darlene Hodik Pub. Jacques Rutten
Prodn. Mgr. .... Tim Hartford
Mechanical Specifications: Type page 11 11/16 x 21 1/2; E - 6 cols, 1 13/16, 3/16 between; A - 6 cols, 1 13/16, 3/16 between; C - 6 cols, 1 13/16, 3/16 between.Equipment & Software: Hardware — 4-APP/Power Mac 6100-66, APP/Mac G4, APP/Mac 8600; Presses — ABD/360, ABD/9870, HI/Kord, 3-G, G/Community; Software — QPS/QuarkXPress 4.0, Adobe/Photoshop 5.0.
Delivery Method: Mail, Newsstand, Racks
Areas Served: Fergus, Petroleum, Judith Basin, Wheatland

LIBBY

KOOTENAI VALLEY RECORD (TUES)
507 Mineral Ave, Libby, MT, 59923-1957, Lincoln, USA; gen tel (406) 293-2424; gen fax (406) 293-5263; disp adv e-mail kvrecord@gmail.com; ed e-mail kvrecord@gmail.com; web site www.facebook.com/pages/Kootenai-Valley-Record/387373364659815
Advertising rate: Open inch rate $5.00
Established: 2007
Publisher/Ad Mgr./Ed. .... Lee Bothman
Reporter .... Chris Nelson
Delivery Method: Mail, Newsstand, Carrier, Racks
Areas Served: Libby, Troy

THE MONTANIAN (WED)
317 California Ave, Libby, MT, 59923-1937, Lincoln, USA; gen tel (406) 293-8202; disp adv e-mail news@montanian.com; class adv e-mail news@montanian.com; ed e-mail news@montanian.com; web site www.facebook.com/The.Montanian
Circulation: 3,400fr; Sworn/Estimate/Non-Audited
Advertising rate: Open inch rate $6
Established: 1989Editions: (3,400)
Owner/Publisher .... Carol J. Latham
Ed. .... David F. Latham
Mechanical Specifications: on requestEquipment & Software: Hardware — Proprietary; Presses — Proprietary; Software — Proprietary
Delivery Method: Newsstand
Areas Served: 59923, 59935

THE WESTERN NEWS (TUES, FRI)
311 California Ave, Libby, MT, 59923-1937, Lincoln, USA; gen tel (406) 293-4124; adv tel (406) 210-1863; gen fax (406) 293-7187; disp adv e-mail sresch@thewesternnews.com; class adv e-mail tjohnston@thewesternnews.com; ed e-mail agerstenecker@thewesternnews.com; web site www.thewesternnews.com - 60,000(views)
Circulation: 2,186pd, 64fr; CAC
Advertising rate: Open inch rate $6.25
Established: 1903
Group: Hagadone Corporation
Digital Platform - Mobile: Apple, Android, Windows, Blackberry
Digital Platform - Tablet: Apple iOS, Android, Windows 7, Blackberry Tablet OS, Kindle, Nook, Kindle Fire
Publisher .... Matt Bunk
Ed. .... Alan Gerstenecker
Prodn. Mgr. .... Paul Sievers
Mechanical Specifications: Type page 13 x 21; E - 6 cols, 2 1/18, 1/6 between; A - 6 cols, 2 1/18, 1/6 between; C - 6 cols, 2 1/18, 1/6 between.Equipment & Software: Hardware — PCs; Presses — G/Community; Software — QPS/QuarkXPress, Archetype/Corel/Draw, Adobe/Photoshop, Adobe/Acrobat.
Delivery Method: Mail, Newsstand, Racks
Areas Served: Lincoln County, Montana

MALTA

THE PHILLIPS COUNTY NEWS (WED)
220 N CENTRAL AVE, Malta, MT, 59538, Phillips, USA; gen tel (406) 654-2020; adv tel (406) 654-2020; gen fax (406) 654-1410; disp adv e-mail sarahpcnews@gmail.com; ed e-mail markpcnews@gmail.com
Circulation: 2,324pd, 52fr; Sworn/Estimate/Non-Audited
Advertising rate: Open inch rate $4.50
Established: 1896
Group: Main Street Media, Inc.
Pub. .... Bonnie Starr
Ed. .... Curtis H. Starr
Delivery Method: Mail, Racks
Areas Served: Phillips

PHILIPSBURG

THE PHILIPSBURG MAIL (THUR)
410 W Broadway St, Philipsburg, MT, 59858, Granite, USA; gen tel (406) 859-3223; disp adv e-mail ads@pburgmail.com; class adv e-mail ads@pburgmail.com; ed e-mail news@pburgmail.com; web site www.pburgmail.com
Circulation: 1,400pd, 13fr; Sworn/Estimate/Non-Audited
Advertising rate: Open inch rate $6.25
Established: 1887
Group: Montana Newspaper Advertising Service, Inc.
Pub./Owner .... Ann Mullen
Ed. .... Emily Petrovski
Mechanical Specifications: Type page 10 1/2 x 16; E - 5 cols, 1 9/10, 1/6 between; A - 5 cols, 1 9/10, 1/6 between; C - 5 cols, 1 9/10, 1/6 between.Equipment & Software: ; Software — Adobe/PageMaker 6.5, Adobe/Photoshop 6.0.
Delivery Method: Mail, Newsstand, Racks
Areas Served: 59722, 59711, 59701, 59858, 59832, 59837, 59801, 59802, 59804, 59808, 59843, 59601

PLAINS

CLARK FORK VALLEY PRESS (WED)
105 Lynch St, Plains, MT, 59859, Sanders, USA; gen tel (406) 826-3402; adv tel (406) 826-3403; ed tel (406) 826-5599; gen fax (406) 826-5577; disp adv e-mail llarson@vp-mi.com; class adv e-mail cminemyer@vp-mi.com; ed e-mail editor@vp-mi.com; web site www.vp-mi.com - 2,500(views) 2,000(visitors)
Circulation: 971pd,; CAC
Advertising rate: Open inch rate $5.25
Group: Hagadone Corporation
Pub. .... Dan Drewry
Adv. Mgr. .... Laurie Ramos
Ed. .... Matt UnrauEquipment & Software: Hardware — APP/Macs; Software — Adobe/PageMaker 6.0.
Delivery Method: Mail, Racks

MINERAL INDEPENDENT (WED)
105 Lynch St, Plains, MT, 59859, Sanders, USA; gen tel (406) 826-3402; gen fax (406) 826-5577; disp adv e-mail llarson@vp-mi.com; class adv e-mail cminemyer@vp-mi.com; ed e-mail editor@vp-mi.com; web site www.vp-mi.com - 2,500(views) 2,000(visitors)
Circulation: 736pd,; CAC
Advertising rate: Open inch rate $6.00
Established: 1910
Group: Hagadone Corporation
Pub. .... Dan Drewry
Adv. Mgr. .... Laurie Ramos
Ed. .... Matt Unrau
Delivery Method: Mail, Racks

PLENTYWOOD

SHERIDAN COUNTY NEWS (THUR)
115 N Main St, Plentywood, MT, 59254-1817, Sheridan, USA; gen tel (406) 765-2190; gen fax (406) 765-3333; disp adv e-mail scnews@nemont.net; ed e-mail scnews@nemont.net
Circulation: 2,418pd, 25fr; Sworn/Estimate/Non-Audited
Advertising rate: Open inch rate $4.88
Established: 1995
Adv. Mgr. .... Tim Polk
Circ. Mgr. .... Angie Tommerup
Ed. .... Joe Nistler
Business Manager .... Deanna Hellegaard
Mechanical Specifications: Type page 13 x 21; E - 6 cols, 2, 3/16 between; A - 6 cols, 2, 3/16 between; C - 6 cols, 2, 3/16 between.
Delivery Method: Mail, Newsstand
Areas Served: 592, 553, 981, 980, 598, 597,595, 596, 594, 593, 853, 852, 800, 591, 970

POLSON

LAKE COUNTY LEADER (THUR)
108 1st St E, Polson, MT, 59860-2310, Lake, USA; gen tel (406) 883-4343; gen fax (406) 883-4349; disp adv e-mail lramos@leader-advertiser.com; class adv e-mail elonnivik@leaderadvertiser.com; ed e-mail editor@leaderadvertiser.com; web site www.leader-advertiser.com
Circulation: 2,339pd, 329fr; CAC
Advertising rate: Open inch rate $14.29
Established: 1910
Group: Hagadone Corporation
Adv. Dir./Gen. Mgr. .... Laurie Ramos
Mechanical Specifications: Type page 12 1/2 x 21.
Delivery Method: Mail, Newsstand, Racks

RED LODGE

CARBON COUNTY NEWS (THUR)
202 S Hauser Ave, Red Lodge, MT, 59068-9128, Carbon, USA; gen tel (406) 446-2222; gen fax (406) 446-2225; disp adv e-mail ads@carboncountynews.com; class adv e-mail ccnsales@carboncountynews.com; ed e-mail news@carboncountynews.com; web site www.carboncountynews.com
Circulation: 3,100pd, 500fr; Sworn/Estimate/Non-Audited
Advertising rate: Open inch rate $8.10
Established: 1909
Group: Yellowstone Communications
Ed. .... Alastair Baker
Publisher .... Frank Perea
Pub. .... Tim Craig
Circ. Mgr. .... Edith Achermann
Adv .... Terri Newby
Mechanical Specifications: Type page 13 x 21; E - 6 cols, 2, 1/6 between; A - 6 cols, 2, 1/6 between; C - 6 cols, 2, 1/6 between.Equipment & Software: Hardware — APP/Mac G3; Software — Adobe/PageMaker 6.5, QPS/QuarkXPress 4.0, Adobe/Photoshop 5.0, Adobe/Acrobat 4.0, Adobe/Illustrator 8.0.
Delivery Method: Mail, Carrier
Areas Served: Carbon, Red Lodge, Bearcreek, Belfry, Boyd, Bridger, Fromberg, Joliet, Luther, Roberts and Roscoe

RONAN

VALLEY JOURNAL (WED)
331 Main St SW, Ste A, Ronan, MT, 59864-2708, Lake, USA; gen tel (406) 676-8989; gen fax (406) 676-8990; disp adv e-mail boone@valleyjournal.net; ed e-mail vjeditor@valleyjournal.net; web site http://www.valleyjournal.net/
Circulation: 8,400fr; Sworn/Estimate/Non-Audited
Advertising rate: 1/16 -$70; 1/8 - $105; 1/4 - $200; 1/3 - $270; 1/2 - $385; Fulll - $750
Established: 2004
Mechanical Specifications: Mission, Jocko and lower Flathead Valley
Delivery Method: Mail, Newsstand, Racks
Areas Served: Lake County, Montana

ROUNDUP

THE ROUNDUP RECORD-TRIBUNE/ WINNETT TIMES (WED)
24 Main St, Roundup, MT, 59072-2828, Musselshell, USA; gen tel (406) 323-1105; gen fax (406) 323-1761; disp adv e-mail rrtnews@midrivers.com; ed e-mail rrtnews@midrivers.com
Circulation: 2,600pd, 88fr; Sworn/Estimate/Non-Audited
Advertising rate: Open inch rate $4.50
Established: 1908
Prodn. Mgr. .... Eric N. Rasmussen
Mechanical Specifications: Type page 15 1/2 x 21.
Delivery Method: Mail
Areas Served: 59072

SCOBEY

DANIELS COUNTY LEADER (THUR)
214 Main St, Scobey, MT, 59263, Daniels, USA; gen tel (406) 487-5303; gen fax (406) 487-5304; disp adv e-mail 2leader@nemont.net; ed e-mail 2leader@nemont.net; web site http://www.danielscountyleader.com
Circulation: 1,540pd,; Sworn/Estimate/Non-Audited
Advertising rate: Open inch rate $5.22
Adv. Mgr. .... Burl Bowler
Ed. .... Milton Gunderson

SEELEY LAKE

SEELEY SWAN PATHFINDER (THUR)
3166 Highway 83 N, Seeley Lake, MT, 59868, Missoula, USA; gen tel (406) 677-2022; adv tel (406) 677-2155; disp adv e-mail pathfinder@seeleylake.com; web site http://www.seeleylake.com/
Circulation: 1,250pd, 50fr; USPS
Advertising rate: Open inch rate $5.00
Established: 1984
Group: Montana Newspaper Advertising Service, Inc.
Editor & Publisher .... Andi Bourne
Mailing & Advertising .... Nathan Bourne
Mechanical Specifications: Type page 10 x 11 1/2; E - 5 cols, 1 3/4, 1/4 between; A - 5 cols, 1 3/4, 1/4 between; C - 5 cols, 1 3/4, 1/4 between.Equipment & Software: Hardware — 3-Mac; Software — Microsoft/Word 6.1.
Delivery Method: Mail, Newsstand
Areas Served: 59868, 59826, 59854, 59823

SHELBY

THE SHELBY PROMOTER (WED)
119 2nd Ave S, Shelby, MT, 59474-1962, Toole, USA; gen tel (406) 434-5171; gen fax (406) 434-5955; disp adv e-mail promoadmgr@3rivers.net; class adv e-mail pressads2@bresnan.net; ed e-mail cbpress@bresnan.net; web site http://cutbankpioneerpress.com/shelby_promoter/
Circulation: 2,125pd, 0fr; Sworn/Estimate/Non-Audited
Advertising rate: Open inch rate $6.50
Group: Montana Newspaper Advertising Service, Inc.
Brian Kavanagh
Leanne KavanaghPub.s
Delivery Method: Mail, Newsstand, Carrier, Racks
Areas Served: Shelby - Toole - 59474

SIDNEY

SIDNEY HERALD (WED, SUN)
310 2nd Ave NE, Sidney, MT, 59270-4404, Richland, USA; gen tel (406)482-2706; gen fax (406) 433-7802; disp adv e-mail heraldsales@sidneyherald.com; class adv e-mail

classifieds@sidneyherald.com; ed e-mail editor@sidneyherald.com; web site www.sidneyherald.com
Circulation: 2,192pd,; VAC
Advertising rate: Open inch rate $11.50
Established: 1907
Group: Wick CommunicationsEditions: (2) Sidney Herald, Plains Reporter
Circ. Mgr....Dawn Steinbeisser
Prodn. Mgr....Ellen Wznick
Adv. Sales Exec....Patti Tornabeni
Adv. Sales Exec....Deb Crossland
Business Office Mgr....Deb Schieffer
Editor....Bill Vander Weele
Sports Editor....Fox Ashleigh
Classified Sales....Stacie Ratliff
Pub....Karen Brown
Pub....Stephanie Spiess
Mechanical Specifications: Type page 11 1/4 x 21; E - 6 cols, 1 5/8, between; A - 6 cols, 1 5/8, between; C - 9 cols, 1 3/16, between. Equipment & Software: ; Software — QPS/QuarkXPress 4.0.
Delivery Method: Mail, Newsstand, Carrier, Racks
Areas Served: 59270, 59221, 59243, 59262, 59217

THE ROUNDUP (WED)
111 E Main St, Sidney, MT, 59270-4107, Richland, USA; gen tel (406) 433-3306; adv tel (406) 433-3306; gen fax (406) 433-4114; disp adv e-mail adsales@esidney.com; class adv e-mail classads@esidney.com; ed e-mail publisher@esidney.com; web site www.roundupweb.com
Circulation: 9,500fr
Advertising rate: Open inch rate $10.25
Established: 1994
Digital Platform - Mobile: Apple, Android
Digital Platform - Tablet: Apple iOS, Android
Pub....Jody Wells
Adv. Mgr....Dianne Swanson
Delivery Method: Newsstand, Carrier
Areas Served: Watford City, Williston, and Sidney

STEVENSVILLE

BITTERROOT STAR (WED)
215 Main St, Stevensville, MT, 59870-2112, Ravalli, USA; gen tel (406) 777-3928; gen fax (406) 777-4265; disp adv e-mail editor@bitterrootstar.com; class adv e-mail editor@bitterrootstar.com; ed e-mail editor@bitterrootstar.com; web site www.bitterrootstar.com - 400,000(views) 150,000(visitors)
Circulation: 400pd, 6,800fr; Sworn/Estimate/Non-Audited
Advertising rate: Open inch rate $10.20
Established: 1985
Digital Platform - Mobile: Apple, Windows
Adv. Sales Consultant....Jean Schurman
Ed....Michael Howell
Prodn. Mgr....Victoria Howell
Mechanical Specifications: Type page 12 7/8 x 21; E - 6 cols, 2, 1/6 between; A - 6 cols, 2, 1/6 between; C - 6 cols, 2, 1/6 between. Equipment & Software: Hardware — APP/Mac Quadra 605, APP/Mac Quadra 900, APP/Mac Performa 6200; Software — QPS/QuarkXPress, Adobe/PageMaker, Adobe/Photoshop, Adobe/Illustrator, Microsoft/Word, Claris/Works.
Delivery Method: Mail, Newsstand, Carrier, Racks
Areas Served: Ravalli County, Montana

TERRY

THE TERRY TRIBUNE (WED)
204 S Logan Ave, Terry, MT, 59349, Prarie, USA; gen tel (406) 635-5513; gen fax (406) 635-2149; disp adv e-mail tribune@midriver.com
Circulation: 856pd, 17fr; Sworn/Estimate/Non-Audited
Advertising rate: Open inch rate $4.00
Established: 1907
Group: Montana Newspaper Advertising Service, Inc.
Yellowstone Communications
Pub....Dan Killoy
Adv. Mgr....Dawn Olson
Ed....Kay Johnson
Mechanical Specifications: Type page 10 1/4 x 13; A - 5 cols, 2, 1/4 between; C - 6 cols, 3/16 between.Equipment & Software: ; Software — QPS/QuarkXPress.
Areas Served: 59326, 59349

THOMPSON FALLS

SANDERS COUNTY LEDGER (THUR)
603 W Main St, Thompson Falls, MT, 59873, Sanders, USA; gen tel (406) 827-3421; gen fax (406) 827-4375; disp adv e-mail advertising@scledger.net; class adv e-mail classifieds@scledger.net; ed e-mail editor@scledger.net; web site http://www.scledger.net/
Circulation: 28,700pd,; Sworn/Estimate/Non-Audited
Advertising rate: 1/4 - $210.00; 1/2 - $375.00; Full - $675.00
Established: 1983
Adv. Mgr....Sherry Hagerman Benton
Ed./Pub....Annie Wooden
Off. Mgr./Classifieds....Tom Eggensperger
Delivery Method: Mail, Newsstand, Racks
Areas Served: 59873, 59859, 59874, 59853, 59844, 59854, 59856

WHITE SULPHUR SPRINGS

THE MEAGHER COUNTY NEWS (THUR)
13 E Main St, White Sulphur Springs, MT, 59645-9000, Meagher, USA; gen tel (406) 547-3831; gen fax (406) 547-3832; disp adv e-mail mcnews@mtintouch.net; ed e-mail mcnews@mtintouch.net; web site www.meagher-county-news.com/
Circulation: 1,200pd,; Sworn/Estimate/Non-Audited
Advertising rate: Open inch rate $5.00
Established: 1889
Ed....Jason Phillips
Mechanical Specifications: Type page 10 3/4 x 13 1/2; E - 5 cols, 2 1/16, 1/8 between; A - 5 cols, 2 1/16, 1/8 between; C - 5 cols, 2 1/16, 1/8 between.Equipment & Software: Hardware — APP/Mac; Software — Microsoft/Word, QPS/QuarkXPress.
Delivery Method: Mail, Newsstand
Areas Served: Meagher

WHITEFISH

THE WHITEFISH PILOT (WED)
312 2nd St E, Whitefish, MT, 59937-2414, Flathead, USA; gen tel (406) 862-3505; adv tel (406) 862-3505; ed tel (406) 862-3505; gen fax (406) 862-3636; disp adv e-mail kfritz@dailyinterlake.com; class adv e-mail classifieds@dailyinterlake.com; ed e-mail editor@whitefishpilot.com; web site www.whitefishpilot.com - 20,000(views)
Circulation: 2,727pd, 66fr; CAC
Advertising rate: Open inch rate $14.18
Established: 1904
Group: Hagadone Corporation
Montana Newspaper Advertising Service, Inc.
Reporter....Heidi Desch
Mechanical Specifications: Type page 13 x 21; E - 6 cols, 2, 1/4 between; A - 6 cols, 2, 1/4 between; C - 6 cols, 2, 1/4 between.
Delivery Method: Mail, Newsstand, Racks
Areas Served: Whitefish

WHITEHALL

WHITEHALL LEDGER (WED)
15 W Legion St, Whitehall, MT, 59759-9784, Jefferson, USA; gen tel (406) 287-5301; gen fax (406) 287-5352; disp adv e-mail advertising@whitehallledger.com; ed e-mail info@whitehallledger.com; web site www.whitehallledger.com
Circulation: 1,400pd, 16fr; Sworn/Estimate/Non-Audited
Advertising rate: Open inch rate $5
Established: 1984
Group: Montana Newspaper Advertising Service, Inc.
Prodn. Mgr....Greg Corr
Mechanical Specifications: Type page 9 7/8 x 15; E - 5 cols, 1 5/6, 1/8 between; A - 5 cols, 1 5/6, 1/8 between; C - 5 cols, 1 5/6, 1/8 between.Equipment & Software: Hardware — APP/Mac; Software — Adobe/InDesign
Delivery Method: Mail, Newsstand, Racks
Areas Served: Whitehall, Pipestone, Cardwell, Silver Star, Waterloo, Boulder

WIBAUX

THE WIBAUX PIONEER-GAZETTE (THUR)
106 1st Ave SE, Wibaux, MT, 59353-8004, Wibaux, USA; gen tel (406) 796-2218; disp adv e-mail wibaux@midrivers.com
Circulation: 880pd,; Sworn/Estimate/Non-Audited
Advertising rate: Open inch rate $4.41
Ed....Frank Datta
Mechanical Specifications: Type page 10 1/4 x 13; E - 5 cols, 2, between; A - 5 cols, 2, between; C - 5 cols, 2, between.Equipment & Software: Hardware — 3-PC; Software — Microsoft/Windows 95, Archetype/Corel, Microsoft/Word 6.0.
Delivery Method: Mail
Areas Served: Wibaux

WOLF POINT

THE HERALD-NEWS (THUR)
408 Main St, Wolf Point, MT, 59201-1534, Roosevelt, USA; gen tel (406) 653-2222; gen fax (406) 653-2221; disp adv e-mail herald@nemont.net; ed e-mail herald@nemont.net; web site www.wolfpointherald.com
Circulation: 2,000pd, 30fr; Sworn/Estimate/Non-Audited
Advertising rate: Open inch rate $6.75
Publisher....Darla Shumway
Ed....Bill Weele
Mechanical Specifications: Type page 11.125 x 21.5; 6 cols, .14" betweenEquipment & Software: Hardware — IBM; Software — Adobe/PageMaker 6.5.
Delivery Method: Mail, Newsstand
Areas Served: Roosevelt, northern McCone, eastern Valley, southern Danielsc counties

NEBRASKA

AINSWORTH

AINSWORTH STAR-JOURNAL (WED)
921 E 4th St, Ainsworth, NE, 69210-1218, Brown, USA; gen tel (402) 387-2844; gen fax (402) 387-1234; disp adv e-mail ainsworthnews@ainsworthnews.com; web site ainsworthnews.com
Circulation: 1,375pd,; Sworn/Estimate/Non-Audited
Advertising rate: Open inch rate $7.00
Group: Great Plains Publishing Co., Inc.
Pub....Rodney Worrell
Ed....Kathy S. Worrell
Mechanical Specifications: 6 column by 21.5" SAUEquipment & Software: Hardware — Apple; Presses — Newsking ; Software — Adobe InDesign Suite
Delivery Method: Mail, Newsstand, Racks
Areas Served: 69210, 69217, 69214, 69135, 69157

ALBION

ALBION NEWS (WED)
328 W Church St, Albion, NE, 68620-1260, Boone, USA; gen tel (402) 395-2115; gen fax (402) 395-2772; disp adv e-mail brachow@frontier.com; class adv e-mail julied@frontiernet.net; ed e-mail albnnuz@frontiernet.net; web site www.albionnewsonline.com
Circulation: 1,850pd,; USPS
Advertising rate: Open inch rate $7.50
Established: 1879
Group: Dickerson Newspapers, Inc.
Digital Platform - Mobile: Windows
Ed and co-pub....Jim Dickerson
Mechanical Specifications: Type page 15 1/2 x 21; E - 7 cols, 2 1/12, 1/6 between; A - 7 cols, 2 1/12, 1/6 between; C - 7 cols, 2 1/12, 1/6 between.
Delivery Method: Mail, Newsstand, Racks
Areas Served: 68620, 68660, 68627, 68652, 68665

PETERSBURG PRESS (WED)
328 W Church St, Albion, NE, 68620-1225, Boone, USA; gen tel (402) 395-2115; gen fax (402) 395-2772; disp adv e-mail albnnuz@frontiernet.net; web site http://www.albionnewsonline.com/category/petersburg-press/
Circulation: 380pd,; USPS
Advertising rate: Open inch rate $3.40
Established: 1888
Group: Dickerson Newspapers, Inc.
co-publisher....Jim Dickerson
Delivery Method: Mail, Newsstand, Racks
Areas Served: Boone

ALMA

HARLAN COUNTY JOURNAL (THUR)
711 Main St, Alma, NE, 68920-2164, Harlan, USA; gen tel (308) 928-2143; gen fax (308) 928-9914; disp adv e-mail journal@frontiernet.net; web site http://www.mainstreetmedia.us/
Circulation: 1,600pd, 67fr; Sworn/Estimate/Non-Audited
Advertising rate: Open inch rate $4.25
Group: Main Street Media, Inc.
Ed....Jack Krier
Delivery Method: Mail, Newsstand, Racks
Areas Served: Harlan

ARAPAHOE

ARAPAHOE PUBLIC MIRROR (WED)
420 Nebraska Ave, Arapahoe, NE, 68922-2762, Furnas, USA; gen tel (308) 962-7261; gen fax (308) 962-7865; disp adv e-mail arapmir@atcjet.net; web site www.arapahoemirror.org
Circulation: 950pd,; Sworn/Estimate/Non-Audited
Advertising rate: Open inch rate 5.99
Established: 18
Pub....T.M. (Ted) Gill
Pub....Gayle L. Schutz
Circ. Mgr....Cheri Gill
Mechanical Specifications: Type page 13 x 21 1/2; E - 6 cols, 2, 1/3 between; A - 6 cols, 2, 1/3 between; C - 6 cols, 2, 1/3 between. Equipment & Software: Hardware — APP/Macs; Software — Adobe/PageMaker, Adobe/Photoshop, Microsoft/Word.
Delivery Method: Mail, Racks

ARNOLD

ARNOLD SENTINEL (THUR)
113 S Walnut, Arnold, NE, 69120-6872, Lincoln, USA; gen tel (308) 848-2511; disp adv e-mail arnoldsentinel@gpcom.net; web site None
Circulation: 800pd,; Sworn/Estimate/Non-Audited
Advertising rate: Open inch rate $5.00

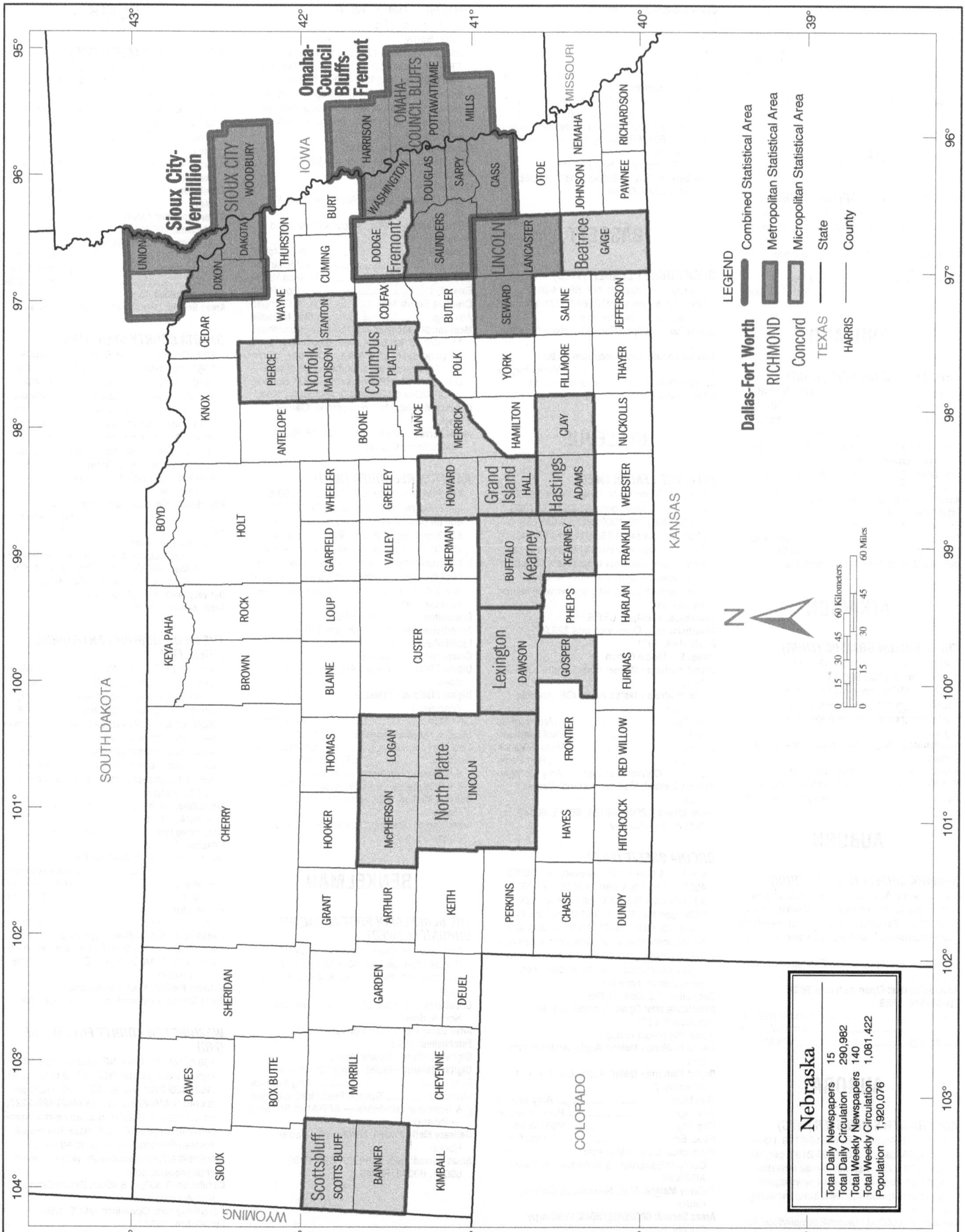
Nebraska
Total Daily Newspapers 15
Total Daily Circulation 290,982
Total Weekly Newspapers 140
Total Weekly Circulation 1,081,422
Population 1,920,076
LEGEND
Dallas-Fort Worth — Combined Statistical Area
RICHMOND — Metropolitan Statistical Area
Concord — Micropolitan Statistical Area
TEXAS — State
HARRIS — County
0 15 30 45 60 Miles
0 15 30 45 60 Kilometers
Omaha-Council Bluffs-Fremont
Sioux City-Vermillion
OMAHA-COUNCIL BLUFFS
SIOUX CITY
LINCOLN
Fremont
Columbus
Norfolk
Grand Island
Hastings
Kearney
Lexington
North Platte
Scottsbluff
Beatrice
SOUTH DAKOTA
IOWA
MISSOURI
KANSAS
COLORADO
WYOMING
UNION
DIXON
DAKOTA
WOODBURY
HARRISON
POTTAWATTAMIE
MILLS
WASHINGTON
DOUGLAS
SARPY
CASS
OTOE
NEMAHA
RICHARDSON
JOHNSON
PAWNEE
DODGE
SAUNDERS
LANCASTER
GAGE
THURSTON
BURT
CUMING
WAYNE
STANTON
COLFAX
BUTLER
SEWARD
SALINE
JEFFERSON
CEDAR
PIERCE
MADISON
PLATTE
POLK
YORK
FILLMORE
THAYER
KNOX
ANTELOPE
BOONE
NANCE
MERRICK
HAMILTON
CLAY
NUCKOLLS
HOLT
WHEELER
GREELEY
HOWARD
HALL
ADAMS
WEBSTER
BOYD
GARFIELD
VALLEY
SHERMAN
BUFFALO
KEARNEY
FRANKLIN
KEYA PAHA
ROCK
LOUP
CUSTER
PHELPS
HARLAN
BROWN
BLAINE
DAWSON
GOSPER
FURNAS
THOMAS
LOGAN
FRONTIER
RED WILLOW
CHERRY
HOOKER
McPHERSON
LINCOLN
HAYES
HITCHCOCK
GRANT
ARTHUR
KEITH
PERKINS
CHASE
DUNDY
SHERIDAN
GARDEN
DEUEL
DAWES
BOX BUTTE
MORRILL
CHEYENNE
SIOUX
SCOTTS BLUFF
BANNER
KIMBALL
95° 96° 97° 98° 99° 100° 101° 102° 103° 104°
43° 42° 41° 40° 39°

Group: The Arnold Sentinel LLC
Circulation....................................Fallon Gibson
Man.Ed. ....Janet Larreau
Pub...Lacy McCarthy
Mechanical Specifications: Type page 11 x 23; E - 6 cols, between; A - 6 cols, between; C - 6 cols, between.
Delivery Method: Mail, Newsstand, Racks
Areas Served: Custer

ARTHUR

THE ARTHUR ENTERPRISE (THUR)
PO Box 165, Arthur, NE, 69121-0165, Arthur, USA; gen tel (308) 764-2402; disp adv e-mail artent@neb-sandhills.net
Circulation: 392pd, 42fr; Sworn/Estimate/Non-Audited
Advertising rate: Open inch rate $3.50
Ed. ....Karen A. Sizer

ASHLAND

THE ASHLAND GAZETTE (THUR)
1432 Silver St, Ashland, NE, 68003-1846, Saunders, USA; gen tel (402) 944-3397; gen fax (402) 944-3398; disp adv e-mail advertising@wahoonewspaper.com; ed e-mail news@ashland-gazette.com; web site www.ashland-gazette.com
Circulation: 1,800pd,; Sworn/Estimate/Non-Audited
Advertising rate: Open inch rate $7.30
Established: 1879
Group: BH Media Group
Ed. ....Suzi Nelson
Exec. Ed...................................Lisa Brichacek
Delivery Method: Mail, Newsstand, Racks

ATKINSON

THE ATKINSON GRAPHIC (THUR)
207 E Main St, Atkinson, NE, 68713, Holt, USA; gen tel (402) 925-5411; gen fax (402) 925-5411; disp adv e-mail advertising@atkinsongraphic.com; ed e-mail editor@atkinsongraphic.com; web site www.atkinsongraphic.com
Circulation: 2,300pd,; Sworn/Estimate/Non-Audited
Advertising rate: Open inch rate $4.50
Pub./Gen. Mgr.............Roxanne Hollingsworth
Ed. ....Jerry Hollingsworth

AUBURN

NEMAHA COUNTY HERALD (THUR)
830 Central Ave, Auburn, NE, 68305-1614, Nemaha, USA; gen tel (402) 274-3185; gen fax (402) 274-3273; disp adv e-mail kendall@anewspaper.net; web site www.anewspaper.net
Circulation: 3,245pd,; Sworn/Estimate/Non-Audited
Advertising rate: Open inch rate $6.25
Established: 1888
Pub...Kendall Neiman
Ed. ....Darrell Wellman
Prodn. Mgr. ....Will McQue

AURORA

AURORA NEWS-REGISTER (WED)
1320 K St, Aurora, NE, 68818-2119, Hamilton, USA; gen tel (402) 694-2131; gen fax (402) 694-2133; disp adv e-mail advertising@hamilton.net; ed e-mail newsregister@hamilton.net; web site www.auroranewsregister.com
Circulation: 3,000pd,; Sworn/Estimate/Non-Audited
Advertising rate: Open inch rate $6.40
Established: 1929
Group: Porchlight Publishing Inc
Pub...Kurt Johnson
Pub...Paula Johnson
Adv. Mgr. ....Dave Bradley
Mng. Ed.......................................Laurie Pfeifer
Prodn. Mgr. ....Marc Russell
Mechanical Specifications: Type page 14 1/4 x 21; E - 6 cols, 2 1/4, 1/6 between; A - 6 cols, 2 1/4, 1/6 between; C - 6 cols, 2 1/4, 1/6 between.Equipment & Software: Hardware — IBM, APP/Macs; Presses — 4-KP/News King.
Delivery Method: Mail, Newsstand
Areas Served: 68818, 68843, 68841, 68865. 68654, 68846, 68854

BASSETT

ROCK COUNTY LEADER (WED)
118 Clark St, Bassett, NE, 68714-6012, Rock, USA; gen tel (402) 684-3771; disp adv e-mail news@rcleader.com
Circulation: 1,500pd,; Sworn/Estimate/Non-Audited
Advertising rate: Open inch rate $4.20
Ed. ....Mariel Fegley
Delivery Method: Mail, Newsstand, Racks
Areas Served: Rock

BELLEVUE

BELLEVUE LEADER (WED)
604 Fort Crook Rd N, Bellevue, NE, 68005-4500, Sarpy, USA; gen tel (402) 733-7300; adv tel (402) 733-7300; ed tel (402) 733-7300; gen fax (402) 733-9116; ed fax (402) 733-9116; disp adv e-mail news@bellevueleader.com; class adv e-mail classifieds@bellevueleader.com; ed e-mail letters@bellevueleader.com; web site www.bellevueleader.com
Circulation: 2,954pd,; USPS
Advertising rate: Open inch rate $23.27
Established: 1971
Group: BH Media Group
Digital Platform - Mobile: Apple, Android, Windows
Digital Platform - Tablet: Apple iOS, Android, Windows 7
Gen Man.......................................Amy McKay
Adv. Mgr. ....Paul Swanson
Circ. Mgr....................................Melissa Vanek
Exec. Ed..Ron Petak
Production Control Manager.......Amy Corrigan
Delivery Method: Mail, Newsstand, Carrier, Racks
Areas Served: 68005, 68123, 68113, 68147, 68157/Sarpy County

GRETNA BREEZE (WED)
604 Fort Crook Rd N, Bellevue, NE, 68005-4557, Sarpy, USA; gen tel (402) 733-7300; adv tel (402) 733-7300; ed tel (402) 332-0592; gen fax (402) 733-9116; adv fax (402) 733-9116; ed fax (402) 733-9116; disp adv e-mail news@bellevueleader.com; class adv e-mail classifieds@bellevueleader.com; ed e-mail letters@bellevueleader.com; web site www.gretnabreeze.com
Circulation: 1,200pd,; USPS
Advertising rate: Open inch rate $11.38
Established: 1971
Group: BH Media Group
Digital Platform - Mobile: Apple, Android, Windows
Digital Platform - Tablet: Apple iOS, Android, Windows 7
Gen Man.......................................Amy McKay
Adv. Mgr. ....Paul Swanson
Circ. Mgr....................................Melissa Vanek
Exec. Ed..Ron Petak
Production Control Manager.....................Amy CorriganEquipment & Software: Hardware — APP/Mac.
Delivery Method: Mail, Newsstand, Carrier, Racks
Areas Served: 68028/68136/68138/Sarpy County

PAPILLION TIMES (WED)
604 Fort Crook Rd N, Bellevue, NE, 68005-4557, Sarpy, USA; gen tel (402) 733-7300; adv tel (402) 444-1242; ed tel (402) 733-7300; gen fax (402) 733-9116; adv fax (402) 444-1592; ed fax (402) 733-9116; disp adv e-mail news@papilliontimes.com; class adv e-mail classifieds@bellevueleader.com; ed e-mail sports@papilliontimes.com; web site www.omaha.com
Circulation: 2,152pd,; USPS
Advertising rate: Open inch rate $16.51
Established: 1874
Group: BH Media Group
Digital Platform - Mobile: Apple, Android, Windows
Digital Platform - Tablet: Apple iOS, Android, Windows 7
General Manager...........................Amy McKay
Mktg. Dir.....................................Paul Swanson
Circ. Mgr....................................Melissa Vanek
Exec. Ed..Ron Petak
Creative Servs. Mgr. ....Amy Corrigan
Adv. Mgr......................................Dan Matuella
Mechanical Specifications: Full Size Broadsheet 11.5x20.75; full page width 6 columns 11 1/2; full page depth 20 3/4; agate line per column inch 14; Equipment & Software: Hardware — Dell, Ultre 94, HP; Presses — 4-KP; Software — QPS/QuarkXPress 4.0, Microsoft/Office.
Delivery Method: Mail, Newsstand, Carrier, Racks
Areas Served: 68046, 68133, 68128, 68059, 68138/Sarpy County

RALSTON RECORDER (WED)
604 Fort Crook Rd N, Bellevue, NE, 68005-4557, Sarpy, USA; gen tel (402) 733-7300; adv tel (402) 444-1248; ed tel (402) 331-6300; gen fax (402) 733-9116; ed fax (402) 733-9116; disp adv e-mail paul.swanson@bellevueleader.com; class adv e-mail classifieds@bellevueleader.com; ed e-mail news@ralstonrecorder.com; web site www.ralstonrecorder.com
Circulation: 727pd, 0fr; USPS
Advertising rate: Open inch rate $10.40
Established: 1963
Group: BH Media Group
Digital Platform - Mobile: Apple, Android, Windows
Digital Platform - Tablet: Apple iOS, Android, Windows 7
Gen Man.......................................Amy McKay
Special Projects Manager..........Paul Swanson
Circ. Mgr....................................Melissa Vanek
Exec. Ed.........................Ron PetakEquipment & Software: Hardware — 24-Dell; Presses — 4-KP; Software — MS/Windows, InDesign
Delivery Method: Mail, Newsstand, Carrier, Racks
Areas Served: Ralston/Douglas/68127 and Sarpy County

BENKELMAN

THE BENKELMAN POST AND NEWS-CHRONICLE (WED)
513 Chief St, Benkelman, NE, 69021-3065, Dundy, USA; gen tel (308) 423-2337; gen fax (308) 423-5555; disp adv e-mail bpost@bwtelcom.net
Circulation: 1,245pd, 35fr; Sworn/Estimate/Non-Audited
Advertising rate: Open inch rate $5.75
Established: 1993
Digital Platform - Mobile: Apple
Digital Platform - Tablet: Apple iOS, Kindle
Pub...Amy Fredrick
Manager ....Trenton FrederickEquipment & Software: Hardware — APP/Mac; Software — indesign
Delivery Method: Mail, Newsstand, Carrier, Racks
Areas Served: 69021, 69027, 69030, 69037, 69041, 69043, 69045

BLAIR

ARLINGTON CITIZEN (THUR)
138 N 16th St, Blair, NE, 68008-1633, Washington, USA; gen tel (402) 426-2121; adv tel (402) 426-2121; ed tel (402) 426-2121; gen fax (402) 426-2227; adv fax (402) 426-2227; ed fax (402) 426-2227; disp adv e-mail mrhoades@enterprisepub.com; class adv e-mail lhansen@enterprisepub.com; ed e-mail online@enterprisepub.com; web site www.enterprisepub.com
Circulation: 575pd,; Sworn/Estimate/Non-Audited
Advertising rate: Open inch rate $8.00
Established: 1954
Group: Enterprise Publishing Co.
Publisher/Owner.......................Mark Rhoades
Sales Manager........................Lynette Hansen
Editor ....Leanna Ellis
Delivery Method: Mail
Areas Served: 68002, 68008, 68034, 68044

DAKOTA COUNTY STAR (THUR)
7990 County Road P35, Blair, NE, 68008-6562, Washington, USA; gen tel (402) 426-9860; adv tel (402) 426-9860; ed tel (402) 426-9860; gen fax (402) 426-9860; adv fax (402) 426-9860; ed fax (402) 426-9860; disp adv e-mail mrhoades@enterprisepub.com; class adv e-mail mrhoades@enterprisepub.com; ed e-mail mrhoades@enterprisepub.com; web site www.dakotacountystar.net
Circulation: 2,200pd, 78fr; Sworn/Estimate/Non-Audited
Advertising rate: Open inch rate $10.25
Owner/Pub...............................Mark Rhoades
Ed. ....Blake Branch
Associate Publisher ....Chris RhoadesEquipment & Software: Hardware — APP/iMac, APP/Mac G4; Presses — 4-KP/NewsKing, Ik, ABD/9810, ABD/9970.
Delivery Method: Mail, Newsstand
Areas Served: 68776

THE PILOT TRIBUNE / ENTERPRISE (TUES, FRI)
138 N 16th St, Blair, NE, 68008-1633, Washington, USA; gen tel (402) 426-2121; adv tel (402) 426-2121; ed tel (402) 426-2121; gen fax (402) 426-2227; adv fax (402) 426-2227; ed fax (402) 426-2227; disp adv e-mail mrhoades@enterprisepub.com; class adv e-mail subscribe@enterprisepub.com; ed e-mail editor@enterprisepub.com; web site www.enterprisepub.com - 112,000(views) 72,000(visitors)
Circulation: 14,900pd, 11,700fr; Sworn/Estimate/Non-Audited
Advertising rate: Open inch rate $17.50
Established: 1869
Group: Enterprise Publishing Co.
Pub...Mark Rhoades
Adv. Mgr. ....Lynette Hansen
Circ. Mgr.. Rich Hain
Prodn. Mgr. ....Jen Stolz
managing editor.........................Katie Rohman
Mechanical Specifications: Type page 11.62 x 21 1/2; E - 6 cols, 2 1/16, 1/6 between; A - 6 cols, 2 1/16, 1/6 between; C - 6 cols, 2 1/16, 1/6 between.
Delivery Method: Mail, Newsstand
Areas Served: Washington county - Blair, NE

WASHINGTON COUNTY ENTERPRISE (FRI)
138 N 16th St, Blair, NE, 68008-1633, Washington, USA; gen tel (402) 426-2121; adv tel (402) 426-2121; ed tel (402) 426-2121; gen fax (402) 426-2227; adv fax (402) 426-2227; ed fax (402) 426-2227; disp adv e-mail lhansen@enterprisepub.com; class adv e-mail lhansen@enterprisepub.com; ed e-mail online@enterprisepub.com; web site www.enterprisepub.com
Circulation: 3,300pd, 8,400fr; Sworn/Estimate/Non-Audited
Advertising rate: Open inch rate $11.50
Established: 1892
Group: Enterprise Publishing Co.
Publisher...................................Mark Rhoades
Sales Manager........................Lynette Hansen

Distribution Manager .... Rich Hain
Mng. Ed...................................... Katie Rohman
Associate Publisher.................. Chris Rhoades
Mechanical Specifications: Type page 13 x 21 1/2; E - 6 cols, 2 1/16, 1/6 between; A - 6 cols, 2 1/16, 1/6 between; C - 6 cols, 2 1/16, 1/6 between.
Delivery Method: Mail, Newsstand
Areas Served: 68008-68002-68029-68034-68023

BLOOMFIELD

THE BLOOMFIELD MONITOR (THUR)

110 N Broadway St, Bloomfield, NE, 68718-4406, Knox, USA; gen tel (402) 373-2332; gen fax (402) 373-2887; disp adv e-mail bmonitor@yahoo.com
Circulation: 1,300pd,; Sworn/Estimate/Non-Audited
Advertising rate: Open inch rate $575
Established: 1890
Gen. Mgr. .... Mary Ellen Skrivan
Ed. .... Joseph M. Skrivan
Mechanical Specifications: Type page 15 x 21; E - 7 cols, 2 1/12, 1/6 between; A - 7 cols, 2 1/12, 1/6 between; C - 7 cols, 2 1/12, 1/6 between.
Delivery Method: Mail, Newsstand

BLUE HILL

BLUE HILL LEADER (THUR)

565 W Gage St, Blue Hill, NE, 68930-8000, Webster, USA; gen tel (402) 756-2077; gen fax (402) 756-2583; disp adv e-mail bluehillleader@gtmc.net; class adv e-mail bluehillleader@gtmc.net; ed e-mail bluehillleader@gtmc.net; web site http://www.mainstreetmedia.us/
Circulation: 950pd,; Sworn/Estimate/Non-Audited
Advertising rate: Open inch rate $5.00
Established: 1887
Group: Main Street Media, Inc.
Publisher..................................... Frank Mercer
Editor .... Rick Houchin
Office Manager/Billing/Advertising........ Melissa Lounsbury
Mechanical Specifications: Type page 11 1/8 x 17; E - 5 cols, 1 15/16, 1/6 between; A - 5 cols, 1 15/16, 1/6 between; C - 5 cols, 1 15/16, 1/6 between.Equipment & Software: Hardware — Mac; Software — Adobe/InDesign 5.0.
Delivery Method: Mail, Newsstand, Racks
Areas Served: 68930, 68925, 68932, 68973, 68950

BRIDGEPORT

BRIDGEPORT NEWS-BLADE (WED)

801 Main St, Bridgeport, NE, 69336-4046, Nebraska, USA; gen tel (308) 262-0675; gen fax (308) 262-0675; disp adv e-mail ads@newsblade.net; class adv e-mail ads@newsblade.net; ed e-mail editor@newsblade.net; web site NewsBlade.com
Circulation: 1,200pd, 50fr; Sworn/Estimate/Non-Audited
Advertising rate: Open inch rate $4.75
Established: 1900
Group: MOCO RENOVO LLC
Ed/Pub....................................... John Erickson
Delivery Method: Mail, Newsstand
Areas Served: Morrill County

BROKEN BOW

CUSTER COUNTY CHIEF (THUR)

305 S 10th Ave, Broken Bow, NE, 68822-2019, Custer, USA; gen tel (308) 872-2471; gen fax (308) 872-2415; disp adv e-mail chiefnews@custercountychief.com; web site www.custercountychief.com
Circulation: 3,900pd,; Sworn/Estimate/Non-Audited
Advertising rate: Open inch rate $7.75
Established: 1892
Group: Horizon Publications Inc.
Exec Ed .... Mona Weatherly
Adv. Mgr. .... Mary Coffman
Mng. Ed................................. Ellen Mortinson
Prodn. Supvr. .... Diane Franzen
Mechanical Specifications: Type page 13 x 21 1/2; E - 6 cols, 2 1/16, 1/72 between; A - 6 cols, 2 1/16, 1/72 between; C - 6 cols, 2 1/16, 1/72 between.
Delivery Method: Mail, Newsstand, Racks
Areas Served: Custer

BURWELL

SARGENT LEADER (THUR)

757 H St, Burwell, NE, 68823-4110, Garfield, USA; gen tel (308) 346-4504; disp adv e-mail bwtrib@tribune2000.com; web site www.tribune2000.com
Circulation: 500pd,; Sworn/Estimate/Non-Audited
Advertising rate: Open inch rate $7.00
Pub..................................... Lawrence Johnson
Delivery Method: Mail, Newsstand, Racks
Areas Served: Custer Valley

THE BURWELL TRIBUNE (WED)

757 H St, Burwell, NE, 68823-4110, Garfield, USA; gen tel (308) 346-4504; disp adv e-mail bwtrib@tribune2000.com; web site www.tribune2000.com
Circulation: 1,400pd,; Sworn/Estimate/Non-Audited
Advertising rate: Open inch rate $8.00
Established: 1896
Ed. .... Lawrence Johnson
Delivery Method: Mail, Newsstand, Racks
Areas Served: Garfield

BUTTE

THE BUTTE GAZETTE (THUR)

PO Box 6, Butte, NE, 6872-20006, Boyd, USA; gen tel (402) 775-2431; gen fax (402) 775-2431; disp adv e-mail advocate@nntc.net
Circulation: 400pd,; Sworn/Estimate/Non-Audited
Advertising rate: Open inch rate $3.00
Ed. .... Sadie Wells

CALLAWAY

THE CALLAWAY COURIER (THUR)

206 E Morse St, Callaway, NE, 68825-2611, Custer, USA; gen tel (308) 836-2200; disp adv e-mail ccourier@gpcom.net
Circulation: 680pd,; Sworn/Estimate/Non-Audited
Advertising rate: Open inch rate $4.00
Established: 1968
Editor/Publisher .... Michael Wendorff
Ed. .... Suzanne Wendorff
Delivery Method: Mail, Racks
Areas Served: 68825, 68860, 68822, 69120, 69130

CAMBRIDGE

CAMBRIDGE CLARION (THUR)

706 Patterson St, Cambridge, NE, 69022-6598, Furnas, USA; gen tel (308) 697-3326; gen fax (308) 697-3326; disp adv e-mail clarion@cambridgeclarion.com; web site www.cambridgeclarion.com
Circulation: 1,100pd, 70fr; Sworn/Estimate/Non-Audited
Advertising rate: Open inch rate $4.00
Established: 1920
Ed. .... Jolene Miller
Mechanical Specifications: Type page 13 1/2 x 21; E - 6 cols, 2, 1/6 between; A - 6 cols, 2, 1/6 between; C - 6 cols, 2, 1/6 between. Equipment & Software: Hardware — APP/Mac Classic, APP/Mac G3 300; Software — Multi-Ad/Creator.
Delivery Method: Mail, Newsstand, Racks
Areas Served: Furnas

CEDAR RAPIDS

CEDAR RAPIDS PRESS (FRI)

206 W Main St, Cedar Rapids, NE, 68627-5600, Boone, USA; gen tel (308) 358-0440; gen fax (308) 358-0440; disp adv e-mail crpress@hotmail.com; class adv e-mail crpress@hotmail.com; ed e-mail crpress@hotmail.com
Circulation: 350pd, 10fr; Sworn/Estimate/Non-Audited
Advertising rate: Open inch rate $4.00
Established: 1947
Ed. .... David Bopp
Location News Reporter........... Kim Schilousky
Mechanical Specifications: Type page 11 x 15.Equipment & Software: Hardware — PC; Presses — HI; Software — Microsoft/Works, Microsoft/Windows 98.
Delivery Method: Mail, Newsstand, Racks
Areas Served: Boone

CENTRAL CITY

REPUBLICAN-NONPAREIL (THUR)

802 C Ave, Central City, NE, 68826-1738, Merrick, USA; gen tel (308) 946-3081; gen fax (308) 946-3614; disp adv e-mail republicannonpareil@gmail.com; web site http://republicannonpareil.com/
Circulation: 1,995pd,; Sworn/Estimate/Non-Audited
Advertising rate: Open inch rate $7.90
Adv. Mgr. .... Penni Jensen
Ed. .... Robert M. Jensen
Mechanical Specifications: Type page 10 x 14; E - 4 cols, 2 1/4, 1/6 between; A - 4 cols, 2 1/4, 1/6 between; C - 4 cols, 2 1/4, 1/6 between. Equipment & Software: Hardware — PCs; Software — Adobe/PageMaker 6.0.

CHADRON

THE CHADRON RECORD (WED)

248 W 2nd St, Chadron, NE, 69337-2337, Dawes, USA; gen tel (308) 432-5511; gen fax (308) 432-2385; disp adv e-mail julie.pfister@lee.net; class adv e-mail raelynn.nuno@lee.net; ed e-mail chadron.record@lee.net; web site www.thechadronnews.com
Circulation: 2,100pd, 4,700fr; Sworn/Estimate/Non-Audited
Advertising rate: Open inch rate $8.30
Established: 1884
Group: Lee Enterprises, Inc.
Ed. .... Kerri Rempp
Adv. Mgr. .... Julie Pfister
Mechanical Specifications: Type page 10x 20,5; E - 6 cols, 1 4/5, 1/8 between; A - 6 cols, 1 4/5, 1/8 between; C - 6 cols, 1 4/5, 1/8 between.Equipment & Software: Hardware — PC; Presses — Headliner
Delivery Method: Mail, Newsstand, Carrier, Racks
Areas Served: 69337, 69339, 69346

CHAPPELL

CHAPPELL REGISTER (THUR)

273 Vincent Ave, Chappell, NE, 69129-9701, Deuel, USA; gen tel (308) 874-2207; gen fax (308) 874-2207; disp adv e-mail chapregister@embarqmail.com
Circulation: 1,000pd,; Sworn/Estimate/Non-Audited
Advertising rate: Open inch rate $4.47
Ed. .... Michael Talbott
Delivery Method: Mail
Areas Served: Deuel

CLARKSON

COLFAX COUNTY PRESS (WED)

242 Pine St, Clarkson, NE, 68629-4093, USA; gen tel (402) 892-3544; gen fax (402) 892-3544; disp adv e-mail ccpress@mega-vision.com
Circulation: 1,397pd,; Sworn/Estimate/Non-Audited
Advertising rate: Open inch rate $3.39
Gen. Mgr. .... Helen Evans
Ed. .... T.A. Evans
Mechanical Specifications: Type page 13 1/2 x 21 1/2; E - 6 cols, 2 1/2, 1/4 between; A - 6 cols, 2 1/2, 1/4 between; C - 6 cols, 2 1/2, 1/4 between.Equipment & Software: Hardware — Compaq.

COLERIDGE

COLERIDGE BLADE (WED)

107 W Broadway St, Coleridge, NE, 68727, Cedar, USA; gen tel (402) 283-4267; gen fax (402) 254-3999; disp adv e-mail advertising@hartel.net; web site http://www.northeastnebraskanews.us/category/cedar-county/coleridge/
Circulation: 445pd, 35fr; Sworn/Estimate/Non-Audited
Advertising rate: Open inch rate $4.86
Group: Northeast Nebraska News Co.
Ed. .... Rob Dump
Mechanical Specifications: Type page 10 1/4 x 15; E - 5 cols, between; A - 5 cols, 2, 1/8 between.Equipment & Software: Hardware — PCs.
Delivery Method: Mail, Newsstand, Racks
Areas Served: Cedar

COZAD

THE TRI-CITY TRIBUNE (WED, THUR)

320 W 8th St, Cozad, NE, 69130-1772, Dawson, USA; gen tel (308) 784-3644; gen fax (308) 784-3647; disp adv e-mail ads@tricitytrib.com; ed e-mail news@tricitytrib.com; web site www.tricitytrib.com
Circulation: 3,450pd,; Sworn/Estimate/Non-Audited
Advertising rate: Open inch rate $8.25
Established: 1965
Pub.. Nancy Dorsey
Mechanical Specifications: Type page 10 x 13; E - 6 cols, between.Equipment & Software: Hardware — APP/Mac.
Delivery Method: Mail, Newsstand, Racks
Areas Served: Dawson, Custer

CRAWFORD

CRAWFORD CLIPPER/HARRISON SUN LLC (WED)

435 2nd St, Crawford, NE, 69339-1099, Dawes, USA; gen tel (308) 665-2310; gen fax (308) 665-1146; disp adv e-mail crawfordclipper@gmail.com
Circulation: 1,050pd, 50fr; Sworn/Estimate/Non-Audited
Advertising rate: Open inch rate $5.00
Established: 1979
Owner/Editor Prodn. Mgr. ..... Jessica Espinoza
Reporter/Photographer.................. Diane Clark
Delivery Method: Mail, Newsstand, Racks
Areas Served: Sioux, Dawes

CREIGHTON

CREIGHTON NEWS (WED)

816 Main St, Creighton, NE, 68729-4003, Knox, USA; gen tel (402) 358-5220; gen fax (402) 358-5132; disp adv e-mail jforbes@creightonnews.com; web site http://www.creightonnews.com/
Circulation: 1,400pd,; Sworn/Estimate/Non-Au-

dited
Advertising rate: Open inch rate $6.75
Group: JD Printing & Publishing Co
Pub. .... Dave Wright
Ed. .... Rhea Landholm
Delivery Method: Mail, Newsstand, Racks
Areas Served: Knox

CRETE

THE CRETE NEWS (WED)
1201 Linden Ave, Crete, NE, 68333-2252, Saline, USA; gen tel (402) 826-2147; gen fax (402) 826-5072; disp adv e-mail ads_pat@cretenews.net; ed e-mail newsdesk@cretenews.net; web site www.cretenews.net
Circulation: 3,500pd,; Sworn/Estimate/Non-Audited
Advertising rate: Open inch rate $8.50
Established: 1871
Pub. .... John Reeves
Adv. Mgr. .... Pat Hire
Mechanical Specifications: Type page 13 x 21 1/2; E - 6 cols, 1/6 between; A - 6 cols, 1/6 between; C - 6 cols, 3/8, 1/6 between.Equipment & Software: Hardware — APP/Mac G3, APP/Mac G4; Presses — 4-KP/News King; Software — QPS/QuarkXPress 4.11, Adobe/Photoshop 7.0.
Delivery Method: Mail, Newsstand, Carrier, Racks
Areas Served: 68333, 68341, 68343, 68359, 68351, 68406, 68464, 68445, 68368, 68338, 68339, 68328

CROFTON

THE CROFTON JOURNAL (TUES)
108 W Main St, Crofton, NE, 68730-3310, USA; gen tel (402) 388-4355; gen fax (402) 388-4336; disp adv e-mail journal@gpcom.net; ed e-mail plainviewnews@nyecom.net; web site http://www.croftonjournal.com/
Circulation: 1,000pd,; Sworn/Estimate/Non-Audited
Advertising rate: Open inch rate $3.50
Pub. .... Kevin Henseler

CURTIS

HI-LINE ENTERPRISE (THUR)
208 Center Ave, Curtis, NE, 69025-3024, Frontier, USA; gen tel (308) 367-4144; gen fax (308) 367-8616; disp adv e-mail advertising@blairnebraska.com; class adv e-mail advertising@blairnebraska.com; ed e-mail editor@hilineenterprise.com; web site www.hilineenterprise.com
Circulation: 1,500pd,; Sworn/Estimate/Non-Audited
Advertising rate: Open inch rate $45.35
Pub. .... Mark Rhoades
Adv. Mgr. .... Lynette Hansen
Mechanical Specifications: Type page 11 9/16 x 21 1/5.

DAVID CITY

THE BANNER-PRESS (THUR)
339 E St, David City, NE, 68632-1635, Butler, USA; gen tel (402) 367-3054; gen fax (402) 367-3055; disp adv e-mail advertising@thebanner-press.com; ed e-mail lpeirce@thebanner-press.com; web site www.thebanner-press.com
Circulation: 2,800pd,; Sworn/Estimate/Non-Audited
Advertising rate: Open inch rate $7.00
Established: 1875
Group: Lee Enterprises, Inc.
Editor .... Larry Peirce
Mechanical Specifications: Type page 12 5/8 x 21 1/2; E - 6 cols, 2, 1/6 between; A - 6 cols, 2, 1/6 between; C - 6 cols, 2, 1/6 between.
Delivery Method: Mail, Newsstand, Racks
Areas Served: Butler

DESHLER

DESHLER RUSTLER (WED)
706 4th St, Deshler, NE, 68340-1801, USA; gen tel (402) 365-7221; gen fax (402) 365-4439; disp adv e-mail deshlerrustler@gpcom.net
Circulation: 1,300pd,; Sworn/Estimate/Non-Audited
Advertising rate: Open inch rate $5.75
Assistant Editor .... Jennifer Czeki
Circ. Mgr., Ad Mgr., Billing .... Dawn Schleif
Ed. .... Lois Struve
Assistant .... Paulette Hynek
Mechanical Specifications: Type page 13 x 21; E - 6 cols, 1 5/6, 1/6 between.Equipment & Software: Hardware — APP/Mac.
Delivery Method: Mail, Newsstand

DODGE

DODGE CRITERION (WED)
140 N Oak St, Dodge, NE, 68633-3094, Dodge, USA; gen tel (402) 693-2415; gen fax (402) 693-2415; disp adv e-mail dodgecriterion@gpcom.net
Circulation: 650pd, 9fr; USPS
Advertising rate: Open inch rate $6.00
Established: 1888
Editor .... Kathleen Kauffold
Ed. .... Ken H. Kauffold
Mechanical Specifications: Type page 13 x 21 1/2; E - 6 cols, 2 1/12, 1/6 between; A - 6 cols, 2 1/12, 1/6 between; C - 2 cols, 2 1/12, 1/6 between.Equipment & Software: Hardware — hp; Software — Microsoft/Publisher 97.
Delivery Method: Mail
Areas Served: 68633, 68641, 68025, 68788, 68500, 680, 687, etc

DONIPHAN

THE DONIPHAN HERALD (THUR)
206 W Walnut St, Doniphan, NE, 68832-8903, Hamilton, USA; gen tel (402) 845-2937; ed e-mail rsadd@hamilton.net; web site www.doniphanherald.com
Circulation: 712pd, 23fr; Sworn/Estimate/Non-Audited
Advertising rate: Open inch rate $5.00
Established: 1972
Ed. .... Randy SaddEquipment & Software: Hardware — APP/Mac IIsi.
Delivery Method: Mail, Newsstand, Racks
Areas Served: Paul, Hamilton, Adams

ELGIN

THE ELGIN REVIEW (WED)
116 S 2nd St, Elgin, NE, 68636-4409, Antelope, USA; gen tel (402) 843-5500; gen fax (402) 843-5422; disp adv e-mail elgnrev@gpcom.net; web site www.elginreview.com
Circulation: 1,043pd,; Sworn/Estimate/Non-Audited
Advertising rate: Open inch rate $6.65
Established: 1897
Lynell Morgan
Dennis MorganEd.s
Delivery Method: Mail

ELKHORN

THE DOUGLAS COUNTY POST GAZETTE (TUES)
2929 N 204th St, Ste 117, Elkhorn, NE, 68022-1230, Douglas, USA; gen tel (402) 289-2329; gen fax (402) 289-0861; disp adv e-mail mike@dcpostgazette.com; class adv e-mail info@dcpostgazette.com; ed e-mail dcpostgazette@dcpostgazette.com; web site www.dcpostgazette.com
Circulation: 3,400pd, 12,200fr; Sworn/Estimate/Non-Audited
Advertising rate: Open inch rate $21.50
Established: 1984
Pub. .... Mike Overmann
Co-Pub. .... Penny Overmann
Circ. Mgr. .... Andrea Whery
Ed. .... Mary Lou Rodgers
Mechanical Specifications: Type page 14 1/4 x 21 1/2; E - 6 cols, 2 1/6, between; A - 6 cols, 2 1/6, between; C - 6 cols, 2 1/6, between.
Delivery Method: Mail, Newsstand
Areas Served: 68022, 68007, 68064, 68069

ELM CREEK

THE BEACON-OBSERVER (THUR)
215 N Tyler St, Elm Creek, NE, 68836-1536, Buffalo, USA; gen tel (308) 856-4770; gen fax (308) 856-0055; ed e-mail happ.michael@gmail.com; web site www.beaconobserver.com
Circulation: 1,380pd, 60fr; Sworn/Estimate/Non-Audited
Advertising rate: Open inch rate $7.35
Established: 1898
Ed. .... Michael HappEquipment & Software: Hardware — APP/Mac G4; Software — Adobe/PageMaker.
Delivery Method: Mail, Newsstand, Racks
Areas Served: Buffalo, Dawson, Phelps

FAIRBURY

FAIRBURY JOURNAL-NEWS (WED)
516 5th St, Fairbury, NE, 68352-2648, Jefferson, USA; gen tel (402) 729-6141; adv tel (402) 300 -0819; gen fax (402) 729-5652; disp adv e-mail Susan@fairburyjournalnews.com; ed e-mail Jim.Headley@fairburyjournalnews.com; web site fairburyjournalnews.com
Circulation: 4,500pd,; Sworn/Estimate/Non-Audited
Advertising rate: Open inch rate $8.25
Established: 1892
Group: Linscott Media, LLC
Adv. Mgr. .... Susan Bartles
Pub./Owner .... Tim Linscott
Delivery Method: Mail, Newsstand, Racks
Areas Served: Jefferson

FALLS CITY

FALLS CITY JOURNAL (TUES)
1709 Stone St, Falls City, NE, 68355-2026, Richardson, USA; gen tel (402) 245-2431; gen fax (402) 245-4404; disp adv e-mail fcjournalads@sentco.net; ed e-mail sschock@sentco.net; web site http://fcjournal.net/
Circulation: 4,100pd,; Sworn/Estimate/Non-Audited
Advertising rate: Open inch rate $6.75
Pub. .... George W. Schock
Book Keeper .... Chelsie Alexander
Adv. Mgr. .... Nikki McKim
Ed. .... Scott Schock
Delivery Method: Mail, Newsstand, Carrier, Racks
Areas Served: Richardson

FRANKLIN

FRANKLIN COUNTY CHRONICLE (WED)
707 15th Ave, Franklin, NE, 68939-1511, Franklin, USA; gen tel (308) 425-3481; gen fax (308) 425-6823; disp adv e-mail frcochron@gtmc.net; web site http://www.mainstreetmedia.us/
Circulation: 1,200pd,; Sworn/Estimate/Non-Audited
Advertising rate: Open inch rate $4.95
Established: 1990
Group: Main Street Media, Inc.
Pub. .... Frank Mercer
Areas Served: Franklin

FRIEND

FRIEND SENTINEL (WED)
108 S Main St, Friend, NE, 68359-1029, Saline, USA; gen tel (402) 947 2391; gen fax (402) 947-2239; disp adv e-mail pcheckett s@sewardindependent.com; ed e-mail jillmartin@sewardindependent.com; web site http://www.friendsentinel.com/
Advertising rate: Open inch rate $5.50
Group: Enterprise Publishing Co.
Delivery Method: Mail, Newsstand, Racks
Areas Served: Saline

GENEVA

NEBRASKA SIGNAL (WED)
131 N 9th St, Geneva, NE, 68361-2017, Fillmore, USA; gen tel (402) 759-3117; gen fax (402) 759-4214; disp adv e-mail signal@thenebraskasignal.com; web site www.thenebraskasignal.com
Circulation: 2,500pd,; Sworn/Estimate/Non-Audited
Advertising rate: Open inch rate $7.15
Established: 1881
Pub., Circ. Mgr., Ed. .... John Edgecombe
Mechanical Specifications: Type page 13 x 21; E - 6 cols, 1, 1/6 between; A - 6 cols, 1, 1/6 between; C - 6 cols, 1, 1/6 between.Equipment & Software: Hardware — APP/Mac; Software — Indesign

GENOA

THE GENOA LEADER-TIMES (WED)
524 Willard Ave, Genoa, NE, 68640-3039, USA; gen tel (402) 993-2205; disp adv e-mail gltimes@cablene.com
Circulation: 600pd,; Sworn/Estimate/Non-Audited
Advertising rate: Open inch rate $3.39
Pub. .... Mary K. Johnson
Gen. Mgr. .... Cindy Mohr

GORDON

SHERIDAN COUNTY JOURNAL STAR (WED)
400 N Main St, Gordon, NE, 69343-1264, Sheridan, USA; gen tel (308) 282-0118; gen fax (866) 309-1774; disp adv e-mail scjsads@gmail.com; class adv e-mail scjsads@gmail.com; ed e-mail scjsnews@gmail.com; web site http://sheridancountyjournalstar.net/
Circulation: 1,700pd,; Sworn/Estimate/Non-Audited
Advertising rate: Open inch rate $6.50
Established: 1891
Managing Editor .... Jordan Huether
Delivery Method: Mail, Newsstand, Racks
Areas Served: Sheridan County, Nebraska

GOTHENBURG

GOTHENBURG TIMES (WED)
406 10th St, Gothenburg, NE, 69138-1922, Dawson, USA; gen tel (308) 537-3636; gen fax (308) 537-7554; disp adv e-mail ads@gothenburgtimes.com; class adv e-mail ads@gothenburgtimes.com; ed e-mail news@gothenburgtimes.com; web site www.gothenburgtimes.com
Circulation: 1,800pd, 0fr; Sworn/Estimate/Non-Audited
Advertising rate: Open inch rate $7.10
Established: 1908
Group: Platte Valley Media LLC
GM .... Ellen Morternsen
Mechanical Specifications: Type page 11 5/8 x 21; E - 6 cols, 1 5/6, 1/6 between; A - 6 cols, 1 5/6, 1/6 between; C - 8 cols, 1 1/3, 1/8 between.Equipment & Software: Hardware

— APP/Mac; Presses — G/Community; Software — Adobe Creative Suite 5
Delivery Method: Mail, Newsstand, Racks
Areas Served: 69138, 69123, 69029

GRANT

THE GRANT TRIBUNE SENTINEL (WED)
PO Box 67, 327 Central Ave., Grant, NE, 69140-0067, Grant, USA; gen tel (308) 352-4311; gen fax (308) 352-4101; disp adv e-mail tribads@gpcom.net; class adv e-mail triboffice@gpcom.net; ed e-mail granttribune@gpcom.net; web site http://www.granttribune.com/
Circulation: 1,200pd,; Sworn/Estimate/Non-Audited
Advertising rate: Open inch rate $7.35
Established: 1897
Group: Johnson Publications
Ed .... Brooke Pankonin
Publication Manager .... Samantha Goff
Office Manager .... Bonnie Becker
Delivery Method: Mail, Newsstand, Racks
Areas Served: Perkins

GRETNA

THE GRETNA GUIDE & NEWS (WED)
620 N Highway 6, Gretna, NE, 68028-8090, Sarpy, USA; gen tel (402) 332-3232; gen fax (402) 332-4733; disp adv e-mail mike@gretnaguide.com; ed e-mail gretnaguide@gretnaguide.com; web site www.gretnaguide.com
Circulation: 1,170pd, 3,380fr; Sworn/Estimate/Non-Audited
Advertising rate: Open inch rate $15.75
Established: 1963
Adv. Mgr. .... Mike Overmann
Ed. .... Andrea Bartman
Mechanical Specifications: Type page 11.5 x 21.5; E - 6 cols,
1 col: 1.778"
2 col: 3.722"
3 col: 5.667"
4 col: 7.611"
5 col: 9.556"
6 col: 11.5"Equipment & Software: Hardware — APP/Mac, PCs; Software — Microsoft/Word Adobe/PageMaker, Indesign Adobe/Photoshop CS2
Delivery Method: Mail, Newsstand
Areas Served: 68028, 68059, 68136

HARTINGTON

CEDAR COUNTY NEWS (WED)
102 W Main St, Hartington, NE, 68739-3005, Cedar, USA; gen tel (402) 254-3997; gen fax (402) 254-3999; disp adv e-mail advertising@hartel.net; ed e-mail ccnews@hartel.net; web site http://www.hartington.net
Circulation: 1,640pd,; Sworn/Estimate/Non-Audited
Advertising rate: Open inch rate $5.85
Established: 1898
Group: Northeast Nebraska News Co.
Pub. .... Peggy Year
Ed. .... Rob Dump
Delivery Method: Mail, Newsstand, Racks
Areas Served: Cedar

HAYES CENTER

HAYES CENTER TIMES REPUBLICAN (THUR)
311 Tate St, Hayes Center, NE, 69032-9747, Hayes, USA; gen tel (308) 286-3325; ed tel (308) 222-0380; disp adv e-mail times@gpcom.net
Circulation: 867pd,; Sworn/Estimate/Non-Audited
Advertising rate: Open inch rate $5.50
Group: Southwest Nebraska News, LLCAlysia MESSERSMITH
Delivery Method: Mail

HEBRON

HEBRON JOURNAL-REGISTER (WED)
318 Lincoln Ave, Hebron, NE, 68370-1524, Thayer, USA; gen tel (402) 768-6602; gen fax (402) 768-7354; disp adv e-mail hebronjr@windstream.net; web site http://www.hebronjournalregister.com
Circulation: 2,500pd,; Sworn/Estimate/Non-Audited
Advertising rate: Open inch rate $7.25
Ed. .... Mike Edgecombe
Delivery Method: Mail, Newsstand, Racks
Areas Served: Thayer

HEMINGFORD

THE LEDGER (THUR)
714 Box Butte Ave, Hemingford, NE, 69348-9706, Box Butte, USA; gen tel (308) 487-3334; gen fax (308) 487-3347; disp adv e-mail news@ledgeronline.com; web site www.ledgeronline.com
Circulation: 1,400pd,; Sworn/Estimate/Non-Audited
Advertising rate: Open inch rate $5.90
Established: 1907
Group: Midland Newspapers Inc
Adv. Mgr. .... Lyle Fodnes
Ed. .... Amber Ningen
Delivery Method: Mail, Newsstand, Racks
Areas Served: Box Butte

HENDERSON

THE HENDERSON NEWS (THUR)
PO Box 606, 1021 N Main, Henderson, NE, 68371-0606, York, USA; gen tel (402) 723-5861; gen fax (402) 723-5863; disp adv e-mail servpress@mainstaycomm.net
Circulation: 350pd, 20fr; Sworn/Estimate/Non-Audited
Advertising rate: Open inch rate $5.00
Established: 1977
Pub. .... Jan Edgecombe
Mechanical Specifications: Type page 11 x 17; E - 5 cols, 2 1/4, 1/6 between; A - 5 cols, 2 1/4, 1/6 between; C - 5 cols, 2 1/4, 1/6 between. Equipment & Software: Hardware — APP/Mac; Presses — ATF/Chief; Software — Multi-Ad/Creator 3.7, Adobe/PageMaker 7.0.
Delivery Method: Mail

HICKMAN

VOICE NEWS (THUR)
114 Locust St, Ste B, Hickman, NE, 68372-9525, Lancaster, USA; gen tel (402) 792-2255; gen fax (402) 792-2256; disp adv e-mail voicenews@inebraska.com; web site www.voicenewsnebraska.com
Circulation: 3,304pd, 260fr; Sworn/Estimate/Non-Audited
Advertising rate: Open inch rate $8.75
Established: 1978
Adv. Mgr. .... Linda Bryant
Ed. .... Bill Bryant
Prod. Mgr. .... Kevin DeValkenaere
Delivery Method: Mail, Racks
Areas Served: 68500, 68400, 68300

HOWELLS

HOWELLS JOURNAL (WED)
122 N 3rd St, Howells, NE, 68641-3087, Colfax, USA; gen tel (402) 986-1777; disp adv e-mail howellsjournal@msn.com; ed e-mail howellsjournal@msn.com; web site http://www.ci.howells.ne.us/commclub.asp
Circulation: 915pd,; Sworn/Estimate/Non-Audited
Advertising rate: Open inch rate $4.75
Pub., Ed. .... Cheryl Sudbeck

HUMBOLDT

HUMBOLDT STANDARD (THUR)
317 W Square St, Humboldt, NE, 68376-6043, Richardson, USA; gen tel (402) 862-2200; gen fax (402) 862-2209; disp adv e-mail hs40231@windstream.net; web site http://humboldtstandard.tripod.com/
Circulation: 1,360pd,; Sworn/Estimate/Non-Audited
Advertising rate: Open inch rate $6.00
Established: 1882
Ed. .... Jack Cooper
Mechanical Specifications: Type page 13 x 21 1/2; E - 6 cols, 2 1/20, between; A - 6 cols, 2 1/20, between; C - 8 cols, 1 2/3, between. Equipment & Software: ; Presses — 2-G/Community; Software — Microsoft/Windows.

HYANNIS

GRANT COUNTY NEWS (THUR)
206 S Grant Ave, Hyannis, NE, 69350, Grant, USA; gen tel (308) 458-2425; gen fax (308) 458-2425; disp adv e-mail gcn@neb-sandhills.net
Circulation: 650pd, 35fr; Sworn/Estimate/Non-Audited
Advertising rate: Open inch rate $3.50
Established: 1896
Ed. .... Sharon M. Wheelock
Delivery Method: Mail, Newsstand, Racks
Areas Served: Grant, Chery, Aurthur, Garden, Keith

IMPERIAL

IMPERIAL REPUBLICAN (THUR)
622 Broadway, Imperial, NE, 69033-3136, Chase, USA; gen tel (308) 882-4453; gen fax (308) 882-5167; disp adv e-mail imperialads@jpipapers.com; class adv e-mail frontdesk@jpipapers.com; ed e-mail schultzjan@jpipapers.com; web site www.imperialrepublican.com
Circulation: 1,614pd, 36fr; Sworn/Estimate/Non-Audited
Advertising rate: Open inch rate $7.45
Established: 1885
Co-Publisher .... Lori Pankonin
Managing editor .... Jan Schultz
Co-Publisher
Russ Pankonin
Ad Rep .... Jana Pribbeno
Accounts Payable manager
Vivian Berry
Pressman .... Alan Carman
Office/Circ Mgr.
Amanda Courter
Production Mgr. .... Hayes Karen
Production Asst
Jenn Huff
Reporter .... Becky KuntzelmanEquipment & Software: Hardware — APP/Mac; Presses — KP/News King; Software — InDesign
Delivery Method: Mail, Newsstand
Areas Served: 690, 691, 807 +

KIMBALL

WESTERN NEBRASKA OBSERVER (THUR)
118 E 2nd St, Kimball, NE, 69145-1209, Kimball, USA; gen tel (308) 235-3631; adv tel (308) 235-3631; gen fax (308) 235-3632; disp adv e-mail ads@westernnebraskaobserver.net; ed e-mail editor@westernnebraskaobserver.net; web site www.westernnebraskaobserver.net
Circulation: 1,910pd,; Sworn/Estimate/Non-Audited
Advertising rate: Open inch rate $6.00
Established: 1885
Editor & Publisher .... Jacob Misener
Mechanical Specifications: Type page 11 5/8 x 21 1/2; E - 6 cols, 1 5/6, 1/8 between; A - 6 cols, 1 5/6, 1/8 between; C - 6 cols, 1 5/6, 1/8 between.Equipment & Software: Hardware — APP/Macs, APP/Power Mac 7500, 2-APP/Power Mac 6100-60, Polaroid/Sprintscan, HP/Flatbed Scanner, Olympus/Digital Camera; Software — Adobe/Photoshop, Microsoft/Word, Adobe/PageMaker.
Delivery Method: Mail
Areas Served: Kimball

LAUREL

LAUREL ADVOCATE (WED) 106 E 2nd St, Laurel, NE, 68745-1990, Cedar, USA; gen tel (402) 256-3200; gen fax (402) 254-3999; disp adv e-mail banners@hartington.net; web site http://www.hartington.net/category/laurel-advocate
Circulation: 950pd,; Sworn/Estimate/Non-Audited
Advertising rate: Open inch rate $4.54
Group: Northeast Nebraska News Co.
Ed. .... Rob Dump
Delivery Method: Mail, Newsstand, Racks
Areas Served: Cedar

LEXINGTON

LEXINGTON CLIPPER-HERALD (WED, SAT)
114 W 5th St, Lexington, NE, 68850-1903, Dawson, USA; gen tel (308) 324-5511; gen fax (308) 324-5240; disp adv e-mail ads@lexch.com; class adv e-mail carol.meyer@lexch.com; ed e-mail malena.ward@lexch.com; web site www.lexch.com
Circulation: 3,000pd, 5,200fr; Sworn/Estimate/Non-Audited
Advertising rate: Open inch rate $10.64
Group: BH Media Group
Circ. Mgr. .... Chrissy Wagener
Mechanical Specifications: Type page 11 1/2 x 21; E - 6 cols, 1 3/16, 1/8 between; A - 6 cols, 1 1/8, 1/8 between; C - 9 cols, 1 3/16, 1/8 between.
Delivery Method: Mail, Carrier, Racks
Areas Served: Dawson & Gosper Counties

LINCOLN

NEIGHBORHOOD EXTRA (SAT)
926 P St, Lincoln, NE, 68508-3615, Lancaster, USA; gen tel (402) 473-7150; adv tel (402) 473-7257; gen fax (402) 473-7159; disp adv e-mail advertising@journalstar.com; ed e-mail dbundy@journalstar.com; web site www.neighborhoodextra.com
Circulation: 33,000pd,; Sworn/Estimate/Non-Audited
Advertising rate: Open inch rate $41.29
Established: 1990
Group: Lee Enterprises, Inc.
Publisher .... Ava Thomas
Circ. Mgr. .... Brady Svendgard
Ed. .... Dennis Buckley
Mechanical Specifications: Type page 9 15/16 x 12; E - 5 cols, 9 15/16, 1/6 between; A - 5 cols, 9 15/16, 1/6 between.Equipment & Software: Hardware — 3-APP/Mac; Software — Multi-Ad.
Delivery Method: Newsstand, Carrier
Areas Served: Lancaster

MADISON

THE MADISON STAR-MAIL (THUR)
211 S Main St, Madison, NE, 68748-6485, Madison, USA; gen tel (402) 454-3818; adv tel (402) 640-1268; ed tel (402) 640-1268; gen fax (402) 454-3893; disp adv e-mail starmail@frontiernet.net; class adv e-mail starmail@frontiernet.net; ed e-mail starmail@frontiernet.net; web site http://www.madisonstar-mail.com/
Circulation: 700pd, 50fr; Sworn/Estimate/Non-Audited
Advertising rate: Open inch rate $5.25
Established: 1878

Pub., Adv. Mgr., Ed. .... Niko Gronenthal
Owners .... Greig Gronenthal
Mechanical Specifications: Type page 13 1/4 x 21 1/2; E - 6 cols, 2 1/24, 1/6 between; A - 6 cols, 2 1/24, 1/6 between; C - 6 cols, 2 1/24, 1/6 between.Equipment & Software: Hardware — APP/Macs; Software — Adobe/PageMaker.
Delivery Method: Mail

MILFORD

MILFORD TIMES (WED)

510 1st St, Milford, NE, 68405-9701, Seward, USA; gen tel (402) 761-2911; gen fax (402) 761-2914; disp adv e-mail patdaehling@sewardindependent.com; ed e-mail news@milfordtimes.net; web site http://www.milford-times.net/
Circulation: 1,100pd, 10fr; Sworn/Estimate/Non-Audited
Advertising rate: Open inch rate $6.15
Group: Enterprise Publishing Co.
Pub... Kevin Zadina
Adv. Mgr...................................... Pat Daehling
Ed. ....Nancy McGill
Mechanical Specifications: Type page 10 1/2 x 15; E - 5 cols, 2, 1/8 between; A - 5 cols, 2, 1/8 between; C - 5 cols, 2, 1/8 between. Equipment & Software: Hardware — APP/Mac Performa; Software — QPS/QuarkXPress.
Delivery Method: Mail, Newsstand, Racks
Areas Served: Seward

MINDEN

THE MINDEN COURIER (WED)

429 N Colorado Ave, Minden, NE, 68959-1654, Kearney, USA; gen tel (308) 832-2220; gen fax (308) 832-2221; disp adv e-mail mindencourier@gtmc.net; web site http://www.themindencourier.com/
Circulation: 2,300pd,; Sworn/Estimate/Non-Audited
Advertising rate: Open inch rate $6.75
Established: mindencourier@gtmc.net
Pub.................................. Michele Edgecombe
Adv. Mgr................................. Jim Edgecombe
Mechanical Specifications: Type page 13 x 21; E - 6 cols, 2, 1/6 between; A - 6 cols, 2, 1/6 between; C - 6 cols, 2, 1/6 between.Equipment & Software: Hardware — APP/Mac.
Delivery Method: Mail, Newsstand, Racks
Areas Served: Kearney

MULLEN

HOOKER COUNTY TRIBUNE (THUR)

306 NW 1st St, Mullen, NE, 69152, Hooker, USA; gen tel (308) 546-2242; gen fax (308) 546-2722; disp adv e-mail tribune@nebnet.net; web site https://www.facebook.com/pages/Hooker-County-Tribune-LLC/127613693099
Circulation: 775pd,; Sworn/Estimate/Non-Audited
Advertising rate: Open inch rate $4.00
Established: 1887
Digital Platform - Mobile: Apple
Ed. ....Gerri Peterson
Delivery Method: Mail, Newsstand
Areas Served: Hooker

NEBRASKA CITY

NEBRASKA CITY NEWS-PRESS (TUES, FRI)

823 Central Ave, Nebraska City, NE, 68410-2408, Otoe, USA; gen tel (402) 873-3334; adv tel (402) 209-8020; ed tel (402) 873-3334; gen fax (402) 873-5436; adv fax (402) 873-5436; ed fax (402) 873-5436; disp adv e-mail ldavis@ncnewspress.com; class adv e-mail classad@ncnewspress.com; ed e-mail kmanion@ncnewspress.com; web site www.ncnewspress.com 20,000(visitors)
Circulation: 2,110pd,; Sworn/Estimate/Non-Audited
Advertising rate: Open inch rate $10.87
Established: 1858
Group: GateHouse Media, Inc.
Digital Platform - Mobile: Apple, Android, Windows
Digital Platform - Tablet: Apple iOS, Android, Windows 7
Gen. Mgr......................... Tammy Schumacher
Sports Ed.......................................Kirt Manion
Classified Adv. Mgr.................Roxanne Schutz
Mechanical Specifications: Type page 12 1/4 x 21 1/2; E - 6 cols, 1 7/8, 3/16 between; A - 6 cols, 1 7/8, 3/16 between; C - 6 cols, 1 7/8, 3/16 between.
Delivery Method: Mail, Newsstand, Racks
Areas Served: Otoe and Fremont County

NELIGH

CLEARWATER RECORD-EWING NEWS (THUR)

419 M St, Neligh, NE, 68756-1422, Antelope, USA; gen tel (402) 887-4840; gen fax (402) 887-4711; disp adv e-mail jwright@neligh-news.com; ed e-mail lschindler@nelighnews.com; web site http://www.nelighnews.com/clearwater_ewing/
Circulation: 600pd,; Sworn/Estimate/Non-Audited
Advertising rate: Open inch rate $5.75
Group: JD Printing & Publishing Co
Pub..Joan Wright
Delivery Method: Mail, Newsstand, Racks
Areas Served: Clearwater, Ewing

THE NELIGH NEWS AND LEADER (WED)

419 M St, Neligh, NE, 68756-1422, Antelope, USA; gen tel (402) 887-4840; gen fax (402) 887-4711; disp adv e-mail jpellatz@neligh-news.com; web site http://www.nelighnews.com/
Circulation: 1,500pd,; Sworn/Estimate/Non-Audited
Advertising rate: Open inch rate $6.75
Group: JD Printing & Publishing Co
Pub..Joan Wright
Ed. .... David Wright
Delivery Method: Mail, Newsstand, Carrier, Racks
Areas Served: Antelope

NELSON

NUCKOLLS COUNTY LOCOMOTIVE-GAZETTE (THUR)

63 E 4th, Nelson, NE, 68961, Nuckolls, USA; gen tel (402) 225-2301; gen fax (402) 225-2301; disp adv e-mail nclgnews@gmail.com
Circulation: 700pd,; Sworn/Estimate/Non-Audited
Advertising rate: Open inch rate $4.00
Established: 1884
Group: Superior Publishing Co
Superior Publishing Company
Ed. ....Mary Statz
Delivery Method: Mail, Newsstand, Racks
Areas Served: Nuckolls

NEWMAN GROVE

NEWMAN GROVE REPORTER (WED)

509 Hale Ave, Newman Grove, NE, 68758-6033, Madison, USA; gen tel (402) 447-6012; disp adv e-mail editor@ngreporter.com; web site ngreporter.com
Circulation: 625pd, 12fr; Sworn/Estimate/Non-Audited
Advertising rate: Open inch rate $5.00
Established: 1882
Owners/Publishers ....Steve & Gail Johnson
Delivery Method: Mail, Newsstand, Racks
Areas Served: 68758

NIOBRARA

NIOBRARA TRIBUNE (THUR)

2544 Park Ave, Niobrara, NE, 68760-7073, Knox, USA; gen tel (402) 857-3737; adv tel (402) 857-3737; gen fax (402) 388-4336; disp adv e-mail niobraratribune@yahoo.com; ed e-mail Editor@atkinsongraphic.com
Circulation: 520pd,; Sworn/Estimate/Non-Audited
Advertising rate: Open inch rate $3.50
Pub...Kevin Henseler
Ed. ....Valerie Zach

NORTH BEND

NORTH BEND EAGLE (WED)

730 Main St, North Bend, NE, 68649-5003, Dodge, USA; gen tel (402) 652-8312; gen fax (402) 652-8312; disp adv e-mail eagleads@gmail.com; class adv e-mail eagleads@gmail.com; ed e-mail nbeagle@gmail.com; web site northbendeagle.com
Circulation: 1,467pd, 10fr; Sworn/Estimate/Non-Audited
Advertising rate: Open inch rate $7.00
Established: 1897
Digital Platform - Mobile: Apple
Digital Platform - Tablet: Apple iOS
Ed & Pub ....Nathan Arneal
Delivery Method: Mail, Newsstand
Areas Served: North Bend, Morse Bluff, Ames, Rogers, etc

O' NEILL

HOLT COUNTY INDEPENDENT (THUR)

114 N 4th St, O' Neill, NE, 68763-1503, Holt, USA; gen tel (402) 336-1220; gen fax (402) 336-1222; disp adv e-mail ads@holtindependent.com; ed e-mail editor@holtindependent.com; web site http://www.holtindependent.com/
Circulation: 3,500pd, 20fr; Sworn/Estimate/Non-Audited
Advertising rate: Open inch rate $4.25
Established: 1880
Ed. .... George A. Miles
Publisher....................................James T. Miles
Editor .... Amanda Sindelar
Areas Served: Holt County, Nebraska

OAKLAND

LYONS MIRROR-SUN (THUR)

217 N Oakland Ave, Oakland, NE, 68045-1338, Burt, USA; gen tel (402) 685-5624; gen fax (402) 685-5625; disp adv e-mail ali@enterprisepub.com; class adv e-mail burtcountysports@gmail.com; ed e-mail lmsun@abbnebraska.com; web site http://burtcountynews.net/
Circulation: 900pd, 30fr; Sworn/Estimate/Non-Audited
Advertising rate: Open inch rate $5.35
Group: Enterprise Publishing Co.
Mechanical Specifications: Type page 13 x 21; E - 3 cols, 4 1/3, 1/6 between; A - 6 cols, 2 1/12, 1/6 between; C - 6 cols, 2 1/12, 1/6 between.
Delivery Method: Mail, Newsstand, Racks
Areas Served: Burt

OAKLAND INDEPENDENT (THUR)

217 N Oakland Ave, Oakland, NE, 68045-1338, Burt, USA; gen tel (402) 685-5624; gen fax (402) 685-5625; disp adv e-mail ali@enterprisepub.com; ed e-mail oindependent@abbnebraska.com; web site http://burtcountynews.net/
Advertising rate: Open inch rate $5.90
Group: Enterprise Publishing Co.
Delivery Method: Mail, Newsstand, Racks
Areas Served: Burt

OGALLALA

KEITH COUNTY NEWS (MON, WED)

116 W A St, Ogallala, NE, 69153-2543, Keith, USA; gen tel (308) 284-4046; gen fax (308) 284-4048; disp adv e-mail newsboy@ogallalakcnews.com; ed e-mail newsboy@ogallalakcnews.com; web site http://ogallalakcnews.com/Welcome.html
Circulation: 3,900pd, 200fr; Sworn/Estimate/Non-Audited
Advertising rate: Open inch rate $9.10
Established: 1885
Bookkepper ....Judy Curtis
Adv. Mgr...............................Marilee Perlinger
Pub...Jeff Headley
Mechanical Specifications: Type page 11 5/8 x 21 1/2; E - 6 cols, 1 13/16, 1/8 between; A - 6 cols, 1 13/16, 1/8 between; C - 9 cols, 1 1/6, 1/8 between.Equipment & Software: Hardware — APP/Mac; Software — Adobe/PageMaker 6.0, Adobe/PageMaker 6.5, Microsoft/Word 6.0.
Delivery Method: Mail, Newsstand, Carrier, Racks
Areas Served: Keith, Deuel, Aurthur, Garden, Perkins

ORCHARD

THE ORCHARD NEWS (THUR)

230 Windom St, Orchard, NE, 68764-5077, Antelope, USA; gen tel (402) 893-2535; gen fax (402) 893-2535; disp adv e-mail orchardnews@juno.com; ed e-mail orchardnews@juno.com
Circulation: 600pd,; Sworn/Estimate/Non-Audited
Advertising rate: Open inch rate $4.00
Prodn. Mgr. .... Lucy Ferguson
Reporter/Videographer..............Logan Lawson
Ed. .... Natalie Bruzon

ORD

THE ORD QUIZ (WED)

305 S 16th St, Ord, NE, 68862-1752, Valley, USA; gen tel (308) 728-3262; gen fax (308) 728-5715; disp adv e-mail quizadv@frontier.com; ed e-mail quizeditor@frontier.com; web site www.ordquiz.com
Circulation: 2,050pd, 40fr; Sworn/Estimate/Non-Audited
Advertising rate: Open inch rate $7.50
Established: 1882
Digital Platform - Mobile: Apple
Pub./Adv. Mgr................................Lynn Griffith
Office Mgr. ....Cori Nickels
Society Ed.................................Bonnie Griffith
Prodn. Mgr. .... Larry Kearns
Ed. .... Nick Hon
Mechanical Specifications: Type page 101/2 x 21; 6 cols
Delivery Method: Mail, Racks

OSHKOSH

GARDEN COUNTY NEWS (THUR)

204 Main St, Oshkosh, NE, 69154-6130, Garden, USA; gen tel (308) 772-3555; gen fax (308) 772-4475; disp adv e-mail gcnews@embarqmail.com; class adv e-mail gcnews@embarqmail.com; ed e-mail kelly@gardencountynews.com; web site http://www.gardencountynews.com/
Circulation: 1,400pd,; Sworn/Estimate/Non-Audited
Advertising rate: Open inch rate $5.00
Established: 1905
Pub...Kelly Reece
Delivery Method: Mail, Newsstand, Racks
Areas Served: Garden, Deuel, part of Cheyenne, Keith, Arthur, Morrill counties

OSMOND

THE OSMOND REPUBLICAN (WED)
340 N State St, Osmond, NE, 68765-5723, Pierce, USA; gen tel (402) 748-3666; gen fax (402) 748-3666; disp adv e-mail osmondnews@abbnebraska.com; web site www.northeastnebraskanews.us/category/cedar-county/osmond/
Circulation: 975pd, 10fr; Sworn/Estimate/Non-Audited
Advertising rate: Open inch rate $4.90
Established: 1890
Group: Northeast Nebraska News Co.
Pub....Rob Dump
Office Mgr....Regina Lorenz
Bernice Blecha
Delivery Method: Mail, Newsstand, Racks
Areas Served: northeast Nebraska, greater Nebraska, other states

OXFORD

OXFORD STANDARD (THUR)
104 W South Railway St, Oxford, NE, 68967, Furnas, USA; gen tel (308) 824-3582; gen fax (308) 824-3582; disp adv e-mail oxstandard@yahoo.com; web site https://www.facebook.com/Oxford-Standard-343679009051590/?ref=page_internal
Circulation: 800pd,; Sworn/Estimate/Non-Audited
Advertising rate: Open inch rate $4.00
Established: 1896Jolene Miller
Delivery Method: Mail, Newsstand, Racks
Areas Served: Furnas

PAWNEE CITY

THE PAWNEE REPUBLICAN (THUR)
600 G St, Pawnee City, NE, 68420, Pawnee, USA; gen tel (402) 852-2575; disp adv e-mail ads@pawneenews.com; ed e-mail ronald@pawneenews.com; web site www.pawneenews.com
Circulation: 1,500pd, 52fr; Sworn/Estimate/Non-Audited
Advertising rate: Open inch rate $6.70
Established: 1867
Group: Sunrise Publications, Inc
Pub....Beverly J. Puhalla
Pub....Ronald J. Puhalla
Ed....Ray Cappel
Mechanical Specifications: Type page 13 x 21; E - 6 cols, 2, 1/6 between; A - 6 cols, 2, 1/6 between; C - 6 cols, 2, 1/6 between.Equipment & Software: Hardware — IBM; Presses — WPC/Web Leader.
Delivery Method: Mail, Newsstand, Racks
Areas Served: Pawnee

PENDER

THE PENDER TIMES (THUR)
313 Main St, Pender, NE, 68047, Thurston, USA; gen tel (402) 385-3013; gen fax (402) 385-3013; disp adv e-mail ptimes@huntel.net; ed e-mail ptimespublisher@abbnebraska.com; web site http://penderthurston.com/
Circulation: 1,450pd, 75fr; Sworn/Estimate/Non-Audited
Advertising rate: Open inch rate $5.12
Ed....Norvin Hansen
Mechanical Specifications: Type page 10 1/2 x 21 1/2.Equipment & Software: Hardware — APP/Mac; Presses — ABD.

PLAINVIEW

THE PLAINVIEW NEWS (WED)
508 W Locust Ave, Plainview, NE, 68769-4119, Pierce, USA; gen tel (402) 582-4921; gen fax (402) 582-4922; disp adv e-mail plainviewnews@nyecom.net; ed e-mail plainviewnews@nyecom.net; web site http://www.theplainviewnews.com/
Circulation: 1,900pd,; Sworn/Estimate/Non-Audited
Advertising rate: Open inch rate $5.75
Established: 1892
Pub....Brook Curtiss
Mechanical Specifications: Type page 15 1/2 x 21 1/4; E - 7 cols, 2 1/12, 1/6 between; A - 7 cols, 2 1/12, 1/6 between; C - 7 cols, 2 1/12, 1/6 between.Equipment & Software: Hardware — IBM; Software — XYQUEST/XyWrite, Adobe/Photoshop, Microsoft/Works.
Delivery Method: Mail, Newsstand, Racks
Areas Served: 68769, 68720, 68737

PLATTSMOUTH

THE PLATTSMOUTH JOURNAL (THUR)
410 Main St, Plattsmouth, NE, 68048-1960, Cass, USA; gen tel (402) 296-2141; gen fax (402) 296-3401; disp adv e-mail caroline.dall@lee.net; class adv e-mail karen.turner@lee.net; ed e-mail pattijo.peterson@lee.net; web site http://fremonttribune.com/cass-news/
Circulation: 5,200pd, 16,250fr; Sworn/Estimate/Non-Audited
Advertising rate: Open inch rate $8.20
Established: 1881
Group: Lee Enterprises, Inc.
Ed....Patti Jo Peterson
Adv. Rep....Caroline Dall
Mechanical Specifications: Type page 14 x 21; E - 6 cols, 2 1/8, between; A - 6 cols, 2 1/8, between; C - 6 cols, 2 1/8, between.Equipment & Software: Hardware — APP/Mac.
Delivery Method: Mail, Newsstand, Racks
Areas Served: Cass

RANDOLPH

THE RANDOLPH TIMES (WED)
121 W Broadway St, Randolph, NE, 68771-2516, Cedar, USA; gen tel (402) 337-0488; gen fax (402) 337-0488; disp adv e-mail randolph@cedarcountynews.net; web site http://www.northeastnebraskanews.us/category/cedar-county/randolph/
Advertising rate: Open inch rate $4.54
Group: Northeast Nebraska News Co.Rob Dump
Delivery Method: Mail, Newsstand, Racks
Areas Served: Cedar

RAVENNA

THE RAVENNA NEWS (WED)
322 Grand Ave, Ravenna, NE, 68869-1398, Buffalo, USA; gen tel (308) 452-3411; gen fax (308) 452-3511; disp adv e-mail ranews@cornhusker.net
Circulation: 1,152pd, 3fr; Sworn/Estimate/Non-Audited
Advertising rate: Open inch rate $7.45
Established: 1886
Pub./Adv. Mgr....T.M. (Ted) Gill
co-publisher....Nancy Jackson
Mechanical Specifications: Type page 11 1/2 x 21; E - 6 cols, 1 5/6, 1/8 between; A - 6 cols, 1 5/6, 1/8 between; C - 6 cols, 1 5/6, 1/8 between.Equipment & Software: Hardware — APP/Mac.
Delivery Method: Mail, Newsstand, Racks
Areas Served: 68869, 68852, 68844, 68866, 68871 Buffalo and Sherman Counties

RED CLOUD

THE RED CLOUD CHIEF (WED)
322 N Webster St, Red Cloud, NE, 68970-2550, Webster, USA; gen tel (402) 746-3700; gen fax (402) 746-2368; disp adv e-mail chief@gpcom.net; web site http://www.mainstreetmedia.us/
Circulation: 1,682pd,; Sworn/Estimate/Non-Audited
Advertising rate: Open inch rate $4.50
Group: Main Street Media, Inc.
Ed....Harriett Zade
Delivery Method: Mail, Newsstand, Racks

SAINT EDWARD

THE ST. EDWARD ADVANCE (THUR)
105 N 3rd St, Saint Edward, NE, 68660-4559, Boone, USA; gen tel (402) 678-2771; gen fax (402) 678-2556; disp adv e-mail advance@gpcom.net; class adv e-mail advance@gpcom.net; ed e-mail advance@gpcom.net
Circulation: 582pd, 8fr; Sworn/Estimate/Non-Audited
Advertising rate: Open inch rate $4.00
Established: 1900
Ed....Stephanie A. Dawson
Mechanical Specifications: Type page 13 x 21; E - 6 cols, 2 1/12, 1/6 between; A - 6 cols, 2 1/12, 1/6 between; C - 6 cols, 2 1/12, 1/6 between.Equipment & Software: Hardware — COM/386, COM/486, Pentium/PC 200+; Software — Adobe/PageMaker 6.5.
Delivery Method: Mail
Areas Served: 68660-68601-68620-68640-68623-68627-68628-68638-68644-68758

SAINT PAUL

THE PHONOGRAPH-HERALD (WED)
406 Howard Ave, Saint Paul, NE, 68873-2141, Howard, USA; gen tel (308) 754-4401; gen fax (308) 754-4498; disp adv e-mail maryjo@phonographherald.com; ed e-mail connie@phonographherald.com
Circulation: 2,452pd,; Sworn/Estimate/Non-Audited
Advertising rate: Open inch rate $8.55
Established: 1873
Pub....Connie M. Thompson
Delivery Method: Mail, Newsstand, Racks
Areas Served: Howard

SCHUYLER

THE SCHUYLER SUN (THUR)
1112 C St, Schuyler, NE, 68661-1914, Colfax, USA; gen tel (402) 352-2424; gen fax (402) 352-3332; disp adv e-mail thesunads@qwestoffice.net; ed e-mail thesun@qwestoffice.net; web site www.schuyler-sun.com - 3,840(views)
Circulation: 3,200pd,; Sworn/Estimate/Non-Audited
Advertising rate: Open inch rate $7
Established: 1871
Group: Lee Enterprises, Inc.
Digital Platform - Mobile: Apple, Windows
Interim Ed....Tyler Ellyson
Delivery Method: Mail
Areas Served: Colfax County, NE

SCOTTSBLUFF

GERING COURIER (THUR)
1405 Broadway, Scottsbluff, NE, 69361-3151, Scotts Bluff, USA; gen tel (308) 436-2222; gen fax (308) 436-7127; disp adv e-mail doug.southard@starherald.com; class adv e-mail class@starherald.com; ed e-mail brad.staman@geringcourier.com; web site www.geringcourier.com
Circulation: 2,118pd,; Sworn/Estimate/Non-Audited
Advertising rate: Open inch rate $7.50
Established: 1887
Group: BH Media Group
Pub....Brad Staman
Ed....Jeff Fielder
Delivery Method: Mail, Newsstand, Racks
Areas Served: Scottsbluff

THE BUSINESS FARMER (FRI)
22 W 17th St, Scottsbluff, NE, 69361-3156, Scotts Bluff, USA; gen tel (308) 635-3110; gen fax (308) 635-7435; disp adv e-mail farmads@thebusinessfarmer.com; ed e-mail farmnews@thebusinessfarmer.com; web site www.thebusinessfarmer.com
Circulation: 2,300pd,; Sworn/Estimate/Non-Audited
Advertising rate: Open inch rate $11.29
Group: News Media Corp.
Pub....Jeff Robertson
Mechanical Specifications: Type page 10 x 13 1/2; E - 6 cols, 1 7/12, 1/6 between; A - 6 cols, 1 7/12, 1/6 between; C - 6 cols, 1 7/12, 1/6 between.Equipment & Software: Hardware — APP/Mac; Software — QPS/QuarkXPress.
Delivery Method: Mail, Newsstand, Racks
Areas Served: Scotts Bluff

TWIN CITY WEEKLY (WED)
1405 Broadway, Scottsbluff, NE, 69361-3151, Scotts Bluff, USA; gen tel (308) 632-9000; gen fax (308) 632-9001; disp adv e-mail doug.southard@starherald.com; ed e-mail bart.schaneman@starherald.com; web site www.starherald.com
Circulation: 5,869pd, 6,528fr; Sworn/Estimate/Non-Audited
Advertising rate: Open inch rate $6.00
Pub....Jim Holland
Gen. Mgr....Roger Tollefson
Adv. Mgr....Doug Southard
Ed....Steve Frederick
Mechanical Specifications: Type page 10 1/6 x 11 1/4; E - 6 cols, 1 1/2, between; A - 6 cols, 1 1/2, between.
Delivery Method: Mail, Newsstand, Carrier, Racks
Areas Served: 69363

SCRIBNER

RUSTLER SENTINEL (WED)
310 Depot Rd, Scribner, NE, 68057-3210, Dodge, USA; gen tel (402) 664-3198; adv tel (402) 654-2218; ed tel (402) 664-3198; gen fax (402) 664-3141; adv fax (40) 254-2130; ed fax (402) 654-2130; disp adv e-mail rustlernews@gpcom.net; ed e-mail rustlersentinel@gpcom.net
Circulation: 1,300pd, 100fr; Sworn/Estimate/Non-Audited
Advertising rate: Open inch rate $7.25
Established: 1884
Pub....Kathy Lodl
Managing Editor....Chris Heitshusen
Reporter....Kathy Buhrman
Mechanical Specifications: Type page 10 x 13; E - 5 cols, 2, 1/6 between; A - 5 cols, 2, 1/6 between; C - 5 cols, 2, 1/6 between.Equipment & Software: Hardware — APP/Mac; Software — Microsoft/Word.
Delivery Method: Mail, Newsstand
Areas Served: 68057 68031 68664 68063

SEWARD

SEWARD COUNTY INDEPENDENT (WED)
129 S 6th St, Seward, NE, 68434-2078, Seward, USA; gen tel (402) 643-3676; gen fax (402) 643-6774; disp adv e-mail pchecks@sewardindependent.com; class adv e-mail classifieds@sewardindependent.com; ed e-mail scinews@sewardindependent.com; web site www.sewardindependent.com
Circulation: 3,200pd, 25fr; Sworn/Estimate/Non-Audited
Advertising rate: 10.45
Established: 1893
Group: Enterprise Publishing Co.
Owner....Mark Rhoades
Pub....Kevin L. Zadina
Adv. Mgr....Patrick Checketts
Bookkeeper....Tammy Leff
Ed....Stephanie Croston
Mechanical Specifications: Type page 15 x 22; E - 6 cols, 2 1/30, 1/6 between; A - 6 cols, 2 1/30, 1/6 between; C - 6 cols, 2 1/30, 1/6

between.Equipment & Software: Hardware — APP/Macs; Software — Adobe/PageMaker 7.0, Adobe/Photoshop 7.0.
Delivery Method: Mail, Newsstand, Racks
Areas Served: Seward/Seward/68434

SHELTON

SHELTON CLIPPER (THUR)
113 C St, Shelton, NE, 68876-9688, Buffalo, USA; gen tel (308) 647-5158; gen fax (308) 647-6953; disp adv e-mail info@clipperpubco.com; web site www.clipperpubco.com
Circulation: 1,001pd,; Sworn/Estimate/Non-Audited
Advertising rate: Open inch rate $7.50
Group: Clipper Publishing, Inc
Gen. Mgr. .... Barb Berglund
Ed. .... Steven L. Glenn
Delivery Method: Mail, Newsstand, Racks
Areas Served: Buffalo, Hall

THE GIBBON REPORTER (THUR)
113 C St, Shelton, NE, 68876-9688, Buffalo, USA; gen tel (308) 647-5158; gen fax (308) 647-6953; disp adv e-mail info@clipperpubco.com; web site www.clipperpubco.com
Circulation: 1,097pd, 36fr; Sworn/Estimate/Non-Audited
Advertising rate: Open inch rate $7.50
Group: Clipper Publishing, Inc
Pub. .... Steven L. Glenn
Ed. .... Barb Berglund
Delivery Method: Mail, Newsstand
Areas Served: Buffalo, Hall

THE WOOD RIVER SUNBEAM (THUR)
113 C St, Shelton, NE, 68876-9688, Buffalo, USA; gen tel (308) 647-5158; gen fax (308) 647-6953; disp adv e-mail info@clipperpubco.com; web site www.clipperpubco.com
Circulation: 1,083pd, 9fr; Sworn/Estimate/Non-Audited
Advertising rate: Open inch rate $7.50
Group: Clipper Publishing, Inc
Pub. .... Steven L. Glenn
Ed. .... Barb Berglund
Delivery Method: Mail, Newsstand
Areas Served: Buffalo, Hall

SIDNEY

SIDNEY SUN-TELEGRAPH (WED, FRI)
817 12th Ave, Sidney, NE, 69162-1625, Cheyenne, USA; gen tel (308) 254-2818; gen fax (308) 254-3925; disp adv e-mail publisher@suntelegraph.com; class adv e-mail publisher@suntelegraph.com; ed e-mail editor@suntelegraph.com; web site www.suntelegraph.com
Circulation: 3,000pd,; Sworn/Estimate/Non-Audited
Advertising rate: Open inch rate $9.00
Established: 1873
Group: Stevenson Newspapers
Digital Platform - Mobile: Apple, Windows
Digital Platform - Tablet: Apple iOS, Windows 7, Blackberry Tablet OS, Kindle, Kindle Fire
Pub. .... Keith Hansen
Mechanical Specifications: Type page 12 x 21 1/2; E - 6 cols, 2, 1/3 between; A - 6 cols, 2, 1/3 between; C - 8 cols, 1/3 between.
Delivery Method: Mail, Newsstand, Carrier, Racks
Areas Served: 69162, 69131, 69133, 69141, 69145, 69149, 69156

SPALDING

SPALDING ENTERPRISE (FRI)
140 S Cedar St, Spalding, NE, 68665, Greeley, USA; gen tel (308) 497-2153; gen fax (308) 497-2153; disp adv e-mail spalding2002@hotmail.com
Circulation: 730pd, 15fr; Sworn/Estimate/Non-Audited
Advertising rate: Open inch rate $3.25
Established: 1900
Ed. ....David BoppEquipment & Software: Hardware — PC; Presses — HI; Software — Microsoft/Windows 98, Microsoft/Works.

SPENCER

THE SPENCER ADVOCATE (THUR)
100 S Thayer St, Spencer, NE, 68777-9784, Boyd, USA; gen tel (402) 589-1010; gen fax (402) 589-1010; disp adv e-mail advocate@nntc.net
Circulation: 1,056pd, 21fr; Sworn/Estimate/Non-Audited
Advertising rate: Open inch rate $3.00
Ed. .... Sadie Wells

SPRINGVIEW

SPRINGVIEW HERALD (WED)
102 S Main St, Springview, NE, 68778-9603, Keya Paha, USA; gen tel (402) 497-3651; gen fax (402) 497-2651; ed e-mail editor@springviewherald.com; web site https://www.facebook.com/SpringviewHerald
Circulation: 750pd, 25fr; Sworn/Estimate/Non-Audited
Advertising rate: Open inch rate $4.75
Established: 1886
Editor .... Amy Johnson
Mechanical Specifications: Type page 11 1/2 x 16; E - 5 cols, 2, 1/16 between; A - 5 cols, 2, 1/16 between; C - 5 cols, 2, 1/16 between. Equipment & Software: Hardware — Compaq/Gateway; Software — Adobe/PageMaker 6.5.
Delivery Method: Mail, Newsstand, Racks
Areas Served: Springview, Keya Paha, 68778

STANTON

STANTON REGISTER (WED)
907 Ivy St, Stanton, NE, 68779-2348, Stanton, USA; gen tel (402) 439-2173; gen fax (402) 439-2273; disp adv e-mail assistregister@stanton.net; ed e-mail register@stanton.net
Circulation: 1,514pd, 20fr; Sworn/Estimate/Non-Audited
Advertising rate: Open inch rate $3.75
Established: 1878
Pub. .... Laura M. Forker
Mechanical Specifications: Type page 13 1/2 x 21; E - 6 cols, 1 1/12, 1/12 between; A - 6 cols, 1 1/12, 1/12 between.Equipment & Software: Hardware — IBM; Software — Microsoft/Word.
Delivery Method: Mail, Carrier
Areas Served: Stanton

STAPLETON

STAPLETON ENTERPRISE (THUR)
238 Main St, Stapleton, NE, 69163-9701, Logan, USA; gen tel (308) 636-2444; gen fax (308) 636-2445; disp adv e-mail creativeprinters@gpcom.net
Circulation: 650pd,; Sworn/Estimate/Non-Audited
Advertising rate: Open inch rate $4.50
Established: 1912
Group: The Arnold Sentinel LLC
Pub. .... Audrey M. French
Gen. Mgr. .... Marcia R. Hora
Circ. Mgr. .... Traci Frey
Mechanical Specifications: Type page 11 1/2 x 21; E - 6 cols, 12 1/2, between; A - 6 cols, between; C - 6 cols, between.Equipment & Software: Hardware — APP/Macs.
Delivery Method: Mail, Newsstand, Racks
Areas Served: Logan, McPherson

THOMAS COUNTY HERALD (THUR)
238 Main St, Stapleton, NE, 69163-9701, Logan, USA; gen tel (308) 636-2444; gen fax (308) 636-2445; disp adv e-mail creativeprinters@gpcom.net
Circulation: 600pd,; Sworn/Estimate/Non-Audited
Advertising rate: Open inch rate $4.50
Group: The Arnold Sentinel LLC
Adv. Mgr. .... Marcia Hora
Ed. .... Traci Frey
Mechanical Specifications: Type page 11 x 16; E - 5 cols, 2, between; A - 5 cols, 2, between; C - 5 cols, 2, between.
Delivery Method: Mail, Newsstand, Racks
Areas Served: Thomas

STROMSBURG

POLK COUNTY NEWS (THUR)
PO Box 365, Stromsburg, NE, 68666-0365, Polk, USA; gen tel (402) 764-5341; gen fax (402) 764-5341; disp adv e-mail polkcountynews@yahoo.com; web site www.polkcountynewspaper.com
Circulation: 1,800pd, 20fr; Sworn/Estimate/Non-Audited
Advertising rate: Open inch rate $6.50
Dave Thompson
Sandy ThompsonPub.s

SUPERIOR

THE SUPERIOR EXPRESS (THUR)
148 E 3rd St, Superior, NE, 68978-1705, Nuckolls, USA; gen tel (402) 879-3291; gen fax (402) 879-3463; disp adv e-mail tse@superiorne.com; web site http://superiorne.com/
Circulation: 2,900pd, 116fr; Sworn/Estimate/Non-Audited
Advertising rate: Open inch rate $4.00
Established: 1900
Group: Superior Publishing Co
Superior Publishing Company
Ed. .... Bill Blauvelt
Mechanical Specifications: Type page 15 x 21; E - 7 cols, 2, 1/6 between; A - 7 cols, 2, 1/6 between; C - 7 cols, 2, 1/6 between.Equipment & Software: Hardware — APP/Mac; Presses — G/Community; Software — Adobe/PageMaker, Microsoft/Word, Macromedia/Freehand, Adobe/Photoshop.
Delivery Method: Mail, Newsstand, Racks
Areas Served: Nuckolls county Nebraska, Jewell County Kansas and adjoining areas

SUTHERLAND

THE COURIER-TIMES (THUR)
824 1st St, Sutherland, NE, 69165-2155, Lincoln, USA; gen tel (308) 386-4617; disp adv e-mail suthcourier@gpcom.net
Circulation: 1,200pd,; USPS
Advertising rate: Open inch rate $6.00
Established: 1895
Ed. .... Trenda Seifer
Mechanical Specifications: Type page 10 x 20; E - 6 cols, 1.5, 1/6 between; A - 6 cols, 1.5, 1/6 between; C - 6 cols, 1.5, 1/6 between.Equipment & Software: Hardware — APP/Mac.
Delivery Method: Mail, Racks
Areas Served: 69165, 69143, 69153, 69101, 69155, 69169, 69132,

SUTTON

CLAY COUNTY NEWS (THUR)
207 N Saunders Ave, Sutton, NE, 68979-2511, Clay, USA; gen tel (402) 773-5576; gen fax (402) 773-5577; disp adv e-mail ccntory@gmail.com; ed e-mail claycountynews@gmail.com; web site http://www.theclaycountynews.com/
Circulation: 2,805pd, 50fr; Sworn/Estimate/Non-Audited
Advertising rate: Open inch rate $6.10
Established: 1875
Ed. .... Tory Duncan
Mechanical Specifications: Type page 12 7/8 x 21; E - 6 cols, 13, 1/6 between; A - 6 cols, 1/6 between; C - 6 cols, 1/6 between.Equipment & Software: Hardware — 6-APP/Mac; Software — Microsoft/98.
Delivery Method: Mail, Newsstand, Racks
Areas Served: Clay

SYRACUSE

SYRACUSE JOURNAL-DEMOCRAT (THUR)
123 W 17th St, Syracuse, NE, 68446, Otoe, USA; gen tel (402) 269-2135; gen fax (402) 269-2392; disp adv e-mail tschumacher@ncnewspress.com; ed e-mail tpearson@ncnewspress.com; web site www.journaldemocrat.com
Circulation: 1,550pd, 74fr; Sworn/Estimate/Non-Audited
Advertising rate: Open inch rate $8.70
Established: 1876
Group: GateHouse Media, Inc.
Gen. Mgr. .... Tammy Schumacher
Exec. Ed. .... Tammy Pearson
Delivery Method: Mail, Newsstand, Racks
Areas Served: 68446

TECUMSEH

THE TECUMSEH CHIEFTAIN (THUR)
241 Clay St, Tecumseh, NE, 68450-2317, Johnson, USA; gen tel (402) 335-3394; gen fax (402) 335-3496; disp adv e-mail ads@tecumsehchieftain.com; ed e-mail news@tecumsehchieftain.com; web site tecumsehchieftain.com
Circulation: 1,630pd,; Sworn/Estimate/Non-Audited
Advertising rate: Open inch rate $7.00
Group: Sunrise Publications, Inc
Owner, Pub. .... Bev Puhalla
Ed. .... Ann Wickett
Mechanical Specifications: Type page 13 x 21 1/2; E - 6 cols, 2 1/16, 1/8 between; A - 6 cols, 2 1/16, between; C - 6 cols, 2 1/16, between.Equipment & Software: Hardware — APP/Mac; Presses — KP/News King; Software — Adobe/PageMaker 6.5.
Delivery Method: Mail, Newsstand, Racks
Areas Served: Johnson

TEKAMAH

BURT COUNTY PLAINDEALER (WED)
707 S 13th St, Tekamah, NE, 68061-1326, Burt, USA; gen tel (402) 374-2226; gen fax (402) 374-2739; disp adv e-mail renee.lombardo@lee.net; ed e-mail katie.novak@lee.net; web site www.burtcountyplaindealer.com
Circulation: 1,057pd, 121fr; Sworn/Estimate/Non-Audited
Advertising rate: Open inch rate $5.85
Established: 1934
Group: Lee Enterprises, Inc.
Gen. Mgr. .... Joe Zink
Circ. Mgr. .... Jodie Jordan
Mechanical Specifications: Type page 9(13/16) x 21; 5-column.
Delivery Method: Mail, Newsstand, Racks
Areas Served: Burt

MIDWEST MESSENGER (BI-MTHLY)
707 S 13th St, Tekamah, NE, 68061-1326, Burt, USA; gen tel (402) 374-2226; adv tel (402) 374-2226; ed tel (402) 374-2226; gen fax (402) 374-2739; adv fax (402) 374-2739; ed fax (402) 374-2739; disp adv e-mail deanna.ray@midwestmessenger.com; class adv e-mail renee.lombardo@midwestmessenger.com; ed e-mail terry.anderson@lee.net; web site www.midwestmessenger.com
Circulation: 0pd, 100,000fr; Sworn/Estimate/Non-Audited
Advertising rate: Open inch rate $18.45
Established: 1968
Group: Lee Enterprises, Inc.Editions: (4) West Edition, North Edition, Iowa Edition, South

Edition
Digital Platform - Mobile: Apple, Android
Digital Platform - Tablet: Apple iOS, Android
News Ed. .... Terry Anderson
Gen. Mgr. .... Joe Zink
Adv. Mgr. .... Deanna Ray
Pub. .... Mike Wood
Delivery Method: Mail, Racks
Areas Served: Nebraska, western Iowa, eastern Wyoming, northeastern Colorado

TRENTON

HITCHOCK COUNTY NEWS (WED)
346 Main St, Trenton, NE, 69044-1809, USA; gen tel (308) 334-5226; gen fax (308) 334-5225
Circulation: 1,142pd, 21fr; Sworn/Estimate/ Non-Audited
Advertising rate: Open inch rate $9.00
Gen. Mgr. .... Amy Frederick
Circ. Mgr. .... Kathy Broz
Prodn. Mgr. .... Jason FrederickEquipment & Software: Hardware — APP/Mac; Software — Aldus/PageMaker.

VALENTINE

VALENTINE MIDLAND NEWS (WED)
146 W 2nd St, Valentine, NE, 69201-1822, Cherry, USA; gen tel (402) 376-2833; gen fax (402) 376-1946; disp adv e-mail valentinenews@valentinenews.com; web site http://valentinenews.com/
Circulation: 2,050pd,; Sworn/Estimate/Non-Audited
Advertising rate: Open inch rate $5.50
Established: 1989
Group: Great Plains Publishing Co., Inc.
Office Mgr. .... Dana Anderson
Ed. .... Laura Vorman
Mechanical Specifications: Type page 15 x 21 3/4; A - 7 cols, 2, 1/6 between; C - 7 cols, 2, 1/6 between.

WAHOO

WAHOO NEWSPAPER (THUR)
564 N Broadway St, Wahoo, NE, 68066-1653, Saunders, USA; gen tel (402) 443-4162; gen fax (402) 443-4459; disp adv e-mail advertising@wahoonewspaper.com; class adv e-mail classifieds@wahoonewspaper.com; ed e-mail news@wahoonewspaper.com; web site www.wahoo-ashland-waverly.com - 40,000(views) 13,000(visitors)
Circulation: 2,850pd,; Sworn/Estimate/Non-Audited
Advertising rate: Open inch rate $9.30
Established: 1886
Group: BH Media Group
Advertising Manager..................... Candi Puren
General Manager.......................... Amy McKay
Mechanical Specifications: Type page 11 5/8 x 21 1/4; E - 6 cols, between; A - 8 cols, 1 1/3, between; C - 8 cols, 1 1/3, between.
Delivery Method: Mail, Newsstand, Carrier, Racks
Areas Served: 68066, 68041, 68073, 68042, 68033, 68017, 68336

WAKEFIELD

THE WAKEFIELD REPUBLICAN (THUR)
224 Main St, Wakefield, NE, 68784-6027, Dixon, USA; gen tel (402) 287-2323; gen fax (402) 287-2323; disp adv e-mail wakenews@huntel.net
Circulation: 1,050pd, 50fr; Sworn/Estimate/ Non-Audited
Advertising rate: Open inch rate $5.00
Established: 1882
Owner (Estate) .... Brad Kurtenbach
Co-Pub............................ Linda H. Richmueller
Co-Pub....................... William H. Rischmueller
Mechanical Specifications: Type page 10 x 15 1/2; E - 5 cols, 1 11/12, 1/8 between; A - 5 cols, 1 11/12, 1/8 between; C - 5 cols, 1 11/12, 1/8 between.
Delivery Method: Mail, Newsstand

WAUNETA

THE WAUNETA BREEZE (THUR)
324 N Tecumseh, Wauneta, NE, 69045-9509, Chase, USA; gen tel (308) 394-5389; gen fax (308) 394-5931; disp adv e-mail breeze.office@jpipapers.com; class adv e-mail breeze.office@jpipapers.com; ed e-mail breeze.editor@jpipapers.com; web site www.waunetanebraska.com
Circulation: 817pd,; Sworn/Estimate/Non-Audited
Advertising rate: 6.60
Established: 1887
Group: Johnson Publications
Co-Publisher.............................. Lori Pankonin
Co-Publisher........................... Russ Pankonin
News Editor .... Christi Christner
Delivery Method: Mail, Racks

WAUSA

THE WAUSA GAZETTE (THUR)
510 E Broadway St, Wausa, NE, 68786-1558, Knox, USA; gen tel (402) 586-2661; gen fax (402) 586-2661; disp adv e-mail wausagazette@gpcom.net; web site http://www.northeastnebraskanews.us/category/wausa-county/
Circulation: 963pd, 2fr; Sworn/Estimate/ Non-Audited
Advertising rate: Open inch rate $4.54
Group: Northeast Nebraska News Co.
Ed. .... Rob Dump
Mechanical Specifications: Type page 13 1/4 x 21 1/2; E - 6 cols, 2, 1/6 between; A - 6 cols, 2, 1/6 between; C - 6 cols, 2, 1/6 between. Equipment & Software: Hardware — HP/LaserJet; Software — Microsoft/Windows, Microsoft/Word.
Delivery Method: Mail, Newsstand, Racks
Areas Served: Knox

WAVERLY

THE NEWS (THUR)
14541 Castlewood St, Ste 300, Waverly, NE, 68462-1526, Lancaster, USA; gen tel (402) 786-2344; gen fax (402) 786-2343; disp adv e-mail news@newswaverly.com; web site www.newswaverly.com
Circulation: 1,810pd, 73fr; Sworn/Estimate/ Non-Audited
Advertising rate: Open inch rate $6.25
News Ed. .... Michael Wunder
Exec. Ed................................... Lisa Brichacek
Mechanical Specifications: Type page 13 3/4 x 22 3/4; E - 6 cols, 2 1/12, 1/8 between; A - 6 cols, 2 1/12, 1/8 between; C - 6 cols, 2 1/12, 1/8 between.Equipment & Software: Hardware — APP/Mac; Presses — 6-KP/Color King; Software — Adobe/PageMaker 6.0.
Areas Served: 68462, 68347, 68304, 68461, 68366, 68017, 68336, 68605

THE WAVERLY NEWS (THUR)
14541 Castlewood St, Ste 300, Waverly, NE, 68462-1526, Lancaster, USA; gen tel (402) 786-2344; gen fax (402) 786-2343; disp adv e-mail advertising@newswaverly.com; class adv e-mail advertising@newswaverly.com; web site www.wahoo-ashland-waverly.com
Circulation: 925pd,; Sworn/Estimate/Non-Audited
Advertising rate: $8.00 pci
Group: BH Media Group
Exec. Ed. .... Lisa Brichacek
Delivery Method: Mail
Areas Served: 68347, 68428, 68462, 68517, 68527, 68017, 6806568516, 68520, 68521

WAYNE

THE WAYNE HERALD (THUR)
114 Main St, Wayne, NE, 68787-1940, Wayne, USA; gen tel (402) 375-2600; gen fax (402) 375-1888; disp adv e-mail melissa@wayneherald.com; class adv e-mail whclass@inebraska.com; ed e-mail sports@wayneherald.com; web site http://mywaynenews.com
Circulation: 2,100pd,; Sworn/Estimate/Non-Audited
Advertising rate: Open inch rate $7.50
Group: Smith Newspapers
Pub.. Kevin Peterson
Gen. Mgr. .... Melissa Urbanec
Ed. .... Michael Carnes
Circ. Mgr.................................. Linda Granfield
Mechanical Specifications: Type page 13 x 21 1/2; E - 6 cols, 2, 1/16 between; A - 6 cols, 2, 1/16 between; C - 6 cols, 2, 1/16 between. Equipment & Software: Hardware — 2-APP/Mac PowerBook 8500; Presses — 4-G; Software — QPS/QuarkXPress 4.1.
Delivery Method: Mail, Newsstand, Racks
Areas Served: Wayne, Cedar, Dixon

WEST POINT

WEST POINT NEWS (WED)
134 E Grove St, West Point, NE, 68788-1823, Cuming, USA; gen tel (402) 372-2461; gen fax (402) 372-3530; disp adv e-mail admanager@wpnews.com; class adv e-mail adrep7@wpnews.com; ed e-mail editor@wpnews.com; web site www.wpnews.com
Circulation: 2,500pd, 165fr; Sworn/Estimate/ Non-Audited
Advertising rate: Open inch rate $13.95
Established: 1869
Pub./Gen. Mgr. .... Tom Kelly
Circ. Mgr................................. Colleen Ernesti
Ed. .... Willis Mahannah
Prodn. Mgr. .... Warren Wesche
Adv. Mgr. ....
Karey RahnEquipment & Software: Hardware — 5-APP/Power Mac, 2-HP/ScanJet, 1-HP/LaserJet 4mv, Compaq/PageMarq 20, APP/Mac LaserWriter 16/600, 2-HP/LaserJet II, 7-PC; Presses — 1-ABD/360, 1-ABD/375 Colorhead, 3-WPC/Web Leader, 1-HI, 4-KP/News King; Software — Caere/OmniPage Pro 7.0, Adobe
Delivery Method: Mail, Newsstand, Racks
Areas Served: Cuming County

WILBER

WILBER REPUBLICAN (WED)
113 W 3rd St, Wilber, NE, 68465-3242, Saline, USA; gen tel (402) 821-2586; gen fax (402) 821-3586; disp adv e-mail pchecketts@sewardindependent.com; ed e-mail jillmartin@sewardindependent.com; web site http://www.wilber-republican.com/
Circulation: 2,000pd, 37fr; Sworn/Estimate/ Non-Audited
Advertising rate: Open inch rate $5.75
Group: Enterprise Publishing Co.
Ed. .... Tim Linscott
Mechanical Specifications: Type page 15 x 21; E - 6 cols, 2, 1/6 between; A - 6 cols, 2, 1/6 between; C - 6 cols, 2, 1/6 between.
Delivery Method: Mail, Newsstand, Racks
Areas Served: Saline

WISNER

WISNER NEWS-CHRONICLE (THUR)
1014 Avenue E, Wisner, NE, 68791-2248, Cuming, USA; gen tel (402) 529-3228; gen fax (402) 529-3279; disp adv e-mail wisnewsad@gpcom.net; ed e-mail wisnews@gpcom.net; web site www.wpnews.com
Circulation: 1,991pd, 30fr; Sworn/Estimate/ Non-Audited
Advertising rate: Open inch rate $7.15
Pub. .... Tom Kelly
Copy Ed. .... Kristy Dunbar
Mechanical Specifications: Type page 13 x 21 1/2; E - 6 cols, 2 1/12, 1/6 between; A - 6 cols, 2 1/12, 1/6 between; C - 6 cols, 2 1/12, 1/6 between.Equipment & Software: Hardware — PC 7300, APP/Mac IIci, APP/Mac LaserPrinter, APP/Mac LaserMaster 1800, APP/Power Mac G3, APP/Power Mac 7400, APP/Mac LaserWriter 8500; Presses — ABD/9800; Software — Adobe/PageMaker, Adobe/Photoshop.
Areas Served: Cuming

WOLBACH

THE WOLBACH MESSENGER (THUR)
PO Box 38, Wolbach, NE, 68882-0038, Greeley, USA; gen tel (308) 754-4401; gen fax (308) 754-4498; disp adv e-mail maryjo@phonographherald.com; ed e-mail connie@phonographherald.com
Circulation: 447pd,; Sworn/Estimate/Non-Audited
Advertising rate: Open inch rate $5.70
Established: 1900
Pub................................. Connie M. Thompson
Delivery Method: Mail, Newsstand, Racks
Areas Served: Greeley, Howard

WYMORE

WYMORE ARBOR STATE (TUES)
204 S 7th St, Wymore, NE, 68466-2102, Gage, USA; gen tel (402) 645-3344; gen fax (402) 645-3345; disp adv e-mail wymorearborstate@windstream.net; web site http://www.wymorearborstate.com/
Circulation: 1,000pd, 78fr; Sworn/Estimate/ Non-Audited
Advertising rate: Open inch rate $5.50
Established: 1882
Ed. .... Dale Crawford

NEVADA

ALAMO

LINCOLN COUNTY RECORD (FRI)
407 Highway 93, Alamo, NV, 89001, Lincoln, USA; gen tel (775) 725-3232; disp adv e-mail contact.lcrecord@gmail.com; class adv e-mail contact.lcrecord@gmail.com; ed e-mail contact.lcrecord@gmail.com ; web site www.lccentral.com - 4,000(views)
Circulation: 1,700pd, 40fr; USPS
Advertising rate: Open inch rate $12.00
Established: 1870
Group: Battle Born Media LLC
Ed. .... Ben Rowley
Mechanical Specifications: Type page BROADSHEET 11 x 20.5; E - 4 cols, 2.6", 3/20 between; A - 4 cols, 2.6", 3/20 between; C - 4 cols, 2.6", 3/20 between.
Delivery Method: Mail, Racks
Areas Served: 89043, 89042, 89017, 89001, 89008

BOULDER CITY

BOULDER CITY REVIEW (THUR)
508 Nevada Way, Ste 1, Boulder City, NV, 89005-2400, Clark, USA; gen tel (702) 201-1940; adv tel (702) 823-1457; ed tel (702) 586-9523; gen fax (702) 586-9565; ed fax (702) 586-9565; disp adv e-mail volsen@bouldercityreview.com; class adv e-mail mgemmill@bouldercityreview.com; ed e-mail hsaylor@bouldercityreview.com; web site http://www.bouldercityreview.com/

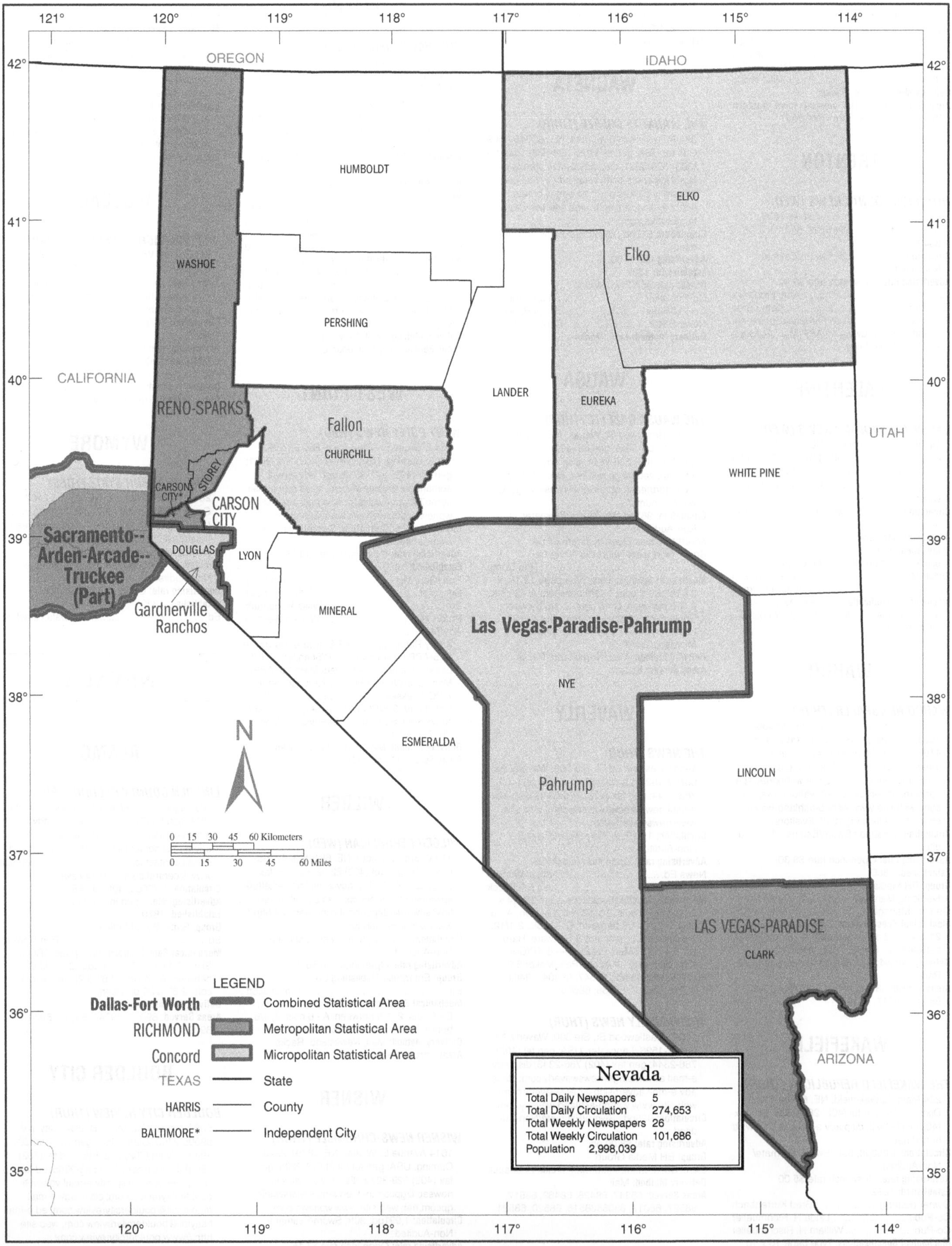
121°
120°
119°
118°
117°
116°
115°
114°
42°
41°
40°
39°
38°
37°
36°
35°
OREGON
IDAHO
CALIFORNIA
UTAH
ARIZONA
HUMBOLDT
ELKO
Elko
WASHOE
PERSHING
LANDER
EUREKA
RENO-SPARKS
Fallon
CHURCHILL
WHITE PINE
CARSON CITY*
STOREY
CARSON CITY
Sacramento--Arden-Arcade--Truckee (Part)
DOUGLAS
LYON
Gardnerville Ranchos
MINERAL
Las Vegas-Paradise-Pahrump
NYE
ESMERALDA
LINCOLN
Pahrump
N
0 15 30 45 60 Kilometers
0 15 30 45 60 Miles
LAS VEGAS-PARADISE
CLARK
LEGEND
Dallas-Fort Worth — Combined Statistical Area
RICHMOND — Metropolitan Statistical Area
Concord — Micropolitan Statistical Area
TEXAS — State
HARRIS — County
BALTIMORE* — Independent City
Nevada
Total Daily Newspapers 5
Total Daily Circulation 274,653
Total Weekly Newspapers 26
Total Weekly Circulation 101,686
Population 2,998,039

Circulation: 2,500pd,; Sworn/Estimate/Non-Audited
Advertising rate: Full - $909; 1/2 - $469; 1/4 - $228; 1/8 - $117
Established: 2009
Group: Las Vegas Review-Journal Inc.
Digital Platform - Mobile: Apple, Android
Digital Platform - Tablet: Apple iOS, Android
Ed .... Hali Bernstein Saylor
Publisher....................................Noah Cusick
Display Advertising Sales Executive..Val Olsen
Office Coordinator ....Michelle Gemmill
Reporter ....Celia Shortt Goodyear
Delivery Method: Mail, Newsstand, Carrier, Racks
Areas Served: Boulder City/Clark/89005

ELY

ELY TIMES (FRI)

515 Murry St, Ely, NV, 89301-1950, White Pine, USA; gen tel (775) 289-4491; gen fax (775) 289-4566; disp adv e-mail elytimes.teresa@gmail.com; class adv e-mail elytimes.linda@gmail.com; ed e-mail elytimes.marty@gmail.com; web site www.elynews.com
Circulation: 2,700pd,; Sworn/Estimate/Non-Audited
Advertising rate: Open inch rate $16.85
Established: 1920
Group: Battle Born Media LLC
Ed. ....Marty Bachman
Pub. ....Sherman Frederick
Mechanical Specifications: Type page 12 x 21; E - 6 cols, 1 3/4, 1/6 between; A - 6 cols, 1 3/4, 1/6 between; C - 9 cols, 1 1/3, 1/9 between. Equipment & Software: Hardware — APP/Mac, 2-APP/Power Mac 6100-66; Presses — 1-G/Community; Software — QPS/QuarkXPress.
Delivery Method: Mail, Newsstand, Carrier, Racks
Areas Served: 89301, 89315, 89311, 89317, 89318, 89319

THE EUREKA SENTINEL (THUR)

515 Murry St, Ely, NV, 89301-1950, White Pine, USA; gen tel (775) 289-4491; gen fax (775) 289-4566; disp adv e-mail elytimes.teresa@gmail.com; class adv e-mail elytimes.linda@gmail.com; ed e-mail elytimes.lukas@gmail.com; web site http://eurekasentinel.com/
Circulation: 500pd, 50fr; Sworn/Estimate/Non-Audited
Advertising rate: Open inch rate $7.60
Established: 1870
Group: Battle Born Media LLC
Ed. ....Gary Cook
Delivery Method: Mail, Newsstand, Carrier, Racks
Areas Served: 89316

FALLON

LAHONTAN VALLEY NEWS & FALLON EAGLE STANDARD (WED, FRI)

37 S Maine St, Fallon, NV, 89406-3301, Churchill, USA; gen tel (775) 423-6041; gen fax (775) 423-0474; disp adv e-mail smason@lahontanvalleynews.com; class adv e-mail classifieds@sierranevadamedia.com; ed e-mail sranson@lahontanvalleynews.com; web site www.lahontanvalleynews.com
Circulation: 3,330pd, 303fr; CAC
Advertising rate: 1/32 Pg $30.00; 1/16 Pg $57.00; 1/12 Pg $86.00
Group: Swift Communications, Inc.
Delivery Method: Mail, Newsstand, Carrier, Racks
Areas Served: Fallon

GARDNERVILLE

THE RECORD-COURIER (WED, FRI, SUN)

1503 US Highway 395 N, Ste G, Gardnerville, NV, 89410-5227, Douglas, USA; gen tel (775) 782-5121; gen fax (775) 782-6132; disp adv e-mail pbridges@nevadaappeal.com; class adv e-mail classifieds@sierranevadamedia.com; ed e-mail pbridges@nevadaappeal.com; web site www.recordcourier.com
Circulation: 6,100pd, 85fr; AAM
Advertising rate: 1/32 Pg $51.75; 1/16 Pg $74.75; 1/12 Pg $92.00
Group: Swift Communications, Inc.
Ed. ....Kurt Hildebrand
Pub... Pat Bridges
Mechanical Specifications: Type page 13 x 21 1/2; E - 6 cols, 2, 1/8 between; A - 6 cols, 2, 1/8 between; C - 9 cols, 1 5/16, 1/8 between.
Delivery Method: Mail, Newsstand, Carrier, Racks
Areas Served: Douglas

HAWTHORNE

MINERAL COUNTY INDEPENDENT NEWS (THUR)

420 3rd St, Hawthorne, NV, 89415, Mineral, USA; gen tel (775) 945-2414; gen fax (775) 945-1270; disp adv e-mail hbunchmcin@gmail.com; ed e-mail mcin.cw@gmail.com; web site http://mcindependentnews.com/
Circulation: 4,500pd, 80fr; Sworn/Estimate/Non-Audited
Advertising rate: Open inch rate $11.25
Established: 1933
Group: Battle Born Media LLC
Web. Ed. ....Ben Rowley
COO ....Kirk Kern
Mechanical Specifications: Type page 14 1/4 x 21; A - 8 cols, 1 5/8, between; C - 8 cols, 1 5/8, between.Equipment & Software: Hardware — APP/Power Mac; Presses — HI, ATF/Chief; Software — Archetype/Corel Draw 6.0, Word Perfect.
Delivery Method: Mail, Newsstand, Carrier, Racks
Areas Served: 89418

HENDERSON

THE SUNDAY (SUN)

2275 Corporate Cir, Henderson, NV, 89074-7719, Clark, USA; web site thesunday.com
Circulation: 54,438fr; VAC
Areas Served: 89074

INCLINE VILLAGE

NORTH LAKE TAHOE BONANZA (THUR)

925 Tahoe Blvd, Ste 206, Incline Village, NV, 89451-7471, Washoe, USA; gen tel (775) 831-4666; gen fax (775) 831-4222; disp adv e-mail scollins@tahoebonanza.com; class adv e-mail classifieds@sierranevadamedia.com; ed e-mail kmacmillan@sierrasun.com; web site www.tahoebonanza.com
Circulation: 0pd, 2,792fr; CAC
Advertising rate: 1/32 Pg $50.00; 1/16 Pg $70.00; 1/12 Pg $90.00
Established: 1970
Group: Swift Communications, Inc.
Ed. ....Kevin MacMillan
Mechanical Specifications: Type page 12 3/4 x 21 1/2; E - 6 cols, 2, 1/10 between; A - 6 cols, 2, 1/10 between; C - 9 cols, 1 5/16, 4/5 between.
Delivery Method: Newsstand, Carrier, Racks
Areas Served: 89450

LAS VEGAS

EL TIEMPO (FRI)

1111 W Bonanza Rd, Las Vegas, NV, 89106-3545, Clark, USA; gen tel (702) 477-3845; adv tel (702) 477-3845; ed tel (702) 47-3846; disp adv e-mail gjuricad@reviewjournal.com; class adv e-mail ddyer@reviewjournal.com; ed e-mail mcmatta@reviewjournal.com; web site http://www.eltiempolv.com/ - 5,000(views) 2,900(visitors)
Circulation: 0pd, 51,878fr; CAC
Advertising rate: Full - $4,090; 1/2 - $2,105; 1/4 - $1,025; 1/8 - $525
Established: 1994
Digital Platform - Mobile: Apple, Android, Windows, Blackberry
Pub./Ed. ....Maria Cristina Matta-Caro
Mechanical Specifications: Full Page 10" x 20.50"
1/2 Page V 4.90" x 20.50" H 10" x 10"
1/4 page Std 4.90 x 10"
1/8 page V 4.90" x 4.875" H 10" x 2.50"
Equipment & Software: Hardware — PC
Delivery Method: Carrier, Racks
Areas Served: Las Vegas Valley, Henderson, North Las Vegas,.

LAS VEGAS BUSINESS PRESS (MON)

1111 W Bonanza Rd, Las Vegas, NV, 89106-3545, Clark, USA; gen tel (702) 383-4617; adv tel (702) 383-4617; ed tel (702) 3830299; disp adv e-mail ddonaldson@lvbusinesspress.com; class adv e-mail ddyer@reviewjournal.com; ed e-mail lcollier@lvbusinesspress.com; web site http://www.businesspress.vegas
Circulation: 365pd, 9,874fr; AAM
Advertising rate: Full - $3,640; 1/2 - $2,184; 1/4 - $1,463; 1/8 - $923
Established: 1983
Group: Las Vegas Review-Journal, Inc.
Digital Platform - Mobile: Apple, Android, Windows
Digital Platform - Tablet: Apple iOS, Android, Windows 7
Editor ....Lyn Collier
Delivery Method: Mail
Areas Served: Southern Nevada
Las Vegas, Henderson, North Las Vegas

NIFTY NICKEL (FRI)

1111 W Bonanza Rd, Las Vegas, NV, 89106-3545, Clark, USA; gen tel (702) 383-0383; adv tel 702-383-0383; gen fax (702) 380-4561; adv fax (702) 383-0389; disp adv e-mail jlevin@reviewjournal.com; class adv e-mail ddyer@reviewjournal.com; ed e-mail ddyer@reviewjournal.com; web site http://www.niftynickel.vegas
Circulation: 0pd, 72,000fr; Sworn/Estimate/Non-Audited
Advertising rate: Full - $1,391; 1/2 - $906; 1/4 - $603; 1/8 - $392
Established: 1967
Group: Review-Journal
Div. Sales Mgr. ....Deidre Dyer
Delivery Method: Newsstand, Carrier, Racks
Areas Served: Las Vegas Valley

VIEW NEIGHBORHOOD NEWSPAPERS (TUES, WED)

1111 W Bonanza Rd, Las Vegas, NV, 89106-3545, Clark, USA; gen tel (702) 380-4589; adv tel (702) 383-0388; ed tel (702) 380-4553; gen fax (702) 477-3852; adv fax (702) 383-0389; disp adv e-mail ctrares@reviewjournal.com; class adv e-mail bnelson@reviewjournal.com; ed e-mail jmosier@viewnews.com; web site www.viewnews.com
Circulation: 97,924pd, 502,633fr; AAM
Advertising rate: Full page = $5,959, Half page = $3,069
Established: 1993Editions: (6) North Las Vegas/Centennial, Sunrise/Whitney, Summerlin/Summerlin South, Spring Vallley/Southwest, Henderson/Anthem, Downtown/Paradise
Digital Platform - Mobile: Apple, Android, Windows
Digital Platform - Tablet: Apple iOS, Android, Windows 7, Blackberry Tablet OS, Kindle, Nook, Kindle Fire
Ed. ....Jeff Mosier
Mechanical Specifications: Full page = 10 in x 25 in
Half page = 10 in x 10 in
JPG or PDF accepted
Delivery Method: Mail, Carrier
Areas Served: 89002,89005,89011,89012,89014,89015,89030,89031,89032,89044,89052,89074,89081,89084,89085,89086,89087,89101,89102,89103,89104,89106,89107,89108,89109,89110,89113,89115,89117,89118,89119,89120,89121,89122,89123,89128,89129,89130,89131,89134,89135,89138,89139,89141,89142,89143,89144,89145,89146,89147,89148,89149,89156,89166,89169,89178,89179,89183

LOGANDALE

MOAPA VALLEY PROGRESS (WED)

2885 N Moapa Valley Blvd, Logandale, NV, 89021, Clark, USA; gen tel (702) 397-6246; gen fax (702) 397-6247; disp adv e-mail progress@mvdsl.com; web site www.mvprogress.com
Circulation: 80pd, 5,600fr; Sworn/Estimate/Non-Audited
Advertising rate: Open inch rate $5.90
Established: 1987
Ed. ....Vernon Robison
Mechanical Specifications: Type page 10 x 12 1/2; E - 5 cols, 2, 3/16 between; A - 5 cols, 2, 3/16 between; C - 6 cols, 1 5/8, 1/8 between. Equipment & Software: ; Software — Adobe/InDesign 3.0.1.
Delivery Method: Mail, Newsstand, Racks
Areas Served: 89040, 89021, 89025

MESQUITE

DESERT VALLEY TIMES (TUES, FRI)

355 W Mesquite Blvd, Ste. C10, Mesquite, NV, 89027-8128, Clark, USA; gen tel (702) 323-7922; gen fax (702) 346-7494; ed e-mail news@dvtnv.com; web site www.dvtonline.com
Circulation: 8,000fr; Sworn/Estimate/Non-Audited
Advertising rate: Open inch rate $7.90
Established: 1986
Group: Gannett
Reporter ....Lucas Thomas
Reporter ....Sarah Gambles
Exec Ed ....Steve Kiggins
Jolene Schwartz Classified Sales
Delivery Method: Mail, Newsstand, Racks
Areas Served: 89027

MESQUITE LOCAL NEWS (THUR)

12 W Mesquite Blvd, Ste 109, Mesquite, NV, 89027-4774, Clark, USA; gen tel (702) 346-6397; adv tel (702) 346-6397; ed tel (702) 346-6397; disp adv e-mail steph.bbm@gmail.com; class adv e-mail steph.bbm@gmail.com; ed e-mail barb@bjellestad.com; web site http://mesquitelocalnews.com/
Circulation: 4pd, 7,500fr; Sworn/Estimate/Non-Audited
Advertising rate: Modular
Established: 2004
Group: Battle Born Media LLC
Class Sales Exec................Stephanie Frehner
Ed ....Barbara Ellestad
Office/Writer/Calendar................Teri Nehrenz
Mechanical Specifications: Full page 10 x 20.5
Delivery Method: Mail, Newsstand, Carrier, Racks
Areas Served: 86432, 89027, 89007, 89034, 89040, 89021, 89025

PAHRUMP

PAHRUMP VALLEY TIMES (WED, FRI)

1570 E HIGHWAY 372, Pahrump, NV, 89048-4638, Nye, USA; gen tel (775) 727-5102; adv tel (702) 383-0388; gen fax (775) 727-5309; adv fax (702) 383-0389; disp adv e-mail Pvtads@pvtimes.com; class adv e-mail pvtads@pvtimes.com; ed e-mail Aknightly@Pvtimes.com; web site http://pvtimes.com/
Circulation: 4,683pd,; AAM
Advertising rate: Full - $901; 1/2 - $451; 1/4 - $226; 1/8 - $116
Established: 1971
Digital Platform - Mobile: Apple, Android
Digital Platform - Tablet: Apple iOS, Android
Ed. ....Arnold Knightly
Publisher......................................Noah Cusick
Mechanical Specifications: Type page 9 3/4 x 12 1/2; E - 6 cols, 1 1/2, 1/8 between; A - 6 cols, 1 1/2, 1/8 between; C - 6 cols, 1 1/2, 1/8

between.Equipment & Software: Hardware — PCs, APP/Power Mac, APP/Mac Performa 6300 CD; Presses — 6-HI/V-15A; Software — Adobe/PageMaker 6.0, Adobe/Illustrator.
Delivery Method: Mail, Newsstand, Carrier, Racks
Areas Served: 89048

RENO

RENO NEWS & REVIEW (THUR)
405 Marsh Ave, Fl 3rd, Reno, NV, 89509-1541, Washoe, USA; gen tel (775) 324-4440; gen fax (775) 324-2515; disp adv e-mail bizmgr@newsreview.com; web site http://www.newsreview.com/reno/home
Circulation: 4pd, 19,062fr; VAC
Advertising rate: 1/20 Pg $188.00; 1/10 Pg $331.00; 1/4 Pg $711.00
Established: 1995
Group: Chico Community Publishing Inc.
Ass. Ed. .... Brad Bynum

SPARKS

SPARKS TRIBUNE (TUES, THUR)
155 Glendale Ave, Ste 10, Sparks, NV, 89431-5751, Washoe, USA; gen tel (775) 358-8062; adv tel (775) 358-8062 ext 238; gen fax (775) 359-3837; disp adv e-mail advertising@dailysparkstribune.com; class adv e-mail carolyn@dailysparkstribune.com; ed e-mail deckles@dailysparkstribune.com
Circulation:; Sworn/Estimate/Non-Audited
Advertising rate: Open inch rate $12.50
Established: 1910
Pub. .... Sherman Frederick
Ed. .... Eric Dahlberg
Delivery Method: Mail, Newsstand, Carrier

TONOPAH

TONOPAH TIMES-BONANZA AND GOLDFIELD NEWS (THUR)
150 Main St, Tonopah, NV, 89049, Nye, USA; gen tel (775) 482-3365; gen fax (775) 482-5042; disp adv e-mail broberts@tonopahtimes.com
Circulation: 1,800pd,; Sworn/Estimate/Non-Audited
Advertising rate: Modular Broadsheet call for pricing.
Established: 1903
Group: GateHouse Media, Inc.
Pub... Marie Wujek
Adv. Mgr.......................... Bobby Jean Roberts
Delivery Method: Mail, Newsstand, Racks
Areas Served: 89049
89013
89045
89010
89409
89022

VIRGINIA CITY

COMSTOCK CHRONICLE (FRI)
66 N B St, Virginia City, NV, 89440, Storey, USA; gen tel (775) 847-0765; gen fax ; disp adv e-mail storeystories@gmail.com
Circulation: 1,000pd,; Sworn/Estimate/Non-Audited
Advertising rate: Open inch rate $5.00
Established: 1988
Pub...Richard Mann
Ed. ....Angela Mann
Delivery Method: Mail, Racks
Areas Served: 89440 89521 89403 89434

WENDOVER

HIGH DESERT ADVOCATE (THUR)
2028 Elko Ave, PO Box 2028, Wendover, NV, 89883-3237, Elko, USA; gen tel (775) 664-3415; gen fax (775) 664-3415; disp adv e-mail advocate@cut.net; class adv e-mail ccopelan@cut.net; ed e-mail advocate@cut.net; web site www.coyote-tv.com
Circulation: 5,500pd,; USPS
Advertising rate: Open inch rate $9.00
Established: 1984
Digital Platform - Mobile: Apple
Digital Platform - Tablet: Apple iOS
Ed. .... Howard Copelan
Prodn. Mgr. ....Corinne Copelan
Mechanical Specifications: Type page 10 x 19.5 1/2; E - 6 cols, 2, 1/8 between; A - 6 cols, 2, 1/8 between; C - 8 cols, 1 7/8, 1/8 between. Equipment & Software: Hardware — various Mac's
system snow leopard; Software — InDesign
Delivery Method: Newsstand, Carrier, Racks
Areas Served: 89883, 84083, 89301, 89801, 89802, 89803

WINNEMUCCA

BATTLE MOUNTAIN BUGLE (WED)
1022 Grass Valley Rd, Winnemucca, NV, 89445-4045, Humboldt, USA; gen tel (775) 635-2230; gen fax (775) 635-2644; disp adv e-mail k.koseck@winnemuccapublishing.net; class adv e-mail bmb.office@winnemuccapublishing.net; ed e-mail editorial@winnemuccapublishing.net; web site www.insidenorthernnevada.com
Advertising rate: Open inch rate $11.00
Established: 1978
Ed. .... Michelle Cook
Delivery Method: Mail, Newsstand, Racks
Areas Served: Lander

LOVELOCK REVIEW-MINER (WED)
1022 Grass Valley Rd, Winnemucca, NV, 89445-4045, Humboldt, USA; gen tel (775) 623-5011; disp adv e-mail l.enget@winnemuccapublishing.net; class adv e-mail lrm.office@winnemuccapublishing.net; ed e-mail editorial@winnemuccapublishing.net ; web site http://insidenorthernnevada.com
Circulation: 1,350pd, 26fr; Sworn/Estimate/Non-Audited
Advertising rate: Open inch rate $11.00
Established: 1904
Ed. .... Michelle Cook
Mechanical Specifications: Type page 11 3/4 x 20 1/2; E - 6 cols, 1 13/16, 1/6 between; A - 6 cols, 2 13/16, 1/6 between; C - 6 cols, 2 13/16, 1/6 between.Equipment & Software: Hardware — PCs; Software — Pagemaker 7.0, Corel Draw.
Delivery Method: Mail, Newsstand, Racks
Areas Served: 89419, 89418

THE HUMBOLDT SUN (WED, SAT)
1022 Grass Valley Rd, Winnemucca, NV, 89445-4045, Humboldt, USA; gen tel (775) 623-5011; gen fax (775) 623-5243; disp adv e-mail r.coleman@winnemuccapublishing.net; web site www.news4nevada.com
Circulation: 3,650pd,; Sworn/Estimate/Non-Audited
Advertising rate: Open inch rate $11.00
Established: 1960
Gen. Mgr............................ Holly Rudy-James
Mechanical Specifications: Type page 13 x 21 1/2; E - 6 cols, 2, 1/6 between; A - 6 cols, 2, 1/6 between; C - 6 cols, 2, 1/6 between. Equipment & Software: Hardware — Zeos/486, Pentium/PC; Presses — 6-G/Community; Software — SunType/Editorial, Ventura/Publisher, QPS/QuarkXPress.
Delivery Method: Mail, Newsstand, Racks
Areas Served: Humboldt

YERINGTON

MASON VALLEY NEWS/THE LEADER-COURIER (FRI)
207 W Goldfield Ave, Yerington, NV, 89447-2349, Lyon, USA; gen tel (775) 463-4242; gen fax (775) 463-5547; disp adv e-mail dhogarth@masonvalleynews.com; class adv e-mail classifieds@masonvalleynews.com; ed e-mail news@masonvalleynews.com; web site www.masonvalleynews.com
Circulation: 3,700pd,; Sworn/Estimate/Non-Audited
Advertising rate: Open inch rate $7.21
Group: Gannett
Adv. Mgr. .... Debora Hogarth
Assoc. Sales Mgr.................... Shannon Burns
Mechanical Specifications: Type page 13 x 21 1/2; E - 6 cols, 2, 1/6 between; A - 6 cols, between; C - 8 cols, between.Equipment & Software: Hardware — APP/Mac; Presses — KP/News King; Software — Claris, Microsoft Adobe/PageMaker.
Delivery Method: Mail, Newsstand, Racks
Areas Served: 89447

NEW HAMPSHIRE

AMHERST

AMHERST CITIZEN (WED, MTHLY)
16 Pine Acres Rd, Amherst, NH, 03031-2710, Hillsborough, USA; gen tel (603) 672-9444; adv tel (603) 672-9444; ed tel (603) 672-9444; gen fax (603) 672-8153; disp adv e-mail ads@amherstcitizen.com; ed e-mail news@amherstcitizen.com; web site http://www.amherstcitizen.com/ - 1,454(views) 930(visitors)
Circulation: 0pd, 6,117fr; USPS
Advertising rate: Open inch rate $13.50
Established: 1992
Group: None
Digital Platform - Mobile: Other
Digital Platform - Tablet: Other
Pub./Ed....................................Cliff Ann Wales
Adv. Dir.......................................James Wales
Mechanical Specifications: PDF's preferredEquipment & Software: Hardware — Mac; Software — Adobe Creative Cloud
Delivery Method: Mail, Newsstand
Areas Served: Hillsborough 03031 03057

BERLIN

THE BERLIN DAILY SUN (TUES, THUR)
164 MAIN ST STE 1, BERLIN, NH, 03570-2477, Coos, USA; gen tel (603) 752-5858; adv tel (603) 733-5808; ed tel (603) 326-6100; gen fax (866) 475-4429; adv fax (603) 356-0435; ed fax (866) 475-4429; disp adv e-mail joyce@conwaydailysun.com; class adv e-mail ads@conwaydailysun.com; ed e-mail barbara@berlindailysun.com; web site www.berlindailysun.com
Circulation: 8,925pd,; Sworn/Estimate/Non-Audited
Advertising rate: Open inch rate $7.00
Established: 1989
Pub...Mark Guerringue
Ass. Pub...................................Joyce Brothers
Ed. .... Adam Hirshan
Prodn. Mgr. ....Frank Haddy
Managing Ed..........................Barbara Tetreault
Adv. Rep.......................................Tee Johnson
Delivery Method: Mail, Newsstand, Carrier, Racks
Areas Served: 03570, 03579, 03581, 03588, 03581

COLEBROOK

THE NEWS AND SENTINEL (WED)
6 Bridge St, Colebrook, NH, 03576-3033, Coos, USA; gen tel (603) 237-5501; gen fax (603) 237-5060; disp adv e-mail sales@colebrooknewsandsentinel.com; ed e-mail editor@colebrooknewsandsentinel.com; web site www.colbsent.com - 1,500(views)
Circulation: 2,687pd, 231fr; USPS
Advertising rate: Full - $485; 1/2 - $242.50; 1/4 - $117
Established: 1870
Editor and Publisher .... Karen Harrigan
Mechanical Specifications: Type page 10 x 15; E - 5 cols, 1 7/8, 1/8 between; A - 5 cols, 1 7/8, 1/8 between; C - 5 cols, 1 7/8, 1/8 between. Equipment & Software: ; Software — QPS/QuarkXPress 4.1.
Delivery Method: Mail, Newsstand, Carrier, Racks
Areas Served: Coos, Vermont, Essex

DERRY

DERRY NEWS (THUR)
46 W Broadway, Derry, NH, 03038-2329, Rockingham, USA; gen tel (603) 437-7000; gen fax (603) 432-4510; disp adv e-mail advertising@derrynews.com; class adv e-mail classifieds@derrynews.com; ed e-mail rford@derrynews.com; web site www.derrynews.com
Circulation: 7,000pd, 26,000fr; Sworn/Estimate/Non-Audited
Advertising rate: Open inch rate $20.13
Established: 1880
Group: Community Newspaper Holdings, Inc.
Pub..Karen Andreas
Adv. Dir... Cathy Goss
Circ. Mgr.. Steve Milone
Mechanical Specifications: Type page 11 5/8 x 21 1/2; E - 6 cols, 1 5/6, 1/8 between; A - 6 cols, 1 5/6, 1/8 between; C - 10 cols, 1 1/16, 1/16 between.
Delivery Method: Mail, Newsstand, Racks
Areas Served: 03038, 03053

DOVER

ROCHESTER TIMES (THUR)
18 Main St, Unit 2D, Dover, NH, 03820-3812, Strafford, USA; gen tel (603) 332-2300; gen fax (603) 330-3162; disp adv e-mail thetimes@fosters.com; web site www.fosters.com
Circulation: 15,000fr; Sworn/Estimate/Non-Audited
Advertising rate: Open inch rate $11.15
Established: 1993
Group: George J. Foster Co., Inc.
Mechanical Specifications: Type page 10 13/16 x 16; E - 5 cols, 2 1/16, 1/6 between; A - 5 cols, 2 1/16, 1/6 between; C - 7 cols, 1 7/16, 1/6 between.Equipment & Software: Hardware — IBM, APP/Mac; Presses — G/Community; Software — Multi-Ad/Creator 4.0.
Delivery Method: Newsstand, Carrier, Racks
Areas Served: Famington, Rochester, Barington, Lee, Dover, Somersworth

HILLSBOROUGH

MESSENGER (FRI)
246 W Main St, Hillsborough, NH, 03244-5251, Hillsborough, USA; gen tel (603) 464-3388; gen fax (603) 464-4106; disp adv e-mail granitequill@mcttelecom.com; web site granitequill.com
Circulation: 25,000fr; Sworn/Estimate/Non-Audited
Advertising rate: Open inch rate $12.50
Pub.. Leigh Bosse
Ed..Joyce Bosse
Mechanical Specifications: Type page 10 1/4 x 16; E - 4 cols, between; A - 4 cols, between; C - 4 cols, between.
Delivery Method: Mail, Newsstand, Carrier, Racks
Areas Served: New Hampshire

HUDSON

HUDSON-LITCHFIELD NEWS (FRI)
1 Campbell Ave, Hudson, NH, 03051-4202,

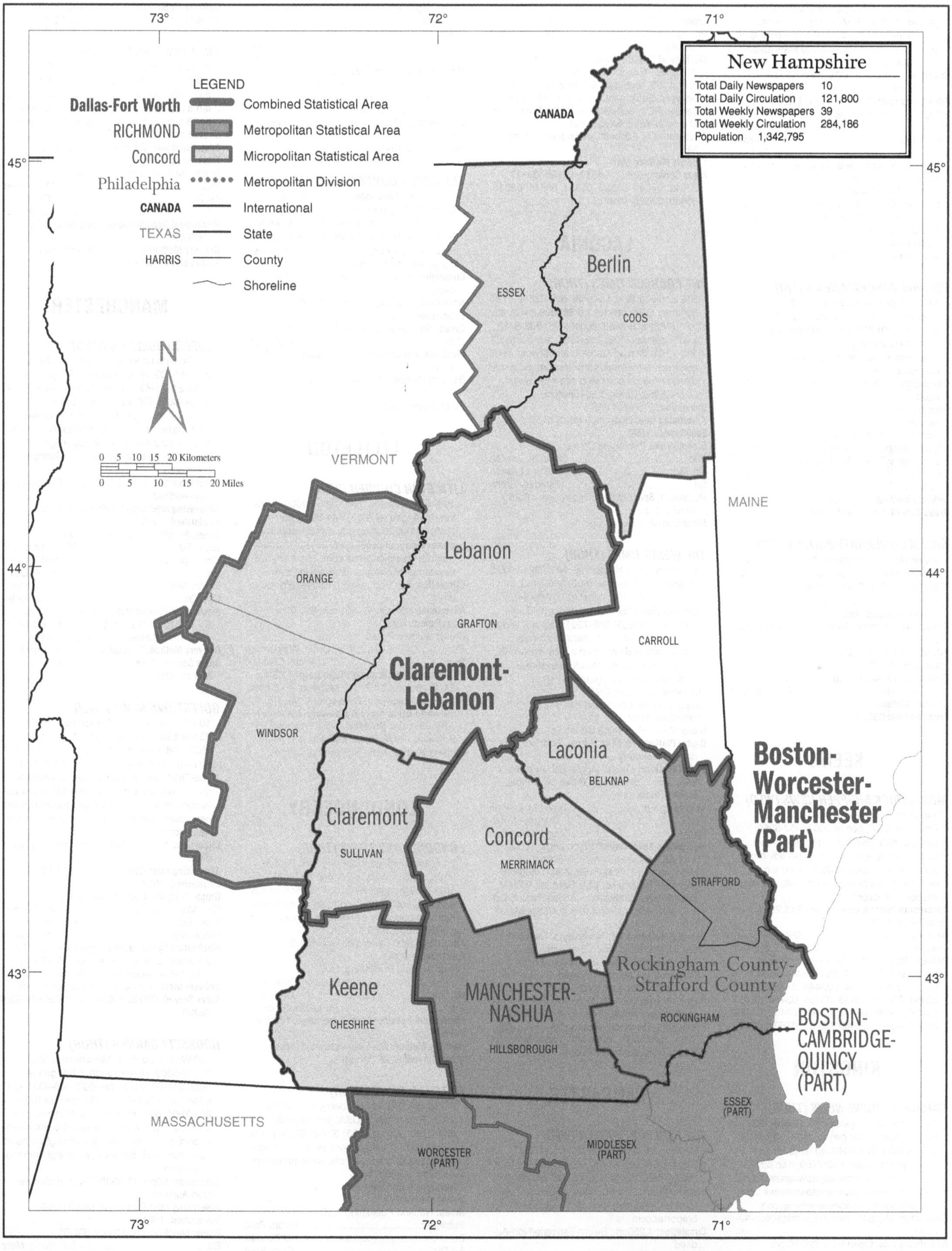
New Hampshire
Total Daily Newspapers 10
Total Daily Circulation 121,800
Total Weekly Newspapers 39
Total Weekly Circulation 284,186
Population 1,342,795
LEGEND
Dallas-Fort Worth Combined Statistical Area
RICHMOND Metropolitan Statistical Area
Concord Micropolitan Statistical Area
Philadelphia Metropolitan Division
CANADA International
TEXAS State
HARRIS County
Shoreline
N
0 5 10 15 20 Kilometers
0 5 10 15 20 Miles
73°
72°
71°
45°
44°
43°
CANADA
VERMONT
MAINE
MASSACHUSETTS
Berlin
ESSEX
COOS
Lebanon
ORANGE
GRAFTON
CARROLL
Claremont-Lebanon
WINDSOR
Laconia
BELKNAP
Boston-Worcester-Manchester (Part)
Claremont
SULLIVAN
Concord
MERRIMACK
STRAFFORD
Rockingham County-Strafford County
Keene
CHESHIRE
MANCHESTER-NASHUA
HILLSBOROUGH
ROCKINGHAM
BOSTON-CAMBRIDGE-QUINCY (PART)
ESSEX (PART)
WORCESTER (PART)
MIDDLESEX (PART)

Hillsborough, USA; gen tel (603) 880-1516; gen fax (603) 879-9707; disp adv e-mail sales@areanewsgroup.com; ed e-mail len@areanewsgroup.com; web site www.areanewsgroup.com
Circulation: 20pd, 13,900fr; Sworn/Estimate/Non-Audited
Advertising rate: Open inch rate $12.25
Group: Area News Group
Pub. .... Len Lathrop
Sales Rep. .... Mike Falzone
Ed. .... Robin Rodgers
Mechanical Specifications: Type page 10 1/4 x 16; E - 6 cols, 1 5/8, 1/16 between; A - 6 cols, 1 5/8, 1/16 between; C - 6 cols, 1 5/8, 1/16 between.Equipment & Software: Hardware — IBM, APP/Macs; Software — ClarisWorks 2.0, Canvas 3.0.
Delivery Method: Mail
Areas Served: 03051, 03052

PELHAM/WINDHAM NEWS (FRI)

1 Campbell Ave, Hudson, NH, 03051-4202, Hillsborough, USA; gen tel (603) 880-1516; gen fax (603) 879-9707; disp adv e-mail sales@areanewsgroup.com; ed e-mail len@areanewsgroup.com; web site www.areanewsgroup.com
Circulation: 10,058fr; Sworn/Estimate/Non-Audited
Advertising rate: Open inch rate $12.25
Established: 2001
Group: Area News Group
Digital Platform - Tablet: Apple iOS, Android, Blackberry Tablet OS, Kindle Fire, Other
Sales Rep .... Sandy Russo
Sales .... Mike FIzone
Delivery Method: Mail, Racks
Areas Served: 03076 and 03087

SALEM COMMUNITY PATRIOT (FRI)

1 Campbell Ave, Hudson, NH, 03051-4202, Hillsborough, USA; gen tel (603) 880-1516; gen fax (603) 879-9707; disp adv e-mail news@areanewsgroup.com; web site www.areanewsgroup.com
Circulation: 14,763fr; Sworn/Estimate/Non-Audited
Advertising rate: $12.25
Established: 2007
Group: Area News Group
customer service .... Mike Falzone
Delivery Method: Mail
Areas Served: 03079

KEENE

MONADNOCK SHOPPER NEWS (WED)

445 West St, Keene, NH, 03431-2448, Cheshire, USA; gen tel (603) 352-5250; gen fax (603) 357-9351; disp adv e-mail sales@shoppernews.com; class adv e-mail classified@shoppernews.com; ed e-mail editorial@shoppernews.com; web site www.shoppernews.com
Advertising rate: Open inch rate $18.28
Established: 1958
Asst. Pub./Ed. .... Michelle Green
Pres./Pub. .... Mitchell G. Shakour
Delivery Method: Mail, Newsstand, Racks
Areas Served: 03602, 03604, 03441, 03443, 03444, 03446, 03447, 03448, 03449, 03450, 03451, 03452, 03453, 03455, 03456, 03457, 03458, 03468, 03470, 03461, 03462, 03466, 03464, 03445, 03469, 03465, 03608, 03467

KINGSTON

CARRIAGE TOWNE NEWS (THUR)

14 Church St, Kingston, NH, 03848-3062, Rockingham, USA; gen tel (603) 642-4499; adv tel (603) 734-9048; ed tel (603) 734-9050; gen fax (603) 642-7750; disp adv e-mail advertise@carriagetownenews.com; ed e-mail elisha@carriagetownenews.com; web site www.carriagetownenews.com
Circulation: 25,354fr; Sworn/Estimate/Non-Audited
Advertising rate: Open Rate $20.50 pci
Established: 1983
Group: Community Newspaper Holdings, Inc.
Ed. .... Elisha Blaisdell
Prod. Mgr. .... Corrinne Lester
Mechanical Specifications: Type page 11 5/8 x 21 1/2; E - 6 cols, 1 4/5, 1/8 between; A - 6 cols, 1 4/5, between; C - 10 cols, 1, 1/16 between.Equipment & Software: Hardware — Lenovo PCs; Software — Adobe/Photoshop, Microsoft/Word. Skyque.net AdobeInCopy, AdobeInDesign,Excel, Paint.NET
Delivery Method: Mail
Areas Served: 03811, 03819, 03826, 03827, 03042, 03044, 03833, 03841, 03848, 03858, 03859, 03865, 03873

LACONIA

THE COCHECO TIMES (THUR)

515 Endicott St N, Laconia, NH, 03246-1725, Belknap, USA; gen tel 1 (888) 308-8463; adv tel 1 (888) 308-8463; ed tel (603) 366-8463 x 317; gen fax (603) 366-7301; adv fax (603) 366-7301; disp adv e-mail sales@weirs.com; class adv e-mail sales@weirs.com; ed e-mail dlawton@weirs.com; web site www.weirs.com - 7,950(views) 3,524(visitors)
Circulation: 27,789fr; VAC
Advertising rate: Open inch rate $12.50
Established: 1992
Group: Weirs Publishing Co Inc.
Pub. .... David M. Lawton
Off. Mgr. .... Starr Lawton
Ed. .... Bredan Smith
Mechanical Specifications: Type page: 10.25 x 12.685; 5 col
Areas Served: Belknap County

THE WEIRS TIMES (THUR)

515 Endicott St N, Laconia, NH, 03246-1725, Belknap, USA; gen tel (603) 366-8463; adv tel (603) 366-8463; ed tel (603) 366-8463; gen fax (603) 366-7301; adv fax (603) 366-7301; ed fax (603) 366-7301; disp adv e-mail advertise@weirs.com; class adv e-mail advertise@weirs.com; ed e-mail dlawton@weirs.com; web site www.theweirstimes.com - 7,950(views) 3,524(visitors)
Circulation: 27,789fr; CVC
Advertising rate: Open inch rate $12.50
Established: 1992
Group: Weirs Publishing Co Inc.
Digital Platform - Mobile: Apple, Android, Windows, Blackberry
Digital Platform - Tablet: Apple iOS, Android, Windows 7, Blackberry Tablet OS, Kindle, Nook, Kindle Fire
Managing Ed. .... David M. Lawton
Ed. .... Brendan Smith
Circ, Mgr. .... Craig Richardson
Mechanical Specifications: Type page: 10.25 x 12.685; 5 col Equipment & Software: Hardware — 1-Acer/P166, 2-AMT/486-50, Microtek/Scanmaker IIXE Scanner, HP/4M LaserPrinter; Software — Adobe/Photoshop 3.0, Adobe/Illustrator 4.0, Aldus/PageMaker 5.0.
Delivery Method: Mail, Newsstand, Racks
Areas Served: Alton, Alton Bay, Ashland, Barnstead, Belmont, Boscawen, Bristol, Canterbury, Center Barnstead, Center Harbor, Chichester, Concord, Franklin, Gilford, Holderness, Laconia, Meredith, Moultonborough, New Hampton, Ossipee, Penacook, Pittsfield, Plymouth, Sanbornton, Sandwich, Tilton,Tuftonboro, Tamworth, Weirs Beach, West Ossipee, and Wolfeboro.

LANCASTER

THE BERLIN REPORTER (WED)

79 Main St, Lancaster, NH, 03584-3027, Coos, USA; gen tel (603) 788-4939; gen fax (603) 788-3022; disp adv e-mail courierreporter@salmonpress.com; ed e-mail courierreporter@salmonpress.com; web site www.breporter.com
Circulation: 4,250pd,; Sworn/Estimate/Non-Audited
Advertising rate: Open inch rate $10.00
Established: 1838
Group: Salmon Press
Ed. .... Darin Wipperman
Pub. .... Frank Chilinski
Mechanical Specifications: Type page 11 3/4 x 21.Equipment & Software: Hardware — APP/Mac; Presses — 4-G/Community; Software — QPS/QuarkXPress.
Delivery Method: Mail, Newsstand, Carrier, Racks
Areas Served: Coos

THE COOS COUNTY DEMOCRAT (WED)

79 Main St, Lancaster, NH, 03584-3027, Coos, USA; gen tel (603) 788-4939; gen fax (603) 788-3022; disp adv e-mail courierreporter@salmonpress.com; ed e-mail courierreporter@salmonpress.com; web site www.cooscountydemocrat.com
Circulation: 5,520pd,; Sworn/Estimate/Non-Audited
Advertising rate: Open inch rate $10.00
Established: 1838
Group: Salmon PressDarin Wipperman
Pub. .... Frank Chilinski
Mechanical Specifications: Type page 15 3/4 x 21.
Delivery Method: Mail, Newsstand, Carrier, Racks
Areas Served: Coos

LITTLETON

LITTLETON COURIER (WED)

16 Mill St, Littleton, NH, 03561-4000, Grafton, USA; gen tel (603) 444-3927; gen fax (603) 444-3920; disp adv e-mail courierreporter@salmonpress.com; ed e-mail courierreporter@salmonpress.com; web site www.newhampshirelakesandmountains.com
Circulation: 6,500pd,; Sworn/Estimate/Non-Audited
Advertising rate: Open inch rate $10.00
Established: 1889
Group: Salmon Press
Ed. .... Darin Wipperman
Pub. .... Frank Chilinski
Mechanical Specifications: Type page 11 3/4 x 21; E - 6 cols, 1 4/5, 1/5 between; A - 6 cols, 1 4/5, 1/5 between; C - 8 cols, 1 1/5, 1/5 between.Equipment & Software: Hardware — APP/iMac G4; Presses — 5-KP/News King; Software — QPS/QuarkXPress 4.1.
Delivery Method: Mail, Newsstand, Carrier, Racks

LONDONDERRY

LONDONDERRY TIMES (THUR)

2 Litchfield Rd, Londonderry, NH, 03053-2625, Rockingham, USA; gen tel (603) 537-2760; gen fax (603) 537-2765; disp adv e-mail dpaul@nutpub.com; ed e-mail lodonnell@nutpub.com; web site www.nutpub.net
Circulation: 0pd, 9,553fr; CVC
Advertising rate: Open inch rate $14.00
Established: 2000
Group: Nutfield Publishing, LLC
Pub. .... Debra Paul
Art Dir. .... Chris Paul
Ed. .... Leslie O'Donnell
Mechanical Specifications: Type page: 10.25 x 13; 6 col
Delivery Method: Mail, Newsstand, Racks
Areas Served: Rockingham

NUTFIELD NEWS (THUR)

2 Litchfield Rd, Londonderry, NH, 03053-2625, Rockingham, USA; gen tel (603) 537-2760; gen fax (603) 537-2765; disp adv e-mail dpaul@nutpub.com; ed e-mail lodonnell@nutpub.com; web site www.nutpub.net
Circulation: 9,996fr; CVC
Advertising rate: Open inch rate $14.00
Established: 2000
Group: Nutfield Publishing, LLC
Publisher .... Debra Paul
Ed. .... Leslie O'Donnell
Art Dir. .... Chris Paul
Delivery Method: Mail, Newsstand, Racks
Areas Served: Type page: 10.25 x 13; 6 col

TRI-TOWN TIMES (THUR)

2 Litchfield Rd, Londonderry, NH, 03053-2625, Rockingham, USA; gen tel (603) 537-2760; gen fax (603) 537-2765; disp adv e-mail dpaul@nutpub.com; ed e-mail lodonnell@nutpub.com; web site www.nutpub.net
Circulation: 8,699fr; CVC
Advertising rate: Open inch rate $14.00
Established: 2006
Group: Nutfield Publishing, LLC
Pub. .... Debra Paul
Art Dir. .... Chris Paul
Ed. .... Leslie O'Donnell
Mechanical Specifications: Type page: 10.25 x 13; 6 col
Delivery Method: Mail, Newsstand, Racks
Areas Served: Rockingham

MANCHESTER

BEDFORD BULLETIN (WED)

100 William Loeb Dr, Manchester, NH, 03109-5309, Hillsborough, USA; gen tel (603) 314-0447; adv tel (603) 668-4321 x241; ed tel (603) 668-4321 x757; gen fax (603) 206-7801; disp adv e-mail ul@unionleader.com; class adv e-mail classified@unionleader.com; ed e-mail editor@yourneighborhoodnews.com; web site www.yourneighborhoodnews.com
Circulation: 56pd, 10,000fr; Sworn/Estimate/Non-Audited
Advertising rate: Open inch rate $14.55
Established: 1970
Group: Neighborhood News (OOB)
Exec. Ed. .... Christine Heiser
Circ. Mgr. .... Robert Bennett
Ed. .... Holly Davis
Prodn. Mgr. .... Pam Young
Circ. Dir. .... Debra Dooley
Mechanical Specifications: Type page 13 x 21; E - 6 cols, 2 1/16, 1/8 between; A - 6 cols, 2 1/16, 1/8 between; C - 9 cols, between.
Delivery Method: Newsstand, Carrier, Racks
Areas Served: Bedford, Amherst, Merrimack, Manchester

GOFFSTOWN NEWS (THUR)

100 William Loeb Dr, Manchester, NH, 03109-5309, Hillsborough, USA; gen tel (603) 206-7800; adv tel (603) 668-4321 x241; ed tel (603) 668-4321 x757; gen fax (603) 206-7801; disp adv e-mail ul@unionleader.com; class adv e-mail classified@unionleader.com; ed e-mail editor@yourneighborhoodnews.com; web site www.yourneighborhoodnews.com
Circulation: 9,000fr; Sworn/Estimate/Non-Audited
Advertising rate: Open inch rate $11.50
Established: 1957
Group: Neighborhood News (OOB)
Circ. Mgr. .... Rob Bennett
Exec. Ed. .... Christine Heiser
Prodn. Mgr. .... Pam Fahey
Mechanical Specifications: Type page 13 x 20; E - 6 cols, 2 1/16, 1/8 between; A - 6 cols, 2 1/16, 1/8 between; C - 9 cols, between.
Delivery Method: Newsstand, Carrier, Racks
Areas Served: 03045 03046 03070 03281 03304 03229

HOOKSETT BANNER (THUR)

100 William Loeb Dr, Manchester, NH, 03109-5309, Hillsborough, USA; gen tel (603) 314-0447; adv tel (603) 668-4321 x241; ed tel (603) 668-4321 x757; gen fax (603) 206-7801; disp adv e-mail ul@unionleader.com; class adv e-mail classified@unionleader.com; ed e-mail editor@yourneighborhoodnews.com; web site www.yourneighborhoodnews.com
Circulation: 50pd, 11,050fr; Sworn/Estimate/Non-Audited
Advertising rate: Open inch rate $12.00
Established: 1961
Group: Neighborhood News (OOB)
Ed. .... Henry Metz

Prodn. Mgr. .... Pam Fahey
Pub./Sales Dir. .... Amy Vellucci
Mechanical Specifications: Type page 13 x 21; E - 6 cols, 2 1/16, 1/8 between; A - 6 cols, 2 1/16, 1/8 between; C - 9 cols, between.
Delivery Method: Newsstand, Carrier, Racks
Areas Served: Hooksett, Allenstown, Pembroke, Epsom, Auburn, Candia, Raymond, Concord, Manchester

MEREDITH

MEREDITH NEWS (THUR)

5 Water St, Meredith, NH, 03253-6233, Belknap, USA; gen tel (603) 279-4516; adv tel (603) 279-4516 x 120; gen fax (603) 279-3331; disp adv e-mail jeffd@salmonpress.com; class adv e-mail jumbo@salmonpress.com; ed e-mail mnews@salmonpress.com; web site www.newhampshirelakesandmountains.com
Circulation: 5,300pd,; Sworn/Estimate/Non-Audited
Advertising rate: Open inch rate $10.00
Established: 1880
Group: Salmon Press
Ed. .... Erin Plummer
Pub. .... Frank Chilinski
Mechanical Specifications: Type page 11 3/4 x 21; E - 6 cols, 1 4/5, 1/5 between; A - 6 cols, 1 4/5, 1/5 between; C - 9 cols, 1 1/5, 1/5 between.Equipment & Software: Hardware — APP/Mac, APP/iMac G4; Software — Microsoft/Word, QPS/QuarkXPress.
Delivery Method: Mail, Newsstand, Carrier, Racks

PLYMOUTH RECORD ENTERPRISE (THUR)

5 Water St, Meredith, NH, 03253-6233, Belknap, USA; gen tel (603) 279-4516; adv tel (603) 279-4516 ext. 132; ed tel (603) 279-4516 ext. 111; gen fax (603) 279-3331; adv fax (603) 279-3331; ed fax (603) 279-3331; disp adv e-mail courierstj@salmonpress.com; class adv e-mail courierstj@salmonpress.com; ed e-mail record@salmonpress.com; web site www.salmonpress.com
Advertising rate: Open inch rate $10.00
Digital Platform - Mobile: Apple, Android, Blackberry
Digital Platform - Tablet: Apple iOS, Android, Blackberry Tablet OS
Ed. .... Brendan Berube
Adv. Mgr. .... Tracy Lewis
Pub. .... Frank Chilinski
Delivery Method: Mail, Racks
Areas Served: Belknap County

THE GILFORD STEAMER (THUR)

5 Water St, Meredith, NH, 03253-6233, Belknap, USA; gen tel (603) 279-4516; adv tel (603) 279-4516 x 120; gen fax (603) 279-3331; disp adv e-mail jeffd@salmonpress.com; class adv e-mail jumbo@salmonpress.com; ed e-mail record@salmonpress.com; web site www.salmonpress.com - 100,000(views) 50,000(visitors)
Circulation: 6,800fr; Sworn/Estimate/Non-Audited
Advertising rate: Open inch rate $10.00
Established: 2004
Group: Salmon Press
Pub. .... Frank Chilnski
Ed. .... Breandan Berube
Jefferey DeFrancesco
Delivery Method: Mail, Newsstand, Carrier, Racks

WINNISQUAM ECHO (THUR)

5 Water St, Meredith, NH, 03253-6233, Belknap, USA; gen tel (603) 279-4516; adv tel (603) 279-4516 x 120; gen fax (603) 279-3331; disp adv e-mail maureen@salmonpress.com; class adv e-mail jumbo@salmonpress.com; ed e-mail record@salmonpress.com; web site www.salmonpress.com
Circulation: 9,200fr; Sworn/Estimate/Non-Audited
Advertising rate: Open inch rate $10.00
Established: 2004
Group: Salmon Press
Pub. .... Frank Chilinski
Ed. .... Breandan Berube
Delivery Method: Mail, Newsstand, Carrier, Racks

MILFORD

BEDFORD JOURNAL (FRI)

54 School St, Milford, NH, 03055-4543, Hillsborough, USA; gen tel (603) 673-3100; adv tel (603) 594-1219; gen fax (603) 673-8250; disp adv e-mail cabnews@cabinet.com; ed e-mail cabnews@cabinet.com; web site www.cabinet.com
Circulation: 9,100fr; Sworn/Estimate/Non-Audited
Advertising rate: Open inch rate $10.61
Established: 1802
Group: Ogden Newspapers Inc.
Managing Ed. .... Sandy Bucknam
Mechanical Specifications: Type page 11 1/2 x 21; E - 6 cols, between; A - 6 cols, between; C - 9 cols, between.
Delivery Method: Mail, Newsstand, Racks
Areas Served: 3110

HOLLIS BROOKLINE JOURNAL (FRI)

54 School St, Milford, NH, 03055-4543, Hillsborough, USA; gen tel (603) 673-3100; adv tel (603) 594-6460; ed tel (603) 673-3100; gen fax (603) 673-8250; adv fax (603) 594-6569; ed fax (603) 673-8250; disp adv e-mail sbucknam@cabinet.com; ed e-mail sbucknam@cabinet.com; web site www.cabinet.com
Circulation: 4,700fr; Sworn/Estimate/Non-Audited
Advertising rate: Open inch rate $7.70
Established: 1802
Group: Independent Publications Inc
Managing Ed. .... Sandy Bucknam
Mechanical Specifications: Type page 10.25x20.5 E - 6 cols, between; A - 6 cols, between; C - 9 cols, between.Equipment & Software: Hardware — APP/Mac; Software — Adobe/PageMaker.
Delivery Method: Mail
Areas Served: 03049, 03033

MERRIMACK JOURNAL (FRI)

54 School St, Milford, NH, 03055-4543, Hillsborough, USA; gen tel (603) 673-3100; gen fax (603) 673-8250; disp adv e-mail sbucknam@cabinet.com; ed e-mail sbucknam@cabinet.com; web site www.cabinet.com
Circulation: 10,400fr; Sworn/Estimate/Non-Audited
Advertising rate: Open inch rate $10.80
Established: 1826
Group: Ogden Newspapers Inc.Sandy Bucknam
Mechanical Specifications: Type page 11 2/3 x 21; E - 6 cols, between; A - 6 cols, between; C - 9 cols, between.
Delivery Method: Mail, Newsstand, Racks
Areas Served: Merrimack, NH

THE MILFORD CABINET (THUR)

54 School St, Milford, NH, 03055-4543, Hillsborough, USA; gen tel (603) 673-3100; gen fax (603) 673-8250; disp adv e-mail sbucknam@cabinet.com; ed e-mail sbucknam@cabinet.com; web site www.cabinet.com
Circulation: 6,700pd, 78fr; Sworn/Estimate/Non-Audited
Advertising rate: Open inch rate $12.50
Established: 1802
Group: Ogden Newspapers Inc.Sandy Bucknam
Mechanical Specifications: Type page 11 1/2 x 21; E - 6 cols, 1 7/8, between; A - 6 cols, 1 7/8, between; C - 9 cols, 1 3/16, between. Equipment & Software: Hardware — APP/Mac; Software — Adobe/PageMaker.
Delivery Method: Mail, Newsstand, Racks
Areas Served: Milford, Amherst, Mont Vernon, Souhegan Valley

NORTH SUTTON

INTERTOWN RECORD (TUES)

1719 Route 114, North Sutton, NH, 3260, Merrimack, USA; gen tel (603) 927-4028; disp adv e-mail info@intertownrecord.com; class adv e-mail info@intertownrecord.com; ed e-mail info@intertownrecord.com; web site www.intertownrecord.com - 1,200(views) 600(visitors)
Circulation: 2,200pd, 100fr; Sworn/Estimate/Non-Audited
Advertising rate: Open inch rate $9
Established: 1993
Digital Platform - Mobile: Other
Digital Platform - Tablet: Other
Pub./Gen. Mgr. .... Annette Vogel
Mechanical Specifications: Type page 10 1/4 x 16; 5 cols, 1.937, .1667 between.Equipment & Software: Hardware — MacBook Pro
iMac
iPhone
Dell; Presses — Upper Valley Press; Software — InDesign, Photoshop, Adobe Creative Cloud, QuarkXPress 8.5, AppleMail, AddressBook, Wordpress, Pages, Fetch, Safari, Google Chrome, Preview, Quickbooks 2013
Delivery Method: Mail, Newsstand, Racks
Areas Served: 03216, 03230, 03233, 03221, 03257, 03255, 03278, 03287, 03284, 03782, 03773, 03751, 03753, 03260

PETERBOROUGH

MONADNOCK LEDGER-TRANSCRIPT (TUES, THUR)

20 Grove St, Ste 120, Peterborough, NH, 03458-1466, Hillsborough, USA; gen tel (603) 924-7172; gen fax (603) 924-3681; adv fax (603) 928-3681; disp adv e-mail ads@ledgertranscript.com; class adv e-mail classifieds@ledgertranscript.com; ed e-mail news@ledgertranscript.com; web site www.ledgertranscript.com - 173,462(views) 31,969(visitors)
Circulation: 4,587pd, 230fr; Sworn/Estimate/Non-Audited
Advertising rate: Open inch rate $10.25
Established: 1849
Group: Newspapers of New England
Pub. .... Heather McKernan
Ed. .... Ben Conant
Circ. Mgr. .... Kimberly Poorte
Mechanical Specifications: Type page 13 x 21; E - 6 cols, 2 1/16, 1/8 between; A - 6 cols, 2 1/16, 1/8 between; C - 6 cols, 2 1/16, 1/8 between.
Delivery Method: Mail, Newsstand, Racks
Areas Served: 03043, 03047, 03048, 03071, 03082, 03084, 03086, 03440, 03442, 03444, 03449, 03452, 03458, 03461

PORTSMOUTH

EXETER NEWS-LETTER (TUES, FRI)

111 NH Ave, Rockingham, Portsmouth, NH, 03801-2864, Rockingham, USA; gen tel (800) 439-0303; gen fax (603) 433-5760; adv fax (603) 427-0550; disp adv e-mail advertising@seacoastonline.com; class adv e-mail advertising@seacoastonline.com; ed e-mail news@seacoastonline.com; web site www.seacoastonline.com
Advertising rate: Open inch rate $26.38
Group: Dow Jones Local Media Group
Seacoast Media Group
Ed. .... Howard Altschiller
Adv. Dir. .... Vince Ciampi
Pub. .... John Tabor
Dennis Thompson
Delivery Method: Newsstand, Carrier, Racks
Areas Served: 03833

THE HAMPTON UNION (TUES, FRI, SUN)

111 NH Ave, Portsmouth, NH, 03801-2864, Rockingham, USA; gen tel (800) 439-0303; gen fax (603) 433-5760; adv fax (603) 427-0550; disp adv e-mail adreps@seacoastonline.com; ed e-mail news@seacoastonline.com; web site www.seacoastonline.com
Circulation: 4,525pd,; Sworn/Estimate/Non-Audited
Advertising rate: Open inch rate $26.30
Group: Dow Jones Local Media Group
Seacoast Media Group
Pub. .... John Tabor
Circ. Dir. .... Dennis Thompson
Exec. Ed. .... Howard Altschiller
Ad Director .... Andrew Chernoff
Delivery Method: Newsstand, Carrier, Racks
Areas Served: 03842

THE YORK WEEKLY (WED)

111 NH Ave, Portsmouth, NH, 03801-2864, Rockingham, USA; gen tel (800) 439-0303; gen fax (603) 433-5760; adv fax (603) 427-0550; disp adv e-mail adreps@seacoastonline.com; ed e-mail news@seacoastonline.com; web site www.seacoastonline.com
Circulation: 3,900pd,; Sworn/Estimate/Non-Audited
Advertising rate: Open inch rate $13.24
Group: Dow Jones Local Media Group
Seacoast Media Group
Pub. .... John Tabor
Circ. Mgr. .... Dennis Thompson
Vince Ciampi
Howard Altschiller
Mechanical Specifications: Type page 11 1/2 x 21; E - 6 cols, 1 3/4, between; A - 6 cols, 1/4 between; C - 9 cols, 1 3/16, 1/8 between. Equipment & Software: Hardware — APP/Macs; Software — Adobe/PageMaker 6.5.
Delivery Method: Mail, Newsstand, Racks
Areas Served: York, ME

YORK COUNTY COAST STAR (THUR)

111 NH Ave, Portsmouth, NH, 03801-2864, Rockingham, USA; gen tel (800) 439-0303; gen fax (603) 433-5760; adv fax (603) 427-0550; disp adv e-mail adreps@seacoastonline.com; ed e-mail news@seacoastonline.com; web site www.seacoastonline.com
Advertising rate: Open inch rate $15.64
Group: Dow Jones Local Media Group
Seacoast Media Group
Ed. .... Howard Altschiller
Adv. Dir. .... Vince Ciampi
Pub. .... John Tabor
Dennis Thompson
Delivery Method: Mail, Newsstand, Racks
Areas Served: York, ME

WOLFEBORO

CARROLL COUNTY INDEPENDENT (THUR)

35 Center St, Clarke Plaza, Wolfeboro, NH, 03894-4324, Carroll, USA; gen tel (603) 569-3126; gen fax (603) 569-4743; disp adv e-mail maureen@salmonpress.com; class adv e-mail jumbo@salmonpress.com; ed e-mail tbeeler@salmonpress.news; web site www.carrollcountyindependent.com
Circulation: 4,500pd,; Sworn/Estimate/Non-Audited
Advertising rate: Open inch rate $10.00
Established: 1881
Group: Salmon Press
Ed. .... Thomas Beeler
Frank Chilinski
Mechanical Specifications: Type page 15 1/4 x 21 3/4; E - 7 cols, 2 1/16, 1/6 between; A - 7 cols, 2 1/16, 1/6 between; C - 9 cols, 1 9/16, 1/12 between.Equipment & Software: Hardware — APP/Mac; Presses — WPC/Web Leader; Software — Word Perfect 3.5, QPS/QuarkXPress.
Delivery Method: Mail, Newsstand, Carrier, Racks
Areas Served: Carroll

GRANITE STATE NEWS (THUR)

35 Center St, Clarke Plaza, Wolfeboro, NH, 03894-4324, Carroll, USA; gen tel (603) 569-3126; gen fax (603) 569-3126; disp adv e-mail maureen@salmonpress.com; class adv e-mail jumbo@salmonpress.com; ed e-mail tbeeler@salmonpress.news; web site

www.granitestatenews.com
Circulation: 5,800pd,; Sworn/Estimate/Non-Audited
Advertising rate: Open inch rate $10.00
Established: 1859
Group: Salmon Press
Pub. ... Frank Chilinski
Ed. ... Thomas Beeler
Mechanical Specifications: Type page 15 1/4 x 21 3/4; E - 7 cols, 2 1/16, 1/6 between; A - 7 cols, 2 1/16, 1/6 between; C - 9 cols, 1 9/16, 1/12 between.Equipment & Software: Hardware — APP/Mac; Presses — WPC/Web Leader; Software — WordPerfect 3.5, QPS/QuarkXPress.
Delivery Method: Mail, Newsstand, Carrier, Racks
Areas Served: Wolfeboro, Tuftonboro, Brookfield and Wakefield NH

WOLFEBORO FALLS

THE BAYSIDER (THUR)

Clark Plaza, Wolfeboro Falls, NH, 3896, Carroll, USA; gen tel (603) 569-3126; gen fax (603) 569-4743; disp adv e-mail maureen@salmonpress.com; class adv e-mail jumbo@salmonpress.com; ed e-mail baysider@salmonpress.com; web site www.salmonpress.com
Advertising rate: Open inch rate $10.00
Established: 2005
Group: Salmon PressFrank Chilinski
Ed. ... Joshua Spaulding
Delivery Method: Mail, Newsstand, Carrier, Racks

NEW JERSEY

ASBURY PARK

COASTER (THUR)

1011 Main St, Ste B, Asbury Park, NJ, 07712-5963, Monmouth, USA; gen tel (732) 775-3010; gen fax (732) 775-8345; class adv e-mail advertising@thecoaster.net; ed e-mail editor@thecoaster.net; web site www.thecoaster.net
Circulation: 5,100pd,; Sworn/Estimate/Non-Audited
Advertising rate: Open inch rate $7.00
Established: 1983
Adv. Mgr. ... Michael Booth
Ed. ... Ellen Carroll
Delivery Method: Mail, Newsstand, Racks
Areas Served: Allenhurst, Asbury Park, Avon, Bradley Beach, Deal, Interlaken, Loch Arbour, Neptune, Neptune City, Ocean Township, Tinton Falls

BAYONNE

BAYONNE COMMUNITY NEWS (WED)

447 Broadway, Bayonne, NJ, 07002-3623, Hudson, USA; gen tel (201) 798-7800; adv tel (201) 798-7800; ed tel (201) 798-7800; gen fax (201) 798-0018; adv fax (201) 798-0018; ed fax (201) 798-0018; disp adv e-mail dunger@hudsonreporter.com; class adv e-mail classified@hudsonreporter.com; ed e-mail editorial@hudsonreporter.com; web site www.hudsonreporter.com
Circulation: 0pd, 45,808fr; CAC
Advertising rate: Open inch rate $20.40
Established: 1978
Group: Hudson Reporter Associates, Lp
Digital Platform - Mobile: Apple, Android, Windows, Blackberry
Digital Platform - Tablet: Apple iOS, Android, Windows 7, Blackberry Tablet OS, Kindle, Nook, Kindle Fire
Co-Pub. ... Lucha Malato
Co-Pub. ... David S. Unger
Ed. ... Cecilia Martinez
Tish Kraszyk
Circ. Dir. ... Roberto Lopez
Mechanical Specifications: Type page 10 1/4 x 15; E - 7 cols, 1 3/8, 1/8 between; A - 7 cols, 1 3/8, 1/8 between; C - 7 cols, 1 3/8, 1/8 between.Equipment & Software: Hardware — APP/Mac Performa 6200, APP/Mac G4; Software — Multi-Ad/Creator, Claris/Draw, Adobe/Photoshop.
Delivery Method: Carrier, Racks
Areas Served: Bayonne/Hudson/07002

MR. (SUN)

447 Broadway, Bayonne, NJ, 07002-3623, Hudson, USA; gen tel (201) 798-7800; gen fax (201) 798-0018; disp adv e-mail dunger@hudsonreporter.com; class adv e-mail dunger@hudsonreporter.com; ed e-mail editorial@hudsonreporter.com; web site www.hudsonreporter.com
Circulation: 0pd, 9,823fr; Sworn/Estimate/Non-Audited
Advertising rate: Open inch rate $20.40
Established: 1983
Digital Platform - Mobile: Apple, Android, Blackberry
Digital Platform - Tablet: Apple iOS, Android, Windows 7, Blackberry Tablet OS, Kindle, Nook, Kindle Fire
Pub. ... Lucha M. Malato
Adv. Dir. ... David S. Unger
Circ. Mgr. ... Roberto Lopez
Ed. ... Caren Matzner
Advt Mgr ... Tish Kraszyk
Mechanical Specifications: Type page 10 3/8 x 13; E - 7 cols, 1 5/16, 1/8 between; A - 7 cols, 1 5/16, 1/8 between; C - 7 cols, 1 5/16, 1/8 between.Equipment & Software: Hardware — PCs, APP/Mac; Software — Archetype/Corel Draw 4.0, QPS/QuarkXPress, Adobe/Photoshop, Adobe/Illustrator, Adobe/PageMaker.
Delivery Method: Carrier, Racks
Areas Served: 07302, 07304, 07305, 07306, 07307, 07310

SECAUCUS REPORTER (SUN)

447 Broadway, Bayonne, NJ, 07002-3623, Hudson, USA; gen tel (201) 798-7800; gen fax (201) 798-0018; disp adv e-mail dunger@hudsonreporter.com; class adv e-mail classified@hudsonreporter.com; ed e-mail editorial@hudsonreporter.com; web site www.hudsonreporter.com
Circulation: 0pd, 33,028fr; CAC
Advertising rate: Open inch rate $20.40
Established: 1983
Group: Hudson Reporter Associates, Lp
Digital Platform - Mobile: Apple, Windows, Blackberry
Digital Platform - Tablet: Apple iOS, Android, Windows 7, Blackberry Tablet OS, Kindle, Nook, Kindle Fire
Co-Pub. ... Lucha Malato
Co-Pub ... David S. Unger
Circ. Mgr. ... Roberto Lopez
Ed. ... Caren Matzner
Mechanical Specifications: Type page 10 3/8 x 15; E - 7 cols, 1 3/8, 1/8 between; A - 7 cols, 1 3/8, 1/8 between; C - 7 cols, 1 3/8, 1/8 between.Equipment & Software: Hardware — PCs, APP/Mac; Software — Archetype/Corel Draw 4.0, QPS/QuarkXPress, Adobe/Photoshop, Adobe/Illustrator, Adobe/PageMaker.
Delivery Method: Carrier, Racks
Areas Served: Secaucus/Hudson/07094

THE HOBOKEN REPORTER (SUN)

447 Broadway, Bayonne, NJ, 07002-3623, Hudson, USA; gen tel (201) 798-7800; adv tel (201) 798-0018; gen fax (201) 798-7800; adv fax 201-798-0018; disp adv e-mail dunger@hudsonreporter.com; class adv e-mail tishk@hudsonreporter.com; ed e-mail editorial@hudsonreporter.com; web site www.hudsonreporter.com
Circulation: 0pd, 11,925fr; CAC
Advertising rate: Open inch rate $20.40
Established: 1983
Group: Hudson Reporter Associates, Lp
Digital Platform - Mobile: Apple, Android, Windows, Blackberry
Digital Platform - Tablet: Apple iOS, Android, Windows 7, Blackberry Tablet OS, Kindle, Nook, Kindle Fire
Pub. ... Lucha M. Malato
Pub. ... David S. Unger
Adv. Mgr. ... Tish Kraszyk
Circ. Mgr. ... Roberto Lopez
Ed. ... Caren Lissner
Mechanical Specifications: Type page 10 1/4 x 15; E - 7 cols, 1 3/8, 1/8 between; A - 7 cols, 1 3/8, 1/8 between; C - 7 cols, 1 3/8, 1/8 between.Equipment & Software: Hardware — PCs, APP/Mac; Software — Archetype/Corel Draw 4.0, QPS/QuarkXPress, Adobe/Photoshop, Adobe/Illustrator, Adobe/PageMaker.
Delivery Method: Carrier, Racks
Areas Served: 07030

THE NORTH BERGEN REPORTER (SUN)

447 Broadway, Bayonne, NJ, 07002-3623, Hudson, USA; gen tel (201) 798-7800; gen fax (201) 798-0018; disp adv e-mail dunger@hudsonreporter.com; class adv e-mail tishk@hudsonreporter.com; ed e-mail editorial@hudsonreporter.com; web site www.hudsonreporter.com
Circulation: 0pd, 12,112fr; CAC
Advertising rate: Open inch rate $20.00
Established: 1983
Group: Hudson Reporter Associates, Lp
Digital Platform - Mobile: Apple, Android, Blackberry
Digital Platform - Tablet: Apple iOS, Android, Windows 7, Blackberry Tablet OS, Kindle, Nook, Kindle Fire
Pub. ... Lucha M. Malato
Pub. ... David S. Unger
Adv. Mgr. ... Tish Kraszyk
Circ. Mgr. ... Roberto Lopez
Ed. ... Caren matzner
Mechanical Specifications: Type page 10 3/8 x 15; E - 7 cols, 1 3/8, 1/8 between; A - 7 cols, 1 3/8, 1/8 between; C - 7 cols, 1 3/8, 1/8 between.Equipment & Software: Hardware — PCs, APP/Mac; Software — Archetype/Corel Draw 4.0, QPS/QuarkXPress, Adobe/Photoshop, Adobe/Illustrator, Adobe/PageMaker.
Delivery Method: Carrier, Racks
Areas Served: North Bergen/Hudson/07047

THE WEEHAWKEN REPORTER (SUN)

447 Broadway, Bayonne, NJ, 07002-3623, Hudson, USA; gen tel (201) 798-7800; gen fax (201) 798-0018; disp adv e-mail dunger@hudsonreporter.com; class adv e-mail classified@hudsonreporter.com; ed e-mail editorial@hudsonreporter.com; web site www.hudsonreporter.com
Circulation: 0pd, 2,986fr; CAC
Advertising rate: Open inch rate $20.40
Established: 1983
Group: Hudson Reporter Associates, Lp
Digital Platform - Mobile: Apple, Android, Windows, Blackberry
Co-Pub. ... Lucha M. Malato
Co-Pub. ... David S. Unger
Circ. Mgr. ... Roberto Lopez
Ed. ... Caren Lissner
Adv. Mgr. ... Tish Kraszyk
Mechanical Specifications: Type page 10 3/8 x 13; E - 7 cols, 1 5/16, 1/8 between; A - 7 cols, 1 5/16, 1/8 between; C - 7 cols, 1 5/16, 1/8 between.Equipment & Software: Hardware — PCs, APP/Mac; Software — Archetype/Corel Draw 4.0, QPS/QuarkXPress, Adobe/Photoshop, Adobe/Illustrator, Adobe/PageMaker.
Delivery Method: Carrier, Racks
Areas Served: Weehawken, NJ 07086

BERNARDSVILLE

BERNARDSVILLE NEWS (THUR)

17-19 Morristown Rd, Bernardsville, NJ, 07924-2372, Somerset, USA; gen tel (908) 766-3900; gen fax (908) 766-5375; disp adv e-mail advertising@newjerseyhills.com; class adv e-mail nicoleb@Newjerseyhills.com; ed e-mail czavalick@Newjerseyhills.com; web site www.recordernewspapers.com
Circulation: 6,488pd, 101fr; Sworn/Estimate/Non-Audited
Advertising rate: Open inch rate $23.00
Established: 1897
Group: New Jersey Hills Media GroupEditions: (2) 2 total; Bernardsville News-East (5,500); Bernardsville News-West (3,500);
Co-Pub. ... Elizabeth K. Parker
Co-Pub. ... Stephen W. Parker
Adv. Dir. ... Jerry O'Donnell
Prodn. Mgr. ... Linda Campbell
Gen. Off. Mgr ... Diane Howard
Ass. Exec. Ed. ... Philip Nardone
Ed. ... Charles Zavalick
Mechanical Specifications: Type page 13 x 22 3/4; E - 6 cols, 2 1/16, between; A - 6 cols, 2 1/16, between; C - 9 cols, 1 1/2, between.
Delivery Method: Mail, Newsstand, Racks
Areas Served: 07921 07978 07931 07938 07934 07977 07924 07920

CHATHAM COURIER (THUR)

17-19 Morristown Rd, Bernardsville, NJ, 07924-2372, Somerset, USA; gen tel (908) 766-3900; adv tel (973) 377-2000; ed tel (973) 377-2000; adv fax (973) 377-7721; ed fax (973) 377-7721; disp adv e-mail advertising@Newjerseyhills.com; class adv e-mail lindap@newjerseyhills.com; ed e-mail eparker@newjerseyhills.com; web site www.recordernewspapers.com
Circulation: 1,856pd, 12fr; CAC
Advertising rate: Open inch rate $11.03
Established: 1945
Group: New Jersey Hills Media Group
Pub. ... Elizabeth K. Parker
Pub. ... Stephen W. Parker
Adv. Dir. ... Doug McBride
Circ. Dir. ... David Nelson
Prodn. Mgr. ... Linda Campbell
Ed. ... Philip Nardone
Delivery Method: Mail, Newsstand, Racks
Areas Served: 07928

ECHOES-SENTINEL (THUR)

17-19 Morristown Rd, Bernardsville, NJ, 07924-2372, Somerset, USA; gen tel (908) 766-3900; adv tel 9087663900 ext 230; ed tel 9087663900 ext 241; gen fax (908) 766-2773; disp adv e-mail advertising@Newjerseyhills.com; class adv e-mail lindap@newjerseyhills.com; ed e-mail eparker@newjerseyhills.com; web site www.echoes-sentinel.com
Circulation: 1,251pd, 11fr; Sworn/Estimate/Non-Audited
Advertising rate: Open inch rate $14.06
Established: 1959
Group: New Jersey Hills Media Group
Pub./Ed. ... Elizabeth K. Parker
Pub. ... Stephen W. Parker
Delivery Method: Mail, Newsstand, Racks
Areas Served: 07059 07933 07946 07980

FLORHAM PARK EAGLE (THUR)

17-19 Morristown Rd, Bernardsville, NJ, 07924-2372, Somerset, USA; gen tel (908) 766-3900; ed tel 9087663900 ext 246; disp adv e-mail advertising@Newjerseyhills.com; class adv e-mail lindap@newjerseyhills.com; ed e-mail eparker@newjerseyhills.com; web site www.florhamparkeagle.com
Circulation: 1,210pd, 5fr; CAC
Advertising rate: Open inch rate $11.03
Established: 1979
Group: New Jersey Hills Media Group
Pub. ... Elizabeth K. Parker
Pub. ... Stephen W. Parker
Adv. Mgr. ... Douglas McBride
Circ. Mgr. ... Dave Nelson
Prodn. Mgr. ... Linda Campbell
Ed. ... Christine Lee
Delivery Method: Mail, Newsstand, Racks
Areas Served: 07932

HANOVER EAGLE (THUR)

17-19 Morristown Rd, Bernardsville, NJ, 07924-2372, Somerset, USA; gen tel (908) 766-3900; gen fax (908) 766-2773; disp adv e-mail advertising@Newjerseyhills.com; class adv e-mail classified@recordernewspapers.com; ed e-mail jlent@Newjerseyhills.com; web site www.recordernewspapers.com
Circulation: 1,645pd, 18fr; CAC
Advertising rate: Open inch rate $9.82
Group: New Jersey Hills Media Group
Pub. ... Elizabeth K. Parker
Pub. ... Stephen W. Parker

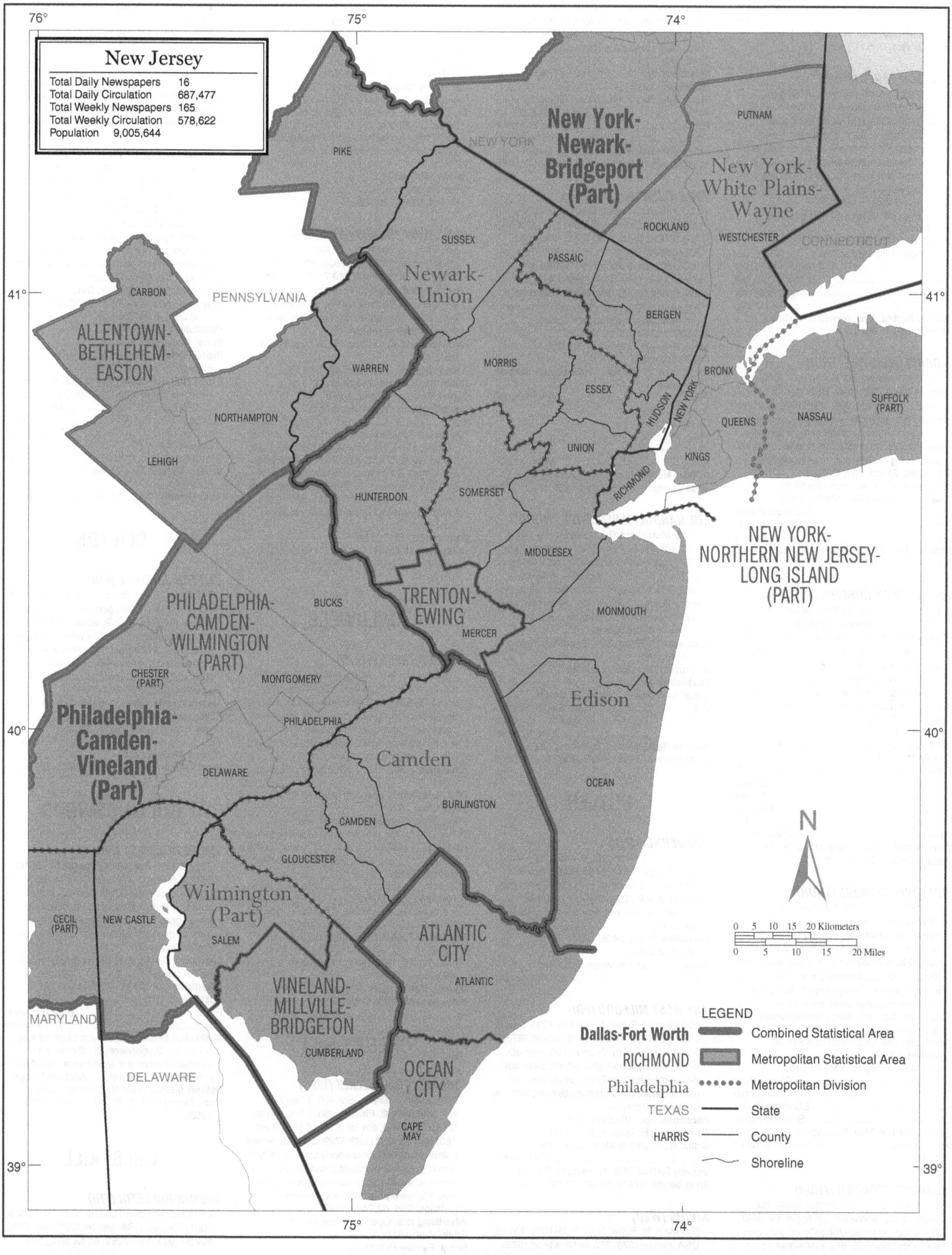
New Jersey
Total Daily Newspapers 16
Total Daily Circulation 687,477
Total Weekly Newspapers 165
Total Weekly Circulation 578,622
Population 9,005,644
New York-Newark-Bridgeport (Part)
New York-White Plains-Wayne
Newark-Union
ALLENTOWN-BETHLEHEM-EASTON
NEW YORK-NORTHERN NEW JERSEY-LONG ISLAND (PART)
TRENTON-EWING
PHILADELPHIA-CAMDEN-WILMINGTON (PART)
Philadelphia-Camden-Vineland (Part)
Edison
Camden
Wilmington (Part)
ATLANTIC CITY
VINELAND-MILLVILLE-BRIDGETON
OCEAN CITY
PIKE
SUSSEX
PUTNAM
ROCKLAND
WESTCHESTER
CONNECTICUT
PASSAIC
BERGEN
CARBON
PENNSYLVANIA
NEW YORK
WARREN
MORRIS
ESSEX
HUDSON
BRONX
QUEENS
NASSAU
SUFFOLK (PART)
KINGS
UNION
RICHMOND
NORTHAMPTON
LEHIGH
HUNTERDON
SOMERSET
MIDDLESEX
MONMOUTH
BUCKS
MERCER
CHESTER (PART)
MONTGOMERY
PHILADELPHIA
DELAWARE
OCEAN
BURLINGTON
CAMDEN
GLOUCESTER
CECIL (PART)
NEW CASTLE
SALEM
ATLANTIC
CUMBERLAND
CAPE MAY
MARYLAND
DELAWARE
N
0 5 10 15 20 Kilometers
0 5 10 15 20 Miles
LEGEND
Dallas-Fort Worth Combined Statistical Area
RICHMOND Metropolitan Statistical Area
Philadelphia Metropolitan Division
TEXAS State
HARRIS County
Shoreline
76°
75°
74°
41°
40°
39°

Circ. Mgr....................................... Dave Nelson
Ed. .... Jim Lent
Delivery Method: Mail, Newsstand, Racks
Areas Served: 07981 07936

MADISON EAGLE (THUR)

17-19 Morristown Rd, Bernardsville, NJ, 07924-2372, Somerset, USA; gen tel (908) 766-3900; ed tel 9087663900 ext 240; gen fax (908) 766-2773; disp adv e-mail advertising@Newjerseyhills.com; class adv e-mail lindap@newjerseyhills.com; ed e-mail gherzog@Newjerseyhills.com; web site www.madisoneagle.com
Circulation: 2,235pd, 60fr; CAC
Advertising rate: Open inch rate $11.03
Established: 1880
Group: BH Media Group
New Jersey Hills Media Group
Pub..................................... Elizabeth K. Parker
Pub...................................... Stephen W. Parker
Adv. Mgr. .... Douglas McBride
Ed. .... Garry Herzog
Delivery Method: Mail, Newsstand, Racks
Areas Served: 079040

MORRIS NEWS-BEE (THUR)

17-19 Morristown Rd, Bernardsville, NJ, 07924-2372, Somerset, USA; gen tel (908) 766-3900; gen fax (908) 766-2773; disp adv e-mail advertising@Newjerseyhills.com; class adv e-mail classified@recordernewspapers.com; ed e-mail jlent@Newjerseyhills.com; web site www.morrisnewsbee.com
Circulation: 714pd, 23fr; CAC
Advertising rate: Open inch rate $9.82
Group: New Jersey Hills Media Group
Pub.. Elizabeth Parker
Adv. Mgr. .... Douglas McBride
Ed. .... Jim Lent
Delivery Method: Mail, Newsstand, Racks
Areas Served: 07960 07927 07950

MOUNT OLIVE CHRONICLE (THUR)

17-19 Morristown Rd, Bernardsville, NJ, 07924-2372, Somerset, USA; gen tel (908) 879-4100; ed tel 9087663900 ext 251; gen fax (908) 879-0799; disp adv e-mail advertising@Newjerseyhills.com; class adv e-mail classified@recordernewspapers.com; ed e-mail pgarber@Newjerseyhills.com; web site www.recordernewspapers.com
Circulation: 2,000pd, 13fr; Sworn/Estimate/Non-Audited
Advertising rate: Open inch rate $11.91
Established: 1979
Group: New Jersey Hills Media Group
Adv. Mgr. .... Allison Spinella
Circ. Mgr...................................... David Nelson
Ed. .... Phil Garber
Co-Pub.................................... Stephen Parker
Co-Pub................................... Elizabeth Parker
Delivery Method: Mail, Newsstand, Racks
Areas Served: 07836, 07828

OBSERVER TRIBUNE (THUR)

17-19 Morristown Rd, Bernardsville, NJ, 07924-2372, Somerset, USA; gen tel (908) 879-4100; ed tel 9087663900 ext 251; gen fax (908) 879-0799; disp adv e-mail advertising@Newjerseyhills.com; class adv e-mail classified@recordernewspapers.com; ed e-mail pgarber@Newjerseyhills.com; web site www.recordernewspapers.com
Circulation: 4,501pd, 53fr; Sworn/Estimate/Non-Audited
Advertising rate: Open inch rate $17.86
Established: 1936
Group: New Jersey Hills Media Group
Circ. Mgr....................................... Dave Nelson
Ed. .... Phil Garber
Co-Pub.................................. Elizabeth Parker
Co-Pub.................................... Stephen Parker
Delivery Method: Mail, Newsstand, Racks
Areas Served: 07870 07853 07930 07945 07935 07976

ROXBURY REGISTER (THUR)

17-19 Morristown Rd, Bernardsville, NJ, 07924-2372, Somerset, USA; gen tel (908) 766-3900; ed tel 9087663900 ext 223; gen fax (908) 766-1083; disp adv e-mail advertising@Newjerseyhills.com; class adv e-mail lindap@newjerseyhills.com; ed e-mail mcondon@Newjerseyhills.com; web site www.recordernewspapers.com
Circulation: 1,213pd, 12fr; CAC
Advertising rate: Open inch rate $11.91
Established: 1988
Group: New Jersey Hills Media Group
Pub.................................... Elizabeth K. Parker
Pub..................................... Stephen W. Parker
Ed. .... Michael Condon
Delivery Method: Mail, Newsstand, Racks
Areas Served: 07850 07852 07876 07847 07856

THE CITIZEN (WED)

17-19 Morristown Rd, Bernardsville, NJ, 07924-2372, Somerset, USA; gen tel (908) 766-3900; adv tel (908) 766-3900; ed tel 9087663900 ext 241; gen fax (908) 766-1083; adv fax (908) 766-6365; disp adv e-mail advertising@newjerseyhills.com; class adv e-mail nicoleb@Newjerseyhills.com; ed e-mail mcondon@newjerseyhills.com; web site www.recordernewspapers.com
Circulation: 2,345pd, 107fr; CAC
Advertising rate: Open inch rate $11.47
Established: 1946
Group: New Jersey Hills Media GroupElizabeth K. Parker
Pub... Stephen Parker
Jerry O'Donnell
Linda Campbell
Philip Nardone
Diane Howard
Ed. .... Mike Condon
Delivery Method: Mail, Newsstand, Racks
Areas Served: 07866 07046 07834 07005 07045

THE RANDOLPH REPORTER (THUR)

17-19 Morristown Rd, Bernardsville, NJ, 07924-2372, Somerset, USA; gen tel (908) 766-3900; ed tel 9087663900 ext 244; gen fax (908) 766-2773; disp adv e-mail advertising@Newjerseyhills.com; class adv e-mail lindap@newjerseyhills.com; ed e-mail mmontalto@newjerseyhills.com; web site www.recordernewspapers.com
Circulation: 1,973pd, 22fr; Sworn/Estimate/Non-Audited
Advertising rate: Open inch rate $12.57
Established: 1978
Group: New Jersey Hills Media Group
Pub... Stephen Parker
Pub................................... Elizabeth K. Parker
Ed. .... Mike Montalto
Delivery Method: Mail, Newsstand, Racks
Areas Served: 07845 07803 07869 07970 07885

BUTLER

AIM VERNON (FRI)

505 Main St, Butler, NJ, 07405-1095, Morris, USA; gen tel (973) 569-7000; adv tel (973) 569-7269; ed tel (973) 569-7100; gen fax (973) 569-7268; disp adv e-mail aim@northjersey.com; web site www.northjersey.com/vernon
Circulation: 0pd, 8,840fr; AAM
Established: 2009
Group: North Jersey Media Group Inc.
Ed. .... Rick Green

AIM WEST MILFORD (FRI)

505 Main St, Butler, NJ, 07405-1095, Morris, USA; gen tel (973) 283-5600; adv tel (973) 569-7269; ed tel (973) 569-7100; disp adv e-mail adhelp@northjersey.com; class adv e-mail marketplace@northjersey.com; ed e-mail newsroom@northjersey.com; web site www.northjersey.com
Circulation: 0pd, 10,051fr; AAM
Advertising rate: Open inch rate $16.75
Group: North Jersey Media Group Inc.
Ed. .... Rick Green
Delivery Method: Mail, Newsstand, Carrier
Areas Served: 07438, 07421, 07435, 07480

ARGUS (WED)

505 Main St, Butler, NJ, 07405-1095, Morris, USA; gen tel (973) 283-5618; adv tel (973) 569-7269; ed tel (973) 569-7100; disp adv e-mail adhelp@northjersey.com; class adv e-mail marketplace@northjersey.com; ed e-mail newsroom@northjersey.com; web site www.northjersey.com
Circulation: 0pd, 9,847fr; AAM
Advertising rate: Open inch rate $8.75
Group: North Jersey Media Group Inc.
Digital Platform - Mobile: Apple, Android, Windows, Blackberry
Digital Platform - Tablet: Apple iOS, Android, Windows 7, Blackberry Tablet OS
Ed. .... Rick Green
Delivery Method: Mail
Areas Served: 07405, 07035, 07440, 07442, 07444, 07457, 07403

SUBURBAN TRENDS (WED, SUN)

505 Main St, Butler, NJ, 07405-1095, Morris, USA; gen tel (973) 283-5600; adv tel (973) 569-7269; ed tel (973) 569-7100; disp adv e-mail adhelp@northjersey.com; class adv e-mail marketplace@northjersey.com; ed e-mail newsroom@northjersey.com; web site www.northjersey.com
Circulation: 9,350pd,; Sworn/Estimate/Non-Audited
Advertising rate: Open inch rate $14.75
Group: North Jersey Media Group Inc.
Digital Platform - Mobile: Apple
Digital Platform - Tablet: Apple iOS
Ed. .... Rick Green
Mechanical Specifications: Type page 13 x 12; E - 6 cols, 1 5/6, 1/4 between; A - 6 cols, 1 5/6, 1/4 between; C - 10 cols, 1 1/2, 1/4 between. Equipment & Software: Hardware — APP/Mac G3; Presses — MHI, MAN, Uniset; Software — QPS/QuarkXPress 4.0, Microsoft/Word 98, Adobe/Photoshop 5.0, Adobe/Illustrator 8.0.
Delivery Method: Carrier
Areas Served: 07405, 07420, 07440, 07442, 07444, 07456, 07421, 07435, 07457, 07465, 07480

CALDWELL

THE PROGRESS (THUR)

6 Brookside Ave, Caldwell, NJ, 07006-5604, Essex, USA; gen tel (973) 978-4809; gen fax (973) 933-2247; disp adv e-mail advertising@Newjerseyhills.com; class adv e-mail classified@recordernewspapers.com; ed e-mail lgreenspan@Newjerseyhills.com; web site www.theprogressnj.com
Circulation: 5,900pd,; Sworn/Estimate/Non-Audited
Advertising rate: Open inch rate $13.13
Established: 1911
Group: New Jersey Hills Media Group
Pub... Steven Parker
Circ. Mgr...................................... Mary Carroll
Lifestyles Ed. .... Rita Annan-Brady
Elizabeth Parker
Reporter .... Megan Crouse
Advertising representative........... Robert Corio
Advertising representative..Theresa Caporizzo
Ed. .... Russ Crespolini
Mechanical Specifications: Type page 13 x 21 1/2; E - 6 cols, 2 1/16, 1/8 between; A - 6 cols, 2 1/16, 1/8 between; C - 6 cols, 2 1/16, 1/8 between.
Delivery Method: Mail, Newsstand, Racks
Areas Served: 07006 07021 07068 07004

CHERRY HILL

PHILADELPHIA WEEKLY (WED)

2 Executive Campus, Ste 400, Cherry Hill, NJ, 08002-4102, Philadelphia, USA; gen tel (215) 563-7400; adv tel (215) 563-7400 ext. 163; gen fax (215) 563-6799; disp adv e-mail dsimms@philadelphiaweekly.com; class adv e-mail jmaguire@philadelphiaweekly.com; ed e-mail abarbalios@philadelphiaweekly.com; web site www.philadelphiaweekly.com
Circulation: 9pd, 62,949fr; VAC
Advertising rate: Open inch rate $45.00
Established: 1971
Group: Review Publishing
Digital Platform - Mobile: Apple, Android, Blackberry
Digital Platform - Tablet: Apple iOS, Android, Windows 7, Blackberry Tablet OS
Pub... John C. Gallo
Adv. Mgr.................................... Deidre Simms
Mng. Ed............................ Anastasia Barbalios
Delivery Method: Mail, Newsstand, Carrier, Racks
Areas Served: 19145, 19146, 19147, 19148

SOUTH PHILLY REVIEW (THUR)

2 Executive Campus, Ste 400, Cherry Hill, NJ, 08002-4102, Camden, USA; gen tel (215) 336-2500; adv tel (215) 336-2500 ext. 129; ed tel (215) 336-2500 ext. 121; gen fax (215) 336-1112; disp adv e-mail dtangi@southphillyreview.com; class adv e-mail epuggi@southphillyreview.com; ed e-mail bgelman@southphillyreview.com; web site www.southphillyreview.com
Circulation: 30pd, 56,555fr; CVC
Advertising rate: 1/16 Pg $190.00; 1/12 Pg $248.00; 1/8 Pg $369.00
Established: 1947
Group: Review Publishing
Digital Platform - Mobile: Apple, Android, Blackberry
Digital Platform - Tablet: Apple iOS, Android, Windows 7, Blackberry Tablet OS
Pub./COO .... John C. Gallo
Adv. Mgr.. Daniel Tangi
Circ. Mgr .... Cathy Semeraro Ed. Joseph Myers
Prod. Mgr. .... Holly Siemon
Delivery Method: Mail, Newsstand, Carrier, Racks
Areas Served: 19145, 19146, 19147, 19148

CLIFTON

CLIFTON JOURNAL (FRI)

777 Passaic Ave, Ste 575, Clifton, NJ, 07012-1873, Passaic, USA; gen tel (973) 778-2500; adv tel (973) 569-7269; ed tel (973) 569-7100; disp adv e-mail adhelp@northjersey.com; class adv e-mail marketplace@northjersey.com; ed e-mail newsroom@northjersey.com; web site www.northjersey.com
Circulation: 0pd, 31,542fr; AAM
Advertising rate: Open inch rate $15.50
Established: 1917
Group: North Jersey Media Group Inc.
Ed. .... Rick Green
Delivery Method: Carrier
Areas Served: 07011, 07012, 07013, 07014

COLLINGSWOOD

THE RETROSPECT (FRI)

732 Haddon Ave, Collingswood, NJ, 08108-3712, Camden, USA; gen tel (856) 854-1400; gen fax (856) 854-8790; disp adv e-mail publisher@theretrospect.com; class adv e-mail graphics@theretrospect.com; ed e-mail editor@theretrospect.com; web site theretrospect.com
Circulation: 5,500pd, 384fr; Sworn/Estimate/Non-Audited
Advertising rate: Open inch rate $14
Established: 1902
Pub... Brett Ainsworth
Bus .... Susan Ainsworth
Mechanical Specifications: Type page 10 x 16; A - 5 cols, 2, between; C - 6 cols, 1 1/2, between.Equipment & Software: Hardware — APP/Mac G5; Software — Adobe/InDesign.
Delivery Method: Mail, Newsstand, Racks
Areas Served: 08108, 08107, 08106, 08033, 08035

CRESSKILL

BOGOTA BULLETIN (FRI)

210 Knickerbocker Rd, Cresskill, NJ, 07626-1801, Bergen, USA; gen tel (201) 894-6700; adv tel (973) 569-7269; ed tel (973) 569-

7100; disp adv e-mail adhelp@northjersey.com; class adv e-mail marketplace@northjersey.com; ed e-mail newsroom@northjersey.com; web site http://www.northjersey.com/bogota/
Circulation: 638fr; AAM
Established: 2007
Group: North Jersey Community Newspapers
Ed. .... Rick Green
Delivery Method: Carrier

CLIFFSIDE PARK CITIZEN (FRI)

210 Knickerbocker Rd, Cresskill, NJ, 07626-1801, Bergen, USA; gen tel (201) 894-6700; adv tel (973) 569-7269; ed tel (973) 569-7100; disp adv e-mail adhelp@northjersey.com; class adv e-mail marketplace@northjersey.com; ed e-mail newsroom@northjersey.com; web site www.northjersey.com
Circulation: 10,618fr; AAM
Advertising rate: Open inch rate $15.45
Established: 2006
Group: North Jersey Media Group
Ed. .... Rick Green
Delivery Method: Carrier
Areas Served: Cliffside Park, NJ

EDGEWATER VIEW (FRI)

210 Knickerbocker Rd, Cresskill, NJ, 07626-1801, Bergen, USA; gen tel (201) 894-6700; adv tel (973) 569-7269; ed tel (973) 569-7100; disp adv e-mail adhelp@northjersey.com; class adv e-mail marketplace@northjersey.com; ed e-mail newsroom@northjersey.com; web site www.northjersey.com/edgewater
Circulation: 6,279fr; AAM
Advertising rate: Open inch rate $14.63
Established: 2004
Group: North Jersey Media Group Inc.
Ed. .... Rick Green
Areas Served: 7020

ENGLEWOOD SUBURBANITE (THUR)

210 Knickerbocker Rd, Cresskill, NJ, 07626-1801, Bergen, USA; gen tel (201) 894-6700; adv tel (973) 569-7269; ed tel (973) 569-7100; disp adv e-mail adhelp@northjersey.com; class adv e-mail marketplace@northjersey.com; ed e-mail newsroom@northjersey.com; web site www.northjersey.com
Circulation: 6,435fr; AAM
Group: North Jersey Media Group Inc.
Ed. .... Rick Green
Delivery Method: Mail

FORT LEE SUBURBANITE (FRI)

210 Knickerbocker Rd, Cresskill, NJ, 07626-1801, Bergen, USA; gen tel (201) 894-6700; adv tel (973) 569-7269; ed tel (973) 569-7100; disp adv e-mail adhelp@northjersey.com; class adv e-mail marketplace@northjersey.com; ed e-mail newsroom@northjersey.com; web site www.northjersey.com/fortlee
Circulation: 17,288fr; AAM
Advertising rate: Open inch rate $17.50
Established: 2003
Group: North Jersey Media Group Inc.
Digital Platform - Mobile: Apple, Android
Digital Platform - Tablet: Apple iOS, Android
Ed. .... Rick Green
Delivery Method: Mail, Racks
Areas Served: Bergen County

HACKENSACK CHRONICLE (FRI)

210 Knickerbocker Rd, Cresskill, NJ, 07626-1801, Bergen, USA; gen tel (201) 894-6700; adv tel (201) 894-6722; ed tel (973) 569-7100; disp adv e-mail adhelp@northjersey.com; class adv e-mail marketplace@northjersey.com; ed e-mail newsroom@northjersey.com; web site www.northjersey.com/hackensack
Circulation: 20,139fr; AAM
Advertising rate: Open inch rate $7.25
Established: 2005
Group: North Jersey Media Group Inc.
Digital Platform - Mobile: Apple, Android
Digital Platform - Tablet: Apple iOS, Android
Ed. .... Rick Green
Delivery Method: Mail, Racks
Areas Served: Bergen County

LEONIA LIFE (FRI)

210 Knickerbocker Rd, Cresskill, NJ, 07626-1801, Bergen, USA; gen tel (201) 894-6700; adv tel (973) 569-7269; ed tel (973) 569-7100; disp adv e-mail adhelp@northjersey.com; class adv e-mail marketplace@northjersey.com; ed e-mail newsroom@northjersey.com; web site www.northjersey.com/leonia
Circulation: 3,354fr; AAM
Advertising rate: Open inch rate $7.95
Established: 2005
Group: North Jersey Community Newspapers
Digital Platform - Mobile: Apple, Android
Digital Platform - Tablet: Apple iOS, Android
Ed. .... Rick Green
Delivery Method: Mail, Racks
Areas Served: Bergen County

LITTLE FERRY LOCAL (FRI)

210 Knickerbocker Rd, Cresskill, NJ, 07626-1801, Bergen, USA; gen tel (201) 894-6700; adv tel (973) 569-7269; ed tel (973) 569-7100; disp adv e-mail adhelp@northjersey.com; class adv e-mail marketplace@northjersey.com; ed e-mail newsroom@northjersey.com; web site www.northjersey.com
Circulation: 879fr; AAM
Advertising rate: Open inch rate $13.00
Established: 2007
Group: North Jersey Community Newspapers
Digital Platform - Mobile: Apple, Android
Digital Platform - Tablet: Apple iOS, Android
Ed. .... Rick Green
Delivery Method: Mail, Racks
Areas Served: Bergen County

NORTHERN VALLEY SUBURBANITE (THUR)

210 Knickerbocker Rd, Cresskill, NJ, 07626-1801, Bergen, USA; gen tel (201) 894-6700; adv tel (973) 569-7269; ed tel (973) 569-7100; disp adv e-mail adhelp@northjersey.com; class adv e-mail marketplace@northjersey.com; ed e-mail newsroom@northjersey.com; web site www.northjersey.com
Circulation: 0pd, 13,116fr; AAM
Advertising rate: Open inch rate $22.28
Group: North Jersey Media Group Inc.
Ed. .... Rick Green
Mechanical Specifications: Type page 9 2/3 x ; E - 5 cols, 1 5/6, 1/6 between; A - 5 cols, 1 5/6, 1/6 between; C - 10 cols, 1 2/28, 1/6 between.Equipment & Software: Hardware — APP/Mac G3, PC; Presses — MAN, Uniset, MHI; Software — QPS/QuarkXPress 4.0, Microsoft/Word 98, Adobe/Photoshop 5.0, Adobe/Illustrator 8.0.
Areas Served: 07620, 07624, 07626, 07627, 07631, 07632, 07640, 07641, 07647

RIDGEFIELD PARK PATRIOT (FRI)

210 Knickerbocker Rd, Cresskill, NJ, 07626-1801, Bergen, USA; gen tel (201) 894-6700; adv tel (973) 569-7269; ed tel (973) 569-7100; disp adv e-mail adhelp@northjersey.com; class adv e-mail marketplace@northjersey.com; ed e-mail newsroom@northjersey.com; web site www.northjersey.com
Circulation: 978fr; AAM
Advertising rate: Open inch rate $13.00
Established: 2006
Group: North Jersey Community Newspapers
Digital Platform - Mobile: Apple, Android
Digital Platform - Tablet: Apple iOS, Android
Ed. .... Rick Green
Delivery Method: Mail, Racks
Areas Served: Bergen County

TEANECK SUBURBANITE (THUR)

210 Knickerbocker Rd, Cresskill, NJ, 07626-1801, Bergen, USA; gen tel (201) 894-6700; adv tel (973) 569-7269; ed tel (973) 569-7100; disp adv e-mail adhelp@northjersey.com; class adv e-mail marketplace@northjersey.com; ed e-mail newsroom@northjersey.com; web site www.northjersey.com/teaneck
Circulation: 0pd, 13,651fr; AAM
Advertising rate: Open inch rate $24.50
Group: North Jersey Media Group Inc.
Ed. .... Rick Green
Delivery Method: Carrier
Areas Served: 07666

TENAFLY SUBURBANITE (THUR)

210 Knickerbocker Rd, Cresskill, NJ, 07626-1801, Bergen, USA; gen tel (201) 894-6700; adv tel (973) 569-7269; ed tel (973) 569-7100; disp adv e-mail adhelp@northjersey.com; class adv e-mail marketplace@northjersey.com; ed e-mail newsroom@northjersey.com; web site www.northjersey.com
Circulation: 4,267fr; CAC
Group: North Jersey Media Group Inc.
Ed. .... Rick Green
Delivery Method: Mail

TWIN-BORO NEWS (THUR)

210 Knickerbocker Rd, Ste 5, Cresskill, NJ, 07626-1801, Bergen, USA; gen tel (201) 894-6700; adv tel (973) 569-7269; ed tel (973) 569-7100; disp adv e-mail adhelp@northjersey.com; class adv e-mail marketplace@northjersey.com; ed e-mail newsroom@northjersey.com; web site www.northjersey.com
Circulation: 0pd, 15,427fr; AAM
Advertising rate: Open inch rate $17.69
Group: North Jersey Media Group Inc.
Pub. .... Janice Friedman
Ed. .... William Slossar
Vice Pres., Prodn. .... Glenn Garvie
Adv. Mgr. .... Ellen Zitis
Mechanical Specifications: Type page 9 2/3 x 12.75; E - 5 cols, 1 5/6, 1/4 between; A - 5 cols, 1 5/6, 1/4 between; C - 5 cols, 1 5/6, 1/4 between.Equipment & Software: Hardware — APP/Mac G3, PC; Presses — MAN, Uniset, MHI; Software — QPS/QuarkXPress 4.0, Adobe/Photoshop 5.0, Adobe/Illustrator 8.0, Microsoft/Word 98.
Delivery Method: Carrier
Areas Served: 07621, 07628, 07646

EGG HARBOR TOWNSHIP

BRIGANTINE BEACHCOMBER (FRI)

206 W Parkway Dr, Egg Harbor Township, NJ, 08234-5106, Atlantic, USA; gen tel (609) 383-8994; disp adv e-mail adpro@thebeachcombernews.com; class adv e-mail adpro@thebeachcombernews.com; web site http://www.thebeachcombernews.com/
Circulation: 3,450fr; CAC
Advertising rate: Open inch rate $16.00
Group: Catamaran Media
Pub. .... Marc Blum
Adv. Dir. .... Steve Mehl
Ed. .... Bill Barlow
Delivery Method: Mail

THE CURRENT (WED)

206 W Parkway Dr, Egg Harbor Township, NJ, 08234-5106, Atlantic, USA; gen tel (609) 383-8994; gen fax (609) 383-0056; disp adv e-mail current@shorenewstoday.com; web site www.shorenewstoday.com
Circulation: 13,957fr; CAC
Advertising rate: Open inch rate $16.00
Group: Catamaran MediaEditions: (6) The Current of Downbeach (8,336); The Current of Egg Harbor Township (13,975); The Current of Galloway/Port Republic (11,238); The Current of Hamilton/Mays Landing (8,077); The Current of Linwood, Northfield & Somers Point (10,073); The Current
Ed. .... Bill Barlow
Mechanical Specifications: Type page 10 x 12 1/2; E - 6 cols, 1 7/12, 1/6 between; A - 6 cols, 1 9/16, 1/6 between; C - 6 cols, 1 1/4, 1/6 between.Equipment & Software: Hardware — PC; Software — Adobe/PageMaker, Microsoft/Word, Adobe/Illustrator, Adobe/Photoshop.
Delivery Method: Mail, Newsstand
Areas Served: 08232 08234 08221 08225 08244 08402 08403 08406 08206 08241 08220 08240 08213 08201 08232 08215 08330

ELMER

ELMER TIMES (THUR)

21 State St, Elmer, NJ, 08318-2145, Salem, USA; gen tel (856) 358-6171; disp adv e-mail elmertimes@hotmail.com
Circulation: 1,900pd,; Sworn/Estimate/Non-Audited
Advertising rate: Open inch rate $5.50
Established: 1885
Pub. .... Mark Foster
Ed. .... Prestons Foster
Mechanical Specifications: Type page 13 3/4 x 21 1/2; E - 8 cols, 1 1/2, 1/4 between; A - 8 cols, 1 1/2, 1/4 between; C - 8 cols, 1 1/2, 1/4 between.
Delivery Method: Mail, Newsstand
Areas Served: 8318

FAIR LAWN

COMMUNITY NEWS (THUR)

12-38 River Rd, Fair Lawn, NJ, 07410-1802, Bergen, USA; gen tel (201) 791-8994; gen fax (201) 794-3259; disp adv e-mail communitynews@northjersey.com; web site http://archive.northjersey.com/community-news
Circulation: 0pd, 66,888fr; AAM
Advertising rate: Open inch rate $16.45
Established: 1948
Adv. Mgr. .... Ellen Zitis
Pub. .... Janice Friedman
Ed. .... Richard Mardekian

THE GAZETTE (THUR)

12-38 River Rd, Fair Lawn, NJ, 07410-1802, Bergen, USA; gen tel (201) 791-8994; adv tel (973) 569-7263; gen fax (201) 794-3259; adv fax (973) 569-7259; disp adv e-mail thegazette@northjersey.com
Circulation: 0pd, 15,918fr; AAM
Advertising rate: Open inch rate $19.44
Established: 1948
Group: North Jersey Media Group
Ed. .... Richard Mardekian
Ad. Director .... Ellen Zitis
Pub. .... Janice Friedman
Delivery Method: Carrier
Areas Served: Hawthorne
Haledon
Prospect Park
North Haledon

FLEMINGTON

HUNTERDON COUNTY DEMOCRAT (THUR)

200 State Route 31, Ste 200, Flemington, NJ, 08822-5819, Hunterdon, USA; gen tel (908) 782-4747; gen fax (908) 782-6572; disp adv e-mail Akratzer@express-times.com; web site www.njnpublishing.info
Circulation: 8,786pd, 8,634fr; AAM
Advertising rate: Open inch rate $28.98
Established: 1847
Group: Advance Publications, Inc.
Circ. Mgr. .... Judith A. Morgan
Mng. Ed. .... Rick Epstein
Ed. .... Jay Langley
Adv. Dir. .... Al Kratzer
VP, Circ. .... Dennis Carletta
Pres./Pub. .... Joseph Gioioso
Mechanical Specifications: Type page 13 x 21; E - 6 cols, 2 1/16, 1/8 between; A - 6 cols, 2 1/16, 1/8 between; C - 9 cols, 1 3/8, 1 between.
Areas Served: Hunterdon County

HUNTERDON OBSERVER (SAT)

8 Minneakoning Rd, Flemington, NJ, 08822-5725, Hunterdon, USA; gen tel (908) 782-4747; gen fax (908) 782-6572; disp adv e-mail news@hcdemocrat.com; web site www.nj.com
Circulation: 48,256fr; Sworn/Estimate/Non-Audited
Advertising rate: Open inch rate $19.95
Established: 1987
Group: NJN Publishing
Circ. Mgr. .... Judy Morgan
Ed. .... Jay Langley
Mng. Ed. .... Rick Epstein
Pub./Adv. Mgr. .... Eileen Bickel
Mechanical Specifications: Type page 10 13/16

x 13; E - 5 cols, 2 1/16, 1/8 between; A - 5 cols, 2 1/16, 1/8 between; C - 7 cols, 1 3/8, 1/8 between.
Areas Served: Annandale, Asbury, Baptistown, Bloomsbury, Califon, Clinton, Flemington, Frenchtown, Glen Gardner, Hampton, High Bridge, Lambertville, Lebanon, Little York, Milford, Oldwick, Pittstown, Quakertown, Readington, Ringoes, Rosemont, Sergeantsville, Stockton, Stanton, Three Bridges, Whitehouse, Whitehouse Station

STAR-GAZETTE (THUR)
8 Minneakoning Rd, Flemington, NJ, 08822-5725, Hunterdon, USA; gen tel (908) 782-6572; gen fax (908) 782-6572; disp adv e-mail news@hcdemocrat.com; web site www.nj.com
Circulation: 336pd, 4fr; Sworn/Estimate/Non-Audited
Advertising rate: Open inch rate $21.00
Group: Advance Publications, Inc.
Exec. Ed....Craig Turpin
Mechanical Specifications: Type page 13 x 21; E - 6 cols, 2 1/16, 1/6 between; A - 6 cols, 2 1/16, 1/6 between; C - 10 cols, 1 1/2, 1/6 between.Equipment & Software: Hardware — APP/Macs, PCs; Software — QPS/QuarkXPress.

THE WARREN REPORTER (FRI)
8 Minneakoning Rd, Flemington, NJ, 08822-5725, Hunterdon, USA; gen tel (908) 782-4747; gen fax (908) 782-6572; disp adv e-mail ourtown@lehighvalleylive.com; web site www.nj.com/warrenreporter/
Circulation: 52,934fr; CVC
Advertising rate: Open inch rate $25.00
Established: 1968
Group: Advance Publications, Inc.
Adv. Dir....Robin Von Ohlsen
Exec. Ed....Craig Turpin
Ed....Kevin Lechiski
News Ed....Jessica King
Prodn. Mgr....Linda Zetterberg
Areas Served: Allamuchy, Belvidere, Broadway, Great Meadows, Hackettstown, Hope, Johnsonburg, Oxford, Phillipsburg, Port Murray, Stewartsville, Washington

GLOUCESTER CITY

GLOUCESTER CITY NEWS (THUR)
34 S Broadway, Gloucester City, NJ, 08030-1710, Camden, USA; gen tel (856) 456-1199; gen fax (856) 456-1330; disp adv e-mail gcneditor@verizon.net; class adv e-mail gcnads@verizon.net; web site www.gloucitynews.com
Circulation: 2,900pd, 200fr; USPS
Advertising rate: Open inch rate $7.00
Established: 1927
Pub./Ed....Albert J. Countryman
Mechanical Specifications: Type page 11 x 16; E - 6 cols, 1 7/12, 1/12 between; A - 6 cols, 1 7/12, 1/12 between; C - 6 cols, 1 7/12, 1/12 between.Equipment & Software: Hardware — Mk; Software — Mk.
Delivery Method: Mail, Newsstand, Racks
Areas Served: 08030, 08031, 08059, 08093, 08078, 08035

HADDONFIELD

BURLINGTON TOWNSHIP SUN (WED)
108 Kings Hwy E, Haddonfield, NJ, 08033-2099, Camden, USA; gen tel (856) 779-3800; adv tel (856) 528-4844; disp adv e-mail jgallo@newspapermediagroup.com; web site burlingtontownshipsun.com
Group: Newspaper Media Group
Adv. Dir.... Arlene Reyes
Mktg. Dir....Angela Smith

CHERRY HILL SUN (WED)
108 Kings Hwy E, Haddonfield, NJ, 08033-2099, Camden, USA; gen tel (856) 779-3800; adv tel (856) 528-4844; disp adv e-mail jgallo@newspapermediagroup.com; web site cherryhillsun.com
Group: Newspaper Media Group
Adv. Dir.... Arlene Reyes
Mktg. Dir....Angela Smith

CINNAMINSON SUN (WED)
108 Kings Hwy E, Haddonfield, NJ, 08033-2099, Camden, USA; gen tel (856) 779-3800; adv tel (856) 528-4844; disp adv e-mail jgallo@newspapermediagroup.com; web site cinnaminsonsun.com
Group: Newspaper Media Group
Adv. Dir.... Arlene Reyes
Mktg. Dir....Angela Smith

HADDONFIELD SUN (WED)
108 Kings Hwy E, Ste 300, Haddonfield, NJ, 08033-2099, Camden, USA; gen tel (856) 779-3800; adv tel (856) 528-4844; disp adv e-mail jgallo@newspapermediagroup.com; web site haddonfieldsun.com
Group: Newspaper Media Group
Adv. Dir.... Arlene Reyes
Mktg. Dir....Angela Smith

MARLTON SUN (WED)
108 Kings Hwy E, Haddonfield, NJ, 08033-2099, Camden, USA; gen tel (856) 779-3800; adv tel (856) 528-4844; disp adv e-mail jgallo@newspapermediagroup.com; web site marltonsun.com
Group: Newspaper Media Group
Adv. Dir.... Arlene Reyes
Mktg. Dir....Angela Smith

MEDFORD SUN (WED)
108 Kings Hwy E, Haddonfield, NJ, 08033-2099, Camden, USA; gen tel (856) 779-3800; adv tel (856) 528-4844; disp adv e-mail jgallo@newspapermediagroup.com; web site medfordsun.com
Group: Newspaper Media Group
Adv. Dir.... Arlene Reyes
Mktg. Dir....Angela Smith

MOORESTOWN SUN (WED)
108 Kings Hwy E, Haddonfield, NJ, 08033-2099, Camden, USA; gen tel (856) 779-3800; adv tel (856) 528-4844; disp adv e-mail jgallo@newspapermediagroup.com; web site moorestownsun.com
Group: Newspaper Media Group
Adv. Dir.... Arlene Reyes
Mktg. Dir....Angela Smith

MT. LAUREL SUN (WED)
108 Kings Hwy E, Haddonfield, NJ, 08033-2099, Camden, USA; gen tel (856) 779-3800; adv tel (856) 528-4844; disp adv e-mail jgallo@newspapermediagroup.com; web site mtlaurelsun.com
Group: Newspaper Media Group
Adv. Dir.... Arlene Reyes
Mktg. Dir....Angela Smith

PALMYRA SUN (WED)
108 Kings Hwy E, Haddonfield, NJ, 08033-2099, Camden, USA; gen tel (856) 779-3800; adv tel (856) 528-4844; disp adv e-mail jgallo@newspapermediagroup.com; web site palmyrasun.com
Group: Newspaper Media Group
Adv. Dir.... Arlene Reyes
Mktg. Dir....Angela Smith

SHAMONG SUN (WED)
108 Kings Hwy E, Haddonfield, NJ, 08033-2099, Camden, USA; gen tel (856) 779-3800; adv tel (856) 528-4844; disp adv e-mail jgallo@newspapermediagroup.com; web site shamongsun.com
Group: Newspaper Media Group
Adv. Dir.... Arlene Reyes
Mktg. Dir....Angela Smith

SICKLERVILLE SUN (WED)
108 Kings Hwy E, Haddonfield, NJ, 08033-2099, Camden, USA; gen tel (856) 779-3800; adv tel (856) 528-4844; disp adv e-mail jgallo@newspapermediagroup.com; web site sicklervillesun.com
Group: Newspaper Media Group
Adv. Dir.... Arlene Reyes
Mktg. Dir....Angela Smith

TABERNACLE SUN (WED)
108 Kings Hwy E, Haddonfield, NJ, 08033-2099, Camden, USA; gen tel (856) 779-3800; adv tel (856) 528-4844; disp adv e-mail jgallo@newspapermediagroup.com; web site tabernaclesun.com
Group: Newspaper Media Group
Adv. Dir.... Arlene Reyes
Mktg. Dir....Angela Smith

THE BERLIN SUN (WED)
108 Kings Hwy E, Ste 300, Haddonfield, NJ, 08033-2099, Camden, USA; gen tel (856) 779-3800; adv tel (856) 528-4844; disp adv e-mail jgallo@newspapermediagroup.com; web site theberlinsun.com
Group: Newspaper Media Group
Adv. Dir.... Arlene Reyes
Mktg. Dir....Angela Smith

VOORHEES SUN (WED)
108 Kings Hwy E, Haddonfield, NJ, 08033-2099, Camden, USA; gen tel (856) 779-3800; adv tel (856) 528-4844; disp adv e-mail jgallo@newspapermediagroup.com; web site voorheessun.com
Group: Newspaper Media Group
Adv. Dir.... Arlene Reyes
Mktg. Dir....Angela Smith

HAMMONTON

ATLANTIC COUNTY RECORD (WED)
115 12th St, Hammonton, NJ, 08037-1521, USA; gen tel (609) 646-0561; gen fax (800) 489-4464
Circulation: 796pd,; Sworn/Estimate/Non-Audited
Advertising rate: Open inch rate $10.16
Group: Gannett
Pub....Charles Nutt
Exec. Ed....Mark Leiser

MAINLAND JOURNAL (WED)
115 12th St, Hammonton, NJ, 08037-1521, USA; gen tel (609) 561-2300; gen fax (609) 567-2249
Circulation: 882pd,; Sworn/Estimate/Non-Audited
Advertising rate: Open inch rate $12.88
Group: Gannett
Adv. Dir....Joe Calchi
Exec. Ed....Mark Leiser

HASBROUCK HEIGHTS

THE OBSERVER (THUR)
PO Box 445, Hasbrouck Heights, NJ, 07604-0445, Bergen, USA; gen tel (201) 288-0333; disp adv e-mail theobsads@verizon.net; class adv e-mail theobsads@verizon.net; ed e-mail theobsnews@verizon.net
Circulation: 2,300pd,; Sworn/Estimate/Non-Audited
Advertising rate: Open inch rate $9.10
Established: 1925
Ed....Connie Doheny
Delivery Method: Mail

HILLSBOROUGH

HILLSBOROUGH BEACON (FRI)
421 US Highway 206, Hillsborough, NJ, 08844-5097, Somerset, USA; gen tel (609) 924-3244; ed tel (609) 874-2163; gen fax (609) 921-2714; adv fax (609) 921-2714; ed fax (609) 924-3842; disp adv e-mail SBriggin@centraljersey.com; ed e-mail amartins@centraljersey.com; web site www.hillsboroughbeacon.com
Circulation: 1,298pd, 2,038fr; Sworn/Estimate/Non-Audited
Advertising rate: Open inch rate $22.57
Established: 1955
Group: Newspaper Media Group
Pub....James B. Kilgore
Mgr Ed....Andrew Martins
Mechanical Specifications: Full page depth 21" 1/8" between
1 col 1.625"
2 col 3.360"
3 col 5.097"
4 col 6.833"
5 col 8.570"
6 col 10.305"

Equipment & Software: ; Presses — G/Community
Delivery Method: Mail, Newsstand, Racks
Areas Served: 08844

HOBOKEN

WEST NEW YORK/UNION CITY REPORTER (SUN)
1400 Washington St, Hoboken, NJ, 07030-9402, Hudson, USA; gen tel (201) 798-7800; gen fax (201) 798-0018; disp adv e-mail dunger@hudsonreporter.com; class adv e-mail classified@hudsonreporter.com; ed e-mail editorial@hudsonreporter.com; web site www.hudsonreporter.com
Circulation: 0pd, 2,285fr; CAC
Advertising rate: Open inch rate $19.60
Established: 1983
Group: Hudson Reporter Associates, Lp
Pub....Lucha M. Malato
Co-Pub....David S. Unger
Circ. Mgr....Roberto Lopez
Advertising Manager....Tish Kraszyk
Mechanical Specifications: Type page 10 3/8 x 13; E - 7 cols, 1 5/16, 1/8 between; A - 7 cols, 1 5/16, 1/8 between; C - 7 cols, 1 5/16, 1/8 between.Equipment & Software: Hardware — PC, APP/Mac; Software — Archetype/Corel Draw 4.0, QPS/QuarkXPress, Adobe/Photoshop, Adobe/Illustrator, Adobe/PageMaker.
Delivery Method: Carrier, Racks
Areas Served: West New York New Jersey

KINGSTON

TOWN TOPICS (WED)
4438 Route 27, Kingston, NJ, 08528-9613, Mercer, USA; gen tel (609) 924-2200; gen fax (609) 924-8818; disp adv e-mail robin.broomer@towntopics.com; class adv e-mail clasifieds@towntopics.com; ed e-mail editor@towntopics.com; web site www.towntopics.com - 1,946(views)
Circulation: 15,000fr; Sworn/Estimate/Non-Audited
Advertising rate: Open inch rate $16.30
Established: 1946
Ed....Lynn A. Smith
Mechanical Specifications: Type page 10 3/8 x 16; E - 6 cols, 1 5/8, between; A - 6 cols, 1 5/8, 1/12 between; C - 6 cols, 1 5/8, 1/12 between.Equipment & Software: Hardware — APP/Macs; Software — DTI/AdSpeed 4.0.
Areas Served: Princeton Borough, Princeton Township, Belle Mead, Hillsborough, Hopewell, Pennington, Skillman

LAWRENCE

BORDENTOWN CURRENT (MTHLY)
15 Princess Rd, Ste K, Lawrence, NJ, 08648-2301, Mercer, USA; gen tel (609)396-1511; adv tel (609)396-1511 x110; ed tel (609)396-1511 x121; disp adv e-mail tfritts@mercerspace.com; ed e-mail ssciarrotta@mercerspace.com; web site bordentowncurrent.com
Circulation: 8,508fr; CVC
Ed.... Samantha Sciarrotta
Areas Served: 08648

COMMUNITY NEWS SERVICE - HAMILTON POST (MTHLY)
15 Princess Rd, Ste K, Lawrence, NJ, 08648-2301, Mercer, USA; gen tel (609)396-1511; gen fax (609)844-0180; disp adv e-mail events@mercerspace.com; web site mercer-space.com
Circulation: 42,101fr; CVC
Established: 1982
Ed. .... Rob Anthes
Areas Served: 08648

LAWRENCE GAZETTE - COMMUNITY NEWS SERVICE (MTHLY)
15 Princess Rd, Ste K, Lawrence, NJ, 08648-2301, Mercer, USA; gen tel (609)396-1511; gen fax (609)844-0180; ed e-mail news@mercerspace.com; web site mercerspace.com
Circulation: 16,856fr; CVC
Ed. .... Samantha Sciarrotta
Areas Served: 08648

LINCOLN PARK

LIFE & LEISURE (THUR)
234 Main St, Ste 2, Lincoln Park, NJ, 07035-1787, Morris, USA; gen tel (973) 696-8008; adv tel (973) 865-8000; ed tel (973) 865-8000; gen fax (973) 556-1991; disp adv e-mail joe@lifeandleisurenj.com; web site www.lifeandleisurenj.com
Circulation: 50,261fr; CVC
Advertising rate: Open inch rate $60.00
Established: 2003Editions: (49,524) zone 1, zone 2 zone 3
Digital Platform - Mobile: Apple, Android
Digital Platform - Tablet: Apple iOS, Android
Pub./Adv. Mgr./Circ, Mgr............. Joe Pellegrino
Prod. Mgr..................................... Robin Banta
Classified Adv. Mgr.................... Kathleen Todd
Delivery Method: Mail
Areas Served: 07470,07035,07440,07444,07045,07403,07457,07405,07442

LITTLE FALLS

SOUTH BERGENITE (THUR)
PO Box 471, Little Falls, NJ, 07424-0471, Passaic, USA; gen tel (201) 933-1166; adv tel (800) 472-0158; gen fax (201) 933-5496; adv fax (973) 569-7440; disp adv e-mail adhelp@northjersey.com; web site www.northjersey.com/southbergen
Circulation: 0pd, 30,071fr; AAM
Established: 1970
Group: North Jersey Media Group Inc.
Ed. .... Rick Green
Mechanical Specifications: Type page 13 x 21; E - 6 cols, 1 5/6, 1/4 between; A - 6 cols, 2 1/12, 1/6 between; C - 6 cols, 1 5/6, 1/4 between.Equipment & Software: Hardware — APP/Mac G3, PC; Presses — MAN, Uniset, MHI; Software — QPS/QuarkXPress 4.0, Microsoft/Word 98, Adobe/Photoshop 5.0, Adobe/Illustrator 8.0.
Areas Served: 07072, 07073, 07071, 07070, 07032

LIVINGSTON

WEST ESSEX TRIBUNE (THUR)
495 S Livingston Ave, Livingston, NJ, 07039-4327, Essex, USA; gen tel (973) 992-1771; gen fax (973) 992-7015; disp adv e-mail tribune.jenny@gmail.com; class adv e-mail WETribune@gmail.com; ed e-mail West-EssexTribune@gmail.com; web site www.westessextribune.net
Circulation: 5,213pd, 197fr; Sworn/Estimate/Non-Audited
Advertising rate: Open inch rate $14.15
Established: 1929
Digital Platform - Mobile: Apple, Android, Windows, Blackberry
Digital Platform - Tablet: Apple iOS, Android, Windows 7, Blackberry Tablet OS, Kindle, Nook, Kindle Fire
Pub.................................Jennifer Cone Chciuk
Mng. Ed............................ Christine Sablynski
Prodn. Mgr. ....Karen Trachtenberg
Editor .... Michelle Bent
Mechanical Specifications: Type page 13 x 21; E - 6 cols, 2, between; A - 6 cols, 2, between; C - 7 cols, 1 3/4, between.Equipment & Software: Hardware — PC; Software — Adobe CS3
Delivery Method: Mail, Newsstand
Areas Served: 07039

MALAGA

THE SENTINEL OF GLOUCESTER COUNTY (THUR)
PO Box 367, 330 Oak Ave, Malaga, NJ, 08328-0903, Gloucester, USA; gen tel (856) 694-1600; gen fax (856) 694-0469; disp adv e-mail ftsentinel@comcast.net; web site www.thenjsentinel.com
Circulation: 1,200pd, 200fr; Sworn/Estimate/Non-Audited
Advertising rate: see website
Established: 1942
Owner/Ed................................... Cindy Merckx
Delivery Method: Mail, Newsstand
Areas Served: All of Gloucester County including Franklin, Elk, Monroe, Washington, Deptford, Mantua, West Deptford Townships, Newfield, Clayton, Glassboro, Pitman, Woodbury.

MANALAPAN

ATLANTICVILLE (THUR)
198 US Highway 9, Ste 100, Manalapan, NJ, 07726-3073, Monmouth, USA; gen tel (732) 358-5200; gen fax (732) 780-4678; disp adv e-mail gmsales@gmnews.com; ed e-mail aville@gmnews.com; web site www.gmnews.com
Circulation: 5pd, 17,595fr; CAC
Advertising rate: Full - $1,037; 1/2 - $584; 1/4 - $322; 1/8 - $188
Group: Newspaper Media Group
Mng. Ed....................................Gloria Stravelli
Delivery Method: Carrier
Areas Served: 07711 07712 07723 07724 07739 07740 07750 07755 07712 07757 07760 07764

EAST BRUNSWICK SENTINEL (THUR)
198 US Highway 9 Ste 100, Suite 100, Manalapan, NJ, 07726-3073, Monmouth, USA; gen tel (732) 358-5200; gen fax (732) 780-4678; disp adv e-mail gmsales@gmnews.com; ed e-mail ebsent@gmnews.com; web site www.gmnews.com
Circulation: 12pd, 32,428fr; CAC
Advertising rate: Full - $1,063; 1/2 - $620; 1/4 - $342; 1/8 - $193
Group: Newspaper Media Group
Pub...Ben Bannizzaro
Adv. Dir... Robert Waitt
Circ. Mgr......................................Debra Parana
Mng. Ed....................................Brian Donohue
Prodn. Mgr. ....Gene Lennon
Mechanical Specifications: Type page 10 x 13; E - 4 cols, 2 3/8, 1/6 between; A - 4 cols, 2 3/8, 1/6 between; C - 8 cols, 1 1/4, between. Equipment & Software: Hardware — APP/Power Mac 9500; Presses — Dev/Horizon 2400; Software — QPS/QuarkXPress 3.32, Adobe/Photoshop 4.0, Multi-Ad/Creator 4.01, Adobe/Illustrator 3.0.
Delivery Method: Carrier
Areas Served: 08816 08828 08831 08850 08882 08884

EDISON/NETUCHEN SENTINEL (WED)
198 US Highway 9, Ste 100, Manalapan, NJ, 07726-3073, Monmouth, USA; gen tel (732) 358-5200; gen fax (732) 780-4678; disp adv e-mail gmsales@gmnews.com; ed e-mail sentnorth@gmnews.com; web site www.gmnews.com
Circulation: 7pd, 24,239fr; CAC
Advertising rate: Full - $1,012; 1/2 - $569; 1/4 - $311; 1/8 - $178
Adv. Mgr..................................... Josef Ornegri
Circ. Mgr.....................................Kathy Herban
Ed. .... Gregory Bean
Mng. Ed.......................................Melissa Kress
Prodn. Mgr. ....Gene Lennon
Mechanical Specifications: Type page 10 x 13; E - 4 cols, 2 3/8, 1/6 between; A - 4 cols, 2 3/8, 1/6 between; C - 8 cols, 1 1/4, between. Equipment & Software: Hardware — APP/Power Mac 9500; Presses — Dev/Horizon 2400; Software — Multi-Ad/Creator 4.01, Adobe/Photoshop 4.0, QPS/QuarkXPress 3.32, Adobe/Illustrator 3.0.
Delivery Method: Carrier
Areas Served: 08817 08820 08837 08863 08840

EXAMINER (THUR)
198 US Highway 9 Ste 100, Suite 100, Manalapan, NJ, 07726-3073, Monmouth, USA; gen tel (732) 358-5200; gen fax (732) 780-4678; disp adv e-mail gmsales@gmnews.com; ed e-mail examiner@gmnews.com; web site www.centraljersey.com
Circulation: 4pd, 7,263fr; CAC
Advertising rate: Full - $533; 1/2 - $306; 1/4 - $172; 1/8 - $106
Group: Newspaper Media Group
Digital Platform - Mobile: Android, Windows
Pub.. Joe Eisele
Delivery Method: Carrier
Areas Served: 08501 08510 08514 08535 07726

NEWS TRANSCRIPT (WED)
198 US Highway 9, Ste 100, Manalapan, NJ, 07726-3073, Monmouth, USA; gen tel (732) 358-5210; gen fax (732) 780-4678; disp adv e-mail gmsales@gmnews.com; ed e-mail gmntnews@gmnews.com; web site www.gmnews.com
Circulation: 13pd, 38,917fr; CAC
Advertising rate: Full - $1,135; 1/2 - $698; 1/4 - $409; 1/8 - $214
Group: Newspaper Media Group
Pub.. Rick Feinblatt
Circ. Mgr....................................Debra Parana
Mng. Ed................................ Mark R. Rosman
Dir., Prodn.................................Gene Lennon
Mechanical Specifications: Type page 10 x 13; E - 4 cols, 2 3/8, 1/6 between; A - 4 cols, 2 3/8, 1/6 between; C - 8 cols, 1 1/4, between. Equipment & Software: Hardware — APP/Power Mac 9500; Presses — Dev/Horizon 2400; Software — Multi-Ad/Creator 4.01, Adobe/Photoshop 4.0, QPS/QuarkXPress 3.32, Adobe/Illustrator 3.0.
Delivery Method: Carrier
Areas Served: 07722 07726 07728 07731 07726 07746 07751

NORTH/SOUTH BRUNSWICK SENTINEL (THUR)
198 US Highway 9 Ste 100, Suite 100, Manalapan, NJ, 07726-3073, Monmouth, USA; gen tel (732) 358-5200; gen fax (732) 780-4678; disp adv e-mail gmsales@gmnews.com; ed e-mail nssent@gmnews.com; web site www.gmnews.com
Circulation: 8pd, 15,884fr; CAC
Advertising rate: Full - $919; 1/2 - $522; 1/4 - $291; 1/8 - $167
Group: Newspaper Media Group
Digital Platform - Mobile: Apple, Android, Windows
Digital Platform - Tablet: Apple iOS, Android, Windows 7
Adv. Director ....Robert D. Waitt
Circ. Dir...................................Richard Klypka
Ed. .... Mark Rosman
Prodn. Mgr. ....Gene Lennon
Publisher.................................Ben Cannizzaro
Mechanical Specifications: Type page 10" x 11.25" - 4 cols, 1col - 2 3/8", 2col - 4 4/8", 3col - 7 3/8"1/6, 4col - 10"Equipment & Software: Hardware — HP Servers, Power Mac, X serve; Presses — Printed by North Jersey Media Group in Rockaway N.J.; Software — QPS/QuarkXPress 7.3, Adobe/Photoshop CS 6, Multi-Ad/Creator 4.0, Adobe/Illustrator CS 6.
Delivery Method: Carrier
Areas Served: 08512 08810 08540 08824 08852 08902

SUBURBAN (THUR)
198 US Highway 9 Ste 100, Suite 100, Manalapan, NJ, 07726-3073, Monmouth, USA; gen tel (732) 358-5200; gen fax (732) 780-4678; disp adv e-mail gmsales@gmnews.com; ed e-mail ebsent@gmnews.com; web site www.gmnews.com
Circulation: 9pd, 29,685fr; CAC
Advertising rate: Full - $1,017; 1/2 - $574; 1/4 - $317; 1/8 - $183
Group: Newspaper Media Group
Pub....................................... Ben Cannizzaro
Promo. Coord.............................Kate Rochelle
Circ. Mgr..Rich Klypka
Mng. Ed....................................Brian Donohue
Prodn. Mgr. ....Gene Lennon
Mechanical Specifications: Type page 10 x 13; E - 4 cols, 2 3/8, 1/6 between; A - 4 cols, 2 3/8, 1/6 between; C - 8 cols, 1 1/4, between. Equipment & Software: Hardware — APP/Power Mac 9500; Presses — Dev/Horizon 2400; Software — QPS/QuarkXPress 3.32, Adobe/Photoshop 4.0, Multi-Ad/Creator 4.01, Adobe/Illustrator 3.0.
Areas Served: 07747 08857 08859 08872 08879

THE HUB (THUR)
198 US Highway 9 Ste 100, Suite 100, Manalapan, NJ, 07726-3073, Monmouth, USA; gen tel (732) 358-5200; gen fax (732) 780-4678; disp adv e-mail gmsales@gmnews.com; ed e-mail hubeditor@gmnews.com; web site www.gmnews.com
Circulation: 6pd, 17,427fr; CAC
Advertising rate: Full - $1,037; 1/2 - $584; 1/4 - $322; 1/8 - $188
Group: Newspaper Media Group
Adv. Dir.. Robert Waitt
Mng. Ed....................................Gloria Stravelli
Delivery Method: Carrier
Areas Served: 07716 07704 07739 07757 07701 07760 07702 07724

THE INDEPENDENT (THUR)
198 US Highway 9 Ste 100, Suite 100, Manalapan, NJ, 07726-3073, Monmouth, USA; gen tel (732) 358-5200; gen fax (732) 780-4678; disp adv e-mail gmsales@gmnews.com; ed e-mail hubeditor@gmnews.com; web site www.gmnews.com
Circulation: 7pd, 32,799fr; CAC
Advertising rate: Full - $1,104; 1/2 - $656; 1/4 - $373; 1/8 - $198
Group: Newspaper Media Group
Pub./Gen. Mgr........................ Ben Cannizzaro
Controller............................John Buonansonti
Dir., Adv. .... Robert D. Waitt
Circ. Dir...................................Richard Klypka
Mng. Ed....................................Gloria Stravelli
News Ed. .... Adele Young
Mechanical Specifications: Type page 10 x 13; E - 4 cols, 2 3/8, 1/6 between; A - 4 cols, 2 3/8, 1/6 between; C - 8 cols, 1 1/4, between. Equipment & Software: Hardware — APP/Power Mac 9500; Presses — Dev/Horizon 2400; Software — QPS/QuarkXPress 3.32, Adobe/Photoshop 4.0, Multi-Ad/Creator 4.01, Adobe/Illustrator 3.0.
Delivery Method: Carrier
Areas Served: 07747 07718 07730 07733 07734 07735 07738 07747 07748 07758 07701

TRI-TOWN NEWS (THUR)
198 US Highway 9 Ste 100, Suite 100, Manalapan, NJ, 07726-3073, Monmouth, USA; gen tel (732) 780-4192; gen fax (732) 780-4678; disp adv e-mail gmsales@gmnews.com; ed e-mail gmntnews@gmnews.com; web site www.gmnews.com
Circulation: 7pd, 27,600fr; CAC
Advertising rate: Full - $904; 1/2 - $579; 1/4 - $332; 1/8 - $173
Group: Newspaper Media Group
Pub....................................... Ben Cannizzaro
Adv. Dir.................................Robert D. Waitt
Exec. Ed..Greg Bean
Mng. Ed....................................... Mark Rosman
Prodn./System Mgr.................... Gene Lennon
Mechanical Specifications: Type page 10 x 13; E - 4 cols, 2 3/8, 1/6 between; A - 4 cols, 2 3/8, 1/6 between; C - 8 cols, 1 1/4, between. Equipment & Software: ; Software — QPS/Quark Xpress 3.32, Adobe/Photoshop 4.0, Adobe/Illustrator 3.0, DEV/Horizon 2400

1991, Multi Adcreator 4.01.
Areas Served: 08514 07727 07731 08527 08701 07726 08533

MANASQUAN

THE COAST STAR (THUR)

13 Broad St, Manasquan, NJ, 08736-2906, Monmouth, USA; gen tel (732) 223-0076; gen fax (732) 223-8212; disp adv e-mail publisher@starnewsgroup.com; web site www.starnewsgroup.com
Circulation: 12,500pd,; Sworn/Estimate/Non-Audited
Advertising rate: Open inch rate $8.50
Established: 1877
Pub....................................James M. Manser
Ed. ....Frederick Tuccillo
General Manager.................Alison Manser Ertl
Mechanical Specifications: Full page is six columns by 21 inches. Page width is 10.875 inchesEquipment & Software: Hardware — APP/Mac; Presses — None; Software — QPS/QuarkXPress 6.5.
Delivery Method: Mail, Newsstand
Areas Served: 08730,08736,08750,07762,08720,07719, 07717,08753

MARMORA

SHORE NEWS TODAY (WED, THUR)

507 Route US 9 S, Marmora, NJ, 08223-1258, Herkimer, USA ; gen tel (609) 624-8900; web site http://www.shorenewstoday.com
Group: BH Media Group
Gen. Mgr. ....Anthony Falduto

WILDWOOD LEADER (FRI)

507 Route US 9 S, Marmora, NJ, 08223-1258, Cape May, USA; gen tel (609) 624-8900 ; disp adv e-mail info@shorenewstoday.com; class adv e-mail susan.dibiasio@shorenewstoday.com; ed e-mail bbarlow@catamaranmedia.com; web site http://www.shorenewstoday.com/wildwood/
Circulation: 3,339fr; CAC
Advertising rate: Open inch rate $12
Group: Shore News Today
Ed ....Bill Barlow
Delivery Method: Mail

MAYWOOD

OUR TOWN (THUR)

19 W Pleasant Ave, Maywood, NJ, 07607-1320, Bergen, USA; gen tel (201) 843-5700; gen fax (201) 843-5781; disp adv e-mail rtownmaywoodrp@aol.com; class adv e-mail rtownmaywoodrp@aol.com; ed e-mail news@ourtownnews.com; web site www.ourtownnewsonline.com
Circulation: 3,800pd, 90fr; Sworn/Estimate/Non-Audited
Advertising rate: Open inch rate $19.30
Established: 1948
Camille Hornes
James HornesEd.s
Mechanical Specifications: Type page 10 1/4 x 16.
Delivery Method: Mail, Newsstand, Racks
Areas Served: 07607, 07662

MEDFORD

THE CENTRAL RECORD (THUR)

32 S Main St, Ste A, Medford, NJ, 08055-2455, Burlington, USA; gen tel (609) 654-5000; ed tel 6096545000 ext 18; gen fax (609) 654-0391; ed e-mail news@medfordcentralrecord.com; web site southjerseylocalnews.com
Circulation: 1,174pd,; AAM
Advertising rate: Open inch rate $14.90
Established: 1896
Group: Digital First MediaEditions: (2) Mariton Edition; Mount Laurel Edition;
Mng. Ed. ....John Berry
Mechanical Specifications: Type page 13 1/2 x 21; E - 6 cols, 2, 1/6 between; A - 6 cols, 2, 1/6 between; C - 10 cols, 1 1/3, 1/6 between. Equipment & Software: Hardware — APP/Mac; Software — Adobe/PageMaker, Adobe/Photoshop.
Delivery Method: Mail, Racks
Areas Served: Berlin, Blackwood, Browns Mills, Clementon, Gloucester Township, Medford, Medford Lakes, Marlton, Mount Laurel, Pemberton, Pemberton Township, Shamong, Southampton, Tabern

MILLBURN

THE ITEM OF MILLBURN AND SHORT HILLS (THUR)

181 Millburn Ave, Ste 201, Millburn, NJ, 07041-1811, Essex, USA; gen tel (973) 921-6451; adv tel (973) 569-7269; ed tel (973) 569-7100; gen fax (973) 921-6458; disp adv e-mail adhelp@northjersey.com; class adv e-mail marketplace@northjersey.com; ed e-mail newsroom@northjersey.com; web site www.theitemonline.com
Circulation: 3,120pd, 696fr; CAC
Advertising rate: Open inch rate $14.20
Established: 1888
Group: North Jersey Media Group Inc.
Ed. ....Rick Green
Delivery Method: Mail, Newsstand
Areas Served: 07041, 07078

MILLVILLE

CUMBERLAND REMINDER (WED)

2 W Vine St, Millville, NJ, 08332-3823, Cumberland, USA; gen tel (856) 825-8811; gen fax (856) 825-0011; disp adv e-mail thereminder@comcast.net; class adv e-mail thereminderqa@comcast.net; ed e-mail Editor@remindernewspaper.net; web site www.reminderusa.net
Circulation: 11pd, 14,864fr; CVC
Advertising rate: N/A
Established: 1992
Digital Platform - Mobile: Apple
Pub..Karen Keirsey
Pub...Darrell Kopp
Pub...Karen L. Keirsey
Pub...Darrell Kopp
Ed. ....Daniel Podehl
Pub.......................................Patricia Haserick
Ed. ....Daniel Podehl
Adv. Mgr...............................Patricia Catalano
Prod. Mgr ....Justine Roque
Mechanical Specifications: Type page: 10 x 12; 8 col Equipment & Software: Hardware — APP/Mac; Software — QPS/QuarkXPress 8.5
Delivery Method: Racks
Areas Served: 08332, 08360, 08361, 08302, 08072,08079,08318,08312,08322,08344,08310,08326,08341,08350,08352,08347,08302,08250,08270,08317,08319,08330,08270,08214,08316,08324,08327,08329,08332,08348,08311,08315,08321,08345,08302,08320,08353,08313

SNJ TODAY NEWSPAPER (WED)

600 G St, Millville, NJ, 08332-2111, Cumberland, USA; gen tel (856) 327-8800; gen fax (856) 457-7816; disp adv e-mail dcongdon@snjtoday.com; class adv e-mail dfrie@snjtoday.com; ed e-mail news@snjtoday.com; web site www.snjtoday.com
Circulation: 23,000fr; USPS
Established: 2008
Group: SNJ Today
Ed. ....Jeffrey Schwachter
Delivery Method: Mail, Newsstand, Racks
Areas Served: South Jersey

MONTCLAIR

THE MONTCLAIR TIMES (THUR)

130 Valley Rd, Montclair, NJ, 07042-2369, Essex, USA; gen tel (973) 233-5000; adv tel (973) 569-7269; ed tel (973) 569-7100; disp adv e-mail adhelp@northjersey.com; class adv e-mail marketplace@northjersey.com; ed e-mail newsroom@northjersey.com; web site www.montclairtimes.com
Circulation: 6,396pd, 466fr; CAC
Advertising rate: Open inch rate $16.90
Established: 1877
Group: North Jersey Media Group Inc.
Ed. ....Rick Green
Delivery Method: Mail, Newsstand
Areas Served: 07042, 07043

VERONA-CEDAR GROVE TIMES (THUR)

130 Valley Rd, Rear, Montclair, NJ, 07042-2369, Essex, USA; gen tel (973) 233-5048; adv tel (973) 569-7269; ed tel (973) 569-7100; disp adv e-mail adhelp@northjersey.com; class adv e-mail marketplace@northjersey.com; ed e-mail newsroom@northjersey.com; web site http://archive.northjersey.com/towns/verona-cedar-grove
Circulation: 2,799pd, 822fr; CAC
Advertising rate: Open inch rate $12.80
Established: 1948
Group: North Jersey Media Group Inc.
Ed. ....Rick Green
Delivery Method: Mail, Newsstand
Areas Served: 07009, 07044

NEPTUNE

BEACH HAVEN TIMES (THUR)

3600 State Route 66, Neptune, NJ, 07753-2605, Monmouth, USA; gen tel (732) 922-6000; disp adv e-mail HTowns@njpressmedia.com; class adv e-mail appclass@gannett.com; ed e-mail lreddington@njpressmedia.com; web site www.app.com
Circulation: 1,279pd, 255fr; AAM
Advertising rate: Open inch rate $15.95
Group: Gannett
Pres./Pub. ....Tom Donovan
Exec. Ed./VP..................................Hollis Towns
Mechanical Specifications: Type page 13 x 21 1/2; E - 6 cols, 2 1/16, 3/16 between; A - 6 cols, 2 1/16, 3/16 between; C - 8 cols, 1 1/2, 1/8 between.

THE BEACON (THUR)

3601 State Route 66, A Publication of the Press, Neptune, NJ, 07753-2604, Monmouth, USA; gen tel (732) 922-6000; ed tel 8008229770v eext t 4110; disp adv e-mail tbeacon@app.com; ed e-mail htowns@gannettnj.com; web site www.app.com
Circulation: 2,554pd, 511fr; AAM
Advertising rate: Open inch rate $15.95
Group: Gannett
Publisher.....................................Tom Donovan
Mechanical Specifications: Type page 13 x 21 1/2; E - 6 cols, 2 1/16, 3/16 between; A - 6 cols, 2 1/16, 3/16 between; C - 8 cols, 1 1/2, 1/8 between.
Delivery Method: Newsstand, Carrier, Racks
Areas Served: southern Ocean County NJ

THE LACEY BEACON (THUR)

3600 State Route 66, Neptune, NJ, 07753-2605, Monmouth, USA; gen tel (732) 922-6000; ed tel 8008229770 ext 4110; gen fax (732) 643-4014; ed e-mail htowns@gannettnj.com; web site www.app.com
Circulation: 1,486pd, 4fr; Sworn/Estimate/Non-Audited
Advertising rate: Open inch rate $15.95
Group: Gannett
Pub..Tom Donovan
Exec. Ed./VP ....Hollis Towns
Vice Pres., Adv...........................Karen Guarasi

TOMS RIVER OBSERVER-REPORTER (THUR)

3600 State Route 66, Neptune, NJ, 07753-2605, Monmouth, USA; gen tel (800) 822-9770; ed tel 8008229770 ext 4110; disp adv e-mail observer@app.com; ed e-mail htowns@gannettnj.com; web site www.app.com
Circulation: 115,000fr; Sworn/Estimate/Non-Audited
Advertising rate: Open inch rate $11.33
Group: Gannett
Pub...................................Thomas M. Donovan
Mechanical Specifications: Type page 10 1/8 x 13; E - 5 cols, 1 5/6, between; A - 5 cols, 1 5/6, between; C - 8 cols, 1 5/8, between.

TUCKERTON BEACON (THUR)

3600 State Route 66, Neptune, NJ, 07753-2605, Monmouth, USA; gen tel (732) 922-6000; gen fax (732) 557-5658; disp adv e-mail tbletter@app.com; ed e-mail htowns@gannettnj.com; web site www.app.com
Circulation: 2,184pd, 2,184fr; Sworn/Estimate/Non-Audited
Advertising rate: Open inch rate $15.95
Established: 1889
Group: Gannett
Pub......................................Thomas Donovan
Ed. ....Hollis Towns
Mechanical Specifications: Type page 11 5/8 x 21; E - 6 cols, 1 5/6, 1/8 between; A - 6 cols, 1 5/6, 1/8 between; C - 10 cols, 1 1/10, between.Equipment & Software: ; Software — Mk.

NEW PROVIDENCE

CRANFORD CHRONICLE (THUR)

309 South St, New Providence, NJ, 07974-2110, Union, USA; gen tel (908) 464-1025; gen fax (908) 464-9085; disp adv e-mail union@njnpublishing.com; web site www.nj.com
Circulation: 3,300pd,; Sworn/Estimate/Non-Audited
Advertising rate: Open inch rate $11.04
Established: 1893
Group: Advance Publications, Inc.
Pub...Eileen Bickel
Circ. Mgr....................................Mary Krovacin
Adv. Dir...Jon Babicz
Mechanical Specifications: Type page 13 x 21; E - 6 cols, 2 1/16, between; A - 6 cols, 2 1/16, between; C - 10 cols, 1 3/16, between.
Areas Served: Cranford, Garwood, Kenilworth

INDEPENDENT PRESS (WED)

309 South St, Ste 1, New Providence, NJ, 07974-2110, Union, USA; gen tel (908) 464-1025; gen fax (908) 464-9085; disp adv e-mail ipeditors@njnpublishing.com; web site www.nj.com/independentpress
Circulation: 496pd, 34,581fr; Sworn/Estimate/Non-Audited
Advertising rate: Open inch rate $21.53
Established: 1964
Group: Advance Publications, Inc.Editions: (5) Independent Press Berkeley Height/New Providence Edition (12,800); Independent Press Chatham Edition (5,664); Independent Press Madison Edition (3,600); Independent Press Milburn/Short Hill Edition (5,816); Independent Press Summit Edition (7,20
Pub.......................................Michael J. Kelly
Circ. Mgr..Lewis King
Ed. ....Patricia E. Meola
Adv. Sales.....................................Eileen Bickle
Mechanical Specifications: Type page 13 x 21; E - 6 cols, 2, 1/6 between; A - 6 cols, 2, 1/6 between; C - 10 cols, 1 1/6, 3/4 between. Equipment & Software: Hardware — 8-APP/Mac; Software — QPS/QuarkXPress, Adobe/Photoshop.
Areas Served: Berkeley Heights, Chatham, Madison, Millburn,New Providence, Plainfield, Short Hills, Summit, Warren

LEDGER SOMERSET OBSERVER (SAT)

309 South St, New Providence, NJ, 07974-2110, Union, USA; gen tel (908) 575-6660; gen fax (908) 575-6726; web site http://www.nj.com/
Circulation: 5,797pd,; CAC
Advertising rate: Open inch rate $19.52

Group: Advance Publications, Inc.
Pub....David Tomasini
Mng. Ed....Craig Turpin
Mechanical Specifications: Type page 13 x 21; E - 6 cols, 2 1/16, between; A - 6 cols, 2 1/16, between; C - 10 cols, 1 3/16, between.

SUBURBAN NEWS (THUR)
309 South St, Ste 1, New Providence, NJ, 07974-2110, Union, USA; gen tel (908) 464-1025; gen fax (908) 464-9085; disp adv e-mail suburbannews@northjersey.com
Circulation: 14pd, 63,972fr; Sworn/Estimate/Non-Audited
Advertising rate: Open inch rate $26.88
Established: 1948
Group: Advance Publications, Inc.Editions: (4) 4 total; Central Zone (25,188); City Zone (17,066); East Zone (26,567); South Zone (23,179);
Vice Pres., Adv....Eileen Bickel
Adv. Dir....Carol Hladun
Circ. Mgr....Ted Meadowcroft
Ed....Ellen Dooley
Sports Ed....Russ Crespolini
Mechanical Specifications: Type page 10 x 13; E - 5 cols, 2 1/16, between; A - 5 cols, 2 1/16, between; C - 8 cols, 1 3/16, between.
Areas Served: Clark, Cranford, Fanwood, Garwood, Kenilworth, Mountainside, New Providence, Rahway, Roselle Park, Scotch Plains, Springfield, Union, Westfield

NEWARK

NEW JERSEY LAW JOURNAL (MON)
24 Commerce St, Ste 425, Newark, NJ, 07102-4005, Essex, USA; gen tel (973) 642-0075; ed tel (973) 854-2950; gen fax (973) 642-0920; disp adv e-mail njladvertising@alm.com; ed e-mail rfleury@alm.com; web site http://www.njlawjournal.com/
Advertising rate: Full - $5,655; 1/2 - $3,640; 1/4 - $2,195
Established: 1878
Group: ALM
Editor-in-Chief....Hank Grezlak
Delivery Method: Mail, Carrier
Areas Served: New Jersey

NUTLEY

BELLEVILLE TIMES (THUR)
90 Centre St, Nutley, NJ, 07110-3720, Essex, USA; gen tel (973) 667-2100; adv tel (973) 233-5007; gen fax (973) 667-3904; disp adv e-mail bellevilletimes@northjersey.com; web site http://www.northjersey.com/towns/belleville
Circulation: 1,317pd, 35fr; CAC
Advertising rate: Open inch rate $16.45
Established: 1909
Group: North Jersey Media Group Inc.
Ed....Rick Green
Delivery Method: Mail, Newsstand
Areas Served: 07109

OCEAN CITY

OCEAN CITY SENTINEL (WED)
801 Asbury Ave, Ste 310, Ocean City, NJ, 08226-3641, Cape May, USA; gen tel (609) 399-5411; adv tel (609) 399-1220; ed tel (609) 399 5492; gen fax (609) 398-6397; adv fax (609) 399-9304; ed fax (609) 399 0416; disp adv e-mail ocsentineladvertising@comcast.net; ed e-mail oceancitysentinel@comcast.net; web site www.ocsentinel.com
Circulation: 10,000pd, 15,000fr; USPS
Advertising rate: Open inch rate $15.50
Established: 1880
Group: Sample Media, Inc.
Sample News Group LLCEditions: Ocean City Sentinel; Sentinel of Somers Point, Linwood & Northfield; Upper Township Sentinel; Ocean City Sure Guide; Southern Sure Guide; Cape May Star & Wave
Editor and Publisher....David Nahan
Delivery Method: Mail, Newsstand, Carrier, Racks
Areas Served: 08226 08244 08225 08221 08223 08230 08250 08225 08243 08248

PLEASANTVILLE

THE GAZETTE (WED, THUR)
1000 W Washington Ave, Pleasantville, NJ, 08232-3861, Cape May, USA; gen tel (609) 624-8900; gen fax (609) 624-3470; disp adv e-mail info@shorenewstoday.com; web site http://archive.northjersey.com/towns/the-gazette
Circulation: 5pd, 6,968fr; CAC
Advertising rate: Open inch rate $15.80
Group: Catamaran MediaEditions: (4) Lower Township Gazette (5,854); Middle Township Gazette (8,147); Ocean City Gazette (6,068); Upper Township Gazette (6,735);
Ed....Bill Barlow
Mechanical Specifications: Type page 10 1/4 x 15 1/2; E - 5 cols, between; A - 6 cols, 1 9/16, between; C - 7 cols, between.Equipment & Software: Hardware — IBM/PCs; Presses — HI/V-ISA.
Delivery Method: Mail, Newsstand

PRINCETON

CRANBURY PRESS (FRI)
300 Witherspoon St, Princeton, NJ, 08542-3401, Mercer, USA; gen tel (609) 924-3244; gen fax (609) 921-2714; adv fax (609) 921-2714; ed fax (609) 924-3842; disp adv e-mail feedback@centraljersey.com; class adv e-mail advertising@centraljersey.com; ed e-mail ckim@centraljersey.com; web site http://www.centraljersey.com/news/the_cranbury_press/
Circulation: 77pd, 1,614fr; CAC
Advertising rate: Open rate $13.60
Established: 1885
Pub....Joe Eisele
Ed....Aubrey Huston
Mechanical Specifications: Full page depth 21" 1/8" between
1 col 1.625"
2 col 3.360"
3 col 5.097"
4 col 6.833"
5 col 8.570"
6 col 10.305"

Delivery Method: Mail, Newsstand, Racks
Areas Served: 08512, 08831

HAMILTON-ROBBINSVILLE OBSERVER (FRI)
300 Witherspoon St, Princeton, NJ, 08542-3401, Mercer, USA; gen tel (609) 924-3244; adv tel (609) 874-2148; ed tel (609) 874-2188; gen fax (609) 921-2714; disp adv e-mail mnesbihal@centraljersey.com; class adv e-mail mnesbihal@centraljersey.com; ed e-mail ahuston@centraljersey.com; web site www.centraljersey.com
Circulation: 3,725pd, 6,107fr; CAC
Advertising rate: Open inch rate$13.15
Ed....Aubrey Huston
Delivery Method: Mail

HOPEWELL VALLEY NEWS (THUR)
300 Witherspoon St, Princeton, NJ, 08542-3401, Mercer, USA; gen tel (609) 924-3244; gen fax (609) 921-2714; adv fax (609) 921-2714; ed fax (609) 924-3842; disp adv e-mail scampo@centraljersey.com; ed e-mail ahuston@centraljersey.com; web site www.hopewellvalleynews.com
Circulation: 167pd, 3,241fr; CAC
Advertising rate: Open inch rate $13.15
Established: 1956
Group: Newspaper Media Group
Pub....Joe Eisele
Ed....Aubrey Huston
Mechanical Specifications: Full page depth 21" 1/8" between
1 col 1.625"
2 col 3.360"
3 col 5.097"
4 col 6.833"
5 col 8.570"
6 col 10.305"

Equipment & Software: ; Presses — G Community
Delivery Method: Mail, Newsstand, Racks
Areas Served: 08534, 08525, 08560

REGISTER-NEWS (THUR)
300 Witherspoon St, Princeton, NJ, 08542-3401, Mercer, USA; gen tel (609) 924-3244; gen fax (609) 924-3842; adv fax (609) 921-2714; ed e-mail ahuston@centraljersey.com; web site www.registernews.com
Circulation: 4,662pd, 54fr; Sworn/Estimate/Non-Audited
Advertising rate: Open inch rate $12.25
Ed....Aubrey Huston
Pub....Joe Eisele
Areas Served: Bordentown, Florence, Springfield, Chesterfield, Mansfield, New Hanover, North Hanover, Fieldsboro

REPORTE HISPANO (FRI)
42 Dorann Ave, Princeton, NJ, 08540-3906, Mercer, USA; gen tel (609) 933-1400; ed tel (609) 933-7367; gen fax (609) 924-5392; adv fax (609) 924-5392; ed fax (609) 924-5392; disp adv e-mail advertising@reportehispano.com; class adv e-mail Publisher@ReporteHispano.com; ed e-mail Kleibeel@ReporteHispano.com ; web site www.reportehispano.com - 250,000(views) 250,000(visitors)
Circulation: 0pd, 54,900fr; CAC
Advertising rate: Open inch rate $65.00
Established: 2006
Pub....Cara Marcano
Ed....Kleibeel Marcano
Mechanical Specifications: 10 inches wide x 11 inches high
Delivery Method: Newsstand, Carrier, Racks
Areas Served: NJ, CT, Pa, NYC

SOUTH BRUNSWICK POST (THUR)
PO Box 350, 300 Witherspoon Street, Princeton, NJ, 08542-0350, Mercer, USA; gen tel (609) 924-3244; gen fax (609) 921-2714; adv fax (609) 921-2714; ed fax (609) 924-3842; disp adv e-mail kparis@centraljersey.com; ed e-mail ahuston@centraljersey.com; web site www.southbrunswickpost.com
Circulation: 1,810pd, 904fr; CAC
Advertising rate: Open inch rate $13.15
Established: 1958
Group: Newspaper Media Group
Pub....Joe Eisele
Mechanical Specifications: Full page depth 21" 1/8" between
1 col 1.625"
2 col 3.360"
3 col 5.097"
4 col 6.833"
5 col 8.570"
6 col 10.305"

Equipment & Software: ; Presses — G-Community
Delivery Method: Mail, Newsstand, Racks
Areas Served: 08824

THE BEACON (THUR)
300 Witherspoon St, Princeton, NJ, 08542-3401, Mercer, USA; gen tel (609) 924-3244; gen fax (609) 921-2714; adv fax (609) 921-2714; ed fax (609) 924-3842; disp adv e-mail msamano@centraljersey.com; class adv e-mail dscarpati@centraljersey.com; ed e-mail ahuston@centraljersey.com; web site www.beaconnews.com
Circulation: 768pd,; Sworn/Estimate/Non-Audited
Advertising rate: Open rate inch $10.45
Established: 1845
Group: Newspaper Media Group
Ed....Aubrey Huston
Pub....Joe Eisele
Mechanical Specifications: Full page depth 21" 1/8" between
1 col 1.625"
2 col 3.360"
3 col 5.097"
4 col 6.833"
5 col 8.570"
6 col 10.305" Equipment & Software: ; Presses — G-Community
Delivery Method: Mail, Newsstand
Areas Served: Lambertville, West Amwell , New Hope (Pa.), Stockton , Solebury (Pa.)

THE LAWRENCE LEDGER (THUR)
300 Witherspoon St, Princeton, NJ, 08542-3401, Mercer, USA; gen tel (609) 924-3244; gen fax (609-921-2714; adv fax (609) 921-2714; ed fax (609) 924-3842; disp adv e-mail mnebbia@centraljersey.com; ed e-mail ahuston@centraljersey.com; web site www.lawrenceledger.com
Circulation: 1,560pd, 452fr; CAC
Advertising rate: Open inch rate $12.70
Established: 1968
Group: Newspaper Media Group
Ed....Aubrey Huston
Mechanical Specifications: Full page depth 21" 1/8" between
1 col 1.625"
2 col 3.360"
3 col 5.097"
4 col 6.833"
5 col 8.570"
6 col 10.305"

Equipment & Software: ; Presses — G/Community
Delivery Method: Mail, Newsstand, Racks
Areas Served: 08648

THE PRINCETON PACKET (TUES, FRI)
PO Box 350, Princeton, NJ, 08542-0350, Mercer, USA; gen tel (609) 924-3244; gen fax (609) 921-2714; adv fax (609) 921-2714; ed fax (609) 924-3842; disp adv e-mail feedback@centraljerseycom; ed e-mail ahuston@centraljersey.com; web site www.centraljersey.com
Circulation: 423pd, 15,151fr; CAC
Advertising rate: Open inch rate Tues $23.22; Fri. $26.82
Established: 1786
Ed....Aubrey Huston
Mechanical Specifications: Full page depth 21" 1/8" between
1 col 1.625"
2 col 3.360"
3 col 5.097"
4 col 6.833"
5 col 8.570"
6 col 10.305" Equipment & Software: Hardware — PCs, HP, Sun/Sparc; Presses — G Community; Software — HI/Pagination, HI/Editorial, Dewar/Classified, CJ/Circulation.
Delivery Method: Mail, Newsstand
Areas Served: 08540, 08550, 08502, 08536, 08558, 08542

WINDSOR-HIGHTS HERALD (FRI)
300 Witherspoon St, Princeton, NJ, 08542-3401, Mercer, USA; gen tel (609) 924-3244; gen fax (609) 921-2714; adv fax (609) 921-2714; ed fax (609) 924-3842; disp adv e-mail Jclerico@centraljersey.com; class adv e-mail classified@centraljersey.com; ed e-mail green@northjersey.com; web site www.windsorhightsherald.com
Circulation: 170pd, 2,302fr; CAC
Advertising rate: Open inch rate $15.40
Established: 1965
Group: Newspaper Media Group
Ed....Rick Green
Mechanical Specifications: Full page depth 21" 1/8" between
1 col 1.625"
2 col 3.360"
3 col 5.097"
4 col 6.833"
5 col 8.570"
6 col 10.305" Equipment & Software: ; Presses — G/Community
Delivery Method: Mail, Newsstand
Areas Served: Mercer

RAHWAY

NJTODAY.NET (FRI)

PO Box 1061, Suite 503, Rahway, NJ, 07065-1061, Union, USA; gen tel (908) 352-3100; adv tel (732) 574-1200; ed tel (908) 352-3100; disp adv e-mail ads@njtoday.net; class adv e-mail sales@njtoday.net; ed e-mail news@njtoday.net; web site www.njtoday.net

Circulation: 136,656pd, 3,344fr; Sworn/Estimate/Non-Audited

Advertising rate: Open inch rate $40.00

Established: 1822

Group: CMD Media LLC

Pub. .... Lisa McCormick

Ed. .... Paul Hadsall

Assc. Pub./Dir. Sales Ops. .... Bob Milici

Mechanical Specifications: Type page 10 1/4 x 13 1/2; E - 5 cols, 2, 1/8 between; A - 5 cols, 2, 1/8 between; C - 7 cols, 1 3/8, 1/8 between. Equipment & Software: ; Software — QPS/QuarkXPress 4.1.

Delivery Method: Mail, Newsstand

Areas Served: Union, Middlesex

RED BANK

THE MONMOUTH JOURNAL (FRI)

212 Maple Ave, Red Bank, NJ, 07701-1758, Monmouth, USA; gen tel (732) 747-7007; gen fax (732) 747-5445; disp adv e-mail ads@themonmouthjournal.com; class adv e-mail classi@themonmouthjournal.com; ed e-mail news@themonmouthjournal.com; web site www.themonmouthjournal.com

Circulation: 11,000fr; Sworn/Estimate/Non-Audited

Advertising rate: Open inch rate $7.85

Established: 2004

Gen. Mgr. .... Susan Paviluk

Ed. .... Gary Chapman

Delivery Method: Newsstand, Racks

Areas Served: Red Bank, Middletown, Rumson, Fair Haven, Atlantic Highlands, Highlands, Little Silver, Monmouth Beach, Sea Bright, Shrewsbury

THE TWO RIVER TIMES (THUR)

75 W Front St, Ste 2, Red Bank, NJ, 07701-1660, Monmouth, USA; gen tel (732) 219-5788; gen fax (732) 747-7213; disp adv e-mail ads@tworivertimes.com; ed e-mail editor@tworivertimes.com; web site http://trtnj.com/

Circulation: 20,000pd, 12,000fr; Sworn/Estimate/Non-Audited

Advertising rate: Open inch rate $11.90

Established: 1990

Gen. Mgr. .... Donna Rovere

Circ. Mgr. .... Melissa McGuire

Ed. .... Eileen Moon

Prodn. Mgr. .... Chris Draper

Publisher .... Ellen McCarthyEquipment & Software: Hardware — APP/Power Mac; Software — QPS/QuarkXPress 3.32, Adobe/Photoshop 3.0, Multi-Ad/CAMS Write Now 2.0.

Delivery Method: Mail, Newsstand, Racks

Areas Served: Red Bank, Fair Haven, Rumson, Little Silver, Shrewsbury, Oceanport, Monmouth Beach, Sea Bright, Highlands, Atlantic Highlands, Middletown, Holmdel, Colts Neck,

RIDGEWOOD

FRANKLIN LAKES/OAKLAND SUBURBAN NEWS (THUR)

41 Oak St, Ridgewood, NJ, 07450-3805, Bergen, USA; gen tel (201) 612-5415; gen fax (201) 612-5421; disp adv e-mail suburbannews@northjersey.com; ed e-mail green@northjersey.com; web site http://archive.northjersey.com/towns/franklin-lakes

Circulation: 7,915fr; CAC

Advertising rate: Open inch rate $12.79

Group: North Jersey Media Group Inc.

Ed. .... Rick Green

Mechanical Specifications: Type page 9 2/3 x 12; E - 5 cols, 1 5/6, 1/4 between; A - 5 cols, 1 5/6, 1/4 between; C - 5 cols, 1 5/6, 1/4 between.

Areas Served: 07417, 07436

GLEN ROCK GAZETTE (FRI)

41 Oak St, Ridgewood, NJ, 07450-3805, Bergen, USA; gen tel (201) 612-5432; gen fax (201) 612-5436; disp adv e-mail glenrock@northjersey.com; web site www.northjersey.com

Circulation: 0pd, 3,904fr; AAM

Advertising rate: Open inch rate $8.58

Group: North Jersey Media Group Inc.

Mng. Ed. .... Cindy Probert

Pub. .... Janice Friedman

Vice Pres., Prodn. .... Glenn Garvie

Adv. Mgr. .... Ellen Zitis

Ed. .... Rick Green

Mechanical Specifications: Type page 13 x 13; E - 5 cols, 2 1/12, 1/4 between; A - 5 cols, 2 1/12, 1/4 between; C - 8 cols, 1 2/9, 1/4 between.Equipment & Software: ; Software — Microsoft/Windows NT 3.51.

Areas Served: 7452

MAHWAH SUBURBAN NEWS (THUR)

41 Oak St, Ridgewood, NJ, 07450-3805, Bergen, USA; gen tel (201) 612-5400; gen fax (201) 612-5421; disp adv e-mail suburbannews@northjersey.com; web site www.northjersey.com

Circulation: 7,442fr; CAC

Advertising rate: Open inch rate $8.13

Group: North Jersey Media Group Inc.Editions: (7) 7 total Franklin Lakes/Oakland Suburban News (7,747); Mahwah Suburban News (5,108); Midland Park Suburban News (2,653); Ramsey Suburban News (4,458); Suburban News/Village Gazette (7,623); Waldwick Suburban News (3,297); Wyckoff Suburban News (5,702);

Pres. .... Stephen Borg

Adv. Mgr. .... Ellen Zitis

Ed. .... Rick Green

Mechanical Specifications: Type page 9 2/3 x 12; E - 5 cols, 1 5/6, 1/8 between; A - 5 cols, 1 5/6, 1/8 between; C - 10 cols, 1 2/25, 1/8 between.Equipment & Software: Hardware — APP/Mac G3; Software — QPS/QuarkXPress 4.0, Adobe/Photoshop 5.0, Microsoft/Word 98, Adobe/Illustrator 8.0.

MIDLAND PARK SUBURBAN NEWS (THUR)

41 Oak St, Ridgewood, NJ, 07450-3805, Bergen, USA; gen tel (201) 612-5415; gen fax (201) 612-5421; disp adv e-mail suburbannews@northjersey.com; ed e-mail green@northjersey.com; web site http://archive.northjersey.com/towns/midland-park

Circulation: 2,400fr; CAC

Advertising rate: Open inch rate $6.13

Group: North Jersey Media Group Inc.

Ed. .... Rick Green

Vice Pres./Pub. .... Janice Friedman

Adv. Mgr. .... Ellen Zitis

Areas Served: 7432

RAMSEY SUBURBAN NEWS (THUR)

41 Oak St, Ridgewood, NJ, 07450-3805, Bergen, USA; gen tel (201) 612-5416; adv tel (973) 569-7269; ed tel (973) 569-7100; gen fax (201) 612-5421; disp adv e-mail adhelp@northjersey.com; class adv e-mail marketplace@northjersey.com; ed e-mail green@northjersey.com; web site www.northjersey.com/ramsey

Circulation: 3,615fr; CAC

Group: North Jersey Media Group Inc.

Ed. .... Rick GreenEquipment & Software: Hardware — PC, APP/Mac; Software — Microsoft/Windows NT 3.5.

Delivery Method: Mail, Carrier

Areas Served: 07463,07446,07430

SUBURBAN NEWS (THUR)

41 Oak St, Ridgewood, NJ, 07450-3805, Bergen, USA; adv tel (973) 569-7269; ed tel (973) 569-7100; disp adv e-mail adhelp@northjersey.com; class adv e-mail marketplace@northjersey.com; ed e-mail green@northjersey.com; web site www.northjersey.com/ridgewood

Circulation: 0pd, 33,730fr; AAM

Advertising rate: Open inch rate $17.52

Group: North Jersey Media Group Inc.

Ed. .... Rick Green

Mechanical Specifications: Type page 9 2/3 x 12; E - 5 cols, 1 5/6, 1/4 between; A - 5 cols, 1 5/6, 1/4 between; C - 5 cols, 1 5/6, 1/4 between.

Delivery Method: Mail

Areas Served: 07450

TOWN JOURNAL (THUR)

41 Oak St, Ridgewood, NJ, 07450-3805, Bergen, USA; gen tel (201) 612-5434; adv tel (973) 569-7269; ed tel (973) 569-7100; gen fax (201) 612-5436; disp adv e-mail adhelp@northjersey.com; class adv e-mail marketplace@northjersey.com; ed e-mail green@northjersey.com

Circulation: 0pd, 6,775fr; CAC

Advertising rate: Open inch rate $15.53

Group: North Jersey Media Group Inc.

Ed. .... Rick Green

Mechanical Specifications: Type page 9 2/3 x 15; E - 5 cols, 1 5/6, 1/4 between; A - 5 cols, 1 5/6, 1/4 between; C - 5 cols, 1 5/6, 1/4 between.

Delivery Method: Mail, Carrier

Areas Served: 07401, 07423, 07458

TOWN NEWS (THUR)

41 Oak St, Ridgewood, NJ, 07450-3805, Bergen, USA; gen tel (201) 612-5426; adv tel (973) 569-7269; ed tel (973) 569-7100; gen fax (201) 612-5421; disp adv e-mail adhelp@northjersey.com; class adv e-mail marketplace@northjersey.com; ed e-mail green@northjersey.com; web site www.northjersey.com/townnews

Circulation: 0pd, 9,069fr; AAM

Advertising rate: Open inch rate $21.61

Group: North Jersey Media Group Inc.Rick Green

Mechanical Specifications: Type page 9 2/3 x 12; E - 5 cols, 1 5/6, 1/4 between; A - 5 cols, 1 5/6, 1/4 between; C - 10 cols, 1 5/6, 1/4 between.

Delivery Method: Carrier

Areas Served: 07649, 07652, 07661

WALDWICK SUBURBAN NEWS (WED)

41 Oak St, Ridgewood, NJ, 07450-3805, Bergen, USA; gen tel (201) 612-5415; adv tel (973) 569-7269; ed tel (973) 569-7100; disp adv e-mail adhelp@northjersey.com; class adv e-mail marketplace@northjersey.com; ed e-mail green@northjersey.com

Circulation: 2,801fr; Sworn/Estimate/Non-Audited

Advertising rate: Open inch rate $6.68

Group: North Jersey Media Group Inc.

Ed. .... Rick Green

Areas Served: 07463

WYCKOFF SUBURBAN NEWS (WED)

41 Oak St, Ridgewood, NJ, 07450-3805, Bergen, USA; gen tel (201) 612-5415; adv tel (973) 569-7269; ed tel (973) 569-7100; gen fax (201) 612-5421; disp adv e-mail adhelp@northjersey.com; class adv e-mail marketplace@northjersey.com; ed e-mail green@northjersey.com

Circulation: 5,569fr; CAC

Advertising rate: Open inch rate $10.41

Group: North Jersey Media Group Inc.

Ed. .... Rick Green

Mechanical Specifications: Type page 9 2/3 x 12; E - 5 cols, 1 5/6, 1/4 between; A - 5 cols, 1 5/6, 1/4 between; C - 5 cols, 1 5/6, 1/4 between.

RIO GRANDE

CAPE MAY COUNTY HERALD TIMES (WED)

1508 Route 47, Rio Grande, NJ, 08242-1413, Cape May, USA; gen tel (609) 886-8600; adv tel 609-886-8600 ext 34; ed tel 609-886-8600 ext 28; gen fax (609) 886-1879; adv fax 609-886-2162; ed fax 609-886-1879; disp adv e-mail advertise@cmcherald.com; class adv e-mail Classified@cmcherald.com; ed e-mail editor@cmcherald.com; web site www.capemaycountyherald.com - 926,501(views) 107,155(visitors)

Circulation: 681pd, 30,243fr; VAC

Advertising rate: Modular: 1x2 $47.00; 1x3 $63.00; 2x2 $83.00; Open inch rate $29.95

Established: 1967

Pub. .... Arthur R. Hall

Ed. .... Al Camtbell

Adv. Sales .... Karen Dickinson

Mechanical Specifications: Type page 10 x 15.5 1/2; E - 7 cols, 1 3/8, 1/8 between; A - 7 cols, 2 7/8, between; C - 7 cols, between. Equipment & Software: Hardware — APP/Mac, IBM.

Delivery Method: Racks

Areas Served: 08202, 08204, 08210, 08214, 08223, 08226, 08242, 08243, 08247, 08251, 08260, 08270

ROCKAWAY

AIM JEFFERSON (FRI)

100 Commons Way, Rockaway, NJ, 07866-2038, Morris, USA; gen tel (973) 586-8195; adv tel (973) 283-5608; ed tel (973) 283-5611; disp adv e-mail adhelp@northjersey.com; web site www.northjersey.com

Circulation: 0pd, 8,196fr; AAM

Advertising rate: Open inch rate $16.75

Group: North Jersey Media Group Inc.

Digital Platform - Mobile: Apple, Android, Windows, Blackberry

Digital Platform - Tablet: Apple iOS, Android, Windows 7, Blackberry Tablet OS

Ed. .... Rick Green

Delivery Method: Mail, Newsstand

Areas Served: 07438, 07435, 07460, 07849, 07885

NEIGHBOR NEWS (WED)

100 Commons Way, Rockaway, NJ, 07866-2038, Morris, USA; gen tel (973) 586-8190; adv tel (973) 586-8195; disp adv e-mail adhelp@northjersey.com; web site www.northjersey.com

Circulation: 0pd, 35,796fr; AAM

Advertising rate: Open inch rate $46.00 Full Run

Established: 1987

Group: North Jersey Media Group Inc.Editions: (4) Edition 1; Denville/Rockaway, Edition 2 - Boonton Twp/Mountain Lks, Edition 3 - Dover Edition, Edition 4 - Montville Twp. Edition

Ed. .... Rick Green

Delivery Method: Mail

Areas Served: 07866, 07834, 07435, 07005, 07046, 07801, 07803, 07885, 07045, 07058, 07082

PARSIPPANY LIFE (WED)

100 Commons Way, Rockaway, NJ, 07866-2038, USA; gen tel (973) 586-8190; gen fax (973) 586-8199; disp adv e-mail parsippany@northjersey.com; web site www.parsippanylife.com

Circulation: 0pd, 12,060fr; AAM

Advertising rate: Open inch rate $14.00

Group: North Jersey Media Group Inc.

Ed. .... Rick Green

Mechanical Specifications: Type page 9 2/3 x 13; E - 5 cols, 1 5/6, 1/4 between; A - 5 cols, 1 5/6, 1/4 between; C - 5 cols, 1 5/6, 1/4 between.

Areas Served: 07054, 07034, 07950

SOUTH PLAINFIELD

SOUTH PLAINFIELD OBSERVER (FRI)

1110 Hamilton Blvd Ste 1B, Ste 1B, South Plainfield, NJ, 07080-2031, Middlesex, USA; gen tel (908) 668-0010; adv tel (908) 668-0010; ed tel (908) 668-0010; gen fax (908) 669-8819; adv fax (908) 668-8819; disp adv e-mail spobserver@comcast.net; class adv

e-mail spobserver@comcast.net; ed e-mail spobserver@comcast.net
Circulation: 3,000pd,; USPS
Advertising rate: $11.95
Established: 1997
Pub....Nancy Grennier
Delivery Method: Mail, Newsstand
Areas Served: South Plainfield, NJ 07080

SPARTA

ADVERTISER NEWS (NORTH EDITION) (THUR)
1A Main St, Ste 9, Sparta, NJ, 07871-1909, Sussex, USA; gen tel (973) 300-0890; adv tel (973) 300-0890; ed tel (973) 300-0890; disp adv e-mail njoffice@strausnews.com; class adv e-mail sales@strausnews.com; ed e-mail njoffice@strausnews.com; web site www.advertisernewsnorth.com
Circulation: 0pd, 10,147fr; CAC
Advertising rate: Open inch rate $9.15
Digital Platform - Mobile: Apple, Android
Digital Platform - Tablet: Apple iOS, Android
Pres....Jeanne Straus
Mng. Ed....Mike Zummo
Delivery Method: Mail, Racks
Areas Served: Sussex County

ADVERTISER NEWS (SOUTH EDITION) (THUR)
1A Main St, Ste 9, Sparta, NJ, 07871-1909, Sussex, USA; gen tel (973) 300-0890; adv tel (973) 300-0890; ed tel (973) 300-0890; disp adv e-mail njoffice@strausnews.com; class adv e-mail sales@strausnews.com; ed e-mail njoffice@strausnews.com; web site www.advertisernewssouth.com
Circulation: 0pd, 8,515fr; CAC
Advertising rate: Open inch rate $9.15
Digital Platform - Mobile: Apple, Android
Digital Platform - Tablet: Apple iOS, Android
Pres....Jeanne Straus
Mng. Ed....Mike Zummo
Delivery Method: Mail, Racks
Areas Served: Sussex County

SPARTA INDEPENDENT (THUR)
1A Main St, Ste 9, Sparta, NJ, 07871-1909, Sussex, USA; gen tel (973) 300-0890; gen fax (973) 726-0018; ed e-mail njoffice@strausnews.com; web site www.strausnews.com
Circulation: 0pd, 2,480fr; CAC
Advertising rate: Open inch rate $15.00
Established: 1986
Group: Straus News
Pres....Jeanne Straus
Mng. Ed....Mike Zummo
Mechanical Specifications: Type page 10 1/4 x 14; E - 6 cols, 1 1/2, between; A - 6 cols, 1 1/2, between; C - 6 cols, 1 1/2, between. Equipment & Software: Hardware — PC; Software — Microsoft/Word, QPS/QuarkXPress.
Delivery Method: Mail, Newsstand
Areas Served: 07871

TOWNSHIP JOURNAL (THUR)
1A Main St, Ste 9, Sparta, NJ, 07871-1909, Sussex, USA; gen tel (973) 300-0890; gen fax (973) 726-0018; ed e-mail njoffice@strausnews.com; web site www.strausnews.com
Circulation: 0pd, 17,037fr; CAC
Advertising rate: Open inch rate $15.00
Established: 1995
Group: Straus News
Pub....Jeanne Straus
Mechanical Specifications: Type page 10 1/4 x 14; E - 6 cols, 1 1/2, between; A - 6 cols, 1 1/2, between; C - 6 cols, 1 1/2, between. Equipment & Software: ; Software — QPS/QuarkXPress.
Delivery Method: Mail, Newsstand
Areas Served: 07821 07821 07860

UNION

BELLEVILLE POST (THUR)
1291 Stuyvesant Ave, Union, NJ, 07083-3854, Union, USA; gen tel (908) 686-7700; gen fax (908) 686-4169; disp adv e-mail ads@thelocalsource.com; class adv e-mail class@thelocalsource.com; ed e-mail editorial@thelocalsource.com; web site www.essexnewsdaily.com
Circulation: 231pd,
Established: 1982
Group: Worrall Community Newspapers, Inc.
Pub....David Worrall
Gen. Mgr....Raymond Worrall
IT / Production Manager
Circulation Manager....Peter Worrall
Nancy Worrall
Mechanical Specifications: Type page 13 x 21; E - 6 cols, 2 1/16, 1/8 between; A - 6 cols, 2 1/16, 1/8 between; C - 6 cols, 2 1/16, 1/8 between.Equipment & Software: Hardware — Mk.
Areas Served: Nutley, Belleville

IRVINGTON HERALD (THUR)
1291 Stuyvesant Ave, Union, NJ, 07083-3854, Union, USA; gen tel (908) 686-7700; gen fax (908) 686-4169; disp adv e-mail ads@thelocalsource.com; class adv e-mail class@thelocalsource.com; ed e-mail editorial@thelocalsource.com; web site www.essexnewsdaily.com
Circulation: 455pd, 46fr; CAC
Advertising rate: Full - $885; 1/2 - $440; 1/4 - $225; 1/8 - $115
Established: 1911
Group: Worrall Community Newspapers, Inc.
Pub....David Worrall
Gen. Mgr....Raymond Worrall
Bus. Mgr....Nancy Worrall
Adv. Mgr....Peter Worrall
Mechanical Specifications: Type page 13 x 21; E - 6 cols, 2 1/16, 1/8 between; A - 6 cols, 2 1/16, 1/8 between; C - 6 cols, 2 1/16, 1/8 between.Equipment & Software: Hardware — Mk.
Delivery Method: Mail, Newsstand
Areas Served: Vailsburg, Irvington

NEWS-RECORD OF MAPLEWOOD & SOUTH ORANGE (THUR)
1291 Stuyvesant Ave, Union, NJ, 07083-3854, Union, USA; gen tel (908) 686-7700; gen fax (908) 686-4169; disp adv e-mail ads@thelocalsource.com; class adv e-mail class@thelocalsource.com; ed e-mail editorial@thelocalsource.com; web site www.essexnewsdaily.com
Circulation: 6,168pd, 148fr; Sworn/Estimate/Non-Audited
Advertising rate: Full - $1,050; 1/2 - $530; 1/4 - $265; 1/8 - $135
Established: 1889
Group: Worrall Community Newspapers, Inc.
Pub....David Worrall
Bus. Mgr....Nancy Worrall
Gen. Mgr....Raymond Worrall
Adv. Mgr....Peter Worrall
Mechanical Specifications: Full page measures 10 1/4 w x 11" DeepEquipment & Software: Hardware — Mk.
Delivery Method: Mail, Newsstand
Areas Served: Maplewood, South Orange

NUTLEY JOURNAL (THUR)
1291 Stuyvesant Ave, Union, NJ, 07083-3854, Union, USA; gen tel (908) 686-7700; gen fax (908) 686-4169; disp adv e-mail ads@thelocalsource.com; class adv e-mail class@thelocalsource.com; ed e-mail essexcty@thelocalsource.com; web site www.essexnewsdaily.com
Circulation: 270pd, 5,122fr; USPS
Advertising rate: Full - $1,050; 1/2 - $530; 1/4 - $265; 1/8 - $135
Established: 1982
Group: Worrall Community Newspapers, Inc.
Pub....David Worrall
Gen. Mgr....Raymond Worrall
Adv. Mgr....Peter Worrall
Controller....Nancy Worrall
Mechanical Specifications: Type page 13 x 21; E - 6 cols, 2 1/16, 1/8 between; A - 6 cols, 2 1/16, 1/8 between; C - 6 cols, 2 1/16, 1/8 between.Equipment & Software: Hardware — Mk.
Delivery Method: Mail, Newsstand
Areas Served: Nutley, Belleville

RECORD-TRANSCRIPT OF EAST ORANGE AND ORANGE (THUR)
1291 Stuyvesant Ave, Union, NJ, 07083-3854, Union, USA; gen tel (908) 686-7700; gen fax (908) 686-4169; disp adv e-mail ads@thelocalsource.com; class adv e-mail class@thelocalsource.com; ed e-mail editorial@thelocalsource.com; web site www.essexnewsdaily.com
Circulation: 2,967pd, 86fr; CAC
Advertising rate: Full - $885; 1/2 - $440; 1/4 - $225; 1/8 - $115
Established: 1899
Group: Worrall Community Newspapers, Inc.
Pub....David Worrall
Gen. Mgr....Raymond Worrall
Adv. Mgr....Peter Worrall
Controller....Nancy Worrall
Mechanical Specifications: Type page 13 x 21; E - 6 cols, 2 1/16, 1/8 between; A - 6 cols, 2 1/16, 1/8 between; C - 6 cols, 2 1/16, 1/8 between.Equipment & Software: Hardware — Mk.
Delivery Method: Mail, Newsstand
Areas Served: East Orange, Orange

THE GLEN RIDGE PAPER (THUR)
1291 Stuyvesant Ave, Union, NJ, 07083-3854, Union, USA; gen tel (908) 686-7700; gen fax (908) 686-4169; disp adv e-mail ads@thelocalsource.com; class adv e-mail class@thelocalsource.com; ed e-mail editorial@thelocalsource.com; web site www.essexnewsdaily.com
Circulation: 679pd,; CAC
Advertising rate: Full - $1,050; 1/2 - $530; 1/4 - $265; 1/8 - $135
Established: 1935
Group: Worrall Community Newspapers, Inc.
Pub....David Worrall
Gen. Mgr....Raymond Worrall
Adv. Mgr....Peter Worrall
Controller....Nancy Worrall
Mechanical Specifications: Type page 13 x 21; E - 6 cols, 2 1/16, 1/8 between; A - 6 cols, 2 1/16, 1/8 between; C - 6 cols, 2 1/16, 1/8 between.Equipment & Software: Hardware — Mk.
Delivery Method: Mail, Newsstand
Areas Served: Bloomfield, Glen Ridge

THE INDEPENDENT PRESS OF BLOOMFIELD (THUR)
1291 Stuyvesant Ave, Union, NJ, 07083-3854, Union, USA; gen tel (908) 686-7700; gen fax (908) 686-4169; disp adv e-mail ads@thelocalsource.com; class adv e-mail class@thelocalsource.com; ed e-mail editorial@thelocalsource.com; web site www.essexnewsdaily.com
Circulation: 2,378pd, 418fr; Sworn/Estimate/Non-Audited
Advertising rate: Full - $1,050; 1/2 - $530; 1/4 - $265; 1/8 - $135
Established: 1883
Group: Worrall Community Newspapers, Inc.
Pub./Pres....David Worrall
Bus. Mgr....Nancy Worrall
Vice Pres., Editorial....Raymond Worrall
Mechanical Specifications: Type page 13 x 21; E - 6 cols, 2 1/16, 1/8 between; A - 6 cols, 2 1/16, 1/8 between; C - 6 cols, 2 1/16, 1/8 between.Equipment & Software: Hardware — Mk.
Delivery Method: Mail, Newsstand
Areas Served: Bloomfield, Glen Ridge

UNION COUNTY LOCAL SOURCE (THUR)
1291 Stuyvesant Ave, Union, NJ, 07083-3854, Union, USA; gen tel (908) 686-7700; gen fax (908) 686-4169; disp adv e-mail ads@thelocalsource.com; class adv e-mail class@thelocalsource.com; ed e-mail editorial@thelocalsource.com; web site www.unionnewsdaily.com
Circulation: 4,156pd, 217fr; Sworn/Estimate/Non-Audited
Advertising rate: Full - $1,380; 1/2 - $695; 1/4 - $350; 1/8 - $175
Established: 1917
Group: Worrall Community Newspapers, Inc.
Pub....David Worrall
Adv. Mgr....Peter Worrall
General Manager....Raymond Worrall
Controller....Nancy Worrall
Mechanical Specifications: Type page 13 x 21; E - 6 cols, 2 1/16, 1/8 between; A - 6 cols, 2 1/16, 1/8 between; C - 6 cols, 2 1/16, 1/8 between.Equipment & Software: Hardware — Mk.; Presses — G/Metroliner
Delivery Method: Mail, Newsstand
Areas Served: Summit, Springfield, Mountainside, Union, Hillside, Kenilworth, Roselle Park, Cranford, Roselle, Winfield, Clark, Rahway, Linden, Elizabeth

WEST ORANGE CHRONICLE (THUR)
1291 Stuyvesant Ave, Union, NJ, 07083-3854, Union, USA; gen tel (908) 686-7700; gen fax (908) 686-4169; disp adv e-mail ads@thelocalsource.com; class adv e-mail class@thelocalsource.com; ed e-mail editorial@thelocalsource.com; web site www.essexnewsdaily.com
Circulation: 2,968pd, 1,272fr; Sworn/Estimate/Non-Audited
Advertising rate: Full - $1,050; 1/2 - $530; 1/4 - $265; 1/8 - $135
Established: 1930
Group: Worrall Community Newspapers, Inc.
Pub....David Worrall
Vice Pres....Raymond Worrall
Prodn. Dir....Peter Worrall
Controller....Nancy Worrall
Mechanical Specifications: Tabloid page 10.25" x 11"; modular sizesEquipment & Software: Hardware — Mk.
Delivery Method: Mail, Newsstand
Areas Served: West Orange

VINELAND

HAMMONTON NEWS (WED)
891 E Oak Rd, Unit A, Vineland, NJ, 08360-2311, USA; gen tel (609) 561-2300; adv tel (609) 561-2300; gen fax (609) 567-2249; disp adv e-mail djclass@gannett.com; web site www.thehammontonnews.com
Circulation: 5,037pd,; Sworn/Estimate/Non-Audited
Advertising rate: Open inch rate $11.31
Group: Gannett
Pub./Pres....Joe Calchi
Ed....John Garrahan

WEST CAPE MAY

CAPE MAY STAR AND WAVE (THUR)
PO Box 2427, West Cape May, NJ, 08204-7427, Cape May, USA; gen tel (609) 884-3466; gen fax (609) 884-2893; disp adv e-mail cmstarwaveadvertise@comcast.net; ed e-mail cmstarwave@comcast.net; web site www.starandwave.com
Circulation: 3,395pd, 386fr; Sworn/Estimate/Non-Audited
Advertising rate: Open inch rate $8.30
Established: 1854
Group: Sample Media Inc
Pub....David Nahan
Adv. Mgr....Rob Elder
Ed....Jack Fichter
Delivery Method: Mail, Newsstand, Racks
Areas Served: Cape May, Lower Township, Wildwood (NJ)

WEST MILFORD

THE WEST MILFORD MESSENGER (FRI)
1499 Union Valley Rd, West Milford, NJ, 07480-1361, Passaic, USA; gen tel (973)728-2200; ed e-mail nyoffice@strausnews.com; web site www.westmilfordmessenger.com

Circulation: 313pd, 10,156fr; AAM
Advertising rate: 1/4P $790, 1/2P $1330
Mng. Ed. .... Mike Zummo
Delivery Method: Mail

WESTFIELD

THE TIMES OF SCOTCH PLAINS-FANWOOD (THUR)

251 North Ave W, Westfield, NJ, 07090-1499, Union, USA; gen tel (908) 232-4407; gen fax (908) 232-0473; disp adv e-mail sales@goleader.com; ed e-mail press@goleader.com; web site www.goleader.com
Circulation: 8,500pd, 42fr; Sworn/Estimate/Non-Audited
Advertising rate: Open inch rate $12.00
Established: 1890
Pub.................................. Horace R. Corbin
Asst. Pub.................................. David Corbin
Ed. .... Paul Peyton
Mechanical Specifications: Type page 13 x 21; E - 6 cols, 2, 1/8 between; A - 6 cols, 2, 1/8 between; C - 6 cols, 2, 1/8 between.Equipment & Software: Hardware — IBM/PC; Software — Microsoft/Word 7.1, Adobe/PageMaker, Microsoft/Windows 95, Adobe/Photoshop, Adobe/Illustrator.
Delivery Method: Mail, Newsstand

THE WESTFIELD LEADER (THUR)

251 North Ave W, Ste 7, Westfield, NJ, 07090-1499, Union, USA; gen tel (908) 232-4407; gen fax (908) 232-0473; disp adv e-mail sales@goleader.com; web site www.goleader.com - 3,752,779(views) 1,364,475(visitors)
Circulation: 8,000pd, 59fr; Sworn/Estimate/Non-Audited
Advertising rate: Open inch rate $12.00
Established: 1890
Pub.................................. Horace R. Corbin
Asst. Pub.................................. David Corbin
Adv. Dir.................................. Fred Lecomte
Mechanical Specifications: pdf see www.goleader.com/presskitEquipment & Software: Hardware — IBM; Software — Adobe, Microsoft, Linux
Delivery Method: Mail, Newsstand, Racks

WESTWOOD

PASCACK VALLEY COMMUNITY LIFE (THUR)

372 Kinderkamack Rd, Ste 5, Westwood, NJ, 07675-1657, Bergen, USA; gen tel (201) 664-2501; gen fax (201) 664-1332; disp adv e-mail pvcommunitylife@northjersey.com
Circulation: 0pd, 11,024fr; AAM
Advertising rate: Open inch rate $21.08
Group: North Jersey Media Group Inc.
Ed. .... Rick Green
Mechanical Specifications: Type page 9 2/3 x 13; E - 5 cols, 1 5/6, 1/4 between; A - 5 cols, 1 5/6, 1/4 between; C - 5 cols, 1 2/25, 1/4 between.Equipment & Software: Hardware — APP/Mac G3, PC; Presses — MAN, Uniset, MHI; Software — QPS/QuarkXPress 4.0, Microsoft/Word 98, Adobe/Photoshop 5.0, Adobe/Illustrator 8.0.
Areas Served: 07630, 07642, 07645, 07656, 07675

WHIPPANY

HUNTERDON REVIEW (WED)

100 S Jefferson Rd, Ste 104, Whippany, NJ, 07981-1009, Hunterdon, USA; gen tel (908) 766-3900; adv tel (908) 766-3900 ext 234; ed tel (908) 7663-900 ext 255; gen fax (908) 766-6365; disp adv e-mail advertising@newjerseyhills.com; class adv e-mail theag@newjerseyhills.com; ed e-mail wobrien@newjerseyhills.com; web site www.hunterdon-review.com
Circulation: 813pd, 35fr; Sworn/Estimate/Non-Audited
Advertising rate: Open inch rate $12.68
Established: 1868
Group: New Jersey Hills Media Group
Digital Platform - Mobile: Apple, Windows
Digital Platform - Tablet: Apple iOS, Android
Pub.................................. Elizabeth K. Parker
Pub.................................. Stephen Parker
Prod. Mgr. .... Linda Campbell
Diane Howard
Ass. Exec. Ed. .... Philip Nardone
Editor, Hunterdon Review and Today in Hunterdon .... Walter O'Brien
Delivery Method: Mail, Newsstand, Racks
Areas Served: 07865 08827 08826 07830 07979 08829 08809 08801 08833 08858 08888 08889 08885

WOODLAND PARK

BLOOMFIELD LIFE (THUR)

1 Garret Mountain Plz, Woodland Park, NJ, 07424-3320, Passaic, USA; gen tel (973) 569-7000; adv tel (973) 233-5007; gen fax (973) 569-7268; disp adv e-mail bloomfieldlife@northjersey.com; web site http://www.northjersey.com/towns/bloomfield
Circulation: 1,500pd, 165fr; CAC
Advertising rate: Open inch rate $16.10
Established: 1981
Group: North Jersey Media Group Inc.
Ed. .... Rick Green
Delivery Method: Mail, Newsstand
Areas Served: 07003

GLEN RIDGE VOICE (THUR)

1 Garret Mountain Plz, Woodland Park, NJ, 07424-3320, Passaic, USA; gen tel (973) 569-7000; adv tel (973) 233-5007; gen fax (973) 569-7268; disp adv e-mail glenridgevoice@northjersey.com; web site http://www.northjersey.com/towns/glen-ridge
Circulation: 620pd, 58fr; CAC
Advertising rate: Open inch rate $13.70
Established: 1995
Group: North Jersey Media Group Inc.
Ed. .... Rick Green
Delivery Method: Mail, Newsstand
Areas Served: 07028

NUTLEY SUN (THUR)

1 Garret Mountain Plz, Woodland Park, NJ, 07424-3320, Passaic, USA; gen tel (973) 569-7000; adv tel (973) 233-5007; gen fax (973) 569-7268; disp adv e-mail nutleysun@northjersey.com; web site http://www.northjersey.com/towns/nutley
Circulation: 2,830pd, 734fr; CAC
Advertising rate: Open inch rate $20.10
Established: 1902
Group: North Jersey Media Group Inc.
Ed. .... Rick Green
Delivery Method: Mail, Newsstand
Areas Served: 07110

PASSAIC VALLEY TODAY (THUR)

1 Garret Mountain Plz, Woodland Park, NJ, 07424-3320, Passaic, USA; gen tel (973) 569-7377; adv tel (973) 569-7201; ed tel (973) 569-7393; disp adv e-mail adhelp@northjersey.com; web site www.northjersey.com
Circulation: 0pd, 11,187fr; AAM
Advertising rate: Open inch rate $10.50
Group: North Jersey Media Group Inc.
Ed. .... Rick Green
Delivery Method: Mail, Carrier
Areas Served: 07424, 07512

THE RIDGEWOOD NEWS (FRI)

1 Garret Mountain Plz, Woodland Park, NJ, 07424-3320, Passaic, USA; gen tel (201) 612-5400; gen fax (201) 612-5410; disp adv e-mail ridgewoodnews@northjersey.com; web site http://archive.northjersey.com/towns/ridgewood
Circulation: 3,310pd, 29fr; AAM
Advertising rate: Open inch rate $21.59
Established: 1889
Group: North Jersey Community Newspapers North Jersey Media Group Inc.
Ed. .... Rick Green
Mechanical Specifications: Type page 13 x 21; E - 6 cols, 2 2/25, 1/8 between; A - 6 cols, 2 2/25, 1/8 between; C - 10 cols, 1 2/25, 1/8 between.Equipment & Software: Hardware — APP/Mac G3; Presses — MAN, Uniset, MHI; Software — QPS/QuarkXPress 4.0, Microsoft/Word 98, Adobe/Photoshop 5.0, Adobe/Illustrator 8.0.
Delivery Method: Mail, Carrier, Racks
Areas Served: 07417, 07452, 07423, 07450, 07481

WAYNE TODAY (THUR)

1 Garret Mountain Plz, Woodland Park, NJ, 07424-3320, Passaic, USA; gen tel (973) 569-7393; gen fax (973) 569-7377; disp adv e-mail today@northjersey.com; class adv e-mail deyoung@northjersey.com; ed e-mail today@northjersey.com; web site www.northjersey.com/wayne
Circulation: 0pd, 18,206fr; CAC
Advertising rate: Open inch rate $14.05
Group: North Jersey Media Group Inc.Editions: (2) 2 total; Passaic Valley (11,236); Wayne (16,482);
Ed. .... Rick Green
Mechanical Specifications: Type page 11 5/8 x 21; E - 6 cols, 1 5/6, 1/8 between; A - 6 cols, 1 5/6, 1/8 between; C - 10 cols, 1 1/2, 1/8 between.Equipment & Software: Hardware — APP/Mac G3; Presses — MHI, MAN, Uniset; Software — QPS/QuarkXPress 4.0, Microsoft/Word 98, Adobe/Photoshop 5.0, Adobe/Illustrator 8.0.
Areas Served: 07424, 07512, 07470

NEW MEXICO

ALBUQUERQUE

ALBUQUERQUE BUSINESS FIRST (FRI)

6565 Americas Pkwy NE Ste 770, Suite 202, Albuquerque, NM, 87110-8177, Bernalillo, USA; gen tel (505) 768-7008; adv tel (505) 348-8326; ed tel (505) 768-7008; gen fax (505) 768-0890; disp adv e-mail dschrimsher@bizjournals.com; ed e-mail cortiz@bizjournals.com; web site www.bizjournals.com/albuquerque
Circulation: 5,400pd,; Sworn/Estimate/Non-Audited
Advertising rate: Full - $5,412; 1/2 - $4,600; 1/4 - $2,575
Established: 1993
Group: ACBJ
Digital Platform - Mobile: Apple, Android
Digital Platform - Tablet: Apple iOS, Android
Pub. .... Candace Beeke
Delivery Method: Mail

HEALTH CITY SUN (FRI)

6300 Montano Rd NW, Ste G3, Albuquerque, NM, 87120-1826, Bernalillo, USA; gen tel (505) 242-3010; gen fax (505) 842-5464; disp adv e-mail legal@healthcitysun.com; web site www.healthcitysun.com
Circulation: 2,000pd, 250fr; Sworn/Estimate/Non-Audited
Advertising rate: Open inch rate $10.00
Established: 1929
Pub.. Jill Stone
Delivery Method: Mail
Areas Served: Bernalillo County, New Mexico

BELEN

VALENCIA COUNTY NEWS-BULLETIN (THUR)

1837 Camino Del Llano, Belen, NM, 87002-2619, Valencia, USA; gen tel (505) 864-4472; gen fax (505) 864-3549; disp adv e-mail jmickelson@numberninemediainc.com; ed e-mail cgarcia@news-bulletin.com; web site www.news-bulletin.com
Circulation: 2,855pd, 12,174fr; Sworn/Estimate/Non-Audited
Advertising rate: Open inch rate $17.98
Established: 1910
Digital Platform - Mobile: Apple, Android
Ed. .... Clara Garcia
Pub .... Joe Mickelson
Mechanical Specifications: Type page 13 x 21 1/2; E - 6 cols, 1 5/6, 1/6 between; A - 6 cols, 1 5/6, 1/6 between; C - 8 cols, 1 1/3, 1/6 between.Equipment & Software: Hardware — APP/Mac; Presses — 5-G/Community; Software — QPS/QuarkXPress, Adobe/Photoshop.
Delivery Method: Mail, Newsstand, Carrier, Racks
Areas Served: Valencia

CARRIZOZO

LINCOLN COUNTY NEWS (THUR)

309 Central Ave, Carrizozo, NM, 88301, Lincoln, USA; gen tel (575) 648-2333; gen fax (575) 648-2333; disp adv e-mail j.p.aguilar44@hotmail.com
Circulation: 1,858pd, 60fr; Sworn/Estimate/Non-Audited
Advertising rate: Open inch rate $5.10
Established: 1905
Prodn. Mgr. .... Peter Aguilar
Pub./Ed...................................... Steve Mathis
office Mgr./Adv. Mgr.................. P. Dawn Mathis
Mechanical Specifications: Type page 13 x 21; E - 6 cols, 2, 1/4 between; A - 6 cols, 2, 1/4 between; C - 6 cols, 2, 1/4 between.
Delivery Method: Mail, Racks
Areas Served: 883 882

CLAYTON

UNION COUNTY LEADER (WED)

15 N 1st St, Clayton, NM, 88415-3501, Union, USA; gen tel (575) 374-2587; gen fax (575) 374-8117; disp adv e-mail ucleader@plateautel.net
Circulation: 2,300pd, 95fr; Sworn/Estimate/Non-Audited
Advertising rate: Open inch rate $5.75
Established: 1928
Group: New Mexico Press Association
Ed. .... Brandy Payton
Ed./Pub. .... Terry Martin
Expeditor .... Susan Richardson
Adv. Mgr./Office Mgr................ Patricia Herrera
Adv. Sales Rep........................ Deborah Snider
Mechanical Specifications: Type page 13 x 21; E - 6 cols, 2 1/16, 1/8 between; A - 6 cols, 2 1/16, 1/8 between; C - 8 cols, 1 1/2, 1/8 between.Equipment & Software: Hardware — PC; Software — Aldus/PageMaker 6.0, WordPerfect.

EDGEWOOD

THE INDEPENDENT (WED)

2005A Old Route 66, Edgewood, NM, 87015, Santa Fe, USA; gen tel (505) 286-1212; disp adv e-mail independent@lobo.net; class adv e-mail independent@lobo.net; ed e-mail independent@lobo.net; web site www.edgewood.news
Circulation: 3,000pd, 500fr; Sworn/Estimate/Non-Audited
Advertising rate: $10 open inch
Established: 1999
Digital Platform - Tablet: Other
Business Manager...................... Debbie Ohler
Editor & Publisher.................... Leota Harriman
Mechanical Specifications: 10x13
Delivery Method: Mail, Newsstand, Racks
Areas Served: 87008, 87015, 87016, 87035, 87036, 87060, 87056, 87061, 87047, 87059, 87123

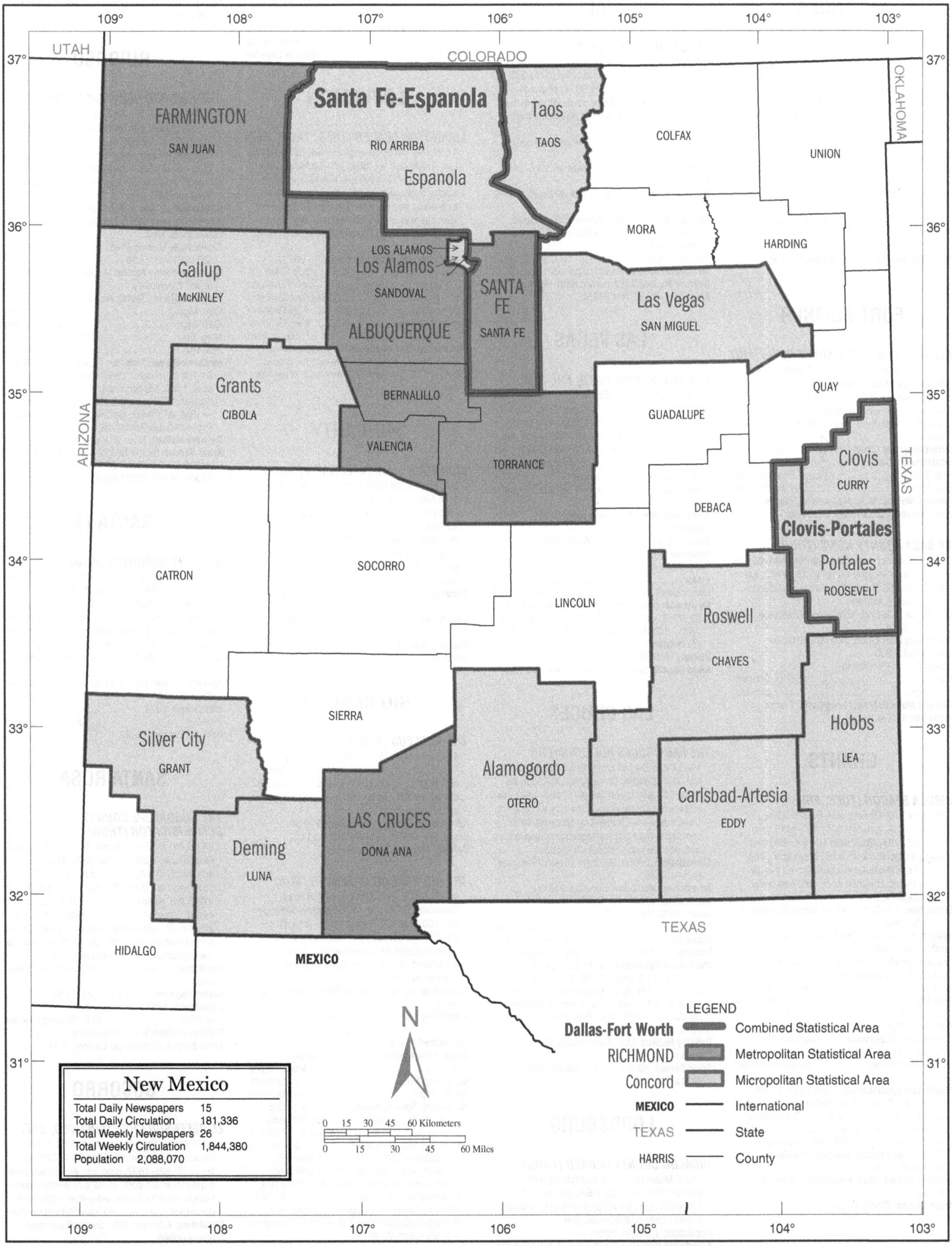
UTAH
COLORADO
OKLAHOMA
ARIZONA
TEXAS
MEXICO
FARMINGTON
SAN JUAN
Santa Fe-Espanola
RIO ARRIBA
Espanola
Taos
TAOS
COLFAX
UNION
MORA
HARDING
LOS ALAMOS
Los Alamos
SANDOVAL
ALBUQUERQUE
SANTA FE
SANTA FE
Gallup
McKINLEY
Las Vegas
SAN MIGUEL
QUAY
Grants
CIBOLA
BERNALILLO
VALENCIA
TORRANCE
GUADALUPE
Clovis
CURRY
DEBACA
Clovis-Portales
Portales
ROOSEVELT
CATRON
SOCORRO
LINCOLN
Roswell
CHAVES
SIERRA
Silver City
GRANT
Hobbs
LEA
Alamogordo
OTERO
Carlsbad-Artesia
EDDY
LAS CRUCES
DONA ANA
Deming
LUNA
HIDALGO
N
LEGEND
Dallas-Fort Worth Combined Statistical Area
RICHMOND Metropolitan Statistical Area
Concord Micropolitan Statistical Area
MEXICO International
TEXAS State
HARRIS County
New Mexico
Total Daily Newspapers 15
Total Daily Circulation 181,336
Total Weekly Newspapers 26
Total Weekly Circulation 1,844,380
Population 2,088,070
0 15 30 45 60 Kilometers
0 15 30 45 60 Miles
109° 108° 107° 106° 105° 104° 103°
37° 36° 35° 34° 33° 32° 31°

ESPANOLA

RIO GRANDE SUN (THUR)

123 N Railroad Ave, Espanola, NM, 87532-2627, Rio Arriba, USA; gen tel (505) 753-2126; gen fax (505) 753-2140; disp adv e-mail rgsunads@riograndesun.com; class adv e-mail classifieds@riograndesun.com; ed e-mail rgsunedit@riograndesun.com; web site www.riograndesun.com

Circulation: 11,500pd,; Sworn/Estimate/Non-Audited

Advertising rate: Open inch rate $9.50

Established: 1956

Pub./Co-owner ..... Robert Trapp

Adv./Mktg. ..... Maria Lopez Garcia

News Ed. ..... Jennifer Garcia

Delivery Method: Newsstand, Racks

Areas Served: Rio Arriba, Arriba, Northern Santa Fe

FORT SUMNER

CLOVIS LIVESTOCK MARKET NEWS (FRI)

181 East Sumner Ave, Fort Sumner, NM, 88119, De Baca, USA; gen tel (575) 355-2462; gen fax (575) 355-7253; disp adv e-mail pecospub@plateautel.net

Circulation: 1,350pd,; Sworn/Estimate/Non-Audited

Advertising rate: Open inch rate $10.60

Established: 1993

Pub./Ed. ..... Scot Stinnett

Bus. Mgr. ..... Lisa Stinnett

Delivery Method: Mail, Newsstand, Racks

Areas Served: Eastern NM and West TX

DE BACA COUNTY NEWS (THUR)

181 E Sumner Ave, Fort Sumner, NM, 88119, De Baca, USA; gen tel (575) 355-2462; gen fax (575) 355-7253; disp adv e-mail pecospub@plateautel.net

Circulation: 1,350pd, 15fr; Sworn/Estimate/Non-Audited

Advertising rate: Open inch rate $10.30

Established: 1900

Group: Pecos Publishing

Pub. ..... Scot Stinnett

Bus. Mgr. ..... Lisa Stinnett

Delivery Method: Mail, Newsstand, Racks

Areas Served: De Baca

GRANTS

CIBOLA BEACON (TUES, FRI)

PO Box 579, Grants, NM, 87020-0579, Cibola, USA; gen tel (505) 287-4411; gen fax (505) 287-7822; disp adv e-mail advertising@cibolabeacon.com; class adv e-mail classifieds@cibolabeacon.com; ed e-mail editor@cibolabeacon.com; web site www.cibolabeacon.com

Circulation: 3,400pd, 5,300fr; Sworn/Estimate/Non-Audited

Advertising rate: Open inch rate $8.00

Established: 1945

Group: New Mexico Press Association Orion El Faro Publishing

Gen. Mgr. ..... Donald Jaramillo

Adv. Mgr. ..... Sylvia Gonzales

Adv. Acct. Mgr. ..... Alaina Jaramillo

Adv. Acct. Mgr. ..... Vanessa Garcia

Composing Supervisor ..... Ramona Montaño

Circulation Dept. Manager ..... Aaryn Tribbey

Senior Staff Writer ..... Rosanne Boyett

Ed. ..... Ham Lujan

Mechanical Specifications: Type page 11 7/8 x 21 1/2; E - 6 cols, 2, 1/3 between; A - 6 cols, 2, 1/3 between; C - 9 cols, 1, 1/3 between. Equipment & Software: Hardware — APP/Mac; Presses — 6-HI/V-15A; Software — QPS/QuarkXPress, Adobe/PageMaker, Multi-Ad/Creator.

Delivery Method: Mail, Newsstand, Carrier, Racks

Areas Served: Cibola County

JAL

THE JAL RECORD (THUR)

101 E Panther, Jal, NM, 88252, Lea, USA; gen tel (575) 395-9970; adv tel (575) 395-9970; gen fax (575) 395-9971; disp adv e-mail Contact-us@jalrecord.net; ed e-mail Contact_us@jalrecord.net; web site www.jalrecordonline.com

Circulation: 1,475pd, 26fr; Sworn/Estimate/Non-Audited

Advertising rate: Open inch rate $5.99

Established: 1939

Digital Platform - Mobile: Apple, Android, Windows, Blackberry

Digital Platform - Tablet: Apple iOS, Android, Windows 7, Blackberry Tablet OS, Kindle, Nook, Kindle Fire

Publisher/ Owner ..... John Chance

Mechanical Specifications: page size 10 x 13

Delivery Method: Mail, Newsstand, Racks

Areas Served: Jal, NM 88252

LAS VEGAS

LAS VEGAS OPTIC (WED, FRI, SUN)

720 University Ave, Ste B, LAS VEGAS, NM, 87701, San Miguel , USA; gen tel (505) 425-6796; adv tel (505) 425-6796; ed tel (505) 425-6796; gen fax (505) 425-1005; adv fax (505) 425-1005; ed fax (505) 425-1005; disp adv e-mail optic@lasvegasoptic.com; web site www.lasvegasoptic.com

Circulation: 3,850pd,; Sworn/Estimate/Non-Audited

Advertising rate: Open inch rate $12.00

Established: 1879

Group: New Mexico Press Association

Advertising Manager

Cynthia Fitch

Editor ..... Jason Brooks

Circulation Coordinator ..... Ashley Ortega

Mechanical Specifications: Type page 10 1/2 x 22 1/2; E - 6 cols, 1 1/2, 1/8 between; A - 6 cols, 1 1/2, 1/8 between; C - 6 cols, 1 1/2, 1/8 between.

Delivery Method: Mail

Areas Served: San Miguel and Mora Counties

LAS CRUCES

THE LAS CRUCES BULLETIN (FRI)

1740 Calle De Mercado, Ste A, Las Cruces, NM, 88005-8254, Dona Ana, USA; gen tel (575) 524-8061; gen fax (575) 526-4621; disp adv e-mail shellie@lascrucesbulletin.com; class adv e-mail jamie@lascrucesbulletin.com; ed e-mail brook@lascrucesbulletin.com; web site www.lascrucesbulletin.com

Circulation: 1,000pd, 20,000fr; Sworn/Estimate/Non-Audited

Advertising rate: Open inch rate $18.00

Established: 1969

Group: OPC News, LLC

Pub. ..... Richard Coltharp

News Ed. ..... Susie Ouderkirk

Managing Editor ..... Brook Stockberger

Mechanical Specifications: Type page 10 5/16 x 12 7/8; E - 6 cols, 1 9/16, 3/16 between; A - 6 cols, 1 9/16, 3/16 between; C - 8 cols, 1 1/8, 3/16 between.Equipment & Software: Hardware — APP/Mac; Software — InDesign 2014, Microsoft/Word 5.1.

Delivery Method: Mail, Newsstand, Carrier, Racks

Areas Served: 88001, 88005, 88007, 88011, 88012

LORDSBURG

HIDALGO COUNTY HERALD (THUR)

212 E Motel Dr, Ste B, Lordsburg, NM, 88045-1906, Hidalgo, USA; gen tel (575) 542-8705; gen fax (575) 542-8837; disp adv e-mail hcherald@hotmail.com

Circulation: 1,500pd, 300fr

Advertising rate: Open inch rate $4.50; Modular rates: 1/8 P $67.50 1/4 P $148.50 1/2 P $283.50 Full $567

Digital Platform - Mobile: Apple

Pub. Ed. ..... Brenda Hood

Adv. Mgr. ..... Glenda Greene

LOVINGTON

LOVINGTON LEADER (TUES, THUR, SAT)

14 W Avenue B, Lovington, NM, 88260-4404, Lea, USA; gen tel (505) 396-2844; gen fax (505) 396-5775; disp adv e-mail lovington-leader@yahoo.com; class adv e-mail leader@leaco.net; ed e-mail leader@leaco.net; web site www.lovingtonleaderonline.com

Circulation: 1,495pd,; Sworn/Estimate/Non-Audited

Advertising rate: Open inch rate $8.00

Adv. Mgr. ..... Joyce Clemens

Ed./Pub. ..... John Graham

Society Ed. ..... Jeanine Graham

Sports Ed. ..... Neil Granath

Prodn. Pressman ..... Hop Graham

Classified Adv. Mgr. ..... Gina Ford

Mechanical Specifications: Type page 13 x 21; E - 6 cols, 2 1/16, 1/8 between; A - 6 cols, 2 1/16, 1/8 between; C - 6 cols, 2 1/16, 1/8 between.

MORIARTY

MOUNTAIN VIEW TELEGRAPH (THUR)

215 Old Route 66 Building 1 Suite 4, Moriarty, NM, 87035, Torrance, USA; gen tel (505) 823-7101; adv tel (505) 823-7108; ed tel (505) 823-7102; gen fax (505) 823-7107; disp adv e-mail btrujillo@mvtelegraph.com; class adv e-mail class@mvtelegraph.com; ed e-mail editor@mvtelegraph.com; web site www.mvtelegraph.com

Circulation: 7,000pd,; Sworn/Estimate/Non-Audited

Advertising rate: Open inch rate $12.02

Ed. ..... Tod Dickson

Delivery Method: Mail, Newsstand, Racks

Areas Served: Torrance, Santa Fe

RIO RANCHO

THE NUCLEUS (THUR)

409 NM Hwy 528, Ste 101, Rio Rancho, NM, 87124, Sandoval, USA; gen tel (505) 892-8080; gen fax (505) 892-5719; disp adv e-mail lross@rrobserver.com; web site www.kafbnucleus.com

Advertising rate: Open inch rate $26.50

Group: RR Community Publishing LLC

Delivery Method: Carrier, Racks

THE RIO RANCHO OBSERVER (SUN)

409 NM 528, Rio Rancho, NM, 87124, Sandoval, USA; gen tel (505) 892-8080; gen fax (505) 892-5719; disp adv e-mail mhartranft @rrobserver.com; class adv e-mail observerclass@rrobserver.com; ed e-mail mhartranft @rrobserver.com; web site www.rrobserver.com

Circulation: 23,500fr; Sworn/Estimate/Non-Audited

Advertising rate: 1/16 Pg $129.60; 1/8 Pg $248.40; 1/4 Pg $432.00

Established: 1973

Group: New Mexico Press Association

Pub. ..... Rockford Hayes

Managing Ed. ..... Mike Hartranft

Prodn. Mgr. ..... Gina Martinez

Mechanical Specifications: Type page 11 5/8 x 21 1/2; E - 6 cols, 1 13/16, 1/8 between; A - 6 cols, 1 13/16, 1/8 between; C - 7 cols, 1 9/16, 13/100 between.Equipment & Software: Hardware — 2-PC 486, 11-Pentium/PC, Xante/Printer 1200 dpi, Mk, ScanMakerII, 2-HP/LaserJet, APP/Power Mac 8100/120, 2-Pentium/PC Celerons, N T Server, APP/iMac; Software — Adobe/PageMaker 6.5, Archetype/Corel Draw 7.0, Adobe/Photoshop 4.0, Microsoft/Word

Delivery Method: Newsstand, Carrier, Racks

Areas Served: 87124, 87114

RUIDOSO

THE RUIDOSO NEWS (WED, FRI)

104 Park Ave, Ruidoso, NM, 88345-6154, Lincoln, USA; gen tel (575) 257-4001; gen fax (575) 257-7053; disp adv e-mail beth-barrett@ruidosonews.com; class adv e-mail jgoodwin@ruidosonews.com; ed e-mail tvestal@ruidosonews.com; web site www.ruidosonews.com

Circulation: 2,194pd, 46fr; AAM

Advertising rate: Open inch rate $13.15

Established: 1946

Group: New Mexico Press AssociationEditions: (20,000) Vamono's

Digital Platform - Mobile: Apple, Android, Windows, Blackberry

Digital Platform - Tablet: Apple iOS, Android

Circ. Mgr. ..... Chris Gonzales

Gen. Mgr. ..... Carol BUrgess

Mng. Ed. ..... Kelly Brooks Vestal

Adv. Dir. ..... Frank Leto

Mechanical Specifications: Type page 12 1/2 x 21 1/4; E - 6 cols, 1 5/6, 1/6 between; A - 6 cols, 1 5/6, 1/6 between; C - 8 cols, 1 1/3, 1/6 between.Equipment & Software: Hardware — IBM, APP/Mac; Software — QPS/QuarkXPress, Adobe/Printshop.

Delivery Method: Mail, Newsstand, Racks

Areas Served: 88301 88312 88316 88318 88323 88338 88324 88336 88341 88343 88345 88346 88348 88351 88355

SANTA FE

SANTA FE REPORTER (WED)

132 E Marcy St, Santa Fe, NM, 87501-2054, Santa Fe, USA; gen tel (505) 988-5541; adv tel (505) 988-5541 x205; gen fax (505) 988-5348; disp adv e-mail advertising@sfreporter.com; ed e-mail editor@sfreporter.com; web site www.sfreporter.com

Circulation: 16,000fr; Sworn/Estimate/Non-Audited

Advertising rate: 1/8 Pg $300; 1/3 Pg $488; Full Page $2310

Established: 1974

Pub./Ed. ..... Julie Ann Grimm

Delivery Method: Racks

SANTA ROSA

THE GUADALUPE COUNTY COMMUNICATOR (THUR)

241 S 4th St, Santa Rosa, NM, 88435-2322, Guadalupe, USA; gen tel (575) 472-3555; adv tel (575) 472-3555; ed tel (575) 472-3555; gen fax (575) 472-5555; adv fax (575) 472-5555; ed fax (575) 472-5555; disp adv e-mail comsilvercom@plateautel.net; class adv e-mail comsilvercom@plateautel.net; ed e-mail menewspaper@hotmail.com; web site www.guadalupecommunicator.com

Circulation: 2,000pd,; Sworn/Estimate/Non-Audited

Advertising rate: Open inch rate $6.30

Established: 1983

Rep./Pub. ..... M.E. Sprengelmeyer

Delivery Method: Mail, Newsstand

Areas Served: Guadalupe County, N.M.

SOCORRO

EL DEFENSOR CHIEFTAIN (WED, SAT)

200 Winkler St, Socorro, NM, 87801-4200, Socorro, USA; gen tel (575) 835-0520; gen fax (575) 835-1837; disp adv e-mail advertising@dchieftain.com; class adv e-mail classifieds@dchieftain.com; ed e-mail editorial@dchieftain.com; web site www.dchieftain.com

Circulation: 4,500pd, 30fr; Sworn/Estimate/Non-Audited

Advertising rate: Open inch rate $10.72
Established: 1860
Pub./Ed. .... Scott Turner
Mechanical Specifications: Type page 11 5/6 x 21 1/2; E - 6 cols, 1 5/6, 1/6 between; A - 6 cols, 1 5/6, 1/6 between; C - 8 cols, 1, 1/6 between.Equipment & Software: Hardware — IBM, APP/Mac; Software — QPS/QuarkXPress 4.4, Adobe/Photoshop 5.0.

TAOS

THE TAOS NEWS (THUR)

226 Albright St, Taos, NM, 87571-6312, Taos, USA; gen tel (575) 758-2241; gen fax (575) 758-9647; disp adv e-mail admanager@taosnews.com; class adv e-mail admanager@taosnews.com; ed e-mail editor@taosnews.com; web site www.taosnews.com
Circulation: 6,871pd, 14fr; VAC
Advertising rate: Open inch rate $18.80
Established: 1959
Editor .... Staci Matlock
Mechanical Specifications: Type page 13 x 21 1/2; E - 6 cols, 2 1/16, between; A - 6 cols, 2 1/16, between; C - 9 cols, 1 1/4, between. Equipment & Software: Hardware — APP/Power Mac G4; Presses — G/Community; Software — QPS/QuarkXPress, Baseview.
Delivery Method: Mail, Newsstand, Carrier, Racks
Areas Served: 87549, 87556, 87558, 87513, 87514, 87519, 87521, 87571, 87525, 87557, 87529, 87553

TRUTH OR CONSEQUENCES

SIERRA COUNTY SENTINEL (FRI)

1747 E 3rd Ave, Truth Or Consequences, NM, 87901-2042, Sierra, USA; gen tel (575) 894-3088; adv tel (575) 894-3088; gen fax (575) 894-3998; adv fax (575) 894-3998; disp adv e-mail sentinel@gpkmedia.com; web site gpkmedia.com
Circulation: 4,580pd, 30fr; Sworn/Estimate/Non-Audited
Advertising rate: Open inch rate $7.50
Established: 1967
Group: New Mexico Press Association
Digital Platform - Tablet: Apple iOS, Android, Windows 7
Pub. .... Frances Luna
Mechanical Specifications: Type page 11 1/2 x 21; E - 8 cols, 1 5/8, 1/6 between; A - 8 cols, 1 5/8, 1/6 between; C - 8 cols, 1 5/8, 1/6 between.Equipment & Software: Hardware — APP/Mac; Software — QPS/QuarkXPress 8.5
Delivery Method: Mail, Newsstand, Carrier, Racks
Areas Served: 87901

THE HERALD (WED)

1204 N Date St, Truth Or Consequences, NM, 87901-1754, Sierra County, USA; gen tel (575) 894-2143; gen fax (575) 894-7824; disp adv e-mail herald@torcherald.com; web site www.theheraldtorc.com
Circulation: 4,000pd,; Sworn/Estimate/Non-Audited
Advertising rate: Open inch rate $3.80
Established: 1928
Group: Herald Newspapers, Inc.
Pub... Mike Tooley
Ed. .... Carlos Padilla
Associate Publisher .... Cindy Tooley-Harrison
Delivery Method: Mail, Newsstand
Areas Served: 87901, 87942, 87935, 87931, 87932, 87943, 87939, 88042, 87930, 87801

TUCUMCARI

QUAY COUNTY SUN (WED, SAT)

902 S 1st St, Tucumcari, NM, 88401-3217, Quay, USA; gen tel (575) 461-1952; ed tel (800) 819-9925; gen fax (575) 461-1965; disp adv e-mail cnjadvertising@cnjonline.com; class adv e-mail rsullivan@cnjonline.com; web site www.qcsunonline.com
Circulation: 4,200pd, 30fr; Sworn/Estimate/Non-Audited
Advertising rate: Open inch rate $7.98
Group: Clovis Media Inc.
Ad. Director .... Viola Gonzales
Classifieds Mgr. .... Lorinda Martinez
Ed. .... David Gragg
Bookkeeper .... Marilyn Parker
PUBLISHER .... ROB LANGRELL
Mechanical Specifications: Type page 13 x 21 1/2; E - 6 cols, 2 1/16, 1/8 between; A - 6 cols, 2 1/16, 1/8 between; C - 9 cols, 1 3/8, 1/8 between.

NEW YORK

ADAMS

JEFFERSON COUNTY JOURNAL (WED)

7 Main St, Adams, NY, 13605-1228, Jefferson, USA; gen tel (315) 232-2141; gen fax (315) 232-4586; disp adv e-mail jcjesfucn@citlink.net
Circulation: 3,500pd,; Sworn/Estimate/Non-Audited
Advertising rate: Open inch rate $4.00
Established: 1844
Ed. .... Karl A. Fowler
Mechanical Specifications: Type page 14 7/8 x 21; A - 8 cols, 1 5/8, between.

AKRON

AKRON BUGLE (THUR)

7263 Downey Rd, Akron, NY, 14001-9714, Erie, USA; gen tel (716) 542-9615; gen fax (716) 210-8947; disp adv e-mail akronbugle@gmail.com; class adv e-mail classifieds@akronbugle.com; ed e-mail editor@akronbugle.com; web site www.akronbugle.com
Circulation: 1,895pd, 15fr; Sworn/Estimate/Non-Audited
Advertising rate: Open inch rate $8.50
Established: 1981
Pub.................................. Marilyn J. Kasperek
Adv. Mgr. .... Kenneth B. Kasperek
Mechanical Specifications: Type page 10 x 15.85; 5 cols, 2
Delivery Method: Mail, Newsstand
Areas Served: 14001 14031 14004 14036 14094

ALBANY

THE LEGISLATIVE GAZETTE (TUES)

PO Box 7329, Albany, NY, 12224-0329, Albany, USA; gen tel (518) 486-6513; adv tel (518) 473-9739; disp adv e-mail gvadney@legislativegazette.com; web site www.legislativegazette.com
Advertising rate: Open inch rate $28.80
Established: 1978
Editor .... James Gormley
Pub... Alan Chartock

ALDEN

ALDEN ADVERTISER (THUR)

13200 Broadway St, Alden, NY, 14004-1313, Erie, USA; gen tel (716) 937-9226; disp adv e-mail aldenadvertiser@rochester.rr.com; ed e-mail aldenadvertiser@rochester.rr.com; web site www.aldenadvertisernews.com
Circulation: 3,550pd, 108fr; Sworn/Estimate/Non-Audited
Advertising rate: Open inch rate $8.50
Established: 1914
Gen. Mgr. & Ed............... Leonard A. Weisbeck
Mechanical Specifications: Type page 10 x 16; E - 5 cols, 1 11/12, 1/6 between; A - 5 cols, 1 11/12, 1/6 between.Equipment & Software: Hardware — APP/Mac; Presses — G/Suburban, HI, ATF/Davidson 501, ATF/Davidson 700; Software — QPS/QuarkXPress.

ALEXANDRIA BAY

THOUSAND ISLAND SUN (WED)

Route 12, Alexandria Bay, NY, 13607, Jefferson, USA; gen tel (315) 482-2581; gen fax (315) 482-6315; disp adv e-mail tisun@gisco.net; web site www.thousandislandssun.net
Circulation: 6,397pd, 25fr; Sworn/Estimate/Non-Audited
Advertising rate: Open inch rate $4.80
Established: 1901
Gen. Mgr. .... Craig Snow
Ed. .... David Swartzentruber
Mechanical Specifications: Type page 16 x 21; E - 7 cols, 2, 1/6 between; A - 7 cols, 2, 1/6 between; C - 7 cols, 2, 1/6 between.Equipment & Software: Hardware — APP/Mac; Software — Aldus/PageMaker.

ALFRED

THE ALFRED SUN (THUR)

764 State Rt 244, Alfred, NY, 14802, Allegany, USA; gen tel (607) 587-8110; adv tel 607-382-5308; disp adv e-mail alfredsun.news@gmail.com; web site n/a
Circulation: 959pd, 50fr; Sworn/Estimate/Non-Audited
Advertising rate: Open inch rate $6.00
Established: 1883
Ed. and Pub. .... David L. Snyder
Mechanical Specifications: Type page 11 x 14; E - 5 cols, 2, between; A - 5 cols, 2, between; C - 6 cols, 1 5/8, between.
Delivery Method: Mail, Newsstand
Areas Served: Alfred/Allegany County/14802

ALTAMONT

THE ALTAMONT ENTERPRISE & ALBANY COUNTY POST (THUR)

120 Maple Ave, Altamont, NY, 12009-7718, Albany, USA; gen tel (518) 861-4026; ed tel (518) 861-5005; gen fax (518) 595-8211; disp adv e-mail ads@altamontenterprise.com; class adv e-mail classifieds@altamontenterprise.com; ed e-mail MHale-Spencer@AltamontEnterprise.com; web site www.altamontenterprise.com
Circulation: 4,757pd, 111fr; Sworn/Estimate/Non-Audited
Advertising rate: Open inch rate $12
Established: 1884
Digital Platform - Mobile: Apple, Android
Digital Platform - Tablet: Apple iOS, Android, Blackberry Tablet OS, Kindle, Kindle Fire
Ed co-pub .... Melissa Hale-Spencer
digital ed, co-pub .... Marcello Iaia
Co-pub .... Gary Spencer
Mechanical Specifications: Type page 11 1/4 x 16; E - 5 cols, 1 7/8, 1/8 between; A - 5 cols, 1 7/8, 1/8 between; C - 5 cols, 1 7/8, 1/8 between.Equipment & Software: Hardware — APP/Mac; Software — Adobe/Photoshop 2.5.1, Adobe/Illustrator 6.0, Adobe/PageMaker 6.5.
Delivery Method: Mail, Newsstand
Areas Served: Albany County, NY

AMITYVILLE

MASSAPEQUA POST (WED)

85 Broadway, Ste A, Amityville, NY, 11701-2778, Suffolk, USA; gen tel (516) 798-5100; adv tel (631) 608-4495; gen fax (631) 264-5310; adv fax (631) 264-5310; disp adv e-mail acjads@optonline.net; class adv e-mail acjads@optonline.net; ed e-mail acjnews@rcn.com; web site www.massapequapost.com
Circulation: 2,800pd, 400fr; Sworn/Estimate/Non-Audited
Advertising rate: Open inch rate $8.50
Established: 1954
Group: CJ Publishers Inc.
Pub.. Alfred James
Exec. Ed.................................. Carolyn James
Mechanical Specifications: Type page 10 x 12; 6 cols, 1.5, 0.125 between
Equipment & Software: Hardware — APP/Mac.; Software — Adobe
Microsoft
Delivery Method: Mail, Newsstand
Areas Served: Massapequa, Massapequa Park, Plainedge, South Farmingdale, Seaford

THE AMITYVILLE RECORD (WED)

85 Broadway, Ste A, Amityville, NY, 11701-2778, Suffolk, USA; gen tel (631) 264-0077; adv tel (631) 608-4495; gen fax (631) 264-5310; adv fax (631) 264-5310; disp adv e-mail acjads@optonline.net; class adv e-mail acjads@optonline.net; ed e-mail acjnews@rcn.com; web site www.amityvillerecord.com
Circulation: 2,800pd, 300fr; Sworn/Estimate/Non-Audited
Advertising rate: Open inch rate $8.50
Established: 1904
Group: CJ Publishers Inc.
Pres./Pub. .... Alfred James
Exec. Ed.................................. Carolyn James
Mechanical Specifications: Type page 10 x 12; 6 cols, 1.5, 0.125 between
Delivery Method: Mail, Newsstand
Areas Served: Amityville Village, North Amityville, Copiague, Lindenhurst

AMSTERDAM

COURIER STANDARD ENTERPRISE (FRI)

1 Venner Rd, Amsterdam, NY, 12010-5617, Montgomery, USA; gen tel (518) 843-1100x103; gen fax (518) 843-1100x103; disp adv e-mail sales@recordernews.com; ed e-mail news@recordernews.com; web site www.courierstandardenterprise.com
Circulation: 2,000pd, 100fr; Sworn/Estimate/Non-Audited
Advertising rate: Open inch rate $9.10
Established: 1876
Group: McClary Media, Inc.
Digital Platform - Mobile: Apple, Android
Digital Platform - Tablet: Apple iOS, Android
Assoc. Pub. .... Geoff Dylong
Pub.. Kevin McClary
Ad. Director .... Brian Krohn
Ed. .... Joshua ThomasEquipment & Software: ; Software — Adobe/PageMaker 8.0.
Delivery Method: Mail, Newsstand
Areas Served: Montgomery County NY

SACANDAGA EXPRESS (WED, FRI)

1 Venner Rd, Amsterdam, NY, 12010-5617, Montgomery, USA; gen tel 1 (518) 843-1100; gen fax (518) 843-1338; web site http://www.sacandagaexpress.com
Circulation: 4,500fr; Sworn/Estimate/Non-Audited
Advertising rate: $5.65 per column inch
Group: Port Jackson Media LLC
Digital Platform - Mobile: Apple, Android
Associate Pub. .... Geoff Dylong
Ed. .... Carla Kolbe
Ad. Director .... Brian Krohn
Delivery Method: Newsstand
Areas Served: Fulton County NY

ARCADE

ARCADE HERALD (THUR)

223 Main St, Arcade, NY, 14009-1209, Wyoming, USA; gen tel (585) 492-2525; gen fax (585) 492-2667; disp adv e-mail heraldads@roadrunner.com; ed e-mail heraldnews@roadrunner.com; web site www.mywnynews.com/arcade_warsaw

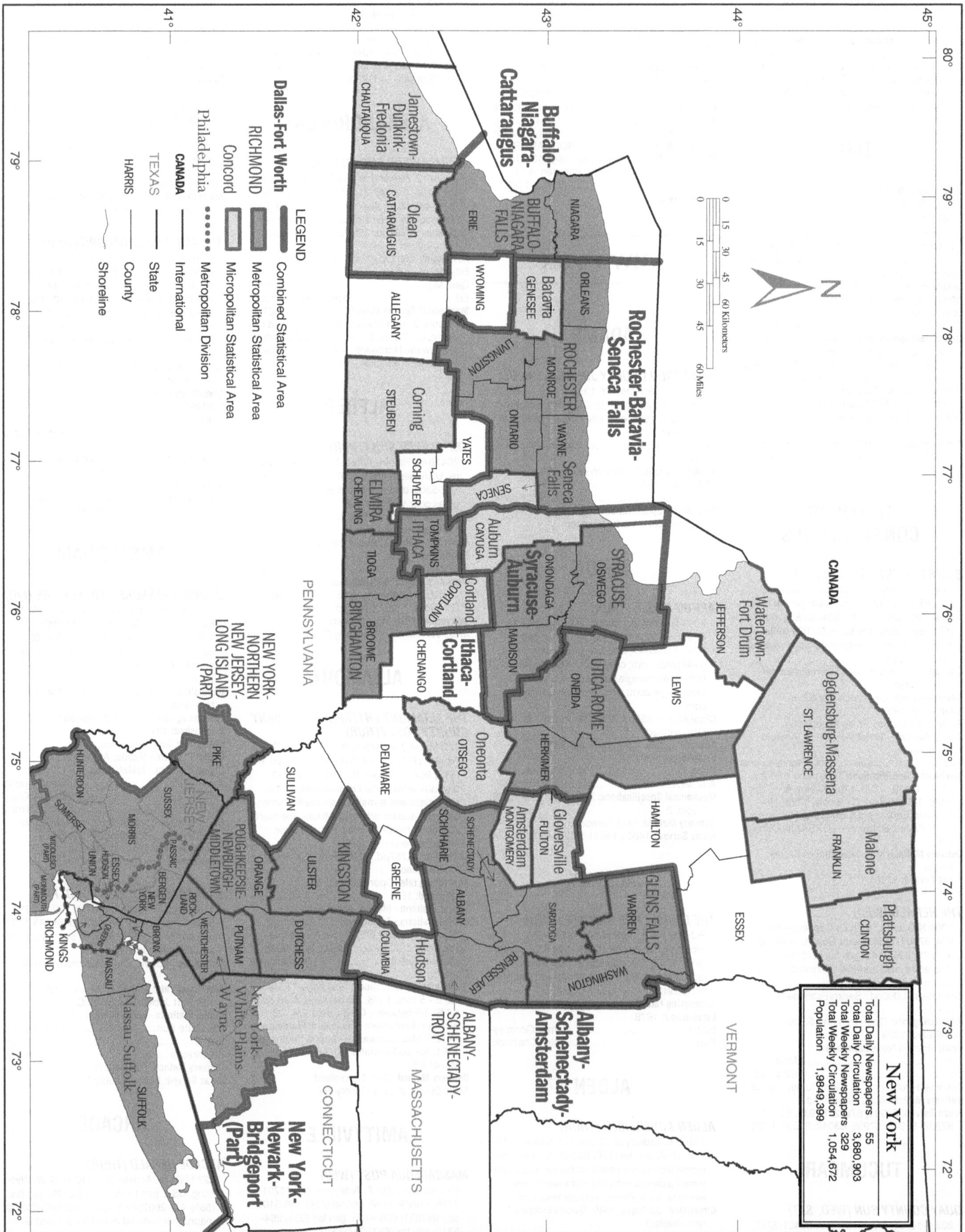
New York
Total Daily Newspapers 55
Total Daily Circulation 3,680,903
Total Weekly Newspapers 329
Total Weekly Circulation 1,054,672
Population 1,9849,399
LEGEND
Dallas-Fort Worth Combined Statistical Area
RICHMOND Metropolitan Statistical Area
Concord Micropolitan Statistical Area
Philadelphia Metropolitan Division
CANADA International
TEXAS State
HARRIS County
Shoreline
0 15 30 45 60 Kilometers
0 15 30 45 60 Miles
N
CANADA
PENNSYLVANIA
VERMONT
MASSACHUSETTS
CONNECTICUT
NEW JERSEY
Buffalo-Niagara-Cattaraugus
Rochester-Batavia-Seneca Falls
Syracuse-Auburn
Ithaca-Cortland
Albany-Schenectady-Amsterdam
New York-Newark-Bridgeport (Part)
NEW YORK-NORTHERN NEW JERSEY-LONG ISLAND (PART)
Jamestown-Dunkirk-Fredonia
CHAUTAUQUA
Olean
CATTARAUGUS
BUFFALO-NIAGARA FALLS
ERIE
NIAGARA
Batavia
GENESEE
ORLEANS
WYOMING
ALLEGANY
ROCHESTER
MONROE
LIVINGSTON
ONTARIO
WAYNE
Seneca Falls
SENECA
YATES
Corning
STEUBEN
SCHUYLER
ELMIRA
CHEMUNG
ITHACA
TOMPKINS
TIOGA
Auburn
CAYUGA
Cortland
CORTLAND
SYRACUSE
OSWEGO
ONONDAGA
MADISON
BINGHAMTON
BROOME
CHENANGO
Watertown-Fort Drum
JEFFERSON
LEWIS
UTICA-ROME
ONEIDA
HERKIMER
Ogdensburg-Massena
ST. LAWRENCE
Malone
FRANKLIN
Plattsburgh
CLINTON
ESSEX
HAMILTON
GLENS FALLS
WARREN
WASHINGTON
SARATOGA
Gloversville
FULTON
Amsterdam
MONTGOMERY
SCHENECTADY
SCHOHARIE
ALBANY
RENSSELAER
ALBANY-SCHENECTADY-TROY
Oneonta
OTSEGO
DELAWARE
GREENE
Hudson
COLUMBIA
KINGSTON
ULSTER
SULLIVAN
POUGHKEEPSIE-NEWBURGH-MIDDLETOWN
ORANGE
DUTCHESS
PUTNAM
WESTCHESTER
ROCKLAND
New York-White Plains-Wayne
PIKE
SUSSEX
PASSAIC
MORRIS
BERGEN
ESSEX
HUDSON
UNION
SOMERSET
HUNTERDON
MIDDLESEX (PART)
MONMOUTH (PART)
NEW YORK
BRONX
QUEENS
KINGS
RICHMOND
Nassau-Suffolk
NASSAU
SUFFOLK

Circulation: 5,000pd,; Sworn/Estimate/Non-Audited
Advertising rate: Open inch rate $11.45
Established: 1891
Group: Neighbor to Neighbor News, Inc.
Pub....................................Grant M. Hamilton
Ad. Mgr...Cyndi Gradi
Mechanical Specifications: Type page 10.5 x 19.5; 5 cols, 2, 0.125 between
Areas Served: Arcade, Delevan, Sardina, Java, Machias, Eagle, Holland, Freedom, Sheldon, Farmersville, Yorkshire

ARKVILLE

CATSKILL MOUNTAIN NEWS (WED)
43414 State Hwy. 28, Arkville, NY, 12406, Delaware, USA; gen tel (845) 586-2601; gen fax (845) 586-2366; disp adv e-mail news@catskillmountainnews.com; web site www.catskillmountainnews.com
Circulation: 4,100pd, 6fr; Sworn/Estimate/Non-Audited
Advertising rate: Open inch rate $7.50
Established: 1863
Circ. Mgr...............................Linda Schebesta
Adv. Mgr.....................................Doris Warner
Ed.....................................Richard D. Sanford
Mechanical Specifications: Type page 12 x 21; E - 6 cols, 1 7/8, 1/8 between; A - 6 cols, 1 7/8, 1/8 between; C - 9 cols, 1 1/4, 1/16 between. Equipment & Software: Hardware — APP/Macs; Presses — MOT; Software — Microsoft/Word 98, QPS/QuarkXPress, Multi-Ad/Creator, Adobe/Photoshop.

AUBURN

THIS WEEK (SAT)
25 Dill St, Auburn, NY, 13021-3605, Cayuga, USA; gen tel (315) 282-2200; adv tel (315) 282-2213; ed tel (315) 282-2231; gen fax (315) 253-6031; disp adv e-mail Jeffrey.Weigand@lee.net; class adv e-mail Jeffrey.Weigand@lee.net; ed e-mail news@auburnpub.com; web site www.skaneatelesjournal.com
Circulation: 7,500fr; Sworn/Estimate/Non-Audited
Advertising rate: Open inch rate $7.50
Group: Cayuga Media
Digital Platform - Mobile: Apple, Android
Digital Platform - Tablet: Apple iOS, Android
Pub..Rob Forcey
Adv. Dir.....................................Daniel Pelletier
Delivery Method: Mail, Newsstand, Carrier, Racks
Areas Served: Western Onondaga County and Syracuse

BABYLON

THE BEACON (THUR)
65 Deer Park Ave, Ste 2, Babylon, NY, 11702-2820, Suffolk, USA; gen tel (631) 587-5612; ed tel same; gen fax (631) 587-0198; disp adv e-mail acjads@optonline.net; class adv e-mail acjads@optonline.net; ed e-mail acjnews@rcn.com; web site www.babylonbeacon.com
Circulation: 2,800pd, 400fr; Sworn/Estimate/Non-Audited
Advertising rate: Open inch rate $9.50
Established: 1966
Group: CJ Publishers Inc.
Digital Platform - Mobile: Apple
Digital Platform - Tablet: Apple iOS
Pub...Alfred James
Pub.......................................Carolyn James
Circ. Mgr...............................Helene Pagano
Adv. Mgr.................................Maryann Heins
Mechanical Specifications: Type page 10 x 12; 6 cols, 1.5, 0.125 between
Delivery Method: Mail, Newsstand, Racks
Areas Served: Babylon Village, North Babylon, West Babylon, West Islip, Deer Park, Lindenhurst

BALLSTON SPA

BALLSTON JOURNAL (THUR)
PO Box 319, Ballston Spa, NY, 12020-0319, Saratoga, USA; gen tel (518) 885-5238; gen fax (518) 885-3752; web site www.theballstonjournal.com
Circulation: 151,000fr; Sworn/Estimate/Non-Audited
Advertising rate: Open inch rate $40.00
Established: 1798
Pub...Patrick J. Smith
Mechanical Specifications: Type page 9 3/4 x 14; E - 6 cols, 1 1/2, 1/3 between; A - 6 cols, between; C - 6 cols, between.

BATAVIA

THE DRUMMER PENNYSAVER (SUN)
2 Apollo Dr, Batavia, NY, 14020-3002, Genesee, USA; gen tel (585) 343-2055; gen fax (585) 344-2050; class adv e-mail batads@batavianews.com; web site www.drummerpennysaver.com
Circulation: 15,200fr; CVC
Advertising rate: Open inch rate $10.13
Established: 1979
Group: Johnson Newspaper Corp.
Pub......................................Michael Messerly
Ad. Dir...Kim Pasierb
Mechanical Specifications: Type page 9.3 x 10.7; 5 cols, 1.625
Delivery Method: Carrier, Racks
Areas Served: 14005, 14013, 14020, 14036, 14040, 14054, 14056, 14058, 14125, 14143, 14416, 14422, 14482, 14557

BATH

STEUBEN COURIER-ADVOCATE (SUN)
10 W Steuben St, Bath, NY, 14810-1512, Steuben, USA; gen tel (607) 776-2121; gen fax (607) 776-3967; disp adv e-mail trounsville@the-leader.com; class adv e-mail sball@steubencourier.com; ed e-mail news@steubencourier.com; web site www.steubencourier.com
Circulation: 11,113fr; CVC
Advertising rate: Open inch rate $8.77
Established: 1968
Group: GateHouse Media, Inc.
Sales Mgr...........................Teresa Rounsville
Ed...Stella DuPree
Circ. Mgr..................................Jamie Stopka
Mechanical Specifications: Type page 10 x 20.5; 6 cols
Equipment & Software: Hardware — APP/Mac; Presses — G; Software — Multi-Ad/Creator, Adobe/PageMaker.
Delivery Method: Mail, Carrier, Racks
Areas Served: 14809, 14810, 14819, 14820, 14821, 14840, 14873, 14874, 14879

BAYSIDE

ASTORIA TIMES (THUR)
4102 Bell Blvd, Bayside, NY, 11361-2792, Queens, USA; gen tel (718) 229-0300; adv tel (718) 229-0300; ed tel (718) 229-0300; gen fax (718) 225-7117; adv fax (718) 225-7117; ed fax (718) 225-7117; disp adv e-mail brice@cnglocal.com; class adv e-mail classified@cnglocal.com; ed e-mail timesledgernews@cnglocal.com; web site www.astoriatimes.com
Circulation: 1,983pd,; Sworn/Estimate/Non-Audited
Advertising rate: Open inch rate $52.00
Group: Queens Village Times (OOB)
Digital Platform - Mobile: Apple, Android, Windows, Blackberry
Digital Platform - Tablet: Apple iOS, Android, Windows 7, Blackberry Tablet OS
Ed...Roz Liston
Mechanical Specifications: Type page 10 1/3 x 14; E - 4 cols, 2 4/9, 1/6 between; A - 4 cols, 2 4/9, 1/6 between; C - 7 cols, 1 5/12, 1/8 between.
Delivery Method: Mail, Racks
Areas Served: Queens County

BAYSIDE TIMES (FRI)
4102 Bell Blvd Ste 1, Ste 1, Bayside, NY, 11361-2794, Queens, USA; gen tel (718) 229-0300; gen fax (718) 224-2934; disp adv e-mail brice@cnglocal.com; class adv e-mail classified@cnglocal.com; ed e-mail timesledgernews@cnglocal.com; web site www.timesledger.com
Circulation: 11,042pd,; Sworn/Estimate/Non-Audited
Advertising rate: Open inch rate $59.00
Established: 1935
Group: Community News Group
Digital Platform - Mobile: Apple, Android, Windows, Blackberry
Digital Platform - Tablet: Apple iOS, Android, Windows 7, Blackberry Tablet OS
Ed...Roz Liston
Mechanical Specifications: Type page 10 1/3 x 14; E - 4 cols, 2 4/9, 1/6 between; A - 4 cols, 2 4/9, 1/6 between; C - 8 cols, 1 1/8, 1/8 between.Equipment & Software: Hardware — APP/Mac; Presses — G/Community, G/Urbanite.
Delivery Method: Mail, Racks
Areas Served: 11360, 11361, 11364, 11362, 11363, 11001, 11004, 11005, 11426, 11040, 11356, 11357

FLUSHING TIMES (THUR)
4102 Bell Blvd, Bayside, NY, 11361-2792, Queens, USA; gen tel (718) 229-0300; adv tel (718) 229-0300; ed tel (718) 229-0300; gen fax (718) 229-7117; adv fax (718) 229-7117; ed fax (718) 229-7117; disp adv e-mail brice@cnglocal.com; class adv e-mail classified@cnglocal.com; ed e-mail timesledgernews@cnglocal.com; web site www.timesledger.com
Circulation: 5,015pd,; Sworn/Estimate/Non-Audited
Advertising rate: 1/8 Pg $248.00; 1/4 Pg $442.00; 1/2 Pg $790.00
Established: 1992
Group: Queens Village Times (OOB)
Digital Platform - Mobile: Apple, Android, Windows, Blackberry
Digital Platform - Tablet: Apple iOS, Android, Windows 7, Blackberry Tablet OS
Mng. Ed...Roz Liston
Display/Online Adv..........................Brian Rice
Mechanical Specifications: Type page 10 1/3 x 14; E - 4 cols, 2 4/9, 1/6 between; A - 4 cols, 2 4/9, 1/6 between; C - 8 cols, 1 1/8, 1/8 between.Equipment & Software: Hardware — APP/Mac, PC; Presses — G/Community, G/Urbanite.
Delivery Method: Mail, Newsstand, Racks
Areas Served: 11354, 11355, 11358, 11367, 11366, 11432

FOREST HILLS LEDGER (THUR)
4102 Bell Blvd, Bayside, NY, 11361-2792, Queens, USA; gen tel (718) 229-0300; gen fax (718) 224-2934; disp adv e-mail brice@cnglocal.com; class adv e-mail classified@cnglocal.com; ed e-mail timesledgernews@cnglocal.com; web site www.timesledger.com
Circulation: 2,503pd,; Sworn/Estimate/Non-Audited
Advertising rate: Open inch rate $6.16
Group: Queens Village Times (OOB)
Ed...Roz Liston
Mechanical Specifications: Type page 10 1/3 x 14; E - 4 cols, 2 4/9, 1/6 between; A - 4 cols, 2 4/9, 1/6 between; C - 7 cols, 1 5/12, 1/8 between.Equipment & Software: Hardware — APP/Mac, PC.

FRESH MEADOWS TIMES (FRI)
4102 Bell Blvd, Bayside, NY, 11361-2792, Queens, USA; gen tel (718) 260-2500; adv tel (718) 260-2500; ed tel (718) 260-2500; gen fax (718) 260-2549; adv fax (718) 260-2549; ed fax (718) 260-2549; disp adv e-mail brice@cnglocal.com; class adv e-mail classified@cnglocal.com; ed e-mail timesledgernews@cnglocal.com; web site www.timesledger.com
Circulation: 21,000pd,; Sworn/Estimate/Non-Audited
Advertising rate: Open inch rate $52.00
Group: Community Newspaper Group
Queens Village Times (OOB)
Digital Platform - Mobile: Apple, Android, Windows, Blackberry
Digital Platform - Tablet: Apple iOS, Android, Windows 7, Blackberry Tablet OS
Ed...Roz Liston
Classified Advertising Director.. Amanda Tarley
Display & Online Advertising .... Brian Rice
Mechanical Specifications: Page- 9.75 x 11 (inches)
E- 6 columns, 1.5 inches/column,1/4 inch between
A-6 columns, 1.5 inches/ column,1/4 inch between
C- 8 columns, 1.1367 inches/column
Delivery Method: Newsstand, Racks
Areas Served: 11412, 11423, 11432, 11434, 11435, 11436, 11413, 11422, 11427, 11429

JACKSON HEIGHTS TIMES (FRI)
4102 Bell Blvd, Bayside, NY, 11361-2792, Queens, USA; gen tel (718) 260-2500; adv tel (718) 260-2500; ed tel (718) 260-2500; gen fax (718) 260-2549; adv fax (718) 260-2549; ed fax (718) 260-2549; disp adv e-mail brice@cnglocal.com; class adv e-mail classified@cnglocal.com; ed e-mail timesledgernews@cnglocal.com; web site www.timesledger.com
Circulation: 21,000pd,; Sworn/Estimate/Non-Audited
Advertising rate: Open inch rate $52.00
Group: Community Newspaper Group
Queens Village Times (OOB)
Digital Platform - Mobile: Apple, Android, Windows, Blackberry
Digital Platform - Tablet: Apple iOS, Android, Windows 7, Blackberry Tablet OS
Ed...Roz Liston
Classified Advertising Director.. Amanda Tarley
Display & Online Advertising............Brian Rice
Mechanical Specifications: Page- 9.75 x 11 (inches)
E- 6 columns, 1.5 inches/column,1/4 inch between
A-6 columns, 1.5 inches/ column,1/4 inch between
C- 8 columns, 1.1367 inches/column
Delivery Method: Newsstand, Racks
Areas Served: 11412, 11423, 11432, 11434, 11435, 11436, 11413, 11422, 11427, 11429

JAMAICA TIMES (FRI)
4102 Bell Blvd, Bayside, NY, 11361-2792, Queens, USA; gen tel (718) 260-2500; adv tel (718) 260-2500; ed tel (718) 260-2500; gen fax (718) 260-2549; adv fax (718) 260-2549; ed fax (718) 260-2549; disp adv e-mail brice@cnglocal.com; class adv e-mail classified@cnglocal.com; ed e-mail timesledgernews@cnglocal.com; web site www.timesledger.com
Circulation: 21,000pd,; Sworn/Estimate/Non-Audited
Advertising rate: Open inch rate $52.00
Group: Community Newspaper Group
Queens Village Times (OOB)
Digital Platform - Mobile: Apple, Android, Windows, Blackberry
Digital Platform - Tablet: Apple iOS, Android, Windows 7, Blackberry Tablet OS
Mng. Ed...Roz Liston
Classified Advertising Director.. Amanda Tarley
Display & Online Advertising
Brian Rice
Mechanical Specifications: Page- 9.75 x 11 (inches)
E- 6 columns, 1.5 inches/column,1/4 inch between
A-6 columns, 1.5 inches/ column,1/4 inch between
C- 8 columns, 1.1367 inches/column
Delivery Method: Newsstand, Racks
Areas Served: 11412, 11423, 11432, 11434, 11435, 11436, 11413, 11422, 11427, 11429

LAURELTON TIMES (FRI)
4102 Bell Blvd, Bayside, NY, 11361-2792, Queens, USA; gen tel (718) 260-2500; adv

tel (718) 260-2500; ed tel (718) 260-2500; gen fax (718) 260-2549; adv fax (718) 260-2549; ed fax (718) 260-2549; disp adv e-mail brice@cnglocal.com; class adv e-mail classified@cnglocal.com; ed e-mail timesledgernews@cnglocal.com; web site www.timesledger.com
Circulation: 21,000pd,; Sworn/Estimate/Non-Audited
Advertising rate: Open inch rate $52.00
Group: Community Newspaper Group
Queens Village Times (OOB)
Digital Platform - Mobile: Apple, Android, Windows, Blackberry
Digital Platform - Tablet: Apple iOS, Android, Windows 7, Blackberry Tablet OS
Ed. .... Roz Liston
Classified Advertising Director.. Amanda Tarley
Display & Online Advertising
Brian Rice
Mechanical Specifications: Page- 9.75 x 11 (inches)
E- 6 columns, 1.5 inches/column,1/4 inch between
A-6 columns, 1.5 inches/ column,1/4 inch between
C- 8 columns, 1.1367 inches/column
Delivery Method: Newsstand, Racks
Areas Served: 11412, 11423, 11432, 11434, 11435, 11436, 11413, 11422, 11427, 11429

RIDGEWOOD LEDGER (FRI)

4102 Bell Blvd, Bayside, NY, 11361-2792, Queens, USA; gen tel (718) 260-2500; adv tel (718) 260-2500; ed tel (718) 260-2500; gen fax (718) 260-2549; adv fax (718) 260-2549; ed fax (718) 260-2549; disp adv e-mail brice@cnglocal.com; class adv e-mail classified@cnglocal.com; ed e-mail timesledgernews@cnglocal.com; web site www.timesledger.com
Circulation: 21,000pd,; Sworn/Estimate/Non-Audited
Advertising rate: Open inch rate $52.00
Group: Community Newspaper Group
Queens Village Times (OOB)
Digital Platform - Mobile: Apple, Android, Windows, Blackberry
Digital Platform - Tablet: Apple iOS, Android, Windows 7, Blackberry Tablet OS
Mng. Ed.. Roz Liston
Classified Advertising Director.. Amanda Tarley
Display & Online Advertising
Brian Rice
Mechanical Specifications: Page- 9.75 x 11 (inches)
E- 6 columns, 1.5 inches/column,1/4 inch between
A-6 columns, 1.5 inches/ column,1/4 inch between
C- 8 columns, 1.1367 inches/column
Delivery Method: Newsstand, Racks
Areas Served: 11412, 11423, 11432, 11434, 11435, 11436, 11413, 11422, 11427, 11429

THE LITTLE NECK LEDGER (THUR)

4102 Bell Blvd, Bayside, NY, 11361-2792, Queens, USA; gen tel (718) 229-0300; gen fax (718) 225-7117; disp adv e-mail news@timesledger.com; class adv e-mail classified@cnglocal.com; ed e-mail timesledgernews@cnglocal.com; web site www.timesledger.com
Circulation: 1,686pd,; Sworn/Estimate/Non-Audited
Advertising rate: Open inch rate $6.16
Group: Queens Village Times (OOB)
Ed. .... Roz Liston
Display & Online Advertising
Brian Rice
Classified Advertising
Amanda Tarley
Mechanical Specifications: Type page 10 1/3 x 14; E - 4 cols, 2 4/9, 1/6 between; A - 4 cols, 2 4/9, 1/6 between; C - 7 cols, 1 5/12, 1/8 between.Equipment & Software: Hardware — APP/Mac, PC.

THE QUEENS COURIER (THUR)

3815 Bell Blvd, Bayside, NY, 11361-2058, Queens, USA; gen tel (718) 224-5863; adv tel (718) 224-5863 ext 231; gen fax (718) 224-5441; disp adv e-mail bbrennan@queenscourier.com; ed e-mail editorial@queenscourier.com; web site www.queenscourier.com
Circulation: 6,000pd, 70,000fr; CAC
Advertising rate: Open inch rate $16.00
Established: 1985Editions: (4) 4 total Courier; Forest Hills Courier; Northwest Courier; Southwest Courier;
Digital Platform - Mobile: Apple, Android, Blackberry
Digital Platform - Tablet: Apple iOS, Android, Blackberry Tablet OS, Kindle, Kindle Fire, Other
Pub.............................. Victoria Schneps-Yunis
Editor-in-chief .... Robert Pozarycki
Mechanical Specifications: Full page 8.75 x 11.5
1/2 page Horizontal 8.75 x 5.6875
1/2 page Vertical 4.313 x 11.5
Strip 8.75 x 1.8125
Quarter page 4.313 x 5.6875
Eighth page 4.313 x 2.78125
Junior page 8.75 x 8.25Equipment & Software: Hardware — APP/Mac; Presses — WPC/Web Leader; Software — QPS/QuarkXPress.
Delivery Method: Mail, Newsstand, Racks
Areas Served: Queens NY

THE WHITESTONE TIMES (THUR)

4102 Bell Blvd, Bayside, NY, 11361-2792, Queens, USA; gen tel (718) 229-0300; adv tel (718) 229-0300; ed tel (718) 229-0300; gen fax (718) 225-7117; adv fax (718) 225-7117; ed fax (718) 225-7117; disp adv e-mail brice@cnglocal.com; class adv e-mail classified@cnglocal.com; ed e-mail timesledgernews@cnglocal.com; web site www.timesledger.com
Circulation: 5,015pd,; Sworn/Estimate/Non-Audited
Advertising rate: Open inch rate $52.00
Group: Queens Village Times (OOB)
Digital Platform - Mobile: Apple, Android, Windows, Blackberry
Digital Platform - Tablet: Apple iOS, Android, Windows 7, Blackberry Tablet OS
Mng. Ed.. Roz Liston
Display & Online Advertising
Brian Rice
Classified Advertising
Amanda Tarley
Mechanical Specifications: Type page 10 1/3 x 14; E - 4 cols, 2 4/9, 1/6 between; A - 4 cols, 2 4/9, 1/6 between; C - 7 cols, 1 5/12, 1/8 between.Equipment & Software: Hardware — APP/Mac, PC.
Delivery Method: Mail, Newsstand, Racks
Areas Served: Queens County

TIMES NEWSWEEKLY (THUR)

3815 Bell Blvd, Bayside, NY, 11361-2058, Queens, USA; gen tel (718) 821-7503; adv tel (718) 821-7500; gen fax (718) 456-0120; adv fax (718) 456-0120; disp adv e-mail info@timesnewsweekly.com; class adv e-mail d.cusick@timesnewsweekly.com; ed e-mail info@timesnewsweekly.com; web site www.timesnewsweekly.com; www.ridgewoodtimes.net
Circulation: 20,000pd, 0fr; USPS
Advertising rate: Open inch rate $16.00
Established: 1908
Pub. .... Victoria Schneps-YunisEquipment & Software: Hardware — APP/Mac; Software — QPS/QuarkXPress.
Delivery Method: Mail, Newsstand
Areas Served: 11385, 11378, 11379, 11374, 11375, 11377, 11416, 11418, 11419, 11420, 11421, 11417, 11414, 11104, 11101, 11103, 11102, 11105, 11370, 11371, 11369, 11368

BEDFORD HILLS

RECORD-REVIEW (FRI)

PO Box 455, Bedford Hills, NY, 10507-0455, Westchester, USA; gen tel (914) 244-0533; gen fax (914) 244-0537; disp adv e-mail flynch@scarsdalenews.com; class adv e-mail gryan@scarsdalenews.com; ed e-mail recordreview@optonline.net; web site www.record-review.com
Circulation: 3,300pd, 100fr; Sworn/Estimate/Non-Audited
Advertising rate: national open rate $12.86/ci
Established: 1995
Pub. .... Deborah White
Ed. .... Ed Baum
Mechanical Specifications: Type page 14 1/16 x 21; E - 6 cols, 2 1/6, 1/6 between; A - 9 cols, 1 5/12, 1/6 between; C - 9 cols, 1 5/12, 1/6 between.Equipment & Software: Hardware — APP/Mac; Software — InDesign; Acrobat; Photoshop
Delivery Method: Mail
Areas Served: 10506, 10507, 10536, 10549, 10576

BOONVILLE

BOONVILLE HERALD & ADIRONDACK TOURIST (WED)

105 E Schuyler St, Boonville, NY, 13309-1103, Oneida, USA; gen tel (315) 942-4449; gen fax (315) 942-4440; disp adv e-mail boonherald@aol.com; web site www.boonvilleherald.com
Circulation: 4,200pd, 217fr; Sworn/Estimate/Non-Audited
Advertising rate: Open inch rate $5.20
Established: 1852
Pub. & Sr. Ed...................................... Joe Kelly
Ed. .... Sandra Hrim
Sales Mgr.. Hal Muthig
Mechanical Specifications: Type page 14 x 21; E - 8 cols, 1 2/3, 1/6 between; A - 8 cols, 1 2/3, 1/6 between; C - 8 cols, 1 2/3, 1/6 between.

BRONX

BRONX PRESS-REVIEW (THUR)

PO Box 1252, Bronx, NY, 10471-0620, Bronx, USA; gen tel (718) 543-5200; gen fax (718) 543-4206; disp adv e-mail rnilva@aol.com; ed e-mail bxny@aol.com; web site www.bronxpresspolitics.blogspot.com
Circulation: 20,000fr; Sworn/Estimate/Non-Audited
Advertising rate: Open inch rate $15.00
Established: 1942
Pub... Andrew Wolf
Prodn. Mgr. .... Joel Pal
Mechanical Specifications: Type page 9 7/8 x 13; E - 5 cols, 5/6, 1/6 between; A - 5 cols, 1 5/6, 1/6 between; C - 5 cols, 1/6 between.
Areas Served: Bronx, NY

BRONX TIMES REPORTER (FRI)

3604 E Tremont Ave, Ste B, Bronx, NY, 10465-2050, Bronx, USA; gen tel (718) 260-4597; adv tel (718) 260-4593; ed tel (718) 742-3396; adv fax (718) 518-0038; disp adv e-mail LGuerriero@cnglocal.com; class adv e-mail classified@cnglocal.com; ed e-mail BronxTimes@cnglocal.com; web site www.bxtimes.com
Circulation: 26,000fr; Sworn/Estimate/Non-Audited
Advertising rate: 1/8 Pg $240.00; 1/4 Pg $480.00; 1/2 Pg $960.00
Group: Community Newspaper Group
Pub. .... Laura Guerriero
Ed. .... John Collazzi
Mechanical Specifications: Type page 9.75 x 11; 6 cols, 1.5, 0.125 between
Areas Served: Allerton, Van Nest, Pelham Parkway North, Pelham Parkway South, Westchester Square, Zerega, Belmont, Waterbury, LaSalle, Pelham Bay, Country Club, Spencer Estate, Edgewater Park, Silver Beach, Locust Beach

CO-OP CITY NEWS (THUR)

135 Dreiser Loop, Bronx, NY, 10475-2704, Bronx, USA; gen tel (718) 320-3071; gen fax (718) 320-7059; disp adv e-mail bronxnews@gmail.com; ed e-mail bronxnews@gmail.com; web site https://sites.google.com/site/citynewsbx/
Circulation: 16,000fr; Sworn/Estimate/Non-Audited
Advertising rate: Open inch rate $9.42
Pub........................... Christopher G. Hagedorn
Ed. .... Mike Horowitz
Mechanical Specifications: Type page 10 x 13; E - 6 cols, 1 3/4, 1/14 between; A - 6 cols, 1 3/4, 1/14 between; C - 6 cols, 1 3/4, 1/14 between.
Delivery Method: Mail

CO-OP CITY TIMES (SAT)

2049 Bartow Ave, Rm 21, Bronx, NY, 10475-4613, Bronx, USA; gen tel (718) 320-3375; adv tel (718) 320-3375 Ext. 3384; ed tel (718) 320-3375 Ext. 3375/6; gen fax (718) 320-2595; disp adv e-mail jflynn@riverbaycorp.com; class adv e-mail jflynn@riverbaycorp.com; ed e-mail rboone@riverbaycorp.com; web site www.riverbaycorp.com
Circulation: 0pd, 18,000fr; Sworn/Estimate/Non-Audited
Established: 1966
Group: Riverbay Corporation
Ed. .... Rozaan Boone
Delivery Method: Carrier
Areas Served: 10475

PARKCHESTER NEWS (FRI)

135 Dreiser Loop, Bronx, NY, 10475-2704, Bronx, USA; gen tel (718) 320-3071; gen fax (718) 320-7059; disp adv e-mail bronxnews@gmail.com; ed e-mail bronxnews@gmail.com; web site https://sites.google.com/site/parkchesternewsbx/
Circulation: 12,200fr; Sworn/Estimate/Non-Audited
Advertising rate: Open inch rate $9.80
Group: Hagedorn Communications
Pub........................... Christopher G. Hagedorn
Ed. .... Daniel Gesslein
Mktg. Dir.. Al Zezula
Mechanical Specifications: Type page 10 x 13; E - 6 cols, 1 3/4, 1/14 between; A - 6 cols, 1 3/4, 1/14 between; C - 6 cols, 1 3/4, 1/14 between.
Delivery Method: Mail

RIVERDALE REVIEW (THUR)

PO Box 1252, Bronx, NY, 10471-0620, Bronx, USA; gen tel (718) 543-5200; gen fax (718) 543-4206; disp adv e-mail Bxny@aol.com; ed e-mail bxny@aol.com; web site www.bronxpresspolitics.blogspot.com
Circulation: 20,000fr; Sworn/Estimate/Non-Audited
Advertising rate: Open inch rate $15.00
Established: 1993
Adv. Mgr. .... Robert Nilva
Ed. .... Andrew Wolf
Prodn. Mgr. .... Joel Pal
Mechanical Specifications: Type page 9 7/8 x 13; E - 5 cols, 1 5/6, 1/6 between; A - 5 cols, 1 5/6, 1/6 between; C - 5 cols, 1 5/6, 1/6 between.
Delivery Method: Carrier, Racks
Areas Served: 10463, 10471

THE BRONX NEWS (THUR)

135 Dreiser Loop, Bronx, NY, 10475-2704, Bronx, USA; gen tel (718) 320-3071; gen fax (718) 320-7059; disp adv e-mail bronxnews@gmail.com; ed e-mail bronxnews@gmail.com; web site https://sites.google.com/site/bronxnews/
Circulation: 6,000pd, 4,000fr; Sworn/Estimate/Non-Audited
Advertising rate: Open inch rate $11.60
Established: 1976
Group: Hagedorn Communications
Pub........................... Christopher G. Hagedorn
Ed. .... Daniel Gesslein
Mktg. Dir.. Al Zezula
Mechanical Specifications: Type page 10 x 13; E - 6 cols, 1 3/4, 1/14 between; A - 6 cols, 1 3/4, 1/14 between; C - 6 cols, 1 3/4, 1/14 between.
Delivery Method: Mail

THE RIVERDALE PRESS (THUR)

5676 Riverdale Ave, Ste 311, Bronx, NY, 10471-2100, Bronx, USA; gen tel (718) 543-6065; gen fax (718) 548-4038; disp adv e-mail newsroom@riverdalepress.com; class adv e-mail classified@riverdalepress.com; ed e-mail mhinman@riverdalepress.com; web site www.riverdalepress.com

Circulation: 8,140pd, 2,500fr; Sworn/Estimate/Non-Audited
Advertising rate: Open inch rate $30.10
Established: 1950
Group: Joseph Jacobs Organization
Richner Communications, Inc.
Mechanical Specifications: Type page 13 x 21; E - 6 cols, 1 7/8, 1/6 between; A - 6 cols, 1 7/8, 1/6 between; C - 8 cols, 1 3/8, between. Equipment & Software: Hardware — APP/Mac; Software — QPS/QuarkXPress 5.0, Microsoft/Works, Microsoft/Word.
Delivery Method: Mail, Newsstand, Racks
Areas Served: 10034, 10463, 10471, 10701, 10704, 10705

BROOKLYN

BAY NEWS (FRI)

1 Metrotech Ctr N, Fl 10, Brooklyn, NY, 11201-3875, Kings, USA; gen tel (718) 260-2500; adv tel (718) 260-2510; adv fax (718) 260-2549; disp adv e-mail JStern@CNGLocal.com; class adv e-mail Classified@CNGLocal.com; ed e-mail editorial@cnglocal.com; web site www.brooklyndaily.com
Circulation: 32,000fr; Sworn/Estimate/Non-Audited
Advertising rate: Open Inch rate $61.00
Group: Community News Group
Courier Life Publications, Inc.
EIC....Vince DiMiceli
Mechanical Specifications: Type page 9.75 x 11; 6 cols, 1.5, 0.125 between
Delivery Method: Carrier, Racks
Areas Served: 11204, 11214, 11223, 11224, 11228, 11229, 11235,

BAY RIDGE COURIER (THUR)

1 Metrotech Ctr N, Fl 10, Brooklyn, NY, 11201-3875, Kings, USA; gen tel (718) 615-2500; gen fax (718) 260-2592; disp adv e-mail jstern@cnglocal.com; class adv e-mail classified@cnglocal.com; ed e-mail editorial@cnglocal.com; web site www.brooklyndaily.com
Circulation: 19,000pd,; Sworn/Estimate/Non-Audited
Advertising rate: 1/12 Pg $78.00; 1/8 Pg $117.00; 1/16 Pg $149.00
Group: Community Newspaper Group
Courier Life Publications, Inc.
Pub....Clifford Luster
Circ. Mgr....Jennifer Stern
Ed....Ken Brown
VP, Display Sales....Ralph D'onofrio
Classified Adv. Mgr....Amanda Tarley
Mechanical Specifications: Type page 11 1/4 x 15; E - 6 cols, 1 1/2, 1/4 between; A - 6 cols, 1 1/2, 1/4 between; C - 7 cols, 1, between.
Delivery Method: Carrier, Racks
Areas Served: 11204 11214 11223 11224 11228 11229 11235 11204 11218 11210 11229 11230 11203 11225 11226 11209 11228 11219 11220

BROOKLYN COURIER (THUR)

1 Metrotech Ctr N, Fl 10, Brooklyn, NY, 11201-3875, Kings, USA; gen tel (718) 260-2500; disp adv e-mail jstern@cnglocal.com; class adv e-mail classified@cnglocal.com; ed e-mail editorial@cnglocal.com; web site www.brooklypaper.com
Advertising rate: Open Inch rate $29.00
Group: Community Newspaper Group
Courier Life Publications, Inc.
Classified Adv. Mgr....Amanda Tarley
Pub....Clifford Luster
Delivery Method: Carrier, Racks
Areas Served: 11215 12217 12237 12218 11201 11217 11231 11211 11226 11220 11323

BROOKLYN HEIGHTS PRESS & COBBLE HILL NEWS (THUR)

16 Court St Ste 3000, Suite 1208, Brooklyn, NY, 11241-1013, Kings, USA; gen tel (718) 858-2300; gen fax (718) 858-4483; disp adv e-mail kat@brooklyneagle.com; class adv e-mail kat@brooklyneagle.com; ed e-mail jdh@brooklyneagle.com; web site www.brooklyneagle.com
Circulation: 12,500pd,; Sworn/Estimate/Non-Audited
Advertising rate: Open inch rate $35.28
Established: 1937
Group: Everything Brooklyn Media
Pub....Dozier Hasty
Adv. Mgr....Pat Higgins
Ed....Henrick Kroquis

CANARSIE COURIER (THUR)

1142 E 92nd St, Brooklyn, NY, 11236-3624, Kings, USA; gen tel (718) 257-0600; gen fax (718) 272-0870; disp adv e-mail canarsiec@aol.com; web site www.canarsiecourier.com
Circulation: 10,000pd,; Sworn/Estimate/Non-Audited
Advertising rate: Open inch rate $26.73
Established: 1921
Pub....Donna M. Marra
Bus. Mgr....Catherine RosaEquipment & Software: Hardware — APP/Mac.
Delivery Method: Mail, Newsstand
Areas Served: 11236, 11234, 11239, 11203, 11229, 11207

CARIBBEAN LIFE (TUES)

1 Metrotech Ctr N, Ste 1001, Brooklyn, NY, 11201-3832, Kings, USA; gen tel (718) 260-2500; adv tel (718) 260-8302; ed tel (718) 260-8318; adv fax (718) 260-2579; disp adv e-mail jstern@cnglocal.com; class adv e-mail classified@cnglocal.com; ed e-mail VDiMiceli@CNGLocal.com; web site www.caribbeanlifenews.com
Circulation: 71,500fr; Sworn/Estimate/Non-Audited
Advertising rate: 1/12 Pg $421.00; 1/8 Pg $632.00; 1/6 Pg $801.00
Group: Community Newspaper Group
Pub....Clifford Luster
VP, Display Sales....Ralph D'onofrio
Mechanical Specifications: Type page 9.75 x 11; 6 cols, 1.5, 0.125 between
Areas Served: Canarsie, Flatbush, Flatlands, Brownsville, Bed Stuyvesant, East New York, East Flatbush, Harlem, Jamaica, Hollis St Albans, Rochdale, Laurelton, Springfield Gardens, Rosedale, Cambria Heights, Queens Village, Richmond Hill, BayChester, Co-op City, Morris Park, Parkchester, Tremont, Soundview, Mt Vernon, Mott Haven, Fleetwood, Pelham Manor, Eastchester, Kingsbridge, Norwood, Wakefield

EAST VILLAGER AND LOWER EAST SIDER (THUR, BI-MTHLY)

1 Metrotech Ctr N, 10th Floor, Brooklyn, NY, 11201-3832, New York, USA; gen tel (212) 229-1890; adv tel (212) 229-1890 x2496; gen fax (212) 229-2790; disp adv e-mail news@thevillager.com; ed e-mail news@thevillager.com; web site www.eastvillagernews.com
Advertising rate: Full - $1,675; 1/2 - $1,045; 1/4 - $655; 1/8 - $420
Group: NYC Community Media, LLCJennifer Goodstein
Scott Stiffler
Areas Served: 1002 10003 10006 1007 10009 10010 10012

HOME REPORTER AND SUNSET NEWS (THUR)

8723 3rd Ave, Brooklyn, NY, 11209-5103, Kings, USA; gen tel (718) 238-6600; gen fax (718) 238-6630; disp adv e-mail ads@homereporternews.com; ed e-mail editorial@homereporternews.com; web site www.homereporter.com
Circulation: 9,696pd,; Sworn/Estimate/Non-Audited
Advertising rate: Open inch rate $1.70
Pub....J. Frank Griffin
Ed....Rick Buttacavoli

MILL-MARINE COURIER & CANARSIE DIGEST (THUR)

1 Metrotech Ctr Ste 1001, Suite 1001, Brooklyn, NY, 11201-3949, Kings, USA; gen tel (718) 260-2500; ed tel (718) 260-8303; gen fax (718) 615-3828; disp adv e-mail JStern@CNGLocal.com; class adv e-mail Classified@CNGLocal.com; ed e-mail Editorial@CNGLocal.com; web site www.brooklyndaily.com
Circulation: 8,645pd, 1,490fr; Sworn/Estimate/Non-Audited
Advertising rate: Open inch rate $11.20
Established: 1959
Group: Courier Life Publications, Inc.
Pub....Clifford Luster
Gen. Mgr....Dan Holt
Circ. Mgr....Jennifer Stern
Ed....Ken Brown
Mechanical Specifications: Type page 11 1/4 x 15; E - 6 cols, 1 1/2, 1/4 between; A - 6 cols, 1 1/2, 1/4 between; C - 7 cols, 1, between.
Delivery Method: Carrier, Racks
Areas Served: 11234 11236 11239

SPRING CREEK SUN (FRI, BI-MTHLY)

1540 Van Siclen Ave Ste 4, Ste. 4, Brooklyn, NY, 11239-2429, Kings, USA; gen tel (718) 240-4554; adv tel (718) 240-4554; ed tel (718) 240-4554; ed fax (718) 240-4599; disp adv e-mail pstern@springcreektowers.com; class adv e-mail pstern@springcreektowers.com; ed e-mail pstern@springcreektowers.com; web site springcreeksunonline.com
Circulation: 8,500fr; Sworn/Estimate/Non-Audited
Established: 1974
Group: Starrett City Inc.
Digital Platform - Mobile: Apple, Android, Windows
Reporter....Amanda Moses
Pamela Stern
Mechanical Specifications: Type page 10 x 14; E - 5 cols, 2, 1/8 between; A - 5 cols, 2, 1/8 between; C - 5 cols, 2, 1/8 between.Equipment & Software: Hardware — PC platform; Software — quarkx, adobe suite
Delivery Method: Mail, Carrier, Racks
Areas Served: 11239

THE BROOKLYN PAPERS (FRI)

1 Metrotech Ctr N, Ste 1001, Brooklyn, NY, 11201-3832, Kings, USA; gen tel (718) 260-2500; adv tel (718) 260-2510; adv fax (718) 260-2579; disp adv e-mail RDonofrio@cnglocal.com; class adv e-mail classified@cnglocal.com; ed e-mail editorial@cnglocal.com; web site www.brooklynpaper.com
Circulation: 25,600fr; Sworn/Estimate/Non-Audited
Advertising rate: Open inch rate $101.00
Group: Community Newspaper GroupEditions: (12) 12 total; Bay Ridge Paper; Bensonhurst Paper; Brooklyn Heights Paper; Carroll Garden-Cobble Hill Paper; Downtown News; Fort Greene-Clinton Hill Paper; Kensington Paper; Midwood Paper; Ocean Parkway Paper; Park Slope Paper; Sunset Park Paper; Windsor Terr
Ed.-in-Chief....Vince DiMirceli
Clifford Luster
Deputy Ed....Nathan Tempey
Mechanical Specifications: Type page 11 x 20.125; 8 cols, 1.27, 0.12 between
Areas Served: Brooklyn Heights, Boerum Hill, Downtown, Dumbo, Metrotech, Vinegar Hill, Carroll Gardens, Cobble Hill, Columbia St. Waterfront District, Red Hook, Gowanus, Greenwood Heights, Park Slope, Prospect Heights, Sunset Park, Windsor Terrace, Bushwick, East Williamsburg, Greenpoint, Williamsburg, Bay Ridge, Dyker Heights

THE BROOKLYN SPECTATOR (FRI)

9733 4th Ave, Brooklyn, NY, 11209-8104, Kings, USA; gen tel (718) 238-6600; gen fax (718) 238-6630; disp adv e-mail clatorre@brooklynreporter.com; class adv e-mail clatorre@brooklynreporter.com; ed e-mail editorial@brooklynreporter.com; web site http://brooklynspectator.com/
Circulation: 800pd, 10,000fr; Sworn/Estimate/Non-Audited
Advertising rate: varies
Group: Schneps Communications
Pub....Joshua Schneps
VP, S&O....Christine LaTorre
EIC....Helen Klein
Delivery Method: Mail, Newsstand, Racks
Areas Served: kings county

THE GREENPOINT GAZETTE (WED)

597 Manhattan Ave, Apt 1, Brooklyn, NY, 11222-3924, Kings, USA; gen tel (718) 389-6067; gen fax (718) 349-3471; disp adv e-mail jeff@greenpointnews.com; ed e-mail jeff@greenpointnews.com; web site www.greenpointnews.com
Circulation: 9,000pd,; Sworn/Estimate/Non-Audited
Advertising rate: (Modular Rates) 2 x 4 - $25 1x
Established: 1973
Ed. & Pub....Jeff Mann
Mechanical Specifications: Type page 10 x 14
Areas Served: Greenpoint, Williamsburg, Bushwick, East Williamsburg, lower Manhattan, Long Island City

THE PHOENIX (FRI)

16 Court St, Ste 1208, Brooklyn, NY, 11241-1012, Kings, USA; gen tel (718) 858-2300; gen fax (718) 858-4483; disp adv e-mail edit@brooklyneagle.net; ed e-mail publisher@BrooklynEagle.com; web site www.brooklyneagle.com
Circulation: 13,000pd,; Sworn/Estimate/Non-Audited
Advertising rate: Open inch rate $35.28
Established: 1972
Group: Everything Brooklyn Media
Pub....J.D. Hasty
Mng. Ed....Samanhta Samel

THE VILLAGER (THUR)

1 Metrotech Ctr Fl 10th, 10th Floor, Brooklyn, NY, 11201-3948, Kings, USA; gen tel (212) 229-1890; adv tel (212) 229-1890 x2496; ed tel (646) 452-2464; gen fax (212) 229-2790; disp adv e-mail atarley@downtownexpress.com; ed e-mail lincoln@thevillager.com; web site www.thevillager.com
Circulation: 20,000pd,; Sworn/Estimate/Non-Audited
Advertising rate: Full - $1,675; 1/2 - $1,045; 1/4 - $655; 1/8 - $420
Established: 1933
Group: NYC Community Media, LLCScott Stiffler
Jennifer Goodstein
Mechanical Specifications: Type page 10 x 14; E - 4 cols, 2 1/4, between; A - 6 cols, 1 1/2, between; C - 6 cols, 1 1/2, between.Equipment & Software: Hardware — PC; Software — Adobe/PageMaker 6.0.
Areas Served: 10001 10003 10012 10013 10014

BUFFALO

BUFFALO BUSINESS FIRST (FRI)

465 Main St, Ste 100, Buffalo, NY, 14203-1717, Erie, USA; gen tel (716) 854-5822; gen fax (716) 854-3394; disp adv e-mail buffalo@bizjournals.com; web site www.buffalo.bizjournals.com
Advertising rate: 1/8 P $1335 1/4 P $2310 1/2 P $3665 Full $5105
Pub....Jack Connors

BUFFALO LAW JOURNAL (MON)

465 Main St, Ste 100, Buffalo, NY, 14203-1717, Erie, USA; gen tel (716) 541-1650; gen fax (716) 854-3826; ed e-mail jconnors@bizjournals.com; web site http://www.lawjournalbuffalo.com
General Mgr....Kim Schaus
Pub....Jack Connors

BUSINESS FIRST OF BUFFALO (FRI)

465 Main St, Ste 100, Buffalo, NY, 14203-1717, Erie, USA; gen tel (716) 541-1600; gen fax (716) 854-3394; disp adv e-mail buffalo@bizjournals.com; web site http://buffalo.bizjournals.com
Advertising rate: 1/8 P $540; 1/2 P $1480; Full $3115
Established: 1984
Digital Platform - Mobile: Apple, Android
Pub....Jack Connors
Delivery Method: Mail, Newsstand

GOWANDA NEWS (SAT)

75 Boxwood Ln, Buffalo, NY, 14227-2707, Erie, USA; gen tel (716) 532-2288; ed tel 7165322288 ext 104; gen fax (716) 532-3056; disp adv e-mail mstockdale@metrowny.com; ed e-mail mpankow@metrowny.com; web site www.metrowny.com - 1,640(views) 1,032(visitors)
Circulation: 9,059fr; CVC
Advertising rate: CP
Established: 1827
Group: Metro Group, Inc.
Digital Platform - Mobile: Apple, Android
Digital Platform - Tablet: Apple iOS, Android, Blackberry Tablet OS, Kindle
Ed. .... Mary Pankow
Ad. Sales .... Maureen Stockdale
Off. Mgr. .... Judy Covert
Pub. .... Gary Durawa
Circ. Mgr .... Bill Marshall
Areas Served: 14034, 14035, 14062, 14070, 14081, 14091, 14111, 14129, 14138, 14719, 14723, 14726

SPRINGVILLE JOURNAL (SAT)

75 Boxwood Ln, Buffalo, NY, 14227-2707, Erie, USA; gen tel (716) 592-4550; ed tel (716) 592-4550 ext. 24; gen fax (716) 592-4663; disp adv e-mail info@springvillejournal.com; ed e-mail lschumer@springvillejournal.com; web site www.metrowny.com - 7,293(views) 5,071(visitors)
Circulation: 0pd, 7,420fr; CVC
Advertising rate: CP
Established: 1939
Group: Metro Group, Inc.
Digital Platform - Mobile: Apple, Android
Digital Platform - Tablet: Apple iOS, Android, Windows 7, Blackberry Tablet OS, Kindle
Pub. .... Denny Guastaferro
Ed. .... Lizz Schumer
Circ. Mgr. .... Sandy Dashnaw
Pub. .... Gary Durawa
Adv. Mgr. .... Judy Beckwith
Circ. Mgr .... Bill Marshall
Mechanical Specifications: Type page: 10.25 x 16; 6 col
Areas Served: Springville, Ashford, Boston, Concord, Sardinia, Colden, and East Otto

CALLICOON

SULLIVAN COUNTY DEMOCRAT (TUES, FRI)

5 Lower Main St, Callicoon, NY, 12723-5000, Sullivan, USA; gen tel (845) 887-5200; gen fax (845) 887-5386; disp adv e-mail lizt@sc-democrat.com; class adv e-mail class@sc-democrat.com; ed e-mail editor@sc-democrat.com; web site http://www.scdemocratonline.com/
Circulation: 9,000pd,; USPS
Advertising rate: Open inch rate $11.72
Established: 1891
Group: Catskill-Delaware Publications
Co-Editor .... Joseph Abraham
Co-Editor .... Matt Shortall
Advertising Director .... Liz Tucker
Publisher .... Fred Stabbert III
Business Manager .... Sue Owens
Mechanical Specifications: Type page 11 1/4 x 21; E - 6 cols, 2, 1/6 between; A - 6 cols, 2, 1/6 between; C - 9 cols, 1 3/8, between.
Delivery Method: Mail, Newsstand, Racks

CAMDEN

QUEEN CENTRAL NEWS (MON)

39 Main St, Camden, NY, 13316-1301, Oneida, USA; gen tel (315)245-1849; gen fax (315)245-1880 ; disp adv e-mail theqcn@gmail.com; ed e-mail theqcn@gmail.com; web site http://www.queencentralnews.com/
Advertising rate: Open inch rate $5.50
Established: 1974
Ed & Owner .... Jim Van Winkle
Ad. Mgr. .... Dori Monteith
Delivery Method: Mail, Racks
Areas Served: 13316, 13437, 13042, 13044, 13401, 13493, 13471, 13028, 13308, 13123, 13157, 13162, 13493, 13483, 13302

CANANDAIGUA

BRIGHTON-PITTSFORD POST (THUR)

73 Buffalo St, Canandaigua, NY, 14424-1001, Ontario, USA; gen tel (585) 394-0770; ed tel (585) 337-4276; gen fax (585) 394-4160; disp adv e-mail bkesel@messengerpostmedia.com; class adv e-mail classifieds@messengerpostmedia.com; ed e-mail bdoane@messengerpostmedia.com; web site www.mpnnow.com - 700,000(views) 200,000(visitors)
Circulation: 147pd, 8,305fr; AAM
Advertising rate: Full Pg $810.00; 1/2 Pg $405.00; 1/4 Pg $203.00; 1/8 Pg $99.00
Group: Messenger Post Media
Pres./Pub. .... Beth Kesel
Mechanical Specifications: Type page 13 x 20 1/2; E - 6 cols, 2 1/12, 1/6 between; A - 6 cols, 2 1/12, 1/6 between; C - 8 cols, 1 1/2, 1/6 between.Equipment & Software: Hardware — APP/Mac; Presses — G/Community, Hamada/11 x 17 665 sheet-fed; Software — QPS/QuarkXPress, Adobe/PageMaker Adobe/Photoshop.
Areas Served: 14534 14610 14618 14620

EAST ROCHESTER-FAIRPORT POST (THUR)

73 Buffalo St, Canandaigua, NY, 14424-1001, Ontario, USA; gen tel (585) 394-0770; gen fax (585) 394-4160; disp adv e-mail bkesel@messengerpostmedia.com; class adv e-mail classifieds@messengerpostmedia.com; ed e-mail byoung@messengerpostmedia.com; web site www.mpnnow.com - 700,000(views) 200,000(visitors)
Circulation: 108pd, 5,179fr; AAM
Advertising rate: Full Pg $810.00; 1/2 Pg $405.00; 1/4 Pg $203.00; 1/8 Pg $99.00
Group: Messenger Post Media
Pres./Pub. .... Beth Kesel
Delivery Method: Mail
Areas Served: 14450 14445

GATES-CHILI POST (THUR)

73 Buffalo St, Canandaigua, NY, 14424-1001, Ontario, USA; gen tel (585) 394-0770; gen fax (585) 394-4160; disp adv e-mail bkesel@messengerpostmedia.com; class adv e-mail classifieds@messengerpostmedia.com; ed e-mail jbattaglia@messengerpostmedia.com; web site www.mpnnow.com - 700,000(views) 200,000(visitors)
Circulation: 52pd, 4,973fr; AAM
Advertising rate: Full - $810; 1/2 - $405; 1/4 - $203; 1/8 - $99
Group: Messenger Post Media
Pres./Pub. .... Beth Kesel
Mechanical Specifications: Type page 11 7/8 x 20 1/2; E - 6 cols, 1 13/16, 1/8 between; A - 6 cols, 1 13/16, 1/8 between; C - 8 cols, 1 3/8, 1/8 between.Equipment & Software: Hardware — APP/Mac; Presses — G/Community; Software — QPS/QuarkXPress, Adobe/Photoshop.
Delivery Method: Mail
Areas Served: 14606 14624

GREECE POST (THUR)

73 Buffalo St, Canandaigua, NY, 14424-1001, Ontario, USA; gen tel (585) 394-0770; gen fax (585) 394-4160; disp adv e-mail bkesel@messengerpostmedia.com; class adv e-mail classifieds@messengerpostmedia.com; ed e-mail bdoane@messengerpostmedia.com; web site www.mpnnow.com - 700,000(views) 200,000(visitors)
Circulation: 88pd, 14,569fr; AAM
Advertising rate: Full - $810; 1/2 - $405; 1/4 - $203; 1/8 - $99
Group: Messenger Post Media
Gen. Mgr./Adv. Dir. .... Beth Kesel
Pres./Pub. .... Brian Doane
Mechanical Specifications: Type page 11 7/8 x 20 1/2; E - 6 cols, 1 13/16, 1/8 between; A - 6 cols, 1 13/16, 1/8 between; C - 8 cols, 1 3/8, 1/8 between.Equipment & Software: Hardware — APP/Mac; Presses — G/Community, Hamada/11 x 17 665 sheet-fed; Software — QPS/QuarkXPress, Adobe/Photoshop.
Delivery Method: Mail
Areas Served: 14612 14616 14626

IRONDEQUOIT POST (THUR)

73 Buffalo St, Canandaigua, NY, 14424-1001, Ontario, USA; gen tel (585) 394-0770; gen fax (585) 394-4160; disp adv e-mail bkesel@messengerpostmedia.com; class adv e-mail classifieds@messengerpostmedia.com; ed e-mail lquinlan@messengerpostmedia.com; web site www.mpnnow.com - 700,000(views) 200,000(visitors)
Circulation: 83pd, 7,104fr; AAM
Advertising rate: Full - $810; 1/2 - $405; 1/4 - $203; 1/8 - $99
Group: Messenger Post MediaBeth Kesel
Brian Doane
Delivery Method: Mail
Areas Served: 14609 14617 14622

MESSENGER POST MEDIA (WED, THUR, FRI)

73 Buffalo St, Canandaigua, NY, 14424-1001, Ontario, USA; gen tel (585) 394-0770; adv tel (585) 394-0770; ed tel (585) 394-0770; gen fax (585) 394-1675; disp adv e-mail bkesel@messengerpostmedia.com; class adv e-mail advertising@messengerpostmedia.com; ed e-mail bkesel@messengerpostmedia.com; web site www.mpnnow.com
Circulation: 0pd, 8,975fr; CVC
Advertising rate: Open inch rate $19.75
Established: 1970
Group: GateHouse Media, Inc.Editions: (3) 3 total Ad Net Community News-Canandaigua (17,353);
Pub. .... Brian Doane
Exe. Ed. .... Brian Doane
Mng. Ed./Content .... Allison Cooper
Mng. Ed./Presentation .... Kevin Frisch
Adv. Dir. .... Beth Kesel
Production Director .... Brian Ambor
Mechanical Specifications: Type page 10 1/4 x 12; E - 5 cols, 2 1/3, 1/6 between; A - 6 cols, 1 3/5, 1/6 between; C - 6 cols, 1 3/5, 1/6 between.Equipment & Software: Hardware — APP/Power Mac, PC, AG/Duoscan Scanner, Elite 808, APP/Mac Laserwriter Pro 630, AG/Accuset 1000; Software — Multi-Ad/Creator 4.02, QPS/QuarkXPress 3.2.
Delivery Method: Mail, Newsstand, Carrier, Racks
Areas Served: 14425

PENFIELD POST (THUR)

73 Buffalo St, Canandaigua, NY, 14424-1001, Ontario, USA; gen tel (585) 394-0770; gen fax (585) 394-4160; disp adv e-mail bkesel@messengerpostmedia.com; class adv e-mail classifieds@mpnewspapers.com; ed e-mail byoung@messengerpostmedia.com; web site www.mpnnow.com - 700,000(views) 200,000(visitors)
Circulation: 94pd, 3,241fr; AAM
Advertising rate: Open inch rate $9.23
Established: 1971
Group: Messenger Post Media
Ed. .... Allison Cooper
Brian Doane
Beth Kesel
Mechanical Specifications: Type page 11 7/8 x 20 1/2; E - 6 cols, 1 13/16, 1/8 between; A - 6 cols, 1 13/16, 1/8 between; C - 8 cols, 1 3/8, 1/8 between.Equipment & Software: Hardware — APP/Mac; Presses — G/Community, Hamada/11 x 17 665 sheet-fed; Software — QPS/QuarkXPress, Adobe/Photoshop.
Delivery Method: Mail
Areas Served: 14526 14625

RUSH-HENRIETTA POST (THUR)

73 Buffalo St, Canandaigua, NY, 14424-1001, Ontario, USA; gen tel (585) 394-0770; gen fax (585) 394-4160; disp adv e-mail bkesel@messengerpostmedia.com; class adv e-mail classifieds@messengerpostmedia.com; ed e-mail mshippers@messengerpostmedia.com; web site www.mpnnow.com - 700,000(views) 200,000(visitors)
Circulation: 68pd, 2,924fr; AAM
Advertising rate: Full - $810; 1/2 - $405; 1/4 - $203; 1/8 - $99
Group: Messenger Post Media
Mng. Ed. .... Allison Cooper
Pub. .... Brian Doane
Beth Kesel
Mechanical Specifications: Type page 11 7/8 x 20 1/2; E - 6 cols, 1 13/16, 1/8 between; A - 6 cols, 1 13/16, 1/8 between; C - 8 cols, 1 3/8, 1/8 between.Equipment & Software: Hardware — APP/Mac; Presses — G/Community, Hamada/11 x 17 665 sheet-fed; Software — QPS/QuarkXPress, Adobe/Photoshop.
Delivery Method: Mail
Areas Served: 14467 14586 14623

VICTOR POST (FRI)

73 Buffalo St, Canandaigua, NY, 14424-1001, Ontario, USA; gen tel (585) 394-0770; gen fax (585) 394-4160; disp adv e-mail bkesel@messengerpostmedia.com; class adv e-mail classifieds@messengerpostmedia.com; ed e-mail bdoane@messengerpostmedia.com; web site www.mpnnow.com - 700,000(views) 200,000(visitors)
Circulation: 16pd, 3,674fr; AAM
Advertising rate: Open inch rate 13.50
Group: GateHouse Media, Inc.
Pres./Pub. .... Brian Doane
General Mgr./Adv. Director .... Beth Kesel
Delivery Method: Mail
Areas Served: 14425 14564

WAYNE POST (WED)

73 Buffalo St, Canandaigua, NY, 14424-1001, Ontario, USA; gen tel (585) 394-0770; gen fax (585) 394-4160; disp adv e-mail bkesel@messengerpostmedia.com; class adv e-mail classifieds@messengerpostmedia.com; ed e-mail bdoane@messengerpostmedia.com; web site www.mpnnow.com - 700,000(views) 200,000(visitors)
Circulation: 1,317pd, 170fr; AAM
Established: 1876
Group: GateHouse Media, Inc.
Gen. Mgr./Adv. Dir. .... Beth Kesel
Pres./Pub. .... Brian Doane
Delivery Method: Mail
Areas Served: 14502 14513 14522

WEBSTER POST (THUR)

73 Buffalo St, Canandaigua, NY, 14424-1001, Ontario, USA; gen tel (585) 394-0770; gen fax (585) 394-4160; disp adv e-mail bkesel@messengerpostmedia.com; class adv e-mail classifieds@messengerpostmedia.com; ed e-mail bdoane@messengerpostmedia.com; web site www.mpnnow.com - 700,000(views) 200,000(visitors)
Circulation: 71pd, 4,750fr; AAM
Advertising rate: Full - $810; 1/2 - $405; 1/4 - $203; 1/8 - $99
Group: Messenger Post Media
Gen. Mgr./Adv. Dir. .... Beth Kesel
Pres./Pub. .... Brian Doane
Mechanical Specifications: Type page 13 x 20 1/2; E - 6 cols, 1 13/16, 1/8 between; A - 6 cols, 1 13/16, 1/8 between; C - 8 cols, 1 3/8, 1/8 between.Equipment & Software: Hardware — APP/Mac; Presses — G/Community, Hamada/11 x 17 665 sheet-fed; Software — QPS/QuarkXPress, Adobe/PageMaker, Adobe/Photoshop.
Delivery Method: Mail
Areas Served: 14580

CANTON

ST. LAWRENCE PLAINDEALER (TUES)

1 Main St, Ste 103, Canton, NY, 13617-1279, St. Lawrence, USA; gen tel (315) 386-8521; gen fax (315) 393-5108; disp adv e-mail pdealer@ogd.com; web site http://www.watertowndailytimes.com/section/news05
Circulation: 156pd, 1fr; AAM
Advertising rate: Open inch rate $6.95
Mng. Ed. .... Pery White

CATSKILL

WINDHAM JOURNAL (THUR)

414 Main St, Catskill, NY, 12414-1303, Greene, USA; gen tel (518) 943-2100; gen fax (518) 943-2063; disp adv e-mail advertising@thedailymail.net; ed e-mail lanander.windhamjournal@registerstar.com; web site http://www.columbiagreenemedia.com/windham_journal/
Circulation: 2,400pd,; Sworn/Estimate/Non-Audited
Advertising rate: Open inch rate $6.50
Established: 1857
Pub....................................... Mark Vinciguerra
Adv. Mgr....................................... Pam Geskie
Ed.. Lori Anander

CHESTER

DIRT MAGAZINE (BI-MTHLY)

20 West Ave, Chester, NY, 10918-1032, Orange, USA; gen tel (845) 469-9000; disp adv e-mail artdept@strausnews.com; class adv e-mail artdept@strausnews.com; ed e-mail editor.dirt@strausnews.com; web site www.dirt-mag.com
Circulation: 20,233fr; AAM
Advertising rate: 1/4P $790, 1/2P $1330
Established: 2011
Group: Straus News
Mng. Ed .... Mike Zummo
Pub..Jeanne Straus
Delivery Method: Mail

PHOTO NEWS (FRI)

20 West Ave, Ste 201, Chester, NY, 10918-1053, Orange, USA; gen tel (845) 469-9000; gen fax (845) 469-9001; disp adv e-mail sales@strausnews.com; ed e-mail nyoffice@strausnews.com; web site www.thephoto-news.com
Circulation: 6,701fr; AAM
Advertising rate: Open inch rate $15.00
Established: 1986
Group: Straus News
Pres. ....Jeanne Straus
Mng. Ed....................................... Mike Zummo
Mechanical Specifications: Type page 10 1/4 x 14; E - 6 cols, 1 1/2, between; A - 6 cols, 1 1/2, between; C - 6 cols, 1 1/2, between. Equipment & Software: Hardware — APP/Mac; Software — QPS/QuarkXPress, Microsoft/Word.
Areas Served: 10950 10917 10930 10926 10987

THE ADVERTISER-NEWS (NORTH) (THUR)

20 West Ave, Ste 101, Chester, NY, 10918-1053, Orange, USA; gen tel (845) 469-9000; gen fax (845) 469-9001; disp adv e-mail njoffice@strausnews.com; web site www.strausnews.com
Circulation: 20,619fr; Sworn/Estimate/Non-Audited
Advertising rate: Open inch rate $21.00
Group: Straus NewsEditions: (2) 2 total Advertiser-News North Edition (10,875); Advertiser-News South Edition (9,744);
Pres. ....Jeanne Straus
Mng. Ed....................................... Mike Zummo
Mechanical Specifications: Type page 10 1/4 x 14; E - 6 cols, 1 1/2, between; A - 6 cols, between; C - 6 cols, between.Equipment & Software: Hardware — APP/Mac; Software — Microsoft/Word, QPS/QuarkXPress.
Areas Served: 07462, 07461, 07416, 07419, 07848

WARWICK ADVERTISER (FRI)

20 West Ave, Ste 201, Chester, NY, 10918-1053, Orange, USA; gen tel (845) 469-9000; gen fax (845) 469-9001; disp adv e-mail sales@strausnews.com; ed e-mail nyoffice@strausnews.com; web site www.warwickadvertiser.com
Circulation: 6,617fr; AAM
Advertising rate: Open inch rate $15.00
Established: 1866
Group: Straus News
Pres. ....Jeanne Straus
Mng. Ed....................................... Mike Zummo
Mechanical Specifications: Type page 10 1/4 x 14; E - 6 cols, 1 1/2, between; A - 6 cols, 1 1/2, between; C - 6 cols, 1 1/2, between. Equipment & Software: Hardware — APP/Mac; Software — Microsoft/Word, QPS/QuarkXPress.
Areas Served: 10990 10921 10969

CLARENCE

BUFFALO ROCKET (THUR)

9195 Main St, Clarence, NY, 14031-1931, Erie, USA; gen tel (716) 861-3304; adv tel (716) 861-3304; ed tel (716) 861-3304; gen fax (716) 873-8586; disp adv e-mail barbarag.gallagherprinting@gmail.com; class adv e-mail barbarag.gallagherprinting@gmail.com; ed e-mail barbarag.gallagherprinting@gmail.com; web site www.buffalorocket.com
Circulation: 14,100fr; Sworn/Estimate/Non-Audited
Advertising rate: Open inch rate $10.00
Established: 1969
Group: Gallagher Printing
Ed. .... Barbara Gilboy
Mechanical Specifications: Type page 10 x 14; 5 cols, 2
Delivery Method: Mail, Newsstand, Carrier
Areas Served: 14216;14207;14213;14214;14222;14217;14202

COBLESKILL

MY SHOPPER - MOHAWK VALLEY EDITION (SAT, SUN)

2403 State Route 7, Ste 4, Cobleskill, NY, 12043-5740, Schoharie, USA; gen tel (518) 234-8215; gen fax (518) 234-8520; disp adv e-mail production@pennysaveronline.com; web site www.myshopperonline.com
Circulation: 11,499fr; CVC
Advertising rate: $9.60
Established: 1987
Group: Snyder Communication Corp.Editions: Mohawk Valley Edition
Corporate Sales Manager ....Russ Foote
Mechanical Specifications: 96 ad units per page 6 col. wide x 16" deep
col. width 1 5/8" or 10 picas
Delivery Method: Carrier
Areas Served: Fort Plain, Canajoharie, St. Johnsville, and portions of Montgomery County in New York State

TIMES-JOURNAL (WED)

108 Division St, Ste A, Cobleskill, NY, 12043-4699, Schoharie, USA; gen tel (518) 234-2515; gen fax (518) 234-7898; disp adv e-mail tjournalads@yahoo.com; class adv e-mail tjournalclassified@yahoo.com; ed e-mail tjournalnews@yahoo.com; web site www.timesjournalonline.com
Circulation: 6,800pd, 76fr; Sworn/Estimate/Non-Audited
Advertising rate: Open inch rate $7.57
Established: 1877
Pub.. James Poole
Ed. .... Patsy Nicosia
Sales manager ....Bruce Tryon
Mechanical Specifications: Type page 10.5 x 21; A - 6 cols, 1.625, 0.0625 between; C - 8 cols, 1.25, 0.0625 between
Delivery Method: Mail, Newsstand
Areas Served: 12043, 12122, 12157, 12149, 13459, 12087, 12092

COLD SPRING

PUTNAM COUNTY NEWS & RECORDER (WED)

3 Stone St, Cold Spring, NY, 10516-3020, NY, USA; gen tel (845) 265-2468; adv tel 845-265-2468; ed tel 845-265-2468; gen fax (845) 265-2144; adv fax 845-265-2144; ed fax 845-265-2144; disp adv e-mail ads@pcnr.com; class adv e-mail ads@pcnr.com; ed e-mail editor@pcnr.com; web site www.pcnr.com
Circulation: 2,100pd,; USPS
Advertising rate: $5.75
Established: 1866
Pub .... Douglas Cunningham
Delivery Method: Mail, Newsstand
Areas Served: Western Putnam County in NY: Cold Spring, 10516; Garrison, 10524; Putnam Valley, 10579; Lake Peekskill, 10537

THE PUTNAM COUNTY COURIER (TUES)

144 Main St, Ste 1, Cold Spring, NY, 10516-2854, Putnam, USA; gen tel (845) 265-2468; adv tel (845) 265-2468; ed tel (845) 265-2468; gen fax (845) 225-1914; adv fax 845-265-2144; ed fax 845-265-2144; disp adv e-mail ads@pcnr.com; class adv e-mail ads@pcnr.com; ed e-mail editor@pcnr.com; web site www.putnamcountycourier.com
Circulation: 2,100pd,; USPS
Advertising rate: Open inch rate $5.75
Established: 1841
Pub. & Editor-in-Chief .... Douglas Cunningham
Mechanical Specifications: Type page 1 1/4 x 21; E - 6 cols, 1 7/8, 1/8 between; A - 6 cols, 1 7/8, 1/8 between; C - 8 cols, 1 4/5, 1/8 between.
Delivery Method: Mail, Newsstand
Areas Served: Carmel, 10512; Brewster, 10509; Patterson, 12563; Pawling, 12564; Stormville, 12582; Mahopac, 10541

CONKLIN

THE COUNTRY COURIER (WED)

1035 Conklin Rd, Conklin, NY, 13748-1102, Broome, USA; gen tel (607) 775-0472; gen fax (607) 775-5863; disp adv e-mail Deinstein@stny.rr.com; web site www.wecoverthetowns.com
Circulation: 1,300pd,; Sworn/Estimate/Non-Audited
Advertising rate: Open inch rate $5.00
Established: 1981
Group: Newspaper Publishers LLC
Pub. & Ad.................................Donald Einstein
Ed. .... Elizabeth Einstein
Mechanical Specifications: Type page 10 x 13.5; 6 cols, 1.5, 0.22 between
Equipment & Software: Hardware — APP/Macs.
Delivery Method: Mail, Newsstand
Areas Served: 13748, 13795, 13903, 13749

THE WINDSOR STANDARD (WED)

1035 Conklin Rd, Conklin, NY, 13748-1102, Broome, USA; gen tel (607) 775-0472; gen fax (607) 775-5863; disp adv e-mail deinstein@stny.rr.com; web site www.wecoverthetowns.com
Circulation: 1,300pd, 73fr; Sworn/Estimate/Non-Audited
Advertising rate: Open inch rate $5.00
Established: 1878
Group: Newspaper Publishers LLC
Pub and Adv. Mgr....................Donald Einstein
Ed. .... Elizabeth Einstein
Mechanical Specifications: Type page 10 x 13.5; 6 cols, 1.5, 0.22 between
Equipment & Software: Hardware — APP/Mac.
Delivery Method: Mail, Newsstand
Areas Served: 13865, 13787, 13795, 13813, 13826, 13833, 13848

VESTAL TOWN CRIER (WED)

1035 Conklin Rd, Conklin, NY, 13748-1102, Broome, USA; gen tel (607) 775-0472; gen fax (607) 775-5863; disp adv e-mail eeinstein7@gmail.com; web site www.wecoverthetowns.com
Circulation: 1,200pd,; Sworn/Estimate/Non-Audited
Advertising rate: Open inch rate $5.00
Established: 1979
Group: Newspaper Publishers LLC
Pub...Donald Einstein
Ed. .... Elizabeth Einstein
Mechanical Specifications: Type page 10 x 13.5; 6 cols, 1.5, 0.22 between
Equipment & Software: Hardware — APP/Macs; Software — CS5, MS Word
Delivery Method: Mail
Areas Served: 13850, 13732

COOPERSTOWN

COOPERSTOWN CRIER (THUR)

21 Railroad Ave, Ste 25, Cooperstown, NY, 13326-1169, Otsego, USA ; gen tel (607) 547-9493; web site http://www.coopercrier.com
Group: Community Newspaper Holdings, Inc.

CORNWALL

THE CORNWALL LOCAL (FRI)

55 Quaker Ave Ste 204, Suite 204, Cornwall, NY, 12518-2026, Orange, USA; gen tel (845) 534-7771; disp adv e-mail joegill@thecornwalllocal.com; ed e-mail kencashman@thecornwalllocal.com; web site www.thecornwalllocal.com
Circulation: 1,676pd, 67fr; Sworn/Estimate/Non-Audited
Advertising rate: Open Rate $10.60
Established: 1888
Group: News of the Highlands Inc.
VP & Pub. ....Joseph V. Gill
Ed. .... Ken Cashman
Mechanical Specifications: Type page 11 x 21; E & A - 6 cols, 1.625, 0.25 between; C - 7 cols, 1.4306, 0.1666 between
Equipment & Software: Hardware — APP/Mac; Software — QPS.
Delivery Method: Mail, Newsstand
Areas Served: 12518, 12520, 12584, 12553, 10917, 10953, 10930, 12577

THE NEWS OF THE HIGHLANDS (FRI)

C/O 55 Quaker Ave., Ste 204, Cornwall, NY, 12518, Orange, USA; gen tel (845) 534-7771; gen fax (845) 534-3855; disp adv e-mail joegill@thecornwalllocal.com; ed e-mail newsofthehighlands@gmail.com; web site www.thenewsofthehighlands.com
Circulation: 919pd, 730fr; Sworn/Estimate/Non-Audited
Established: 1891
Group: News of the Highlands Inc.
VP & Gen. Mgr.............................Joseph V. Gill
Ed. .... Mary Jane Pitt
Mechanical Specifications: Type page 11 x 21; E & A - 6 cols, 1.625, 0.25 between; C - 7 cols, 1.4306, 0.1666 between
Delivery Method: Mail, Newsstand
Areas Served: 10928, 10996, 10922

CROPSEYVILLE

THE EASTWICK PRESS (FRI)

13 Babcock Lake Rd, Cropseyville, NY, 12052-2200, Rensselaer, USA; gen tel (518) 491-1613; adv tel (518) 491-1613; ed tel (518) 491-1613; gen fax (518) 658-0013; adv fax (518) 658-0013; ed fax (518) 658-0013; disp adv e-mail ads@eastwickpress.com; class adv e-mail ads@eastwickpress.com; ed e-mail news@eastwickpress.com; web site www.eastwickpress.com
Advertising rate: Open inch rate $8.00
Established: 2017
Group: Eastwick Press LLC
Digital Platform - Mobile: Apple, Android, Blackberry
Digital Platform - Tablet: Apple iOS, Android, Blackberry Tablet OS
Publisher, editor....................Doug La Rocque
Graphic Design, Reporter............Alex Brooks
Copy Editor.............................. Bea Peterson
Publisher, Advertising...........Tom Withcuskey
Photo Journalist.........................Steve Bradley
Photo Journalist........................Thaddeus Flint
Photo Journalist........................ Amy Modesti
Delivery Method: Mail, Racks

Areas Served: Petersburgh, Hoosick, Berlin, Grafton, and Stephentown Brunswick,Pittstown, New Lebanon

CUBA

CUBA PATRIOT & FREE PRESS (WED)

25 W Main St, Cuba, NY, 14727-1403, Allegany, USA; gen tel (585) 968-2580; gen fax (585) 968-2622; disp adv e-mail sales@cubapatriot.com; ed e-mail mail@cubapatriot.com; web site www.cubapatriot.com
Circulation: 3,870pd,; Sworn/Estimate/Non-Audited
Advertising rate: Open inch rate $8.70
Established: 1862
Managing Ed....Melodie Farwell
Pub....Christina Arden-Hopkins
Ad. Sales....Donna Falandys
Mechanical Specifications: Type page 10 x 16; 5 cols, 1.891, 0.128 between
Equipment & Software: Hardware — APP/Mac; Software — Adobe/PageMaker 4.2, Microsoft/Word, Multi-Ad.

DANSVILLE

GENESEE COUNTRY EXPRESS (THUR)

113 Main St, Ste 2, Dansville, NY, 14437-1611, Livingston, USA; gen tel (585) 335-2271; gen fax (585) 335-6957; disp adv e-mail lesbowen@dansvilleonline.com; class adv e-mail kellyschecter@dansvilleonline.com; ed e-mail lesbowen@dansvilleonline.com; web site www.dansvilleonline.com
Circulation: 2,500pd, 6fr; Sworn/Estimate/Non-Audited
Advertising rate: Open inch rate $7.50
Established: 1851
Group: GateHouse Media, Inc.Editions: (1) Genesee Country Express
Advertising Director....Melissa VanSkiver
Regional Publisher....Rick Emanuel
Editor....John Anderson
Multi-Media Sales Executive Judy Smith-Cronk
Mechanical Specifications: Type page 13 x 21; E - 6 cols, 1 7/8, 1/16 between; A - 6 cols, 1 7/8, 1/16 between; C - 6 cols, 1 7/8, 1/16 between.Equipment & Software: Hardware — APP/Mac; Software — MultiAd/Creator, QPS/QuarkXPress.
Delivery Method: Mail, Newsstand
Areas Served: 14435, 14572, 14454, 14510, 14517, 14529, 14560, 14572, 14822, 14826, 14437

DELHI

THE REPORTER (WED)

97 Main St, Ste 5, Delhi, NY, 13753-1231, Delaware, USA; gen tel (607) 865-4131; gen fax (607) 865-8689; disp adv e-mail sales@waltonreporter.com; ed e-mail news@waltonreporter.com; web site http://www.the-reporter.net/
Circulation: 6,800pd, 50fr; Sworn/Estimate/Non-Audited
Advertising rate: Open inch rate $10.35
Established: 1881
Pub./Ed....Randy Shepard
Adv. Sales....Bernice Bates
Mechanical Specifications: Type page 10 3/8 x 15 1/2; A - 5 cols, 1 7/8, 1/4 between; C - 6 cols, 1 1/2, 1/4 between.Equipment & Software: Hardware — IBM, APP/Power Mac; Presses — ABD/9850, HI/18-25; Software — QPS/QuarkXPress, Adobe/PageMaker, Adobe/Photoshop, Adobe/Illustrator, Archetype/Corel Graphics.

DELMAR

COLONIE/LOUDONVILLE SPOTLIGHT (WED)

341 Delaware Ave, Delmar, NY, 12054-1920, Albany, USA; gen tel (518) 439-4949; gen fax (518) 439-5198; disp adv e-mail Advertise@spotlightnews.com; class adv e-mail classified@spotlightnews.com ; ed e-mail news@spotlightnews.com; web site www.spotlightnews.com
Circulation: 10,000pd,; CVC
Advertising rate: 1/8 Pg $155.00; 1/4 Pg $320.00; 1/2 Pg $645.00
Established: 1955
Group: Community Media GroupEditions: (3) The Spotlight, Colonie Spotlight, Loudonville Spotlight
Pub....John McIntyre
VP of Sales....Bo Berezansky
Mng. Ed....Michael Hallisey
Mechanical Specifications: Type page 10 x 15.5; 6 cols, 1.5625, 0.125 between
Delivery Method: Mail, Newsstand, Racks
Areas Served: 12205, 12204, 12110, 12211, 12128

SPOTLIGHT NEWSPAPERS (WED)

341 Delaware Ave, Delmar, NY, 12054-1920, USA; gen tel (518) 439-4949; gen fax (518) 439-5198; disp adv e-mail news@spotlightnews.com; web site www.spotlightnews.com
Circulation: 5,520pd, 13,273fr; VAC
Pub....John McIntyre
VP of Advertising....Bo Berezansky
Mng. Ed....Hallisey Michael

THE SPOTLIGHT (WED)

341 Delaware Ave, Delmar, NY, 12054-1920, Albany, USA; gen tel (518) 439-4949; gen fax (518) 439-5198; disp adv e-mail advertise@spotlightnews.com; class adv e-mail classified@spotlightnews.com; ed e-mail news@spotlightnews.com; web site www.spotlightnews.com
Circulation: 7,270pd, 18,983fr; CVC
Advertising rate: 1/8 Pg $155.00; 1/4 Pg $320.00; 1/2 Pg $645.00; Open inch rate $17.00
Established: 1955
Group: Community Media GroupEditions: (5)
Pub....John McIntyre
Ad....Bo Berezansky
Ed....Michael Hallisey
Mechanical Specifications: Type page 10 x 15.5; 6 cols, 1.5625, 0.125 between
Equipment & Software: Hardware — APP/Mac; Software — Adobe/PageMaker 6.5.
Delivery Method: Mail, Newsstand, Racks
Areas Served: 12054, 12067, 12084, 12085, 12077, 12158, 12143, 12156

DEPOSIT

THE DEPOSIT COURIER (WED)

24 Laurel Bank Ave, Ste 2, Deposit, NY, 13754-1251, Broome & Delaware, USA; gen tel (607) 467-3600; gen fax (607) 467-5330; disp adv e-mail couriernews@tds.net; class adv e-mail couriernews@tds.net
Circulation: 2,050pd, 32fr; Sworn/Estimate/Non-Audited
Advertising rate: Open inch rate $.20
Established: 1848
Adv. Mgr....Ann Schmitz
Ed....Hilton A. EvansEquipment & Software: Hardware — APP/Mac, PC; Software — Adobe/PageMaker.
Areas Served: 13754,13783,13756,13765

DOBBS FERRY

THE RIVERTOWNS ENTERPRISE (FRI)

95 Main St, Dobbs Ferry, NY, 10522-1673, Westchester, USA; gen tel (914) 478-2787; adv tel 9144782787 x12; ed tel 9144782787 x11; gen fax (914) 478-2863; disp adv e-mail displayads@rivertownsenterprise.net; class adv e-mail classifiedads@rivertownsenterprise.net; ed e-mail tlamorte@rivertownsenterprise.net; web site www.rivertownsenterprise.net
Circulation: 6,000pd, 200fr; Sworn/Estimate/Non-Audited
Advertising rate: 1x4 $57.50; 2x3.5 $100.00; 2x5 $143.75
Established: 1975
Pub....Deborah G. White
Ed....Timothy LaMorte
Mechanical Specifications: Type page 9.3125 x 14; 4 cols, 2.1875, 0.25 between
Areas Served: Hastings-on-Hudson, Dobbs Ferry, Ardsley and Irvington

EAST AURORA

EAST AURORA ADVERTISER (THUR)

710 Main St, East Aurora, NY, 14052-2406, Erie, USA; gen tel (716) 652-0320; gen fax (716) 652-8383; disp adv e-mail ads@eastaurorany.com; ed e-mail eanews@eastaurorany.com; web site www.my-wnynews.com/east_aurora_advertiser
Circulation: 4,440pd, 340fr; Sworn/Estimate/Non-Audited
Advertising rate: Open inch rate $16.15
Established: 1872
Group: Neighbor to Neighbor News, Inc.
Mng. Ed....Adam Zeremski
Mechanical Specifications: Type page 10.5 x 19.5; 5 cols, 2, 0.125 between
Areas Served: East Aurora, Aurora, Elma, Marilla, Wales, West Falls, Holland

ELMA REVIEW (THUR)

710 Main St, East Aurora, NY, 14052-2406, Erie, USA; gen tel (716) 652-0320; gen fax (716) 652-8383; disp adv e-mail ads@eastaurorany.com; ed e-mail eanews@eastaurorany.com; web site www.my-wnynews.com/east_aurora_advertiser
Circulation: 1,030pd,; Sworn/Estimate/Non-Audited
Advertising rate: Open inch rate $10.60
Established: 1979
Group: Neighbor to Neighbor News, Inc.Grant M. Hamilton
Ed....Adam Zeremski
Mechanical Specifications: Type page 10.5 x 19.5; 5 cols, 2, 0.125 between
Areas Served: Elma, Marilla, Wales

EAST HAMPTON

THE EAST HAMPTON STAR (THUR)

153 Main St, East Hampton, NY, 11937-2716, Suffolk, USA; gen tel (631) 324-0002; gen fax (631) 324-7943; disp adv e-mail ads@ehstar.com; class adv e-mail classy@easthamptonstar.com; ed e-mail editor@easthamptonstar.com; web site www.easthamptonstar.com - 530,000(views) 53,000(visitors)
Circulation: 11,000pd, 612fr; Sworn/Estimate/Non-Audited
Advertising rate: 1/64 Pg $50.00; 1/32 Pg $102.00; 1/24 Pg $136.00
Established: 1885
Pub....Helen S. Rattray
Adv. Mgr....Isabel Hefner
Ed....David E. Rattray
Prodn. Mgr....Kathy Kovach
Mechanical Specifications: Type page 13.667 x 20.917; 6 cols, 2.139, 0.166 between.
Equipment & Software: Hardware — APP/Macs, PCs.
Areas Served: Shinnecock Canal, Southampton, Water Mill, Noyac, Bridgehampton, Sagaponack, Wainscott, North Haven, Sag Harbor, Northwest, East Hampton, Springs, Amagansett, Napeague, Montauk

THE INDEPENDENT (WED)

74 Montauk Hwy, Unit 16, East Hampton, NY, 11937-3268, Suffolk, USA; gen tel (631) 324-2500; gen fax (631) 324-2544; disp adv e-mail ads@indyeastend.com; class adv e-mail classifieds@indyeastend.com; ed e-mail news@indyeastend.com; web site www.indyeastend.com
Circulation: 12pd, 14,000fr; Sworn/Estimate/Non-Audited
Advertising rate: 1/16 Pg $282.00; 1/8 Pg $499.00; 1/4 Pg $881.00
Established: 1993
Group: East Hampton Media Holdings llcEditions: (1)
Ed....Rick Murphy
Pub....James Mackin
Adv. Sales....Joanna Froschl
Mechanical Specifications: Type page 8.75 x 11.25; 4 cols, 2.094, 0.125 between
Equipment & Software: Hardware — APP/Mac G4, Lazermaster/11x17; Presses — G/Community; Software — QPS/QuarkXPress 4.1, Adobe/Photoshop 6.0, Adobe/Illustrator 9.0.
Delivery Method: Mail, Racks
Areas Served: East Hampton, Southampton, Riverhead, Southold, Shelter Island

ELIZABETHTOWN

THE ADIRONDACK JOURNAL SUN (SAT)

14 Hand Ave, Elizabethtown, NY, 12932, Essex, USA; gen tel (518) 873-6368; adv tel (518) 585-9173; gen fax (518) 873-6360; adv fax (518) 585-9175; disp adv e-mail ads@suncommunitynews.com; class adv e-mail susan@suncommunitynews.com; ed e-mail johng@suncommunitynews.com; web site www.suncommmunitynews.com - 9,508(views) 1,882(visitors)
Circulation: 94pd, 8,087fr; VAC
Advertising rate: Open inch rate $19.50
Established: 1878
Group: Sun Community News, Published by:Denton Publications, Inc.
Pres./Pub....Daniel E. Alexander
Pres./Pub....Edward Coats
Ed....Thom Randall
Ed....John Gereau
Prodn. Mgr....Bill Coats
Adv. Mgr....Scarlette Merfeld
Circ. Mgr....Jennifer Tower
Office Mgr....Susan Zackarenko
Mechanical Specifications: Type page: 10 x 16; 6 col
Delivery Method: Mail, Racks
Areas Served: 12808 12810 12811 12812 12814 12815 12817 12824 12842 12843 12845 12847 12853 12856 12860 12862 12878 12885 12886

THE NEWS ENTERPRISE SUN (SAT)

14 Hand Ave, Elizabethtown, NY, 12932, Essex, USA; gen tel (518) 873-6368; adv tel (518) 585-9173; gen fax (518) 873-6360; disp adv e-mail ads@suncommunitynews.com; class adv e-mail susan@suncommunitynews.com; ed e-mail johng@suncommunitynews.com; web site www.suncommunitynews.com - 18,747(views) 2,534(visitors)
Circulation: 39pd, 3,414fr; VAC
Advertising rate: Open inch rate $19.50
Established: 1948
Group: Sun Community News, Published by:Denton Publications, Inc.
Digital Platform - Mobile: Apple, Android, Windows
Digital Platform - Tablet: Apple iOS, Android, Windows 7, Kindle
Pub....Daniel E. Alexander
Assoc. Pub....Edward Coats
Adv. Dir....Ashley Alexander
Gen. Mgr....Dan Alexander
Mng. Ed....John Gereau
Plant Operations Mgr....William Coats
Southern Adirondacks Publishing Group Manager....Scarlette Merfeld
Circ. Mgr....Jennifer Tower
Mechanical Specifications: Type page 10 x 16; E - 6 cols, 1 1/2, between; A - 6 cols, 1 1/2, between.Equipment & Software: Hardware — APP/Mac, PC; Presses — 17-G/Community
Delivery Method: Mail, Racks
Areas Served: 12811,12812, 12842, 12843, 12847, 12851, 12852, 12853, 12856, 12857, 12862, 12886,

THE NORTH COUNTRYMAN SUN (SAT)

14 Hand Ave, Elizabethtown, NY, 12932, Essex, USA; gen tel (518) 873-6368; gen fax (518) 873-6360; disp adv e-mail ashley@suncommunitynews.com; class adv e-mail ashley@suncommunitynews.com; ed e-mail pete@suncommunitynews.com;

web site www.suncommunitynews.com - 25,249(views) 9,893(visitors)
Circulation: 37pd, 8,281fr; VAC
Advertising rate: Open inch rate $19.50
Established: 1927
Group: Sun Community News, Published by:Denton Publications, Inc.
Digital Platform - Mobile: Apple, Android, Windows
Digital Platform - Tablet: Apple iOS, Android, Windows 7, Kindle
Pub.................................. Daniel E. Alexander
Prodn. Mgr. .... Bill Coats
Mgr Ed .... Pete DeMola
Advt Dir .... Ashley Alexander
Associate Pub.......................... Edward Coats
Adv. Mgr............................ Scarlette Merfeld
Circ. Mgr .... Jennifer Tower
Mechanical Specifications: Type page 10 x 10; E - 4 cols, 1 1/2, 1/3 between.Equipment & Software: Hardware — APP/Mac G4, PC; Presses — 17 Unit Goss Community
Delivery Method: Mail, Racks
Areas Served: Serving Clinton, Essex, Warren, Franklin and Washington Counties

THE TIMES OF TI SUN (SAT)
14 Hand Ave, Elizabethtown, NY, 12932, Essex, USA; gen tel (518) 873-6368; adv tel (518) 585-9173; gen fax (518) 873-6360; adv fax (518) 585-9175; disp adv e-mail ads@suncommunitynews.com; class adv e-mail ads@suncommunitynews.com; ed e-mail johng@suncommunitynews.com; web site www.suncommunitynews.com - 18,747(views) 2,534(visitors)
Circulation: 77pd, 7,214fr; VAC
Advertising rate: Open inch rate $19.50
Established: 1948
Group: Sun Community News, Published by:Denton Publications, Inc.
Digital Platform - Mobile: Apple, Android, Windows
Digital Platform - Tablet: Apple iOS, Android, Windows 7, Kindle
Pub.................................. Daniel E. Alexander
Assoc. Pub............................... Edward Coats
Adv. Dir................................ Ashley Alexander
Prod. Mgr. .... Dan Alexander
Mng. Ed...................................... John Gereau
Plant Operations Mgr................. William Coats
Southern Adirondacks Publishing Group Mgr/ Ad. Mgr .... Scarlette Merfeld
Circ. Mgr .... Jennifer Tower
Mechanical Specifications: Type page 10 x 16; E - 6 cols, 1 1/2, between; A - 6 cols, 1 1/2, between.Equipment & Software: Hardware — APP/Mac, PC; Presses — 17-G/Community
Delivery Method: Mail, Racks
Areas Served: 12836 12841 12851 12852 12855 12858 12857 12861 12872 12870 12874 12883 12928 12956 12960 12961 12974

THE VALLEY NEWS SUN (SAT)
14 Hand Ave, Elizabethtown, NY, 12932, Essex, USA; gen tel (518) 873-6368; gen fax (518) 873-6360; disp adv e-mail ashley@suncommunitynews.com; class adv e-mail ashley@suncommunitynews.com; ed e-mail johng@suncommunitynews.com; web site www.suncommunitynews.com - 10,315(views) 1,745(visitors)
Circulation: 67pd, 15,249fr; VAC
Advertising rate: Open inch rate $19.50
Established: 1948
Group: Sun Community News, Published by:Denton Publications, Inc.
Digital Platform - Mobile: Apple, Android, Windows
Digital Platform - Tablet: Apple iOS, Android, Windows 7, Kindle
Mng. Ed...................................... John Gereau
Plant Operations Mgr......................... Bill Coats
Adv. Dir................................ Ashley Alexander
Pub.................................. Daniel E. Alexander
Ad. Mgr .... Scarlette Merfeld
Circ. Mgr .... Jennifer Tower
Asst Mgr Ed .... Pete Demola
Mechanical Specifications: Type page 10 x 10; E - 4 cols, 1 1/2, 1/3 between.Equipment & Software: Hardware — APP/Mac ; Presses — 17 Unit Goss Community
Delivery Method: Mail, Racks
Areas Served: 12932 12950 12964 12993 12996 12936 12912 12944 12975 12941 12987 12997 12942 12943 12913 12945 12946 12977 12983 12989 12986 12973 12970 12976 12939

ELLENVILLE

SHAWANGUNK JOURNAL (THUR)
PO Box 669, Ellenville, NY, 12428-0669, Ulster, USA; gen tel (845) 647-9190; gen fax (845) 647-8713; disp adv e-mail ads@gunkjournal.com; ed e-mail info@gunkjournal.com; web site www.shawangunkjournal.com
Advertising rate: (Modular Rates) 1/16 page, 3.25 x 2 - $30 1x
Established: 1849
Exec. Ed... Alex Shiffer
Mgn. Ed.. Paul Smart
Sales & Marketing .... Tara Dalton
Mechanical Specifications: Type page 10.25 x 15
Delivery Method: Mail, Racks
Areas Served: Accord, Bloomingburg, Cragsmoor, Ellenville, High Falls, Kerhonkson, Napanoch, Phillipsport, Pine Bush, Shawangunk, Spring Glen, Stone Ridge, Summitville, Walker Valley, Wallkill, Wawarsing, Wurtsboro

FULTON

THE PALLADIUM-TIMES (SAT)
67 S 2nd St, Fulton, NY, 13069-1725, Oswego, USA; gen tel (315) 592-2459; gen fax (315) 598-6618; disp adv e-mail tbarnes@palltimes.com; class adv e-mail adesantis@palltimes.com; ed e-mail apoole@palltimes.com; web site www.valleynewsonline.com
Circulation: 8,230pd, 5,000fr; Sworn/Estimate/ Non-Audited
Advertising rate: Open inch rate $8.92
Pub.. Jon Spaulding
Ad. Mgr....................................... Andrew Poole
Mechanical Specifications: Type page 10.3125 x 16; 6 cols
Delivery Method: Mail
Areas Served: 13069, 13135

THE VALLEY NEWS (WED, SAT)
67 S 2nd St, Fulton, NY, 13069-1259, Oswego, USA; gen tel (315) 598-6397; gen fax (315) 598-6618; class adv e-mail classifieds@valleynewsonline.com; ed e-mail colin@fultonvalleynews.com; web site www.valleynewsonline.com
Circulation: 8,105pd, 5,000fr; Sworn/Estimate/ Non-Audited
Advertising rate: Open inch rate $10.95
Established: 1947
Ed. .... Colin Hogan
Mechanical Specifications: Type page 10 1/4 x 15 3/4; E - 4 cols, 2 5/12, 1/3 between; A - 4 cols, 2 3/8, 1/3 between; C - 4 cols, 2 5/12, 1/3 between.
Delivery Method: Mail
Areas Served: 13069, 13135

GARDEN CITY

BALDWIN HERALD (THUR)
2 Endo Blvd, Garden City, NY, 11530-6707, Nassau, USA; gen tel (516) 569-4000; adv tel (516) 569-400 x250; gen fax (516) 569-4942; disp adv e-mail baldwineditor@liherald.com; class adv e-mail sales@liherald.com; web site www.liherald.com
Circulation: 5,291pd,; Sworn/Estimate/Non-Audited
Advertising rate: Open inch rate $17.50
Group: Richner Communications, Inc.
Pub.. Clifford Richner
VP, Ops./Gen. Mgr................. Michael Bologna
Adv. Mgr............................ Rhonda Glickman
Mechanical Specifications: Type page 9 3/4 x 13 3/4; E - 4 cols, 2 1/3, 1/6 between; A - 6 cols, 1 1/2, 1/6 between; C - 6 cols, 1 1/2, 1/6 between.Equipment & Software: Hardware — APP/Mac, PCs, APP/Appleshare, Novell/ Server; Presses — G/Community; Software — QPS/QuarkXPress, Microsoft/Word.
Delivery Method: Mail, Newsstand, Racks
Areas Served: 11510

BELLMORE HERALD (THUR)
2 Endo Blvd, Garden City, NY, 11530-6707, Nassau, USA; gen tel (516) 569-4000; gen fax (516) 569-4942; disp adv e-mail sales@liherald.com; web site www.liherald.com
Circulation: 5,251pd,; Sworn/Estimate/Non-Audited
Advertising rate: Open inch rate $20.73
Group: Richner Communications, Inc.
Pub.. Clifford Richner
Pub... Stuart Richner
Gen. Mgr. .... Michael Bologna
Adv. Mgr. .... Rhonda Glickman
Mechanical Specifications: Type page 9 3/4 x 13 3/4; E - 4 cols, 2 1/3, 1/6 between; A - 6 cols, 1 1/2, 1/6 between; C - 6 cols, 1 1/2, 1/6 between.Equipment & Software: Hardware — APP/Mac, PC; Presses — G/Community; Software — QPS/QuarkXPress, Microsoft/ Word.
Delivery Method: Mail, Newsstand, Racks
Areas Served: 11710

EAST MEADOW HERALD (THUR)
2 Endo Blvd, Garden City, NY, 11530-6707, Nassau, USA; gen tel (516) 569-4000; gen fax (516) 569-4942; disp adv e-mail sales@liherald.com; ed e-mail emeadoweditor@liherald.com; web site www.liherald.com
Circulation: 4,068pd, 225fr; Sworn/Estimate/ Non-Audited
Advertising rate: Open inch rate $20.73
Group: Richner Communications, Inc.
Pub.. Clifford Richner
Pub... Stuart Richner
Gen. Mgr. .... Michael Bologna
Adv. Mgr. .... Rhonda Glickman
Ed. .... Stefany Reyes
Mechanical Specifications: Type page 9 3/4 x 13 3/4; E - 4 cols, 2 1/3, 1/6 between; A - 6 cols, 1 1/2, 1/6 between; C - 6 cols, 1 1/2, 1/6 between.Equipment & Software: Hardware — APP/Mac, PCs; Presses — G/Community; Software — Adobe/PageMaker, MS/Word.
Delivery Method: Mail, Newsstand, Racks
Areas Served: 11554, 11590, 11756

FRANKLIN SQUARE/ELMONT HERALD (THUR)
2 Endo Blvd, Garden City, NY, 11530-6707, Nassau, USA; gen tel (516) 569-4000; adv tel 5165694000 x 250; ed tel 5165694000 x 214; gen fax (516) 569-4942; disp adv e-mail sales@liherald.com; class adv e-mail sales@liherald.com; web site www.liherald.com
Circulation: 6,096pd,; USPS
Advertising rate: Open inch rate $17.91
Group: Richner Communications, Inc.
Executive Ed................................ Jeff Bessen
Adv. Mgr............................ Rhonda Glickman
Mechanical Specifications: Type page 9 3/4 x 13 3/4; E - 4 cols, 2 1/3, 1/6 between; A - 6 cols, 1 1/2, 1/6 between; C - 6 cols, 1 1/2, 1/6 between.
Delivery Method: Mail, Newsstand, Carrier, Racks
Areas Served: 11010, 11003

GARDEN CITY NEWS (FRI)
821 Franklin Ave, Ste 208, Garden City, NY, 11530-4519, Nassau, USA; gen tel (516) 294-8900; adv tel (516) 294-8900; ed tel (516) 294-8900; gen fax (516) 294-8924; adv fax (516) 294-8924; ed fax (516) 294-8924; disp adv e-mail kpiltz@gcnews.com; class adv e-mail sdaly@gcnews.com; ed e-mail editor@gcnews.com; web site www.gcnews.com
Circulation: 8,481pd,; Sworn/Estimate/Non-Audited
Advertising rate: Open inch rate $17.91
Group: Litmor Publishing
Digital Platform - Mobile: Apple, Android
Digital Platform - Tablet: Apple iOS, Android
Ed./Pub. .... Meg Morgan Norris
Adv. Sales... Ken Piltz
Mechanical Specifications: Type page 8.75 x 11.5; 6 cols, 1.325, 0.183 between
Delivery Method: Mail, Racks
Areas Served: 11530

HICKSVILLE MID-ISLAND TIMES (FRI)
821 Franklin Ave, Ste 206, Garden City, NY, 11530-4519, Nassau, USA; gen tel (516) 294-8900; adv tel (516) 294-8900; ed tel (516) 294-8900; gen fax (516) 294-8924; adv fax (516) 294-8924; ed fax (516) 294-8924; disp adv e-mail kpiltz@gcnews.com; class adv e-mail sdaly@gcnews.com; ed e-mail editor@gcnews.com; web site www.gcnews.com
Circulation: 2,765pd,; Sworn/Estimate/Non-Audited
Advertising rate: Open inch rate $12.75
Group: Litmor Publishing
Digital Platform - Mobile: Apple, Android, Windows, Blackberry
Digital Platform - Tablet: Apple iOS, Android, Windows 7, Blackberry Tablet OS
Pub.................................. Meg Morgan Norris
Adv. Mgr... Ken Piltz
Mechanical Specifications: Type page 8.75 x 11.5; 6 cols, 1.325, 0.183 between Equipment & Software: Hardware — APP/Mac; Presses — G/Community; Software — QPS/ QuarkXPress 3.32, Adobe/Photoshop 3.2, Adobe/Illustrator 5.1.
Delivery Method: Mail, Racks
Areas Served: 11756, 11801, 11802, 11803, 11804

JERICHO NEWS JOURNAL (FRI)
821 Franklin Ave, Ste 206, Garden City, NY, 11530-4519, Nassau, USA; gen tel (516) 294-8900; adv tel (516) 294-8900; ed tel (516) 294-8900; gen fax (516) 294-8924; adv fax (516) 294-8924; ed fax (516) 294-8924; disp adv e-mail kpiltz@gcnews.com; class adv e-mail sdaly@gcnews.com; ed e-mail editor@gcnews.com; web site www.gcnews.com
Circulation: 2,727pd,; Sworn/Estimate/Non-Audited
Advertising rate: Open inch rate $7.00
Group: Litmor Publishing
Digital Platform - Mobile: Apple, Android
Digital Platform - Tablet: Apple iOS, Android
Ed. .... Meg Morgan Norris
Adv. Dir.. Ken Piltz
Mechanical Specifications: Type page 8.75 x 11.5; 6 cols, 1.325, 0.183 between
Delivery Method: Mail, Racks
Areas Served: 11753, 11545, 11732

LONG BEACH HERALD (THUR)
2 Endo Blvd, Garden City, NY, 11530-6707, Nassau, USA; gen tel (516) 569-4000; gen fax (516) 569-4942; disp adv e-mail sales@liherald.com; ed e-mail lbeditor@liherald.com; web site www.liherald.com
Circulation: 6,544pd, 1,356fr; Sworn/Estimate/ Non-Audited
Advertising rate: Open inch rate $21.69
Group: Richner Communications, Inc.
Pub.. Clifford Richner
Pub... Stuart Richner
Gen. Mgr. .... Michael Bologna
Adv. Mgr. .... Rhonda Glickman
Mechanical Specifications: Type page 9 3/4 x 13 3/4; E - 4 cols, 2 1/3, 1/6 between; A - 6 cols, 1 1/2, 1/6 between; C - 6 cols, 1 1/2, 1/6 between.Equipment & Software: Hardware — APP/Mac, PC; Presses — G/Community; Software — QPS/QuarkXPress, Microsoft/ Word.
Delivery Method: Mail, Newsstand, Racks
Areas Served: 11509, 11561, 11569

LYNBROOK/EAST ROCKAWAY HERALD (THUR)
2 Endo Blvd, Garden City, NY, 11530-6707, Nassau, USA; gen tel (516) 569-4000; adv tel 5165694000 x250; ed tel 5165694000 x202; gen fax (516) 569-4942; disp adv e-mail sales@liherald.com; web site www.liherald.com
Circulation: 5,272pd, 1,293fr; Sworn/Estimate/ Non-Audited
Advertising rate: Open inch rate $21.69
Group: Richner Communications, Inc.
Pub.. Clifford Richner
Pub... Stuart Richner
Gen. Mgr. .... Michael Bologna
Adv. Mgr. .... Rhonda Glickman

Mechanical Specifications: Type page 9 3/4 x 13 3/4; E - 4 cols, 2 1/3, 1/6 between; A - 6 cols, 1 1/2, 1/6 between; C - 6 cols, 1 1/2, 1/6 between.
Equipment & Software: Hardware — APP/Mac, PC; Presses — G/Community; Software — QPS/QuarkXPress, Microsoft/Word.
Delivery Method: Mail, Newsstand, Racks
Areas Served: 11563, 11518

MALVERNE/WEST HEMPSTEAD HERALD (THUR)

2 Endo Blvd, Garden City, NY, 11530-6707, Nassau, USA; gen tel (516) 569-4000; adv tel 5165694000 x250; gen fax (516) 569-4942; disp adv e-mail sales@liherald.com; ed e-mail ahackmack@liherald.com; web site www.liherald.com
Circulation: 3,286pd,; Sworn/Estimate/Non-Audited
Advertising rate: Open inch rate $17.91
Group: Richner Communications, Inc.
Pub. .... Clifford Richner
Pub. .... Stuart Richner
Adv. Mgr. .... Rhonda Glickman
Gen. Mgr. .... Michael Bologna
Mechanical Specifications: Type page 9 3/4 x 13 3/4; E - 4 cols, 2 1/3, 1/6 between; A - 6 cols, 1 1/2, 1/6 between; C - 6 cols, 1 1/2, 1/6 between.Equipment & Software: Hardware — APP/Mac, PC; Presses — G/Community; Software — QPS/QuarkXPress, Microsoft/Word.
Delivery Method: Mail, Newsstand, Racks
Areas Served: 11565, 11552

MERRICK HERALD (THUR)

2 Endo Blvd, Garden City, NY, 11530-6707, Nassau, USA; gen tel (516) 569-4000; gen fax (516) 569-4942; disp adv e-mail sales@liherald.com; web site www.liherald.com
Circulation: 3,846pd,; Sworn/Estimate/Non-Audited
Advertising rate: Open inch rate $20.73
Group: Richner Communications, Inc.
Pub. .... Clifford Richner
Pub. .... Stuart Richner
Gen. Mgr. .... Michael Bologna
Adv. Mgr. .... Rhonda Glickman
Ed. .... Scott Brinton
Mechanical Specifications: Type page 9 1/2 x 13 3/4; E - 4 cols, 2 1/3, 1/6 between; A - 6 cols, 1 1/2, 1/6 between; C - 6 cols, 1 1/2, 1/6 between.Equipment & Software: Hardware — APP/Mac, PC; Presses — G/Community; Software — QPS/QuarkXPress, Microsoft/Word.
Delivery Method: Mail, Newsstand, Racks
Areas Served: 11566

NASSAU HERALD (THUR)

2 Endo Blvd, Garden City, NY, 11530-6707, Nassau, USA; gen tel (516) 569-4000; adv tel 5165694000 x250; ed tel 5165694000 x201; gen fax (516) 569-4942; disp adv e-mail sales@liherald.com; web site www.liherald.com
Circulation: 8,771pd,; Sworn/Estimate/Non-Audited
Advertising rate: Open inch rate $25.16
Group: Richner Communications, Inc.
Pub. .... Clifford Richner
Pub. .... Stuart Richner
Gen. Mgr. .... Michael Bologna
Adv. Mgr. .... Rhonda Glickman
Ed. .... Jeff Bessen
Mechanical Specifications: Type page 9 3/4 x 13 3/4; E - 4 cols, 2 1/3, 1/6 between; A - 6 cols, 1 1/2, 1/6 between; C - 6 cols, 1 1/2, 1/6 between.
Delivery Method: Mail, Newsstand, Racks
Areas Served: 11509, 11516, 11557, 11559, 11581, 11598, 11096

OCEANSIDE-ISLAND PARK HERALD (THUR)

2 Endo Blvd, Garden City, NY, 11530-6707, Nassau, USA; gen tel (516) 569-4000; gen fax (516) 569-4942; disp adv e-mail sales@liherald.com; ed e-mail oceaneditor@liherald.com; web site www.liherald.com
Circulation: 5,015pd, 1,281fr; Sworn/Estimate/Non-Audited
Advertising rate: Open inch rate $21.69
Group: Richner Communications, Inc.
Pub. .... Clifford Richner
Ed. .... Ben Strack
Mechanical Specifications: Type page 9 3/4 x 13 3/4; E - 4 cols, 2 1/3, 1/6 between; A - 6 cols, 1 1/2, 1/6 between; C - 6 cols, 1 1/2, 1/6 between.Equipment & Software: Hardware — APP/Mac, PC; Presses — G/Community; Software — QPS/QuarkXPress, Microsoft/Word.
Delivery Method: Mail, Newsstand, Racks
Areas Served: 11572, 11558

OYSTER BAY GUARDIAN (FRI)

2 Endo Blvd, Garden City, NY, 11530-6707, Nassau, USA; gen tel (516) 922-4215 X327; adv tel (516) 569-4000 x272; gen fax (516) 922-4227; disp adv e-mail llane@oysterbayguardian.com.; web site www.oysterbayguardian.com
Circulation: 3,500pd, 50fr; Sworn/Estimate/Non-Audited
Advertising rate: Open inch rate $.64
Established: 1899
Group: Richner Communications, Inc.
Ed. .... Laura Lane
Pub. .... Clifford Richner
Ad. Mgr. .... Rhonda Glickman
Delivery Method: Mail, Newsstand

ROCKVILLE CENTRE HERALD (THUR)

2 Endo Blvd, Garden City, NY, 11530-6707, Nassau, USA; gen tel (516) 569-4000; gen fax (516) 569-4942; disp adv e-mail sales@liherald.com; ed e-mail rvceditor@liherald.com; web site www.liherald.com
Circulation: 6,367pd, 1,646fr; Sworn/Estimate/Non-Audited
Advertising rate: Open inch rate $21.69
Group: Richner Communications, Inc.
Pub. .... Clifford Richner
Pub. .... Stuart Richner
Gen. Mgr. .... Michael Bologna
Adv. Mgr. .... Rhonda Glickman
Ed. .... Brian Kacharaba
Mechanical Specifications: Type page 9 3/4 x 13 3/4; E - 4 cols, 2 1/3, 1/6 between; A - 6 cols, 1 1/2, 1/6 between; C - 6 cols, 1 1/2, 1/6 between.Equipment & Software: Hardware — APP/Mac, PC; Presses — G/Community; Software — QPS/QuarkXPress, Microsoft/Word.
Delivery Method: Mail, Newsstand, Racks
Areas Served: 11570

GENESEO

THE LIVINGSTON COUNTY NEWS (THUR)

122 Main St, Geneseo, NY, 14454-1230, Livingston, USA; gen tel (585) 243-0296; adv tel (585) 243-0296; ed tel (585) 243-0296; gen fax (585) 243-0348; adv fax (585) 243-0348; ed fax (585) 243-0348; disp adv e-mail jzambito@batavianews.com; class adv e-mail jzambito@batavianews.com; ed e-mail ben@livingstonnews.com; web site www.thelcn.com
Circulation: 5,789pd,; USPS
Advertising rate: Open inch rate $7.50
Group: Johnson Newspaper Corporation
Digital Platform - Mobile: Apple, Android, Windows
Digital Platform - Tablet: Apple iOS, Android, Windows 7
Gen Mgr/Mng. Ed. .... Ben Beagle
Sales Rep. .... Kim Roberts
Sports Ed. .... Chris Metcalf
Reporter .... Matt Leader
Advt Dir. .... Gary Durawa
Delivery Method: Mail, Newsstand, Racks
Areas Served: Livingston County

GHENT

THE COLUMBIA PAPER (THUR)

PO Box 482, Ghent, NY, 12075-0482, Columbia, USA; gen tel (518) 392-1122; disp adv e-mail ads@columbiapaper.com; class adv e-mail ads@columbiapaper.com; ed e-mail letters@columbiapaper.com; web site www.columbiapaper.com - 25,400(views) 6,400(visitors)
Circulation: 2,200pd,; USPS
Advertising rate: Open inch rate $10.00
Established: 2009
Associate Ed. .... Diane Valden
Ed. & Pub. .... Parry Teasdale
Deputy Pub. .... Emilia Teasdale
Mechanical Specifications: Type page 10 x 16; 5 cols, 1.83, 0.2 between
Delivery Method: Mail, Newsstand
Areas Served: Columbia County, NY

GLEN COVE

GOLD COAST GAZETTE (THUR)

57 Glen St, Glen Cove, NY, 11542-2755, Nassau, USA; gen tel (516) 671-2360; gen fax (516) 569-4942; disp adv e-mail mail@goldcoastgazette.net; web site goldcoastherald.com
Group: Richner Communications, Inc.
Ed./Pub. .... Kevin Horton

GLENS FALLS

THE CHRONICLE (THUR)

15 Ridge St, Glens Falls, NY, 12801-3608, Warren, USA; gen tel (518) 792-1126; adv tel (518) 792-1126; ed tel (518) 792-1126; gen fax (518) 793-1587; disp adv e-mail ads@loneoak.com; class adv e-mail ads@loneoak.com; ed e-mail chronicle@loneoak.com; web site www.readthechronicle.com
Circulation: 500pd, 28,000fr; Sworn/Estimate/Non-Audited
Advertising rate: Open inch rate $21.00
Established: 1980
Owner/Pub. .... Mark Frost
News Ed. .... Gordon Woodworth
Mng. Ed. .... Cathy DeDe
Chief Operating Officer .... Sandra Hutchinson
Advertising Sales Guru .... Valerie Erceg
Mechanical Specifications: Type page 10 x 16; E - 4 cols, 2 1/3, 1/4 between; A - 4 cols, 2 1/3, 1/4 between; C - 6 cols, 1 1/2, 1/4 between.
Delivery Method: Mail, Newsstand, Racks
Areas Served: Glens Falls, Lake George region, northern New York State

GOUVERNEUR

THE GOUVERNEUR TRIBUNE-PRESS (FRI)

74 Trinity Ave, Gouverneur, NY, 13642-1126, Saint Lawrence, USA; gen tel (315) 287-2100; gen fax (315) 287-2397; disp adv e-mail tribunepress@verizon.net; web site www.gouverneurtribunepress.com
Circulation: 3,724pd, 301fr; Sworn/Estimate/Non-Audited
Advertising rate: Open inch rate $5.35
Pub. .... M. Dan McClelland
Ed. .... Rachel Hunter
Ad. .... Curran Wade

GRAND ISLAND

ISLAND DISPATCH (FRI)

1859 Whitehaven Rd, Grand Island, NY, 14072-1803, Erie, USA; gen tel (716) 773-7676; gen fax (716) 773-7190; disp adv e-mail majoraccounts@wnypapers.com; class adv e-mail Grandislandsales@wnypapers.com; ed e-mail dispatch@wnypapers.com; web site www.wnypapers.com
Circulation: 1,550pd, 0fr; Sworn/Estimate/Non-Audited
Advertising rate: Open inch rate $12.77
Established: 1944
Group: Niagara Frontier Publications
Digital Platform - Mobile: Apple, Android, Windows, Blackberry
Digital Platform - Tablet: Apple iOS, Android, Windows 7, Blackberry Tablet OS, Kindle, Nook, Kindle Fire
Pub. .... A. Skip Mazenauer
Ed. .... Larry Austin
Mng. Ed. .... Terry Duffy
editor .... Josh Maloney
Mechanical Specifications: Type page 10 1/2 x 15.75; E - 5 cols, 2, 1/8 between; A - 5 cols, 2, 1/8 between; C - 5 cols, 2, 1/8 between. Equipment & Software: Hardware — APP/Power Mac 7200-120, APP/Power Mac 7200-90, Umax/Astra 610s Scanner, Unity 1800XL-Plus Printer; Software — QPS/QuarkXPress 5.0, Adobe/Photoshop 3.0, Adobe/Illustrator 5.0.
Delivery Method: Mail, Newsstand
Areas Served: 14072

LEWISTON-PORTER SENTINEL (SAT)

1859 Whitehaven Rd, Grand Island, NY, 14072-1803, Erie, USA; gen tel (716) 773-7676; gen fax (716) 773-7190; disp adv e-mail majoraccounts@wnypapers.com; class adv e-mail Sentinelsales@wnypapers.com; ed e-mail sentinel@wnypapers.com; web site www.wnypapers.com
Circulation: 0pd,; Sworn/Estimate/Non-Audited
Advertising rate: Open inch rate $23.94
Established: 1987
Group: Niagara Frontier Publications
Digital Platform - Mobile: Apple, Android, Windows, Blackberry
Digital Platform - Tablet: Apple iOS, Android, Windows 7, Blackberry Tablet OS, Kindle, Nook, Kindle Fire
PubCEO .... A. Skip Mazenauer
Mng. Ed. .... Terry Duffy
Josh Malone
Mechanical Specifications: Type page 10 3/4 x 15.75; E - 5 cols, 2, 1/8 between; A - 5 cols, 2, 1/8 between; C - 5 cols, 2, 1/8 between. Equipment & Software: Hardware — APP/Power Mac 7200-120, Umax/Astra 610S Scanner, Unity 1800XL-Plus Printer, APP/Power Mac 7200-90; Software — QPS/QuarkXPress 5.0, Adobe/Photoshop 3.0, Adobe/Illustrator 5.0.
Delivery Method: Carrier, Racks
Areas Served: 14092; 14174; 14172; 14012; 14108, Niagara County

NIAGARA-WHEATFIELD TRIBUNE (THUR)

1859 Whitehaven Rd, Grand Island, NY, 14072-1803, Erie, USA; gen tel (716) 773-7676; gen fax (716) 773-7190; disp adv e-mail majoraccounts@wnypapers.com; class adv e-mail tribunesales@wnypapers.com; ed e-mail tribune@wnypapers.com; web site www.wnypapers.com
Circulation: 11,500fr; Sworn/Estimate/Non-Audited
Advertising rate: Open inch rate $23.94 as of Nov 1, 2016
Established: 1944
Group: Niagara Frontier Publications
Digital Platform - Mobile: Apple, Android, Windows, Blackberry
Digital Platform - Tablet: Apple iOS, Android, Windows 7, Blackberry Tablet OS, Kindle, Nook, Kindle Fire
Pub. .... A. Skip Mazenauer
Mng. Ed. .... Terry Duffy
editor .... David Yarger
Mechanical Specifications: Type page 10 .5 x 15.75; E - 5 cols, 2, 1/8 between; A - 5 cols, 2, 1/8 between; C - 5 cols, 2, 1/8 between. Equipment & Software: Hardware — APP/Power Mac 7200-120, UMax/Astra 610S Scanner, APP/Power Mac 7200-90, UMAX/Astra 1220s Scanner, HP/Laser Jet 5000 Printer; Software — QPS/QuarkXPress 5.0, Adobe/Photoshop 3.0, Adobe/Illustrator 5.0.
Delivery Method: Carrier
Areas Served: Town of Niagara, Town of Wheatfield, part of Niagara Falls, part of No. Tonawanda.

GRANVILLE

NORTHSHIRE FREE PRESS (FRI)

14 E Main St, Granville, NY, 12832-1334,

Washington, USA; gen tel (518) 642-1234; adv tel (518) 642-1234; ed tel (518) 642-1234; gen fax (518) 642-1344; adv fax (518) 642-1344; ed fax (518) 642-1344; disp adv e-mail advertising@manchesternewspapers.com; class adv e-mail classifieds@manchesternewspapers.com; ed e-mail publisher@manchesternewspapers.com; web site www.manchesternewspapers.com
Circulation: 0pd, 7,030fr; CVC
Advertising rate: Open inch rate $11.70
Established: 1995
Group: Manchester Newspapers, Inc.
Digital Platform - Mobile: Apple, Android, Windows, Blackberry
Digital Platform - Tablet: Apple iOS, Android, Windows 7, Blackberry Tablet OS
Exec. VP .... Lisa Manchester
Pub./ Nat'l Adv. Mgr.......... John MacArthur Manchester
Ed. .... Bill Toscano
Circ. Mgr .... Ann Hilder
Prodn. Mgr./Adv. Mgr.......... Jane Cosey
Mechanical Specifications: Type page 10.5 x 16; 5 cols, 2, 0.125 between
Delivery Method: Mail, Racks
Areas Served: 12809, 12816, 12821, 12823, 12827, 12831, 12834, 12838, 12848, 12865, 12866, 12871, 12873, 12884, 12028, 12057, 12089, 12090, 12094, 12133, 12154, 12170, 12185, 05468, 05776

THE GRANVILLE SENTINEL (WED, THUR)
14 E Main St, Granville, NY, 12832-1334, Washington, USA; gen tel (518) 642-1234; adv tel (518) 642-1234; ed tel (518) 642-1234; gen fax (518) 642-1344; adv fax (518) 642-1344; ed fax (518) 642-1344; disp adv e-mail advertising@manchesternewspapers.com; class adv e-mail classifieds@manchesternewspapers.com; ed e-mail publisher@manchesternewspapers.com; web site www.manchesternewspapers.com
Circulation: 2,800pd,; USPS
Advertising rate: Open inch rate $12.30
Established: 1875
Group: Manchester Newspapers, Inc.
Digital Platform - Mobile: Apple, Android, Windows, Blackberry
Digital Platform - Tablet: Apple iOS, Android, Windows 7, Blackberry Tablet OS
Pub.......... John MacArthur Manchester
Exec. VP .... Lisa Manchester
Prodc. Mgr & Ad.......... Jane Casey
Mechanical Specifications: Type page 10.5 x 16; 5 cols, 2, 0.125 between
Equipment & Software: Hardware — PC; Software — Adobe/PageMaker 6.5.
Delivery Method: Mail, Newsstand
Areas Served: Middle Granville, Granville, Wells, West Pawlet, Pawlet, Hartford

THE LAKES REGION FREE PRESS (FRI)
14 E Main St, Granville, NY, 12832-1334, Washington, USA; gen tel (518) 642-1234; adv tel (518) 642-1234; ed tel (518) 642-1234; gen fax (518) 642-1344; adv fax (518) 642-1344; ed fax (518) 642-1344; disp adv e-mail advertising@manchesternewspapers.com; class adv e-mail classifieds@manchesternewspapers.com; ed e-mail publisher@manchesternewspapers.com; web site www.manchesternewspapers.com
Circulation: 8,039fr; VAC
Advertising rate: Open inch rate $29.45
Established: 1995
Group: Manchester Newspapers, Inc.
Digital Platform - Mobile: Apple, Android, Windows, Blackberry
Digital Platform - Tablet: Apple iOS, Android, Windows 7, Blackberry Tablet OS
Pub./Nat'l Adv. Mgr.......... John Manchester
Vice Pres. .... Lisa Manchester
Prodn. Mgr. .... Jane Cosey
Ed. .... Bill Toscano
Circ. Mgr .... Ann Hilder
Mechanical Specifications: Type page 10.5 x 16; 5 cols, 2, 0.125 between
Delivery Method: Mail
Areas Served: 05731, 05732, 05735, 05741, 05743, 05750, 05757, 05761, 05764, 05774, 05775, 12837

THE NORTH COUNTRY FREE PRESS (FRI)
14 E Main St, Granville, NY, 12832-1334, Washington, USA; gen tel (518) 642-1234; adv tel (518) 642-1234; ed tel (518) 642-1234; gen fax (518) 642-1344; adv fax (518) 642-1344; ed fax (518) 642-1344; disp adv e-mail advertising@manchesternewspapers.com; class adv e-mail classifieds@manchesternewspapers.com; ed e-mail publisher@manchesternewspapers.com; web site www.manchesternewspapers.com
Circulation: 17,172fr; VAC
Advertising rate: Open inch rate $14.50
Established: 1995
Group: Manchester Newspapers, Inc.
Digital Platform - Mobile: Apple, Android, Windows, Blackberry
Digital Platform - Tablet: Apple iOS, Android, Windows 7, Blackberry Tablet OS
Exec. VP .... Lisa Manchester
Pub.......... John MacArthur Manchester
Prodn. Mgr./Adv. Mgr.......... Jane Cosey
Circ. Mgr .... Ann Hilder
Mechanical Specifications: Type page 10.5 x 16; 5 cols, 2, 0.125 between
Delivery Method: Mail, Racks
Areas Served: 12809, 12816, 12821, 12823, 12827, 12831, 12834, 12838, 12848, 12865, 12866, 12871, 12873, 12884, 12028, 12057, 12089, 12090, 12094, 12133, 12154, 12170, 12185, 05468, 05776

THE WEEKENDER (FRI)
14 E Main St, Granville, NY, 12832-1334, Washington, USA; gen tel (518) 642-1234; adv tel (518) 642-1234; ed tel (518) 642-1234; gen fax (518) 642-1344; adv fax (518) 642-1344; ed fax (518) 642-1344; disp adv e-mail advertising@manchesternewspapers.com; class adv e-mail classifieds@manchesternewspapers.com; ed e-mail publisher@manchesternewspapers.com; web site www.manchesternewspapers.com
Circulation: 5,517fr; VAC
Advertising rate: Open inch rate $11.70
Established: 1995
Group: Manchester Newspapers, Inc.
Digital Platform - Mobile: Apple, Android, Windows, Blackberry
Digital Platform - Tablet: Apple iOS, Android, Windows 7, Blackberry Tablet OS
Exec. VP .... Lisa Manchester
Pub.......... John MacArthur Manchester
Prodn. Mgr./Adv. Mgr.......... Jane Cosey
Circ. Mgr .... Ann Hilder
Mechanical Specifications: Type page 10.5 x 16; 5 cols, 2, 0.125 between
Delivery Method: Mail, Racks
Areas Served: 12809, 12816, 12821, 12823, 12827, 12831, 12834, 12838, 12848, 12865, 12866, 12871, 12873, 12884, 12028, 12057, 12089, 12090, 12094, 12133, 12154, 12170, 12185, 05468, 05776

THE WHITEHALL TIMES (THUR)
14 E Main St, Granville, NY, 12832-1334, Washington, USA; gen tel (518) 642-1234; gen fax (518) 642-1344; disp adv e-mail advertising@manchesternewspapers.com; class adv e-mail classifieds@manchesternewspapers.com; ed e-mail publisher@manchesternewspapers.com; web site www.manchesternewspapers.com
Circulation: 1,400pd,; USPS
Advertising rate: Open inch rate $12.30
Established: 1815
Group: Manchester Newspapers, Inc.
Ed. .... John MacArthur Manchester
Exec. VP .... Lisa Manchester
Prodc. Mgr. & Ad.......... Jane Casey
Mechanical Specifications: Type page 10.5 x 16; 5 cols, 2, 0.125 between
Delivery Method: Mail, Newsstand
Areas Served: Whitehall, Putnam

GREENE

THE CHENANGO AMERICAN/WHITNEY POINT REPORTER/OXFORD REVIEW-TIMES (THUR)
9 1/2 S Chenango St, Greene, NY, 13778-1212, Chenango, USA; gen tel (607) 656-4511; gen fax (607) 656-8544; disp adv e-mail hometownnews@frontiernet.net; ed e-mail hometownnews@frontiernet.net; web site www.tritownnews.com
Circulation: 2,100pd, 131fr; Sworn/Estimate/Non-Audited
Advertising rate: Open inch rate $3.50
Ed. .... Allison Collins
Pub .... Ken Paden
Mechanical Specifications: Type page 10 3/8 x 16; 6 cols, 1.625, 0.125 between
Delivery Method: Mail, Newsstand

GREENWICH

THE GREENWICH JOURNAL-SALEM PRESS (THUR)
35 Salem St, Greenwich, NY, 12834-1320, Washington, USA; gen tel (518) 692-2204; gen fax (518) 692-2205; disp adv e-mail news@greenwichjournalsalempress.com; web site http://www.greenwichjournalsalempress.com/
Circulation: 2,000pd, 103fr; Sworn/Estimate/Non-Audited
Advertising rate: Open inch rate $7.50
Established: 1842
Mng. Ed.......... Sally B. Tefft

HAMBURG

THE SUN AND ERIE COUNTY INDEPENDENT (THUR)
141 Buffalo St, Hamburg Village Plaza, Hamburg, NY, 14075-5010, Erie, USA; gen tel (716) 649-4040; ed tel 7166494040 ext 255; gen fax (716) 649-3231; disp adv e-mail news@thesunnews.net; ed e-mail jowen@thesunnews.net; web site www.thesunnews.net - 11,799(views) 8,535(visitors)
Circulation: 10,000pd,; CVC
Advertising rate: Open inch rate $12.00
Established: 1875
Group: Metro Group, Inc.
Dist. Mgr .... Teri Scott
Editor .... Lizz Schumer
Pub .... Denny Guastaferro
Assoc. Ed.......... Felice Krycia
Sports Ed.......... Michael Petro
Community Reporter .... Michael Canfield
Delivery Method: Mail
Areas Served: Hamburg, Boston, Eden, North Collins, Brant and surrounding areas

HANCOCK

THE HANCOCK HERALD (WED)
102 E Front St, Hancock, NY, 13783-1200, Delaware, USA; gen tel (607) 637-3591; gen fax (607) 637-4383; disp adv e-mail jill@hancockherald.com; class adv e-mail Mary@hancockherald.com; ed e-mail hancockherald@hancock.net; web site www.hancockherald.com
Circulation: 2,000pd,; Sworn/Estimate/Non-Audited
Advertising rate: Open inch rate $4.00
Established: 1873
Digital Platform - Mobile: Windows
Pub./Ed. .... Sally Zegers
Mechanical Specifications: Type page 15 1/2 x 21 1/2; E - 8 cols, 1 5/6, 1/6 between; A - 8 cols, 1 5/6, 1/6 between; C - 8 cols, 1 5/6, 1/6 between.Equipment & Software: Hardware — PC
Delivery Method: Mail, Newsstand
Areas Served: 13783, 13754, 18439, 18437, 18461 etc

HEMPSTEAD

EAST MEADOW BEACON (FRI)
5 Centre St, Hempstead, NY, 11550-2422, Nassau, USA; gen tel (516) 481-5400; gen fax (516) 481-8773; disp adv e-mail thebeaconnews5@aol.com
Circulation: 5,600pd,; Sworn/Estimate/Non-Audited
Advertising rate: Open inch rate $4.90
Group: Nassau County Publications
Pub.......... Kathleen Hoegl
Ed. .... Barbara Yohe
Mechanical Specifications: Type page 10 x 14.

THE HEMPSTEAD BEACON (FRI)
5 Centre St, Ste 3, Hempstead, NY, 11550-2422, Nassau, USA; gen tel (516) 481-5400; gen fax (516) 481-8773; disp adv e-mail thebeaconnews5@aol.com
Circulation: 4,800pd,; Sworn/Estimate/Non-Audited
Advertising rate: Open inch rate $4.35
Group: Nassau County Publications
Pub.......... Kathleen Hoegl
Ed. .... Barbara Yohe

THE MERRICK BEACON (FRI)
5 Centre St, Ste 3, Hempstead, NY, 11550-2422, Nassau, USA; gen tel (516) 481-5400; gen fax (516) 481-8773; disp adv e-mail thebeaconnews5@aol.com
Circulation: 3,700pd,; Sworn/Estimate/Non-Audited
Advertising rate: Open inch rate $4.75
Established: 1950
Group: Nassau County Publications
Pub.......... Kathleen Hoegl
Ed. .... Barbara Yohe

THE UNIONDALE BEACON (FRI)
5 Centre St, Ste 3, Hempstead, NY, 11550-2422, Nassau, USA; gen tel (516) 481-5400; gen fax (516) 481-8773; disp adv e-mail thebeaconnews5@aol.com
Circulation: 5,000pd,; Sworn/Estimate/Non-Audited
Advertising rate: Open inch rate $4.90
Group: Nassau County Publications
Pub.......... Kathleen Hoegl
Ed. .... Barbara Yohe

WEST HEMPSTEAD BEACON (FRI)
5 Centre St, Ste 3, Hempstead, NY, 11550-2422, Nassau, USA; gen tel (516) 481-5400; gen fax (516) 481-8773; disp adv e-mail thebeaconnews5@aol.com
Circulation: 5,200pd,; Sworn/Estimate/Non-Audited
Advertising rate: Open inch rate $4.90
Group: Nassau County Publications
Pub.......... Katherine Hoegl
Ed. .... Barbara Yohr

HOWARD BEACH

THE FORUM (THUR)
15519 Lahn St, Howard Beach, NY, 11414-2858, Queens, USA; gen tel (718) 845-3221; gen fax (718) 738-7645; disp adv e-mail forumsouth@gmail.com; ed e-mail michael@theforumnewsgroup.com; web site www.theforumnewsgroup.com
Circulation: 25,000fr; Sworn/Estimate/Non-Audited
Advertising rate: Open inch rate $7.00
Group: The Forum Newspaper, Inc.
Editor-in-Chief.......... Michael Cusenza
Mechanical Specifications: Howard Beach, Ozone Park, Broad Channel, Richmond Hill, Woodhaven

HUDSON

CHATHAM COURIER (THUR)
1 Hudson City Ctr, Ste 202, Hudson, NY, 12534-2355, Columbia, USA; gen tel (518) 828-1616; adv tel (518) 828-1616; ed tel (518) 828-1616; gen fax (518) 671-6043; adv fax (518) 671-6043; ed fax (518) 671-6043; disp adv e-mail advertising@registerstar.com; class adv e-mail classifieds@registerstar.com; ed e-mail chathamcourier@

registerstar.com; web site www.chatham-courier.net
Circulation: 1,200pd,; Sworn/Estimate/Non-Audited
Advertising rate: Open inch rate $7.25
Established: 1862
Group: Johnson Newspaper Corp.
Digital Platform - Mobile: Apple, Android
Digital Platform - Tablet: Apple iOS, Android
Pub.......................................Mark Vinciguerra
Ed. .... Karrie Allen
Managing editor.......................... Lori Anander
Delivery Method: Mail, Newsstand, Carrier, Racks
Areas Served: Columbia County

GREENE COUNTY NEWS (THUR)
1 Hudson City Ctr, Ste 202, Hudson, NY, 12534-2355, Columbia, USA; gen tel (518) 828-1616; ed tel (518) 828-1616; gen fax (518) 671-6043; ed fax (518) 828-3870; disp adv e-mail advertising@registerstar.com; class adv e-mail Classifieds@registerstar.com; ed e-mail lanander.windhamjournal@registerstar.com; web site www.registerstar.com/greene_county_news
Circulation: 668pd,; Sworn/Estimate/Non-Audited
Advertising rate: Open inch rate $7.25
Established: 1907
Pub.... Mark VinciguerraEquipment & Software: Hardware — Apple; Software — Quark 6.52, Photoshop CS2
Delivery Method: Mail, Newsstand, Carrier
Areas Served: Greene, Columbia, Albany

HUNTINGTON

THE LONG-ISLANDER NEWS (THUR)
14 Wall St, Ste A, Huntington, NY, 11743-7622, Suffolk, USA; gen tel (631) 427-7000; adv tel (631) 427-7000; ed tel (631) 427-7000; gen fax (631) 427-5820; adv fax (631) 427-5820; ed fax (631) 427-5820; disp adv e-mail info@longislandernews.com; class adv e-mail info@longislandernews.com; ed e-mail psloggatt@longislandernews.com; web site www.longislandernews.com
Circulation: 24,000pd,; Sworn/Estimate/Non-Audited
Advertising rate: Open inch rate $9.00
Established: 1838
Group: Tribco LLC
Digital Platform - Mobile: Apple, Android
Digital Platform - Tablet: Apple iOS, Android
Pub./Mng.Ed. .... Peter Sloggatt
Ed. ....Andrew Wroblewski
Mechanical Specifications: Type page 10 1/4 x 13 7/8; E - 4 cols, 2 1/2, 1/4 between; A - 4 cols, 2 1/2, 1/4 between; C - 6 cols, 1 1/2, 1/6 between.Equipment & Software: ; Software — QPS/QuarkXPress, Adobe/Photoshop, Microsoft/Word.
Delivery Method: Mail, Newsstand
Areas Served: 11743, 11746, 11721, 11724, 11749, 11746, 11768, 11731

THE NORTHPORT JOURNAL (THUR)
14 Wall St, Huntington, NY, 11743-7622, Suffolk, USA; gen tel (631) 427-7000; gen fax (631) 427-5820; disp adv e-mail info@longislandernews.com; web site www.longislandernews.com
Circulation: 1,200pd,; Sworn/Estimate/Non-Audited
Advertising rate: Open inch rate $5.60
Group: Tribco LLC
Pres./Pub.........................Andrew Wroblewski
Mng. Ed.................... Peter SloggattEquipment & Software: ; Software — QPS/QuarkXPress, Adobe/Photoshop, Microsoft/Word.

THE RECORD (THUR)
14 Wall St, Huntington, NY, 11743-7622, Suffolk, USA; gen tel (631) 427-7000; adv tel (631) 427-7000; ed tel (631) 427-7000; gen fax (631) 427-5820; adv fax (631) 427-5820; ed fax (631) 427-5820; disp adv e-mail info@longislandernews.com; class adv e-mail info@longislandernews.com; ed e-mail psloggatt@longislandernews.com; web site www.longislandernews.com
Circulation: 5,500pd,; Sworn/Estimate/Non-Audited
Advertising rate: Open inch rate $9.00
Established: 1838
Group: Tribco LLC
Digital Platform - Mobile: Apple, Android
Digital Platform - Tablet: Apple iOS, Android
Pub./Mng. Ed. .... Peter Sloggatt
Ed. ....Andrew Wroblewski
Adv. Mgr. ....David Viejo
Circ. Mgr................................ George Wallace
Prodn. Mgr. ....Rob Nieter
Mechanical Specifications: Type page 10 1/4 x 13 7/8; E - 4 cols, 2 1/2, 1/4 between; A - 4 cols, 2 1/2, 1/4 between; C - 6 cols, 1 1/2, 1/6 between.Equipment & Software: Hardware — APP/Mac; Software — QPS/QuarkXPress, Adobe/Photoshop, Microsoft/Word.
Delivery Method: Mail, Newsstand
Areas Served: 11743, 11746, 11721, 11724, 11749, 11746, 11768, 11731

HYDE PARK

HUDSON VALLEY NEWS (WED)
PO Box 268, Hyde Park, NY, 12538-0268, Dutchess, USA; gen tel (845) 233-4651; disp adv e-mail advertising@thehudsonvalleynews.com; ed e-mail editorial@thehudsonvalleynews.com; web site www.thehudsonvalleynews.com
Advertising rate: (Modular Rates)
Exec. Ed...Jim Langan
Adv. Dir.......................................Mahlon Goer
Pub..Caroline Carey
Mechanical Specifications: Type page 11.375 x 12; 4 cols, 2.5
Areas Served: Dutchess

ITHACA

ITHACA TIMES (WED)
109 N Cayuga St, Ste A, Ithaca, NY, 14850-4340, Tompkins, USA; gen tel (607) 277-7000; gen fax (607) 277-1012 ; disp adv e-mail jbilinski@ithacatimes.com; web site www.ithaca.com
Circulation: 22,936fr; Sworn/Estimate/Non-Audited
Delivery Method: Newsstand
Areas Served: 14850,14886, 14882,13053

NEWFIELD NEWS (WED)
1009 N Cayuage St, Ithaca, NY, 14850, Tompkins, USA; gen tel (607) 277-7000; gen fax (607) 277-1012; disp adv e-mail tolson@ithacatimes.com; ed e-mail editor@flcn.org; web site www.ithaca.com
Circulation: 475pd, 30fr; Sworn/Estimate/Non-Audited
Advertising rate: 3/4 - $551; 1/2 - $379; 1/4 - $205;1/8 - $104
Group: Finger Lakes Community Newspapers
Pub..James Bilinski
Ed. ....Nick Reynolds
Delivery Method: Mail

OVID GAZETTE (WED)
109 N Cayuga St, Ithaca, NY, 14850-4341, Tompkins, USA; gen tel (607) 277-7000; gen fax (607) 277 1012; disp adv e-mail jbilinski@ithacatimes.com; ed e-mail editor@flcn.org; web site www.ithaca.com
Circulation: 575pd, 63fr; Sworn/Estimate/Non-Audited
Established: 1801
Group: Finger Lakes Community Newspapers
Pub..James Bilinski
Delivery Method: Mail
Areas Served: seneca City

SPENCER RANDOM HARVEST WEEKELY (WED)
109 N Cayuga St, Ithaca, NY, 14850-4341, Ithaca, USA; gen tel (607) 277-7000; gen fax (607) 277-1012; disp adv e-mail jbilinski@ithacatimes.com; ed e-mail editor@flcn.org; web site www.ithaca.com
Circulation: 826pd,; Sworn/Estimate/Non-Audited
Established: 1980
Group: Finger Lakes Community Newspapers
Pub...James Bilinski
Delivery Method: Mail
Areas Served: Spencer NY Tioga County

THE CANDOR CHRONICLE (WED)
109 N Cayuga St, Ithaca, NY, 14850-4341, Tompkins, USA; gen tel (607) 277-7700; gen fax (607) 277-1012; web site http://www.ithaca.com/news/candor/
Group: Finger Lakes Community Newspapers
Ed. ....Nick Reynolds

THE DRYDEN COURIER (WED)
109 N Cayuga St, Ithaca, NY, 14850-4341, Tompkins, USA; gen tel (607) 277-7700; gen fax (607) 277-1012; web site http://www.ithaca.com/news/candor/
Group: Finger Lakes Community Newspapers
Ed. ....Nick Reynolds

THE INTERLAKEN REVIEW (WED)
1009 N Cayuage St, Ithaca, NY, 14850, Tompkins, USA; gen tel (607) 277-7000; gen fax (607) 277-1012; disp adv e-mail tolson@ithacatimes.com; ed e-mail editor@flcn.org; web site www.ithaca.com
Circulation: 351pd, 42fr; Sworn/Estimate/Non-Audited
Advertising rate: 3/4 - $551; 1/2 - $379; 1/4 - $205;1/8 - $104
Group: Finger Lakes Community Newspapers
Pub...James Bilinski
Mng. Ed. ....Nick Reynolds
Delivery Method: Mail

THE LANSING LEDGER (WED)
109 N Cayuga St, Ithaca, NY, 14850-4341, Tompkins, USA; gen tel (607) 277-7700; gen fax (607) 277-1012; web site http://www.ithaca.com/news/lansing/
Group: Finger Lakes Community Newspapers

THE TRUMANSBURG FREE PRESS (WED)
109 N Cayuga St, Ithaca, NY, 14850-4341, Tompkins, USA; gen tel (607) 277-7000; gen fax (607) 387-9421; disp adv e-mail tolson@ithacatimes.com; ed e-mail editor@flcn.org; web site www.ithaca.com
Circulation: 1,100pd, 85fr; Sworn/Estimate/Non-Audited
Advertising rate: 3/4 - $551; 1/2 - $379; 1/4 - $205;1/8 - $104
Established: 1865
Group: Finger Lakes Community Newspapers
Pub...James Bilinski
Mng. Ed......................................Bill Chaisson
Mng. Ed...Glynis Hart
Delivery Method: Mail
Areas Served: 14886

KINGSTON

KINGSTON TIMES (THUR)
322 Wall St, Kingston, NY, 12401-3820, Ulster, USA; gen tel (845) 334-8200; gen fax (845) 334-8202; disp adv e-mail info@ulsterpublishing.com; class adv e-mail classifieds@ulsterpublishing.com; ed e-mail kingstontimes@ulsterpublishing.com; web site www.kingstonx.com
Circulation: 1,550pd,; Sworn/Estimate/Non-Audited
Advertising rate: Open inch rate $17.00
Group: Ulster Publishing
Ed. ....Dan Barton
Adv. Dir./Circ Mgr./Classified Adv........... Genia Wickwire
Pub.......................................Brian Hollander
Mechanical Specifications: Type page 10 x 15.5; 3 cols, 3, 0.5 between
Areas Served: Kingston, Ulster

SAUGERTIES TIMES (THUR)
322 Wall St, Kingston, NY, 12401-3820, Ulster, USA; gen tel (845) 334-8200; gen fax (845) 334-8202; disp adv e-mail info@ulsterpublishing.com; class adv e-mail classifieds@ulsterpublishing.com; ed e-mail saugertiestimes@ulsterpublishing.com; web site www.saugertiesx.com
Circulation: 1,700pd,; Sworn/Estimate/Non-Audited
Advertising rate: Open inch rate $17.00
Group: Ulster Publishing
Ed. ....Brian Hollander
Ed. ....Dan Barton
Ad. Dir. ....Genia Wickwire
Mechanical Specifications: Type page 10 x 15.5; 3 cols, 3, 0.5 between
Areas Served: Saugerties

WOODSTOCK TIMES (THUR)
322 Wall St, Kingston, NY, 12401-3820, Ulster, USA; gen tel (845) 334-8200 ; gen fax (845) 334-8202; disp adv e-mail info@ulsterpublishing.com; class adv e-mail classifieds@ulsterpublishing.com; ed e-mail wtedit@gmail.com; web site www.woodstockx.com
Circulation: 4,400pd,; Sworn/Estimate/Non-Audited
Advertising rate: Open inch rate $17.00
Group: Ulster Publishing
Ed. ....Brian Hollander
Ad. Director.............................Genia Wickwire
Mechanical Specifications: Type page 10 x 15.5; 3 cols, 3, 0.5 between
Areas Served: Woodstock, West Hurley, Kingston, Saugerties, Olive, Phoenicia

LOWVILLE

CARTHAGE REPUBLICAN TRIBUNE (THUR)
7567 S STATE ST, LOWVILLE, NY, 13367-1512, Jefferson, USA; gen tel (315) 493-1270; adv tel (315) 376-4997; ed tel (315) 493-1270; gen fax (315) 376-4136; disp adv e-mail tribunenews@lowville.com; class adv e-mail caucter@lowville.com; ed e-mail jpapineau@lowville.com; web site http://www.carthagerepublicantribune.com/
Circulation: 66pd,; AAM
Advertising rate: Open inch rate $4.70
Established: 1860
Group: Johnson Newspaper Corp.
Managing Editor ....Jeremiah Papineau
Mechanical Specifications: Type page 13 1/8 x 20 1/4; E - 6 cols, 2, 1/6 between; A - 6 cols, 2, 1/6 between; C - 6 cols, 2, 1/6 between. Equipment & Software: Hardware — APP/Power Mac.
Delivery Method: Mail, Newsstand, Carrier

LACKAWANNA

SOUTH BUFFALO NEWS (WED)
2703 S Park Ave, Lackawanna, NY, 14218-1511, Erie, USA; gen tel (716) 823-8222; disp adv e-mail frontpagegroupinc@gmail.com; ed e-mail newsroomfpg@wny.twcbc.com
Circulation: 3,000pd,; Sworn/Estimate/Non-Audited
Advertising rate: Open inch rate $7.50
Group: Front Page Group Inc
Ex Ed ....Darryl McPherson
Mechanical Specifications: Type page 10 1/16 x 16; E - 5 cols, 1 7/8, 1/6 between; A - 5 cols, 1 7/8, 1/6 between; C - 5 cols, 1 7/8, 1/6 between.Equipment & Software: Hardware — IBM; Software — Adobe/PageMaker 6.0.
Delivery Method: Mail, Newsstand
Areas Served: 14210, 14220

LAKE PLACID

THE LAKE PLACID NEWS (FRI)
6179 Sentinel Rd, Lake Placid, NY, 12946-3509, Essex, USA; gen tel (518) 523-4401; adv tel (518) 891-2600; ed tel (518) 523-4401; disp adv e-mail advertising@lakeplacidnews.com; class adv e-mail classifieds@

adirondackdailyenterprise.com; ed e-mail news@lakeplacidnews.com; web site www.lakeplacidnews.com
Circulation: 2,500pd,; Sworn/Estimate/Non-Audited
Advertising rate: Open inch rate $15.30
Established: 1905
Group: Ogden Newspapers Inc.
Pub....................................... Catherine Moore
Mechanical Specifications: Type page 11 4/5 x 21; E - 6 cols, 1 4/5, between; A - 6 cols, 3 4/5, between; C - 8 cols, 1 1/3, between. Equipment & Software: Hardware — APP/Mac; Presses — G/Community; Software — QPS/QuarkXPress 4.0, Adobe/Photoshop.
Delivery Method: Mail, Newsstand, Racks
Areas Served: Essex County

LATHAM

ALBANY BUSINESS REVIEW (FRI)
40 British American Blvd, Ste 9, Latham, NY, 12110-1424, Albany, USA; gen tel (518) 640-6800; adv tel (518) 640-6820; ed tel (518) 640-6808; gen fax (518) 640-6801; disp adv e-mail tgiroux@bizjournals.com; ed e-mail mhendricks@bizjournals.com; web site www.albany.bizjournals.com
Advertising rate: Open inch rate $97
Editor-in-Chief......................... Mike Hendricks
Mgn. Editor .... Melissa Mangini

LE ROY

LE ROY PENNYSAVER & NEWS (MON)
1 Church St, Le Roy, NY, 14482-1017, Genesee, USA; gen tel (585) 768-2201; adv tel (585) 768-2201; ed tel (585) 768-2201; gen fax (585) 768-6334; adv fax (585) 768-6334; ed fax (585) 768-6334; disp adv e-mail pennysaver@leroyny.com; class adv e-mail office@leroyny.com; ed e-mail editor@leroyny.com; web site www.leroyny.com - 2,783(views) 938(visitors)
Circulation: 7,263fr; CVC
Advertising rate: Open inch rate $9.91
Established: 1935
Group: Dray Enterprises Inc. Editions: (1) Le Roy Pennysaver & News
Pub./Ed.................................... David Grayson
Prod. Mgr.................................... Terry Guilford
Mechanical Specifications: Type page 8.5 x 12, 4 cols, 1.75, 0.5 between
Delivery Method: Mail, Carrier
Areas Served: 14143, 14414, 14416, 14422, 14423, 14482, 14511, 14525, 14592

LOCUST VALLEY

THE LEADER (WED)
336 Forest Ave, Locust Valley, NY, 11560-2122, Nassau, USA; gen tel (516) 676-1434; gen fax (516) 676-1414; disp adv e-mail advertising@theleaderonline.com; class adv e-mail classifieds@theleaderonline.com; ed e-mail news@theleaderonline.com; web site www.theleaderonline.com
Circulation: 3,200pd, 80fr; Sworn/Estimate/Non-Audited
Advertising rate: (Modular Rates) 1/12 page, 2.375 x 4.6 - $90 1x
Pub.. Lawrence Lally
Mng. Ed.. LC Colgate
Mechanical Specifications: Type page 10 x 14; E - 5 cols, 2, 1/6 between; A - 5 cols, 2, 1/6 between; C - 5 cols, 2, 1/6 between.
Areas Served: Locust Valley, Oyster Bay, Glen Cove, Bayville, Centre Island, Cove Neck, Lattingtown, Matinecock, The Brookvilles, Muttontown

LOWVILLE

JOURNAL AND REPUBLICAN (WED)
7567 S State St, Lowville, NY, 13367-1512, Lewis, USA; gen tel (315) 376-3525; adv tel (315) 376-4997; ed tel (315) 376-6851; gen fax (315) 376-4136; adv fax (315) 376-4136; disp adv e-mail caucter@lowville.com; class adv e-mail dfinster@lowville.com; ed e-mail jpapineau@lowville.com; web site www.journalandrepublican.com
Circulation: 4,106pd, 22fr; Sworn/Estimate/Non-Audited
Advertising rate: Open inch rate $9.40
Established: 1830
Group: Johnson Newspaper Corp.
Managing Editor .... Jeremiah Papineau
Mechanical Specifications: Type page 13 x 21; E - 6 cols, 2, 3/8 between; A - 6 cols, 2, 3/8 between; C - 9 cols, 1 5/8, 1/8 between. Equipment & Software: Hardware — APP/Mac; Software — Microsoft/Word, Multi-Ad/Creator.
Delivery Method: Mail, Newsstand, Carrier
Areas Served: 13305, 13309, 13312, 13620, 13325, 13626, 13367, 13327

MAHOPAC

PUTNAM COUNTY PRESS (WED)
PO Box 608, Mahopac, NY, 10541-0608, Putnam, USA; gen tel (845) 628-8400; adv tel (845) 628-8400; ed tel (845) 628-8401; gen fax (845) 628-8400; adv fax (845) 628-8400; ed fax (845) 628-8400; disp adv e-mail advertising@putnampresstimes.com; class adv e-mail advertising@putnampresstimes.com; ed e-mail putnampress@aol.com; web site www.putnampresstimes.com
Circulation: 3,200pd,; Sworn/Estimate/Non-Audited
Advertising rate: Open inch rate $9.57
Digital Platform - Mobile: Apple, Android, Windows, Blackberry
Digital Platform - Tablet: Apple iOS, Android, Windows 7, Blackberry Tablet OS
Pub.. Don Hall
Ed-in-Chief.. Holly Toal
Adv. Mgr................................ Christine Groppe
Delivery Method: Mail, Racks
Areas Served: Brewster, Carmel, Kent, Mahopac, Patterson, Philipstown, and Putnam Valley

PUTNAM COUNTY TIMES (WED)
PO Box 608, Mahopac, NY, 10541-0608, Putnam, USA; gen tel (845) 628-8400; adv tel (845) 628-8400; ed tel (845) 628-8400; gen fax (845) 628-8400; adv fax (845) 628-8400; ed fax (845) 628-8400; disp adv e-mail advertising@putnampresstimes.com; class adv e-mail advertising@putnampresstimes.com; ed e-mail putnampress@aol.com; web site www.putnampresstimes.com
Advertising rate: Open inch rate $9.57
Digital Platform - Mobile: Apple, Android, Windows, Blackberry
Digital Platform - Tablet: Apple iOS, Android, Windows 7, Blackberry Tablet OS
Pub.. Don Hall
Ed-in-Chief.. Holly Toal
Adv. Mgr./Graphic Designer... Christine Groppe
Delivery Method: Mail, Racks
Areas Served: Brewster, Carmel, Kent, Mahopac, Patterson, Philipstown, and Putnam Valley

MASPETH

FOREST HILLS/REGO PARK TIMES (THUR)
6960 Grand Ave, Maspeth, NY, 11378-1828, Queens, USA; gen tel (718) 639-7000; gen fax (718) 429-1234; disp adv e-mail ads@queensledger.com; ed e-mail news@queensledger.com; web site www.foresthillstimes.com
Circulation: 18,000pd, 165fr; Sworn/Estimate/Non-Audited
Advertising rate: Full - $709; 1/2 - $362; 1/4 - $202; 1/8 - $104
Established: 1995
Group: BQE Publishing Inc.
Digital Platform - Mobile: Apple, Android
Digital Platform - Tablet: Apple iOS, Android
Pub.................................... Walter H. Sanchez
Gen. Mgr. .... Tammy Sanchez
Delivery Method: Mail, Newsstand, Racks
Areas Served: 11375 11374 11415

GLENDALE REGISTER (THUR)
6960 Grand Ave, Maspeth, NY, 11378-1828, Queens, USA; gen tel (718) 639-7000; gen fax (718) 429-1234; disp adv e-mail ads@queensledger.com; ed e-mail news@queensledger.com; web site www.queensledger.com
Circulation: 1,320pd, 165fr; Sworn/Estimate/Non-Audited
Advertising rate: Full - $709; 1/2 - $362; 1/4 - $202; 1/8 - $104
Established: 1935
Group: BQE Publishing Inc.
Digital Platform - Mobile: Apple, Android
Digital Platform - Tablet: Apple iOS, Android
Gen. Mgr. .... Tammy Sanchez
Ed. .... Walter H. Sanchez
Mechanical Specifications: Type page 10 x 14; E - 4 cols, 2 3/8, 1/4 between; A - 4 cols, 2 3/8, 1/4 between; C - 5 cols, 1 15/16, 1/4 between.Equipment & Software: Hardware — APP/Mac; Software — APP/Mac System 7.5, Adobe/PageMaker 5.0.
Delivery Method: Mail, Newsstand, Racks
Areas Served: 11385

QUEENS LEDGER (THUR)
6960 Grand Ave, Maspeth, NY, 11378-1828, Queens, USA; gen tel (718) 639-7000; gen fax (718) 429-1234; disp adv e-mail ads@queensledger.com; ed e-mail news@queensledger.com; web site www.queensledger.com
Circulation: 10,890pd,; Sworn/Estimate/Non-Audited
Advertising rate: Full - $709; 1/2 - $362; 1/4 - $202; 1/8 - $104
Established: 1873
Group: BQE Publishing Inc.
Digital Platform - Mobile: Apple, Android
Digital Platform - Tablet: Apple iOS, Android
Pub.................................... Walter H. Sanchez
Gen. Mgr. .... Tammy Sanchez
Ed. .... Shane Miller
Delivery Method: Mail, Newsstand, Racks
Areas Served: 11378 11379 11377 11373 11385 11355

THE LEADER-OBSERVER OF WOODHAVEN (THUR)
6960 Grand Ave, Maspeth, NY, 11378-1828, Queens, USA; gen tel (718) 639-7000; gen fax (718) 429-1234; disp adv e-mail ads@queensledger.com; ed e-mail news@queensledger.com; web site www.leaderobserver.com
Circulation: 25,000pd,; Sworn/Estimate/Non-Audited
Advertising rate: Full - $709; 1/2 - $362; 1/4 - $202; 1/8 - $104
Established: 1909
Group: BQE Publishing Inc.
Digital Platform - Mobile: Apple, Android
Digital Platform - Tablet: Apple iOS, Android
Gen. Mgr. .... Tammy Sanchez
Ed. .... Walter H. Sanchez
Delivery Method: Mail, Newsstand, Racks
Areas Served: 11421 11414 11417 4418 11415 11420 11432

MATTITUCK

RIVERHEAD NEWS-REVIEW (THUR)
7785 Main Rd, Mattituck, NY, 11952-1518, Suffolk, USA; gen tel (631) 298-3200; adv tel (631) 354-8043; ed tel (631) 354-8045; gen fax (631) 298-3287; disp adv e-mail jtumminello@timesreview.com; class adv e-mail classifieds@timesreview.com; ed e-mail mwhite@timesreview.com; web site http://riverheadnewsreview.timesreview.com/ - 215,000(views) 22,000(visitors)
Circulation: 5,255pd, 61fr; Sworn/Estimate/Non-Audited
Advertising rate: (Modular Rates)
Established: 1868
Group: Time Review Newsgroup
Pub.. Andrew Olsen
Exec. Ed...................................... Grant Parpan
Sales & Marketing Dir. .... Sonja Reinholt Derr
Mechanical Specifications: Type page 9.75 x 13.75; E&A - 4 cols, 2.25, 0.25 between; C - 5 cols, 1.875, 0.105 between. Equipment & Software: Hardware — APP/Mac, PC.
Delivery Method: Mail, Racks
Areas Served: Wading River, Calverton, Northville, Aquebogue, Riverhead, Jamesport

THE SUFFOLK TIMES (THUR)
7785 Main Rd, Mattituck, NY, 11952-1518, Suffolk, USA; gen tel (631) 298-3200; adv tel (631) 354-8053; ed tel (631) 354-8045; gen fax (631) 298-3287; disp adv e-mail tvolinski@timesreview.com; class adv e-mail classifieds@timesreview.com; ed e-mail mwhite@timesreview.com; web site www.suffolktimes.com - 230,000(views) 23,000(visitors)
Circulation: 8,723pd, 200fr; Sworn/Estimate/Non-Audited
Advertising rate: (Modular Rates)
Established: 1857
Group: Times Review Newsgroup
Pub.. Andrew Olsen
Sales & Marketing Dir. .... Sonja Reinholt Derr
Exec. Ed...................................... Grant Parpan
Mechanical Specifications: Type page 9.75 x 13.75; E&A - 4 cols, 2.25, 0.25 between; C - 5 cols, 1.875, 0.105 between.
Equipment & Software: Hardware — APP/Mac, PC; Software — QPS/QuarkXPress, Adobe/Photoshop, Microsoft/Word.
Delivery Method: Mail
Areas Served: Laurel, New Suffolk, Mattituck, Cutchague, Peconic, Southold, Greenport, East Marion, Orient

MECHANICVILLE

THE EXPRESS (THUR)
30 Walnut St, Fl 1, Mechanicville, NY, 12118-1040, Saratoga, USA; gen tel (518) 664-3335; adv tel (518) 664-3335; ed tel (518) 664-3335; disp adv e-mail info.expresspaper@gmail.com; class adv e-mail info.expresspaper@gmail.com; ed e-mail info.expresspaper@gmail.com; web site www.theexpressweeklynews.com - 4,000(views) 3,500(visitors)
Circulation: 2,700pd, 0fr; USPS
Advertising rate: Open inch rate $8.00
Established: 1981
Digital Platform - Mobile: Apple
Owner/Ed................................ Cindy Mahoney
Owner & Pub............................ Tom Mahoney
V.P. Sales and Marketing .... Melissa LeMay
Mechanical Specifications: Type page 10.25 x 14; 6 cols, 1.5, 0.25 between
Equipment & Software: Hardware — ; Software — In design
Delivery Method: Mail, Newsstand
Areas Served: 12118,12170,12065,12154,12194,12121,12020, 12188,12866

MEXICO

INDEPENDENT MIRROR (FRI)
80 N Jefferson St, Mexico, NY, 13114-3001, Oswego, USA; gen tel (315) 963-7813; gen fax (315) 963-4087; disp adv e-mail ocwadvertising@cnymail.com; class adv e-mail ocwadvertising@cnymail.com; ed e-mail ocweeklies@cnymail.com; web site www.oswegocountyweeklies.com
Circulation: 3,260pd,; Sworn/Estimate/Non-Audited
Advertising rate: Open inch rate $7.50
Established: 1861
Mng. Ed.............................. Rose Ann Parsons
Areas Served: 13114, 13131, 13126, 13069, 13142, 13121, 13107

PHOENIX REGISTER (FRI)
80 N Jefferson St, Mexico, NY, 13114-3001, Oswego, USA; gen tel (315) 963-7813; gen fax (315) 963-4087; disp adv e-mail ocwadvertising@cnymail.com; class adv e-mail

ocwadvertising@cnymail.com; ed e-mail ocweeklies@cnymail.com; web site www.oswegocountyweeklies.com
Circulation: 2,272pd,; Sworn/Estimate/Non-Audited
Advertising rate: Open inch rate $7.50
Established: 1858
Mng. Ed.............................. Rose Ann Parsons
Areas Served: 13135, 13132, 13069

SALMON RIVER NEWS (FRI)
80 N Jefferson St, Mexico, NY, 13114-3001, Oswego, USA; gen tel (315) 963-7813; gen fax (315) 963-4087; disp adv e-mail ocwadvertising@cnymail.com; class adv e-mail ocwadvertising@cnymail.com; ed e-mail ocweeklies@cnymail.com; web site www.oswegocountyweeklies.com
Circulation: 5,145pd,; Sworn/Estimate/Non-Audited
Advertising rate: Open inch rate $7.50
Established: 1973
Mgn. Ed.............................. Rose Ann Parsons

THE CITIZEN OUTLET (FRI)
80 N Jefferson St, Mexico, NY, 13114-3001, Oswego, USA; gen tel (315) 963-7813; gen fax (315) 963-4087; disp adv e-mail ocwadvertising@cnymail.com; class adv e-mail ocwadvertising@cnymail.com; ed e-mail rparsons@oswegonews.com; web site www.oswegocountyweeklies.com
Circulation: 4,889pd,; Sworn/Estimate/Non-Audited
Advertising rate: Open inch rate $7.50
Established: 1950
Mng. Ed.............................. Rose Ann Parsons
Areas Served: 13036, 13029, 13167, 13044, 13076, 13042. 13028

MILLERTON

THE MILLERTON NEWS (THUR)
16 Century Blvd, Millerton, NY, 12546-5274, Dutchess, USA; gen tel (518) 789-4401; gen fax (518) 789-9247; disp adv e-mail advertising@lakevillejournal.com; class adv e-mail classifieds@lakevillejournal.com; ed e-mail editor@millertonnews.com; web site www.millertonnews.com
Circulation: 1,292pd, 32fr; CAC
Advertising rate: Open inch rate $11.00
Adv. Mgr.......................... Elizabeth Castrodad
Circ. Mgr....................................... Helen Testa
Pub./Ed.-in-Chief .... Janet Manko
Ed. .... Whitney Joseph
Mechanical Specifications: Type page 15 x 21; E - 7 cols, 2 1/16, between; A - 7 cols, 2 1/16, between; C - 8 cols, between.Equipment & Software: Hardware — APP/Mac; Software — Adobe/PageMaker.
Areas Served: Amenia, Ancram, Copake, Dover, Millerton, North East, Pine Plains, Rhinebeck, Red Hook, Millbrook, Poughkeepsie, Wassaic

MINEOLA

FARMINGDALE OBSERVER (THUR)
132 E 2nd St, Mineola, NY, 11501-3522, Nassau, USA; gen tel (516) 747-8282; gen fax (516) 742-5867; disp adv e-mail advertising@antonnews.com; class adv e-mail classified@antonnews.com; ed e-mail frizzo@antonmediagroup.com; web site http://farmingdale-observer.com/
Circulation: 5,130pd,; Sworn/Estimate/Non-Audited
Advertising rate: 1/8 Pg $489.00; 1/6 Pg $625.00; 1/4 Pg $812.00
Established: 1960
Group: Anton Community Newspapers
Pub.................................. Angela Susan Anton
Adv. Mgr... Iris Picone
Circ. Mgr.................................... Joy DiDonato
Ed. .... Frank Rizzo
Mng. Ed.................................... Carrie Seaman
Delivery Method: Mail, Newsstand
Areas Served: Farmingdale, Bethpage & Melville

GARDEN CITY LIFE (THUR)
132 E 2nd St, Mineola, NY, 11501-3522, Nassau, USA; gen tel (516) 747-8282; gen fax (641) 742-5867; disp adv e-mail advertising@antonnews.com; class adv e-mail classified@antonnews.com; ed e-mail gardencitylife@antonnews.com; web site http://gardencity-life.com/
Circulation: 6,010pd,; Sworn/Estimate/Non-Audited
Advertising rate: 1/8 Pg $489.00; 1/6 Pg $625.00; 1/4 Pg $812.00
Established: 1985
Group: Anton Community Newspapers
Pub.................................. Angela Susan Anton
Adv. Mgr.. Iris Picone
Circ. Mgr.................................... Joy DiDonato
Ed. .... Dave Gil de Rubio
Mng. Ed.. Cary Sieman
Delivery Method: Mail, Newsstand
Areas Served: Garden City, Stewart Minor

GLEN COVE RECORD-PILOT (THUR)
132 E 2nd St, Mineola, NY, 11501-3522, Nassau, USA; gen tel (516) 747-8282; gen fax (516) 742-5867; disp adv e-mail advertising@antonnews.com; class adv e-mail classified@antonnews.com; ed e-mail jnossa@antonmediagroup.com; web site www.antonnews.com
Circulation: 5,344pd, 1,128fr; Sworn/Estimate/Non-Audited
Advertising rate: 1/8 Pg $489.00; 1/6 Pg $625.00; 1/4 Pg $812.00
Established: 1953
Group: Anton Community Newspapers
Pub.................................. Angela Susan Anton
Adv. Mgr.. Iris Picone
Circ. Mgr.................................... Joy DiDonato
Ed. .... Jill Nossa
Mng. Ed.........Cary SeamanEquipment & Software: Hardware — APP/Mac, PC, Postscript Level 2; Presses — WPC; Software — QPS/QuarkXPress 3.32.
Delivery Method: Mail, Newsstand
Areas Served: Glen Cove, Brookville, Glenwood Landing, Locust Valley, Old Brookville, Sea Cliff

GREAT NECK RECORD (THUR)
132 E 2nd St, Mineola, NY, 11501-3522, Nassau, USA; gen tel (516) 747-8282; gen fax (516) 482-4491; disp adv e-mail advertising@antonnews.com; class adv e-mail classified@antonnews.com; ed e-mail sarbitaljacoby@antonmediagroup.com; web site http://greatneckrecord.com/
Circulation: 6,998pd, 988fr; Sworn/Estimate/Non-Audited
Advertising rate: Full - $583; 1/2 - $327; 1/4 - $190; 1/8 - $113
Established: 1933
Group: Anton Community Newspapers
Pub.. Angela S. Anton
Circ. Mgr.................................... Joy DiDonato
Mng. Ed........................... Sheri ArbitalJacoby
Prod. Dir.................................. Karen Mengel
Mechanical Specifications: Type page 10 1/4 x 14; E - 4 cols, 2 3/8, 3/8 between; A - 4 cols, 2 3/8, 3/8 between; C - 6 cols, 1 9/16, 3/16 between.Equipment & Software: Hardware — APP/Mac, PC, Postscript Level 2; Presses — MAN; Software — QPS/QuarkXPress 3.32.
Delivery Method: Mail, Newsstand
Areas Served: Great Neck, Great Neck Estates, Great Neck Plaza, Kesington, Kings Point, Lake Success, Russell Gardens, Saddle Rock, Thomaston

HICKSVILLE ILLUSTRATED NEWS (THUR)
132 E 2nd St, Mineola, NY, 11501-3522, Nassau, USA; gen tel (516) 747-8282; gen fax (516) 742-5867; disp adv e-mail advertising@antonnews.com; class adv e-mail classified@antonnews.com; ed e-mail frizzo@antonmediagroup.com; web site www.antonnews.com
Circulation: 5,000pd,; Sworn/Estimate/Non-Audited
Advertising rate: 1/8 Pg $489.00; 1/6 Pg $625.00; 1/4 Pg $812.00
Established: 1986
Group: Anton Community Newspapers
Pub.................................. Angela Susan Anton
Circ. Mgr.................................... Joy DiDonato
Ed. .... Frank Rizzo
Delivery Method: Mail, Newsstand
Areas Served: Hicksville

LEVITTOWN TRIBUNE (THUR)
132 E 2nd St, Mineola, NY, 11501-3522, Nassau, USA; gen tel (516) 747-8282; gen fax (516) 742-5867; disp adv e-mail advertising@antonnews.com; class adv e-mail classified@antonnews.com; ed e-mail jfauci@antonmediagroup.com; web site http://levittown-tribune.com/
Circulation: 3,290pd, 764fr; Sworn/Estimate/Non-Audited
Advertising rate: 1/8 Pg $489.00; 1/6 Pg $625.00; 1/4 Pg $812.00
Established: 1948
Group: Anton Community Newspapers
Pub.. Angela Anton
Ed. .... Jennifer Fauci
Circ. Mgr......... Joy DiDonatoEquipment & Software: Hardware — APP/Mac, PC, Postscript Level 2; Presses — WPC; Software — QPS/QuarkXPress 3.32.
Delivery Method: Mail, Newsstand
Areas Served: Levittown, Island trees, North Wantagh

MANHASSET PRESS (THUR)
132 E 2nd St, Mineola, NY, 11501-3522, Nassau, USA; gen tel (516) 747-8282; gen fax (516) 742-5867; disp adv e-mail advertising@antonnews.com; class adv e-mail classified@antonnews.com; ed e-mail ejohnson@antonmediagroup.com; web site www.antonnews.com
Circulation: 3,801pd, 304fr; Sworn/Estimate/Non-Audited
Advertising rate: 1/8 Pg $489.00; 1/6 Pg $625.00; 1/4 Pg $812.00
Established: 1934
Group: Anton Community Newspapers
Pub.. Angela Anton
Ed. .... Elizabeth JohnsonEquipment & Software: Hardware — APP/Mac, PC; Presses — WPC; Software — QPS/QuarkXPress 3.32.
Delivery Method: Mail, Newsstand
Areas Served: Manhasset, Munsey Park, Plandome Manor, Flower Hill

MASSAPEQUAN OBSERVER (THUR)
132 E 2nd St, Mineola, NY, 11501-3522, Nassau, USA; gen tel (516) 747-8282; gen fax (516) 742-5867; disp adv e-mail advertising@antonnews.com; class adv e-mail classified@antonnews.com; ed e-mail smosco@antonmediagroup.com; web site http://www.massapequaobserver.com/
Circulation: 4,920pd, 631fr; Sworn/Estimate/Non-Audited
Advertising rate: 1/8 Pg $489.00; 1/6 Pg $625.00; 1/4 Pg $812.00
Established: 1959
Group: Anton Community Newspapers
Pub.. Angela Anton
Ed. .... Jennifer Fauci
Delivery Method: Mail, Newsstand
Areas Served: Massapequa, Massapequa Park

MINEOLA AMERICAN (WED)
132 E 2nd St, Mineola, NY, 11501-3522, Nassau, USA; gen tel (516) 747-8282; gen fax (516) 742-5867; disp adv e-mail advertising@antonnews.com; class adv e-mail classified@antonnews.com; ed e-mail mineola@antonnews.com; web site http://mineolaamerican.com/
Circulation: 4,873pd,; Sworn/Estimate/Non-Audited
Advertising rate: 1/8 Pg $489.00; 1/6 Pg $625.00; 1/4 Pg $812.00
Established: 1952
Group: Anton Community Newspapers
Pub................ Angela AntonEquipment & Software: Hardware — APP/Mac, PC, Postscript Level 2; Presses — WPC; Software — QPS/QuarkXPress 3.32.
Delivery Method: Mail, Newsstand
Areas Served: Mineola, Williston Park, Albertson

NEW HYDE PARK ILLUSTRATED (THUR)
132 E 2nd St, Mineola, NY, 11501-3522, Nassau, USA; gen tel (516) 747-8282; gen fax (516) 742-5867; disp adv e-mail advertising@antonnews.com; class adv e-mail classified@antonnews.com; ed e-mail jscotchie@antonmediagroup.com; web site http://newhydeparkillustrated.com/
Circulation: 4,200pd, 847fr; Sworn/Estimate/Non-Audited
Advertising rate: 1/8 Pg $489.00; 1/6 Pg $625.00; 1/4 Pg $812.00
Established: 1930
Group: Anton Community Newspapers
Pub.. Angela Anton
Circ. Mgr.................................... Joy DiDonato
Ed. .... Joe ScotchieEquipment & Software: Hardware — APP/Mac, PC, Postscript Level 2; Presses — WPC; Software — QPS/QuarkXPress 3.32.
Delivery Method: Mail, Newsstand
Areas Served: Floral Park, Bellerose, Stewart Manor, South Floral Park, Bellerose Terrace, Elmont, Franklin Square, North Valley Stream, South Floral Park, West Hempstead, New Hyde Park Garden City Park

OYSTER BAY ENTERPRISE PILOT (THUR)
132 E 2nd St, Mineola, NY, 11501-3522, Nassau, USA; gen tel (516) 747-8282; gen fax (516) 742-5867; disp adv e-mail advertising@antonnews.com; class adv e-mail classified@antonnews.com; ed e-mail smosco@antonmediagroup.com; web site http://oysterbayenterprisepilot.com/
Circulation: 1,892pd, 492fr; Sworn/Estimate/Non-Audited
Advertising rate: 1/8 Pg $489.00; 1/6 Pg $625.00; 1/4 Pg $812.00
Established: 1882
Group: Anton Community Newspapers
Pub.. Angela Anton
Ed. .... Steve MoscoEquipment & Software: Hardware — APP/Mac, PC, Postscript Level 2; Presses — WPC; Software — QPS/QuarkXPress 3.32.
Delivery Method: Mail, Newsstand
Areas Served: Oysterbay, Oyster Bay Cove, East Norwich, Bayville

PLAINVIEW/OLD BETHPAGE HERALD (THUR)
132 E 2nd St, Mineola, NY, 11501-3522, Nassau, USA; gen tel (516) 747-8282; gen fax (516) 742-5867; disp adv e-mail advertising@antonnews.com; class adv e-mail classified@antonnews.com; ed e-mail plainview@antonnews.com; web site www.antonnews.com
Circulation: 3,225pd, 447fr; Sworn/Estimate/Non-Audited
Advertising rate: 1/8 Pg $489.00; 1/6 Pg $625.00; 1/4 Pg $812.00
Established: 1956
Group: Anton Community Newspapers
Pub.. Angela Anton
Mng. Ed..................................... Cary Seaman
Delivery Method: Mail, Newsstand
Areas Served: Plainview, Old Bethpage

ROSLYN NEWS (THUR)
132 E 2nd St, Mineola, NY, 11501-3522, Nassau, USA; gen tel (516) 747-8282; gen fax (516) 742-5867; disp adv e-mail advertising@antonnews.com; class adv e-mail classified@antonnews.com; ed e-mail jscotchie@antonmediagroup.com; web site http://roslyn-news.com/
Circulation: 4,800pd, 821fr; Sworn/Estimate/Non-Audited
Advertising rate: 1/8 Pg $489.00; 1/6 Pg $625.00; 1/4 Pg $812.00
Established: 1877
Group: Anton Community Newspapers
Pub.. Angela Anton
Ed. .... Joe ScotchieEquipment & Software: Hardware — APP/Mac, PC, Postscript Level 2; Presses — WPC; Software — QPS/QuarkXPress 3.32.
Delivery Method: Mail, Newsstand
Areas Served: Roslyn, East Hills, Greenvale, Albertson

SYOSSET/JERICHO TRIBUNE (THUR)
132 E 2nd St, Mineola, NY, 11501-3522, Nassau, USA; gen tel (516) 747-8282; gen fax (516) 742-5867; disp adv e-mail advertising@antonnews.com; class adv e-mail classified@antonnews.com; ed e-mail nlockwood@AntonMediaGroup.com; web site http://syossetjerichotribune.com/
Circulation: 4,220pd, 753fr; Sworn/Estimate/Non-Audited
Advertising rate: 1/8 Pg $489.00; 1/6 Pg $625.00; 1/4 Pg $812.00
Established: 1958
Group: Anton Community Newspapers
Pub. .... Angela Anton
Circ. Mgr. .... Joy DiDonato
Ed. .... Nicole Lockwood
Delivery Method: Mail, Newsstand
Areas Served: Syosset, Woodbury, Jericho, Brookville, Old Brookville, Muttontown

WESTBURY TIMES (THUR)
132 E 2nd St, Mineola, NY, 11501-3522, Nassau, USA; gen tel (516) 747-8282; gen fax (516) 742-5867; disp adv e-mail advertising@antonnews.com; class adv e-mail classified@antonnews.com; ed e-mail babraham@antonmediagroup.com; web site http://thewestburytimes.com/
Circulation: 3,445pd,; Sworn/Estimate/Non-Audited
Advertising rate: 1/8 Pg $489.00; 1/6 Pg $625.00; 1/4 Pg $812.00
Established: 1933
Group: Anton Community Newspapers
Pub. .... Angela Anton
Ed. .... Betsy AbrahamEquipment & Software: Hardware — APP/Mac, PC, Postscript Level 2; Presses — WPC; Software — QPS/QuarkXPress 3.32.
Delivery Method: Mail, Newsstand
Areas Served: Westbury, Carle Place, Salisbury, Old Westbury

MOUNT KISCO

THE EXAMINER (TUES)
PO Box 611, Mount Kisco, NY, 10549-0611, Westchester, USA; gen tel (914) 864-0878; adv tel (914) 864-0878; ed tel (914) 419-0390; disp adv e-mail advertising@theexaminernews.com; class adv e-mail astone@theexaminernews.com; ed e-mail mwilbur@theexaminernews.com; web site www.theexaminernews.com
Circulation: 0pd, 6,475fr; CVC
Advertising rate: 1/16 Pg $55.00; 1/8 Pg $110.00; 1/4 Pg $220.00
Established: 2007
Group: Examiner Media
Digital Platform - Mobile: Apple, Android, Windows, Blackberry
Digital Platform - Tablet: Apple iOS, Android, Windows 7, Blackberry Tablet OS
Pub. .... Adam Stone
Ed. .... Martin Wilbur
Delivery Method: Mail, Newsstand, Racks
Areas Served: Westchester County

THE NORTHERN WESTCHESTER EXAMINER (TUES)
PO Box 611, Mount Kisco, NY, 10549-0611, Westchester, USA; gen tel (914) 864-0878; adv tel (914) 864-0878; ed tel (914) 729-4242; disp adv e-mail advertising@theexaminernews.com; class adv e-mail astone@theexaminernews.com; ed e-mail rpezzullo@theexaminernews.com; web site www.theexaminernews.com
Circulation: 0pd, 7,360fr; CVC
Advertising rate: 1/16 Pg $55.00; 1/8 Pg $110.00; 1/4 Pg $220.00
Established: 2007
Group: Examiner Media
Digital Platform - Mobile: Apple, Android, Windows, Blackberry
Digital Platform - Tablet: Apple iOS, Android, Windows 7, Blackberry Tablet OS
Pub. .... Adam Stone
Ed. .... Rick Pezzullo
Delivery Method: Mail, Newsstand, Racks
Areas Served: Westchester County

THE PUTNAM EXAMINER (TUES)
PO Box 611, Mount Kisco, NY, 10549-0611, Westchester, USA; gen tel (914) 864-0878; adv tel (914) 864-0878; ed tel (914) 671-5595; disp adv e-mail advertising@theexaminernews.com; class adv e-mail astone@theexaminernews.com; ed e-mail dpropper@theexaminernews.com; web site www.theexaminernews.com
Circulation: 0pd, 5,841fr; CVC
Advertising rate: 1/16 Pg $55.00; 1/8 Pg $110.00; 1/4 Pg $220.00
Established: 2007
Group: Examiner Media
Digital Platform - Mobile: Apple, Android, Windows, Blackberry
Digital Platform - Tablet: Apple iOS, Android, Windows 7, Blackberry Tablet OS
Pub. .... Adam Stone
Ed. .... David Propper
Delivery Method: Mail, Newsstand, Racks
Areas Served: Westchester County

THE WHITE PLAINS EXAMINER (TUES)
PO Box 611, Mount Kisco, NY, 10549-0611, Westchester, USA; gen tel (914) 864-0878; adv tel (914) 864-0878; ed tel (914) 588-5583; disp adv e-mail advertising@theexaminernews.com; class adv e-mail astone@theexaminernews.com; ed e-mail pcasey@theexaminernews.com; web site www.theexaminernews.com
Circulation: 0pd, 5,226fr; CVC
Advertising rate: 1/16 Pg $55.00; 1/8 Pg $110.00; 1/4 Pg $220.00
Established: 2007
Group: Examiner Media
Digital Platform - Mobile: Apple, Android, Windows, Blackberry
Digital Platform - Tablet: Apple iOS, Android, Windows 7, Blackberry Tablet OS
Pub. .... Adam Stone
Ed. .... Pat Casey
Delivery Method: Mail, Newsstand, Racks
Areas Served: Westchester County

NANUET

ROCKLAND COUNTY TIMES (THUR)
119 Main St, Nanuet, NY, 10954-2882, Rockland, USA; gen tel (845) 627-1414; gen fax (845) 627-1411; disp adv e-mail editor@rocklandcountytimes.com; ed e-mail editor@rocklandcountytimes.com; web site www.rocklandtimes.com
Circulation: 3,100pd, 4,400fr; Sworn/Estimate/Non-Audited
Advertising rate: Open inch rate $12.50
Established: 1888
Group: Citizens Publishing Corporation of Rockland
Digital Platform - Mobile: Blackberry
Digital Platform - Tablet: Other
Ed. in Chief/Pub. .... Dylan Skriloff
Mechanical Specifications: Type page 13 x 20; E - 9 cols, 1 5/16, 1/6 between; A - 9 cols, 1 5/16, 1/6 between; C - 9 cols, 1 5/16, 1/6 between.Equipment & Software: Hardware — APP/Mac; Software — Adobe/Photoshop 6.0, Adobe/Acrobat 4.0, QPS/QuarkXPress 4.0.
Delivery Method: Mail, Newsstand, Carrier, Racks
Areas Served: 10954, 10913, 10920, 10923, 10927, 10931, 10952, 10956, 10960, 10962, 10965, 10968, 10970, 10974, 10976, 10977, 10980, 10901, 10982, 10983, 10984, 10986, 10989, 10994

NARROWSBURG

THE RIVER REPORTER (THUR)
93 Erie Ave, Narrowsburg, NY, 12764-6423, Sullivan, USA; gen tel (845) 252-7414; adv tel (845) 25207414 ext. 34; ed tel 845-252-7414, ext. 28; gen fax (845) 252-3298; disp adv e-mail sales@riverreporter.com; class adv e-mail eileen@riverreporter.com; ed e-mail editor@riverreporter.com; web site www.riverreporter.com
Circulation: 3,000pd, 265fr; Sworn/Estimate/Non-Audited
Advertising rate: 1/12 Pg $50.00; 1/8 Pg $80.00; 1/6 Pg $110.00
Established: 1975
Group: Stuart Communications Inc.
Pub. .... Laurie Stuart
Ed. .... Fritz Mayer
Prod. Mgr. .... Amanda Reed
Mechanical Specifications: Type page 10 1/4 x 10 1/2; E - 6 cols, 1 1/2, between; A - 6 cols, 1 1/2, between; C - 6 cols, 1 1/2, between. Equipment & Software: ; Software — Adobe/InDesign CS5
Delivery Method: Mail
Areas Served: Upper Delaware River Valley

NEW PALTZ

NEW PALTZ TIMES (THUR)
29 S Chestnut St, New Paltz, NY, 12561-1948, Ulster, USA; gen tel (845) 255-7000; gen fax (845) 255-7005; disp adv e-mail ads@ulsterpublishing.com; class adv e-mail classifieds@ulsterpublishing.com; ed e-mail newpaltztimes@ulsterpublishing.com; web site www.newpaltzx.com
Circulation: 4,850pd,; Sworn/Estimate/Non-Audited
Advertising rate: Open inch rate $17.00
Group: Ulster Publishing
Owner/Pub. .... Geddy Sveikauskas
Ad. Dir. .... Genia Wickwire
Ed. .... Debbie Alexsa
Mechanical Specifications: Type page 10 x 15.5; 3 cols, 3, 0.5 between
Areas Served: New Paltz, Gardiner, Rosendale, High Falls, Stone Ridge

NEW YORK

CHELSEA CLINTON NEWS (THUR)
242 W 30th St, New York, NY, 10001-4903, New York, USA; gen tel (212) 868-0190; gen fax (212) 268-2935; disp adv e-mail sales@strausnews.com; ed e-mail nyoffice@strausnews.com; web site www.nypress.com
Circulation: 138pd,; AAM
Advertising rate: 5 Newspapers: 1/8 Pg $1360.00; 1/6 Pg $1690.00; 1/4 Pg $2420.00
Established: 1939
Pres. .... Jeanne Straus
Ed-in-Chief .... Alexis Gelber
Mechanical Specifications: Type page 10.333 x 11
Areas Served: Chelsea Clinton, Midtown West

CHELSEA NOW (FRI)
515 Canal St, Unit 1C, New York, NY, 10013-1330, New York, USA; gen tel (212) 229-1890; adv tel (212) 229-1890 x2496; gen fax (212) 229-2790; disp adv e-mail ads@thevillager.com; class adv e-mail francesco@downtownexpress.com; ed e-mail letters@chelseanow.com; web site www.chelseanow.com
Circulation: 20,000pd,; Sworn/Estimate/Non-Audited
Advertising rate: Full - $1,675; 1/2 - $1,045; 1/4 - $655; 1/8 - $420
Established: 1933
Group: NYC Community Media, LLC
Pub. .... Jennifer Goodstein
Associate Ed. .... Scott Stiffler
Mechanical Specifications: Type page 10 x 14; E - 4 cols, 2 1/4, between; A - 6 cols, 1 1/2, between; C - 6 cols, 1 1/2, between.Equipment & Software: Hardware — PC; Software — Adobe/PageMaker 6.0.
Areas Served: 10001 10011 10016 10018 10019

FORWARD NEWSPAPER (FRI)
125 Maiden Ln, Fl 8, New York, NY, 10038-5015, New York, USA; gen tel (212) 889-8200; adv tel (212) 453-9420; adv fax (212) 689-4255; ed fax (212) 447-6406; disp adv e-mail advertising@forward.com; class adv e-mail classified@forward.com; ed e-mail newsdesk@forward.com; web site www.forward.com
Circulation: 29,479pd,; AAM
Advertising rate: Open inch rate $72.00
Established: 1897
CEO/Pub. .... Samuel Norich
Ed. .... Jane Eisner
Managing Ed. .... Dan Friedman
Adv. Dir. .... Kim Rosenberg Amzallag
Mktg. Dir. .... Bob Goldfarb
Mechanical Specifications: Type page 11.5 x 18.3; 6 cols, 1.78, 0.16 between

THE BRONX FREE PRESS (WED, THUR)
5030 Broadway, Ste 801, New York, NY, 10034-1666, New York, USA; gen tel (212) 569-5800; adv tel (212) 569-5800; ed tel (212) 569-5800; gen fax (212) 544-9545; adv fax (212) 544-9545; ed fax (212) 544-9545; disp adv e-mail sales@thebronxfreepress.com; class adv e-mail sales@thebronxfreepress.com; ed e-mail editor@thebronxfreepress.com; web site www.thebronxfreepress.com
Advertising rate: Open inch rate $472.00 (1/8P)
Digital Platform - Mobile: Apple, Android
Digital Platform - Tablet: Apple iOS, Android
Ed. .... Debralee Santos
Pub. .... Roberto Ramirez
Pub. .... Luis Miranda
Pub. .... David Keisman
Mechanical Specifications: Type page 10 x 11.25; 4 cols
Delivery Method: Mail, Racks
Areas Served: 10034

THE DOWNTOWN EXPRESS (FRI)
515 Canal St, Unit 1C, New York, NY, 10013-1330, New York, USA; gen tel (212) 229-1890; adv tel (212) 229-1890 x2496; gen fax (212) 229-2790; disp adv e-mail ads@thevillager.com; ed e-mail news@downtownexpress.com; web site www.downtownexpress.com
Circulation: 40,000fr; Sworn/Estimate/Non-Audited
Advertising rate: Full - $1,675; 1/2 - $1,045; 1/4 - $655; 1/8 - $420
Group: NYC Community Media, LLCJennifer Goodstein
Ed. .... Scott Stiffler
Mechanical Specifications: Type page 10 x 14; E - 4 cols, 2 1/4, between; A - 6 cols, 2 1/2, between; C - 6 cols, 1 1/2, between.
Areas Served: 10002 10004 10007 10014 10038 10280

THE NEW YORK OBSERVER (WED)
321 W 44th St, Fl 6th, New York, NY, 10036-5404, USA; gen tel (212) 755-2400; adv tel (212) 407-9328; gen fax (212) 668-4889; disp adv e-mail Jbodager@observer.com; ed e-mail editorial@observer.com; web site www.observer.com
Circulation: 52,000pd,; Sworn/Estimate/Non-Audited
Advertising rate: 1/9 Pg $25000.00; 1/6 Pg $3500.00; 1/4 Pg $4400.00
Established: 1987
Pub. .... Joseph Meyer

THE WESTSIDER (THUR)
63 W 38th St, New York, NY, 10018-3818, New York, USA; gen tel (212) 868-0190; gen fax (212) 268-2935; disp adv e-mail sales@strausnews.com; ed e-mail nyoffice@strausnews.com; web site www.nypress.com
Circulation: 326pd,; AAM
Advertising rate: 1/16 Pg $165.00; 1/8 Pg $287.00; 1/4 Pg $508.00
Established: 1972
Pres. .... Jeanne Straus
Ed.-in-Chief .... Alex Gelber
Mechanical Specifications: Type page 10.333 x 11
Areas Served: Upper West Side, Midtown West

WEST SIDE SPIRIT (THUR)
28th St and 7th Ave, New York, NY, 10001, New York, USA; gen tel (212) 868-190; gen fax (212) 268-0503; disp adv e-mail sales@

strausnews.com; ed e-mail nyoffice@strausnews.com; web site http://www.westsidespirit.com/
Circulation:; AAM
Advertising rate: 1/8 Pg $450.00 1/6 Pg $550.00; 1/4 Pg $800.00
Established: 1985
Group: Straus News
Pres .... Jeanne Straus
Ed-in-chief .... Alexis Gelber
Mechanical Specifications: Type page 10.333 x 11
Areas Served: Upper West Side, Midtown West

NEWBURGH

HUDSON VALLEY PRESS (WED)

PO Box 2160, Newburgh, NY, 12550-0332, Orange, USA; gen tel (845) 562-1313; gen fax (845) 562-1348; disp adv e-mail sales@hvpress.net; class adv e-mail ads@hvpress.net; ed e-mail editor@hypress.net; web site www.hvpress.net
Advertising rate: (Modular Rates)
Established: 1983
Exec. Ed & Pub. .... Chuck Stewart
Mechanical Specifications: Type page 11 x 12; 6 cols, 1.5, 0.2 between
Areas Served: Ulster, Sullivan, Dutchess, Orange, Rockland, Westchester

MID-HUDSON TIMES (WED)

300 Stony Brook Ct, Ste B, Newburgh, NY, 12550-6535, Orange, USA; gen tel (845) 561-0170; adv tel (845) 561-0170; gen fax (845) 561-3967; class adv e-mail advertising@tcnewspapers.com; ed e-mail editor@tcnewspapers.com; web site www.timescommunitypapers.com
Circulation: 2,700pd, 100fr; Sworn/Estimate/Non-Audited
Advertising rate: Open inch rate $10.00
Established: 1989
Group: Times Community Newspapers
Ed. & Pub. .... Carl J. Aiello
Mechanical Specifications: Type page 10.25 x 11; 6 cols, 1.5, 0.25 between
Equipment & Software: Hardware — APP/Mac; Software — Adobe InDesign
Delivery Method: Mail, Newsstand, Racks
Areas Served: 12518, 12550, 12551, 12552, 12553, 12584

WALLKILL VALLEY TIMES (WED)

300 Stony Brook Ct, Newburgh, NY, 12550-6534, Orange, USA; gen tel (845) 561-0170; gen fax (845) 561-3967; disp adv e-mail advertising@tcnewspapers.com; class adv e-mail classifieds@tcnewspapers.com; ed e-mail editor@tcnewspapers.com; web site www.timescommunitypapers.com
Circulation: 5,000pd, 53fr; Sworn/Estimate/Non-Audited
Advertising rate: Open inch rate $10.00
Established: 1983
Group: Times Community Newspapers
Editor & Publisher .... Carl J. Aiello
Mechanical Specifications: Type page 10.25 x 11; 6 cols, 1.5, 0.25 between
Equipment & Software: Hardware — APP/Mac; Software — Adobe/InDesign
Delivery Method: Mail, Newsstand, Racks
Areas Served: 10915, 10919, 10924, 10940, 10941, 12525, 12543, 12549, 12566, 12575, 12586, 12588, 12589, 12721, 12722

NORWICH

THE NEW BERLIN GAZETTE (FRI)

29 Lackawanna Ave, Norwich, NY, 13815-1404, Chenango, USA; gen tel (607) 847-6131; gen fax (607) 334-8273; disp adv e-mail jsmith@evesun.com; ed e-mail jgenung@evesun.com; web site www.evesun.com
Circulation: 800pd,; Sworn/Estimate/Non-Audited
Advertising rate: Open inch rate $3.80
Established: 1871
Group: Snyder Communications
Pres. & Pub. .... Richard Snyder
Mng. Ed. .... Ashley Babbitt
Production Mgr. .... Jeff Smith
Mechanical Specifications: Type page 10.75 x 16; 6 cols, 1.625, 0.2 between
Equipment & Software: Hardware — APP/Mac; Software — Baseview/NewsEdit Pro, QPS/QuarkXPress.
Areas Served: New Berlin, South New Berlin, Edmeston, South Edmeston, Burlington Flats, West Burlington, West Edmeston, Pittsfield, Morris, Gilbertsville, Garrattsville, Mt. Upton, Norwich, Butternuts, New Lisbon, Sherburne, Columbus

OGDENSBURG

ADVANCE NEWS (SUN)

308 Isabella St, Ogdensburg, NY, 13669-1409, Saint Lawrence, USA; gen tel (315) 393-1003; gen fax (315) 393-5108; disp adv e-mail journal@ogd.com; class adv e-mail class@ogd.com; web site http://www.ogd.com
Circulation: 10,700pd,; Sworn/Estimate/Non-Audited
Advertising rate: Open inch rate $9.00
Adv. Mgr. .... Barb Ward
Ed. .... Charles W. Kelly

NORTH COUNTRY CATHOLIC (WED)

622 Washington St, Ogdensburg, NY, 13669-1724, St. Lawrence, USA; gen tel (315) 608-7556; ed e-mail mkilian@dioogdensburg.org; web site www.northcountrycatholic.org
Advertising rate: Open inch rate $11.00
Established: 1946
Group: Diocese of Ogdensburg
Pub. .... Bishop Robert J. Cunningham
Adv. Dir. .... Susan Stewart
Ed. .... Mary Lou Killian
Mechanical Specifications: Type page 8.75 x 10.75; 5 cols, 1.75

OLD FORGE

THE ADIRONDACK EXPRESS (TUES)

2955 St. RT. 28, Old Forge, NY, 13420, Herkimer, USA; gen tel (315) 369-2237; gen fax (315) 369-3378; disp adv e-mail dgraydon@adirondackexpress.com; class adv e-mail office@adirondackexpress.com; ed e-mail editor@adirondackexpress.com; web site www.adirondackexpress.com
Circulation: 2,000pd, 12,500fr; Sworn/Estimate/Non-Audited
Advertising rate: Open inch rate $5.90
Group: McClary Media
Pub. .... Kevin McClary
Dir., Adv./Mktg. .... Brian Krohn
Adv. Sales Mgr. .... Debbie Graydon
Ed .... M. Lisa Monroe

THE WEEKLY ADIRONDACK (THUR)

Route 28, Old Forge, NY, 13420, Herkimer, USA; gen tel (315) 369-9982; adv tel (315) 369-9982; ed tel (315) 369-9982; gen fax (315) 369-9983; adv fax (315) 369-9983; ed fax (315) 369-9983; disp adv e-mail weeklyadk@yahoo.com; class adv e-mail weeklyadk@yahoo.com; ed e-mail weeklyadk@yahoo.com; web site www.weeklyadk.com
Advertising rate: Open inch rate $18.00
Digital Platform - Mobile: Apple, Android, Blackberry
Digital Platform - Tablet: Apple iOS, Android, Blackberry Tablet OS
Pub./Ed./Adv. Mgr. .... Jay Lawson
Adv. Sales Rep. .... Marianne Christy
Delivery Method: Mail, Racks
Areas Served: Old Forge, Inlet, Eagle Bay, Big Moose, Otter Lake, White Lake, Woodgate, Forestport, Raquette Lake, Blue Mountain Lake, and Long Lake

ONEIDA

THE ONEIDA DAILY DISPATCH (TUES, THUR, SUN)

130 Broad St, Oneida, NY, 13421-1696, Oneida, USA; gen tel (315) 363-5100; adv tel (315) 363-5100; ed tel (315) 363-5100; gen fax (315) 363-9832; adv fax (315) 363-9832; ed fax (315) 363-9832; disp adv e-mail kalvord@oneidadispatch.com; class adv e-mail advertising@oneidadispatch.com; ed e-mail newsroom@oneidadispatch.com; web site www.oneidadispatch.com
Circulation: 4,042pd, 1,984fr; AAM
Advertising rate: Open inch rate $14.99
Established: 1873
Group: Digital First Media
Adv. Dir. .... Karen Alvord
Mng. Ed. .... Bob O'Leary
Circulation Supervisor .... Sabrina Sharkey
Production Mgr. .... Phil Hudson
Mechanical Specifications: 1 col. 1.557", 2 co9l. 3.223", 3 col. 4.89", 4 col. 6.557", 5 col. 8.223", 6 col. 9.89"
Delivery Method: Mail, Newsstand, Carrier, Racks
Areas Served: 13421, 13032, 13035, 13037, 13054, 13157, 13163, 13310, 13354, 13346, 13402, 13408, 13409, 13461, 13476, 13478

PALATINE BRIDGE

COUNTRY FOLKS - EAST ZONE (MON)

6113 State Highway 5, Palatine Bridge, NY, 13428-2809, Montgomery, USA; gen tel (518) 673-3763; adv tel (518) 673-0104; ed tel (518) 673-0143; gen fax (518) 673-2381; disp adv e-mail info@leepub.com; class adv e-mail classifieds@leepub.com; ed e-mail cfeditor@leepub.com; web site www.countryfolks.com
Circulation: 8,900pd, 1,100fr; USPS
Advertising rate: Open inch rate $14.75
Established: 1970
Group: Lee Enterprises, Inc.
Digital Platform - Mobile: Apple, Android, Windows, Blackberry
Digital Platform - Tablet: Apple iOS, Android, Windows 7, Blackberry Tablet OS, Kindle, Nook, Kindle Fire
Ed. .... Joan Kark-Wren
Ed. .... Gary Elliott
Ad. Sales .... Bruce Button
Mechanical Specifications: Type page 10.25 x 13; 6 cols, 1.5625
Delivery Method: Mail
Areas Served: 110-139

PATCHOGUE

ISLIP BULLETIN (THUR)

20 Medford Ave, Ste 112, Patchogue, NY, 11772-1220, Suffolk, USA; gen tel (631) 475-1000; adv tel (631) 475-1000 x17; ed tel (631) 475-1000 x13; gen fax (631) 475-1565; disp adv e-mail ttlia@optonline.net; ed e-mail scnibletter@optonline.net; web site www.islipbulletin.net
Circulation: 1,500pd,; Sworn/Estimate/Non-Audited
Advertising rate: 1/16 Pg $79.00; 1/12 Pg $106.00; 1/8 Pg $131.00
Established: 1948
Pub. .... John T. Tuthill
Gen. Mgr. .... Joanne LaBarca
Editor .... Liz Finnigan
Asst. Pub. .... Terry Tuthill
Ad. .... Monica Musetti-Carlin
Mechanical Specifications: Type page 10 x 13.75; 4 cols, 2.25, 0.25 between
Delivery Method: Mail, Newsstand, Racks
Areas Served: 11795, 11706, 11751, 11730, 11739

LONG ISLAND ADVANCE (THUR)

20 Medford Ave, Ste 112, Patchogue, NY, 11772-1220, Suffolk, USA; gen tel (631) 475-1000; adv tel (631) 475-1000 x28; ed tel (631) 475-1000 x21; gen fax (631) 475-1565; disp adv e-mail ttlia@optonline.net; class adv e-mail ttlia@optonline.net; ed e-mail advletters@optonline.net; web site www.longislandadvance.net
Circulation: 5,000pd,; Sworn/Estimate/Non-Audited
Advertising rate: 1/16 Pg $104.00; 1/12 Pg $119.00; 1/8 Pg $153.00
Established: 1871
Digital Platform - Mobile: Apple, Android, Windows, Blackberry
Digital Platform - Tablet: Apple iOS, Android, Windows 7, Blackberry Tablet OS, Kindle, Nook, Kindle Fire
Pub. .... John T. Tuthill
Asst. Pub. .... Terry Tuthill
Display Adv. Mgr. .... Rory Upton
Gen. Mgr. .... Joanne Solowey-LaBarca
Editor .... Nicole Allegrezza
Mechanical Specifications: Type page 10 x 13.75; 4 cols, 2.25, 0.25 between
Delivery Method: Mail, Newsstand, Racks
Areas Served: 11715, 11772, 11713, 11763, 11967, 11951, 11950, 11934, 11940,11719,11955,11980

SUFFOLK COUNTY NEWS (THUR)

20 Medford Ave, Ste 112, Patchogue, NY, 11772-1220, Suffolk, USA; gen tel (631) 475-1000; adv tel (631) 475-1000 x17; ed tel (631) 475-1000 x13; gen fax (631) 475-1565; disp adv e-mail ibscnsales@suffolkcountynews.net; ed e-mail scnibletter@optonline.net; web site www.suffolkcountynews.net
Circulation: 53,000pd,; Sworn/Estimate/Non-Audited
Advertising rate: 1/16 Pg $84.00; 1/12 Pg $111.00; 1/8 Pg $138.00
Established: 1884
Pub. .... John T. Tuthill
Gen. Mgr. .... Joanne LaBarca
Ed. .... Liz Finnigan
Monica Musetti-Carlin
Mechanical Specifications: Type page 10 x 13.75; 4 cols, 2.25, 0.25 between
Delivery Method: Mail, Newsstand, Racks
Areas Served: 11769, 11782, 11716, 11705

PEARL RIVER

OUR TOWN EASTSIDE (THUR)

110 W Crooked Hill Rd, Pearl River, NY, 10965-1012, Rockland, USA; gen tel (845) 735-1342; gen fax (845) 620-9533; disp adv e-mail ads@ourtownnews.com; ed e-mail news@ourtownnews.com; web site http://www.ourtownnews.com/
Circulation: 0pd, 19,999fr; CAC
Advertising rate: (Modular Rates) 1/8 page, 5.081 x 2.64 - $550 1x
Established: 1970
Group: Straus News
Pres. .... Jeanne Straus
Mng. Ed. .... Kate Raffa
Mechanical Specifications: Type page 10.333 x 11
Areas Served: Upper East Side, Midtown East

PENN YAN

THE CHRONICLE-EXPRESS (WED, SUN)

138 Main St, Penn Yan, NY, 14527-1299, Yates, USA; gen tel (315) 536-4422; gen fax (315) 536-0682; disp adv e-mail CandyScutt@chronicle-express.com; class adv e-mail CandyScutt@chronicle-express.com; ed e-mail News@chronicle-express.com; web site www.chronicle-express.com
Circulation: 3,200pd, 11,245fr; Sworn/Estimate/Non-Audited
Advertising rate: Open inch rate $13.25
Established: 1824
Group: GateHouse Media, Inc.
Pub. .... Karen Morris
Ad. Mgr .... Candy Scutt
Ed. .... Gwen Chamberlain
Mechanical Specifications: Type page 10 x 16; 6 cols, 1.75
Delivery Method: Mail, Newsstand, Racks

Areas Served: 14527, 14418, 14441, 14837, 14461, 14842, 14544, 14507, 14415, 14478, 14463, 14561

THE OBSERVER (WED)

270 Lake St, Ste 11, Penn Yan, NY, 14527-1832, Yates, USA; gen tel (607) 243-7600; gen fax (607) 243-5833; disp adv e-mail obsrev@gmail.com; ed e-mail obsrev@gmail.com; web site www.observer-review.com
Circulation: 1,400pd, 300fr; USPS
Advertising rate: Open inch rate $6.85
Established: 1878
Group: Finger Lakes Media, Inc.
Pres. and Pub. .... George Lawson
Bus. Mgr. .... Debbie Lawson
Mechanical Specifications: Type page 11 x 17; E - 5 cols, 1 14/15, 1/6 between; A - 5 cols, 1 14/15, 1/6 between; C - 5 cols, 1 14/15, 1/6 between.Equipment & Software: Hardware — Macs; Software — Adobe/InDesign 6.0, Claris 4.0.
Delivery Method: Mail, Newsstand

PERRY

PERRY HERALD (THUR)

7851 State Route 39, Perry, NY, 14530-9534, Wyoming, USA; gen tel (585) 237-6310; gen fax (585) 237-6868; disp adv e-mail perryherald@frontiernet.net; web site www.perryshopper.com
Circulation: 772pd, 7fr; Sworn/Estimate/Non-Audited
Advertising rate: Open inch rate $6.00
Established: 1878
Ed. ....
Lorraine SturmEquipment & Software: Hardware — APP/Mac G3; Presses — Davidson; Software — Adobe/PageMaker 6.5.
Areas Served: 14530, 14427, 14066, 14550

PORT CHESTER

WESTMORE NEWS (FRI)

38 Broad St, Port Chester, NY, 10573-4152, Westchester, USA; gen tel (914) 939-6864; adv tel (914) 939-6864; ed tel (914) 939-6864; gen fax (914) 939-6877; adv fax (914) 939-6877; disp adv e-mail publisher@westmorenews.com; class adv e-mail publisher@westmorenews.com; ed e-mail editor@westmorenews.com; web site www.westmorenews.com
Circulation: 2,433pd, 983fr; USPS
Advertising rate: 1/16 Pg $111.77; 1/8 Pg $158.83; 1/4 Pg $270.60
Established: 1964Editions: (2) 2 total; Port Chester Edition (2,000); Rye Brook Edition (1,400);
Publisher .... Richard Abel
Editor .... Jananne Abel
Mechanical Specifications: Type page 10 x 16; E - 5 cols, 1 5/6, 1/6 between; A - 5 cols, 1 5/6, 1/6 between; C - 6 cols, 1 1/2, 1/6 between. Equipment & Software: Hardware — PCs; Software — Adobe/PageMaker 6.0.
Delivery Method: Mail, Newsstand, Racks
Areas Served: Port Chester/Westchester/New York/10573
and
Rye Brook/Westchester/New York/10573

PORT WASHINGTON

PORT WASHINGTON NEWS (THUR)

270 Main St, Port Washington, NY, 11050-2753, Nassau, USA; gen tel (516) 747-8282; gen fax (516) 767-0036; disp adv e-mail advertising@antonnews.com; class adv e-mail classified@antonnews.com; ed e-mail portwashington@antonnews.com; web site www.antonnews.com
Circulation: 6,501pd, 329fr; Sworn/Estimate/Non-Audited
Advertising rate: Full - $583; 1/2 - $327; 1/4 - $190; 1/8 - $113
Established: 1903
Group: Anton Community Newspapers
Pub. .... Angela Anton
Circ. Mgr. .... Joy DiDonato
Ed. .... Elizabeth JohnsonEquipment & Software: Hardware — APP/Mac, PC, Postscript Level 2; Presses — WPC; Software — QPS/QuarkXPress 3.32.
Delivery Method: Mail, Newsstand
Areas Served: Port Washington, Sands Point, Baxter Estates, Port Washington North, Flower Hill, Manorhaven

POTSDAM

NORTH COUNTRY THIS WEEK (WED, SAT)

19 Depot St, Ste 1, Potsdam, NY, 13676-1143, St. Lawrence, USA; gen tel (315) 265-1000; adv tel (315) 265-1000; ed tel (315) 265-1000; gen fax (315) 268-8701; adv fax (315) 268-8701; ed fax (315) 268-8701; disp adv e-mail thisweek@northcountrynow.com; class adv e-mail thisweek@northcountrynow.com; ed e-mail news@northcountrynow.com; web site www.northcountrynow.com - 2,444,371(views) 214,503(visitors)
Circulation: 13pd, 19,489fr; CVC
Advertising rate: Open inch rate $12.70
Established: 1984
Digital Platform - Mobile: Apple, Android
Digital Platform - Tablet: Apple iOS, Android
Pub. .... Bill Shumway
Adv. Mgr. .... John Basham
Mechanical Specifications: Type page 10.8336 x 16; 5 cols, 2.014, 0.18 between
Equipment & Software: Hardware — APP/Mac G4, APP/Mac G4, Microsoft/Windows XP Server, GCC/Elite XL; Software — QPS/QuarkXPress 4.1, Adobe/PageMaker 6.5, Adobe/Photoshop 5.02, Microsoft/Word 98.
Delivery Method: Mail, Carrier, Racks
Areas Served: 12965, 12967, 13613, 13617, 13621, 13625, 13630, 13646, 13647, 13649, 13654, 13655, 13658, 13660, 13662, 13664, 13667, 13668, 13669, 13672, 13676, 13678, 13680, 13694, 13696, 13697, 13699

RAVENA

THE RAVENA NEWS-HERALD (THUR)

PO Box 178, Ravena, NY, 12143-0178, Albany, USA; gen tel (518) 828-1616; adv tel (518) 828-1616; ed tel (518) 828-1616; gen fax (518)671-6043; adv fax 518-671-6043; disp adv e-mail advertisingregisterstar.com; class adv e-mail classifieds@wdt.net; ed e-mail editorial@registerstar.com; web site www.hudsonvalley360.com - 1,048,368(views) 162,011(visitors)
Circulation: 514pd,; Sworn/Estimate/Non-Audited
Advertising rate: Open inch rate $7.25
Established: 2010
Group: Johnson Newspaper Corp.
Digital Platform - Mobile: Apple, Android
Digital Platform - Tablet: Apple iOS, Android
Pub. .... Mark Vinciguerra
Ed. .... Melanie Lekocevic
Multi-Media Consultant .... Marlene McTigue
Personnel Administrator .... Tammi Ullrich
Delivery Method: Mail, Racks
Areas Served: Greene and Albany counties

RED CREEK

POST-HERALD (WED)

6784 Main St., Red Creek, NY, 13143, Wayne, USA; gen tel (315) 754-6229; gen fax (315) 754-6431; disp adv e-mail advertising@wayuga.com; ed e-mail editor@wayuga.com; web site www.wayuga.com
Circulation: 1,884pd, 23fr; Sworn/Estimate/Non-Audited
Advertising rate: Open inch rate $5.25
Pub. & Adv. Mgr. .... Charles Palermo
Ed. .... Tammy Whitacre
Mechanical Specifications: Type page 10 x 16; E - 5 cols, 1 7/8, 1/4 between; A - 5 cols, 1 7/8, 1/4 between; C - 6 cols, 1 5/8, 1/4 between. Equipment & Software: Hardware — IBM, APP/Mac, QMS/PS; Presses — G/Suburban; Software — Adobe/PageMaker 6.0.

ROCHESTER

ROCHESTER BUSINESS JOURNAL (FRI)

45 East Ave, Ste 500, Rochester, NY, 14604-2200, Monroe, USA; gen tel (585) 546-8303; gen fax (585) 546-3398; disp adv e-mail jgeiger@rbj.net; ed e-mail pericson@rbj.net; web site www.rbj.net
Advertising rate: 1/16 Pg $474.00; 1/8 Pg $907.00; 1/4 Pg $1438.00
Group: New Media Investment Group
VP & Editor .... Paul Ericson
President & Pub. .... Susan Holliday
Jo Ann Geiger
Mechanical Specifications: Type page 10 x 14

ROCKAWAY BEACH

THE WAVE (FRI)

8808 Rockaway Beach Blvd, Rockaway Beach, NY, 11693-1608, Queens, USA; gen tel (718) 634-4000; gen fax (718) 945-0913; disp adv e-mail ads@rockawave.com; class adv e-mail classifieds@rockawave.com; ed e-mail editor@rockawave.com; web site www.rockawave.com
Circulation: 9,000pd, 100fr; Sworn/Estimate/Non-Audited
Advertising rate: Open inch rate $10.70
Established: 1893
Pub. .... Susan B. Locke
Gen. Mgr. .... Sanford Bernstein
Adv. Mgr. .... Felicia Scarola-Edwards
Managing Editor .... Mark Healey
Mechanical Specifications: Type page 9 3/4 x 14; E - 4 cols, 2 1/3, 1/6 between; A - 4 cols, 2 1/3, 1/6 between; C - 5 cols, 1 5/6, 1/6 between.Equipment & Software: Hardware — PC; Software — QPS/QuarkXPress 7.5, Microsoft/Word, Microsoft/Windows.
Delivery Method: Mail, Newsstand
Areas Served: 11691, 11692, 11693, 11694, 11695, 11697

RONKONKOMA

LONG ISLAND BUSINESS NEWS (FRI)

2150 Smithtown Ave, Ste 7, Ronkonkoma, NY, 11779-7348, Suffolk, USA; gen tel (631) 737-1700; adv tel (631) 913-4233; ed tel (631) 913-4257; disp adv e-mail jgiametta@libn.com; ed e-mail editor@libn.com; web site libn.com
Circulation: 4,000pd, 1,000fr; VAC
Established: 1953
Group: Long Island Business News
GateHouse Media, Inc.
Digital Platform - Mobile: Apple
Digital Platform - Tablet: Apple iOS
Bus. Mgr. .... Joe Dowd
Scott Schoen
Delivery Method: Mail, Newsstand, Racks
Areas Served: Nassau and Suffolk counties, New York

SAG HARBOR

SAG HARBOR EXPRESS (THUR)

22 Division Street, Sag Harbor, NY, 11963, Suffolk, USA; gen tel (631) 725-1700; gen fax (631) 725-1584; disp adv e-mail advertising@sagharboronline.com; class adv e-mail classifieds@sagharboronline.com; ed e-mail kmenu@sagharboronline.com; web site www.sagharboronline.com
Circulation: 3,000pd, 1,000fr; Sworn/Estimate/Non-Audited
Advertising rate: (Modular Rates) 1/32 page, 4.5 x 2 - $82 1x
Established: 1859
Ad. Dir. .... Gavin Menu
Ed .... Kathryn Menu
Mechanical Specifications: Type page 13.75 x 20.25; E & A - 6 cols, 2.125, 0.2 between; C - 7 cols, 1.875, 0.104 between.
Delivery Method: Mail, Newsstand
Areas Served: 11963, 11937, 11932, 11968

SALAMANCA

THE SALAMANCA PRESS (THUR)

36 River St, Salamanca, NY, 14779-1474, Cattaraugus, USA; gen tel (716) 945-1644; adv tel (716) 945-1644; ed tel (716) 945-1644; gen fax (716) 945-4285; adv fax (716) 945-4285; ed fax (716) 945-4285; disp adv e-mail salpressads@gmail.com; class adv e-mail salpressclass@gmail.com; ed e-mail salamanacapress@gmail.com; web site www.salamancapress.com
Circulation: 1,200pd, 0fr; Sworn/Estimate/Non-Audited
Advertising rate: Open inch rate $7.03
Established: 1867
Group: Bradford Publishing
Digital Platform - Mobile: Apple, Android, Windows, Blackberry
Digital Platform - Tablet: Apple iOS, Android, Windows 7, Blackberry Tablet OS, Kindle, Nook, Kindle Fire
Gen Mgr./Mng. Ed. .... Rich Place
Delivery Method: Mail, Racks
Areas Served: Cattaraugus County

SARATOGA SPRINGS

COMMUNITY NEWS (FRI)

20 Lake Ave, Saratoga Springs, NY, 12866-2314, Saratoga, USA; gen tel (518) 583-8729 ext 224; adv tel (518) 583-8716; gen fax (518) 371-0933; disp adv e-mail cnews@saratogian.com; cnews@nycap.rr.com; ed e-mail cnews@saratogian.com; web site www.cnweekly.com
Circulation: 26,000fr; Sworn/Estimate/Non-Audited
Advertising rate: Open inch rate $12.00
Group: Digital First Media
Mng. Ed. .... Charlie Kraebel
Pub. .... Michael O'Sullivan
Mechanical Specifications: Type page 12 x 21; E - 5 cols, 1/6 between; A - 6 cols, 1 7/8, 1/6 between; C - 9 cols, 1 1/5, 1/6 between. Equipment & Software: Hardware — APP/Mac.
Areas Served: 12065

SARATOGA TODAY (FRI)

5 Case St, Saratoga Springs, NY, 12866-3501, Saratoga, USA; gen tel (518) 581-2480; adv tel (518) 581-2480 x 209; ed tel (518) 581-2480 x 212; gen fax (518) 581-2487; disp adv e-mail jdaley@saratogapublishing.com; ed e-mail cbeatty@saratogapublishing.com; web site www.saratogatodaynewspaper.com - 500,000(views)
Circulation: 10,000fr; Sworn/Estimate/Non-Audited
Advertising rate: Open inch rate $21.45
Established: 2006
Pub & Ed .... Chad Beatty
Ad. .... Jim Daley
Mechanical Specifications: Type page 10.5 x 13; 5 cols, 1.9, 0.3 between
Delivery Method: Mail, Racks
Areas Served: Saratoga, Ballston Spa, Malta, Mitlon, Wilton

SETAUKET

THE PORT TIMES-RECORD (THUR)

185 Main St, Ste 4, Setauket, NY, 11733-2870, Suffolk, USA; gen tel (631) 751-7744; adv tel ext 118; ed tel ext 130; gen fax (631) 751-4165; disp adv e-mail kjm@tbrnewspapers.com; class adv e-mail class@tbrnews-

papers.com; ed e-mail news@tbrnewspapers.com; web site www.tbrnewsmedia.com
Circulation: 8,814pd,; Sworn/Estimate/Non-Audited
Advertising rate: Open inch rate $15..88
Established: 1989
Group: Times Beacon Record News Media
Pub....................................... Leah S. Dunaief
Gen. Mgr. .... Johness Watts Kuisel
Adv. Mgr. .... Kathryn Mandracchia
Delivery Method: Mail, Newsstand
Areas Served: 11777, 11776,

THE VILLAGE TIMES HERALD (THUR)
185 Main St, Ste 4, Setauket, NY, 11733-2870, Suffolk, USA; gen tel (631) 751-7744; adv tel ext 118; ed tel ext 130; gen fax (631) 751-4165; disp adv e-mail kjm@tbrnewspapers.com; class adv e-mail class@tbrnewspapers.com; ed e-mail news@tbrnewspapers.com; web site www.tbrnewsmedia.com
Circulation: 10,060pd,; Sworn/Estimate/Non-Audited
Advertising rate: Open inch rate $15.88
Established: 1976
Pub....................................... Leah S. Dunaief
Gen. Mgr. .... Johness Watts Kuisel
Adv. Dir. .... Kathryn Mandracchia
Delivery Method: Mail, Newsstand
Areas Served: 11733, 11790, 11720

SHELTER ISLAND

SHELTER ISLAND REPORTER (THUR)
50 N Ferry Rd, Shelter Island, NY, 11964, Suffolk, USA; gen tel (631) 749-1000; adv tel (631) 749-1000 x14; ed tel (631) 749-1000 x18; gen fax (631) 749-0144; disp adv e-mail sales@sireporter.com; class adv e-mail classifieds@timesreview.com; ed e-mail a.clancy@sireporter.com; web site http://shelterislandreporter.timesreview.com/ - 50,000(views) 7,000(visitors)
Circulation: 2,191pd,; Sworn/Estimate/Non-Audited
Advertising rate: (Modular Rates)
Group: Times Review Newsgroup
Pub....................................... Andrew Olsen
Exec. Ed.................................... Grant Parpan
Mechanical Specifications: Type page 9.75 x 13.75; E&A - 4 cols, 2.25, 0.25 between; C - 5 cols, 1.875, 0.105 between.
Equipment & Software: Hardware — APP/Mac, PC.
Delivery Method: Mail, Newsstand
Areas Served: Shelter Island

SHERBURNE

SHERBURNE NEWS (THUR)
17 E State St, Sherburne, NY, 13460-9751, Chenango, USA; gen tel (607) 674-6071; gen fax (607) 264-2436; disp adv e-mail thesherburnenews@gmail.com; class adv e-mail shernews@frontiernet.net; ed e-mail info@sherburnenews.net; web site www.sherburnenews.net
Circulation: 2,000pd,; Sworn/Estimate/Non-Audited
Advertising rate: Open inch rate $4.00
Established: 1864
Adv. Mgr. .... James McDaniel
Mechanical Specifications: Type page 12 x 20; E - 6 cols, 2, between; A - 6 cols, 2, between.
Delivery Method: Mail, Racks
Areas Served: Chenango

SIDNEY

TRI-TOWN NEWS (WED)
5 Winkler Rd, Sidney, NY, 13838-1057, Delaware, USA; gen tel (607) 561-3526; gen fax (607) 563-8999; disp adv e-mail ttnews@tritownnews.com; class adv e-mail advertising@tritownnews.com; web site www.tritownnews.com
Circulation: 3,400pd,; Sworn/Estimate/Non-Audited
Advertising rate: Open inch rate $5.85
Established: 1856
Ed. .... Allison Collins
Sales and Office Manager........... Ryan Dalpiaz
Ad. Director .... Anna Ritchey
Delivery Method: Mail, Newsstand
Areas Served: Sidney, Bainbridge, Unadilla, Afton, Harpursville

SMITHTOWN

BROOKHAVEN REVIEW (THUR)
27 W Main St, Smithtown, NY, 11787-2602, Suffolk, USA; gen tel (631) 265-3500; gen fax (631) 265-3504; disp adv e-mail messenger127e@aol.com
Circulation: 2,415pd, 835fr; Sworn/Estimate/Non-Audited
Advertising rate: $4.00 per column inch
Group: P & S News Group
Pub... Phillip Sciarillo
Areas Served: Lake Grove, North Centereach, Centereach, Coram, Selden

SMITHTOWN MESSENGER (THUR)
27 W Main St, Smithtown, NY, 11787-2602, Suffolk, USA; gen tel (631) 265-3500; gen fax (631) 265-3504; disp adv e-mail messenger127e@aol.com
Circulation: 8,500pd,; Sworn/Estimate/Non-Audited
Advertising rate: Open inch rate $7.60
Established: 1887
Group: P & S News Group
Pub...................................... Phillip L. Sciarillo
Areas Served: Ft. Salonga, Kings Park, Nissequogue, Head of the Harbor, St. James, The Branch, Smithtown, Hauppauge, Commack

THE SMITHTOWN NEWS (THUR)
1 Brooksite Dr, Smithtown, NY, 11787-3454, Suffolk, USA; gen tel (631) 265-2100; gen fax (631) 265-6237; disp adv e-mail ads@smithtownnews.com; class adv e-mail ads@smithtownnews.com; ed e-mail info@smithtownnews.com; web site www.thesmithtownnews.northshorenewsgroup.com
Circulation: 10,647pd,; Sworn/Estimate/Non-Audited
Advertising rate: Open inch rate $7.85
Pres. .... Jennifer Paley
Ed. .... Bernard Paley
Mechanical Specifications: Type page 9 7/8 x 13 7/8; E - 5 cols, 1 7/8, between; A - 5 cols, 1 7/8, between; C - 6 cols, between.Equipment & Software: Hardware — APP/Mac; Software — Adobe/PageMaker 6.0.
Delivery Method: Mail
Areas Served: SmithtownTowhnship/Suffolk/11787/11754/11780/11767/11725

SOMERS

MAHOPAC NEWS (THUR)
334 Route 202, # 1, Somers, NY, 10589-3207, Putnam, USA; gen tel (845) 208-0774; adv tel (845) 621-1116; ed tel (845) 208-0774; disp adv e-mail forhan@halstonmedia.com; class adv e-mail forhan@halstonmedia.com; ed e-mail marschhauser@halstonmedia.com; web site www.mahopacnews.com
Advertising rate: Open inch rate $14.50
Digital Platform - Mobile: Apple, Android, Windows, Blackberry
Digital Platform - Tablet: Apple iOS, Android, Windows 7, Blackberry Tablet OS
Pub... Brett Freeman
Ed. .... Marc Weinreich
Adv. Mgr. .... Shelley Kilcoyne
Delivery Method: Mail, Newsstand, Racks
Areas Served: Putnam County

YORKTOWN NEWS, MAHOPAC NEWS, THE SOMERS RECORD, NORTH SALEM NEWS (THUR)
334 Route 202, Bailey Court, Somers, NY, 10589-3207, Westchester, USA; gen tel (845)621-1116; adv tel (845)621-1116; ed tel (845)208-8151; disp adv e-mail ads@halstonmedia.com; class adv e-mail kilcoyne@halstonmedia.com; ed e-mail freeman@halstonmedia.com; web site www.tapintoyorktown.net - 35,000(views)
Circulation: 25,500fr; USPS
Established: 2015
Group: Halston Media LLC
Digital Platform - Mobile: Apple, Android, Windows
Digital Platform - Tablet: Apple iOS, Android, Windows 7
Pub.. Brett Freeman
Delivery Method: Mail
Areas Served: Northern Westchester & Putnam Counties

SOUTHAMPTON

DAN'S PAPERS LLC (FRI)
158 County Road 39, Ste 2, Southampton, NY, 11968-5252, Suffolk, USA; gen tel (631) 537-0500; gen fax (631) 537-6374; disp adv e-mail display@danspapers.com; class adv e-mail adinfo@danspapers.com; ed e-mail editor@danspapers.com; web site www.danspapers.com - 1,000,000(views) 200,000(visitors)
Circulation: 32,940fr; AAM
Advertising rate: (Modular Rates) 1/24 page, 3 x 1.313 - $200 1x
Established: 1960
Group: Manhattan Media LLCEditions: (51)
Sr. Ed. .... Stacy Dermont
Pres./ Ed. .... Dan Rattiner
Mechanical Specifications: Type page 9.375 x 12.25
Delivery Method: Mail, Racks
Areas Served: Westhampton Beach, North Fork, Southampton, Sag Harbor, East Hampton, Amagansett, Montauk, Shelter Island, Southold, Riverhead, doorman Buildings in Manhattan's Upper east Side and Westside

THE SOUTHAMPTON PRESS (THUR)
135 Windmill Ln, Southampton, NY, 11968-4840, Suffolk, USA; gen tel (631) 283-4100; gen fax (631) 283-4927; disp adv e-mail ads@pressnewsgroup.com; ed e-mail joeshaw@pressnewsgroup.com; web site www.southamptonpress.com
Circulation: 8,382pd, 209fr; Sworn/Estimate/Non-Audited
Advertising rate: 1/64 Pg $77.00; 1/32 Pg $131.00; 1/16 Pg $234.00
Established: 1897Editions: (2) 2 total; Eastern Edition (9,313); Western Edition (6,738);
Pub.............................. Joseph P. Louchheim
Ed. .... Joseph P. Shaw
Sales Mgr. .... Paul Conroy
Mechanical Specifications: Type page 11.125 x 20.5; 6 cols, 1.715, 0.167 between
Delivery Method: Mail, Newsstand
Areas Served: Water Mill, Sag Harbor, Southampton, Bridgehamption

SPECULATOR

HAMILTON COUNTY EXPRESS (WED)
2892 State Route 30, Speculator, NY, 12164, Hamilton, USA; gen tel (518) 843-1100; ed tel (518) 843-1100 x312; gen fax (518) 843-6580; ed fax (518) 843-6580; disp adv e-mail briankrohn@recordernews.com; class adv e-mail advertising@recordernews.com; ed e-mail editor@hamiltoncountyexpress.com; web site www.hamiltoncountyexpress.com
Circulation: 2,681pd, 81fr; Sworn/Estimate/Non-Audited
Advertising rate: Open inch rate $8
Established: 1949
Group: Port Jackson Media LLC
Pub... Kevin McClary
Mktg. Dir .... Brian Krohn
Ed. .... Gwendolyn Girsdansky
Mechanical Specifications: Type page 11 x 17; E - 5 cols, 2, 3/5 between; A - 5 cols, 2, 3/5 between; C - 5 cols, 2, 3/5 between.Equipment & Software: Hardware — APP/Mac.
Delivery Method: Mail, Newsstand
Areas Served: Hamilton County NY

SPENCERPORT

HAMLIN CLARKSON HERALD (SUN)
1776 Hilton Parma Corners Rd, Spencerport, NY, 14559-9501, Monroe, USA; gen tel (585) 352-3411; adv tel (585) 352-3411 ext. 128; ed tel (585) 352-3411 ext. 127; gen fax (585) 352-4811; disp adv e-mail production@westsidenewsny.com; class adv e-mail classified.advertising@westsidenewsny.com; ed e-mail editor@westsidenewsny.com; web site www.westsidenewsonline.com
Circulation: 10pd, 5,915fr; VAC
Advertising rate: 1/8 Pg $139.20; 1/4 Pg $258.00; 1/3 Pg $344.00; Open inch rate $26.75
Established: 1988
Group: Westside NewsEditions: (1)
Pub... Keith Ryan
Editor .... Evelyn Dow
Ad. & Production Manager.............. Karen Fien
Mechanical Specifications: Type page 10.25 x 16; 6 cols, 1.5, 0.25 betweenEquipment & Software: Hardware — 10 macs; Software — Adobe InDesign, Photoshop, Illustrator, Acrobat, Microsoft Word, Excel, Powerpoint
Delivery Method: Mail, Newsstand, Carrier, Racks
Areas Served: 14464, 14420, 14476

SUBURBAN NEWS NORTH (SUN)
1776 Hilton Parma Corners Rd, Spencerport, NY, 14559-9501, Monroe, USA; gen tel (585) 352-3411; adv tel 5853523411 ext 128; ed tel 5853523411 ext 127; gen fax (585) 352-4811; disp adv e-mail production@westsidenewsny.com; class adv e-mail classified.advertising@westsidenewsny.com; ed e-mail editor@westsidenewsny.com; web site www.westsidenewsonline.com
Circulation: 6pd, 7,094fr; CVC
Advertising rate: Open inch rate $26.75
Established: 1953
Group: Westside NewsEditions: (1)
Publisher.. Keith Ryan
Editor .... Evelyn Dow
Production manager .... Karen Fien
Mechanical Specifications: Type page 10.25 x 16; 6 cols, 1.5, 0.25 between
Equipment & Software: Hardware — 10 macs; Presses — none; Software — Adobe InDesign, Photoshop, Illustrator, Acrobat, Microsoft Word, Excel, Powerpoint
Delivery Method: Mail, Newsstand, Carrier, Racks
Areas Served: 14468, 14559

SUBURBAN NEWS SOUTH (SUN)
1776 Hilton Parma Corners Rd, Spencerport, NY, 14559-9501, Monroe, USA; gen tel (585) 352-3411; adv tel 5853523411 ext 128; ed tel 5853523411 ext 127; gen fax (585) 352-4811; disp adv e-mail production@westsidenewsny.com; class adv e-mail classified.advertising@westsidenewsny.com; ed e-mail editor@westsidenewsny.com; web site www.westsidenewsonline.com
Circulation: 38pd, 11,887fr; CVC
Advertising rate: Open inch rate $26.75
Established: 1988
Group: Westside NewsEditions: (1)
Publisher.. Keith Ryan
Editor .... Evelyn Dow
Production manager .... Karen Fien
Mechanical Specifications: Type page 10.25 x 16; 6 cols, 1.5, 0.25 between
Equipment & Software: Hardware — 10 macs; Presses — none; Software — Adobe InDesign, Photoshop, Illustrator, Acrobat, Microsoft Word, Excel, Powerpoint
Delivery Method: Mail, Newsstand, Carrier, Racks
Areas Served: 14559, 14624, 14428, 14514

SUBURBAN NEWS WEST (SUN)
1776 Hilton Parma Corners Rd, Spencerport, NY, 14559-9501, Monroe, USA; gen tel (585) 352-3411; adv tel 5853523411 ext 128; ed tel 5853523411 ext 127; gen fax (585) 352-

4811; disp adv e-mail production@westsidenewsny.com; class adv e-mail classified.advertising@westsidenewsny.com; ed e-mail editor@westsidenewsny.com; web site www.westsidenewsonline.com
Circulation: 8pd, 8,817fr; CVC
Advertising rate: Open inch rate $26.75
Established: 1989
Group: Westside NewsEditions: (1)
Publisher....Keith Ryan
Editor....Evelyn Dow
Production manager....Karen Fien
Mechanical Specifications: Type page 10.25 x 16; 6 cols, 1.5, 0.25 between
Equipment & Software: Hardware — 10 macs; Presses — none; Software — Adobe InDesign, Photoshop, Illustrator, Acrobat, Microsoft Word, Excel, Powerpoint
Delivery Method: Mail, Newsstand, Carrier, Racks
Areas Served: 14420, 14470, 14413

STAMFORD

MOUNTAIN EAGLE (FRI)

9 Railroad Ave, Stamford, NY, 12167-1229, Delaware, USA; gen tel (607) 652-5252; adv tel 518-763-6854; ed tel 518-763-6854; gen fax (607) 652-5253; adv fax 607-652-5253; ed fax 607-652-5253; disp adv e-mail mountaineaglenews@gmail.com; class adv e-mail mountaineaglenews@gmail.com; ed e-mail mountaineaglenews@gmail.com; web site www.the-mountaineagle.com - 80,000(views) 50,000(visitors)
Circulation: 1,400pd, 300fr; Sworn/Estimate/Non-Audited
Advertising rate: Open inch rate $7.25
Established: 1982
Group: Schoharie News LLC
Ed.... Mathew AvitabileEquipment & Software: Hardware — Apple; Software — Quark 6.52, Photoshop CS2
Delivery Method: Mail, Newsstand, Carrier
Areas Served: Delaware, Greene, and Schoharie counties

SUNNYSIDE

WOODSIDE HERALD (FRI)

4311 Greenpoint Ave, Sunnyside, NY, 11104-2605, Queens, USA; gen tel (718) 729-3772; disp adv e-mail SherilynSabba@WoodsideHerald.com; ed e-mail Rob@WoodsideHerald.com; web site www.woodsideherald.com
Circulation: 14,000pd, 5,000fr; Sworn/Estimate/Non-Audited
Advertising rate: (Modular Rates) 1/16 page, 2 x 4 - $40.00 1x
Prodn. Mgr....Sharilyn Sabba
Mechanical Specifications: Type page 10 1/2 x 14; E - 2 cols, 4 1/4, 1/6 between.Equipment & Software: Hardware — APP/Mac; Software — Adobe/Photoshop 6.0, Adobe/PageMaker 6.52.

SYOSSET

LONG ISLAND PRESS (MTHLY)

6901 Jericho Tpke, Ste 215, Syosset, NY, 11791-4447, Nassau, USA; gen tel (516) 284-3300; gen fax (516) 284-3310; disp adv e-mail felice@longislandpress.com; web site www.longislandpress.com
Circulation: 40,000fr; Sworn/Estimate/Non-Audited
Group: Schneps Communications
Pub....John Kominicki
Mechanical Specifications: Type page 8.75 x 11.25
Areas Served: Nassau & Suffolk

SYRACUSE

BALDWINSVILLE MESSENGER (WED)

2501 James St, Ste 100, Syracuse, NY, 13206-2996, Onondaga, USA; gen tel (315) 434-8889; gen fax (315) 434-8883; disp adv e-mail messenger@cnylink.com; web site http://www.baldwinsvillemessenger.com/
Circulation: 6,100pd,; Sworn/Estimate/Non-Audited
Advertising rate: Open inch rate $12.00
Pub....Dave Tyler
Adv. Dir....Jack Gardner
Prodn. Mgr....Lori Newcomb
Circ. Mgr....Mac Green
Mechanical Specifications: Type page 10 13/16 x 16; E - 5 cols, 2 1/16, 1/8 between; A - 5 cols, 2 1/16, 1/8 between; C - 7 cols, 1 1/2, between.
Delivery Method: Mail, Newsstand, Carrier
Areas Served: 13027

CAZENOVIA REPUBLICAN (WED)

2501 James St, Ste 100, Syracuse, NY, 13206-2996, Madison, USA; gen tel (315) 434-8889; gen fax (315) 434-8883; disp adv e-mail llewis@eaglenewsonline.com; ed e-mail editor@cazenoviarepublican.com; web site www.cazenoviarepublican.com
Circulation: 103pd, 3,294fr; VAC
Advertising rate: Open inch rate $12.50
Established: 1854
Ed....Jason Emerson
Adv. Mgr....Lori Lewis
Pub....David Tyler
Circ. Mgr....Lori Newcomb
Mechanical Specifications: Type page 10 13/16 x 16; E - 5 cols, 2 1/16, 1/8 between; A - 5 cols, 2 1/16, 1/8 between; C - 7 cols, 1 1/2, between.
Delivery Method: Mail, Newsstand, Racks

EAGLE BULLETIN (WED)

2501 James St, Ste 100, Syracuse, NY, 13206-2996, Onondaga, USA; gen tel (315) 434-8889; gen fax (315) 434-8883; disp adv e-mail llewis@eaglenewsonline.com; ed e-mail editor@eaglebulletin.com; web site www.eaglebulletin.com
Circulation: 56pd, 5,902fr; VAC
Advertising rate: Open inch rate $12.50
Gen. Mgr....Lori Newcomb
Pub....David Tyler
Ed....Jason Emerson
Advt rep
Lori Lewis
Mechanical Specifications: Type page 10 13/16 x 16; E - 5 cols, 2 1/16, 1/8 between; A - 5 cols, 2 1/16, 1/8 between; C - 7 cols, 1 1/2, between.
Delivery Method: Mail, Newsstand, Carrier
Areas Served: 13057 13066 13078 13082 13104 13116 13214

EAGLE OBSERVER (WED)

2501 James St, Ste 100, Syracuse, NY, 13206-2996, Onondaga, USA; ed e-mail dtyler@eaglenewsonline.com; web site http://www.eagle-observer.com/
Advertising rate: Open inch rate $12.00
Pub....David Tyler
Delivery Method: Mail, Newsstand, Carrier
Areas Served: 13031 13108 13110 13214 13219

EAGLE STAR REVIEW (WED)

2501 James St, Ste 100, Syracuse, NY, 13206-2996, Onondaga, USA; gen tel (315) 434-8889; gen fax (315) 434-8883; disp adv e-mail newsroom@eaglenewsonline.com; ed e-mail editor@eaglestarreview.com; web site www.eaglenewsonline.com
Circulation: 21pd, 5,542fr; VAC
Advertising rate: Open inch rate $12.50
Pub....David Tyler
Mechanical Specifications: Type page 10 13/16 x 16; E - 5 cols, 2 1/6, 1/8 between; A - 5 cols, 2 1/6, 1/8 between; C - 7 cols, 1 1/3, 1/8 between.
Delivery Method: Mail
Areas Served: 13090, 13041, 13212, 13029, 13039, 13088, 13089, 13031

ONONDAGA VALLEY NEWS (MON)

750 W Genesee St, Syracuse, NY, 13204-2306, Onondaga, USA; gen tel (315) 472-7825; gen fax (315) 478-1434; ed e-mail editorial@scotsmanpress.com; web site www.scotsmanonline.com
Circulation: 22pd, 7,903fr; Sworn/Estimate/Non-Audited
Advertising rate: Open inch rate $7.42
Established: 1990
Group: Scotsman Press
Pub....A. Loren Colburn
Adv. Mgr....Thomas C. Cuskey
Ed....Deb Lum
Mechanical Specifications: Type page 10 5/16 x 13; E - 6 cols, 1 5/8, 1/8 between; A - 6 cols, 1 5/8, 1/8 between; C - 6 cols, 1 5/8, 1/8 between.

SKANEATELES PRESS (WED)

2501 James St, Ste 100, Syracuse, NY, 13206-2996, Onondaga, USA; gen tel (315) 685-8338; gen fax (315) 685-8338; disp adv e-mail press_observer@cnylink.com; ed e-mail editor@skaneatelespress.com; web site www.eaglenewsonline.com
Circulation: 146pd, 2,973fr; VAC
Advertising rate: Open inch rate $12.50
Pres....Richard K. Keene
Adv. Mgr....Matt Green
Prodn. Mgr....Lori Newcomb
Pub....David Tyler
Mechanical Specifications: Type page 10 13/16 x 16; E - 5 cols, 2 1/6, 1/8 between; A - 5 cols, 2 1/16, 1/8 between; C - 7 cols, 1 1/3, 1/8 between.
Delivery Method: Mail, Newsstand, Carrier
Areas Served: 13152

SYRACUSE NEW TIMES (WED)

1415 W Genesee St, Ste 1, Syracuse, NY, 13204-2185, Onondaga, USA; gen tel (315) 422-7011 ; disp adv e-mail advertising@syracusenewtimes.com; class adv e-mail advertising@syracusenewtimes.com; ed e-mail editorial@syracusenewtimes.com; web site www.syracusenewtimes.com
Circulation: 37,185fr; CVC
Advertising rate: 1/12 Pg $260.00; 1/8 Pg $385.00; 1/6 Pg $515.00
Pub....William Brod
Ed....Bill DeLapp
Mechanical Specifications: Type page 9.32 x 10.62; 4 cols, 1.875
Delivery Method: Racks
Areas Served: 13021, 13027, 13029, 13030, 13031, 13032, 13035, 13036, 13037, 13039, 13041, 13044, 13045, 13057, 13060, 13063, 13066, 13069, 13077, 13078, 13084, 13088, 13090, 13104, 13108, 13116, 13120, 13126, 13132, 13135, 13138, 13141, 13152, 13153, 13157, 13159, 13162, 13163, 13164, 13166, 13202, 13203, 13204, 13205, 13206, 13207, 13208, 13209, 13210, 13211, 13212, 13214, 13215, 13219, 13220, 13224, 13244, 13290, 13346, 13403, 13408, 13413, 13421, 13440, 13461, 13478, 13501, 13502

THE CENTRAL NEW YORK BUSINESS JOURNAL (FRI)

269 W Jefferson St, Syracuse, NY, 13202-2334, Onondaga, USA; gen tel (315) 579-3900; adv tel (315) 579-3907; ed tel (315) 579-3902; disp adv e-mail mlamacchia@cnybj.com; ed e-mail arombel@cnybj.com; web site www.cnybj.com - 39,000(views) 8,700(visitors)
Advertising rate: (Modular Rates) 1/8 page, 4.875 x 3.125 - $1,335 1x
Ed.-in-Chief....Adam Rombel
Pub....Norman Poltenson
Mechanical Specifications: Type page 10 x 12.75

THE EAGLE (WED, THUR)

2501 James St, Ste 100, Syracuse, NY, 13206-2996, Onondaga, USA; gen tel (315) 434-8889; adv tel 3154348889 x312; ed tel 3154348889 x320; gen fax (315) 434-8883; disp adv e-mail news@theeaglenewspaper.com; class adv e-mail EagleNews@gmail.com; web site www.theeaglecny.com
Circulation: 1pd, 4,850fr; USPS
Advertising rate: 1/8 Pg $94.50; 1/4 Pg $187.00; 1/2 Pg $375.00David Tyler
Ed....Jennifer Wing
Ad....James Robison
Mechanical Specifications: Type page 10 x 16; 6 cols, 1.5, 0.25 between
Delivery Method: Mail, Newsstand, Carrier
Areas Served: Syracuse

TROY

GREENBUSH LIFE (THUR)

270 River Triangle, Suite 202B, Troy, NY, 12180, Rensselaer, USA; gen tel (518) 270-1200; adv tel (518) 290-3896; ed tel (518) 290-3909; gen fax (518) 270-1251; adv fax (518) 583-8014; disp adv e-mail ttergeoglou@freemanonline.com; class adv e-mail aschaal@digitalfirstmedia.com; ed e-mail ckraebel@digitalfirstmedia.com; web site www.troyrecord.com/greenbush
Advertising rate: Open inch rate $12.75
Regional Advertising Director....Timothy Tergeoglou
Ed....Charlie Krabel
Michael O'Sullivan
Mechanical Specifications: Type page ; A - 6 cols, 1.883, 0.125 between; C - 10 cols, 1.09, 0.08 bewteen

LATHAM LIFE (THUR)

270 River Triangle, Suite 202B, Troy, NY, 12180, Rensselaer, USA; gen tel (518) 270-1200; adv tel (518) 270-1204; ed tel (518) 290-3909; adv fax (518) 583-8014; disp adv e-mail letters@troyrecord.com; ed e-mail llewis@troyrecord.com; web site http://www.troyrecord.com/
Advertising rate: Open inch rate $12.75
Ad. Sales Mgr....Timothy Tergeoglou
Ed....Charlie Krabel
Pub....Michael O'Sullivan
Mechanical Specifications: Type page ; A - 6 cols, 1.883, 0.125 between; C - 10 cols, 1.09, 0.08 bewteen
Areas Served: Rensselaer, Watervliet

TUPPER LAKE

TUPPER LAKE FREE PRESS (WED)

136 Park St, Tupper Lake, NY, 12986-1818, Franklin, USA; gen tel (518) 359-2166; gen fax (518) 359-2295; disp adv e-mail tlfreepress@yahoo.com; web site www.tupperlakepress.com
Circulation: 3,800pd, 89fr; Sworn/Estimate/Non-Audited
Advertising rate: Open inch rate $5.46
Established: 1931
Gen. Mgr./Adv. Mgr....Judy McClelland
Pub....M. Dan McClelland
Ed....Sue Mitchell

UTICA

MID YORK WEEKLY (THUR)

221 Oriskany St E, Utica, NY, 13501-1201, Oneida, USA; gen tel (315)792-5000; adv tel (315)792-5107; ed tel (315)792-5008; gen fax (315)792-5017; disp adv e-mail epittman@uticaod.com; class adv e-mail pzehr@uticaod.com; ed e-mail rjohns1@uticaod.com; web site uticaod.com
Circulation: 1,984pd, 0fr
Established: 2004
Pub....Terry Cascioli
Areas Served: 13501

UTICA PHOENIX (MTHLY)

1113 Linwood Pl, Utica, NY, 13501-3911, Oneida, USA; gen tel (315) 797-2417; gen fax (315) 797-7025; disp adv e-mail uticaphoenix@gmail.com; web site www.uticaphoenix.net
Circulation: 365fr; Sworn/Estimate/Non-Audited
Established: 2002
Office and Distribution Manager, Online Editor

Theresa Mancuso
Pub......................Cassandra Harris-Lockwood
Mechanical Specifications: Type page 9.75 x 15
Delivery Method: Racks
Areas Served: Oneida County- Utica, New Hartford, Clinton, Yorkville, Washington Mills, Rome, Vernon, Sherrill, Marcy. Herkimer County Frankfort, Herkimer, Ilion

YOUR VALLEY (THUR)

221 Oriskany St E, Utica, NY, 13501-1201, Oneida, USA; gen tel (315) 792-5000; adv tel (315) 792-5103; ed tel (315) 792-5004; adv fax (315) 792-5085; ed fax (315) 792-5033; disp adv e-mail epittman@uticaod.com; ed e-mail kworrell@uticaod.com; web site www.uticaod.com/pennysaver
Circulation: 0pd, 9,895fr; VAC
Advertising rate: Open inch rate $4.00
Established: 2006
Group: GateHouse Media, Inc.
Ed. ....Kris Worrell
Ad. Dir ....Erin Pittman
Circ. Mgr ....Robert Gall
Prod. Mgr ....Zoran Music
Pub. ....Terry Cascioli
Mechanical Specifications: Type page 10.12 x 21; 6 cols, 1.3125
Delivery Method: Mail, Racks
Areas Served: 13329, 13340, 13350, 13357, 13365, 13406, 13407, 13416, 13431, 13439, 13501

VAILS GATE

ORANGE COUNTY POST (WED)

PO Box 406, Vails Gate, NY, 12584-0406, Orange, USA; gen tel (845) 496-9997; gen fax (845) 496-9949; class adv e-mail ocpads@frontiernet.net; ed e-mail ocpnews@frontiernet.net; web site www.ocpostsentinel.com
Circulation: 2,400pd, 150fr; Sworn/Estimate/Non-Audited
Advertising rate: Open inch rate $4.95
Established: 1936
Group: EWSmith Publishing
Editor ....Howard JP Spear
Delivery Method: Mail, Newsstand, Carrier
Areas Served: 10914, 10916, 10918, 10940, 10992, 12575, 12577

THE SENTINEL (FRI)

PO Box 406, Vails Gate, NY, 12584-0406, Orange, USA; gen tel (845) 562-1218; gen fax (845) 562-0488; disp adv e-mail sentinelnews@hvcbiz.rr.com; web site www.thesentinel-online.com
Circulation: 7,000pd,; Sworn/Estimate/Non-Audited
Advertising rate: Open inch rate $8.00
Established: 1979
Ed. ....Everett W. Smith

WADING RIVER

COMMUNITY JOURNAL (WED)

2042 N Country Rd, Ste 204, Wading River, NY, 11792-1639, Suffolk, USA; gen tel (631) 929-8882; gen fax (631) 929-4560; ed e-mail LettersCJ25A@aol.com
Circulation: 7,500pd,; Sworn/Estimate/Non-Audited
Advertising rate: Open inch rate $7.00
Ed. ....Bernadette S. Budd

WAPPINGERS FALLS

BEACON FREE PRESS (WED)

84 E Main St, Wappingers Falls, NY, 12590-2504, Dutchess, USA; gen tel (845) 297-3723; gen fax (845) 297-6810; disp adv e-mail sdnadvertising@aol.com; ed e-mail newsplace@aol.com; web site www.sdutchessnews.com
Circulation: 8,002fr; Sworn/Estimate/Non-Audited
Advertising rate: Open inch rate $12.50
Group: Southern Dutchess News
Pub..Albert M. Osten
Ed. ....Ray Fashona
Ad. ....Janet Way
Ad. ....Roxane Hoffman
Mechanical Specifications: Type page 9.875 x 16; E&A - 6 cols, 2.375, 0.125 between; C - 7 cols, 1.3125, 0.125 between
Equipment & Software: Hardware — PC, APP/Mac; Presses — WPC/Web Leader, G/Community; Software — Adobe/PageMaker 6.0, Adobe/Photoshop, Microsoft/Word 6.0, Accuset/Accumail 5.0, Arclist 2.2.
Delivery Method: Mail
Areas Served: Beacon

NORTHERN DUTCHESS NEWS (WED)

84 E Main St, Wappingers Falls, NY, 12590-2599, Dutchess, USA; gen tel (845) 297-3723; gen fax (845) 297-6810; disp adv e-mail sdnadvertising@aol.com; ed e-mail northerndutchess@sdutchessnews.com; web site www.sdutchessnews.com
Advertising rate: Open inch rate $12.50
Group: Southern Dutchess News
Ed. ....Ray Fashona
Pub..Albert M. Osten
Mechanical Specifications: Type page 9.875 x 16; E&A - 6 cols, 2.375, 0.125 between; C - 7 cols, 1.3125, 0.125 between
Delivery Method: Mail
Areas Served: Amenia, Clinton, Hyde Park, Milan, Millbrook, Pleasant Valley, Pine Plains, Stanford, Rhinebeck, Red Hook

SOUTHERN DUTCHESS NEWS (WED)

84 E Main St, Wappingers Falls, NY, 12590-2599, Dutchess, USA; gen tel (845) 297-3723; gen fax (845) 297-6810; disp adv e-mail sdnadvertising@aol.com; ed e-mail newsplace@aol.com; web site www.sdutchessnews.com
Circulation: 7,947pd,; Sworn/Estimate/Non-Audited
Advertising rate: Open inch rate $12.50
Established: 1952
Group: Southern Dutchess News
Pub..Albert M. Osten
Ad. ....Janet Way
Ed. ....Ray Fashona
Ad. ....Roxane Hoffman
Mechanical Specifications: Type page 9.875 x 16; E&A - 6 cols, 2.375, 0.125 between; C - 7 cols, 1.3125, 0.125 between
Equipment & Software: Hardware — PC, APP/Mac; Presses — WPC/Web Leader, G/Community; Software — Adobe/PageMaker 6.0, Adobe/Photoshop, Microsoft/Word 6.0, Accuset/Accumail 5.0, Arclist 2.2.
Delivery Method: Mail
Areas Served: Arlington, Beekman, Chelsea, Dover, Fishkill, East, Fishkill, Hopewell Junction, Hughsonville, LaGrange, New Hamburg, Pawling, Spackenkill, Stormville, Town of Poughkeepsie, Town of Wappinger, Union Vale, Village of Wappingers Falls

WARSAW

WARSAW PENNYSAVER (SUN)

72 N Main St, Warsaw, NY, 14569-1329, Wyoming, USA; gen tel (585) 786-8161; gen fax (585) 786-5159; disp adv e-mail ads@warsawpennysaver.com; class adv e-mail ads@warsawpennysaver.com; web site www.warsawpennysaver.com
Circulation: 9,280pd,; CVC
Advertising rate: (Modular Rates) 3.625 x 1.5 - $22.00
Established: 1943
Treasurer
Co-owner..............................Colleen Kennedy
President
Co-owner......................Christine Kennedy-Till
Mechanical Specifications: Type page 7.5 x 11
Delivery Method: Mail
Areas Served: Bliss, Castile, Dale, Fillmore, Gainesville, Hume, Johnsonburg, North Java, Pavilion-(partial), Portageville, Rock Glen, Sheldon-(partial), Silver Springs, Varysburg, Warsaw, Wiscoy, Wyoming

WARSAW'S COUNTRY COURIER (THUR)

11 S Main St, Warsaw, NY, 14569-1501, Wyoming, USA; gen tel (585) 786-3080; gen fax (585) 786-3083; disp adv e-mail tammy-courierads@roadrunner.com; ed e-mail news@couriercountry.com; web site www.mywnynews.com/arcade_warsaw
Advertising rate: Open inch rate $8.65
Established: 1997
Group: Neighbor to Neighbor News, Inc.
Ad. Director.............................Tammy Hobson
Pub.....................................Grant M. Hamilton
Mng. Ed.......................................Julia Merulla
Mechanical Specifications: Type page 10.5 x 19.5; 5 cols, 2, 0.125 between
Areas Served: Warsaw, Perry, Castile, Wyoming

WARWICK

WARWICK VALLEY DISPATCH (WED)

2 Oakland Ave, Warwick, NY, 10990-1530, Orange, USA; gen tel (845) 986-2216; gen fax (845) 987-1180; disp adv e-mail ads@wvdispatch.com; ed e-mail editor@wvdispatch.com; web site www.wvdispatch.com
Circulation: 2,500pd, 50fr; Sworn/Estimate/Non-Audited
Advertising rate: Open inch rate $7.00
Established: 1885
Publisher/Owner...................F. Eugene Wright
Adv. Mgr...Lon Tytell
Ed. ....Jennifer O'Connor
Mng. Ed..................................Marion Maroski
Prodn. Mgr. ....David DeWitt
Mechanical Specifications: Type page 10 3/8 x 15; E - 6 cols, 1 5/8, 1/8 between; A - 6 cols, 1 5/8, 1/8 between; C - 6 cols, 1 5/8, 1/8 between.
Areas Served: 10990

WATERLOO

THE REVEILLE/BETWEEN THE LAKES (THUR)

5 Walnut St S, Waterloo, NY, 13165-1337, Seneca, USA; gen tel (315) 651-4372; adv tel (315) 224-2768; ed tel (315) 224-2768; gen fax (315) 873-3540; disp adv e-mail revbetweenthelakes@gmail.com; class adv e-mail revbetweenthelakes@gmail.com; ed e-mail revbetweenthelakes@gmail.com
Circulation: 1,100pd, 400fr; Sworn/Estimate/Non-Audited
Advertising rate: Open inch rate $9.75 national / $6.50 local
Established: 1855
Pub ....John Stoughtenger
CFO ....Constance Stoughtenger
Mechanical Specifications: Type page 10 x 14; E - 5 cols, 1 5/6, 1/6 between; A - 5 cols, 1 5/6, 1/6 between; C - 6 cols, 1 1/2, 1/6 between.Equipment & Software: Hardware — Gateway, HP/LaserJet 4V; Software — QPS/QuarkXPress 3.3, Adobe/Photoshop 3.0.
Delivery Method: Mail, Newsstand
Areas Served: 13065, 13148, 13165, 14521, 14541, 14588, 14847, 14860

WATERVILLE

THE WATERVILLE TIMES (WED)

129 W Main St, Waterville, NY, 13480-1165, Oneida, USA; gen tel (315) 841-4105; gen fax (315) 841-4104; disp adv e-mail advertising@cnymail.com; ed e-mail watervilletimes@cnymail.com; web site www.watervilleny.com/timesindex.htm
Circulation: 2,516pd, 73fr; Sworn/Estimate/Non-Audited
Advertising rate: Open inch rate $6.00
Established: 1856
Pub... Patricia Louise
Adv. Mgr. ....Kristi Kosmoski
Office Mgr. ....Kim Kupris
Mechanical Specifications: Type page 10 x 16; 5 cols, 1.8125, 0.1875 between
Equipment & Software: ; Software — QPS/QuarkXPress 4.0.
Delivery Method: Mail
Areas Served: Augusta, Brookfield, Deansboro, Knoxboro, North Brookfield, Madison, Oriskany Falls, Paris Hill, Sauquoit, Waterville and West Edmeston

WATKINS GLEN

THE WATKINS REVIEW & EXPRESS (WED)

PO Box 207, Watkins Glen, NY, 14891-0207, Schuyler, USA; gen tel (607) 535-1500; gen fax (607) 243-5833; disp adv e-mail obsrev@gmail.com; web site www.observer-review.com
Circulation: 1,350pd, 300fr; USPS
Advertising rate: Open inch rate $6.85
Established: 1854
Group: Finger Lakes Media. Inc.
Pres. and Pub. ....George Lawson
Delivery Method: Mail, Newsstand

WEBSTER

WAYNE COUNTY MAIL (THUR)

46 North Ave, Webster, NY, 14580-3008, Monroe, USA; gen tel (585) 671-1533; gen fax (585) 671-7067; disp adv e-mail wcmail@empirestateweeklies.com
Circulation: 2,500pd, 200fr; Sworn/Estimate/Non-Audited
Advertising rate: 1/8 Pg $60.00; 1/4 Pg $105.00; 1/3 Pg $128.00
Established: 1901
Group: Empire State Weeklies
Pub..W. David Young
Ed. ....Mike Sorenson
Mechanical Specifications: Type page 10 x 16; E - 4 cols, 2 1/3, 1/6 between; A - 4 cols, 2 1/3, 1/6 between; C - 6 cols, 1 1/2, 1/6 between. Equipment & Software: Hardware — APP/Mac; Presses — WPC; Software — Adobe/PageMaker 6.0.

WEBSTER HERALD (WED)

46 North Ave, Webster, NY, 14580-3008, Monroe, USA; gen tel (585) 671-1533; gen fax (585) 671-7067; disp adv e-mail websterherald@empirestateweeklies.com
Circulation: 4,000pd, 800fr; Sworn/Estimate/Non-Audited
Advertising rate: 1/8 Pg $75.00; 1/4 Pg $130.00; 1/2 Pg $215.00
Group: Empire State Weeklies
Pub...W. David Young
Mng. Ed....................................Mike Sorenson
Mechanical Specifications: Type page 10 x 16; E - 4 cols, 2 2/5, between; C - 6 cols, between.Equipment & Software: Hardware — APP/Mac; Presses — WPC; Software — Adobe/PageMaker, Microsoft/Word 6.0.

WESTFIELD

THE WESTFIELD REPUBLICAN (THUR, SAT)

41 E Main St, Westfield, NY, 14787-1303, Chautauqua, USA; gen tel (716) 326-3163; gen fax (716) 326-3165; disp adv e-mail jsaxton@westfieldrepublican.com; class adv e-mail ads@westfieldrepublican.com; ed e-mail editorial@westfieldrepublican.com; web site www.westfieldrepublican.com
Circulation: 2,100pd, 5,256fr; Sworn/Estimate/Non-Audited
Advertising rate: Business card $50.00; Rectangle $95.00; Block $135.00
Group: Ogden Newspapers Inc.
Publisher...Mike Bird
General Manager & Ad. Dir.............Jim Saxton

WESTFIELD REPUBLICAN (THUR)

41 E Main St, Westfield, NY, 14787-1303, Chautauqua, USA; gen tel (716) 326-3163; gen fax (716) 326-3165; disp adv e-mail jsaxton@westfieldrepublican.com; class adv e-mail ads@westfieldrepublican.com; ed

e-mail editorial@westfieldrepublican.com; web site www.westfieldrepublican.com
Circulation: 900pd, 25fr; Sworn/Estimate/Non-Audited
Advertising rate: Business card $50.00; Rectangle $95.00; Block $135.00
Group: Ogden Newspapers Inc.
BM & Ad. Dir. ..... Jim Saxton
Pub. ..... Mike Bird
Delivery Method: Mail, Newsstand

WHITE PLAINS

FAIRFIELD COUNTY BUSINESS JOURNAL (MON)

3 Gannett Dr, Ste G7, White Plains, NY, 10604-3402, Westchester, USA; gen tel (914) 694-3600; adv tel (914) 694-3600; ed tel (914) 358-0745; gen fax (914) 694-3699; adv fax (914) 694-3699; ed fax (914) 694-3680; disp adv e-mail dee@westfairinc.com; class adv e-mail mrose@westfairinc.com; ed e-mail bobr@westfairinc.com; web site www.westfaironline.com
Circulation: 1,453pd, 3,757fr; VAC
Advertising rate: Open inch rate $4,922.00 (Full-Page)
Group: Westfair Communications Inc.
Digital Platform - Mobile: Apple, Android, Windows, Blackberry
Digital Platform - Tablet: Apple iOS, Android, Windows 7, Blackberry Tablet OS, Kindle, Nook, Kindle Fire
Pub. ..... Dee DelBello
Mng. Ed. ..... Bob Rozycki
Circ. Mgr. ..... Sylvia Sikoutris
Delivery Method: Mail, Newsstand, Racks
Areas Served: Fairfield County

NORTHERN WESTCHESTER EXPRESS (THUR)

1 Gannett Dr, White Plains, NY, 10604-3402, Westchester, USA; gen tel (914) 694-9300; adv tel (914) 694-5158; ed tel (914) 694-9300; disp adv e-mail gpaganodec@lohud.com; class adv e-mail gtroyano@lohud.com; ed e-mail jhasson@lohud.com; web site www.lohud.com/Westchester
Circulation: 86,008fr; AAM
Advertising rate: Open inch rate $16.50
Digital Platform - Mobile: Apple
Digital Platform - Tablet: Apple iOS
Vice Pres. ..... George Troyano
Ed. ..... Kathleen Ryan O'Conner
Consumer Exper. Dir
Ed Forbes
Mechanical Specifications: Type page 10 x 20.75; A - 6 cols, 1.562, 0.126 between; C - 10 cols, 0.95, 0.095 between
Delivery Method: Mail, Racks
Areas Served: Northern Westchester

PUTNAM EXPRESS (THUR)

1 GANNETT DR, White Plains, NY, 10604, Westchester, USA; gen tel (914) 694-9300; adv tel (914) 694-5158; ed tel (914) 694-9300; disp adv e-mail gtroyano@lohud.com; class adv e-mail gtroyano@lohud.com; ed e-mail jhasson@lohud.com; web site www.lohud.com/Putnam
Advertising rate: Open inch rate $8.00
Digital Platform - Mobile: Apple
Digital Platform - Tablet: Apple iOS
Vice Pres. ..... George Troyano
Adv. Dir. ..... Ed Forbes
Ed. ..... Kathleen Ryan O'Conner
Mechanical Specifications: Type page 10 x 20.75; A - 6 cols, 1.562, 0.126 between; C - 10 cols, 0.95, 0.095 between
Delivery Method: Mail, Newsstand
Areas Served: Putnam County

ROCKLAND COUNTY EXPRESS (THUR)

1 Gannett Dr, White Plains, NY, 10604-3402, Westchester, USA; gen tel (914) 694-9300; adv tel (914) 694-5158; ed tel (914) 694-9300; disp adv e-mail gpaganodec@lohud.com; class adv e-mail gtroyano@lohud.com; ed e-mail jhasson@lohud.com; web site www.lohud.com/Rockland
Circulation: 59,176fr; AAM
Advertising rate: Open inch rate $16.50
Group: Gannett
Digital Platform - Mobile: Apple
Digital Platform - Tablet: Apple iOS
Vice Pres. ..... George Troyano
Adv. Mgr. ..... Ed Forbes
Ed. ..... Kathleen Ryan O'Conner
Mechanical Specifications: Type page 10 x 20.75; A - 6 cols, 1.562, 0.126 between; C - 10 cols, 0.95, 0.095 between
Delivery Method: Mail, Racks
Areas Served: 10604

WESTCHESTER COUNTY BUSINESS JOURNAL (MON)

3 Gannett Dr, Ste G7, White Plains, NY, 10604-3402, Westchester, USA; gen tel (914) 694-3600; adv tel (914) 694-3600; ed tel (914) 358-0745; gen fax (914) 694-3699; adv fax (914) 694-3699; ed fax (914) 694-3680; disp adv e-mail dee@westfairinc.com; class adv e-mail mrose@westfairinc.com; ed e-mail bobr@westfairinc.com; web site www.westfaironline.com
Circulation: 1,697pd, 4,496fr; VAC
Advertising rate: Open inch rate $4,922.00 (Full-Page)
Group: Westfair Communications Inc.
Digital Platform - Mobile: Apple, Android, Windows, Blackberry
Digital Platform - Tablet: Apple iOS, Android, Windows 7, Blackberry Tablet OS, Kindle, Nook, Kindle Fire
Pub. ..... Dee DelBello
Mng. Ed. ..... Bob Rozycki
Circ. Mgr. ..... Sylvia Sikoutris
Delivery Method: Mail, Newsstand, Racks
Areas Served: Westchester County

WHITESTONE

QUEENS TRIBUNE (THUR)

15050 14th Rd, Ste 2, Whitestone, NY, 11357-2607, Queens, USA; gen tel (718) 357-7400; gen fax (718) 357-9417; disp adv e-mail news@queenstribune.com; ed e-mail editor@queenstribune.com; web site www.queenstribune.com
Circulation: 2,000pd, 147,000fr; Sworn/Estimate/Non-Audited
Advertising rate: Open inch rate $75.00
Group: Tribco LLC
Pub. ..... Michael Nussbaum
Editor-in-Chief ..... Steven Ferrari
Adv. Admin. ..... Maureen Coppola

THE PRESS OF SOUTHEAST QUEENS (FRI)

15050 14th Rd, Whitestone, NY, 11357-2609, Queens, USA; gen tel (718) 357-7400; gen fax (718) 357-9417; disp adv e-mail sales@queenstribune.com; class adv e-mail sales@queenstribune.com; ed e-mail editor@queenstribune.com; web site www.queenstribune.com
Circulation: 25,000fr; Sworn/Estimate/Non-Audited
Advertising rate: 1/8 Pg $280.00; 1/4 Pg $432.00; 1/2 Pg $665.00
Group: Tribco LLC
Pub. ..... Michael Nussbaum
Ed. ..... Steven Ferrari
Adv. Admin. ..... Maureen Coppola
Areas Served: 11411, 11412, 11413, 11418, 11420, 11422, 11425, 11427, 11428, 11429, 11430, 11431, 11432, 11433, 11434, 11433, 11434, 11435, 11436

WILLIAMSVILLE

AMHERST BEE (WED)

5564 Main St, Williamsville, NY, 14221-5473, Erie, USA; gen tel (716) 632-4700; adv tel (716) 204-4934; gen fax (716) 633-8601; disp adv e-mail salesdept@beenews.com; class adv e-mail classified@beenews.com; ed e-mail kdepriest@beenews.com; web site www.beenews.com
Circulation: 5,000pd, 25,000fr; Sworn/Estimate/Non-Audited
Advertising rate: Open inch rate $17.83
Established: 1879
Group: Bee Group Newspapers
Pub. ..... Trey Measer
Exec. Vice Pres. ..... Michael Measer
Ed. ..... Keaton DePriest
Adv. Dir. ..... Mary Anne Cappon
Sales Mgr. ..... David Passalugo
Classifieds Mgr. ..... Holly Schiferle
Mechanical Specifications: Type page 10 1/2 x 14; E - 5 cols, 2, 1/8 between; A - 5 cols, 2, 1/8 between; C - 6 cols, between.
Delivery Method: Mail, Newsstand, Racks
Areas Served: Ahmerst, Village of Williamsville

CHEEKTOWAGA BEE (THUR)

5564 Main St, Williamsville, NY, 14221-5410, Erie, USA; gen tel (716) 632-4700; adv tel (716) 204-4934; gen fax (716) 633-8601; disp adv e-mail Salesdept@BeeNews.com; class adv e-mail classified@beenews.com; ed e-mail bjackson@beenews.com; web site www.beenews.com
Circulation: 1,800pd,; Sworn/Estimate/Non-Audited
Advertising rate: Open inch rate $17.83
Established: 1977
Group: Bee Group Newspapers
Ed. ..... Bryan Jackson
Pub. ..... Trey Measer
Exec. Vice Pres. ..... Michael Measer
Adv. Sales Dir. ..... Mary Ann Cappon
Mechanical Specifications: Type page 10 1/2 x 14; E - 5 cols, 2, 1/8 between; A - 5 cols, 2, 1/8 between; C - 6 cols, between.
Delivery Method: Mail, Newsstand, Racks
Areas Served: Cheektowaga

CLARENCE BEE (WED)

5564 Main St, Williamsville, NY, 14221-5410, Erie, USA; gen tel (716) 632-4700; adv tel (716) 204-4934; gen fax (716) 633-8601; disp adv e-mail Salesdept@BeeNews.com; class adv e-mail classified@beenews.com; ed e-mail epowers@beenews.com; web site www.beenews.com
Circulation: 3,700pd, 16fr; Sworn/Estimate/Non-Audited
Advertising rate: Open inch rate $20.47
Established: 1937
Group: Bee Group Newspapers
Pub. ..... Trey Measer
Exec. Vice Pres. ..... Michael Measer
Ed. ..... Ethan Powers
Mechanical Specifications: Type page 10 1/2 x 14; E - 5 cols, 2, 1/8 between; A - 5 cols, 2, 1/8 between; C - 6 cols, between.
Delivery Method: Mail, Newsstand, Racks
Areas Served: Clarence

DEPEW BEE (THUR)

5564 Main St, Williamsville, NY, 14221-5410, Erie, USA; gen tel (716) 632-4700; adv tel (716) 204-4934; gen fax (716) 633-8601; disp adv e-mail Salesdept@BeeNews.com; class adv e-mail classified@beenews.com; ed e-mail julieh@beenews.com; web site www.beenews.com
Circulation: 3,700pd, 0fr; Sworn/Estimate/Non-Audited
Advertising rate: Open inch rate $20.66
Established: 1893
Group: Bee Group Newspapers
Pub. ..... Trey Measer
Vice Pres. ..... Michael Measer
Mechanical Specifications: Type page 10 1/2 x 14; E - 5 cols, 2, 1/8 between; A - 5 cols, 2, 1/8 between; C - 6 cols, between.
Delivery Method: Mail, Newsstand, Racks
Areas Served: Village of Depew

EAST AURORA BEE (THUR)

5564 Main St, Williamsville, NY, 14221-5410, Erie, USA; gen tel (716) 632-4700; adv tel (716) 204-4934; gen fax (716) 633-8601; disp adv e-mail Salesdept@BeeNews.com; class adv e-mail classified@beenews.com; ed e-mail katep@beenews.com; web site www.beenews.com
Circulation: 2,100pd,; Sworn/Estimate/Non-Audited
Advertising rate: Open inch rate $16.37
Established: 1987
Group: Bee Group Newspapers
Pub./Pres. ..... Trey Measer
Adv. Sales Dir. ..... Mary Anne Cappon
Adv. Sales ..... Scott Patterson
Sales Mgr. ..... David Passalugo
Exec. Vice Pres. ..... Michael Measer
Ed. ..... Kate Pelczynski
Mng. Ed. ..... David Sherman
Copy Ed. ..... Beth Hutchinson
Prodn. Mgr. ..... Karl Scheitheir
Mechanical Specifications: Type page 10 1/2 x 14; E - 5 cols, 2, 1/8 between; A - 5 cols, 2, 1/8 between; C - 6 cols, between.
Delivery Method: Mail, Newsstand, Racks
Areas Served: East Aurora

KEN-TON BEE (WED)

5564 Main St, Williamsville, NY, 14221-5410, Erie, USA; gen tel (716) 632-4700; adv tel (716) 204-4934; gen fax (716) 633-8601; disp adv e-mail Salesdept@BeeNews.com; class adv e-mail classified@beenews.com; ed e-mail awalters@beenews.com; web site www.beenews.com
Circulation: 1,800pd, 10fr; Sworn/Estimate/Non-Audited
Advertising rate: Open inch rate $17.66
Established: 1982
Group: Bee Group Newspapers
Exec. Vice Pres. ..... Michael Measer
Pub. ..... Trey Measer
Adv. Mgr. ..... David Passalugo
Circ. Mgr. ..... Mike Measer
Ed. ..... Anna Waiters
Mechanical Specifications: Type page 10 1/2 x 14; E - 5 cols, 2, 1/8 between; A - 5 cols, 2, 1/8 between; C - 6 cols, between.
Delivery Method: Mail, Newsstand, Racks
Areas Served: Tonawanda, Village of Kenmore

LANCASTER BEE (THUR)

5564 Main St, Williamsville, NY, 14221-5410, Erie, USA; gen tel (716) 632-4700; adv tel (716) 204-4934; gen fax (716) 633-8601; disp adv e-mail Salesdept@BeeNews.com; class adv e-mail classified@beenews.com; ed e-mail arobb@beenews.com; web site www.beenews.com
Circulation:; Sworn/Estimate/Non-Audited
Advertising rate: Open inch rate $20.66
Established: 1877
Group: Bee Group Newspapers
Pub ..... Trey Measer
Exec. Vice Pres. ..... Michael Measer
Delivery Method: Mail, Newsstand, Racks
Areas Served: Lancaster, Village of Lancaster

ORCHARD PARK BEE (THUR)

5564 Main St, Williamsville, NY, 14221-5410, Erie, USA; gen tel (716) 632-4700; adv tel (716) 204-4934; gen fax (716) 633-8601; disp adv e-mail Salesdept@BeeNews.com; class adv e-mail classified@beenews.com; ed e-mail cgraham@beenews.com; web site www.beenews.com
Circulation: 2,140pd,; Sworn/Estimate/Non-Audited
Advertising rate: Open inch rate $16.39
Established: 1986
Group: Bee Group Newspapers
Exec. Vice Pres. ..... Michael Measer
Pub. ..... Trey Measer
Adv. Mgr. ..... Dean Hutter
Circ. Mgr. ..... Mike Measer
Ed. ..... Chris Graham
Mechanical Specifications: Type page 10 1/2 x 14; E - 5 cols, 2, 1/8 between; A - 5 cols, 2, 1/8 between; C - 6 cols, between.
Delivery Method: Mail, Newsstand, Racks
Areas Served: Orchard Park, Village of Orchard Park

WEST SENECA BEE (THUR)

5564 Main St, Williamsville, NY, 14221-5410, Erie, USA; gen tel (716) 632-4700; adv tel (716) 204-4934; gen fax (716) 633-8601; disp adv e-mail Salesdept@BeeNews.com; class adv e-mail classified@beenews.com; ed e-mail jwaters@beenews.com; web site www.beenews.com
Circulation: 5,200pd, 14fr; Sworn/Estimate/Non-Audited

Advertising rate: Open inch rate $20.66
Established: 1980
Group: Bee Group Newspapers
Exec. Vice Pres....................... Michael Measer
Pub.. Trey Measer
Ed. .... Jenee Waters
Mechanical Specifications: Type page 10 1/2 x 14; E - 5 cols, 2, 1/8 between; A - 5 cols, 2, 1/8 between; C - 6 cols, between.
Delivery Method: Mail, Newsstand, Racks
Areas Served: West Seneca

WILLISTON PARK

GREAT NECK NEWS (FRI)
105 Hillside Ave, Ste I, Williston Park, NY, 11596-2311, Nassau, USA; gen tel (516) 307-1045; adv tel (516) 307-1045 Ext. 212; ed tel (516) 307-1045 Ext. 201; gen fax (516) 307-1046; disp adv e-mail mspitalnick@theislandnow.com; class adv e-mail lmatinale@theislandnow.com; ed e-mail sblank@theislandnow.com; web site www.theislandnow.com - 116,000(views) 38,000(visitors)
Circulation: 4,033pd,; Sworn/Estimate/Non-Audited
Advertising rate: Open inch rate $16.00
Established: 1926
Group: Blank Slate Media LLCEditions: (5) Great Neck News, New Hyde Park Herald Courier, Wiliston Times, Roslyn Times, and Manhasset Times
Digital Platform - Mobile: Apple, Android
Digital Platform - Tablet: Apple iOS, Android
Ed & Pub .... Steven Blank
Circulation Mgr .... Holly Blank
Reporter .... Joe Nikic
ACCT EXECUTIVE .... Melissa Spitalnick
Mechanical Specifications: Type page 8.75 x 11.5; 6 cols, 1.325, 0.183 between
Delivery Method: Mail, Newsstand, Racks
Areas Served: 11020, 11021, 11022, 11023, 11024, 11026, 11027

MANHASSET TIMES (MON, TUES, FRI)
105 Hillside Ave, Ste I, Williston Park, NY, 11596-2311, Nassau, USA; web site https://theislandnow.comSteven Blank

NEW HYDE PARK HERALD COURIER (FRI)
105 Hillside Ave, Ste I, Williston Park, NY, 11596-2311, Nassau, USA; gen tel (516) 307-1045; adv tel (516) 307-1045 Ext. 201; ed tel (516) 307-1045 Ext. 201; gen fax (516) 307-1046; adv fax (516) 307-1046; ed fax (516) 307-1046; disp adv e-mail sshaughnessy@theislandnow.com; class adv e-mail lmatinale@theislandnow.com; ed e-mail sblank@theislandnow.com; web site www.theislandnow.com
Circulation: 4,381pd,; Sworn/Estimate/Non-Audited
Advertising rate: Open inch rate $16.00
Established: 1936
Group: Blank Slate Media LLC
Digital Platform - Mobile: Apple, Android
Digital Platform - Tablet: Apple iOS, Android
Pub .... Steven Blank
Circ. Mgr.. Holly Blank
Adv. Dir............................ Stacy Shaughnessy
Mechanical Specifications: Type page 8.75 x 11.5; 6 cols, 1.325, 0.183 between
Delivery Method: Mail, Racks
Areas Served: 11001, 11040, 11042,11011

PORT WASHINGTON TIMES (MON, WED, FRI)
105 Hillside Ave, Ste I, Williston Park, NY, 11596-2311, Nassau, USA; web site https://theislandnow.comSteven Blank

ROSLYN TIMES (WED)
105 Hillside Ave, Ste I, Williston Park, NY, 11596-2311, Nassau, USA; gen tel (516) 307-1045; gen fax 516-307-1046; web site https://theislandnow.com
Circulation:; Sworn/Estimate/Non-Audited
Ed/Pub.. steven blank
Areas Served: 11020, 11021, 11022, 11023, 11024, 11025, 11026, 11027

WILLISTON TIMES (FRI)
105 Hillside Ave, Ste I, Williston Park, NY, 11596-2311, Nassau, USA; gen tel (516) 307-1045; adv tel (516) 307-1045 Ext. 201; ed tel (516) 307-1045 Ext. 201; gen fax (516) 307-1046; adv fax (516) 307-1046; disp adv e-mail pcamp@theislandnow.com; class adv e-mail lmatinale@theislandnow.com; ed e-mail sblank@theislandnow.com; web site www.theislandnow.com
Circulation: 4,284pd,; Sworn/Estimate/Non-Audited
Advertising rate: $11.00 per column inch
Established: 1940
Group: Blank Slate Media LLC
Ed. .... Steven Blank
Cir. Mgr.. Holly Blank
Acct Exc... Gail Hicka
Mechanical Specifications: Type page 8.75 x 11.5; 6 cols, 1.325, 0.183 between
Delivery Method: Mail, Newsstand, Racks
Areas Served: 11501, 11507, 11514, 11596

WOODSIDE

BROOKLYN DOWNTOWN STAR (THUR)
4523 47th St, Woodside, NY, 11377-5225, Queens, USA; gen tel (718) 639-7000; disp adv e-mail ads@queensledger.com; ed e-mail news@queensledger.com; web site www.BrooklynDowntownstar.com
Circulation: 500pd, 14,500fr; Sworn/Estimate/Non-Audited
Advertising rate: Full - $709; 1/2 - $362; 1/4 - $202; 1/8 - $104
Established: 2004
Group: BQE Publishing Inc.
Digital Platform - Mobile: Apple, Android
Digital Platform - Tablet: Apple iOS, Android
Gen. Mgr.............................. Tammy Sanchez
Ed. .... Walter H. Sanchez
director of marketing.................. John Sanchez
Mechanical Specifications: 13"high by 10"wide
Delivery Method: Mail, Newsstand, Racks
Areas Served: 11206 11205 11217 11201

ECUADOR NEWS (TUES)
6403 Roosevelt Ave, Fl 2, Woodside, NY, 11377-3643, Queens, USA; gen tel (718) 205-7014; gen fax (718) 205-6580 ; ed e-mail ecuanews@inch.com; web site www.ecuadornews.com.ec
Advertising rate: Open inch rate $21.54
Established: 1996
CEO & Editor-in-Chief .... Marcelo Segovia
Business Rep.......................... Leonardo Ottati
Adv. Mgr.............................. Carmen Arboleda
Mechanical Specifications: Type page 5 cols x 13.5

GREENPOINT STAR & NORTHSIDE WEEKLY NEWS (THUR)
4523 47th St, Woodside, NY, 11377-5225, Queens, USA; gen tel (718) 639-7000; disp adv e-mail ads@queensledger.com; ed e-mail news@queensledger.com; web site www.greenpointstar.com
Circulation: 2,000pd, 13,000fr; Sworn/Estimate/Non-Audited
Advertising rate: Full - $709; 1/2 - $362; 1/4 - $202; 1/8 - $104
Established: 1898
Group: BQE Publishing Inc.Editions: (1)
Digital Platform - Mobile: Apple, Android
Digital Platform - Tablet: Apple iOS, Android
Gen. Mgr.............................. Tammy Sanchez
Ed. .... Walter H. Sanchez
Mechanical Specifications: 13" high by 10" high
Delivery Method: Mail, Newsstand, Racks
Areas Served: 11211 11222 11206 11378

LONG ISLAND CITY/ASTORIA/JACKSON HEIGHTS JOURNAL (THUR)
4523 47th St, Woodside, NY, 11377-5225, Queens, USA; gen tel (718) 639-7000; disp adv e-mail ads@queensledger.com; ed e-mail news@queensledger.com; web site www.LICJournal.com
Circulation: 1,100pd, 17,000fr; Sworn/Estimate/Non-Audited
Advertising rate: Full - $709; 1/2 - $362; 1/4 - $202; 1/8 - $104
Established: 1986
Group: BQE Publishing Inc.
Digital Platform - Mobile: Apple, Android
Digital Platform - Tablet: Apple iOS, Android
Gen. Mgr.............................. Tammy Sanchez
Ed. .... Walter H. Sanchez
director of marketing.................. John Sanchez
Mechanical Specifications: 13" high by 10" wide
Delivery Method: Mail, Newsstand, Racks
Areas Served: 11101 11102 11103 1104 1105 11106 111368 111372 111369 111373

THE QUEENS EXAMINER (THUR)
454-23 47 Street, Woodside, NY, 11377, Queens, USA; gen tel (718) 639-7000; disp adv e-mail ads@queensledger.com; ed e-mail news@queensledger.com; web site www.queensexaminer.com
Circulation: 5,000pd, 12,000fr; Sworn/Estimate/Non-Audited
Advertising rate: Full - $709; 1/2 - $362; 1/4 - $202; 1/8 - $104
Established: 1999
Group: BQE Publishing Inc.
Digital Platform - Mobile: Apple, Android
Digital Platform - Tablet: Apple iOS, Android
Gen. Mgr.............................. Tammy Sanchez
Ed. .... Walter H. Sanchez
Director of marketing .... John Sanchez
Mechanical Specifications: 13" high by 10" high
Delivery Method: Mail, Newsstand, Racks
Areas Served: 11355 11356 11357 11361 11363 11365

YONKERS

YONKERS RISING (FRI)
25 Warburton Ave, Yonkers, NY, 10701-7079, Westchester, USA; gen tel (914) 965-4000; gen fax (914) 965-2892; disp adv e-mail pgerken@risingmediagroup.com; ed e-mail dmurphy@risingmediagroup.com; web site www.yonkersrising.com
Circulation: 16,476fr; Sworn/Estimate/Non-Audited
Advertising rate: Open inch rate $10.50
Pub... Nick Sprayregen
Ed. in Chief .... Daniel Murphy
Ad. Sales .... Paul Gerken
Mechanical Specifications: Type page 13 x 21 1/2; E - 6 cols, 2 1/16, 1/8 between; A - 6 cols, 2 1/16, 1/8 between.Equipment & Software: ; Presses — G/Community; Software — Adobe/PageMaker 5.0, Archetype/Corel WordPerfect 4.0.

NORTH CAROLINA

AHOSKIE

GATES COUNTY INDEX (WED)
801 Parker Ave E, Ahoskie, NC, 27910-3641, USA; gen tel (252) 332-2123; adv tel (252) 332-7217; ed tel (252) 332-7207; gen fax (252) 332-3940; adv fax (252) 332-3940; ed fax (252) 332-3940; disp adv e-mail judy.farmer@r-cnews.com; class adv e-mail anna.phipps@r-cnews.com; ed e-mail cal.bryant@r-cnews.com; web site www.roanoke-chowannewsherald.com
Circulation: 1,500pd,; USPS
Advertising rate: Open inch rate $9.38
Group: Boone Newspapers, Inc.
Ed. .... Cal Bryant
Pub .... Tony Clark
Delivery Method: Mail, Racks
Areas Served: Gates County

ROANOKE-CHOWAN NEWS-HERALD (TUES, THUR, SAT)
801 Parker Ave E, Ahoskie, NC, 27910-3641, Hertford, USA; gen tel (252) 332-2123; adv tel (252) 332-2123; ed tel (252) 332-7207; gen fax (252) 332-3940; adv fax (252) 332-3940; ed fax (252) 332-3940; disp adv e-mail judy.farmer@r-cnews.com; class adv e-mail anna.phipps@r-cnews.com; ed e-mail cal.bryant@r-cnews.com; web site www.r-cnews.com
Circulation: 6,800pd, 5,000fr; USPS
Advertising rate: Open inch rate $13.50
Established: 1914
Group: Boone Newspapers, Inc.
Digital Platform - Mobile: Windows
Digital Platform - Tablet: Windows 7
Ed. .... Cal Bryant
Production Mgr........................... Sarah Morris
Mktg. Consult................................ Judy Farmer
Delivery Method: Mail, Carrier, Racks
Areas Served: Hertford, Northampton, Bertie and Gates counties in northeastern North Carolina.

ALBEMARLE

THE STANLY NEWS & PRESS (TUES, THUR, SUN)
237 W North St, Albemarle, NC, 28001-3923, USA; gen tel (704) 982-2121; gen fax (704) 986-2627; adv fax (704) 982-8736; disp adv e-mail talmond@stanlynewspress.com; class adv e-mail talmond@stanlynewspress.com; ed e-mail bj@stanlynewspress.com; web site www.thesnaponline.com
Circulation: 7,000pd, 13,000fr; Sworn/Estimate/Non-Audited
Advertising rate: Open inch rate $9.98
Established: 1880
Group: Boone Newspapers, Inc.Editions: (1) The Advantage
Editor .... B.J. Drye
Pub.. Sandy Selvy
Adv. Mgr.................................. Tracey Almond
Mechanical Specifications: Type page 11 10/16 x 21 1/2; E - 6 cols, 1 13/16, between; A - 6 cols, 1 13/16, between; C - 6 cols, 1 13/16, between.Equipment & Software: ; Presses — G/Community.
Delivery Method: Mail, Newsstand, Carrier, Racks
Areas Served: 28001, 28002, 27306, 28009, 28127, 28128, 28129, 28137, 28163

ANDREWS

ANDREWS JOURNAL (THUR)
995 Main St, Nantahala Suite, Andrews, NC, 28901-7087, Cherokee, USA; gen tel (828) 321-4271; gen fax (828) 321-5890; disp adv e-mail advertising@myandrewsjournal.com; class adv e-mail news@myandrewsjournal.com; ed e-mail news@myandrewsjournal.com; web site www.myandrewsjournal.com - 2,453(views)
Circulation: 1,600pd, 50fr; Sworn/Estimate/Non-Audited
Advertising rate: Open inch rate $11.00
Established: 1959
Group: Community Newspapers, Inc.
Pub... David Brown
Ed. .... Matthew Osborne
Mechanical Specifications: Type page 13 x 21 1/2; E - 6 cols, 2, between; A - 6 cols, 2, between; C - 6 cols, 2, between.
Delivery Method: Mail, Newsstand, Racks
Areas Served: 28901, 28905, 28781, 28906

BAYBORO

THE COUNTY COMPASS (THUR)
PO Box 460, Bayboro, NC, 28515-0460, Pamlico, USA; gen tel (252) 745-3155; adv tel (252) 745-3155; ed tel (252) 670-0447; gen fax (252) 745-3220; disp adv e-mail flora@compassnews360.com; class adv e-mail jeff@compassnews360.com; ed e-mail jeff@

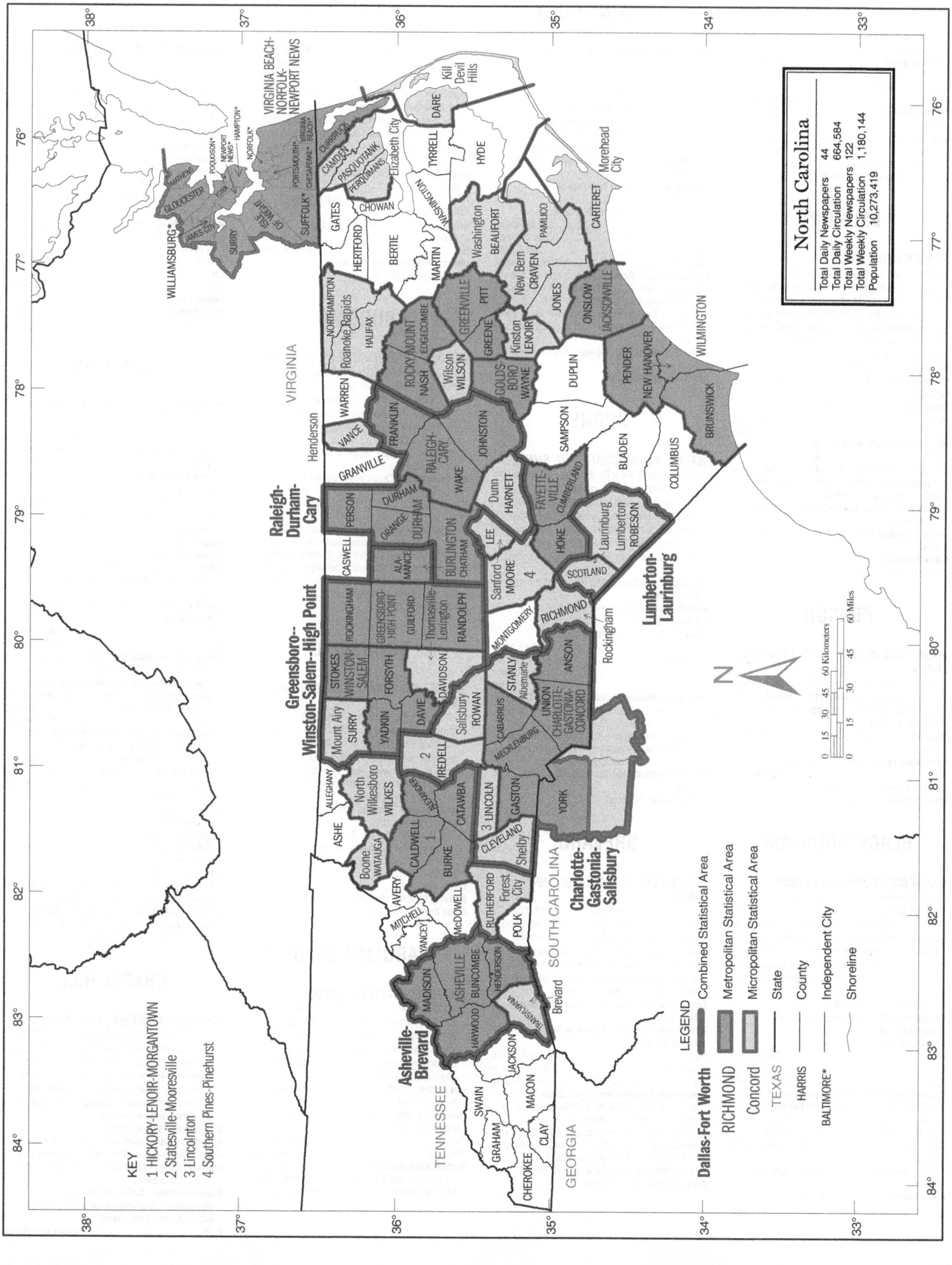
North Carolina
Total Daily Newspapers 44
Total Daily Circulation 664,584
Total Weekly Newspapers 122
Total Weekly Circulation 1,180,144
Population 10,273,419
KEY
1 HICKORY-LENOIR-MORGANTOWN
2 Statesville-Mooresville
3 Lincolnton
4 Southern Pines-Pinehurst
LEGEND
Dallas-Fort Worth Combined Statistical Area
RICHMOND Metropolitan Statistical Area
Concord Micropolitan Statistical Area
TEXAS State
HARRIS County
BALTIMORE* Independent City
Shoreline
Raleigh-Durham-Cary
Greensboro--Winston-Salem--High Point
Lumberton-Laurinburg
Charlotte-Gastonia-Salisbury
Asheville-Brevard
VIRGINIA BEACH-NORFOLK-NEWPORT NEWS
VIRGINIA
SOUTH CAROLINA
TENNESSEE
GEORGIA

compassnews360.com; web site http://www.compassnews360.com
Circulation: 500pd, 19,500fr; Sworn/Estimate/Non-Audited
Advertising rate: Full - $400; 1/2 - $225; 1/4 - $135; 1/8 - $75
Established: 2009
Pub./Ed....................................... Jeff Aydelette
Delivery Method: Mail, Newsstand, Carrier, Racks
Areas Served: Counties of Pamlico, Beaufort, Craven, and
Carteret in eastern North Carolina. Growing rapidly, and free to the reader.

BELMONT

BANNER NEWS (THUR)

128 N Main St, Belmont, NC, 28012-3166, Gaston, USA; gen tel (704) 739-7496; gen fax (704) 825-0894; disp adv e-mail alan.bannernews@gmail.com; class adv e-mail pat.bannernews@gmail.com; ed e-mail alan.bannernews@gmail.com; web site www.banner-news.com
Circulation: 0pd, 3,827fr; CVC
Advertising rate: Open inch rate $10.90
Established: 1936
Group: Gemini Newspapers
Pub.. Wendy Isbell
Ed. .... Alan Hodge
Mechanical Specifications: Type page 13 x 21 1/2; E - 6 cols, 2, 3/16 between; A - 6 cols, 2, 3/16 between; C - 6 cols, 2, 3/16 between. Equipment & Software: Hardware — APP/Mac; Software — QPS/QuarkXPress, Multi-Ad/Creator, Microsoft/Word, Adobe/Photoshop.
Delivery Method: Mail, Newsstand, Carrier, Racks
Areas Served: Belmont, Mt Holly, Stanely, Cramerton, McAdenville

BENSON

FOUR OAKS-BENSON NEWS IN REVIEW (WED)

113 S Market St, Benson, NC, 27504-1520, Johnston, USA; gen tel (919) 894-3331; gen fax (919) 894-1069; disp adv e-mail fobnews@aol.com
Circulation: 4,500pd,; Sworn/Estimate/Non-Audited
Advertising rate: Open inch rate $8.50
Pub.. Norman Delano
Delivery Method: Mail, Newsstand
Areas Served: Johnston

BLACK MOUNTAIN

BLACK MOUNTAIN NEWS (THUR)

111 Richardson Blvd, Black Mountain, NC, 28711-3526, Buncombe, USA; gen tel (828) 669-8727; gen fax (828) 669-8619; disp adv e-mail becky@blackmountainnews.com; class adv e-mail jennifer@blackmountainnews.com; ed e-mail jennifer@blackmountainnews.com; web site www.blackmountainnews.com
Circulation: 3,000pd, 135fr; USPS
Advertising rate: Open inch rate $8.50
Established: 1945
Group: Gannett
Pub... David Neill
Ed. .... Paul Clark
Adv. Rep .... Becky Andrade
Mechanical Specifications: Type page 11 1/16 x 21; E - 6 cols, 1 13/16, 1/8 between; A - 6 cols, 1 13/16, 1/8 between; C - 8 cols, 1 5/16, 1/8 between.Equipment & Software: Hardware — APP/Mac G4; Software — QPS/QuarkXPress 4.1.
Delivery Method: Mail, Newsstand, Carrier, Racks
Areas Served: 28711, 28778, 28757, 28770

BLOWING ROCK

THE BLOWING ROCKET (THUR)

452-1 Sunset Dr Hwy 321, Blowing Rock, NC, 28605, Watauga, USA; gen tel (919) 932-2003; gen fax (919) 932-8799; disp adv e-mail charlie.price@mountaintimes.com; class adv e-mail classifieds@mountaintimes.com; ed e-mail newpaper@mountaintimes.com; web site www.blowingrocket.com
Circulation: 2,700pd, 36fr; Sworn/Estimate/Non-Audited
Advertising rate: Open inch rate $4.82
Established: 1932
Group: Adams Publishing Group, LLC
Pub.. Gene Fowler
Adv. Mgr./Mktg. Dir. .... Charlie Price
Ed. .... Jeff Eason
Class Adv. Mgr. .... Brenda Minton
Mechanical Specifications: Type page 13 1/2 x 21; E - 6 cols, 2, 3/16 between; A - 6 cols, 2, 3/16 between; C - 9 cols, 1 5/16, 1/8 between.Equipment & Software: Hardware — APP/Mac; Software — QPS/QuarkXPress 3.2.
Delivery Method: Mail, Newsstand, Carrier, Racks
Areas Served: Watauga

BOONE

WATAUGA DEMOCRAT (WED, SUN)

474 Industrial Park Dr, Boone, NC, 28607-3937, Watauga, USA; gen tel (828) 264-3612; gen fax (828) 262-0282; disp adv e-mail charlie.price@mountaintimes.com; class adv e-mail classifieds@mountaintimes.com; ed e-mail community@wataugademocrat.com; web site www.wataugademocrat.com
Circulation: 3,800pd, 296fr; Sworn/Estimate/Non-Audited
Advertising rate: Open inch rate $19.81
Established: 1888
Group: Adams Publishing Group, LLC
Pub.. Gene Fowler
Circ. Mgr...................................... Andy Gainey
Ed. .... Tom Mayer
Adv. Dir.. Charlie Price
Mechanical Specifications: Type page 13 x 21; E - 6 cols, 2 1/16, 1/8 between; A - 6 cols, 2 1/6, 1/8 between; C - 9 cols, 1 3/8, 1/8 between.Equipment & Software: Hardware — APP/Macs; Presses — G/Community; Software — Adobe CS
Delivery Method: Mail, Newsstand, Carrier, Racks
Areas Served: Watauga

BREVARD

THE TRANSYLVANIA TIMES (MON, THUR)

37 N Broad St, Brevard, NC, 28712-3725, Transylvania, USA; gen tel (828) 883-8156; gen fax (828) 883-8158; disp adv e-mail shirsh@transylvaniatimes.com; class adv e-mail classifieds@transylvaniatimes.com; ed e-mail info@transylvaniatimes.com; web site www.transylvaniatimes.com
Circulation: 8,200pd, 80fr; Sworn/Estimate/Non-Audited
Advertising rate: Open inch rate $8.50
Established: 1887
Pub... Stella A. Trapp
Adv. Exec. .... John Connelly
Ed. .... John Lanier
Mechanical Specifications: Type page 11 5/8 x 21; E - 6 cols, 1 13/16, 1/16 between; A - 6 cols, 1 13/16, 1/16 between; C - 6 cols, 1 13/16, 1/16 between.Equipment & Software: Hardware — APP/Mac; Software — Microsoft/Word 4.0, Multi-Ad/Creator 2.5.
Delivery Method: Mail, Newsstand, Racks
Areas Served: Transylvania

BRYSON CITY

THE SMOKY MOUNTAIN TIMES (THUR)

1 River St, Ste 3, Bryson City, NC, 28713-6982, Swain, USA; gen tel (828) 488-2189; gen fax (828) 488-0315; disp adv e-mail adrep@thesmokymountaintimes.com; class adv e-mail classifieds@thesmokymountaintimes.com; ed e-mail news@thesmokymountaintimes.com; web site www.thesmokymountaintimes.com
Circulation: 3,900pd,; Sworn/Estimate/Non-Audited
Advertising rate: Open inch rate $13.00
Established: 1883
Group: Community Newspapers, Inc.
Publisher.................................. Ashley Butcher
Ed. .... Jessica Webb
Delivery Method: Mail, Racks
Areas Served: 28713

BURGAW

PENDER-TOPSAIL POST & VOICE (WED)

108 W WILMINGTON ST, Burgaw, NC, 28425, Pender, USA; gen tel (910) 259-9111; gen fax (910) 259-9112; disp adv e-mail advertising@post-voice.com; ed e-mail posteditor@thependerpost.com; web site http://www.post-voice.com/
Circulation: 5,000pd, 400fr; Sworn/Estimate/Non-Audited
Advertising rate: Open inch rate $7.00
Ad. Director.................................. Brenda Todd
Pub.. Les High
Ed. .... Andy Pettigrew
Mechanical Specifications: Type page 13 x 21 1/2; E - 6 cols, 2, 1/6 between; A - 6 cols, 2, 1/6 between; C - 6 cols, 2, 1/6 between. Equipment & Software: Hardware — APP/Mac; Software — Abbott Systems/Ready, Set, Go, Adobe/PageMaker.
Areas Served: 28425

BURNSVILLE

YANCEY COMMON TIMES JOURNAL (WED)

22 N Main St, Burnsville, NC, 28714-2925, Yancey, USA; gen tel (828) 682-2120; gen fax (828) 682-3701; disp adv e-mail pat@yanceypaper.com; ed e-mail jody@yanceypaper.com; web site www.yanceytimesjournal.com
Advertising rate: Open inch rate $7.25
Group: Trib Publications
Digital Platform - Mobile: Apple, Android, Windows, Blackberry
Digital Platform - Tablet: Apple iOS, Android, Windows 7, Blackberry Tablet OS
Pub./Ed. .... Jody Higgins
Pub./Adv. Dir. .... Pat Randolph
Circ. Mgr.................................... Audria Briggs
Delivery Method: Mail, Newsstand, Racks
Areas Served: Yancey

CAROLINA BEACH

THE ISLAND GAZETTE (WED)

1003 Bennet Ln, Ste F, Carolina Beach, NC, 28428-5770, New Hanover, USA; gen tel (910) 458-8156; gen fax (910) 458-0267; disp adv e-mail islandgazette@aol.com; ed e-mail editor@islandgazette.net; web site www.islandgazette.net
Circulation: 7,000pd, 325fr; Sworn/Estimate/Non-Audited
Advertising rate: Open inch rate $12.00
Established: 1978
Pub... Roger McKee
Mng. Ed.............................. Williard H. Killough
Mechanical Specifications: Type page 13 x 21.Equipment & Software: Hardware — APP/Mac; Software — QPS/QuarkXPress 3.1.

CARY

SOUTHWEST WAKE NEWS (WED, SUN)

122 E Chatham St, Ste 230, Cary, NC, 27511-3360, Wake, USA; gen tel (919) 460-2600; disp adv e-mail placeads@newsobserver.com; class adv e-mail caryclassads@newsobserver.com; ed e-mail carynews@newsobserver.com; web site www.southwestwakenews.com
Circulation: 53,190fr; CAC
Established: 2009
Group: The News & Observer Publishing Co.
Digital Platform - Mobile: Apple, Android, Windows, Blackberry
Digital Platform - Tablet: Apple iOS, Android, Blackberry Tablet OS, Kindle, Nook, Kindle Fire, Other
Adv Dir....................................... Kaki Berkeley
Ed .... Jessica Banov
Pub... Sara Glines
Delivery Method: Carrier
Areas Served: Apex, Cary, Fuquay-Varina, Holly Springs

CASHIERS

CROSSROADS CHRONICLE (WED)

196 Burns St., Ste. 1, Cashiers, NC, 28717, Jackson, USA; gen tel (828) 743-5101; gen fax (828) 743-4173; disp adv e-mail mhenry@CrossroadsChronicle.com; class adv e-mail Classifieds@CrossroadsChronicle.com; ed e-mail Editor@CrossroadsChronicle.com; web site http://www.crossroadschronicle.com - 4,038(views) 2,244(visitors)
Circulation: 2,200pd,; USPS
Advertising rate: Open inch rate $13.00
Established: 1983
Group: Community Newspapers, Inc.
Digital Platform - Mobile: Apple, Android, Windows
Digital Platform - Tablet: Apple iOS, Android, Windows 7, Kindle
Pub.. Mike Henry
Editor .... Don Richeson
Mechanical Specifications: Camera ready adsmust be a PDF, JPG or TIF file with all images, fonts, etc. embedded and RGB/PMS spot colors converted to either Grayscale or CMYK. InDesign files that are packaged with fonts and links may be submitted. Publisher and Word files will NOT be accepted. Resolution for both submitted ads and photos should be a minimum of 300 dpi. The Chronicle will not be held responsible for ads and/or photos that do not print clearly as a result of low resolution.
Width Picas Inches
1 Column 10p 1.667
2 Columns 20p9 3.458
3 Columns 31p6 5.25
4 Columns 42p3 7.042
5 Columns 52p12 8.833
6 Columns 63p9 10.625 Equipment & Software: ; Software — Indesign CS3
Delivery Method: Mail, Newsstand, Racks
Areas Served: 28717, 28723, 28736, 28741, 28747, 28774, 28779, 28783

CHAPEL HILL

THE DURHAM NEWS (WED, SUN)

505 W Franklin St, Chapel Hill, NC, 27516-2315, Orange, USA; gen tel (919) 932-2003; gen fax (919) 932-8799; disp adv e-mail kberkeley@newsobserver.com; class adv e-mail drogers@newsobserver.com; ed e-mail editor@newsobserver.com; web site www.thedurhamnews.com
Circulation: 75,594fr; CAC
Advertising rate: Open inch rate $23.24
Group: The News & Observer Publishing Co.
Digital Platform - Mobile: Apple, Android, Windows, Blackberry
Digital Platform - Tablet: Apple iOS, Android, Windows 7, Blackberry Tablet OS, Kindle, Nook, Kindle Fire, Other
Pub...................................... Felicia Gressette

Ed .... Mark Schultz
Adv. Mgr. .... Kaki Berkeley
Adv. Dir. .... Doug Rogers
Delivery Method: Carrier
Areas Served: Durham

CHARLOTTE

CHARLOTTE BUSINESS JOURNAL (FRI)

550 S Caldwell St Ste 910, Suite 910, Charlotte, NC, 28202-2881, Mecklenburg, USA; gen tel (704) 973-1100; gen fax (704) 973-1102; ed e-mail kpitts@bizjournals.com; web site www.charlottebusinessjournal.com
Advertising rate: Modular: 1/8 - $1665; 1/4 - $3085; 1/2 - $4855; Full - $7890
Ed .... Robert Morris
Pres/Pub .... Kevin Pitts
Delivery Method: Mail

NORTH CAROLINA LAWYERS WEEKLY (MON)

1611 E 7th St, Charlotte, NC, 28204-2411, Mecklenburg, USA; gen tel (800) 876-5297; adv tel (704) 817-1341; ed tel (704) 817-1351; disp adv e-mail andrea.mounts@nclawyersweekly.com; class adv e-mail katherine.lewis@nclawyersweekly.com; ed e-mail amber.nimocks@nclawyersweekly.com; web site http://nclawyersweekly.com
Advertising rate: Full - $2452; Jr - $1510; 1/2 - $1454; 1/4 - $785; 1/8 - $495;
Established: 1987
Group: The Dolan Company
Digital Platform - Mobile: Apple, Android, Windows, Blackberry
Digital Platform - Tablet: Apple iOS, Android, Windows 7, Blackberry Tablet OS
Ed .... Amber Nimocks
Ad. Dir .... Andrea Mounts
Pub .... Paul Fletcher
Delivery Method: Mail

SOUTH CHARLOTTE WEEKLY (FRI)

9506 Monroe Rd, Charlotte, NC, 28270-1527, Mecklenburg, USA; gen tel (704) 849-2261; gen fax (704) 849-2504; disp adv e-mail adsales@carolinaweeklynewspapers.com; ed e-mail editor@thecharlotteweekly.com; web site www.thecharlotteweekly.com
Circulation: 5pd, 23,877fr; CVC
Advertising rate: 1/8 Pg $124.00; 1/6 Pg $174.00; 1/4 Pg $247.00
Established: 2002
Group: Carolina Media GroupEditions: (2) 2 total; North Charlotte Weekly (12,000); South Charlotte Weekly (32,000);
Ed. .... Justin Vick
Mechanical Specifications: Type page: 9.875 x 12.5; 4 col
Delivery Method: Mail, Newsstand, Carrier, Racks
Areas Served: Mecklenberg

THE CHARLOTTE POST (THUR)

1531 Camden Rd, Charlotte, NC, 28203-4753, Mecklenburg, USA; gen tel (704) 376-0496; gen fax (704) 342-2160; disp adv e-mail advertising@thecharlottepost.com; class adv e-mail classified@thecharlottepost.com; ed e-mail herb.white@thecharlottepost.com; web site http://www.thecharlottepost.com
Circulation: 10,695pd, 6,083fr; Sworn/Estimate/Non-Audited
Advertising rate: Open inch rate $22.50
Established: 1974
Ed. .... Herbert White
Adv. Dir. .... Jeri Thompson
Office Mgr. .... Betty Potts
Delivery Method: Mail, Newsstand, Racks
Areas Served: Mecklenburg

THE MATTHEWS-MINT HILL (FRI)

9506 Monroe Rd, Charlotte, NC, 28270-1527, Mecklenburg, USA; gen tel (704) 849-2261; adv tel (704) 849-2261; gen fax (704) 849-2504; disp adv e-mail adsales@carolinaweeklynewspapers.com; class adv e-mail brent@cmgweekly.com; ed e-mail mike@matthewsminthillweekly.com; web site http://www.matthewsminthillweekly.com/
Circulation: 1pd, 12,976fr; VAC
Advertising rate: 1/8 Pg $122.00; 1/4 Pg $243.00; 1/2 Pg $472.00; Full $858.00
Established: 2007
Group: Carolina Media Group
Ed. .... Justin Vick
Pub .... Kelly Wright
Mechanical Specifications: Type page: 9.875 x 12.5; 4 col
Delivery Method: Mail, Newsstand, Carrier, Racks
Areas Served: Mecklenberg

THE MECKLENBURG TIMES (TUES, FRI)

130 N McDowell St, Ste B, Charlotte, NC, 28204-2268, Mecklenburg, USA; gen tel (704) 247-2900; gen fax (704) 377-2458; disp adv e-mail andrea.mounts@nclawyersweekly.com; ed e-mail sharon.roberts@mecktimes.com; web site www.mecktimes.com
Circulation: 965pd, 45fr; Sworn/Estimate/Non-Audited
Advertising rate: 1/8 Pg $225.00; 1/4 Pg $400.00; 1/2 Pg $700.00
Established: 1923
Group: The Dolan Company
Digital Platform - Mobile: Apple, Android, Windows, Blackberry
Digital Platform - Tablet: Apple iOS, Android, Windows 7, Blackberry Tablet OS
Pub .... Paul Fletcher
Adv. Dir. .... Andrea Mounts
Delivery Method: Mail, Racks
Areas Served: Mecklenberg, Gaston, Iredale, Catawba, Cabarrus, Lincoln, Union,

THE UNION COUNTY WEEKLY (FRI)

9506 Monroe Rd, Charlotte, NC, 28270-1527, Mecklenburg, USA; gen tel (704) 849-2261; gen fax (704) 849-2504; disp adv e-mail kelly@cmgweekly.com; class adv e-mail brent@cmgweekly.com; ed e-mail justin@cmgweekly.com; web site http://www.unioncountyweekly.com/
Circulation: 18,417fr; CVC
Advertising rate: Modular Rates: 1/8 P $160 1/4 P $318 1/2 P $617 Full $1122
Established: 2005
Group: Carolina Media Group
Ed. .... Justin Vick
Pub .... Kelly Wright
Mechanical Specifications: Type page: 9.875 x 12.5; 4 col
Delivery Method: Mail, Newsstand, Carrier, Racks
Areas Served: Union

CHERRYVILLE

THE CHERRYVILLE EAGLE (WED)

107 E Main St, # 12, Cherryville, NC, 28021-3406, Gaston, USA; gen tel (704) 435-6752; adv tel (704) 300-3493; ed tel (704) 435-6752; gen fax (704) 435-8293; ed fax (704) 435-8293; disp adv e-mail michael.cherryvilleeagle@gmail.com; class adv e-mail michael.cherryvilleeagle@gmail.com; ed e-mail michael.cherryvilleeagle@gmail.com; web site cherryvilleeagle.com
Circulation: 2,750pd,; Sworn/Estimate/Non-Audited
Advertising rate: Open inch rate $10.90
Established: 1906
Group: Community First Media, Inc.
Ed. .... Michael Powell
Sales Rep. .... Mark Blanton
Mechanical Specifications: Type page 13 x 21 1/2; E - 6 cols, 2, 3/16 between; A - 6 cols, 2, 3/16 between; C - 6 cols, 2, 3/16 between. Equipment & Software: Hardware — APP/Mac; Software — QPS/QuarkXPress, Multi-Ad/Creator, Microsoft/Word, Adobe/Photoshop.
Delivery Method: Mail, Carrier, Racks
Areas Served: 28021

CLEMMONS

THE CLEMMONS COURIER (THUR)

3600 Clemmons Rd, Clemmons, NC, 27012-9104, Forsyth, USA; gen tel (336) 766-4126; gen fax (336) 766-7350; disp adv e-mail courier9@bellsouth.net; web site http://www.clemmonscourier.net/
Circulation: 2,700pd, 50fr; Sworn/Estimate/Non-Audited
Advertising rate: Open inch rate $8.00
Group: SalisburyNewsMedia
Evening Post Publishing Newspaper Group
Pub./Ed. .... Dwight Sparks
Adv. Mgr. .... Christy Clark
Mechanical Specifications: Type page 13 x 21; A - 6 cols, between; C - 6 cols, between.
Areas Served: Clemmons 27012, Lewisville 27023

CONCORD

INDEPENDENT TRIBUNE (WED, FRI, SUN)

363 Church St N, Concord, NC, 28025-4589, Cabarrus, USA; gen tel (704) 782-3155; adv tel (704) 789-9125; ed tel (704) 789-9103; gen fax (704) 786-0645; adv fax (704) 789-9159; ed fax (704) 786-0645; disp adv e-mail jdunham@independenttribune.com; ed e-mail mplemmons@independenttribune.com; web site www.independenttribune.com - 77,684(views) 4,381(visitors)
Circulation: 7,992pd, 100fr; CAC
Advertising rate: Open inch rate $16.75
Established: 1996
Group: BH Media Group
Digital Platform - Mobile: Apple, Android
Digital Platform - Tablet: Apple iOS, Android
Bus Mgr .... Rhonda Hargenrader
Ed. .... Mark Plemmons
Mechanical Specifications: Type page 13 x 21 1/2; E - 6 cols, 2 1/16, 1/8 between; A - 6 cols, 2 1/16, 1/8 between; C - 9 cols, 1 3/8, 1/16 between.
Delivery Method: Mail, Newsstand, Racks
Areas Served: Concord, Kannapolis, Harrisburg, Cabarrus & southern Rowan counties

CREEDMOOR

THE BUTNER-CREEDMOOR NEWS (THUR)

418 N Main St, Ste 20, Creedmoor, NC, 27522-8809, Granville, USA; gen tel (919) 528-2393; gen fax (919) 528-0288; disp adv e-mail bcnews@mindspring.com; web site www.butnercreedmoornews.org
Circulation: 5,400pd,; Sworn/Estimate/Non-Audited
Advertising rate: Open inch rate $10.00
Pub./Ed. .... Elizabeth Coleman
Adv. Mgr. .... Penny Carpenter
Mechanical Specifications: Type page 11 1/2 x 21 1/2; E - 6 cols, 1 3/4, 1/6 between; A - 6 cols, 1 3/4, 1/6 between; C - 6 cols, 1 3/4, 1/6 between.Equipment & Software: Hardware — Mac/G4; Software — Adobe/Pagemaker 7.0.
Areas Served: 27522

DURHAM

CHAPEL HILL NEWS (WED, SUN)

1530 N Gregson St, Ste 2A, Durham, NC, 27701-1164, Orange, USA; gen tel (919) 932-2003; adv tel (919) 932-8776; gen fax (919) 932-8799; disp adv e-mail chdisplay@newsobserver.com; class adv e-mail drogers@newsobserver.com; ed e-mail editor@newsobserver.com; web site www.chapelhillnews.com
Circulation: 2pd, 44,233fr; CAC
Advertising rate: Open inch rate $36.63
Established: 1932
Group: The News & Observer Publishing Co.
Digital Platform - Mobile: Apple, Android, Windows, Blackberry
Digital Platform - Tablet: Apple iOS, Android, Windows 7, Blackberry Tablet OS, Kindle, Nook, Kindle Fire, Other
Pub. .... Mark Schultz
Adv. Dir. .... Mark Alston
Adv. Dir. .... Doug Rogers
Mechanical Specifications: Type page 13 1/8 x 21; E - 6 cols, 2 1/16, 1/8 between; A - 6 cols, 2 1/16, 1/8 between; C - 6 cols, 2 1/16, 1/8 between.Equipment & Software: Hardware — APP/Mac; Presses — G/Community; Software — QPS/QuarkXPress.
Delivery Method: Carrier
Areas Served: 27514

INDY WEEK (WED)

201 W Main St, Ste 101, Durham, NC, 27701-3228, USA; gen tel (919) 286-1972; gen fax (919) 286-4274; disp adv e-mail eroberts@indyweek.com; class adv e-mail classy@indyweek.com; ed e-mail jbillman@indyweek.com; web site http://www.indyweek.com
Circulation: 45,000fr; Sworn/Estimate/Non-Audited
Advertising rate: 1/8 Pg $75.00; 1/2 Pg $130.00; Full $210.00;
Pub. .... Susan Harper
Ed. .... Jeffery Billman
Bus. Mgr. .... Alex Rogers

EDENTON

THE CHOWAN HERALD (TUES, THUR, SAT)

423 S Broad St, Edenton, NC, 27932-1935, USA; gen tel (252) 332-2123; adv tel (252) 332-7203; ed tel (252) 332-7207; gen fax (252) 482-4410; disp adv e-mail chowanherald@nccox.com; class adv e-mail chowanadvertising@nccox.com; ed e-mail cal.bryant@r-cnews.com
Circulation: 5,000pd,; Sworn/Estimate/Non-Audited
Advertising rate: Open inch rate $11.24
Group: Cooke Communications North Carolina, LLC
Ed. .... Cal Bryant
Prod. Mgr. .... Sarah Morris
Sales Coord. .... Judy Farmer
Mechanical Specifications: Type page 13 x 21 1/2; E - 6 cols, 2 1/4, between; A - 6 cols, 2 1/4, between; C - 8 cols, 1 1/2, between. Equipment & Software: Hardware — APP/Mac; Software — Microsoft/Word 6.0.1, Aldus/PageMaker.

ELIZABETHTOWN

BLADEN JOURNAL (TUES, FRI)

138 W BROAD ST, Elizabethtown, NC, 28337, Bladen, USA; gen tel (910) 862-4163; gen fax (910) 862-6602; disp adv e-mail ads@bladenjournal.com; class adv e-mail cjudson@civitasmedia.com; ed e-mail cvincent@civitasmedia.com; web site www.bladenjournal.com
Circulation: 4,400pd, 3,800fr; Sworn/Estimate/Non-Audited
Advertising rate: Open inch rate $11.80
Established: 1978
Group: Champion Media
Ed./Gen. Mgr. .... Curt Vincent
Adv. Sales Rep. .... Charlotte Smith
Adv. Dir. .... David Perkins
Mechanical Specifications: Type page 11 5/8 x 21 1/2; E - 6 cols, 1 4/5, 1/8 between; A - 6 cols, 1 4/5, 1/8 between; C - 9 cols, 1 5/16, 1/11 between.
Delivery Method: Mail, Carrier
Areas Served: Bladen

ELKIN

THE TRIBUNE (MON, WED, FRI)

214 E Main St, Elkin, NC, 28621-3431, Surry, USA; gen tel (336) 835-1513; gen fax (336)

835-8742; disp adv e-mail hlamm@elkintribune.com; ed e-mail wbyerly-wood@elkintribune.com; web site www.elkintribune.com
Circulation: 6,000pd,; Sworn/Estimate/Non-Audited
Advertising rate: Open inch rate $12.50
Established: 1911
Content Mgr./Ed.....Wendy Wood
Sr. Ad. Rep.....Holly Lamm
Staff Reporter.....Beanie Taylor
Staff Report.....Kristian Russell
Customer Service Rep.....Dawn Bagale
Advertising Rep.....Scott Belcher
PublisherSandy HurleyEquipment & Software: ; Presses — 4-G/Community, 3-HI/Orient.
Delivery Method: Carrier, Racks
Areas Served: Surry, Yadkin and Wilkes counties

FARMVILLE

THE FARMVILLE ENTERPRISE (WED)

3754 S Main St, Farmville, NC, 27828-8546, Pitt, USA; gen tel (252) 753-4126; gen fax (252) 753-4126; ed e-mail farmvilleed@nccox.com; web site https://www.facebook.com/pages/The-Farmville-Enterprise/178388739633
Circulation: 2,500pd,; Sworn/Estimate/Non-Audited
Advertising rate: Open inch rate $8.25
Established: 1910
Group: Cooke Communications North Carolina, LLC
Pub.....Mitchell Oakley
Mechanical Specifications: Type page 13 x 21 1/2.Equipment & Software: Hardware — APP/Mac; Software — Microsoft/Word 6.0.1, Aldus/PageMaker.
Delivery Method: Mail
Areas Served: Pitt

FAYETTEVILLE

UP & COMING WEEKLY (WED)

208 Rowan St, Fayetteville, NC, 28301-4922, Cumberland, USA; gen tel (910) 484-6200; gen fax (910) 484-9218; web site www.upandcomingweekly.com
Circulation: 0pd, 8,648fr; CVC
Advertising rate: 1/16 Pg $114.00; 1/8 Pg $203.00; 1/4 Pg $371.00
Established: 1996
Pub./Adv. Mgr.....Bill Bowman
Associate Pub.....Joy G. Crowe
Associate Pub.....Janice Burton
Mktg. Mgr.....Sam Lum
Vice Pres., Opns.....Jean Bolton
Circ. Mgr.....Laurel Handforth
Mktg. Rep.....Mary Beth Leiby
Office Mgr.....Tracy McCullough
Mechanical Specifications: Type page 9 3/4 x 12; E - 6 cols, 2 1/4, 2/3 between; A - 4 cols, 2 1/4, 2/3 between; C - 6 cols, 1 1/2, 2/3 between.
Areas Served: Fayetheville, Fort Bragg, Cumberland

FOREST CITY

RUTHERFORD WEEKLY (THUR)

369 Butler Rd, Forest City, NC, 28043-6106, Rutherford, USA; gen tel (828) 248-1408; ed tel (828) 248-1496; gen fax (828) 245-7013; disp adv e-mail mike@rutherfordweekly.com; class adv e-mail www.advertising@rutherfordweekly.com; ed e-mail www.events@rutherfordweekly.com; web site www.rutherfordweekly.com
Circulation: 15,807fr; CVC
Advertising rate: Open inch rate $21.00
Established: 1991
Group: Community Newspaper Holdings, Inc.
Editions: (15) Rutherford weekly
Digital Platform - Mobile: Apple
Digital Platform - Tablet: Apple iOS
Gen. Mgr.....Mike Marlow
Circ. Mgr.....Les Wood
Prod. Mgr.....Jan Sailors
Mechanical Specifications: 6 columns 10.333 wide by 15 inches tall Equipment & Software: Hardware — mac ; Presses — walton press; Software — indesign
Delivery Method: Racks
Areas Served: 28043 28150 28139 28017 28018 2801928024 28040

FRANKLIN

THE FRANKLIN PRESS (WED, FRI)

40 Depot St, Franklin, NC, 28734-2704, Franklin, USA; gen tel (828) 524-2010; adv tel (828) 524-2010; gen fax (828) 524-8821; disp adv e-mail addirector@thefranklinpress.com; class adv e-mail classifieds@thefranklinpress.com; ed e-mail editor@thefranklinpress.com; web site www.thefranklinpress.com
Circulation: 8,524pd, 21fr; Sworn/Estimate/Non-Audited
Advertising rate: Open inch rate $15.45
Established: 1886
Group: Community Newspapers, Inc.
Pub.....Rachael Hopkins
Ed.....Barbara McRae
M.A. Lewis
Corp. Mktg. Dir.....Joel Jenkins
Mechanical Specifications: Type page 13 1/2 x 21 1/2; E - 6 cols, 2, 1/6 between; A - 6 cols, 2, 1/6 between; C - 9 cols, 1 1/3, 1/8 between.Equipment & Software: Hardware — APP/Mac, APP/Power Mac; Presses — 8-G/Community; Software — Adobe/PageMaker 6.5, Adobe/Photoshop 5.0.
Delivery Method: Mail

GRAHAM

THE ALAMANCE NEWS (THUR)

114 W Elm St, Graham, NC, 27253-2802, Alamance, USA; gen tel (336) 228-7851; gen fax (336) 229-9602; disp adv e-mail alamanacenews@mail.com; web site http://www.alamancenews.us
Circulation: 4,000pd,; Sworn/Estimate/Non-Audited
Advertising rate: Open inch rate $11.28
Pub./Ed.....Thomas E. Boney
Mechanical Specifications: Type page 11.6 x 21; E - 6 cols, 1.8; Equipment & Software: ; Presses — G/Community
Delivery Method: Mail, Newsstand, Racks
Areas Served: Alamance County, NC

GREENSBORO

THE BUSINESS JOURNAL (FRI)

100 S Elm St, Ste 400, Greensboro, NC, 27401-2641, Guilford, USA; gen tel (336) 271- 6539; adv tel (336) 370-2890; ed tel (336) 370-2895; disp adv e-mail aforesman@bizjournals.com; class adv e-mail gjohnston@bizjournals.com; ed e-mail rtroyer@bizjournals.com; web site http://www.bizjournals.com/triad/
Advertising rate: 1/4 P - $1553; 1/2 P- $2719;Full - $4026
Established: 1998
Digital Platform - Mobile: Apple, Android, Windows
Digital Platform - Tablet: Apple iOS, Android, Windows 7
Pres./Pub.....Ollie Chandhok
Ed.....Rebecca Troyer
Delivery Method: Mail, Newsstand, Racks
Areas Served: 27000 - 27499

YES! WEEKLY (WED)

5500 Adams Farm Ln, Ste 204, Greensboro, NC, 27407-7059, Guilford, Forsyth, USA; gen tel (336) 316-1231 ; gen fax (336) 316-1930; disp adv e-mail publisher@yesweekly.com; class adv e-mail publisher@yesweekly.com; ed e-mail katie@yesweekly.com; web site www.yesweekly.com - 850,000(views) 65,000(visitors)
Circulation: 20,000fr; Sworn/Estimate/Non-Audited
Advertising rate: Open inch rate $20
Established: 2005
Group: Womack Newspapers, Inc
Digital Platform - Mobile: Apple, Android
Digital Platform - Tablet: Apple iOS, Android
Mechanical Specifications: 9.9 x 10.2Equipment & Software: Hardware — Apple; Presses — NA; Software — Adobe
Delivery Method: Newsstand, Racks
Areas Served: Guilford, Forsyth, Alamance, Davidson

GRIFTON

THE TIMES-LEADER (WED)

6904 S. Highland Ave., Grifton, NC, 28530, Lenoir, Pitt, USA; gen tel (252) 524-4376; gen fax (252) 524-3312; disp adv e-mail kstephens@ncweeklies.com; ed e-mail timesleader@ncweeklies.com; web site https://www.facebook.com/timesleader.newspaper - 1,912(views)
Circulation: 2,200pd,; Sworn/Estimate/Non-Audited
Advertising rate: Open inch rate $8.25
Established: 1912
Group: Community Newspaper Holdings, Inc.
Cooke Communications North Carolina, LLC
Pub.....Kyle Stephens
Ed.....Angela Harne
Mechanical Specifications: Type page 11 5/8 x 21 1/2; E - 6 cols, 1 7/8, 1/8 between; A - 6 cols, 1 7/8, 1/8 between; C - 6 cols, 1 7/8, 1/8 between.Equipment & Software: Hardware — APP/Mac; Software — Microsoft/Word 6.0.1, Aldus/PageMaker.
Delivery Method: Mail, Newsstand, Racks
Areas Served: 28513 28590 28530

HAVELOCK

THE HAVELOCK NEWS (THUR)

230 Stonebridge Sq, Havelock, NC, 28532-9505, Craven, USA; gen tel (252) 444-1999; gen fax (252) 447-0897; disp adv e-mail taylor.shannon@havenews.com; class adv e-mail havenews@havenews.com; ed e-mail ken.buday@havenews.com; web site www.havenews.com
Circulation: 1,200pd, 21fr; Sworn/Estimate/Non-Audited
Advertising rate: Open inch rate $6.00
Established: 1986
Group: Halifax Media
Ed./Gen. Mgr.....Ken Buday
Adv. Consult.....Taylor Shannon
Mechanical Specifications: Type page 13 x 21 1/2.
Delivery Method: Mail, Newsstand
Areas Served: 28532

HAYESVILLE

CLAY COUNTY PROGRESS (THUR)

43 Main St, Hayesville, NC, 28904-5808, Clay, USA; gen tel (828) 389-8431; gen fax (828) 389-9997; disp adv e-mail ads@claycountyprogress.com; class adv e-mail classifieds@claycountyprogress.com; ed e-mail news@claycountyprogress.com; web site www.claycountyprogress.com
Circulation: 4,400pd,; Sworn/Estimate/Non-Audited
Advertising rate: Open inch rate $10.75
Established: 1980
Group: Community Newspapers, Inc.
Adv. Mgr.....Tracy Smith
Circ. Mgr.....Danny Hughes
Pub.....Becky Long
Corp. Mktg. Dir.....Joel Jenkins
Mechanical Specifications: Type page 13 x 21; E - 6 cols, 2, between; A - 6 cols, 2, between; C - 6 cols, 2, between.Equipment & Software: Hardware — APP/Mac.
Delivery Method: Mail, Newsstand, Carrier
Areas Served: Clay

HERTFORD

PERQUIMANS WEEKLY (WED)

111 W Market St, Hertford, NC, 27944-1150, Perquimans, USA; gen tel (252) 426-5728; adv tel (252) 426-5728; ed tel (252) 426-5728; gen fax (252) 426-4625; disp adv e-mail balexander@ncweeklies.com; class adv e-mail balexander@ncweeklies.com; ed e-mail pwilliams@ncweeklies.com; web site http://www.dailyadvance.com/communities/perquimans
Circulation: 1,733pd,; Sworn/Estimate/Non-Audited
Advertising rate: Unknown
Established: 1932
Group: Cooke Communications North Carolina, LLC
Digital Platform - Mobile: Apple, Windows
Pub.....Michael Goodman
Mng Ed.....Julian Eure
Ad. Dir.....Sean O'Brian
Mechanical Specifications: Type page 11 5/8 x 21; E - 6 cols, 1 5/6, 1/8 between; C - 9 cols, 1 3/16, 1/8 between.Equipment & Software: Hardware — APP/Mac; Software — Microsoft/Word 6.0.1, Aldus/PageMaker.
Delivery Method: Mail, Carrier, Racks
Areas Served: Perquimans County

HIGH POINT

ARCHDALE TRINITY NEWS (THUR)

213 Woodbine St, High Point, NC, 27260-8339, Guilford, USA; gen tel (336) 434-2716 ; adv tel (336) 888-3625; ed tel (336) 434-2716 ; disp adv e-mail csaunders@hpenews.com; class adv e-mail classified@hpenews.com; ed e-mail jseabolt@atnonline.net; web site www.atnonline.net
Circulation: 3,500pd, 15fr; Sworn/Estimate/Non-Audited
Advertising rate: Open inch rate $16.09
Established: 1978
Digital Platform - Mobile: Apple, Android
Digital Platform - Tablet: Apple iOS, Android
Adv. Dir.....John McClure
Pub.....Rick Bean
Mechanical Specifications: Type page 13 x 21; E - 6 cols, 2 1/16, 1/16 between; A - 6 cols, 2 1/16, 1/16 between; C - 9 cols, 1 3/8, 1/16 between.
Delivery Method: Mail, Racks
Areas Served: Guilford and Randolph County

THOMASVILLE TIMES (WED, SAT)

213 Woodbine St, High Point, NC, 27260-8339, Davidson, USA; gen tel (336) 888-3590; gen fax (336) 888-3632; disp adv e-mail aduncan@hpenews.com; class adv e-mail classified@hpenews.com; ed e-mail editor@tvilletimes.com; web site http://www.tvilletimes.com/
Circulation: 5,500pd, 334fr; Sworn/Estimate/Non-Audited
Advertising rate: Open inch rate $9.50
Established: 1890
Group: Paxton Media Group, LLC
Adv. Mgr.....John McClure
Circ. Mgr.....Donte Owens
Mechanical Specifications: Type page 13 x 21; E - 6 cols, 2, 1/6 between; A - 6 cols, 2, 1/6 between; C - 9 cols, 1 1/3, 1/6 between. Equipment & Software: Hardware — 3-APP/Power Mac 7500; Presses — 8-G/Community; Software — QPS/QuarkXPress 3.2, Adobe/PageMaker 5.0, Multi-Ad/Creator.
Delivery Method: Mail, Newsstand, Racks
Areas Served: Thomasville

HIGHLANDS

THE HIGHLANDER (THUR)

34 N Fifth St, Highlands, NC, 28741, Macon, USA; gen tel (828) 526-4114; adv tel (828) 526-4114; gen fax (828) 526-3658; disp adv e-mail ads@highlandsnews.com; class adv e-mail classifieds@highlandsnews.com; ed

e-mail editor@highlandsnews.com; web site www.highlandsnews.com
Circulation: 3,500pd, 60fr; Sworn/Estimate/Non-Audited
Advertising rate: Open inch rate $12.35
Established: 1958
Group: Community Newspapers, Inc.
Pub.. Eric Nesmith
Mktg. Dir..Joel JenkinsEquipment & Software: ; Software — Adobe/PageMaker 6.5.
Delivery Method: Mail

HILLSBOROUGH

THE NEWS OF ORANGE COUNTY (WED)

109 E King St, Hillsborough, NC, 27278-2570, Orange, USA; gen tel (919) 732-2171; gen fax (919) 732-4852; disp adv e-mail k.coleman@newsoforange.com; class adv e-mail advertising@newsoforange.com; ed e-mail charles.pogacar@gmail.com; web site http://www.newsoforange.com/
Circulation: 4,200pd,; Sworn/Estimate/Non-Audited
Advertising rate: Open inch rate $9.45
Established: 1893
Group: Womack Publishing Co.
Adv./Gen. Mgr........................... Keith Coleman
Ed... Vanessa Shortley
Mechanical Specifications: Type page 13 x 21 1/2; E - 6 cols, 1 5/6, 1/8 between; A - 6 cols, 1 5/6, 1/8 between; C - 6 cols, 1 5/6, 1/8 between.Equipment & Software: Hardware — APP/Macs; Software — Adobe/PageMaker 6.0, Microsoft/Word, QPS/QuarkXPress.
Areas Served: 27278, 27231, 27243, 27514, 27516, 27572, 27302, 27510, 27583, 27541, 27603, 27705

JAMESTOWN

JAMESTOWN NEWS (WED)

206 E Main St, Ste 1A, Jamestown, NC, 27282-8005, Guilford, USA; gen tel (336) 841-4933; gen fax (336) 841-4953; disp adv e-mail publisher@yesweeekly.com; class adv e-mail jamestownnews@northstate.net; ed e-mail jamestownnews@northstate.net; web site www.jamestownnews.com
Circulation: 4,000pd, 10fr; Sworn/Estimate/Non-Audited
Advertising rate: Open inch rate $8.00
Established: 1978
Group: Womack Newspapers
Pub.................................... Charles A. Womack
Editor... Carol Brooks
Delivery Method: Mail, Racks
Areas Served: 27282

KENANSVILLE

DUPLIN TIMES (THUR)

102 Front St, Kenansville, NC, 28349, Duplin, USA; gen tel (910) 296-0239; gen fax (910) 296-9545; disp adv e-mail duplinads@ncweeklies.com; ed e-mail tnormile@ncweeklies.com; web site http://theduplintimes.com
Circulation: 6,100pd, 11,125fr; Sworn/Estimate/Non-Audited
Advertising rate: Open inch rate $10.00
Established: 1935
Group: Cooke Communications North Carolina, LLC
Digital Platform - Mobile: Apple, Android, Windows, Blackberry
Digital Platform - Tablet: Apple iOS, Android, Windows 7, Blackberry Tablet OS
Editor....................................... Trevor Normile
Mechanical Specifications: 6 column format, 10.125" x 21"
Classified is 8 col format, 10.125" x 21"Equipment & Software: Hardware — APP/Mac; Software — Microsoft/Word 6.0.1, Adobe CS2 (Indesign, etc).
Delivery Method: Mail, Newsstand, Racks
Areas Served: 28349,28398, 28341, 28365, 28325, 28453, 28458, 28464, 28466, 28508, 28518, 28521, 28525, 28572, 28574

KENLY

KENLY NEWS (WED)

201 W 2ND ST, Kenly, NC, 27542, Johnston, USA; gen tel (919) 284-2295; gen fax (919) 284-6397; disp adv e-mail debra@kenly-news.com; ed e-mail rstewart@kenlynews.com; web site www.kenlynews.com
Circulation: 3,200pd, 180fr; Sworn/Estimate/Non-Audited
Advertising rate: Open inch rate $6.80
Established: 1973Editions: (1) Kenly News-Pine Level
Pub... Rick Stewart
News Ed. .... Keith Barnes
Adv. Dir.Debra MalarchikEquipment & Software: Hardware — 6-APP/Mac; Software — Adobe/PageMaker, Adobe/Photoshop, Microsoft/Word.
Delivery Method: Mail, Newsstand, Racks

KERNERSVILLE

KERNERSVILLE NEWS (TUES, THUR, SAT)

300 E Mountain St, Kernersville, NC, 27284-2943, Forsyth, USA; gen tel (336) 993-2161; gen fax (336) 993-0931; disp adv e-mail ad_director@kernersvillenews.com; class adv e-mail classifieds@kernersvillenews.com; ed e-mail editor@kernersvillenews.com; web site www.kernersvillenews.com
Circulation: 6,000pd, 17,850fr; Sworn/Estimate/Non-Audited
Advertising rate: Open inch rate $18.50
Established: 1938
Assist. Pub/Ed .... Meredith Harrell
Adv. Dir .... Tracy Cardwell
Ed.. John Owensby
Vice Pres./Bus. Mgr ....Connie OwensbyEquipment & Software: Hardware — PC; Presses — 4-KP/NewsKing; Software — Adobe/PageMaker.
Delivery Method: Mail, Newsstand, Carrier, Racks
Areas Served: 27284

KING

THE STOKES NEWS (THUR)

122 S Main St, King, NC, 27021-9011, Stokes, USA; gen tel (336) 591-8191; adv tel (336) 779-4036; gen fax (336) 591-4379; disp adv e-mail sstanley@civitasmedia.com; class adv e-mail cmabe@civitasmedia.com; web site www.thestokesnews.com
Circulation: 8,400pd, 21fr; Sworn/Estimate/Non-Audited
Advertising rate: Open inch rate $13.50
Established: 1872
Group: Champion Media
Office Mgr. .... Anna Holcomb
Ed.. Amanda Dodson
Sports Ed................................ Robert Money
Mechanical Specifications: Type page 11 9/16 x 21 1/2; E - 6 cols, 1 3/4, between; A - 6 cols, 1 3/4, between; C - 9 cols, 1 3/4, between. Equipment & Software: ; Presses — G/Community.
Delivery Method: Mail, Racks
Areas Served: 27021

KINGS MOUNTAIN

KINGS MOUNTAIN HERALD (WED)

700 E Gold St, Kings Mountain, NC, 28086-3135, Cleveland & Gaston, USA; gen tel (704) 739-7496; gen fax (704) 739-0611; disp adv e-mail rick.kmherald@gmail.com; class adv e-mail kathy.kmherald@gmail.com; ed e-mail lib.kmherald@gmail.com; web site kmherald.com
Circulation: 1,200pd, 1,000fr; Sworn/Estimate/Non-Audited
Advertising rate: Open inch rate $8.00
Established: 1886
Group: Community First Media
Ed.. Elizabeth Stewart
Adv. Rep .... Mark Blanton
Mechanical Specifications: Type page 13 x 20; E - 6 cols, 2, 3/16 between; A - 6 cols, 2, 3/16 between; C - 6 cols, 2, 3/16 between. 10" x 21" - 6 col.Equipment & Software: Hardware — APP/Mac; Software — QPS/QuarkXPress, Microsoft/Word, Adobe/Photoshop.
Delivery Method: Mail, Newsstand, Racks
Areas Served: 28086, 28021, 28012, 28120, 28016, 28023

LA GRANGE

WEEKLY GAZETTE (WED)

108 S Caswell St, La Grange, NC, 28551-1794, Lenoir, USA; gen tel (252) 521-2065; gen fax (252) 566-5318; disp adv e-mail theweeklygazette@embarqmail.com; web site https://www.facebook.com/The-Weekly-Gazette-246109135408722/?ref=page_internal
Circulation: 1,500pd, 25fr; USPS
Advertising rate: Open inch rate $7.00
Digital Platform - Mobile: Windows
Digital Platform - Tablet: Windows 7
Ed... Glenn Penuel
Mechanical Specifications: Type page 13 1/2 x 21 1/2; E - 6 cols, 1 3/4, 1/8 between; A - 6 cols, 1 3/4, 1/8 between; C - 6 cols, 1 3/4, 1/8 between.
Delivery Method: Mail, Racks
Areas Served: 28551, 28501

LENOIR

CALDWELL WEEKLY (WED)

123 Pennton Ave NW, Lenoir, NC, 28645-4313, Caldwell, USA; gen tel (828) 758-7381; gen fax (828) 754-0110; disp adv e-mail mtyree@newstopic.com; class adv e-mail mtyree@newstopic.net; ed e-mail guylucas@newstopic.net; web site www.newstopic.net
Circulation: 10,500fr; USPS
Advertising rate: Open inch rate $5.40Editions: (1) Caldwell Weekly
Pub.. Terese Almquist
Circ. Dir. .... Mike Lambert
Ed. .... Guy Lucas
Mechanical Specifications: Type page 10 x 21 1/2; E - 6 cols, 1 5/6, 1/8 between; A - 6 cols, 1 5/6, 1/8 between.Equipment & Software: Hardware — APP/Mac; Presses — G/Community; Software — Baseview, Multi-Ad/Creator, QPS/QuarkXPress, InDesign.
Delivery Method: Carrier
Areas Served: 28645, 28638, 28630, 28611

LILLINGTON

HARNETT COUNTY NEWS (WED)

407 MAIN ST, Lillington, NC, 27546, Harnett, USA; gen tel (910) 893-5121; gen fax (910) 893-6128; ed e-mail editor@harnettcountynews.com; web site harnettcountynews.com
Circulation: 2,118pd, 11fr; Sworn/Estimate/Non-Audited
Advertising rate: Open inch rate $8.70
Pub.. Bart S. Adams
Ed... Tom Woerner
Mechanical Specifications: Type page 11 3/5 x 21; E - 6 cols, 1 4/5, 1/8 between.Equipment & Software: ; Software — MS/Word.

LINCOLNTON

LINCOLN TIMES-NEWS (MON, WED, FRI)

119 W Water St, Lincolnton, NC, 28092-2623, Lincoln, USA; gen tel (704) 735-3031; adv tel (704) 735-3031; gen fax (704) 735-3037; adv fax (704) 735-3996; ed fax (704) 735-1278; disp adv e-mail advertising@lincolntimesnews.com; class adv e-mail classifieds@lincolntimesnews.com; ed e-mail editor@lincolntimesnews.com; web site www.lincolntimesnews.com
Circulation: 10,500pd,; Sworn/Estimate/Non-Audited
Advertising rate: Open inch rate $10.00
Established: 1873
Group: Western Publishing Co
Pub... Jerry G. Leedy
Adv. Mgr.................................... Lisa Matthews
Mng. Ed................................ Michael Gebelein
Mechanical Specifications: Type page 13 x 21 1/2; E - 6 cols, 2 1/16, 1/8 between; A - 6 cols, 2 1/16, 1/8 between; C - 9 cols, 1 5/12, 1/8 between.Equipment & Software: Hardware — Dell; Presses — KP/News King, KP/Color King with folder; Software — Archetype/Corel Draw 7.0, Adobe/PageMaker 6.5.
Delivery Method: Mail, Newsstand, Carrier, Racks
Areas Served: Lincoln

LITTLETON

LAKE GASTON GAZETTE-OBSERVER (WED)

378 Lizard Creek Rd, Littleton, NC, 27850-8390, Warren, USA; gen tel (252) 586-2700; gen fax (252) 586-3522; disp adv e-mail ads@lakegastongazette-observer.com; ed e-mail news@lakegastongazette-observer.com; web site http://www.lakegastongazette-observer.com/
Advertising rate: Open inch rate $9.70
Established: 1955
Group: Womack Publishing Co.Della Rose
Office Mgr......................................Carol Griffin
Adv. Mgr................................ Mary Lou Cheek
Delivery Method: Mail, Newsstand, Racks
Areas Served: Warren, Northampton, Brunswick, Mecklenburg, Halifax

MARSHALL

NEWS-RECORD AND SENTINEL (WED)

58 Back St., Marshall, NC, 28753, Madison, USA; gen tel (828) 649-1075; gen fax (828) 649-9426; ed e-mail info@newsrecordsentinel.com
Circulation: 6,500pd, 50fr; Sworn/Estimate/Non-Audited
Advertising rate: 1/8 Pg $108.00; 1/6 Pg $142.00; 1/4 Pg $211.00
Established: 1901
Group: Gannett
Gen. Mgr./Ed.............................. Christina Rice
Delivery Method: Mail, Racks

MARSHVILLE

THE HOME NEWS (THUR)

123 E Union St, Marshville, NC, 28103-1142, Union, USA; gen tel (704) 624-5068; gen fax (704) 624-2371; disp adv e-mail homenewseditor@aol.com; ed e-mail ourhomepaper@gmail.com; web site https://ourhomepaper.wordpress.com/
Circulation: 2,850pd,; Sworn/Estimate/Non-Audited
Advertising rate: Open inch rate $5.50
Established: 1892
Pub.................................... John H. Edmonson
Office Mgr. .... Brenda Thomas
Mechanical Specifications: Type page 13 x 21 1/2; E - 6 cols, 2 1/16, 1/8 between; A - 6 cols, 2 1/16, 1/8 between; C - 8 cols, 1 1/2, 1/8 between.Equipment & Software: Hardware — APP/Mac; Software — Adobe/PageMaker 3.0.
Delivery Method: Mail, Newsstand, Racks
Areas Served: Union, Anson, Mecklenburg

MEBANE

THE MEBANE ENTERPRISE (WED)
106 N Fourth St, Mebane, NC, 27302-2428, Alamance, USA; gen tel (919) 563-3555; gen fax (919) 563-9242; disp adv e-mail j.brown@mebaneenterprise.com; class adv e-mail c.manion@mebaneenterprise.com; ed e-mail editor@mebaneenterprise.com; web site www.mebaneenterprise.com
Circulation: 3,100pd, 81fr; Sworn/Estimate/Non-Audited
Advertising rate: Open inch rate $9.45
Established: 1908
Group: Womack Publishing Co.
Adv./Gen. Mgr. ....Jackie Brown
Ed. .... Karen Carter
Mechanical Specifications: 6 col x 21.5 "
1 col - 1.56
2 col - 3.25"
3 col - 4.93"
4 col - 6.63"
5 col - 8.31"
6 col - 10"Equipment & Software: Hardware — APP/Mac; Software — QPS/QuarkXPress 4.1, Adobe/Photoshop, Adobe/PageMaker.
Delivery Method: Mail, Newsstand, Racks
Areas Served: Alamance County, Orange County, Caswell Co

MOCKSVILLE

DAVIE COUNTY ENTERPRISE-RECORD (THUR)
171 S Main St, Mocksville, NC, 27028-2424, Davie, USA; gen tel (336) 751-2120; gen fax (336) 751-9760; disp adv e-mail erads2@davie-enterprise.com; class adv e-mail classifieds@salisburypost.com; ed e-mail ernews@davie-enterprise.com; web site http://www.ourdavie.com/
Circulation: 8,500pd, 32fr; Sworn/Estimate/Non-Audited
Advertising rate: Open inch rate $9.25
Established: 1899
Group: Salisbury Newsmedia
Mng Ed. .... Mike Barnhardt
Adv. Dir.. Ray Tutterow
Ed. ....Dwight Sparks
Delivery Method: Mail, Racks
Areas Served: Davie County, 27028, 27006

MONROE

THE ENQUIRER-JOURNAL (WED, FRI, SUN)
1508 Skyway Dr, Monroe, NC, 28110-3008, Union, USA; gen tel (704) 289-1541; adv tel (704) 261-2208; ed tel (704) 261-2220; gen fax (704) 289-2929; disp adv e-mail apurser@theej.com; class adv e-mail adcopy@theej.com; ed e-mail jerrysnow@theej.com; web site www.enquirerjournal.com - 203,000(views) 26,337(visitors)
Circulation: 5,392pd, 4,000fr; USPS
Advertising rate: $20.00
Established: 1873
Group: Paxton Media Group, LLC
Digital Platform - Mobile: Apple, Android
Digital Platform - Tablet: Apple iOS, Android
Mng. Ed.......................................Stan Hojnacki
Sports Ed.......................................Jerry Snow
Adv. Mgr..................................Sharon Jimenez
Pub...Randy Lohrenz
Delivery Method: Mail, Newsstand, Carrier, Racks
Areas Served: 28079, 28103, 28104, 28105, 28110, 28112, 28133, 28173, 28174, 29728

MOORESVILLE

MOORESVILLE TRIBUNE (WED, SUN)
147 E Center Ave, Mooresville, NC, 28115-2513, Iredell, USA; gen tel (704) 664-5554; adv tel (704) 562-9067; ed tel (704) 696-2941; gen fax (704) 664-3614; disp adv e-mail advertising@mooresvilletribune.com; class adv e-mail classified@mooresvilletribune.com; ed e-mail dgowing@mooresvilletribune.com; web site www.mooresvilletribune.com
Circulation: 921pd, 10,910fr; CAC
Advertising rate: Open inch rate $10.86
Established: 1937
Group: BH Media Group
World Media Enterprises Inc.
Adv. Mgr. .... LeAnna Dunlap
Circ. Mgr...Bud Welch
Ed .... Dale Gowing
Delivery Method: Mail, Newsstand, Carrier, Racks
Areas Served: Iredell

MOREHEAD CITY

CARTERET COUNTY NEWS-TIMES (WED, FRI, SUN)
4206 Bridges St, Morehead City, NC, 28557-2942, Carteret, USA; gen tel (252) 726-7081; adv tel (252) 726-7081 x263; gen fax (252) 726-6016; disp adv e-mail kim@thenewstimes.com; class adv e-mail classifieds@thenewstimes.com; ed e-mail beth@thenewstimes.com; web site http://www.carolinacoastonline.com/
Circulation: 10,230pd,; USPS
Advertising rate: Open inch rate $13.50
Established: 1942
Group: Carteret Publishing Co.
Pub..................................... Lockwood Phillips
Adv. Dir.. Kim Moseley
Ed. .... Walter D. Phillips
Mng. Ed..Beth Blake
Mechanical Specifications: Type page 13 1/8 x 21 1/2; E - 6 cols, 2 1/16, 1/4 between; A - 6 cols, 2 1/16, 1/4 between; C - 8 cols, 1 1/2, 3/16 between.Equipment & Software: Hardware — APP/Mac; Presses — 8-G/Community (2-color decks); Software — Indesign
Delivery Method: Mail, Newsstand, Carrier, Racks
Areas Served: 28511,28512,28516,28520,28524,25828,28531,28532,28553,28557,28570,m28575,28577,28579,28581,28584,28589,28594

MOUNT OLIVE

MOUNT OLIVE TRIBUNE (MON)
214 N Center St, Mount Olive, NC, 28365-1702, Wayne, USA; gen tel (919) 658-9456; gen fax (919) 658-9559; disp adv e-mail ads@mountolivetribune.com; ed e-mail editor@mountolivetribune.com; web site www.mountolivetribune.com
Circulation: 2,000pd, 49fr; Sworn/Estimate/Non-Audited
Advertising rate: Open inch rate $13.50
Established: 1904
Pub .... Barry Merrill
Mechanical Specifications: Type page 13 x 21 1/2; E - 6 cols, 2 1/16, between; A - 6 cols, 2 1/16, between; C - 6 cols, 2 1/16, between. Equipment & Software: Hardware — PC; Presses — G/Community; Software — Adobe/PageMaker, Microsoft/Word, QPS/QuarkXPress.
Delivery Method: Mail, Newsstand, Carrier, Racks
Areas Served: Wayne, Duplin

MURPHY

CHEROKEE SCOUT (WED)
89 Sycamore St, Murphy, NC, 28906-2954, Cherokee, USA; gen tel (828) 837-5122; gen fax (828) 837-5832; disp adv e-mail advertising@cherokeescout.com; class adv e-mail classifieds@cherokeescout.com; ed e-mail news@cherokeescout.com; web site www.cherokeescout.com - 34,000(views) 10,000(visitors)
Circulation: 8,000pd, 100fr; Sworn/Estimate/Non-Audited
Advertising rate: $14.50
Established: 1889
Group: Community Newspapers, Inc.
Pub..David Brown
Adv. Mgr. ....Donna Cook
Ed. .... Matthew Osborne
Mechanical Specifications: Type page 13 x 21 1/2; E - 6 cols, 2, 1/6 between; A - 6 cols, 2, 1/6 between; C - 6 cols, 2, 1/6 between. Equipment & Software: Hardware — APP/Mac; Presses — G/Community; Software — Adobe Creative Suite 2, Interlink, Microsoft Office
Delivery Method: Mail, Newsstand, Racks
Areas Served: Cherokee County, (28901, 28904, 28905, 28906)

NAGS HEAD

OUTER BANKS SENTINEL (WED)
PO Box 546, Nags Head, NC, 27959-0546, Dare, USA; gen tel (252) 480-2234; gen fax (252) 480-1146; disp adv e-mail donna@obsentinel.com; class adv e-mail classifieds@obsentinel.com; ed e-mail mark@obsentinel.com; web site www.obsentinel.com
Circulation: 5,000pd,; Sworn/Estimate/Non-Audited
Advertising rate: Open inch rate $9.00
Established: 1996
Group: SLAM Publications
Ed. .... Neel Keller
Pub...Mark Jurkowitz
Delivery Method: Mail
Areas Served: 27954

NASHVILLE

THE NASHVILLE GRAPHIC (THUR)
203 W Washington St, Nashville, NC, 27856-1263, Nash, USA; gen tel (252) 459-7101; gen fax (252) 459-3052; disp adv e-mail ads@nashvillegraphic.com; class adv e-mail classifieds@nashvillegraphic.com; ed e-mail news@nashvillegraphic.com; web site www.nashvillegraphic.com - 600,000(views) 14,000(visitors)
Circulation: 3,328pd, 3,800fr; Sworn/Estimate/Non-Audited
Advertising rate: Open inch rate $7.50
Established: 1895
Pub./Adv. Mgr.........................Jo Anne Cooper
Mechanical Specifications: Type page 11 5/8 x 21 1/2; E - 6 cols, 2 1/16, 1/6 between; A - 6 cols, 2 1/16, 1/6 between.
Delivery Method: Mail, Newsstand, Racks
Areas Served: Nash

NEWLAND

THE AVERY JOURNAL-TIMES (THUR)
335 Linville St, Newland, NC, 28657-8037, Avery, USA; gen tel (828) 733-2448; gen fax (828) 733-0639; disp adv e-mail cindy.zuercher@averyjournal.com; class adv e-mail classifieds@averyjournal.com; ed e-mail editor@averyjournal.com; web site www.averyjournal.com
Circulation: 5,300pd, 415fr; Sworn/Estimate/Non-Audited
Advertising rate: Open inch rate $7.57
Established: 1959
Group: Adams Publishing Group, LLC
Pub.. Gene Fowler
Class Adv. Mgr. ....Brenda Minton
Adv. Mgr....................................... Charlie Price
Mechanical Specifications: Type page 13 x 21; E - 6 cols, 2, 1/6 between; A - 6 cols, 2, 1/6 between; C - 9 cols, 1 1/2, 1/12 between.Equipment & Software: Hardware — APP/Mac.
Delivery Method: Mail, Newsstand, Racks
Areas Served: 28657

NORTH WILKESBORO

THE WILKES JOURNAL-PATRIOT (TUES, FRI)
711 Main St, North Wilkesboro, NC, 28659-4211, Wilkes, USA; gen tel (336) 838-4117; gen fax (336) 838-9864; disp adv e-mail narchibald@journalpatriot.com; class adv e-mail wjpads@wilkes.net; ed e-mail wilkesjp@wilkes.net; web site www.journalpatriot.com
Circulation: 11,000pd,; Sworn/Estimate/Non-Audited
Advertising rate: Open inch rate $6.75
Established: 1906
Adv. Mgr. ....Nellie Archibald
Circ. Mgr.................................... Debby Church
Pub..Jule Hubbard
Mechanical Specifications: Type page 13 x 21 1/2; A - 6 cols, 2 1/16, 1/8 between.
Delivery Method: Mail, Newsstand, Carrier, Racks
Areas Served: Wilkes

OXFORD

OXFORD PUBLIC LEDGER (MON, THUR)
200 W Spring St, Oxford, NC, 27565-3247, Granville, USA; gen tel (919) 693-2646; gen fax (919) 693-3704; disp adv e-mail oplronnieadvertising@earthlink.net; class adv e-mail oplchristyadvertising@earthlink.net; ed e-mail opllynnallred@earthlink.net
Circulation: 6,500pd, 60fr; Sworn/Estimate/Non-Audited
Advertising rate: Open inch rate $6.50
Established: 1881
Pub..Charles Critcher
Adv. Mgr.................................Ronald Critcher
Ed. ....Al Carson

PILOT MOUNTAIN

THE PILOT (WED)
11 W. Main St., Pilot Mountain, NC, 27041, Surry, USA; gen tel (336) 415-4739; disp adv e-mail pilnews@civitasmedia.com; web site pilotmountainnews.com
Group: Adams Publishing Group, LLC
Sr. Adv. Rep. .... Sherry Stanley
Pub...Ron Clausen

PITTSBORO

THE CHATHAM RECORD (THUR)
19 Hillsboro St, Pittsboro, NC, 27312-5891, Chatham, USA; gen tel (919) 542-3013; gen fax (919) 542-2590; disp adv e-mail advertising@thechathamnews.com; ed e-mail jhunter@thechathamnews.com; web site www.thechathamnews.com
Circulation: 2,100pd, 30fr; Sworn/Estimate/Non-Audited
Advertising rate: Open inch rate $7.25
Group: The Chatham News Publishing Co, Inc.
Ed. ....Randall Rigsbee
Mechanical Specifications: Type page 13 x 21 1/2; E - 6 cols, 2 1/16, 1/8 between; A - 6 cols, 2 1/16, 1/8 between; C - 6 cols, 2 1/16, 1/8 between.
Delivery Method: Mail, Newsstand, Racks
Areas Served: 27312 27514 27502 27559 27562 27344 27207 27339 27615 27707 27511 27215

PLYMOUTH

THE ROANOKE BEACON (WED)
212 W Water St, Plymouth, NC, 27962-1212, Washington, USA; gen tel (252) 793-2123; adv tel (252) 793-2123; gen fax (252) 793-5365; disp adv e-mail sales@roanokebeacon.com; ed e-mail news@roanokebeacon.com; web site www.roanokebeacon.com
Circulation: 2,226pd, 334fr; Sworn/Estimate/Non-Audited
Advertising rate: Open inch rate $7.00
Established: 1889
Group: Wayne Printing

Pub./Ed. .... Mary Wayt
Mechanical Specifications: Type page 10.04 x 20 1/2; E - 6 cols, 1 4/5, 1/8 between; A - 6 cols, 1 4/5, 1/8 between; C - 6 cols, 1 4/5, 1/8 between.
Delivery Method: Mail, Newsstand, Racks
Areas Served: 27962, 27970, 27928, 27846, 27925

PRINCETON

PRINCETON NEWS-LEADER (THUR)
119 W Edwards St, Princeton, NC, 27569-7374, Johnston, USA; gen tel (919) 936-9891; gen fax (919) 936-2065; disp adv e-mail debra@kenlynews.com; class adv e-mail ads@newsleadernow.com; ed e-mail kbarnes@kenlynews.com; web site www.johnstoniannews.com
Circulation: 1,500pd, 267fr; Sworn/Estimate/Non-Audited
Advertising rate: Open inch rate $6.95
Pub .... Rick Stewart
Delivery Method: Mail, Newsstand
Areas Served: Johnston, Wayne

RAEFORD

THE NEWS-JOURNAL (WED)
119 W Elwood Ave, Raeford, NC, 28376-2801, Hoke, USA; gen tel (910) 875-2121; gen fax (910) 875-7256; disp adv e-mail ads@thenews-journal.com; class adv e-mail wendy@thenews-journal.com; ed e-mail ken@thenews-journal.com; web site www.thenews-journal.com
Circulation: 3,100pd, 10,000fr; Sworn/Estimate/Non-Audited
Advertising rate: Open inch rate $7.90
Established: 1905
Group: Dickson Press, IncEditions: (1) The ECHO
Digital Platform - Mobile: Blackberry
Digital Platform - Tablet: Other
Ed. .... Ken MacDonald
Sales Manager .... Sue Ogas
Office Manager .... Ashley Brock
Mechanical Specifications: Type page 13 x 21; E - 6 cols, 2 1/16, 1/6 between; A - 6 cols, 2 1/16, 1/6 between; C - 8 cols, 1 1/2, 1/6 between.Equipment & Software: ; Presses — G/Community.
Delivery Method: Mail, Newsstand, Racks
Areas Served: 28376,28386,28315,28377

RALEIGH

CLAYTON NEWS-STAR (WED, SUN)
215 S McDowell St, Raleigh, NC, 27601-1331, Johnston, USA; gen tel (919) 829-4500; adv tel (919) 836-5680; ed tel (919) 836-5747; gen fax (919) 553-5858; disp adv e-mail gsmith@newsobserver.com; ed e-mail jdrescher@newsobserver.com; web site www.claytonnewsstar.com
Circulation: 19pd, 18,699fr; CAC
Advertising rate: Open inch rate $23.24
Established: 1911
Group: The News & Observer Publishing Co.
Digital Platform - Mobile: Apple, Android, Windows, Blackberry
Digital Platform - Tablet: Apple iOS, Android, Windows 7, Blackberry Tablet OS, Kindle, Nook, Kindle Fire, Other
Adv. Dir. .... Kaki Berkeley
Delivery Method: Carrier
Areas Served: Clayton, Western Johnston

EASTERN WAKE NEWS (WED, SUN)
215 S McDowell St, Raleigh, NC, 27601-1331, Johnston, Wake, USA; gen tel (919) 269-6101; adv tel (919) 553-7234; ed tel (919) 829-4823; gen fax (919) 269-8383; disp adv e-mail smcleod@newsobserver.com; class adv e-mail ewnewsads@nando.com; ed e-mail jwhitfield@newsobserver.com; web site www.easternwakenews.com
Circulation: 7pd, 24,416fr; CAC
Advertising rate: Open inch rate $32.17
Established: 1925
Group: The News & Observer Publishing Co.
Digital Platform - Mobile: Apple, Android, Windows, Blackberry
Digital Platform - Tablet: Apple iOS, Android, Windows 7, Blackberry Tablet OS, Kindle, Nook, Kindle Fire, Other
Adv. Mgr. .... Kaki Berkeley
Mng. Ed. .... Jhonny Whitfield
Mechanical Specifications: Type page 13 x 21 1/4; E - 6 cols, between; A - 6 cols, between; C - 10 cols, between.Equipment & Software: Hardware — APP/Mac; Software — QPS/QuarkXPress, Baseview.
Delivery Method: Carrier
Areas Served: 27597, 27557, 27591

GARNER-CLEVELAND RECORD (WED, SUN)
215 S McDowell St, Raleigh, NC, 27601-1331, Wake, USA; gen tel (919) 829-4500; disp adv e-mail smcleod@newsobserver.com; ed e-mail jwhitfield@newsobserver.com; web site www.garnercleveland.com
Circulation: 33,870fr; CAC
Advertising rate: Open inch rate $23.24
Group: The News & Observer Publishing Co.
Digital Platform - Mobile: Apple, Android, Windows, Blackberry
Digital Platform - Tablet: Apple iOS, Android, Windows 7, Blackberry Tablet OS, Kindle, Nook, Kindle Fire, Other
Adv. Dir. .... Kaki Berkeley
Ed. .... Johnny Whitfield
Delivery Method: Carrier
Areas Served: Garner, Cleveland

MIDTOWN RALEIGH NEWS (WED, SUN)
215 S McDowell St, Raleigh, NC, 27601-1331, Wake, USA; gen tel (919) 829-4500; adv tel (919) 836-5909; disp adv e-mail ptompkins@newsobserver.com; class adv e-mail sbewley@newsobserver.com; ed e-mail nrnews@newsobserver.com; web site www.midtownraleighnews.com
Circulation: 75,189fr; CAC
Advertising rate: Open inch rate $37.18
Group: The News & Observer Publishing Co.
Digital Platform - Mobile: Apple, Android, Windows, Blackberry
Digital Platform - Tablet: Apple iOS, Android, Windows 7, Blackberry Tablet OS, Kindle, Nook, Kindle Fire, Other
Adv Sales Mgr .... Shelley Bewley
Delivery Method: Carrier
Areas Served: Wake

NORTH RALEIGH NEWS (WED, SUN)
215 S McDowell St, Raleigh, NC, 27601-1331, Wake, USA; gen tel (919) 829-4500; adv fax (919) 829-4589; disp adv e-mail trevor.holland@newsobserver.com; class adv e-mail brookie.holloway@newsobserver.com; ed e-mail nrnews@newsobserver.com; web site www.northraleighnews.com
Circulation: 73,782fr; CAC
Advertising rate: Open inch rate $37.18
Established: 2003
Group: The News & Observer Publishing Co.
Digital Platform - Mobile: Apple, Android, Windows, Blackberry
Digital Platform - Tablet: Apple iOS, Android, Windows 7, Blackberry Tablet OS, Kindle, Kindle Fire, Other
Ed. .... Dan Barkin
Adv. Dir. .... Peter Tompkins
Delivery Method: Carrier
Areas Served: Wake

THE CARY NEWS (WED, SUN)
215 S McDowell St, Raleigh, NC, 27601-1331, Wake, USA; gen tel (919) 460-2600; disp adv e-mail placeads@newsobserver.com; ed e-mail carynews@newsobserver.com; web site www.carynews.com
Circulation: 6pd, 55,997fr; CAC
Established: 1963
Group: The McClatchy Company
Digital Platform - Mobile: Apple, Android, Windows, Blackberry
Digital Platform - Tablet: Apple iOS, Android, Windows 7, Blackberry Tablet OS, Kindle, Nook, Kindle Fire, Other
Ad. Dir. .... Kaki Berkeley
Mechanical Specifications: Type page 13 x 21; E - 6 cols, 2 1/16, 1/8 between; A - 6 cols, 2 1/16, 1/8 between; C - 10 cols, 1 3/16, 1/8 between.Equipment & Software: Hardware — APP/Mac; Presses — Flexographic.
Delivery Method: Carrier
Areas Served: Cary, Morrisville, Apex, Holly Springs, Fuquay-Varina

TRIANGLE BUSINESS JOURNAL (FRI)
3600 Glenwood Ave, Ste 100, Raleigh, NC, 27612-4951, Wake, USA; gen tel (919) 878-0010; ed tel (919) 327-1000; gen fax (919) 954-4898; disp adv e-mail dcampbell@bizjournals.com; class adv e-mail dcampbell@bizjournals.com; ed e-mail triangle@bizjournals.com; web site www.bizjournals.com/triangle
Advertising rate: Full - $6065; 1/2 - $3635; 1/4 - $2440; 1/8 - 1615
Established: 1985
Digital Platform - Mobile: Apple, Android, Windows, Blackberry
Digital Platform - Tablet: Apple iOS
Pub. .... Bryan Hamilton
Delivery Method: Mail
Areas Served: Wake

RED SPRINGS

THE RED SPRINGS CITIZEN (WED)
131 S Main St, Red Springs, NC, 28377-1511, Robeson, USA; gen tel (910) 843-4631; gen fax (910) 843-8171; disp adv e-mail aoxendine@civitasmedia.com; web site http://www.redspringscitizen.com/
Circulation: 2,300pd,; Sworn/Estimate/Non-Audited
Advertising rate: Open inch rate $6.00
Established: 1889
Group: Civitas Media, LLC-OOB
Pub. .... Joe Craig
Adv .... Ashley Oxendine
Ed. .... Scott Witten
Mechanical Specifications: Type page 13 x 21; E - 6 cols, 2 1/16, 1/4 between; A - 6 cols, 2 1/16, 1/4 between; C - 6 cols, 2 1/16, 1/4 between.
Delivery Method: Mail, Newsstand, Carrier, Racks
Areas Served: Robeson

REIDSVILLE

ROCKINGHAM NOW (WED, SUN)
1921 Vance St, Reidsville, NC, 27320-3254, Rockingham, USA ; gen tel (800) 323-2951; ed e-mail ghunt@caswellmessenger.com; web site http://www.rockinghamnow.com
Group: BH Media Group
Pub. .... Jeff Gauger
Ed .... Gerri Hunt

THE EDEN NEWS (WED, SUN)
1921 Vance St, Reidsville, NC, 27320-3254, Rockingham, USA; gen tel (336) 349-4331; gen fax (336) 342-2513; disp adv e-mail pdurham@reidsvillereview.com; ed e-mail news@reidsvillereview.com; web site http://www.rockinghamnow.com
Advertising rate: Open inch rate $8.50
Group: BH Media Group
Group Ed. .... Amanda K Lehmert
Adv. Dir. .... Pam Durham
Pub. .... Steven W. Kaylor
Delivery Method: Mail, Newsstand, Carrier, Racks
Areas Served: Rockingham

THE MESSENGER (WED)
1921 Vance St, Reidsville, NC, 27320-3254, Rockingham, USA; gen tel (336) 349-4331; gen fax (336) 342-2513; disp adv e-mail pdurham@reidsvillereview.com; ed e-mail news@reidsvillereview.com; web site http://www.rockinghamnow.com
Circulation: 4,475pd, 75fr; Sworn/Estimate/Non-Audited
Advertising rate: Open inch rate $7.50
Established: 1915
Group: BH Media Group
Adv. Dir. .... Pam Durham
Office Mgr. .... Amanda K Lehmert
Ed .... Steven W. Kaylor
Mechanical Specifications: Type page 11 1/2 x 21 1/2; E - 6 cols, 1/8 between; A - 6 cols, 1/8 between; C - 9 cols, 1/8 between.Equipment & Software: Hardware — APP/Mac, Power PCs; Software — Multi-Ad/Creator 3.7, Microsoft/Word 5.1, QPS/QuarkXPress 3.31.
Delivery Method: Mail, Newsstand, Carrier, Racks
Areas Served: Rockingham

THE REIDSVILLE REVIEW (WED, SUN)
1921 Vance St, Reidsville, NC, 27320-3254, Rockingham, USA; gen tel (336) 349-4331; adv tel (434) 385-5505; ed tel (336) 349-4331; gen fax (336) 342-2513; adv fax (336) 342-2513; ed fax (336) 342-2513; disp adv e-mail pdurham@reidsvillereview.com; class adv e-mail pdurham@reidsvillereview.com; ed e-mail news@reidsvillereview.com; web site http://www.news-record.com/rockingham_now/
Circulation: 5,195pd,; Sworn/Estimate/Non-Audited
Advertising rate: Open inch rate $9.88
Established: 1928
Group: BH Media Group
Pub. .... Steven K. Kaylor
Ed. .... Amanda K Lehmert
Ad. Dir. .... Pam Durham
Mechanical Specifications: Type page 13 x 21 1/2; E - 6 cols, 2 1/16, 1/8 between; A - 6 cols, 2 1/16, 1/8 between; C - 9 cols, 1 5/16, 1/8 between.
Delivery Method: Mail, Newsstand, Carrier, Racks
Areas Served: Rockingham

ROBBINSVILLE

THE GRAHAM STAR (THUR)
720 Tallulah Rd, Robbinsville, NC, 28771-9461, Graham, USA; gen tel (828) 479-3383; gen fax (828) 479-1044; disp adv e-mail ads@grahamstar.com; ed e-mail editor@grahamstar.com; web site www.grahamstar.com
Circulation: 3,500pd, 24fr; Sworn/Estimate/Non-Audited
Advertising rate: Open inch rate $10.75
Established: 1955
Group: Community Newspapers, Inc.
Pub .... James Budd
Corp. Mktg. Dir. .... Joel Jenkins
Ed .... Sam Marlow
Areas Served: 28771

ROXBORO

THE COURIER-TIMES (WED, SAT)
109 Clayton Ave, Roxboro, NC, 27573-4611, Person, USA; gen tel (336) 599-0162; gen fax (336) 597-2773; disp adv e-mail learussell@roxboro-courier.com; class adv e-mail ctreception@roxboro-courier.com; ed e-mail tchandler@roxboro-courier.com; web site http://www.personcountylife.com/
Circulation: 8,509pd, 95fr; Sworn/Estimate/Non-Audited
Advertising rate: Open inch rate $12.00
Established: 1881
Pub .... Brinn Clayton
Circ. Mgr. .... Eric Whitt
Ed. .... Tim Chandler
Mechanical Specifications: Type page 13 x 21 1/2; E - 6 cols, 2 1/16, 1/6 between; A - 6 cols, 2 1/16, 1/6 between; C - 8 cols, 1 1/2, 1/8 between.Equipment & Software: Hardware — APP/Mac; Presses — 7-HI/V15A; Software — Adobe/PageMaker 7.0.
Areas Served: 27573, 27541, 27583, 27343, 27572, 27291

SAINT PAULS

THE ST. PAULS REVIEW (THUR)

218 W Broad St, Saint Pauls, NC, 28384-1534, Robeson, USA; gen tel (910) 865-4179; gen fax (910) 865-4995; disp adv e-mail dmckenzie@civitasmedia.com; class adv e-mail aoxendine@civitasmedia.com; web site www.stpaulsreview.com
Circulation: 2,500pd,; Sworn/Estimate/Non-Audited
Advertising rate: Open inch rate $5.25
Established: 1922
Group: Civitas Media, LLC-OOB
Adv. Mgr.. Mark Moses
Ed. .... Paul Terry

SHALLOTTE

THE BRUNSWICK BEACON (THUR)

208 Smith Ave, Shallotte, NC, 28470-4458, Brunswick, USA; gen tel (910) 754-6890; gen fax (910) 754-5407; disp adv e-mail addirector@brunswickbeacon.com; class adv e-mail classified@brunswickbeacon.com; ed e-mail editor@brunswickbeacon.com; web site www.brunswickbeacon.com
Circulation: 17,700pd, 2fr; Sworn/Estimate/Non-Audited
Advertising rate: Open inch rate $16.82
Established: 1962
Group: Landmark Communications, Inc.
Landmark Community Newspapers, LLC
Pub.. Scott Harrell
Adv. Mgr.. Angie Sutton
Ed. .... Stacey Manning
Mechanical Specifications: Type page 13 x 21; E - 6 cols, 2, 1/6 between; A - 6 cols, 2, 1/6 between; C - 6 cols, 2, 1/6 between.Equipment & Software: Hardware — APP/Mac; Presses — G/Community; Software — QPS/QuarkXPress 3.32.
Areas Served: 28459, 28470, 28467, 28468, 28469, 28462, 28422, 28420, 28479, 28452

SILER CITY

THE CHATHAM NEWS (THUR)

303 W Raleigh St, Siler City, NC, 27344-3725, Chatham, USA; gen tel (919) 663-3232; gen fax (919) 663-4042; disp adv e-mail advertising@thechathamnews.com; ed e-mail rigsbee@thechathamnews.com; web site www.thechathamnews.com
Circulation: 9,200pd, 395fr; Sworn/Estimate/Non-Audited
Advertising rate: Open inch rate $7.25
Group: The Chatham News Publishing Co, Inc.
Mng. Ed.................................Randall Rigsbee
Prodn. Mgr. .... Steve Roberts
Mechanical Specifications: Type page 13 x 21 1/2; E - 6 cols, 2 1/16, 1/8 between; A - 6 cols, 2 1/16, 1/8 between; C - 6 cols, 2 1/16, 1/8 between.
Delivery Method: Mail, Newsstand, Racks
Areas Served: 27344 275252 27207 27208 28213 27312 27355 2749 27330 27316 27298 27215 27203 27405 27511

SOUTHERN PINES

THE PILOT (WED, SUN)

145 W Pennsylvania Ave, Southern Pines, NC, 28387-5428, Moore, USA; gen tel (910) 692-7271; adv tel (919) 693-2505; ed tel (919) 693-2462; gen fax (910) 692-9382; disp adv e-mail pat@thepilot.com; class adv e-mail classified@thepilot.com; ed e-mail dsinclair@thepilot.com; web site www.thepilot.com - 1,400,000(views) 335,000(visitors)
Circulation: 15,005pd, 312fr; Sworn/Estimate/Non-Audited
Advertising rate: Open inch rate $15.75
Established: 1920
Pub.. David Woronoff
Adv. Dir .... Pat Taylor
Ed. ....John Nagy
Gen. Mgr. .... Kit McKinley
Circ. Dir. Darlene StarkEquipment & Software: ; Presses — KP.
Delivery Method: Mail, Newsstand, Carrier, Racks
Areas Served: Moore

SOUTHPORT

THE STATE PORT PILOT (WED)

114 E Moore St, Southport, NC, 28461-3926, Brunswick, USA; gen tel (910) 457-4568; gen fax (910) 457-9427; disp adv e-mail carol@stateportpilot.com; class adv e-mail kim@stateportpilot.com; ed e-mail pilot@stateportpilot.com; web site www.stateportpilot.com
Circulation: 7,400pd, 0fr; Sworn/Estimate/Non-Audited
Advertising rate: Open inch rate $9.00
Established: 1928
Group: The State Port Pilot
Ed./Pub. .... Ed Harper
Associate Editor.............................Terry Pope
Adv. Dir.....................................Carol Magnani
Jan Keyes
Kim Adams
Morgan Harper
Mechanical Specifications: Type page 11 1/2 x 21; E - 6 cols, 1 3/4, between; A - 6 cols, 1 3/4, between; C - 6 cols, 1 3/4, between. Equipment & Software: Hardware — APP/Mac; Presses — G; Software — Abobe InDesign 5.5
Delivery Method: Mail, Newsstand, Racks
Areas Served: 28461, 28465, 28422

SPARTA

THE ALLEGHANY NEWS (WED)

20 S Main St, Sparta, NC, 28675-9643, Alleghany, USA; gen tel (336) 372-8999; gen fax (336) 372-5707; disp adv e-mail ads@alleghanynews.com; class adv e-mail classifieds@alleghanynews.com; ed e-mail news@alleghanynews.com; web site www.alleghanynews.com - 18,000(views)
Circulation: 3,800pd, 50fr; USPS
Advertising rate: Open inch rate $6.00
Established: 1889
Digital Platform - Tablet: Other
Gen. Mgr./Adv. Dir.......................... Ron Brown
Circ. Mgr....................................Nancy Greene
Ed. .... Coby LaRue
Ed Assit...................................... Sarah Maynor
Sports Ed.................................. Mark Ketchum
Ed .... Bob Bamberg
Mechanical Specifications: Type page 10.125"x 21.5"; E - 6 cols, A - 6 cols, 0.125 inches gutterEquipment & Software: ; Software — QPS/QuarkXPress 4.1, Multi-Ad/Creator 6. Indesign
Delivery Method: Mail, Newsstand, Racks
Areas Served: Sparta/Alleghany

SPRING HOPE

SPRING HOPE ENTERPRISE & THE BAILEY NEWS (THUR)

113 N Ash St, Spring Hope, NC, 27882-7711, Nash, USA; gen tel (252) 478-3651; adv tel (252) 478-3651; gen fax (252) 478-3075; disp adv e-mail Springhopeads@embarqmail.com; ed e-mail shenterprise@embarqmail.com; web site www.springhopeenterprise.com
Circulation: 2,400pd, 600fr; Sworn/Estimate/Non-Audited
Advertising rate: Open inch rate $7.50
Established: 1947
Circ. Mgr.................................Joseph Burnette
Ed. .... Ken Ripley
Mechanical Specifications: Type page 11 x 21 1/2; E - 6 cols, 2, 1/6 between; A - 6 cols, 2, 1/6 between.Equipment & Software: Hardware — APP/Mac; Software — Microsoft/Word 5.0, Adobe/PageMaker 6.0.
Delivery Method: Mail, Racks
Areas Served: Southern Nash County, including 27882, 27807, and 27557

SPRUCE PINE

MITCHELL NEWS-JOURNAL (WED)

261 Locust St, Spruce Pine, NC, 28777-2713, Mitchell, USA; gen tel (828) 765-2071; gen fax (828) 765-1616; disp adv e-mail adrep@mitchellnews.com; ed e-mail editor@mitchellnews.com; web site www.mitchellnews.com
Circulation: 4,922pd, 135fr; Sworn/Estimate/Non-Audited
Advertising rate: Open inch rate $12.60
Established: 1927
Group: Community Newspapers, Inc.
Adv. Mgr.................................... Cindy Lindsey
Mktg. Dir....................................... Joel Jenkins
Mechanical Specifications: Type page 13 x 21 1/2; E - 6 cols, 2, 1/6 between; A - 6 cols, 2, 1/6 between; C - 6 cols, 2, 1/6 between.
Delivery Method: Mail, Carrier
Areas Served: Mitchell

SWANSBORO

TIDELAND NEWS (WED)

774 W Corbett Ave, Swansboro, NC, 28584-8452, Onslow, USA; gen tel (910) 326-5066; gen fax (910) 326-1165; disp adv e-mail jennifer@tidelandnews.com; class adv e-mail michelle@tidelandnews.com; ed e-mail jimmy@tidelandnews.com; web site www.tidelandnews.com
Circulation: 3,000pd, 500fr; Sworn/Estimate/Non-Audited
Advertising rate: Open inch rate $6.20
Established: 1979
Group: Carteret Publishing Co.
Pub... Walter Phillips
Adv. Mgr................................. Jennifer Pearce
Mechanical Specifications: Type page 11 1/2 x 21 1/2; E - 6 cols, 1 3/4, 1/6 between; A - 6 cols, 1 3/4, 1/6 between; C - 8 cols, 1 1/2, 1/6 between.Equipment & Software: Hardware — APP/Mac; Software — Multi-Ad/Creator 3.7.
Delivery Method: Mail, Newsstand, Carrier, Racks
Areas Served: 28584, 28594, 28582, 28570, 28539

SYLVA

THE SYLVA HERALD & RURALITE (THUR)

539 W Main St, Sylva, NC, 28779-5551, Jackson, USA; gen tel (828) 586-2611; adv tel (866) 572-3150; gen fax (828) 586-2637; disp adv e-mail margo@thesylvaherald.com; class adv e-mail classifieds@thesylvaherald.com; ed e-mail news@thesylvaherald.com; web site www.thesylvaherald.com
Circulation: 7,300pd, 42fr; Sworn/Estimate/Non-Audited
Advertising rate: Open inch rate $12.05
Established: 1926
Pub... Steven B. Gray
Adv. Mgr.. Margo Gray
Ed. .... Lynn Hotaling
Corp. Mktg. Dir. .... Joel Jenkins
Mechanical Specifications: Type page 13 1/16 x 21 1/2; E - 6 cols, 2 1/16, 1/8 between; A - 6 cols, 2 1/16, 1/8 between; C - 6 cols, 2 1/16, 1/8 between.Equipment & Software: Hardware — APP/Macs; Presses — 8-G/Community; Software — Adobe/PageMaker, QPS/QuarkXPress, Adobe/Photoshop, Adobe/Illustrator.
Delivery Method: Mail, Newsstand
Areas Served: 28723, 28717, 28779, 28789

TABOR CITY

TABOR-LORIS TRIBUNE (WED)

PO Box 67, 102 Avon Street, Tabor City, NC, 28463-0067, Columbus, USA; gen tel (910) 653-3153; ed tel (910) 653-7442; gen fax (910) 653-5818; disp adv e-mail tribpenny@tabor-loris.com; class adv e-mail tribpenny@tabor-loris.com; ed e-mail tribdeuce@tabor-loris.com; web site www.tabor-loris.com
Circulation: 3,000pd, 200fr; Sworn/Estimate/Non-Audited
Advertising rate: $5.50
Established: 1946
Group: Atlantic Corp.
Gen. Mgr./Ed..................................... Deuce Niven
Advertising Manager.................Penny Holmes
Adv./Reporter........................ Joyce Sammons
Mechanical Specifications: Type page 13 x 21; E - 6 cols, 2, 1/6 between; A - 6 cols, 2, 1/6 between; C - 6 cols, 2, 1/6 between.Equipment & Software: Hardware — iMac
MacBook Air; Presses — Outsourced/Goss Community; Software — Adobe Creative Suite
Microsoft Office
Misc.
Delivery Method: Mail, Newsstand, Racks
Areas Served: Columbus County, NC
Horry County, SC

TAYLORSVILLE

THE TAYLORSVILLE TIMES (WED)

24 E Main Ave, Taylorsville, NC, 28681-2541, Alexander, USA; gen tel (828) 632-2532; gen fax (828) 632-8233; disp adv e-mail ads@taylorsvilletimes.com; class adv e-mail classifieds@taylorsvilletimes.com; ed e-mail taylorsvilletimes@taylorsvilletimes.com; web site www.taylorsvilletimes.com
Circulation: 5,002pd, 49fr; USPS
Advertising rate: Open inch rate $6.80
Established: 1886Editions: (1) The Bethlehem Star
Pub... Lee Sharpe
Ed. .... Micah Henry
Adv. Mgr....................................... Steve Garland
Mechanical Specifications: Type page 10 x 21 1/2; E - 6 cols, 1/6 between; A - 6 cols, 1/6 between; C - 6 cols, 1/6 between.Equipment & Software: Hardware — PC, ECR; Presses — 6-KP/NewsKing; Software — QPS/QuarkXPress 4.0.
Delivery Method: Mail, Newsstand, Racks
Areas Served: 28681, 28636

TROY

MONTGOMERY HERALD (WED)

139 Bruton St, Troy, NC, 27371-2815, Montgomery, USA; gen tel (910) 576-6051; gen fax (910) 576-1050; disp adv e-mail advertise@montgomeryhrald.com; class adv e-mail advertise@montgomeryhrald.com; ed e-mail sendnews@montgomeryherald.com; web site www.montgomeryherald.com
Circulation: 4,700pd, 556fr; Sworn/Estimate/Non-Audited
Advertising rate: Open inch rate $10.70
Established: 1880s
Group: Womack Publishing Co.
Publisher..Tammy Dunn
Office Manager...............................Josh Bowles
Sports Editor.. Jon GallowayEquipment & Software: Hardware — APP/Mac; Presses — G/Community; Software — Adobe/PageMaker 5.0.
Delivery Method: Mail, Racks
Areas Served: Montgomery County NC

WADESBORO

THE ANSON RECORD (WED)

123 E Martin St, Ste 400, Wadesboro, NC, 28170-2276, Anson, USA; gen tel (704) 694-2161; adv tel (910) 817-2667; gen fax (704) 694-7060; disp adv e-mail dspencer@civitasmedia.com; class adv e-mail miprice@civitasmedia.com; ed e-mail acavenaugh@civitasmedia.com; web site www.ansonrecord.com
Circulation: 5,000pd, 1,000fr; Sworn/Estimate/

Non-Audited
Advertising rate: Open inch rate $15.15
Established: 1881
Group: Champion Media
Digital Platform - Mobile: Apple, Android
Digital Platform - Tablet: Apple iOS, Kindle
Ed. .... Corey Friedman
Mechanical Specifications: Type page 13 x 21 1/2; E - 6 cols, between; A - 6 cols, between; C - 6 cols, between.Equipment & Software: Hardware — APP/Mac 7400CD; Presses — KP; Software — Adobe/PageMaker 6.0.
Delivery Method: Mail, Racks
Areas Served: 28007, 28091, 28102, 28103, 28119, 28133, 28135, 28170

WAKE FOREST

THE WAKE WEEKLY (THUR)
229 E Owen Ave, Wake Forest, NC, 27587-2717, Wake, USA; gen tel (919) 556-3182; gen fax (919) 556-2233; disp adv e-mail advertising@wakeweekly.com; class adv e-mail classifieds@wakeweekly.com; ed e-mail editor@wakeweekly.com; web site www.wakeweekly.com
Circulation: 8,900pd,; Sworn/Estimate/Non-Audited
Advertising rate: Open inch rate $11.00
Established: 1947Editions: (3) The Wake Forest Weekly, The Rolesville Wake Crossroads Weekly, The Franklin Weekly
Ed./Assit. Pub. .... Clellie Allen
Pub. .... Todd F. Allen
Ad. Dir. .... Kathleen Jackson
Prod. Mgr. .... Al Merritt
Delivery Method: Mail, Newsstand, Racks
Areas Served: 27587, 27588, 27549, 27596, 27614, 27571, 27525, 27616

WALNUT COVE

THE WEEKLY INDEPENDENT (FRI)
1072 N Main St, Walnut Cove, NC, 27052-9312, Stokes, USA; gen tel (336) 983-3109; gen fax (336) 591-4379; disp adv e-mail sfenner@civitasmedia.com
Circulation: 5,000pd, 263fr; Sworn/Estimate/Non-Audited
Advertising rate: Open inch rate $7.30
Established: 1985
Group: Civitas Media, LLC-OOB
Ed .... Nicholas Elmes
Mechanical Specifications: Type page 10 1/4 x 21 1/2; E - 6 cols, between; A - 6 cols, between; C - 9 cols, between.
Delivery Method: Mail, Racks
Areas Served: Forsyth

WARRENTON

WARREN RECORD (WED)
112 N Main St, Warrenton, NC, 27589-1922, Warren, USA; gen tel (252) 257-3341; gen fax (252) 257-1413; disp adv e-mail ads@warrenrecord.com; ed e-mail news@warrenrecord.com; web site www.warrenrecord.com
Circulation: 5,600pd, 113fr; Sworn/Estimate/Non-Audited
Advertising rate: Open inch rate $9.00
Established: 1896
Group: Womack Publishing Co.
Ed./Gen. Mgr. .... Jennifer Harris
Asst. Ed. .... Luci Weldon
Office Mgr. .... Brandy Carter
Mechanical Specifications: Type page 13 x 21 1/2; E - 6 cols, 2, 1/6 between; A - 6 cols, 2, 1/6 between; C - 6 cols, 2, 1/6 between.
Delivery Method: Newsstand

WAYNESVILLE

SMOKY MOUNTAIN NEWS (WED)
144 Montgomery St, Waynesville, NC, 28786-3720, Haywood, USA; gen tel (828) 452-4251; gen fax (828) 452-3585; disp adv e-mail ads@smokymountainnews.com; class adv e-mail classads@smokymountainnews.com; ed e-mail news@smokymountainnews.com; web site http://www.smokymountain-news.com
Circulation: 0pd, 15,485fr; CVC
Advertising rate: N/A
Adv. Dir. .... Greg Boothroyd
News Ed. .... Becky Johnson
Pub. .... Scott McLeod
Circ. Mgr. .... Scott Collier
Delivery Method: Racks
Areas Served: Haywood, Jackson, Macon, Swain

THE MOUNTAINEER (MON, WED, FRI)
220 N Main St, Waynesville, NC, 28786-3812, Haywood, USA; gen tel (828) 452-0661; gen fax (828) 452-0665; disp adv e-mail info@themountaineer.com; ed e-mail news@themountaineer.com; web site http://themountaineer.com
Circulation:; Sworn/Estimate/Non-Audited
Advertising rate: Open inch rate $17.85
Adv. Dir. .... Susan DuFour
Mng. Ed .... Vicki Hyatt
Pub. .... Jonathan W. Key
Delivery Method: Mail, Newsstand, Carrier, Racks

WEAVERVILLE

THE WEAVERVILLE TRIBUNE (THUR)
113 N Main St, Weaverville, NC, 28787-8444, Buncombe, USA; gen tel (828) 252-5804; adv tel (828) 252-5804; ed tel (828) 252-5804; gen fax (828) 252-5817; adv fax (828) 252-5817; ed fax (828) 252-5817; disp adv e-mail starnesp@att.net; class adv e-mail advertising@weavervilletribune.com; ed e-mail editor@weavervilletribune.com; web site www.weavervilletribune.com
Advertising rate: Open inch rate $13.50
Established: 2003
Digital Platform - Mobile: Apple, Android
Digital Platform - Tablet: Apple iOS, Android
Pub./Ed. .... Clint Parker
Adv. Dir. .... Pat Starnes
Delivery Method: Mail, Newsstand, Racks
Areas Served: Bumcombe County

WEST JEFFERSON

JEFFERSON POST (TUES, FRI)
203 S. 2nd Ave., West Jefferson, NC, 28694, Ashe, USA; gen tel (336) 846-7164; gen fax (336) 846-7165; disp adv e-mail tlaws@civitasmedia.com; ed e-mail editorial@jeffersonpost.com; web site www.jeffersonpost.com
Circulation: 6,500pd,; Sworn/Estimate/Non-Audited
Advertising rate: Open inch rate $7.20
Established: 1931
Group: Champion Media
Ed. .... Cliff Clark
Pub. .... Cabot Hamilton
Gen. Mgr. .... Teresa Laws
Pub. .... Ron ClausenEquipment & Software: Hardware — APP/Mac; Software — QPS/QuarkXPress.
Areas Served: 28694

THE ASHE MOUNTAIN TIMES (THUR)
7 E Main St, West Jefferson, NC, 28694, Ashe, USA; gen tel (336) 246-6397; gen fax (336) 246-3240; disp adv e-mail ron.brown@mountaintimes.com; class adv e-mail classifieds@mountaintimes.com; ed e-mail ron.brown@mountaintimes.com; web site http://www.ashemountaintimes.com
Circulation: 9,553fr; VAC
Advertising rate: $10.87 per column inch
Group: Adams Publishing Group, LLC
Adv./Gen. Mgr. .... Ron Brown

WHITEVILLE

THE NEWS REPORTER (MON, THUR)
127 W Columbus St, Whiteville, NC, 28472-4023, Columbus, USA; gen tel (910) 642-4104; gen fax (910) 642-1856; disp adv e-mail deanlewis@nrcolumbus.com; class adv e-mail hannerichards@nrcolumbus.com; ed e-mail leshigh@nrcolumbus.com; web site www.nrcolumbus.com
Circulation: 10,100pd, 235fr; Sworn/Estimate/Non-Audited
Advertising rate: Open inch rate $10.50
Established: 1890
Digital Platform - Mobile: Apple
Pub/owner .... James C. High
Ed .... Les High
Ed. .... Clara Cartrette
Barbara Milligan
Clarissa Hamilton
Laura Worthington
Adv. Dir. .... Mickey Greer
Mechanical Specifications: Type page 11 1/2 x 21; E - 6 cols, 1 13/16, 1/6 between; A - 6 cols, 1 13/16, 1/6 between; C - 6 cols, 1 13/16, 1/6 between.Equipment & Software: Hardware — APP/Macs; Presses — Goss Community six unit with Orient color deck; Software — Lastest Adobe suite, MS Word, other
Delivery Method: Mail, Newsstand, Carrier, Racks
Areas Served: 28472, 28431, 28439, 28450, 28463, 28424, 28442, 28455, 28430, 28432, 28438, 28423 28456, 28436, 28433, 28320

WILLIAMSTON

ENTERPRISE & WEEKLY HERALD (TUES, FRI)
106 W Main St, Williamston, NC, 27892-2471, Martin, USA; gen tel (252) 792-1181; gen fax (252) 792-1921; disp adv e-mail lavan@ncweeklies.com; ed e-mail kstephens@ncweeklies.com; web site https://www.facebook.com/pages/The-Enterprise/171082442937848
Circulation: 5,100pd, 21fr; Sworn/Estimate/Non-Audited
Advertising rate: Open inch rate $7.50
Established: 1899
Group: Cooke Communications North Carolina, LLC
Adv. .... Lou Ann VanLandingham
Gen. Mgr. .... Jay Jenkins
Mechanical Specifications: Type page 11 5/8 x 21; E - 6 cols, 1 5/6, 1/6 between; A - 6 cols, 1 5/6, 1/6 between; C - 9 cols, 1 18/100, 1/6 between.Equipment & Software: Hardware — APP/Mac; Presses — G/Community; Software — Microsoft/Word 6.0.1, Aldus/PageMaker.
Delivery Method: Mail, Newsstand, Carrier, Racks
Areas Served: Martin

WILMINGTON

LUMINA NEWS (THUR)
7232 Wrightsville Ave, Wilmington, NC, 28403-7223, New Hanover, USA; gen tel (910) 256-6569; adv tel (910) 256-6569; gen fax (910) 256-6512; disp adv e-mail szmiller980@gmail.com; ed e-mail pub@luminanews.com; web site http://www.luminanews.com
Advertising rate: Open inch rate $9.00
Ed. .... Marimar McNaughton
Account Exec. .... Jill Sabourin
Pub./Circ. Mgr. .... Pat Bradford
Delivery Method: Mail, Racks
Areas Served: New Hanover

WINDSOR

BERTIE LEDGER-ADVANCE (WED)
105 E Granville St, Windsor, NC, 27983-6753, Bertie, USA; gen tel (252) 794-3185; gen fax (252) 794-2835; disp adv e-mail jmobley@ncweeklies.com; ed e-mail twhite@ncweeklies.com; web site https://www.facebook.com/Bertie-Ledger-Advance-540014596016586/about/?ref=page_internal
Circulation: 4,200pd,; Sworn/Estimate/Non-Audited
Advertising rate: Open inch rate $6.10
Established: 1930
Group: Cooke Communications North Carolina, LLC
Pub. .... Jay Jenkins
Ed .... Thadd White
Mechanical Specifications: Type page 12 3/4 x 21; E - 6 cols, 2 1/16, 1/8 between; A - 6 cols, 2 1/16, 1/8 between; C - 9 cols, 1 3/8, 1/8 between.Equipment & Software: Hardware — APP/Mac; Software — Microsoft/Word 6.0.1, Aldus/PageMaker 5.0.
Delivery Method: Mail, Newsstand, Carrier, Racks
Areas Served: Bertie

WINSTON SALEM

THE CHRONICLE (THUR)
617 N Liberty St, Winston Salem, NC, 27101-2912, Forsyth, USA; gen tel (336) 722-8624; adv tel (336) 722-8624 ext. 101; ed tel (336) 722-8624 ext. 113; gen fax (336) 723-9173; disp adv e-mail ssmith@wschronicle.com; class adv e-mail adv@wschronicle.com; ed e-mail drogers@wschronicle.com; web site http://www.wschronicle.com - 40,000(views) 15,000(visitors)
Circulation: 5,000pd, 2,000fr; CVC
Advertising rate: Open inch rate $16.20
Established: 1974
Digital Platform - Mobile: Windows
Digital Platform - Tablet: Windows 7
Ed .... Donna Rogers
Office Mgr. .... Paulette Moore
Bus. Mgr. .... Elaine Pitt
Mechanical Specifications: 9.889" X 21"
Delivery Method: Mail, Newsstand, Carrier, Racks
Areas Served: Forsyth

YADKINVILLE

THE YADKIN RIPPLE (THUR)
115 S Jackson St, Yadkinville, NC, 27055-7714, Yadkin, USA; gen tel (336) 679-2341; adv tel (336) 258-4030; ed tel (336) 258-4035; gen fax (336) 679-2340; disp adv e-mail hlamm@civitasmedia.com; class adv e-mail kball@civitasmedia.com; ed e-mail wbyerly-wood@civitasmedia.com; web site www.yadkinripple.com
Circulation: 6,000pd, 40fr; Sworn/Estimate/Non-Audited
Advertising rate: Open inch rate $12.99
Established: 1892
Group: Champion Media
Gen. Mgr. .... Holly Lamm
Pub. .... Ron Clausen
Mechanical Specifications: Type page 13 x 21 1/2; E - 6 cols, 2 1/20, between; A - 6 cols, 2 1/20, between; C - 6 cols, 2 1/20, between.
Areas Served: 27055

YANCEYVILLE

CASWELL MESSENGER (WED)
137 MAIN ST, Yanceyville, NC, 27379, Caswell, USA; gen tel (336) 694-4145; gen fax (336) 694-5637; disp adv e-mail ads@caswellmessenger.com; class adv e-mail cmofficemanager@caswellmessenger.com; ed e-mail editor@caswellmessenger.com; web site www.caswellmessenger.com
Circulation: 4,000pd, 142fr; Sworn/Estimate/Non-Audited
Advertising rate: Open inch rate $10.70
Established: 1926
Group: Womack Publishing Co.

Office Mgr. .... Patricia Cheek
Ed. .... Patti O'Keefe
Acc. Exec. .... Jonathan Pettiford
Delivery Method: Mail, Newsstand, Racks
Areas Served: 27379

NORTH DAKOTA

ASHLEY

THE ASHLEY TRIBUNE (WED)
115 W Main St, Ashley, ND, 58413-7003, McIntosh, USA; gen tel (701) 288-3531; gen fax (701) 288-3532; disp adv e-mail redhead@drtel.net; web site http://www.centraldakotanews.com/newspapers/ashley-tribune/
Circulation: 1,600pd,; Sworn/Estimate/Non-Audited
Advertising rate: Open inch rate $7.00
Ed. .... Tony Bender
Mechanical Specifications: Type page 13 x 21 1/2; E - 6 cols, 2, 1/8 between; A - 6 cols, 2, 1/8 between; C - 6 cols, 2, 1/8 between. Equipment & Software: Hardware — PCs; Software — Adobe/PageMaker 5.0.

BEACH

BILLINGS COUNTY PIONEER (THUR)
22 Central Ave, Beach, ND, 58621, Golden Valley, USA; gen tel (701) 872-3755; gen fax (701) 872-3756; disp adv e-mail goldenandbillings@gmail.com
Circulation: 325pd,; Sworn/Estimate/Non-Audited
Advertising rate: Open inch rate $4.90
Group: Nordmark Publishing
Pub. .... Jason Nordmark
Ed. .... Richard Volesky
Mechanical Specifications: Type page 13 x 21; E - 6 cols, 2, 1/6 between; A - 6 cols, 2, 1/6 between; C - 6 cols, 2, 1/6 between.Equipment & Software: Hardware — APP/Mac; Software — QPS/QuarkXPress.
Delivery Method: Mail, Newsstand

THE GOLDEN VALLEY NEWS (THUR)
22 Central Ave Ste 1, Beach, ND, 58621, Golden Valley, USA; gen tel (701) 872-3755; gen fax (701) 872-3756; disp adv e-mail gvnews@midstate.net; ed e-mail goldenandbillings@gmail.com
Circulation: 879pd,; Sworn/Estimate/Non-Audited
Advertising rate: Open inch rate $6.50
Group: Nordmark Publishing
Pub. .... Jason Nordmark
Ed. / Ad Mgr. .... Richard Volesky
Mechanical Specifications: Type page 13 x 21; E - 6 cols, 2, 1/6 between; A - 6 cols, 2, 1/6 between; C - 6 cols, 2, 1/6 between.Equipment & Software: Hardware — APP/Macs; Software — QPS/QuarkXPress 2.0.
Delivery Method: Mail, Newsstand
Areas Served: Golden Valley

BELCOURT

TURTLE MOUNTAIN TIMES (MON)
PO Box 1270, Belcourt, ND, 58316-1270, Rolette, USA; gen tel (701)477-6670; gen fax (701)477-6875; disp adv e-mail thetimes@utma.com
Circulation: 3,000pd,; Sworn/Estimate/Non-Audited
Advertising rate: Open inch rate $5.50
Established: 1993
Circ. Mgr. .... Neva M. E. Rainey
Gen. Mgr. .... Eugene L. Trottier
Mechanical Specifications: Type page 13 15/16 x 22 3/4; E - 6 cols, 2, 1/8 between; A - 6 cols, 1 7/8, 1/8 between; C - 6 cols, 1 7/8, 1/8 between.Equipment & Software: Hardware — APP/Macs; Software — QPS/QuarkXPress.
Delivery Method: Mail, Newsstand, Racks
Areas Served: Rolette

BEULAH

BEULAH BEACON (THUR)
324 2nd Ave NE, Beulah, ND, 58523-6613, Mercer, USA; gen tel (701) 873-4381; gen fax (701) 873-2383; disp adv e-mail coalnews@westriv.com; web site www.bhgnews.com
Circulation: 2,000pd, 81fr; Sworn/Estimate/Non-Audited
Advertising rate: Open inch rate $6.20
Group: BHG, Inc.
Pub., Owner .... Mike Gackle
Adv. Mgr., Gen. Mgr. .... Ken Beauchamp
Ed. .... Kate Johnson
Mechanical Specifications: Type page 11 x 17; E - 5 cols, 2, 1/6 between; A - 5 cols, 2, 1/6 between; C - 5 cols, 2, 1/6 between.

CENTER REPUBLICAN (THUR)
324 2nd Ave NE, Beulah, ND, 58523-6613, Mercer, USA; gen tel (701) 748-2255; gen fax (701) 748-5768; disp adv e-mail star@westriv.com; ed e-mail coalnews@westriv.com; web site www.bhgnews.com
Circulation: 555pd, 18fr; Sworn/Estimate/Non-Audited
Advertising rate: Open inch rate $6.20
Group: BHG, Inc.
Ed. .... Annette Tait

BOTTINEAU

BOTTINEAU COURANT (TUES)
419 Main St, Bottineau, ND, 58318-1229, Bottineau, USA; gen tel (701) 228-2605; gen fax (701) 228-5864; disp adv e-mail courant3@utma.com; class adv e-mail courant4@utma.com; ed e-mail courant@utma.com; web site www.bottineaunewspaper.com
Circulation: 3,000pd,; Sworn/Estimate/Non-Audited
Advertising rate: Open inch rate $6.05
Delivery Method: Mail

BOWBELLS

BURKE COUNTY TRIBUNE (WED)
104 Railway St. SE, Bowbells, ND, 58721, USA; gen tel (701) 377-2626; gen fax (701) 377-2717; disp adv e-mail tribune@nccray.net; web site online.burkecountytribune.com
Circulation: 1,000pd, 30fr; Sworn/Estimate/Non-Audited
Advertising rate: Open inch rate $9.50
Pub. .... Kristi Bohl
office manager .... Lyann Olson
secretary .... Michelle Redmer
Mechanical Specifications: Type page 13 x ; E - 6 cols, 2, 1/6 between; A - 6 cols, 2, 1/6 between; C - 6 cols, 2, 1/6 between.Equipment & Software: Hardware — Gateway; Software — Adobe/PageMaker, Adobe/Photoshop.
Areas Served: Burke County

BOWMAN

BOWMAN COUNTY PIONEER (FRI)
203 7th Ave NW, 7th Ave NW, Bowman, ND, 58623-4443, Bowman, USA; gen tel (701) 523-5623; adv tel (701) 523-5623; gen fax (701) 523-3441; disp adv e-mail finderads@countrymedia.net; class adv e-mail pioneer-info@countrymedia.net; ed e-mail cbenz@countrymedia.net; web site http://www.bowmanextra.com
Circulation: 1,300pd, 300fr; ODC
Advertising rate: Open inch rate $6.60
Established: 1907
Group: Country Media Inc.
Pub. .... Frank Perea II
Ed.Cole BenzEquipment & Software: Hardware — APP/Mac; Software — QPS/QuarkXPress 3.3.
Delivery Method: Mail
Areas Served: 58623

CANDO

TOWNER COUNTY RECORD-HERALD (SAT)
423 Main St, Cando, ND, 58324-6309, Towner, USA; gen tel (701) 968-3223; gen fax (701) 968-3345; disp adv e-mail tcrhads@gondtc.com; class adv e-mail tcrhads@gondtc.com; ed e-mail tcrheditor@gondtc.com
Advertising rate: Open inch rate $6.00
Group: Nordmark Publishing
Ed. .... Jason Nordmark
Delivery Method: Mail, Newsstand, Racks
Areas Served: Towner

CARRINGTON

FOSTER COUNTY INDEPENDENT (MON)
1191 Main St, Carrington, ND, 58421-1523, Foster, USA; gen tel (701) 652-3181; gen fax (701) 652-3286; disp adv e-mail fosterconews@daktel.com; web site http://www.fostercountyindependent.com
Circulation: 3,000pd,; Sworn/Estimate/Non-Audited
Advertising rate: Open inch rate $6.00
Established: 1883
Circ. Mgr. .... Pattie Stock
Ed. .... Allen Stock
Delivery Method: Mail, Newsstand
Areas Served: Foster

CASSELTON

CASS COUNTY REPORTER (WED)
122 6th Ave N, Casselton, ND, 58012-3232, Cass, USA; gen tel (701) 347-4493; gen fax (701) 347-4495; disp adv e-mail ads@ccreporter.com; ed e-mail news@ccreporter.com; web site www.ccreporter.com
Circulation: 2,600pd,; Sworn/Estimate/Non-Audited
Advertising rate: Open inch rate $6.50
Established: 1880
Pub./Ed. .... Sean W. Kelly
Front Off. .... Trish Priewe
Cir. Mgr. .... Randy Buntrock
Adv. Mgr.
Jacqueline Baarstad
Reporter .... Angela Kolden
Graphic Designer .... Angela Ecklund
Delivery Method: Mail, Newsstand, Racks
Areas Served: Cass

CAVALIER

THE CAVALIER CHRONICLE (WED)
207 Main St W, Cavalier, ND, 58220-4503, Pembina, USA; gen tel (701) 265-8844; gen fax (701) 265-8089; disp adv e-mail tim@cavchronicle.com; class adv e-mail tim@cavchronicle.com; ed e-mail lynn@cavchronicle.com; web site www.cavalierchronicle.com
Circulation: 2,500pd,; Sworn/Estimate/Non-Audited
Advertising rate: Open inch rate $6.00
Established: 1885
Cir. Mgr. .... Delores Kemp
Ed. .... Lynn Schroeder
Pub. Emeritus .... Theodore Schroeder

COOPERSTOWN

GRIGGS COUNTY COURIER (FRI)
809 Burrel Ave NW, Cooperstown, ND, 58425-7106, Griggs, USA; gen tel (701) 797-3331; gen fax (701) 797-3476; disp adv e-mail calbert@ncppub.com; class adv e-mail calbert@ncppub.com; ed e-mail chetland@ncppub.com
Circulation: 1,600pd, 106fr; Sworn/Estimate/Non-Audited
Advertising rate: Open inch rate $5.77
Established: 1883
Group: New Century Press
Off. Mgr. .... Nicole Henton
Ed. .... Caitlin Hetland
Ad. Mgr. .... Catherine Albert
Mechanical Specifications: Type page 15 3/16 x 21 1/2; E - 5 cols, 1 3/4, 1/6 between; A - 5 cols, 1 3/4, 1/6 between; C - 5 cols, 1 3/4, 1/6 between.Equipment & Software: Hardware — APP/Mac; Software — QPS/QuarkXPress 3.1.
Delivery Method: Mail, Newsstand, Racks
Areas Served: Griggs

CROSBY

THE JOURNAL (WED)
117 North Main, Crosby, ND, 58730, Divide, USA; gen tel (701) 965-6088; gen fax (701) 965-6089; disp adv e-mail journalads@crosbynd.com ; class adv e-mail journalads@crosbynd.com ; ed e-mail cecilew@crosbynd.com; web site www.journaltrib.com
Circulation: 2,500pd, 30fr; Sworn/Estimate/Non-Audited
Advertising rate: Open inch rate $7.20
Established: 1904
Group: Journal Publishing
Pub. / Ed. .... Cecile Krimm
Prod. .... Jenny Bummer
Cir. .... Holly Anderson
Mechanical Specifications: Type page 13 x 21 1/2; E - 6 cols, 2, 1/6 between; A - 6 cols, 2, 1/6 between; C - 6 cols, 2, 1/6 between. Equipment & Software: Hardware — PC; Software — Adobe/Photoshop, Adobe/PageMaker.

DICKINSON

ADVERTIZER (WED)
1815 1st St W, Dickinson, ND, 58601-2463, Stark, USA; gen tel (701) 225-8111; adv tel (701) 456-1220; ed tel (701) 456-1205; gen fax (701) 225-4205; ed fax (701) 225-6653; disp adv e-mail reilts@thedickinsonpress.com; class adv e-mail ssacks@thedickinsonpress.com; ed e-mail DMonke@thedickinsonpress.com; web site http://www.thedickinsonpress.com
Circulation: 25,848fr; VAC
Advertising rate: Open inch rate $13.50
Established: 1980
Group: Forum Communications Co.
Pub. .... Harvey Brock
Cir. Mgr. .... John Hodges
Adv. Dir. .... Bob Carruth
Mng. Ed. .... Dustin Monke
Bus. Mgr. .... Joy Schoch
Delivery Method: Mail, Newsstand, Racks
Areas Served: Stark

DRAYTON

VALLEY NEWS & VIEWS (THUR)
206 Almeron Ave, Drayton, ND, 58225, Pembina, USA; gen tel (701) 454-6333; gen fax (701)454-6333; disp adv e-mail valleynv@polarcomm.com
Circulation: 600pd,; Sworn/Estimate/Non-Audited
Advertising rate: Open inch rate $5.00
Established: 1981
Editor/Owner .... Lesa Van Camp
Delivery Method: Mail, Newsstand

EDGELEY

EDGELEY MAIL (WED)
516 MAIN ST, Edgeley, ND, 58433, LaMoure,

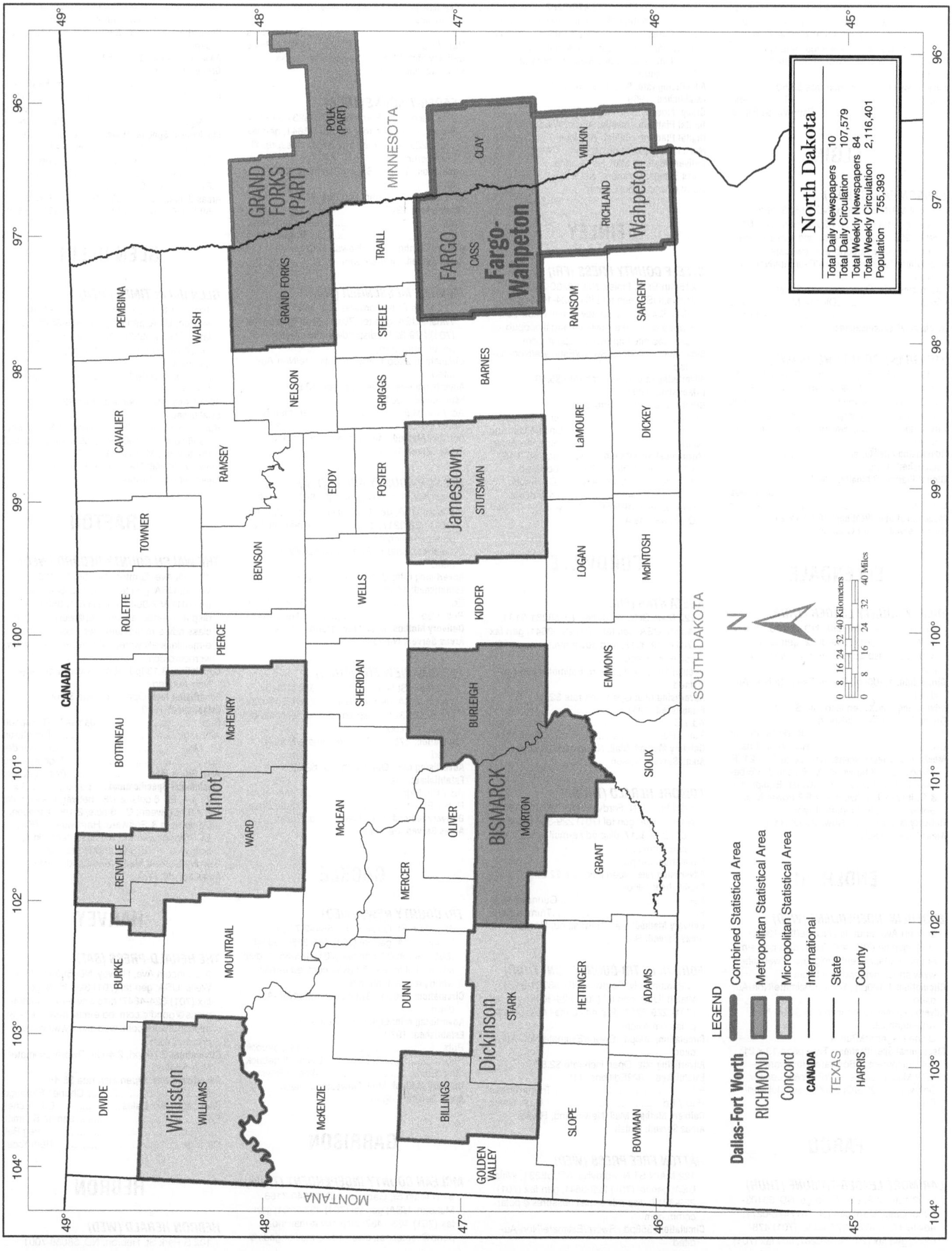
North Dakota
Total Daily Newspapers 10
Total Daily Circulation 107,579
Total Weekly Newspapers 84
Total Weekly Circulation 2,116,401
Population 755,393
LEGEND
Dallas-Fort Worth Combined Statistical Area
RICHMOND Metropolitan Statistical Area
Concord Micropolitan Statistical Area
CANADA International
TEXAS State
HARRIS County
0 8 16 24 32 40 Kilometers
0 8 16 24 32 40 Miles
N
CANADA
MINNESOTA
SOUTH DAKOTA
MONTANA
GRAND FORKS (PART)
POLK (PART)
CLAY
WILKIN
FARGO
Fargo-Wahpeton
CASS
RICHLAND
Wahpeton
PEMBINA
WALSH
GRAND FORKS
TRAILL
STEELE
RANSOM
SARGENT
CAVALIER
NELSON
GRIGGS
BARNES
LaMOURE
DICKEY
RAMSEY
EDDY
FOSTER
Jamestown
STUTSMAN
TOWNER
BENSON
WELLS
KIDDER
LOGAN
McINTOSH
ROLETTE
PIERCE
SHERIDAN
BURLEIGH
EMMONS
BOTTINEAU
McHENRY
Minot
WARD
McLEAN
OLIVER
BISMARCK
MORTON
SIOUX
RENVILLE
MERCER
GRANT
BURKE
MOUNTRAIL
DUNN
Dickinson
STARK
HETTINGER
ADAMS
DIVIDE
Williston
WILLIAMS
McKENZIE
BILLINGS
SLOPE
BOWMAN
GOLDEN VALLEY
49°
48°
47°
46°
45°
96°
97°
98°
99°
100°
101°
102°
103°
104°

USA; gen tel (701) 493-2261; disp adv e-mail advertising@drtel.net; class adv e-mail classifieds@drtel.net; ed e-mail edgeleymail@drtel.net; web site www.edgeleynd.com
Circulation: 1,000pd,; Sworn/Estimate/Non-Audited
Advertising rate: Open inch rate $5.50
Circ. Mgr....................................... Tausha Dide
Ed. .... Patty Wood Bartle

ELGIN

CARSON PRESS (WED)
119 N MAIN ST, Elgin, ND, 58533, Grant, USA; gen tel (701) 584-2900; gen fax (701) 584-2900; disp adv e-mail gcn@westriv.com; web site www.carsonpressnewspaper.com
Circulation: 1,000pd,; Sworn/Estimate/Non-Audited
Advertising rate: Open inch rate $5.50
Cir. Mgr.......................... Dianne Mutschelknaus
Ed. .... Jill Friesz
Mechanical Specifications: 10.625 x 21

THE GRANT COUNTY NEWS (WED)
119 Main St., Elgin, ND, 58533, Grant, USA; gen tel (701) 584-2900; gen fax (701) 584-2900; disp adv e-mail gcn@westriv.com; web site www.grantcountynewsnewspaper.com
Circulation: 1,500pd,; Sworn/Estimate/Non-Audited
Advertising rate: Open inch rate $5.50
Established: 1955
Digital Platform - Mobile: Windows
Ed. .... Jill Friesz
Circ. Mgr....................................... John Schultz
Mechanical Specifications: 10.625 x 21
Areas Served: Grant County

ELLENDALE

DICKEY COUNTY LEADER (THUR)
216 Main Ave, Ellendale, ND, 58436, Dickey, USA; gen tel (701) 349-3222; gen fax (701) 349-3229; disp adv e-mail dcleader@drtel.net
Circulation: 1,200pd,; Sworn/Estimate/Non-Audited
Advertising rate: Open inch rate $7.50
Group: Nordmark Publishing
Pub....................................... Jason Nordmark
Ed. .... Roberta Johnson
Mechanical Specifications: Type page 14 x 21; E - 6 cols, 2, 1/6 between; A - 6 cols, 2, 1/6 between; C - 6 cols, 2, 1/6 between.Equipment & Software: Hardware — APP/Power Mac; Software — QPS/QuarkXPress.
Delivery Method: Mail, Newsstand, Racks
Areas Served: Dickey

ENDERLIN

ENDERLIN INDEPENDENT (WED)
209 4th Ave, Enderlin, ND, 58027-1300, USA; gen tel (701) 437-3131; disp adv e-mail enderlinindependent@mlgc.com; web site www.enderlinindependent.com
Circulation: 1,100pd,; Sworn/Estimate/Non-Audited
Advertising rate: Open inch rate $4.50
Art Hagebock
Diane HagebockPub. s
Mechanical Specifications: Type page 13 x 21 1/4.Equipment & Software: Hardware — APP/Mac; Presses — WPC/Web Leader; Software — QPS/QuarkXPress, Multi-Ad/Creator.

FARGO

LARIMORE LEADER-TRIBUNE (THUR)
2802 15th St S, Unit C, Fargo, ND, 58103-5958, Cass, USA; gen tel (701) 478-0277; adv tel (701) 478-0277; ed tel (701) 478-0277; gen fax (701) 478-0287; adv fax (701) 478-0287; ed fax (701) 478-0287; disp adv e-mail larimoreleader@cableone.net; class adv e-mail larimoreleader@cableone.net; ed e-mail larimoreleader@cableone.net
Circulation: 525pd, 25fr; Sworn/Estimate/Non-Audited
Advertising rate: $4.50 column inch
Established: 1969
Group: Ness Press, Inc.
Digital Platform - Mobile: Apple, Windows
Digital Platform - Tablet: Windows 7
Mechanical Specifications: Photo Offset
Delivery Method: Mail, Newsstand
Areas Served: Larimore, ND & Rural Grand Forks County

FINLEY

STEELE COUNTY PRESS (FRI)
215 4th St W, Finley, ND, 58230-3000, Steele, USA; gen tel (701) 524-1640; gen fax (701) 524-2221; disp adv e-mail calbert@ncppub.com; ed e-mail ldefrang@ncppub.com; web site http://www.ncppub.com
Circulation: 1,400pd,; Sworn/Estimate/Non-Audited
Advertising rate: Open inch rate $5.50
Established: 1897
Group: New Century Press
Cir. Mgr....................................... Lisa Midstokke
Ed. .... Lindsie Defrang
Sales....................................... Catherine Albert
Mechanical Specifications: Type page 10 3/16 x 16 1/2; E - 5 cols, 1 7/8, 1/6 between; A - 5 cols, 1 7/8, 1/6 between; C - 5 cols, 1 7/8, 1/6 between.Equipment & Software: Hardware — APP/Macs; Software — QPS/QuarkXPress 4.1.

FORDVILLE

ANETA STAR (FRI)
122 Main St N, Fordville, ND, 58231-3134, Walsh, USA; gen tel (701) 229-3641; gen fax (701) 229-3217; disp adv e-mail nesspres@polarcomm.com
Circulation: 350pd,; Sworn/Estimate/Non-Audited
Advertising rate: Open inch rate $2.87
Established: 1951
Ad. / Cir. .... Truman Ness
Pub. / Ed. .... Ness Press
Delivery Method: Mail, Newsstand, Racks
Areas Served: Nelson

EDMORE HERALD (THUR)
122 Main St N, Fordville, ND, 58231-3134, Walsh, USA; gen tel (701) 229-3641; gen fax (701) 229-3217; disp adv e-mail nesspres@polarcomm.com,
Circulation: 245pd,
Advertising rate: Open inch rate $2.87
Established: 1960
Pub....................................... Gunnard Ness
Ed. .... Truman Ness
Delivery Method: Mail, Newsstand, Racks
Areas Served: Ramsey

FORDVILLE TRI-COUNTY SUN (THUR)
122 Main St N, Fordville, ND, 58231-3134, Walsh, USA; gen tel (701) 229-3641; gen fax (701) 229-3217; disp adv e-mail nesspres@polarcomm.com
Circulation: 500pd,; Sworn/Estimate/Non-Audited
Advertising rate: Open inch rate $2.87
Established: 1922Editions: (1)
Ed. .... Truman Ness
Pub. / Ed. .... Ness Press
Delivery Method: Mail, Newsstand, Racks
Areas Served: Walsh

HATTON FREE PRESS (WED)
122 MAIN ST N, Fordville, ND, 58231, Walsh, USA; gen tel (701) 229-3641; gen fax (701) 229-3217; disp adv e-mail nesspres@polarcomm.com
Circulation: 358pd,; Sworn/Estimate/Non-Audited
Advertising rate: Open inch rate $2.87
Established: 1910
Ed. .... Truman Ness
Pub. / Ed. .... Ness Press
Delivery Method: Mail, Newsstand, Racks
Areas Served: Traill

LEADER-TRIBUNE (THUR)
122 Main St N, Fordville, ND, 58231-3134, Walsh, USA; gen tel (701) 229-3641; gen fax (701) 229-3217; disp adv e-mail nesspres@polarcomm.com
Circulation: 525pd,; Sworn/Estimate/Non-Audited
Advertising rate: Open inch rate $2.87
Established: 1978
Pub....................................... Gunnard Ness
Ed. .... Truman Ness
Delivery Method: Mail, Newsstand, Racks
Areas Served: Grand Forks

MCVILLE MESSENGER (THUR)
122 Main St N, Fordville, ND, 58231-3134, Walsh, USA; gen tel (701) 229-3641; gen fax (701) 229-3217; disp adv e-mail nesspres@polarcomm.com
Circulation: 220pd,; Sworn/Estimate/Non-Audited
Advertising rate: Open inch rate $2.87
Established: 1981
Ad. / Cir. Mgr. .... Truman Ness
Pub. / Ed. .... Ness Press
Delivery Method: Mail, Newsstand, Racks
Areas Served: Nelson

NELSON COUNTY ARENA (FRI)
122 Main St N, Fordville, ND, 58231-3134, Walsh, USA; gen tel (701) 229-3641; gen fax (701) 229-3217; disp adv e-mail nesspres@polarcomm.com
Circulation: 420pd,; Sworn/Estimate/Non-Audited
Advertising rate: Open inch rate $2.87
Established: 1908
Ed. .... Truman Ness
Pub. / Ed. .... Ness Press
Delivery Method: Mail, Newsstand, Racks
Areas Served: Nelson

PEMBINA NEW ERA (THUR)
122 Main St N, Fordville, ND, 58231-3134, Walsh, USA; gen tel (701) 229-3641; gen fax (701) 229-3217; disp adv e-mail nesspres@polarcomm.com
Circulation: 375pd,; Sworn/Estimate/Non-Audited
Advertising rate: Open inch rate $2.87
Established: 1922
Ad. / Cir. Mgr. .... Truman Ness
Pub. / Ed. .... Ness Press
Delivery Method: Mail, Newsstand, Racks
Areas Served: Pembina

GACKLE

TRI COUNTY NEWS (WED)
321 Main St, Gackle, ND, 58442-7109, Logan, USA; gen tel (701) 485-3550; ed tel (605) 999-4607; gen fax (701) 485-3551; disp adv e-mail tcnews@daktel.com; ed e-mail wendy@dakotafire.net
Circulation: 750pd,; Sworn/Estimate/Non-Audited
Advertising rate: Open inch rate $5.00
Established: 1970
Pub. .... Art Hagebock
Pub. .... Diane Hagebock
Mng. Ed....................................... Wendy Royston
Delivery Method: Mail, Newsstand, Racks
Areas Served: Logan

GARRISON

MCLEAN COUNTY INDEPENDENT (THUR)
91 N Main St, Garrison, ND, 58540-7166, McLean, USA; gen tel (701) 463-2201; gen fax (701) 463-7487; disp adv e-mail independ@restel.net; class adv e-mail bhgads@nd-bhginc.com; ed e-mail editors@bhgnews.com; web site www.nd-bhginc.com
Circulation: 3,000pd,; Sworn/Estimate/Non-Audited
Advertising rate: Open inch rate $6.00
Group: BHG, Inc.
Pub....................................... Mike Gackle
Gen. Mgr. .... Jill Denning Gackle
Ed. .... Stu Merry
Ad. Mgr....................................... Sarah Chase
Mechanical Specifications: Type page 11 x 17; E - 4 cols, 2 3/8, 1/6 between; A - 5 cols, 2, 1/6 between; C - 5 cols, 2, 1/6 between. Equipment & Software: Hardware — PCs; Presses — G/Community.
Areas Served: 58540, 58759, 58756, 58735, 58723, 58716, 58779, 58778, 58775, 58579

GLEN ULLIN

GLEN ULLIN TIMES (WED)
105 B St S, Glen Ullin, ND, 58631-7110, Morton, USA; gen tel (701) 348-3325; gen fax (701) 348-3325; disp adv e-mail gutimes@westriv.com; web site http://www.glenullintimes.com
Circulation: 1,000pd, 50fr; Sworn/Estimate/Non-Audited
Advertising rate: Open inch rate $3.50
Established: 1904
Pub. / Ed. Nancy BittnerEquipment & Software: ; Software — Adobe/PageMaker 6.5, Adobe/Photoshop, Microsoft/Word 6.0.
Delivery Method: Mail, Newsstand, Racks
Areas Served: Morton

GRAFTON

THE WALSH COUNTY RECORD (WED)
402 Hill Ave, Grafton, ND, 58237-1002, Walsh, USA; gen tel (701) 352-0640; adv tel (701) 352-0640; ed tel (701) 352-0641; disp adv e-mail advertising@wcrecord.com; class adv e-mail brianl@wcrecord.com; ed e-mail jackie@wcrecord.com; web site www.wcrecord.com
Circulation: 3,136pd, 100fr; Sworn/Estimate/Non-Audited
Advertising rate: Open inch rate $5.00
Established: 1923
Pub....................................... Jackie L. Thompson
Adv. Mgr. .... Tim Martin
Cir. Mgr....................................... Deb Bender
Ed. .... Todd Kjelland
Adv. Sales Rep....................................... Brian LeClerc
Mechanical Specifications: Type page 13 3/8 x 21 1/4; E - 6 cols, 2 1/8, between; A - 6 cols, 2 1/8, between; C - 6 cols, 2 1/8, between. Equipment & Software: Hardware — PCs, ECR/Imaginesetter, HP/LaserJet 5 simx; Software — QPS/QuarkXPress 4.0.
Delivery Method: Mail, Newsstand, Racks
Areas Served: Walsh

HARVEY

THE HERALD-PRESS (SAT)
913 Lincoln Ave, Harvey, ND, 58341-1523, Wells, USA; gen tel (701) 324-4646; gen fax (701) 324-4647; disp adv e-mail herald-press@gondtc.com; ed e-mail heraldpress@midconetwork.com; web site www.herald-pressnd.com
Circulation: 2,700pd, 2,400fr; Sworn/Estimate/Non-Audited
Advertising rate: Open inch rate $5.45
Pub....................................... Charles Eldredge
Gen. Mgr. / Ad. Sales....................................... Edie Schell
Ed. .... Janine Schmitz
Copy Ed....................................... Peg Bell
Cir. Mgr. .... Ruth Yoder

HEBRON

HEBRON HERALD (WED)
102 S Park St, Hebron, ND, 58638-7001,

Morton, USA; gen tel (701) 878-4494; gen fax (701) 878-4498; disp adv e-mail hherald@westriv.com
Circulation: 1,100pd, 50fr; Sworn/Estimate/Non-Audited
Advertising rate: Open inch rate $4.25
Established: 1898
Pub. / Ed. ....Jane Brandt
Mechanical Specifications: Type page 9 x 14.
Delivery Method: Mail, Newsstand, Racks
Areas Served: Morton

RICHARDTON MERCHANT (MON, BI-MTHLY)
102 S Park St, Hebron, ND, 58638-7001, Morton, USA; gen tel (701) 878-4494; gen fax (701) 878-4498; disp adv e-mail hherald@westriv.com
Circulation: 75pd, 1,100fr; Sworn/Estimate/Non-Audited
Advertising rate: Open inch rate $4.25
Established: 1973
Pub. / Ed. ....Jane Brandt
Delivery Method: Mail, Newsstand, Racks
Areas Served: Stark

HETTINGER

ADAMS COUNTY RECORD (FRI)
116 S Main St, Hettinger, ND, 58639-7031, Adams, USA; gen tel (701) 567-2424 ; gen fax (701) 567-2425; disp adv e-mail adamscountyrecord@countrymedia.net; class adv e-mail adamscountyrecord@countrymedia.net; web site www.adamscountyextra.com
Circulation: 1,232pd,; Sworn/Estimate/Non-Audited
Advertising rate: Open inch rate $7.05
Group: Country Media Inc.
Country Media
Digital Platform - Mobile: Apple, Android, Windows, Blackberry
Ed. .... Cole Benz
Pub. .... Stacy Swenson
Off. Mgr. .... Jayden Ragsdale
Ad. Mgr. .... Patricia Lewton
Delivery Method: Mail, Newsstand, Racks
Areas Served: Adams County ND, Perkins County SD

HILLSBORO

HILLSBORO BANNER (FRI)
20 W Caledonia Ave, Hillsboro, ND, 58045-4205, Traill, USA; gen tel (701) 636-4241; gen fax (701) 636-4245; disp adv e-mail hbanner@rrv.net; web site www.hillsboro-banner.com
Circulation: 1,350pd,; Sworn/Estimate/Non-Audited
Advertising rate: Open inch rate $5.00
Established: 1879
Pub. .... Cheryl Kelly
Pub. .... Shawn Kelly
Cir. Mgr. .... Alyssa Short
Ed. .... Cole Short
Mechanical Specifications: Type page 14 x 21; E - 6 cols, 2, 1/6 between; A - 6 cols, 2, 1/6 between; C - 6 cols, 2, 1/6 between.

KENMARE

THE KENMARE NEWS (WED)
20 2nd St NW, Kenmare, ND, 58746-7114, Ward, USA; gen tel (701) 385-4275; gen fax (701) 385-4395; disp adv e-mail news@kenmarend.com; web site www.kenmarend.com
Circulation: 1,800pd, 28fr; Sworn/Estimate/Non-Audited
Advertising rate: Open inch rate $4.50
Established: 1898
Cir. Mgr. .... Fay Froseth
Pub. / Ed. .... Terry Froseth
Pub. Emeritus .... Glen Froseth
Prod. Asst. .... Elsa Condit

KILLDEER

DUNN COUNTY HERALD (FRI)
26 Central Ave S, Killdeer, ND, 58640-4000, Dunn, USA; gen tel (701) 764-5312; gen fax (701) 764-5049; disp adv e-mail dcherald@countrymedia.net; web site http://www.dunncountyextra.com/
Circulation: 1,334pd,; Sworn/Estimate/Non-Audited
Advertising rate: Open inch rate $7.05
Group: Country Media Inc.
Office Mgr .... Carol Hicks
Mechanical Specifications: Type page 10 1/2 x 16; E - 5 cols, 2, 1/3 between.Equipment & Software: Hardware — APP/Mac; Software — QPS/QuarkXPress 4.0.
Delivery Method: Mail, Newsstand

KULM

KULM MESSENGER (WED)
6 MAIN AVE S, Kulm, ND, 58456, USA; gen tel (701) 647-2411; gen fax (701) 647-2398; disp adv e-mail kulm@drtel.net
Circulation: 900pd, 37fr; Sworn/Estimate/Non-Audited
Advertising rate: Open inch rate $4.25
Art Hagebock
Diane HagebockPub.sEquipment & Software: Hardware — APP/Mac; Software — QPS/QuarkXPress 3.31.

LAKOTA

LAKOTA AMERICAN (THUR)
PO Box 507, Lakota, ND, 58344-0507, Nelson, USA; gen tel (701)247-2482; gen fax (701)247-2483; disp adv e-mail lamerican@polarcomm.com; class adv e-mail lamerican@polarcomm.com; ed e-mail lamerican@polarcomm.com
Circulation: 798pd, 24fr; Sworn/Estimate/Non-Audited
Advertising rate: Open inch rate $5.50
Established: 1901
Pub. .... Denise Westad
Ed. .... Sara Plum
Delivery Method: Mail, Newsstand
Areas Served: Nelson County and surrounding area

LAMOURE

LA MOURE CHRONICLE (WED)
20 1ST ST SW, Lamoure, ND, 58458, USA; gen tel (701) 883-5393; gen fax (701) 883-5076; disp adv e-mail chronicle@drtel.net
Circulation: 2,456pd, 15fr; Sworn/Estimate/Non-Audited
Advertising rate: Open inch rate $4.50
Pub. .... Art Hagebock
Pub. / Cir. Mgr. .... Diane Hagebock
Mechanical Specifications: Type page 13 x 21; E - 6 cols, 2, 1/6 between; A - 6 cols, 2, 1/6 between; C - 6 cols, 2, 1/6 between.Equipment & Software: Hardware — APP/Mac; Software — QPS/QuarkXPress 4.0.

LANGDON

CAVALIER COUNTY REPUBLICAN (MON)
618 3rd St, Langdon, ND, 58249-2622, Cavalier, USA; gen tel (701) 256-5311; gen fax (701) 256-5841; disp adv e-mail ccr@utma.com; web site www.cavaliercountyextra.com
Circulation: 1,800pd,; Sworn/Estimate/Non-Audited
Advertising rate: Open inch rate $7.00
Established: 1888
Group: Country Media Inc.
Cir. Mgr. .... Lori Peterson
Melissa Anderson
Delivery Method: Mail
Areas Served: Cavalier County 58249

LINTON

EMMONS COUNTY RECORD (THUR)
201 N Broadway St, Linton, ND, 58552-7020, Emmons, USA; gen tel (701) 254-4537; gen fax (701) 254-4909; disp adv e-mail info@lintonnd.com; ed e-mail info@lintonnd.com; web site www.ecrecord.com
Circulation: 3,012pd, 163fr; Sworn/Estimate/Non-Audited
Advertising rate: Open inch rate $7.60
Established: 1884
Publisher/Editor .... Leah P. Burke
Adv. Mgr. .... Julie Brandner
Pub. Emeritus .... Allan C. Burke
Mechanical Specifications: Type page 11 3/4 x 21 3/8; E - 6 cols, 1 3/16, 3/16 between; A - 6 cols, 2 1/16, 1/8 between; C - 6 cols, 2 1/16, 1/8 between.Equipment & Software: Hardware — 2-APP/Mac; Presses — WPC; Software — Adobe/PageMaker 6.0, Adobe/Photoshop.
Delivery Method: Mail, Newsstand
Areas Served: 58552, 58544, 58573, 58542, 57648, 58579

LISBON

THE RANSOM COUNTY GAZETTE (MON)
410 Main St, Lisbon, ND, 58054-4142, Ransom, USA; gen tel (701) 683-4128; gen fax (701) 683-4129; disp adv e-mail info@rcgazette.com; web site www.rcgazette.com
Circulation: 3,000pd,; Sworn/Estimate/Non-Audited
Advertising rate: Open inch rate $5.75
Adv. Mgr. .... Cheryl Kelly
Ed. .... Sean W. Kelly
Mng. Ed. .... Terri BartaEquipment & Software: Hardware — APP/Mac; Software — QPS/QuarkXPress, Adobe/Photoshop, Multi-Ad.

LITCHVILLE

THE LITCHVILLE BULLETIN (WED)
505 3RD AVE, Litchville, ND, 58461, Barnes, USA; gen tel (701) 762-4267; gen fax (701) 762-4267; disp adv e-mail bulletin@drtel.net
Circulation: 1,025pd,; Sworn/Estimate/Non-Audited
Advertising rate: Open inch rate $4.50
Established: 1901
Ed. .... Ruth E. McCleerey
Pub. .... Art Hagebock
Pub. .... Diane Hagebock

MANDAN

MANDAN NEWS (FRI)
414 W Main St, Mandan, ND, 58554-3145, Morton, USA; gen tel (701) 250-8250; adv tel (701) 250-8805; ed tel (701) 250-8250; gen fax (701) 223-2063; ed e-mail editor@mandan-news.com; web site mandan-news.com
Circulation: 1,900pd,; Sworn/Estimate/Non-Audited
Advertising rate: Open inch rate $6.50
Established: 1976
Group: Lee Enterprises, Inc.
Mandan News Ed./Reporter .... Tyana JohnsonEquipment & Software: Hardware — APP/Mac; Presses — HI; Software — Multi-Ad 4.01, Adobe/PageMaker 5.0.
Delivery Method: Mail, Newsstand, Racks
Areas Served: Mandan

MAYVILLE

TRAILL COUNTY TRIBUNE (SAT)
12 3rd St SE, Mayville, ND, 58257-1414, Traill, USA; gen tel (701) 788-3281; gen fax (701) 788-3287; disp adv e-mail tribune@tctribune.net
Circulation: 2,600pd,; Sworn/Estimate/Non-Audited
Advertising rate: Open inch rate $5.00
Pub. .... Sean W. Kelly
Gen. Mgr. .... Thomas A. Monilaws
Graph. Des. / Adv. .... Gail Mooney
Mechanical Specifications: Type page 15 1/8 x 21 1/2; E - 7 cols, 2, 1/6 between; A - 7 cols, 2, 1/6 between; C - 7 cols, 2, 1/6 between. Equipment & Software: Hardware — APP/Mac; Software — QPS/QuarkXPress 3.3, Multi-Ad/Creator 3.8, Adobe/PageMaker 6.0.

MCCLUSKY

MCCLUSKY GAZETTE (THUR)
203 Main St, McClusky, ND, 58463, Sheridan, USA; gen tel (701) 363-2492; gen fax (701) 363-2698; disp adv e-mail gazette@westriv.com; web site www.nd-bhginc.com
Circulation: 900pd, 50fr; Sworn/Estimate/Non-Audited
Advertising rate: Open inch rate $5.50
Group: BHG, Inc.
Editor/Office Supervisor .... Alllan Tinker
Ad Manager .... Betty Jean Dockter
Delivery Method: Mail, Newsstand
Areas Served: Sheridan County

MCLEAN COUNTY JOURNAL (THUR)
203 Main St S, McClusky, ND, 58463-4000, Sheridan, USA; gen tel (701) 363-2276; adv tel Same; ed tel (701) 363-2276; gen fax (701) 363-2698; ed fax (701) 363-2276; disp adv e-mail turtle@westriv.com; web site www.bhgnews.com
Circulation: 700pd, 46fr; Sworn/Estimate/Non-Audited
Advertising rate: Open inch rate $6.50
Established: 1905
Group: BHG, Inc.
Digital Platform - Mobile: Windows
Digital Platform - Tablet: Windows 7
Ed. .... Allan Tinker
Ad. Mgr. .... Betty Jean Dockter
Mechanical Specifications: Type page 10 3/4 x 16; E - 5 cols, 2 1/16, 1/6 between; A - 5 cols, 2 1/16, 1/6 between; C - 5 cols, 2 1/16, 1/6 between.Equipment & Software: Hardware — PC; Software — Microsoft/Word, Ventura.
Delivery Method: Mail, Newsstand
Areas Served: McLean County

MILNOR

THE SARGENT COUNTY TELLER (FRI)
PO Box 247, Milnor, ND, 58060-0247, Sargent, USA; gen tel (701)427-9472; gen fax (701)427-9492; disp adv e-mail info@thescteller.com; class adv e-mail info@thescteller.com; ed e-mail info@thescteller.com
Circulation: 1,600pd, 150fr; USPS
Advertising rate: 6.25
Established: 1883
Group: Kelly Ink, Inc.
Digital Platform - Mobile: Apple
Digital Platform - Tablet: Apple iOS
Co-pub. .... Cheryl Kelly
Pub. / Ed. .... Sean Kelly
Mechanical Specifications: 11 pica, 1pica gutter, 21 inches deep
Delivery Method: Mail, Newsstand
Areas Served: Gwinner, Milnor, Forman, Rutland, Lidgerwood, Geneseo, (serving all of Sargent County, North Dakota

MINNEWAUKAN

BENSON COUNTY FARMERS PRESS (THUR)
120 B Ave, Minnewaukan, ND, 58351-5208, Benson, USA; gen tel (701) 473-5436; gen fax (701) 473-5736; disp adv e-mail farmerspress@gondtc.com; class adv e-mail farmerspress@gondtc.com; ed e-mail

farmerspress@gondtc.com; web site www.bensoncountynews.com
Circulation: 2,098pd, 77fr; Sworn/Estimate/Non-Audited
Advertising rate: Open inch rate $6.50 net
Established: 1884
Digital Platform - Mobile: Windows
Digital Platform - Tablet: Windows 7
Owner/Pub. .... Denise Westad
Ed. .... Sara J. Plum
Mechanical Specifications: Type page 13 x 21; E - 6 cols, 2, 1/6 between; A - 6 cols, 2, 1/6 between; C - 6 cols, 2, 1/6 between.Equipment & Software: Hardware — PC Pentium II, PC Pentium III; Software — 8-WordPerfect, Caere/OmniPage 10, Adobe/Photoshop 7, Adobe/PageMaker 6.5, InterLink, Windows XP.
Delivery Method: Mail, Newsstand
Areas Served: Benson County and surrounding area

MOHALL

RENVILLE COUNTY FARMER (WED)

110 Main St E, Mohall, ND, 58761-4058, Renville, USA; gen tel (701) 756-6363; gen fax (701) 756-7136; disp adv e-mail rcf1@ndak.net
Circulation: 875pd, 51fr; Sworn/Estimate/Non-Audited
Advertising rate: Open inch rate $5.50
Established: 1901
Digital Platform - Mobile: Windows
Digital Platform - Tablet: Windows 7
Ed. .... LaVonne L. Erickson
Mechanical Specifications: Type page 13 x 22; E - 6 cols, 2, 1/4 between.Equipment & Software: Hardware — PC; Software — QPS/QuarkXPress.
Delivery Method: Mail, Newsstand
Areas Served: 58761, 58750, 58782, 58787, 58711, 58740,

NAPOLEON

NAPOLEON HOMESTEAD (WED)

323 Main Ave, Napoleon, ND, 58561-7108, Logan, USA; gen tel (701) 754-2212; gen fax (701) 754-2212; disp adv e-mail homestead@napoleonnd.com; web site http://www.centraldakotanews.com/?id=1049
Circulation: 1,550pd, 20fr; Sworn/Estimate/Non-Audited
Advertising rate: Open inch rate $6.5
Established: 1886
Cir. Mgr. .... Christine Schwartzenberger
Pub. / Ed. .... Terry Schwartzenberger
Mechanical Specifications: Type page 10 1/2 x 21 1/2; E - 6 cols, 2 1/8, 3/16 between; A - 6 cols, 2 1/8, 3/16 between; C - 6 cols, 2 1/8, 3/16 between.Equipment & Software: Hardware — APP/Mac, IBM; Software — Microsoft/Windows 3.0.
Delivery Method: Mail, Newsstand, Racks
Areas Served: Logan

NEW ENGLAND

THE HERALD (FRI)

724 Main St, New England, ND, 58647-7000, Hettinger, USA; gen tel (701) 579-4530; gen fax (701) 579-4180; disp adv e-mail therald@countrymedia.net; web site http://www.newenglandextra.com
Circulation: 1,100pd,; Sworn/Estimate/Non-Audited
Advertising rate: Open inch rate $7.05
Group: Country Media Inc.
Pub. .... Norma Peterson
Ed. .... Cole Benz
Off. Mgr .... Jaden Ragsdale
Delivery Method: Carrier

NEW ROCKFORD

NEW ROCKFORD TRANSCRIPT (MON)

6 8th St N, New Rockford, ND, 58356-1518, Eddy, USA; gen tel (701) 947-2417; gen fax (701) 947-2418; disp adv e-mail nrtranscript@gmail.com; class adv e-mail nrtranscript@gmail.com; ed e-mail amywobbema@gmail.com; web site www.newrockfordtranscript.com
Circulation: 1,000pd, 2,000fr; Sworn/Estimate/Non-Audited
Advertising rate: Open inch rate $6.25
Established: 1883
Pub. /Ed. .... Amy Wobbema
Mechanical Specifications: Type page 11 3/4 x 21 1/2; E - 6 cols, 1 4/5, 1/6 between; A - 6 cols, 1 4/5, 1/6 between; C - 6 cols, 1 4/5, 1/6 between.
Delivery Method: Mail, Newsstand
Areas Served: New Rockford/Eddy County

NEW SALEM

NEW SALEM JOURNAL (WED)

1201 N. 8th St., New Salem, ND, 58563, Morton, USA; gen tel (701) 843-7567; gen fax (701) 843-7623; disp adv e-mail newsalemjournal@gmail.com
Circulation: 900pd,; Sworn/Estimate/Non-Audited
Advertising rate: Open inch rate $4.00
Pub. / Ed. .... Robyn Thiel
Delivery Method: Mail
Areas Served: Morton

NEW TOWN

MOUNTRAIL COUNTY RECORD (THUR)

372 Main St, New Town, ND, 58763-4001, Mountrail, USA; gen tel (701) 627-4829; gen fax (701) 627-4021; disp adv e-mail ntsales@nd-bhginc.com; ed e-mail nteditor@bhgnews.com; web site www.bhgnews.com
Circulation: 750pd, 46fr; Sworn/Estimate/Non-Audited
Advertising rate: Open inch rate $6.00
Group: BHG, Inc.
Adv. Mgr. .... Jodi Iberson
Ed. .... Jerry Kram

NEW TOWN NEWS (FRI)

PO Box 730, New Town, ND, 58763-0730, Mountrail, USA; gen tel (701) 627-4829; gen fax (701) 627-4021; disp adv e-mail ntsales@nd-bhginc.com; ed e-mail nteditor@bhgnews.com; web site www.bhgnews.com
Circulation: 1,047pd, 37fr; Sworn/Estimate/Non-Audited
Advertising rate: $7.15 per column inch
Group: BHG, Inc.
Editor .... Jerry Kram
Adv. Mgr. .... Jodie Iverson
Areas Served: 58763

NORTHWOOD

THE GLEANER (MON)

22 N Main St, Northwood, ND, 58267-4005, Grand Forks, USA; gen tel (701) 587-6126; gen fax (701) 587-5219; disp adv e-mail gleaner@invisimax.com
Circulation: 900pd,; Sworn/Estimate/Non-Audited
Advertising rate: Open inch rate $5.50
Pub. .... Beth Johnson
Ed. .... Karen Bilden

OAKES

THE OAKES TIMES (THUR)

501 Main Ave, Oakes, ND, 58474-1241, Dickey, USA; gen tel (701) 742-2361; gen fax (701) 742-2207; disp adv e-mail oakestms@drtel.net
Circulation: 2,800pd, 15fr; Sworn/Estimate/Non-Audited
Advertising rate: Open inch rate $6.00
Established: 1884
Group: Nordmark Publishing
Pub. .... Jason Nordmark
Editor .... Ethel Erickson
Adv. Mgr. .... Alexis MarthallerEquipment & Software: Hardware — APP/Mac; Software — InDesign CS5
Delivery Method: Mail, Newsstand
Areas Served: 58474, 58458, 58441, 58436, 58490, 58017, 58032, 58040, 58054, 58072, 58075

PARK RIVER

THE WALSH COUNTY PRESS (WED)

401 Briggs Ave S, Ste 2, Park River, ND, 58270-4023, Walsh, USA; gen tel (701) 284-6333; gen fax (701) 284-6091; disp adv e-mail wcpress@polarcomm.com
Circulation: 1,100pd,; Sworn/Estimate/Non-Audited
Advertising rate: Open inch rate $4.85
Established: 1884
Group: Nordmark Publishing
Pub. .... Jason Nordmark
Prodn. Mgr. .... Sue Steinke
Sports .... Kevin Skavhaug
Ed. .... Allison Olimb
Delivery Method: Mail, Newsstand, Racks
Areas Served: Walsh

PICK CITY

THE HAZEN STAR (THUR)

26 Main Rd E, Pick City, ND, 58545-7034, Mercer, USA; gen tel (701) 748-2255; gen fax (701) 748-5768; disp adv e-mail star@westriv.com; web site www.nd-bhginc.com
Circulation: 2,000pd, 34fr; Sworn/Estimate/Non-Audited
Advertising rate: Open inch rate $6.20
Group: BHG, Inc.
Adv. Mgr. .... Dareen Ost
Ed. .... Daniel Arens
Cir. Mgr. .... Sharon Olander
Mechanical Specifications: Type page 10 1/2 x 16; E - 5 cols, 1 11/12, 1/6 between; A - 5 cols, 1 11/12, 1/6 between; C - 5 cols, 1 11/12, 1/6 between.

ROLLA

LAKE METIGOSHE MIRROR (WED)

11 1st Ave NE, Rolla, ND, 58367-7125, Bottineau, USA; gen tel (866)476-5253; adv tel (701) 477-6495; gen fax (701)477-3182; disp adv e-mail metigosh@utma.com
Advertising rate: Open inch rate $5.60
Established: 2005Jason Nordmark
Bus. Mgr. .... Holly Cammack
Cir. Mgr. .... Alvin LaFromboise
Adv. Mgr. .... Jenee Munro
Delivery Method: Mail, Newsstand, Racks
Areas Served: Bottineau

TURTLE MOUNTAIN STAR (MON)

11 1st Ave NE, Rolla, ND, 58367-7125, Rolette, USA; gen tel (701) 477-6495; gen fax (701) 477-3182; disp adv e-mail tmstar@utma.com
Circulation: 3,600pd,; Sworn/Estimate/Non-Audited
Advertising rate: Open inch rate $5.60
Group: Nordmark Publishing
Pub. / Ed. .... Jason Nordmark
Delivery Method: Mail, Newsstand, Racks
Areas Served: Rolette

RUGBY

PIERCE COUNTY TRIBUNE (SAT)

219 S Main Ave, Rugby, ND, 58368-1720, Pierce, USA; gen tel (701) 776-5252; gen fax (701) 776-2159; disp adv e-mail cholm@thepiercecountytribune.com; class adv e-mail business@thepiercecountytribune.com ; web site www.thepiercecountytribune.com
Circulation: 2,700pd,; Sworn/Estimate/Non-Audited
Advertising rate: Open inch rate $7.15
Group: Ogden Newspapers Inc.
Adv. Acct. Exec. .... Cheryl Holm
Off. Mgr. .... Ruby Allen
Ed. / Mgr. .... J.T. Pelt
Mechanical Specifications: Type page 13 x 21 1/4; E - 6 cols, 2, 1/6 between; A - 6 cols, 2, 1/6 between; C - 6 cols, 2, 1/6 between. Equipment & Software: ; Software — QPS/QuarkXPress, Write Now, Adobe/Photoshop.

STANLEY

MOUNTRAIL COUNTY PROMOTER (WED)

117 S Main St, Stanley, ND, 58784-4003, USA; gen tel (701) 628-2333; gen fax (701) 628-2694; disp adv e-mail promoter@midstatetel.com; web site www.mountrailcountypromoter.com
Circulation: 2,100pd,; Sworn/Estimate/Non-Audited
Advertising rate: Open inch rate $5.00
Established: 1906
Ed. .... Mary Kilen
Mechanical Specifications: Type page 13 x 21; E - 3 cols, 4 1/5, 1/4 between; A - 6 cols, 2, 1/4 between; C - 6 cols, 2, 1/4 between.

STEELE

STEELE OZONE AND KIDDER COUNTY PRESS (WED)

115 1st Ave SE, Steele, ND, 58482-7131, Steele, USA; gen tel (701) 475-2513; gen fax (701) 475-2329; disp adv e-mail sop@bektel.com; web site http://www.steeleozonend.com/
Advertising rate: $5.50 per column inch
Ed. / Pub. .... Paul Erdelt

TIOGA

TIOGA TRIBUNE (WED)

101 2nd Street, Tioga, ND, 58852, Williams, USA; gen tel (701) 664-2222; gen fax (701) 664-3333; disp adv e-mail advertising@tiogand.com; ed e-mail cecilew@crosbynd.com; web site http://www.journaltrib.com/
Circulation: 1,400pd,; Sworn/Estimate/Non-Audited
Advertising rate: Open inch rate $7.20
Established: 1951
Group: Journal Publishing
Pub. .... Cecile Krimm
Delivery Method: Mail, Newsstand

TOWNER

THE MOUSE RIVER JOURNAL (WED)

PO Box 268, Towner, ND, 58788-0268, McHenry, USA; gen tel (701) 537-5610; gen fax (701) 537-5493; disp adv e-mail msrvrjnl@ndak.net; ed e-mail msrvrjnl@srt.com; web site http://mouseriverjournal.weebly.com/
Circulation: 1,200pd,; Sworn/Estimate/Non-Audited
Advertising rate: Open inch rate $4.85
Group: Nordmark Publishing
Pub. .... Jason Nordmark
Ed. .... Billy Joe Eriksmoen

UNDERWOOD

UNDERWOOD NEWS (THUR)
216 Lincoln Ave, Underwood, ND, 58576-4005, McLean, USA; gen tel (701) 442-5535; gen fax (701) 462-8128; disp adv e-mail bhgnews@westriv.com; web site http://www.bhgnews.com/
Circulation: 529pd, 22fr; Sworn/Estimate/Non-Audited
Advertising rate: Open inch rate $6.80
Group: BHG, Inc.
Adv. Mgr. .... Don Winter
Ed. .... Suzanne Werre
Delivery Method: Mail, Newsstand, Carrier, Racks

VELVA

VELVA AREA VOICE (THUR)
1 Main St N, Velva, ND, 58790-7304, McHenry, USA; gen tel (701) 338-2599; gen fax (701) 338-2705; disp adv e-mail yournews@srt.com; web site www.nd-bhginc.com
Circulation: 1,000pd,; Sworn/Estimate/Non-Audited
Advertising rate: Open inch rate $6.20
Group: BHG, Inc.
Ed. .... Courtney Graves

WAHPETON

NEWS-MONITOR (TUES)
601 Dakota Ave, Wahpeton, ND, 58075-4325, Richland, USA; gen tel (701) 642-8585; gen fax (701) 642-6068; disp adv e-mail tarak@wahpetondailynews.com; class adv e-mail classifieds@wahpetondailynews.com; ed e-mail newsmonitor@wahpetondailynews.com; web site http://www.wahpetondaily-news.com/news_monitor
Circulation: 1,750pd,; Sworn/Estimate/Non-Audited
Advertising rate: Open inch rate $7.30
Established: 1991
Group: Wick Communications
Pub. .... Ken Harty
Adv. Mgr. .... Tara Klostreich
Mng. ed. .... Karen Speidel
Mechanical Specifications: Type page 13 x 21; E - 6 cols, 2 1/16, 3/16 between; A - 6 cols, 2 1/16, 3/16 between; C - 8 cols, 1 1/2, 3/16 between.Equipment & Software: Hardware — APP/Mac; Presses — G/Community; Software — QPS/QuarkXPress.
Delivery Method: Mail, Newsstand, Racks
Areas Served: Hankinson, Lidgerwood, Wyndmere, Fairmount

WALHALLA

WALHALLA MOUNTAINEER (WED)
1001 Central Ave, Walhalla, ND, 58282, Pembina, USA; gen tel (701)549-2580; disp adv e-mail mtneer@utma.com
Advertising rate: $4.00 per column inch

WASHBURN

LEADER-NEWS (THUR)
607 Main Avenue, Washburn, ND, 58577, McLean, USA; gen tel (701) 462-8126; gen fax (701)462-8128; disp adv e-mail bhgnews@westriv.com; ed e-mail leadernews@westriv.com; web site www.bhgnews.com
Circulation: 1,735pd, 55fr; Sworn/Estimate/Non-Audited
Advertising rate: Open inch rate $6.50
Group: BHG, Inc.
Ed. .... Don Winter
Editor .... Alyssa Meier

WATFORD CITY

MCKENZIE COUNTY FARMER (WED)
109 N Main St, Watford City, ND, 58854-7101, McKenzie, USA; gen tel (701) 842-2351; gen fax (701) 842-2352; disp adv e-mail mcf@watfordcitynd.com; web site www.watfordcitynd.com
Circulation: 2,400pd, 26fr; Sworn/Estimate/Non-Audited
Advertising rate: Open inch rate $8.00
Established: 1908
Ed. .... Neal A. Shipman
Mechanical Specifications: Type page 13 x 21 1/2; E - 6 cols, 2 1/16, 1/8 between; A - 6 cols, 2 1/16, 1/8 between; C - 6 cols, 2 1/16, 1/8 between.Equipment & Software: Hardware — PCs; Software — Adobe/PageMaker 6.5, Adobe/Photoshop 5.0, Adobe/Illustrator 7.0.
Delivery Method: Mail, Newsstand, Racks
Areas Served: 58854, 58831, 58835, 58757, 58634, 58838, 58847, 58801, 58640, 58763,

WEST FARGO

WEST FARGO PIONEER (WED)
3124 41st Street S, West Fargo, ND, 58078, Cass, USA; gen tel (701) 451-5718; ed tel (701) 241-5579; gen fax (701) 241-5487; disp adv e-mail news@westfargopioneer.com; web site www.westfargopioneer.com
Circulation: 1,000pd,; Sworn/Estimate/Non-Audited
Advertising rate: Open inch rate $12.00
Group: Forum Communications Co.
Assistant Ed. .... Wendy Reuer
Ed. .... Matthew Von Pinnon
Mechanical Specifications: Type page 10 1/4 x 16 1/2; E - 5 cols, 1 3/4, 1/6 between; A - 5 cols, 1 3/4, 1/6 between; C - 5 cols, 1 3/4, 1/6 between.Equipment & Software: Hardware — PCs; Presses — G/Community.

WESTHOPE

WESTHOPE STANDARD (WED)
150 MAIN ST, Westhope, ND, 58793, Bottineau, USA; gen tel (701) 245-6461; gen fax (701) 245-6461; disp adv e-mail standard@srt.com; web site www.cndnews.com
Circulation: 800pd,; Sworn/Estimate/Non-Audited
Advertising rate: Open inch rate $4.00
Established: 1901
Ed. .... Ginny Heth
Mechanical Specifications: Type page 14 x 21.Equipment & Software: Hardware — APP/Mac LC 580, IBM; Software — QPS/QuarkXPress, Claris/Works, Print Shop.
Delivery Method: Mail, Newsstand, Racks
Areas Served: Bottineau

WILLISTON

THE PLAINS REPORTER (WED)
14 4th St W, Williston, ND, 58801-5308, Williams, USA; gen tel (701) 572-2165; gen fax (701) 572-1965; disp adv e-mail advertising@willstonherald.com; ed e-mail news@willistonherald.com; web site www.willistonherald.com
Circulation: 15,500fr; Sworn/Estimate/Non-Audited
Advertising rate: Open inch rate $9.10
Publisher .... Ken Harty
Managing Editor .... Jamie Kelly
Mechanical Specifications: Type page 13 x 21; E - 6 cols, 2 1/16, 1/8 between; A - 6 cols, 2 1/16, 1/8 between.Equipment & Software: Hardware — APP/Mac; Presses — HI/V15A; Software — QPS/QuarkXPress, DTI/AdBuilder, Baseview/NewsEditPro.

WISHEK

THE WISHEK STAR (WED)
24 N Centennial St, Wishek, ND, 58495-0275, McIntosh, USA; gen tel (701) 452-2331; gen fax (701) 452-2340; disp adv e-mail wishekstar@gmail.com; class adv e-mail wishekstar@gmail.com; ed e-mail wishekstar@gmail.com; web site mcintosh-star-tribune.com
Circulation: 1,000pd,; Sworn/Estimate/Non-Audited
Advertising rate: Open inch rate $7.75
Established: 1901
Group: Redhead Publishing, Inc
Editorial Dir. .... Francis Materi
Mechanical Specifications: Type page 10 x 16; E - 6 cols, 1 3/4, 1/8 between; A - 6 cols, 1 3/4, 1/8 between; C - 6 cols, 1 3/4, 1/8 between. Equipment & Software: Hardware — APP/Mac, APP/iMac; Presses — 4-G/Community; Software — QPS/QuarkXPress 4.0, Adobe/Quandra 610.
Delivery Method: Mail, Newsstand, Racks

OHIO

ADA

THE ADA HERALD (THUR)
229 N Main St, Ada, OH, 45810-1109, Hardin, USA; gen tel (419) 634-6055; adv tel (419) 634-6055 ext. 203; ed tel (419) 634-6055 ext. 201; gen fax (419) 634-0912; adv fax (419) 634-0912; ed fax (419) 634-0912; disp adv e-mail kpickens@putnamsentinel.com ; class adv e-mail kpickens@putnamsentinel.com ; ed e-mail sgriffis@adaherald.com; web site www.adaherald.com
Circulation: 3,000pd,; Sworn/Estimate/Non-Audited
Advertising rate: Open inch rate $10.00
Established: 1885
Group: Delphos Herald, Inc.
Digital Platform - Mobile: Apple, Android, Windows, Blackberry
Digital Platform - Tablet: Apple iOS, Android, Windows 7, Blackberry Tablet OS, Kindle, Nook, Kindle Fire
Pub. .... David Thornberry
Ed. .... Anne Coburn-Griffis
Adv. Mgr. .... Kristen Pickens
Mechanical Specifications: Type page 13 x 21; E - 6 cols, 2, 1/4 between; A - 6 cols, 2, 1/4 between; C - 8 cols, 1 1/4, 1/4 between. Equipment & Software: Hardware — 6-APP/Mac; Software — QPS/QuarkXPress 3.3, Adobe/Photoshop, Caere/OmniPage.
Delivery Method: Mail, Newsstand, Racks
Areas Served: Hardin County

AKRON

THE SUBURBANITE (SUN)
3577 S Arlington Rd, Ste B, Akron, OH, 44312-5268, Summit, USA; gen tel (330) 899-2872; adv tel (330) 899-2872 ext. 12; ed tel (330) 899-2872 ext. 14; gen fax (330) 896-7633; adv fax (330) 896-7633; ed fax (330) 896-7633; disp adv e-mail suburbanite@thesuburbanite.com; class adv e-mail suburbanite@thesuburbanite.com; ed e-mail greg.kohntopp@thesuburbanite.com; web site www.thesuburbanite.com
Circulation: 69pd, 33,046fr; Sworn/Estimate/Non-Audited
Advertising rate: Open inch rate $16.25
Established: 1965
Group: GateHouse Media, Inc.
Digital Platform - Mobile: Apple, Android
Digital Platform - Tablet: Apple iOS, Android, Windows 7
Ed. .... Greg kohntopp
Adv. Mgr. .... Carol CooneyEquipment & Software: Hardware — APP/Power Mac G4; Software — QPS/QuarkXPress 4.0.
Delivery Method: Mail, Newsstand, Racks
Areas Served: 44203, 44319, 44216, 44232, 44312, 44685, 44720, 44250, 44306

ANTWERP

ANTWERP BEE-ARGUS (OTHER)
1`13 Main, Antwerp, OH, 45813, Paulding, USA; gen tel (419) 258-8161; ed tel (419) 258-8161; gen fax (419) 258-9365; class adv e-mail an; ed e-mail antwerpbeeargus@frontier.com; web site www.antwerpbeeargus.com
Circulation:; Sworn/Estimate/Non-Audited
Advertising rate: Open inch rate $5.50 (Local); $6.50 (National)
Established: 1883
Digital Platform - Mobile: Apple
Digital Platform - Tablet: Apple iOS
Pub./Ed. .... June L. Temple
Ed. .... Sandra K. Temple
Mng. Ed. .... Rodger S. Temple
Mechanical Specifications: Type page 13 x ; E - 6 cols, 2, 1 between; A - 6 cols, 2, between; C - 6 cols, 2, between.

ARCHBOLD

ARCHBOLD BUCKEYE (WED)
207 N Defiance St, Archbold, OH, 43502-1187, Fulton, USA; gen tel (419) 445-4466; adv tel (419) 445-4466; ed tel (419) 445-4466; adv fax (419) 445-4177; disp adv e-mail advertising@archboldbuckeye.com; class adv e-mail advertising@archboldbuckeye.com; ed e-mail buckeye@archboldbuckeye.com; web site www.archboldbuckeye.com
Circulation: 1,956pd, 56fr; Sworn/Estimate/Non-Audited
Advertising rate: Open inch rate $11.40 (Local); $13.42 (National)
Established: 1905
Digital Platform - Mobile: Apple, Android, Windows, Blackberry
Digital Platform - Tablet: Apple iOS, Android, Windows 7, Blackberry Tablet OS, Kindle, Nook, Kindle Fire
Pub. .... Ross William Taylor
Adv. Dir. .... Mary Huber
Ed. .... David Pugh
Prodn. Mgr. .... Brent Taylor
Mechanical Specifications: Type page 11 1/2 x 21; E - 6 cols, 1.66, 1/8 between; A - 6 cols, 1.66, 1/8 between; C - 6 cols, 1.66, 1/8 between.Equipment & Software: Hardware — APP/iMac; Software — Microsoft/Creator/InDesign
Delivery Method: Mail, Newsstand
Areas Served: Fulton County

FARMLAND NEWS (TUES)
104 Depot St, Archbold, OH, 43502-1235, Fulton, USA; gen tel (419) 445-9456; adv tel (419) 445-9456; ed tel (419) 445-9456; gen fax (419) 445-4444; adv fax (419) 445-4444; ed fax (419) 445-4444; disp adv e-mail Ads@FarmlandNews.com; class adv e-mail Ads@FarmlandNews.com; ed e-mail News1@FarmlandNews.com
Circulation: 2,300pd, 100fr; Sworn/Estimate/Non-Audited
Advertising rate: Open inch rate $12.50
Established: 1959
Digital Platform - Mobile: Apple, Android
Digital Platform - Tablet: Apple iOS, Android, Windows 7
Circulation Mgr/Sales .... Larkin Wise-Chappuis
Pub/Adv. Mgr. .... Dianne Lantz
Ed .... Judy Short
Mechanical Specifications: Type page 10 3/4 x 12 3/4; E - 5 cols, 2, 1/6 between; A - 5 cols, 2, 1/6 between; C - 6 cols, 1 2/3, 1/6 between. Equipment & Software: Hardware — APP/Mac; Software — Multi-Ad/Creator 4.0.1.
Delivery Method: Mail, Newsstand
Areas Served: Counties in Ohio: Williams, De-

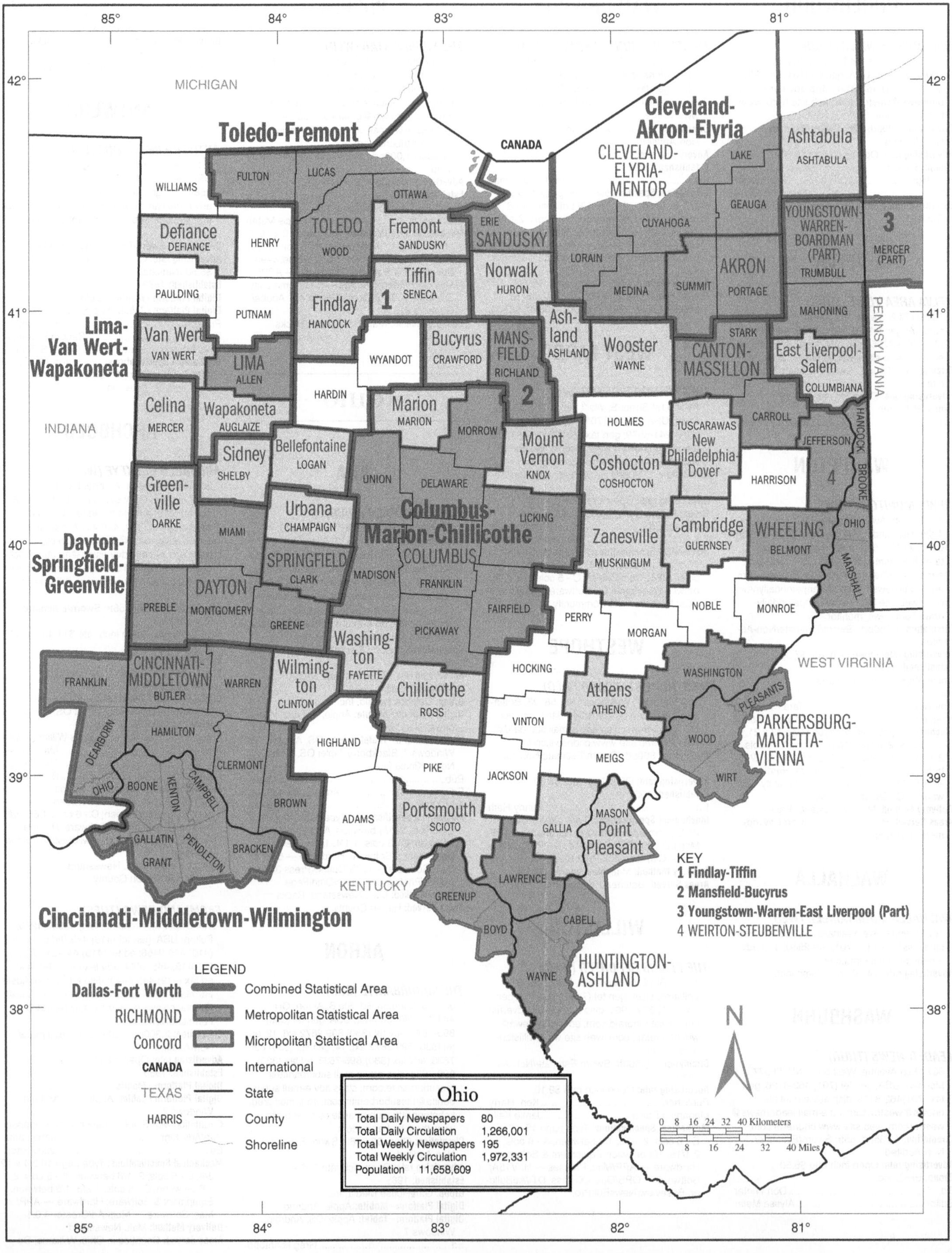

85°
84°
83°
82°
81°
42°
41°
40°
39°
38°
MICHIGAN
INDIANA
KENTUCKY
WEST VIRGINIA
PENNSYLVANIA
CANADA
Toledo-Fremont
Cleveland-Akron-Elyria
Lima-Van Wert-Wapakoneta
Dayton-Springfield-Greenville
Columbus-Marion-Chillicothe
Cincinnati-Middletown-Wilmington
CLEVELAND-ELYRIA-MENTOR
YOUNGSTOWN-WARREN-BOARDMAN (PART)
PARKERSBURG-MARIETTA-VIENNA
HUNTINGTON-ASHLAND
WILLIAMS
FULTON
LUCAS
TOLEDO
WOOD
OTTAWA
Fremont
SANDUSKY
ERIE
SANDUSKY
Defiance
DEFIANCE
HENRY
PAULDING
PUTNAM
Tiffin
SENECA
Findlay
HANCOCK
Norwalk
HURON
LORAIN
MEDINA
CUYAHOGA
SUMMIT
AKRON
PORTAGE
GEAUGA
LAKE
Ashtabula
ASHTABULA
TRUMBULL
MERCER (PART)
MAHONING
Van Wert
VAN WERT
LIMA
ALLEN
WYANDOT
Bucyrus
CRAWFORD
MANSFIELD
RICHLAND
Ashland
ASHLAND
Wooster
WAYNE
STARK
CANTON-MASSILLON
East Liverpool-Salem
COLUMBIANA
HARDIN
Celina
MERCER
Wapakoneta
AUGLAIZE
Marion
MARION
MORROW
HOLMES
TUSCARAWAS
New Philadelphia-Dover
CARROLL
JEFFERSON
HANCOCK
BROOKE
Sidney
SHELBY
Bellefontaine
LOGAN
UNION
DELAWARE
Mount Vernon
KNOX
Coshocton
COSHOCTON
HARRISON
Greenville
DARKE
MIAMI
Urbana
CHAMPAIGN
LICKING
Zanesville
MUSKINGUM
Cambridge
GUERNSEY
WHEELING
BELMONT
OHIO
MARSHALL
SPRINGFIELD
CLARK
MADISON
COLUMBUS
FRANKLIN
PREBLE
DAYTON
MONTGOMERY
GREENE
Washington
FAYETTE
PICKAWAY
FAIRFIELD
PERRY
NOBLE
MONROE
MORGAN
FRANKLIN
CINCINNATI-MIDDLETOWN
BUTLER
WARREN
Wilmington
CLINTON
Chillicothe
ROSS
HOCKING
Athens
ATHENS
WASHINGTON
PLEASANTS
DEARBORN
HAMILTON
HIGHLAND
VINTON
WOOD
MEIGS
OHIO
BOONE
KENTON
CAMPBELL
CLERMONT
PIKE
JACKSON
WIRT
BROWN
ADAMS
Portsmouth
SCIOTO
GALLIA
MASON
Point Pleasant
GALLATIN
GRANT
PENDLETON
BRACKEN
LAWRENCE
GREENUP
BOYD
CABELL
WAYNE
KEY
1 Findlay-Tiffin
2 Mansfield-Bucyrus
3 Youngstown-Warren-East Liverpool (Part)
4 WEIRTON-STEUBENVILLE
LEGEND
Dallas-Fort Worth Combined Statistical Area
RICHMOND Metropolitan Statistical Area
Concord Micropolitan Statistical Area
CANADA International
TEXAS State
HARRIS County
Shoreline
N
0 8 16 24 32 40 Kilometers
0 8 16 24 32 40 Miles
Ohio
Total Daily Newspapers 80
Total Daily Circulation 1,266,001
Total Weekly Newspapers 195
Total Weekly Circulation 1,972,331
Population 11,658,609

fiance, Paulding, Van Wert, Fulton, Henry, Lucas,, Wood & Putnam
Michigan Counties: Lenawee & Hillsdale

ATHENS

ATHENS NEWS (MON, THUR)

14 N Court St, Ste 1, Athens, OH, 45701-2429, Athens, USA; gen tel (740) 594-8219; gen fax (740) 592-5695; disp adv e-mail hilary@athensnews.com; class adv e-mail amy@athensnews.com; ed e-mail news@athensnews.com; web site www.athensnews.com - 63,653(views) 54,914(visitors)
Circulation: 12,000fr; CVC
Advertising rate: n/a - modular
Established: 1977
Group: APG Ohio
Digital Platform - Mobile: Apple, Android
Digital Platform - Tablet: Apple iOS, Android, Windows 7
Ed. and Pub. .... Terry Smith
Mechanical Specifications: One page 10 x 10; E - 4 cols, 2.4", 1/6 between; A - 4 cols, 2.4, 1/6 between; C - 6 cols, 1.58, 1/6 between. Equipment & Software: Hardware — APP/Macs; Software — APP/Mac System, Adobe/InDesign
Delivery Method: Racks
Areas Served: Athens County

ATTICA

ATTICA HUB (THUR)

202 N Main St, Attica, OH, 44807-9484, Seneca, USA; gen tel (419) 426-3491; adv tel (419) 426-3491; ed tel (419) 426-3491; gen fax (419) 426-2003; adv fax (419) 426-2003; ed fax (419) 426-2003; disp adv e-mail sales@atticahub.com; class adv e-mail auctions@atticahub.com; ed e-mail news@atticahub.com; web site www.atticahub.com
Circulation: 4,400pd,; Sworn/Estimate/Non-Audited
Advertising rate: Open inch rate $4.50
Established: 1896
Digital Platform - Mobile: Apple, Android, Windows, Blackberry
Digital Platform - Tablet: Apple iOS, Android, Windows 7, Blackberry Tablet OS, Kindle, Nook, Kindle Fire
Owner/Pub. .... Deb Cook
Adv. Mgr. .... Tammy Collins
Mechanical Specifications: Type page 13 x 21; E - 6 cols, 2 1/16, between; A - 6 cols, 2 1/16, between; C - 6 cols, 2 1/16, between. Equipment & Software: Hardware — IBM; Software — QPS/QuarkXPress.
Delivery Method: Mail, Newsstand, Racks
Areas Served: Ashland, Crawford, Erie, Hardin, Huron, Knox, Ottawa, Richland, Sandusky, Seneca, and Wyandot County

AVON LAKE

NORTH RIDGEVILLE PRESS (WED)

158 Lear Rd, Avon Lake, OH, 44012-1982, Lorain, USA; gen tel (440) 933-5100; adv tel (440) 933-5100; ed tel (440) 933-5100; gen fax (440) 933-7904; adv fax (440) 933-7904; ed fax (440) 933-7904; disp adv e-mail NRNews@2presspapers.com; class adv e-mail nrpclass@dceye.com; ed e-mail editor@2presspapers.com; web site www.2presspapers.com
Circulation: 2,000pd, 1,000fr; USPS
Advertising rate: Open inch rate $9.15
Established: 1980
Group: Douthit Communications, Inc.
Lorain County Printing & Publishing Co.
Digital Platform - Mobile: Apple, Android, Windows, Blackberry
Digital Platform - Tablet: Apple iOS, Android, Windows 7, Blackberry Tablet OS, Kindle, Nook, Kindle Fire
Pub. .... Harold K. Douthit
Ed. .... Peter Comings
Adv. Mgr./Gen. Mgr. .... Janet L. Sanner
Mechanical Specifications: Type page 10 3/8 x 16; A - 6 cols, 1 5/8, 1/4 between; C - 6 cols, 1 5/8, 1/4 between.Equipment & Software: Hardware — PC; Presses — Offset; Software — QPS/QuarkXPress 4.1, Macromedia/Freehand 9, Microsoft/Word 6, Adobe/Photoshop 5.5.
Delivery Method: Mail, Racks
Areas Served: 44039

THE PRESS (WED)

158 Lear Rd, Avon Lake, OH, 44012-1982, Lorain, USA; gen tel (440) 933-5100; adv tel (440) 933-5100; ed tel (440) 933-5100; gen fax (440) 933-7904; adv fax (440) 933-7904; ed fax (440) 933-7904; disp adv e-mail advertising@2presspapers.com; class adv e-mail alpclass@dceye.com; ed e-mail editor@2presspapers.com; web site www.2presspapers.com
Circulation: 4,000pd, 2,500fr; USPS
Advertising rate: Open inch rate $14.50
Established: 1951
Group: Douthit Communications, Inc.
Digital Platform - Mobile: Apple, Android, Windows, Blackberry
Digital Platform - Tablet: Apple iOS, Android, Windows 7, Blackberry Tablet OS, Kindle, Nook, Kindle Fire
Ed. .... Larry Limpf
Mechanical Specifications: Type page 10 1/2 x 16; A - 6 cols, 1 5/8, 1/4 between; C - 6 cols, 1 5/8, 1/4 between.Equipment & Software: Hardware — PC; Software — Microsoft/Word 6, QPS/QuarkXPress 4.1, Macromedia/Freehand 9.0, Adobe/Photoshop 5.5.
Delivery Method: Mail, Newsstand, Racks
Areas Served: 44011, 44012, 44054

BARBERTON

THE BARBERTON HERALD (THUR)

70 4th St NW, Ste 1, Barberton, OH, 44203-8283, Summit, USA; gen tel (330) 753-1068; adv tel (330) 753-1068; ed tel (330) 753-1068; gen fax (330) 753-1021; adv fax (330) 753-1021; ed fax (330) 753-1021; disp adv e-mail jimc@barbertonherald.com; class adv e-mail classifieds@barbertonherald.com; ed e-mail news@barbertonherald.com; web site www.barbertonherald.com
Circulation: 7,800pd, 33,618fr; Sworn/Estimate/Non-Audited
Advertising rate: Open inch rate $19.00
Established: 1923
Digital Platform - Mobile: Apple, Android, Windows, Blackberry
Digital Platform - Tablet: Apple iOS, Android, Windows 7, Blackberry Tablet OS, Kindle, Nook, Kindle Fire
Pub. .... Cheryl Vespoint
Adv. Dir. .... Jim Colombo
Ed. .... Rich Muller
Delivery Method: Mail, Newsstand, Racks
Areas Served: Barberton and Norton

BARNESVILLE

BARNESVILLE ENTERPRISE (WED)

166 E Main St, Barnesville, OH, 43713-1004, Belmont, USA; gen tel (740) 425-1912; adv tel (740) 425-1912; ed tel (740) 425-1912; gen fax (740) 425-2545; adv fax (740) 425-2545; ed fax (740) 425-2545; disp adv e-mail bstephen@barnesville-enterprise.com; class adv e-mail enterprise@barnesville-enterprise.com; ed e-mail enterprise@barnesville-enterprise.com; web site www.barnesville-enterprise.com
Circulation: 4,613pd, 30fr; Sworn/Estimate/Non-Audited
Advertising rate: Open inch rate $6.80
Established: 1866
Group: Jeffersonian Advantage
Digital Platform - Mobile: Apple, Android, Windows, Blackberry
Digital Platform - Tablet: Apple iOS, Android, Windows 7, Blackberry Tablet OS, Kindle, Nook, Kindle Fire
Pub. .... Andrew Dix
Ed. .... Cathryn Stanley
Mng. Ed. .... Ray Booth
Advertising .... Beth Stephens
Mechanical Specifications: Type page 13 x 21 1/2; E - 6 cols, 2 1/16, 1/8 between; A - 6 cols, 2 1/16, 1/8 between; C - 9 cols, 1 3/8, 1/16 between.
Delivery Method: Mail, Newsstand
Areas Served: 43713, 43719, 43759, 43716, 43773, 43718

BATAVIA

THE CLERMONT SUN (THUR, SUN)

465 E Main St, Batavia, OH, 45103-3003, Clermont, USA; gen tel (513) 732-2511; adv tel (513) 732-2511; ed tel (513) 732-2511; gen fax (513) 732-6344; adv fax (513) 732-6344; ed fax (513) 732-6344; disp adv e-mail ckeith@clermontsun.com; class adv e-mail tadams@clermontsun.com; ed e-mail ahunter@clermontsun.com; web site www.clermontsun.com
Circulation: 2,500pd, 18,000fr; Sworn/Estimate/Non-Audited
Advertising rate: Open inch rate $9.80
Established: 1828
Group: MCM Ohio LLC
Digital Platform - Mobile: Apple, Android
Digital Platform - Tablet: Apple iOS, Android, Windows 7
Pub. .... Tony Adams
Owner .... Scott Champion
Mechanical Specifications: Type page 11 1/2 x 21 1/2; E - 6 cols, 1 3/4, between; A - 6 cols, 1 3/4, between; C - 8 cols, 1 1/4, between.
Delivery Method: Mail, Newsstand, Racks
Areas Served: 45103, 45106, 45157, 45160, 45150, 45120, 45176, 45245

BELLEVUE

OTTAWA COUNTY EXPONENT (FRI)

250 Castalia St, Ste E, Bellevue, OH, 44811-1200, Huron, USA; gen tel (419) 898-5361; adv tel (419) 898-5361; ed tel (419) 898-5361; gen fax (419) 898-0501; adv fax (419) 898-0501; ed fax (419) 898-0501; disp adv e-mail rmiller@civitasmedia.com; class adv e-mail rmiller@civitasmedia.com; ed e-mail ocenews@civitasmedia.com; web site www.exponentnews.com
Circulation: 2,500pd, 200fr; Sworn/Estimate/Non-Audited
Advertising rate: Open inch rate $8.65
Group: Civitas Media, LLC-OOB
Digital Platform - Mobile: Apple, Android, Windows, Blackberry
Digital Platform - Tablet: Apple iOS, Android, Windows 7, Blackberry Tablet OS, Kindle, Nook, Kindle Fire
Ed. .... Rick Miller
Adv. Mgr. .... Gina Miller
Office Mgr./Prod. Dir. .... Christine Dials
Mechanical Specifications: Type page 12 3/4 x 21 1/2; E - 6 cols, 2, between; A - 6 cols, 2, between; C - 6 cols, 2, between.Equipment & Software: Hardware — APP/Mac Centris 610, APP/Mac Performa 475, APP/Mac Performa 200, NewGen/Scanner; Software — Microsoft/Word 5.0, Aldus/PageMaker, Fox Pro/Quicken 3.0.
Delivery Method: Mail, Newsstand, Racks
Areas Served: Ottawa County

BELLVILLE

BELLVILLE STAR & TRI-FORKS PRESS (THUR)

107 Main St, Bellville, OH, 44813-1020, Richland, USA; gen tel (419) 886-2291; adv tel (419) 886-2291; ed tel (419) 886-2291; gen fax (419) 886-2704; adv fax (419) 886-2704; ed fax (419) 886-2704; disp adv e-mail bellvillestar@ohcommedia.com; class adv e-mail bellvillestar@ohcommedia.com; ed e-mail Dsharp@ohcommedia.com; web site http://thebellvillestar.com/
Circulation: 2,100pd, 16fr; Sworn/Estimate/Non-Audited
Advertising rate: Open inch rate $9.30
Group: AIM Media Indiana
Ed. .... Diana Sharp
Mechanical Specifications: Type page 13 x 20 1/2; C - 6 cols, between.
Delivery Method: Mail, Newsstand
Areas Served: Richland County

BLUFFTON

THE BLUFFTON NEWS (THUR)

101 N Main St, Bluffton, OH, 45817-1245, Allen, USA; gen tel (419) 358-8010; adv tel (419) 358-8010; ed tel (419) 358-8010; gen fax (419) 358-8020; adv fax (419) 358-8020; ed fax (419) 358-8020; disp adv e-mail editor@blufftonnews.com; class adv e-mail editor@blufftonnews.com; ed e-mail editor@blufftonnews.com; web site www.blufftonnews.com
Circulation: 2,900pd,; Sworn/Estimate/Non-Audited
Advertising rate: Open inch rate $8.50
Established: 1876
Digital Platform - Mobile: Apple, Android, Windows, Blackberry
Digital Platform - Tablet: Apple iOS, Android, Windows 7, Blackberry Tablet OS, Kindle
Pub. .... Thomas M. Edwards
Ed. .... Austin Arnold
Adv. Mgr. .... Sean Burgie
Mechanical Specifications: Type page 11 5/8 x ; E - 6 cols, 1 3/16, between; A - 6 cols, 2, between; C - 6 cols, 2, between.Equipment & Software: Hardware — APP/Power Macs; Software — QPS/QuarkXPress, Adobe/Photoshop, Adobe/Illustrator.
Delivery Method: Mail, Newsstand
Areas Served: Allen County

BOARDMAN

BOARDMAN NEWS (THUR)

8302 Southern Blvd, Ste 2, Boardman, OH, 44512-6353, Mahoning, USA; gen tel (330) 758-6397; adv tel (330) 758-6397; ed tel (330) 758-6397; gen fax (330) 758-2658; adv fax (330) 758-2658; ed fax (330) 758-2658; disp adv e-mail bnews@zoominternet.net; class adv e-mail bnews@zoominternet.net; ed e-mail bnews@zoominternet.net; web site www.boardmannews.net
Circulation: 8,000pd, 100fr; USPS
Advertising rate: Open inch rate $10.00
Established: 1947
Digital Platform - Mobile: Apple, Android
Digital Platform - Tablet: Apple iOS, Android, Windows 7
Pub. Emeritus .... Jack A. Darnell
Ed. .... John A. Darnell
Adv. Mgr. .... Gwen Darnell
Mechanical Specifications: Type page 13 x 20; E - 8 cols, 1 5/8, 1/6 between; A - 8 cols, 1 5/8, 1/6 between; C - 8 cols, 1 5/8, 1/6 between. Equipment & Software: Hardware — 2-APP/Mac, APP/PowerBook; Software — Adobe/PageMaker 5.0.
Photoshop
In Design
Delivery Method: Mail, Newsstand, Carrier
Areas Served: 44512, 44511, 44514, 44406

BROOKVILLE

BROOKVILLE STAR (WED)

14 Mulberry St, Brookville, OH, 45309-1828, Montgomery, USA; gen tel (937) 833-2545; adv tel (937) 833-2545; ed tel (937) 833-2545; gen fax (937) 833-2546; adv fax (937) 833-2546; ed fax (937) 833-2546; disp adv e-mail ads@brookvillestar.net; class adv e-mail ads@brookvillestar.net; ed e-mail news@brookvillestar.net; web site www.brookvillestar.net
Circulation: 3,500pd,; Sworn/Estimate/Non-Audited

Advertising rate: Open inch rate $7.00
Established: 1891
Digital Platform - Mobile: Apple, Android, Windows, Blackberry
Digital Platform - Tablet: Apple iOS, Android, Windows 7, Blackberry Tablet OS, Kindle, Nook, Kindle Fire
Pub./Ed. ....Jim Hoffman
Adv. Mgr./Circ. Mgr. ....Mark Gordon
Mechanical Specifications: Type page 13 x 21 1/2; E - 6 cols, 1 13/16, between; A - 6 cols, 1 13/16, between; C - 8 cols, 1 5/16, between.
Delivery Method: Mail, Racks
Areas Served: 45309, 45345, 45354, 45378, 45338

BUCKEYE LAKE

THE BUCKEYE LAKE BEACON (SAT)

4675 Walnut Rd, Buckeye Lake, OH, 43008-7770, Licking, USA; gen tel (740) 928-5541; adv tel (740) 928-5541; ed tel (740) 928-5541; gen fax (740) 928-7960; adv fax (740) 928-7960; ed fax (740) 928-7960; disp adv e-mail charlesprince@buckeyelakebeacon.net; class adv e-mail art@buckeyelakebeacon.net; ed e-mail charlesprince@buckeyelakebeacon.net; web site www.buckeyelakebeacon.net
Circulation: 15fr; Sworn/Estimate/Non-Audited
Advertising rate: Open inch rate $6.95
Established: 1996
Digital Platform - Mobile: Apple, Android, Windows, Blackberry
Digital Platform - Tablet: Apple iOS, Android, Windows 7, Blackberry Tablet OS, Kindle, Nook, Kindle Fire
Pub./Ed./Adv. Mgr. ....Charles Prince
Bus. Mgr. ....Mary Prince
Mechanical Specifications: Type page 10 3/16 x 16; E - 5 cols, 1 7/8, between; A - 5 cols, 1 7/8, between.Equipment & Software: Hardware — HP/LaserWriter 4MV 600 dpi; Software — InDesign, Photoshop, Illustrator, Word
Delivery Method: Carrier, Racks
Areas Served: 43008, 43025, 43046, 43076, 43062, 43076, 43105, 43148

CADIZ

HARRISON NEWS-HERALD (WED, THUR, SAT)

144 S Main St, Ste 1, Cadiz, OH, 43907-1165, Harrison, USA; gen tel (740) 942-2118; adv tel (740) 942-2118; ed tel (740) 942-2118; gen fax (740) 942-4667; adv fax (740) 942-4667; ed fax (740) 942-4667; disp adv e-mail andrea@harrisonnewsherald.com; class adv e-mail andrea@harrisonnewsherald.com; ed e-mail newsroom@harrisonnewsherald.com; web site www.harrisonnewsherald.com
Circulation: 6,000pd, 40fr; Sworn/Estimate/Non-Audited
Advertising rate: Open inch rate $9.95
Established: 1819
Group: Schloss Media, Inc.
Digital Platform - Mobile: Apple, Android, Windows
Digital Platform - Tablet: Apple iOS, Android, Windows 7
Pub. ....David G. Schloss
Ed. ....Emily J. Schloss
Editor ....Mike Sieber
Mechanical Specifications: Type page 13 x 21 1/2; E - 6 cols, 2, 1/5 between; A - 6 cols, 2, 1/5 between; C - 9 cols, 1 1/4, 1/5 between.
Delivery Method: Mail, Newsstand, Racks
Areas Served: 43907
44615
45309

CALDWELL

THE JOURNAL & NOBLE COUNTY LEADER (MON)

309 Main St, Caldwell, OH, 43724-1321, Noble, USA; gen tel (740) 732-2341; adv tel (740) 732-2341; ed tel (740) 732-2341; gen fax (740) 732-7288; adv fax (740) 732-7288; ed fax (740) 732-7288; disp adv e-mail news@journal-leader.com; class adv e-mail news@journal-leader.com; ed e-mail news@journal-leader.com; web site www.journal-leader.com
Circulation: 4,500pd,; Sworn/Estimate/Non-Audited
Advertising rate: Open inch rate $7.50
Established: 1859
Digital Platform - Mobile: Apple, Android, Windows
Digital Platform - Tablet: Apple iOS, Android, Windows 7
Pub./Ed./Adv. Dir. ....Anne Chlovechok
Delivery Method: Mail, Racks
Areas Served: Noble County

CAMBRIDGE

NEW CONCORD AREA LEADER (SUN)

831 Wheeling Ave, Cambridge, OH, 43725-2316, Guernsey, USA; gen tel (740) 439-3531; adv tel (740) 439-3531; ed tel (740) 439-3531; gen fax (740) 432-6219; adv fax (740) 439-3533; ed fax (740) 432-6219; disp adv e-mail Lynn@daily-jeff.com; class adv e-mail ads@daily-jeff.com; ed e-mail newsroom@daily-jeff.com; web site www.newconcordleader.com
Circulation: 1,150pd,; Sworn/Estimate/Non-Audited
Advertising rate: Open inch rate $3.00
Group: Jeffersonian Advantage
Digital Platform - Mobile: Apple, Android, Windows, Blackberry
Digital Platform - Tablet: Apple iOS, Android, Windows 7, Blackberry Tablet OS, Kindle, Nook, Kindle Fire
Pub. ....Andrew Dix
Exec. Ed. ....Ray Booth
Mechanical Specifications: Type page 13 x 21 1/2; E - 6 cols, 2 1/16, 1/6 between; A - 6 cols, 2 1/16, 1/6 between; C - 9 cols, 1 3/8, between.Equipment & Software: Hardware — APP/Macs; Presses — G/Community; Software — QPS/QuarkXPress, Multi-Ad, Adobe/Photoshop.
Delivery Method: Mail, Newsstand
Areas Served: Guernsey County
Muskingum County

CAREY

THE MOHAWK LEADER (WED)

1198 E Findlay St, Carey, OH, 43316-9760, Wyandot, USA; gen tel (419) 396-7567; adv tel (419) 396-7567; ed tel (419) 396-7567; gen fax (419) 396-7527; adv fax (419) 396-7527; ed fax (419) 396-7527; disp adv e-mail Ads@theprogressortimes.com ; class adv e-mail Amy@theprogressortimes.com; ed e-mail Steve@theprogressortimes.com ; web site www.theprogressortimes.com
Circulation: 4,000pd,; Sworn/Estimate/Non-Audited
Advertising rate: Open inch rate $6.80
Established: 1894
Digital Platform - Mobile: Apple, Android, Windows, Blackberry
Digital Platform - Tablet: Apple iOS, Android, Windows 7, Blackberry Tablet OS, Kindle, Nook, Kindle Fire
Pub./Ed. ....Stephen C. Zender
Adv. Dir. ....Amy Yeater
Circ. Mgr. ....Jenny Freeman
Mechanical Specifications: Type page 13 x 21; E - 6 cols, 2 1/16, 1/8 between; A - 6 cols, 2 1/16, 1/8 between.Equipment & Software: Hardware — APP/Mac; Software — QPS/QuarkXPress.
Delivery Method: Mail, Newsstand
Areas Served: Wyandot County

THE PROGRESSOR TIMES (WED)

1198 E Findlay St, Carey, OH, 43316-9760, Wyandot, USA; gen tel (419) 396-7567; adv tel (419) 396-7567; ed tel (419) 396-7567; gen fax (419) 396-7527; adv fax (419) 396-7527; ed fax (419) 396-7527; disp adv e-mail Ads@theprogressortimes.com ; class adv e-mail Amy@theprogressortimes.com; ed e-mail Steve@theprogressortimes.com ; web site www.theprogressortimes.com
Circulation: 4,000pd,; Sworn/Estimate/Non-Audited
Advertising rate: Open inch rate $6.80
Established: 1873
Digital Platform - Mobile: Apple, Android, Windows, Blackberry
Digital Platform - Tablet: Apple iOS, Android, Windows 7, Blackberry Tablet OS, Kindle, Nook, Kindle Fire
Pub./Ed. ....Stephen C. Zender
Adv. Dir. ....Amy Yeater
Circ. Mgr. ....Jenny Freeman
Mechanical Specifications: Type page 13 x 21; E - 6 cols, 2 1/16, 1/8 between; A - 6 cols, 2 1/16, 1/8 between.Equipment & Software: Hardware — APP/Mac; Software — QPS/QuarkXPress.
Delivery Method: Mail, Newsstand
Areas Served: Wyandot County

CARROLLTON

THE FREE PRESS STANDARD (THUR)

43 E Main St, Carrollton, OH, 44615-1221, Carroll, USA; gen tel (330) 627-5591; adv tel (330) 627-5591; ed tel (330) 627-5591; gen fax (330) 627-3195; adv fax (330) 627-3195; ed fax (330) 627-3195; disp adv e-mail adfps44615@yahoo.com; class adv e-mail ctrushel@freepressstandard.com; ed e-mail fps44615@yahoo.com; web site www.freepressstandard.com - 100,000(views)
Circulation: 4,500pd, 700fr; Sworn/Estimate/Non-Audited
Advertising rate: Open inch rate $10.81
Established: 1831
Digital Platform - Mobile: Apple, Android
Digital Platform - Tablet: Apple iOS, Android, Windows 7
Ed. ....Carol McIntire
Adv. Mgr. ....Connie Trushel
publisher ....David Schloss
Mechanical Specifications: Type page 13 x 21 1/2; E - 6 cols, 2, 1/6 between; A - 6 cols, 2, 1/6 between; C - 9 cols, 1 1/3, 1/6 between. Equipment & Software: Hardware — APP/Mac; Software — WordPerfect, QPS/QuarkXPress 3.3.
Delivery Method: Mail, Newsstand
Areas Served: Carroll, Stark, Harrison, Columbiana, Jefferson, and Tuscarawas County

CHAGRIN FALLS

CHAGRIN VALLEY TIMES (THUR)

525 Washington St, Chagrin Falls, OH, 44022-4455, Geauga, USA; gen tel (440) 247-5335; adv tel (440) 247-5335; ed tel (440) 247-5335; gen fax (440) 247-5615; adv fax (440) 247-5615; ed fax (440) 247-5615; disp adv e-mail sales@chagrinvalleytimes.com; class adv e-mail myad@chagrinvalleytimes.com; ed e-mail editor@chagrinvalleytimes.com; web site www.chagrinvalleytoday.com
Circulation: 4,487pd, 5,179fr; AAM
Advertising rate: Open inch rate $20.75
Established: 1971
Group: Douthit Communications, Inc.
Digital Platform - Mobile: Apple, Android
Digital Platform - Tablet: Apple iOS, Android, Windows 7
Pub. ....Harold K. Douthit
Ed. ....Ellen J Kleinerman
Mechanical Specifications: Type page 10 1/4 x 16; E - 4 cols, 2 3/8, 1/4 between; A - 6 cols, 1 5/8, between; C - 6 cols, 1 5/8, between. Equipment & Software: Hardware — IBM; Software — QPS/QuarkXPress, Adobe/Illustrator.
Delivery Method: Mail, Newsstand, Racks
Areas Served: Eastern Cuyahoga and Western Geauga County

GEAUGA COURIER (FRI)

525 Washington St, Chagrin Falls, OH, 44022-4455, Geauga, USA; gen tel (440) 247-5335; adv tel (440) 247-5335; ed tel (440) 247-5335; gen fax (440) 247-5615; adv fax (440) 247-5615; ed fax (440) 247-5615; disp adv e-mail sales@chagrinvalleytimes.com; class adv e-mail myad@chagrinvalleytimes.com; ed e-mail editor@chagrinvalleytimes.com; web site www.chagrinvalleytoday.com
Circulation: 2,500pd, 2,500fr; Sworn/Estimate/Non-Audited
Advertising rate: Open inch rate $20.75
Established: 1998
Group: Douthit Communications, Inc.
Digital Platform - Mobile: Apple, Android
Digital Platform - Tablet: Apple iOS, Android, Windows 7
Pub. ....H. Kenneth Douthit III
Editor ....Ellen J Kleinerman
Mechanical Specifications: Type page 10 1/4 x 16; E - 4 cols, 2 3/8, between; A - 6 cols, 1 5/8, between; C - 6 cols, 1 5/8, between.
Delivery Method: Mail, Newsstand, Racks
Areas Served: 44024, 44065, 44021, 44026

SOLON TIMES (THUR)

525 Washington St, Chagrin Falls, OH, 44022-4455, Geauga, USA; gen tel (440) 247-5335; adv tel (440) 247-5335; ed tel (440) 247-5335; gen fax (440) 247-5615; adv fax (440) 247-5615; ed fax (440) 247-5615; disp adv e-mail sales@chagrinvalleytimes.com; class adv e-mail myad@chagrinvalleytimes.com; ed e-mail editor@chagrinvalleytimes.com; web site www.chagrinvalleytoday.com
Circulation: 1,900pd, 1,000fr; Sworn/Estimate/Non-Audited
Advertising rate: Open inch rate $24.40
Established: 1978
Group: Douthit Communications, Inc.
Digital Platform - Mobile: Apple, Android
Digital Platform - Tablet: Apple iOS, Android, Windows 7
Pub. ....H. Kenneth Douthit III
Editor ....Ellen Kleinerman
Classifieds Mgr. ....Diana Nicolanti
Mechanical Specifications: Type page 10 1/4 x 16; E - 4 cols, 2 3/8, between; A - 6 cols, 1 5/8, between; C - 6 cols, 1 5/8, between. Equipment & Software: Hardware — IBM; Software — QPS/QuarkXPress, Adobe/Illustrator.
Delivery Method: Mail, Newsstand, Racks
Areas Served: 44139

CHARDON

GEAUGA COUNTY MAPLE LEAF (THUR)

101 South St, Chardon, OH, 44024-1336, Geauga, USA; gen tel (440) 285-2013; adv tel (440) 285-2013; ed tel (440) 285-2013; gen fax (440) 285-2015; adv fax (440) 285-2015; ed fax (440) 285-2015; disp adv e-mail ads@geaugamapleleaf.com; class adv e-mail ads@geaugamapleleaf.com; ed e-mail editor@geaugamapleleaf.com; web site www.geaugamapleleaf.com
Circulation: 4,200pd, 508fr; Sworn/Estimate/Non-Audited
Advertising rate: Open inch rate $11.00
Established: 1993
Digital Platform - Mobile: Apple, Android
Digital Platform - Tablet: Apple iOS, Android, Windows 7
Pub. ....Jeff Karlovec
Ed. ....John Karlovec
News Ed. ....Cassandra Shofar
Mechanical Specifications: Type page 8 1/4 x 10 1/2; E - 4 cols, 1 3/5, 1/8 between; A - 4 cols, 1 3/5, 1/8 between; C - 4 cols, 1 3/5, 1/8 between.Equipment & Software: ; Presses — HI.
Delivery Method: Mail, Newsstand, Racks
Areas Served: Geauga County, OH

CINCINNATI

COMMUNITY JOURNAL CLERMONT (WED)

312 Elm St, Cincinnati, OH, 45202-2739, Clermont, USA; gen tel (513) 248-8600; adv tel (513) 248-8600; ed tel (513) 248-8600; gen fax (513) 248-1938; adv fax (513) 248-1938; ed fax (513) 248-1938; disp adv e-mail acumby@communitypress.com; class adv e-mail acumby@communitypress.com; ed e-mail therron@communitypress.com; web site www.cincinnati.com
Circulation: 10,835fr; CAC
Advertising rate: Open inch rate $7.40
Group: Gannett
Digital Platform - Mobile: Apple, Android, Windows, Blackberry
Digital Platform - Tablet: Apple iOS, Android, Windows 7, Blackberry Tablet OS, Kindle, Nook, Kindle Fire
Editor .... Richard Maloney
Pres./Pub. .... Margaret Buchanan
Adv. Mgr. .... Alison Cumby
Delivery Method: Mail, Newsstand, Carrier, Racks
Areas Served: 45102, 45103, 45122, 45140, 45145, 45147, 45150, 45150, 45157, 45158, 45160, 45176, 45244, 45245

DELHI PRESS (WED)

312 Elm St, Cincinnati, OH, 45202-2739, Hamilton, USA; gen tel (513) 923-3111; adv tel (513) 923-3111; ed tel (513) 923-3111; gen fax (513) 923-1806; adv fax (513) 923-1806; ed fax (513) 923-1806; disp adv e-mail chahn@enquirer.com; class adv e-mail mwoodruff@enquirer.com; ed e-mail memral@communitypress.com; web site www.cincinnati.com
Circulation: 10,091pd, 8,241fr; CAC
Advertising rate: Open inch rate $16.83
Group: Gannett
Digital Platform - Mobile: Apple, Android, Windows, Blackberry
Digital Platform - Tablet: Apple iOS, Android, Windows 7, Blackberry Tablet OS, Kindle, Nook, Kindle Fire
Pres./Pub. .... Margaret Buchanan
Exec. Ed. .... Carolyn Washburn
Editor .... Richard Maloney
Adv. VP .... Carol Hahn
Circ. Mgr. .... Sharon Schachleiter
Mechanical Specifications: Type page 13 x 20 3/4; A - 6 cols, 2 1/16, 1/8 between; C - 10 cols, 1 3/16, 1/8 between.
Delivery Method: Mail, Newsstand, Carrier
Areas Served: Hamilton County

EASTERN HILLS JOURNAL (WED)

312 Elm St, Cincinnati, OH, 45202-2739, Clermont, USA; gen tel (513) 248-8600; adv tel (513) 248-8600; ed tel (513) 248-8600; gen fax (513) 248-1938; adv fax (513) 248-1938; ed fax (513) 248-1938; disp adv e-mail acumby@communitypress.com; class adv e-mail acumby@communitypress.com; ed e-mail espangler@communitypress.com; web site www.cincinnati.com
Circulation: 10,835fr; CAC
Advertising rate: Open inch rate $13.20
Group: Gannett
Digital Platform - Mobile: Apple, Android, Windows, Blackberry
Digital Platform - Tablet: Apple iOS, Android, Windows 7, Blackberry Tablet OS, Kindle, Nook, Kindle Fire
Community Recorder Editor .... Nancy Daly
Pres./Pub. .... Margaret Buchanan
Adv. Mgr. .... Alison Cumby
Delivery Method: Mail, Newsstand, Carrier, Racks
Areas Served: 45174, 45208, 45209, 45227

FOREST HILLS JOURNAL (WED)

312 Elm St, Cincinnati, OH, 45202-2739, Clermont, USA; gen tel (513) 248-8600; adv tel (513) 248-8600; ed tel (513) 248-8600; gen fax (513) 248-1938; adv fax (513) 248-1938; ed fax (513) 248-1938; disp adv e-mail acumby@communitypress.com; class adv e-mail acumby@communitypress.com; ed e-mail espangler@communitypress.com; web site www.cincinnati.com
Circulation: 10,835fr; CAC
Advertising rate: Open inch rate $16.20
Group: Gannett
Digital Platform - Mobile: Apple, Android, Windows, Blackberry
Digital Platform - Tablet: Apple iOS, Android, Windows 7, Blackberry Tablet OS, Kindle, Nook, Kindle Fire
Ed. .... Nancy Daly
Pres./Pub. .... Margaret Buchanan
Adv. Mgr. .... Alison Cumby
Delivery Method: Mail, Newsstand, Carrier, Racks
Areas Served: Clermont County

HILLTOP PRESS (WED)

312 Elm St, Cincinnati, OH, 45202-2739, Hamilton, USA; gen tel (513) 768-8200; adv tel (513) 923-3111; ed tel (513) 923-3111; gen fax (513) 923-1806; adv fax (513) 923-1806; ed fax (513) 923-1806; disp adv e-mail chahn@enquirer.com; class adv e-mail mwoodruff@enquirer.com; ed e-mail rmaloney@communitypress.com; web site www.cincinnati.com
Circulation: 10,091pd, 8,241fr; CAC
Advertising rate: Open inch rate $15.30
Group: Gannett
Digital Platform - Mobile: Apple, Android, Windows, Blackberry
Digital Platform - Tablet: Apple iOS, Android, Windows 7, Blackberry Tablet OS, Kindle, Nook, Kindle Fire
Pres./Pub. .... Margaret Buchanan
Exec. Ed. .... Carolyn Washburn
Mng. Ed. .... Richard Maloney
Adv. VP .... Carol Hahn
Circ. Mgr. .... Sharon Schachleiter
Mechanical Specifications: Type page 13 x 20 3/4; A - 6 cols, 2 1/16, 1/8 between; C - 10 cols, 1 3/16, 1/8 between.
Delivery Method: Mail, Newsstand, Carrier
Areas Served: Hamilton County

MILFORD-MIAMI ADVERTISER (WED)

312 Elm St, Cincinnati, OH, 45202-2739, Clermont, USA; gen tel (513) 248-8600; adv tel (513) 248-8600; ed tel (513) 248-8600; gen fax (513) 248-1938; adv fax (513) 248-1938; ed fax (513) 248-1938; disp adv e-mail acumby@communitypress.com; class adv e-mail acumby@communitypress.com; ed e-mail therron@communitypress.com; web site www.cincinnati.com
Circulation: 10,835fr; CAC
Advertising rate: Open inch rate $11.75
Group: Gannett
Digital Platform - Mobile: Apple, Android, Windows, Blackberry
Digital Platform - Tablet: Apple iOS, Android, Windows 7, Blackberry Tablet OS, Kindle, Nook, Kindle Fire
Ed. .... Richard Maloney
Pres./Pub. .... Margaret Buchanan
Adv. Mgr. .... Alison Cumby
Delivery Method: Mail, Newsstand, Carrier, Racks
Areas Served: Clermont County

NORTHWEST PRESS (WED)

5556 Cheviot Rd, Ste A, Cincinnati, OH, 45247-5202, Hamilton, USA; gen tel (513) 923-3111; adv tel (513) 923-3111; ed tel (513) 923-3111; gen fax (513) 923-1806; adv fax (513) 923-1806; ed fax (513) 923-1806; disp adv e-mail chahn@enquirer.com; class adv e-mail mwoodruff@enquirer.com; ed e-mail cwashburn@enquirer.com; web site www.cincinnati.com
Circulation: 12,176pd,; Sworn/Estimate/Non-Audited
Advertising rate: Open inch rate $15.75
Established: 1921
Group: Gannett
Digital Platform - Mobile: Apple, Android, Windows, Blackberry
Digital Platform - Tablet: Apple iOS, Android, Windows 7, Blackberry Tablet OS, Kindle, Nook, Kindle Fire
Pres./Pub. .... Margaret Buchanan
Ed. .... Carolyn Washburn
Adv. VP .... Carol Hahn
Account Mgr. .... Adele Baston
Mechanical Specifications: 10"x17.25 full pg; 10"x8.5" 1/2 pg H;8.5 1/4 pg
Delivery Method: Mail, Newsstand, Carrier
Areas Served: Hamilton County

PRICE HILL PRESS (WED)

312 Elm St, Cincinnati, OH, 45202-2739, Hamilton, USA; gen tel (513) 923-3111; adv tel (513) 923-3111; ed tel (513) 923-3111; gen fax (513) 923-1806; adv fax (513) 923-1806; ed fax (513) 923-1806; disp adv e-mail chahn@enquirer.com; class adv e-mail mwoodruff@enquirer.com; ed e-mail memral@communitypress.com; web site www.cincinnati.com
Circulation: 10,091pd, 8,241fr; CAC
Advertising rate: Open inch rate $18.00
Group: Gannett
Digital Platform - Mobile: Apple, Android, Windows, Blackberry
Digital Platform - Tablet: Apple iOS, Android, Windows 7, Blackberry Tablet OS, Kindle, Nook, Kindle Fire
Pres./Pub. .... Margaret Buchanan
Exec. Ed. .... Carolyn Washburn
Mng. Ed. .... Richard Maloney
Adv. VP .... Carol Hahn
Circ. Mgr. .... Sharon Schachleiter
Mechanical Specifications: Type page 13 x 20 3/4; A - 6 cols, 2 1/16, 1/8 between; C - 10 cols, 1 3/16, 1/8 between.
Delivery Method: Mail, Newsstand, Carrier
Areas Served: Hamilton County

TRI-COUNTY PRESS (WED)

312 Elm St, Cincinnati, OH, 45202-2739, Clermont, USA; gen tel (513) 248-8600; adv tel (513) 248-8600; ed tel (513) 248-8600; gen fax (513) 248-1938; adv fax (513) 248-1938; ed fax (513) 248-1938; disp adv e-mail acumby@communitypress.com; class adv e-mail acumby@communitypress.com; ed e-mail espangler@communitypress.com; web site www.cincinnati.com
Circulation: 10,835fr; CAC
Advertising rate: Open inch rate $9.20
Group: Gannett
Digital Platform - Mobile: Apple, Android, Windows, Blackberry
Digital Platform - Tablet: Apple iOS, Android, Windows 7, Blackberry Tablet OS, Kindle, Nook, Kindle Fire
Ed. .... Nancy Daly
Pres./Pub. .... Margaret Buchanan
Adv. Mgr. .... Alison Cumby
Delivery Method: Mail, Newsstand, Carrier, Racks
Areas Served: 45231, 45240, 45246

WESTERN HILLS PRESS (WED)

312 Elm St, Cincinnati, OH, 45202-2739, Hamilton, USA; gen tel (513) 923-3111; adv tel (513) 923-3111; ed tel (513) 923-3111; gen fax (513) 923-1806; adv fax (513) 923-1806; ed fax (513) 923-1806; disp adv e-mail chahn@enquirer.com; class adv e-mail mwoodruff@enquirer.com; ed e-mail memral@communitypress.com; web site www.cincinnati.com
Circulation: 10,091pd, 8,241fr; CAC
Advertising rate: Open inch rate $17.77
Group: Gannett
Digital Platform - Mobile: Apple, Android, Windows, Blackberry
Digital Platform - Tablet: Apple iOS, Android, Windows 7, Blackberry Tablet OS, Kindle, Nook, Kindle Fire
Pres./Pub. .... Margaret Buchanan
Exec. Ed. .... Carolyn Washburn
Mng. Ed. .... Richard Maloney
Adv. VP .... Carol Hahn
Circ. Mgr. .... Sharon Schachleiter
Mechanical Specifications: Type page 13 x 20 3/4; A - 6 cols, 2 1/16, 1/8 between; C - 10 cols, 1 3/16, 1/8 between.
Delivery Method: Mail, Newsstand, Carrier
Areas Served: 45001, 45002, 45052, 45211, 45233, 45238, 45247, 45248

CLEVELAND

CLEVELAND SCENE (WED)

737 Bolivar Rd, Ste 4100, Cleveland, OH, 44115-1259, Cuyahoga, USA; gen tel (216) 241-7550; adv tel (216) 802-7258; ed tel (216) 802-7254; gen fax (216) 802-7212; adv fax (216) 802-7212; ed fax (216) 802-7212; disp adv e-mail scene@clevescene.com; class adv e-mail gkelley@clevescene.com; ed e-mail vgrzegorek@clevescene.com; web site www.clevescene.com
Circulation: 43,359fr; VAC
Advertising rate: Open inch rate $53.00
Established: 1970
Digital Platform - Mobile: Apple, Android
Digital Platform - Tablet: Apple iOS, Android
Pub. .... Chris Keating
Ed. .... Vince Grzegorek
Adv. Dir. .... Shayne Rose
Delivery Method: Mail, Newsstand, Racks
Areas Served: Cuyahoga County

SUN NEWS (THUR)

5510 Cloverleaf Pkwy, Cleveland, OH, 44125-4815, Cuyahoga, USA; gen tel (216) 986-2600; adv tel (216) 986-2460; ed tel (216) 986-6070; gen fax (216) 986-2340; adv fax (216) 986-2340; ed fax (216) 986-2340; disp adv e-mail sun@sunnews.com; class adv e-mail mmorilak@sunnews.com; ed e-mail ckovach@sunnews.com; web site www.sunnews.com
Circulation: 137,284pd,; AAM
Advertising rate: Open inch rate $18.20
Established: 1969
Group: Advance Publications, Inc.Editions: (11) Brunswick Sun; Chagrin Solon Sun; Medina Sun; News Sun; Sun messenger; Sun Post; Sun Post-Herald; Sun Press; Sun Sentinel; Sun Star-Courier; West Shore Sun
Digital Platform - Mobile: Apple, Android, Windows, Blackberry
Digital Platform - Tablet: Apple iOS, Android, Windows 7, Blackberry Tablet OS
Exec. Ed. .... Linda Kinsey
Ed. .... Mark Morilak
Mng. Ed. .... Carol Kovach
Asst. Ed. .... Rodney Bengston
Mechanical Specifications: Type page 11 5/8 x 19 5/8; E - 6 cols, between; A - 6 cols, between; C - 10 cols, between.Equipment & Software: Hardware — HI; Software — HI.
Delivery Method: Mail, Newsstand, Carrier, Racks
Areas Served: Cuyahoga County

COLUMBIA STATION

THE RURAL-URBAN RECORD (MON)

24487 Squire Rd, Columbia Station, OH, 44028-9672, Lorain, USA; gen tel (440) 236-8982; adv tel (440) 236-8982; ed tel (440) 236-8982; gen fax (440) 236-9198; adv fax (440) 236-9198; ed fax (440) 236-9198; disp adv e-mail news@rural-urbanrecord.com; class adv e-mail news@rural-urbanrecord.com; ed e-mail news@rural-urbanrecord.com; web site www.rural-urbanrecord.com
Circulation: 35pd, 22,439fr; VAC
Advertising rate: Open inch rate $15.50
Established: 1955
Digital Platform - Mobile: Apple, Android, Windows, Blackberry
Digital Platform - Tablet: Apple iOS, Android, Windows 7, Blackberry Tablet OS, Kindle, Nook, Kindle Fire
Pub./Ed./Gen. Mgr. .... Lee Boise
Circ. Mgr. .... Cheryl Mikoletic
Graphic Artist/News Ed .... Randi MacWilliams
Sales Rep .... Stephanie Sayles
Graphic Artist .... Stephanie Humphrey
Mechanical Specifications: Type page 10 5/16 x 16; E - 6 cols, 1 9/16, between; A - 6 cols, 1 9/16, between; C - 6 cols, 1 9/16, between. Equipment & Software: Hardware — IBM; Software — Archetype/Corel Draw, Adobe/Photoshop, Ventura, XYQUEST/XyWrite.
Delivery Method: Mail, Newsstand, Racks
Areas Served: Lorain County

COLUMBUS

COLUMBUS BUSINESS FIRST (FRI)

303 W Nationwide Blvd, Columbus, OH, 43215-2309, Franklin, USA; gen tel (614) 461-4040; adv tel (614) 461-4040; ed tel (614) 461-4040; gen fax (614) 365-2980; adv fax (614) 365-2980; ed fax (614) 365-2980; disp adv e-mail ddeppero@bizjournals.com; class adv e-mail dbuchanan@bizjournals.com; ed e-mail dcappa@bizjournals.com; web site www.bizjournals.com/columbus

Advertising rate: Open inch rate $6.945.00 (Full-Page)
Digital Platform - Mobile: Apple, Android, Windows, Blackberry
Digital Platform - Tablet: Apple iOS, Android, Windows 7, Blackberry Tablet OS
Pres./Pub. .... Nick Fortine
Ed. .... Dominic Cappa
Digital/Online Mng. Ed. .... Doug Buchanan
Delivery Method: Mail, Newsstand, Racks
Areas Served: Franklin County

EASTSIDE MESSENGER (SUN)

3500 Sullivant Ave, Columbus, OH, 43204-1105, Franklin, USA; gen tel (614) 272-5422; adv tel (614) 272-5422; ed tel (614) 272-5422; gen fax (614) 272-0684; adv fax (614) 272-0684; ed fax (614) 272-0684; disp adv e-mail phildaubel@columbusmessenger.com; class adv e-mail phildaubel@columbusmessenger.com; ed e-mail eastside@columbusmessenger.com; web site www.columbusmessenger.com

Circulation: 0pd, 15,405fr; CVC
Advertising rate: Open inch rate $59.55
Established: 1974
Group: Columbus Messenger Newspapers
Digital Platform - Mobile: Apple, Android, Windows, Blackberry
Digital Platform - Tablet: Apple iOS, Android, Windows 7, Blackberry Tablet OS
Pub./Gen. Mgr. .... Philip F. Daubel
Adv. Mgr. .... Fred Schenk
Ed. .... Rick Palsgrove
Circ. Mgr .... Doug Henry
Mechanical Specifications: Type page 10 1/2 x 16; E - 8 cols, 1 13/16, 3/16 between; A - 8 cols, 1 13/16, 3/16 between; C - 8 cols, 1 13/16, 3/16 between.Equipment & Software: Hardware — APP/Mac; Software — QPS/QuarkXPress 4.0.
Delivery Method: Carrier
Areas Served: 43068, 43110, 43147

MADISON MESSENGER (SUN)

3500 Sullivant Ave, Columbus, OH, 43204-1105, Franklin, USA; gen tel (740) 852-0809; adv tel (740) 852-0809; ed tel (740) 852-0809; gen fax (740) 852-0814; adv fax (740) 852-0814; ed fax (740) 852-0814; disp adv e-mail phildaubel@columbusmessenger.com; class adv e-mail phildaubel@columbusmessenger.com; ed e-mail madison@columbusmessenger.com; web site www.columbusmessenger.com

Circulation: 15,095fr; CVC
Advertising rate: Open inch rate $59.55
Established: 1984
Group: Columbus Messenger Newspapers
Digital Platform - Mobile: Apple, Android, Windows, Blackberry
Digital Platform - Tablet: Apple iOS, Android, Windows 7, Blackberry Tablet OS
Pub./Gen. Mgr. .... Philip F. Daubel
Adv. Mgr. .... Fred Schenk
Ed. .... Rick Palsgrove
Circ. Mgr .... Doug Henry
Mechanical Specifications: Type page 10 1/2 x 16; E - 8 cols, 1 13/16, 3/16 between; A - 8 cols, 1 13/16, 3/16 between; C - 8 cols, 1 13/16, 3/16 between.Equipment & Software: Hardware — APP/Mac; Software — QPS/QuarkXPress 4.0.
Delivery Method: Carrier
Areas Served: 43140, 43143, 43153, 43162, 43064, 43119

SOUTHEAST MESSENGER (SUN)

3500 Sullivant Ave, Columbus, OH, 43204-1105, Franklin, USA; gen tel (614) 272-5422; adv tel (614) 272-5422; ed tel (614) 272-5422; gen fax (614) 272-0684; adv fax (614) 272-0684; ed fax (614) 272-0684; disp adv e-mail phildaubel@columbusmessenger.com; class adv e-mail phildaubel@columbusmessenger.com; ed e-mail southeast@columbusmessenger.com; web site www.columbusmessenger.com

Circulation: 20,664fr; CVC
Advertising rate: Open inch rate $59.55
Established: 1974
Group: Columbus Messenger Newspapers
Digital Platform - Mobile: Apple, Android, Windows, Blackberry
Digital Platform - Tablet: Apple iOS, Android, Windows 7, Blackberry Tablet OS
Pub./Gen. Mgr. .... Philip F. Daubel
Ed. .... Rick Palsgrove
Adv. Mgr.
Fred Schenk
Circ. Mgr .... Doug Henry
Mechanical Specifications: Type page 10 1/2 x 11.5; E - 8 cols, 1 3/16, 3/16 between; A - 8 cols, 1 3/16, 3/16 between; C - 8 cols, 1 3/16, 3/16 between.Equipment & Software: Hardware — APP/Mac; Software — QPS/QuarkXPress 4.0.
Delivery Method: Carrier
Areas Served: 43207, 43232, 43125, 43110, 43068

SOUTHWEST MESSENGER (SUN)

3500 Sullivant Ave, Columbus, OH, 43204-1105, Franklin, USA; gen tel (614) 272-5422; adv tel (614) 272-5422; ed tel (614) 272-5422; gen fax (614) 272-0684; adv fax (614) 272-0684; ed fax (614) 272-0684; disp adv e-mail phildaubel@columbusmessenger.com; class adv e-mail phildaubel@columbusmessenger.com; ed e-mail southwest@columbusmessenger.com; web site www.columbusmessenger.com

Circulation: 21,388fr; CVC
Advertising rate: Open inch rate $59.55
Established: 1974
Group: Columbus Messenger Newspapers
Digital Platform - Mobile: Apple, Android, Windows, Blackberry
Digital Platform - Tablet: Apple iOS, Android, Windows 7, Blackberry Tablet OS
Pub./Gen. Mgr. .... Philip F. Daubel
Adv. Mgr. .... Fred Schenk
Ed. .... Rick Palsgrove
Circ. Mgr .... Doug Henry
Mechanical Specifications: Type page 10 1/2 x 16; E - 8 cols, 1 3/16, 3/16 between; A - 8 cols, 1 3/16, 3/16 between; C - 8 cols, 1 3/16, 3/16 between.Equipment & Software: Hardware — APP/Mac; Software — QPS/QuarkXPress 4.0.
Delivery Method: Carrier
Areas Served: 43123, 43140, 43146

WESTSIDE MESSENGER (SUN)

3500 Sullivant Ave, Columbus, OH, 43204-1105, Franklin, USA; gen tel (614) 272-5422; adv tel (614) 272-5422; ed tel (614) 272-5422; gen fax (614) 272-0684; adv fax (614) 272-0684; ed fax (614) 272-0684; disp adv e-mail phildaubel@columbusmessenger.com; class adv e-mail phildaubel@columbusmessenger.com; ed e-mail westside@columbusmessenger.com; web site www.columbusmessenger.com

Circulation: 0pd, 22,404fr; CVC
Advertising rate: Open inch rate $59.55
Established: 1974
Group: Columbus Messenger Newspapers
Digital Platform - Mobile: Apple, Android, Windows, Blackberry
Digital Platform - Tablet: Apple iOS, Android, Windows 7, Blackberry Tablet OS
Pub./Gen. Mgr. .... Philip F. Daubel
Adv. Mgr. .... Fred Schenk
Ed. .... Rick Palsgrove
Circ. Mgr .... Doug Henry
Mechanical Specifications: Type page 10 x 13; E - 4 cols, 2 3/8, 1/6 between; A - 4 cols, 2 3/8, 1/6 between; C - 8 cols, 1 1/4, between. Equipment & Software: Hardware — APP/Mac; Software — QPS/QuarkXPress 4.0.
Delivery Method: Carrier
Areas Served: 43204, 43223, 43228, 43119

CRESTLINE

THE CRESTLINE ADVOCATE (WED)

312 N Seltzer St, Crestline, OH, 44827-1403, Crawford, USA; gen tel (419) 683-3355; adv tel (419) 683-3355; ed tel (419) 683-3355; gen fax (419) 683-0175; adv fax (419) 683-0175; ed fax (419) 683-0175; disp adv e-mail crestlineadvocate@yahoo.com; class adv e-mail crestlineadvocate@yahoo.com; ed e-mail crestlineadvocate@midohio.twcbc.com

Circulation: 2,300pd, 100fr; Sworn/Estimate/Non-Audited
Advertising rate: Open inch rate $6.00
Established: 1869
Pub./Gen. Mgr. .... Joseph Polito
Ed. .... Kim Ross-Polito
Mechanical Specifications: Type page 12 1/2 x 20 1/2; E - 6 cols, 1 3/4, 1/6 between; A - 6 cols, 1 3/4, 1/6 between; C - 6 cols, 1 3/4, 1/6 between.Equipment & Software: Hardware — 2-APP/iMac, 1-APP/Server; Software — QPS/QuarkXPress, Adobe/Photoshop 4.0, Adobe/Acrobat.
Delivery Method: Mail, Newsstand
Areas Served: 44820 to 44999

DALTON

THE DALTON GAZETTE & KIDRON NEWS (WED)

41 W Main St, Dalton, OH, 44618, Wayne, USA; gen tel (330) 828-8401; adv tel (330) 828-8401; ed tel (330) 828-8401; gen fax (330) 828-8401; adv fax (330) 828-8401; ed fax (330) 828-8401; disp adv e-mail daltonkidronnews@sbcglobal.net; class adv e-mail daltonkidronnews@sbcglobal.net; ed e-mail daltonkidronnews@sbcglobal.net; web site www.daltongazette.com

Circulation: 1,505pd, 5fr; Sworn/Estimate/Non-Audited
Advertising rate: Open inch rate $7.50
Established: 1875
Digital Platform - Mobile: Apple, Android
Digital Platform - Tablet: Apple iOS, Android
Pub./Ed. .... Francis Woodruff
Mechanical Specifications: Type page 10 x 16; E - 5 cols, 1 7/8, 1/8 between.Equipment & Software: Hardware — Mac computers
Delivery Method: Mail, Newsstand
Areas Served: 44618, 44667, 44636, 44646, 44666, 44606, 44691, 44667

DAYTON

THE OAKWOOD REGISTER (WED)

435 Patterson Rd, Dayton, OH, 45419-4309, Montgomery, USA; gen tel (937) 294-2662; adv tel (937) 294-2662; ed tel (937) 294-2662; gen fax (937) 294-8375; adv fax (937) 294-8375; ed fax (937) 294-8375; disp adv e-mail adrates@oakwoodregister.com; class adv e-mail classifieds@oakwoodregister.com; ed e-mail editor@oakwoodregister.com; web site www.oakwoodregister.com

Circulation: 120pd, 6,500fr; Sworn/Estimate/Non-Audited
Advertising rate: Open inch rate $14.00
Established: 1991
Group: Winkler Publishing
Digital Platform - Mobile: Apple
Digital Platform - Tablet: Apple iOS
Prodn. Mgr. .... Tom Girard
Advertising Sales .... Richard Brame
Advertising Sales .... Vicky Holloway
Office Manager .... Robin Burnam
Mechanical Specifications: Type page 10 1/4 x 14; E - 5 cols, 2, 1/6 between; C - 7 cols, 1 3/8, 1/6 between.Equipment & Software: Hardware — APP/Mac, 2-APP/Power Mac, 1-APP/Mac G4; Presses — G/Web; Software — QPS/QuarkXPress 4.0, Adobe/PageMaker 6.5, Adobe/Photoshop.
Delivery Method: Mail, Carrier, Racks
Areas Served: 45419, 45409

DELAWARE

THE SUNBURY NEWS (THUR)

40 N Sandusky St, Ste 202, Delaware, OH, 43015-1973, Delaware, USA; gen tel (740) 363-1161; adv tel (740) 363-1161; ed tel (740) 363-1161; gen fax (740) 363-6262; adv fax (740) 363-6262; ed fax (740) 363-6262; disp adv e-mail rburns@civitasmedia.com; class adv e-mail rburns@civitasmedia.com; ed e-mail ghenery@civitasmedia.com; web site www.sunburynews.com

Circulation: 2,997pd, 43fr; Sworn/Estimate/Non-Audited
Advertising rate: Open inch rate $6.70
Digital Platform - Mobile: Apple, Android
Digital Platform - Tablet: Apple iOS, Android
Pub. .... Gary Merrell
Managing Ed. .... Gary Budzak
Asst. Mgr. .... Rick Burns
Mechanical Specifications: Type page 13 x 21; E - 6 cols, 2 1/16, 1/8 between; A - 6 cols, 2 1/16, 1/8 between; C - 6 cols, 2 1/16, 1/8 between.Equipment & Software: Hardware — APP/Mac; Software — QPS/QuarkXPress 3.3, Multi-Ad/Creator.
Delivery Method: Mail, Newsstand, Racks
Areas Served: Delaware County

DELTA

THE DELTA ATLAS (TUES)

212 Main St, Delta, OH, 43515-1312, Fulton, USA; gen tel (419) 822-3231; adv tel (419) 822-3231; ed tel (419) 822-3231; gen fax (419) 822-3289; adv fax (419) 822-3289; ed fax (419) 822-3289; disp adv e-mail deltaatlas@windstream.net; class adv e-mail deltaatlas@windstream.net; ed e-mail deltaatlas@windstream.net

Circulation: 1,507pd, 254fr; Sworn/Estimate/Non-Audited
Advertising rate: Open inch rate $3.25
Established: 1898
Pub./Ed. .... Thomas W. Mack
Delivery Method: Mail, Newsstand
Areas Served: Fulton County

DESHLER

THE DESHLER FLAG (THUR)

107 E Main St, Ste A, Deshler, OH, 43516-1288, Henry, USA; gen tel (419) 278-2816; adv tel (419) 278-2816; ed tel (419) 278-2816; gen fax (419) 278-2816; adv fax (419) 278-2816; ed fax (419) 278-2816; disp adv e-mail dflagads@embarqmail.com; class adv e-mail dflagads@embarqmail.com; ed e-mail dflagnews@embarqmail.com; web site www.deshlerflag.embarqspace.com

Circulation: 1,400pd,; Sworn/Estimate/Non-Audited
Advertising rate: Open inch rate $5.60
Established: 1876
Group: Mickens, Inc.
Digital Platform - Mobile: Windows
Digital Platform - Tablet: Windows 7
Editor .... Heather Spratt
Publisher/Editor .... Don Mickens
Mechanical Specifications: Type page 13 1/4 x 21; E - 6 cols, 2 1/16, between; A - 6 cols, 2 1/16, between; C - 6 cols, 2 1/16, between. Equipment & Software: Hardware — APP/Macs; Software — Adobe/PageMaker, Microsoft/Word.
Delivery Method: Mail, Newsstand
Areas Served: Henry County

EATON

THE REGISTER-HERALD (WED, SAT)

532 N Barron St, Ste 105, Eaton, OH, 45320-1710, Preble, USA; gen tel (937) 456-5553; adv tel (937) 456-5553 ext. 120; ed tel (937) 456-5553 ext. 130; gen fax (937) 456-3558; adv fax (937) 456-3558; ed fax (937) 456-

3558; disp adv e-mail bkemp@civitasmedia.com; class adv e-mail lcollins@civitasmedia.com; ed e-mail emowen@civitasmedia.com; web site www.registerherald.com
Circulation: 5,300pd, 12,000fr; Sworn/Estimate/Non-Audited
Advertising rate: Open inch rate $11.00 (Wed); $12.00 (Sat)
Established: 1918
Group: AIM Media Indiana
Digital Platform - Mobile: Apple, Android, Windows, Blackberry
Digital Platform - Tablet: Apple iOS, Android, Windows 7, Blackberry Tablet OS
Ed. .... Eddie Mowen Jr.
Gen. Mgr. .... Leslie Collins
Adv. Mgr. .... Betsy Kemp
Delivery Method: Mail, Newsstand, Carrier, Racks
Areas Served: Preble County

EDGERTON

THE EDGERTON EARTH (THUR)

114 S Michigan Ave, Edgerton, OH, 43517-9801, Williams, USA; gen tel (419) 298-2369; adv tel (419) 298-2369; ed tel (419) 298-2369; gen fax (419) 386-2829; adv fax (419) 386-2829; ed fax (419) 386-2829; disp adv e-mail edgertonearth@edgertonearth.com; class adv e-mail edgertonearth@edgertonearth.com; ed e-mail edgertonearth@edgertonearth.com; web site www.edgertonearth.com
Circulation: 1,301pd,; Sworn/Estimate/Non-Audited
Advertising rate: Open inch rate $5.25
Digital Platform - Mobile: Apple
Digital Platform - Tablet: Apple iOS
Pub./Ed. .... Cindy Thiel
Adv. Mgr. .... Barb Imm
Office Mgr. .... Karrie Kimpel
Delivery Method: Mail, Newsstand
Areas Served: Williams County

FINDLAY

THE COURIER ADVANTAGE (MON)

701 W Sandusky St, Findlay, OH, 45840-2325, Hancock, USA; gen tel (419) 422-5151; adv tel (419) 422-5151; ed tel (419) 422-5151; gen fax (419) 422-2937; adv fax (419) 422-2937; ed fax (419) 422-2937; disp adv e-mail advertising@thecourier.com; class adv e-mail advertising@thecourier.com; ed e-mail news@thecourier.com; web site www.thecourier.com
Circulation: 10,000fr; Sworn/Estimate/Non-Audited
Advertising rate: Open inch rate $6.60
Established: 1836
Group: Findlay Publishing Co.
Digital Platform - Mobile: Apple, Android
Digital Platform - Tablet: Apple iOS, Android, Windows 7
Pub. .... Karl L. Heminger
Adv. Mgr. .... Kari May-Faulkner
Mng. Ed. .... Jim Harrold
Mechanical Specifications: Type page 11 5/8 x 21 1/4; A - 6 cols, 1 13/16, 1/8 between; C - 8 cols, 1 5/8, 1/8 between.Equipment & Software: Hardware — 40-Gateway GP6 Clients, 2-Sun/Ultra 60 Servers; Presses — HI/845; Software — HI/NME NMP 2.08.
Delivery Method: Mail, Racks
Areas Served: 45840

FOSTORIA

THE FOSTORIA FOCUS (SUN)

112 N Main St, Fostoria, OH, 44830-2223, Seneca, USA; gen tel (419) 435-6397; adv tel (419) 435-6397; ed tel (419) 435-6397; gen fax (419) 435-0101; adv fax (419) 435-0101; ed fax (419) 435-0101; disp adv e-mail sales@fostoriafocus.com; class adv e-mail salestony@fostoriafocus.com; ed e-mail news@fostoriafocus.com; web site www.fostoriafocus.com
Circulation: 5pd, 10,680fr; CVC
Advertising rate: Open inch rate $10.50
Established: 1994
Digital Platform - Mobile: Apple, Android
Digital Platform - Tablet: Apple iOS, Android, Windows 7
Pub. .... Judy Miller
Pub. .... Donald Miller
Adv. Mgr. .... Tony Klima
Adv. Mgr. .... Julie Heldman
Prod. Mgr. .... Linda Wagner
Delivery Method: Carrier
Areas Served: Hancock County

GALION

GALION INQUIRER (WED, SAT)

129 Harding Way E, Galion, OH, 44833-1902, Crawford, USA; gen tel (419) 468-1117; gen fax (419) 468-7255; disp adv e-mail vtaylor@civitasmedia.com; class adv e-mail vtaylor@civitasmedia.com; ed e-mail vtaylor@galnews@civitasmedia.com; web site www.galioninquirer.com
Circulation: 1,800pd,; Sworn/Estimate/Non-Audited
Advertising rate: Open inch rate $9.50
Group: AIM Media Indiana
Digital Platform - Mobile: Apple, Android
Digital Platform - Tablet: Apple iOS, Android
Pub. .... Vicki Taylor
Sports Ed. .... John Kleinknecht
Mechanical Specifications: Type page 13 x 21 1/2; E - 6 cols, 2, 1/6 between; A - 6 cols, 2, 1/6 between; C - 8 cols, 1 1/2, 7/50 between.
Delivery Method: Mail, Newsstand, Carrier, Racks
Areas Served: 44833, 43338, 44827, 43325, 44820

GALLIPOLIS

SUNDAY TIMES-SENTINEL (SUN)

825 3rd Ave, Gallipolis, OH, 45631-1624, Gallia, USA; gen tel (740) 446-2342; gen fax (740) 446-3008; disp adv e-mail jmitchell@civitasmedia.com; class adv e-mail kcade@civitasmedia.com; ed e-mail mjohnsoncivitasmedia.com; web site www.mydailytribune.com
Advertising rate: Open inch rate $17.90
Group: Civitas Media, LLC-OOB
Digital Platform - Mobile: Apple, Android, Windows, Blackberry
Digital Platform - Tablet: Apple iOS, Android, Windows 7, Blackberry Tablet OS
Ed. .... Beth Sergent
Pub. .... Bud Hunt
Delivery Method: Mail, Newsstand, Carrier, Racks
Areas Served: Gallia County

TRI-COUNTY MARKETPLACE (SAT)

825 3rd Ave, Gallipolis, OH, 45631-1624, Gallia, USA; gen tel (740) 446-2342; gen fax (740) 446-3008; disp adv e-mail jmitchell@civitasmedia.com; class adv e-mail kcade@civitasmedia.com; ed e-mail mjohnson@civitasmedia.com; web site www.mydailytribune.com
Circulation: 18,000fr; Sworn/Estimate/Non-Audited
Advertising rate: Open inch rate $7.20
Group: Civitas Media, LLC-OOB
Digital Platform - Mobile: Apple, Android, Windows, Blackberry
Digital Platform - Tablet: Apple iOS, Android, Windows 7, Blackberry Tablet OS
Adv. Mgr. .... Beth Sergent
Sales .... Matt RodgersEquipment & Software: Hardware — APP/Mac; Presses — G/Urbanite; Software — Baseview.
Delivery Method: Carrier
Areas Served: Gallia County

GEORGETOWN

THE RIPLEY BEE (THUR)

111 E State St, Georgetown, OH, 45121-1412, Brown, USA; gen tel (937) 378-6161; adv tel (937) 392-4321; ed tel (937) 392-4321; gen fax (937) 378-2004; adv fax (937) 378-2004; ed fax (937) 378-2004; disp adv e-mail striplett@newsdemocrat.com; class adv e-mail classifieds@newsdemocrat.com; ed e-mail news@newsdemocrat.com; web site www.ripleybee.com
Circulation: 1,400pd, 183fr; Sworn/Estimate/Non-Audited
Advertising rate: Open inch rate $5.50
Established: 1842
Group: Civitas Media, LLC-OOB
Digital Platform - Mobile: Apple, Android
Digital Platform - Tablet: Apple iOS, Android, Windows 7
Pub./Adv. Mgr. .... Steven Triplett
Bus. Mgr. .... Julie Richmond
Ed. .... Bryan Peck
Mechanical Specifications: Type page 9.889 x 21; E - 6 cols, 2, .111 between; A - 6 cols, 2, 3/16 between; C - 7 cols, 1.302, .111 between. Equipment & Software: Hardware — Apple/Mac G4; Software — QPS/QuarkXPress, Adobe/Photoshop.
Delivery Method: Mail, Newsstand, Racks
Areas Served: 45167, 45101, 45134, 45171

THE NEWS DEMOCRAT (THUR, SUN)

111 E State St, Georgetown, OH, 45121-1412, Brown, USA; gen tel (937) 378-6161; adv tel (937) 378-6161; ed tel (937) 378-6161; gen fax (937) 378-2004; adv fax (937) 378-2004; ed fax (937) 378-2004; disp adv e-mail striplett@newsdemocrat.com; class adv e-mail classifieds@newsdemocrat.com; ed e-mail news@newsdemocrat.com; web site www.newsdemocrat.com
Circulation: 3,200pd, 17,000fr; Sworn/Estimate/Non-Audited
Advertising rate: Open inch rate $7.25 (Thur); $9.22 (Sun)
Established: 1888
Group: Champion Media
Digital Platform - Mobile: Apple, Android
Digital Platform - Tablet: Apple iOS, Android, Windows 7
Pub./Adv. Mgr. .... Steven Triplett
Ed. .... Bryan Peck
Bus. Mgr. .... Julie Richmond
Circ. Mgr. .... Shirley Ross
Mechanical Specifications: Type page 9.889 x 21; E - 6 cols, .111 between columns; A - 6 cols, 1 5/6, 1/8 between; C - 7 cols, 1.302, .111 between.Equipment & Software: ; Presses — G/Community; Software — QPS/QuarkXPress 4.1.
Delivery Method: Mail, Newsstand, Carrier, Racks
Areas Served: 45121, 45101, 45107, 45118, 45130, 45131, 45154, 45167, 45168, 45171, 45697

GREENVILLE

THE EARLY BIRD (SAT, SUN)

5312 Sebring Warner Rd, Greenville, OH, 45331-8787, Darke, USA; gen tel (937) 548-3330; adv tel (937) 548-3330; ed tel (937) 548-3330; gen fax (937) 548-3376; disp adv e-mail asanders@earlybirdpaper.com; class adv e-mail jkaiser@earlybirdpaper.com; ed e-mail rberry@earlybirdpaper.com; web site www.bluebagmedia.com
Circulation: 20pd, 27,965fr; VAC
Advertising rate: Open inch rate $18.00
Established: 1968
Group: Brothers Publishing Co.
Digital Platform - Mobile: Apple, Android
Digital Platform - Tablet: Apple iOS, Android
Pres./Pub. .... Keith Foutz
Mng. Ed. .... Ryan Berry
Prod. Mgr. .... Shannie Denny
Circ. Mgr .... Becky Snyder
webmaster .... Clinton Randall
Mkt Dir .... Annette Sanders
Mechanical Specifications: Type page 12 1/2 x 20 7/8; E - 6 cols, 2, 1/6 between; A - 6 cols, 2, 1/6 between; C - 9 cols, 1 1/3, 1/6 between.
Delivery Method: Mail, Carrier
Areas Served: 45304, 45358, 45331, 45378, 45361, 45382, 45321, 45337, 45308, 45328, 45346, 45332, 45331, 45346, 47390, 45350, 45351, 45362, 45303, 45348, 45310, 45390, 45380, 45388

WEEKEND ADVOCATE (SUN)

428 S Broadway St, Greenville, OH, 45331-1926, Darke, USA; gen tel (937) 548-3151; adv tel (937) 548-3151; ed tel (937) 548-3151; gen fax (937) 548-3913; adv fax (937) 548-3913; ed fax (937) 548-3913; disp adv e-mail info@dailyadvocate.com; class adv e-mail info@dailyadvocate.com; ed e-mail cchalmers@dailyadvocate.com; web site www.dailyadvocate.com
Circulation: 25,296fr; AAM
Advertising rate: Open inch rate $22.00
Group: Versa Capital Management LLC
Digital Platform - Mobile: Apple, Android, Windows, Blackberry
Digital Platform - Tablet: Apple iOS, Android, Windows 7, Blackberry Tablet OS
Adv. Mgr. .... Christie Randall
Circ. Mgr. .... Barbara Wilson
Ed. .... Bob Robinson
Asst. Ed. .... Linda Moody
News Ed. .... Mike Buckmaster
Sports Ed. .... Kyle Shaner
Christina Chalmers
Mechanical Specifications: Type page 13 3/4 x 21 1/2; E - 6 cols, 1 3/4, 1/8 between; A - 6 cols, 1 3/4, 1/8 between; C - 8 cols, 1 5/16, 1/8 between.
Delivery Method: Mail, Newsstand, Racks
Areas Served: Darke County

HARTVILLE

THE HARTVILLE NEWS (WED)

316 E Maple St, Hartville, OH, 44632-8880, Stark, USA; gen tel (330) 877-9345; gen fax (330) 877-1364; disp adv e-mail knowlespres_rh@sbcglobal.net; class adv e-mail knowlespress_comp@sbcglobal.net; ed e-mail knowlespress_rh@sbcglobal.net; web site www.knowlespress.com
Circulation: 2,000pd, 37fr; Sworn/Estimate/Non-Audited
Advertising rate: Open inch rate $7.25
Established: 1930
Digital Platform - Mobile: Windows
Digital Platform - Tablet: Windows 7
Ed. .... Rosalee Haines
Mng. Ed. .... Jackie Vaughn
Circ. Mgr. .... Lindalee Sourini
Mechanical Specifications: Type page 9 13/16 x 15 1/4; E - 5 cols, 1 13/16, 1/6 between; A - 5 cols, 1 13/16, 1/6 between; C - 5 cols, 1 13/16, 1/6 between.Equipment & Software: Hardware — APP/Mac 7500, APP/G4; Software — QPS/QuarkXPress 4.04, Word Perfect 6.1, Adobe/Illustrator 6.0, Adobe/Photoshop 5.5.
Delivery Method: Mail, Racks
Areas Served: 44632, 44685, 44601, 44641, 44720, 44721, 44201, 44260, 44312

HICKSVILLE

THE NEWS-TRIBUNE (WED)

147 E High St, Hicksville, OH, 43526-1168, Defiance, USA; gen tel (419) 542-7764; adv tel (419) 542-7764; ed tel (419) 542-7764; gen fax (419) 542-7370; adv fax (419) 542-7370; ed fax (419) 542-7370; disp adv e-mail maryann@hicksvillenewstribune.com; class adv e-mail maryann@hicksvillenewstribune.com; ed e-mail maryann@hicksvillenewstribune.com; web site www.hicksvillenewstribune.com
Circulation: 2,157pd, 50fr; Sworn/Estimate/Non-Audited
Advertising rate: Open inch rate $6.50
Established: 1886
Digital Platform - Mobile: Windows
Digital Platform - Tablet: Windows 7

Pub./Ed. .... Mary Ann Barth
Ed. .... Michael G. Barth
Mng. Ed.............. Jan HeffelfingerEquipment & Software: Hardware — APP/Mac, APP/Mac Scanner; Software — Claris, Multi-Ad.
Delivery Method: Mail, Newsstand
Areas Served: 43526, 43512, 45813, 43506, 45821, 43517, 43520, 43536, 43549, 45879, 43556, 46721, 46706, 46741, 43788, 46743

JACKSON

THE JACKSON COUNTY TIMES-JOURNAL (TUES, THUR, SUN)

1 Acy Ave, Ste D, Jackson, OH, 45640-9563, Jackson, USA; gen tel (740) 286-2187; adv tel (740) 286-2187 ext. 302; ed tel (740) 286-2187 ext. 329; gen fax (740) 286-5854; adv fax (740) 286-5854; ed fax (740) 286-5854; disp adv e-mail tmaynard@timesjournal.com; class adv e-mail amontgomery@timesjournal.com; ed e-mail jhughes@timesjournal.com; web site www.jacksoncountydaily.com
Circulation: 5,600pd, 11,500fr; Sworn/Estimate/Non-Audited
Advertising rate: Open inch rate $11.50
Established: 1847
Group: ACM Ohio LLC
Digital Platform - Mobile: Apple, Android
Digital Platform - Tablet: Apple iOS, Android
Pub.. Norman Gilliland
Mng. Ed.................................. Jennifer Hughes
Adv. Dir... Teresa Bryan
Circ. Mgr... Ken Cris
Mechanical Specifications: Type page 14 x 21 1/2; E - 6 cols, 1 5/6, 1/6 between; A - 6 cols, 1 5/6, 1/6 between; C - 8 cols, 1 5/6, 1/6 between.Equipment & Software: Hardware — APP/Mac; Software — Multi-Ad 3.7.2, QPS/QuarkXPress.
Delivery Method: Mail, Newsstand, Carrier, Racks
Areas Served: 45640, 45656, 45692

THE TELEGRAM (WED, SAT)

920 Veterans Dr, Unit D, Jackson, OH, 45640-2175, Jackson, USA; gen tel (740) 286-3604; gen fax (740) 286-0167; disp adv e-mail jgillum@jcbipaper.com; class adv e-mail bowens@jcbipaper.com; ed e-mail skeller@jcbipaper.com; web site www.the-telegramnews.com
Circulation: 6,000pd,; Sworn/Estimate/Non-Audited
Advertising rate: Open inch rate $8.25
Established: 2005
Digital Platform - Mobile: Apple, Android
Digital Platform - Tablet: Apple iOS, Android, Windows 7
Exec. Ed... Pete Wilson
Mng. Ed.................................... Steven P. Keller
Gen. Mgr. .... Jerry Mossbarger
Adv. Mgr. .... Jeanne Gillum
Admin.................... Rayanna PuckettEquipment & Software: Hardware — IBM; Software — Adobe/PageMaker 4.0, Adobe/Photoshop.
Delivery Method: Mail, Newsstand, Carrier, Racks
Areas Served: Jackson County and Vinton County

JEFFERSON

LAKE COUNTY TRIBUNE (FRI)

46 W Jefferson St, Jefferson, OH, 44047-1028, Ashtabula, USA; gen tel (440) 576-9125; adv tel (440) 576-9125 x102; ed tel (440) 576-9125 x107; gen fax (440) 576-2778; disp adv e-mail beckecreed@gazettenews.com; class adv e-mail beckecreed@gazettenews.com; ed e-mail tribune@gazettenews.com; web site www.gazettenews.com
Circulation: 2,266pd,; USPS
Advertising rate: Open inch rate $8.00
Established: 1992
Group: Gazette Newspapers, Inc.
Digital Platform - Mobile: Apple, Android, Windows, Blackberry
Digital Platform - Tablet: Apple iOS, Android, Windows 7, Blackberry Tablet OS
Pres./Pub. .... William Creed
Editor .... Kathy Vaci
Director of Operations/Adv. Mgr... Becke Creed
Mechanical Specifications: 1 col. - 1.5"
2 col - 3.25"
3 col - 5"
4 col. - 6.75"
5 col. - 8.5"
6 col. - 10.25"Equipment & Software: Hardware — APP/Mac; Presses — Goss Community; Software — Adobe/Pagemaker.
Delivery Method: Mail, Newsstand
Areas Served: Eastern Lake County, Madison, Perry, Painesville, and Mentor

THE COURIER (THUR)

46 W Jefferson St, Jefferson, OH, 44047-1028, Ashtabula, USA; gen tel (440) 576-9125; adv tel (440) 576-9125 x102; ed tel (440) 576-9125 x116; gen fax (440) 576-2778; adv fax (440) 576-2778; ed fax (440) 576-2778; disp adv e-mail beckecreed@gazettenews.com; class adv e-mail beckecreed@gazettenews.com; ed e-mail courier@gazettenews.com; web site www.gazettenews.com
Circulation: 2,600pd,; Sworn/Estimate/Non-Audited
Advertising rate: Open inch rate 8.00
Established: 1992
Group: Gazette Newspapers, Inc.
Digital Platform - Mobile: Apple, Android, Windows, Blackberry
Digital Platform - Tablet: Apple iOS, Android, Windows 7, Blackberry Tablet OS
Pres./Pub. .... William Creed
Editor .... Martha Sorohan
Director of Operations/Advert. Man. .... Becke Creed
Mechanical Specifications: Type page 10.25 x 16Equipment & Software: Hardware — APP/Mac, PC; Presses — G/Community; Software — Adobe/PageMaker.
Delivery Method: Mail, Newsstand
Areas Served: Conneaut and Kingsville

THE GAZETTE (WED)

46 W Jefferson St, Jefferson, OH, 44047-1028, Ashtabula, USA; gen tel (440) 576-9125; adv tel (440) 576-9125 x102; ed tel (440) 576-9125 x107; gen fax (440) 576-2778; disp adv e-mail beckecreed@gazettenews.com; class adv e-mail beckecreed@gazettenews.com; ed e-mail gazette@gazettenews.com; web site www.gazettenews.com
Circulation: 3,955pd,; USPS
Advertising rate: Open inch rate $8.00
Established: 1876
Group: Gazette Newspapers, Inc.
Digital Platform - Mobile: Apple, Android, Windows, Blackberry
Digital Platform - Tablet: Apple iOS, Android, Windows 7, Blackberry Tablet OS
Pres./Pub. .... William Creed
senior editor.......................... Stefanie Wessell
Director of operations/Adv. Mgr.... Becke Creed
Mechanical Specifications: Type page 10.25 x 16Equipment & Software: Hardware — PC, APP/Mac; Presses — G/Community; Software — Adobe/PageMaker.
Delivery Method: Mail, Newsstand
Areas Served: Jefferson, Ashtabula, and Geneva

THE NEWS (FRI)

46 W Jefferson St, Jefferson, OH, 44047-1028, Ashtabula, USA; gen tel (440) 576-9125; adv tel (440) 576-9125 X102; ed tel (440) 576-9125 X107; gen fax (440) 576-2778; disp adv e-mail beckecreed@gazettenews.com; class adv e-mail classifieds@gazettenews.com; ed e-mail dcook@gazettenews.com; web site www.gazettenews.com
Circulation: 1,568pd,; USPS
Advertising rate: Open inch rate $8.00
Established: 1890
Group: Gazette Newspapers, Inc.
Digital Platform - Mobile: Apple, Android, Windows, Blackberry
Digital Platform - Tablet: Apple iOS, Android, Windows 7, Blackberry Tablet OS
Pres./Pub. .... William Creed
Ed. .... Doris Cook
Director of Operations/Adv. Mgr... Becke Creed
Mechanical Specifications: 6 columns x 16" format (10.25" x 16")Equipment & Software: Hardware — Mac; Presses — Goss Community; Software — Pagemaker
Delivery Method: Mail, Newsstand
Areas Served: Andover and Orwell

THE SHORES NEWS (MTHLY)

46 W Jefferson St, Jefferson, OH, 44047-1028, Ashtabula, USA; gen tel (440) 576-9125 ; adv tel (440) 576-9125 x102; ed tel (440) 576-9125 x107; gen fax (440) 576-2778; disp adv e-mail beckecreed@gazettenews.com; class adv e-mail classifieds@gazettenews.com; ed e-mail shoresnews@gazettenews.com; web site www.gazettenews.com
Circulation: 1,329pd,; USPS
Advertising rate: Open inch rate $8.00
Established: 1992
Group: Gazette Newspapers, Inc.
Digital Platform - Mobile: Apple, Android, Windows, Blackberry
Digital Platform - Tablet: Apple iOS, Android, Windows 7, Blackberry Tablet OS
Pres./Pub. .... William Creed
Ed. .... Stefanie Wessell
Director of Operations/Adv. Mgr... Becke Creed
Mechanical Specifications: 6 column x 16" format 10.25" x 16"Equipment & Software: Hardware — Mac; Presses — Goss Community; Software — pagemaker
Delivery Method: Mail, Newsstand
Areas Served: Roaming Shores

KENT

AURORA ADVOCATE (WED)

1050 W Main St, Kent, OH, 44240-2006, Portage, USA; gen tel (330) 541-9400; adv tel (330) 541-9400; ed tel (330) 541-9400; gen fax (330) 296-2698; adv fax (330) 296-2698; ed fax (330) 296-2698; disp adv e-mail Ads@recordpub.com; class adv e-mail class@recordpub.com; ed e-mail editor@recordpub.com; web site www.auroraadvocate.com
Circulation: 180pd, 5,440fr; AAM
Advertising rate: Open inch rate $12.24
Established: 1830
Group: GateHouse Media, Inc.
Digital Platform - Mobile: Apple, Android, Windows, Blackberry
Digital Platform - Tablet: Apple iOS, Android, Windows 7, Blackberry Tablet OS
Pub... David E. Dix
Ed. .... Ken Lahmers
Adv. Mgr. .... Harry Newman
Gen. Mgr. .... Ron Waite
Prod. Mgr. .... Joe Filippini
Mechanical Specifications: Type page 9 1/8 x 14; E - 5 cols, 1 13/16, between; A - 5 cols, 1 13/16, between; C - 5 cols, 1 13/16, between.Equipment & Software: Hardware — APP/Mac
Delivery Method: Carrier
Areas Served: 44202

CUYAHOGA FALLS NEWS-PRESS (SUN)

1050 W Main St, Kent, OH, 44240-2006, Portage, USA; gen tel (330) 541-9400; adv tel (330) 541-9400; ed tel (330) 541-9400; gen fax (330) 296-2698; adv fax (330) 296-2698; ed fax (330) 296-2698; disp adv e-mail Ads@recordpub.com; class adv e-mail class@recordpub.com; ed e-mail editor@recordpub.com; web site www.fallsnewspress.com
Circulation: 342pd, 21,540fr; AAM
Advertising rate: Open inch rate $14.04
Established: 1830
Group: GateHouse Media, Inc.
Digital Platform - Mobile: Apple, Android, Windows, Blackberry
Digital Platform - Tablet: Apple iOS, Android, Windows 7, Blackberry Tablet OS
Pub... David E. Dix
Ed. .... Phil Keren
Mechanical Specifications: Type page 9 1/8 x 143/16, between; C - 5 cols, 1 13/16, between.Equipment & Software: Hardware — APP/Mac; Presses — G/Urbanite; Software — Baseview/EditPro.
Delivery Method: Carrier
Areas Served: Portage County

HUDSON HUB-TIMES (WED, SUN)

1050 W Main St, Kent, OH, 44240-2006, Portage, USA; gen tel (330) 541-9427; gen fax (330) 296-2698; disp adv e-mail Ads@recordpub.com; class adv e-mail class@recordpub.com; ed e-mail editor@recordpub.com; web site www.hudsonhubtimes.com
Circulation: 259pd, 8,950fr; AAM
Advertising rate: Open inch rate $9.60
Established: 1830
Group: GateHouse Media, Inc.
Digital Platform - Mobile: Apple, Android, Windows, Blackberry
Digital Platform - Tablet: Apple iOS, Android, Windows 7, Blackberry Tablet OS
Pub... David E. Dix
Ed. .... Andrew Adam
Adv. Mgr. .... Harry Newman
Gen. Mgr. .... Ron Waite
Circ. Mgr.............................. Margaret Gotschall
Mechanical Specifications: Type page 9 5/8 x 16; E - 5 cols, 1 13/16, between; A - 5 cols, 1 13/16, between; C - 5 cols, 1 13/16, between.Equipment & Software: Hardware — APP/Mac; Presses — G/Urbanite; Software — Baseview.
Delivery Method: Carrier
Areas Served: Summit County
Portage County

NORDONIA HILLS NEWS LEADER (WED)

1050 W Main St, Kent, OH, 44240-2006, Portage, USA; gen tel (330) 541-9400; adv tel (330) 541-9400; ed tel (330) 541-9400; gen fax (330) 296-2698; adv fax (330) 296-2698; ed fax (330) 296-2698; disp adv e-mail Ads@recordpub.com; class adv e-mail class@recordpub.com; ed e-mail editor@recordpub.com; web site www.the-news-leader.com
Circulation: 316pd, 12,568fr; CAC
Advertising rate: Open inch rate $12.72
Established: 1830
Group: Record Publishing Company, LLC
Digital Platform - Mobile: Apple, Android, Windows, Blackberry
Digital Platform - Tablet: Apple iOS, Android, Windows 7, Blackberry Tablet OS
Pub... David E. Dix
Ed. .... Eric Marotta
Circ. Mgr. .... Margaret Gotchell
Mechanical Specifications: Type page 9 1/8 x 14Equipment & Software: Hardware — APP/Macs; Presses — G/Urbanite; Software — Baseview.
Delivery Method: Carrier
Areas Served: 44056, 44067

STOW SENTRY (SUN)

1050 W Main St, Kent, OH, 44240-2006, Portage, USA; gen tel (330) 541-9400; adv tel (330) 673-3500; ed tel (330) 541-9400 Ext. 4178; gen fax (330) 296-2698; adv fax (330) 296-2698; ed fax (330) 296-2698; disp adv e-mail Ads@recordpub.com; class adv e-mail legals@recordpub.com; ed e-mail editor@recordpub.com; web site www.stowsentry.com
Circulation: 320pd, 14,083fr; CAC
Advertising rate: Open inch rate $10.20
Established: 1830
Group: GateHouse Media, Inc.
Digital Platform - Mobile: Apple, Android, Windows, Blackberry
Digital Platform - Tablet: Apple iOS, Android, Windows 7, Blackberry Tablet OS
Pub... David E. Dix
Sr. Ed. .... Marsha McKenna
Cir. Mgr.............................. Margaret Gottschall
Gen. Mgr. .... Ron Waite
Adv. Mgr. .... Diane Ringer
Mechanical Specifications: Type page 9 5/8 x 16; E - 5 cols, 1 13/16, between; A - 5 cols, 1 13/16, between; C - 5 cols, 1 13/16, between.Equipment & Software: Hardware — APP/Macs; Presses — G; Software — Baseview.
Delivery Method: Carrier
Areas Served: Portage County

TALLMADGE EXPRESS (SUN)

1050 W Main St, Kent, OH, 44240-2006, Por-

tage, USA; gen tel (330) 541-9400; adv tel (330) 541-9400; ed tel (330) 541-9400; gen fax (330) 296-2698; adv fax (330) 296-2698; ed fax (330) 296-2698; disp adv e-mail Ads@recordpub.com; class adv e-mail class@recordpub.com; ed e-mail editor@recordpub.com; web site www.tallmadgeexpress.com
Circulation: 219pd, 7,202fr; CAC
Advertising rate: Open inch rate $12.24
Established: 1830
Group: Record Publishing Company, LLC
Digital Platform - Mobile: Apple, Android, Windows, Blackberry
Digital Platform - Tablet: Apple iOS, Android, Windows 7, Blackberry Tablet OS
Pub....... David E. Dix
Exec. Ed....... Erica Peterson
Ed....... Jaime Gerard
Gen. Mgr....... Ron Walte
Mechanical Specifications: Type page 9 1/8 x 14; E - 5 cols, 1 13/16, between; A - 5 cols, 1 13/16, between; C - 5 cols, 1 13/16, between.Equipment & Software: Hardware — APP/Macs
Delivery Method: Carrier
Areas Served: Portage County

TWINSBURG BULLETIN (THUR)

1050 W Main St, Kent, OH, 44240-2006, Portage, USA; gen tel (330) 541-9400; adv tel (330) 541-9400 Ext. 4114; ed tel (330) 541-9400 Ex. 4172; gen fax (330) 296-2698; adv fax (330) 296-2698; ed fax (330) 296-2698; disp adv e-mail Ads@recordpub.com; class adv e-mail jgasper@recordpub.com; ed e-mail aschunk@recordpub.com; web site www.twinsburgbulletin.com
Circulation: 162pd, 8,293fr; CAC
Advertising rate: Open inch rate $9.50
Established: 1830
Group: Record Publishing Company, LLC
Digital Platform - Mobile: Apple, Android, Windows, Blackberry
Digital Platform - Tablet: Apple iOS, Android, Windows 7, Blackberry Tablet OS
Pub....... David E. Dix
Ed....... Andrew Schunk
Adv. Sales Mgr....... Joe Gasper
Gen. Mgr....... Ron Waite
Cir. Dir....... Gary Hurst
Cir. Mgr....... Margaret Gotschall
Mechanical Specifications: Type page 10 3/8 x 16; E - 5 cols, 1 7/8, between; A - 5 cols, 1 7/8, between; C - 5 cols, 1 7/8, between. Equipment & Software: Hardware — APP/Macs; Presses — G/Urbanite; Software — Baseview.
Delivery Method: Carrier
Areas Served: Portage County

LEIPSIC

THE LEIPSIC MESSENGER (THUR)

117 E Main St, Leipsic, OH, 45856-1428, Putnam, USA; gen tel (419) 943-2590; gen fax (419) 943-2590; web site www.leipsic-messenger.com
Circulation: 1,300pd,; Sworn/Estimate/Non-Audited
Advertising rate: Open inch rate $5.60
Digital Platform - Mobile: Apple, Android, Windows, Blackberry
Digital Platform - Tablet: Apple iOS, Android, Windows 7, Blackberry Tablet OS
Pub....... Keith Mickens
Adv. Mgr....... Susan Mickens
Mechanical Specifications: Type page 10 1/2 x 21; E - 6 cols, 2, 1/4 between; A - 6 cols, 2, 1/4 between; C - 6 cols, 2, 1/4 between.
Delivery Method: Mail, Newsstand
Areas Served: 45856

LEWIS CENTER

THISWEEK BEXLEY NEWS (THUR)

7801 N Central Dr, Lewis Center, OH, 43035-9407, Delaware, USA; gen tel (740) 888-6000; adv tel (740) 888-6007; ed tel (740) 888-6100; gen fax (740) 888-6006; adv fax (740) 888-6001; ed fax (740) 888-6006; disp adv e-mail advertising@thisweeknews.com; class adv e-mail classified@thisweeknews.com; ed e-mail lcochran@thisweeknews.com; web site www.thisweeknews.com
Circulation: 7,691fr; AAM
Advertising rate: 1/20 Pg $64.00; 1/12 Pg $94.00; 1/10 Pg $125.00
Established: 1990
Group: ThisWeek Community News Consumer News Service Inc.
Digital Platform - Mobile: Apple, Android, Windows, Blackberry
Digital Platform - Tablet: Apple iOS, Android, Windows 7, Blackberry Tablet OS
Pres./Pub....... Bradley Harmon
Mng. Ed....... Lee Cochran
Adv. Dir....... Doug Dixon
Mechanical Specifications: 9.5" x 13.3"; 6-columns, 1.438" w eachEquipment & Software: Hardware — APP/Mac; Presses — TKS; Software — QPS/QuarkXPress.
Delivery Method: Carrier, Racks
Areas Served: Central Ohio

THISWEEK CLINTONVILLE BOOSTER (THUR)

7801 N Central Dr, Lewis Center, OH, 43035-9407, Delaware, USA; gen tel (740) 888-6000; adv tel (740) 888-6007; ed tel (740) 888-6100; gen fax (740) 888-6006; adv fax (740) 888-6001; ed fax (740) 888-6006; disp adv e-mail advertising@thisweeknews.com; class adv e-mail classified@thisweeknews.com; ed e-mail editorial@thisweeknews.com; web site www.thisweeknews.com
Circulation: 14,250fr; Sworn/Estimate/Non-Audited
Advertising rate: Open inch rate $15.25
Established: 1990
Group: ThisWeek Community News Consumer News Service Inc.
Digital Platform - Mobile: Apple, Android, Windows, Blackberry
Digital Platform - Tablet: Apple iOS, Android, Windows 7, Blackberry Tablet OS
Pub....... Bradley Harmon
Mng. Ed....... Lee Cochran
Adv. Dir....... Doug Dixon
Mechanical Specifications: 9.5" x 13.3"; 6-columns, 1.438" w eachEquipment & Software: Hardware — APP/Mac; Presses — TKS; Software — QPS/QuarkXPress.
Delivery Method: Carrier, Racks
Areas Served: Central Ohio

THISWEEK DELAWARE NEWS (SUN)

7801 N Central Dr, Lewis Center, OH, 43035-9407, Delaware, USA; gen tel (740) 888-6000; adv tel (740) 888-6007; ed tel (740) 888-6100; gen fax (740) 888-6006; adv fax (740) 888-6001; ed fax (740) 888-6006; disp adv e-mail advertising@thisweeknews.com; class adv e-mail classified@thisweeknews.com; ed e-mail editorial@thisweeknews.com; web site www.thisweeknews.com
Circulation: 16,520fr; AAM
Advertising rate: 1/20 Pg $75.00; 1/12 Pg $111.00; 1/10 Pg $147.00
Established: 1990
Group: ThisWeek Community News Consumer News Service Inc.
Digital Platform - Mobile: Apple, Android, Windows, Blackberry
Digital Platform - Tablet: Apple iOS, Android, Windows 7, Blackberry Tablet OS
Pub....... Bradley Harmon
Mng. Ed....... Lee Cochran
Adv. Dir....... Doug Dixon
Mechanical Specifications: 9.5" x 13.3"; 6-columns, 1.438" w eachEquipment & Software: Hardware — APP/Mac; Presses — TKS; Software — QPS/QuarkXPress.
Delivery Method: Carrier, Racks
Areas Served: Central Ohio

THISWEEK DUBLIN VILLAGER (THUR)

7801 N Central Dr, Lewis Center, OH, 43035-9407, Delaware, USA; gen tel (740) 888-6000; adv tel (740) 888-6007; ed tel (740) 888-6100; gen fax (740) 888-6006; adv fax (740) 888-6001; ed fax (740) 888-6006; disp adv e-mail advertising@thisweeknews.com; class adv e-mail classified@thisweeknews.com; ed e-mail editorial@thisweeknews.com; web site www.thisweeknews.com
Circulation: 19,462fr; AAM
Advertising rate: 1/20 Pg $81.00
Established: 1990
Group: ThisWeek Community News Consumer News Service Inc.
Digital Platform - Mobile: Apple, Android, Windows, Blackberry
Digital Platform - Tablet: Apple iOS, Android, Windows 7, Blackberry Tablet OS
Pub....... Bradley Harmon
Adv. Dir....... Doug Dixon
Mng. Ed....... Lee Cochran
Mechanical Specifications: 9.5" x 13.3"; 6-columns, 1.438" w eachEquipment & Software: Hardware — APP/Mac; Presses — TKS; Software — QPS/QuarkXPress.
Delivery Method: Carrier, Racks
Areas Served: Central Ohio

THISWEEK GERMAN VILLAGE GAZETTE (THUR)

7801 N Central Dr, Lewis Center, OH, 43035-9407, Delaware, USA; gen tel (740) 888-6000; adv tel (740) 888-6007; ed tel (740) 888-6100; gen fax (740) 888-6006; adv fax (740) 888-6001; ed fax (740) 888-6006; disp adv e-mail advertising@thisweeknews.com; class adv e-mail classified@thisweeknews.com; ed e-mail editorial@thisweeknews.com; web site www.thisweeknews.com
Circulation: 4,316fr; AAM
Advertising rate: 1/20 Pg $49.00; 1/12 Pg $72.00; 1/10 Pg $94.00
Established: 1990
Group: ThisWeek Community News Consumer News Service Inc.
Digital Platform - Mobile: Apple, Android, Windows, Blackberry
Digital Platform - Tablet: Apple iOS, Android, Windows 7, Blackberry Tablet OS
Pub....... Bradley Harmon
Mng. Ed....... Lee Cochran
Adv. Dir....... Doug Dixon
Mechanical Specifications: 9.5" x 13.3"; 6-columns, 1.438" w eachEquipment & Software: Hardware — APP/Mac; Presses — TKS; Software — QPS/QuarkXPress.
Delivery Method: Carrier, Racks
Areas Served: Central Ohio

THISWEEK GROVE CITY RECORD (THUR)

7801 N Central Dr, Lewis Center, OH, 43035-9407, Delaware, USA; gen tel (740) 888-6000; adv tel (740) 888-6007; ed tel (740) 888-6100; gen fax (740) 888-6006; adv fax (740) 888-6001; ed fax (740) 888-6006; disp adv e-mail advertising@thisweeknews.com; class adv e-mail classified@thisweeknews.com; ed e-mail editorial@thisweeknews.com; web site www.thisweeknews.com
Circulation: 14,614fr; AAM
Advertising rate: 1/20 Pg $49.00; 1/12 Pg $72.00; 1/10 Pg $94.00
Established: 1990
Group: ThisWeek Community News Consumer News Service Inc.
Digital Platform - Mobile: Apple, Android, Windows, Blackberry
Digital Platform - Tablet: Apple iOS, Android, Windows 7, Blackberry Tablet OS
Pub....... Bradley Harmon
Mng. Ed....... Lee Cochran
Adv. Dir....... Doug Dixon
Mechanical Specifications: 9.5" x 13.3"; 6-columns, 1.438" w eachEquipment & Software: Hardware — APP/Mac; Presses — TKS; Software — QPS/QuarkXPress.
Delivery Method: Carrier, Racks
Areas Served: Central Ohio

THISWEEK HILLIARD NORTHWEST NEWS (THUR)

7801 N Central Dr, Lewis Center, OH, 43035-9407, Delaware, USA; gen tel (740) 888-6000; adv tel (740) 888-6007; ed tel (740) 888-6100; gen fax (740) 888-6006; adv fax (740) 888-6001; ed fax (740) 888-6006; disp adv e-mail advertising@thisweeknews.com; class adv e-mail classified@thisweeknews.com; ed e-mail editorial@thisweeknews.com; web site www.thisweeknews.com
Circulation: 21,859fr; AAM
Advertising rate: 1/20 Pg $81.00; 1/12 Pg $118.00; 1/10 Pg $156.00
Established: 1990
Group: ThisWeek Community News Consumer News Service Inc.
Digital Platform - Mobile: Apple, Android, Windows, Blackberry
Digital Platform - Tablet: Apple iOS, Android, Windows 7, Blackberry Tablet OS
Pub....... Bradley Harmon
Mng. Ed....... Lee Cochran
Adv. Dir....... Doug Dixon
Mechanical Specifications: 9.5" x 13.3"; 6-columns, 1.438" w eachEquipment & Software: Hardware — APP/Mac; Presses — TKS; Software — QPS/QuarkXPress.
Delivery Method: Carrier, Racks
Areas Served: Central Ohio

THISWEEK JOHNSTOWN INDEPENDENT (SUN)

7801 N Central Dr, Lewis Center, OH, 43035-9407, Delaware, USA; gen tel (740) 888-6000; adv tel (740) 888-6007; ed tel (740) 888-6100; gen fax (740) 888-6006; adv fax (740) 888-6001; ed fax (740) 888-6006; disp adv e-mail advertising@thisweeknews.com; class adv e-mail classified@thisweeknews.com; ed e-mail editorial@thisweeknews.com; web site www.thisweeknews.com
Circulation: 6,448fr; AAM
Advertising rate: 1/20 Pg $54.00; 1/10 Pg $79.00; 1/5 Pg $151.00
Established: 1990
Group: ThisWeek Community News Consumer News Service Inc.
Digital Platform - Mobile: Apple, Android, Windows, Blackberry
Digital Platform - Tablet: Apple iOS, Android, Windows 7, Blackberry Tablet OS
Pub....... Bradley Harmon
Mng. Ed....... Lee Cochran
Adv. Dir....... Doug Dixon
Mechanical Specifications: 9.5" x 13.3"; 6-columns, 1.438" w eachEquipment & Software: Hardware — APP/Mac; Presses — TKS; Software — QPS/QuarkXPress.
Delivery Method: Carrier, Racks
Areas Served: Central Ohio

THISWEEK LICKING COUNTY NEWS (SUN)

7801 N Central Dr, Lewis Center, OH, 43035-9407, Delaware, USA; gen tel (740) 888-6000; adv tel (740) 888-6007; ed tel (740) 888-6100; gen fax (740) 888-6006; adv fax (740) 888-6001; ed fax (740) 888-6006; disp adv e-mail advertising@thisweeknews.com; class adv e-mail classified@thisweeknews.com; ed e-mail editorial@thisweeknews.com; web site www.thisweeknews.com
Circulation: 14,403fr; AAM
Advertising rate: 1/20 Pg $81.00; 1/12 Pg $118.00; 1/10 Pg $156.00
Established: 1990
Group: ThisWeek Community News Consumer News Service Inc.
Digital Platform - Mobile: Apple, Android, Windows, Blackberry
Digital Platform - Tablet: Apple iOS, Android, Windows 7, Blackberry Tablet OS
Pub....... Bradley Harmon
Mng. Ed....... Lee Cochran
Adv. Dir....... Doug Dixon
Mechanical Specifications: 9.5" x 13.3"; 6-columns, 1.438" w eachEquipment & Software: Hardware — APP/Mac; Presses — TKS; Software — QPS/QuarkXPress.
Delivery Method: Carrier, Racks
Areas Served: Central Ohio

THISWEEK MARYSVILLE NEWS (SUN)

7801 N Central Dr, Lewis Center, OH, 43035-9407, Delaware, USA; gen tel (740) 888-6000; adv tel (740) 888-6007; ed tel (740) 888-6100; gen fax (740) 888-6006; adv fax (740) 888-6001; ed fax (740) 888-6006; disp adv e-mail advertising@thisweeknews.com; class adv e-mail classified@thisweeknews.com; ed e-mail editorial@thisweeknews.com; web site www.thisweeknews.com
Circulation: 10,126fr; AAM
Advertising rate: 1/20 Pg $81.00; 1/12 Pg $118.00; 1/10 Pg $156.00
Established: 1990

Group: ThisWeek Community News
Consumer News Service Inc.
Digital Platform - Mobile: Apple, Android, Windows, Blackberry
Digital Platform - Tablet: Apple iOS, Android, Windows 7, Blackberry Tablet OS
Pub....Bradley Harmon
Mng. Ed....Lee Cochran
Adv. Dir....Doug Dixon
Mechanical Specifications: 9.5" x 13.3"; 6-columns, 1.438" w eachEquipment & Software: Hardware — APP/Mac; Presses — TKS; Software — QPS/QuarkXPress.
Delivery Method: Carrier, Racks
Areas Served: Central Ohio

THISWEEK NEW ALBANY NEWS (THUR)

7801 N Central Dr, Lewis Center, OH, 43035-9407, Delaware, USA; gen tel (740) 888-6000; adv tel (740) 888-6007; ed tel (740) 888-6100; gen fax (740) 888-6006; adv fax (740) 888-6001; ed fax (740) 888-6006; disp adv e-mail advertising@thisweeknews.com; class adv e-mail classified@thisweeknews.com; ed e-mail editorial@thisweeknews.com; web site www.thisweeknews.com
Circulation: 7,219fr; Sworn/Estimate/Non-Audited
Advertising rate: 1/20 Pg $81.00; 1/12 Pg $118.00; 1/10 Pg $156.00
Established: 1990
Group: ThisWeek Community News
Consumer News Service Inc.
Digital Platform - Mobile: Apple, Android, Windows, Blackberry
Digital Platform - Tablet: Apple iOS, Android, Windows 7, Blackberry Tablet OS
Pub....Bradley Harmon
Mng. Ed....Lee Cochran
Adv. Dir....Doug Dixon
Mechanical Specifications: 9.5" x 13.3"; 6-columns, 1.438" w eachEquipment & Software: Hardware — APP/Mac; Presses — TKS; Software — QPS/QuarkXPress.
Delivery Method: Carrier, Racks
Areas Served: Central Ohio

THISWEEK NORTHLAND NEWS (THUR)

7801 N Central Dr, Lewis Center, OH, 43035-9407, Delaware, USA; gen tel (740) 888-6000; adv tel (740) 888-6007; ed tel (740) 888-6100; gen fax (740) 888-6006; adv fax (740) 888-6001; ed fax (740) 888-6006; disp adv e-mail advertising@thisweeknews.com; class adv e-mail classified@thisweeknews.com; ed e-mail editorial@thisweeknews.com; web site www.thisweeknews.com
Circulation: 14,294fr; AAM
Advertising rate: 1/20 Pg $81.00; 1/12 Pg $118.00; 1/10 Pg $156.00
Established: 1990
Group: ThisWeek Community News
Consumer News Service Inc.
Digital Platform - Mobile: Apple, Android, Windows, Blackberry
Digital Platform - Tablet: Apple iOS, Android, Windows 7, Blackberry Tablet OS
Pub....Bradley Harmon
Mng. Ed....Lee Cochran
Adv. Dir....Doug Dixon
Mechanical Specifications: 9.5" x 13.3"; 6-columns, 1.438" w eachEquipment & Software: Hardware — APP/Mac; Presses — TKS; Software — QPS/QuarkXPress.
Delivery Method: Carrier, Racks
Areas Served: Central Ohio

THISWEEK NORTHWEST NEWS (THUR)

7801 N Central Dr, Lewis Center, OH, 43035-9407, Delaware, USA; gen tel (740) 888-6000; adv tel (740) 888-6007; ed tel (740) 888-6100; gen fax (740) 888-6006; adv fax (740) 888-6001; ed fax (740) 888-6006; disp adv e-mail advertising@thisweeknews.com; class adv e-mail classified@thisweeknews.com; ed e-mail editorial@thisweeknews.com; web site www.thisweeknews.com
Circulation: 3,344fr; AAM
Advertising rate: 1/20 Pg $81.00; 1/12 Pg $118.00; 1/10 Pg $156.00
Established: 1990
Group: ThisWeek Community News
Consumer News Service Inc.
Digital Platform - Mobile: Apple, Android, Windows, Blackberry
Digital Platform - Tablet: Apple iOS, Android, Windows 7, Blackberry Tablet OS
Pub....Bradley Harmon
Mng. Ed....Lee Cochran
Adv. Dir....Doug Dixon
Mechanical Specifications: 9.5" x 13.3"; 6-columns, 1.438" w eachEquipment & Software: Hardware — APP/Mac; Presses — TKS; Software — QPS/QuarkXPress.
Delivery Method: Carrier, Racks
Areas Served: Central Ohio

THISWEEK OLENTANGY VALLEY NEWS (THUR)

7801 N Central Dr, Lewis Center, OH, 43035-9407, Delaware, USA; gen tel (740) 888-6000; adv tel (740) 888-6007; ed tel (740) 888-6100; gen fax (740) 888-6006; adv fax (740) 888-6001; ed fax (740) 888-6006; disp adv e-mail advertising@thisweeknews.com; class adv e-mail classified@thisweeknews.com; ed e-mail editorial@thisweeknews.com; web site www.thisweeknews.com
Circulation: 20,103fr; AAM
Advertising rate: 1/20 Pg $81.00; 1/12 Pg $118.00; 1/10 Pg $156.00
Established: 1990
Group: ThisWeek Community News
Consumer News Service Inc.
Digital Platform - Mobile: Apple, Android, Windows, Blackberry
Digital Platform - Tablet: Apple iOS, Android, Windows 7, Blackberry Tablet OS
Pub....Bradley Harmon
Mng. Ed....Lee Cochran
Adv. Dir....Doug Dixon
Mechanical Specifications: 9.5" x 13.3"; 6-columns, 1.438" w eachEquipment & Software: Hardware — APP/Mac; Presses — TKS; Software — QPS/QuarkXPress.
Delivery Method: Carrier, Racks
Areas Served: Central Ohio

THISWEEK PICKERINGTON TIMES-SUN (THUR)

7801 N Central Dr, Lewis Center, OH, 43035-9407, Delaware, USA; gen tel (740) 888-6000; adv tel (740) 888-6007; ed tel (740) 888-6100; gen fax (740) 888-6006; adv fax (740) 888-6001; ed fax (740) 888-6006; disp adv e-mail advertising@thisweeknews.com; class adv e-mail classified@thisweeknews.com; ed e-mail editorial@thisweeknews.com; web site www.thisweeknews.com
Circulation: 12,805fr; Sworn/Estimate/Non-Audited
Advertising rate: 1/20 Pg $75.00; 1/12 Pg $111.00; 1/10 Pg $147.00
Established: 1990
Group: ThisWeek Community News
Consumer News Service Inc.
Digital Platform - Mobile: Apple, Android, Windows, Blackberry
Digital Platform - Tablet: Apple iOS, Android, Windows 7, Blackberry Tablet OS
Pub....Bradley Harmon
Mng. Ed....Lee Cochran
Adv. Dir....Doug Dixon
Mechanical Specifications: 9.5" x 13.3"; 6-columns, 1.438" w eachEquipment & Software: Hardware — APP/Mac; Presses — TKS; Software — QPS/QuarkXPress.
Delivery Method: Carrier, Racks
Areas Served: Central Ohio

THISWEEK REYNOLDSBURG NEWS (THUR)

7801 N Central Dr, Lewis Center, OH, 43035-9407, Delaware, USA; gen tel (740) 888-6000; adv tel (740) 888-6007; ed tel (740) 888-6100; gen fax (740) 888-6006; adv fax (740) 888-6001; ed fax (740) 888-6006; disp adv e-mail advertising@thisweeknews.com; class adv e-mail classified@thisweeknews.com; ed e-mail editorial@thisweeknews.com; web site www.thisweeknews.com
Circulation: 11,110fr; AAM
Advertising rate: 1/20 Pg $64.00; 1/12 Pg $94.00; 1/10 Pg $125.00
Established: 1990
Group: ThisWeek Community News
Consumer News Service Inc.
Digital Platform - Mobile: Apple, Android, Windows, Blackberry
Digital Platform - Tablet: Apple iOS, Android, Windows 7, Blackberry Tablet OS
Pub....Bradley Harmon
Mng. Ed....Lee Cochran
Adv. Dir....Doug Dixon
Mechanical Specifications: 9.5" x 13.3"; 6-columns, 1.438" w eachEquipment & Software: Hardware — APP/Mac; Presses — TKS; Software — QPS/QuarkXPress.
Delivery Method: Carrier, Racks
Areas Served: Central Ohio

THISWEEK ROCKY FORK ENTERPRISE (THUR)

7801 N Central Dr, Lewis Center, OH, 43035-9407, Delaware, USA; gen tel (740) 888-6000; adv tel (740) 888-6007; ed tel (740) 888-6100; gen fax (740) 888-6006; adv fax (740) 888-6001; ed fax (740) 888-6006; disp adv e-mail advertising@thisweeknews.com; class adv e-mail classified@thisweeknews.com; ed e-mail editorial@thisweeknews.com; web site www.thisweeknews.com
Circulation: 14,419fr; AAM
Advertising rate: 1/20 Pg $64.00; 1/12 Pg $94.00; 1/10 Pg $125.00
Established: 1990
Group: ThisWeek Community News
Consumer News Service Inc.
Digital Platform - Mobile: Apple, Android, Windows, Blackberry
Digital Platform - Tablet: Apple iOS, Android, Windows 7, Blackberry Tablet OS
Pub....Bradley Harmon
Mng. Ed....Lee Cochran
Adv. Dir....Doug Dixon
Mechanical Specifications: 9.5" x 13.3"; 6-columns, 1.438" w eachEquipment & Software: Hardware — APP/Mac; Presses — TKS; Software — QPS/QuarkXPress.
Delivery Method: Carrier, Racks
Areas Served: Central Ohio

THISWEEK THE CANAL WINCHESTER TIMES (THUR)

7801 N Central Dr, Lewis Center, OH, 43035-9407, Delaware, USA; gen tel (740) 888-6000; adv tel (740) 888-6007; ed tel (740) 888-6100; gen fax (740) 888-6006; adv fax (740) 888-6001; ed fax (740) 888-6006; disp adv e-mail advertising@thisweeknews.com; class adv e-mail classified@thisweeknews.com; ed e-mail editorial@thisweeknews.com; web site www.thisweeknews.com
Circulation: 9,580fr; Sworn/Estimate/Non-Audited
Advertising rate: Open inch rate $15.25
Established: 1990
Group: ThisWeek Community News
Consumer News Service Inc.
Digital Platform - Mobile: Apple, Android, Windows, Blackberry
Digital Platform - Tablet: Apple iOS, Android, Windows 7, Blackberry Tablet OS
Pub....Bradley Harmon
Mng. Ed....Lee Cochran
Adv. Dir....Doug Dixon
Mechanical Specifications: 9.5" x 13.3"; 6-columns, 1.438" w eachEquipment & Software: Hardware — APP/Mac; Presses — TKS; Software — QPS/QuarkXPress.
Delivery Method: Carrier, Racks
Areas Served: Central Ohio

THISWEEK TRI-VILLAGE NEWS (THUR)

7801 N Central Dr, Lewis Center, OH, 43035-9407, Delaware, USA; gen tel (740) 888-6000; adv tel (740) 888-6007; ed tel (740) 888-6100; gen fax (740) 888-6006; adv fax (740) 888-6001; ed fax (740) 888-6006; disp adv e-mail advertising@thisweeknews.com; class adv e-mail classified@thisweeknews.com; ed e-mail editorial@thisweeknews.com; web site www.thisweeknews.com
Circulation: 4,669fr; AAM
Advertising rate: 1/20 Pg $49.00; 1/12 Pg $72.00; 1/10 Pg $94.00
Established: 1990
Group: ThisWeek Community News
Consumer News Service Inc.
Digital Platform - Mobile: Apple, Android, Windows, Blackberry
Digital Platform - Tablet: Apple iOS, Android, Windows 7, Blackberry Tablet OS
Pub....Bradley Harmon
Mng. Ed....Lee Cochran
Adv. Dir....Doug Dixon
Mechanical Specifications: 9.5" x 13.3"; 6-columns, 1.438" w eachEquipment & Software: Hardware — APP/Mac; Presses — TKS; Software — QPS/QuarkXPress.
Delivery Method: Carrier, Racks
Areas Served: Central Ohio

THISWEEK UPPER ARLINGTON NEWS (THUR)

7801 N Central Dr, Lewis Center, OH, 43035-9407, Delaware, USA; gen tel (740) 888-6000; adv tel (740) 888-6007; ed tel (740) 888-6100; gen fax (740) 888-6006; adv fax (740) 888-6001; ed fax (740) 888-6006; disp adv e-mail advertising@thisweeknews.com; class adv e-mail classified@thisweeknews.com; ed e-mail editorial@thisweeknews.com; web site www.thisweeknews.com
Circulation: 18,473fr; AAM
Advertising rate: 1/20 Pg $64.00; 1/12 Pg $94.00; 1/10 Pg $125.00
Established: 1990
Group: ThisWeek Community News
Consumer News Service Inc.
Digital Platform - Mobile: Apple, Android, Windows, Blackberry
Digital Platform - Tablet: Apple iOS, Android, Windows 7, Blackberry Tablet OS
Pub....Bradley Harmon
Mng. Ed....Lee Cochran
Adv. Dir....Doug Dixon
Mechanical Specifications: 9.5" x 13.3"; 6-columns, 1.438" w eachEquipment & Software: Hardware — APP/Mac; Presses — TKS; Software — QPS/QuarkXPress.
Delivery Method: Carrier, Racks
Areas Served: Central Ohio

THISWEEK WEST SIDE NEWS (SUN)

7801 N Central Dr, Lewis Center, OH, 43035-9407, Delaware, USA; gen tel (740) 888-6000; adv tel (740) 888-6007; ed tel (740) 888-6100; gen fax (740) 888-6006; adv fax (740) 888-6001; ed fax (740) 888-6006; disp adv e-mail advertising@thisweeknews.com; class adv e-mail classified@thisweeknews.com; ed e-mail editorial@thisweeknews.com; web site www.thisweeknews.com
Circulation: 7,850fr; AAM
Advertising rate: 1/20 Pg $75.00; 1/12 Pg $111.00; 1/10 Pg $147.00
Established: 1990
Group: ThisWeek Community News
Consumer News Service Inc.
Digital Platform - Mobile: Apple, Android, Windows, Blackberry
Digital Platform - Tablet: Apple iOS, Android, Windows 7, Blackberry Tablet OS
Pub....Bradley Harmon
Mng. Ed....Lee Cochran
Adv. Dir....Doug Dixon
Mechanical Specifications: 9.5" x 13.3"; 6-columns, 1.438" w eachEquipment & Software: Hardware — APP/Mac; Presses — TKS; Software — QPS/QuarkXPress.
Delivery Method: Carrier, Racks
Areas Served: Central Ohio

THISWEEK WESTERVILLE NEWS & PUBLIC OPINION (THUR)

7801 N Central Dr, Lewis Center, OH, 43035-9407, Delaware, USA; gen tel (740) 888-6000; adv tel (740) 888-6007; ed tel (740) 888-6100; gen fax (740) 888-6006; adv fax (740) 888-6001; ed fax (740) 888-6006; disp adv e-mail advertising@thisweeknews.com; class adv e-mail classified@thisweeknews.com; ed e-mail editorial@thisweeknews.com; web site www.thisweeknews.com
Circulation: 25,825fr; AAM
Advertising rate: 1/20 Pg $81.00; 1/12 Pg $118.00; 1/10 Pg $156.00
Established: 1990
Group: ThisWeek Community News
Consumer News Service Inc.
Digital Platform - Mobile: Apple, Android, Windows, Blackberry
Digital Platform - Tablet: Apple iOS, Android, Windows 7, Blackberry Tablet OS
Pub....Bradley Harmon

Mng. Ed.. Lee Cochran
Adv. Dir... Doug Dixon
Mechanical Specifications: 9.5" x 13.3"; 6-columns, 1.438" w eachEquipment & Software: Hardware — APP/Mac; Presses — TKS; Software — QPS/QuarkXPress.
Delivery Method: Carrier, Racks
Areas Served: Central Ohio

THISWEEK WHITEHALL NEWS (THUR)
7801 N Central Dr, Lewis Center, OH, 43035-9407, Delaware, USA; gen tel (740) 888-6000; adv tel (740) 888-6007; ed tel (740) 888-6100; gen fax (740) 888-6006; adv fax (740) 888-6001; ed fax (740) 888-6006; disp adv e-mail advertising@thisweeknews.com; class adv e-mail classified@thisweeknews.com; ed e-mail editorial@thisweeknews.com; web site www.thisweeknews.com
Circulation: 5,110fr; Sworn/Estimate/Non-Audited
Advertising rate: 1/20 Pg $64.00; 1/12 Pg $94.00; 1/10 Pg $125.00
Established: 1990
Group: ThisWeek Community News
Consumer News Service Inc.
Digital Platform - Mobile: Apple, Android, Windows, Blackberry
Digital Platform - Tablet: Apple iOS, Android, Windows 7, Blackberry Tablet OS
Pub... Bradley Harmon
Mng. Ed.. Lee Cochran
Adv. Dir... Doug Dixon
Mechanical Specifications: 9.5" x 13.3"; 6-columns, 1.438" w eachEquipment & Software: Hardware — APP/Mac; Presses — TKS; Software — QPS/QuarkXPress.
Delivery Method: Carrier, Racks
Areas Served: Central Ohio

THISWEEK WORTHINGTON NEWS (THUR)
7801 N Central Dr, Lewis Center, OH, 43035-9407, Delaware, USA; gen tel (740) 888-6000; adv tel (740) 888-6007; ed tel (740) 888-6100; gen fax (740) 888-6006; adv fax (740) 888-6001; ed fax (740) 888-6006; disp adv e-mail advertising@thisweeknews.com; class adv e-mail classified@thisweeknews.com; ed e-mail editorial@thisweeknews.com; web site www.thisweeknews.com
Circulation: 17,875fr; AAM
Advertising rate: 1/20 Pg $81.00; 1/12 Pg $118.00; 1/10 Pg $156.00
Established: 1990
Group: ThisWeek Community News
Consumer News Service Inc.
Digital Platform - Mobile: Apple, Android, Windows, Blackberry
Digital Platform - Tablet: Apple iOS, Android, Windows 7, Blackberry Tablet OS
Pub... Bradley Harmon
Mng. Ed.. Lee Cochran
Adv. Dir... Doug Dixon
Mechanical Specifications: 9.5" x 13.3"; 6-columns, 1.438" w eachEquipment & Software: Hardware — APP/Mac; Presses — TKS; Software — QPS/QuarkXPress.
Delivery Method: Carrier, Racks
Areas Served: Central Ohio

LIBERTY TOWNSHIP

THE OXFORD PRESS (FRI)
6752 Cincinnati Dayton Rd Ste 205, Suite 205, Liberty Township, OH, 45044-9374, Butler, USA; gen tel (513) 755-5060; adv tel (513) 483-5225; ed tel (513) 755-5060; gen fax (513) 483-5252; adv fax (513) 483-5252; ed fax (513) 483-5252; disp adv e-mail oxfordeditor@coxinc.com; class adv e-mail oxfordeditor@coxinc.com; ed e-mail oxfordeditor@coxinc.com; web site www.Journal-News.com/Oxford
Circulation: 1,646pd, 32fr; AAM
Advertising rate: Open inch rate $9.00
Established: 1932
Group: Cox Media Group Ohio
Digital Platform - Mobile: Apple, Android
Digital Platform - Tablet: Apple iOS, Android, Windows 7
Editor.................................... Jennifer Burcham
Mechanical Specifications: Type page 13 x 21 1/2; E - 6 cols, 2 1/16, between; A - 6 cols, 2 1/16, between; C - 10 cols, 1 3/16, between. Equipment & Software: Hardware — Mac Clone; Software — QPS/QuarkXPress.
Delivery Method: Mail, Racks
Areas Served: Oxford/Butler County

TODAY'S PULSE (SUN)
7320 Yankee Rd, Liberty Township, OH, 45044-9168, Butler, USA; gen tel (513) 755-5060; adv tel (513) 483-5225; ed tel (513) 755-5060; gen fax (513) 483-5252; adv fax (513) 483-5252; ed fax (513) 483-5252; disp adv e-mail kathy.lane@coxinc.com; ed e-mail Jennifer.Burcham@coxinc.com; web site www.todayspulse.com
Circulation: 45,400fr; AAM
Advertising rate: Open inch rate $9.50
Group: Cox Media Group OhioEditions: (2) Today's Pulse - Butler County; Today's Pulse - Warren County
Digital Platform - Mobile: Apple, Android
Digital Platform - Tablet: Apple iOS, Android, Windows 7
Editor.................................... Jennifer Burcham
Ed.. Jennifer Collins
Mechanical Specifications: Type page 13 x 21 1/2; E - 6 cols, 2 1/16, between; A - 6 cols, 2 1/16, between; C - 10 cols, 1 1/4, between. Equipment & Software: ; Software — DTI 5.0.
Delivery Method: Carrier, Racks
Areas Served: Butler and Warren County

LIMA

THE419 (OTHER)
672 Kiowa Trl, THE419, Lima, OH, 45805-4115, Allen, USA; gen tel (855) 451-1018; disp adv e-mail contact@the419.com; class adv e-mail advertising@the419.com; web site the419.com
Circulation: 35,000fr
Advertising rate: sold by 100,000 impressions
Established: 2014
Pub. & CEO.......................... Stephen Johnson
Brand Mgr............................... Taylor Johnson
Areas Served: Lim / Allen County / Ohio

LONDON

PLAIN CITY ADVOCATE (SAT)
55 W High St, London, OH, 43140-1074, Madison, USA; gen tel (740) 852-1616; adv tel (740) 852-1616 ext. 27; ed tel (740) 852-1616 ext. 21; gen fax (740) 852-1620; adv fax (740) 852-1620; ed fax (740) 852-1620; disp adv e-mail afugate@civitasmedia.com; class adv e-mail spowers@civitasmedia.com; ed e-mail amckinney@civitasmedia.com; web site www.plaincity-advocate.com
Circulation: 1,315pd, 4,695fr; Sworn/Estimate/Non-Audited
Advertising rate: Open inch rate $7.20
Established: 1923
Group: Civitas Media, LLC-OOB
Digital Platform - Mobile: Apple, Android, Windows, Blackberry
Digital Platform - Tablet: Apple iOS, Android, Windows 7, Blackberry Tablet OS, Kindle, Nook, Kindle Fire
Ed.. Andrea McKinney
Mechanical Specifications: Type page 13 x 21 1/4; E - 6 cols, 2 1/16, between; A - 6 cols, 2 1/16, between; C - 8 cols, between.Equipment & Software: Hardware — APP/Mac; Presses — G; Software — QPS/QuarkX-Press, Multi-Ad/Creator.
Delivery Method: Mail, Newsstand, Carrier
Areas Served: 43162, 43064, 43040

THE TRIBUNE (OTHER)
55 W High St, London, OH, 43140-1074, Madison, USA
Circulation: 0pd,
Areas Served: Madison County

LOUDONVILLE

THE LOUDONVILLE TIMES (TUES)
263 W Main St, Loudonville, OH, 44842-1135, Holmes, USA; gen tel (419) 994-5600; gen fax (419) 994-5826; disp adv e-mail advertising@theloudonvilletimes.com; class adv e-mail advertising@theloudonvilletimes.com; ed e-mail news@theloudonvilletimes.com; web site www.theloudonvilletimes.com
Circulation: 2,100pd, 50fr; Sworn/Estimate/Non-Audited
Advertising rate: Open inch rate $7.50
Established: 1873
Group: Ashland Publishing Co. LLC
Digital Platform - Mobile: Apple, Android, Windows, Blackberry
Digital Platform - Tablet: Apple iOS, Android, Windows 7, Blackberry Tablet OS
Editor.......................... Lance WhiteEquipment & Software: Hardware — 2-APP/Mac 5500; Presses — G/Community.
Delivery Method: Mail, Newsstand, Racks
Areas Served: Holmes County
Ashland County
Knox County

LOUISVILLE

THE LOUISVILLE HERALD (THUR)
308 S Mill St, Louisville, OH, 44641-1643, Stark, USA; gen tel (330) 875-5610; adv tel (330) 875-5610; ed tel (330) 875-5610; gen fax (330) 875-4475; adv fax (330) 875-4475; ed fax (330) 875-4475; disp adv e-mail heraldads@mac.com; class adv e-mail officemgr@louisvilleherald.com; ed e-mail theherald@mac.com; web site www.louisvilleherald.com
Circulation: 2,100pd, 0fr; Sworn/Estimate/Non-Audited
Advertising rate: Open inch rate $7.50
Established: 1887
Digital Platform - Mobile: Apple, Android
Digital Platform - Tablet: Apple iOS, Android
Pub./Ed................................. Frank H. Clapper
Adv. Mgr.................................. Jackie Clapper
Office Manager.......................... Rhonda Griffin
Mechanical Specifications: Type page 13 x 21 1/2; E - 6 cols, 2, 1/6 between; A - 6 cols, 2, 1/6 between; C - 8 cols, 1 1/2, 1/6 between. Equipment & Software: Hardware — APP/Power Macs; Software — Claris/Draw, Microsoft/Word, Adobe/Photoshop.
Delivery Method: Mail, Newsstand
Areas Served: 44641, 44730, 44669, 44670, 44650, 44634, 44720, 44601, 44718

LOVELAND

BETHEL JOURNAL (WED)
394 Wards Corner Rd, Ste 170, Loveland, OH, 45140-8333, Clermont, USA; gen tel (513) 248-8600; adv tel (513) 248-8600; ed tel (513) 248-8600; gen fax (513) 248-1938; adv fax (513) 248-1938; ed fax (513) 248-1938; disp adv e-mail acumby@communitypress.com; class adv e-mail acumby@communitypress.com; ed e-mail therron@communitypress.com; web site www.cincinnati.com
Circulation: 10,835fr; CAC
Advertising rate: Open inch rate $5.20
Group: Gannett
Digital Platform - Mobile: Apple, Android, Windows, Blackberry
Digital Platform - Tablet: Apple iOS, Android, Windows 7, Blackberry Tablet OS, Kindle, Nook, Kindle Fire
Ed.. Richard Maloney
Pres./Pub.......................... Margaret Buchanan
Adv. Mgr.................................... Alison Cumby
Delivery Method: Mail, Newsstand, Carrier, Racks
Areas Served: Clermont County

INDIAN HILL JOURNAL (WED)
394 Wards Corner Rd, Ste 170, Loveland, OH, 45140-8333, Clermont, USA; gen tel (513) 248-8600; adv tel (513) 248-8600; ed tel (513) 248-8600; gen fax (513) 248-1938; adv fax (513) 248-1938; ed fax (513) 248-1938; disp adv e-mail acumby@communitypress.com; class adv e-mail acumby@communitypress.com; ed e-mail espangler@communitypress.com; web site www.cincinnati.com
Circulation: 10,835fr; CAC
Advertising rate: Open inch rate $7.40
Group: Gannett
Digital Platform - Mobile: Apple, Android, Windows, Blackberry
Digital Platform - Tablet: Apple iOS, Android, Windows 7, Blackberry Tablet OS, Kindle, Nook, Kindle Fire
Ed.. Nancy Daly
Pres./Pub.......................... Margaret Buchanan
Adv. Mgr.................................... Alison Cumby
Delivery Method: Mail, Newsstand, Carrier, Racks
Areas Served: Clermont County

LOVELAND HERALD (WED)
394 Wards Corner Rd, Ste 170, Loveland, OH, 45140-8333, Clermont, USA; gen tel (513) 248-8600; adv tel (513) 248-8600; ed tel (513) 248-8600; gen fax (513) 248-1938; adv fax (513) 248-1938; ed fax (513) 248-1938; disp adv e-mail acumby@communitypress.com; class adv e-mail acumby@communitypress.com; ed e-mail espangler@communitypress.com; web site www.cincinnati.com
Circulation: 10,835fr; CAC
Advertising rate: Open inch rate $7.40
Group: Gannett
Digital Platform - Mobile: Apple, Android, Windows, Blackberry
Digital Platform - Tablet: Apple iOS, Android, Windows 7, Blackberry Tablet OS, Kindle, Nook, Kindle Fire
Ed.. Nancy Daly
Pres./Pub.......................... Margaret Buchanan
Adv. Mgr.................................... Alison Cumby
Delivery Method: Mail, Newsstand, Carrier, Racks
Areas Served: Clermont County

MANCHESTER

THE MANCHESTER SIGNAL (THUR)
414 E 7th St, Manchester, OH, 45144-1402, Adams, USA; gen tel (937) 549-2800; gen fax (937) 549-3611; disp adv e-mail thesignal1@frontier.com; class adv e-mail thesignal1@frontier.com; ed e-mail thesignal1@frontier.com
Circulation: 5,200pd, 20fr; USPS
Advertising rate: Open inch rate $9.24
Established: 1883
Digital Platform - Mobile: Blackberry
Digital Platform - Tablet: Other
Owner/Pub./Ed. William G. WoolardEquipment & Software: Hardware — IBM Dell; Presses — ABDicks; Software — Microsoft/Windows 95.
Delivery Method: Mail, Newsstand, Carrier, Racks
Areas Served: Adams, Brown, Higland and Scioto Counties

MARBLEHEAD

THE PENINSULA NEWS (FRI)
211 W Main St, Marblehead, OH, 43440-2245, Ottawa, USA; gen tel (419) 798-5731; adv tel (419) 798-5731; ed tel (419) 798-5731; gen fax (419) 798-5731; adv fax (419) 798-5731; ed fax (419) 798-5731; disp adv e-mail pennews@wcnet.org; class adv e-mail pennews@wcnet.org; ed e-mail pennews@wcnet.org; web site www.thepennews.com
Circulation: 1,884pd,; Sworn/Estimate/Non-Audited
Advertising rate: Open inch rate $6.45
Established: 1890
Digital Platform - Mobile: Apple, Android, Windows, Blackberry

Digital Platform - Tablet: Apple iOS, Android, Windows 7, Blackberry Tablet OS
Pub./Circ. Mgr. .... Rick Miller
Ed. .... Patricia Lukac
Delivery Method: Mail
Areas Served: 43440

MARYSVILLE

THE RICHWOOD GAZETTE (WED)

PO Box 226, Marysville, OH, 43040-0226, Union, USA; gen tel (740) 943-2214; adv tel (740) 943-2214; ed tel (740) 943-2214; gen fax (740) 943-3595; adv fax (740) 943-3595; ed fax (740) 943-3595; disp adv e-mail rgads@rgnews.biz; class adv e-mail slsheets@rgnews.biz; ed e-mail slsheets@rgnews.biz; web site www.rgnews.biz
Circulation: 2,000pd, 11fr; USPS
Advertising rate: Open inch rate $7.60
Established: 1872
Digital Platform - Mobile: Apple, Android
Digital Platform - Tablet: Apple iOS, Android, Windows 7
Editor .... Daniel E. Behrens
Adv. Dir. .... Marie Woodford
Office Mgr. .... Sherryl Sheets
Publisher .... Kevin Behresn
Delivery Method: Mail, Newsstand
Areas Served: Union County

MC ARTHUR

THE VINTON COUNTY COURIER (WED)

103 S Market St, Mc Arthur, OH, 45651-1219, Vinton, USA; gen tel (740) 596-5393; adv tel (740) 596-5393; ed tel (740) 596-5393; gen fax (740) 596-4226; adv fax (740) 596-4226; ed fax (740) 596-4226; disp adv e-mail tfaught@timesjournal.com; class adv e-mail pjohnson@vintoncourier.com; ed e-mail tbuchanan@vintoncourier.com; web site www.vintoncourier.com
Circulation: 2,500pd,; Sworn/Estimate/Non-Audited
Advertising rate: Open inch rate $7.50
Established: 1971
Group: Adams Publishing Group, LLC
Digital Platform - Mobile: Apple, Android, Windows, Blackberry
Digital Platform - Tablet: Apple iOS, Android, Windows 7, Blackberry Tablet OS, Kindle, Nook, Kindle Fire
Office Mgr. .... Pam Johnson
Pub. .... Monica Nieporte
Ed .... Tyler Buchanan
Acct Exec. .... Tonya Faught
Mechanical Specifications: Type page 13 x 21 1/2; E - 6 cols, 2 1/3, 1/6 between; A - 6 cols, 2 1/3, 1/6 between; C - 9 cols, 1 1/3, 1/6 between.
Delivery Method: Mail, Racks
Areas Served: Vinton County

MCCONNELSVILLE

MORGAN COUNTY HERALD (WED)

89 W Main St, McConnelsville, OH, 43756-1264, Morgan, USA; gen tel (740) 962-3377; adv tel (740) 962-3377; ed tel (740) 962-3377; gen fax (740) 962-6861; adv fax (740) 962-6861; ed fax (740) 962-6861; disp adv e-mail advertising@mchnews.com; class adv e-mail classifieds@mchnews.com; ed e-mail newsroom@mchnews.com; web site www.mchnews.com
Circulation: 3,054pd, 49fr; USPS
Advertising rate: Open inch rate $10.00
Established: 1844
Digital Platform - Mobile: Apple, Android
Digital Platform - Tablet: Apple iOS, Android, Windows 7
Publisher .... Jack L. Barnes
General Manager .... David Keller
Mechanical Specifications: Type page 12 x 21; E - 6 cols, 2 1/30, 1/6 between; A - 6 cols, 2 1/30, 1/6 between; C - 6 cols, 2 1/30, 1/6 between.Equipment & Software: Hardware — APP/Power Mac G3; Software — QPS/QuarkXPress 4.1, NewsEdit Pro 3.2.3, Baseview.
Delivery Method: Mail, Racks
Areas Served: Morgan County

MEDINA

THE POST NEWSPAPERS - BRUNSWICK (SAT)

5146 Normandy Park Dr, Ste 100, Medina, OH, 44256-9608, Medina, USA; gen tel (330) 721-7678; adv tel (330) 721-7678; ed tel (330) 721-7678; gen fax (330) 722-9875; adv fax (330) 722-9875; ed fax (330) 722-9875; disp adv e-mail sales@thepostnewspapers.com; class adv e-mail classifieds@thepostnewspapers.com; ed e-mail news@thepostnewspapers.com; web site www.thepostnewspapers.com
Circulation: 0pd, 10,217fr; VAC
Advertising rate: Open inch rate $90.00
Established: 1975
Group: The Post Newspapers
Digital Platform - Mobile: Apple, Android, Windows, Blackberry
Digital Platform - Tablet: Apple iOS, Android, Windows 7, Blackberry Tablet OS
Pub. .... Bruce M. Trogdon
Exec. Ed. .... Michael Trogdon
Mng. Ed. .... Michelle Farnham
Adv. Mgr. .... Tara Leffel
Adv. Mgr. .... Tami Cassidy
Circ. Mgr .... Greg Studer
Delivery Method: Mail, Newsstand, Racks
Areas Served: Medina County

THE POST NEWSPAPERS - EASTERN MEDINA (SAT)

5146 Normandy Park Dr, Ste 100, Medina, OH, 44256-9608, Medina, USA; gen tel (330) 721-7678; adv tel (330) 721-7678; ed tel (330) 721-7678; gen fax (330) 722-9875; adv fax (330) 722-9875; ed fax (330) 722-9875; disp adv e-mail sales@thepostnewspapers.com; class adv e-mail classifieds@thepostnewspapers.com; ed e-mail news@thepostnewspapers.com; web site www.thepostnewspapers.com
Circulation: 3,611fr; VAC
Advertising rate: Open inch rate $90.00
Established: 1975
Group: The Post Newspapers
Digital Platform - Mobile: Apple, Android, Windows, Blackberry
Digital Platform - Tablet: Apple iOS, Android, Windows 7, Blackberry Tablet OS
Pub. .... Bruce M. Trogdon
Exec. Ed. .... Michael Trogdon
Mng. Ed. .... Michelle Farnham
Adv. Mgr. .... Tara Leffel
Adv. Mgr. .... Tami Cassidy
Circ. Mgr .... Greg Studer
Delivery Method: Mail, Newsstand, Racks
Areas Served: Medina County

THE POST NEWSPAPERS - MEDINA (SAT)

5146 Normandy Park Dr, Ste 100, Medina, OH, 44256-9608, Medina, USA; gen tel (330) 721-7678; adv tel (330) 721-7678; ed tel (330) 721-7678; gen fax (330) 722-9875; adv fax (330) 722-9875; ed fax (330) 722-9875; disp adv e-mail sales@thepostnewspapers.com; class adv e-mail classifieds@thepostnewspapers.com; ed e-mail news@thepostnewspapers.com; web site www.thepostnewspapers.com
Circulation: 10,640fr; VAC
Advertising rate: Open inch rate $90.00
Established: 1975
Group: The Post Newspapers
Digital Platform - Mobile: Apple, Android, Windows, Blackberry
Digital Platform - Tablet: Apple iOS, Android, Windows 7, Blackberry Tablet OS
Pub. .... Bruce M. Trogdon
Exec. Ed. .... Michael Trogdon
Managing Editor .... Michelle Farnham
Adv. Mgr. .... Tara Leffel
Adv. Mgr. .... Tami Cassidy
Circ. Mgr .... Greg Studer
Graphic Designer .... Michelle Arnst
Managing Editor .... David Sickels
Delivery Method: Mail, Newsstand, Racks
Areas Served: Medina County

THE POST NEWSPAPERS - NORTHERN WAYNE (SAT)

5164 Normandy Park Dr, Medina, OH, 44256-5901, Medina, USA; gen tel (330) 721-7678; adv tel (330) 721-7678; ed tel (330) 721-7678; gen fax (330) 722-9875; adv fax (330) 722-9875; ed fax (330) 722-9875; disp adv e-mail btrogdon@thepostnewspapers.com; class adv e-mail btrogdon@thepostnewspapers.com; ed e-mail btrogdon@thepostnewspapers.com; web site www.thepostnewspapers.com
Circulation: 9,225fr; CVC
Advertising rate: Open inch rate $90.00
Established: 1975
Group: The Post Newspapers
Digital Platform - Mobile: Apple, Android, Windows, Blackberry
Digital Platform - Tablet: Apple iOS, Android, Windows 7, Blackberry Tablet OS
Pub. .... Bruce M. Trogdon
Exec. Ed. .... Michael Trogdon
Mng. Ed. .... Michelle Farnham
Adv. Mgr. .... Tara Leffel
Adv. Mgr. .... Tami Cassidy
Circ. Mgr .... Greg Studer
Delivery Method: Mail, Newsstand, Racks
Areas Served: Medina County

THE POST NEWSPAPERS - NORTON (SAT)

5164 Normandy Park Dr, Ste 100, Medina, OH, 44256-5903, Medina, USA; gen tel (330) 721-7678; adv tel (330) 721-7678; ed tel (330) 721-7678; gen fax (330) 722-9875; adv fax (330) 722-9875; ed fax (330) 722-9875; disp adv e-mail sales@thepostnewspapers.com; class adv e-mail classifieds@thepostnewspapers.com; ed e-mail news@thepostnewspapers.com; web site www.thepostnewspapers.com
Circulation: 3,004fr; VAC
Advertising rate: Open inch rate $90.00
Established: 1975
Group: The Post Newspapers
Digital Platform - Mobile: Apple, Android, Windows, Blackberry
Digital Platform - Tablet: Apple iOS, Android, Windows 7, Blackberry Tablet OS
Pub. .... Bruce M. Trogdon
Exec. Ed. .... Michael Trogdon
Mng. Ed. .... Michelle Farnham
Adv. Mgr. .... Tara Leffel
Delivery Method: Mail, Newsstand, Racks
Areas Served: Medina County

THE POST NEWSPAPERS - SOUTHERN MEDINA (SAT)

5146 Normandy Park Dr, Ste 100, Medina, OH, 44256-9608, Medina, USA; gen tel (330) 721-7678; adv tel (330) 721-7678; ed tel (330) 721-7678; gen fax (330) 722-9875; adv fax (330) 722-9875; ed fax (330) 722-9875; disp adv e-mail sales@thepostnewspapers.com; class adv e-mail classifieds@thepostnewspapers.com; ed e-mail news@thepostnewspapers.com; web site www.thepostnewspapers.com
Circulation: 8,003fr; VAC
Advertising rate: Open inch rate $90.00
Established: 1975
Group: The Post Newspapers
Digital Platform - Mobile: Apple, Android, Windows, Blackberry
Digital Platform - Tablet: Apple iOS, Android, Windows 7, Blackberry Tablet OS
Pub. .... Bruce M. Trogdon
Exec. Ed. .... Michael Trogdon
Mng. Ed. .... Michelle Farnham
Adv. Mgr. .... Tara Leffel
Adv. Mgr. .... Tami Cassidy
Circ. Mgr .... Greg Studer
Delivery Method: Mail, Newsstand, Racks
Areas Served: Medina County

THE POST NEWSPAPERS - STRONGSVILLE (SAT)

5146 Normandy Park Dr, Ste 100, Medina, OH, 44256-9608, Medina, USA; gen tel (330) 721-7678; adv tel (330) 721-7678; ed tel (330) 721-7678; gen fax (330) 722-9875; adv fax (330) 722-9875; ed fax (330) 722-9875; disp adv e-mail sales@thepostnewspapers.com; class adv e-mail classifieds@thepostnewspapers.com; ed e-mail news@thepostnewspapers.com; web site www.thepostnewspapers.com
Circulation: 9,095fr; CVC
Advertising rate: Open inch rate $90.00
Established: 1975
Group: The Post Newspapers
Digital Platform - Mobile: Apple, Android, Windows, Blackberry
Digital Platform - Tablet: Apple iOS, Android, Windows 7, Blackberry Tablet OS
Pub. .... Bruce M. Trogdon
Exec. Ed. .... Michael Trogdon
Mng. Ed. .... Michelle Farnham
Adv. Mgr. .... Tara Leffel
Circ. Mgr .... Greg Studer
Adv. Mgr. .... Tami Cassidy
Delivery Method: Mail, Newsstand, Racks
Areas Served: Medina County

THE POST NEWSPAPERS - WADSWORTH (SAT)

5146 Normandy Park Dr, Ste 100, Medina, OH, 44256-9608, Medina, USA; gen tel (330) 721-7678; adv tel (330) 721-7678; ed tel (330) 721-7678; gen fax (330) 722-9875; adv fax (330) 722-9875; ed fax (330) 722-9875; disp adv e-mail sales@thepostnewspapers.com; class adv e-mail classifieds@thepostnewspapers.com; ed e-mail news@thepostnewspapers.com; web site www.thepostnewspapers.com
Circulation: 9,066fr; VAC
Advertising rate: Open inch rate $90.00
Established: 1975
Group: The Post Newspapers
Digital Platform - Mobile: Apple, Android, Windows, Blackberry
Digital Platform - Tablet: Apple iOS, Android, Windows 7, Blackberry Tablet OS
Pub. .... Bruce M. Trogdon
Exec. Ed. .... Michael Trogdon
Mng. Ed. .... Michelle Farnham
Adv. Mgr. .... Tara Leffel
Adv. Mgr. .... Tami Cassidy
Circ. Mgr .... Greg Studer
Delivery Method: Mail, Newsstand, Racks
Areas Served: Medina County

MIAMISBURG

FRANKLIN CHRONICLE (THUR)

230 S 2nd St, Miamisburg, OH, 45342-2925, Montgomery, USA; gen tel (937) 866-3331; adv tel (937) 866-3331; ed tel (937) 866-3331; gen fax (937) 866-6011; adv fax (937) 866-6011; ed fax (937) 866-6011; disp adv e-mail franklinchronicle@miller-publishing.com; class adv e-mail franklinchronicle@miller-publishing.com; ed e-mail franklinchronicle@miller-publishing.com
Circulation: 1,214pd, 2,000fr; Sworn/Estimate/Non-Audited
Advertising rate: Open inch rate $10.00
Pub./Ed. .... Don Miller
Mng. Ed. .... Steve Sandlin
Mechanical Specifications: Type page 13 x 21 1/2; E - 6 cols, 2 1/16, 1/8 between; A - 6 cols, 2 1/16, 1/8 between; C - 6 cols, 1 3/16, 1/8 between.
Delivery Method: Mail, Newsstand
Areas Served: Franklin and Warren County

MIAMISBURG NEWS (THUR)

230 S 2nd St, Miamisburg, OH, 45342-2925, Montgomery, USA; gen tel (937) 866-3331; adv tel (937) 866-3331; ed tel (937) 866-3331; gen fax (937) 866-6011; adv fax (937) 866-6011; ed fax (937) 866-6011; disp adv e-mail news@miamivalleynewspapers.com; class adv e-mail news@miamivalleynewspapers.com; ed e-mail news@miamivalleynewspapers.com
Circulation: 3,000pd, 37fr; Sworn/Estimate/Non-Audited
Advertising rate: Open inch rate $10.00

Pub..Don Miller
Mng. Ed.......................................Steve Sandlin
Mechanical Specifications: Type page 13 x 21; E - 6 cols, 2 1/16, 1/8 between; A - 6 cols, 2 1/16, 1/8 between; C - 10 cols, 1 3/16, 1/8 between.Equipment & Software: Hardware — APP/Mac; Software — QPS/QuarkXPress, Microsoft/Excel, Claris/MacWrite.
Delivery Method: Mail, Newsstand
Areas Served: Franklin and Warren County

THE GERMANTOWN PRESS (THUR)
230 S 2nd St, Miamisburg, OH, 45342-2925, Montgomery, USA; gen tel (937) 866-3331; gen fax (937) 866-6011; disp adv e-mail ads@miamivalleynewspapers.com; class adv e-mail ads@miamivalleynewspapers.com; ed e-mail news@miamivalleynewspapers.com
Circulation: 3,000pd,; Sworn/Estimate/Non-Audited
Advertising rate: Open inch rate $8.30
Established: 1874
Group: Miami Valley Newspapers
Pub./Adv. Mgr..............................Donald Miller
Ed. .... Ben MerschEquipment & Software: Hardware — APP/Mac 7.5; Software — QPS/QuarkXPress 4.0.
Delivery Method: Mail, Newsstand
Areas Served: 45327

MILLBURY

THE PRESS (MON)
1550 Woodville Rd, Millbury, OH, 43447-9619, Wood, USA; gen tel (419) 836-2221; adv tel (419) 836-2221; ed tel (419) 836-2221; gen fax (419) 836-1319; adv fax (419) 836-1319; ed fax (419) 836-1319; disp adv e-mail mperkins@presspublications.com; class adv e-mail mperkins@presspublications.com; ed e-mail news@presspublications.com; web site www.presspublications.com - 40,365(views) 14,852(visitors)
Circulation: 0pd, 33,965fr; VAC
Advertising rate: Open inch rate $31.15
Established: 1972
Group: Douthit Communications, Inc.Editions: (2) Metro Edition (17,588); Suburban Edition (16,457);
Digital Platform - Mobile: Windows
Digital Platform - Tablet: Windows 7
Pub..Harold K. Douthit
General Manager........................Mary Perkins
Circ. Mgr ....Jordan Szozda
Prod. Mgr ....Tammy Payne
Mechanical Specifications: Type page 10 1/4 x 16; E - 4 cols, 2 3/8, 1/10 between; A - 6 cols, 1 5/8, 1/10 between; C - 6 cols, 1 5/8, 1/10 between.Equipment & Software: ; Software — Microsoft/Windows Corel Draw, In Design
Delivery Method: Carrier, Racks
Areas Served: 43605, 43616, 43618, 43619, 43430, 43447, 43449, 43416, 43450, 43465, 43469

MILLERSBURG

HOLMES COUNTY JOURNAL (THUR)
7368 County Road 623, Millersburg, OH, 44654-9256, Holmes, USA; gen tel (330) 674-2300; adv tel (330) 674-2300; ed tel (330) 674-2300; gen fax (888) 769-3960 ; adv fax (888) 769-3960 ; ed fax (888) 769-3960 ; disp adv e-mail calguire@gpubs.com; class adv e-mail calguire@gpubs.com; ed e-mail tmosser@gpubs.com; web site www.gpubs.com
Advertising rate: Open inch rate $9.50
Group: Graphic Publications Inc.
Digital Platform - Mobile: Apple, Android, Windows, Blackberry
Digital Platform - Tablet: Apple iOS, Android, Windows 7, Blackberry Tablet OS, Kindle, Nook, Kindle Fire
Pres. ....Michael Mast
Ed. ....Tami Mosser
Adv. Dir...Clint Alguire
Delivery Method: Mail, Racks
Areas Served: Holmes County

THE HOLMES COUNTY HUB SHOPPER (THUR)
25 N Clay St, Millersburg, OH, 44654-1117, Holmes, USA; gen tel (330) 674-1811; adv tel (330) 674-1811; ed tel (330) 674-5676; gen fax (330) 674-3780; adv fax (330) 674-3780; ed fax (330) 674-3780; disp adv e-mail anixon@the-daily-record.com; class adv e-mail bpolen@the-daily-record.com; ed e-mail bbower@the-daily-record.com; web site www.holmescountyshopper.com
Circulation: 4,253pd, 155fr; Sworn/Estimate/Non-Audited
Advertising rate: Open inch rate $7.50
Group: Wooster Republican Printing Co.
Digital Platform - Mobile: Apple, Android, Windows, Blackberry
Digital Platform - Tablet: Apple iOS, Android, Windows 7, Blackberry Tablet OS
Mng. Ed.......................................Lance White
Mechanical Specifications: Type page 13 x 21 1/2; E - 6 cols, 2, 1/3 between; A - 6 cols, 2, 1/3 between; C - 6 cols, 2, 1/3 between. Equipment & Software: Hardware — APP/Power Mac; Software — Microsoft/Word 5.1, QPS/QuarkXPress 3.3.
Delivery Method: Mail, Carrier, Racks
Areas Served: Holmes County

WOOSTER WEEKLY NEWS (MON)
7368 County Road 623, Millersburg, OH, 44654-9256, Holmes, USA; gen tel (330) 674-2300; gen fax (888) 769-3960 ; ed e-mail kvalentini@alonovus.com; web site www.alonovus.com - 12,043(views) 5,027(visitors)
Circulation: 0pd, 8,625fr; Sworn/Estimate/Non-Audited
Advertising rate: Open inch rate $11.99
Established: 2002
Group: AloNovus Corp.
Digital Platform - Mobile: Apple, Android, Windows, Blackberry
Digital Platform - Tablet: Apple iOS, Android, Windows 7, Blackberry Tablet OS, Kindle, Nook, Kindle Fire
Pres. ....Michael Mast
Circ. Mgr ....Rick Festi
Delivery Method: Racks
Areas Served: 44691

MINERVA

THE NEWS LEADER (THUR)
604 Valley St, Minerva, OH, 44657-1580, Carroll, USA; gen tel (330) 868-3408; adv tel (330) 868-5222; ed tel (330) 868-3408; gen fax (330) 868-3273; adv fax (330) 868-3273; ed fax (330) 868-3273; disp adv e-mail jkaplan@the-review.com; class adv e-mail ccarle@the-review.com; ed e-mail klewis@the-review.com; web site www.tnl-news.com
Circulation: 4,400pd, 25fr; Sworn/Estimate/Non-Audited
Advertising rate: Open inch rate $6.50
Digital Platform - Mobile: Apple, Android, Windows, Blackberry
Digital Platform - Tablet: Apple iOS, Android, Windows 7, Blackberry Tablet OS, Kindle, Nook, Kindle Fire
Pub...G. Charles Dix
Ed. ....Rob Todor
Adv. Dir...Jeff Kaplan
Delivery Method: Mail, Racks
Areas Served: Minerva, Malvern, and the Tri-County Area

THE PRESS-NEWS (THUR)
604 Valley St, Minerva, OH, 44657-1580, Carroll, USA; gen tel (330) 868-3408; adv tel (330) 868-5222; ed tel (330) 868-3408; gen fax (330) 868-3273; adv fax (330) 868-3273; ed fax (330) 868-3273; disp adv e-mail jkaplan@the-review.com; class adv e-mail ccarle@the-review.com; ed e-mail kmundy@the-review.com; web site www.the-pressnews.com
Circulation: 2,200pd,; Sworn/Estimate/Non-Audited
Advertising rate: Open inch rate $5.45
Digital Platform - Mobile: Apple, Android, Windows, Blackberry
Digital Platform - Tablet: Apple iOS, Android, Windows 7, Blackberry Tablet OS, Kindle, Nook, Kindle Fire
Pub...G. Charles Dix
Ed. ....Rob Todor
Adv. Dir...Jeff Kaplan
Delivery Method: Mail, Racks
Areas Served: Southeastern Stark County

MINSTER

THE COMMUNITY POST (THUR)
326 N Main St Ste 200, Minster, OH, 45865, Auglaize, USA; gen tel (419) 628-2369; adv tel (419) 628-2369; ed tel (419) 628-2369; gen fax (419) 628-4712; adv fax (419) 628-4712; ed fax (419) 628-4712; disp adv e-mail publisher@nktelco.net; class adv e-mail publisher@nktelco.net; ed e-mail reporter@nktelco.net; web site www.minstercommunitypost.com
Circulation: 1,500pd,; Sworn/Estimate/Non-Audited
Advertising rate: Open inch rate $5.92
Established: 1896
Group: Horizon Publications Inc.
Digital Platform - Mobile: Apple, Android
Digital Platform - Tablet: Apple iOS, Android
Pub..Deb Zwez
Adv. Mgr...Carol Kohn
Mechanical Specifications: Type page 13 x 21 1/2; E - 6 cols, 2 1/12, between; A - 6 cols, 2 1/12, between; C - 9 cols, 1 1/6, between.
Delivery Method: Mail, Racks
Areas Served: 45865, 45869, 45822

MONTPELIER

THE LEADER-ENTERPRISE (WED)
319 W Main St, Montpelier, OH, 43543-1017, Williams, USA; gen tel (419) 485-3113; adv tel (419) 485-3113; ed tel (419) 485-3113; gen fax (419) 485-3114; adv fax (419) 485-3114; ed fax (419) 485-3114; disp adv e-mail leaderadvertising@frontier.com; class adv e-mail leaderenterprise@frontier.com; ed e-mail jward.leaderenterprise@frontier.com; web site http://myplace.frontier.com/~leaderenterprise
Circulation: 1,000pd, 55fr; Sworn/Estimate/Non-Audited
Advertising rate: Open inch rate $7.25
Established: 1923
Ed. ....Jamie Ward
Asst. Ed....................................Nancy Jackson
Adv. Mgr. ....Joie Hills
Delivery Method: Mail, Newsstand
Areas Served: Montpelier, Pioneer, and Holiday City

MOUNT GILEAD

THE MORROW COUNTY SENTINEL (WED)
46 S Main St, Mount Gilead, OH, 43338-1433, Morrow, USA; gen tel (419) 946-3010; gen fax (419) 947-7241; disp adv e-mail vtaylor@civitasmedia.com; class adv e-mail vtaylor@civitasmedia.com; ed e-mail rwagner@civitasmedia.com; web site www.morrowcountysentinel.com
Circulation: 2,750pd,; Sworn/Estimate/Non-Audited
Advertising rate: Open inch rate $11.00
Group: Civitas Media, LLC-OOB
Digital Platform - Mobile: Apple, Android, Windows, Blackberry
Digital Platform - Tablet: Apple iOS, Android, Windows 7, Blackberry Tablet OS
Gen. Mgr. ....Vicki Taylor
Ed. ....Randa Wagner
Sports Ed..................................Rob Hamilton
Ed. ....Anthony Conchel
Delivery Method: Mail, Newsstand, Racks
Areas Served: Morrow County

MOUNT ORAB

THE BROWN COUNTY PRESS (SUN)
219 S High St, Mount Orab, OH, 45154-9039, Brown, USA; gen tel (937) 444-3441; adv tel (937) 444-3441; ed tel (937) 444-3441; gen fax (937) 444-2652; adv fax (937) 444-2652; ed fax (937) 444-2652; disp adv e-mail bcpress@frontier.com; class adv e-mail bcpress@frontier.com; ed e-mail bcpress@frontier.com; web site www.browncountypress.com - 8,448(views) 1,891(visitors)
Circulation: 0pd, 18,775fr; VAC
Advertising rate: Open inch rate $9.50
Established: 1973
Group: MCM Ohio LLC
Digital Platform - Mobile: Apple, Android, Windows, Blackberry
Digital Platform - Tablet: Apple iOS, Android, Windows 7, Blackberry Tablet OS, Kindle, Nook, Kindle Fire
Ed. ....Wayne Gates
Pub..Tony Adams
Circ. Mgr ....Ruby Martin
Mechanical Specifications: Type page 11 3/5 x 21 1/2; E - 6 cols, 1 4/5, 1/8 between; A - 6 cols, 1 4/5, 1/8 between; C - 8 cols, 1 1/4, 1/8 between.
Delivery Method: Mail, Newsstand, Racks
Areas Served: Brown County

NEW LEXINGTON

PERRY COUNTY TRIBUNE (WED)
116 S Main St, New Lexington, OH, 43764-1376, Perry, USA; gen tel (740) 342-4121; adv tel (740) 342-4121 ext. 104; ed tel (740) 342-4121 ext. 106; gen fax (740) 342-4131; disp adv e-mail pdennis@perrytribune.com; class adv e-mail bcarney@perrytribune.com; ed e-mail dhutmire@perrytribune.com; web site www.perrytribune.com
Circulation: 4,000pd, 16,400fr; Sworn/Estimate/Non-Audited
Advertising rate: Open inch rate $10.20
Established: 1893
Group: Adams Publishing Group, LLC
Digital Platform - Mobile: Apple, Android, Windows, Blackberry
Digital Platform - Tablet: Apple iOS, Android, Windows 7, Blackberry Tablet OS, Kindle, Nook, Kindle Fire
Ed. ....Deb Hutmire
Adv. Dir...Pete Dennis
Delivery Method: Mail, Newsstand
Areas Served: Perry County

NEW LONDON

FIRELANDS FARMER (MON)
43 E Main St, New London, OH, 44851-1213, Huron, USA; gen tel (419) 929-8043; adv tel (419) 929-8043; ed tel (419) 929-8043; gen fax (419) 929-8210; adv fax (419) 929-8210; ed fax (419) 929-8210; disp adv e-mail globe@sdgnewsgroup.com; class adv e-mail globe@sdgnewsgroup.com; ed e-mail globe@sdgnewsgroup.com; web site www.sdgnewsgroup.com
Advertising rate: Open inch rate $6.95
Group: SDGNewsgroup
Digital Platform - Mobile: Apple, Android, Windows, Blackberry
Digital Platform - Tablet: Apple iOS, Android, Windows 7, Blackberry Tablet OS
Pub..Scott Gove
Ed. ....Terry Wilson
Adv. Dir..Karla Souslin
Delivery Method: Mail, Racks
Areas Served: Huron County

NEW LONDON RECORD (THUR)
43 E Main St, New London, OH, 44851-1213, Huron, USA; gen tel (419) 929-3411; adv tel (419) 929-3411; ed tel (419) 929-3411; gen fax (419) 929-8210; adv fax (419) 929-8210; ed fax (419) 929-8210; disp adv e-mail re-

cord@sdgnewsgroup.com; class adv e-mail record@sdgnewsgroup.com; ed e-mail record@sdgnewsgroup.com; web site www.sdgnewsgroup.com
Circulation: 2,000pd,; Sworn/Estimate/Non-Audited
Advertising rate: Open inch rate $6.95
Group: SDGNewsgroup
Digital Platform - Mobile: Apple, Android, Windows, Blackberry
Digital Platform - Tablet: Apple iOS, Android, Windows 7, Blackberry Tablet OS, Kindle, Nook, Kindle Fire
Pub.. Scott Gove
Ed. .... Terry Wilson
Adv. Dir...Karla Souslin
Delivery Method: Mail, Racks
Areas Served: Huron County

NEW WASHINGTON

THE NEW WASHINGTON HERALD (THUR)

625 S Kibler St, New Washington, OH, 44854-9541, Crawford, USA; gen tel (419) 492-2133; adv tel (419) 492-2133; ed tel (419) 492-2133; gen fax (419) 492-2128; adv fax (419) 492-2128; ed fax (419) 492-2128; disp adv e-mail backerman@theheraldinc.com; class adv e-mail backerman@theheraldinc.com; ed e-mail backerman@herald-print.com; web site www.theheraldinc.com
Circulation: 1,600pd, 75fr; Sworn/Estimate/Non-Audited
Advertising rate: Open inch rate $6.35
Established: 1881
Digital Platform - Mobile: Windows
Digital Platform - Tablet: Windows 7
Pub./Ed. .... David Stump
Adv. Dir.................................Bonnie Ackerman
Mechanical Specifications: Type page 10 1/4 x 16; E - 5 cols, 1 5/6, 1/6 between; A - 5 cols, 1 5/6, 1/6 between; C - 5 cols, 1 5/6, 1/6 between.Equipment & Software: Hardware — APP/Mac Network with NT Server; Presses — MAN; Software — Adobe/PageMaker 6.5, QPS/QuarkXPress 3.3.
Delivery Method: Mail, Newsstand
Areas Served: Crawford County

NEWARK

THE GRANVILLE SENTINEL (THUR)

22 N 1st St, Newark, OH, 43055-5608, Licking, USA; gen tel (740) 587-3397; adv tel (740) 328-8502; ed tel (740) 328-8820; gen fax (740) 587-3398; adv fax (740) 587-3398; ed fax (740) 587-3398; disp adv e-mail atrabitz@newarkadvocate.com; class adv e-mail rangreen@newarkadvocate.com; ed e-mail mshearer@newarkadvocate.com; web site www.granvillesentinel.com
Circulation: 2,300pd,; Sworn/Estimate/Non-Audited
Advertising rate: Open inch rate $7.10
Group: Gannett
Digital Platform - Mobile: Apple, Android, Windows, Blackberry
Digital Platform - Tablet: Apple iOS, Android, Windows 7, Blackberry Tablet OS
Exec. Ed.................................Michael Shearer
Mng. Ed..................................Craig McDonald
Adv. Dir......................................Adam Trabitz
Mechanical Specifications: Type page 13 x 16; E - 5 cols, 2 1/4, between; A - 5 cols, 2 1/4, between; C - 5 cols, 2 1/4, between.Equipment & Software: Hardware — APP/Mac.
Delivery Method: Mail, Racks
Areas Served: Licking County

THE PATASKALA STANDARD (THUR)

22 N 1st St, Newark, OH, 43055-5608, Licking, USA; gen tel (740) 927-2991; adv tel (740) 328-8502; ed tel (740) 328-8820; gen fax (740) 927-2930; adv fax (740) 927-2930; ed fax (740) 927-2930; disp adv e-mail atrabitz@newarkadvocate.com; class adv e-mail rangreen@newarkadvocate.com; ed e-mail mshearer@newarkadvocate.com; web site www.pataskalastandard.com
Circulation: 3,100pd, 25fr; Sworn/Estimate/Non-Audited
Advertising rate: Open inch rate $7.10
Group: Gannett
Digital Platform - Mobile: Apple, Android, Windows, Blackberry
Digital Platform - Tablet: Apple iOS, Android, Windows 7, Blackberry Tablet OS
Exec. Ed.................................Michael Shearer
Mng. Ed..................................Craig McDonald
Adv. Dir......................................Adam Trabitz
Delivery Method: Mail, Racks
Areas Served: Licking County

NEWCOMERSTOWN

NEWCOMERSTOWN NEWS (WED)

140 W Main St, Newcomerstown, OH, 43832-1041, Tuscarawas, USA; gen tel (740) 498-7117; adv tel (740) 498-7117; ed tel (740) 498-7117; gen fax (740) 498-5624; adv fax (740) 498-5624; ed fax (740) 498-5624; disp adv e-mail gjohnson@newcomerstown-news.com; class adv e-mail jtrzop@newcomerstown-news.com; ed e-mail nwolfe@newcomerstown-news.com; web site www.newcomerstown-news.com
Circulation: 3,500pd, 24fr; Sworn/Estimate/Non-Audited
Advertising rate: Open inch rate $8.50
Established: 1898
Group: Jeffersonian Advantage
Digital Platform - Mobile: Apple, Android, Windows, Blackberry
Digital Platform - Tablet: Apple iOS, Android, Windows 7, Blackberry Tablet OS, Kindle, Nook, Kindle Fire
Pub...Andrew Dix
Ed. ....Niki Wolfe
Mng. Ed.......................................Ray H. Booth
Adv. Mgr.................................Peggy Morgatroyd
Mechanical Specifications: Type page 13 x 21; E - 6 cols, 2, 1/6 between; A - 6 cols, 2, 1/6 between; C - 9 cols, between.Equipment & Software: Hardware — APP/Mac; Software — Baseview, QPS/QuarkXPress.
Delivery Method: Mail, Newsstand
Areas Served: Tuscarawas County

OBERLIN

AMHERST NEWS-TIMES (THUR)

42 S Main St, Oberlin, OH, 44074-1627, Lorain, USA; gen tel (440) 988-2801; adv tel (440) 775-1611; ed tel (440) 775-1611; gen fax (440) 988-2802; adv fax (440) 774-2167; ed fax (440) 774-2167; disp adv e-mail rward@civitasmedia.com; class adv e-mail aduncan@civitasmedia.com; ed e-mail news@theoberlinnews.com; web site www.theamherstnewstimes.com
Circulation: 1,300pd, 199fr; Sworn/Estimate/Non-Audited
Advertising rate: Open inch rate $9.75
Established: 1919
Group: AIM Media Indiana
Digital Platform - Mobile: Apple, Android, Windows, Blackberry
Digital Platform - Tablet: Apple iOS, Android, Windows 7, Blackberry Tablet OS
Reg. Rev. Dir. ....Tom Hutson
Ed. ....Jason Hawk
Bus. Mgr./Adv. Rep.........................Robin Ward
Delivery Method: Mail, Newsstand
Areas Served: Lorain County

OBERLIN NEWS-TRIBUNE (TUES)

42 S Main St, Oberlin, OH, 44074-1627, Lorain, USA; gen tel (440) 988-2801; adv tel (440) 775-1611; ed tel (440) 775-1611; gen fax (440) 988-2802; adv fax (440) 774-2167; ed fax (440) 774-2167; disp adv e-mail rward@civitasmedia.com; class adv e-mail jyoder@civitasmedia.com; ed e-mail news@theoberlinnews.com; web site www.theoberlinnewstribune.com
Circulation: 2,000pd, 10,000fr; Sworn/Estimate/Non-Audited
Advertising rate: Open inch rate $7.50
Established: 1930
Group: Civitas Media, LLC-OOB
Digital Platform - Mobile: Apple, Android, Windows, Blackberry
Digital Platform - Tablet: Apple iOS, Android, Windows 7, Blackberry Tablet OS
Pub./Reg. Rev. Dir..........................Tom Hutson
Ed. ....Jason Hawk
Bus. Mgr./Adv. Rep..
Robin WardEquipment & Software: Hardware — Baseview; Presses — G/Doublewire.
Delivery Method: Mail, Newsstand
Areas Served: Lorain County

WELLINGTON ENTERPRISE (THUR)

42 S Main St, Oberlin, OH, 44074-1627, Lorain, USA; gen tel (440) 988-2801; adv tel (440) 775-1611; ed tel (440) 775-1611; gen fax (440) 988-2802; adv fax (440) 774-2167; ed fax (440) 774-2167; disp adv e-mail rward@civitasmedia.com; class adv e-mail aduncan@civitasmedia.com; ed e-mail news@theoberlinnews.com; web site www.thewellingtonenterprise.com
Circulation: 1,358pd, 62fr; Sworn/Estimate/Non-Audited
Advertising rate: Open inch rate $9.75
Established: 1864
Group: Civitas Media, LLC-OOB
Digital Platform - Mobile: Apple, Android, Windows, Blackberry
Digital Platform - Tablet: Apple iOS, Android, Windows 7, Blackberry Tablet OS
Reg. Rev. Dir.................................Tom Hutson
Ed. ....Jason Hawk
Bus. Mgr./Adv. Rep.........................Robin Ward
Mechanical Specifications: Type page 9.889 x 21 1/2; E - 6 cols, 2 1/8, between; A - 6 cols, 2 1/8, between; C - 6 cols, 2 1/8, between.
Delivery Method: Mail, Newsstand
Areas Served: 44090, 44880

ONTARIO

TRIBUNE COURIER & MADISON TRIBUNE (THUR)

347 Allen Dr, Ontario, OH, 44906-1001, Richland, USA; gen tel (419) 529-2847; gen fax (419) 529-2847; disp adv e-mail kim@tribune-courier.com; class adv e-mail betty@tribune-courier.com; ed e-mail frank@tribune-courier.com; web site www.tribune-courier.com
Circulation: 2,600pd, 5fr; Sworn/Estimate/Non-Audited
Advertising rate: Open inch rate $7.95 (Local); $11.50 (National)
Established: 1961
Group: Stumbo Publishing Co.
Digital Platform - Mobile: Windows
Digital Platform - Tablet: Windows 7
Pub./Ed. ....Frank Stumbo
Treasurer .... Betty E. Stumbo
Adv. Mgr. .... Kim Knapp
Mechanical Specifications: Type page 11 1/2 x 20 1/2; E - 6 cols, 1 3/4, 1/8 between; A - 6 cols, 1 3/4, 1/8 between; C - 6 cols, 1 3/4, 1/8 between.Equipment & Software: Hardware — APP/Mac G3, APP/Mac G4, APP/Mac G5; Software — QPS/QuarkXPress 4.1, Adobe/Photoshop, Adobe/Acrobat 5.0.
Delivery Method: Mail, Newsstand, Racks
Areas Served: Richland County

OTTAWA

PUTNAM COUNTY SENTINEL (WED, SAT)

224 E Main St, Ottawa, OH, 45875-1944, Putnam, USA; gen tel (419) 523-5709; adv tel (419) 523-5709 ext. 225; ed tel (419) 523-5709 ext. 231; gen fax (419) 523-3512; adv fax (419) 523-3512; ed fax (419) 523-3512; disp adv e-mail kpickens@putnamsentinel.com ; class adv e-mail gbogart@putnamsentinel.com; ed e-mail news@putnamsentinel.com; web site www.putnamsentinel.com
Circulation: 7,800pd, 107fr; Sworn/Estimate/Non-Audited
Advertising rate: Open inch rate $11.00
Established: 1855
Group: Delphos Herald, Inc.
Digital Platform - Mobile: Apple, Android, Windows, Blackberry
Digital Platform - Tablet: Apple iOS, Android, Windows 7, Blackberry Tablet OS
Pub...Doug Nutter
Ed. ....Anne Coburn-Griffis
Sports Ed..........................Charlie Warnimont
Circ. Mgr......................................Mark Ranes
Adv. Mgr. ....Cheryl Andres
Adv. Rep..................................Kim Andreasen
Adv. Rep....................................Crystal Dunlap
Mechanical Specifications: Type page 11 5/8 x 20 1/2; E - 6 cols, 2, between; A - 9 cols, 1 3/16, between; C - 9 cols, 1 3/16, between.
Delivery Method: Mail, Newsstand, Racks
Areas Served: Putnam County

PUTNAM COUNTY VIDETTE (THUR)

224 E Main St, Ottawa, OH, 45875-1944, Putnam, USA; gen tel (419) 523-5709; adv tel (419) 523-5709 ext. 225; ed tel (419) 523-5709 ext. 231; gen fax (419) 523-3512; adv fax (419) 523-3512; ed fax (419) 523-3512; disp adv e-mail kpickens@putnamsentinel.com ; class adv e-mail gbogart@putnamsentinel.com ; ed e-mail news@putnamsentinel.com; web site www.putnamsentinel.com
Advertising rate: Open inch rate $5.70
Group: Delphos Herald, Inc.
Digital Platform - Mobile: Apple, Android, Windows, Blackberry
Digital Platform - Tablet: Apple iOS, Android, Windows 7, Blackberry Tablet OS
Pub...Doug Nutter
Adv. Mgr. ....Cheryl Andres
Delivery Method: Mail, Newsstand, Racks
Areas Served: Columbus Grove

PAULDING

THE PAULDING PROGRESS (WED)

113 S Williams St, Paulding, OH, 45879-1429, Paulding, USA; gen tel (419) 399-4015; adv tel (419) 399-4015; ed tel (419) 399-4015; gen fax (419) 399-4030; adv fax (419) 399-4030; ed fax (419) 399-4030; disp adv e-mail advertising@progressnewspaper.org; class adv e-mail dnutter@progressnewspaper.org; ed e-mail progress@progressnewspaper.org; web site www.progressnewspaper.org
Circulation: 4,000pd, 10,000fr; Sworn/Estimate/Non-Audited
Advertising rate: Open inch rate $9.25
Group: Delphos Herald, Inc.
Digital Platform - Mobile: Apple, Android, Windows, Blackberry
Digital Platform - Tablet: Apple iOS, Android, Windows 7, Blackberry Tablet OS
Pub./Adv. Mgr.................................Doug Nutter
Ed. .... Melinda Krick
Delivery Method: Mail, Newsstand, Racks
Areas Served: Paulding County

PERRYSBURG

HOLLAND-SPRINGFIELD JOURNAL (TUES)

130 Louisiana Ave, Perrysburg, OH, 43551-1457, Wood, USA; gen tel (419) 874-2528; adv tel (419) 874-4491; ed tel (419) 874-4491; gen fax (419) 874-7311; adv fax (419) 874-7311; ed fax (419) 874-7311; disp adv e-mail matt@welchpublishing.com; class adv e-mail publisher@perrysburg.com; ed e-mail editor@hollandsfj.us; web site www.hollandsfj.us
Circulation: 5,000fr; Sworn/Estimate/Non-Audited
Advertising rate: Open inch rate $11.80
Established: 2003
Group: Welch Publishing Company
Digital Platform - Mobile: Apple, Android, Windows, Blackberry
Digital Platform - Tablet: Apple iOS, Android, Windows 7, Blackberry Tablet OS, Kindle, Nook, Kindle Fire
Pres .... Matthew H. Welch
Ed. ....Jane Maiolo
Mechanical Specifications: Type page 15 1/4 x 21 1/2; E - 9 cols, 1 9/16, 1/12 between.

Equipment & Software: Hardware — APP/Mac, IBM, COM; Presses — WPC/Web Leader; Software — QPS/QuarkXPress 4.0, Microsoft/Office.
Delivery Method: Mail, Newsstand, Racks
Areas Served: Lucas Co.

PERRYSBURG MESSENGER JOURNAL (WED)

117 E 2nd St, Perrysburg, OH, 43551-2172, Wood, USA; gen tel (419) 874-4491; adv tel (419) 874-4491; ed tel (419) 874-4491; gen fax (419) 874-7311; adv fax (419) 874-7311; ed fax (419) 874-7311; disp adv e-mail matt@welchpublishing.com; class adv e-mail publisher@perrysburg.com; ed e-mail editor@perrysburg.com; web site www.perrysburg.com
Circulation: 5,676pd, 6,882fr; USPS
Advertising rate: Open inch rate $11.80
Established: 1853
Group: Welch Publishing Company
Digital Platform - Mobile: Apple, Android, Windows, Blackberry
Digital Platform - Tablet: Apple iOS, Android, Windows 7, Blackberry Tablet OS, Kindle, Nook, Kindle Fire
Pub. .... John B. Welch
Adv. Mgr. .... Matthew H. Welch
Ed. .... Deb Buker
Mechanical Specifications: Type page 15 1/4 x 21 1/2; E - 9 cols, 1 9/16, 1/12 between. Equipment & Software: Hardware — APP/Mac, IBM, COM; Presses — WPC/Web Leader; Software — QPS/QuarkXPress 4.0, Microsoft/Office.
Delivery Method: Mail, Newsstand, Racks
Areas Served: 43551, 43552

PORT CLINTON

THE BEACON (THUR)

205 SE Catawba Rd, Ste G, Port Clinton, OH, 43452-2669, Ottawa, USA; gen tel (419) 732-2154; adv tel (419) 732-2154; ed tel (419) 732-2154; gen fax (419) 734-5382; adv fax (419) 734-5382; ed fax (419) 734-5382; disp adv e-mail advertising@thebeacon.net; class adv e-mail angied@thebeacon.net; ed e-mail editor@thebeacon.net; web site www.thebeacon.net
Circulation: 6pd, 14,238fr; CVC
Advertising rate: Open inch rate $18.50
Established: 1983
Group: Schaffner Publications, Inc.Editions: (3) 3 total; Catawba Island Beacon; Lakeside/Marblehead Beacon; Oak Harbor Beacon;
Digital Platform - Mobile: Apple, Android, Windows, Blackberry
Digital Platform - Tablet: Apple iOS, Android, Windows 7, Blackberry Tablet OS, Kindle, Nook, Kindle Fire
Pub. .... John Schaffner
Ed. .... Jasmine Cupp
Adv. Mgr. .... Connie Roberts
Circ. Mgr. .... Bruce Dinse
Mechanical Specifications: Type page 11 1/16 x 21 1/2; E - 6 cols, 1 2/3, 1/6 between; A - 6 cols, 1 2/3, 1/6 between; C - 9 cols, 1 1/16, 1/6 between.Equipment & Software: Hardware — APP/Mac; Software — QPS/QuarkXPress 4.1, Adobe/Photoshop.
Delivery Method: Mail, Racks
Areas Served: Ottawa County

PORTSMOUTH

THE COMMUNITY COMMON (SUN)

637 6th St, Portsmouth, OH, 45662-3924, Scioto, USA; gen tel (740) 353-1151; adv tel (740) 353-1151; ed tel (740) 353-1151; gen fax (740) 353-5848; adv fax (740) 353-5848; ed fax (740) 353-5848; disp adv e-mail bwarnock@civitasmedia.com; class adv e-mail bwarnock@civitasmedia.com; ed e-mail news@communitycommon.com; web site www.communitycommon.com
Advertising rate: Open inch rate $14.70
Established: 1982
Group: Civitas Media, LLC-OOB
Digital Platform - Mobile: Apple, Android
Digital Platform - Tablet: Apple iOS, Android, Windows 7
Pub. .... Hope ComerEquipment & Software: Hardware — APP/Mac; Software — Multi-Ad/CAMS.
Delivery Method: Mail, Racks
Areas Served: 45662

ROCKY RIVER

WEST LIFE (WED)

19071 Old Detroit Rd, Rocky River, OH, 44116-1767, Cuyahoga, USA; gen tel (440) 871-5797; adv tel (440) 933-5100; ed tel (440) 871-5797; gen fax (440) 871-3824; adv fax (440) 871-0157; ed fax (440) 871-3824; disp adv e-mail bkohler@2presspapers.com; class adv e-mail bkohler@westlifenews.com; ed e-mail editor@westlifenews.com; web site www.westlifenews.com
Circulation: 12,000pd, 750fr; Sworn/Estimate/Non-Audited
Advertising rate: Open inch rate $17.50
Established: 1959
Group: Douthit Communications, Inc.
Digital Platform - Mobile: Apple, Android, Windows, Blackberry
Digital Platform - Tablet: Apple iOS, Android, Windows 7, Blackberry Tablet OS, Kindle, Nook, Kindle Fire
Pub. .... Harold K. Douthit
Managing Editor .... Susan Love
Mechanical Specifications: Type page 10 3/8 x 16; E - 6 cols, 1 1/2, between; A - 6 cols, 1 1/2, between; C - 6 cols, 1 1/2, between. Equipment & Software: Hardware — PC; Software — QPS/QuarkXPress 4.1, Macromedia/Freehand 9, Microsoft/Word 6, Adobe/Photoshop 5.5.
Delivery Method: Mail, Newsstand, Racks
Areas Served: Westlake, Bay Village, North Olmsted, Rocky River, Lakewood and Fairview Park

ROSSFORD

ROSSFORD RECORD JOURNAL (THUR)

215 Osborne St, Rossford, OH, 43460-1238, Wood, USA; gen tel (419) 874-4491; adv tel (419) 874-4491; ed tel (419) 874-4491; gen fax (419) 874-7311; adv fax (419) 874-7311; ed fax (419) 874-7311; disp adv e-mail matt@welchpublishing.com; class adv e-mail publisher@perrysburg.com; ed e-mail editor@rossford.com; web site www.rossford.com
Circulation: 1,759pd, 1,800fr; USPS
Advertising rate: Open inch rate $6.10
Established: 1940
Group: Welch Publishing Company
Digital Platform - Mobile: Apple, Android, Windows, Blackberry
Digital Platform - Tablet: Apple iOS, Android, Windows 7, Blackberry Tablet OS, Kindle, Nook, Kindle Fire
Pub. .... John B. Welch
Adv. Mgr. .... Matthew H. Welch
Ed. .... Beth Church
Mechanical Specifications: Type page 15 1/4 x 21 1/2; E - 9 cols, 1 9/16, 1/12 between; A - 9 cols, 1 9/16, 1/12 between; C - 9 cols, 1 9/16, 1/12 between.Equipment & Software: Hardware — APP/Mac, IBM, COM; Presses — WPC/Web Leader; Software — QPS/QuarkXPress 4.0, Adobe/Photoshop 3.3, Microsoft/Office.
Delivery Method: Mail, Newsstand, Racks
Areas Served: Wood County

SPENCERVILLE

THE JOURNAL NEWS (THUR)

PO Box 8, Spencerville, OH, 45887-0008, Allen, USA; gen tel (419) 733-855; adv tel (419) 733-0855; ed tel (419) 733-0855; disp adv e-mail news@spencervillenews.com; class adv e-mail news@spencervillenews.com; ed e-mail news@spencervillenews.com
Circulation: 2,100pd,; Sworn/Estimate/Non-Audited
Advertising rate: Open inch rate $6.00
Established: 1879Editions: (52)
Digital Platform - Mobile: Apple, Android
Digital Platform - Tablet: Apple iOS, Android, Windows 7, Kindle Fire
Manager .... Cassandra Helmstetter
Mechanical Specifications: 1 column = 1.68 inches wide
2 columns = 3.48 inches wide
3 columns = 5.27 inches wide
4 columns = 7.07 inches wide
5 columns = 8.87 inches wide
6 columns = 10.66 inches wide
Full Page = 6 columns wide x 21 inches deep
Quarter Fold
Delivery Method: Mail, Racks
Areas Served: Allen County

STRUTHERS

HOMETOWN JOURNAL (THUR)

32 State St, Ste 204, Struthers, OH, 44471-1952, Mahoning, USA; gen tel (330) 755-2155; disp adv e-mail news@hometownjournal.biz; class adv e-mail news@hometownjournal.biz; ed e-mail news@hometownjournal.biz; web site www.hometownjournal.biz
Circulation: 4,000pd, 1,000fr; Sworn/Estimate/Non-Audited
Advertising rate: Open inch rate $8.00
Established: 1928
Digital Platform - Mobile: Apple, Android, Windows
Digital Platform - Tablet: Apple iOS, Android, Windows 7
Pub./Ed. .... Nancy Johngrass
Delivery Method: Mail, Newsstand, Racks
Areas Served: Mahoning County

SUGARCREEK

THE BUDGET (WED)

134 N Factory St, Sugarcreek, OH, 44681, Tuscarawas, USA; gen tel (330) 852-4634; adv tel (330) 852-4634; ed tel (330) 852-4634; gen fax (330) 852-4421; adv fax (330) 852-4421; ed fax (330) 852-4421; disp adv e-mail mmiller@thebudgetnewspaper.com; class adv e-mail classifieds@thebudgetnewspaper.com; ed e-mail localnews@thebudgetnewspaper.com; web site www.thebudgetnewspaper.com
Circulation: 18,875pd, 1,161fr; USPS
Advertising rate: Open inch rate $8.70
Established: 1890
Digital Platform - Mobile: Apple, Android
Digital Platform - Tablet: Apple iOS, Android
National Edition Ed. .... Fannie Erb-Miller
Local Edition Ed. .... Beverly Keller
Adv. Dir. .... Miller Milo
Delivery Method: Mail, Newsstand, Racks
Areas Served: Tuscarawas County

TOLEDO

POINT & SHORELAND JOURNAL (TUES)

2930 131st St, Toledo, OH, 43611-2325, Lucas, USA; gen tel (419) 874-2528; adv tel (419) 874-4491; ed tel (419) 874-4491; gen fax (419) 874-7311; adv fax (419) 874-7311; ed fax (419) 874-7311; disp adv e-mail matt@welchpublishing.com; class adv e-mail publisher@perrysburg.com; ed e-mail publisher@perrysburg.com; web site www.pointandshoreland.com
Circulation: 5,676pd, 6,882fr; USPS
Advertising rate: Open inch rate $11.80
Group: Welch Publishing Company
Digital Platform - Mobile: Apple, Android, Windows, Blackberry
Digital Platform - Tablet: Apple iOS, Android, Windows 7, Blackberry Tablet OS, Kindle, Nook, Kindle Fire
Pub. .... John B. Welch
Adv. Mgr. .... Matthew H. Welch
Mechanical Specifications: Type page 15 1/4 x 21 1/2; E - 9 cols, 1 9/16, 1/12 between. Equipment & Software: Hardware — APP/Mac, IBM, COM; Presses — WPC/Web Leader; Software — QPS/QuarkXPress 4.0, Microsoft/Office.
Delivery Method: Mail, Newsstand, Racks
Areas Served: Lucas County

TROY

MIAMI COUNTY ADVOCATE (SUN)

224 S Market St, Troy, OH, 45373-3327, Miami, USA; gen tel (937) 440-5275; adv tel (937) 440-5275; ed tel (937) 335-5634; gen fax (937) 440-5286; adv fax (937) 440-5286; ed fax (937) 440-5286; disp adv e-mail wrheditor@gmail.com; class adv e-mail wrheditor@gmail.com; ed e-mail wrheditor@gmail.com
Circulation: 22,000fr; Sworn/Estimate/Non-Audited
Advertising rate: Open inch rate $9.00
Established: 1975
Group: AIM Media IndianaEditions: (4) Miami Valley Weekly (9,627); Piqua Weekly (12,567); Sidney Weekly (10,175); Tipp City Weekly (3,790);
Editor .... Christina Chalmers
Ed. .... Joyell Nevins
News Ed. .... Jan Burns
Mechanical Specifications: Type page 13 x 21 1/2; E - 6 cols, 2 1/16, between; A - 6 cols, 2 1/16, between; C - 9 cols, 1 15/16, between. Equipment & Software: Hardware — APP/Mac; Presses — G/Urbanite; Software — Multi-Ad/Creator, QPS/QuarkXPress.
Delivery Method: Mail, Carrier, Racks
Areas Served: 45373, 45383, 45389, 45371, 45359, 45356, 45339, 45337, 45326, 45318, 45317, 45312, 45308, 43072

WEEKLY RECORD HERALD (SUN)

224 S Market St, Troy, OH, 45373-3327, Miami, USA; gen tel (937) 440-5275; adv tel (937) 440-5275; ed tel (937) 335-5634; gen fax (937) 440-5286; adv fax (937) 440-5286; ed fax (937) 440-5286; disp adv e-mail wrheditor@gmail.com; class adv e-mail wrheditor@gmail.com; ed e-mail wrheditor@gmail.com; web site www.weeklyrecordherald.com
Circulation: 3,000pd,; Sworn/Estimate/Non-Audited
Advertising rate: Open inch rate $5.30
Established: 2008
Group: Ohio Community Media, LLC
Digital Platform - Mobile: Apple, Android
Digital Platform - Tablet: Apple iOS, Android
Ed. .... Joyell Nevins
News Ed. ... Jan BurnsEquipment & Software: ; Software — Microsoft/Windows 97.
Delivery Method: Mail, Carrier, Racks
Areas Served: Bethel Township, Tipp City, and West Milton

URBANA

THE MECHANICSBURG TELEGRAM (WED)

1637 E US Highway 36, Ste 10, Urbana, OH, 43078-9156, Champaign, USA; gen tel (937) 652-1331; adv tel (937) 652-1331 ext. 206; ed tel (937) 652-1331ext. 221; gen fax (937) 652-1336; adv fax (937) 652-1336; ed fax (937) 652-1336; disp adv e-mail lmoon@civitasmedia.com; class adv e-mail cherring@civitasmedia.com; ed e-mail jmiller@civitasmedia.com; web site www.burgtelegram.com
Circulation: 52pd, 2,255fr; Sworn/Estimate/Non-Audited
Advertising rate: Open inch rate $6.80
Established: 1902
Group: Civitas Media, LLC-OOB
Pub./Adv. Dir. .... Lane Moon
Ed. .... Justin Miller
Retail Adv. Rep. .... Jessica Kinzer
Classified Adv. Rep. .... Carol Herring
Mechanical Specifications: Type page 13 x 21; E - 6 cols, 1.556, between; A - 6 cols, 1.556,

between; C - 6 cols, between.Equipment & Software: ; Presses — G
Delivery Method: Mail
Areas Served: 43044

UTICA

THE UTICA HERALD (THUR)

60 N Main St, Utica, OH, 43080-7704, Licking, USA; gen tel (740) 892-2771; adv tel (740) 892-2771; ed tel (740) 892-2771; disp adv e-mail theuticaherald@Aol.com; class adv e-mail theuticaherald@aol.com; ed e-mail theuticaherald@aol.com
Circulation: 2,100pd,; Sworn/Estimate/Non-Audited
Advertising rate: Open inch rate $7.00
Established: 1878
Group: Heartland Communications
Pub.................................. Randy Almendinger
Mechanical Specifications: Type page 13 x 21; E - 6 cols, 2, 1/6 between; A - 6 cols, 2, 1/6 between; C - 8 cols, 1 1/2, 1/6 between. Equipment & Software: Hardware — Pentium II; Presses — ABD; Software — Microsoft/ Windows.
Delivery Method: Mail, Newsstand
Areas Served: 43080, 43055, 43071, 43027, 43005, 43037

VANDALIA

ENGLEWOOD INDEPENDENT (THUR)

694 W National Rd, Vandalia, OH, 45377-1032, Montgomery, USA; gen tel (937) 236-4990; adv tel (937) 836-2619; ed tel (937) 836-2619; gen fax (937) 836-1940; adv fax (937) 836-1940; ed fax (937) 836-1940; disp adv e-mail kbelcher@civitasmedia.com; class adv e-mail pbeattie@civitasmedia.com; ed e-mail Rnunnari@civitasmedia.com; web site www.englewoodindependent.com
Circulation: 5,800pd, 1,000fr; Sworn/Estimate/ Non-Audited
Advertising rate: Open inch rate $8.66
Established: 1975
Group: AIM Media Indiana
Digital Platform - Mobile: Apple, Android, Windows, Blackberry
Digital Platform - Tablet: Apple iOS, Android, Windows 7, Blackberry Tablet OS
Mng. Ed....................................... Ron Nunnari
Adv. Mgr.................................. Pamela Beattie
Mechanical Specifications: Type page 13 1/2 x 21.
Delivery Method: Mail, Newsstand, Racks
Areas Served: 45322, 45315, 45415, 45354, 45309

HUBER HEIGHTS COURIER (THUR)

694 W National Rd, Vandalia, OH, 45377-1032, Montgomery, USA; gen tel (937) 236-4990; adv tel (937) 236-4990; ed tel (937) 236-4990; gen fax (937) 236-4176; adv fax (937) 236-4176; ed fax (937) 236-4176; disp adv e-mail kbelcher@civitasmedia.com; class adv e-mail kbelcher@civitasmedia.com; ed e-mail dwacker@civitasmedia.com; web site www.hhcourier.com
Circulation: 6,000pd, 4,130fr; Sworn/Estimate/ Non-Audited
Advertising rate: Open inch rate $8.66
Established: 1973
Group: AIM Media Indiana
Digital Platform - Mobile: Apple, Android, Windows, Blackberry
Digital Platform - Tablet: Apple iOS, Android, Windows 7, Blackberry Tablet OS
Mng. Ed....................................... Ron Nunnari
Adv. Mgr.................................. Pamela Beattie
Delivery Method: Mail, Newsstand, Racks
Areas Served: Montgomery County

VANDALIA DRUMMER NEWS (THUR)

694 W National Rd, Vandalia, OH, 45377-1032, Montgomery, USA; gen tel (937) 236-4990; adv tel (937) 890-6030; ed tel (937) 890-6030; gen fax (937) 890-9153; adv fax (937) 890-9153; ed fax (937) 890-9153; disp adv e-mail kbelcher@civitasmedia.com; class adv e-mail kbelcher@civitasmedia.com; ed e-mail dwacker@civitasmedia.com; web site www.vandaliadrummernews.com
Circulation: 4,200pd, 1,000fr; Sworn/Estimate/ Non-Audited
Advertising rate: Open inch rate $8.66
Established: 1979
Group: Civitas Media, LLC-OOB
Digital Platform - Mobile: Apple, Android, Windows, Blackberry
Digital Platform - Tablet: Apple iOS, Android, Windows 7, Blackberry Tablet OS
Mng. Ed....................................... Ron Nunnari
Adv. Mgr.................................. Pamela Beattie
Mechanical Specifications: Type page 13 3/4 x 22; E - 6 cols, 2, 1/8 between; A - 6 cols, 2, 1/8 between; C - 8 cols, 1 1/2, 1/8 between. Equipment & Software: Hardware — APP/ Mac LC III, APP/Mac Server 8550-200; Presses — 2-HI/V-15A, Atlas; Software — QPS/QuarkXPress 3.31, Microsoft 5.1, Adobe/Photoshop 3.0.
Delivery Method: Mail, Newsstand, Racks
Areas Served: Montgomery County

VERMILION

VERMILION PHOTOJOURNAL (THUR)

630 Main St, Vermilion, OH, 44089-1047, Erie, USA; gen tel (440) 967-5268; adv tel (440) 967-5268; ed tel (440) 967-5268; gen fax (440) 967-2535; adv fax (440) 967-2535; ed fax (440) 967-2535; disp adv e-mail info@vermilion-news.com; class adv e-mail info@vermilion-news.com; ed e-mail info@vermilion-news.com
Circulation: 3,000pd, 486fr; Sworn/Estimate/ Non-Audited
Advertising rate: Open inch rate $9.25
Group: Douthit Communications, Inc.
Ed./Gen. Mgr.......................... Karen Cornelius
Adv. Dir....................................... Susan Borso
News Ed .... Melanie Williamson
Delivery Method: Mail, Newsstand
Areas Served: Erie County

VERSAILLES

VERSAILLES POLICY (WED)

308 N West St, Versailles, OH, 45380-1360, Darke, USA; gen tel (937) 526-9131; adv tel (937) 526-9131; ed tel (937) 526-9131; disp adv e-mail vpolicy@roadrunner.com; class adv e-mail vpolicy@roadrunner.com; ed e-mail vpolicy@roadrunner.com
Circulation: 2,000pd,; USPS
Advertising rate: Open inch rate $7.00
Established: 1875
Pub./Ed./Adv. Mgr. .... Scott Langston
Mechanical Specifications: Type page 13 x 21 1/2; E - 6 cols, 2, 1/5 between; A - 6 cols, 2, 1/5 between; C - 9 cols, 1 3/8, 1/5 between. Equipment & Software: Hardware — PC; Software — Adobe/PageMaker 6.5, Adobe/ InDesign 1.5.
Delivery Method: Mail, Newsstand
Areas Served: 45380

WAPAKONETA

AUGLAIZE MERCHANDISER (TUES)

520 Industrial Dr, Wapakoneta, OH, 45895-9200, Auglaize, USA; gen tel (419) 738-2128; gen fax (419) 738-5352; disp adv e-mail marketingetc@wapakwdn.com; class adv e-mail classified@wapakwdn.com; ed e-mail editor@wapakwdn.com; web site www.wapakdailynews.com
Circulation: 7,030fr; Sworn/Estimate/Non-Audited
Advertising rate: Open inch rate $16
Established: 1905
Group: Horizon Publications Inc.
Pub... Deb Zwez
Adv. Dir................................ Gayle Masonbrink
Mechanical Specifications: Type page 13 x 21 1/2; E - 6 cols, 2 1/16, 1/8 between; A - 6 cols, 2 1/16, 1/8 between; C - 9 cols, 1 5/16, 1/8 between.
Delivery Method: Mail, Carrier
Areas Served: Auglaize County

WARREN

AUSTINTOWN TOWN CRIER (THUR)

240 Franklin St SE, Warren, OH, 44483-5711, Trumbull, USA; gen tel (330) 629-6200; adv tel (330) 841-1620; ed tel (330) 629-6200; gen fax (330) 629-6210; adv fax (330) 629-6210; ed fax (330) 629-6210; disp adv e-mail kbergman@tribtoday.com; class adv e-mail kbergman@tribtoday.com; ed e-mail editor@towncrieronline.com; web site www.towncrieronline.com
Circulation: 16,206fr; Sworn/Estimate/Non-Audited
Advertising rate: Open inch rate $13.05
Established: 1993
Group: Ogden Newspapers Inc.
Digital Platform - Mobile: Apple, Android, Windows, Blackberry
Digital Platform - Tablet: Apple iOS, Android, Windows 7, Blackberry Tablet OS
Ed./Gen. Mgr................................ Amy Wilson
Adv. Dir....................................... Kim Bergman
Mechanical Specifications: Type page 9 7/8 x 11 1/2; E - 5 cols, 1 7/8, between; A - 5 cols, 1 7/8, between; C - 7 cols, 1 13/16, between.Equipment & Software: Hardware — IBM/486; Software — CText.
Delivery Method: Mail, Newsstand, Racks
Areas Served: 44511, 44512, 44515, 44514

BOARDMAN TOWN CRIER (THUR)

240 Franklin St SE, Warren, OH, 44483-5711, Trumbull, USA; gen tel (330) 629-6200; adv tel (330) 841-1620; ed tel (330) 629-6200; gen fax (330) 629-6210; adv fax (330) 629-6210; ed fax (330) 629-6210; disp adv e-mail kbergman@tribtoday.com; class adv e-mail kbergman@tribtoday.com; ed e-mail editor@towncrieronline.com; web site www.towncrieronline.com
Circulation: 35,000fr; Sworn/Estimate/Non-Audited
Advertising rate: Open inch rate $14.00
Established: 1993
Group: Ogden Newspapers Inc.
Digital Platform - Mobile: Apple, Android, Windows, Blackberry
Digital Platform - Tablet: Apple iOS, Android, Windows 7, Blackberry Tablet OS
Ed./Gen. Mgr................................ Amy Wilson
Adv. Dir....................................... Kim Bergman
Mechanical Specifications: Type page 9 7/8 x 11 1/2; E - 5 cols, 1 7/8, between; A - 5 cols, 1 7/8, between; C - 7 cols, 1 13/16, between.Equipment & Software: Hardware — IBM/486; Software — CText.
Delivery Method: Mail, Newsstand, Racks
Areas Served: 44511, 44512, 44515, 44514

CANFIELD TOWN CRIER (THUR)

240 Franklin St SE, Warren, OH, 44483-5711, Trumbull, USA; gen tel (330) 629-6200; adv tel (330) 841-1620; ed tel (330) 629-6200; gen fax (330) 629-6210; adv fax (330) 629-6210; ed fax (330) 629-6210; disp adv e-mail kbergman@tribtoday.com; class adv e-mail kbergman@tribtoday.com; ed e-mail editor@towncrieronline.com; web site www.towncrieronline.com
Circulation: 35,000fr; Sworn/Estimate/Non-Audited
Advertising rate: Open inch rate $10.15
Established: 1993
Group: Ogden Newspapers Inc.
Digital Platform - Mobile: Apple, Android, Windows, Blackberry
Digital Platform - Tablet: Apple iOS, Android, Windows 7, Blackberry Tablet OS
Ed./Gen. Mgr................................ Amy Wilson
Adv. Dir....................................... Kim Bergman
Mechanical Specifications: Type page 9 7/8 x 11 1/2; E - 5 cols, 1 7/8, between; A - 5 cols, 1 7/8, between; C - 7 cols, 1 13/16, between.Equipment & Software: Hardware — IBM/486; Software — CText.
Delivery Method: Mail, Newsstand, Racks
Areas Served: 44406

POLAND TOWN CRIER (THUR)

240 Franklin St SE, Warren, OH, 44483-5711, Trumbull, USA; gen tel (330) 629-6200; adv tel (330) 841-1620; ed tel (330) 629-6200; gen fax (330) 629-6210; adv fax (330) 629-6210; ed fax (330) 629-6210; disp adv e-mail kbergman@tribtoday.com; class adv e-mail kbergman@tribtoday.com; ed e-mail editor@towncrieronline.com; web site www.towncrieronline.com
Circulation: 35,000fr; Sworn/Estimate/Non-Audited
Advertising rate: Open inch rate $10.15
Established: 1993
Group: Ogden Newspapers Inc.
Digital Platform - Mobile: Apple, Android, Windows, Blackberry
Digital Platform - Tablet: Apple iOS, Android, Windows 7, Blackberry Tablet OS
Ed./Gen. Mgr................................ Amy Wilson
Adv. Dir....................................... Kim Bergman
Mechanical Specifications: Type page 9 7/8 x 11 1/2; E - 5 cols, 1 7/8, between; A - 5 cols, 1 7/8, between; C - 7 cols, 1 13/16, between.Equipment & Software: Hardware — IBM/486; Software — CText.
Delivery Method: Mail, Newsstand, Racks
Areas Served: 44511, 44512, 44515, 44514

WAUSEON

FULTON COUNTY EXPOSITOR (TUES, THUR)

1270 N Shoop Ave, Ste A, Wauseon, OH, 43567-2211, Fulton, USA; gen tel (419) 335-2010; adv tel (419) 335-2010; ed tel (419) 335-2010; gen fax (419) 335-2030; adv fax (419) 335-2030; ed fax (419) 335-2030; disp adv e-mail fceadvertising@civitasmedia.com ; class adv e-mail fceadvertising@civitasmedia.com ; ed e-mail fcenews@civitasmedia.com ; web site www.fcnews.org
Circulation: 4,236pd, 51fr; Sworn/Estimate/ Non-Audited
Advertising rate: Open inch rate $8.95
Established: 1874
Digital Platform - Mobile: Apple, Android, Windows, Blackberry
Digital Platform - Tablet: Apple iOS, Android, Windows 7, Blackberry Tablet OS
Ed. .... Drew Stambaugh
Sports Ed............................. Max Householder
Delivery Method: Mail, Newsstand
Areas Served: Fulton County

SWANTON ENTERPRISE (TUES)

1270 N Shoop Ave, Ste A, Wauseon, OH, 43567-2211, Fulton, USA; gen tel (419) 335-2010; adv tel (419) 335-2010; ed tel (419) 335-2010; gen fax (419) 335-2030; adv fax (419) 335-2030; ed fax (419) 335-2030; disp adv e-mail TSEnews@civitasmedia.com; class adv e-mail TSEnews@civitasmedia.com; ed e-mail dstambaugh@civitasmedia.com; web site www.swantonenterprise.com
Circulation: 810pd,; Sworn/Estimate/Non-Audited
Advertising rate: Open inch rate $8.50
Established: 1887
Group: Civitas Media, LLC-OOB
Digital Platform - Mobile: Apple, Android, Windows, Blackberry
Digital Platform - Tablet: Apple iOS, Android, Windows 7, Blackberry Tablet OS
Ed. .... Drew Stambaugh
Sports Ed............................. Max Householder
Delivery Method: Mail, Newsstand
Areas Served: 43558

WAVERLY

THE PIKE COUNTY NEWS WATCHMAN (WED, SUN)

14532 US Highway 23, Ste A, Waverly, OH, 45690-8011, Pike, USA; gen tel (740) 947-2149; adv tel (740) 947-2149 ext. 104; ed tel (740) 947-2149 ext. 110; gen fax (740)

947-1344; adv fax (740) 947-1344; ed fax (740) 947-1344; disp adv e-mail ngilliland@newswatchman.com; class adv e-mail tbryan@newswatchman.com; ed e-mail dmagill@newswatchman.com; web site www.pikecountydaily.com
Circulation: 3,800pd, 11,500fr; Sworn/Estimate/Non-Audited
Advertising rate: Open inch rate $8.96
Established: 1832
Group: ACM Ohio LLC
Digital Platform - Mobile: Apple, Android, Windows, Blackberry
Digital Platform - Tablet: Apple iOS, Android, Windows 7, Blackberry Tablet OS, Kindle, Nook, Kindle Fire
Pub. .... Norman Gilliland
Ed. .... Matt Lucas
Adv. Mgr. .... Teresa Bryan
Circ. Mgr. .... Ken Crisp
Media Rep. .... Rebecca Hedges
Ed. .... Stephanie Stanley
Mechanical Specifications: Type page 13 x 21 1/2; E - 6 cols, 2 1/3, 1/6 between; A - 6 cols, 2 1/3, 1/6 between; C - 9 cols, 2 1/3, 1/6 between.
Delivery Method: Mail, Newsstand, Carrier, Racks
Areas Served: 45612, 45613, 45626, 45661, 45642, 45646, 45690, 45683, 45687

WEST ALEXANDRIA

THE ADVERTISER (TUES)
10 S Main St, West Alexandria, OH, 45381-1216, Preble, USA; gen tel (937) 839-4733; adv tel (937) 839-4733; ed tel (937) 839-4733; gen fax (937) 839-5351; adv fax (937) 839-5351; ed fax (937) 839-5351; disp adv e-mail twinvpub@infinet.com; class adv e-mail information@onlinetvp.com; ed e-mail twinvpub@infinet.com; web site www.twinvalleypublications.com
Circulation: 400pd, 8,000fr; Sworn/Estimate/Non-Audited
Advertising rate: Open inch rate $7.50
Established: 1934
Group: Twin Valley Publications
Digital Platform - Mobile: Apple, Android
Digital Platform - Tablet: Apple iOS, Android
Pub./Ed. .... Sam Shortes
Gen. Mgr. .... Cindy Shortes
Adv. Mgr. .... Angie Donohoo
Mechanical Specifications: Type page 10 1/3 x 12; E - 6 cols, 1 7/10, 1/6 between; A - 6 cols, 1 7/10, 1/6 between; C - 6 cols, 1 7/10, 1/6 between.Equipment & Software: Hardware — APP/Mac; Software — Abbott Systems/Ready, Set, Go 7.0.
Delivery Method: Mail, Newsstand, Racks
Areas Served: Preble County

THE LEWISBURG LEADER (TUES)
10 S Main St, West Alexandria, OH, 45381-1216, Preble, USA; gen tel (937) 839-4733; adv tel (937) 839-4733; ed tel (937) 839-4733; gen fax (937) 839-5351; adv fax (937) 839-5351; ed fax (937) 839-5351; disp adv e-mail twinvpub@infinet.com; class adv e-mail information@onlinetvp.com; ed e-mail twinvpub@infinet.com; web site www.twinvalleypublications.com
Circulation: 400pd, 8,000fr; Sworn/Estimate/Non-Audited
Advertising rate: Open inch rate $7.50
Established: 1934
Group: Twin Valley Publications
Digital Platform - Mobile: Apple, Android
Digital Platform - Tablet: Apple iOS, Android
Pub./Ed. .... Sam Shortes
Gen. Mgr. .... Cindy Shortes
Adv. Mgr. .... Angie Donohoo
Mechanical Specifications: Type page 10 1/3 x 12; E - 6 cols, 1 7/10, 1/6 between; A - 6 cols, 1 7/10, 1/6 between; C - 6 cols, 1 7/10, 1/6 between.Equipment & Software: Hardware — APP/Mac; Software — Abbott Systems/Ready, Set, Go 7.0.
Delivery Method: Mail, Newsstand, Racks
Areas Served: Preble County

THE TWIN VALLEY NEWS (TUES)
10 S Main St, West Alexandria, OH, 45381-1293, Preble, USA; gen tel (937) 839-4733; adv tel (937) 839-4733; ed tel (937) 839-4733; gen fax (937) 839-5351; adv fax (937) 839-5351; ed fax (937) 839-5351; disp adv e-mail twinvpub@infinet.com; class adv e-mail information@onlinetvp.com; ed e-mail twinvpub@infinet.com; web site www.twinvalleypublications.com
Circulation: 400pd, 8,000fr; Sworn/Estimate/Non-Audited
Advertising rate: Open inch rate $7.50
Established: 1934 **Group:** Twin Valley Publications
Digital Platform - Mobile: Apple, Android
Digital Platform - Tablet: Apple iOS, Android
Pub./Ed. .... Sam Shortes
Gen. Mgr. .... Cindy Shortes
Adv. Mgr. .... Angie Donohoo
Mechanical Specifications: Type page 10 1/3 x 12; E - 6 cols, 1 7/10, 1/6 between; A - 6 cols, 1 7/10, 1/6 between; C - 6 cols, 1 7/10, 1/6 between.Equipment & Software: Hardware — APP/Mac; Software — Abbott Systems/Ready, Set, Go 7.0.
Delivery Method: Mail, Newsstand, Racks
Areas Served: Preble County

WEST UNION

THE PEOPLE'S DEFENDER (WED)
PO Box 308, West Union, OH, 45693-0308, Adams, USA; gen tel (937) 544-2391; adv tel (937) 544-2391; ed tel (937) 544-2391; gen fax (937) 544-2298; adv fax (937) 544-2298; ed fax (937) 544-2298; disp adv e-mail trigdon@peoplesdefender.com; class adv e-mail pniswander@peoplesdefender.com; ed e-mail lhuffman@peoplesdefender.com; web site www.peoplesdefender.com
Circulation: 8,500pd, 12,800fr; Sworn/Estimate/Non-Audited
Advertising rate: Open inch rate $8.75
Established: 1866
Group: Civitas Media, LLC-OOB
Digital Platform - Mobile: Apple, Android, Windows, Blackberry
Digital Platform - Tablet: Apple iOS, Android, Windows 7, Blackberry Tablet OS
Pub./Ed. .... Lee Huffman
Adv. Mgr. .... Terry Rigdon
Bus. Mgr. .... Peggy Niswander
Delivery Method: Mail, Newsstand
Areas Served: Adams County

WHEELERSBURG

THE SCIOTO VOICE (THUR)
8366 Downtown Hayport Rd, Wheelersburg, OH, 45694, Scioto, USA; gen tel (740) 574-8494; adv tel (740) 574-8494; ed tel (740) 574-8494; gen fax (740) 574-2329; adv fax (740) 574-2329; ed fax (740) 574-2329; disp adv e-mail info@thesciotovoice.com; class adv e-mail jessica@thesciotovoice.com; ed e-mail debbie@thesciotovoice.com; web site www.thesciotovoice.com
Circulation: 3,000pd,; USPS
Advertising rate: Open inch rate $5.25
Established: 1973
Digital Platform - Mobile: Apple, Android, Windows, Blackberry
Digital Platform - Tablet: Apple iOS, Android, Windows 7, Blackberry Tablet OS, Kindle, Nook, Kindle Fire
Pub./Ed. .... Debora Allard
Mechanical Specifications: Full Page 6 col x 21.5 inches
1 column =1.56 inches, 2 Col =3.22, 3 col = 4.889, 4 col = 6.556, 5 col =8.222, 6 col = 9.889
Delivery Method: Mail, Newsstand
Areas Served: Scioto, Jackson, and Lawrence County

WILLARD

GREENWICH ENTERPRISE REVIEW (TUES)
211 S Myrtle Ave, Willard, OH, 44890-1407, Huron, USA; gen tel (419) 935-0184; gen fax (419) 933-2031; disp adv e-mail willardtj@hmcltd.net; class adv e-mail willardtj@hmcltd.net; ed e-mail willardtj@hmcltd.net
Circulation: 14,200fr; Sworn/Estimate/Non-Audited
Advertising rate: Open inch rate $8.75
Established: 1950
Assoc. Pub. .... Karla Souslin
Ed. .... Lynne Phillips
Areas Served: 44837, 44878, 44855

THE WILLARD TIMES-JUNCTION (TUES, THUR)
211 S Myrtle Ave, Willard, OH, 44890-1407, Huron, USA; gen tel (419) 935-0184; adv tel (419) 935-0184; ed tel (419) 935-0184; gen fax (419) 933-2031; adv fax (419) 933-2031; ed fax (419) 933-2031; disp adv e-mail globe@sdgnewsgroup.com; class adv e-mail globe@sdgnewsgroup.com; ed e-mail globe@sdgnewsgroup.com; web site www.sdgnewsgroup.com
Circulation: 3,600pd, 50fr; Sworn/Estimate/Non-Audited
Advertising rate: Open inch rate $10.80
Group: SDGNewsgroup
Digital Platform - Mobile: Apple, Android, Windows, Blackberry
Digital Platform - Tablet: Apple iOS, Android, Windows 7, Blackberry Tablet OS
Pub. .... Scott Gove
Ed. .... Terry Wilson
Adv. Dir. .... Karla Souslin
Mechanical Specifications: Type page 13 x 21 1/2; E - 6 cols, 2, between; A - 6 cols, 2, between; C - 6 cols, between.Equipment & Software: Hardware — APP/Mac; Software — Microsoft/Word 6.0, QPS/QuarkXPress.
Delivery Method: Mail, Racks
Areas Served: Huron County

WILLSHIRE

WILLSHIRE PHOTO STAR (WED)
307 State St., Willshire, OH, 45898, Van Wert, USA; gen tel (419) 495-2696; adv tel (419) 495-2696; ed tel (419) 495-2696; gen fax (419) 495-2143; adv fax (419) 495-2143; ed fax (419) 495-2143; disp adv e-mail photostarnews@verizon.net; class adv e-mail photostarnews@verizon.net; ed e-mail photostarnews@verizon.net
Circulation: 165pd, 11,025fr; Sworn/Estimate/Non-Audited
Advertising rate: Open inch rate $8.00
Established: 1895
Pub./Ed. .... Judith Bunner
Co-Pub./Ed. .... John D. Bunner
Mechanical Specifications: Type page 10 1/4 x 16.
Delivery Method: Mail, Newsstand, Racks
Areas Served: Van Wert County

WILMINGTON

NEWS JOURNAL STAR (MON)
761 S Nelson Ave, Wilmington, OH, 45177-2517, Clinton, USA; gen tel (937) 382-2574; adv tel (937) 382-2574; ed tel (937) 382-2574; gen fax (937) 382-4392; adv fax (937) 382-4392; ed fax (937) 382-4392; disp adv e-mail skersey@civitasmedia.com; class adv e-mail bvandeventer@civitasmedia.com; ed e-mail rgraf@civitasmedia.com; web site www.wnewsj.com
Circulation: 17,000fr; Sworn/Estimate/Non-Audited
Advertising rate: Open inch rate $13.25
Established: 1838
Group: AIM Media Indiana
Digital Platform - Mobile: Apple, Android
Digital Platform - Tablet: Apple iOS, Android, Windows 7
Pub. .... Randy Graf
Ed. .... Tom Barr
Mechanical Specifications: Type page 13 x 21; E - 6 colsEquipment & Software: Hardware — APP/Mac; Presses — G/Community; Software — QPS/QuarkXPress.
Delivery Method: Mail, Carrier
Areas Served: Clinton County

WOODSFIELD

MONROE COUNTY BEACON (THUR)
103 E Court St, Woodsfield, OH, 43793-1110, Monroe, USA; gen tel (740) 472-0734; adv tel (740) 472-0734; ed tel (740) 472-0734; gen fax (740) 472-0735; adv fax (740) 472-0735; ed fax (740) 472-0735; disp adv e-mail monroecountybeacon@sbcglobal.net; class adv e-mail monroecountybeacon@sbcglobal.net; ed e-mail monroecountybeacon@sbcglobal.net; web site www.mcbeacon.com
Circulation: 4,950pd, 15fr; Sworn/Estimate/Non-Audited
Advertising rate: Open inch rate $9.50 (Local); $12.73 (National)
Established: 1884
Group: Delphos Herald, Inc.
Digital Platform - Mobile: Apple, Android
Digital Platform - Tablet: Apple iOS, Android
Ed./Gen. Mgr. .... Darin Brown
News Ed. .... Linsey Colvin
Mechanical Specifications: Type page 12 x 21 1/2; E - 6 cols, 1 3/4, 1/6 between; A - 6 cols, 1 3/4, 1/6 between; C - 8 cols, 1 1/2, 1/6 between.Equipment & Software: Hardware — 5-APP/Mac; Software — QPS/QuarkXPress 3.32.
Delivery Method: Mail, Newsstand, Racks
Areas Served: Monroe County

XENIA

BEAVERCREEK NEWS-CURRENT (THUR)
1836 W Park Sq, Xenia, OH, 45385-2668, Greene, USA; gen tel (937) 372-4444; adv tel (937) 372-4444 ext 200; ed tel (937) 372-4444; gen fax (937) 372-3385; adv fax (937) 372-3385; ed fax (937) 372-1951; disp adv e-mail tpease@civitasmedia.com; class adv e-mail tpease@civitasmedia.com; ed e-mail editor@xeniagazette.com; web site www.beavercreeknewscurrent.com
Circulation: 3,805pd,; Sworn/Estimate/Non-Audited
Advertising rate: Open inch rate $11.90
Ed. .... Diane Chiddister
Adv. Mgr. .... Robert Hasek
Mechanical Specifications: Type page 13 x 21 - 1/2; E - 6 cols, 1/6 between; A - 6 cols, 1/6 between; C - 9 cols, 1/6 between.
Areas Served: Beavercreek (OH)

SUGARCREEK BELLBROOK TIMES (THUR)
1836 W Park Sq, Xenia, OH, 45385-2668, Greene, USA; gen tel (937) 294-7000; adv tel (937) 294-7000; ed tel (937) 294-7000; gen fax (937) 294-2981; adv fax (937) 294-2981; ed fax (937) 294-2981; disp adv e-mail jmilburn@tcnewsnet.com; class adv e-mail tcnewsnet@tcnewsnet.com; ed e-mail jmilburn@tcnewsnet.com; web site www.bellbrooktimes.com
Advertising rate: Open inch rate $7.50
Group: Ohio Community Media, LLC
Digital Platform - Mobile: Apple, Android, Windows, Blackberry
Digital Platform - Tablet: Apple iOS, Android, Windows 7, Blackberry Tablet OS
Ed. .... Jodi Milburn
Sales .... Don Yeazell
Sales .... Amber Campbell
Mechanical Specifications: Type page 13 x 21 1/2; E - 6 cols, 2 1/16, between; A - 6 cols, 2 1/16, between; C - 9 cols, between.
Delivery Method: Mail, Newsstand, Racks
Areas Served: Bellbrook and Sugarcreek Township

YELLOW SPRINGS

THE YELLOW SPRINGS NEWS (THUR)

253 1/2 Xenia Ave, Yellow Springs, OH, 45387-1832, Greene, USA; gen tel (937) 767-7373; adv tel (937) 767-7373; ed tel (937) 767-7373; gen fax (937) 767-2254; adv fax (937) 767-2254; ed fax (937) 767-2254; disp adv e-mail advert@ysnews.com; class adv e-mail classifieds@ysnews.com; ed e-mail ysnews@ysnews.com; web site www.ysnews.com

Circulation: 1,841pd, 39fr; Sworn/Estimate/Non-Audited
Advertising rate: Open inch rate $9.00
Established: 1880
Digital Platform - Mobile: Apple, Android, Windows, Blackberry
Digital Platform - Tablet: Apple iOS, Android, Windows 7, Blackberry Tablet OS, Kindle, Nook, Kindle Fire
Ed. .... Diane Chiddister
Assc. Ed. .... Lauren Heaton
Adv. Mgr. .... Robert Hasek
Mechanical Specifications: Type page 13 x 21 1/2; E - 5 cols, 2 5/12, 1/6 between; A - 5 cols, 2 5/12, 1/6 between; C - 5 cols, 2 5/12, 1/6 between.Equipment & Software: Hardware — APP/Mac; Software — Adobe/PageMaker.
Delivery Method: Mail, Newsstand, Racks
Areas Served: Greene County

OKLAHOMA

ALLEN

THE ALLEN ADVOCATE (THUR)

101 W Broadway, Allen, OK, 74825-3209, Pontotoc, USA; gen tel (580) 857-2687; gen fax (580) 857-2573; disp adv e-mail cindy@allennewspaper.com; ed e-mail dianna@allennewspaper.com; web site www.allennewspaper.com

Circulation: 1,350pd,; Sworn/Estimate/Non-Audited
Advertising rate: Open inch rate $4.00
Pub./Ed .... Dianna Brannan
Adv. Mgr .... Cindy Davis

ALVA

ALVA REVIEW-COURIER (FRI, SUN)

620 Choctaw St, Alva, OK, 73717-1626, Woods, USA; gen tel (580) 327-2200; gen fax (580) 327-2454; disp adv e-mail sales@alvareviewcourier.net; class adv e-mail manager@alvareviewcourier.net; ed e-mail news@alvareviewcourier.net; web site www.alvareviewcourier.com

Circulation: 1,300pd,; Sworn/Estimate/Non-Audited
Advertising rate: Open inch rate $5.60
Ed .... Marione Martin
Publisher .... Lynn L. Martin
Ad Rep. .... Bill Springer
Ad Rep. .... Amanda Galindo
Office Manager .... Linda Toone
Mechanical Specifications: Type page 11 x 17; E - 5 cols, 2 1/16, 1/8 between; A - 5 cols, 2 1/16, 1/8 between; C - 5 cols, 2 1/16, 1/8 between.
Delivery Method: Mail, Newsstand, Carrier
Areas Served: Woods County, Oklahoma

ANTLERS

ANTLERS AMERICAN (THUR)

110 E Main St, Antlers, OK, 74523-3254, Pushmataha, USA; gen tel (580) 298-3314; gen fax (580) 298-3316; disp adv e-mail comp.antlers.amer@sbcglobal.net; class adv e-mail class.antlers.amer@sbcglobal.net; ed e-mail ed.antlersamer@sbcglobal.net; web site www.theantlersamerican.com

Circulation: 2,703pd,; Sworn/Estimate/Non-Audited
Advertising rate: Open inch rate $9.00
Established: 1895
Group: Heritage Publications (2003) Inc. Horizon Publications Inc.
Adv. Mgr. .... Shelley Baskin
Pub/Ed/Gen. Mgr .... Steffenson Tracy
Class/Legal Clerk .... Van Meter Michelle
Delivery Method: Mail, Newsstand, Racks
Areas Served: Antlers and all of Pushmataha County

APACHE

THE APACHE NEWS (THUR)

120 E Evans Ave, Apache, OK, 73006-9190, Caddo, USA; gen tel (580) 588-3862; gen fax (580) 588-3862; disp adv e-mail apachenews@pldi.net

Circulation: 1,250pd,; Sworn/Estimate/Non-Audited
Advertising rate: Open inch rate $4.00
Established: 1901
Digital Platform - Mobile: Apple
Digital Platform - Tablet: Apple iOS
Ed. .... Joye Wright
Mechanical Specifications: Type page 13 3/4 x 21; E - 6 cols, 2 1/8, 1/4 between; A - 6 cols, 2 1/6, 1/4 between; C - 8 cols, 1 2/3, between.Equipment & Software: Hardware — APP/Mac G3; Software — Adobe/PageMaker, Adobe/Photoshop.
Delivery Method: Mail, Newsstand
Areas Served: Caddo County

ATOKA

ATOKA COUNTY TIMES (WED)

894 W 13th St, Atoka, OK, 74525-3426, Atoka, USA; gen tel (580) 889-3319; adv tel (580) 889-3310; gen fax (580) 889-2300; disp adv e-mail rlinscott@atokaspeedynet.net; ed e-mail dstuart@atokaspeedynet.net; web site atokacountytimes.com

Circulation: 3,600pd,; Sworn/Estimate/Non-Audited
Advertising rate: Open inch rate $7.15
Established: 1950
Digital Platform - Mobile: Apple
Digital Platform - Tablet: Apple iOS
Pub. .... Louise Cain
Adv. Mgr. .... Ron Linscott
Ed .... Deanna Stuart
Mechanical Specifications: Type page 11 5/8 x 21 1/4; A - 6 cols, 1 5/6, 1/8 between; C - 8 cols, 1/8 between.
Delivery Method: Mail, Racks
Areas Served: Atoka County

BARNSDALL

BIGHEART TIMES (THUR)

116 N 5th St, Barnsdall, OK, 74002-6616, Osage, USA; gen tel (918) 847-2916; gen fax (918) 847-2654; disp adv e-mail marlyn@bighearttime.com; ed e-mail louise@bigheart-time.com; web site www.bighearttimes.com

Circulation: 1,500pd,; Sworn/Estimate/Non-Audited
Advertising rate: Open inch rate $4.50
Established: 1919
Group: Fully Involved Inc
Digital Platform - Mobile: Apple, Android
Digital Platform - Tablet: Apple iOS, Android, Kindle
Owner/Pub/Ed .... Louise Red Corn
Adv. .... Marlyn Slone
Mechanical Specifications: Type page 10 x 21 1/2- 6 cols
Delivery Method: Mail, Newsstand, Racks
Areas Served: Osage

BEAVER

THE HERALD-DEMOCRAT (THUR)

108 Douglas Ave, Beaver, OK, 73932-9620, Beaver, USA; gen tel (580) 625-3241; gen fax (580) 625-4269; ed e-mail bvrnews@gmail.com; web site http://www.bvrcowchipnews.com/

Circulation: 1,500pd,; Sworn/Estimate/Non-Audited
Advertising rate: Open inch rate $4.00
Digital Platform - Mobile: Windows
Digital Platform - Tablet: Windows 7
Co-pub. .... Joe Lansden
Mechanical Specifications: 6 column format 11 1/2 by 21 inches
Delivery Method: Mail, Newsstand
Areas Served: Beaver County

BETHANY

THE BETHANY TRIBUNE (FRI)

6728 NW 38th St, Bethany, OK, 73008-3360, Oklahoma, USA; gen tel (405) 789-1962; gen fax (405) 789-4253; disp adv e-mail ads@OKCTribune.com; ed e-mail news@OKCTribune.com; web site www.bethanytribuneonline.com

Circulation: 3,500pd,; Sworn/Estimate/Non-Audited
Advertising rate: Open inch rate $18.04
Established: 1923
Asst. Pub .... Stacie Henderson-Harrington
Ed/Adv .... Matt Montgomery
Office Mgr. .... Teresa Wardell
Areas Served: Oklahoma County

BLACKWELL

BLACKWELL JOURNAL-TRIBUNE (TUES, FRI)

PO Box 760, Blackwell, OK, 74631-0760, Kay, USA; gen tel (580) 363-3370; gen fax (580) 363-4415; disp adv e-mail ads@grcnet.com; class adv e-mail classifieds@blackwelljournaltribune.net; ed e-mail ngoff@blackwelljournaltribune.net; web site http://www.blackwelljournaltribune.net

Circulation: 2,475pd, 3fr; Sworn/Estimate/Non-Audited
Advertising rate: Open inch rate $19.00
Established: 1915
Group: American Hometown Publishing
News Ed. .... Nixie Goff
Class. Adv. .... Jennifer Nice
Pub./Ed. .... Belinda Ramsey
Adv. .... Tina Allen
Mechanical Specifications: Type page 13 x 21 1/2; E - 6 cols, 2 1/16, 1/8 between; A - 6 cols, 2 1/16, 1/8 between; C - 8 cols, 1 1/2, 1/16 between.

BOISE CITY

THE BOISE CITY NEWS (WED)

105 W Main, Boise City, OK, 73933, Cimarron, USA; gen tel (580) 544-2222; gen fax (580) 544-3281; disp adv e-mail blackmesapub@yahoo.com; ed e-mail bcnews@ptsi.net; web site https://boisecitynews2.wordpress.com/

Circulation: 1,750pd,; Sworn/Estimate/Non-Audited
Advertising rate: Open inch rate $4.75
Adv. Mgr .... Linda Gray
Ed. .... C.F. David

BRISTOW

BRISTOW NEWS (WED, FRI)

112 W 6th Ave, Bristow, OK, 74010-2810, Creek, USA; gen tel (918) 367-2282; gen fax (918) 367-2724; disp adv e-mail bristownews@sbcglobal.net; web site bristownews.com

Circulation: 3,000pd,; Sworn/Estimate/Non-Audited
Advertising rate: Open inch rate $6.15
Established: 1889
Group: Central Oklahoma Publishing
Adv. .... Tabatha Shadow
Class Acct. .... Angie Gentry
J. D. Meisner
Rick Vyper
Mechanical Specifications: Type page 13 x 21; E - 6 cols, 2 1/8, 1/8 between; A - 6 cols, 2 1/8, 1/8 between; C - 6 cols, 2 1/8, 1/8 between. Equipment & Software: Hardware — APP/Mac; Presses — G/Community; Software — Adobe/PageMaker.
Delivery Method: Mail, Newsstand, Racks
Areas Served: Creek County

CARNEGIE

CARNEGIE HERALD (WED)

14 W Main, Carnegie, OK, 73015, Caddo, USA; gen tel (580) 654-1443; gen fax (580) 654-1608; disp adv e-mail lcooper@timescall.com; ed e-mail news@carnegieherald.com; web site www.carnegieherald.com

Circulation: 1,405pd,; Sworn/Estimate/Non-Audited
Advertising rate: Open inch rate $6.00
Established: 1903
Pub./Adv. Dir./Ed. .... Donald Cooper
Pub./Adv. Dir./Managing Ed. .... Lori Cooper
Mechanical Specifications: Type page 11.67" x 21" 6 cols
Delivery Method: Mail, Newsstand
Areas Served: 73015

CHELSEA

CHELSEA REPORTER (THUR)

245 W 6th St, Chelsea, OK, 74016-1833, Rogers, USA; gen tel (918) 789-2331; gen fax (918) 789-2333; ed e-mail chelsea_reporter@sbcgoble.net; web site https://www.facebook.com/ChelseaReporter

Circulation: 1,850pd,; Sworn/Estimate/Non-Audited
Advertising rate: Open inch rate $5.00
Pub. ....
Linda LordEquipment & Software: Hardware — APP/Mac; Software — Microsoft/Word, Adobe/PageMaker, Adobe/Photoshop.
Areas Served: Rogers County

CHEROKEE

THE CHEROKEE MESSENGER & REPUBLICAN (THUR)

216 S Grand Ave, Cherokee, OK, 73728-2030, Alfalfa, USA; gen tel (580) 596-3344; gen fax (580) 596-2959; disp adv e-mail ads@cherokeenewspaper.com; class adv e-mail Info@cherokeenewspaper.com; ed e-mail news@cherokeenewspaper.com; web site www.cherokeemessengerrepublican.com

Circulation: 1,900pd, 250fr; USPS
Advertising rate: Open inch rate $7.00
Established: 1900
Gen. Mgr. .... Marsha Tucker
Adv. Dir. .... Heather Gilley
Ed .... Kyle Spade
Pub .... Hoby Hammer
Mechanical Specifications: Broadsheet
6 columns by 21 inches
13 inches by 21 inches
12.2 picas per column
2.028 inches per column
Equipment & Software: Hardware — APP/Mac; Software — InDesign CS6
Delivery Method: Mail, Racks
Areas Served: Cherokee County

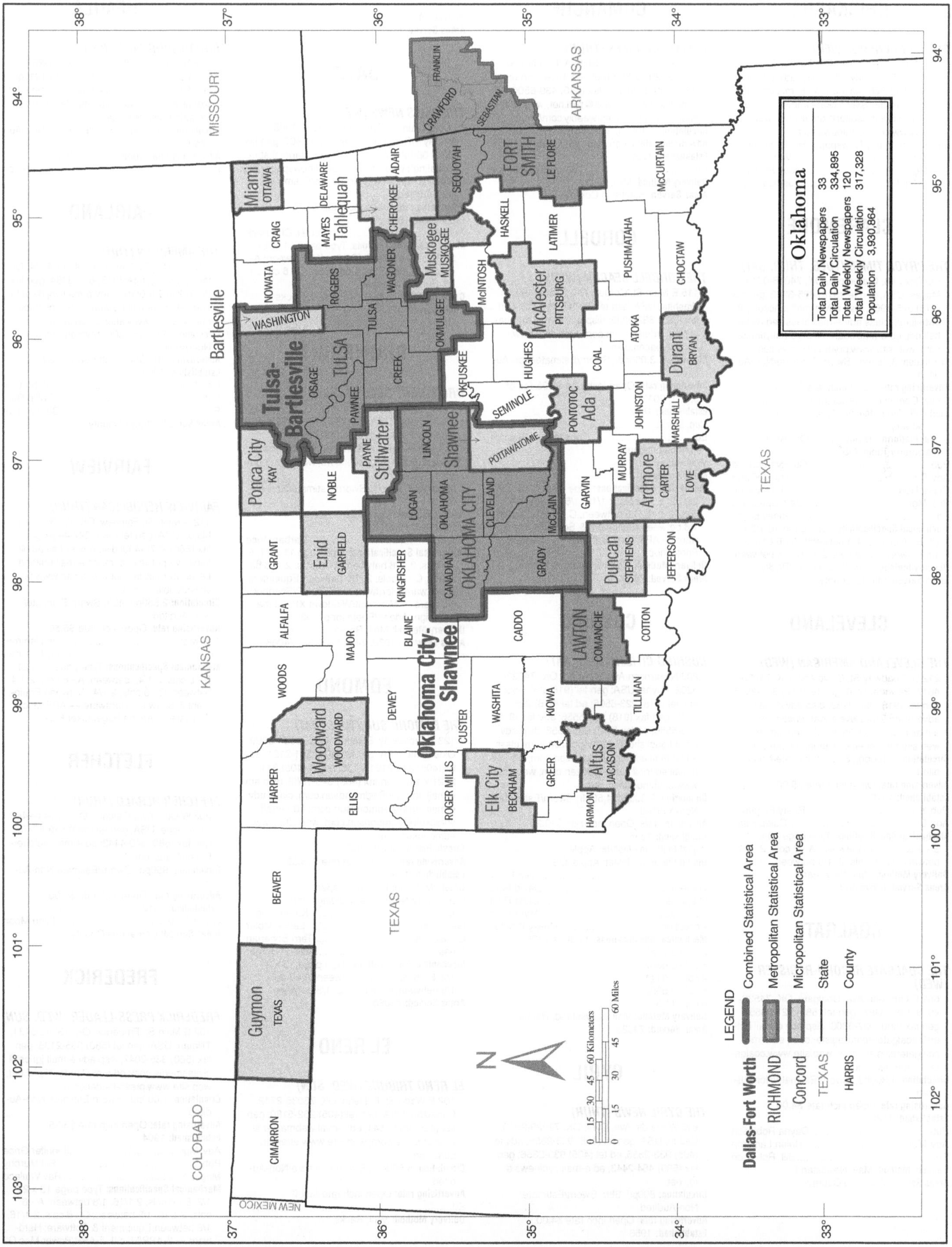
Oklahoma
Total Daily Newspapers 33
Total Daily Circulation 334,895
Total Weekly Newspapers 120
Total Weekly Circulation 317,328
Population 3,930,864
LEGEND
Dallas-Fort Worth Combined Statistical Area
RICHMOND Metropolitan Statistical Area
Concord Micropolitan Statistical Area
TEXAS State
HARRIS County
0 15 30 45 60 Miles
0 15 30 45 60 Kilometers
N
Tulsa-Bartlesville
Oklahoma City-Shawnee
Bartlesville
Tahlequah
Miami
Ponca City
Enid
Stillwater
Shawnee
Muskogee
McAlester
Ada
Ardmore
Durant
Duncan
Lawton
Altus
Elk City
Woodward
Guymon
FORT SMITH
OKLAHOMA CITY
TULSA
KANSAS
MISSOURI
ARKANSAS
TEXAS
COLORADO
NEW MEXICO
CIMARRON
TEXAS
BEAVER
HARPER
WOODS
ALFALFA
GRANT
KAY
OSAGE
WASHINGTON
NOWATA
CRAIG
OTTAWA
DELAWARE
MAYES
ROGERS
CHEROKEE
ADAIR
SEQUOYAH
WAGONER
MUSKOGEE
OKMULGEE
CREEK
PAWNEE
NOBLE
GARFIELD
MAJOR
WOODWARD
ELLIS
DEWEY
BLAINE
KINGFISHER
LOGAN
PAYNE
LINCOLN
OKLAHOMA
CANADIAN
CUSTER
ROGER MILLS
BECKHAM
WASHITA
CADDO
GRADY
McCLAIN
CLEVELAND
POTTAWATOMIE
SEMINOLE
OKFUSKEE
McINTOSH
HASKELL
LE FLORE
LATIMER
PITTSBURG
HUGHES
PONTOTOC
COAL
ATOKA
PUSHMATAHA
McCURTAIN
CHOCTAW
BRYAN
JOHNSTON
MARSHALL
MURRAY
GARVIN
CARTER
LOVE
STEPHENS
JEFFERSON
COMANCHE
COTTON
TILLMAN
KIOWA
GREER
JACKSON
HARMON
CRAWFORD
SEBASTIAN
FRANKLIN
38°
37°
36°
35°
34°
33°
94°
95°
96°
97°
98°
99°
100°
101°
102°
103°

CHICKASHA

CHICKASHA NEWS (WED)
411 W Chickasha Ave, Chickasha, OK, 73018-2505, Grady, USA; disp adv e-mail advertising@chickashanews.com; class adv e-mail classifieds@chickashanews.com; ed e-mail chickashaeditor@gmail.com; web site http://www.chickashanews.com
Group: Community Newspaper Holdings, Inc.
Circ. Dir. .... Vonnie Clark
Adv. Mgr .... Lindsey Palesano
Ed. in Chief .... James Bright

CLAREMORE

THE PRYOR TIMES (TUES, THUR, SAT)
PO Box 248, Claremore, OK, 74018-0248, Mayes, USA; gen tel (918) 825-3292; gen fax (918) 825-1965; disp adv e-mail amccurry@swbell.net; class adv e-mail classifieds@swbell.net; ed e-mail cbaron@pryordailytimes.com; web site www.pryordailytimes.com
Circulation: 3,787pd,; Sworn/Estimate/Non-Audited
Advertising rate: Open inch rate $13.66
Group: Community Newspaper Holdings, Inc.
Digital Platform - Mobile: Apple, Android, Blackberry
Digital Platform - Tablet: Apple iOS, Android, Blackberry Tablet OS
Pub. .... Carolyn Ashford
Adv. Dir. .... Ara McCurry
Class. Rep. .... Ginny Free
Bus. Mgr .... Beth Spaulding
Ed .... Cydney Baron
Mechanical Specifications: Type page 16 1/2 x 21; E - 6 cols, 2, 1/8 between; A - 6 cols, 2, 1/8 between; C - 8 cols, 2 1/16, 1/8 between.
Delivery Method: Mail, Newsstand, Racks
Areas Served: Mayes County

CLEVELAND

THE CLEVELAND AMERICAN (WED)
212 S Broadway St, Cleveland, OK, 74020-4617, Pawnee, USA; gen tel (918) 358-2553; gen fax (918) 358-2182; disp adv e-mail advertising@theclevelandamerican.com; ed e-mail news@theclevelandamerican.com; web site http://theclevelandamerican.com
Circulation: 2,150pd,; Sworn/Estimate/Non-Audited
Advertising rate: Open inch rate $5.00
Established: 1919
Pub./Ed. .... Rusty Ferguson
Adv. Dir .... Caleb Head
Mechanical Specifications: Type page 13 x 21; E - 6 cols, 2, 1/6 between; A - 6 cols, 2, 1/6 between; C - 8 cols, 2, 1/6 between.
Delivery Method: Mail, Newsstand
Areas Served: Cleveland

COALGATE

THE COALGATE RECORD-REGISTER (WED)
602 E Lafayette Ave, Coalgate, OK, 74538-4018, Coal, USA; gen tel (580) 927-2355; gen fax (580) 927-3800; disp adv e-mail helen@coalgaterecordregister.com; ed e-mail coalgaterec@aol.com; web site www.coalgaterecordregister.com
Circulation: 1,800pd,; Sworn/Estimate/Non-Audited
Advertising rate: Open inch rate $4.00
Established: 1988
Pub. .... Dayna Robinson
Adv. Mgr. .... Helen Langdon
Ed. .... Bill Robinson
Delivery Method: Mail, Newsstand
Areas Served: Coalgate County

COMANCHE

COMANCHE TIMES (THUR)
513 Hillery Rd Ste A, Suite A, Comanche, OK, 73529-1200, Stephens, USA; gen tel (580) 439-6500; gen fax (580) 439-6500; ed e-mail comanchetimes@pldi.net; web site http://comanchetimes.weebly.com/
Circulation: 1,100pd, 35fr; USPS
Advertising rate: Open inch rate $4.95
Established: 1992
Ed. .... Steve Bolton
Delivery Method: Mail, Racks
Areas Served: Stephens County

CORDELL

THE CORDELL BEACON (WED)
115 E Main St, Cordell, OK, 73632-4897, Washita, USA; gen tel (580) 832-3333; gen fax (580) 832-3335; disp adv e-mail thebeacon@cordellbeacon.com; web site www.cordellbeacon.com
Circulation: 3,000pd,; Sworn/Estimate/Non-Audited
Advertising rate: Open inch rate $5.95 (as of Jan. 1, 2017)
Established: 1897
Circ. Mgr. .... Cindy Banks
Ed. .... Zonelle Cox Rainbolt
Penelope Gibbons
Vicki Salley
Mary Anderson
Mechanical Specifications: Type page 12 31/32 x 21 1/2; E - 6 cols, 2 1/16, 1/6 between; A - 6 cols, 2 1/16, 1/6 between; C - 6 cols, 2 1/16, 1/6 between.Equipment & Software: Hardware — APP/Mac; Software — InDesign, Photoshop
Delivery Method: Mail, Newsstand, Racks
Areas Served: 73632

CUSHING

CUSHING CITIZEN (WED, SAT)
202 N Harrison Ave, Cushing, OK, 74023-3302, Payne, USA; gen tel (918) 285-5555; adv tel (918) 223-6566; ed tel (918) 285-5555; gen fax (918) 285-5556; adv fax (918) 285-5556; ed fax (918) 285-5556; disp adv e-mail publisher@cushingcitizen.com; class adv e-mail ads@cushingcitizen.com; ed e-mail editor@cushingcitizen.com; web site www.cushingcitizen.com
Circulation: 2,300pd, 4,500fr; Sworn/Estimate/Non-Audited
Advertising rate: Open inch rate $10.20
Established: 1895
Digital Platform - Mobile: Apple
Digital Platform - Tablet: Apple iOS
Ed. .... Jim Perry
Owner/Pub. .... David Reid
Graphics .... Chris Reid
Accounting .... Myra Reid
Receptionist .... Crissy Kindley
Mechanical Specifications: 1 col - 1.7778"
2 col - 3.7222"
3 col - 5.6667"
4 col - 7.6111"
5 col - 9.5556"
6 col - 11.5"
Delivery Method: Mail, Newsstand, Racks
Areas Served: 74023

CYRIL

THE CYRIL NEWS (THUR)
815 W Windle Ave, Cyril, OK, 73029-2900, Caddo, USA; gen tel (405) 933-2356; adv tel (405) 933-2356; ed tel (405) 933-2356; gen fax (580) 464-2443; ed e-mail cyrilnews@tds.net
Circulation: 800pd, 38fr; Sworn/Estimate/Non-Audited
Advertising rate: Open inch rate $4.00
Established: 1956
Owner/Ed. .... Robbie Snider
Delivery Method: Mail, Newsstand
Areas Served: Caddo County

DAVIS

THE DAVIS NEWS (WED)
400 E Main St, Davis, OK, 73030-1908, Murray, USA; gen tel (580) 369-2807; gen fax (580) 369-2807; ed e-mail davispaper@sbcglobal.net; web site www.davisnewspaper.net
Circulation: 1,500pd, 39fr; Sworn/Estimate/Non-Audited
Advertising rate: Open inch rate $4.75
Established: 1894
Pub./Ed. .... Sharon R. Chadwick
Mechanical Specifications: Type page 11 5/8 x 21 1/2; E - 6 cols, 1 13/16, 1/16 between; A - 6 cols, 1 13/16, 1/16 between; C - 6 cols, 1 13/16, 1/16 between.
Delivery Method: Mail, Newsstand, Racks
Areas Served: 73030

DRUMRIGHT

DRUMRIGHT GUSHER (WED)
129 E Broadway St, Drumright, OK, 74030-3801, Creek, USA; gen tel (918) 352-2284; disp adv e-mail ads@drumrightgusher.com; ed e-mail pub@drumrightgusher.com, news@drumrightgusher.com; web site Drumright Gusher
Circulation: 1,192pd,; Sworn/Estimate/Non-Audited
Advertising rate: Open inch rate $5.60
Established: 1989
Pub./Ed. .... Barbara Vice
Mechanical Specifications: Type page 11 x 21; E - 6 cols, 2, 1/6 between; A - 6 cols, 2, 1/6 between; C - 6 cols, 2, 1/6 between.Equipment & Software: Hardware — PCs, HP/Scanner; Software — Microsoft/Windows XP, Adobe InDesign, Adobe/Photoshop CS3
Delivery Method: Mail, Racks
Areas Served: 74030, 74023, 74052, 74068

EDMOND

THE EDMOND SUN (TUES, SAT)
123 S Broadway, Edmond, OK, 73034-3899, Oklahoma, USA; gen tel (405) 341-2121; adv tel (405) 341-2121 x 135; ed tel (405) 341-2121 x 110; gen fax (405) 340-7363; disp adv e-mail aburger@edmondsun.com; class adv e-mail terrib@edmondsun.com; ed e-mail sbrackett@edmondsun.com; web site www.edmondsun.com
Circulation: 3,540pd,; VAC
Advertising rate: Open inch rate $15.55
Established: 1889
Group: McNaughton Newspapers
Community Newspaper Holdings, Inc.
Pub. .... Karen Ediger
Gen. Mgr. .... Lance Moler
Classi. Adv. .... Terri Bohanan
Sales .... Allison Burger
Mechanical Specifications: Type page 13 x 21 1/2; E - 6 cols, 2, 1/8 between; A - 6 cols, 2, 1/8 between; C - 9 cols, 2, 1/8 between.
Areas Served: 73083

EL RENO

EL RENO TRIBUNE (WED, SUN)
102 E Wade St, El Reno, OK, 73036-2742, Canadian, USA; gen tel (405) 262-5180; gen fax (405) 262-3541; ed e-mail webmaster@elrenotribune.com; web site www.elrenotribune.com
Circulation: 5,500pd,; Sworn/Estimate/Non-Audited
Advertising rate: Open inch rate $5.50
Ed. .... Ray T. Dyer
Delivery Method: Mail, Racks

EUFAULA

INDIAN JOURNAL (THUR)
109 S Main St, Eufaula, OK, 74432-2875, McIntosh, USA; gen tel (918) 689-2191; gen fax (918) 689-2377; ed e-mail ijdemolegals@bigbasinllc.com; web site http://www.eufaula-indianjournal.com/site/
Circulation: 3,600pd,; Sworn/Estimate/Non-Audited
Advertising rate: Open inch rate $9.00
Ed. .... Donna Pearce

FAIRLAND

THE AMERICAN (THUR)
7 N Main St, Fairland, OK, 74343-4744, Ottawa, USA; gen tel (918) 676-3484; gen fax (918) 256-7100; disp adv e-mail vdj@cableone.net; ed e-mail nowatastarl@sbcglobal.net; web site www.aftonamerican.com
Circulation: 1,050pd, 20fr; Sworn/Estimate/Non-Audited
Advertising rate: Open inch rate $16.39
Established: 1906
Gen Mgr. .... John Link
Pub .... Phillp Reid
Ed .... Becky Clark
Areas Served: Ottawa County

FAIRVIEW

FAIRVIEW REPUBLICAN (THUR)
112 N Main St, Fairview, OK, 73737-1621, Major, USA; gen tel (580) 227-4439; gen fax (580) 227-4430; disp adv e-mail ads@fairviewrepublican.com; ed e-mail editor@fairviewrepublican.com; web site www.fairviewrepublican.com
Circulation: 2,850pd, 45fr; Sworn/Estimate/Non-Audited
Advertising rate: Open inch rate $6.50
Adv. Mgr. .... Jo Hammer
Ed. .... Hoby Hammer
Mechanical Specifications: Type page 13 x 21; E - 6 cols, 2 1/4, between; A - 6 cols, 2 1/4, between; C - 6 cols, 2 1/4, between.Equipment & Software: Hardware — APP/Mac; Software — Adobe/PageMaker 6.52.

FLETCHER

FLETCHER HERALD (THUR)
203 W Cole Ave, Fletcher, OK, 73541-9462, Comanche, USA; gen tel (580) 549-6045; gen fax (580) 549-4443; ed e-mail lfletcherherald@aol.com
Circulation: 950pd,; Sworn/Estimate/Non-Audited
Advertising rate: Open inch rate $4.00
Established: 1912
Owner/Pub. .... Lynn Moon
Areas Served: Comanche County

FREDERICK

FREDERICK PRESS-LEADER (WED, SUN)
102 S Main St, Frederick, OK, 73542-5431, Tillman, USA; gen tel (580) 335-2188; gen fax (580) 335-2047; disp adv e-mail jgrice@civitasmedia.com; ed e-mail press@pldi.net; web site www.press-leader.com
Circulation: 1,000pd,; Sworn/Estimate/Non-Audited
Advertising rate: Open inch rate $8.25
Established: 1904
Adv. Mgr. .... Jennifer Grice
Pub. .... Bill Murphy
Mng. Ed. .... Ray Wallace
Mechanical Specifications: Type page 13 x 21 1/2; E - 6 cols, 2 1/16, 1/8 between; A - 6 cols, 2 1/16, 1/8 between; C - 6 cols, 2 1/16, 1/8 between.Equipment & Software: Hardware — 3-APP/Mac II, 5-APP/Power Mac G3;

Software — Baseview.
Areas Served: 73542, 73530, 73570

FREEDOM

THE FREEDOM CALL (THUR)

1575 Greer Rd, Freedom, OK, 73842, Woods, USA; gen tel (580) 621-3578; gen fax (580) 621-3472; ed e-mail freedomcall@pldi.net
Circulation: 500pd,; Sworn/Estimate/Non-Audited
Advertising rate: Open inch rate $4.00
Established: 1959
Ed. .... Donna Hodgson
Areas Served: Woods County

GARBER

GARBER-BILLINGS NEWS (THUR)

516 Main St, Garber, OK, 73738, Garfield, USA; gen tel (580) 863-2240; gen fax 5808632240; ed e-mail gbnews@pldi.net
Circulation: 700pd,; Sworn/Estimate/Non-Audited
Advertising rate: Open inch rate $4.00
Established: 1899
Ed. .... Lacey Deeds
Delivery Method: Mail, Newsstand
Areas Served: Garfield and Noble County

GEARY

GEARY STAR (THUR)

116 S Broadway, Geary, OK, 73040-2409, Blaine, USA; gen tel (405) 884-2476; gen fax (580) 623-4925; disp adv e-mail ads@TheGearyStar.com; class adv e-mail ads@watongarepublican.com; ed e-mail Editor@TheGearyStar.com; web site http://www.thegearystar.com
Circulation: 1,250pd,; Sworn/Estimate/Non-Audited
Advertising rate: Open inch rate $3.36
Ed .... Eric Warsinskey
Adv Rep .... Kimberly Jenkins

GROVE

GROVE SUN (TUES, FRI)

16 W 3rd St, Grove, OK, 74344-3223, Delaware, USA; gen tel (918) 786-2228; gen fax (918) 786-2156; disp adv e-mail khutchison@grovesun.com; class adv e-mail sedwards@grovesun.com; ed e-mail khutson@grovesun.com; web site www.grandlakenews.com
Circulation: 2,800pd,; Sworn/Estimate/Non-Audited
Advertising rate: Open inch rate $8.50
Established: 1898
Digital Platform - Mobile: Apple
Digital Platform - Tablet: Apple iOS
Pub .... Cheryl Franklin
Mng. Ed .... Kaylea Hutson
Ed .... Kaylea Hutson-Miller
Circ. Mgr .... Dylan Elliott
Delivery Method: Mail, Newsstand, Racks
Areas Served: 74344, 74346, 74370, 74343, 74331

GUTHRIE

GUTHRIE NEWS LEADER (TUES, THUR, SAT)

PO Box 879, Guthrie, OK, 73044-0879, Logan, USA; gen tel (405) 282-2222; gen fax (405) 282-7378 ; disp adv e-mail gnlsales@guthrienewsleader.net; class adv e-mail gnlnews@yahoo.com; ed e-mail publisher@guthrienewsleader.net; web site http://www.guthrienewsleader.net
Circulation: 5,649pd,; Sworn/Estimate/Non-Audited
Advertising rate: Open inch rate $9.30
Established: 1898
Group: American Hometown Publishing
Adv. Dir .... Mona Robinson
Pub .... Rochelle Stidham
Office Mgr .... Kala Plagg
Mechanical Specifications: Type page 13 x 21 1/2; E - 6 cols, 2 1/8, 1/6 between; A - 6 cols, 2 1/8, 1/6 between; C - 6 cols, 2 1/8, 1/6 between.

HEALDTON

THE HEALDTON HERALD (THUR)

11207 Highway 76, Healdton, OK, 73438-1725, Carter, USA; gen tel (580) 229-0147; gen fax (580) 229-0132; ed e-mail hherald@cablerocket.com
Circulation: 1,500pd, 21fr; Sworn/Estimate/Non-Audited
Advertising rate: Open inch rate $4.30
Established: 1917
Ed .... Cindy Dickerson
Mechanical Specifications: Type page 11 5/8 x 21; E - 6 cols, 1 5/6, 1/8 between; A - 6 cols, 1 5/6, 1/8 between; C - 6 cols, 1 5/6, 1/8 between.Equipment & Software: Hardware — APP/Mac; Software — Adobe/PageMaker 6.5+, Adobe/Photoshop LE 4.0.
Delivery Method: Mail, Newsstand, Racks
Areas Served: Carter County

WILSON POST-DEMOCRAT (THUR)

11204 Highway 76, Healdton, OK, 73438-1724, Carter, USA; gen tel (580) 229-0147; gen fax (580) 229-0132; ed e-mail healdton-herald@att.net
Circulation: 800pd, 10fr; Sworn/Estimate/Non-Audited
Advertising rate: Open inch rate $3.75
Established: 1917
Pub .... Christi Blakemore
Ed. .... Cindy Dickerson
Mechanical Specifications: Type page 11 3/5 x 21; E - 6 cols, 1 5/6, 1/8 between; A - 6 cols, 1 5/6, 1/5 between; C - 6 cols, 1 5/6, 1/8 between.Equipment & Software: Hardware — APP/Mac; Software — Adobe/PageMaker 6.5 +, Adobe/Photoshop LE 4.0.
Delivery Method: Mail, Newsstand

HEAVENER

THE HEAVENER LEDGER (WED)

507 E 1st St, Heavener, OK, 74937-3203, LeFlore, USA; gen tel (918) 653-2425; adv tel (918) 653-2425; ed tel (918) 653-2425; gen fax (918) 653-7305; disp adv e-mail heavenerledger@windstream.net; class adv e-mail heavenerledgerchris@windstream.net; web site heavenerledger.com - 20,000(views) 7,500(visitors)
Circulation: 1,200pd,; Sworn/Estimate/Non-Audited
Advertising rate: Open inch rate $5.00
Established: 1904
Group: Heavener Ledger, Inc.
Legals .... Karen Toney
Classified .... Chris Lessley
Delivery Method: Mail, Newsstand, Racks
Areas Served: Le Flore County

HENNESSEY

THE HENNESSEY CLIPPER (THUR)

117 S Main St, Hennessey, OK, 73742-1402, Kingfisher, USA; gen tel (405) 853-4888; gen fax (405) 853-4890; disp adv e-mail tracie@hennesseyclipper.com; class adv e-mail linda@hennesseyclipper.com; ed e-mail barb@hennesseyclipper.com; web site www.hennesseyclipper.com
Circulation: 1,650pd, 140fr; Sworn/Estimate/Non-Audited
Advertising rate: Open inch rate $5.50
Established: 1890
Ed. .... Barbara A. Walter
Pub .... Maria Laubach
Areas Served: Kingfisher County

HENRYETTA

HENRYETTA FREE-LANCE (WED, SUN)

302 W Main St, Henryetta, OK, 74437-4240, Okmulgee, USA; gen tel (918) 652-3311; gen fax (918) 652-7347; disp adv e-mail advertising@henryettanewspaper.com; class adv e-mail hflclassified@bigbasinllc.com; ed e-mail news@henryettanewspaper.com; web site http://www.henryettafree-lance.com/
Circulation: 2,000pd,; Sworn/Estimate/Non-Audited
Advertising rate: Open inch rate $12.50
Established: 1901
Adv. Dir .... Stephanie Grist
Mng. Ed .... Valerie RiceEquipment & Software: Hardware — Software ½ QPS/QuarkXPress, Baseview/NewsEdit.; Software — QPS/QuarkXPress, Baseview/NewsEdit.
Areas Served: 74437

HINTON

HINTON RECORD (WED)

116 W MAIN ST, Hinton, OK, 73047, Caddo, USA; gen tel (405) 542-6644; gen fax (405) 542-3120; disp adv e-mail ads@HintonRecord.com; ed e-mail Editor@HintonRecord.com; web site www.hintonrecord.com
Circulation: 1,025pd, 6fr; Sworn/Estimate/Non-Audited
Advertising rate: Open inch rate $3.40
Ed .... Eric Warsinskey
Adv. Rep .... Kimberly Jenkins
Delivery Method: Mail, Newsstand
Areas Served: Caddo County (Oklahoma) Blaine County (Oklahoma)

HOLDENVILLE

HOLDENVILLE TRIBUNE (WED)

114 N Broadway St, Holdenville, OK, 74848-3248, Hughes, USA; gen tel (405) 379-5184; disp adv e-mail bill@holdenvilletribune.com; ed e-mail dayna@holdenvilletribune.com; web site www.holdenvilletribune.com
Advertising rate: Open inch rate $4.00
Pub./Ed .... Dayna Robinson
Areas Served: Hughes County

HOLLIS

THE HOLLIS NEWS (THUR)

204 E Vivian St, Hollis, OK, 73550-1840, Harmon, USA; gen tel (580) 688-3376; gen fax (580) 688-2261; ed e-mail hollisnews@pldi.net; web site http://redriversun.com/index117.htm
Circulation: 1,200pd,; Sworn/Estimate/Non-Audited
Advertising rate: Open inch rate $3.75
Established: 1938
Group: Blackburn Media Group
Ed. .... Everett Brazil
Delivery Method: Mail, Newsstand, Carrier, Racks
Areas Served: Harmon County

HOMINY

THE HOMINY NEWS-PROGRESS (WED)

115 W Main St, Hominy, OK, 74035-1031, Osage, USA; gen tel (918) 885-2101; adv tel (918) 885-2101; ed tel (918) 885-2101; gen fax (918) 885-4596; adv fax (918) 885-4596; ed fax (918) 885-4596; disp adv e-mail hominynews2@gmail.com; class adv e-mail hominyews2@gmail.com; ed e-mail same; web site None
Circulation: 1,400pd,; USPS
Advertising rate: Open inch rate $5.00
Established: 1918
Group: American Chief Co.
Digital Platform - Mobile: Apple
Digital Platform - Tablet: Apple iOS
Gen Mgr .... Vickie Denny
Office Mgr .... Treca Carter
Mechanical Specifications: Type page 10.625 x21 1/2 - 6 cols
Delivery Method: Mail, Newsstand, Racks
Areas Served: Hominy, Osage County and Pawnee County

HUGO

HUGO NEWS (TUES, FRI)

128 E Jackson St, Hugo, OK, 74743-4082, Choctaw, USA; gen tel (580) 326-3311; adv tel (580) 326-3311; ed tel (580) 326-3311; gen fax (580) 326-6397; adv fax (580) 326-6397; ed fax (580) 326-6397; disp adv e-mail linda@hugonews.com; class adv e-mail hdnadv@sbcglobal.net; ed e-mail hugonews@sbcglobal.net; web site www.hugonews.com
Circulation: 2,600pd,; Sworn/Estimate/Non-Audited
Advertising rate: Open inch rate $6.50
Established: 1907
Group: Hugo Publishing Co.
VP, Acct .... Judy Stamper
Adv. Dir .... Linda Packard
Pres./Pub./Ed .... Stan Stamper
Prodn. Mgr. .... Homer Garrison
Ed .... Krystle Taylor
Mechanical Specifications: Type page 13 x 21 1/2; E - 6 cols, 2 1/16, 1/8 between; A - 6 cols, 2 1/16, 1/8 between; C - 6 cols, 2 1/16, 1/8 between.
Delivery Method: Mail, Newsstand, Racks
Areas Served: Choctaw County (OK)

IDABEL

BROKEN BOW NEWS (WED, SUN)

107 S Central Ave, Idabel, OK, 74745-4847, McCurtain, USA; gen tel (580) 584-6210; gen fax (580) 286-2208; disp adv e-mail ads@mccurtain.com; ed e-mail paper@mccurtain.com; web site www.mccurtain.com
Circulation: 1,232pd,; Sworn/Estimate/Non-Audited
Advertising rate: Open inch rate $3.80
Pub .... Bruce Willingham
Adv. Dir .... Hallee Deramus

JAY

DELAWARE COUNTY JOURNAL (WED)

254 N 5TH ST, Jay, OK, 74346, Delaware, USA; gen tel (918) 253-4322; gen fax (918) 253-4380; disp adv e-mail khutchison@grovesun.com; class adv e-mail sedwards@grovesun.com; ed e-mail khutson@grovesun.com; web site grandlakenews.com
Circulation: 2,200pd, 30fr; Sworn/Estimate/Non-Audited
Advertising rate: Open inch rate $6.50
Established: 1922
Ed. .... Janet Barber
Pub .... Cheryl Franklin
Ed .... Kaylea Hutson-Miller
Circ. Mgr .... Dylan Elliott
Delivery Method: Mail, Newsstand, Racks
Areas Served: Delaware

KINGFISHER

THE KINGFISHER TIMES & FREE PRESS (WED, SUN)

323 N Main St, Kingfisher, OK, 73750-2749, Kingfisher, USA; gen tel (405) 375-3220; gen fax (405) 375-3222; disp adv e-mail kfrtimesads@pldi.net; class adv e-mail kfrnews@pldi.net; ed e-mail editor@kingfisherpress.net; web site www.kingfisherpress.net
Circulation: 3,750pd, 50fr; USPS

Advertising rate: Open inch rate $5.95
Established: 1889
Pub. Emeritus ....Gary Reid
Pub...Barry Reid
Sr. Ed. ....Christine Reid
Mng./Sports Ed......................Michael Swisher
Ad Mng. ....Robin Johnston
Delivery Method: Mail, Newsstand, Racks
Areas Served: 73750

KONAWA

KONAWA LEADER (THUR)

102 N Broadway St, Konawa, OK, 74849-2232, Seminole, USA; gen tel (580) 925-3187; gen fax (580) 925-3187; ed e-mail konawaleader@sbcglobal.net; web site http://konawa.net
Circulation: 1,500pd,; Sworn/Estimate/Non-Audited
Advertising rate: Open inch rate $4.16
Pub..Stu Phillips

LINDSAY

LINDSAY NEWS (THUR)

117 S Main St, Lindsay, OK, 73052-5631, Garvin, USA; gen tel (405) 756-4045; gen fax (405) 756-2729; disp adv e-mail dustin@cableprinting.com; class adv e-mail dustin@cableprinting.com; ed e-mail gina@cableprinting.com; web site www.cableprinting.com
Circulation: 2,500pd,; Sworn/Estimate/Non-Audited
Advertising rate: Open inch rate $3.95
Established: 1902
Pub...Darrell Cable
Ed. ....Gina Cable
Mechanical Specifications: Type page 13 x 21; E - 6 cols, 2, between; A - 6 cols, 2, between; C - 6 cols, 2, between.
Areas Served: Garvin County

MADILL

MADILL RECORD (THUR)

211 Plaza, Madill, OK, 73446-2250, Marshall, USA; gen tel (580) 795-3355; gen fax (580) 795-3530; disp adv e-mail madillrecord@sbcglobal.net; ed e-mail recordeditorial@sbcglobal.net; web site www.madillrecord.net
Circulation: 3,900pd, 50fr; Sworn/Estimate/Non-Audited
Advertising rate: Open inch rate $7.00
Established: 1895
Group: Cordell Beacon Co. Inc.
Digital Platform - Mobile: Apple, Android, Windows
Digital Platform - Tablet: Apple iOS, Android, Windows 7, Blackberry Tablet OS, Nook, Kindle Fire
General Manager.......................Tiffani Stewart
Advertising Specialist ....Lori Robinson
Advertising Sales........................Janice Jurden
Reporter ....Tina Firquain
Mechanical Specifications: Type page 11.625 x 21; E - 6 cols, 1.833, 1/8 between; A - 6 cols, 1.833, 1/8 between; C - 8 cols, 1.344, 1/8 between.Equipment & Software: Hardware — IBM, APP/Mac, APP/Mac; Presses — 9-HI; Software — Creative Suites 5.5
Areas Served: Marshall County

MANGUM

THE MANGUM STAR-NEWS (THUR)

121 S Oklahoma Ave, Mangum, OK, 73554-4274, Greer, USA; gen tel (580) 782-3321; gen fax (580) 782-2198; ed e-mail mangumnews@gmail.com; web site www.mangumstarnews.net
Circulation: 2,000pd,; Sworn/Estimate/Non-Audited
Advertising rate: Open inch rate $4.50
Established: 1887
Ed. ....Casey Paxton
Mechanical Specifications: Type page 13 x 21 1/2.
Areas Served: Greer County

MARIETTA

MARIETTA MONITOR (FRI)

104 W Main St, Marietta, OK, 73448-2832, Love, USA; gen tel (580) 276-3255; gen fax (580) 276-2118; ed e-mail monitorok@sbcglobal.net; web site https://www.facebook.com/mariettamonitor.newspaper/
Circulation: 3,000pd, 30fr; Sworn/Estimate/Non-Audited
Advertising rate: Open inch rate $4.25
Established: 1895
Pub..Willis Choate
Ed. ....Norene Choate
Delivery Method: Mail
Areas Served: Marietta & Love County

MARLOW

THE MARLOW REVIEW (THUR)

316 W Main St, Marlow, OK, 73055-2442, Stephens, USA; gen tel (580) 658-6657; gen fax (580) 658-6659; disp adv e-mail advertising@marlowreview.com; class adv e-mail classifieds@marlowreview.com; ed e-mail news@marlowreview.com; web site www.marlowreview.com
Circulation: 3,700pd,; Sworn/Estimate/Non-Audited
Advertising rate: Open inch rate $6.70
Established: 1892
Ed. ....Todd Brooks
Pub...Judy Keller
Mechanical Specifications: 1 col = 1.8194"
2 col = 3.8056"
3 col = 5.7917"
4 col = 7.7778"
5 col = 9.7639"
6 col = 11.75"Equipment & Software: ; Software — InDesign, Interlink, MS Office
Delivery Method: Mail, Newsstand, Racks
Areas Served: Stephens County

MAYSVILLE

THE GARVIN COUNTY NEWS STAR (FRI)

402 Williams, Maysville, OK, 73057-3683, Garvin, USA; gen tel (405) 867-4457; gen fax (405) 867-5115; disp adv e-mail news@gcnews-star.com; class adv e-mail news@gcnews-star.com; ed e-mail publisher@gcnews-star.com; web site www.gcnews-star.com
Circulation: 1,800pd,; Sworn/Estimate/Non-Audited
Advertising rate: Open inch rate $5.50
Established: 2008
Co-Pub./Co-Own./Ed.......................Jeff Shultz
Co-Pub./Co-Own....................... Nanette Shultz
Office Mgr. ....Judy Baker
Office worker .... Tessa Widmer
Mechanical Specifications: Type page 13 x 21; E - 6 cols, 2 1/24, 1/6 between; A - 6 cols, 2 1/24, 1/6 between; C - 6 cols, 2 1/24, 1/6 between.
Delivery Method: Mail, Racks
Areas Served: Garvin County

MEDFORD

THE MEDFORD PATRIOT-STAR AND GRANT COUNTY JOURNAL (WED)

116 12 W CHEROKEE ST, Medford, OK, 73759, USA; gen tel (580) 395-2212; disp adv e-mail patriotstar@att.net; class adv e-mail patriotstar@att.net; web site
Circulation: 1,500pd, 0fr; Sworn/Estimate/Non-Audited
Advertising rate: Open inch rate $7.00
Established: 1896
Ed. .... Ken Kiser
Mechanical Specifications: Type page 14 15/16 x 21 1/2.Equipment & Software: Hardware — Gateway, Mk; Software — Adobe/Photoshop 5.0, WordPerfect 9.0.
Delivery Method: Mail, Newsstand, Racks
Areas Served: Grant County, Oklahoma

MIDWEST CITY

MIDWEST CITY BEACON (FRI)

1500 S Midwest Blvd, Ste 202, Midwest City, OK, 73110-4944, Oklahoma, USA; gen tel (405) 455-1110; adv tel (405) 376-6688; ed tel (405) 455-1110; gen fax (405) 455-1126; disp adv e-mail ads@midwestcitybeacon.com; class adv e-mail ads@midwestcitybeacon.com; ed e-mail news@midwestcitybeacon.com; web site www.midwestcitybeacon.com
Circulation: 1,500pd, 0fr; Sworn/Estimate/Non-Audited
Advertising rate: Open inch rate $24.47
Established: 1936
Group: Mustang Times LLC
Mng Ed .... Jeff Harrison
Areas Served: Oklahoma County

MOORELAND

MOORELAND LEADER (THUR)

202 N Main St, Mooreland, OK, 73852-9217, Woodward, USA; gen tel (580) 994-5410; gen fax (580) 994-5409; ed e-mail leader2@pldi.net; web site http://www.moorelandleader.com
Circulation: 800pd, 45fr; Sworn/Estimate/Non-Audited
Advertising rate: Open inch rate $3.75
Established: 1903
Ed. ....Tim Schnoebelen
Mechanical Specifications: Type page 13 x 21; E - 6 cols, 2, between; A - 6 cols, 2, between; C - 6 cols, 2, between.Equipment & Software: Hardware — APP/Mac IIsi, APP/Mac SE 30, APP/Power Mac 7500-100; Presses — 4-KP/News King.
Areas Served: Woodward County

MORRIS

THE MORRIS NEWS (THUR)

421 E Ozark St Ste A, Suite A, Morris, OK, 74445-4853, Okmulgee, USA; gen tel (918) 733-4898; gen fax (888) 701-3188; ed e-mail morrisnews@windstream.net; web site www.themorrisnews.wordpress.com/
Circulation: 800pd,; Sworn/Estimate/Non-Audited
Advertising rate: Open inch rate $4.00
Established: 1910
Ed. .... Herman L. Thompson
Pub.. Patsy Thompson
Mechanical Specifications: Type page 13 x 21 1/2; E - 6 cols, 2 1/12, between; A - 6 cols, 2 1/12, between; C - 6 cols, 2 1/12, between.
Areas Served: Okmulgee County

MOUNTAIN VIEW

THE MOUNTAIN VIEW NEWS (THUR)

319 Main St, Mountain View, OK, 73062-9557, Kiowa, USA; gen tel (580) 347-2231; ed e-mail news@westok.net; web site http://www.themountainviewnews.com
Advertising rate: $5.70 per column inch
Co-Pub..Jyl Hobbs

MUSTANG

THE MUSTANG NEWS (THUR)

120 E Trade Center Ter Ste 102, Suite #102, Mustang, OK, 73064-4410, Canadian, USA; gen tel (405) 376-4571; gen fax (405) 376-5312; disp adv e-mail dsettle@mustangnews.info; class adv e-mail rlerma@mustangnews.info; ed e-mail vmiddleton@mustangnews.info; web site http://www.theyukonreview.com/mustang-news/
Circulation: 4,000pd,; Sworn/Estimate/Non-Audited
Advertising rate: Open inch rate $5.00
Established: 1982
Group: El Reno Tribune
Ed ....Victoria Middleton
Pub ....John Settle
Adv./Ops Dir.................................David Settle
Office Mgr. ....Andrea Griffin
Delivery Method: Mail, Newsstand, Racks
Areas Served: Canadian County

THE TUTTLE TIMES (THUR)

553 N Mustang Rd, Mustang, OK, 73064-7002, Canadian, USA; gen tel (405) 376-6688; gen fax (405) 376-3565; disp adv e-mail mustangpublisher@sbcglobal.net; ed e-mail editor@tuttletimes.com; web site www.mustangpaper.com/the-tuttle-times/
Circulation: 2,400pd, 40fr; Sworn/Estimate/Non-Audited
Advertising rate: Open inch rate $4.25
Established: 1905
Group: Community Newspaper Holdings, Inc.
Digital Platform - Mobile: Windows
Pub...Steven Kizzias
Circ. Mgr.....................................Angie Russell
Ed. ....Jeff Harrison
Mechanical Specifications: Type page 13 x 21; E - 6 cols, 2 1/16, between; A - 6 cols, 2 1/16, between; C - 6 cols, 2 1/16, between. Equipment & Software: Hardware — IBM; Presses — 6-G/Suburban; Software — Microsoft/Windows 95.
Delivery Method: Mail, Newsstand
Areas Served: Grady County

NEWCASTLE

NEWCASTLE PACER (THUR)

120 NE 2nd St Ste 102, Suite 102, Newcastle, OK, 73065-4185, McClain, USA; gen tel (405) 387-5277; gen fax (405) 387-9863; disp adv e-mail peg@newcastlepacer.com; ed e-mail darla@newcastlepacer.com; web site www.newcastlepacer.com
Circulation: 1,800pd, 72fr; Sworn/Estimate/Non-Audited
Advertising rate: Open inch rate $7.25
Established: 1978
Gen. Mgr. ....Clarence Wright
Ed ....Darla Welchel
Adv. Sales .... Peggy Brian
Areas Served: McClain County

NEWKIRK

THE NEWKIRK HERALD JOURNAL (THUR)

121 N Main St, Newkirk, OK, 74647-2217, Kay, USA; gen tel (580) 362-2140; gen fax (580) 362-2348; disp adv e-mail adv@newkirkherald.com; class adv e-mail class@newkirkherald.com; ed e-mail news@newkirkherald.com; web site www.newkirkherald.com
Circulation: 1,450pd, 100fr; Sworn/Estimate/Non-Audited
Advertising rate: Open inch rate $6.45
Ed./Pub. .... Scott Cloud
Mktg. Dir.....................................Dixie Colquhon
Class./Legal Dir...........................Cindy Daigle
Circ./Office Mgr. ....Theda Sheets
Mechanical Specifications: Type page 13 x 21 1/2; E - 6 cols, 2 1/8, 1/8 between; A - 6 cols, 2 1/8, 1/8 between; C - 8 cols, 1 1/2, 1/8 between.Equipment & Software: Hardware — APP/Mac; Software — Adobe/Photoshop 5.0, Adobe/PageMaker 6.5.
Areas Served: Kay County

NORMAN

MOORE AMERICAN (TUES)
215 E Comanche St, Norman, OK, 73069-6007, Cleveland, USA; gen tel (405) 321-1800; adv tel (405) 366-3504; ed tel (405) 366-3542; gen fax (405) 366-3516; disp adv e-mail tjgriffis@normantranscript.com; class adv e-mail rrasor@normantranscript.com; ed e-mail editor@normantranscript.com; web site www.mooreamerican.com
Circulation: 4,500pd, 13,000fr; Sworn/Estimate/Non-Audited
Advertising rate: Open inch rate $9.00
Group: Community Newspaper Holdings, Inc.
Pub....Mark Millsap
Ed....Shana Adkisson
Circ. Dir....Vonnie Clark
Bus. Mgr....Tammy Griffis
Prod. Mgr....Rob Rasor
Mechanical Specifications: Type page 13 x 21; E - 6 cols, 2, 1/8 between; A - 6 cols, 2, 1/8 between; C - 6 cols, 2, 1/8 between.Equipment & Software: Hardware — APP/Mac; Software — QPS/QuarkXPress.
Areas Served: Cleveland County

NOWATA

THE NOWATA STAR (WED)
126 E Cherokee Ave, Nowata, OK, 74048-2702, Nowata, USA; gen tel (918) 273-2446; gen fax (918) 273-0537; disp adv e-mail vdj@cableone.net; ed e-mail nowatastar@sbcglobal.net; web site http://www.nowatastaronline.com
Circulation: 2,800pd,; Sworn/Estimate/Non-Audited
Advertising rate: Open inch rate $7.50
Established: 1909
Advertising rep....Michelle Milner
Gen. Mgr....John Link
Pub....Phillip Red
Delivery Method: Mail, Newsstand
Areas Served: Nowata

OKEENE

OKEENE RECORD (THUR)
211 N Main St, Okeene, OK, 73763-9447, Blaine, USA; gen tel (580) 822-4401; adv tel (580) 822-4401; ed tel (580) 822-4401; gen fax (877) 420-6331; ed fax (877) 420-6331; disp adv e-mail bcpub@pldi.net; class adv e-mail bcpub@pldi.net; ed e-mail bcpub@pldi.net; web site www.okeenerecord.com
Circulation: 750pd,; Sworn/Estimate/Non-Audited
Advertising rate: Open inch rate $9.00
Established: 1918
Group: Trail Miller Co., LLC
Managing Editor....Toni Goforth
Delivery Method: Mail, Racks
Areas Served: Blaine County

OKEMAH

OKEMAH NEWS LEADER (THUR)
115 W Broadway St, Okemah, OK, 74859-2616, Okfuskee, USA; gen tel (918) 623-0123; adv tel (918) 623-0123; ed tel (918) 623-0123; gen fax (918) 623-1024; disp adv e-mail Ads@okemahnewsleader.com; web site www.okemahnewsleader.com
Circulation: 2,700pd, 22fr; Sworn/Estimate/Non-Audited
Advertising rate: Open inch rate $4.50
Established: 1921
Digital Platform - Mobile: Android, Blackberry
Pub./Ed....Lynn Thompson
Ed./Adv. Dir....Roger Thompson
Office Mgr....Kay Thompson
Reporter....Shakara Shepard
Pamela Thompson
Mechanical Specifications: Type page 13 x 21; E - 6 cols, 2, 1/6 between; A - 6 cols, 2, 1/6 between; C - 6 cols, 2, 1/6 between.Equipment & Software: Hardware — APP/Mac SE; Software — Microsoft/Word, Adobe/PageMaker.
Delivery Method: Mail, Newsstand, Carrier, Racks
Areas Served: Okfuskee County

OKLAHOMA CITY

OKCBIZ (MON)
3701 N Shartel Ave, Oklahoma City, OK, 73118-7102, Oklahoma, USA; gen tel (405) 605-6789; gen fax (405) 621-2909; disp adv e-mail cduane@okgazette.com; class adv e-mail svanhorn@okgazette.com; ed e-mail jchancellor@okgazette.com; web site www.okc.biz
Circulation: 789pd, 3,056fr; Sworn/Estimate/Non-Audited
Advertising rate: Open inch rate $68.50
CEO/Pres/Pub....Bill Bleakley
Mktg. Mgr....Kelsey Lowe
Adv. Dir....Christy Duane
Ed....Jennifer Chancellor
Circ. Mgr....Chad Bleakley
Areas Served: Oklahoma County

OKLAHOMA CITY FRIDAY (FRI)
10801 Quail Plaza Dr, Oklahoma City, OK, 73120-3118, Oklahoma, USA; gen tel (405) 755-3311; gen fax (405) 755-3315; disp adv e-mail lovina@okcfriday.com; class adv e-mail rebecca@okcfriday.com; ed e-mail rose@okcfriday.com; web site www.okcfriday.com
Circulation: 8,200pd, 100fr; Sworn/Estimate/Non-Audited
Advertising rate: Open inch rate $25.00
CEO/Pub....Vicki Gourley
Ed/Co-Pub....Rose Lane
Class./Legal Mgr....Rebecca Hall
Prod. Mgr....Jason Jewell
Circ. Mgr....Jennifer Clark
Adv. Sales....Lovina Morgan
Mechanical Specifications: Type page 13 1/8 x 21 1/2; E - 6 cols, 2 1/10, 1/6 between; A - 6 cols, 2 1/10, 1/6 between; C - 6 cols, 2 1/10, 1/6 between.Equipment & Software: Hardware — 14-PC; Presses — WPC/Web Leader; Software — QPS/QuarkXPress, Microsoft/Windows 98, Microsoft/Windows NT, Microsoft/Office 97.
Areas Served: 73112, 73118, 73116, 73120, 73132, 73162

THE CITY SENTINEL (THUR, MTHLY)
PO Box 60876, Oklahoma City, OK, 73146-0876, Oklahoma, USA; gen tel (405) 740-8687; disp adv e-mail sales@city-sentinel.com; ed e-mail news@city-sentinel; web site www.city-sentinel.com
Circulation: 10,000pd, 10,000fr; Sworn/Estimate/Non-Audited
Advertising rate: Open inch rate $12.50
Established: 2000
Digital Platform - Mobile: Windows
Pub./Ed....Patrick McGuigan
Creative. Dir....Vincent Lee
Reporter....Darla Shelden
Delivery Method: Racks
Areas Served: Oklahoma County

OOLOGAH

OOLOGAH LAKE LEADER (THUR)
109 S Maple St, Oologah, OK, 74053-3299, Rogers, USA; gen tel (918) 443-2428; gen fax (918) 443-2429; disp adv e-mail Carolyn.Estes@sbcglobal.net; class adv e-mail OologahInfo@sbcglobal.net; ed e-mail LakeLeader@sbcglobal.net; web site http://oologahonline.com/ - 15,000(views) 8,500(visitors)
Circulation: 2,700pd, 5,501fr; Sworn/Estimate/Non-Audited
Advertising rate: Open inch rate $6.50 (subject to change)
Established: 1982
Group: Oologah Lake Leader LLCEditions: (1)
Digital Platform - Mobile: Windows
Digital Platform - Tablet: Apple iOS, Android, Windows 7
Co-Pub./Gen. Mgr....Faith Wylie
Mktg. Dir....Carolyn Estes
Co-Pub./Ed....John Wylie
Mechanical Specifications: Type page 10 x 21 1/2, 6 col Equipment & Software: Hardware — PCs; Software — Adobe/PageMaker 6.5, Adobe/Photoshop 5.5.
Delivery Method: Mail, Newsstand, Racks
Areas Served: Northwest Rogers County and the Oologah-Talala School District, Oologah, Talala, Tacora Hills, Briarcliff, Canyon Oasis, parts of rural Claremore. All of 74053, 74080, 74017, 74018, 74019

OWASSO

OWASSO REPORTER (THUR)
202 E 2nd Ave Ste 101, Suite 101, Owasso, OK, 74055-3131, Tulsa, USA; gen tel (918) 272-1155; adv tel (918) 259-7527; ed tel (918) 272-1155 x 402; gen fax (918) 272-0642; disp adv e-mail Aeron.Taylor@owassoreporter.com; class adv e-mail Ashley.Roop@owassoreporter.com; ed e-mail art.haddaway@owassoreporter.com; web site www.owassoreporter.com - 48,393(views) 14,315(visitors)
Circulation: 3,934pd, 348fr; CVC
Advertising rate: 1/24 Pg $50.40; 1/16 Pg $88.20; 1/8 Pg $152.25
Established: 1964
Group: Community Publishers, Inc.
Pub....Mike Brown
Ed....Art Haddaway
Mktg....Aeron Taylor
Mechanical Specifications: Type page 11 3/4 x 21 1/2; E - 6 cols, 1 13/16, 1/6 between; A - 6 cols, 1 13/16, 1/6 between; C - 9 cols, 1 13/16, 1/6 between.Equipment & Software: Hardware — APP/Mac; Presses — G; Software — QPS/QuarkXPress 4.1.
Areas Served: Rogers, Tulsa County

PAULS VALLEY

PAULS VALLEY DEMOCRAT (TUES, THUR, SUN)
108 S Willow St, Pauls Valley, OK, 73075-3834, Garvin, USA; gen tel (405) 238-6464; gen fax (405) 238-3042; disp adv e-mail jdavenport@pvdemocrat.com; class adv e-mail charris@pvdemocrat.com; ed e-mail marie@pvdemocrat.com; web site www.paulsvalleydailydemocrat.com
Circulation: 2,950pd,; Sworn/Estimate/Non-Audited
Advertising rate: 1/8 Pg $101.25; 1/4 Pg $196.13; 1/2 Pg $377.25
Established: 1904
Group: Community Newspaper Holdings, Inc.
Class./Legal....Christy Harris
Circ....Sheila Johnson
Ed....Mike Arie
Gen. Mgr....Sara Fisher
Mechanical Specifications: Type page 13 1/2 x 21 1/2; E - 6 cols, 2 1/16, 1/8 between; A - 6 cols, 2 1/16, 1/8 between; C - 8 cols, 1 1/2, 1/8 between.
Delivery Method: Mail, Newsstand, Racks
Areas Served: 73075, 73074,73052,73057,7309 8,73433,74872

PAWHUSKA

PAWHUSKA JOURNAL-CAPITAL (WED)
1020 Lynn Ave, # A, Pawhuska, OK, 74056-3062, Osage, USA; gen tel (918) 287-1590; gen fax (918) 287-1804; disp adv e-mail jstrachan@examiner-enterprise.com; class adv e-mail classads@pawhuskajournalcapital.com; ed e-mail cday@examiner-enterprise.com; web site www.pawhuskajournalcapital.com
Circulation: 3,500pd,; Sworn/Estimate/Non-Audited
Advertising rate: Open inch rate $6.36
Established: 1867
Pub....Matthew Tranquill
Adv....Jeannie Strachan
Office Mgr....Tammy Green
Circ. Mgr....Robert Dye
Ed....Chris Day
Mechanical Specifications: Type page 11 7/10 x 21 1/2; A - 6 cols, 1 5/6, between; C - 9 cols, 1 1/6, between.
Areas Served: Osage County

PAWNEE

PAWNEE CHIEF (WED)
556 Illinois St, Pawnee, OK, 74058-2011, Pawnee, USA; gen tel (918) 762-2552; gen fax (918) 762-2554; ed e-mail news@pawneechief.net; web site http://pawneechief.net/
Circulation: 2,300pd, 101fr; Sworn/Estimate/Non-Audited
Advertising rate: Open inch rate $5.00
Established: 1941
Group: American Chief Co.
Pub./Ed....Vickie Denny
Mechanical Specifications: Type page 11 5/8 x 20 1/2; E - 6 cols, 1 4/5, between; A - 6 cols, 1 4/5, between; C - 6 cols, 1 4/5, between. Equipment & Software: Hardware — APP/Mac; Software — Microsoft/Works, Adobe/PageMaker.
Delivery Method: Mail
Areas Served: 74058, 74038, 74045, 75061, 74650, 74020

PERKINS

PERKINS JOURNAL (THUR)
222 N Main St, Perkins, OK, 74059-3630, Payne, USA; gen tel (405) 547-2411; gen fax (405) 547-2419; ed e-mail publisher@thejournalok.com; web site www.thejournalok.com
Circulation: 3,500pd,; Sworn/Estimate/Non-Audited
Advertising rate: Open inch rate $6.25
Established: 1892
Pub....David Sasser
Sports Ed....Rick Lomenick
Mechanical Specifications: Type page 13 x 21; E - 6 cols, 2, 1/3 between; A - 6 cols, 2, 1/3 between; C - 6 cols, 2, 1/3 between.Equipment & Software: Hardware — APP/Mac; Software — Adobe/PageMaker 5.0.
Areas Served: Payne County

PIEDMONT

CHIEFTAIN (THUR)
109 Monroe Ave NW, Piedmont, OK, 73078-8521, Canadian, USA; gen tel (405) 373-1616; gen fax (405) 373-1636; disp adv e-mail orkarchechieftain@sbcglobal.net; ed e-mail editor@piedmontnewsonline.com
Circulation: 700pd, 15fr; Sworn/Estimate/Non-Audited
Advertising rate: Open inch rate $3.95
Pub....Roger Pugh
Mng. Ed...... Erik BergerEquipment & Software: Hardware — APP/Mac; Software — Adobe/PageMaker, Adobe/Photoshop.

THE PIEDMONT-SURREY GAZETTE (THUR)
109 Monroe Ave NW, Piedmont, OK, 73078-8521, Canadian, USA; gen tel (405) 373-1616; gen fax (405) 373-1636; ed e-mail piedmontgazette@sbcglobal.net; web site www.piedmontsurreygazette.com
Circulation: 1,475pd, 10fr; Sworn/Estimate/Non-Audited
Advertising rate: Open inch rate $5.50
Established: 1976
Pub....Roger Pugh
Mng. Ed...... Eric BergerEquipment & Software: Hardware — APP/Mac; Software — Adobe/PageMaker, Adobe/Photoshop.

PRAGUE

THE PRAGUE TIMES-HERALD (THUR)
1123 N Jim Thorpe Blvd, Prague, OK, 74864-3524, Lincoln, USA; gen tel (405) 567-3933; gen fax (405) 567-3934; ed e-mail praguetimes@windstream.net; web site https://www.facebook.com/Prague-Times-Herald-127645500614437/?ref=page_internal
Circulation: 2,500pd,; Sworn/Estimate/Non-Audited
Advertising rate: Open inch rate $3.50
Established: 1972
Pub .... Sharon Lee
Mechanical Specifications: Type page 10.625 x 21.
Areas Served: 74864

PRYOR

THE PAPER (MON)
3 N Adair St, Ste 7, Pryor, OK, 74361-2480, Mayes, USA; gen tel (918) 825-2860; adv tel (918) 825-2860; ed tel (918) 825-2860; gen fax (918) 825-2862; disp adv e-mail legals@mayescounty.com; ed e-mail paull@mayescounty.com; web site www.thepaper.mayescounty.com
Advertising rate: Open inch rate $6.00
Established: 1999
Ed. .... Paul Lewis
Ads./Class./Legals .... Andrea Finney
Areas Served: Mayes County

PURCELL

THE PURCELL REGISTER (THUR)
225 W Main St, Purcell, OK, 73080-4221, McClain, USA; gen tel (405) 527-2126; adv tel (405) 527-2126; ed tel (405) 527-2126; gen fax (405) 527-3299; disp adv e-mail purcellregister@gmail.com; class adv e-mail advertising@purcellregister.com; ed e-mail jdmontgomery70@gmail.com; web site www.purcellregister.com
Circulation: 2,316pd, 29fr; USPS
Advertising rate: Open inch rate $8.00
Established: 1887
Ed./Pub. .... John D. Montgomery
Mechanical Specifications: Type page 13 x 21; E - 6 cols, 2 1/12, 1/6 between; A - 6 cols, 2 1/12, 1/6 between; C - 6 cols, 2 1/12, 1/6 between.Equipment & Software: Hardware — APP/Mac; Presses — HI/Cotrell V-15A; Software — Adobe/PageMaker, Adobe/Photoshop, Microsoft/Word.
Delivery Method: Mail, Newsstand, Racks
Areas Served: 73080, 73051, 73093, 73095, 73069, 73072, 73075, 73071, 73030

RINGLING

THE RINGLING EAGLE (THUR)
103 E Main St, Ringling, OK, 73456-1117, Jefferson, USA; gen tel (580) 662-2221; ed e-mail ringlingeagle@sbcglobal.net; web site http://ringlingeagle.com/The_Ringling_Eagle/Home.html
Circulation: 739pd, 22fr; Sworn/Estimate/Non-Audited
Advertising rate: Open inch rate $4.00
Established: 1920
Pub./Ed. .... Melissa Grace
Mechanical Specifications: Type page 11 5/8 x 21; E - 6 cols, 1 5/6, between; A - 6 cols, 1 5/6, between; C - 6 cols, 1 5/6, between. Equipment & Software: Hardware — APP/Mac; Software — Indesign
Delivery Method: Mail, Newsstand

RUSH SPRINGS

THE RUSH SPRINGS GAZETTE (THUR)
220 W Blakely St, Rush Springs, OK, 73082-1709, Grady, USA; gen tel (580) 476-2525; gen fax (580) 476-2526; ed e-mail rsgazette@sbcglobal.net
Circulation: 1,200pd, 25fr; Sworn/Estimate/Non-Audited
Advertising rate: Open inch rate $5.00
Ed. .... Karen Goodwin
Areas Served: Grady County

SALLISAW

SEQUOYAH COUNTY TIMES (WED, FRI)
111 N Oak St, Sallisaw, OK, 74955-4637, Sequoyah, USA; gen tel (918) 775-4433; gen fax (918) 775-3023; disp adv e-mail advertising@seqcotimes.com; ed e-mail news@seqcotimes.com; web site www.sequoyahcountytimes.com
Circulation: 4,627pd, 96fr; Sworn/Estimate/Non-Audited
Advertising rate: Open inch rate $7.50
Established: 1893
Publisher .... James Mayo
Gen. Mgr. /Assoc. Pub .... Jeff Mayo
Advertising Manager .... Carrie Carberry
Mechanical Specifications: Type page 13 x 21 1/2; E - 6 cols, 2 1/12, 1/8 between; A - 6 cols, 2 1/12, 1/8 between; C - 6 cols, 2 1/12, 1/8 between.Equipment & Software: Hardware — APP/Power Mac 8500, 2-APP/Power Mac G3, APP/Power Mac 7200, 5-APP/iMac, 2-Nikon/Scanner, Flatbed Scanner; Presses — Goss-DGM; Software — Microsoft/Word 98, Adobe/PageMaker 6.5, Adobe/Photoshop 5.0.
Delivery Method: Mail, Racks
Areas Served: 74427, 74931, 74435, 74936, 74945, 74948, 74945, 74954, 74955, 74962, 74470, 74946, 74962

SAYRE

THE BECKHAM COUNTY RECORD (WED)
112 E Main St, Sayre, OK, 73662-2914, Beckham, USA; gen tel (580) 928-5540 ; gen fax (580) 928-5547; ed e-mail sayrerecord@cableone.net; web site www.sayrerecord.com
Circulation: 2,300pd, 100fr; Sworn/Estimate/Non-Audited
Advertising rate: Open inch rate $4.75
Established: 1987
Digital Platform - Mobile: Other
Digital Platform - Tablet: Other
Co-Pub .... Brad Spitzer
Ed. .... Dayva Spitzer
Mechanical Specifications: Type page 11.5 x 21 1/2; E - 6 cols, 2, between; A - 6 cols, 2, between; C - 6 cols, 2, between.Equipment & Software: Hardware — APP/Mac.
Delivery Method: Mail, Newsstand, Racks
Areas Served: Sayre, Elk City, Erick and Sweetwater communities, Beckham county

SEILING

THE DEWEY COUNTY RECORD (THUR)
207 N Main St, Seiling, OK, 73663-6676, Dewey, USA; gen tel (580) 922-4296; adv tel (580) 922-4296; ed tel (580) 922-4296; gen fax (877) 420-6331; disp adv e-mail dcpub@pldi.net; class adv e-mail dcpub@pldi.net; ed e-mail dcpub@pldi.net; web site http://deweycountyrecord.com/
Circulation: 1,325pd, 6fr; Sworn/Estimate/Non-Audited
Advertising rate: $6.50 a column inch
Established: 1972
Group: Trail Miller Co. LLC
Asst. Ed & Office Mgr .... Amy Tune
Delivery Method: Mail, Newsstand, Racks
Areas Served: Dewey County

SENTINEL

SENTINEL LEADER (THUR)
307 E Main St, Sentinel, OK, 73664-9800, Washita, USA; gen tel (580) 393-4348; gen fax (580) 393-4349; ed e-mail sleader@pldi.net; web site www.thesentinelleader.com
Circulation: 1,200pd,; Sworn/Estimate/Non-Audited
Advertising rate: Open inch rate $3.75
Established: 1902
Digital Platform - Mobile: Apple
Pub./Ed. .... Jolene Wolfenbarger
Mechanical Specifications: Type page 11.625 x 21 1/2; E - 6 cols, 2, 1/8 between; A - 6 cols, 2, 1/8 between; C - 6 cols, 2, 1/8 between. Equipment & Software: Hardware — PC; Software — Adobe/PageMaker 6.5.
Delivery Method: Mail, Racks
Areas Served: Sentinel, Washita County, Southwest Oklahoma

SHATTUCK

NORTHWEST OKLAHOMAN (THUR)
329 S Main St, Shattuck, OK, 73858-8804, Ellis, USA; gen tel (580) 938-2533; ed tel (580) 938-2533; gen fax (580) 938-5240; disp adv e-mail nwopaper@podi.net; ed e-mail nwopaper@podi.net; web site http://www.northwestoklahoman.com/
Circulation: 1,350pd,; Sworn/Estimate/Non-Audited
Advertising rate: Open inch rate $3.00
Established: 1931
Pub .... Jeff Schnoebelen
Areas Served: Ellis County

SHIDLER

SHIDLER REVIEW (THUR)
234 S Cosden Ave, Shidler, OK, 74652-5198, Osage, USA; gen tel (918) 793-3841; ed tel (918) 793-3841; gen fax (918) 793-3842
Circulation: 1,100pd,; Sworn/Estimate/Non-Audited
Advertising rate: Open inch rate $3.50
Established: 1925
Pub./Adv. Dir./Managing Ed. ..... Marlene Fields
Ed .... Julia Ross
Mechanical Specifications: Type page 13 x 21 1/2; E - 6 cols, 1 9/10, 1/8 between; A - 6 cols, 1 9/10, 1/8 between; C - 6 cols, 1 9/10, 1/8 between.Equipment & Software: Hardware — HP, Gateway; Software — Microsoft/Works, WordPerfect.
Areas Served: Osage County

SKIATOOK

SKIATOOK JOURNAL (FRI)
500 W Rogers Blvd, Skiatook, OK, 74070-1081, Osage, USA; gen tel (918) 396-1616; adv tel (918) 259-7527; ed tel (918) 272-1155 x 402; gen fax (918) 396-1618; disp adv e-mail bruce.hugill@skiatookjournal.com; ed e-mail john.ferguson@baledger.com; web site www.skiatookjournal.com - 23,552(views) 5,679(visitors)
Circulation: 1,965pd, 126fr; CVC
Advertising rate: 1/24 Pg $49.35; 1/16 Pg $70.35; 1/8 Pg $140.70
Established: 1903
Group: Community Publishers, Inc.
Pub .... Mike Brown
Ed .... Lindsey Renuard
Mktg .... Bruce Hugill
Mechanical Specifications: Type page 13 x 21 1/2; E - 6 cols, 1 13/16, 1/6 between; A - 6 cols, 1 13/16, 1/6 between; C - 9 cols, 1 3/16, 1/6 between.Equipment & Software: Hardware — G; Software — QPS/QuarkXPress 4.1.
Areas Served: Skiatook and Sperry, OK

SNYDER

KIOWA COUNTY DEMOCRAT (THUR)
530 E St, Snyder, OK, 73566-1626, Kiowa, USA; gen tel (580) 569-2684; adv tel (580) 569-2684; ed tel (580) 569-2684; gen fax (580) 569-2640; adv fax (580) 569-2640; ed fax (580) 569-2640; disp adv e-mail ads@kiowacountydemocrat.com; class adv e-mail ads@kiowacountydemocrat.com; ed e-mail dee@kiowacountydemocrat.com
Circulation: 1,000pd, 25fr; Sworn/Estimate/Non-Audited
Advertising rate: Open inch rate $7.39
Established: 1905
Owner/Ed./Pub .... Dee Richardson
Office Mgr/Advertising Manager Jenny Stouder
Mechanical Specifications: Pass columns
Delivery Method: Mail, Newsstand, Racks
Areas Served: Southern Kiowa County 73566, 73564, 73559, 73549, 73570, 73555, 73552

SPIRO

SPIRO GRAPHIC (THUR)
212 S Main St, Spiro, OK, 74959-2506, Le Flore, USA; gen tel (918) 962-2075; gen fax (918) 962-3531; disp adv e-mail spirographic@sbcglobal.net; ed e-mail ttowner@bataviannews.com
Circulation: 2,850pd, 75fr; Sworn/Estimate/Non-Audited
Advertising rate: Open inch rate $6.00
Established: 1962
Pub .... Jim Fienup
Gen. Mgr./Ed. .... Michael Messerly
Areas Served: Le Flore County

STIGLER

STIGLER NEWS-SENTINEL (THUR)
204 S Broadway St, Stigler, OK, 74462-2320, Haskell, USA; gen tel (918) 967-4655; gen fax (918) 967-4289; disp adv e-mail summer@stiglernews.com; ed e-mail editor@stiglernews.com; web site www.stiglernews.com
Circulation: 3,953pd, 53fr; Sworn/Estimate/Non-Audited
Advertising rate: Open inch rate $7.44
Established: 1980Editions: Doug Russell
Digital Platform - Mobile: Apple
Owner/Pub. .... Linus G.Jr. Williams
Asst. Pub./Adv. Mgr. .... Summer Long
Mng. Ed. .... Anita Reding
Mechanical Specifications: Type page 11.75 x 21 1/2.Equipment & Software: Hardware — APP/Macs; Presses — V-25— 21 units; Software — Adobe/Photoshop, Adobe/indesign, Microsoft.
Delivery Method: Mail, Newsstand
Areas Served: Haskell County

STILWELL

STILWELL DEMOCRAT JOURNAL (WED)
118 N 2nd St, Stilwell, OK, 74960-3028, Adair, USA; gen tel (918) 696-2228; gen fax (918) 696-7066; disp adv e-mail stilwelldj@windstream.net
Circulation: 5,000pd,; Sworn/Estimate/Non-Audited
Advertising rate: Open inch rate $8.30
Established: 1898
Group: Community Newspaper Holdings, Inc.
Pub .... Gary Jackson
Ed./Adv. .... Keith Neale
Reporter .... Darrell Neale
Composing .... Chris Fuson
Office Mgr .... Brittany Tatum
Sydney Asbill
Clerk .... Noveena Littlejohn
Delivery Method: Mail, Newsstand
Areas Served: 74960

STROUD

STROUD AMERICAN (THUR)
315 W Main St, Stroud, OK, 74079-3611, Lincoln, USA; gen tel (918) 968-2581; adv

tel (918) 968-2581; ed tel (918) 968-2581; gen fax (918) 968-3864; disp adv e-mail stroudamerican@brightok.net; ed e-mail stroudamerican@cotc.net; web site https://www.facebook.com/stroudamerican/
Circulation: 2,100pd,; Sworn/Estimate/Non-Audited
Advertising rate: Open inch rate $15.00
Established: 1898
Ed. .... Michael Brown
Office Mgr. .... Alicia Brown
Delivery Method: Mail, Racks
Areas Served: Creek, Lincoln County

SULPHUR

SULPHUR TIMES-DEMOCRAT (WED, THUR)
115 W Muskogee Ave, Sulphur, OK, 73086-4809, Murray, USA; gen tel (580) 622-2102; gen fax (580) 622-2937; ed e-mail jcjohn@sulphurtimes.com; web site www.sulphurtimes.com
Circulation: 3,400pd, 160fr; Sworn/Estimate/Non-Audited
Advertising rate: Open inch rate $5.05
Digital Platform - Mobile: Apple
Digital Platform - Tablet: Apple iOS
Ed. .... James John
Mechanical Specifications: Type page 12X21Equipment & Software: Hardware — APP/Mac; Software — Aldus/PageMaker/InDesign
Delivery Method: Mail, Newsstand
Areas Served: 73086

TALIHINA

TALIHINA AMERICAN (THUR)
205 2nd St, Talihina, OK, 74571-2323, Le Flore, USA; gen tel (918) 567-2390; gen fax (918) 465-2170; disp adv e-mail tricountypubinc@sbcglobal.net
Circulation: 1,700pd,; Sworn/Estimate/Non-Audited
Advertising rate: Open inch rate $3.50
Established: 1918
Ed .... Mark Showell
Areas Served: Le Flore County

TECUMSEH

COUNTYWIDE & SUN (THUR)
108 E Washington St, 108 E. Washington St., Tecumseh, OK, 74873-3242, Pottawatomie, USA; gen tel (405) 598-3793; gen fax (405) 598-3891; ed e-mail editor@countywidenews.com; web site www.countywidenews.com
Circulation: 1,798pd, 250fr; Sworn/Estimate/Non-Audited
Advertising rate: Open inch rate $7.50
Established: 1923
Digital Platform - Mobile: Apple
Digital Platform - Tablet: Apple iOS
Pres./Co-Pub. .... Wayne Trotter
Co-Pub./Ed. .... Gloria Trotter
Mktg. Dir. .... Suzie Campbell
Advertising Executive .... Aaron McDonald
Mechanical Specifications: Type page 10 1/2 x 14; E - 3 cols, 3 1/3, 1/6 between; A - 5 cols, 2 1/2, 1/6 between; C - 7 cols, 1 1/2, 1/6 between.Equipment & Software: Hardware — APP/Mac, Nikon/Coolscan; Software — Adobe/PageMaker 6.0, Adobe/Photoshop 3.0, Adobe/Illustrator 6.0.
Delivery Method: Mail, Newsstand, Racks
Areas Served: Pottawatomie County, OK

THOMAS

THE THOMAS TRIBUNE (THUR)
115 W Orient, Thomas, OK, 73669, Custer, USA; gen tel (580) 661-3524; gen fax (580) 661-3324; ed e-mail thethomastribune@yahoo.com
Circulation: 1,150pd,; Sworn/Estimate/Non-Audited
Advertising rate: Open inch rate $4.20
Established: 1902
Digital Platform - Mobile: Other
Digital Platform - Tablet: Windows 7, Other
Editor .... Jessica Braun
Mechanical Specifications: Type page 12x21
Delivery Method: Mail, Newsstand
Areas Served: Custer, Blaine & Dewey Counties

TISHOMINGO

JOHNSTON COUNTY CAPITAL-DEMOCRAT (WED)
103 N Neshoba St, Tishomingo, OK, 73460-1739, Johnston, USA; gen tel (405) 371-2356; gen fax (405) 371-9648; ed e-mail ray.lokey@capital-democrat.com; web site johnstoncountycapital-democrat.com
Circulation: 3,023pd, 25fr; Sworn/Estimate/Non-Audited
Advertising rate: Open inch rate $3.00
Pub .... Ray Lokey
Ed. .... Jenny Lokey

TONKAWA

THE TONKAWA NEWS (THUR)
108 N 7th St, Tonkawa, OK, 74653-3578, Kay, USA; gen tel (580) 628-2532; gen fax (580) 628-4044; disp adv e-mail ads@tonkawanews.com; ed e-mail news@tonkawanews.com; web site www.tonkawanews.com
Circulation: 1,708pd, 23fr; Sworn/Estimate/Non-Audited
Advertising rate: Open inch rate $5.00
Ed. .... H. Lyle Becker
Mechanical Specifications: Type page 13 x 21 1/2; E - 6 cols, 2, between; A - 6 cols, 2, between; C - 8 cols, 1 1/2, between.Equipment & Software: Hardware — APP/Mac; Software — QPS/QuarkXPress.

TULSA

BROKEN ARROW LEDGER (WED)
PO Box 1770, Tulsa, OK, 74102-1770, Tulsa, USA; gen tel (918) 259-7500; disp adv e-mail melissa.lambert@baledger.com; ed e-mail john.ferguson@baledger.com; web site http://www.tulsaworld.com/communities/brokenarrow - 77,292(views) 22,449(visitors)
Circulation: 1,444pd, 16,424fr; CVC
Advertising rate: Open inch rate $71.00
Established: 1903
Group: Community Publishers, Inc.
Ed .... John Ferguson
Mktg. .... Melissa Lambert
Areas Served: 74012

CATOOSA TIMES (WED)
315 S Boulder Ave, Tulsa, OK, 74103-3401, Tulsa, USA; gen tel (918) 272-1155; adv tel (918) 259-7527; ed tel (918) 272-1155 x 402; gen fax (918) 272-0642; disp adv e-mail advertising@tulsaworld.com; ed e-mail news@tulsaworld.com; web site CatoosaWorld.com
Circulation: 1,300pd,; Sworn/Estimate/Non-Audited
Advertising rate: Open inch rate $47.00
Pub .... Mike Brown
Ed .... Art Haddaway
Areas Served: 74055

COLLINSVILLE NEWS (WED)
315 S Boulder Ave, Tulsa, OK, 74103-3401, Tulsa, USA; gen tel (918) 371-9666; gen fax (918) 371-9668; disp adv e-mail advertising@tulsaworld.com; ed e-mail news@tulsaworld.com; web site http://www.tulsaworld.com/communities/collinsville/ - 7,224(views) 2,668(visitors)
Circulation: 1,223pd, 131fr; CVC
Advertising rate: 1/24 Pg $47.25; 1/16 Pg $68.25; 1/8 Pg $136.50
Established: 1903
Group: Community Publishers, Inc.
Pub. .... Mike Brown
Ed .... Josh Burton
Circ. Dirc .... Robert Robertson
Adv. Dir. .... Jamey Honeycutt
Mechanical Specifications: Type page 11 3/4 x 21 1/2; E - 6 cols, 1 13/16, 1/6 between; A - 6 cols, 1 13/16, 1/6 between; C - 9 cols, 1 3/16, 1/6 between.Equipment & Software: Hardware — APP/Mac; Presses — G; Software — QPS/QuarkXPress 4.1.
Delivery Method: Mail, Newsstand, Racks
Areas Served: North Tulsa County and Collinsville, 74021

OWASSO RAMBLER (MTHLY)
7116 S Mingo Rd Ste 103, Suite 103, Tulsa, OK, 74133-3268, Tulsa, USA; gen tel (918) 254-1515; adv tel (918) 254-1515; gen fax (918) 254-1515; disp adv e-mail fcameron@gtrnews.com; class adv e-mail fcameron@gtrnews.com; ed e-mail fcameron@gtrnews.com; web site http://www.gtrnews.com/owasso-rambler/
Circulation: 1pd, 1,974fr; VAC
Advertising rate: N/A
Established: 1992
Group: Greater Tulsa Reporter Newspapers Union Boundry Inc.
Digital Platform - Mobile: Apple, Android
Digital Platform - Tablet: Apple iOS, Android
Pub./CEO .... Forrest Cameron
Adv. Dir. .... Sharon Cameron
Circ. Mgr .... Dan Cameron
Delivery Method: Mail, Racks
Areas Served: Tulsa County

SAND SPRINGS LEADER (WED)
PO Box 1770, Tulsa, OK, 74102-1770, Tulsa, USA; gen tel (918) 245-6634; adv tel (918) 259-7527; gen fax (918) 241-3610; disp adv e-mail samantha.ferguson@sandspringsleader.com; ed e-mail kirk.mccracken@sandspringsleader.com; web site www.sandspringsleader.com - 58,193(views) 15,233(visitors)
Circulation: 929pd, 10fr; Sworn/Estimate/Non-Audited
Advertising rate: Open inch rate $7.20
Established: 1903
Group: Community Publishers, Inc.
Pub. .... Mike Brown
CSR .... Chala DeSelm
Mng. Ed. .... Kirk McCracken
Mktg. .... Samantha Ferguson
Mechanical Specifications: Type page 11 3/4 x 21 1/2; E - 6 cols, 1 13/16, 1/6 between; A - 6 cols, 1 13/16, 1/6 between; C - 9 cols, 1 3/16, 1/6 between.Equipment & Software: Hardware — APP/Mac; Presses — G; Software — QPS/QuarkXPress 4.1.
Areas Served: 74044

TULSA BEACON (THUR)
6784 S 67th East Ave, Tulsa, OK, 74133-1723, Tulsa, USA; gen tel (918) 523-4425; gen fax (918) 523-4408; disp adv e-mail orders@tulsabeacon.com; ed e-mail charlesbiggs@tulsabeacon.com; web site www.tulsabeacon.com
Advertising rate: Open inch rate $8.00
Ed. .... Charles Biggs
Areas Served: 74153

TULSA COUNTY NEWS (WED)
315 S Boulder Ave, Tulsa, OK, 74103-3401, Tulsa, USA; gen tel (918) 582-0921; disp adv e-mail stephanie.knight@tulsaworld.com; class adv e-mail advertising@tulsaworld.com; ed e-mail news@tulsaworld.com; web site http://www.tulsaworld.com/news/
Circulation: 942pd, 10fr; Sworn/Estimate/Non-Audited
Advertising rate: Open inch rate $8.30
Established: 1965
Pub. .... Gary Percefull
Mechanical Specifications: Type page 10 x 13; E - 5 cols, 1 13/16, 1/6 between; A - 5 cols, 1 13/16, 1/6 between; C - 7 cols, 1 3/16, 1/6 between.Equipment & Software: Hardware — APP/Mac; Presses — G; Software — QPS/QuarkXPress 4.1.
Areas Served: 74017, 74131, 74132

VALLIANT

THE VALLIANT LEADER (WED)
119 N DALTON ST, Valliant, OK, 74764, McCurtian, USA; gen tel (580) 933-4579; gen fax (580) 933-4900; disp adv e-mail valeader@valliant.net
Circulation: 1,800pd,; USPS
Advertising rate: Open inch rate $4.20
Established: 1982
Ed. .... Peter A. Wilson
Mechanical Specifications: Full pg - 62 picas x 62 p3 (6 col x 21 inches)
1 col - 10 picas w/ gutter 0p8.9Equipment & Software: Hardware — Mac computers; Software — indesign
Delivery Method: Mail, Racks
Areas Served: McCurtain, Pushmataha, Choctaw counties, & others

WAGONER

WAGONER TRIBUNE (THUR)
221 E Cherokee St, Wagoner, OK, 74467-4703, Wagoner, USA; gen tel (918) 485-5505; ed tel (918) 485-5505; gen fax (918) 485-8442; disp adv e-mail Shelby.stockton@wagonercountyat.com; class adv e-mail Channing.Wedel@wagonercountyat.com; ed e-mail christy.wheeland@wagonercountyat.com; web site www.wagonertribune.com - 44,807(views) 9,215(visitors)
Circulation: 2,115pd, 217fr; CVC
Advertising rate: 1/24 Pg $28.35; 1/16 Pg $40.95; 1/8 Pg $81.90
Established: 1903
Group: Community Publishers, Inc.
Ed .... Christy Wheeland
Mktg. .... Laura Schnee
Class./Inside Sales .... Channing Wedel
Mechanical Specifications: Type page 11 3/4 x 21 1/2; E - 6 cols, 1 13/16, 1/6 between; A - 6 cols, 1 13/16, 1/6 between; C - 9 cols, 1 3/16, 1/6 between.Equipment & Software: Hardware — APP/Mac; Presses — G; Software — QPS/QuarkXPress 4.1.
Areas Served: 74467

WALTERS

WALTERS HERALD (THUR)
112 S Broadway St, Walters, OK, 73572-2033, Cotton, USA; gen tel (580) 875-3326; gen fax (580) 875-3150; disp adv e-mail waltersheraldads@sbcglobal.net; class adv e-mail waltersheraldads@sbcglobal.net; ed e-mail cottoncountylegals@sbcglobal.net; web site http://www.waltersherald.com
Circulation: 173pd, 25fr; Sworn/Estimate/Non-Audited
Advertising rate: Open inch rate $4.30
Established: 1901
Ed. Adv./Gen Mgr. .... Beth Davis
Adv. Mgr./Circ. Mgr. .... Kim Hicklin
Delivery Method: Mail, Newsstand, Racks
Areas Served: 73572;73568;73562;73531;73528 ;73529; 73548;73543; 73501; 73505; 73507 ; 76354 ; 76308 ; 76308

WATONGA

THE WATONGA REPUBLICAN (WED)
104 E Main St, Watonga, OK, 73772-3831, Blaine, USA; gen tel (580) 623-4922; gen fax (580) 623-4925; disp adv e-mail Ian@WatongaRepublican.com; class adv e-mail ads@wrnews.net; ed e-mail Editor@WatongaRepublican.com; web site http://thewatongarepublican.com/
Circulation: 2,950pd, 17fr; Sworn/Estimate/Non-Audited
Advertising rate: Open inch rate $5.60
Established: 1892

Group: Central Oklahoma Publishing
Digital Platform - Mobile: Blackberry
Digital Platform - Tablet: Windows 7
Chief Ed................................. Eric Warsinskey
News Ed..Ian Pribanic
Adv.......................................Kimberly Jenkins
Mechanical Specifications: Type page 11.61 x 21; 6 colEquipment & Software: Hardware — PC; Software — QPS/QuarkXPress 5.0./ In Design
Delivery Method: Mail, Newsstand, Racks
Areas Served: 73036, 73501, 73772, 73040, 73763, 73724

WESTVILLE

WESTVILLE REPORTER (THUR)

118 N 2nd St, Westville, OK, 74965, Adair, USA; gen tel (918) 723-5445; gen fax (918) 696-7066; disp adv e-mail stilwelldj@windstream.net; ed e-mail westvillereporter@yahoo.com
Circulation: 2,100pd, 400fr; Sworn/Estimate/Non-Audited
Advertising rate: Open inch rate $7.15
Established: 1931
Group: Community Newspaper Holdings, Inc.
Pub..Gary Jackson
Ed...Keith Neale
Delivery Method: Mail, Newsstand
Areas Served: 74965

WETUMKA

THE HUGHES COUNTY TIMES (THUR)

501 E Highway 9, Wetumka, OK, 74883-6048, Hughes, USA; gen tel (405) 452-3294; adv tel (405) 4523294; ed tel (405) 452-3294; gen fax (405) 452-3574; disp adv e-mail hughescountytimes@sbcglobal.net; ed e-mail hughescountytimes@sbcglobal.net; web site www.hughescountytimes.com
Circulation: 1,500pd, 20fr; Sworn/Estimate/Non-Audited
Advertising rate: Open inch rate $5.90
Established: 1908
Group: ROBINSON PUBLISHING CO., INC.
Digital Platform - Mobile: Apple
Off. mng...................................Jade Robinson
Mechanical Specifications: Type page10 x 21.5; E - 6 cols, 2, 1/6 between; A - 6 cols, 2, 1/6 between; C - 6 cols, 2, 1/6 between.Equipment & Software: Hardware — APP/Mac.
Delivery Method: Mail, Racks
Areas Served: Hughes County

WEWOKA

WEWOKA TIMES (WED)

210 S Wewoka Ave, Wewoka, OK, 74884-2640, Seminole, USA; gen tel (405) 257-3341; gen fax (405) 257-3342; disp adv e-mail ads@seminoleproducer.com; class adv e-mail lovina@okcfriday.com; ed e-mail stu@seminoleoklahoma.com; web site wewokatimes.com
Circulation: 1,200pd,; Sworn/Estimate/Non-Audited
Advertising rate: Open inch rate $3.50
Established: 1920
Mng. Ed...Donny Cofer
Adv. Dir...Mike Gifford
Adv. Sales Rep........................Lovina Morgan
Pub..Stu Phillips
Mechanical Specifications: Type page 13 x 21; E - 6 cols, 2, 1/6 between; A - 6 cols, 2, 1/6 between; C - 8 cols, 2, 1/6 between.Equipment & Software: Hardware — COM.
Delivery Method: Mail, Newsstand
Areas Served: Wewoka

WILBURTON

LATIMER COUNTY NEWS-TRIBUNE (THUR)

111 W Ada Ave, Wilburton, OK, 74578-2416, Latimer, USA; gen tel (918) 465-2321; gen fax (918) 465-3011; disp adv e-mail lcntads@att.net; class adv e-mail lcntclassifieds@att.net; ed e-mail lcnt@att.net
Circulation: 2,400pd, 40fr; Sworn/Estimate/Non-Audited
Advertising rate: Open inch rate $6.00
Established: 1915
Ed...Mark Showell
Office Mgr...............................Brenda Showell
Class./Legals...........................Malissa Evans
Mechanical Specifications: Type page 14 x 21 1/2.
Delivery Method: Mail, Newsstand

WYNNEWOOD

WYNNEWOOD GAZETTE (THUR)

210 S Dean A McGee Ave, Wynnewood, OK, 73098-7810, Garvin, USA; gen tel (405) 665-4333; adv tel (405) 665-4333; ed tel (405) 665-4333; gen fax (405) 665-4333; disp adv e-mail info@wwgazette.news
Circulation: 1,700pd, 60fr; Sworn/Estimate/Non-Audited
Advertising rate: Open inch rate $5.00
Established: 1902
Group: Victory Publishing LLC
Digital Platform - Mobile: Apple, Android, Windows, Blackberry
Digital Platform - Tablet: Apple iOS, Android, Windows 7
Advertising Manager.. Tara BrownEquipment & Software: Hardware — APP/Power Mac G3, APP/Mac Performa, APP/G4; Software — Adobe/PageMaker 6.0, Adobe/Photoshop LE 4.0, Claris/Works 4.0.
Areas Served: Garvin County

YUKON

THE YUKON REVIEW (WED, SAT)

110 S 5th St, Yukon, OK, 73099-2601, Canadian, USA; gen tel (405) 354-5264; gen fax (405) 354-3044; disp adv e-mail dsettle@theyukonreview.com; class adv e-mail rreynolds@theyukonreview.com; ed e-mail editor@theyukonreview.com; web site www.yukonreview.net
Circulation: 4,321pd, 4,800fr; VAC
Advertising rate: Open inch rate $6.00
Group: Black Press Group Ltd.
Gen. Mgr...............................Bart Nicholson
Adv./Ops Dir.................................David Settle
Pub..John Settle
Ed...Kyle Salomon
Mechanical Specifications: Type page 13 x 21.

OREGON

BAKER CITY

BAKER CITY HERALD (MON, WED, FRI)

1915 1st St, Baker City, OR, 97814-3338, Baker, USA; gen tel (541) 523-3673; adv tel (541) 523-3673; ed tel (541) 523-3673; gen fax (541) 523-6426; adv fax (541) 523-6426; ed fax (541) 523-6426; disp adv e-mail ads@bakercityherald.com; class adv e-mail ads@bakercityherald.com; ed e-mail news@bakercityherald.com; web site www.bakercityherald.com - 154,900(views) 35,900(visitors)
Circulation: 1,998pd, 87fr; CVC
Advertising rate: Open inch rate $11.99
Established: 1870
Group: Western Communications, Inc.
Pub...Kari Borgen
Ed...Jayson Jacoby
Photo Ed...................................S. John Collins
Prodn. Mgr..............................Frank Everidge
Circ. Mgr..Kelli Craft
Advt Dir...................................Karrine Brogoitti
Mechanical Specifications: Type page 11.75 x 21 1/2; E - 6 cols, 2 1/16, 1/8 between; A - 6 cols, 2 1/16, 1/8 between; C - 6 cols, 1 9/16, 1/16 between.
Delivery Method: Mail, Newsstand, Carrier, Racks
Areas Served: 97814, 97833, 97834, 97877

THE RECORD-COURIER (THUR)

1718 Main St, Baker City, OR, 97814-3447, Baker, USA; gen tel (541) 523-5353; gen fax (541) 523-5353; disp adv e-mail ads@therconline.com; ed e-mail news@therconline.com; web site www.therconline.com
Circulation: 3,200pd, 58fr; Sworn/Estimate/Non-Audited
Advertising rate: Open inch rate $5.75
Established: 1901
Pub...Greg Brinton
Adv. Mgr...Dave Conn
Mechanical Specifications: Type page 16 x 21.

BANDON

BANDON WESTERN WORLD (WED, THUR)

1185 BALTIMORE AVE SE, Bandon, OR, 97411, Coos County, USA; gen tel (541) 347-2423; gen fax (541) 347-2424; disp adv e-mail mike.hrycko@theworldlink.com; class adv e-mail jeannie.smith@theworldlink.com; ed e-mail larry.campbell@theworldlink.com; web site www.bandonwesternworld.com
Circulation: 1,059pd,; Sworn/Estimate/Non-Audited
Advertising rate: Open inch rate $7.95
Established: 1912
Group: Southwestern Oregon Publishing Company
Prod. Supv..................................Dan Gordon
Editor..Amy Strong
Circulation....................................Mike Hrycko
Publisher..Chris Rush
Mechanical Specifications: Type page 13 x 21; E - 6 cols, 2 1/2, 1/6 between; A - 6 cols, 2 1/2, 1/6 between; C - 8 cols, 1 1/3, 1/4 between. Equipment & Software: Hardware — APP/Mac; Software — Adobe/PageMaker, Claris/Draw, Write Now.
Delivery Method: Mail, Newsstand, Racks
Areas Served: 97411

BEAVERTON

BEAVERTON LEADER (WED)

4800 SW Griffith Dr, Ste 230, Beaverton, OR, 97005-8709, Washington, USA; gen tel (503) 221-8351; gen fax (503) 294-4191; disp adv e-mail advertise@oregonian.com; class adv e-mail classified@oregonian.com; ed e-mail newclerk@oregonian.com; web site www.oregonlive.com//beavertonleader - 20,000,000(views) 3,000,000(visitors)
Circulation: 64,397fr; AAM
Advertising rate: 1/8 Pg $694.13; 1/4 Pg $1315.44; 1/2 Pg $2300.63
Established: 2013
Group: Advance Publications, Inc.
Digital Platform - Mobile: Apple, Android, Windows, Blackberry
Pub.......................................Chris Anderson
VP, Mktg.......................................Mike Burns
Delivery Method: Newsstand
Areas Served: 97005, 97006, 97007, 97008, 97223, 97225, 97229

BEND

SOURCE WEEKLY (WED)

704 NW Georgia Ave, Bend, OR, 97703-3243, Deschutes, USA; gen tel (541) 383-0800; disp adv e-mail amanda@bendsource.com; ed e-mail editor@bendsource.com; web site http://www.bendsource.com/
Circulation: 325pd,; Sworn/Estimate/Non-Audited
Advertising rate: Modular rates
Established: 1997
Pub...Aaron Switzer
Adv. Dir...................................Amanda Klingman
Ed...Nicole Vulcan
Areas Served: 97702, 97703, 97701,

BROOKINGS

CURRY COASTAL PILOT (WED, SAT)

507 Chetco Ave, Brookings, OR, 97415-8011, Curry, USA; gen tel (541) 469-3123; gen fax (541) 469-4679; disp adv e-mail mail@currypilot.com; class adv e-mail mail@currypilot.com; ed e-mail news@currypilot.com; web site www.currypilot.com
Circulation: 4,759pd, 87fr; CVC
Advertising rate: Open inch rate $14.90
Established: 1946
Group: Western Communications, Inc.
Circ. Mgr.................................Jenna Steineke
Ed...Scott Graves
Pub...Charles Kocher
Prod. Mgr.......................................Aura Wright
Circ. Mgr.....................................David Jeffcoat
Mechanical Specifications: Type page 10 1/2 x 21 1/2; E - 6 colsEquipment & Software: Hardware — APP/Mac; Presses — G/Community; Software — QPS/QuarkXPress 3.2, InDesign 5.5
Delivery Method: Mail, Newsstand, Carrier, Racks
Areas Served: 97415, 97444, 95567

BROWNSVILLE

THE TIMES (WED)

343 N MAIN ST, Brownsville, OR, 97327, Linn, USA; gen tel (541) 466-5311; gen fax (541) 466-5312; disp adv e-mail thetimes@peak.org; ed e-mail thetimes089@centurytel.net; web site www.thebrownsvilletimes.com
Circulation: 1,200pd, 62fr; Sworn/Estimate/Non-Audited
Advertising rate: Open inch rate $6.00
Established: 1888
Ed...Don Ware
Owner/Pub.................................Vance Parrish
Mechanical Specifications: Type page 11 3/4 x 17 1/2; E - 5 cols, 1/6, between; C - 6 cols, 1/12 between.
Delivery Method: Mail, Newsstand
Areas Served: Brookings, Sheriden and Brownsville

BURNS

BURNS TIMES-HERALD (WED)

355 N Broadway Ave, Burns, OR, 97720-1704, Harney, USA; gen tel (541) 573-2022; gen fax (541) 573-3915; disp adv e-mail addrop@burnstimesherald.info; ed e-mail editor@burnstimesherald.info; web site www.burnstimesherald.info
Circulation: 3,008pd, 46fr; Sworn/Estimate/Non-Audited
Advertising rate: Open inch rate $8.25
Established: 1887
Group: Survival Media LLC
Gen. Mgr.................................Sue Pedersen
Circ. Mgr.......................................Jeff Graham
Ed...Jennifer Jenks
Mechanical Specifications: Type page 11 5/6 x 20 1/2; E - 6 cols, 1 5/6, 1/6 between; A - 6 cols, 1 5/6, 1/6 between; C - 8 cols, 1 1/3, 1/6 between.Equipment & Software: Hardware — APP/Mac; Software — QPS/QuarkXPress 3.31.

CANBY

THE CANBY HERALD (WED)

241 N Grant St, Canby, OR, 97013-3629, Clackamas, USA; gen tel (503) 266-6831; gen fax (503) 266-6836; disp adv e-mail sstorey@canbyherald.com; web site www.canbyherald.com
Circulation: 5,100pd,; Sworn/Estimate/Non-Au-

Oregon
Total Daily Newspapers 16
Total Daily Circulation 349,211
Total Weekly Newspapers 88
Total Weekly Circulation 692,164
Population 4,142,776
LEGEND
Dallas-Fort Worth Combined Statistical Area
RICHMOND Metropolitan Statistical Area
Concord Micropolitan Statistical Area
TEXAS State
HARRIS County
Shoreline
0 15 30 45 60 Kilometers
0 15 30 45 60 Miles
N
WASHINGTON
IDAHO
NEVADA
CALIFORNIA
Astoria
CLATSOP
COLUMBIA
CLARK
SKAMANIA
MULTNOMAH
PORTLAND-VANCOUVER-BEAVERTON
CLACKAMAS
WASHINGTON
YAMHILL
TILLAMOOK
POLK
SALEM
MARION
BENTON
CORVALLIS
LINCOLN
LINN
Albany-Corvallis-Lebanon
Albany-Lebanon
LANE
EUGENE-SPRINGFIELD
Hood River
HOOD RIVER
WASCO
City of The Dalles
SHERMAN
GILLIAM
MORROW
UMATILLA
Pendleton-Hermiston
UNION
La Grande
WALLOWA
BAKER
GRANT
WHEELER
JEFFERSON
CROOK
Prineville
Bend-Prineville
BEND
DESCHUTES
MALHEUR
Ontario
PAYETTE
HARNEY
LAKE
KLAMATH
Klamath Falls
DOUGLAS
Roseburg
COOS
Coos Bay
CURRY
Brookings
JOSEPHINE
Grants Pass
JACKSON
MEDFORD
46°
45°
44°
43°
42°
41°
115°
116°
117°
118°
119°
120°
121°
122°
123°
124°
125°
126°

dited
Advertising rate: Open inch rate $11.25
Established: 1906
Group: Pamplin Media Group
Pamplin Media Group
Ed. ....John Baker
Adv .... Sandy Storey
Pub...Georgia Newton
Mechanical Specifications: Type page 13 x 21 1/2; E - 6 cols, 2 1/12, 1/3 between; A - 6 cols, 2 1/12, 1/3 between; C - 9 cols, 1 1/3, 1/6 between.Equipment & Software: Hardware — PC.
Delivery Method: Mail, Newsstand
Areas Served: 97013, 97002, 97045

CAVE JUNCTION

ILLINOIS VALLEY NEWS (WED)

221 S REDWOOD HWY, Cave Junction, OR, 97523, Josephine, USA; gen tel (541) 592-2541; gen fax (541) 592-433; disp adv e-mail dan@illinoies-valley-news.com; class adv e-mail zbooth@illinois-valley-news.com; ed e-mail newsroom1@frontiernet.net; web site www.illinois-valley-news.com
Circulation: 3,500pd, 25fr; Sworn/Estimate/Non-Audited
Advertising rate: Open inch rate $5.50
Established: 1937
Group: W. H. Alltheway, LLC
Pub ....Dan Mancuso
Mechanical Specifications: Type page 11 1/2 x 20 1/4; E - 6 cols, 1 3/4, 1/4 between; A - 6 cols, 1 3/4, 1/4 between; C - 8 cols, 1 1/4, 1/4 between.Equipment & Software: Hardware — PC.

CLATSKANIE

THE CHIEF (FRI)

148 N Nehalem St, Clatskanie, OR, 97016-7435, Columbia, USA; gen tel (503) 728-3350; gen fax (503) 308-6791; disp adv e-mail lressler@countrymedia.net; ed e-mail cmann@countrymedia.net; web site www.thechiefnews.com
Circulation: 2,750pd,; Sworn/Estimate/Non-Audited
Advertising rate: Open inch rate $6.00
Established: 1891
Group: Country Media Inc.
Gen. Mgr. ....Lora Ressler
Ed ....Cody Mann
Mechanical Specifications: Type page 12 3/4 x 21; E - 6 cols, 2, 1/6 between; A - 6 cols, 2, 1/6 between; C - 8 cols, 1 1/2, 1/6 between. Equipment & Software: Hardware — APP/iMac.
Delivery Method: Mail, Newsstand

CONDON

THE TIMES-JOURNAL (THUR)

319 S Main St, Condon, OR, 97823-7647, Gilliam, USA; gen tel (541) 384-2421; gen fax (541) 384-2411; disp adv e-mail times-journal@jncable.com
Circulation: 1,400pd, 40fr; Sworn/Estimate/Non-Audited
Advertising rate: Open inch rate $5.25
Established: 1886
Group: Macro Graphics of Condon, LLC
Digital Platform - Mobile: Windows
Pub.....................................Janet L. Stinchfield
Ed. .... McLaren E. Stinchfield
Class. Mgr............................Cody Bettencourt
Mechanical Specifications: Type page 13 x 21; E - 6 cols, 2 1/16, 1/8 between; A - 6 cols, 2 1/16, 1/8 between.
Delivery Method: Mail, Newsstand
Areas Served: Newspaper of Record for Gilliam, Wheeler and Sherman counties in north-central Oregon

COOS BAY

THE UMPQUA POST (WED)

350 Commercial Ave, Coos Bay, OR, 97420-2269, Douglas, USA; gen tel (541) 271-7474; adv tel (541) 271-7474; ed tel (541) 269-1222; gen fax (541) 271-2821; disp adv e-mail amanda.johnson@theworldlink.com; class adv e-mail umpquapost@theworldlink.com; ed e-mail shelby.case@theworldlink.com; web site www.theUmpquapost.com
Circulation: 750pd,; Sworn/Estimate/Non-Audited
Advertising rate: Open inch rate $8.15
Established: 1996
Group: Southwestern Oregon Publishing Company
Digital Platform - Mobile: Apple, Android
Digital Platform - Tablet: Apple iOS, Android
Delivery Method: Mail, Newsstand, Racks
Areas Served: 97467

COQUILLE

THE SENTINEL (WED)

61 E 1st St, Coquille, OR, 97423-1846, Coos, USA; gen tel (541) 396-3191; gen fax (541) 396-3624; ed e-mail coquillevalley-sentinel@mycomspan.com; web site www.thecoquillevalleysentniel.com
Circulation: 2,500pd, 63fr; Sworn/Estimate/Non-Audited
Advertising rate: Open inch rate $8.50
Established: 1882
Ed. ....Jean Ivy
Mechanical Specifications: Type page 14 3/4 x 21; E - 6 cols, 2, 3/16 between; A - 6 cols, 2, 3/16 between; C - 6 cols, 2, 3/16 between. Equipment & Software: Hardware — APP/Mac; Software — QPS 5.0.
Areas Served: 97423, 97420, 97459, 97411, 97467

CORVALLIS

THE PHILOMATH EXPRESS (WED)

1835 NW Circle Blvd, Corvallis, OR, 97330-1310, USA; gen tel (541) 753-2641; adv tel (541) 758-9581
Circulation:; Sworn/Estimate/Non-Audited
Group: Lee Enterprises, Inc.
Gen. Mngr. .... Mike McInally
Controller....................................... Doug Byers
Ed. .... Brad Fuqua
Areas Served: Philomath OR

COTTAGE GROVE

COTTAGE GROVE SENTINEL (WED)

116 N 6th St, Cottage Grove, OR, 97424-1601, Lane, USA; gen tel (541) 942-3325; gen fax (541) 942-3328; disp adv e-mail cgnews@cgsentinel.com; class adv e-mail legals@cgsentinel.com; ed e-mail cgnews@cgsentinel.com; web site www.cgsentinel.com
Circulation: 2,500pd, 225fr; Sworn/Estimate/Non-Audited
Advertising rate: Open inch rate $6.50
Established: 1889
Group: News Media Corp.
Pub...Jessica Baker
Ed. ....Jon Stinnett
Gen. Mgr. .... Gary Manly
Circ./Class. Mgr .... Carla Williams
Delivery Method: Mail, Racks
Areas Served: Cottage Grove, OR; Lane County

CRESWELL

THE CRESWELL CHRONICLE (THUR)

34 W Oregon Ave, Creswell, OR, 97426-9259, Lane, USA; gen tel (541) 895-2197; gen fax (541) 895-2361; disp adv e-mail olson@thecreswellchronicle.com; web site www.thecreswellchronicle.com
Circulation: 1,050pd, 50fr; Sworn/Estimate/Non-Audited
Advertising rate: Open inch rate $9.00
Established: 1965
Group: SJ Olson Publishing, Inc
Pub............Scott OlsonEquipment & Software: Hardware — APP/Mac; Software — Adobe/PageMaker 6.5.
Delivery Method: Mail, Newsstand, Racks

DALLAS

THE POLK COUNTY ITEMIZER-OBSERVER (WED)

147 SE Court St, Dallas, OR, 97338-3158, Polk, USA; gen tel (503) 623-2373; gen fax (503) 623-2395; disp adv e-mail iosales@polkio.com; class adv e-mail ioads@polkio.com; ed e-mail ionews@polkio.com; web site www.polkio.com
Circulation: 4,800pd, 8,500fr; USPS
Advertising rate: $10.25 col incn
Established: 1875
Group: Eagle Newspapers, Inc.
Pub ....Nancy Adams
Ed. .... Kurt Holland
Adv. LeaderHeidi LeppinEquipment & Software: ; Software — QPS/QuarkXPress.
Delivery Method: Mail
Areas Served: Polk County, Oregon —primary zips are: 97338, 97351, 97361, 97344, 97371, 97347 & 97304

DRAIN

DRAIN ENTERPRISE (THUR)

309 N First St, Drain, OR, 97435-0268, Douglas, USA; gen tel (541) 836-2241; gen fax (541) 836-2243; ed e-mail drainenterprise@earthlink.net; web site www.354.com/drain/enterprise.htm
Circulation: 900pd, 20fr; Sworn/Estimate/Non-Audited
Advertising rate: Open inch rate $4.00
Established: 1950
Pub./Owner.............................. Sue Anderson
Mechanical Specifications: Type page 11 x 16; E - 5 cols, 2, 1/8 between; A - 5 cols, 2, between; C - 5 cols, 2, between.Equipment & Software: ; Presses — ATF/15, ATF/22; Software — Adobe/PageMaker 6.5.
Areas Served: 97435, 97436, 97499, 97424

EAGLE POINT

UPPER ROGUE INDEPENDENT (TUES)

11136 Highway 62, Eagle Point, OR, 97524-9779, Jackson, USA; gen tel (541) 826-7700; gen fax (541) 826-1340; ed e-mail editor@urindependent.com; web site www.urindependent.com
Circulation: 2,000pd, 0fr; Sworn/Estimate/Non-Audited
Advertising rate: Open inch rate $8.00
Established: 1976
Owner/Ed............................. Ralph McKechnie
Mechanical Specifications: Type page 10 1/4 x 13 1/2.Equipment & Software: Hardware — PCs; Software — Microsoft/Windows 8, Adobe/indesign, Archetype/Corel Draw, Adobe/Photoshop 4.0.
Delivery Method: Mail, Racks

ENTERPRISE

WALLOWA COUNTY CHIEFTAIN (WED)

209 NW 1st St, Enterprise, OR, 97828-1003, Wallowa, USA; gen tel (541) 426-4567; gen fax (541) 426-3921; disp adv e-mail jsackett@wallowa.com; class adv e-mail cjenkins@wallowa.com; ed e-mail editor@wallowa.com; web site www.wallowacounty-chieftain.com
Circulation: 4,000pd,; Sworn/Estimate/Non-Audited
Advertising rate: Open inch rate $8.40
Established: 1884
Group: East Oregonian
Pub....................................... Marissa Williams
Ed. .... Roberth Ruth
Adv Sales .... Jim Sackett
Class/Circ. Mgr........................ Cheryl Jenkkins
Mechanical Specifications: Type page 12 3/4 x 21; E - 6 cols, 2 1/12, 1/6 between; A - 6 cols, 2 1/12, 1/6 between; C - 9 cols, 1 1/2, 1/6 between.Equipment & Software: Hardware — PC; Presses — 10-G/Community; Software — Adobe 6.5.

ESTACADA

ESTACADA NEWS (THUR)

307 SW Highway 224, Estacada, OR, 97023-7026, Clackamas, USA; gen tel (503) 630-3241; gen fax (503) 630-5840; disp adv e-mail email@estacadanews.com; ed e-mail editor@estacadanews.com; web site www.estacadanews.com
Circulation: 2,000pd, 35fr; Sworn/Estimate/Non-Audited
Advertising rate: Open inch rate $37.00
Established: 1904
Group: Pamplin Media Group
Pres. .... Mark Garber
VP .... Brian Monahan
Adv... Karen Tamburina
Areas Served: 97022, 97023

FLORENCE

SIUSLAW NEWS (WED, SAT)

148 Maple St, Florence, OR, 97439-9656, Lane, USA; gen tel (541) 997-3441; ed tel (541) 902-3520; gen fax (541) 997-7979; disp adv e-mail s.gutierrez@thesiuslawnews.com; ed e-mail editor@thesiuslawnews.com; web site www.thesiuslawnews.com
Circulation: 6pd, 125fr; Sworn/Estimate/Non-Audited
Advertising rate: Open inch rate $14.80
Established: 1890
Group: News Media Corp.
Adv. Mgr. .... Susan Gutierrez
Publisher..................................... Jenna Bartlett
Sales person......................... Jeanna Petersen
Mechanical Specifications: Type page 13 1/4 x 21; E - 6 cols, 2 1/12, 1/6 between; A - 6 cols, 2 1/12, 1/6 between; C - 8 cols, 1 1/2, 1/6 between.Equipment & Software: Hardware — APP/Mac, Imagesetter; Presses — 6-G/Community; Software — QPS/QuarkXPress 4.0.
Delivery Method: Mail, Newsstand, Racks
Areas Served: 97430, 97439, 97493, 97453, 97467, 97480, 97498

FOREST GROVE

FOREST GROVE NEWS-TIMES (WED)

2038 Pacific Ave, Forest Grove, OR, 97116-2357, Washington, USA; gen tel (503) 357-3181; adv tel (503) 357-3181; ed tel (503) 357-3181; disp adv e-mail advertising@fgnewstimes.com; ed e-mail news@fgnewstimes.com; web site www.forestgrovenewstimes.com
Circulation: 3,800pd, 600fr; Sworn/Estimate/Non-Audited
Advertising rate: Open inch rate $12.50
Established: 1886
Group: Pamplin Media Group
Clas. Adv........................... Rebecca Mansfield
Circ. Mgr..Kim Stephens
Prodn. Mgr. .... Maureen Zoebelein
Publ... Nikki DeBuse
Public Notice................................. Marc Caplan
Advertising Sales........................... Toni Ashby
Editor .... Jill SmithEquipment & Software: ; Software — QPS/QuarkXPress 4.1, Microsoft/Word.
Delivery Method: Mail, Newsstand, Racks
Areas Served: 97116, 97113, 97106, 97117,

97119, 97133, 97123, 97125

THE HILLSBORO TRIBUNE (FRI)
2038 Pacific Ave, Forest Grove, OR, 97116-2357, Washington, USA; gen tel (503) 357-3181; disp adv e-mail info@hillsborotribune.com; ed e-mail news@hillsborotribune.com; web site www.hillsborotribune.com
Circulation: 3,500pd, 2,500fr; Sworn/Estimate/Non-Audited
Advertising rate: Open inch rate $17.50
Established: 2012
Group: Pamplin Media Group
Editor....................................Geoff Pursinger
Delivery Method: Mail, Racks
Areas Served: 97123, 97124, 97006, 97007, 97133, 97229

GOLD BEACH

CURRY COUNTY REPORTER (WED)
29822 ELLENSBURG AVE, Gold Beach, OR, 97444, Curry, USA; gen tel (541) 247-6643; gen fax (541) 247-6644; disp adv e-mail micki@currycountyreporter.com; ed e-mail currycountyreporter@gmail.com; web site www.currycountyreporter.com
Circulation: 2,748pd,; AAM
Advertising rate: Open inch rate $8.75
Established: 1914
Co-Pub....................................Matt Hall
Co-Pub/Adv....................................Molly Walker
Mechanical Specifications: Type page 13 x 21 1/2.Equipment & Software: Hardware — APP/Mac; Software — Microsoft/Office 98, Adobe/PageMaker 6.0, QPS/QuarkXPress 4.0.
Delivery Method: Mail, Racks
Areas Served: Curry and Coos counties.

GRANTS PASS

ROGUE RIVER PRESS (WED)
8991 Rogue River Hwy, Grants Pass, OR, 97527-4377, Jackson, USA; gen tel (541) 582-1707; gen fax (541) 582-0201; disp adv e-mail rrpress@rogueriverpress.com; class adv e-mail marketing@rogueriverpress.com; ed e-mail editor@rogueriverpress.com; web site www.rogueriverpress.com
Circulation: 2,000pd,; Sworn/Estimate/Non-Audited
Advertising rate: Open inch rate $9.50 + 25% color
Established: 1915
Group: Valley Pride Publications, Llc
Circ/Web Mgr....................................Leif Birdsall
Admin....................................Pam Birdsall
Sports Ed....................................Brian Mortenson
Mechanical Specifications: Type page 10 1/4 x 13 1/2; E - 4 cols, 2 1/2, 1/8 between; A - 4 cols, 2 1/2, between; C - 6 cols, 1 3/20, between. Equipment & Software: Hardware — APP/Power Mac 7500, APP/Mac G4, APP/Mac G3 Powerbook; Software — QPS/QuarkXPress 4.0, Adobe/Photoshop 3.0.
Delivery Method: Mail, Newsstand, Racks
Areas Served: Jackson County

GRESHAM

BOOM! BOOMERS AND BEYOND (WED, MTHLY)
1190 NE Division St, Gresham, OR, 97030-5727, Multnomah, USA; gen tel (503) 665-2181; gen fax (503) 665-2187; adv fax (503) 669-2760; disp adv e-mail cmoore@commnewspapers.com; ed e-mail jschrag@pamplinmedia.com; web site www.boomnw.com
Advertising rate: Open inch rate $42.00
Ed....................................John Schrag
Circ. Mgr....................................Kim Stephens
Adv. Dir....................................Christine Moore

SANDY POST (WED)
584 NE 8TH ST, Gresham, OR, 97030, Clackamas, USA; gen tel (503) 668-5548; adv tel (503) 665-2181; gen fax (503) 668-0748; adv fax (503) 668-5549; disp adv e-mail aapplegate@theoutlookonline.com; class adv e-mail dbeauchamp@pamplinmedia.com; ed e-mail sbrown@theoutlookonline.com; web site http://pamplinmedia.com/sandy-post-news/
Circulation: 3,500pd, 28fr; Sworn/Estimate/Non-Audited
Advertising rate: Open inch rate $37.00
Established: 1937
Group: Pamplin Media Group
Pamplin Media Group
Pres....................................Mark Garber
Pub/Ed....................................Steve Brown
Adv. Mgr....................................Alisa Applegate
Circ. Mgr....................................Kim Stephens
Mechanical Specifications: Type page 13 x 21 1/2; E - 6 cols, 2 1/16, 1/6 between; A - 6 cols, 2 1/16, 1/6 between.Equipment & Software: Hardware — APP/Mac; Presses — G/Community; Software — QPS/QuarkXPress 4.0, Adobe/Photoshop.
Areas Served: 97009, 97011, 97019, 97028, 97049, 97055, 97067

THE OUTLOOK (TUES, FRI)
1190 NE Division St, Gresham, OR, 97030-5727, Multnomah, USA; gen tel (503) 665-2181; gen fax (503) 665-2187; disp adv e-mail todell@theoutlookonline.com; ed e-mail todell@theoutlookonline.com; web site portlandtribune.com/gresham-outlook-news/
Advertising rate: Open inch rate $37.00
Established: 1911
Group: Pamplin Media Group
VP....................................J. Brian Monihan
Ed....................................Tiffaney O'Dell
Circ. Mgr....................................Kim Stephens

HALFWAY

HELLS CANYON JOURNAL (WED)
145 N Main St, Halfway, OR, 97834-2018, Baker, USA; gen tel (541) 742-7900; gen fax (541) 742-7933; disp adv e-mail hcjads@pinetel.com; class adv e-mail hcjads@pinetel.com; ed e-mail hcj@pinetel.com; web site http://orenews.com/halfway
Circulation: 1,000pd,; Sworn/Estimate/Non-Audited
Advertising rate: Open inch rate $4.60
Established: 1983
Group: Hells Canyon Publishing, Inc.
Adv. Dir....................................Cindy Thayer
Circ. Mgr....................................Julie Bishop
Pub./Ed/Prod. Mgr....................................Steve Backstrom
Mechanical Specifications: Type page 11 3/4 x 21; E - 6 cols, 1 3/4, 1/6 between; A - 6 cols, 1 3/4, 1/6 between; C - 6 cols, 1 3/4, 1/6 between.Equipment & Software: Hardware — Pentium/PC; Software — Adobe/PageMaker 7.0, Adobe/Photoshop 6.0.
Areas Served: Baker County, Oregon

HEPPNER

HEPPNER GAZETTE-TIMES (WED)
188 W Willow St, Heppner, OR, 97836-2070, Morrow, USA; gen tel (541) 676-9228; gen fax (541) 676-9211; disp adv e-mail david@rapidserve.net; ed e-mail editor@rapidserve.net; web site www.heppner.net/gazette
Circulation: 2,000pd,; Sworn/Estimate/Non-Audited
Advertising rate: Open inch rate $5.00
Established: 1883
Group: Sykes Publishing, LLC
Ed....................................Andrea Di Salvo

HERMISTON

HERMISTON HERALD (WED, SAT)
333 E Main St, Hermiston, OR, 97838-1869, Umatilla County, USA; gen tel (541) 567-6457; gen fax (541) 567-1764; disp adv e-mail addirector@hermistonherald.com; ed e-mail gwest@hermistonherald.com; web site www.hermistonherald.com
Circulation: 4,322pd, 6,200fr; Sworn/Estimate/Non-Audited
Advertising rate: Open inch rate $10.50
Established: 1906
Group: EO Media Group
Adv. Dir....................................Marissa Williams
Circ. Mgr....................................Dawn Hendricks
Ed....................................Gary West
Mechanical Specifications: Type page 13 x 21 1/2; E - 6 cols, 2 1/16, between; A - 6 cols, 2 1/16, between; C - 8 cols, 1 1/2, between. Equipment & Software: Hardware — APP/Mac; Presses — 5-G/Community; Software — QPS/QuarkXPress 3.2, Adobe/Photoshop 5, Adobe/Acrobat 4.
Areas Served: 97838

THE HERMISTON HERALD (WED)
333 E Main St, Hermiston, OR, 97838-1869, Umatilla, USA; gen tel (541) 567-6457; ed e-mail newsroom@hermistonherald.com; web site www.hermistonherald.com
Circulation: 10,000pd, 156fr; Sworn/Estimate/Non-Audited
Established: 1906
Group: EO Media Group
Adv. Sales....................................Jeanne Jewett
Mechanical Specifications: Type page 13 x 21 1/2; E - 6 cols, 2, 1/6 between; A - 6 cols, 2, 1/6 between; C - 7 cols, 1 1/3, 1/6 between. Equipment & Software: Hardware — APP/Mac; Presses — 7-G/Community; Software — QPS/QuarkXPress 4.0, Adobe/Photoshop 5.0.
Delivery Method: Mail, Newsstand
Areas Served: Umatilla County/Morrow County

HOOD RIVER

HOOD RIVER NEWS (WED, SAT)
419 State St, Ste 1, Hood River, OR, 97031-2075, Hood River, USA; gen tel (541) 386-1234; gen fax (541) 386-6796; disp adv e-mail jthompson@hoodrivernews.com; class adv e-mail hrnews@hoodrivernews.com; ed e-mail kneumann-rea@hoodrivernews.com; web site www.hoodrivernews.com
Circulation: 5,300pd, 98fr; Sworn/Estimate/Non-Audited
Advertising rate: Open inch rate $11.50
Established: 1905
Group: Eagle Newspapers, Inc.
Digital Platform - Mobile: Apple, Android, Windows, Blackberry
Digital Platform - Tablet: Apple iOS, Android, Windows 7, Blackberry Tablet OS, Kindle, Nook, Kindle Fire
Pub....................................Joe Petshow
Circ. Mgr....................................Esther Smith
Ed....................................Kirby Neumann-Rea
Adv. Mgr....................................Jody Thompson
Mechanical Specifications: 6 columns - Each column 1.583 inches wide with 0.125 inch gutters. Depth: 21 inches.Equipment & Software: ; Presses — Quad Stack; Goss
Delivery Method: Mail, Newsstand, Carrier, Racks
Areas Served: 97031 97014 97044 97041 97040

JOHN DAY

BLUE MOUNTAIN EAGLE (WED)
195 N Canyon Blvd, John Day, OR, 97845-1187, Grant, USA; gen tel (541) 575-0710; gen fax (541) 575-1244; disp adv e-mail kim@bmeagle.com; class adv e-mail trista@bmeagle.com; ed e-mail editor@bluemountaineagle.com; web site www.myeaglenews.com
Circulation: 3,500pd, 75fr; Sworn/Estimate/Non-Audited
Advertising rate: Open inch rate $9.00
Established: 1868
Group: East Oregonian
Ed....................................Scotta Calister
Pub....................................Marissa Williams
Adv. Rep....................................Kim Kell
Class./Circ....................................Trista Cox
Mechanical Specifications: Type page 12 x 21 1/2; E - 6 cols, 1 3/4, 1/6 between; A - 6 cols, 1 3/4, 1/6 between; C - 6 cols, 1 3/4, 1/6 between.
Areas Served: 97845, 97865, 97869, 97820, 97856, 97825, 97864

JUNCTION CITY

TRI-COUNTY NEWS (WED)
225 W 6th Ave, Junction City, OR, 97448-1605, lane, USA; gen tel (541) 234-2111; ed tel (541) 234-2111; disp adv e-mail ads@tctrib.com; ed e-mail news@tctrib.com; web site www.yourtribunenews.com
Circulation: 2,000pd,; Sworn/Estimate/Non-Audited
Advertising rate: Open inch rate $8.00
Established: 1977
Digital Platform - Mobile: Apple, Android, Windows, Blackberry
Digital Platform - Tablet: Apple iOS, Android, Windows 7, Blackberry Tablet OS
Pub....................................Steve Rowland
Ed....................................Gini Barmlett
Mng. Editor....................................Sayde Moser
Bus. Mgr....................................Kyle Krenik
Delivery Method: Mail, Newsstand
Areas Served: 97404, 97448, 97446, 97408, 97456

KEIZER

KEIZERTIMES (FRI)
142 Chemawa Rd N, Keizer, OR, 97303-5356, Marion, USA; gen tel (503) 390-1051; gen fax (503) 390-8023; disp adv e-mail advertising@keizertimes.com; publisher@keizertimes.com; class adv e-mail classifieds@keizertimes.com; ed e-mail editor@keizertimes.com; web site www.keizertimes.com
Circulation: 1,900pd, 0fr; Sworn/Estimate/Non-Audited
Advertising rate: Open inch rate $13.95
Established: 1979
Group: Wheatland Publishing Corp.Editions: (1) Keizertimes
Pub....................................Lyndon Zaitz
Legal Notices....................................Laurie Painter
Prod./Clas....................................Andrew Jackson
News Ed....................................Eric A. Howald
Assoc. Ed....................................Derek Wiley
Adv. Acc. Rep....................................Paula Moseley
Mechanical Specifications: 1 column = 1.667 inches
2 columns = 3.45 inches
3 columns = 5.25 inches
4 columns = 7.04 inches
5 columns = 8.83 inches
6 columns = 10.62 inches
21.25 inches tallEquipment & Software: Hardware — Macintosh; Presses — None; Software — InDesign, Adobe platforms
Delivery Method: Mail, Racks
Areas Served: 97303

LA GRANDE

THE OBSERVER (MON, WED, FRI)
1406 5th St, La Grande, OR, 97850-2402, Union, USA; gen tel (541) 963-3161; adv tel (541) 963-3161; ed tel (541) 963-3161; gen fax (541) 963-7804; adv fax (541) 963-7804; ed fax (541) 963-7804; disp adv e-mail ads@lagrandeobserver.com; class adv e-mail ads@lagrandeobserver.com; ed e-mail news@lagrandeobserver.com; web site www.lagrandeobserver.com - 253,700(views) 54,500(visitors)
Circulation: 3,801pd, 174fr; CVC
Advertising rate: Open inch rate $14.93
Established: 1896
Group: Western Communications, Inc.
Circ. Mgr....................................Kelli Craft
Ed/Pub....................................Andrew Cutler
Gen Mgr, Operations....................................Frank Everidge
Advt Dir....................................Karrine Brogoitti
Mechanical Specifications: Type page 11.75 x

21 1/2; E - 6 cols, 2 1/16, 1/8 between; A - 6 cols, 2 1/16, 1/8 between; C - 6 cols, 1 9/16, 1/16 between.
Delivery Method: Mail, Newsstand, Carrier, Racks
Areas Served: 97850; 97883; 97827; 97841; 97824; 97828;97846; 97885; 97867; 97857

LAKE OSWEGO

REGAL COURIER (THUR, MTHLY)

400 2nd St, Lake Oswego, OR, 97034-3127, Clackamas, USA; gen tel (503) 639-5414; adv tel (971) 204-7771; ed tel (503) 639-5414; gen fax (503) 635-8817; adv fax (503) 620-3433; ed fax (503) 635-8817; disp adv e-mail cmoore@pamplinmediia.com; class adv e-mail rmansfield@pamplin meda.com; ed e-mail editor@theregalcourier.com; web site www.portlandtribune.com/regal-courier-news
Circulation: 4,800fr; Sworn/Estimate/Non-Audited
Advertising rate: Open inch rate $9.85
Established: 1977
Group: Pamplin Media Group
Digital Platform - Mobile: Apple, Android
Digital Platform - Tablet: Apple iOS, Android
Pub.. Christine Moore
Delivery Method: Mail, Newsstand, Racks
Areas Served: Washington County

SOUTHWEST COMMUNITY CONNECTION (THUR, MTHLY)

400 2nd St, Lake Oswego, OR, 97034-3127, Clackamas, USA; gen tel (503) 639-5414; adv tel (503) 546-9883; gen fax (503) 635-8817; disp adv e-mail cmoore@commnewspapers.com; class adv e-mail lbernards@commnewspapers.com; ed e-mail kelseyo@pamplinmedia.com; web site www.swcommconnection.com
Advertising rate: Open inch rate $9.85
Established: 1994
Group: Pamplin Media Group
Pamplin Media Group
Digital Platform - Mobile: Apple, Android
Digital Platform - Tablet: Apple iOS, Android
Pub.. Brian Monihan
Adv. Dir.. Christine Moore
Ed.. Kelsey O'Halloran
Delivery Method: Mail, Newsstand, Racks
Areas Served: Southwest Portland

THE LAKE OSWEGO REVIEW (THUR)

400 2nd St, Lake Oswego, OR, 97034-3127, Clackamas, USA; gen tel (503) 635-8811; adv tel (503) 546-0771; gen fax (503) 635-8817; disp adv e-mail cmoore@commnewspapers.com; class adv e-mail callsop@commnewspapers.com; ed e-mail gstein@lakeoswegoreview.com; web site www.portlandtribune.com/lake-oswego-review-news
Circulation: 7,600pd,; Sworn/Estimate/Non-Audited
Advertising rate: Open inch rate $37.00
Established: 1920
Group: Pamplin Media Group
Pamplin Media Group
Pub.. J. Brian Monihan
Adv Dir.. Christine Moore
Class Sales Mgr.. Charlotte Allsop
Circ. Mgr.. Gini Kraemer
Ed.. Gary Stein
Delivery Method: Mail, Newsstand
Areas Served: 97034, 97035, 97219

WEST LINN TIDINGS (THUR)

400 2nd St, Lake Oswego, OR, 97034-3127, Clackamas, USA; gen tel (503) 635-8811; adv tel (503) 684-0360; gen fax (503) 635-8817; disp adv e-mail cmoore@commnewspapers.com; class adv e-mail bmonihan@westlinntidings.com; ed e-mail gstein@lakeoswegoreview.com; web site www.westlinntidings.com
Circulation: 3,750pd,; USPS
Advertising rate: Open inch rate $37.00
Established: 1981
Group: Pamplin Media Group
Pub.. J. Brian Monihan
Ed.. Gary Stein
Adv. Dir.. Christine Moore
Delivery Method: Mail, Newsstand
Areas Served: 97068

WILSONVILLE SPOKESMAN (WED)

400 2nd St, Lake Oswego, OR, 97034-3127, Clackamas, USA; gen tel (503) 682-3935; adv tel (503) 684-0360; gen fax (503) 682-6265; disp adv e-mail cmoore@commnewspapers.com; ed e-mail gstein@lakeoswegoreview.com; web site www.wilsonvillespokesman.com
Circulation: 3,350pd, 2,500fr; Sworn/Estimate/Non-Audited
Advertising rate: Open inch rate $37.00
Established: 1985
Group: Pamplin Media Group
Pub.. J. Brian Monihan
Adv. Dir.. Christine Moore
Ed.. Gary Stein
Mechanical Specifications: Type page 11 7/8 x 21 1/2; E - 6 cols, 1 7/8, 1/8 between; A - 6 cols, 1 7/8, 1/8 between; C - 9 cols, 1 1/4, 1/8 between.
Areas Served: 97070, 97140, 97002

LAKEVIEW

LAKE COUNTY EXAMINER (WED)

739 N 2nd St, Lakeview, OR, 97630-1512, Lake, USA; gen tel (541) 947-3378; gen fax (541) 947-4359; disp adv e-mail ads@lakecountyexam.com; ed e-mail news@lakecountyexam.com; web site www.lakecountyexam.com
Circulation: 2,150pd, 4,300fr; Sworn/Estimate/Non-Audited
Advertising rate: Open inch rate $7.55
Established: 1880
Group: Adams Publishing Group, LLC
Ed.. Tillie Flynn
Circ. Mgr.. Jolie Murphy
Adv.. Kristin Keiser
Mechanical Specifications: Type page 10.5 x 20.25; E - 6 cols, 1 5/6, 3/16 between; A - 6 cols, 1.6458, 3/16 between; C - 6 cols, 1.6458, 3/16 between.Equipment & Software: Hardware — APP/Mac; Software — InDesigns
Adobe/Photoshop, Adobe/Illustrator.
Delivery Method: Mail
Areas Served: 97630- 97635

LEBANON

LEBANON EXPRESS (WED)

90 E Grant St, Lebanon, OR, 97355-3201, Linn, USA; gen tel (541) 258-3151; gen fax (541) 259-3569; disp adv e-mail lebanon.express@lee.net; web site www.lebanon-express.com
Circulation: 2,664pd,; Sworn/Estimate/Non-Audited
Advertising rate: Open inch rate $8.00
Established: 1887
Group: Lee Enterprises, Inc.
Ed.. Matt DeBow
Adv. Dir.. Cyndi Sprinkel-Hart
Dir. of Ops.. Bill Draper

LINCOLN CITY

OREGON COAST TODAY (FRI)

800 SE Highway 101, Lincoln City, OR, 97367-2755, Lincoln, USA; gen tel (541) 921-0413; disp adv e-mail greg@oregoncoasttoday.com; ed e-mail patrick@oregoncoasttoday.com; web site www.oregoncoasttoday.com
Circulation: 17,000fr; Sworn/Estimate/Non-Audited
Group: EO Media Group
Adv. Rep.. Greg Robertson
Ed.. Patrick Alexander

THE NEWS GUARD (WED)

1818 N E. 21st St., Lincoln City, OR, 97367, Lincoln, USA; gen tel (541) 994-2178; gen fax (541) 994-7613; disp adv e-mail newsguardads@countrymedia.net; class adv e-mail classifieds@thenewsguard.com; ed e-mail newsguardeditor@countrymedia.net; web site www.thenewsguard.com
Circulation: 6,000pd,; Sworn/Estimate/Non-Audited
Advertising rate: Open inch rate $10.85
Established: 1927
Group: Country Media Inc.
Country Media, Inc
Pub.. Joe Warren
Mechanical Specifications: Type page 11 1/8 x 21 1/2; E - 6 cols, 1 5/6, 1/8 between; A - 6 cols, 1 5/6, 1/8 between; C - 9 cols, 1 5/6, 1/8 between.
Delivery Method: Mail, Newsstand, Racks
Areas Served: 97149, 97368, 97367, 97388, 97341

MADRAS

THE MADRAS PIONEER (WED)

345 SE 5th St, Madras, OR, 97741-1501, Jefferson, USA; gen tel (541) 475-2275; gen fax (541) 475-3710; disp adv e-mail tahern@eaglenewspapers.com; web site www.madraspioneer.com
Circulation: 3,300pd, 125fr; USPS
Advertising rate: Open inch rate $37.00
Established: 1904
Group: Pamplin Media Group
Pub.. Tony Ahern
Ed.. Susan Matheny
News Ed.. Holly Gill
Adv. Dir.. Joy DeHaan
Circ. Dir.. Joey Lantz
Comp. Supv..
Becky JohnsonEquipment & Software: Hardware — PCs; Software — QPS/QuarkXPress 4.0, Archetype/Corel Draw.
Areas Served: 97741, 97761, 97734

MANZANITA

NORTH COAST CITIZEN (THUR, BI-MTHLY)

PO Box 355, Manzanita, OR, 97130-0355, Tillamook, USA; gen tel (503) 842-7535; ed tel editor@northcoastcitizen.com; gen fax (503) 842-8842; disp adv e-mail jwarren@countrymedia.net; web site www.northcoastcitizen.com
Circulation: 1,200pd, 50fr; Sworn/Estimate/Non-Audited
Established: 1996
Group: Country Media Inc.
Managing Editor.. Brian Cameron
Delivery Method: Mail, Newsstand, Racks
Areas Served: Manzanita, Wheeler and Nehalem Oregon

MCKENZIE BRIDGE

MCKENZIE RIVER REFLECTIONS (THUR)

59059 Old McKenzie Hwy, McKenzie Bridge, OR, 97413-9615, Lane, USA; gen tel (541) 822-3358; gen fax (541) 663-4550; disp adv e-mail rivref@aol.com; class adv e-mail rivref@aol.com; ed e-mail rivref@aol.com; web site mckenzieriverreflectionsnewspaper.com
Circulation: 800pd,; Sworn/Estimate/Non-Audited
Advertising rate: Open inch rate $6.65
Established: 1978
Digital Platform - Mobile: Apple
Digital Platform - Tablet: Apple iOS
Pub.. Kenneth Engelman
Mng. Ed.. Louise Engelman
Mechanical Specifications: 10.25"w X 16.5"h - 5 columns
Delivery Method: Mail, Newsstand
Areas Served: 97478, 97489, 97488, 97413

MCMINNVILLE

NEWS-REGISTER (TUES, FRI)

611 NE 3rd St, McMinnville, OR, 97128-4518, Yamhill, USA; gen tel (503) 472-5114; gen fax (503) 472-9151; disp adv e-mail rsudeith@oregonlitho.com; class adv e-mail classified@newsregister.com; ed e-mail sbagwell@newsregister.com; web site www.newsregister.com
Circulation: 8,291pd, 300fr; Sworn/Estimate/Non-Audited
Advertising rate: Open inch rate $18.46
Established: 1866
Group: Bladine Family
Pres./Pub.. Jeb Bladine
Mng. Ed.. Steve Bagwell
Sale/Mktg. Dir.. Robert Sudeith
Mechanical Specifications: Type page 11 5/8 x 21 1/2; A - 6 cols, 1 3/4, 1/3 between; C - 6 cols, 1 3/4, 1/3 between.Equipment & Software: Hardware — APP/Mac; Presses — 18-G/Community; Software — APT
Delivery Method: Mail, Newsstand, Racks
Areas Served: 97218, 97114, 97111, 97101, 97115, 97378, 97396, 97127, 97148

MILTON FREEWATER

VALLEY HERALD (FRI)

408 N Main St, Milton Freewater, OR, 97862-1724, Umatilla, USA; gen tel (541) 938-6688; gen fax (541) 938-6689; ed e-mail s.widmer.valleyherald@gmail.com; web site http://www.mfvalleyherald.net/
Circulation: 2,500pd,; Sworn/Estimate/Non-Audited
Advertising rate: Open inch rate $7.50
Established: 2001
Circ. Mgr.. Melanie Hall
Pub.. Sherrie Widmer

MOLALLA

MOLALLA PIONEER (WED)

217 E Main St, Molalla, OR, 97038-8128, Clackamas, USA; gen tel (503) 829-2301; gen fax (503) 829-2317; disp adv e-mail tnizer@canbyherald.com; class adv e-mail rmansfield@pamplinmedia.com; ed e-mail psavage@molallapioneer.com; web site www.molallapioneer.com
Circulation: 3,800pd, 2,900fr; Sworn/Estimate/Non-Audited
Advertising rate: Open inch rate $37.00
Established: 1913
Group: Pamplin Media Group
Pamplin Media Group
Ed.. Peggy Savage
Pub.. Georgia Newton
Circ. Mgr.. Linda Baker
Areas Served: 97038, 97017, 97042, 97004

MYRTLE CREEK

THE DOUGLAS COUNTY MAIL (THUR)

325 NE 1st Ave, Myrtle Creek, OR, 97457-9063, Douglas, USA; gen tel (541) 863-5233; gen fax (541) 863-5234; ed e-mail dcmail@dcmail.info
Circulation: 2,000pd, 20fr; Sworn/Estimate/Non-Audited
Advertising rate: Open inch rate $7.00
Established: 1902
Group: Myrtle Tree Press, Inc.
Pub./Ed.. Robert L. Chaney
Mechanical Specifications: Type page 13 x 21 1/2; E - 6 cols, 2, 1/6 between; A - 6 cols, 2, 1/6 between; C - 6 cols, 2, 1/6 between.
Areas Served: 97410, 97417, 97429, 97442, 97457, 97469, 97496, 97479

MYRTLE POINT

MYRTLE POINT HERALD (THUR)
408 Spruce St, Myrtle Point, OR, 97458-1062, Coos, USA; gen tel (541) 572-2717; gen fax (541) 572-2828; disp adv e-mail mpherald@harborside.com; ed e-mail myrtlepointherald@gmail.com
Circulation: 2,100pd,; Sworn/Estimate/Non-Audited
Advertising rate: Open inch rate $7.50
Established: 1889
Ed. .... Mary Schamehorn
Owner/Adv. Mgr. .... Sherry Anderson
Mechanical Specifications: Type page 13 x 21; E - 6 cols, 2 1/12, 1/6 between; A - 6 cols, 2 1/12, 1/16 between; C - 6 cols, 2 1/12, 1/6 between.

NEWBERG

THE NEWBERG GRAPHIC (WED, SAT)
PO Box 700, Newberg, OR, 97132-0700, Yamhill, USA; gen tel (503) 538-2181; gen fax (503) 538-1632; disp adv e-mail pbecker@newberggraphic.com; class adv e-mail rmansfield@pamplinmedia.com; ed e-mail gallen@newberggraphic.com; web site www.newberggraphic.com
Circulation: 5,500pd,; Sworn/Estimate/Non-Audited
Advertising rate: Open inch rate $37.00
Established: 1888
Group: Pamplin Media Group
Pamplin Media Group
Pub .... Allen Herriges
Ed. .... Gary Allen
Adv. .... Paula Becker
Mechanical Specifications: Type page 11 7/8 x 21 1/2; E - 6 cols, 1 7/8, 1/6 between; A - 6 cols, 1 7/8, 1/6 between; C - 9 cols, 1 3/16, 1/6 between.Equipment & Software: ; Presses — G/Community; Software — QPS/QuarkXPress.
Areas Served: 97132, 97115, 97137

NEWPORT

NEWS-TIMES (WED, FRI)
831 NE Avery St, Newport, OR, 97365-3033, Lincoln, USA; gen tel (541) 265-8571; gen fax (541) 265-3103; disp adv e-mail bmoore@newportnewstimes.com; class adv e-mail dlacroix@newportnewstimes.com; ed e-mail whaupt@newportnewstimes.com; web site www.newportnewstimes.com
Circulation: 10,100pd, 301fr; Sworn/Estimate/Non-Audited
Advertising rate: Open inch rate $20.76
Established: 1882
Group: News Media Corp.
Adv. Dir. .... Barbara Moore
Pub .... Jamie Rand
Ed. .... Wyatt Haupt
Circ. Mgr. .... David Liulamaga
Mechanical Specifications: Type page 12 x 21 1/2; E - 6 cols, 1 7/8, 3/20 between; A - 6 cols, 1 7/8, 3/20 between; C - 9 cols, 1 1/4, 3/20 between.Equipment & Software: Hardware — APP/Mac; Presses — 6-G/Community; Software — QPS/QuarkXPress, Adobe/Photoshop.
Areas Served: 97365, 97366, 97369, 97367, 97388, 97391, 97394, 97398

OAKRIDGE

DEAD MOUNTAIN ECHO (THUR)
48013 Highway 58, Oakridge, OR, 97463-9523, Lane, USA; gen tel (541) 782-4241; gen fax (541) 782-3323; ed e-mail lroberts@efn.org; web site https://www.facebook.com/DeadMountainEcho/
Circulation: 650pd, 2,400fr; Sworn/Estimate/Non-Audited
Advertising rate: Open inch rate $11.00
Established: 1973
Group: Echo Publishing, Inc.
Ed./Pub .... Larry D. Roberts
Mechanical Specifications: Type page 10 1/4 x 16; E - 5 cols, 11 5/16, 1/6 between; A - 5 cols, 11 5/16, 1/6 between; C - 7 cols, 1 1/3, 1/6 between.
Delivery Method: Mail, Newsstand
Areas Served: 97463, 97492

PENDLETON

THE PENDLETON RECORD (THUR)
PO Box 69, 809 SE Court Ave, Pendleton, OR, 97801-0069, Umatilla, USA; gen tel (541) 276-2853; disp adv e-mail penrecor@uci.net
Circulation: 1,000pd,; Sworn/Estimate/Non-Audited
Advertising rate: Open inch rate $7.50
Established: 1911
Adv. Mgr. .... Marguerite Maznaritz
Ed. .... Sam Westover
Mechanical Specifications: Type page 13 x 21.

PORT ORFORD

PORT ORFORD NEWS (WED)
519 10th St, Port Orford, OR, 97465-8765, Curry, USA; gen tel (541) 260-3638; ed e-mail portorfordnews@gmail.com; web site www.portorfordnews.net
Circulation: 1,200pd, 9fr; Sworn/Estimate/Non-Audited
Advertising rate: Open inch rate $6.00
Established: 1958
Pub .... Matt HallEquipment & Software: Hardware — APP/Mac G3; Software — Adobe/PageMaker, Microsoft/Office.

PORTLAND

BUSINESS JOURNAL OF PORTLAND (FRI)
851 SW 6th Ave Ste 500, Suite 500, Portland, OR, 97204-1342, Multnomah, USA; gen tel (503) 274-8733; gen fax (503) 219-3450; disp adv e-mail avangordon@bizjournals.com; class adv e-mail athomas@bizjournals.com; ed e-mail sstevens@bizjournals.com; web site http://www.bizjournals.com/portland/
Advertising rate: 1/8 page 52x $427; 1/2 page 52x $1504; Full page 52x $2791
Established: 1984
Digital Platform - Mobile: Apple, Android
Digital Platform - Tablet: Apple iOS, Android
Pub .... Craig Wessel
Adv. Coord. .... Angela Thomas
Ed .... Suzanne Stevenson
Delivery Method: Mail, Newsstand, Racks
Areas Served: Multnomah, Clackamas, Washington

DAILY JOURNAL OF COMMERCE (MON, WED, FRI)
921 SW Washington St Ste 210, Suite 210, Portland, OR, 97205-2810, Multnomah, USA; gen tel (503) 226-1311; disp adv e-mail bbeyer@djcOregon.com; class adv e-mail sales@djcoregon.com; ed e-mail stephanie.basalyga@djcoregon.com; web site www.djcoregon.com
Advertising rate: Open inch rate $19.00
Established: 1872
Group: The Dolan Company
Pub .... Nick Bjork
Adv. Mgr. .... Bill Beyer
Ed .... Stephanie Basalyga
Mechanical Specifications: 10" x 16" full page
Delivery Method: Mail

FOREST GROVE LEADER (WED)
1500 SW 1st Ave, Ste 400, Portland, OR, 97201-5828, Multnomah, USA; gen tel (503) 648-1131; gen fax (503) 294-4191; disp adv e-mail advertise@oregonian.com; class adv e-mail classified@oregonian.com; ed e-mail newsclerk@oregonian.com; web site www.oregonlive.com//forestgroveleader - 20,000,000(views) 3,000,000(visitors)
Circulation: 18,035fr; AAM
Advertising rate: 1/8 Pg $196.38; 1/6 Pg $260.14; 1/4 Pg $384.85
Established: 2013
Group: Advance Publications, Inc.
Digital Platform - Mobile: Apple, Android, Windows, Blackberry
Pub .... Chris Anderson
Adv. Sales .... Monica Butler
Ed. .... Samantha Swindler
VP, Sales/Multimedia .... Barbara Swanson
Delivery Method: Newsstand
Areas Served: 97116, 97117, 97119, 97125, 97113, 97109, 97106

HILLSBORO ARGUS (WED, FRI)
1515 SW 5th Ave, Ste 1000, Portland, OR, 97201-5615, Washington, USA; gen tel (503) 648-1131; gen fax (503) 294-4191; disp adv e-mail mbutler@hillsboroargus.com; class adv e-mail argusclassifieds@hillsboroargus.com; ed e-mail mkatches@oregonian.com; web site www.oregonlive.com/hillsboroargus - 20,000,000(views) 3,000,000(visitors)
Circulation: 1,040pd, 17,335fr; AAM
Advertising rate: 1/8 Pg $275.76; 1/7 Pg $306.40; 1/6 Pg $367.68
Established: 1873
Group: Advance Publications, Inc.
Digital Platform - Mobile: Apple, Android, Windows, Blackberry
Digital Platform - Tablet: Apple iOS, Android, Windows 7, Blackberry Tablet OS, Kindle, Nook, Kindle Fire
Adv. Dir. .... Monica Butler
Ed .... Mark Katches
Pres .... John Maher
Mechanical Specifications: Type page 11 7/8 x 21 1/2; E - 6 cols, 1 7/8, 1/4 between; A - 6 cols, 1 7/8, 1/4 between; C - 8 cols, 1, 1/4 between.Equipment & Software: Hardware — 12-Mk, 13-APP/Mac; Presses — G/Suburban; Software — QPS/QuarkXPress 4.1, Adobe/Photoshop 3.0, Macromedia/Freehand 4.
Delivery Method: Newsstand, Carrier, Racks
Areas Served: 97006. 97007, 97229, 97123, 97124, 97133

OREGON CITY NEWS (WED)
6605 SE Lake Rd, Portland, OR, 97222-2161, Portland, USA; gen tel (503) 684-0360; gen fax (503) 620-3433; disp adv e-mail kschaub@clackamasreview.com; class adv e-mail dbeauchamp@pamplinmedia.com; ed e-mail rrendleman@clackamasreview.com; web site www.oregoncitynewsonline.com
Circulation: 3,500pd,; Sworn/Estimate/Non-Audited
Advertising rate: Open inch rate $37.00
Group: Pamplin Media Group
Pub .... Angela Fox
Ed .... Raymond Rendleman
Adv. Rep .... Kathy Schaub
Areas Served: 97045, 97015, 97222, 97267, 97027

PORTLAND MERCURY (THUR)
115 SW Ash St Ste 600, Suite 600, Portland, OR, 97204-3549, Multnomah, USA; gen tel (503) 294-0840; gen fax (503) 294-0844; disp adv e-mail salesinfo@portlandmercury.com; ed e-mail news@portlandmercury.com; web site www.portlandmercury.com
Circulation: 8pd, 35,645fr; VAC
Advertising rate: 1/4 Pg $604.00; 1/2 Pg $1208.00; Jr Pg $1812.00; Full Pg $2416.00
Established: 2001
Group: Index Newspapers, Inc
Digital Platform - Mobile: Android, Windows, Blackberry
Digital Platform - Tablet: Android, Windows 7, Blackberry Tablet OS, Kindle, Nook, Kindle Fire
Pub .... Rob Thompson
Adv. Dir. .... James Deeley
Ed. .... Steve Humphrey
Areas Served: Portland Metro Area , Beaverton, Gresham

SUSTAINABLE LIFE (THUR, MTHLY)
6605 SE Lake Rd, Portland, OR, 97222-2161, Multnomah, USA; gen tel (503) 226-6397; adv tel (503) 546-0771; ed tel (503) 546-5139; gen fax (503) 546-0727; adv fax (503) 620-3433; ed fax (503) 546-0727; disp adv e-mail cmoore@commnewspapers.com; class adv e-mail classifiedadvertising@commnewspapers.com; ed e-mail kharden@commnewspapers.com; web site http://portlandtribune.com/portland-tribune-sustainable-life - 69,137(views) 12,643(visitors)
Circulation: 80,000pd, 97,000fr
Advertising rate: Open inch rate $65.00
Established: 2006
Group: Pamplin Media Group
Digital Platform - Mobile: Apple, Android, Windows, Blackberry
Digital Platform - Tablet: Apple iOS, Android, Windows 7, Blackberry Tablet OS
Pres. .... Mark Garber
Adv. Dir. .... Christine Moore
Exec. Ed. .... Kevin Harden
Circ. Mgr .... Kim Stephens
Delivery Method: Mail, Racks
Areas Served: 97222

THE BEAVERTON VALLEY TIMES (THUR)
6605 SE Lake Rd, Portland, OR, 97222-2161, Clackamas, USA; gen tel (503) 684-0360; gen fax (503) 620-3433; disp adv e-mail cmoore@pamplinmedia.com; class adv e-mail rmansfield@pamplinmedia.com; ed e-mail dhaynes@pamplinmedia.com; web site beavertonvalleytimes.com
Circulation: 7,000pd,; Sworn/Estimate/Non-Audited
Advertising rate: Open inch rate $16.17
Established: 1921
Group: Pamplin Media Group
Pamplin Media Group
Adv. Dir .... Christine Moore
Circ. Mgr .... Kim Stephens
Pub .... Mark Garber
Ed. .... Dana HaynesEquipment & Software: ; Software — QPS/QuarkXPress, Adobe/InDesign, Macromedia Freehand, Adobe/Illustrator, Adobe/Photoshop, Microsoft/Word.
Delivery Method: Mail, Newsstand, Racks
Areas Served: 97005, 97006, 97007, 97008, 97225, 97229

THE BEE (WED, MTHLY)
1837 SE Harold St, Portland, OR, 97202-4932, Multnomah, USA; gen tel (503) 232-2326; gen fax (503) 232-9787; web site www.thebeenews.com
Advertising rate: Open inch rate $37.00
Established: ReadTheBee@myexcel.com
Group: Pamplin Media Group
Pub .... J. Brian Monihan
Ed./Gen. Mgr. .... Eric Norberg
Areas Served: 97202, 97206

THE CLACKAMAS REVIEW (WED)
6605 SE Lake Rd, Portland, OR, 97222-2161, Multnomah, USA; gen tel (503) 684-0360; gen fax (503) 620-3433; disp adv e-mail kschaub@clackamasreview.com; class adv e-mail dbeauchamp@pamplinmedia.com; ed e-mail RRendleman@clackamasreview.com; web site www.clackamasreview.com
Circulation: 1,000pd, 33,300fr; Sworn/Estimate/Non-Audited
Advertising rate: Open inch rate $37.00
Group: Pamplin Media Group
Pub .... Angela Fox
Ed .... Raymond Rendleman
Circ. Mgr. .... Kim Stephens
Adv. Rep. .... Kathy Schaub
Mechanical Specifications: Type page 9 3/4 x 15; E - 5 cols, 1 13/16, 1/4 between; A - 5 cols, 1 13/16, 1/4 between; C - 7 cols, 1 1/4, between.
Equipment & Software: Hardware — APP/Mac; Presses — G/Community; Software — QPS/QuarkXPress 3.31, Claris/FileMaker Pro, Adobe/Photoshop, Microsoft/Word 5.0.
Areas Served: 97045, 97015, 97222, 97267, 97027

THE PORTLAND TRIBUNE (THUR)
6605 SE Lake Rd, Portland, OR, 97222-2161, Clackamas, USA; gen tel (503) 226-6397; adv tel (503) 546-0771; ed tel (503) 546-5167; gen fax (503) 620-3433; disp adv e-mail cmoore@commnewspapers.com; class adv e-mail dbeauchamp@pamplinmedia.com; ed e-mail jschrag@pamplinmedia.com; web site www.portlandtribune.com
Advertising rate: Open inch rate $75.00
Established: 2001
Group: Pamplin Media Group
Pamplin Media Group
Digital Platform - Mobile: Apple, Android, Windows, Blackberry
Digital Platform - Tablet: Apple iOS, Android, Windows 7, Blackberry Tablet OS
Pres. .... Mark Garber
Ed. .... John Schrag
Adv. Dir. .... Christine Moore
Circ. Mgr .... Kim Stephens
Delivery Method: Mail, Newsstand, Racks
Areas Served: Portland

THE SOUTHEAST EXAMINER (SAT)
PO Box 33663, Portland, OR, 97292-3663, Multnomah, USA; gen tel (503) 254-7550; gen fax (503) 254-7545; ed e-mail examiner@inseportland.com; web site http://www.southeastexaminer.com
Circulation: 25,975fr; CVC
Advertising rate: Open inch rate $32.45
Established: 1988
Digital Platform - Mobile: Apple
Pub./Circ. Mgr. .... Nancy Tannler
Delivery Method: Mail, Racks
Areas Served: inner se portland

THE TIMES (TIGARD/TUALATIN TIMES) (THUR)
6605 SE Lake Rd, Portland, OR, 97222-2161, Clackamas, USA; gen tel (503) 546-0771; adv tel (503) 546-0771; ed tel (503) 546-0771; gen fax (503) 620-3433; disp adv e-mail cmoore@pamplinmedia.com; class adv e-mail rmanffield@pamplinmedia.com; ed e-mail dhaynes@pamplinmedia.com; web site www.tigardtimes.com
Circulation: 7,000pd,; Sworn/Estimate/Non-Audited
Advertising rate: Open inch rate $16.17
Established: 1956
Group: Pamplin Media Group
Adv. Dir .... Christine Moore
Circ. Mgr .... Kim Stephens
Ed. .... Dana HaynesEquipment & Software: ; Software — QPS/QuarkXPress, Adobe/InDesign, Adobe/Illustrator, Macromedia/Freelance, Adobe/Photoshop, Microsoft/Word.
Delivery Method: Mail, Newsstand, Racks
Areas Served: 97223, 97224, 97062, 97140

PRINEVILLE

CENTRAL OREGONIAN (TUES, FRI)
558 N Main St, Prineville, OR, 97754-1199, Crook, USA; gen tel (541) 447-6205; gen fax (541) 447-1754; disp adv e-mail advertising@centraloregonian.com; class adv e-mail classifieds@centraloregonian.com; ed e-mail jchaney@centraloregonian.com; web site www.centraloregonian.com
Circulation: 3,753pd,; Sworn/Estimate/Non-Audited
Advertising rate: Open inch rate $8.90
Established: 1881
Group: Pamplin Media Group
Gen. Mgr. .... Teresa Tooley
Pub. .... Tony Ahern
Ed. .... Jason Chaney
Mechanical Specifications: Type page 11 5/8 x 21; E - 6 cols, 1 5/6, 1/10 between; A - 6 cols, 1 5/6, 1/10 between; C - 8 cols, 1 1/5, 1/10 between.Equipment & Software: Hardware — 13-PC; Presses — 6-G/Community; Software — Microsoft Word, QPS/QuarkXPress, Photoshop, Adobe Illustrator.
Delivery Method: Mail
Areas Served: Crook County, Oregon

REDMOND

THE REDMOND SPOKESMAN (WED)
226 NW 6th St, Redmond, OR, 97756-1718, Deschutes, USA; gen tel (541) 548-2184; ed tel (541) 548-2186; gen fax (541) 548-3203; disp adv e-mail adv@redmondspokesman.com; class adv e-mail classified@redmonspokesman.com; ed e-mail news@redmondspokesman.com; web site www.redmondspokesman.com
Circulation: 2,243pd, 953fr; VAC
Advertising rate: Open inch rate $19.95
Established: 1911
Group: Western Communications, Inc.
Adv. Mgr. .... Denise Duval
Circ. Mgr. .... Amy Husted
Pub. .... Steve Hawes
Senior Reporter .... Geoff Folsom
Reporter .... Colby Brown
Mechanical Specifications: Type page 11 5/6 x 20 1/2; E - 6 cols, 1 4/5, 3/16 between; A - 6 cols, 1 4/5, 3/16 between; C - 9 cols, 1 2/9, 1/8 between.Equipment & Software: ; Software — InDesign
Delivery Method: Mail, Carrier, Racks
Areas Served: 97756, 97760, 97753

SAINT HELENS

THE CHRONICLE (WED)
1805 Columbia Blvd, Saint Helens, OR, 97051-6220, Columbia, USA; gen tel (503) 397-0116; gen fax (503) 397-4093; disp adv e-mail chronicleads@countrymedia.net; class adv e-mail chronicleclassifieds@countrymedia.net; ed e-mail dpatterson@countrymedia.net; web site http://www.thechronicleonline.com/
Circulation: 3,100pd, 7,349fr; USPS
Advertising rate: Open inch rate $6.55
Established: 1881
Group: Country Media, Inc
Pub./Ed. .... Don Patterson
Adv. Sales .... Amy Johnson
Mechanical Specifications: Type page 11 5/8 x 21; E - 6 cols, 1 5/6, between; A - 6 cols, 1 5/6, between; C - 8 cols, 1 1/3, between. Equipment & Software: Hardware — APP/Mac; Software — QPS/QuarkXPress 4.0.
Delivery Method: Mail
Areas Served: 97051, 97056, 97054, 97053, 97018, 97048

SALEM

APPEAL TRIBUNE (WED)
340 Vista Ave SE, Salem, OR, 97302-4546, Marion, USA; gen tel (503) 399-6611; disp adv e-mail golocal@statesmanjournal.com; class adv e-mail ads@statesmanjournal.com; ed e-mail ccrosby@statesmanjournal.com; web site http://www.silvertonappeal.com/
Circulation: 1,009pd, 0fr; AAM
Advertising rate: Open inch rate $13.71
Established: 1880
Group: Gannett
Pres. .... Ryan Kedzierski
Circ. Dir. .... Paul Nettland
Ed .... Cherrill Crosby
Delivery Method: Carrier
Areas Served: Silverton, Oregon, Marion County, 97381

CAPITAL PRESS (FRI)
1400 Broadway St NE, Salem, OR, 97301-0504, Marion, USA; gen tel (503) 364-4431; gen fax (503) 370-4383; disp adv e-mail bsell@capitalpress.com; class adv e-mail jsperry@eomediagroup.com; ed e-mail jbeach@capitalpress.com; web site http://www.capitalpress.com/oregon - 180,000(views) 54,000(visitors)
Circulation: 26,415pd, 1,120fr; AAM
Advertising rate: Open inch rate $30.98
Established: 1924
Group: EO Media Group
Digital Platform - Mobile: Apple, Android
Digital Platform - Tablet: Apple iOS, Android
Ed. .... Joe Beach
Adv. Dir. .... Beth Sell
Circ. Dir. .... Samantha McLaren
Mechanical Specifications: Type page 10 1/2 x 21 1/4; E - 6 cols, 3/16; A - 6 cols, C - 8 cols
Delivery Method: Mail, Newsstand, Racks
Areas Served: Western United States

STAYTON MAIL (WED)
340 Vista Ave SE, Salem, OR, 97302-4546, Marion, USA; gen tel (503) 399-6611; disp adv e-mail golocal@statesmanjournal.com; class adv e-mail ads@statesmanjournal.com; ed e-mail ccrosby@statesmanjournal.com; web site www.staytonmail.com
Circulation: 765pd, 0fr; AAM
Advertising rate: Open inch rate $53.60
Established: 1894
Group: Gannett
Pres. .... Ryan Kedzierski
Circ. Dir. .... Paul Nettland
Ed .... Cherrill Crosby
Mechanical Specifications: Type page 13 x 21 1/2; E - 6 cols, 2, between; A - 6 cols, 2, between; C - 9 cols, 1 5/16, between.
Delivery Method: Carrier
Areas Served: Stayton, Oregon, Marion County, 97383

SCAPPOOSE

THE SOUTH COUNTY SPOTLIGHT (FRI)
33548 Edward Ln, Ste 110, Scappoose, OR, 97056-3838, Columbia, USA; gen tel (503) 543-6387; gen fax (503) 543-6380; disp adv e-mail dswan@spotlightnews.net; ed e-mail news@spotlightnews.net; web site www.spotlightnews.net
Circulation: 4,500pd,; Sworn/Estimate/Non-Audited
Advertising rate: Open inch rate $37.00
Established: 1961
Group: Pamplin Media Group
Pamplin Media Group
Pub. .... Darryl Swan
Circ. Mgr. .... Kim Stephens
Graphic Designer .... Chelsea Tull
News Reporter .... Nicole Thill
News Reporter .... Courtney Vaughn
Office Coord .... Rose Zimnicki
Sports Ed. .... Jake McNeal
Advt Sales .... Dawn Britton
Mechanical Specifications: Type page 11 3/4 x 17 1/2; E - 5 cols, 1/6, between; C - 6 cols, 1/12 between.Equipment & Software: Hardware — PC, APP/Mac; Software — QPS/QuarkXPress, Adobe/PageMaker.
Delivery Method: Mail, Newsstand, Racks
Areas Served: 97018, 97051, 97053, 97056

SEASIDE

SEASIDE SIGNAL (THUR)
1555 N Roosevelt Dr, Seaside, OR, 97138-7143, Clatsop, USA; gen tel (503) 738-5561; gen fax (503) 738-9285; disp adv e-mail bsmith@dailyastorian.com; class adv e-mail rherren@dailyastorian.com; ed e-mail rmarx@seasidesignal.com; web site http://www.dailyastorian.com/signal
Circulation: 3,500pd,; Sworn/Estimate/Non-Audited
Advertising rate: Open inch rate $37.00
Established: 1905
Group: Country Media, Inc
Adv. Mgr. .... Betty Smith
Office Coord .... Rebecca Herren
Ed .... R.J. Marx
Mechanical Specifications: Type page 10 1/4 x 16 1/2; E - 5 cols, 2, 1/6 between; A - 5 cols, 2, 1/6 between; C - 7 cols, 1 1/2, 1/6 between. Equipment & Software: Hardware — APP/Mac; Software — QPS/QuarkXPress 4.0.

SPRINGFIELD

SPRINGFIELD TIMES (FRI)
216 Main St, Ste 5, Springfield, OR, 97477-5370, Lane, USA; gen tel (541) 741-7368; gen fax (541) 741-7380; disp adv e-mail Joan.Springfieldtimes@hotmail.com; ed e-mail rick@springfieldtimes.net; web site www.springfieldtimes.net
Circulation: 1,443pd, 25fr; USPS
Advertising rate: Open inch rate $10.50
Established: 2008
Group: S. J. Olson Publishing, Inc.
Pub. .... Amber Deyo
Ed .... Rick Morgan
Adv. Rep .... Joan Schryvers
Office Mgr. .... Joann Purcelley Equipment & Software: ; Presses — No; Software — Adobe Create Suite 5
Delivery Method: Mail
Areas Served: 97477, 97478

SWEET HOME

THE NEW ERA (WED)
1313 Main St, Sweet Home, OR, 97386-1611, Linn, USA; gen tel (541) 367-2135; gen fax (541) 367-2137; disp adv e-mail mirian@sweethomenews.com; class adv e-mail advertising@sweethomenews.com; ed e-mail news@sweethomenews.com; web site www.sweethomenews.com
Circulation: 2,000pd, 6,625fr; Sworn/Estimate/Non-Audited
Advertising rate: Open inch rate $10.25
Established: 1929
Pub .... Scott Swanson
Adv. Dir .... Miriam Swanson
Class. Mgr. .... Firiel Severns
Mechanical Specifications: 1.95/ 1 column
4.05 / 2 column
6.16 / 3 column
8.27 / 4 column
10.38 / 5 colum
maximum height of ad 16.5"
Delivery Method: Mail, Racks
Areas Served: 97386, 97345, 97355,

TILLAMOOK

HEADLIGHT-HERALD (WED)
1908 2nd St, Tillamook, OR, 97141-2206, Tillamook, USA; gen tel (503) 842-7535; gen fax (503) 842-8842; disp adv e-mail headlightads@countrymedia.net; class adv e-mail classifieds@orcoastnews.com; ed e-mail jwolfe@countrymedia.net; web site www.tillamookheadlightherald.com
Circulation: 8,500pd, 86fr; Sworn/Estimate/Non-Audited
Advertising rate: Open inch rate $8.25
Established: 1888
Group: Country Media, Inc
Pub .... Joe Warren
Ed .... Jordan Wolfe
Circ. Mgr. .... Brian Humphrey
Mechanical Specifications: Type page 11 5/8 x 21 1/2; E - 6 cols, 1 5/6, 1/8 between; A - 6 cols, 1 5/6, 1/8 between; C - 9 cols, 1 3/16, 1/8 between.Equipment & Software: Hardware — APP/Mac; Software — QPS/QuarkXPress.

VALE

MALHEUR ENTERPRISE (WED)
289 A St W, Vale, OR, 97918-1303, Malheur, USA; gen tel (541) 473-3377; gen fax (541) 473-3268; disp adv e-mail business@malheurenterprise.com; ed e-mail scotta@malheurenterprise.com; web site http://malheurenterprise.com/
Circulation: 1,300pd, 40fr; Sworn/Estimate/Non-Audited
Advertising rate: Open inch rate $7.50
Established: 1909
Pub/Ed .... Scotta Callister

Gen. Mgr. .... Lyndon Zaitz
Bus. Mgr. ....Bobbi ButticeEquipment & Software: Hardware — PC, APP/Mac; Software — Adobe InDesign, Adobe/Illustrator 7.0, Microsoft/Works 4.0, Caere/OmniPage Pro 6.0, WordPerfect, Microsoft/Windows, Interlink/PageMaker.
Delivery Method: Mail, Racks
Areas Served: Malheur County

WARRENTON

THE COLUMBIA PRESS (FRI)

5 N Highway 101, # 500, Warrenton, OR, 97146-9313, Clatsop, USA; gen tel (503) 861-3331; gen fax (503) 325-1477; disp adv e-mail ads@thecolumbiapress.net; ed e-mail editor@thecolumbiapress.com; web site www.thecolumbiapress.com
Circulation: 1,200pd,; USPS
Advertising rate: Open inch rate $7.00
Established: 1922
Digital Platform - Mobile: Apple
Pub./Ed. .... Cindy Yingst
Mechanical Specifications: Type page 10.3x10.5
Delivery Method: Mail, Newsstand, Racks
Areas Served: Warrenton, Astoria, Seaside. Clatsop County

WOODBURN

WOODBURN INDEPENDENT (WED)

650 N 1st St, Woodburn, OR, 97071-4002, Marion, USA; gen tel (503) 981-3441; gen fax (503) 981-1253; disp adv e-mail Klang@woodburnindependent.com; class adv e-mail rmansfield@pamplinmedia.com; ed e-mail Lkeefer@woodburnindependent.com; web site www.woodburnindependent.com
Circulation: 4,692pd, 163fr; Sworn/Estimate/Non-Audited
Advertising rate: Open inch rate $37.00
Established: 1888
Group: Pamplin Media Group
Ed. .... Lindsay Keefer
Pub... Al Herriges
Circ. Mgr......................................Kim Stephens
Areas Served: 97071, 97032, 97026, 97137, 97362

PENNSYLVANIA

ALLENTOWN

BETHLEHEM PRESS (WED)

1633 N 26th St, Ste 102, Allentown, PA, 18104-1805, Northampton, USA; gen tel (610) 625-2121; adv tel (610) 740-0944; ed tel (610) 740-0944; gen fax (610) 625-2126; adv fax (610) 740-9908; ed fax (610) 740-0947; disp adv e-mail mstocking@tnonline.com; ed e-mail gtaylor@tnonline.com; web site www.bethlehem.thelehighvalleypress.com
Circulation: 5,046pd,; Sworn/Estimate/Non-Audited
Advertising rate: Open inch rate $8.95 per column inch
Established: 2005
Group: Times News, LLC
Digital Platform - Mobile: Apple, Android
Digital Platform - Tablet: Apple iOS, Android
Adv. Mgr. .... Peg Stocking
Ed. .... George Taylor
Delivery Method: Mail, Newsstand, Carrier, Racks
Areas Served: 18015, 18017, 18018, 18020, 18045, 18055, 18104

CATASAUQUA PRESS (THUR)

1633 N 26th St, Allentown, PA, 18104-1805, Lehigh, USA; gen tel (610) 740-0944; adv tel (610) 740-0944; ed tel (610) 740-0944; gen fax (610) 740-0947; adv fax (610) 740-9908; ed fax (610) 740-0947; disp adv e-mail mstocking@tnonline.com; class adv e-mail mstocking@tnonline.com; ed e-mail lwojciechowski@tnonline.com; web site www.catasauqua.thelehighvalleypress.com
Circulation: 1,380pd,; Sworn/Estimate/Non-Audited
Advertising rate: Open inch rate $8.95 per column inch
Established: 2003
Group: Times News, LLC
Adv. Mgr. .... Peg Stocking
Gen. Mgr. .... Scott Masenheimer
Assoc. Ed......................... Linda Wojciechowski
Delivery Method: Mail, Newsstand, Carrier, Racks
Areas Served: 18032, 18052, 18067, 18104

EAST PENN PRESS (WED)

1633 N 26th St, Ste 102, Allentown, PA, 18104-1805, Lehigh, USA; gen tel (610) 740-0944; gen fax (610) 740-9908; ed fax (610) 740-0947; disp adv e-mail mstocking@tnonline.com; ed e-mail dgalbraith@tnonline.com; web site http://eastpenn.thelehighvalleypress.com
Circulation: 5,159pd,; Sworn/Estimate/Non-Audited
Advertising rate: Open inch rate $8.95 per column inch
Established: 1959
Group: Times News, LLC
Ed. .... Debra Galbraith
Adv. Mgr.. Peg StockingEquipment & Software: Hardware — APP/Mac
Delivery Method: Mail, Newsstand, Carrier, Racks
Areas Served: 18011, 18031, 18049, 18062, 18092, 18103, 18104, 18106

NORTHAMPTON PRESS (THUR)

1633 N 26th St, Ste 102, Allentown, PA, 18104-1805, Lehigh, USA; gen tel (610) 740-0944; gen fax (610) 740-0947; adv fax (610) 740-9908; disp adv e-mail mstocking@tnonline.com; ed e-mail jbillings@tnonline.com; web site http://northampton.thelehighvalleypress.com
Circulation: 2,770pd,; Sworn/Estimate/Non-Audited
Advertising rate: Open inch rate $8.95 per column inch
Established: 1998
Group: Times News, LLC
Gen. Mgr. .... Scott Masenheimer
Adv. Mgr. .... Peg Stocking
Delivery Method: Mail, Newsstand, Carrier, Racks
Areas Served: 18014, 18017, 18035, 18038, 18052, 18067, 18088, 18104

NORTHWESTERN PRESS (THUR)

1633 N 26th St, Ste 102, Allentown, PA, 18104-1805, Lehigh, USA; gen tel (610) 740-0944; gen fax (610) 740-0947; adv fax (610) 740-9908; disp adv e-mail mstocking @tnonline.com; class adv e-mail mstocking@tnonline.com; ed e-mail dpalmieri@tnonline.com; web site http://northwestern.thelehighvalleypress.comhelehighvalleypress.com
Circulation: 2,344pd,; Sworn/Estimate/Non-Audited
Advertising rate: Open inch rate $8.95 per column inch
Established: 1994
Group: Times News, LLC
Adv. Mgr. .... Peg Stocking
Ed .... Debbie Palmieri
Delivery Method: Mail, Newsstand, Carrier, Racks
Areas Served: 18031, 18051, 18053, 18066, 18069, 18078, 18080, 18104, 19529, 19530

PARKLAND PRESS (THUR)

1633 N 26th St, Ste 102, Allentown, PA, 18104-1805, Lehigh, USA; gen tel (610) 740-0944; gen fax (610) 740-0947; adv fax (610) 740-9908; disp adv e-mail mstocking@tnonline.com; ed e-mail dpalmieri@tnonline.com; web site http://parkland.thelehighvalleypress.com
Circulation: 4,174pd,; Sworn/Estimate/Non-Audited
Advertising rate: Open inch rate $8.95 per column inch
Established: 1989
Group: Times News, LLC
Adv. Mgr. .... Peg Stocking
Ed. ...... Debbie PalmieriEquipment & Software: Hardware — APP/Mac; Presses — MAN/Uniman 2x2; Software — QPS/QuarkXPress.
Delivery Method: Mail, Newsstand, Carrier, Racks
Areas Served: 18031, 18037, 18051, 18052, 18059, 18065, 18069, 18078, 18080, 18103, 18104, 18106

SALISBURY PRESS (WED)

1633 N 26th St, Ste 102, Allentown, PA, 18104-1805, Lehigh, USA; gen tel (610) 740-0944; gen fax (610) 740-0947; adv fax (610) 740-9908; disp adv e-mail mstocking@tnonline.com; ed e-mail dgalbraith@tnonline.com; web site http://salisbury.thelehighvalleypress.com
Circulation: 1,868pd,; Sworn/Estimate/Non-Audited
Advertising rate: Open inch rate $8.95
Established: 2000
Group: Times News, LLC
Adv. Mgr. .... Peg Stocking
Ed. .... Deb Galbraith
Delivery Method: Mail, Newsstand, Carrier, Racks
Areas Served: 18015, 18049, 18103, 18104

WHITEHALL-COPLAY PRESS (THUR)

1633 N 26th St, Ste 102, Allentown, PA, 18104-1805, Lehigh, USA; gen tel (610) 740-0944; gen fax (610) 740-0947; adv fax (610) 740-9908; disp adv e-mail mstocking@tnonline.com; class adv e-mail smasenheimer@tnonline.com; ed e-mail klutterschmidt@tnonline.com; web site http://whitehallcoplay.thelehighvalleypress.com
Circulation: 3,014pd,; Sworn/Estimate/Non-Audited
Advertising rate: Open inch rate $8.95
Established: 1992
Group: Times News, LLC
Adv. Mgr. .... Peg Stocking
Circ. Mgr.................................. Kathy Carpenter
Gen. Mgr. .... Scott Masenheimer
Ed .... Kelly Lutterschmidt
Mechanical Specifications: Type page 13 x 21; E - 6 cols, 2 1/12, 1/8 between; A - 6 cols, 2 1/12, 1/8 between; C - 9 cols, 1 1/3, 1/8 between.Equipment & Software: Hardware — APP/Mac; Presses — MAN/Uniman 2x2; Software — QPS/QuarkXPress 3.3.
Delivery Method: Mail, Newsstand, Carrier, Racks
Areas Served: 18037, 18052, 18067, 18104

ARDMORE

MAIN LINE SUBURBAN LIFE (SUN)

110 Ardmore Ave, Ardmore, PA, 19003-1339, Montgomery, USA; gen tel (610) 642-4300; ed tel (610) 642-4300 ext. 82523; gen fax (610) 645-7620; ed fax (610) 642-9704; disp adv e-mail paadvertising@digitalfirstmedia.com; class adv e-mail brsmith@21st-century-media.com; ed e-mail sgreenspon@mainlinemedianews.com; web site http://www.mainlinemedianews.com/mainlinesuburbanlife/
Circulation: 2,283pd, 64fr; CAC
Advertising rate: Open inch rate $35.40
Established: 1987
Group: Digital First Media
Digital Platform - Mobile: Apple, Android
Digital Platform - Tablet: Apple iOS, Android
Exec. Ed.. Andy Stettler
Adv. Mgr. .... Brad Smith
Circ. Mgr. .... Larry Butts
Ed. .... Susan Greenspon
Ryan Wells
Mechanical Specifications: Type page 11 5/8 x 20 1/2; E - 6 cols, 2, 1/6 between; A - 6 cols, 2, 1/6 between; C - 10 cols, 1/6 between. Equipment & Software: Hardware — APP/Mac; Presses — G; Software — QPS/QuarkXPress.
Delivery Method: Mail, Newsstand, Carrier, Racks
Areas Served: 19301, 19312, 19333

MAIN LINE TIMES (SUN)

110 Ardmore Ave, Ardmore, PA, 19003-1339, Montgomery, USA; gen tel (610) 642-4300; ed tel (610) 642-4300 ext. 82524; gen fax (610) 645-7620; ed fax (610) 642-9704; disp adv e-mail paadvertising@digitalfirstmedia.com; class adv e-mail brsmith@21st-centurymedia.com; ed e-mail sgreenspon@mainlinemedianews.com; web site www.mainlinetimes.com
Circulation: 2,452pd, 76fr; CAC
Advertising rate: Open inch rate $35.40
Group: Digital First Media
Digital Platform - Mobile: Apple, Android
Digital Platform - Tablet: Apple iOS, Android
Adv. Mgr. .... Brad Smith
Mng. Ed................................ Susan Greenspon
Circ. Dir. .... Phillp Metz
Mechanical Specifications: Type page 13 x 21 1/2; E - 6 cols, 2 1/16, 1/4 between; A - 6 cols, 2 1/16, 1/4 between; C - 8 cols, 1 5/8, 1/4 between.Equipment & Software: Hardware — APP/Mac; Presses — G/Urbanite.
Delivery Method: Mail, Newsstand, Carrier, Racks
Areas Served: Montgomery County

ASPINWALL

THE HERALD (THUR)

101 Emerson Ave Ste 13, Suite 13, Aspinwall, PA, 15215-3252, Allegheny, USA; gen tel (412) 782-2121; adv tel (724) 459-6100; gen fax (412) 782-1195; adv fax (724) 459-7366; disp adv e-mail dfellabaum@tribweb.com; class adv e-mail jpaschl@tribweb.com; ed e-mail lfabregas@tribweb.com; web site www.tribLIVE.com
Circulation: 2,251pd,; AAM
Advertising rate: Open inch rate $20.00
Group: Trib Total Media, Inc.
Digital Platform - Mobile: Apple, Android
Digital Platform - Tablet: Apple iOS, Android
Adv. Mgr. .... Jill Paschl
Exec. Ed... Frank Craig
Ed. .... Luis Fábregas
Delivery Method: Mail, Newsstand
Areas Served: Allegheny County

BEDFORD

BEDFORD GAZETTE (FRI)

424 W Penn St, Bedford, PA, 15522-1230, Bedford, USA; gen tel (814) 623-1151; gen fax (814) 623-5055; disp adv e-mail sgrowden@bedfordgazette.com; class adv e-mail classifieds@bedfordgazette.com; ed e-mail ecoyle@bedfordgazette.com; web site www.bedfordgazette.com
Circulation: 200pd,; Sworn/Estimate/Non-Audited
Advertising rate: Open inch rate $12.77 (Local); $15.73 (National)
Established: 1805
Group: Bedford Gazette LLC
Digital Platform - Mobile: Apple, Android
Digital Platform - Tablet: Apple iOS, Android
Pub.. Joseph Beegle
Bus. Mgr.................................. Rebecca Smith
Ed. .... Elizabeth Coyle
Circ. .... Susan May
Delivery Method: Mail, Newsstand, Carrier, Racks
Areas Served: Bedford County

BENSALEM

NORTHEAST TIMES (WED)

3412 Progress Dr, Ste C, Bensalem, PA, 19020-5817, Bucks, USA; gen tel (215) 355-9009; adv tel (215) 354-3058; ed tel (215) 354-3030; gen fax (215) 355-4812; disp adv e-mail kstuski@bsmphilly.com; class adv

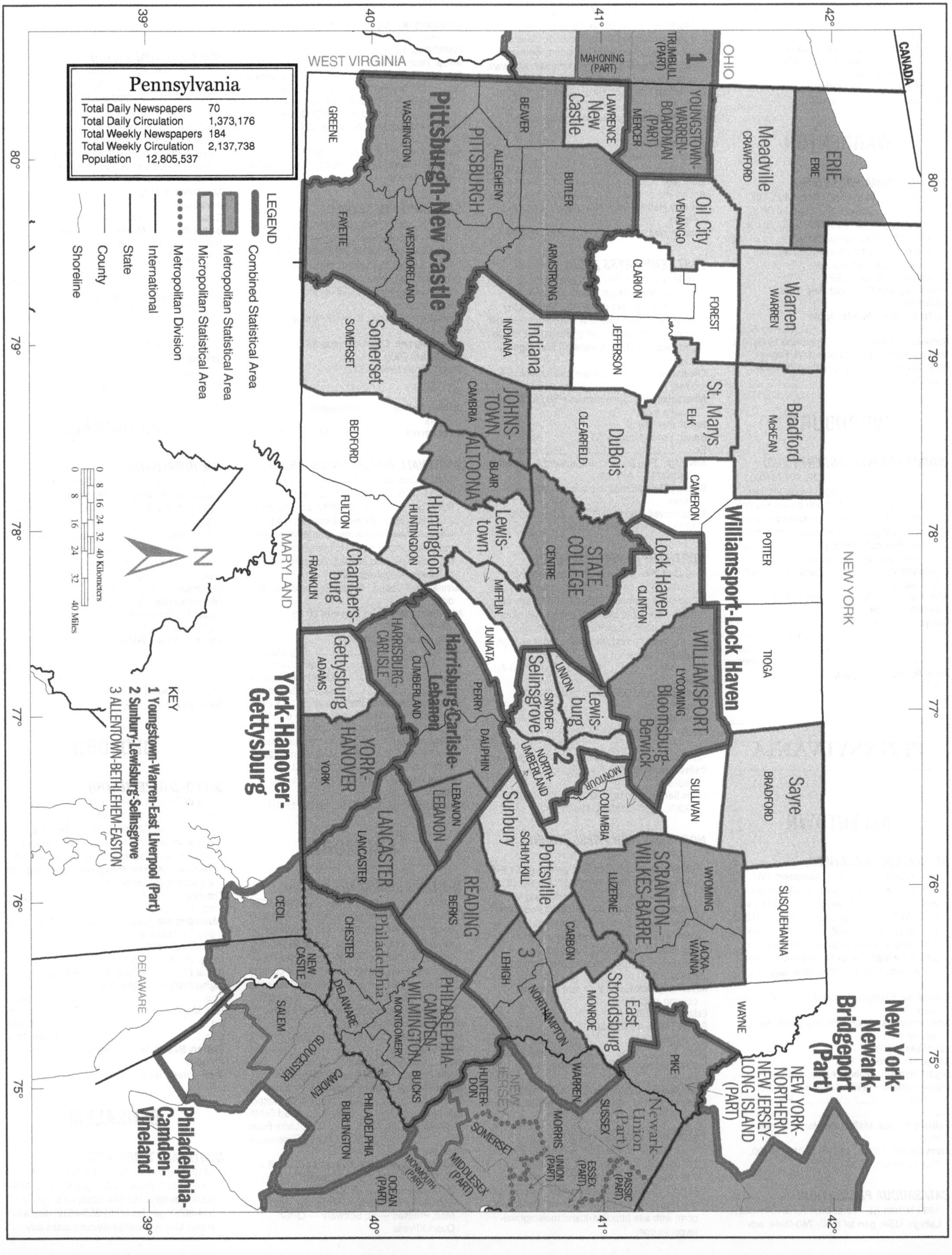
Pennsylvania
Total Daily Newspapers 70
Total Daily Circulation 1,373,176
Total Weekly Newspapers 184
Total Weekly Circulation 2,137,738
Population 12,805,537
LEGEND
Combined Statistical Area
Metropolitan Statistical Area
Micropolitan Statistical Area
Metropolitan Division
International
State
County
Shoreline
KEY
1 Youngstown-Warren-East Liverpool (Part)
2 Sunbury-Lewisburg-Selinsgrove
3 ALLENTOWN-BETHLEHEM-EASTON
0 8 16 24 32 40 Kilometers
0 8 16 24 32 40 Miles
N
Pittsburgh-New Castle
PITTSBURGH
Erie
Meadville
Oil City
Warren
Bradford
St. Marys
DuBois
Indiana
Somerset
JOHNSTOWN
ALTOONA
Huntingdon
Lewistown
STATE COLLEGE
Lock Haven
Williamsport-Lock Haven
WILLIAMSPORT
Bloomsburg-Berwick
Lewisburg
Selinsgrove
Sunbury
Pottsville
Sayre
SCRANTON-WILKES-BARRE
East Stroudsburg
Chambersburg
Gettysburg
York-Hanover-Gettysburg
YORK-HANOVER
Harrisburg-Carlisle-Lebanon
HARRISBURG-CARLISLE
LEBANON
LANCASTER
READING
Philadelphia
PHILADELPHIA-CAMDEN-WILMINGTON
Philadelphia-Camden-Vineland
New York-Newark-Bridgeport (Part)
NEW YORK-NORTHERN NEW JERSEY-LONG ISLAND (PART)
Newark-Union (Part)
YOUNGSTOWN-WARREN-BOARDMAN (PART)
New Castle
MAHONING (PART)
TRUMBULL (PART)
ERIE
CRAWFORD
MERCER
LAWRENCE
VENANGO
WARREN
McKEAN
POTTER
TIOGA
BRADFORD
SUSQUEHANNA
WAYNE
FOREST
ELK
CAMERON
CLARION
JEFFERSON
CLEARFIELD
CLINTON
LYCOMING
SULLIVAN
WYOMING
LACKAWANNA
PIKE
BEAVER
BUTLER
ARMSTRONG
ALLEGHENY
WASHINGTON
GREENE
FAYETTE
WESTMORELAND
INDIANA
CAMBRIA
SOMERSET
BEDFORD
BLAIR
CENTRE
HUNTINGDON
FULTON
FRANKLIN
MIFFLIN
JUNIATA
UNION
SNYDER
NORTHUMBERLAND
MONTOUR
COLUMBIA
LUZERNE
CARBON
MONROE
PERRY
CUMBERLAND
ADAMS
YORK
DAUPHIN
LEBANON
SCHUYLKILL
LANCASTER
BERKS
LEHIGH
NORTHAMPTON
CHESTER
DELAWARE
MONTGOMERY
BUCKS
PHILADELPHIA
NEW CASTLE
CECIL
SALEM
GLOUCESTER
CAMDEN
BURLINGTON
HUNTERDON
WARREN
SUSSEX
MORRIS
SOMERSET
MIDDLESEX (PART)
MONMOUTH (PART)
OCEAN (PART)
UNION (PART)
ESSEX (PART)
PASSAIC (PART)
NEW JERSEY
OHIO
WEST VIRGINIA
MARYLAND
DELAWARE
NEW YORK
CANADA
39°
40°
41°
42°
80°
79°
78°
77°
76°
75°

e-mail kstuski@bsmphilly.com; ed e-mail lswanson@bsmphilly.com; web site www.bsmphilly.com
Circulation: 1,025pd, 109,074fr; VAC
Advertising rate: Open inch rate $35.31
Established: 1937
Group: Broad Street MediaEditions: (8) Northeast Times-Bustleton (22,325); Northeast Times-Far Northeast (11,645); Northeast Times-Frankford (3,200); Northeast Times-Lawndale (11,794); Northeast Times-Mayfair (22,000); Northeast Times-Oxford Circle (5,400); Northeast Times-Rhawnhurst
Digital Platform - Mobile: Apple, Android
Digital Platform - Tablet: Apple iOS, Android
Pub.. Perry Corsetti
Circ. Mgr.. Pearl Harta
Ed.. Lillian Swanson
Mechanical Specifications: 9.5"w x 10.66"h
Delivery Method: Carrier
Areas Served: 19135, 19136, 19149, 19152, 19114, 19115, 19111, 19116, 19154

STAR COMMUNITY NEWSWEEKLY (WED, THUR)
3412 Progress Dr, Ste C, Bensalem, PA, 19020-5817, Philadelphia, USA; gen tel (215) 354-3000; adv tel (215) 354-3070; ed tel (215) 354-3113; gen fax (215) 244-1406; adv fax (215) 244-1406; ed fax (215) 244-1406; disp adv e-mail mmcdevitt@bsmphilly.com; class adv e-mail pbuzine@bsmphilly.com; ed e-mail star@bsmphilly.com; web site http://www.starnewsphilly.com/
Circulation: 27,275fr; VAC
Advertising rate: Open inch rate $7.20 (ROP); $30.00 (Class Display)
Established: 1982
Group: Broad Street MediaEditions: (2) Star 8 Northern Liberties and Fishtown / Star 9 Port Richmond and Bridesburg
Pub.. Perry Corsetti
Adv. Sales Mgr.......................... Michelle McDevitt
Adv. Sales Rep.......................... Patti Buzine
Adv. Sales Rep.......................... Carmen Ferugean
Circ. Mgr.. Pearl Harta
Mechanical Specifications: 10" x 10" full page
Delivery Method: Carrier
Areas Served: 19123, 19125, 19122, 19134, 19137

THE MIDWEEK WIRE (WED)
3412 Progress Dr, Ste C, Bensalem, PA, 19020-5817, Bucks, USA; gen tel (215) 354-3000; adv tel (215) 354-3058; ed tel (215) 354-3030; gen fax (215) 355-4812; disp adv e-mail pawirenews@bsmphilly.com; class adv e-mail kstuski@bsmphilly.com; ed e-mail pawirenews@bsmphilly.com; web site www.bsmphilly.com
Circulation: 178,628fr; VAC
Advertising rate: Open inch rate $116.00
Established: 1987
Group: Broad Street Media
Mng. Ed.. Ted Bordelon
Pub.. Perry Corsetti
Circ. Mgr.. Pearl Harta
Mechanical Specifications: Type page 10 5/16 x 13; E - 6 cols, 1 9/16, between; A - 6 cols, 1 9/16, between; C - 8 cols, 1 1/4, between. Equipment & Software: Hardware — APP/Mac; Software — QPS/QuarkXPress.
Delivery Method: Mail
Areas Served: Bucks and Montgomery County

BETHLEHEM

LEHIGH VALLEY BUSINESS (MON)
65 E Elizabeth Ave Ste 400, Suite 700, Bethlehem, PA, 18018-6515, Northampton, USA; gen tel (610) 807-9619; adv tel (610) 807-9619 ext. 107; ed tel (610) 807-9619 ext. 115; gen fax (610) 807-9612; disp adv e-mail johnc@LVB.com; class adv e-mail morourke@lvb.com; ed e-mail billk@lvb.com; web site www.LVB.com - 150,000(views) 30,000(visitors)
Circulation: 2,425pd, 6,210fr; CVC
Advertising rate: Open inch rate $8.75
Established: 2012
Group: GateHouse Media, Inc.
Digital Platform - Mobile: Apple, Android
Digital Platform - Tablet: Apple iOS, Android
Pub.. Michael O'Rourke
Editor.. Bill Kline
Sales Mgr.. Tom Vrana
Delivery Method: Mail
Areas Served: Greater Lehigh Valley

BLAIRSVILLE

BLAIRSVILLE DISPATCH (FRI)
116 E Market St, Blairsville, PA, 15717-1326, Indiana, USA; gen tel (724) 459-6100; ed tel (724) 459-6100 ext. 13; gen fax (724) 459-7366; disp adv e-mail dfellabaum@tribweb.com; class adv e-mail jpaschl@tribweb.com; ed e-mail jhimler@tribweb.com; web site www.tribLIVE.com
Circulation: 16,500pd, 1,500fr; Sworn/Estimate/Non-Audited
Advertising rate: Open inch rate $18.00
Group: Sample Media Group
Digital Platform - Mobile: Apple, Android
Digital Platform - Tablet: Apple iOS, Android
Adv. Mgr.. Jill Paschl
Ed.. Jeffrey Himler
Delivery Method: Mail, Newsstand
Areas Served: Blairsville, Derry, Homer City, Indiana, New Alexandria, New Florence, and Seward

BLAKESLEE

JOURNAL OF THE POCONO PLATEAU (MON)
Route 940, Blakeslee, PA, 18610, Monroe, USA; gen tel (570) 443-8321; adv tel (570) 443-9131 ext. 302; ed tel (570) 443-9131 ext. 304; gen fax (570) 443-8142; disp adv e-mail journalnews@pa.metrocast.net; class adv e-mail journalads@pa.metrocast.net; ed e-mail journalnews@pa.metrocast.net; web site www.pocononewspapers.com
Circulation: 35pd, 9,465fr; CVC
Advertising rate: Open inch rate $13.00
Established: 1995
Digital Platform - Mobile: Apple
Digital Platform - Tablet: Apple iOS
Ed. & Pub.. Ruth Isenberg
Gen. Mgr.. Seth Isenberg
Mechanical Specifications: 9.98"w x 12.9"hEquipment & Software: Hardware — Mac; Software — mix
Delivery Method: Mail, Racks
Areas Served: 18661, 18255, 18610, 18346, 18347, 18348, 18350, 18466, 18210, 18219, 18222, 18224, 18707, 18229

BRADFORD

BRADFORD JOURNAL-MINER (THUR)
69 Garlock Holw, Bradford, PA, 16701-3420, McKean, USA; gen tel (814) 465-3468; gen fax (814) 465-3468; ed e-mail bradfordjournal@bradfordjournalonline.com; web site www.bradfordjournal.com
Circulation: 5,500pd,; Sworn/Estimate/Non-Audited
Advertising rate: Open inch rate $8.32
Established: 1940
Digital Platform - Mobile: Apple, Android
Digital Platform - Tablet: Apple iOS, Android, Kindle, Nook, Kindle Fire
Pub.. Grant Nichols
Ed.. Debi Nichols
Mechanical Specifications: Type page 10 1/4 x 16; E - 6 cols, 1 9/16, 1/6 between; A - 6 cols, 1 9/16, 1/6 between; C - 6 cols, 1 9/16, 1/6 between.Equipment & Software: Hardware — APP/Mac, Laser Plus, APP/Mac SE, APP/Mac II, APP/iMac, Lexmark; Software — Microsoft 3.0, 5.1A.
Delivery Method: Mail, Newsstand, Racks
Areas Served: McKean County

BRISTOL

BRISTOL PILOT (THUR)
220 Radcliffe St, St 2, Bristol, PA, 19007-5014, Bucks, USA; gen tel (215) 788-1682; adv tel (215) 542-0200 ext. 153; ed tel (215) 542-0200 ext. 157; gen fax (215) 788-6328; disp adv e-mail mburns@buckslocalnews.com; class adv e-mail buckscalss@buckslocalnews.com; ed e-mail advance@buckslocalnews.com; web site www.bristolpilot.com
Circulation: 1,197pd, 5fr; CAC
Advertising rate: Open inch rate $13.10
Group: Digital First Media
Digital Platform - Mobile: Apple, Android
Digital Platform - Tablet: Apple iOS, Android
Pub.. Bill Murray
Adv. Mgr.. Tammy Darmiento
Ed.. Jeff Werner
Mechanical Specifications: Type page 10 x 16; E - 6 cols, 1 1/2, 1/6 between; A - 6 cols, 1 1/2, 1/6 between; C - 6 cols, 1 1/2, 1/6 between.Equipment & Software: Hardware — APP/Mac; Presses — G; Software — QPS/QuarkXPress.
Delivery Method: Mail, Newsstand, Carrier
Areas Served: Bucks County of Pennsylvania, and Hunterdon and Mercer County of New Jersey

BROOKVILLE

JEFFERSONIAN DEMOCRAT (WED)
301 Main St, Apt 1, Brookville, PA, 15825-1204, Jefferson, USA; gen tel (814) 849-5339; adv tel (814) 849-6737 ext. 25; ed tel (814) 849-6737 ext. 28; gen fax (814) 849-4333; disp adv e-mail jeffdem@windstream.net; ed e-mail rbartley@thecourierexpress.com; web site http://www.thecourierexpress.com/jeffersonian_democrat/
Circulation: 3,342pd,; AAM
Advertising rate: Open inch rate $7.45
Established: 1873
Group: Community Media Group
McLean Publishing Co.
Digital Platform - Mobile: Apple, Android
Digital Platform - Tablet: Apple iOS, Android
Ed.. Randon W. Bartley
Pub.. Pat Patterson
Mechanical Specifications: Type page 12 x 21 1/2; E - 6 cols, 1 13/16, 3/16 between; A - 6 cols, 1 13/16, 3/16 between; C - 8 cols, 1 7/16, 1/16 between.Equipment & Software: Hardware — 6-APP/Mac; Presses — Web Leader; Software — Baseview, QPS/QuarkXPress 4.1.
Delivery Method: Mail, Newsstand, Carrier
Areas Served: 15864, 15829, 15825, 15860, 15824, 15828, 16214, 16217, 16233, 16258, 15767

CANTON

THE CANTON INDEPENDENT SENTINEL (THUR)
10 W Main St, Canton, PA, 17724-1503, Bradford, USA; gen tel (570) 673-5151; gen fax (570) 673-5152; disp adv e-mail advertise@myweeklysentinel.com; class adv e-mail cisnews@frontiernet.net; ed e-mail editor@myweeklysentinel.com; web site www.thecantonsentinel.com
Circulation: 3,700pd,; Sworn/Estimate/Non-Audited
Advertising rate: Open inch rate $4.00
Established: 1941
Group: Troy Gazette-Register
Digital Platform - Mobile: Apple, Android
Digital Platform - Tablet: Apple iOS, Android
News Ed.. Andrea Sutton
Ed.. John Shaffer
Adv.......... Amy BellowsEquipment & Software: Hardware — APP/Mac; Software — Fullwrite.
Delivery Method: Mail, Newsstand, Carrier, Racks
Areas Served: 17724, 17765, 17743, 17768, 17763, 16910, 16947, 16925, 16926, 17735

CLARION

CLARION NEWS (TUES, THUR)
860 S 5th Ave, Ste 4, Clarion, PA, 16214-8601, Clarion, USA; gen tel (814) 226-7000; gen fax (814) 226-7518; disp adv e-mail clarionnews.circulation@gmail.com; class adv e-mail cnclassifieds@gmail.com; ed e-mail rsherman.theclarionnews@gmail.com; web site www.theclarionnews.com
Circulation: 7,000pd, 64fr; Sworn/Estimate/Non-Audited
Advertising rate: Open inch rate $12.40
Established: 1840
Digital Platform - Mobile: Apple, Android
Digital Platform - Tablet: Apple iOS, Android, Kindle, Nook, Kindle Fire
Pub.. Patrick C. Boyle
Ed.. Rodney Sherman
Adv. Mgr.. Mary Louise Loque
Circ. Mgr.. Jeff McLaughlin
Mechanical Specifications: Type page 13 x 21; E - 6 cols, 2 1/16, 3/8 between; A - 6 cols, 2 1/16, 3/8 between; C - 9 cols, 1 3/8, 1/8 between.
Delivery Method: Mail, Newsstand, Carrier, Racks
Areas Served: Clarion County

CLARKS SUMMIT

ABINGTON JOURNAL (WED)
211 S State St, Clarks Summit, PA, 18411-1546, Lackawanna, USA; gen tel (570) 587-1148; adv tel (570) 829-7293; ed tel (570) 585-1604; gen fax (570) 586-3980; adv fax (570) 829-2002; ed fax (570) 829-5537; disp adv e-mail aspina@civitasmedia.com; class adv e-mail lbyrnes@civitasmedia.com; ed e-mail dmartin@timesleader.com; web site www.theabingtonjournal.com
Circulation: 1,955pd, 229fr; AAM
Advertising rate: Open inch rate $8.25
Established: 1947
Digital Platform - Mobile: Apple, Android
Digital Platform - Tablet: Apple iOS, Android, Windows 7
Ed.. Dotty Martin
Media Dir.. Anthony Spina
Pub.. Mike Murray
Mechanical Specifications: Type page 13 x 21; E - 6 cols, 2, between; A - 6 cols, 2, between; C - 9 cols, 1 3/8, between.Equipment & Software: Hardware — APP/Mac; Software — Adobe/PageMaker 6.0.
Delivery Method: Mail, Newsstand, Carrier
Areas Served: Lackawanna County

COUDERSPORT

POTTER LEADER-ENTERPRISE (WED)
6 W 2nd St, Coudersport, PA, 16915-1131, Potter, USA; gen tel (814) 274-8044; gen fax (814) 274-8120; disp adv e-mail sharon@tiogapublishing.com; class adv e-mail adsleader@tiogapublishing.com; ed e-mail blake@tiogapublishing.com; web site www.potterleaderenterprise.com
Circulation: 7,000pd, 200fr; Sworn/Estimate/Non-Audited
Advertising rate: Open inch rate $9.60
Established: 1874
Digital Platform - Mobile: Apple, Android
Digital Platform - Tablet: Apple iOS, Android, Blackberry Tablet OS, Kindle, Nook, Kindle Fire
Ed.......... Blake BachoEquipment & Software: Hardware — APP/Mac; Software — Adobe InDesign CS4
Delivery Method: Mail, Newsstand, Racks
Areas Served: Potter County

CRANBERRY TOWNSHIP

THE CRANBERRY EAGLE (WED, SUN)
20701 Route 19, Cranberry Township, PA,

16066-6009, Butler, USA; gen tel (724) 776-4270; adv tel (724) 776-4270 ext. 15; gen fax (724) 776-0211; disp adv e-mail mjurysta@butlereagle.com; class adv e-mail macepavelek@butlereagle.com; ed e-mail pgrubbs@butlereagle.com; web site www.thecranberryeagle.com
Circulation: 21,600fr; AAM
Advertising rate: Open inch rate $8.00
Established: 1987
Group: Eagle Publications, Inc.
Digital Platform - Mobile: Apple, Android, Windows
Digital Platform - Tablet: Apple iOS, Android, Windows 7
Gen. Mgr. .... Mace Pavelek
Circ. Dir. .... Alice Lunn
Adv. Mgr. .... Michelle Jurysta
Ed .... Paula Grubbs
Delivery Method: Mail, Newsstand
Areas Served: Butler County

DILLSBURG

DILLSBURG BANNER (THUR)

31 S Baltimore St, Dillsburg, PA, 17019-1228, York, USA; gen tel (717) 432-3456; gen fax (717) 432-1518; disp adv e-mail sara@dillsburgbanner.net; ed e-mail dillsburgbanner@dillsburgbanner.net; web site www.dillsburgbanner.net
Circulation: 3,900pd,; Sworn/Estimate/Non-Audited
Advertising rate: Open inch rate $11.29
Established: 1987
Digital Platform - Mobile: Windows
Digital Platform - Tablet: Windows 7
Pres./Pub./Ed. .... Marie Chomicki
Delivery Method: Mail, Newsstand
Areas Served: York County

DREXEL HILL

RIDLEY PRESS (THUR)

3245 Garrett Rd, Apt 3, Drexel Hill, PA, 19026-2338, Delaware, USA; gen tel (610) 259-4141; disp adv e-mail mail@presspublishing.org; class adv e-mail mail@presspublishing.org; ed e-mail mail@presspublishing.org
Circulation:; Sworn/Estimate/Non-Audited
Advertising rate: Open inch rate $7.00
Established: 1960
Mng. Ed. .... P.A. Girard
Mechanical Specifications: Type page 10 x 15 3/4; E - 5 cols, 1 5/6, 1/6 between; A - 5 cols, 1 5/6, 1/6 between; C - 5 cols, 1 5/6, 1/6 between.
Delivery Method: Mail, Newsstand
Areas Served: 19033, 19033, 19094, 19018, 19078

THE YEADON TIMES (THUR)

3245 Garrett Rd, Apt 3, Drexel Hill, PA, 19026-2338, Delaware, USA; gen tel (610) 259-4141; disp adv e-mail mail@presspublishing.org; class adv e-mail mail@presspublishing.org; ed e-mail mail@presspublishing.org
Circulation:; Sworn/Estimate/Non-Audited
Advertising rate: Open inch rate $7.00
Established: 1929
Ed. .... Philippe A. Girard
Mechanical Specifications: Type page 10 x 15 3/4; E - 5 cols, 1 5/6, 1/6 between; A - 5 cols, 1 5/6, 1/6 between; C - 5 cols, 1 5/6, 1/6 between.Equipment & Software: ; Presses — G/Community
Delivery Method: Mail, Newsstand
Areas Served: 19050

UPPER DARBY PRESS (THUR)

3245 Garrett Rd, Apt 3, Drexel Hill, PA, 19026-2338, Delaware, USA; gen tel (610) 259-4141; disp adv e-mail mail@presspublishing.org; class adv e-mail mail@presspublishing.org; ed e-mail mail@presspublishing.org
Circulation:; Sworn/Estimate/Non-Audited
Established: 1926
Ed. .... Philippe A. Girard
Mechanical Specifications: Type page 10 x 15 3/4; E - 5 cols, 1 5/6, 1/6 between; A - 5 cols, 1 5/6, 1/6 between; C - 5 cols, 1 5/6, 1/6 between.
Delivery Method: Mail, Newsstand
Areas Served: 19082, 19026

DU BOIS

TRI-COUNTY SUNDAY (SUN)

500 Jeffers St, Du Bois, PA, 15801-2430, Clearfield, USA; gen tel (814) 371-4200; gen fax (814) 371-3241; ed e-mail newspaper@thecourierexpress.com; web site http://www.thecourierexpress.com/tri_county_sunday/
Advertising rate: Open inch rate $15.30
Established: 1993
Group: Community Media Group
Digital Platform - Mobile: Apple, Android
Digital Platform - Tablet: Apple iOS, Android
Pub. .... Devin Hamilton
Ed. .... Joy Norwood
Delivery Method: Mail, Newsstand, Carrier, Racks
Areas Served: Clearfield, Cameron, Southern McKean, Clarion, and Forest County

DUSHORE

THE SULLIVAN REVIEW (WED)

211 Water St, Dushore, PA, 18614, Sullivan, USA; gen tel (570) 928-8403; adv tel 570-928-8403; ed tel 570-928-8403; gen fax (570) 928-8006; disp adv e-mail ads@thesullivanreview.com; ed e-mail news@thesullivanreview.com; web site https://www.thesullivanreview.com/
Circulation: 6,727pd, 63fr; Sworn/Estimate/Non-Audited
Advertising rate: Open inch rate $6.40
Established: 1878
Pub. .... John Shoemaker
Mechanical Specifications: Type page 13 x 21 1/2; E - 6 cols, 2 1/12, 1/8 between; A - 6 cols, 2 1/12, 1/8 between; C - 8 cols, 1 7/12, 1/12 between.Equipment & Software: Hardware — PC.
Delivery Method: Mail, Newsstand
Areas Served: Sullivan County

EASTON

THE US (WED)

18 Centre Sq, Easton, PA, 18042-7746, Northampton, USA; gen tel (610) 258-7171; gen fax (610) 559-7240; disp adv e-mail news@express-times.com; class adv e-mail advertising@express-times.com; web site www.lehighvalleylive.com/the-us
Circulation: 21,000fr; Sworn/Estimate/Non-Audited
Advertising rate: Open inch rate $15.00
Established: 1980
Group: Advance Publications, Inc.
Pub .... Martin K. Till
Ed. .... Jim Deegan
Mechanical Specifications: 9.046"x10.875"
5 columnsEquipment & Software: Hardware — APP/Mac; Presses — G; Software — QPS/QuarkXPress 3.32.
Delivery Method: Carrier, Racks
Areas Served: 18014, 18064, 18020, 18045, 18085, 18083, 18091

EBENSBURG

MAINLINE EXTRA (THUR)

975 Rowena Dr, Ebensburg, PA, 15931-2077, Cambria, USA; gen tel (814) 472-4110; gen fax (814) 472-2275; ed e-mail mainlinenews@verizon.net; web site www.mainline-news.com
Circulation: 10,130fr; Sworn/Estimate/Non-Audited
Advertising rate: Open inch rate $14.75
Group: Mainline Newspapers
Digital Platform - Mobile: Apple, Android, Blackberry
Digital Platform - Tablet: Apple iOS, Android, Windows 7, Blackberry Tablet OS
Pub. .... William Anderson
Ed. .... Paula Varner
Delivery Method: Mail, Newsstand
Areas Served: Cambria County

THE DISPATCH (SUN)

975 Rowena Dr, Ebensburg, PA, 15931-2077, Cambria, USA; gen tel (814) 472-2275; gen fax (814) 472-4110; ed e-mail mainlinenews@verizon.net; web site www.mainline-news.com
Circulation: 1,928pd, 10,451fr; AAM
Advertising rate: Open inch rate $14.75
Group: Mainline Newspapers
Digital Platform - Mobile: Apple, Android, Blackberry
Digital Platform - Tablet: Apple iOS, Android, Windows 7, Blackberry Tablet OS
Pub. .... William Anderson
Ed. .... Paula Varner
Delivery Method: Mail, Newsstand
Areas Served: Portage, Beaverdale, Cassandra, St. Michael, Salix, Sidman, South Fork, Summerhill, and Wilmore

THE JOURNAL (THUR)

975 Rowena Dr, Ebensburg, PA, 15931-2077, Cambria, USA; gen tel (814) 472-4110; gen fax (814) 472-2275; ed e-mail mainlinenews@verizon.net; web site www.mainline-news.com
Circulation: 2,300pd,; Sworn/Estimate/Non-Audited
Advertising rate: Open inch rate $14.75
Group: Mainline Newspapers
Digital Platform - Mobile: Apple, Android, Blackberry
Digital Platform - Tablet: Apple iOS, Android, Windows 7, Blackberry Tablet OS
Pub. .... William Anderson
Ed. .... Paula Varner
Delivery Method: Mail, Newsstand
Areas Served: Nanty Glo, Vintondale, Belsano, Mineral Point, Mundys Corner, Strongstown, and Twin Rocks

THE MAINLINER (THUR)

975 Rowena Dr, Ebensburg, PA, 15931-2077, Cambria, USA; gen tel (814) 472-4110; gen fax (814) 472-2275; ed e-mail mainlinenews@verizon.net; web site www.mainline-news.com
Circulation: 2,700pd,; Sworn/Estimate/Non-Audited
Advertising rate: Open inch rate $14.75
Group: Mainline Newspapers
Digital Platform - Mobile: Apple, Android, Blackberry
Digital Platform - Tablet: Apple iOS, Android, Windows 7, Blackberry Tablet OS
Pub. .... William Anderson
Ed. .... Paula Varner
Delivery Method: Mail, Newsstand
Areas Served: Cresson, Gallitzin, Ashville, Chest Springs, Coupon, Lilly, Loretto, and Tunnelhil

THE MOUNTAINEER-HERALD (THUR)

975 Rowena Dr, Ebensburg, PA, 15931-2077, Cambria, USA; gen tel (814) 472-4110; gen fax (814) 472-2275; ed e-mail mainlinenews@verizon.net; web site www.mainline-news.com
Circulation: 3,013pd,; Sworn/Estimate/Non-Audited
Advertising rate: Open inch rate $14.75
Group: Mainline Newspapers
Sample News Group LLC
Digital Platform - Mobile: Apple, Android, Blackberry
Digital Platform - Tablet: Apple iOS, Android, Windows 7, Blackberry Tablet OS
Pub. .... William Anderson
Ed. .... Paula Varner
Mechanical Specifications: Type page 13 x 21 1/2.Equipment & Software: Hardware — APP/Mac.
Delivery Method: Mail, Newsstand
Areas Served: Ebensburg, Colver, Revloc, and Cambria Township

EIGHTY FOUR

THE WEEKLY RECORDER (FRI)

1056 Route 519, Eighty Four, PA, 15330-2812, Washington, USA; gen tel (724) 884-1498; gen fax (724) 884-0006; disp adv e-mail recorderads01@gmail.com; class adv e-mail recorderads02@gmail.com; ed e-mail jessicaashley@theweeklyrecorder.com; web site www.theweeklyrecorder.info
Circulation: 3,000pd, 10fr; Sworn/Estimate/Non-Audited
Advertising rate: Open inch rate $10.00
Established: 1888
Digital Platform - Mobile: Apple, Android
Digital Platform - Tablet: Apple iOS, Android, Windows 7, Blackberry Tablet OS
Owner/Pub./Ed. .... Jessica Dernosek
Adv. Mgr. .... Christina Luna
Mechanical Specifications: Type page 10 x 13; E - 4 cols, 2 5/12, 1/6 between; A - 4 cols, 2 5/12, 1/6 between; C - 4 cols, 2 5/12, 1/6 between.Equipment & Software: Hardware — PC; Software — Aldus/PageMaker 4.0.
Delivery Method: Mail, Newsstand
Areas Served: Washington County

ELIZABETHTOWN

THE ELIZABETHTOWN ADVOCATE (THUR)

9 S Market St, Elizabethtown, PA, 17022-2308, Lancaster, USA; gen tel (717) 361-0340; adv tel (717)481-7321; disp adv e-mail drobrish@lnpnews.com; class adv e-mail bkent.eph@lnpnews.com; ed e-mail drobrish@lnpnews.com ; web site www.etownpa.com
Circulation: 6,250pd,; Sworn/Estimate/Non-Audited
Advertising rate: Open inch rate $5.75 per column inch
Established: 2010
Editor .... Dan Robrish
Delivery Method: Mail, Newsstand, Racks
Areas Served: 17022, 17502, 17552

EMLENTON

THE PROGRESS NEWS (TUES)

410 Main St, Emlenton, PA, 16373, Venango, USA; gen tel (724) 867-1112; adv tel 724-867-1112; gen fax (724) 867-1356; adv fax 724-867-1356; disp adv e-mail dstaab@myprogressnews.com; class adv e-mail ads@myprogressnews.com; ed e-mail news@myprogressnews.com; web site www.myprogressnews.com
Circulation: 14,000fr; Sworn/Estimate/Non-Audited
Advertising rate: Open inch rate $14.00
Established: 1885
Group: Staab Typographic
Digital Platform - Mobile: Windows
Digital Platform - Tablet: Windows 7
Pub./Ed. .... David J. Staab
Mechanical Specifications: Full Page - 6 col x 21 inches
1 col. 9 pica 9 points; 2 col. 20 pica 2 points
3 col. 30 pica 6 points; 4 col. 41 pica
5 col. 51 pica; 6 col. 61 pica 6 points
Delivery Method: Mail, Racks
Areas Served: 16373, 16232, 16319, 16054, 16036, 16049, 16028, 16025, 16041, 16050, 16022, 16048, 16030, 16372, 16375, 16020, 16061, 16048

EMPORIUM

CAMERON COUNTY ECHO (WED)

300 S Broad St, Ste 1, Emporium, PA, 15834-1495, Cameron, USA; gen tel (814) 486-3711; gen fax (814) 486-0990; ed e-mail ccecho@zitomedia.net; web site www.camer-

oncountyecho.net
Circulation: 3,761pd, 48fr; Sworn/Estimate/Non-Audited
Advertising rate: Open inch rate $6.22
Pub.. David A. Brown
Delivery Method: Mail, Newsstand
Areas Served: Cameron County

EPHRATA

LANCASTER FARMING (SAT)
1 E Main St, Ephrata, PA, 17522-2713, Lancaster, USA; gen tel (717) 733-6397; adv tel (717) 721-4400; ed tel (717) 733-6397; gen fax (717) 733-6058; adv fax (717) 733-6058; ed fax (717) 733-6058; disp adv e-mail jherr.eph@lnpnews.com; class adv e-mail khoffer.eph@lnpnews.com; ed e-mail dlarison.eph@lnpnews.com; web site www.lancasterfarming.com
Circulation: 59,454pd, 529fr; Sworn/Estimate/Non-Audited
Advertising rate: Open inch rate $18.98
Established: 1955
Group: LNP
LNP Media Group, Inc.
Lancaster Newspapers Inc.
Digital Platform - Mobile: Apple, Android
Digital Platform - Tablet: Apple iOS, Android, Kindle, Nook, Kindle Fire
President and publisher................. Bill Burgess
Vice President .... Peter Lindquist
Editor .... Dennis Larison
Delivery Method: Mail, Newsstand, Carrier, Racks
Areas Served: Pennsylvania, New Jersey, Ohio, Maryland, New York, Delaware, Virginia, West Virginia, Massachusetts, Connecticut, Rhode Island, Vermont, New Hampshire, Maine

LITITZ RECORD EXPRESS (THUR)
1 E Main St, Ephrata, PA, 17522-2713, Lancaster, USA; gen tel (717) 733-6397; gen fax (717) 733-6058; disp adv e-mail bkent@lnpnews.com; class adv e-mail mreidenbach.eph@lnpnews.com; ed e-mail afasnacht.eph@lnpnews.com; web site www.lititzrecordexpress.com
Circulation: 8,200pd,; Sworn/Estimate/Non-Audited
Advertising rate: Open inch rate $12.59
Established: 1877
Group: LNP
LNP Media Group, Inc.
Digital Platform - Mobile: Apple, Android
Digital Platform - Tablet: Apple iOS, Android, Kindle, Nook, Kindle Fire
Adv. Mgr....................................... Beverly Kent
Ed. .... Andrew Fasnacht
Mechanical Specifications: Type page 13 x 21 1/2; E - 6 cols, 2 1/16, 1/8 between; A - 6 cols, 2 1/16, 1/8 between; C - 8 cols, 1 1/2, 1/8 between.Equipment & Software: Hardware — APP/Mac, PC, AU/Lino Imaging System; Presses — G/Community; Software — APP/System 7, Multi-Ad/Creator 4.0, QPS/QuarkXPress 4.0, Adobe/Photoshop, Adobe/PageMaker, HI.
Delivery Method: Mail, Newsstand, Racks
Areas Served: Lancaster County

THE EPHRATA REVIEW (WED)
1 E Main St, Ephrata, PA, 17522-2713, Lancaster, USA; gen tel (717) 733-6397; gen fax (717) 733-6058; disp adv e-mail bkent@lnpnews.com; class adv e-mail mreidenbach.eph@lnpnews.com; ed e-mail afasnacht.eph@lnpnews.com; web site www.ephratareview.com
Circulation: 7,485pd, 70fr; Sworn/Estimate/Non-Audited
Advertising rate: Open inch rate $17.29
Established: 1878
Group: LNP
LNP Media Group, Inc.
Digital Platform - Mobile: Apple, Android
Digital Platform - Tablet: Apple iOS, Android, Kindle, Nook, Kindle Fire
Pres./Pub...................................... Bill Burgess
Vice Pres./Asst. Gen. Mgr......... Peter Lindquist
Ed. .... Andrew Fasnacht
Adv. Mgr....................................... Beverly Kent
Mechanical Specifications: Type page 13 x 21 1/2; E - 6 cols, 2 1/16, between; A - 6 cols, 2 1/16, between; C - 8 cols, 1 1/2, between.
Delivery Method: Mail, Newsstand, Racks
Areas Served: Lancaster County

THE SHOPPING NEWS OF LANCASTER COUNTY (WED)
615 E Main St, Ephrata, PA, 17522-2537, Lancaster, USA; gen tel (717) 738-1151; adv tel (717) 738-1151 ext. 225; gen fax (717) 733-3900; disp adv e-mail dfoose@snews.com; class adv e-mail tmarxen@snews.com; ed e-mail hwenger@snews.com; web site www.snews.com - 62,944(views) 6,230(visitors)
Circulation: 2pd, 37,813fr; VAC
Advertising rate: Open inch rate $13.25
Established: 1965
Group: Hocking Printing Co., Inc.Editions: (1) The Shopping News
Digital Platform - Mobile: Apple, Android
Digital Platform - Tablet: Apple iOS, Android
Pub./Gen. Mgr.......................... Harold Wenger
Ed. .... Julie Hocking
Delivery Method: Carrier
Areas Served: Northern Lancaster County

FOREST CITY

THE FOREST CITY NEWS (WED)
636 Main St, Forest City, PA, 18421-1430, Susquehanna, USA; gen tel (570) 785-3800; gen fax (570) 785-9840; disp adv e-mail jennifer@forestcitynews.com; ed e-mail patricia@forestcitynews.com; web site www.forestcitynews.com
Circulation: 3,500pd, 140fr; Sworn/Estimate/Non-Audited
Advertising rate: Open inch rate $6.00
Established: 1887
Pub./Ed............................ Patricia M. Striessky
Adv. Sales.................................. Jennifer Butler
Office Mgr.............................. Jean Matoushek
Mechanical Specifications: Type page 13 x 21; E - 7 cols, 1 3/4, 1 1/2 between; A - 7 cols, 1 3/4, between; C - 7 cols, 1 3/4, between. Equipment & Software: Hardware — APP/Macs; Software — Microsoft/Word, Adobe/PageMaker.
Delivery Method: Mail, Newsstand
Areas Served: Susquehanna, Wayne, and Lackawanna County

FORT WASHINGTON

GLENSIDE NEWS (SUN)
290 Commerce Dr, Fort Washington, PA, 19034-2400, Montgomery, USA; gen tel (215) 542-0200; adv tel (215) 542-0200 ext. 150; ed tel (215) 542-0200 ext. 264; gen fax (215) 643-9475; disp adv e-mail sanderer@montgomerynews.com; class adv e-mail classified@montgomerynews.com; ed e-mail editorial@montgomerynews.com; web site www.montgomerynews.com
Circulation: 573pd, 62fr; AAM
Advertising rate: 1/20 Pg $232.00; 1/16 Pg $270.00; 1/12 Pg $332.00
Established: 1894
Group: Montgomery Newspapers
Digital First Media
Digital Platform - Mobile: Apple, Android, Blackberry
Digital Platform - Tablet: Apple iOS, Android, Windows 7, Blackberry Tablet OS
Circ. Mgr .... Joe Flenders
Adv. Mgr....................................... Beth Douglas
Ed .... Thomas Celona
Mechanical Specifications: Type page 12 3/4 x 21 1/2; E - 6 cols, 2, 1/6 between; A - 6 cols, 2, 1/6 between; C - 10 cols, 1 1/3, 1/6 between. Equipment & Software: Hardware — APP/Mac; Presses — G/Offset; Software — QPS/QuarkXPress.
Delivery Method: Mail, Newsstand, Carrier, Racks
Areas Served: 19038

MONTGOMERY LIFE (THUR)
290 Commerce Dr, Fort Washington, PA, 19034-2400, Montgomery, USA; gen tel (215) 542-0200; adv tel (215) 542-0200 ext. 150; ed tel (215) 542-0200 ext. 264; gen fax (215) 643-9475; disp adv e-mail sanderer@montgomerynews.com; class adv e-mail classified@montgomerynews.com; ed e-mail editorial@montgomerynews.com; web site www.montgomerynews.com
Circulation: 220pd, 151fr; CAC
Advertising rate: 1/20 Pg $232.00; 1/16 Pg $270.00; 1/12 Pg $332.00
Group: Digital First Media
Digital Platform - Mobile: Apple, Android, Blackberry
Digital Platform - Tablet: Apple iOS, Android, Windows 7, Blackberry Tablet OS
Exec. Ed.................................. Thomas Celona
Adv. Mgr.................................... Beth Douglas
Circ. Mgr .... Joe Flenders
Mechanical Specifications: Type page 12 3/4 x 21 1/2; E - 6 cols, 2, 1/6 between; A - 6 cols, 2, 1/6 between; C - 10 cols, 1 1/3, 1/6 between. Equipment & Software: Hardware — APP/Mac; Presses — G/Offset; Software — QPS/QuarkXPress.
Delivery Method: Mail, Newsstand, Carrier, Racks
Areas Served: Montgomery County

NORTH PENN LIFE (SUN)
290 Commerce Dr, Fort Washington, PA, 19034-2400, Montgomery, USA; gen tel (215) 542-0200; adv tel (215) 542-0200 ext. 150; ed tel (215) 542-0200 ext. 264; gen fax (215) 643-9475; disp adv e-mail sanderer@montgomerynews.com; class adv e-mail classified@montgomerynews.com; ed e-mail dgodshalk@montgomerynews.com; web site www.montgomerynews.com
Circulation: 570pd, 168fr; CAC
Advertising rate: 1/20 Pg $232.00; 1/16 Pg $270.00; 1/12 Pg $332.00
Group: Montgomery Newspapers
Digital First Media
Digital Platform - Mobile: Apple, Android, Blackberry
Digital Platform - Tablet: Apple iOS, Android, Windows 7, Blackberry Tablet OS
Circ. Dir....................................... Joe Flenders
Adv. Mgr....................................... Beth Douglas
Thomas Celona
Mechanical Specifications: Type page 12 3/4 x 21 1/2; E - 6 cols, 2, 1/6 between; A - 6 cols, 2, 1/6 between; C - 10 cols, 1 1/3, 1/6 between. Equipment & Software: Hardware — APP/Mac; Presses — G/Offset; Software — QPS/QuarkXPress.
Delivery Method: Mail, Newsstand, Carrier, Racks
Areas Served: 19440, 19446, 19454

PERKASIE NEWS-HERALD (SUN)
290 Commerce Dr, Fort Washington, PA, 19034-2400, Montgomery, USA; gen tel (215) 257-6839; adv tel (215) 542-0200 ext. 150; ed tel (215) 542-0200 ext. 264; gen fax (215) 643-9475; disp adv e-mail sanderer@montgomerynews.com; class adv e-mail classified@montgomerynews.com; ed e-mail editorial@montgomerynews.com; web site www.perkasienewsherald.com
Circulation: 929pd,; CAC
Advertising rate: 1/20 Pg $202.00; 1/16 Pg $232.00; 1/12 Pg $282.00
Group: Montgomery Newspapers
Digital First Media
Digital Platform - Mobile: Apple, Android, Blackberry
Digital Platform - Tablet: Apple iOS, Android, Windows 7, Blackberry Tablet OS
Ed. .... Thomas Celona
Adv. Mgr.................................... Beth Douglas
Circ. Mgr .... Joe Flenders
Mechanical Specifications: Type page 11 5/8 x 20 1/2; E - 6 cols, 1 5/6, 1/6 between; A - 6 cols, 1 5/6, 1/6 between; C - 9 cols, between. Equipment & Software: Hardware — APP/Mac; Software — QPS/QuarkXPress.
Delivery Method: Mail, Newsstand, Carrier, Racks
Areas Served: 18911, 18944, 18960, 18962, 18910, 18917, 18927

PUBLIC SPIRIT (SUN)
290 Commerce Dr, Fort Washington, PA, 19034-2400, Montgomery, USA; gen tel (215) 542-0200; adv tel (215) 542-0200 ext. 150; ed tel (215) 542-0200 ext. 414; gen fax (215) 643-9475; disp adv e-mail sanderer@montgomerynews.com; class adv e-mail classified@montgomerynews.com; ed e-mail sroman@montgomerynews.com; web site www.montgomerynews.com
Circulation: 299pd, 63fr; CAC
Advertising rate: 1/20 Pg $202.00; 1/16 Pg $232.00; 1/12 Pg $282.00
Established: 1957
Group: Digital First Media
Digital Platform - Mobile: Apple, Android, Blackberry
Digital Platform - Tablet: Apple iOS, Android, Windows 7, Blackberry Tablet OS
Ed .... Thomas Celona
Circ. Mgr...................................... Joe Flenders
Adv. Mgr.................................... Beth Douglas
Mechanical Specifications: Type page 12 3/4 x 21 1/2; E - 6 cols, 2, 1/6 between; A - 6 cols, 2, 1/6 between; C - 10 cols, 1 1/3, 1/6 between. Equipment & Software: Hardware — APP/Mac; Presses — G/Offset; Software — QPS/QuarkXPress.
Delivery Method: Mail, Newsstand, Carrier, Racks
Areas Served: 19040, 19044

SOUDERTON INDEPENDENT (SUN)
290 Commerce Dr, Fort Washington, PA, 19034-2400, Montgomery, USA; gen tel (215) 542-0200; adv tel (215) 542-0200 ext. 150; ed tel (215) 542-0200 ext. 414; gen fax (215) 643-9475; adv fax (215) 643-9475; ed fax (215) 643-9475; disp adv e-mail sanderer@montgomerynews.com; class adv e-mail classified@montgomerynews.com; ed e-mail tcelona@montgomerynews.com; web site www.montgomerynews.com
Circulation: 8,113pd, 784fr; CAC
Advertising rate: 1/20 Pg $202.00; 1/16 Pg $232.00; 1/12 Pg $282.00
Established: 1957
Group: Digital First Media
Montgomery Newspapers
Digital Platform - Mobile: Apple, Android, Blackberry
Digital Platform - Tablet: Apple iOS, Android, Windows 7, Blackberry Tablet OS
Pub....................................... Elizabeth Wilson
News Ed.................................. Thomas Celona
Mechanical Specifications: Type page 12 3/4 x 21 1/2; E - 6 cols, 2, 1/6 between; A - 6 cols, 2, 1/6 between; C - 10 cols, 1 1/3, 1/6 between. Equipment & Software: Hardware — APP/Mac; Presses — G/offset; Software — QPS/QuarkXPress.
Delivery Method: Mail, Newsstand, Carrier, Racks
Areas Served: 18964, 18969, 19438

SPRINGFIELD SUN (SUN)
290 Commerce Dr, Fort Washington, PA, 19034-2400, Montgomery, USA; gen tel (215) 542-0200; adv tel (215) 542-0200 ext. 150; ed tel (215) 542-0200 ext. 279; gen fax (215) 643-9475; disp adv e-mail sanderer@montgomerynews.com; class adv e-mail classified@montgomerynews.com; ed e-mail mross@montgomerynews.com; web site www.montgomerynews.com
Circulation: 1,047pd,; CAC
Advertising rate: 1/20 Pg $232.00; 1/16 Pg $270.00; 1/12 Pg $332.00
Established: 1957
Group: Montgomery Newspapers
Digital First Media
Digital Platform - Mobile: Apple, Android, Blackberry
Digital Platform - Tablet: Apple iOS, Android, Windows 7, Blackberry Tablet OS
Circ. Mgr...................................... Joe Flenders
Adv. Mgr.................................... Beth Douglas
Ed .... Thomas Celona
Mechanical Specifications: Type page 12 3/4 x 21 1/2; E - 6 cols, 2, 1/6 between; A - 6 cols, 2, 1/6 between; C - 10 cols, 1 1/3, 1/6 between. Equipment & Software: Hardware — APP/Mac; Presses — G/Offset; Software — QPS/QuarkXPress.

Delivery Method: Mail, Newsstand, Carrier, Racks
Areas Served: 19031, 19075, 19118

THE COLONIAL (SUN)

290 Commerce Dr, Fort Washington, PA, 19034-2400, Montgomery, USA; gen tel (215) 542-0200; adv tel (215) 542-0200 ext. 150; ed tel (215) 542-0200 ext. 279; gen fax (215) 643-9475; disp adv e-mail sanderer@montgomerynews.com; class adv e-mail classified@montgomerynews.com; ed e-mail tcelona@montgomerynews.com; web site www.montgomerynews.com
Circulation: 791pd, 125fr; CAC
Advertising rate: Open inch rate $14.95
Digital Platform - Mobile: Apple, Android, Blackberry
Digital Platform - Tablet: Apple iOS, Android, Windows 7, Blackberry Tablet OS
Ed. .... Thomas Celona
Adv. Mgr. .... Beth Douglas
Circ. Mgr. .... Joe Flenders
Mechanical Specifications: Type page 12 3/4 x 21 1/2; E - 6 cols, 2, 1/6 between; A - 6 cols, 2, 1/6 between; C - 10 cols, 1 1/3, 1/6 between. Equipment & Software: Hardware — APP/Mac; Presses — G/Offset; Software — QPS/QuarkXPress.
Delivery Method: Mail, Newsstand, Carrier, Racks
Areas Served: 19444, 19462, 19428

THE GLOBE (SUN)

290 Commerce Dr, Fort Washington, PA, 19034-2400, Montgomery, USA; gen tel (215) 542-0200; adv tel (215) 542-0200 ext. 150; ed tel (215) 542-0200 ext. 279; gen fax (215) 643-9475; disp adv e-mail sanderer@montgomerynews.com; class adv e-mail classified@montgomerynews.com; ed e-mail mross@montgomerynews.com; web site www.montgomerynews.com
Circulation: 226pd, 62fr; CAC
Advertising rate: 1/20 Pg $232.00; 1/16 Pg $270.00; 1/12 Pg $332.00
Group: Digital First Media
Digital Platform - Mobile: Apple, Android, Blackberry
Digital Platform - Tablet: Apple iOS, Android, Windows 7, Blackberry Tablet OS
Circ. Mgr. .... Joe Flenders
Ed .... Thomas Celona
Adv. Mgr. .... Beth Douglas
Mechanical Specifications: Type page 12 3/4 x 21 1/2; E - 6 cols, 2, 1/6 between; A - 6 cols, 2, 1/6 between; C - 10 cols, 1 1/3, 1/6 between. Equipment & Software: Hardware — APP/Mac; Presses — G/Offset; Software — QPS/QuarkXPress.
Delivery Method: Mail, Newsstand, Carrier, Racks
Areas Served: 19006

TIMES CHRONICLE (SUN)

290 Commerce Dr, Fort Washington, PA, 19034-2400, Montgomery, USA; gen tel (215) 542-0200; adv tel (215) 542-0200 ext. 150; ed tel (215) 542-0200 ext. 279; gen fax (215) 643-9475; disp adv e-mail sanderer@montgomerynews.com; class adv e-mail classified@montgomerynews.com; ed e-mail mross@montgomerynews.com; web site www.montgomerynews.com
Circulation: 1,064pd, 63fr; CAC
Advertising rate: 1/20 Pg $232.00; 1/16 Pg $270.00; 1/12 Pg $332.00
Established: 1957
Group: Digital First Media
Digital Platform - Mobile: Apple, Android, Blackberry
Digital Platform - Tablet: Apple iOS, Android, Windows 7, Blackberry Tablet OS
Ed .... Thomas Celona
Adv. Mgr. .... Beth Douglas
Circ. Mgr. .... Joe Flenders
Mechanical Specifications: Type page 12 3/4 x 21 1/2; E - 6 cols, 2, 1/6 between; A - 6 cols, 2, 1/6 between; C - 10 cols, 1 1/3, 1/6 between.Equipment & Software: Hardware — APP/Mac; Presses — G; Software — QPS/QuarkXPress.
Delivery Method: Mail, Newsstand, Carrier, Racks
Areas Served: 19001, 19012, 19117, 19046

WILLOW GROVE GUIDE (SUN)

290 Commerce Dr, Fort Washington, PA, 19034-2400, Montgomery, USA; gen tel (215) 542-0200; adv tel (215) 542-0200 ext. 150; ed tel (215) 542-0200 ext. 414; gen fax (215) 643-9475; disp adv e-mail sanderer@montgomerynews.com; class adv e-mail classified@montgomerynews.com; ed e-mail sroman@montgomerynews.com; web site www.montgomerynews.com
Circulation: 144pd, 62fr; CAC
Advertising rate: 1/20 Pg $202.00; 1/16 Pg $232.00; 1/12 Pg $282.00
Group: Digital First Media
Digital Platform - Mobile: Apple, Android, Blackberry
Digital Platform - Tablet: Apple iOS, Android, Windows 7, Blackberry Tablet OS
Circ. Mgr .... Joe Flenders
Ed. .... Thomas Celona
Adv. Mgr. .... Beth Douglas
Mechanical Specifications: Type page 12 3/4 x 21 1/2; E - 6 cols, 2, 1/6 between; A - 6 cols, 2, 1/6 between; C - 10 cols, 1 1/3, 1/6 between. Equipment & Software: Hardware — APP/Mac; Presses — G/Offset; Software — QPS/QuarkXPress.
Delivery Method: Mail, Newsstand, Carrier, Racks
Areas Served: 19090

GREENCASTLE

THE ECHO-PILOT (WED)

PO Box 159, 24 E. Baltimore St, Greencastle, PA, 17225-0159, Franklin, USA; gen tel (717) 597-2164; gen fax (717) 597-3754; disp adv e-mail agreen@echo-pilot.com; ed e-mail news@echo-pilot.com; web site www.echo-pilot.com
Circulation: 2,700pd,; Sworn/Estimate/Non-Audited
Advertising rate: Open inch rate $6.80
Established: 1849
Group: GateHouse Media, Inc.
Digital Platform - Mobile: Apple, Android
Digital Platform - Tablet: Apple iOS, Android
Ed. .... Joyce Nowell
Adv. Mgr .... Alice Green
Delivery Method: Mail, Newsstand
Areas Served: Franklin County

GREENSBURG

THE JEANNETTE SPIRIT (THUR)

622 Cabin Hill Dr, Greensburg, PA, 15601-1657, Westmoreland, USA; gen tel (724) 838-5154; gen fax (724) 838-5171; disp adv e-mail bcornali@tribweb.com; ed e-mail jdeflitch@tribweb.com; web site http://triblive.com/local/westmoreland/
Circulation: 1,351pd,; AAM
Advertising rate: Open inch rate $12.42
Established: 1983
Group: Trib Total Media, Inc.
Digital Platform - Mobile: Apple, Android
Digital Platform - Tablet: Apple iOS, Android
Ed .... Jerry Deflitch
Mechanical Specifications: Type page 11 1/2 x 21 1/2; E - 6 cols, 1 13/16, 1/8 between; A - 6 cols, 1 13/16, 1/8 between; C - 10 cols, 1 1/16, 1/8 between.Equipment & Software: Hardware — PCs, Compaq/Server; Presses — HI; Software — QPS/QuarkXPress 4.0.
Delivery Method: Mail, Newsstand
Areas Served: Westmoreland County

GROVE CITY

ALLIED NEWS (WED, SAT)

201 Erie St, Ste A, Grove City, PA, 16127-1659, Mercer, USA; gen tel (724) 458-5010; adv tel (724) 458-5010; ed tel (724) 458-5010; gen fax (724) 458-1609; adv fax (724) 458-1609; ed fax (724) 458-1609; disp adv e-mail alliednews@gmail.com; class adv e-mail alliednews@gmail.com; ed e-mail alliednewspaper@gmail.com; web site www.alliednews.com
Circulation: 1,929pd, 7,665fr; Sworn/Estimate/Non-Audited
Advertising rate: Open inch rate $15.35
Established: 1872
Group: Community Newspaper Holdings, Inc.
Digital Platform - Mobile: Apple, Android
Digital Platform - Tablet: Apple iOS, Android
Pub .... Sharon Sorg
Delivery Method: Mail, Newsstand, Carrier, Racks
Areas Served: Mercer County, Butler County, Venango County

HANOVER

THE EVENING SUN (TUES, THUR, SUN)

135 Baltimore St, Hanover, PA, 17331-3142, York, USA; gen tel (717) 637-3736; adv tel (717) 637-3736; ed tel (717) 637-3736 ; gen fax (717) 637-7730; adv fax (717) 264-2009; ed fax (717) 637-0900; disp adv e-mail info@eveningsun.com; class adv e-mail advertising@eveningsun.com; ed e-mail ejones@eveningsun.com; web site www.eveningsun.com
Circulation: 6,815pd, 929fr; AAM
Advertising rate: Open inch rate $45.58
Group: Gannett
Metro Ed. .... Janelle Coolbaugh
Circ. Mgr. .... Robert Trazkovich
Community Sun Ed .... Kim Sterner
Sports Ed. .... Charles Curley
Style Ed. .... Ann Diviney
Online Mgr. .... Bryan Byers
Prod. Foreman, Press .... David Myers
Pub .... Sara Glines
Pub .... Fred Uffelman
Nat'l Sales .... Breanne Packard
Adv. & Marketing Dir. .... Katie Hoyt
Mechanical Specifications: Type page 13 x 21 1/2; E - 6 cols, 2 1/16, 1/8 between; A - 6 cols, 2 1/16, 1/8 between; C - 6 cols, 2 1/16, 1/8 between.

HARRISBURG

CENTRAL PENN BUSINESS JOURNAL (FRI)

1500 Paxton St, Fl 3, Harrisburg, PA, 17104-2626, Dauphin, USA; gen tel (717) 236-4300; gen fax (717) 236-6803; disp adv e-mail natet@centralpennbusiness.com; class adv e-mail marks@centralpennbusiness.com; ed e-mail editorial@centralpennbusiness.com; web site www.centralpennbusiness.com
Circulation: 10,000pd,; Sworn/Estimate/Non-Audited
Advertising rate: Open inch rate $4150.00 (Full-Run)
Established: 1984
Group: Journal Multimedia
Digital Platform - Mobile: Apple, Android
Digital Platform - Tablet: Apple iOS, Android
CEO .... David Schankweiler
Pub .... Douglas Cooper
Mng. Ed .... Amy Gulli
Sales Mgr .... ShaunJude McCoach
Delivery Method: Mail, Carrier
Areas Served: Dauphin, Cumberland, Lebanon, Lancaster, and York County

HELLERTOWN

THE VALLEY VOICE (FRI)

1188 Main St, Hellertown, PA, 18055-1319, Northampton, USA; gen tel (610) 838-2066; gen fax (610) 838-2239; ed e-mail valleyvoice@verizon.net; web site www.hellertown.patch.com/listings/the-valley-voice
Circulation: 4,317pd, 451fr; Sworn/Estimate/Non-Audited
Advertising rate: Open inch rate $12.50
Established: 1988
Pub./Adv. Mgr. .... Ann Marie Gonsalves
Ed. .... Paul Bealer
Mechanical Specifications: Type page 10 x 13; E - 5 cols, 2, between; A - 5 cols, 2, between; C - 5 cols, 2, between.Equipment & Software: Hardware — Gateway; Software — Adobe/PageMaker 6.5.
Delivery Method: Mail, Newsstand, Carrier
Areas Served: 18055, 18015, 18017, 18018, 18020

HONESDALE

CARBONDALE NEWS (FRI)

220 8th St, Honesdale, PA, 18431-1854, Wayne, USA; gen tel (570) 253-3055; adv tel (570) 253-3055 ext. 301; ed tel (570) 253-3055 ext: 329; gen fax (570) 253-5387; adv fax (570) 253-5387; ed fax (570) 253-5387; disp adv e-mail mfleece@wayneindependent.com; class adv e-mail pjordan@wayneindependent.com; ed e-mail mleet@wayneindependent.com; web site www.thecarbondalenews.com
Circulation: 1,315pd,; USPS
Advertising rate: Open inch rate $10.74
Established: 1851
Group: GateHouse Media, Inc.
Digital Platform - Mobile: Apple, Android
Digital Platform - Tablet: Apple iOS, Android
Pres./Pub/Adv. Sales Mgr. .... Michelle Fleece
Managing Editor .... Melissa Lee
Circulation Coordinator .... Marcia Barrera
Mechanical Specifications: Type page 13 x 21 1/4; E - 6 cols, 2 1/24, 5/36 between; A - 6 cols, 2 1/24, 5/36 between; C - 8 cols, 1 1/2, 11/72 between.Equipment & Software: Hardware — APP/Power Mac; Software — Adobe/PageMaker 6.0, Adobe/Photoshop.
Delivery Method: Mail, Newsstand, Racks
Areas Served: Lackawanna County

THE MOSCOW VILLAGER (FRI)

220 8th St, Honesdale, PA, 18431-1854, Wayne, USA; gen tel (570) 253-3055; adv tel (570) 253-3055 ext. 301; ed tel (570) 253-3055 ext: 329; gen fax (570) 253-5387; adv fax (570) 253-5387; ed fax (570) 253-5387; disp adv e-mail mfleece@wayneindependent.com; class adv e-mail pjordan@wayneindependent.com; ed e-mail mleet@wayneindependent.com; web site www.moscowvillager.com - 19,137(views) 5,318(visitors)
Circulation: 500pd, 0fr; USPS
Advertising rate: Open inch rate $10.74
Established: 1961
Group: GateHouse Media, Inc.
Digital Platform - Mobile: Apple, Android, Windows, Blackberry
Pres./Pub./Adv. Dir. .... Michelle Fleece
Mechanical Specifications: Type page 10.333" x 21"; E - 6 cols, 1.583" each; A - 4 cols, standard SAU format; C - 6 cols, 1.583" each. Equipment & Software: Hardware — APP/Power Mac, PC; Software — Adobe/PageMaker 6.0, Adobe/Photoshop, DOS.
Delivery Method: Mail, Racks
Areas Served: 18444, 18424, 18436, 18445

THE NEWS EAGLE (WED, SAT)

8 Silk Mill Drive Suite 101, Honesdale, PA, 18431, Wayne, USA; gen tel (570) 253-3055; adv tel (570) 253-3055 ext. 301; ed tel (570) 226-4547 ext. 107; gen fax (570) 226-4548; adv fax (570) 253-5387; ed fax (570) 226-4548; disp adv e-mail mfleece@wayneindependent.com; class adv e-mail pjordan@wayneindependent.com; ed e-mail pbecker@neagle.com; web site www.neagle.com
Circulation: 1,294pd,; USPS
Advertising rate: Open inch rate $17.21
Established: 1950
Group: GateHouse Media, Inc.
Digital Platform - Mobile: Apple, Android, Windows, Blackberry, Other
Digital Platform - Tablet: Other
Pub .... Michelle Fleee
Managing Editor .... Peter Becker
Mechanical Specifications: Type page 13 1/4 x 21; E - 6 cols, 1 3/4, 1/6 between; A - 6 cols, 1 3/4, 1/6 between; C - 8 cols, 1 1/2, 1/6 between.Equipment & Software: Hardware — APP/Mac; Presses — G/Suburban; Software

— Baseview/News Edit Pro, Adobe/Illustrator, QPS/QuarkXPress.
Delivery Method: Mail, Newsstand, Racks
Areas Served: Wayne and Pike County

HUGHESVILLE

THE LUMINARY (WED)
1025 Route 405 Hwy, Hughesville, PA, 17737-9069, Lycoming, USA; gen tel (570) 584-0111; gen fax (570) 584-5399; disp adv e-mail advertising@muncyluminary.com; ed e-mail bbarrett@muncyluminary.com; web site www.muncyluminary.com
Circulation: 1,300pd, 12fr; Sworn/Estimate/ Non-Audited
Advertising rate: Open inch rate $4.32 (Local); $10.00 (National)
Group: Ogden Newspapers Inc.
Digital Platform - Mobile: Apple, Android
Digital Platform - Tablet: Apple iOS, Android
Pub....................................Bernard Oravec
Mng. Ed....................................Barbara Barrett
Mechanical Specifications: Type page 13 x 21 1/2; E - 6 cols, 2 1/12, 1/6 between; A - 6 cols, 2 1/12, 1/6 between; C - 9 cols, 1 5/12, between.Equipment & Software: Hardware — APP/Mac IIsi; Software — QPS/QuarkXPress.
Delivery Method: Mail, Newsstand, Racks
Areas Served: Muncy, Hughesville, and Montgomery

HUMMELSTOWN

THE SUN (THUR)
18 E Main St, Hummelstown, PA, 17036-1613, Dauphin, USA; gen tel (717) 566-3251; gen fax (717) 566-6196; disp adv e-mail ads@thesunontheweb.com; class adv e-mail ads@thesunontheweb.com; ed e-mail news@thesunontheweb.com; web site www.thesunontheweb.com
Circulation: 8,000pd,; USPS
Advertising rate: Open inch rate $11.00
Established: 1871
Digital Platform - Mobile: Apple, Android, Blackberry
Digital Platform - Tablet: Apple iOS, Android, Windows 7, Blackberry Tablet OS
Adv. Mgr....................................Amber Topper
Owner....................................Dave Buffington
Editor....................................Drew Weidman
Mechanical Specifications: Type page 13 3/4 x 21 1/2; E - 8 cols, 1 7/12, 1/6 between; A - 8 cols, 1 7/12, 1/6 between; C - 8 cols, 1 7/12, 1/6 between.Equipment & Software: Hardware — PC, APP/Mac, APP/Power Mac G3; Software — Adobe/PageMaker, WordPerfect, QPS/QuarkXPress, Adobe/Photoshop, Microsoft Word.
Delivery Method: Mail, Newsstand, Racks
Areas Served: 17022, 17028, 17033, 17036, 17057, 17078, 17502, 17545, 17547

HUNTINGDON

THE VALLEY LOG (WED)
PO Box 384, Huntingdon, PA, 16652-0384, Huntingdon, USA; gen tel (814) 447-5506; gen fax (814) 447-3050; disp adv e-mail ads@thevalleylog.net; ed e-mail news@thevalleylog.net
Circulation: 2,716pd, 78fr; Sworn/Estimate/ Non-Audited
Advertising rate: Open inch rate $4.00
Established: 1980
Group: Joseph F. Biddle Publishing Co.
Pub. C. Arnold McClureEquipment & Software: Hardware — APP/Mac; Software — Adobe/ PageMaker 6.5, QPS/QuarkXPress.
Delivery Method: Mail, Newsstand, Racks
Areas Served: Southern Huntingdon, Fulton, and Mifflin County

JOHNSONBURG

THE JOHNSONBURG PRESS (WED)
517 Market St, Johnsonburg, PA, 15845-1294, Elk, USA; gen tel (814) 965-2503; gen fax (814) 965-2504; ed e-mail jbgpress@windstream.net; web site www.jonestownship.com/bul/jbgpress.htm
Circulation: 2,004pd, 25fr; Sworn/Estimate/ Non-Audited
Advertising rate: Open inch rate $8.25
Gen. Mgr....................................John E. Fowler
Ed....................................Frances Fowler
Mechanical Specifications: Type page 13 x 21 1/2; A - 6 cols, 2 1/16, 1/6 between; C - 6 cols, 2 1/16, 1/6 between.Equipment & Software: Hardware — IBM; Software — Adobe/ PageMaker 6.0.
Delivery Method: Mail, Newsstand
Areas Served: Elk County

LAHASKA

BUCKS COUNTY HERALD (THUR)
PO Box 685, 5761 Lower York Road, Lahaska, PA, 18931-0685, Bucks, USA; gen tel (215) 794-1096; adv tel (215) 794-1096; ed tel (215) 794-1096; gen fax (215) 794-1109; adv fax (215) 794-1109; ed fax (215) 794-1109; disp adv e-mail jgwingert@buckscountyherald.com; class adv e-mail jgwingert@buckscountyherald.com; ed e-mail jgwingert@buckscountyherald.com; web site www.buckscountyherald.com
Circulation: 25,000fr; Sworn/Estimate/Non-Audited
Advertising rate: Open inch rate $22.00
Established: 2002
Digital Platform - Mobile: Apple, Android, Windows
Digital Platform - Tablet: Apple iOS, Android, Windows 7, Blackberry Tablet OS, Kindle, Nook, Kindle Fire
Ed....................................Bridget Wingert
Mng. Ed....................................Dave Campbell
Associate Pub....................................Joseph Wingert
Delivery Method: Mail, Newsstand, Racks
Areas Served: Bucks County

LANSDALE

ADVANCE OF BUCKS COUNTY (THUR)
307 Derstine Ave, Lansdale, PA, 19446-3532, Montgomery, USA; gen tel (215) 542-0200; adv tel (215) 785-5960 ext. 113; ed tel (215) 542-0200 ext. 157; gen fax (215) 648-1120; adv fax (215) 785-0283; disp adv e-mail tdarmiento@buckslocalnews.com; class adv e-mail bucksclass@buckslocalnews.com; ed e-mail advance@buckslocalnews.com; web site http://www.buckslocalnews.com
Circulation: 2,400pd, 18fr; CAC
Advertising rate: Open inch rate $9.25
Group: Digital First Media
Digital Platform - Mobile: Apple, Android
Digital Platform - Tablet: Apple iOS, Android
Pub....................................Bill Murray
Adv. Mgr....................................Tammy Darmiento
Ed....................................Jeff Werner
Mechanical Specifications: Type page 10 x 11 1/2; E - 6 cols, 1 1/2, 1/6 between; A - 6 cols, 1 1/2, 1/6 between; C - 6 cols, 1 1/2, 1/6 between.Equipment & Software: Hardware — APP/Mac; Presses — G; Software — QPS/ QuarkXPress.
Delivery Method: Mail, Newsstand, Carrier
Areas Served: Bucks County

AMBLER GAZETTE (SUN)
307 Derstine Ave, Lansdale, PA, 19446-3532, Montgomery, USA; gen tel (215) 542-0200; adv tel (215) 542-0200; ed tel (215) 542-0200; gen fax (215) 648-1120; disp adv e-mail bdouglas@21st-centurymedia.com; class adv e-mail classified@montgomerynews.com; ed e-mail editorial@montgomerynews.com; web site www.montgomerynews.com
Circulation: 2,478pd, 597fr; AAM
Advertising rate: 1/20 Pg $232.00; 1/16 Pg $270.00; 1/12 Pg $332.00
Established: 1957
Group: Montgomery Newspapers
Digital First Media
Digital Platform - Mobile: Apple, Android, Blackberry
Digital Platform - Tablet: Apple iOS, Android, Windows 7, Blackberry Tablet OS
Exec. Ed....................................Thomas Celona
Adv. Mgr....................................Beth Douglas
Circ. Mgr....................................Joe Flenders
Mechanical Specifications: Type page 12 3/4 x 21 1/2; E - 6 cols, 2, 1/6 between; A - 6 cols, 2, 1/6 between; C - 10 cols, 1 1/3, 1/6 between. Equipment & Software: Hardware — APP/ Mac; Presses — G/Offset; Software — QPS/ QuarkXPress.
Delivery Method: Mail, Newsstand, Carrier, Racks
Areas Served: 19002, 19422, 19034, 19025

MONTGOMERY MEDIA (SUN)
307 Derstine Ave, Lansdale, PA, 19446-3532, Montgomery, USA; gen tel (215) 542-0200; gen fax (215) 648-1120; disp adv e-mail tdarmiento@buckslocalnews.com; class adv e-mail bucksclass@buckslocalnews.com; ed e-mail advance@buckslocalnews.com; web site www.buckslocalnews.com
Circulation: 10,853pd, 1,129fr; AAM
Group: Digital First Media
Ed....................................Jeff Werner

NEWTOWN ADVANCE (THUR)
307 Derstine Ave, Lansdale, PA, 19446-3532, Montgomery, USA; gen tel (215) 968-2244; adv tel (215) 542-0200 ext. 153; ed tel (215) 542-0200 ext. 157; gen fax (215) 643-9475; disp adv e-mail mburns@buckslocalnews.com; class adv e-mail bucksclass@buckslocalnews.com; ed e-mail advance@buckslocalnews.com; web site www.buckslocalnews.com
Circulation: 2,400pd, 18fr; CAC
Advertising rate: Modular rate $162.00 per week (1/15 pg); $202.00 per week (1/10 pg)
Group: Digital First Media
Digital Platform - Mobile: Apple, Android
Digital Platform - Tablet: Apple iOS, Android
Pub....................................Bill Murray
Adv. Mgr....................................Marcia Burns
Ed....................................Jeff Werner
Delivery Method: Mail, Newsstand, Carrier, Racks
Areas Served: Bucks County

LEBANON

LEBANON VALLEY REVIEW (SUN)
718 Poplar St, Lebanon, PA, 17042-6755, Lebanon, USA; gen tel (717) 272-5611; adv tel (717) 272-5611 ext. 105; ed tel (717) 272-5611 ext. 138; gen fax (717) 274-1608 ; adv fax (717) 270-9503; disp adv e-mail trprice@mediaonepa.com; class adv e-mail eweidman@mediaonepa.com; ed e-mail andrearich@ldnews.com; web site www.ldnews.com - 8,137,364(views) 1,603,024(visitors)
Circulation: 22,300fr; Sworn/Estimate/Non-Audited
Advertising rate: Open inch rate $8.85
Established: 1872
Digital Platform - Mobile: Apple, Android
Digital Platform - Tablet: Apple iOS, Android, Kindle, Nook, Kindle Fire
Pub....................................Scott Downs
News Ed....................................Rahn Forney
Managing Ed....................................Andrea Rich
Delivery Method: Mail, Newsstand, Carrier
Areas Served: 17042, 17046, 17003, 17067, 17078, 17038

LIGONIER

THE LIGONIER ECHO (THUR)
112 W Main St, Ligonier, PA, 15658-1243, Westmoreland, USA; gen tel (724) 238-2111; adv tel (724) 838-5154; gen fax (724) 887-5115; adv fax (724) 887-5115; disp adv e-mail dfellabaum@tribweb.com; class adv e-mail jpaschl@tribweb.com; ed e-mail echo@tribweb.com; web site www.tribLIVE.com
Circulation: 3,331pd,; AAM
Advertising rate: Open inch rate $24.00
Established: 1888
Group: Trib Total Media, Inc.
Digital Platform - Mobile: Apple, Android
Digital Platform - Tablet: Apple iOS, Android
Adv. Mgr....................................Jill Paschl
Ed....................................Deborah Brehun
Pub....................................Joseph F. Soforic
Mechanical Specifications: Type page 11 1/2 x 21 1/12; E - 6 cols, 1 13/16, 1/8 between; A - 6 cols, 1 13/16, 1/8 between; C - 10 cols, 1 1/16, 1/8 between.Equipment & Software: Hardware — PCs, Compaq/Server; Presses — HI; Software — QPS/QuarkXPress 4.0.
Delivery Method: Mail, Newsstand
Areas Served: Ligonier

MARTINSBURG

MORRISONS COVE HERALD (THUR)
113 N Market St, Martinsburg, PA, 16662-1207, Blair, USA; gen tel (814) 793-2144; adv tel (814) 793-2144; ed tel (814) 793-2144; gen fax (814) 793-4882; adv fax (814) 793-4882; ed fax (814) 793-4882; disp adv e-mail advertising@mcheraldonline.com; class adv e-mail advertising@mcheraldonline.com; ed e-mail editor@mcheraldonline.com
Circulation: 7,609pd, 114fr; Sworn/Estimate/ Non-Audited
Advertising rate: Open inch rate $7.89
Established: 1885
Publisher....................................Allan Bassler
Acct Mgr....................................Martin Bakner
Mechanical Specifications: Type page 13 x 21 1/2; E - 6 cols, 2 1/12, 1/6 between; A - 6 cols, 2 1/12, 1/6 between; C - 6 cols, 2 1/12, 1/6 between.Equipment & Software: Hardware — 6-APP/Mac; Software — QPS/ QuarkXPress.
Delivery Method: Mail, Newsstand
Areas Served: 16662, 16673, 16693, 16695, 16664, 16664, 16659, 16625, 16635, 16637, 16650, 16648, 16655

MC CONNELLSBURG

FULTON COUNTY NEWS (THUR)
PO Box 635, 417 E Market St, Mc Connellsburg, PA, 17233-0635, Fulton, USA; gen tel (717) 485-3811; gen fax (717) 485-5187; disp adv e-mail Newsads@comcast.net; class adv e-mail ; ed e-mail fultoncountynews@comcast.net; web site www.fultoncountynews.com - 332,733(views) 10,733(visitors)
Circulation: 5,100pd, 15fr; Sworn/Estimate/ Non-Audited
Advertising rate: Open inch rate $7.20
Established: 1899
Digital Platform - Mobile: Apple, Android, Windows
Digital Platform - Tablet: Apple iOS, Android, Windows 7, Blackberry Tablet OS, Kindle, Nook, Kindle Fire
Pub. / Adv. Mgr....................................Jamie S. Greathead
Circ. Mgr....................................Trudy Gelvin
Ed....................................Lindsay Mellott
Madison Romig
Mechanical Specifications: Type page 10 1/2 x 21; 1 1/2 inch columns with 1/8 between; 6 columns = 10 1/4Equipment & Software: Hardware — APP/Mac G4; Software — QPS/ QuarkXPress 4.11.
Delivery Method: Mail, Newsstand, Racks
Areas Served: Fulton County

MECHANICSBURG

THE PATRIOT-NEWS (TUES, THUR, SUN)
2020 Technology Pkwy, Ste 300, Mechanicsburg, PA, 17050-9412, Cumberland, USA;

gen tel (717) 255-8100; adv tel (717) 255-8190; ed tel (717) 255-4127; gen fax (717) 255-8456; adv fax (717) 255-8450; ed fax (717) 255-8456; disp adv e-mail verticalsupport@pennlive.com; class adv e-mail bizsupport@pennlive.com; ed e-mail business@pennlive.com; web site www.pennlive.com 1,523,000(visitors)
Circulation: 51,772pd, 2,857fr; Sworn/Estimate/Non-Audited
Advertising rate: Modular rates apply
Established: 1852
Group: Advance Publications, Inc.
National Adv. Sales............. Shannon Garman
Director of Operations .... Kurt Hower
President .... D. Lee Carlson
VP of Sales................................Susan Chieca
VP of Content ....Cate Barron
VP & General Manager .... Paul Thomas
Director of Circulation & Audience Development..Dan Christ
Mechanical Specifications: Type page 11 5/8 x 21; E - 6 cols, 1 13/16, 1/6 between; A - 6 cols, 1 13/16, 1/6 between; C - 10 cols, 1 1/32, 1/8 between.
Delivery Method: Mail, Newsstand, Carrier, Racks
Areas Served: Dauphin, Cumberland, Perry, Lebanon & Northern York Counties

MERCERSBURG

MERCERSBURG JOURNAL (WED)

120 N Main St, Mercersburg, PA, 17236-1724, Franklin, USA; gen tel (717) 307-2430; adv tel (717) 307-2432; ed tel (717) 307-2440; gen fax (717) 485-0341; adv fax (717) 307-2240; ed fax (717) 307-2240; disp adv e-mail ads@mercersburgjournal.com; class adv e-mail classifieds@mercersburgjournal.com; ed e-mail news@mercersburgjournal.com
Circulation: 2,700pd, 5,950fr; Sworn/Estimate/Non-Audited
Advertising rate: Open inch rate $7.50
Established: 1843
Publisher & Editor............................Ken Bustin
Mng Ed. ....Tom Stapleford
Office Mgr ....Valerie Dykes
Sales Dir. .... Oram Lawry
Circ. Mgr ....Simon Blodgett
Delivery Method: Mail, Newsstand
Areas Served: Franklin County, PA
Portions of Fulton County, PA

MEYERSDALE

THE NEW REPUBLIC (THUR)

145 Center St, Meyersdale, PA, 15552-1320, Somerset, USA; gen tel (814) 634-8321; gen fax (814) 634-5556; disp adv e-mail ads@tnrnewspaper.com; class adv e-mail classifieds@tnrnewspaper.com; ed e-mail editorial@tnrnewspaper.com; web site www.tnrnewspaper.com
Circulation: 5,000pd,; Sworn/Estimate/Non-Audited
Advertising rate: Open inch rate $7.67
Established: 1900
Group: The New Republuc
Digital Platform - Mobile: Apple, Android
Digital Platform - Tablet: Apple iOS, Android
Pub./Gen. Mgr............. Linda A. Gindlesperger
Ed. .... Denise Kester
Mechanical Specifications: Type page 15 x 22; E - 8 cols, 1 5/8, 3/16 between; A - 8 cols, 1 5/8, 3/16 between; C - 8 cols, 1 5/8, 3/16 between.Equipment & Software: Hardware — APP/Mac; Software — QPS/QuarkXPress.
Delivery Method: Mail, Newsstand, Racks
Areas Served: Somerset County

MIDDLEBURG

SNYDER COUNTY TIMES (SAT)

405 E Main St, Middleburg, PA, 17842-1215, Snyder, USA; gen tel (570) 837-6065; gen fax (570) 837-0776; disp adv e-mail scuc@ptd.net; ed e-mail sctimes6065@gmail.com; web site www.thesnydercountytimes.com
Circulation: 26,000pd,; Sworn/Estimate/Non-Audited
Advertising rate: Open inch rate $7.50
Established: 1997
Group: Snyder County Times, Inc.
Pres./Pub./Ed............................Susan Weaver
Mechanical Specifications: Type page 13 x 21 1/2; E - 6 cols, 2 1/16, 1/8 between; A - 6 cols, 2 1/16, 1/8 between; C - 8 cols, 1 1/2, 1/8 between.Equipment & Software: Hardware — PCs; Presses — Offset; Software — Adobe/PageMaker, Microsoft/Windows, Adobe/Photoshop.
Delivery Method: Mail, Newsstand
Areas Served: Snyder County

MIDDLETOWN

PRESS AND JOURNAL (TUES, WED)

20 S Union St, Middletown, PA, 17057-1466, Dauphin, USA; gen tel (717) 944-4628; adv tel (717) 944-4628; ed tel (717) 944-4628; gen fax (717) 944-2083; adv fax (717) 944-2083; ed fax (717) 944-2083; disp adv e-mail sales@pressandjournal.com; class adv e-mail info@pressandjournal.com; ed e-mail editor@pressandjournal.com; web site www.pressandjournal.com
Circulation: 8,000pd, 1,000fr; Sworn/Estimate/Non-Audited
Advertising rate: Open inch rate $13.00
Established: 1854
Digital Platform - Mobile: Apple
Digital Platform - Tablet: Apple iOS
Pub.......................................Joseph G. Sukle
Adv. Mgr. ....David Brown
Gen. Mgr. ....Maxine Etter
Sukle Louise
Editor ....Jason Maddux
Delivery Method: Mail, Newsstand, Racks
Areas Served: Dauphin County

MIFFLINBURG

MIFFLINBURG TELEGRAPH (THUR)

358 Walnut St, Mifflinburg, PA, 17844-1123, Union, USA; gen tel (570) 966-2255; gen fax (570) 966-0062; disp adv e-mail heidi@mifflinburgtelegraph.com; class adv e-mail john@mifflinburgtelegraph.com; ed e-mail heidi@mifflinburgtelegraph.com; web site www.mifflinburgtelegraph.com
Circulation: 500pd,; Sworn/Estimate/Non-Audited
Advertising rate: Open inch rate $5.00
Established: 1862
Group: Mifflinburg Telegraph, Inc.
Digital Platform - Mobile: Apple, Android
Digital Platform - Tablet: Apple iOS, Android
Pub...John Stamm
Ed. .... Heidi Criswell
Mechanical Specifications: Type page 9 5/8 x 12 7/16; E - 5 cols, 1 3/4, 3/16 between; A - 5 cols, 1 3/4, 3/16 between.
Delivery Method: Mail, Newsstand
Areas Served: Union County

MIFFLINTOWN

JUNIATA SENTINEL (WED)

1806 WILLIAM PENN HWY, Mifflintown, PA, 17059, Juniata, USA; gen tel (717) 436-8206; adv tel (717) 582-4305; gen fax (717) 436-5174; adv fax (717) 582-7933; disp adv e-mail displayads@juniata-sentinel.com; ed e-mail csmith@juniata-sentinel.com; web site www.juniata-sentinel.com
Circulation: 3,617pd, 49fr; Sworn/Estimate/Non-Audited
Advertising rate: Open inch rate $6.50
Established: 1846
Group: Advance Publications, Inc.
Pub...Curt Dreibelbis
Ed. ....Carol Smith
Circ. Mgr.......................................Bryan Smith
Adv.......................................Melanie Campbell
Mechanical Specifications: Type page 11 5/8 x 21; E - 6 cols, 1 5/6, 1/8 between; A - 6 cols, 1 5/6, 1/8 between; C - 8 cols, 1 3/8, 1/8 between.Equipment & Software: Hardware — APP/Mac; Software — Adobe/PageMaker 6.5.
Delivery Method: Mail, Newsstand, Racks
Areas Served: Juniata County

MILFORD

PIKE COUNTY DISPATCH (THUR)

105 W Catherine St, Milford, PA, 18337-1417, Pike, USA; gen tel (570) 296-6641; gen fax (570) 296-2610; disp adv e-mail ads@pikedispatch.com; class adv e-mail Classifieds@pikeduspatch.com; ed e-mail editor@pikedispatch..com; web site www.pikedispatch.com - 36,000(views)
Circulation: 6,500pd, 21,174fr; USPS
Advertising rate: Open inch rate $16.95
Established: 1826
Digital Platform - Mobile: Apple, Windows
Digital Platform - Tablet: Apple iOS, Windows 7
Pub... Sue Doty-Lloyd
Ed. ....Chris Jones
Prod. Mgr ....Christina Hoiffman
Mechanical Specifications: Type page 13 x 21; E - 6 cols, 1 3/4, 1/8 between; A - 6 cols, 2 1/16, 1/8 between; C - 9 cols, 1 5/16, 1/8 between.Equipment & Software: Hardware — APP/Mac; Software — Adobe/PageMaker, Microsoft/Word.
Delivery Method: Mail, Newsstand
Areas Served: 18337, 18324, 18328, 18336, 18340, 18425, 12551, 18464, 18458, 18451, 18445, 18428, 07860, 07461, 07827, 07484,10940,10998

MILLERSBURG

UPPER DAUPHIN SENTINEL (TUES)

510 Union St, Millersburg, PA, 17061-1470, Dauphin, USA; gen tel (717) 692-4737; adv tel (717) 692-4737 ext. 113; ed tel (717) 692-4737 ext. 104; gen fax (717) 692-2420; disp adv e-mail ads@sentinelnow.com; class adv e-mail classifieds@sentinelnow.com; ed e-mail dgood@sentinelnow.com; web site www.sentinelnow.com
Circulation: 8,683pd,; Sworn/Estimate/Non-Audited
Advertising rate: Open inch rate $10.80
Digital Platform - Mobile: Apple
Digital Platform - Tablet: Apple iOS
Pub... Ben L. Kocher
Ed. .... Duane E. Good
Adv. Mgr.. Sue King
Delivery Method: Mail, Newsstand
Areas Served: Dauphin County

MONROEVILLE

NORTH JOURNAL (SUN)

610 Beatty Rd, Monroeville, PA, 15146-1558, Allegheny, USA; gen tel (412) 856-7400; adv tel (724) 567-5656; gen fax (412) 856-7954; adv fax (724) 568-1729; disp adv e-mail dfellabaum@tribweb.com; class adv e-mail jpaschl@tribweb.com; ed e-mail jcuddy@tribweb.com; web site www.tribLIVE.com
Circulation: 59pd, 18,759fr; AAM
Advertising rate: Open inch rate $12.42
Group: Trib Total Media, Inc.
Digital Platform - Mobile: Apple, Android
Digital Platform - Tablet: Apple iOS, Android
Ed. .... Frank Craig
Mng. Ed...Jim Cuddy
Mechanical Specifications: Type page 10 13/16 x 16; A - 5 cols, 2 1/16, between; C - 7 cols, 1 5/16, between.
Delivery Method: Mail, Newsstand
Areas Served: McCandless, Pine, Richland, and Marshall

MONTROSE

THE SUSQUEHANNA COUNTY INDEPENDENT (WED)

231 Church St, Montrose, PA, 18801-1272, Susquehanna, USA; gen tel (570) 278-6397; gen fax (570) 278-4305; ed e-mail indynews@independentweekender.com; web site http://www.susqcoindy.com/PS/contact/
Circulation: 3,700pd, 173fr; CAC
Advertising rate: Open inch rate $8.40
Established: 1816
Adv. Mgr......................................Vicki Wooden
Mechanical Specifications: Type page 10 3/8 x 15 1/2.Equipment & Software: Hardware — APP/Macs, PCs; Software — Adobe/PageMaker, Adobe/Photoshop, Caere/OmniPage.
Delivery Method: Mail, Newsstand
Areas Served: Susquehanna County

MOUNT JOY

ENGLE - COLUMBIA / WRIGHTSVILLE MERCHANDISER (WED)

1425 W Main St, Mount Joy, PA, 17552-9589, Lancaster, USA; gen tel (717) 653-1833; gen fax (717) 492-2580; disp adv e-mail sales@engleonline.com; class adv e-mail jhemperly@engleonline.com; ed e-mail jpengle@engleonline.com; web site www.engleonline.com
Circulation: 0pd, 4,826fr; VAC
Advertising rate: Open inch rate $4.50 - $25.75
Established: 1959
Group: Engle Printing & Publishing Co., Inc.
CEO/Pres./Pub. ....Charles A. Engle
Prod. Mgr. ....Jeremy Engle
Sales Mgr.................................John Hemperly
Circ. Mgr.......................................Mark Malloy
Mechanical Specifications: Type page 10 3/8 x 16; E - 6 cols, 1 3/8, between; A - 6 cols, 1 3/8, between; C - 6 cols, 1 3/8, between. Equipment & Software: Hardware — APP/Mac; Presses — Printed on our own in-house coldset web presses; Software — QPS/QuarkXPress 4.0, Adobe/Illustrator 8.0, Adobe/Photoshop 7.0, Adobe/InDesign.
Delivery Method: Mail
Areas Served: 17313, 17356, 17366, 17402, 17315, 17318, 17345, 17347, 17358, 17365, 17370, 17401, 17404, 17302, 17309, 17314, 17321, 17322, 17327, 17407, 17342, 17349, 17352, 17361, 17360, 17363, 17403, 17403, 17401, 17403, 17404, 17361, 17349

ENGLE - CONESTOGA VALLEY / PEQUEA VALLEY PENNY SAVER (WED)

1425 W Main St, Mount Joy, PA, 17552-9589, Lancaster, USA; gen tel (717) 653-1833; gen fax (717) 492-2580; disp adv e-mail sales@engleonline.com; class adv e-mail jhemperly@engleonline.com; ed e-mail jpengle@engleonline.com; web site www.engleonline.com
Circulation: 0pd, 7,335fr; VAC
Advertising rate: Open inch rate $4.50 - $25.75
Established: 1959
Group: Engle Printing & Publishing Co., Inc.
CEO/Pres./Pub. ....Charles A. Engle
Prod. Mgr. ....Jeremy Engle
Sales Mgr.................................John Hemperly
Circ. Mgr.......................................Mark Malloy
Mechanical Specifications: Type page 10 3/8 x 16; E - 6 cols, 1 3/8, between; A - 6 cols, 1 3/8, between; C - 6 cols, 1 3/8, between. Equipment & Software: Hardware — APP/Mac; Presses — Printed on our own in-house coldset web presses; Software — QPS/QuarkXPress 4.0, Adobe/Illustrator 8.0, Adobe/Photoshop 7.0, Adobe/InDesign.
Delivery Method: Mail
Areas Served: 17313, 17356, 17366, 17402, 17315, 17318, 17345, 17347, 17358, 17365, 17370, 17401, 17404, 17302, 17309, 17314, 17321, 17322, 17327, 17407, 17342, 17349, 17352, 17361, 17360, 17363, 17403, 17403, 17401, 17403, 17404, 17361, 17349

ENGLE - DOWNINGTOWN / EXTON /

COMMUNITY COURIER (WED)
1425 W Main St, Mount Joy, PA, 17552-9589, Lancaster, USA; gen tel (717) 653-1833; gen fax (717) 492-2580; disp adv e-mail sales@engleonline.com; class adv e-mail jhemperly@engleonline.com; ed e-mail jpengle@engleonline.com; web site www.engleonline.com

Circulation: 0pd, 51,760fr; VAC
Advertising rate: Open inch rate $4.50 - $25.75
Established: 1959
Group: Engle Printing & Publishing Co., Inc.
CEO/Pres./Pub. .... Charles A. Engle
Prod. Mgr. .... Jeremy Engle
Sales Mgr. .... John Hemperly
Circ. Mgr. .... Mark Malloy
Mechanical Specifications: Type page 10 3/8 x 16; E - 6 cols, 1 3/8, between; A - 6 cols, 1 3/8, between; C - 6 cols, 1 3/8, between. Equipment & Software: Hardware — APP/Mac; Presses — Printed on our own in-house coldset web presses; Software — QPS/QuarkXPress 4.0, Adobe/Illustrator 8.0, Adobe/Photoshop 7.0, Adobe/InDesign.
Delivery Method: Mail
Areas Served: 17313, 17356, 17366, 17402, 17315, 17318, 17345, 17347, 17358, 17365, 17370, 17401, 17404, 17302, 17309, 17314, 17321, 17322, 17327, 17407, 17342, 17349, 17352, 17361, 17360, 17363, 17403, 17403, 17401, 17403, 17404, 17361, 17349

ENGLE - ELIZABETHTOWN / MOUNT JOY MERCHANDISER (WED)
1425 W Main St, Mount Joy, PA, 17552-9589, Lancaster, USA; gen tel (717) 653-1833; gen fax (717) 492-2580; disp adv e-mail sales@engleonline.com; class adv e-mail jhemperly@engleonline.com; ed e-mail jpengle@engleonline.com; web site www.engleonline.com

Circulation: 0pd, 13,123fr; VAC
Advertising rate: Open inch rate $4.50 - $25.75
Established: 1959
Group: Engle Printing & Publishing Co., Inc.
CEO/Pres./Pub. .... Charles A. Engle
Prod. Mgr. .... Jeremy Engle
Sales Mgr. .... John Hemperly
Circ. Mgr. .... Mark Malloy
Mechanical Specifications: Type page 10 3/8 x 16; E - 6 cols, 1 3/8, between; A - 6 cols, 1 3/8, between; C - 6 cols, 1 3/8, between. Equipment & Software: Hardware — APP/Mac; Presses — Printed on our own in-house coldset web presses; Software — QPS/QuarkXPress 4.0, Adobe/Illustrator 8.0, Adobe/Photoshop 7.0, Adobe/InDesign.
Delivery Method: Mail
Areas Served: 17313, 17356, 17366, 17402, 17315, 17318, 17345, 17347, 17358, 17365, 17370, 17401, 17404, 17302, 17309, 17314, 17321, 17322, 17327, 17407, 17342, 17349, 17352, 17361, 17360, 17363, 17403, 17403, 17401, 17403, 17404, 17361, 17349

ENGLE - GAP / OXFORD COMMUNITY COURIER (WED)
1425 W Main St, Mount Joy, PA, 17552-9589, Lancaster, USA; gen tel (717) 653-1833; gen fax (717) 492-2580; disp adv e-mail sales@engleonline.com; class adv e-mail jhemperly@engleonline.com; ed e-mail jpengle@engleonline.com; web site www.engleonline.com

Circulation: 0pd, 15,834fr; VAC
Advertising rate: Open inch rate $4.50 - $25.75
Established: 1959
Group: Engle Printing & Publishing Co., Inc.
CEO/Pres./Pub. .... Charles A. Engle
Prod. Mgr. .... Jeremy Engle
Sales Mgr. .... John Hemperly
Circ. Mgr. .... Mark Malloy
Mechanical Specifications: Type page 10 3/8 x 16; E - 6 cols, 1 3/8, between; A - 6 cols, 1 3/8, between; C - 6 cols, 1 3/8, between. Equipment & Software: Hardware — APP/Mac; Presses — Printed on our own in-house coldset web presses; Software — QPS/QuarkXPress 4.0, Adobe/Illustrator 8.0, Adobe/Photoshop 7.0, Adobe/InDesign.
Delivery Method: Mail
Areas Served: 17313, 17356, 17366, 17402, 17315, 17318, 17345, 17347, 17358, 17365, 17370, 17401, 17404, 17302, 17309, 17314, 17321, 17322, 17327, 17407, 17342, 17349, 17352, 17361, 17360, 17363, 17403, 17403, 17401, 17403, 17404, 17361, 17349

ENGLE - HEMPFIELD / MOUNTVILLE MERCHANDISER (WED)
1425 W Main St, Mount Joy, PA, 17552-9589, Lancaster, USA; gen tel (717) 653-1833; gen fax (717) 492-2580; disp adv e-mail sales@engleonline.com; class adv e-mail jhemperly@engleonline.com; ed e-mail jpengle@engleonline.com; web site www.engleonline.com

Circulation: 0pd, 19,463fr; VAC
Advertising rate: Open inch rate $4.50 - $25.75
Established: 1959
Group: Engle Printing & Publishing Co., Inc.
CEO/Pres./Pub. .... Charles A. Engle
Prod. Mgr. .... Jeremy Engle
Sales Mgr. .... John Hemperly
Circ. Mgr. .... Mark Malloy
Mechanical Specifications: Type page 10 3/8 x 16; E - 6 cols, 1 3/8, between; A - 6 cols, 1 3/8, between; C - 6 cols, 1 3/8, between. Equipment & Software: Hardware — APP/Mac; Presses — Printed on our own in-house coldset web presses; Software — QPS/QuarkXPress 4.0, Adobe/Illustrator 8.0, Adobe/Photoshop 7.0, Adobe/InDesign.
Delivery Method: Mail
Areas Served: 17313, 17356, 17366, 17402, 17315, 17318, 17345, 17347, 17358, 17365, 17370, 17401, 17404, 17302, 17309, 17314, 17321, 17322, 17327, 17407, 17342, 17349, 17352, 17361, 17360, 17363, 17403, 17403, 17401, 17403, 17404, 17361, 17349

ENGLE - HERSHEY / HUMMELSTOWN / PALMYRA COMMUNITY COURIER (WED)
1425 W Main St, Mount Joy, PA, 17552-9589, Lancaster, USA; gen tel (717) 653-1833; gen fax (717) 492-2580; disp adv e-mail sales@engleonline.com; class adv e-mail jhemperly@engleonline.com; ed e-mail jpengle@engleonline.com; web site www.engleonline.com

Circulation: 0pd, 29,199fr; VAC
Advertising rate: Open inch rate $4.50 - $25.75
Established: 1959
Group: Engle Printing & Publishing Co., Inc.
CEO/Pres./Pub. .... Charles A. Engle
Prod. Mgr. .... Jeremy Engle
Sales Mgr. .... John Hemperly
Circ. Mgr. .... Mark Malloy
Mechanical Specifications: Type page 10 3/8 x 16; E - 6 cols, 1 3/8, between; A - 6 cols, 1 3/8, between; C - 6 cols, 1 3/8, between. Equipment & Software: Hardware — APP/Mac; Presses — Printed on our own in-house coldset web presses; Software — QPS/QuarkXPress 4.0, Adobe/Illustrator 8.0, Adobe/Photoshop 7.0, Adobe/InDesign.
Delivery Method: Mail
Areas Served: 17313, 17356, 17366, 17402, 17315, 17318, 17345, 17347, 17358, 17365, 17370, 17401, 17404, 17302, 17309, 17314, 17321, 17322, 17327, 17407, 17342, 17349, 17352, 17361, 17360, 17363, 17403, 17403, 17401, 17403, 17404, 17361, 17349

ENGLE - MANHEIM / LITITZ MERCHANDISER (WED)
1425 W Main St, Mount Joy, PA, 17552-9589, Lancaster, USA; gen tel (717) 653-1833; gen fax (717) 492-2580; disp adv e-mail sales@engleonline.com; class adv e-mail jhemperly@engleonline.com; ed e-mail jpengle@engleonline.com; web site www.engleonline.com

Circulation: 0pd, 22,578fr; CVC
Advertising rate: Open inch rate $9.00 - $21.00
Established: 1959
Group: Engle Printing & Publishing Co., Inc.
CEO/Pres./Pub. .... Charles A. Engle
Prod. Mgr. .... Jeremy Engle
Sales Mgr. .... John Hemperly
Circ. Mgr. .... Mark Malloy
Mechanical Specifications: Type page 10 3/8 x 16; E - 6 cols, 1 3/8, between; A - 6 cols, 1 3/8, between; C - 6 cols, 1 3/8, between. Equipment & Software: Hardware — APP/Mac; Presses — Printed on our own in-house coldset web presses; Software — QPS/QuarkXPress 4.0, Adobe/Illustrator 8.0, Adobe/Photoshop 7.0, Adobe/InDesign.
Delivery Method: Mail
Areas Served: 17313, 17356, 17366, 17402, 17315, 17318, 17345, 17347, 17358, 17365, 17370, 17401, 17404, 17302, 17309, 17314, 17321, 17322, 17327, 17407, 17342, 17349, 17352, 17361, 17360, 17363, 17403, 17403, 17401, 17403, 17404, 17361, 17349

ENGLE - MANHEIM TOWNSHIP MERCHANDISER (WED)
1425 W Main St, Mount Joy, PA, 17552-9589, Lancaster, USA; gen tel (717) 653-1833; gen fax (717) 492-2580; disp adv e-mail sales@engleonline.com; class adv e-mail jhemperly@engleonline.com; ed e-mail jpengle@engleonline.com; web site www.engleonline.com

Circulation: 0pd, 14,985fr; VAC
Advertising rate: Open inch rate $4.50 - $25.75
Established: 1959
Group: Engle Printing & Publishing Co., Inc.
CEO/Pres./Pub. .... Charles A. Engle
Prod. Mgr. .... Jeremy Engle
Sales Mgr. .... John Hemperly
Circ. Mgr. .... Mark Malloy
Mechanical Specifications: Type page 10 3/8 x 16; E - 6 cols, 1 3/8, between; A - 6 cols, 1 3/8, between; C - 6 cols, 1 3/8, between. Equipment & Software: Hardware — APP/Mac; Presses — Printed on our own in-house coldset web presses; Software — QPS/QuarkXPress 4.0, Adobe/Illustrator 8.0, Adobe/Photoshop 7.0, Adobe/InDesign.
Delivery Method: Mail
Areas Served: 17313, 17356, 17366, 17402, 17315, 17318, 17345, 17347, 17358, 17365, 17370, 17401, 17404, 17302, 17309, 17314, 17321, 17322, 17327, 17407, 17342, 17349, 17352, 17361, 17360, 17363, 17403, 17403, 17401, 17403, 17404, 17361, 17349

ENGLE - MIDDLETOWN SHOPPER (WED)
1425 W Main St, Mount Joy, PA, 17552-9589, Lancaster, USA; gen tel (717) 653-1833; gen fax (717) 492-2580; disp adv e-mail sales@engleonline.com; class adv e-mail jhemperly@engleonline.com; ed e-mail jpengle@engleonline.com; web site www.engleonline.com

Circulation: 0pd, 9,787fr; VAC
Advertising rate: Open inch rate $4.50 - $25.75
Established: 1959
Group: Engle Printing & Publishing Co., Inc.
CEO/Pres./Pub. .... Charles A. Engle
Prod. Mgr. .... Jeremy Engle
Sales Mgr. .... John Hemperly
Circ. Mgr. .... Mark Malloy
Mechanical Specifications: Type page 10 3/8 x 16; E - 6 cols, 1 3/8, between; A - 6 cols, 1 3/8, between; C - 6 cols, 1 3/8, between. Equipment & Software: Hardware — APP/Mac; Presses — Printed on our own in-house coldset web presses; Software — QPS/QuarkXPress 4.0, Adobe/Illustrator 8.0, Adobe/Photoshop 7.0, Adobe/InDesign.
Delivery Method: Mail
Areas Served: 17313, 17356, 17366, 17402, 17315, 17318, 17345, 17347, 17358, 17365, 17370, 17401, 17404, 17302, 17309, 17314, 17321, 17322, 17327, 17407, 17342, 17349, 17352, 17361, 17360, 17363, 17403, 17403, 17401, 17403, 17404, 17361, 17349

ENGLE - MILLERSVILLE ADVERTISER (WED)
1425 W Main St, Mount Joy, PA, 17552-9589, Lancaster, USA; gen tel (717) 653-1833; gen fax (717) 492-2580; disp adv e-mail sales@engleonline.com; class adv e-mail jhemperly@engleonline.com; ed e-mail jpengle@engleonline.com; web site www.engleonline.com

Circulation: 0pd, 18,310fr; CVC
Advertising rate: Open inch rate $9.00 - $21.00
Established: 1959
Group: Engle Printing & Publishing Co., Inc.
CEO/Pres./Pub. .... Charles A. Engle
Prod. Mgr. .... Jeremy Engle
Sales Mgr. .... John Hemperly
Circ. Mgr. .... Mark Malloy
Mechanical Specifications: Type page 10 3/8 x 16; E - 6 cols, 1 3/8, between; A - 6 cols, 1 3/8, between; C - 6 cols, 1 3/8, between. Equipment & Software: Hardware — APP/Mac; Presses — Printed on our own in-house coldset web presses; Software — QPS/QuarkXPress 4.0, Adobe/Illustrator 8.0, Adobe/Photoshop 7.0, Adobe/InDesign.
Delivery Method: Mail
Areas Served: 17313, 17356, 17366, 17402, 17315, 17318, 17345, 17347, 17358, 17365, 17370, 17401, 17404, 17302, 17309, 17314, 17321, 17322, 17327, 17407, 17342, 17349, 17352, 17361, 17360, 17363, 17403, 17403, 17401, 17403, 17404, 17361, 17349

ENGLE - MORGANTOWN / HONEY BROOK COMMUNITY COURIER (WED)
1425 W Main St, Mount Joy, PA, 17552-9589, Lancaster, USA; gen tel (717) 653-1833; gen fax (717) 492-2580; disp adv e-mail sales@engleonline.com; class adv e-mail jhemperly@engleonline.com; ed e-mail jpengle@engleonline.com; web site www.engleonline.com

Circulation: 0pd, 15,251fr; VAC
Advertising rate: Open inch rate $4.50 - $25.75
Established: 1959
Group: Engle Printing & Publishing Co., Inc.
CEO/Pres./Pub. .... Charles A. Engle
Prod. Mgr. .... Jeremy Engle
Sales Mgr. .... John Hemperly
Circ. Mgr. .... Mark Malloy
Mechanical Specifications: Type page 10 3/8 x 16; E - 6 cols, 1 3/8, between; A - 6 cols, 1 3/8, between; C - 6 cols, 1 3/8, between. Equipment & Software: Hardware — APP/Mac; Presses — Printed on our own in-house coldset web presses; Software — QPS/QuarkXPress 4.0, Adobe/Illustrator 8.0, Adobe/Photoshop 7.0, Adobe/InDesign.
Delivery Method: Mail
Areas Served: 17313, 17356, 17366, 17402, 17315, 17318, 17345, 17347, 17358, 17365, 17370, 17401, 17404, 17302, 17309, 17314, 17321, 17322, 17327, 17407, 17342, 17349, 17352, 17361, 17360, 17363, 17403, 17403, 17401, 17403, 17404, 17361, 17349

ENGLE - NEW HOLLAND PENNYSAVER (WED)
1425 W Main St, Mount Joy, PA, 17552-9589, Lancaster, USA; gen tel (717) 653-1833; gen fax (717) 492-2580; disp adv e-mail sales@engleonline.com; class adv e-mail jhemperly@engleonline.com; ed e-mail jpengle@engleonline.com; web site www.engleonline.com

Circulation: 0pd, 13,721fr; CVC
Advertising rate: Open inch rate $9.00 - $21.00
Established: 1959
Group: Engle Printing & Publishing Co., Inc.
CEO/Pres./Pub. .... Charles A. Engle
Prod. Mgr. .... Jeremy Engle
Sales Mgr. .... John Hemperly
Circ. Mgr. .... Mark Malloy
Mechanical Specifications: Type page 10 3/8 x 16; E - 6 cols, 1 3/8, between; A - 6 cols, 1 3/8, between; C - 6 cols, 1 3/8, between. Equipment & Software: Hardware — APP/Mac; Presses — Printed on our own in-house coldset web presses; Software — QPS/QuarkXPress 4.0, Adobe/Illustrator 8.0, Adobe/Photoshop 7.0, Adobe/InDesign.
Delivery Method: Mail
Areas Served: 17313, 17356, 17366, 17402, 17315, 17318, 17345, 17347, 17358, 17365, 17370, 17401, 17404, 17302, 17309, 17314, 17321, 17322, 17327, 17407, 17342, 17349, 17352, 17361, 17360, 17363, 17403, 17403, 17401, 17403, 17404, 17361, 17349

ENGLE - QUARRYVILLE ADVERTISER (WED)
1425 W Main St, Mount Joy, PA, 17552-9589, Lancaster, USA; gen tel (717) 653-1833; gen fax (717) 492-2580; disp adv e-mail sales@engleonline.com; class adv e-mail jhemperly@engleonline.com; ed e-mail jpengle@engleonline.com; web site www.engleonline.com

Circulation: 0pd, 12,027fr; CVC
Advertising rate: Open inch rate $9.00 - $21.00
Established: 1959
Group: Engle Printing & Publishing Co., Inc.
CEO/Pres./Pub. .... Charles A. Engle
Prod. Mgr. .... Jeremy Engle

Sales Mgr.................................John Hemperly
Circ. Mgr.......................................Mark Malloy
Mechanical Specifications: Type page 10 3/8 x 16; E - 6 cols, 1 3/8, between; A - 6 cols, 1 3/8, between; C - 6 cols, 1 3/8, between. Equipment & Software: Hardware — APP/ Mac; Presses — Printed on our own in-house coldset web presses; Software — QPS/ QuarkXPress 4.0, Adobe/Illustrator 8.0, Adobe/Photoshop 7.0, Adobe/InDesign.
Delivery Method: Mail
Areas Served: 17313, 17356, 17366, 17402, 17315, 17318, 17345, 17347, 17358, 17365, 17370, 17401, 17404, 17302, 17309, 17314, 17321, 17322, 17327, 17407, 17342, 17349, 17352, 17361, 17360, 17363, 17403, 17403, 17401, 17403, 17404, 17361, 17349

ENGLE - WEST CHESTER COMMUNITY COURIER (WED)

1425 W Main St, Mount Joy, PA, 17552-9589, Lancaster, USA; gen tel (717) 653-1833; gen fax (717) 492-2580; disp adv e-mail sales@engleonline.com; class adv e-mail jhemperly@engleonline.com; ed e-mail jpengle@engleonline.com; web site www.engleonline.com
Circulation: 0pd, 19,987fr; CVC
Advertising rate: Open inch rate $9.00 - $21.00
Established: 1959
Group: Engle Printing & Publishing Co., Inc.
CEO/Pres./Pub......................Charles A. Engle
Prod. Mgr...................................Jeremy Engle
Sales Mgr.................................John Hemperly
Circ. Mgr.......................................Mark Malloy
Mechanical Specifications: Type page 10 3/8 x 16; E - 6 cols, 1 3/8, between; A - 6 cols, 1 3/8, between; C - 6 cols, 1 3/8, between. Equipment & Software: Hardware — APP/ Mac; Presses — Printed on our own in-house coldset web presses; Software — QPS/ QuarkXPress 4.0, Adobe/Illustrator 8.0, Adobe/Photoshop 7.0, Adobe/InDesign.
Delivery Method: Mail
Areas Served: 17313, 17356, 17366, 17402, 17315, 17318, 17345, 17347, 17358, 17365, 17370, 17401, 17404, 17302, 17309, 17314, 17321, 17322, 17327, 17407, 17342, 17349, 17352, 17361, 17360, 17363, 17403, 17403, 17401, 17403, 17404, 17361, 17349

ENGLE - WILLOW STREET STRASBURG ADVERTISER (WED)

1425 W Main St, Mount Joy, PA, 17552-9589, Lancaster, USA; gen tel (717) 653-1833; gen fax (717) 492-2580; disp adv e-mail sales@engleonline.com; class adv e-mail jhemperly@engleonline.com; ed e-mail jpengle@engleonline.com; web site www.engleonline.com
Circulation: 0pd, 9,327fr; CVC
Advertising rate: Open inch rate $4.50 - $25.75
Established: 1959
Group: Engle Printing & Publishing Co., Inc.
CEO/Pres./Pub......................Charles A. Engle
Prod. Mgr...................................Jeremy Engle
Sales Mgr.................................John Hemperly
Circ. Mgr.......................................Mark Malloy
Mechanical Specifications: Type page 10 3/8 x 16; E - 6 cols, 1 3/8, between; A - 6 cols, 1 3/8, between; C - 6 cols, 1 3/8, between. Equipment & Software: Hardware — APP/ Mac; Presses — Printed on our own in-house coldset web presses; Software — QPS/ QuarkXPress 4.0, Adobe/Illustrator 8.0, Adobe/Photoshop 7.0, Adobe/InDesign.
Delivery Method: Mail
Areas Served: 17313, 17356, 17366, 17402, 17315, 17318, 17345, 17347, 17358, 17365, 17370, 17401, 17404, 17302, 17309, 17314, 17321, 17322, 17327, 17407, 17342, 17349, 17352, 17361, 17360, 17363, 17403, 17403, 17401, 17403, 17404, 17361, 17349

ENGLE - YORK COMMUNITY COURIER EAST EDITION (WED)

1425 W Main St, Mount Joy, PA, 17552-9589, Lancaster, USA; gen tel (717) 653-1833; gen fax (717) 492-2580; disp adv e-mail sales@engleonline.com; class adv e-mail jhemperly@engleonline.com; ed e-mail jpengle@engleonline.com; web site www.engleonline.com
Circulation: 0pd, 37,165fr; VAC
Advertising rate: Open inch rate $4.50 - $25.75
Established: 1959
Group: Engle Printing & Publishing Co., Inc.Editions: (3) 3 total York Community Courier
CEO/Pres./Pub......................Charles A. Engle
Prod. Mgr...................................Jeremy Engle
Sales Mgr.................................John Hemperly
Circ. Mgr.......................................Mark Malloy
Mechanical Specifications: Type page 10 3/8 x 16; E - 6 cols, 1 3/8, between; A - 6 cols, 1 3/8, between; C - 6 cols, 1 3/8, between. Equipment & Software: Hardware — APP/ Mac; Presses — Printed on our own in-house coldset web presses; Software — QPS/ QuarkXPress 4.0, Adobe/Illustrator 8.0, Adobe/Photoshop 7.0, Adobe/InDesign.
Delivery Method: Mail
Areas Served: 17313, 17356, 17366, 17402, 17315, 17318, 17345, 17347, 17358, 17365, 17370, 17401, 17404, 17302, 17309, 17314, 17321, 17322, 17327, 17407, 17342, 17349, 17352, 17361, 17360, 17363, 17403, 17403, 17401, 17403, 17404, 17361, 17349

ENGLE - YORK COMMUNITY COURIER SOUTH EDITION (WED)

1425 W Main St, Mount Joy, PA, 17552-9589, Lancaster, USA; gen tel (717) 653-1833; gen fax (717) 492-2580; disp adv e-mail sales@engleonline.com; class adv e-mail jhemperly@engleonline.com; ed e-mail jpengle@engleonline.com; web site www.engleonline.com
Circulation: 0pd, 27,503fr; VAC
Advertising rate: Open inch rate $4.50 - $25.75
Established: 1959
Group: Engle Printing & Publishing Co., Inc.Editions: (3) 3 total York Community Courier
CEO/Pres./Pub......................Charles A. Engle
Prod. Mgr...................................Jeremy Engle
Sales Mgr.................................John Hemperly
Circ. Mgr.......................................Mark Malloy
Mechanical Specifications: Type page 10 3/8 x 16; E - 6 cols, 1 3/8, between; A - 6 cols, 1 3/8, between; C - 6 cols, 1 3/8, between. Equipment & Software: Hardware — APP/ Mac; Presses — Printed on our own in-house coldset web presses; Software — QPS/ QuarkXPress 4.0, Adobe/Illustrator 8.0, Adobe/Photoshop 7.0, Adobe/InDesign.
Delivery Method: Mail
Areas Served: 17313, 17356, 17366, 17402, 17315, 17318, 17345, 17347, 17358, 17365, 17370, 17401, 17404, 17302, 17309, 17314, 17321, 17322, 17327, 17407, 17342, 17349, 17352, 17361, 17360, 17363, 17403, 17403, 17401, 17403, 17404, 17361, 17349

ENGLE - YORK COMMUNITY COURIER WEST EDITION (WED)

1425 W Main St, Mount Joy, PA, 17552-9589, Lancaster, USA; gen tel (717) 653-1833; gen fax (717) 492-2580; disp adv e-mail sales@engleonline.com; class adv e-mail jhemperly@engleonline.com; ed e-mail jpengle@engleonline.com; web site www.engleonline.com
Circulation: 0pd, 37,639fr; VAC
Advertising rate: Open inch rate $4.50 - $25.75
Established: 1959
Group: Engle Printing & Publishing Co., Inc.Editions: (3) 3 total York Community Courier
CEO/Pres./Pub......................Charles A. Engle
Prod. Mgr...................................Jeremy Engle
Sales Mgr.................................John Hemperly
Circ. Mgr.......................................Mark Malloy
Mechanical Specifications: Type page 10 3/8 x 16; E - 6 cols, 1 3/8, between; A - 6 cols, 1 3/8, between; C - 6 cols, 1 3/8, between. Equipment & Software: Hardware — APP/ Mac; Presses — Printed on our own in-house coldset web presses; Software — QPS/ QuarkXPress 4.0, Adobe/Illustrator 8.0, Adobe/Photoshop 7.0, Adobe/InDesign.
Delivery Method: Mail
Areas Served: 17313, 17356, 17366, 17402, 17315, 17318, 17345, 17347, 17358, 17365, 17370, 17401, 17404, 17302, 17309, 17314, 17321, 17322, 17327, 17407, 17342, 17349, 17352, 17361, 17360, 17363, 17403, 17403, 17401, 17403, 17404, 17361, 17349

MOUNT PLEASANT

THE MOUNT PLEASANT JOURNAL (THUR)

23 S Church St, # 33, Mount Pleasant, PA, 15666-1831, Westmoreland, USA; gen tel (724) 547-5722; adv tel (724) 779-6959; gen fax (724) 887-5115; adv fax (724) 568-1729; disp adv e-mail jpaschl@tribweb.com; class adv e-mail mzigarovich@tribweb.com; ed e-mail apanian@tribweb.com; web site www.tribLIVE.com
Circulation: 2,812pd,; AAM
Advertising rate: Open inch rate $12.42
Established: 1873
Group: Trib Total Media, Inc.
Digital Platform - Mobile: Apple, Android
Digital Platform - Tablet: Apple iOS, Android
Adv. Dir..Jill Paschl
Ed..A.J. Panian
Mechanical Specifications: Type page 11 1/2 x 21 1/2; E - 6 cols, 1 13/16, 1/8 between; A - 6 cols, 1 13/16, 1/8 between; C - 10 cols, 1 1/16, 1/8 between.Equipment & Software: Hardware — PCs, Compaq/Server; Presses — HI; Software — QPS/QuarkXPress 4.0.
Delivery Method: Mail, Newsstand
Areas Served: Mount Pleasant

MOUNTAIN TOP

MOUNTAINTOP EAGLE (WED)

85 S Main St, Mountain Top, PA, 18707-1962, Luzerne, USA; gen tel (570) 474-6397; gen fax (570) 474-9272; disp adv e-mail mteagle@ptd.net; class adv e-mail steffie@ptd.net; ed e-mail news@mteagle.com; web site www.mteagle.com
Circulation: 2,500pd, 3fr; Sworn/Estimate/ Non-Audited
Advertising rate: Open inch rate $14.98
Established: 1970
Digital Platform - Mobile: Apple, Android, Windows, Blackberry
Digital Platform - Tablet: Apple iOS, Android, Windows 7, Blackberry Tablet OS, Kindle, Nook, Kindle Fire
Pub.....................................Stephanie Grubert
Ed..Kathy Flower
Delivery Method: Mail, Newsstand
Areas Served: Luzerne County

MUNHALL

THE VALLEY MIRROR (THUR)

3315 Main St Ste A, Ste 2, Munhall, PA, 15120-3200, Allegheny, USA; gen tel (412) 462-0626; gen fax (412) 462-1847; ed e-mail valleymirror@comcast.net; web site http://www.valleymirror.com/
Circulation: 5,000pd,; Sworn/Estimate/Non-Audited
Advertising rate: Open inch rate $8.00
Established: 1981
Group: Laughing Dog Media LLC
Digital Platform - Mobile: Apple, Android
Digital Platform - Tablet: Apple iOS, Android
Pub./Ed...............................Marilyn Schiavoni
Mechanical Specifications: Type page 10 1/4 x 13 3/4; E - 5 cols, 2, between; A - 5 cols, 2, between; C - 6 cols, 1 9/16, between. Equipment & Software: Hardware — I Mac; Software — Adobe/CS5
Delivery Method: Mail, Racks
Areas Served: 15104, 15112, 15218, 15120,15122, 15145, 15207, 15221,15235

MURRYSVILLE

PENN FRANKLIN NEWS (MON, WED)

4021 Old William Penn Hwy, Murrysville, PA, 15668-1846, Westmoreland, USA; gen tel (724) 327-3471; gen fax (724) 325-4591; disp adv e-mail admanager@penn-franklin.com; ed e-mail news@penn-franklin.com; web site www.penn-franklin.com
Advertising rate: Open inch rate $6.41
Established: 1947
Group: Penn Franklin Publishing Co.
Digital Platform - Mobile: Apple, Android, Windows
Digital Platform - Tablet: Apple iOS, Android, Windows 7
Pub./Ed....................................Charlene Word
Delivery Method: Mail, Newsstand, Carrier
Areas Served: Murrysville, Export Borough, Delmont Borough, Penn Township, Trafford Borough, Salem Township, and Manor Borough

NEW BETHLEHEM

THE LEADER-VINDICATOR (WED)

435 Broad St, New Bethlehem, PA, 16242-1194, Clarion, USA; gen tel (814) 275-3131; adv tel (814) 275-3131 ext. 224; gen fax (814) 275-3531; disp adv e-mail rwells@thecourierexpress.com; class adv e-mail mcraig@thecourierexpress.com; ed e-mail jwalzak@thecourierexpress.com; web site www.thecourierexpress.com/the_leader_vindicator
Circulation: 4,899pd, 46fr; Sworn/Estimate/ Non-Audited
Advertising rate: Open inch rate $9.85
Established: 1873
Group: Community Media Group
Digital Platform - Mobile: Apple, Android
Digital Platform - Tablet: Apple iOS, Android
Pub..Devin Hamilton
Ed...Josh Walzak
Gen. Mgr.................................. Randy Bartley
Mechanical Specifications: Type page 12 x 21; E - 6 cols, 1 13/16, 1/7 between; A - 6 cols, 1 13/16, 1/7 between; C - 6 cols, 1 13/16, 1/7 between.Equipment & Software: Hardware — APP/Mac; Presses — ATF/Chief 17; Software — QPS/QuarkXPress, Multi-Ad/Creator.
Delivery Method: Mail, Newsstand, Carrier, Racks
Areas Served: 16242, 15829, 15864, 16214, 16216, 16222, 16223, 16224, 16230, 16245, 16246, 16248, 16253, 16254, 16255, 16256, 16259, 16261

NEW BLOOMFIELD

DUNCANNON RECORD (THUR)

51 Church St, New Bloomfield, PA, 17068-9683, Perry, USA; gen tel (717) 582-4305; gen fax (717) 582-7933; disp adv e-mail advertising@perrycountytimes.com; class adv e-mail advertising@perrycountytimes.com; ed e-mail editor@perrycountytimes.com; web site pennlive.com/perry-county-times
Circulation: 1,611pd, 18fr; Sworn/Estimate/ Non-Audited
Advertising rate: Open inch rate $4.00
Group: Advance Publications, Inc.
Pub...Curt Dreibelbis
Adv. Mgr...................................George Roche
Editorial Consultant
Wade Fowler
Ed. ....Gary Thomas
Circulation Manager .... Brittany Ciccocioppo
Mechanical Specifications: Type page 11 5/8 x 21 1/2; E - 6 cols, 1 5/6, 1/8 between; A - 6 cols, 1 5/6, 1/8 between; C - 8 cols, 1 3/8, 1/8 between.
Delivery Method: Mail, Newsstand
Areas Served: Perry County

PERRY COUNTY TIMES (THUR)

51 Church St, New Bloomfield, PA, 17068-9683, Perry, USA; gen tel (717) 582-4305; gen fax (717) 582-7933; disp adv e-mail advertising@perrycountytimes.com; class adv e-mail advertising@perrycountytimes.com; ed e-mail editor@perrycountytimes.com; web site
Circulation: 3,741pd, 39fr; Sworn/Estimate/ Non-Audited
Advertising rate: Open inch rate $5.15
Established: 1886
Group: Advance Publications, Inc.
Pub...Curt Dreibelbis
Adv. Mgr...................................George Roche

Editorial Consultant .... Wade Fowler
Ed. .... Gary Thomas
Circulation Manager .... Brittany Ciccocioppo
Mechanical Specifications: Type page 11 5/8 x 21; E - 6 cols, 1 5/6, 1/8 between; A - 6 cols, 1 5/6, 1/8 between; C - 8 cols, 1 3/8, 1/8 between.Equipment & Software: Hardware — APP/Mac; Software — Adobe/Indesign
Delivery Method: Mail, Newsstand
Areas Served: Perry County

THE NEWS-SUN (WED)

51 Church St, New Bloomfield, PA, 17068-9683, Perry, USA; gen tel (717) 582-4305; adv tel (717) 582-4305; ed tel (717) 582-4305; gen fax (717) 582-7933; adv fax (717) 582-7933; ed fax (717) 582-7933; disp adv e-mail advertising@perrycountytimes.com; class adv e-mail advertising@perrycountytimes.com; ed e-mail editor@perrycountytimes.com
Circulation: 2,304pd, 34fr; Sworn/Estimate/Non-Audited
Advertising rate: Open inch rate $4.55
Group: Advance Publications, Inc.
Adv. Mgr..................................... George Roche
Editorial Consultant .... Wade Fowler
Ed. .... Gary Thomas
Publisher.................................. Curt Dreibelbis
Circulation Manager .... Brittany Ciccocioppo
Mechanical Specifications: Type page 11 5/8 x 21 1/2; E - 6 cols, 1 5/6, 1/8 between; A - 6 cols, 1 5/6, 1/8 between; C - 8 cols, 1 3/8, 1/8 between.
Delivery Method: Mail, Newsstand
Areas Served: Perry County, PA

NEW WILMINGTON

THE GLOBE LEADER (THUR)

129 W Neshannock Ave, Ste C, New Wilmington, PA, 16142-1183, Lawrence, USA; gen tel (724) 946-8098; gen fax (724) 946-2097; disp adv e-mail globepaper@aol.com; ed e-mail globeleaderparrish@gmail.com; web site www.globe-leader.com
Circulation: 2,000pd,; Sworn/Estimate/Non-Audited
Advertising rate: Open inch rate $8.00
Established: 1880
Pub.. Frank Parrish
Mng. Ed............................. Darlinda McDonald
Delivery Method: Mail, Newsstand, Racks
Areas Served: Lawrence County

NORTHERN CAMBRIA

THE STAR-COURIER (THUR)

520 Philadelphia Ave, Northern Cambria, PA, 15714-1630, Cambria, USA; gen tel (814) 948-6210; gen fax (814) 948-7563; ed e-mail mainlinenews@verizon.net; web site www.mainline-news.com
Circulation: 4,500pd,; Sworn/Estimate/Non-Audited
Advertising rate: Open inch rate $8.30
Established: 1900
Group: Mainline Newspapers
Sample News Group LLC
Digital Platform - Mobile: Apple, Android, Blackberry
Digital Platform - Tablet: Apple iOS, Android, Windows 7, Blackberry Tablet OS
Pub...................................... William Anderson
Ed. .... Paula Varner
Adv. Mgr...................................... Katie Hanlon
Delivery Method: Mail, Newsstand
Areas Served: Northern Cambria, Patton, Carrolltown, and Hastings

PENNSBURG

TOWN AND COUNTRY (THUR)

2508 Kutztown Rd, Pennsburg, PA, 18073-1914, Montgomery, USA; gen tel (215) 679-5060; gen fax (215) 679-5077; disp adv e-mail wsuhl.ljrpublishing@gmail.com; class adv e-mail mkoder.ljrpublishing@gmail.com; ed e-mail lroeder.ljrpublishing@gmail.com; web site www.upvnews.com
Circulation: 5,900pd, 100fr; USPS
Advertising rate: Open inch rate $8.50
Established: 1899
Digital Platform - Mobile: Apple, Android
Digital Platform - Tablet: Apple iOS, Android
Pub./Ed....................................... Larry Roeder
Adv. Mgr....................................... Wayne Suhl
Graphics Editor...................... Robert Esposito
Staff Writer........................... Bradlwy Schlegel
Mechanical Specifications: 5 col. tab. 10" x 12 1/4" .167 gutter.
Delivery Method: Mail, Newsstand
Areas Served: Montgomery County
Berks County
Bucks County
Lehigh County

PHILADELPHIA

CHESTNUT HILL LOCAL (THUR)

8434 Germantown Ave, Ste 1, Philadelphia, PA, 19118-3386, Philadelphia, USA; gen tel (215) 248-8800; gen fax (215) 248-8814; disp adv e-mail sonia@chestnuthilllocal.com; class adv e-mail classifieds@chestnuthilllocal.com; ed e-mail pete@chestnuthilllocal.com; web site www.chestnuthilllocal.com - 130,070(views) 50,000(visitors)
Circulation: 6,000pd, 300fr; Sworn/Estimate/Non-Audited
Advertising rate: $17/col."
Established: 1958
Digital Platform - Mobile: Apple, Android
Digital Platform - Tablet: Apple iOS, Android
Assc. Pub............................ Larry Hochberger
Ed. .... Peter Mazzaccaro
Adv. Mgr....................................... Sonia Leones
Circ. Mgr.................................... Cheryl Massaro
Mechanical Specifications: Type page 10 13/16 x 16; E - 5 cols, 2 1/16, 1/8 between; A - 5 cols, 2 1/16, 1/8 between; C - 5 cols, 2 1/16, 1/8 between.Equipment & Software: Hardware — APP/Mac; Software — QPS/QuarkXPress 4.0.
Delivery Method: Mail, Newsstand, Racks
Areas Served: 19118, 19119, 19038, 19031,19075, 19444

JUNIATA NEWS (TUES)

E Erie Ave, Philadelphia, PA, 19124, Philadelphia, USA; gen tel (215) 435-3909; gen fax (215) 887-3716; ed e-mail juniatanews@comcast.net
Advertising rate: Open inch rate $8.24
Established: 1934
Pub./Ed.............................. Thomas Lineman
Delivery Method: Mail, Newsstand
Areas Served: Philadelphia County

PHILADELPHIA BUSINESS JOURNAL (FRI)

400 Market St Ste 1200, Suite 1200, Philadelphia, PA, 19106-2501, Philadelphia, USA; gen tel (215) 238-1450; gen fax (215) 238-9489; disp adv e-mail rmaver@bizjournals.com; class adv e-mail pdemo@bizjournals.com; ed e-mail cey@bizjournals.com; web site www.pbj.com
Advertising rate: Open inch rate $8132.00 (Full-Page)
Established: 1982
Digital Platform - Mobile: Apple, Android, Windows, Blackberry
Digital Platform - Tablet: Apple iOS, Android, Windows 7, Blackberry Tablet OS, Kindle, Nook, Kindle Fire
Pub... Lyn Kremer
Ed. .... Craig Ey
Mng. Ed.. Dell Poncet
Adv. Mgr... Ron Maver
Delivery Method: Mail, Newsstand, Carrier
Areas Served: Delaware Valley

PHILADELPHIA FREE PRESS (WED)

218 S 45th St, Philadelphia, PA, 19104-2919, Philadelphia, USA; gen tel (215) 222-2846; adv tel (215) 222-2846; ed tel (215) 222-2846; gen fax (215) 222-2378; adv fax (215) 222-2378; ed fax (215) 222-2378; disp adv e-mail cchristian@pressreview.net; class adv e-mail cchristian@pressreview.net; ed e-mail editor@pressreview.net; web site www.phillyfreepress.com - 25,200(views)
Circulation: 15,000fr; CVC
Advertising rate: Open inch rate $24.15
Established: 1988
Group: University City Review, Inc.
Digital Platform - Mobile: Apple, Android, Blackberry
Digital Platform - Tablet: Apple iOS, Android, Windows 7, Blackberry Tablet OS
Pub./Ed.................................. Robert Christian
News Reporter........................ Nicole Contosta
Adv. Mgr............................... Claudia Christian
Circ. Mgr............................... George Chavame
Delivery Method: Mail, Carrier, Racks
Areas Served: 19102, 19103, 19106, 19107, 19130, 19146, 19147

THE PHILADELPHIA PUBLIC RECORD (THUR)

325 Chestnut St Ste 1110, Suite 1110, Philadelphia, PA, 19106-2611, Philadelphia, USA; gen tel (215) 755-2000; gen fax (215) 689-4099; disp adv e-mail editor@phillyrecord.com; class adv e-mail mbarrett@phillyrecord.com; web site www.phillyrecord.com
Circulation: 4,000pd, 25,000fr; Sworn/Estimate/Non-Audited
Advertising rate: Open inch rate $20.00
Established: 1999
Group: City & State PAEditions: (8) Senior salute, Labor Day, State of Port, Columbus Weekend, Memorial Day Weekend, July 4th,Health, Education, Thanksgiving and Christmas
Digital Platform - Mobile: Windows, Blackberry
Digital Platform - Tablet: Apple iOS, Windows 7
Adv. Dir..................................... Melissa Barrett
Mechanical Specifications: Full page= Width 9.12" Height: 9.87"Equipment & Software: Hardware — PC; Presses — Philadelphia Inquirer; Software — Quark
Delivery Method: Mail, Carrier, Racks
Areas Served: All Philadelphia and General Assembly in Harrisburg, PA

THE REVIEW (WED)

6220 Ridge Ave, Philadelphia, PA, 19128-2750, Philadelphia, USA; gen tel (215) 483-7300; adv tel (215) 483-7300 ext. 218; ed tel (215) 483-7300 ext. 210; gen fax (215) 483-2073; disp adv e-mail cswider@ingnews.com; class adv e-mail noleary@ingnews.com; ed e-mail review@ingnews.com; web site www.roxreview.com
Circulation: 16,000pd, 9,500fr; Sworn/Estimate/Non-Audited
Advertising rate: Modular rate $442.00 (1/4 P); $802.00 (1/2 P); $1522.00 (Full)
Group: Digital First Media
Digital Platform - Mobile: Apple, Android, Blackberry
Digital Platform - Tablet: Apple iOS, Android, Windows 7, Blackberry Tablet OS
Pub.. Elizabeth Wilson
Ed. .... George Beetham
Adv. Mgr.. Kathy Zapp
Mechanical Specifications: Type page 13 1/4 x 21; E - 8 cols, 1 1/2, 1/6 between; A - 8 cols, 1 1/2, 1/6 between; C - 8 cols, 1 1/2, 1/6 between.Equipment & Software: Hardware — APP/Mac, PC; Presses — G; Software — QPS/QuarkXPress.
Delivery Method: Mail, Newsstand, Carrier, Racks
Areas Served: Roxborough, Manayunk, Andorra, Wissahickon, and East Falls

UNIVERSITY CITY REVIEW (WED)

218 S 45th St, Philadelphia, PA, 19104-2919, Philadelphia, USA; gen tel (215) 222-2846; gen fax (215) 222-2378; disp adv e-mail cchristian@pressreview.net; ed e-mail editor@pressreview.net; web site www.ucreview.com - 17,200(views)
Circulation: 29,467fr; VAC
Advertising rate: Open inch rate $23.00
Digital Platform - Mobile: Apple, Android, Blackberry
Digital Platform - Tablet: Apple iOS, Android, Windows 7, Blackberry Tablet OS
Pub./Ed.................................. Robert Christian
Adv. Mgr.............................. Claudia Christian
Delivery Method: Mail, Newsstand
Areas Served: 19104, 19139, 19143

PITTSBURGH

BUTTERMILK FALLS (THUR)

460 Rodi Rd, Pittsburgh, PA, 15235-4547, Allegheny, USA; gen tel (412) 871-2345; adv tel (724) 567-5656; gen fax (724) 568-1729; disp adv e-mail jpaschl@tribweb.com; class adv e-mail mzigarovich@tribweb.com; ed e-mail smcfarland@tribweb.com; web site http://tribtotalmedia.com/
Circulation: 16,600fr; CVC
Advertising rate: Open inch rate $14.97
Group: Trib Total Media, Inc.
Digital Platform - Mobile: Apple, Android
Digital Platform - Tablet: Apple iOS, Android
Ed. .... Susan McFarland
Adv. Dir.. Jill Paschl
Delivery Method: Mail, Newsstand
Areas Served: Apollo, North Apollo, Hyde Park, East Vandergrift, Leechburg, Vandergrift, Avonmore, Salina, saltsburg, Schenley, Spring Church, New Kensington, Freeport, and Ford City.

MURRYSVILLE STAR (THUR)

460 Rodi Rd, Pittsburgh, PA, 15235-4547, Allegheny, USA; gen tel (412) 856-7400; adv tel (724) 567-5656; gen fax (412) 856-7954; disp adv e-mail jpaschl@tribweb.com; class adv e-mail mzigarovich@tribweb.com; ed e-mail smcfarland@tribweb.com; web site www.tribLIVE.com
Circulation: 68pd, 11,299fr; AAM
Advertising rate: Open inch rate $11.58
Group: Trib Total Media, Inc.
Digital Platform - Mobile: Apple, Android
Digital Platform - Tablet: Apple iOS, Android
Ed. .... Brian Estadt
Adv. Dir.. Jill Paschl
Mechanical Specifications: Type page 13 x 21 1/2; A - 6 cols, 2 1/16, between; C - 9 cols, 1 5/16, between.
Delivery Method: Mail, Newsstand
Areas Served: Murrysville, Export, Delmont

NORWIN STAR (THUR)

460 Rodi Rd, Pittsburgh, PA, 15235-4547, Allegheny, USA; gen tel (412) 856-7400; adv tel (724) 567-5656; ed tel (412) 856-7400 ext. 8627; gen fax (412) 856-7954; disp adv e-mail jpaschl@tribweb.com; class adv e-mail mzigarovich@tribweb.com; ed e-mail awallace@tribweb.com; web site www.tribLIVE.com
Circulation: 134pd, 16,170fr; AAM
Advertising rate: Open inch rate $14.97
Group: Trib Total Media, Inc.
Digital Platform - Mobile: Apple, Android
Digital Platform - Tablet: Apple iOS, Android
Adv. Dir.. Jill Paschl
Ed. .... Alan Wallace
Mechanical Specifications: Type page 13 x 21 1/2; A - 6 cols, 2 1/16, between; C - 9 cols, 1 5/16, between.
Delivery Method: Mail, Newsstand
Areas Served: Westmoreland City, Wendel, Irwin/North Huntington, Herminie, Rilton, Ardara, and Larimer

PENN-TRAFFORD STAR (THUR)

460 Rodi Rd, Pittsburgh, PA, 15235-4547, Allegheny, USA; gen tel (412) 856-7400; adv tel (724) 567-5656; ed tel (412) 856-7400 ext. 8680; gen fax (412) 856-7954; disp adv e-mail jpaschl@tribweb.com; class adv e-mail mzigarovich@tribweb.com; ed e-mail b.estadt@gatewaynewspapers.com; web site www.tribLIVE.com
Circulation: 170pd, 8,138fr; AAM
Advertising rate: Open inch rate $8.79
Group: Trib Total Media, Inc.
Digital Platform - Mobile: Apple, Android
Digital Platform - Tablet: Apple iOS, Android
Ed. .... Brian Estadt
Adv. Dir.. Jill Paschl
Delivery Method: Mail, Newsstand

Areas Served: Trafford, Harrison City, North Huntington, Manor, and Penn

PITTSBURGH BUSINESS TIMES (FRI)

424 S 27th St Ste 211, Suite 211, Pittsburgh, PA, 15203-2380, Allegheny, USA; gen tel (412) 481-6397; gen fax (412) 481-9956; disp adv e-mail rvaccarelli@bizjournals.com; class adv e-mail amcgrath@bizjournals.com; ed e-mail hburns@bizjournals.com; web site www.amcity.com/pittsburgh
Advertising rate: Open inch rate $6769.00 (Full-Page)
Established: 1981
Digital Platform - Mobile: Apple, Android, Windows, Blackberry
Digital Platform - Tablet: Apple iOS, Android, Windows 7, Blackberry Tablet OS, Kindle, Nook, Kindle Fire
Pub.. Alan Robertson
Ed. .... Howard Burns
Adv. Dir...................................... Rick Vaccarelli
Mng. Ed....................................... Jennifer Curry
Delivery Method: Mail, Newsstand, Carrier
Areas Served: Allegheny County

PLUM ADVANCE LEADER (THUR)

460 Rodi Rd, Pittsburgh, PA, 15235-4547, Allegheny, USA; gen tel (412) 856-7400; adv tel (724) 567-5656; gen fax (412) 856-7954; disp adv e-mail jpaschl@tribweb.com; class adv e-mail mzigarovich@tribweb.com; ed e-mail fcraig@tribweb.com; web site www.tribLIVE.com
Circulation: 95pd, 10,657fr; AAM
Advertising rate: Open inch rate $11.58
Group: Trib Total Media, Inc.
Digital Platform - Mobile: Apple, Android
Digital Platform - Tablet: Apple iOS, Android
Exec. Ed....................................... Frank Craig
Adv. Dir/ .... Jill Paschl
Delivery Method: Mail, Newsstand
Areas Served: Plum

SOUTH HILLS RECORD (THUR)

503 Martindale St, Pittsburgh, PA, 15212-5746, Allegheny, USA; gen tel (412) 388-5805; adv tel (412) 324-1400; gen fax (412) 388-0900; adv fax (412) 324-1401; disp adv e-mail jpaschl@tribweb.com; class adv e-mail mzigarovich@tribweb.com; ed e-mail jcuddy@tribweb.com; web site www.tribLIVE.com
Circulation: 3,114pd,; AAM
Advertising rate: Open inch rate $5.09
Group: Trib Total Media, Inc.
Digital Platform - Mobile: Apple, Android
Digital Platform - Tablet: Apple iOS, Android
Adv. Dir.. Jill Paschl
Mng. Ed... Jim Cuddy
Mechanical Specifications: Type page 10 13/16 x 16; A - 5 cols, 2 1/16, between; C - 7 cols, 1 5/16, between.
Delivery Method: Mail, Newsstand
Areas Served: Brentwood, Baldwin, Whitehall, Pleasant Hills, Jefferson, Baldwin Twp.

THE ALMANAC (WED)

2600 Boyce Plaza Rd, Ste 142, Pittsburgh, PA, 15241-3949, Washington, USA; gen tel (724) 941-7725; gen fax (724) 941-8685; disp adv e-mail jhott@observer-reporter.com; class adv e-mail cslota@observer-reporter.com; ed e-mail mjones@observer-reporter.com; web site www.thealmanac.net
Circulation: 63pd, 43,448fr; CAC
Advertising rate: Open inch rate $28.75
Established: 1965
Group: Observer Publishing Co.Editions: (2) 2 Total: Almanac-Zone 1 (27,028); Almanac-Zone 2 (29,042)
Digital Platform - Mobile: Apple, Android, Windows
Digital Platform - Tablet: Apple iOS, Android, Windows 7
Circ. Mgr.. Judi Smith
Prod. Mgr. .... Jeannie Robinson
Ed. .... Katie Green
Adv. Mgr................................ Jasmine Blussick
Mechanical Specifications: Type page 13 x 21; E - 6 cols, 2, 1/8 between; A - 6 cols, 2, 1/8 between; C - 6 cols, 2, 1/8 between.Equipment & Software: Hardware — APP/Mac; Presses — WPC; Software — QPS/QuarkXPress 3.32, Microsoft/Word.
Delivery Method: Carrier, Racks
Areas Served: 15017, 15102, 15216, 15220, 15234, 15317, 15228, 15241

THE NORTHSIDE CHRONICLE (WED, MTHLY)

922 Middle St, Pittsburgh, PA, 15212-7200, Allegheny, USA; gen tel (412) 321-3919; gen fax (412) 321-1447; disp adv e-mail editor@thenorthsidechronicle.com; web site www.thenorthsidechronicle.com
Circulation:; Sworn/Estimate/Non-Audited
Advertising rate: Modular rates: 1/8 P $56 1/4 P $118 1/2 P $229 Full $452
Established: 1985
Advertising Manager................ Lauren Stauffer
Delivery Method: Mail, Newsstand, Carrier
Areas Served: Northside, Pittsburgh, Pennsylvania

THE SIGNAL ITEM (THUR)

503 Martindale St, Pittsburgh, PA, 15212-5746, Allegheny, USA; gen tel (412) 388-5801; gen fax (412) 388-0900; disp adv e-mail jpaschl@tribweb.com; class adv e-mail mzigarovich@tribweb.com; ed e-mail bridgeville.news@gatewaynewspapers.com; web site www.tribLIVE.com
Circulation: 270pd, 8,664fr; AAM
Advertising rate: Open inch rate $8.79
Group: Trib Total Media, Inc.
Digital Platform - Mobile: Apple, Android
Digital Platform - Tablet: Apple iOS, Android
Adv. Dir.. Jill Paschl
Ed. .... Bob Pastin
Mechanical Specifications: Type page 10 13/16 x 16; A - 5 cols, 2 1/16, between; C - 7 cols, 1 5/16, between.
Delivery Method: Mail, Newsstand
Areas Served: Carnegie

THE TIMES EXPRESS (THUR)

460 Rodi Rd, Pittsburgh, PA, 15235-4547, Allegheny, USA; gen tel (412) 856-7400; gen fax (412) 856-7954; disp adv e-mail jpaschl@tribweb.com; class adv e-mail mzigarovich@tribweb.com; ed e-mail jcuddy@tribweb.com; web site www.tribLIVE.com
Circulation: 137pd, 15,766fr; AAM
Advertising rate: Open inch rate $12.42
Group: Trib Total Media, Inc.
Digital Platform - Mobile: Apple, Android
Digital Platform - Tablet: Apple iOS, Android
Adv. Dir .... Jill Paschl
Mng. Ed.. Jim Cuddy
Mechanical Specifications: Type page 13 x 21 1/2; A - 6 cols, 2 1/16, between; C - 9 cols, 1 5/16, between.
Delivery Method: Mail, Newsstand
Areas Served: Monroeville, Pitcairn, and Wilmerding

PITTSTON

SUNDAY DISPATCH (SUN)

71 N Main St, Pittston, PA, 18640-1915, Luzerne, USA; gen tel (570) 655-1418; adv tel (570) 829-7293; ed tel (570) 602-0715; gen fax (570) 602-0184; adv fax (570) 829-2002; disp adv e-mail tspina@timesleader.com; class adv e-mail classifieds@timesleader.com; ed e-mail eackerman@psdispatch.com; web site www.psdispatch.com
Circulation: 5,501pd, 121fr; AAM
Advertising rate: Open inch rate $14.80
Group: Civitas Media, LLC-OOB impreMedia LLC
Digital Platform - Mobile: Apple, Android
Digital Platform - Tablet: Apple iOS, Android
Pub.. Richard Connor
Ed. .... Dotty Martin
Delivery Method: Mail, Newsstand, Carrier, Racks
Areas Served: Luzerne County

PORT ROYAL

THE TIMES (WED)

410 MILFORD ST, Port Royal, PA, 17082, Juniata, USA; gen tel (717) 436-9900; gen fax (717) 436-8300; ed e-mail thetimes@nmax.net; web site www.timesnewspaper.com
Circulation: 3,650pd, 15fr; Sworn/Estimate/Non-Audited
Advertising rate: Open inch rate $3.75
Owner/Ed................................. Donna Swartz
Delivery Method: Mail
Areas Served: Juniata County and surrounding communities in Pennsylvania

POTTSTOWN

BERKSMONT NEWS (WED)

24 N Hanover St, Pottstown, PA, 19464-5410, Montgomery, USA; gen tel (610) 970-3218; ed tel (610) 970-3218 ext. 625; gen fax (610) 369-0233; disp adv e-mail denice@berksmontnews.com; class adv e-mail wordad@berksmontnews.com; ed e-mail ethiel@berksmontnews.com; web site www.berksmontnews.com
Circulation: 395pd, 5,500fr; Sworn/Estimate/Non-Audited
Advertising rate: Modular rate $275.00 (1/4 P); $519.00 (1/2 P); $976.00 (Full)
Established: 1885
Group: Berks-Mont Newspapers, Inc. Digital First Media
Digital Platform - Mobile: Apple, Android, Blackberry
Digital Platform - Tablet: Apple iOS, Android, Windows 7, Blackberry Tablet OS
Gen. Mgr.. Patti Paul
Adv. Mgr. .... Denice Schaeffer
Ed. .... Emily Thiel
Mechanical Specifications: Type page 11 5/8 x 20 1/2; E - 6 cols, 1 5/6, 1/8 between; A - 6 cols, 1 5/6, 1/8 between; C - 9 cols, 1 3/16, 1/8 between.Equipment & Software: Hardware — 3-APP/Mac G4, 7-APP/iMac; Software — QPS/QuarkXPress 4.1, Adobe/Photoshop 6.0, Adobe/Illustrator 9.0, Adobe/Acrobat 5.0.
Delivery Method: Mail, Newsstand, Carrier, Racks
Areas Served: 19508, 19518, 19606, 19548, 19520

MERCURY SAMPLER (WED, SAT)

24 N Hanover St, Pottstown, PA, 19464-5410, Montgomery, USA; gen tel (610) 323-3000; adv tel (610) 970-4451; ed tel (610) 970-4455; gen fax (610) 327-3308; ed fax (610) 323-0682; disp adv e-mail sbatten@pottsmerc.com; class adv e-mail classified@pottsmerc.com; ed e-mail letters@pottsmerc.com; web site www.pottsmerc.com
Circulation: 24,244fr; Sworn/Estimate/Non-Audited
Advertising rate: Open inch rate $4.10
Digital Platform - Mobile: Apple, Android
Digital Platform - Tablet: Apple iOS, Android
Pub... Edward Condra
Adv. Mgr....................................... Steve Batten
Ed. .... Nancy March
Pub .... Thomas Abbott
Mechanical Specifications: Type page 13 x 22; E - 6 cols, 2 1/16, between; A - 6 cols, 2 1/16, between.Equipment & Software: ; Presses — G/Letter Press.
Delivery Method: Mail, Newsstand, Racks
Areas Served: 19464

THE BOYERTOWN AREA TIMES (THUR)

24 N Hanover St, Pottstown, PA, 19464-5410, Montgomery, USA; gen tel (610) 970-3218; adv tel (610) 970-3218 ext. 632; ed tel (610) 970-3218 ext. 623; gen fax (610) 369-0233; disp adv e-mail denice@berksmontnews.com; class adv e-mail wordad@berksmontnews.com; ed e-mail rblanchard@berksmontnews.com; web site www.berksmontnews.com
Circulation: 5,820pd, 488fr; Sworn/Estimate/Non-Audited
Advertising rate: Open inch rate $16.11
Established: 1857
Group: Berks-Mont Newspapers, Inc. Digital First Media
Digital Platform - Mobile: Apple, Android
Digital Platform - Tablet: Apple iOS, Android, Kindle, Nook, Kindle Fire
Pub... Patti Paul
Gen. Mgr. .... Denice Schaeffer
Ed. .... Rebecca Blanchard
Mechanical Specifications: Type page 11 5/8 x 21 1/2; E - 6 cols, 1 5/6, 1/8 between; A - 6 cols, 1 5/6, 1/8 between; C - 9 cols, 1 3/16, 1/8 between.Equipment & Software: Hardware — 3-APP/Mac G4, 7-APP/iMac; Software — QPS/QuarkXPress 6.1, Adobe/Illustrator 11.0, Adobe/Photoshop 8.0.
Delivery Method: Mail, Newsstand, Carrier, Racks
Areas Served: 19503, 19504, 19505, 19512, 19519, 19525, 19545, 19547, 19472, 19435

THE COMMUNITY CONNECTION (FRI)

24 N Hanover St, Pottstown, PA, 19464-5410, Montgomery, USA; gen tel (610) 970-3218; adv tel (610) 970-3218 ext. 632; ed tel (610) 970-3218 ext. 640; gen fax (610) 369-0233; disp adv e-mail denice@berksmontnews.com; class adv e-mail wordad@berksmontnews.com; ed e-mail mreichl@berksmontnews.com; web site www.berksmontnews.con
Circulation: 7,000fr; Sworn/Estimate/Non-Audited
Advertising rate: $4.00 per column inch
Group: Berks-Mont Newspapers, Inc. Digital First Media
Digital Platform - Mobile: Apple, Android
Digital Platform - Tablet: Apple iOS, Android, Kindle, Nook, Kindle Fire
Ed. .... Lisa Mitchell
Gen. Mgr............................... Denice Schaeffer
Delivery Method: Mail, Newsstand, Carrier, Racks
Areas Served: Modular rate $32.00 (1/60 pg); $48.00 (1/40 pg)

THE HAMBURG AREA ITEM (WED)

24 N Hanover St, Pottstown, PA, 19464-5410, Berks, USA; gen tel (610) 562-7515; adv tel (610) 970-3218 ext. 632; gen fax (610) 562-4644; disp adv e-mail denice@berksmontnews.com; class adv e-mail wordad@berksmontnews.com; ed e-mail ssingley@berksmontnews.com; web site http://www.berksmontnews.com/local-news-hamburg-area-item
Advertising rate: Open inch rate $11.96
Group: Digital First Media Berks-Mont Newspapers, Inc.
Digital Platform - Mobile: Apple, Android
Digital Platform - Tablet: Apple iOS, Android, Kindle, Nook, Kindle Fire
Ed. .... Shea SingleyEquipment & Software: Hardware — 5-PC; Software — Archetype/Corel Draw 8.0.
Delivery Method: Mail, Newsstand
Areas Served: Berks County

THE KUTZTOWN AREA PATRIOT (THUR)

24 N Hanover St, Pottstown, PA, 19464-5410, Montgomery, USA; gen tel (610) 562-7515; gen fax (610) 562-4644; disp adv e-mail denice@berksmontnews.com; class adv e-mail wordad@berksmontnews.com; ed e-mail lmitchell@berksmontnews.com; web site www.berksmontnews.com
Circulation: 3,100pd, 336fr; Sworn/Estimate/Non-Audited
Advertising rate: Modular rate $275.00 (1/4 P); $519.00 (1/2 P); $976.00 (Full)
Established: 1874
Group: Berks-Mont Newspapers, Inc.
Digital Platform - Mobile: Apple, Android
Digital Platform - Tablet: Apple iOS, Android, Kindle, Nook, Kindle Fire
Pub... Patti Paul
Gen. Mgr. .... Denice Schaeffer
Ed. .... Lisa Mitchell
Mechanical Specifications: Type page 11 5/8 x 21 1/2; E - 6 cols, 1 5/6, 1/8 between; A - 6 cols, 1 5/6, 1/8 between; C - 9 cols, 1 3/16, 1/8 between.Equipment & Software: Hardware — 2-APP/Mac G4, 2-APP/iBooks, 2-APP/iMac;

Software — QPS/QuarkXPress 4.1, Adobe/PhotoShop 6.0, Adobe/Illustrator 8.0.
Delivery Method: Mail, Newsstand, Carrier, Racks
Areas Served: 19530, 19539, 19562, 19510, 19522, 19534, 19529, 19511, 19536, 19538, 19564

THE PHOENIX REPORTER & ITEM (SUN)
24 N Hanover St, Pottstown, PA, 19464-5410, Montgomery, USA; gen tel (610) 933-8926; ed tel (610) 933-8926 ext. 633; gen fax (610) 933-1187; disp adv e-mail ppaul@21st-centurymedia.com; class adv e-mail jfinneran@21st-centurymedia.com; ed e-mail editor@phoenixvillenews.com; web site www.phoenixvillenews.com
Circulation: 2,566pd,; Sworn/Estimate/Non-Audited
Advertising rate: 1/60 Pg $30.00
Established: 2013
Group: Digital First Media
Digital Platform - Mobile: Apple, Android, Blackberry
Digital Platform - Tablet: Apple iOS, Android, Windows 7, Blackberry Tablet OS, Kindle, Nook, Kindle Fire
Pub..Patricia Paul
Ed. ....Leann Pettit
Mechanical Specifications: Type page 12 3/4 x 21 1/2; E - 6 cols, 2, 1/6 between; A - 6 cols, 2, 1/6 between; C - 10 cols, 1 1/3, 1/6 between. Equipment & Software: Hardware — APP/Mac; Presses — G/Offset; Software — QPS/QuarkXPress.
Delivery Method: Mail, Newsstand, Racks
Areas Served: 19473, 19426, 19478, 194330, 19474, 19492, 18074

TRI-COUNTY RECORD (TUES)
24 N Hanover St, Pottstown, PA, 19464-5410, Lancaster, USA; gen tel (610) 286-0162; ed tel (610) 286-0162 ext. 25; gen fax (610) 369-0233; disp adv e-mail denice@berksmontnews.com; class adv e-mail wordad@berksmontnews.com; ed e-mail jfinneran@tricountyrecord.com; web site www.tricountyrecord.com
Circulation: 20,100fr; Sworn/Estimate/Non-Audited
Advertising rate: Modular rate $408.00 (1/4 P); $770.00 (1/2 P); $1450.00 (Full)
Group: Berks-Mont Newspapers, Inc.
Digital First Media
Digital Platform - Mobile: Apple, Android
Digital Platform - Tablet: Apple iOS, Android, Kindle, Nook, Kindle Fire
Pub...Patti Paul
Adv. Mgr. .... Denice Schaeffer
Ed. .... Justin Finneran
Mechanical Specifications: Type page 10 3/8 x 13; E - 6 cols, 1 2/3, between; A - 6 cols, 1 2/3, between.Equipment & Software: Hardware — APP/Mac IIsi; Software — Multi-Ad/Creator 3.7.
Delivery Method: Mail, Newsstand, Carrier, Racks
Areas Served: Lancaster County

RENOVO

THE RECORD (THUR)
12423 Renovo Rd, Renovo, PA, 17764-1335, Clinton, USA; gen tel (570) 923-1500; adv tel (570) 858-5688; gen fax (570) 923-1572; disp adv e-mail clintoncountyrecord@yahoo.com; class adv e-mail lgavlock@verizon.net; ed e-mail clintoncountyrecord@comcast.net; web site www.therecord-online.com
Circulation: 2,000pd,; Sworn/Estimate/Non-Audited
Advertising rate: Open inch rate $5.00
Established: 1871
Group: Clinton County Publishing Company
Publisher...John Lipez
Editor .... Lynn Gavlock
Advertising...............................Jeannine Lipez
Billing/Subscriptions ....Tracy Embick
Delivery Method: Mail, Newsstand
Areas Served: Clinton County

SCHUYLKILL HAVEN

SOUTH SCHUYLKILL NEWS (THUR)
960 E Main St, Ste 1, Schuylkill Haven, PA, 17972-9752, Schuylkill, USA; gen tel (570) 385-3120; gen fax (570) 385-0725; disp adv e-mail dschaeffer@southschuylkillnews.com; class adv e-mail classified@southschuylkill-news.com; ed e-mail news@southschuylkill.net; web site www.southschuylkill.com
Circulation: 3,140pd, 8fr; USPS
Advertising rate: Open inch rate $17.00
Established: 1891
Group: South Schuylkill Printing & Publishing
Digital Platform - Mobile: Apple, Android
Digital Platform - Tablet: Apple iOS, Android
Pub./Ed./Adv. Dir..................William K. Knecht
Adv.......................................Denice Schaeffer
Mechanical Specifications: Type page 9.875 x 21; E - 6 cols, 2 1/16, 1/6 between; A - 6 cols, 2 1/16, 1/6 between.
Delivery Method: Mail, Newsstand
Areas Served: Schuylkill County, Blue Moutain, Pine Grove Area, Schuylkill Haven Area and Williams Valley

SCRANTON

NORTHEAST PENNSYLVANIA BUSINESS JOURNAL (WED, MTHLY)
149 Penn Ave, Ofc, Scranton, PA, 18503-2056, Lackawanna, USA; gen tel (570) 207-9001; adv tel (570) 207-9001 ext. 5425; ed tel (570) 207-9001 ext. 5415; gen fax (570) 207-3448; disp adv e-mail kbrislin@timesshamrock.com; class adv e-mail jgregg@timesshamrock.com; ed e-mail ezygmunt@timesshamrock.com; web site www.npbj.com
Advertising rate: Open inch rate $2,466.00 (Full-Page)
Group: Times Shamrock Communications
Digital Platform - Mobile: Apple, Android
Digital Platform - Tablet: Apple iOS, Android
Ed. .... Elizabeth Zygmunt
Adv. Mgr.......................................Kevin Brislin
Adv. Exec..Judy Gregg
Delivery Method: Mail, Carrier, Racks
Areas Served: Northeast Pennsylvania

SEWICKLEY

SEWICKLEY HERALD (THUR)
504 Beaver St, Sewickley, PA, 15143-1753, Allegheny, USA; gen tel (412) 324-1400; gen fax (412) 324-1401; disp adv e-mail jpaschl@tribweb.com; class adv e-mail mzigarovich@tribweb.com; ed e-mail jcuddy@tribweb.com; web site www.tribLIVE.com
Circulation: 431pd, 7,981fr; AAM
Advertising rate: Open inch rate $8.79
Established: 1903
Group: Trib Total Media, Inc.
Digital Platform - Mobile: Apple, Android
Digital Platform - Tablet: Apple iOS, Android
Adv. Dir...Jill Paschl
Ed. .... Frank Craig
Mechanical Specifications: Type page 10 13/16 x 16; A - 5 cols, 2 1/16, between; C - 7 cols, 1 5/16, between.
Delivery Method: Mail, Newsstand
Areas Served: Sewickley

SHIPPENSBURG

THE SHIPPENSBURG NEWS-CHRONICLE (TUES, FRI)
22 E King St, Shippensburg, PA, 17257-1308, Cumberland/Franklin, USA; gen tel (717) 532-4101; adv tel (717) 532-4101 ext. 225; ed tel (717) 532-4101 ext. 222; gen fax (717) 532-3020; disp adv e-mail advertising@shipnewschronicle.com; ed e-mail nceditor@gmail.com; web site www.shipnc.com
Circulation: 5,100pd, 100fr; Sworn/Estimate/Non-Audited
Advertising rate: Open inch rate $6.00
Established: 1844
Group: Sample News Group LLC
Digital Platform - Mobile: Apple, Android
Digital Platform - Tablet: Apple iOS, Android
Gen. Mgr./Adv. Dir.................John Zimmerman
Mng. Ed......................................Dale Heberlig
Delivery Method: Mail, Racks
Areas Served: Cumberland and Franklin County

THE VALLEY TIMES-STAR (WED)
22 E King St, Shippensburg, PA, 17257-1308, Cumberland/Franklin, USA; gen tel (717) 532-4101; adv tel (717) 532-4101 ext. 225; ed tel (717) 532-4101 ext. 222; gen fax (717) 532-3020; disp adv e-mail advertising@shipnewschronicle.com; ed e-mail nceditor@gmail.com; web site www.shipnc.com
Circulation: 3,017pd, 75fr; Sworn/Estimate/Non-Audited
Advertising rate: Open inch rate $4.00
Digital Platform - Mobile: Apple, Android
Digital Platform - Tablet: Apple iOS, Android
Mng. Ed......................................Dale Heberlig
Gen. Mgr./Adv. Dir.................John Zimmerman
Delivery Method: Mail, Racks
Areas Served: Cumberland and Franklin County

SOUDERTON

COURIER NEWS WEEKLY (WED)
70 Souderton Hatfield Pike, Ste 250, Souderton, PA, 18964-1939, Montgomery, USA; gen tel (267) 663-6300; gen fax (215) 799-2226; disp adv e-mail slapp@buxmontmedia.com; class adv e-mail classifieds@buxmontmedia.com; ed e-mail editorial@buxmontmedia.com; web site www.buxmontmedia.com
Circulation: 10pd, 48,656fr; CVC
Advertising rate: 1/32 Pg $45.00; 1/16 Pg $74.00; 1/8 Pg $138.00
Established: 1947
Group: Buxmont Media, LLCEditions: (5) 5 zoned edtion - Named for areas
Digital Platform - Mobile: Windows
Digital Platform - Tablet: Windows 7
Pub...Susan Lapp
Gen. Mgr. ....Thomas O'Donnell
Mechanical Specifications: Type page 10 x 12 7/16; E - 4 cols, 1 1/2, between; A - 4 cols, 1 1/2, between; C - 8 cols, 1 1/2, between.
Delivery Method: Mail
Areas Served: Central Montgomery and Bucks County

SOUTH WILLIAMSPORT

WEBB WEEKLY (WED)
280 Kane St, Ste 2, South Williamsport, PA, 17702-7166, Lycoming, USA; gen tel (570) 326-9322; adv tel (570) 419-9826; ed tel (570) 337-0759; gen fax (570) 326-9383; disp adv e-mail Rmingle@webbweekly.com; class adv e-mail classifieds@webbweekly.com; ed e-mail sturi@webbweekly.com; web site www.webbweekly.com
Circulation: 0pd, 57,940fr; VAC
Advertising rate: 1/8 Pg $185.00; 1/4 Pg $250.00; 3/8 Pg $435.00
Pub..................................James A. Jr. Webb
Gen. Mgr...................................Larry Andrews
Prod. Mgr.................................Eric Nordstrom
Delivery Method: Mail, Newsstand
Areas Served: Lycoming County

SUNBURY

SCRAPBOOK (FRI)
200 Market St, Sunbury, PA, 17801-3402, Northumberland, USA; gen tel (570) 286-5671; gen fax (570) 286-2570; disp adv e-mail sdiads@dailyitem.com; class adv e-mail pbennett@dailyitem.com; ed e-mail dhilliard@dailyitem.com; web site www.dailyitem.com - 1,700,000(views)
Circulation: 24,000fr; Sworn/Estimate/Non-Audited
Advertising rate: Open inch rate $12.00
Group: The Daily Item
Digital Platform - Mobile: Apple, Android
Digital Platform - Tablet: Apple iOS, Android, Windows 7, Blackberry Tablet OS, Kindle
Pub.. Gary Grossman
Mng. Ed.......................................David Hilliard
Adv. Dir....................................... Patty Bennett
Mechanical Specifications: Type page 13 1/4 x 21; E - 6 cols, 2, between; A - 6 cols, 2, between; C - 9 cols, 1 5/16, between. Equipment & Software: Hardware — 40-PC, 4-APP/Mac, 2-AU/Image Setter; Presses — 5-TKS/Double width, 1-TKS/Half deck; Software — Microsoft/Windows 3.11.
Delivery Method: Mail, Newsstand, Carrier
Areas Served: 17801

SUSQUEHANNA

SUSQUEHANNA COUNTY TRANSCRIPT (WED)
36 Exchange St, Susquehanna, PA, 18847-2610, Susquehanna, USA; gen tel (570) 853-3134; gen fax (570) 853-4707; ed e-mail susqtran@epix.net; web site susquehanna-transcript.com
Circulation: 6,257pd, 251fr; Sworn/Estimate/Non-Audited
Advertising rate: Open inch rate $7.90 (Local); $10.90 (National)
Digital Platform - Mobile: Apple, Android
Digital Platform - Tablet: Apple iOS, Android
Ed. .... Charles Ficarro
Mechanical Specifications: Type page 10 1/4 x 15 1/4; A - 6 cols, 1 5/16, 1/8 between.Equipment & Software: Hardware — APP/Macs; Presses — Hamada; Software — Adobe/Photoshop, Adobe/PageMaker, Microsoft/Word, QPS/QuarkXPress, Adobe/Illustrator.
Delivery Method: Mail, Newsstand
Areas Served: Susquehanna County

SWARTHMORE

COUNTY PRESS (WED)
639 S Chester Rd, Swarthmore, PA, 19081-2315, Delaware, USA; gen tel (610) 583-4432; adv tel (610) 583-4432 ext. 116; ed tel (610) 583-4432 ext. 120; gen fax (610) 583-0503; disp adv e-mail rcrowe@21st-centurymedia.com; class adv e-mail classified@delconewsnetwork.com; ed e-mail cparker@delconewsnetwork.com; web site www.delconewsnetwork.com
Circulation: 4,375pd, 450fr; Sworn/Estimate/Non-Audited
Advertising rate: Open inch rate $12.36
Established: 1931
Group: Digital First Media
21st Century Media
Digital Platform - Mobile: Apple, Android
Digital Platform - Tablet: Apple iOS, Android
Pub./Adv. Dir. .... Richard L. Crowe
Ed ....Peg DeGrassa
Mechanical Specifications: Type page 9.86 x 15.75; E - 6 cols, 1 1/2, 1/6 between; A - 6 cols, 1 1/2, 1/6 between; C - 6 cols, 1 1/2, 1/6 between.Equipment & Software: Hardware — APP/Mac; Presses — G; Software — QPS/QuarkXPress.
Delivery Method: Mail, Newsstand
Areas Served: 19073, 19008, 19063

GARNET VALLEY PRESS (WED)
639 S Chester Rd, Swarthmore, PA, 19081-2315, Delaware, USA; gen tel (610) 235-2679; adv tel (610) 915-2223; ed tel (610) 915-2250; gen fax (610) 622-8829; disp adv e-mail rcrowe@21st-centurymedia.com; class adv e-mail classified@delconewsnetwork.com; ed e-mail pdegrassa@delconewsnetwork.com; web site www.delconewsnetwork.com
Circulation: 1,050pd, 75fr; USPS
Advertising rate: Open inch rate $10.36
Established: 1992
Group: Digital First Media
21st Century Media
Digital Platform - Mobile: Apple, Android

Digital Platform - Tablet: Apple iOS, Android
Adv Mgr................................ Richard L. Crowe
Ed...Peg DeGrassa
Mechanical Specifications: Type page 9.89" x20"; E - 6 cols, 1.56", 1/6 between; A - 6 cols, 1.56", 1/6 between; C - 6 cols, 1.56", 1/6 between.Equipment & Software: Hardware — APP/Mac; Software — QPS/QuarkXPress 3.3.
Delivery Method: Mail, Newsstand
Areas Served: 19342, 19331, 19061, 19017, 19373

NEWS OF DELAWARE COUNTY, TOWN TALK, GARNET VALLEY PRESS, SPRINGFIELD PRESS, COUNTY PRESS (THUR)

21 S Swarthmore Ave, 5, Swarthmore, PA, 19081, Delaware, USA; gen tel 610-915-2223; adv tel (610) 915-2223; ed tel (610) 306-6171; gen fax (610) 583-0503; disp adv e-mail advertising@delconewsnetwork.com; class adv e-mail classified@delconewsnetwork.com; ed e-mail pdegrassa@delconewsnetwork.com; web site www.delconewsnetwork.com
Circulation: 137,214pd,; Sworn/Estimate/Non-Audited
Advertising rate: Open inch rate $31.00
Group: Digital First Media
21st Century MediaEditions: (2) Boroughs; Haverford; Upper Darby/Drexel Hill **Digital Platform - Mobile:** Apple, Android
Digital Platform - Tablet: Apple iOS, Android
Pub./Adv. Mgr........................ Richard L. Crowe
Mng. Ed.................................. David Bjorkgren
Mechanical Specifications: Type page 9.86 x 20; E - 6 cols, 2 1/16, 1/8 between; A - 6 cols, 2 1/16, 1/8 between; C - 8 cols, 1 1/2, 1/8 between.Equipment & Software: Hardware — APP/Mac, IBM; Presses — G/Urbanite; Software — QPS/QuarkXPress 3.3, Adobe/Photoshop 2.5, Intertext.
Delivery Method: Mail, Newsstand, Carrier
Areas Served: Delaware County

SPRINGFIELD PRESS (WED)

639 S Chester Rd, Swarthmore, PA, 19081-2315, Delaware, USA; gen tel (610) 583-4432; adv tel (610) 583-4432 ext. 108; ed tel (610) 583-4432 ext. 110; gen fax (610) 583-0503; disp adv e-mail rcrowe@21st-centurymedia.com; class adv e-mail classified@delconewsnetwork.com; ed e-mail awinnemore@delconewsnetwork.com; web site www.delconewsnetwork.com
Circulation: 4,700pd, 525fr; Sworn/Estimate/Non-Audited
Advertising rate: Open inch rate $12.36
Established: 1931
Digital Platform - Mobile: Apple, Android
Digital Platform - Tablet: Apple iOS, Android
Adv. Mgr.............................. Richard L. Crowe
Mng. Ed..................................Amy Winnemore
Mechanical Specifications: Type page 10 1/4 x 16; E - 6 cols, 1 5/8, 3/16 between; A - 6 cols, 1 5/8, 3/16 between; C - 6 cols, 1 5/8, 3/16 between.Equipment & Software: Hardware — APP/Macs; Presses — G/Community.
Delivery Method: Mail, Newsstand
Areas Served: 19064, 19070

THE SWARTHMOREAN (FRI)

112 Park Ave, Swarthmore, PA, 19081-1724, Delaware, USA; gen tel (610) 543-0900; gen fax (610) 543-3790; disp adv e-mail diane@swarthmorean.com; ed e-mail chris@swarthmorean.com; web site http://www.swarthmorean.com/
Circulation: 2,200pd,; Sworn/Estimate/Non-Audited
Advertising rate: Open inch rate $9.00
Established: 1893
Adv. Mgr..................................Diane Madison
Ed.......................... Chris ReynoldsEquipment & Software: Hardware — APP/Mac Centris; Software — Adobe/PageMaker 5.0.
Delivery Method: Mail, Newsstand
Areas Served: Delaware County

TOWN TALK NEWSPAPERS (WED)

639 S Chester Rd, Swarthmore, PA, 19081-2315, Pennsylvania, USA; gen tel (610) 915-2223; adv tel (610) 915-2223; ed tel (610) 915-2247; gen fax 610-622-8829; disp adv e-mail rcrowe@21st-centurymedia.com; class adv e-mail classified@delconewsnetwork.com; web site www.delconewsnetwork.com
Circulation: 28,500fr; Sworn/Estimate/Non-Audited
Advertising rate: Open inch rate $21.48
Established: 1961
Group: 21st Century Media
Digital Platform - Mobile: Apple, Android
Digital Platform - Tablet: Apple iOS, Android
Ed..................................Margaret DeGrasssa
Adv. Mgr.............................. Richard L. Crowe
Delivery Method: Carrier, Racks
Areas Served: Delaware County

TIONESTA

FOREST PRESS (WED)

165 Elm St, Tionesta, PA, 16353-9704, Forest, USA; gen tel (814) 755-4900; gen fax (814) 755-4429; disp adv e-mail info@visitANF.com; ed e-mail forestpress1@yahoo.com; web site http://www.titusvilleherald.com/eedition_myforestpress/
Circulation: 3,800pd,; Sworn/Estimate/Non-Audited
Advertising rate: Open inch rate $5.00
Established: 1867
Adv. Mgr......................................Tina Mohrey
Ed..Cathy Culver
Mechanical Specifications: Type page 10 x 13.
Delivery Method: Mail, Newsstand, Carrier, Racks
Areas Served: Titusville, Oil City, Tidioute, Marienville, Tionesta, Pleasantville, East and West Hickory

TUNKHANNOCK

WYOMING COUNTY PRESS EXAMINER (TUES, FRI)

16 E Tioga St, Tunkhannock, PA, 18657-1599, Wyoming, USA; gen tel (570) 836-2123; adv tel (570) 836-2123 ext. 26; ed tel (570) 836-2123 ext. 33; gen fax (570) 836-3378; disp adv e-mail bromanski@wcexaminer.com; class adv e-mail classifieds@wcexaminer.com; ed e-mail bbaker@wcexaminer.com; web site www.wcexaminer.com
Circulation: 5,570pd, 120fr; Sworn/Estimate/Non-Audited
Advertising rate: Open inch rate $11.00
Established: 1865
Group: Times-Shamrock Communications
Digital Platform - Mobile: Apple, Android
Digital Platform - Tablet: Apple iOS, Android
Pub..Greg Zyla
Ed...Robert L. Baker
Delivery Method: Mail, Newsstand
Areas Served: 18657, 18414, 18419, 18446, 18612, 18615, 18618, 18623, 18625, 18629, 18630, 18536, 18844

VALLEY VIEW

THE CITIZEN-STANDARD (THUR)

104 W Main St, Valley View, PA, 17983-9423, Schuylkill, USA; gen tel (570) 682-9081; gen fax (570) 682-8734; disp adv e-mail ads@citizenstandard.com; class adv e-mail stacy-h@citizenstandard.com; ed e-mail news@citizenstandard.com; web site www.citizenstandard.com
Circulation: 4,800pd,; Sworn/Estimate/Non-Audited
Advertising rate: Open inch rate $9.37
Established: 1929
Sales Mgr.................................. Stacy Hoover
Mng. Ed.............................. Rebecca Zemenick
Ed...Vicki Terwilliger
Adv. Consultant........................Jessica Witmer
Mechanical Specifications: Type page 13 x 21 1/2; E - 6 cols, 2, between; A - 6 cols, 2, between.Equipment & Software: Hardware — PC, APP/Mac; Presses — KP/News King; Software — Adobe/Illustrator, Baseview.
Delivery Method: Mail, Newsstand, Racks
Areas Served: Schuylkill, Dauphin, Northumberland, and seven school districts including Halifax, Line Mountain, Millersburg, Pine Grove, Tri-Valley, Upper Dauphin and Wiliams Valley.

VANDERGRIFT

KISKI VALLEY NEWS (THUR)

151 Grant Ave, Vandergrift, PA, 15690-1201, Westmoreland, USA; gen tel (724) 567-5656; gen fax (724) 568-1729; disp adv e-mail dfellabaum@tribweb.com; class adv e-mail jpaschl@tribweb.com; ed e-mail smcfarland@tribweb.com; web site www.tribLIVE.com
Advertising rate: Open inch rate $14.97
Digital Platform - Mobile: Apple, Android
Digital Platform - Tablet: Apple iOS, Android
Ed.......................................Susan McFarland
Adv. Mgr..Jill Paschl
Delivery Method: Mail, Newsstand
Areas Served: Apollo, North Apollo, Hyde Park, East Vandergrift, Leechburg, Vandergrift, Avonmore, Salina, saltsburg, Schenley, Spring Church, New Kensington, Freeport, and Ford City.

WALNUTPORT

THE HOME NEWS (THUR)

4685 Lehigh Dr, Ste 2, Walnutport, PA, 18088-9574, Northampton, USA; gen tel (610) 923-0382; gen fax (610) 923-0383; disp adv e-mail info@homenewspa.com; class adv e-mail advertising@homenewspa.com; ed e-mail editorial@homenewspa.com; web site www.homenewspa.com
Circulation: 3,500pd,; Sworn/Estimate/Non-Audited
Advertising rate: Open inch rate $5.80
Established: 1942
Group: Innovative Designs & Publishing
Pub...Paul Prass
Ed................................ William J. Halbfoerster
Mechanical Specifications: Type page 10 1/2 x 14; E - 5 cols, 2 1/20, 1/6 between; A - 5 cols, 2 1/20, 1/6 between; C - 5 cols, 2 1/20, 1/6 between.Equipment & Software: Hardware — APP/Power Mac; Software — In Design
Delivery Method: Mail, Newsstand, Racks
Areas Served: 18014, 18067, 18064, 18038, 18088, 18091

WARRENDALE

CRANBERRY JOURNAL (SUN)

535 Keystone Dr, Warrendale, PA, 15086-7538, Allegheny, USA; gen tel (724) 772-8742; adv tel (412) 838-5131; gen fax (724) 779-6911; disp adv e-mail bdawson@tribweb.com; class adv e-mail dsciotto@tribweb.com; ed e-mail kpalmiero@tribweb.com; web site www.yourcranberry.com
Circulation: 52pd, 16,295fr; AAM
Advertising rate: Open inch rate $7.47
Group: Trib Total Media, Inc.
Digital Platform - Mobile: Apple, Android
Digital Platform - Tablet: Apple iOS, Android
Mng. Ed...............................Kimberly Palmiero
Mechanical Specifications: 10.625 inches wide x 11.25 inches deep
6 columns
.125 inches between columns
Delivery Method: Mail, Racks
Areas Served: Warrendale (15086), Mars (16046), and Cranberry Township (16066)

PINE CREEK JOURNAL (SUN)

535 Keystone Dr, Warrendale, PA, 15086-7538, Allegheny, USA; gen tel (412) 856-7400; adv tel (724) 567-5656; ed tel (412) 782-2121; gen fax (412) 856-7954; adv fax (724) 568-1729; disp adv e-mail jpaschl@tribweb.com; class adv e-mail mzigarovich@tribweb.com; ed e-mail DMcElhinny@tribweb.com; web site www.tribLIVE.com
Circulation: 309pd, 9,619fr; AAM
Advertising rate: Open inch rate $14.97
Digital Platform - Mobile: Apple, Android
Digital Platform - Tablet: Apple iOS, Android
Ed..Dave McElhinny
Senior Advertising Sales Director..... Jill Paschl
Delivery Method: Mail, Newsstand
Areas Served: Hampton and Gibsonia

WAYNE

KING OF PRUSSIA COURIER (SUN)

134 N Wayne Ave, Wayne, PA, 19087-3349, Delaware, USA; gen tel (610) 642-4300; ed tel (610) 642-4300 ext. 82524; gen fax (610) 645-7620; ed fax (610) 642-9704; disp adv e-mail cwert@mainlinemedianews.com; class adv e-mail brsmith@21st-centurymedia.com; ed e-mail sgreenspon@mainlinemedianews.com; web site www.mainlinemedianews.com
Circulation: 6,446fr; Sworn/Estimate/Non-Audited
Advertising rate: Open inch rate $30.58
Digital Platform - Mobile: Apple, Android
Digital Platform - Tablet: Apple iOS, Android
Exec. Ed...................................... Andy Stettler
Mng. Ed...............................Susan Greenspon
Adv. Mgr...Brad Smith
Pub.. Elizabeth Wilson
Mechanical Specifications: Type page 12 x 21 1/2; E - 6 cols, 2 1/16, 1/6 between; A - 6 cols, 2 1/16, 1/6 between; C - 8 cols, 1 1/2, 1/6 between.
Delivery Method: Mail, Newsstand, Carrier, Racks
Areas Served: Delaware County

WAYNESBURG

GREENE COUNTY MESSENGER (FRI)

95 E High St Ste 107, Suite 107, Waynesburg, PA, 15370-1853, Greene, USA; gen tel (724) 852-2251; adv tel (724) 425-7213; gen fax (724) 852-2271; adv fax (724) 438-7528; disp adv e-mail info@greenecountymessenger.com; class adv e-mail dbehary@heraldstandard.com; ed e-mail steve@greenemessenger.com; web site www.greenecountymessenger.com
Circulation: 7,000pd, 150fr; Sworn/Estimate/Non-Audited
Advertising rate: Open inch rate $13.50
Established: 1990
Group: Calkins Media
Ed... Steve Barrett
Gen. Mgr.......................................Jane Adams
Mechanical Specifications: Type page 12 1/2 x 21 1/2; E - 6 cols, 2, 1/6 between; A - 6 cols, 2, 1/6 between; C - 6 cols, 2, 1/6 between. Equipment & Software: Hardware — APP/Mac G4, APP/Mac G3, 7-APP/iMac; Software — QPS/QuarkXPress 4.11.
Delivery Method: Mail, Newsstand, Carrier, Racks
Areas Served: Greene County

GREENESPEAK (THUR, MTHLY)

PO Box 1003, Waynesburg, PA, 15370-3003, Greene, USA; gen tel (724) 344-7980; adv tel (724) 344-7980; ed tel (724) 344-7980; gen fax (724) 267-3911; adv fax (724) 267-3911; ed fax (724) 267-3911; disp adv e-mail cindy@greenespeak.com; class adv e-mail cindy@greenespeak.com; ed e-mail cindy@greenespeak.com; web site www.greenespeak.com
Circulation: 4,000fr; Sworn/Estimate/Non-Audited
Advertising rate: Open inch rate $50.00 (1/8 pg); $100.00 (1/4 pg); $175.00 (1/2 pg); $350.00 (Full)
Established: 2004
Pub./Ed....................................... Cindy Bailey
Delivery Method: Newsstand, Racks
Areas Served: Greene and Washington County

WELLSBORO

FREE PRESS-COURIER (WED)

25 East Ave, Wellsboro, PA, 16901-1618, Tioga, USA; gen tel (814) 367-2230; gen fax (570) 724-2278; disp adv e-mail palmer@tiogapublishing.com; class adv e-mail slapoint@tiogapublishing.com; ed e-mail nkennedy@tiogapublishing.com; web site www.tiogapublishing.com
Circulation: 2,735pd,; Sworn/Estimate/Non-Audited
Advertising rate: Open inch rate $6.75
Group: Community Media Group
Tioga Publishing Company
Digital Platform - Mobile: Apple, Android
Digital Platform - Tablet: Apple iOS, Android, Kindle, Nook, Kindle Fire
Ed. .... Natalie Kennedy
Ed./Pub. .... David Sullens
Delivery Method: Mail, Newsstand, Racks
Areas Served: Tioga County

THE WELLSBORO GAZETTE (THUR)

25 East Ave, Wellsboro, PA, 16901-1618, Tioga, USA; gen tel (570) 724-2287; gen fax (570) 724-2278; disp adv e-mail dsullens@tiogapublishing.com; class adv e-mail slapoint@tiogapublishing.com; ed e-mail nkennedy@tiogapublishing.com; web site www.tiogapublishing.com - 180,000(views) 40,000(visitors)
Circulation: 5,500pd,; Sworn/Estimate/Non-Audited
Advertising rate: Open inch rate $12.25
Established: 1874
Group: Community Media Group
Tioga Publishing Company
Digital Platform - Mobile: Apple, Android, Blackberry
Digital Platform - Tablet: Apple iOS, Android, Windows 7, Blackberry Tablet OS
Ed./Pub. .... David Sullens
Mechanical Specifications: Type page 13 x 21 1/2; E - 6 cols, 2 1/16, 1/6 between; A - 6 cols, 2, 1/6 between; C - 8 cols, 1 3/8, 1/6 between.Equipment & Software: Hardware — APP/Mac; Software — Adobe/PageMaker 6.5.
Delivery Method: Mail, Newsstand, Racks
Areas Served: Tioga County

WEST CHESTER

AVON GROVE SUN (THUR)

250 N Bradford Ave, West Chester, PA, 19382-1912, Chester, USA; gen tel (610) 430-6961; gen fax (610) 430-1192; disp adv e-mail tjohnston@dailylocal.com; ed e-mail andyh@dailylocal.com; web site www.avongrovesun.com
Circulation: 2,428pd,; AAM
Advertising rate: Modular rate $725.00 (1/4 P); $1420.00 (1/2 P); $2845.00 (Full)
Digital Platform - Mobile: Apple, Android
Digital Platform - Tablet: Apple iOS, Android, Windows 7
Pub. .... Edward Condra
Ed. .... Andrew Hachadorian
Delivery Method: Mail, Newsstand, Carrier, Racks
Areas Served: Kennett Square, Chadds Ford, Avon Grove, and Oxford

THE KENNETT PAPER (THUR)

250 N Bradford Ave, West Chester, PA, 19382-1912, Chester, USA; gen tel (610) 430-6590; adv tel (610) 430-6961; gen fax (610) 430-1192; adv fax (610) 430-1192; disp adv e-mail tjohnston@dailylocal.com; class adv e-mail kennettpaper@gmail.com; ed e-mail andyh@dailylocal.com; web site www.kennettpaper.com
Circulation: 5,000pd,; Sworn/Estimate/Non-Audited
Advertising rate: Modular rate $725.00 (1/4 P); $1420.00 (1/2 P); $2845.00 (Full)
Digital Platform - Mobile: Apple, Android
Digital Platform - Tablet: Apple iOS, Android, Windows 7
Pub. .... Edward Condra
Ed. .... Andrew Hachadorian
Adv. .... Tricia Johnston
Mechanical Specifications: Type page 11 x 17; E - 6 cols, 1 7/8, 1/6 between; A - 6 cols, 1 7/8, 1/6 between; C - 9 cols, 1 1/4, 1/12 between. Equipment & Software: Hardware — APP/Mac IIci, APP/Mac Quadra 840, APP/Mac Centris 650; Software — QPS/QuarkXPress 3.31, Adobe/Photoshop 4.0, Adobe/Illustrator 5.5.
Delivery Method: Mail, Newsstand, Carrier, Racks
Areas Served: 19311, 19317, 19348, 19350, 19360, 19375, 19390

WEST GROVE

CHESTER COUNTY PRESS (WED)

144 S Jennersville Rd, West Grove, PA, 19390-9430, Chester, USA; gen tel (610) 869-5533; gen fax (610) 869-9628; disp adv e-mail info@chestercounty.com; class adv e-mail adsales@chestercounty.com; ed e-mail editor@chestercounty.com; web site www.chestercounty.com
Circulation: 13,125pd, 1,441fr; USPS
Advertising rate: Open inch rate $14.70
Established: 1866
Group: Ad Pro Inc.
Digital Platform - Mobile: Apple, Android
Digital Platform - Tablet: Apple iOS, Android
Pub. .... Randall S. Lieberman
Adv. Mgr. .... Alan Turns
Ed. .... Steve Hoffman
Mechanical Specifications: Type page 13 x 21 1/2; E - 6 cols, 2 1/4, 1/4 between; A - 6 cols, 2 1/4, 1/4 between; C - 9 cols, 1 3/8, 1/4 between.Equipment & Software: Hardware — PC Network; Presses — G/Urbanite; Software — Microsoft, Archetype/Corel Draw, Adobe Creative Suite
Delivery Method: Mail, Newsstand, Carrier, Racks
Areas Served: Avondale, Chadds Ford, Chatham, Cochranville, Jennersville, Kelton, Kemblesville, Kennett Square, Landenberg, Lewisville, Lincoln University, Longwood, Lenape, West Grove, Mendenhall, New London, Nottingham, Oxford, Toughkenamon, Unionville and the neighboring communities in Southern Lancaster County, Hockessin, Delaware and Rising Sun, Maryland

WEST NEWTON

THE TIMES-SUN (THUR)

205 E Main St, West Newton, PA, 15089-1519, Westmoreland, USA; gen tel (724) 872-6800; gen fax (724) 887-5115; disp adv e-mail jpaschl@tribweb.com; class adv e-mail mzigarovich@tribweb.com; ed e-mail bzirkle@tribweb.com; web site www.tribLIVE.com
Circulation: 1,648pd,; AAM
Advertising rate: Open inch rate $12.42
Established: 1878
Group: Trib Total Media, Inc.
Digital Platform - Mobile: Apple, Android
Digital Platform - Tablet: Apple iOS, Android
Ed. .... William Zirkle
Adv. Dir. .... Jill Paschl
Mechanical Specifications: Type page 11 1/2 x 21 1/2; E - 6 cols, 1 13/16, 1/8 between; A - 6 cols, 1 13/16, 1/8 between; C - 10 cols, 1 1/16, 1/8 between.Equipment & Software: Hardware — PCs, Compaq/Server; Presses — HI; Software — QPS/QuarkXPress 4.0.
Delivery Method: Mail, Newsstand
Areas Served: West Newton

WHITE HAVEN

THE JOURNAL-HERALD (THUR)

211 Main St, White Haven, PA, 18661-1406, Luzerne, USA; gen tel (570) 443-8321; ed tel (570) 443-9131 x304; gen fax (570) 443-8142; disp adv e-mail journalads@pa.metrocast.net; class adv e-mail journalads@pa.metrocast.net; ed e-mail journalnews@pa.metrocast.net; web site www.pocononewspapers.com
Circulation: 845pd, 36fr; Sworn/Estimate/Non-Audited
Advertising rate: Open inch rate $6.00
Established: 1878
Ptr. .... Seth Isenberg
Ed. .... Ruth Isenberg
Heather Maslo
Mechanical Specifications: Type page 10 x 12; E - 5 cols, 1.865", 1/8 between; A - 5 cols, 1.865", 1/8 between; C - 7 cols, 1 3/4, 1/8 between.Equipment & Software: Hardware — APP/Mac.; Software — Adobe
Delivery Method: Mail, Newsstand, Carrier
Areas Served: 18661, 18255

WILKES BARRE

THE DALLAS POST (SUN)

15 N Main St, Wilkes Barre, PA, 18701-2604, Luzerne, USA; gen tel (570) 675-5211; adv tel (570) 970-7153; ed tel (570) 970-7440; gen fax (570) 675-3650; adv fax (570) 829-2002; disp adv e-mail advertising@timesleader.com; class adv e-mail classifieds@timesleader.com; ed e-mail dmartin@mydallaspost.com; web site www.mydallaspost.com
Circulation: 4,665pd, 20fr; AAM
Advertising rate: Open inch rate $16.50
Established: 1889
Group: impreMedia LLC
Digital Platform - Mobile: Apple, Android
Digital Platform - Tablet: Apple iOS, Android, Windows 7
Adv. Dir. .... Susan Kahlau
Ed. .... Matt Golas
Pub. .... Jayson McAree
Mechanical Specifications: Type page 11 5/8 x 20 3/4; E - 6 cols, 1 13/16 between; A - 6 cols, 1 13/16 between; C - 10 cols, 1 1/16 between. Equipment & Software: Hardware — APP/Mac; Software — QPS/QuarkXPress 4.0.
Delivery Method: Mail, Newsstand, Carrier
Areas Served: 18612, 18627, 18639, 18708

WYALUSING

THE ROCKET-COURIER (THUR)

302 State St, Wyalusing, PA, 18853, Bradford, USA; gen tel (570) 746-1217; gen fax (570) 746-7737; disp adv e-mail rocket@epix.net; class adv e-mail rocket@epix.net; ed e-mail rocket@epix.net; web site www.rocket-courier.com
Circulation: 4,000pd, 100fr; USPS
Advertising rate: Open inch rate $10.25
Established: 1887
Digital Platform - Mobile: Apple, Android, Windows, Blackberry
Digital Platform - Tablet: Apple iOS, Android, Windows 7, Blackberry Tablet OS
Reporter .... Cain Chamberlain
Delivery Method: Mail, Newsstand, Racks
Areas Served: 18853, 18848, 18623, 18630, 18829, 18810, 18614, 18833, 18801, 18840, 18846, 18854

RHODE ISLAND

BLOCK ISLAND

THE BLOCK ISLAND TIMES (FRI)

PO Box 278, Ocean Ave, Block Island, RI, 02807-0278, Washington, USA; gen tel (401) 466-2222; adv tel (401) 466-2222; ed tel (401) 466-2222; gen fax (401) 466-8804; adv fax (401) 466-8804; ed fax (401) 466-8804; disp adv e-mail ads@blockislandtimes.com; class adv e-mail classifieds@blockislandtimes.com; ed e-mail ltrodson@blockislandtimes.com; web site www.blockislandtimes.com
Circulation: 4,000pd,; Sworn/Estimate/Non-Audited
Advertising rate: Open inch rate $14.50
Established: 1970
Group: Central Connecticut Communications LLC
Digital Platform - Mobile: Apple, Android
Digital Platform - Tablet: Apple iOS, Android, Windows 7, Kindle
Co-Pub. .... Fraser Lang
Co-Pub./Adv. Dir. .... Betty Lang
Adv. Mgr./Prodn. Mgr. .... John Barry
Ed. .... Lars R. Trodson
Ed. of Special Publications .... Lisa Stiepock
Mechanical Specifications: Type page 11 x 17; E - 4 cols, 2 5/16, 1/4 between; A - 4 cols, 2 5/16, 1/4 between; C - 4 cols, 2 5/16, 1/4 between.Equipment & Software: Hardware — APP/Mac G4; Software — Incopy/ Indesign
Delivery Method: Mail, Newsstand, Carrier
Areas Served: 02807

BRISTOL

BARRINGTON TIMES (WED)

1 Bradford St, Bristol, RI, 02809-1906, Bristol, USA; gen tel (401) 253-6000; adv tel (401) 424-9146; ed tel (401) 253-6000; gen fax (401) 253-6055; adv fax (401) 253-6055; ed fax (401) 253-6055; disp adv e-mail tnuttall@eastbaynewspapers.com; class adv e-mail spitocchelli@eastbaynewspapers.com; ed e-mail jbickford@eastbaynewspapers.com; web site www.eastbayri.com
Circulation: 2,593pd, 0fr; CVC
Advertising rate: Open inch rate $18.50
Established: 1958
Group: East Bay Newspapers
Digital Platform - Mobile: Apple, Android
Digital Platform - Tablet: Apple iOS, Android, Windows 7
Pub. .... Matthew D. Hayes
Ed. .... Josh Bickford
Adv. Dir. .... Toni Nuttall
Classified Mgr. .... Steve Pitocchelli
Mechanical Specifications: Type page 10 3/4 x 16 3/4.
Delivery Method: Mail, Newsstand
Areas Served: Bristol County

BRISTOL PHOENIX (THUR)

1 Bradford St, Bristol, RI, 02809-1906, Bristol, USA; gen tel (401) 253-6000; adv tel (401) 424-9146; ed tel (401) 253-6000; gen fax (401) 253-6055; adv fax (401) 253-6055; ed fax (401) 253-6055; disp adv e-mail tnuttall@eastbaynewspapers.com; class adv e-mail spitocchelli@eastbaynewspapers.com; ed e-mail jbickford@eastbaynewspapers.com; web site www.eastbayri.com
Circulation: 3,423pd, 15fr; CVC
Advertising rate: Open inch rate $18.50
Established: 1837
Group: East Bay Newspapers
Digital Platform - Mobile: Apple, Android
Digital Platform - Tablet: Apple iOS, Android, Windows 7
Pub. .... Matthew D. Hayes
Ed. .... Josh Bickford
Adv. Dir. .... Toni Nuttall
Classified Mgr. .... Steve Pitocchelli
Mechanical Specifications: Type page 10 3/4 x 16 3/4; E - 5 cols, 2 1/16, between; A - 5 cols, 2 1/16, between; C - 6 cols, 1 5/8, between.
Delivery Method: Mail, Newsstand
Areas Served: Bristol County

PORTSMOUTH TIMES (THUR)

1 Bradford St, Bristol, RI, 02809-1906, Bristol, USA; gen tel (401)253-6000; adv tel (401)424-9129; ed tel (401)424-9144; disp adv e-mail info@eastbaynewspapers.com; web site eastbayri.com
Circulation: 4,320fr; CVC
Delivery Method: Newsstand
Areas Served: 02809

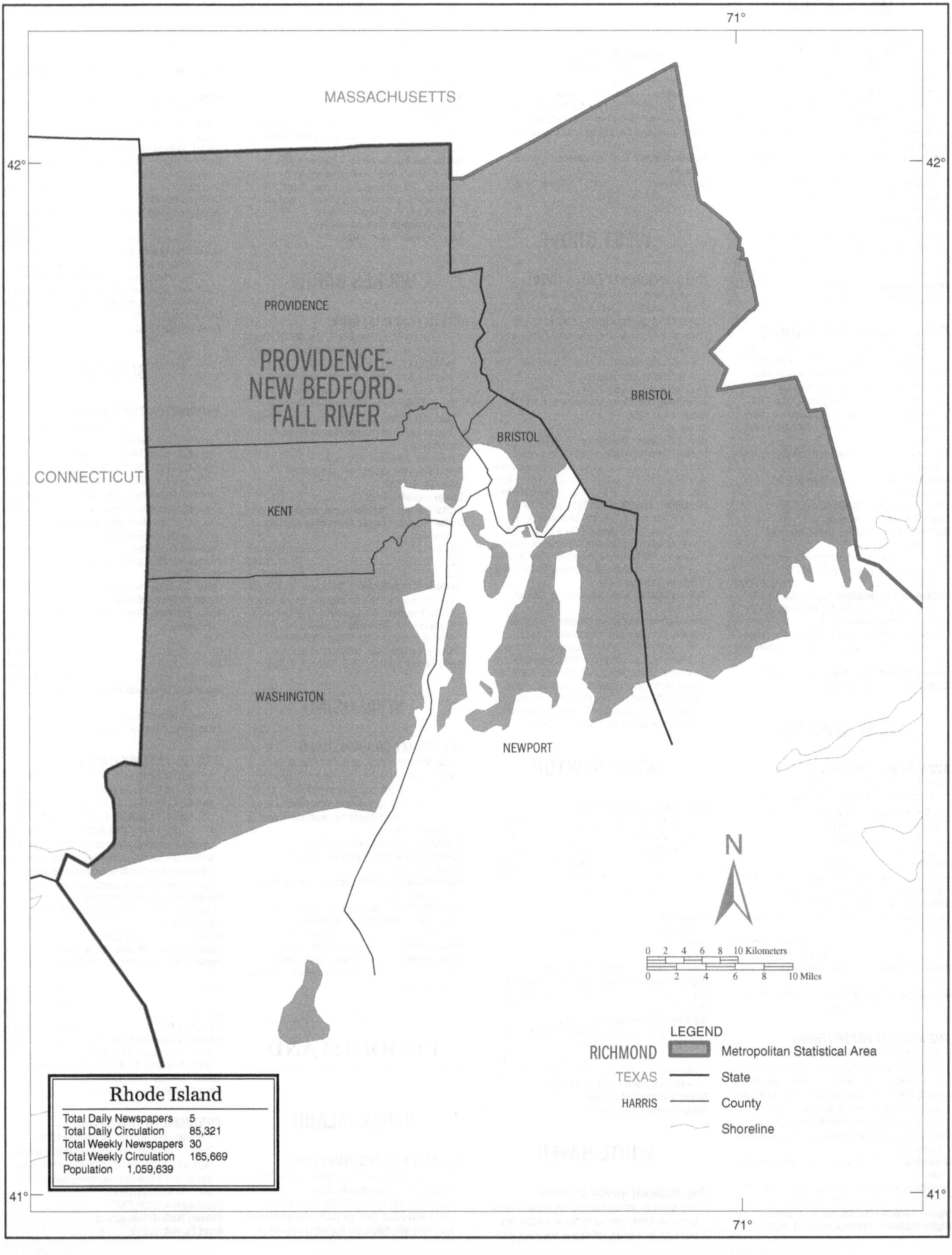

Rhode Island

Total Daily Newspapers	5
Total Daily Circulation	85,321
Total Weekly Newspapers	30
Total Weekly Circulation	165,669
Population	1,059,639

SAKONNET TIMES (THUR)
1 Bradford St, Bristol, RI, 02809-1906, Bristol, USA; gen tel (401) 253-6000; adv tel (401) 424-9146; ed tel (401) 424-9120; gen fax (401) 253-6055; adv fax (401) 253-6055; ed fax (401) 253-6055; disp adv e-mail tnuttall@eastbaynewspapers.com; class adv e-mail spitocchelli@eastbaynewspapers.com; ed e-mail bburdett@eastbaynewspapers.com; web site www.eastbayri.com
Circulation: 2,842pd, 0fr; CVC
Advertising rate: Open inch rate $18.50
Established: 1967
Group: East Bay Newspapers
Digital Platform - Mobile: Apple, Android
Digital Platform - Tablet: Apple iOS, Android, Windows 7
Pub....................................Matthew D. Hayes
Ed...Bruce Burdett
Adv. Dir...Toni Nuttall
Classified Mgr.......................Steve Pitocchelli
Mechanical Specifications: Type page 10 3/4 x 16 3/4; E - 5 cols, 2 1/16, between; A - 5 cols, 2 1/16, between; C - 6 cols, 1 5/8, between.
Delivery Method: Mail, Newsstand, Racks
Areas Served: 02871, 02878, 02837

THE POST (THUR)
1 Bradford St, Bristol, RI, 02809-1906, Bristol, USA; gen tel (401) 253-6000; gen fax (401) 253-6055; adv fax (401) 253-6055; ed fax (401) 253-6055; disp adv e-mail mnascimento@eastbaynewspapers.com; class adv e-mail ; ed e-mail mrego@eastbaynewspapers.com; web site www.eastbayri.com
Circulation: 8,324fr; VAC
Advertising rate: Open inch rate $7.15
Group: East Bay Newspapers
Digital Platform - Mobile: Apple, Android
Digital Platform - Tablet: Apple iOS, Android, Windows 7
Pub....................................Matthew D. Hayes
Ed...Mike Rego
Ad Rep...............................Mary Nascimento
Mechanical Specifications: Type page 10 3/4 x 16 3/4.
Delivery Method: Newsstand
Areas Served: East Providence, Rumford and Riverside

WARREN TIMES-GAZETTE (WED)
1 Bradford St, Bristol, RI, 02809-1906, Bristol, USA; gen tel (401) 253-6000; adv tel (401) 424-9146; ed tel (401) 935-2738; gen fax (401) 253-6055; adv fax (401) 253-6055; ed fax (401) 253-6055; disp adv e-mail tnuttall@eastbaynewspapers.com; class adv e-mail spitocchelli@eastbaynewspapers.com; ed e-mail thayes@eastbaynewspapers.com; web site www.eastbayri.com
Circulation: 1,508pd, 0fr; CVC
Advertising rate: Open inch rate $18.50
Established: 1866
Group: East Bay Newspapers
Digital Platform - Mobile: Apple, Android
Digital Platform - Tablet: Apple iOS, Android, Windows 7
Pub....................................Matthew D. Hayes
Ed...Ted Hayes
Mng. Ed.................................Scott Pickering
Adv. Dir...Toni Nuttall
Gen. Mgr...Lisa Carro
Prodn. Mgr....................................Jock Hayes
Mechanical Specifications: Type page 10 3/4 x 16 3/4; E - 5 cols, 2 1/16, between; A - 5 cols, 2 1/16, between; C - 6 cols, 1 5/8, between.
Delivery Method: Mail, Newsstand
Areas Served: Bristol County

WESTPORT SHORELINES (THUR)
1 Bradford St, Bristol, RI, 02809-1906, Bristol, USA; gen tel (401) 253-6000; adv tel (401) 424-9146; ed tel (401) 424-9120; gen fax (401) 253-6055; adv fax (401) 253-6055; ed fax (401) 253-6055; disp adv e-mail tnuttall@eastbaynewspapers.com; class adv e-mail spitocchelli@eastbaynewspapers.com; ed e-mail bburdett@eastbaynewspapers.com; web site www.eastbayri.com
Circulation: 1,179pd, 0fr; CVC
Advertising rate: Open inch rate $18.50
Established: 1994
Group: East Bay Newspapers
Digital Platform - Mobile: Apple, Android
Digital Platform - Tablet: Apple iOS, Android, Windows 7
Pub....................................Matthew D. Hayes
Ed...Bruce Burdett
Mng. Ed.................................Scott Pickering
Adv. Dir...Toni Nuttall
Gen. Mgr...Lisa Carro
Prodn. Mgr....................................Jock Hayes
Mechanical Specifications: Type page 10 3/4 x 16 3/4.
Delivery Method: Mail, Newsstand
Areas Served: Bristol County

JAMESTOWN

THE JAMESTOWN PRESS (THUR)
45 Narragansett Ave, Jamestown, RI, 02835-1150, Newport, USA; gen tel (401) 423-3200; adv tel (401) 423-3200; ed tel (401) 423-3200; disp adv e-mail robert@jamestownpress.com; class adv e-mail robert@jamestownpress.com; ed e-mail news@jamestownpress.com; web site www.jamestownpress.com
Circulation: 150pd, 5,500fr; Sworn/Estimate/Non-Audited
Advertising rate: Open inch rate $11
Established: 1989
Group: Write Way Media
Digital Platform - Mobile: Apple, Android, Windows, Blackberry
Digital Platform - Tablet: Apple iOS, Android, Windows 7, Blackberry Tablet OS
Ed...Tim Riel
Mechanical Specifications: Type page 10 1/4 x 16; E - 5 cols, 1 11/12, between; A - 5 cols, between; C - 5 cols, between.
Delivery Method: Mail, Racks
Areas Served: 02835

LINCOLN

THE NORTH PROVIDENCE BREEZE (WED)
6 Blackstone Valley Pl, Ste 204, Lincoln, RI, 02865-1112, USA; gen tel (401)334-9555; adv tel (401)334-9555 x 153; ed tel (401)334-9555 x122; gen fax (401)334-9994; disp adv e-mail cindy@valleybreeze.com; class adv e-mail donna@valleybreeze.com; ed e-mail mgreen@valleybreeze.com; web site valleybreeze.com
Circulation: 2pd, 7,749fr; CVC
Group: Breeze Publications Inc.
Pub..Tom Ward
Dep. Pub.......................................Jamie Quinn
Accounting/HR.......................Barbara Phinney
Adv. Dir.....................................Karen Buckley
Ed.-in-Chief................................Marcia Green
Delivery Method: Newsstand
Areas Served: 02865

THE VALLEY BREEZE & OBSERVER (THUR)
6 Blackstone Valley Pl Ste 204, Suite 204, Lincoln, RI, 02865-1112, Providence, USA; gen tel (401)334-9555; gen fax (401)334-9994; disp adv e-mail karen@valleybreeze.com; web site valleybreeze.com
Circulation: 4pd, 10,657fr; VAC
Group: Breeze Publications Inc.
Pub..Tom Ward
Deputy Pub...................................Jamie Quinn
Adv. Dir, ...Karen Buckley
Ed.-in-Chief................................Marcia Green
Accounting/HR.......................Barbara Phinney
Delivery Method: Newsstand
Areas Served: 02865

THE VALLEY BREEZE - CUMBERLAND/ LINCOLN (THUR)
6 Blackstone Valley Pl Ste 204, Ste. 204, Lincoln, RI, 02865-1112, Providence, USA; gen tel (401) 334-9555; gen fax (401) 334-9994; disp adv e-mail tward@valleybreeze.com; web site www.valleybreeze.com
Circulation: 9pd, 17,014fr; VAC
Advertising rate: Open inch rate $21.00-60.00
Established: 1996
Group: Breeze Publications Inc.
Digital Platform - Mobile: Apple, Android
Digital Platform - Tablet: Apple iOS, Android
Pub...Thomas V. Ward
Ed..Marcia Green
Adv. Dir.....................................Karen Buckley
Prodn. Mgr...............................James E. Quinn
Circ. Mgr ....Rhonda Hanson
Delivery Method: Mail, Racks
Areas Served: North Providence

THE VALLEY BREEZE - PAWTUCKET (WED)
6 Blackstone Valley Pl, Ste 204, Lincoln, RI, 02865-1112, USA; gen tel (401)334-9555; gen fax (401)334-9994; disp adv e-mail karen@valleybreeze.com; web site valleybreeze.com
Circulation: 3pd, 9,083fr; VAC
Pub..Tom Ward
Dep. Pub.......................................Jamie Quinn
Accounting/HR.......................Barbara Phinney
Adv. Dir.....................................Karen Buckley
Ed.-in-Chief................................Marcia Green
Delivery Method: Newsstand
Areas Served: 02865

THE VALLEY BREEZE - WOONSOCKET/ NORTH SMITHFIELD (THUR)
6 Blackstone Valley Pl Ste 204, Suite 204, Lincoln, RI, 02865-1112, Providence, USA; gen tel (401) 334-9555; adv tel ((401) 334-9555 ext. 142; ed tel ((401) 334-9555 ext. 122; gen fax (401) 334-9994; disp adv e-mail karen@valleybreeze.com; class adv e-mail donna@valleybreeze.com; ed e-mail mgreen@valleybreeze.com; web site valleybreeze.com
Circulation: 7pd, 16,421fr; VAC
Pub..Tom Ward
Dep. Pub.......................................Jamie Quinn
Acounting/HR.........................Barbara Phinney
Adv. Dir.....................................Karen Buckley
Ed.-in-Chief................................Marcia Green
Delivery Method: Newsstand
Areas Served: 02865

NEWPORT

NEWPORT MERCURY (FRI)
101 Malbone Rd, Newport, RI, 02840-1340, Newport, USA; gen tel (401) 849-3300; adv tel (401) 380-2319; ed tel (401) 380-2371; gen fax (401) 849-3335; adv fax (401) 849-3335; ed fax (401) 849-3335; disp adv e-mail marketing@newportri.com; class adv e-mail mercury@newportmercury.com; ed e-mail editor@newportmercury.com; web site www.newportmercury.com
Advertising rate: Open inch rate $18.50
Established: 1758
Group: The Edward A. Sherman Publishing Co.
Digital Platform - Mobile: Apple, Android, Windows, Blackberry
Digital Platform - Tablet: Apple iOS, Android, Windows 7, Blackberry Tablet OS
Pub...William F. Lucey
Ed...Janine Weisman
Adv. Dir..............................Annemarie Brisson
Delivery Method: Mail, Newsstand
Areas Served: Newport County

NEWPORT NAVALOG (WED)
101 Malbone Rd, Newport, RI, 02840-1340, Newport, USA; gen tel (401) 849-3300; adv tel (401) 849-3300 ext. 212; ed tel (401) 849-3300; gen fax (401) 849-3335; adv fax (401) 849-3335; ed fax (401) 849-3335; disp adv e-mail brisson@newportri.com; class adv e-mail marketing@newportri.com; ed e-mail editor@newportri.com; web site www.newportri.com
Advertising rate: Open inch rate $18.50
Established: 1901
Digital Platform - Mobile: Apple, Android, Windows, Blackberry
Digital Platform - Tablet: Apple iOS, Android, Windows 7, Blackberry Tablet OS
Pub...William F. Lucey
Exec. Ed............................Sheila L. Mullowney
Adv. Dir..............................Annemarie Brisson
Delivery Method: Mail, Newsstand
Areas Served: Naval Station Newport in Newport and Middletown

NEWPORT THIS WEEK (THUR)
86 Broadway, Newport, RI, 02840-2750, Newport, USA; gen tel (401) 847-7766; adv tel (401) 847-7766; ed tel (401) 847-7766; gen fax (401) 846-4974; adv fax (401) 846-4974; ed fax (401) 846-4974; disp adv e-mail kirby@newportthisweek.net; class adv e-mail nila@newportthisweek.net; ed e-mail news@newportthisweek.net; web site www.newportthisweek.com - 300,000(views)
Circulation: 0pd, 14,758fr; VAC
Advertising rate: Open inch rate $40.00
Established: 1973
Digital Platform - Mobile: Apple, Android, Windows, Blackberry
Digital Platform - Tablet: Apple iOS, Android, Windows 7, Blackberry Tablet OS
Pub...Lynne Tungett
Web Pub.....................................Tom Shevlin
Adv. Dir.....................................Kirby Varacalli
Adv. Exec.......................................Nila Asciolla
Gen. Mgr..Diana Oehrli
Ed..Lisette Prince
Mechanical Specifications: Type page 10 3/4 x 16 3/4.
Delivery Method: Mail, Racks
Areas Served: Newport, Middletown, and Jamestown

THE INDEPENDENT (THUR)
101 Malbone Rd, Newport, RI, 02840-1340, Newport, USA; gen tel (401) 789-6000; adv tel (401) 380-2317; ed tel (401) 380-2394; gen fax (401) 849-3306; adv fax (401) 849-3335; ed fax (401) 849-3306; disp adv e-mail abrams@newportri.com; class adv e-mail classified@independentri.com; ed e-mail editorial@scindependent.com; web site www.independentri.com
Circulation: 5,907pd, 510fr; CVC
Advertising rate: Open inch rate $15.00
Established: 1997
Group: The Edward A. Sherman Publishing Co.
Digital Platform - Mobile: Apple, Android
Digital Platform - Tablet: Apple iOS, Android, Windows 7
Pub...William F. Lucey
Adv. Sales Mgr.............................Lynn Abrams
Mng. Ed....................................Liz Boardman
Circ. Mgr......................................Kevin Shoen
Managing Editor.........................Liz Boardman
Adv. Dir..............................Annemarie Brisson
Sports Editor.....................William Geoghegan
Delivery Method: Mail, Newsstand, Racks
Areas Served: North Kingstown, Narragansett, South Kingstown

PROVIDENCE

PROVIDENCE BUSINESS NEWS (FRI)
400 Westminster St, Ste 600, Providence, RI, 02903-3222, Providence, USA; gen tel (401) 273-2201; adv tel (401) 680-4800; ed tel (401) 680-4820; gen fax (401) 274-6580; adv fax (401) 274-0270; ed fax (401) 274-0670; disp adv e-mail advertising@pbn.com; class adv e-mail ahlers@pbn.com; ed e-mail editor@pbn.com; web site www.pbn.com
Circulation: 3,400pd, 1,900fr; VAC
Advertising rate: Open inch rate $4900.00 (Full-Page)
Established: 1986
Digital Platform - Mobile: Apple, Android, Windows, Blackberry
Digital Platform - Tablet: Apple iOS, Android, Windows 7, Blackberry Tablet OS
Pub...................................Roger Bergenheim
Ed..Mark Murphy
Mng. Ed....................................Michael Mello
Dir of Sales & Mktg...........Annemarie Brisson
Delivery Method: Mail
Areas Served: Providence County

WAKEFIELD

CHARIHO TIMES (THUR)

187 Main St, Wakefield, RI, 02879-3504, Washington, USA; gen tel (401) 789-9744; adv tel (401) 789-9744; ed tel (401) 789-9744; gen fax (401) 789-1550; adv fax (401) 789-1550; ed fax (401) 789-1550; disp adv e-mail jboucher@ricentral.com; class adv e-mail jboucher@ricentral.com; ed e-mail mwunsch@ricentral.com; web site www.ricentral.com

Circulation: 426pd, 117fr; AAM
Advertising rate: Open inch rate $9.11
Established: 1992
Group: Southern Rhode Island Newspapers RISN Operations Inc.
Digital Platform - Mobile: Apple, Android
Digital Platform - Tablet: Apple iOS, Android
Adv. Mgr./Pub. .... Jody Boucher
Matt Wunsch
Circ. Mgr. .... Phil Rowell
Delivery Method: Mail, Newsstand, Racks
Areas Served: 02892, 02813, 02812, 02804, 02898, 02894, 02832

COVENTRY COURIER (FRI)

187 Main St, Wakefield, RI, 02879-3504, Washington, USA; gen tel (401) 789-9744; adv tel (401) 789-9744; ed tel (401) 789-9744; gen fax (401) 789-1550; adv fax (401) 789-1550; ed fax (401) 789-1550; disp adv e-mail jboucher@ricentral.com; class adv e-mail jboucher@ricentral.com; ed e-mail jryan@ricentral.com; web site www.ricentral.com

Circulation: 282pd, 58fr; AAM
Advertising rate: Open inch rate $12.08
Established: 1996
Group: Southern Rhode Island Newspapers RISN Operations Inc.
Digital Platform - Mobile: Apple, Android
Digital Platform - Tablet: Apple iOS, Android
Regional Pub./Adv. Dir. .... Jody Boucher
Circ. Mgr. .... Phil Rowell
Ed. .... Jeremiah Ryan
Delivery Method: Mail, Newsstand, Racks
Areas Served: Washington County

EAST GREENWICH PENDULUM (THUR)

187 Main St, Wakefield, RI, 02879-3504, Washington, USA; gen tel (401) 789-9744; adv tel (401) 789-9744; ed tel (401) 789-9744; gen fax (401) 789-1550; adv fax (401) 789-1550; ed fax (401) 789-1550; disp adv e-mail jboucher@ricentral.com; class adv e-mail ediggins@ricentral.com; ed e-mail mwunsch@ricentral.com; web site www.ricentral.com

Circulation: 741pd, 61fr; AAM
Advertising rate: Open inch rate $11.69
Established: 1854
Group: Southern Rhode Island Newspapers RISN Operations Inc.
Digital Platform - Mobile: Apple, Android
Digital Platform - Tablet: Apple iOS, Android
Circ. Mgr. .... Phil Rowell
Adv. Dir. .... Jody Boucher
Editor .... Matt Wunsch
Delivery Method: Newsstand, Carrier, Racks
Areas Served: 02818

NARRAGANSETT TIMES (WED, FRI)

187 Main St, Wakefield, RI, 02879-3504, Washington, USA; gen tel (401) 789-9744; adv tel (401) 789-9744; ed tel (401) 789-9744; gen fax (401) 789-1550; adv fax (401) 789-1550; ed fax (401) 789-1550; disp adv e-mail jboucher@ricentral.com; class adv e-mail jboucher@ricentral.com; ed e-mail mwunsch@ricentral.com; web site www.ricentral.com

Circulation: 1,920pd, 172fr; CAC
Advertising rate: Open inch rate $18.42
Established: 1855
Group: Southern Rhode Island Newspapers RISN Operations Inc.
Digital Platform - Mobile: Apple, Android
Digital Platform - Tablet: Apple iOS, Android
Adv. Mgr./Pub. .... Jody Boucher
Ed. .... Matt Wunsch
Circ. Mgr. .... Phil Rowell
Delivery Method: Mail, Newsstand, Racks
Areas Served: 02879, 02882, 02813

STANDARD-TIMES (THUR)

187 Main St, Wakefield, RI, 02879-3504, Washington, USA; gen tel (401) 789-9744; adv tel (401) 789-9744; ed tel (401) 789-9744; gen fax (401) 789-1550; adv fax (401) 789-1550; ed fax (401) 789-1550; disp adv e-mail jboucher@ricentral.com; class adv e-mail jboucher@ricentral.com; ed e-mail pspetrini@ricentral.com; web site www.ricentral.com

Circulation: 1,536pd, 86fr; CAC
Advertising rate: Open inch rate $14.77
Established: 1888
Group: RISN Operations Inc. Southern Rhode Island Newspapers
Digital Platform - Mobile: Apple, Android
Digital Platform - Tablet: Apple iOS, Android
Adv. Mgr. .... Jody Boucher
Ed. .... Paul Spetrini
Circ. Mgr. .... Phil Rowell
Pub. .... Nanci Batson
Mechanical Specifications: Type page 12 x 21; E - 6 cols, 1 15/16, 1/8 between; A - 6 cols, 1 15/16, 1/8 between; C - 8 cols, 1 5/8, 1/8 between.Equipment & Software: Hardware — PC, APP/Power Mac 7100; Software — WordPerfect 5.1, Multi-Ad/Creator 3.7.
Delivery Method: Newsstand, Carrier, Racks
Areas Served: North Kingstown, Exeter, and West Greenwich

WARWICK

BEACON COMMUNICATIONS, INC (TUES, THUR)

1944 Warwick Ave, Warwick, RI, 02889-2448, Kent, USA; gen tel (401) 732-3100; gen fax (401) 732-3110; web site www.warwickonline.com

Circulation: 13,519pd, 8,997fr; CVC
Established: 1968
Publisher .... John Howell
General Manager .... Richard Fleischer

CRANSTON HERALD (THUR)

1944 Warwick Ave, Warwick, RI, 02889-2448, Kent, USA; gen tel (401) 732-3100; adv tel (401) 732-3100; ed tel (401) 732-3100; gen fax (401) 732-3110; adv fax (401) 732-3110; ed fax (401) 732-3110; disp adv e-mail suzannew@rhodybeat.com; class adv e-mail sueh@rhodybeat.com; ed e-mail johnh@rhodybeat.com; web site www.cranstononline.com

Circulation: 2,079pd, 99fr; VAC
Advertising rate: Open inch rate $9.83
Established: 1928
Group: Beacon Communications, Inc
Digital Platform - Mobile: Apple, Android
Digital Platform - Tablet: Apple iOS, Android, Windows 7
Pub. .... John I. Howell
Ed. .... Tracey O'Neill
Gen. Mgr. .... Richard G. Fleischer
Mechanical Specifications: 6 cols. x 21" (10.5" x 21") each column 1.65"Equipment & Software: Hardware — PC Based; Software — InDesign 5
Delivery Method: Mail, Newsstand, Carrier
Areas Served: 02920, 02921, 02910, 02905

JOHNSTON SUN RISE (THUR)

1944 Warwick Ave, Warwick, RI, 02889-2448, Kent, USA; gen tel (401) 732-3100; adv tel (401) 732-3100; ed tel (401) 732-3100; gen fax (401) 732-3100; adv fax (401) 732-3100; ed fax (401) 732-3100; disp adv e-mail suzannew@rhodybeat.com; class adv e-mail sueh@rhodybeat.com; ed e-mail johnh@rhodybeat.com; web site www.johnstonsunrise.net

Circulation: 0pd, 8,175fr; VAC
Advertising rate: Open inch rate $9.83
Group: Beacon Communications, Inc
Digital Platform - Mobile: Apple, Android
Digital Platform - Tablet: Apple iOS, Android, Windows 7
Pub./Ed. .... John I. Howell
Ed. .... Tracey O'Neill
Gen. Mgr. .... Richard G. Fleischer
Adv. Sales .... Gina Fugere
Classified Adv. Mgr. .... Sue Howarth
Delivery Method: Mail, Newsstand, Carrier
Areas Served: Kent County

WARWICK BEACON (TUES, THUR)

1944 Warwick Ave, Ste 4, Warwick, RI, 02889-2400, Kent, USA; gen tel (401) 529-0947; adv tel (401) 529-0947; ed tel (401) 529-0947; gen fax (401) 732-3110; adv fax (401) 732-3110; ed fax (401) 732-3110; disp adv e-mail lisab@rhodybeat.com; class adv e-mail richardf@rhodybeat.com; ed e-mail johnh@rhodybeat.com; web site www.warwickonline.com - 220,000(views) 17,000(visitors)

Circulation: 5,720pd, 403fr; VAC
Advertising rate: Open inch rate $13.60
Established: 1954
Group: Beacon Communications, Inc
Digital Platform - Mobile: Android
Digital Platform - Tablet: Android, Windows 7
Pub./Ed. .... John I. Howell
Gen. Mgr. .... Richard G. Fleischer
Credit Mgr. .... Lynne Taylor
Mechanical Specifications: 6 cols. x 21" (10.5" wide) Each column measures 1.65"Equipment & Software: Hardware — PC; Software — InDesign
Delivery Method: Mail, Newsstand, Carrier
Areas Served: 02886, 02887, 02888, 02889, 02818

WESTERLY

CHARLESTOWN PRESS (THUR)

56 Main St, Westerly, RI, 02891-2113, Washington, USA; gen tel (401) 348-1000; adv tel (860) 495-8265; ed tel (860) 495-8224; gen fax (401) 348-3080; adv fax (401) 348-3080; ed fax (401) 348-3080; disp adv e-mail jlayton@thewesterlysun.com; class adv e-mail classified@thewesterlysun.com; ed e-mail dsmith@thewesterlysun.com; web site www.thewesterlysun.com

Advertising rate: Open inch rate $18.00
Group: Sun Publishing Company
Ed. .... David Smith
Vice Pres./Adv. Dir. .... Kelly Tremaine
Delivery Method: Mail, Racks
Areas Served: Washington County

WOOD RIVER PRESS (THUR)

56 Main St, Westerly, RI, 02891-2113, Washington, USA; gen tel (401) 348-1000; adv tel (860) 495-8265; ed tel (860) 495-8224; gen fax (401) 348-3080; adv fax (401) 348-3080; ed fax (401) 348-3080; disp adv e-mail jlayton@thewesterlysun.com; class adv e-mail classified@thewesterlysun.com; ed e-mail dsmith@thewesterlysun.com; web site www.thewesterlysun.com

Advertising rate: Open inch rate $18.00
Group: Sun Publishing Company
Ed. .... David Smith
Vice Pres./Adv. Dir. .... Kelly Tremaine
Delivery Method: Mail, Racks
Areas Served: Washington County

SOUTH CAROLINA

ABBEVILLE

THE PRESS & BANNER (WED)

107 W Pickens St, Abbeville, SC, 29620-2415, Abbeville, USA; gen tel (864) 366-5461; adv tel (864) 366-5461; ed tel (864) 366-5461; gen fax (864) 366-5463; adv fax (864) 366-5463; ed fax (864) 366-5463; disp adv e-mail pb@bannercorp.net; class adv e-mail pb@bannercorp.net; ed e-mail pb@bannercorp.net

Circulation: 7,000pd,; USPS
Advertising rate: Open inch rate $9.50
Established: 1844
Pub./Ed. .... John R. West
Prod. Mgr. .... Lamar West
Delivery Method: Mail, Newsstand, Racks
Areas Served: Abbeville County

BAMBERG

THE ADVERTIZER-HERALD (WED)

369 McGee St, Bamberg, SC, 29003-1338, Bamberg, USA; gen tel (803) 245-5204; adv tel (803) 245-5204; ed tel (803) 245-5204; gen fax (803) 245-3900; adv fax (803) 245-3900; ed fax (803) 245-3900; disp adv e-mail ahpublisher@bellsouth.net; class adv e-mail ahpublisher@bellsouth.net; ed e-mail ahpublisher@bellsouth.net; web site www.advertizerherald.com

Circulation: 2,450pd,; Sworn/Estimate/Non-Audited
Advertising rate: Open inch rate $6.75
Digital Platform - Tablet: Windows 7
Pub./Gen. Mgr. .... Joyce Searson
Mechanical Specifications: Type page 13 x 20 1/2; E - 6 cols, 2, between; A - 6 cols, 2, between; C - 6 cols, 2, between.Equipment & Software: Hardware — APP/Mac; Presses — G; Software — Adobe/PageMaker 6.5.
Delivery Method: Mail, Newsstand
Areas Served: Bamberg County

BARNWELL

THE PEOPLE-SENTINEL (WED)

10481 DUNBARTON BLVD, Barnwell, SC, 29812, Barnwell, USA; gen tel (803) 259-3501; gen fax (803) 259-2703; disp adv e-mail laura.mckenzie@morris.com; class adv e-mail ads@thepeoplesentinel.com; ed e-mail jonathan.vickery@morris.com; web site www.thepeoplesentinel.com

Circulation: 3,985pd, 73fr; Sworn/Estimate/Non-Audited
Advertising rate: Open inch rate $13.55
Established: 1852
Digital Platform - Mobile: Apple, Android
Digital Platform - Tablet: Apple iOS, Android, Windows 7
Pub. .... Laura J. McKenzie
Mng. Ed. .... Jonathan Vickery
Mechanical Specifications: .... 46" Web
broadsheet .... BPS
Full width 10.5
Gutter width 0.167
Columns 6

1 col 1.6458
2 col 3.4167
3 col 5.1875
4 col 6.9583
5 col 8.7292
6 col 10.5

Depth **19.75

46" Web
Tab .... BPS
Full width 8.7292
Gutter width 0.167
Columns 5

1 col 1.6458
2 col 3.4167
3 col 5.1875
4 col 6.9583
5 col 8.7292
6 col ....

Depth **10.25
Doubletruck 21.5
Spine 0.05
Equipment & Software: Hardware — APP/Mac; Presses — G; Software — QPS/QuarkXPress.
Delivery Method: Mail, Newsstand, Racks
Areas Served: Barnwell County: 29812, 29853, 29826, 29817, 29813, 29843, 29836, 29042 Allendale County: 29810, 29827, 29846,

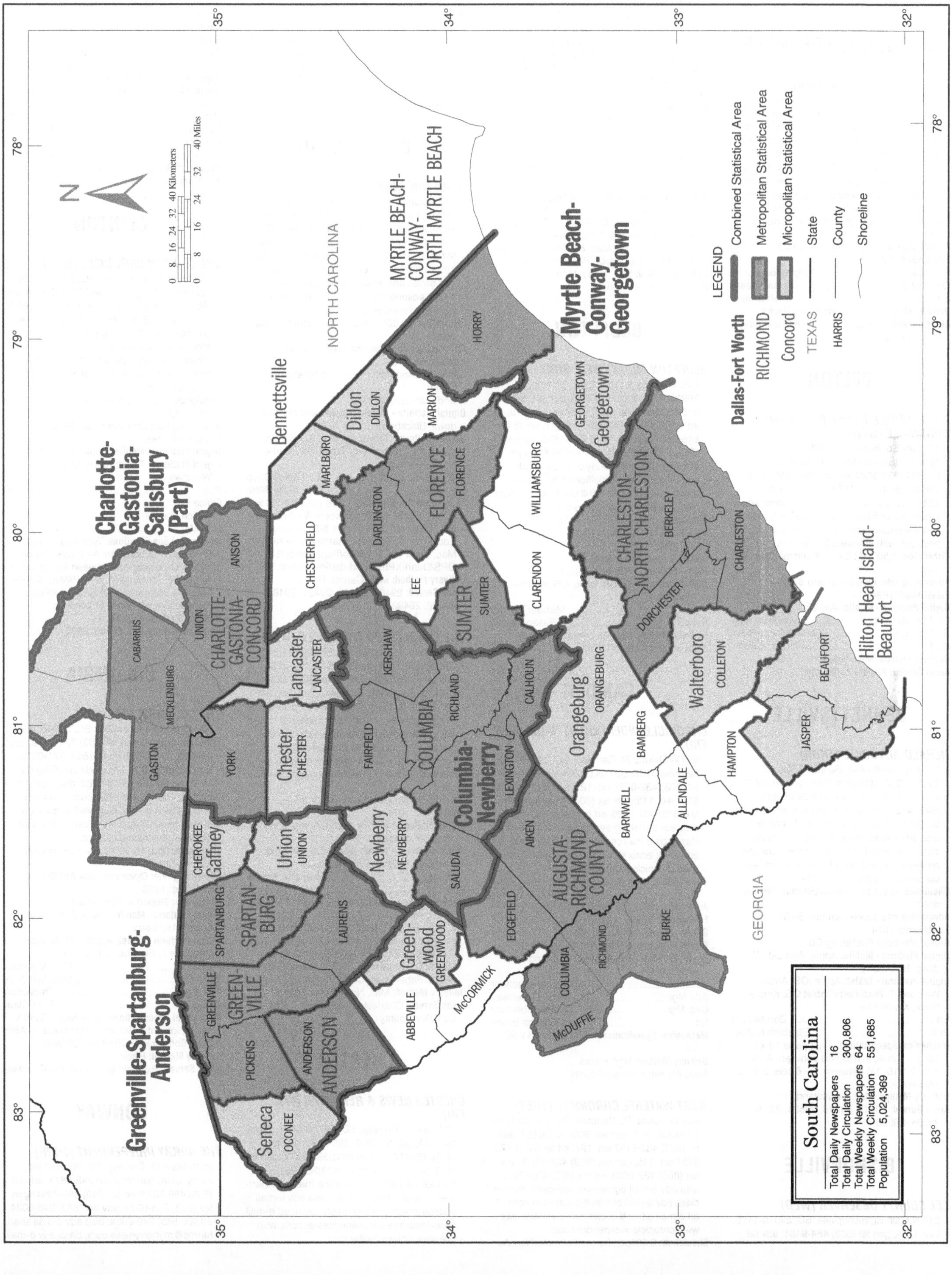
South Carolina
Total Daily Newspapers 16
Total Daily Circulation 300,806
Total Weekly Newspapers 64
Total Weekly Circulation 551,685
Population 5,024,369
LEGEND
Dallas-Fort Worth Combined Statistical Area
RICHMOND Metropolitan Statistical Area
Concord Micropolitan Statistical Area
TEXAS State
HARRIS County
Shoreline
NORTH CAROLINA
GEORGIA
Charlotte-Gastonia-Salisbury (Part)
Greenville-Spartanburg-Anderson
Columbia-Newberry
Myrtle Beach-Conway-Georgetown
MYRTLE BEACH-CONWAY-NORTH MYRTLE BEACH
CHARLOTTE-GASTONIA-CONCORD
CHARLESTON-NORTH CHARLESTON
AUGUSTA-RICHMOND COUNTY
Hilton Head Island-Beaufort
Bennettsville
Dillon
Georgetown
Walterboro
Orangeburg
Sumter
Florence
Columbia
Lancaster
Chester
Union
Gaffney
Newberry
Greenwood
Spartanburg
Greenville
Anderson
Seneca
0 8 16 24 32 40 Kilometers
0 8 16 24 32 40 Miles

29849, 29911

BATESBURG LEESVILLE

THE TWIN-CITY NEWS (THUR)
114 E Columbia Ave, Batesburg Leesville, SC, 29006-2130, Lexington, USA; gen tel (803) 532-6203; adv tel (803) 532-6203; ed tel (803) 532-6203; gen fax (803) 532-6204; adv fax (803) 532-6204; ed fax (803) 532-6204; disp adv e-mail bltwincitynews@gmail.com; class adv e-mail bltwincitynews@gmail.com; ed e-mail bltwincitynews@gmail.com; web site http://www.twin-citynews.com/
Circulation: 2,675pd, 39fr; Sworn/Estimate/Non-Audited
Advertising rate: Open inch rate $6.00
Established: 1925
Publisher.............................Douglas Bruner III
Office Mgr. ....Teresa Shealy
Editor ....Leah Bruner
Delivery Method: Mail, Newsstand, Racks
Areas Served: Lexington County, Aiken County, Saluda County

BELTON

THE BELTON & HONEA PATH NEWS-CHRONICLE (WED)
310 City Sq, Belton, SC, 29627-1435, Anderson, USA; gen tel (864) 338-6124; adv tel (864) 338-6124; ed tel (864) 338-6124; gen fax (864) 338-1109; adv fax (864) 338-1109; ed fax (864) 338-1109; disp adv e-mail elaine@bhpnc.com; class adv e-mail elaine@bhpnc.com; ed e-mail elaine@bhpnc.com; web site www.bhpnc.com
Circulation: 2,500pd,; Sworn/Estimate/Non-Audited
Advertising rate: Open inch rate $7.25
Established: 1894
Digital Platform - Mobile: Apple
Co-Pub./Bus. Mgr.....................Lynn Robinson
Co-Pub./Ed. ....Elaine Ellison-Rider
Co-Pub..................................Doris E. Ellison
Delivery Method: Mail, Newsstand, Racks
Areas Served: Anderson County

BENNETTSVILLE

HERALD-ADVOCATE (THUR)
100 Fayetteville Ave, Bennettsville, SC, 29512-4022, Marlboro, USA; gen tel (843) 479-3815; adv tel (843) 479-3815; ed tel (843) 479-3815; gen fax (843) 479-7671; adv fax (843) 479-7671; ed fax (843) 479-7671; disp adv e-mail ads@heraldadvocate.com; class adv e-mail ads@heraldadvocate.com; ed e-mail news@heraldadvocate.com; web site www.heraldadvocate.com
Circulation: 6,800pd,; Sworn/Estimate/Non-Audited
Advertising rate: Open inch rate $6.00
Established: 1874
Group: Marlboro Publishing Co.
Digital Platform - Mobile: Apple, Android, Windows, Blackberry
Digital Platform - Tablet: Apple iOS, Android, Windows 7, Blackberry Tablet OS, Kindle, Nook, Kindle Fire
Ed. .... Dan McNiel
Pub.......................................Elizabeth McNiel
Mechanical Specifications: Type page 13 x 21 1/2; E - 6 cols, 2 1/16, 1/6 between; A - 6 cols, 2 1/16, 1/6 between; C - 6 cols, 2 1/16, 1/6 between.
Delivery Method: Mail, Newsstand
Areas Served: 29512, 29516, 29525, 29570, 29594, 29596

BISHOPVILLE

LEE COUNTY OBSERVER (WED)
218 N Main St, Bishopville, SC, 29010-1416, Lee, USA; gen tel (803) 484-9431; adv tel (803) 484-9431; ed tel (803) 484-9431; gen fax (803) 484-5055; adv fax (803) 484-5055; ed fax (803) 484-5055; disp adv e-mail advertise@sc.rr.com; class adv e-mail observer@sc.rr.com; ed e-mail editor@sc.rr.com
Circulation: 3,100pd, 25fr; Sworn/Estimate/Non-Audited
Advertising rate: Open inch rate $7.45
Established: 1902
Group: Morris Multimedia, Inc.
Pub......................................Michael Mischner
Office Mgr. ....Nancy Wilson
Adv. Sales Mgr. ....Millie Scott
Circ. Mgr..BG Maize
Mng. Ed......................................Gee Atkinson
Mechanical Specifications: Type page 13 x 21 1/2; E - 6 cols, 1 7/8, 1/8 between; A - 6 cols, 1 7/8, 1/8 between; C - 6 cols, 1 7/8, 1/8 between.Equipment & Software: Hardware — APP/Mac, APP/iMac; Software — Adobe/PageMaker 6.5, Adobe/Photoshop 5.0.
Delivery Method: Mail, Newsstand
Areas Served: Lee County

BLUFFTON

BLUFFTON TODAY (WED, SUN)
6 Promenade St, Unit 1005, Bluffton, SC, 29910-7051, Beaufort, USA; gen tel (843) 815-0800; adv tel (843) 815-0800 ext. 18; ed tel (843) 815-0800 ext. 19; gen fax (843) 815-0828; adv fax (843) 815-0828; ed fax (843) 815-0828; disp adv e-mail Kathryn.goodman@blufftontoday.com; class adv e-mail Mary.Ryan@blufftontoday.com; ed e-mail lawrence.conneff@blufftontoday.com; web site www.blufftontoday.com
Circulation: 396pd, 18,600fr; AAM
Advertising rate: Modular Rates
Established: 2005
Group: GateHouse Media, Inc.
Digital Platform - Mobile: Apple, Android
Digital Platform - Tablet: Apple iOS, Android, Windows 7
Pub...Michael Traynor
Exec. Ed....................................Susan Catron
Delivery Method: Mail, Newsstand, Carrier
Areas Served: Beaufort County, Jasper County

CAMDEN

CHRONICLE-INDEPENDENT (MON, WED, FRI)
909 W Dekalb St, Camden, SC, 29020-4259, Kershaw, USA; gen tel (803) 432-6157; adv tel (803) 432-6157 ext. 127; ed tel (803) 432-6157 ext. 115; gen fax (803) 432-7609; adv fax (803) 432-7609; ed fax (803) 432-7609; disp adv e-mail bgreenway@ci-camden.com; class adv e-mail csmith@ci-camden.com ; ed e-mail editor@ci-camden.com; web site www.chronicle-independent.com
Circulation: 6,500pd,; Sworn/Estimate/Non-Audited
Advertising rate: Open inch rate $12.15
Established: 1889
Group: Morris Multimedia, Inc.
Digital Platform - Mobile: Apple, Android
Digital Platform - Tablet: Apple iOS, Android, Windows 7
Pub......................................Michael Mischner
Adv. Mgr. ....Betsy Greenway
Circ. Mgr...............................Debbie Albertson
Ed. ....Martha Bruce
Mechanical Specifications: Type page 13 x 20 1/2.
Delivery Method: Mail, Racks
Areas Served: Kershaw County

WEST WATEREE CHRONICLE (TUES)
909 W Dekalb St, Camden, SC, 29020-4259, Kershaw, USA; gen tel (803) 432-6157; adv tel (803) 432-6157 ext. 127; ed tel (803) 432-6157 ext. 115; gen fax (803) 432-7609; adv fax (803) 432-7609; ed fax (803) 432-7609; disp adv e-mail bgreenway@ci-camden.com; class adv e-mail csmith@ci-camden.com ; ed e-mail editor@ci-camden.com; web site www.chronicle-independent.com
Circulation: 6,500pd,; Sworn/Estimate/Non-Audited
Advertising rate: Open inch rate $12.15
Established: 1889
Pub......................................Michael Mischner
Adv. Mgr. ....Betsy Greenway
Circ. Mgr...............................Debbie Albertson
Ed. ....Martha Bruce
Delivery Method: Mail, Racks
Areas Served: Kershaw County

CHARLESTON

MOULTRIE NEWS (WED)
134 Columbus St, Charleston, SC, 29403-4809, Charleston, USA; gen tel (843) 958-7480; adv tel (843) 958-7485; ed tel (843) 958-7482; gen fax (843) 958-7490; adv fax (843) 958-7490; ed fax (843) 958-7490; disp adv e-mail ads@moultrienews.com; class adv e-mail ads@moultrienews.com; ed e-mail editor@moultrienews.com; web site www.moultrienews.com
Circulation: 28,000fr; Sworn/Estimate/Non-Audited
Advertising rate: Open inch rate $12.50
Established: 1964
Group: Evening Post Publishing Newspaper Group
Island Publications, Inc.
Digital Platform - Mobile: Apple, Android, Windows, Blackberry
Digital Platform - Tablet: Apple iOS, Android, Windows 7, Blackberry Tablet OS, Kindle, Nook, Kindle Fire
Pub... Vickey Boyd
Ed. .... Sully Witte
Mechanical Specifications: Type page 11 5/8 x 21; E - 6 cols, 1 5/6, between; A - 6 cols, 1 5/6, between; C - 6 cols, 1 5/6, between. Equipment & Software: Hardware — APP/Mac; Software — Adobe/PageMaker 6.0, QPS/QuarkXPress, Adobe/Photoshop 5.0.
Delivery Method: Mail, Carrier, Racks
Areas Served: 29464, 29466, 29451, 29482, 29492, 29492

THE CHARLESTON CHRONICLE (WED)
1111 King St, Charleston, SC, 29403-3761, Charleston, USA; gen tel (843) 723-2785; adv tel (843) 723-2785; ed tel (843) 723-2785; gen fax (843) 737-5443; adv fax (843) 737-5443; ed fax (843) 737-5443; disp adv e-mail sales@charlestonchronicle.net ; class adv e-mail publisher@charlestonchronicle.net ; ed e-mail news@charlestonchronicle.net ; web site www.charlestonchronicle.net
Circulation: 6,000pd,; Sworn/Estimate/Non-Audited
Advertising rate: Open inch rate $15.10
Established: 1971
Digital Platform - Mobile: Apple, Android, Windows, Blackberry
Digital Platform - Tablet: Apple iOS, Android, Windows 7, Blackberry Tablet OS
Circ. Mgr..................................Nanette Smalls
Pub...James J. French
Mechanical Specifications: Type page 13 x 21; E - 6 cols, 2 1/16, 1/4 between; A - 6 cols, 2 1/16, 1/4 between; C - 6 cols, 2 1/16, 1/4 between.Equipment & Software: Hardware — APP/Power Mac 6100-66, APP/Power Mac 8500; Software — QPS/QuarkXPress, Adobe/PageMaker, Claris/Works.
Delivery Method: Mail, Newsstand, Racks
Areas Served: Charleston, Dorchester, and Berkeley County

CHESTER

CHESTER NEWS & REPORTER (WED, FRI)
104 York St, Chester, SC, 29706-1427, Chester, USA; gen tel (803) 385-3177; adv tel (803)385-3177; ed tel (803)385-3177; gen fax (803) 581-2518; adv fax (803)581-2518; ed fax (803)581-2518; disp adv e-mail addepartment@onlinechester.com; class adv e-mail addepartment@onlinechester.com; ed e-mail newsdepartment@onlinechester.com; web site www.onlinechester.com
Circulation: 7,175pd,; Sworn/Estimate/Non-Audited
Advertising rate: Open inch rate $10.34
Established: 1869
Group: Landmark Communications, Inc.
Landmark Community Newspapers, LLC
Digital Platform - Mobile: Apple, Android
Digital Platform - Tablet: Apple iOS, Android, Windows 7
Pub.....................................William J. Aultman
Ed./Adv. Sales Rep. ....Nancy Pearsons
Adv. Rep.. Fran Dodds
Classified Mgr. .... Karen Graham
Delivery Method: Mail, Newsstand
Areas Served: Chester County

CLINTON

THE CLINTON CHRONICLE (WED)
513 N Broad St, Clinton, SC, 29325-1705, Laurens, USA; gen tel (864)833-1900; adv tel (864)833-1900; ed tel (864)833-1900; gen fax (864)833-1902; adv fax (864)833-1902; ed fax (864)833-1902; disp adv e-mail sales1@clintonchronicle.net; class adv e-mail janice@clintonchronicle.net; ed e-mail news@clintonchronicle.net; web site www.clintonchronicle.com
Circulation: 3,250pd, 150fr; Sworn/Estimate/Non-Audited
Advertising rate: Open inch rate $8.35
Established: 1900
Digital Platform - Mobile: Apple, Android
Digital Platform - Tablet: Apple iOS, Android, Windows 7
Pub..Larry Franklin
Office Mgr.
Janice Franklin
Adv. Mgr. ....Shirley Pace
Mechanical Specifications: Type page 6 x 21; E - 6 cols, 1/6 between; A - 6 cols, 1/6 between; C - 6 cols, 1/6 between.Equipment & Software: Hardware — 4-APP/iMac, 2-APP/Mac G4; Software — QPS/QuarkXPress, Microsoft/Word, Adobe/Photoshop.
Delivery Method: Mail, Racks
Areas Served: 29325, 29360, 29351

COLUMBIA

THE COLUMBIA STAR (FRI)
723 Queen St, Columbia, SC, 29205-1723, Richland, USA; gen tel (803) 771-0219; adv tel (803) 771-0219; ed tel (803) 771-0219; gen fax (866) 608-1782; adv fax (866) 608-1782; ed fax (866) 608-1782; disp adv e-mail GailT@TheColumbiaStar.com; class adv e-mail Pams@TheColumbiaStar.com; ed e-mail mimim@thecolumbiastar.com; web site www.thecolumbiastar.com
Circulation: 0pd, 15,000fr; Sworn/Estimate/Non-Audited
Advertising rate: Open inch rate $11.00
Established: 1963
Group: Star Reporter Corporation
Digital Platform - Mobile: Apple, Android, Windows, Blackberry
Digital Platform - Tablet: Apple iOS, Android, Windows 7, Blackberry Tablet OS
Pub...Mimi Maddock
Exec. Ed.......................................Mike Maedock
Adv. Mgr. ....Gail Trebuchon
Office Mgr. .... Pam Clark
Mechanical Specifications: Type page 10 2/5 x 14.Equipment & Software: Hardware — APP/Mac; Software — QPS/QuarkXPress.
Delivery Method: Racks
Areas Served: Richland and Lexington Counties

CONWAY

THE HORRY INDEPENDENT (THUR)
2510 Main St, Conway, SC, 29526-3365, Horry, USA; gen tel (843) 248-6671; adv tel (843) 488-7234; ed tel (843) 488-7241; gen fax (843) 248-6024; adv fax (843) 248-6024; ed fax (843) 248-6024; disp adv e-mail shari.harms@myhorrynews.com; class adv e-mail

shari.harms@myhorrynews.com; ed e-mail kathy.ropp@myhorrynews.com; web site www.myhorrynews.com
Circulation: 6,000pd, 125fr; Sworn/Estimate/Non-Audited
Advertising rate: Open inch rate $10.50
Established: 1980
Group: Waccamaw Publishers, Inc.
Digital Platform - Mobile: Apple, Android, Windows, Blackberry
Digital Platform - Tablet: Apple iOS, Android, Windows 7, Blackberry Tablet OS, Kindle, Nook, Kindle Fire
Owner/Pub.............................. Steve Robertson
Ed. .... Kathy Ropp
Business Mgr. ....Adrian Robertson
Editor ....Tom O'Dare
Mechanical Specifications: Type page 10.62 x 21.Equipment & Software: Hardware — APP/Mac; Presses — Orient; Software — Microsoft/Word 5.0, Adobe/PageMaker 6.5, Multi-Ad/Creator 3.8, QPS/QuarkXPress 6.5.
Delivery Method: Mail, Newsstand, Racks
Areas Served: 29526, 29527, 29569, 29511, 29544, 29568, 29577, 29579

THE LORIS SCENE (WED)

2510 Main St, Conway, SC, 29526-3365, Horry, USA; gen tel (843) 248-6671; adv tel (843) 488-7234; ed tel (843) 488-7250; gen fax (843) 248-6024; adv fax (843) 248-6024; ed fax (843) 248-6024; disp adv e-mail shari.harms@myhorrynews.com; class adv e-mail shari.harms@myhorrynews.com; ed e-mail annette.norris@myhorrynews.com; web site www.myhorrynews.com
Circulation: 1,800pd,; Sworn/Estimate/Non-Audited
Advertising rate: Open inch rate $9.40
Established: 190
Group: Horry News & Shopper
Waccamaw Publishers, Inc
Digital Platform - Mobile: Apple, Android, Windows, Blackberry
Digital Platform - Tablet: Apple iOS, Android, Windows 7, Blackberry Tablet OS, Kindle, Nook, Kindle Fire
Owner/Pub.............................. Steve Robertson
Ed. ....Annette Norris
Business Mgr. ....Adrian Robertson
Advertising Director ....Shari Harms
Mechanical Specifications: Type page 10 x 16; E - 6 cols, 1 1/2, between; A - 6 cols, 1 1/2, between; C - 6 cols, 1 1/2, between. Equipment & Software: Hardware — APP/Mac; Software — Adobe/PageMaker, Adobe/Photoshop, Microsoft/Word.
Delivery Method: Mail, Newsstand, Racks
Areas Served: Horry County

DARLINGTON

THE NEWS & PRESS (WED)

1175 S MAIN ST, Darlington, SC, 29532, Darlington, USA; gen tel (843)393-3811; adv tel (843)393-3811; ed tel (843)393-3811; gen fax (843)393-6811; adv fax (843)393-6811; ed fax (843)393-6811; disp adv e-mail ads@newsandpressonline.com; class adv e-mail sales@newsandpressonline.com; ed e-mail editor@newsandpressonline.com; web site www.newsandpressonline.com
Circulation: 6,000pd,; Sworn/Estimate/Non-Audited
Advertising rate: Open inch rate $8.95
Established: 1874
Digital Platform - Mobile: Apple, Android
Digital Platform - Tablet: Apple iOS, Android, Windows 7
Gen. Mgr. .... Morrell Thomas
Ed. ....Jana Pye
Adv. Mgr. .... Charlotte Berger
Office Mgr. ....Judy Rogers
Delivery Method: Mail, Newsstand, Racks
Areas Served: 29532, 29540, 29550, 29069, 29501

DILLON THE DILLON HERALD (TUES, THUR)

505 Highway 301 N, Dillon, SC, 29536-2957, Dillon, USA; gen tel (843)774-3311; adv tel (843)774-3311; ed tel (843)774-3311; gen fax (843)841-1930; adv fax (843)841-1930; ed fax (843)841-1930; disp adv e-mail jd@the-dillonherald.com; class adv e-mail jd@thedillonherald.com; ed e-mail bf@thedillonherald.com; web site www.thedillonherald.com
Circulation: 7,485pd,; Sworn/Estimate/Non-Audited
Advertising rate: Open inch rate $8.19
Established: 1894
Digital Platform - Tablet: Windows 7
Gen. Mgr./Adv. Mgr................. Johnnie Daniels
Pub./Ed. .... Betsy Finklea
Mechanical Specifications: Type page 11 5/8 x 20 1/2; E - 6 cols, 1 13/16, 1/8 between; A - 6 cols, 1 13/16, 1/8 between; C - 6 cols, 1 13/16, 1/8 between.Equipment & Software: Hardware — APP/Mac; Presses — G; Software — QPS/QuarkXPress 6.0, Microsoft/Word.
Delivery Method: Mail, Newsstand, Carrier, Racks
Areas Served: 29536, 29563, 29565, 29547, 28383, 29571, 29520, 29567, 29543, 29581, 29512, 29516, 29525, 29571, 29574, 29592, ETC.

EASLEY

THE EASLEY PROGRESS (WED, FRI)

201 W Main St, Easley, SC, 29640-2040, Pickens, USA; gen tel (864) 855-0355; adv tel (864) 855-0355; ed tel (864) 855-0355; gen fax (864) 855-6825; adv fax (864) 855-6825; ed fax (864) 855-6825; disp adv e-mail cwyatt@civitasmedia.com; class adv e-mail ryoungblood@civitasmedia.com; ed e-mail ladamson@civitasmedia.com; web site www.theeasleyprogress.com
Circulation: 7,401pd,; Sworn/Estimate/Non-Audited
Advertising rate: Open inch rate $10.54
Established: 1902
Group: Civitas Media, LLC-OOB
Digital Platform - Mobile: Apple, Android
Digital Platform - Tablet: Apple iOS, Android, Windows 7
Gen. Mgr./Media Dir.................Christine Wyatt
Customer Ser Rep. .... Rhonda Youngblood
Mechanical Specifications: Type page 13 x 21; E - 6 cols, 2 1/16, 1/6 between; A - 6 cols, 2 1/16, 1/6 between; C - 6 cols, 2 1/16, 1/6 between.Equipment & Software: Hardware — APP/Mac; Presses — KP; Software — Multi-Ad/Creator 3.7.
Delivery Method: Mail, Newsstand
Areas Served: 29640, 29641, 29642, 29671, 29657

THE PICKENS SENTINEL (WED)

714-D S PENDLETON ST, Easley, SC, 29640-3526, Pickens, USA; gen tel (864) 855-0355; adv tel (864) 855-0355; ed tel (864) 855-0355; gen fax (864) 855-6825; adv fax (864) 855-6825; ed fax (864) 855-6825; disp adv e-mail cwyatt@civitasmedia.com; class adv e-mail ryoungblood@civitasmedia.com; ed e-mail ladamson@civitasmedia.com; web site www.pickenssentinel.com
Circulation: 6,800pd,; Sworn/Estimate/Non-Audited
Advertising rate: Open inch rate $7.75
Established: 1871
Group: Champion Media
Digital Platform - Mobile: Apple, Android
Digital Platform - Tablet: Apple iOS, Android, Windows 7
Gen. Mgr./Ed........................... Lonnie Adamson
Adv. Mgr. ....Christine Wyatt
Circ. Mgr./Classified.......... Rhonda Youngblood
Mechanical Specifications: Type page 11 1/2 x 21; E - 6 cols, 1 3/4, 1/3 between; A - 6 cols, 1 3/4, 1/3 between; C - 6 cols, 1 3/4, 1/3 between.Equipment & Software: Hardware — PC; Software — WordPerfect 5.0, Archetype/Corel Draw 4.0, Microsoft/Windows, Adobe/PageMaker.
Delivery Method: Mail, Newsstand, Racks
Areas Served: 29671, 29657, 29640, 29641, 29642, 29630

EDGEFIELD

THE EDGEFIELD ADVERTISER (WED)

117 Courthouse Sq, Edgefield, SC, 29824-1319, Edgefield, USA; gen tel (803) 637-3540; adv tel (803) 637-3540; ed tel (803) 637-3540; gen fax (803) 637-0602; adv fax (803) 637-0602; ed fax (803) 637-0602; disp adv e-mail sharon@edgefieldadvertiser.com; class adv e-mail sandra@edgefieldadvertiser.com; ed e-mail suzanne@edgefieldadvertiser.com; web site www.edgefieldadvertiser.com
Circulation: 4,000pd,; Sworn/Estimate/Non-Audited
Advertising rate: Open inch rate $7.00
Established: 1836
Digital Platform - Mobile: Apple, Blackberry
Digital Platform - Tablet: Apple iOS, Android, Windows 7, Blackberry Tablet OS
Owner/Pub./Ed...... Suzanne Gile Mims Derrick
Online Ed.......................................Robert Norris
Office Mgr. ....Sandra Reece
Adv. Mgr. ....Sharon Nunamaker
Mechanical Specifications: Type page 14 x 21; E - 8 cols, 1 3/5, between.Equipment & Software: ; Presses — G/Community.
Delivery Method: Mail, Newsstand, Racks
Areas Served: 29824, 29847, 29832, 29138, 29129, 29105, 29835, 29845, 29838, 29841, 29829

FLORENCE

LAKE CITY NEWS & POST (WED)

310 S Dargan St, Florence, SC, 29506-2537, Florence, USA; gen tel (843) 317-6397; adv fax (843) 317-7290; ed fax (843) 317-7292; disp adv e-mail news@scnow.com; web site www.scnow.com/newsandpost
Group: BH Media Group
Acct. Exec...............................Donna Wiggins
Ed. .... Shamira McCray

MARION STAR & MULLINS ENTERPRISE (WED)

310 S Dargan St, Florence, SC, 29506-2537, Florence, USA; gen tel (843) 317-6397; adv tel (843) 423-2050; ed tel (843) 317-6397; gen fax (843) 423-2542; adv fax (843) 423-2542; ed fax (843) 423-2542; disp adv e-mail starandenterprise@scnow.com; class adv e-mail starandenterprise@scnow.com; ed e-mail news@scnow.com; web site http://www.scnow.com/starandenterprise/
Circulation: 4,000pd, 20,000fr; Sworn/Estimate/Non-Audited
Advertising rate: Open inch rate $8.00
Established: 1846
Digital Platform - Mobile: Apple, Android
Digital Platform - Tablet: Apple iOS, Android, Windows 7
Pub...Joe Craig
Ed. .... Naeem McFadden
Adv. Account Exec. .... Kathy Sawyer
Mechanical Specifications: Type page 13 x 21 1/2; E - 6 cols, 2 1/16, 1/6 between; A - 6 cols, 2 1/16, 1/6 between; C - 6 cols, 2 1/16, 1/6 between.Equipment & Software: Hardware — APP/Mac; Presses — 6-G/Community; Software — Adobe/PageMaker 6.5.
Delivery Method: Mail, Newsstand, Racks
Areas Served: 29571, 29574, 29581, 29519, 29592, 29546, 29536

THE FLORENCE NEWS JOURNAL (WED)

312 Railroad Ave, Florence, SC, 29506-2583, Florence, USA; gen tel (843)667-9656; adv tel (843)667-9656; ed tel (843)667-9656; gen fax (843)661-7102; adv fax (843)661-7102; ed fax (843)661-7102; disp adv e-mail powersc@myflorencetoday.com; class adv e-mail classifieds@florencenewsjournal.com; ed e-mail bharrison@florencenewsjournal.com; web site www.florencenewsjournal.com - 26,037(views) 10,254(visitors)
Circulation: 9pd, 16,212fr; CVC
Advertising rate: Open inch rate $15.00
Established: 1982
Group: Swartz Media, LLC
Digital Platform - Mobile: Apple, Android
Digital Platform - Tablet: Apple iOS, Android, Windows 7
Pub.. Don Swartz
Ed. ....Brenda Harrison
Prodn. Mgr. .... Beth Strett
Mechanical Specifications: Type page 11 1/2 x 21; E - 6 cols, 2 1/16, 1/6 between; A - 6 cols, 2 1/16, 1/6 between; C - 9 cols, 1 7/16, 1/12 between.Equipment & Software: Hardware — APP/Mac; Software — QPS/QuarkXPress, Adobe/Photoshop, Microsoft/Word.
Delivery Method: Mail, Newsstand, Racks
Areas Served: Florence County

THE WEEKLY OBSERVER (WED)

310 S Dargan St, Florence, SC, 29506-2537, Florence, USA; gen tel (843) 558-3323; adv tel (843) 558-3323; ed tel (843) 558-3323; gen fax (843) 558-9601; adv fax (843) 558-9601; ed fax (843) 558-9601; disp adv e-mail jdavis@florencenews.com; class adv e-mail jdavis@florencenews.com; ed e-mail cmckagen@florencenews.com; web site www.scnow.com/observer
Circulation: 2,300pd,; Sworn/Estimate/Non-Audited
Advertising rate: Open inch rate $5.00
Established: 1973
Digital Platform - Mobile: Apple, Android
Digital Platform - Tablet: Apple iOS, Android, Windows 7
Pub... Mark Laskowski
Ed. .... Chris McKagen
Account Exec.................................John Davis
Delivery Method: Mail, Newsstand
Areas Served: Williamsburg County

GAFFNEY

THE GAFFNEY LEDGER (MON, WED, FRI)

1604 W Floyd Baker Blvd, Gaffney, SC, 29341-1206, Cherokee, USA; gen tel (864) 489-1131; gen fax (864) 487-7667; disp adv e-mail greg@gaffneyledger.com; class adv e-mail wilson@gaffneyledger.com; ed e-mail editor@gaffneyledger.com; web site www.gaffneyledger.com - 93,363(views) 14,858(visitors)
Circulation: 6,200pd, 24,000fr; Sworn/Estimate/Non-Audited
Advertising rate: Open inch rate $10.50
Established: 1894
Digital Platform - Mobile: Apple, Android, Windows, Blackberry
Digital Platform - Tablet: Apple iOS, Android, Windows 7, Blackberry Tablet OS, Kindle, Nook, Kindle Fire
Pub...Cody Sossamon
Ed. .... Klonie Jordan
Advt Mgr ....Greg Moore
Features/Lifestyles Editor......Abbie Sossamon
Mechanical Specifications: Type page 10.5 x 21 1/2; E - 6 cols, 2 1/16, 3/16 between; A - 6 cols, 2 1/16, 3/16 between; C - 9 cols, 1 1/3, 1/8 between.Equipment & Software: Hardware — APP/Power Mac; Presses — G/Community; Software — QPS/QuarkXPress 9.3, Adobe/Illustrator 6.0, Adobe/Photoshop CS5.1.
Delivery Method: Mail, Newsstand, Carrier, Racks
Areas Served: 25500, 29340, 29341, 29342, 29702, 29330, 29323, 29372

GEORGETOWN

THE GEORGETOWN TIMES (MON, WED, FRI)

615 Front St, Georgetown, SC, 29440-3623, Georgetown, USA; gen tel (843) 546-4148; adv tel (843) 546-4148 ext. 237; ed tel (843) 546-4148 ext. 230; gen fax (843) 546-2395; adv fax (843) 546-2395; ed fax (843) 546-2395; disp adv e-mail jcioni@gtowntimes.com; class adv e-mail classifieds@gtowntimes.com; ed e-mail thoward@gtowntimes.com; web site www.gtowntimes.com
Circulation: 9,223pd, 22,000fr; Sworn/Estimate/Non-Audited

Advertising rate: Open inch rate $8.50
Established: 1798
Group: Evening Post Publishing Newspaper Group
Digital Platform - Mobile: Apple, Android, Windows, Blackberry
Digital Platform - Tablet: Apple iOS, Android, Windows 7, Blackberry Tablet OS
Pub....John Carr
Bus. Mgr....Christel Newton
Ed....Tommy Howard
Sales Mgr....Dale Lambert
Mechanical Specifications: Type page 11 5/8 x 21; E - 6 cols, 1 5/6, 1/8 between; A - 6 cols, 1 5/6, 1/8 between; C - 9 cols, 1 3/16, 1/8 between.Equipment & Software: ; Presses — 12-G/Community
Delivery Method: Mail, Racks
Areas Served: Georgetown County

WACCAMAW TIMES (WED, FRI)

615 Front St, Georgetown, SC, 29440-3623, Georgetown, USA; gen tel (843) 546-4148; adv tel (843) 546-4148; ed tel (843) 546-4148; gen fax (843) 545-8928; adv fax (843) 545-8928; ed fax (843) 545-8928; disp adv e-mail jcioni@southstrandnews.com; class adv e-mail classifieds@southstrandnews.com; ed e-mail mstevens@southstrandnews.com; web site southstrandnews.com
Circulation: 6,208pd, 0fr; Sworn/Estimate/Non-Audited
Advertising rate: $10.34
Established: 1798
Group: Evening Post Publishing Newspaper GroupChristel Newton
Delivery Method: Mail, Racks
Areas Served: Georgetown County

GREENVILLE

TRIBUNE-TIMES (WED)

305 S Main St, Greenville, SC, 29601-2605, Greenville, USA; gen tel (864) 298-4100; adv tel (864) 298-4342; ed tel (864) 298-4100; gen fax (864) 298-4395; adv fax (864) 298-4395; ed fax (864) 298-4395; disp adv e-mail dfoster3@gannett.com; class adv e-mail dfoster3@gannett.com; ed e-mail khardy1@greenvillenews.com ; web site www.greenvilleonline.com
Circulation: 37,674fr; Sworn/Estimate/Non-Audited
Advertising rate: Open inch rate $9.90
Group: Gannett
Digital Platform - Mobile: Apple, Android, Windows, Blackberry
Digital Platform - Tablet: Apple iOS, Android, Windows 7, Blackberry Tablet OS, Kindle, Nook, Kindle Fire
Exec. Ed....John S. Pittman
News Dir....Bill Fox
Marketing VP....Maggie Krost
Mechanical Specifications: Type page 12 x 21; E - 6 cols, 2, 1/6 between; A - 6 cols, 2, 1/6 between; C - 10 cols, between.
Delivery Method: Mail, Newsstand
Areas Served: Greenville County

GREER

THE GREER CITIZEN (WED)

317 Trade St, Greer, SC, 29651-3431, Greenville, USA; gen tel (864) 877-2076; adv tel (864) 877-2076 ext. 100; ed tel (864) 877-2076 ext. 103; gen fax (864) 877-3563; adv fax (864) 877-3563; ed fax (864) 877-3563; disp adv e-mail sblackwell@greercitizen.com; class adv e-mail sreider@greercitizen.com; ed e-mail billy@greercitizen.com; web site www.greercitizen.com
Circulation: 6,300pd,; Sworn/Estimate/Non-Audited
Advertising rate: Open inch rate $9.50
Established: 1918
Digital Platform - Mobile: Apple, Android
Digital Platform - Tablet: Apple iOS, Android, Windows 7
Pub./Adv. Mgr....Steve Blackwell
Ed....Billy Cannada

Mechanical Specifications: Type page 13 x 21 1/2; E - 6 cols, 2 1/16, between; A - 6 cols, 2 1/16, between; C - 6 cols, 2 1/16, between. Equipment & Software: Hardware — APP/Mac; Presses — 6-KP/News King; Software — Adobe/PageMaker, Adobe/Photoshop.
Delivery Method: Mail, Newsstand
Areas Served: 29650, 29651, 29652, 29365, 29687, 29334, 29385, 29369, 29388, 29375

HAMPTON

HAMPTON COUNTY GUARDIAN (THUR)

306 Lee Ave, Hampton, SC, 29924-3442, Hampton, USA; gen tel (803) 943-4645; adv tel (803) 943-4645; ed tel (803) 943-4645; gen fax (803) 943-9365; adv fax (803) 943-9365; ed fax (803) 943-9365; disp adv e-mail ads@hamptoncountyguardian.com; class adv e-mail news@hamptoncountyguardian.com; ed e-mail news@hamptoncountyguardian.com; web site www.hamptoncountyguardian.com
Circulation: 5,200pd,; Sworn/Estimate/Non-Audited
Advertising rate: Open inch rate $12.28
Established: 1879
Digital Platform - Mobile: Apple, Android
Digital Platform - Tablet: Apple iOS, Android, Windows 7
Pub....Michael DeWitt
Circ. Mgr....Angie Crosby
Adv. Sales....Catina Gadson
Mechanical Specifications: Type page 13 x 21; E - 6 cols, 2, between; A - 6 cols, 2, between; C - 6 cols, 2, between.Equipment & Software: Hardware — APP/Mac; Software — Write Now, Adobe/PageMaker.
Delivery Method: Mail, Newsstand
Areas Served: Hampton County

HARTSVILLE

THE HARTSVILLE MESSENGER (WED)

212 Swift Creek Rd, Hartsville, SC, 29550-4383, Darlington, USA; gen tel (843) 332-6545; adv tel (843) 332-6545 ext. 10; ed tel (843) 332-6545 ext. 16; gen fax (843) 332-1341; adv fax (843) 332-1341; ed fax (843) 332-1341; disp adv e-mail dwiggins@hartsvillemessenger.com; class adv e-mail swyatt@hartsvillemessenger.com; ed e-mail rsloan@hartsvillemessenger.com; web site www.scnow.com
Circulation: 3pd, 14,640fr; CVC
Advertising rate: Open inch rate $10.00
Established: 1893
Group: Media General, Inc. (OOB)
BH Media Group
Digital Platform - Mobile: Apple, Android, Windows, Blackberry
Digital Platform - Tablet: Apple iOS, Android, Windows 7, Blackberry Tablet OS, Kindle, Nook, Kindle Fire
Pub./Ed....Robert Sloan
Account Exec....Donna Wiggins
Account Exec....Sara Wyatt
Mechanical Specifications: Type page 13 x 21; E - 6 cols, 2, 1/6 between; A - 6 cols, 2, 1/6 between; C - 8 cols, 1 2/3, 1/6 between. Equipment & Software: Hardware — APP/Mac; Presses — G; Software — QPS/QuarkXPress.
Delivery Method: Mail, Carrier, Racks
Areas Served: 29550, 29551, 29501, 29540, 29532

HOLLY HILL

THE OBSERVER (WED)

8513 OLD STATE RD, Holly Hill, SC, 29059, Orangeburg, USA; gen tel (803) 496-3242; adv tel (803) 496-3242; ed tel (803) 496-3242; gen fax (803) 496-3051; adv fax (803) 496-3051; ed fax (803) 496-3051; disp adv e-mail retailads@bellsouth.net; class adv e-mail retailads@bellsouth.net; ed e-mail newseditor@bellsouth.net

Circulation: 1,300pd,; Sworn/Estimate/Non-Audited
Advertising rate: Open inch rate $5.15
Pub....Joyce Searson
Ed....Doug Rogers
Delivery Method: Mail, Newsstand
Areas Served: Orangeburg County

IRMO

THE LAKE MURRAY NEWS (THUR)

PO Box 175, Irmo, SC, 29063-0175, Lexington, USA; gen tel (803) 772-5584; adv tel (803) 772-5584; ed tel (803) 772-5584; gen fax (803) 772-7795; adv fax (803) 772-7795; ed fax (803) 772-7795; disp adv e-mail lakemurraynews@aol.com; class adv e-mail lakemurraynews@aol.com; ed e-mail lakemurraynews@aol.com; web site www.thelakemurraynews.net
Circulation: 9,000pd,; Sworn/Estimate/Non-Audited
Advertising rate: Open inch rate $9.80
Digital Platform - Mobile: Apple, Android
Digital Platform - Tablet: Apple iOS, Android, Windows 7
Owner/Pub....Kirk Luther
Co-Pub./Ed....Rod Shealy Jr.
Delivery Method: Mail, Newsstand
Areas Served: Lexington County

KINGSTREE

THE NEWS (WED)

511 N Longstreet St, Kingstree, SC, 29556-3301, Williamsburg, USA; gen tel (843) 355-6397; adv tel (843) 355-7454; ed tel (843) 355-6397; gen fax (843) 355-6530; adv fax (843) 355-6530; ed fax (843) 355-6530; disp adv e-mail advertising@kingstreenews.com; class adv e-mail classifieds@kingstreenews.com; ed e-mail trodgers@kingstreenews.com; web site www.kingstreenews.com
Circulation: 4,800pd,; Sworn/Estimate/Non-Audited
Advertising rate: Open inch rate $6.90
Group: Evening Post Publishing Newspaper Group
Digital Platform - Mobile: Apple, Android
Digital Platform - Tablet: Apple iOS, Android, Windows 7
Pub./Ed....Tami Rodgers
Circ. Mgr....Patricia McCrea
Adv. Rep....Beth Ward
Mechanical Specifications: Type page 13 x 21; E - 6 cols, 2 1/24, 1/6 between; A - 6 cols, 2 1/24, 1/6 between; C - 9 cols, between. Equipment & Software: Hardware — APP/Mac; Software — Microsoft/Word 6.0, QPS/QuarkXPress 3.31, Adobe/Photoshop 3.0, Adobe/Acrobat.
Delivery Method: Mail, Newsstand
Areas Served: Williamsburg County

LAKE CITY

NEWS & POST (WED)

107 N Acline St, Lake City, SC, 29560-2129, Florence, USA; gen tel (843) 394-3571; adv tel (843) 394-3571; ed tel (843) 394-3571; gen fax (843) 394-5057; adv fax (843) 394-5057; ed fax (843) 394-5057; disp adv e-mail newsandpost@florencenews.com; class adv e-mail newsandpost@florencenews.com; ed e-mail newsandpost@florencenews.com; web site www.scnow.com
Circulation: 2,500pd,; Sworn/Estimate/Non-Audited
Advertising rate: Open inch rate $7.38
Group: World Media Enterprises Inc.
Digital Platform - Mobile: Apple, Android, Windows, Blackberry
Digital Platform - Tablet: Apple iOS, Android, Windows 7, Blackberry Tablet OS, Kindle, Nook, Kindle Fire
Pub./Ed....Donna Tracy
Circ. Mgr....David Johnson
Mechanical Specifications: Type page 13 x 21 1/2; E - 6 cols, between; A - 6 cols, between; C - 6 cols, between.Equipment & Software: Hardware — APP/Mac.
Delivery Method: Mail, Carrier, Racks
Areas Served: Florence County

LANCASTER

LANCASTER NEWS (WED, FRI, SUN)

701 N White St, Lancaster, SC, 29720-2174, Lancaster, USA; gen tel (803) 283-1133; adv tel (803) 283-1133; ed tel (803) 283-1133; gen fax (803) 283-8969; adv fax (803) 283-8969; ed fax (803) 283-8969; disp adv e-mail news@thelancasternews.com; class adv e-mail news@thelancasternews.com; ed e-mail news@thelancasternews.com; web site www.thelancasternews.com
Circulation: 12,500pd,; Sworn/Estimate/Non-Audited
Advertising rate: Open inch rate $16.87
Established: 1852
Group: Landmark Communications, Inc.
Landmark Community Newspapers, LLC
Digital Platform - Mobile: Apple, Android
Digital Platform - Tablet: Apple iOS, Android, Windows 7
Pub....Susan Rowell
Adv. Mgr....Leigh Airington
Circ. Mgr....Angela Vincent
Ed....Barbara Howell
Mng. Ed....Jane Alford
Prodn. Mgr....Bruce Adams
Mechanical Specifications:
Delivery Method: Mail, Newsstand, Racks
Areas Served: Lancaster County

LAURENS

LAURENS COUNTY ADVERTISER (WED, SAT)

226 W Laurens St, Laurens, SC, 29360-2960, Laurens, USA; gen tel (864) 984-2586; adv tel (864) 984-2586; ed tel (864) 984-2586; gen fax (864) 984-4039; adv fax (864) 984-4039; ed fax (864) 984-4039; disp adv e-mail advertising@lcadvertiser.com; class adv e-mail classifieds@lcadvertiser.com; ed e-mail news@lcadvertiser.com; web site www.laurenscountyadvertiser.net
Circulation: 250fr; Sworn/Estimate/Non-Audited
Advertising rate: Open inch rate $9.25
Digital Platform - Mobile: Apple, Android, Windows, Blackberry
Digital Platform - Tablet: Apple iOS, Android, Windows 7, Blackberry Tablet OS, Kindle, Nook, Kindle Fire
Adv. Mgr....James Brown
Prodn. Mgr....Marc Brown
Mechanical Specifications: Type page 13 x 21 1/2; E - 6 cols, 2 1/24, 1/6 between; A - 6 cols, 2 1/24, 1/6 between; C - 6 cols, 2 1/24, 1/6 between.Equipment & Software: Hardware — APP/Mac; Presses — 8-KP/ColorKing; Software — QPS/QuarkXPress, Adobe/Photoshop, Multi-Ad/Creator.
Delivery Method: Mail, Newsstand
Areas Served: Laurens County

LEXINGTON

LEXINGTON COUNTY CHRONICLE & THE DISPATCH-NEWS (THUR)

131 Swartz Rd, Lexington, SC, 29072-3623, Lexington, USA; gen tel (803) 359-7633; adv tel (803) 359-7633; ed tel (803) 359-7633; gen fax (803) 359-2936; disp adv e-mail lexingtonchronicle@gmail.com; class adv e-mail lexingtonchronicle@gmail.com; ed e-mail lexingtonchronicle@gmail.com; web site www.lexingtonchronicle.com
Circulation: 3,500pd, 6,000fr; Sworn/Estimate/Non-Audited
Advertising rate: Open inch rate $13.00
Established: 1870
Group: Lexington Publishing Co, Inc.
Digital Platform - Mobile: Apple, Android, Windows

Digital Platform - Tablet: Apple iOS, Android, Windows 7
Adv. Mgr. .... MacLeod Bellune
Ed. Emer. .... Jerry Bellune
Associate Publisher .... Ashley Steele
Metro Editor .... Hal Millard
Advertising Manager .... Linda Sauls
Managing Editor .... Mark Bellune
Advertising Representative .... Holly Vaucher
News Editor .... Rob Cottingham
Sports Editor .... Thomas Grant
Advertising Representative .... Roxanne Moore
Mechanical Specifications: Type page 10 1/2 x 21; E - 6 cols, 1.6458, .125 between;
Equipment & Software: Hardware — PC; Software — Adobe/InDesign 5.5
Delivery Method: Mail, Newsstand, Racks
Areas Served: 29033, 29036, 29063, 29070, 29072, 29073, 29123, 29160, 29169, 29170, 29172, 29212, 29210

MANNING

THE MANNING TIMES (THUR)
230 E Boyce St, Manning, SC, 29102-3441, Clarendon, USA; gen tel (803) 435-8422; gen fax (803) 435-4189; disp adv e-mail manningsctimes@gmail.com; class adv e-mail manningsctimes@gmail.com; ed e-mail editorial@manninglive.com; web site manninglive.com - 7,000(views) 150,000(visitors)
Circulation: 4,000pd, 14,000fr; Sworn/Estimate/Non-Audited
Advertising rate: Open inch rate $6.75
Established: 1882
Digital Platform - Mobile: Apple, Android
Digital Platform - Tablet: Apple iOS, Android, Windows 7
Ed. .... Robert Baker
Pub. .... Leigh Ann Maynard
Delivery Method: Mail, Newsstand, Racks
Areas Served: Clarendon County

MARION

MARION COUNTY NEWS JOURNAL (WED)
800 N MAIN ST, Marion, SC, 29571-2519, Marion, USA; gen tel (843) 423-7336 ; adv tel (843) 423-7336 ; ed tel (843) 423-7336 ; gen fax (843) 423-7111; adv fax (843) 423-7111; ed fax (843) 423-7111; disp adv e-mail advertising@marionnewsjournal.com; class adv e-mail classifiedads@marioncountynewsjournal.com ; ed e-mail mcnj@marioncountynewsjournal.com; web site www.marioncountynewsjournal.com - 23,458(views) 7,942(visitors)
Circulation: 6pd, 11,297fr; CVC
Advertising rate: Open inch rate $8.00
Established: 1996
Group: Swartz Media, LLC
Digital Platform - Mobile: Apple, Android, Windows, Blackberry
Digital Platform - Tablet: Apple iOS, Android, Windows 7, Blackberry Tablet OS, Kindle, Nook, Kindle Fire
Pub./Ed. .... Don Swartz
Adv. Dir. .... Kay Byrd
Web Mgr. .... Catherine Moreno
Prod. Mgr .... Beth Strett
Delivery Method: Mail, Newsstand, Racks
Areas Served: Marion County

MC CORMICK

MCCORMICK MESSENGER (THUR)
120 S Main St, Mc Cormick, SC, 29835-8345, McCormick, USA; gen tel (864) 852-3311; adv tel (864) 852-3311; ed tel (864) 852-3311; gen fax (864) 852-3528; adv fax (864) 852-3528; ed fax (864) 852-3528; disp adv e-mail mccmess@wctel.net; class adv e-mail mccmess@wctel.net; ed e-mail mccmess@wctel.net; web site www.themccormickmessenger.com
Circulation: 2,200pd,; Sworn/Estimate/Non-Audited
Advertising rate: Open inch rate $5.75
Established: 1902
Gen. Mgr. .... Vicki Dorn
Adv. Mgr. .... Ashley Creswell
Office Mgr. .... Karen Bowick
Mechanical Specifications: Type page 12 x 21 1/2; E - 6 cols, 2, 1/4 between; A - 6 cols, 2, 1/4 between; C - 6 cols, 2, 1/4 between. Equipment & Software: Hardware — APP/Mac Performa 6360, APP/iMac; Software — Microsoft/Word 6.01, Adobe/PageMaker 6.5.
Delivery Method: Mail, Newsstand
Areas Served: McCormick County

MYRTLE BEACH

CAROLINA FOREST CHRONICLE (THUR)
4761 Highway 501, Ste 3, Myrtle Beach, SC, 29579-9457, Horry, USA; gen tel (843) 236-4810; adv tel (843) 488-7234; ed tel (843) 488-7259; gen fax (843) 448-4860; adv fax (843) 448-4860; ed fax (843) 448-4860; disp adv e-mail shari.harms@myhorrynews.com; class adv e-mail shari.harms@myhorrynews.com; ed e-mail michael.smith@myhorrynews.com; web site www.myhorrynews.com
Circulation: 5,000pd, 125fr; Sworn/Estimate/Non-Audited
Advertising rate: Open inch rate $14.60
Established: 2007
Group: Waccamaw Publishers Inc.
Digital Platform - Mobile: Apple, Android, Windows, Blackberry
Digital Platform - Tablet: Apple iOS, Android, Windows 7, Blackberry Tablet OS, Kindle, Nook, Kindle Fire
Owner/Pub. .... Steve Robertson
Prod. Mgr. .... Betty Moses
Editor .... charles Perry
Advertising Director .... Shari Harms
Mechanical Specifications: Type page 10.62 x 21.Equipment & Software: Hardware — APP/Mac; Presses — Orient; Software — Microsoft/Word 5.0, Adobe/PageMaker 6.5, Multi-Ad/Creator 3.8, QPS/QuarkXPress 6.5.
Delivery Method: Mail, Newsstand, Racks
Areas Served: Horry County 29579

MYRTLE BEACH HERALD (FRI)
4761 Highway 501, Ste 3, Myrtle Beach, SC, 29579-9457, Horry, USA; gen tel (843) 236-4810; adv tel (843) 488-7234; ed tel (843) 488-7258; gen fax (843) 448-4860; adv fax (843) 448-4860; ed fax (843) 448-4860; disp adv e-mail shari.harms@myhorrynews.com; class adv e-mail shari.harms@myhorrynews.com; ed e-mail charles.perry@myhorrynews.com; web site www.myhorrynews.com
Circulation: 5,600pd, 125fr; Sworn/Estimate/Non-Audited
Advertising rate: Open inch rate $10.50
Established: 2009
Group: Waccamaw Publishers, Inc
Digital Platform - Mobile: Apple, Android, Windows, Blackberry
Digital Platform - Tablet: Apple iOS, Android, Windows 7, Blackberry Tablet OS, Kindle, Nook, Kindle Fire
Owner/Pub. .... Steve Robertson
Ed. .... Tom O'Dare
Advertising Directo .... Shari Harms
Mechanical Specifications: Type page 10.62 x 21.Equipment & Software: Hardware — APP/Mac; Presses — Orient; Software — Microsoft/Word 5.0, Adobe/PageMaker 6.5, Multi-Ad/Creator 3.8, QPS/QuarkXPress 6.5.
Delivery Method: Mail, Newsstand, Racks
Areas Served: Horry County 29577 29575 29572

NEWBERRY

THE NEWBERRY OBSERVER (MON, WED, FRI)
1716 Main St, Newberry, SC, 29108-3548, Newberry, USA; gen tel (803) 276-0625; adv tel (803) 276-0625; ed tel (803) 276-0625; gen fax (803) 276-1517; adv fax (803) 276-1517; ed fax (803) 276-1517; disp adv e-mail news@newberryobserver.com; class adv e-mail news@newberryobserver.com; ed e-mail news@newberryobserver.com; web site www.newberryobserver.com
Circulation: 7,000pd,; Sworn/Estimate/Non-Audited
Advertising rate: Open inch rate $8.40
Established: 1883
Group: Champion Media
Digital Platform - Mobile: Apple, Android
Digital Platform - Tablet: Apple iOS, Android, Windows 7
Pub. .... Ty Ransdell
Circ. Mgr. .... Tiffany Lancaster
Ed. .... Holly Astwood
Prodn. Mgr. .... Michelle Cromer
Mechanical Specifications: Type page 13 x 21 1/2; E - 6 cols, 1 1/2, 1/8 between; A - 6 cols, 1 1/2, 1/8 between; C - 8 cols, 1 1/8, 1/8 between.Equipment & Software: Hardware — APP/Mac; Presses — 8-G/Community; Software — QPS/QuarkXPress.
Delivery Method: Mail, Newsstand
Areas Served: Newberry County

NORTH AUGUSTA

THE STAR (THUR)
404 E Martintown Rd, Ste 2, North Augusta, SC, 29841-4236, Aiken, USA; gen tel (803) 279-2793; adv tel (803) 279-2793; ed tel (803) 279-2793; gen fax (803) 278-4070; adv fax (803) 278-4070; ed fax (803) 278-4070; disp adv e-mail rdallas@northaugustastar.com; class adv e-mail thargrove@northaugustastar.com; ed e-mail editor@northaugustastar.com; web site www.northaugustastar.com
Circulation: 4,000pd, 33fr; Sworn/Estimate/Non-Audited
Advertising rate: Open inch rate $7.34
Established: 1954
Group: Aiken Communications, Inc.
Evening Post Publishing Newspaper Group
Digital Platform - Mobile: Apple, Android
Digital Platform - Tablet: Apple iOS, Android, Windows 7
Exec. Ed. .... Melissa Hanna
News Ed. .... Scott Rodgers
Account Exec. Adv. .... Rechelle Dallas
Delivery Method: Mail, Newsstand
Areas Served: 29841, 29861, 29860

NORTH MYRTLE BEACH

NORTH MYRTLE BEACH TIMES (THUR)
203 Highay 17 North, North Myrtle Beach, SC, 29582, Horry, USA; gen tel (843) 249-3525; gen fax (843) 249-7012; disp adv e-mail nmbtimes@sc.rr.com; class adv e-mail nmbtimes@sc.rr.com; ed e-mail nmbtimes@sc.rr.com; web site www.nmbtimes.com
Circulation: 12,598pd, 200fr; USPS
Advertising rate: Open inch rate $9.00
Established: 1971
Digital Platform - Mobile: Apple, Windows
Digital Platform - Tablet: Apple iOS, Windows 7
Pub./Ed. .... Polly Lowman
Mechanical Specifications: Type page 11.5 x 21; E - 6 cols, between; A - 6 cols, between; C - 6 cols, between.
Delivery Method: Mail, Newsstand
Areas Served: Horry County

PAGELAND

PAGELAND PROGRESSIVE-JOURNAL (TUES)
28825 HIGHWAY 9, Pageland, SC, 29728, Chesterfield, USA; gen tel (843) 672-2358; ed tel (843) 672-3002; gen fax (843) 672-5593; disp adv e-mail dstokes@thelancasternews.com; class adv e-mail mcraig@thelancasternews.com; ed e-mail editor@pagelandprogressive.com; web site www.pagelandprogressive.com
Circulation: 3,000pd,; Sworn/Estimate/Non-Audited
Advertising rate: Open inch rate $6.00
Group: Landmark Communications, Inc.
Landmark Community Newspapers, LLC
Digital Platform - Mobile: Apple, Android, Windows, Blackberry
Digital Platform - Tablet: Apple iOS, Android, Windows 7, Blackberry Tablet OS, Kindle, Nook, Kindle Fire
Pub. .... Susan Rowell
Editor .... Kimberly Harrington
Office manager .... Sheila Whitaker
Sales consultant .... Donna Stokes
Reporter .... Vanessa Brewer-Tyson
Mechanical Specifications: Type page 13 x 21 1/2; E - 6 cols, 2, 1/5 between; A - 6 cols, 2, 1/5 between; C - 6 cols, 2, 1/5 between. Equipment & Software: Hardware — 1-APP/Mac G3, 2-APP/iMac; Software — InDesign 6, Adobe/Photoshop 5.0.
Delivery Method: Mail, Newsstand, Racks
Areas Served: 29728, 29718, 29727, 29741

PAWLEYS ISLAND

COASTAL OBSERVER (THUR)
97 Commerce Dr, Pawleys Island, SC, 29585-6011, Georgetown, USA; gen tel (843) 237-8438; adv tel (843) 237-8438; ed tel (843) 237-8438; gen fax (843) 235-0084; adv fax (843) 235-0084; ed fax (843) 235-0084; disp adv e-mail coastalobserverads@gmail.com; class adv e-mail coastalobserverads@gmail.com; ed e-mail editor@coastalobserver.com; web site www.coastalobserver.com
Circulation: 5,000pd,; Sworn/Estimate/Non-Audited
Advertising rate: Open inch rate $8.15
Established: 1982
Digital Platform - Mobile: Apple, Android, Windows, Blackberry
Digital Platform - Tablet: Apple iOS, Android, Windows 7, Blackberry Tablet OS
Pub. .... M.P. Swenson
Ed. .... Charles R. Swenson
Mechanical Specifications: Type page 13 x 21; E - 6 cols, 1 3/16, 5/36 between; A - 6 cols, 1 13/16, 5/36 between; C - 6 cols, 1 13/16, 5/36 between.
Delivery Method: Mail, Newsstand
Areas Served: Georgetown County

RIDGELAND

JASPER COUNTY SUN (WED)
138 S RAILROAD AVE, Ridgeland, SC, 29936, Jasper, USA; gen tel (843) 726-6161; adv tel (843) 726-6161; ed tel (843) 726-6161; gen fax (843) 726-8661; adv fax (843) 726-8661; ed fax (843) 726-8661; disp adv e-mail news@jaspercountysun.com; class adv e-mail news@jaspercountysun.com; ed e-mail news@jaspercountysun.com; web site www.jaspercountysun.com
Circulation: 6,000pd,; Sworn/Estimate/Non-Audited
Advertising rate: Open inch rate $8.00
Digital Platform - Mobile: Apple, Android
Digital Platform - Tablet: Apple iOS, Android
Ed. .... Anthony Garzilli
Sales Rep. .... Wanda Phillips
Office Mgr. .... Nancy White
Mechanical Specifications: Type page 13 x 21; E - 6 cols, 2, 1/6 between; A - 6 cols, 2, 1/6 between; C - 8 cols, 1 1/2, 1/6 between.
Delivery Method: Mail, Racks
Areas Served: Ridgeland and Jasper County

ROCK HILL

FORT MILL TIMES (WED)
132 W Main St, Rock Hill, SC, 29730-4430, York, USA; gen tel (803) 326-4315; adv tel (803) 326-4313; ed tel (803) 326-4315; disp adv e-mail gkerosetz@heraldonline.com ; class adv e-mail myoung@heraldonline.com ; ed e-mail news@fortmilltimes.com; web site www.fortmilltimes.com
Circulation: 24,000fr; Sworn/Estimate/Non-Audited

Advertising rate: Open inch rate $16.75
Established: 1892
Group: The McClatchy Company
Digital Platform - Mobile: Apple, Android, Blackberry
Digital Platform - Tablet: Apple iOS, Android, Windows 7, Blackberry Tablet OS
Ed. .... Michael Harrison
Reporter .... John Marks
Mechanical Specifications: Type page 11 1/2 x 21 1/2; E - 6 cols, 1 5/6, 3/20 between; A - 6 cols, 1 5/6, 3/20 between; C - 6 cols, 1 5/6, 3/20 between.Equipment & Software: Hardware — APP/Mac, APP/Mac G4; Software — Macromedia/Freehand 9.0, QPS/QuarkXPress 4.0, Adobe/Photoshop 4.0, Microsoft 5.0, Adobe/Illustrator 5.5.
Delivery Method: Mail, Newsstand, Carrier, Racks
Areas Served: York County
Lancaster County

SAINT GEORGE

THE EAGLE-RECORD (THUR)

5549 Memorial Blvd, Saint George, SC, 29477-2473, Dorchester, USA; gen tel (843) 563-3121; adv tel (843) 563-3121; ed tel (843) 563-3121; gen fax (843) 563-5355; adv fax (843) 563-5355; ed fax (843) 563-5355; disp adv e-mail eagle_record@bellsouth.net; class adv e-mail eagle_record@bellsouth.net; ed e-mail eagle_record@bellsouth.net; web site www.theeaglerecord.com
Circulation: 3,100pd,; Sworn/Estimate/Non-Audited
Advertising rate: Open inch rate $5.00
Established: 1899
Digital Platform - Mobile: Apple, Android, Windows, Blackberry
Digital Platform - Tablet: Apple iOS, Android, Windows 7, Blackberry Tablet OS
Pub./Ed. .... Andrew Gentry
Office Mgr./Circ. Mgr. .... Elizabeth Gentry
Adv. Dir. .... Victoria M. Owens
Prod. Mgr. .... Julie McAlhany
Mechanical Specifications: Type page 13 x 21 1/2; E - 2 cols, 4 1/4, between; A - 6 cols, 2 1/16, between; C - 8 cols, 1 1/2, between. Equipment & Software: Hardware — PCs; Software — Ami Pro.
Delivery Method: Mail, Newsstand
Areas Served: Dorchester County

SAINT MATTHEWS

THE CALHOUN TIMES (THUR)

1632 Bridge St, Saint Matthews, SC, 29135-1373, Calhoun, USA; gen tel (803) 874-3137; adv tel (803) 874-3137; ed tel (803) 874-3137; gen fax (803) 874-1588; adv fax (803) 874-1588; ed fax (803) 874-1588; disp adv e-mail thecalhountimes@windstream.net; class adv e-mail thecalhountimes@windstream.net; ed e-mail thecalhountimes@windstream.net
Circulation: 2,200pd, 20fr; Sworn/Estimate/Non-Audited
Advertising rate: Open inch rate $5.00
Established: 1929
Group: Rome News-Tribune
Pub. .... Edwin C. Morris
Ed. .... Edwin C. Sr.
Mechanical Specifications: Type page 13 1/8 x 21 1/2; E - 6 cols, 2, 1/4 between; A - 6 cols, 2, 1/4 between; C - 6 cols, 2, 1/4 between.
Delivery Method: Mail, Newsstand
Areas Served: Calhoun County

SALUDA

STANDARD SENTINEL (THUR)

302 N Main St, Saluda, SC, 29138-1353, Saluda, USA; gen tel (864) 445-2527; adv tel (864) 445-2527; ed tel (864) 445-2527; gen fax (864) 445-8679; adv fax (864) 445-8679; ed fax (864) 445-8679; disp adv e-mail sentinel@saludasc.com; class adv e-mail sentinel@saludasc.com; ed e-mail sentinel@saludasc.com; web site www.saludastandard-sentinel.com
Circulation: 4,200pd,; Sworn/Estimate/Non-Audited
Advertising rate: Open inch rate $4.80
Digital Platform - Tablet: Windows 7
Pub./Ed. .... Ralph B. Shealy
Mechanical Specifications: Type page 13 1/2 x 21 1/2; E - 6 cols, 2 1/20, between; A - 6 cols, 2 1/20, between; C - 6 cols, 2 1/20, between.Equipment & Software: Hardware — PC, 4-IBM; Software — Adobe/PageMaker 6.5, Archetype/Corel Draw 5.0.
Delivery Method: Mail, Newsstand
Areas Served: Saluda County

SUMMERVILLE

BERKELEY INDEPENDENT (WED)

104 E Doty Ave, Summerville, SC, 29483-6300, Berkeley, USA; gen tel (843) 761-6397; adv tel (843) 873-9424; ed tel (843) 761-6397; gen fax (843) 899-6996; adv fax (843) 899-6996; ed fax (843) 899-6996; disp adv e-mail amack@berkeleyind.com; class adv e-mail landerson@berkeleyind.com; ed e-mail dbrown@berkeleyind.com; web site www.berkeleyind.com
Circulation: 4,500pd,; Sworn/Estimate/Non-Audited
Advertising rate: Open inch rate $7.00
Established: 1987
Group: Evening Post Publishing Newspaper Group
Digital Platform - Mobile: Apple, Android, Windows, Blackberry
Digital Platform - Tablet: Apple iOS, Android, Windows 7, Blackberry Tablet OS, Kindle, Nook, Kindle Fire
Pub. .... Ellen Priest
Ed. .... Frank Johnson
Adv. Dir. .... Chris Zoeller
Bus. Mgr. .... Cheryl Cargill
Mechanical Specifications: Type page 13 x 21 1/4; E - 6 cols, 2, 1/4 between; A - 6 cols, 2, 1/4 between; C - 8 cols, 1 1/2, 1/4 between. Equipment & Software: Hardware — APP/Mac; Software — QPS/QuarkXPress 3.11, Microsoft/Word 5.0.
Delivery Method: Mail, Racks
Areas Served: Berkeley County

SUMMERVILLE JOURNAL-SCENE (WED, FRI)

104 E Doty Ave, Ste C, Summerville, SC, 29483-6394, Dorchester, USA; gen tel (843) 873-9424; adv tel (843) 873-9424; ed tel (843) 873-9424; gen fax (843) 873-9432; adv fax (843) 873-9432; ed fax (843) 873-9432; disp adv e-mail czoeller@journalscene.com; class adv e-mail nick@journalscene.com; ed e-mail jwatts@journalscene.com; web site www.journalscene.com
Circulation: 5,200pd, 21,500fr; Sworn/Estimate/Non-Audited
Advertising rate: Open inch rate $8.00
Established: 1972
Group: Evening Post Publishing Newspaper Group
Digital Platform - Mobile: Apple, Android, Windows, Blackberry
Digital Platform - Tablet: Apple iOS, Android, Windows 7, Blackberry Tablet OS, Kindle, Nook, Kindle Fire
Exec. Ed. .... Judy Watts
Adv. Dir. .... Chris Zoeller
Pub. .... Michael Chauvin
Bus. Mgr. .... Chloe Brothers
Mechanical Specifications: Type page 14 1/4 x 20 1/2; E - 6 cols, 2, 1/8 between; A - 6 cols, 2, 1/8 between; C - 6 cols, 2, 1/8 between.
Delivery Method: Mail, Racks
Areas Served: 29483, 29484, 29485, 29488, 29477, 29472

THE GAZETTE (THUR)

104 E Doty Ave Ste C, Summerville, Summerville, SC, 29483-6300, Dorchester, USA; gen tel (843) 873-9424; adv tel (843) 873-9424; ed tel (843) 873-9424; gen fax (843) 873-9432; adv fax (843) 873-9432; ed fax (843) 873-9432; disp adv e-mail czoeller@journalscene.com; class adv e-mail jasmine@ourgazette.com ; ed e-mail fjohnson@ourgazette.com; web site www.ourgazette.com
Circulation: 77pd, 15,000fr; Sworn/Estimate/Non-Audited
Advertising rate: Open inch rate $10.50
Group: Evening Post Publishing Newspaper Group
Digital Platform - Mobile: Apple, Android, Windows, Blackberry
Digital Platform - Tablet: Apple iOS, Android, Windows 7, Blackberry Tablet OS, Kindle, Nook, Kindle Fire
Pub. .... Ellen Priest
Ed. .... Frank Johnson
Adv. Dir. .... Chris Zoeller
Mechanical Specifications: Type page 13 x ; E - 6 cols, 2 1/8, 3/16 between; A - 6 cols, 1 1/2, 3/16 between; C - 8 cols, 1 1/2, 3/16 between.Equipment & Software: Hardware — APP/Mac; Software — Simple Text, QPS/QuarkXPress.
Delivery Method: Mail, Racks
Areas Served: Goose Creek and Hanahan

WALHALLA

KEOWEE COURIER (WED)

118 S College St, Walhalla, SC, 29691-2258, Oconee, USA; gen tel (864) 638-5856; adv tel (864) 638-5856; ed tel (864) 638-5856; gen fax (864) 638-5857; adv fax (864) 638-5857; ed fax (864) 638-5857; disp adv e-mail keoweecourier@bellsouth.net; class adv e-mail westnews@bellsouth.net; ed e-mail westnews@bellsouth.net; web site www.laserbuddy.com/news/kc.htm
Circulation: 2,300pd, 206fr; Sworn/Estimate/Non-Audited
Advertising rate: Open inch rate $6.00
Established: 1849
Group: Keowee Publications, Inc.
Digital Platform - Mobile: Apple, Android
Digital Platform - Tablet: Apple iOS, Android, Windows 7
Pub. .... Robert E. Tribble
Ed. .... Ashton Hester
Delivery Method: Mail, Newsstand
Areas Served: Walhalla, West Union, Salem, Tamassee, Keowee Community, Keowee Key, and Mountain Rest

WALTERBORO

THE PRESS AND STANDARD (THUR)

1025 Bells Hwy, Walterboro, SC, 29488-2507, Colleton, USA; gen tel (843) 549-2586; adv tel (843) 549-2586; ed tel (843) 549-2586; gen fax (843) 549-2446; adv fax (843) 549-2446; ed fax (843) 549-2446; disp adv e-mail pressadvertisiing@lowcountry.com; class adv e-mail pressadvertising@lowcountry.com; ed e-mail editor@lowcountry.com; web site walterborolive.com
Circulation: 4,500pd,; Sworn/Estimate/Non-Audited
Advertising rate: Open inch rate $10.00
Established: 1877
Digital Platform - Mobile: Apple, Android, Windows, Blackberry
Digital Platform - Tablet: Apple iOS, Android, Windows 7, Blackberry Tablet OS
Pub. .... Barry Moore
Mechanical Specifications: Type page 10 1/16 x 21 1/2; E - 6 cols, 1 13/16, 1/6 between; A - 6 cols, 1 13/16, 1/6 between; C - 6 cols, 1 3/8, 1/6 between.Equipment & Software: Hardware — APP/Mac G3s; Software — QPS/QuarkXPress 4.0.
Delivery Method: Mail, Newsstand, Racks
Areas Served: Colleton County

WARE SHOALS

THE WARE SHOALS OBSERVER (WED)

730 N Greenwood Ave, Ware Shoals, SC, 29692-1233, Abbeville, USA; gen tel (864) 456-7772; adv tel (864) 456-7772; ed tel (864) 456-7772; gen fax (864) 456-7122; adv fax (864) 456-7122; ed fax (864) 456-7122; disp adv e-mail theobserver@embarqmail.com; class adv e-mail theobserver@embarqmail.com; ed e-mail theobserver@embarqmail.com
Circulation: 2,950pd, 50fr; Sworn/Estimate/Non-Audited
Advertising rate: Open inch rate $3.50
Pub. .... S. Daniel Branyon
Ed. .... Faye Branyon
Delivery Method: Mail, Newsstand
Areas Served: Abbeville County

WESTMINSTER

THE WESTMINSTER NEWS (WED)

100 E Main St, Westminster, SC, 29693-1715, Oconee, USA; gen tel (864) 647-5404; adv tel (864) 647-5404; ed tel (864) 647-5404; gen fax (864) 647-5405; adv fax (864) 647-5405; ed fax (864) 647-5405; disp adv e-mail westnews@bellsouth.net; class adv e-mail westnews@bellsouth.net; ed e-mail westnews@bellsouth.net; web site www.westminstersc.com
Circulation: 2,500pd, 50fr; Sworn/Estimate/Non-Audited
Advertising rate: Open inch rate $5.75
Established: 1954
Group: Trib Publications
Digital Platform - Mobile: Windows
Digital Platform - Tablet: Windows 7
Pres./Pub. .... Robert E. Tribble
Mng. Ed. .... Mary Beth King
Ed. .... Rolann Lee
Delivery Method: Mail, Newsstand
Areas Served: Westminster, Long Creek, Oakway, Madison, Pleasant Grove, Hopewell, Holly Springs, Toxaway, and Weldon Road

WILLIAMSTON

THE JOURNAL (WED)

106 W Main St, Williamston, SC, 29697-1404, Anderson, USA; gen tel (864) 847-7361; adv tel (864) 847-7361; ed tel (864) 847-7361; gen fax (864) 847-9879; adv fax (864) 847-9879; ed fax (864) 847-9879; disp adv e-mail tina@thejournalonline.com; class adv e-mail tina@thejournalonline.com; ed e-mail editor@thejournalonline.com; web site www.thejournalonline.com
Circulation: 2,500pd,; USPS
Advertising rate: Open inch rate $11.50 (Commissionable); $10.00 (Local)
Established: 1955
Digital Platform - Mobile: Apple, Android
Digital Platform - Tablet: Apple iOS, Android, Windows 7
Mng. Ed. .... David C. Meade
Prod. Mgr. .... Richard A. Meade
Graphics/Layout/Legal Adv. Mgr. .... Tina WilliamsEquipment & Software: Hardware — APP/Mac, PC; Presses — 7-WPC/Web, KP/News King; Software — Adobe/PageMaker 7.0.
Delivery Method: Mail, Newsstand, Racks
Areas Served: 29697, 29669, 29673
NE Anderson County

WINNSBORO

THE HERALD INDEPENDENT (TUES, FRI)

127 N Congress St, Winnsboro, SC, 29180-1118, Fairfield, USA; gen tel (803) 635-4016; adv tel (803) 276-0625; ed tel (803) 635-4016; gen fax (803) 635-2948; adv fax (803) 635-2948; ed fax (803) 635-2948; disp adv e-mail demmons@civitasmedia.com; class adv e-mail mwainscott@civitasmedia.com; ed e-mail hieditor@heraldindependent.com; web site www.heraldindependent.com
Circulation: 3,000pd,; Sworn/Estimate/Non-Audited

Advertising rate: Open inch rate $10.80
Established: 1982
Group: Civitas Media, LLC-OOB
Digital Platform - Mobile: Apple, Android
Digital Platform - Tablet: Apple iOS, Android, Windows 7
Pub./Ed./Gen. Mgr....................James Denton
Regional Sales Dir....................David Emmons
Classified Exec....................Martha Wainscott
Mechanical Specifications: Type page 13 x 21 1/2; E - 6 cols, 2, 1/6 between; A - 6 cols, 2, 1/6 between; C - 6 cols, 2, 1/6 between. Equipment & Software: Hardware — APP/Mac; Software — Adobe/PageMaker 6.0.
Delivery Method: Mail, Newsstand
Areas Served: Fairfield County

SOUTH DAKOTA

ABERDEEN

FARM FORUM (FRI)
124 S 2nd St, Aberdeen, SD, 57401-4010, Brown, USA; gen tel (605)225-4100; adv tel (605)622-2264; ed tel (605)622-2318; disp adv e-mail farmforum@aberdeennews.com; class adv e-mail farmforum@aberdeennews.com; ed e-mail farmforum@aberdeennews.com; web site www.farmforum.net
Circulation: 35,409fr; CAC
Group: Schurz Communications Inc
Ed....................Stan Wise
Adv. Dir....................Christy Orwig
Delivery Method: Mail

ALCESTER

ALCESTER UNION & HUDSONITE (THUR)
110 E First St, Alcester, SD, 57001, Union, USA; gen tel (605) 934-2640; adv tel (605) 934-2640; ed tel (605) 934-2640; gen fax (605) 934-2096; adv fax (605) 934-2096; ed fax (605) 934-2096; disp adv e-mail advertising@ahenews.com; class adv e-mail info@ahenews.com; ed e-mail publisher@ahenews.com; web site www.ahenews.com
Circulation: 890pd, 35fr; USPS
Advertising rate: Open inch rate $4.45 (Local); $5.62 (National)
Established: 1889
Group: Paragon Publishing
Digital Platform - Mobile: Windows
Digital Platform - Tablet: Windows 7
Pub./Ed....................Paul Buum
Circ. Mgr....................Michele Buum
Mechanical Specifications: Type page 10.25" x 16", 5 col., 1 pica gutterEquipment & Software: Hardware — PC's; Software — InDesign, Photoshop, Illustrator, Microsoft Office
Delivery Method: Mail, Racks
Areas Served: 57001, 57034, 57004, 51001, 51023

ALEXANDRIA

THE ALEXANDRIA HERALD (THUR)
531 Main St, Alexandria, SD, 57311-2286, Hanson, USA; gen tel (605) 239-4521; adv tel (605) 239-4521; ed tel (605) 239-4521; gen fax (605) 449-4430; adv fax (605) 449-4430; ed fax (605) 449-4430; disp adv e-mail ementerprise@triotel.net; class adv e-mail ementerprise@triotel.net; ed e-mail ementerprise@triotel.net; web site www.anderson-publications.com
Circulation: 430pd, 15fr; Sworn/Estimate/Non-Audited
Advertising rate: Open inch rate $3.73
Pub./Ed....................Matt Anderson
Mng. Ed....................Terry Janssen
Mechanical Specifications: Type page 9 3/4 x 16; E - 5 cols, 1 13/16, 3/16 between.Equipment & Software: Hardware — APP/iMac; Presses — ABD; Software — Adobe/PageMaker, Adobe/Photoshop.
Delivery Method: Mail, Newsstand
Areas Served: 57311, 57340, 57332

ARLINGTON

THE ARLINGTON SUN (THUR)
208 S Main St, Arlington, SD, 57212-8000, Kingsbury, USA; gen tel (605) 983-5491; adv tel (605) 983-5491; ed tel (605) 983-5491; gen fax (866) 314-4217; adv fax (866) 314-4217; ed fax (866) 314-4217; disp adv e-mail asn@mchsi.com; class adv e-mail asn@mchsi.com; ed e-mail asn@mchsi.com; web site www.rfdnewsgroup.com
Circulation: 900pd,; Sworn/Estimate/Non-Audited
Advertising rate: Open inch rate $5.00
Established: 1885
Digital Platform - Mobile: Apple, Windows
Digital Platform - Tablet: Apple iOS, Windows 7
Pub....................Chris Schumacher
Co-Pub....................Linda Schumacher
Adv. Mgr....................Aggie Cleveland
Ed....................Frank Crisler
Delivery Method: Mail, Newsstand, Racks
Areas Served: 57212, 57214, 57244, 57071, 57061, 57051, 57248, 57249, 57220

ARMOUR

THE ARMOUR CHRONICLE (TUES)
624 MAIN AVE, Armour, SD, 57313, Douglas, USA; gen tel (605) 724-2747; adv tel (605) 724-2747; ed tel (605) 724-2747; gen fax (605) 724-2947; adv fax (605) 724-2947; ed fax (605) 724-2947; disp adv e-mail chronicle@unitelsd.com; class adv e-mail chronicle@unitelsd.com; ed e-mail chronicle@unitelsd.com
Circulation: 913pd, 10fr; Sworn/Estimate/Non-Audited
Advertising rate: Open inch rate $6.25
Digital Platform - Mobile: Windows
Digital Platform - Tablet: Windows 7
Editor/Publisher....................Gerri Olson
Delivery Method: Mail, Racks
Areas Served: 57313, 57330, 57328

THE DELMONT RECORD (TUES)
624 MAIN AVE, Armour, SD, 57313, Douglas, USA; gen tel (605) 724-2747; adv tel (605) 724-2747; ed tel (605) 724-2747; gen fax (605) 724-2947; adv fax (605) 724-2947; ed fax (605) 724-2947; disp adv e-mail chronicle@unitelsd.com; class adv e-mail chronicle@unitelsd.com; ed e-mail chronicle@unitelsd.com
Circulation: 220pd, 10fr; Sworn/Estimate/Non-Audited
Advertising rate: Open inch rate $6.25
Digital Platform - Mobile: Windows
Digital Platform - Tablet: Windows 7
Editor/Publisher....................Gerri Olson
Delivery Method: Mail, Racks
Areas Served: 57313, 57330, 57328

AVON

AVON CLARION (WED)
103 MAIN ST N, Avon, SD, 57315, Bon Homme, USA; gen tel (605) 286-3919; adv tel (605) 286-3919; ed tel (605) 286-3919; gen fax (605) 286-3507; adv fax (605) 286-3507; ed fax (605) 286-3507; disp adv e-mail theavonclarion@yahoo.com; class adv e-mail theavonclarion@yahoo.com; ed e-mail theavonclarion@yahoo.com; web site www.avonsd.com
Circulation: 800pd,; Sworn/Estimate/Non-Audited
Advertising rate: Open inch rate $5.00
Pub./Ed./Adv. Mgr....................Jackson S. Brodeen
Delivery Method: Mail, Racks
Areas Served: 57315, 57062, 57066, 57380, 57329, 57078

BERESFORD

BERESFORD REPUBLIC (THUR)
111 N 3rd St, Beresford, SD, 57004-1741, Union, USA; gen tel (605) 763-2006; adv tel (605) 763-2006; ed tel (605) 763-2006; gen fax (605) 763-5503; adv fax (605) 763-5503; ed fax (605) 763-5503; disp adv e-mail republic@bmtc.net; class adv e-mail republic@bmtc.net; ed e-mail republic@bmtc.net
Circulation: 1,200pd,; Sworn/Estimate/Non-Audited
Advertising rate: Open inch rate $4.50
Established: 1894
Group: Star Publishing Co.
Pub....................Shane Hill
Pub./Ed....................Allyson Hill
Delivery Method: Mail, Newsstand, Racks
Areas Served: 57004, 57001, 57014, 57013

BISON

THE BISON COURIER (THUR)
122A W Main St, Bison, SD, 57620, Perkins, USA; gen tel (605) 244-7199; adv tel (605) 244-7199; ed tel (605) 244-7199; gen fax (605) 244-7198; adv fax (605) 244-7198; ed fax (605) 244-7198; disp adv e-mail courier@sdplains.com; class adv e-mail courier@sdplains.com; ed e-mail courier@sdplains.com; web site www.ravellettepublications.com
Circulation: 750pd, 25fr; Sworn/Estimate/Non-Audited
Advertising rate: Open inch rate $4.70
Digital Platform - Mobile: Apple, Android
Digital Platform - Tablet: Apple iOS, Android, Windows 7
Pub....................Don Ravellette
Gen. Mgr....................Marsha Veal
Mechanical Specifications: Type page 12 x 16; A - 2 cols, between.Equipment & Software: ; Software — Microsoft/Windows 3.1, WordPerfect, Adobe/PageMaker.
Delivery Method: Mail, Racks
Areas Served: 57620, 57644, 57649

BRANDON

BRANDON VALLEY CHALLENGER (WED)
1400 E Cedar St, Brandon, SD, 57005-1604, Minnehaha, USA; gen tel (605) 582-6025; adv tel (605) 582-6025; ed tel (605) 582-6025; gen fax (605) 582-7184; adv fax (605) 582-7184; ed fax (605) 582-7184; disp adv e-mail aschultz@argusleader.com; class adv e-mail aschultz@argusleader.com; ed e-mail apthiele@argusleader.com; web site www.brandoninfo.com
Circulation: 1,200pd, 5,700fr; Sworn/Estimate/Non-Audited
Advertising rate: Open inch rate $5.35
Group: Gannett
Digital Platform - Mobile: Apple, Android
Digital Platform - Tablet: Apple iOS, Android, Windows 7
Ed....................Jill Meier
Adv. Mgr....................Andrea Schultz
Delivery Method: Mail, Racks
Areas Served: 57317, 57335, 57571

BRIDGEWATER

BRIDGEWATER TRIBUNE (THUR)
440 N Main St, Bridgewater, SD, 57319, McCook, USA; gen tel (605) 425-2361; adv tel (605) 425-2361; ed tel (605) 425-2361; gen fax (605) 425-2547; adv fax (605) 425-2547; ed fax (605) 425-2547; disp adv e-mail tschwans@triotel.net; class adv e-mail tschwans@triotel.net; ed e-mail tschwans@triotel.net; web site www.salemspecial.com
Circulation: 350pd, 50fr; Sworn/Estimate/Non-Audited
Advertising rate: Open inch rate $4.20
Digital Platform - Mobile: Windows
Digital Platform - Tablet: Windows 7
Ed....................Troy Schwans
Delivery Method: Mail, Racks
Areas Served: 57319, 57332, 57311, 57374, 57029, 57023, 57058, 57012

BRITTON

LANGFORD BUGLE (WED)
706 Seventh St, Britton, SD, 57430, Marshall, USA; gen tel (605) 448-2281; gen fax (605) 448-2282; disp adv e-mail hgnice@brittonsd.com; class adv e-mail kbuhl@brittonsd.com; ed e-mail dcard@brittonsd.com; web site www.marshallcountyjournal.com
Circulation: 485pd,; Sworn/Estimate/Non-Audited
Advertising rate: Open inch rate $6.10
Digital Platform - Mobile: Apple, Android, Windows, Blackberry
Digital Platform - Tablet: Apple iOS, Android, Windows 7, Blackberry Tablet OS
Pub./Ed....................Douglas M. Card
Adv. Mgr....................Helen Nice
Delivery Method: Mail, Racks
Areas Served: 57454, 57468, 57432, 57430, 57401

THE BRITTON JOURNAL (WED)
706 Seventh St, Britton, SD, 57430, Marshall, USA; gen tel (605) 448-2281; adv tel (605) 448-2281; ed tel (605) 448-2281; gen fax (605) 448-2282; adv fax (605) 448-2282; ed fax (605) 448-2282; disp adv e-mail hgnice@brittonsd.com; class adv e-mail journal@brittonsd.com; ed e-mail dcard@brittonsd.com; web site www.marshallcountyjournal.com
Circulation: 1,779pd, 50fr; Sworn/Estimate/Non-Audited
Advertising rate: Open inch rate $6.50
Digital Platform - Mobile: Apple, Android, Windows, Blackberry
Digital Platform - Tablet: Apple iOS, Android, Windows 7, Blackberry Tablet OS
Pub./Ed....................Douglas M. Card
Ann Stiegelmeier
Stephanie Elsaas
Delivery Method: Mail, Racks
Areas Served: 57421, 57430, 57432, 57232, 57247, 57454, 57446, 57270, 58017, 58043

BRYANT

THE BRYANT DAKOTAN (WED)
110 W Main St, Bryant, SD, 57221-2058, Hamlin, USA; gen tel (605) 628-2551; adv tel (605) 628-2551; ed tel (605) 628-2551; gen fax (605) 881-4008; adv fax (605) 881-4008; ed fax (605) 881-4008; disp adv e-mail dakotan@datatruck.com; class adv e-mail dakotan@datatruck.com; ed e-mail dakotan@datatruck.com
Circulation: 504pd, 30fr; Sworn/Estimate/Non-Audited
Advertising rate: Open inch rate $4.00
Established: 1979
Pub./Ed....................Stephanie Bawdon
Mechanical Specifications: Type page 9 3/4 x 13 3/4.Equipment & Software: Hardware — APP/Mac; Software — QPS/QuarkXPress.
Delivery Method: Mail
Areas Served: 57221, 57241, 57248, 57233, 57242, 57271, 57278

BUFFALO

NATION'S CENTER NEWS (WED)
PO Box 107, Buffalo, SD, 57720-0107, Harding, USA; gen tel (605) 642-2761; adv tel (605) 642-2761; ed tel (605) 642-2761; gen fax (605) 642-9060; adv fax (605) 642-9060; ed fax (605) 642-9060; disp adv e-mail Dru@bhpioneer.com; class adv e-mail classifieds@bhpioneer.com; ed e-mail news@bhpioneer.com; web site www.bhpioneer.com
Circulation: 1,200pd,; Sworn/Estimate/Non-Audited
Advertising rate: Open inch rate $3.50

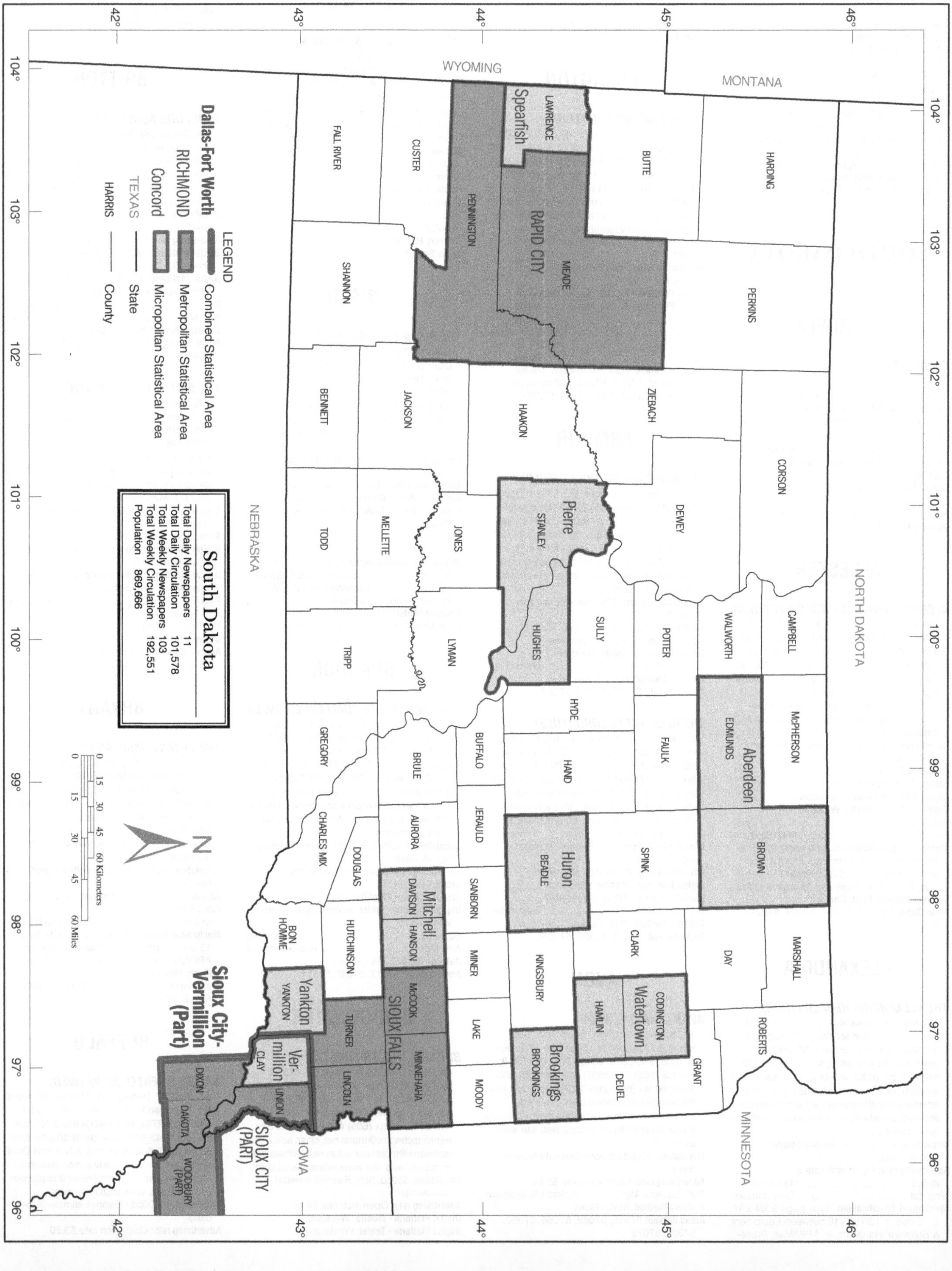
South Dakota
Total Daily Newspapers 11
Total Daily Circulation 101,578
Total Weekly Newspapers 103
Total Weekly Circulation 192,551
Population 869,666
LEGEND
Dallas-Fort Worth Combined Statistical Area
RICHMOND Metropolitan Statistical Area
Concord Micropolitan Statistical Area
TEXAS State
HARRIS County
WYOMING
MONTANA
NORTH DAKOTA
MINNESOTA
IOWA
NEBRASKA
RAPID CITY
Spearfish
Pierre
Aberdeen
Huron
Mitchell
Watertown
Brookings
Yankton
Vermillion
SIOUX FALLS
Sioux City-Vermillion (Part)
SIOUX CITY (PART)
LAWRENCE
BUTTE
HARDING
PERKINS
MEADE
PENNINGTON
CUSTER
FALL RIVER
SHANNON
JACKSON
BENNETT
HAAKON
ZIEBACH
CORSON
DEWEY
STANLEY
JONES
MELLETTE
TODD
TRIPP
LYMAN
HUGHES
SULLY
POTTER
WALWORTH
CAMPBELL
McPHERSON
EDMUNDS
FAULK
HYDE
HAND
BUFFALO
BRULE
GREGORY
CHARLES MIX
AURORA
JERAULD
BEADLE
SPINK
BROWN
DAY
MARSHALL
ROBERTS
GRANT
CODINGTON
CLARK
HAMLIN
DEUEL
KINGSBURY
BROOKINGS
MINER
SANBORN
DAVISON
HANSON
DOUGLAS
HUTCHINSON
BON HOMME
YANKTON
McCOOK
LAKE
MOODY
MINNEHAHA
TURNER
LINCOLN
CLAY
UNION
DIXON
DAKOTA
WOODBURY (PART)
0 15 30 45 60 Kilometers
0 15 30 45 60 Miles
N

Established: 1978
Digital Platform - Mobile: Apple, Windows
Digital Platform - Tablet: Apple iOS, Windows 7
Pub. .... Letitia Lister
Ed. .... Mark Watson
Adv. Mgr. .... Dru Thomas
Delivery Method: Mail, Racks
Areas Served: 57720, 57785, 57649, 57654, 57717, 57701, 58649, 57651, 58633, 58639

BURKE

THE BURKE GAZETTE (WED)

825 Main St, Burke, SD, 57523, Gregory, USA; gen tel (605) 775-2612; adv tel (605) 775-2612; ed tel (605) 775-2612; gen fax (605) 775-2612; adv fax (605) 775-2612; ed fax (605) 775-2612; disp adv e-mail burkegaz@gwtc.net; class adv e-mail burkegaz@gwtc.net; ed e-mail burkegaz@gwtc.net; web site www.burkegazette.com
Circulation: 1,250pd,; USPS
Advertising rate: Open inch rate $4.00
Established: 1904
Digital Platform - Mobile: Apple
Digital Platform - Tablet: Apple iOS
Pub./Ed. .... C.J. Fahrenbacher
Mechanical Specifications: Type page 10 1/2 x 13; E - 5 cols, 2 , 1/8 between; A - 5 cols, 2 , 1/8 between; C - 5 cols, 2 , 1/8 between. Equipment & Software: Hardware — APP/Mac; Software — Adobe/PageMaker 5.0.
Delivery Method: Mail, Newsstand
Areas Served: 57523, 57533, 57317, 57538, 57335, 57529, 68755

CANISTOTA

CANISTOTA CLIPPER (THUR)

210 W Main St, Canistota, SD, 57012, McCook, USA; gen tel (605) 296-3181; adv tel (605) 296-3181; ed tel (605) 296-3181; gen fax (605) 296-3289; adv fax (605) 296-3289; ed fax (605) 296-3289; disp adv e-mail ads@andersonpublications.com; class adv e-mail ads@andersonpublications.com; ed e-mail news@andersonpublications.com
Circulation: 625pd,; Sworn/Estimate/Non-Audited
Advertising rate: Open inch rate $2.25
Pub./Ed. .... Matt Anderson
Gen. Mgr. .... Jelene Olsen
Delivery Method: Mail, Racks
Areas Served: 57012, 57043, 57047, 57058, 57319, 57048, 57023

MONTROSE HERALD (THUR)

210 W Main St, Canistota, SD, 57012, McCook, USA; gen tel (605) 296-3181; adv tel (605) 296-3181; ed tel (605) 296-3181; gen fax (605) 296-3289; adv fax (605) 296-3289; ed fax (605) 296-3289; disp adv e-mail ads@andersonpublications.com; class adv e-mail ads@andersonpublications.com; ed e-mail news@andersonpublications.com
Circulation: 518pd,; Sworn/Estimate/Non-Audited
Advertising rate: Open inch rate $3.00
Pub./Ed. .... Matt Anderson
Gen. Mgr. .... Jelene Olsen
Delivery Method: Mail, Racks
Areas Served: 57012, 57043, 57047, 57058, 57319, 57048, 57023

THE HARTFORD AREA NEWS (THUR)

210 W Main St, Canistota, SD, 57012, McCook, USA; gen tel (605) 296-3181; adv tel (605) 296-3181; ed tel (605) 296-3181; gen fax (605) 296-3289; adv fax (605) 296-3289; ed fax (605) 296-3289; disp adv e-mail ads@andersonpublications.com; class adv e-mail ads@andersonpublications.com; ed e-mail news@andersonpublications.com
Circulation: 636pd,; Sworn/Estimate/Non-Audited
Advertising rate: Open inch rate $3.25
Pub./Ed. .... Matt Anderson
Gen. Mgr. .... Jelene Olsen
Delivery Method: Mail, Racks
Areas Served: 57012, 57043, 57047, 57058, 57319, 57048, 57023

THE HUMBOLDT JOURNAL (THUR)

210 W Main St, Canistota, SD, 57012, McCook, USA; gen tel (605) 296-3181; adv tel (605) 296-3181; ed tel (605) 296-3181; gen fax (605) 296-3289; adv fax (605) 296-3289; ed fax (605) 296-3289; disp adv e-mail ads@andersonpublications.com; class adv e-mail ads@andersonpublications.com; ed e-mail news@andersonpublications.com
Circulation: 399pd,; Sworn/Estimate/Non-Audited
Advertising rate: Open inch rate $3.25
Pub./Ed. .... Matt Anderson
Gen. Mgr. .... Jelene Olsen
Delivery Method: Mail, Racks
Areas Served: 57012, 57043, 57047, 57058, 57319, 57048, 57023

CANTON

SIOUX VALLEY NEWS (THUR)

213 E 5th St, Canton, SD, 57013-1733, Lincoln, USA; gen tel (605) 764-2000; adv tel (605) 764-2000; ed tel (605) 764-2000; gen fax (605) 764-6397; adv fax (605) 764-6397; ed fax (605) 764-6397; disp adv e-mail svn@SiouxValleyNewsOnline.com; class adv e-mail svn@SiouxValleyNewsOnline.com; ed e-mail svn@SiouxValleyNewsOnline.com; web site www.siouxvalleynewsonline.com
Circulation: 1,680pd, 0fr; Sworn/Estimate/Non-Audited
Advertising rate: Open inch rate $6.50/$7.50 Classifieds
Established: 1872
Digital Platform - Mobile: Apple, Android
Digital Platform - Tablet: Apple iOS, Android, Windows 7
Pub./Ed. .... Andy Wilcox
Delivery Method: Mail, Newsstand, Racks
Areas Served: 57013, 57077, 57034, 57032, 57027, 51240

CASTLEWOOD

HAMLIN COUNTY REPUBLICAN (WED)

123 E Main St, Castlewood, SD, 57223, Hamlin, USA; gen tel (605) 793-2293; adv tel (605) 793-2293; ed tel (605) 793-2293; gen fax (605) 793-9140; adv fax (605) 793-9140; ed fax (605) 793-9140; disp adv e-mail hcp@itctel.com; class adv e-mail hcp@itctel.com; ed e-mail hcp@itctel.com; web site www.hamlincountypublishing.com
Circulation: 800pd,; Sworn/Estimate/Non-Audited
Advertising rate: Open inch rate $5.00
Group: Hamlin County Publishing, Inc.
Digital Platform - Mobile: Windows
Digital Platform - Tablet: Windows 7
Pub. .... LeeAnne Dufek
News Ed. .... Jenna Aderhold
Adv. Mgr. .... Doug Kruiter
Delivery Method: Mail
Areas Served: 57223, 57201, 57226, 57241, 57006, 57234

CENTERVILLE

CENTERVILLE JOURNAL (THUR)

1000 Washington St, Centerville, SD, 57014-2218, Turner, USA; gen tel (605) 563-2351; adv tel (605) 563-2351; ed tel (605) 563-2351; gen fax (605) 326-5333; adv fax (605) 326-5333; ed fax (605) 326-5333; disp adv e-mail journal@iw.net; class adv e-mail journal@iw.net; ed e-mail journal@iw.net
Circulation: 810pd,; Sworn/Estimate/Non-Audited
Advertising rate: Open inch rate $3.85
Group: Star Publishing Co.
Pub. .... Shane Hill
Ed. .... Allyson Hill
Mechanical Specifications: Type page 10 x 15; E - 5 cols, 1 5/6, 1/6 between; A - 5 cols, 1 5/6, 1/6 between; C - 5 cols, 1 5/6, 1/6 between. Equipment & Software: Hardware — APP/Mac; Software — Adobe/PageMaker 6.5, Adobe/Photoshop 4.0.
Delivery Method: Mail
Areas Served: 57014, 57004

CLARK

CLARK COUNTY COURIER (WED)

119 1st Ave E, Clark, SD, 57225-1712, Clark, USA; gen tel (605) 532-3654; adv tel (605) 532-3654; ed tel (605) 532-3654; gen fax (605) 532-5424; adv fax (605) 532-5424; ed fax (605) 532-5424; disp adv e-mail courier@itctel.com; class adv e-mail courier@itctel.com; ed e-mail courier@itctel.com; web site www.clarkcountypublishing.com
Circulation: 2,400pd, 33fr; Sworn/Estimate/Non-Audited
Advertising rate: Open inch rate $4.50
Established: 1885
Digital Platform - Mobile: Apple, Android
Digital Platform - Tablet: Apple iOS, Android, Windows 7
Pub./Ed. .... Bill Krikac
Delivery Method: Mail, Newsstand, Racks
Areas Served: 57225, 57217, 57322, 57236, 57243, 57350, 57258, 57271, 57278

CLEAR LAKE

CLEAR LAKE COURIER (WED)

416 3rd Ave S, Clear Lake, SD, 57226, Deuel, USA; gen tel (605) 874-2499; adv tel (605) 874-2499; ed tel (605) 874-2499; gen fax (605) 874-2642; adv fax (605) 874-2642; ed fax (605) 874-2642; disp adv e-mail clprint@itctel.com; class adv e-mail clprint@itctel.com; ed e-mail clprint@itctel.com
Circulation: 1,500pd, 25fr; Sworn/Estimate/Non-Audited
Advertising rate: Open inch rate $5.75
Pub./Ed. .... Kenneth Reiste
Adv. Mgr. .... Nancy A. Greene
Mechanical Specifications: Type page 13 x 21 1/2; E - 6 cols, 2 1/16, 1/6 between; A - 6 cols, 2 1/16, 1/6 between; C - 6 cols, 2 1/16, 1/6 between.
Delivery Method: Mail, Newsstand
Areas Served: 57226, 57218, 57237, 57238, 57268

CONDE

TIMES-RECORD (WED)

165 2nd St SW, Conde, SD, 57434-2014, Spink, USA; gen tel (605) 382-5627; adv tel (605) 382-5627; ed tel (605) 382-5627; gen fax (605) 382-5629; adv fax (605) 382-5629; ed fax (605) 382-5629; disp adv e-mail eastarea@nvc.net; class adv e-mail eastarea@nvc.net; ed e-mail eastarea@nvc.net
Circulation: 807pd,; USPS
Advertising rate: Open inch rate $3.25
Pub./Ed./Adv. Mgr. .... Tina Sanderson
News Ed. .... Amy Hearnen
Delivery Method: Mail
Areas Served: 57440, 57436, 57447, 57434, 57258

CORSICA

THE CORSICA GLOBE (TUES)

215 Main St, Corsica, SD, 57328, Douglas, USA; gen tel (605) 946-5489; adv tel (605) 946-5489; ed tel (605) 946-5489; gen fax (605) 946-5179; adv fax (605) 946-5179; ed fax (605) 946-5179; disp adv e-mail globe@siouxvalley.net; class adv e-mail globe@siouxvalley.net; ed e-mail globe@siouxvalley.net; web site www.corsicaglobe.blogspot.com
Circulation: 1,093pd, 51fr; Sworn/Estimate/Non-Audited
Advertising rate: Open inch rate $6.75
Digital Platform - Mobile: Windows
Digital Platform - Tablet: Windows 7
Pub./Ed./Adv. Mgr. .... Mary Neugebauer
Pub. .... Dennis Neugebauer
Delivery Method: Mail, Racks
Areas Served: 57328, 57344, 57364, 57375, 57313

CUSTER

CUSTER COUNTY CHRONICLE (WED)

522 Mount Rushmore Rd, Custer, SD, 57730-1930, Custer, USA; gen tel (605) 673-2217; adv tel (605) 673-2217; ed tel (605) 673-2217; gen fax (605) 673-3321; adv fax (605) 673-3321; ed fax (605) 673-3321; disp adv e-mail custerchronicle@gwtc.net; class adv e-mail custerads@gwtc.net; ed e-mail custernews@gwtc.net; web site www.custercountynews.com
Circulation: 1,800pd,; Sworn/Estimate/Non-Audited
Advertising rate: Open inch rate $7.00
Established: 1880
Digital Platform - Mobile: Apple, Android
Digital Platform - Tablet: Apple iOS, Android, Windows 7
Ed. .... Norma G. Najacht
Gen. Mgr. .... Jason Ferguson
Pub./Adv. Mgr. .... Charles W. Najacht
Reporter .... Jacy Glazier
Mechanical Specifications: Type page 10 x 21; E - 6 cols, 1.5, 1/6 between; A - 6 cols, 1.5, 1/6 between; C - 6 cols, 1.5, 1/6 between. Equipment & Software: Hardware — APP/Mac; Presses — None; Software — QPS/QuarkXPress 7.0.
Delivery Method: Mail, Newsstand
Areas Served: 57730, 57747, 57745, 57738, 57722, 57744, 57773

DE SMET

THE DE SMET NEWS (WED)

220 Calumet Ave SE, De Smet, SD, 57231-3100, Kingsbury, USA; gen tel (605) 854-3331; adv tel (605) 854-3331; ed tel (605) 854-3331; gen fax (605) 854-9977; adv fax (605) 854-9977; ed fax (605) 854-9977; disp adv e-mail mail@desmetnews.com; class adv e-mail mail@desmetnews.com; ed e-mail mail@desmetnews.com; web site www.desmetnews.com - 14,000(views) 2,700(visitors)
Circulation: 1,315pd, 20fr; Sworn/Estimate/Non-Audited
Advertising rate: Open inch rate $6.35
Established: 1880
Group: Blegen Publishing Inc.
Digital Platform - Mobile: Apple, Android, Windows, Blackberry
Digital Platform - Tablet: Apple iOS, Android, Windows 7, Blackberry Tablet OS, Kindle, Nook, Kindle Fire
Pub. .... Dale Blegen
Ed. .... David Tritle
Office Mgr. .... Jessica Jung
Mechanical Specifications: Type page 14 3/4 x 21 1/4; E - 6 cols, 2 1/3, 1/6 between; A - 6 cols, 2 1/3, 1/6 between; C - 5 cols, 1 5/6, 1/6 between.Equipment & Software: Hardware — APP/Mac; Software — Adobe/PageMaker 6.5, Microsoft/Word 5.1.
Delivery Method: Mail, Newsstand, Racks
Areas Served: 57212, 57221, 57323, 57349, 57386, 57278, 57231, 57249, 57233, 57051

DELL RAPIDS

BALTIC BEACON (WED)

414 E 4th St, Dell Rapids, SD, 57022-1928, Minnehaha, USA; gen tel (605) 428-5441; adv tel (605) 428-5441; ed tel (605) 428-5441; gen fax (605) 428-5992; adv fax (605) 428-5992; ed fax (605) 428-5992; disp adv e-mail tribune@dellrapids.net; class adv e-mail tribune@dellrapids.net; ed e-mail

editor@dellrapidsinfo.com; web site www.dellrapidsinfo.com
Circulation: 320pd, 6,100fr; Sworn/Estimate/Non-Audited
Advertising rate: Open inch rate $5.35
Group: Gannett
Digital Platform - Mobile: Apple, Android, Windows, Blackberry
Digital Platform - Tablet: Apple iOS, Android, Windows 7, Blackberry Tablet OS
Pub....Randell Beck
Ed....Brent Vell
Delivery Method: Mail, Newsstand, Racks
Areas Served: 57003, 57030, 57065, 57020

DELL RAPIDS TRIBUNE (WED)
414 E 4th St, Dell Rapids, SD, 57022-1928, Minnehaha, USA; gen tel (605) 428-5441; adv tel (605) 428-5441; ed tel (605) 428-5441; gen fax (605) 428-5992; adv fax (605) 428-5992; ed fax (605) 428-5992; disp adv e-mail tribune@dellrapids.net; class adv e-mail tribune@dellrapids.net; ed e-mail editor@dellrapidsinfo.com; web site www.dellrapidsinfo.com
Circulation: 1,300pd, 34fr; Sworn/Estimate/Non-Audited
Advertising rate: Open inch rate $5.65
Group: Gannett
Digital Platform - Mobile: Apple, Android, Windows, Blackberry
Digital Platform - Tablet: Apple iOS, Android, Windows 7, Blackberry Tablet OS
Pub....Randell Beck
Office Mgr....Carolyn Lamberty
Ed....Luke Tatge
Delivery Method: Mail, Newsstand, Racks
Areas Served: 57022, 57003

EAGLE BUTTE

WEST RIVER EAGLE (THUR)
317 South Main Street, Eagle Butte, SD, 57625, Dewey, USA; gen tel (605) 964-2100; adv tel (605) 964-2100; ed tel (605) 964-2100; gen fax (605) 964-2110; adv fax (605) 964-2110; ed fax (605) 964-2110; disp adv e-mail wreagle@westrivereagle.com; class adv e-mail wreagle@westrivereagle.com; ed e-mail wreagle@westrivereagle.com; web site www.westrivereagle.com
Circulation: 2,100pd,; Sworn/Estimate/Non-Audited
Advertising rate: Open inch rate $7.30
Established: 1910
Group: Bridge City Publishing, Inc.
Digital Platform - Mobile: Apple, Android, Windows, Blackberry
Digital Platform - Tablet: Apple iOS, Android, Windows 7, Blackberry Tablet OS, Kindle, Nook, Kindle Fire
Pub....Larry Atkinson
Gen. Mgr....Nancy Anderson
Customer Service
Justice Garreau
Advertising Sales
Cadyn Dupris
Editor....Jody Rust
Mechanical Specifications: Type page 11 x 16; E - 5 cols, 2 1/12, 5/36 between; A - 5 cols, 2 1/12, 5/36 between; C - 5 cols, 2 1/12, 5/36 between.Equipment & Software: Hardware — APP/Mac; Software — Microsoft/Word 5.1, QPS/QuarkXPress 3.31.
Delivery Method: Mail, Newsstand, Racks
Areas Served: 57652, 57625, 57623, 57442, 57656, 57636

EDGEMONT

EDGEMONT HERALD TRIBUNE (THUR)
410 2nd Ave, Edgemont, SD, 57735-4910, Custer, USA; gen tel (605) 662-7201; adv tel (605) 662-7201; ed tel (605) 662-7201; gen fax (605) 662-7202; adv fax (605) 662-7202; ed fax (605) 662-7202; disp adv e-mail tribune@gwtc.net; class adv e-mail tribune@gwtc.net; ed e-mail tribune@gwtc.net; web site www.edgemonttribune.com
Circulation: 800pd,; Sworn/Estimate/Non-Audited
Advertising rate: Open inch rate $4.85
Established: 1923
Digital Platform - Mobile: Apple, Android
Digital Platform - Tablet: Apple iOS, Android, Windows 7
Mng. Ed....Amber Schumacher
Mechanical Specifications: Type page 10" x 21"; E - 6 cols, 1.56", 1/8" between; A - 6 cols, 1.56", 1/8" between; C - 6 cols, 1.56", 1/8" between.Equipment & Software: Hardware — 2-IBM; Software — QPS/QuarkXPress 5.0.
Delivery Method: Mail, Newsstand
Areas Served: 57735, 57747, 57763, 57774

ELK POINT

SOUTHERN UNION COUNTY LEADER-COURIER (THUR)
108 W Main St, Elk Point, SD, 57025-2314, Union, USA; gen tel (605) 356-2632; adv tel (605) 356-2632; ed tel (605) 356-2632; gen fax (605) 356-3626; adv fax (605) 356-3626; ed fax (605) 356-3626; disp adv e-mail leader2@iw.net; class adv e-mail leader2@iw.net; ed e-mail leader1@iw.net; web site www.leadercourier-times.com
Circulation: 1,150pd, 19fr
Advertising rate: Open inch rate $8.00
Digital Platform - Mobile: Apple, Android, Windows, Blackberry
Digital Platform - Tablet: Apple iOS, Android, Windows 7, Blackberry Tablet OS, Kindle, Nook, Kindle Fire
Pub....Bruce Odson
Gen. Mgr....Susan Odson
Delivery Method: Mail
Areas Served: 57010, 57025, 57038, 57004, 57001, 57069, 57049, 51001, 51103, 51109

ELKTON

THE ELKTON RECORD (THUR)
205 Elk St, Elkton, SD, 57026-2193, Brookings, USA; gen tel (605) 542-4831; adv tel (605) 542-4831; ed tel (605) 542-4831; gen fax (605) 542-1306; adv fax (605) 542-1306; ed fax (605) 542-1306; disp adv e-mail ern@itctel.com; class adv e-mail ern@itctel.com; ed e-mail ern@itctel.com; web site www.rfdnewsgroup.com
Circulation: 600pd, 57fr; Sworn/Estimate/Non-Audited
Advertising rate: Open inch rate $5.00
Established: 1884
Group: Clear Lake Courier
Digital Platform - Mobile: Apple, Windows
Digital Platform - Tablet: Apple iOS, Windows 7
Pub./Ed....Linda Schumacher
Mechanical Specifications: Type page 9 3/4 x 15; E - 5 cols, 1/6 between; A - 5 cols, 1/6 between; C - 5 cols, 1/6 between.Equipment & Software: Hardware — APP/Mac G4, APP/Mac G3; Software — Aldus PageMaker 6.0, Aldus PageMaker 6.5, Adobe/PhotoShop.
Delivery Method: Mail, Newsstand, Racks
Areas Served: 57026, 57074, 57002

ESTELLINE

ESTELLINE JOURNAL (WED)
214 Main St, Estelline, SD, 57234, Hamlin, USA; gen tel (605) 873-2475; adv tel (605) 873-2475; ed tel (605) 793-2293; gen fax (605) 793-9140; adv fax (605) 793-9140; ed fax (605) 793-9140; disp adv e-mail hcp@itctel.com; class adv e-mail hcp@itctel.com; ed e-mail hcp@itctel.com; web site www.hamlincountypublishing.com
Circulation: 650pd,; Sworn/Estimate/Non-Audited
Advertising rate: Open inch rate $5.00
Digital Platform - Mobile: Apple, Android
Digital Platform - Tablet: Apple iOS, Android, Windows 7
Pub....Lee Anne Dufek
Ed....Jenna Aderhold
Adv. Mgr....Doug Kruiter
Delivery Method: Mail, Racks

EUREKA

NORTHWEST BLADE (THUR)
810 G Avenue, Eureka, SD, 57437, McPherson, USA; gen tel (605) 284-2631; disp adv e-mail nwblade@valleytel.net; class adv e-mail nwblade@valleytel.net; ed e-mail nwblade@valleytel.net; web site www.eurekanorthwestblade.blogspot.com
Circulation: 1,125pd, 25fr; Sworn/Estimate/Non-Audited
Advertising rate: Open inch rate $4.95
Group: Pride Publications
Digital Platform - Mobile: Windows
Digital Platform - Tablet: Windows 7
Pub....Tara Beitelspacher
Mechanical Specifications: Type page 13 1/2 x 21 1/2.Equipment & Software: Hardware — 4-COM; Presses — G.
Delivery Method: Mail, Newsstand
Areas Served: 57437, 57456, 57457, 57448, 57432, 57632

FAITH

THE FAITH INDEPENDENT (WED)
106 Main St, Faith, SD, 57626, Meade, USA; gen tel (605) 967-2161; adv tel (605) 967-2161; ed tel (605) 967-2161; gen fax (605) 967-2160; adv fax (605) 967-2160; ed fax (605) 967-2160; disp adv e-mail faithind@faithsd.com; class adv e-mail faithind@faithsd.com; ed e-mail faithind@faithsd.com; web site www.ravellettepublications.com
Circulation: 1,000pd,; Sworn/Estimate/Non-Audited
Advertising rate: Open inch rate $4.35
Digital Platform - Mobile: Apple, Windows
Digital Platform - Tablet: Apple iOS, Windows 7
Pub./Ed....Don Ravellette
Office Mgr....Diane Isaacs
Delivery Method: Mail, Racks
Areas Served: 57626, 57718, 57747, 57623, 57629, 57792, 57765, 57636, 57777, 57644, 57785, 57737

FAULKTON

FAULK COUNTY RECORD (WED)
121 8th Ave S, Faulkton, SD, 57438-2116, Faulk, USA; gen tel (605) 598-6525; adv tel (605) 598-6525; ed tel (605) 598-6525; gen fax (605) 598-4355; adv fax (605) 598-4355; ed fax (605) 598-4355; disp adv e-mail info@faulkcountyrecord.com; class adv e-mail info@faulkcountyrecord.com; ed e-mail info@faulkcountyrecord.com; web site www.faulkcountyrecord.com
Circulation: 1,420pd, 8fr; Sworn/Estimate/Non-Audited
Advertising rate: Open inch rate $4.00
Established: 1882
Digital Platform - Mobile: Apple, Android, Windows, Blackberry
Digital Platform - Tablet: Apple iOS, Android, Windows 7, Blackberry Tablet OS
Pub./Ed....James Moritz
Co-Pub....Jody Moritz
Mechanical Specifications: 5 columns, tab, page size 10.5" x 13.75"
Delivery Method: Mail, Newsstand
Areas Served: 57438, 57435, 57467, 57470, 57473, 57466, 57465

FLANDREAU

MOODY COUNTY ENTERPRISE (WED)
107 W 2nd Ave, Flandreau, SD, 57028-1149, Moody, USA; gen tel (605) 997-3725; adv tel (605) 997-3725; ed tel (605) 997-3725; gen fax (605) 997-3194; adv fax (605) 997-3194; ed fax (605) 997-3194; disp adv e-mail mce6@mcisweb.com; class adv e-mail mce3@mcisweb.com; ed e-mail mce6@mcisweb.com; web site www.moodycountyenterprise.com
Circulation: 3,300pd, 1,200fr; Sworn/Estimate/Non-Audited
Advertising rate: Open inch rate $5.00
Established: 1878
Group: News Media Corp.
Digital Platform - Mobile: Apple, Android, Windows, Blackberry
Digital Platform - Tablet: Apple iOS, Android, Windows 7, Blackberry Tablet OS, Kindle, Nook, Kindle Fire
Pub....William McMacken
Ed....M.L. Headrick
Gen. Mgr....Roger Janssen
Mechanical Specifications: Type page 13 x 21; E - 6 cols, between.Equipment & Software: Hardware — APP/Macs; Software — Microsoft/Word, Adobe/PageMaker, Adobe/Photoshop.
Delivery Method: Mail, Newsstand, Racks
Areas Served: 57028, 57017, 57022, 57024, 57026, 57065, 57074, 56164

FREEMAN

THE FREEMAN COURIER (THUR)
308 S Main St, Freeman, SD, 57029-2302, Hutchinson, USA; gen tel (605) 925-7033; gen fax (605) 925-4684; disp adv e-mail courier@gwtc.net; class adv e-mail courier@gwtc.net; ed e-mail courier@gwtc.net; web site www.freemansd.com
Circulation: 1,500pd,; Sworn/Estimate/Non-Audited
Advertising rate: Open inch rate $5.60
Established: 1901
Group: Second Century Publishing Inc.
Digital Platform - Mobile: Apple, Android, Windows, Blackberry
Digital Platform - Tablet: Apple iOS, Android, Windows 7, Blackberry Tablet OS, Kindle, Nook, Kindle Fire
Former publisher....Tim Waltner
Publisher....Jeremy Waltner
Adv. Mgr....Jason Scharberg
Graphic Designer....Tabitha Schoenwald
Office Manager....Linda VonEye
Delivery Method: Mail, Newsstand
Areas Served: 57029, 57043, 57045, 57319

GEDDES

CHARLES MIX COUNTY NEWS (THUR)
308 Main St, Geddes, SD, 57342, Charles Mix, USA; gen tel (605) 337-2571; adv tel (605) 337-2571; ed tel (605) 337-2571; gen fax (605) 337-2363; adv fax (605) 337-2363; ed fax (605) 337-2363; disp adv e-mail cmcountynews@midstatesd.net; class adv e-mail cmcountynews@midstatesd.net; ed e-mail cmcountynews@midstatesd.net
Circulation: 685pd, 1fr; Sworn/Estimate/Non-Audited
Advertising rate: Open inch rate $5.25
Pub./Ed....Rhonda Blair
Co-Pub....Wayne Blair
Delivery Method: Mail, Racks
Areas Served: 57342, 57369, 57356, 57313

GETTYSBURG

POTTER COUNTY NEWS (THUR)
110 S Exene St, Gettysburg, SD, 57442-1520, Potter, USA; gen tel (605) 765-2464; adv tel (605) 765-2464; ed tel (605) 765-2464; gen fax (605) 765-2465; adv fax (605) 765-2465; ed fax (605) 765-2465; disp adv e-mail pcnews@pottercountynews.com; class adv e-mail lacey@pottercountynews.com; ed e-mail pcnews@pottercountynews.com; web site www.pottercountynews.com - 13,000(views)
Circulation: 1,600pd,; Sworn/Estimate/Non-Audited
Advertising rate: Open inch rate $5.90
Established: 1883

Digital Platform - Mobile: Apple, Android, Windows, Blackberry
Digital Platform - Tablet: Apple iOS, Android, Windows 7, Blackberry Tablet OS, Kindle, Nook, Kindle Fire
Pub. .... Larry Atkinson
Ed. .... Molly McRoberts
Adv. Mgr. .... Lacey Johnson
Mechanical Specifications: Type page 11 x 17; E - 5 cols, 2 1/12, 5/36 between; A - 5 cols, 2 1/12, 5/36 between; C - 5 cols, 2 1/12, 5/36 between.Equipment & Software: Hardware — APP/Mac; Software — Adobe/Acrobat 4.0, Microsoft/Word 98, Adobe/PageMaker 6.5.
Delivery Method: Mail, Newsstand, Racks
Areas Served: 57625, 57442, 57450, 57455, 57475

GREGORY

GREGORY TIMES-ADVOCATE (WED)
119 E 7th St, Gregory, SD, 57533-1412, Gregory, USA; gen tel (605) 835-8089; adv tel (605) 835-8089; ed tel (605) 835-8089; gen fax (605) 835-8467; adv fax (605) 835-8467; ed fax (605) 835-8467; disp adv e-mail gregorynews@gregorynews.com; class adv e-mail gregorynews@gregorynews.com; ed e-mail gregorynews@gregorynews.com; web site www.ainsworthnews.com
Circulation: 2,000pd,; Sworn/Estimate/Non-Audited
Advertising rate: Open inch rate $5.75
Established: 1904
Digital Platform - Mobile: Apple, Android, Windows, Blackberry
Digital Platform - Tablet: Apple iOS, Android, Windows 7, Blackberry Tablet OS, Kindle, Nook, Kindle Fire
Pub./Ed. .... Cheryl Sperl
Adv. Mgr. .... Sue Brozik
Delivery Method: Mail, Newsstand, Racks
Areas Served: 57533, 57523, 57317, 57529, 68744, 68778, 68743, 68755

GROTON

GROTON INDEPENDENT (WED)
21 N Main St., Groton, SD, 57445, Brown, USA; gen tel (605) 397-6397; adv tel (605) 397-6397; ed tel (605) 397-6397; gen fax (775) 459-6259; adv fax (775) 459-6259; ed fax (775) 459-6259; disp adv e-mail office@grotonsd.net; class adv e-mail office@grotonsd.net; ed e-mail paperpaul@grotonsd.net; web site www.397news.com
Circulation: 400pd,; Sworn/Estimate/Non-Audited
Advertising rate: Open inch rate $6.10
Established: 1883
Group: Next Generation Publications, Inc.
Finger Lakes Community Newspapers
Digital Platform - Mobile: Windows
Digital Platform - Tablet: Windows 7
Pub. .... Paul Irvin Kosel
Office Mgr. .... Tina Kosel
Mechanical Specifications: Type page 13 1/4 x 21 1/2; E - 6 cols, 2 1/16, 1/8 between; A - 6 cols, 2 1/16, 1/8 between; C - 6 cols, 2 1/16, 1/8 between.Equipment & Software: Hardware — Pentium/PC; Software — Adobe/PageMaker 5.0.
Delivery Method: Mail, Newsstand
Areas Served: 57422, 57427, 57432, 57433, 57434, 57439, 57455, 57474, 57454, 57401, 57441, 57445, 57449

HAYTI

HERALD-ENTERPRISE (WED)
PO Box 207, Hayti, SD, 57241-0207, Hamlin, USA; gen tel (605) 783-3636; adv tel (605) 783-3636; ed tel (605) 783-3636; gen fax (605) 793-9140; adv fax (605) 793-9140; ed fax (605) 793-9140; disp adv e-mail hcp@itctel.com; class adv e-mail hcp@itctel.com; ed e-mail hcp@itctel.com; web site www.hamlincountypublishing.com
Circulation: 750pd, 35fr; Sworn/Estimate/Non-Audited
Advertising rate: Open inch rate $5.00
Group: Hamlin County Publishing, Inc.Editions: (50)
Digital Platform - Mobile: Apple, Android
Digital Platform - Tablet: Apple iOS, Android, Windows 7
Pub./Ed./Adv. Mgr. .... Lee Anne Dufek
Delivery Method: Mail
Areas Served: 57241, 57223, 57234, 57221, 57242, 57248, 57271

HIGHMORE

HIGHMORE HERALD (THUR)
211 Iowa Ave N, Highmore, SD, 57345-2101, Faulk, USA; gen tel (605) 852-2927; adv tel (605) 852-2927; ed tel (605) 852-2927; gen fax (605) 852-2927; adv fax (605) 852-2927; ed fax (605) 852-2927; disp adv e-mail hiherald@venturecomm.net; class adv e-mail hiherald@venturecomm.net; ed e-mail hiherald@venturecomm.net
Circulation: 1,450pd,; Sworn/Estimate/Non-Audited
Advertising rate: Open inch rate $5.00
Established: 1882
Pub./Ed. .... Mary Ann Morford
Adv. Mgr. .... Mary Hamlin
Delivery Method: Mail, Racks
Areas Served: 57345, 57536, 57540, 57371

HILL CITY

HILL CITY PREVAILER-NEWS (WED)
333 Main St, # 7, Hill City, SD, 57745-3003, Pennington, USA; gen tel (605) 574-2538; adv tel (605) 574-2538; ed tel (605) 574-2538; gen fax (605) 574-4409; adv fax (605) 574-4409; ed fax (605) 574-4409; disp adv e-mail prevailer@goldenwest.net; class adv e-mail custerads@gwtc.net; ed e-mail prevailer@goldenwest.net; web site www.hillcityprevailernews.blogspot.com
Circulation: 700pd,; Sworn/Estimate/Non-Audited
Advertising rate: Open inch rate $6.50
Established: 1971
Group: Southern Hills Publishing, Inc.
Digital Platform - Mobile: Windows
Digital Platform - Tablet: Windows 7
Pub. .... Charles W. Najacht
Ed. .... Kacie Svoboda
Adv. Mgr. .... Stacy Swenson
Mechanical Specifications: Type page 10 x 21; E - 6 cols, 1 1/2, between; A - 6 cols, 1 1/2, between; C - 6 cols, 1 1/2, between.Equipment & Software: Hardware — APP/Mac; Software — Quark 7.0
Delivery Method: Mail, Racks
Areas Served: 57745, 57701, 57730, 57709

HOT SPRINGS

HOT SPRINGS STAR (TUES)
107 N Chicago St, Hot Springs, SD, 57747-1631, Fall River, USA; gen tel (605) 745-4170; gen fax (605) 745-3161; disp adv e-mail starads@lee.net; class adv e-mail hsstar@lee.net; ed e-mail hsstar@lee.net; web site www.hotspringsstar.com
Circulation: 1,900pd, 25fr; Sworn/Estimate/Non-Audited
Advertising rate: Open inch rate $8.30
Established: 1886
Group: Lee Enterprises, Inc.
Digital Platform - Mobile: Apple, Android, Windows, Blackberry
Digital Platform - Tablet: Apple iOS, Android, Windows 7, Blackberry Tablet OS
Pub. .... Brett Nachtigall
Prod. Mgr. .... Sheryl Grimes
Mechanical Specifications: Type page 10 1/2 x 16; E - 5 cols, 2, 1/6 between; A - 5 cols, 2, 1/6 between; C - 7 cols, 1 1/2, 1/6 between.
Delivery Method: Mail, Newsstand, Carrier, Racks
Areas Served: 57747, 57715, 57722, 57735, 57763, 57766, 57774, 57782, 57735

HOVEN

THE HOVEN REVIEW (THUR)
69 2nd Ave E, Hoven, SD, 57450, Potter, USA; gen tel (605) 948-2110; adv tel (605) 948-2110; ed tel (605) 948-2110; gen fax (605) 948-2578; adv fax (605) 948-2578; ed fax (605) 948-2578; disp adv e-mail hoven@venturecomm.net; class adv e-mail hoven@venturecomm.net; ed e-mail hoven@venturecomm.net
Circulation: 650pd, 9fr; Sworn/Estimate/Non-Audited
Advertising rate: Open inch rate $5.35
Pub. .... Kyle Krueger
Ed. .... Janel Lehman
Delivery Method: Mail
Areas Served: 57475, 57450, 57455, 57466, 57442

HOWARD

MINER COUNTY PIONEER (THUR)
120 S Main St, Howard, SD, 57349-9058, Miner, USA; gen tel (605) 772-5644; adv tel (605) 772-5644; ed tel (605) 772-5644; gen fax (605) 772-5645; adv fax (605) 772-5645; ed fax (605) 772-5645; disp adv e-mail ads@minercountypioneer.com; class adv e-mail ads@minercountypioneer.com; ed e-mail news@minercountypioneer.com
Circulation: 1,902pd, 65fr; Sworn/Estimate/Non-Audited
Advertising rate: Open inch rate $4.28
Pub./Ed. .... Carla Poulson
Managing Editor/Office Manager .... Heather Poulson
Delivery Method: Mail, Racks
Areas Served: 57349, 57321, 57076, 57337, 57323, 57042, 57301

IPSWICH

IPSWICH TRIBUNE (WED)
419 S 5th St, Ipswich, SD, 57451-2500, Edmunds, USA; gen tel (605) 426-6471; gen fax (605) 426-6202; disp adv e-mail iptribune@valleytel.net; class adv e-mail iptribune@valleytel.net; ed e-mail iptribune@valleytel.net
Circulation: 941pd, 3fr; Sworn/Estimate/Non-Audited
Advertising rate: Open inch rate $3.35
Digital Platform - Mobile: Windows
Digital Platform - Tablet: Windows 7
Pub. .... Dwain Gibson
Managing Ed. .... Tena Gibson
Mechanical Specifications: Type page 9 3/4 x 13; E - 5 cols, 1 3/4, 1 pica between; A - 5 cols, 1 3/4, 1 pica between; C - 5 cols, 1 3/4, 1 pica between.Equipment & Software: ; Software — QPS/QuarkXPress
Delivery Method: Mail, Racks
Areas Served: 57451, 57471, 57448

ROSCOE-HOSMER INDEPENDENT (WED)
419 S 5th St, Ipswich, SD, 57451-2500, Edmunds, USA; gen tel (605) 426-6471; gen fax (605) 426-6202; disp adv e-mail iptribune@valleytel; class adv e-mail iptribune@valleytel.net; ed e-mail iptribune@valleytel.net
Circulation: 605pd,; Sworn/Estimate/Non-Audited
Advertising rate: Open inch rate $3.35
Digital Platform - Mobile: Windows
Digital Platform - Tablet: Windows 7
Pub. .... Dwain Gibson
Managing Ed. .... Tena Gibson
Mechanical Specifications: Type page 9 3/4 x 13; E - 5 cols, 1 3/4, 1 pica between; A - 5 cols, 1 3/4, 1 pica between; C - 5 cols, 1 3/4, 1 pica between.Equipment & Software: Hardware — APP/Macs; Software — QPS/QuarkXPress
Delivery Method: Mail, Racks
Areas Served: 57471, 57448,

IRENE

THE TRI-COUNTY NEWS (THUR)
303 W Main St, Irene, SD, 57037, Yankton, USA; gen tel (605) 263-3339; adv tel (605) 263-3339; ed tel (605) 263-3339; gen fax (605) 263-2425; adv fax (605) 263-2425; ed fax (605) 263-2425; disp adv e-mail thenews@iw.net; class adv e-mail thenews@iw.net; ed e-mail thenews@iw.net
Circulation: 560pd, 23fr; Sworn/Estimate/Non-Audited
Advertising rate: Open inch rate $4.75
Group: Clear Lake Courier
Pub./Ed. .... Allyson Hill
Co-Pub. .... Shane Hill
Mechanical Specifications: Type page 9 3/4 x 15; E - 5 cols, 1 5/6, between; A - 5 cols, 1 5/6, between; C - 5 cols, 1 5/6, between.
Delivery Method: Mail
Areas Served: 57037, 57070, 57073, 57078, 57072

ISABEL

THE ISABEL DAKOTAN (THUR)
403 N Main St, Isabel, SD, 57633, Dewey, USA; gen tel (605) 466-2258; adv tel (605) 466-2258; ed tel (605) 466-2258; gen fax (605) 446-2258; adv fax (605) 446-2258; ed fax (605) 446-2258; disp adv e-mail dakotan@lakotanetwork.com; class adv e-mail dakotan@lakotanetwork.com; ed e-mail dakotan@lakotanetwork.com
Circulation: 750pd,; Sworn/Estimate/Non-Audited
Advertising rate: Open inch rate $4.00
Pub./Adv. Dir. .... Robert Slocum
Ed. .... Barbara Begeman
Delivery Method: Mail, Racks
Areas Served: 57656, 57628, 57623, 57633, 57625

KADOKA

KADOKA PRESS (THUR)
915 S Main St, Kadoka, SD, 57543, Jackson, USA; gen tel (605) 837-2259; adv tel (605) 837-2259; ed tel (605) 837-2259; gen fax (605) 837-2312; adv fax (605) 837-2312; ed fax (605) 837-2312; disp adv e-mail press@kadokatelco.com; class adv e-mail press@kadokatelco.com; ed e-mail editor@kadokatelco.com; web site www.ravellettepublications.com
Circulation: 1,100pd,; Sworn/Estimate/Non-Audited
Advertising rate: Open inch rate $4.80
Digital Platform - Mobile: Apple, Windows
Digital Platform - Tablet: Apple iOS, Windows 7
Pub. .... Don Ravellette
Ed. .... Rhonda Dennis
Delivery Method: Mail, Racks
Areas Served: 57543, 57577, 57547, 57521, 57560, 57775, 57750

LAKE PRESTON

LAKE PRESTON TIMES (WED)
301 N Main St, Lake Preston, SD, 57249, Kingsbury, USA; gen tel (605) 847-4421; adv tel (605) 847-4421; ed tel (605) 847-4421; gen fax (605) 847-4421; adv fax (605) 847-4421; ed fax (605) 847-4421; disp adv e-mail mail@lakeprestontimes.net; class adv e-mail mail@lakeprestontimes.net; ed e-mail mail@lakeprestontimes.net; web site www.lakeprestontimes.net
Circulation: 1,104pd, 37fr; Sworn/Estimate/Non-Audited
Advertising rate: Open inch rate $5.65
Group: Blegen Publishing Inc.
Pub. .... Dale Blegen
Editor .... Donna Palmlund
Mechanical Specifications: Type page 9 x 15; E - 4 cols, 2 1/3, 1/6 between; A - 4 cols, 2 1/3,

1/6 between; C - 5 cols, 1 3/4, 1/6 between. Equipment & Software: Hardware — APP/Mac; Presses — ABD/385, ABD/9880; Software — Adobe/PageMaker 4.0, Microsoft/Word 5.1.
Delivery Method: Mail, Newsstand, Racks
Areas Served: 57249, 57051, 57231, 57212, 57244, 57233, 57221, 57054

LEMMON

THE LEMMON LEADER (FRI)

213 Main Ave, Lemmon, SD, 57638-1119, Perkins, USA; gen tel (605) 374-3751; adv tel (605) 374-3751; ed tel (605) 374-3751; gen fax (605) 374-5295; adv fax (605) 374-5295; ed fax (605) 374-5295; disp adv e-mail leader@sdplains.com; class adv e-mail leader@sdplains.com; ed e-mail leader@sdplains.com; web site www.lemmonleader.net
Circulation: 604pd,; Sworn/Estimate/Non-Audited
Advertising rate: Open inch rate $7.05
Digital Platform - Mobile: Apple, Android
Digital Platform - Tablet: Apple iOS, Android, Windows 7
Pub./Adv. Dir. .... Tanya Mitchell
Ed. .... Jamie Spainhower
Office Mgr. .... Jennifer Marxsen
Delivery Method: Mail
Areas Served: 57620, 57634, 57635, 57644, 57645, 57649, 57638

LENNOX

THE LENNOX INDEPENDENT (THUR)

116 S Main St, Lennox, SD, 57039-2096, Lincoln, USA; gen tel (605) 647-2284; adv tel (605) 647-2284; ed tel (605) 647-2284; gen fax (605) 647-2218; adv fax (605) 647-2218; ed fax (605) 647-2218; disp adv e-mail ads@lennoxnews.com; class adv e-mail ads@lennoxnews.com; ed e-mail editor@lennoxnews.com; web site www.lennoxnews.com
Circulation: 1,500pd, 35fr; Sworn/Estimate/Non-Audited
Advertising rate: Open inch rate $4.25
Established: 1885
Group: Independent Publishing Co.
Digital Platform - Mobile: Apple, Android, Windows, Blackberry
Digital Platform - Tablet: Apple iOS, Android, Windows 7, Blackberry Tablet OS, Kindle, Nook, Kindle Fire
Co-Pub./Ed .... Kelli Bultena
Co-Pub./Business manager.....Debbie Schmidt
Sports Ed.................................... Anne Homan
Mechanical Specifications: Type page 12 1/2 x 22 1/2; E - 6 cols, 1, between.Equipment & Software: Hardware — APP/Mac.
Delivery Method: Mail, Newsstand
Areas Served: 57039, 57015, 57064, 57021, 57077, 57101, 57032, 57036

LEOLA

MCPHERSON COUNTY HERALD (WED)

1203 Moulton St, Leola, SD, 57456-2214, McPherson, USA; gen tel (605) 439-3131; adv tel (605) 439-3131; ed tel (605) 439-3131; disp adv e-mail herald@valleytel.net; class adv e-mail herald@valleytel.net; ed e-mail herald@valleytel.net
Circulation: 375pd,; Sworn/Estimate/Non-Audited
Advertising rate: Open inch rate $3.50
Established: 1890
Digital Platform - Mobile: Windows
Digital Platform - Tablet: Windows 7
Pub./Ed. .... Jeremy Cox
Delivery Method: Mail
Areas Served: 57456, 57457, 57401, 57437, 57481, 58439

MARION

MARION RECORD (THUR)

403 N Broadway, Marion, SD, 57043, Turner, USA; gen tel (605) 648-3821; gen fax (605) 648-3920; disp adv e-mail mrecord@gwtc.net; class adv e-mail mrecord@gwtc.net; ed e-mail mrecord@gwtc.net
Circulation: 500pd,; Sworn/Estimate/Non-Audited
Advertising rate: Open inch rate $4.00
Established: 1900
Group: Anderson Publications Inc
Mechanical Specifications: Type page 13 1/8 x 21; E - 6 cols, 2 1/16, 1/8 between; A - 6 cols, 2 1/16, 1/8 between; C - 6 cols, 2 1/16, 1/8 between.Equipment & Software: Hardware — APP/Mac; Software — Adobe/PageMaker 6.0, Microsoft/Word 6.0, Adobe/Photoshop 3.0.
Delivery Method: Mail
Areas Served: 57043, 57053, 57047, 57023, 57029

MARTIN

BENNETT COUNTY BOOSTER II (WED)

502 2nd Ave, Martin, SD, 57551-8502, Bennett, USA; gen tel (605) 685-6866; adv tel (605) 685-6866; ed tel (605) 685-6866; gen fax (605) 685-6535; adv fax (605) 685-6535; ed fax (605) 685-6535; disp adv e-mail booster@gwtc.net; class adv e-mail booster@gwtc.net; ed e-mail booster@gwtc.net; web site www.bennettcountyboostersd.com
Circulation: 2,250pd,; Sworn/Estimate/Non-Audited
Advertising rate: Open inch rate $5.75
Digital Platform - Mobile: Apple, Android, Windows, Blackberry
Digital Platform - Tablet: Apple iOS, Android, Windows 7, Blackberry Tablet OS, Kindle, Nook, Kindle Fire
Pub./Ed. .... Tim Huether
Adv. Mgr./News Ed......................... Marj Oleske
Gen. Mgr. .... Mandy SchererEquipment & Software: Hardware — APP/Mac, IBM; Presses — G; Software — QPS/QuarkXPress, Adobe/Photoshop.
Delivery Method: Mail, Newsstand, Racks
Areas Served: 57551, 57574, 57756, 57714, 57716, 57752, 57577, 57772, 57547, 57560

MC LAUGHLIN

CORSON SIOUX COUNTY NEWS MESSE (THUR)

PO Box 788, 202 W 1st Ave, Mc Laughlin, SD, 57642-0788, Corson, USA; gen tel (605) 823-4490; adv tel (605) 823-4490; ed tel (605) 823-4490; gen fax (605) 823-4632; disp adv e-mail macnews@westriv.com; class adv e-mail macnews@westriv.com; ed e-mail macnews@westriv.com; web site www.siouxcountynewsmessenger.blogspot.com
Circulation: 1,000pd, 12fr; Sworn/Estimate/Non-Audited
Advertising rate: Open inch rate $4.25
Established: 1915
Digital Platform - Mobile: Windows
Digital Platform - Tablet: Windows 7
Ed.itor .... Zach Buechler
Delivery Method: Mail, Racks
Areas Served: 57642, 58568, 57641, 57660, 57645, 57634

MENNO

THE HUTCHINSON HERALD (WED)

203 S 5th St, Menno, SD, 57045-2127, Hutchinson, USA; gen tel (605) 387-5158; adv tel (605) 387-5158; ed tel (605) 387-5158; gen fax (605) 387-5148; adv fax (605) 387-5148; ed fax (605) 387-5148; disp adv e-mail scpi.adv@gwtc.net; class adv e-mail hherald@gwpc.net; ed e-mail hherald@gwpc.net; web site www.mennosd.com
Circulation: 700pd,; Sworn/Estimate/Non-Audited
Advertising rate: Open inch rate $4.50
Established: 1882
Group: Second Century Publishing Inc.
Digital Platform - Mobile: Apple, Android, Windows, Blackberry
Digital Platform - Tablet: Apple iOS, Android, Windows 7, Blackberry Tablet OS
Pub... Tim Waltner
Ed. .... Erik Kaufman
Adv. Dir.................................. Jason Scharberg
Mechanical Specifications: Type page 13 x 21Equipment & Software: Hardware — APP/Mac; Software — Microsoft/Word, Indesign, Photoshop
Delivery Method: Mail, Newsstand
Areas Served: 57045, 57052, 57059, 57029, 57040

MILBANK

GRANT COUNTY REVIEW (WED)

225 S Main St, Milbank, SD, 57252-1808, Grant, USA; gen tel (605) 432-4516; adv tel (605) 432-4516; ed tel (605) 432-4516; gen fax (605) 432-5042; adv fax (605) 432-5042; ed fax (605) 432-5042; disp adv e-mail gcreview@itcmilbank.com; class adv e-mail gcreview@itcmilbank.com; ed e-mail gcreview@itcmilbank.com; web site www.grantcountyreview.com
Circulation: 3,600pd, 68fr; Sworn/Estimate/Non-Audited
Advertising rate: Open inch rate $7.00
Established: 1880
Digital Platform - Mobile: Apple, Android, Windows, Blackberry
Digital Platform - Tablet: Apple iOS, Android, Windows 7, Blackberry Tablet OS, Kindle, Nook, Kindle Fire
Pub./Ed. .... Phyllis Dolan Justice
Co-Pub. .... Clarence Justice
Gen. Mgr. .... Deb Hemmer
Adv. Mgr. .... Holli Seehafer
Mechanical Specifications: Type page 13 5/6 x 21 1/2; E - 6 cols, 2 1/6, 1/6 between; A - 6 cols, 1/6 between; C - 6 cols, 1/6 between. Equipment & Software: Hardware — 6-APP/Mac; Software — Adobe/Photoshop QuarkXPress.
Delivery Method: Mail
Areas Served: 57252, 57279, 57227, 57216, 57251, 57264, 57266, 57265, 57256, 57269

MILLER

THE MILLER PRESS (WED)

114 W 3rd St, Miller, SD, 57362-1325, Hand, USA; gen tel (605) 853-3575; adv tel (605) 853-3575; ed tel (605) 853-3575; gen fax (605) 853-2478; adv fax (605) 853-2478; ed fax (605) 853-2478; disp adv e-mail advertising@themillerpress.com; class adv e-mail advertising@themillerpress.com; ed e-mail publisher@themillerpress.com; web site www.themillerpress.com
Circulation: 2,050pd,; Sworn/Estimate/Non-Audited
Advertising rate: Open inch rate $6.30
Established: 1882
Digital Platform - Mobile: Apple, Android, Windows, Blackberry
Digital Platform - Tablet: Apple iOS, Android, Windows 7, Blackberry Tablet OS, Kindle, Nook, Kindle Fire
Pub./Ed. .... Mike Caviness
Adv. Dir...................................... Janice Erfman
Mechanical Specifications: Type page 13 x 21 1/2; E - 6 cols, 2 1/16, 1/6 between; A - 6 cols, 2 1/16, 1/6 between; C - 8 cols, 1 1/2, 1/8 between.Equipment & Software: Hardware — APP/Mac G3, APP/iMacs; Software — Adobe/PageMaker 7.0, Adobe/Photoshop 6.0.
Delivery Method: Mail, Newsstand
Areas Served: 57362, 57373, 57371, 57467, 57231, 57345, 57256, 57540, 57467, 57381

MISSION

TODD COUNTY TRIBUNE (WED)

W Highway 18, Mission, SD, 57555, Todd, USA; gen tel (605) 856-4469; adv tel (605) 856-4469; ed tel (605) 856-4469; gen fax (605) 856-2428; adv fax (605) 856-2428; ed fax (605) 856-2428; disp adv e-mail tribnews@gwtc.net; class adv e-mail tribnews@gwtc.net; ed e-mail tribnews@gwtc.net; web site www.trib-news.com
Circulation: 2,200pd,; Sworn/Estimate/Non-Audited
Advertising rate: Open inch rate $5.92
Digital Platform - Mobile: Apple, Android, Windows, Blackberry
Digital Platform - Tablet: Apple iOS, Android, Windows 7, Blackberry Tablet OS, Kindle, Nook, Kindle Fire
Pub... Tim Huether
Office Mgr. .... Elaine Emery
Mechanical Specifications: Type page 13 x 21 1/2; E - 6 cols, 2 1/16, 1/8 between; A - 6 cols, 2 1/16, 1/8 between.Equipment & Software: Hardware — 3-APP/Mac, 1-APP/Mac G4, APP/Mac 7600; Software — QPS/QuarkXPress, Adobe/Photoshop, Claris/Works.
Delivery Method: Mail, Newsstand, Racks
Areas Served: 57555, 57570, 57579, 57585, 57572, 57566, 57563, 69201, 57560

MOBRIDGE

MOBRIDGE TRIBUNE (WED)

1413 E Grand Xing, Mobridge, SD, 57601-2905, Walworth, USA; gen tel (605) 845-3646; adv tel (605) 845-3646; ed tel (605) 845-3646; gen fax (605) 845-7659; adv fax (605) 845-7659; ed fax (605) 845-7659; disp adv e-mail ads@mobridgetribune.com; class adv e-mail office@mobridgetribune.com; ed e-mail news@mobridgetribune.com; web site www.mobridgetribune.com
Circulation: 2,417pd,; Sworn/Estimate/Non-Audited
Advertising rate: Open inch rate $9.20
Established: 1909
Group: Bridge City Publishing, Inc.
Digital Platform - Mobile: Apple, Android, Windows, Blackberry
Digital Platform - Tablet: Apple iOS, Android, Windows 7, Blackberry Tablet OS, Kindle, Nook, Kindle Fire
Pub .... Larry Atkinson
Ed. .... Katie Zerr
Gen. Mgr. .... Linda Meyer
Adv. Specialties/Printing Mgr. ...... Arden Nelson
Web Printing Mgr. .... Lance St. John
Sports Ed... Jay Davis
Sales Mgr .... Risa Fryhling
Bus. Mgr.................................... Kelsey Majeski
Composition Mgr.......................... Jane Bachman
Circulation Mgr............................. Breezy Kuehl
Webmaster/Photoshop .... Justin Petersen
Mechanical Specifications: Type page 10 3/4 x 16; E - 5 cols, 2 1/6, 1/8 between; A - 5 cols, 2 1/6, 1/8 between; C - 5 cols, 2 1/6, 1/8 between.Equipment & Software: Hardware — APP/Mac; Presses — 6-G/Community; Software — Adobe/Creative Suite 3
Delivery Method: Mail, Newsstand, Carrier, Racks
Areas Served: 57601, 57648, 57632, 57646, 57631, 57472, 57420, 57452, 57428, 58538, 57641, 57642, 57643, 57658, 57639, 57657, 57661, 57630, 57656, 57628, 57633, 57450, 57623, 57634, 57622

MURDO

MURDO COYOTE (THUR)

210 Main St, Murdo, SD, 57559-2022, Jones, USA; gen tel (605) 669-2271; adv tel (605) 669-2271; ed tel (605) 669-2271; gen fax (605) 669-2744; adv fax (605) 669-2744; ed fax (605) 669-2744; disp adv e-mail coyoteads@gwtc.net; class adv e-mail coyoteads@gwtc.net; ed e-mail mcoyote@gwtc.

net; web site www.ravellettepublications.com
Circulation: 550pd, 10fr; Sworn/Estimate/ Non-Audited
Advertising rate: Open inch rate $5.00
Established: 1906
Digital Platform - Mobile: Apple, Windows
Digital Platform - Tablet: Apple iOS, Windows 7
Pub. .... Don Ravellette
Gen. Mgr. .... Kelly Penticoff
Adv. Mgr. .... Karlee Barnes
Mechanical Specifications: Type page 13 x 21 1/2.Equipment & Software: ; Software — Quark 6
Delivery Method: Mail, Racks
Areas Served: 57559, 57531, 57562

ONIDA

ONIDA WATCHMAN (THUR)

106 S Main St, Onida, SD, 57564-2178, Sully, USA; gen tel (605) 258-2604; adv tel (605) 258-2604; ed tel (605) 258-2604; gen fax (605) 258-2572; adv fax (605) 258-2572; ed fax (605) 258-2572; disp adv e-mail amanda.fanger@onidawatchman.com; class adv e-mail curt.olson@onidawatchman.com; ed e-mail marileen.tilberg@onidawatchman.com; web site www.onidawatchman.com
Circulation: 1,037pd, 30fr; Sworn/Estimate/ Non-Audited
Advertising rate: Open inch rate $3.65
Established: 1883
Digital Platform - Mobile: Apple, Android, Windows, Blackberry
Digital Platform - Tablet: Apple iOS, Android, Windows 7, Blackberry Tablet OS
Pub. .... Curt Olson
Ed. .... Marileen Tilberg
Adv. Mgr. .... Amanda Fanger
Mechanical Specifications: Type page 13 x 21 1/2.
Delivery Method: Mail
Areas Served: 57564, 57520, 57522, 57536, 57442, 57501

PARKER

THE (MOORHEAD, MN) EXTRA (THUR)

133 N Main St, Parker, SD, 57053, Turner, USA; gen tel (605) 297-4419; adv tel (605) 297-4419; ed tel (605) 297-4419; gen fax (605) 297-4015; adv fax (605) 297-4015; ed fax (605) 297-4015; disp adv e-mail ads@ncppub.com; class adv e-mail rschneider@ncppub.com; ed e-mail sebeling@ncppub.com; web site www.thenewera-online.com
Circulation: 0pd, 5,635fr; CVC
Advertising rate: Open inch rate $5.97
Established: 1875
Group: New Century Press
Digital Platform - Mobile: Apple, Android
Digital Platform - Tablet: Apple iOS, Android, Windows 7
Pub. .... Michael Ohop
Ed. .... Sarah Eveling
Adv. Mgr. .... Paul Harms
Mechanical Specifications: Type page 13 x 21; E - 6 cols, 2, 1/6 between; A - 6 cols, 2, 1/6 between; C - 6 cols, 2, 1/6 between.Equipment & Software: Hardware — APP/Mac Performa 638; Software — QPS/QuarkXPress.
Delivery Method: Mail, Racks
Areas Served: 57047, 57043, 57070, 57036, 57039, 57029, 57053, 57015, 57023, 57021, 57014, 57037

PARKSTON

THE PARKSTON ADVANCE (WED)

205 W Main St, Parkston, SD, 57366, Hutchinson, USA; gen tel (605) 928-3111; adv tel (605) 928-3111; ed tel (605) 928-3111; gen fax (605) 928-3111; adv fax (605) 928-3111; ed fax (605) 928-3111; disp adv e-mail advance@santel.net; class adv e-mail advance@santel.net; ed e-mail advance@santel.net; web site www.parkstonadvance.com
Circulation: 1,100pd,; Sworn/Estimate/Non-Audited
Advertising rate: Open inch rate $5.59
Digital Platform - Mobile: Apple, Android
Digital Platform - Tablet: Apple iOS, Android, Windows 7
Pub. .... Scott E. Ehler
Mng. Ed. .... Wendy Royston
Adv. Mgr. .... Kevin Geppert
Delivery Method: Mail, Racks
Areas Served: 57366, 57331

PHILIP

THE PIONEER-REVIEW (THUR)

105 Wood Ave, Philip, SD, 57567-4100, Haakon, USA; gen tel (605) 859-2516; adv tel (605) 859-2516; ed tel (605) 859-2516; gen fax (605) 859-2410; adv fax (605) 859-2410; ed fax (605) 859-2410; disp adv e-mail ads@pioneer-review.com; class adv e-mail ads@pioneer-review.com; ed e-mail newsdesk@pioneer-review.com; web site www.pioneer-review.com
Circulation: 1,650pd, 35fr; Sworn/Estimate/ Non-Audited
Advertising rate: Open inch rate $7.00
Digital Platform - Mobile: Apple, Windows
Digital Platform - Tablet: Apple iOS, Windows 7
Pub. .... Don Ravellette
Ed. .... Del Bartels
Gen. Mgr. .... Kelly Penticoff
Delivery Method: Mail, Racks
Areas Served: 57567, 57543, 57552, 57553, 57729, 57531, 57790, 57775, 57537, 57521, 57736, 57750, 57559, 57562, 57626, 57551

PLANKINTON

SOUTH DAKOTA MAIL (THUR)

116 N Main St, Plankinton, SD, 57368-2015, Aurora, USA; gen tel (605) 942-7770; adv tel (605) 942-7770; ed tel (605) 942-7770; gen fax (605) 942-7770; adv fax (605) 942-7770; ed fax (605) 942-7770; disp adv e-mail sdmail@siouxvalley.net; class adv e-mail sdmail@siouxvalley.net; ed e-mail sdmail@siouxvalley.net
Circulation: 950pd,; Sworn/Estimate/Non-Audited
Advertising rate: Open inch rate $5.30
Pub. .... Gayle Van Genderen
Ed. .... J.P. Studeny
Delivery Method: Mail, Racks
Areas Served: 57375, 57383, 57368, 57363, 57382, 57301

PLATTE

THE PLATTE ENTERPRISE (THUR)

511 S Main St, Platte, SD, 57369-2130, Charles Mix, USA; gen tel (605) 337-3101; gen fax (605) 337-3433; disp adv e-mail eprise@midstatesd.net; class adv e-mail eprise@midstatesd.net; ed e-mail eprise@midstatesd.net; web site www.platteenterprise.blogspot.com
Circulation: 1,890pd,; Sworn/Estimate/Non-Audited
Advertising rate: Open inch rate $5.25
Established: 1900
Digital Platform - Mobile: Windows
Digital Platform - Tablet: Windows 7
Pub./Gen. Mgr. .... Sharon Huizenga
Adv. Mgr. .... Jason Huizenga
Delivery Method: Mail, Racks
Areas Served: 57369, 57342, 57364, 57344, 57310

POLLOCK

PRAIRIE PIONEER (THUR)

117 Main St, Pollock, SD, 57648-8616, Campbell, USA; gen tel (605) 889-2320; adv tel (605) 889-2320; ed tel (605) 889-2320; gen fax (605) 889-2361; adv fax (605) 889-2361; ed fax (605) 889-2361; disp adv e-mail ads@valleytel.net; class adv e-mail ads@valleytel.net; ed e-mail pioneer@valleytel.net; web site www.ppioneer.com
Circulation: 1,500pd,; Sworn/Estimate/Non-Audited
Advertising rate: Open inch rate $6.85
Established: 1883
Digital Platform - Mobile: Apple, Android, Windows, Blackberry
Digital Platform - Tablet: Apple iOS, Android, Windows 7, Blackberry Tablet OS, Kindle, Nook, Kindle Fire
Pub. .... Leah P. Burke
Adv. Dir. .... Julie Brandner
Ed. .... Orland Geigle
Sports Ed. .... Waynette Geigle
Delivery Method: Mail, Newsstand, Racks
Areas Served: 57648, 57646, 57632, 57423, 57437, 58542, 58581, 58573, 57631

PRESHO

LYMAN COUNTY HERALD (WED)

223 N MAIN AVE, Presho, SD, 57568, Lyman, USA; gen tel (605) 895-6397; adv tel (605) 895-6397; ed tel (605) 895-6397; gen fax (605) 895-6377; adv fax (605) 895-6377; ed fax (605) 895-6377; disp adv e-mail news@lcherald.com; class adv e-mail news@lcherald.com; ed e-mail news@lcherald.com; web site www.lcherald.com
Circulation: 962pd,; Sworn/Estimate/Non-Audited
Advertising rate: Open inch rate $5.60
Digital Platform - Mobile: Apple, Android, Windows, Blackberry
Digital Platform - Tablet: Apple iOS, Android, Windows 7, Blackberry Tablet OS, Kindle, Nook, Kindle Fire
Pub./Ed./Adv. Mgr. .... Lucy Halverson
Co-Pub. .... Kim Halverson
Delivery Method: Mail
Areas Served: 57568, 57544, 57576, 57569, 57531

RAPID CITY

BUTTE COUNTY POST (WED)

PO Box 450, Rapid City, SD, 57709-0450, Butte, USA; gen tel (605) 892-2528; adv tel (605) 892-2528; ed tel (605) 892-2528; gen fax (605) 892-2529; adv fax (605) 892-2529; ed fax (605) 892-2529; disp adv e-mail mona.heimbaugh@rapidcityjournal.com; class adv e-mail mona.heimbaugh@rapidcityjournal.com; ed e-mail bcpnews@rapidcityjournal.com; web site www.buttecountypost.com
Circulation: 1,587pd,; Sworn/Estimate/Non-Audited
Advertising rate: Open inch rate $8.30
Established: 2008
Digital Platform - Mobile: Apple, Android, Windows, Blackberry
Digital Platform - Tablet: Apple iOS, Android, Windows 7, Blackberry Tablet OS
Gen Mgr .... Mona Heimbaugh
Publisher .... Eugene Jackson
NH Editor .... Deb HollNS
Delivery Method: Mail, Newsstand, Carrier, Racks
Areas Served: 57717, 57760, 57742, 57762, 57776, 57783, 82729, 82710, 82720, 59311, 39316, 87720, 59324, 57788

REDFIELD

THE REDFIELD PRESS (WED)

16 E 7th Ave, Redfield, SD, 57469-1206, Spink, USA; gen tel (605) 472-0822; adv tel (605) 472-0822; ed tel (605) 472-0822; gen fax (605) 472-3634; adv fax (605) 472-3634; ed fax (605) 472-3634; disp adv e-mail sales.redpress@midconetwork.com; class adv e-mail advertising.redpress@midconetwork.com; ed e-mail editor.redpress@midconetwork.com; web site www.redfieldpress.com
Circulation: 1,950pd,; Sworn/Estimate/Non-Audited
Advertising rate: Open inch rate $6.45
Group: News Media Corp.
Digital Platform - Mobile: Apple, Android, Windows, Blackberry
Digital Platform - Tablet: Apple iOS, Android, Windows 7, Blackberry Tablet OS, Kindle, Nook, Kindle Fire
Pub. .... Mark Davis
Adv. Sales Mgr. .... Parry Sterner
Mng. Ed. .... Derek E. Keeling
Mechanical Specifications: Type page 11 1/4 x 13 3/4; E - 5 cols, 1 7/8, between.Equipment & Software: Hardware — 5-APP/Mac; Software — QPS/QuarkXPress 4.0.
Delivery Method: Mail, Newsstand, Racks
Areas Served: 57469, 57424, 57429, 57434, 57436, 57438, 57440, 57460, 57461, 57465, 57467, 57470, 57476, 57477, 57348

ROSHOLT

THE ROSHOLT REVIEW (WED)

104 Park Place, Rosholt, SD, 57260, Roberts, USA; gen tel (605) 537-4276; adv tel (605) 537-4276; ed tel (605) 537-4276; gen fax (605) 537-4858; adv fax (605) 537-4858; ed fax (605) 537-4858; disp adv e-mail review@tnics.com; class adv e-mail review@tnics.com; ed e-mail review@tnics.com; web site www.rosholtreview.blogspot.com
Circulation: 1,280pd, 25fr; Sworn/Estimate/ Non-Audited
Advertising rate: Open inch rate $3.35
Digital Platform - Mobile: Windows **Digital Platform - Tablet:** Windows 7
Pub./Ed./Adv. Dir. .... Calvin Ceroll
Delivery Method: Mail, Racks
Areas Served: 57260, 57255, 57262, 58030, 58041, 56296, 56219

SALEM

SALEM SPECIAL (THUR)

135 S Main St, Salem, SD, 57058-8514, McCook, USA; gen tel (605) 425-2361; adv tel (605) 425-2361; ed tel (605) 425-2361; gen fax (605) 425-2547; adv fax (605) 425-2547; ed fax (605) 425-2547; disp adv e-mail tschwans@triotel.net; class adv e-mail tschwans@triotel.net; ed e-mail tschwans@triotel.net; web site www.salemspecial.com
Circulation: 1,200pd,; Sworn/Estimate/Non-Audited
Advertising rate: Open inch rate $4.40
Established: 1890
Pub./Ed. .... Troy Schwans
McKillop LuAnn
Delivery Method: Mail, Newsstand, Racks
Areas Served: 57076, 57029, 57058, 57319, 57012, 57321, 57374, 57048, 57311, 57332

SCOTLAND

SCOTLAND JOURNAL (WED)

630 1st St, Scotland, SD, 57059, Bon Homme, USA; gen tel (605) 583-4419; gen fax (605) 583-4406; disp adv e-mail scotnews@gwtc.net; class adv e-mail scotnews@gwtc.net; ed e-mail scotnews@gwtc.net
Circulation: 900pd, 60fr; Sworn/Estimate/ Non-Audited
Advertising rate: Open inch rate $5.48
Established: 1894
Group: B&H Publishing, Inc.
Pub. .... Becky Tycz
Ed./Adv. Dir. .... Peggy Schelske
Circ. .... Billie Jo Hayes
Mechanical Specifications: Type page 13 x 21 1/2.
Delivery Method: Mail
Areas Served: 57059, 57354, 57066, 57052, 57040, 57045, 57376

SELBY

SELBY RECORD (THUR)
4411 Main St, Selby, SD, 57472-2010, Walworth, USA; gen tel (605) 649-7866; adv tel (605) 649-7866; ed tel (605) 649-7866; gen fax (605) 649-1126; adv fax (605) 649-1126; ed fax (605) 649-1126; disp adv e-mail selbyrec@venturecomm.net; class adv e-mail selbyrec@venturecomm.net; ed e-mail selbyrec@venturecomm.net
Circulation: 1,000pd, 10fr; Sworn/Estimate/Non-Audited
Advertising rate: Open inch rate $3.93
Pub. .... Sharon Wolff
Ed. .... Sandy Bond
Delivery Method: Mail, Newsstand, Racks
Areas Served: 57472, 57420, 57631, 57646, 57428, 57452

SISSETON

SISSETON COURIER (TUES)
117 E Oak St, Sisseton, SD, 57262-1413, Roberts, USA; gen tel (605) 698-7642; adv tel (605) 698-7642; ed tel (605) 698-7642; gen fax (605) 698-3641; adv fax (605) 698-3641; ed fax (605) 698-3641; disp adv e-mail ads@sissetoncourier.com; class adv e-mail design@sissetoncourier.com; ed e-mail news@sissetoncourier.com; web site www.sissetoncourier.com
Circulation: 3,201pd, 90fr; Sworn/Estimate/Non-Audited
Advertising rate: Open inch rate $6.25
Digital Platform - Mobile: Apple, Android
Digital Platform - Tablet: Apple iOS, Android, Windows 7
Pub./Ed. .... Kevin Deutsch
Office Mgr. .... Sylvia Deutsch
Adv. Dir. .... Jennie Evenson
Delivery Method: Mail, Newsstand, Racks
Areas Served: 57262, 57255, 57270, 57257, 57266, 57260, 56219, 57224, 57232

SPRINGFIELD

SPRINGFIELD TIMES (WED)
712 8TH ST, Springfield, SD, 57062, Bon Homme, USA; gen tel (605) 369-2441; adv tel (605) 369-2441; ed tel (605) 589-3242; gen fax (605) 369-2793; adv fax (605) 369-2793; ed fax (605) 369-2793; disp adv e-mail times@gwtc.net; class adv e-mail times@gwtc.net; ed e-mail times@gwtc.net
Circulation: 850pd,; Sworn/Estimate/Non-Audited
Advertising rate: Open inch rate $4.52
Established: 1871
Pub./Adv. Dir. .... Rebecca Tycz
Ed. .... Sheila Kremer
Delivery Method: Mail, Racks
Areas Served: 57062, 57066, 57315, 57063

STURGIS

MEADE COUNTY TIMES-TRIBUNE (WED)
1010 Ballpark Rd, Ste 1, Sturgis, SD, 57785-2208, Meade, USA; gen tel (605) 347-2503; adv tel (605) 892-2528; ed tel (605) 347-2503; gen fax (605) 347-2321; adv fax (605) 347-2321; ed fax (605) 347-2321; disp adv e-mail mona.heimbaugh@rapidcityjournal.com; class adv e-mail mona.heimbaugh@rapidcityjournal.com; ed e-mail deb.holland@rapidcityjournal.com; web site www.meadecountytimes.com
Circulation: 2,800pd, 5,000fr; Sworn/Estimate/Non-Audited
Advertising rate: Open inch rate $8.00
Established: 1907
Group: Lee Enterprises, Inc.
Digital Platform - Mobile: Apple, Android
Digital Platform - Tablet: Apple iOS, Android, Windows 7
Ed. .... Deb Holland
Inside sales/news clerk .... Alisa Harlan
Mechanical Specifications: Type page 10 x 16; E - 5 cols, 2, between; A - 5 cols, 2, between; C - 5 cols, 2, between.
Delivery Method: Mail, Newsstand, Carrier, Racks
Areas Served: 57785, 57765, 57787, 57784, 57719, 57760, 57736, 57748, 57762, 57761, 57737, 57793, 57718, 57769, 57741, 57779, 57758

TIMBER LAKE

TIMBER LAKE TOPIC (THUR)
806 Main St, Timber Lake, SD, 57656, Dewey, USA; gen tel (605) 865-3546; adv tel (605) 865-3546; ed tel (605) 865-3546; gen fax (605) 865-3787; adv fax (605) 865-3787; ed fax (605) 865-3787; disp adv e-mail timtopic@lakotanetwork.com; class adv e-mail timtopic@lakotanetwork.com; ed e-mail timtopic@lakotanetwork.com; web site www.timberlakesouthdakota.com
Circulation: 1,450pd, 31fr; Sworn/Estimate/Non-Audited
Advertising rate: Open inch rate $5.00
Established: 1910
Digital Platform - Mobile: Apple, Android
Digital Platform - Tablet: Apple iOS, Android, Windows 7
Pub./Ed./Adv. Dir. .... Jim Nelson
Pub./Ed. ....
Kathy Snyder NelsonEquipment & Software: Hardware — APP/Mac; Software — Adobe/PageMaker 6.5.
Delivery Method: Mail, Newsstand, Racks
Areas Served: 57656, 57657, 57633, 57630, 57628, 57625, 57652, 57601

TRIPP

TRIPP STAR-LEDGER (WED)
PO Box D, Tripp, SD, 57376-0454, Hutchinson, USA; gen tel (605) 928-3111; adv tel (605) 928-3911; ed tel (605) 928-3111; gen fax (605) 928-3111; adv fax (605) 928-3111; ed fax (605) 928-3111; disp adv e-mail advance@santel.net; class adv e-mail advance@santel.net; ed e-mail advance@santel.net; web site www.parkstonadvance.com
Circulation: 606pd,; Sworn/Estimate/Non-Audited
Advertising rate: Open inch rate $5.59
Digital Platform - Mobile: Apple, Android
Digital Platform - Tablet: Apple iOS, Android, Windows 7
Pub. .... Scott Ehler
Mng. Ed. .... Wendy Royston
Adv. Dir. .... Kevin Geppert
Delivery Method: Mail, Racks
Areas Served: 57376, 57366

VERMILLION

VERMILLION PLAIN TALK (FRI)
201 W Cherry St, Vermillion, SD, 57069-1109, Clay, USA; gen tel (605) 624-2695; adv tel (605) 624-4429 ext. 103; ed tel (605) 624-4429 ext. 105; gen fax (605) 624-2696; adv fax (605) 624-2696; ed fax (605) 624-2696; disp adv e-mail gary.wood@plaintalk.net; class adv e-mail michele.schievelbein@plaintalk.net; ed e-mail david.lias@plaintalk.net; web site www.plaintalk.net
Circulation: 2,275pd, 30fr; Sworn/Estimate/Non-Audited
Advertising rate: Open inch rate $8.63
Established: 1886
Digital Platform - Mobile: Apple, Android, Windows, Blackberry
Digital Platform - Tablet: Apple iOS, Android, Windows 7, Blackberry Tablet OS
Pub./Ed. .... Gary Wood
Ed. .... David Lias
Adv. Dir. .... Micki Schievelbein
Ed. .... Shauna Marlette
Delivery Method: Mail, Newsstand, Racks
Areas Served: 57069, 57004, 57010, 57025, 57044, 57073

VIBORG

VIBORG ENTERPRISE/HURLEY LEADER (THUR)
100 N Main St, Viborg, SD, 57070-2102, Turner, USA; gen tel (605) 766-7827; adv tel (605) 766-7827; ed tel (605) 766-7827; gen fax (605) 766-7828; adv fax (605) 766-7828; ed fax (605) 766-7828; disp adv e-mail enterprise@iw.net; class adv e-mail enterprise@iw.net; ed e-mail leader@iw.net
Circulation: 583pd, 22fr; Sworn/Estimate/Non-Audited
Advertising rate: Open inch rate $4.60
Group: Star Publishing Co.
Pub./Ed. .... Shane Hill
Pub./Gen. Mgr. .... Allyson Hill
Mechanical Specifications: Type page 9 3/4 x 15; E - 5 cols, 1 5/6, between; A - 5 cols, 1 5/6, between; C - 5 cols, 1 5/6, between.Equipment & Software: Hardware — APP/Mac; Software — Adobe/PageMaker 6.5, Adobe/Photoshop 4.01.
Delivery Method: Mail
Areas Served: 57070, 57036, 57037, 57021

VOLGA

THE VOLGA TRIBUNE (THUR)
207 Kasan Ave, Volga, SD, 57071, Brookings, USA; gen tel (605) 627-9471; adv tel (605) 627-9471; ed tel (605) 627-9471; gen fax (605) 627-9310; adv fax (605) 627-9310; ed fax (605) 627-9310; disp adv e-mail chris.rfdnews@mchsi.com; class adv e-mail chris.rfdnews@mchsi.com; ed e-mail rfdnews@mchsi.com; web site www.rfdnewsgroup.com
Circulation: 1,800pd,; Sworn/Estimate/Non-Audited
Advertising rate: Open inch rate $5.00
Established: 1882
Group: Clear Lake Courier
Digital Platform - Mobile: Apple, Windows
Digital Platform - Tablet: Apple iOS, Windows 7
Pub. .... Chris Schumacher
Ed. .... David KeithEquipment & Software: Hardware — 1-APP/Mac G3, 1-APP/Mac G4; Software — Adobe/PageMaker 6.5.
Delivery Method: Mail, Racks
Areas Served: 57071, 57220, 57061, 57006

WAGNER

LAKE ANDES WAVE (WED)
209 S Main Ave, Wagner, SD, 57380-1727, Charles Mix, USA; gen tel (605) 384-5616; adv tel (605) 384-5616; ed tel (605) 384-5616; gen fax (605) 384-5955; adv fax (605) 384-5955; ed fax (605) 384-5955; disp adv e-mail announcer@hcinet.net; class adv e-mail announcer@hcinet.net; ed e-mail announcer@hcinet.net; web site www.thelakeandeswave.com
Circulation: 440pd,; Sworn/Estimate/Non-Audited
Advertising rate: Open inch rate $5.50
Group: Star Publishing Co.
Digital Platform - Mobile: Apple, Android, Windows
Digital Platform - Tablet: Apple iOS, Android, Windows 7
Pub./Ed. .... Barb Pechous
Delivery Method: Mail
Areas Served: 57356, 57357, 57342, 57367, 57380, 57313, 57361

THE WAGNER POST (WED)
209 S Main Ave, Wagner, SD, 57380-1727, Charles Mix, USA; gen tel (605) 384-5616; adv tel (605) 384-5616; ed tel (605) 384-5616; gen fax (605) 384-5955; adv fax (605) 384-5955; ed fax (605) 384-5955; disp adv e-mail announcer@hcinet.net; class adv e-mail announcer@hcinet.net; ed e-mail announcer@hcinet.net; web site www.postandwave.com
Circulation: 1,800pd, 6,500fr; Sworn/Estimate/Non-Audited
Advertising rate: Open inch rate $6.50
Digital Platform - Mobile: Apple, Android, Windows
Digital Platform - Tablet: Apple iOS, Android, Windows 7
Pub./Ed. .... Barb Pechous
Delivery Method: Mail, Racks
Areas Served: 57380, 57329, 57357, 57356, 57361, 57315, 57062, 57330, 57313, 57342, 57335

WAUBAY

WAUBAY CLIPPER (SAT)
122 N Main St, Waubay, SD, 57273, Day, USA; gen tel (605) 947-4501; adv tel (605)947-4501; ed tel (605)947-4501; gen fax (605) 947-4501; adv fax (605)947-4501; ed fax (605)947-4501; disp adv e-mail linda@waubayclipper.com; class adv e-mail linda@waubayclipper.com; ed e-mail linda@waubayclipper.com; web site www.waubayclipper.blogspot.com
Circulation: 875pd, 26fr; Sworn/Estimate/Non-Audited
Advertising rate: Open inch rate $6.00
Digital Platform - Tablet: Apple iOS
Pub./Ed./Adv. Dir. .... Linda M. Walters
Delivery Method: Mail, Newsstand
Areas Served: 57273, 57256, 57274, 57266

WEBSTER

REPORTER & FARMER (MON)
516 Main St, Webster, SD, 57274-1719, Day, USA; gen tel (605) 345-3356; adv tel (605) 345-3356; ed tel (605) 345-3356; gen fax (605) 345-3739; adv fax (605) 345-3739; ed fax (605) 345-3739; disp adv e-mail news@reporterandfarmer.com; class adv e-mail sports@reporterandfarmer.com; ed e-mail news@reporterandfarmer.com; web site www.reporterandfarmer.com
Circulation: 3,200pd,; Sworn/Estimate/Non-Audited
Advertising rate: Open inch rate $6.30
Established: 1881
Digital Platform - Mobile: Apple, Android, Windows, Blackberry
Digital Platform - Tablet: Apple iOS, Android, Windows 7, Blackberry Tablet OS
Pub./Ed. .... LeAnn Suhr
Adv. Mgr. .... John SuhrEquipment & Software: Hardware — APP/Macs, IBM; Software — QPS/QuarkXPress, Adobe/Photoshop.
Delivery Method: Mail, Newsstand, Racks
Areas Served: 57274, 57239, 57250, 57256, 57468, 57422, 57261, 57273, 57217, 57219, 57222, 57232

WESSINGTON SPRINGS

TRUE DAKOTAN (TUES)
113 E Main St, Wessington Springs, SD, 57382, Jerauld, USA; gen tel (605) 539-1281; adv tel (605) 539-1281; ed tel (605) 539-1281; gen fax (605) 539-9315; adv fax (605) 539-9315; ed fax (605) 539-9315; disp adv e-mail news@truedakotan.com; class adv e-mail delia@truedakotan.com; ed e-mail kristi@truedakotan.com; web site www.truedakotan.com
Circulation: 1,400pd,; Sworn/Estimate/Non-Audited
Advertising rate: Open inch rate $6.25
Established: 1975
Group: Kristi Publishing, Inc.
Digital Platform - Mobile: Apple, Windows
Digital Platform - Tablet: Apple iOS, Windows 7
Editor/Publisher .... Kristi HineEquipment & Software: ; Software — Venture/Publisher 2000.
Delivery Method: Mail, Newsstand, Racks
Areas Served: 57382, 57312, 57358, 57341, 57381, 57385, 57383

WHITE

THE TRI-CITY STAR (THUR)

PO Box 341, White, SD, 57276-0341, Brookings, USA; gen tel (605) 629-2052; adv tel (605) 629-2052; ed tel (605) 629-2052; gen fax (605) 629-1303; adv fax (605) 629-1303; ed fax (605) 629-1303; disp adv e-mail t.c.s@mchsi.com; class adv e-mail t.c.s@mchsi.com; ed e-mail t.c.s@mchsi.com; web site www.rfdnewsgroup.com
Circulation: 1,800pd,; Sworn/Estimate/Non-Audited
Advertising rate: Open inch rate $5.00
Established: 1884
Digital Platform - Mobile: Apple, Windows
Digital Platform - Tablet: Apple iOS, Windows 7
Pub. .... Chris Schumacher
Ed. .... Paul Ekren
Delivery Method: Mail, Racks
Areas Served: 57268, 57213, 57276

WHITE LAKE

THE STICKNEY ARGUS (WED)

PO Box 216, White Lake, SD, 57383-0216, Aurora, USA; gen tel (605) 249-2420; adv tel (605) 249-2420; ed tel (605) 249-2420; gen fax (855) 303-3153; disp adv e-mail info@auroracountynews.net; class adv e-mail info@auroracountynews.net; ed e-mail info@auroracountynews.net
Circulation: 400pd, 31fr; Sworn/Estimate/Non-Audited
Advertising rate: Open inch rate $5.75
Established: 1906
Group: Standard Publishing Inc.
Owner .... Kim Ehlers
Delivery Method: Mail, Racks
Areas Served: 57383, 57368, 57375, 57301, 57382

WHITE RIVER

MELLETTE COUNTY NEWS (WED)

416 N MAIN ST, White River, SD, 57579, Mellette, USA; gen tel (605) 259-3642; adv tel (605) 259-3642; ed tel (605) 259-3642; gen fax (605) 259-3497; adv fax (605) 259-3497; ed fax (605) 259-3497; disp adv e-mail mcnews@gwtc.net; class adv e-mail mcnews@gwtc.net; ed e-mail mcnews@gwtc.net; web site www.mellettecountynews.com
Circulation: 500pd,; Sworn/Estimate/Non-Audited
Advertising rate: Open inch rate $5.50
Established: 1912
Digital Platform - Mobile: Apple, Android
Digital Platform - Tablet: Apple iOS, Android, Windows 7
Pub. .... Tim Huether
Ed. .... Kristan Krogman
Mechanical Specifications: Type page 11.75 x 21; 1 pica gutter; 1 col - 1.82"Equipment & Software: ; Software — InDesign, Adobe/Photoshop
Delivery Method: Mail
Areas Served: 57555, 57570, 57579, 57585, 57572, 57566, 57563, 57560, 69201

WILMOT

WILMOT ENTERPRISE (THUR)

805 Main St, Wilmot, SD, 57279, Roberts, USA; gen tel (605) 938-4651; adv tel (605) 938-4651; ed tel (605) 938-4651; gen fax (605) 938-4683; adv fax (605) 938-4683; ed fax (605) 938-4683; disp adv e-mail wilnews@tnics.com; class adv e-mail wilnews@tnics.com; ed e-mail wilnews@tnics.com; web site www.wilmotenterprise.blogspot.com
Circulation: 850pd,; Sworn/Estimate/Non-Audited
Advertising rate: Open inch rate $4.50
Established: 1884
Pub./Ed./Adv. Dir... Nancy KimmelEquipment & Software: Hardware — 1-APP/Mac G4, APP/Mac 6200; Software — Adobe/PageMaker 6.0, Adobe/Photoshop 5.0.
Delivery Method: Mail
Areas Served: 57279, 57227, 57251, 57257, 57266, 57269

WINNER

WINNER ADVOCATE (WED)

125 W 3rd St, Winner, SD, 57580-1707, Tripp, USA; gen tel (605) 842-1481; adv tel (605)842-1481; ed tel (605)842-1481; gen fax (605) 842-1979; adv fax (605)842-1979; ed fax (605)842-1979; disp adv e-mail winneradvocate@hotmail.com; class adv e-mail winneradvocate@hotmail.com; ed e-mail charley.najacht@thewinneradvocate.com; web site www.thewinneradvocate.com
Circulation: 2,600pd,; Sworn/Estimate/Non-Audited
Advertising rate: Open inch rate $6.85
Established: 1910
Digital Platform - Mobile: Apple, Android, Windows, Blackberry
Digital Platform - Tablet: Apple iOS, Android, Windows 7, Blackberry Tablet OS
Pub. .... Charley Najacht
Ed. .... Dan Bechtold
Gen. Mgr. .... Rick Hoover
Adv. Mgr. .... Laura Brown
Delivery Method: Mail, Newsstand, Racks
Areas Served: 57580, 57584, 57528, 57526, 57523, 57541, 57530, 57533, 57529, 57534, 57542, 57553, 57555, 57578, 57579, 57585

WOONSOCKET

SANBORN WEEKLY JOURNAL (THUR)

506 W 6th St, Woonsocket, SD, 57385, Sanborn, USA; gen tel (605) 796-4221; adv tel (605) 796-4221; ed tel (605) 796-4221; gen fax (605) 796-4221; adv fax (605) 796-4221; ed fax (605) 796-4221; disp adv e-mail swj124@mac.com; class adv e-mail swj124@mac.com; ed e-mail swj124@mac.com; web site www.sanbornjournal.com
Circulation: 1,201pd, 38fr; Sworn/Estimate/Non-Audited
Advertising rate: Open inch rate $4.85
Established: 1883
Pub./Ed. .... Hillary Lutter
Mng. Ed. .... Bryan Lutter
Mechanical Specifications: Type page 13 x 21; E - 6 cols, 2, 1/6 between; A - 6 cols, 2, 1/6 between; C - 6 cols, 2, 1/6 between.Equipment & Software: Hardware — APP/Mac; Software — QPS/QuarkXPress, Claris.
Delivery Method: Mail, Racks
Areas Served: 57385, 57359, 57314, 57350, 57301, 57349, 57382, 57338, 57337, 57358

YANKTON

THE YANKTON COUNTY OBSERVER (FRI)

308 Douglas Ave, Yankton, SD, 57078-4432, Yankton, USA; gen tel (605) 665-0484; adv tel (605) 665-0484; ed tel (605) 665-0484; gen fax (605) 665-2263; adv fax (605) 665-2263; ed fax (605) 665-2263; disp adv e-mail kathy@ycobserver.com; class adv e-mail ads@ycobserver.com; ed e-mail kathy@ycobserver.com; web site www.ycobserver.com
Circulation: 2,700pd, 60fr; Sworn/Estimate/Non-Audited
Advertising rate: Open inch rate $7.00
Established: 1978
Digital Platform - Mobile: Apple, Android, Windows, Blackberry
Digital Platform - Tablet: Apple iOS, Android, Windows 7, Blackberry Tablet OS, Kindle, Nook, Kindle Fire
Pub./Ed. .... Kathy Church
Adv. Mgr. .... Jim Anderson
Mechanical Specifications: Type page 10.3 x 15.875; All pages - 5 cols, 1.926, 1/6 between.Equipment & Software: Hardware — APP/Mac.
Delivery Method: Mail, Newsstand, Racks
Areas Served: 57078, 57031, 57037, 57046, 57067, 57072, 57040, 57063

TENNESSEE

ALAMO

THE CROCKETT COUNTY TIMES (THUR)

46 W Main St, Alamo, TN, 38001-1614, Crockett, USA; gen tel (731) 696-4558; adv tel (731) 696-4558; ed tel (731) 696-4558; gen fax (731) 696-4550; adv fax (731) 696-4550; ed fax (731) 696-4550; disp adv e-mail thetimes@crockettnet.com; class adv e-mail thetimes@crockettnet.com; ed e-mail thetimes@crockettnet.com; web site www.magicvalleypublishing.com
Circulation: 4,200pd,; Sworn/Estimate/Non-Audited
Advertising rate: Open inch rate $7.35
Established: 1873
Digital Platform - Mobile: Apple, Android, Windows, Blackberry
Digital Platform - Tablet: Apple iOS, Android, Windows 7, Blackberry Tablet OS, Kindle, Nook, Kindle Fire
Pub. .... Dennis Richardson
Ed. .... Hope Riley
Adv. Dir. .... Keshia Richardson
Mechanical Specifications: Type page 11 5/8 x 21; E - 6 cols, 1 5/6, 1/8 between; A - 6 cols, 1 5/6, 1/8 between; C - 6 cols, 1 5/6, 1/8 between.Equipment & Software: ; Software — Adobe/PageMaker.
Delivery Method: Mail, Racks
Areas Served: Crockett County

ASHLAND CITY

ASHLAND CITY TIMES (WED)

202 N Main St, Ste A, Ashland City, TN, 37015-1318, Cheatham, USA; gen tel (615) 792-4230; adv tel (615) 792-4230; ed tel (615) 792-4230; gen fax (615) 792-3671; adv fax (615) 792-3671; ed fax (615) 792-3671; disp adv e-mail jward@tennessean.com; class adv e-mail pdyates@tennessean.com; ed e-mail madowney@tennessean.com; web site www.ashlandcitytimes.com
Circulation: 5,000pd,; Sworn/Estimate/Non-Audited
Advertising rate: Open inch rate $13.85
Group: Gannett
The Tennessean
TN Media
Digital Platform - Mobile: Apple, Android
Digital Platform - Tablet: Apple iOS, Android, Windows 7
Mng. Ed. .... Meg Downey
Sales VP .... John Ward
Circ. Mgr. .... Shirley Bradley
Delivery Method: Mail, Racks
Areas Served: Cheatham County

BARTLETT

COLLIERVILLE INDEPENDENT (WED)

2850 Stage Village Cv, Ste 5, Bartlett, TN, 38134-4682, Shelby, USA; gen tel (901) 388-1500; adv tel (901) 388-1500; ed tel (901) 388-1500; gen fax (901) 529-7687; adv fax (901) 529-7687; ed fax (901) 529-7687; disp adv e-mail graham.sweeney@journalinc.com; class adv e-mail graham.sweeney@journalinc.com; ed e-mail graham.sweeney@journalinc.com; web site www.colliervilleindependent.com
Circulation: 14,000fr; Sworn/Estimate/Non-Audited
Advertising rate: Open inch rate $16.35
Digital Platform - Mobile: Apple, Android
Digital Platform - Tablet: Apple iOS, Android, Windows 7
Pub./Ed./Adv. Dir. .... Graham Sweeney
Mechanical Specifications: Type page 13 x 21 1/2; E - 6 cols, 2 1/12, 1/6 between; A - 6 cols, 2 1/12, 1/6 between; C - 6 cols, 2 1/12, 1/6 between.
Delivery Method: Mail, Newsstand, Racks
Areas Served: Shelby County

SHELBY SUN TIMES (THUR)

2850 Stage Village Cv, Ste 5, Bartlett, TN, 38134-4682, Shelby, USA; gen tel (901) 388-1500; adv tel (901) 388-1500; ed tel (901) 388-1500; gen fax (901) 529-7687; adv fax (901) 529-7687; ed fax (901) 529-7687; disp adv e-mail graham.sweeney@journalinc.com; class adv e-mail graham.sweeney@journalinc.com; ed e-mail graham.sweeney@journalinc.com; web site www.shelby-news.com
Circulation: 30,000fr; Sworn/Estimate/Non-Audited
Advertising rate: Open inch rate $22.44
Established: 1987
Digital Platform - Mobile: Apple, Android
Digital Platform - Tablet: Apple iOS, Android, Windows 7
Pub./Ed./Adv. Dir. .... Graham Sweeney
Mechanical Specifications: Type page 9 13/16 x 14 1/2; E - 6 cols, 1 1/2, between; A - 6 cols, 1 1/2, between; C - 6 cols, 1 1/2, between.
Delivery Method: Mail, Newsstand, Racks
Areas Served: 38138, 38139, 38018, 38017, 38133, 38016

THE BARTLETT EXPRESS (THUR)

2850 Stage Village Cv, Ste 5, Bartlett, TN, 38134-4682, Shelby, USA; gen tel (901) 433-9138; adv tel (901) 433-9138; ed tel (901) 433-9138; gen fax (901) 529-7687; adv fax (901) 529-7687; ed fax (901) 529-7687; disp adv e-mail vickie.clark@journalinc.com; class adv e-mail felicia.watkins@journalinc.com; ed e-mail carolyn.bahm@journalinc.com; web site www.bartlett-express.com
Circulation: 3,045pd,; Sworn/Estimate/Non-Audited
Advertising rate: Open inch rate $10.50
Established: 1978
Group: Journal West 10 Media, LLC
Digital Platform - Mobile: Apple, Android
Digital Platform - Tablet: Apple iOS, Android, Windows 7
Ed .... Carolyn Bahm
Sales Mgr .... Vickie Clark
Sales .... Whitney Fisher
Sales .... Lyn Whitson
Mechanical Specifications: Type page 13 x 21 1/2; E - 6 cols, 2, 1/3 between; A - 6 cols, 2, 1/3 between; C - 9 cols, 1 1/2, 1/6 between. Equipment & Software: Hardware — APP/Macs; Presses — HI/V-15A; Software — QPS/QuarkXPress, Adobe/Photoshop, Adobe/PageMaker.
Delivery Method: Mail, Newsstand, Carrier, Racks
Areas Served: 38133, 38134, 38135, 38184, 38002

BEAN STATION

GRAINGER TODAY (WED)

691 Main St, Bean Station, TN, 37708-4242, Grainger, USA; gen tel (865) 993-0713; adv tel (865)993-0713; ed tel (865)993-0713; gen fax (865) 993-6474; adv fax (865)993-6474; ed fax (865)993-6474; disp adv e-mail editor@graingertoday.com; class adv e-mail classified@graingertoday.com; ed e-mail editor@graingertoday.com; web site www.graingertoday.com
Circulation: 6,003pd,; Sworn/Estimate/Non-Audited
Advertising rate: Modular broadsheet sizes
Established: 2004
Digital Platform - Mobile: Apple, Android, Windows, Blackberry
Digital Platform - Tablet: Apple iOS, Android, Windows 7, Blackberry Tablet OS, Kindle, Nook, Kindle Fire
Pub. .... Ann Cason

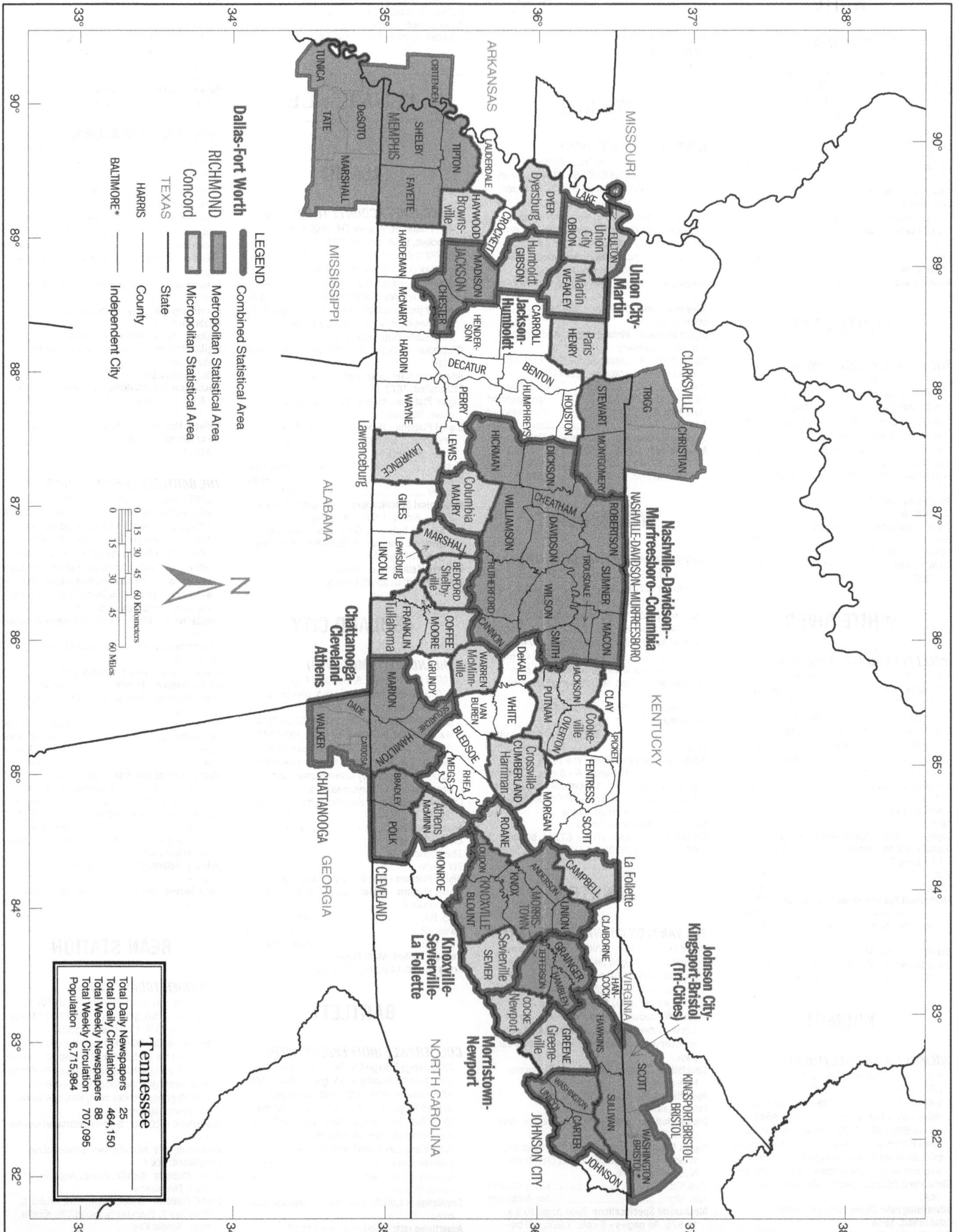
Tennessee
Total Daily Newspapers 25
Total Daily Circulation 464,150
Total Weekly Newspapers 88
Total Weekly Circulation 707,095
Population 6,715,984
LEGEND
Dallas-Fort Worth Combined Statistical Area
RICHMOND Metropolitan Statistical Area
Concord Micropolitan Statistical Area
TEXAS State
HARRIS County
BALTIMORE* Independent City
N
0 15 30 45 60 Kilometers
0 15 30 45 60 Miles
Union City-Martin
Jackson-Humboldt
Nashville-Davidson--Murfreesboro--Columbia
NASHVILLE-DAVIDSON--MURFREESBORO
CLARKSVILLE
Chattanooga-Cleveland-Athens
CHATTANOOGA
CLEVELAND
Knoxville-Sevierville-La Follette
La Follette
Johnson City-Kingsport-Bristol (Tri-Cities)
KINGSPORT-BRISTOL-BRISTOL
JOHNSON CITY
Morristown-Newport
Lawrenceburg
MISSOURI
KENTUCKY
VIRGINIA
ARKANSAS
MISSISSIPPI
ALABAMA
GEORGIA
NORTH CAROLINA
90° 89° 88° 87° 86° 85° 84° 83° 82°
33° 34° 35° 36° 37° 38°

Mng. Ed..Tracey Wolfe
Associate Publisher........................Krista Etter
Senior Sales Rep..........................Ashley Miller
Delivery Method: Mail, Racks
Areas Served: 37861, 37708, 37709, 37881, 37811, 37888, 37857, 37814, 37815, 37813, 37760, 37879, 37824, 37825, 37721

BENTON

POLK COUNTY NEWS/CITIZEN ADVANCE (WED)

3 Main St, Benton, TN, 37307, Polk, USA; gen tel (423) 338-2818; adv tel (423) 338-2818; ed tel (423) 338-2818; gen fax (423) 338-4574; adv fax (423) 338-4574; ed fax (423) 338-4574; disp adv e-mail advertising@thepolkcountynews.com; class adv e-mail advertising@thepolkcountynews.com; ed e-mail news@thepolkcountynews.com; web site www.polknewsonline.com
Circulation: 3,800pd,; Sworn/Estimate/Non-Audited
Advertising rate: Open inch rate $5.75
Established: 1883
Group: The Newspaper Publishing Company, LLC
Digital Platform - Mobile: Blackberry
Digital Platform - Tablet: Other
Pub..Cheryl Buehler
Ed. ....Richmond Clayton
Mechanical Specifications: Type page 10 x 21; 6 cols, 1.56, 1/8 between;Equipment & Software: Hardware — APP/Mac; Software — InDesign, Photoshop, Acrobat
Delivery Method: Mail, Newsstand, Racks
Areas Served: 37307, 37325, 37369, 37361, 37362, 37317, 37371, 37326, 37333

BOLIVAR

BULLETIN-TIMES (WED)

PO Box 438, Bolivar, TN, 38008-0438, Hardeman, USA; gen tel (731) 658-3691; adv tel (731) 658-3691; ed tel (731) 658-3691; gen fax (731) 658-7222; adv fax (731) 658-7222; ed fax (731) 658-7222; disp adv e-mail editor@hardemancountyjournal.com; class adv e-mail editor@hardemancountyjournal.com; ed e-mail editor@hardemancountyjournal.com; web site www.bulletintimesnews.com
Circulation: 5,000pd, 15,000fr; Sworn/Estimate/Non-Audited
Advertising rate: Open inch rate $8.30
Established: 1865
Group: Delphos Herald, Inc.
Digital Platform - Mobile: Apple, Android, Windows, Blackberry
Digital Platform - Tablet: Apple iOS, Android, Windows 7, Blackberry Tablet OS
Pub./Ed. ....Richard Fry
Account Exec./Circ. Mgr............ Shasity Mynatt
Mechanical Specifications: Type page 13 x 21 1/2; E - 6 cols, 1 13/16, 1/6 between; A - 6 cols, 1 13/16, 1/6 between; C - 6 cols, 1 13/16, 1/6 between.Equipment & Software: Hardware — APP/Mac; Software — QPS/QuarkXPress 4.0, Adobe/Photoshop 5.0.
Delivery Method: Mail, Newsstand, Racks
Areas Served: Hardeman County

BROWNSVILLE

BROWNSVILLE STATES-GRAPHIC (THUR)

20 N Washington Ave, Brownsville, TN, 38012-2555, Haywood, USA; gen tel (731) 772-1172; adv tel (731) 772-1172; ed tel (731) 772-1172; gen fax (731) 772-8306; adv fax (731) 772-8306; ed fax (731) 772-8306; disp adv e-mail advertising@statesgraphic.com; class adv e-mail advertising@statesgraphic.com; ed e-mail mmatlock@statesgraphic.com; web site www.statesgraphic.com
Circulation: 4,600pd, 50fr; Sworn/Estimate/Non-Audited
Advertising rate: Open inch rate $7.20
Established: 1867
Group: American Hometown Publishing
Digital Platform - Mobile: Apple, Android, Windows, Blackberry
Digital Platform - Tablet: Apple iOS, Android, Windows 7, Blackberry Tablet OS, Kindle, Nook, Kindle Fire
Editor...Jennifer Willis
Adv. Mgr. ....Kristine Osteen
Sports Ed..
Jeff IrelandEquipment & Software: Hardware — APP/Mac; Software — Microsoft/Word, Adobe/PageMaker, Adobe/Photoshop.
Delivery Method: Mail, Racks
Areas Served: Haywood County

BYRDSTOWN

PICKETT COUNTY PRESS (THUR)

23 Courthouse Sq, Byrdstown, TN, 38549-2253, Pickett, USA; gen tel (931) 864-3675; adv tel (931) 864-3675; ed tel (931) 864-3675; gen fax (931) 864-3695; adv fax (931) 864-3695; ed fax (931) 864-3695; disp adv e-mail pickettpress@twlakes.net; class adv e-mail pickettpress@twlakes.net; ed e-mail pickettpress@twlakes.net; web site www.pickettcountypress.com
Circulation: 2,100pd, 11fr; Sworn/Estimate/Non-Audited
Advertising rate: Open inch rate $5.00
Established: 1962
Digital Platform - Mobile: Apple, Android
Digital Platform - Tablet: Apple iOS, Android, Windows 7
Pub./Ed. ....Amanda Bond
Adv. Dir./Office Mgr......................Lora Presley
Admin. Assistant.......................Heather Smith
Mechanical Specifications: Type page 13 x 21 1/2; E - 6 cols, 2, between; A - 6 cols, 2, between.Equipment & Software: Hardware — APP/Mac.
Delivery Method: Mail, Newsstand
Areas Served: Pickett County

CAMDEN

THE CAMDEN CHRONICLE (THUR)

144 W Main St, Camden, TN, 38320-1786, Benton, USA; gen tel (731) 584-7200; adv tel (731) 584-7200; ed tel (731) 584-7200; gen fax (731) 584-4943; adv fax (731) 584-4943; ed fax (731) 584-4943; disp adv e-mail bentonco@usit.net; class adv e-mail bentonco@usit.net; ed e-mail bentonco@usit.net; web site www.magicvalleypublishing.com/camden-chronicle
Circulation: 6,000pd,; Sworn/Estimate/Non-Audited
Advertising rate: Open inch rate $8.10
Established: 1890
Digital Platform - Mobile: Apple, Android, Windows, Blackberry
Digital Platform - Tablet: Apple iOS, Android, Windows 7, Blackberry Tablet OS, Kindle, Nook, Kindle Fire
Pub....................................Dennis Richardson
Ed. ....Lisa Richardson
Prodn. Mgr. ....Vanessa Witt
Daniel Richardson
Mechanical Specifications: Type page 13 x 21 1/2; E - 6 cols, 2, 1/6 between; A - 6 cols, 2, 1/6 between; C - 6 cols, 2, 1/6 between. Equipment & Software: Hardware — APP/Mac.
Delivery Method: Mail, Racks
Areas Served: Benton County

CARTHAGE

CARTHAGE COURIER (THUR)

509 Main St N, Carthage, TN, 37030-1270, Smith, USA; gen tel (615) 735-1110; adv tel (615) 735-1110; ed tel (615) 735-1110; gen fax (615) 735-0635; adv fax (615) 735-0635; ed fax (615) 735-0635; disp adv e-mail advertising@carthagecourier.com; class adv e-mail production@carthagecourier.com; ed e-mail news@carthagecourier.com; web site www.carthagecourier.com
Circulation: 5,500pd,; Sworn/Estimate/Non-Audited
Advertising rate: Open inch rate $6.00
Established: 1913
Digital Platform - Mobile: Apple, Android, Windows, Blackberry
Digital Platform - Tablet: Apple iOS, Android, Windows 7, Blackberry Tablet OS, Kindle, Nook, Kindle Fire
Pub./Adv. Dir. ....Scott Winfree
Ed. ....Eddie West
Delivery Method: Mail, Newsstand, Racks
Areas Served: Smith County

CHATTANOOGA

HAMILTON COUNTY HERALD (FRI)

1412 McCallie Ave, Chattanooga, TN, 37404-2935, Hamilton, USA; gen tel (423) 602-9270; adv tel (423) 602-9267; ed tel (423) 602-9268; gen fax (423) 602-9269; disp adv e-mail gm@hamiltoncountyherald.com; class adv e-mail gm@hamiltoncountyherald.com; ed e-mail editor@HamiltonCountyHerald.com; web site www.hamiltoncountyherald.com
Circulation: 3,733pd,; Sworn/Estimate/Non-Audited
Advertising rate: Open inch rate $18.00
Established: 1913
Group: The Daily News Publishing Co., Inc
Digital Platform - Mobile: Apple, Android, Windows, Blackberry
Digital Platform - Tablet: Apple iOS, Android, Windows 7, Blackberry Tablet OS
Gen. Mgr./Adv. Dir....................Susanne Reed
Ed. ....David Laprad
Pub, CEO.......................................Eric Barnes
Delivery Method: Mail, Newsstand, Racks
Areas Served: Hamilton County

CLARKSVILLE

ROBERTSON COUNTY TIMES (WED)

200 Commerce St, Clarksville, TN, 37040-5101, Robertson, USA; gen tel (615) 384-3567; adv tel (615) 384-3567; ed tel (615) 384-3567; gen fax (615) 384-1221; adv fax (615) 384-1221; ed fax (615) 384-1221; disp adv e-mail slupton@tennessean.com; ed e-mail ebmiller@mtcngroup.com; web site http://www.tennessean.com/counties/robertson/ - 173,576(views) 47,907(visitors)
Circulation: 13,946pd,; Sworn/Estimate/Non-Audited
Advertising rate: Full Page Rate $1200. Modular ad sizes only
Established: 1922
Group: Gannett
The Tennessean
TN Media
Digital Platform - Mobile: Apple, Android
Digital Platform - Tablet: Apple iOS, Android, Windows 7
Pub.................................Laura Hollingsworth
VP of Advertising................Jamie McPherson
Editor...Nicole Young
Mechanical Specifications: All pages 6 column, 10"x21". Gutter between columns .167Equipment & Software: ; Software — QPS/QuarkXPress 4.11.
Delivery Method: Mail, Newsstand, Carrier, Racks
Areas Served: Robertson

CLINTON

THE COURIER NEWS (WED)

233 N Hicks St, Clinton, TN, 37716-2919, Anderson, USA; gen tel (865) 457-2515; gen fax (865) 457-1586; disp adv e-mail jwright@mycouriernews.com; class adv e-mail classifieds@hometownclinton.com; ed e-mail editor@hometownclinton.com; web site www.mycouriernews.com
Circulation: 4,000pd,; USPS
Advertising rate: 2x3 $47.00; 2x6 $95.00; 3x6 $142.00
Established: 1887
Group: Republic Newspapers
Digital Platform - Mobile: Apple, Android
Digital Platform - Tablet: Apple iOS, Android, Windows 7
Ed. ....Ken Leinhart
Retail Adv.............................Allison McKeehn
Business Mgr. ....Penny Sullivan
Classified Adv. ....Brenda Foster
Kim Webber
Sports ed.................................Richard Evans
Gen. Assignment Reporter.........Heather Miller
Mailroom Supervisor .... Denise Wrasman
Publisher.......................................John Wright
Mechanical Specifications: Type page 13 x 21 1/2; E - 6 cols, 1 5/6, between; A - 6 cols, 1 5/6, between; C - 9 cols, 1 3/16, between. Equipment & Software: Hardware — APP/Mac; Software — Microsoft/Word 5.1, Adobe/PageMaker 6.5.
Delivery Method: Mail, Newsstand, Carrier, Racks
Areas Served: 37716

COLLIERVILLE

THE COLLIERVILLE HERALD (THUR)

165 N Main St, Ste 107, Collierville, TN, 38017-2654, Shelby, USA; gen tel (901) 853-2241; adv tel (901) 853-2241; ed tel (901) 853-2241 ext. 107; disp adv e-mail publisher@colliervilleherald.net; class adv e-mail ads@colliervilleherald.net; ed e-mail editor@colliervilleherald.net; web site www.colliervilleherald.net
Circulation: 1,575pd, 300fr; Sworn/Estimate/Non-Audited
Advertising rate: Open inch rate $13.00
Established: 1870
Group: American Hometown Publishing
Digital Platform - Mobile: Apple, Android
Digital Platform - Tablet: Apple iOS, Android, Windows 7
Pub...Toni Rowan
Office Manager.........................Gena Bumpas
Editor.....................................Kelly Josephson
Production/Graphics........... Jennifer DeShazo
Mechanical Specifications: Type page 13 3/4 x 21 1/2; E - 6 cols, 2 1/12, 1/4 between; A - 6 cols, 2 1/12, 1/4 between; C - 6 cols, 2 1/12, 1/4 between.
Delivery Method: Mail, Racks
Areas Served: Shelby County

CROSSVILLE

CROSSVILLE CHRONICLE (TUES, WED, FRI)

125 West Ave, Crossville, TN, 38555-4478, Cumberland, USA; gen tel (931) 484-5145; adv tel (931) 484-5145; ed tel (931) 484-5145; gen fax (931) 456-7683; adv fax (931) 456-7683; ed fax (931) 456-7683; disp adv e-mail batkinson@crossville-chronicle.com; class adv e-mail batkinson@crossville-chronicle.com; ed e-mail mmoser@crossville-chronicle.com; web site www.crossville-chronicle.com
Circulation: 8,500pd, 10,200fr; Sworn/Estimate/Non-Audited
Advertising rate: Open inch rate $7.75
Established: 1886
Group: Community Newspaper Holdings, Inc.
Digital Platform - Mobile: Apple, Android
Digital Platform - Tablet: Apple iOS, Android, Windows 7
Pub......................................Pauline D. Sherrer
Ed. ....Mike Moser
Asst. Ed.................................Heather Mullinix
Prodn. Mgr. ....Jimmy Burks
GM/Marketing Director ....Bill Atkinson
Mechanical Specifications: Type page 13 x 21 1/2; E - 6 cols, between; A - 6 cols, between; C - 8 cols, between.Equipment & Software: Hardware — APP/Mac; Presses — G/Community; Software — Multi-Ad, QPS/QuarkXPress, InDesign
Delivery Method: Mail, Racks
Areas Served: Cumberland County

DAYTON

THE HERALD-NEWS (WED, SUN)
3687 Rhea County Hwy, Dayton, TN, 37321-5819, Rhea, USA; gen tel (423) 775-6111; adv tel (423) 775-6111; ed tel (423) 775-6111; gen fax (423) 775-8218; adv fax (423) 775-8259; ed fax (423) 775-8218; disp adv e-mail keith.locke@rheaheraldnews.com; class adv e-mail sarajane.locke@rheaheraldnews.com; ed e-mail reed.johnson@rheaheraldnews.com; web site www.rheaheraldnews.com
Circulation: 9,700pd, 9fr; Sworn/Estimate/Non-Audited
Advertising rate: Open inch rate $10.00
Established: 1898
Group: Adams Publishing Group, LLC
Digital Platform - Mobile: Apple, Android
Digital Platform - Tablet: Apple iOS, Android, Windows 7
Pub. .... Sara Jane Locke
Ed. .... Reed Johnson
Gen. Mgr. .... Diane Emens
Adv. Mgr. .... Kerth Locke
Circ. Mgr. .... Lynne Spivey
Prodn. Mgr. .... June Yarbrough
Mechanical Specifications: Type page 11 5/8 x 21; E - 6 cols, 1 3/4, 1/6 between; A - 6 cols, 1 3/4, 1/6 between; C - 9 cols, between. Equipment & Software: Hardware — APP/Macs; Software — Adobe/Photoshop, QPS/QuarkXPress 4.1.
Delivery Method: Mail, Newsstand, Racks
Areas Served: 37321, 37381, 37338, 37332, 37395, 37337, 37308, 37373

DICKSON

THE DICKSON HERALD (WED, FRI)
104 Church St, Dickson, TN, 37055-1826, Dickson, USA; gen tel (615) 446-2811; adv tel (615) 446-2811; ed tel (615) 446-2811; ed fax (615) 446-5560; disp adv e-mail slupton@tennessean.com; class adv e-mail slupton@tennessean.com; ed e-mail news@dicksonherald.com; web site www.dicksonherald.com - 122,450(views) 45,001(visitors)
Circulation: 17,453pd,; Sworn/Estimate/Non-Audited
Advertising rate: Full Page Rate $800
Established: 1907
Group: Gannett
The Tennessean
TN Media
Digital Platform - Mobile: Apple, Android
Digital Platform - Tablet: Apple iOS, Android, Windows 7
Pres./Pub. .... Laura Hollingsworth
National Adv. Mgr. .... Sean Lupton
Ed. .... Chris Gadd
Mechanical Specifications: All pages 6 column, 10"x21". Gutter between columns .167Equipment & Software: Hardware — APP/Mac 7300, APP/Mac G3; Software — Microsoft/Word 8.0, Adobe/Photoshop 4.0, QPS/QuarkXPress 4.1.
Delivery Method: Mail, Newsstand, Racks
Areas Served: Dickson County

DOVER

STEWART-HOUSTON TIMES (TUES)
310 Spring St, Dover, TN, 37058-3233, Stewart, USA; gen tel (931) 232-5421; adv tel (931) 232-5421; ed tel (931) 232-5421; gen fax (931) 232-8224; adv fax (931) 232-8224; ed fax (931) 232-8224; disp adv e-mail shirellefine@theleafchronicle.com; class adv e-mail jbolin@theleafchronicle.com; ed e-mail rstevens@theleafchronicle.com; web site www.thestewarthoustontimes.com
Circulation: 6,000pd, 5,300fr; Sworn/Estimate/Non-Audited
Advertising rate: Open inch rate $17.85
Established: 1888
Group: Gannett
The Tennessean
TN Media
Digital Platform - Mobile: Apple, Android
Digital Platform - Tablet: Apple iOS, Android, Windows 7
Pub. .... Loretta Threatt
Ed./Gen. Mgr. .... Richard V. Stevens
Adv. Mgr. .... Shirelle Fine
Delivery Method: Mail, Carrier, Racks
Areas Served: Stewart County

DUNLAP

THE DUNLAP TRIBUNE (TUES, THUR)
15331 Rankin Ave, Dunlap, TN, 37327-7048, Sequatchie, USA; gen tel (423) 949-2505; adv tel (423) 949-2505; ed tel (423) 949-2505; gen fax (423) 949-5297; adv fax (423) 949-5297; ed fax (423) 949-5297; disp adv e-mail valleypubincads@bledsoe.net; class adv e-mail valleypubinc@bledsoe.net; ed e-mail valleypubincnews@bledsoe.net; web site www.thedunlap-tribune.com
Circulation: 3,250pd, 12,477fr; Sworn/Estimate/Non-Audited
Advertising rate: Open inch rate $3.25
Established: 1889
Group: Valley Publishing Company, Inc
Digital Platform - Mobile: Apple
Digital Platform - Tablet: Apple iOS
Pub. .... Amy S. Hale
Mng. Ed./Adv. Mgr. .... Sandy Dodson
Mechanical Specifications: 6 column (11.625 inches) by 21 inchesEquipment & Software: Hardware — iMacs; Software — Microsoft/Word; Creative Suites with InDesign, Photoshop, Illustrator; InCoopy
Delivery Method: Mail, Newsstand
Areas Served: 37327

DYER

THE TRI-CITY REPORTER (THUR)
121 S Main St, Dyer, TN, 38330-1815, Gibson, USA; gen tel (731) 692-3506; adv tel (731) 692-3506; ed tel (731) 692-3506; gen fax (731) 692-4844; adv fax (731) 692-4844; ed fax (731) 692-4844; disp adv e-mail mindy@tricityreporter.net; class adv e-mail news@tricityreporter.net; ed e-mail ceast@tricityreporter.net; web site www.milanmirror-exchange.com
Circulation: 3,000pd, 203fr; Sworn/Estimate/Non-Audited
Advertising rate: Open inch rate $4.50 (Local); $7.50 (National)
Established: 1892
Group: American Hometown Publishing
Digital Platform - Mobile: Apple, Android, Windows, Blackberry
Digital Platform - Tablet: Apple iOS, Android, Windows 7, Blackberry Tablet OS
Pub. .... April Jackson
Mng. Ed. .... Cindy East
Mechanical Specifications: Type page 13 x 21; E - 6 cols, 2, 1/4 between; A - 6 cols, 2, 1/4 between; C - 6 cols, 2, 1/4 between.Equipment & Software: Hardware — 4-APP/Mac.
Delivery Method: Mail, Racks
Areas Served: Dyer, Rutherford, Kenton, and Yorkville

DYERSBURG

DYERSBURG NEWS (WED)
294 US Highway 51 Byp N, Dyersburg, TN, 38024-3659, Dyer, USA; gen tel (731) 285-4091; adv tel (731) 285-4091 ext. 116; ed tel (731) 285-4091 ext. 121; gen fax (731) 285-9747; adv fax (731) 285-9747; ed fax (731) 285-9747; disp adv e-mail sruse@stategazette.com; class adv e-mail cdawson@stategazette.com; ed e-mail jcannon@stategazette.com; web site www.stategazette.com
Circulation: 16,985fr; Sworn/Estimate/Non-Audited
Advertising rate: Open inch rate $11.50
Established: 1865
Digital Platform - Mobile: Apple, Android
Digital Platform - Tablet: Apple iOS, Android, Windows 7
Pub./Gen. Mgr. .... Shelia Rouse
Ed. .... Jason Cannon
Adv. Dir. .... Charles Dawson
Mechanical Specifications: Type page 13 x 21 1/2; E - 6 cols, 2, 1/8 between; A - 6 cols, 2, 1/8 between; C - 9 cols, 1 1/2, 1/8 between. Equipment & Software: Hardware — APP/Mac; Software — QPS/QuarkXPress, Adobe/Photoshop, Adobe/Illustrator, Multi-Ad/Creator, Microsoft/Word, Macromedia/Freehand, Microsoft/Excel.
Delivery Method: Mail, Racks
Areas Served: Dyer County

ERWIN

THE ERWIN RECORD (WED)
218 Gay St, Erwin, TN, 37650-1230, Unicoi, USA; gen tel (423) 743-4112; adv tel (423) 743-4112; ed tel (423) 743-4112; gen fax (423) 743-6125; adv fax (423) 743-6125; ed fax (423) 743-6125; disp adv e-mail dhiggins@erwinrecord.net; class adv e-mail dhiggins@erwinrecord.net; ed e-mail kwhitson@erwinrecord.net; web site www.erwinrecord.net
Circulation: 4,200pd, 40fr; Sworn/Estimate/Non-Audited
Advertising rate: Open inch rate $7.00
Established: 1928
Group: Sandusky Newspapers, Inc.
Digital Platform - Mobile: Apple, Android
Digital Platform - Tablet: Apple iOS, Android
Publisher .... Keith Whitson
Managing Editor .... Keeli Parkey
Advertising Director .... Damaris Higgins
Graphic Design .... David Sheets
Staff Writer/Sports Writer .... Curtis Carden
Mechanical Specifications: Type page 11 1/2 x 21 1/2; E - 6 cols, 1 3/4, 1/6 between; A - 6 cols, 1 3/4, 1/6 between; C - 8 cols, 1, 1/6 between.Equipment & Software: Hardware — APP/Mac; Software — Macromedia/Freehand 8.0.
Delivery Method: Mail, Newsstand, Carrier, Racks
Areas Served: 37692, 37601, 37659, 37643, 37650

FAIRVIEW

FAIRVIEW OBSERVER (TUES)
1874 Fairview Blvd, Ste A, Fairview, TN, 37062-9412, Williamson, USA; gen tel (615) 799-8565; adv tel (615) 799-8565; ed tel (615) 799-8565; gen fax (615) 799-8728; adv fax (615) 799-8728; ed fax (615) 799-8728; disp adv e-mail ssullivan2@mtcngroup.com; class adv e-mail ssullivan2@mtcngroup.com; ed e-mail fvoeditor@mtcngroup.com; web site www.fairviewobserver.com
Circulation: 1,350pd,; Sworn/Estimate/Non-Audited
Advertising rate: Open inch rate $7.80
Established: 1989
Group: Gannett
The Tennessean
TN Media
Digital Platform - Mobile: Apple, Android, Windows, Blackberry
Digital Platform - Tablet: Apple iOS, Android, Windows 7, Blackberry Tablet OS, Kindle, Nook, Kindle Fire
Pres./Pub. .... Laura Hollingsworth
Gen. Mgr. .... Becky Moran
Ed. .... Nancy Phillips Stephens
Adv. Mgr. .... Megan Wren
Mechanical Specifications: ROP: Full Page 10" x 21", 1 column 1.528 inches, 2 column 3.222 inches, 3 column 4.917 inches, 4 column 6.611 inches, 5 column 8.306 inches, 6 column 10". Classified: 1 column 0.94 inches, 2 column 1.95 inches, 3 column 2.96 inches, 4 column 3.96 inches, 5 column 4.97 inches, 6 column 5.97 icnhes, 7 column 6.98 inches, 8 column 7.98 inches, 9 column 8.99 inches, 10 columns 10 inchesEquipment & Software: ; Software — Adobe/Photoshop, QPS/QuarkXPress.
Delivery Method: Mail
Areas Served: 37062

FARRAGUT

FARRAGUT PRESS (THUR)
11863 Kingston Pike, Farragut, TN, 37934-3833, Knox, USA; gen tel (865) 675-6397; adv tel (865)675-6397 ext. 8877; ed tel (865)675-6397 ext. 8876; gen fax (865) 675-1675; adv fax (865)675-1675; ed fax (865)675-1675; disp adv e-mail egrove@farragutpress.com; class adv e-mail egrove@farragutpress.com; ed e-mail dbarile@farragutpress.com; web site www.farragutpress.com
Circulation: 401pd, 14,541fr; CVC
Advertising rate: Open inch rate $12.50
Established: 1988
Group: Republic Newspapers, Inc.
Digital Platform - Mobile: Apple
Digital Platform - Tablet: Apple iOS, Android, Windows 7
Pub./Ed. .... Dan Barile
Adv. Mgr. .... Elaine Grove
Advertising Sales .... Julie Gunter
Advertising Sales .... Kathy Hartman
Advertising Sales .... Laura Sayers
Receptionist .... Lori Timmis
Sales .... Scott Hamstead
Circ. Mgr. .... Linda Gildner
Advertising Sales .... Sherry Long
Adverstising Sales .... Shannon Diane
Mechanical Specifications: Type page 13 x 21 1/2; E - 6 cols, 2, 3/16 between; A - 6 cols, 2, 3/16 between; C - 6 cols, 2, 3/16 between. Equipment & Software: Hardware — APP/Mac; Software — QPS/QuarkXPress, Multi-Ad/Creator, Microsoft/Word, Adobe/Photoshop.
Delivery Method: Mail, Carrier, Racks
Areas Served: Knox County

FAYETTEVILLE

THE ELK VALLEY TIMES (WED)
418 Elk Ave N, 418 Elk Ave N, Fayetteville, TN, 37334-2512, Lincoln, USA; gen tel (931) 433-6151; gen fax (931) 433-6040; disp adv e-mail evtadmgr@lcs.net; class adv e-mail evtad1@lcs.net; ed e-mail evtnews@lcs.net; web site www.elkvalleytimes.com
Circulation: 9,600pd, 124fr; Sworn/Estimate/Non-Audited
Advertising rate: Open inch rate $13.37
Established: 1850
Group: Lakeway Publishers, Inc.
Digital Platform - Mobile: Apple, Android
Digital Platform - Tablet: Apple iOS, Android
CEO/Pub./Ed. .... Lucy Williams
Mng. Ed. .... Sandy Williams
Advertising Manager .... Janie Herrin
Mechanical Specifications: Full Page/ROP/10"x21.5"
Delivery Method: Mail, Newsstand, Racks
Areas Served: 37334, 37144, 37328, 37335, 37348, 37359, 38453, 38488, 38449

GALLATIN

GALLATIN NEWS EXAMINER (WED, FRI)
1 Examiner Ct, Gallatin, TN, 37066-7111, Sumner, USA; gen tel (615) 452-2561; adv tel (615) 575-7141; ed tel (615) 575-7161; gen fax (615) 575-7181; adv fax (615) 575-7181; ed fax (615) 575-7181; disp adv e-mail slupton@tennessean.com; class adv e-mail pdyates@tennessean.com; ed e-mail mdevarenne@tennessean.com; web site www.gallatinnewsexaminer.com - 100,000(views)
Advertising rate: Open inch rate $16.90
Established: 1840
Group: Gannett
The Tennessean
TN Media
Digital Platform - Mobile: Apple, Android
Digital Platform - Tablet: Apple iOS, Android, Windows 7

Retail Adv. Mgr. .... Robyn Williams
Sports Ed. .... Cecil Joyce
Gen. Mgr. .... Roger Watson
Ed. .... Mealand Ragland-Hudgins
Gen. Mgr... Josh CrossEquipment & Software: Hardware — APP/Mac; Presses — 8-WPC/King; Software — QPS/QuarkXPress 4.1.
Delivery Method: Mail, Newsstand, Racks
Areas Served: Sumner County

THE HENDERSONVILLE STAR NEWS (WED, FRI)

1 Examiner Ct, Gallatin, TN, 37066-7111, Sumner, USA; gen tel (615) 824-8480; adv tel (615) 824-8480; ed tel (615) 824-8480; gen fax (615) 824-3126; adv fax (615) 824-3126; ed fax (615) 824-3126; disp adv e-mail slupton@tennessean.com; class adv e-mail pdyates@tennessean.com; ed e-mail mdevarenne@tennessean.com; web site www.tennessean.com/section/hendersonville
Circulation: 15,850fr; Sworn/Estimate/Non-Audited
Advertising rate: Open inch rate $17.20
Group: Gannett
The Tennessean
TN Media
Digital Platform - Mobile: Apple, Android
Digital Platform - Tablet: Apple iOS, Android, Windows 7
Pres./Pub. .... Laura Hollingsworth
Exec. Ed./Vice Pres. .... Maria De Varenne
National Adv. Mgr. .... Sean Lupton
Adv. Dir./Gen. Mgr./Adv. SalesRachel Biggirstaff
Delivery Method: Mail, Newsstand, Racks
Areas Served: Sumner County

GERMANTOWN

GERMANTOWN NEWS (WED)

7545 North St, Germantown, TN, 38138-3822, Shelby, USA; gen tel (901) 754-0337; gen fax (901) 754-2961; disp adv e-mail advertising@germantownnews.com; class adv e-mail classified@germantownnews.com; ed e-mail news@germantownnews.com; web site www.germantownnews.com
Circulation: 7,500pd,; Sworn/Estimate/Non-Audited
Advertising rate: Open inch rate $14.95
Established: 1974
Group: Crittenden Publishing Co.
Digital Platform - Mobile: Apple, Android
Digital Platform - Tablet: Apple iOS, Android, Windows 7
Mng. Ed. .... Rebekah Yearout
Mechanical Specifications: Type page 11 3/4 x 21 1/2; E - 6 cols, 1 3/4, 1/8 between; A - 6 cols, 1 3/4, 1/8 between; C - 9 cols, 1 1/4, between.
Delivery Method: Mail, Newsstand, Racks
Areas Served: 38138, 38139, 38120, 38119, 38125

HARTSVILLE

THE HARTSVILLE VIDETTE (THUR)

206 River St, Hartsville, TN, 37074-1709, Trousdale, USA; gen tel (615) 374-3556; adv tel (615) 374-3556; ed tel (615) 374-3556; gen fax (615) 374-2211; adv fax (615) 374-2211; ed fax (615) 374-2211; disp adv e-mail thevidette@bellsouth.net; class adv e-mail thevidette@bellsouth.net; ed e-mail thevidette@bellsouth.net; web site www.hartsvillevidette.com
Circulation: 2,300pd,; Sworn/Estimate/Non-Audited
Advertising rate: Open inch rate $5.10
Established: 1862
Group: Sandusky Newspapers, Inc.
Digital Platform - Mobile: Apple, Android, Windows, Blackberry
Digital Platform - Tablet: Apple iOS, Android, Windows 7, Blackberry Tablet OS, Kindle, Nook, Kindle Fire
Pub. .... Joe Adams
Mng. Ed. .... Laurie Everett
Adv. Mgr. .... Roger Wells
Classified Mgr. .... Melanie Ray
Delivery Method: Mail, Newsstand
Areas Served: 37074, 37031, 37057, 37066, 37083, 37087, 37151, 37186

HENDERSON

CHESTER COUNTY INDEPENDENT (THUR)

218 S Church Ave, Henderson, TN, 38340-2638, Chester, USA; gen tel (731) 989-4624; adv tel (731) 989-4624; ed tel (731) 989-4624; gen fax (731) 989-5008; adv fax (731) 989-5008; ed fax (731) 989-5008; disp adv e-mail mcroom@chestercountyindependent.com; class adv e-mail news@chestercountyindependent.com; ed e-mail jwebb@chestercountyindependent.com; web site www.chestercountyindependent.com
Circulation: 5,100pd, 6fr; Sworn/Estimate/Non-Audited
Advertising rate: Open inch rate $8.61
Established: 1865
Group: American Hometown Publishing
Digital Platform - Mobile: Apple, Android, Windows, Blackberry
Digital Platform - Tablet: Apple iOS, Android, Windows 7, Blackberry Tablet OS
Publisher .... Scott Whaley
Ed./Circ. Dir. .... James A. Webb
Adv. Dir. .... Marvin Croom
Ed. .... Scott Whaley
Delivery Method: Mail, Newsstand, Racks
Areas Served: Henderson/Chester/38340
Enville/Chester/38332
Jacks Creek/Chester/38347

HOHENWALD

LEWIS COUNTY HERALD (THUR)

31 E Linden Ave, Hohenwald, TN, 38462-1415, Lewis, USA; gen tel (931) 796-3191; gen fax (931) 796-2153; disp adv e-mail lewisherald@bellsouth.net; class adv e-mail lewisherald@bellsouth.net; ed e-mail lewisherald@bellsouth.net; web site www.lewisherald.com
Circulation: 3,251pd, 18fr; USPS
Advertising rate: Open inch rate $6.50
Established: 1898
Digital Platform - Mobile: Apple, Android
Digital Platform - Tablet: Apple iOS, Android, Windows 7
Ed./Adv. Mgr. .... Walton Dunn
Mng. Ed./Prod. Mgr. .... Hulon Dunn
Circ. Mgr. .... Marne Carroll
Graphic Artist .... Julie Reeves
Reporter/Photographer .... Glenda Atkinson
Pressman .... Michael HinsonEquipment & Software: Hardware — APP/Mac.; Presses — Goss Community 5 units; Software — Adobe InDesign CS5
Delivery Method: Mail, Racks
Areas Served: 38462, 38401, 38464, 38474, 37053

HUMBOLDT

THE HUMBOLDT CHRONICLE (TUES)

2606 Eastend Dr, Ste A, Humboldt, TN, 38343-2265, Gibson, USA; gen tel (731) 784-2531; adv tel (731) 784-2531; ed tel (731) 784-2531; gen fax (731) 784-2533; adv fax (731) 784-2533; ed fax (731) 784-2533; disp adv e-mail ads@hchronicle.net; class adv e-mail ads@hchronicle.net; ed e-mail dwade@hchronicle.net; web site www.hchronicle.net
Circulation: 2,000pd, 400fr; Sworn/Estimate/Non-Audited
Advertising rate: Open inch rate $7.25
Established: 1886
Group: Gibson County Publishing
Digital Platform - Mobile: Apple, Android
Digital Platform - Tablet: Apple iOS, Android, Windows 7
Ed. .... Danny WadeEquipment & Software: Hardware — Mac; Presses — N/A; Software — Adobe, Microsoft
Delivery Method: Mail, Racks
Areas Served: Gibson County

HUNTINGDON

CARROLL COUNTY NEWS-LEADER (TUES)

165 Court Sq, Ste 2, Huntingdon, TN, 38344-3703, Carroll, USA; gen tel (731) 986-2253; adv tel (731) 986-2253; ed tel (731) 986-2253; gen fax (731) 986-3585; adv fax (731) 986-3585; ed fax (731) 986-3585; disp adv e-mail daniel@newsleaderonline.com; class adv e-mail daniel@newsleaderonline.com; ed e-mail daniel@newsleaderonline.com; web site www.magicvalleypublishing.com
Circulation: 2,800pd,; Sworn/Estimate/Non-Audited
Advertising rate: Open inch rate $8.50
Established: 1868
Group: Magic Valley Publishing Co., Inc
Digital Platform - Mobile: Apple, Android, Windows, Blackberry
Digital Platform - Tablet: Apple iOS, Android, Windows 7, Blackberry Tablet OS, Kindle, Nook, Kindle Fire
Owner .... Dennis M. Richardson
Ed. .... Shirley Nanney
Pub .... Daniel Richardson
Sports Ed. .... Ron Park
Society Ed .... Lindsey Bell
Art Director .... Christy SlamanEquipment & Software: Hardware — Macs; Presses — none; Software — Adobe suite
Delivery Method: Mail, Newsstand, Carrier, Racks
Areas Served: 38301, 38344, 38327, 38328

JAMESTOWN

FENTRESS COURIER (WED)

114 White Oak St, Jamestown, TN, 38556-4204, Fentress, USA; gen tel (931) 879-4040; gen fax (931) 879-7716; disp adv e-mail fencourier@twlakes.net; class adv e-mail fencourier@twlakes.net; ed e-mail fencourier@twlakes.net; web site fentresscouriernews.com
Circulation: 4,700pd,; Sworn/Estimate/Non-Audited
Advertising rate: Open inch rate $6.00
Established: 1946
Digital Platform - Mobile: Apple, Android
Digital Platform - Tablet: Apple iOS, Android, Windows 7
Pub./Ed. .... Bill Bowden
Mechanical Specifications: 6 columns (1.833") per page.
Page size 11.625 x 21.5"Equipment & Software: Hardware — APP/Max G5; Software — QPS/QuarkXPress, Adobe/Photoshop, Adobe/Illustrator, Adobe/Freehand.
Delivery Method: Mail, Newsstand, Racks
Areas Served: 38556, 38553, 38504, 38565, 38577

JEFFERSON CITY

THE STANDARD BANNER (TUES, THUR)

122 W Old Andrew Johnson Hwy, Jefferson City, TN, 37760-1996, Jefferson, USA; gen tel (865) 475-2081; gen fax (865) 475-8539; disp adv e-mail info@standardbanner.com; ed e-mail news@standardbanner.com; web site www.standardbanner.com
Circulation: 6,000pd, 10fr; Sworn/Estimate/Non-Audited
Advertising rate: Open inch rate $6.75
Established: 1928
Digital Platform - Mobile: Apple, Android, Windows, Blackberry
Digital Platform - Tablet: Apple iOS, Android, Windows 7, Blackberry Tablet OS, Kindle, Nook, Kindle Fire
Pub./Ed. .... Dale Gentry
Adv. Mgr. .... Shane Cook
Sports Ed. .... Dave Gentry
Mechanical Specifications: Type page 13 x 21; E - 6 cols, 2 1/16, between; A - 6 cols, 2 1/16, between; C - 6 cols, 2 1/16, between.Equipment & Software: Hardware — APP/Mac, APP/Power Macs, PCs; Presses — Web Leader; Software — Adobe/InDesign CS6, Adobe Photoshop CS 5.1,
Delivery Method: Mail, Newsstand, Racks
Areas Served: 37760, 37820, 37725, 37890, 37877, 37871

JOHNSON CITY

JOHNSON CITY NEWS & NEIGHBOR (WED)

1114 Sunset Dr, Ste 1, Johnson City, TN, 37604-2969, Washington, USA; gen tel (423) 979-1300; adv tel (423) 979-1300; ed tel (423) 979-1300; gen fax (423) 979-1307; adv fax (423) 979-1307; ed fax (423) 979-1307; disp adv e-mail marketing@jcnewsandneighbor.com; class adv e-mail marketing@jcnewsandneighbor.com; ed e-mail news@jcnewsandneighbor.com; web site www.jcnewsandneighbor.com - 9,195(views) 2,746(visitors)
Circulation: 1,100pd, 29,690fr; CVC
Advertising rate: Open inch rate $18.55
Established: 1997
Group: Derby Publishing LLCEditions: (2) Johnson City News & Neighbor; Johnson City News
Digital Platform - Mobile: Apple
Digital Platform - Tablet: Apple iOS
Pub./Ed. .... Bill Derby
Circ. Mgr. .... Roy Jenkins
Assoc. Publisher .... Jeff Derby
Mechanical Specifications: 1 col. width 1.7"; 2 col. width 3.525"; 3 col. width 5.35"; 4 col. width 7.175"; 5 col. width 9"; 6 col. width 10.825" (6 col. x 21.5" deep)
Delivery Method: Carrier
Areas Served: 37601, 37604, 37659, 37615, 37686

JONESBOROUGH

HERALD & TRIBUNE (WED)

702 W Jackson Blvd, Jonesborough, TN, 37659-5264, Washington, USA; gen tel (423) 753-3136; adv tel (423) 753-3136; ed tel (423) 753-3136; gen fax (423) 753-6528; adv fax (423) 753-6528; ed fax (423) 753-6528; disp adv e-mail ads@heraldandtribune.com; class adv e-mail bcasey@heraldandtribune.com; ed e-mail kswing@heraldandtribune.com; web site www.heraldandtribune.com
Circulation: 4,500pd, 195fr; Sworn/Estimate/Non-Audited
Advertising rate: Open inch rate $8.25
Established: 1869
Group: Sandusky Newspapers, Inc.
Digital Platform - Mobile: Apple, Android
Digital Platform - Tablet: Apple iOS, Android, Windows 7Krystal Hawkins
Gen Asst .... Collin Brooks
Adv Mgr .... Marcella Peeks
Gen Mgr & Ed .... Lisa Whaley
Mechanical Specifications: Type page 12 1/2 x 22; E - 6 cols, 1 5/6, 1/8 between; A - 6 cols, 1 5/6, 1/8 between; C - 9 cols, 1 3/16, 1/8 between.Equipment & Software: Hardware — 5-APP/Mac; Presses — Harris/V 15A Offset; Software — Adobe/PageMaker 6.52.
Adobe/InDesign 5.0
Delivery Method: Mail, Newsstand, Carrier, Racks
Areas Served: 37659, 37605, 37604, 37605, 37603, 37602, 37601, 37614, 37615, 37690, 37681, 37656

KINGSTON

ROANE COUNTY NEWS (MON, WED, FRI)

204 Franklin St, Kingston, TN, 37763-2625, Roane, USA; gen tel (865) 376-3481; ed tel (865) 376-3481 ext. 320; gen fax (865) 376-1945; disp adv e-mail kkile@roanecounty.com; class adv e-mail tyeary@roanecounty.

com; ed e-mail hwillett@roanecounty.com; web site www.roanecounty.com
Circulation: 8,609pd, 45fr; Sworn/Estimate/Non-Audited
Advertising rate: Open inch rate $14.62
Established: 1957
Group: Landmark Community Newspapers, LLC
Digital Platform - Mobile: Apple, Android
Digital Platform - Tablet: Apple iOS, Android, Windows 7
Adv. Mgr. .... Kevin Kile
Circ. Mgr. .... Neva Peters
Delivery Method: Mail, Racks
Areas Served: Roane County

LA FOLLETTE

LA FOLLETTE PRESS (THUR)

225 N 1st St, La Follette, TN, 37766-2462, Campbell, USA; gen tel (423) 562-8468; adv tel (423) 562-8468; ed tel (423) 562-8468; gen fax (423) 566-7060; adv fax (423) 566-7060; ed fax (423) 566-7060; disp adv e-mail ads@lafollettepress.com; class adv e-mail classifieds@lafollettepress.com; ed e-mail bschanding@lafollettepress.com; web site www.lafollettepress.com
Circulation: 10,300pd, 150fr; Sworn/Estimate/Non-Audited
Advertising rate: Open inch rate $10.04 (Local); $12.36 (National)
Established: 1910
Group: Landmark Community Newspapers, LLC
Digital Platform - Mobile: Apple, Android, Windows, Blackberry
Digital Platform - Tablet: Apple iOS, Android, Windows 7, Blackberry Tablet OS, Kindle, Nook, Kindle Fire
Adv. Mgr. .... Ann Rutherford
Pub. .... Linn Hudson
Adv. Sales .... Mae Clotfelter
Adv. Sales .... Tilbert McCrary
Office Mgr. .... Karen Cumorich
Delivery Method: Mail, Newsstand, Racks
Areas Served: Campbell County

LAFAYETTE

MACON COUNTY TIMES (THUR)

200 Times Ave, Lafayette, TN, 37083-1244, Macon, USA; gen tel (615) 666-2440; adv tel (615) 666-2440; ed tel (615) 666-2440; gen fax (615) 666-4909; adv fax (615) 666-4909; ed fax (615) 666-4909; disp adv e-mail cturner@civitasmedia.com; class adv e-mail ldallas@civitasmedia.com; ed e-mail tcryar@civitasmedia.com; web site www.maconcountytimes.com - 25,000(views) 13,000(visitors)
Circulation: 4,000pd, 18fr; Sworn/Estimate/Non-Audited
Advertising rate: Open inch rate $6.85
Established: 1919
Group: AIM Media Indiana
Digital Platform - Mobile: Apple, Android, Windows, Blackberry
Digital Platform - Tablet: Apple iOS, Android, Windows 7, Blackberry Tablet OS, Kindle, Nook, Kindle Fire
Publisher .... Lane Moon
Mechanical Specifications: Type page 10.112" x 21 1/2"; E - 6 cols, 1.546", 1/8 between; A - 6 cols, 1.546", 1/8 between; C - 6 cols, 1.546", 1/8 between.Equipment & Software: Hardware — APP/Mac; Presses — 3-KP.
Delivery Method: Mail, Newsstand, Racks
Areas Served: Macon County

LAWRENCEBURG

LAWRENCE COUNTY ADVOCATE (WED, SUN)

121 N Military Ave, Lawrenceburg, TN, 38464-3323, Lawrence, USA; gen tel (931) 762-1726; adv tel (931) 762-1726; ed tel (931) 762-1726; gen fax (931) 762-7874; adv fax (931) 762-7874; ed fax (931) 762-7874; disp adv e-mail lawcoadv@bellsouth.net; class adv e-mail lawcoadv@bellsouth.net; ed e-mail advocateeditor@bellsouth.net; web site www.lawrencecountyadvocate.net
Circulation: 202pd, 31,876fr; CVC
Advertising rate: Open inch rate $6.20
Established: 1986
Digital Platform - Mobile: Apple, Android, Windows, Blackberry
Digital Platform - Tablet: Apple iOS, Android, Windows 7, Blackberry Tablet OS, Kindle, Nook, Kindle Fire
Pub. .... Sam Kennedy
Adv. Mgr. .... Janice Butler
Circ. Mgr. .... Dorothy Adams
Prodn. Mgr.John FinneyEquipment & Software: Hardware — IBM; Presses — KP/News King; Software — Microsoft/Windows 95, Adobe/PageMaker 6.5, Microsoft/Word 4.0.
Delivery Method: Mail, Newsstand, Racks
Areas Served: Lawrence County

THE DEMOCRAT-UNION (TUES, FRI)

238 Hughes St, Lawrenceburg, TN, 38464-3364, Lawrence, USA; gen tel (931) 762-2222; adv tel (931) 762-2222; ed tel (931) 762-2222; gen fax (931) 762-4191; adv fax (931) 762-4191; ed fax (931) 762-4191; disp adv e-mail duadv@bellsouth.net; class adv e-mail duadv@bellsouth.net; ed e-mail dunews@bellsouth.net; web site www.lawrenceburg.com/du
Circulation: 7,600pd,; Sworn/Estimate/Non-Audited
Advertising rate: Open inch rate $6.95
Established: 1884
Pub./Ed. .... Jim Crawford
Assc. Ed. .... Bobby Crawford
Assc. Ed. .... Charlie Crawford
Delivery Method: Mail, Racks
Areas Served: Lawrence County

LEBANON

MT. JULIET NEWS (WED)

402 N Cumberland St, Lebanon, TN, 37087-2306, Wilson, USA; gen tel (615) 754-6397; adv tel (615) 754-6397; ed tel (615) 754-6397; gen fax (615) 754-6398; adv fax (615) 754-6398; ed fax (615) 754-6398; disp adv e-mail mtjulietnews@tds.net; class adv e-mail mtjulietnews@tds.net; ed e-mail mtjulietnews@tds.net; web site www.mtjulietnews.com
Circulation: 2,000pd, 12,500fr; Sworn/Estimate/Non-Audited
Advertising rate: Open inch rate $9.85
Established: 1987
Group: Sandusky Newspapers, Inc.
Digital Platform - Mobile: Apple, Android, Windows, Blackberry
Digital Platform - Tablet: Apple iOS, Android, Windows 7, Blackberry Tablet OS, Kindle, Nook, Kindle Fire
Pub. .... Joe Adams
Mng. Ed. .... Laurie Everett
Adv. Dir. .... Roger Wells
Prod. Mgr. Mark RogersEquipment & Software: Hardware — APP/Mac IIsi, APP/Mac Quadra 610; Software — QPS/QuarkXPress.
Delivery Method: Mail, Newsstand
Areas Served: Wilson County

THE WILSON POST (WED)

223 N Cumberland St, Ste A, Lebanon, TN, 37087-2869, Wilson, USA; gen tel (615) 444-6008; adv tel (615) 444-6008; ed tel (615) 444-6008; gen fax (615) 444-6018; adv fax (615) 444-6018; ed fax (615) 444-6018; disp adv e-mail mhazelwood@mainstreetmediatn.com; class adv e-mail classifieds@wilsonpost.com; ed e-mail news@wilsonpost.com; web site www.wilsonpost.com
Circulation: 10,000pd,; USPS
Advertising rate: Open inch rate $11.75
Established: 1978
Group: Main Street Media of Tennessee
Digital Platform - Mobile: Apple, Android, Windows
Digital Platform - Tablet: Apple iOS, Android, Windows 7
Pres./Pub. .... Dave Gould
Editor .... Sabrina Garrett
Managing Editor
Brian Harville
Sports Editor .... Tommy Bryan
Advertising Account Executive .... Debby Mabry
Photographer .... Dallus Whitfield
Office Manager .... Shelley Satterfield
Ad Designer .... Mary Anne Ferrell
Graphic Designer .... Carrie Tomlin
Mechanical Specifications: Type page 11 1/2 x 21; E - 6 cols, 2 1/4, 1/4 between; A - 6 cols, between; C - 6 cols, between.Equipment & Software: ; Software — Adobe/PageMaker 7.0.
Delivery Method: Mail, Newsstand
Areas Served: 37087, 37088, 37184, 37122, 37071, 37136

LENOIR CITY

NEWS-HERALD (WED)

201 Simpson Rd, Lenoir City, TN, 37771-6567, Loudon, USA; gen tel (865) 986-6581; adv tel (865) 986-6581; ed tel (865) 986-6581; gen fax (865) 988-3261; adv fax (865) 988-3261; ed fax (865) 988-3261; disp adv e-mail amanda.kimbrell@news-herald.net; class adv e-mail classifieds@news-herald.net; ed e-mail news@news-herald.net; web site www.news-herald.net
Circulation: 3,450pd, 250fr; Sworn/Estimate/Non-Audited
Advertising rate: Open inch rate $15.25
Established: 1885
Group: Adams Publishing Group, LLC
Digital Platform - Mobile: Apple, Android
Digital Platform - Tablet: Apple iOS, Android
Pub./Ed. .... Steve Meadows
Business Manager .... Amanda Kimbrell
News Editor .... Jonathan Herrmann
Mechanical Specifications: Full page: 10 inches by 20.5 inches
Type page 10 x 11 1/16 x ; E - 5 cols, 1 2/28, between; A - 5 cols, 1 2/28, between; C - 1 cols, 1 2/28, between.Equipment & Software: Hardware — Mac for editorial and production, PC for business office; Presses — Off-site printing; Software — CS3, Microsoft Office Suite
Delivery Method: Mail, Newsstand, Carrier, Racks
Areas Served: 37771, 37772, 37774, 37742, 37846

THE CONNECTION (WED)

201 Simpson Rd, Lenoir City, TN, 37771-6567, Loudon, USA; gen tel (865) 986-6581; adv tel (865) 986-6581; ed tel (865) 986-6581; gen fax (865) 988-3261; adv fax (865) 988-3261; ed fax (865) 988-3261; disp adv e-mail amanda.kimbrell@news-herald.net; class adv e-mail classifieds@news-herald.net; ed e-mail news@news-herald.net; web site www.tellicovillageconnection.com
Circulation: 4,050fr; Sworn/Estimate/Non-Audited
Advertising rate: Open inch rate $15.64
Established: 1993
Group: APG Media of Tennessee/North Carolina
Digital Platform - Mobile: Apple, Android
Digital Platform - Tablet: Apple iOS, Android
Pub./Ed. .... Steve Meadows
News Ed. .... Jonathan Herrmann
Business Manager .... Amanda Kimbrell
Mechanical Specifications: Full page: 10 inches by 20.5 inches
Type page 10 x 11 1/16 x ; E - 5 cols, 1 2/28, between; A - 5 cols, 1 2/28, between; C - 1 cols, 1 2/28, between.Equipment & Software: Hardware — Mac for editorial and production, PC for business office; Presses — Off-site printing; Software — CS3, Microsoft Office Suite
Delivery Method: Mail
Areas Served: 37774, 37885

LEWISBURG

MARSHALL COUNTY TRIBUNE (WED, FRI)

111 W Commerce St, Lewisburg, TN, 37091-3343, Marshall, USA; gen tel (931) 359-1188; adv tel (931) 359-1188 ext. 24; ed tel (931) 359-1188 ext. 26; gen fax (931) 359-1847; adv fax (931) 359-1847; ed fax (931) 359-1847; disp adv e-mail jward@marshalltribune.com; class adv e-mail lbrown@marshalltribune.com; ed e-mail mteditor@marshalltribune.com; web site www.marshalltribune.com
Circulation: 4,025pd, 21fr; Sworn/Estimate/Non-Audited
Advertising rate: Open inch rate $9.50
Established: 1873
Group: Rust CommunicationsEditions: Marshall County Tribune
Digital Platform - Mobile: Apple, Android
Digital Platform - Tablet: Apple iOS, Android, Windows 7
Pub. .... Hugh Jones
Adv. Mgr./Gen. Mgr. .... Jim Ward
Ed. .... Karen Hall
Delivery Method: Mail, Newsstand, Racks
Areas Served: Marshall County

LEXINGTON

LEXINGTON PROGRESS (WED)

508 S Broad St, Lexington, TN, 38351-2211, Henderson, USA; gen tel (731) 968-6397; adv tel (731) 968-6397; ed tel (731) 968-6397; gen fax (731) 968-9560; adv fax (731) 968-9560; ed fax (731) 968-9560; disp adv e-mail advertising@lexingtonprogress.com; class adv e-mail advertising@lexingtonprogress.com; ed e-mail news@lexingtonprogress.com; web site www.lexingtonprogress.com
Circulation: 7,300pd, 2,000fr; Sworn/Estimate/Non-Audited
Advertising rate: Open inch rate $7.50
Established: 1884
Digital Platform - Mobile: Apple, Android
Digital Platform - Tablet: Apple iOS, Android, Windows 7
Pub. .... Tom Franklin
Ed. .... Mike Reed
Adv. Dir. .... Susan Small
Delivery Method: Mail, Newsstand, Racks
Areas Served: Henderson County

LINDEN

BUFFALO RIVER REVIEW (WED)

115 S Mill St, Linden, TN, 37096-6457, Perry, USA; gen tel (931) 589-2169; adv tel (931) 589-2169; ed tel (931) 589-2169; gen fax (931) 589-3858; adv fax (931) 589-3858; ed fax (931) 589-3858; disp adv e-mail brreview@tds.net; class adv e-mail brreview@tds.net; ed e-mail brreditor@tds.net; web site www.buffaloriverreview.com
Circulation: 3,000pd,; Sworn/Estimate/Non-Audited
Advertising rate: Open inch rate $3.75
Established: 1976
Group: Kennedy Newspapers
Digital Platform - Mobile: Windows
Digital Platform - Tablet: Windows 7
Pub. .... Sam Kennedy
VP .... John Finney
Gen. Mgr. .... Sherri Groom
Ed. .... Randy Mackin
Mechanical Specifications: Type page 12 2/3 x 21; E - 6 cols, 2, between; A - 6 cols, 2, between; C - 6 cols, 2, between.Equipment & Software: Hardware — IBM; Software — Adobe/PageMaker 6.5.
Delivery Method: Mail, Racks
Areas Served: 37096, 37097

LIVINGSTON

OVERTON COUNTY NEWS (WED)

415 W Main St, Livingston, TN, 38570-1831, Overton, USA; gen tel (931) 823-6485; adv tel (931) 823-6485; ed tel (931) 823-6485; gen fax (931) 823-6486; adv fax (931) 823-6486; ed fax (931) 823-6486; disp adv e-mail carson@overtoncountynews.com; class adv

e-mail darren@overtoncountynews.com; ed e-mail news@overtoncountynews.com; web site www.overtoncountynews.com
Circulation: 5,600pd, 60fr; Sworn/Estimate/Non-Audited
Advertising rate: Open inch rate $6.80
Established: 1967
Digital Platform - Mobile: Apple, Android
Digital Platform - Tablet: Apple iOS, Android, Windows 7
Owner/Pub./Nat'l Adv. Mgr. .... Carson Oliver
Ed. .... Dewain Peek
Adv. Mgr. .... Darren Oliver
Mechanical Specifications: Type page 13 x 21; E - 6 cols, 2, 1/8 between; A - 6 cols, 2, between; C - 6 cols, 2, between.
Delivery Method: Mail, Newsstand, Racks
Areas Served: Overton County

LYNCHBURG

MOORE COUNTY NEWS (THUR)

30 Hiles St, Lynchburg, TN, 37352-8355, Moore, USA; gen tel (931) 759-7302; adv tel (931) 759-7302; ed tel (931) 759-7302; gen fax (931) 759-6838; adv fax (931) 759-6838; ed fax (931) 759-6838; disp adv e-mail mcnpub@lcs.net; class adv e-mail mcnpub@lcs.net; ed e-mail mcnpub@lcs.net; web site www.themoorecountynews.com
Circulation: 2,500pd, 19fr; Sworn/Estimate/Non-Audited
Advertising rate: Open inch rate $6.11
Established: 1928
Group: Lakeway Publishers, Inc.
Digital Platform - Mobile: Apple, Android
Digital Platform - Tablet: Apple iOS, Android, Windows 7
Pub./Ed. .... Tabitha Moore
Adv. Mgr. .... Barbara Green
Mechanical Specifications: Type page 13 x 21 1/2; E - 5 cols, 1 5/6, 1/8 between; A - 5 cols, 1 5/6, 1/8 between; C - 5 cols, 1 5/6, 1/8 between.Equipment & Software: ; Software — Adobe/PageMaker 6.5, QPS/QuarkXPress, Microsoft/Word.
Delivery Method: Mail, Racks
Areas Served: 37352, 37388, 37334, 37398, 37160, 37334, 37155, 37359, 37360, 37183, 37330, 37129, 37306

MANCHESTER

MANCHESTER TIMES (WED)

300 N Spring St, Manchester, TN, 37355-1567, Coffee, USA; gen tel (931) 728-7577; adv tel (931) 728-7577; ed tel (931) 728-7577; gen fax (931) 728-7614; adv fax (931) 728-7614; ed fax (931) 728-7614; disp adv e-mail mtpub@lcs.net; class adv e-mail mtclass@lcs.net; ed e-mail lnunez@manchestertimes.com; web site www.manchestertimes.com
Circulation: 4,880pd,; USPS
Advertising rate: Open inch rate $11.20
Established: 1881
Group: Lakeway Publishers, Inc.
Digital Platform - Mobile: Apple, Android
Digital Platform - Tablet: Apple iOS, Android, Windows 7
Pub. .... Josh Peterson
Delivery Method: Mail, Racks
Areas Served: Coffee County

MARTIN

WEAKLEY COUNTY PRESS (TUES, THUR)

235 S Lindell St, Martin, TN, 38237-2438, Weakley, USA; gen tel (731) 587-3144; adv tel (731) 587-3144; ed tel (731) 587-3144; gen fax (731) 587-3147; adv fax (731) 587-3147; ed fax (731) 587-3147; disp adv e-mail lcwagster@frontiernet.net; class adv e-mail classifieds@wcpnews.com; ed e-mail editor@wcpnews.com; web site www.nwtn-today.com
Circulation: 3,150pd,; Sworn/Estimate/Non-Audited
Advertising rate: Open inch rate $8.95
Established: 1884
Digital Platform - Mobile: Apple, Android, Windows, Blackberry
Digital Platform - Tablet: Apple iOS, Android, Windows 7, Blackberry Tablet OS, Kindle, Nook, Kindle Fire
Gen. Mgr. .... Lynette Calhoun Wagster
Editorial Cartoonist
Graphic Design .... Beth Cravens
Delivery Method: Mail, Newsstand, Carrier, Racks
Areas Served: Weakley County

MAYNARDVILLE

THE UNION NEWS LEADER (TUES)

3755 Maynardville Hwy, Maynardville, TN, 37807-3437, Union, USA; gen tel (865) 992-3392; adv tel (865) 992-3392; ed tel (865) 992-3392; gen fax (865) 992-6861; adv fax (865) 992-6861; ed fax (865) 992-6861; disp adv e-mail enewspaper@aol.com; class adv e-mail enewspaper@aol.com; ed e-mail enewspaper@aol.com; web site www.uc-newsleader.com
Circulation: 3,000pd,; Sworn/Estimate/Non-Audited
Advertising rate: Open inch rate $7.50
Established: 1990
Digital Platform - Mobile: Apple, Android
Digital Platform - Tablet: Apple iOS, Android, Windows 7
Pub. .... Chris Upton
Mng. Ed./Adv. Dir. .... Elbra Davis
Delivery Method: Mail, Newsstand, Racks
Areas Served: Union County and portions of surrounding counties

MC KENZIE

MCKENZIE BANNER (TUES)

3 Banner Row, Mc Kenzie, TN, 38201-2230, Carroll, USA; gen tel (731) 352-3323; adv tel (731) 352-3323; ed tel (731) 352-3323; gen fax (731) 352-3322; adv fax (731) 352-3322; ed fax (731) 352-3322; disp adv e-mail jennifer@mckenziebanner.com; class adv e-mail jennifer@mckenziebanner.com; ed e-mail washburn@mckenziebanner.com; web site www.mckenziebanner.com
Circulation: 4,500pd,; Sworn/Estimate/Non-Audited
Advertising rate: Open inch rate $6.75
Established: 1870
Group: Tri-County Publishing, Inc.
Digital Platform - Mobile: Apple, Android
Digital Platform - Tablet: Apple iOS, Android, Windows 7
Ed. .... Joel T. Washburn
Adv. Mgr. .... Jennifer Sims
Mechanical Specifications: Type page 13 1/4 x 21; E - 6 cols, 2 1/4, between; A - 6 cols, 2 1/4, between.
Delivery Method: Mail, Newsstand, Racks
Areas Served: Carroll County/38201

MCMINNVILLE

SOUTHERN STANDARD (WED, FRI, SUN)

105 College St, McMinnville, TN, 37110-2573, Warren, USA; gen tel (931) 473-2191; adv tel (931) 473-2191; ed tel (931) 473-2191; gen fax (931) 473-6823; adv fax (931) 473-6823; ed fax (931) 473-6823; disp adv e-mail advertising@southernstandard.com; class adv e-mail classifieds@southernstandard.com; ed e-mail editor@southernstandard.com; web site www.southernstandard.com
Circulation: 9,500pd, 409fr; Sworn/Estimate/Non-Audited
Advertising rate: Open inch rate $8.85
Established: 1879
Group: Morris Multimedia, Inc.
Digital Platform - Mobile: Apple, Android
Digital Platform - Tablet: Apple iOS, Android, Windows 7
Pub. .... Patricia Zechman
Circ. Mgr. .... Dale Stubblefield
Ed. .... James Clark
Adv. Mgr. .... Sharon Patrick
Circ. Mgr. .... Bill Cathcart
Delivery Method: Mail, Racks
Areas Served: Warren County

MEMPHIS

MEMPHIS BUSINESS JOURNAL (FRI)

80 Monroe Ave, Ste 600, Memphis, TN, 38103-2440, Shelby, USA; gen tel (901) 523-1000; adv tel (901) 523-1000; ed tel (901) 259-1721; gen fax (901) 526-5240; adv fax (901) 526-5240; ed fax (901) 526-5240; disp adv e-mail schamblin@bizjournals.com; class adv e-mail thollahan@bizjournals.com; ed e-mail bwellborn@bizjournals.com; web site www.bizjournals.com/memphis
Circulation: 5,196pd,; Sworn/Estimate/Non-Audited
Advertising rate: Open inch rate $5,560.00 (Full-Page)
Established: 1979
Digital Platform - Mobile: Apple, Android, Windows, Blackberry
Digital Platform - Tablet: Apple iOS, Android, Windows 7, Blackberry Tablet OS
Pub. .... Stuart Chamblin
Ed. .... Bill Wellborn
Managing Editor .... Mary Cashiola
Delivery Method: Mail, Racks
Areas Served: Shelby County

THE MEMPHIS NEWS (FRI)

193 Jefferson Ave, Memphis, TN, 38103-2322, Shelby, USA; gen tel (901) 523-1561; adv tel (901) 528-8122; ed tel (901) 528-8625; gen fax (901) 526-5813; adv fax (901) 526-5813; ed fax (901) 526-5813; disp adv e-mail dwaggener@memphisdailynews.com; class adv e-mail dfancher@memphisdailynews.com; ed e-mail lallen@memphisdailynews.com; web site www.thememphisnews.com
Circulation: 21,229fr; CVC
Advertising rate: 1/8 Pg $165.00; 1/4 Pg $330.00; 1/2 Pg $660.00
Established: 2008
Group: The Daily News Publishing Co.
Digital Platform - Mobile: Apple, Android
Digital Platform - Tablet: Apple iOS, Android, Windows 7
Pub. .... Eric Barnes
Gen. Mgr. .... Jennifer Shields
Circ. Coordinator .... Kaye Kerr
Managing Ed. .... Jane Donahoe
Delivery Method: Mail, Racks
Areas Served: 38103

THE MILLINGTON STAR (WED)

2850 Stage Village Cv, Ste 5, Memphis, TN, 38134-4682, Shelby, USA; gen tel (901) 872-2286; adv tel (901) 872-2286; ed tel (901) 872-2286; gen fax (901) 872-2965; adv fax (901) 872-2965; ed fax (901) 872-2965; disp adv e-mail sheri.williams@journalinc.com; class adv e-mail felicia.watkins@journalinc.com; ed e-mail sheri.williams@journalinc.com; web site www.millington-news.com
Circulation: 6,000pd,; Sworn/Estimate/Non-Audited
Advertising rate: Open inch rate $10.00
Established: 1950
Digital Platform - Mobile: Apple, Android
Digital Platform - Tablet: Apple iOS, Android, Windows 7
Pub./Adv. Dir. .... Brian Boom
Copy Ed. .... Bill Short
Mechanical Specifications: Type page 13 x 21 1/4; E - 6 cols, between; A - 6 cols, between; C - 9 cols, between.Equipment & Software: Hardware — APP/Power Mac, APP/Mac Performa; Software — Adobe/PageMaker 6.5, Adobe/Photoshop.
Delivery Method: Mail, Racks
Areas Served: 38053, 38058, 38004, 38011, 38019, 38023

MILAN

MILAN MIRROR-EXCHANGE (TUES)

1104 S Main St, Milan, TN, 38358-2726, Gibson, USA; gen tel (731) 686-1632; adv tel (731) 686-1632; ed tel (731) 686-1632; gen fax (731) 686-9005; adv fax (731) 686-9005; ed fax (731) 686-9005; disp adv e-mail scarlet@milanmirrorexchange.com; class adv e-mail melissa@milanmirrorexchange.com; ed e-mail victor@milanmirrorexchange.com; web site www.milanmirrorexchange.com
Circulation: 5,600pd,; Sworn/Estimate/Non-Audited
Advertising rate: Open inch rate $6.00
Established: 1964Editions: (1)
Digital Platform - Mobile: Apple, Android, Windows, Blackberry
Digital Platform - Tablet: Apple iOS, Android, Windows 7, Blackberry Tablet OS, Kindle, Nook, Kindle Fire
Pub. .... Dorris Parkins
Ed. .... Victor Parkins
Mng. Ed. .... Melanie Day
Adv. Mgr. .... Scarlet Elliott
Mechanical Specifications: Type page 13 x 21; E - 6 cols, 2, between; A - 6 cols, 2, between. Equipment & Software: Hardware — APP/Mac.
Delivery Method: Mail, Racks
Areas Served: Gibson and Carroll County

MOUNT JULIET

THE CHRONICLE OF MT. JULIET (WED)

11509 Lebanon Rd, Mount Juliet, TN, 37122-5500, Wilson, USA; gen tel (615) 754-6111; adv tel (615) 754-6111; ed tel (615) 754-6111; gen fax (615) 754-8203; adv fax (615) 754-8203; ed fax (615) 754-8203; disp adv e-mail doyle@thechronicleofmtjuliet.com; class adv e-mail thechronicle@thechronicleofmtjuliet.com; ed e-mail editor@thechronicleofmtjuliet.com; web site www.thechronicleofmtjuliet.com
Circulation: 13,000pd, 11,600fr; Sworn/Estimate/Non-Audited
Advertising rate: Open inch rate $10.99
Established: 1980
Digital Platform - Mobile: Apple, Android, Windows, Blackberry
Digital Platform - Tablet: Apple iOS, Android, Windows 7, Blackberry Tablet OS, Kindle, Nook, Kindle Fire
Vice Pres. .... Phyllis Robinson
Pub. .... Bill Robinson
Assc. Pub. .... Michael Robinson
Ed. .... Kenny Howell
Sales Mgr. .... Doyle Wood
Mechanical Specifications: Type page 9 3/4 x 14; E - 5 cols, 1 5/6, 1/6 between; A - 5 cols, 1 5/6, 1/6 between; C - 5 cols, 1 5/6, 1/6 between.Equipment & Software: Hardware — PC; Software — QPS/QuarkXPress 5.0, Adobe/Photoshop 4.0.
Delivery Method: Mail, Newsstand, Racks
Areas Served: 37138, 37122

MOUNTAIN CITY

THE TOMAHAWK (WED)

118 S Church St, Mountain City, TN, 37683-1502, Johnson, USA; gen tel (423) 727-6121; adv tel (423) 727-6121; ed tel (423) 727-6121; gen fax (423) 727-4833; adv fax (423) 727-4833; ed fax (423) 727-4833; disp adv e-mail advertise@thetomahawk.com; class adv e-mail classifieds@thetomahawk.com; ed e-mail editor@thetomahawk.com; web site www.thetomahawk.com
Circulation: 5,700pd,; Sworn/Estimate/Non-Audited
Advertising rate: Open inch rate $9.40
Established: 1874
Group: Sandusky Newspapers, Inc.
Digital Platform - Mobile: Apple, Android, Windows
Digital Platform - Tablet: Apple iOS, Android, Windows 7

Pub...Bill Thomas
Ed. ....Angie Gambill
Adv. Mgr. .... Ann Badal
Classified Adv. Mgr.........................Paula Walter
Office Manager........................ David Holloway
Delivery Method: Mail, Newsstand, Carrier, Racks
Areas Served: Upper East Tennessee, Western North Carolina, and Southwest Virginia

MURFREESBORO

THE MURFREESBORO POST (MON)

307 N Walnut St, Ste 2, Murfreesboro, TN, 37130-3656, Rutherford, USA; gen tel (615) 869-0800; adv tel (615) 869-0800; ed tel (615) 869-0800; gen fax (615) 869-0849; adv fax (615) 869-0849; ed fax (615) 869-0849; disp adv e-mail retailads@murfreesboropost.com; class adv e-mail retailads@murfreesboropost.com; ed e-mail editor@murfreesboropost.com; web site www.murfreesboropost.com
Circulation: 0pd, 10,000fr; Sworn/Estimate/Non-Audited
Advertising rate: Open inch rate $12.00
Established: 2006
Group: Main Street Media of Tennessee
Digital Platform - Mobile: Apple, Android, Windows, Blackberry
Digital Platform - Tablet: Apple iOS, Android, Windows 7, Blackberry Tablet OS, Kindle, Nook, Kindle Fire
Ed .... Zack Owensby
Asst News Ed .... Cat Murphy
Sports Ed.......................................Monte Hale
Class Mgr .... Lisa Peters
Delivery Method: Racks
Areas Served: Rutherford County

NASHVILLE

NASHVILLE BUSINESS JOURNAL (FRI)

1800 Church St, Ste 300, Nashville, TN, 37203-2224, Davidson, USA; gen tel (615) 248-2222; adv tel (615) 248-2222; ed tel (615) 248-2222; gen fax (615) 248-6246; adv fax (615) 248-6246; ed fax (615) 248-6246; disp adv e-mail aharris@bizjournals.com; class adv e-mail mfriedenberg@bizjournals.com; ed e-mail lbecker@bizjournals.com; web site www.bizjournals.com/nashville
Advertising rate: Open inch rate $9,695.00 (Full-Page)
Digital Platform - Mobile: Apple, Android, Windows, Blackberry
Digital Platform - Tablet: Apple iOS, Android, Windows 7, Blackberry Tablet OS
Pres./Pub. ....Kate Herman
Ed. in Chief ....Lori Becker
Mng. Ed.. Eric Snyder
Adv. Dir... Amy Harris
Delivery Method: Mail, Racks
Areas Served: Davidson County

NASHVILLE LEDGER (FRI)

222 2nd Ave N, Ste 101, Nashville, TN, 37201-1693, Davidson, USA; gen tel (615) 254-5522; adv tel (615) 254-5522; ed tel (615) 254-5522; gen fax (615) 254-5525; adv fax (615) 254-5525; ed fax (615) 254-5525; disp adv e-mail dchambers@nashvilleledger.com; class adv e-mail kkale@nashvilleledger.com; ed e-mail lgraves@nashvilleledger.com; web site www.nashvilleledger.com
Circulation: 10,000pd,; Sworn/Estimate/Non-Audited
Advertising rate: 1/8 Pg $150.00; 1/4 Pg $300.00; 1/2 Pg $600.00
Established: 1978
Group: The Daily News Publishing Co.
Digital Platform - Mobile: Apple, Android, Windows, Blackberry
Digital Platform - Tablet: Apple iOS, Android, Windows 7, Blackberry Tablet OS, Kindle, Nook, Kindle Fire
Pub./Ed. .... Lyle Graves
Adv. Mgr. .... Dianna Chambers
Public Notice Adv........................ Don Fancher
Mechanical Specifications: Type page 13 x 21; E - 6 cols, 1 7/8, 1/8 between; A - 6 cols, 1 7/8, 1/8 between; C - 6 cols, 1 7/8, 1/8 between. Equipment & Software: Hardware — PC, APP/Mac; Software — QPS/QuarkXPress, Adobe/PageMaker, Archetype/Corel.
Delivery Method: Mail, Newsstand, Racks
Areas Served: Davidson County

NEWPORT

THE NEWPORT PLAIN TALK (TUES, THUR, SUN)

145 E Broadway, Newport, TN, 37821-2324, Cocke, USA; gen tel (423) 623-6171; gen fax (423) 625-1995; class adv e-mail ads@newportplaintalk.com; ed e-mail seth.butler@newportplaintalk.com; web site www.newportplaintalk.com - 140,000(views) 35,000(visitors)
Circulation: 6,000pd,; Sworn/Estimate/Non-Audited
Advertising rate: Open inch rate $21.90
Established: 1900
Group: Adams Publishing Group, LLC
Digital Platform - Mobile: Apple, Android
Digital Platform - Tablet: Apple iOS, Android
Pub. Ed. .... Seth Butler
News Editor ....Matt Winter
Assistant Editor.............................Duay O'Neil
Staff Writer.................................Alison Brooks
Sports Editor......................... Dennis Barker Jr
Advertising..............................Sharon Bryant
Advertising...............................Vickie Mason
Classifieds Manager............. Sandy Freshour
Circulation Manager ....Larry Davis
District Manager Circulation .... Lynn Crum
Business Manager..................Claudine Harris
Delivery Method: Mail, Newsstand, Carrier, Racks
Areas Served: Newport/Cocke/37821
Parrottsville/Cocke
Cosby/Cocke
Bybee/Cocke
Del Rio/Cocke

ONEIDA

SCOTT COUNTY NEWS (THUR)

18289 Alberta St, Oneida, TN, 37841-2059, Scott, USA; gen tel (423) 569-8351; adv tel (423) 569-8351; ed tel (423) 569-8351; gen fax (423) 569-4500; adv fax (423) 569-4500; ed fax (423) 569-4500; disp adv e-mail nikita@scnoneida.net; class adv e-mail trish@scnoneida.net; ed e-mail nikita@scnoneida.net; web site www.scnoneida.com
Circulation: 5,000pd,; Sworn/Estimate/Non-Audited
Advertising rate: Open inch rate $6.00
Established: 1916
Pub... Mike Erwin
Delivery Method: Mail, Newsstand, Racks
Areas Served: Scott County

PARSONS

THE NEWS LEADER (WED)

24 W Main St, Parsons, TN, 38363-2012, Decatur, USA; gen tel (731) 847-6354; adv tel (731) 847-6354; ed tel (731) 847-6354; gen fax (731) 847-9120; adv fax (731) 847-9120; ed fax (731) 847-9120; disp adv e-mail thenewsleader@netease.net; class adv e-mail thenewsleader@netease.net; ed e-mail thenewsleader@netease.net; web site www.readtheleader.com
Circulation: 3,500pd,; Sworn/Estimate/Non-Audited
Advertising rate: Open inch rate $3.75
Established: 1926
Digital Platform - Mobile: Apple, Android
Digital Platform - Tablet: Apple iOS, Android, Windows 7
Pub./Ed. .... Danny Haynes
Mechanical Specifications: Type page 12 1/2 x 21 1/2; E - 6 cols, 2, between; A - 6 cols, 1 3/4, 1/8 between; C - 8 cols, 1 9/16, 1/8 between.Equipment & Software: Hardware — APP/Mac; Software — Adobe/PageMaker 6.0, Microsoft/Word.
Delivery Method: Mail
Areas Served: Decatur County

PIKEVILLE

THE BLEDSONIAN-BANNER (THUR)

399 Spring St, Pikeville, TN, 37367-5624, Bledsoe, USA; gen tel (423) 447-2996; adv tel (423) 447-2996; ed tel (423) 447-2996; gen fax (423) 447-2997; adv fax (423) 447-2997; ed fax (423) 447-2997; disp adv e-mail valleypubicads@bledsoe.net; class adv e-mail valleypubincads@bledsoe.net; ed e-mail valleypubincnews@bledsoe.net; web site www.thebledsonian-banner.net
Circulation: 3,000pd, 0fr; Sworn/Estimate/Non-Audited
Advertising rate: Open inch rate $4.00
Established: 1891
Group: Valley Publishing Company, Inc
Digital Platform - Mobile: Apple
Digital Platform - Tablet: Apple iOS
Pub... Amy Sue Hale
Ed./Adv. Mgr. .... Sandy Dodson
Mechanical Specifications: 6 col (11.625 inches) x 21 inch, 1 col=1.83 inchesEquipment & Software: ; Software — Adobe Creative Suites - InDesign, Photoshop, Illustrator; InCopy, Microsoft Word
Delivery Method: Mail, Newsstand
Areas Served: Bledsoe County (37367)

PORTLAND

THE PORTLAND LEADER (WED)

109 S Broadway St, Portland, TN, 37148-1303, Sumner, USA; gen tel (615) 325-9241; adv tel (615) 325-9241; ed tel (615) 325-9241; gen fax (615) 325-9243; adv fax (615) 325-9243; ed fax (615) 325-9243; disp adv e-mail sales@portlandleader.net; class adv e-mail customerservice@portlandleader.net; ed e-mail editor@portlandleader.net; web site www.portlandleader.net
Circulation: 3,000pd, 50fr; Sworn/Estimate/Non-Audited
Advertising rate: Open inch rate $6.00
Established: 1958
Digital Platform - Mobile: Apple, Android
Digital Platform - Tablet: Apple iOS, Android, Windows 7
Pub./Gen. Mgr. ....Jamie Johnson
Ed. .... Sonya Thompson
Office Mgr. ....April Barton
Sales Mgr......................................Jared Wilber
Mechanical Specifications: Type page 13 x 21 1/2; E - 6 cols, between; A - 6 cols, between; C - 8 cols, between.
Delivery Method: Mail, Racks
Areas Served: Sumner County

PULASKI

PULASKI CITIZEN (WED)

955 W College St, Pulaski, TN, 38478-3600, Giles, USA; gen tel (931) 363-3544; adv tel (931) 363-3544 ext. 115; ed tel (931) 363-3544 ext. 131; gen fax (931) 363-4312; adv fax (931) 424-2828; ed fax (931) 363-8656; disp adv e-mail bob@pulaskicitizen.com; class adv e-mail rebecca.brooks@pulaskicitizen.com; ed e-mail cary.malone@pulaskicitizen.com; web site www.pulaskicitizen.com
Circulation: 4,848pd, 524fr; Sworn/Estimate/Non-Audited
Advertising rate: Open inch rate $9.00
Established: 1854
Digital Platform - Mobile: Apple, Android, Windows, Blackberry
Digital Platform - Tablet: Apple iOS, Android, Windows 7, Blackberry Tablet OS, Kindle, Nook, Kindle Fire
EIC..Cary Jane Malone
Pub
Circ. Mgr. .... Scott Stewart
Advt Mgr .... Bob Dunnavant
Sports Ed....................................... Mark Mize
Staff Writer/Photographer........Trea Dunnavant
Advertising Rep ....Alan Faulkner
Equipment & Software: Hardware — APP/Mac; Presses — HI/Cotrell V-15A; Software — Adobe/PageMaker 6.0, QPS/QuarkXPress 3.3, Microsoft/Word 6.0.1, Adobe/Photoshop 4.0.
Delivery Method: Mail, Newsstand, Racks
Areas Served: Giles County

RIPLEY

THE LAUDERDALE COUNTY ENTERPRISE (THUR)

145 E Jackson Ave, Ripley, TN, 38063-1556, Lauderdale, USA; gen tel (731) 635-1771; adv tel (731) 635-1771; ed tel (731) 635-1771; gen fax (731) 635-2111; adv fax (731) 635-2111; ed fax (731) 635-2111; disp adv e-mail LCENEWS@YAHOO.COM; class adv e-mail LCENEWS@YAHOO.COM; ed e-mail LCENEWS@YAHOO.COM
Circulation: 4,600pd, 43fr; Sworn/Estimate/Non-Audited
Advertising rate: Open inch rate $6.20
Established: 1885
Pub./Gen. Mgr. ....Beverly Hutcherson
Delivery Method: Mail, Racks
Areas Served: Lauderdale County

THE LAUDERDALE VOICE (WED)

127 N Main St, Ripley, TN, 38063-1307, Lauderdale, USA; gen tel (731) 635-1238; adv tel (731) 635-1238; ed tel (731) 635-1238; gen fax (731) 635-3394; adv fax (731) 635-3394; ed fax (731) 635-3394; disp adv e-mail news@lauderdalevoice.com; class adv e-mail news@lauderdalevoice.com; ed e-mail news@lauderdalevoice.com
Circulation: 3,500pd, 4fr; Sworn/Estimate/Non-Audited
Advertising rate: Open inch rate $3.50
Established: 1977
Ed. ....Jay Heath
Adv. Dir./Circ. Dir. .... Rose Heath
Delivery Method: Mail, Racks
Areas Served: Lauderdale County

ROGERSVILLE

THE ROGERSVILLE REVIEW (WED, SAT)

316 E Main St, Rogersville, TN, 37857-3355, Hawkins, USA; gen tel (423) 272-7422; adv tel (423) 272-7422; ed tel (423) 272-7422; gen fax (423) 272-7889; adv fax (423) 272-7889; ed fax (423) 272-7889; disp adv e-mail ads@therogersvillereview.com; class adv e-mail classifieds@therogersvillereview.com; ed e-mail news@therogersvillereview.com; web site www.therogersvillereview.com
Circulation: 5,775pd, 3,308fr; USPS
Advertising rate: Open inch rate $12.00 (Wed); $14.00 (Sat)
Established: 1885
Group: Adams Publishing Group, LLC
Digital Platform - Mobile: Apple, Android
Digital Platform - Tablet: Apple iOS, Android
Pub./Ed. .... Tommy Campbell
Adv. Exec. ....Buffy Torres
Adv. Exec. ....Abby Swearingen
Classified Adv. Mgr. ....Christy Alvis
Mechanical Specifications: Type page 13 x 21 1/2; E - 6 cols, 2 1/16, 1/8 between; A - 6 cols, 2 1/16, 1/8 between; C - 9 cols, 1 5/16, 1/8 between.Equipment & Software: Hardware — APP/Mac Quadra 360, APP/Mac LaserWriter Pro, Color One/Scanner; Software — Adobe/PageMaker 4.2, QPS/QuarkXPress 3.3, Adobe/Photoshop.
Delivery Method: Mail, Racks
Areas Served: Hawkins, Hancock, and Sullivan County

SAVANNAH

THE COURIER (THUR)
375 Main St, Savannah, TN, 38372-2056, Hardin, USA; gen tel (731) 925-6397; adv tel (731) 925-6397; ed tel (731) 925-6397; gen fax (731) 925-6310; adv fax (731) 925-6310; ed fax (731) 925-6310; disp adv e-mail advertising@courieranywhere.com; class adv e-mail advertising@courieranywhere.com; ed e-mail info@courieranywhere.com; web site www.courieranywhere.com - 45,000(views) 11,200(visitors)
Circulation: 6,400pd, 52fr; Sworn/Estimate/Non-Audited
Advertising rate: Open inch rate $5.50
Established: 1884
Digital Platform - Mobile: Apple, Android
Digital Platform - Tablet: Apple iOS, Android, Windows 7
Pub....Joseph Hurd
Ed....Ron Schaming
Mechanical Specifications: Type page 13 x 21; E - 6 cols, 2 1/12, 1/6 between; A - 6 cols, 2 1/12, 1/6 between; C - 6 cols, 2 1/12, 1/6 between.Equipment & Software: ; Presses — KP; Software — Adobe/PageMaker, Archetype/Corel Draw.
Delivery Method: Mail, Racks
Areas Served: 38372, 38310

SMITHVILLE

SMITHVILLE REVIEW (WED)
106 S 1st St, Ste A, Smithville, TN, 37166-1744, DeKalb, USA; gen tel (615) 597-5485; gen fax (615) 597-5489; disp adv e-mail angie@smithvillereview.com ; class adv e-mail angie@smithvillerevice.com; ed e-mail news@smithvillereview.com ; web site www.smithvillereview.com
Circulation: 3,500pd, 0fr; Sworn/Estimate/Non-Audited
Advertising rate: Open inch rate $5.60
Established: 1892
Digital Platform - Mobile: Apple, Android
Digital Platform - Tablet: Apple iOS, Android, Windows 7
Pub./Gen. Mgr./Adv. Dir....Angie Meadows
Ed....Reed Vanderpool
Delivery Method: Mail, Newsstand, Racks
Areas Served: DeKalb County

SOUTH PITTSBURG

JASPER JOURNAL (TUES)
307 Elm Ave, South Pittsburg, TN, 37380-1337, Marion, USA; gen tel (423) 837-6312; adv tel (423) 837-6312; ed tel (423) 837-6312; gen fax (423) 837-8715 ; adv fax (423) 837-8715 ; ed fax (423) 837-8715 ; disp adv e-mail classifiedworks@marioncountynewstn.com; class adv e-mail classifiedworks@marioncountynewstn.com; ed e-mail mcnews@marioncountynewstn.com; web site www.marioncountynewstn.com
Circulation: 2,500pd,; Sworn/Estimate/Non-Audited
Advertising rate: Open inch rate $7.00
Established: 1938
Digital Platform - Mobile: Apple, Android
Digital Platform - Tablet: Apple iOS, Android, Windows 7
Pub....Melissa Brown
Adv. Dir....Deborah Keahey
Managing Ed....Kathie Tierney
Christy Sacks
Delivery Method: Mail, Newsstand
Areas Served: Marion County

SOUTH PITTSBURG HUSTLER (THUR)
307 Elm Ave, South Pittsburg, TN, 37380-1337, Marion, USA; gen tel (423) 837-6312; gen fax (423) 837-8715; disp adv e-mail classifiedworks@marioncountynewstn.com; class adv e-mail classifiedworks@marioncountynewstn.com; ed e-mail mcnews@marioncountynewstn.com; web site www.marioncountynewstn.com
Circulation: 1,500pd, 8,600fr; Sworn/Estimate/Non-Audited
Advertising rate: Open inch rate $7.10
Established: 1899
Digital Platform - Mobile: Apple, Android
Digital Platform - Tablet: Apple iOS, Android, Windows 7
Gen. Mgr....Melissa Brown
Office Mgr....Debbie Keahey
Managing Ed....Kathie Tierney
Composer....Christy Sacks
Delivery Method: Mail, Newsstand, Carrier, Racks
Areas Served: Marion County

SPARTA

THE EXPOSITOR (MON, THUR)
34 W Bockman Way, Sparta, TN, 38583-2015, White, USA; gen tel (931) 836-3284; adv tel (931) 836-3284; ed tel (931) 836-3284; gen fax (931) 836-3948; adv fax (931) 836-3948; ed fax (931) 836-3948; disp adv e-mail kim@myspartanews.com; class adv e-mail cristie@myspartanews.com; ed e-mail editor@myspartanews.com; web site www.spartalive.com
Circulation: 5,000pd, 6,900fr; Sworn/Estimate/Non-Audited
Advertising rate: Open inch rate $8.50
Established: 1876
Group: Smith Newspaper, Inc.
Digital Platform - Mobile: Apple, Android, Windows, Blackberry
Digital Platform - Tablet: Apple iOS, Android, Windows 7, Blackberry Tablet OS
Pub....Jim Shanks
Ed....Kim Wood
Gen. Mgr....Cristie Hatmaker
Delivery Method: Mail, Newsstand, Carrier, Racks
Areas Served: White County

SWEETWATER

THE ADVOCATE & DEMOCRAT (WED, SUN)
609 E North St, Sweetwater, TN, 37874-3137, Monroe, USA; gen tel (423) 337-7101; adv tel (423) 337-7101; ed tel (423) 337-7101; gen fax (423) 337-5932; adv fax (423) 337-5932; ed fax (423) 337-5932; disp adv e-mail sharon.livingston@advocateanddemocrat.com; class adv e-mail tommy.wilson@advocateanddemocrat.com; ed e-mail editor@advocateanddemocrat.com; web site www.advocateanddemocrat.com
Circulation: 4,533pd, 12,000fr; Sworn/Estimate/Non-Audited
Advertising rate: Open inch rate $13.50 (Wed); $16.00 (Sun)
Established: 1896
Group: Adams Publishing Group, LLC
Digital Platform - Mobile: Apple, Android
Digital Platform - Tablet: Apple iOS, Android, Windows 7
Ed....Tommy Millsaps
Adv. Mgr....Sharon Livingston
Ed....Mia Rhodarmer
Circ. Mgr....David Smith
Pub....Jeff Schumacher
Mechanical Specifications: Type page 13 x 21 1/2; E - 6 cols, 2, between; A - 6 cols, 2, between; C - 9 cols, 1 5/16, between. Equipment & Software: Hardware — APP/Mac; Presses — Oriient; Software — QPS/QuarkXPress 4.1, Adobe/PageMaker. In-design
Delivery Method: Mail, Newsstand, Carrier, Racks
Areas Served: Monroe County

TAZEWELL

CLAIBORNE PROGRESS (WED)
1705 Main St, Tazewell, TN, 37879-3413, Claiborne, USA; gen tel (423) 626-3222; adv tel (423) 626-3222; ed tel (423) 626-3222; gen fax (423) 626-6868; adv fax (423) 626-6868; ed fax (423) 626-6868; disp adv e-mail editor@claiborneprogress.net; class adv e-mail editor@claiborneprogress.net; ed e-mail editor@claiborneprogress.net; web site www.claiborneprogress.net
Circulation: 7,000pd,; Sworn/Estimate/Non-Audited
Advertising rate: Open inch rate $7.85
Established: 1887
Group: Boone Newspapers, Inc.
Digital Platform - Mobile: Apple, Android, Windows, Blackberry
Digital Platform - Tablet: Apple iOS, Android, Windows 7, Blackberry Tablet OS, Kindle, Nook, Kindle Fire
Adv. Dir....Pat Cheek
Publisher....Cynthia Orr
Delivery Method: Mail, Newsstand, Racks
Areas Served: Claiborne County

TIPTONVILLE

THE LAKE COUNTY BANNER (WED)
315 Church St, Tiptonville, TN, 38079-1147, Lake, USA; gen tel (731) 253-6666; adv tel (731) 253-6666; ed tel (731) 253-6666; gen fax (731) 253-6667; adv fax (731) 253-6667; ed fax (731) 253-6667; disp adv e-mail banner@lakecountybanner.com; class adv e-mail banner@lakecountybanner.com; ed e-mail wilmforr@gmail.com; web site www.lakecountybanner.com
Circulation: 3,400pd, 160fr; Sworn/Estimate/Non-Audited
Advertising rate: Open inch rate $8.00
Established: 1923
Group: Magic Valley Publishing
Digital Platform - Mobile: Apple
Digital Platform - Tablet: Apple iOS, Windows 7
Ed., Typesetting, Photo./Reporter, Adv.Matthew Forrest
Gen. Mgr....Matthew Richardson
Office Mgr/Circ....Jordan PriceEquipment & Software: Hardware — 4-APP/Mac, 1-Mitsubishi/Diamond Pro.
Delivery Method: Mail, Newsstand, Racks
Areas Served: 38079, 38077, 38080, 38232, 38240, 38254, 38007, 38024

TRACY CITY

GRUNDY COUNTY HERALD (THUR)
65 Oak St, Tracy City, TN, 37387-5048, Grundy, USA; gen tel (931) 592-2781; adv tel (931) 592-2781; ed tel (931) 592-2781; gen fax (931) 598-5812; adv fax (931) 592-9241 ; ed fax (931) 598-5812; disp adv e-mail gcherald@lcs.net; class adv e-mail gcherald@lcs.net; ed e-mail gcherald@lcs.net; web site www.grundycountyherald.com
Circulation: 5,100pd,; Sworn/Estimate/Non-Audited
Advertising rate: Open inch rate $9.46
Established: 1929
Group: Lakeway Publishers, Inc.
Digital Platform - Mobile: Apple, Android, Windows, Blackberry
Digital Platform - Tablet: Apple iOS, Android, Windows 7, Blackberry Tablet OS, Kindle, Nook, Kindle Fire
Pub./Ed....Joy Caldwell
Adv. Dir....Chris Cooper
Mandy Phillips
Delivery Method: Mail, Newsstand, Racks
Areas Served: Grundy County

TULLAHOMA

THE TULLAHOMA NEWS (WED, FRI, SUN)
505 Lake Way Pl, Tullahoma, TN, 37388-4710, Coffee, USA; gen tel (931) 455-4545; adv tel (931) 455-4545; ed tel (931) 455-4545; gen fax (931) 455-9299; adv fax (931) 455-9299; ed fax (931) 455-9299; disp adv e-mail tnads@lcs.net; class adv e-mail tnclass@lcs.net; ed e-mail tnedit@lcs.net; web site www.tullahomanews.com - 1,700,000(views) 76,000(visitors)
Circulation: 8,252pd, 9,500fr; USPS
Advertising rate: Open inch rate $15.12
Established: 1881
Group: Lakeway Publishers, Inc.
Digital Platform - Mobile: Apple, Android, Windows
Digital Platform - Tablet: Apple iOS, Android, Windows 7, Kindle, Kindle Fire
Pub....Jeff Fishman
Editor....Susan Campbell
Mechanical Specifications: Type page 10 x 21 1/2; E - 6 cols, 2, 1/12 between; A - 6 cols, 1.5, 1/12 between; C - 8 cols, between. Equipment & Software: ; Presses — 8-G/Community; Software — Adobe InDesign; Falcon for editorial
Delivery Method: Mail, Racks
Areas Served: Coffee County

WARTBURG

MORGAN COUNTY NEWS (WED)
202 N MAIDEN ST, Wartburg, TN, 37887, Morgan, USA; gen tel (423) 346-6225; adv tel (423) 346-6225; ed tel (423) 346-6225; gen fax (423) 346-5788; adv fax (423) 346-5788; ed fax (423) 346-5788; disp adv e-mail kkile@roanecounty.com; class adv e-mail kkile@roanecounty.com; ed e-mail jbyrge@morgancountynews.net; web site www.morgancountynews.net
Circulation: 5,377pd, 49fr; Sworn/Estimate/Non-Audited
Advertising rate: Open inch rate $9.20
Established: 1917
Group: Landmark Communications, Inc.
Landmark Community Newspapers, LLC
Digital Platform - Mobile: Apple, Android, Windows, Blackberry
Digital Platform - Tablet: Apple iOS, Android, Windows 7, Blackberry Tablet OS, Kindle, Nook, Kindle Fire
Gen. Mgr....Johnny Teglas
Adv. Mgr....Kevin Kile
Editor....John "Goose" Lindsay
Delivery Method: Mail, Racks
Areas Served: Morgan County

WAVERLY

THE NEWS-DEMOCRAT (FRI)
302A W Main St, Waverly, TN, 37185-1513, Humphreys, USA; gen tel (931) 296-2426; adv tel (931) 296-2426; ed tel (931) 296-2426; gen fax (931) 296-5156; adv fax (931) 296-5156; ed fax (931) 296-5156; disp adv e-mail kerrylampley@bellsouth.net; class adv e-mail newsdemocrat@bellsouth.net; ed e-mail newsdemocrat@bellsouth.net; web site www.thenews-democrat.com
Circulation: 4,000pd, 165fr; Sworn/Estimate/Non-Audited
Advertising rate: Open inch rate $6.00
Established: 1871
Group: Kennedy Newspapers Co., Inc
Digital Platform - Mobile: Apple
Digital Platform - Tablet: Apple iOS
Pub....Ward Phillips
Ed....Grey Collier
Adv. Mgr....Kerry Lamplet
Mechanical Specifications: Type page 10" x 21 1/2"; E - 6 cols, 2, 1/8 between; A - 6 cols, 2, 1/8 between; C - 6 cols, 2, 1/8 between. Equipment & Software: Hardware — APP/Mac; Software — Adobe/PageMaker 5.0, Microsoft/Word 4.0, Adobe/Photoshop 2.5.
Delivery Method: Mail, Racks
Areas Served: 37185, 37101, 37134, 37078

TEXAS

ALBANY

ALBANY NEWS (THUR)
49 S Main St, Albany, TX, 76430, Shackelford, USA; gen tel (325) 762-2201; adv tel (325) 762-2201; ed tel (325) 762-2201; gen fax (325) 762-3201; adv fax (325) 762-3201; ed fax (325) 762-3201; disp adv e-mail dlucas@thealbanynews.net; class adv e-mail ads@thealbanynews.net; ed e-mail melinda@thealbanynews.net; web site www.thealbanynews.net
Circulation: 1,350pd,; Sworn/Estimate/Non-Audited
Advertising rate: Open inch rate $6.50
Established: 1875
Digital Platform - Mobile: Apple
Digital Platform - Tablet: Apple iOS
Pub. .... Donnie Lucas
Ed. .... Melinda LucasEquipment & Software: Hardware — Macintosh; Software — Adobe CS4
Delivery Method: Mail, Racks
Areas Served: 76430, 76464

ALEDO

THE COMMUNITY NEWS (FRI)
203 Pecan Dr, Aledo, TX, 76008, Parker, USA; gen tel (817) 441-7661; adv tel (817) 441-7661; ed tel (817) 441-7661; gen fax (817) 441-5419; adv fax (817) 441-5419; ed fax (817) 441-5419; disp adv e-mail business@community-news.com; class adv e-mail business@community-news.com; ed e-mail news@community-news.com; web site www.community-news.com
Circulation: 2,244pd,; Sworn/Estimate/Non-Audited
Advertising rate: Open inch rate $8.00
Established: 1995
Digital Platform - Mobile: Apple, Android, Windows, Blackberry
Digital Platform - Tablet: Apple iOS, Android, Windows 7, Blackberry Tablet OS, Kindle, Nook, Kindle Fire
Pub./Ed. .... Randy Keck
Adv. Dir. .... Loydale Schmid
Phil Major
Delivery Method: Mail, Newsstand, Racks
Areas Served: 76008, 76108, 76087, 76126

ALICE

ALICE ECHO-NEWS JOURNAL (WED, SUN)
405 E Main St, Alice, TX, 78332-4968, Jim Wells, USA; gen tel (361) 664-6588; adv tel (361) 664-6588 ext. 212; ed tel (361) 664-6588; gen fax (361) 668-1030; adv fax (361) 668-1030; ed fax (361) 668-1030; disp adv e-mail gdelaney@gatehousemedia.com; class adv e-mail ssalaiz@aliceechonews.com; ed e-mail ohunter@aliceechonews.com; web site www.alicetx.com
Circulation: 3,107pd, 500fr; Sworn/Estimate/Non-Audited
Advertising rate: Open inch rate $10.00
Established: 1894
Group: GateHouse Media, Inc.
Digital Platform - Mobile: Apple, Android
Digital Platform - Tablet: Apple iOS, Android, Windows 7
Ed. .... Ofelia Hunter
Sports Ed. .... Pete Garcia
National/Major acciunts .... Russel Gruber
Mechanical Specifications: Type page 10.5 x 16 ; E - 6 cols, 2 1/16, 1/8 between; A - 6 cols, 2 1/16, 1/8 between; C - 8 cols, 1 1/2, 1/8 between.
Delivery Method: Mail, Newsstand, Carrier, Racks
Areas Served: Jim Wells County

NUECES COUNTY RECORD-STAR (THUR)
405 E Main St, Alice, TX, 78332-4968, Jim Wells, USA; gen tel (361) 664-6588; adv tel (361) 664-6588 ext. 214; ed tel (361) 664-6588; gen fax (361) 668-1030; adv fax (361) 668-1030; ed fax (361) 668-1030; disp adv e-mail bweaver@aliceechonews.com; class adv e-mail bweaver@aliceechonews.com; ed e-mail news@recordstar.com; web site www.recordstar.com
Circulation: 3,100pd,; Sworn/Estimate/Non-Audited
Advertising rate: Open inch rate $6.60
Established: 1910
Group: GateHouse Media, Inc.
Digital Platform - Mobile: Apple, Android, Windows, Blackberry
Digital Platform - Tablet: Apple iOS, Android, Windows 7, Blackberry Tablet OS, Kindle, Nook, Kindle Fire
Pub./Ed. .... Bill Weaver
Exec. Ed. .... Ofelia Garcia Hunter
Mechanical Specifications: Type page 13 x 21; E - 6 cols, 2, 1/6 between; A - 6 cols, 2, 1/6 between; C - 6 cols, 2, 1/6 between.Equipment & Software: Hardware — APP/Mac; Software — Aldus/PageMaker 6.0, Adobe/Photoshop, Microsoft/Word.
Delivery Method: Mail, Newsstand, Carrier
Areas Served: 78410, 78460, 78409

ALPINE

ALPINE AVALANCHE (THUR)
118 N 5th St, Alpine, TX, 79830-4602, Brewster, USA; gen tel (432) 837-3334; adv tel (432) 837-3334; ed tel (432) 837-3334; gen fax (432)837-7181; adv fax (432)837-7181; ed fax (432)837-7181; disp adv e-mail publisher@alpineavalanche.com; class adv e-mail bookkeeping@alpineavalanche.com; ed e-mail editor@alpineavalanche.com; web site www.alpineavalanche.com - 60,000(views) 19,000(visitors)
Circulation: 1,930pd, 373fr; CVC
Advertising rate: Open inch rate $7.50
Established: 1891
Digital Platform - Mobile: Apple, Android, Windows
Digital Platform - Tablet: Apple iOS, Android, Windows 7, Kindle, Nook, Kindle Fire
Publisher and editor .... Gwin Grimes
Mechanical Specifications: Type page 13 x 21 3/4; E - 6 cols, 2, 1/6 between; A - 6 cols, 2, 1/6 between; C - 6 cols, 2, 1/6 between. Equipment & Software: Hardware — APP/Mac; Software — WordPerfect, Adobe/PageMaker, QPS/QuarkXPress, Microsoft/Word.
Delivery Method: Mail, Newsstand, Racks
Areas Served: Brewster County and the Big Bend region

ALVIN

ALVIN SUN-ADVERTISER (WED, SUN)
570 Dula St, Alvin, TX, 77511-2942, Brazoria, USA; gen tel (281) 331-4421; adv tel (281) 331-4421; ed tel (281) 331-4421; gen fax (281) 331-4424; adv fax (281) 331-4424; ed fax (281) 331-4424; disp adv e-mail ads@alvinsun.net; class adv e-mail ads@alvinsun.net; ed e-mail editor@alvinsun.net; web site www.alvinsun.net
Circulation: 350pd, 14,500fr; Sworn/Estimate/Non-Audited
Advertising rate: Open inch rate $12.47
Established: 1892
Group: Hartman News LLP
Digital Platform - Mobile: Apple, Android
Digital Platform - Tablet: Apple iOS, Android, Windows 7
Bus. Mgr. .... Donna Hopkins
Publisher .... David Rupkalvis
Delivery Method: Mail, Newsstand, Carrier, Racks
Areas Served: 77511, 77578, 77583, 77577, 77510

ANAHUAC

THE ANAHUAC PROGRESS (WED)
306 Willcox St, Anahuac, TX, 77514, Chambers, USA; gen tel (409) 267-6131; gen fax (409) 267-4157; disp adv e-mail theprogress@theanahuacprogress.com; class adv e-mail theprogress@theanahuacprogress.com; ed e-mail theprogress@theanahuacprogress.com; web site www.theanahuacprogress.com
Circulation: 647pd, 0fr; USPS
Advertising rate: Open inch rate $5.25
Established: 1908
Group: Granite Publishing Partners LLC
Digital Platform - Mobile: Apple, Android, Windows
Digital Platform - Tablet: Apple iOS, Android, Windows 7, Blackberry Tablet OS, Kindle, Nook, Kindle Fire
Mng. Ed./Gen. Mgr. .... Dayna Haynes
Mechanical Specifications: Type page 10.25 x 21; E - 6 cols, 1.625", 1.250" between; A - 6 cols, 1.625", 1.25" between; C - 9 cols, 9.000", 1.250" between.
Delivery Method: Mail, Newsstand, Racks
Areas Served: Chambers County

ANDREWS

ANDREWS COUNTY NEWS (THUR, SUN)
210 E Broadway St, Andrews, TX, 79714-6586, Andrews, USA; gen tel (432) 523-2085; adv tel (432) 523-2085; ed tel (432) 523-2085; gen fax (432) 523-9492; adv fax (432) 523-9492; ed fax (432) 523-9492; disp adv e-mail publisher@basinbroadband.com; class adv e-mail ads@basinbroadband.com; ed e-mail editor@basinbroadband.com; web site www.andrewscountynews.com
Circulation: 3,100pd, 135fr; Sworn/Estimate/Non-Audited
Advertising rate: Open inch rate $9.80
Established: 1934
Digital Platform - Mobile: Apple, Android, Blackberry
Digital Platform - Tablet: Apple iOS, Android, Windows 7, Blackberry Tablet OS
Pub. .... Kandi Roberts
Ed. .... Sam Kaufman
Adv. Dir. .... Priscilla Rider
Delivery Method: Mail, Newsstand, Carrier, Racks
Areas Served: 79714

ANGLETON

THE BULLETIN (TUES)
PO Box 2426, Angleton, TX, 77516-2426, Brazoria, USA; gen tel (979) 849-5407; adv tel (979) 849-5407; ed tel (979) 849-5407; gen fax (866) 844-5288; adv fax (866) 844-5288; ed fax (866) 844-5288; disp adv e-mail sharon.bulletin@gmail.com; class adv e-mail sharon.bulletin@gmail.com; ed e-mail john.bulletin@gmail.com; web site www.mybulletinnewspaper.com
Circulation: 6,000fr; Sworn/Estimate/Non-Audited
Advertising rate: Open inch rate $8.00 local, $14 national
Established: 1994
Group: J&S Communications
Digital Platform - Mobile: Apple, Android, Windows, Blackberry
Digital Platform - Tablet: Apple iOS, Android, Windows 7, Blackberry Tablet OS, Kindle, Nook, Kindle Fire
Co-Publisher /Advertising Director Sharon Toth
Ed. .... John Toth
Mechanical Specifications: Type page 10 1/2 x 12 3/4; E - 5 cols, 2, 1/8 between; A - 5 cols, 2, 1/8 between; C - 5 cols, 2, 1/8 between. Equipment & Software: Hardware — IBM; Presses — HI; Software — CompuWorks/Publisher.
Delivery Method: Racks
Areas Served: Brazoria Co, Tx, 77515, 77566, 77531, 77541, 77422, 77486, 77511, 77512, 77534, 77480

ANSON

WESTERN OBSERVER (WED)
1120 W Court Plz, Anson, TX, 79501-4315, Jones, USA; gen tel (325) 823-3253; adv tel (325) 823-3253; ed tel (325) 823-3253; gen fax (325) 823-2957; adv fax (325) 823-2957; ed fax (325) 823-2957; disp adv e-mail westobserver@sbcglobal.net; class adv e-mail westobserver@sbcglobal.net; ed e-mail westobserver@sbcglobal.net
Circulation: 2,100pd,; Sworn/Estimate/Non-Audited
Advertising rate: Open inch rate $4.05
Established: 1883
Pub./Ed./Adv. Dir. .... Tiffany Waddell
Delivery Method: Mail, Newsstand
Areas Served: Jones County

ARANSAS PASS

ARANSAS PASS PROGRESS (WED)
346 S Houston St, Aransas Pass, TX, 78336-2515, San Patricio, USA; gen tel (361) 758-5391; adv tel (361) 758-5391; ed tel (361) 758-5391; gen fax (361) 758-5393; adv fax (361) 758-5393; ed fax (361) 758-5393; disp adv e-mail mattie@aransaspassprogress.com; class adv e-mail classifieds@aransaspassprogress.com; ed e-mail publisher@aransaspassprogress.com; web site www.aransaspassprogress.com
Circulation: 1,854pd,; Sworn/Estimate/Non-Audited
Advertising rate: Open inch rate $8.00
Established: 1909
Digital Platform - Mobile: Apple, Android
Digital Platform - Tablet: Apple iOS, Android, Windows 7
Pub./Ed./Adv. Dir. .... Brenda Burr
Bus. Mgr. .... Amanda Torres
Delivery Method: Mail, Newsstand, Racks
Areas Served: San Patricio

THE INGLESIDE INDEX (WED)
346 S Houston St, Aransas Pass, TX, 78336-2515, San Patricio, USA; gen tel (361) 758-5391; adv tel (361) 758-5391; ed tel (361) 758-5391; gen fax (361) 758-5393; adv fax (361) 758-5393; ed fax (361) 758-5393; disp adv e-mail mattie@aransaspassprogress.com; class adv e-mail classifieds@aransaspassprogress.com; ed e-mail publisher@aransaspassprogress.com; web site www.inglesideindex.com
Circulation: 1,500pd, 46fr; Sworn/Estimate/Non-Audited
Advertising rate: Open inch rate $6.50
Established: 1953
Digital Platform - Mobile: Apple, Android
Digital Platform - Tablet: Apple iOS, Android, Windows 7
Pub./Ed. .... Brenda Burr
Bus. Mgr. .... Amanda Torres
Mechanical Specifications: Type page 13 x 21; E - 6 cols, 2 1/16, 1/6 between; A - 6 cols, 2 1/16, 1/6 between; C - 9 cols, 1 1/2, between.Equipment & Software: Hardware — APP/Mac; Software — QPS/QuarkXPress.
Delivery Method: Mail, Newsstand
Areas Served: San Patricio County

ARCHER CITY

ARCHER COUNTY NEWS (THUR)
104 E Walnut, Archer City, TX, 76351, Archer, USA; gen tel (940) 574-4569; adv tel (940) 574-4569; ed tel (940) 574-4569; gen fax (940) 574-4234; adv fax (940) 574-4234; ed fax (940) 574-4234; disp adv e-mail archernews@yahoo.com; class adv e-mail archernews@yahoo.com; ed e-mail acjennyg@gmail.com; web site www.archercountynews.com
Circulation: 1,300pd,; Sworn/Estimate/Non-Au-

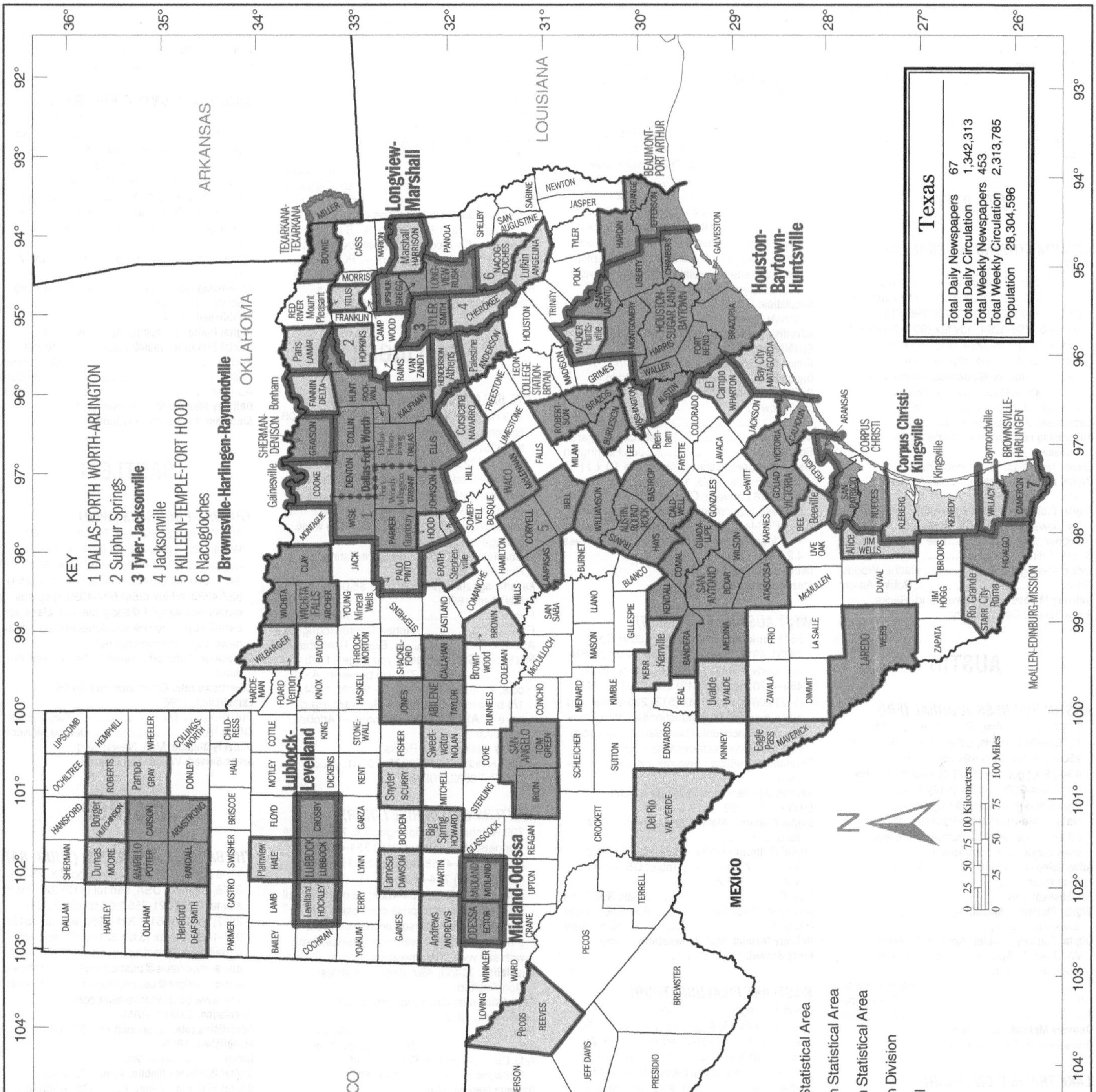
KEY
1 DALLAS-FORTH WORTH-ARLINGTON
2 Sulphur Springs
3 Tyler-Jacksonville
4 Jacksonville
5 KILLEEN-TEMPLE-FORT HOOD
6 Nacogdoches
7 Brownsville-Harlingen-Raymondville
Texas
Total Daily Newspapers 67
Total Daily Circulation 1,342,313
Total Weekly Newspapers 453
Total Weekly Circulation 2,313,785
Population 28,304,596
LEGEND
Dallas-Fort Worth Combined Statistical Area
RICHMOND Metropolitan Statistical Area
Concord Micropolitan Statistical Area
Philadelphia Metropolitan Division
MEXICO International
TEXAS State
HARRIS County
Shoreline
0 25 50 75 100 Miles
0 25 50 75 100 Kilometers
N
OKLAHOMA
ARKANSAS
LOUISIANA
NEW MEXICO
MEXICO
Longview-Marshall
Houston-Baytown-Huntsville
Corpus Christi-Kingsville
Lubbock-Levelland
Midland-Odessa
McALLEN-EDINBURG-MISSION

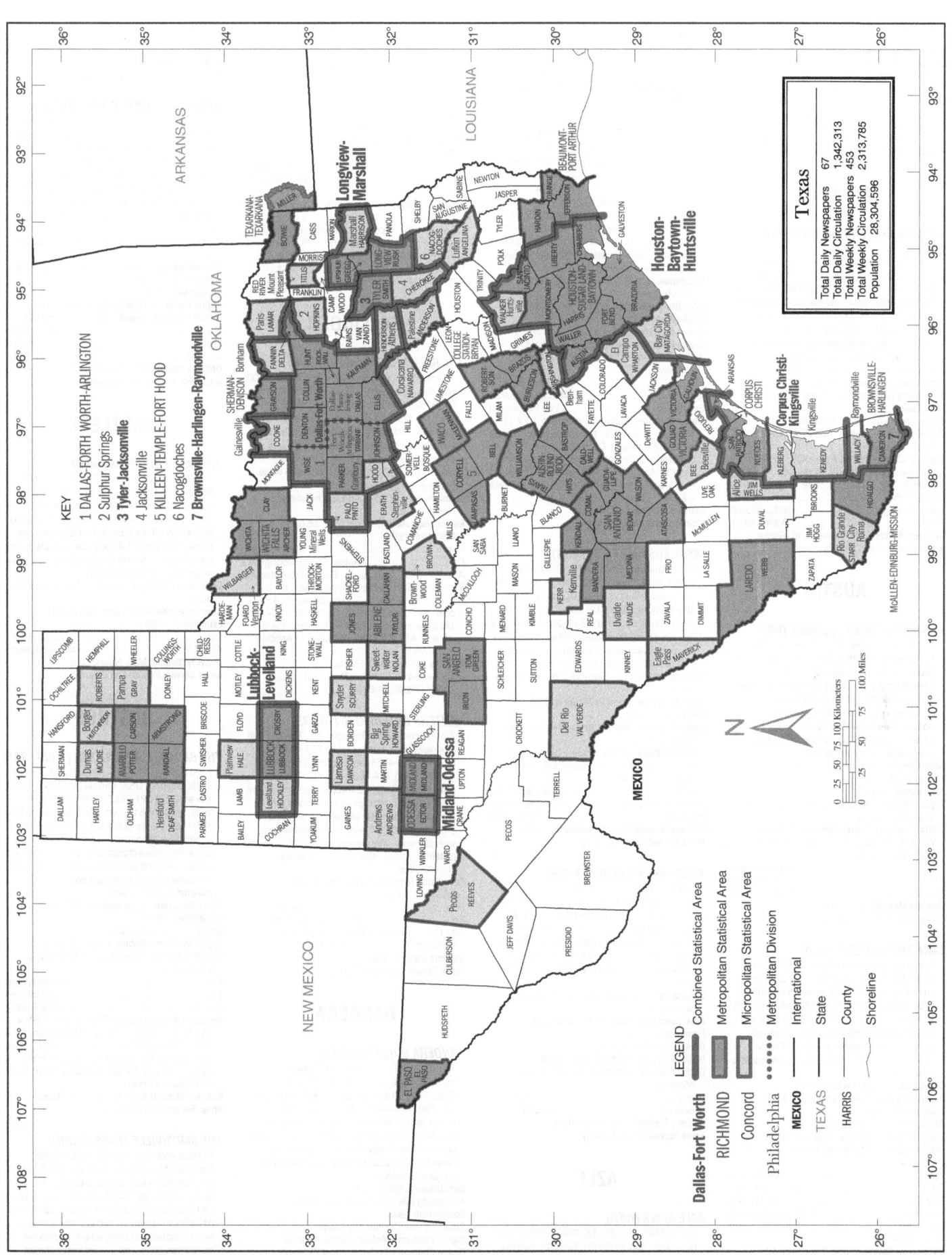

dited
Advertising rate: Open inch rate $5.00
Established: 1908
Digital Platform - Mobile: Windows
Digital Platform - Tablet: Windows 7
Pres./Ed./Adv. Dir.....................Barbara Phillips
Co-Pub.. Jerry Phillips
Assistant Editor....................Mandy Kinnaman
Delivery Method: Mail, Racks
Areas Served: 76351, 76366, 76301, 76389, 76370, 76379

ATLANTA

ATLANTA CITIZENS JOURNAL (WED, SUN)

306 W Main St, Atlanta, TX, 75551-2523, Cass, USA; gen tel (903) 796-7133; adv tel (903) 796-7133; ed tel (903) 796-7133; gen fax (903) 796-3294; adv fax (903) 796-3294; ed fax (903) 796-3294; disp adv e-mail production@casscountynow.com; class adv e-mail production@casscountynow.com; ed e-mail raaron@casscountynow.com; web site www.atlantacitizensjournal.com
Circulation: 3,100pd, 51fr; USPS
Advertising rate: Open inch rate $7.95
Established: 1879
Group: Northeast Texas Publishing
Digital Platform - Mobile: Apple, Android, Windows, Blackberry
Digital Platform - Tablet: Apple iOS, Android, Windows 7, Blackberry Tablet OS
Designer............................Lee Ellen Benjamin
Sports Editor................................Tim Emmons
Office Manager..........................Rachel Woods
Editor..Robin Aaron
Delivery Method: Mail, Newsstand, Racks
Areas Served: Cass County

AUSTIN

AUSTIN BUSINESS JOURNAL (FRI)

111 Congress Ave, Ste 750, Austin, TX, 78701-4074, Travis, USA; gen tel (512) 494-2500; adv tel (512) 494-2500; ed tel (512) 494-2500; gen fax (512) 494-2525; adv fax (512) 494-2525; ed fax (512) 494-2525; disp adv e-mail austin@bizjournals.com; class adv e-mail austin@bizjournals.com; ed e-mail austin@bizjournals.com; web site www.bizjournals.com/austin
Advertising rate: Open inch rate $6880.00 (Full-Page)
Established: 1981
Digital Platform - Mobile: Apple, Android, Windows, Blackberry
Digital Platform - Tablet: Apple iOS, Android, Windows 7, Blackberry Tablet OS, Kindle, Nook, Kindle Fire
Pub...Heather Ledage
Ed. .... Colin Pope
Adv. Dir.................................. Doug Pogemiller
Delivery Method: Mail, Racks
Areas Served: Travis County

LAKE TRAVIS VIEW (THUR)

305 S Congress Ave, Austin, TX, 78704-1200, Travis, USA; gen tel (512) 263-1100; adv tel (512) 263-1100; ed tel (512) 263-1100; gen fax (512) 263-3583; adv fax (512) 263-3583; ed fax (512) 263-3583; disp adv e-mail news@statesman.com; class adv e-mail news@statesman.com; ed e-mail news@statesman.com; web site www.statesman.com
Circulation: 438pd, 1,476fr; AAM
Advertising rate: Open inch rate $14.20
Established: 1985
Group: Cox Media Group
Digital Platform - Mobile: Apple, Android
Digital Platform - Tablet: Apple iOS, Android, Windows 7
Pub...Jay Plotkin
Ed. ....Ed Allen
Adv. Dir...Ken Brown
Adv. Mgr.................................Danny Esposito
Sports Ed................................ Max Thompson
Devin Monk
Mechanical Specifications: Type page 10 x 11 1/2; E - 5 cols, 1 15/16, 1/8 between; A - 5 cols, 1 15/16, 1/8 between.Equipment & Software: Hardware — Dell/Optiplex; Software — QPS/QuarkXPress 4.1, Adobe/Photoshop 6.0, Microsoft/Word, Adobe/Acrobat 4.0.
Delivery Method: Mail, Newsstand, Racks
Areas Served: Travis County

THE PFLUGERVILLE PFLAG (WED)

305 S Congress Ave, Austin, TX, 78704-1200, USA; gen tel (512) 255-5827; adv tel (512) 255-5827; ed tel (512) 255-5827; gen fax (512) 251-6221; adv fax (512) 251-6221; ed fax (512) 251-6221; disp adv e-mail communityadvertising@statesman.com; class adv e-mail classified@statesman.com; ed e-mail mguajardo@archive.pflugervillepflag.com; web site www.statesman.com/s/news/local/pflugerville-pflag
Circulation: 0pd, 8,547fr; Sworn/Estimate/Non-Audited
Advertising rate: Open inch rate $13.80
Established: 1980
Group: Cox Media Group
Digital Platform - Mobile: Apple, Android
Digital Platform - Tablet: Apple iOS, Android, Windows 7
Pub...Terry Schaub
Mng. Ed.................................Marcial Guajardo
Sports Ed................................. Joe Harrington
Mechanical Specifications: Type page 10 x 11 1/2; E - 5 cols, 1 7/8, 1/6 between; A - 5 cols, 1 7/8, 1/6 between; C - 5 cols, 1 7/8, 1/6 between.Equipment & Software: Hardware — APP/Mac G3, APP/Power Mac; Software — Adobe/Photoshop 5.5, QPS/QuarkXPress 4.2.
Delivery Method: Mail, Racks
Areas Served: 78660, 78691

WEST AUSTIN NEWS (THUR)

5511 Parkcrest Dr, Ste 105, Austin, TX, 78731-4917, Travis, USA; gen tel (512) 459-4070; adv tel (512) 459-4070; ed tel (512) 459-4070; gen fax (512) 206-0704; adv fax (512) 206-0704; ed fax (512) 206-0704; disp adv e-mail ads@westaustinnews.com; class adv e-mail accounts@westaustinnews.com; web site www.westaustinnews.com
Circulation: 1,880pd,; Sworn/Estimate/Non-Audited
Advertising rate: Open inch rate $18.50
Established: 1986
Digital Platform - Mobile: Apple, Android, Windows, Blackberry
Digital Platform - Tablet: Apple iOS, Android, Windows 7, Blackberry Tablet OS, Kindle, Nook, Kindle Fire
Pub./Ed.....................................Bart Stephens
Adv. Mgr./Office Mgr............... Rachelle Topete
Prodn. Mgr. ....Kim Bader
Delivery Method: Mail, Newsstand, Racks
Areas Served: Travis County

WESTLAKE PICAYUNE (THUR)

305 S Congress Ave, Austin, TX, 78704-1200, Travis, USA; gen tel (512) 327-2990; adv tel (512) 445-3742; ed tel (512) 912-2502; disp adv e-mail communityadvertising@statesman.com; class adv e-mail classified@statesman.com; ed e-mail editor@statesman.com; web site www.statesman.com
Circulation: 463pd, 3,415fr; Sworn/Estimate/Non-Audited
Advertising rate: Open inch rate $12.00
Established: 1976
Group: Cox Media Group
Digital Platform - Mobile: Apple, Android
Digital Platform - Tablet: Apple iOS, Android, Windows 7
Pub./Ed...Ed Allen
Sports Ed...................................Habeab Kurdi
Delivery Method: Mail, Newsstand
Areas Served: Travis County

AZLE

AZLE NEWS (WED)

321 W Main St, Azle, TX, 76020-2903, Tarrant, USA; gen tel (817) 270-3340; gen fax (817) 270-5300; disp adv e-mail johnna@azlenews.net; class adv e-mail publisher@azlenews.net; ed e-mail markcampbell@azlenews.net; web site www.azlenews.net
Circulation: 3,939pd, 112fr; Sworn/Estimate/Non-Audited
Advertising rate: Open inch rate $6.50
Established: 1959
Digital Platform - Mobile: Apple, Android
Digital Platform - Tablet: Apple iOS, Android, Windows 7
Pub./Adv. Dir. .... Kim Ware
Ed. ....Mark Campbell
Adv. Mgr..................................Johnna Bridges
Mechanical Specifications: Type page 13 x 21; E - 5 cols, 2 1/2, 1/6 between; A - 6 cols, 2, 1/6 between; C - 6 cols, 2, 1/6 between.Equipment & Software: Hardware — PCs; Software — WordPerfect 6.5, Adobe/PageMaker 5.0.
Delivery Method: Mail, Newsstand, Racks
Areas Served: 76020, 76082, 76086, 76135

BALLINGER

THE BALLINGER LEDGER (THUR)

709 Hutchins Ave, Ballinger, TX, 76821-5608, Runnels, USA; gen tel (325) 365-3501; adv tel (325) 365-3501; ed tel (325) 365-3501; gen fax (325) 365-5389; adv fax (325) 365-5389; ed fax (325) 365-5389; disp adv e-mail news@ballingerledger.com; class adv e-mail news@ballingerledger.com; ed e-mail news@ballingerledger.com; web site www.ballingerledger.com
Circulation: 2,500pd, 13fr; Sworn/Estimate/Non-Audited
Advertising rate: Open inch rate $6.00
Established: 1886
Pub...Juliet LeMond
Ed. .... Ruben Cantu-Rodriguez
Adv. Dir.............................. Brandi Rosenbaum
Mechanical Specifications: Type page 11 7/8 x 21 1/2; E - 6 cols, 1 7/8, 1/6 between; A - 6 cols, 1 7/8, 1/6 between; C - 9 cols, 1 1/4, 1/6 between.Equipment & Software: Hardware — APP/Mac G4; Software — Adobe/PageMaker 6.5.
Delivery Method: Mail, Racks
Areas Served: 76821, 76875, 76861, 76866, 79567, 76882, 76865

WINTERS ENTERPRISE (THUR)

709 Hutchins Ave, Ballinger, TX, 76821-5608, Runnels, USA; gen tel (325) 754-4958; adv tel (325) 754-4958; ed tel (325) 754-4958; gen fax (325) 754-4628; adv fax (325) 754-4628; ed fax (325) 754-4628; disp adv e-mail news@wintersenterprise.com; class adv e-mail news@wintersenterprise.com; ed e-mail chawkinds@wintersenterprise.com; web site www.wintersenterprise.com
Circulation: 714pd, 48fr; Sworn/Estimate/Non-Audited
Advertising rate: Open inch rate $4.25
Established: 1905
Pub...Juliet LeMond
Ed. .... Ruben Cantu-Rodriguez
Adv. Dir...........Brandi RosenbaumEquipment & Software: Hardware — APP/Mac.
Delivery Method: Mail
Areas Served: Runnels County

BANDERA

BANDERA BULLETIN (WED)

1110 MAIN ST, Bandera, TX, 78003, Bandera, USA; gen tel (830) 796-3718; adv tel (830) 796-3718; ed tel (830) 796-3718; gen fax (830) 796-4885; adv fax (830) 796-4885; ed fax (830) 796-4885; disp adv e-mail jessica@banderabulletin.com; class adv e-mail jessica@banderabulletin.com; ed e-mail news@banderabulletin.com; web site www.banderabulletin.com
Circulation: 2,193pd,; CVC
Advertising rate: Open inch rate $9.00
Established: 1945
Group: Fenice Community Media
Digital Platform - Mobile: Apple, Android
Digital Platform - Tablet: Apple iOS, Android, Windows 7
Pub./Ed. ....Jessica Hawley-Jerome
Adv. Dir...James Taylor
Delivery Method: Mail, Newsstand
Areas Served: Bandera County

BANDERA COUNTY COURIER (THUR)

302 Dallas St, Bandera, TX, 78003-5819, Bandera, USA; gen tel (830) 796-9799; adv tel (830) 796-9799; ed tel (830) 796-9799; gen fax (830) 796-9399; adv fax (830) 796-9399; ed fax (830) 796-9399; disp adv e-mail bccourier@sbcglobal.net; class adv e-mail bccclass@sbcglobal.net; ed e-mail bcceditor@sbcglobal.net; web site www.bccourier.com
Circulation: 2,000pd,; Sworn/Estimate/Non-Audited
Advertising rate: Open inch rate $7.00 (Local); $8.00 (National)
Established: 2004
Digital Platform - Mobile: Apple, Android
Digital Platform - Tablet: Apple iOS, Android
Pub..Gail Joiner
Editor ....Bev Barr
Adv. Dir...Dee Russ
Delivery Method: Mail, Newsstand
Areas Served: Bandera County

BARTLETT

TRIBUNE-PROGRESS (WED)

108 W Clark St, Bartlett, TX, 76511-4371, Williamson, USA; gen tel (254) 527-4424; adv tel (254) 527-4424; ed tel (254) 527-4424; gen fax (254) 527-4333; adv fax (254) 527-4333; ed fax (254) 527-4333; disp adv e-mail newslady01@sbcglobal.net; class adv e-mail newslady01@sbcglobal.net; ed e-mail newslady01@sbcglobal.net
Circulation: 1,259pd,; Sworn/Estimate/Non-Audited
Advertising rate: Open inch rate $4.95
Established: 1886
Pub./Ed./Adv. Dir...........................Gayle Bielss
Office Mgr. .... Debbie McKeon
Delivery Method: Mail, Newsstand
Areas Served: Williamson County

BASTROP

THE BASTROP ADVERTISER (THUR, SAT)

1106 College St, Ste C, Bastrop, TX, 78602-3948, Bastrop, USA; gen tel (512) 321-2557; adv tel (512) 321-2557; ed tel (512) 321-2557; gen fax (512) 321-1680; adv fax (512) 321-1680; ed fax (512) 321-1680; disp adv e-mail news@bastropadvertiser.com; class adv e-mail news@bastropadvertiser.com; ed e-mail cwright@bastropadvertiser.com; web site www.bastropadvertiser.com
Circulation: 3,091fr; AAM
Advertising rate: Open inch rate $13.65
Established: 1853
Group: Cox Media Group
Digital Platform - Mobile: Apple, Android
Digital Platform - Tablet: Apple iOS, Android, Windows 7
Pub.......................................Emmett McKinley
Ed. .... Cyndi Wright
Adv. Dir......................................Debbie Denny
Mechanical Specifications: Type page 11 5/8 x 20 1/2; E - 6 cols, 1 13/16, 1/8 between; A - 6 cols, 1 5/6, 1/8 between; C - 10 cols, 1 13/16, 1/9 between.Equipment & Software: Hardware — PCs; Software — Microsoft/Word, QPS/QuarkXPress.
Delivery Method: Mail, Newsstand, Racks
Areas Served: Bastrop County

THE SMITHVILLE TIMES (THUR)

PO Box 459, Bastrop, TX, 78602-0459, Bastrop, USA; gen tel (512) 237-4655; adv tel (512) 237-4655; ed tel (512) 237-4655; gen fax (512) 237-5443; adv fax (512) 237-5443; ed fax (512) 237-5443; disp adv e-mail news@statesman.com; class adv e-mail news@statesman.com; ed e-mail news@statesman.com; web site www.statesman.

com
Circulation: 1,359fr; AAM
Advertising rate: Open inch rate $10.75
Established: 1895
Group: Cox Media Group
Digital Platform - Mobile: Apple, Android
Digital Platform - Tablet: Apple iOS, Android, Windows 7
Vice Pres. .... Tammy Moore
Pub. .... Mark Gwin
Ed. .... Cyndi Wright
Mechanical Specifications: Type page 11 5/8 x 20 1/2; E - 6 cols, 2, 1/6 between; A - 6 cols, 1 5/6, 1/8 between; C - 10 cols, 2, 1/9 between.
Delivery Method: Mail, Newsstand
Areas Served: Bastrop County

BAY CITY

THE BAY CITY TRIBUNE (WED, SUN)

2901 Carey Smith Blvd, Bay City, TX, 77414-3768, Matagorda, USA; gen tel (979) 245-5555; adv tel (979) 245-5555; ed tel (979) 245-5555; gen fax (979) 244-5908; adv fax (979) 244-5908; ed fax (979) 244-5908; disp adv e-mail angie.pagel@baycitytribune.com; class adv e-mail support@baycitytribune.com; ed e-mail news@baycitytribune.com; web site www.baycitytribune.com
Circulation: 2,520pd, 917fr; CAC
Advertising rate: Open inch rate $10.00
Established: 1845
Group: Southern Newspapers Inc.
Digital Platform - Mobile: Apple, Android, Windows, Blackberry
Digital Platform - Tablet: Apple iOS, Android, Windows 7, Blackberry Tablet OS, Kindle, Nook, Kindle Fire
Ed. .... Shelly Story
Pub./Retail Adv. Mgr. .... Angie Pagel
Bus. Mgr. .... Jessica Wright
Brandon Cox
Classified Adv. Dir. .... Christi Lara
Circ. Mgr. .... Andre Moore
Prod. Dir. .... Natalie Perez
Mechanical Specifications: Type page 13 x 21 1/2; E - 6 cols, 2 1/16, 1/8 between; A - 6 cols, 2 1/16, 1/8 between; C - 9 cols, 1 7/16, 1/16 between.Equipment & Software: Hardware — Mk, APP/Mac IIsi, 2-APP/Mac SE30; Software — Baseview, Aldus/PageMaker.
Delivery Method: Newsstand, Carrier, Racks
Areas Served: Matagorda County

BEAUMONT

THE HARDIN COUNTY NEWS (WED)

380 Main St, Beaumont, TX, 77701-2331, Hardin, USA; gen tel (409) 755-4912; adv tel (409) 755-4912; ed tel (409) 755-4912; gen fax (409) 755-7731; adv fax (409) 755-7731; ed fax (409) 755-7731; disp adv e-mail jreedy@hearstnp.com; class adv e-mail jreedy@hearstnp.com; ed e-mail dlisenby@beaumontenterprise.com; web site www.beaumontenterprise.com
Circulation: 19,000fr; Sworn/Estimate/Non-Audited
Advertising rate: Open inch rate $9.25
Established: 1970
Group: Hearst Communications, Inc.
Digital Platform - Mobile: Apple, Android
Digital Platform - Tablet: Apple iOS, Android, Windows 7
Pub. .... Jeffrey T. Reedy
Ed. .... David Lisenby
Mechanical Specifications: Type page 13 x 21 1/2; E - 6 cols, 2 1/16, 1/8 between; A - 6 cols, 2 1/16, 1/8 between; C - 9 cols, 1 3/8, 1/8 between.
Delivery Method: Mail, Racks
Areas Served: Hardin County

BEEVILLE

BEEVILLE BEE-PICAYUNE (WED, SAT)

111 N Washington St, Beeville, TX, 78102-4508, Bee, USA; gen tel (361) 358-2550; adv tel (361) 358-2550; ed tel (361) 358-2550; gen fax (361) 358-5323; adv fax (361) 358-5323; ed fax (361) 358-5323; disp adv e-mail news@mysoutex.com; class adv e-mail karneseditor@mysoutex.com; ed e-mail news@mysoutex.com; web site www.mySouTex.com
Circulation: 4,158pd,; Sworn/Estimate/Non-Audited
Advertising rate: Open inch rate $9.00
Established: 1886
Digital Platform - Mobile: Apple, Android, Windows, Blackberry
Digital Platform - Tablet: Apple iOS, Android, Windows 7, Blackberry Tablet OS, Kindle, Nook, Kindle Fire
Co-Pub. .... Chip Latcham
Co-Pub. .... Jeff Latcham
Ed. .... Jason Collins
Adv. Dir. .... Karl Arnst
Delivery Method: Mail, Newsstand
Areas Served: Bee County

BELLVILLE

THE BELLVILLE TIMES (THUR)

106 E Palm St, Bellville, TX, 77418-1544, Austin, USA; gen tel (979) 865-3131; adv tel (979) 865-3131; ed tel (979) 865-3131; gen fax (979) 865-3132; adv fax (979) 865-3132; ed fax (979) 865-3132; disp adv e-mail bvtimes@sbcglobal.net; class adv e-mail bvtimes@sbcglobal.net; ed e-mail bvtimes@sbcglobal.net; web site www.bellvilletimes.com
Circulation: 4,100pd, 44fr; Sworn/Estimate/Non-Audited
Advertising rate: Open inch rate $7.50
Established: 1879
Pub./Ed. .... Bruce White
Adv. Dir. .... Angie Grawunder
Delivery Method: Mail, Newsstand
Areas Served: Austin County

BELTON

THE BELTON JOURNAL (THUR)

210 N Penelope St, Belton, TX, 76513-3159, Bell, USA; gen tel (254) 939-5754; gen fax (254) 939-2333; disp adv e-mail david@beltonjournal.com; class adv e-mail david@beltonjournal.com; ed e-mail editor@beltonjournal.com; web site www.beltonjournal.com
Circulation: 4,090pd,; Sworn/Estimate/Non-Audited
Advertising rate: Open inch rate $7.00
Established: 1866
Digital Platform - Mobile: Apple, Android
Digital Platform - Tablet: Apple iOS, Android, Windows 7
Pub. .... David Tuma
Ed. .... Matthew Girard
Adv. Dir. .... Susan Gibson
Delivery Method: Mail, Newsstand, Racks
Areas Served: Bell County

BIG LAKE

BIG LAKE WILDCAT (THUR)

707 N Florida Ave, Big Lake, TX, 76932-4139, Reagan, USA; gen tel (325) 884-2215; adv tel (325) 884-2215; ed tel (325) 884-2215; gen fax (325) 884-5771; adv fax (325) 884-5771; ed fax (325) 884-5771; disp adv e-mail editor@mybiglake.com; class adv e-mail editor@mybiglake.com; ed e-mail editor@mybiglake.com; web site www.mybiglake.com
Circulation: 890pd,; Sworn/Estimate/Non-Audited
Advertising rate: Open inch rate $6.00
Established: 1925
Digital Platform - Mobile: Apple, Android
Digital Platform - Tablet: Apple iOS, Android, Windows 7
Pub. .... Randy Mankin
Ed. .... Marla Daugherty
Adv. Dir. .... J.L. Mankin
Delivery Method: Mail, Newsstand, Racks
Areas Served: Reagan County

BIG SANDY

BIG SANDY-HAWKINS JOURNAL (WED)

102 N TYLER ST, Big Sandy, TX, 75755, Upshur, USA; gen tel (903) 636-4351; adv tel (903) 636-4351; ed tel (903) 636-4351; gen fax (903) 636-5091; adv fax (903) 636-5091; ed fax (903) 636-5091; disp adv e-mail BSHjournal@aol.com; class adv e-mail BSHjournal@aol.com; ed e-mail BSHjournal@aol.com; web site www.thejournal.biz
Circulation: 1,153pd,; Sworn/Estimate/Non-Audited
Advertising rate: Open inch rate $8.00
Established: 1949
Group: Texas Community Media LLC
Pub. .... Jim Bardwell
Adv. Dir. .... Vicky Himel
Mgr. .... Danielle Dupree
Delivery Method: Mail, Newsstand
Areas Served: Upshur County

BLANCO

BLANCO COUNTY NEWS (WED)

714 4th St, Ste 102, Blanco, TX, 78606-5569, Blanco, USA; gen tel (830) 833-4812; adv tel (830) 833-4812; ed tel (830) 833-4812; gen fax (830) 833-4246; adv fax (830) 833-4246; ed fax (830) 833-4246; disp adv e-mail news@blanconews.com; class adv e-mail scottwesner@hotmail.com; ed e-mail editor@blanconews.com
Circulation: 3,200pd, 35fr; Sworn/Estimate/Non-Audited
Advertising rate: Open inch rate $4.75
Established: 1883
Digital Platform - Mobile: Apple, Android
Digital Platform - Tablet: Apple iOS, Android, Windows 7
Pub. .... Scott Wesner
Ed. .... Charles Willgren
Adv. Dir. .... Jill Hunter
Mechanical Specifications: Type page 11 5/8 x 21; E - 6 cols, 1 7/8, 1/6 between; A - 6 cols, 1 7/8, 1/6 between; C - 6 cols, 1 7/8, 1/6 between.Equipment & Software: Hardware — Adobe/Pagemaker
Delivery Method: Mail, Newsstand
Areas Served: Blanco County

BOERNE

BOERNE STAR (TUES, FRI)

941 N School St, Boerne, TX, 78006-5922, Kendall, USA; gen tel (830) 249-2441; adv tel (830) 249-2441; ed tel (830) 249-2441; gen fax (830) 249-4607; adv fax (830) 249-4607; ed fax (830) 249-4607; disp adv e-mail frank@boernestar.com; class adv e-mail kolleen@boernestar.com; ed e-mail briancartwright@boernestar.com; web site www.boernestar.com
Circulation: 4,179pd, 1,401fr; CVC
Advertising rate: Open inch rate $7.50
Established: 1906
Group: Fenice Community Media
Digital Platform - Mobile: Apple, Android
Digital Platform - Tablet: Apple iOS, Android, Windows 7
Pub./Ed. .... Brian Cartwright
Adv. Dir. .... Frank Shubert
Office Mgr. .... Sandra Pfeiffer
Circ. Mgr. .... Stephen Bartell
Dana Smith
Mechanical Specifications: Type page 13 x 21; E - 6 cols, 1 5/6, 1/8 betweenEquipment & Software: Hardware — APP/Power Mac; Software — QPS/QuarkXPress.
Delivery Method: Mail, Newsstand, Racks
Areas Served: Kendall County

BOGATA

BOGATA NEWS-TALCO TIMES (THUR)

Highway 271, Bogata, TX, 75417, Red River, USA; gen tel (903) 632-5322; adv tel (903) 632-5322; ed tel (903) 632-5322; gen fax (903) 652-6041; adv fax (903) 652-6041; ed fax (903) 652-6041; disp adv e-mail tppub@1starnet.com; class adv e-mail tppub@1starnet.com; ed e-mail nnichols@1starnet.com
Circulation: 1,249pd, 10fr; Sworn/Estimate/Non-Audited
Advertising rate: Open inch rate $6.00
Established: 1910
Group: Thunder Prairie Publishing
Pub. .... Nanalee Nichols
Ed. .... Nancy Brown
Adv. Dir. .... Thomas Nichols
Mechanical Specifications: Type page 13 x 21; E - 6 cols, 2 1/12, between; A - 6 cols, 2 1/12, between; C - 8 cols, between.Equipment & Software: Hardware — APP/Power Mac 4400-200; Software — Adobe/Photoshop, Adobe/PageMaker 6.5.
Delivery Method: Mail, Racks
Areas Served: Red River County

BOOKER

BOOKER NEWS (THUR)

PO Box 807, Booker, TX, 79005-0807, Lipscomb, USA; gen tel (806) 658-4732; disp adv e-mail bookernews@amaonline.com; class adv e-mail bnews@ptsi.net; ed e-mail bnews@ptsi.net
Circulation: 758pd,; USPS
Advertising rate: Open inch rate $5.50
Established: 1927
Advertising Director .... Kayla Parvin
Delivery Method: Mail, Newsstand
Areas Served: Lipscomb and Ochiltree County

BOWIE

THE BOWIE NEWS (WED, SAT)

213 W Wise St, Bowie, TX, 76230-5036, Montague, USA; gen tel (940) 872-2247; adv tel (940) 872-2247; ed tel (940) 872-2247; gen fax (940) 872-4812; adv fax (940) 872-4812; ed fax (940) 872-4812; disp adv e-mail ads@bowienewsonline.com; class adv e-mail classifieds@bowienewsonline.com; ed e-mail editor@bowienewsonline.com; web site www.bowienewsonline.com
Circulation: 4,700pd, 550fr; Sworn/Estimate/Non-Audited
Advertising rate: Open inch rate $6.25
Established: 1922
Digital Platform - Mobile: Apple, Android
Digital Platform - Tablet: Apple iOS, Android, Windows 7
Owner/Pub. .... Michael Winter
Ed. .... Barbara Beckwith GreenEquipment & Software: Hardware — assorted PC; Software — Adobe/Indesign, Photoshop
Delivery Method: Mail, Racks
Areas Served: Montague

BRADY

BRADY STANDARD-HERALD (WED)

201 S Bridge St, Brady, TX, 76825-4917, McCulloch, USA; gen tel (325) 597-2959; adv tel (325) 597-2959; ed tel (325) 597-2959; gen fax (888) 908-4741; adv fax (888) 908-4741; ed fax (888) 908-4741; disp adv e-mail publisher@bradystandard.com; class adv e-mail advertise@bradystandard.com; ed e-mail newseditor@bradystandard.com ; web site www.bradystandard.com
Circulation: 3,800pd, 68fr; Sworn/Estimate/Non-Audited
Advertising rate: Open inch rate $4.25
Established: 1909
Digital Platform - Mobile: Apple, Android

Digital Platform - Tablet: Apple iOS, Android, Windows 7
Pub./Ed. .... James Stewart
Pub. Emeritus .... Larry B. Smith
Adv. Dir. .... Holly Stewart
Office Mgr. .... Kathy Smith
News Ed. .... Amanda Howell
Delivery Method: Mail, Newsstand, Racks
Areas Served: McCulloch

BRECKENRIDGE

BRECKENRIDGE AMERICAN (WED, SAT)

114 E Elm St, Breckenridge, TX, 76424-3613, Stephens, USA; gen tel (254) 559-5412; adv tel (254) 559-5412; ed tel (254) 559-5412; gen fax (254) 559-3491; adv fax (254) 559-3491; ed fax (254) 559-3491; disp adv e-mail admgr@breckenridgeamerican.com; class adv e-mail classified@breckenridgeamerican.com; ed e-mail editor@breckenridgeamerican.com; web site www.breckenridgeamerican.com
Circulation: 1,904pd, 25fr; Sworn/Estimate/Non-Audited
Advertising rate: Open inch rate $10.56
Established: 1920
Group: Moser Community Media, LLCEditions: Final
Digital Platform - Mobile: Apple, Android
Digital Platform - Tablet: Apple iOS, Android, Windows 7
Publisher.. Tyler Patton
Managing Editor .... Jimmy Potts
Mechanical Specifications: Page size: 12.5 inches by 22.5 inches
Columns: 6
1 col = 1.75 inches
2 col = 3.75 inches
3 col = 5.6875 inches
4 col = 7.635 inches
5 col = 9.5625 inches
6 col = 11.50 inches
Full Page charged at 6 cols x 20.5 inchesEquipment & Software: Hardware — APP/Mac 64; Presses — 4-KP/News King; Software — Adobe/PageMaker 7.0.
Delivery Method: Mail, Newsstand, Racks
Areas Served: 76424, 76429, 76430, 46738, 76448, 76470, 76475

BREMOND

THE BREMOND PRESS (FRI)

301 S Main St, Bremond, TX, 76629, Robertson, USA; gen tel (254) 746-7033; adv tel (254) 746-7033; ed tel (254) 746-7033; gen fax (254) 746-7089; adv fax (254) 746-7089; ed fax (254) 746-7089; disp adv e-mail bremondpress@earthlink.net; class adv e-mail bremondpress@earthlink.net; ed e-mail bremondpress@earthlink.net
Circulation: 1,319pd,; Sworn/Estimate/Non-Audited
Advertising rate: Open inch rate $4.00
Established: 1922
Pub./Ed. .... Betty Yezak
Adv. Dir. .... George Yezak
Delivery Method: Mail, Newsstand
Areas Served: Robertson County

BRIDGEPORT

BRIDGEPORT INDEX (THUR)

916 Halsell St, Bridgeport, TX, 76426-3028, Wise, USA; gen tel (940) 683-4021; adv tel (940) 683-4021; ed tel (940) 683-4021; gen fax (940) 683-3841; adv fax (940) 683-3841; ed fax (940) 683-3841; disp adv e-mail bridwellk@bridgeportindex.com; class adv e-mail ads@bridgeportindex.com; ed e-mail news@bridgeportindex.com; web site www.bridgeportindex.com
Circulation: 2,690pd, 30fr; Sworn/Estimate/Non-Audited
Advertising rate: Open inch rate $6.50
Established: 1894
Digital Platform - Mobile: Apple, Android
Digital Platform - Tablet: Apple iOS, Android, Windows 7
Pub./Adv. Dir. .... Keith Bridwell
Ed. .... Jay Bridwell
Prodn. Dir. .... Francine West
Delivery Method: Mail, Newsstand
Areas Served: Wise County

CHICO TEXAN (THUR)

916 Halsell St, Bridgeport, TX, 76426-3028, Wise, USA; gen tel (940) 683-4021; adv tel (940) 683-4021; ed tel (940) 683-4021; gen fax (940) 683-3841; adv fax (940) 683-3841; ed fax (940) 683-3841; disp adv e-mail bridwellk@bridgeportindex.com; class adv e-mail bridwellk@bridgeportindex.com; ed e-mail news@bridgeportindex.com; web site www.chicotexan.com
Circulation: 700pd,; Sworn/Estimate/Non-Audited
Advertising rate: Open inch rate $5.00
Established: 1894
Digital Platform - Mobile: Apple, Android, Windows, Blackberry
Digital Platform - Tablet: Apple iOS, Android, Windows 7, Blackberry Tablet OS
Pub./Adv. Dir. .... Keith Bridwell
Ed. .... Jay Bridwell
Prod. Mgr. .... Francine West
Mechanical Specifications: Type page 13 x 21 1/2; E - 6 cols, 2 1/2, 1/6 between; A - 6 cols, 2 1/2, 1/6 between; C - 6 cols, 2 1/2, 1/6 between.Equipment & Software: Hardware — APP/Mac IIci, APP/Mac si, APP/Mac LC III, APP/Mac 7200-100; Software — QPS/QuarkXPress 3.31, Adobe/PageMaker 6.5.
Delivery Method: Mail, Newsstand
Areas Served: Wise County

BROOKSHIRE

THE TIMES TRIBUNE (THUR)

921 Cooper St, Brookshire, TX, 77423, Waller, USA; gen tel (281) 934-4949; adv tel (281) 934-4949; ed tel (281) 934-4949; gen fax (281) 934-2012; adv fax (281) 934-2012; ed fax (281) 934-2012; disp adv e-mail news.trib@timestribune.com; class adv e-mail news.trib@timestribune.com; ed e-mail news.trib@timestribune.com; web site www.timestribune.com
Circulation: 1,100pd,; Sworn/Estimate/Non-Audited
Advertising rate: Open inch rate $5.00
Established: 1993
Group: Community Newspaper Holdings, Inc.
Digital Platform - Tablet: Windows 7
Pub./Ed. .... Jan Mincy
Adv. Dir. .... Lillie Ruby
Delivery Method: Mail, Newsstand
Areas Served: Walker County

BROWNFIELD

BROWNFIELD NEWS (WED, SUN)

409 W Hill St, Brownfield, TX, 79316-3203, Terry, USA; gen tel (806) 637-4535; adv tel (806) 637-4535; ed tel (806) 637-4535; gen fax (806) 637-3795; adv fax (806) 637-3795; ed fax (806) 637-3795; disp adv e-mail advertising@brownfieldonline.com; class adv e-mail ads2@brownfieldonline.com; ed e-mail news@brownfieldonline.com; web site www.brownfieldonline.com
Circulation: 3,100pd, 60fr; Sworn/Estimate/Non-Audited
Advertising rate: Open inch rate $7.00
Established: 1904
Digital Platform - Mobile: Apple, Android, Windows, Blackberry
Digital Platform - Tablet: Apple iOS, Android, Windows 7, Blackberry Tablet OS
Pub./Ed. .... Lynn Brisendine
Adv. Dir. .... Russ McKee
Brian Brisendine
Delivery Method: Mail, Racks
Areas Served: Terry County

BROWNWOOD

BROWNWOOD BULLETIN (WED, FRI, SUN)

700 Carnegie St, Brownwood, TX, 76801-7040, Brown, USA; gen tel (325) 646-2541; adv tel (325)641-3122; ed tel (325) 641-3112; gen fax (325) 646-6835; adv fax (325)646-6835; ed fax (325)646-6835; disp adv e-mail mhorton@gatehousemedia.com; class adv e-mail mhorton@gatehousemedia.com; ed e-mail derrick.stuckly@brownwoodbulletin.com; web site www.brownwoodtx.com
Circulation: 3,000pd,; Sworn/Estimate/Non-Audited
Advertising rate: Open inch rate $15.25
Established: 1900
Group: New Media Investment Group
Digital Platform - Mobile: Apple, Android
Digital Platform - Tablet: Apple iOS, Android
Assistant Editor/Sports Editor... Derrick Stuckly
Mechanical Specifications: Type page 12 x 21 1/2; E - 6 cols, 1 5/6, 1/8 between; A - 6 cols, 1 5/6, 1/8 between; C - 10 cols, 1 1/25, 1/8 between.
Areas Served: Brown County and surrounding area

BUFFALO

BUFFALO EXPRESS (TUES)

912 E Commerce, Buffalo, TX, 75831, Leon, USA; gen tel (903) 322-6009; adv tel (903) 322-6009; ed tel (903) 322-6009; gen fax (903) 322-7215; adv fax (903) 322-7215; ed fax (903) 322-7215; disp adv e-mail buffaloexpress@windstream.net; class adv e-mail buffaloexpress@windstream.net; ed e-mail buffaloexpress@windstream.net; web site www.buffaloexpressnews.com
Circulation: 1,695pd,; Sworn/Estimate/Non-Audited
Advertising rate: Open inch rate $5.25
Established: 2000
Pub./Adv. Dir. .... Mary Ann Vaughn
Ed. .... Lee Gayle Boettcher
Delivery Method: Mail, Racks
Areas Served: Leon County

THE BUFFALO PRESS (WED)

924 W Commerce, Buffalo, TX, 75831, Leon, USA; gen tel (903) 322-4248; adv tel (903) 322-4248; ed tel (903) 322-4248; gen fax (903) 322-4023; adv fax (903) 322-4023; ed fax (903) 322-4023; disp adv e-mail buffalopress@gmail.com; class adv e-mail buffalopress@gmail.com; ed e-mail buffalopress@gmail.com; web site www.leoncountytoday.com
Circulation: 3,000pd, 2,500fr; Sworn/Estimate/Non-Audited
Advertising rate: Open inch rate $4.05
Established: 1931
Digital Platform - Mobile: Apple, Android, Windows, Blackberry
Digital Platform - Tablet: Apple iOS, Android, Windows 7, Blackberry Tablet OS, Kindle, Nook, Kindle Fire
Pub. .... Mac Shadix
Sales Dir. .... Richard Moran
Prodn. Mgr. .... Linda Smith
Delivery Method: Mail, Newsstand
Areas Served: Leon County

BUNA

THE BUNA BEACON (WED)

566 TX State Highway 62, Buna, TX, 77612-6472, Jasper, USA; gen tel (409) 994-2218; adv tel (409) 994-2218; ed tel (409) 994-2218; gen fax (409) 994-0228; adv fax (409) 994-0228; ed fax (409) 994-0228; disp adv e-mail publisher@bunabeacon.com; class adv e-mail advertising@bunabeacon.com; ed e-mail editor@bunabeacon.com; web site www.bunabeacon.com
Circulation: 1,601pd,; Sworn/Estimate/Non-Audited
Advertising rate: Open inch rate $7.00
Established: 1990
Digital Platform - Mobile: Apple, Android
Digital Platform - Tablet: Apple iOS, Android, Windows 7
Co-Pub./Mng. Ed. .... Barbara Davis
Co-Pub./Adv. Dir. .... Terry Wells
Delivery Method: Mail, Newsstand, Racks
Areas Served: Jasper County

BURKBURNETT

BURKBURNETT INFORMER STAR (THUR)

417 Avenue C, Burkburnett, TX, 76354-3424, Wichita, USA; gen tel (940) 569-2191; adv tel (940) 569-2191; ed tel (940) 569-2191; gen fax (940) 569-0704; adv fax (940) 569-0704; ed fax (940) 569-0704; disp adv e-mail jeff@burknews.com; class adv e-mail linda@burknews.com; ed e-mail jeff@burknews.com; web site www.burknews.com
Circulation: 2,850pd,; Sworn/Estimate/Non-Audited
Advertising rate: Open inch rate $4.25
Established: 1908
Digital Platform - Mobile: Apple, Android, Windows, Blackberry
Digital Platform - Tablet: Apple iOS, Android, Windows 7, Blackberry Tablet OS
Pub. .... Bret McCormick
Ed. .... Jeff Bromley
Adv. Mgr. .... Linda Ingram
Delivery Method: Mail, Racks
Areas Served: Wichita County

BURLESON

BURLESON STAR (WED, SUN)

327 NW Renfro St, Burleson, TX, 76028-3421, Johnson, USA; gen tel (817) 295-0486; adv tel (817) 295-0486; ed tel (817) 295-0486; gen fax (817) 295-5278; adv fax (817) 295-5278; ed fax (817) 295-5278; disp adv e-mail ads@thestargroup.com; class adv e-mail classified@thestargroup.com; ed e-mail btinsley@live.com; web site www.burlesonstar.net
Circulation: 3,328pd, 259fr; Sworn/Estimate/Non-Audited
Advertising rate: Open inch rate $10.00
Established: 1964
Group: Moser Community Media, LLC
Digital Platform - Mobile: Apple, Android, Windows, Blackberry, Other
Digital Platform - Tablet: Apple iOS, Android, Windows 7, Blackberry Tablet OS, Kindle, Nook, Kindle Fire
Pub. .... Dan Taylor
Ed. .... Brian Porter
Adv. Dir. .... Cathy Smith
Delivery Method: Mail, Newsstand, Racks
Areas Served: 76028, 76036, 76058

KEENE STAR (WED)

319 N Burleson Blvd, Burleson, TX, 76028-3907, Johnson, USA; gen tel (817) 295-0486; adv tel (817) 295-0486 ext. 21; ed tel (817) 295-0486 ext. 19; gen fax (817) 295-5278; disp adv e-mail ads@thestargroup.com; class adv e-mail classified@thestargroup.com; ed e-mail keenestar@thestargroup.com; web site www.keenestar.net
Circulation: 950pd, 1,106fr; Sworn/Estimate/Non-Audited
Advertising rate: Open inch rate $8.50
Established: 1993
Digital Platform - Mobile: Apple, Android, Windows, Blackberry
Digital Platform - Tablet: Apple iOS, Android, Windows 7, Blackberry Tablet OS, Kindle, Nook, Kindle Fire
Pub. .... Dan Taylor
Ed. .... Paul Gnadt
Adv. Dir. .... Cathy Smith
Delivery Method: Mail, Newsstand, Carrier
Areas Served: 76059, 76033

BURNET

BURNET BULLETIN (WED)

220 S Main St, Burnet, TX, 78611-3107, Burnet, USA; gen tel (512) 756-6136; adv tel (512) 756-6136; ed tel (512) 756-6136; gen fax (512) 756-8911; adv fax (512) 756-8911; ed fax (512) 756-8911; disp adv e-mail publisher@burnetbulletin.com; class adv e-mail publisher@burnetbulletin.com; ed e-mail editorial@burnetbulletin.com; web site www.burnetbulletin.com - 16,500(views) 8,700(visitors)
Circulation: 5,115pd,; USPS
Advertising rate: Open inch rate $9.00
Established: 1873
Group: Highland Lakes Newspapers
Digital Platform - Mobile: Apple, Android
Digital Platform - Tablet: Apple iOS, Android
Adv. Consultant.......................... Lora Cheney
Burnet Community Ed... James Herbert Walker
Ed. / Pub.................................. Frank Shubert
Bus. Mgr......... Sharon PelkyEquipment & Software: Hardware — APP/Mac, PCs; Presses — Quad stack; Software — InDesign, Adobe/Photoshop 5.5.,Account Scout
Delivery Method: Mail, Newsstand, Racks
Areas Served: 78611, 78605, 78608, 78609, 78642

CITIZENS GAZETTE (WED)

106 Linsey Cv, Burnet, TX, 78611-5886, Burnet, USA; gen tel (512) 756-6640; adv tel (512) 756-6640; ed tel (512) 756-6640; gen fax (512) 756-6640; adv fax (512) 756-6640; ed fax (512) 756-6640; disp adv e-mail cgazette@tstar.net; class adv e-mail cgazette@tstar.net; ed e-mail cgazette@tstar.net
Circulation: 1,000pd,; Sworn/Estimate/Non-Audited
Advertising rate: Open inch rate $7.00
Established: 1991
Ed./Pub./Adv. Dir.......................... Rick Espitia
Delivery Method: Mail, Newsstand
Areas Served: Burnet County

CALDWELL

BURLESON COUNTY TRIBUNE (THUR)

306 W Highway 21, Caldwell, TX, 77836-1122, Burleson, USA; gen tel (979) 567-3286; adv tel (979)567-3286; ed tel (979)567-3286; gen fax (979) 567-7898; adv fax (979)567-7898; ed fax (979)567-7898; disp adv e-mail news@bctribune.com; class adv e-mail ads@bctribune.com; ed e-mail news@bctribuine.com; web site www.bctribune.com
Circulation: 4,300pd, 40fr; Sworn/Estimate/Non-Audited
Advertising rate: Open inch rate $11.00
Established: 1884
Pub... Sam Preuss
Ed.. Roy Sanders
Ad. Director............................ Amber Campise
Mechanical Specifications: Type page 13 x 21; E - 6 cols, 2 1/16, 1/8 between; A - 6 cols, 2 1/16, 1/8 between; C - 8 cols, 1 1/2, 1/8 between.
Delivery Method: Mail, Newsstand

CAMERON

THE CAMERON HERALD (THUR)

108 E 1st St, Cameron, TX, 76520-3341, Milam, USA; gen tel (254) 697-6671; adv tel (254) 697-6671; ed tel (254) 697-6671; gen fax (254) 697-4902; adv fax (254) 697-4902; ed fax (254) 697-4902; disp adv e-mail herald@cameronherald.com; class adv e-mail classifieds@cameronherald.com; ed e-mail publisher@cameronherald.com; web site www.cameronherald.com
Circulation: 1,943pd, 123fr; CVC
Advertising rate: Open inch rate $9.25
Established: 1860
Digital Platform - Mobile: Apple, Android
Digital Platform - Tablet: Apple iOS, Android, Windows 7
Pub./Ed.. Phil Major
Interim Pub. .... Candace Velvin
Adv. Mgr............................. Elissa Hernandez
Office Mgr............................... Clydell Seaton
Mechanical Specifications: Type page 11 5/8 x 21 1/2; E - 6 cols, 1 5/6, 1/8 between; A - 6 cols, 1 5/6, 1/8 between; C - 9 cols, 1 1/8, 1/16 between.Equipment & Software: Hardware — APP/Mac, APP/iMac G3; Software — QPS/QuarkXPress 5.1.
Delivery Method: Mail, Newsstand
Areas Served: Milam County

THORNDALE CHAMPION (THUR)

108 E 1st St, Cameron, TX, 76520-3341, Milam, USA; gen tel (254) 455-0144; adv tel (254) 455-0144; ed tel (254) 455-0144; gen fax (254) 697-4902; adv fax (254) 697-4902; ed fax (254) 697-4902; disp adv e-mail tdchamp@cameronherald.com; class adv e-mail tdchamp@cameronherald.com; ed e-mail tdchamp@cameronherald.com; web site www.cameronherald.com/thorndale
Circulation: 490pd,; Sworn/Estimate/Non-Audited
Advertising rate: Open inch rate $3.15
Established: 1898
Digital Platform - Tablet: Windows 7
Pub./Ed.. Phil Major
Adv. Dir............................... Elissa Hernandez
Delivery Method: Mail

CANADIAN

THE CANADIAN RECORD (THUR)

211 Main St, Canadian, TX, 79014-2212, Hemphill, USA; gen tel (806) 323-6461; adv tel (806) 323-6461; ed tel (806) 323-6461; gen fax (806) 323-5738; adv fax (806) 323-5738; ed fax (806) 323-5738; disp adv e-mail ray@canadianrecord.com; class adv e-mail mary@canadianrecord.com; ed e-mail laurie@canadianrecord.com; web site www.canadianrecord.com
Circulation: 1,750pd, 35fr; Sworn/Estimate/Non-Audited
Advertising rate: Open inch rate $11.15
Established: 1893
Digital Platform - Mobile: Apple, Android, Windows, Blackberry
Digital Platform - Tablet: Apple iOS, Android, Windows 7, Blackberry Tablet OS, Kindle, Nook, Kindle Fire
Pub./Ed.......................... Laurie Ezzell Brown
Bus. Mgr.............................. Mary L. Smithee
Adv. Mgr.. Ray Weeks
Adv. Sales.............................. Jaquita Adcock
Sports Ed...................................... Peyton Aufill
News Ed.................................. Cathy Ricketts
Mechanical Specifications: Type page 9 5/8 x 13 1/2; E - 4 cols, 2 1/2, 1/6 between; A - 4 cols, 2 1/2, 1/6 between; C - 4 cols, 2 1/2, 1/6 between.Equipment & Software: Hardware — PCs; Software — Archetype/Corel Ventura, Novell, Adobe/InDesign 2.0, Adobe/Photoshop 7.0, Corel/Draw 12.
Delivery Method: Mail, Newsstand
Areas Served: 79014

CANTON

CANTON HERALD (THUR)

103 E Tyler St, Canton, TX, 75103-1413, Van Zandt, USA; gen tel (903) 567-4000; adv tel (903) 567-4000; ed tel (903) 567-4000; gen fax (903) 567-6076; adv fax (903) 567-6076; ed fax (903) 567-6076; disp adv e-mail brad@vanzandtnews.com; class adv e-mail brad@vanzandtnews.com; ed e-mail vznews@aol.com; web site www.thecantonherald.com
Circulation: 5,000pd,
Advertising rate: Open inch rate $7.25
Established: 1882
Digital Platform - Mobile: Apple, Android
Digital Platform - Tablet: Apple iOS, Android, Windows 7
Delivery Method: Mail, Newsstand
Areas Served: Van Zandt County

THE QUINLAN-TAWAKONI NEWS (FRI)

103 E Tyler St, Canton, TX, 75103-1413, Van Zandt, USA; gen tel (903) 567-4000; adv tel (903) 567-4000; gen fax (903) 567-6076; adv fax (903) 567-6076; disp adv e-mail brad@vanzandtnews.com; class adv e-mail brad@vanzandtnews.com; ed e-mail brad@vanzandtnews.com; web site www.quinlan-tawakoninews.com
Circulation: 3,000pd,
Advertising rate: Open inch rate $5.00
Established: 1963
Delivery Method: Mail, Newsstand
Areas Served: Hunt County

CANYON

THE CANYON NEWS (THUR, SUN)

1500 5th Ave, Canyon, TX, 79015-3830, Randall, USA; gen tel (806) 655-7121; adv tel (806) 655-7121; ed tel (806) 655-7121; gen fax (806) 655-0823; adv fax (806) 655-0823; ed fax (806) 655-0823; disp adv e-mail marketing@canyonnews.com; class adv e-mail marketing@canyonnews.com; ed e-mail news@canyonnews.com; web site www.canyonnews.com
Circulation: 3,900pd, 300fr; Sworn/Estimate/Non-Audited
Advertising rate: Open inch rate $6.00
Established: 1896
Group: Hearst Communications, Inc.
Digital Platform - Mobile: Apple, Android
Digital Platform - Tablet: Apple iOS, Android
Pub.. Debbie Aylesworth
Ed... James Barrington
Mechanical Specifications: Type page 13 x 21; E - 6 cols, 1/6 between; A - 6 cols, 1/6 between; C - 8 cols, 1/6 between.Equipment & Software: Hardware — PC; Presses — G/Suburban; Software — Microsoft/Office 98, Adobe/PageMaker 6.51, Archetype/Corel Ventura 8.0, Adobe/Photoshop 4.0.
Delivery Method: Mail, Newsstand
Areas Served: Randall County

CANYON LAKE

BULVERDE STANDARD (WED)

1850 Old Sattler Rd, Canyon Lake, TX, 78132-1874, Comal, USA; gen tel (830) 899-3137; adv tel (830) 237-7313; ed tel (830) 899-3137; disp adv e-mail dougkirk@moment.net; class adv e-mail dougkirk@moment.net; ed e-mail dougkirk@moment.net
Circulation: 2,000fr; Sworn/Estimate/Non-Audited
Advertising rate: Open inch rate $14.00
Established: 1985
Pub./Ed.. Douglas Kirk
Mechanical Specifications: 6 column Broad sheet, 21" H X 10"W Printable SpaceEquipment & Software: Hardware — PC; Software — QPS/QuarkXPress.
Delivery Method: Racks
Areas Served: Comal County

CANYON LAKE WEEK (WED)

1850 Old Sattler Rd, Canyon Lake, TX, 78132-1874, Comal, USA; gen tel (830) 899-3137; adv tel (830) 237-7313; ed tel (830) 899-3137; disp adv e-mail dougkirk@gvtc.com; class adv e-mail dougkirk@gvtc.com; ed e-mail dougkirk@gvtc.com; web site No Website
Circulation: 3,200fr; Sworn/Estimate/Non-Audited
Advertising rate: Open inch rate $14.00
Established: 1985
Ed... Douglas Kirk
Mechanical Specifications: 6 column Broad sheet, 21" H X 10"W Printable SpaceEquipment & Software: Hardware — PC; Software — QPS/QuarkXPress.
Delivery Method: Racks
Areas Served: Comal County

COMAL COUNTY BEACON (WED)

1850 Old Sattler Rd, Canyon Lake, TX, 78132-1874, Comal, USA; gen tel (830) 899-3137; adv tel (830) 237-7313; ed tel (830) 899-3137; disp adv e-mail dougkirk@gvtc.com; class adv e-mail dougkirk@gvtc.com; ed e-mail dougkirk@gvtc.com; web site www.LookForMeIWillFindYou.com
Circulation: 3,500fr; Sworn/Estimate/Non-Audited
Advertising rate: Open inch rate $14.50
Established: 1985
Pub./Ed....................................... Douglas Kirk
Mechanical Specifications: 6 column Broad sheet, 21" H X 10"W Printable SpaceEquipment & Software: Hardware — PC; Software — QPS/QuarkXPress.
Delivery Method: Racks
Areas Served: Comal County

CARRIZO SPRINGS

CARRIZO SPRINGS JAVELIN (WED)

604 N 1st St, Carrizo Springs, TX, 78834-2602, Dimmit, USA; gen tel (830) 876-2318; adv tel (830) 876-2318; ed tel (830) 876-2318; gen fax (830) 876-2620; adv fax (830) 876-2620; ed fax (830) 876-2620; disp adv e-mail csjavelin@yahoo.com; class adv e-mail csjavelin@yahoo.com; ed e-mail csjdigital@yahoo.com; web site www.carrizospringsjavelin.com
Circulation: 2,100pd, 100fr; USPS
Advertising rate: Open inch rate $4.00
Established: 1884
Digital Platform - Mobile: Apple, Android, Windows, Blackberry
Digital Platform - Tablet: Apple iOS, Android, Windows 7, Blackberry Tablet OS, Kindle, Nook, Kindle Fire
Co-Pub./Ed./Adv. Dir............. Claudia McDaniel
Delivery Method: Mail, Newsstand
Areas Served: Dimmit County

CARTHAGE

THE PANOLA WATCHMAN (WED, SAT)

109 W Panola St, Carthage, TX, 75633-2631, Panola, USA; gen tel (903) 693-7888; adv tel (903) 693-7888; ed tel (903) 693-7888; gen fax (903) 693-5857; adv fax (903) 693-5857; ed fax (903) 693-5857; disp adv e-mail msweeney@panolawatchman.com; class adv e-mail tpeel@panolawatchman.com; ed e-mail bbarlish@panolawatchman.com; web site www.panolawatchman.com
Circulation: 4,826pd, 80fr; Sworn/Estimate/Non-Audited
Advertising rate: Open inch rate $7.95
Established: 1873
Digital Platform - Mobile: Apple, Android
Digital Platform - Tablet: Apple iOS, Android, Windows 7
Pub./Adv. Dir. .... Bill Holder
Ed. .... Becky Barlish
Classified Mgr. .... Tammy Peel
Mechanical Specifications: Type page 13 x 21 1/2; E - 6 cols, 2, 1/6 between; A - 6 cols, 2, 1/6 between; C - 6 cols, 2, 1/6 between. Equipment & Software: Hardware — PC; Software — QPS/QuarkXPress, Microsoft/Word 5.0.
Delivery Method: Mail, Newsstand, Racks
Areas Served: Panola County

CASTROVILLE

CASTROVILLE NEWS BULLETIN (THUR)

1105 Fiorella St, Castroville, TX, 78009-4577, Medina, USA; gen tel (830) 538-2556; adv tel (830) 538-2556; ed tel (830) 538-2556; gen fax (830) 931-3450; adv fax (830) 931-3450; ed fax (830) 931-3450; disp adv e-mail cornerstoneads@sbcglobal.net; class adv e-mail cornerstoneads@sbcglobal.net; ed e-mail cornerstonenews@sbcglobal.net; web site www.cornerstonenewspapers.com
Circulation: 1,991pd, 9fr; Sworn/Estimate/Non-Audited
Advertising rate: Open inch rate $5.75

Established: 1958
Group: McNaughton Newspapers
Digital Platform - Tablet: Windows 7
Pub./Ed./Adv. Dir. .... Natalie Spencer
Adv. Mgr. .... Lori Black
News Ed.Alicia RamirezEquipment & Software: Hardware — APP/Mac.
Delivery Method: Mail, Newsstand
Areas Served: Medina County

LEADER NEWS (THUR)

1105 Fiorella St, Castroville, TX, 78009-4577, Medina, USA; gen tel (830) 931-9698; adv tel (830) 931-9698; ed tel (830) 931-9698; gen fax (830) 931-3450; adv fax (830) 931-3450; ed fax (830) 931-3450; disp adv e-mail cornerstonenews@sbcglobal.net; class adv e-mail cornerstonenews@sbcglobal.net; ed e-mail cornerstonenews@sbcglobal.net
Circulation: 2,300pd,; Sworn/Estimate/Non-Audited
Advertising rate: Open inch rate $36.10
Established: 1999
Group: Burge Publishing Corp.Editions: (4) 4 total: Castroville (1,000); Devine Natalia (1,000); Lytle (1,000); Pleasanton (1,000)
Adv. Dir. .... Natalie Spencer
Ed. .... James La Combe
Pub. .... Frank Vasquez
Circ. Mgr. .... Jane Broyles
Mechanical Specifications: Type page 13 x 21; E - 6 cols, 2, 5/16 between; A - 6 cols, 2, 5/16 between; C - 6 cols, 2, 5/16 between. Equipment & Software: ; Software — QPS/QuarkXPress 5.0.
Delivery Method: Mail, Racks
Areas Served: Atascosa County

MEDINA VALLEY TIMES (THUR)

1105 Fiorella St, Castroville, TX, 78009-4577, Medina, USA; gen tel (830) 538-2556; adv tel (830) 538-2556; ed tel (830) 538-2556; gen fax (830) 931-3450; adv fax (830) 931-3450; ed fax (830) 931-3450; disp adv e-mail cornerstoneads@sbcglobal.net; class adv e-mail cornerstoneads@sbcglobal.net; ed e-mail cornerstonenews@sbcglobal.net; web site www.cornerstonenewspapers.com
Circulation: 3,255pd, 44fr; Sworn/Estimate/Non-Audited
Advertising rate: Open inch rate $5.85
Established: 1977
Digital Platform - Mobile: Apple, Android
Digital Platform - Tablet: Apple iOS, Android, Windows 7
Pub./Adv. Dir. .... Natalie Spencer
News Ed. .... Alicia Ramirez
Mechanical Specifications: Type page 13 x 21; E - 6 cols, 2 1/16, 1/8 between; A - 6 cols, 2 1/16, 1/8 between; C - 6 cols, 2 1/16, 1/8 between.Equipment & Software: Hardware — APP/Mac.
Delivery Method: Mail, Newsstand
Areas Served: Atascosa County

CEDAR PARK

HILL COUNTRY NEWS (THUR)

715 Discovery Blvd, Ste 304, Cedar Park, TX, 78613-2289, Williamson, USA; gen tel (512) 259-4449; gen fax (512) 259-8889; disp adv e-mail publisher@hillcountrynews.com; class adv e-mail classifieds@hillcountrynews.com; ed e-mail news@hillcountrynews.com; web site www.hillcountrynews.com - 546,019(views) 201,046(visitors)
Circulation: 988pd, 15,910fr; USPS
Advertising rate: Open inch rate $23.00
Established: 1968
Group: Fenice Community Media
Digital Platform - Mobile: Apple, Android, Windows
Digital Platform - Tablet: Apple iOS, Android, Windows 7
Pub. .... Scott Coleman
Classifieds .... Shelly Stamport
Adv. .... Roger Munford
Managing Editor .... Nick Brothers
Sports Editor .... Zach Smith
Mechanical Specifications: Type page 10 x 21 1/2; E - 6 cols, 2 1/16, between; A - 6 cols, 2 1/16, between; C - 9 cols, 1 3/8, between.
Delivery Method: Mail, Newsstand, Carrier, Racks
Areas Served: 78613, 78641, 78750, 78759, 78729, 78726

CENTER

THE LIGHT & CHAMPION (TUES, FRI)

137 San Augustine St, Center, TX, 75935-3951, Shelby, USA; gen tel (936) 598-3377; adv tel (936)598-3377; ed tel (936)598-3377; gen fax (936) 598-6394; adv fax (936)598-6394; ed fax (936)598-6394; disp adv e-mail steve.fountain@lightandchampion.com; class adv e-mail cgilcrease@lightandchampion.com; ed e-mail steve.fountain@lightandchampion.com; web site www.lightandchampion.com
Circulation: 2,496pd, 29fr; CVC
Advertising rate: Open inch rate $7.85
Established: 1877
Group: Fenice Community Media
PTS, Inc.
Digital Platform - Mobile: Apple, Android
Digital Platform - Tablet: Apple iOS, Android, Windows 7
Pub. .... Dale Buie
Managing editor .... Leah Dolan
Delivery Method: Mail, Newsstand, Racks
Areas Served: Shelby County

CENTERVILLE

CENTERVILLE NEWS (WED)

204 E Main St, Centerville, TX, 75833, Leon, USA; gen tel (903) 536-2015; adv tel (903) 536-2015; ed tel (903) 536-2015; gen fax (903) 536-2329; adv fax (903) 536-2329; ed fax (903) 536-2329; disp adv e-mail centervillenewspaper@gmail.com; class adv e-mail centervillenewspaper@gmail.com; ed e-mail centervillenewspaper@gmail.com
Circulation: 1,140pd, 45fr; Sworn/Estimate/Non-Audited
Advertising rate: Open inch rate $3.50
Established: 1980
Publisher .... Christie Stanford
Delivery Method: Mail, Racks
Areas Served: Leon County

CHANDLER

CHANDLER & BROWNSBORO STATESMAN (THUR)

300 Second St, Chandler, TX, 75758-2238, Henderson, USA; gen tel (903) 849-3333; adv tel (903) 849-3333; ed tel (903) 849-3333; gen fax NA; adv fax NA; ed fax NA; disp adv e-mail advertising@c-bstatesman.com; class adv e-mail advertising@c-bstatesman.com; ed e-mail editor@c-bstatesman.com; web site www.c-bstatesman.com
Circulation: 979pd,; USPS
Advertising rate: Open inch rate $6.40
Established: 1976
Group: Faith 3 Media, LLC
Digital Platform - Mobile: Apple, Android, Windows, Blackberry
Digital Platform - Tablet: Apple iOS, Android, Windows 7, Blackberry Tablet OS, Kindle, Nook, Kindle Fire
Owner / Publisher .... Betty Abendroth
Circulation / Distribution .... Amanda Wilcox
Delivery Method: Mail, Newsstand
Areas Served: Henderson County

CISCO

CISCO PRESS (THUR, SUN)

700 Conrad Hilton Blvd, Cisco, TX, 76437-3140, Eastland, USA; gen tel (254) 442-2244; adv tel (254) 442-2244; ed tel (254) 442-2244; gen fax (254) 629-2092; adv fax (254) 629-2092; ed fax (254) 629-2092; disp adv e-mail ecn@att.net; class adv e-mail ecn@att.net; ed e-mail ecn@att.net; web site www.eastlandcountytoday.com
Circulation: 965pd,; Sworn/Estimate/Non-Audited
Advertising rate: Open inch rate $8.00
Established: 1919
Group: Eastland County Newspapers
Digital Platform - Mobile: Apple, Android
Digital Platform - Tablet: Apple iOS, Android, Windows 7
Pub. .... Houston V. O'Brien
Ed. .... Ladonna Latham
Adv. Dir. .... Rebecca McCrary
Delivery Method: Mail, Racks
Areas Served: Eastland County

CLARENDON

CLARENDON ENTERPRISE (THUR)

105 Kearney St, Clarendon, TX, 79226-6051, Donley, USA; gen tel (806) 874-2259; gen fax (806) 874-2423; disp adv e-mail news@clarendononline.com; class adv e-mail news@clarendononline.com; ed e-mail news@clarendononline.com; web site www.clarendonlive.com
Circulation: 1,325pd,; Sworn/Estimate/Non-Audited
Advertising rate: Open inch rate $5.25
Established: 1878
Digital Platform - Mobile: Apple, Android
Digital Platform - Tablet: Apple iOS, Android, Windows 7
Pub./Ed. .... Roger A. Estlack
Adv. Dir. .... Tara Hogan
Mechanical Specifications: Type page 13 x 20; E - 6 cols, between; A - 6 cols, between; C - 6 cols, between.Equipment & Software: Hardware — Pentium/PC; Software — Adobe/InDesign 1.5.
Delivery Method: Mail, Newsstand, Racks
Areas Served: Clarendon, Hedley, Howardwick, and Lelia Lake

CLARKSVILLE

CLARKSVILLE TIMES (THUR)

106 E Main St, Clarksville, TX, 75426-3936, Red River, USA; gen tel (903) 427-4567; adv tel (903) 427-4567; ed tel (903) 427-4567; gen fax (903) 427-4567; adv fax (903) 427-4567; ed fax (903) 427-4567; disp adv e-mail theclarksvilletimes@gmail.com; class adv e-mail theclarksvilletimes@gmail.com; ed e-mail theclarksvilletimes@gmail.com
Circulation: 2,042pd, 24fr; Sworn/Estimate/Non-Audited
Advertising rate: Open inch rate $11.00
Established: 1873
Group: Red River Media
Digital Platform - Mobile: Apple, Android
Digital Platform - Tablet: Apple iOS, Android, Windows 7
Managing Editor .... Lou Antonelli
Delivery Method: Mail, Newsstand
Areas Served: Red River County

CLAUDE

THE CLAUDE NEWS (FRI)

119 N Trice St, Claude, TX, 79019, Armstrong, USA; gen tel (806) 226-4500; adv tel (806) 226-4500; ed tel (806) 226-4500; gen fax (806) 222-0023; adv fax (806) 222-0023; ed fax (806) 222-0023; disp adv e-mail editor@claudenews.com; class adv e-mail editor@claudenews.com; ed e-mail editor@claudenews.com; web site www.claudenews.com
Circulation: 700pd,; Sworn/Estimate/Non-Audited
Advertising rate: Open inch rate $4.25
Established: 1890
Digital Platform - Mobile: Apple, Android
Digital Platform - Tablet: Apple iOS, Android, Windows 7
Co-Pub./Ed./Adv. Dir. ...... Jessica Montgomery
Co-Pub. .... Will MontgomeryEquipment & Software: Hardware — PCs; Presses — ABD; Software — Adobe/PageMaker 5.0, Archetype/Corel Draw 5.0.
Delivery Method: Mail, Racks
Areas Served: Armstrong County

CLEVELAND

EASTEX ADVOCATE (WED)

106 W Hanson St, Cleveland, TX, 77327-4406, Liberty, USA; gen tel (281) 592-2626; adv tel (281) 592-2626; ed tel (281) 592-2626; gen fax (281) 592-2629; adv fax (281) 592-2629; ed fax (281) 592-2629; disp adv e-mail dbrady@hcnonline.com; class adv e-mail dbrady@hcnonline.com; ed e-mail vbrashier@hcnonline.com; web site www.YourEastexNews.com/eastex
Circulation: 10,523fr; CVC
Advertising rate: $8.25
Established: 1917
Group: 1013 Communications
Hearst Communications, Inc.
Digital Platform - Mobile: Apple, Android, Windows, Blackberry
Digital Platform - Tablet: Apple iOS, Android, Windows 7
Pub. .... Brenda Miller-Fergerson
Ed. .... Vanesa Brashier
Adv. Dir. .... Dianne Brady
Pub/Ad Dir .... Corey Turner
Mechanical Specifications: 10.388" x 20.5"
Delivery Method: Carrier, Racks
Areas Served: Liberty County & San Jacinto County

CLIFTON

THE CLIFTON RECORD (WED)

310 W 5th St, Clifton, TX, 76634-1611, Bosque, USA; gen tel (254) 675-3336; adv tel (254) 675-3336; ed tel (254) 675-3336; gen fax (254) 675-4090; adv fax (254) 675-4090; ed fax (254) 675-4090; disp adv e-mail Bvoss@cliftonrecord.com; class adv e-mail Joyce@meridiantribune.com; ed e-mail Simone@cliftonrecord.com; web site www.cliftonrecord.com
Circulation: 2,303pd,; Sworn/Estimate/Non-Audited
Advertising rate: Open inch rate $7.25
Established: 1895
Digital Platform - Mobile: Apple, Android
Digital Platform - Tablet: Apple iOS, Android, Windows 7
Pub./Ed. .... Brett Voss
Delivery Method: Mail, Newsstand
Areas Served: Bosque County

CLYDE

BAIRD BANNER (WED)

312 N 1st St, Clyde, TX, 79510-4729, Callahan, USA; gen tel (325) 893-4244; adv tel (325) 893-4244; ed tel (325) 893-4244; gen fax (325) 893-2780; disp adv e-mail clydejournal@earthlink.net; class adv e-mail clydejournal@earthlink.net; ed e-mail clydejournal@earthlink.net; web site www.clydenewspaper.com
Circulation: 525pd, 30fr; Sworn/Estimate/Non-Audited
Advertising rate: Open inch rate $3.30
Established: 1997
Digital Platform - Mobile: Apple, Android
Digital Platform - Tablet: Apple iOS, Android, Windows 7
Ed./Adv. Dir. .... Lyn Walker
Editor .... Danny Tabor
Delivery Method: Mail, Newsstand
Areas Served: Callahan County

CLYDE JOURNAL (WED)

312 N 1st St, Clyde, TX, 79510-4729, Callahan, USA; gen tel (325) 893-4244; gen fax (325) 893-2780; disp adv e-mail

clydejournal@earthlink.net; class adv e-mail clydejournal@earthlink.net; ed e-mail clydejournal@earthlink.net; web site www.clydenewspaper.com
Circulation: 2,250pd, 40fr; Sworn/Estimate/Non-Audited
Advertising rate: Open inch rate $4.55
Established: 1972
Digital Platform - Mobile: Apple, Android
Digital Platform - Tablet: Apple iOS, Android, Windows 7
Ed .... Daniel Tabor
Adv Dir .... Lyn Walker
Melinda Kevil
Delivery Method: Mail, Newsstand
Areas Served: Callahan County

COLEMAN

CHRONICLE & DEMOCRAT-VOICE (WED)
208 W Pecan St, Coleman, TX, 76834-4148, Coleman, USA; gen tel (325) 625-4128; adv tel (325) 625-4128; ed tel (325) 625-4128; gen fax (325) 625-4129; adv fax (325) 625-4129; ed fax (325) 625-4129; disp adv e-mail mail@colemannews.com; class adv e-mail mail@colemannews.com; ed e-mail mail@colemannews.com; web site www.colemannews.com
Circulation: 2,945pd, 80fr; Sworn/Estimate/Non-Audited
Advertising rate: Open inch rate $4.10
Established: 1881
Digital Platform - Mobile: Apple
Digital Platform - Tablet: Apple iOS, Windows 7
Pub .... Brett Autry
Ed./Adv. Dir. .... Amber HardinEquipment & Software: Hardware — APP/Mac; Software — QPS/QuarkXPress.
Delivery Method: Mail, Newsstand
Areas Served: Coleman County

COLORADO CITY

COLORADO CITY RECORD (THUR)
257 E 2nd St, Colorado City, TX, 79512-6431, Mitchell, USA; gen tel (325) 728-3413; adv tel (325) 728-3413; ed tel (325) 728-3413; gen fax (325) 728-3414; adv fax (325) 728-3414; ed fax (325) 728-3414; disp adv e-mail coloradorecord@yahoo.com; class adv e-mail coloradorecord@yahoo.com; ed e-mail coloradorecord@yahoo.com; web site www.coloradorecord.com
Circulation: 3,000pd, 100fr; Sworn/Estimate/Non-Audited
Advertising rate: Open inch rate $5.00
Established: 1905
Digital Platform - Mobile: Apple, Android
Digital Platform - Tablet: Apple iOS, Android, Windows 7
Adv. Mgr. .... Earl Plagens
Pub .... Sheila Plagens
Editor .... Stephanie Perez
Delivery Method: Mail, Racks
Areas Served: Mitchell County

COLUMBUS

THE BANNER PRESS NEWSPAPER (THUR)
1217 Bowie St, Columbus, TX, 78934-2343, Colorado, USA; gen tel (979) 732-6243; gen fax (979) 732-6245; disp adv e-mail banneroffice@sbcglobal.net; class adv e-mail london1214@sbcglobal.net; ed e-mail bannercolumbus@sbcglobal.net; web site www.bannerpresspaper.com
Circulation: 4,250pd, 50fr; USPS
Advertising rate: Open inch national rate $9.59
Established: 1985
Digital Platform - Mobile: Apple, Android
Digital Platform - Tablet: Apple iOS, Android, Windows 7
Pub./Ed. .... Chad Ferguson
Bookkeeper .... Ramona Ferguson
Classified Sales .... London Ferguson
Mechanical Specifications: Type page 13 3/4 x 21; E - 7 cols, 1 3/4, between; A - 7 cols, 1 3/4, between; C - 7 cols, 1 3/4, between. Equipment & Software: Hardware — APP/Mac; Software — Adobe/Illustrator 8.0, Adobe/PageMaker 6.5, Adobe/Photoshop 5.0, Microsoft/Office 98.
Delivery Method: Mail, Newsstand, Racks
Areas Served: Austin, Colorado and Fayette Counties

THE COLORADO COUNTY CITIZEN (WED)
2024 Highway 71 S, Columbus, TX, 78934-2820, Colorado, USA; gen tel (979) 732-2304; adv tel (979) 732-2304; ed tel (979) 732-2304; gen fax (979) 732-8804; adv fax (979) 732-8804; ed fax (979) 732-8804; disp adv e-mail publisher@coloradocountycitizen.com; class adv e-mail ads@coloradocountycitizen.com; ed e-mail editor@coloradocountycitizen.com; web site www.coloradocountycitizen.com
Circulation: 2,868pd, 50fr; CVC
Advertising rate: Open inch rate $11.00
Established: 1857
Group: Fenice Community Media
Digital Platform - Mobile: Apple, Android
Digital Platform - Tablet: Apple iOS, Android, Windows 7
Pub .... Michelle Banse
John Brown
Adv. Dir. .... Roxanne Glover
Bookkeeper ...., Gina Sides
Delivery Method: Mail, Newsstand
Areas Served: Colorado County

COMANCHE

THE COMANCHE CHIEF (THUR)
203 W Grand Ave, Comanche, TX, 76442-2316, Comanche, USA; gen tel (325) 356-2636; adv tel (325) 356-2636; ed tel (325) 356-2636; gen fax (325) 356-5380; adv fax (325) 356-5380; ed fax (325) 356-5380; disp adv e-mail editor@thecomanchechief.com; class adv e-mail editor@thecomanchechief.com; ed e-mail editor@thecomanchechief.com; web site www.thecomanchechief.com
Circulation: 3,200pd,; Sworn/Estimate/Non-Audited
Advertising rate: Open inch rate $6.00
Established: 1873
Digital Platform - Mobile: Apple, Android, Windows
Digital Platform - Tablet: Apple iOS, Android, Windows 7
Bradley Wilkerson
Lance WilkersonEditors
Delivery Method: Mail, Newsstand, Racks
Areas Served: Comanche/Comanche/76442

COMFORT

THE COMFORT NEWS (THUR)
504B Sixth St, Comfort, TX, 78013-2318, Kendall, USA; gen tel (830) 995-3634; gen fax (830) 995-2075; disp adv e-mail dukecomfort@hctc.net; class adv e-mail dukecomfort@hctc.net; ed e-mail dukecomfort@hctc.net; web site thecomfortnews.com
Circulation: 1,146pd,; Sworn/Estimate/Non-Audited
Advertising rate: Open inch rate $10.69
Established: 1904
Group: The Comfort News & Print, Inc.
Co-Pub .... Deborah Hawkins
Co-Pub./Ed. .... Michael Hawkins
Features editor and photographer ...... Bill Terry
Office Mgr. .... Michele Coover
Delivery Method: Mail, Newsstand, Racks
Areas Served: Kendall County

CONROE

ATASCOCITA OBSERVER (WED)
100 Avenue A, Conroe, TX, 77301-2946, Harris, USA; gen tel (281) 378-1060; adv tel (281) 378-1071; ed tel (281) 378-1064; gen fax (281) 446-6901; adv fax (281) 446-6901; ed fax (281) 446-6901; disp adv e-mail cturner@hcnonline.com; class adv e-mail cturner@hcnonline.com; ed e-mail jsummer@hcnonline.com; web site www.asascocitaobserver.com
Circulation: 0pd, 17,998fr; CVC
Advertising rate: Open inch rate $13.04
Established: 2003
Group: Hearst Communications, Inc.
Times Media Group
Digital Platform - Mobile: Apple, Android, Windows
Digital Platform - Tablet: Apple iOS, Android, Windows 7
Pub .... Brenda Miller-Fergerson
Gen. Sales Mgr. .... Corey Turner
Pub .... Jason Joseph
Adv. Mgr. .... Charles Lee
Circ. Mgr .... Rick Flores
Prod. Mgr .... Angela Hicks
Mechanical Specifications: 10.388" x 20.5"
Delivery Method: Carrier, Racks
Areas Served: 77044, 77346, 77396

CLEVELAND ADVOCATE (WED)
100 Avenue A, Ste 600, Conroe, TX, 77301-2946, Liberty, USA; gen tel (281) 592-2626; adv tel (281) 592-2626; ed tel (281) 592-2626; gen fax (281) 592-2629; adv fax (281) 592-2629; ed fax (281) 592-2629; disp adv e-mail dbrady@hcnonline.com; class adv e-mail dbrady@hcnonline.com; ed e-mail vbrashier@hcnonline.com; web site www.hcndaytonnews.com
Circulation: 4,152pd,; CVC
Advertising rate: Open inch rate $12.89
Established: 1917
Group: Times Media Group
Digital Platform - Mobile: Apple, Android, Windows
Digital Platform - Tablet: Apple iOS, Android, Windows 7
Pub .... Brenda Miller-Fergerson
Ed. .... Vanesa Brashier
Adv. Dir. .... Dianne Brady
Pub .... Jason Joseph
Adv. Mgr. .... Charles Lee
Circ. Mgr .... Rick Flores
Prod. Mgr .... Angela Hicks
Mechanical Specifications: 10.388" x 20.5"
Delivery Method: Mail, Newsstand, Carrier, Racks
Areas Served: 77327, 77328, 77331, 77371, 77372, 77575

DAYTON NEWS (WED)
100 Avenue A, Conroe, TX, 77301-2946, Liberty, USA; gen tel (281) 592-2626; adv tel (281) 592-2626; ed tel (281) 592-2626; gen fax (281) 592-2629; adv fax (281) 592-2629; ed fax (281) 592-2629; disp adv e-mail dbrady@hcnonline.com; class adv e-mail dbrady@hcnonline.com; ed e-mail vbrashier@hcnonline.com; web site www.yourdaytonnews.com
Circulation: 0pd, 6,177fr; CVC
Advertising rate: Open inch rate $8.66
Established: 2004
Group: Times Media Group
Digital Platform - Mobile: Apple, Android, Windows
Digital Platform - Tablet: Apple iOS, Android, Windows 7
Pub .... Brenda Miller-Fergerson
Ed. .... Vanesa Brashier
Adv. Dir. .... Dianne Brady
Prod. Mgr .... Angela Hicks
Pub .... Jason Joseph
Adv. Mgr. .... Charles Lee
Circ. Mgr .... Rick Flores
Pub/Ad Dir .... Corey Turner
Delivery Method: Carrier, Racks
Areas Served: 77535
77575

FORT BEND SUN (THUR)
100 Avenue A, Conroe, TX, 77301-2946, Montgomery, USA; gen tel (281) 378-1900; adv tel (281) 378-1908; ed tel (281) 378-1911; gen fax (713) 520-1193; adv fax (713) 520-1193; ed fax (713) 520-1193; disp adv e-mail rdavis@hcnonline.com; class adv e-mail tisaacks@hcnonline.com; ed e-mail rgraham@hcnonline.com
Circulation: 0pd, 30,633fr; CVC
Advertising rate: Open inch rate $14.73
Established: 1967
Group: Hearst Communications, Inc.
Digital Platform - Mobile: Apple, Android
Digital Platform - Tablet: Apple iOS, Android, Windows 7
Pub .... Richard Davis
Ed. .... Rusty Graham
Pub .... Jason Joseph
Adv. Mgr. .... Charles Lee
Circ. Mgr .... Rick Flores
Delivery Method: Mail, Newsstand, Racks
Areas Served: Harris County

FRIENDSWOOD JOURNAL (WED)
100 Avenue A, Conroe, TX, 77301-2946, Harris, USA; gen tel (281) 378-1920; adv tel (281) 378-1922; ed tel (281) 378-1930; gen fax (281) 922-4499; adv fax (281) 922-4499; ed fax (281) 922-4499; disp adv e-mail cwentz@hcnonline.com; class adv e-mail cwentz@hcnonline.com; ed e-mail jmolony@hcnonline.com; web site www.yourfriendswoodnews.com
Circulation: 724pd, 7,995fr; CVC
Advertising rate: Open inch rate $6.73
Established: 1975
Group: Hearst Communications, Inc.
Times Media Group
Digital Platform - Mobile: Apple, Android, Windows
Digital Platform - Tablet: Apple iOS, Android, Windows 7
Pub .... Brenda Miller-Fergerson
Ed. .... Jim Molony
Adv. Dir. .... Charles Lee
Pub .... Jason Joseph
Circ. Mgr .... Rick Flores
Prod. Mgr .... Carol Taylor
Advt Sales Mgr .... Cheryl Wentz
Mechanical Specifications: 10.388" x 20.5"
Delivery Method: Mail, Newsstand, Carrier, Racks
Areas Served: Harris County

HUMBLE OBSERVER (WED)
100 Avenue A, # B, Conroe, TX, 77301-2946, Harris, USA; gen tel (281) 378-1060; adv tel (281) 378-1071; ed tel (281) 378-1064; gen fax (281) 446-6901; adv fax (281) 446-6901; ed fax (281) 446-6901; disp adv e-mail cturner@hcnonline.com; class adv e-mail cturner@hcnonline.com; ed e-mail jsummer@hcnonline.com; web site www.yourhumblenews.com
Circulation: 0pd, 11,977fr; CVC
Advertising rate: Open inch rate $8.99
Established: 1975
Group: Hearst Communications, Inc.
Times Media Group
Digital Platform - Mobile: Apple, Android, Windows
Digital Platform - Tablet: Apple iOS, Android, Windows 7
Pub .... Brenda Miller-Fergerson
Gen. Sales Mgr. .... Corey Turner
Ed. .... Melecio C. Franco
Pub .... Jason Joseph
Adv. Mgr. .... Charles Lee
Circ. Mgr .... Rick Flores
Prod. Mgr .... Angela Hicks
Mechanical Specifications: 10.388" x 20.5"
Delivery Method: Mail, Newsstand, Racks
Areas Served: 77338
77346
77396

KINGWOOD OBSERVER (WED)
100 Avenue A, # B, Conroe, TX, 77301-2946, Harris, USA; gen tel (281) 378-1060; adv tel (281) 378-1071; ed tel (281) 378-1064; gen fax (281) 446-6901; adv fax (281) 446-6901; ed fax (281) 446-6901; disp adv e-mail cturner@hcnonline.com; class adv e-mail cturner@hcnonline.com; ed e-mail jsummer@hcnonline.com; web site www.yourkingwoodnews.com
Circulation: 0pd, 20,580fr; CVC
Advertising rate: Open inch rate $17.32
Established: 1977
Group: Hearst Communications, Inc.
Times Media Group

Digital Platform - Mobile: Apple, Android, Windows
Digital Platform - Tablet: Apple iOS, Android, Windows 7
Pub.......... Brenda Miller-Fergerson
Gen. Sales Mgr.......... Corey Turner
Ed. .... Melecio C. Franco
Pub. .... Jason Joseph
Adv. Mgr.......... Charles Lee
Circ. Mgr .... Rick Flores
Prod. Mgr .... Angela Hicks
Mechanical Specifications: 10.388" x 20.5"
Delivery Method: Carrier, Racks
Areas Served: 77339
77345
77346

LAKE HOUSTON OBSERVER (WED)

100 Avenue A, Conroe, TX, 77301-2946, Harris, USA; gen tel (281) 378-1060; adv tel (281) 378-1071; ed tel (281) 378-1064; gen fax (281) 446-6901; adv fax (281) 446-6901; ed fax (281) 446-6901; disp adv e-mail cturner@hcnonline.com; class adv e-mail cturner@hcnonline.com; ed e-mail jsummer@hcnonline.com; web site www.yourlakehouston.com
Circulation: 0pd, 7,270fr; CVC
Advertising rate: Open inch rate $17.04
Established: 1981
Group: Hearst Communications, Inc.
Times Media Group
Digital Platform - Mobile: Apple, Android
Digital Platform - Tablet: Apple iOS, Android, Windows 7
Pub.......... Brenda Miller-Fergerson
Gen. Sales Mgr.......... Corey Turner
Prod. Mgr .... Angela Hicks
Pub.......... Jason Joseph
Adv. Mgr.......... Charles Lee
Circ. Mgr .... Rick Flores
Mechanical Specifications: 10.388" x 20.5"
Delivery Method: Carrier, Racks
Areas Served: 77336
77532

MAGNOLIA POTPOURRI (WED)

100 Avenue A, Conroe, TX, 77301-2946, Harris, USA; gen tel (281) 378-1080; adv tel (281) 378-1082; ed tel (281) 378-1087; gen fax (281) 320-2005; adv fax (281) 320-2005; ed fax (281) 320-2005; disp adv e-mail rdavis@hcnonline.com; class adv e-mail srovegno@hcnonline.com; ed e-mail rkent@hcnonline.com; web site www.thetomballpotpourri.com
Circulation: 0pd, 13,545fr; CVC
Advertising rate: 1/16 Pg $152.00; 1/8 Pg $271.00; 1/4 Pg $513.00; Per Inch Rate $16.14
Established: 1986
Group: Hearst Communications, Inc.
Times Media Group
Digital Platform - Mobile: Apple, Android
Digital Platform - Tablet: Apple iOS, Android, Windows 7
Ed. .... Roy Kent
Sales Mgr.......... Susan Rovegno
Pub.......... Jason Joseph
Adv. Mgr.......... Charles Lee
Circ. Mgr .... Rick Flores
Major Sr. Acct. Mgr.......... Tom Legg
Mktg. Mgr.......... Megan O'Sullivan
Delivery Method: Mail, Newsstand, Racks
Areas Served: Harris County

MEMORIAL EXAMINER (THUR)

100 Avenue A, Ste 200, Conroe, TX, 77301-2946, Montgomery, USA; gen tel (281) 378-1900; adv tel (281) 378-1904; ed tel (281) 378-1911; gen fax (713) 520-1193; adv fax (713) 520-1193; ed fax (713) 520-1193; disp adv e-mail rdavis@hcnonline.com; class adv e-mail ljohnson@hcnonline.com; ed e-mail rgraham@hcnonline.com; web site www.examinernews.com/memorial
Circulation: 0pd, 27,451fr; CVC
Advertising rate: 1/16 Pg $152.00; 1/8 Pg $271.00; 1/4 Pg $513.00; Per Inch Rate $23.11
Established: 2004
Group: Hearst Communications, Inc.
Times Media Group
Digital Platform - Mobile: Apple, Android
Digital Platform - Tablet: Apple iOS, Android, Windows 7
Pub.......... Richard Davis
Ed. .... Rusty Graham
Pub.......... Jason Joseph
Adv. Mgr.......... Charles Lee
Circ. Mgr .... Rick Flores
Prod. Mgr.......... Clayton Harris
Mktg. Mgr.......... Megan O'Sullivan
Major Sr. Acct. Mgr.......... Tom Legg
Delivery Method: Mail, Newsstand, Racks
Areas Served: Harris County

PEARLAND JOURNAL (THUR)

100 Avenue A, Conroe, TX, 77301-2946, Montgomery, USA; gen tel (281) 378-1920; adv tel (281) 378-1922; ed tel (281) 378-1930; gen fax (281) 922-4499; adv fax (281) 922-4499; ed fax (281) 922-4499; disp adv e-mail bmiller-fergerson@hcnonline.com; class adv e-mail bcrainer@hcnonline.com ; ed e-mail jmolony@hcnonline.com; web site www.pearlandjournal.com - 56,000(views)
Circulation: 1,125pd, 19,330fr; CVC
Advertising rate: 1/16 Pg $152.00; 1/8 Pg $271.00; 1/4 Pg $513.00; Per Inch $16.14
Established: 1975
Group: Times Media Group
Digital Platform - Mobile: Apple, Android, Windows, Blackberry
Digital Platform - Tablet: Apple iOS, Android, Windows 7, Blackberry Tablet OS, Kindle, Nook, Kindle Fire
Pub.......... Brenda Miller-Fergerson
Ed. .... Jim Molony
Sales Mgr.......... Dean West
Pub. .... Jason Joseph
Adv. Mgr.......... Charles Lee
Circ. Mgr .... Rick Flores
Prod. Mgr.......... Carol Taylor
Major Sr. Acct. Mgr.......... Tom Legg
Mktg. Mgr.......... Megan O'Sullivan
Delivery Method: Mail, Newsstand, Carrier, Racks
Areas Served: 77581, 77584

TOMBALL POTPOURRI (WED)

100 Avenue A, Conroe, TX, 77301-2946, Harris, USA; gen tel (281) 378-1080; adv tel (281) 378-1082; ed tel (281) 378-1087; gen fax (281) 320-2005; adv fax (281) 320-2005; ed fax (281) 320-2005; disp adv e-mail rdavis@hcnonline.com; class adv e-mail srovegno@hcnonline.com; ed e-mail rkent@hcnonline.com; web site www.hcnonline.com
Circulation: 0pd, 17,490fr; CVC
Advertising rate: 1/16 Pg $152.00; 1/8 Pg $271.00; 1/4 Pg $513.00; Open inch rate $15.15
Established: 1986
Group: Hearst Communications, Inc.
Times Media Group
Digital Platform - Mobile: Apple, Android
Digital Platform - Tablet: Apple iOS, Android, Windows 7
Pub.......... Richard Davis
Ed. .... Roy Kent
Sales Mgr.......... Susan Rovegno
Pub.......... Jason Joseph
Charles Lee
Circ. Mgr .... Rick Flores
Mktg. Mgr.......... Megan O'Sullivan
Major Sr. Acct. Mgr.......... Tom Legg
Mechanical Specifications: Type page 10 x 13; E - 6 cols, 1 1/2, 1/8 between; A - 6 cols, 1 1/2, 1/8 between; C - 6 cols, 1 1/2, 1/8 between. Equipment & Software: Hardware — APP/Mac; Software — Adobe/PageMaker.
Delivery Method: Mail, Newsstand, Racks
Areas Served: Harris County

SPRING OBSERVER (THUR)

100 Avenue A, Ste 108, Conroe, TX, 77301-2946, Montgomery, USA; gen tel (936) 521-3400; adv tel (936) 521-3422; ed tel (396) 521-3400; gen fax (936) 521-3392; adv fax (936) 521-3392; disp adv e-mail tlegg@hcnonline.com; class adv e-mail lelizade@hcnonline.com; ed e-mail adubois@hcnonline.com; web site www.yourhoustonnews.com
Circulation: 0pd, 18,167fr; CVC
Advertising rate: Modular - full = $2306.30;3/4 =$1700.00; 1/2 = $1,275.00; 1/3 =$880;1/4 =675, 1/8 =$356;1/16 =$200 ; Per Inch $19.39
Established: 2004
Group: Times Media Group
Digital Platform - Mobile: Apple, Android
Digital Platform - Tablet: Apple iOS, Android, Windows 7
Pub./Adv. Dir. .... Richard Davis
Exec. Ed.......... Andy DuBois
Mng. Ed.......... Catherine Dominguez
Pub. .... Jason Joseph
Adv. Mgr.......... Charles Lee
Circ. Mgr .... Rick Flores
Prod. Mgr.......... Angela Hicks
Majors Sr. Acct. Mgr.......... Tom Legg
Mktg. Mgr.......... Megan O'Sullivan
Mechanical Specifications: 6 columns (10.388") x 20.5"
Delivery Method: Mail, Newsstand, Carrier, Racks
Areas Served: 77014, 77373

THE EXAMINERS (THUR)

100 Avenue A, Ste 200, Conroe, TX, 77301-2946, Montgomery, USA; gen tel (281) 378-1900; adv tel (281) 378-1906; ed tel (281) 378-1911; gen fax (713) 520-1193; adv fax (713) 520-1193; ed fax (713) 520-1193; disp adv e-mail rdavis@hcnonline.com; class adv e-mail pstewart@hcnonline.com; ed e-mail rgraham@hcnonline.com; web site www.Examinernews.com
Circulation: 0pd, 33,286fr; CVC
Advertising rate: 1/16 Pg $152.00; 1/8 Pg $271.00; 1/4 Pg $513.00; Per Inch $13.55
Established: 2001
Group: Hearst Communications, Inc.
Digital Platform - Mobile: Apple, Android
Digital Platform - Tablet: Apple iOS, Android, Windows 7
Pub.......... Richard Davis
Ed. .... Rusty Graham
Pub.......... Jason Joseph
Adv. Mgr.......... Charles Lee
Circ. Mgr .... Rick Flores
Prod. Mgr.......... Clayton Harris
Major Sr. Acct. Mgr.......... Tom Legg
Mktg. Mgr.......... Megan O'Sullivan
Delivery Method: Mail, Newsstand, Racks
Areas Served: Harris County

THE RANCHER (THUR)

100 Avenue A, Conroe, TX, 77301-2946, Montgomery, USA; gen tel (281) 378-1900; adv tel (281) 378-1908; ed tel (281) 378-1911; gen fax (713) 520-1193; adv fax (713) 520-1193; ed fax (713) 520-1193; disp adv e-mail rdavis@hcnonline.com; class adv e-mail tisaacks@hcnonline.com; ed e-mail rgraham@hcnonline.com; web site www.katysun.com
Circulation: 0pd, 26,985fr; CVC
Advertising rate: Open inch rate $20.24
Established: 1953
Group: Hearst Communications, Inc.
Times Media Group
Digital Platform - Mobile: Apple, Android
Digital Platform - Tablet: Apple iOS, Android, Windows 7
Pub.......... Richard Davis
Ed. .... Rusty Graham
Pub.......... Jason Johnson
Adv. Mgr.......... Charles Lee
Circ. Mgr .... Rick Flores
Prod. Mgr.......... Tom Stamper
Delivery Method: Mail, Newsstand, Racks
Areas Served: Harris County

THE WOODLANDS VILLAGER (THUR)

100 Avenue A, Ste 190, Conroe, TX, 77301-2946, Montgomery, USA; gen tel (281) 378-1040; adv tel (281) 378-1042; ed tel (281) 378-1049; gen fax (281) 363-3299; adv fax (281) 363-3299; ed fax (281) 363-3299; disp adv e-mail rdavis@hcnonline.com; class adv e-mail lelizade@hcnonline.com; ed e-mail adubois@hcnonline.com; web site www.thewoodlandsvillager.com
Circulation: 0pd, 44,200fr; CVC
Advertising rate: Modular -full =2768; 3/4 =$2040;1/2 = $1056; 1/3 =$1056; 1/4 =$810; 1/8 =$428; 1/16 =$240; Open inch rate $26.17
Established: 1977
Group: Times Media Group
Digital Platform - Mobile: Apple, Android
Digital Platform - Tablet: Apple iOS, Android, Windows 7
Pub./Adv. Dir. .... Richard Davis
Exec. Ed.......... Andy DuBois
Mng. Ed.......... Catherine Dominguez
Pub.......... Jason Joseph
Adv. Mgr.......... Charles Lee
Circ. Mgr .... Rick Flores
Mktg. Mgr.......... Megan O'Sullivan
Major Sr. Acct. Mgr.......... Tom Legg
Mechanical Specifications: 6 columns (10.388") x 20.5"
Delivery Method: Mail, Newsstand, Carrier, Racks
Areas Served: 77380, 77381, 77382, 77384, 77385, 77386, 77389

COOPER

COOPER REVIEW (THUR)

50 E Side Sq, Cooper, TX, 75432-1935, Delta, USA; gen tel (903) 395-2175; adv tel (903) 395-2175; ed tel (903) 395-2175; gen fax (903) 395-0424; adv fax (903) 395-0424; ed fax (903) 395-0424; disp adv e-mail ads@cooperreview.com; class adv e-mail ads@cooperreview.com; ed e-mail news@cooperreview.com; web site www.cooperreview.com
Circulation: 1,550pd, 100fr; Sworn/Estimate/Non-Audited
Advertising rate: Open inch rate $5.00
Established: 1880
Digital Platform - Mobile: Apple, Android
Digital Platform - Tablet: Apple iOS, Android, Windows 7
Pub./Adv. Dir. .... Jim Butler
Ed. .... Cindy Roller
Office Mgr. .... Sally Butler
Mechanical Specifications: Type page 12 x 21 1/2; E - 6 cols, 2 1/16, 1/8 between; A - 6 cols, 2 1/16, 1/8 between; C - 6 cols, 2 1/16, 1/8 between. Equipment & Software: Hardware — PC; Software — Windows 98/ Indesign
Delivery Method: Mail, Racks
Areas Served: 75432, 75448, 75450, 75428, 75441, 75415, 75469, 75460, 75462, 75482

COPPELL

CITIZENS' ADVOCATE (FRI)

509 W Bethel Rd, Coppell, TX, 75019-4481, Dallas, USA; gen tel (972) 462-8192; adv tel (972) 462-8192; ed tel (972) 462-8192; disp adv e-mail citizensadvocate2000@yahoo.com; class adv e-mail citizensadvocate2000@yahoo.com; ed e-mail citizensadvocate2000@yahoo.com; web site www.coppellcitizensadvocate.com
Circulation: 5,000pd,; Sworn/Estimate/Non-Audited
Advertising rate: Open inch rate $12.00
Established: 1984
Digital Platform - Mobile: Apple, Android
Digital Platform - Tablet: Apple iOS, Android, Windows 7
Pub./Ed.......... Jean Murph
Adv. Dir.......... Kathryn Walker
Delivery Method: Mail, Racks
Areas Served: Coppell, Texas

COPPERAS COVE

COPPERAS COVE LEADER-PRESS (TUES, FRI)

2210 E Business 190, Ste 1, Copperas Cove, TX, 76522-2523, Coryell, USA; gen tel (254) 547-4207; adv tel (254) 547-4207; ed tel (254) 547-4207; gen fax (254) 542-3299; adv fax (254) 542-3299; ed fax (254) 542-3299; disp adv e-mail advertising@coveleaderpress.com; class adv e-mail jhauk@coveleaderpress.com; ed e-mail news@coveleaderpress.com; web site www.coveleaderpress.com
Circulation: 3,650pd, 56fr; Sworn/Estimate/Non-Audited

Advertising rate: Open inch rate $6.75
Established: 1894
Digital Platform - Mobile: Apple, Android, Windows, Blackberry
Digital Platform - Tablet: Apple iOS, Android, Windows 7, Blackberry Tablet OS, Kindle, Nook, Kindle Fire
Pub.. Larry Hauk
Adv. Dir...Joyce Hauk
Pub..David Morris
Delivery Method: Mail, Newsstand, Racks
Areas Served: 76522, 76538

CORRIGAN

CORRIGAN TIMES (THUR)

202 E Front St, Corrigan, TX, 75939-2589, Polk, USA; gen tel (936) 398-2535; adv tel (936) 398-2535; ed tel (936) 398-2535; gen fax (936) 327-7156; adv fax (936) 327-7156; ed fax (936) 327-7156; disp adv e-mail polknews@livingston.net; class adv e-mail polknews@livingston.net; ed e-mail polknews@livingston.net; web site www.EastTexasNews.com
Circulation: 1,350pd,; Sworn/Estimate/Non-Audited
Advertising rate: Open inch rate $3.70
Established: 1953
Group: Polk County Publishing Co.
Digital Platform - Mobile: Apple, Android
Digital Platform - Tablet: Apple iOS, Android
Ed.. Kim Popham
Adv. Dir.. Linda Holley
Delivery Method: Mail, Newsstand
Areas Served: Polk County

CRANE

CRANE NEWS (THUR)

401 S Gaston St, Crane, TX, 79731-2621, Crane, USA; gen tel (432) 558-3541; adv tel (432) 558-3541; ed tel (432) 558-3541; gen fax (432) 558-2676; adv fax (432) 558-2676; ed fax (432) 558-2676; disp adv e-mail newspub@nwol.net; class adv e-mail newspub@nwol.net; ed e-mail newspub@nwol.net
Circulation: 1,780pd, 70fr; Sworn/Estimate/Non-Audited
Advertising rate: Open inch rate $6.00
Established: 1879
Pub./Ed.......................................Dennis Greer
Adv. Dir.................................. Mandy Timmons
Mechanical Specifications: Type page 13 x 21.Equipment & Software: Hardware — 4-Gateway/Pentium; Software — Adobe/PageMaker 6.0, Archetype/Corel Draw 5.0, Microsoft/Office.
Delivery Method: Mail, Racks
Areas Served: Crane County

CROCKETT

HOUSTON COUNTY COURIER (THUR, SUN)

102 S 7th St, Crockett, TX, 75835-2146, Houston, USA; gen tel (936) 544-2238; adv tel (936) 544-2238; ed tel (936) 544-2238; gen fax (936) 544-4088; adv fax (936) 544-4088; ed fax (936) 544-4088; disp adv e-mail lreynolds@houstoncountycourier.com; class adv e-mail joycel@houstoncountycourier.com; ed e-mail news@houstoncountycourier.com; web site www.houstoncountycourier.com
Circulation: 5,763pd,; Sworn/Estimate/Non-Audited
Advertising rate: Open inch rate $7.20
Established: 1890
Group: Polk County Publishing Co.
Digital Platform - Mobile: Apple, Android
Digital Platform - Tablet: Apple iOS, Android, Windows 7
Owner.. Alvin Holley
Pub...Larry Reynolds
Ed. ....Lynda Jones
Adv. Dir./Gen. Mgr.................Jeannine Rhone
Delivery Method: Mail, Newsstand, Racks
Areas Served: Houston County

CROSS PLAINS

CROSS PLAINS REVIEW (THUR)

116 E 1st St, Cross Plains, TX, 76443-2464, Callahan, USA; gen tel (254) 725-6111; gen fax (254) 725-7225; disp adv e-mail clydejournal@earthlink.net; class adv e-mail clydejournal@earthlink.net; ed e-mail clydejournal@earthlink.net
Circulation: 1,300pd, 35fr; Sworn/Estimate/Non-Audited
Advertising rate: Open inch rate $3.30
Established: 1908
Pub...Betty Tabor
Ed
Becky Tabor
Delivery Method: Mail, Newsstand
Areas Served: Callahan County

CROWELL

FOARD COUNTY NEWS (THUR)

108 S 1st St, Crowell, TX, 79227, Foard, USA; gen tel (940) 684-1355; adv tel (940) 684-1355; ed tel (940) 684-1355; gen fax (940) 684-1700; adv fax (940) 684-1700; ed fax (940) 684-1700; disp adv e-mail fcnews@srcaccess.net; class adv e-mail fcnews@srcaccess.net; ed e-mail fcnews@srcaccess.net
Circulation: 727pd,; Sworn/Estimate/Non-Audited
Advertising rate: Open inch rate $3.00
Established: 1891
Leslie Hopkins
Lisa HopkinsPub./Ed./Adv. Dir.s
Delivery Method: Mail

CRYSTAL CITY

ZAVALA COUNTY SENTINEL (THUR)

202 E Nueces St, Crystal City, TX, 78839-3325, Zavala, USA; gen tel (830) 374-3465; adv tel (830) 374-3465; ed tel (830) 374-3465; gen fax (830) 374-5771; adv fax (830) 374-5771; ed fax (830) 374-5771; disp adv e-mail zcsentinel@sbcglobal.net; class adv e-mail zcsentinel@sbcglobal.net; ed e-mail zcsentinel@sbcglobal.net; web site www.zavalacountysentinel.net
Circulation: 2,300pd, 50fr; Sworn/Estimate/Non-Audited
Advertising rate: Open inch rate $4.15
Established: 1911
Group: Winter Garden Publishing Co., Inc.
Digital Platform - Mobile: Apple, Android
Digital Platform - Tablet: Apple iOS, Android, Windows 7
Co-Pub..................................Ricardo Sanchez
Co-Pub...Jerry Mata
Managing Ed./Circ. Mgr. .... Mary Rodriquez
Adv. Mgr....................................... Rosa Rocha
Pub... Tomas Aguilar
District Mgr. Alberto LiraEquipment & Software: Hardware — APP/Mac; Software — Adobe/PageMaker 6.0, Microsoft/Word.
Delivery Method: Mail, Racks
Areas Served: Zavala County

CUERO

THE CUERO RECORD (WED)

119 E Main St, Cuero, TX, 77954-3021, DeWitt, USA; gen tel (361) 275-3464; adv tel (361) 275-3464; ed tel (361) 275-3464; gen fax (361) 275-3131; adv fax (361) 275-3131; ed fax (361) 275-3131; disp adv e-mail cuerorecord@cuerorecord.com; class adv e-mail cuerorecord@cuerorecord.com; ed e-mail cuerorecord@cuerorecord.com; web site www.cuerorecord.com
Circulation: 2,445pd, 2,685fr; USPS
Advertising rate: Open inch rate $14.50
Established: 1894
Group: Moser Community Media
Digital Platform - Mobile: Apple, Android, Windows, Blackberry
Digital Platform - Tablet: Apple iOS, Android, Windows 7, Blackberry Tablet OS, Kindle, Nook, Kindle Fire
Pub./Ed. ....Glenn Rea
Adv. Dir.................................... Sonya Timpone
Delivery Method: Mail, Newsstand, Racks
Areas Served: DeWitt County

DAINGERFIELD

THE BEE (WED)

106 Webb St, Daingerfield, TX, 75638-1648, Morris, USA; gen tel (903) 645-3948; adv tel (903) 645-3948; ed tel (903) 645-3948; gen fax (903) 645-3731; adv fax (903) 645-3731; ed fax (903) 645-3731; disp adv e-mail thebee@etcnonline.com; class adv e-mail beenewspaper@etcnonline.com; ed e-mail alewter@steelcountrybee.com; web site www.steelcountrybee.com
Circulation: 3,100pd, 3,068fr; Sworn/Estimate/Non-Audited
Advertising rate: Open inch rate $9.30
Established: 1965
Group: Northeast Texas Publishing
Digital Platform - Mobile: Apple, Android, Windows, Blackberry
Digital Platform - Tablet: Apple iOS, Android, Windows 7, Blackberry Tablet OS, Kindle, Nook, Kindle Fire
Ed. .... Susan Taft
Adv. Dir................................Keilani Gonzalez
Delivery Method: Mail, Newsstand, Racks
Areas Served: Morris County

DALHART

DALHART TEXAN (TUES, FRI)

410 Denrock Ave, Dalhart, TX, 79022-2628, Dallam, USA; gen tel (806) 244-4511; adv tel (806)244-4511; ed tel (806)244-4511; gen fax (806) 244-2395; adv fax (806)244-2395; ed fax (806)244-2395; disp adv e-mail advertising@thedalharttexan.com; class adv e-mail classifieds@thedalharttexan.com; ed e-mail publisher@thedalharttexan.com; web site www.thedalharttexan.com
Circulation: 2,300pd,; Sworn/Estimate/Non-Audited
Advertising rate: Open inch rate $7.30
Established: 1901
Digital Platform - Mobile: Apple, Android
Digital Platform - Tablet: Apple iOS, Android
Owner/Co-Pub...............................Scott Wood
Owner/Co-Pub............................Scott Wesner
Ed./Adv. Dir. .... Tammi Kate Ledford
Mechanical Specifications: Type page 15 x 21; E - 6 cols, 2 1/16, 1/8 between; A - 6 cols, 2 1/16, 1/8 between; C - 6 cols, 2 1/16, 1/8 between.Equipment & Software: Hardware — 7-IBM/486 workstation, 1-IBM/486DX file-server; Presses — 3-KP/NewsKing; Software — Novell/Netware.
Delivery Method: Mail, Newsstand, Racks
Areas Served: Hartley and Dallam County

DALLAS

DALLAS BUSINESS JOURNAL (FRI)

2515 McKinney Ave, Ste 100, Dallas, TX, 75201-7675, Dallas, USA; gen tel (214) 696-5959; adv tel (214) 696-5959; ed tel (214) 696-5959; gen fax (214) 696-1486; adv fax (214) 696-1486; ed fax (214) 696-1486; disp adv e-mail dallas@bizjournals.com; class adv e-mail tphillips@bizjournals.com; ed e-mail dallas@bizjournals.com; web site www.bizjournals.com/dallas
Circulation: 11,847pd,; Sworn/Estimate/Non-Audited
Advertising rate: Open inch rate $9745.00 (Full-Page)
Established: 1977
Digital Platform - Mobile: Apple, Android, Windows, Blackberry
Digital Platform - Tablet: Apple iOS, Android, Windows 7, Blackberry Tablet OS, Kindle, Nook, Kindle Fire
Pub...Lisa Bormaster
Ed. ....Juan Elizondo Jr.
Adv. Dir.......................................Bob Baranski
Delivery Method: Mail, Racks
Areas Served: Dallas County

LONE STAR OUTDOOR NEWS (FRI)

PO Box 551695, Dallas, TX, 75355-1695, Dallas, USA; gen tel (214) 361-2276; adv tel (214) 361-2276; ed tel (214) 361-2276; gen fax (214) 501-0509; adv fax (214) 501-0509; ed fax (214) 501-0509; disp adv e-mail cnyhus@lonestaroutdoornews.com; class adv e-mail dsams@lonestaroutdoornews.com; ed e-mail editor@lonestaroutdoornews.com; web site www.lsonews.com
Circulation: 5,242pd, 35,519fr; VAC
Advertising rate: Open inch rate $16.50
Established: 2004
Digital Platform - Mobile: Apple, Android
Digital Platform - Tablet: Apple iOS, Android, Windows 7
Founder/CEO ....David J. Sams
Exec. Ed.......................................Craig Nyhus
Mng. Ed.................................. Conor Harrison
Delivery Method: Mail, Newsstand, Racks
Areas Served: All Texas

PARK CITIES NEWS (THUR)

4136 Greenbrier Dr, Ste 575, Dallas, TX, 75225-6635, Dallas, USA; gen tel (214) 369-7570; adv tel (214) 369-7570; ed tel (214) 369-7570; gen fax (214) 369-7736; adv fax (214) 369-7736; ed fax (214) 369-7736; disp adv e-mail advertising@peoplenewspapers.com; class adv e-mail pcn@parkcitiesnews.com; ed e-mail pcn@parkcitiesnews.com; web site www.parkcitiesnews.com
Circulation: 5,000pd, 250fr; Sworn/Estimate/Non-Audited
Advertising rate: 1/12 Pg $455.00; 1/8 Pg $650.00; 1/6 Pg $845.00
Established: 1938
Pub......................................Marjorie B. Waters
Ed./Gen. Mgr...................... Thomas R. Waters
Ed./Adv. Dir. .... Peter H. Waters
Mechanical Specifications: Type page 13 x 21; E - 6 cols, 2, between; A - 6 cols, 2, between; C - 5 cols, 2 1/2, between.Equipment & Software: Hardware — APP/Mac.
Delivery Method: Mail
Areas Served: Highland Park, University Park, Preston Hollow, Bluff View, Turtle Creek, Greenway Parks and far North Dallas

PARK CITIES PEOPLE (MTHLY)

750 N Saint Paul St, Ste 2100, Dallas, TX, 75201-3214, Dallas, USA; gen tel (214) 739-2244; adv tel (214) 739-2244; ed tel (214) 739-2244 ext. 257; gen fax (214) 594-5779; adv fax (214) 594-5779; ed fax (214) 594-5779; disp adv e-mail advertising@peoplenewspapers.com; class adv e-mail gabrielle.reese@peoplenewspapers.com; ed e-mail editor@peoplenewspapers.com; web site www.parkcitiespeople.com - 55,000(views) 12,500(visitors)
Circulation: 301pd, 20,651fr; CVC
Advertising rate: Open inch rate $58.00
Established: 1981
Group: D Magazine Partners LPEditions: (2) Preston Hollow People
Digital Platform - Mobile: Apple, Android, Windows, Blackberry
Digital Platform - Tablet: Apple iOS, Android, Windows 7, Blackberry Tablet OS
Pub...Patricia Martin
Editor ....Todd Jorgenson
Mechanical Specifications: 5 column x 14" page size
1 column 1.85"
2 column 3.88"
3 column 5.92"
4 column 7.96"
5 column 10.00"
Delivery Method: Mail, Newsstand, Racks
Areas Served: 75205, 75209, 75219, 75220, 75225, 75229, 75230

PRESTON HOLLOW PEOPLE (MTHLY)
750 N Saint Paul St, Ste 2100, Dallas, TX, 75201-3214, Dallas, USA; gen tel (214) 739-2244; adv tel (214) 523-5228; ed tel (214) 739-2244 ext. 242; gen fax (214) 594-5779; disp adv e-mail advertising@peoplenewspapers.com; class adv e-mail classifieds@peoplenewspapers.com; ed e-mail editor@peoplenewspapers.com; web site www.parkcitiespeople.com - 11,000(views) 4,000(visitors)
Circulation: 109pd, 25,041fr; CVC
Advertising rate: Open inch rate $58.00
Established: 1981
Group: D Magazine Partners LP
Digital Platform - Mobile: Apple, Android
Digital Platform - Tablet: Apple iOS, Android, Windows 7
Pub....Patricia Martin
Marketing Coordinator....Gabrielle Reese
Mechanical Specifications: 5 column x 14" page size
1 column 1.85"
2 column 3.88"
3 column 5.92"
4 column 7.96"
5 column 10.00"
Delivery Method: Mail, Newsstand, Racks
Areas Served: 75209, 75220, 75225, 75229, 75230

TEXAS JEWISH POST (THUR)
7920 Belt Line Rd, Ste 680, Dallas, TX, 75254-8150, Dallas, USA; gen tel (972) 458-7283; gen fax (214) 466-2633; disp adv e-mail susanw@tjpnews.com; class adv e-mail susanw@tjpnews.com; ed e-mail sharon@tjpnews.com; web site www.tjpnews.com
Circulation: 3,569pd, 455fr; CVC
Advertising rate: Open inch rate $35.00
Established: 1947
Group: Joseph Jacobs Organization
Digital Platform - Mobile: Apple, Android, Windows, Blackberry
Digital Platform - Tablet: Apple iOS, Android, Windows 7, Blackberry Tablet OS
Pub./Ed....Sharon Wisch-Ray
VP, Sales/Mktg....Amy Doty
VP Sales and Circ....Susan Wisch
Mechanical Specifications: Type page 10 1/8 x 12 1/2; E - 6 cols, between; A - 6 cols, between.Equipment & Software: Hardware — APP/Mac.
Delivery Method: Mail, Newsstand, Racks
Areas Served: Dallas County

TEXAS LAWYER (MON)
1412 Main St, Dallas, TX, 75202-4014, Dallas, USA; gen tel (214) 744-9300; adv tel (214) 744-7751; ed tel (214) 744-7721; gen fax (214) 741-2325; adv fax (214) 741-2325; ed fax (214) 741-2325; disp adv e-mail ccollins@alm.com; class adv e-mail ccollins@alm.com; ed e-mail ccollins@alm.com; web site www.texaslawyer.com
Circulation: 3,694pd,; Sworn/Estimate/Non-Audited
Advertising rate: Open inch rate $25.00
Established: 1985
Digital Platform - Mobile: Apple, Android, Windows, Blackberry
Digital Platform - Tablet: Apple iOS, Android, Windows 7, Blackberry Tablet OS, Kindle, Nook, Kindle Fire
Pub....Cathy Collins
Ed. in Chief....Heather D Nevitt
Delivery Method: Mail, Racks
Areas Served: Dallas County

DE LEON

DE LEON FREE PRESS (THUR)
324 S Texas St, De Leon, TX, 76444-1946, Comanche, USA; gen tel (254) 893-6868; adv tel (254) 893-6868; ed tel (254) 893-6868; gen fax (254) 893-3550; adv fax (254) 893-3550; ed fax (254) 893-3550; disp adv e-mail news@deleontexas.com; class adv e-mail news@deleontexas.com; ed e-mail news@deleontexas.com; web site www.deleonfreepress.com
Circulation: 2,000pd,; Sworn/Estimate/Non-Audited
Advertising rate: Open inch rate $4.30
Established: 1890
Digital Platform - Mobile: Windows
Digital Platform - Tablet: Windows 7
Pub....Jon Awbrey
Ed....Laura Kestner
Adv. Mgr....Betty Wofford
Delivery Method: Mail, Newsstand
Areas Served: Comanche County

DECATUR

WISE COUNTY MESSENGER (WED, SAT)
115 S Trinity St, Decatur, TX, 76234-1819, Wise, USA; gen tel (940) 627-5987; adv tel (940) 627-5987; ed tel (940) 627-5987; gen fax (940) 627-1004; adv fax (940) 627-1004; ed fax (940) 627-1004; disp adv e-mail webmaster@wcmessenger.com; class adv e-mail webmaster@wcmessenger.com; ed e-mail news@wcmessenger.com; web site www.wcmessenger.com
Circulation: 7,745pd, 34fr; Sworn/Estimate/Non-Audited
Advertising rate: Open inch rate $8.95
Established: 1880
Digital Platform - Mobile: Apple, Android, Windows, Blackberry
Digital Platform - Tablet: Apple iOS, Android, Windows 7, Blackberry Tablet OS
Pres./Pub....Roy J. Eaton
Exec. Ed....Bob Buckel
Sp. Project Mgr....Brian Knox
Adv. Mgr....Lisa Davis
Prod. Mgr....Todd Griffith
Gen. Mgr./VP, Adv....Mark Jordan
Ed....Kristin TribeEquipment & Software: Hardware — Mk, APP/Mac; Presses — Offset; Software — Adobe/PageMaker, QPS/QuarkXPress, Baseview.
Delivery Method: Mail, Racks
Areas Served: 76234, 76426, 76225, 76023, 76431, 76246, 76078, 76267, 76073, 76071

DELL CITY

HUDSPETH COUNTY HERALD (FRI)
290 S Main, Dell City, TX, 79837, Hudspeth, USA; gen tel (915) 964-2426; adv tel (915) 964-2426; ed tel (915) 964-2426; gen fax (915) 964-2426; adv fax (915) 964-2426; ed fax (915) 964-2426; disp adv e-mail hcherald@dellcity.com; class adv e-mail hcherald@dellcity.com; ed e-mail hcherald@dellcity.com
Circulation: 602pd,; Sworn/Estimate/Non-Audited
Advertising rate: Open inch rate $6.50
Established: 1956
Pub....James Lynch
Ed....Shannon Martin-Stewart
Delivery Method: Mail, Newsstand
Areas Served: Hudspeth County

DENVER CITY

DENVER CITY PRESS (SUN)
321 N Main Ave, Denver City, TX, 79323-3249, Yoakum, USA; gen tel (806) 592-2141; adv tel (806) 592-2141; ed tel (806) 592-2141; gen fax (806) 592-8233; adv fax (806) 592-8233; ed fax (806) 592-8233; disp adv e-mail dcpress@midtech.net; class adv e-mail dcpress@midtech.net; ed e-mail dcpress@midtech.net
Circulation: 1,600pd, 3fr; Sworn/Estimate/Non-Audited
Advertising rate: Open inch rate $5.00
Established: 1939
Pub....John Graham
Ed....JP Landry
Delivery Method: Mail, Newsstand
Areas Served: Yoakum County

DEPORT

DEPORT TIMES-BLOSSOM TIMES (THUR)
161 Main St, Deport, TX, 75435, Lamar, USA; gen tel (903) 652-4205; adv tel (903) 652-4205; ed tel (903) 652-4205; gen fax (903) 652-6041; adv fax (903) 652-6041; ed fax (903) 652-6041; disp adv e-mail tppub@1starnet.com; class adv e-mail tppub@1starnet.com; ed e-mail tppub@1starnet.com
Circulation: 783pd, 10fr; Sworn/Estimate/Non-Audited
Advertising rate: Open inch rate $5.20
Established: 1909
Group: Thunder Prairie Publishing
Pub./Ed....Nanalee Nichols
Adv. Mgr....Thomas Nichols
Office Mgr....Cindy Allen
Mechanical Specifications: Type page 13 x 21 1/2; E - 6 cols, 1 13/16, between; C - 8 cols, between.Equipment & Software: Hardware — APP/Power Mac; Software — Adobe/PageMaker 4.02.
Delivery Method: Mail, Racks
Areas Served: 75435, 75434, 75436, 75468, 75460

DETROIT WEEKLY (THUR)
161 Main St, Deport, TX, 75435, Lamar, USA; gen tel (903) 652-4205; adv tel (903) 652-4205; ed tel (903) 652-4205; gen fax (903) 652-6041; adv fax (903) 652-6041; ed fax (903) 652-6041; disp adv e-mail tppub@1starnet.com; class adv e-mail tppub@1starnet.com; ed e-mail tppub@1starnet.com
Circulation: 614pd,; Sworn/Estimate/Non-Audited
Advertising rate: Open inch rate $3.80
Established: 1982
Group: Thunder Prairie Publishing
Pub....Nanalee Nichols
Adv. Mgr....Thomas Nichols
Ed....Liz Irwin
Delivery Method: Mail, Newsstand
Areas Served: Red River County

DEVINE

DEVINE NEWS (THUR)
216 S Bright Dr, Devine, TX, 78016-3202, Medina, USA; gen tel (830) 665-2211; adv tel (830) 665-2211; ed tel (830) 665-2211; gen fax (830) 663-3686; adv fax (830) 663-3686; ed fax (830) 663-3686; disp adv e-mail ads@devinenews.com; class adv e-mail kk@devinenews.com; ed e-mail news@devinenews.com; web site www.devinenews.com
Advertising rate: Open inch rate $8.00
Established: 1897
Digital Platform - Mobile: Apple, Android, Windows, Blackberry
Digital Platform - Tablet: Apple iOS, Android, Windows 7, Blackberry Tablet OS
Pub./Gen. Mgr....Kathleen DuBose Calame
Adv. Sales Rep....Linda Sherrell
Ed./Office Mgr....Kayleen Holden
Delivery Method: Mail, Newsstand, Racks
Areas Served: Medina County

DIBOLL

DIBOLL FREE PRESS (WED)
PO Box 339, Diboll, TX, 75941-0339, Angelina, USA; gen tel (936) 829-3313; adv tel (936) 829-3313; ed tel (936) 829-3313; gen fax (936) 829-3321; adv fax (936) 829-3321; ed fax (936) 829-3321; disp adv e-mail ads@dibollfreepress.com; class adv e-mail web@dibollfreepress.com; ed e-mail editor@dibollfreepress.com; web site www.dibollfreepress.com
Circulation: 3,526pd, 187fr; Sworn/Estimate/Non-Audited
Advertising rate: Open inch rate $8.54
Established: 1952
Group: Temple-Inland Forest Products Corp.
Digital Platform - Mobile: Apple, Android
Digital Platform - Tablet: Apple iOS, Android, Windows 7
Online Media Dir....Hunter McLeroy
Pub....Bill Woodall
Ed....Jerry Gaudling
Mechanical Specifications: Type page 13 x 21; E - 6 cols, between; A - 6 cols, between; C - 8 cols, between.Equipment & Software: Hardware — APP/Mac; Presses — MAN; Software — QPS/QuarkXPress 3.32.
Delivery Method: Mail, Newsstand
Areas Served: Angelina County

DIMMITT

THE CASTRO COUNTY NEWS (THUR)
108 W Bedford St, Dimmitt, TX, 79027-2504, Castro, USA; gen tel (806) 647-1234; adv tel (806) 647-1234; ed tel (806) 647-1234; gen fax (866) 563-8728; adv fax (866) 563-8728; ed fax (866) 563-8728; disp adv e-mail thecastrocountynews@yahoo.com; class adv e-mail newspaperjeff@yahoo.com; ed e-mail thecastrocountynews@yahoo.com; web site www.thecastrocountynews.com/
Circulation: 1,500pd, 62fr; Sworn/Estimate/Non-Audited
Advertising rate: Open inch rate $5.00
Established: 1924
Digital Platform - Mobile: Apple, Android
Digital Platform - Tablet: Apple iOS, Android, Windows 7
Adv. Dir....Jeff Blackmon
Assoc. Pub....Bill Holland
Pub....Brett Wesner
Mechanical Specifications: Type page 11 11/16 x 21; E - 6 cols, 1 13/16, 3/16 between; A - 6 cols, 1 13/16, 3/16 between; C - 6 cols, 1 13/16, 3/16 between.Equipment & Software: Hardware — PCs, HP/LaserPrinter, APP/Mac LaserPrinter; Software — Photoshop, InDesign
Delivery Method: Mail
Areas Served: 79027, 79043, 79063

DUBLIN

THE DUBLIN CITIZEN (THUR)
938 N Patrick St, Dublin, TX, 76446-1128, Erath, USA; gen tel (254) 445-2515; adv tel (254)445-2515; ed tel (254)445-2515; gen fax (254) 445-4116; adv fax (254)445-4116; ed fax (254)445-4116; disp adv e-mail publisher@dublincitizen.com; class adv e-mail classifieds@dublincitizen.com; ed e-mail publisher@dublincitizen.com; web site www.dublincitizen.com
Circulation: 2,400pd,; Sworn/Estimate/Non-Audited
Advertising rate: Open inch rate $5.00
Established: 1990
Digital Platform - Mobile: Other
Digital Platform - Tablet: Other
Pub./Ed./Owner....Mac McKinnon
Bus. Mgr....Cindy Combs
Mechanical Specifications: 11.625 x 21
Delivery Method: Mail, Newsstand, Racks
Areas Served: Erath County

DUMAS

THE MOORE COUNTY NEWS-PRESS (THUR, SUN)
702 S Meredith Ave, Dumas, TX, 79029-4444, Moore, USA; gen tel (806) 935-4111; adv tel (806) 935-4111; ed tel (806) 935-4111; gen fax (806) 935-2348; adv fax (806) 935-2348; ed fax (806) 935-2348; disp adv e-mail advertising@moorenews.com; class adv e-mail classifieds@moorenews.com; ed e-mail editor@moorenews.com; web site www.moorenews.com
Circulation: 3,480pd,; Sworn/Estimate/Non-Audited
Advertising rate: Open inch rate $7.95
Established: 1927

Group: Lancaster Management, Inc.
Digital Platform - Mobile: Apple, Android
Digital Platform - Tablet: Apple iOS, Android, Windows 7
Pub. .... Wanda Brooks
Ed. .... Michael Wright
Bus. Mgr. .... Robin Patterson
Mechanical Specifications: Type page 12 1/2 x 20; E - 6 cols, 1 15/16, 1/8 between; A - 6 cols, 1 15/16, 1/8 between; C - 8 cols, 1 1/2, 1/8 between.Equipment & Software: ; Software — QPS/QuarkXPress, Microsoft/Word, Adobe/Photoshop.
Delivery Method: Mail, Newsstand, Carrier, Racks
Areas Served: Moore County

EAGLE LAKE

EAGLE LAKE HEADLIGHT (THUR)

220 E Main St, Eagle Lake, TX, 77434-2426, Colorado, USA; gen tel (979) 234-5521; adv tel (979) 234-5521; ed tel (979) 234-5521; gen fax (979) 234-5522; adv fax (979) 234-5522; ed fax (979) 234-5522; disp adv e-mail eaglelakeheadlight@sbcglobal.net; class adv e-mail eaglelakeheadlight@sbcglobal.net; ed e-mail eaglelakeheadlight@sbcglobal.net; web site www.eaglelakeheadlight.com
Circulation: 2,057pd,; Sworn/Estimate/Non-Audited
Advertising rate: Open inch rate $4.15
Established: 1903
Digital Platform - Mobile: Apple, Android, Windows, Blackberry
Digital Platform - Tablet: Apple iOS, Android, Windows 7, Blackberry Tablet OS
Pub./Ed. .... Doug Beal
Adv. Dir. .... Alesia Davis
Delivery Method: Mail, Racks
Areas Served: Colorado County

EASTLAND

CALLAHAN COUNTY STAR (THUR)

215 S Seaman St, Eastland, TX, 76448-2745, Eastland, USA; gen tel (254) 629-1707; adv tel (254) 629-1707; ed tel (254) 629-1707; gen fax (254) 629-2092; adv fax (254) 629-2092; ed fax (254) 629-2092; disp adv e-mail ecn@att.net; class adv e-mail ecn@att.net; ed e-mail ecn@att.net; web site www.eastlandcountytoday.com
Circulation: 579pd,; Sworn/Estimate/Non-Audited
Advertising rate: Open inch rate $5.00
Established: 1887
Digital Platform - Mobile: Apple, Android, Windows, Blackberry
Digital Platform - Tablet: Apple iOS, Android, Windows 7, Blackberry Tablet OS, Kindle, Nook, Kindle Fire
Pub./Ed. .... Houston V. O'Brien
Adv. Dir. .... Rebecca McCrary
Delivery Method: Mail
Areas Served: Callahan County

EASTLAND TELEGRAM (THUR, SUN)

215 S Seaman St, Eastland, TX, 76448-2745, Eastland, USA; gen tel (254) 629-1707; adv tel (254) 629-1707; ed tel (254) 629-1707; gen fax (254) 629-2092; adv fax (254) 629-2092; ed fax (254) 629-2092; disp adv e-mail ecn@att.net; class adv e-mail ecn@att.net; ed e-mail ecn@att.net; web site www.eastlandcountytoday.com
Circulation: 1,825pd,; Sworn/Estimate/Non-Audited
Advertising rate: Open inch rate $8.00
Established: 1925
Group: Eastland County Newspapers
Digital Platform - Mobile: Apple, Android
Digital Platform - Tablet: Apple iOS, Android, Windows 7
Pub. .... Houston V. O'Brien
Ed. .... Amy Glenn
Circ. Mgr. .... Margaret Hallmark
Adv. Dir. .... McCrary Rebecca
Mechanical Specifications: Type page 14 x 21; E - 8 cols, 1 7/12, 1 between; A - 8 cols, 1 7/12, 1 between.Equipment & Software: Hardware — APP/Mac; Presses — 4-KP/News King.
Delivery Method: Mail, Racks
Areas Served: Eastland County

RANGER TIMES (THUR, SUN)

215 S Seaman St, Eastland, TX, 76448-2745, Eastland, USA; gen tel (254) 629-1707; adv tel (254) 629-1707; ed tel (254) 629-1707; gen fax (254) 629-2092; adv fax (254) 629-2092; ed fax (254) 629-2092; disp adv e-mail ecn@att.net; class adv e-mail ecn@att.net; ed e-mail ecn@att.net; web site www.eastlandcountytoday.com
Circulation: 538pd,; Sworn/Estimate/Non-Audited
Advertising rate: Open inch rate $6.25
Established: 1919
Group: Eastland County Newspapers
Digital Platform - Mobile: Apple, Android, Windows, Blackberry
Digital Platform - Tablet: Apple iOS, Android, Windows 7, Blackberry Tablet OS, Kindle, Nook, Kindle Fire
Pub. .... Houston V. O'Brien
Ed. .... Margaret Hetrick
Adv. Dir. .... Rebecca McCrary
Delivery Method: Mail
Areas Served: Eastland County

RISING STAR (THUR)

PO Box 29, Eastland, TX, 76448-0029, Eastland, USA; gen tel (254) 629-1707; adv tel (254) 629-1707; ed tel (254) 629-1707; gen fax (254) 629-2092; adv fax (254) 629-2092; ed fax (254) 629-2092; disp adv e-mail ecn@att.net; class adv e-mail ecn@att.net; ed e-mail ecn@att.net; web site www.eastlandcountytoday.com
Circulation: 550pd, 41fr; Sworn/Estimate/Non-Audited
Advertising rate: Open inch rate $16.00
Group: Eastland County Newspapers
Digital Platform - Mobile: Apple, Android
Digital Platform - Tablet: Apple iOS, Android, Windows 7
Pub. .... Houston V. O'Brien
Mechanical Specifications: Type page 14 x 23; E - 8 cols, 1 1/2, 1/4 between; A - 8 cols, 1 1/2, 1/4 between; C - 8 cols, 1 1/2, 1/4 between. Equipment & Software: Hardware — APP/Mac; Software — Claris/MacWrite 3.0.
Delivery Method: Mail, Racks
Areas Served: Eastland County

EDEN

THE EDEN ECHO (THUR)

131 Market St, Eden, TX, 76837, Concho, USA; gen tel (325) 869-5717; adv tel (325) 869-5717; ed tel (325) 869-5717; disp adv e-mail edenecho@wcc.net; class adv e-mail edenecho@wcc.net; ed e-mail edenecho@wcc.net; web site EDENECHO.NET
Circulation: 610pd, 30fr; USPS
Advertising rate: Open inch rate $4.00
Established: 1906
Group: EDEN APPLE TREE ENTERPRISES LLCEditions: (1,000)
Pub./Ed./Adv. Dir. .... A.J. Dolle
Ed. .... Lillian HarrodEquipment & Software: Hardware — computers
Delivery Method: Mail, Racks
Areas Served: Concho County

EDNA

JACKSON COUNTY HERALD-TRIBUNE (WED)

306 N Wells St, Edna, TX, 77957-2729, Jackson, USA; gen tel (361) 782-3547; adv tel (361) 782-3547; ed tel (361) 782-3547; gen fax (361) 782-6002; adv fax (361) 782-6002; ed fax (361) 782-6002; disp adv e-mail advertising@jacksonconews.com; class adv e-mail Sales@jacksonconews.com; ed e-mail news@jacksonconews.com; web site www.jacksonconews.com
Circulation: 2,700pd, 35fr; Sworn/Estimate/Non-Audited
Advertising rate: Open inch rate $8.50
Established: 1906
Group: Moser community Media
Digital Platform - Mobile: Apple, Android, Windows, Blackberry
Digital Platform - Tablet: Apple iOS, Android, Windows 7, Blackberry Tablet OS, Kindle, Nook, Kindle Fire
Publisher .... Chris Lundstrom
Adv. Dir. .... Pam Harvey
Delivery Method: Mail, Newsstand
Areas Served: Jackson County

EL CAMPO

EL CAMPO LEADER-NEWS (WED, SAT)

203 E Jackson St, El Campo, TX, 77437-4413, Wharton, USA; gen tel (979) 543-3363; adv tel (979) 543-3363; ed tel (979) 543-3363; gen fax (979) 543-0097; adv fax (979) 543-0097; ed fax (979) 543-0097; disp adv e-mail publisher@leader-news.com; class adv e-mail classified@leader-news.com; ed e-mail publisher@leader-news.com; web site www.leader-news.com
Circulation: 4,583pd, 115fr; Sworn/Estimate/Non-Audited
Advertising rate: Open inch rate $8.32
Established: 1885
Group: Hartman Newspapers LP
Digital Platform - Mobile: Apple, Android, Windows
Digital Platform - Tablet: Apple iOS, Android, Windows 7
Pub./Ed. .... Jay T. Strasner
Office Mgr. .... Diana David
Keri Mahalitc
Mechanical Specifications: Type page 13 x 21; E - 6 cols, 2 1/20, 1/6 between; A - 6 cols, 2 1/20, 1/6 between; C - 6 cols, 2 1/20, 1/6 between.Equipment & Software: Hardware — Mk, APP/Mac; Software — QPS/QuarkXPress, Adobe/Photoshop, Claris/Works, Microsoft/Office, Microsoft/Works, Baseview/NewsEdit Pro.
Delivery Method: Mail, Newsstand, Racks
Areas Served: 77437, 77488, 77442, 77460

ELDORADO

ELDORADO SUCCESS (THUR)

204 SW Main St, Eldorado, TX, 76936, Schleicher, USA; gen tel (325) 853-3125; adv tel (325) 853-3125; ed tel (325) 853-3125; gen fax (325) 853-3378; adv fax (325) 853-3378; ed fax (325) 853-3378; disp adv e-mail kathy@myeldorado.net; class adv e-mail lupe@myeldorado.net; ed e-mail success@myeldorado.net; web site www.myeldorado.net
Circulation: 1,100pd,; Sworn/Estimate/Non-Audited
Advertising rate: Open inch rate $6.00
Established: 1901
Group: Masked Rider Publishing, Inc.
Digital Platform - Mobile: Apple, Android
Digital Platform - Tablet: Apple iOS, Android, Windows 7
Pub. .... Randy Mankin
Gen. Mgr./Adv. Dir. .... Kathy Mankin
Circ. Mgr. .... Lupe Elizondo
Delivery Method: Mail, Newsstand, Racks
Areas Served: Schleicher County

ELECTRA

ELECTRA STAR-NEWS (THUR)

207 N Waggoner St, Electra, TX, 76360-2440, Wichita, USA; gen tel (940) 495-2149; adv tel (940) 495-2149; ed tel (940) 495-2149; gen fax (940) 495-2627; adv fax (940) 495-2627; ed fax (940) 495-2627; disp adv e-mail electrastarnews@electratel.net; class adv e-mail electrastarnews@electratel.net; ed e-mail electrastarnews@electratel.net
Circulation: 2,000pd, 79fr; Sworn/Estimate/Non-Audited
Advertising rate: Open inch rate $3.00
Established: 1907
Pub. .... Ted Miller
Ed. .... Jeannette Miller
Adv. Dir. .... Ann Wright
Delivery Method: Mail, Newsstand
Areas Served: Wichita County

ELGIN

ELGIN COURIER (WED)

105 N Main St, Elgin, TX, 78621-2618, Bastrop, USA; gen tel (512) 285-3333; adv tel (512)285-3333; ed tel (512)285-3333; gen fax (512) 285-9406; adv fax (512)285-9406; ed fax (512)392-9406; disp adv e-mail publisher@elgincourier.com; class adv e-mail publisher@elgincourier.com; ed e-mail elgincourier@elgincourier.com; web site www.elgincourier.com
Circulation: 2,007pd, 220fr; CVC
Advertising rate: Open inch rate $9.00
Established: 1890
Group: Fenice Community Media
Digital Platform - Mobile: Apple, Android
Digital Platform - Tablet: Apple iOS, Android, Windows 7
Adv. Mgr. .... Marie Ott
Publisher .... Dan Kleiner
Ed. .... Charles Wood
Circ. Mgr .... Heather Romine
Prod. Mgr .... Patricia FinneyEquipment & Software: Hardware — APP/Mac; Software — QuarkXPress 8.5
Delivery Method: Mail, Newsstand, Racks
Areas Served: Bastrop County

EMORY

RAINS COUNTY LEADER (TUES)

239 N Texas St, Emory, TX, 75440-2405, Rains, USA; gen tel (903) 473-2653; adv tel (903) 473-2653; ed tel (903) 473-2653; gen fax (903) 473-0050; adv fax (903) 473-0050; ed fax (903) 473-0050; disp adv e-mail rainsleader@earthlink.net; class adv e-mail ads@rainscountyleader.com; ed e-mail news@rainscountyleader.com; web site www.rainscountyleader.com
Circulation: 2,400pd, 79fr; Sworn/Estimate/Non-Audited
Advertising rate: Open inch rate $6.00
Established: 1887Editions: (900) RainsCountyLeader.com
Digital Platform - Mobile: Apple, Android
Digital Platform - Tablet: Apple iOS, Android, Windows 7
Pub. .... Earl C. Hill
Circ. Mgr. .... Nancy Fenter
Ed. .... Earl, III Hill
Adv. Mgr. .... Kay Thompson
Mechanical Specifications: Type page 13 x 21; E - 6 cols, 2, 1/4 between; A - 6 cols, 2, 1/4 between; C - 6 cols, 2, 1/4 between.Equipment & Software: Hardware — 7-mini macs, Xante/Accel-a-Writer, GCC/Elite 20/200 Printer; Presses — print off site; Software — Adobe/Illustrator 9.0, Adobe/Photoshop 5.0, Microsoft/Word 5.0, Adobe/InDesign 1.5, Adobe/Go Live 5.0.
Delivery Method: Mail, Newsstand, Racks
Areas Served: 75440, 75453, 75472, 75410

FAIRFIELD

FREESTONE COUNTY TIMES (WED)

401 E Commerce St, Fairfield, TX, 75840-1603, Freestone, USA; gen tel (903) 389-6397; adv tel (903) 389-6397; ed tel (903) 389-6397; gen fax (903) 389-2636; adv fax (903) 389-2636; ed fax (903) 389-2636; disp adv e-mail ads@freestonecountytimes.com; class adv e-mail ads@freestonecountytimes.com; ed e-mail news@freestonecountytimes.com; web site www.freestonecountytimes.com 12,284(visitors)
Circulation: 2,840pd, 52fr; Sworn/Estimate/Non-Audited

Advertising rate: Open inch rate $8.20
Established: 2002
Digital Platform - Mobile: Apple, Android
Digital Platform - Tablet: Apple iOS, Android, Windows 7
Pub./Adv. Dir. .... Scott Marster Sr.
Ed. ....Karen Leidy
Sales Exec......................Sherry Schoeneberg
Adv. Sales............Jennifer LockeEquipment & Software: ; Software — Adobe InDesign
Delivery Method: Mail, Newsstand
Areas Served: Freestone County

THE FAIRFIELD RECORDER (THUR)
101 E Commerce St, Fairfield, TX, 75840-1507, Freestone, USA; gen tel (903) 389-3334; gen fax (903) 389-8255; disp adv e-mail office@fairfield-recorder.com; class adv e-mail classifieds@fairfield-recorder.com; ed e-mail news@fairfield-recorder.com; web site www.fairfield-recorder.com
Circulation: 2,000pd,; Sworn/Estimate/Non-Audited
Advertising rate: Open inch rate $6
Established: 1876
Group: Freestone County Publishing LP
Digital Platform - Mobile: Apple, Android, Windows, Blackberry
Digital Platform - Tablet: Apple iOS, Android, Windows 7, Blackberry Tablet OS
Office Mgr. .... Tanya Lee
Mechanical Specifications: Type page 13 x 21; E - 6 cols, between.
Delivery Method: Mail, Newsstand, Racks
Areas Served: 75840, 75859, 75860, and surrounding areas

FALFURRIAS

FALFURRIAS FACTS (THUR)
219 E Rice St, Falfurrias, TX, 78355-3621, Brooks, USA; gen tel (361) 325-2200; adv tel (361) 325-2200; ed tel (361) 325-2200; gen fax (361) 325-2200; adv fax (361) 325-2200; ed fax (361) 325-2200; disp adv e-mail falfacts@yahoo.com; class adv e-mail falfacts@yahoo.com; ed e-mail falfacts@yahoo.com
Circulation: 3,000pd,; Sworn/Estimate/Non-Audited
Advertising rate: Open inch rate $5.00
Established: 1906
Pub./Ed. .... Marcelo Silva
Adv. Dir............................San Juanita Olivarez
Mechanical Specifications: 1 col. = 1.6111"
2 col. = 3.3889"
3 col. = 5.1667"
4 col. = 6.9444"
5 col. = 8.7222"
6 col. = 10.5"
Delivery Method: Mail, Newsstand
Areas Served: Brooks, Jim Wells, Jim Hogg, and Kenedy

FARMERSVILLE

FARMERSVILLE TIMES (THUR)
101 S Main St, Farmersville, TX, 75442-2207, Collin, USA; gen tel (972) 784-6397; adv tel (972) 442.5515 x29; ed tel (972) 784.6397 x30; disp adv e-mail advertising@csmediatexas.com; class adv e-mail classifieds@csmediatexas.com; ed e-mail news@farmersvilletimes.com; web site www.farmersvilletimes.com
Circulation: 3,500pd,; USPS
Advertising rate: Open inch rate $8.25
Established: 1885
Group: C&S Media, Inc.
Digital Platform - Mobile: Apple, Android, Windows, Blackberry
Digital Platform - Tablet: Apple iOS, Android, Windows 7, Blackberry Tablet OS, Kindle, Kindle Fire
Pub./Ed./Adv. Mgr. .. Chad EngbrockEquipment & Software: Hardware — Apple; Software — inDesign
Delivery Method: Mail, Newsstand, Carrier, Racks
Areas Served: Collin County

PRINCETON HERALD (THUR)
101 S Main St, Farmersville, TX, 75442-2207, Collin, USA; gen tel (972) 784-6397; adv tel (972) 784-6397; ed tel (972) 784-6397; gen fax (972) 782-7023; adv fax (972) 782-7023; ed fax (972) 782-7023; disp adv e-mail advertising@csmediatexas.com; class adv e-mail advertising@csmediatexas.com; ed e-mail news@princetonherald.com; web site www.princetonherald.com
Circulation: 1,799pd, 27fr; Sworn/Estimate/Non-Audited
Advertising rate: Open inch rate $8.00
Established: 1970
Group: C&S Media, Inc.
Digital Platform - Mobile: Apple, Android, Windows, Blackberry
Digital Platform - Tablet: Apple iOS, Android, Windows 7, Blackberry Tablet OS, Kindle, Nook, Kindle Fire
Pub./Ed./Adv. Dir..................... Chad Engbrock
Mechanical Specifications: Type page 11.5 x 21; E - 6 cols, 1.778 between; A & B sections - 6 cols C section - 8 cols, 1 3/4, 1/6 between.
Delivery Method: Mail, Newsstand, Racks
Areas Served: 75407

FARWELL

THE STATE LINE TRIBUNE (FRI)
404 3rd St, Farwell, TX, 79325-4670, Parmer, USA; gen tel (806) 481-3681; adv tel (806) 481-3681; ed tel (806) 481-3681; disp adv e-mail tribune@plateautel.net; class adv e-mail tribune@plateautel.net; ed e-mail tribune@plateautel.net; web site www.statelinetribune.com
Circulation: 1,500pd, 0fr; Sworn/Estimate/Non-Audited
Advertising rate: Open inch rate $4.20
Established: 1911
Digital Platform - Mobile: Apple, Android
Digital Platform - Tablet: Apple iOS, Android
Pub./Ed./Adv. Dir..........................Rob Pomper
Delivery Method: Mail, Racks
Areas Served: Parmer County, Bailey County, Curry County. 79325, 79009, 79035, 79347, 79053, 88135, 88101,

FERRIS

RED OAK RECORD (THUR)
208 S Central St, Ferris, TX, 75125-2622, Ellis, USA; gen tel (972) 544-2369; gen fax (972) 544-8150; disp adv e-mail publisher@redoakrecord.com; class adv e-mail ads@elliscountypress.com; ed e-mail charles@redoakrecord.com; web site www.redoakrecord.com
Circulation: 640pd, 340fr; Sworn/Estimate/Non-Audited
Advertising rate: Open inch rate $14.00
Established: 2006
Group: County Press Enterprises, LLC
Digital Platform - Mobile: Apple, Android, Windows
Digital Platform - Tablet: Apple iOS, Android, Windows 7
Pub./Ed..........................Charles D. Hatfield Jr.
Mechanical Specifications: Page Size 11.5 Wide x 21" Deep
Gutter 0.15"
1 Col = 1.719 inches
2 Col = 3.570 inches
3 Col = 5.438 inches
4 Col = 7.289 inches
5 Col = 9.156 inches
6 Col = 11.00 inchesEquipment & Software: Hardware — PC - Windows; Software — Adobe Series
Delivery Method: Mail, Newsstand, Racks
Areas Served: 75154

THE ELLIS COUNTY PRESS (THUR)
208 S Central St, Ferris, TX, 75125-2622, Ellis, USA; gen tel (972) 544-2369; gen fax (972) 544-8150; disp adv e-mail press@elliscountypress.com; class adv e-mail press@elliscountypress.com; ed e-mail charles@elliscountypress.com; web site www.elliscountypress.com
Circulation: 3,500pd, 500fr; Sworn/Estimate/Non-Audited
Advertising rate: Open inch rate $15.00
Established: 1992
Group: County Press Enterprises, LLC
Digital Platform - Mobile: Apple, Android, Windows, Blackberry
Digital Platform - Tablet: Apple iOS, Android, Windows 7, Blackberry Tablet OS
Pub./Owner/Ed...............Charles D. Hatfield Jr.
Inside Ad Sales.....................Shirley Habingga
Creative Director..................... Greg Chapman
Mechanical Specifications: Type page 11 1/2 x 21 1/2; E - 6 cols, 1 7/8, 1/8 between; A - 6 cols, 1 7/8, 1/8 between; C - 9 cols, 1 1/4, 1/8 between.Equipment & Software: Hardware — 5 PCs, 3 scanners, 3 color laser printers; Software — Microsoft/Windows XP & 7, Adobe Indesign 5, Adobe Photoshop CS5
Delivery Method: Mail, Newsstand, Racks
Areas Served: Ellis County

FLATONIA

THE FLATONIA ARGUS (THUR)
212 S Penn Ave, Flatonia, TX, 78941, Fayette, USA; gen tel (361) 865-3510; adv tel (361) 865-3510; ed tel (361) 865-3510; gen fax (361) 865-3510; adv fax (361) 865-3510; ed fax (361) 865-3510; disp adv e-mail admanager@flatoniaargus.com; class adv e-mail admanager@flatoniaargus.com; ed e-mail newspaper@flatoniaargus.com; web site www.flatoniaargus.com
Circulation: 940pd, 38fr; Sworn/Estimate/Non-Audited
Advertising rate: Open inch rate $3.90
Established: 1875
Digital Platform - Mobile: Apple, Windows
Digital Platform - Tablet: Apple iOS, Windows 7
Pub./Ed./Adv. Dir...................... Paul A. Prause
Office Mgr./Reporter/Photo......Melanie Berger
Mechanical Specifications: Type page 16 x 20 1/2; E - 8 cols, 1 5/6, 1/3 between; A - 8 cols, 1 5/6, 1/3 between; C - 8 cols, 1 5/6, 1/3 between.Equipment & Software: ; Software — WordPerfect.
Delivery Method: Mail, Newsstand
Areas Served: Fayette County

FLORESVILLE

WILSON COUNTY NEWS (WED)
1012 C St, Floresville, TX, 78114-2224, Wilson, USA; gen tel (830) 216-4519; adv tel (830)216-4519; ed tel (830)216-4519; gen fax (830) 393-3219; adv fax (830)393-3219; ed fax (830)393-3219; disp adv e-mail display@wcn-online.com; class adv e-mail classifieds@wcn-online.com; ed e-mail editor@wcn-online.com; web site www.wilsoncountynews.com - 4,000,000(views) 300,000(visitors)
Circulation: 8,190pd, 1,074fr; Sworn/Estimate/Non-Audited
Advertising rate: Open inch rate $12.83
Established: 1973
Group: WCN, Inc.
Digital Platform - Mobile: Apple, Android
Digital Platform - Tablet: Apple iOS, Android, Kindle
Publisher................................ Elaine Kolodziej
Ed. .... Nannette Kilbey-Smith
Op. Dir.......................................Kristen Weaver
Mechanical Specifications: 9.94" x 20.75"Equipment & Software: Hardware — APP/Mac; Software — Adobe/Photoshop/InDesign
Delivery Method: Mail, Newsstand
Areas Served: 78053, 78101, 78112, 78113, 78114, 78121, 78143, 78147, 78152, 78160, 78161, 78223, 78263

FLOYDADA

FLOYD COUNTY HESPERIAN-BEACON (THUR)
201 W California St, Ste A, Floydada, TX, 79235-2700, Floyd, USA; gen tel (806) 983-3737; adv tel (806) 983-3737; ed tel (806) 983-3737; gen fax (806) 983-3141; adv fax (806) 983-3141; ed fax (806) 983-3141; disp adv e-mail fchb.editor@yahoo.com; class adv e-mail fchblockney@yahoo.com; ed e-mail fchb.editor@yahoo.com; web site www.hesperianbeacononline.com
Circulation: 2,600pd, 23fr; Sworn/Estimate/Non-Audited
Advertising rate: Open inch rate $3.75
Established: 1896
Digital Platform - Mobile: Apple, Android, Windows, Blackberry
Digital Platform - Tablet: Apple iOS, Android, Windows 7, Blackberry Tablet OS, Kindle, Nook, Kindle Fire
Owner.....................................Chris Bleckburn
Ed. ....Jennifer Harbin
Adv. Dir................................Barbara Anderson
Delivery Method: Mail, Racks
Areas Served: Floyd County

FORNEY

FORNEY MESSENGER (THUR)
201 W Broad St, Forney, TX, 75126-9161, Kaufman, USA; gen tel (972) 564-3121; adv tel (972) 564-3121; ed tel (972) 564-3121; gen fax (972) 552-3599; adv fax (972) 552-3599; ed fax (972) 552-3599; disp adv e-mail messengerads@sbcglobal.net; class adv e-mail messengerads@sbcglobal.net; ed e-mail messengernews@sbcglobal.net; web site www.yourforneymessenger.com
Circulation: 3,600pd,; Sworn/Estimate/Non-Audited
Advertising rate: Open inch rate $4.00
Established: 1896
Digital Platform - Mobile: Apple, Android, Windows, Blackberry
Digital Platform - Tablet: Apple iOS, Android, Windows 7, Blackberry Tablet OS
Pub...Cary L. Griffin
Ed. ....Judy Griffin
Graphic Designer..........................Jeff Cannon
Delivery Method: Mail, Newsstand
Areas Served: Kaufman County

FORT DAVIS

JEFF DAVIS COUNTY MT. DISPATCH (THUR)
100 Court Ave, Fort Davis, TX, 79734, Jeff Davis, USA; gen tel (432) 426-3077; adv tel (432) 426-3077; ed tel (432) 426-3077; gen fax (432) 426-3077; adv fax (432) 426-3077; ed fax (432) 426-3077; disp adv e-mail dispatch@mztv.net; class adv e-mail dispatch@mztv.net; ed e-mail dispatch@mztv.net; web site www.jdcmountaindispatch.com
Circulation: 1,500pd,; Sworn/Estimate/Non-Audited
Advertising rate: Open inch rate $5.50
Established: 1983
Business Manager...................... Christi Dillard
Ed. .... Bob Dillard
Adv. Dir.. Kristi Huffman
Delivery Method: Mail, Newsstand
Areas Served: Jeff Davis County

FORT STOCKTON

THE FORT STOCKTON PIONEER (THUR)
210 N Nelson St, Fort Stockton, TX, 79735-6724, Pecos, USA; gen tel (432) 336-2281; adv tel (432) 336-2281; ed tel (432) 336-2281; gen fax (432) 336-6432; adv fax (432) 336-6432; ed fax (432) 336-6432; disp adv e-mail publisher@fspioneer.com; class adv e-mail publisher@fspioneer.com; ed e-mail pioneer@fspioneer.com; web site www.fortstocktonpioneer.com
Circulation: 3,365pd,; Sworn/Estimate/Non-Audited
Advertising rate: Open inch rate $7.25
Established: 1908

Group: Fenice Community Media
Digital Platform - Mobile: Apple, Windows
Digital Platform - Tablet: Apple iOS, Windows 7
Pub./Adv. Dir./Ed. .... Pam Palileo
Mechanical Specifications: Type page 11 1/2 x 21 1/2; E - 6 cols, 1 5/6, 1/10 between; A - 6 cols, 1 5/6, 1/10 between; C - 9 cols, 1 1/6, 1/10 between.Equipment & Software: Hardware — APP/Mac; Software — QPS/QuarkXPress 3.31.
Delivery Method: Mail, Newsstand, Racks
Areas Served: Pecos County

FORT WORTH

FORT WORTH BUSINESS PRESS (MON)

101 Summit Ave, Ste 803, Fort Worth, TX, 76102-2622, Tarrant, USA; gen tel (817) 336-8300; adv tel (817) 336-8300; ed tel (817) 336-8300; gen fax (817) 332-3038; adv fax (817) 332-3038; ed fax (817) 332-3038; disp adv e-mail nkaranges@bizpress.net; class adv e-mail bizpress@bizpress.net; ed e-mail nkaranges@bizpress.net; web site www.fortworthbusiness.com
Circulation: 631pd, 3,446fr; VAC
Advertising rate: Open inch rate $4275.00
Established: 1988
Digital Platform - Mobile: Apple, Android, Windows, Blackberry
Digital Platform - Tablet: Apple iOS, Android, Windows 7, Blackberry Tablet OS
Pub. .... Nick Karanges
Ed. .... Robert Francis
Adv. Dir. .... Mary Schlegel
Delivery Method: Mail, Newsstand, Racks
Areas Served: Tarrant County

THE KELLER CITIZEN (WED)

PO Box 1870, Fort Worth, TX, 76101-1870, Tarrant, USA; gen tel (817) 431-2231; adv tel (817) 431-2231; ed tel (817) 431-2231; gen fax (817) 431-5534; adv fax (817) 431-5534; ed fax (817) 431-5534; disp adv e-mail mshreve@star-telegram.com; class adv e-mail weeklyclassifieds@star-telegram.com; ed e-mail editor@star-telegram.com; web site www.star-telegram.com
Circulation: 44,322fr; AAM
Advertising rate: Open inch rate $19.48
Established: 1980
Group: The McClatchy Company
Digital Platform - Mobile: Apple, Android, Windows, Blackberry
Digital Platform - Tablet: Apple iOS, Android, Windows 7, Blackberry Tablet OS
Ed. .... Alice Murray
Adv. Mgr. .... Steffanie Harnitchek
Pres. / Pub. .... Gary Wortel
Mechanical Specifications: Type page 11 5/8 x 20 7/8; E - 6 cols, 1 5/6, 1/8 between; A - 6 cols, 1 5/6, 1/8 between; C - 10 cols, 1/10 between.Equipment & Software: Hardware — APP/Power Mac G4, APP/Mac LaserWriter 16-600, APP/Power Mac G3, Xante/Accel-a-Writer 3N, APP/iMac; Software — QPS/QuarkXPress 5.0, Adobe/Acrobat 5.0, Adobe/Photoshop 7.0, Adobe/Illustrator 10.0.
Delivery Method: Mail, Racks
Areas Served: 76052, 76177, 76244, 76248, 76262, 76178

FRANKLIN

FRANKLIN NEWS WEEKLY (THUR)

107 E Decherd St, Franklin, TX, 77856-3747, Robertson, USA; gen tel (979) 828-1520; gen fax (979) 828-1525; disp adv e-mail FranklinNewsWeekly@gmail.com; class adv e-mail FranklinNewsWeekly@gmail.com; ed e-mail FranklinNewsWeekly@gmail.com
Circulation: 1,000pd,; Sworn/Estimate/Non-Audited
Advertising rate: Open inch rate $4.00
Established: 1970
Pub./Ed./Adv. Dir. .... Sharon Jean Russell
Delivery Method: Mail, Newsstand, Racks
Areas Served: Robertson County
all over the USA

FRANKSTON

FRANKSTON CITIZEN (THUR)

142 W Main St, Frankston, TX, 75763-3519, Anderson, USA; gen tel (903) 876-2218; adv tel (903) 876-2218; ed tel (903) 876-2218; gen fax (903) 876-4974; adv fax (903) 876-4974; ed fax (903) 876-4974; disp adv e-mail sales@frankstoncitizen.com; class adv e-mail sales@frankstoncitizen.com; ed e-mail news@frankstoncitizen.com; web site www.frankstoncitizen.com
Circulation: 1,901pd, 88fr; Sworn/Estimate/Non-Audited
Advertising rate: Open inch rate $4.35
Established: 1910
Digital Platform - Mobile: Apple, Android, Windows
Digital Platform - Tablet: Apple iOS, Android, Windows 7
Ed. .... Jay Graham
Adv. Dir. .... J. Tom Graham
Mechanical Specifications: Type page 11 3/8 x 21 1/2; E - 6 cols, 1 3/4, 1/8 between; A - 6 cols, 1 3/4, 1/8 between; C - 8 cols, 1 5/16, 3/32 between.Equipment & Software: Hardware — Apple computers; Software — Adobe/InDesign 2.02.
Delivery Method: Mail, Racks
Areas Served: Anderson County
Henderson County

FREDERICKSBURG

FREDERICKSBURG STANDARD-RADIO POST (WED)

712 W Main St, Fredericksburg, TX, 78624-3134, Gillespie, USA; gen tel (830) 997-2155; adv tel (830) 997-2155; ed tel (830) 997-2155; gen fax (830) 990-0036; adv fax (830) 990-0036; ed fax (830) 990-0036; disp adv e-mail fbgads@fredericksburgstandard.com; class adv e-mail kim@fredericksburgstandard.com; ed e-mail ken@fredericksburgstandard.com; web site www.fredericksburgstandard.com
Circulation: 7,999pd,; Sworn/Estimate/Non-Audited
Advertising rate: Open inch rate $11
Established: 1907
Group: Moser Community Media, LLC
Digital Platform - Mobile: Apple, Android
Digital Platform - Tablet: Apple iOS, Android
Pub. .... Ken Esten Cooke
Adv. Dir. .... Kimberly Jung
Circ. Mgr. .... Sherrie Geistweidt
Mng Ed .... Yvonne Hartmann
Delivery Method: Mail, Newsstand, Carrier, Racks
Areas Served: 78624, 78618, 78631, 78028, 78013, 78606

FRIONA

THE FRIONA STAR (THUR)

916 Main St, Friona, TX, 79035-2042, Parmer, USA; gen tel (806) 250-2211; gen fax (806) 250-5127; disp adv e-mail frionastar@wtrt.net; class adv e-mail frionastar@wtrt.net; ed e-mail frionastar@wtrt.net; web site www.frionaonline.com
Circulation: 1,350pd,; Sworn/Estimate/Non-Audited
Advertising rate: Open inch rate $4.50
Established: 1925
Digital Platform - Mobile: Apple
Digital Platform - Tablet: Apple iOS, Windows 7
Mng Ed. .... Dana Jameson
Delivery Method: Mail, Newsstand
Areas Served: Parmer County

FRITCH

THE EAGLE PRESS (FRI)

None, Fritch, TX, 79036, Hutchinson, USA; gen tel (806) 275-0015; disp adv e-mail tara.eaglepress@ymail.com; class adv e-mail tara.eaglepress@ymail.com; ed e-mail tara.eaglepress@ymail.com
Circulation: 808pd,; Sworn/Estimate/Non-Audited
Advertising rate: Open inch rate $5.00
Established: 1987
Pub./Ed./Adv. Dir. .... Tara Huff
Delivery Method: Mail, Newsstand, Racks
Areas Served: Hutchinson County

GATESVILLE

GATESVILLE MESSENGER AND STAR FORUM (WED, SAT)

116 S 6th St, Gatesville, TX, 76528-2052, Coryell, USA; gen tel (254) 865-5212; adv tel (254) 865-5212; ed tel (254) 865-5212; gen fax (254) 865-2361; adv fax (254) 865-2361; ed fax (254) 865-2361; disp adv e-mail advertising@gatesvillemessenger.com; class adv e-mail classifieds@gatesvillemessenger.com; ed e-mail editor@gatesvillemessenger.com; web site www.gatesvillemessenger.com
Circulation: 3,400pd,; USPS
Advertising rate: Open inch rate $7.60
Established: 1881Editions: (104)
Digital Platform - Mobile: Windows
Digital Platform - Tablet: Windows 7
Pub. .... Marshall Day
Ed. .... Larry Kennedy
Mechanical Specifications: 11.625" X 21"
6 col. format
Delivery Method: Mail, Newsstand, Racks
Areas Served: 76528

GEORGETOWN

SUNDAY SUN (SUN)

707 S Main St, Georgetown, TX, 78626-5700, Williamson, USA; gen tel (512) 930-4824; adv tel (512) 930-4824 ext. 205; ed tel (512) 930-4824 ext. 217 ; gen fax (512) 863-2474; adv fax (512) 863-2474; ed fax (512) 863-2474; disp adv e-mail ads@wilcosun.com; class adv e-mail class@wilcosun.com; ed e-mail editor@wilcosun.com; web site www.wilcosun.com
Circulation: 9,000pd,; Sworn/Estimate/Non-Audited
Advertising rate: Open inch rate $10.00
Established: 1974
Digital Platform - Mobile: Apple, Android
Digital Platform - Tablet: Apple iOS, Android, Windows 7
Pub. .... Clark Thurmond
Co-Pub./Ed. .... Linda Scarbrough
Mng. Ed. .... Will Anderson
Adv. Mgr. .... Teri Gray
Delivery Method: Mail, Racks
Areas Served: 78626, 78627, 78628, 78633

THE WILLIAMSON COUNTY SUN (WED)

707 S Main St, Georgetown, TX, 78626-5700, Williamson, USA; gen tel (512) 930-4824; adv tel (512) 930-4824 ext. 205; ed tel (512) 930-4824 ext. 217; gen fax (512) 868-0314; adv fax (512) 868-0314; ed fax (512) 868-0314; disp adv e-mail ads@wilcosun.com; class adv e-mail class@wilcosun.com; ed e-mail editor@wilcosun.com; web site www.wilcosun.com
Circulation: 9,000pd,; Sworn/Estimate/Non-Audited
Advertising rate: Open inch rate $11.00
Established: 1877
Digital Platform - Mobile: Apple, Android
Digital Platform - Tablet: Apple iOS, Android, Windows 7
Pub. .... Clark Thurmond
Co-Pub./Ed. .... Linda Scarbrough
Adv. Dir. .... Teri Gray
Mng. Ed. .... Will Anderson
Mechanical Specifications: Type page 11 x 21; E - 6 cols, 2 1/16, 1/6 between; A - 6 cols, 2 1/16, 1/6 between; C - 8 cols, 1 1/2, 1/6 between.Equipment & Software: Hardware — APP/Macs; Presses — G/Community
Delivery Method: Mail, Racks
Areas Served: 78626, 78627, 78628

GIDDINGS

GIDDINGS TIMES & NEWS (THUR)

170 N Knox Ave, Giddings, TX, 78942-3439, Lee, USA; gen tel (979) 542-2222; adv tel (979) 542-2222; ed tel (979) 542-2222; gen fax (979) 542-9410; adv fax (979) 542-9410; ed fax (979) 542-9410; disp adv e-mail gtimes@verizon.net; class adv e-mail gtimes@verizon.net; ed e-mail gtimes@verizon.net; web site www.giddingstimes.com
Advertising rate: Open inch rate $12.00
Established: 1888
Pub./Ed./Adv. Dir. .... David True
Delivery Method: Mail, Newsstand, Racks
Areas Served: Lee County

GILMER

GILMER MIRROR (THUR)

214 E Marshall St, Gilmer, TX, 75644-2228, Upshur, USA; gen tel (903) 843-2503; adv tel (903) 843-2503; ed tel (903) 843-2503; gen fax (903) 843-5123; adv fax (903) 843-5123; ed fax (903) 843-5123; disp adv e-mail gilmermirror@yahoo.com; class adv e-mail gilmermirrorclassifieds@yahoo.com; ed e-mail gilmermirror@gmail.com; web site www.gilmermirror.com
Circulation: 3,500pd, 23fr; Sworn/Estimate/Non-Audited
Advertising rate: Open inch rate $6.50
Established: 1877
Group: Greeneway Enterprises, Inc.
Digital Platform - Mobile: Apple, Android
Digital Platform - Tablet: Apple iOS, Android, Windows 7
Pub. .... William R. Greene
Adv. Mgr. .... Suzanne Patterson
Tabitha McCainEquipment & Software: Hardware — APP/Mac; Software — Adobe/PageMaker 5.0, Adobe/Photoshop.
Delivery Method: Mail, Racks
Areas Served: 75644

GLADEWATER

GLADEWATER MIRROR (WED)

211 N Main St, Gladewater, TX, 75647-2335, Gregg, USA; gen tel (903) 845-2235; gen fax (903) 845-2237; disp adv e-mail gladewatermirror@aol.com; class adv e-mail gladewatermirror@aol.com; ed e-mail gladewatermirror@aol.com; web site www.gladewatermirror.com
Circulation: 1,750pd,; Sworn/Estimate/Non-Audited
Advertising rate: Open inch rate $7.00
Established: 1928
Group: Bardwell Ink LLC
Digital Platform - Mobile: Apple, Android
Digital Platform - Tablet: Apple iOS, Android, Windows 7
Pub./Ed. .... Jim Bardwell
Delivery Method: Mail, Newsstand, Racks
Areas Served: Gregg County & Upshur County

GOLDTHWAITE

GOLDTHWAITE EAGLE (WED)

1002 Fisher St, Goldthwaite, TX, 76844-2159, Mills, USA; gen tel (325) 648-2244; adv tel (325) 648-2244; ed tel (325) 648-2244; gen fax (325) 648-2024; adv fax (325) 648-2024; ed fax (325) 648-2024; disp adv e-mail goldnews@centex.net; class adv e-mail goldedit@centex.net; ed e-mail goldpub@centex.net; web site www.goldthwaiteeagle.com
Circulation: 1,975pd,; Sworn/Estimate/Non-Audited
Advertising rate: Open inch rate $6.00
Established: 1894
Digital Platform - Mobile: Apple, Android
Digital Platform - Tablet: Apple iOS, Android, Windows 7

Ed./Pub./Adv. Dir.................Steven W. Bridges
Delivery Method: Mail, Newsstand, Racks
Areas Served: Mills County

GOLIAD

GOLIAD ADVANCE-GUARD (THUR)

202 S Commercial St, Goliad, TX, 77963-4189, Goliad, USA; gen tel (361) 645-2330; adv tel (361) 645-2330; ed tel (361) 645-2330; adv fax (361) 645-2812; disp adv e-mail advertising@mysoutex.com; class adv e-mail advertising@mysoutex.com; ed e-mail goliad@mysoutex.com; web site www.mysoutex.com
Circulation: 2,000pd,; Sworn/Estimate/Non-Audited
Advertising rate: Open inch rate $14.00
Established: 1913
Group: Beeville Publishing Co. Inc
Digital Platform - Mobile: Apple, Android
Digital Platform - Tablet: Apple iOS, Android, Windows 7
Co-Pub..Jeff Latcham
Co-Pub.......................................Chip Latcham
Ed...Bill Clough
Delivery Method: Mail, Racks
Areas Served: Goliad County

GONZALES

THE GONZALES CANNON (THUR)

901 N Saint Joseph St, Gonzales, TX, 78629-3566, Gonzales, USA; gen tel (830) 672-7100; adv tel (830)672-7100; ed tel (830)672-7100; gen fax (830) 672-7111; adv fax (830)672-7111; ed fax (830)672-7111; disp adv e-mail advertising@gonzalescannon.com; class adv e-mail subscriptions@gonzalescannon.com; ed e-mail news@gonzalescannon.com; web site www.gonzalescannon.com
Circulation: 2,500pd, 500fr; Sworn/Estimate/Non-Audited
Advertising rate: Open inch rate $7.50
Established: 2009
Digital Platform - Mobile: Windows
Digital Platform - Tablet: Windows 7Sanya Harkey
Mark Lube
Dorothy Gast
News Editor..........................Kathryn Penrose
Reporter...................................Chris Johnson
Pub..................................Michael McCracken
Mechanical Specifications: 9.875x21
Delivery Method: Mail, Newsstand, Racks
Areas Served: 78629, 78632, 78959, 77984, 77975, 77964, 77995, 77954, 77994, 78159, 78614

THE GONZALES INQUIRER (TUES, FRI)

622 Saint Paul St, Gonzales, TX, 78629-3552, Gonzales, USA; gen tel (830) 672-2861; adv tel (830) 672-2861; ed tel (830) 672-2861; gen fax (830) 672-7029; adv fax (830) 672-7029; ed fax (830) 672-7029; disp adv e-mail publisher@gonzalesinquirer.com; class adv e-mail ads@gonzalesinquirer.com; ed e-mail news@gonalesinquirer.com; web site www.gonzalesinquirer.com
Circulation: 1,189pd, 1,088fr; CVC
Advertising rate: Open inch rate $7.60
Established: 1853
Group: Fenice Community Media
Digital Platform - Mobile: Apple, Android, Windows, Blackberry
Digital Platform - Tablet: Apple iOS, Android, Windows 7, Blackberry Tablet OS, Kindle, Nook, Kindle Fire
Ed./Pub...Brandi Guy
Office Mgr....................................Kim Brewer
Adv. Mgr..Jessie Hott
Classifieds Adv. Sales..............Cammy Lewis
Adv. Sales..................................Shane Taylor
Reporter..Rob Ford
Jose Torres
Valerie ReddellEquipment & Software: Hardware — APP/Mac; Software — QPS/QuarkXPress.
Delivery Method: Mail, Newsstand, Racks

GRAHAM

THE GRAHAM LEADER (WED, SUN)

620 Oak St, Graham, TX, 76450-3040, Young, USA; gen tel (940) 549-7800; adv tel (940) 549-7800; ed tel (940) 549-7800; gen fax (940) 549-4364; adv fax (940) 549-4364; ed fax (940) 549-4364; disp adv e-mail advmgr@grahamleader.com; class adv e-mail classified@grahamleader.com; ed e-mail editor@grahamleader.com; web site www.grahamleader.com
Circulation: 3,400pd, 50fr; Sworn/Estimate/Non-Audited
Advertising rate: Open inch rate $11.70
Established: 1876
Group: Moser Community Media, LLC
Digital Platform - Mobile: Apple, Android
Digital Platform - Tablet: Apple iOS, Android, Windows 7
Publisher.......................................Tyler Patton
Ed...Brenda Sommer
Delivery Method: Mail, Newsstand, Racks
Areas Served: Young County

GRANBURY

HOOD COUNTY NEWS (WED, SAT)

1501 S Morgan St, Granbury, TX, 76048-2791, Hood, USA; gen tel (817) 573-7066; adv tel (817) 573-7066 ext. 272; ed tel (817) 573-7066 ext. 245; gen fax (817) 279-8371; adv fax (817) 279-8371; ed fax (817) 279-8371; disp adv e-mail advertising@hcnews.com; class adv e-mail classads@hcnews.com; ed e-mail editor@hcnews.com; web site www.hcnews.com
Circulation: 8,959pd,; Sworn/Estimate/Non-Audited
Advertising rate: Open inch rate $11.00
Established: 1886
Digital Platform - Mobile: Apple, Android, Windows, Blackberry
Digital Platform - Tablet: Apple iOS, Android, Windows 7, Blackberry Tablet OS, Kindle, Nook, Kindle Fire
Pub..Jerry Tidwell
Ed...Roger Enlow
Adv. Dir...Rick Craig
Delivery Method: Mail, Newsstand, Racks
Areas Served: Hood County

GRAND SALINE

GRAND SALINE SUN (THUR)

116 N Main St, Grand Saline, TX, 75140-1844, Van Zandt, USA; gen tel (903) 962-4275; gen fax (903) 962-3660; disp adv e-mail amoore@grandsalinesun.com; class adv e-mail amoore@grandsalinesun.com; ed e-mail wcallaway@grandsalinesun.com; web site www.grandsalinesun.com
Circulation: 1,200pd, 54fr; Sworn/Estimate/Non-Audited
Advertising rate: Open inch rate $7.95
Established: 1893
Group: Lake Country Media, LLC
Digital Platform - Mobile: Apple, Android, Windows, Blackberry
Digital Platform - Tablet: Apple iOS, Android, Windows 7, Blackberry Tablet OS
Pub..Dan Moore
Ed...Wendi Callaway
Adv. Dir./Bus. Mgr..........................Ann Moore
Mechanical Specifications: 1 Column 1.58 inches
2 Column 3.343 inches
3 Column 5.121 inches
4 Column 6.922 inches
5 Column 8.716 inches
6 Column 10.507 inches
Delivery Method: Mail, Newsstand, Racks
Areas Served: Grand Saline, Fruitvale, Edgewood, and Canton

GRANDVIEW

GRANDVIEW TRIBUNE (FRI)

104 E Criner St, Grandview, TX, 76050-2179, Johnson, USA; gen tel (817) 866-3391; adv tel (817) 866-3391; ed tel (817) 866-3391; gen fax (817) 866-3869; adv fax (817) 866-3869; ed fax (817) 866-3869; disp adv e-mail darladudley@windstream.net; class adv e-mail tribune-sales@windstream.net; ed e-mail tribune-editor@windstream.net
Circulation: 1,200pd,; Sworn/Estimate/Non-Audited
Advertising rate: Open inch rate $4.00
Established: 1896
Owner/Pub..................................Darla Dudley
Ed...Janeen Roberts
Adv. Dir...............................Janet MacDonald
Delivery Method: Mail, Newsstand
Areas Served: Johnson, Ellis, and Hill County

GRAPELAND

THE MESSENGER (THUR, SUN)

202 S Main St, Grapeland, TX, 75844-2404, Houston, USA; gen tel (936) 687-2424; adv tel (936) 687-2424; ed tel (936) 687-2424; gen fax (936) 687-3441; adv fax (936) 687-3441; ed fax (936) 687-3441; disp adv e-mail news@messenger-news.com; class adv e-mail news@messenger-news.com; ed e-mail kboothe@messenger-news.com; web site www.messenger-news.com
Circulation: 2,376pd,; Sworn/Estimate/Non-Audited
Advertising rate: Open inch rate $5.35
Established: 1899
Group: Nicol Publishing
Digital Platform - Mobile: Apple, Android
Digital Platform - Tablet: Apple iOS, Android, Windows 7
Pub...Tom Nicol
Ed..Kay Boothe
Copy Editor / Composing............Cheril Vernon
Reporter......................................Will Johnson
Office Manager/Sales............Lesia Rounsavall
Sales......................................Ansel Bradshaw
Delivery Method: Mail, Newsstand, Racks
Areas Served: Houston County
Anderson County

GREENVILLE

COMMERCE JOURNAL (THUR)

2305 King St, Greenville, TX, 75401-3257, Hunt, USA; gen tel (903) 455-4220; adv tel (903) 455-4220 ext. 311; ed tel (903) 455-4220 ext. 324; gen fax (903) 455-6281; adv fax (903) 455-6281; ed fax (903) 455-6281; disp adv e-mail advertising@heraldbanner.com; class adv e-mail smorgan@heraldbanner.com; ed e-mail editor@heraldbanner.com; web site www.commercejournal.com
Circulation: 2,000pd, 67fr; Sworn/Estimate/Non-Audited
Advertising rate: Open inch rate $6.88
Established: 1889
Group: Community Newspaper Holdings, Inc.
Digital Platform - Mobile: Apple, Android
Digital Platform - Tablet: Apple iOS, Android, Windows 7
Pub...Lisa Chappell
Ed...Derek Price
Adv. Dir.....................................Rita Haldeman
Delivery Method: Mail, Newsstand
Areas Served: Hunt County

ROCKWALL COUNTY HERALD BANNER (FRI)

2305 King St, Greenville, TX, 75401-3257, Hunt, USA; gen tel (903) 455-4220; adv tel (903) 455-4220, Ext. 312; gen fax (903) 455-6281; disp adv e-mail advertising@heraldbanner.com; class adv e-mail advertising@heraldbanner.com; web site http://www.rockwallheraldbanner.com
Group: Community Newspaper Holdings, Inc.
Ed...Caleb Slinkard

ROYSE CITY HERALD BANNER (WED)

2305 King St, Greenville, TX, 75401-3257, USA; gen tel (903) 455-4220; adv tel (903) 455-4220, Ext. 312; gen fax (903) 455-6281; disp adv e-mail advertising@heraldbanner.com; class adv e-mail advertising@heraldbanner.com; web site http://www.roysecityheraldbanner.com
Group: Community Newspaper Holdings, Inc.
Caleb Slinkard
Mary Standfield

GROESBECK

GROESBECK JOURNAL (THUR)

115 N Ellis St, Groesbeck, TX, 76642-1308, Limestone, USA; gen tel (254) 729-5103; adv tel (254) 729-5103; ed tel (254) 729-5103; gen fax (254) 729-8310; adv fax (254) 729-8310; ed fax (254) 729-8310; disp adv e-mail groesbeckads@groesbeckjournal.com; class adv e-mail groesbeckads@groesbeckjournal.com; ed e-mail news@groesbeckjournal.com; web site www.groesbeckjournal.com
Circulation: 2,550pd, 50fr; Sworn/Estimate/Non-Audited
Advertising rate: Open inch rate $6.00
Established: 1892
Group: Moser Community Media, LLC
Digital Platform - Mobile: Apple, Android, Windows, Blackberry
Digital Platform - Tablet: Apple iOS, Android, Windows 7, Blackberry Tablet OS, Kindle, Nook, Kindle Fire
General Manager.............................Kim Smith
Delivery Method: Mail, Newsstand
Areas Served: Limestone County

GROOM

GROOM / MCLEAN / LEFORS (THUR)

84 BROADWAY AVE, Groom, TX, 79039, Carson, USA; gen tel (806) 248-7333; adv tel (806) 248-7333; ed tel (806) 248-7333; gen fax (806) 822-7333; adv fax (806) 822-7333; ed fax (806) 822-7333; disp adv e-mail thegroomnews@gmail.com; class adv e-mail thegroomnews@gmail.com; ed e-mail thegroomnews@gmail.com
Advertising rate: Open inch rate $4.15
Established: 1925
Pub./Adv. Dir.............................Donna Burton
Ed...Bob Glass
Ed..Janet Glass
Delivery Method: Mail, Newsstand
Areas Served: Carson County

GROVETON

GROVETON NEWS (THUR)

134 E 1st St, Groveton, TX, 75845-4809, Trinity, USA; gen tel (936) 642-1726; gen fax (936) 642-1195; disp adv e-mail grovetonnews@gmail.com; class adv e-mail grovetonnews@gmail.com; ed e-mail grovetonnews@gmail.com; web site www.grovetonnews.com
Circulation: 2,000pd,; Sworn/Estimate/Non-Audited
Advertising rate: Open inch rate $6.00
Established: 1905
Group: Polk County Publishing Co.
Digital Platform - Mobile: Apple, Android
Digital Platform - Tablet: Apple iOS, Android, Windows 7
Pub./Adv. Dir.................................Alvin Holley
Composition/News Ed.................Darlene Pyle
Asst Ed/Writer...........................Chris Edwards
Delivery Method: Mail, Newsstand
Areas Served: Trinity County

HALE CENTER

HALE CENTER AMERICAN (FRI)

616 S Main St, Hale Center, TX, 79041-9586, Hale, USA; gen tel (806) 285-7766; adv tel

(806) 285-7766; ed tel (806) 285-7766; gen fax (866) 641-2816; adv fax (866) 641-2816; ed fax (866) 641-2816; disp adv e-mail halecenterpaper@hotmail.com; class adv e-mail halecenterpaper@hotmail.com; ed e-mail halecenterpaper@hotmail.com; web site www.southplainsplus.com
Circulation: 300pd,; Sworn/Estimate/Non-Audited
Advertising rate: Open inch rate $5.00
Established: 1922
Group: Triple S Media
Digital Platform - Mobile: Apple, Android, Windows, Blackberry
Digital Platform - Tablet: Apple iOS, Android, Windows 7, Blackberry Tablet OS, Nook, Kindle Fire, Other
Pub./Ed. .... Phillip Hamilton
Adv. Dir. .... Ursula Hamilton
Mechanical Specifications: 25 inch Web - 6 col.=11.625 in.Equipment & Software: Hardware — Apple editorial
PC circulation; Presses — None; Software — Adobe Creative Cloud - editorial
Apple - editorial
Interlink - Circulation
Delivery Method: Mail, Newsstand
Areas Served: 79041, 79021

HALLETTSVILLE

HALLETTSVILLE TRIBUNE-HERALD (WED)
108 S Texana St, Hallettsville, TX, 77964-2847, Lavaca, USA; gen tel (361) 798-2481; adv tel (361) 798-2481; ed tel (361) 798-2481; gen fax (361) 798-9902; adv fax (361) 798-9902; ed fax (361) 798-9902; disp adv e-mail tribuneherald@sbcglobal.net; class adv e-mail tribuneads@sbcglobal.net; ed e-mail tribuneherald@sbcglobal.net
Circulation: 3,100pd,; USPS
Advertising rate: Open inch rate $7.80
Established: 1875
Pub. .... L.M. Preuss III
Adv. Dir. .... Kristie Bludau
Delivery Method: Mail, Newsstand
Areas Served: Lavaca County

HAMILTON

HAMILTON HERALD-NEWS (THUR)
112 E Main St, Hamilton, TX, 76531-1954, Hamilton, USA; gen tel (254) 386-3145; adv tel (254) 386-3145; ed tel (254) 386-3145; gen fax (254) 386-3001; adv fax (254) 386-3001; ed fax (254) 386-3001; disp adv e-mail lthompson@thehamiltonherald-news.com; class adv e-mail classifieds@thehamiltonherald-news.com; ed e-mail kmiller@thehamiltonherald-news.com; web site www.theHamiltonHerald-News.com
Circulation: 3,200pd,; Sworn/Estimate/Non-Audited
Advertising rate: Open inch rate $4.00
Established: 1875
Digital Platform - Mobile: Apple, Android
Digital Platform - Tablet: Apple iOS, Android, Windows 7
Pub./Ed./Adv. Dir. .... Kenneth Miller
Delivery Method: Mail, Newsstand
Areas Served: Hamilton County

HAMLIN

HAMLIN HERALD (THUR)
350 S Central Ave, Hamlin, TX, 79520-4832, Jones, USA; gen tel (325) 576-3606; gen fax (325) 576-3606; disp adv e-mail pipernews@sbcglobal.net; class adv e-mail pipernews@sbcglobal.net; ed e-mail pipernews@sbcglobal.net
Circulation: 1,200pd,; USPS
Advertising rate: Open inch rate $5.95
Established: 1905
Digital Platform - Mobile: Windows, Other
Digital Platform - Tablet: Windows 7, Other
Owner .... Rudy Martinez
Delivery Method: Mail, Newsstand, Racks
Areas Served: Fisher, Jones County and Stonewall

HART

HART BEAT (FRI)
407 Broadway, Hart, TX, 79043, Castro, USA; gen tel (806) 938-2640; adv tel (806) 938-2640; ed tel (806) 938-2640; gen fax (806) 938-2216; adv fax (806) 938-2216; ed fax (806) 938-2216; disp adv e-mail hbeat@amaonline.com; class adv e-mail hbeat@amaonline.com; ed e-mail hbeat@amaonline.com
Circulation: 342pd, 40fr; Sworn/Estimate/Non-Audited
Advertising rate: Open inch rate $3.00
Established: 1962
Pub./Ed./Adv. Dir. .... Neoma Wall Williams
Mechanical Specifications: Type page 10 13/16 x 13; E - 5 cols, 2 1/16, 1/8 between.Equipment & Software: Hardware — APP/Mac II; Software — Adobe/PageMaker 3.02.
Delivery Method: Mail, Newsstand
Areas Served: Castro County

THE PULSE (FRI)
407 Broadway, Hart, TX, 79043, Castro, USA; gen tel (806) 938-2640; adv tel (806) 938-2640; ed tel (806) 938-2640; gen fax (806) 938-2216; adv fax (806) 938-2216; ed fax (806) 938-2216; disp adv e-mail hbeat@amaonline.com; class adv e-mail hbeat@amaonline.com; ed e-mail hbeat@amaonline.com; web site www.thepulsenews.net
Circulation: 185pd,; Sworn/Estimate/Non-Audited
Advertising rate: Open inch rate $3.00
Established: 1962
Pub./Ed./Adv. Dir. .... Neoma Wall Williams
Delivery Method: Mail, Newsstand
Areas Served: Castro County

HEARNE

FRANKLIN ADVOCATE (THUR)
114 W 4th St, Hearne, TX, 77859-2506, Robertson, USA; gen tel (979) 279-3411; adv tel (979)279-3411; ed tel (979)279-3411; gen fax 979-279-5401; adv fax (979)279-5401; ed fax (979)279-5401; disp adv e-mail ads@robconews.com; class adv e-mail ads@robconews.com; ed e-mail news@robconews.com; web site www.franklin-advocate.com
Circulation: 494pd, 6fr; Sworn/Estimate/Non-Audited
Advertising rate: 6.50
Established: 1982 - Reestablished 2014
Group: Moser Community Media
Publisher .... Dennis Phillips
Delivery Method: Mail, Newsstand, Racks
Areas Served: Robertson County, Texas

ROBERTSON COUNTY NEWS (THUR)
114 W 4th St, Hearne, TX, 77859-2506, Robertson, USA; gen tel (979) 279-3411; adv tel (979) 279-3411; ed tel (979) 279-3411; gen fax (979) 279-5401; adv fax (979) 279-5401; ed fax (979) 279-5401; disp adv e-mail ads@robconews.com; class adv e-mail ads@robconews.com; ed e-mail news@robconews.com; web site www.robconews.com
Circulation: 2,146pd, 92fr; Sworn/Estimate/Non-Audited
Advertising rate: Open inch rate $7.25
Established: 1889
Group: Moser Community Media
Digital Platform - Mobile: Apple, Android
Digital Platform - Tablet: Apple iOS, Android, Windows 7
Pub./Ed. .... Dennis Phillips
Adv. Dir. .... Teresa Phillips
Delivery Method: Mail, Newsstand, Racks
Areas Served: Robertson County

HEBBRONVILLE

HEBBRONVILLE VIEW (WED)
212 E Galbraith St, Hebbronville, TX, 78361-3404, Jim Hogg, USA; gen tel (361) 527-4272; adv tel (361) 527-4272; ed tel (361) 527-4272; gen fax (361) 527-5271; adv fax (361) 527-5271; ed fax (361) 527-5271; disp adv e-mail hebview@gmail.com; class adv e-mail hebview@gmail.com; ed e-mail hebview@gmail.com
Circulation: 1,400pd,; Sworn/Estimate/Non-Audited
Advertising rate: Open inch rate $5.00
Established: 1985
Pub./Ed. .... Carlos Vela
Adv. Dir. .... Vanessa Saenz
Delivery Method: Mail, Newsstand
Areas Served: Jim Hogg County

JIM HOGG COUNTY ENTERPRISE (WED)
304 E Galbraith St, Hebbronville, TX, 78361-3402, Jim Hogg, USA; gen tel (361) 527-3261; adv tel (361) 527-3261; ed tel (361) 527-3261; gen fax (361) 527-4545; adv fax (361) 527-4545; ed fax (361) 527-4545; disp adv e-mail enterprise78361@aol.com; class adv e-mail enterprise78361@aol.com; ed e-mail enterprise78361@aol.com
Advertising rate: Open inch rate $5.00
Established: 1926
Digital Platform - Mobile: Windows
Digital Platform - Tablet: Windows 7
Pub. .... Tony Salinas
Ed. .... Poncho Hernandez
Adv. Dir. .... Maribel Guerrero
Delivery Method: Mail, Newsstand
Areas Served: Jim Hogg County

HEMPHILL

THE SABINE COUNTY REPORTER (WED)
610 Worth St, Hemphill, TX, 75948-7258, Sabine, USA; gen tel (409) 787-2172; gen fax (409) 787-4300; disp adv e-mail screporter@yahoo.com; web site www.sabinecountyreporter.com
Circulation: 2,100pd,; USPS
Advertising rate: Open inch rate $4.50
Established: 1883
Digital Platform - Mobile: Apple, Windows
Digital Platform - Tablet: Apple iOS, Windows 7
Ed. .... Brandy Meurer
Delivery Method: Mail, Newsstand, Racks
Areas Served: Sabine County

HENDERSON

OVERTON NEWS (WED)
1711 US Highway 79 S, Henderson, TX, 75654-4509, Rusk, USA; gen tel (903) 657-2501; gen fax (903) 657-2452; ed fax (903) 657-0056; disp adv e-mail leslinebarger@hendersondailynews.com; class adv e-mail classifieds@hendersondailynews.com; ed e-mail mprosser@hendersondailynews.com; web site www.hendersondailynews.com
Circulation: 7,000pd, 6,400fr; Sworn/Estimate/Non-Audited
Advertising rate: Open inch rate $3.65
Established: 1930Editions: (2) Henderson Daily News, Overton News (Weekly)
Digital Platform - Mobile: Apple, Android, Windows, Blackberry
Digital Platform - Tablet: Apple iOS, Android, Windows 7, Blackberry Tablet OS, Kindle, Kindle Fire
Pub. .... Les Linebarger
Ed. .... Matthew Prosser
Circ. Mgr. .... John Garrison
Mechanical Specifications: Type page 13 x 21 1/2; E - 6 cols, 2 1/16, between; A - 6 cols, 2 1/16, between; C - 8 cols, 1 1/2, between. Equipment & Software: ; Presses — 6-HI/V-15A.
Delivery Method: Mail, Newsstand, Carrier, Racks
Areas Served: Henderson, Overton, New London, and Rusk County

HENRIETTA

CLAY COUNTY LEADER (THUR)
114 W Ikard St, Henrietta, TX, 76365-2827, Clay, USA; gen tel (940) 538-4333; adv tel (940) 538-4333; ed tel (940) 538-4333; gen fax (940) 538-4542; adv fax (940) 538-4542; ed fax (940) 538-4542; disp adv e-mail ads@claycountyleader.com; class adv e-mail ads@claycountyleader.com; ed e-mail news@claycountyleader.com; web site www.claycountyleader.com
Advertising rate: Open inch rate $5.00
Established: 1932
Digital Platform - Mobile: Apple, Android, Windows, Blackberry
Digital Platform - Tablet: Apple iOS, Android, Windows 7, Blackberry Tablet OS, Kindle, Nook, Kindle Fire
Pub. .... Bret McCormick
Ed. .... Mike Chacanaca
Delivery Method: Mail, Newsstand
Areas Served: Clay County

HEREFORD

THE HEREFORD BRAND (WED, SUN)
PO Box 673, Hereford, TX, 79045-0673, Deaf Smith, USA; gen tel (806) 364-2030; adv tel (806)364-2030; ed tel (806)364-2030; gen fax (806) 364-8364; adv fax (806)364-8364; ed fax (806)364-8364; disp adv e-mail retail@herefordbrand.com; class adv e-mail class@herefordbrand.com; ed e-mail editor@herefordbrand.com; web site www.herefordbrand.com
Circulation: 2,100pd,; Sworn/Estimate/Non-Audited
Advertising rate: Open inch rate $8.00
Established: 1901
Group: Roberts Publishing
Digital Platform - Mobile: Apple, Android, Windows
Digital Platform - Tablet: Apple iOS, Android, Windows 7
Editor/Gen. Mgr. .... Lynda Work
Adv. Dir. .... Raymond Gonzales
Sports Ed. .... John Daigle
Lifestyle Ed. .... Tyler Jameson
Staff News Writer .... Mary Freeman
Lifestyles Writer .... Kaylee Sparkman
Classifieds/Circulation .... Laura Foster
Accountant .... Paige Arnold
Mechanical Specifications: Type page 13 x 21; E - 6 cols, 2 1/16, 1/8 between; A - 6 cols, 2 1/16, 1/8 between; C - 6 cols, 2 1/16, 1/8 between.
Delivery Method: Mail, Newsstand, Carrier, Racks
Areas Served: 79045

HICO

HICO NEWS REVIEW (THUR)
110 E Second St, Hico, TX, 76457-6433, Hamilton, USA; gen tel (254) 796-4325; adv tel (254) 796-4325; ed tel (254) 796-4325; gen fax (254) 796-2548; adv fax (254) 796-2548; ed fax (254) 796-2548; disp adv e-mail hiconews@gmail.com; class adv e-mail hiconews@gmail.com; ed e-mail hiconews@gmail.com; web site www.thehiconewsreview.com
Circulation: 1,550pd,; Sworn/Estimate/Non-Audited
Advertising rate: Open inch rate $4.95
Established: 1895
Digital Platform - Mobile: Apple, Android
Digital Platform - Tablet: Apple iOS, Android, Windows 7
Pub. .... Jerry McAdams
Managing Editor, Production Coordinator. Traci Till
Delivery Method: Mail, Racks
Areas Served: Hamilton County

HILLSBORO

HILLSBORO REPORTER (MON, THUR)

335 Country Club Rd, Hillsboro, TX, 76645-2318, Hill, USA; gen tel (254) 582-3431; adv tel (254) 582-3431; ed tel (254) 582-3431; gen fax (254) 582-3800; adv fax (254) 582-3800; ed fax (254) 582-3800; disp adv e-mail ads@hillsbororeporter.com; class adv e-mail ads@hillsbororeporter.com; ed e-mail news@hillsbororeporter.com; web site www.hillsbororeporter.com
Circulation: 4,250pd,; Sworn/Estimate/Non-Audited
Advertising rate: Open inch rate $8.15 (Local); $10.85 (National)
Established: 1963
Digital Platform - Mobile: Apple, Android
Digital Platform - Tablet: Apple iOS, Android, Windows 7
Pub./Adv. Dir. ....Roger Galle
Ed. .... Rick Bailey
Delivery Method: Mail, Newsstand, Racks
Areas Served: Hill County, West, Milford, and Lake Whitney

HONDO

HONDO ANVIL HERALD (THUR)

1601 Avenue K, Hondo, TX, 78861-1838, Medina, USA; gen tel (830) 426-3346; gen fax (830) 426-3348; disp adv e-mail anvil1@hondo.net; class adv e-mail anvil2@hondo.net; ed e-mail anvil4@hondo.net; web site www.hondoanvilherald.com
Circulation: 4,521pd, 10fr; Sworn/Estimate/Non-Audited
Advertising rate: Open inch rate $7.50
Established: 1886
Digital Platform - Mobile: Apple, Android
Digital Platform - Tablet: Apple iOS, Android, Windows 7
Pub./Ed. .... Jeff Berger
Adv. Mgr. .... Lois Davis
Mechanical Specifications: Type page 13 x 21 1/2; E - 6 cols, 2, 1/4 between; A - 6 cols, 2, 1/4 between; C - 9 cols, 1 1/2, 1/4 between. Equipment & Software: Hardware — APP/Mac.
Delivery Method: Mail, Newsstand
Areas Served: Medina County

HONEY GROVE

THE WEEKLY GAZETTE (THUR)

511 5th St, Honey Grove, TX, 75446-1901, Fannin, USA; gen tel (903) 378-3558; adv tel (903) 378-3558; ed tel (903) 378-3558; gen fax (903) 378-3588; adv fax (903) 378-3588; ed fax (903) 378-3588; disp adv e-mail hgwcnews@sbcglobal.net; class adv e-mail hgwcnews@sbcglobal.net; ed e-mail hgwcnews@sbcglobal.net; web site www.honeygroveweeklygazette.com
Circulation: 1,500pd,; Sworn/Estimate/Non-Audited
Advertising rate: Open inch rate $4.00
Established: 1999
Digital Platform - Mobile: Apple, Android, Windows, Blackberry
Digital Platform - Tablet: Apple iOS, Android, Windows 7, Blackberry Tablet OS, Kindle, Nook, Kindle Fire
Pub./Ed. .... Lorrie Page
Adv. Dir. .... JoAnn Page
Delivery Method: Mail, Newsstand
Areas Served: Fannin County

HORIZON CITY

WEST TEXAS COUNTY COURIER (THUR)

15344 Werling Ct, Horizon City, TX, 79928-7012, El Paso, USA; gen tel (915) 852-3235; adv tel (915) 852-3235; ed tel (915) 852-3235; gen fax (915) 852-0123; adv fax (915) 852-0123; ed fax (915) 852-0123; disp adv e-mail wtxcc@wtxcc.com; class adv e-mail wtxcc@wtxcc.com; ed e-mail wtxcc@wtxcc.com; web site www.wtxcc.com
Circulation: 11,000fr; Sworn/Estimate/Non-Audited
Advertising rate: Open inch rate $25.00
Established: 1973
Digital Platform - Mobile: Apple, Android, Windows, Blackberry
Digital Platform - Tablet: Apple iOS, Android, Windows 7, Blackberry Tablet OS, Kindle, Nook, Kindle Fire
Pub./Ed./Adv. Dir. .... Rick Shrum
Mechanical Specifications: Type page 10 1/2 x 15 3/4; E - 5 cols, 2, 1/8 between; A - 5 cols, 2, 1/8 between; C - 6 cols, 1 3/5, 1/8 between. Equipment & Software: Hardware — APP/Mac; Software — Microsoft/Word 5.0, Adobe/PageMaker 4.2.
Delivery Method: Mail, Newsstand, Racks
Areas Served: Anthony, Vinton, Canutillo, East Montana, Horizon, Socorro, Clint, Fabens, San Elizario, and Tornillo

HOUSTON

BELLAIRE EXAMINER (THUR)

7613 Katy Fwy, Ste C, Houston, TX, 77024-2007, Harris, USA; gen tel (281) 378-1900; adv tel (281) 378-1906; ed tel (281) 378-1911; gen fax (713) 520-1193; adv fax (713) 520-1193; ed fax (713) 520-1193; disp adv e-mail rdavis@hcnonline.com; class adv e-mail pstewart@hcnonline.com; ed e-mail rgraham@hcnonline.com; web site www.hcnonline.com/bellaire_examiner
Circulation: 13,998fr; Sworn/Estimate/Non-Audited
Advertising rate: 1/16 Pg $240.00; 1/8 Pg $428.00; 1/4 Pg $810.00
Group: Hearst Communications, Inc.
Times Media Group
Digital Platform - Mobile: Apple, Android
Digital Platform - Tablet: Apple iOS, Android, Windows 7
Pub. ....Richard Davis
Major Sr. Acct. Mgr. .... Tom Legg
Adv. Dir. .... Charles Lee
Ed. .... David Taylor
Delivery Method: Mail, Newsstand, Racks
Areas Served: Harris County

CYPRESS CREEK MIRROR (WED)

21901 State Highway 249, Ste 500, Houston, TX, 77070-1545, Harris, USA; gen tel (281) 378-1080; adv tel (281) 378-1082; ed tel (281) 378-1087; gen fax (281) 320-2005; adv fax (281) 320-2005; ed fax (281) 320-2005; disp adv e-mail rdavis@hcnonline.com; class adv e-mail srovegno@hcnonline.com; ed e-mail rkent@hcnonline.com; web site www.hcnonline.com
Circulation: 0pd, 34,741fr; CVC
Advertising rate: 1/16 pg $200.00; 1/8 Pg $356.00; 1/4 Pg $675.00; per inch $15.81
Established: 2003
Group: Hearst Communications, Inc.
Times Media Group
Digital Platform - Mobile: Apple, Android
Digital Platform - Tablet: Apple iOS, Android, Windows 7
Pub. ....Richard Davis
Ed. .... Roy Kent
Sales Mgr. .... Susan Rovegno
Mktg. Mgr. .... Megan O'Sullivan
Major Sr. Acct. Mgr. .... Tom Legg
Adv. Dir. .... Charles Lee
Delivery Method: Mail, Newsstand, Racks
Areas Served: Harris County

HIGHLANDS STAR / CROSBY COURIER (THUR)

5906 Star Ln, Houston, TX, 77057-7118, Harris, USA; gen tel (281) 328-9605; adv tel (281) 328-9605; ed tel (281) 328-9605; gen fax (713) 977-1188; adv fax (713) 977-1188; ed fax (713) 977-1188; disp adv e-mail grafikstar@aol.com; class adv e-mail grafikstar@aol.com; ed e-mail grafikstar@aol.com; web site www.starcouriernews.com
Circulation: 4,400pd, 3,400fr; USPS
Advertising rate: Open inch rate $6.00
Established: 1955
Group: Grafikpress Corp.Editions: (2) Barbers Hill Dayton Press
Digital Platform - Mobile: Apple, Android
Digital Platform - Tablet: Apple iOS, Android, Windows 7
Pub./Ed. .... Gilbert Hoffman
Adv. Dir. .... Lewis Spearman
Mechanical Specifications: Broadsheet 12.5 x 22.75
Column width 1.833 inches
6 col x 21 = 11.62 x 21Equipment & Software: Hardware — Mac/PC; Presses — King Press 5 unit; Software — Pagemaker, Photoshop, Ind
Delivery Method: Mail, Newsstand, Carrier, Racks
Areas Served: 77562, 77532, 77336, 77520, 77521, 77522, 77523, 77580, 77535

HOUSTON BUSINESS JOURNAL (FRI)

5444 Westheimer Rd, Ste 1700, Houston, TX, 77056-5349, Harris, USA; gen tel (713) 688-8811; adv tel (713) 688-8811; ed tel (713) 688-8811; gen fax (713) 963-0482; adv fax (713) 963-0482; ed fax (713) 963-0482; disp adv e-mail jbeddow@bizjournals.com; class adv e-mail jbeddow@bizjournals.com; ed e-mail houston@bizjournals.com; web site www.bizjournals.com/houston - 1,300,000(views) 300,000(visitors)
Circulation: 17,000pd, 3,500fr; AAM
Advertising rate: Open inch rate $7615.00 (Full-Page)
Established: 1971
Digital Platform - Mobile: Apple, Android, Windows
Digital Platform - Tablet: Apple iOS, Android, Windows 7
Pub. .... John Beddow
Ed. .... B. Candace Beeke
Adv. Dir. .... Nancy Brown
Delivery Method: Mail, Newsstand
Areas Served: Greater Houston Area

HOUSTON FORWARD TIMES (WED)

4411 Almeda Rd, Houston, TX, 77004-4999, Harris, USA; gen tel (713) 526-4727; adv tel (713) 526-4727; ed tel (713) 526-4727; gen fax (713) 526-3170; adv fax (713) 526-3170; ed fax (713) 526-3170; disp adv e-mail forwardtimes@forwardtimes.com; class adv e-mail forwardtimes@forwardtimes.com; ed e-mail forwardtimes@forwardtimes.com; web site www.forwardtimes.com
Circulation: 35,089pd,; Sworn/Estimate/Non-Audited
Advertising rate: Open inch rate $28.00 (Local); $36.00 (National)
Established: 1960
Group: Houston Forward Times Publishing Co.
Digital Platform - Mobile: Apple, Android, Windows, Blackberry
Digital Platform - Tablet: Apple iOS, Android, Windows 7, Blackberry Tablet OS
Pub./Ed. .... Karen Carter Richards
Adv. Dir. .... Henrietta Wilson
Delivery Method: Mail, Newsstand, Carrier, Racks
Areas Served: Harris County

JEWISH HERALD-VOICE (THUR)

3403 Audley St, Houston, TX, 77098-1923, Harris, USA; gen tel (713) 630-0391; adv tel (713) 630-0391; ed tel (713) 630-0391; gen fax (713) 630-0404; adv fax (713) 630-0404; ed fax (713) 630-0404; disp adv e-mail advertising@jhvonline.com; class adv e-mail classified@jhvonline.com; ed e-mail editor@jhvonline.com; web site www.jhvonline.com
Circulation: 5,000pd,; USPS
Advertising rate: Open inch rate $40.00
Established: 1908
Digital Platform - Mobile: Apple, Android, Windows, Blackberry
Digital Platform - Tablet: Apple iOS, Android, Windows 7, Blackberry Tablet OS
Pub./Ed. .... Jeanne Samuels
Adv. Dir. .... Vicki Samuels
Mechanical Specifications: 9.79" X 15.5" FULL PAGE
Delivery Method: Mail, Newsstand
Areas Served: All Texas

NORTHEAST NEWS (TUES)

5906 Star Ln, Houston, TX, 77057-7118, Harris, USA; gen tel (281) 449-9945; adv tel (281) 449-9945; ed tel (281) 449-9945; gen fax (713) 977-1188; adv fax (713) 977-1188; ed fax (713) 977-1188; disp adv e-mail nenewsroom@aol.com; class adv e-mail nenewsroom@aol.com ; ed e-mail nenewsroom@aol.com ; web site www.nenewsroom.com
Circulation: 30,000fr; Sworn/Estimate/Non-Audited
Advertising rate: Open inch rate $12.00
Established: 1977
Group: Grafikpress Corp.
Digital Platform - Mobile: Apple, Android
Digital Platform - Tablet: Apple iOS, Android, Windows 7
Pub./Gen. Mgr./Adv. Mgr. .... Gilbert Hoffman
Ed .... Tom Thornburgh
Lewis Spearman
Mechanical Specifications: Type page 13 x 21; E - 7 cols, 1 3/4, 1/8 between; A - 7 cols, 1 3/4, 1/8 between; C - 9 cols, 1 3/8, 1/8 between. Equipment & Software: Hardware — Mac/PC; Presses — King Press 5 unit; Software — Pagemaker, Photoshop, InDesign
Delivery Method: Mail, Newsstand, Carrier, Racks
Areas Served: 77039, 77093, 77037, 77060, 77076, 77032

RIVER OAKS EXAMINER (THUR)

7613 Katy Fwy, Ste C, Houston, TX, 77024-2007, Harris, USA; gen tel (281) 378-1900; adv tel (281) 378-1906; ed tel (281) 378-1911; gen fax (713) 520-1193; adv fax (713) 520-1193; ed fax (713) 520-1193; disp adv e-mail rdavis@hcnonline.com; class adv e-mail pstewart@hcnonline.com; ed e-mail rgraham@hcnonline.com; web site www.hcnonline.com/river_oaks_examiner
Circulation: 12,027fr; Sworn/Estimate/Non-Audited
Advertising rate: 1/16 Pg $240.00; 1/8 Pg $428.00; 1/4 Pg $810.00
Group: Times Media Group
Hearst Communications, Inc.
Digital Platform - Mobile: Apple, Android
Digital Platform - Tablet: Apple iOS, Android, Windows 7
Pub. ....Richard Davis
Ed. .... Rusty Graham
Mktg. Mgr. .... Megan O'Sullivan
Major Sr. Acct. Mgr. .... Tom Legg
Adv. Dir. .... Charles Lee
Delivery Method: Mail, Newsstand, Racks
Areas Served: Harris County

SUGAR LAND SUN (THUR)

21901 State Highway 249, Ste 500, Houston, TX, 77070-1545, Harris, USA; gen tel (281) 378-1900; adv tel (281) 378-1908; ed tel (281) 378-1911; gen fax (713) 520-1193; adv fax (713) 520-1193; ed fax (713) 520-1193; disp adv e-mail rdavis@hcnonline.com; class adv e-mail tisaacks@hcnonline.com; ed e-mail rgraham@hcnonline.com; web site www.yourhoustonnews.com/sugar_land
Circulation: 27,081fr; Sworn/Estimate/Non-Audited
Advertising rate: 1/16 Pg $152.00; 1/8 Pg $271.00; 1/4 Pg $513.00
Group: Times Media Group
Hearst Communications, Inc.
Digital Platform - Mobile: Apple, Android
Digital Platform - Tablet: Apple iOS, Android, Windows 7
Pub. ....Richard Davis
Ed. .... Rusty Graham
Adv. Dir. .... Charles Lee
Mktg. Mgr. .... Megan O'Sullivan
Majors Sr. Acct. Mgr. .... Tom Legg
Delivery Method: Mail, Newsstand, Racks
Areas Served: Harris County

THE LEADER (SAT)

3500 E T C Jester Blvd, Ste A, Houston, TX, 77018-6020, Harris, USA; gen tel (713) 686-8494; adv tel (713) 686-8494; ed tel (713) 686-8494; gen fax (713) 686-0970; adv fax (713) 686-0970; ed fax (713) 686-0970; disp adv e-mail ads@theleadernews.com;

class adv e-mail ads@theleadernews.com; ed e-mail news@theleadernews.com; web site www.theleadernews.com - 23,794(views) 8,425(visitors)
Circulation: 17pd, 33,935fr; VAC
Advertising rate: Open inch rate $36.10
Established: 1954Editions: (2) 2
Digital Platform - Mobile: Apple, Android, Windows, Blackberry
Digital Platform - Tablet: Apple iOS, Android, Windows 7, Blackberry Tablet OS, Kindle, Nook, Kindle Fire
Pub. .... Terry Burge
Ed. .... Greg Densmore
Circ. Mgr. .... Jane Broyles
Pub. .... Jonathan McElvy
Prod. Mgr .... Jake Dukate
Mechanical Specifications: Type page 10 1/8 x 14; E - 6 cols, 1 1/2, 1/6 between; A - 6 cols, 1 1/2, 1/6 between; C - 7 cols, 1 1/2, 1/12 between.
Delivery Method: Mail, Newsstand, Racks
Areas Served: Northwest Houston

WEST UNIVERSITY EXAMINER (THUR)
21901 State Highway 249, Ste 500, Houston, TX, 77070-1545, Harris, USA; gen tel (281) 378-1900; gen fax (713) 520-1193; disp adv e-mail kkonter@hcnonline.com; class adv e-mail clee@hcnonline.com; ed e-mail rkent@hcnonline.com; web site http://www.yourhoustonnews.com
Circulation:; CVC
Group: Times Media Group
Advt Sales Mgr .... Kathy Konter
Ed .... Roy Kent

HUBBARD

HUBBARD CITY NEWS (THUR)
205 NW 6th St, Hubbard, TX, 76648-2016, Hill, USA; gen tel (254) 576-2978; adv tel (254) 576-2978; ed tel (254) 576-2978; gen fax (254) 576-5076; adv fax (254) 576-5076; ed fax (254) 576-5076; disp adv e-mail bminzenews@hillsboro.net; class adv e-mail bminzenews@hillsboro.net; ed e-mail bminzenews@hillsboro.net
Circulation: 1,050pd,; Sworn/Estimate/Non-Audited
Advertising rate: Open inch rate $3.60
Established: 1881
Pub./Ed./Adv. Dir. .... Barbara Minze
Delivery Method: Mail, Racks
Areas Served: Hill County

HUMBLE

EAST MONTGOMERY COUNTY OBSERVER (WED)
907 E Main St, Humble, TX, 77338-4749, Harris, USA; gen tel (281) 378-1060; adv tel (281) 378-1071; ed tel (281) 378-1062; gen fax (281) 446-6901; adv fax (281) 446-6901; ed fax (281) 446-6901; disp adv e-mail cturner@hcnonline.com; class adv e-mail cturner@hcnonline.com; ed e-mail jsummer@hcnonline.com; web site www.YourEMCNews.com
Circulation: 0pd, 10,498fr; CVC
Advertising rate: $11.39
Established: 1982
Group: Hearst Communications, Inc.
Times Media Group
Digital Platform - Mobile: Apple, Android
Digital Platform - Tablet: Apple iOS, Android, Windows 7
Pub. .... Brenda Miller-Fergerson
Pub/Ad Dir .... Corey Turner
Mechanical Specifications: 10.388" x 20.5"
Delivery Method: Carrier, Racks
Areas Served: Montgomery County

IDALOU

IDALOU BEACON (FRI)
207 Main St, Idalou, TX, 79329-9127, Lubbock, USA; gen tel (806) 892-2233; gen fax (806) 892-2233; disp adv e-mail beacon@windstream.net; class adv e-mail beacon@windstream.net; ed e-mail beacon@windstream.net
Circulation: 800pd,; Sworn/Estimate/Non-Audited
Advertising rate: Open inch rate $6.35
Established: 1955
Pub./Ed./Adv. Dir. .... Jona Janet
Mechanical Specifications: Type page 11.5 x 21.25; E - 6 cols, 1.76, 1/6 between; A - 6 cols, 1.76, 1/6 between; C - 6 cols, 1.76, 1/6 between.
Delivery Method: Mail, Newsstand
Areas Served: Lubbock County

INGRAM

WEST KERR CURRENT (THUR)
107 Highway 39, Ste A, Ingram, TX, 78025-3286, Kerr, USA; gen tel (830) 367-3501; adv tel (830) 367-3501; ed tel (830) 367-3501; gen fax (830) 367-3064; adv fax (830) 367-3501; ed fax (830) 367-3501; disp adv e-mail wkcurrent@classicnet.net; class adv e-mail wkcurrent@classicnet.net; ed e-mail wkcurrent@classicnet.net; web site www.wkcurrent.com
Circulation: 1,400pd, 25fr; Sworn/Estimate/Non-Audited
Advertising rate: Open inch rate $6.00
Established: 2003
Digital Platform - Mobile: Apple, Android, Windows, Blackberry
Digital Platform - Tablet: Apple iOS, Android, Windows 7, Blackberry Tablet OS, Kindle, Nook, Kindle Fire
Pub./Ed. .... Clint Schroeder
reporter, ad sales .... Irene Van Winkle
Advertising Director .... Nancy Schroeder
Delivery Method: Mail, Newsstand, Racks
Areas Served: 78024, 78025, 78058, 78028

IOWA PARK

IOWA PARK LEADER (THUR)
112 W Cash St, Iowa Park, TX, 76367-2824, Wichita, USA; gen tel (940) 592-4431; adv tel (940) 592-4431; ed tel (940) 592-4431; gen fax (940) 592-4431; adv fax (940) 592-4431; ed fax (940) 592-4431; disp adv e-mail kcollins@iowaparkleader.com; class adv e-mail kcollins@iowaparkleader.com; ed e-mail dhamilton@iowaparkleader.com; web site www.iowaparkleader.com
Circulation: 2,700pd,; Sworn/Estimate/Non-Audited
Advertising rate: Open inch rate $4.50
Established: 1969
Digital Platform - Mobile: Apple, Android
Digital Platform - Tablet: Apple iOS, Android, Windows 7
Ed./Pub. .... Dolores Hamilton
Sports Ed. .... Kevin Hamilton
Adv. Mgr. .... Kari Collins
reporter/photographer
Sherrie Williams
Delivery Method: Mail, Newsstand
Areas Served: Wichita County

IRVING

THE IRVING RAMBLER (SAT)
627 S Rogers Rd, Irving, TX, 75060-3753, Dallas, USA; gen tel (972) 870-1992; adv tel (214) 675-6493; ed tel (214) 675-6493; disp adv e-mail johns@ramblernewspapers.net; class adv e-mail laurier@ramblernewspapers.net; ed e-mail staceys@ramblernewspapers.net; web site www.irvingrambler.com
Circulation: 4,400pd, 1,900fr; Sworn/Estimate/Non-Audited
Advertising rate: Open inch rate $18.40
Established: 2003
Group: Rambler Newspapers
Digital Platform - Mobile: Apple, Android
Digital Platform - Tablet: Apple iOS, Android, Windows 7
Pub. .... John Starkey
Ed. .... Stacey Starkey
Office Mgr .... Laurie Reeter-Brown
Delivery Method: Mail, Newsstand, Carrier, Racks
Areas Served: 70560, 75061, 75062, 75063, 75038, 75039, 75019

JACKSBORO

JACKSBORO HERALD-GAZETTE (FRI)
212 N Church St, Jacksboro, TX, 76458-1800, Jack, USA; gen tel (940) 567-2616; adv tel (940) 567-2616; ed tel (940) 567-2616; gen fax (940) 567-2071; adv fax (940) 567-2071; ed fax (940) 567-2071; disp adv e-mail editor@jacksboronewspapers.com; class adv e-mail editor@jacksboronewspapers.com; ed e-mail editor@jacksboronewspapers.com; web site www.jacksboronewspapers.com
Circulation: 1,500pd, 11fr; Sworn/Estimate/Non-Audited
Advertising rate: Open inch rate $7.35
Established: 1880
Group: Moser Community Media
Digital Platform - Mobile: Apple, Android, Windows, Blackberry
Digital Platform - Tablet: Apple iOS, Android, Windows 7, Blackberry Tablet OS, Kindle, Nook, Kindle Fire
Staff Writer .... Brian Smith
Ad manager .... Mary Jo Watson
Mechanical Specifications: Type page 12 1/2 x 20 1/2; E - 6 cols, 1 15/16, 1/6 between; A - 6 cols, 1 15/16, 1/6 between; C - 6 cols, 1 15/16, 1/6 between.Equipment & Software: Hardware — APP/Mac; Software — Adobe/PageMaker 6.5, Adobe/Photoshop 7.0.
Delivery Method: Mail, Racks
Areas Served: 76458, 76459, 76486

JACKSONVILLE

JACKSONVILLE DAILY PROGRESS (TUES, THUR, SAT)
525 E Commerce St, Jacksonville, TX, 75766-4909, Cherokee, USA; gen tel (903) 586-2236; adv tel (903) 586-2236; ed tel (903) 586-2236; gen fax (903) 586-0987; adv fax (903) 586-0987; ed fax (903) 586-0987; disp adv e-mail publisher@jacksonvilleprogress.com; class adv e-mail publisher@jacksonvilleprogress.com; ed e-mail editor@jacksonvilleprogress.com; web site www.jacksonvilleprogress.com
Circulation: 3,000pd,; Sworn/Estimate/Non-Audited
Advertising rate: Open inch rate $10.10 (Mon-Fri); $10.50 (Sat)
Established: 1910
Group: CNHI, LLC
Community Newspaper Holdings, Inc.
Digital Platform - Mobile: Apple, Android
Digital Platform - Tablet: Apple iOS, Android
Sports Ed. .... Jay Neal
Pub. .... Lange Svehlak
Adv. Asst. .... Sharon Claxton
Ed. .... April Barbe
Mechanical Specifications: Type page 12 1/2 x 21 1/2; E - 6 cols, 1 5/6, 1/8 between; A - 6 cols, 1 5/6, 1/8 between; C - 9 cols, 1 3/16, 1/8 between.
Delivery Method: Mail, Carrier
Areas Served: Jacksonville and Cherokee County

JASPER

JASPER NEWSBOY (WED)
702 S Wheeler St, Jasper, TX, 75951-4544, Jasper, USA; gen tel (409) 384-3441; adv tel (409) 384-3441; ed tel (409) 384-3441; gen fax (409) 384-8803; adv fax (409) 384-8803; ed fax (409) 384-8803; disp adv e-mail plinares@hearstnp.com; class adv e-mail jhidalgo@hearstnp.com; ed e-mail tkelly@hearstnp.com; web site www.beaumonterprise.com
Circulation: 6,100pd,; Sworn/Estimate/Non-Audited
Advertising rate: Open inch rate $7.10
Established: 1865
Digital Platform - Mobile: Apple, Android, Windows, Blackberry
Digital Platform - Tablet: Apple iOS, Android, Windows 7, Blackberry Tablet OS, Kindle, Nook, Kindle Fire
Pub. .... Mark Adkins
Ed. .... Timothy M. Kelly
Adv. Dir. .... Sharon Friedes
Delivery Method: Mail, Newsstand
Areas Served: Jasper County

JEFFERSON

JEFFERSON JIMPLECUTE (THUR)
120 N Vale St, Jefferson, TX, 75657-2256, Marion, USA; gen tel (903) 665-2462; adv tel (903)665-2462; ed tel (903)665-2462; gen fax (903) 705-4326; adv fax (903)705-4326; ed fax (903)705-4326; disp adv e-mail ads@jimplecute.com; class adv e-mail ads@jimplecute.com; ed e-mail editor@jimplecute.com; web site www.jimplecute1848.com
Circulation: 2,000pd, 75fr; Sworn/Estimate/Non-Audited
Advertising rate: Open inch rate $5.85
Established: 1848
Group: Red River MediaEditions: (10) Mardi Gras, Candlelight, Christmas Seasons, Bull dog Football
Digital Platform - Mobile: Apple, Android
Digital Platform - Tablet: Apple iOS, Android, Windows 7
Pub. .... Bob Palmer
Gen. Mgr. .... Hugh Lewis
Ed. .... Sara Whitaker
Delivery Method: Mail, Newsstand, Carrier, Racks
Areas Served: 75657, 75455, 75657, 75671, 75752, 75480, 75630, 75686, 75044, 75601, 75671, 75672, 75670

JEWETT

JEWETT MESSENGER (WED)
223 Cameron St, Jewett, TX, 75846-4612, Leon, USA; gen tel (903) 626-4296; adv tel (903) 626-4296; ed tel (903) 626-4296; gen fax (903) 626-5248; adv fax (903) 626-5248; ed fax (903) 626-5248; disp adv e-mail jmessenger46@sbcglobal.net; class adv e-mail jmessenger46@sbcglobal.net; ed e-mail jmessenger46@sbcglobal.net; web site www.jewettmessengeronline.com
Circulation: 1,800pd, 24fr; Sworn/Estimate/Non-Audited
Advertising rate: Open inch rate $3.50
Established: 1885
Pub./Ed./Adv. Dir. ....
David CluteEquipment & Software: Hardware — APP/Mac; Software — QPS/QuarkXPress.
Delivery Method: Mail, Newsstand
Areas Served: Leon County

JOHNSON CITY

JOHNSON CITY RECORD-COURIER (THUR)
110 E Main St, Ste B, Johnson City, TX, 78636-4239, Blanco, USA; gen tel (830) 868-7181; adv tel (830) 868-7181; ed tel (830) 868-7181; gen fax (830) 868-7182; adv fax (830) 868-7182; ed fax (830) 868-7182; disp adv e-mail jcrecordcourier@verizon.net; class adv e-mail jcrecordcourier@verizon.net; ed e-mail jcrecordcourier@verizon.net; web site www.jcrecordcourier.com
Circulation: 1,600pd, 200fr; Sworn/Estimate/Non-Audited
Advertising rate: Open inch rate $5.25
Established: 1880
Digital Platform - Mobile: Apple, Android
Digital Platform - Tablet: Apple iOS, Android, Windows 7

Pub..Scott Wesner
Ed./Adv. Dir. .... Emily Zbytovsky
Delivery Method: Mail, Newsstand
Areas Served: Blanco County

JUNCTION

THE JUNCTION EAGLE (WED)

215 N 6th St, Junction, TX, 76849-4123, Kimble, USA; gen tel (325) 446-2610; adv tel (325) 446-2610; ed tel (325) 446-2610; gen fax (325) 446-4025; adv fax (325) 446-4025; ed fax (325) 446-4025; disp adv e-mail ashley@junctioneagle.com; class adv e-mail asia@junctioneagle.com; ed e-mail editor@junctioneagle.com; web site www.junction-eagle.com
Circulation: 2,000pd,; Sworn/Estimate/Non-Audited
Advertising rate: Open inch rate $5.00
Established: 1882
Digital Platform - Mobile: Apple, Android, Windows, Blackberry
Digital Platform - Tablet: Apple iOS, Android, Windows 7, Blackberry Tablet OS, Kindle, Nook, Kindle Fire
Pub./Ed..........................Debbie Cooper Kistler
Ed. ....Jimmy Kistler
Admin. Assistant.........................Asia Happner
Adv. Director ....Ashley Lundy
Delivery Method: Mail, Newsstand, Racks
Areas Served: Kimble County

KARNES CITY

THE KARNES COUNTYWIDE (WED)

106 N Esplanade St, Karnes City, TX, 78118-2942, Karnes, USA; gen tel (830) 583-0283; adv tel (830) 583-0283; ed tel (830) 583-0283; gen fax (830) 583-0285; adv fax (830) 583-0285; ed fax (830) 583-0285; disp adv e-mail karneseditor@mysoutex.com; class adv e-mail karneseditor@mysoutex.com; ed e-mail karneseditor@mysoutex.com; web site www.mysoutex/.com
Circulation: 4,000pd,; Sworn/Estimate/Non-Audited
Advertising rate: Open inch rate $7.00
Established: 1891
Digital Platform - Mobile: Apple, Android
Digital Platform - Tablet: Apple iOS, Android, Windows 7
Co-Pub...Jeff Latcham
Co-Pub.......................................Chip Latcham
Ed. ....Joe Baker
Adv. Dir........................ Karl ArnstEquipment & Software: ; Software — Adobe/InDesign 1.5, Adobe/Photoshop 5.0, Microsoft/Word.
Delivery Method: Mail, Newsstand
Areas Served: Karnes County

KATY

THE KATY TIMES (THUR)

5319 E 5th St, Katy, TX, 77493-2520, Harris, USA; gen tel (281) 391-3141; adv tel (281) 391-3141; ed tel (281) 391-3141; gen fax (281) 391-2030; adv fax (281) 391-2030; ed fax (281) 391-2030; disp adv e-mail jennifer@katytimes.com; class adv e-mail lindsay@katytimes.com; ed e-mail news@katytimes.com; web site www.katytimes.com - 80,000(views) 2,500(visitors)
Circulation: 4,300pd, 0fr; Sworn/Estimate/Non-Audited
Advertising rate: Open inch rate $10.75
Established: 1912
Group: Hartman Newspapers LP
Digital Platform - Mobile: Apple, Android, Windows, Blackberry
Digital Platform - Tablet: Apple iOS, Android, Windows 7, Blackberry Tablet OS, Kindle, Nook, Kindle Fire
Pub..Terry Schaub
Mgr. Ed.................................... Greg Densmore
Circulation............................. Quincey Prickett
Delivery Method: Mail, Newsstand, Carrier, Racks
Areas Served: Harris County

KAUFMAN

THE KAUFMAN HERALD (THUR)

300 N Washington St, Kaufman, TX, 75142-1345, Kaufman, USA; gen tel (972) 932-2171; adv tel (972) 932-2171; ed tel (972) 932-2171; gen fax (972) 932-2172; adv fax (972) 932-2172; ed fax (972) 932-2172; disp adv e-mail sales@kaufmanherald.com; class adv e-mail classifieds@kaufmanherald.com; ed e-mail mlewis@kaufmanherald.com; web site www.kaufmanherald.com
Circulation: 2,972pd, 277fr; CVC
Advertising rate: Open inch rate $12.90
Established: 1885
Group: Hartman Newspapers LP
Digital Platform - Mobile: Apple, Android, Blackberry
Digital Platform - Tablet: Apple iOS, Android, Blackberry Tablet OS
Pub./Ed./Adv. Dir........................ Monica Lewis
Retail Adv. Mgr.............................. Amy Fowler
Classified Adv. Mgr............. Kathy Lynn Dieken
Mechanical Specifications: Full page 21.50 inches by 11.25
Delivery Method: Mail, Racks
Areas Served: Kaufman County

KERMIT

THE WINKLER COUNTY NEWS (THUR)

109 S Poplar St, Kermit, TX, 79745-3027, Winkler, USA; gen tel (432) 586-2561; adv tel (432) 586-2561; ed tel (432) 586-2561; gen fax (432) 586-2562; adv fax (432) 586-2562; ed fax (432) 586-2562; disp adv e-mail gfreepress@sbcglobal.net; class adv e-mail gfreepress@sbcglobal.net; ed e-mail gfreepress@sbcglobal.net
Circulation: 1,500pd,; Sworn/Estimate/Non-Audited
Advertising rate: Open inch rate $4.20
Established: 1936
Co-Pub.. Denise Hannah
Co-Pub.. Tom Beckham
Ed. ....Phil Parks
Adv. Dir.....................................Phyllis Thomas
Delivery Method: Mail, Newsstand
Areas Served: Winkler County

KERRVILLE

HILL COUNTRY COMMUNITY JOURNAL (WED)

303 Earl Garrett St, Kerrville, TX, 78028-4529, Kerr, USA; gen tel (830) 257-2828; adv tel (830) 257-2828; ed tel (830) 257-2828; gen fax (830) 896-9444; adv fax (830) 896-9444; ed fax (830) 896-9444; disp adv e-mail journal@ktc.com; class adv e-mail journal@ktc.com; ed e-mail journal@ktc.com; web site www.hccommunityjournal.com
Advertising rate: Open inch rate $5.00
Established: 2005
Digital Platform - Mobile: Apple
Digital Platform - Tablet: Apple iOS, Windows 7
Pub./Ed...Tammy Prout
Adv. Dir.. Linda Wise
Delivery Method: Mail, Newsstand
Areas Served: Kerr County

KILGORE

BULLARD BANNER NEWS (WED)

610 E Main St, Kilgore, TX, 75662-2612, Smith, USA; gen tel (903) 894-9306; adv tel (903) 894-9306; ed tel (903) 894-9306; gen fax (903) 894-9308; adv fax (903) 894-9308; ed fax (903) 894-9308; disp adv e-mail advertising@bullardnews.com; class adv e-mail classifieds@kilgorenewsherald.com; ed e-mail news1@bullardnews.com; web site www.bullardnews.com
Circulation: 1,800pd,; Sworn/Estimate/Non-Audited
Advertising rate: Open inch rate $6.55
Established: 1996
Group: Bluebonnet Publishing, LLC
Digital Platform - Mobile: Apple, Android, Windows, Blackberry
Digital Platform - Tablet: Apple iOS, Android, Windows 7, Blackberry Tablet OS, Kindle, Nook, Kindle Fire
Pub./Ed. .... Bill Woodall
Co-Pub.................................. Jessica Woodall
Adv. Dir...Jamie Mims
Delivery Method: Mail, Racks
Areas Served: 75757, 75703, 75762

KILGORE NEWS HERALD (WED, SAT)

610 E Main St, Kilgore, TX, 75662-2612, Gregg, USA; gen tel (903) 984-2593; adv tel (903) 984-2593; ed tel (903) 984-2593; gen fax (903) 984-7462; adv fax (903) 984-7462; ed fax (903) 984-7462; disp adv e-mail bwoodall@kilgorenewsherald.com; class adv e-mail addirector@kilgorenewsherald.com; ed e-mail news1@kilgorenewsherald.com; web site www.kilgorenewsherald.com - 161,000(views) 60,000(visitors)
Circulation: 2,770pd, 1,200fr; Sworn/Estimate/Non-Audited
Advertising rate: Open inch rate $10.97
Established: 1935
Group: Bluebonnet Publishing, LLC
Digital Platform - Mobile: Apple, Android, Blackberry
Digital Platform - Tablet: Apple iOS, Android, Blackberry Tablet OS
Co-Pub./Ed. .... Bill Woodall
Co-Pub.................................. Jessica Woodall
News Ed. .... James Draper
Sports Ed.....................................Mitch Lucas
Prod. Mgr. .... Charlotte Smith
Mechanical Specifications: Type page 11 1/2 x 21 1/2; E - 6 cols, 2 1/16, 1/8 between; A - 6 cols, 2 1/16, 1/8 between; C - 8 cols, 1 1/2, 1/8 between.
Delivery Method: Mail, Newsstand, Carrier, Racks
Areas Served: Gregg and Rusk County

KINGSVILLE

KINGSVILLE RECORD & BISHOP NEWS (WED, SUN)

1831 W Santa Gertrudis St, Kingsville, TX, 78363-3447, Kleberg, USA; gen tel (361) 592-4304; adv tel (361) 592-4304; ed tel (361) 592-4304; gen fax (361) 592-1015; adv fax (361) 592-1015; ed fax (361) 592-1015; disp adv e-mail cjmaher@king-ranch.com; class adv e-mail cjmaher@king-ranch.com; ed e-mail cjmaher@king-ranch.com; web site www.KingsvilleRecord.com
Circulation:; Sworn/Estimate/Non-Audited
Advertising rate: Open inch rate $8.00
Established: 1906
Pub./Ed............................. Christopher Maher
Ad. Director.................................... Tracy Pena
Delivery Method: Mail, Newsstand
Areas Served: Kleberg County, Nueces County

KIRBYVILLE

KIRBYVILLE BANNER (WED)

104 N Kellie Ave, Kirbyville, TX, 75956-1824, Jasper, USA; gen tel (409) 423-2696; adv tel (409) 423-2696; ed tel (409) 423-2696; gen fax (409) 423-4793; adv fax (409) 423-4793; ed fax (409) 423-4793; disp adv e-mail kbannerads@sbcglobal.net; class adv e-mail kbannerads@sbcglobal.net; ed e-mail kbanner@sbcglobal.net
Circulation: 1,770pd, 9fr; Sworn/Estimate/Non-Audited
Advertising rate: Open inch rate $6.10
Established: 1906
Pub .... Danny Reneau
Adv. Dir... Karen Kilmer
Reporter .... Sallie Solly
Delivery Method: Mail, Newsstand
Areas Served: Jasper County

KYLE

HAYS FREE PRESS (WED)

113 W Center St, Kyle, TX, 78640-9450, TX, USA; gen tel (512) 268-7862; gen fax (512) 268-0262; disp adv e-mail tracy@haysfreepress.com; class adv e-mail david@haysfreepress.com; ed e-mail news@haysfreepress.com; web site www.haysfreepress.com 35,000(visitors)
Circulation: 3,205pd, 454fr; Sworn/Estimate/Non-Audited
Advertising rate: Open inch rate $12.50
Established: 1903
Group: Barton Publications, Inc.
Digital Platform - Mobile: Apple, Android
Digital Platform - Tablet: Apple iOS, Android
Pub.................................. Cyndy Slovak-Barton
Ed. ....Moses Leos III
Bus. Mgr. .... Connie Brewer
Adv. Mgr. ....Tracy Mack
Circ. Mgr...................................Suzanne Hallam
Prodn. Mgr. .... David WhiteEquipment & Software: Hardware — APP/Mac, PC; Software — Adobe/InDesign.
Delivery Method: Mail, Newsstand, Racks
Areas Served: 78666, 78610, 78640, 78619, 78652

LA FERIA

LA FERIA NEWS (WED)

102 S Main St, La Feria, TX, 78559-5005, Cameron, USA; gen tel (956) 797-9920; adv tel (956) 797-9920; ed tel (956) 797-9920; gen fax (956) 797-9921; adv fax (956) 797-9921; ed fax (956) 797-9921; disp adv e-mail drwpops@aol.com; class adv e-mail laferianews2@aol.com; ed e-mail laferianews@aol.com; web site www.laferianews.net
Circulation: 5,000pd,; Sworn/Estimate/Non-Audited
Advertising rate: Open inch rate $8.00
Established: 1923
Digital Platform - Mobile: Apple, Windows
Digital Platform - Tablet: Apple iOS, Windows 7
Pub./Adv. Dir. .... Don Wright
Ed. .... Mary Beth Wright
Delivery Method: Mail, Newsstand
Areas Served: Cameron County

LA GRANGE

THE FAYETTE COUNTY RECORD (TUES, FRI)

127 S Washington St, La Grange, TX, 78945-2628, Fayette, USA; gen tel (979) 968-3155; adv tel (979) 968-3155; ed tel (979) 968-3155; gen fax (979) 968-6767; adv fax (979) 968-6767; ed fax (979) 968-6767; disp adv e-mail becky@fayettecountyrecord.com; class adv e-mail jackie@fayettecountyrecord.com; ed e-mail regina@fayettecountyrecord.com; web site www.fayettecountyrecord.com
Circulation: 5,477pd, 51fr; Sworn/Estimate/Non-Audited
Advertising rate: Open inch rate $8.25
Established: 1922
Group: Fayette County Record, Inc.
Digital Platform - Mobile: Apple, Android, Windows, Blackberry
Digital Platform - Tablet: Apple iOS, Android, Windows 7, Blackberry Tablet OS, Kindle, Nook, Kindle Fire
Pub...Regina Keilers
Ed. ....Jeff Wick
Adv. Dir.. Becky Weise
Classified Mgr. ....Jackie Daniels
Circ. Mgr...............................Theresia Karstedt
Office Mgr. ....Aileen Loehr
Prod. Mgr. ....John Castaneda
Mechanical Specifications: Type page 13 1/2 x 21.Equipment & Software: Hardware — APP/Mac; Software — InDesign, Photoshop
Delivery Method: Mail, Newsstand, Racks
Areas Served: 78945, 78940, 78954, 78956, 78941, 78932, 78949

LA VERNIA

LA VERNIA NEWS (THUR)
112 E Chihuahua St, La Vernia, TX, 78121-5898, Wilson, USA; gen tel (830) 779-3751; gen fax (210) 855-4848; disp adv e-mail reader@lavernianews.com; class adv e-mail reader@lavernianews.com; ed e-mail reader@lavernianews.com; web site www.lavernianews.com
Circulation: 1,284pd, 529fr; Sworn/Estimate/Non-Audited
Advertising rate: Open inch rate $4.50
Established: 1969
Group: WCN, Inc.
Digital Platform - Mobile: Apple, Android, Blackberry
Digital Platform - Tablet: Apple iOS, Android, Windows 7, Blackberry Tablet OS
Publisher................................ Elaine Kolodziej
Adv. Dir.....................................Kristen Weaver
Ed. .... Nannette Kilbey-Smith
Delivery Method: Mail, Newsstand
Areas Served: Wilson County

LAMESA

LAMESA PRESS REPORTER (WED, SUN)
523 N 1st St, Lamesa, TX, 79331-5405, Dawson, USA; gen tel (806) 872-2177; gen fax (806) 872-2623; disp adv e-mail adsales@pressreporter.com; class adv e-mail classifieds@pressreporter.com; ed e-mail editor@pressreporter.com; web site www.pressreporter.com
Circulation: 1,970pd, 83fr; Sworn/Estimate/Non-Audited
Advertising rate: Open inch rate $7.00
Established: 1905
Digital Platform - Mobile: Apple, Android
Digital Platform - Tablet: Apple iOS, Android, Windows 7
Pub... Russel Skiles
Ed. .... Herrel Hallmark
Bookkeeper .... Heather Allen
ad manager ....Kelsey Odom
Mechanical Specifications: Type page 12.625 x 21; E - 6 cols, 1.83, 1/8 between; A - 6 cols, 1.83, 1/8 between; C - 6 cols, 1.83, 1/8 between.Equipment & Software: Hardware — PC; Software — WordPerfect 8.0, InDesign
Delivery Method: Mail, Newsstand, Carrier
Areas Served: 79331, 79713, 79351, 79377,79738

LAMPASAS

LAMPASAS DISPATCH RECORD (TUES, FRI)
416 S Live Oak St, Lampasas, TX, 76550-2940, Lampasas, USA; gen tel (512) 556-6262; adv tel (512) 556-6262; ed tel (512) 556-6262; gen fax (512) 556-3278; adv fax (512) 556-3278; ed fax (512) 556-3278; disp adv e-mail ads@lampasasdispatchrecord.com; class adv e-mail ads@lampasasdispatchrecord.com; ed e-mail news@lampasas.com; web site www.lampasasdispatchrecord.com
Circulation: 2,941pd, 37fr; Sworn/Estimate/Non-Audited
Advertising rate: Open inch rate $7.70
Established: 1955
Digital Platform - Mobile: Apple, Android, Windows, Blackberry
Digital Platform - Tablet: Apple iOS, Android, Windows 7, Blackberry Tablet OS, Kindle, Nook, Kindle Fire
Co-Pub./Ed. ....James Lowe
Co-Pub...Gail Lowe
Adv. Dir...................................Teresa Thornton
Mechanical Specifications: Type page 13 x 21; E - 6 cols, 2 1/16, 3/16 between; A - 6 cols, 2 1/16, 3/16 between; C - 6 cols, 2 1/16, 3/16 between.
Delivery Method: Mail, Newsstand, Racks
Areas Served: 76550, 76539, 76853

LEONARD

LEONARD GRAPHIC (THUR)
100 E Collin St, Ste 201, Leonard, TX, 75452-2561, Fannin, USA; gen tel (903) 587-2850; adv tel (903) 587-2853; ed tel (903) 587-2850; gen fax (903) 587-0297; adv fax (903) 587-0297; ed fax (903) 587-0297; disp adv e-mail ava@theleonardgraphic.com; class adv e-mail ava@theleonardgraphic.com; ed e-mail betsy@theleonardgraphic.com; web site www.theleonardgraphic.com
Circulation: 724pd,; Sworn/Estimate/Non-Audited
Advertising rate: Open inch rate $20.00
Established: 1890
Digital Platform - Mobile: Apple, Android, Windows, Blackberry
Digital Platform - Tablet: Apple iOS, Android, Windows 7, Blackberry Tablet OS
Pub./Ed. .... Betsy Blevins
Adv. Dir.. Ava Barlow
Delivery Method: Mail, Newsstand, Racks
Areas Served: Fannin County

LEVELLAND

LEVELLAND & HOCKLEY COUNTY NEWS-PRESS (WED, SUN)
711 Austin St, Levelland, TX, 79336-4523, Hockley, USA; gen tel (806) 894-3121; adv tel (806) 894-3121; ed tel (806) 894-3121; gen fax (806) 894-7957; adv fax (806) 894-7957; ed fax (806) 894-7957; disp adv e-mail levellandads@valornet.com; class adv e-mail levellandads@valornet.com; ed e-mail levellandnews@valornet.com; web site www.levellandnews.net
Circulation: 4,300pd, 50fr; Sworn/Estimate/Non-Audited
Advertising rate: Open inch rate $7.75
Established: 1928
Group: Stephen & Pat Enterprises
Digital Platform - Mobile: Apple, Android, Windows, Blackberry
Digital Platform - Tablet: Apple iOS, Android, Windows 7, Blackberry Tablet OS
Pub......................................Stephen A. Henry
Pub... Pat Henry
News Ed .... Kati Walker
Adv. Mgr. ....Michelle Davis
Mechanical Specifications: Type page PASSEquipment & Software: Hardware — Mac & PC; Software — Aldus/PageMaker 8.0, Archetype/Corel Draw, Q&A 4.0, Adobe/Photoshop, WordPerfect 8.0-12.
Delivery Method: Mail, Newsstand, Carrier, Racks
Areas Served: 79336, 79338, 79372, 79380, 79379, 79358, 79346, 79367, 79353, 79313,

LEXINGTON

LEXINGTON LEADER (THUR)
612 Wheatley St, Lexington, TX, 78947-9401, Lee, USA; gen tel (979) 773-3022; adv tel (979) 773-3022; ed tel (979) 773-3022; gen fax (979) 773-4125; adv fax (979) 773-4125; ed fax (979) 773-4125; disp adv e-mail editor@lexingtonleader.com; class adv e-mail editor@lexingtonleader.com; ed e-mail editor@lexingtonleader.com; web site www.lexingtonleader.com
Circulation: 1,500pd,; Sworn/Estimate/Non-Audited
Advertising rate: Open inch rate $7.25
Established: 1997
Digital Platform - Mobile: Apple, Android
Digital Platform - Tablet: Apple iOS, Android, Windows 7
Ed. .... Cindy Terrell
Delivery Method: Mail, Newsstand, Carrier, Racks
Areas Served: Lexington/Lee County/78947

LIBERTY

THE VINDICATOR (THUR)
1939 Trinity St, Ste A, Liberty, TX, 77575-4851, Liberty, USA; gen tel (936) 336-3611; adv tel (936) 336-3611; ed tel (936) 336-3611; gen fax (936) 336-3345; adv fax (936) 336-3345; ed fax (936) 336-3345; disp adv e-mail publisher@thevindicator.com; class adv e-mail ads@thevindicator.com; ed e-mail editor@thevindicator.com; web site www.thevindicator.com - 62,689(views) 25,327(visitors)
Circulation: 1,019pd, 732fr; CVC
Advertising rate: Open inch rate $6.50
Established: 1887
Group: Fenice Community Media
Digital Platform - Mobile: Apple, Android, Windows
Digital Platform - Tablet: Apple iOS, Android, Windows 7, Blackberry Tablet OS, Kindle, Nook, Kindle Fire
Pub...Carol Skewes
Adv. Mgr. .... Kim Marlow
Circ. Mgr ....Rodger Slusher
Office Mgr. .... Jennfier Gray
Sports Ed...................................Jerry Michalsky
Mechanical Specifications: Type page 10.25 x 21; E - 6 cols, 1.625", 1.250" between; A - 6 cols, 1.625", 1.25" between; C - 9 cols, 9.000", 1.250" between.
Delivery Method: Mail, Racks
Areas Served: Liberty County

LIBERTY HILL

THE LIBERTY HILL INDEPENDENT (THUR)
14251 W State Highway 29, Ste B, Liberty Hill, TX, 78642-5843, Williamson, USA; gen tel (512) 778-5577; disp adv e-mail news@LHIndependent.com; web site www.LHIndependent.com - 6,500(views) 4,200(visitors)
Circulation: 1,850pd,; Sworn/Estimate/Non-Audited
Advertising rate: Open inch rate $7.00
Established: 1987
Group: Free State Media Group
Digital Platform - Mobile: Apple, Android
Digital Platform - Tablet: Apple iOS, Android, Windows 7
Pub./Owner..............................Shelly Wilkison
Delivery Method: Mail, Newsstand, Racks
Areas Served: 78642, 78641, 78605, 78628

LINDALE

THE LINDALE NEWS & TIMES (THUR)
104 N Main St, Lindale, TX, 75771-6294, Smith, USA; gen tel (903) 882-8880; gen fax (903) 882-8234; disp adv e-mail mattaway@lindalenews-times.com; class adv e-mail advertising@lindalenews-times.com; ed e-mail news@lindalenews-times.com; web site www.lindalenews-times.com
Circulation: 2,127pd,; Sworn/Estimate/Non-Audited
Advertising rate: Open inch rate $8.20
Established: 1900
Group: Bluebonnet Publishing, LLC
Digital Platform - Mobile: Apple, Android, Windows, Blackberry
Digital Platform - Tablet: Apple iOS, Android, Windows 7, Blackberry Tablet OS, Kindle, Nook, Kindle Fire
Pub..Joyce Hathcock
Ed. .... Terry Cannon
Adv. Dir.......................................Maria Attaway
Office Mgr. .... Angela` Houston
Delivery Method: Mail, Newsstand, Racks
Areas Served: Smith County

LINDEN

THE CASS COUNTY SUN (WED)
122 W Houston St, Linden, TX, 75563-5556, Cass, USA; gen tel (903) 756-7396; adv tel (903) 756-7396; ed tel (903) 756-7396; gen fax (903) 756-3038; adv fax (903) 756-3038; ed fax (903) 756-3038; disp adv e-mail aguillory@casscountynow.com; class adv e-mail aguillory@casscountynow.com; ed e-mail bwoods@casscountynow.com; web site www.casscountynow.com
Circulation: 1,100pd, 1,075fr; Sworn/Estimate/Non-Audited
Advertising rate: Open inch rate $12.50
Established: 1876
Group: Northeast Texas Publishing
Digital Platform - Mobile: Apple, Android, Windows, Blackberry
Digital Platform - Tablet: Apple iOS, Android, Windows 7, Blackberry Tablet OS
Ad Mgr...................................... Angela Guillory
Editor ....Ben Woods
General Manager.......................Rachel Woods
Delivery Method: Mail, Newsstand, Racks
Areas Served: Cass County

LINDSAY

LINDSAY LETTER (FRI)
117 E Main St, Lindsay, TX, 76250-2105, Cooke, USA; gen tel (940) 668-8788; adv tel (940) 668-8788; ed tel (940) 668-8788; gen fax (940) 668-6677; adv fax (940) 668-6677; ed fax (940) 668-6677; disp adv e-mail news@lindsayletter.net; class adv e-mail news@lindsayletter.net; ed e-mail news@lindsayletter.net; web site www.lindsayletter.net
Advertising rate: Open inch rate $5.00
Established: 2007
Digital Platform - Mobile: Apple, Windows
Digital Platform - Tablet: Apple iOS, Windows 7
Pub./Ed. ....Joe Warren
Adv. Dir..Karen Corley
Delivery Method: Mail, Newsstand
Areas Served: Cooke County

LITTLEFIELD

LAMB COUNTY LEADER-NEWS (WED, SUN)
313 W 4th St, Littlefield, TX, 79339-3313, Lamb, USA; gen tel (806) 385-4481; gen fax (806) 385-4640; disp adv e-mail ads@lambcountyleadernews.com; class adv e-mail classifieds@lambcountyleadernews.com; ed e-mail news@lambcountyleadernews.com
Circulation:; USPS
Advertising rate: Open inch rate $8.00
Established: 1918
Adv. Dir......................................Grata Reber
Pub...Brett Wesner
Classified Adv. Mgr./Circ. Mgr. .....Melissa Silva
Delivery Method: Mail, Newsstand, Carrier
Areas Served: Lamb County

LIVINGSTON

POLK COUNTY ENTERPRISE (THUR, SUN)
100 E Calhoun St, Livingston, TX, 77351-2908, Polk, USA; gen tel (936) 327-4357; adv tel (936) 327-4357; ed tel (936) 327-4357; gen fax (936) 327-7156; adv fax (936) 327-7156; ed fax (936) 327-7156; disp adv e-mail enterprise@easttexasnews.com; class adv e-mail enterprise@easttexasnews.com; ed e-mail enterprise@easttexasnews.com; web site www.easttexasnews.com
Circulation: 7,673pd, 83fr; Sworn/Estimate/Non-Audited
Advertising rate: Open inch rate $9.00
Established: 1904
Group: Polk County Publishing Co.
Digital Platform - Mobile: Apple, Android
Digital Platform - Tablet: Apple iOS, Android, Windows 7
Pub.. Alvin Holley
Ed. ....Valerie Reddell
Adv. Mgr. .... Linda Holley
Delivery Method: Mail, Newsstand, Carrier,

Racks
Areas Served: Polk County

SAN JACINTO NEWS-TIMES (THUR)
100 E Calhoun St, Livingston, TX, 77351-2908, Polk, USA; gen tel (936) 628-6851; adv tel (936) 327-4357; ed tel (936) 628-6851; gen fax (936) 327-7156; adv fax (936) 327-7156; ed fax (936) 327-7156; disp adv e-mail enterprise@easttexasnews.com; class adv e-mail enterprise@easttexasnews.com; ed e-mail enterprise@easttexasnews.com; web site www.easttexasnews.com
Circulation: 2,450pd, 17fr; Sworn/Estimate/Non-Audited
Advertising rate: Open inch rate $3.45
Established: 1904
Group: Polk County Publishing Co.
Digital Platform - Mobile: Apple, Android
Digital Platform - Tablet: Apple iOS, Android, Windows 7
Pub....Alvin Holley
Ed....Martha Charrey
Adv. Dir....Linda Holley
Delivery Method: Mail, Racks
Areas Served: San Jacinto County

LLANO

THE LLANO NEWS (WED)
813 Berry St, Llano, TX, 78643-1907, Llano, USA; gen tel (325) 247-4433; adv tel (325) 247-4433; ed tel (325) 247-4433; gen fax (325) 247-3338; adv fax (325) 247-3338; ed fax (325) 247-3338; disp adv e-mail thenews@verizon.net; class adv e-mail thenews@verizon.net; ed e-mail thenews@verizon.net; web site www.llanonews.com
Advertising rate: Open inch rate $6.00
Established: 1889
Digital Platform - Mobile: Apple, Android
Digital Platform - Tablet: Apple iOS, Android
Pub....Ken Wesner
Ed....Heather Wagner
Adv. Dir....Scott Wesner
Delivery Method: Mail, Newsstand
Areas Served: Llano County

LOCKHART

LOCKHART POST-REGISTER (THUR)
111 S Church St, Lockhart, TX, 78644-2641, Caldwell, USA; gen tel (512) 398-4886; disp adv e-mail news@post-register.com; class adv e-mail advertising@post-register.com; ed e-mail kathibliss@post-register.com; web site www.post-register.com
Circulation: 3,086pd, 177fr; USPS
Advertising rate: Open inch rate $8.20
Established: 1872
Digital Platform - Mobile: Apple, Android
Digital Platform - Tablet: Apple iOS
Pub....Dana Garrett
Mng. Ed....Kathi Bliss
Mechanical Specifications: Type page 10x 21; E - 6 cols, 1.562, 1/8 betweenEquipment & Software: Hardware — APP/Mac; Software — QPS/QuarkXPress.
Delivery Method: Mail, Newsstand
Areas Served: Lockhart, Caldwell County, 78644

LULING

THE LULING NEWSBOY AND SIGNAL (THUR)
415 E Davis St, Luling, TX, 78648-2316, Caldwell, USA; gen tel (830) 875-2116; adv tel (830)875-2116; ed tel (830)875-2116; gen fax (830) 875-2124; adv fax (830)875-2124; ed fax (830)875-2124; disp adv e-mail slulingnewsboy@austin.rr.com; class adv e-mail slulingnewsboy@austin.rr.com; ed e-mail slulingnewsboy@austin.rr.com; web site lulingnewsboy.com
Circulation: 1,500pd, 39fr; Sworn/Estimate/Non-Audited
Advertising rate: Open inch rate $6.50
Established: 1878
Group: Luling Publishing Co., Inc.Editions: (52)
Pub./Ed./Adv. Dir....Karen G. McCrary
Mechanical Specifications: 5-6 columns news 7 columns classy
Delivery Method: Mail, Newsstand
Areas Served: 78648, 78629, 78661, 78638

MABANK

LAKE AREA LEADER (WED)
1316 S 3rd St, Ste 108, Mabank, TX, 75147-7680, Henderson, USA; gen tel (903) 887-4511; adv tel (903) 887-4511; ed tel (903) 887-4511; gen fax (903) 887-4510; adv fax (903) 887-4510; ed fax (903) 887-4510; disp adv e-mail advertising@themonitor.net; class adv e-mail advertising@themonitor.net; ed e-mail publisher@themonitor.net; web site www.themonitor.net
Circulation: 26,000fr; Sworn/Estimate/Non-Audited
Advertising rate: Open inch rate $8.50
Established: 1974
Group: Van Zandt Newspapers LLC
Digital Platform - Mobile: Apple, Android
Digital Platform - Tablet: Apple iOS, Android, Windows 7
General Manager....Susan Harrison
Gen. Mgr....Susan Harrison
Ed....Pearl CantrellEquipment & Software: ; Software — Adobe/PageMaker 6.0, Adobe/Photoshop 5.0.
Delivery Method: Mail
Areas Served: Cedar Creek Lake Area

THE KERENS TRIBUNE (FRI)
1316 S 3rd St, Mabank, TX, 75147-7680, Henderson, USA; gen tel (903) 887-4511; adv tel (903) 887-4511; ed tel (903) 887-4511; gen fax (903) 887-4510; adv fax (903) 887-4510; ed fax (903) 887-4510; disp adv e-mail kteditor07@yahoo.com; class adv e-mail kteditor07@yahoo.com; ed e-mail kteditor07@yahoo.com
Circulation: 905pd, 78fr; Sworn/Estimate/Non-Audited
Advertising rate: Open inch rate $4
Established: 1892
Pub....John Buzzetta
Ed....Erik Walsh
Adv. Dir....Keron Walker
Delivery Method: Mail, Newsstand
Areas Served: Navarro County

THE MONITOR (THUR, SUN)
1316 S 3rd St, Ste 108, Mabank, TX, 75147-7680, Kaufman, USA; gen tel (903) 887-4511; adv tel (903) 887-4511; ed tel (903) 887-4511; gen fax (903) 887-4510; adv fax (903) 887-4510; ed fax (903) 887-4510; disp adv e-mail advertising@themonitor.net; class adv e-mail classifieds@themonitor.net; ed e-mail publisher@themonitor.net; web site www.themonitor.net
Advertising rate: Open inch rate $8.00
Established: 1974
Digital Platform - Mobile: Apple, Android, Windows, Blackberry
Digital Platform - Tablet: Apple iOS, Android, Windows 7, Blackberry Tablet OS, Kindle, Nook, Kindle Fire
Pub....Susan Harrison
Ed....Pearl Cantrell
Adv. Dir....Keron Walker
Delivery Method: Mail, Newsstand, Racks
Areas Served: Kaufman County

MADISONVILLE

MADISONVILLE METEOR (WED)
205 N Madison St, Madisonville, TX, 77864-1509, Madison, USA; gen tel (936) 348-3505; gen fax (936) 348-3338; disp adv e-mail classifieds@madisonvillemeteor.com; class adv e-mail classifieds@madisonvillemeteor.com; ed e-mail editor@madisonvillemeteor.com; web site www.madisonvillemeteor.com
Circulation: 1,197pd, 37fr; CVC
Advertising rate: Open inch rate $7.75
Established: 1894
Group: Fenice Community Media
Digital Platform - Mobile: Apple, Android, Windows, Blackberry
Digital Platform - Tablet: Apple iOS, Android, Windows 7, Blackberry Tablet OS, Kindle, Nook, Kindle Fire
Ed./Pub....Tony Farkas
Advertising Manager....Tammy Farkas
Sports writer....Campbell Atkins
Office Manager....Kim McKee
Mechanical Specifications: 10" x 21"
Delivery Method: Mail
Areas Served: Madison County

MALAKOFF

THE MALAKOFF NEWS (FRI)
815 E Royall Blvd, Ste 6, Malakoff, TX, 75148-9273, Henderson, USA; gen tel (903) 887-4511; adv tel (903) 887-4511; ed tel (903) 887-4511; gen fax (903) 887-4510; adv fax (903) 887-4510; ed fax (903) 887-4510; disp adv e-mail thenews.hendersonco@yahoo.com; class adv e-mail thenews.hendersonco@yahoo.com; ed e-mail thenews.hendersonco@yahoo.com; web site www.malakoffnews.net
Circulation: 2,000pd, 200fr; Sworn/Estimate/Non-Audited
Advertising rate: Open inch rate $5.00
Established: 1903
Digital Platform - Mobile: Apple
Digital Platform - Tablet: Apple iOS, Windows 7
Pub....John Buzzetta
Ed....Michael Hannigan
Adv. Dir....Keron Walker
Delivery Method: Mail, Newsstand
Areas Served: Henderson County

MANSFIELD

MANSFIELD NEWS-MIRROR (WED)
PO Box 337, Mansfield, TX, 76063-0337, Tarrant, USA; gen tel (817) 473-4451; adv tel (817) 987-6303; ed tel (817) 473-4451; gen fax (817) 473-0730; adv fax (817) 473-0730; ed fax (817) 473-0730; disp adv e-mail kmordecai@star-telegram.com; class adv e-mail kmordecai@star-telegram.com; ed e-mail arogers@mansfieldnewsmirror.com; web site www.star-telegram.com/mansfieldnewsmirror
Circulation: 32,158fr; AAM
Advertising rate: Open inch rate $15.97
Group: The McClatchy Company
Digital Platform - Mobile: Apple, Android, Blackberry
Digital Platform - Tablet: Apple iOS, Android, Blackberry Tablet OS
Pub./Ed....Amanda Rogers
Adv. Dir....Karen Mordecai
Adv. Mgr....Baker Haynes
Delivery Method: Mail, Racks
Areas Served: Tarrant County

MARBLE FALLS

THE HIGHLANDER (TUES, FRI)
304 Highlander Cir, Marble Falls, TX, 78654-6322, Burnet, USA; gen tel (830) 693-4367; adv tel (830) 693-4367; ed tel (830) 693-4367; gen fax (830) 693-3650; adv fax (830) 693-3650; ed fax (830) 693-3650; disp adv e-mail advertising@highlandernews.com; class adv e-mail classifieds@highlandernews.com; ed e-mail roy.bode@highlandernews.com; web site www.highlandernews.com - 79,800(views) 12,100(visitors)
Circulation: 6,159pd,; USPS
Advertising rate: Open inch rate $9.00
Established: 1959
Group: Highland Lakes NewspapersEditions: Tuesday & Friday/Weekend
Digital Platform - Mobile: Apple, Android
Digital Platform - Tablet: Apple iOS, Android
Pub./Ed....Roy Bode
Exec. Ed....Phil Schoch
Adv. Dir....Tina PhillipsEquipment & Software: Hardware — APP/Power Mac, APP/Mac G4, PCs; Presses — Quad Stack; Software — QPS/Indesign CS2, Adobe/Photoshop 4.5.
Delivery Method: Mail, Newsstand, Racks
Areas Served: 78654, 78657, 78669, 78643, 78663, 78639, 78636

THE PICAYUNE (WED)
1007 Avenue K, Marble Falls, TX, 78654-5039, Texas, USA; gen tel (830) 693-7152; gen fax (830) 693-3085; disp adv e-mail advertising@thepicayune.com; class adv e-mail classifieds@thepicayune.com; ed e-mail editor@thepicayune.com; web site https://www.101highlandlakes.com
Circulation: 0pd, 25,194fr; CVC
Advertising rate: Open inch rate $15.60
Established: 1991
Group: Victory Publising Co., Ltd.
Digital Platform - Mobile: Apple, Android, Windows, Blackberry
Digital Platform - Tablet: Apple iOS, Android, Windows 7, Blackberry Tablet OS
Owner....Dan Alvey
Owner....Lee Alvey
COO/Pub....Amber Weems
Adv. Mgr....Mandi Wyatt
Ed....Thomas Edwards
Prodn. Mgr....Florence Edwards
Ed....Daniel Clifton
Mechanical Specifications: Type page 11 7/8 x 21; E - 6 cols, 1 7/8, 1/6 between; A - 6 cols, 1 7/8, 1/6 between; C - 6 cols, 1 7/8, 1/6 between.Equipment & Software: Hardware — APP/Mac; Presses — G/Community; Software — QPS/QuarkXPress 4.0, Multi-Ad/Creator, Adobe/Photoshop.
Delivery Method: Carrier, Racks
Areas Served: 78654, 78657, 78663, 78669, 78636, 78611, 78609, 78639, 78643, 78672, 78607

MARFA

THE BIG BEND SENTINEL (THUR)
110 N Highland Ave, Marfa, TX, 79843-6500, Presidio, USA; gen tel (432) 729-4342; adv tel (432) 729-4342; ed tel (432) 729-4342; disp adv e-mail rosario@bigbendsentinel.com; class adv e-mail rosario@bigbendsentinel.com; ed e-mail editor@bigbendsentinel.com; web site www.bigbendnow.com
Circulation: 2,658pd, 25fr; Sworn/Estimate/Non-Audited
Advertising rate: Open inch rate $7.50
Established: 1926
Digital Platform - Mobile: Apple, Android, Windows, Blackberry
Digital Platform - Tablet: Apple iOS, Android, Windows 7, Blackberry Tablet OS, Kindle, Nook, Kindle Fire
Pub./Ed....Robert L. Halpern
CFO/Adv. Dir....Rosario Halpern-Salgado
Mechanical Specifications: Type page 13 x 21.Equipment & Software: Hardware — Dell; Software — Microsoft/Word, Adobe/PageMaker, Adobe/Photoshop.
Delivery Method: Mail, Newsstand, Racks
Areas Served: Presidio County
Brewster County
Jeff Davis County

MARLIN

THE MARLIN DEMOCRAT (WED)
211 Fortune St, Marlin, TX, 76661-2799, Falls, USA; gen tel (254) 883-2554; adv tel (256) 604-7381; ed tel (256) 604-7381; gen fax (254) 883-6553; disp adv e-mail advertising@marlindemocrat.com; class adv e-mail advertising@marlindemocrat.com; ed e-mail publisher@marlindemocrat.com; web site www.marlindemocrat.com
Circulation: 2,300pd, 70fr; Sworn/Estimate/Non-Audited
Advertising rate: 7.25
Established: 1890
Group: Moser Community Media
Digital Platform - Mobile: Apple, Android, Win-

dows, Blackberry
Digital Platform - Tablet: Apple iOS, Android, Windows 7, Blackberry Tablet OS, Kindle, Nook, Kindle Fire
Publisher.................................. Dennis Phillips
Mechanical Specifications: 6x21.5 on 1.53-inch column widthEquipment & Software: Hardware — APP/Mac Quadra; Software — QPS/QuarkXPress, Adobe/Photoshop 3.0.
Delivery Method: Mail, Newsstand, Racks
Areas Served: Falls County

MART

THE MART MESSENGER (THUR)
105 S Pearl St, Mart, TX, 76664-1424, McLennan, USA; gen tel (254) 876-3939; adv tel (254) 876-3939; ed tel (254) 876-3939; gen fax (254) 876-3942; adv fax (254) 876-3942; ed fax (254) 876-3942; disp adv e-mail lhauk@aol.com; class adv e-mail martmessenger@yahoo.com; ed e-mail martmessenger@yahoo.com
Circulation: 1,800pd,; Sworn/Estimate/Non-Audited
Advertising rate: Open inch rate $3.50
Established: 1993
Pub.. Larry Hauk
Ed./Adv. Dir. .... Carolyn Potts
Mechanical Specifications: Type page 21 1/2 x 13; E - 6 cols, between; A - 6 cols, between; C - 6 cols, between.
Delivery Method: Mail, Newsstand
Areas Served: 76664, 76682, 76624, 76605

MASON

MASON COUNTY NEWS (WED)
122 S Live Oak, Mason, TX, 76856, Mason, USA; gen tel (325) 347-5757; adv tel (325) 347-5757; ed tel (325) 347-5757; gen fax (325) 347-5668; adv fax (325) 347-5668; ed fax (325) 347-5668; disp adv e-mail mcnads@hctc.net; class adv e-mail mcnads@hctc.net; ed e-mail mcnnews@hctc.net; web site www.masoncountynews.com
Circulation: 2,188pd,; Sworn/Estimate/Non-Audited
Advertising rate: Open inch rate $4.00
Established: 1877
Digital Platform - Mobile: Apple, Android
Digital Platform - Tablet: Apple iOS, Android, Windows 7
Pub...Scott Wesner
Ed. .... Gerry Gamel
Adv. Dir...T.J. Schmidt
Delivery Method: Mail, Newsstand
Areas Served: Mason County

MATHIS

MATHIS NEWS (THUR)
620 E San Patricio Ave, Mathis, TX, 78368-2429, San Patricio, USA; gen tel (361) 547-3274; adv tel (361) 547-3274; ed tel (361) 547-3274; gen fax (361) 547-3275; adv fax (361) 547-3275; ed fax (361) 547-3275; disp adv e-mail Mathisnews@mysoutex.com; class adv e-mail Mathisoffice@mysoutex.com; ed e-mail Mathisnews@mysoutex.com; web site www.mysoutex.com.com
Circulation: 2,000pd, 35fr; Sworn/Estimate/Non-Audited
Advertising rate: Open inch rate $7.20
Established: 1924
Group: San Patricio Publishing Co., Inc.
Digital Platform - Tablet: Windows 7???? ????
Delivery Method: Mail, Newsstand, Carrier, Racks
Areas Served: San Patricio County

MC GREGOR

MCGREGOR MIRROR & CRAWFORD SUN (THUR)
311 S Main St, Mc Gregor, TX, 76657-1608, McLennan, USA; gen tel (254) 840-2091; gen fax (254) 840-2097; disp adv e-mail bonnie@mcgregormirror.com; class adv e-mail bonnie@mcgregormirror.com; ed e-mail charles@mcgregormirror.com; web site www.mcgregormirror.com
Circulation: 1,700pd, 7fr; Sworn/Estimate/Non-Audited
Advertising rate: Open inch rate $6.00
Established: 1892
Digital Platform - Mobile: Apple, Android, Windows, Blackberry
Digital Platform - Tablet: Apple iOS, Android, Windows 7, Blackberry Tablet OS, Kindle, Nook, Kindle Fire
Co-Pub./Adv. Mgr.................... Bonnie Mullens
Co-Pub./Ed. ....Charles Mooney
Circ. Mgr./Bus. Mgr....................Mynette Taylor
Delivery Method: Mail, Newsstand
Areas Served: 76657, 76638, 75651

MCALLEN

EDINBURG REVIEW (WED)
1811 N 23rd St, McAllen, TX, 78501-6121, Hidalgo, USA; gen tel (956) 682-2423; adv tel (956) 682-2423; ed tel (956) 682-2423; gen fax (956) 630-6371; disp adv e-mail lmedrano@valleytowncrier.com; class adv e-mail sales@valleytowncrier.com; ed e-mail pperez@valleytowncrier.com; web site www.edinburgreview.com
Circulation: 24,041fr; CVC
Advertising rate: Open inch rate $13.00
Established: 1914
Group: GateHouse Media, Inc.
Digital Platform - Mobile: Apple, Android, Windows, Blackberry
Digital Platform - Tablet: Apple iOS, Android, Windows 7, Blackberry Tablet OS, Kindle, Nook, Kindle Fire
Pub./Reg. Op. Dir. ....Linda Medrano
Ed. .... Pedro Perez
Majors/Nationals Representative.........Claudia Garcia
Mechanical Specifications: Type page 13 x 21 1/2; E - 6 cols, 2 1/16, 1/8 between; A - 6 cols, 2 1/16, 1/8 between; C - 9 cols, 1 3/8, 1/16 between.
Delivery Method: Carrier, Racks
Areas Served: 78539, 78540, 78541

VALLEY TOWN CRIER (WED)
1811 N 23rd St, McAllen, TX, 78501-6196, Hidalgo, USA; gen tel (956) 682-2423; adv tel (956)682-2423 x 260; ed tel (956)682-2423 x 220; gen fax (956) 630-6371; adv fax (956)630-6371; ed fax (956)630-6371; disp adv e-mail rdeluna@valleytowncrier.com; class adv e-mail rdeluna@valleytowncrier.com; ed e-mail pperez@valleytowncrier.com; web site www.yourvalleyvoice.com - 76,521(views) 11,611(visitors)
Circulation: 15,000fr; VAC
Advertising rate: Open inch rate $43.00
Established: 1964
Group: GateHouse Media, Inc.
Digital Platform - Mobile: Apple, Android, Windows, Blackberry
Digital Platform - Tablet: Apple iOS, Android, Windows 7, Blackberry Tablet OS, Kindle, Nook, Kindle Fire
Pub./Reg. Op. Dir. ....Linda Medrano
Ed. .... Pedro Perez
Circ. Mgr .... Ernesto Sanchez
Business Manager.........................Holly Reyes
Production Director....................Jimmy Rocha
Mechanical Specifications: Type page 10.5" x 16"; E - 6 cols, 1.68", A - 6 cols,1.68"
Delivery Method: Carrier, Racks
Areas Served: 78501, 78503, 78504, 78516, 78537, 78539, 78557, 78572, 78577, 78589

MCKINNEY

COLLIN COUNTY COMMERCIAL RECORD (TUES)
202 W Louisiana St, Ste 202, McKinney, TX, 75069-4459, Collin, USA; gen tel (972) 562-0606; adv tel (972) 562-0606; ed tel (972) 562-0606; gen fax (972) 562-2919; adv fax (972) 562-2919; ed fax (972) 562-2919; disp adv e-mail cccr@collincountycommercialrecord.com; class adv e-mail cccr@collincountycommercialrecord.com; ed e-mail cccr@collincountycommercialrecord.com; web site www.collincountycommercialrecord.com
Advertising rate: Open inch rate $3.00
Established: 1982
Digital Platform - Mobile: Apple, Android, Windows, Blackberry
Digital Platform - Tablet: Apple iOS, Android, Windows 7, Blackberry Tablet OS
Pub.. E. Nuel Cates
Ed. ....Emily Cates
Delivery Method: Newsstand
Areas Served: Collin County

MEMPHIS

HALL COUNTY HERALD (WED)
617 W Main St, Memphis, TX, 79245-3303, Hall, USA; gen tel (806) 259-2441; adv tel (806) 259-2441; ed tel (806) 259-2441; gen fax (806) 259-2798; adv fax (806) 259-2798; ed fax (806) 259-2798; disp adv e-mail hallcountyherald@yahoo.com; class adv e-mail hallcountyherald@yahoo.com; ed e-mail editor@myhallcounty.com; web site www.hallcountyherald.com
Circulation: 2,000pd, 65fr; Sworn/Estimate/Non-Audited
Advertising rate: Open inch rate $3.45
Established: 1890
Digital Platform - Mobile: Apple, Android, Windows, Blackberry
Digital Platform - Tablet: Apple iOS, Android, Windows 7, Blackberry Tablet OS, Kindle, Nook, Kindle Fire
Pub............................... Christopher Blackburn
Ed. .... Ryan Mills
Adv. Dir................................. Rebekah Dietrich
Delivery Method: Mail, Newsstand
Areas Served: Hall County

MENARD

MENARD NEWS AND MESSENGER (THUR)
220 Gay St, Menard, TX, 76859, Menard, USA; gen tel (325) 396-2243; adv tel (325) 396-2243; ed tel (325) 396-2243; gen fax (325) 396-2739; adv fax (325) 396-2739; ed fax (325) 396-2739; disp adv e-mail menardnews@verizon.net; class adv e-mail menardnews@verizon.net; ed e-mail menardnews@verizon.net
Advertising rate: Open inch rate $4.00
Established: 1936
Pub./Ed./Adv. Dir..................... Dan Feather Jr.
Delivery Method: Mail, Newsstand
Areas Served: Menard County

MERCEDES

MERCEDES ENTERPRISE (WED)
805 S Missouri Ave, Mercedes, TX, 78570-3441, Hidalgo, USA; gen tel (956) 565-2425; adv tel (956) 565-2425; ed tel (956) 565-2425; gen fax (956) 565-2570; adv fax (956) 565-2570; ed fax (956) 565-2570; disp adv e-mail mercedesenterprise@sbcglobal.net; class adv e-mail mercedesenterprise@sbcglobal.net; ed e-mail mercedesenterprise@sbcglobal.net
Circulation: 2,000pd,; Sworn/Estimate/Non-Audited
Advertising rate: Open inch rate $5.15
Established: 1907
Group: Mercedes Publishing
Publisher/OwnerDr. Barbara Baggerly-Hinojosa
Sales/Owner.......................... C.A. Hinojosa, III
Office Manager.......... Cristina Cantu-Gutierrez
Editor ....Carlos Cardenas
Delivery Method: Mail, Newsstand
Areas Served: Hidalgo County

MERIDIAN

MERIDIAN TRIBUNE (WED)
114 N MAIN, Meridian, TX, 76665, Bosque, USA; gen tel (254) 435-6333; adv tel (254) 435-6333; ed tel (254) 435-6333; gen fax (254) 435-6348; adv fax (254) 435-6348; ed fax (254) 435-6348; disp adv e-mail brett@meridiantribune.com; class adv e-mail design@meridiantribune.com; ed e-mail news@meridiantribune.com; web site www.meridiantribune.com
Circulation: 1,780pd,; Sworn/Estimate/Non-Audited
Advertising rate: Open inch rate $6.95
Established: 1893
Digital Platform - Mobile: Apple, Android, Windows, Blackberry
Digital Platform - Tablet: Apple iOS, Android, Windows 7, Blackberry Tablet OS, Kindle, Nook, Kindle Fire
Pub./Ed. ....Brett Voss
Delivery Method: Mail, Newsstand, Racks
Areas Served: Bosque County

MERKEL

THE MERKEL MAIL (WED)
912 N 1st, Merkel, TX, 79536-3815, Taylor, USA; gen tel (325) 928-5712; adv tel (325) 928-5712; ed tel (325) 928-5712; gen fax (325) 928-5899; adv fax (325) 928-5899; ed fax (325) 928-5899; disp adv e-mail merkelmail@windstream.net; class adv e-mail merkelmail@windstream.net; ed e-mail merkelmail@windstream.net
Circulation: 1,046pd, 20fr; Sworn/Estimate/Non-Audited
Advertising rate: Open inch rate $4.25
Established: 1890
Pub./Ed./Adv. Dir........................ John Starbuck
Delivery Method: Mail
Areas Served: Taylor County

MEXIA

THE MEXIA NEWS (TUES, THUR, SAT)
214 N Railroad St, Mexia, TX, 76667-2850, Limestone, USA; gen tel (254) 562-2868; adv tel (254) 562-2868; ed tel (254) 562-2868; gen fax (254) 562-3121; adv fax (254) 562-3121; ed fax (254) 562-3121; disp adv e-mail mike@themexianews.com; class adv e-mail classifieds@themexianews.com; ed e-mail news@themexianews.com; web site www.mexiadailynews.com
Circulation: 2,350pd,; USPS
Advertising rate: Open inch rate $5.00
Established: 1899
Group: Moser Community Media, LLC
Digital Platform - Mobile: Apple, Android, Windows, Blackberry
Digital Platform - Tablet: Apple iOS, Android, Windows 7, Blackberry Tablet OS, Kindle, Nook, Kindle Fire
Pub.. Mike Eddleman
Ed. ....Brenda Sommer
Adv. Dir.................................... Jennifer Bynum
Mechanical Specifications: One col. 1.637Equipment & Software: Hardware — MACS; Presses — Goss Community; Software — Quark Express, Photoshop, Illustrator
Delivery Method: Mail, Newsstand, Carrier, Racks
Areas Served: 76667, 76642, 75860, 76693, 76686, 76635

MIDLAND

GREENWOOD RANGER (THUR)
10703 FM 307, Midland, TX, 79706-5319, Midland, USA; gen tel (432) 756-2090; adv tel (432) 756-2090; ed tel (432) 756-2090;

gen fax (432) 756-2090; adv fax (432) 756-2090; ed fax (432) 756-2090; disp adv e-mail gwranger@crcom.net; class adv e-mail gwranger@crcom.net; ed e-mail gwranger@crcom.net
Circulation: 1,400pd,; Sworn/Estimate/Non-Audited
Advertising rate: Open inch rate $4.75
Pub. Bob Dillard
Ed. Tate Dillard
Delivery Method: Mail
Areas Served: Midland County

MILES

MILES MESSENGER (THUR)

104 Robinson St, Miles, TX, 76861, Tom Green, USA; gen tel (325) 468-3611; adv tel (325) 468-3611; ed tel (325) 468-3611; gen fax (325) 468-3611; adv fax (325) 468-3611; ed fax (325) 468-3611; disp adv e-mail shortcake56@verizon.net; class adv e-mail shortcake56@verizon.net; ed e-mail shortcake56@verizon.net
Advertising rate: Open inch rate $4.10
Established: 1903
Pub./Ed./Adv. Dir. Donna Glass
Delivery Method: Mail, Newsstand
Areas Served: Runnels County

THE CONCHO HERALD (THUR)

104 Robinson St, Miles, TX, 76861, Tom Green, USA; gen tel (325) 468-3611; adv tel (325) 468-3611; ed tel (325) 468-3611; gen fax (325) 468-3611; adv fax (325) 468-3611; ed fax (325) 468-3611; disp adv e-mail shortcake56@verizon.net; class adv e-mail shortcake56@verizon.net; ed e-mail shortcake56@verizon.net
Circulation: 200pd,; Sworn/Estimate/Non-Audited
Advertising rate: Open inch rate $3.50
Established: 1890
Pub./Ed./Adv. Dir. Donna Glass
Mechanical Specifications: Type page 10 1/4 x 15; E - 5 cols, 2, 1/8 between; A - 5 cols, 2, 1/8 between; C - 5 cols, 2, 1/8 between. Equipment & Software: Hardware — MGD/22.
Delivery Method: Mail
Areas Served: Concho County

THE ROWENA PRESS (THUR)

Robinson St, Miles, TX, 76861, Tom Green, USA; gen tel (325) 468-3611; adv tel (325) 468-3611; ed tel (325) 468-3611; gen fax (325) 468-3611; adv fax (325) 468-3611; ed fax (325) 468-3611; disp adv e-mail shortcake56@verizon.net; class adv e-mail shortcake56@verizon.net; ed e-mail shortcake56@verizon.net
Advertising rate: Open inch rate $3.00
Established: 1936
Pub./Ed./Adv. Dir. Donna Glass
Delivery Method: Mail
Areas Served: Runnels County

MINEOLA

WOOD COUNTY MONITOR (WED)

715 Mimosa Dr, Mineola, TX, 75773-2611, Wood, USA; gen tel (903) 569-2442; gen fax (903) 569-6836; disp adv e-mail advertising@woodcountymonitor.com; class adv e-mail classifieds@woodcountymonitor.com; ed e-mail news@woodcountymonitor.com; web site www.thewoodcountymonitor.com
Circulation: 3,800pd,; Sworn/Estimate/Non-Audited
Advertising rate: Open inch rate $10
Established: 1876
Group: Bluebonnet Publishing, LLC
Digital Platform - Mobile: Apple, Android, Windows, Blackberry
Digital Platform - Tablet: Apple iOS, Android, Windows 7, Blackberry Tablet OS, Kindle, Nook, Kindle Fire
Pub. Joyce Hathcock
Ed. Doris Newman
Delivery Method: Mail, Racks
Areas Served: 75773, 75783, 75410, 75444

MISSION

PROGRESS TIMES (FRI)

1217 N Conway Ave, Mission, TX, 78572-4112, Hidalgo, USA; gen tel (956) 585-4893; adv tel (956) 585-4893; ed tel (956) 585-4893; gen fax (956) 585-2304; adv fax (956) 585-2304; ed fax (956) 585-2304; disp adv e-mail ads@progresstimes.net; class adv e-mail info@progresstimes.net; ed e-mail news@progresstimes.net; web site www.progresstimes.net - 11,011(views) 3,874(visitors)
Circulation: 2,905pd, 7,095fr; Sworn/Estimate/Non-Audited
Advertising rate: Open inch rate $15.25
Established: 1972
Group: Mission Publishing Co
Digital Platform - Mobile: Apple, Android, Windows, Blackberry
Digital Platform - Tablet: Apple iOS, Android, Windows 7, Blackberry Tablet OS, Kindle, Nook, Kindle Fire
Pub./Ed. Jim Brunson
Office Mgr. Sharon Sanchez
Advertising Manager Dee Rendon
Advertising Representative Maria Smith
Mechanical Specifications: 10.5" x 19.75" Full Page Dimension
1 Column - 1.61"
2 Column - 3.39"
3 Column - 5.17"
4 Column - 6.94"
5 Column - 8.72"
6 Column - 10.5"
Delivery Method: Mail, Newsstand, Carrier, Racks
Areas Served: Hidalgo County

MONAHANS

THE MONAHANS NEWS (MON, THUR)

107 W 2nd St, Monahans, TX, 79756-4235, Ward, USA; gen tel (432) 943-4313; adv tel (432) 943-4313; ed tel (432) 943-4313; gen fax (432) 943-4314; adv fax (432) 943-4314; ed fax (432) 943-4314; disp adv e-mail editor@monahansnews.net; class adv e-mail editor@monahansnews.net; ed e-mail editor@monahansnews.net
Advertising rate: Open inch rate $7.00
Established: 1931
Pub. Smokey Briggs
Ed. Paula Bard
Adv. Dir. Bob Rice
Delivery Method: Mail, Newsstand
Areas Served: Ward County

MOULTON

THE MOULTON EAGLE (THUR)

208B W Moore, Moulton, TX, 77975-5513, Lavaca, USA; gen tel (361) 596-4871; adv tel (361) 596-4871; ed tel (361) 596-4871; gen fax (361) 596-7562; adv fax (361) 596-7562; ed fax (361) 596-7562; disp adv e-mail moultoneagle@sbcglobal.net; class adv e-mail moultoneagle@sbcglobal.net; ed e-mail moultoneagle@sbcglobal.net
Circulation: 1,350pd,; Sworn/Estimate/Non-Audited
Advertising rate: Open inch rate $3.45
Established: 1914
Pub. Bob Anderson
Ed. Kristie Bludau
Adv. Mgr. Margaret Pozzi
Circ. Mgr. Stef Demorie
Delivery Method: Mail, Newsstand
Areas Served: Lavaca County

MOUNT VERNON

MOUNT VERNON OPTIC-HERALD (THUR)

108 Kaufman St S, Mount Vernon, TX, 75457-2833, Franklin, USA; gen tel (903) 537-2228; adv tel (903) 537-2228; ed tel (903) 537-2228; gen fax (903) 537-2227; adv fax (903) 537-2227; ed fax (903) 537-2227; disp adv e-mail optic@mt-vernon.com; class adv e-mail optic@mt-vernon.com; ed e-mail optic@mt-vernon.com; web site www.mt-vernon.com
Circulation: 2,500pd,
Advertising rate: Open inch rate $7.50
Established: 1874
Digital Platform - Mobile: Apple, Android
Digital Platform - Tablet: Apple iOS, Android, Windows 7
Pub. Susan Reeves
Ed. Lillie M. Bush-Reeves
John Reeves
Terri Cruit
Delivery Method: Mail, Racks
Areas Served: Franklin County

MUENSTER

MUENSTER ENTERPRISE (FRI)

117 E 1st St, Muenster, TX, 76252-2788, Cooke, USA; gen tel (940) 759-4311; gen fax (940) 759-4110; disp adv e-mail advertising@ntin.net; class adv e-mail advertising@ntin.net; ed e-mail swood@ntin.net
Circulation: 1,700pd, 36fr; Sworn/Estimate/Non-Audited
Advertising rate: Open inch rate $6.00
Established: 1936
Pub./Owner Deborah Wood
Ed. Scott Wood
Mechanical Specifications: Type page 11 5/8 x 21 1/2; E - 6 cols, 1 13/16, 1/8 between; A - 6 cols, 1 13/16, 1/8 between; C - 8 cols, 1 3/8, between.Equipment & Software: Hardware — APP/Mac, APP/Power Mac G3; Software — Adobe/PageMaker 6.0.
Delivery Method: Mail, Newsstand
Areas Served: Cooke County

MULESHOE

MULESHOE JOURNAL (THUR)

201 W Avenue C, Muleshoe, TX, 79347-3530, Bailey, USA; gen tel (806) 272-4536; adv tel (806) 272-4536; ed tel (806) 272-4536; gen fax (806) 272-3567; adv fax (806) 272-3567; ed fax (806) 272-3567; disp adv e-mail adsales@muleshoejournal.com; class adv e-mail circulation@muleshoejournal.com; ed e-mail editor@muleshoejournal.com; web site www.muleshoejournal.com
Circulation: 1,600pd, 50fr; Sworn/Estimate/Non-Audited
Advertising rate: Open inch rate $5.50
Established: 1924
Group: Hearst Communications, Inc.
Digital Platform - Mobile: Apple, Windows
Digital Platform - Tablet: Apple iOS, Windows 7
Pub. David Wedel
Adv. Dir. Rhea Gonzales
CIRCULATON/BOOK KEEPING APRIL CISNEROS
Mechanical Specifications: 6 column broadsheet 10" x 21.5"
Delivery Method: Mail, Newsstand, Carrier, Racks
Areas Served: 79347

MUNDAY

KNOX COUNTY NEWS-COURIER (THUR)

121 East B St, Munday, TX, 76371, Knox, USA; gen tel (940) 422-5350; adv tel (940) 422-5350; ed tel (940) 422-5350; gen fax (866) 863-1118; adv fax (866) 400-1083; ed fax (866) 863-1118; disp adv e-mail kcnewscourier@gmail.com; class adv e-mail kcnewscourier@gmail.com; ed e-mail kcnewscourier@gmail.com; web site www.kcnewscourier.com
Circulation: 934pd,; Sworn/Estimate/Non-Audited
Advertising rate: Open inch rate $5.50
Established: 2011
Group: Blackburn Media Group
Digital Platform - Mobile: Apple, Android, Windows, Blackberry
Digital Platform - Tablet: Apple iOS, Android, Windows 7, Blackberry Tablet OS, Kindle, Nook, Kindle Fire
Pub. Christopher Blackburn
Delivery Method: Mail, Racks
Areas Served: Knox County

STONEWALL COUNTY COURIER (THUR)

111 East B St, Munday, TX, 76371, Knox, USA; gen tel (877) 308-9684; adv tel (877) 308-9684; ed tel (877) 308-9684; gen fax (877) 811-4754; adv fax (877) 811-4754; ed fax (877) 811-4754; disp adv e-mail courier@westex.net; class adv e-mail courier@westex.net; ed e-mail webmaster@stonewallcountycourier.com
Circulation: 900pd, 60fr; Sworn/Estimate/Non-Audited
Advertising rate: Open inch rate $5.00
Established: 1985
Digital Platform - Tablet: Windows 7
Pub./Ed./Adv. Dir. Jay White
Delivery Method: Mail
Areas Served: Stonewall County

TWIN CITIES NEWS (THUR)

111 East B St, Munday, TX, 76371, Knox, USA; gen tel (940) 422-4314; adv tel (940) 422-4314; ed tel (940) 422-4314; gen fax (940) 422-4333; adv fax (940) 422-4333; ed fax (940) 422-4333; disp adv e-mail mcourier@westex.net; class adv e-mail mcourier@westex.net; ed e-mail mcourier@westex.net; web site www.smalltownpapers.com
Circulation: 772pd, 17fr; Sworn/Estimate/Non-Audited
Advertising rate: Open inch rate $3.00
Digital Platform - Tablet: Windows 7
Pub./Ed./Adv. Dir. Jay WhiteEquipment & Software: Hardware — APP/Mac.
Delivery Method: Mail
Areas Served: Stonewall and Knox County

NAPLES

THE MONITOR (THUR)

110 Main St, Naples, TX, 75568, Morris, USA; gen tel (903) 897-2281; adv tel (903) 897-2281; ed tel (903) 897-2281; gen fax (903) 897-2095; adv fax (903) 897-2095; ed fax (903) 897-2095; disp adv e-mail themonitor@valornet.com; class adv e-mail themonitor@valornet.com; ed e-mail themonitor@valornet.com
Circulation: 2,000pd, 50fr; USPS
Advertising rate: Open inch rate $6.58
Established: 1886
Pub./Ed. Morris Craig
Adv. Dir. Melody Alford
Circ. Mgr. Denise Summerlin
Bookkeeper Jennifer Adams
Photographer/Reporter Jeremy Craig
Mechanical Specifications: 6 col x 21-inch page
Delivery Method: Mail, Racks
Areas Served: Morris, Cass, Bowie, and Titus County

NAVASOTA

THE NAVASOTA EXAMINER (WED)

115 S RAILROAD ST, Navasota, TX, 77868, Grimes, USA; gen tel (936) 825-6484; adv tel (936) 825-6484; ed tel (936) 825-6484; gen fax (936) 825-2230; adv fax (936) 825-2230; ed fax (936) 825-2230; disp adv e-mail publisher@navasotaexaminer.com; class adv e-mail ads@navasotaexaminer.com; ed e-mail news@navasotaexaminer.com; web site www.navasotaexaminer.com

Circulation: 3,616pd, 370fr; CVC
Advertising rate: Open inch rate $8.40
Established: 1894
Group: Fenice Community Media
Digital Platform - Mobile: Apple, Android
Digital Platform - Tablet: Apple iOS, Android, Windows 7
Adv. Dir. .... Ana Cosino
Bookkeeper .... Carrie Little
Staff writer .... Nicole Shupe
Mechanical Specifications: Type page 11 5/8 x 21; E - 6 cols, 1 5/6, between; A - 6 cols, 1 5/6, between; C - 9 cols, 1 1/4, between. Equipment & Software: Hardware — 7-APP/Mac 610, APP/Power Mac 7500; Software — Adobe/PageMaker 5.0, Adobe/Photoshop 3.2.
Delivery Method: Mail, Newsstand, Carrier, Racks
Areas Served: Grimes County

NEEDVILLE

THE GULF COAST TRIBUNE (THUR)

3115 School St, Needville, TX, 77461-8446, Fort Bend, USA; gen tel (979) 793-6560; adv tel (979) 793-6560; ed tel (979) 793-6560; gen fax (979) 793-4260; adv fax (979) 793-4260; ed fax (979) 793-4260; disp adv e-mail advertising@consolidated.net; class adv e-mail advertising@consolidated.net; ed e-mail gctribune@consolidated.net; web site www.fbherald.com
Circulation: 1,200pd, 67fr; Sworn/Estimate/Non-Audited
Advertising rate: Open inch rate $5.00
Established: 1962
Digital Platform - Mobile: Apple, Android
Digital Platform - Tablet: Apple iOS, Android, Windows 7
Pub .... David E. Toney
Ed. .... Rebecca Hutchinson
Adv. Dir. .... Dale McFarland
Mechanical Specifications: Type page 6X21; E - 6 cols, 1.833", between; C - 9 cols, between.Equipment & Software: Hardware — APP/Mac; Software — Abbott Systems/Ready, Set, Go.
Delivery Method: Mail, Newsstand
Areas Served: Fort Bend County

NEW BOSTON

BOWIE COUNTY CITIZEN TRIBUNE (WED)

129N NE FRONT ST, New Boston, TX, 75570-2906, Bowie, USA; gen tel (903) 628-5801; adv tel (903) 628-5801; ed tel (903) 628-5801; gen fax (903) 628-8272; adv fax (903) 628-8272; ed fax (903) 628-8272; disp adv e-mail alewter@bowiecountynow.com; class adv e-mail alewter@bowiecountynow.com; ed e-mail tribunenews@bowiecountynow.com; web site www.bowiecountynow.com
Circulation: 5,700pd,; Sworn/Estimate/Non-Audited
Advertising rate: Open inch rate $7.95 (Local); $9.47 (National)
Established: 1885
Group: Northeast Texas Publishing
Digital Platform - Mobile: Apple, Android
Digital Platform - Tablet: Apple iOS, Android, Windows 7
Adv. Dir. .... Melanie Pyle
Gen. Mgr. .... Kenny Mitchell
Class. & Circ. .... LeAnna Stephenson
Mechanical Specifications: Type page 11 7/8 x 21; E - 6 cols, 1 7/8, 1/16 between; A - 6 cols, 1 7/8, 1/16 between; C - 6 cols, 1 7/8, 1/16 between.Equipment & Software: Hardware — APP/Mac; Software — Adobe/PageMaker.
Delivery Method: Mail, Newsstand
Areas Served: Bowie County

NEW ULM

THE NEW ULM ENTERPRISE (THUR)

910 FM 109, New Ulm, TX, 78950, Austin, USA; gen tel (979) 992-3351; adv tel (979) 992-3351; ed tel (979) 992-3351; gen fax (979) 992-3352; adv fax (979) 992-3352; ed fax (979) 992-3352; disp adv e-mail nuent@industryinet.com; class adv e-mail nuent@industryinet.com; ed e-mail editor@industryinet.com
Circulation: 1,031pd, 16fr; Sworn/Estimate/Non-Audited
Advertising rate: Open inch rate $4.75
Established: 1910
Pub .... Maridel Dungen
Mechanical Specifications: 11.625 x 21Equipment & Software: Hardware — APP/Mac Performa 6116 CD; Software — Adobe/PageMaker.
Delivery Method: Mail, Racks
Areas Served: 78950, 78944, 78940, 77833, 78934, 77418, 77474, 78931, 78933, 78945, 77485

NEWTON

NEWTON COUNTY NEWS (WED)

112 GLOVER DR, Newton, TX, 75966, Newton, USA; gen tel (409) 379-2416; adv tel (409) 379-2416; ed tel (409) 379-2416; gen fax (409) 379-2416; adv fax (409) 379-2416; ed fax (409) 379-2416; disp adv e-mail newtonnews@valornet.com; class adv e-mail newtonnews@valornet.com; ed e-mail newtonnews@valornet.com; web site www.newtonnews.com
Circulation: 1,500pd,; Sworn/Estimate/Non-Audited
Advertising rate: Open inch rate $5.00
Established: 1969
Digital Platform - Mobile: Apple
Digital Platform - Tablet: Apple iOS, Windows 7, Kindle Fire
Co-Pub .... Jay Wilkerson
Co-Pub./Adv. Dir. .... Shawn Wilkerson
Office Mgr./Classifieds .... Karyn Lobb
Delivery Method: Mail, Newsstand, Racks
Areas Served: 75966, 75951, 75933, 75956, 75932, 75928

NIXON

COW COUNTRY COURIER (THUR)

2652 FM 2922, Nixon, TX, 78140-5245, Gonzales, USA; gen tel (830) 582-1740; adv tel (830) 582-1740; ed tel (830) 582-1740; gen fax (830) 582-2123; adv fax (830) 582-2123; ed fax (830) 582-2123; disp adv e-mail wscott@gvec.net; class adv e-mail wscott@gvec.net; ed e-mail wscott@gvec.net
Circulation: 850pd,; Sworn/Estimate/Non-Audited
Advertising rate: Open inch rate $4.50
Established: 1993
Pub./Ed./Owner .... Scott Wendle
Delivery Method: Newsstand
Areas Served: Gonzales County

NOCONA

NOCONA NEWS (THUR)

115 Cooke St, Nocona, TX, 76255-2107, Montague, USA; gen tel (940) 825-3201; adv tel (940) 825-3201; ed tel (940) 825-3201; gen fax (940) 825-3202; adv fax (940) 825-3202; ed fax (940) 825-3202; disp adv e-mail advertising@noconanews.net; class adv e-mail advertising@noconanews.net; ed e-mail news@noconanews.net ; web site www.noconanews.net
Advertising rate: Open inch rate $6.10
Established: 1905
Digital Platform - Mobile: Apple, Android
Digital Platform - Tablet: Apple iOS, Android, Windows 7
Co-Pub./Ed. .... Tracy Mesler
Co-Pub./Adv. Dir. .... Linda Mesler
Delivery Method: Mail, Newsstand, Racks
Areas Served: Montague County

NORMANGEE

THE NORMANGEE STAR (WED)

202 HEATH ST, Normangee, TX, 77871, Leon, USA; gen tel (936) 396-3391; adv tel (936) 396-3391; ed tel (936) 396-3391; gen fax (936) 396-2478; adv fax (936) 396-2478; ed fax (936) 396-2478; disp adv e-mail publisher@texasbb.com; class adv e-mail publisher@texasbb.com; ed e-mail publisher@texasbb.com; web site www.normangeestar.com
Circulation: 1,400pd, 50fr; Sworn/Estimate/Non-Audited
Advertising rate: Open inch rate $3.75
Established: 1912
Digital Platform - Mobile: Apple, Android
Digital Platform - Tablet: Apple iOS, Android, Windows 7
Pub./Ed./Adv. Dir. .... Hank Hargrave
Mechanical Specifications: Type page 11 5/8 x 21; E - 6 cols, 1 5/6, 1/8 between; A - 6 cols, 1 5/6, 1/8 between; C - 6 cols, 1 5/6, 1/8 between.Equipment & Software: ; Software — QPS/QuarkXPress 4.1, Adobe/Photoshop 5.5, Microsoft/Word 98, Adobe/Acrobat 5.0.
Delivery Method: Mail, Newsstand
Areas Served: 77871

ODONNELL

O'DONNELL INDEX-PRESS (WED)

1629 FM 2053, Odonnell, TX, 79351-3205, Lynn, USA; gen tel (806) 428-3591; adv tel (806) 428-3591; ed tel (806) 428-3591; gen fax (806) 428-3360; adv fax (806) 428-3360; ed fax (806) 428-3360; disp adv e-mail indexpress@poka.com; class adv e-mail indexpress@poka.com; ed e-mail indexpress@poka.com
Circulation: 400pd, 20fr; Sworn/Estimate/Non-Audited
Advertising rate: Open inch rate $5.00
Established: 1923
Pub./Adv. Dir. .... Sharon Wells
Ed./Adv. Dir. .... John Wells
Mechanical Specifications: Type page 10 x ; E - 5 cols, 2, 1/4 between.
Delivery Method: Mail, Newsstand, Racks
Areas Served: 79351, 79331

OLNEY

THE OLNEY ENTERPRISE (THUR)

213 E Main St, Olney, TX, 76374-1923, Young, USA; gen tel (940) 564-5558; adv tel (940) 564-5558; ed tel (940) 564-5558; gen fax (940) 564-3992; adv fax (940) 564-3992; ed fax (940) 564-3992; disp adv e-mail advertising@olneyenterprise.com; class adv e-mail classified@olneyenterprise.com; ed e-mail editor@olneyenterprise.com; web site www.olneyenterprise.com
Circulation: 1,218pd, 15fr; Sworn/Estimate/Non-Audited
Advertising rate: Open inch rate $8.93
Established: 1908
Group: Moser Community Media, LLC
Digital Platform - Mobile: Apple, Android
Digital Platform - Tablet: Apple iOS, Android, Windows 7
Group Pub. .... Robb Krecklow
Ed. .... Mindi Kimbro
Adv. Mgr. .... Karen Harris
Circ. Mgr. .... Tommy Leeman
Pub. .... Roy G. Robinson
Managing Editor .... Jimmy Potts
Mechanical Specifications: Page size: 12.5 inches by 22.5 inches
Columns: 6
1 col = 1.75 inches
2 col = 3.75 inches
3 col = 5.6875 inches
4 col = 7.635 inches
5 col = 9.5625 inches
6 col = 11.50 inches
Full Page charged at 6 cols x 20.5 inchesEquipment & Software: Hardware — APP/Mac; Software — Adobe/PageMaker, Adobe/Photoshop.
Delivery Method: Mail, Newsstand, Racks
Areas Served: 76359, 76350, 76372, 76374

OLTON

THE OLTON ENTERPRISE (FRI)

520 Eighth St, Olton, TX, 79064, Lamb, USA; gen tel (806) 285-7766; adv tel (806) 285-7766; ed tel (806) 285-7766; gen fax (866) 641-2816; adv fax (866) 641-2816; ed fax (866) 641-2816; disp adv e-mail oltonenterprise@hotmail.com; class adv e-mail oltonenterprise@hotmail.com; ed e-mail oltonenterprise@hotmail.com; web site www.southplainsplus.com
Circulation: 1,000pd, 20fr; Sworn/Estimate/Non-Audited
Advertising rate: Open inch rate $5
Established: 1926
Group: Triple S Media
Digital Platform - Mobile: Apple, Android, Windows, Blackberry
Digital Platform - Tablet: Apple iOS, Android, Windows 7, Blackberry Tablet OS, Nook, Kindle Fire, Other
Pub./Ed. .... Phillip Hamilton
Adv. Dir. .... Ursula Hamilton
Mechanical Specifications: 25-inch web 6 col = 11.625 inchEquipment & Software: Hardware — Apple-editorial
Circulation-PC; Software — Adobe Creative Cloud - Editorial
Apple - Editorial
Interlink - Circulation
Delivery Method: Mail, Newsstand, Racks
Areas Served: 79064, 79031, 79082

ORANGE

THE ORANGE LEADER (WED, SAT)

841B Dal Sasso Dr, Orange, TX, 77630-4825, Orange, USA; gen tel (409) 883-3571; adv tel (409) 883-3571; ed tel (409) 883-3571; disp adv e-mail candice.trahan@orangeleader.com; class adv e-mail candice.trahan@orangeleader.com; ed e-mail news@orangeleader.com; web site www.orangeleader.com
Circulation: 2,967pd,; Sworn/Estimate/Non-Audited
Advertising rate: Open inch rate $14.75
Established: 1875
Group: Boone's Newspapers
Digital Platform - Mobile: Apple, Android, Windows, Blackberry
Digital Platform - Tablet: Apple iOS, Android, Windows 7, Blackberry Tablet OS
Ed .... Dawn Burleigh
Pub .... Bobby Tingle
Sports Ed. .... Van Wade
Inside Sales .... Candice Trahan
Mechanical Specifications: Type page 11 5/8 x 21 1/2; E - 6 cols, 1 13/16, 1/8 between; A - 6 cols, 1 13/16, 1/8 between; C - 9 cols, 1 13/16, 1/8 between.
Delivery Method: Mail, Newsstand, Racks
Areas Served: Orange County

OZONA

OZONA STOCKMAN (WED)

1000 Avenue E, Ozona, TX, 76943, Crockett, USA; gen tel (325) 392-2551; adv tel (325) 392-2551; ed tel (325) 392-2551; gen fax (325) 392-2439; adv fax (325) 392-2439; ed fax (325) 392-2439; disp adv e-mail susan@ozonastockman.com; class adv e-mail susan@ozonastockman.com; ed e-mail publisher@ozonastockman.com; web site www.ozonastockman.com
Circulation: 1,755pd, 20fr; Sworn/Estimate/Non-Audited
Advertising rate: Open inch rate $5.50 (Local); $7.00 (National)
Established: 1913
Digital Platform - Mobile: Apple, Android, Windows, Blackberry

Digital Platform - Tablet: Apple iOS, Android, Windows 7, Blackberry Tablet OS, Kindle, Nook, Kindle Fire
Pub./Ed. .... Melissa Perner
Adv. Dir. .... Susan Calloway
Delivery Method: Mail, Newsstand, Racks
Areas Served: Crockett County

PADUCAH

PADUCAH POST (TUES)

819 8th St, Paducah, TX, 79248, Cottle, USA; gen tel (806) 492-3585; adv tel (806) 492-3585; ed tel (806) 492-3585; gen fax (806) 492-3585; adv fax (806) 492-3585; ed fax (806) 492-3585; disp adv e-mail jtaylor1@caprock-spur.com; class adv e-mail jtaylor1@caprock-spur.com; ed e-mail jtaylor1@caprock-spur.com
Advertising rate: Open inch rate $3.00
Established: 1906
Pub./Ed./Adv. Dir. .... Jimmye C. Taylor
Mng. Ed. .... Chad Piper
Delivery Method: Mail, Newsstand
Areas Served: Cottle County

PALACIOS

PALACIOS BEACON (WED)

310 5th St, Palacios, TX, 77465-4702, Matagorda, USA; gen tel (361) 972-3009; adv tel (361) 972-3009; ed tel (361) 972-3009; gen fax (361) 972-2610; adv fax (361) 972-2610; ed fax (361) 972-2610; disp adv e-mail brandi.palaciosbeacon@gmail.com; class adv e-mail carolyn.beacon@gmail.com; ed e-mail ryan.palaciosbeacon@gmail.com; web site www.palaciosbeacon.com
Circulation: 1,600pd,; Sworn/Estimate/Non-Audited
Advertising rate: Open inch rate $5.50
Established: 1907
Group: City by the Sea Publishing, LLC
Digital Platform - Mobile: Apple, Android
Digital Platform - Tablet: Apple iOS, Android, Windows 7
Adv. Mgr. .... Carolyn White
Ryan West
Brandi West
Alan Schulman
Mechanical Specifications: Type page 11.5 x 21 1/2; E - 6 cols, 1.75 between; A - 6 cols, 2, 1/16 between; C - 6 cols, 2, 1/16 between. Equipment & Software: Hardware — APP/Mac; Software — Microsoft/Word 98, Adobe/PageMaker 6.5.
Delivery Method: Mail, Newsstand
Areas Served: 77465

PANHANDLE

PANHANDLE HERALD / WHITE DEER NEWS (THUR)

319 Main, Panhandle, TX, 79068, Carson, USA; gen tel (806) 537-3634; adv tel (806) 537-3634; ed tel (806) 537-3634; gen fax (806) 537-3634; adv fax (806) 537-3634; ed fax (806) 537-3634; disp adv e-mail shaun@panhandleherald.com; class adv e-mail shaun@panhandleherald.com; ed e-mail panhandleherald@hotmail.com; web site www.panhandleherald.com/
Circulation: 1,251pd, 19fr; USPS
Advertising rate: Open inch rate $4.25
Established: 1887Editions: (51) Panhandle Herald & White Deer News
Digital Platform - Mobile: Windows, Other
Digital Platform - Tablet: Windows 7, Other
Ed./Pub./Adv. Dir./Owner .... Shaun Wink
Co-Pub. .... Frank Wink
Mechanical Specifications: Type page Tabloid=10.35 inches x 11.75 inches; E - 6 cols; 1 column=1.6 inches; 2 column=3.35 inches (with .15 inch (gutter) between); 3 column=5.1 inches (with .30 inch between); 4 column=6.85 inches (with .45 inch between); 5 column=8.6 inches (with .60 inch between); 6 columns=10.35 (with .75 inch between) Equipment & Software: ; Software — WordPerfect 5.0.
Delivery Method: Mail, Racks
Areas Served: Panhandle, White Deer, Skellytown, and Groom

PEARLAND

FRIENDSWOOD REPORTER NEWS (WED)

2404 Park Ave, Pearland, TX, 77581-4234, Galveston, USA; gen tel (281) 485-7501; adv tel (281) 485-7501; ed tel (281) 485-7501; gen fax (281) 485-6397; adv fax (281) 485-6397; ed fax (281) 485-6397; disp adv e-mail laurae3009@yahoo.com; class adv e-mail laurae3009@yahoo.com; ed e-mail laurae3009@yahoo.com
Circulation: 2,300pd, 5fr; Sworn/Estimate/Non-Audited
Advertising rate: Open inch rate $8.50
Established: 1969
Adv. Mgr. .... Laura Emmons
Circ. Mgr. .... Randy Emmons
Prodn. Mgr. .... Kathy Pulpan
Delivery Method: Mail, Racks
Areas Served: 77511, 77546, 77581, 77584, 77586

PEARLAND REPORTER NEWS (WED)

2404 Park Ave, Pearland, TX, 77581-4234, Brazoria, USA; gen tel (281) 485-7501; adv tel (281) 485-7501; ed tel (281) 485-7501; gen fax (281) 485-6397; adv fax (281) 485-6397; ed fax (281) 485-6397; disp adv e-mail laurae3009@yahoo.com; class adv e-mail laurae3009@yahoo.com; ed e-mail laurae3009@yahoo.com
Circulation: 28,000pd,; Sworn/Estimate/Non-Audited
Advertising rate: Open inch rate $11.50
Established: 1971
Pub. / Exec. Ed. .... Laura Emmons
Circ. Mgr. .... Randy Emmons
Prodn. Mgr. .... Kathy Pulpan
Delivery Method: Mail, Newsstand, Racks
Areas Served: 77511, 77546, 77581, 77584, 77586

PEARSALL

FRIO-NUECES CURRENT (THUR)

321 E San Marcos St, Pearsall, TX, 78061-3223, Frio, USA; gen tel (830) 334-3644; adv tel (830)334-3644; ed tel (830)334-3644; gen fax (830) 334-3647; adv fax (830)334-3647; ed fax (830)334-3647; disp adv e-mail currentads@att.net; class adv e-mail currentads@att.net; ed e-mail currenteditor@att.net; web site www.frio-nuecescurrent.com
Circulation: 3,453pd, 75fr; Sworn/Estimate/Non-Audited
Advertising rate: Open inch rate $8.00
Established: 1896
Pub. .... Craig Garnett
Ed. .... Marc Robertson
Gen. Mgr. .... Logan Garnett
Adv. Dir. .... Michelle Frausto
Delivery Method: Mail, Newsstand
Areas Served: Frio County

PECOS

PECOS ENTERPRISE (TUES, FRI)

324 S Cedar St, Pecos, TX, 79772-3211, Reeves, USA; gen tel (432) 445-5475; adv tel (432) 445-5475; ed tel (432) 445-5475; gen fax (432) 445-4321; adv fax (432) 445-4321; ed fax (432) 445-4321; disp adv e-mail smokey@pecos.net; class adv e-mail news@pecos.net; ed e-mail jon@pecos.net; web site www.pecos.net/news
Circulation: 1,700pd,; Sworn/Estimate/Non-Audited
Advertising rate: Open inch rate $8.21
Established: 1887
Digital Platform - Mobile: Apple, Android
Digital Platform - Tablet: Apple iOS, Android, Windows 7
Pub. .... Smokey Briggs
Ed. .... Jon Fulbright
Adv. Dir. .... Christina Bitolas
Bus. Mgr. .... Lorna Navarette
Classified Adv. Mgr. .... Laura Rodriguez
Mechanical Specifications: Type page 13 x 21 1/2; E - 6 cols, 2 1/16, 1/8 between; A - 6 cols, 2 1/16, 1/8 between; C - 6 cols, 2 1/16, 1/8 between.Equipment & Software: Hardware — PC; Presses — 4-G/Community; Software — Adobe/PageMaker 6.5.
Delivery Method: Mail, Newsstand
Areas Served: Reeves County

PERRYTON

PERRYTON HERALD (THUR, SUN)

401 S Amherst St, Perryton, TX, 79070-3012, Ochiltree, USA; gen tel (806) 435-3631; adv tel (806) 435-3631; ed tel (806) 435-3631; gen fax (806) 435-2420; adv fax (806) 435-2420; ed fax (806) 435-2420; disp adv e-mail dclardy@ptsi.net; class adv e-mail wlarmon@ptsi.net; ed e-mail mhdudley@ptsi.net; web site www.perrytonherald.com
Circulation: 3,500pd,; Sworn/Estimate/Non-Audited
Advertising rate: Open inch rate $5.50
Established: 1917
Pub. .... Jim Hudson
Ed. .... Mary H. Dudley
Adv. Dir. .... Doris Clardy
Classified Mgr. .... Meagan Rogers
Delivery Method: Mail, Newsstand
Areas Served: Ochiltree County

PHARR

ADVANCE NEWS JOURNAL (WED)

217 W Newcombe Ave, Pharr, TX, 78577-4742, Hidalgo, USA; gen tel (956) 783-0036; adv tel (956) 783-0036; ed tel (956) 783-0036; gen fax (956) 787-8824; adv fax (956) 787-8824; ed fax (956) 787-8824; disp adv e-mail advancenews@aol.com; class adv e-mail advancenews@aol.com; ed e-mail advancenews@aol.com; web site www.anjournal.com
Advertising rate: Open inch rate $8.00
Established: 1978
Pub. .... Gregg Wendorf
Ed. .... Ruben Acosta
Adv. Dir. .... Jan Wendorf
Delivery Method: Mail, Newsstand, Racks
Areas Served: Hidalgo County

PILOT POINT

PILOT POINT POST SIGNAL (FRI)

111 E Main St, Pilot Point, TX, 76258-4532, Denton, USA; gen tel (940) 686-2169; adv tel (940) 686-2169; ed tel (940) 686-2169; gen fax (940) 686-2437; adv fax (940) 686-2437; ed fax (940) 686-2437; disp adv e-mail creid@postsignal.com; class adv e-mail rgreene@postsignal.com; ed e-mail editor@postsignal.com; web site www.postsignal.com
Circulation: 2,030pd,; Sworn/Estimate/Non-Audited
Advertising rate: Open inch rate $6.00
Established: 1878
Digital Platform - Mobile: Apple, Windows
Digital Platform - Tablet: Apple iOS, Windows 7
Adv. Mgr. .... Cathy Reid
Mng. Ed. .... Richard Greene
Pub./Ed. .... David Lewis
Delivery Method: Mail, Newsstand, Racks
Areas Served: Denton County

PITTSBURG

PITTSBURG GAZETTE (THUR)

112 Quitman St, Pittsburg, TX, 75686-1322, Camp, USA; gen tel (903) 856-6629; adv tel (903) 856-6629; ed tel (903) 856-6629; gen fax (903) 856-0510; adv fax (903) 856-0510; ed fax (903) 856-0510; disp adv e-mail iperez@campcountynow.com; class adv e-mail iperez@campcountynow.com; ed e-mail dknox@campcountynow.com; web site www.campcountynow.com
Circulation: 3,100pd, 33fr; Sworn/Estimate/Non-Audited
Advertising rate: Open inch rate $8.00
Established: 1884
Group: Northeast Texas Publishing
Digital Platform - Mobile: Apple, Android, Windows, Blackberry
Digital Platform - Tablet: Apple iOS, Android, Windows 7, Blackberry Tablet OS, Kindle, Nook, Kindle Fire
Pub. .... Debbie Knox
Ed. .... Susan Taft
Adv. Mgr. .... Brittany York
Delivery Method: Mail, Newsstand, Racks
Areas Served: Camp County

PLANO

ALLEN AMERICAN (THUR)

624 Krona Dr, Ste 170, Plano, TX, 75074-8304, Collin, USA; gen tel (972) 398-4200; adv tel (972) 398-4471; ed tel (972) 398-4200; gen fax (972) 398-4470; adv fax (972) 398-4470; ed fax (972) 398-4470; disp adv e-mail llibby@starlocalnews.com; class adv e-mail dhemphill@starlocalnews.com; ed e-mail swright@starlocalnews.com; web site www.starlocalmedia.com - 546,019(views) 201,046(visitors)
Circulation: 849pd, 18,161fr; VAC
Advertising rate: Open inch rate $35.30
Established: 1969
Group: S.A.W. Advisors, LLC
Digital Platform - Mobile: Apple, Android
Digital Platform - Tablet: Apple iOS, Android, Windows 7
Group Pub. .... Mike Miller
National Adv. Dir. .... Danny James
Mng. Ed. .... Rick Mann
Adv. Mgr. .... Leanne Libby
Circ. Mgr. .... Melissa Rougeot
Mechanical Specifications: Type page 13 x 21 1/2; E - 6 cols, 2 1/16, 1/8 between; A - 6 cols, 2 1/16, 1/8 between; C - 8 cols, 1 1/2, 1/8 between.
Delivery Method: Mail, Newsstand
Areas Served: Collin County

CARROLLTON LEADER (SUN)

624 Krona Dr, Ste 170, Plano, TX, 75074-8304, Collin, USA; gen tel (972) 398-4200; adv tel (972) 398-4471; ed tel (972) 398-4200; gen fax (972) 398-4470; adv fax (972) 398-4470; ed fax (972) 398-4470; disp adv e-mail llibby@starlocalnews.com; class adv e-mail dhemphill@starlocalnews.com; ed e-mail mmiller@starlocalnews.com; web site www.carrolltonleader.com - 546,019(views) 201,046(visitors)
Circulation: 251pd, 1,772fr; VAC
Advertising rate: Open inch rate $35.30
Established: 2001
Group: S.A.W. Advisors, LLC
Digital Platform - Mobile: Apple, Android
Digital Platform - Tablet: Apple iOS, Android, Windows 7
Group Pub. .... Mike Miller
National Adv. Dir. .... Danny James
Mng. Ed. .... Rick Mann
Adv. Mgr. .... Leanne Libby
Circ. Mgr. .... Melissa Rougeot
Classified Adv. Mgr. .... Della Hemphill
Mechanical Specifications: Type page 13 x 21 1/2; E - 6 cols, 2 1/16, 1/8 between; A - 6 cols, 2 1/16, 1/8 between; C - 8 cols, 1 1/2, 1/8 between.
Delivery Method: Mail, Newsstand
Areas Served: Collin County

CELINA RECORD (FRI)

624 Krona Dr, Ste 170, Plano, TX, 75074-8304, Collin, USA; gen tel (972) 398-4200; adv tel (972) 398-4471; ed tel (972) 398-4200; gen fax (972) 398-4470; adv fax (972)

398-4470; ed fax (972) 398-4470; disp adv e-mail llibby@starlocalnews.com; class adv e-mail dhemphill@starlocalnews.com; ed e-mail mmiller@starlocalnews.com; web site www.celinarecord.com - 546,019(views) 201,046(visitors)
Circulation: 327pd, 86fr; VAC
Advertising rate: Open inch rate $35.30
Established: 1901
Group: S.A.W. Advisors, LLC
Digital Platform - Mobile: Apple, Android
Digital Platform - Tablet: Apple iOS, Android, Windows 7
Group Pub....................Mike Miller
National Adv. Dir....................Danny James
Mng. Ed....................Rick Mann
Adv. Mgr....................Leanne Libby
Circ. Mgr....................Melissa Rougeot
Della Hemphill
Mechanical Specifications: Type page 13 x 21 1/2; E - 6 cols, 2 1/16, 1/8 between; A - 6 cols, 2 1/16, 1/8 between; C - 8 cols, 1 1/2, 1/8 between.
Delivery Method: Mail, Newsstand
Areas Served: Collin County

COLONY-COURIER LEADER (SUN)

624 Krona Dr, Ste 170, Plano, TX, 75074-8304, Collin, USA ; gen tel (972)398-4200; adv tel (972) 398-4471; ed tel (972)424-9504; gen fax (972)398-4470; adv fax (972)398-4470; ed fax (972)398-4470; disp adv e-mail llibby@starlocalmedia.com; class adv e-mail dhemphill@starlocalmedia.com; ed e-mail swright@starlocalnews.com; web site www.starlocalmedia.com
Group: Times Media Group
Star Community Newspapers
Exec. Ed....................Liz McGathey

COPPELL GAZETTE (SUN)

624 Krona Dr, Ste 170, Plano, TX, 75074-8304, Collin, USA; gen tel (972) 398-4200; adv tel (972) 398-4471; ed tel (972) 398-4200; gen fax (972) 398-4470; adv fax (972) 398-4470; ed fax (972) 398-4470; disp adv e-mail llibby@starlocalmedia.com; class adv e-mail dhemphill@starlocalmedia.com; ed e-mail swright@starlocalmedia.com; web site www.coppellgazette.com - 546,019(views) 201,046(visitors)
Circulation: 219pd, 9,287fr; VAC
Advertising rate: Open inch rate $35.30
Established: 1981
Group: S.A.W. Advisors, LLC
Digital Platform - Mobile: Apple, Android
Digital Platform - Tablet: Apple iOS, Android, Windows 7
Group Pub....................Mike Miller
National Adv. Dir....................Danny James
Mng. Ed....................Rick Mann
Adv. Mgr....................Leanne Libby
Circ. Mgr....................Melissa Rougeot
Classified Adv. Mgr....................Della Hemphill
Mechanical Specifications: Type page 13 x 21 1/2; E - 6 cols, 2 1/16, 1/8 between; A - 6 cols, 2 1/16, 1/8 between; C - 8 cols, 1 1/2, 1/8 between.
Delivery Method: Mail, Newsstand
Areas Served: Collin County

FLOWER MOUND LEADER (WED, SAT)

624 Krona Dr, Ste 170, Plano, TX, 75074-8304, Collin, USA; gen tel (972) 398-4200; adv tel (972) 398-4471; ed tel (972) 398-4200; gen fax (972) 398-4470; adv fax (972) 398-4470; ed fax (972) 398-4470; disp adv e-mail llibby@starlocalnews.com; class adv e-mail dhemphill@starlocalnews.com; ed e-mail mmiller@starlocalnews.com; web site www.scntx.com/flower_mound_leader
Circulation: 767pd, 29,274fr; CVC
Advertising rate: Open inch rate $35.30
Group: S.A.W. Advisors, LLC
Digital Platform - Mobile: Apple, Android
Digital Platform - Tablet: Apple iOS, Android, Windows 7
Group Pub....................Mike Miller
Nat'l Adv. Mgr....................Danny James
Mng. Ed....................Rick Mann
Classifieds....................Della Hemphill
Mechanical Specifications: Type page 13 x 21 1/2; E - 6 cols, 2 1/16, 1/8 between; A - 6 cols, 2 1/16, 1/8 between; C - 8 cols, 1 1/2, 1/8 between.
Delivery Method: Mail, Newsstand
Areas Served: Collin County

FRISCO ENTERPRISE (FRI)

624 Krona Dr, Ste 170, Plano, TX, 75074-8304, Collin, USA; gen tel (972) 398-4200; adv tel (972) 398-4471; ed tel (972) 398-4200; gen fax (972) 398-4470; adv fax (972) 398-4470; ed fax (972) 398-4470; disp adv e-mail llibby@starlocalmedia.com; class adv e-mail dhemphill@starlocalmedia.com; ed e-mail swright@starlocalmedia.com; web site www.friscoenterprise.com - 546,019(views) 201,046(visitors)
Circulation: 621pd, 25,900fr; VAC
Advertising rate: Open inch rate $35.30
Established: 1957
Group: S.A.W. Advisors, LLC
Digital Platform - Mobile: Apple, Android
Digital Platform - Tablet: Apple iOS, Android, Windows 7
Group Pub....................Mike Miller
National Adv. Dir....................Danny James
Mng. Ed....................Rick Mann
Adv. Mgr....................Leanne Libby
Circ. Mgr....................Melissa Rougeot
Classified Adv. Mgr....................Della Hemphill
Mechanical Specifications: Type page 13 x 21 1/2; E - 6 cols, 2 1/16, 1/8 between; A - 6 cols, 2 1/16, 1/8 between; C - 8 cols, 1 1/2, 1/8 between.
Delivery Method: Mail, Newsstand
Areas Served: Collin County

LAKE CITIES SUN (SUN)

624 Krona Dr, Ste 170, Plano, TX, 75074-8304, Collin, USA; gen tel (940) 497-4141; adv tel (940) 497-4141; ed tel (940) 497-4141; gen fax (940) 497-2273; adv fax (940) 497-2273; ed fax (940) 497-2273; disp adv e-mail llibby@starlocalmedia.com; class adv e-mail dhemphill@starlocalmedia.com; ed e-mail swright@starlocalmedia.com; web site www.starlocalmedia.com
Circulation: 221pd, 5,189fr; VAC
Advertising rate: Open inch rate $30.00
Established: 1974
Group: S.A.W. Advisors, LLC
Digital Platform - Mobile: Apple, Android
Digital Platform - Tablet: Apple iOS, Android, Windows 7
Pub./Ed....................Terry Lantrip
Adv. Dir....................Pauline Mounger
Pub....................Mike Miller
Adv. Mgr....................Leanne Libby
Circ. Mgr....................Melissa Rougeot
Delivery Method: Mail, Newsstand
Areas Served: Denton County

LEWISVILLE LEADER (SUN)

624 Krona Dr, Ste 170, Plano, TX, 75074-8304, Collin, USA; gen tel (972) 398-4200; adv tel (972) 398-4471; ed tel (972) 398-4200; gen fax (972) 398-4470; adv fax (972) 398-4470; ed fax (972) 398-4470; disp adv e-mail llibby@starlocalmedia.com; class adv e-mail dhemphill@starlocalmedia.com; ed e-mail swright@starlocalmedia.com; web site www.starlocalmedia.com
Circulation: 225pd, 11,333fr; VAC
Advertising rate: Open inch rate $35.30
Group: S.A.W. Advisors, LLC
Digital Platform - Mobile: Apple, Android
Digital Platform - Tablet: Apple iOS, Android, Windows 7
Group Pub....................Mike Miller
National Adv. Dir....................Danny James
Mng. Ed....................Rick Mann
Adv. Mgr....................Leanne Libby
Circ. Mgr....................Melissa Rougeot
Classifieds....................Della Hemphill
Mechanical Specifications: Type page 13 x 21 1/2; E - 6 cols, 2 1/16, 1/8 between; A - 6 cols, 2 1/16, 1/8 between; C - 8 cols, 1 1/2, 1/8 between.
Delivery Method: Mail, Newsstand
Areas Served: Collin County

LITTLE ELM JOURNAL (FRI)

624 Krona Dr, Ste 170, Plano, TX, 75074-8304, Collin, USA; gen tel (972) 398-4200; adv tel (972) 398-4471; ed tel (972) 398-4200; gen fax (972) 398-4470; adv fax (972) 398-4470; ed fax (972) 398-4470; disp adv e-mail llibby@starlocalmedia.com; class adv e-mail dhemphill@starlocalmedia.com; ed e-mail swright@starlocalmedia.com; web site www.starlocalmedia.com - 546,019(views) 201,046(visitors)
Circulation: 126pd, 5,933fr; VAC
Advertising rate: Open inch rate $35.30
Established: 1993
Group: S.A.W. Advisors, LLC
Digital Platform - Mobile: Apple, Android
Digital Platform - Tablet: Apple iOS, Android, Windows 7
Group Pub....................Mike Miller
National Adv. Dir....................Danny James
Mng. Ed....................Rick Mann
Circ. Mgr....................Melissa Rougeot
Adv. Mgr....................Leanne Libby
Mechanical Specifications: Type page 13 x 21 1/2; E - 6 cols, 2 1/16, 1/8 between; A - 6 cols, 2 1/16, 1/8 between; C - 8 cols, 1 1/2, 1/8 between.
Delivery Method: Mail, Newsstand
Areas Served: Collin County

MCKINNEY COURIER-GAZETTE (SUN)

624 Krona Dr, Ste 170, Plano, TX, 75074-8304, Collin, USA; gen tel (972) 398-4200; adv tel (972) 398-4471; ed tel (972) 398-4200; gen fax (972) 398-4470; adv fax (972) 398-4470; ed fax (972) 398-4470; disp adv e-mail llibby@starlocalmedia.com; class adv e-mail dhemphill@starlocalmedia.com; ed e-mail swright@starlocalmedia.com; web site www.courier-gazette.com - 546,019(views) 201,046(visitors)
Circulation: 861pd, 29,344fr; VAC
Advertising rate: Open inch rate $35.30
Established: 1991
Group: S.A.W. Advisors, LLC
Digital Platform - Mobile: Apple, Android
Digital Platform - Tablet: Apple iOS, Android, Windows 7
Group Pub....................Mike Miller
National Adv. Dir....................Danny James
Community Ed....................Chris Beattie
Adv. Mgr....................Leanne Libby
Circ. Mgr....................Melissa Rougeot
Classifieds....................Della Hemphill
Mechanical Specifications: Type page 13 x 21 1/2; E - 6 cols, 2 1/16, 1/8 between; A - 6 cols, 2 1/16, 1/8 between; C - 8 cols, 1 1/2, 1/8 between.
Delivery Method: Mail, Newsstand
Areas Served: Collin County

MESQUITE NEWS (THUR)

624 Krona Dr, Ste 170, Plano, TX, 75074-8304, Collin, USA; gen tel (972) 398-4200; adv tel (972) 398-4471; ed tel (972) 398-4200; gen fax (972) 398-4470; adv fax (972) 398-4470; ed fax (972) 398-4470; disp adv e-mail llibby@starlocalmedia.com; class adv e-mail dhemphill@starlocalmedia.com; ed e-mail swright@starlocalmedia.com; web site www.starlocalmedia.com - 546,019(views) 201,046(visitors)
Circulation: 268pd, 23,418fr; VAC
Advertising rate: Open inch rate $35.30
Established: 1882
Group: S.A.W. Advisors, LLC
Digital Platform - Mobile: Apple, Android
Digital Platform - Tablet: Apple iOS, Android, Windows 7
Group Pub....................Mike Miller
National Adv. Dir....................Danny James
Mng. Ed....................Rick Mann
Adv. Mgr....................Leanne Libby
Circ. Mgr....................Melissa Rougeot
Classifieds....................Della Hemphill
Mechanical Specifications: Type page 13 x 21 1/2; E - 6 cols, 2 1/16, 1/8 between; A - 6 cols, 2 1/16, 1/8 between; C - 8 cols, 1 1/2, 1/8 between.
Delivery Method: Mail, Newsstand
Areas Served: Collin County

PLANO STAR-COURIER (THUR, SUN)

624 Krona Dr, Ste 170, Plano, TX, 75074-8304, Collin, USA; gen tel (972) 398-4200; adv tel (972) 398-4471; ed tel (972) 398-4200; gen fax (972) 398-4470; adv fax (972) 398-4470; ed fax (972) 398-4470; disp adv e-mail llibby@starlocalmedia.com; class adv e-mail dhemphill@starlocalmedia.com; ed e-mail swright@starlocalmedia.com; web site www.starlocalmedia.com - 546,019(views) 201,046(visitors)
Circulation: 526pd, 44,216fr; VAC
Advertising rate: Open inch rate $35.30
Established: 1889
Group: Times Media Group
Digital Platform - Mobile: Apple, Android
Digital Platform - Tablet: Apple iOS, Android, Windows 7
Group Pub....................Mike Miller
National Adv. Dir....................Danny James
Mng. Ed....................Rick Mann
Classifieds....................Della Hemphill
Mechanical Specifications: Type page 13 x 21 1/2; E - 6 cols, 2 1/16, 1/8 between; A - 6 cols, 2 1/16, 1/8 between; C - 8 cols, 1 1/2, 1/8 between.
Delivery Method: Mail, Newsstand
Areas Served: Collin County

ROWLETT LAKESHORE TIMES (THUR)

624 Krona Dr, Ste 170, Plano, TX, 75074-8304, Collin, USA; gen tel (972) 398-4200; adv tel (972) 398-4471; ed tel (972) 398-4200; gen fax (972) 398-4470; adv fax (972) 398-4470; ed fax (972) 398-4470; disp adv e-mail llibby@starlocalmedia.com; class adv e-mail dhemphill@starlocalmedia.com; ed e-mail swright@starlocalmedia.com; web site www.starlocalmedia.com - 546,019(views) 201,046(visitors)
Circulation: 206pd, 6,242fr; VAC
Advertising rate: Open inch rate $35.30
Established: 1982
Group: S.A.W. Advisors, LLC
Digital Platform - Mobile: Apple, Android
Digital Platform - Tablet: Apple iOS, Android, Windows 7
Group Pub....................Mike Miller
National Adv. Dir....................Danny James
Mng. Ed....................Rick Mann
Adv. Mgr....................Leanne Libby
Circ. Mgr....................Melissa Rougeot
Classifieds....................Della Hemphill
Mechanical Specifications: Type page 13 x 21 1/2; E - 6 cols, 2 1/16, 1/8 between; A - 6 cols, 2 1/16, 1/8 between; C - 8 cols, 1 1/2, 1/8 between.
Delivery Method: Mail, Newsstand
Areas Served: Collin County

SUNNYVALE VIEW (SUN)

624 Krona Dr, Ste 170, Plano, TX, 75074-8304, Collin, USA; gen tel (972) 398-4471; adv tel (972) 398-4471; ed tel (972) 398-4471; gen fax (972) 398-4470; adv fax (972) 398-4470; ed fax (972) 398-4470; disp adv e-mail llibby@starlocalmedia.com; class adv e-mail dhemphill@starlocalmedia.com; ed e-mail swright@starlocalmedia.com; web site www.starlocalmedia.com - 546,019(views) 201,046(visitors)
Circulation: 21pd, 1,740fr; CVC
Advertising rate: Open inch rate $35.30
Established: 1998
Group: American Community Newspapers LLC
Digital Platform - Mobile: Apple, Android
Digital Platform - Tablet: Apple iOS, Android, Windows 7
Group Pub....................Mike Miller
National Adv. Dir....................Danny James
Mng. Ed....................Rick Mann
Classifieds....................Della Hemphill
Mechanical Specifications: Type page 13 x 21 1/2; E - 6 cols, 2 1/16, 1/8 between; A - 6 cols, 2 1/16, 1/8 between; C - 8 cols, 1 1/2, 1/8 between.
Delivery Method: Mail, Newsstand
Areas Served: Collin County

THE COLONY COURIER LEADER (SUN)

624 Krona Dr, Ste 170, Plano, TX, 75074-8304, Collin, USA; gen tel (972) 398-4200; adv tel (972) 398-4471; ed tel (972) 398-4200; gen fax (972) 398-4470; adv fax (972) 398-4470; ed fax (972) 398-4470; disp adv e-mail llibby@starlocalnews.com; class adv e-mail dhemphill@starlocalnews.com; ed e-mail mmiller@starlocalnews.com; web site

www.starlocalnews.com - 546,019(views) 201,046(visitors)
Circulation: 260pd, 6,447fr; VAC
Advertising rate: Open inch rate $35.30
Established: 1981
Group: S.A.W. Advisors, LLC
Digital Platform - Mobile: Apple, Android
Digital Platform - Tablet: Apple iOS, Android, Windows 7
Group Pub....................................... Mike Miller
National Adv. Dir. .... Danny James
Mng. Ed... Rick Mann
Adv. Mgr...................................... Leanne Libby
Circ. Mgr .... Melissa Rougeot
Cklassifieds .... Della Hemphill
Mechanical Specifications: Type page 13 x 21 1/2; E - 6 cols, 2 1/16, 1/8 between; A - 6 cols, 2 1/16, 1/8 between; C - 8 cols, 1 1/2, 1/8 between.
Delivery Method: Mail, Newsstand
Areas Served: Collin County

PLEASANTON

PLEASANTON EXPRESS (WED)

114 E Goodwin St, Pleasanton, TX, 78064-4124, Atascosa, USA; gen tel (830) 281-2341; gen fax (830) 569-6100; disp adv e-mail mgallegos@pleasantonexpress.com; class adv e-mail classifieds@pleasantonexpress.com; ed e-mail sbrown@pleasantonexpress.com; web site www.pleasantonexpress.com
Circulation: 8,400fr; Sworn/Estimate/Non-Audited
Advertising rate: Open inch rate $14.20
Established: 1909
Digital Platform - Mobile: Apple, Android, Windows, Blackberry
Digital Platform - Tablet: Apple iOS, Android, Windows 7, Blackberry Tablet OS, Kindle, Nook, Kindle Fire
Pub... Judith Wilkerson
Editor .... Sue Brown
Adv. Dir....................................... Mary Gallegos
Business Manager, Classifieds Manager .... Rhonda Chancellor
Ad Sales .... Megan Benishek
Associate Pub............. Noel Wilkerson Holmes
Delivery Method: Mail, Newsstand, Racks
Areas Served: Atascosa County

PORT ARANSAS

PORT ARANSAS SOUTH JETTY (THUR)

141 W Cotter Ave, Port Aransas, TX, 78373-4034, Nueces, USA; gen tel (361) 749-5131; adv tel (361) 749-5131; ed tel (361) 749-5131; gen fax (361) 749-5137; adv fax (361) 749-5137; ed fax (361) 749-5137; disp adv e-mail displayads@portasouthjetty.com; class adv e-mail classifiedads@portasouthjetty.com; ed e-mail southjetty@centurytel.net; web site www.portasouthjetty.com
Circulation: 3,730pd, 56fr; Sworn/Estimate/Non-Audited
Advertising rate: Open inch rate $10.75
Established: 1971Editions: (52) Port Aransas South Jetty
Digital Platform - Mobile: Apple, Android, Windows, Blackberry, Other
Digital Platform - Tablet: Apple iOS, Android, Windows 7, Blackberry Tablet OS, Kindle, Nook, Kindle Fire, Other
Co-Pub./Adv. Dir........................ Murray Judson
Co-Pub./Ed.............................. Mary Judson
Mechanical Specifications: 1 column = 1.5 inches
2 columns = 3.2 inches
3 columns = 4.9 inches
4 columns = 6.6 inches
5 columns = 8.25 inches
6 columns = 9.91 inches
Delivery Method: Mail, Newsstand, Racks
Areas Served: Port Aransas and Corpus Christi, Nueces County, TX are locally distributed by mail at a lower rate than all other states in U.S.

PORT ISABEL

PORT ISABEL-SOUTH PADRE PRESS (THUR)

101 E Maxan St, Port Isabel, TX, 78578-4504, Cameron, USA; gen tel (956) 943-5545; adv tel (956) 943-5545; ed tel (956) 943-5545; gen fax (956) 943-4782; adv fax (956) 943-4782; ed fax (956) 943-4782; disp adv e-mail rayq@portisabelsouthpadre.com; class adv e-mail rayq@portisabelsouthpadre.com; ed e-mail editor@portisabelsouthpadre.com; web site www.portisabelsouthpadre.com
Circulation: 30,000pd, 0fr; USPS
Advertising rate: Open inch rate $9.55
Established: 1952
Digital Platform - Mobile: Apple
Digital Platform - Tablet: Apple iOS, Windows 7
Pub./Ed.. Ray Quiroga
Delivery Method: Mail, Newsstand, Racks
Areas Served: Port Isabel, Laguna Vista, South Padre Island, Cameron County

PORT LAVACA

PORT LAVACA WAVE (WED, SAT)

107 E Austin St, Port Lavaca, TX, 77979-4402, Calhoun, USA; gen tel (361) 552-9788; adv tel (361) 552-9788; ed tel (361) 552-9788; gen fax (361) 552-3108; adv fax (361) 552-3108; ed fax (361) 552-3108; disp adv e-mail tfrench@plwave.com; class adv e-mail tfrench@plwave.com; ed e-mail tfrench@plwave.com; web site www.portlavacawave.com
Circulation: 4,200pd, 2,300fr; Sworn/Estimate/Non-Audited
Advertising rate: Open inch rate $8.40
Established: 1890
Group: Hartman Newspapers LP
Digital Platform - Mobile: Apple, Windows
Digital Platform - Tablet: Apple iOS, Windows 7, Kindle
Pub./Ed....................................... Tania French
Delivery Method: Mail, Newsstand, Racks
Areas Served: 77979, 77978, 77982, 77983

PORTLAND

PORTLAND NEWS (THUR)

1105 Railroad Dr, Ste B, Portland, TX, 78374-1759, San Patricio, USA; gen tel (361) 643-1566; adv tel (361) 643-1566; ed tel (361) 643-1566; gen fax (361) 643-1400; adv fax (361) 643-1400; ed fax (361) 643-1400; disp adv e-mail advertising@mysoutex.com; class adv e-mail receptionist@mysoutex.com; ed e-mail editor@mysoutex.com
Circulation: 2,500pd, 50fr; Sworn/Estimate/Non-Audited
Advertising rate: Open inch rate $7.75
Established: 1964
Group: San Patricio Publishing Co., Inc.
Digital Platform - Tablet: Windows 7
Co-Pub...................................... James F. Tracy
Co-Pub./Adv. Mgr....................... John H. Tracy
Ed. .... Diana Stone
Mechanical Specifications: Type page 13 x 21.Equipment & Software: Hardware — APP/Mac; Presses — HI/V-15A.
Delivery Method: Mail, Newsstand
Areas Served: San Patricio County

THE COASTAL BEND HERALD (THUR)

1011 US Highway 181, Ste 6, Portland, TX, 78374-1733, San Patricio, USA; gen tel (361) 729-1828; adv tel (361) 729-1828; ed tel (361) 729-1828; gen fax (361) 729-9060; adv fax (361) 729-9060; ed fax (361) 729-9060; disp adv e-mail theherald@the-i.net; class adv e-mail kriley@the-i.net; ed e-mail tmacek@theheraldonline.com
Circulation: 4,250pd, 125fr; Sworn/Estimate/Non-Audited
Advertising rate: Open inch rate $6.85
Established: 1974
Digital Platform - Mobile: Apple, Android
Digital Platform - Tablet: Apple iOS, Android, Windows 7
Pub./Ed... Kerry Riley
Adv. Mgr................................ Michelle Perdue
Prodn. Mgr. .... Bettye Landers
Web Mgr....................................... Todd Macek
Mechanical Specifications: Type page 13 x 21; E - 6 cols, 2 5/16, 1/8 between; A - 6 cols, 2 5/16, 1/8 between; C - 8 cols, 1 1/2, 1/8 between.Equipment & Software: Hardware — APP/Mac.
Delivery Method: Mail, Newsstand
Areas Served: 77990, 78381, 78382, 78358, 78336, 78373, 78362, 78374, 77979

POST

THE POST DISPATCH (FRI)

123 E Main St, Post, TX, 79356-3229, Garza, USA; gen tel (806) 495-2816; adv tel (806) 495-2816; ed tel (806) 495-2816; gen fax (806) 495-2059; adv fax (806) 495-2059; ed fax (806) 495-2059; disp adv e-mail thepostcitydispatch@gmail.com; class adv e-mail thepostcitydispatch@gmail.com; ed e-mail thepostcitydispatch@gmail.com; web site www.thepostdispatchonline.com
Circulation: 1,550pd,; Sworn/Estimate/Non-Audited
Advertising rate: Open inch rate $8.00
Established: 1926
Digital Platform - Mobile: Apple, Android, Windows, Blackberry
Digital Platform - Tablet: Apple iOS, Android, Windows 7, Blackberry Tablet OS, Kindle, Nook, Kindle Fire
Pub.............................. Christopher Blackburn
Ed./Adv. Dir. .... Wayne Hodgin
Delivery Method: Mail, Newsstand
Areas Served: Garza County

PRESIDIO

THE PRESIDIO INTERNATIONAL (THUR)

110 N Highland Avenue, Presidio, TX, 79845, Presidio, USA; gen tel (432) 729-4342; adv tel (432) 729-4342; ed tel (432) 729-4342; ed fax (432) 729-4601; disp adv e-mail rosario@bigbendnow.com; class adv e-mail rosario@bigbendnow.com; ed e-mail editor@bigbendnow.com; web site www.bigbendnow.com
Circulation: 900pd,; Sworn/Estimate/Non-Audited
Advertising rate: Open inch rate $7.50
Established: 1986
Pub./Ed............................... Robert L. Halpern
Adv. Dir.................... Rosario Salgado-Halpern
Mechanical Specifications: Type page 13 x 21; E - 6 cols, 2, 1/6 between; A - 6 cols, 2, 1/6 between; C - 6 cols, 2, 1/6 between.Equipment & Software: Hardware — Dell; Software — Microsoft/Word, Adobe/PageMaker, Adobe/Photoshop.
Delivery Method: Mail, Newsstand, Racks
Areas Served: Presidio County

QUANAH

QUANAH TRIBUNE-CHIEF (FRI)

PO Box 481, Quanah, TX, 79252-0481, Hardeman, USA; gen tel (940) 663-5333; gen fax (940) 663-5073; disp adv e-mail editor@quanahtribunechief.com; class adv e-mail editor@quanahtribunechief.com; ed e-mail editor@quanahtribunechief.com; web site www.quanahtribunechief.com
Circulation: 1,500pd, 19fr; Sworn/Estimate/Non-Audited
Advertising rate: Open inch rate $7.00
Established: 1889
Digital Platform - Mobile: Apple, Android, Windows, Blackberry
Digital Platform - Tablet: Apple iOS, Android, Windows 7, Blackberry Tablet OS, Kindle, Nook, Kindle Fire
Pub.. Bret McCormick
Ed. .... Carol Whitmire
Mechanical Specifications: Type page 13 x 21; E - 6 cols, 2 1/16, 1/8 between; A - 6 cols, 2 1/16, 1/8 between; C - 6 cols, 2 1/16, 1/8 between.
Delivery Method: Mail, Newsstand, Racks
Areas Served: 79252, 79225, 73537

QUITAQUE

THE VALLEY TRIBUNE (WED)

205 Cypress, Quitaque, TX, 79255, Briscoe, USA; gen tel (806) 455-1101; gen fax (806) 455-1101; disp adv e-mail thevalleytribune@yahoo.com; class adv e-mail thevalleytribune@yahoo.com; ed e-mail thevalleytribune@yahoo.com
Circulation: 1,000pd,; Sworn/Estimate/Non-Audited
Advertising rate: Open inch rate $5.00
Established: 1926
Pub./Adv. Dir. .... Brandei Taylor
Mechanical Specifications: Type page 13 x 21.
Delivery Method: Mail, Newsstand
Areas Served: Briscoe County

QUITMAN

WOOD COUNTY MONITOR (WED)

310 E Goode St, Ste C, Quitman, TX, 75783-2502, Wood, USA; gen tel (903) 763-4522; adv tel (903) 763-4522; ed tel (903) 763-4522; gen fax (903) 763-2313; adv fax (903) 763-2313; ed fax (903) 763-2313; disp adv e-mail advertising@thewoodcountymonitor.com; class adv e-mail classifieds@thewoodcountymonitort.com; ed e-mail news@thewoodcountydemocrat.com; web site www.thewoodcountymonitor.com
Circulation: 3,065pd,; Sworn/Estimate/Non-Audited
Advertising rate: Open inch rate $8.20
Established: 1893
Group: Bluebonnet Publishing, LLC
Digital Platform - Mobile: Apple, Android, Windows, Blackberry
Digital Platform - Tablet: Apple iOS, Android, Windows 7, Blackberry Tablet OS, Kindle, Nook, Kindle Fire
News Editor .... Larry Tucker
Ed. .... Maggie Fraser
Adv. Dir.. Kiki Bettis
Delivery Method: Mail, Newsstand, Racks
Areas Served: Wood County

RALLS

CROSBY COUNTY NEWS (FRI)

817 Main, Ralls, TX, 79357, Crosby, USA; gen tel (806) 253-0211; adv tel (806) 253-0211; ed tel (806) 253-0211; gen fax (806) 253-0211; adv fax (806) 253-0211; ed fax (806) 253-0211; disp adv e-mail crosbycountynews@windstream.net; class adv e-mail crosbycountynews@windstream.net; ed e-mail crosbycountynews@windstream.net
Circulation: 1,000pd,; Sworn/Estimate/Non-Audited
Advertising rate: Open inch rate $4.00
Established: 1985
Pub./Ed....................................... John Valentine
Adv. Dir.................................. Brenda Valentine
Delivery Method: Mail, Carrier, Racks
Areas Served: Crosby County (79357, 79322, 79343)

RAYMONDVILLE

RAYMONDVILLE CHRONICLE & WILLACY COUNTY NEWS (WED)

PO Box 369, 192 N 4th St, Raymondville, TX, 78580-0369, Willacy, USA; gen tel (956) 689-2421; gen fax (956) 689-6575; disp adv e-mail erica@raymondvillechroniclenews.com; class adv e-mail erica@raymondvillechroniclenews.com; ed e-mail chroniclenews@msn.com; web site www.raymondvil-

lechroniclenews.com
Circulation: 2,500pd,; Sworn/Estimate/Non-Audited
Advertising rate: Open inch rate $9.80
Established: 1920
Digital Platform - Mobile: Apple, Android, Windows, Blackberry
Digital Platform - Tablet: Apple iOS, Android, Windows 7, Blackberry Tablet OS, Kindle, Nook, Kindle Fire
Pub./Ed. .... Paul E. Whitworth
Adv. Dir. .... Carlos Martinez
Reporter .... Antonio Vindell
Sec./Office Mgr. .... Erica Ysasi
Graphics Designer .... Eric Aguirre
Mechanical Specifications: SAU 6 cols. x 20 inches
Delivery Method: Mail, Newsstand, Racks
Areas Served: 78580, 78569

REFUGIO

REFUGIO COUNTY PRESS (THUR)

412 N Alamo St, Refugio, TX, 78377-2504, Refugio, USA; gen tel (361) 526-2397; gen fax (361) 526-2398; disp adv e-mail sales@mysoutex.com; class adv e-mail classifieds@mysoutex.com; ed e-mail refugiocountypress@mysoutex.com; web site www.mySouTex.com
Circulation: 2,200pd, 0fr; USPS
Advertising rate: Open inch rate $6.80
Established: 1959
Group: Beeville Publishing Company, Inc.
Digital Platform - Mobile: Apple, Android, Windows, Blackberry
Digital Platform - Tablet: Apple iOS, Android, Windows 7, Blackberry Tablet OS, Kindle, Nook, Kindle Fire
Co-Pub. .... Jeff Latcham
Co-Pub. .... Chip Latcham
Adv. Dir. .... Karl Arnst
Ed. .... Tim Delaney
Delivery Method: Mail, Newsstand, Racks
Areas Served: Refugio County, Refugio, Woodsboro, Austwell/Tivoli

ROBERT LEE

THE OBSERVER/ENTERPRISE (FRI)

707 Austin St, Robert Lee, TX, 76945, Coke, USA; gen tel (325) 453-2433; adv tel (325) 453-2433; ed tel (325) 453-2433; gen fax (325) 453-4643; adv fax (325) 453-4643; ed fax (325) 453-4643; disp adv e-mail o-e@wcc.net; class adv e-mail o-e@wcc.net; ed e-mail o-e@wcc.net; web site www.observer-enterprise.com
Circulation: 1,553pd, 32fr; Sworn/Estimate/Non-Audited
Advertising rate: Open inch rate $6.00
Established: 1898
Digital Platform - Mobile: Apple, Android
Digital Platform - Tablet: Apple iOS, Android, Windows 7
Pub./Ed./Adv. Dir. .... Melinda McCutchen
Classified Ed. .... Amber Sawyer
Mechanical Specifications: Type page 10 x 16; E - 5 cols, 1 11/12, between; A - 5 cols, 1 11/12, between; C - 5 cols, 1 11/12, between.Equipment & Software: Hardware — APP/Mac.
Delivery Method: Mail, Newsstand
Areas Served: Coke County

ROCKDALE

ROCKDALE REPORTER (THUR)

221 E Cameron Ave, Rockdale, TX, 76567-2972, Milam, USA; gen tel (512) 446-5838; adv tel (512) 446-5838; ed tel (512) 446-5838; gen fax (512) 446-5317; adv fax (512) 446-5317; ed fax (512) 446-5317; disp adv e-mail kathy@rockdalereporter.com; class adv e-mail linda@rockdalereporter.com; ed e-mail mike@rockdalereporter.com; web site www.rockdalereporter.com
Advertising rate: Open inch rate $8.00
Established: 1893
Digital Platform - Mobile: Apple, Android, Windows, Blackberry
Digital Platform - Tablet: Apple iOS, Android, Windows 7, Blackberry Tablet OS, Kindle, Nook, Kindle Fire
Pub./Adv. Dir. .... Kathy Cooke
Ed. .... Mike Brown
Delivery Method: Mail, Newsstand
Areas Served: Milam County

ROCKPORT

THE ROCKPORT PILOT (WED, SAT)

1002 E Wharf St, Rockport, TX, 78382-2662, Aransas, USA; gen tel (361) 729-9900; adv tel (361) 729-9900; ed tel (361) 729-9900; gen fax (361) 729-8903; adv fax (361) 729-8903; ed fax (361) 729-8903; disp adv e-mail displayadvertising@rockportpilot.com; class adv e-mail classifieds@rockportpilot.com; ed e-mail publisher@rockportpilot.com; web site www.rockportpilot.com
Advertising rate: Open inch rate $8.00
Established: 1869
Group: Hartman Newspapers LP
Digital Platform - Mobile: Apple, Android, Windows, Blackberry
Digital Platform - Tablet: Apple iOS, Android, Windows 7, Blackberry Tablet OS, Kindle, Nook, Kindle Fire
Pub./Ed. .... Mike Probst
Mng. Ed. .... Norma Martinez
Adv. Dir. .... Kim Gove
Delivery Method: Mail, Newsstand, Racks
Areas Served: Edwards County

ROCKSPRINGS

TEXAS MOHAIR WEEKLY (THUR)

108 N Well St, Rocksprings, TX, 78880, Edwards, USA; gen tel (830) 683-3130; adv tel (830) 683-3130; ed tel (830) 683-3130; gen fax (830) 683-3230; adv fax (830) 683-3230; ed fax (830) 683-3230; disp adv e-mail tmw@swtexas.net; class adv e-mail tmw@swtexas.net; ed e-mail tmw@swtexas.net; web site www.rockspringsrecord.com
Circulation: 1,100pd,; Sworn/Estimate/Non-Audited
Advertising rate: Open inch rate $5.00
Established: 1893
Digital Platform - Mobile: Apple, Android
Digital Platform - Tablet: Apple iOS, Android, Windows 7
Co-Pub./Co-Ed./Adv. Dir. .... Carolyn Anderson
Co-Ed./Co-Pub. .... Dean Anderson
Delivery Method: Mail, Newsstand
Areas Served: Edwards County

ROCKWALL

ROCKWALL COUNTY NEWS (THUR)

107 W Bourn St, Rockwall, TX, 75087-4108, Rockwall, USA; gen tel (972) 722-3099; adv tel (972) 722-3099; ed tel (972) 722-3099; gen fax (972) 722-2199; adv fax (972) 722-2199; ed fax (972) 722-2199; disp adv e-mail rcn.news@yahoo.com; class adv e-mail rcn.news@yahoo.com; ed e-mail rcn.news@yahoo.com; web site www.rockwallcountynews.com
Circulation: 4,000pd,; Sworn/Estimate/Non-Audited
Advertising rate: Open inch rate $10.00
Established: 1986
Digital Platform - Mobile: Apple, Android
Digital Platform - Tablet: Apple iOS, Android, Windows 7
Pub./Ed. .... Wesley Burnett
Adv. Dir. .... Mike Moore
Delivery Method: Mail, Newsstand
Areas Served: Rockwall County

ROMA

SOUTH TEXAS REPORTER (THUR)

101 E La Fragua Ave, Roma, TX, 78584-5593, Starr, USA; gen tel (956) 271-4500; gen fax (956) 267-9322; disp adv e-mail southtexasreporter@ymail.com; class adv e-mail southtexasreporter@ymail.com; ed e-mail southtexasreporter@ymail.com
Circulation: 10,000fr; Sworn/Estimate/Non-Audited
Advertising rate: Open inch rate $5.50
Established: 1971
Pub./Ed. .... Raul Guerra
Chief Ed. .... Larry Hoelter
Mechanical Specifications: Type page 13 x 21; E - 6 cols, between.
Delivery Method: Mail, Racks
Areas Served: Starr County

ROSEBUD

THE ROSEBUD NEWS (THUR)

229 W Main St, Rosebud, TX, 76570, Falls, USA; gen tel (254) 583-7811; adv tel (254) 583-7811; ed tel (254) 583-7811; gen fax (254) 583-2493; adv fax (254) 583-2493; ed fax (254) 583-2493; disp adv e-mail rnprint@valornet.com; class adv e-mail rnprint@valornet.com; ed e-mail rnprint@valornet.com; web site www.marlindemocrat.com/rosebud
Circulation: 1,800pd, 15fr; Sworn/Estimate/Non-Audited
Advertising rate: Open inch rate $8.00
Established: 1893
Digital Platform - Mobile: Apple, Android
Digital Platform - Tablet: Apple iOS, Android, Windows 7
Adv. Dir. .... Pegy Roberson
Adv. Sales Rep. .... Loren Vega
Gen Mgr. .... Kazia Conway
Pub. .... Hank Hargrave
Mechanical Specifications: Type page 15 3/16 x 21; E - 7 cols, 2 1/16, 1/8 between; A - 7 cols, 2 1/16, 1/8 between; C - 8 cols, 1 13/16, 1/8 between.Equipment & Software: Hardware — APP/Mac; Software — Adobe/PageMaker 4.0.
Delivery Method: Mail, Newsstand, Racks
Areas Served: Falls County

ROTAN

DOUBLE MOUNTAIN CHRONICLE (FRI)

114 E Sammy Baugh Ave, Rotan, TX, 79546-4522, Fisher, USA; gen tel (325) 735-2562; adv tel (325) 735-2562; ed tel (325) 735-2562; gen fax (325) 735-2230; adv fax (325) 735-2230; ed fax (325) 735-2230; disp adv e-mail advertising@dmchronicle.com; class adv e-mail publisher@dmchronicle.com; ed e-mail editor@dmchronicle.com; web site doublemountainchronicle.com
Circulation: 1,038pd,; USPS
Advertising rate: Open inch rate $8.00
Established: 1907
Editor .... Jeff Hurt
Advertising/Reporting .... Kyndra Vaught
Business .... Pat Porter
Delivery Method: Mail, Newsstand
Areas Served: Fisher, Kent & Stonewall Counties

ROUND ROCK

ROUND ROCK LEADER (THUR, SAT)

1111 N Interstate 35, Ste 230, Round Rock, TX, 78664-4244, Williamson, USA; gen tel (512) 255-5827; adv tel (512) 255-5827; ed tel (512) 255-5827; gen fax (512) 248-2736; adv fax (512) 248-2736; ed fax (512) 248-2736; disp adv e-mail editor@rrleader.com; class adv e-mail editor@rrleader.com; ed e-mail editor@rrleader.com; web site www.statesman.com
Circulation: 6,010fr; AAM
Advertising rate: Open inch rate $17.00
Established: 1877
Digital Platform - Mobile: Apple, Android
Digital Platform - Tablet: Apple iOS, Android, Windows 7
Pub. .... Terry Schaub
Ed. .... Brad Stutzman
Classified Rep. .... Michelle Collins
Distribution Mgr. .... Lorna Woeishen
Mechanical Specifications: Type page 13 x 21; E - 6 cols, 2 1/16, 1/6 between; A - 6 cols, 2 1/16, 1/6 between; C - 6 cols, 2 1/16, 1/6 between.Equipment & Software: Hardware — APP/Mac; Presses — 6-G/Community; Software — QPS/QuarkXPress 3.32, Adobe/PageMaker 6.5, Adobe/Photoshop 5.0, Adobe/Illustrator.
Delivery Method: Mail, Newsstand
Areas Served: 78664, 78681, 78680, 78682, 78717, 78729, 78750, 78759

RUSK

CHEROKEEAN HERALD (WED)

140 N Main St, Rusk, TX, 75785-1326, Cherokee, USA; gen tel (903) 683-2257; adv tel (903) 683-2257 ext. 105; ed tel (903) 683-2257 ext. 107; gen fax (903) 683-5104; adv fax (903) 683-5104; ed fax (903) 683-5104; disp adv e-mail advertising@mediactr.com; class adv e-mail classifiedads@mediactr.com ; ed e-mail herald@mediactr.com; web site www.thecherokeean.com
Circulation: 4,500pd, 200fr; Sworn/Estimate/Non-Audited
Advertising rate: Open inch rate $6.75
Established: 1850
Group: Cherokeean Herald KTLU LLC
Digital Platform - Mobile: Apple, Android, Windows, Blackberry
Digital Platform - Tablet: Apple iOS, Android, Windows 7, Blackberry Tablet OS
Pub. .... Marie Whitehead
Ed. .... Terrie Gonzalez
Adv. Dir. .... Robert Gonzalez
Managing Ed. .... Quinten Boyd
Mechanical Specifications: 6 col-11.1528 inches 1 col - 1.7778 gutter.125Equipment & Software: Hardware — APP/Macs; Software — Adobe/InDesign 2.0.
Delivery Method: Mail, Newsstand, Racks
Areas Served: 75785, 75925, 75976, 75766

SAINT JO

THE SAINT JO TRIBUNE (FRI)

105 E Howell St, Saint Jo, TX, 76265-2228, Montague, USA; gen tel (940) 995-2586; adv tel (940) 995-2586; ed tel (940) 995-2586; gen fax (940) 995-2586; adv fax (940) 995-2586; ed fax (940) 995-2586; disp adv e-mail saintjotribune@embarqmail.com; class adv e-mail saintjotribune@embarqmail.com; ed e-mail saintjotribune@embarqmail.com
Circulation: 832pd, 51fr; Sworn/Estimate/Non-Audited
Advertising rate: Open inch rate $5.35
Established: 1898
Co-Pub./Ed. .... C.E. Cole
Co-Pub./Mng. Ed. .... Dee Cole
Delivery Method: Mail, Newsstand
Areas Served: Montague County

SALADO

SALADO VILLAGE VOICE (THUR)

213 Mill Creek Dr, Ste 125, Salado, TX, 76571-4939, Bell, USA; gen tel (254) 947-5321; adv tel (254) 947-5321; ed tel (254) 947-5321; disp adv e-mail advertising@saladovillagevoice.com; class adv e-mail classifieds@saladovillagevoice.com; ed e-mail news@saladovillagevoice.com; web site www.saladovillagevoice.com
Circulation: 1,500pd,; USPS
Advertising rate: Open inch rate $6.00
Established: 1979
Group: Salado Village Voice Inc.
Digital Platform - Mobile: Apple, Android

Digital Platform - Tablet: Apple iOS, Android, Windows 7
Pub./Ed. .... Tim Fleischer
Pub./Adv. Mgr. .... Marilyn Fleischer
Mechanical Specifications: 6 Columns/Print area 10" x 21.5"
Delivery Method: Mail, Newsstand, Racks
Areas Served: Salado, Bell County (76571)

SAN ANTONIO

BROOKS DISCOVERY NEWS (FRI, SUN)

301 Avenue E, San Antonio, TX, 78205-2006, Bexar, USA; gen tel (210) 250-3711; adv tel (210) 250-2500; ed tel (210) 250-3195; gen fax (210) 250-3715; adv fax (210) 250-2565; ed fax (210) 250-3105; disp adv e-mail rca-plan@express-news.net; class adv e-mail communitysupport@express-news.net; ed e-mail editors@express-news.net; web site www.express-news.com
Advertising rate: Open inch rate $346.77
Digital Platform - Mobile: Apple, Android
Digital Platform - Tablet: Apple iOS, Android, Windows 7
Vice Pres., Finance .... Fred Mergele
Vice Pres., HR .... Susan Ehrman
Sales Dir. ...... Rebecca Named Chavez-Becker
Adv. Mgr., Automotive .... Doug Bennight
Adv. Mgr., Telemktg./Classified .... Roxanne Beavers
Adv. Mgr., Telemktg./Retail .... Pat Harvey
Vice Pres., Mktg. .... Dean Aitken
Vice Pres., Mktg. .... Patrick Magallanes
Target Mktg. Mgr. .... Liz English
Circ. Sr. Vice Pres. .... Scott Frantzen
Circ. Dir., Admin. .... Paul Borrego
Dir., Metro Home Delivery .. Sammy Aburumuh
New Publications & Special Projects Ed... Terry Scott-Bertling
Ed. .... Michael Leary
Mng. Ed .... Jamie Stockwell
Mechanical Specifications: Type page 11 5/8 x 21; E - 6 cols, 2 1/16, 1/8 between; A - 6 cols, 2 1/16, 1/8 between; C - 10 cols, 1 5/16, 1/16 between.
Delivery Method: Mail, Newsstand
Areas Served: Bexar County

BULVERDE NEWS (THUR)

301 Avenue E, San Antonio, TX, 78205-2006, Bexar, USA; gen tel (210) 250-3711; adv tel (210) 250-2500; ed tel (210) 250-3195; gen fax (210) 250-3715; adv fax (210) 250-2565; ed fax (210) 250-3105; disp adv e-mail communitysupport@express-news.net; class adv e-mail communitysupport@express-news.net; ed e-mail editors@express-news.net; web site www.express-news.com
Circulation: 35pd, 3,285fr; VAC
Advertising rate: Open inch rate $346.77
Digital Platform - Mobile: Apple, Android
Digital Platform - Tablet: Apple iOS, Android, Windows 7
Pres./Pub. .... Thomas A. Stephenson
Vice Pres., Finance .... Fred Mergele
Vice Pres., HR .... Susan Ehrman
Vice Pres., Classified Adv. .... Charlotte Aaron
Sales Dir. ...... Rebecca Named Chavez-Becker
Adv. Mgr., Automotive .... Doug Bennight
Adv. Mgr., Telemktg./Classified .... Roxanne Beavers
Adv. Mgr., Telemktg./Retail .... Pat Harvey
Vice Pres., Mktg. .... Dean Aitken
Vice Pres., Mktg. .... Patrick Magallanes
Target Mktg. Mgr. .... Liz English
Circ. Sr. Vice Pres. .... Scott Frantzen
Circ. Dir., Admin. .... Paul Borrego
Dir., Metro Home Delivery .. Sammy Aburumuh
Ed. .... Robert Rivard
Mng. Ed .... Brett Thacker
Asst. Mng. Ed., Features.... Terry Scott-Bertling
Asst. Mng. Ed., Graphics/Design/Photo... Hallie Paul
Asst. Mng. Ed., News .... Craig Thomason
Mechanical Specifications: Type page 11 5/8 x 21; E - 6 cols, 2 1/16, 1/8 between; A - 6 cols, 2 1/16, 1/8 between; C - 10 cols, 1 5/16, 1/16 between.
Delivery Method: Mail, Newsstand
Areas Served: Bexar County

FORT SAM NEWS LEADER (THUR)

301 Avenue E, San Antonio, TX, 78205-2006, Bexar, USA; gen tel (210) 250-3000; adv tel (210) 250-2500; ed tel (210) 250-3195; gen fax (210) 221-1198; adv fax (210) 250-2565; ed fax (210) 250-3105; disp adv e-mail USAF.jbsa.502-ABW.Mbx.502-abw-pa@mail.mil; class adv e-mail communitysupport@express-news.net; ed e-mail editors@express-news.net; web site www.express-news.com
Circulation: 0pd, 0fr; VAC
Advertising rate: Open inch rate $346.77
Digital Platform - Mobile: Apple, Android
Digital Platform - Tablet: Apple iOS, Android, Windows 7
Pres./Pub. .... Thomas A. Stephenson
Vice Pres., Finance .... Fred Mergele
Vice Pres., HR .... Susan Ehrman
Vice Pres., Classified Adv. .... Charlotte Aaron
Sales Dir. ...... Rebecca Named Chavez-Becker
Adv. Mgr., Automotive .... Doug Bennight
Adv. Mgr., Telemktg./Classified .... Roxanne Beavers
Adv. Mgr., Telemktg./Retail .... Pat Harvey
Vice Pres., Mktg. .... Dean Aitken
Vice Pres., Mktg. .... Patrick Magallanes
Target Mktg. Mgr. .... Liz English
Circ. Sr. Vice Pres. .... Scott Frantzen
Circ. Dir., Admin. .... Paul Borrego
Dir., Metro Home Delivery .. Sammy Aburumuh
Ed. .... Robert Rivard
Mng. Ed .... Brett Thacker
Asst. Mng. Ed., Features.... Terry Scott-Bertling
Asst. Mng. Ed., Graphics/Design/Photo... Hallie Paul
Asst. Mng. Ed., News .... Craig Thomason
Mechanical Specifications: Type page 11 5/8 x 21; E - 6 cols, 2 1/16, 1/8 between; A - 6 cols, 2 1/16, 1/8 between; C - 10 cols, 1 5/16, 1/16 between.
Delivery Method: Mail, Newsstand
Areas Served: Bexar County

KELLY OBSERVER (THUR)

301 Avenue E, San Antonio, TX, 78205-2006, Bexar, USA; gen tel (210) 250-3711; adv tel (210) 250-2500; ed tel (210) 250-3195; gen fax (210) 250-3715; adv fax (210) 250-2565; ed fax (210) 250-3105; disp adv e-mail communitysupport@express-news.net; class adv e-mail communitysupport@express-news.net; ed e-mail editors@express-news.net; web site www.express-news.com
Circulation: 10pd, 6,934fr; VAC
Advertising rate: Open inch rate $346.77
Digital Platform - Mobile: Apple, Android
Digital Platform - Tablet: Apple iOS, Android, Windows 7
Pres./Pub. .... Thomas A. Stephenson
Vice Pres., Finance .... Fred Mergele
Vice Pres., HR .... Susan Ehrman
Vice Pres., Classified Adv. .... Charlotte Aaron
Sales Dir. ...... Rebecca Named Chavez-Becker
Adv. Mgr., Automotive .... Doug Bennight
Adv. Mgr., Telemktg./Classified .... Roxanne Beavers
Adv. Mgr., Telemktg./Retail .... Pat Harvey
Vice Pres., Mktg. .... Dean Aitken
Vice Pres., Mktg. .... Patrick Magallanes
Target Mktg. Mgr. .... Liz English
Circ. Sr. Vice Pres. .... Scott Frantzen
Circ. Dir., Admin. .... Paul Borrego
Dir., Metro Home Delivery .. Sammy Aburumuh
Ed. .... Robert Rivard
Mng. Ed .... Brett Thacker
Asst. Mng. Ed., Features.... Terry Scott-Bertling
Asst. Mng. Ed., Graphics/Design/Photo... Hallie Paul
Asst. Mng. Ed., News .... Craig Thomason
Mechanical Specifications: Type page 11 5/8 x 21; E - 6 cols, 2 1/16, 1/8 between; A - 6 cols, 2 1/16, 1/8 between; C - 10 cols, 1 5/16, 1/16 between.
Delivery Method: Mail, Newsstand
Areas Served: Bexar County

MEDICAL PATRIOT (THUR)

301 Avenue E, San Antonio, TX, 78205-2006, Bexar, USA; gen tel (210) 250-3711; adv tel (210) 250-2500; ed tel (210) 250-3195; gen fax (210) 250-3715; adv fax (210) 250-2565; ed fax (210) 250-3105; disp adv e-mail communitysupport@express-news.net; class adv e-mail communitysupport@express-news.net; ed e-mail editors@express-news.net; web site www.express-news.com
Circulation: 10pd, 4,898fr; VAC
Advertising rate: Open inch rate $346.77
Digital Platform - Mobile: Apple, Android
Digital Platform - Tablet: Apple iOS, Android, Windows 7
Pres./Pub. .... Thomas A. Stephenson
Vice Pres., Finance .... Fred Mergele
Vice Pres., HR .... Susan Ehrman
Vice Pres., Classified Adv. .... Charlotte Aaron
Sales Dir. ...... Rebecca Named Chavez-Becker
Adv. Mgr., Automotive .... Doug Bennight
Adv. Mgr., Telemktg./Classified .... Roxanne Beavers
Adv. Mgr., Telemktg./Retail .... Pat Harvey
Vice Pres., Mktg. .... Dean Aitken
Vice Pres., Mktg. .... Patrick Magallanes
Target Mktg. Mgr. .... Liz English
Circ. Sr. Vice Pres. .... Scott Frantzen
Circ. Dir., Admin. .... Paul Borrego
Dir., Metro Home Delivery .. Sammy Aburumuh
Ed. .... Robert Rivard
Mng. Ed .... Brett Thacker
Asst. Mng. Ed., Features.... Terry Scott-Bertling
Asst. Mng. Ed., Graphics/Design/Photo... Hallie Paul
Asst. Mng. Ed., News .... Craig Thomason
Mechanical Specifications: Type page 11 5/8 x 21; E - 6 cols, 2 1/16, 1/8 between; A - 6 cols, 2 1/16, 1/8 between; C - 10 cols, 1 5/16, 1/16 between.
Delivery Method: Mail, Newsstand
Areas Served: Bexar County

NORTH CENTRAL NEWS (THUR)

301 Avenue E, San Antonio, TX, 78205-2006, Bexar, USA; gen tel (210) 250-3711; adv tel (210) 250-2500; ed tel (210) 250-3195; gen fax (210) 250-3715; adv fax (210) 250-2565; ed fax (210) 250-3105; disp adv e-mail communitysupport@express-news.net; class adv e-mail communitysupport@express-news.net; ed e-mail editors@express-news.net; web site www.express-news.com
Circulation: 10pd, 28,141fr; VAC
Advertising rate: Open inch rate $346.77
Digital Platform - Mobile: Apple, Android
Digital Platform - Tablet: Apple iOS, Android, Windows 7
Pres./Pub. .... Thomas A. Stephenson
Vice Pres., Finance .... Fred Mergele
Vice Pres., HR .... Susan Ehrman
Vice Pres., Classified Adv. .... Charlotte Aaron
Sales Dir. ...... Rebecca Named Chavez-Becker
Adv. Mgr., Automotive .... Doug Bennight
Adv. Mgr., Telemktg./Classified .... Roxanne Beavers
Adv. Mgr., Telemktg./Retail .... Pat Harvey
Vice Pres., Mktg. .... Dean Aitken
Vice Pres., Mktg. .... Patrick Magallanes
Target Mktg. Mgr. .... Liz English
Circ. Sr. Vice Pres. .... Scott Frantzen
Circ. Dir., Admin. .... Paul Borrego
Dir., Metro Home Delivery .. Sammy Aburumuh
Ed. .... Robert Rivard
Mng. Ed .... Brett Thacker
Asst. Mng. Ed., Features.... Terry Scott-Bertling
Asst. Mng. Ed., Graphics/Design/Photo... Hallie Paul
Asst. Mng. Ed., News .... Craig Thomason
Mechanical Specifications: Type page 11 5/8 x 21; E - 6 cols, 2 1/16, 1/8 between; A - 6 cols, 2 1/16, 1/8 between; C - 10 cols, 1 5/16, 1/16 between.
Delivery Method: Mail, Newsstand
Areas Served: Bexar County

NORTHEAST HERALD (THUR)

301 Avenue E, San Antonio, TX, 78205-2006, Bexar, USA; gen tel (210) 250-3711; adv tel (210) 250-2500; ed tel (210) 250-3195; gen fax (210) 250-3715; adv fax (210) 250-2565; ed fax (210) 250-3105; disp adv e-mail communitysupport@express-news.net; class adv e-mail communitysupport@express-news.net; ed e-mail mleary@express-news.net; web site www.express-news.com
Circulation: 13,990fr; AAM
Advertising rate: Open inch rate $346.77
Digital Platform - Mobile: Apple, Android
Digital Platform - Tablet: Apple iOS, Android, Windows 7
Pres./Pub. .... Thomas A. Stephenson
Vice Pres., Finance .... Fred Mergele
Vice Pres., HR .... Susan Ehrman
Vice Pres., Classified Adv. .... Charlotte Aaron
Sales Dir. ...... Rebecca Named Chavez-Becker
Adv. Mgr., Automotive .... Doug Bennight
Adv. Mgr., Telemktg./Classified .... Roxanne Beavers
Adv. Mgr., Telemktg./Retail .... Pat Harvey
Vice Pres., Mktg. .... Dean Aitken
Vice Pres., Mktg. .... Patrick Magallanes
Target Mktg. Mgr. .... Liz English
Circ. Sr. Vice Pres. .... Scott Frantzen
Circ. Dir., Admin. .... Paul Borrego
Dir., Metro Home Delivery .. Sammy Aburumuh
Ed. .... Robert Rivard
Mng. Ed .... Brett Thacker
Asst. Mng. Ed., Features.... Terry Scott-Bertling
Asst. Mng. Ed., Graphics/Design/Photo... Hallie Paul
Asst. Mng. Ed., News .... Craig Thomason
Mechanical Specifications: Type page 11 5/8 x 21; E - 6 cols, 2 1/16, 1/8 between; A - 6 cols, 2 1/16, 1/8 between; C - 10 cols, 1 5/16, 1/16 between.
Delivery Method: Mail, Newsstand
Areas Served: Bexar County

NORTHWEST WEEKLY (THUR)

301 Avenue E, San Antonio, TX, 78205-2006, Bexar, USA; gen tel (210) 250-3711; adv tel (210) 250-2500; ed tel (210) 250-3195; gen fax (210) 250-3715; adv fax (210) 250-2565; ed fax (210) 250-3105; disp adv e-mail communitysupport@express-news.net; class adv e-mail communitysupport@express-news.net; ed e-mail editors@express-news.net; web site www.express-news.com
Circulation: 10pd, 22,617fr; VAC
Advertising rate: Open inch rate $346.77
Digital Platform - Mobile: Apple, Android
Digital Platform - Tablet: Apple iOS, Android, Windows 7
Pres./Pub. .... Thomas A. Stephenson
Vice Pres., Finance .... Fred Mergele
Vice Pres., HR .... Susan Ehrman
Vice Pres., Classified Adv. .... Charlotte Aaron
Sales Dir. ...... Rebecca Named Chavez-Becker
Adv. Mgr., Automotive .... Doug Bennight
Adv. Mgr., Telemktg./Classified .... Roxanne Beavers
Adv. Mgr., Telemktg./Retail .... Pat Harvey
Vice Pres., Mktg. .... Dean Aitken
Vice Pres., Mktg. .... Patrick Magallanes
Target Mktg. Mgr. .... Liz English
Circ. Sr. Vice Pres. .... Scott Frantzen
Circ. Dir., Admin. .... Paul Borrego
Dir., Metro Home Delivery .. Sammy Aburumuh
Ed. .... Robert Rivard
Mng. Ed .... Brett Thacker
Asst. Mng. Ed., Features.... Terry Scott-Bertling
Asst. Mng. Ed., Graphics/Design/Photo... Hallie Paul
Asst. Mng. Ed., News .... Craig Thomason
Mechanical Specifications: Type page 11 5/8 x 21; E - 6 cols, 2 1/16, 1/8 between; A - 6 cols, 2 1/16, 1/8 between; C - 10 cols, 1 5/16, 1/16 between.
Delivery Method: Mail, Newsstand
Areas Served: Bexar County

RANDOLPH WINGSPREAD (FRI)

301 Avenue E, San Antonio, TX, 78205-2006, Bexar, USA; gen tel (210) 250-3000; adv tel (210) 250-2500; ed tel (210) 250-3195; gen fax (210) 250-3715; adv fax (210) 250-2565; ed fax (210) 250-3105; disp adv e-mail communitysupport@express-news.net; class adv e-mail communitysupport@express-news.net; ed e-mail editors@express-news.net; web site www.express-news.com
Circulation: 0pd, 0fr; VAC
Advertising rate: Open inch rate $346.77
Digital Platform - Mobile: Apple, Android
Digital Platform - Tablet: Apple iOS, Android, Windows 7
Pres./Pub. .... Thomas A. Stephenson
Vice Pres., Finance .... Fred Mergele
Vice Pres., HR .... Susan Ehrman
Vice Pres., Classified Adv. .... Charlotte Aaron
Sales Dir. ...... Rebecca Named Chavez-Becker
Adv. Mgr., Automotive .... Doug Bennight
Adv. Mgr., Telemktg./Classified .... Roxanne Beavers
Adv. Mgr., Telemktg./Retail .... Pat Harvey
Vice Pres., Mktg. .... Dean Aitken

Vice Pres., Mktg..................Patrick Magallanes
Target Mktg. Mgr..............................Liz English
Circ. Sr. Vice Pres.....................Scott Frantzen
Circ. Dir., Admin...........................Paul Borrego
Dir., Metro Home Delivery .. Sammy Aburumuh
Ed..Robert Rivard
Mng. Ed.......................................Brett Thacker
Asst. Mng. Ed., Features.... Terry Scott-Bertling
Asst. Mng. Ed., Graphics/Design/Photo... Hallie Paul
Asst. Mng. Ed., News..............Craig Thomason
Mechanical Specifications: Type page 11 5/8 x 21; E - 6 cols, 2 1/16, 1/8 between; A - 6 cols, 2 1/16, 1/8 between; C - 10 cols, 1 5/16, 1/16 between.
Delivery Method: Mail, Newsstand
Areas Served: Bexar County

SAN ANTONIO BUSINESS JOURNAL (FRI)

8200 W Interstate 10, Ste 820, San Antonio, TX, 78230-3877, Bexar, USA; gen tel (210) 341-3202; adv tel (210) 341-3202; ed tel (210) 341-3202; gen fax (210) 342-4443; adv fax (210) 342-4443; ed fax (210) 342-4443; disp adv e-mail sanantonio@bizjournals.com; class adv e-mail sanantonio@bizjournals.com; ed e-mail sanantonio@bizjournals.com; web site www.bizjournals.com/sanantonio
Advertising rate: Open inch rate $6,815.00 (Full-Page)
Established: 1987
Digital Platform - Mobile: Apple, Android, Windows, Blackberry
Digital Platform - Tablet: Apple iOS, Android, Windows 7, Blackberry Tablet OS, Kindle, Nook, Kindle Fire
Pub...Kent Krauss
Ed...Bill Conroy
Adv. Dir...Mary Jonas
Delivery Method: Mail, Newsstand, Racks
Areas Served: Bexar County

SOUTHSIDE REPORTER (WED)

301 Avenue E, San Antonio, TX, 78205-2006, Bexar, USA; gen tel (210) 250-3000; adv tel (210) 250-2500; ed tel (210) 250-3171; gen fax (210) 250-3105; adv fax (210) 250-3360; ed fax (210) 250-3105; disp adv e-mail dbrennan@primetimenewspapers.com; class adv e-mail dbrennan@primetimenewspapers.com; ed e-mail mleary@express-news.net; web site www.mysanantonio.com
Circulation: 16,352fr; AAM
Advertising rate: Open inch rate $20.75
Established: 1935
Pres.......................................Tom Stephenson
Vice. Pres. Sales........................Johnny Flores
Prodn. Mgr.................................Aunna Wright
Mng. Ed...................................Jamie Stockwell
Mechanical Specifications: 1 column 1.54" 2 column 3.22", 3 column 4.90" 4 column 6.58", 5 column 8.26" 6 column 9.94"Equipment & Software: Hardware — APP/Mac IIci; Software — QPS/QuarkXPress.
Delivery Method: Mail, Carrier, Racks
Areas Served: 78210

SAN AUGUSTINE

SAN AUGUSTINE TRIBUNE (THUR)

807 E Columbia St, San Augustine, TX, 75972-2213, San Augustine, USA; gen tel (936) 275-2181; gen fax (936) 275-0572; disp adv e-mail mail@sanaugustinetribune.com; class adv e-mail mail@sanaugustinetribune.com; ed e-mail mail@sanaugustinetribune.com; web site www.sanaugustinetribune.com
Circulation: 3,000pd, 300fr; Sworn/Estimate/Non-Audited
Advertising rate: Open inch rate $6.00
Established: 1916
Digital Platform - Mobile: Apple, Android, Windows, Blackberry
Digital Platform - Tablet: Apple iOS, Android, Windows 7, Blackberry Tablet OS, Kindle, Nook, Kindle Fire
Pub./Ed./Adv. Dir.........................Stephen Hays
Mechanical Specifications: Type page 13 x 21 1/2; E - 6 cols, 2 1/16, 1/8 between; A - 6 cols, 2 1/16, 1/8 between; C - 8 cols, 1 1/6, between.Equipment & Software: Hardware — PC.
Delivery Method: Mail, Racks
Areas Served: San Augustine County

SAN BENITO

SAN BENITO NEWS (SUN)

PO Box 1791, San Benito, TX, 78586-0017, Cameron, USA; gen tel (956) 399-2436; adv tel (956) 399-2436; ed tel (956) 399-2436; gen fax (956) 399-2430; adv fax (956) 399-2430; ed fax (956) 399-2430; disp adv e-mail publisher@sbnewspaper.com; class adv e-mail publisher@sbnewspaper.com; ed e-mail editor@sbnewspaper.com; web site www.sbnewspaper.com
Circulation: 3,933pd, 231fr; Sworn/Estimate/Non-Audited
Advertising rate: Open inch rate $9.55
Established: 1929
Digital Platform - Mobile: Apple, Android, Windows, Blackberry
Digital Platform - Tablet: Apple iOS, Android, Windows 7, Blackberry Tablet OS, Kindle, Nook, Kindle Fire
Adv. Dir./Circ. Mgr..........................Rudy Pena
Publisher.......................................Ray Quiroga
Mechanical Specifications: Type page 13 1/8 x 21 1/4; E - 6 cols, 2 1/16, between; A - 6 cols, 2 1/16, between; C - 6 cols, 2 1/16, between. Equipment & Software: Hardware — APP/Mac; Presses — 7-KP/News King.
Delivery Method: Mail, Newsstand
Areas Served: San Benito, Rio Hondo, Los Indios, Harlingen Cameron County 78586

SAN SABA

SAN SABA NEWS & STAR (THUR)

505 E Wallace St, San Saba, TX, 76877-3603, San Saba, USA; gen tel (325) 372-5115; adv tel (325) 372-5115; ed tel (325) 372-5115; gen fax (325) 372-3973; adv fax (325) 372-3973; ed fax (325) 372-3973; disp adv e-mail sabanews@centex.net; class adv e-mail sabanews@centex.net; ed e-mail sabanews@centex.net; web site www.sansabanews.com
Circulation: 2,394pd, 70fr; Sworn/Estimate/Non-Audited
Advertising rate: Open inch rate $4.00
Established: 1873
Digital Platform - Mobile: Apple, Android, Windows, Blackberry
Digital Platform - Tablet: Apple iOS, Android, Windows 7, Blackberry Tablet OS, Kindle, Nook, Kindle Fire
Pub..Ken Wesner
Pub./Ed...Karen Faught
Adv. Dir..............................Yvonne Contreras
Delivery Method: Mail, Newsstand
Areas Served: San Saba County

SANGER

SANGER NEWS (THUR)

412 Bolivar St, Sanger, TX, 76266-8961, Denton, USA; gen tel (940) 458-8515; adv tel (940) 458-8515; ed tel (940) 458-8515; gen fax (940) 458-8011; adv fax (940) 458-8011; ed fax (940) 458-8011; disp adv e-mail sanger@lemonspublications.com; class adv e-mail sanger@lemonspublications.com; ed e-mail sanger@lemonspublications.com; web site www.lemonspublications.com
Circulation: 1,513pd,; Sworn/Estimate/Non-Audited
Advertising rate: Open inch rate $5.25
Established: 2012
Group: Lemons Publications
Digital Platform - Mobile: Apple, Android, Windows, Blackberry
Digital Platform - Tablet: Apple iOS, Android, Windows 7, Blackberry Tablet OS, Kindle, Nook, Kindle Fire
Pub...Blake Lemons
Ed./Adv. Dir..........................Lee Ann Lemons
Delivery Method: Mail, Racks
Areas Served: Denton County

SCHULENBURG

THE SCHULENBURG STICKER (THUR)

405 N Main St, Schulenburg, TX, 78956-1561, Fayette, USA; gen tel (979) 743-3450; adv tel (979) 743-3450; ed tel (979) 743-3450; gen fax (979) 743-4609; adv fax (979) 743-4609; ed fax (979) 743-4609; disp adv e-mail stickerads@cmaaccess.com; class adv e-mail stickerads@cmaaccess.com; ed e-mail sticker@cmaaccess.com; web site www.schulenburgsticker.com
Circulation: 2,823pd, 34fr; Sworn/Estimate/Non-Audited
Advertising rate: Open inch rate $3.90 (Local); $5.00 (National)
Established: 1894
Digital Platform - Mobile: Apple, Android, Windows, Blackberry
Digital Platform - Tablet: Apple iOS, Android, Windows 7, Blackberry Tablet OS
Adv. Mgr...................................Carla Riscicar
Ed..Diane Prause
Mng. Ed.....................................Darrell Vyvjala
Mechanical Specifications: Type page 13 x 21; E - 6 cols, 2 1/16, 1/8 between; A - 6 cols, 2 1/16, 1/8 between; C - 6 cols, 2 1/16, 1/8 between.Equipment & Software: Hardware — APP/Mac; Software — Adobe/PageMaker 6.0.
Delivery Method: Mail, Newsstand
Areas Served: Fayette County

SEAGRAVES

TRI COUNTY TRIBUNE (THUR)

202 Main St, Seagraves, TX, 79359, Gaines, USA; gen tel (806) 332-5501; adv tel (806) 332-5501; ed tel (806) 332-5501; gen fax (806) 387-3582; adv fax (806) 387-3582; ed fax (806) 387-3582; disp adv e-mail thetrib@crosswind.net; class adv e-mail thetrib@crosswind.net; ed e-mail thetrib@crosswind.net
Circulation: 229pd,; Sworn/Estimate/Non-Audited
Advertising rate: Open inch rate $3.00
Established: 2001
Pub./Ed./Adv. Dir..............................Lane Mills
Delivery Method: Mail, Newsstand
Areas Served: Gaines County

SEALY

THE SEALY NEWS (THUR)

193 Schmidt Rd, Sealy, TX, 77474-9320, Austin, USA; gen tel (979) 885-3562; adv tel (979) 885-3562; ed tel (979) 885-3562; gen fax (979) 885-3564; adv fax (979) 885-3564; ed fax (979) 885-3564; disp adv e-mail advertising@sealynews.com; class adv e-mail classifieds@sealynews.com; ed e-mail publisher@sealynews.com; web site www.sealynews.com
Circulation: 3,972pd, 94fr; Sworn/Estimate/Non-Audited
Advertising rate: Open inch rate $7.75
Established: 1887
Group: Fenice Community Media
Digital Platform - Mobile: Apple, Android
Digital Platform - Tablet: Apple iOS, Android, Windows 7
Adv. Mgr.......................................Karen Lopez
Mechanical Specifications: Type page 13 x 21 1/2; E - 6 cols, 2 1/16, 1/8 between; A - 6 cols, 2 1/16, 1/8 between; C - 9 cols, 1 3/8, 1/16 between.Equipment & Software: Hardware — APP/Macs, Umax/Scanner; Software — QPS/QuarkXPress 3.31, Microsoft/Word 5.1, Adobe/Photoshop 3.0.4.
Delivery Method: Mail, Newsstand
Areas Served: Austin County

SEMINOLE

SEMINOLE SENTINEL (WED, SUN)

406 S Main St, Seminole, TX, 79360-5058, Gaines, USA; gen tel (432) 758-3667; adv tel (432) 758-3667; ed tel (432) 758-3667; gen fax (432) 758-2136; adv fax (432) 758-2136; ed fax (432) 758-2136; disp adv e-mail ads@seminolesentinel.com; class adv e-mail ads@seminolesentinel.com; ed e-mail news@seminolesentinel.com; web site www.seminolesentinel.com
Circulation: 2,100pd,; Sworn/Estimate/Non-Audited
Advertising rate: Open inch rate $10.00 - $17.00
Established: 1907
Group: Roberts Publishing
Digital Platform - Mobile: Apple, Android
Digital Platform - Tablet: Apple iOS, Android, Windows 7
Ed...Dustin Wright
Office Mgr.................................Christy Hawkins
Adv. Dir.....................................Misty Ramirez
Mechanical Specifications: Type page 13 x 21; E - 4 cols, 3, 1/8 between; A - 6 cols, 2 1/16, between; C - 6 cols, 2 1/16, between. Equipment & Software: Hardware — 8-PC 486s; Software — Adobe/PageMaker 7.0, WordPerfect 6.0.
Delivery Method: Mail, Newsstand, Carrier
Areas Served: Gaines County

SEYMOUR

BAYLOR COUNTY BANNER (THUR)

109 E Morris St, Seymour, TX, 76380-2140, Baylor, USA; gen tel (940) 889-2616; adv tel (940) 889-2616; ed tel (940) 889-2616; gen fax (940) 889-3610; adv fax (940) 889-3610; ed fax (940) 889-3610; disp adv e-mail banner@srcaccess.net; class adv e-mail banner@srcaccess.net; ed e-mail banner@srcaccess.net; web site www.baylorbanner.com
Circulation: 2,500pd, 26fr; Sworn/Estimate/Non-Audited
Advertising rate: Open inch rate $4.00
Established: 1895
Co-Pub.......................................Suzette Gwinn
Co-Pub./Ed....................................Matt Gwinn
Adv. Dir...Lisa Torrez
Mechanical Specifications: Type page 11 5/8 x 21; E - 6 cols, 1 5/6, 1/8 between; A - 6 cols, 1 5/6, 1/8 between; C - 6 cols, 1 5/6, 1/8 between.
Delivery Method: Mail, Racks
Areas Served: Baylor County

SHAMROCK

COUNTY STAR NEWS (THUR)

212 N Main St, Shamrock, TX, 79079-2228, Wheeler, USA; gen tel (806) 256-2070; adv tel (806) 256-2070; ed tel (806) 256-2070; gen fax (806) 256-2071; adv fax (806) 256-2071; ed fax (806) 256-2071; disp adv e-mail Jeff@countystarnews.com; class adv e-mail Jeff@countystarnews.com; ed e-mail thecastrocountynews@yahoo.com; web site www.countystarnews.com
Circulation: 2,400pd,; Sworn/Estimate/Non-Audited
Advertising rate: Open inch rate $5.00
Established: 1993
Digital Platform - Mobile: Apple, Android
Digital Platform - Tablet: Apple iOS, Android, Windows 7
Pub./Ed./Adv. Dir........................Jeff Blackmon
Delivery Method: Mail, Racks
Areas Served: Wheeler County

SHERMAN

TEXOMA MARKETING AND MEDIA GROUP, PUBLISHER OF THE VAN

ALSTYNE LEADER (FRI)

603 S Sam Rayburn Fwy, Sherman, TX, 75090-7258, Grayson, USA; gen tel (903) 893-8181; adv tel 903-893-8181; ed tel 903-893-8181; gen fax NA; adv fax NA; ed fax NA; disp adv e-mail kmason@herald-democrat.com; class adv e-mail jsewell@hearlddemocrat.com; ed e-mail jcannon@heralddemocrat.com; web site www.vanalstyneleader.com
Circulation: 969pd,; Sworn/Estimate/Non-Audited
Advertising rate: Open inch rate $5.00
Established: 1892
Group: texoma marketing and media group
Digital Platform - Mobile: Apple, Android
Digital Platform - Tablet: Apple iOS, Android, Windows 7
Senior Group Publisher .... Nate Rodriguez
Delivery Method: Mail, Newsstand, Racks
Areas Served: Van Alstyne, Howe, and Gunter

THE ANNA-MELISSA TRIBUNE (THUR)

603 S Sam Rayburn Fwy, Sherman, TX, 75090-7258, Grayson, USA; gen tel (903) 893-8181; adv tel (903) 893-8181; ed tel (903) 893-8181; disp adv e-mail gmiller@heralddemocrat.com; class adv e-mail jsewell@heralddemocrat.com; ed e-mail gmiller@heralddemocrat.com; web site www.amtrib.com
Circulation: 9,000fr; Sworn/Estimate/Non-Audited
Advertising rate: Open inch rate $8.50
Established: 2002
Group: texoma marketing and media group
Digital Platform - Mobile: Apple, Android
Digital Platform - Tablet: Apple iOS, Android, Windows 7
senior group publisher............... nate rodriguez
Delivery Method: Newsstand, Carrier, Racks
Areas Served: Anna, Melissa, and Westminster

SHINER

THE SHINER GAZETTE (THUR)

713 N Avenue D, Shiner, TX, 77984-5210, Lavaca, USA; gen tel (361) 594-3346; adv tel (361) 594-3346; ed tel (361) 594-3346; gen fax (361) 594-2655; adv fax (361) 594-2655; ed fax (361) 594-2655; disp adv e-mail shinergazette@sbcglobal.net; class adv e-mail shinergazette@sbcglobal.net; ed e-mail shinergazette@sbcglobal.net
Circulation: 2,250pd,; Sworn/Estimate/Non-Audited
Advertising rate: Open inch rate $11.00
Established: 1892
Mechanical Specifications: Type page 13 x 21; E - 6 cols, 2, 3/16 between; A - 6 cols, 2, 3/16 between; C - 6 cols, 2, 3/16 between.Equipment & Software: Hardware — APP/Mac; Software — Adobe/PageMaker.
Delivery Method: Mail, Newsstand, Racks
Areas Served: Lavaca County

SILSBEE

SILSBEE BEE (WED)

404 Highway 96 S, Silsbee, TX, 77656-4810, Hardin, USA; gen tel (409) 385-5278; adv tel (409) 385-5278; ed tel (409) 385-5278; gen fax (409) 385-5270; adv fax (409) 385-5270; ed fax (409) 385-5270; disp adv e-mail publisher@silsbeebee.com; class adv e-mail publisher@silsbeebee.com; ed e-mail editor@silsbeebee.com; web site www.silsbeebee.com
Circulation: 4,709pd, 25fr; Sworn/Estimate/Non-Audited
Advertising rate: Open inch rate $6.75
Established: 1919
Group: Reneau
Digital Platform - Mobile: Apple, Android, Windows, Blackberry
Digital Platform - Tablet: Apple iOS, Android, Windows 7, Blackberry Tablet OS, Kindle, Nook, Kindle Fire
Pub.. Danny Reneau
Ed. .... Daniel Elizondo
Adv. Dir...................................... Janet Reneau
Delivery Method: Mail, Newsstand
Areas Served: Hardin County

SILVERTON

BRISCOE COUNTY NEWS (WED)

BOX CLOSED, Silverton, TX, 79257-0130, Briscoe, USA; gen tel (806) 823-2333; adv tel (806) 823-2333; ed tel (806) 847-7803; disp adv e-mail briscoenews@gmail.com; class adv e-mail briscoenews@gmail.com; ed e-mail briscoenews@gmail.com; web site www.caprockcourier.com
Circulation: 1,500pd,; Sworn/Estimate/Non-Audited
Advertising rate: Open inch rate $3.00
Established: 1912
Digital Platform - Mobile: Apple, Android, Windows, Blackberry
Digital Platform - Tablet: Apple iOS, Android, Windows 7, Blackberry Tablet OS, Kindle, Nook, Kindle Fire
Pub./Ed.. Sally Arnold
Mng. Ed.................................... Brenda Hutson
Reporter/Photographer......................... Tori Fry
Delivery Method: Mail, Racks
Areas Served: Briscoe, Hall, and Motley County

SINTON

SAN PATRICIO COUNTY NEWS (THUR)

104 N Sehorn St, Sinton, TX, 78387-2550, San Patricio, USA; gen tel (361) 364-1270; adv tel (361) 364-1270; ed tel (361) 364-1270; gen fax (361) 364-3833; adv fax (361) 364-3833; ed fax (361) 364-3833; disp adv e-mail advertising@sanpatpublishing.com; class adv e-mail receptionist@sanpatpublishing.com; ed e-mail editor@sanpatpublishing.com; web site www.sanpatpublishing.com
Circulation: 2,500pd,; Sworn/Estimate/Non-Audited
Advertising rate: Open inch rate $7.55
Established: 1901
Group: San Patricio Publishing Co., Inc.
Digital Platform - Tablet: Windows 7
Co-Pub./Ed. .... James F. Tracy
Co-Pub./Adv. Dir.............................. John Tracy
Mechanical Specifications: Type page 107/8 x 211/2Equipment & Software: Hardware — APP/Mac
Delivery Method: Mail, Newsstand, Racks
Areas Served: San Patricio County

THE ODEM - EDROY TIMES (THUR)

117 S Rachal St, Sinton, TX, 78387-2545, San Patricio, USA; gen tel (361) 364-1270; adv tel (361) 364-1270; ed tel (361) 364-1270; gen fax (361) 364-3833; adv fax (361) 364-3833; ed fax (361) 364-3833; disp adv e-mail advertising@sanpatpublishing.com; class adv e-mail receptionist@sanpatpublishing.com; ed e-mail editor@sanpatpublishing.com; web site www.sanpatpublishing.com
Advertising rate: Open inch rate $5.50
Established: 1948
Digital Platform - Tablet: Windows 7
Co-Pub./Ed. .... James Tracy
Co-Pub./Adv. Dir.............................. John Tracy
Delivery Method: Mail, Newsstand, Racks
Areas Served: San Patricio County

SLATON

THE SLATONITE (THUR)

139 S 9th St, Slaton, TX, 79364-4121, Lubbock, USA; gen tel (806) 828-6201; adv tel (806) 828-6201; ed tel (806) 828-6201; gen fax (806) 828-6202; adv fax (806) 828-6202; ed fax (806) 828-6202; disp adv e-mail slatonite@sbcglobal.net; class adv e-mail slatonite@sbcglobal.net; ed e-mail slatonite@sbcglobal.net; web site www.slatonitenews.com
Circulation: 1,900pd, 25fr; USPS
Advertising rate: Open inch rate $5.35 (Local); $6.25 (National)
Established: 1911
Group: Slaton Media, LLC
Publisher/Ed. .... Ken Richardson
James Villanueva
Mechanical Specifications: New SAUEquipment & Software: Hardware — Mac; Software — Adobe Indesign
Delivery Method: Mail, Racks
Areas Served: 79364, 79366, 79356, 79481

SONORA

DEVIL'S RIVER NEWS (THUR)

224 E Main St, Sonora, TX, 76950-2605, Sutton, USA; gen tel (325) 387-2507; adv tel (325) 387-2507; ed tel (325) 387-2507; gen fax (325) 387-5691; adv fax (325) 387-5691; ed fax (325) 387-5691; disp adv e-mail editor@sonoratx.net; class adv e-mail editor@sonoratx.net; ed e-mail editor@sonoratx.net; web site www.devilsriver.news
Advertising rate: Open inch rate $5.00
Established: 1890
Pub./Ed. .... Ben Taylor
Adv. Dir.................................... Rhonda Wilson
Delivery Method: Mail, Newsstand
Areas Served: Sutton County

SPEARMAN

THE HANSFORD COUNTY REPORTER-STATESMAN (THUR)

213 Main St, Spearman, TX, 79081-2065, Hansford, USA; gen tel 806-659-3434; adv tel (806) 659-3434; ed tel (806) 659-3434; disp adv e-mail reporterstatesman@gmail.com; class adv e-mail reporterstatesman@gmail.com; ed e-mail reporterstatesman@gmail.com; web site www.reporterstatesman.com
Circulation: 1,400pd, 300fr; Sworn/Estimate/Non-Audited
Advertising rate: Open inch rate $5.75
Established: 1901
Digital Platform - Mobile: Apple, Android
Digital Platform - Tablet: Apple iOS, Android
Pub./Ed./Adv. Dir..................... Catherine Smith
Ass. Ed./Phot. .... Ernie BowenEquipment & Software: Hardware — APP/Macs; Software — QuarkXpress 9.0
Delivery Method: Mail, Newsstand, Racks
Areas Served: 79081, 79040, 79062

SPRINGTOWN

SPRINGTOWN EPIGRAPH (WED)

109 E 1ST ST, Springtown, TX, 76082, Parker, USA; gen tel (817) 220-7217; adv tel (817) 220-7217; ed tel (817) 270-3370; gen fax (817) 523-4457; adv fax (817) 270-5300; ed fax (817) 270-5300; disp adv e-mail publisher@azlenews.net; class adv e-mail kimware@azlenews.net; ed e-mail markcampbell@azlenews.net; web site www.springtown-epigraph.net/
Circulation: 2,000pd, 10fr; Sworn/Estimate/Non-Audited
Advertising rate: Open inch rate $8.50
Established: 1964
Digital Platform - Mobile: Apple
Digital Platform - Tablet: Apple iOS
Pub./Adv. Dir. .... Kim Ware
Ed. .... Mark Campbell
Delivery Method: Mail, Newsstand, Racks
Areas Served: 76020, 76023, 76073, 76082, 76085, 76087, 76088, 76098, 76487

SPUR

THE TEXAS SPUR (THUR)

PO Box 430, Spur, TX, 79370-0430, Dickens, USA; gen tel (806) 271-3381; adv tel (806) 271-3381; ed tel (806) 271-3381; gen fax (806) 271-3966; adv fax (806) 271-3966; ed fax (806) 271-3966; disp adv e-mail display@thetexasspur.com; class adv e-mail classified@thetexasspur.com; ed e-mail news@thetexasspur.com; web site www.thetexasspur.com
Circulation: 1,200pd,; Sworn/Estimate/Non-Audited
Advertising rate: Open inch rate $4.60
Established: 1909
Digital Platform - Mobile: Apple
Pub.. Cindi Taylor
Asst. Ed./Adv. Dir.
Kassi AtkinsonEquipment & Software: Hardware — APP/Mac; Software — Adobe InDesign
Delivery Method: Mail, Newsstand
Areas Served: 79220, 79370, 79229, 79518, 79528, 79243

STAFFORD

FORT BEND STAR (WED)

3944 Bluebonnet Dr, Stafford, TX, 77477-3952, Fort Bend, USA; gen tel (281) 690-4200; adv tel (281) 690-4200; ed tel (281) 690-4200; gen fax (281) 690-4250; adv fax (281) 690-4250; ed fax (281) 690-4250; disp adv e-mail ads@fortbendstar.com; class adv e-mail starnews@fortbendstar.com; ed e-mail starnews@fortbendstar.com; web site www.fortbendstar.com
Circulation: 200pd, 34,775fr; VAC
Advertising rate: Open inch rate $22.00
Digital Platform - Mobile: Apple, Android, Windows, Blackberry
Digital Platform - Tablet: Apple iOS, Android, Windows 7, Blackberry Tablet OS
Pub.................................. Michael Fredrickson
Ed. .... Jean Sandlin
Acct. Exec. .... B.K. Carter
Mechanical Specifications: Type page 13 x 21 1/2; E - 6 cols, 2 1/16, between; A - 6 cols, 2 1/16, between; C - 10 cols, 1 1/6, 1/12 between.Equipment & Software: Hardware — APP/Mac, COM; Software — Adobe/PageMaker, QPS/QuarkXPress.
Delivery Method: Mail, Newsstand, Racks
Areas Served: Fort Bend County

STAMFORD

THE NEW STAMFORD AMERICAN (FRI)

102 S Swenson St, Stamford, TX, 79553-4624, Jones, USA; gen tel (325) 773-5550; adv tel (325) 773-5550; ed tel (325) 773-5550; gen fax (325) 773-5551; adv fax (325) 773-5551; ed fax (325) 773-5551; disp adv e-mail ads@stamfordamerican.net; class adv e-mail cmetler@stamfordamerican.net; ed e-mail editor@stamfordamerican.net; web site www.stamfordamerican.net
Circulation: 526pd,; Sworn/Estimate/Non-Audited
Advertising rate: Open inch rate $4.20
Established: 2009
Digital Platform - Mobile: Apple, Android
Digital Platform - Tablet: Apple iOS, Android, Windows 7
Pub.................................. Callie Metler-Smith
Adv. Dir./Ed. .... Debbie Heald
Ed. .... Jennifer Prichard
Delivery Method: Mail, Newsstand
Areas Served: Jones County

THE STAMFORD STAR (FRI)

202 E Hamilton St, Stamford, TX, 79553-4730, Jones, USA; gen tel (325) 773-5100; adv tel (325) 773-5100; ed tel (325) 773-5100; gen fax (325) 773-5105; adv fax (325) 773-5105; ed fax (325) 773-5105; disp adv e-mail audra@thestamfordstar.com; class adv e-mail cheyenne@thestamfordstar.com; ed e-mail cheyenne@thestamfordstar.com; web site www.thestamfordstar.com
Circulation: 1,500pd, 200fr; Sworn/Estimate/Non-Audited
Advertising rate: Open inch rate $5.00
Established: 2006
Group: The Stamford StarEditions: (1) The Haskell Star
Digital Platform - Mobile: Apple, Windows

Digital Platform - Tablet: Windows 7
Pub./Ed. .... Cheyenne Bereuter
Adv. Dir. .... Audra Arendall
Delivery Method: Mail, Newsstand, Racks
Areas Served: Stamford, Jones County and Haskell, Haskell County

STANTON

MARTIN COUNTY MESSENGER (THUR)

210 Saint Peter, Stanton, TX, 79782, Martin, USA; gen tel (432) 756-2090; adv tel (432) 756-2090; ed tel (432) 756-2090; disp adv e-mail ncmessenger@crcom.net; class adv e-mail ncmessenger@crcom.net; ed e-mail ncmessenger@crcom.net; web site www.martincountymessenger.com
Circulation: 1,500pd,; Sworn/Estimate/Non-Audited
Advertising rate: Open inch rate $4.90
Established: 1925
Pub./Ed. .... Bob Dillard
Adv. Dir. .... David Butler
Delivery Method: Mail, Newsstand
Areas Served: Martin County

STEPHENVILLE

GLEN ROSE REPORTER (FRI)

702 E South Loop, Stephenville, TX, 76401-5314, Erath, USA; gen tel (254) 897-2282; adv tel (225)323-4383; ed tel (254)965-3124; gen fax (254) 897-9423; adv fax (254)897-9423; ed fax (254)897-9423; disp adv e-mail advertising@theglenrosereporter.com; class adv e-mail advertising@theglenrosereporter.com; ed e-mail news@theglenrosereporter.com; web site www.yourglenrosetx.com
Circulation: 3,000pd,; Sworn/Estimate/Non-Audited
Advertising rate: Open inch rate $2.55
Established: 1887
Group: GateHouse Media, Inc.
Digital Platform - Mobile: Apple, Android, Windows, Blackberry
Digital Platform - Tablet: Apple iOS, Android, Windows 7, Blackberry Tablet OS, Kindle, Nook, Kindle Fire
Gen. Mgr. .... Todd Franz
Sports Ed. .... Tye Chandler
Adv. Exec. .... Haley Thompson
Mng. Ed. .... Travis Smith
Delivery Method: Mail, Newsstand, Racks
Areas Served: Somervell County

STRATFORD

STRATFORD STAR (THUR)

805 Purnell Ave, Stratford, TX, 79084-5006, Sherman, USA; gen tel (806) 366-5885; adv tel (806) 366-5885; ed tel (806) 366-5885; gen fax (806) 366-5884; adv fax (806) 366-5884; ed fax (806) 366-5884; disp adv e-mail stardm@xit.net; class adv e-mail stardm@xit.net; ed e-mail stardm@xit.net
Circulation: 529pd,; Sworn/Estimate/Non-Audited
Advertising rate: Open inch rate $3.50
Established: 1901
Pub./Ed. .... Martha Robertson
Delivery Method: Mail
Areas Served: Sherman County

TAHOKA

LYNN COUNTY NEWS (THUR)

1617 Main St, Tahoka, TX, 79373, Lynn, USA; gen tel (806) 561-4888; adv tel (806) 561-4888; ed tel (806) 561-4888; gen fax (806) 561-6308; adv fax (806) 561-6308; ed fax (806) 561-6308; disp adv e-mail LCNpam@poka.com; class adv e-mail LCNpam@poka.com; ed e-mail lynnconews@poka.com
Circulation: 1,150pd, 10fr; Sworn/Estimate/Non-Audited
Advertising rate: Open inch rate $5.25
Established: 1903
Pub .... Juanell Jones
Mechanical Specifications: Type page 11.6 x 21; E - 6 cols, 1.75, 1/6 between; A - 6 cols, 1.75, 1/6 between; C - 6 cols, 1.75, 1/6 between. Equipment & Software: Hardware — APP/iMac; Software — Adobe/Creative Suite 5.1
Delivery Method: Mail, Newsstand
Areas Served: Lynn County

TATUM

TRAMMEL TRACE TRIBUNE (THUR, MTHLY)

245 W Johnson St, Tatum, TX, 75691, Rusk, USA; gen tel (903) 240-9226; adv tel (903) 240-9226; ed tel (903) 240-9226; disp adv e-mail info@tatumnews.com; class adv e-mail info@tatumnews.com; ed e-mail info@tatumnews.com
Circulation: 560pd, 440fr; Sworn/Estimate/Non-Audited
Advertising rate: Open inch rate $5.00
Established: 1976
Pub. .... Amy Haden
Co-Pub./Ed./Adv. Dir. .... Byron Haden
Delivery Method: Mail, Newsstand
Areas Served: Rusk County

TAYLOR

TAYLOR PRESS (WED, SUN)

211 W 3rd St, Taylor, TX, 76574-3518, Williamson, USA; gen tel (512) 3528535; disp adv e-mail publisher@taylorpress.net; ed e-mail news@taylorpress.net; web site www.taylorpress.net - 110,000(views) 40,000(visitors)
Circulation: 2,233pd, 172fr; CVC
Advertising rate: Open inch rate $9.75
Established: 1911
Group: Fenice Community Media
Digital Platform - Mobile: Apple
Prodn. Mgr., Pre-press .... Grace Rangel
Adv. Mgr. .... Scott Rucker
Pub./Ed. .... Richard Stone
News Ed. .... Jason Hennington
Mechanical Specifications: Type page 10 x 21; E - 6 cols, 2 1/16, 1/8 between; A - 6 cols, 2 1/16, 1/8 between; C - 9 cols, 1 3/8, 1/16 between.
Delivery Method: Mail, Newsstand, Racks
Areas Served: AUSTIN—SAN MARCOS, TX MSA

THE HUTTO NEWS (WED)

211 W 3rd St, Taylor, TX, 76574-3518, Williamson, USA; gen tel (512) 578-5229; adv tel (512)578-5229; ed tel (512)578-5229; gen fax (512) 352-2227; adv fax (512)352-2227; ed fax (512)352-2227; disp adv e-mail scott@taylorpress.net; class adv e-mail classified@taylorpress.net; ed e-mail scott@taylorpress.net; web site www.thehuttonews.com
Circulation: 100pd, 6,500fr; Sworn/Estimate/Non-Audited
Advertising rate: Open inch rate $7.00
Group: Fenice Community Media
Digital Platform - Mobile: Apple, Android
Digital Platform - Tablet: Apple iOS, Android
Classified Adv. Mgr. .... Laura Bachmeyer
Adv. .... Scott Rucker
Sports Ed. .... Reagan Roehl
Pub. .... Richard Stone
Mechanical Specifications: Type page 11 5/8 x 21 1/2; E - 6 cols, between; A - 6 cols, between; C - 6 cols, between.
Delivery Method: Carrier, Racks
Areas Served: Williamson County

TEAGUE

TEAGUE CHRONICLE (THUR)

319 Main St, Teague, TX, 75860-1621, Freestone, USA; gen tel (254) 739-2141; adv tel (254) 739-2141; ed tel (254) 739-2141; gen fax (254) 739-2144; adv fax (254) 739-2144; ed fax (254) 739-2144; disp adv e-mail teaguechronicle@sbcglobal.net; class adv e-mail teaguechronicle@sbcglobal.net; ed e-mail teaguechronicle@sbcglobal.net; web site www.teaguechronicle.com
Circulation: 2,500pd,; Sworn/Estimate/Non-Audited
Advertising rate: Open inch rate $4.25
Established: 1906
Digital Platform - Mobile: Apple, Android
Digital Platform - Tablet: Apple iOS, Android, Windows 7
Pub./Ed. .... Steve Massey
Adv. Mgr. .... Paula Swinburn
Mechanical Specifications: Type page 13 x 21; E - 6 cols, 2 1/16, 1/8 between; A - 6 cols, 2 1/16, 1/8 between; C - 6 cols, 2 1/16, 1/8 between.
Delivery Method: Mail, Newsstand, Racks
Areas Served: Freestone County

TERRELL

THE TERRELL TRIBUNE (WED, SAT)

150 9th St, Terrell, TX, 75160-3061, Kaufman, USA; gen tel (972) 563-6476; adv tel (972) 563-6476; ed tel (972) 563-6476; gen fax (972) 563-0340; adv fax (972) 563-0340; ed fax (972) 563-0340; disp adv e-mail pbarringer@terrelltribune.com; class adv e-mail classifieds@terrelltribune.com; ed e-mail news@terrelltribune.com; web site www.terrelltribune.com
Circulation: 2,300pd, 10,500fr; Sworn/Estimate/Non-Audited
Advertising rate: Open inch rate $11.00
Established: 1898
Group: Van Zandt Newspapers, LLC
Digital Platform - Mobile: Apple, Android, Windows, Blackberry
Digital Platform - Tablet: Apple iOS, Android, Blackberry Tablet OS, Kindle, Kindle Fire
Bus Mgr/Circu/Inserts .... Vickie Painter
Mechanical Specifications: Type page 11.625 x 21, 6 cols.
Delivery Method: Mail, Newsstand, Carrier, Racks
Areas Served: DALLAS—FORT WORTH, TX CMSA

THREE RIVERS

THE PROGRESS (WED)

501 N Harborth Ave., Suite D, Three Rivers, TX, 78071, Live Oak, USA; gen tel (361)786-3022; adv tel (361) 343-5214; ed tel (361) 786-3022; disp adv e-mail theprogress@mysoutex.com; class adv e-mail sales4@mysoutex.com; ed e-mail theprogress@mysoutex.com; web site www.mysoutex.com
Circulation: 3,173pd, 13fr; Sworn/Estimate/Non-Audited
Advertising rate: Open inch rate $5.50
Established: 1928
Group: Beeville Publishing Co. Inc.
Digital Platform - Mobile: Apple, Android
Digital Platform - Tablet: Apple iOS, Android, Windows 7
Office Manager .... Delia Soto
Mechanical Specifications: Type page 13 x 21 1/4; E - 6 cols, 2, 1/4 between; A - 6 cols, 2, 1/4 between; C - 6 cols, 2, 1/4 between.
Delivery Method: Mail, Newsstand, Racks
Areas Served: Live Oak County, McMullen County

THROCKMORTON

THROCKMORTON TRIBUNE (THUR)

140 N Minter Ave, Ste 109, Throckmorton, TX, 76483-5344, Throckmorton, USA; gen tel (940) 849-0147; adv tel (940) 849-0147; ed tel (940) 849-0147; gen fax (940) 849-0149; adv fax (940) 849-0149; ed fax (940) 849-0149; disp adv e-mail throckmortontribune@gmail.com; class adv e-mail throckmortontribune@gmail.com; ed e-mail throckmortontribune@gmail.com
Circulation: 1,051pd, 214fr; Sworn/Estimate/Non-Audited
Advertising rate: Open inch rate $14.00
Established: 1886
Pub./Ed. .... Dobbi Makovy
Mechanical Specifications: Type page 13 1/4 x 21; E - 6 cols, 2, between.
Delivery Method: Mail
Areas Served: Throckmorton, Woodson, and Elbert in Throckmorton County

TIMPSON

TIMPSON & TENAHA NEWS (THUR)

150 Park Plz, Timpson, TX, 75975, Shelby, USA; gen tel (936) 254-3618; gen fax (936) 254-3206; disp adv e-mail ttnews@ttnewsinc.com; class adv e-mail ttnews@ttnewsinc.com; ed e-mail ttnews@ttnewsinc.com; web site www.ttnewsinc.com
Circulation: 2,001pd, 6fr; USPS
Advertising rate: Open inch rate $6.00
Established: 1885
Digital Platform - Mobile: Apple
Digital Platform - Tablet: Apple iOS
Ed./Pub. .... Hilda Pena
Adv. Mgr. .... Rhonda Samford
Delivery Method: Mail, Racks
Areas Served: Predominately Shelby, Nacogdoches, and Panola County, but we have subscribers thruout Texas and even other states

TRENTON

TRENTON TRIBUNE (THUR)

115 Hamilton St, Trenton, TX, 75490-2610, Fannin, USA; gen tel (903) 989-2325; adv tel (903) 989-2325; ed tel (903) 989-2325; gen fax (903) 989-2923; adv fax (903) 989-2923; ed fax (903) 989-2923; disp adv e-mail trentontribune@texoma.net; class adv e-mail trentontribune@texoma.net; ed e-mail trentontribune@texoma.net; web site www.texomaliving.com
Circulation: 1,215pd,; Sworn/Estimate/Non-Audited
Advertising rate: Open inch rate $4.00
Pub./Ed./Adv. Dir. .... Tom M. Holmes
Delivery Method: Mail
Areas Served: Fannin County

TRINITY

THE TRINITY STANDARD (THUR)

106 E Main St, Trinity, TX, 75862, Trinity, USA; gen tel (936) 594-2126; adv tel (936) 594-2126; ed tel (936) 594-2126; gen fax (936) 594-7547; adv fax (936) 594-7547; ed fax (936) 594-7547; disp adv e-mail trinity.standard@gmail.com; class adv e-mail trinity.standard@gmail.com; ed e-mail trinity.standard@gmail.com; web site www.easttexasnews.com
Circulation: 2,800pd,; Sworn/Estimate/Non-Audited
Advertising rate: Open inch rate $5.30
Established: 1928
Group: Polk County Publishing Co.
Digital Platform - Mobile: Apple, Android
Digital Platform - Tablet: Apple iOS, Android, Windows 7
Pub. .... Alvin Holley
Ed. .... Gregory Peak
Adv. Mgr. .... Linda Holley
Office Mgr. .... Mary McClure
Mechanical Specifications: Type page 13 x 21; E - 6 cols, between; A - 6 cols, between; C - 6 cols, between.
Delivery Method: Mail, Newsstand, Racks
Areas Served: Trinity County

TULIA

SWISHER COUNTY NEWS (THUR)
109 S Austin Ave, Tulia, TX, 79088-2802, Swisher, USA; gen tel (806) 995-0052; adv tel (806) 995-0052; ed tel (806) 995-0052; ed fax (806) 995-0011
Circulation: 1,184pd,; Sworn/Estimate/Non-Audited
Advertising rate: Open inch rate $5.00
Established: 2009
Digital Platform - Mobile: ApplePatrice Sims
Delivery Method: Mail, Racks
Areas Served: Swisher County

TURKEY

MOTLEY COUNTY TRIBUNE (THUR)
904 Childress Ave, Turkey, TX, 79261-2022, Hall, USA; gen tel (806) 402-0120; adv tel (806) 402-0120; ed tel (806) 402-0120; disp adv e-mail caprockcourier@gmail.com; class adv e-mail caprockcourier@gmail.com; ed e-mail caprockcourier@gmail.com
Circulation: 669pd,; Sworn/Estimate/Non-Audited
Advertising rate: Open inch rate $5.00
Established: 1891
Ed .... Tori Minick
Delivery Method: Mail, Newsstand
Areas Served: 79244, 79256, 79255, 79261, 79248

TUSCOLA

THE JIM NED JOURNAL (THUR)
334 Butterfield Trail Rd, Tuscola, TX, 79562-2566, Taylor, USA; gen tel (325) 572-3716; adv tel (325) 572-3716; ed tel (325) 572-3716; gen fax (325) 480-4196; adv fax (325) 480-4196; ed fax (325) 480-4196; disp adv e-mail jimnedjournal@taylortel.net; class adv e-mail jimnedjournal@taylortel.net; ed e-mail jimnedjournal@taylortel.net
Circulation: 440pd,; Sworn/Estimate/Non-Audited
Advertising rate: Open inch rate $5.15
Established: 1986
Pub./Ed. .... Bill Broyles
Adv. Dir. .... Grace Broyles
Delivery Method: Mail
Areas Served: Taylor County

UVALDE

UVALDE LEADER-NEWS (THUR, SUN)
110 N East St, Uvalde, TX, 78801-5312, Uvalde, USA; gen tel (830) 278-3335; gen fax (830) 278-9191; disp adv e-mail sbalke@uvaldeleadernews.com; class adv e-mail nybarra@uvaldeleadernews.com; ed e-mail cgarnett@uvaldeleadernews.com; web site www.uvaldeleadernews.com
Circulation: 4,741pd,; Sworn/Estimate/Non-Audited
Advertising rate: Open inch rate $10.00
Established: 1879
Digital Platform - Mobile: Apple, Android, Windows, Blackberry
Digital Platform - Tablet: Apple iOS, Android, Windows 7, Blackberry Tablet OS, Kindle, Nook, Kindle Fire
Pub./Ed. .... Craig Garnett
Adv. Dir. .... Steve Balke
Managing Ed. .... Meghann Garcia
Delivery Method: Mail, Newsstand, Racks
Areas Served: Uvalde County

VALLEY MILLS

VALLEY MILLS PROGRESS (THUR)
403 E Avenue A, Valley Mills, TX, 76689-4424, Bosque, USA; gen tel (254) 932-6450; adv tel (254) 932-6450; ed tel (254) 932-6450; gen fax (254) 932-6450; adv fax (254) 932-6450; ed fax (254) 932-6450; disp adv e-mail vmprogress.tx@gmail.com; class adv e-mail vmprogress.tx@gmail.com; ed e-mail vmprogress.tx@gmail.com; web site none
Circulation: 675pd,; Sworn/Estimate/Non-Audited
Advertising rate: Open inch rate $7.00
Established: 1989
Pub./Ed./Adv. Dir. .... Mark Grear
Delivery Method: Mail, Racks
Areas Served: Bosque County

VAN HORN

THE VAN HORN ADVOCATE (THUR)
701 W Broadway, Van Horn, TX, 79855, Culberson, USA; gen tel (432) 283-2003; adv tel (432) 283-2003; ed tel (432) 283-2003; gen fax (432) 283-1070; adv fax (432) 283-1070; ed fax (432) 283-1070; disp adv e-mail Lmorton@thevanhornadvocate.com; class adv e-mail Lmorton@thevanhornadvocate.com; ed e-mail rmorales@thevanhornadvocate.com; web site www.thevanhornadvocate.com
Circulation: 985pd,; Sworn/Estimate/Non-Audited
Advertising rate: Open inch rate $7
Established: 1910
Digital Platform - Tablet: Windows 7
Pub./Ed. .... Robert Morales
Adv. Dir. .... Lisa Morton
Delivery Method: Mail, Racks
Areas Served: Culberson County

VEGA

VEGA ENTERPRISE (THUR)
116 S Main St, Vega, TX, 79092, Oldham, USA; gen tel (806) 267-2230; adv tel (806) 267-2230; ed tel (806) 267-2230; gen fax (806) 267-2889; adv fax (806) 267-2889; ed fax (806) 267-2889; disp adv e-mail vegaent@arn.net; class adv e-mail vegaent@arn.net; ed e-mail vegaent@arn.net
Circulation: 900pd,; Sworn/Estimate/Non-Audited
Advertising rate: Open inch rate $3.20
Established: 1948
Pub./Ed./Adv. Dir. .... Quincy Taylor
Delivery Method: Mail
Areas Served: Oldham County

VIDOR

VIDOR VIDORIAN (THUR)
450 W Bolivar St, Vidor, TX, 77662-4724, Orange, USA; gen tel (409) 769-5428; adv tel (409) 769-5428; ed tel (409) 769-5428; gen fax (409) 769-2600; adv fax (409) 769-2600; ed fax (409) 769-2600; disp adv e-mail vidorian1@sbcglobal.net; class adv e-mail vidorian1@sbcglobal.net; ed e-mail vidorian1@sbcglobal.net
Circulation: 1,502pd, 11,275fr; Sworn/Estimate/Non-Audited
Advertising rate: Open inch rate $5.00
Established: 1959
Pub. .... Adair Luker
Ed./Adv. Dir. .... Randall Luker
Mechanical Specifications: Type page 13 x 21; E - 6 cols, 1 13/16, 1/8 between; A - 6 cols, 1 13/16, 1/8 between; C - 9 cols, 1, 1/8 between.Equipment & Software: Hardware — APP/Mac 7200-120; Presses — 6-KP; Software — QPS/QuarkXPress 3.2.
Delivery Method: Mail, Racks
Areas Served: 77662, 77630

WACO

RIESEL RUSTLER (FRI)
412 S 16th St, Waco, TX, 76706-1802, McLennan, USA; gen tel (254) 753-3871; adv tel (254) 753-3871; ed tel (254) 753-3871; gen fax (254) 753-3884; adv fax (254) 753-3884; ed fax (254) 753-3884; disp adv e-mail rustler@jonesprint.com; class adv e-mail rustler@jonesprint.com; ed e-mail rustler@jonesprint.com
Circulation: 564pd,; Sworn/Estimate/Non-Audited
Advertising rate: Open inch rate $4.25
Established: 1896
Pub./Adv. Dir. .... Roger Jones
Ed. .... Becky Wiese
Delivery Method: Mail
Areas Served: McLennan County

WALLIS

WALLIS NEWS-REVIEW (THUR)
256 Cedar St, Wallis, TX, 77485-9787, Austin, USA; gen tel (979) 478-6412; adv tel (979) 478-6412; ed tel (979) 478-6412; ed fax (979) 478-2198; disp adv e-mail joanie@wallisnews.com; class adv e-mail joanie@wallisnews.com; ed e-mail johnny@wallisnews.com; web site www.wallisnews.com
Circulation: 800pd, 25fr; USPS
Advertising rate: Open inch rate $6.00
Established: 1974
Digital Platform - Mobile: Apple, Android, Windows, Blackberry
Digital Platform - Tablet: Apple iOS, Android, Windows 7, Blackberry Tablet OS, Kindle, Nook, Kindle Fire
Pub./Adv. Dir. .... Joanie Griffin
Ed. .... Johnny Griffin
Mechanical Specifications: Type page 13 x 21; E - 6 cols, 2 1/8, between; A - 6 cols, 2 1/8, between.Equipment & Software: ; Software — Adobe/PageMaker.
Delivery Method: Mail, Newsstand
Areas Served: Austin County

WAXAHACHIE

THE MIDLOTHIAN MIRROR (WED)
200 W Marvin Ave, Waxahachie, TX, 75165-3040, Ellis, USA; gen tel (972) 775-3322; adv tel (972) 775-3322; ed tel (972) 775-3322; gen fax (972) 775-4669; adv fax (972) 775-4669; ed fax (972) 775-4669; disp adv e-mail news@midlothianmirror.com; class adv e-mail midlothianmirror@sbcglobal.net; ed e-mail bkurtz@waxahachietx.com; web site www.midlothianmirror.com
Circulation: 6,000pd,; Sworn/Estimate/Non-Audited
Advertising rate: Open inch rate $14.17
Established: 1882
Digital Platform - Mobile: Apple, Android, Windows, Blackberry
Digital Platform - Tablet: Apple iOS, Android, Windows 7, Blackberry Tablet OS, Kindle, Nook, Kindle Fire
Pub./Rgl Mgr. .... Jeffrey Parra
Ed. .... Neal White
Adv. Mgr. .... Donna McFarland
Circ. Mgr. .... Brian Jones
Adv. Sales Rep. .... Larissa Hinton
Mechanical Specifications: Type page 13 x 21; E - 6 cols, 1 5/6, between; A - 10 cols, 1 2/25, between; C - 6 cols, 1 5/6, between. Equipment & Software: Hardware — APP/Mac; Presses — 6-G/Community; Software — QPS/QuarkXPress 3.2.
Delivery Method: Mail, Racks
Areas Served: Ellis County

WEBSTER

BAY AREA CITIZEN (THUR)
12554 Highway 3, Webster, TX, 77598-5426, Harris, USA; gen tel (281) 378-1920; adv tel (281) 378-1922; ed tel (281) 378-1930; gen fax (281) 668-1103; adv fax (281) 668-1103; ed fax (281) 668-1103; disp adv e-mail cwentz@hcnonline.com; class adv e-mail cwentz@hcnonline.com; ed e-mail jmolony@hcnonline.com; web site www.YourBayAreaNews.com
Circulation: 28,523fr; CVC
Advertising rate: $14.25
Established: 1961
Group: Hearst Communications, Inc.
Times Media Group
Digital Platform - Mobile: Apple, Android, Windows
Digital Platform - Tablet: Apple iOS, Android, Windows 7
Pub. .... Brenda Miller-Fergerson
Ed. .... Jim Molony
Adv. Dir. .... Charles Lee
Advt Sales Mgr .... Cheryl Wentz
Mechanical Specifications: 10.388" x 20.5"
Delivery Method: Carrier, Racks
Areas Served: 77058, 77059, 77062, 77573, 77586, 77598

DEER PARK BROADCASTER (THUR)
12554 Highway 3, Webster, TX, 77598-5426, Harris, USA; gen tel (281) 378-1920; disp adv e-mail cwentz@hcnonline.com; class adv e-mail clee@hcnonline.com; ed e-mail jmolony@hcnonline.com; web site http://www.yourhoustonnews.com/deer_park/
Circulation: 11,100fr; CVC
Group: Hearst Communications, Inc.
Times Media Group
Pub .... Brenda Miller-Fergerson
Advt Sales Mgr .... Cheryl Wentz
Delivery Method: Carrier

PASADENA CITIZEN (THUR, SUN)
12554 Highway 3, Webster, TX, 77598-5426, Harris, USA; gen tel (281) 378-1920; adv tel (281) 378-1922; ed tel (281) 378-1930; gen fax (281) 922-4499; adv fax (281) 922-4499; ed fax (281) 922-4499; disp adv e-mail cwentz@hcnonline.com; class adv e-mail cwentz@hcnonline.com; ed e-mail jmolony@hcnonline.com; web site www.YourPasadenaNews.com
Circulation: 3,472pd, 10,000fr; CVC
Advertising rate: $14.25
Established: 1947
Group: Hearst Communications, Inc.
Times Media Group
Digital Platform - Mobile: Apple, Android, Windows
Digital Platform - Tablet: Apple iOS, Android, Windows 7
Pub. .... Brenda Miller-Fergerson
Ed. .... Jim Molony
Adv. Dir. .... Charles Lee
Advt Sales Mgr .... Cheryl Wentz
Mechanical Specifications: 10.388" x 20.5"
Delivery Method: Mail, Carrier, Racks
Areas Served: 77017, 77502, 77503, 77504, 77505, 77506, 77536, 77587

WEIMAR

THE WEIMAR MERCURY (THUR)
200 W Main St, Weimar, TX, 78962-2013, Colorado, USA; gen tel (979) 725-9595; gen fax (979) 725-9051; disp adv e-mail mercuryads@weimarmercury.com; class adv e-mail mercuryads@weimarmercury.com; ed e-mail mercury@weimarmercury.com; web site www.weimarmercury.com
Circulation: 3,205pd, 146fr; Sworn/Estimate/Non-Audited
Advertising rate: Open inch rate $3.40
Established: 1888
Digital Platform - Mobile: Apple, Android
Digital Platform - Tablet: Apple iOS, Android, Windows 7
Pub./Ed./Adv. Dir. .... Bruce Beal
Mechanical Specifications: Type page 13 x 21; E - 6 cols, 2, 1/3 between; A - 6 cols, 2, 1/3 between; C - 6 cols, 2, 1/3 between.
Delivery Method: Mail, Newsstand, Racks
Areas Served: Colorado County

WESLACO

THE MID-VALLEY TOWN CRIER (THUR, SUN)
401 S Kansas Ave, Ste C2, Weslaco, TX,

78596-6382, Hidalgo, USA; gen tel (956) 969-2543; adv tel (956) 969-2543; ed tel (956) 969-2543; gen fax (956) 968-0855; adv fax (956) 968-0855; ed fax (956) 968-0855; disp adv e-mail ads@mvtcnews.com; class adv e-mail ads@mvtcnews.com; ed e-mail mrodriguez@mvtcnews.com; web site www.midvalleytowncrier.com
Circulation: 21,750fr; CAC
Advertising rate: Open inch rate $18.89
Established: 1967
Group: Times Media Group
Digital Platform - Mobile: Apple, Android, Windows, Blackberry
Digital Platform - Tablet: Apple iOS, Android, Windows 7, Blackberry Tablet OS, Kindle, Nook, Kindle Fire
Pub. .... John Greider
Ed. .... Matt Lynch
Nat'l Adv. Mgr. .... Benita Mendell
Delivery Method: Mail, Racks
Areas Served: Weslaco, Mercedes, Donna, Progreso, Edcouch,
Elsa, and La Villa

WEST

THE WEST NEWS (THUR)

214 W Oak St, West, TX, 76691-1443, McLennan, USA; gen tel (254) 826-3718; adv tel (254) 826-3718; ed tel (254) 826-3718; gen fax (254) 826-3719; adv fax (254) 826-3719; ed fax (254) 826-3719; disp adv e-mail westnews@sbcglobal.net; class adv e-mail westnews@sbcglobal.net; ed e-mail westnews@sbcglobal.net
Circulation: 3,000pd,; Sworn/Estimate/Non-Audited
Advertising rate: Open inch rate $4.25
Established: 1889
Pub. .... Linn A. Pescaia
Ed. .... Larry Knapek
Adv. Dir. .... Scott Knapek
Mechanical Specifications: Type page 13 x 21; E - 6 cols, 1 5/6, 1/6 between.
Delivery Method: Mail, Racks
Areas Served: McLennan County

WEST COLUMBIA

THE BRAZORIA COUNTY NEWS (THUR)

113 E Bernard St, West Columbia, TX, 77486-3213, Brazoria, USA; gen tel (979) 345-3127; adv tel (979) 345-3127; ed tel (979) 345-3127; gen fax (979) 345-5308; adv fax (979) 345-5308; ed fax (979) 345-5308; disp adv e-mail thenews@brazoriacountynews.com; class adv e-mail gctribune@consolidated.net; ed e-mail thenews@brazoriacountynews.com; web site www.brazoriacountynews.com
Circulation: 11,000fr; Sworn/Estimate/Non-Audited
Advertising rate: Open inch rate $7.00
Established: 1962
Digital Platform - Mobile: Apple, Android, Windows, Blackberry
Digital Platform - Tablet: Apple iOS, Android, Windows 7, Blackberry Tablet OS, Kindle, Nook, Kindle Fire
Pub. .... David E. Toney
Ed. .... Becky Toney Hutchinson
Mechanical Specifications: Type page 11 5/8 x 21; E - 6 cols, 1 5/6, 1/8 between; A - 6 cols, 1 5/6, 1/8 between; C - 9 cols, 1 3/16, 1/8 between.
Delivery Method: Mail, Racks
Areas Served: 77422, 77430, 77431, 77463, 77480, 77486

WHARTON

EAST BERNARD EXPRESS (THUR)

115 W Burleson St, Wharton, TX, 77488-5003, Wharton, USA; gen tel (979) 532-0095; adv tel (979) 532-0095; ed tel (979) 532-0095; gen fax (979) 532-8845; adv fax (979) 532-8845; ed fax (979) 532-8845; disp adv e-mail bwallace@journal-spectator.com; class adv e-mail bwallace@journal-spectator.com; ed e-mail bwallace@journal-spectator.com; web site www.smalltownpapers.com
Circulation: 1,000pd,; Sworn/Estimate/Non-Audited
Advertising rate: Open inch rate $4.00
Established: 1949
Group: Hartman Newspapers LP
Pub./Ed./Adv. Dir. .... Bill Wallace
Delivery Method: Mail, Racks
Areas Served: 77435

WHARTON JOURNAL-SPECTATOR (WED, SAT)

115 W Burleson St, Wharton, TX, 77488-5090, Wharton, USA; gen tel (979) 532-8840; adv tel (979) 532-8840; ed tel (979) 532-8840; gen fax (979) 532-8845; adv fax (979) 532-8845; ed fax (979) 532-8845; disp adv e-mail awatson@journal-spectator.com; class adv e-mail classified@journal-spectator.com; ed e-mail bwallace@journal-spectator.com; web site www.journal-spectator.com
Circulation: 4,500pd,; Sworn/Estimate/Non-Audited
Advertising rate: Open inch rate $7.30
Established: 1889
Group: Hartman Newspapers LP
Digital Platform - Mobile: Apple, Android, Windows, Blackberry
Digital Platform - Tablet: Apple iOS, Android, Windows 7, Blackberry Tablet OS, Kindle, Nook, Kindle Fire
Pub./Ed. .... Bill Wallace
Mng. Ed. .... Keith Magee
Retail Adv. Mgr. .... Ann Watson
Classified Adv. Mgr. .... Helen Sevier
Mechanical Specifications: 1 - column = 1.833 inches
2 - column = 3.792 inches
3 - column = 5.750 inches
4 - column = 7.708 inches
5 - column = 9.667 inches
6 - column = 11.625 inches
Delivery Method: Mail, Newsstand, Carrier, Racks
Areas Served: 77488, 77420, 77448, 77435, 77443, 77436

WHEELER

THE WHEELER TIMES (THUR)

110 E Texas Ave, Wheeler, TX, 79096, Wheeler, USA; gen tel (806) 826-3123; adv tel (806) 826-3123; ed tel (806)826-3123; disp adv e-mail wtimes@windstream.net; class adv e-mail wtimes@windstream.net; ed e-mail wtimes@windstream.net
Circulation: 973pd,; Sworn/Estimate/Non-Audited
Advertising rate: Open inch rate $3.00
Established: 1933
Pub./Ed./Adv. Dir. .... Louis C. Stas
Delivery Method: Mail
Areas Served: Wheeler County

WHITE OAK

WHITE OAK INDEPENDENT (THUR)

100 N White Oak Rd, White Oak, TX, 75693-1243, Gregg, USA; gen tel (903) 845-5349; adv tel (903) 845-5349; ed tel (903) 845-5349; gen fax (903) 845-5349; adv fax (903) 845-5349; ed fax (903) 845-5349; disp adv e-mail newman5608@suddenlink.net; class adv e-mail newman5608@suddenlink.net; ed e-mail newman5608@suddenlink.net
Circulation: 745pd,; Sworn/Estimate/Non-Audited
Advertising rate: Open inch rate $4.20
Established: 1990
Pub./Ed. .... Winnie Newman
Adv. Mgr. .... Candy Miller
Delivery Method: Mail
Areas Served: Gregg County

WHITEHOUSE

TRI COUNTY LEADER (THUR)

304 State Highway 110 N, Whitehouse, TX, 75791-3112, Smith, USA; gen tel (903) 839-2353; adv tel (903) 839-2353; ed tel (903) 839-2353; gen fax (903) 839-8519; adv fax (903) 839-8519; ed fax (903) 839-8519; disp adv e-mail ads@tricountyleader.com; class adv e-mail classifieds@kilgorenewsherald.com; ed e-mail reporter@tricountyleader.com; web site www.tricountyleader.com
Circulation: 2,600pd,; Sworn/Estimate/Non-Audited
Advertising rate: Open inch rate $5.25
Established: 1988
Group: Bluebonnet Publishing
Digital Platform - Mobile: Apple, Android, Windows, Blackberry
Digital Platform - Tablet: Apple iOS, Android, Windows 7, Blackberry Tablet OS, Kindle, Nook, Kindle Fire
Pub./Adv. Dir. .... Bill Woodall
Co-Pub. .... Jessica Woodall
Ed. .... Don Treul
Staff Writer .... Suzanne Loudamy
Delivery Method: Mail, Racks
Areas Served: Smith County

WHITESBORO

WHITESBORO NEWS-RECORD (THUR)

130 E Main St, Whitesboro, TX, 76273-1705, Grayson, USA; gen tel (903) 564-3565; adv tel (903) 564-3565; ed tel (903) 564-3565; gen fax (903) 564-9655; adv fax (903) 564-9655; ed fax (903) 564-9655; disp adv e-mail ads@whitesboroneews.com; class adv e-mail ads@whitesboroneews.com; ed e-mail news@whitesboronews.com; web site www.whitesboronews.com
Circulation: 3,000pd, 38fr; Sworn/Estimate/Non-Audited
Advertising rate: Open inch rate $5.00
Established: 1877
Pub./Ed. .... Scott Wood
Prod. Mgr. .... Jaquita Lewter
Reporter .... Mary Jane Farmer
Sports writer .... Vic Riley
Mechanical Specifications: Type page 11 1/2 x 21 1/2; E - 6 cols, 1 13/16, 1/4 between; A - 6 cols, 1 13/16, 1/4 between; C - 6 cols, 1 13/16, 1/4 between.Equipment & Software: Hardware — APP/Mac; Software — Adobe/PageMaker 4.0.
Delivery Method: Mail, Newsstand, Racks
Areas Served: Grayson County

WHITEWRIGHT

WHITEWRIGHT SUN (THUR)

PO Box 218, 121 W Grand, Whitewright, TX, 75491-0218, Grayson, USA; gen tel (903) 364-2276; disp adv e-mail whitewrightsun@cableone.net; class adv e-mail whitewrightsun@cableone.net; ed e-mail whitewrightsun@cableone.net
Circulation: 1,100pd, 50fr; Sworn/Estimate/Non-Audited
Advertising rate: Open inch rate $6.00
Established: 1884
Pub./Adv. Dir. .... Roger Palmer
Ed. .... Kim Palmer
Delivery Method: Mail, Newsstand, Racks
Areas Served: Grayson County

WILLS POINT

VAN BANNER (THUR)

109 N 5th St, Wills Point, TX, 75169-2058, Van Zandt, USA; gen tel (903) 567-4000; adv tel (903) 567-4000; ed tel (903) 567-4000; gen fax (903) 567-6076; adv fax (903) 567-6076; ed fax (903) 567-6076; disp adv e-mail brad@vanzandtnews.com; class adv e-mail brad@vanzandtnews.com; ed e-mail brad@vanzandtnews.com; web site www.vanbanner.com
Circulation: 694pd,; Sworn/Estimate/Non-Audited
Advertising rate: Open inch rate $4.25 **Established:** 1998
Digital Platform - Mobile: Apple, Android, Windows, Blackberry
Digital Platform - Tablet: Apple iOS, Android, Windows 7, Blackberry Tablet OS, Kindle, Nook, Kindle Fire
Pub. .... John Buzzetta
Ed. .... Julie Vaughan
Adv. Dir. .... Kelli Baxter
Delivery Method: Mail
Areas Served: Van Zandt County

VAN ZANDT NEWS (SUN)

109 N 5th St, Wills Point, TX, 75169-2058, Van Zandt, USA; gen tel (903) 873-2525; adv tel (903) 873-2525; ed tel (903) 873-2525; gen fax (903) 873-4321; adv fax (903) 873-4321; ed fax (903) 873-4321; disp adv e-mail vzads@aol.com; class adv e-mail vzads@aol.com; ed e-mail vznews@aol.com; web site www.vanzandtnews.com
Circulation: 5,500pd, 100fr; Sworn/Estimate/Non-Audited
Advertising rate: Open inch rate $7.25
Established: 1982
Group: Van Zandt Newspapers LLC
Digital Platform - Mobile: Apple, Android, Windows, Blackberry
Digital Platform - Tablet: Apple iOS, Android, Windows 7, Blackberry Tablet OS, Kindle, Nook, Kindle Fire
Mechanical Specifications: Type page 11 1/2 x 21 1/2; E - 6 cols, 1 13/16, between; A - 6 cols, 1 13/16, between; C - 8 cols, 1 5/16, between.
Delivery Method: Mail, Newsstand
Areas Served: Van Zandt County

WILLS POINT CHRONICLE (FRI)

109 N 5th St, Wills Point, TX, 75169-2058, Van Zandt, USA; gen tel (903) 873-2525; adv tel (903) 873-2525; ed tel (903) 873-2525; gen fax (903) 873-4321; adv fax (903) 873-4321; ed fax (903) 873-4321; disp adv e-mail brad@vanzandtnews.com; class adv e-mail brad@vanzandtnews.com; ed e-mail vznews@aol.com; web site www.willspointchronicle.com
Circulation: 3,051pd, 500fr; Sworn/Estimate/Non-Audited
Advertising rate: Open inch rate $7.25
Established: 1879
Digital Platform - Mobile: Apple, Android, Windows, Blackberry
Digital Platform - Tablet: Apple iOS, Android, Windows 7, Blackberry Tablet OS, Kindle, Nook, Kindle Fire
Delivery Method: Mail, Newsstand, Racks
Areas Served: Van Zandt County

WIMBERLEY

CENTURY NEWS (WED)

PO Box 49, Wimberley, TX, 78676-0049, Hays, USA; gen tel (512) 847-2202; adv tel (512) 847-2202; ed tel (512) 847-2202; gen fax (512) 847-9054; adv fax (512) 847-9054; ed fax (512) 847-9054; disp adv e-mail dscenturynews@gmail.com; class adv e-mail dscenturynews@gmail.com; ed e-mail dscenturynews@gmail.com
Circulation: 300pd,; Sworn/Estimate/Non-Audited
Advertising rate: Open inch rate $8.25
Pub. .... Mary V. Saunders
Ed. .... Anne Drabicky
Adv. Mgr. .... Gina McClure
Prodn. Mgr. .... Jim Gore
Mechanical Specifications: Type page 13 x 21; E - 6 cols, 2, 3/16 between; A - 6 cols, 2, 3/16 between; C - 9 cols, 1 3/8, between. Equipment & Software: ; Software — Adobe/PageMaker 6.0, Adobe/Photoshop 5.0, Microsoft/Word 6.0, Caere/OmniPage Pro, QPS/QuarkXPress 3.31, Macromedia/Freehand.
Delivery Method: Mail
Areas Served: Hays County

WIMBERLEY VIEW (THUR)
101 FM 3237, Ste A, Wimberley, TX, 78676-5371, Hays, USA; gen tel (512) 847-2202; gen fax (512) 847-9054; disp adv e-mail wimberleyview@gmail.com; class adv e-mail wimberleyview@gmail.com; ed e-mail dsweat@wimberleyview.com; web site wimberleyview.com
Circulation: 2,100pd,; Sworn/Estimate/Non-Audited
Advertising rate: Open inch rate $10.00
Established: 1976
Group: San Marcos Publishing
Digital Platform - Mobile: Apple, Android, Windows, Blackberry
Digital Platform - Tablet: Apple iOS, Android, Windows 7, Blackberry Tablet OS
GM/Ed....Dalton Sweat
Sales Rep....Susan Sisson
ReporterGary ZupancicEquipment & Software: ; Presses — San Marcos Publishing
Delivery Method: Mail, Racks
Areas Served: Hays County

WINNIE

HOMETOWN PRESS (THUR)
336 Broadway, Winnie, TX, 77665-7829, Chambers, USA; gen tel (409) 296-9988; adv tel (409) 296-9988; ed tel (409) 296-9988; gen fax (409) 296-9987; adv fax (409) 296-9987; ed fax (409) 296-9987; disp adv e-mail htpress99@windstream.net; class adv e-mail htpress99@windstream.net; ed e-mail htpress99@windstream.net
Circulation: 2,000pd,; Sworn/Estimate/Non-Audited
Advertising rate: Open inch rate $6.25
Established: 1991
Pub./Ed....Scott Reese Willey
Adv. Mgr....Crystal Estes
Gen. Mgr....Jennifer BrownEquipment & Software: Hardware — APP/Mac; Software — QPS/QuarkXPress.
Delivery Method: Mail, Newsstand, Racks
Areas Served: 77665, 77514, 77622, 77705

WINNSBORO

THE WINNSBORO NEWS (THUR)
105 Locust St, Winnsboro, TX, 75494-2519, Wood, USA; gen tel (903) 342-5247; adv tel (903) 342-5247; ed tel (903) 342-5247; gen fax (903) 342-3266; adv fax (903) 342-3266; ed fax (903) 342-3266; disp adv e-mail winnsboronews@suddenlinkmail.com; class adv e-mail winnsboronews@suddenlinkmail.com; ed e-mail winnsboronews@suddenlinkmail.com
Circulation: 4,010pd, 8fr; Sworn/Estimate/Non-Audited
Advertising rate: Open inch rate $6.50
Established: 1908
Pub./Ed....Thomas F. Pendergast
Mng. Ed....Karen W. Pendergast
Adv. Mgr....Linda Henry
Prodn. Mgr....Ross Hunter
Mechanical Specifications: Type page 13 x 21; E - 6 cols, 2 1/30, 1/6 between; A - 6 cols, 2 1/30, 1/6 between; C - 6 cols, 2 1/30, 1/6 between.Equipment & Software: Hardware — APP/Mac, IBM; Presses — 5-G; Software — Adobe/PageMaker, Microsoft/Windows.
Delivery Method: Mail, Newsstand, Racks
Areas Served: Wood County

WOODVILLE

TYLER COUNTY BOOSTER (THUR)
205 W Bluff St, Woodville, TX, 75979-5221, Tyler, USA; gen tel (409) 283-2516; adv tel (409)283-2516; ed tel (409)283-2516; gen fax (409) 283-2560; adv fax (409)283-2560; ed fax (409)283-2560; disp adv e-mail advertising@tylercountybooster.com; class adv e-mail classified@tylercountybooster.com; ed e-mail editor@tylercountybooster.com; web site www.tylercountybooster.com
Circulation: 3,750pd, 1,000fr; Sworn/Estimate/Non-Audited
Advertising rate: Open inch rate $9
Established: 1930
Group: Polk County Publishing Co.
Digital Platform - Mobile: Apple, Android, Windows, Blackberry
Digital Platform - Tablet: Apple iOS, Android, Windows 7, Blackberry Tablet OS
Mgr....Kelli Barnes
Ed....Jim Powers
Delivery Method: Mail, Newsstand, Racks
Areas Served: Tyler County

WYLIE

MURPHY MONITOR (THUR)
110 N Ballard Ave, Wylie, TX, 75098-4467, Collin, USA; gen tel (972) 442-5515; adv tel (972) 442-5515; ed tel (972) 442-5515; gen fax (972) 442-4318; adv fax (972) 442-4318; ed fax (972) 442-4318; disp adv e-mail news@murphymonitor.com; class adv e-mail advertising@csmediatexas.com; ed e-mail news@murphymonitor.com; web site www.murphymonitor.com
Circulation: 2,179pd, 0fr; USPS
Advertising rate: Open inch rate $11.16
Established: 2005
Group: C&S Media, Inc.Editions: (52)
Digital Platform - Mobile: Apple, Android, Windows, Blackberry
Digital Platform - Tablet: Apple iOS, Android, Windows 7, Blackberry Tablet OS, Kindle, Kindle Fire
Pub./Ed./Adv. Dir....Chad B. Engbrock
Mechanical Specifications: 11.5 x 21Equipment & Software: Hardware — Mac; Presses — n/a; Software — In Design
Delivery Method: Mail, Newsstand, Carrier, Racks
Areas Served: 75094

SACHSE NEWS (THUR)
110 N Ballard Ave, Wylie, TX, 75098-4467, Collin, USA; gen tel (972) 442-5515; adv tel (972) 442-5515; ed tel (972) 442-5515; gen fax (972) 442-4318; adv fax (972) 442-4318; ed fax (972) 442-4318; disp adv e-mail advertising@csmediatexas.com; class adv e-mail cengbrock@csmediatexas.com; ed e-mail news@sachsenews.com; web site www.sachsenews.com
Circulation: 1,533pd,; Sworn/Estimate/Non-Audited
Advertising rate: Open inch rate $14.15
Established: 2005
Digital Platform - Mobile: Apple, Android, Windows, Blackberry
Digital Platform - Tablet: Apple iOS, Android, Windows 7, Blackberry Tablet OS, Kindle, Nook, Kindle Fire
Pub./Ed./Adv. Dir....Chad B. Engbrock
Delivery Method: Mail, Newsstand, Racks
Areas Served: Dallas County

THE WYLIE NEWS (WED)
110 N Ballard Ave, Wylie, TX, 75098-4467, Collin, USA; gen tel (972) 442-5515; adv tel (972) 442-5515; ed tel (972) 442-5515; gen fax (972) 442-4318; adv fax (972) 442-4318; ed fax (972) 442-4318; disp adv e-mail advertising@wylienews.com; class adv e-mail classifieds@wylienews.com; ed e-mail cengbrock@wylienews.com; web site www.wylienews.com
Circulation: 3,856pd,; Sworn/Estimate/Non-Audited
Advertising rate: Open inch rate $14.00
Established: 1948
Digital Platform - Mobile: Apple, Android, Windows, Blackberry
Digital Platform - Tablet: Apple iOS, Android, Windows 7, Blackberry Tablet OS, Kindle, Nook, Kindle Fire
Pub....Chad B. Engbrock
Delivery Method: Mail, Newsstand, Racks
Areas Served: Collin County

YOAKUM

YOAKUM HERALD-TIMES (WED)
312 Lott St, Yoakum, TX, 77995-2798, Lavaca, USA; gen tel (361) 293-5266; adv tel (361) 293-5266; ed tel (361) 293-5266; gen fax (361) 293-5267; adv fax (361) 293-5267; ed fax (361) 293-5267; disp adv e-mail heraldtimes@sbcglobal.net; class adv e-mail heraldtimes@sbcglobal.net; ed e-mail heraldtimes@sbcglobal.net; web site www.levacacountytoday.com
Circulation: 3,200pd,; Sworn/Estimate/Non-Audited
Advertising rate: Open inch rate $6.95
Established: 1892
Pub./Ed./Adv. Dir....Mike McCracken
Mechanical Specifications: Type page 13 x 21; E - 6 cols, 2, 1/6 between; A - 6 cols, 2, 1/6 between; C - 6 cols, 2, 1/6 between.Equipment & Software: Hardware — APP/Mac; Software — Adobe/PageMaker 5.0.
Delivery Method: Mail, Racks
Areas Served: Lavaca County

YORKTOWN

YORKTOWN NEWS-VIEW (WED)
133 E MAIN ST, Yorktown, TX, 78164, DeWitt, USA; gen tel (361) 564-2242; adv tel (361) 564-2242; ed tel (361) 564-2242; gen fax (361) 564-9290; adv fax (361) 564-9290; ed fax (361) 564-9290; disp adv e-mail yorktownnews@sbcglobal.net; class adv e-mail yorktownnews@sbcglobal.net; ed e-mail yorktownnews@sbcglobal.net; web site www.yorktownnews-view.com
Circulation: 2,700pd, 75fr; Sworn/Estimate/Non-Audited
Advertising rate: Open inch rate $4.35
Established: 1895
Digital Platform - Mobile: Apple, Android, Windows, Blackberry
Digital Platform - Tablet: Apple iOS, Android, Windows 7, Blackberry Tablet OS, Kindle, Nook, Kindle Fire
Pub./Ed....Glenn Rea
Adv. Dir....Sonya Timpone
Office Mgr....Mari Gohlke
News Ed....Elizabeth Rodriguez
Delivery Method: Mail, Racks
Areas Served: DeWitt County

ZAPATA

ZAPATA COUNTY NEWS (THUR)
2765 US Highway 83, Zapata, TX, 78076-4239, Zapata, USA; gen tel (956) 765-6931; gen fax (956) 765-9058; disp adv e-mail zapatarates@sbcglobal.net; class adv e-mail zapatamngr@gmail.com; ed e-mail zapatarates@sbcglobal.net
Circulation: 2,500pd, 66fr; Sworn/Estimate/Non-Audited
Advertising rate: Open inch rate $6.25
Established: 1976
Pub....Karran Westerman
Adv. Dir....Danielle WestermanEquipment & Software: Hardware — APP/Mac G4, APP/iMac, APP/Mac G3; Presses — KP/News King; Software — QPS/QuarkXPress 4.1, Microsoft/Word, Adobe/Acrobat, Adobe/Photoshop.
Delivery Method: Mail, Newsstand, Racks
Areas Served: Zapata County/Webb County/Austin/McAllen/Dallas/Out of State

UTAH

BOUNTIFUL

THE DAVIS CLIPPER (THUR)
PO Box 267, 1370 S 500 West, Bountiful, UT, 84011-0267, Davis, USA; gen tel (801) 295-2251; adv tel (801) 295-2251; ed tel (801) 295-2251; gen fax (801) 295-3044; adv fax (801) 295-3044; ed fax (801) 295-3044; disp adv e-mail tgunn@davisclipper.com; class adv e-mail tgunn@davisclipper.com; ed e-mail jwardell@davisclipper.com; web site www.davisclipper.com
Circulation: 32,633fr; Sworn/Estimate/Non-Audited
Advertising rate: Open inch rate $11.95
Established: 1891
Group: Spectrum Press Inc.
Pub./Gen. Mgr....Tom Gunn
Adv. Mgr....Gene R. Milne
Circ. Mgr....Roy Millard
Ed....R. Gail Stahle
Mng. Ed....Judith Jensen
Prodn. Mgr....Hayes Rowell
Mechanical Specifications: Type page 13 x 21 1/2; E - 6 cols, 2, 1/6 between; A - 6 cols, 2, 1/6 between; C - 8 cols, 1 1/2, 1/6 between. Equipment & Software: Hardware — APP/Mac, Panther/Pro Imagesetter; Presses — 12-G/Suburban; Software — QPS/QuarkXPress 3.32.
Delivery Method: Mail, Newsstand
Areas Served: South Davis County

BRIGHAM CITY

BOX ELDER NEWS JOURNAL (WED)
55 S 100 W, Brigham City, UT, 84302-2540, Box Elder, USA; gen tel (435) 723-3471; adv tel (435) 723-3471; ed tel (435) 723-3471; gen fax (435) 723-5247; adv fax (435) 723-5247; ed fax (435) 723-5247; disp adv e-mail casey@benewsjournal.com; class adv e-mail casey@benewsjournal.com; ed e-mail casey@benewsjournal.com; web site www.benewsjournal.com
Circulation: 4,200pd, 8,500fr; USPS
Advertising rate: Open inch rate $10.50
Established: 1896
Digital Platform - Mobile: Apple, Android, Windows
Digital Platform - Tablet: Apple iOS, Android, Windows 7, Blackberry Tablet OS, Kindle, Nook, Kindle Fire
Pub....Casey Claybaugh
Ed....Sean Hales
Advertising Manager....Jamie Hester
Classifieds Manager....Carson Barnhart
Mechanical Specifications: Type page 13 x 21 1/2; E - 6 cols, 2, 1/6 between; A - 6 cols, 2, 1/6 between; C - 6 cols, 2, 1/6 between. Equipment & Software: Hardware — APP/Mac; Presses — 8 UNIT HARRIS V-15D WEB PRESS; Software — Adobe
Delivery Method: Mail, Newsstand, Racks
Areas Served: Box Elder County

CASTLE DALE

EMERY COUNTY PROGRESS (TUES)
410 E Main St, Castle Dale, UT, 84513-4506, Emery, USA; gen tel (435) 381-2431; adv tel (435) 637-0732; ed tel (435) 381-2431; gen fax (435) 381-5431; adv fax (435) 381-5431; ed fax (435) 381-5431; disp adv e-mail ads@ecprogress.com; class adv e-mail ads@ecprogress.com; ed e-mail editor@ecprogress.com; web site www.ecprogress.com
Circulation: 1,805pd, 2,675fr; Sworn/Estimate/Non-Audited
Advertising rate: Open inch rate $6.83
Established: 1900
Group: Brehm Communications, Inc.

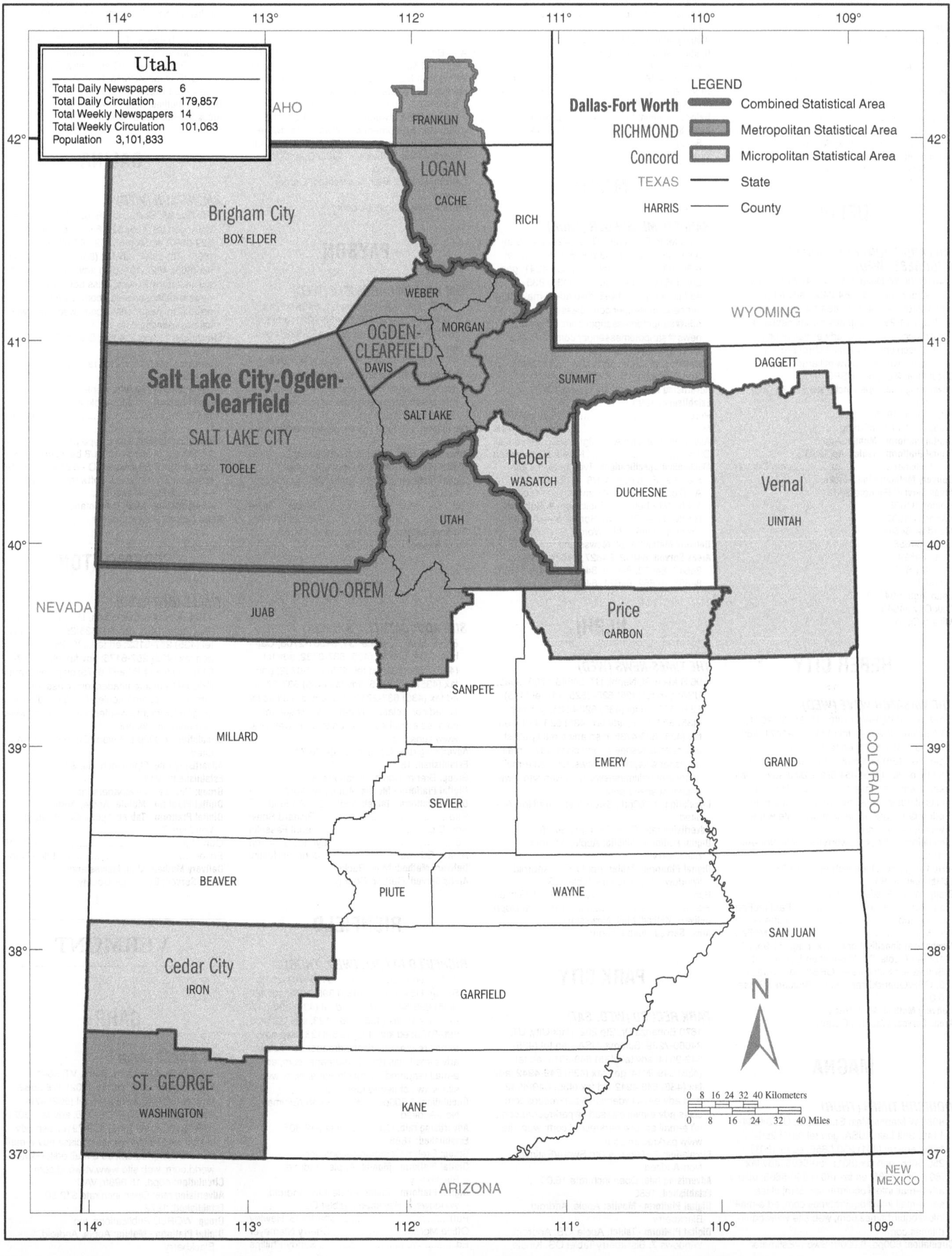
Utah
Total Daily Newspapers 6
Total Daily Circulation 179,857
Total Weekly Newspapers 14
Total Weekly Circulation 101,063
Population 3,101,833
LEGEND
Dallas-Fort Worth Combined Statistical Area
RICHMOND Metropolitan Statistical Area
Concord Micropolitan Statistical Area
TEXAS State
HARRIS County
114° 113° 112° 111° 110° 109°
42° 41° 40° 39° 38° 37°
IDAHO
WYOMING
NEVADA
COLORADO
ARIZONA
NEW MEXICO
FRANKLIN
LOGAN
CACHE
RICH
Brigham City
BOX ELDER
WEBER
MORGAN
OGDEN-CLEARFIELD
DAVIS
Salt Lake City-Ogden-Clearfield
SALT LAKE CITY
SUMMIT
DAGGETT
SALT LAKE
TOOELE
Heber
WASATCH
DUCHESNE
Vernal
UINTAH
UTAH
PROVO-OREM
JUAB
Price
CARBON
SANPETE
MILLARD
EMERY
GRAND
SEVIER
BEAVER
PIUTE
WAYNE
SAN JUAN
Cedar City
IRON
GARFIELD
ST. GEORGE
WASHINGTON
KANE
N
0 8 16 24 32 40 Kilometers
0 8 16 24 32 40 Miles

Digital Platform - Mobile: Apple, Android, Blackberry
Digital Platform - Tablet: Apple iOS, Android, Windows 7, Blackberry Tablet OS
Pub.. Rick Shaw
Office Mgr. .... Linda Thayn
Adv. Dir....................................... Jenni Fasselin
Circ. Mgr... Darla Lee
Ed. .... Patsy Stoddard
Mechanical Specifications: Type page 12 x 21 1/2.Equipment & Software: Hardware — PC; Software — Adobe/PageMaker.
Delivery Method: Mail, Newsstand
Areas Served: Emery County

DELTA

MILLARD COUNTY CHRONICLE PROGRESS (WED)

40 N 300 W, Delta, UT, 84624-8505, Millard, USA; gen tel (435) 864-2400; adv tel (435) 864-2400; ed tel (435) 864-2400; gen fax (775) 514-2931; disp adv e-mail debbie@millardccp.com; class adv e-mail debbie@millardccp.com; ed e-mail chronpro@millard-ccp.com; web site www.millardccp.com
Circulation: 2,600pd,; USPS
Advertising rate: Open inch rate $13.75 (Full Color)
Established: 1910
Group: DuMor Publishing
Digital Platform - Mobile: Apple
Digital Platform - Tablet: Apple iOS
Co-Publisher............................... Lewis Dutson
Delivery Method: Mail, Racks
Areas Served: Fillmore 84631
Holden 84636
Kanosh 84637
Meadow 84644
Scipio 84656
Delta 84624
Hinckley 84635
Lynndyl 84640
Leamington 84638
Oak City 84649
Millard County

HEBER CITY

THE WASATCH WAVE (WED)

165 S 100 W, Heber City, UT, 84032-2001, Wasatch, USA; gen tel (435) 654-1471; adv tel (435) 654-1471; ed tel (435) 654-1471; gen fax (435) 654-5085; adv fax (435) 654-5085; ed fax (435) 654-5085; disp adv e-mail kari@wasatchwave.com; class adv e-mail classifieds@wasatchwave.com; ed e-mail editor@wasatchwave.com; web site www.wasatchwave.com
Circulation: 4,200pd,; Sworn/Estimate/Non-Audited
Advertising rate: Open inch rate $13.28
Established: 1889
Group: Wave Publishing, Inc.
Gen. Mgr./Co.-Pub. .... Paul McFee
Ed./Co. Pub.................................. Laurie Wynn
Adv. Mgr... Kari McFee
Mechanical Specifications: Type page 11.9 x 21 1/2; A - 6 cols, 2, 1/4 between.Equipment & Software: ; Software — QPS/QuarkXPress 9, QPS/QuarkXPress 5., QPS/QuarkXPress 6.0.
Delivery Method: Mail, Racks
Areas Served: Wasatch County

MAGNA

OQUIRRH TIMES (THUR)

8980 W Magna Main St, Magna, UT, 84044-1149, Salt Lake, USA; gen tel (801) 250-5656; adv tel (801) 250-5656; ed tel (801) 250-5656; gen fax (801) 250-5685; adv fax (801) 250-5685; ed fax (801) 250-5685; disp adv e-mail info@oquirrhtimes.com; class adv e-mail info@oquirrhtimes.com; ed e-mail info@oquirrhtimes.com; web site www.oquirrhtimes.com
Circulation: 800pd, 8,000fr; Sworn/Estimate/Non-Audited
Advertising rate: Open inch rate $10.95
Established: 1906
Digital Platform - Mobile: Apple, Android
Digital Platform - Tablet: Apple iOS, Android
Owner/Pub./Ed......................... Howard Stahle
Owner/Adv. Mgr.......................... Bonnie Stahle
Prod. Mgr.Tyler PetersonEquipment & Software: Hardware — APP/Mac.
Delivery Method: Mail, Newsstand, Racks
Areas Served: 84044, 84120, 84119, 84118, 84128

MANTI

SANPETE MESSENGER (THUR)

35 S Main St, Manti, UT, 84642-1350, Sanpete, USA; gen tel (435) 835-4241; adv tel (435) 835-4241; ed tel (435) 835-4241; gen fax (435) 835-1493; adv fax (435) 835-1493; ed fax (435) 835-1493; disp adv e-mail ads@sanpetemessenger.com; class adv e-mail ads@sanpetemessenger.com; ed e-mail news@sanpetemessenger.com; web site www.sanpetemessenger.com
Circulation: 2,000pd, 100fr; Sworn/Estimate/Non-Audited
Advertising rate: Open inch rate $9.00
Established: 1893
Pub.. Suzanne Dean
Mng Ed .... Robert Stevens
Associate Pub and Advt Mgr........... Lloyd Call
Office Mgr .... Karen Christensen
Mechanical Specifications: Type page 12 1/2 x 21 1/2; E - 6 cols, 1 1/8, 1/12 between; A - 6 cols, 1 1/8, 1/12 between; C - 6 cols, 1 1/8, 1/12 between.Equipment & Software: Hardware — Pentium; Software — Adobe Creative Suite 3, MS/Word.
Delivery Method: Mail, Newsstand
Areas Served: 84642, 84627, 84634, 84622, 84647, 84632, 84630, 84629, 84646, 84667, 84665, 84662, 84621, 84643

NEPHI

THE TIMES-NEWS (WED)

96 S Main St, Nephi, UT, 84648-1708, Juab, USA; gen tel (435) 623-0525; adv tel (435) 623-0525; ed tel (435) 623-0525; gen fax (435) 623-4735; adv fax (435) 623-4735; ed fax (435) 623-4735; disp adv e-mail publisher@nephitimesnews.com; class adv e-mail publisher@nephitimesnews.com; ed e-mail editor@nephitimesnews.com; web site www.nephitimesnews.com
Circulation: 1,700pd,; Sworn/Estimate/Non-Audited
Advertising rate: Open inch rate $4.95
Digital Platform - Mobile: Apple, Android, Blackberry
Digital Platform - Tablet: Apple iOS, Android, Windows 7, Blackberry Tablet OS
Pub.. Allan R. Gibson
Ed. .... Rebecca Dopp
Delivery Method: Mail, Newsstand
Areas Served: Juab County

PARK CITY

PARK RECORD (WED, SAT)

1670 Bonanza Dr, Ste 202, Park City, UT, 84060-7239, Summit, USA; gen tel (435) 649-9014; adv tel (435) 649-9014; ed tel (435) 649-9014; gen fax (435) 649-4942; adv fax (435) 649-4942; ed fax (435) 649-4942; disp adv e-mail vdeming@parkrecord.com; class adv e-mail classads@parkrecord.com; ed e-mail editor@parkrecord.com; web site www.parkrecord.com
Circulation: 7,800pd, 300fr; Sworn/Estimate/Non-Audited
Advertising rate: Open inch rate 16.00
Established: 1880
Digital Platform - Mobile: Apple, Android, Blackberry
Digital Platform - Tablet: Apple iOS, Android, Windows 7, Blackberry Tablet OS, Kindle, Nook, Kindle Fire
Pub.. Andy Bernhard
Circ. Mgr...................................... Lacy Brundy
Ed. .... Nan Chalat-Noaker
Adv. Dir... Valerie Spung
Classified Mgr. .... Jennifer Lynch
Production Mgr.............................. Lisa Powell
Mechanical Specifications: Type page 12 13/16 x 21 1/2; E - 6 cols, 2, 1/8 between; A - 6 cols, 2, 1/8 between; C - 9 cols, 1 3/8, 1/8 between.Equipment & Software: Hardware — APP/Mac; Presses — WPC/Web Leader, G/Community; Software — QPS/QuarkXPress, Adobe/Photoshop.
Delivery Method: Mail, Newsstand, Carrier, Racks
Areas Served: Summit County

PAYSON

THE PAYSON CHRONICLE (WED)

145 E Utah Ave, Payson, UT, 84651-2248, Utah, USA; gen tel (801) 465-9221; adv tel (801) 465-9221; ed tel (801) 465-9221; gen fax (801) 465-9221; adv fax (801) 465-9221; ed fax (801) 465-9221; disp adv e-mail thepaysonchronicle@msn.com; class adv e-mail thepaysonchronicle@msn.com; ed e-mail thepaysonchronicle@msn.com; web site www.paysonads.com
Circulation: 2,000pd,; Sworn/Estimate/Non-Audited
Advertising rate: Open inch rate $4.50
Digital Platform - Mobile: Apple, Android
Digital Platform - Tablet: Apple iOS, Android, Windows 7
Pub./Ed.................................... Michael Olson
Mng. Ed.................................. Denise Windley
Delivery Method: Mail, Newsstand, Racks
Areas Served: Utah County

PRICE

SUN ADVOCATE (TUES, THUR)

845 E Main St, Price, UT, 84501-2708, Carbon, USA; gen tel (435) 637-0732; adv tel (435) 637-0732; ed tel (435) 637-0732; gen fax (435) 637-2716; adv fax (435) 637-2716; ed fax (435) 637-2716; disp adv e-mail ads@sunad.com; class adv e-mail ads@sunad.com; ed e-mail editor@sunad.com; web site www.sunad.com
Advertising rate: Open inch rate $8.74
Established: 1891
Group: Brehm Communications, Inc.
Digital Platform - Mobile: Apple, Android
Digital Platform - Tablet: Apple iOS, Android
Pub.. Richard Shaw
Adv. Dir...................................... Jenni Fasselin
Ed. .... Lynnda Johnson
Assoc. Ed................................ John Serfustini
Delivery Method: Mail, Racks
Areas Served: Carbon County

RICHFIELD

RICHFIELD REAPER (WED, THUR)

65 W Center St, Richfield, UT, 84701-2546, Sevier, USA; gen tel (435) 896-5476; adv tel (435) 896-5476 ext. 18; ed tel (435) 896-5476 ext. 21; gen fax (435) 896-8123; adv fax (435) 896-8123; ed fax (435) 896-8123; disp adv e-mail reaperad@richfieldreaper.com; class adv e-mail class@richfieldreaper.com; ed e-mail reapered@richfieldreaper.com; web site www.richfieldreaper.com
Circulation: 5,300pd, 6,300fr; Sworn/Estimate/Non-Audited
Advertising rate: Open inch rate $12.50
Established: 1888
Group: Brehm Communications, Inc.
Digital Platform - Mobile: Apple, Android, Blackberry
Digital Platform - Tablet: Apple iOS, Android, Windows 7, Blackberry Tablet OS
Pub..................................... Charles G. Hawley
Office Mgr. .... Cherry Niemeyer
Ed. .... Sandy Phillips
Assoc. Ed................................ David Anderson
Mechanical Specifications: Type page 13 x 21 1/2; E - 6 cols, 2 1/16, between; A - 6 cols, 2 1/16, between; C - 9 cols, 1 2/5, between. Equipment & Software: Hardware — APP/Mac; Presses — G/Community; Software — QPS/QuarkXPress, Multi-Ad, Baseview/NewsEdit Pro.
Delivery Method: Mail, Newsstand, Racks
Areas Served: Sevier County

SALINA

SALINA SUN (WED)

PO Box 85, Salina, UT, 84654-0085, Sevier, USA; gen tel (435) 529-6397; adv tel (435) 529-6397; ed tel (435) 529-6397; gen fax (866) 492-5194; adv fax (866) 492-5194; ed fax (866) 492-5194; disp adv e-mail news@salinasunonline.com; class adv e-mail news@salinasunonline.com; ed e-mail news@salinasunonline.com; web site www.salinasunonline.com
Circulation: 750pd, 2,400fr; Sworn/Estimate/Non-Audited
Advertising rate: Open inch rate $6.25
Established: 1911
Digital Platform - Mobile: Apple
Digital Platform - Tablet: Apple iOS
Adv. Dir./Pub. .... Laura Fielding
Ed. .... Troy Fielding
Mechanical Specifications: Type page 13 1/2 x 21 1/2; E - 6 cols, 2 1/8, 1/8 between; A - 6 cols, 2 1/8, 1/8 between; C - 6 cols, 2 1/8, 1/8 between.Equipment & Software: ; Software — Adobe/PageMaker 6.1.
Delivery Method: Mail, Newsstand
Areas Served: Sevier County

TREMONTON

THE LEADER (WED)

119 E Main St, Tremonton, UT, 84337-1645, Box Elder, USA; gen tel (435)257-5182; adv tel (435) 257-5182; ed tel (435) 257-5182; gen fax (435) 257-6175; adv fax (435) 257-6175; ed fax (435) 257-6175; disp adv e-mail jodiev@tremontonleader.com; class adv e-mail info@tremontonleader.com; ed e-mail gregm@tremontonleader.com; web site www.tremontonleader.com
Circulation: 7,000pd,; Sworn/Estimate/Non-Audited
Advertising rate: Open inch rate $9.00
Established: 1914
Group: Pioneer Newspapers Inc
Digital Platform - Mobile: Apple, Android
Digital Platform - Tablet: Apple iOS, Android, Windows 7
Gen Mgr... Jodie V.
Editor .... Ellen Cook
Delivery Method: Mail, Newsstand
Areas Served: Box Elder County

VERMONT

BARRE

THE WORLD (WED)

403 US Rt 302-Berlin, Barre, VT, 5641, Washington, USA; gen tel (802) 479-2582; adv tel (802) 479-2582; ed tel (802) 479-2582; gen fax (802) 479-7916; adv fax (802) 479-7916; ed fax (802) 479-7916; disp adv e-mail sales@vt-world.com; class adv e-mail sales@vt-world.com; ed e-mail editor@vt-world.com; web site www.vt-world.com
Circulation: 40pd, 15,898fr; VAC
Advertising rate: Open inch rate $12.50
Established: 1972
Group: WORLD Publications, Inc.
Digital Platform - Mobile: Apple, Android, Blackberry

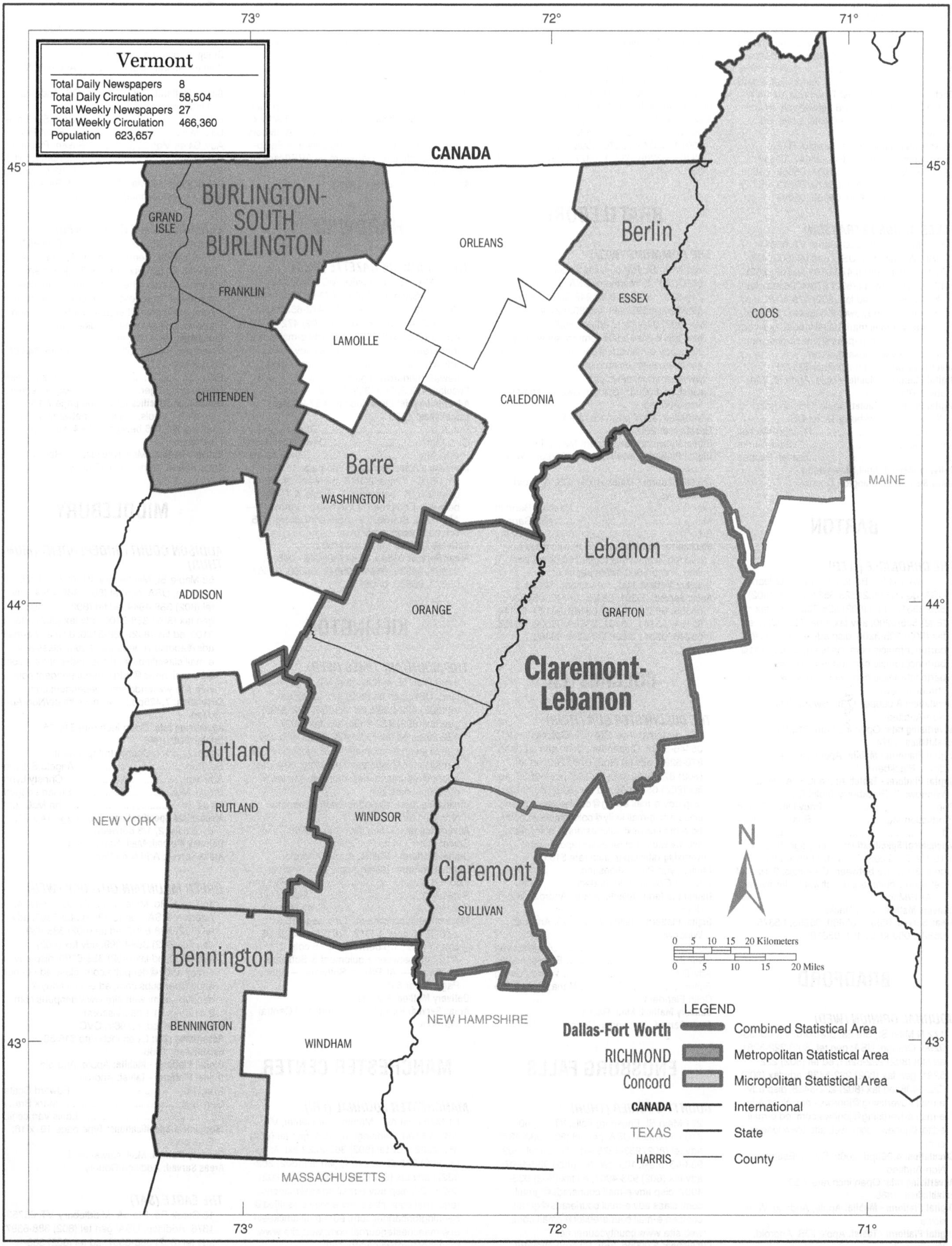
Vermont
Total Daily Newspapers 8
Total Daily Circulation 58,504
Total Weekly Newspapers 27
Total Weekly Circulation 466,360
Population 623,657
CANADA
BURLINGTON-SOUTH BURLINGTON
GRAND ISLE
FRANKLIN
ORLEANS
Berlin
ESSEX
COOS
LAMOILLE
CHITTENDEN
CALEDONIA
Barre
WASHINGTON
MAINE
Lebanon
ADDISON
ORANGE
GRAFTON
Claremont-Lebanon
Rutland
RUTLAND
NEW YORK
WINDSOR
Claremont
SULLIVAN
Bennington
BENNINGTON
WINDHAM
NEW HAMPSHIRE
MASSACHUSETTS
N
0 5 10 15 20 Kilometers
0 5 10 15 20 Miles
LEGEND
Dallas-Fort Worth Combined Statistical Area
RICHMOND Metropolitan Statistical Area
Concord Micropolitan Statistical Area
CANADA International
TEXAS State
HARRIS County
73°
72°
71°
45°
44°
43°

Digital Platform - Tablet: Apple iOS, Android, Blackberry Tablet OS
Co-Pub./owner.................................Gary Hass
Co-Pub./owner........................Deborah Phillips
Prodn. Mgr. .... Christine Richardson
Circ. ....Aeletha Kelly
Ed .... Aaron Retherford
Mechanical Specifications: Type page 10 1/4 x 16; E - 6 cols, 1 5/8, 1/6 between; A - 6 cols, 1 5/8, 1/6 between; C - 6 cols, 1 5/8, 1/6 between.
Delivery Method: Mail, Newsstand, Racks
Areas Served: 05640, 05641, 05647, 05648, 05649, 05650, 05651, 05654, 05658, 05602, 05660, 05661, 05663, 05670, 05673, 05675, 05676, 05678, 05679, 05680, 05682

TIMES ARGUS EXTRA (SUN)

47 N Main St, Ste 200, Barre, VT, 05641-4168, Washington, USA; gen tel (802) 479-0191 ; adv tel (802) 479-0191 ; ed tel (802) 479-0191 ; gen fax (802) 479-4096; adv fax (802) 776-5600; ed fax (802) 479-4096; disp adv e-mail mandy.dwinell@timesargus.com; class adv e-mail marineau@timesargus.com; ed e-mail steven.pappas@timesargus.com; web site www.timesargus.com
Advertising rate: Open inch rate $11.00
Digital Platform - Mobile: Apple, Android, Windows, Blackberry
Digital Platform - Tablet: Apple iOS, Android, Windows 7, Blackberry Tablet OS
Pres./Pub. ....R. John Mitchell
Adv. Exec. .... Sean Burke
Ed. ....Steven Pappas
Delivery Method: Mail, Newsstand
Areas Served: Washington County

BARTON

THE CHRONICLE (WED)

133 WATER ST, Barton, VT, 5822, Orleans, USA; gen tel (802) 525-3531; adv tel (802) 525-3531; ed tel (802) 525-3531; gen fax (802) 525-3200; adv fax (802) 525-3200; ed fax (802) 525-3200; disp adv e-mail ads@bartonchronicle.com; class adv e-mail ads@bartonchronicle.com; ed e-mail news@bartonchronicle.com; web site www.bartonchronicle.com
Circulation: 8,000pd, 173fr; Sworn/Estimate/Non-Audited
Advertising rate: Open inch rate $12.25
Established: 1974
Digital Platform - Mobile: Apple, Android, Windows, Blackberry
Digital Platform - Tablet: Apple iOS, Android, Windows 7, Blackberry Tablet OS
Pub..................................... Tracy Davis Pierce
Production Mgr.........................Brianne Nichols
Ed. .... Tena Starr
Mechanical Specifications: Type page 10.25 x 15 1/2; E - 3 cols, 3 1/4, 1/4 between; A - 3 cols, 3 1/4, 1/8 between; C - 4 cols, 2 1/2, 1/4 between.Equipment & Software: Hardware — APP/Mac.
Delivery Method: Mail, Racks
Areas Served: 05822, 05860, 05855, 05875, 05829, 05830, 05851, 05819

BRADFORD

JOURNAL OPINION (WED)

172 N Main St, Ste 23, Bradford, VT, 05033-9290, Orange, USA; gen tel (802) 222-5281; adv tel (802) 222-5281; ed tel (802) 222-5281; gen fax (802) 222-5438; adv fax (802) 222-5438; ed fax (802) 222-5438; disp adv e-mail advertising@jonews.com; class adv e-mail advertising@jonews.com; ed e-mail editor@jonews.com; web site www.jonews.com
Circulation: 4,000pd, 200fr; Sworn/Estimate/Non-Audited
Advertising rate: Open inch rate 7.50
Established: 1865
Digital Platform - Mobile: Apple, Android, Windows
Digital Platform - Tablet: Apple iOS, Android, Windows 7
Owner/Pub..............................Connie Sanville
Adv. Mgr.............................Michele Sherburne
Mng. Ed..............................Alex Nuti-De Biasi
Mechanical Specifications: Type page 12 x 21; E - 6 cols, 2, 1/12 between; A - 6 cols, 2, 1/12 between; C - 6 cols, 2, 1/12 between. Equipment & Software: ; Software — Adobe/PageMaker, Adobe/Photoshop.
Delivery Method: Mail, Newsstand
Areas Served: 05033, 03785, 05821, 05039, 05042, 05043, 05045, 05051, 05054, 05069, 05074, 05075, 05076, 05081, 05085, 03740, 03765, 03768, 03771, 03774, 03777, 03779, 03780, 03279

BRATTLEBORO

THE COMMONS (WED)

139 Main St, Rm 604, Brattleboro, VT, 05301-2871, Windham, USA; gen tel (802) 246-6397; adv tel (802) 246-6397; ed tel (802) 246-6397; gen fax (802) 246-1319; adv fax (802) 246-1319; ed fax (802) 246-1319; disp adv e-mail ads@commonsnews.org; class adv e-mail ads@commonsnews.org; ed e-mail news@commonsnews.org; web site www.commonsnews.org
Circulation: 500pd, 10,500fr; Sworn/Estimate/Non-Audited
Advertising rate: Open inch rate $16.50
Established: 2006
Group: Vermont Independent Media, Inc.
Digital Platform - Mobile: Apple, Android, Windows
Digital Platform - Tablet: Apple iOS, Android, Windows 7
Adv. Dir.................................. Raechel Bennett
Mgr... Mia Gannon
Ed. ....Jeff Potter
Mechanical Specifications: PDF with fonts embedded, continuous tones 150 pixels per inch, line art 600 pixels per inch.
Delivery Method: Mail, Newsstand, Racks
Areas Served: 05301, 03451, 05345, 05353, 05359, 05355, 05343, 05148, 05143, 05146, 05154, 05141, 05101, 03609, 03608, 05158, 05346, 05341, 05363, 05354, 03466

COLCHESTER

THE COLCHESTER SUN (THUR)

462 Hegeman Ave, Ste 105, Colchester, VT, 05446-3187, Chittenden, USA; gen tel (802) 878-5282; adv tel (802) 878-5282; ed tel (802) 878-5282; gen fax (802) 651-9635; adv fax (802) 651-9635; ed fax (802) 651-9635; disp adv e-mail ewing@colchestersun.com; class adv e-mail kelly@colchestersun.com; ed e-mail news@colchestersun.com; web site www.colchester.essexreporter.com
Advertising rate: Open inch rate $10.00
Group: Lynn Publications Inc.
Addison County Independent
Digital Platform - Mobile: Apple, Android, Windows
Digital Platform - Tablet: Apple iOS, Android, Windows 7
Co-Pub...Angelo Lynn
Co-Pub......................................Emerson Lynn
Adv. Dir.......................................Wendy Ewing
Editor ....Maria Archangelo
Colin Flanders
Delivery Method: Mail, Racks
Areas Served: Chittenden County

ENOSBURG FALLS

COUNTY COURIER (THUR)

271 Main St, Enosburg Falls, VT, 05450-6109, Franklin, USA; gen tel (802) 933-4375; adv tel (802) 933-4375 ext. 100; ed tel (802) 933-4375 ext. 105; gen fax (802) 933-4907; adv fax (802) 933-4907; ed fax (802) 933-4907; disp adv e-mail courierads@gmail.com; class adv e-mail courierads@gmail.com; ed e-mail couriereditor@gmail.com; web site www.countycourier.net
Circulation: 3,000pd, 76fr; Sworn/Estimate/Non-Audited
Advertising rate: Open inch rate $8.40
Established: 1878
Digital Platform - Mobile: Apple, Android, Windows
Digital Platform - Tablet: Apple iOS, Android, Windows 7
Ed./Pub. .... Ed Shamy
Adv. Rep..Dan Rico
Mechanical Specifications: Type page 10 3/16 x 16; E - 5 cols, 11 1/2, 1/6 between; A - 5 cols, 1/6 between; C - 5 cols, 1/6 between.Equipment & Software: Hardware — APP/Macs.
Delivery Method: Mail
Areas Served: Franklin County

HARDWICK

THE HARDWICK GAZETTE (WED)

42 S MAIN ST, Hardwick, VT, 5843, Caledonia, USA; gen tel (802) 472-6521; adv tel (802) 472-6521; ed tel (802) 472-6521; gen fax (802) 472-6522; adv fax (802) 472-6522; ed fax (802) 472-6522; disp adv e-mail ads@thehardwickgazette.com; class adv e-mail ads@thehardwickgazette.com; ed e-mail news@thehardwickgazette.com
Circulation: 2,300pd, 35fr; USPS
Advertising rate: Open inch rate $7.25, net
Established: 1889
Pub./Ed. ....Ross Connelly
Circ. Mgr............................... Dawn Gustafson
Prodn. Mgr. ....Sandy Atkins
Mechanical Specifications: Type page 15 1/8 x 21 1/8; E - 7 cols, 2 1/16, between; A - 7 cols, 2 1/16, between; C - 7 cols, 2 1/16, between.Equipment & Software: Hardware — APP/Mac; Software — Adobe/InDdesign 5.5 Adobe/Photoshop 5.1
Delivery Method: Mail, Newsstand
Areas Served: 05843, 05647, 05648, 05826, 05827, 05836, 05841, 05842, 05658, 05667, 05873, 05680, 05681

KILLINGTON

THE MOUNTAIN TIMES (WED)

5465 ROUTE 4, Killington, VT, 5751, Rutland, USA; gen tel (802) 422-2399; adv tel (802) 422-2399; ed tel (802) 422-2399; gen fax (802) 422-2395; adv fax (802) 422-2395; ed fax (802) 422-2395; disp adv e-mail jason@mountaintimes.info; class adv e-mail jason@mountaintimes.info; ed e-mail editor@mountaintimes.info; web site www.mountaintimes.info
Circulation: 0pd, 10,000fr; Sworn/Estimate/Non-Audited
Advertising rate: Open inch rate $12.58
Group: Outer Limits Publishing
Digital Platform - Mobile: Apple, Android
Digital Platform - Tablet: Apple iOS, Android
Pub./Ed. ....Polly Lynn
Sales Mgr....................................Jason Mikula
Bus. Mgr.................................Erica Harrington
Mechanical Specifications: Type page 10 5/16 x 16; E - 6 cols, 1 7/12, 1/6 between; A - 6 cols, 1 7/12, 1/6 between; C - 6 cols, 1 7/12, 1/6 between.Equipment & Software: Hardware — APP/Mac; Software — Adobe/PageMaker 5.0.
Delivery Method: Mail, Racks
Areas Served: Killington, Rutland, and Central Vermont

MANCHESTER CENTER

MANCHESTER JOURNAL (FRI)

51 Memorial Ave, Manchester Center, VT, 05255-5100, Bennington, USA; gen tel (802) 362-2222; adv tel (802) 362-2222 ext. 4; ed tel (802) 362-2222 ext. 1; gen fax (802) 362-5327; adv fax (802) 362-5327; ed fax (802) 362-5327; disp adv e-mail news@manchesterjournal.com; class adv e-mail classified@benningtonbanner.com; ed e-mail amckeever@manchesterjournal.com; web site www.manchesternewspapers.com
Circulation: 15,000fr; Sworn/Estimate/Non-Audited
Advertising rate: Open inch rate $12.00
Established: 1861
Group: Birdland Acquisition LLC.
Digital Platform - Mobile: Apple, Android, Windows
Digital Platform - Tablet: Apple iOS, Android, Windows 7
Ed. .... Greg Sukiennik
Circ. Mgr.......................................Evan Pringle
Adv. Sales Mgr..................... Susan Plaisance
Pub...Alan English
Pres. .... Fredric Rutberg
Delivery Method: Mail, Newsstand, Racks
Areas Served: Bennington County

VERMONT NEWS GUIDE (WED)

105A BONNET ST, Manchester Center, VT, 05255-4488, Bennington, USA; gen tel (802) 362-3535; gen fax (802) 362-5368; disp adv e-mail jmurren@hersamacornvt.com; class adv e-mail dburgess@hersamacornvt.com; ed e-mail editor@hersamacornvt.com; web site www.vermontnews-guide.com
Circulation: 15,419fr; VAC
Advertising rate: Smallest modular rate: $48.00
Established: 1972
Ed. .... Liz Schafer
General Manager.......................Angie Leonard
Mechanical Specifications: Type page 7 1/2 x 9 3/4; E - 4 cols, 1 3/4, 1/6 between; A - 4 cols, 1 3/4, 1/6 between; C - 4 cols, 1 3/4, between.
Delivery Method: Mail, Newsstand, Racks
Areas Served: Bennington County

MIDDLEBURY

ADDISON COUNTY INDEPENDENT (MON, THUR)

58 Maple St, Middlebury, VT, 05753-1276, Addison, USA; gen tel (802) 388-4944; adv tel (802) 388-4944; ed tel (802) 388-4944; gen fax (802) 388-3100; adv fax (802) 388-3100; ed fax (802) 388-3100; disp adv e-mail ads@addisonindependent.com; class adv e-mail classifieds@addisonindependent.com; ed e-mail news@addisonindependent.com; web site www.addisonindependent.com
Circulation: 7,425pd,; Sworn/Estimate/Non-Audited
Advertising rate: Open inch rate $10.75
Established: 1946
Group: Addison County Independent
Ed./Pub. ....Angelo S. Lynn
Adv. Mgr. ....Christy Lynn
Prodn. Mgr. ....Susan Leggett
News Ed. ....John McCright
Mechanical Specifications: Type page 14 x 21; E - 6 cols, 2, 1/8 between.
Delivery Method: Mail, Newsstand
Areas Served: Addison County

GREEN MOUNTAIN OUTLOOK (WED)

16 Creek Rd, Middlebury, VT, 05753-1574, Addison, USA; gen tel (802) 388-6397; adv tel (802) 388-6397; ed tel (802) 388-6397; gen fax (802) 388-6399; adv fax (802) 388-6399; ed fax (802) 388-6399; disp adv e-mail andy@denpubs.com; class adv e-mail andy@denpubs.com; ed e-mail andy@denpubs.com; web site www.denpubs.com - 2,418(views) 1,059(visitors)
Circulation: 47pd, 6,766fr; CVC
Advertising rate: Open inch rate $16.50
Established: 1966
Digital Platform - Mobile: Apple, Android
Digital Platform - Tablet: Android
Pres./Pub. .... Edward Coats
Gen. Mgr. .... Mark Brady
Ed. ....Louis Varricchio
Mechanical Specifications: Type page 10 x 16; E - 6 cols
Delivery Method: Mail, Newsstand
Areas Served: Addison County

THE EAGLE (SAT)

16 Creek Rd, Ste 5A, Middlebury, VT, 05753-1376, Addison, USA; gen tel (802) 388-6397; adv tel (802) 388-6397; ed tel (802) 388-

6397; gen fax (802) 388-6399; adv fax (802) 388-6399; ed fax (802) 388-6399; disp adv e-mail addisoneagle@verizon.net; class adv e-mail addisoneagle@verizon.net; ed e-mail addisoneagle@verizon.net; web site www.suncommunitynews.com
Circulation: 176pd, 12,239fr; VAC
Advertising rate: Open inch rate $16.50
Established: 2000
Group: Sun Community News, Published by:Denton Publications, Inc.
Digital Platform - Mobile: Apple, Android
Digital Platform - Tablet: Android
Gen. Mgr. .... Mark Brady
Pub .... David Tyler
Adv. Consultant .... James Robinson
Circ. Mgr .... Jennifer Valenze
Managing Ed .... Louis Varricchio
Mechanical Specifications: Type page 10 x 16; 6 col
Delivery Method: Mail, Newsstand
Areas Served: Middlebury

MILTON

MILTON INDEPENDENT (THUR)
PO Box 163, Milton, VT, 05468-0163, Chittenden, USA; gen tel (802) 893-2028; adv tel (802) 893-2028 ext. 103; ed tel (802) 893-2028; gen fax (802) 893-7467; adv fax (802) 893-7467; ed fax (802) 893-7467; disp adv e-mail dillon@samessenger.com; class adv e-mail classifieds@samessenger.com; ed e-mail courtney@miltonindependent.com; web site www.miltonindependent.com
Advertising rate: Open inch rate $10.00
Established: 1993
Group: Addison County Independent
Digital Platform - Mobile: Windows
Digital Platform - Tablet: Windows 7
Pub .... Emerson Lynn
Ed. .... Courtney Lamdin
Delivery Method: Mail, Racks
Areas Served: Chittenden County

MORRISVILLE

NEWS & CITIZEN (TUES)
417 Brooklyn St, Morrisville, VT, 05661-8510, Lamoille, USA; gen tel (802) 888-2212; gen fax (802) 888-2173; disp adv e-mail irene@newsandcitizen.com; class adv e-mail news@newsandcitizen.com ; ed e-mail edit@newsandcitizen.com; web site www.newsandcitizen.com
Circulation: 2,700pd, 28fr; Sworn/Estimate/Non-Audited
Advertising rate: Open inch rate $6.50
Established: 1881
Digital Platform - Mobile: Windows
Digital Platform - Tablet: Windows 7
Pub .... Bradley A. Limoge
Ed. .... J.B. McKinley
Display Adv. Mgr. .... Irene NuzzoEquipment & Software: Hardware — APP/Mac; Presses — 4-G/Community; Software — Adobe/PageMaker, Adobe/Photoshop, Adobe/Illustrator.
Delivery Method: Mail, Newsstand, Racks
Areas Served: Lamoille County

THE TRANSCRIPT (THUR)
417 Brooklyn St, Morrisville, VT, 05661-8510, Lamoille, USA; gen tel (802) 888-2212; gen fax (802) 888-2173; disp adv e-mail irene@newsandcitizen.com; class adv e-mail news@newsandcitizen.com ; ed e-mail edit@newsandcitizen.com; web site www.newsandcitizen.com/transcript
Circulation: 15,559fr; USPS
Advertising rate: Open inch rate $8.50
Digital Platform - Mobile: Windows
Digital Platform - Tablet: Windows 7
Pub .... Bradley A. Limoge
Ed. .... J.B. McKinley
Display Adv. Mgr. .... Irene Nuzzo
Delivery Method: Mail, Newsstand, Racks
Areas Served: North Central Vermont

NORTHFIELD

THE NORTHFIELD NEWS (THUR)
PO Box 43, Northfield, VT, 05663-0043, Washington, USA; gen tel (802) 485-6397; adv tel (802) 485-6397; ed tel (802) 485-6397; disp adv e-mail northfieldnewsads@gmail.com; class adv e-mail northfieldnewsads@gmail.com; ed e-mail thenorthfieldnews@gmail.com; web site www.thenorthfieldnews.com
Circulation: 1,600pd,; Sworn/Estimate/Non-Audited
Advertising rate: Open inch rate $6.43
Established: 1878
Group: Northfield News Publishing, LLC.
Digital Platform - Mobile: Apple, Android, Windows, Blackberry
Digital Platform - Tablet: Apple iOS, Android, Windows 7, Blackberry Tablet OS
Ed. .... John Cruickshank
Adv. Dir .... Rob Wills
Sports Ed, Photographer .... Bill Croney
Mechanical Specifications: Type page 9 3/4 x 15; E - 5 cols, 1 5/6, 1/6 between; A - 5 cols, 1 5/6, 1/6 between; C - 5 cols, 1 5/6, 1/6 between.Equipment & Software: Hardware — APP/Mac; Software — APP/Mac System 7.5.
Delivery Method: Mail, Racks
Areas Served: Washington County

RANDOLPH

THE HERALD OF RANDOLPH (THUR)
30 Pleasant St, Randolph, VT, 05060-1156, Orange, USA; gen tel (802) 728-3232; adv tel (802) 728-3232; ed tel (802) 728-3232; gen fax (802) 728-9275; adv fax (802) 728-9275; ed fax (802) 728-9275; disp adv e-mail ads@ourherald.com; class adv e-mail ads@ourherald.com; ed e-mail news@ourherald.com; web site www.OurHerald.com
Circulation: 5,000pd,; Sworn/Estimate/Non-Audited
Advertising rate: Open inch rate $12.06
Established: 1874
Digital Platform - Mobile: Apple, Android, Windows, Blackberry
Digital Platform - Tablet: Apple iOS, Android, Windows 7, Blackberry Tablet OS
Editor Emeritus .... M. Dickey Drysdale
Mgr Ed .... Sandy Cooch
Ed & Pub .... Tim Calabro
Mechanical Specifications: Type page 13 x 20 1/2; E - 6 cols, 2 1/16, between; A - 6 cols, 2 1/16, between; C - 6 cols, 2 1/16, between. Equipment & Software: ; Software — In-Design
Microsoft Word
Delivery Method: Mail, Newsstand
Areas Served: Orange County and Windsor County

SAINT ALBANS

THE ESSEX REPORTER (THUR)
281 N Main St, Saint Albans, VT, 05478-2503, Chittenden, USA; gen tel (802) 878-5282; gen fax (802) 651-9635; disp adv e-mail ewing@essexreporter.com; class adv e-mail classified@essexreporter.com; ed e-mail news@essexreporter.com; web site www.essexreporter.com
Circulation: 8,800fr
Advertising rate: Open inch rate $10.00
Group: Lynn Publications Inc.
Addison County Independent
Digital Platform - Mobile: Apple, Android, Windows
Digital Platform - Tablet: Apple iOS, Android, Windows 7
Co-Pub .... Angelo Lynn
Co-Pub .... Emerson Lynn
Adv. Man. .... Wendy Ewing
Ed. and Co-publisher .... Maria Archangelo
Sports Ed .... Colin Flanders
Ed. .... Elsie Lynn
Delivery Method: Mail, Carrier, Racks
Areas Served: Chittenden County

SHELBURNE

SHELBURNE NEWS (THUR)
PO Box 1149, 233 Falls Road, Shelburne, VT, 05482-1149, Chittenden, USA; gen tel (802) 985-3091; adv tel (802) 985-3091; ed tel (802) 985-3091; gen fax n/a; adv fax n/a; ed fax n/a; disp adv e-mail wendy@sheburnenews.com; class adv e-mail wendy@sheburnenews.com; ed e-mail editor@sheburnenews.com; web site www.shelburnenews.com
Circulation: 0pd, 5,000fr; USPS
Advertising rate: modular
Established: 1982
Group: Stowe Reporter LLC
Digital Platform - Mobile: Windows
Digital Platform - Tablet: Windows 7
Adv. Dir .... Wendy Ewing
Ed. .... Lisa Scagliotti
Mechanical Specifications: Type page 10 1/4 x 15 3/4; E - 5 cols, between; A - 4 cols, 2 7/16, 1/5 between; C - 6 cols, 1 9/10, 1/4 between. Equipment & Software: Hardware — Micron, Vektron, Memtek; Presses — 3-G/486MFP; Software — Microsoft/Windows 98.
Delivery Method: Mail, Racks
Areas Served: Shelburne/Chittenden/05482

SOUTH BURLINGTON

THE OTHER PAPER (THUR)
1340 Williston Rd, Ste 201, South Burlington, VT, 05403-6469, Chittenden, USA; gen tel (802) 864-6670; adv tel (802) 864-6670; ed tel (802) 864-6670; gen fax (802) 864-3379; adv fax (802) 864-3379; ed fax (802) 864-3379; disp adv e-mail judy@otherpapersbvt.com; class adv e-mail classifieds@otherpapersbvt.com; ed e-mail editor@otherpapersbvt.com; web site www.otherpapersbvt.com
Advertising rate: Open inch rate $4.00
Established: 1977
Group: Burlington Area Newspaper Group
Digital Platform - Mobile: Apple, Android, Windows, Blackberry
Digital Platform - Tablet: Apple iOS, Android, Windows 7, Blackberry Tablet OS
Pub./Adv. Mgr .... Judy Kearns
Mng. Ed .... Nina Fedrizzi
Ed. .... Penne Tompkins
Delivery Method: Mail, Racks
Areas Served: Chittenden County

STOWE

STOWE REPORTER (THUR)
49 School St, Stowe, VT, 05672-4447, Lamoille, USA; gen tel (802) 253-2101; adv tel (802) 253-2101 ext. 13; ed tel (802) 253-2101 ext. 11; gen fax (802) 253-8332; disp adv e-mail ads@stowereporter.com; class adv e-mail classified@stowereporter.com; ed e-mail news@stowereporter.com; web site www.stowetoday.com
Circulation: 4,700pd,
Advertising rate: Open inch rate $9.28
Established: 1958
Group: Burlington Area Newspaper Group
Digital Platform - Mobile: Apple, Android, Blackberry
Digital Platform - Tablet: Apple iOS, Android, Blackberry Tablet OS
Publisher .... Greg Popa
Ed. .... Tom Kearney
Tommy Gardner
Delivery Method: Mail, Newsstand
Areas Served: Lamoille County

WATERBURY RECORD (THUR)
49 School St, Stowe, VT, 05672-4447, Lamoille, USA; gen tel (802) 253-2101; adv tel (802) 253-2101 ext. 13; ed tel (802) 253-2101 ext. 11; gen fax (802) 253-8332; adv fax (802) 253-8332; ed fax (802) 253-8332; disp adv e-mail sales@stowereporter.com; class adv e-mail ads@waterburyrecord.com; ed e-mail news@waterburyrecord.com; web site www.waterburyrecord.com
Circulation: 4,500fr; Sworn/Estimate/Non-Audited
Advertising rate: Open inch rate $7.65
Established: 2007
Digital Platform - Mobile: Apple, Android
Digital Platform - Tablet: Apple iOS, Android
Pub .... Greg Popa
Delivery Method: Mail, Newsstand
Areas Served: Washington County towns of Waterbury, Waterbury Center and Duxbury

WAITSFIELD

THE VALLEY REPORTER (THUR)
5222 Main St, Waitsfield, VT, 05673-4445, Washington, USA; gen tel (802) 496-3928; gen fax (802) 496-4703; disp adv e-mail ads@valleyreporter.com; class adv e-mail classifiedads@valleyreporter.com; ed e-mail lisa@valleyreporter.com; web site www.thevalleyreporter.com
Circulation: 3,200pd, 98fr; Sworn/Estimate/Non-Audited
Advertising rate: Open inch rate $8.72
Established: 1971
Group: Burlington Area Newspaper Group
Digital Platform - Mobile: Apple, Android, Windows
Digital Platform - Tablet: Apple iOS, Android, Windows 7
Pub .... Patricia A. Clark
Adv. Dir .... Jeff Knight
Ed. .... Lisa Loomis
Delivery Method: Mail, Newsstand, Racks
Areas Served: Duxbury, Warren, Waitsfield, Fayston, and Moretown

WILLISTON

WILLISTON OBSERVER (THUR)
300 Cornerstone Dr, Ste 330, Williston, VT, 05495-4045, Chittenden, USA; gen tel (802) 872-9000; adv tel (802) 872-9000 ext. 118; ed tel (802) 872-9000 ext. 117; gen fax (802) 872-0151; adv fax (802) 872-0151; ed fax (802) 872-0151; disp adv e-mail marianne@willistonobserver.com; class adv e-mail marianne@willistonobserver.com; ed e-mail editor@willistonobserver.com; web site www.willistonobserver.com
Circulation: 7,000fr; Sworn/Estimate/Non-Audited
Established: 1985
Group: Williston Publishing
Burlington Area Newspaper Group
Digital Platform - Mobile: Apple, Android
Digital Platform - Tablet: Apple iOS, Android
Sales Mgr .... Marianne Apfelbaum
Editor .... Jason Starr
Mechanical Specifications: Type page 10 1/4 x 16; E - 5 cols, 2, between; A - 5 cols, 2, between.Equipment & Software: ; Software — Adobe/PageMaker 6.5.
Delivery Method: Mail, Racks
Areas Served: Williston

WOODSTOCK

THE VERMONT STANDARD (WED)
PO Box 88, 43 Central Street, Woodstock, VT, 05091-0088, Windsor, USA; gen tel (802) 457-1313; gen fax (802) 457-3639; disp adv e-mail jestey@thevermontstadard.com; class adv e-mail pwebster@thevermontstandard.com; ed e-mail editor@thevermontstandard.com; web site www.thevermontstandard.com
14,000(visitors)
Circulation: 5,400pd,; Sworn/Estimate/Non-Audited
Advertising rate: Open inch rate $10.00
Established: 1853
Digital Platform - Mobile: Apple, Android, Windows
Digital Platform - Tablet: Apple iOS, Android, Windows 7
Pub .... Phillip Camp,Sr.
Gen. Mgr. .... Jon Estey

Ed. .... Gareth Henderson
Prodn. Mgr. .... Lisa Wright
Bus. Mgr. .... Jean Maynes
Adv. Rep. .... Jim Kelly
Office Coordinator .... Pattie Webster
Circ./ Bus. Columnist .... Mary Camp
Webmaster/Calendar/eEdition........Kat Fulcher
Advertising Representative..... Melanie Hanson
Delivery Method: Mail, Newsstand, Racks
Areas Served: Barnard, Bridgewater, Hartland, Killington, Plymouth, Pomfret, Reading, Quechee, West Windsor, and Woodstock

VIRGINIA

ACCOMAC

CHINCOTEAGUE BEACON (THUR)

23079 Courthouse Ave, Accomac, VA, 23301-1505, Accomack, USA; gen tel (757) 787-1200; adv tel (757)787-1200; ed tel (757)787-1200; gen fax (757) 787-2370; adv fax (757)787-2370; ed fax (757)787-2370; disp adv e-mail mmlewis@dmg.gannett.com; class adv e-mail krowan@dmg.gannett.com; ed e-mail tshockle@dmg.gannett.com; web site www.delmarvanow.com
Circulation: 10,000fr; Sworn/Estimate/Non-Audited
Advertising rate: Open inch rate $9.95
Established: 1956
Group: Gannett
Digital Platform - Mobile: Apple, Android, Windows, Blackberry
Digital Platform - Tablet: Apple iOS, Android, Windows 7, Blackberry Tablet OS
Exec. Ed. .... Mike Kilian
Mng. Ed. .... Ted Shockley
Adv. Dir. .... Robb Scott
VA Adv. Mgr. .... Megan Lewis
Delivery Method: Mail, Newsstand, Racks
Areas Served: Accomack County

ALEXANDRIA

ALEXANDRIA GAZETTE PACKET (THUR)

1606 King St, Alexandria, VA, 22314-2719, Alexandria City, USA; gen tel (703) 778-9410; adv tel (703) 778-9444; ed tel (703) 778-9433; gen fax (703) 778-9445; adv fax (703) 778-9445; ed fax (703) 778-9445; disp adv e-mail dfunk@connectionnewspapers.com; class adv e-mail sales@connectionnewspapers.com; ed e-mail mkimm@connectionnewspapers.com; web site www.connectionnewspapers.com - 502,543(views) 73,776(visitors)
Circulation: 105pd, 10,114fr; CVC
Advertising rate: 1/10 Pg $280.00; 1/5 Pg 460.00; 1/3 Pg $653.00
Established: 1784
Group: Connection Publishing, Inc.
Digital Platform - Mobile: Apple, Android, Windows, Blackberry
Digital Platform - Tablet: Apple iOS, Android, Windows 7, Blackberry Tablet OS
Pub./Ed. .... Mary Kimm
Exec. Vice Pres. .... Jerry Vernon
Adv. Dir. .... Debbie Funk
Circ. Mgr. .... Linda Pecquex
Editor-in-Chief .... Steven Mauren
Prod. Mgr .... Jean Card
Delivery Method: Mail, Newsstand
Areas Served: Fairfax County

ARLINGTON CONNECTION (THUR)

1606 King St, Alexandria, VA, 22314-2719, Alexandria City, USA; gen tel (703) 778-9410; adv tel (703) 778-9444; ed tel (703) 778-9433; gen fax (703) 778-9445; adv fax (703) 778-9445; ed fax (703) 778-9445; disp adv e-mail dfunk@connectionnewspapers.com; class adv e-mail sales@connectionnewspapers.com; ed e-mail mkimm@connectionnewspapers.com; web site www.connectionnewspapers.com - 502,543(views) 73,776(visitors)
Circulation: 0pd, 5,556fr; CVC
Advertising rate: 1/10 Pg $140.00; 1/5 Pg $230.00; 1/2 Pg $505.00
Established: 1988
Group: Connection Publishing, Inc.
Digital Platform - Mobile: Apple, Android, Windows, Blackberry
Digital Platform - Tablet: Apple iOS, Android, Windows 7, Blackberry Tablet OS
Pub./Ed. .... Mary Kimm
Exec. Vice Pres. .... Jerry Vernon
Nat'l Adv. Sales .... Debbie Funk
Circ. Mgr. .... Linda Pecquex
CEO/Pres. .... Peter C. Labovitz
Prod. Mgr .... Jean Card
Delivery Method: Mail, Newsstand
Areas Served: Fairfax County

BURKE CONNECTION (THUR)

1606 King St, Alexandria, VA, 22314-2719, Alexandria City, USA; gen tel (703) 778-9410; adv tel (703) 778-9444; ed tel (703) 778-9433; gen fax (703) 778-9445; adv fax (703) 778-9445; ed fax (703) 778-9445; disp adv e-mail dfunk@connectionnewspapers.com; class adv e-mail sales@connectionnewspapers.com; ed e-mail mkimm@connectionnewspapers.com; web site www.connectionnewspapers.com - 502,543(views) 73,776(visitors)
Circulation: 0pd, 5,963fr; CVC
Advertising rate: 1/10 Pg $140.00; 1/5 Pg $230.00; 1/2 Pg $505.00
Established: 1988
Group: Connection Publishing, Inc.
Digital Platform - Mobile: Apple, Android, Windows, Blackberry
Digital Platform - Tablet: Apple iOS, Android, Windows 7, Blackberry Tablet OS
Pub./Ed. .... Mary Kimm
Exec. Vice Pres. .... Jerry Vernon
Adv. Dir. .... Debbie Funk
Circ. Mgr. .... Linda Pecquex
Pres./CEO .... Peter C. Labovitz
Prod. Mgr .... Jean Card
Delivery Method: Mail, Newsstand
Areas Served: Fairfax County

CENTRE VIEW (THUR)

1606 King St, Alexandria, VA, 22314-2719, Alexandria City, USA; gen tel (703) 778-9410; adv tel (703) 778-9444; ed tel (703) 778-9433; gen fax (703) 778-9445; adv fax (703) 778-9445; ed fax (703) 778-9445; disp adv e-mail dfunk@connectionnewspapers.com; class adv e-mail sales@connectionnewspapers.com; ed e-mail mkimm@connectionnewspapers.com; web site www.connectionnewspapers.com - 502,543(views) 73,776(visitors)
Circulation: 2pd, 4,745fr; CVC
Advertising rate: 1/10 Pg $140.00; 1/5 Pg $230.00; 1/2 Pg $505.00
Established: 1988
Group: Connection Publishing, Inc.
Digital Platform - Mobile: Apple, Android, Windows, Blackberry
Digital Platform - Tablet: Apple iOS, Android, Windows 7, Blackberry Tablet OS
Pub./Ed. .... Mary Kimm
Exec. Vice Pres. .... Jerry Vernon
Adv. Dir. .... Debbie Funk
Circ. Mgr. .... Linda Pecquex
Pres./CEO .... Peter C. Labovitz
Prod. Mgr .... Jean Card
Delivery Method: Mail, Newsstand
Areas Served: Fairfax County

FAIRFAX CONNECTION (THUR)

1606 King St, Alexandria, VA, 22314-2719, Alexandria City, USA; gen tel (703) 778-9410; adv tel (703) 778-9444; ed tel (703) 778-9433; gen fax (703) 778-9445; adv fax (703) 778-9445; ed fax (703) 778-9445; disp adv e-mail dfunk@connectionnewspapers.com; class adv e-mail sales@connectionnewspapers.com; ed e-mail mkimm@connectionnewspapers.com; web site www.connectionnewspapers.com - 502,543(views) 73,776(visitors)
Circulation: 0pd, 4,952fr; CVC
Advertising rate: 1/10 Pg $140.00; 1/5 Pg $230.00; 1/2 Pg $505.00
Established: 1986
Group: Connection Publishing, Inc.
Digital Platform - Mobile: Apple, Android, Windows, Blackberry
Digital Platform - Tablet: Apple iOS, Android, Windows 7, Blackberry Tablet OS
Pub./Ed. .... Mary Kimm
Exec. Vice Pres. .... Jerry Vernon
Adv. Dir. .... Debbie Funk
CEO/Pub. .... Peter C. Labovitz
Prod. Mgr .... Jean Card
Circ. Mgr .... Linda Pecquex
Delivery Method: Mail, Newsstand
Areas Served: Fairfax County

FAIRFAX STATION/CLIFTON/LORTON CONNECTION (THUR)

1606 King St, Alexandria, VA, 22314-2719, Alexandria City, USA; gen tel (703) 778-9410; adv tel (703) 778-9444; ed tel (703) 778-9433; gen fax (703) 778-9445; adv fax (703) 778-9445; ed fax (703) 778-9445; disp adv e-mail dfunk@connectionnewspapers.com; class adv e-mail sales@connectionnewspapers.com; ed e-mail mkimm@connectionnewspapers.com; web site www.connectionnewspapers.com - 502,543(views) 73,776(visitors)
Circulation: 0pd, 6,594fr; CVC
Advertising rate: 1/10 Pg $140.00; 1/5 Pg $230.00; 1/2 Pg $505.00
Established: 1988
Group: Connection Publishing, Inc.
Digital Platform - Mobile: Apple, Android, Windows, Blackberry
Digital Platform - Tablet: Apple iOS, Android, Windows 7, Blackberry Tablet OS
Pub./Ed. .... Mary Kimm
Exec. Vice Pres. .... Jerry Vernon
Adv. Dir. .... Debbie Funk
Pres./CEO .... Peter C. Labovitz
Circ. Mgr .... Linda Pecquex
Prod. Mgr .... Jean Card
Delivery Method: Mail, Newsstand
Areas Served: Fairfax County

GREAT FALLS CONNECTION (THUR)

1606 King St, Alexandria, VA, 22314-2719, Alexandria City, USA; gen tel (703) 778-9410; adv tel (703) 778-9444; ed tel (703) 778-9433; gen fax (703) 778-9445; adv fax (703) 778-9445; ed fax (703) 778-9445; disp adv e-mail dfunk@connectionnewspapers.com; class adv e-mail sales@connectionnewspapers.com; ed e-mail mkimm@connectionnewspapers.com; web site www.connectionnewspapers.com - 502,543(views) 7(visitors)
Circulation: 1pd, 6,088fr; CVC
Advertising rate: 1/10 Pg $140.00; 1/5 Pg $230.00; 1/2 Pg $505.00
Established: 1988
Group: Connection Publishing, Inc.
Digital Platform - Mobile: Apple, Android, Windows, Blackberry
Digital Platform - Tablet: Apple iOS, Android, Windows 7, Blackberry Tablet OS
Pub./Ed. .... Mary Kimm
Exec. Vice Pres. .... Jerry Vernon
Adv. Dir. .... Debbie Funk
Pres./CEO .... Peter C. Labovitz
Circ. Mgr .... Linda Pecquex
Prod. Mgr .... Jean Card
Delivery Method: Mail, Newsstand
Areas Served: Fairfax County

MCLEAN CONNECTION (THUR)

1606 King St, Alexandria, VA, 22314-2719, Alexandria City, USA; gen tel (703) 778-9410; adv tel (703) 778-9444; ed tel (703) 778-9433; gen fax (703) 778-9445; adv fax (703) 778-9445; ed fax (703) 778-9445; disp adv e-mail dfunk@connectionnewspapers.com; class adv e-mail sales@connectionnewspapers.com; ed e-mail mkimm@connectionnewspapers.com; web site www.connectionnewspapers.com - 502,543(views) 73,776(visitors)
Circulation: 0pd, 6,987fr; CVC
Advertising rate: 1/10 Pg $140.00; 1/5 Pg $230.00; 1/2 Pg $505.00
Established: 1988
Group: Connection Publishing, Inc.
Digital Platform - Mobile: Apple, Android, Windows, Blackberry
Digital Platform - Tablet: Apple iOS, Android, Windows 7, Blackberry Tablet OS
Pub./Ed. .... Mary Kimm
Exec. Vice Pres. .... Jerry Vernon
Adv. Dir. .... Debbie Funk
Pres./CEO .... Peter C. Labovitz
Prod. Mgr .... Jean Card
Circ. Mgr .... Linda Pecquex
Delivery Method: Mail, Newsstand
Areas Served: Fairfax County

MOUNT VERNON GAZETTE (THUR)

1606 King St, Alexandria, VA, 22314-2719, Alexandria City, USA; gen tel (703) 778-9410; adv tel (703) 778-9444; ed tel (703) 778-9433; gen fax (703) 778-9445; adv fax (703) 778-9445; ed fax (703) 778-9445; disp adv e-mail dfunk@connectionnewspapers.com; class adv e-mail sales@connectionnewspapers.com; ed e-mail mkimm@connectionnewspapers.com; web site www.connectionnewspapers.com - 502,543(views) 73,776(visitors)
Circulation: 27pd, 8,724fr; CVC
Advertising rate: 1/10 Pg $140.00; 1/5 Pg $230.00; 1/2 Pg $505.00
Established: 1989
Group: Connection Publishing, Inc.
Digital Platform - Mobile: Apple, Android, Windows, Blackberry
Digital Platform - Tablet: Apple iOS, Android, Windows 7, Blackberry Tablet OS
Pub./Ed. .... Mary Kimm
Exec. Vice Pres. .... Jerry Vernon
Adv. Dir. .... Debbie Funk
Pres./CEO .... Peter C. Labovitz
Circ. Mgr .... Linda Pecquex
Prod. Mgr .... Jean Card
Delivery Method: Mail, Newsstand
Areas Served: Fairfax County

OAK HILL/HERNDON CONNECTION (THUR)

1606 King St, Alexandria, VA, 22314-2719, Alexandria City, USA; gen tel (703) 778-9410; adv tel (703) 778-9444; ed tel (703) 778-9433; gen fax (703) 778-9445; adv fax (703) 778-9445; ed fax (703) 778-9445; disp adv e-mail dfunk@connectionnewspapers.com; class adv e-mail sales@connectionnewspapers.com; ed e-mail mkimm@connectionnewspapers.com; web site www.connectionnewspapers.com - 502,543(views) 73,776(visitors)
Circulation: 0pd, 3,450fr; CVC
Advertising rate: 1/10 Pg $140.00; 1/5 Pg $230.00; 1/2 Pg $505.00
Established: 1988
Group: Connection Publishing, Inc.
Digital Platform - Mobile: Apple, Android, Windows, Blackberry
Digital Platform - Tablet: Apple iOS, Android, Windows 7, Blackberry Tablet OS
Pub./Ed. .... Mary Kimm
Exec. Vice Pres. .... Jerry Vernon
Adv. Dir. .... Debbie Funk
Pres./CEO .... Peter C. Labovitz
Prod. Mgr .... Jean Card
Circ. Mgr .... Linda Pecquex
Delivery Method: Mail, Newsstand
Areas Served: Fairfax County

POTOMAC ALMANAC (THUR)

1606 King St, Alexandria, VA, 22314-2719, Alexandria City, USA; gen tel (703) 778-9410; adv tel (703) 778-9444; ed tel (703) 778-9433; gen fax (703) 778-9445; adv fax (703) 778-9445; ed fax (703) 778-9445; disp adv e-mail dfunk@connectionnewspapers.com; class adv e-mail sales@connectionnewspapers.com; ed e-mail mkimm@connectionnewspapers.com; web site www.connectionnewspapers.com - 502,543(views) 73,776(visitors)
Circulation: 0pd, 6,528fr; CVC
Advertising rate: 1/10 Pg $140.00; 1/5 Pg $230.00; 1/2 Pg $505.00
Established: 1957
Group: Connection Publishing, Inc.

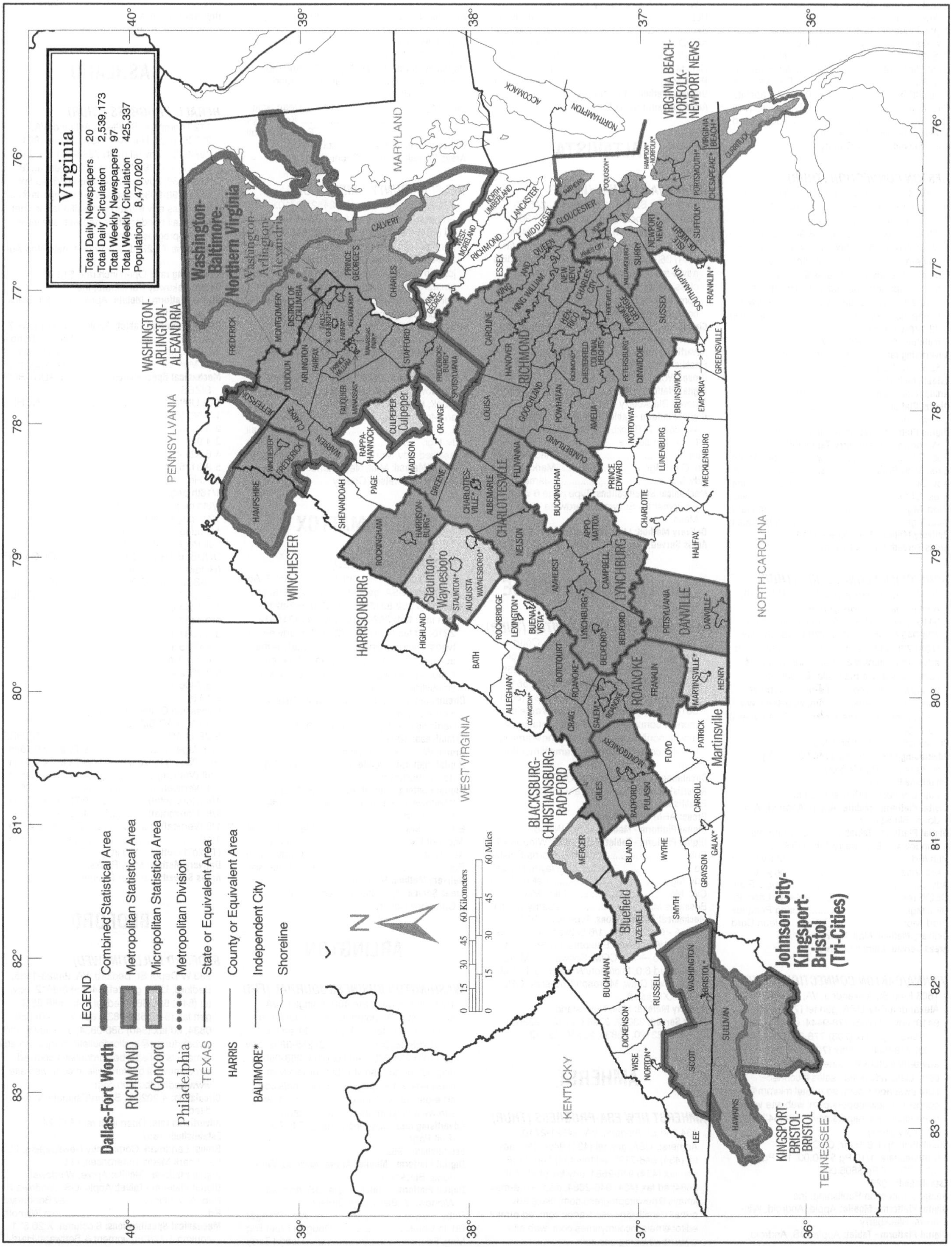
Virginia
Total Daily Newspapers 20
Total Daily Circulation 2,539,173
Total Weekly Newspapers 97
Total Weekly Circulation 425,337
Population 8,470,020
LEGEND
Dallas-Fort Worth Combined Statistical Area
RICHMOND Metropolitan Statistical Area
Concord Micropolitan Statistical Area
Philadelphia Metropolitan Division
TEXAS State or Equivalent Area
HARRIS County or Equivalent Area
BALTIMORE* Independent City
Shoreline
0 15 30 45 60 Kilometers
0 15 30 45 60 Miles
Washington-Baltimore-Northern Virginia
Washington-Arlington-Alexandria
WASHINGTON-ARLINGTON-ALEXANDRIA
WINCHESTER
HARRISONBURG
Staunton-Waynesboro
Culpeper
CHARLOTTESVILLE
RICHMOND
LYNCHBURG
DANVILLE
ROANOKE
Martinsville
BLACKSBURG-CHRISTIANSBURG-RADFORD
Bluefield
Johnson City-Kingsport-Bristol (Tri-Cities)
KINGSPORT-BRISTOL-BRISTOL
VIRGINIA BEACH-NORFOLK-NEWPORT NEWS
PENNSYLVANIA
MARYLAND
WEST VIRGINIA
KENTUCKY
TENNESSEE
NORTH CAROLINA
76°
77°
78°
79°
80°
81°
82°
83°
36°
37°
38°
39°
40°

Digital Platform - Mobile: Apple, Android, Windows, Blackberry
Digital Platform - Tablet: Apple iOS, Android, Windows 7, Blackberry Tablet OS
Pub./Ed. .... Mary Kimm
Exec. Vice Pres. .... Jerry Vernon
Adv. Dir. .... Debbie Funk
Pres./CEO .... Peter C. Labovitz
Circ. Mgr .... Linda Pecquex
Prod. Mgr .... Jean Card
Delivery Method: Mail, Newsstand
Areas Served: Fairfax County

RESTON CONNECTION (THUR)

1606 King St, Alexandria, VA, 22314-2719, Alexandria City, USA; gen tel (703) 778-9410; adv tel (703) 778-9444; ed tel (703) 778-9433; gen fax (703) 778-9445; adv fax (703) 778-9445; ed fax (703) 778-9445; disp adv e-mail dfunk@connectionnewspapers.com; class adv e-mail sales@connectionnewspapers.com; ed e-mail mkimm@connectionnewspapers.com; web site www.connectionnewspapers.com - 502,543(views) 73,776(visitors)
Circulation: 0pd, 6,650fr; CVC
Advertising rate: 1/10 Pg $140.00; 1/5 Pg $230.00; 1/2 Pg $505.00
Established: 1988
Group: Connection Publishing, Inc.
Digital Platform - Mobile: Apple, Android, Windows, Blackberry
Digital Platform - Tablet: Apple iOS, Android, Windows 7, Blackberry Tablet OS
Pub./Ed. .... Mary Kimm
Exec. Vice Pres. .... Jerry Vernon
Adv. Dir. .... Debbie Funk
Pres./CEO .... Peter C. Labovitz
Prod. Mgr .... Jean Card
Circ. Mgr .... Linda Pecquex
Delivery Method: Mail, Newsstand
Areas Served: Fairfax County

SPRINGFIELD CONNECTION (THUR)

1606 King St, Alexandria, VA, 22314-2719, Alexandria City, USA; gen tel (703) 778-9410; adv tel (703) 778-9444; ed tel (703) 778-9433; gen fax (703) 778-9445; adv fax (703) 778-9445; ed fax (703) 778-9445; disp adv e-mail dfunk@connectionnewspapers.com; class adv e-mail sales@connectionnewspapers.com; ed e-mail mkimm@connectionnewspapers.com; web site www.connectionnewspapers.com - 502,543(views) 73,776(visitors)
Circulation: 3pd, 4,610fr; CVC
Advertising rate: 1/10 Pg $140.00; 1/5 Pg $230.00; 1/2 Pg $505.00
Established: 1995
Group: Connection Publishing, Inc.
Digital Platform - Mobile: Apple, Android, Windows, Blackberry
Digital Platform - Tablet: Apple iOS, Android, Windows 7, Blackberry Tablet OS
Pub./Ed. .... Mary Kimm
Exec. Vice Pres. .... Jerry Vernon
Adv. Dir. .... Debbie Funk
CEO/Pres. .... Peter C. Labovitz
Circ. Mgr .... Linda Pecquex
Prod. Mgr .... Jean Card
Delivery Method: Mail, Newsstand
Areas Served: Fairfax County

VIENNA/OAKTON CONNECTION (THUR)

1606 King St, Alexandria, VA, 22314-2719, Alexandria City, USA; gen tel (703) 778-9410; adv tel (703) 778-9444; ed tel (703) 778-9433; gen fax (703) 778-9445; adv fax (703) 778-9445; ed fax (703) 778-9445; disp adv e-mail dfunk@connectionnewspapers.com; class adv e-mail sales@connectionnewspapers.com; ed e-mail mkimm@connectionnewspapers.com; web site www.connectionnewspapers.com - 502,543(views) 73,776(visitors)
Circulation: 1pd, 6,180fr; CVC
Advertising rate: 1/10 Pg $140.00; 1/5 Pg $230.00; 1/2 Pg $505.00
Established: 1988
Group: Connection Publishing, Inc.
Digital Platform - Mobile: Apple, Android, Windows, Blackberry
Digital Platform - Tablet: Apple iOS, Android, Windows 7, Blackberry Tablet OS
Pub./Ed. .... Mary Kimm
Exec. Vice Pres. .... Jerry Vernon
Adv. Dir. .... Debbie Funk
Pres./CEO .... Peter C. Labovitz
Circ. Mgr .... Linda Pecquex
Prod. Mgr .... Jean Card
Delivery Method: Mail, Newsstand
Areas Served: Fairfax County

ALTAVISTA

ALTAVISTA JOURNAL (WED)

1007 Main St, # A, Altavista, VA, 24517-1530, Campbell, USA; gen tel (434) 369-6688; adv tel (434) 369-6688; ed tel (434) 369-6688; gen fax (434) 369-6689; adv fax (434) 369-6689; ed fax (434) 369-6689; disp adv e-mail j.wood@altavistajournal.com; class adv e-mail aljournal@altavistajournal.com; ed e-mail m.thomas@altavistajournal.com; web site www.altavistajournal.com
Circulation: 16,200pd, 120fr; Sworn/Estimate/Non-Audited
Advertising rate: Open inch rate $10.25
Established: 1909
Group: Womack Publishing Co.
Digital Platform - Mobile: Apple, Android, Windows, Blackberry
Digital Platform - Tablet: Apple iOS, Android, Windows 7, Blackberry Tablet OS, Kindle, Nook, Kindle Fire
Pub .... Chad Harrison
Ed./Gen. Mgr. .... Mark Thomas
Adv. Mgr. .... Jamie Glass
Mechanical Specifications: Type page 6 x 21 1/2. Equipment & Software: Hardware — APP/Macs.
Delivery Method: Mail, Newsstand, Racks
Areas Served: Campbell County

AMELIA COURT HOUSE

THE AMELIA BULLETIN MONITOR (THUR)

16311 Goodes Bridge Rd, Amelia Court House, VA, 23002-4837, Amelia, USA; gen tel (804) 561-3655; adv tel (804) 561-3655; ed tel (804) 561-3655; gen fax (804) 561-2065; adv fax (804) 561-2065; ed fax (804) 561-2065; disp adv e-mail bekki@ameliamonitor.com; class adv e-mail contactus@ameliamonitor.com; ed e-mail ann@ameliamonitor.com; web site www.ameliamonitor.com
Circulation: 2,000pd, 8,500fr; USPS
Advertising rate: Open inch rate $8.25
Established: 1972
Group: ABM Enterprises Inc.
Digital Platform - Mobile: Apple, Windows
Digital Platform - Tablet: Apple iOS, Windows 7
Pub .... Ann B. Morris-Salster
Ed. .... Wayne Russell
Adv. Mgr. .... Bekki Morris
Circ. Mgr. .... Julee McConnell
Business Mgr. .... Cathy Banton
Mechanical Specifications: Type page 10 3/8 x 16; A - 6 cols, 1 2/3, 1/6 between; C - 6 cols, 1 2/3, 1/6 between.Equipment & Software: Hardware — PC, COM; Software — Microsoft/Word 6.0, Microsoft/Windows 3.1, Archetype/Corel Draw, Microsoft/Publisher, QPS/QuarkXPress 5.
Delivery Method: Mail, Newsstand
Areas Served: 23002, 23083, 23105, 23966, 23930, 23120, 23833, 23850, 23832

AMHERST

AMHERST NEW ERA-PROGRESS (THUR)

134 2nd St, Amherst, VA, 24521-2710, Amherst, USA; gen tel (434) 946-7195; adv tel (434) 946-7195; ed tel (434) 946-7196; gen fax (434) 946-2684; adv fax (434) 946-2684; ed fax (434) 946-2684; disp adv e-mail kmays@neweraprogress.com; class adv e-mail dsmith@newsadvance.com; ed e-mail editor@nelsoncountytimes.com; web site www.neweraprogress.com
Circulation: 3,943pd,; AAM
Advertising rate: Open inch rate $6.10
Group: World Media Enterprises Inc.
Digital Platform - Mobile: Apple, Android, Windows, Blackberry
Digital Platform - Tablet: Apple iOS, Android, Windows 7, Blackberry Tablet OS, Kindle, Nook, Kindle Fire
Gen. Mgr. .... Dean Smith
Adv. Dir. .... Kelly Mays
Ed. .... Scott Marshall
Delivery Method: Mail, Newsstand
Areas Served: Amherst County

NELSON COUNTY TIMES (THUR)

134 2nd St, Amherst, VA, 24521-2710, Amherst, USA; gen tel (434) 385-5450; adv tel (434) 946-7195; ed tel (434) 946-7196; gen fax (434) 946-2684; adv fax (434) 946-2684; ed fax (434) 946-2684; disp adv e-mail jobrien@newsadvance.com; class adv e-mail cmarsh@neweraprogress.com; ed e-mail editor@nelsoncountytimes.com; web site www.nelsoncountytimes.com
Advertising rate: Open inch rate $9.20
Group: World Media Enterprises Inc.
Digital Platform - Mobile: Apple, Android, Windows, Blackberry
Digital Platform - Tablet: Apple iOS, Android, Windows 7, Blackberry Tablet OS, Kindle, Nook, Kindle Fire
Gen. Mgr. .... Dean Smith
Ed. .... Scott Marshall
Adv. Mgr. .... Jeffrey O'Brien
Classified Adv. Mgr. .... Cathy Marsh
Delivery Method: Mail, Newsstand
Areas Served: Nelson County

APPOMATTOX

TIMES-VIRGINIAN (WED)

589 COURT ST, Appomattox, VA, 24522, Appomattox, USA; gen tel (434) 352-8215; adv tel (434) 352-8215; ed tel (434) 352-8215; gen fax (434) 352-2216; adv fax (434) 352-2216; ed fax (434) 352-2216; disp adv e-mail tvads@timesvirginian.com; class adv e-mail accounts@timesvirginian.com; ed e-mail editor@timesvirginian.com; web site www.timesvirginian.com
Circulation: 4,000pd, 4,800fr; Sworn/Estimate/Non-Audited
Advertising rate: Open inch rate $9.75
Established: 1892
Group: Womack Publishing Co.
Digital Platform - Mobile: Apple, Android, Windows, Blackberry
Digital Platform - Tablet: Apple iOS, Android, Windows 7, Blackberry Tablet OS, Kindle, Nook, Kindle Fire
Ed./Gen. Mgr. .... Marvin Hamlet
Account Exec. .... Lisa Irvin
Adv. Mgr. .... Cindy Smith
Pub .... Chad Harrison
Delivery Method: Mail, Racks
Areas Served: Appomattox, Buckingham, and Campbell County

ARLINGTON

WASHINGTON BUSINESS JOURNAL (FRI)

1555 Wilson Blvd, Ste 400, Arlington, VA, 22209-2405, Arlington, USA; gen tel (703) 258-0800; adv tel (703) 258-0800; ed tel (703) 258-0820; gen fax (703) 258-0802; adv fax (703) 258-0802; ed fax (703) 258-0802; disp adv e-mail ssmith@bizjournals.com; class adv e-mail skaplan@bizjournals.com; ed e-mail dfruehling@bizjournals.com; web site www.bizjournals.com/washington
Advertising rate: Open inch rate $7,840.00 (Full-Page)
Established: 1982
Digital Platform - Mobile: Apple, Android, Windows, Blackberry
Digital Platform - Tablet: Apple iOS, Android, Windows 7, Blackberry Tablet OS
Pub .... Alex Orfinger
Ed. In Chief .... Douglas Fruehling
Mng. Ed .... Robert Terry
Adv. Dir. .... Sandy Smith
Delivery Method: Mail, Racks
Areas Served: Arlington County

ASHLAND

HERALD-PROGRESS (THUR)

112 Thompson St, Ste C, Ashland, VA, 23005-1527, Hanover, USA; gen tel (804) 798-9031; adv tel (804) 798-9031 ext. 220; ed tel (804) 798-9031 ext. 203; gen fax (804) 798-9036; adv fax (804) 798-9036; ed fax (804) 798-9036; disp adv e-mail hpads@lcs.net; class adv e-mail hpclassifieds@lcs.net; ed e-mail hpeditor@lcs.net; web site www.herald-progress.com
Circulation: 7,527pd,; Sworn/Estimate/Non-Audited
Advertising rate: Open inch rate $18.00
Group: Lakeway Publishers, Inc.
Digital Platform - Mobile: Apple, Android, Blackberry, Other
Digital Platform - Tablet: Apple iOS, Windows 7
Pub .... William Trimble
Ed. .... Greg Glassner
Adv. Mgr. .... Julia Wigginton
Mechanical Specifications: DISPLAY ADS: ROP SIZES
COLUMNS .... INCHES
1 1.5625 in
2 3.25 in
3 4.9375 in
4 6.625 in
5 8.3125 in
6 10 in
1/16th page 2 col x 4 in
1/8th page 3 col x 5.25 in
1/4th page 3 col x 10.5 in
1/2 page 6 col x 10.5 in
Full Page - 6 col x 21 in
DOUBLE TRUCK 21 in X 21 in + FOLIO LINE
(Retail Gutter: .125)
CLASSIFIED 8 COLUMN WIDTH SIZES:
COLUMNS .... INCHES
1 1.1844 in
2 2.4437 in
3 3.7031 in
4 4.9625 in
5 6.2219 in
6 7.4812 in
7 8.7406 in
8 10 in
(Classified Gutter: .075 in)
TABLOID AD SIZES:
SIZE of AD .... INCHES
Full Page .... 9.75 in x 9.75 in
Half Page (Horizontal) .... 9.75 in x 4.75 in
Half (Vertical) .... 4.75 in x 9.75 in
1/4 (Vertical) .... 4.75 in x 4.75 in
1/4 (Horizontal) .... 9.75 in x 2.25 in
1/8 (Horizontal) .... 4.75 in x 2.25 in
1/8 (Vertical) .... 2.25 in x 4.5 in
1/16 .... 4.75 in x 1 in
(Tabloid Gutter: .125 in)
Delivery Method: Mail, Racks
Areas Served: Hanover County

BEDFORD

BEDFORD BULLETIN (WED)

233 W Depot St, Bedford, VA, 24523-1935, Bedford, USA; gen tel (540) 586-8612; adv tel (540) 586-8612; ed tel (540) 586-8612; gen fax (540) 586-0834; adv fax (540) 586-0834; ed fax (540) 586-0834; disp adv e-mail jaybondurant@bedfordbulletin.com; class adv e-mail classified@bedfordbulletin.com; ed e-mail news@bedfordbulletin.com; web site www.bedfordbulletin.com
Circulation: 4,202pd,; Sworn/Estimate/Non-Audited
Advertising rate: Open inch rate $12.24
Established: 1857
Group: Landmark Community Newspapers, LLC Landmark Media Enterprises, LLC
Digital Platform - Mobile: Apple, Windows
Digital Platform - Tablet: Apple iOS, Windows 7
Pub./Adv. Mgr. .... Jay Bondurant
Ed. .... Tom Wilmoth
Mechanical Specifications: 6 column X 20.5" 1 coulmn 1.778"Equipment & Software: Hard-

ware — Editorial and graphics Macintosch; Software — Indesign
Delivery Method: Mail, Newsstand, Racks
Areas Served: 24523, 24122, 24174, 24179, 24101, 24095, 24121, 24104, 24551, 24556, 24526

BIG STONE GAP

THE POST (THUR)
215 Wood Ave E, Big Stone Gap, VA, 24219-2823, Wise, USA; gen tel (276) 523-1141; gen fax (276) 523-1175; disp adv e-mail ktate@coalfield.com ; web site thecoalfield-progress.com
Account Exec....Karen Tate
Office Mgr....Marilyn Young
Circ. Mgr....Becky McElroy
News Ed....Glen Gannaway
Sports Ed....Sam Dixon

BLACKSTONE

COURIER-RECORD (WED)
111 W Maple St, Blackstone, VA, 23824-1707, Nottoway, USA; gen tel (434) 292-3019; adv tel (434) 292-3019; ed tel (434) 292-6397; gen fax (434) 292-5966; adv fax (434) 292-5966; ed fax (434) 292-5966; disp adv e-mail john@courier-record.com; class adv e-mail ads@courier-record.com; ed e-mail news@courier-record.com; web site www.courier-record.com
Circulation: 5,219pd, 0fr; Sworn/Estimate/Non-Audited
Advertising rate: Open inch rate $7.00
Established: 1890
Group: Nottoway Publishing Company
Digital Platform - Mobile: Apple, Android, Windows, Blackberry
Digital Platform - Tablet: Apple iOS, Android, Windows 7, Blackberry Tablet OS, Kindle, Nook, Kindle Fire
Publisher....James Coleburn
Advertising Manager....John Coleburn
Editor....William Coleburn
Advertising Department / Graphic DesignerJeff Martin
Advertising Representative....Scott Matthew
Advertising Representative....Jeff Clements
Office Manager....Donna Pridemore
Assistant Office Manager....Karlie Smith
Mechanical Specifications: Type page 13 x 20; 5 column formatEquipment & Software: Hardware — APP/Mac; Presses — G/Community; Software — Adobe/PageMaker 6.0.
Delivery Method: Mail, Newsstand
Areas Served: Nottoway County; Lunenburg County; Dinwiddie County; Amelia County; Brunswick County; Prince Edward County

BOWLING GREEN

THE CAROLINE PROGRESS (THUR)
204 N Main St, Bowling Green, VA, 22427-9416, Caroline, USA; gen tel (804) 633-5005; adv tel (804) 633-5005; ed tel (804) 633-5005; gen fax (804) 633-6740; adv fax (804) 633-6740; ed fax (804) 633-6740; disp adv e-mail cpadvertising@lcs.net; class adv e-mail cpclassifieds@lcs.net; ed e-mail cpeditor@lcs.net; web site www.caroline-progress.com
Circulation: 2,800pd, 30fr; Sworn/Estimate/Non-Audited
Advertising rate: Open inch rate $14.45
Group: Lakeway Publishers, Inc.
Digital Platform - Mobile: Apple, Android, Windows, Blackberry
Digital Platform - Tablet: Apple iOS, Android, Windows 7, Blackberry Tablet OS, Kindle, Nook, Kindle Fire
Publisher....Mosby Wigginton
Editor....Constance Snow
Delivery Method: Mail, Newsstand, Racks
Areas Served: Caroline County

BROOKNEAL

THE UNION STAR (WED)
241 MAIN ST, Brookneal, VA, 24528, Campbell, USA; gen tel (434) 376-2795; adv tel (434) 376-2795; ed tel (434) 376-2795; gen fax (434) 376-2676; adv fax (434) 376-2676; ed fax (434) 376-2676; disp adv e-mail ads@altavistajournal.com; class adv e-mail ads@theunionstar.com; ed e-mail news@theunion-star.com; web site www.theunionstar.com
Circulation: 2,850pd, 50fr; Sworn/Estimate/Non-Audited
Advertising rate: Open inch rate $9.95
Established: 1906
Group: Womack Publishing Co.
Digital Platform - Mobile: Apple, Android, Windows, Blackberry
Digital Platform - Tablet: Apple iOS, Android, Windows 7, Blackberry Tablet OS, Kindle, Nook, Kindle Fire
Mechanical Specifications: Type page 11 11/16 x 21; E - 6 cols, 1 5/6, 1/8 between; A - 6 cols, 1 5/6, 1/8 between; C - 6 cols, 1 5/6, 1/8 between.Equipment & Software: Hardware — APP/Mac; Software — Adobe/PageMaker 6.5, QPS/QuarkXPress 4.0.
Delivery Method: Mail, Racks
Areas Served: Campbell County

CHARLOTTESVILLE

RURAL VIRGINIAN (WED)
685 Rio Rd W, Charlottesville, VA, 22901-1413, Fluvanna, Buckingham, Albemarle, Nelson, USA; gen tel (434) 978-7216; adv tel (434) 978-7216; ed tel (434) 978-7216; gen fax (434) 978-7204; adv fax (434) 978-7204; ed fax (434) 978-7204; disp adv e-mail srhodes@dailyprogress.com; class adv e-mail dhubbard@dailyprogress.com; ed e-mail rv@dailyprogress.com; web site www.dailyprogress.com
Circulation: 12,000fr; Sworn/Estimate/Non-Audited
Advertising rate: Open inch rate $12.50
Established: 1971
Digital Platform - Mobile: Apple, Android, Windows, Blackberry
Digital Platform - Tablet: Apple iOS, Android, Windows 7, Blackberry Tablet OS
Aaron Richardson
Terry BeigieEd.s
Delivery Method: Mail, Racks
Areas Served: Fluvanna, Buckingham, Nelson, and Southern Albemarle County

CHATHAM

STAR-TRIBUNE (WED)
30 S Main St, Chatham, VA, 24531-5436, Pittsylvania, USA; gen tel (434) 432-2791; adv tel (434) 432-2791; ed tel (434) 432-2791; gen fax (434) 432-4033; adv fax (434) 432-4033; ed fax (434) 432-4033; disp adv e-mail advertising@chathamstartribune.com; class adv e-mail legals@chathamstartribune.com; ed e-mail s.light@chathamstartribune.com; web site www.chathamstartribune.com
Circulation: 8,217pd, 275fr; Sworn/Estimate/Non-Audited
Advertising rate: Open inch rate $10.60
Established: 1869
Group: Womack Publishing Co.
Digital Platform - Mobile: Apple, Android, Windows, Blackberry
Digital Platform - Tablet: Apple iOS, Android, Windows 7, Blackberry Tablet OS, Kindle, Nook, Kindle Fire
Pub....Chad Harrison
Ed....Susan Light
Account Exec....Johnathan Pettiford
Sports Ed....Eddy Lloyd
Mechanical Specifications: Type page 13 x 21 1/2; E - 6 cols, 2 1/16, between; A - 6 cols, 2 1/16, between; C - 6 cols, 2 1/16, between. Equipment & Software: Hardware — APP/Mac; Presses — KP, G; Software — Adobe/PageMaker 5.0, Microsoft/Word 6.0.
Delivery Method: Mail, Racks
Areas Served: Pittsylvania County

CHESTER

VILLAGE NEWS (WED)
11801 Centre St, Chester, VA, 23831-1781, Chesterfield, USA; gen tel (804) 751-0421; disp adv e-mail news@villagenewsonline.com; web site villagenewsonline.com
Pub....Linda Fausz

CHRISTIANSBURG

THE RADFORD NEWS JOURNAL (WED, SAT)
302 W Main St, Ste B, Christiansburg, VA, 24073-2981, Montgomery, USA; gen tel (540) 382-6171; gen fax (540) 382-3009; disp adv e-mail lward@ourvalley.org; class adv e-mail lward@ourvalley.org; ed e-mail editor@ourvalley.org; web site www.ourvalley.org
Circulation: 3,250pd,; Sworn/Estimate/Non-Audited
Advertising rate: Open inch rate $9.75
Established: 1884
Group: Mountain Media
Digital Platform - Mobile: Apple, Android, Windows, Blackberry
Digital Platform - Tablet: Apple iOS, Android, Windows 7, Blackberry Tablet OS
Adv. Mgr....Larry Ward
Ed....Brian Perdue
Community reporter....Sam Wall
Mechanical Specifications: Type page 11 5/8 x 21; E - 6 cols, 1 5/6, 1/8 between; A - 6 cols, 1 5/6, 1/8 between; C - 8 cols, 1 5/6, 1/8 between.
Delivery Method: Mail, Newsstand, Racks
Areas Served: City of Redford, Fairlawn

CLINTWOOD

THE DICKENSON STAR (WED)
250 Main St, Clintwood, VA, 24228, Dickenson, USA; gen tel (276) 926-8816; adv tel (276) 926-8816; ed tel (276) 926-8816; gen fax (276) 926-8827; adv fax (276) 926-8827; ed fax (276) 926-8827; disp adv e-mail csutherland@coalfield.com; class adv e-mail dlawson@coalfield.com; ed e-mail ptate@coalfield.com; web site www.coalfield.com
Circulation: 4,000pd, 125fr; Sworn/Estimate/Non-Audited
Advertising rate: Open inch rate $6.15
Established: 1982
Group: American Hometown Publishing
Digital Platform - Mobile: Apple, Android, Windows, Blackberry
Digital Platform - Tablet: Apple iOS, Android, Windows 7, Blackberry Tablet OS, Kindle, Nook, Kindle Fire
Pub....Jenay Tate
Adv. Mgr....Karen Tate
Mng. Ed....Paula Tate
Circ....Becky McElroy
Account Exec....Candacee Watkins
Sports Ed....Sam Dixon
Mechanical Specifications: Type page 13 x 21; E - 6 cols, 2 1/16, between; A - 6 cols, 2 1/16, between; C - 8 cols, 1 1/2, between. Equipment & Software: Hardware — APP/Mac; Presses — G/Community; Software — QPS/QuarkXPress.
Delivery Method: Mail, Racks
Areas Served: Dickenson County

COVINGTON

VIRGINIAN REVIEW (TUES, THUR, SAT)
128 N Maple Ave, Covington, VA, 24426-1545, Alleghany, USA; gen tel (540) 962-2121; adv tel (540) 962-2121; ed tel (540) 962-2121; gen fax (540) 962-6966; adv fax (540) 962-6966; ed fax (540) 962-6966; disp adv e-mail Advertising@thevirginianreview.com; class adv e-mail Classified@thevirginianreview.com; ed e-mail Newsroom@thevirginianreview.com; web site www.thevirginianreview.com/
Circulation: 7,119pd,; Sworn/Estimate/Non-Audited
Advertising rate: Open inch rate $10.00
Established: 1914
Vice Pres....Ewell S. Beirne
Adv. Dir....Mary Ann Beirne
News Ed....Horton P. Beirne
Sports Ed....Adam Crawford
Online Mgr....David Crosier
Prodn. Mgr., Pressroom...Coite Charles Beirne
Mechanical Specifications: Type page 11 5/8 x 21; E - 6 cols, 1 13/16, 3 1/14 between; A - 6 cols, 1 13/16, 3/16 between; C - 8 cols, 1 3/8, 1/8 between.
Delivery Method: Mail, Newsstand, Carrier, Racks

CULPEPER

CULPEPER TIMES (THUR)
206 S Main St, Ste 301, Culpeper, VA, 22701-3138, Culpeper, USA; gen tel (540) 812-2282; adv tel (540) 812-2282; ed tel (540) 812-2282; gen fax (540) 812-2117; adv fax (540) 812-2117; ed fax (540) 812-2117; disp adv e-mail tspargur@culpepertimes.com; class adv e-mail ecobert@virginianews-group.com; ed e-mail anita@culpepertimes.com; web site www.culpepertimes.com
Circulation: 11,000fr; Sworn/Estimate/Non-Audited
Advertising rate: Open inch rate $22.00
Established: 2006
Group: Rappahannock Media LLC
Digital Platform - Mobile: Apple, Android
Digital Platform - Tablet: Apple iOS, Android, Windows 7, Kindle
Ed....Anita Sherman
Group Sales Dir....Tom Spargur
Delivery Method: Mail, Newsstand, Racks
Areas Served: Culpeper County

DRAKES BRANCH

THE CHARLOTTE GAZETTE (WED)
4789 Drakes Main St, Drakes Branch, VA, 23937, Charlotte, USA; gen tel (434) 568-3341; adv tel (434) 808-0614; gen fax (434) 392-3366; disp adv e-mail jackie.newman@thecharlottegazette.com; web site thecharlottegazette.com
Pub....Betty Ramsey
Dir. of Ops....Staci Bridge
Adv. Dir....Jackie Newman
Circ. Dir....Rhonda Finch
Community Ed....Italia Gregory

ELKTON

THE VALLEY BANNER (THUR)
157 W Spotswood Ave, Elkton, VA, 22827-1118, Rockingham, USA; gen tel (540) 298-9444; adv tel (540) 298-9444; ed tel (540) 298-9444; gen fax (540) 298-2560; adv fax (540) 298-2560; ed fax (540) 298-2560; disp adv e-mail vbads@comcast.net; class adv e-mail vbads@comcast.net; ed e-mail vbnews@comcast.net; web site www.shenvalleynow.com
Circulation: 29,896pd,; AAM
Advertising rate: Open inch rate $12.25
Established: 1966
Group: Rockingham Publishing Co.
Digital Platform - Mobile: Apple, Android
Digital Platform - Tablet: Apple iOS, Android, Windows 7
Ed....Travis Long
Gen. Mgr....Peter Yates
Adv. Mgr....Carol Campbell
Circ. Mgr....Tommy Bridges
Prod. Mgr....James Deboer
Mechanical Specifications: Type page 11 5/8 x 21 1/4; E - 6 cols, 1 5/6, 1/8 between; A - 6

cols, 1 5/6, 1/8 between; C - 9 cols, 1 1/4, 1/10 between.Equipment & Software: Hardware — 12-APP/Mac G4, 2-APP/Mac 8600, 2-APP/Mac 7600, LC/III; Software — Adobe/PageMaker 6.5, Microsoft/Excel 5.0, Adobe/Photoshop 5.0.
Delivery Method: Mail, Racks
Areas Served: Page, Rockingham, Shenandoah, and Warren County

EMPORIA

THE PRINCE GEORGE JOURNAL (WED)
111 Baker St, Emporia, VA, 23847-1703, Greensville, USA; gen tel (434) 634-4153; gen fax (434) 634-0783; disp adv e-mail shanbury26@gmail.com; web site theprincegeorgejournal.com
Reg. Ed.. Roger Bell
Adv. Mgr..................................Sarah Hanbury

FALLS CHURCH

FALLS CHURCH NEWS-PRESS (THUR)
200 Little Falls St, Ste 508, Falls Church, VA, 22046-4302, Falls Church City, USA; gen tel (703) 532-3267; adv tel (703) 532-3267; ed tel (703) 532-3267; gen fax (703) 342-0347; adv fax (703) 342-0347; ed fax (703) 342-0347; disp adv e-mail fcnp@fcnp.com; class adv e-mail ads@fcnp.com; ed e-mail nfbenton@fcnp.com; web site www.fcnp.com
Circulation: 15,000fr; Sworn/Estimate/Non-Audited
Advertising rate: Open inch rate $35.00
Established: 1991
Group: Benton Communications Inc.
Digital Platform - Mobile: Apple
Digital Platform - Tablet: Apple iOS
Owner/Pub./Ed.................. Nicholas F. Benton
Mng. Ed....................................... Jody Fellows
Adv. Dir.. Joe Fridling
Adv. Sales.. Nick Gatz
Adv. Sales.................................Melissa Morse
Writer... Leslie Poster
Sports Ed......................................Mike Hume
Mechanical Specifications: Type page 10 1/4 x 13 1/2; E - 5 cols, 1 7/8, 1/8 between; A - 5 cols, 1 7/8, 1/8 between; C - 5 cols, 1 7/8, 1/8 between.Equipment & Software: Hardware — PC; Software — WordPerfect.
Delivery Method: Mail, Newsstand, Carrier, Racks
Areas Served: 22040, 22046, 22205, 22043, 22041

FARMVILLE

THE FARMVILLE HERALD (WED, FRI)
114 North St, Farmville, VA, 23901-1312, Prince Edward, USA; gen tel (434) 392-4151; adv tel (434)392-4151; ed tel (434)392-4151; gen fax (434) 392-3366; disp adv e-mail jackie.newman@farmvilleherald.com; class adv e-mail jackie.newman@farmvilleherald.com; ed e-mail martin.cahn@farmvilleherald.com; web site www.farmvilleherald.com
Established: 1890
Group: Boone Newspapers, Inc.
Adv. Mgr. ....Jackie Newman
Mng. Ed.. Martin Cahn
Dir. of Ops...................................... Staci Bridge
Circ. Mgr...................................Rhonda Finch
Sports Ed..................................... Titus Mohler

FINCASTLE

THE FINCASTLE HERALD (WED)
7 S. Roanoke St, Fincastle, VA, 24090, Botetourt, USA; gen tel (540) 473-2741; adv tel (540) 761-7019; ed tel (540) 473-2741; gen fax (540) 473-2742; adv fax (540) 473-2742; ed fax (540) 473-2742; disp adv e-mail tfrye@ourvalley.org; class adv e-mail customerservice@ourvalley.org; ed e-mail edmccoy@ourvalley.org; web site www.fincastleherald.com
Circulation: 5,500pd,; Sworn/Estimate/Non-Audited
Advertising rate: Open inch rate $10.75
Established: 1866
Group: Virginia Media Inc.
Digital Platform - Mobile: Apple, Android, Windows, Blackberry
Digital Platform - Tablet: Apple iOS, Android, Windows 7, Blackberry Tablet OS
Ed. .... Edwin L. McCoy
Advertising.................................... Tucker Frye
General Manager............................Lynn Hurst
Publisher..................................Michael Stowe
Mechanical Specifications: Type page 11 5/8 x 21; E - 6 cols, 1 5/6, 1/8 between; A - 6 cols, 1 5/6, 1/8 between; C - 8 cols, 1 1/3, 1/8 between.
Delivery Method: Mail, Newsstand, Racks
Areas Served: Botetourt County

FLOYD

THE FLOYD PRESS (THUR)
710 E Main St, Floyd, VA, 24091-2620, Floyd, USA; gen tel (540) 745-2127; adv tel (540) 745-2127; ed tel (540) 745-2127; gen fax (540) 745-2123; adv fax (540) 745-2123; ed fax (540) 745-2123; disp adv e-mail bsewell@wythenews.com.com; class adv e-mail wcombs@wythenews.com; ed e-mail news@floydpress.com; web site www.floydpress.com
Circulation: 5,200pd, 63fr; Sworn/Estimate/Non-Audited
Advertising rate: Open inch rate $11.25
Group: BH Media Group
Digital Platform - Mobile: Apple, Android
Digital Platform - Tablet: Apple iOS, Android, Windows 7
Pub...Samuel Cooper
Group Ed. .... Mark Sage
Ed. .... Wanda Combs
Adv. Mgr.................................Barbara Sewell
Circ. Mgr.....................................Kristi Griffith
Mechanical Specifications: Type page 13 x 21 1/2; E - 6 cols, 2, 1/4 between; A - 6 cols, 2, 1/4 between; C - 6 cols, 2, 1/4 between. Equipment & Software: Hardware — Epson, Samtron, HP; Software — Adobe/PageMaker, Microsoft/Word.
Delivery Method: Mail, Newsstand, Racks
Areas Served: Floyd County

FRANKLIN

THE TIDEWATER NEWS (WED, FRI, SUN)
1000 Armory Dr, Franklin, VA, 23851-1852, Southampton, USA; gen tel (757) 562-3187; adv tel (757) 562-3187; ed tel (757) 562-3187; gen fax (757) 562-6795; adv fax (757) 562-6795; ed fax (757) 562-6795; disp adv e-mail mitzi.lusk@tidewaternews.com; class adv e-mail kate.archer@tidewaternews.com; ed e-mail cain.madden@tidewaternews.com; web site www.tidewaternews.com
Circulation: 5,058pd, 1,500fr; Sworn/Estimate/Non-Audited
Advertising rate: Open inch rate $12.39
Established: 1905
Group: Boone Newspapers, Inc.
Digital Platform - Mobile: Apple, Android, Windows
Digital Platform - Tablet: Apple iOS, Android, Windows 7, Blackberry Tablet OS, Nook, Kindle Fire
Pres./Pub..................................Steve Stewart
Assc. Pub.....................................Tony Clark
Mng. Ed......................................Cain Madden
Adv. Dir..Mitzi Lusk
Office Mgr. ....Michelle Gray
Mechanical Specifications: Type page 10.5" x 21.5; E - 6 cols, 1.6167 , 1/8 between; A - 6 cols, 1.6167, 1/8 between; C - 6 cols, 1.6167, 1/8 between.Equipment & Software: Hardware — APP/iMac, APP/Mac G4; Presses — 4-KP/News King; Software — Adobe/PageMaker 6.0, Multi-Ad/Creator, QPS/QuarkXPress 3.2, Adobe/Photoshop 4.0.
Delivery Method: Mail, Newsstand, Racks
Areas Served: Southampton County

FRONT ROYAL

THE WARREN SENTINEL (THUR)
429 N Royal Ave, Front Royal, VA, 22630-2619, Warren, USA; gen tel (540) 635-4174; adv tel (540) 635-4174; ed tel (540) 635-4174; gen fax (540) 635-7478; adv fax (540) 635-7478; ed fax (540) 635-7478; disp adv e-mail linda@thewarrensentinel.com; class adv e-mail heidi@thewarrensentinel.com; ed e-mail kolmstead@thewarrensentinel.com; web site www.ShenValleyNow.com
Circulation: 3,638pd,; AAM
Advertising rate: Open inch rate $11.50
Established: 1869
Group: Ogden Newspapers Inc.
Digital Platform - Mobile: Apple, Android
Digital Platform - Tablet: Apple iOS, Android, Windows 7
Pub......................................Thomas T. Byrd
Ed./Gen. Mgr..........................Randy Arrington
Mng. Ed.................................Kevin Olmstead
Office Mgr. ....Heidi Anderson
Adv. Mgr.. Linda York
Prod. Mgr. ....Todd AllenEquipment & Software: Hardware — APP/Mac; Software — Adobe/PageMaker, Macromedia/Freehand.
Delivery Method: Mail, Newsstand, Carrier, Racks
Areas Served: Page, Rockingham, Shenandoah and Warren County

GALAX

GALAX GAZETTE (MON, WED, FRI)
108 W Stuart Dr, Galax, VA, 24333-2114, Galax City, USA; gen tel (276) 236-5178; gen fax (276) 236-0756; disp adv e-mail ads@galaxgazette.com; class adv e-mail classifieds@galaxgazette.com; ed e-mail editor@galaxgazette.com; web site www.galaxgazette.com
Circulation: 7,170pd,; Sworn/Estimate/Non-Audited
Advertising rate: Open inch rate $12.79
Established: 1876
Group: Landmark Community Newspapers, LLC
Digital Platform - Mobile: Apple, Android, Windows, Blackberry
Digital Platform - Tablet: Apple iOS, Android, Windows 7, Blackberry Tablet OS, Kindle, Nook, Kindle Fire
Pub...Chuck Burress
Ed. .... Brian Funk
Adv. Mgr....................................Randy Kegley
Delivery Method: Mail
Areas Served: 24333, 24343, 24348, 24381, 24330, 24317, 24326, 24328, 24352

GATE CITY

SCOTT COUNTY VIRGINIA STAR (WED)
255 W Jackson St, Gate City, VA, 24251-4129, Scott, USA; gen tel (276) 386-6300; gen fax (276) 386-2354; disp adv e-mail info@virginiastar.org; class adv e-mail classifieds@virginiastar.org; ed e-mail news@virginiastar.org; web site www.virginiastar.net
Circulation: 6,500pd, 103fr; Sworn/Estimate/Non-Audited
Advertising rate: Open inch rate $6.00
Established: 1903
Group: Scott County Herald-Virginia Inc.Editions: (6,548) Scott County Virginia Star
Digital Platform - Mobile: Apple, Windows
Digital Platform - Tablet: Apple iOS, Windows 7
Pub./Ed.......................................Lisa McCarty
Circ. Dir....................................Emily McCarty
Advt Dir.. Rex McCarty
Delivery Method: Mail
Areas Served: 24221, 24244, 24245, 24250, 24251, 24258, 24271, 24290, 37660, 37662, 37663, 37664, 37665

GRUNDY

THE VIRGINIA MOUNTAINEER (WED)
1122 Grundy Plaza Dr, STE 2400, Grundy, VA, 24614, Buchanan, USA; gen tel (276) 935-2123; adv tel (276) 935-2123; ed tel (276) 935-2123; gen fax (276) 935-2125; adv fax (276) 935-2125; ed fax (276) 935-2125; disp adv e-mail VirginiaMountaineer@gmail.com; class adv e-mail VirginiaMountaineer@gmail.com; ed e-mail VirginiaMountaineer@gmail.com; web site www.virginiamountaineer.com
Circulation: 6,300pd, 100fr; USPS
Advertising rate: Open inch rate $7.98
Established: 1922
Digital Platform - Mobile: Windows
Digital Platform - Tablet: Windows 7
Pub./Ed...................................... Sam Bartley
Mng. Ed...................................Scotty Wampler
Gen. Mgr.....................................Joe St. Clair
Mechanical Specifications: Type page 13 x 21 1/2; E - 6 cols, 2, 1/6 between; A - 6 cols, 2, 1/6 between; C - 8 cols, 1 1/2, 1/6 between. Equipment & Software: Hardware — APP/Mac; Presses — G/Community; Software — Adobe/PageMaker.
Delivery Method: Mail, Newsstand
Areas Served: Buchanan County

HARRISONBURG

THE JOURNAL (WED)
231 S Liberty St, Harrisonburg, VA, 22801-3621, Rockingham, USA; gen tel (540) 574-6265; adv tel (540) 574-6229; ed tel (540) 578-3812; gen fax (540) 433-9112; adv fax (540) 433-9112; ed fax (540) 433-9112; disp adv e-mail sturner@dnronline.com; class adv e-mail pyates@dnronline.com; ed e-mail kkersey@dnronline.com; web site www.northforkjournal.com
Circulation: 12,500fr; Sworn/Estimate/Non-Audited
Advertising rate: Open inch rate $24.00
Digital Platform - Mobile: Apple, Android
Digital Platform - Tablet: Apple iOS, Android, Windows 7
Pub.. Peter Yates
Adv. Dir.....................................Steven Turner
Circ. Mgr...................................Tommy Bridges
Ed. ....Kate Kersey
Prodn. Mgr. ....Joyce Hansbrough
Mechanical Specifications: Type page 9 13/16 x 11 1/2; E - 5 cols, 1 7/8, 1/8 between; A - 5 cols, 1 7/8, 1/8 between; C - 5 cols, 1 3/16, 1/16 between.Equipment & Software: Hardware — PC, APP/Mac/Mac; Presses — G/Community; Software — APT.
Delivery Method: Mail, Racks
Areas Served: 22844, 22834, 22830, 22815, 22853

HILLSVILLE

THE CARROLL NEWS (WED)
804 N MAIN ST, Hillsville, VA, 24343, Carroll, USA; gen tel (276) 728-7311; adv tel (276) 728-7311; ed tel (276) 728-7311; gen fax (276) 728-4119; adv fax (276) 728-4119; ed fax (276) 728-4119; disp adv e-mail sstanley@civitasmedia.com; class adv e-mail sstanley@civitasmedia.com; ed e-mail aworrell@civitasmedia.com; web site www.thecarrollnews.com
Circulation: 6,700pd, 10fr; Sworn/Estimate/Non-Audited
Advertising rate: Open inch rate $10.70
Established: 1920
Group: Champion Media
Digital Platform - Mobile: Apple, Android
Digital Platform - Tablet: Apple iOS, Android, Windows 7
Ed. .... Allen Worrell
Adv. Mgr................................... Sherry Stanley
Pub... Ron Clausen
Class./Circ. ....Amber Dowell
Mechanical Specifications: Type page 11 1/2 x 21 1/2; E - 6 cols, 1 3/4, between; A - 6 cols,

1 3/4, between.Equipment & Software: Hardware — APP/Power Mac, APP/Mac IIci.
Delivery Method: Mail, Racks
Areas Served: 24343

HOPEWELL

THE HOPEWELL NEWS (TUES, THUR, SAT)

516 E Randolph Rd, Hopewell, VA, 23860-2652, USA; gen tel (804) 458-8511; adv tel (804) 458-8511; ed tel (804) 458-8511; gen fax (804) 458-7556; adv fax (804) 458-7556; ed fax (804) 458-7556; disp adv e-mail advertising@hpcmedia.net; class adv e-mail classifieds@hpcmedia.net; ed e-mail editor@hpcmedia.net; web site www.hopewellnews.com
Circulation: 56pd, 5,325fr; Sworn/Estimate/Non-Audited
Advertising rate: Open inch rate $9.00
Group: Lancaster Management, Inc.
Digital Platform - Mobile: Apple, Android
Digital Platform - Tablet: Apple iOS, Android, Windows 7
Pub.......... Mike Davis
Gen. Mgr.......... Freda Cook-Snyder
Adv. Mgr.......... Pat Cook
Mng. Ed.......... Adrienne Wallace
Mechanical Specifications: Type page 13 x 21 1/2; E - 6 cols, 2 1/16, 1/8 between; A - 6 cols, 2 1/16, 1/8 between; C - 9 cols, 1 3/8, 1/8 between.
Delivery Method: Mail, Racks
Areas Served: 23860

LAWRENCEVILLE

BRUNSWICK TIMES-GAZETTE (WED)

213 N Main St, Lawrenceville, VA, 23868-1807, Brunswick, USA; gen tel (434) 848-2114; adv tel (434) 848-2114; ed tel (434) 848-2114; gen fax (434) 848-2115; adv fax (434) 848-2115; ed fax (434) 848-2115; disp adv e-mail ads@brunswicktimes-gazette.com; class adv e-mail classifieds@brunswicktimes-gazette.com; ed e-mail news@brunswicktimes-gazette.com; web site www.brunswicktimes-gazette.com
Advertising rate: Open inch rate $7.00
Established: 1894
Group: Womack Publishing Co.
Digital Platform - Mobile: Apple, Android
Digital Platform - Tablet: Apple iOS, Android
Pub.......... Chad Harrison
Acct. Exec.......... Tom Childrey
Ed.......... Sylvia Allen
Delivery Method: Mail, Newsstand, Racks
Areas Served: Brunswick County

LEESBURG

PRINCE WILLIAM TIMES (WED)

9 E Market St, Leesburg, VA, 20176-3013, Loudoun, USA; gen tel (703) 777-1111; gen fax (703) 771-1285; disp adv e-mail skeyes@virginianewsgroup.com; web site http://www.northernvatimes.com/gainesville
Established: 1963
Group: Piedmont Media
Executive Assistant to Chairman/CEO.... Shari Keyes

LEXINGTON

THE NEWS-GAZETTE (WED)

20 W Nelson St, Lexington, VA, 24450-2034, Rockbridge, USA; gen tel (540) 463-3113; adv tel (540) 463-3113; ed tel (540) 463-3113; gen fax (540) 463-1925; adv fax (540) 463-1925; ed fax (540) 463-1925; disp adv e-mail advertising@thenews-gazette.com; class adv e-mail classified@thenews-gazette.com; ed e-mail editor@thenews-gazette.com; web site www.thenews-gazette.com
Circulation: 6,796pd, 115fr; USPS
Advertising rate: Open inch rate $15.00
Established: 1801
Digital Platform - Mobile: Android, Windows
Digital Platform - Tablet: Android, Windows 7, Kindle
Classified Adv. Dir.......... Tonia Watterson
Ed.......... Darryl Woodson
Circ. Mgr.......... April Mikels
Adv. Coord.......... Gay Lea Goodbar
Circulation Manager.......... Lucretia VanBrocklin
publisher.......... Matthew Paxton
Mechanical Specifications: Type page 11.00 x 19.75; E - 6 cols, 1.66, .18 between; A - 6 cols, 1.66, .18 between; C - 6 cols, 1.66, .18 between.Equipment & Software: Hardware — Various Manufacture PCs; Presses — N/A; Software — Quark 7.0, Quark 8.0, Adobe CS3
Delivery Method: Mail, Newsstand, Racks
Areas Served: 24415, 24416, 24435, 24439, 24450, 24472, 24473, 24483, 24555, 24578, 24579,

LOUISA

THE CENTRAL VIRGINIAN (THUR)

89 Rescue Ln, Louisa County Industrial Air Park, Louisa, VA, 23093-4105, Louisa, USA; gen tel (540) 967-0368; adv tel (540) 967-0368; ed tel (540) 967-0368; gen fax (540) 967-0457; adv fax (540) 967-0457; ed fax (540) 967-3847; disp adv e-mail tcvads@lcs.net; class adv e-mail tcvclass@lcs.net; ed e-mail tcveditor@lcs.net; web site www.thecentralvirginian.com
Circulation: 8,128pd, 391fr; USPS
Advertising rate: Open inch rate $13.85
Established: 1912
Group: Lakeway Publishers, Inc.
Digital Platform - Mobile: Apple, Android, Windows, Blackberry, Other
Digital Platform - Tablet: Apple iOS, Android, Windows 7, Blackberry Tablet OS
Adv. Mgr.......... Kelly Seay
Community News Editor.......... Paula Parrish
Associate Editor.......... David Holtzman
Reporter.......... Joseph Haney
Publisher.......... Steve Weddle
Mechanical Specifications: Type page 13 x 21 1/2; E - 6 cols, 2, 1/6 between; A - 6 cols, 2, 1/6 between; C - 8 cols, 1 1/2, 1/12 between. Equipment & Software: Hardware — APP/Mac; Software — Microsoft/Word, Adobe/PageMaker, Adobe/Photoshop.
Delivery Method: Mail, Newsstand, Racks
Areas Served: Lake Anna and Louisa County

LURAY

PAGE NEWS & COURIER (THUR)

17 S Broad St, Luray, VA, 22835-1904, Page, USA; gen tel (540) 743-5123; adv tel (540) 743-5123; ed tel (540) 743-5123; gen fax (540) 743-4779; adv fax (540) 743-4779; ed fax (540) 743-4779; disp adv e-mail pncads@gmail.com; class adv e-mail classified@pagenewspaper.com; ed e-mail editor@pagenewspaper.com; web site www.ShenValleyNow.com
Circulation: 6,746pd,; AAM
Advertising rate: Open inch rate $11.30
Established: 1867
Group: Ogden Newspapers Inc.
Digital Platform - Mobile: Apple, Android
Digital Platform - Tablet: Apple iOS, Android, Windows 7
Ed./Gen. Mgr.......... Randy Arrington
Adv. Mgr.......... Kelli Bailey
Circ. Mgr.......... China Martin
Delivery Method: Mail, Racks
Areas Served: Page, Rockingham, Shenandoah and Warren County

MADISON

MADISON COUNTY EAGLE (THUR)

201 N Main St, Madison, VA, 22727-3053, Madison, USA; gen tel (540) 948-5121; adv tel (434) 975-7112; ed tel (540) 948-5121; gen fax (540) 948-3045; adv fax (540) 948-3045; ed fax (540) 948-3045; disp adv e-mail ccullen@dailyprogress.com; class adv e-mail fkern@orangenews.com; ed e-mail news@madison-news.com; web site www.madison-news.com
Circulation: 4,500pd, 10fr; Sworn/Estimate/Non-Audited
Advertising rate: Open inch rate $13.09
Established: 1910
Digital Platform - Mobile: Apple, Android
Digital Platform - Tablet: Apple iOS, Android, Windows 7
Pub.......... Lawrence McConnell
Ed.......... Don Richeson
Managing Editor.......... Jeff Poole
Adv. Dir.......... Carolyn Cullen
Delivery Method: Mail, Racks
Areas Served: Madison County

MARION

SMYTH COUNTY NEWS & MESSENGER (WED, SAT)

119 S Sheffey St, Marion, VA, 24354-2523, Smyth, USA; gen tel (276) 783-5121; gen fax (276) 783-9713; disp adv e-mail cbiertzer@smythnews.com; ed e-mail sportern@wythenews.com; web site www.swvatoday.com
Circulation: 2,652pd,; USPS
Advertising rate: Call for rates
Established: 1884
Group: BH Media Group
Digital Platform - Mobile: Apple, Android
Digital Platform - Tablet: Apple iOS, Android, Windows 7
Mng. Ed.......... Stephanie Porter-Nichols
Circ. Mgr.......... Sonny Corpus
Sports Ed.......... Jerry Orr
Adv. Dir.......... Randy Thompson
Group Ed.......... Mark Sage
Delivery Method: Mail, Newsstand, Carrier, Racks
Areas Served: Smyth County

MC LEAN

SUN GAZETTE (THUR)

6704 Old McLean Village Dr, Ste 200, Mc Lean, VA, 22101-3906, Fairfax, USA; gen tel (703) 738-2520; adv tel (703) 738-2523; ed tel (703) 738-2520; gen fax (703) 738-2530; adv fax (703) 738-2530; ed fax (703) 738-2530; disp adv e-mail dmartin@sungazette.net; class adv e-mail tfields@sungazette.net; ed e-mail smccaffrey@sungazette.net; web site www.sungazette.net
Circulation: 37pd, 34,420fr; AAM
Advertising rate: 1/16 Pg $159.00; 1/8 Pg $269.00; 1/4 Pg $349.00
Established: 1935
Group: Northern Virginia Media Services
Digital Platform - Mobile: Apple, Android
Digital Platform - Tablet: Apple iOS, Android, Windows 7
Pub.......... Norm Styer
Ed.......... Scott McCaffrey
Adv. Mgr.......... Debbie Martin
COO.......... Bruce Potter
Classified Adv. Mgr.......... Paula Grose
Mechanical Specifications: Type page 10 x 13; E - 5 cols, 1 7/8, 1/6 between; A - 5 cols, 1 7/8, 1/6 between; C - 6 cols, 1 5/12, 1/6 between. Equipment & Software: Hardware — APP/Mac G3; Presses — WPC/Web Leader, G/Urbanite, G/Community; Software — QPS/QuarkXPress 4.1, Adobe/Photoshop 5.0.
Delivery Method: Mail, Newsstand, Racks
Areas Served: Arlington, McLean, Great Falls, Vienna and Oakton

MECHANICSVILLE

GOOCHLAND GAZETTE (THUR)

8460 Times Dispatch Blvd, Mechanicsville, VA, 23116-2029, Hanover, USA; gen tel (804) 746-1235; adv tel (804) 814-7780; ed tel (804) 746-1235 ext. 22; gen fax (804) 730-0476; adv fax (804) 775-4051; ed fax (804) 819-5584; disp adv e-mail schildrey@mechlocal.com; class adv e-mail cgrant@mechlocal.com; ed e-mail mkinser@mechlocal.com; web site www.richmond.com
Circulation: 47pd, 5,910fr; AAM
Advertising rate: Open inch rate $12.30
Established: 1955
Group: BH Media Group
World Media Enterprises Inc.
Digital Platform - Mobile: Apple, Windows
Digital Platform - Tablet: Apple iOS, Windows 7
Pub.......... Joy Monopoli
Managing Ed.......... Melody Kinser
Sports Ed.......... Charlie Leffler
Delivery Method: Mail, Racks
Areas Served: 23038, 23039, 23063, 23065, 23093, 23102, 23103, 23117, 23129, 23146, 23153, 23233, 23238

MECHANICSVILLE LOCAL (WED)

8460 Times Dispatch Blvd, Mechanicsville, VA, 23116-2029, Hanover, USA; gen tel (804) 746-1235; adv tel (804) 746-1235; ed tel (804) 746-1235 ext. 22; gen fax (804) 730-0476; adv fax (804) 819-5529; ed fax (804) 819-5584; disp adv e-mail sales@mechlocal.com; class adv e-mail cgrant@mechlocal.com; ed e-mail mkinser@mechlocal.com; web site www.richmond.com
Circulation: 28pd, 23,098fr; CAC
Advertising rate: Open inch rate $30.00
Established: 1984
Group: BH Media Group
World Media Enterprises Inc.
Digital Platform - Mobile: Apple, Windows
Digital Platform - Tablet: Apple iOS, Windows 7
Pub.......... Joy Monopoli
Melody Kinser
Delivery Method: Mail, Racks
Areas Served: 23111, 23116, 23069, 23162

MIDDLEBURG

MIDDLEBURG LIFE (MTHLY)

112 W Washington St, Middleburg, VA, 20118, Loudoun, USA; gen tel (540) 687-6059; adv tel (540)687-6059; ed tel (540)687-6059; disp adv e-mail info@middleburglife.com; class adv e-mail tfields@insidenova.com; ed e-mail info@middleburglife.com; web site middleburglife.com
Group: Greenhill Media
Advertising.......... Vicky Moon

MONTROSS

WESTMORELAND NEWS (WED)

15692 Kings Hwy, Montross, VA, 22520, Westmoreland, USA; gen tel (804) 493-8096; adv tel (804) 493-8096; ed tel (804) 493-8096; gen fax (804) 493-8009; adv fax (804) 493-8009; ed fax (804) 493-8009; disp adv e-mail wmnads@lcs.net; class adv e-mail wmnads@lcs.net; ed e-mail wmneditor@lcs.net; web site www.westmorelandnews.net
Circulation: 7,608pd,; Sworn/Estimate/Non-Audited
Established: 1948
Group: Lakeway Publishers, Inc.
Digital Platform - Mobile: Apple, Android, Windows, Blackberry
Digital Platform - Tablet: Apple iOS, Android, Windows 7, Blackberry Tablet OS
Pub.......... Bill Trimble
Ed.......... Lee Francis
Mechanical Specifications: Type page 13 x 21 1/2; E - 6 cols, 2, between; A - 6 cols, 2, between; C - 9 cols, 1 1/3, between.Equipment & Software: Hardware — APP/Mac Classic, APP/Mac Quadra, APP/Power Mac G3.
Delivery Method: Mail, Newsstand, Racks
Areas Served: Westmoreland County

NEWPORT NEWS

THE VIRGINIA GAZETTE (WED, SAT)
703 Mariners Row, Newport News, VA, 23606-4432, James City, USA; gen tel (757) 220-1736; adv tel (757) 220-1736; ed tel (757) 220-1736; gen fax (757) 220-1766; adv fax (757) 220-1766; ed fax (757) 220-1766; disp adv e-mail jcunnison@dailypress.com; class adv e-mail jcunnison@dailypress.com; ed e-mail pbellow@vagazette.com; web site www.vagazette.com
Circulation: 14,000pd,; Sworn/Estimate/ Non-Audited
Advertising rate: 1/64 Pg $24.00; 1./32 Pg $45.00; 1/16 Pg $75.00
Established: 1930
Group: Tronc, Inc.
Digital Platform - Mobile: Apple, Android, Windows, Blackberry
Digital Platform - Tablet: Apple iOS, Android, Windows 7, Blackberry Tablet OS
Adv. Mgr. .... Olivia Hartman
Advertising Manager............ Jennifer Cunnison
Delivery Method: Mail, Newsstand, Carrier, Racks
Areas Served: Williamsburg

NORFOLK

INSIDE BUSINESS, THE HAMPTON ROADS BUSINESS JOURNAL (MON)
150 W Brambleton Ave, Norfolk, VA, 23510-2018, Norfolk City, USA; gen tel (757) 222-5353; adv tel (757) 222-3165; ed tel (757) 222-5349; gen fax (757) 222-5359; adv fax (757) 222-5359; ed fax (757) 222-5359; disp adv e-mail ski.miller@insidebiz.com; class adv e-mail ski.miller@insidebiz.com; ed e-mail ron.crow@insidebiz.com; web site www.insidebiz.com
Circulation: 4,048pd, 3,468fr; VAC
Advertising rate: Open inch rate $3,450 (Full-Page)
Established: 1996
Group: Landmark Media Enterprises, LLC The Virginian-Pilot
Digital Platform - Mobile: Apple, Android
Digital Platform - Tablet: Apple iOS, Android, Kindle, Nook, Kindle Fire
Pub.................. Mike Herron
Editor.................. Ron Crow
Mechanical Specifications: Full page - 9.6" x 13.25"
Delivery Method: Mail, Newsstand
Areas Served: 23168-23851

NORTON

THE COALFIELD PROGRESS (TUES, FRI)
725 Park Ave NE, Norton, VA, 24273-1007, Wise, USA; gen tel (276) 679-1101; gen fax (276) 679-5922; disp adv e-mail ktate@coalfield.com; web site thecoalfieldprogress.com
Office Mgr. .... Debbie Belcher
Circ. .... Becky McElroy
Adv. Mgr. .... Karen Tate
News Ed. .... Jeff Lester
Sports Ed. .... Sam Dixon

ORANGE

ORANGE COUNTY REVIEW (THUR)
146 Byrd St, Orange, VA, 22960-1631, Orange, USA; gen tel (540) 672-1266; adv tel (540) 672-1266 ext. 14; ed tel (540) 672-1266 ext. 23; gen fax (540) 672-7481; adv fax (540) 672-7481; ed fax (540) 672-7481; disp adv e-mail news@orangenews.com; class adv e-mail jstrader@orangenews.com; ed e-mail jpoole@orangenews.com; web site www.dailyprogress.com
Circulation: 7,000pd, 18fr; Sworn/Estimate/ Non-Audited
Advertising rate: Open inch rate $18.30
Group: BH Media Group
Digital Platform - Mobile: Apple, Android
Digital Platform - Tablet: Apple iOS, Android, Windows 7
Pub.................. Lawrence McConnell
Mng. Ed. .... Jeff Poole
Adv. Mgr. .... John Strader
Delivery Method: Mail, Racks
Areas Served: Orange County

PALMYRA

FLUVANNA REVIEW (THUR)
2987 Lake Monticello Rd, Palmyra, VA, 22963-4820, Fluvanna, USA; gen tel (434) 591-1000; adv tel (434) 207-0222; ed tel (434) 207-0224; gen fax (434) 589-1704; adv fax (434) 589-1704; ed fax (434) 589-1704; disp adv e-mail sales@fluvannareview.com; class adv e-mail edee@fluvannareview.com; ed e-mail carlos@fluvannareview.com; web site www.fluvannareview.com - 10,000(views) 6,000(visitors)
Circulation: 15pd, 6,200fr; VAC
Advertising rate: 1/16 Pg $45.00; 1/8 Pg $82.00; 1/4 Pg $130.00
Established: 1979
Group: Valley PublishingEditions: (1)
Digital Platform - Mobile: Apple, Android, Windows, Blackberry
Digital Platform - Tablet: Apple iOS, Android, Windows 7, Blackberry Tablet OS, Kindle, Nook, Kindle Fire
Pub./Ed./Circ. Mgr. .... Carlos Santos
Adv. Mgr. .... Lisa Hurdle
Prod. Mgr .... Kathy Zeek
Delivery Method: Mail, Carrier, Racks
Areas Served: Fluvanna County

POWHATAN

POWHATAN TODAY (WED)
3229 Anderson Hwy, Ste 200, Powhatan, VA, 23139-7340, Powhatan, USA; gen tel (804) 598-4305; adv tel (804) 598-4305 ext. 14; ed tel (804) 598-4305 ext. 13; gen fax (804) 598-7757; disp adv e-mail sales@powhatantoday.com; class adv e-mail bweeks@powhatantoday.com; ed e-mail lmcfarland@powhatantoday.com; web site www.powhatantoday.com
Circulation: 72pd, 11,167fr; CAC
Advertising rate: Open inch rate $8.75/ mass mailer $11
Established: 1986
Group: BH Media Group
Digital Platform - Mobile: Apple, Android, Windows, Blackberry
Digital Platform - Tablet: Apple iOS, Android, Windows 7, Blackberry Tablet OS, Kindle, Nook, Kindle Fire
Pub.................. Joy Monopoli
Ed. .... Melody Kinser
Adv. Mgr. .... Birgit Weeks
Delivery Method: Mail, Racks
Areas Served: Powhatan County

RICHLANDS

RICHLANDS NEWS-PRESS (WED)
1945 2nd St, Richlands, VA, 24641-2303, Tazewell, USA; gen tel (276) 963-1081; adv tel (800) 655-1406 ext. 31; ed tel (276) 963-1081; gen fax (276) 963-0202; adv fax (276) 963-0202; ed fax (276) 963-0202; disp adv e-mail bsewell@wythenews.com; class adv e-mail jsage@wythenews.com; ed e-mail jtalbert@richlands-news-press.com; web site www.richlands-news-press.com
Circulation: 7,000pd, 172fr; Sworn/Estimate/ Non-Audited
Advertising rate: Open inch rate $22.00
Group: BH Media Group
Digital Platform - Mobile: Apple, Android
Digital Platform - Tablet: Apple iOS, Android, Windows 7
Pub.................. Mark Sage
Ed. .... Jim Talbert Adv. Dir. Barbara Sewell
Delivery Method: Mail, Newsstand, Racks
Areas Served: Tazewell County

ROCKY MOUNT

THE FRANKLIN NEWS-POST (MON, WED, FRI)
310 S Main St, Rocky Mount, VA, 24151-1711, Franklin, USA; gen tel (540) 483-5113; adv tel (540) 483-5113; ed tel (540) 483-5113; gen fax (540) 483-8013; adv fax (540) 483-8013; ed fax (540) 483-8013; disp adv e-mail fnpevents@franklinnews-post.com; class adv e-mail fnpcharles@franklinnews-post.com; ed e-mail fnpcharles@franklinnewspost.com; web site www.thefranklinnewspost.com
Circulation: 8,300pd, 25fr; Sworn/Estimate/ Non-Audited
Advertising rate: Open inch rate $12.83
Group: BH Media Group
Digital Platform - Mobile: Apple, Android
Digital Platform - Tablet: Apple iOS, Android, Windows 7
Ed. .... Andy Williamson
Steven Marsh
Staff Writer.................. Stacey Hairston
Classifeids .... Robin Miller
Circulation.................. Pat Baraty
Adv . Stephanie BradleyEquipment & Software: Hardware — APP/Mac 7200; Presses — G; Software — QPS/QuarkXPress, APP/Mac Write Pro.
Delivery Method: Mail, Racks
Areas Served: Franklin County

SALEM

SALEM TIMES-REGISTER (THUR)
1633 W Main St, Salem, VA, 24153-3115, Salem, USA; gen tel (540) 389-9355; adv tel (540) 389-9355; ed tel (540) 389-9355; gen fax (540) 389-2930; adv fax (540) 389-2930; ed fax (540) 389-2930; disp adv e-mail wendicraig@gmail.com; class adv e-mail customerservice@ourvalley.org; ed e-mail shawn.nowlin@ourvalley.org; web site www.ourvalley.org
Circulation: 2,800pd,; USPS
Advertising rate: Open inch rate $10.75
Established: 1884
Group: Virginia Media, LLC
Digital Platform - Mobile: Apple, Android, Windows, Blackberry
Digital Platform - Tablet: Apple iOS, Android, Windows 7, Blackberry Tablet OS
General Manager.................. Lynn Hurst
Mechanical Specifications: Type page 11 5/8 x 21; E - 6 cols, 1 5/6, 1/8 between; A - 6 cols, 1 5/6, 1/8 between; C - 6 cols, 1 5/6, 1/8 between.Equipment & Software: Hardware — APP/Mac; Presses — G/Community; Software — Adobe/PageMaker 6.0, Microsoft/ Word 5.0, Microsoft/Excel 3.0.
Delivery Method: Mail, Racks
Areas Served: 24153

SOUTH BOSTON

THE GAZETTE-VIRGINIAN (MON, WED, FRI)
3201 Halifax Rd, South Boston, VA, 24592-4907, Halifax, USA; gen tel (434) 572-3945; adv tel (434) 572-3945; ed tel (434) 572-3945; gen fax (434) 572-1173; adv fax (434) 572-1173; ed fax (434) 572-1173; disp adv e-mail pseat@gazettevirginian.com; class adv e-mail classifieds@gazettevirginian.com; ed e-mail pbryant@gazettevirginian.com; web site www.gazettevirginian.com
Circulation: 9,100pd,; Sworn/Estimate/Non-Audited
Advertising rate: Open inch rate $7.50
Digital Platform - Mobile: Apple, Android, Windows, Blackberry
Digital Platform - Tablet: Apple iOS, Android, Windows 7, Blackberry Tablet OS
Pub.................. Linda Shelton
Ed. .... Paula Bryant
Patricia Seat
Mechanical Specifications: Type page 13 x 21 1/2; E - 6 cols, 2, between; A - 6 cols, 2, between; C - 6 cols, 2, between.Equipment & Software: Hardware — APP/Mac; Presses — KP; Software — Adobe/PageMaker, Adobe/ Photoshop.
Delivery Method: Mail, Newsstand, Carrier, Racks
Areas Served: 24592

SOUTH HILL

MECKLENBURG REPORTER (SUN)
PO Box 60, South Hill, VA, 23970-0060, Mecklenburg, USA; gen tel (434) 447-3178; gen fax (434) 447-5931; disp adv e-mail tbrowder@womackpublishing.com; web site mecklenburgreporter.com
Gen. Mgr. .... Randy Velvin
Mng. Ed. .... Patrick Love
News Ed. .... Dallas Weston
Acct. Exec. .... Tina Browder
Acct. Exec. .... Teresa Elliott

SOUTH HILL ENTERPRISE (WED)
914 W Danville St, South Hill, VA, 23970, Mecklenburg, USA; gen tel (434) 447-3178; gen fax (434) 447-5931; disp adv e-mail editor@southhillenterprise.com; web site southhillenterprise.com
Group: Womack Publishing Co.
Gen. Mgr. .... Randy Velvin
Mng. Ed. .... Patrick Love
Office Mgr. .... Barbara Arthur

SPRINGFIELD

FEDERAL TIMES (MON)
6883 Commercial Dr, Springfield, VA, 22159-0002, Fairfax, USA; gen tel (703) 642-7330; adv tel (703) 642-7330; ed tel (703) 642-7330; gen fax (703) 642-7386; adv fax (703) 642-7386; ed fax (703) 642-7386; disp adv e-mail advertising@federaltimes.com; class adv e-mail advertising@militarytimes.com; ed e-mail swatkins@federaltimes.com; web site www.federaltimes.com
Advertising rate: Open inch rate $7,680.00 (Full-Page)
Established: 1965
Group: Gannett
Digital Platform - Mobile: Apple, Android, Windows, Blackberry
Digital Platform - Tablet: Apple iOS, Android, Windows 7, Blackberry Tablet OS
Ed. .... Jill Aitoro
Delivery Method: Mail, Newsstand, Racks
Areas Served: Fairfax County

STANARDSVILLE

THE GREENE COUNTY RECORD (THUR)
113 Main St, Stanardsville, VA, 22973-2970, Greene, USA; gen tel (434) 985-2315; adv tel (434) 985-2315; ed tel (434) 985-2315; gen fax (434) 985-8356; adv fax (434) 985-8356; ed fax (434) 985-8356; disp adv e-mail lmcconnell@dailyprogress.com; class adv e-mail ccullen@dailyprogress.com; ed e-mail pfitzgerald@greene-news.com; web site www.dailyprogress.com
Circulation: 3,000pd,; Sworn/Estimate/Non-Audited
Advertising rate: Open inch rate $12.00
Established: 1895
Group: BH Media Group
Digital Platform - Mobile: Apple, Android
Digital Platform - Tablet: Apple iOS, Android, Windows 7
Pub.................. Lawrence McConnell
Adv. Mgr. .... Nancy Embree
Ed. .... Pat Fitzgerald
Mechanical Specifications: Type page 13 x 21 1/2; E - 6 cols, 2, 1/6 between; A - 6 cols, 2, 1/6 between; C - 9 cols, 1 1/3, between. Equipment & Software: ; Software — Micro-

soft/Windows 95, QPS/QuarkXPress, Adobe/Photoshop.
Delivery Method: Mail, Racks
Areas Served: Greene County

STERLING

FAIRFAX COUNTY TIMES (FRI)
20 Pidgeon Hill Dr, Ste 201, Sterling, VA, 20165-6134, Loudoun, USA; gen tel (703) 437-5400; adv tel (571) 323-6212; ed tel (571) 323-6224; gen fax (703) 437-6019; adv fax (703) 437-6019; ed fax (703) 437-6019; disp adv e-mail kwashburn@fairfaxtimes.com; class adv e-mail kwashburn@fairfaxtimes.com; ed e-mail gmacdonald@fairfaxtimes.com; web site www.fairfaxtimes.com - 80,000(views) 15,000(visitors)
Circulation: 102,157fr; VAC
Advertising rate: Open inch rate $54.00
Established: 1964
Group: Whip It Media, Inc.
Digital Platform - Mobile: Apple, Android, Windows, Blackberry
Digital Platform - Tablet: Apple iOS, Android, Windows 7, Blackberry Tablet OS, Kindle, Nook, Kindle Fire
Exec. Ed ....Gregg MacDonald
Delivery Method: Newsstand, Carrier, Racks
Areas Served: Fairfax County

STUART

THE ENTERPRISE (WED)
129 N Main St, Stuart, VA, 24171-8802, Patrick, USA; gen tel (276) 694-3101; adv tel (276) 694-3101; ed tel (276) 694-3101; gen fax (276) 694-5110; adv fax (276) 694-5110; ed fax (276) 694-5110; disp adv e-mail mail@theenterprise.net; class adv e-mail mail@theenterprise.net; ed e-mail mail@theenterprise.net; web site www.theenterprise.net
Circulation: 5,900pd,; Sworn/Estimate/Non-Audited
Advertising rate: Open inch rate $7.00
Established: 1876
Digital Platform - Mobile: Windows
Digital Platform - Tablet: Windows 7
Pub...Gail M. Harding
Adv. Mgr...Pam Hall
Ed...Nancy Lindsey
Delivery Method: Mail, Racks
Areas Served: Patrick County

SUTHERLAND

DINWIDDIE MONITOR (WED)
20121 Cox Rd, Sutherland, VA, 23885-9457, Dinwiddie, USA; gen tel (804) 733-8636; adv tel (804) 733-8636; ed tel (804) 733-8636; gen fax (804) 732-6322; adv fax (804) 732-6322; ed fax (804) 732-6322; disp adv e-mail dmmonitor@earthlink.net; class adv e-mail dmmonitor@earthlink.net; ed e-mail dmmonitor@earthlink.net; web site www.dinwiddie-monitor.com
Circulation: 5,200pd, 4,100fr; Sworn/Estimate/Non-Audited
Advertising rate: Open inch rate $7.00
Digital Platform - Mobile: Windows
Digital Platform - Tablet: Windows 7
Pub...Evan Jones
Managing Ed.......................Adrienne Wallace
Mechanical Specifications: Type page 13 x 21 1/2; E - 6 cols, 2 1/16, 1/8 between; A - 6 cols, 2 1/16, 1/8 between; C - 6 cols, 2 1/16, 1/8 between.Equipment & Software: Hardware — APP/Mac; Presses — KP/King; Software — Adobe/PageMaker, Adobe/Photoshop, QPS/QuarkXPress.
Delivery Method: Mail, Racks
Areas Served: Dinwiddie County

TAPPAHANNOCK

RAPPAHANNOCK TIMES (WED)
622 Charlotte St, Tappahannock, VA, 22560, Essex, USA; gen tel (804) 443-2200; adv tel (804) 443-2200; ed tel (804) 443-2200; gen fax (804) 443-9684; adv fax (804) 443-9684; ed fax (804) 443-9684; disp adv e-mail julie@rappnews.com; class adv e-mail julie@rappnews.com; ed e-mail raptimes@verizon.net
Circulation: 4,926pd, 74fr; Sworn/Estimate/Non-Audited
Advertising rate: Open inch rate $16.82
Established: 1850
Adv. Mgr...............................Catherine Wells
Pub./Chairman...........................Walter Nicklin
Pres...Dennis Brack
Gen. Mgr./Circ. Mgr.................Jan Clatterbuck
Adv. Dir...Patrice Indig
Delivery Method: Mail
Areas Served: Essex County

TASLEY

EASTERN SHORE NEWS (WED, SAT)
PO Box 288, Tasley, VA, 23441-0288, Accomack, USA; gen tel (757) 787-1200; gen fax (757) 787-2370; disp adv e-mail mmlewis@dmg.gannett.com; class adv e-mail krowan@dmg.gannett.com; ed e-mail tschockley@dmg.gannett.com; web site www.easternshorenews.com
Circulation: 8,700pd, 55fr; Sworn/Estimate/Non-Audited
Advertising rate: Open inch rate $17.68
Established: 1897
Group: Gannett
Digital Platform - Mobile: Apple, Android, Windows, Blackberry
Digital Platform - Tablet: Apple iOS, Android, Windows 7, Blackberry Tablet OS
Exec. Ed...Mike Kilian
Mng. Ed...Ted Shockley
Adv. Dir...Robb Scott
VA Adv. Mgr.......................................Megan Lewis
Mechanical Specifications: Type page 13 x 20 1/2; E - 6 cols, 2, 1/6 between; A - 6 cols, 2, 1/6 between; C - 9 cols, 1 1/3, 1/6 between. Equipment & Software: Hardware — APP/Mac; Software — QPS/QuarkXPress 3.32.
Delivery Method: Mail, Newsstand, Racks
Areas Served: Accomack County

URBANNA

SOUTHSIDE SENTINEL (THUR)
276 Virginia St, Urbanna, VA, 23175-2041, Middlesex, USA; gen tel (804) 758-2328; adv tel (804) 758-2328 ext. 104; ed tel (804) 758-2328 ext. 109; gen fax (804) 758-5896; adv fax (804) 758-5896; ed fax (804) 758-5896; disp adv e-mail wpayne@ssentinel.com; class adv e-mail classifieds@ssentinel.com; ed e-mail editor@ssentinel.com; web site www.SSentinel.com
Circulation: 4,394pd, 141fr; Sworn/Estimate/Non-Audited
Advertising rate: Open inch rate $9.25
Established: 1896
Digital Platform - Mobile: Apple, Android, Windows, Blackberry
Digital Platform - Tablet: Apple iOS, Android, Windows 7, Blackberry Tablet OS
Pub...............................Frederick A. Gaskins
Ed...............................John Thomas Hardin
Adv. Dir...Wendy Payne
Circ. Mgr./Classified Mgr.........Peggy Baughan
Art Dir...Julie Burwood
IT/Web Mgr...............................Joseph Gaskins
Customer Acct. Mgr.................Geanie Longest
Mechanical Specifications: Type page 10.955 inch x 19.8 inch; 6 cols, 1.7217 inch, 0.125 inch gutters.Equipment & Software: Hardware — Epson/Scanners, Macintosh G4s and G5s, Powerbooks, Dell PCs, Xante and HP printers.; Software — Adobe CS3, Interlink, Fake Brains AccountScout
Delivery Method: Mail, Newsstand
Areas Served: Middlesex County

VICTORIA

THE KENBRIDGE-VICTORIA DISPATCH (WED)
1404 Nottoway Boulevard, Victoria, VA, 23974, Lunenburg, USA; gen tel (434) 696-5550; gen fax (434) 696-2958; disp adv e-mail jackie.newman@kenbridgevictoriadispatch.com; web site kenbridgevictoriadispatch.com
Pub...Betty Ramsey
Mng. Ed...Jordan Miles
Dir. of Ops...Staci Bridge
Community Ed.......................................Wanda Fix
Adv. Dir...Jackie Newman
Circ. Dir...Rhonda Finch
Sports Ed...Titus Mohler

VIENNA

AIR FORCE TIMES (MON)
1919 Gallows Rd, Ste 400, Vienna, VA, 22182-4038, Fairfax, USA; gen tel (703) 642-7330; adv tel (703) 642-7330; ed tel (703) 642-7330; gen fax (703) 642-7386; adv fax (703) 642-7386; ed fax (703) 642-7386; disp adv e-mail advertising@militarytimes.com; class adv e-mail airlet@airforcetimes.com; ed e-mail riannotta@militarytimes.com; web site www.airforcetimes.com
Advertising rate: Open inch rate $7,680.00 (Full-Page)
Established: 1947
Group: Gannett
Digital Platform - Mobile: Apple, Android, Windows, Blackberry
Digital Platform - Tablet: Apple iOS, Android, Windows 7, Blackberry Tablet OS
Ed...Becky Iannotta
Delivery Method: Mail, Newsstand, Racks
Areas Served: Fairfax County

ARMY TIMES (MON)
1919 Gallows Rd, Ste 400, Vienna, VA, 22182-4038, Fairfax, USA; gen tel (703) 642-7330; adv tel (703) 642-7330; ed tel (703) 642-7330; gen fax (703) 642-7386; adv fax (703) 642-7386; ed fax (703) 642-7386; disp adv e-mail advertising@militarytimes.com; class adv e-mail armylet@armytimes.com; ed e-mail rsandza@militarytimes.com; web site www.armytimes.com
Advertising rate: Open inch rate $7,680.00 (Full-Page)
Established: 1940
Group: Gannett
Digital Platform - Mobile: Apple, Android, Windows, Blackberry
Digital Platform - Tablet: Apple iOS, Android, Windows 7, Blackberry Tablet OS
Ed...Richard Sandza
Delivery Method: Mail, Newsstand, Racks
Areas Served: Fairfax County

MARINE CORPS TIMES (MON)
1919 Gallows Rd, Ste 400, Vienna, VA, 22182-4038, Fairfax, USA; gen tel (703) 642-7330; adv tel (703) 642-7330; ed tel (703) 642-7330; gen fax (703) 642-7386; adv fax (703) 642-7386; ed fax (703) 642-7386; disp adv e-mail advertising@militarytimes.com; class adv e-mail marinelet@marinecorpstimes.com; ed e-mail adegrandpre@militarytimes.com; web site www.marinecorpstimes.com
Advertising rate: Open inch rate $7,680.00 (Full-Page)
Established: 1999
Group: Gannett
Digital Platform - Mobile: Apple, Android, Windows, Blackberry
Digital Platform - Tablet: Apple iOS, Android, Windows 7, Blackberry Tablet OS
Ed...Andrew DeGrandpre
Delivery Method: Mail, Newsstand, Racks
Areas Served: Fairfax County

WAKEFIELD

THE SUSSEX-SURRY DISPATCH (WED)
111 Railroad Avenue, Wakefield, VA, 23888, Sussex, USA; gen tel (757) 899-3551; gen fax (757) 899-7312; disp adv e-mail ads@dinwiddie-monitor.com; web site www.sussexsurrydispatch.com
Circulation: 6,800pd,; Sworn/Estimate/Non-Audited
Advertising rate: Open inch rate $7.90
Digital Platform - Mobile: Windows
Digital Platform - Tablet: Windows 7
News Ed...Ben May
Pub...Evan Jones
Delivery Method: Mail, Newsstand, Racks
Areas Served: Sussex and Surry County

WARRENTON

FAUQUIER TIMES (WED)
39 Culpeper St, Warrenton, VA, 20186-3319, Fauquier, USA; gen tel (540) 347-4222; adv tel (540) 351-1166; ed tel (540) 351-1663; gen fax (540) 349-8676; disp adv e-mail psymington@fauquier.com; class adv e-mail kgodfrey@fauquier.com; ed e-mail kpugh@fauquier.com; web site www.fauquier.com
Circulation: 9,447pd,; AAM
Advertising rate: Open inch rate $28.82
Established: 1905
Group: Piedmont Media
Digital Platform - Mobile: Apple, Android
Digital Platform - Tablet: Apple iOS, Android, Windows 7, Kindle
Chairman/CEO.......................Peter W. Arundel
Gen. Mgr.......................Pamela Symington
Piedmont Adv. Supervisor.........Kathy Godfrey
Dist. Mgr.......................................Nancy Keyser
Managing Ed.......................Mark Grandstaff
Exec. Ed.......................................Steve Campbell
Delivery Method: Mail, Newsstand, Racks
Areas Served: 20187

WARSAW

NORTHERN NECK NEWS (WED)
132 COURT CIR, Warsaw, VA, 22572, Richmond, USA; gen tel (804) 333-6397; gen fax (804) 333-0033; disp adv e-mail nnnads@lcs.net; class adv e-mail nnnclassifieds@lcs.net; ed e-mail nnneditor@lcs.net; web site www.northernnecknews.com
Circulation: 8,300pd,; Sworn/Estimate/Non-Audited
Advertising rate: Open inch rate $10.58
Group: Lakeway Publishers, Inc.
Digital Platform - Mobile: Apple, Android, Windows, Blackberry
Digital Platform - Tablet: Apple iOS, Android, Windows 7, Blackberry Tablet OS
Adv. Dir.......................................Janice Bryant
Prodn. Mgr.......................................Cheryl Angelia
Pub.................................Cary WebbEquipment & Software: Hardware — APP/Mac; Software — QPS/QuarkXPress.
Delivery Method: Mail, Racks
Areas Served: Richmond County

NORTHUMBERLAND ECHO (WED)
132 COURT CIR, Warsaw, VA, 22572, Northumberland, USA; gen tel (804) 580-3444; adv tel (804) 580-3444; ed tel (804) 580-3444; gen fax (804) 333-0033 ; adv fax (804) 333-0033 ; ed fax (804) 333-0033 ; disp adv e-mail chamilton@northumberlandecho.com; class adv e-mail chamilton@northumberlandecho.com; ed e-mail rriddell@northumberlandecho.com; web site www.northumberlandecho.com
Circulation: 2,800pd,; Sworn/Estimate/Non-Audited
Advertising rate: Open inch rate $6.86
Established: 1902
Group: Lakeway Publishers, Inc.
Digital Platform - Mobile: Apple, Android
Digital Platform - Tablet: Apple iOS, Android, Windows 7

Pub..Bill Trimble
Mng. Ed..Lee Francis
Adv. Mgr................................Debbie Mulvena
Delivery Method: Mail, Racks
Areas Served: Northumberland County

WEST POINT

THE TIDEWATER REVIEW (WED)
425 12th St, West Point, VA, 23181, King William, USA; gen tel (804) 843-2282; adv tel (804) 843-2282; ed tel (804) 843-2282; gen fax (804) 843-4404; adv fax (804) 843-4404; ed fax (804) 843-4404; disp adv e-mail Jhaynes@tidewaterreview.com; class adv e-mail Sfrench@tidewaterreview.com; ed e-mail Rlawson@tidewaterreview.com
Circulation: 5,000pd, 121fr; Sworn/Estimate/Non-Audited
Advertising rate: 1/8 Pg $155.00; 1/4 Pg $301.00; 1/2 Pg $568.00
Digital Platform - Mobile: Apple, Android, Windows, Blackberry
Digital Platform - Tablet: Apple iOS, Android, Windows 7, Blackberry Tablet OS
Gen. Mgr./Ed.............................Robin Lawson
Adv. Mgr.................................Jennifer Haynes
Delivery Method: Mail, Racks
Areas Served: King and Queen, New Kent, West Point, and King William County

WOODBRIDGE

INSIDENOVA/NORTH STAFFORD (FRI)
1372 Old Bridge Rd, Ste 101, Woodbridge, VA, 22192-2755, Prince William, USA; gen tel ; adv tel ; ed tel 571-208-8059; gen fax ; disp adv e-mail bpowell@insidenova.com; class adv e-mail ; ed e-mail adolzenko@insidenova.com; web site www.insidenova.com
Circulation: 21pd, 19,811fr; Sworn/Estimate/Non-Audited
Advertising rate:
Established: 1990
Group: rappahannock media
Digital Platform - Mobile: Apple, Android, Windows, Blackberry
Digital Platform - Tablet: Apple iOS, Android, Windows 7
Aleks Dolzenko
Mechanical Specifications: Type page 12 x 20 1/2; E - 5 cols, 2 1/2, between; A - 6 cols, 2, between; C - 10 cols, 1 1/6, between. Equipment & Software: Hardware — APP/Mac; Presses — 2-MAN/4; Software — QPS/QuarkXPress 4.1.
Delivery Method: Mail, Carrier, Racks
Areas Served: Stafford County, virginia

INSIDENOVA/PRINCE WILLIAM (FRI)
1372 Old Bridge Rd, Ste 101, Woodbridge, VA, 22192-2755, Prince William, USA; gen tel (703) 993-9933; adv tel (703) 303-8713; ed tel 571-208-8059; disp adv e-mail cfields@princewilliamtoday.com; class adv e-mail ; ed e-mail adolzenko@insidenova.com; web site www.insidenova.com
Circulation: 280pd, 14,785fr; CVC
Advertising rate: 1/16 Pg $145.00; 1/8 Pg $205.00; 1/4 Pg $305.00
Established: 2013
Group: rappahannock media
Digital Platform - Mobile: Apple, Android
Digital Platform - Tablet: Apple iOS, Android
Rgl. VP...Bruce Potter
Sr. Ed..Kari Pugh
Adv. Mgr......................................Connie Fields
Ed..Aleks Dolzenko
Delivery Method: Mail, Racks
Areas Served: Prince William County

WOODSTOCK

THE SHENANDOAH VALLEY-HERALD (FRI)
136 W Court St, Woodstock, VA, 22664-1490, Shenandoah, USA; gen tel (540) 459-4078; adv tel (540) 459-4078; ed tel (540) 459-4078; gen fax (540) 459-4077; adv fax (540) 459-4077; ed fax (540) 459-4077; disp adv e-mail editor@pagenewspaper.com; class adv e-mail svhads@dnronline.com; ed e-mail editor@pagenewspaper.com; web site www.ShenValleyNow.com
Circulation: 2,503pd,; AAM
Advertising rate: Open inch rate $11.70
Established: 1806
Group: Ogden Newspapers Inc.
Digital Platform - Mobile: Apple, Android
Digital Platform - Tablet: Apple iOS, Android, Windows 7
Ed./Gen. Mgr..........................Randy Arrington
Advt Sales ....Toni Allen
Mechanical Specifications: Type page 13 x 21 1/2.
Delivery Method: Mail, Newsstand, Carrier, Racks
Areas Served: 22664

WYTHEVILLE

BLAND COUNTY MESSENGER (WED)
460 W Main St, Wytheville, VA, 24382-2207, Wythe, USA; gen tel (276) 228-6611; adv tel (800) 655-1406 ext. 31; ed tel (800) 655-1406 ext. 19; gen fax (276) 228-7260; adv fax (276) 228-7260; ed fax (276) 228-7260; disp adv e-mail bsewell@wythenews.com; class adv e-mail jsage@wythenews.com; ed e-mail jsimmons@wythenews.com; web site www.blandcountynews.com
Circulation: 2,500pd, 64fr; Sworn/Estimate/Non-Audited
Advertising rate: Open inch rate $12.40
Group: BH Media Group
Digital Platform - Mobile: Apple, Android
Digital Platform - Tablet: Apple iOS, Android, Windows 7
Group Ed.......................................Mark Sage
Mng. Ed......................................Jeff Simmons
Pub...Sam Cooper
Adv. Dir.......................................Linda Crigger
Delivery Method: Mail, Racks
Areas Served: Bland County

WASHINGTON COUNTY NEWS (WED)
460 W Main St, Wytheville, VA, 24382-2207, Washington, USA; gen tel (276) 628-7101; adv tel (276) 628-7101; ed tel (800) 655-1406 ext. 16; gen fax (276) 628-1195; adv fax (276) 628-1195; ed fax (276) 628-1195; disp adv e-mail jmaxwell@bristolnews.com; class adv e-mail bsewell@wythenews.com; ed e-mail jsage@wythenews.com; web site www.swvat.com
Circulation: 4,255pd, 287fr; Sworn/Estimate/Non-Audited
Advertising rate: Open inch rate $13.95
Group: World Media Enterprises Inc.
Digital Platform - Mobile: Apple, Android, Windows, Blackberry
Digital Platform - Tablet: Apple iOS, Android, Windows 7, Blackberry Tablet OS
Pub..James Maxwell
Ed..Mark Sage
Adv. Mgr...................................Barbara Sewell
Circ. Dir......................................Sonny Corpus
Production Mgr.............................Hilda Foster
Mechanical Specifications: Type page 13 x 21 1/2; E - 6 cols, 2 1/16, 1/9 between; A - 6 cols, 2 1/16, 1/9 between; C - 8 cols, 1 1/2, 1/9 between.
Delivery Method: Mail, Newsstand, Racks
Areas Served: Richlands, Wytheville, Floyd, Smyth, Washington, and Bland County

WYTHEVILLE ENTERPRISE (WED, SAT)
460 W Main St, Wytheville, VA, 24382-2207, Wythe, USA; gen tel (276) 228-6611; adv tel (800) 655-1406 ext. 31; ed tel (800) 655-1406 ext. 19; gen fax (276) 228-7260; adv fax (276) 228-7260; ed fax (276) 228-7260; disp adv e-mail bsewell@wythenews.com; class adv e-mail jsage@wythenews.com; ed e-mail jsimmons@wythenews.com; web site www.wythenews.com
Circulation: 6,700pd,; Sworn/Estimate/Non-Audited
Advertising rate: Open inch rate $11.00
Group: BH Media Group
Digital Platform - Mobile: Apple, Android
Digital Platform - Tablet: Apple iOS, Android, Windows 7
Group Ed.......................................Mark Sage
Mng. Ed.....................................Jeff Simmons
Adv. Dir....................................Barbara Sewell
Retail Adv. Mgr...........................Donna Akers
Delivery Method: Mail, Newsstand, Racks
Areas Served: Wythe County

YORKTOWN

YORK TOWN CRIER/THE POQUOSON POST (THUR)
3526 George Washington Mem Hwy, Yorktown, VA, 23693-3371, York, USA; gen tel (757) 766-1776; adv tel (757) 766-1776; ed tel (757) 766-1776; gen fax (757) 766-1788; adv fax (757) 766-1788; ed fax (757) 766-1788; disp adv e-mail rob@yorktowncrier.com; class adv e-mail rob@yorktowncrier.com; ed e-mail news@yorktowncrier.com; web site www.yorktowncrier.com
Circulation: 4,000pd,; Sworn/Estimate/Non-Audited
Advertising rate: Open inch rate $9.30
Established: 1978
Digital Platform - Mobile: Apple, Android, Windows, Blackberry
Digital Platform - Tablet: Apple iOS, Android, Windows 7, Blackberry Tablet OS, Kindle, Nook, Kindle Fire
Pub./Mng. Ed......................Elizabeth Meisner
Adv. Mgr.......................................Rob Meisner
Mechanical Specifications: Type page 13 x 21 1/2; E - 6 cols, 2 1/16, 1/6 between; A - 6 cols, 2 1/16, 1/6 between; C - 6 cols, 2 1/16, 1/6 between.Equipment & Software: Hardware — APP/Mac; Presses — 6-G/Community; Software — QPS/QuarkXPress 3.31.
Delivery Method: Mail, Racks
Areas Served: York County

WASHINGTON

ABERDEEN

THE DAILY WORLD (TUES, THUR, SAT)
315 S Michigan St, Aberdeen, WA, 98520-6037, Grays Harbor, USA; gen tel (360) 532-4000; adv tel (360) 532-4000; ed tel (360) 532-4000; gen fax (360) 533-1328; adv fax (360) 533-1328; ed fax (360) 533-6039; disp adv e-mail mspezia@thedailyworld.com; class adv e-mail advert@thedailyworld.com; ed e-mail editor@thedailyworld.com; web site www.thedailyworld.com
Circulation: 5,596pd, 749fr; AAM
Advertising rate: Open inch rate $19.85
Group: Black Press Group Ltd.
Adv. Mgr.......................................Mike Spezia
Circ. Dir...................................Gerald Atkinson
City Ed.......................................Bill Lindstrom
Asst. City Ed..............................Dan Jackson
Entertainment Ed., Preview Magazine.......Jeff Burlingame
Photo Dept. Mgr...........................Kathy Quigg
Religion Ed..................................Tommi Gatlin
Sports Ed..................................Rick Anderson
Mgr., Distr...................................Ryan Parson
Prodn. Mgr., Pre Press Systems.. David Dutton
Prodn. Foreman, Pressroom...Larry Schoening
Publisher...................................Stanley Woody
Editor...Doug Barker
Mechanical Specifications: Type page 13 x 21 1/2; E - 6 cols, 2 1/16, 1/8 between; A - 6 cols, 2 1/16, 1/8 between; C - 9 cols, 1 3/8, 1/16 between.

ANACORTES

ANACORTES AMERICAN (WED)
901 6th St, Anacortes, WA, 98221-1716, Skagit, USA; gen tel (360) 293-3122; adv tel (360) 293-3122; ed tel (360) 293-3122 ext. 1040; disp adv e-mail ads@skagitpublishing.com; class adv e-mail classified@skagitpublishing.com; ed e-mail news@goanacortes.com; web site www.goanacortes.com
Circulation: 2,355pd, 40fr; CAC
Advertising rate: Open inch rate $12.00
Established: 1890
Group: Adams Publishing Group, LLC
Digital Platform - Mobile: Apple, Android, Windows, Blackberry
Digital Platform - Tablet: Apple iOS, Android, Windows 7, Blackberry Tablet OS, Kindle, Nook, Kindle Fire
Pub./Ed.......................................Jack Darnton
Ed. / Gen. Mgr..........................Colette Weeks
Display Adv. Mgr..................Deb Davis Bundy
Delivery Method: Carrier, Racks
Areas Served: Skagit County

BAINBRIDGE ISLAND

BAINBRIDGE ISLAND REVIEW (FRI)
PO Box 10817, Bainbridge Island, WA, 98110-0817, Kitsap, USA; gen tel (206) 842-6613; adv tel (206) 842-6613; ed tel (206) 842-6613; disp adv e-mail publisher@bainbridgereview.com; class adv e-mail publisher@bainbridgereview.com; ed e-mail editor@bainbridgereview.com; web site www.bainbridgereview.com
Circulation: 2,062pd, 471fr; AAM
Advertising rate: Open inch rate $22.40
Established: 1923
Group: Black Press Group Ltd.
Sound Publishing, Inc.
Digital Platform - Mobile: Apple, Android, Windows, Blackberry
Digital Platform - Tablet: Apple iOS, Android, Windows 7, Blackberry Tablet OS, Kindle, Nook, Kindle Fire
Pub...Donna Etchey
Ed..Brian Kelly
Nat'l Sales Dir........................Stephen Barrett
Nat'l/Rgl Acct. Mgr...............Theresa Eskridge
Market Develop. Admin..............Clare Ortblad
Delivery Method: Mail, Newsstand, Racks
Areas Served: Kitsap County

BATTLE GROUND

THE REFLECTOR (WED)
208 SE 1ST ST, Battle Ground, WA, 98604, Clark, USA; gen tel (360) 687-5151; gen fax (360) 687-5162; disp adv e-mail ads@thereflector.com; class adv e-mail legals@thereflector.com; ed e-mail news@thereflector.com; web site www.thereflector.com - 41,169(views) 11,732(visitors)
Circulation: 816pd, 28,206fr; Sworn/Estimate/Non-Audited
Advertising rate: Open inch rate $16.25
Established: 1909
Group: Lafromboise Communications, Inc.
Digital Platform - Mobile: Apple, Android, Windows, Blackberry
Digital Platform - Tablet: Apple iOS, Android, Windows 7, Blackberry Tablet OS, Kindle, Nook, Kindle Fire
Pub...Laura Venneri
Mechanical Specifications: 9.98" x 20.43" 5 column retail
7 column classified.
Delivery Method: Mail, Newsstand, Carrier, Racks
Areas Served: North Clark County and South Cowlitz County

BELLEVUE

BELLEVUE REPORTER (FRI)
2700 Richards Rd, Ste 201, Bellevue, WA,

Washington
Total Daily Newspapers 20
Total Daily Circulation 556,185
Total Weekly Newspapers 117
Total Weekly Circulation 1,243,712
Population 7,405,473
LEGEND
Dallas-Fort Worth Combined Statistical Area
RICHMOND Metropolitan Statistical Area
Concord Micropolitan Statistical Area
Philadelphia Metropolitan Division
CANADA International
TEXAS State
HARRIS County
Shoreline
CANADA
IDAHO
OREGON
Seattle-Tacoma-Olympia
BELLINGHAM
WHATCOM
MOUNT VERNON-ANACORTES
SKAGIT
Oak Harbor
ISLAND
SAN JUAN
SNOHOMISH
Seattle-Bellevue-Everett
KING
SEATTLE-TACOMA-BELLEVUE
Tacoma
PIERCE
KITSAP
BREMERTON-SILVERDALE
OLYMPIA
THURSTON
Shelton
MASON
JEFFERSON
Port Angeles
CLALLAM
Aberdeen
GRAYS HARBOR
PACIFIC
WAHKIAKUM
Centralia
LEWIS
LONGVIEW
COWLITZ
SKAMANIA
CLARK
PORTLAND-VANCOUVER-BEAVERTON
MULTNOMAH
CLACKAMAS
COLUMBIA
WASHINGTON
YAMHILL
KLICKITAT
YAKIMA
Ellensburg
KITTITAS
WENATCHEE
CHELAN
DOUGLAS
OKANOGAN
Moses Lake
GRANT
KENNEWICK-RICHLAND-PASCO
BENTON
FRANKLIN
Walla Walla
WALLA WALLA
COLUMBIA
GARFIELD
ASOTIN
LEWISTON
NEZ PERCE
Pullman
WHITMAN
ADAMS
LINCOLN
SPOKANE
FERRY
STEVENS
PEND OREILLE
N
0 15 30 45 60 Kilometers
0 15 30 45 60 Miles
49°
48°
47°
46°
45°
116°
117°
118°
119°
120°
121°
122°
123°
124°
125°

98005-4200, King, USA; gen tel (425) 453-4270; adv tel (425) 453-4623; ed tel (425) 453-4233; disp adv e-mail jgralish@bellevuereporter.com; class adv e-mail mdevere@soundpublishing.com; ed e-mail editor@bellevuereporter.com; web site www.bellevuereporter.com
Circulation: 15pd, 35,074fr; AAM
Advertising rate: Open inch rate $34.85
Established: 1930
Group: Black Press Group Ltd.
Sound Publishing, Inc.
Digital Platform - Mobile: Apple, Android, Windows, Blackberry
Digital Platform - Tablet: Apple iOS, Android, Windows 7, Blackberry Tablet OS, Kindle, Nook, Kindle Fire
Pub./Ed. .... Craig Groshart
Adv. Mgr. .... Jen Gralish
Market Develop. Admin. .... Clare Ortblad
Nat'l Sales Dir. .... Stephen Barrett
Delivery Method: Mail, Newsstand, Racks
Areas Served: King County

ISSAQUAH/SAMMAMISH REPORTER (FRI)

2700 Richards Rd, Ste 201, Bellevue, WA, 98005-4200, King, USA; gen tel (425) 391-0363; adv tel (425) 391-0363; ed tel (425) 391-0363; disp adv e-mail scravens@issaquahreporter.com; class adv e-mail jsuman@bellevuereporter.com; ed e-mail cgroshart@issaquahreporter.com; web site www.issaquah-reporter.com
Circulation: 10pd, 1,442fr; AAM
Advertising rate: Open inch rate $28.05
Group: Black Press Group Ltd.
Sound Publishing, Inc.
Digital Platform - Mobile: Apple, Android, Windows, Blackberry
Digital Platform - Tablet: Apple iOS, Android, Windows 7, Blackberry Tablet OS, Kindle, Nook, Kindle Fire
Pub. .... William Shaw
Ed. .... Craig Groshart
Adv. Mgr. .... Sally Cravens
Nat'l Sales Dir. .... Stephen Barrett
Delivery Method: Mail, Newsstand, Racks
Areas Served: King County

MERCER ISLAND REPORTER (WED)

2700 Richards Rd, Ste 201, Bellevue, WA, 98005-4200, King, USA; gen tel (206) 232-1215; adv tel (206) 232-1215 ext. 3050; ed tel (206) 232-1215 ext. 1050; gen fax (206) 232-1284; adv fax (206) 232-1284; ed fax (206) 232-1284; disp adv e-mail wshaw@soundpublishing.com; class adv e-mail tbaumann@mi-reporter.com; ed e-mail editor@mi-reporter.com; web site www.mi-reporter.com
Circulation: 6,498pd, 35,864fr; AAM
Advertising rate: Open inch rate $14.50
Established: 1947
Group: Black Press Group Ltd.
Sound Publishing, Inc.
Digital Platform - Mobile: Apple, Android, Windows, Blackberry
Digital Platform - Tablet: Apple iOS, Android, Windows 7, Blackberry Tablet OS, Kindle, Nook, Kindle Fire
Pub. .... William Shaw
Ed. .... Mary L. Grady
Nat'l Sales Dir. .... Stephen Barrett
Mechanical Specifications: Type page 13 1/2 x 23; E - 6 cols, 2 1/5, between; A - 6 cols, 2 1/5, between.
Delivery Method: Mail
Areas Served: King County

BELLINGHAM

BELLINGHAM BUSINESS JOURNAL (THUR, MTHLY)

1909 Cornwall Ave, Bellingham, WA, 98225-3659, Whatcom, USA; gen tel (360) 647-8805; adv tel (360) 647-8805; ed tel (360) 647-8805; gen fax (360) 647-0502; adv fax (360) 647-0502; ed fax (360) 647-0502; disp adv e-mail tbouchard@bbjtoday.com; class adv e-mail sales@bbjtoday.com; ed e-mail editor@bbjtoday.com; web site www.bbjtoday.com
Advertising rate: Open inch rate $23.85
Established: 1994
Group: Black Press Group Ltd.
Sound Publishing, Inc.
Digital Platform - Mobile: Apple, Android, Windows, Blackberry
Digital Platform - Tablet: Apple iOS, Android, Windows 7, Blackberry Tablet OS, Kindle, Nook, Kindle Fire
Adv. Mgr. .... Tony Bouchard
News Ed. .... Evan Marczynski
Delivery Method: Mail, Newsstand, Racks
Areas Served: Whatcom County

BLAINE

THE NORTHERN LIGHT (THUR)

225 Marine Dr, Ste 200, Blaine, WA, 98230-4052, Whatcom, USA; gen tel (360) 332-1777; adv tel (360) 332-1777; ed tel (360) 332-1777; gen fax (360) 332-2777; adv fax (360) 332-2777; ed fax (360) 332-2777; disp adv e-mail sales@thenorthernlight.com; class adv e-mail info@thenorthernlight.com; ed e-mail editor@thenorthernlight.com; web site www.thenorthernlight.com
Circulation: 17pd, 10,458fr; VAC
Advertising rate: 1/4 pg $410.00; Full Pg $1500.00
Established: 1995
Group: Point Roberts Press, Inc.
Digital Platform - Mobile: Apple, Android, Windows, Blackberry
Digital Platform - Tablet: Apple iOS, Android, Windows 7, Blackberry Tablet OS
Pub./Mng. Ed. .... Patrick J. Grubb
Adv. Mgr. .... Louise H. Mugar
Mechanical Specifications: Type page 10 1/4 x 15 1/4; E - 5 cols, 2, 1/6 between; A - 5 cols, 2, 1/6 between; C - 6 cols, 1 1/2, 1/6 between.Equipment & Software: Hardware — APP/Mac.
Delivery Method: Mail, Racks
Areas Served: Blaine and Birch Bay/98230

BURIEN

FEDERAL WAY NEWS (WED, FRI)

14006 1st Ave S, Ste B, Burien, WA, 98168-3402, King, USA; gen tel (206) 708-1378; adv tel (206) 387-3873; ed tel (425)-238-4616; gen fax (206) 453-5041; disp adv e-mail donao@robinsonnews.com; class adv e-mail classifieds@robinsonnews.com; ed e-mail kenr@robinsonnews.com; web site www.federalwaynews.net
Circulation:; Sworn/Estimate/Non-Audited
Advertising rate: Open inch rate $40.00
Established: 1953
Group: Robinson Newspapers
Digital Platform - Mobile: Apple, Android, Windows, Blackberry
Digital Platform - Tablet: Apple iOS, Android, Windows 7, Blackberry Tablet OS
Assoc. Pub. .... Tim Robinson
Mng. Ed. .... Ken Robinson
Adv. Mgr. .... Dona Ozier
Mechanical Specifications: Type page 13 x 21 1/2; E - 6 cols, 2 1/16, 1/8 between; A - 6 cols, 2 1/16, 1/8 between; C - 10 cols, 1 1/4, 1/16 between.Equipment & Software: Hardware — APP/Mac Quadra, APP/Power Mac, APP/Mac Centris, CD Writer; Presses — G/Urbanite; Software — Multi-Ad/Creator 3.62, QPS/QuarkXPress 5.0, Adobe/Photoshop, Adobe/Illustrator.
Delivery Method: Mail, Newsstand, Racks
Areas Served: King County

HIGHLINE TIMES (FRI)

14006 1st Ave S, Ste B, Burien, WA, 98168-3402, King, USA; gen tel (425) 238-4616; adv tel (206) 387-3873; ed tel (425)-238-4616; gen fax (206) 453-5041; adv fax (206) 453-5041; ed fax (206) 453-5041; disp adv e-mail donao@robinsonnews.com; class adv e-mail classifieds@robinsonnews.com; ed e-mail kenr@robinsonnews.com; web site www.highlinetimes.com
Circulation: 15,000pd,; Sworn/Estimate/Non-Audited
Advertising rate: Open inch rate $24.00
Established: 1945
Group: Robinson Newspapers
Digital Platform - Mobile: Apple, Android, Windows, Blackberry
Digital Platform - Tablet: Apple iOS, Android, Windows 7, Blackberry Tablet OS
Pub. .... Jerry Robinson
Assoc. Pub. .... Tim Robinson
Mng. Ed. .... Ken Robinson
Adv. Mgr. .... Dona Ozier
Delivery Method: Mail, Newsstand, Racks
Areas Served: 98166, 98168, 98146, 98148, 98188, 98198

CAMAS

CAMAS-WASHOUGAL POST RECORD (TUES)

425 NE 4th Ave, Camas, WA, 98607-2129, Clark, USA; gen tel (360) 834-2141; adv tel (360) 735-4670; ed tel (360) 735-4674; gen fax (360) 834-3423; adv fax (360) 834-3423; ed fax (360) 834-3423; disp adv e-mail heather.acheson@camaspostrecord.com; class adv e-mail shelly.atwell@camaspostrecord.com; ed e-mail heather.acheson@camaspostrecord.com; web site www.camaspostrecord.com
Circulation: 10,000pd,; Sworn/Estimate/Non-Audited
Advertising rate: Open inch rate $11.50
Digital Platform - Mobile: Apple, Android, Windows
Digital Platform - Tablet: Apple iOS, Android, Windows 7
Pub./Adv. Mgr. .... Mike Gallagher
Circ. Mgr. .... Shelly Atwell
Mng. Ed. .... Heather Acheson
Mechanical Specifications: Type page 13 x 21; E - 6 cols, 2 1/16, 1/8 between; A - 6 cols, 2 1/16, 1/8 between; C - 9 cols, 1 1/4, 1/8 between.Equipment & Software: Hardware — APP/Mac; Software — QPS/QuarkXPress, Claris/MacWrite.
Delivery Method: Mail, Racks
Areas Served: Clark County

CASHMERE

CASHMERE VALLEY RECORD (WED)

201 Cottage Ave, Ste 4, Cashmere, WA, 98815-1616, Chelan, USA; gen tel (509) 782-3781; adv tel (509) 548-5286; ed tel (509) 782-3781; gen fax (509) 782-9074; adv fax (509) 548-4789; ed fax (509) 782-9074; disp adv e-mail carol@leavenworthecho.com; class adv e-mail classifieds@leavenworthecho.com; ed e-mail reporter@cashmerevalleyrecord.com; web site www.cashmerevalleyrecord.com - 7,741(views) 6,834(visitors)
Circulation: 1,000pd,; Sworn/Estimate/Non-Audited
Advertising rate: Open inch rate 7.74
Established: 1905
Group: NCW Media, Inc.Editions: (52) Cashmere Valley Record
Digital Platform - Mobile: Apple, Android, Blackberry
Digital Platform - Tablet: Apple iOS, Android, Kindle, Kindle Fire
CEO/Pub. .... Bill Forhan
Adv. Mgr. .... Carol Forhan
Mechanical Specifications: Super Tab - 11 5/8" X 17"
6 col. print 10 1/4" X 16"Equipment & Software: Hardware — Apple; Presses — 5-G/Community; Software — InDesign, Media Span Ad Mgr Pro, Interlink, 1Up!
Delivery Method: Mail, Newsstand, Racks
Areas Served: 98815, 98821, 98836

WENATCHEE BUSINESS JOURNAL (MON, MTHLY)

201 Cottage Ave, Ste 4, Cashmere, WA, 98815-1616, Chelan, USA; gen tel (509) 782-3781; adv tel (509) 548-5286; ed tel (509) 782-3781; gen fax (509) 782-9074; adv fax (509) 548-4789; ed fax (509) 782-9074; disp adv e-mail carol@leavenworthecho.com; class adv e-mail classifieds@leavenworthecho.com; ed e-mail wbjeditor@gmail.com; web site www.ncwbusiness.com
Circulation: 1,600pd, 2,900fr; Sworn/Estimate/Non-Audited
Advertising rate: Open inch rate $24.00
Established: 1987
Group: NCW Media, Inc.Editions: (12) Wenatchee Business Journal
Digital Platform - Mobile: Apple, Android, Windows
Digital Platform - Tablet: Apple iOS, Kindle, Kindle Fire
Mng. Ed. .... Gary BeginEquipment & Software: Hardware — Apple; Presses — N/A; Software — InDesign, Media Span Ad Manager Pro, Interlink, 1Up!
Delivery Method: Mail, Newsstand
Areas Served: Chelan County, Okanogan County, Douglas County

CATHLAMET

WAHKIAKUM COUNTY EAGLE (THUR)

77 Main St, Cathlamet, WA, 98612-4201, Wahkiakum, USA; gen tel (360) 795-3391; adv tel (360) 795-3391; ed tel (360) 795-3391; gen fax (360) 795-3983; adv fax (360) 795-3983; ed fax (360) 795-3983; disp adv e-mail kathi@waheagle.com; class adv e-mail geri@waheagle.com; ed e-mail ernelson@teleport.com; web site www.waheagle.com
Circulation: 1,660pd, 33fr; Sworn/Estimate/Non-Audited
Advertising rate: Open inch rate $8.08
Established: 1891
Digital Platform - Mobile: Apple, Android, Windows
Digital Platform - Tablet: Apple iOS, Android, Windows 7
Pub./Ed. .... Rick Nelson
Adv. Mgr./Prod. Mgr. .... Geri R. Florek
Adv. Account Mgr. .... Kathi Howell
Mechanical Specifications: Type page 10 1/2 x 21; E - 6 cols, 1 7/8, 1/8 between; A - 6 cols, 1 7/8, 1/8 between; C - 6 cols, 1 7/8, 1/8 between.
Delivery Method: Mail, Newsstand
Areas Served: 98612, 98647, 98621, 98643, 98638

CENTRALIA

THE CHRONICLE (TUES, THUR, SAT)

321 N Pearl St, Centralia, WA, 98531-4323, Lewis, USA; gen tel (360) 736-3311; gen fax (360)807-8258; disp adv e-mail bwatson@chronline.com; class adv e-mail classified@chronline.com; ed e-mail letters@chronline.com; web site www.chronline.com
Circulation: 10,200pd,; Sworn/Estimate/Non-Audited
Advertising rate: Open inch rate $16.74
Established: 1966
Group: Lafromboise Communications, Inc.
Digital Platform - Mobile: Apple, Android, Windows, Blackberry
Digital Platform - Tablet: Apple iOS, Android, Windows 7, Blackberry Tablet OS, Kindle, Nook, Kindle Fire
Pub. .... Christine Fossett
Regional Exec. Ed. .... Michael Wagar
Editor .... Eric Schwartz
Sports Ed. .... Aaron Van Tuyl
Circ. Mgr. .... Anita Freeborn
Sales Dir. .... Brian Watson
Business Mgr. .... Mary Jackson
Mechanical Specifications: Type page 9.98"x20.43" 5 column, classifieds 7 column
Delivery Method: Mail, Newsstand, Carrier, Racks
Areas Served: 98531,98532,98579,98589,98596,98591,98572,98522,98565,98570,98582,98564,98356,98377,98361

CHELAN

LAKE CHELAN MIRROR (WED)

310 E Johnson Ave, Chelan, WA, 98816, Chelan, USA; gen tel (509) 682-2213; adv tel (509) 548-5286; ed tel (509) 682-2213; gen fax (509) 682-4209; adv fax (509) 548-4789; ed fax (509) 682-4209; disp adv e-mail carol@leavenworthecho.com; class adv e-mail classifieds@leavenworthecho.com; ed e-mail editor@lakechelanmirror.com; web site www.lakechelanmirror.com
Circulation: 1,800pd, 1,200fr; Sworn/Estimate/Non-Audited
Advertising rate: Open inch rate $16.00
Established: 1891
Group: NCW Media, Inc.Editions: (52) Lake Chelan Mirror
Digital Platform - Mobile: Apple, Android
Digital Platform - Tablet: Apple iOS, Android
Pub/CEO
Bill Forhan
VP, Adv.... Carol ForhanEquipment & Software: Hardware — Apple, CTP, Kansa; Presses — Goss Community; Software — InDesign, Media Span Ad Manager Pro, Interlink, 1Up!
Delivery Method: Mail, Newsstand, Racks
Areas Served: 98816, 98817, 98822

QUAD CITY HERALD (THUR)

310 E Johnson Ave, Chelan, WA, 98816, Chelan, USA; gen tel (509) 682-2213; adv tel (509) 548-5286; ed tel (509) 682-2213; gen fax (509) 682-4209; adv fax (509) 682-4209; ed fax (509) 682-4209; disp adv e-mail carol@leavenworthecho.com; class adv e-mail classifieds@leavenworthecho.com; ed e-mail reporter@qcherald.com; web site www.qcherald.com
Circulation: 1,500pd,; Sworn/Estimate/Non-Audited
Advertising rate: Open inch rate $10.86
Established: 1907
Group: NCW Media, Inc.Editions: (52) Quad City Herald
Digital Platform - Mobile: Apple, Android
Digital Platform - Tablet: Apple iOS, Android
Pub./Adv. Mgr.............Carol ForhanEquipment & Software: Hardware — Apple; Presses — 5 unit Goss community; Software — In Design, Baseview, Interlink, 1Up!
Delivery Method: Mail, Newsstand, Racks
Areas Served: Okanogan County

CHENEY

CHENEY FREE PRESS (THUR)

1616 W 1st St, Cheney, WA, 99004-8800, Spokane, USA; gen tel (509) 235-6184; adv tel (509) 235-6184; ed tel (509) 235-6184; gen fax (509) 235-2887; adv fax (509) 235-2887; ed fax (509) 235-2887; disp adv e-mail info@cheneyfreepress.com; class adv e-mail info@cheneyfreepress.com; ed e-mail info@cheneyfreepress.com; web site www.cheneyfreepress.com
Advertising rate: Open inch rate $11.50
Established: 1896
Digital Platform - Mobile: Apple, Android
Digital Platform - Tablet: Apple iOS, Android, Windows 7
Pub./Ed. .... William Ifft
Delivery Method: Mail, Racks
Areas Served: Spokane County

CHEWELAH

THE INDEPENDENT (THUR)

401 S Park St, Ste A, Chewelah, WA, 99109-9337, Stevens, USA; gen tel (509) 935-8422; adv tel (509) 935-8422; ed tel (509) 935-8422; gen fax (509) 935-4755; adv fax (509) 935-4755; ed fax (509) 935-4755; disp adv e-mail theindependent@centurytel.net; class adv e-mail theindependent@centurytel.net; ed e-mail theindependent@centurytel.net; web site www.chewelahindependent.com
Circulation: 2,100pd, 500fr; USPS
Advertising rate: Open inch rate $8.00
Established: 1903
Group: Chewelah Independent, Inc.Editions: (1) The Independent
Digital Platform - Mobile: Apple, Android
Digital Platform - Tablet: Apple iOS, Android, Windows 7
Pub.. Jared Arnold
Office Mgr. .... Andrea Arnold
Managing Editor .... Brandon Hansen
Delivery Method: Mail, Racks
Areas Served: 99109, 99141, 99114, 99101, 99181, 99173

CLE ELUM

NORTHERN KITTITAS COUNTY TRIBUNE (THUR)

807 W Davis St, Ste A101, Cle Elum, WA, 98922-1027, Kittitas, USA; gen tel (509) 674-2511; gen fax (509) 674-5571; disp adv e-mail ads@nkctribune.com; ed e-mail tribune@nkctribune.com; web site www.nkctribune.com
Circulation: 3,000pd,; Sworn/Estimate/Non-Audited
Advertising rate: Open inch rate $13.00
Established: 1953
Group: Oahe Publishing Corporation
Digital Platform - Mobile: Apple, Android, Windows, Blackberry
Digital Platform - Tablet: Apple iOS, Android, Windows 7, Blackberry Tablet OS
Pub./Ed. ....Jana Stoner
Pub... Terry Hamberg
Delivery Method: Mail, Newsstand, Racks
Areas Served: Kittitas County

COLFAX

WHITMAN COUNTY GAZETTE (THUR)

211 N Main St, Colfax, WA, 99111-1816, Whitman, USA; gen tel (509) 397-4333; adv tel (509) 397-4333; ed tel (509) 397-4333; gen fax (509) 397-4527; adv fax (509) 397-4527; ed fax (509) 397-4527; disp adv e-mail WCGAZETTE@GMAIL.COM; class adv e-mail WCGAZETTE@GMAIL.COM; ed e-mail WCGAZETTE@GMAIL.COM; web site www.wcgazette.com
Advertising rate: Open inch rate $7.35
Established: 1877
Digital Platform - Mobile: Apple, Android, Windows, Blackberry
Digital Platform - Tablet: Apple iOS, Android, Windows 7, Blackberry Tablet OS
Sally Ousley
Gordon ForgeyNews Ed.s
Delivery Method: Mail
Areas Served: Whitman County

COLVILLE

STATESMAN EXAMINER (TUES, WED)

220 S Main St, Colville, WA, 99114-2408, Stevens, USA; gen tel (509) 684-4567; adv tel (509) 684-4567; ed tel (509) 684-4567; gen fax (509) 684-3849; adv fax (509) 684-3849; ed fax (509) 684-3849; disp adv e-mail bonni@statesmanexaminer.com; class adv e-mail classified@statesmanexaminer.com; ed e-mail reporter@statesmanexaminer.com; web site www.statesmanexaminer.com
Advertising rate: Open inch rate $8.00
Established: 1948
Group: Horizon Publications Inc.
Digital Platform - Mobile: Apple, Android
Digital Platform - Tablet: Apple iOS, Android
Adv. Mgr. .... Bonni Haskell
Regional Publisher .... Jesse Mullen
Delivery Method: Mail, Newsstand, Racks
Areas Served: Stevens County

COULEE CITY

THE NEWS & STANDARD (WED)

405 W Main St, Coulee City, WA, 99115, Grant, USA; gen tel (509) 632-5402; adv tel (509) 632-5402; ed tel (509) 632-5402; disp adv e-mail tns@accima.com; class adv e-mail tns@accima.com; ed e-mail tns@accima.com; web site www.smalltownpapers.com
Circulation: 800pd,; Sworn/Estimate/Non-Audited
Advertising rate: Open inch rate $5.00
Established: 1890
Ed./Pub. ....Shirley Rae Maes
Delivery Method: Mail
Areas Served: 99115, 99135, 99103, 99133

COUPEVILLE

SOUTH WHIDBEY RECORD (WED, SAT)

PO Box 1200, Coupeville, WA, 98239-1200, Island, USA; gen tel (360) 221-5300; adv tel (360) 221-5300; ed tel (360) 221-5300; gen fax (360) 221-6474; adv fax (360) 221-6474; ed fax (360) 221-6474; disp adv e-mail kwinjum@whidbeynewsgroup.com; class adv e-mail Classifieds@whidbeynewsgroup.com; ed e-mail kgraves@whidbeynewsgroup.com; web site www.southwhidbeyrecord.com
Circulation: 2,711pd,; CAC
Advertising rate: Open inch rate $16.65
Established: 1921
Group: Black Press Group Ltd.
Sound Publishing, Inc.
Digital Platform - Mobile: Apple, Android, Windows, Blackberry
Digital Platform - Tablet: Apple iOS, Android, Windows 7, Blackberry Tablet OS, Kindle, Nook, Kindle Fire
Pub./Exec. Ed. .... Keven R. Graves
Assc. Pub. .... Kimberlly Winjum
Ed. .... Justin Burnett
Nat'l Sales Dir. ....Stephen Barrett
Delivery Method: Mail, Newsstand, Racks
Areas Served: Island County

THE WHIDBEY EXAMINER (WED)

6 NW Coveland St, Coupeville, WA, 98239, Island, USA; gen tel (360) 678-8060; adv tel (360) 678-8060; ed tel (360) 678-8060; gen fax (360) 678-6073; adv fax (360) 678-6073; ed fax (360) 678-6073; disp adv e-mail news@whidbeyexaminer.com; class adv e-mail news@whidbeyexaminer.com; ed e-mail editor@whidbeyexaminer.com; web site www.whidbeyexaminer.com
Circulation: 983pd, 40fr; AAM
Advertising rate: Open inch rate $9.75
Established: 1994
Group: Black Press Group Ltd.
Sound Publishing, Inc.
Digital Platform - Mobile: Apple, Android, Windows, Blackberry
Digital Platform - Tablet: Apple iOS, Android, Windows 7, Blackberry Tablet OS, Kindle, Nook, Kindle Fire
Ed./Pub. .... Kasia Pierzga
Nat'l Sales Dir. ....Stephen Barrett
Nat'l/Rgl Acct. Mgr. ....Theresa Eskridge
Delivery Method: Mail, Newsstand, Racks
Areas Served: 98239, 98277, 98236, 98249, 98260, 98253

WHIDBEY CROSSWIND (MTHLY)

107 S Main St Ste E101, Suite E 101, Coupeville, WA, 98239-3569, Island, USA; gen tel (360) 675-6611; adv tel (360) 675-6611; ed tel (360) 675-6611; disp adv e-mail kreed@whidbeycrosswind.com; class adv e-mail kreed@whidbeycrosswind.com; ed e-mail editor@whidbeycrosswind.com; web site www.whidbeycrosswind.com
Circulation: 13,394pd, 309,003fr; CAC
Advertising rate: Open inch rate $20.60
Digital Platform - Mobile: Apple, Android, Windows, Blackberry
Digital Platform - Tablet: Apple iOS, Android, Windows 7, Blackberry Tablet OS, Kindle, Nook, Kindle Fire
Pub./Ed. .... K. Reed
Nat'l Sales Dir. ....Stephen Barrett
Delivery Method: Mail, Racks
Areas Served: Island County

DAVENPORT

DAVENPORT TIMES (THUR)

506 Morgan St, Davenport, WA, 99122-5213, Lincoln, USA; gen tel (509) 725-0101; adv tel (509) 725-0101; ed tel (509) 725-0101; gen fax (509) 725-0009; adv fax (509) 725-0009; ed fax (509) 725-0009; disp adv e-mail davenporttimes@centurytel.net; class adv e-mail davenporttimes@centurytel.net; ed e-mail davenporttimes@centurytel.net
Circulation: 2,200pd,; Sworn/Estimate/Non-Audited
Advertising rate: Open inch rate $5.00
Pub.. Bill Ifft
Adv. Mgr. .... Marcia Smith
Ed. .... Mark Smith
Mechanical Specifications: Type page 13 x 21; E - 6 cols, 2 1/36, 1/6 between; A - 6 cols, 2 1/36, 1/6 between; C - 6 cols, 2 1/36, 1/6 between.Equipment & Software: ; Software — Adobe/PageMaker 6.5, Microsoft/Word 7.0.
Delivery Method: Mail
Areas Served: Lincoln County

DAYTON

DAYTON CHRONICLE (WED)

163 E Main St, Dayton, WA, 99328-1350, Columbia, USA; gen tel (509) 382-2221; adv tel (509) 382-2221; ed tel (509) 382-2221; gen fax (509) 382-1546; adv fax (509) 382-1546; ed fax (509) 382-1546; disp adv e-mail daytonchronicle@hotmail.com; class adv e-mail daytonchronicle@hotmail.com; ed e-mail daytonchronicle@hotmail.com
Circulation: 1,700pd,; Sworn/Estimate/Non-Audited
Advertising rate: Open inch rate $8.30
Established: 1878
Pub./Ed. .... Jack Williams
Delivery Method: Mail
Areas Served: Columbia County

DEER PARK

DEER PARK TRIBUNE (WED)

104 N Main St, Deer Park, WA, 99006-5086, Spokane, USA; gen tel (509) 276-5043 ; adv tel (509) 276-5043 ; ed tel (509) 276-5043 ; gen fax (509) 276-2041; adv fax (509) 276-2041; ed fax (509) 276-2041; disp adv e-mail sales@dptribune.com; class adv e-mail classifieds@dptribune.com; ed e-mail tom@dptribune.com ; web site www.dptribune.biz
Advertising rate: Open inch rate $8.00
Established: 1906
Group: Horizon Publications Inc.
Digital Platform - Mobile: Apple, Android
Digital Platform - Tablet: Apple iOS, Android, Windows 7
Pub./Ed. ....Thomas Costigan
Gen. Mgr. ....Theresa Douvia
Adv. Mgr. .... Jeanne Flugel
Delivery Method: Mail, Racks
Areas Served: Spokane County

EAST WENATCHEE

DOUGLAS COUNTY EMPIRE PRESS (THUR)

2290 Grand Ave, East Wenatchee, WA, 98802-8253, Douglas, USA; gen tel (509) 886-8668; adv tel (509) 886-8668; ed tel (509) 886-8668; gen fax (509) 665-1183; adv fax (509) 665-1183; ed fax (509) 665-1183; disp adv e-mail weekly@empire-press.com; class adv e-mail legals@empire-press.com; ed e-mail weekly@empire-press.com; web site www.empire-press.com
Circulation: 925pd, 10fr; Sworn/Estimate/

Non-Audited
Advertising rate: Open inch rate $17.00
Established: 1888
Digital Platform - Mobile: Apple, Android
Digital Platform - Tablet: Apple iOS, Android
Pub...Joe Pitt
Ed. .... Linda Barta
Delivery Method: Mail, Racks
Areas Served: Waterville, Rock Island, Orondo, Bridgeport, Brewster, Mansfield, Douglas, Palisades, East Wenatchee, and Douglas County

EASTSOUND

THE ISLANDS' SOUNDER (WED)
217 Main St, Eastsound, WA, 98245-5510, San Juan, USA; gen tel (360) 376-4500; adv tel (360) 376-4500; ed tel (360) 376-4500; gen fax (360) 376-4501; adv fax (360) 376-4501; ed fax (360) 376-4501; disp adv e-mail publisher@islandssounder.com; class adv e-mail carmstrong@islandssounder.com; ed e-mail cbagby@islandssounder.com; web site www.islandssounder.com
Circulation: 13,394pd,; CAC
Advertising rate: Open inch rate $14.70
Established: 1964
Group: Black Press Group Ltd.
Sound Publishing, Inc.
Digital Platform - Mobile: Apple, Android, Windows, Blackberry
Digital Platform - Tablet: Apple iOS, Android, Windows 7, Blackberry Tablet OS, Kindle, Nook, Kindle Fire
Pub.....................................Colleen Armstrong
Circ. Mgr.......................... Nicole Matisse Duke
Nat'l Sales Dir. ....Stephen BarrettEquipment & Software: Hardware — APP/Mac; Software — QPS/QuarkXPress, Multi-Ad/Creator.
Delivery Method: Mail
Areas Served: San Juan County

EATONVILLE

THE EATONVILLE DISPATCH (THUR)
133 Mashell Ave N, Eatonville, WA, 98328, Pierce, USA; gen tel (360) 832-4411; adv tel (360) 832-4411; ed tel (360) 832-4411; disp adv e-mail advertising@dispatchnews.com; class adv e-mail officemanager@dispatchnews.com; ed e-mail editor@dispatchnews.com; web site www.dispatchnews.com
Advertising rate: Open inch rate $11.00
Established: 1893
Digital Platform - Mobile: Apple, Android, Windows, Blackberry
Digital Platform - Tablet: Apple iOS, Android, Windows 7, Blackberry Tablet OS
Pub.. Cliff Wright
Ed. .... Pat Jenkins
Adv. Mgr..................................... Joni L. Eades
Delivery Method: Mail, Racks
Areas Served: Pierce County

ENUMCLAW

THE COURIER-HERALD (WED)
1627 Cole St, Enumclaw, WA, 98022-3509, King, USA; gen tel (360) 825-2555; adv tel (360) 825-2555; ed tel (360) 802-8205; disp adv e-mail tbeitinger@courierherald.com; class adv e-mail jtribbett@courierherald.com; ed e-mail dbox@soundpublishing.com; web site http://www.courierherald.com/
Circulation: 924pd, 24,468fr; AAM
Advertising rate: Open inch rate $23.45
Established: 2003
Group: Sound Publishing, Inc.
Digital Platform - Mobile: Apple, Android, Windows, Blackberry
Digital Platform - Tablet: Apple iOS, Android, Windows 7, Blackberry Tablet OS, Kindle, Nook, Kindle Fire
Ed. ....Dennis Box
Delivery Method: Mail, Newsstand, Racks
Areas Served: Pierce County

THE ENUMCLAW COURIER-HERALD (WED)
1627 Cole St, Enumclaw, WA, 98022-3509, Pierce, USA; gen tel (360) 825-2555; adv tel (360) 825-2555; ed tel (360) 802-8205; disp adv e-mail dbox@courierherald.com; class adv e-mail swehmann@courierherald.com; ed e-mail editor@courierherald.com; web site www.courierherald.com
Circulation: 924pd, 24,468fr; AAM
Advertising rate: Open inch rate $17.60
Group: Black Press Group Ltd.
Sound Publishing, Inc.
Digital Platform - Mobile: Apple, Android, Windows, Blackberry
Digital Platform - Tablet: Apple iOS, Android, Windows 7, Blackberry Tablet OS, Kindle, Nook, Kindle Fire
Ed./Sr. Writer ....Kevin Hanson
Ed. ....Dennis Box
Nat'l Sales Dir. ....Stephen Barrett
Delivery Method: Mail, Newsstand, Racks
Areas Served: Pierce County

FEDERAL WAY

FEDERAL WAY MIRROR (FRI)
31919 1st Ave S Ste 101, Ste. 101, Federal Way, WA, 98003-5258, King, USA; gen tel (253) 925-5565; ed tel (253) 925-5565 ext. 5050; gen fax (253) 925-5750; disp adv e-mail publisher@federalwaymirror.com; class adv e-mail janderson@federalwaymirror.com; ed e-mail editor@fedwaymirror.com; web site www.federalwaymirror.com
Circulation: 1,006pd, 27,750fr; AAM
Advertising rate: Open inch rate $28.50
Established: 1998
Group: Black Press Group Ltd.
Sound Publishing, Inc.
Digital Platform - Mobile: Apple, Android, Windows, Blackberry
Digital Platform - Tablet: Apple iOS, Android, Windows 7, Blackberry Tablet OS, Kindle, Nook, Kindle Fire
Carrie Rodriguez
Andy HobbsEd.s
Mechanical Specifications: Type page 13 x 21 1/2; E - 5 cols, 2 1/8, 1/8 between; A - 6 cols, 1 3/4, 1/8 between; C - 10 cols, 1 1/16, 1/16 between.
Delivery Method: Mail, Newsstand, Racks
Areas Served: 98001, 98003, 98023, 98032, 98198, 98422

FERNDALE

FERNDALE RECORD (WED)
2004 Main St, Ferndale, WA, 98248-9468, Whatcom, USA; gen tel (360) 384-1411; gen fax (360) 384-1417; disp adv e-mail jan@ferndalerecord.com; class adv e-mail jan@ferndalerecord.com; ed e-mail news@ferndalerecord.com; web site www.ferndalerecord.com
Circulation: 1,150pd, 4,700fr; Sworn/Estimate/Non-Audited
Advertising rate: Open inch rate $15.95
Established: 1885
Group: Lewis Publishing Co., Inc.
Digital Platform - Mobile: Apple, Android, Windows, Blackberry
Digital Platform - Tablet: Apple iOS, Android, Windows 7, Blackberry Tablet OS
News Editor ....Brent Lindquist
Adv. Mgr..Jan Brownr
Reporter, Social Media editor.....Ashley Hiruko
Mechanical Specifications: Page size 11" wide x 21" tall. Column width is 1.694" w/ .167" gutters.
Delivery Method: Mail, Newsstand, Racks
Areas Served: 98248, 98240, 98226

FIFE

TACOMA WEEKLY (THUR)
2588 Pacific Hwy E, Fife, WA, 98424-1016, Pierce, USA; gen tel (253) 922-5317; adv tel (253) 922-5317; ed tel (253) 922-5317; gen fax (253) 922-5305; adv fax (253) 922-5305; ed fax (253) 922-5305; disp adv e-mail rose@tacomaweekly.com; class adv e-mail cmcdonald@tacomaweekly.com; ed e-mail jweymer@tacomaweekly.com; web site www.tacomaweekly.com
Advertising rate: Open inch rate $18.00
Established: 1986
Group: Pierce County Community Newspaper Group
Digital Platform - Mobile: Apple, Android, Windows, Blackberry
Digital Platform - Tablet: Apple iOS, Android, Windows 7, Blackberry Tablet OS
Pub./Ed.....................................John Weymer
Adv. Mgr..Rose Thiele
Delivery Method: Mail, Newsstand, Racks
Areas Served: Pierce County

FORKS

FORKS FORUM (THUR)
490 S Forks Ave, Forks, WA, 98331-9155, Clallam, USA; gen tel (360) 374-3311; adv tel (360) 374-3311; ed tel (360) 374-3311; gen fax (360) 374-5739; adv fax (360) 374-5739; ed fax (360) 374-5739; disp adv e-mail cbaron@forksforum.com; class adv e-mail dwebb@peninsuladailynews.com; ed e-mail editor@forksforum.com; web site www.forksforum.com
Circulation: 150pd, 4,258fr; AAM
Advertising rate: Open inch rate $10.25
Established: 1930
Group: Black Press Group Ltd.
Sound Publishing, Inc.
Digital Platform - Mobile: Apple, Android, Windows
Digital Platform - Tablet: Apple iOS, Android, Windows 7
Mechanical Specifications: 5X12.5
1/col. = 11pd (1.83")
Delivery Method: Mail, Racks
Areas Served: Clallam and Jefferson County

FRIDAY HARBOR

THE JOURNAL OF THE SAN JUAN ISLANDS (WED)
640 Mullis St, Friday Harbor, WA, 98250-7940, San Juan, USA; gen tel (360) 378-5696; adv tel (360) 378-5696; ed tel (360) 378-5696; gen fax (360) 378-5128; adv fax (360) 378-5128; ed fax (360) 378-5128; disp adv e-mail publisher@sanjuanjournal.com; class adv e-mail classifieds@soundpublishing.com; ed e-mail editor@sanjuanjournal.com; web site www.sanjuanjournal.com - 70,000(views) 25,000(visitors)
Circulation: 873pd, 25fr; AAM
Advertising rate: Open inch rate $14.70
Established: 1906
Group: Black Press Group Ltd.
Sound Publishing, Inc.Editions: (2,394)
Digital Platform - Mobile: Apple, Android, Windows, Blackberry
Digital Platform - Tablet: Apple iOS, Android, Windows 7, Blackberry Tablet OS, Kindle, Nook, Kindle Fire
Pub.. Roxanne Angel
Ed. ....Scott Rasmussen
Nat'l Sales Dir. ....Stephen Barrett
Mechanical Specifications: Type page 10 3/4 x 16; E - 5 cols, 1 11/12, 1/6 between; A - 5 cols, 1 11/12, 1/6 between; C - 5 cols, 1 11/12, 1/6 between.Equipment & Software: Hardware — APP/Mac.
Delivery Method: Mail, Racks
Areas Served: San Juan County

GIG HARBOR

THE PENINSULA GATEWAY (WED)
3226 Rosedale St NW, Ste 100, Gig Harbor, WA, 98335-1806, Pierce, USA; gen tel (253) 358-4141; adv tel (253) 358-4130; ed tel (253) 358-4150; disp adv e-mail rob.white@thenewstribune.com; ed e-mail tyler.hemstreet@gateline.com; web site www.thenewstribune.com/gigharbor
Circulation: 4,718pd, 275fr; Sworn/Estimate/Non-Audited
Advertising rate: Open inch rate $25.85
Established: 1917
Group: The McClatchy Company
Digital Platform - Mobile: Apple, Android
Digital Platform - Tablet: Apple iOS, Android
Ed./Pub..................................Tyler Hemstreet
Delivery Method: Mail
Areas Served: Pierce County

GOLDENDALE

GOLDENDALE SENTINEL (WED)
117 W Main St, Goldendale, WA, 98620-9526, Klickitat, USA; gen tel (509) 773-3777; adv tel (509) 773-3777; ed tel (509) 773-3777; gen fax (509) 314-4201; adv fax (509) 314-4201; ed fax (509) 314-4201; disp adv e-mail ads@goldendalesentinel.com; class adv e-mail ads@goldendalesentinel.com; ed e-mail news@goldendalesentinel.com ; web site www.goldendalesentinel.com - 9,200(views) 6,400(visitors)
Circulation: 3,200pd,; Sworn/Estimate/Non-Audited
Advertising rate: Open inch rate $9.00
Established: 1879
Group: Tartan Publications, Inc.
Digital Platform - Mobile: Apple, Android
Digital Platform - Tablet: Apple iOS, Android, Kindle
Ed./Pub...................................... Lou Marzeles
Bookkeeper ....Joel Jennings
Reporter .... Max EriksonEquipment & Software: Hardware — PC; Software — QPS/QuarkXPress.
Delivery Method: Mail, Newsstand, Carrier, Racks
Areas Served: Klickitat County

GRAND COULEE

THE STAR (WED)
3 MIDWAY AVE, Grand Coulee, WA, 99133, Grant, USA; gen tel (509) 633-1350; adv tel (509) 633-1350; ed tel (509) 633-1350; gen fax (509) 633-3828; adv fax (509) 633-3828; ed fax (509) 633-3828; disp adv e-mail ads@grandcoulee.com; class adv e-mail ads@grandcoulee.com; ed e-mail scott@grandcoulee.com; web site www.grandcoulee.com
Circulation: 1,720pd, 3,000fr; Sworn/Estimate/Non-Audited
Advertising rate: Open inch rate 9.25
Established: 1945
Group: Star Publishing Inc
Digital Platform - Mobile: Apple, Android
Digital Platform - Tablet: Apple iOS, Android
Ed./Pub.......................................Scott Hunter
Prod. Mgr. ....Gwen Hilson
Reporter ....Roger Lucas
Mechanical Specifications: Type page 13.75 x 21.5; E - 6 cols, 2.152, 1/6 between; A - 6 cols, 2 1/4, 1/6 between; C - 6 cols, 2 1/4, 1/6 between.Equipment & Software: Hardware — APP/Mac; Presses — G/Community; Software — Adobe/PageMaker 6.0.
Delivery Method: Mail, Racks
Areas Served: 99133, 99116, 99124, 99123, 99155, 99140, 99185, 99103, 99135, 99115, 98830

ISSAQUAH

NEWCASTLE NEWS (MTHLY)
PO Box 1328, Issaquah, WA, 98027-0053, King, USA; gen tel (425) 392-6434; adv tel (425) 392-6434; ed tel (425) 392-6434; gen fax (425) 392-1695; adv fax (425) 392-1695; ed fax (425) 392-1695; disp adv e-mail admanager@isspress.com; class adv e-mail classifieds@isspress.com; ed e-mail news@isspress.com; web site newcastle-news.com
Circulation: 46pd, 5,778fr; Sworn/Estimate/

Non-Audited
Established: 1999
Group: The Seattle Times
Editor .... Scott Stoddard
Delivery Method: Mail, Carrier, Racks
Areas Served: Newcastle/King/98056 Newcastle/King/98059

SAMMAMISH REVIEW (WED)

1085 12th Ave NW, Ste D1, Issaquah, WA, 98027-8988, King, USA; gen tel (425) 392-6434; adv tel (425) 392-6434 ext. 229; ed tel (425) 392-6434 ext. 233; gen fax (425) 392-1695; adv fax (425) 392-1695; ed fax (425) 392-1695; disp adv e-mail admanager@isspress.com; class adv e-mail classifieds@isspress.com; ed e-mail samrev@isspress.com; web site www.sammamishreview.com
Circulation: 400pd, 14,300fr; Sworn/Estimate/ Non-Audited
Advertising rate: Open inch rate $22.00
Established: 1992
Group: The Seattle Times
Issaquah Press Inc.
Digital Platform - Mobile: Apple, Android, Windows
Digital Platform - Tablet: Apple iOS, Android, Windows 7
Ed. .... Ari Cetron
Adv. Mgr. .... Dan DeLong
Mechanical Specifications: 10.5" x 13" page; 1 col + 1.65"Equipment & Software: Hardware — APP Mac
PCs; Software — InDesign CS5.5
Delivery Method: Mail, Newsstand, Carrier
Areas Served: King County

SNOVALLEY STAR (THUR)

1085 12th Ave NW, Ste D1, Issaquah, WA, 98027-8988, King, USA; gen tel (425) 392-6434; adv tel (425) 392-6434 ext. 229; ed tel (425) 392-6434 ext. 233; gen fax (425) 392-1695; adv fax (425) 392-1695; ed fax (425) 392-1695; disp adv e-mail admanager@isspress.com; class adv e-mail classifieds@isspress.com; ed e-mail editor@snovalleystar.com; web site www.snovalleystar.com
Advertising rate: Open inch rate $19.00
Established: 2008
Group: Issaquah Press Inc.
The Seattle Times
Digital Platform - Mobile: Apple, Android, Windows
Digital Platform - Tablet: Apple iOS, Android, Windows 7
Ed. .... Sherry Grindeland
Adv. Mgr. .... Dan DeLong
Gen. Mgr. .... Joe Heslet
Delivery Method: Mail, Newsstand, Racks
Areas Served: King County

THE ISSAQUAH PRESS (THUR)

1085 12th Ave NW, Ste D1, Issaquah, WA, 98027-8988, King, USA; gen tel (425) 392-6434; adv tel (425) 392-6434; ed tel (425) 392-6434; gen fax (425) 392-1695; adv fax (425) 392-1695; ed fax (425) 392-1695; disp adv e-mail admanager@isspress.com; class adv e-mail classifieds@isspress.com; ed e-mail editor@isspress.com; web site www.issaquahpress.com
Circulation: 1,382pd, 12,738fr; Sworn/Estimate/ Non-Audited
Established: 1900
Group: The Seattle TimesEditions: (112)
Digital Platform - Mobile: Apple, Android, Windows
Digital Platform - Tablet: Apple iOS, Android, Windows 7
Editor .... Scott Stoddard
Mechanical Specifications: Type page 10.5 x 21; E - 6 cols, 1.65", .12" betweenEquipment & Software: Hardware — APP/Mac OSX
PCs; Software — InDesign CS 5.5
Adobe Creative Suite
Delivery Method: Mail, Newsstand, Carrier, Racks
Areas Served: King County

KENT

COVINGTON-MAPLE VALLEY-BLACK DIAMOND REPORTER (FRI)

19426 68th Ave S, Kent, WA, 98032-1193, King, USA; gen tel (425) 432-1209; adv tel (425) 432-1209; ed tel (425) 432-1209 ext. 5050; disp adv e-mail pshepherd@kentreporter.com; class adv e-mail khill@maplevalleyreporter.com; ed e-mail dbox@maplevalleyreporter.com; web site www.maplevalleyreporter.com
Circulation: 9pd, 24,041fr; Sworn/Estimate/ Non-Audited
Advertising rate: Open inch rate $23.45
Established: 2005
Group: Black Press Group Ltd.
Sound Publishing, Inc.
Digital Platform - Mobile: Apple, Android, Windows, Blackberry
Digital Platform - Tablet: Apple iOS, Android, Windows 7, Blackberry Tablet OS, Kindle, Nook, Kindle Fire
Pub. .... Polly Shepherd
Ed. .... Dennis Box
Editor .... Sarah Brenden
Advertising Manager .... Natalie Routh
Delivery Method: Mail, Newsstand, Racks
Areas Served: King County

KENT REPORTER (FRI)

19426 68th Ave S, Ste A, Kent, WA, 98032-1193, King, USA; gen tel (253) 872-6600; adv tel (253) 833-0218; ed tel (253) 872-6600; disp adv e-mail khenry@auburn-reporter.com; class adv e-mail dblood@auburn-reporter.com; ed e-mail mklaas@auburn-reporter.com; web site www.auburn-reporter.com
Circulation: 16pd, 24,808fr; CAC
Advertising rate: Open inch rate $23.45
Established: 1998
Group: Black Press Group Ltd.
Sound Publishing, Inc.
Digital Platform - Mobile: Apple, Android, Windows, Blackberry
Digital Platform - Tablet: Apple iOS, Android, Windows 7, Blackberry Tablet OS, Kindle, Nook, Kindle Fire
Reg. Ed. .... Mark Klaas
Delivery Method: Mail, Newsstand, Racks
Areas Served: King County

RENTON REPORTER (FRI)

19426 68th Ave S, Kent, WA, 98032-1193, King, USA; gen tel (253) 255-3484; adv tel (253) 255-3484; ed tel (253) 255-3484 ext. 1050; disp adv e-mail lyaskus@rentonreporter.com; class adv e-mail jhughes@soundpublishing.com; ed e-mail sbrenden@rentonreporter.com; web site www.rentonreporter.com
Circulation: 27pd, 24,814fr; CAC
Advertising rate: Open inch rate $28.05
Group: Black Press Group Ltd.
Sound Publishing, Inc.
Digital Platform - Mobile: Apple, Android, Windows, Blackberry
Digital Platform - Tablet: Apple iOS, Android, Windows 7, Blackberry Tablet OS, Kindle, Nook, Kindle Fire
Multi Media Consultant .... Lisa Yaskus
Delivery Method: Mail, Carrier, Racks
Areas Served: King County

TUKWILA REPORTER (MTHLY)

19426 68th Ave S, Ste A, Kent, WA, 98032-1193, King, USA; gen tel (253) 872-6600; disp adv e-mail marketing@soundpublishing.com; web site http://www.tukwilareporter.com
Circulation: 10,366fr; CAC
Advertising rate: Open inch rate $17.60
Group: Black Press Group Ltd.
Sound Publishing, Inc.
Nat'l Sales Dir. .... Stephen Barrett

KIRKLAND

BOTHELL/KENMORE REPORTER (BI-MTHLY)

11630 Slater Ave NE, Ste 9, Kirkland, WA, 98034-4100, King, USA; gen tel (425) 483-3732; adv tel (425) 483-3732; ed tel (425) 483-3732 ext. 5050; disp adv e-mail sallison@soundpublishing.com; class adv e-mail sallison@soundpublishing.com; ed e-mail editor@bothell-reporter.com; web site www.bothell-reporter.com
Circulation: 38pd, 20,442fr; CAC
Advertising rate: Open inch rate $23.45
Group: Black Press Group Ltd.
Sound Publishing, Inc.
Digital Platform - Mobile: Apple, Android, Windows, Blackberry
Digital Platform - Tablet: Apple iOS, Android, Windows 7, Blackberry Tablet OS, Kindle, Nook, Kindle Fire
Nat'l Sales Dir. .... Stephen Barrett
Delivery Method: Mail, Newsstand, Racks
Areas Served: King County

KIRKLAND REPORTER (FRI)

11630 Slater Ave NE, Ste 8-9, Kirkland, WA, 98034-4100, King, USA; gen tel (425) 822-9166; adv tel (425) 822-9166; ed tel (425) 822-9166; disp adv e-mail pbrown@kirklandreporter.com; class adv e-mail pbrown@kirklandreporter.com; ed e-mail editor@kirklandreporter.com; web site www.kirklandreporter.com and www.bothell-reporter.com
Circulation: 14pd, 25,358fr; CAC
Advertising rate: Open inch rate $28.05
Established: 1978
Group: Black Press Group Ltd.
Sound Publishing, Inc.
Digital Platform - Mobile: Apple, Android, Windows, Blackberry
Digital Platform - Tablet: Apple iOS, Android, Windows 7, Blackberry Tablet OS, Kindle, Nook, Kindle Fire
Nat'l Sales Dir. .... Stephen Barrett
Delivery Method: Mail, Newsstand, Racks
Areas Served: King County

REDMOND REPORTER (FRI)

11630 Slater Ave NE, Ste 8-9, Kirkland, WA, 98034-4100, King, USA; gen tel (425) 867-0353; adv tel (425) 867-0353; ed tel (425) 296-3276; disp adv e-mail cfreese@redmond-reporter.com; ed e-mail anystrom@redmond-reporter.com; web site www.redmond-reporter.com
Circulation: 10pd, 22,635fr; CAC
Advertising rate: Open inch rate $28.05
Established: 2001
Group: Black Press Group Ltd.
Sound Publishing, Inc.
Digital Platform - Mobile: Apple, Android, Windows, Blackberry
Digital Platform - Tablet: Apple iOS, Android, Windows 7, Blackberry Tablet OS, Kindle, Nook, Kindle Fire
Ed. .... Andy Nystrom
Aaron Kunkler
Cynthia Freese
Delivery Method: Mail, Newsstand, Racks
Areas Served: King County

THE OTHELLO OUTLOOK (WED)

10518 NE 37th Cir, Kirkland, WA, 98033-7920, Adams, USA; gen tel (509) 488-3342; adv tel (509) 488-3342; ed tel (509) 488-3342; gen fax (509) 488-3345; adv fax (509) 488-3345; ed fax (509) 488-3345; disp adv e-mail admanager@othellooutlook.com; class adv e-mail officemanager@othellooutlook.com; ed e-mail editor@othellooutlook.com; web site www.smalltownpapers.com
Circulation: 800pd, 5,000fr; Sworn/Estimate/ Non-Audited
Advertising rate: Open inch rate $10.30
Established: 1947
Group: Basin Publishing Co.
Digital Platform - Mobile: Apple, Android
Digital Platform - Tablet: Apple iOS, Android
Ed. .... Briana Alzola
LuAnn Morgan
Mechanical Specifications: Type page 14 x 21 1/2; E - 6 cols, 2 1/8, 1/4 between; A - 6 cols, 2 1/8, 1/4 between; C - 8 cols, 1 9/16, 3/16 between.Equipment & Software: Hardware — APP/Mac; Software — Adobe/PageMaker 6.0.1, Microsoft/Word 3.02.
Delivery Method: Mail, Newsstand
Areas Served: Adams County

LA CONNER

LA CONNER WEEKLY NEWS (WED)

119 N 3rd St, La Conner, WA, 98257, Skagit, USA; gen tel (360) 466-3315; adv tel (360) 466-3315; ed tel (360) 466-3315; disp adv e-mail production@laconnernews.com; class adv e-mail production@laconnernews.com; ed e-mail news@laconnernews.com; web site www.laconnerweeklynews.com - 5,000(views) 4,800(visitors)
Circulation: 1,500pd, 50fr; USPS
Advertising rate: Open inch rate $9.25
Established: 2006
Group: La Conner News LLC
Digital Platform - Mobile: Apple, Android, Windows, Blackberry
Digital Platform - Tablet: Apple iOS, Android, Windows 7, Kindle, Kindle Fire
Co-Pub./ Ed. .... Sandy Stokes
Gen. Mgr./Co-Pub. .... Cindy Vest
Mechanical Specifications: 20.75" page height 1 col 1.83" 2 col 3.8" 3 col 5.75" 4 col 7.71" 5 col 9.66" and 6 col 11.63" wide
Delivery Method: Mail, Racks
Areas Served: Skagit County

LEAVENWORTH

THE LEAVENWORTH ECHO (WED)

215 14th St, Leavenworth, WA, 98826-1411, Chelan, USA; gen tel (509) 548-5286; adv tel (509) 548-5286; ed tel (509) 548-5286; gen fax (509) 548-4789; ed fax (509) 548-4789; disp adv e-mail carol@leavenworthecho.com; class adv e-mail classifieds@leavenworthecho.com; ed e-mail editor@leavenworthecho.com; web site www.leavenworthecho.com - 11,030(views) 8,189(visitors)
Circulation: 1,600pd,; Sworn/Estimate/Non-Audited
Advertising rate: Open inch rate $11.50
Established: 1904
Group: NCW Media, Inc.Editions: (52) The Leavenworth Echo
Digital Platform - Mobile: Apple, Android, Blackberry
Digital Platform - Tablet: Apple iOS, Android, Blackberry Tablet OS, Kindle
Pub. .... Bill Forhan
Ed. .... Ian Dunn
Adv. Dir. .... Carol Forhan
Mechanical Specifications: Super tab - 11 5/8" X 17 "
Print specs - 6 col. format prints over 10 1/4" X 16"
Quarter forldedEquipment & Software: Hardware — Apple, kansa; Presses — 5 unit goss community; Software — InDesign, Media Span Ad Mgr Pro, Interlink, 1Up!
Delivery Method: Mail, Newsstand, Racks
Areas Served: 98826, 98847

LIBERTY LAKE

LIBERTY LAKE SPLASH (THUR, MTHLY)

2310 N Molter Rd, Ste 305, Liberty Lake, WA, 99019-8630, Spokane, USA; gen tel (509) 242-7752; adv tel (509) 242-7752; ed tel (509) 242-7752; gen fax (509) 927-2190; adv fax (509) 927-2190; ed fax (509) 927-2190; disp adv e-mail advertise@libertylakesplash.com; class adv e-mail josh@libertylakesplash.com; ed e-mail editor@libertylakesplash.com; web site www.libertylakesplash.com
Circulation: 100pd, 6,900fr; Sworn/Estimate/ Non-Audited
Advertising rate: Modular Rate $62.00 (1/16P); $124.00 (1/8P)
Established: 1999
Digital Platform - Mobile: Windows
Digital Platform - Tablet: Windows 7
Pub./Ed. .... Josh Johnson

Gen. Mgr. .... Tammy Kimberley
Delivery Method: Mail, Racks
Areas Served: 99019, 99016

LONG BEACH

CHINOOK OBSERVER (WED)

205 Bolstad Ave E, Ste 2, Long Beach, WA, 98631-9200, Pacific, USA; gen tel (360) 642-8181; adv tel (360) 642-8181; ed tel (360) 642-8181; gen fax (360) 642-8105; adv fax (360) 642-8105; ed fax (360) 642-8105; disp adv e-mail advertising@chinookobserver.com; class adv e-mail classifieds@chinookobserver.com; ed e-mail mwinters@chinookobserver.com; web site www.chinookobserver.com
Circulation: 6,800pd,; Sworn/Estimate/Non-Audited
Advertising rate: Open inch rate $15.55
Established: 1900
Group: EO Media Group
Digital Platform - Mobile: Apple, Android, Windows, Blackberry
Digital Platform - Tablet: Apple iOS, Android, Windows 7, Blackberry Tablet OS, Kindle, Nook, Kindle Fire
Pub./Ed. .... Matt Winters
Adv. Mgr. .... Andrew Renwick
Office Mgr. .... Marlene Quillin
Delivery Method: Mail, Newsstand, Racks
Areas Served: Pacific County

LOPEZ ISLAND

THE ISLANDS' WEEKLY (TUES)

131 Weeks Rd, Lopez Island, WA, 98261-5530, San Juan, USA; gen tel (360) 376-4500; adv tel (360) 468-4242; ed tel (360) 468-4242; gen fax (360) 468-4900; adv fax (360) 468-4900; ed fax (360) 468-4900; disp adv e-mail cbagby@islandsweekly.com; class adv e-mail cbagby@islandsweekly.com; ed e-mail publisher@islandsweekly.net; web site www.islandsweekly.com
Circulation: 14pd, 1,878fr; AAM
Advertising rate: Open inch rate $14.70
Established: 1982
Group: Black Press Group Ltd.
Sound Publishing, Inc.
Digital Platform - Mobile: Apple, Android, Windows, Blackberry
Digital Platform - Tablet: Apple iOS, Android, Windows 7, Blackberry Tablet OS, Kindle, Nook, Kindle Fire
Pub. .... Roxannne Angel
Ed./Adv. Mgr. .... Cali Bagby
Nat'l Sales Dir. .... Stephen Barrett
Delivery Method: Mail
Areas Served: San Juan County

LYNDEN

LYNDEN TRIBUNE (WED)

113 6th St, Lynden, WA, 98264-1901, Whatcom, USA; gen tel (360) 354-4444; gen fax (360) 354-4445; disp adv e-mail mitze@lyndentribune.com; class adv e-mail mitze@lyndentribune.com; ed e-mail editor@lyndentribune.com; web site www.lyndentribune.com - 34,450(views) 5,100(visitors)
Circulation: 5,050pd, 7,100fr; Sworn/Estimate/Non-Audited
Advertising rate: Open inch rate $21.50
Established: 1888
Group: Lewis Publishing Co., Inc.
Digital Platform - Mobile: Apple, Android, Windows
Digital Platform - Tablet: Apple iOS, Android, Windows 7
Pub. .... Michael D. Lewis
Adv. Dir. .... Mary Jo Lewis
Adv. Mgr. .... Mitze Kester
Ed. .... Calvin Bratt
Assistant Ed. .... Brent Lindquist
Sports Ed. .... Nick Elges
Circulation Mgr .... Karina Vance
Reporter Ashley HirukoEquipment & Software: ; Presses — 12-unit Goss Community Newspaper press with twin 4-color towers
Delivery Method: Mail, Newsstand, Carrier, Racks
Areas Served: 98264, 98247, 98295, 98276

MAPLE VALLEY

VOICE OF THE VALLEY (TUES)

PO Box 307, Maple Valley, WA, 98038-0307, King, USA; gen tel (425) 432-9696; adv tel (425) 432-9696; ed tel (425) 432-9696; gen fax (866) 423-9203; adv fax (866) 423-9203; ed fax (866) 423-9203; disp adv e-mail advertising@voiceofthevalley.com; class adv e-mail advertising@voiceofthevalley.com; ed e-mail news@voiceofthevalley.com; web site www.voiceofthevalley.com
Advertising rate: Open inch rate $17.50
Established: 1969
Digital Platform - Mobile: Apple, Android
Digital Platform - Tablet: Apple iOS, Android
Pub./Ed. .... Donna Hayes
Delivery Method: Mail
Areas Served: King County

MARYSVILLE

NORTH COUNTY OUTLOOK (TUES)

1331 State Ave, Ste A, Marysville, WA, 98270-3604, Snohomish, USA; gen tel (360) 659-1100; gen fax (360) 658-7536; disp adv e-mail sue@northcountyoutlook.com; class adv e-mail sales@northcountyoutlook.com; ed e-mail editor@northcountyoutlook.com; web site www.northcountyoutlook.com
Circulation: 21,337fr; AAM
Advertising rate: Open inch rate $26.50
Established: 2007
Digital Platform - Mobile: Apple, Android, Windows, Blackberry
Digital Platform - Tablet: Apple iOS, Android, Windows 7, Blackberry Tablet OS, Kindle, Nook, Kindle Fire
Co-Pub./Adv. Mgr. .... Sue Stevenson
Delivery Method: Mail, Newsstand, Racks
Areas Served: Snohomish County

THE ARLINGTON TIMES (WED, SUN)

1085 Cedar Ave, Marysville, WA, 98270-4232, WA, USA; gen tel (360) 654-4157; adv tel (360) 659-1300; ed tel (360) 654-4157; gen fax (360) 658-0350; adv fax (360) 658-0350; ed fax (360) 435-0350; disp adv e-mail jknoblich@soundpublishing.com; class adv e-mail jknoblich@soundpublishing.com; ed e-mail editor@marysvilleglobe.com; web site www.arlingtontimes.com
Circulation: 137pd, 4,949fr; AAM
Advertising rate: Open inch rate $23.45
Established: 1887
Group: Black Press Group Ltd.
Sound Publishing, Inc.
Digital Platform - Mobile: Apple, Android, Windows, Blackberry
Digital Platform - Tablet: Apple iOS, Android, Windows 7, Blackberry Tablet OS, Kindle, Nook, Kindle Fire
Mechanical Specifications: Type page 12 7/8 x 21 1/2; E - 6 cols, 2, 1/8 between; A - 6 cols, 2, 1/8 between; C - 9 cols, 1 3/8, 1/8 between. Equipment & Software: ; Presses — G/Community; Software — QPS/QuarkXPress 4.0.
Delivery Method: Mail, Newsstand, Racks
Areas Served: 98223, 98241, 98287

THE MARYSVILLE GLOBE (SUN)

1085 Cedar Ave, Marysville, WA, 98270-4232, Snohomish, USA; gen tel (360) 654-4157; adv tel (360) 659-1300; ed tel (360) 654-4157; gen fax (360) 658-0350; adv fax (360) 658-0350; ed fax (360) 658-0350; disp adv e-mail jknoblich@soundpublishing.com; class adv e-mail 360-654-4157; ed e-mail editor@marysvilleglobe.com; web site www.marysvilleglobe.com
Circulation: 74pd, 15,000fr; AAM
Advertising rate: Open inch rate $23.45
Established: 1892
Group: Black Press Group Ltd.
Sound Publishing, Inc.
Digital Platform - Mobile: Apple, Android, Windows, Blackberry
Digital Platform - Tablet: Apple iOS, Android, Windows 7, Blackberry Tablet OS, Kindle, Nook, Kindle Fire
Managing Ed. .... Steve Powell
Delivery Method: Mail, Newsstand, Carrier, Racks
Areas Served: Snohomish County

MONTESANO

THE VIDETTE (THUR)

109 W Marcy Ave, Montesano, WA, 98563-3615, Grays Harbor, USA; gen tel (360) 249-3311; adv tel (360) 537-3918; ed tel (360) 249-3311; gen fax (360) 249-5636; disp adv e-mail cgerber@thedailyworld.com; class adv e-mail kfrank@thedailyworld.com; ed e-mail editor@thevidette.com; web site www.thevidette.com
Circulation: 5,583pd, 749fr; CAC
Established: 1883
Digital Platform - Mobile: Apple, Android
Digital Platform - Tablet: Apple iOS, Android
Publisher .... Stanley Woody
Delivery Method: Mail, Newsstand, Racks
Areas Served: Grays Harbor County

MORTON

THE EAST COUNTY JOURNAL (WED)

278 W MAIN ST, Morton, WA, 98356, Lewis, USA; gen tel (360) 496-5993; adv tel (360) 496-5993; ed tel (360) 496-5993; gen fax (360) 496-5110; adv fax (360) 496-5110; ed fax (360) 496-5110; disp adv e-mail ecjeditor@devaulpublishing.com; class adv e-mail ecjeditor@devaulpublishing.com; ed e-mail ecjeditor@devaulpublishing.com; web site www.devaulpublishing.com/eastcounty
Circulation: 7,979fr; AAM
Advertising rate: Open inch rate $11.00
Established: 1936
Group: DeVaul Publishing Inc.
Digital Platform - Mobile: Windows
Digital Platform - Tablet: Windows 7
Co-Pub. .... Frank DeVaul
Co-Pub./Adv. Vice Pres. .... Judy DeVaul
Ed. .... Kevin Westrick
Mechanical Specifications: Type page 13 x 21 1/2; E - 6 cols, 2, 1/6 between; A - 6 cols, 2, 1/6 between; C - 6 cols, 2, 1/6 between. Equipment & Software: Hardware — APP/Mac; Software — Multi-Ad/Creator, Adobe/PageMaker, QPS/QuarkXPress.
Delivery Method: Mail
Areas Served: Lewis County

MOSES LAKE

BASIN BUSINESS JOURNAL FARM NEWS (THUR)

815 W 3rd Ave, Moses Lake, WA, 98837-2008, Grant, USA; gen tel (509) 765-8549; adv tel (509)765-8549; ed tel (509)765-8549; disp adv e-mail bbjagnews@basinbusinessjournal.com; class adv e-mail bbjagnews@basinbusinessjournal.com; ed e-mail bbjagnews@basinbusinessjournal.com; web site www.basinbusinessjournal.com
Group: Hagadone Corporation
Pub. .... Judy Nelson

MOUNT VERNON

THE ARGUS (WED)

1215 Anderson Rd, Mount Vernon, WA, 98274-7615, Skagit, USA; gen tel (360) 424-3251; adv tel (360) 424-3251; ed tel (360) 424-3251; gen fax (360) 424-5300; adv fax (360) 424-5300; ed fax (360) 424-5300; disp adv e-mail dbundy@skagitpublishing.com; class adv e-mail mdobie@skagitpublishing.com; ed e-mail kboyd@skagitpublishing.com; web site www.goskagit.com
Circulation: 3,200pd, 6,300fr; Sworn/Estimate/Non-Audited
Advertising rate: Open inch rate $13.55
Group: Pioneer Newspapers Inc
Digital Platform - Mobile: Windows
Digital Platform - Tablet: Windows 7
Pres. .... Leighton Wood
Adv. Mgr. .... Deb Davis Bundy
Ed. .... Kathy Boyd
Mechanical Specifications: Type page 10 1/4 x 16 1/2; E - 5 cols, 2 1/12, between; A - 5 cols, 2 1/12, between; C - 5 cols, 2 1/12, between. Equipment & Software: Hardware — APP/Mac; Software — Adobe/PageMaker 4.0.
Delivery Method: Mail
Areas Served: Skagit County

MUKILTEO

EDMONDS BEACON (THUR)

806 5th St, Mukilteo, WA, 98275-1628, Snohomish, USA; gen tel (425) 347-1711; adv tel (425) 347-1711; ed tel (425) 347-1711; gen fax (425) 347-6077; adv fax (425) 347-6077; ed fax (425) 347-6077; disp adv e-mail edmondssales@yourbeacon.net; class adv e-mail classifieds@yourbeacon.net; ed e-mail publisher@yourbeacon.net; web site www.edmondsbeacon.com
Circulation: 100pd, 10,000fr; Sworn/Estimate/Non-Audited
Advertising rate: Open inch rate $24.00
Established: 1986
Group: Beacon Publishing Inc.
Digital Platform - Mobile: Apple, Android
Digital Platform - Tablet: Apple iOS, Android
Pub./Ed. .... Paul Archipley
Adv. Dir. .... Linda Chittim
Circ. Mgr. .... Carol Norton
Mechanical Specifications: print size: 10"x16" 1 col: 1.875" (11 picas) 2 col: 3.875" (23 picas) 3 col: 5.875" (35 picas) 4 col: 7.875" (47 picas) 5 col: 10" (60 picas)
Delivery Method: Carrier, Racks
Areas Served: 98020, 98026

MUKILTEO BEACON (WED)

806 5th St, Mukilteo, WA, 98275-1628, Snohomish, USA; gen tel (425) 347-5634; adv tel (425) 347-5634; ed tel (425) 347-5634; gen fax (425) 347-6077; adv fax (425) 347-6077; ed fax (425) 347-6077; disp adv e-mail mukilteosales@yourbeacon.net; class adv e-mail classifieds@yourbeacon.net; ed e-mail mukilteoeditor@yourbeacon.net; web site www.mukilteobeacon.com
Circulation: 166pd, 10,000fr; CVC
Advertising rate: Open inch rate $24.00
Established: 1991
Group: Beacon Publishing Inc.
Digital Platform - Mobile: Apple, Android
Digital Platform - Tablet: Apple iOS, Android
Pub. .... Paul Archipley
Gen. Mgr. .... Linda Chittim
Ed. .... Sara Bruestle
Adv. Mgr. .... Doug Kimball
Graphics .... Doug Warren
Circ. Mgr. .... Carol Norton
Mechanical Specifications: print size: 10"x16"
1 col: 1.875" (11 picas)
2 col: 3.875" (23 picas)
3 col: 5.875" (35 picas)
4 col: 7.875" (47 picas)
5 col: 10" (60 picas)
Delivery Method: Carrier, Racks
Areas Served: 98275, 98208, 98204

NEWPORT

NEWPORT MINER (WED)

421 S Spokane Ave, Newport, WA, 99156-7039, Pend Oreille, USA; gen tel (509) 447-2433; gen fax (509) 447-9222; disp adv e-mail mineradvertising@povn.com; class adv e-mail minerclassifieds@povn.com; ed e-mail minernews@povn.com; web site www.pendoreillerivervalley.com

Circulation: 6,000pd, 11,000fr; Sworn/Estimate/Non-Audited
Advertising rate: Open inch rate $12.90
Established: 1891
Digital Platform - Mobile: Apple, Android, Windows, Blackberry
Digital Platform - Tablet: Apple iOS, Android, Windows 7, Blackberry Tablet OS, Kindle, Nook, Kindle Fire
Pub......Fred J. Willenbrock
Mng. Ed......Michelle Nedved
Adv. Mgr......Lindsay Guscott
Circ. Mgr......Susan Willenbrock
Delivery Method: Mail, Newsstand
Areas Served: Pend Oreille County, WA

THE GEM STATE MINER (WED)

421 S Spokane Ave, Newport, WA, 99156-7039, W. Bonner County, USA; gen tel (509) 447-2433; gen fax (509) 447-9222; disp adv e-mail mineradvertising@povn.com; class adv e-mail minerclassifieds@povn.com; ed e-mail minernews@povn.com; web site www.pendoreillerivervalley.com
Circulation: 6,000pd, 11,000fr; Sworn/Estimate/Non-Audited
Advertising rate: Open inch rate $12.90
Established: 1891
Digital Platform - Mobile: Apple, Android, Windows, Blackberry
Digital Platform - Tablet: Apple iOS, Android, Windows 7, Blackberry Tablet OS, Kindle, Nook, Kindle Fire
Pub......Fred J. Willenbrock
Mng. Ed......Michelle Nedved
Adv. Mgr......Lindsay Guscott
Circ. Mgr......Susan Willenbrock
Delivery Method: Mail, Newsstand
Areas Served: W.Bonner County, Idaho

OCEAN SHORES

NORTH COAST NEWS (THUR)

668 Ocean Shores Blvd NW, Ocean Shores, WA, 98569-9346, Grays Harbor, USA; gen tel (360) 289-2441; adv tel (360) 537-3955; ed tel (360) 289-3968; disp adv e-mail editor@northcoastnews.com; class adv e-mail editor@northcoastnews.com; ed e-mail editor@northcoastnews.com; web site www.northcoastnews.com
Circulation: 1,224pd, 21fr; CAC
Advertising rate: Open inch rate $7.10
Established: 1989
Digital Platform - Mobile: Apple, Android, Windows
Digital Platform - Tablet: Apple iOS, Android, Windows 7
Pub./Ed......Angelo Bruscas
Publisher......Stanley Woody
Delivery Method: Mail
Areas Served: Ocean Shores, Ocean City, Copalis Beach, Iron Springs, Seabrook, Pacific Beach, Moclips, and Taholah

ODESSA

THE ODESSA RECORD (THUR)

1 W 1st Ave, Odessa, WA, 99159-7004, Lincoln, USA; gen tel (509) 982-2632; adv tel (509) 982-2632; ed tel (509) 982-2632; gen fax (509) 982-2651; adv fax (509) 982-2651; ed fax (509) 982-2651; disp adv e-mail therecordads@odessaoffice.com; class adv e-mail therecord@odessaoffice.com; ed e-mail therecord@odessaoffice.com; web site www.odessarecord.com
Circulation: 1,250pd,; Sworn/Estimate/Non-Audited
Advertising rate: Open inch rate $5.50
Established: 1901
Digital Platform - Mobile: Windows
Digital Platform - Tablet: Windows 7
Co-Pub. Edward CrosbyEquipment & Software: ; Software — Microsoft/Windows 3.1, Adobe/PageMaker 4.0.
Delivery Method: Mail
Areas Served: 99159, 99169, 98837

OMAK

OMAK-OKANOGAN COUNTY CHRONICLE (WED, SUN)

PO Box 553, Omak, WA, 98841-0553, Okanogan, USA; gen tel (509) 826-1110; adv tel (509)826-1110; ed tel (509)826-1110; gen fax (509) 826-5819; adv fax (509)826-5819; ed fax (509)826-5819; disp adv e-mail ads@omakchronicle.com; class adv e-mail classifieds@omakchronicle.com; ed e-mail news@omakchronicle.com; web site www.omakchronicle.com
Circulation: 6,600pd, 300fr; Sworn/Estimate/Non-Audited
Advertising rate: Open inch rate $12.50
Established: 1910
Group: Eagle Newspapers, Inc.
Digital Platform - Mobile: Android, Windows
Digital Platform - Tablet: Apple iOS, Android, Windows 7
Publisher and editor......Roger Harnack
Mailroom Manager......Howard Thompson
Advertising Manager......Teresa Myers
Circulation/classified manager......Julie Bock
Delivery Method: Mail, Newsstand, Carrier, Racks
Areas Served: Okanogan, Ferry, Douglas, and Grant County

OROVILLE

OKANOGAN VALLEY GAZETTE-TRIBUNE (THUR)

1422 Main St, Oroville, WA, 98844-9385, Okanogan, USA; gen tel (509) 476-3602; adv tel (509) 476-3054; ed tel (509) 476-3054; gen fax (509) 476-3602; adv fax (509) 476-3602; ed fax (509) 476-3602; disp adv e-mail gary@gazette-tribune.com; class adv e-mail gary@gazette-tribune.com; ed e-mail editor@gazette-tribune.com; web site www.gazette-tribune.com
Circulation: 1,421pd,; CAC
Advertising rate: Open inch rate $11.50
Established: 1905
Group: Black Press Group Ltd.
Sound Publishing, Inc.
Digital Platform - Mobile: Apple, Android, Windows, Blackberry
Digital Platform - Tablet: Apple iOS, Android, Windows 7, Blackberry Tablet OS, Kindle, Nook, Kindle Fire
Pub./Ed......Gary DeVon
Reporter......Brent Baker
Nat'l Sales Dir......Stephen Barrett
Delivery Method: Mail, Newsstand
Areas Served: Okanogan County

OTHELLO

THE SUN TRIBUNE (WED)

705 E Hemlock St, Othello, WA, 99344-1425, Adams, USA; gen tel (509) 765-8549; adv tel (509) 765-8549; ed tel (509) 765-8549; gen fax (509) 765-8659; adv fax (509) 765-8659; ed fax (509) 765-8659; disp adv e-mail publisher@suntribunenews.com; class adv e-mail publisher@suntribunenews.com; ed e-mail editor@suntribunenews.com; web site www.suntribunenews.com
Circulation: 1,250pd, 0fr; Sworn/Estimate/Non-Audited
Advertising rate: $15.34
Established: 2012
Group: Hagadone Corporation
Publisher......Bob Richardson
Delivery Method: Mail, Newsstand, Racks

POMEROY

EAST WASHINGTONIAN (THUR)

742 Main St, Pomeroy, WA, 99347, Garfield, USA; gen tel (509) 843-1313; adv tel (509) 843-1313; ed tel (509) 843-1313; gen fax (509) 843-3911; adv fax (509) 843-3911; ed fax (509) 843-3911; disp adv e-mail e-dub@pomeroy-wa.com; class adv e-mail e-dub@pomeroy-wa.com; ed e-mail e-dub@pomeroy-wa.com
Advertising rate: Open inch rate $6.10
Established: 1882
Pub./Ed......Mike Tom
Delivery Method: Mail
Areas Served: Garfield County

PORT ORCHARD

PORT ORCHARD INDEPENDENT (FRI)

2497 Bethel Rd SE, Ste 102, Port Orchard, WA, 98366-4889, Kitsap, USA; gen tel (360) 876-4414; adv tel (360) 876-4414; ed tel (360) 876-4414; gen fax (360) 876-4458; adv fax (360) 876-4458; ed fax (360) 876-4458; disp adv e-mail lmay@portorchardindependent.com; class adv e-mail smcdonald@soundpublishing.com; ed e-mail editor@portorchardindependent.com; web site www.portorchardindependent.com
Circulation: 891pd, 16,522fr; CAC
Advertising rate: Open inch rate $22.40
Established: 1890
Group: Black Press Group Ltd.
Sound Publishing, Inc.
Digital Platform - Mobile: Apple, Android, Windows, Blackberry
Digital Platform - Tablet: Apple iOS, Android, Windows 7, Blackberry Tablet OS, Kindle, Nook, Kindle Fire
Pub......Sean McDonald
Ed......Dannie Oliveaux
Nat'l Sales Dir......Stephen BarrettEquipment & Software: Hardware — APP/Mac; Presses — WPC/Web Leader; Software — QPS/QuarkXPress, Multi-Ad/Creator.
Delivery Method: Newsstand, Carrier
Areas Served: 98312, 98359, 98366, 98367, 98528

PORT TOWNSEND

PORT TOWNSEND & JEFFERSON COUNTY LEADER (WED)

226 Adams St, Port Townsend, WA, 98368-5706, Jefferson, USA; gen tel (360) 385-2900; adv tel (360) 385-2900 ext. 122; ed tel (360) 385-2900 ext. 107; gen fax (360) 385-3422; adv fax (360) 385-3422; ed fax (360) 385-3422; disp adv e-mail cbrewer@ptleader.com; class adv e-mail classifieds@ptleader.com; ed e-mail lloyd@ptleader.com; web site www.ptleader.com
Circulation: 6,504pd, 561fr; CAC
Advertising rate: Open inch rate $15.30
Established: 1889
Digital Platform - Mobile: Apple, Android, Windows, Blackberry
Digital Platform - Tablet: Apple iOS, Android, Windows 7, Blackberry Tablet OS, Kindle, Nook, Kindle Fire
Pub......Scott Wilson
Mng. Ed......Patrick Sullivan
Adv. Dir......Catherine Brewer
John Stanger
Delivery Method: Mail, Racks
Areas Served: Jefferson County

POULSBO

CENTRAL KITSAP REPORTER (FRI)

19351 8th Ave NE, Ste 205, Poulsbo, WA, 98370-8710, Kitsap, USA; gen tel (360) 308-9161; adv tel (360) 308-9161; ed tel (360) 308-9161 ext. 5050; gen fax (360) 308-9363; adv fax (360) 308-9363; ed fax (360) 308-9363; disp adv e-mail smcdonald@soundpublishing.com; class adv e-mail rnicholson@soundpublishing.com; ed e-mail editor@soundpublishing.com; web site www.kitsapdailynews.com
Circulation: 254pd, 14,934fr; AAM
Advertising rate: Open inch rate $27.50
Group: Black Press Group Ltd.
Sound Publishing, Inc.
Digital Platform - Mobile: Apple, Android, Windows, Blackberry
Digital Platform - Tablet: Apple iOS, Android, Windows 7, Blackberry Tablet OS, Kindle, Nook, Kindle Fire
Pub......Sean McDonald
Ed......Leslie Kelly
Office Mgr......Jessica Ginet
Adv. Rep......Wayne Nelson
Nat'l Sales Dir......Stephen Barrett
Mechanical Specifications: Type page 10 1/4 x 15; E - 6 cols, 1 9/16, 1/6 between; A - 6 cols, 1 9/16, 1/6 between; C - 7 cols, 1 3/8, 1/12 between.Equipment & Software: Hardware — APP/Mac; Presses — WPC/Atlas; Software — QPS/QuarkXPress, Multi-Ad/Creator.
Delivery Method: Newsstand, Carrier
Areas Served: Central Kitsap County

KINGSTON COMMUNITY NEWS (MTHLY)

PO Box 278, Poulsbo, WA, 98370-0278, Kitsap, USA; gen tel (360) 779-4464; adv tel (360) 779-4464; ed tel (360) 779-4464; disp adv e-mail publisher@kingstoncommunitynews.com; class adv e-mail publisher@kingstoncommunitynews.com; ed e-mail rwalker@northkitsapherald.com; web site www.kitsapdailynews.com
Circulation: 8,942fr; CAC
Advertising rate: Open inch rate $12.50
Group: Postmedia Network Inc.
Sound Publishing, Inc.
Digital Platform - Mobile: Apple, Android, Windows, Blackberry
Digital Platform - Tablet: Apple iOS, Android, Windows 7, Blackberry Tablet OS, Kindle, Nook, Kindle Fire
Pub......Donna Etchey
Ed......Richard Walker
Nat'l Sales Dir......Stephen Barrett
Delivery Method: Mail
Areas Served: Kingston, Eglon, Hansville, Indianola, Little Boston, and Port Gamble

NORTH KITSAP HERALD (FRI)

19351 8th Ave NE, Ste 205, Poulsbo, WA, 98370-8710, Kitsap, USA; gen tel (360) 779-4464; adv tel (360) 779-4464; ed tel (360) 779-4464; gen fax (360) 779-8276; adv fax (360) 779-8276; ed fax (360) 779-8276; disp adv e-mail publisher@northkitsapherald.com; class adv e-mail rwalker@northkitsapherald.com; ed e-mail editor@northkitsapherald.com; web site www.kitsapdailynews.com
Circulation: 536pd, 11,265fr; CAC
Advertising rate: Open inch rate $22.40
Established: 1901
Group: Sound Publishing, Inc.
Digital Platform - Mobile: Apple, Android, Windows, Blackberry
Digital Platform - Tablet: Apple iOS, Android, Windows 7, Blackberry Tablet OS, Kindle, Nook, Kindle Fire
Pub......Donna Etchey
Ed......Richard Walker
Circ. Mgr......Christy Dano
Nat'l Sales Dir......Stephen Barrett
Mechanical Specifications: Type page 10 3/8 x 15; E - 6 cols, 1 3/5, 1/6 between; A - 6 cols, 1 3/5, 1/6 between; C - 7 cols, 1 2/5, 1/12 between.Equipment & Software: Hardware — APP/Mac, IBM; Software — QPS/QuarkXPress.
Delivery Method: Mail, Newsstand, Carrier, Racks
Areas Served: Kitsap County

PROSSER

PROSSER RECORD-BULLETIN (WED)

613 7th St, Prosser, WA, 99350-1459, Benton, USA; gen tel (509) 786-1711; adv tel (509) 786-1711; ed tel (509) 786-1711; gen fax (509) 786-1779; adv fax (509) 786-1779; ed fax (509) 786-1779; disp adv e-mail ads@recordbulletin.com; class adv e-mail office@recordbulletin.com; ed e-mail editor@recordbulletin.com; web site www.recordbulletin.com
Circulation:; Sworn/Estimate/Non-Audited
Advertising rate: Open inch rate $8.90
Established: 1920

Digital Platform - Mobile: Windows
Digital Platform - Tablet: Windows 7
Pub....Danielle Fournier
Ed. ....Victoria Walker
Adv. Mgr....Dianne Buxton
Delivery Method: Mail, Racks
Areas Served: Benton County

PUYALLUP

THE PUYALLUP HERALD (THUR)

510 E Main, Puyallup, WA, 98372-5698, Pierce, USA; gen tel (253) 841-2481; adv tel (253) 841-2481; ed tel (253) 841-2481; gen fax (253) 840-8249; adv fax (253) 840-8249; ed fax (253) 840-8249; disp adv e-mail jim.appelgate@gateline.com; class adv e-mail brian.mclean@puyallupherald.com; ed e-mail editor@puyallupherald.com; web site www.thenewstribune.com
Circulation: 27,000pd,; Sworn/Estimate/Non-Audited
Advertising rate: Open inch rate $10.22
Group: The McClatchy Company
Digital Platform - Mobile: Apple, Android
Digital Platform - Tablet: Apple iOS, Android
Pub./Ed....Brian McLean
Adv. Dir....Jim Appelgate
Delivery Method: Mail, Racks
Areas Served: Puyallup, South Hill, Edgewood, Sumner, and Bonney Lake

QUINCY

THE QUINCY VALLEY POST-REGISTER (THUR)

305 Central Ave S, Quincy, WA, 98848-1227, Grant, USA; gen tel (509) 787-4511; adv tel (509) 787-4511; ed tel (509) 787-4511; gen fax (509) 787-2682; adv fax (509) 787-2682; ed fax (509) 787-2682; disp adv e-mail qvprads@gmail.com; class adv e-mail qvpr-classifieds@gmail.com; ed e-mail qvpreditor@gmail.com; web site www.qvpr.com
Advertising rate: Open inch rate $11
Established: 1949
Group: The Wenatchee World
Digital Platform - Mobile: Windows
Digital Platform - Tablet: Windows 7
Delivery Method: Mail, Newsstand, Carrier, Racks
Areas Served: Grant County

RITZVILLE

THE RITZVILLE ADAMS COUNTY JOURNAL (THUR)

216 W Railroad Ave, Ritzville, WA, 99169-2309, Adams, USA; gen tel (509) 659-1020; adv tel (509) 659-1020; ed tel (509) 659-1020; gen fax (509) 659-0842; adv fax (509) 659-0842; ed fax (509) 659-0842; disp adv e-mail advertising@ritzvillejournal.com; class adv e-mail davidson@ritzvillejournal.com; ed e-mail davidson@ritzvillejournal.com; web site www.ritzvillejournal.com
Circulation: 2,100pd, 46fr; Sworn/Estimate/Non-Audited
Advertising rate: Open inch rate $6.90
Established: 1886
Digital Platform - Mobile: Apple, Android, Windows
Digital Platform - Tablet: Apple iOS, Android, Windows 7
Pub./Ed....Steven McFaden
Reporter/News Ed....Katelin Davidson
Mechanical Specifications: Type page 12 3/4 x 21 1/4; E - 6 cols, 2, 1/6 between; A - 6 cols, 2, 1/6 between; C - 6 cols, 2, 1/6 between. Equipment & Software: Hardware — APP/Mac; Software — Adobe/PageMaker.
Delivery Method: Mail
Areas Served: Adams County

SAINT JOHN

THE COMMUNITY CURRENT (THUR, MTHLY)

15 E Front St, Saint John, WA, 99171-8775, Whitman, USA; gen tel (509) 648-3264; adv tel (509) 648-3264; ed tel (509) 648-3264; disp adv e-mail becky@communitycurrentnewspaper.com; class adv e-mail becky@communitycurrentnewspaper.com; ed e-mail becky@communitycurrentnewspaper.com; web site www.communitycurrentnewspaper.com
Advertising rate: Open inch rate $7.25
Established: 1994
Digital Platform - Mobile: Windows
Digital Platform - Tablet: Windows 7
Pub./Ed....Becky Dickerson
Delivery Method: Mail
Areas Served: Whitman County

SEATTLE

BALLARD NEWS-TRIBUNE (WED, FRI)

PO Box 66769, Seattle, WA, 98166-0769, King, USA; gen tel (425) 238-4616; adv tel (206) 387-3873; ed tel (425)-238-4616; gen fax (206) 453-5041; adv fax (206) 453-5041; disp adv e-mail donao@robinsonnews.com; class adv e-mail classifieds@robinsonnews.com; ed e-mail kenr@robinsonnews.com; web site www.westsideweekly.com
Circulation: 10,351pd,; Sworn/Estimate/Non-Audited
Advertising rate: Open inch rate $30.00
Established: 1898
Group: Robinson Newspapers
Digital Platform - Mobile: Apple, Android, Windows, Blackberry
Digital Platform - Tablet: Apple iOS, Android, Windows 7, Blackberry Tablet OS
Co-Pub....Ken Robinson
Assoc. Pub....Tim Robinson
Mng. Ed....Ken Robinson
Adv. Mgr....Dona Ozier
Delivery Method: Mail, Newsstand, Racks
Areas Served: 98177, 98117, 98107, 98103

CITY LIVING SEATTLE (THUR, MTHLY)

636 S Alaska St, Seattle, WA, 98108-1727, King, USA; gen tel (206) 461-1300; adv tel (206) 461-1322; ed tel (206) 461-1346; disp adv e-mail ppcadmanager@nwlink.com; class adv e-mail class1@nwlink.com; ed e-mail CityLivingEditor@nwlink.com; web site www.citylivingseattle.com
Circulation: 3,500pd, 18,000fr; VAC
Advertising rate: Open inch rate $28.00
Group: Pacific Publishing Co. Inc.
Digital Platform - Mobile: Apple, Android, Windows, Blackberry
Digital Platform - Tablet: Apple iOS, Android, Windows 7, Blackberry Tablet OS, Kindle, Nook, Kindle Fire
Ed....Vera Chan-Pool
Adv. Mgr....Terry FainEquipment & Software: Hardware — APP/Mac, PC; Presses — WPC/Web Leader; Software — Adobe/PageMaker 6.5, Microsoft/Word 6.0.
Delivery Method: Mail, Newsstand, Carrier, Racks
Areas Served: 98144, 98108, 98118, 98178

PUGET SOUND BUSINESS JOURNAL (FRI)

801 2nd Ave, Ste 210, Seattle, WA, 98104-1528, King, USA; gen tel (206) 876-5500; adv tel (206) 876-5450; ed tel (206) 876-5431; gen fax (206) 447-8510; adv fax (206) 447-8510; ed fax (206) 447-8510; disp adv e-mail mgeoghegan@bizjournals.com; class adv e-mail mwall@bizjournals.com; ed e-mail gerb@bizjournals.com; web site www.bizjournals.com/seattle
Advertising rate: Open inch rate $8,120.00 (Full-Page)
Established: 1980
Digital Platform - Mobile: Apple, Android, Windows, Blackberry
Digital Platform - Tablet: Apple iOS, Android, Windows 7, Blackberry Tablet OS, Kindle, Nook, Kindle Fire
Pub....Gordon Prouty
Ed. ....George Erb
Adv. Mgr....Martha Geoghegan
Delivery Method: Mail, Newsstand, Racks
Areas Served: King County

QUEEN ANNE & MAGNOLIA NEWS (WED)

636 S Alaska St, Seattle, WA, 98108-1727, King, USA; gen tel (206) 461-1300; adv tel (206) 461-1322; ed tel (206) 461-1346; gen fax (206) 461-1285; adv fax (206) 461-1285; ed fax (206) 461-1285; disp adv e-mail PPC-sales@nwlink.com; class adv e-mail class-mgr@nwlink.com; ed e-mail QAMagNews@nwlink.com; web site www.queenannenews.com
Circulation: 1,898pd, 5,102fr; Sworn/Estimate/Non-Audited
Advertising rate: Open inch rate $32.00
Established: 1919
Group: Pacific Publishing Co. Inc.
Digital Platform - Mobile: Apple, Android, Windows
Digital Platform - Tablet: Apple iOS, Android, Windows 7
Ed....Vera Chan-Pool
Sales Mgr....Terry Fain
Gen. Mgr....Robert Munford
Mechanical Specifications: Type page 10 3/4 x 16; E - 5 cols, 2 1/16, between; A - 5 cols, 2 1/16, between; C - 7 cols, 1 1/3, between.
Delivery Method: Newsstand, Carrier, Racks
Areas Served: 98119, 98109, 98199

THE CAPITOL HILL TIMES (THUR)

4000 Aurora Ave N, Ste 100, Seattle, WA, 98103-7853, King, USA; gen tel (425) 213-5579; adv tel (425) 213-5579; ed tel (425) 213-5579; disp adv e-mail advertising@capitolhilltimes.com; class adv e-mail info@capitolhilltimes.com; ed e-mail editor@capitolhilltimes.com; web site www.capitolhilltimes.com
Advertising rate: Open inch rate $28.00
Established: 1926
Group: RIM Publications
Digital Platform - Mobile: Apple, Android, Windows, Blackberry
Digital Platform - Tablet: Apple iOS, Android, Windows 7, Blackberry Tablet OS
Ed....Gina Luna
Designer/Adv. Mgr....Angela Nickerson
Delivery Method: Mail, Newsstand, Racks
Areas Served: King County

THE MONROE MONITOR & VALLEY NEWS (TUES)

PO Box 80156, Seattle, WA, 98108-0156, Snohomish, USA; gen tel (360) 794-7116; adv tel (360) 794-7116; ed tel (360) 794-7116; gen fax (360) 794-6202; adv fax (360) 794-6202; ed fax (360) 794-6202; disp adv e-mail sfreshman@monroemonitor.com; class adv e-mail kathie@monroemonitor.com; ed e-mail editor@monroemonitor.com; web site www.monroemonitor.com
Circulation: 4,000pd,; Sworn/Estimate/Non-Audited
Advertising rate: Open inch rate $15.75
Established: 1899
Group: RIM Publications
Digital Platform - Mobile: Apple, Android, Windows
Digital Platform - Tablet: Apple iOS, Android, Windows 7
Pub./Ed....Polly Keary
Office Mgr....Kathie Savelesky
Delivery Method: Mail, Newsstand
Areas Served: Snohomish County

WESTSIDE SEATTLE (FRI)

PO Box 66769, Seattle, WA, 98166-0769, King, USA; gen tel (206) 251-3220; adv tel (206) 387-3873; ed tel (425) 238-4616; disp adv e-mail donao@robinsonnews.com; class adv e-mail classifieds@robinsonnews.com; ed e-mail kenr@robinsonnews.com; web site www.westsideseattle.com
Circulation:; Sworn/Estimate/Non-Audited
Advertising rate: Open inch rate $40.00
Established: 1923
Group: Robinson Communications, Inc.
Digital Platform - Mobile: Apple, Android, Windows, Blackberry
Digital Platform - Tablet: Apple iOS, Android, Windows 7, Blackberry Tablet OS
Pub....Tim Robinson
Mng. Ed....Ken Robinson
Mechanical Specifications: Type page 10 7/8 x 16; E - 5 cols, 2 1/6, between; A - 5 cols, 2 1/6, between; C - 8 cols, between.Equipment & Software: Hardware — APP/Mac
Delivery Method: Mail, Newsstand, Racks
Areas Served: 98106, 98116, 98126, 98136, 98146, 98168 98166

SEQUIM

THE SEQUIM GAZETTE (WED)

147 W Washington St, Ste A, Sequim, WA, 98382-3372, Clallam, USA; gen tel (360) 683-3311; adv tel (360) 683-3311 ext. 1050; ed tel (360) 683-3311 ext. 5050; gen fax (360) 683-6670; adv fax (360) 683-6670; ed fax (360) 683-6670; disp adv e-mail dlahmeyer@sequimgazette.com; class adv e-mail classified@sequimgazette.com; ed e-mail editor@sequimgazette.com; web site www.sequimgazette.com
Circulation: 3,875pd,; AAM
Advertising rate: Open inch rate $16.25
Established: 1988
Group: Black Press Group Ltd.
Sound Publishing, Inc.
Digital Platform - Mobile: Android, Windows
Digital Platform - Tablet: Android, Windows 7
Ed....Mike Dashiell
Gen. Mgr./Adv. Mgr....Debi Lahmeyer
Circ. Mgr....Bob Morris
Nat'l Sales Dir....Stephen Barrett
Mechanical Specifications: Type page 10 1/2 x 21 1/col. = 9p8 (1.61")Equipment & Software: Hardware — APP/Mac; Software — Adobe/PageMaker 6.5, Adobe/Photoshop 6.0, Multi-Ad/Creator 4.0.5, QPS/QuarkXPress 4.0, Adobe/Illustrator 8.0.
Delivery Method: Mail, Newsstand, Carrier, Racks
Areas Served: 98382

SHELTON

SHELTON-MASON COUNTY JOURNAL (THUR)

227 W Cota St, Shelton, WA, 98584-2263, Mason, USA; gen tel (360) 426-4412; gen fax (360) 426 9399; disp adv e-mail ads@masoncounty.com; class adv e-mail dave@masoncounty.com; ed e-mail news@masoncounty.com; web site www.masoncounty.com
Circulation: 7,100pd, 100fr; USPS
Established: 1887
Digital Platform - Mobile: Apple
Digital Platform - Tablet: Apple iOS
EIC....Adam Rudnick
Adv. Mgr....Dave Pierik
Pub....
Tom MullenEquipment & Software: Hardware — Mac OS; Presses — Goss Community ; Software — Adobe CS4
Delivery Method: Mail, Newsstand, Racks
Areas Served: 98584, 98524, 98528, 98546, 98548, 98555, 98557, 98588, 98592

SNOHOMISH

EVERETT NEW TRIBUNE (WED)

127 Avenue C, Ste B, Snohomish, WA, 98290-2768, Snohomish, USA; gen tel (360) 568-4121; adv tel (360) 568-4121; ed tel (360) 568-4121; gen fax (360) 568-1484; adv fax (360) 568-1484; ed fax (360) 568-1484; disp adv e-mail becky@snoho.com; class adv e-mail classad.tribune@snoho.com; ed e-mail editor.tribune@snoho.com; web site www.snoho.com
Circulation: 15,000pd, 3,500fr; Sworn/Estimate/Non-Audited
Advertising rate: Open inch rate $18.00

Established: 1892
Digital Platform - Mobile: Apple, Android
Digital Platform - Tablet: Apple iOS, Android, Windows 7
Pub. / Adv. Mgr. .... Becky Reed
Editor .... Michael Whitney
Mechanical Specifications: Type page 10 7/8 x 16 1/2; E - 5 cols, 2 1/16, between; A - 5 cols, 2 1/16, between; C - 7 cols, 1 3/8, between.
Delivery Method: Mail, Newsstand
Areas Served: 98201, 98203, 98204, 98206, 98208

SNOHOMISH COUNTY TRIBUNE (WED)
127 Avenue C, Ste B, Snohomish, WA, 98290-2768, Snohomish, USA; gen tel (360) 568-4121; adv tel (360) 568-4121; ed tel (360) 568-4121; gen fax (360) 568-1484; adv fax (360) 568-1484; ed fax (360) 568-1484; disp adv e-mail becky@snoho.com; class adv e-mail classad.tribune@snoho.com; ed e-mail editor.tribune@snoho.com; web site www.snoho.com
Circulation: 8,500pd, 8,000fr; Sworn/Estimate/ Non-Audited
Advertising rate: Open inch rate $18.00
Established: 1892
Digital Platform - Mobile: Apple, Android
Digital Platform - Tablet: Apple iOS, Android, Windows 7
Pub. / Adv. Mgr. .... Becky Reed
Editor .... Michael Whitney
Delivery Method: Mail, Newsstand
Areas Served: 98290, 98291, 98296, 98272, 98205

SNOQUALMIE

SNOQUALMIE VALLEY RECORD (WED)
8124 Falls Ave SE, Snoqualmie, WA, 98065, King, USA; gen tel (425) 888-2311; adv tel (425) 888-2311; ed tel (425) 888-2311; gen fax (425) 888-2427; adv fax (425) 888-2427; ed fax (425) 888-2427; disp adv e-mail wshaw@valleyrecord.com; class adv e-mail dhamilton@soundpublishing.com; ed e-mail editor@valleyrecord.com; web site www.valleyrecord.com
Circulation: 412pd, 10,872fr; AAM
Advertising rate: Open inch rate $17.60
Established: 1913
Group: Black Press Group Ltd.
Sound Publishing, Inc.
Digital Platform - Mobile: Apple, Android, Windows, Blackberry
Digital Platform - Tablet: Apple iOS, Android, Windows 7, Blackberry Tablet OS, Kindle, Nook, Kindle Fire
Pub. .... William Shaw
Ed. .... Seth Truscott
Nat'l Sales Dir. .... Stephen Barrett
Mechanical Specifications: Type page 11 3/5 x 21; E - 6 cols, 2, 1/6 between; A - 6 cols, 2, 1/6 between; C - 7 cols, 1 7/12, 1/6 between. Equipment & Software: Hardware — APP/ Mac; Software — QPS/QuarkXPress.
Delivery Method: Mail, Newsstand, Racks
Areas Served: King County

SPOKANE

SPOKANE JOURNAL OF BUSINESS (THUR)
429 E 3rd Ave, Spokane, WA, 99202-1414, Spokane, USA; gen tel (509) 456-5257; adv tel (509) 344-1278; ed tel (509) 344-1263; gen fax (509) 893-5481; adv fax (509) 893-5481; ed fax (509) 893-5481; disp adv e-mail publisher@spokanejournal.com; class adv e-mail jenniferz@spokanejournal.com; ed e-mail editor@spokanejournal.com; web site www.spokanejournal.com
Circulation: 7,676pd, 6,011fr; Sworn/Estimate/ Non-Audited
Advertising rate: Open inch rate $2,450.00 (Full-Page)
Established: 1986
Group: Cowles Co.
Digital Platform - Mobile: Apple, Android, Windows, Blackberry
Digital Platform - Tablet: Apple iOS, Android, Windows 7, Blackberry Tablet OS, Kindle
Pub. .... Paul Read
Ed. .... Kim Crompton
Delivery Method: Mail, Newsstand
Areas Served: Spokane County

SPOKANE VALLEY

SPOKANE VALLEY NEWS HERALD (FRI)
1212 N Argonne Rd, Spokane Valley, WA, 99212-2799, Spokane, USA; gen tel (509) 924-2440; adv tel (509) 924-2440; ed tel (509) 924-2440; gen fax (509) 927-1154; adv fax (509) 927-1154; ed fax (509) 927-1154; disp adv e-mail vnh@onemain.com; class adv e-mail vnh@onemain.com; ed e-mail vnh@onemain.com; web site www.spokanevalleyonline.com
Circulation: 5,500pd,; Sworn/Estimate/Non-Audited
Advertising rate: Open inch rate $10.00
Group: Free Press Publishing Inc.
Digital Platform - Mobile: Windows
Digital Platform - Tablet: Windows 7
Pub./Adv. Mgr. .... Harlan Schelleberger
Mng. Ed. .... Mike Huffman
Delivery Method: Mail
Areas Served: Spokane County

STANWOOD

STANWOOD CAMANO NEWS (TUES)
9005 271st St NW, Stanwood, WA, 98292-5998, USA; gen tel (360) 629-2155; disp adv e-mail newsroom@scnews.com
Circulation: 2,247pd,; CAC
Established: 1895
Group: Adams Publishing Group, LLC
Gen. Mgr/ Ed. .... Kathy Boyd

STEVENSON

SKAMANIA COUNTY PIONEER (WED)
198 SW 2ND ST, Stevenson, WA, 98648, Skamania, USA; gen tel (509) 427-8444; adv tel (509) 427-8444; ed tel (509) 427-8444; gen fax (509) 427-4229; adv fax (509) 427-4229; ed fax (509) 427-4229; disp adv e-mail scpioneerads@gorge.net; class adv e-mail scpioneer@gorge.net; ed e-mail scpioneernews@gorge.net
Circulation: 2,600pd,; Sworn/Estimate/Non-Audited
Advertising rate: Open inch rate $6.85
Established: 1898
Pub. .... Frank DeVaul
Pub. .... Judy DeVaul
Ed. .... Philip Watness
Office Mgr./Sports Ed. .... Jean Foster
Adv. Mgr. .... Angela Rogers
Circ. Mgr. .... Bridget Callahan
Delivery Method: Mail, Newsstand
Areas Served: 98648

TACOMA

SOUTH SOUND BIZ (MTHLY)
15 Oregon Ave, Ste L2, Tacoma, WA, 98409-7411, Pierce, USA; gen tel (253) 404-0891; adv tel (253) 404-0891; ed tel (253) 404-0891; gen fax (253) 345-5705; adv fax (253) 345-5705; ed fax (253) 345-5705; disp adv e-mail jrounce@BusinessExaminer.com; ed e-mail news@BusinessExaminer.com; web site www.businessexaminer.com
Circulation: 1,072pd, 6,000fr; CVC
Advertising rate: Open inch rate $3,500 (Full-Page)
Established: 1985
Digital Platform - Mobile: Apple, Android, Windows, Blackberry
Digital Platform - Tablet: Apple iOS, Android, Windows 7, Blackberry Tablet OS
Pub./CEO .... Jeff Rounce
Delivery Method: Mail
Areas Served: Pierce, Thurston, and King County

TENINO

THE TENINO INDEPENDENT (WED)
297 Sussex Ave W, Tenino, WA, 98589-9360, Thurston, USA; gen tel (360) 264-2500; adv tel (360) 748-6848; ed tel (360) 264-2500; gen fax (360) 264-2955; adv fax (360) 748-3666; ed fax (360) 264-2955; disp adv e-mail independent@devaulpublishing.com; class adv e-mail sales2@devaulpublishing.com; ed e-mail independent@devaulpublishing.com; web site www.devaulpublishing.com
Circulation: 1,200pd,; Sworn/Estimate/Non-Audited
Advertising rate: Open inch rate $10.35
Established: 1922
Digital Platform - Mobile: Windows
Digital Platform - Tablet: Windows 7
Pub. .... Frank DeVaul
Pub. .... Judy DeVaul
Ed. .... Dan Fisher
Mechanical Specifications: Type page 10 1/2 x 16; E - 5 cols, 1 5/6, 1/6 between; A - 5 cols, 1 5/6, 1/6 between; C - 5 cols, 1 5/6, 1/6 between.
Delivery Method: Mail, Newsstand, Racks
Areas Served: 98589, 98579, 98530

TOPPENISH

REVIEW INDEPENDENT (WED)
218 W 1st Ave, Toppenish, WA, 98948-1526, Yakima, USA; gen tel (509) 314-6400; adv tel (509) 314-6400; ed tel (509) 314-6400; gen fax (509) 314-6402; adv fax (509) 314-6402; ed fax (509) 314-6402; disp adv e-mail sales@yvpub.com; class adv e-mail tmitzel@yvpub.com; ed e-mail news@yvpub.com; web site www.reviewindependent.com
Circulation: 2,000pd,; Sworn/Estimate/Non-Audited
Advertising rate: Open inch rate $8.50
Established: 1904
Group: Yakima Valley Newspapers LLC
Digital Platform - Mobile: Windows
Digital Platform - Tablet: Windows 7
Pub. .... Bruce Smith
Ed. .... Erick Peterson
Delivery Method: Mail, Newsstand
Areas Served: Toppenish, Zillah, Wapato, Granger, White Swan, and Harrah

TWISP

METHOW VALLEY NEWS (WED)
502 Glover St S, Twisp, WA, 98856-5818, Okanogan, USA; gen tel (509) 997-7011; adv tel (509) 997-7011; ed tel (509) 997-7011; gen fax (509) 997-3277; adv fax (509) 997-3277; ed fax (509) 997-3277; disp adv e-mail sales@methowvalleynews.com; class adv e-mail advertising@methowvalleynews.com; ed e-mail editor@methowvalleynews.com; web site www.methowvalleynews.com
Circulation: 3,000pd, 35fr; Sworn/Estimate/ Non-Audited
Advertising rate: Open inch rate $8.50
Established: 1903
Group: MVN Publishing LLC
Digital Platform - Mobile: Apple, Android, Windows
Digital Platform - Tablet: Apple iOS, Android, Windows 7
Pub./Ed. .... Don Nelson
Mechanical Specifications: Type page 12 x 21; E - 6 cols, 2, 1/4 between; A - 6 cols, 2, 1/4 between; C - 6 cols, 2, 1/4 between.Equipment & Software: Hardware — 7-IBM; Software — InDesign CS 5.5
Delivery Method: Mail, Newsstand
Areas Served: 98856, 98862, 98834, 98833, 98814, 98846

VASHON

VASHON-MAURY ISLAND BEACHCOMBER (WED)
17141 Vashon Hwy SW, Ste B, Vashon, WA, 98070-4603, King, USA; gen tel (206) 463-9195; adv tel (206) 463-9195; ed tel (206) 463-9195; gen fax (206) 673.8288; adv fax (206) 463-6122; ed fax (206) 673.8288; disp adv e-mail publisher@vashonbeachcomber.com; class adv e-mail sriemer@vashonbeachcomber.com; ed e-mail editor@vashonbeachcomber.com; web site www.vashonbeachcomber.com
Circulation: 2,807pd, 20fr; CAC
Advertising rate: Open inch rate $14.52
Established: 1957
Group: Black Press Group Ltd.
Sound Publishing, Inc.
Digital Platform - Mobile: Apple, Android, Windows, Blackberry
Digital Platform - Tablet: Apple iOS, Android, Windows 7, Blackberry Tablet OS, Kindle, Nook, Kindle Fire
Pub. .... Daralyn Anderson
Nat'l Sales Dir. .... Stephen Barrett
Mechanical Specifications: Type page 10 1/4 x 21; E - 6 cols, 1 7/12, between; A - 6 cols, 1 7/12, between; C - 10 cols, 1 1/3, between. Equipment & Software: Hardware — APP/ iMac; Presses — WPC; Software — QPS/ QuarkXPress.
Delivery Method: Mail, Newsstand, Carrier, Racks
Areas Served: King County

WAITSBURG

THE TIMES (THUR)
PO Box 97, Waitsburg, WA, 99361-0097, Walla Walla, USA; gen tel (509) 337-6631; adv tel (509) 337-6631; ed tel (509) 337-6631; gen fax (509) 337-6045; adv fax (509) 337-6045; ed fax (509) 337-6045; disp adv e-mail advertising@waitsburgtimes.com; class adv e-mail publisher@waitsburgtimes.com; ed e-mail editor@waitsburgtimes.com; web site www.waitsburgtimes.com
Advertising rate: Open inch rate $6.95
Established: 1877
Digital Platform - Mobile: Apple, Android, Windows, Blackberry
Digital Platform - Tablet: Apple iOS, Android, Windows 7, Blackberry Tablet OS
Pub. .... Imbert Matthee
Ed. .... Ken Graham
Adv. Mgr. .... Larry Davidson
Delivery Method: Mail, Racks
Areas Served: Walla Walla County

WESTPORT

SOUTH BEACH BULLETIN (THUR)
PO Box 1395, Westport, WA, 98595-1395, Grays Harbor, USA; gen tel (360) 268-0736; adv tel (360) 537-3920; ed tel (360) 268-0736; disp adv e-mail mbagwell@southbeachbulletin.com; class adv e-mail baue@southbeachbulletin.com; ed e-mail southbeachbulletin@comcast.net; web site www.southbeachbulletin.com
Circulation: 4,490fr; CAC
Advertising rate: Open inch rate $7.25
Established: 1993
Group: Sound Publishing Inc.
Digital Platform - Mobile: Apple
Digital Platform - Tablet: Apple iOS
Ed./Gen. Mgr. .... Barb Aue
Adv. Dir. .... Mary Anne Bagwell
Publisher .... Stanley Woody
Mechanical Specifications: Standard Broadsheet
Delivery Method: Racks
Areas Served: Grays Harbor and North Pacific County

WHITE SALMON

THE ENTERPRISE (THUR)
220 E Jewett Blvd, White Salmon, WA, 98672-3000, Klickitat, USA; gen tel (509) 493-2112; adv tel (509) 493-2112; ed tel (509) 493-2112; gen fax (509) 493-2399; adv fax (509) 493-2399; ed fax (509) 493-2399; disp adv e-mail ebakke@eaglenewspapers.com; class adv e-mail amarra@whitesalmonenterprise.com; ed e-mail amarra@whitesalmonenterprise.com; web site www.whitesalmonenterprise.com
Advertising rate: Open inch rate $6.30
Established: 1903
Group: Eagle Newspapers, Inc.
Digital Platform - Mobile: Apple, Android, Windows
Digital Platform - Tablet: Apple iOS, Android, Windows 7
Pub. ..... Elaine Bakke
Ed. / Sports Ed. ..... Sverre Bakke
Class. / Circ. Mgr. ..... Janet Barnes
Reporter ..... Michelle Scott
Delivery Method: Mail, Newsstand
Areas Served: White Salmon and Bingen

WILBUR

WILBUR REGISTER (THUR)
110 NE Main St, Wilbur, WA, 99185-5115, Lincoln, USA; gen tel (509) 647-5551; gen fax (509) 647-5552; disp adv e-mail wilburregister@centurytel.net; class adv e-mail wilburregister@centurytel.net; ed e-mail wilburregister@centurytel.net
Circulation: 1,000pd,; Sworn/Estimate/Non-Audited
Advertising rate: Open inch rate $5.50
Established: 1889
Pub. ..... Frank Stedman
Delivery Method: Mail, Newsstand
Areas Served: Lincoln County

WOODINVILLE

THE WOODINVILLE WEEKLY (MON)
16932 Wdnvl Red Rd NE, Ste A101, Woodinville, WA, 98072-6980, King, USA; gen tel (425) 483-0606; adv tel (425) 483-0606; ed tel (425) 483-0606; gen fax (425) 486-7593; adv fax (425) 486-7593; ed fax (425) 486-7593; disp adv e-mail sales@woodinville.com; class adv e-mail sales@woodinville.com; ed e-mail editor@woodinville.com; web site www.nwnews.com
Circulation: 17,700fr; Sworn/Estimate/Non-Audited
Advertising rate: Open inch rate $20.25
Established: 1976
Digital Platform - Mobile: Apple, Android, Windows, Blackberry
Digital Platform - Tablet: Apple iOS, Android, Windows 7, Blackberry Tablet OS, Kindle, Nook, Kindle Fire
Pub. ..... Julie Boselly
Mechanical Specifications: Type page 10 1/4 x 16; 6 cols, 1 1/2, 1/4 between
Delivery Method: Mail, Racks
Areas Served: 98072, 98077, 98014, 98019, 98011, 98021

YAKIMA

YAKIMA VALLEY BUSINESS TIMES (FRI)
416 S 3rd St, Yakima, WA, 98901-2834, Yakima, USA; gen tel (509) 457-4886; adv tel (509) 457-4886; ed tel (509) 457-4886; gen fax (509) 457-5214; adv fax (509) 457-5214; ed fax (509) 457-5214; disp adv e-mail sales@yvpub.com; class adv e-mail ads@yvpub.com; ed e-mail news@yvpub.com; web site www.yvpub.com
Advertising rate: Open inch rate $8.50
Established: 1997
Group: Yakima Valley Newspapers LLC
Digital Platform - Mobile: Windows
Digital Platform - Tablet: Windows 7
Pub. ..... Bruce Smith
Ed. ..... Erick Peterson
Delivery Method: Mail, Racks
Areas Served: Yakima County

YELM

NISQUALLY VALLEY NEWS (FRI)
106 Plaza Dr SE, Yelm, WA, 98597-8841, Thurston, USA; gen tel (360) 458-2681; adv tel (360) 458-2681; ed tel (360) 458-2681; gen fax (360) 458-5741; adv fax (360) 458-5741; ed fax (360) 458-5741; disp adv e-mail advertise@yelmonline.com; class adv e-mail class2@yelmonline.com; ed e-mail mwagar@yelmonline.com; web site www.yelmonline.com
Circulation: 4,000pd,; Sworn/Estimate/Non-Audited
Advertising rate: Open inch rate $19.44
Established: 1922
Digital Platform - Mobile: Apple, Android, Windows, Blackberry
Digital Platform - Tablet: Apple iOS, Android, Windows 7, Blackberry Tablet OS, Kindle, Nook, Kindle Fire
Pub./Ed. ..... Michael Wagar
Assistant Ed. ..... Tyler Huey
Adv. Mgr. ..... Angie Evans
Office Mgr. ..... Kim Proffit
Pub./Ed. ..... Keven R. Graves
Production Lead ..... Nicole Kiourkas
Mechanical Specifications: Type page 11 3/5 x ; E - 6 cols, 2, between; A - 6 cols, 3 3/4, between; C - 8 cols, 1 1/3, between.Equipment & Software: Hardware — APP/Mac.
Delivery Method: Mail, Newsstand, Racks
Areas Served: 98597, 98576, 98580, 98589, 98328

WEST VIRGINIA

BERKELEY SPRINGS

THE MORGAN MESSENGER (WED)
16 N Mercer St, Berkeley Springs, WV, 25411-1587, Morgan, USA; gen tel (304) 258-1800; gen fax (304) 258-8441; disp adv e-mail ads@morganmessenger.com; class adv e-mail ads@morganmessenger.com; ed e-mail news@morganmessenger.com; web site www.morganmessenger.com
Circulation: 4,800pd,; Sworn/Estimate/Non-Audited
Advertising rate: Open inch rate $7.50
Established: 1893
Digital Platform - Mobile: Apple, Android, Windows, Blackberry
Digital Platform - Tablet: Apple iOS, Android, Windows 7, Blackberry Tablet OS, Kindle, Nook, Kindle Fire
Adv. Mgr./Mng. Ed. ..... Sandy Buzzerd
Ed. ..... Kate Shunney
Mechanical Specifications: Type page 12 1/2 x 21; E - 6 cols, 1 3/4, 3/16 between; A - 6 cols, 1 3/4, 3/16 between; C - 8 cols, 1 1/4, 3/16 between.Equipment & Software: Hardware — APP/Mac; Presses — WPC/Web Leader; Software — QPS/QuarkXPress 7
Delivery Method: Mail, Newsstand
Areas Served: Morgan County

BUCKHANNON

THE RECORD DELTA (MON, WED, FRI)
2B Clarksburg Rd, Buckhannon, WV, 26201-8461, Upshur, USA; gen tel (304) 472-2800; adv tel (304) 472-2800; ed tel (304) 472-2800 ext. 24; gen fax (304) 472-0537; adv fax (304) 472-0537; ed fax (304) 472-0537; disp adv e-mail ads@recorddeltaonline.com; class adv e-mail ads@recorddeltaonline.com; ed e-mail brian@recorddeltaonline.com; web site www.therecorddelta.com
Circulation: 4,304pd,; Sworn/Estimate/Non-Audited
Advertising rate: Open inch rate $13.30
Group: News Media Corp.
Digital Platform - Mobile: Apple, Android, Windows, Blackberry
Digital Platform - Tablet: Apple iOS, Android, Windows 7, Blackberry Tablet OS, Kindle, Nook, Kindle Fire
Pub. ..... Tammy Lyons
Ed. ..... Brian Bergsstrom
Prodn. Mgr. ..... Carol Atkins
Delivery Method: Mail, Newsstand
Areas Served: Upshur County

CHARLES TOWN

SPIRIT OF JEFFERSON (WED)
114 N Charles St, Charles Town, WV, 25414-1508, Jefferson, USA; gen tel (304) 725-2046; adv tel (304) 725-2046; ed tel (304) 725-2046; gen fax (304) 728-6856; adv fax (304) 728-6856; ed fax (304) 728-6856; disp adv e-mail mary@spiritofjefferson.com; class adv e-mail ads@spiritofjefferson.com; ed e-mail editor@spiritofjefferson.com; web site www.spiritofjefferson.com
Circulation: 5,000pd, 63fr; Sworn/Estimate/Non-Audited
Advertising rate: Open inch rate $6.75
Established: 1844
Group: Jefferson Publishing Co.Editions: (52)
Digital Platform - Mobile: Apple, Android, Windows, Blackberry
Digital Platform - Tablet: Apple iOS, Android, Windows 7, Blackberry Tablet OS, Kindle, Nook, Kindle Fire
Pres./Pub. ..... Craig E. See
Ed. ..... Robert Snyder
Adv. Mgr. ..... Mary BurnsEquipment & Software: Hardware — APP/iMac, APP/Mac G4; Software — Adobe/PageMaker 6.5.
Delivery Method: Mail, Newsstand, Carrier, Racks
Areas Served: Jefferson County

CLAY

CLAY COUNTY FREE PRESS (WED)
136 MAIN ST, Clay, WV, 25043, Clay, USA; gen tel (304) 587-4250; adv tel (304) 587-4250; ed tel (304) 587-4250; gen fax (304) 587-7300; adv fax (304) 587-7300; ed fax (304) 587-7300; disp adv e-mail news@claycountyfreepress.com; class adv e-mail advertising@claycountyfreepress.com; ed e-mail news@claycountyfreepress.com; web site www.claycountyfreepress.com
Circulation: 3,500pd,; Sworn/Estimate/Non-Audited
Advertising rate: Open inch rate $6.00
Group: Mountain Media
Digital Platform - Mobile: Windows
Pub./Ed. ..... Marti Marshall
Mechanical Specifications: Type page 13 x 21; E - 6 cols, 2, between; A - 6 cols, 2, between; C - 7 cols, 1 3/4, between.Equipment & Software: Hardware — PCs; Software — In Design CS3, Microsoft/Windows 98.
Delivery Method: Mail, Newsstand
Areas Served: Clay County

ELIZABETH

WIRT COUNTY JOURNAL (WED)
1 Midway Plaza, Elizabeth, WV, 26143, Wirt, USA; gen tel (304) 275-8981; adv tel (304) 275-8981; ed tel (304) 275-8981; gen fax (304) 275-8981; adv fax (304) 275-8981; ed fax (304) 275-8981; disp adv e-mail advertising@wirtjournal.com; class adv e-mail advertising@wirtjournal.com; ed e-mail news@wirtjournal.com; web site www.wirtjournal.com
Circulation: 2,600pd, 60fr; USPS
Advertising rate: Open inch rate $3.50
Established: 1907
Digital Platform - Mobile: Apple, Android, Windows, Blackberry
Digital Platform - Tablet: Apple iOS, Android, Windows 7, Blackberry Tablet OS, Kindle, Nook, Kindle Fire
Pub. ..... James McGoldrick
Mechanical Specifications: 13"x21/5"
Delivery Method: Mail, Newsstand
Areas Served: Wirt County

GLENVILLE

THE GLENVILLE DEMOCRAT/ PATHFINDER (THUR)
PO Box 458, 208 N Court St, Glenville, WV, 26351-0458, Gilmer, USA; gen tel (304) 462-7309; adv tel (304) 462-7309; ed tel (304) 462-7309; gen fax (304) 462-7300; adv fax (304) 462-7300; ed fax (304) 462-7300; disp adv e-mail glenvillenews@gmail.com; class adv e-mail rockbender@hotmail.com; ed e-mail glenvillenews@gmail.com; web site www.glenvillenews.com
Circulation: 3,200pd, 500fr; Sworn/Estimate/Non-Audited
Advertising rate: Open inch rate $5.00
Established: 1892
Digital Platform - Mobile: Apple, Windows
Pub./Sr. Ed./Owner ..... David H. Corcoran Sr.
General Manager ..... David Corcoran Jr.
Bus. Mgr. ..... Patricia Golden
Receptionist/Circulation Manager.... Sara Wise
Mechanical Specifications: Type page 13 x 21 1/2; E - 5 cols, 2 3/8, 1/6 between; A - 6 cols, 2, 1/6 between; C - 6 cols, 2, 1/6 between.
Delivery Method: Mail, Newsstand, Carrier
Areas Served: Gilmer County and surrounding counties

THE GLENVILLE PATHFINDER (THUR)
108 N Court St, Glenville, WV, 26351-1215, Gilmer, USA; gen tel (304) 462-7309; adv tel (304) 462-7309; ed tel (304) 462-7309; gen fax (304) 462-7300; adv fax (304) 462-7300; ed fax (304) 462-7300; disp adv e-mail glenvillenews@gmail.com; class adv e-mail glenvillenews@gmail.com; ed e-mail glenvillenews@gmail.com; web site www.glenvillenews.com
Circulation: 1,500pd, 300fr; Sworn/Estimate/Non-Audited
Advertising rate: Open inch rate $5.00
Established: 1892
Digital Platform - Mobile: Apple, Windows
Pub./Sr. Ed./Owner ..... David H. Corcoran Sr.
Gen. Mgr. ..... David Corcoran Jr.
Bus. Mgr. ..... Patricia Golden
Receptionist/Circulation Clerk ..... Sara Wise
Mechanical Specifications: Type page 13 1/2 x 21 1/2; E - 5 cols, 2 3/8, 1/6 between; A - 6 cols, 2, 1/6 between; C - 6 cols, 2, 1/6 between. Equipment & Software: Hardware — Mac Computers and Printers
Delivery Method: Mail, Newsstand, Carrier
Areas Served: WV, OH, PA, VA, TN, TX, WA, WI, FL, MD, DC, NY zip codes

GRAFTON

MOUNTAIN STATESMAN (MON, WED, FRI)
914 W Main St, Grafton, WV, 26354-1028, Taylor, USA; gen tel (304) 265-3333; adv tel (304) 265-3333 ext. 20; ed tel (304) 265-3333; gen fax (304) 265-3342; adv fax (304) 265-3342; ed fax (304) 265-3342; disp adv e-mail gftemail@aol.com; class adv e-mail gftemail@aol.com; ed e-mail editor@mountainstatesman.com; web site www.mountainstatesman.com
Circulation: 3,300pd, 20fr; Sworn/Estimate/Non-Audited
Advertising rate: Open inch rate $12.53
Group: News Media Corp.
Digital Platform - Mobile: Apple, Android, Windows
Digital Platform - Tablet: Apple iOS, Android, Windows 7, Blackberry Tablet OS, Kindle,

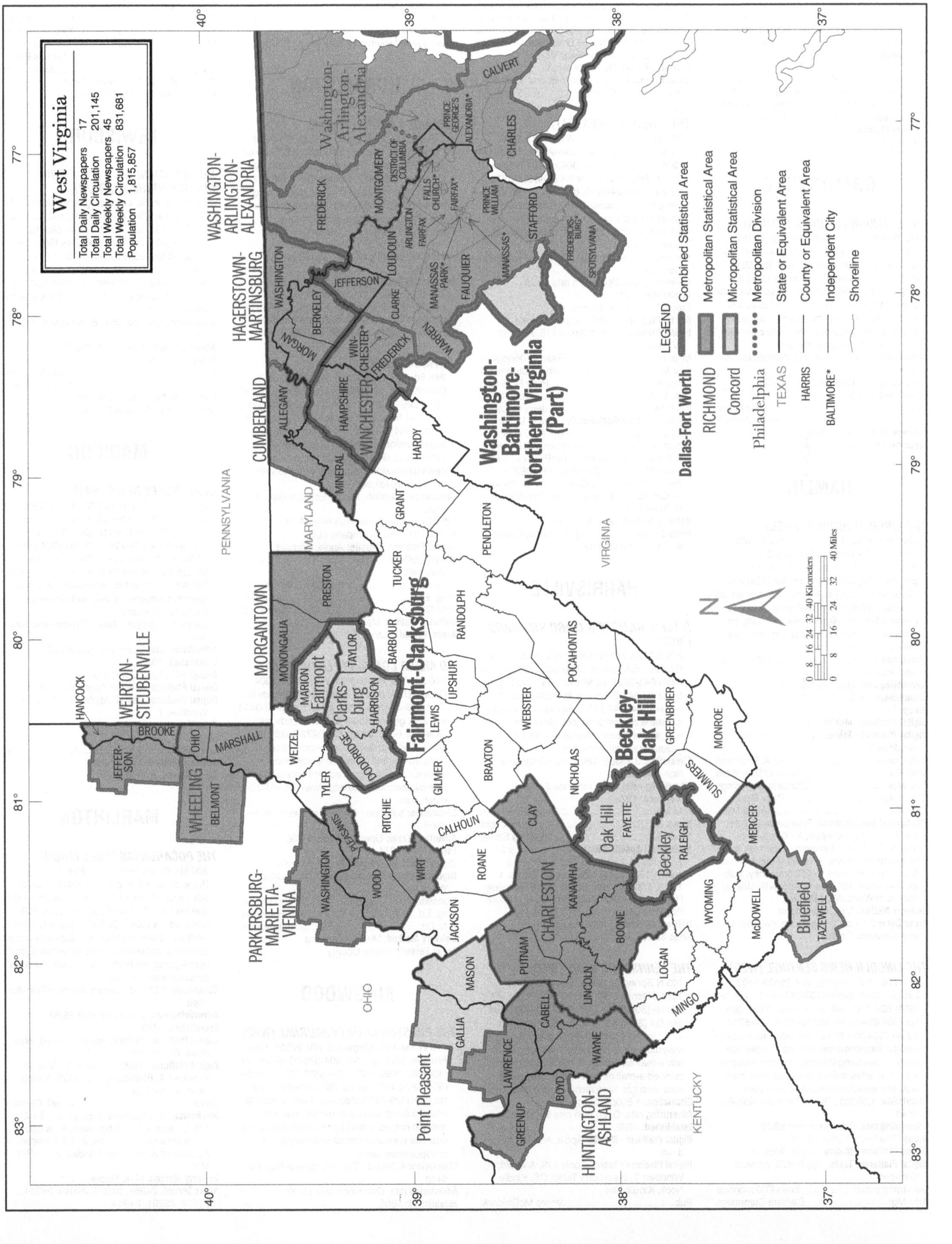
West Virginia
Total Daily Newspapers 17
Total Daily Circulation 201,145
Total Weekly Newspapers 45
Total Weekly Circulation 831,681
Population 1,815,857
LEGEND
Dallas-Fort Worth Combined Statistical Area
RICHMOND Metropolitan Statistical Area
Concord Micropolitan Statistical Area
Philadelphia Metropolitan Division
TEXAS State or Equivalent Area
HARRIS County or Equivalent Area
BALTIMORE* Independent City
Shoreline
Washington-Baltimore-Northern Virginia (Part)
Washington-Arlington-Alexandria
WASHINGTON-ARLINGTON-ALEXANDRIA
HAGERSTOWN-MARTINSBURG
CUMBERLAND
WINCHESTER
MORGANTOWN
WEIRTON-STEUBENVILLE
WHEELING
Fairmont-Clarksburg
Fairmont
Clarks-burg
PARKERSBURG-MARIETTA-VIENNA
CHARLESTON
Beckley-Oak Hill
Oak Hill
Beckley
Bluefield
Point Pleasant
HUNTINGTON-ASHLAND
PENNSYLVANIA
MARYLAND
VIRGINIA
OHIO
KENTUCKY
0 8 16 24 32 40 Kilometers
0 8 16 24 32 40 Miles
N

Nook, Kindle Fire
Pub.. Jean Metz
Ed. ....Robert Jennings
Circ. Mgr.............................. Monica Robinson
Mechanical Specifications: Type page 13 x 21 1/2; E - 6 cols, 2 1/10, between; A - 6 cols, 2 1/10, between; C - 8 cols, 1 1/2, between. Equipment & Software: Hardware — APP/ Power Mac 8100, IBM/486; Presses — WPC/ Web Leader; Software — APP/Mac System.
Delivery Method: Mail, Newsstand
Areas Served: Taylor County

GRANTSVILLE

THE CALHOUN CHRONICLE (THUR)

PO Box 400, Grantsville, WV, 26147-0400, Calhoun, USA; gen tel (304) 354-6917; adv tel (304) 354-6917; ed tel (304) 354-6917; gen fax (304) 354-6917; adv fax (304) 354-6917; ed fax (304) 354-6917; disp adv e-mail contact@calhounchronicle.com; class adv e-mail office@calhounchronicle.com; ed e-mail contact@calhounchronicle.com; web site www.calhounchronicle.com
Circulation: 2,800pd,; Sworn/Estimate/Non-Audited
Advertising rate: Open inch rate $4.00
Established: 1883
Pub.. Helen Morris
Ed. .... Newton Nichols
Delivery Method: Mail, Racks
Areas Served: Calhoun County

HAMLIN

THE LINCOLN JOURNAL (WED)

328 Walnut St, Hamlin, WV, 25523-1403, Lincoln, USA; gen tel (304) 824-5101; adv tel (304) 824-5101; ed tel (304) 824-5101; gen fax (304) 824-5210; adv fax (304) 824-5210; ed fax (304) 824-5210; disp adv e-mail advertising@lincolnjournal.com; class adv e-mail advertising@lincolnjournal.com; ed e-mail editor@lincolnjournal.com; web site www.lincolnjournal.com
Circulation: 5,625pd, 12,875fr; Sworn/Estimate/ Non-Audited
Advertising rate: Open inch rate $9.90
Established: 1903
Group: The Lincoln Journal, Inc.
Digital Platform - Mobile: Apple, Android
Digital Platform - Tablet: Apple iOS, Android, Windows 7
Pub./Owner......................Thomas A. Robinson
Mng. Ed.............................. Sean O'Donoghue
Adv. Mgr............................ Barbara Cummings
Office Mgr. ....Patty Robinson
Circ. Mgr...................................... Verona Miller
Mechanical Specifications: Type page 12 x 21 1/2; E - 6 cols, between; A - 6 cols, between; C - 9 cols, between.Equipment & Software: Hardware — 6-APP/Mac, Motorola/ Mac Clone; Presses — G/Community; Software — Multi-Ad/Creator, Adobe/Illustrator, Microsoft/Word, Word Perfect.
Delivery Method: Mail, Newsstand
Areas Served: Lincoln, Logan, Boone, Cabell, and Kanawha County

THE LINCOLN NEWS SENTINEL (WED)

328 Walnut St, Hamlin, WV, 25523-1403, Lincoln, USA; gen tel (304)824-5101; adv tel (304) 824-5101; ed tel (304)824-5101; gen fax (304)824-5210; adv fax (304)824-5210; ed fax (304)824-5210; disp adv e-mail advertising@lincolnnewssentinel.com; class adv e-mail advertising@lincolnnewssentinel.com; ed e-mail editor@lincolnnewssentinel.com; web site www.lincolnnewssentinel.com
Circulation: 1,350pd,; Sworn/Estimate/Non-Audited
Advertising rate: Open inch rate $9.25
Group: The Lincoln Journal, Inc.
Digital Platform - Mobile: Apple, Android
Digital Platform - Tablet: Apple iOS, Android, Windows 7
Managing Editor .... Sean O'Donoghue
Adv. Mgr............................ Barbara Cummings
Office Mgr. ....Patty Robinson
Circ. Mgr.................. Verona MillerEquipment & Software: Hardware — 6-APP/Mac, Motorola/ Mac Clone; Presses — G; Software — QPS/ QuarkXPress, Adobe/PageMaker.
Delivery Method: Mail, Newsstand
Areas Served: Lincoln, Logan, Boone, Cabell, and Kanawha County

THE LINCOLN TIMES (SAT)

328 Walnut St, Hamlin, WV, 25523-1403, Lincoln, USA; gen tel (304)824-5101; adv tel (304)824-5101; ed tel (304)824-5101; gen fax (304)824-5210; adv fax (304)824-5210; ed fax (304)824-5210; disp adv e-mail advertising@lincolnjournal.com; class adv e-mail advertising@lincolnjournal.com; ed e-mail editor@lincolnjournal.com; web site www.lincolnjournal.com
Circulation: 5,461pd, 12,638fr; Sworn/Estimate/ Non-Audited
Advertising rate: Open inch rate $9.25
Established: 1901
Group: The Lincoln Journal, Inc.
Digital Platform - Mobile: Apple, Android
Digital Platform - Tablet: Apple iOS, Android, Windows 7
Mng. Ed.............................. Sean O'Donoghue
Adv. Mgr............................ Barbara Cummings
Office Mgr. ....Patty Robinson
Circ. Mgr...................................... Verona Miller
Publisher................................ Jerry G. Leedy
Mechanical Specifications: Type page 13 1/4 x 21 1/2; E - 6 cols, between; A - 6 cols, between; C - 10 cols, between.Equipment & Software: Hardware — 8-APP/Mac, 1-Motorola/Mac Clone, Zip drive, XYQUEST/ drives; Presses — G/Community; Software — QPS/QuarkXPress, Adobe/PageMaker, Multi-Ad/Creator.
Delivery Method: Mail, Newsstand
Areas Served: Lincoln, Logan, Boone, Cabell, and Kanawha County

HARRISVILLE

RITCHIE GAZETTE & CAIRO STANDARD (WED)

200 E Main St, Harrisville, WV, 26362-1204, Ritchie, USA; gen tel (304) 643-2221; adv tel (304) 643-2221; ed tel (304) 643-2221; gen fax (304) 643-2156; adv fax (304) 643-2156; ed fax (304) 643-2156; disp adv e-mail ads-gazette@zoominternet.net; class adv e-mail adsgazette@zoominternet.net; ed e-mail gazette@zoominternet.net
Circulation: 3,333pd, 18fr; Sworn/Estimate/ Non-Audited
Advertising rate: Open inch rate $4.75
Established: 1873
Adv. Mgr................................Debbie Frederick
News Ed. ....Torie Knight
Prodn. Mgr. ....Denise Shiflet
Mechanical Specifications: Type page 12 x 21; E - 6 cols, 1 13/16, 5/32 between; A - 6 cols, 1 13/16, 5/32 between; C - 6 cols, 1 13/16, 5/32 between.Equipment & Software: Hardware — APP/Mac; Software — Adobe/ PageMaker 6.5.
Delivery Method: Mail, Newsstand
Areas Served: Ritchie County

THE PENNSBORO NEWS (WED)

103 N Spring St, Harrisville, WV, 26362-1274, Ritchie, USA; gen tel (304)643-4947; adv tel (304)643-4947; ed tel (304)643-4947; gen fax (304)643-4717; adv fax (304)643-4717; ed fax (304)643-4717; disp adv e-mail advertising@ritchiecountynews.com; class adv e-mail advertising@ritchiecountynews.com; ed e-mail news@ritchiecountynews.com; web site www.ritchiecountynews.com
Circulation: 4,800pd, 32fr; USPS
Advertising rate: Open inch rate $4.50
Established: 1892
Digital Platform - Mobile: Apple, Android, Windows
Digital Platform - Tablet: Apple iOS, Android, Windows 7, Blackberry Tablet OS, Kindle, Nook, Kindle Fire
Pub.................................... James McGoldrick
Mechanical Specifications: 6 cols. (13) x 21.5 SAU
Delivery Method: Mail, Newsstand
Areas Served: Ritchie County

HUNTINGTON

HERALD & DISPATCH (SAT)

946 5th Ave, Huntington, WV, 25701-2004, Cabell, USA; gen tel (304) 526-2753; adv tel (304) 526-6696; ed tel (304) 526-2787; gen fax (304) 526-2857; adv fax (304) 526-2863; disp adv e-mail news@herald-dispatch.com; ed e-mail editor@herald-dispatch.com; web site http://www.herald-dispatch.com/
Circulation: 1,044pd, 6fr; Sworn/Estimate/ Non-Audited
Advertising rate: Open inch rate $6.20
Pub./Ed. ....Ed Dawson
Mechanical Specifications: Type page 13 x 20 1/2; E - 6 cols, 1 1/4, 1/6 between; A - 6 cols, 2, 1/6 between; C - 10 cols, 1 1/4, 1/12 between.Equipment & Software: Hardware — APP/Mac; Software — QPS/QuarkXPress.

PUTNAM HERALD (SAT)

946 5th Ave, Huntington, WV, 25701-2004, Cabell, USA; gen tel (304) 526-4000; adv tel (304) 526-2836; ed tel (304) 526-2798; gen fax (304) 526-2858; adv fax (304) 526-2858; ed fax (304) 526-2858; disp adv e-mail cjes-sup@heralddispatch.com; class adv e-mail LWADDELL@heralddispatch.com; ed e-mail news@heralddispatch.com; web site www.herald-dispatch.com
Circulation: 20,000fr; Sworn/Estimate/Non-Audited
Advertising rate: Open inch rate $6.30
Group: HD Media Company LLC
Digital Platform - Mobile: Apple, Android
Digital Platform - Tablet: Apple iOS, Android, Windows 7
Pub./Ed. ....Ed Dawson
Mng. Ed...Les Smith
Adv. Dir..Amy Howat
Delivery Method: Mail, Racks
Areas Served: Putnam County

HD MEDIA COMPANY LLC (WED, SAT)

946 5th Ave, Huntington, WV, 25701-2004, Cabell, USA; gen tel (304) 526-2798; adv tel (304)272-3433 ext. 234; ed tel (304)272-3433 ext. 232; gen fax (304) 526-2857; adv fax (304)272-6516; ed fax (304)272-6516; disp adv e-mail ruth@waynecountynews.com; class adv e-mail classified@waynecountynews.com; ed e-mail editor@waynecountynews.com; web site http://www.herald-dispatch.com
Circulation: 5,800pd,; Sworn/Estimate/Non-Audited
Advertising rate: Open inch rate $7.36
Established: 1874
Digital Platform - Mobile: Apple, Android
Digital Platform - Tablet: Apple iOS, Android, Windows 7
Consultant .... Tom George
Mng. Ed...................................... Rob Robinson
Adv. Dir...Ruth Adkins
Delivery Method: Mail, Newsstand
Areas Served: Wayne County

KINGWOOD

THE PRESTON COUNTY JOURNAL (WED)

110 W Main St, Kingwood, WV, 26537-1108, Preston, USA; gen tel (304)329-0090; adv tel (304)329-0090; ed tel (304)329-0090; gen fax (304)329-2450; adv fax (304)329-2450; ed fax (304)329-2450; disp adv e-mail ppitina@atlanticbb.net; class adv e-mail ppitina@atlanticbb.net; ed e-mail ppitina@atlanticbb.net; web site www.prestoncountynewspapers.com/ppi/index.shtml
Circulation: 4,700pd,; Sworn/Estimate/Non-Audited
Advertising rate: Open inch rate $5.00
Established: 1866
Group: Preston Publications, Inc.
Pub..Gary A. Bolyard
Ed. ....Tina M. Bolyard
Mng. Ed..Carol Peters
Gen. Mgr. .... Dennis Peters
Editor ....John Dahlia
Delivery Method: Mail, Newsstand
Areas Served: Preston County

LEWISBURG

SHINNSTON NEWS & HARRISON COUNTY JOURNAL (THUR)

122 N Court St, Lewisburg, WV, 24901-1159, Greenbrier, USA; gen tel (304) 592-1030; adv tel (304) 592-1030; ed tel (304) 592-1030; gen fax (304) 592-0603; adv fax (304) 592-0603; ed fax (304) 592-0603; disp adv e-mail leah@mountainmedianews.com; class adv e-mail leah@mountainmedianews.com; ed e-mail newsandjournal@yahoo.com; web site www.shinnstonnews.com
Circulation: 3,800pd, 25fr; Sworn/Estimate/ Non-Audited
Advertising rate: Open inch rate $7.00
Group: Mountain Media
Ed. .... Leigh Merrifield
Publisher................................ Michael Showell
Delivery Method: Mail, Newsstand
Areas Served: Harrison County

MADISON

COAL VALLEY NEWS (WED)

350 Main St, Madison, WV, 25130-1293, Boone, USA; gen tel (304)369-1165; adv tel (304)369-1165; ed tel (304)369-1165; gen fax (304)369-1166; adv fax (304)369-1166; ed fax (304)369-1166; disp adv e-mail MBush@civitasmedia.com; class adv e-mail SChampion@civitasmedia.com; ed e-mail fpace@civitasmedia.com; web site www.coalvalleynews.com
Circulation: 5,000pd,; Sworn/Estimate/Non-Audited
Advertising rate: Open inch rate $5.50
Established: 1925
Group: HD Media Company LLC
Digital Platform - Mobile: Apple, Android
Digital Platform - Tablet: Apple iOS, Android, Windows 7
Pub./Ed. ....Fred Pace
Mng. Ed.. Jani Newan
Gen. Mgr. ....Angie Alexander
Delivery Method: Mail, Racks
Areas Served: Boone County

MARLINTON

THE POCAHONTAS TIMES (THUR)

206 8th St, Marlinton, WV, 24954-1031, Pocahontas, USA; gen tel (304)799-4973; adv tel (304)799-4973; ed tel (304)799-4973; gen fax (304)799-6466; adv fax (304)799-6466; ed fax (304)799-6466; disp adv e-mail jnh@pocahontastimes.com; class adv e-mail clj@pocahotnastimes.com; ed e-mail jsgraham@pocahontastimes.com; web site www.pocahontastimes.com
Circulation: 4,500pd,; Sworn/Estimate/Non-Audited
Advertising rate: Open inch rate $5.87
Established: 1883
Digital Platform - Mobile: Apple, Android, Windows, Blackberry
Digital Platform - Tablet: Apple iOS, Android, Windows 7, Blackberry Tablet OS, Kindle, Nook, Kindle Fire
Editor ....Jaynell Graham
Mechanical Specifications: Type page 13 x 21 1/2; E - 6 cols, 2, 1/5 between; A - 6 cols, 2, 1/5 between; C - 6 cols, 2, 1/5 between. Equipment & Software: Hardware — APP/ Mac.
Delivery Method: Mail, Racks
Areas Served: 24954, 24924, 24946, 24934, 26209, 26291, 24944

MULLENS

MULLENS ADVOCATE (WED)
217 Moran Ave, Mullens, WV, 25882-1426, Wyoming, USA; gen tel (304)294-4144; adv tel (304) 294-4144; ed tel (304)294-4144; disp adv e-mail mullensadvocate@yahoo.com; class adv e-mail mullensadvocate@yahoo.com; ed e-mail mullensadvocate@yahoo.com
Circulation: 1,700pd,; Sworn/Estimate/Non-Audited
Advertising rate: Open inch rate $2.90
Established: 1913
Publisher.................................. Melissa Nester
Assistant Legal Editor............. Miranda Austin
Mechanical Specifications: Type page 12 x 21 1/2; E - 6 cols, 2, 1/4 between; A - 6 cols, 2, 1/4 between; C - 6 cols, 2, 1/4 between.
Delivery Method: Mail, Newsstand
Areas Served: Wyoming County

NEW MARTINSVILLE

WETZEL CHRONICLE (WED)
1100 3rd St, New Martinsville, WV, 26155-1500, Wetzel, USA; gen tel (304)455-3300; adv tel (304)455-3300; ed tel (304)455-3300; gen fax (304)455-1275; adv fax (304)455-1275; ed fax (304)455-1275; disp adv e-mail advertising@wetzelchronicle.com; class adv e-mail lnorthcraft@wetzelchronicle.com; ed e-mail bclutter@wetzelchronicle.com; web site www.wetzelchronicle.com
Circulation: 6,000pd, 106fr; Sworn/Estimate/Non-Audited
Advertising rate: Open inch rate $6.81
Group: Ogden Newspapers Inc.
Digital Platform - Mobile: Apple, Android
Digital Platform - Tablet: Apple iOS, Android, Windows 7
Pub... Brian Clutter
Ed.. Amy Witschey
Adv. Mgr.................................. Lisa Northcraft
Mechanical Specifications: Type page 13 x 22; E - 6 cols, 2 1/8, 1/8 between; A - 6 cols, 2 1/8, 1/8 between; C - 6 cols, 2 1/8, 1/8 between. Equipment & Software: Hardware — APP/Mac; Software — QPS/QuarkXPress 3.3.
Delivery Method: Mail, Newsstand
Areas Served: Wetzel County

OAK HILL

MONTGOMERY HERALD (WED)
417 Main St., Oak Hill, WV, 25901, Fayette, USA; gen tel (304) 442-4156; adv tel (304) 442-4156; ed tel (304) 442-4156; gen fax (304) 442-8753; adv fax (304) 442-8753; ed fax (304) 442-8753; disp adv e-mail fwood@register-herald.com; class adv e-mail mhnews@register-herald.com; ed e-mail ckeenan@register-herald.com; web site www.montgomery-herald.com
Circulation: 1,500pd, 184fr; Sworn/Estimate/Non-Audited
Advertising rate: Open inch rate $7.79
Group: Community Newspaper Holdings, Inc.
Digital Platform - Mobile: Apple, Android
Digital Platform - Tablet: Apple iOS, Android, Windows 7
Pub... Frank Wood
Ed.. Cheryl Keenan
Delivery Method: Mail, Newsstand
Areas Served: Fayette County

THE FAYETTE TRIBUNE (MON, THUR)
417 Main St, Oak Hill, WV, 25901, Fayette, USA; gen tel (304)469-3373; adv tel (304)469-3373; ed tel (304)469-3373; gen fax (304)469-4105; adv fax (304)469-4105; ed fax (304)469-4105; disp adv e-mail fwood@register-herald.com; class adv e-mail fwood@register-herald.com; ed e-mail ckeenan@register-herald.com; web site www.fayettetribune.com
Circulation: 2,200pd,; Sworn/Estimate/Non-Audited
Advertising rate: Open inch rate $7.79
Group: Community Newspaper Holdings, Inc.
Digital Platform - Mobile: Apple, Android
Digital Platform - Tablet: Apple iOS, Android, Windows 7
Pub... Frank Wood
Ed.. Cheryl Keenan
Retail Mgr................................ Debbie Maxwell
Delivery Method: Mail, Newsstand
Areas Served: Fayette County

PETERSBURG

GRANT COUNTY PRESS (TUES, SAT)
47 S Main St, Petersburg, WV, 26847-1766, Grant, USA; gen tel (304)257-1844; adv tel (304)257-1844; ed tel (304) 257-4833; gen fax (304)257-1691; adv fax (304)257-1691; ed fax (304) 257-1691; disp adv e-mail ads@grantcountypress.com; class adv e-mail ads@grantcountypress.com; ed e-mail news@grantcountyexpress.com; web site www.grantcountypress.com
Circulation: 3,700pd, 6,200fr; Sworn/Estimate/Non-Audited
Advertising rate: Open inch rate $10.00
Established: 1896
Digital Platform - Mobile: Apple
Digital Platform - Tablet: Other
Circ. Mgr.................................. Mary Simmons
Advertising Manager......................... Tara Pratt
Managing Editor..................... Camille Howard
Business Manager................... Peggy Hughes
Mechanical Specifications: Type page 13 x 21 1/2; E - 6 cols, 2 1/8, between; A - 6 cols, 2 1/8, between; C - 9 cols, 1 1/4, between. Equipment & Software: Hardware — MACs; Software — Phoitoshop, Quark Express. Multi Ad Creator,Dream Weaver
Delivery Method: Mail, Racks
Areas Served: 26847, 26855, 26833, 26731, 26726, 26866, 26884, 26814, 26886, 26804, 26710, 26743, 26739, 26720, 26707

PHILIPPI

THE BARBOUR DEMOCRAT (WED)
113 CHURCH ST, Philippi, WV, 26416, Barbour, USA; gen tel (304)457-2222; adv tel (304)457-2222; ed tel (304)457-2222; gen fax (304)457-2235; adv fax (304)457-2235; ed fax (304)457-2235; disp adv e-mail ads@barbourdemocratwv.com; class adv e-mail ads@barbourdemocratwv.com; ed e-mail news@barbourdemocratwv.com; web site www.barbourdemocratwv.com - 1,000(views)
Circulation: 5,301pd, 300fr; Sworn/Estimate/Non-Audited
Advertising rate: Open inch rate $4.75
Established: 1893
Owner.. Eric Cutright
Delivery Method: Mail, Newsstand
Areas Served: Barbour County

PINEVILLE

THE INDEPENDENT HERALD (WED)
PO Box 100, 100 Appalachian Hwy, Pineville, WV, 24874-0100, Wyoming, USA; gen tel (304)732-6060; adv tel (304)732-6060; ed tel (304)732-6060; gen fax (304)664-8225; adv fax (304)664-8225; ed fax (304)664-8225; disp adv e-mail MBush@civitasmedia.com; class adv e-mail SChampion@civitasmedia.com; ed e-mail fpace@civitasmedia.com; web site www.independentherald.com
Circulation: 2,500pd,; Sworn/Estimate/Non-Audited
Advertising rate: Open inch rate $4.25
Established: 1968
Group: HD Media Company LLC
Digital Platform - Mobile: Apple, Android
Digital Platform - Tablet: Apple iOS, Android, Windows 7
Pub./Ed.. Fred Pace
Delivery Method: Mail, Racks
Areas Served: Wyoming County

PRINCETON

PRINCETON TIMES (FRI)
213 S Walker St, Princeton, WV, 24740-2746, Mercer, USA; gen tel (304)425-8191; adv tel (304)327-2816; ed tel (304)425-2185; gen fax (304)487-1632; adv fax (304)487-1632; ed fax (304)487-1632; disp adv e-mail princetontimes@gmail.com; class adv e-mail princetontimes@gmail.com; ed e-mail ttoler@ptonline.net; web site www.ptonline.net
Circulation: 4,900pd,; Sworn/Estimate/Non-Audited
Advertising rate: Open inch rate $19.00
Group: Community Newspaper Holdings, Inc.
Digital Platform - Mobile: Apple, Android
Digital Platform - Tablet: Apple iOS, Android, Windows 7
Pub./Gen. Mgr............................. Tammie Toler
Adv. Dir.. Terri Hale
Pub.. Darryl Husdon
Delivery Method: Mail, Newsstand
Areas Served: Mercer County

RAVENSWOOD

JACKSON HERALD (TUES, THUR, SAT)
PO Box 38, 305 N Church St, Ravenswood, WV, 26164-0038, Jackson, USA; gen tel (304) 372-4222; adv tel (304) 372-4222; ed tel (304) 372-4222; gen fax (304) 372-5544; adv fax (304) 372-5544; ed fax (304) 372-5544; disp adv e-mail tmandrake@jacksonnewspapers.com; class adv e-mail classified@jacksonnewspapers.com; ed e-mail gmatics@jacksonnewspapers.com; web site www.jacksonnewspapers.com
Circulation: 6,500pd,; Sworn/Estimate/Non-Audited
Advertising rate: Open inch rate $7.00
Established: March 1, 1876
Group: GateHouse Media, Inc.
Digital Platform - Mobile: Apple
Digital Platform - Tablet: Apple iOS
Ed/Gen Mgr................................. Greg Matics
Website Mgr........................ Jennifer Patterson
Delivery Method: Mail, Carrier, Racks
Areas Served: Jackson County

THE JACKSON STAR NEWS (THUR, SAT)
PO Box 38, Ravenswood, WV, 26164-0038, Jackson, USA; gen tel (304) 372-4222; adv tel (304) 372-4222; ed tel (304) 372-4222; gen fax (304) 372-5544; adv fax (304) 372-5544; ed fax (304) 372-5544; disp adv e-mail tmandrake@jacksonnewspapers.com; class adv e-mail classified@jacksonnewspapers.com; ed e-mail editor@jacksonnewspapers.com; web site www.jacksonnewspapers.com
Circulation: 6,000pd, 50fr; Sworn/Estimate/Non-Audited
Advertising rate: Open inch rate $7.00
Established: January 1, 1868
Group: GateHouse Media, Inc.
Digital Platform - Mobile: Apple
Digital Platform - Tablet: Apple iOS
Ed/Gen Mgr............................ Gregory Matics
Website Mgr........................ Jennifer Patterson
Delivery Method: Mail, Carrier, Racks
Areas Served: Jackson County

SAINT MARYS

PLEASANTS COUNTY LEADER (SAT)
206 George St, Saint Marys, WV, 26170-1024, Pleasants, USA; gen tel (304)684-2424; adv tel (304)684-2424; ed tel (304) 684-2424; disp adv e-mail advertising@oracleandleader.com; class adv e-mail advertsing@oracleandleader.com; ed e-mail news@oracleandleader.com ; web site www.oracleandleader.com
Circulation: 2,100pd,; USPS
Advertising rate: Open inch rate $6.50
Established: 1899
Digital Platform - Mobile: Apple, Android, Windows
Digital Platform - Tablet: Apple iOS, Android, Windows 7, Blackberry Tablet OS, Kindle, Nook, Kindle Fire
Pub..................................... James McGoldrick
Gen. Mgr.................................... Randa Gregg
Mechanical Specifications: Type page 13 x 21 1/2; E - 6 cols, 2, 1/6 between; A - 6 cols, 2, 1/6 between; C - 6 cols, 2, 1/6 between.
Delivery Method: Mail, Newsstand
Areas Served: Pleasants County

SHEPHERDSTOWN

THE SHEPHERDSTOWN CHRONICLE (FRI)
123C S Duke St, Shepherdstown, WV, 25443-1828, Jefferson, USA; gen tel (304)876-3380; adv tel (304)263-8931 ext. 121; ed tel (304)876-3380; gen fax (304)876-1957; adv fax (304)876-1957; ed fax (304)876-1957; disp adv e-mail kspielman@journal-news.net; class adv e-mail kcambrel@shepherdstownchronicle.com; ed e-mail tmilbourne@shepherdstownchronicle.com; web site www.shepherdstownchronicle.com
Advertising rate: Open inch rate $7.00
Group: Ogden Newspapers Inc.
Digital Platform - Mobile: Apple, Android
Digital Platform - Tablet: Apple iOS, Android
Ed.. Toni Milbourne
Ed. Assistant.............................. Kelly Cambrel
Adv. Rep............................. Karleen Spielman
Delivery Method: Mail, Newsstand, Racks
Areas Served: Berkeley and Jefferson County

SISTERSVILLE

TYLER STAR NEWS (WED)
720 Wells St, Sistersville, WV, 26175-1326, Tyler, USA; gen tel (304)652-4141; adv tel (304)652-4141; ed tel (304)652-4141; gen fax (304)652-1454; adv fax (304)652-1454; ed fax (304)652-1454; disp adv e-mail lnorthcraft@tylerstarnews.com ; class adv e-mail bclutter@tylerstarnews.com; ed e-mail editor@tylerstarnews.com; web site www.tylerstarnews.com
Circulation: 4,000pd,; Sworn/Estimate/Non-Audited
Advertising rate: Open inch rate $4.89
Group: Ogden Newspapers Inc.
Digital Platform - Mobile: Apple, Android
Digital Platform - Tablet: Apple iOS, Android, Windows 7
Pub... Brian Clutter
Ed.. Amy Witschey
Adv. Mgr.................................. Lisa Northcraft
Mechanical Specifications: Type page 13 x 22; E - 6 cols, 2 1/8, 1/8 between; A - 6 cols, 2 1/8, 1/8 between; C - 6 cols, 2 1/8, 1/8 between. Equipment & Software: Hardware — APP/Mac; Software — QPS/QuarkXPress 3.0.
Delivery Method: Mail, Newsstand
Areas Served: Tyler County

SPENCER

ROANE COUNTY REPORTER (THUR)
210 E Main St, Spencer, WV, 25276-1602, Roane, USA; gen tel (304)927-2360; adv tel (304)927-2360; ed tel (304)927-2360; gen fax (304)927-2361; adv fax (304)927-2361; ed fax (304)927-2361; disp adv e-mail dhedges@thetimesrecord.net; class adv e-mail sales@thetimesrecord.net; ed e-mail jcoop@thetimesrecord.net; web site www.smalltown-papers.com
Circulation: 3,145pd, 100fr; Sworn/Estimate/Non-Audited
Advertising rate: Open inch rate $6.78
Established: 1915
Group: Spencer Newspapers Inc.
Pub.. David J. Hedges
Ed.. Jim Cooper
Prodn. Mgr............................ Andrew Hedges
Sales Mgr.................................. Annie Hedges
Adv. Mgr.. Jim Lemon
Mechanical Specifications: 6 col (SAU) 13 inches

by 21-1/2 inchesEquipment & Software: Hardware — MacIntosh; Presses — King four-unit with four-high color stack; Software — adobe Creative Suite
Delivery Method: Mail, Newsstand
Areas Served: Roane County

THE TIMES RECORD (THUR)
210 E Main St, Spencer, WV, 25276-1602, Roane, USA; gen tel (304) 927-2360; adv tel (304) 927-2360; ed tel (304) 927-2360; gen fax (304) 927-2361; adv fax (304) 927-2361; ed fax (304) 927-2361; disp adv e-mail sales@thetimesrecord.net; class adv e-mail starr@thetimesrecord.net; ed e-mail jcoop@thetimesrecord.net
Circulation: 2,075pd, 25fr; Sworn/Estimate/Non-Audited
Advertising rate: Open inch rate $6.78
Established: 1888
Pub. .... David J. Hedges
Ed. .... Jim Cooper
Prod. Mgr. .... Andrew Hedges
Sales Mgr .... Annie Hedges
Mechanical Specifications: Type page 13 x 21 1/2; E - 6 cols, 2 1/16, 1/8 between; A - 6 cols, 2 1/16, 1/8 between; C - 6 cols, 2 1/16, 1/8 between.Equipment & Software: Hardware — APP/Mac; Presses — 6-KP; Software — Indesign/Photoshop
Delivery Method: Mail, Newsstand
Areas Served: Spencer/Roane County/25276

SUTTON

BRAXTON CITIZENS' NEWS (TUES)
501 Main St, Sutton, WV, 26601-1320, Braxton, USA; gen tel (304)765-5193; adv tel (304)765-5193; ed tel (304)765-5193; gen fax (304)765-2754; adv fax (304)765-2754; ed fax (304)765-2754; disp adv e-mail stevie@bcn-news.com; class adv e-mail stevie@bcn-news.com; ed e-mail editor@bcn-news.com; web site www.bcn-news.com
Circulation: 6,150pd,; Sworn/Estimate/Non-Audited
Advertising rate: Open inch rate $6.62
Established: 1976
Digital Platform - Mobile: Apple, Android
Digital Platform - Tablet: Apple iOS, Android, Windows 7
Pub./Ed. .... Ed Given
Delivery Method: Mail, Newsstand
Areas Served: Braxton County

BRAXTON DEMOCRAT-CENTRAL (FRI)
201 2nd St, Sutton, WV, 26601-1349, Braxton, USA; gen tel (304)765-5555; adv tel (304) 765-5555; ed tel (304) 765-5555; disp adv e-mail braxton@wvdsl.net; class adv e-mail braxton@wvdsl.net; ed e-mail braxton@mountain.net
Circulation: 4,900pd, 100fr; Sworn/Estimate/Non-Audited
Advertising rate: Open inch rate $3.65
Established: 1883
Pub. .... Craig A. Smith
Adv. Mgr. .... Brenda Tingler
Ed. .... Joan BiasEquipment & Software: Hardware — APP/Mac.
Delivery Method: Mail, Newsstand
Areas Served: Braxton County

UNION

MONROE WATCHMAN (THUR)
430 Main St, Union, WV, 24983, Monroe, USA; gen tel (304)772-3016; adv tel (304)772-3016; ed tel (304)772-3016; gen fax (304)772-4421; adv fax (304)772-4421; ed fax (304)772-4421; disp adv e-mail watchman2@earthlink.net; class adv e-mail watchman2@earthlink.net; ed e-mail watchman2@earthlink.net
Circulation: 4,050pd, 15fr; Sworn/Estimate/Non-Audited
Advertising rate: Open inch rate $6.00
Established: 1872
Pub./Gen. Mgr. .... Dale Mohler
Ed. .... H. Craig
Delivery Method: Mail, Newsstand
Areas Served: Monroe County

WEBSTER SPRINGS

WEBSTER ECHO (WED)
219 Back Fork St, Webster Springs, WV, 26288-1034, Webster, USA; gen tel (304)847-5828; adv tel (304)847-5828; ed tel (304)847-5828; gen fax (304)847-5991; adv fax (304)847-5991; ed fax (304)847-5991; disp adv e-mail websterecho@citlink.net; class adv e-mail websterecho@citlink.net; ed e-mail websterecho@citlink.net
Circulation: 2,825pd,; Sworn/Estimate/Non-Audited
Advertising rate: Open inch rate $3.80
Ed. .... Tom Clark
Delivery Method: Mail, Newsstand
Areas Served: Webster County

WEBSTER REPUBLICAN (WED)
219 Back Fork St, Webster Springs, WV, 26288-1034, Webster, USA; gen tel (304)847-5828; adv tel (304)847-5828; ed tel (304)847-5828; gen fax (304)847-5991; adv fax (304)847-5991; ed fax (304)847-5991; disp adv e-mail websterecho@citlink.net; class adv e-mail websterecho@citlink.net; ed e-mail websterecho@citlink.net
Circulation: 994pd,; Sworn/Estimate/Non-Audited
Advertising rate: Open inch rate $3.80
Ed. .... Tom Clark
Delivery Method: Mail, Newsstand
Areas Served: Webster County

WELCH

THE INDUSTRIAL NEWS (WED)
PO Box 569, Welch, WV, 24801-0569, McDowell, USA; gen tel (304)938-2142; adv tel (304)938-2142; ed tel (304)938-2142; gen fax (304)436-3146; adv fax (304)436-3146; ed fax (304)436-3146; disp adv e-mail rubyfmccoy@yahoo.com; class adv e-mail rubyfmccoy@yahoo.com; ed e-mail rubyfmccoy@yahoo.com
Circulation: 2,000pd,; Sworn/Estimate/Non-Audited
Advertising rate: Open inch rate $2.85
Established: 1926
Mng. Ed. .... Ruby McCoy
Adv. Mgr. .... Sheila Bailey
Pub. .... Gregory Spinella
Adv. Mgr. .... Missy Price
Delivery Method: Mail, Newsstand
Areas Served: McDowell County

THE WELCH NEWS (MON, WED, FRI)
125 Wyoming St, Welch, WV, 24801-2220, McDowell, USA; gen tel (304)436-3144; adv tel (304)436-3144; ed tel (304)436-3144; gen fax (304)436-3146; adv fax (304)436-3146; ed fax (304)436-3146; disp adv e-mail welchnews@frontiernet.net; class adv e-mail welchnews@frontiernet.net; ed e-mail welchnews@frontiernet.net
Circulation: 4,764pd,; Sworn/Estimate/Non-Audited
Advertising rate: Open inch rate $6.15
Pub. .... Gregory Spinella
Mng. Ed. .... Andrea Moorehead
Adv. Dir. .... Melissa McKinney
Circ. Mgr. .... Tom Molin
Mechanical Specifications: Type page 13 x 21 1/2; E - 6 cols, 2 1/16, 1/8 between; A - 6 cols, 2 1/16, 1/8 between; C - 9 cols, 1 3/8, 1/16 between.Equipment & Software: Hardware — APP/Mac; Presses — 5-G/Community.
Delivery Method: Mail, Newsstand
Areas Served: McDowell County

WEST UNION

THE HERALD RECORD (TUES)
177 Main St, West Union, WV, 26456-2019, Doddridge, USA; gen tel (304)873-1600; adv tel (304)873-1600; ed tel (304)873-1600; gen fax (304)873-2811; adv fax (304)873-2811; ed fax (304)873-2811; disp adv e-mail theheraldrecord1@gmail.com; class adv e-mail theheraldrecord1@gmail.com; ed e-mail theheraldrecord1@gmail.com
Circulation: 2,721pd, 31fr; Sworn/Estimate/Non-Audited
Advertising rate: Open inch rate $2.50
Established: 1878
Pub./Ed. .... Virginia Nicholson
Delivery Method: Mail, Newsstand
Areas Served: 26456, 26426, 26301, 26415, 26439, 26101, 26202

WESTON

WESTON DEMOCRAT (WED)
306 Main Ave, Weston, WV, 26452-2046, Lewis, USA; gen tel (304)269-1600; adv tel (304)269-1600; ed tel (304)269-1600; gen fax (304)269-4035; adv fax (304)269-4035; ed fax (304)269-4035; disp adv e-mail ads@westondemocrat.com; class adv e-mail classifiedlineads@westondemocrat.com; ed e-mail news@westondemocrat.com; web site www.westondemocrat.com
Circulation: 7,000pd, 88fr; Sworn/Estimate/Non-Audited
Advertising rate: Open inch rate $6.30
Established: 1867
Group: News Media Corp.
Digital Platform - Mobile: Apple, Android
Digital Platform - Tablet: Apple iOS, Android
Adv. Mgr. .... Connie Posey
Editor .... Melissa Toothman
Reporter .... Dusty Metzgar
Reporter .... Rebecca Young
Sports Reporter .... Alli Clark
Sports Reporter .... Tom Hall
Production Assistant .... Donna Prunty
Mechanical Specifications: Type page 13 5/8 x 20 1/2; E - 6 cols, 2 1/8, between; A - 6 cols, 2 1/8, between; C - 6 cols, 2 1/8, between. Equipment & Software: Hardware — APP/Mac, IBM; Software — Adobe/PageMaker 5.0, Adobe/Photoshop 5.0, Adobe/Acrobat Reader.
Delivery Method: Mail, Newsstand, Racks
Areas Served: 26452

WISCONSIN

AMERY

AMERY FREE PRESS (TUES)
215 Keller Ave S, Amery, WI, 54001-1275, Polk, USA; gen tel (715) 268-8101; adv tel (715) 268-8101; ed tel (715) 268-8101; gen fax (715) 268-5300; adv fax (715) 268-5300; ed fax (715) 268-5300; disp adv e-mail phumpal@theameryfreepress.com; class adv e-mail classifieds@theameryfreepress.com; ed e-mail editor@theameryfreepress.com; web site theameryfreepress.com
Circulation: 5,000pd,; Sworn/Estimate/Non-Audited
Advertising rate: Open inch rate $8.50
Established: 1895
Pub./Gen. Mgr. .... Steven R. Sondreal
Pub. .... Jerry Sondreal
Adv. Mgr. .... Pam Humpal
Mechanical Specifications: Type page 16 1/2 x 23.Equipment & Software: Hardware — APP/Mac; Presses — G; Software — Adobe/PageMaker.
Delivery Method: Mail, Newsstand
Areas Served: Polk County

APPLETON

NEWS-RECORD (WED)
306 W Washington St, Appleton, WI, 54911-5452, Outagamie, USA; gen tel (920)993-1000; adv tel (920)996-7224; ed tel (920)920-7224 x254; gen fax (920)722-4938; adv fax (920)722-4938; ed fax (920)722-4938; disp adv e-mail publisher@postcrescent.com; class adv e-mail gmagno@postcrescent.com; ed e-mail jmara@postcrescent.com; web site www.postcrescent.com
Circulation: 23,991fr; CVC
Advertising rate: Open inch rate $16.38
Established: 1961
Group: Gannett
Digital Platform - Mobile: Apple, Android
Digital Platform - Tablet: Apple iOS, Android, Windows 7
Exec. Ed. .... Dan Flannery
Mng. Ed. .... Jamie Mara
Sr. Dir. .... Amy Leitzke
Circ. Mgr .... Mark Johnson
Aud. Analyst. .... Larry Gallup
Pres. / Pub. .... Pamela Henson
Mechanical Specifications: Type page 11 x 13; E - 5 cols, between; A - 5 cols, between. Equipment & Software: Hardware — IBM, APP/Mac; Software — QPS/QuarkXPress.
Delivery Method: Mail, Racks
Areas Served: Winnebago County

ASHLAND

BAYFIELD COUNTY JOURNAL (THUR)
122 3rd St W, Ashland, WI, 54806-1661, Ashland, USA; gen tel (715) 682-2313; adv tel (715)682-2213; ed tel (715)682-2313; disp adv e-mail pressclass@ashlanddailypress.net; class adv e-mail pressclass@ashlanddailypress.net; ed e-mail pressclass@ashlanddailypress.net; web site www.apg-wi.com
Group: Adams Publishing Group, LLCJonathan Johnston

THE DAILY PRESS: COUNTY JOURNAL (THUR)
122 3rd St W, Ashland, WI, 54806-1661, Ashland, USA; gen tel (715) 682-2313; adv tel (715) 682-2313; ed tel (715) 682-2313; gen fax (715) 682-4699; adv fax (715) 682-4699; ed fax (715) 682-4699; disp adv e-mail pressclass@ashlanddailypress.net; class adv e-mail pressclass@ashlanddailypress.net; ed e-mail pressclass@ashlanddailypress.net; web site www.apg-wi.com
Circulation: 3,950pd, 25fr; Sworn/Estimate/Non-Audited
Advertising rate: Open inch rate $6.80
Digital Platform - Mobile: Apple, Android, Windows, Blackberry
Digital Platform - Tablet: Apple iOS, Android, Windows 7, Blackberry Tablet OS
Mng. Ed. .... Seth Carlson
Reg. Sales Mgr. .... David Thornberry
Mechanical Specifications: Type page 13 x 21 1/2; E - 6 cols, 2 1/16, 1/8 between; A - 6 cols, 2 1/16, 1/8 between; C - 6 cols, 2 1/16, 1/8 between.
Delivery Method: Mail
Areas Served: Bayfield County

BALDWIN

THE BALDWIN BULLETIN (TUES)
805 MAIN ST, Baldwin, WI, 54002, Saint Croix, USA; gen tel (715) 684-2484; adv tel (715) 684-2484; ed tel (715) 684-2484; gen fax (715) 684-4937; adv fax (715) 684-4937; ed fax (715) 684-4937; disp adv e-mail pehaw@baldwin-telecom.net; class adv e-mail pehaw@baldwin-telecom.net; ed e-mail pehaw@baldwin-telecom.net; web site www.baldwin-bulletin.com
Circulation: 2,050pd,; Sworn/Estimate/Non-Audited
Advertising rate: Open inch rate $7.50
Established: 1873

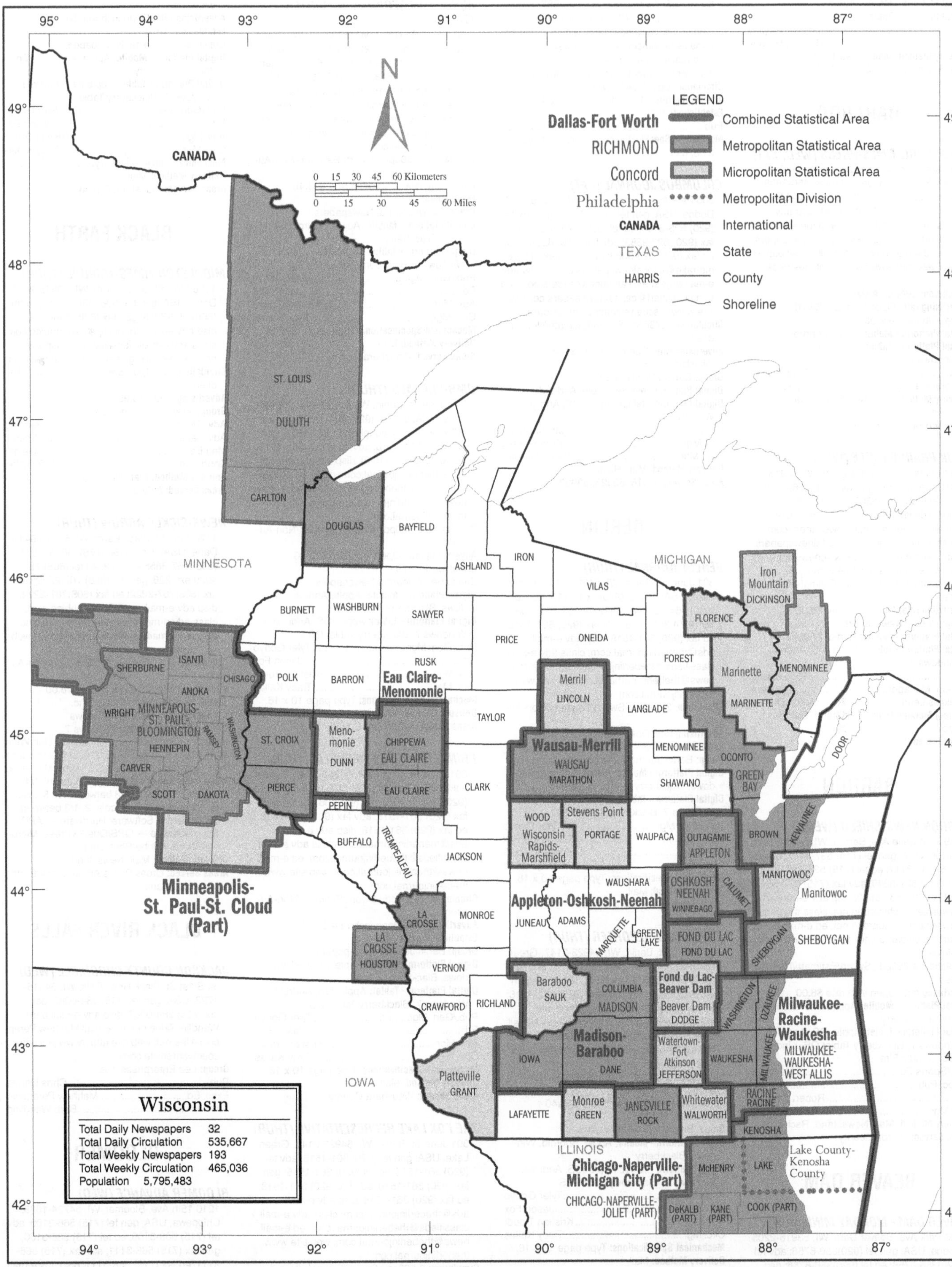
N
0 15 30 45 60 Kilometers
0 15 30 45 60 Miles
LEGEND
Dallas-Fort Worth Combined Statistical Area
RICHMOND Metropolitan Statistical Area
Concord Micropolitan Statistical Area
Philadelphia Metropolitan Division
CANADA International
TEXAS State
HARRIS County
Shoreline
CANADA
MINNESOTA
MICHIGAN
IOWA
ILLINOIS
ST. LOUIS
DULUTH
CARLTON
DOUGLAS
BAYFIELD
ASHLAND
IRON
VILAS
Iron Mountain
DICKINSON
FLORENCE
BURNETT
WASHBURN
SAWYER
PRICE
ONEIDA
FOREST
Marinette
MENOMINEE
MARINETTE
SHERBURNE
ISANTI
CHISAGO
ANOKA
WRIGHT
MINNEAPOLIS-ST. PAUL-BLOOMINGTON
HENNEPIN
RAMSEY
WASHINGTON
CARVER
SCOTT
DAKOTA
POLK
BARRON
RUSK
Eau Claire-Menomonie
Merrill
LINCOLN
LANGLADE
TAYLOR
ST. CROIX
PIERCE
Menomonie
DUNN
CHIPPEWA
EAU CLAIRE
Wausau-Merrill
WAUSAU
MARATHON
MENOMINEE
OCONTO
DOOR
SHAWANO
GREEN BAY
CLARK
PEPIN
BUFFALO
TREMPEALEAU
JACKSON
WOOD
Wisconsin Rapids-Marshfield
Stevens Point
PORTAGE
WAUPACA
OUTAGAMIE
APPLETON
BROWN
KEWAUNEE
MANITOWOC
Manitowoc
WAUSHARA
OSHKOSH-NEENAH
WINNEBAGO
CALUMET
Minneapolis-St. Paul-St. Cloud (Part)
LA CROSSE
MONROE
Appleton-Oshkosh-Neenah
JUNEAU
ADAMS
MARQUETTE
GREEN LAKE
FOND DU LAC
SHEBOYGAN
HOUSTON
VERNON
Baraboo
SAUK
COLUMBIA
MADISON
Fond du Lac-Beaver Dam
Beaver Dam
DODGE
WASHINGTON
OZAUKEE
Milwaukee-Racine-Waukesha
CRAWFORD
RICHLAND
Madison-Baraboo
IOWA
DANE
Watertown-Fort Atkinson
JEFFERSON
WAUKESHA
MILWAUKEE
MILWAUKEE-WAUKESHA-WEST ALLIS
Platteville
GRANT
LAFAYETTE
Monroe
GREEN
JANESVILLE
ROCK
Whitewater
WALWORTH
RACINE
KENOSHA
Chicago-Naperville-Michigan City (Part)
McHENRY
LAKE
Lake County-Kenosha County
CHICAGO-NAPERVILLE-JOLIET (PART)
DeKALB (PART)
KANE (PART)
COOK (PART)
Wisconsin
Total Daily Newspapers 32
Total Daily Circulation 535,667
Total Weekly Newspapers 193
Total Weekly Circulation 465,036
Population 5,795,483

Digital Platform - Mobile: Apple
Digital Platform - Tablet: Apple iOS
Pub...Peter Hawley
Ed. ....Thomas Hawley
Delivery Method: Mail, Newsstand
Areas Served: 54002, 54028, 54015

BARABOO

REEDSBURG TIMES-PRESS (WED, SAT)

714 Matts Ferry Rd, Baraboo, WI, 53913-3152, Sauk, USA; gen tel (608) 356-3808; adv tel (608) 745-3500; ed tel (608) 356-3808; adv fax (608) 745-3530; disp adv e-mail nfoesch@capitalnewspapers.com; class adv e-mail jdenk@capitalnewspapers.com; ed e-mail tkrysiak@capitalnewspapers.com; web site www.reedsburgtimespress.com
Circulation: 966pd,; AAM
Advertising rate: Open inch rate $8.70
Group: Capital Newspapers
Digital Platform - Mobile: Apple, Android
Digital Platform - Tablet: Apple iOS, Android, Windows 7
Editor ....Todd Krysiak
General Manager..............................Jon Denk
Delivery Method: Mail, Newsstand, Carrier, Racks
Areas Served: Sauk County

SAUK PRAIRIE EAGLE (WED)

714 Matts Ferry Rd, Baraboo, WI, 53913-3152, Sauk, USA; gen tel (608) 356-4808; adv tel (608) 745-3500; ed tel (608) 356-4808; adv fax (608) 745-3530; disp adv e-mail mbudde@capitalnewspapers.com; class adv e-mail jdenk@capitalnewspapers.com; ed e-mail jcuevas@wiscnews.com; web site www.saukprairieeagle.com
Circulation: 2,000pd,; Sworn/Estimate/Non-Audited
Advertising rate: Open inch rate $6.00
Group: Capital Newspapers
Digital Platform - Mobile: Apple, Android
Digital Platform - Tablet: Apple iOS, Android, Windows 7
Ed. ....Todd Krisiak
General Manager..............................Jon Denk
Weeklies Lead...........................Jason Cuevas
Delivery Method: Mail, Newsstand, Carrier, Racks
Areas Served: Sauk County

BARRON

BARRON NEWS-SHIELD (WED)

219 E La Salle Ave, Barron, WI, 54812-1426, Barron, USA; gen tel (715) 537-3117; adv tel (715) 537-3117; ed tel (715) 537-3117; gen fax (715) 537-5640; adv fax (715) 537-5640; ed fax (715) 537-5640; disp adv e-mail ads.newsshield@chibardun.net; class adv e-mail newsshield@chibardun.net; ed e-mail editor.barron@chibardun.net; web site www.news-shield.com
Circulation: 4,250pd,; Sworn/Estimate/Non-Audited
Advertising rate: Open inch rate $6.00
Digital Platform - Mobile: Apple, Android, Windows, Blackberry
Digital Platform - Tablet: Apple iOS, Android, Windows 7, Blackberry Tablet OS, Kindle, Nook, Kindle Fire
Pub./Sports Ed..................................Mark Bell
Assoc. Pub...Jim Bell
Ed. ....Robert Zientara
Adv. Mgr.......................................Jennifer Cox
Delivery Method: Mail, Newsstand, Racks
Areas Served: Barron County

BEAVER DAM

BEAVER DAM - MONDAY MINI (MON)

805 Park Ave, Beaver Dam, WI, 53916-2205, Dodge, USA; gen tel (920)356-6756; adv tel (920)356-6756; ed tel (920)356-6756; gen fax (920)887-8790; adv fax (920)887-8790; ed fax (920)887-8790; disp adv e-mail szeinemann@capitalnewspapers.com; class adv e-mail szeienmann@capitalnewspapers.com; ed e-mail szeinemann@capitalnewspapers.com; web site www.capitalnewspapers.com
Circulation: 0pd, 5,647fr; VAC
Advertising rate: Open inch rate $12.00
Established: 1986
Pub...James Kelsh
Mechanical Specifications: Type page: 9.8889 x 21.5; 6 col

COLUMBUS JOURNAL (SAT)

805 Park Ave, Beaver Dam, WI, 53916-2205, Dodge, USA; gen tel (920) 623-3160; adv tel (920) 623-3160; ed tel (920) 623-3160; gen fax (920) 623-9383; adv fax (920) 623-9383; ed fax (920) 623-9383; disp adv e-mail kpremo-rake@capitalnewspapers.com; class adv e-mail ddykstra@capitalnewspapers.com; ed e-mail pscharf@capitalnewspapers.com; web site www.wiscnews.com/columbusjournal
Circulation: 1,736pd,; Sworn/Estimate/Non-Audited
Advertising rate: Open inch rate $7.40
Established: 1855
Group: Capital Newspapers
Digital Platform - Mobile: Apple, Android
Digital Platform - Tablet: Apple iOS, Android, Windows 7
Ed. .... Megan Sheridan
Adv. Mgr.............................. Kara Premo-Rake
Gen. Mgr.................................. Diane Dykstra
Delivery Method: Mail, Racks
Areas Served: 53916, 53925, 53932

BERLIN

BERLIN JOURNAL (THUR)

301 June St, Berlin, WI, 54923-2147, Green Lake, USA; gen tel (920) 361-1515; adv tel (920) 361-1515; ed tel (920) 361-1515; gen fax (920) 361-1518; adv fax (920) 361-1518; ed fax (920) 361-1518; disp adv e-mail ads@theberlinjournal.com; class adv e-mail classifieds@theberlinjournal.com; ed e-mail news@theberlinjournal.com; web site www.theberlinjournal.com
Circulation: 3,500pd,; Sworn/Estimate/Non-Audited
Advertising rate: Open inch rate $13.40
Established: 1870
Group: Berlin Journal Newspapers
Digital Platform - Mobile: Apple, Android, Windows, Blackberry
Digital Platform - Tablet: Apple iOS, Android, Windows 7, Blackberry Tablet OS
Pub./Gen. Mgr...............................Tyler Gonyo
Ed. ....Jason Fox
Adv. Mgr...................................Kristian Troudt
Circ. Mgr..Tracy Kallas
Mechanical Specifications: Type page 10 x 16.
Delivery Method: Mail
Areas Served: Waushara County

GREEN LAKE REPORTER (THUR)

301 June St, Berlin, WI, 54923-2147, Green Lake, USA; gen tel (920) 361-1515; adv tel (920) 361-1515; ed tel (920) 361-1515; gen fax (920) 361-1518; adv fax (920) 361-1518; ed fax (920) 361-1518; disp adv e-mail ads@theberlinjournal.com; class adv e-mail classifieds@theberlinjournal.com; ed e-mail news@theberlinjournal.com; web site www.theberlinjournal.com
Circulation: 3,500pd,; Sworn/Estimate/Non-Audited
Advertising rate: Open inch rate $13.40
Established: 1870
Group: Berlin Journal Newspapers
Digital Platform - Mobile: Apple, Android, Windows, Blackberry
Digital Platform - Tablet: Apple iOS, Android, Windows 7, Blackberry Tablet OS
Pub./Gen. Mgr...............................Tyler Gonyo
Ed. ....Jason Fox
Adv. Mgr...................................Kristian Troudt
Circ. Mgr..Tracy Kallas
Mechanical Specifications: Type page 10 x 16.
Delivery Method: Mail
Areas Served: Waushara County

MARKESAN REGIONAL REPORTER (THUR)

301 June St, Berlin, WI, 54923-2147, Green Lake, USA; gen tel (920) 361-1515; adv tel (920) 361-1515; ed tel (920) 361-1515; gen fax (920) 361-1518; adv fax (920) 361-1518; ed fax (920) 361-1518; disp adv e-mail ads@theberlinjournal.com; class adv e-mail classifieds@theberlinjournal.com; ed e-mail news@theberlinjournal.com; web site www.theberlinjournal.com
Circulation: 3,500pd,; Sworn/Estimate/Non-Audited
Advertising rate: Open inch rate $13.40
Established: 1870
Group: Berlin Journal Newspapers
Digital Platform - Mobile: Apple, Android, Windows, Blackberry
Digital Platform - Tablet: Apple iOS, Android, Windows 7, Blackberry Tablet OS
Pub./Gen. Mgr...............................Tyler Gonyo
Ed. ....Jason Fox
Adv. Mgr...................................Kristian Troudt
Circ. Mgr..Tracy Kallas
Mechanical Specifications: Type page 10 x 16.
Delivery Method: Mail
Areas Served: Waushara County

OMRO HERALD (THUR)

301 June St, Berlin, WI, 54923-2147, Green Lake, USA; gen tel (920) 361-1515; adv tel (920) 361-1515; ed tel (920) 361-1515; gen fax (920) 361-1518; adv fax (920) 361-1518; ed fax (920) 361-1518; disp adv e-mail ads@theberlinjournal.com; class adv e-mail classifieds@theberlinjournal.com; ed e-mail news@theberlinjournal.com; web site www.theberlinjournal.com
Circulation: 3,500pd,; Sworn/Estimate/Non-Audited
Advertising rate: Open inch rate $13.40
Established: 1870
Group: Berlin Journal Newspapers
Digital Platform - Mobile: Apple, Android, Windows, Blackberry
Digital Platform - Tablet: Apple iOS, Android, Windows 7, Blackberry Tablet OS
Pub./Gen. Mgr...............................Tyler Gonyo
Ed. ....Jason Fox
Adv. Mgr...................................Kristian Troudt
Circ. Mgr..Tracy Kallas
Mechanical Specifications: Type page 10 x 16.
Delivery Method: Mail
Areas Served: Waushara County

PRINCETON TIMES-REPUBLIC (THUR)

301 June St, Berlin, WI, 54923-2147, Green Lake, USA; gen tel (920) 361-1515; adv tel (920) 361-1515; ed tel (920) 361-1515; gen fax (920) 361-1518; adv fax (920) 361-1518; ed fax (920) 361-1518; disp adv e-mail ads@theberlinjournal.com; class adv e-mail classifieds@theberlinjournal.com; ed e-mail news@theberlinjournal.com; web site www.theberlinjournal.com
Circulation: 3,500pd,; Sworn/Estimate/Non-Audited
Advertising rate: Open inch rate $13.40
Established: 1870
Group: Berlin Journal Newspapers
Digital Platform - Mobile: Apple, Android, Windows, Blackberry
Digital Platform - Tablet: Apple iOS, Android, Windows 7, Blackberry Tablet OS
Pub./Gen. Mgr...............................Tyler Gonyo
Ed. ....Jason Fox
Adv. Mgr...................................Kristian Troudt
Circ. Mgr..Tracy Kallas
Mechanical Specifications: Type page 10 x 16.
Delivery Method: Mail
Areas Served: Waushara County

THE FOX LAKE REPRESENTATIVE (THUR)

301 June St, Berlin, WI, 54923-2147, Green Lake, USA; gen tel (920) 361-1515; adv tel (920) 361-1515; ed tel (920) 361-1515; gen fax (920) 361-1518; adv fax (920) 361-1518; ed fax (920) 361-1518; disp adv e-mail ads@theberlinjournal.com; class adv e-mail classifieds@theberlinjournal.com; ed e-mail news@theberlinjournal.com; web site www.theberlinjournal.com
Circulation: 3,500pd,; Sworn/Estimate/Non-Audited
Advertising rate: Open inch rate $13.40
Established: 1870
Group: Berlin Journal Newspapers
Digital Platform - Mobile: Apple, Android, Windows, Blackberry
Digital Platform - Tablet: Apple iOS, Android, Windows 7, Blackberry Tablet OS
Pub./Gen. Mgr...............................Tyler Gonyo
Ed. ....Jason Fox
Adv. Mgr....................................Kristian Troudt
Circ. Mgr...Tracy Kallas
Mechanical Specifications: Type page 10 x 16.
Delivery Method: Mail
Areas Served: Waushara County

BLACK EARTH

MIDDLETON TIMES-TRIBUNE (THUR)

1126 Mills St, Black Earth, WI, 53515-9419, Dane, USA; gen tel (608) 836-1601; adv tel (608) 358-7958; gen fax (608) 836-3759; disp adv e-mail khenning@newspubinc.com; class adv e-mail classifieds@newspubinc.com; ed e-mail mgeieger@newspubinc.com
Circulation: 1,844pd,; Sworn/Estimate/Non-Audited
Advertising rate: $13.95 ci
Group: News Publishing, Co., Inc.
Adv. Sales.................................Karin Henning
Adv. Sales...................................Brian Palzkill
Mng Ed. ....Matt Geiger
Sports Ed....................................Rob Reischel
Delivery Method: Mail, Newsstand
Areas Served: 53562

NEWS-SICKLE-ARROW (THUR)

1126 Mills St, Black Earth, WI, 53515-9419, Dane, USA; gen tel (608) 767-3655; adv tel (608) 767-3655 ext. 242; ed tel (608) 767-4029 ext. 226; gen fax (608) 767-2222; adv fax (608)767-2222; ed fax (608)767-2222; disp adv e-mail marc@newspubinc.com; class adv e-mail classifieds@newspubinc.com; ed e-mail nsa@newspubinc.com; web site www.nsarrow.com
Circulation: 2,012pd,; Sworn/Estimate/Non-Audited
Advertising rate: Open inch rate $16.00
Group: News Publishing, Co., Inc.
Digital Platform - Mobile: Windows
Digital Platform - Tablet: Windows 7
Pub.. Dan Witte
Mng. Ed..................................John Donaldson
Adv. Mgr...................................Marc Mickelson
Mechanical Specifications: Type page 10 1/4 x 16; E - 5 cols, 2, 1/3 between; A - 5 cols, 2, 1/3 between; C - 5 cols, 2, 1/3 between. Equipment & Software: Hardware — APP/Mac; Software — QPS/QuarkXPress, Microsoft/Word, Adobe/Photoshop.
Delivery Method: Mail, Newsstand
Areas Served: Cross Plains,Arena, Black Earth, and Mazomanie

BLACK RIVER FALLS

JACKSON COUNTY CHRONICLE (WED)

34 S 1st St, Black River Falls, WI, 54615-1722, USA; gen tel (715) 284-0085; gen fax (715) 284-0087; disp adv e-mail barb.Wandling@lee.net; ed e-mail Matthew.Perenchio@lee.net; web site http://www.jacksoncountychronicle.com/
Group: Lee Enterprises, Inc.
Pub...Chris Hardie
Exec. Ed.............................. Matthew Perenchio
Adv. Mgr....................................Barb Wandling

BLOOMER

BLOOMER ADVANCE (WED)

1210 15th Ave, Bloomer, WI, 54724-1668, Chippewa, USA; gen tel (715) 568-3100; adv tel (715) 568-3100; ed tel (715) 568-3100; gen fax (715) 568-3111; adv fax (715) 568-3111; ed fax (715) 568-3111; disp adv e-mail

ads@bloomeradvance.com; class adv e-mail badvance@bloomer.net; ed e-mail editor@bloomeradvance.com; web site www.bloomeradvance.com
Circulation: 2,310pd, 29fr; USPS
Advertising rate: Open inch rate $5.75
Established: 1886
Pub....................Jim Bell
Ed./Gen. Mgr....................Barry Hoff
Sports Ed....................Dave Boyea
Circ. Mgr....................Sandra Metcalf
Adv. Production....................Lana Durch
Delivery Method: Mail, Newsstand, Racks
Areas Served: Bloomer/Chippewa County/54724
New Auburn/Chippewa County/54757
New Auburn/Barron County/54757

BOSCOBEL

THE BOSCOBEL DIAL (THUR)

901 Wisconsin Ave, Boscobel, WI, 53805-1531, Grant, USA; gen tel (608) 375-4458; adv tel (608)375-4458; ed tel (608)375-4458; gen fax (608) 375-2369; adv fax (608)375-2369; ed fax (608)375-2369; disp adv e-mail dialads@boscobeldial.net; class adv e-mail advertising@boscobeldial.net; ed e-mail dialeditor@boscobeldial.net; web site www.swnews4u.com
Circulation: 5,100pd,; Sworn/Estimate/Non-Audited
Advertising rate: Open inch rate $6.50
Established: 1872
Group: Morris Multimedia, Inc.
Digital Platform - Mobile: Apple, Android
Digital Platform - Tablet: Apple iOS, Android
Ed....................David Krier
Adv. Mgr./Gen. Mgr....................Jean Roth
Delivery Method: Mail, Newsstand, Racks
Areas Served: Grant, Crawford, and Richland County

BRILLION

THE BRILLION NEWS (THUR)

425 W Ryan St, Brillion, WI, 54110-1037, Calumet, USA; gen tel (920) 756-2222; adv tel (920)756-2222; ed tel (920)756-2222; gen fax (920) 756-2701; adv fax (920)756-2701; ed fax (920)756-2701; disp adv e-mail kris@zanderpressinc.com; class adv e-mail lisa@zanderpressinc.com; ed e-mail editor@thebrillionnews.com; web site www.thebrillionnews.com - 10,000(views) 2,200(visitors)
Circulation: 2,100pd, 5fr; USPS
Advertising rate: Open inch rate $9.03
Established: 1894
Group: Zander Press Inc.Editions: (6,288) The Brillion News
Digital Platform - Mobile: Apple, Android, Windows, Blackberry
Digital Platform - Tablet: Apple iOS, Android, Windows 7, Blackberry Tablet OS, Kindle, Nook, Kindle Fire
Pub....................Beth Wenzel
Ed....................David Nordby
Adv. Mgr....................Kris Bastian
Reporter....... Ed ByrneEquipment & Software: Hardware — APP/Mac; Software — Adobe Creative Suite 6
Delivery Method: Mail, Newsstand
Areas Served: Brillion, Reedsville, Hilbert, and Wrightstown. Parts of Calumet, Brown and Manitowoc Counties

BRODHEAD

THE INDEPENDENT REGISTER (THUR)

922 W Exchange St, Brodhead, WI, 53520-1469, Green, USA; gen tel (608) 897-2193; adv tel (608) 897-2193; ed tel (608) 897-2193; gen fax (608) 897-4137; adv fax (608) 897-4137; ed fax (608) 897-4137; disp adv e-mail ads@indreg.com; class adv e-mail paper@indreg.com; ed e-mail sschwartzlow@indreg.com; web site www.indreg.com
Circulation: 5,166fr; VAC
Advertising rate: Open inch rate $9.28
Established: 1860
Digital Platform - Mobile: Apple, Android
Digital Platform - Tablet: Apple iOS, Android, Windows 7
Ed....................Dan Moeller
Adv. Mgr....................Shirley Sauer
Office Mgr....................Joyce Chrisbaum
Pub./Gen. Mgr....................Randy Johnson
Mechanical Specifications: Type page 9 7/8 x 16; E - 5 cols, 1 5/6, 1/6 between; A - 5 cols, 1 5/6, 1/6 between; C - 5 cols, 1 5/6, 1/6 between.Equipment & Software: Hardware — APP/Mac; Presses — HI/V-15A; Software — QPS/QuarkXPress, Adobe/PageMaker.
Delivery Method: Mail, Newsstand
Areas Served: Brodhead, Albany, Juda, Orfordville, Monroe, and Evansville

BROWN DEER

GERMANTOWN EXPRESS NEWS (SAT)

8990 N 51st St, Brown Deer, WI, 53223-2402, Milwaukee, USA; gen tel (262) 238-6397; adv tel (262) 238-6397; ed tel (262) 238-6397; gen fax (262) 242-9450; adv fax (262) 242-9450; ed fax (262) 242-9450; disp adv e-mail advertising@discoverhometown.com; class adv e-mail jonesjf@discoverhometown.com; ed e-mail thomasj@discoverhometown.com; web site www.discoverhometown.com
Circulation: 11,006fr; VAC
Advertising rate: 1/8 Pg $176.00; 1/4 Pg $328.00; 1/2 Pg $640.00
Established: 1994
Group: Hometown Publications, Inc.
Pres./Pub....................Ken Ubert
Mng. Ed....................Thomas McKillen
Prod. Mgr./Adv. Mgr....................Holly Potter
Adv. Sales Rep....................Russ Schliepp
Delivery Method: Mail, Racks
Areas Served: Washington County

HARTFORD EXPRESS NEWS (THUR, SAT)

8990 N 51st St, Brown Deer, WI, 53223-2402, Washington, USA; gen tel (262) 238-6397; adv tel (262) 238-6397; ed tel (262) 238-6397; gen fax (262) 242-9450; adv fax (262) 242-9450; ed fax (262) 242-9450; disp adv e-mail advertising@discoverhometown.com; class adv e-mail jonesjf@discoverhometown.com; ed e-mail thomasj@discoverhometown.com; web site www.discoverhometown.com
Circulation: 3,909fr; VAC
Advertising rate: 1/8 Pg $176.00; 1/4 Pg $328.00; 1/2 Pg $640.00
Established: 1994
Group: Hometown Publications, Inc.
Pres./Pub....................Ken Ubert
Mng. Ed....................Thomas McKillen
Prod. Mgr./Adv. Mgr....................Holly Potter
Adv. Sales Rep....................Russ Schliepp
Delivery Method: Mail, Racks
Areas Served: Washington County

JACKSON EXPRESS NEWS (THUR, SAT)

8990 N 51st St, Brown Deer, WI, 53223-2402, Washington, USA; gen tel (262) 238-6397; adv tel (262) 238-6397; ed tel (262) 238-6397; gen fax (262) 242-9450; adv fax (262) 242-9450; ed fax (262) 242-9450; disp adv e-mail advertising@discoverhometown.com; class adv e-mail jonesjf@discoverhometown.com; ed e-mail thomasj@discoverhometown.com; web site www.discoverhometown.com
Circulation: 4,878fr; CVC
Advertising rate: 1/8 Pg $176.00; 1/4 Pg $328.00; 1/2 Pg $640.00
Established: 1994
Group: Hometown Publications, Inc.
Pres./Pub....................Ken Ubert
Mng. Ed....................Thomas McKillen
Prod. Mgr./Adv. Mgr....................Holly Potter
Adv. Sales Rep....................Russ Schliepp
Delivery Method: Mail, Racks
Areas Served: Washington County

MENOMONEE FALLS EXPRESS NEWS (SAT)

8990 N 51st St, Brown Deer, WI, 53223-2402, Milwaukee, USA; gen tel (262) 238-6397; adv tel (262) 238-6397; ed tel (262) 238-6397; gen fax (262) 242-9450; adv fax (262) 242-9450; ed fax (262) 242-9450; disp adv e-mail advertising@discoverhometown.com; class adv e-mail jonesjf@discoverhometown.com; ed e-mail thomasj@discoverhometown.com; web site www.discoverhometown.com
Circulation: 12,496fr; VAC
Advertising rate: 1/8 Pg $176.00; 1/4 Pg $328.00; 1/2 Pg $640.00
Established: 1994
Group: Hometown Publications, Inc.
Pres./Pub....................Ken Ubert
Mng. Ed....................Thomas McKillen
Prod. Mgr./Adv. Mgr....................Holly Potter
Adv. Sales Rep....................Russ Schliepp
Delivery Method: Mail, Racks
Areas Served: Washington County

MILWAUKEE EXPRESS NEWS (THUR, SAT)

8990 N 51st St, Brown Deer, WI, 53223-2402, Washington, USA; gen tel (262) 238-6397; adv tel (262) 238-6397; ed tel (262) 238-6397; gen fax (262) 242-9450; adv fax (262) 242-9450; ed fax (262) 242-9450; disp adv e-mail advertising@discoverhometown.com; class adv e-mail jonesjf@discoverhometown.com; ed e-mail thomasj@discoverhometown.com; web site www.discoverhometown.com
Circulation: 4,878fr; CVC
Advertising rate: 1/8 Pg $176.00; 1/4 Pg $328.00; 1/2 Pg $640.00
Established: 1994
Group: Hometown Publications, Inc.
Pres./Pub....................Ken Ubert
Mng. Ed....................Thomas McKillen
Prod. Mgr./Adv. Mgr....................Holly Potter
Adv. Sales Rep....................Russ Schliepp
Delivery Method: Mail, Racks
Areas Served: Washington County

SLINGER EXPRESS NEWS (THUR, SAT)

8990 N 51st St, Brown Deer, WI, 53223-2402, Washington, USA; gen tel (262) 238-6397; adv tel (262) 238-6397; ed tel (262) 238-6397; gen fax (262) 242-9450; adv fax (262) 242-9450; ed fax (262) 242-9450; disp adv e-mail advertising@discoverhometown.com; class adv e-mail jonesjf@discoverhometown.com; ed e-mail thomasj@discoverhometown.com; web site www.discoverhometown.com
Circulation: 3,909fr; VAC
Advertising rate: 1/8 Pg $176.00; 1/4 Pg $328.00; 1/2 Pg $640.00
Established: 1994
Group: Hometown Publications, Inc.
Pres./Pub....................Ken Ubert
Mng. Ed....................Thomas McKillen
Prod. Mgr./Adv. Mgr....................Holly Potter
Adv. Sales Rep....................Russ Schliepp
Delivery Method: Mail, Racks
Areas Served: Washington County

SUSSEX EXPRESS NEWS (SAT)

8990 N 51st St, Brown Deer, WI, 53223-2402, Milwaukee, USA; gen tel (262) 238-6397; adv tel (262) 238-6397; ed tel (262) 238-6397; gen fax (262) 242-9450; adv fax (262) 242-9450; ed fax (262) 242-9450; disp adv e-mail advertising@discoverhometown.com; class adv e-mail jonesjf@discoverhometown.com; ed e-mail thomasj@discoverhometown.com; web site www.discoverhometown.com
Circulation: 12,496fr; VAC
Advertising rate: 1/8 Pg $176.00; 1/4 Pg $328.00; 1/2 Pg $640.00
Established: 1994
Group: Hometown Publications, Inc.
Pres./Pub....................Ken Ubert
Mng. Ed....................Thomas McKillen
Prod. Mgr./Adv. Mgr....................Holly Potter
Adv. Sales Rep....................Russ Schliepp
Delivery Method: Mail, Racks
Areas Served: Washington County

WAUWATOSA EXPRESS NEWS (THUR, SAT)

8990 N 51st St, Brown Deer, WI, 53223-2402, Washington, USA; gen tel (262) 238-6397; adv tel (262) 238-6397; ed tel (262) 238-6397; gen fax (262) 242-9450; adv fax (262) 242-9450; ed fax (262) 242-9450; disp adv e-mail advertising@discoverhometown.com; class adv e-mail jonesjf@discoverhometown.com; ed e-mail thomasj@discoverhometown.com; web site www.discoverhometown.com
Circulation: 4,878fr; CVC
Advertising rate: 1/8 Pg $176.00; 1/4 Pg $328.00; 1/2 Pg $640.00
Established: 1994
Group: Hometown Publications, Inc.
Pres./Pub....................Ken Ubert
Mng. Ed....................Thomas McKillen
Prod. Mgr./Adv. Mgr....................Holly Potter
Adv. Sales Rep....................Russ Schliepp
Delivery Method: Mail, Racks
Areas Served: Washington County

WEST ALLIS EXPRESS NEWS (THUR, SAT)

8990 N 51st St, Brown Deer, WI, 53223-2402, Washington, USA; gen tel (262) 238-6397; adv tel (262) 238-6397; ed tel (262) 238-6397; gen fax (262) 242-9450; adv fax (262) 242-9450; ed fax (262) 242-9450; disp adv e-mail advertising@discoverhometown.com; class adv e-mail jonesjf@discoverhometown.com; ed e-mail thomasj@discoverhometown.com; web site www.discoverhometown.com
Circulation: 4,878fr; CVC
Advertising rate: 1/8 Pg $176.00; 1/4 Pg $328.00; 1/2 Pg $640.00
Established: 1994
Group: Hometown Publications, Inc.
Pres./Pub....................Ken Ubert
Mng. Ed....................Thomas McKillen
Prod. Mgr./Adv. Mgr....................Holly Potter
Adv. Sales Rep....................Russ Schliepp
Delivery Method: Mail, Racks
Areas Served: Washington County

WEST BEND EXPRESS NEWS (SAT)

8990 N 51st St, Brown Deer, WI, 53223-2402, Milwaukee, USA; gen tel (262) 238-6397; adv tel (262) 238-6397; ed tel (262) 238-6397; gen fax (262) 242-9450; adv fax (262) 242-9450; ed fax (262) 242-9450; disp adv e-mail advertising@discoverhometown.com; class adv e-mail jonesjf@discoverhometown.com; ed e-mail thomasj@discoverhometown.com; web site www.discoverhometown.com
Circulation: 4,433fr; VAC
Advertising rate: 1/8 Pg $176.00; 1/4 Pg $328.00; 1/2 Pg $640.00
Established: 1994
Group: Hometown Publications, Inc.
Digital Platform - Mobile: Apple, Android
Digital Platform - Tablet: Apple iOS, Android
Pres./Pub....................Ken Ubert
Mng. Ed....................Thomas McKillen
Prod. Mgr./Adv. Mgr....................Holly Potter
Adv. Sales Rep....................Russ Schliepp
Delivery Method: Mail, Racks
Areas Served: Washington County

BURLINGTON

BURLINGTON STANDARD PRESS (THUR)

700 N Pine St, Burlington, WI, 53105-1472, Racine, USA; gen tel (262) 763-3330; adv tel (262) 763-3330; ed tel (262) 763-3330 ext. 148; gen fax (262) 763-2238; adv fax (262) 763-2238; ed fax (262) 763-2238; disp adv e-mail karend@standardpress.com; class adv e-mail dee@southernlakesnewspapers.com; ed e-mail jeisenbart@southernlakesnewspapers.com; web site www.southernlakesnewspapers.com
Circulation: 3,900pd, 4,801fr; Sworn/Estimate/Non-Audited
Advertising rate: Open inch rate $9.50
Group: Southern Lakes Newspapers LLC
Digital Platform - Mobile: Windows

Digital Platform - Tablet: Windows 7
Pub....Jack Cruger
Ed. in Chief....Ed Nadolski
Mng. Ed....Jennifer Eisenbart
Adv. Mgr....Jamie Wambach
Mechanical Specifications: Type page 13 x 21.
Delivery Method: Mail
Areas Served: Racine County

WATERFORD POST (FRI)
700 N Pine St, Burlington, WI, 53105-1472, Racine, USA; gen tel (262) 763-3330; adv tel (262) 763-3330; ed tel (262) 763-3330 ext. 160; gen fax (262) 763-2238; adv fax (262) 763-2238; ed fax (262) 763-2238; disp adv e-mail dfossey@southernlakesnewspapers.com; class adv e-mail dee@southernlakesnewspapers.com; ed e-mail bogumil@southernlakesnewspapers.com; web site www.southernlakesnewspapers.com
Circulation: 1,900pd, 527fr; Sworn/Estimate/Non-Audited
Advertising rate: Open inch rate $7.95
Group: Southern Lakes Newspapers LLC
Digital Platform - Mobile: Windows
Digital Platform - Tablet: Windows 7
Ed. in Chief....Ed Nadolski
Adv. Mgr....Dee Fladwood
Mng. Ed....Patricia Bogumil
Gen. Mgr....Cyndi Jensen
Mechanical Specifications: Type page 13 x 21.
Delivery Method: Mail
Areas Served: Racine County

CAMBRIDGE

THE CAMBRIDGE NEWS & THE INDEPENDENT (THUR)
201 W North St, Cambridge, WI, 53523-8714, Dane, USA; gen tel (608) 423-3213; adv tel (920) 297-2064; ed tel (608) 423-3213; gen fax (608) 423-7802; adv fax (920) 648-8187; ed fax (608) 423-7802; disp adv e-mail jyanko@hngnews.com; class adv e-mail classifies@hngnews.com; ed e-mail deerfield@hngnews.com ; web site www.cambridgeenews.com
Circulation: 1,443pd, 17fr; Sworn/Estimate/Non-Audited
Advertising rate: Open inch rate $11.68
Established: 1894
Group: Hometown News Group
Digital Platform - Mobile: Apple, Android
Digital Platform - Tablet: Apple iOS, Android, Windows 7
Pub....Brian Knox
Managing Editor....Amy Alder
Mechanical Specifications: Type page 6 x 21; E - 6 cols, 2 1/2, 1/6 between; A - 6 cols, 2 1/2, 1/6 between; C - 8 cols, 1 1/2, 1/6 between.
Delivery Method: Mail, Racks
Areas Served: 53523, 53531

CAMPBELLSPORT

CAMPBELLSPORT NEWS (THUR)
101 N Fond Du Lac Ave, Campbellsport, WI, 53010-3542, Fond Du Lac, USA; gen tel (920) 533-8338; adv tel (920)533-8338; ed tel (920) 533-8338; gen fax (920) 533-5579; adv fax (920) 533-5579; ed fax (920) 533-5579; disp adv e-mail sales@thecampbellsportnews.com; class adv e-mail frontdesk@thecampbellsportnews.com; ed e-mail editor@thecampbellsportnews.com; web site www.thecampbellsportnews.com
Circulation: 2,000pd, 11fr; Sworn/Estimate/Non-Audited
Advertising rate: Open inch rate $6.03
Established: 1906
Group: Wisconsin Free Press, Inc.
Digital Platform - Mobile: Apple, Android, Windows, Blackberry
Digital Platform - Tablet: Apple iOS, Android, Windows 7, Blackberry Tablet OS, Kindle, Kindle Fire
Pub....Andrew Johnson
Ed....Andrea Hansen Abler
office/production....Rebecca Van Beek
Adv....Tracy Dieckman
Production....Andrea Steger
Delivery Method: Mail, Newsstand
Areas Served: 53010, 53019, 54935, 53040

CASHTON

THE CASHTON RECORD (WED)
713 Broadway St, Cashton, WI, 54619-2013, Monroe, USA; gen tel (608) 654-7330; adv tel (608) 654-7330; ed tel (608) 654-7330; gen fax (608) 654-7324; adv fax (608) 654-7324; ed fax (608) 654-7324; disp adv e-mail cashtonrecord@centurytel.net; class adv e-mail cashtonrecord@centurytel.net; ed e-mail cashtonrecord@centurytel.net
Circulation: 1,600pd,; Sworn/Estimate/Non-Audited
Advertising rate: Open inch rate $5.11
Pub....Paul Fanning
Ed....Kim Fanning
Mechanical Specifications: Type page 10 x 15; E - 5 cols, 2, 1/6 between; A - 5 cols, 2, 1/6 between; C - 5 cols, 2, 1/6 between.Equipment & Software: Hardware — APP/Power Mac; Software — Adobe/PageMaker 5.0, Claris/MacWrite.
Delivery Method: Mail
Areas Served: Monroe County

CEDARBURG

NEWS GRAPHIC (TUES, THUR)
W61N306 Washington Ave, Ste 1, Cedarburg, WI, 53012-2451, Ozaukee, USA; gen tel (262) 375-5100; adv tel (262) 375-5100; ed tel (262) 375-5100; gen fax (262) 375-5107; adv fax (262) 375-5107; ed fax (262) 375-5107; disp adv e-mail hrogge@conleynet.com; class adv e-mail agannon@conleynet.com; ed e-mail jrockley@conleynet.com; web site www.gmtoday.com
Circulation: 7,218pd, 232fr; VAC
Advertising rate: Open inch rate $14.18
Established: 1883
Group: Conley Media LLC
Digital Platform - Mobile: Apple, Android, Windows, Blackberry
Digital Platform - Tablet: Apple iOS, Android, Windows 7, Blackberry Tablet OS, Kindle, Nook, Kindle Fire
Mng. Ed....Lisa Curtis
Pub./Adv. Dir....Heather Rogge
Delivery Method: Mail, Newsstand, Racks
Areas Served: Ozaukee County

CHETEK

THE CHETEK ALERT (WED)
312 Knapp St, Chetek, WI, 54728-4129, Barron, USA; gen tel (715) 924-4118; adv tel (715) 924-4118; ed tel (715) 924-4118; gen fax (715) 924-4122; adv fax (715) 924-4122; ed fax (715) 924-4122; disp adv e-mail jim@thechetekalert.com; class adv e-mail julie@thechetekalert.com; ed e-mail editor@thechetekalert.com; web site www.chetekalert.com
Circulation: 3,000pd, 20fr; Sworn/Estimate/Non-Audited
Advertising rate: Open inch rate $7.00 (Local); $8.10 (National)
Established: 1882
Digital Platform - Mobile: Apple, Android, Windows, Blackberry
Digital Platform - Tablet: Apple iOS, Android, Windows 7, Blackberry Tablet OS, Kindle, Nook, Kindle Fire
Pub./Ed....Jim Bell
News Ed....Ryan Urban
Sales Mgr....Julie LeMoine
Delivery Method: Mail, Newsstand
Areas Served: Barron County

CHILTON

CHILTON TIMES-JOURNAL (THUR)
19 E Main St, Chilton, WI, 53014-1427, Calumet, USA; gen tel (920) 849-4551; adv tel (920) 849-4551; ed tel (920) 849-4551; gen fax (920) 849-4651; adv fax (920) 849-4651; ed fax (920) 849-4651; disp adv e-mail calumetadvertiser@charter.net; class adv e-mail marilynmcgrew@yahoo.com; ed e-mail timesjournal@charter.net; web site www.chiltontimesjournal.com
Circulation: 5,020pd, 50fr; Sworn/Estimate/Non-Audited
Advertising rate: Open inch rate $9.00
Established: 1857
Group: Calumet Publishing, Inc.
Digital Platform - Mobile: Apple, Android
Digital Platform - Tablet: Apple iOS, Android
Pub....James Moran
Adv. Mgr....Betty Schilling
Office Mgr....Marilyn McGrew
Ed....Patrick Mares
Mechanical Specifications: Type page 6 x 16.Equipment & Software: Hardware — APP/Mac; Presses — KP/News King.
Delivery Method: Mail, Racks
Areas Served: Calumet County

CHIPPEWA FALLS

THE DUNN COUNTY NEWS (WED, SAT)
321 Frenette Dr, Chippewa Falls, WI, 54729-3372, Dunn, USA; gen tel (800) 224-7744; adv tel (715) 738-1644; ed tel (715) 738-1619; gen fax (715) 723-9644; disp adv e-mail paul.pehler@lee.net; class adv e-mail ads@lacrossetribune.com; ed e-mail editor@dunnconnect.com; web site www.dunnconnect.com
Circulation: 2,047pd,; Sworn/Estimate/Non-Audited
Established: 1860
Group: Lee Enterprises, Inc.
Digital Platform - Mobile: Apple, Android, Windows, Blackberry
Digital Platform - Tablet: Apple iOS, Android, Windows 7, Blackberry Tablet OS, Kindle
Ed....Barbara Lyon
Publisher....Bob Fleck Fleck
Mechanical Specifications: Type page 12 x 21 1/2; E - 6 cols, 2, between; A - 6 cols, 2, between.Equipment & Software: Hardware — APP/Power Mac G3; Software — QPS/QuarkXPress.
Delivery Method: Mail, Newsstand, Racks
Areas Served: Dunn County

CLINTON

THE CLINTON TOPPER (THUR)
407 Church St, Clinton, WI, 53525-9494, Rock, USA; gen tel (608) 676-4111; adv tel (608) 676-4111; ed tel (608) 676-4111; gen fax (608) 676-4664; adv fax (608) 676-4664; ed fax (608) 676-4664; disp adv e-mail theclintontopper@aol.com; class adv e-mail theclintontopper@aol.com; ed e-mail theclintontopper@aol.com; web site www.indreg.com
Circulation: 1,650pd, 44fr; Sworn/Estimate/Non-Audited
Advertising rate: Open inch rate $7.30
Established: 1938
Group: Rock Valley Publishing LLC
Digital Platform - Mobile: Apple, Android
Digital Platform - Tablet: Apple iOS, Android, Windows 7
Pub....Jack Cruger
Ed....Dawn Martin
Adv. Mgr....Celesce Lightner-Greenwalt
Mechanical Specifications: Type page 10 x 15 1/2; E - 5 cols, 1 7/8, 3/16 between; A - 5 cols, 1 7/8, 3/16 between; C - 5 cols, 1 7/8, 3/16 between.Equipment & Software: Hardware — IBM; Software — Microsoft/Word 98.
Delivery Method: Mail, Newsstand
Areas Served: Rock County

COLFAX

THE COLFAX MESSENGER (WED)
511 E Railroad Ave, Colfax, WI, 54730-9187, Dunn, USA; gen tel (715) 962-3535; adv tel (715) 962-3535; ed tel (715) 962-3535; gen fax (715) 962-3413; adv fax (715) 962-3413; ed fax (715) 962-3413; disp adv e-mail messenger@dewittmedia.com; class adv e-mail messenger@dewittmedia.com; ed e-mail messenger@dewittmedia.com; web site www.ColfaxMessenger.com
Circulation: 1,100pd, 15fr; Sworn/Estimate/Non-Audited
Advertising rate: Open inch rate $6.00
Established: 1897
Group: DeWitt Media Inc.
Digital Platform - Mobile: Apple, Android, Windows, Blackberry
Digital Platform - Tablet: Apple iOS, Android, Windows 7, Blackberry Tablet OS, Kindle
Pub./Ed....Carlton DeWitt
Mng. Ed....Shawn DeWitt
Delivery Method: Mail, Newsstand
Areas Served: Dunn County

CORNELL

COURIER SENTINEL (THUR)
121 Main St, Cornell, WI, 54732-8386, Chippewa, USA; gen tel (715) 239-6688; adv tel (715) 289-4978; ed tel (715) 239-6688; gen fax (715) 239-6200; adv fax (715) 239-6200; ed fax (715) 239-6200; disp adv e-mail cornellcourier@centurytel.net; class adv e-mail cadottsentinel@centurytel.net; ed e-mail cornellcourier@centurytel.net; web site www.couriersentinelnews.com
Circulation: 3,200pd, 59fr; Sworn/Estimate/Non-Audited
Advertising rate: Open inch rate $6.25
Established: 1958
Group: Trygg J. Hansen Publications Inc.
Digital Platform - Mobile: Apple, Android
Digital Platform - Tablet: Apple iOS, Android, Windows 7
Pub....Trygg Hansen
Ed....John Marder
Cadott Mgr....Monique Westaby
Gen. Mgr....Kris O'Leary
Business Mgr....Rebecca Lindquist
Mechanical Specifications: Type page 13 x 21; E - 6 cols, 2 1/16, between; A - 6 cols, 2 1/16, between; C - 6 cols, 2 1/16, between.
Delivery Method: Mail, Racks
Areas Served: Cadott, Cornell, and Lake Holcombe

COTTAGE GROVE

MCFARLAND THISTLE (TUES, THUR)
213 W Cottage Grove Rd, Ste 9, Cottage Grove, WI, 53527-9330, Dane, USA; gen tel (608)838-6435; adv tel (608)838-6435; ed tel (608)838-6435; disp adv e-mail pjohnson@hngnews.com; class adv e-mail pjohnson@hngnews.com; ed e-mail agerber@hngnews.com; web site www.hngnews.com/mcfarland_thistle
Advertising rate: Open inch rate $12.24
Group: Hometown News Group
Managing Ed....Amber Gerber
Adv. Mgr....Pat Johnson
Circ. Mgr....Luann Neabling
Areas Served: McFarland

CRANDON

FLORENCE MINING NEWS (THUR)
103 S Hazeldell Ave, Crandon, WI, 54520-1453, Florence, USA; gen tel (715) 528-3276; adv tel (715)528-3276; ed tel (715)528-3276; gen fax (715) 528-5976; adv fax (715)528-5976; ed fax (715)528-5976; disp adv e-mail upnorth2@borderlandnet.net; class adv e-mail upnorth2@borderlandnet.net; ed

e-mail upnorth2@borderlandnet.net; web site www.florence-forestnews.com
Pub./Ed. ....Hank Murphy
Ad. Design .... Dianne Olive
Adv. Mgr. ....Teresa Broullire

THE FOREST REPUBLICAN (THUR)

103 S Hazeldell Ave, Crandon, WI, 54520-1453, Forest, USA; gen tel (715) 478-3315; adv tel (715)478-3315; ed tel (715)478-3315; gen fax (715) 478-5385; adv fax (715)478-5385; ed fax (715)478-5385; disp adv e-mail news@forestrepublican.com; class adv e-mail news@forestrepublican.com; ed e-mail news@forestrepublican.com; web site www.florence-forestnews.com
Circulation: 2,500pd, 50fr; USPS
Advertising rate: Open inch rate $5.15
Established: 1886
Group: Borderland Publishing Inc.
Digital Platform - Mobile: Apple, Android, Windows, Blackberry
Digital Platform - Tablet: Apple iOS, Android, Windows 7, Blackberry Tablet OS, Kindle, Nook, Kindle Fire
Gen. Mgr. .... Deb Sivertsen
Owner/Pub./Ed. ....Hank Murphy
Delivery Method: Mail, Newsstand, Carrier
Areas Served: Forest County & surrounding area

CUBA CITY

TRI-COUNTY PRESS (THUR)

223 S Main St, Cuba City, WI, 53807-1543, Grant, USA; gen tel (608) 744-2107; adv tel (608) 744-2107; ed tel (608) 744-2107; gen fax (608) 744-2108; adv fax (608) 744-2108; ed fax (608) 744-2108; disp adv e-mail tcpads@yousq.net; class adv e-mail tcpads@yousq.net; ed e-mail tcpnews@yousq.net; web site www.swnews4u.com
Circulation: 2,667pd, 17fr; Sworn/Estimate/Non-Audited
Advertising rate: 1/8 Pg $63.00; 1/4 Pg $126.00; 1/2 Pg $252.00
Established: 1894
Group: Morris Multimedia, Inc.
Digital Platform - Mobile: Apple, Android
Digital Platform - Tablet: Apple iOS, Android
Pub. .... John Ingebritsen
Adv. Mgr. ....Brian Muldoon
Mechanical Specifications: Type page 11 x 17; E - 6 cols, 1 5/8, 3/16 between; A - 6 cols, 1 5/8, 3/16 between; C - 6 cols, 1 5/8, 3/16 between.
Delivery Method: Mail, Newsstand
Areas Served: 53807, 53811, 53808, 53586, 53818

CUMBERLAND

CUMBERLAND ADVOCATE (WED)

1375 2nd Ave, Cumberland, WI, 54829-7211, Barron, USA; gen tel (715)822-4429; adv tel (715)822-4429; ed tel (715)822-4429; gen fax (715)822-4451; adv fax (715)822-4451; ed fax (715)822-4451; disp adv e-mail news@cumberland-advocate.com; class adv e-mail news@cumberland-advocate.com; ed e-mail news@cumberland-advocate.com
Circulation: 2,550pd,; Sworn/Estimate/Non-Audited
Advertising rate: Open inch rate $7.00
Established: 1882
Group: B&H Publishing, Inc.
Pub./Adv. Mgr. .... Paul Bucher

DARLINGTON

REPUBLICAN JOURNAL (THUR)

316 Main St, Darlington, WI, 53530-1426, Lafayette, USA; gen tel (608) 776-4425; gen fax (608) 776-4301; disp adv e-mail rjads@centurytel.net; class adv e-mail rjclassified@centurytel.net; ed e-mail rjeditor@centurytel.net; web site www.myrjonline.com
Circulation: 2,907pd,; USPS
Advertising rate: Open inch rate $5.95
Established: 1861
Group: Morris Multimedia, Inc.
Digital Platform - Mobile: Apple, Android
Digital Platform - Tablet: Apple iOS, Android, Windows 7
Pub. .... Brian Lund
Ed. .... Tallitha Reese
Adv. Mgr. .... Adam Ploessl
Mechanical Specifications: 10 5/8" x16 full
Delivery Method: Mail, Racks
Areas Served: 53530, 53586, 53510, 53541, 53587

DELAVAN

JANESVILLE MESSENGER (WED, SUN)

120 S Wright St, Delavan, WI, 53115-2012, Rock, USA; gen tel (608) 752-0777; adv tel (608) 752-0777; ed tel (608) 752-0777; gen fax (608) 754-8038; adv fax (608) 754-8038; ed fax (608) 754-8038; disp adv e-mail messenger@janesvillemessenger.com; class adv e-mail messenger@janesvillemessenger.com; ed e-mail danp@communityshoppers.com; web site www.communityshoppers.com - 16,529(views) 7,140(visitors)
Circulation: 0pd, 64,640fr; CVC
Advertising rate: Open inch rate $20.40
Established: 1983
Group: CSI Media, LLC
Digital Platform - Mobile: Apple, Android, Windows, Blackberry
Digital Platform - Tablet: Apple iOS, Android, Windows 7, Blackberry Tablet OS, Kindle, Nook, Kindle Fire
VP/Gen. Mgr. .... Dan White
Adv. Sales Mgr. .... Heidi Springer
Circ. Mgr ....Christopher Wilhelms
Mechanical Specifications: Type page: 10.375 x 16; 7 col
Delivery Method: Mail, Newsstand
Areas Served: Rock County

LAKE GENEVA TIMES (THUR)

1102 Ann St, Delavan, WI, 53115-1938, Walworth, USA; gen tel (262) 728-3411; adv tel (262) 763-2575 ext. 128; ed tel (262) 763-3330 ext. 123; gen fax (262) 728-6844; adv fax (262) 728-6844; ed fax (262) 763-2238; disp adv e-mail dee@southernlakesnewspapers.com; class adv e-mail jstearns@southernlakesnewspapers.com; ed e-mail enadolski@standardpress.com; web site www.standardpress.com
Circulation: 1,206fr; CVC
Advertising rate: Open inch rate $7.90
Group: Southern Lakes Newspapers LLC
Digital Platform - Mobile: Windows
Digital Platform - Tablet: Windows 7
Pub./Gen. Mgr. .... Cyndi Jensen
Ed. in Chief .... Edward Nadolski
Asst. Adv. Dir. .... Dee Fladwood
Adv. Dir .... Vicki Vanderwerff
Circ. Mgr ....Tom Flatow
Prod. Mgr. ....Jessica Franzene
Delivery Method: Mail
Areas Served: Walworth County

PADDOCK LAKE REPORT (SAT)

1102 Ann St, Delavan, WI, 53115-1938, Walworth, USA; gen tel (262) 728-3411; adv tel (262) 763-2575 ext. 128; ed tel (262) 763-3330 ext. 123; gen fax (262) 728-6844; adv fax (262) 728-6844; ed fax (262) 763-2238; disp adv e-mail dee@southernlakesnewspapers.com; class adv e-mail jstearns@southernlakesnewspapers.com; ed e-mail enadolski@standardpress.com; web site www.standardpress.com
Circulation: 1,496fr; VAC
Advertising rate: Open inch rate $11.15
Group: Southern Lakes Newspapers LLC
Digital Platform - Mobile: Windows
Digital Platform - Tablet: Windows 7
Pub./Gen. Mgr. .... Cyndi Jensen
Ed. in Chief .... Edward Nadolski
Adv. Dir. .... Dee Fladwood
Adv. Mgr .... Vicki Vanderwerff
Circ. Mgr ....Tom Flatow
Prod. Mgr ....Sue Lange
Delivery Method: Mail
Areas Served: Walworth County

PALMYRA ENTERPRISE (FRI)

1102 Ann St, Delavan, WI, 53115-1938, Walworth, USA; gen tel (262) 728-3411; adv tel (262) 728-3411; ed tel (262) 728-3411; gen fax (262) 725-7702; adv fax (262) 725-7702; ed fax (262) 725-7702; disp adv e-mail cjensen@rvpublishing.com; class adv e-mail cjensen@rvpublishing.com; ed e-mail cjensen@rvpublishing.com
Circulation: 1,400pd, 700fr; Sworn/Estimate/Non-Audited
Advertising rate: Open inch rate $6.60
Group: Southern Lakes Newspapers LLC
Pub. ....Jack Crueger
Ed. in Chief .... Ed Nadolski
Gen. Mgr. .... Cyndi Jensen
Delivery Method: Mail, Newsstand
Areas Served: Walworth County

THE DELAVAN ENTERPRISE (THUR)

1102 Ann St, Delavan, WI, 53115-1938, Walworth, USA; gen tel (262) 728-3411; adv tel (262) 725-7701 ext. 132; ed tel (262) 725-7701 ext. 130; gen fax (262) 728-6844; adv fax (262) 728-6844; ed fax (262) 728-6844; disp adv e-mail jstearns@southernlakesnewspapers.com; class adv e-mail delavanassistant@southernlakesnewspapers.com; ed e-mail delavaneditor@southernlakesnewspapers.com; web site www.southernlakesnewspapers.com
Circulation: 4,500pd,; Sworn/Estimate/Non-Audited
Advertising rate: Open inch rate $9.35
Established: 1878
Group: Southern Lakes Newspapers LLC
Digital Platform - Mobile: Windows
Digital Platform - Tablet: Windows 7
Pub./Ed. .... Vicky Wedig-Farence
Adv. Mgr. .... Jackie Stearns
Mechanical Specifications: Type page 13 x 21 1/2.Equipment & Software: Hardware — APP/Mac.
Delivery Method: Mail, Newsstand
Areas Served: 53115

DENMARK

THE DENMARK NEWS (THUR)

116 Main St, Denmark, WI, 54208-9683, Brown, USA; gen tel (920) 863-2700; adv tel (920) 713-2047; ed tel (920) 863-2700; gen fax (920) 863-2710; adv fax (920) 863-2710; ed fax (920) 863-2710; disp adv e-mail jc@thedenmarknews.com; class adv e-mail karen@thedenmarknews.com; ed e-mail ryan@thedenmarknews.com; web site www.thedenmarknews.com
Circulation: 2,900pd, 43fr; Sworn/Estimate/Non-Audited
Advertising rate: Open inch rate $7.35
Established: 2009
Digital Platform - Mobile: Windows
Digital Platform - Tablet: Windows 7
Pub. ....Ryan Radue
Adv. Mgr. ....JC Marquez
Office Mgr. .... Karen Nelsen
Mechanical Specifications: Type page 11 1/2 x 21 1/2; E - 6 cols, 1 13/16, 1/8 between; A - 6 cols, 1 13/16, 1/8 between; C - 9 cols, 1 1/16, 1/8 between.Equipment & Software: Hardware — APP/Mac; Software — QPS/QuarkXPress.
Delivery Method: Mail, Racks
Areas Served: 54208, 54227

DODGEVILLE

THE DODGEVILLE CHRONICLE (THUR)

106 W Merrimac St, Dodgeville, WI, 53533-1440, Iowa, USA; gen tel (608) 935-2331; adv tel (608) 935-2331 ext. 20; ed tel (608) 935-2331 ext. 22; gen fax (608) 935-9531; adv fax 608 935-9531; ed fax same; disp adv e-mail sroh@thedodgevillechronicle.com; class adv e-mail mreilly@thedodgevillechronicle.com; ed e-mail preilly@thedodgevillechronicle.com; web site www.thedodgevillechronicle.com
Circulation: 4,700pd, 75fr; Sworn/Estimate/Non-Audited
Advertising rate: Open inch rate $9.75
Established: 1862
Digital Platform - Mobile: Apple, Android
Digital Platform - Tablet: Apple iOS, Android, Windows 7
Co-Pub./Ed. .... Patrick Reilly
Co-Pub./Ed. ....Michael Reilly
Adv. Mgr. ....Shelly Roh
Ed. .... Brooke Bechen
Delivery Method: Mail, Newsstand, Racks
Areas Served: Iowa County

DURAND

THE COURIER-WEDGE (THUR)

103 W Main St, Durand, WI, 54736-1144, Pepin, USA; gen tel (715) 672-4252; adv tel (715) 672-4252; ed tel (715) 672-4252; gen fax (715) 672-4254; adv fax (715) 672-4254; ed fax (715) 672-4254; disp adv e-mail thewedge@nelson-tel.net; class adv e-mail thewedge@nelson-tel.net; ed e-mail thewedge@nelson-tel.net
Circulation: 4,300pd, 36fr; Sworn/Estimate/Non-Audited
Advertising rate: Open inch rate $8.50
Pub. .... Michael Stumpf
Ed. .... Deb Claxton
Delivery Method: Mail
Areas Served: Pepin County

EAGLE RIVER

THREE LAKES NEWS (WED)

425 W Mill St, Eagle River, WI, 54521-8002, Vilas, USA; gen tel (715) 479-4421; adv tel (715) 479-4421; ed tel (715) 479-4421; gen fax (715) 479-6242; adv fax (715) 479-6242; ed fax (715) 479-6242; disp adv e-mail kurtk@vcnewsreview.com; class adv e-mail maryjoa@vcnewsreview.com; ed e-mail garyr@vcnewsreview.com; web site www.vcnewsreview.com
Circulation: 8,000pd,; USPS
Advertising rate: Open inch rate $15.00
Established: 1881
Group: Delphos Herald, Inc.
Pub. .... Kurt Krueger
Ed. ....Gary Ridderbusch
Circ. Mgr. .... Liz Schmidt
Assist. Editor ....Doug Etten
Delivery Method: Mail, Newsstand
Areas Served: Vilas and Oneida County

VILAS COUNTY NEWS-REVIEW (WED)

425 W Mill St, Eagle River, WI, 54521-8002, Vilas, USA; gen tel (715) 479-4421; adv tel (715) 479-4421; ed tel (715) 479-4421; gen fax (715) 479-6242; adv fax (715) 479-6242; ed fax (715) 479-6242; disp adv e-mail kurtk@vcnewsreview.com; class adv e-mail maryjoa@vcnewsreview.com; ed e-mail garyr@vcnewsreview.com; web site www.vcnewsreview.com - 50,200(views) 9,800(visitors)
Circulation: 8,000pd,; USPS
Advertising rate: Open inch rate $14.90
Established: 1881
Digital Platform - Mobile: Apple, Android, Windows, Blackberry
Digital Platform - Tablet: Apple iOS, Android, Windows 7, Blackberry Tablet OS
Pub. .... Kurt Krueger
Ed. ....Gary Ridderbusch
Assit. Editor ....Doug Etten
Delivery Method: Mail, Newsstand
Areas Served: Vilas and Oneida County

EAU CLAIRE

THE COUNTRY TODAY (WED)

701 S Farwell St, Eau Claire, WI, 54701-3831, Eau Claire, USA; gen tel (715) 833-

9270; adv tel (715) 833-9276; ed tel (715) 833-9275; gen fax (715) 858-7307; adv fax (715) 858-7307; ed fax (715) 858-7307; disp adv e-mail sue.bauer@ecpc.com; class adv e-mail mary.brownell@ecpc.com; ed e-mail nathan.jackson@ecpc.com; web site www.thecountrytoday.com
Circulation: 25,000pd, 1,124fr; Sworn/Estimate/Non-Audited
Advertising rate: Open inch rate $19.71
Digital Platform - Mobile: Apple, Android, Windows, Blackberry
Digital Platform - Tablet: Apple iOS, Android, Windows 7, Blackberry Tablet OS, Kindle, Nook, Kindle Fire
Reg. Ed./Prod. Coord................. Nate Jackson
Adv. Mgr.. Sue Bauer
Delivery Method: Mail, Newsstand, Racks
Areas Served: Eau Claire County

EDGERTON

EDGERTON REPORTER (WED)

21 N Henry St, Edgerton, WI, 53534-1859, Rock, USA; gen tel (608) 884-3367; adv tel (608) 884-3367; ed tel (608) 884-3367; gen fax (608) 884-8187; adv fax (608) 884-8187; ed fax (608) 884-8187; disp adv e-mail ereport@ticon.net; class adv e-mail ereport@ticon.net; ed e-mail ereport@ticon.net; web site www.edgertonreporter.com
Circulation: 3,000pd, 2,122fr; Sworn/Estimate/Non-Audited
Advertising rate: Open inch rate $11.00
Established: 1874
Digital Platform - Mobile: Apple, Android, Windows, Blackberry
Digital Platform - Tablet: Apple iOS, Android, Windows 7, Blackberry Tablet OS, Kindle, Nook, Kindle Fire
Ed.. Helen V. Everson
Delivery Method: Mail
Areas Served: 53534

ELKHORN

STATELINE NEWS (WED, SUN)

220B Commerce Ct, Elkhorn, WI, 53121-4371, Rock, USA; gen tel (608) 365-1663; adv tel (608) 365-1663; ed tel (608) 365-1663; gen fax (608) 365-7045; adv fax (608) 365-7045; ed fax (608) 365-7045; disp adv e-mail statelinenews@statelinenews.com; class adv e-mail danp@communityshoppers.com; ed e-mail statelinenews@communityshoppers.com; web site www.communityshoppers.com - 16,529(views) 7,140(visitors)
Circulation: 0pd, 33,740fr; VAC
Advertising rate: Open inch rate $20.40
Established: 1968
Group: CSI Media, LLC
Digital Platform - Mobile: Apple, Android, Windows, Blackberry
Digital Platform - Tablet: Apple iOS, Android, Windows 7, Blackberry Tablet OS, Kindle, Nook, Kindle Fire
Gen. Mgr.. Dan Pyfer
Sales Mgr.................................. Heidi Springer
Ed.. Lynn Vollbrecht
Circ. Mgr......................... Christopher Wilhelms
Prod. Mgr.............................. Dave Chiuilicek
Mechanical Specifications: Type page 10 3/8 x 16; E - 7 cols, 1 1/3, 1/6 between; A - 7 cols, 1 1/3, 1/6 between; C - 7 cols, 1 1/3, 1/6 between.Equipment & Software: Hardware — APP/Mac; Presses — 14-KP; Software — Multi-Ad/Creator, Adobe/Illustrator, QPS/QuarkXPress.
Delivery Method: Mail, Newsstand
Areas Served: Rock County

THE ELKHORN INDEPENDENT (THUR)

812 N Wisconsin St, Elkhorn, WI, 53121-1137, Walworth, USA; gen tel (262) 723-2250; adv tel (262) 723-2250; ed tel (262) 723-2250; gen fax (262) 723-7424; adv fax (262) 723-7424; ed fax (262) 723-7424; disp adv e-mail assistant@elkhornindependent.com; class adv e-mail phansen@standard-press.com; ed e-mail elkinde@elkhornindependent.com; web site www.mywalworthcounty.com
Circulation: 2,911pd, 18fr; Sworn/Estimate/Non-Audited
Advertising rate: Open inch rate $8.95
Established: 1853
Group: Southern Lakes Newspapers LLC
Digital Platform - Mobile: Apple, Android, Windows, Blackberry
Digital Platform - Tablet: Apple iOS, Android, Windows 7, Blackberry Tablet OS, Kindle, Nook, Kindle Fire
Pub... Jack Cruger
Ed... Ed Nadolski
Ed. Assistant.......................... Kellen Olshefski
Adv. Mgr.................................... Pete Hansen
Mechanical Specifications: Type page 13 x 21.
Delivery Method: Mail, Racks
Areas Served: Walworth County

WALWORTH COUNTY SUNDAY (SUN)

120 Wright St, Elkhorn, WI, 53121-1935, Walworth, USA; gen tel (262) 728-3424; adv tel (262) 728-3424; ed tel (262) 728-3424; gen fax (262) 728-5479; adv fax (262) 728-5479; ed fax (262) 728-5479; disp adv e-mail jvina@communityshoppers.com; class adv e-mail jvina@communityshoppers.com; ed e-mail danp@communityshoppers.com; web site www.communityshoppers.com
Circulation: 0pd, 39,009fr; VAC
Advertising rate: Open inch rate $20.40
Established: 1926
Group: CSI Media, LLC
Digital Platform - Mobile: Apple, Android, Windows, Blackberry
Digital Platform - Tablet: Apple iOS, Android, Windows 7, Blackberry Tablet OS, Kindle, Nook, Kindle Fire
Ed... Dan Plutchak
Gen. Mgr... Dan Pyfer
Adv. Mgr... Jose Vina
Sales Mgr................................. Heidi Springer
Circ. Mgr........................ Christopher Wilhelms
Prod. Mgr.............................. Dave Chvilicek
Mechanical Specifications: Type page: 10.375 x 16; 7 col
Delivery Method: Mail, Newsstand
Areas Served: 53115, 53545, 53511, 61080

ELLSWORTH

PIERCE COUNTY HERALD (WED)

126 S Chestnut St, Ellsworth, WI, 54011-4117, Pierce, USA; gen tel (715) 273-4334; adv tel (715) 426-1052; ed tel (715) 273-4334; gen fax (715) 273-4335; adv fax (715) 273-4335; ed fax (715) 273-4335; disp adv e-mail pfrebault@rivertowns.net; class adv e-mail classifieds@rivertowns.net; ed e-mail pch@rivertowns.net; web site www.piercecountyherald.com
Circulation: 3,000pd, 28fr; Sworn/Estimate/Non-Audited
Advertising rate: Open inch rate $9.82
Group: Forum Communications Co.
Digital Platform - Mobile: Apple, Android, Windows, Blackberry
Digital Platform - Tablet: Apple iOS, Android, Windows 7, Blackberry Tablet OS, Kindle, Kindle Fire
Pub.. Steve Dzubay
Ed... Bill Kirk
Adv. Dir...................................... Phil Frebault
Gen. Mgr.................................. Victoria Howe
Mechanical Specifications: Type page 13 x 21 1/2; E - 6 cols, 2, 3/16 between; A - 6 cols, 2, 3/16 between; C - 6 cols, 2, 3/16 between.
Delivery Method: Mail, Newsstand
Areas Served: Ellsworth, Spring Valley, Prescott, Hager City, Bay City, Plum City, Elmwood, and Pierce County

ELROY

MESSENGER OF JUNEAU COUNTY (THUR)

229 Main St, Elroy, WI, 53929-1251, Juneau, USA; gen tel (608) 462-4902; adv tel (608)462-4902; ed tel (608)462-4902; disp adv e-mail themessenger@centurytel.net; class adv e-mail themessenger@centurytel.net; ed e-mail themessenger@centurytel.net; web site www.juneaumessenger.com

EVANSVILLE

EVANSVILLE REVIEW (WED)

8409 N US Highway 14, Evansville, WI, 53536-9263, Rock, USA; gen tel (608) 882-5220; adv tel (608) 882-5220; ed tel (608) 882-5220; gen fax (608) 882-5221; adv fax (608) 882-5221; ed fax (608) 882-5221; disp adv e-mail gildner@litewire.net; class adv e-mail gildner@litewire.net; ed e-mail gildner@litewire.net; web site www.evansvillereview.com
Circulation: 3,000pd, 2,295fr; Sworn/Estimate/Non-Audited
Advertising rate: Open inch rate $7.00
Established: 1862
Pub.. Stan Gildner
Ed.. Kelly Gildner
Delivery Method: Mail, Newsstand
Areas Served: 53536, 53502, 52521, 53545

FENNIMORE

FENNIMORE TIMES (THUR)

1150 Lincoln Ave, Fennimore, WI, 53809-1746, Grant, USA; gen tel (608) 822-3912; adv tel (608) 822-3912; ed tel (608) 822-3912; gen fax (608) 822-3916; adv fax (608) 822-3916; ed fax (608) 822-3916; disp adv e-mail tcpads@yousq.net ; class adv e-mail fennimoretimes@tds.net; ed e-mail timeseditor@tds.net ; web site www.swnews4u.com
Circulation: 1,600pd, 20fr; Sworn/Estimate/Non-Audited
Advertising rate: Open inch rate $5.10
Established: 1889
Group: Morris Multimedia, Inc.
Digital Platform - Mobile: Apple, Android
Digital Platform - Tablet: Apple iOS, Android
Pub..................................... John Ingebritsen
Ed...................................... Robert Callahan
Adv. Mgr.................................. Hannah Rupp
Office Mgr............................... Heather Copus
Mechanical Specifications: Type page 14 x 21 1/4; E - 6 cols, 2 1/8, between; A - 6 cols, 2 1/8, between; C - 8 cols, 1 1/2, between.
Delivery Method: Mail, Newsstand
Areas Served: Grant County

FOND DU LAC

ACTION ADVERTISER (WED)

N6637 Rolling Meadows Dr, Fond Du Lac, WI, 54937-9471, Fond du Lac, USA; gen tel (920) 922-4600; adv tel (920) 907-7901; ed tel (920) 922-4600; gen fax (920) 922-0125; adv fax (920) 922-0125; ed fax (920) 922-0125; disp adv e-mail twhicher@fdlreporter.com; class adv e-mail hbradwin@gannett.com; ed e-mail pbreister@fdlreporter.com; web site www.actiononline.net
Circulation: 33,164fr; VAC
Advertising rate: Open inch rate $17.40
Established: 1970
Group: Gannett
Digital Platform - Mobile: Apple, Android
Digital Platform - Tablet: Apple iOS, Android
Ed.. Peggy Breister
Admin. Assistant....................... Tami Whicher
Adv. Mgr............................... Heather Bradwin
Pub... Karen Befus
Prod. Mgr........................... Barb Rosenberger
Mechanical Specifications: Type page: 10.375 x 16; 6 col
Delivery Method: Carrier, Racks
Areas Served: Fond du Lac County

ACTION SUNDAY (SUN)

N6637 Rolling Meadows Dr, Fond Du Lac, WI, 54937-9471, Fond Du Lac, USA; gen tel (920) 922-4600; adv tel (920) 907-7901; ed tel (920) 922-4600; gen fax (920) 922-0125; adv fax (920) 922-0125; ed fax (920) 922-0125; disp adv e-mail twhicher@fdlreporter.com; class adv e-mail hbradwin@gannett.com; ed e-mail pbreister@fdlreporter.com; web site www.actiononline.net
Circulation: 43,069fr; VAC
Advertising rate: Open inch rate $17.40
Established: 1988
Group: Gannett
Digital Platform - Mobile: Apple, Android
Digital Platform - Tablet: Apple iOS, Android
Ed.. Peggy Breister
Admin. Assistant....................... Tami Whicher
Adv. Mgr............................... Heather Bradwin
Mechanical Specifications: Type page: 10.375 x 16; 6 col
Delivery Method: Carrier, Racks
Areas Served: Fond du Lac County

FREDERIC

INTER-COUNTY LEADER (WED)

303 Wisconsin Ave N, Frederic, WI, 54837-9048, USA; gen tel (715) 327-4236; gen fax (715) 327-4117; disp adv e-mail iccpaonline@centurytel.net; ed e-mail editor@leaderregister.com; web site www.leaderregister.com
Circulation: 6,870pd, 0fr; Sworn/Estimate/Non-Audited
Advertising rate: Open inch rate $9.10
Established: 1933
Group: Inter-County Cooperative Publishing Association
Manager.................................. Douglas Panek
Ed... Gary B. King
Delivery Method: Mail, Newsstand
Areas Served: Burnett and Polk counties

GAYS MILLS

CRAWFORD COUNTY INDEPENDENT & KICKAPOO SCOUT (THUR)

320 Main St, Gays Mills, WI, 54631-8278, Crawford, USA; gen tel (608) 735-4413; adv tel (608)735-4413; ed tel (608)735-4413; gen fax (608) 735-4413; adv fax (608)735-4413; ed fax (608)735-4413; disp adv e-mail jinge@tds.net; class adv e-mail jinge@tds.net; ed e-mail jinge@tds.net; web site www.swnews4u.com
Group: Morris Multimedia, Inc.Charley Preusser

GLENWOOD CITY

TRIBUNE PRESS REPORTER (WED)

105 Misty Ct, Glenwood City, WI, 54013-8574, Saint Croix, USA; gen tel (715) 265-4646; adv tel (715) 265-4646; ed tel (715) 265-4646; gen fax (715) 265-7496; adv fax (715) 265-7496; ed fax (715) 265-7496; disp adv e-mail tribune@dewittmedia.com; class adv e-mail tribune@dewittmedia.com; ed e-mail tribune@dewittmedia.com; web site www.dewittmedia.com
Circulation: 2,785pd, 37fr; Sworn/Estimate/Non-Audited
Advertising rate: Open inch rate $6.00
Established: 1889
Group: DeWitt Media Inc.
Digital Platform - Mobile: Apple, Android, Windows, Blackberry
Digital Platform - Tablet: Apple iOS, Android, Windows 7, Blackberry Tablet OS, Kindle
Pub./Ed.................................... Carlton DeWitt
Mng. Ed..................................... Shawn DeWitt
Delivery Method: Mail, Newsstand
Areas Served: 54013

GRANTSBURG

BURNETT COUNTY SENTINEL (WED)

114 W Madison Ave, Grantsburg, WI, 54840-7022, Burnett, USA; gen tel (715) 463-2341;

gen fax (715) 463-5138; disp adv e-mail stacy@burnettcountysentinel.com; class adv e-mail stacy@burnettcountysentinel.com; ed e-mail editor@burnettcountysentinel.com; web site www.burnettcountysentinel.com
Circulation: 2,425pd,; USPS
Advertising rate: Open inch rate $7.50
Established: 1875
Group: Sentinel Publications
Digital Platform - Mobile: Apple, Android
Digital Platform - Tablet: Apple iOS, Android
Office Mgr. .... Teresa Nordrum
Publisher .... Tom Stangl
Advertising Agent .... Stacy Coy
Editor .... Sean Devlin
Mechanical Specifications: Type page 13 1/8 x 21 1/2; E - 6 cols, 2, between; A - 6 cols, 2, between; C - 6 cols, 2, between.Equipment & Software: Hardware — APP/Mac.
Delivery Method: Mail, Racks
Areas Served: Burnett County

HARTLAND

KETTLE MORAINE INDEX (THUR)

1010 Richards Rd, Hartland, WI, 53029-8301, Waukesha, USA; gen tel (262) 367-3272; adv tel (262) 367-3272; ed tel (262) 367-3272; gen fax (262) 367-7414; adv fax (262) 367-7414; ed fax (262) 367-1136; disp adv e-mail slyles@jrn.com; class adv e-mail mbilke@jrn.com; ed e-mail lakenews@jcp-group.com; web site www.livinglakecountry.com
Circulation: 653pd, 0fr; AAM
Advertising rate: Open inch rate $20.50 (Tue); $21.10 (Thur)
Group: Lake County Publications
JCP Group
Pub./Adv. Dir./Gen. Mgr. .... Steve Lyles
Mng. Ed. .... Scott Peterson
Office Mgr. .... Katie Zurn
Adv. Coord. .... Britani Zambo
Delivery Method: Mail, Newsstand
Areas Served: Waukesha County

LAKE COUNTRY REPORTER (TUES, WED, THUR)

1010 Richards Rd, Hartland, WI, 53029-8301, Waukesha, USA; gen tel (262) 367-3272; adv tel (262) 367-3272; ed tel (262) 367-3272; gen fax (262) 367-7414; adv fax (262) 367-7414; ed fax (262) 367-1136; disp adv e-mail slyles@jrn.com; class adv e-mail mbilke@jrn.com; ed e-mail lakenews@jcp-group.com; web site www.livinglakecountry.com
Circulation: 5,050pd,; AAM
Advertising rate: Open inch rate $20.50 (Tue); $21.10 (Thur)
Group: Lake County Publications
JCP Group
Digital Platform - Mobile: Apple, Android, Windows
Digital Platform - Tablet: Apple iOS, Android, Windows 7
Pub./Adv. Dir./Gen. Mgr. .... Steve Lyles
Mng. Ed. .... Scott Peterson
Office Mgr. .... Katie Zurn
Adv. Coord. .... Britani Zambo
Mechanical Specifications: Type page 9 3/4 x 13 3/4; E - 4 cols, 2 1/4, 1/6 between; A - 4 cols, 2 1/4, 1/6 between.Equipment & Software: Hardware — PC; Presses — G/Community; Software — QPS/QuarkXPress 3.1.
Delivery Method: Mail, Newsstand
Areas Served: Waukesha County

OCONOMOWOC FOCUS (TUES, THUR)

1010 Richards Rd, Hartland, WI, 53029-8301, Waukesha, USA; gen tel (262) 367-3272; adv tel (262) 367-3272; ed tel (262) 367-3272; gen fax (262) 367-7414; adv fax (262) 367-7414; ed fax (262) 367-1136; disp adv e-mail slyles@jrn.com; class adv e-mail mbilke@jrn.com; ed e-mail lakenews@jcp-group.com; web site www.livinglakecountry.com
Circulation: 1,303pd,; AAM
Advertising rate: Open inch rate $20.50 (Tue); $21.10 (Thur)
Group: Lake County Publications
JCP Group
Pub./Adv. Dir./Gen. Mgr. .... Steve Lyles
Mng. Ed. .... Scott Peterson
Office Mgr. .... Katie Zurn
Adv. Coord. .... Britani Zambo
Delivery Method: Mail, Newsstand
Areas Served: Waukesha County

SUSSEX SUN (WED)

1010 Richards Rd, Hartland, WI, 53029-8301, Waukesha, USA; gen tel (262) 367-3272; adv tel (262) 367-3272; ed tel (262) 367-3272; gen fax (262) 367-7414; adv fax (262) 367-7414; ed fax (262) 367-1136; disp adv e-mail slyles@jrn.com; class adv e-mail mbilke@jrn.com; ed e-mail lakenews@jcp-group.com; web site www.livinglakecountry.com
Circulation: 1,239pd,; AAM
Advertising rate: Open inch rate $20.50 (Tue); $21.10 (Thur)
Group: JCP Group
Pub./Adv. Dir./Gen. Mgr. .... Steve Lyles
Mng. Ed. .... Scott Peterson
Office Mgr. .... Katie Zurn
Adv. Coord. .... Britani Zambo
Delivery Method: Mail, Newsstand
Areas Served: Waukesha County

HAYWARD

SAWYER COUNTY RECORD (WED)

15617B US Highway 63, Hayward, WI, 54843-4244, Sawyer, USA; gen tel (715) 634-4881; adv tel (715) 634-4881; ed tel (715) 634-4881; gen fax (715) 634-8191; adv fax (715) 634-8191; ed fax (715) 634-8191; disp adv e-mail dlaporte@sawyercountyrecord.net; class adv e-mail denise.p@sawyercountyrecord.net; ed e-mail akurth@sawyercountyrecord.net; web site www.apg-wi.com
Circulation: 4,000pd, 44fr; CAC
Advertising rate: Open inch rate $14.70
Established: 1893
Group: Adams Publishing Group, LLC
Digital Platform - Mobile: Apple, Android, Windows, Blackberry
Digital Platform - Tablet: Apple iOS, Android, Windows 7, Blackberry Tablet OS, Kindle, Nook, Kindle Fire
Pub. .... Janet Krokson
Mng. Ed. .... Anna Kurth
Adv. Mgr. .... David LaPorte
Mechanical Specifications: Type page 11 1/16 x 21; E - 6 cols, 1 5/6, 1/8 between; A - 6 cols, 1 5/6, 1/8 between; C - 6 cols, 1 5/6, 1/8 between.
Delivery Method: Mail, Newsstand, Racks
Areas Served: Sawyer County

HILLSBORO

HILLSBORO SENTRY-ENTERPRISE (THUR)

839 Water Ave, Hillsboro, WI, 54634-6213, Vernon, USA; gen tel (608) 489-2264; gen fax (608) 489-2348; disp adv e-mail observerads@mwt.net; class adv e-mail observerads@mwt.net; ed e-mail sentry@mwt.net ; web site www.swnews4u.com
Circulation: 1,694pd, 108fr; Sworn/Estimate/Non-Audited
Advertising rate: Open inch rate $6.50
Established: 1885
Group: Morris Multimedia, Inc.
Digital Platform - Mobile: Apple, Android
Digital Platform - Tablet: Apple iOS, Android
Reg. Pub. .... John Ingebritsen
Adv. Dir. .... Dave McGowan
Office Mgr. .... Mary Sterba
Managing Editor .... Harvey Leverenz
Mechanical Specifications: Type page 11 x 16; E - 5 cols, 2, 1/4 between; A - 5 cols, 2, 1/4 between; C - 5 cols, 2, 1/4 between.Equipment & Software: Hardware — APP/Mac; Software — QPS/QuarkXPress.
Delivery Method: Mail, Newsstand
Areas Served: 54634

HURLEY

IRON COUNTY MINER (THUR)

216 Copper St, Hurley, WI, 54534-1339, Iron, USA; gen tel (715) 561-3405; adv tel (715) 561-3405; ed tel (715) 561-3405; gen fax (715) 561-3799; adv fax (715) 561-3799; ed fax (715) 561-3799; disp adv e-mail icm@ironcountyminer.com; class adv e-mail icm@ironcountyminer.com; ed e-mail icm@ironcountyminer.com; web site www.ironcountyminer.com
Circulation: 2,430pd, 114fr; Sworn/Estimate/Non-Audited
Advertising rate: Open inch rate $5.30
Established: 1884
Digital Platform - Mobile: Windows
Digital Platform - Tablet: Windows 7
Pub./Ed. .... Ernest Moore
Delivery Method: Mail, Newsstand
Areas Served: Iron County

JUNEAU

DODGE COUNTY INDEPENDENT-NEWS (THUR)

122 S Main St, Juneau, WI, 53039-1018, Dodge, USA; gen tel (920)386-2421; adv tel (920)386-2421; ed tel (920)386-2421; gen fax (920)386-2422; adv fax (920)386-2422; ed fax (920)386-2422; disp adv e-mail dcind@charterinternet.com; class adv e-mail dcind@charterinternet.com; ed e-mail dcind@charterinternet.com
Circulation: 1,000pd, 27fr; Sworn/Estimate/Non-Audited
Advertising rate: Open inch rate $5.55
Pub. .... James M. Clifford
Gen. Mgr. .... Kevin C. Clifford
Ed. .... Thomas L. Schultz
Mechanical Specifications: Type page 13 1/4 x 21 1/2; E - 6 cols, 2 1/2, between; A - 6 cols, 2 1/2, between; C - 8 cols, 1 1/2, between. Equipment & Software: Hardware — APP/Mac; Presses — G/Community; Software — QPS/QuarkXPress.
Delivery Method: Mail
Areas Served: Dodge County

KAUKAUNA

THE TIMES-VILLAGER (WED, SAT)

1900 Crooks Ave, Kaukauna, WI, 54130-3248, Outagamie, USA; gen tel (920) 759-2000; adv tel (920) 759-2000; ed tel (920) 759-2000; gen fax (920) 759-7344; adv fax (920) 759-7344; ed fax (920) 759-7344; disp adv e-mail sales@timesvillager.com; class adv e-mail classifieds@timesvillager.com; ed e-mail editor@timesvillager.com; web site www.timesvillager.com
Circulation: 5,000pd, 500fr; Sworn/Estimate/Non-Audited
Advertising rate: Open inch rate $10.50
Established: 1880
Group: News Publishing Inc.
Digital Platform - Mobile: Windows
Digital Platform - Tablet: Windows 7
Ed. .... Brian Roebke
Sales .... Kim Reynebeau
Sports .... Dustin Riese
Mechanical Specifications: Type page 9 3/4 x 13 3/4; E - 4 cols, between; A - 4 cols, between; C - 8 cols, between.Equipment & Software: Hardware — PC; Software — QPS/QuarkXPress, Adobe/PageMaker, InDesign
Delivery Method: Mail
Areas Served: 54130, 54136, 54140, 54113, 54915, 54129

KEWAUNEE

KEWAUNEE COUNTY STAR-NEWS (SAT)

203 Ellis St, Kewaunee, WI, 54216-1051, Kewaunee, USA; gen tel (920)388-3175; adv tel (920)304-3300; ed tel (920)388-3175; gen fax (920)388-0198; adv fax (920)388-0198; ed fax (920)388-0198; disp adv e-mail pharkema@gokewauneecounty.com; class adv e-mail ddana@gokewauneecounty.com; ed e-mail editorial@gokewauneecounty.com; web site www.gokewauneecounty.com
Circulation: 11,060fr; VAC
Advertising rate: Open inch rate $13.00
Established: 1859
Group: Gannett
Digital Platform - Mobile: Apple, Android
Digital Platform - Tablet: Apple iOS, Android, Windows 7
Assoc. Ed. .... Warren Bluhm
Adv. Assistant .... Deb Dana
Pub. .... Scott Johnson
Circ. Mgr .... Scott Domalick
Prod. Mgr .... Diane Nolan
Adv. Sales Rep. .... Leah Clover
Classified Mgr. .... Laurie Bolle
Mechanical Specifications: Type page 11 5/8 x 20 3/16; E - 6 cols, 1 13/16, 1/6 between; A - 6 cols, 1 13/16, 1/6 between; C - 9 cols, 1 1/16, 1/12 between.Equipment & Software: Hardware — APP/Mac; Software — InDesign
Delivery Method: Carrier
Areas Served: 52401, 52405, 54208, 54213, 54216, 54217, 54229

LA CROSSE

COULEE NEWS (THUR)

401 3rd St N, La Crosse, WI, 54601-3267, La Crosse, USA; gen tel (608)782-9710; adv tel (608)791-8260; ed tel (608)791-8219; gen fax (608)786-1670; adv fax (608)786-1670; ed fax (608)786-1670; disp adv e-mail barb.formanek@lee.net; class adv e-mail ads@lacrossetribune.com; ed e-mail mike.burns@lee.net; web site www.couleenews.com
Circulation: 1,743pd, 4fr; Sworn/Estimate/Non-Audited
Advertising rate: Open inch rate $9.50
Group: Lee Enterprises, Inc.
Digital Platform - Mobile: Apple, Android
Digital Platform - Tablet: Apple iOS, Android, Windows 7
Pub. .... Chris Hardie
Ed. .... Randy Erickson
Mechanical Specifications: Type page 11 2/3 x 21 1/2; E - 6 cols, 1 1/4, 1/6 between; A - 6 cols, 1 1/4, 1/6 between; C - 6 cols, 1 1/4, 1/6 between.Equipment & Software: Hardware — ACT/Pentium 3/Gateway; Software — QPS/QuarkXPress 4.0.
Delivery Method: Mail, Newsstand
Areas Served: La Crosse County

HOUSTON COUNTY NEWS (THUR)

401 3rd St N, La Crosse, WI, 54601-3267, La Crosse, USA; gen tel (608)791-8411; adv tel (608)791-8411; ed tel (608)791-8411; gen fax (608)791-8238; adv fax (608)791-8238; ed fax (608)791-8238; disp adv e-mail Shari.Holliday@lacrossetribune.com; class adv e-mail ads@lacrossetribune.com; ed e-mail mike.burns@lee.net; web site www.houstonconews.com
Circulation: 1,953pd, 36fr; Sworn/Estimate/Non-Audited
Advertising rate: Open inch rate $7.45
Established: 1968
Digital Platform - Mobile: Apple, Android
Digital Platform - Tablet: Apple iOS, Android, Windows 7
Pub. .... Chris Hardie
Ed. .... Ryan Henry
Mechanical Specifications: Type page 6 x 21 1/2; E - 3 cols, 3 1/4, 1/4 between; A - 3 cols, 3 1/4, 1/4 between.Equipment & Software: Hardware — APP/Mac; Presses — G/Community; Software — QPS/QuarkXPress 4.0.
Delivery Method: Mail, Newsstand
Areas Served: 55947, 55941, 55943, 55919, 55925

ONALASKA HOLMEN COURIER-LIFE (FRI)

401 3rd St N, La Crosse, WI, 54601-3267, La Crosse, USA; gen tel (608)782-9710; adv tel (608)791-8257; ed tel (608)791-8219; gen fax (608)782-9723; adv fax (608)791-8213; ed fax (608)782-9723; disp adv e-mail barb.

formanek@lee.net; class adv e-mail ads@lacrossetribune.com; ed e-mail mike.burns@lee.net; web site www.courierlifenews.com
Circulation: 3,026pd,; Sworn/Estimate/Non-Audited
Advertising rate: Open inch rate $7.80
Established: 2008
Group: Lee Enterprises, Inc.
Digital Platform - Mobile: Apple, Android
Digital Platform - Tablet: Apple iOS, Android, Windows 7
Ed. .... Randy Erickson
Mechanical Specifications: Type page 11 5/8 x 21 1/2; E - 6 cols, 1/8 between; A - 6 cols, 1 5/6, 1/8 between; C - 9 cols, 1 15/16, 3/20 between.Equipment & Software: ; Presses — Goss Urbanite and Dauphin Graphic Machine 850
Delivery Method: Mail, Newsstand
Areas Served: 54601, 54603, 54636, 54650

LADYSMITH

LADYSMITH NEWS (THUR)

120 W 3rd St S, Ladysmith, WI, 54848-1764, Rusk, USA; gen tel (715) 532-5591; adv tel (715) 532-5591; ed tel (715) 532-5591; gen fax (715) 532-6644; adv fax (715) 532-6644; ed fax (715) 532-6644; disp adv e-mail adsales@ladysmithnews.com; class adv e-mail advertise@ladysmithnews.com; ed e-mail editor@ladysmithnews.com; web site www.ladysmithnews.com
Circulation: 5,750pd,; Sworn/Estimate/Non-Audited
Advertising rate: Open inch rate $8.25
Established: 1895
Digital Platform - Mobile: Apple, Android, Windows, Blackberry
Digital Platform - Tablet: Apple iOS, Android, Windows 7, Blackberry Tablet OS, Kindle, Nook, Kindle Fire
Pub. .... James L. Bell
Accts. Mgr. .... Marleen Harmon
Editor .... Luke Klink
Brian Joles
Mechanical Specifications: Type page 13 x 21 1/4; E - 6 cols, 2, 3/16 between; A - 6 cols, 2, 3/16 between; C - 6 cols, 2, 3/16 between. Equipment & Software: Hardware — APP/Mac G4; Presses — G.
Delivery Method: Mail, Racks
Areas Served: Rusk County

LAKE GENEVA

LAKE GENEVA REGIONAL NEWS (THUR)

315 Broad St, Lake Geneva, WI, 53147-1811, Walworth, USA; gen tel (262) 248-4444; adv tel (262)248-4444; ed tel (262)248-8096; gen fax (262) 248-4476; adv fax (262)248-4476; ed fax (242)248-4476; disp adv e-mail rireland@lakegenevanews.net; class adv e-mail sue@lakegenevanews.net; ed e-mail newsroom@lakegenevanews.net; web site www.lakegenevanews.net
Circulation: 4,000pd,; Sworn/Estimate/Non-Audited
Advertising rate: Open inch rate $11.75
Established: 1872
Group: United Communications Corporation
Digital Platform - Mobile: Apple, Android
Digital Platform - Tablet: Apple iOS, Android
Mng. Ed. .... Robert Ireland
Office Mgr. .... Sue Hinske
Mechanical Specifications: Type page 11.125 x 19.75; E - 6 cols, 2 1/16, 1/8 between; A - 6 cols, 2 1/16, 1/8 between; C - 6 cols, 2 1/16, 1/8 between.Equipment & Software: Hardware — PC
Delivery Method: Mail, Newsstand
Areas Served: Lake Geneva

LAKE MILLS

THE LAKE MILLS LEADER (THUR)

320 N Main St, Lake Mills, WI, 53551-1137, Jefferson, USA; gen tel (920)648-2334; adv tel 608-478-2517; ed tel (920)648-2334; disp adv e-mail mfeiler@hngnews.com; class adv e-mail classifieds@hngnews.com; ed e-mail leadereditor@hngnews.com; web site www.lakemillsleader.com
Circulation: 2,100pd,; USPS
Advertising rate: Open inch rate $13.95
Established: 1878
Group: Hometown News Group
Digital Platform - Mobile: Apple, Android
Digital Platform - Tablet: Apple iOS, Android
Pub .... Brian Knox
Managing Editor .... Chris Frost
Advertising Manager .... Missy Feiler
Business Manager .... Chris Drake
Circulation Director .... Brian Knox II
General Manager .... Robb Grindstaff
Mechanical Specifications: Type page 14 1/2 x 21; E - 6 cols, 2 1/16, 1/6 between; A - 6 cols, 2 1/16, 1/6 between; C - 6 cols, 2 1/16, 1/6 between.Equipment & Software: Hardware — APP/Mac; Presses — WPC/Web Leader; Software — Adobe/PageMaker 6.5, Adobe/Photoshop 5.5, Adobe/Illustrator 8.0, QPS/QuarkXPress 4.0.
Delivery Method: Mail, Newsstand, Racks
Areas Served: 53551

LANCASTER

GRANT COUNTY HERALD INDEPENDENT (THUR)

208 W Cherry St, Lancaster, WI, 53813-1629, Grant, USA; gen tel (608) 723-2151; adv tel (608) 723-2151; ed tel (608) 723-2151; gen fax (608) 723-7272; adv fax (608) 723-7272; ed fax (608) 723-7272; disp adv e-mail kkads@tds.net; class adv e-mail jinge@tds.net; ed e-mail newseditor@tds.net ; web site www.swnews4u.com
Circulation: 3,400pd,; Sworn/Estimate/Non-Audited
Advertising rate: Open inch rate $7.61
Established: 1843
Digital Platform - Mobile: Apple, Android
Digital Platform - Tablet: Apple iOS, Android
Reg. Pub. .... John Ingebritsen
Reg. Adv. Dir. .... Kevin Kelly
Ed. .... David Timmerman
Delivery Method: Mail, Newsstand
Areas Served: Lancaster, Bloomington, Cassville, Potosi, Patch Grove, Beetown, Bagley, Glen Haven, Mt. Hope, Mt. Ida, Woodman, Stitzer, Tennyson, North Andover, Burton, Ellenboro, and Wyalusing

LODI

LODI ENTERPRISE & POYNETTE PRESS (THUR)

105 S Main St, Ste H, Lodi, WI, 53555-1140, Columbia, USA; gen tel (606)592-3261; adv tel (606)592-3261; ed tel (608)729-3366; adv fax (606)592-3866; ed fax (606)592-3866; disp adv e-mail mfeiler@hngnews.com; class adv e-mail classifieds@hngnews.com; ed e-mail tmyers@hngnews.com; web site www.hngnews.com
Circulation: 2,725pd,; USPS
Advertising rate: Open inch rate $14.95
Group: Hometown News Group
Digital Platform - Mobile: Windows
Digital Platform - Tablet: Windows 7
Publisher .... Brian Knox
Managing Editor .... Tamar Myers
Advertising Manager .... Missy Feiler
Circulation Director .... Brian Knox II
General Manager .... Robb Grindstaff
Business Manager .... Chris Drake
Delivery Method: Mail, Newsstand, Racks
Areas Served: Columbia and Dane County

LOYAL

THE TRIBUNE RECORD-GLEANER (WED)

318 N Main St, Loyal, WI, 54446-9407, Clark, USA; gen tel (715)255-8531; adv tel (715)255-8531; ed tel (715)255-8531; gen fax (715)255-8357; adv fax (715)255-8357; ed fax (715)255-8357; disp adv e-mail news@trgnews.com; class adv e-mail news@trgnews.com; ed e-mail news@trgnews.com; web site www.centralwinews.com
Circulation: 3,100pd,; Sworn/Estimate/Non-Audited
Advertising rate: Open inch rate $10.30
Established: 1969
Ed. .... Dean Lesar
Delivery Method: Mail
Areas Served: Clark County

THE TRIBUNE-PHONOGRAPH (WED)

318 N Main St, Loyal, WI, 54446-9407, Clark, USA; gen tel (715)223-2342; adv tel (715)223-2342; ed tel (715)223-2342; gen fax (715)255-8357; adv fax (715)255-8357; ed fax (715)255-8357; disp adv e-mail tpads@tpprinting.com; class adv e-mail tpads@tpprinting.com; ed e-mail tp@tpprinting.com; web site www.centralwinews.com
Circulation: 3,100pd,; Sworn/Estimate/Non-Audited
Advertising rate: Open inch rate $10.30
Established: 1969
Ed. .... Dean Lesar
Delivery Method: Mail
Areas Served: Clark County

MADISON

THE CAPITAL TIMES (WED)

1901 Fish Hatchery Rd, Madison, WI, 53713-1248, Dane, USA; gen tel (608) 252-6400; adv tel (608) 252-6274; gen fax (608) 252-6445; adv fax (608) 252-6333; ed fax (608) 252-6445; disp adv e-mail jallen@madison.com; class adv e-mail jallen@madison.com; ed e-mail citydesk@madison.com; web site http://host.madison.com/ct/
Circulation: 61,000pd, 8,000fr; Sworn/Estimate/Non-Audited
Established: 1917
Digital Platform - Mobile: Apple, Android
Digital Platform - Tablet: Apple iOS, Kindle, Kindle Fire
Publisher .... Clayton Frink
Ed. .... Dave Zweifel
Books Ed. .... Lynn Danielson
Editor .... Paul Fanlund
Food Writer .... Debra Carr-Elsing
Chris Murphy
Katie Dean
Jason Joyce
Rob Thomas
Pam Wells
Steven Elbow
Brandon Raygo
Amber Walker
Lisa Speckhard
Katelyn Ferral
Abigail Becker
Jessie Opoien
Pat Schneider
Michelle Stocker
Saiyna Bashir
John Nichols
Lindsay Christians
Delivery Method: Mail, Carrier, Racks

THE CHEESE REPORTER (WED)

2810 Crossroads Dr, Ste 3000, Madison, WI, 53718-7972, Dane, USA; gen tel (608)246-8430; adv tel (608)246-8430; ed tel (608)246-8430; gen fax (608)246-8431; adv fax (608)246-8431; ed fax (608)246-8431; disp adv e-mail advertisers@cheesereporter.com; class adv e-mail advertisers@cheesereporter.com; ed e-mail dgroves@cheesereporter.com; web site www.cheesereporter.com
Pub./Ed. .... Dick Groves
Asst. Ed. .... Moira Crowley
Mktg. Dir./Adv. Mgr. .... Kevin Thome
Subscriptions .... Betty Merkes

THE MADISON TIMES (FRI)

313 W Beltline Hwy, Ste 132, Madison, WI, 53713-2679, Dane, USA; gen tel (608)270-9470; adv tel (608)270-9470; ed tel (608)270-9470; disp adv e-mail sales@madtimes.com; class adv e-mail sales@madtimes.com; ed e-mail news@madtimes.com; web site themadisontimes.themadent.com
Circulation: 250pd, 8,750fr; Sworn/Estimate/Non-Audited
Advertising rate: Open inch rate $26.80
Established: 1991
Sales Manager .... Bri Breunig
Areas Served: Madison, Dane County, WI

MANITOWOC

LAKESHORE CHRONICLE (WED, SUN)

902 Franklin St, Manitowoc, WI, 54220-4514, Manitowoc, USA; gen tel (920)684-4433; adv tel (920)684-4433; ed tel (920)686-2138; gen fax (920)686-2103; adv fax (920)686-2103; ed fax (920)686-2103; disp adv e-mail ljohnson@htrnews.com; class adv e-mail dmahloch@htrnews.com; ed e-mail breid@gannett.com; web site www.htrnews.com
Circulation: 28,473fr; VAC
Advertising rate: Open inch rate $30.59
Group: Gannett
Digital Platform - Mobile: Apple, Android
Digital Platform - Tablet: Apple iOS, Android, Windows 7
Ed. .... Pat Pankratz
Pub. .... Lowell Johnson
Circ. Mgr .... Dave Sielski
Prod. Mgr .... Greg Fiorito
Delivery Method: Mail, Newsstand
Areas Served: Manitowoc County

MAUSTON

JUNEAU COUNTY STAR-TIMES (WED, SAT)

201 E State St, Mauston, WI, 53948-1390, Juneau, USA; gen tel (608)847-7341; adv tel (608)847-7341 ext. 222; ed tel (608)847-7341; gen fax (608)847-4867; adv fax (608)745-3530; ed fax (608)847-4867; disp adv e-mail mmeyers@capitalnewspapers.com; class adv e-mail jcst-news@capitalnewspapers.com; ed e-mail jcuevas@capitalnewspapers.com; web site www.wiscnews.com
Circulation: 2,771pd,; AAM
Advertising rate: Open inch rate $12.80
Established: 1857
Group: Capital Newspapers
Digital Platform - Mobile: Apple, Android
Digital Platform - Tablet: Apple iOS, Android, Windows 7
Gen. Mgr. .... Matt Meyers
Ed. .... Jason Cuevas
Delivery Method: Mail, Racks
Areas Served: Elroy, Mauston, Necedah, New Lisbon, and Wonewoc

MAYVILLE

THE DODGE COUNTY PIONEER (THUR)

126 Bridge St, Mayville, WI, 53050-1634, Dodge, USA; gen tel (920) 387-2211; adv tel (920) 387-2211; ed tel (920) 387-2211; gen fax (920) 387-5515; adv fax (920) 387-5515; ed fax (920) 387-5515; disp adv e-mail salesmgr@dodgecountypionier.com; class adv e-mail salemgr@dodgecountypionier.com; ed e-mail mayville@dodgecountypionier.com; web site www.dodgecountypionier.com
Circulation: 3,221pd,; USPS
Advertising rate: Open inch rate $11.88
Established: 1892
Digital Platform - Mobile: Apple, Android
Digital Platform - Tablet: Apple iOS, Android, Kindle, Kindle Fire
Pub. .... Andrew Johnson
Mechanical Specifications: Type page 13 7/8 x 12 1/2; E - 8 cols, 1 2/3, 1/12 between; A - 8 cols, 1 2/3, 1/12 between; C - 8 cols, 1 2/3, 1/12 between.Equipment & Software: Hardware — I-macs and pc's; Presses — no web full color digital sheet; Software — Adobe Suites, Quark, Office

Delivery Method: Mail
Areas Served: 53050, 53032, 53035, 53922, 53099, 53048, 53091, 53006

MERRILL

FOTO NEWS (WED)
807 E 1st St, Merrill, WI, 54452-2412, Lincoln, USA; gen tel (715) 536-7121; adv tel (715) 536-7121; ed tel (715) 536-7121; gen fax (715) 539-3686; adv fax (715) 539-3686; ed fax (715) 539-3686; disp adv e-mail fotonewsads@mmclocal.com ; class adv e-mail bpatterson@mmclocal.com; ed e-mail clueck@mmclocal.com ; web site www.merrillfotonews.com
Circulation: 172pd, 15,949fr; VAC
Advertising rate: Open inch rate $28.30
Established: 1955
Group: Multi Media Channels
Digital Platform - Mobile: Apple, Android, Windows, Blackberry
Digital Platform - Tablet: Apple iOS, Android, Windows 7, Blackberry Tablet OS, Kindle, Nook, Kindle Fire
Gen. Mgr. .... Tim Schreiber
Ed. .... Colin Lueck
Mechanical Specifications: Type page 9 3/4 x 11; E - 6 cols, 2 13/40, 1/4 between; A - 4 cols, 2 13/40, 1/4 between; C - 8 cols, 1 1/2, 1/4 between.Equipment & Software: Hardware — APP/Mac; Presses — KP/News King, HI/ Sheet-fed press; Software — Adobe/PageMaker 5.0.
Delivery Method: Mail, Newsstand, Racks
Areas Served: 54401, 54403, 54411, 54435, 54438, 54442, 54448, 54451, 54452, 54455, 54470, 54474, 54476, 54481, 54487, 54501, 54564

MERRILL COURIER (WED)
14027 E. Main St., Merrill, WI, 54452, Lincoln, USA; gen tel (715) 536-5843; adv tel (715)536-5843; ed tel (715)536-5843; gen fax (715)539-3686; adv fax (715)539-3686; ed fax (715)339-3686; disp adv e-mail jgartman@mmclocal.com; class adv e-mail jgartman@mmclocal.com; ed e-mail clueck@mmclocal.com; web site www.merrillcourier.net
Group: Multi-Media ChannelsSusan Hovind

MILTON

THE MILTON COURIER (THUR)
513 Vernal Ave, Milton, WI, 53563-1144, Rock, USA; gen tel (608)868-2442; adv tel (608)868-2442; ed tel (608)868-2442; gen fax (608)868-4664; adv fax (608)868-4664; ed fax (608)868-4664; disp adv e-mail courierads@hngnews.com; class adv e-mail milton@hngnews.com; ed e-mail couriereditor@hngnews.com; web site www.hngnews.com
Circulation: 3,450pd, 58fr; Sworn/Estimate/ Non-Audited
Advertising rate: Open inch rate $10.30
Established: 1878
Group: Hometown News Group
Digital Platform - Mobile: Apple, Android
Digital Platform - Tablet: Apple iOS, Android, Windows 7
Pub. .... Brian Knox
Mng. Ed. .... James Debilzen
Adv. Mgr. .... Paul McMurray
Gen. Mgr. .... Barb Trimble
Graphics/Prod. Coord. .... Susan Angell
Sports Ed. .... Michael Gouvion
Office Clerk. .... Judy Lippincott
Mechanical Specifications: 12 inch. x 21 inch.
Delivery Method: Mail, Newsstand
Areas Served: 53563, 53546

MILWAUKEE

MILWAUKEE BUSINESS JOURNAL (FRI)
825 N Jefferson St Ste 200, Suite 200, Milwaukee, WI, 53202-3720, Milwaukee, USA; gen tel (414) 277-8181; adv tel (414) 336-7112; ed tel (414) 336-7116; gen fax (414) 277-8191; disp adv e-mail jon.armstrong@biztimes.com; class adv e-mail robert.bahillo@biztimes.com; ed e-mail andrew.weiland@biztimes.com; web site www.bizjournals.com/milwaukee
Circulation: 413pd, 11,258fr; Sworn/Estimate/ Non-Audited
Advertising rate: Open inch rate $7,950.00 (Full-Page)
Established: 1995
Group: BizTimes Media LLC
Digital Platform - Mobile: Apple, Android
Digital Platform - Tablet: Apple iOS, Android, Windows 7
Pub. .... Dan Meyer
Pub. .... Mark Sabljak
Exec. Ed. .... Steve Jagler
Ed. in Chief .... Mark Kass
Adv. Mgr. .... Kristy Leutermann
Delivery Method: Mail, Newsstand, Racks
Areas Served: Southeastern Wisconsin

MILWAUKEE POST (FRI)
3397 S Howell Ave, Milwaukee, WI, 53207-2743, Milwaukee, USA; gen tel (414)744-6370; adv tel (414)744-6370; ed tel (414)744-6370; gen fax (414)375-7070; adv fax (414)375-7070; ed fax (414)375-7070; disp adv e-mail mkepost@conleynet.com; class adv e-mail mkepost@conleynet.com; ed e-mail dmuck@conleynet.com; web site www.gmtoday.com
Group: Conley Media LLC
Ed. .... Dan Muckelbauer

MINERAL POINT

DEMOCRAT TRIBUNE (THUR)
334 High St, Mineral Point, WI, 53565-1219, Iowa, USA; gen tel (608) 987-2141; adv tel (608) 987-2141; ed tel (608) 987-2141; gen fax (608) 935-9531; adv fax (608) 935-9531; ed fax (608) 935-9531; disp adv e-mail jdoye@thedodgevillechronicle.com; class adv e-mail jdoye@thedodgevillechronicle.com; ed e-mail jdoye@thedodgevillechronicle.com
Circulation: 1,200pd, 15fr; Sworn/Estimate/ Non-Audited
Advertising rate: Open inch rate $7.25
Established: 1848
Pub. .... J. Patrick Reilly
Pub. .... T. Michael Reilly
Ed. .... Joelle Doye
Delivery Method: Mail, Newsstand
Areas Served: Mineral Point

MINOCQUA

LAKELAND TIMES (TUES, FRI)
510 Chippewa St, Minocqua, WI, 54548-9395, Oneida, USA; gen tel (715) 356-5236; adv tel (715) 356-5236; ed tel (715) 356-5236; gen fax (715) 358-2121; adv fax (715) 358-2121; ed fax (715) 358-2121; disp adv e-mail sales@lakelandtimes.com; class adv e-mail classifieds@lakelandtimes.com; ed e-mail editor@lakelandtimes.com; web site www.lakelandtimes.com
Circulation: 9,873pd,; Sworn/Estimate/Non-Audited
Advertising rate: Open inch rate $6.75
Established: 1891
Digital Platform - Mobile: Apple, Android
Digital Platform - Tablet: Apple iOS, Android, Windows 7
Gen. Mgr. .... Gregg Walker
Adv. Mgr. .... Tony Loomis
Assoc. Ed. .... Ray Rivard
Mechanical Specifications: Type page 10 1/2 x 16; E - 6 cols, 1 7/12, 1/6 between; A - 6 cols, 1 7/12, 1/6 between; C - 6 cols, 1 7/12, 1/6 between.Equipment & Software: Hardware — APP/Mac; Software — QPS/QuarkXPress.
Delivery Method: Mail, Racks
Areas Served: Oneida County

MONDOVI

TRI-COUNTY NEWS (THUR)
123 W Main St, Mondovi, WI, 54755-1523, Buffalo, USA; gen tel (715) 597-3313; adv tel (715) 597-3313; ed tel (715) 597-3313; gen fax (715) 597-2705; adv fax (715) 597-2705; ed fax (715) 597-2705; disp adv e-mail patrick@media-md.net; class adv e-mail patrick@media-md.net; ed e-mail tricountynews@media-md.net
Circulation: 1,418pd, 10fr; Sworn/Estimate/ Non-Audited
Advertising rate: Open inch rate $8.50
Mng. Ed. .... Brian Sheridan
Graphic Design .... Erika Bjerstedt
Adv. Mng. .... Patrick Milliren
Pub. .... Michael Stumpf
Mechanical Specifications: Type page 13 x 21 1/2; E - 6 cols, 2, between; A - 6 cols, 2, between; C - 6 cols, 2, between.Equipment & Software: Hardware — APP/Mac; Presses — G/Community; Software — Adobe/ PageMaker 6.0.
Delivery Method: Mail, Racks
Areas Served: Trempealeau County

MONTELLO

THE MARQUETTE COUNTY TRIBUNE (THUR)
120 Underwood Ave, Montello, WI, 53949-9354, Marquette, USA; gen tel (608) 297-2424; gen fax (608) 297-9293; disp adv e-mail marquettetribune@newspubinc.com; class adv e-mail marquettetribune@newspubinc.com; ed e-mail marquettetribune@newspubinc.com; web site www.marquettecountytribune.com
Circulation: 3,203pd, 12fr; Sworn/Estimate/ Non-Audited
Advertising rate: Open inch rate $8.40
Group: News Publishing Company, Inc.
Digital Platform - Mobile: Apple, Android
Pub. .... Daniel Witte
Pub. .... Mark Witte
Prodn. Mgr. .... Mary Faltz
Mechanical Specifications: Type page 10 x 16; E - 6 cols, 1.569, 1/8 between; A - 6 cols, 1.569, 1/8 between; C - 6 cols, 1.569, 1/8 between.Equipment & Software: Hardware — Macintosh iMac G5; Software — Microsoft/ Word 2011, QPS/QuarkXPress 9.3, Adobe/ Photoshop CS5.
Delivery Method: Mail, Newsstand
Areas Served: 53949, 53952, 53953, 53964, 53930, 54960, 53920

MOSINEE

MOSINEE TIMES (THUR)
407 3rd St, Mosinee, WI, 54455-1426, Marathon, USA; gen tel (715) 693-2300; gen fax (715) 693-1574; disp adv e-mail motimes@mtc.net; class adv e-mail motimes@mtc.net; ed e-mail motimes@mtc.net
Circulation: 2,100pd,; USPS
Advertising rate: Open inch rate $6.95
Established: 1895
Pub. .... James Kress
Publisher and Editor .... Susan Durst
Mechanical Specifications: Type page 13 x 21; E - 6 cols, 2, 1/8 between; A - 6 cols, 2, 1/8 between; C - 6 cols, 2, 1/8 between.Equipment & Software: Hardware — PC, APP/ Mac, APP/Power Mac; Software — Adobe/ PageMaker 6.0, Claris/Works.
Delivery Method: Mail, Newsstand, Racks
Areas Served: 54455

NEW GLARUS

POST MESSENGER RECORDER (THUR)
109 5th Ave, New Glarus, WI, 53574, Green, USA; gen tel (608) 527-5252; adv tel (608) 358-7958; gen fax (608) 527-5285; disp adv e-mail khenning@newspubinc.com; class adv e-mail pmr@newspubinc.com; ed e-mail pmreditor@newspubinc.com
Circulation: 1,721pd,; Sworn/Estimate/Non-Audited
Advertising rate: $11.40 ci
Group: News Publishing, Co., Inc.
Adv. Sales .... Karin Henning
Ed. .... Sue Moen
Classifieds/Subscriptions .... Katie Pederson
Delivery Method: Mail, Newsstand
Areas Served: Belleville, Monticello, New Glarus

NEW RICHMOND

NEW RICHMOND NEWS (THUR)
127 S Knowles Ave, New Richmond, WI, 54017-1726, Saint Croix, USA; gen tel (715) 246-6881; adv tel (715) 426-1052; ed tel (715) 243-7767 ext. 241; gen fax (715) 246-7117; adv fax (715) 246-7117; ed fax (715) 246-7117; disp adv e-mail pfrebault@rivertowns.net; class adv e-mail classifieds@rivertowns.net; ed e-mail nrneditor@rivertowns.net; web site www.newrichmond-news.net
Circulation: 5,000pd, 100fr; Sworn/Estimate/ Non-Audited
Advertising rate: Open inch rate $13.63
Established: 1869
Group: Forum Communications Co.
Digital Platform - Mobile: Apple, Android, Windows, Blackberry
Digital Platform - Tablet: Apple iOS, Android, Windows 7, Blackberry Tablet OS, Kindle, Nook, Kindle Fire
Ed Dir. .... Chad Richardson
Delivery Method: Mail, Newsstand
Areas Served: St. Croix County

OCONTO

OCONTO COUNTY REPORTER (WED)
PO Box 200, Oconto, WI, 54153-0200, Oconto, USA; gen tel (920)834-4242; adv tel (920-834-4242; ed tel (920) 834-4242; gen fax (920) 834-4878; disp adv e-mail ckruse@OcontoCountyReporter.com; class adv e-mail classified@wisinfo.com; ed e-mail ktempus@gannett.com; web site www.ocontocountyreporter.com
Circulation: 5,000pd, 50fr; Sworn/Estimate/ Non-Audited
Advertising rate: Open inch rate $7.75
Established: 1871
Group: Gannett
Digital Platform - Mobile: Apple, Android
Digital Platform - Tablet: Apple iOS, Android, Windows 7
Pres./Pub. .... Scott Johnson
Ed. .... Kent Tempus
Account executive .... Christina Kruse
Mechanical Specifications: Type page 10 x 20; E - 6 cols, 1 1/2, between; A - 6 cols, 1 1/2, between; C - 6 cols, 1 1/2, between.
Delivery Method: Mail, Racks
Areas Served: Oconto County

ONTARIO

THE COUNTY LINE (THUR)
207 N Garden St, Ontario, WI, 54651-6532, Vernon, USA; gen tel (608) 337-4232; gen fax (608) 338-0472; disp adv e-mail sales@thecountyline.net; ed e-mail countyline@centurytel.net; web site thecountyline.net
Areas Served: Kendall, Ontario, Norwalk, Wilton, Elroy

OREGON

OREGON OBSERVER (THUR)
125 N Main St, Oregon, WI, 53575-1430, Dane, USA; gen tel (608) 845-9559; adv tel (608) 845-9559; ed tel (608) 845-9559; gen fax (608) 835-0130; adv fax (608)

835-0130; ed fax (608) 835-0130; disp adv e-mail oregonsales@wcinet.com; class adv e-mail ungclassified@wcinet.com; ed e-mail veronapress@wcinet.com; web site www.connectoregonwi.com
Circulation: 1,987pd,; USPS
Advertising rate: Open inch rate $10.25
Established: 1880
Group: Woodward Communications, Inc.
Digital Platform - Mobile: Android
Digital Platform - Tablet: Android
Group Ed. .... Jim Ferolie
General manager........................Lee Borkowski
Mechanical Specifications: Type page 10 5/8 x 16; E - 6 cols, 1 5/8, 1/8 between; A - 6 cols, 1 5/8, 1/8 between; C - 6 cols, 1 5/8, 1/8 between.Equipment & Software: Hardware — APP/Mac
Delivery Method: Mail, Racks
Areas Served: Dane Co.

OSCEOLA

THE SUN (WED)

108 N Cascade St, Osceola, WI, 54020, Polk, USA; gen tel (715) 294-2314; adv tel (715) 294-2314; ed tel (715) 294-2314; gen fax (715) 755-3314; adv fax (715) 755-3314; ed fax (715) 755-3314; disp adv e-mail sales@osceolasun.com; class adv e-mail office@osceolasun.com; ed e-mail editor@osceolasun.com; web site www.osceolasun.com
Circulation: 1,800pd,; USPS
Advertising rate: Open inch rate $6.50
Established: 1897
Group: Sentinel Publication
Digital Platform - Mobile: Apple, Android
Digital Platform - Tablet: Apple iOS, Android
Pub .... Tom StanglEquipment & Software: Hardware — APP/Mac; Software — Adobe/PageMaker.
Delivery Method: Mail, Newsstand
Areas Served: 54020, 54009, 54024, 54026, 54025

PHILLIPS

PARK FALLS HERALD (THUR)

115 N Lake Ave, Phillips, WI, 54555-1220, Price, USA; gen tel (715) 339-3036; adv tel (715) 339-3036; ed tel (715) 339-3036; gen fax (715) 339-4300; adv fax (715) 339-4300; ed fax (715) 339-4300; disp adv e-mail skelley@thephillipsbee.com; class adv e-mail lhaskins@thephillipsbee.com; ed e-mail eknudson@thephillipsbee.com; web site www.pricecountydaily.com
Circulation: 4,367pd, 6,200fr; Sworn/Estimate/Non-Audited
Advertising rate: Open inch rate $8.65
Established: 1900
Group: Adams Publishing Group, LLC
Digital Platform - Mobile: Apple, Android, Windows, Blackberry
Digital Platform - Tablet: Apple iOS, Android, Windows 7, Blackberry Tablet OS, Kindle, Nook, Kindle Fire
Ed. .... Eric Knudson
Adv. Dir. .... Susan Kelley
Circ. Mgr...................................... Linda Haskins
Pub./Gen. Mgr.........................Kenneth Dischler
Delivery Method: Mail, Racks
Areas Served: 54552, 54555, 54556, 54515, 54459, 54514, 54513

PRICE COUNTY REVIEW (THUR)

115 N Lake Ave, Phillips, WI, 54555-1220, Price, USA; gen tel (715) 339-3036
Circulation: 100pd,
Group: Adams Publishing Group, LLC
Areas Served: Price

THE BEE (THUR)

115 N Lake Ave, Phillips, WI, 54555-1220, Price, USA; gen tel (715) 339-3036; adv tel (715) 339-3036; ed tel (715) 339-3036; gen fax (715) 339-4300; adv fax (715) 339-4300; ed fax (715) 339-4300; disp adv e-mail skelley@thephillipsbee.com; class adv e-mail lhaskins@thephillipsbee.com; ed e-mail eknudson@thephillipsbee.com; web site www.pricecountydaily.com
Circulation: 4,367pd, 6,200fr; Sworn/Estimate/Non-Audited
Advertising rate: Open inch rate $7.40
Established: 1884
Digital Platform - Mobile: Apple, Android, Windows, Blackberry
Digital Platform - Tablet: Apple iOS, Android, Windows 7, Blackberry Tablet OS, Kindle, Nook, Kindle Fire
Ed. .... Eric Knudson
Adv. Dir. .... Susan Kelley
Circ. Mgr...................................... Linda Haskins
Delivery Method: Mail, Racks
Areas Served: 54552, 54555, 54556, 54515, 54459, 54514, 54513

PLATTEVILLE

THE PLATTEVILLE JOURNAL (WED)

25 E Main St, Platteville, WI, 53818-3216, Grant, USA; gen tel (608) 348-3006; adv tel (608) 348-3006; ed tel (608) 348-3006; gen fax (608) 348-7979; adv fax (608) 348-7979; ed fax (608) 348-7979; disp adv e-mail ads@theplattevillejournal.com; class adv e-mail ads@theplattevillejournal.com; ed e-mail editor@theplattevillejournal.com; web site www.swnews4u.com
Circulation: 4,300pd, 17,665fr; Sworn/Estimate/Non-Audited
Advertising rate: Open inch rate $6.05
Established: 1899
Group: Morris Multimedia, Inc.
Digital Platform - Mobile: Apple, Android
Digital Platform - Tablet: Apple iOS, Android, Windows 7
Publisher................................. John Ingebritsen
Adv. Mgr...Ann Rupp
Ed. .... Steve Prestegard
Sports Ed..................................... Jason Nihles
Mechanical Specifications: Type page 15 3/4 x 21 1/2; E - 8 cols, 1 5/6, 1/6 between; A - 8 cols, 1 5/6, 1/6 between; C - 8 cols, 1 5/6, 1/6 between.Equipment & Software: Hardware — APP/Mac; Presses — G/Community; Software — Adobe InDesign
Delivery Method: Mail, Newsstand, Racks
Areas Served: 53818

PLYMOUTH

THE REVIEW (TUES, THUR)

113 E Mill St, Plymouth, WI, 53073-1703, Sheboygan, USA; gen tel (920) 893-6411; adv tel (920) 893-6411; ed tel (920) 893-6411; gen fax (920) 893-5505; adv fax (920) 893-5505; ed fax (920) 893-5505; disp adv e-mail displayads@plymouth-review.com; class adv e-mail reviewclassifieds@gmail.com; ed e-mail reply@plymouth-review.com; web site www.plymouth-review.com
Circulation: 5,308pd, 33fr; Sworn/Estimate/Non-Audited
Advertising rate: Open inch rate $6.50
Established: 1895
Digital Platform - Mobile: Apple, Android, Windows, Blackberry
Digital Platform - Tablet: Apple iOS, Android, Windows 7, Blackberry Tablet OS
Pub.. Barry S. Johanson
Pub.............................. M. Christine Johanson
Assoc. Pub................................... Ian Johanson
Circ. Mgr.....................................Debbie Mueller
Ed. ....Emmitt Feldner
Mechanical Specifications: Type page 10 1/2 x 15 3/16; E - 5 cols, 2 1/16, 1/8 between; A - 5 cols, 2 1/16, 1/8 between; C - 5 cols, 2 1/16, 1/8 between.Equipment & Software: Hardware — PC, APP/Mac; Software — XYQUEST/XyWrite, Multi-Ad/Creator.
Delivery Method: Mail, Newsstand
Areas Served: Sheboygan County

THE SHEBOYGAN FALLS NEWS (WED)

113 E Mill St, Plymouth, WI, 53073-1703, Sheboygan, USA; gen tel (920) 893-6411; adv tel (920) 893-6411; ed tel (920) 893-6411; gen fax (920) 893-5505; adv fax (920) 893-5505; ed fax (920) 893-5505; disp adv e-mail displayads@plymouth-review.com; class adv e-mail reviewclassifieds@gmail.com; ed e-mail fallsnews@plymouth-review.com; web site www.plymouth-review.com
Circulation: 2,133pd,; Sworn/Estimate/Non-Audited
Advertising rate: Open inch rate $3.20
Established: 1895
Digital Platform - Mobile: Apple, Android, Windows, Blackberry
Digital Platform - Tablet: Apple iOS, Android, Windows 7, Blackberry Tablet OS
Pub.. Barry S. Johanson
Pub.............................. M. Christine Johanson
Assoc. Pub................................... Ian Johanson
Circ. Mgr.....................................Debbie Mueller
Ed. ....Jeff Pederson
Mechanical Specifications: Type page 10 1/4 x 15; E - 5 cols, 2, 1/8 between; A - 5 cols, 2, 1/8 between; C - 7 cols, 2, 1/8 between. Equipment & Software: Hardware — IBM, APP/Mac; Software — Multi-Ad/Creator.
Delivery Method: Mail, Newsstand
Areas Served: Sheboygan County

PORT WASHINGTON

OZAUKEE PRESS (TUES, THUR)

125 E Main St, Port Washington, WI, 53074-1915, Ozaukee, USA; gen tel (262) 284-3494; adv tel (262) 284-3494 ext. 1102; ed tel (262) 284-3494; gen fax (262) 284-0067; adv fax (262) 284-0067; ed fax (262) 284-0067; disp adv e-mail news@ozaukeepress.com; class adv e-mail news@ozaukeepress.com; ed e-mail news@ozaukeepress.com; web site www.ozaukeepress.com
Circulation: 6,295pd, 215fr; CVC
Advertising rate: Open inch rate $18.50
Established: 1940
Digital Platform - Mobile: Apple, Android
Digital Platform - Tablet: Apple iOS, Android, Windows 7
Pub./Ed.................................William F. Schanen
Adv. Mgr......Holly OstermanEquipment & Software: Hardware — APP/Mac; Presses — G/Community; Software — QPS/QuarkXPress, Adobe/Photoshop, Adobe/Illustrator.
Delivery Method: Mail, Newsstand, Racks
Areas Served: Ozaukee County

PORTAGE

WISCONSIN DELLS EVENTS (WED, SAT)

1640 La Dawn Dr, Portage, WI, 53901-8822, Columbia, USA; gen tel (608)254-8327; adv tel (608)745-3500; ed tel (608)745-3567; gen fax (608)742-8346; adv fax (608)745-3562; ed fax (608)742-8346; disp adv e-mail jdenk@capitalnewspapers.com; class adv e-mail jdenk@capitalnewspapers.com; ed e-mail wde-news@capitalnewspapers.com; web site www.wiscnews.com
Circulation: 2,305pd, 100fr; Sworn/Estimate/Non-Audited
Advertising rate: Open inch rate $11.08
Established: 1903
Group: Capital Newspapers
Digital Platform - Mobile: Android, Windows
Digital Platform - Tablet: Apple iOS
Ed. .... Kay Lapp James
Circ. Mgr.................................. Teresa Klinger
Gen. Mgr. ....Jon Denk
Sports Ed.................................... Travis Houslet
Mechanical Specifications: Type page 11 x 22 1/2; E - 6 cols, 2 1/4, 2/9 between; A - 6 cols, 2 1/4, 2/9 between; C - 8 cols, between.
Delivery Method: Mail, Newsstand, Carrier, Racks
Areas Served: Wisconsin Dells, Columbia, Adams, Sauk, and Juneau counties. Also portions of Marquette County

PRAIRIE DU CHIEN

COURIER-PRESS (MON)

132 S Beaumont Rd, Prairie Du Chien, WI, 53821-1415, Crawford, USA; gen tel (608)326-2441; adv tel (608)326-2441; ed tel (608)326-2441; gen fax (608)326-2443; adv fax (608)326-2443; ed fax (608)326-2443; disp adv e-mail howeads@mhtc.net; class adv e-mail howeads@mhtc.net; ed e-mail howenews@mhtc.net; web site www.guttenbergpress.com
Group: Clayton County Register

RANDOM LAKE

THE SOUNDER (THUR)

405 2nd St, Random Lake, WI, 53075-1824, Sheboygan, USA; gen tel (920) 994-9244; gen fax (920) 994-4817; ed e-mail editor@thesounder.com; web site www.thesounder.com
Circulation: 0fr; Sworn/Estimate/Non-Audited
Established: 1918
Ed. .... Gary Feider
Office Mgr. .... Katie Cramer
Delivery Method: Mail
Areas Served: Southern Sheboygan County & Northern Ozaukee County, Wisconsin

RHINELANDER

STAR JOURNAL (SUN)

24 W Rives St, Rhinelander, WI, 54501-3164, Oneida, USA; gen tel (715) 369-3331; adv tel (715) 369-3331; ed tel (715) 369-3331; gen fax (715) 369-4859; adv fax (715) 369-4859; ed fax (715) 369-4859; disp adv e-mail pdaniels@mmclocal.com; class adv e-mail hodagads@mmclocal.com; ed e-mail starjournal@mmclocal.com; web site www.starjournalnow.com - 21,974(views) 5,083(visitors)
Circulation: 5pd, 15,940fr; VAC
Advertising rate: Open inch rate $18.60
Established: 1977
Group: Multi Media Channels LLC
Digital Platform - Mobile: Apple, Android, Windows, Blackberry
Digital Platform - Tablet: Apple iOS, Android, Windows 7, Blackberry Tablet OS
Pub... Peter Daniels
Circ. Mgr...................................... Cathy Oelrich
Prod. Mgr .... Ernie Neuenfeldt
Mechanical Specifications: Type page: 9.75 x 11; 6 col
Delivery Method: Newsstand, Carrier, Racks
Areas Served: 54501, 54487, 54529, 54548, 54568, 54531, 54562, 54539, 54463, 54558, 54520, 54521

RICE LAKE

RICE LAKE CHRONOTYPE (WED)

28 S Main St, Rice Lake, WI, 54868-2232, USA; gen tel (715) 234-2121; gen fax (715) 234-5232; disp adv e-mail bdorrance@chronotype.com; ed e-mail bdorrance@chronotype.com; web site http://www.apg-wi.com/rice_lake_chronotype/
Circulation: 7,176pd,; Sworn/Estimate/Non-Audited
Advertising rate: Open inchr ate $11.25
Established: 1874
Group: Adams Publishing Group, LLC
Pub.. Warren Dorrance
Managing Ed................................Sam Finazzo
Nat'l Adv. Mgr.............................Bob Dorrance

RICHLAND CENTER

THE RICHLAND OBSERVER (THUR)

172 E Court St, Richland Center, WI, 53581-2339, Richland, USA; gen tel (608) 647-

6141; gen fax (608) 647-6143; web site http://www.swnews4u.com/
Established: 1864
Group: Morris Multimedia, Inc.
Areas Served: Richland

RIPON

RIPON COMMONWEALTH PRESS (WED)

656 S Douglas St, Ripon, WI, 54971-9044, Fond du Lac, USA; gen tel (920) 748-3017; adv tel (920) 748-3017; ed tel (920) 748-3017; gen fax (920) 748-3028; adv fax (920) 748-3028; ed fax (920) 748-3028; disp adv e-mail TimL@riponprinters.com; class adv e-mail rcpads@riponprinters.com; ed e-mail rcpnews@riponprinters.com; web site www.riponpress.com
Circulation: 3,400fr; Sworn/Estimate/Non-Audited
Advertising rate: Open inch rate $10.20
Established: 1864
Digital Platform - Mobile: Apple, Android
Digital Platform - Tablet: Apple iOS, Android, Windows 7
Pub.......... Tim Lyke
Ed.......... Ian Stepleton
Adv. Mgr.......... Bob Chikowski
Circ.......... Kelly Schmude
Delivery Method: Mail, Racks
Areas Served: Fond du Lac County

THE COMMONWEALTH EXPRESS (TUES)

656 S Douglas St, Ripon, WI, 54971-9044, Fond du Lac, USA; gen tel (920)748-3017; adv tel (920)748-3017; ed tel (920)748-3017; gen fax (920)748-3028; adv fax (920)748-3028; ed fax (920)748-3028; disp adv e-mail TimL@riponprinters.com; class adv e-mail TimL@riponprinters.com; ed e-mail TimL@riponprinters.com; web site www.riponpress.com
Circulation: 17,540fr; VAC
Advertising rate: Open inch rate $10.00
Pub.......... Tim Lyke

RIVER FALLS

RIVER FALLS JOURNAL (THUR)

2815 Prairie Dr, River Falls, WI, 54022-5211, Saint Croix, USA; gen tel (715)425-1561; adv tel (715)426-1052; ed tel (715)426-1050; gen fax (715)425-5666; adv fax (715)425-5666; ed fax (715)425-5666; disp adv e-mail sengelhart@rivertowns.net; class adv e-mail classifieds@rivertowns.net; ed e-mail ajacboson@rivertowns.net; web site www.riverfallsjournal.com
Circulation: 2,839pd,; Sworn/Estimate/Non-Audited
Advertising rate: Open inch rate $13.19
Established: 1858
Group: Forum Communications Co.
Digital Platform - Mobile: Apple, Android, Windows, Blackberry
Digital Platform - Tablet: Apple iOS, Android, Windows 7, Blackberry Tablet OS, Kindle
Publisher.......... Neal Ronquist
Advertising Director.......... Steve Engelhart
Editor.......... Anne Jacobson
Circulation Director
Production Director.......... Dave Pevonka
Delivery Method: Mail, Newsstand
Areas Served: 54022, 54016

THE HUDSON STAR-OBSERVER (THUR)

2815 Prairie Dr, River Falls, WI, 54022-5211, Saint Croix, USA; gen tel (715)386-9333; adv tel (715)426-1052; ed tel (715)808-8600; gen fax (715)386-9891; adv fax (715)386-9891; ed fax (715)386-9891; disp adv e-mail pfrebault@rivertowns.net; class adv e-mail classifieds@rivertowns.net; ed e-mail hsoeditor@rivertowns.net; web site www.hudsonstarobserver.com
Circulation: 7,275pd, 50fr; Sworn/Estimate/Non-Audited
Advertising rate: Open inch rate $15.83
Established: 1854
Group: Forum Communications Co.
Digital Platform - Mobile: Apple, Android, Windows, Blackberry
Digital Platform - Tablet: Apple iOS, Android, Windows 7, Blackberry Tablet OS, Kindle
Pub.......... Neal Ronquist
Ed.......... Doug Stohlberg
Adv. Dir.......... Steve Engelhart
Delivery Method: Mail, Newsstand
Areas Served: Pierce County

ROBERTS

CENTRAL ST. CROIX NEWS (THUR)

500 West Blvd, Lowr Level, Roberts, WI, 54023-9637, USA; gen tel (715) 749-3331; ed e-mail editor@centralstcroixnews.com; web site http://centralstcroixnews.publish-path.com
Group: CSCN Holdings, LLC
Pub.......... Jeffrey Redmon
Gen. Mgr./EIC.......... Michele DeLong
Areas Served: 54015
54023

SAUK CITY

SAUK PRAIRIE STAR (THUR)

801 Water St, Sauk City, WI, 53583-1502, Sauk, USA; gen tel (608) 643-3444; adv tel (608) 643-3444; ed tel (608) 643-3444; gen fax (608) 643-4988; adv fax (608) 643-4988; ed fax (608) 643-4988; disp adv e-mail homenewsales@newspubinc.com; class adv e-mail spstar@newspubinc.com; ed e-mail mikesps@newspubinc.com; web site www.newspubinc.com
Circulation: 2,800pd, 40fr; Sworn/Estimate/Non-Audited
Advertising rate: Open inch rate $11.00
Group: News Publishing, Co., Inc.
Digital Platform - Mobile: Apple
Digital Platform - Tablet: Apple iOS
Pub.......... Dan Witte
Pub.......... Mark Witte
Ed.......... Mike Carignan
Delivery Method: Mail
Areas Served: Sauk County

SEYMOUR

ADVERTISER COMMUNITY NEWS (MON)

800 E Factory St, Seymour, WI, 54165-1210, Outagamie, USA; gen tel (920) 833-0420; adv tel (920) 833-0420; ed tel (920) 833-0420; gen fax (920) 833-0423; adv fax (920) 833-0423; ed fax (920) 833-0423; disp adv e-mail ken.h@adcommnews.com; class adv e-mail becky.m@adcommnews.com; ed e-mail keith.s@adcommnews.com; web site www.advertisercommunitynews.com - 6,811(views) 1,900(visitors)
Circulation: 103pd, 8,853fr; VAC
Advertising rate: Open inch rate $17.20 includes full color
Established: 2009
Digital Platform - Mobile: Apple, Android, Windows, Blackberry
Digital Platform - Tablet: Apple iOS, Android, Windows 7, Blackberry Tablet OS
Pub./Owner.......... Ken Hodgden
Circ. Mgr.......... Becky Mueller
Ed.......... Keith Skenadore
Mechanical Specifications: 6 Col 9.75" wide by 13.75 " Tab
Delivery Method: Mail, Newsstand, Carrier
Areas Served: 54165, 54106, 54170, 54152, 54155, 54162, 54131, 54107

SHELL LAKE

WASHBURN COUNTY REGISTER (WED)

11 5th Ave, Ste 103, Shell Lake, WI, 54871, Washburn, USA; gen tel (715) 468-2314; adv tel (715) 468-2314; ed tel (715) 468-2314; gen fax (715) 468-4900; adv fax (715) 468-4900; ed fax (715) 468-4900; disp adv e-mail wcregister@centurytel.net; class adv e-mail wcregister@centurytel.net; ed e-mail wcregister@centurytel.net; web site www.wcregister.net
Circulation: 1,900pd, 20fr; Sworn/Estimate/Non-Audited
Advertising rate: Open inch rate $7.30
Established: 1889
Digital Platform - Mobile: Apple, Android, Windows, Blackberry
Digital Platform - Tablet: Apple iOS, Android, Windows 7, Blackberry Tablet OS, Kindle, Nook, Kindle Fire
Pub./Gen. Mgr.......... Doug Panek
Ed.......... Gary B. King
Adv. Sales Coord.......... Sue Buck
Mechanical Specifications: Type page 10 3/8 x 13; E - 5 cols, 2, 1/6 between; A - 5 cols, 2, 1/6 between; C - 5 cols, 2, 1/6 between. Equipment & Software: Hardware — PC; Software — Archetype/Corel Draw 9.0.
Delivery Method: Mail, Newsstand
Areas Served: 54871, 54801, 54870, 54813

SPARTA

MONROE COUNTY HERALD (MON, THUR)

1302 River Rd, Sparta, WI, 54656-2498, Monroe, USA; gen tel (608) 269-3186; adv tel (608) 269-3186; ed tel (608) 269-3186; gen fax (608) 269-6876; adv fax (608) 269-6876; ed fax (608) 269-6876; disp adv e-mail kyle@monroecountyherald.com; class adv e-mail kyle@monroecountyherald.com; ed e-mail pat@monroecountyherald.com; web site www.monroecountyherald.com
Circulation: 5,000pd, 35fr; Sworn/Estimate/Non-Audited
Advertising rate: Open inch rate $9.50
Established: 1857
Group: Evans Print & Media Group
Digital Platform - Mobile: Windows
Digital Platform - Tablet: Windows 7
Pub.......... Evans Greg
Mechanical Specifications: Type page 13 x 21 1/2; E - 6 cols, 2 1/16, 3/16 between; A - 6 cols, 2 1/16, 3/16 between; C - 9 cols, 1 5/16, 3/16 between.Equipment & Software: Hardware — APP/Mac; Presses — G/Community; Software — Adobe/PageMaker.
Delivery Method: Mail, Newsstand, Racks
Areas Served: Monroe County

THE SPARTA HERALD (MON)

1302 River Rd, Sparta, WI, 54656-2498, Monroe, USA; gen tel (608) 269-3186; adv tel (608) 269-3186; ed tel (608) 269-3186; gen fax (608) 269-6876; adv fax (608) 269-6876; ed fax (608) 269-6876; disp adv e-mail mcp2006@centurytel.net; class adv e-mail mcp2006@centurytel.net; ed e-mail sadtad@centurytel.net; web site www.spartanewspapers.com
Circulation: 4,650pd, 35fr; Sworn/Estimate/Non-Audited
Advertising rate: Open inch rate $9.50
Group: Monroe County Publishers, Inc.
Digital Platform - Mobile: Windows
Digital Platform - Tablet: Windows 7
Pub./Gen. Mgr.......... Theodore Radde
Adv. Mgr.......... Dan Elliott
Ed.......... Pat Malviney
Mechanical Specifications: Type page 13 x 21 1/2; E - 6 cols, 2 1/16, 3/8 between; A - 6 cols, 2 1/16, 3/8 between; C - 9 cols, 1 5/16, 3/8 between.Equipment & Software: Hardware — APP/Mac; Presses — G/Community; Software — Adobe/PageMaker.
Delivery Method: Mail, Racks
Areas Served: Monroe County

SPOONER

SPOONER ADVOCATE (THUR)

251 E Maple St, Spooner, WI, 54801-9698, Washburn, USA; gen tel (715) 635-2181; adv tel (715) 635-2181 ext. 29; ed tel (715) 635-2181; gen fax (715) 635-2186; adv fax (715) 635-2186; ed fax (715) 635-2186; disp adv e-mail mcarlson@spooneradvocate.com; class adv e-mail ads@spooneradvocate.com; ed e-mail news@spooneradvocate.com; web site www.spooneradvocate.com
Circulation: 3,000pd,; Sworn/Estimate/Non-Audited
Advertising rate: Open inch rate $9.50
Established: 1901
Group: Adams Publishing Group, LLC
Digital Platform - Mobile: Apple, Android, Windows, Blackberry
Digital Platform - Tablet: Apple iOS, Android, Windows 7, Blackberry Tablet OS, Kindle, Nook, Kindle Fire
Pub./Ed./Gen. Mgr.......... Janet I. Krokson
Assc. Ed.......... Bill Thornley
Adv. Mgr.......... Michelle Carlson
Prod. Mgr.......... Janis Redman
News editor.......... Julie Hustvet
Advertising consultant.......... Deb Fosberg
Office manager.......... Kelie Kuffel
Mechanical Specifications: Type page 11 5/8 x 21 1/2; E - 6 cols, 11 5/8, 1/8 between; A - 6 cols, 11 5/8, 1/8 between; C - 6 cols, 11 5/8, 1/8 between.Equipment & Software: Hardware — APP/Mac; Software — InDesign CS5
Delivery Method: Mail
Areas Served: Washburn County

SPRING GREEN

SPRING GREEN HOME NEWS (WED)

120 N Worcester St, Spring Green, WI, 53588-8015, Sauk, USA; gen tel (608)588-2508; adv tel (608)588-2508; ed tel (608)588-2508; gen fax (608)588-3536; adv fax (608)588-3536; ed fax (608)588-3536; disp adv e-mail homenewssales@newspubinc.com; class adv e-mail classifieds@newspubinc.com; ed e-mail nsa@newspubinc.com; web site www.newspubinc.com
Circulation: 2,700pd,; Sworn/Estimate/Non-Audited
Advertising rate: Open inch rate $10.15
Group: News Publishing, Co., Inc.
CFO/Controller.......... Tom Finger
Mng. Ed.......... John Donaldson
Delivery Method: Mail, Racks
Areas Served: Sauk County

SPRING VALLEY

SUN-ARGUS (THUR)

W2855 730th Ave, Spring Valley, WI, 54767-8512, Pierce, USA; gen tel (715) 778-4990; ed tel (715) 778-4990; gen fax (715) 778-4996; disp adv e-mail editor@mygatewaynews.com; class adv e-mail admins@mygatewaynews.com; ed e-mail editor@mygatewaynews.com; web site www.mygatewaynews.com
Circulation: 800pd, 2fr; Sworn/Estimate/Non-Audited
Advertising rate: Open inch rate $7.45
Established: 1892
Group: Gateway Publishing, Inc.
Digital Platform - Mobile: Apple, Android, Windows, Blackberry
Digital Platform - Tablet: Apple iOS, Android, Windows 7, Blackberry Tablet OS, Kindle, Nook, Kindle Fire
Ed./Pub.......... Paul Seeling
Mechanical Specifications: Broadsheet. 6 column wide (2" column width) x 21" tall
Delivery Method: Mail, Newsstand
Areas Served: Spring Valley, Elmwood, Wilson, Pierce & St. Croix Counties, 54767, 54740, 54027, 54028

WOODVILLE LEADER (THUR)

W2855 730th Ave, Spring Valley, WI, 54767-8512, Pierce, USA; gen tel (715) 778-4990; ed tel (715) 778-4990; gen fax (715) 778-4996; disp adv e-mail editor@mygatewaynews.com; class adv e-mail admins@mygatewaynews.com; ed e-mail editor@mygatewaynews.com; web site www.mygatewaynews.com

Circulation: 196pd, 2fr; Sworn/Estimate/Non-Audited
Advertising rate: Open inch rate $7.45
Established: 1929
Group: Gateway Publishing, Inc.
Digital Platform - Mobile: Apple, Android, Windows, Blackberry
Digital Platform - Tablet: Apple iOS, Android, Windows 7, Blackberry Tablet OS, Kindle, Nook, Kindle Fire
Ed./Pub. ....Paul Seeling
Mechanical Specifications: Broadsheet. 6 columns wide x 21" tall with 2" wide columns
Delivery Method: Mail, Newsstand
Areas Served: 54028, 54002, 54767, 57027,54740

STANLEY

THE STANLEY REPUBLICAN (THUR)

131 E 1st Ave, Stanley, WI, 54768-1202, Chippewa, USA; gen tel (715) 644-5452; adv tel (715) 644-5452; ed tel (715) 644-5452; gen fax (715) 644-5459; adv fax (715) 644-5459; ed fax (715) 644-5459; disp adv e-mail therepublican@charterinternet.com; class adv e-mail therepublican@charterinternet.com; ed e-mail therepublican@charterinternet.com
Circulation: 2,600pd,; Sworn/Estimate/Non-Audited
Advertising rate: Open inch rate $6.75
Pub./Ed. ....John McLoone
Mechanical Specifications: Type page 13 x 21 1/2; E - 6 cols, 2 1/16, 1/6 between; A - 6 cols, 2 1/16, 1/6 between; C - 6 cols, 2 1/16, 1/6 between.Equipment & Software: Hardware — APP/Mac; Presses — G, Hamada; Software — Adobe/PageMaker 4.2.
Delivery Method: Mail
Areas Served: Stanley and Boyd

STEVENS POINT

THE PORTAGE COUNTY GAZETTE (FRI)

1024 Main St, Stevens Point, WI, 54481-2859, Portage, USA; gen tel (715)343-8045; adv tel (715)343-8045; ed tel (715)343-8045; gen fax (715)343-8048; adv fax (715)343-8048; ed fax (715)343-8048; disp adv e-mail ads@pcgazette.com; class adv e-mail subscriptions@pcgazette.com; ed e-mail pcgazette@g2a.net ; web site www.pcgazette.com
Established: 1878
Managing Ed........................Nathanael Enwald
Adv. Rep...Joey Hetzel
Sports Ed.................................John Kemmeter
Adv. Rep...Matt Clucas
Assoc. Ed...............................Sarah McQueen
Gen. Mgr. ....Gary Glennon
Prod. Coord.................................Paula O'Kray
CFO ....Norb Tepp
Circ./Classifieds........................Nancy Kramer
Circ./Classifieds........................ Amy McKenzie
Delivery Method: Newsstand, Racks

STOUGHTON

STOUGHTON COURIER HUB (THUR)

135 W Main St Ste 102, Ste. 102, Stoughton, WI, 53589-2135, Dane, USA; gen tel (608)873-6671; adv tel (608)873-6671; ed tel (608)873-6671; gen fax (608)873-3473; adv fax (608)873-3473; ed fax (608)873-3473; disp adv e-mail stoughtonsales@wcinet.com; class adv e-mail ungclassified@wcinet.com; ed e-mail stoughtoneditor@wcinet.com; web site connectstoughton.com
Circulation: 2,458pd,; USPS
Advertising rate: Open inch rate $10.50
Established: 1879
Group: Woodward Communications, Inc.
Digital Platform - Mobile: Blackberry
Digital Platform - Tablet: Kindle
Group Ed. .... Jim Ferolie
Gen. Mgr.....................................David Enstad
Mechanical Specifications: Type page 10 5/8 x 16; E - 6 cols, 1 5/8, 1/8 between; A - 6 cols, 1 5/8, 1/8 between; C - 6 cols, 1 5/8, 1/8 between.Equipment & Software: Hardware — APP/Mac
Delivery Method: Mail, Racks
Areas Served: Dane County

STURGEON BAY

DOOR COUNTY ADVOCATE (WED, SAT)

235 N 3rd Ave, Sturgeon Bay, WI, 54235-2417, Door, USA; gen tel (800) 500-5321; adv tel (920) 743-3321; ed tel (920) 743-3321; gen fax (920) 743-8908; adv fax (920) 743-8908; ed fax (920) 743-8908; disp adv e-mail thaen@gannett.com; class adv e-mail Advocate@doorcountyadvocate.com; ed e-mail cclough@doorcountyadvocate.com; web site www.doorcountyadvocate.com - 32,482(views) 3,937(visitors)
Circulation: 7,108pd, 280fr; VAC
Advertising rate: Open inch rate $14.00
Established: 1862
Group: Gannett
Digital Platform - Mobile: Apple, Android, Windows
Digital Platform - Tablet: Apple iOS, Android, Windows 7
Your Key to the Door Weekly Editor......... Chris Clough
Reporter ....Liz Welter
Circulation Operations Coordinator.......... Lynn Schroeder
Operations Manager......................Terrie Haen
Mechanical Specifications: Type page 10 x 20 1/4; 6 colEquipment & Software: Hardware — APP/Mac; Presses — G/Community; Software — QPS/QuarkXPress 4.0, Adobe/Illustrator 8.0.
Delivery Method: Mail, Newsstand, Racks
Areas Served: 54201, 54202, 54204, 54209, 54210, 54211, 54212, 54234, 54235

SUN PRAIRIE

THE STAR (TUES, FRI)

804 Liberty Blvd, Ste 201, Sun Prairie, WI, 53590-4643, Dane, USA; gen tel (608) 837-2521; adv tel (608) 837-2521; ed tel (608) 837-2521; disp adv e-mail mfeiler@hngnews.com; class adv e-mail classifieds@hngnews.com; ed e-mail spedit@hngnews.com; web site www.sunprairiestar.com
Circulation: 3,550pd,; USPS
Advertising rate: Open inch rate $16.95
Established: 1877
Group: Hometown News Group
Digital Platform - Mobile: Apple, Android
Digital Platform - Tablet: Apple iOS, Android, Windows 7
Mng. Ed... Chris Mertes
Adv Mgr ....Missy Feiler
Gen Mgr.................................Robb Grindstaff
Pub .... Brian Knox
Mechanical Specifications: Type page 13 x 21.
Delivery Method: Mail, Newsstand, Racks
Areas Served: 53590

SUPERIOR

SUPERIOR TELEGRAM (TUES, FRI)

1410 Tower Ave, Superior, WI, 54880-1590, Superior, USA; gen tel (715) 395-5000; adv tel (715) 395-5000; ed tel (715) 395-5000; gen fax (715) 395-5002; adv fax (715) 395-5002; ed fax (715) 395-5002; disp adv e-mail telegram@superiortelegram.com; ed e-mail editorial@superiortelegram.com; web site www.superiortelegram.com
Circulation: 4,456pd,; Sworn/Estimate/Non-Audited
Advertising rate: Open inch rate $27.84
Group: Forum Communications Co.
Human Resources Manager........Deb Williams
Editor ....Shelley Nelson
Adv. Dir.......................................Megan Wedel
Circulation Director.......................Rich Roxbury
Mechanical Specifications: Type page 12 1/2 x 21 1/2; E - 6 cols, 2 1/16, 1/8 between; A - 6 cols, 2 1/16, 1/8 between; C - 9 cols, 1 3/8, 1/16 between.
Delivery Method: Mail, Newsstand, Carrier, Racks
Areas Served: Superior, WI

THORP

THORP COURIER (WED)

403 N Washington St, Thorp, WI, 54771-9538, Clark, USA; gen tel (715) 669-5525; adv tel (715) 669-5525; ed tel (715) 669-5525; gen fax (715) 669-5596; adv fax (715) 669-5596; ed fax (715) 669-5596; disp adv e-mail thorpcourier@centurytel.net; class adv e-mail thorpcourier@centurytel.net; ed e-mail thorpcourier@centurytel.net
Circulation: 2,100pd, 35fr; Sworn/Estimate/Non-Audited
Advertising rate: Open inch rate $6.83
Established: 1883
Pub./Ed. ....Mark J. LaGasse
Delivery Method: Mail, Newsstand
Areas Served: Clark County

TOMAH

THE TOMAH JOURNAL (MON, THUR)

903 Superior Ave, Ste 1, Tomah, WI, 54660-2060, Monroe, USA; gen tel (608)372-4123; adv tel (608)791-8260; ed tel (608)374-7785; gen fax (608)372-2791; adv fax (608)372-2791; ed fax (608)372-2791; disp adv e-mail barb.formanek@lee.net; class adv e-mail wendy.rasmussen@lee.net; ed e-mail mike.burns@lee.net; web site www.lacrossetribune.com
Circulation: 5,200pd,; Sworn/Estimate/Non-Audited
Advertising rate: Open inch rate $7.98
Digital Platform - Mobile: Apple, Android
Digital Platform - Tablet: Apple iOS, Android, Windows 7
Pub..Chris Hardie
Exec. Ed.............................Matthew Perenchio
Ed. ....Steve Rundio
Adv. Mgr. ....Barb FormanekEquipment & Software: Hardware — APP/Mac; Software — QPS/QuarkXPress.
Delivery Method: Mail, Racks
Areas Served: Monroe County

TOMAHAWK

TOMAHAWK LEADER (TUES)

315 W Wisconsin Ave, Tomahawk, WI, 54487-1133, Lincoln, USA; gen tel (715) 453-2151; adv tel (715) 453-2151; ed tel (715) 453-2151; gen fax (715) 453-1865; adv fax (715) 453-1865; ed fax (715) 453-1865; disp adv e-mail sales@tomahawkleader.com; class adv e-mail sales@tomahawkleader.com; ed e-mail news@tomahawkleader.com; web site www.tomahawkleader.com
Circulation: 3,200pd, 5,300fr; USPS
Advertising rate: Open inch rate $12.95
Established: 1887
Digital Platform - Mobile: Apple, Android
Digital Platform - Tablet: Apple iOS, Android, Blackberry Tablet OS, Nook, Kindle Fire
Co-Pub./Ed. ....Kathleen A. Tobin
Co-Publisher..................................Larry Tobin
Sales Consultant ....Tatum Evans
Mechanical Specifications: Type page 11 x 21; E - 6 cols, 1.65", 1/8 between.Equipment & Software: Hardware — APP/Mac; Software — Adobe/InDesign, Photoshop
Delivery Method: Mail, Newsstand
Areas Served: 54487, 54442, 54564, 54459, 54531, 54529, 54513, 54435, 54532

TWIN LAKES

WESTOSHA REPORT (SAT)

147 E Main St, Twin Lakes, WI, 53181-9679, Kenosha, USA; gen tel (262) 877-2813; adv tel (262) 945-5728; ed tel (262) 877-2813; gen fax (262) 877-3619; adv fax (262) 877-3619; ed fax (262) 877-3619; disp adv e-mail advertising@westoshareport.com; class adv e-mail assistant@westoshareport.com; ed e-mail annette@westoshareport.com; web site www.westoshareport.com
Circulation: 0pd, 1,208fr; CVC
Advertising rate: Open inch rate $11.95
Group: Southern Lakes Newspapers LLC
Digital Platform - Mobile: Apple, Android
Digital Platform - Tablet: Apple iOS, Android
Ed. ....Edward Nadolski
Creative Dept. Dir........................Sue Z. Lange
Adv. Dir.................................. Vicki Vanderwerff
Pub...Cyndi Jensen
Circ. Mgr...Tom Flatow
Delivery Method: Mail, Newsstand
Areas Served: Dane County

VERONA

THE FITCHBURG STAR (MTHLY)

PO Box 930427, 133 Enterprise Drive, Verona, WI, 53593-0427, Dane, USA; gen tel (608) 845-9559; disp adv e-mail fitchburgstar@wcinet.com; web site connectfitchburg.com
Circulation: 13,277fr
Advertising rate: $11.75
Group: Unified Newspaper Group
Gen. Mgr......................................Lee Borkowski
Ed. ....Jim Ferolie
Ad. Sales ....Catherine Stang
Advertising & Marketing Manager...........Kathy Neumeister
Delivery Method: Mail
Areas Served: Fitchburg WI / Dane County 53575; 53593; 53711; 53713; 53719

THE VERONA PRESS (THUR)

133 Enterprise Dr, Verona, WI, 53593-9122, Dane, USA; gen tel (608) 845-9559; adv tel (608) 845-9559; ed tel (608) 845-9559; gen fax (608) 845-9550; adv fax (608) 845-9550; ed fax (608) 845-9550; disp adv e-mail kathy.neumeister@wcinet.com; class adv e-mail ungclassified@wcinet.com; ed e-mail veronapress@wcinet.com; web site www.connectverona.com
Circulation: 2,100pd,; Sworn/Estimate/Non-Audited
Advertising rate: Open inch rate $10.25
Established: 1965
Group: Woodward Communications, Inc.
Digital Platform - Mobile: Android
Digital Platform - Tablet: Android
Group Ed. ....James Ferolie
Gen. Mgr. ....David Enstad
Mechanical Specifications: Type page 10 5/8 x 16; E - 6 cols, 1 5/8, 1/8 between; A - 6 cols, 1 5/8, 1/8 between; C - 6 cols, 1 5/8, 1/8 between.
Delivery Method: Mail, Racks
Areas Served: Dane County

VIROQUA

VERNON COUNTY BROADCASTER (THUR)

124 W Court St, Viroqua, WI, 54665-1505, Vernon, USA; gen tel (608)637-3137; adv tel (608)791-8223; ed tel (608)637-3137; gen fax (608)637-8557; adv fax (608)637-8557; ed fax (608)637-8557; disp adv e-mail barb.formanek@lee.net; class adv e-mail chardie@rivervalleynewspapers.com; ed e-mail mike.burns@lee.net; web site www.vernonbroadcaster.com
Circulation: 5,336pd, 23fr; Sworn/Estimate/Non-Audited
Advertising rate: Open inch rate $14.05
Established: 1854
Digital Platform - Mobile: Apple, Android
Digital Platform - Tablet: Apple iOS, Android, Windows 7
Pub..Chris Hardie
Adv. Mgr. .... Barb Formanek
Mng. Ed....................................... Matt Johnson

Mechanical Specifications: Type page 15 3/4 x 21 1/2; E - 6 cols, 1 3/4, 3/8 between; A - 6 cols, 1 3/4, 3/8 between; C - 6 cols, 1 3/4, 3/8 between.Equipment & Software: Hardware — APP/Mac; Software — QPS/QuarkXPress, Adobe/Photoshop.
Delivery Method: Mail, Racks
Areas Served: Vernon County

WASHINGTON ISLAND

WASHINGTON ISLAND OBSERVER (WED)

1253 Main Rd, Washington Island, WI, 54246-9009, Washington Island, USA; gen tel (920)847-2661; adv tel (920)847-2661; ed tel (920)847-2661; gen fax (920)847-2141; adv fax (920)847-2141; ed fax (920)847-2141; disp adv e-mail info@washingtonislandobserver.com; class adv e-mail info@washingtonislandobserver.com; ed e-mail info@washingtonislandobserver.com; web site www.washingtonislandobserver.com
Areas Served: Washington Island

WATERLOO

THE WATERLOO/MARSHALL COURIER (THUR)

123 N Monroe St, Waterloo, WI, 53594-1124, Jefferson, USA; gen tel (920)478-2188; adv tel (608) 478-2517; ed tel (920)478-2188; gen fax (920)478-3618; disp adv e-mail mfeiler@hngnews.com; class adv e-mail classifieds@hngnews.com; ed e-mail dgraff@hngnews.com; web site www.courierenews.com
Circulation: 1,500pd,; USPS
Advertising rate: Open inch rate $7.60
Established: 1871
Group: Hometown News Limited Partnership
Digital Platform - Mobile: Apple, Android
Digital Platform - Tablet: Apple iOS, Android, Windows 7
Managing Editor ....Diane Graff
Advertising Manager.....................Missy Feiler
Circulation Director......................Brian Knox II
General Manager....................Robb Grindstaff
Publisher..Brian Knox
Delivery Method: Mail, Newsstand, Racks
Areas Served: Jefferson County

WAUKESHA

BAY VIEW NOW (THUR)

1741 Dolphin Dr, Ste A, Waukesha, WI, 53186-1493, Waukesha, USA; gen tel (414) 224-2100; adv tel (414) 224-2498; ed tel (414) 224-2100 ext. 5; gen fax (262) 446-6646; adv fax (262) 446-6646; ed fax (262) 446-6646; disp adv e-mail alaffe@jrn.com; class adv e-mail btschacher@jrn.com; ed e-mail speterson@jrn.com; web site www.bayviewnow.com
Advertising rate: Open inch rate $55.60
Established: 1956
Group: Community Newspapers, Inc.
Journal Media Group
Digital Platform - Mobile: Apple, Android, Windows
Digital Platform - Tablet: Apple iOS, Android, Windows 7
Chief Ed.................................... Scott Peterson
Design/Interactive Content Dir....Matt Newman
Ed. ....Jim Riccioli
Mechanical Specifications: 1.729" width, 11" depth. 5 columns, full page image 5x11. Ads over 9" deep will be billed at full page depth of 11"
Delivery Method: Carrier
Areas Served: Waukesha County

BROOKFIELD-ELM GROVE NOW (THUR)

1741 Dolphin Dr, Ste A, Waukesha, WI, 53186-1493, Waukesha, USA; gen tel (414) 224-2100; adv tel (414) 224-2498; ed tel (414) 224-2100 ext. 5; gen fax (262) 446-6646; adv fax (262) 446-6646; ed fax (262) 446-6646; disp adv e-mail alaffe@jrn.com; class adv e-mail btschacher@jrn.com; ed e-mail speterson@jrn.com; web site www.brookfieldnow.com
Advertising rate: Open inch rate $26.00
Established: 1956
Group: Community Newspapers, Inc.
Journal Media Group
Digital Platform - Mobile: Apple, Android, Windows
Digital Platform - Tablet: Apple iOS, Android, Windows 7
Chief Ed.................................... Scott Peterson
Design/Interactive Content Dir....Matt Newman
Mechanical Specifications: 1.729" width, 11" depth. 5 columns, full page image 5x11. Ads over 9" deep will be billed at full page depth of 11"
Delivery Method: Carrier
Areas Served: Waukesha County

CUDAHY NOW (THUR)

1741 Dolphin Dr, Ste A, Waukesha, WI, 53186-1493, Waukesha, USA; gen tel (414) 224-2100; adv tel (414) 224-2498; ed tel (414) 224-2100 ext. 5; gen fax (262) 446-6646; adv fax (262) 446-6646; ed fax (262) 446-6646; disp adv e-mail alaffe@jrn.com; class adv e-mail btschacher@jrn.com; ed e-mail speterson@jrn.com; web site www.cudahynow.com
Advertising rate: Open inch rate $55.60
Established: 1956
Group: Community Newspapers, Inc.
Journal Media Group
Digital Platform - Mobile: Apple, Android, Windows
Digital Platform - Tablet: Apple iOS, Android, Windows 7
Chief Ed.................................... Scott Peterson
Design/Interactive Content Dir....Matt Newman
Mechanical Specifications: 1.729" width, 11" depth. 5 columns, full page image 5x11. Ads over 9" deep will be billed at full page depth of 11"
Delivery Method: Carrier
Areas Served: Waukesha County

ELM GROVE NOW (THUR)

1741 Dolphin Dr, Ste A, Waukesha, WI, 53186-1493, Waukesha, USA; gen tel (414) 224-2100; adv tel (414) 224-2498; ed tel (414) 224-2100 ext. 5; gen fax (262) 446-6646; adv fax (262) 446-6646; ed fax (262) 446-6646; disp adv e-mail alaffe@jrn.com; class adv e-mail btschacher@jrn.com; ed e-mail speterson@jrn.com; web site www.elmgrovenow.com
Advertising rate: Open inch rate $55.60
Established: 1956
Group: Community Newspapers, Inc.
Journal Media Group
Digital Platform - Mobile: Apple, Android, Windows
Digital Platform - Tablet: Apple iOS, Android, Windows 7
Chief Ed.................................... Scott Peterson
Design/Interactive Content Dir....Matt Newman
Mechanical Specifications: 1.729" width, 11" depth. 5 columns, full page image 5x11. Ads over 9" deep will be billed at full page depth of 11"
Delivery Method: Carrier
Areas Served: Waukesha County

FOX POINT NOW (THUR)

1741 Dolphin Dr, Ste A, Waukesha, WI, 53186-1493, Waukesha, USA; gen tel (414) 224-2100; adv tel (414) 224-2498; ed tel (414) 224-2100 ext. 5; gen fax (262) 446-6646; adv fax (262) 446-6646; ed fax (262) 446-6646; disp adv e-mail alaffe@jrn.com; class adv e-mail btschacher@jrn.com; ed e-mail speterson@jrn.com; web site www.myfoxpointnow.com
Advertising rate: Open inch rate $55.60
Established: 1956
Group: Community Newspapers, Inc.
Journal Media Group
Digital Platform - Mobile: Apple, Android, Windows
Digital Platform - Tablet: Apple iOS, Android, Windows 7
Chief Ed.................................... Scott Peterson
Design/Interactive Content Dir....Matt Newman
Mechanical Specifications: 1.729" width, 11" depth. 5 columns, full page image 5x11. Ads over 9" deep will be billed at full page depth of 11"
Delivery Method: Carrier
Areas Served: Waukesha County

FRANKLIN NOW (THUR)

1741 Dolphin Dr, Ste A, Waukesha, WI, 53186-1493, Waukesha, USA; gen tel (414) 224-2100; adv tel (414) 224-2498; ed tel (414) 224-2100 ext. 5; gen fax (262) 446-6646; adv fax (262) 446-6646; ed fax (262) 446-6646; disp adv e-mail alaffe@jrn.com; class adv e-mail btschacher@jrn.com; ed e-mail speterson@jrn.com; web site www.franklinnow.com
Advertising rate: Open inch rate $55.60
Established: 1956
Group: Community Newspapers, Inc.
Journal Media Group
Digital Platform - Mobile: Apple, Android, Windows
Digital Platform - Tablet: Apple iOS, Android, Windows 7
Chief Ed.................................... Scott Peterson
Design/Interactive Content Dir....Matt Newman
Mechanical Specifications: 1.729" width, 11" depth. 5 columns, full page image 5x11. Ads over 9" deep will be billed at full page depth of 11"
Delivery Method: Carrier
Areas Served: Waukesha County

GERMANTOWN NOW (THUR)

1741 Dolphin Dr, Ste A, Waukesha, WI, 53186-1493, Waukesha, USA; gen tel (414) 224-2100; adv tel (414) 224-2498; ed tel (414) 224-2100 ext. 5; gen fax (262) 446-6646; adv fax (262) 446-6646; ed fax (262) 446-6646; disp adv e-mail alaffe@jrn.com; class adv e-mail btschacher@jrn.com; ed e-mail speterson@jrn.com; web site www.germantownnow.com
Advertising rate: Open inch rate $55.60
Established: 1956
Group: Community Newspapers, Inc.
Journal Media Group
Digital Platform - Mobile: Apple, Android, Windows
Digital Platform - Tablet: Apple iOS, Android, Windows 7
Chief Ed.................................... Scott Peterson
Design/Interactive Content Dir....Matt Newman
Mechanical Specifications: 1.729" width, 11" depth. 5 columns, full page image 5x11. Ads over 9" deep will be billed at full page depth of 11"
Delivery Method: Carrier
Areas Served: Waukesha County

GLENDALE NOW (THUR)

1741 Dolphin Dr, Ste A, Waukesha, WI, 53186-1493, Waukesha, USA; gen tel (414) 224-2100; adv tel (414) 224-2498; ed tel (414) 224-2100 ext. 5; gen fax (262) 446-6646; adv fax (262) 446-6646; ed fax (262) 446-6646; disp adv e-mail alaffe@jrn.com; class adv e-mail btschacher@jrn.com; ed e-mail speterson@jrn.com; web site www.glendalenow.com
Advertising rate: Open inch rate $55.60
Established: 1956
Group: Community Newspapers, Inc.
Journal Media Group
Digital Platform - Mobile: Apple, Android, Windows
Digital Platform - Tablet: Apple iOS, Android, Windows 7
Chief Ed.................................... Scott Peterson
Design/Interactive Content Dir....Matt Newman
Mechanical Specifications: 1.729" width, 11" depth. 5 columns, full page image 5x11. Ads over 9" deep will be billed at full page depth of 11"
Delivery Method: Carrier
Areas Served: Waukesha County

GREATER MILWAUKEE JOBS (THUR)

801 N Barstow St, Waukesha, WI, 53186-4801, Waukesha, USA; gen tel (262) 542-2500; gen fax (262) 542-6082; web site http://conley.pro.adicio.com/
Group: Conley Media LLC
Ed. ....Dwayne Butler

GREENFIELD-WEST ALLIS NOW (THUR)

1741 Dolphin Dr, Ste A, Waukesha, WI, 53186-1493, Waukesha, USA; gen tel (414) 224-2100; adv tel (414) 224-2498; ed tel (414) 224-2100 ext. 5; gen fax (262) 446-6646; adv fax (262) 446-6646; ed fax (262) 446-6646; disp adv e-mail alaffe@jrn.com; class adv e-mail btschacher@jrn.com; ed e-mail speterson@jrn.com; web site www.greenfieldnow.com
Advertising rate: Open inch rate $28.00
Established: 1956
Group: Community Newspapers, Inc.
Journal Media Group
Digital Platform - Mobile: Apple, Android, Windows
Digital Platform - Tablet: Apple iOS, Android, Windows 7
Chief Ed.................................... Scott Peterson
Design/Interactive Content Dir....Matt Newman
Mechanical Specifications: 1.729" width, 11" depth. 5 columns, full page image 5x11. Ads over 9" deep will be billed at full page depth of 11"
Delivery Method: Carrier
Areas Served: Waukesha County

HALES CORNERS NOW (THUR)

1741 Dolphin Dr, Ste A, Waukesha, WI, 53186-1493, Waukesha, USA; gen tel (414) 224-2100; adv tel (414) 224-2498; ed tel (414) 224-2100 ext. 5; gen fax (262) 446-6646; adv fax (262) 446-6646; ed fax (262) 446-6646; disp adv e-mail alaffe@jrn.com; class adv e-mail btschacher@jrn.com; ed e-mail speterson@jrn.com; web site www.myhalescornersnow.com
Advertising rate: Open inch rate $55.60
Established: 1956
Group: Community Newspapers, Inc.
Journal Media Group
Digital Platform - Mobile: Apple, Android, Windows
Digital Platform - Tablet: Apple iOS, Android, Windows 7
Chief Ed.................................... Scott Peterson
Design/Interactive Content Dir....Matt Newman
Mechanical Specifications: 1.729" width, 11" depth. 5 columns, full page image 5x11. Ads over 9" deep will be billed at full page depth of 11"
Delivery Method: Carrier
Areas Served: Waukesha County

MENOMONEE FALLS-GERMANTOWN NOW (THUR)

1741 Dolphin Dr, Ste A, Waukesha, WI, 53186-1493, Waukesha, USA; gen tel (414) 224-2100; adv tel (414) 224-2498; ed tel (414) 224-2100 ext. 5; gen fax (262) 446-6646; adv fax (262) 446-6646; ed fax (262) 446-6646; disp adv e-mail alaffe@jrn.com; class adv e-mail btschacher@jrn.com; ed e-mail speterson@jrn.com; web site www.menomoneefallsnow.com
Advertising rate: Open inch rate $16.00
Established: 1956
Group: Community Newspapers, Inc.
Journal Media Group
Digital Platform - Mobile: Apple, Android, Windows
Digital Platform - Tablet: Apple iOS, Android, Windows 7
Chief Ed.................................... Scott Peterson
Design/Interactive Content Dir....Matt Newman
Mechanical Specifications: 1.729" width, 11" depth. 5 columns, full page image 5x11. Ads over 9" deep will be billed at full page depth of 11"
Delivery Method: Carrier
Areas Served: Waukesha County

MEQUON NOW (THUR)

1741 Dolphin Dr, Ste A, Waukesha, WI, 53186-1493, Waukesha, USA; gen tel (414) 224-2100; adv tel (414) 224-2498; ed tel (414) 224-2100 ext. 5; gen fax (262) 446-6646; adv fax (262) 446-6646; ed fax (262) 446-6646; disp adv e-mail alaffe@jrn.com; class adv e-mail btschacher@jrn.com; ed

e-mail speterson@jrn.com; web site www.mequonnow.com
Advertising rate: Open inch rate $55.60
Established: 1956
Group: Community Newspapers, Inc.
Journal Media Group
Digital Platform - Mobile: Apple, Android, Windows
Digital Platform - Tablet: Apple iOS, Android, Windows 7
Chief Ed.................................... Scott Peterson
Design/Interactive Content Dir....Matt Newman
Mechanical Specifications: 1.729" width, 11" depth. 5 columns, full page image 5x11. Ads over 9" deep will be billed at full page depth of 11"
Delivery Method: Carrier
Areas Served: Waukesha County

MUSKEGO-NEW BERLIN NOW (THUR)

1741 Dolphin Dr, Ste A, Waukesha, WI, 53186-1493, Waukesha, USA; gen tel (414) 224-2100; adv tel (414) 224-2498; ed tel (414) 224-2100 ext. 5; gen fax (262) 446-6646; adv fax (262) 446-6646; ed fax (262) 446-6646; disp adv e-mail alaffe@jrn.com; class adv e-mail btschacher@jrn.com; ed e-mail speterson@jrn.com; web site www.mymuskegonow.com
Advertising rate: Open inch rate $15.00
Established: 1956
Group: Community Newspapers, Inc.
Journal Media Group
Digital Platform - Mobile: Apple, Android, Windows
Digital Platform - Tablet: Apple iOS, Android, Windows 7
Chief Ed.................................... Scott Peterson
Design/Interactive Content Dir....Matt Newman
Mechanical Specifications: 1.729" width, 11" depth. 5 columns, full page image 5x11. Ads over 9" deep will be billed at full page depth of 11"
Delivery Method: Carrier
Areas Served: Waukesha County

NEW BERLIN NOW (THUR)

1741 Dolphin Dr, Ste A, Waukesha, WI, 53186-1493, Waukesha, USA; gen tel (414) 224-2100; adv tel (414) 224-2498; ed tel (414) 224-2100 ext. 5; gen fax (262) 446-6646; adv fax (262) 446-6646; ed fax (262) 446-6646; disp adv e-mail alaffe@jrn.com; class adv e-mail btschacher@jrn.com; ed e-mail speterson@jrn.com; web site www.newberlinnow.com
Advertising rate: Open inch rate $55.60
Established: 1956
Group: Community Newspapers, Inc.
Journal Media Group
Digital Platform - Mobile: Apple, Android, Windows
Digital Platform - Tablet: Apple iOS, Android, Windows 7
Chief Ed.................................... Scott Peterson
Design/Interactive Content Dir....Matt Newman
Mechanical Specifications: 1.729" width, 11" depth. 5 columns, full page image 5x11. Ads over 9" deep will be billed at full page depth of 11"
Delivery Method: Carrier
Areas Served: Waukesha County

NORTH SHORE NOW (THUR)

1741 Dolphin Dr, Ste A, Waukesha, WI, 53186-1493, Waukesha, USA; gen tel (414) 224-2100; adv tel (414) 224-2498; ed tel (414) 224-2100 ext. 5; gen fax (262) 446-6646; adv fax (262) 446-6646; ed fax (262) 446-6646; disp adv e-mail alaffe@jrn.com; class adv e-mail btschacher@jrn.com; ed e-mail speterson@jrn.com
Advertising rate: Open inch rate $29.00
Established: 1956
Group: Community Newspapers, Inc.
Journal Media Group
Chief Ed.................................... Scott Peterson
Design/Interactive Content Dir....Matt Newman
Delivery Method: Newsstand, Racks
Areas Served: Bayside, Brown Deer, Fox Point, Glendale,
Mequon/Thiensville, Milwaukee (53224), River Hills, Shorewood, Whitefish Bay

OAK CREEK NOW (THUR)

1741 Dolphin Dr, Ste A, Waukesha, WI, 53186-1493, Waukesha, USA; gen tel (414) 224-2100; adv tel (414) 224-2498; ed tel (414) 224-2100 ext. 5; gen fax (262) 446-6646; adv fax (262) 446-6646; ed fax (262) 446-6646; disp adv e-mail alaffe@jrn.com; class adv e-mail btschacher@jrn.com; ed e-mail speterson@jrn.com; web site www.oakcreeknow.com
Advertising rate: Open inch rate $55.60
Established: 1956
Group: Community Newspapers, Inc.
Journal Media Group
Digital Platform - Mobile: Apple, Android, Windows
Digital Platform - Tablet: Apple iOS, Android, Windows 7
Ed.. Scott Peterson
Design/Interactive Content Dir....Matt Newman
Mechanical Specifications: 1.729" width, 11" depth. 5 columns, full page image 5x11. Ads over 9" deep will be billed at full page depth of 11"
Delivery Method: Carrier
Areas Served: Waukesha County

OAK CREEK-FRANKLIN-GREENDALE-HALES CORNERS NOW (THUR)

1741 Dolphin Dr, Ste A, Waukesha, WI, 53186-1493, Waukesha, USA; gen tel (414) 224-2100; adv tel (414) 224-2498; ed tel (414) 224-2100 ext. 5; gen fax (262) 446-6646; adv fax (262) 446-6646; ed fax (262) 446-6646; disp adv e-mail alaffe@jrn.com; class adv e-mail btschacher@jrn.com; ed e-mail speterson@jrn.com; web site www.greendalenow.com
Advertising rate: Open inch rate $18.00
Established: 1956
Group: Community Newspapers, Inc.
Journal Media Group
Digital Platform - Mobile: Apple, Android, Windows
Digital Platform - Tablet: Apple iOS, Android, Windows 7
Chief Ed.................................... Scott Peterson
Design/Interactive Content Dir....Matt Newman
Mechanical Specifications: 1.729" width, 11" depth. 5 columns, full page image 5x11. Ads over 9" deep will be billed at full page depth of 11"
Delivery Method: Carrier
Areas Served: Waukesha County

OCONOMOWOC ENTERPRISE (THUR)

801 N Barstow St, Waukesha, WI, 53186-4801, Waukesha, USA; gen tel (262) 567-5511; web site www.gmtoday.com
Circulation: 3,627pd, 210fr; VAC
Advertising rate: Open inch rate $11.60
Established: 1888
Group: Conley Media LLC
Publisher.. Bill Yorth
Advertising Manager..................Jim Baumgart
Circulation Manager......................Barb Parker
Production Manager........................Pat School
Mechanical Specifications: Type page: 10.6 x 21; 6 col

SOUTH MILWAUKEE NOW (THUR)

1741 Dolphin Dr, Ste A, Waukesha, WI, 53186-1493, Waukesha, USA; gen tel (414) 224-2100; adv tel (414) 224-2498; ed tel (414) 224-2100 ext. 5; gen fax (262) 446-6646; adv fax (262) 446-6646; ed fax (262) 446-6646; disp adv e-mail alaffe@jrn.com; class adv e-mail btschacher@jrn.com; ed e-mail speterson@jrn.com; web site www.southmilwaukeenow.com
Advertising rate: Open inch rate $20.00
Established: 1956
Group: Community Newspapers, Inc.
Journal Media Group
Digital Platform - Mobile: Apple, Android, Windows
Digital Platform - Tablet: Apple iOS, Android, Windows 7
Chief Ed.................................... Scott Peterson
Design/Interactive Content Dir....Matt Newman
Mechanical Specifications: 1.729" width, 11" depth. 5 columns, full page image 5x11. Ads over 9" deep will be billed at full page depth of 11"
Delivery Method: Carrier
Areas Served: Bay View, St. Francis, South Milwaukee, Cudahy

ST. FRANCIS NOW (THUR)

1741 Dolphin Dr, Ste A, Waukesha, WI, 53186-1493, Waukesha, USA; gen tel (414) 224-2100; adv tel (414) 224-2498; ed tel (414) 224-2100 ext. 5; gen fax (262) 446-6646; adv fax (262) 446-6646; ed fax (262) 446-6646; disp adv e-mail alaffe@jrn.com; class adv e-mail btschacher@jrn.com; ed e-mail speterson@jrn.com; web site www.stfrancisnow.com
Advertising rate: Open inch rate $55.60
Established: 1956
Group: Community Newspapers, Inc.
Journal Media Group
Digital Platform - Mobile: Apple, Android, Windows
Digital Platform - Tablet: Apple iOS, Android, Windows 7
Chief Ed.................................... Scott Peterson
Design/Interactive Content Dir....Matt Newman
Mechanical Specifications: 1.729" width, 11" depth. 5 columns, full page image 5x11. Ads over 9" deep will be billed at full page depth of 11"
Delivery Method: Carrier
Areas Served: Waukesha County

WAUWATOSA NOW (THUR)

1741 Dolphin Dr, Ste A, Waukesha, WI, 53186-1493, Waukesha, USA; gen tel (414) 224-2100; adv tel (414) 224-2498; ed tel (414) 224-2100 ext. 5; gen fax (262) 446-6646; adv fax (262) 446-6646; ed fax (262) 446-6646; disp adv e-mail alaffe@jrn.com; class adv e-mail btschacher@jrn.com; ed e-mail speterson@jrn.com; web site www.wauwatosanow.com
Advertising rate: Open inch rate $55.60
Established: 1956
Group: Community Newspapers, Inc.
Journal Media Group
Digital Platform - Mobile: Apple, Android, Windows
Digital Platform - Tablet: Apple iOS, Android, Windows 7
Chief Ed.................................... Scott Peterson
Design/Interactive Content Dir....Matt Newman
Mechanical Specifications: 1.729" width, 11" depth. 5 columns, full page image 5x11. Ads over 9" deep will be billed at full page depth of 11"
Delivery Method: Carrier
Areas Served: Waukesha County

WEST ALLIS NOW (THUR)

1741 Dolphin Dr, Ste A, Waukesha, WI, 53186-1493, Waukesha, USA; gen tel (414) 224-2100; adv tel (414) 224-2498; ed tel (414) 224-2100 ext. 5; gen fax (262) 446-6646; adv fax (262) 446-6646; ed fax (262) 446-6646; disp adv e-mail alaffe@jrn.com; class adv e-mail btschacher@jrn.com; ed e-mail speterson@jrn.com; web site www.westallisnow.com
Advertising rate: Open inch rate $55.60
Established: 1956
Group: Community Newspapers, Inc.
Journal Media Group
Digital Platform - Mobile: Apple, Android, Windows
Digital Platform - Tablet: Apple iOS, Android, Windows 7
Chief Ed.................................... Scott Peterson
Design/Interactive Content Dir....Matt Newman
Mechanical Specifications: 1.729" width, 11" depth. 5 columns, full page image 5x11. Ads over 9" deep will be billed at full page depth of 11"
Delivery Method: Carrier
Areas Served: Waukesha County

WAUNAKEE

WAUNAKEE TRIBUNE (THUR)

105 South St, Waunakee, WI, 53597-1343, Dane, USA; gen tel (608) 849-5227; adv tel (608) 467-1945; ed tel (608) 729-3697; gen fax (608) 849-4225; adv fax (608) 849-4225; ed fax (608) 849-4225; disp adv e-mail dmcguigan@hngnews.com; class adv e-mail classifieds@hngnews.com; ed e-mail tribnews@hngnews.com; web site www.waunakeetribune.com
Circulation: 3,500pd,; Sworn/Estimate/Non-Audited
Advertising rate: Open inch rate $12.72
Established: 1920
Group: Hometown News Group
Digital Platform - Mobile: Apple, Android
Digital Platform - Tablet: Apple iOS, Android, Windows 7
Mng. Ed.................................Roberta Baumann
Advertising representative........Dan McGuigan
Gen. Mgr..................................Robb Grindstaff
Pub.. Brian Knox
Delivery Method: Mail, Newsstand, Racks
Areas Served: Dane County

WAUPACA

WAUPACA COUNTY POST (WED)

1990 Godfrey Dr, Waupaca, WI, 54981-7908, Waupaca, USA; gen tel (920) 217-3309; adv tel (920) 217-3309; ed tel (920) 217-3309; gen fax (715) 258-8162; disp adv e-mail dwood@mmclocal.com; class adv e-mail dwood@mmclocal.com; ed e-mail dwood@mmclocal.com; web site www.waupacanow.com - 22,000(views) 10,000(visitors)
Circulation: 5,054pd, 16,828fr; CVC
Advertising rate: Open inch rate $19.80
Established: 2009
Group: Multi Media Channels, LLC
Digital Platform - Mobile: Apple, Android, Windows
Digital Platform - Tablet: Apple iOS, Android, Windows 7
Ed. ....Robert Cloud
Adv. Mgr..Matt Rice
General Manager...........................Dave Wood
Mechanical Specifications: Type page: 9.5 x 11.5; 5 col Equipment & Software: Hardware — APP/Mac; Presses — WPC/Web Leader 9; Software — QPS/QuarkXPress 6.0, Claris, Adobe/PageMaker.
Delivery Method: Mail, Newsstand
Areas Served: Waupaca County

WISCONSIN STATE FARMER (FRI)

600 Industrial Dr, Waupaca, WI, 54981-8814, Waupaca, USA; gen tel (715)258-5546; adv tel (715)258-5546; ed tel (715)258-5546; gen fax (844)271-6834; adv fax (844)271-6834; ed fax (844)271-6834; disp adv e-mail carla.gunst@jrn.com; class adv e-mail heather.weasner@jmg.com; ed e-mail carla.gunst@jrn.com; web site www.wisfarmer.com
Circulation: 16,669pd, 511fr; AAM
Advertising rate: Open inch rate $23.00
Established: 1956
Group: Journal Media Group
Digital Platform - Mobile: Apple, Windows
Digital Platform - Tablet: Apple iOS, Windows 7
Pub..Trey Foerster
Ed. .... Carla GunstEquipment & Software: Hardware — APP/Mac; Presses — 9-WPC/Web Leader; Software — QPS/QuarkXPress 6.0, Claris, Adobe/PageMaker.
Delivery Method: Mail, Newsstand
Areas Served: statewide Wisconsin, portions of Minnesota, Michigan, Illinois, Iowa.

WAUTOMA

WAUSHARA ARGUS (WED)

W7781 Hwy 21 & 73 E, Wautoma, WI, 54982, Waushara, USA; gen tel (920) 787-3334; adv tel (920) 787-3334; ed tel (920) 787-3334; gen fax (920) 787-2883; adv fax (920) 787-2883; ed fax (920) 787-2883; disp adv e-mail argus@waushararagus.com; class adv e-mail argusmarge@wausharaargus.com; ed e-mail argusmary@wausharaargus.com; web site www.wausharaargus.com
Circulation: 5,400pd, 40fr; Sworn/Estimate/Non-Audited

Advertising rate: Open inch rate $8.50
Established: 1859
Group: Delphos Herald, Inc.
Digital Platform - Mobile: Apple, Windows
Digital Platform - Tablet: Apple iOS, Windows 7
Production Manager..............Marjorie Williams
Sales..Karla Perkins
Publisher.......................................Jon Gneiser
Senior Publisher..............Mary KunaschEquipment & Software: Hardware — Mk, APP/Mac; Software — QPS/QuarkXPress, Adobe.
Delivery Method: Mail, Newsstand, Racks
Areas Served: Waushara, North Portage, Northeast Waupaca, East Winnebago, South Green Lake, South Marquette, and West Adams County

WEST BEND

THE HARTFORD TIMES PRESS (SUN)

100 S 6th Ave, West Bend, WI, 53095-3309, Washington, USA; gen tel (262) 375-5100; adv tel (262) 375-5100; ed tel (262) 375-5100; gen fax (262) 670-6689; adv fax (262) 670-6689; ed fax (262) 670-6689; disp adv e-mail jvan@conleynet.com; class adv e-mail jvan@conleynet.com; ed e-mail jvan@conleynet.com; web site www.gmtoday.com
Circulation: 13,779fr; VAC
Advertising rate: Open inch rate $10.09
Established: 1867
Group: Conley Media LLC
Digital Platform - Mobile: Windows
Digital Platform - Tablet: Windows 7
Pub..Heather Rogge
Ed. .... Sarah Mann
Adv. Mgr. .... Mary Meyer
Circ. Mgr ....Kim Kleba
Prod. Mgr...................................Scott Wiesner
Mechanical Specifications: Type page: 10.6 x 10.5; 6 col
Delivery Method: Mail
Areas Served: Washington County

WASHINGTON COUNTY POST (SUN)

100 S 6th Ave, West Bend, WI, 53095-3309, Washington, USA; gen tel (262) 306-5000; adv tel (262) 306-5000; ed tel 262-306-5000; gen fax (262) 338-5271; adv fax (262) 338-5271; ed fax (262) 338-5271; disp adv e-mail hrogge@conleynet.com; class adv e-mail cshaske@conleynet.com; ed e-mail hrogge@conleynet.com; web site www.gmtoday.com
Circulation: 0pd, 47,203fr; CVC
Advertising rate: Open inch rate $18.31
Established: 1950
Group: Conley Media LLC
Pub & Adv Dir..........................Heather Rogge
Call Center Dir. ....Cindy Shaske
Delivery Method: Carrier
Areas Served: Washington County, Wisconsin

WESTBY

THE WESTBY TIMES (THUR)

PO Box 28, Westby, WI, 54667-0028, Vernon, USA; gen tel (608)634-4317; adv tel (608)634-4317; ed tel (608)634-4317; gen fax (608)634-6499; adv fax (608)634-6499; ed fax (608)634-6499; disp adv e-mail barb.formanek@lee.net; class adv e-mail chardie@rivervalleynewspapers.com; ed e-mail mike.burns@lee.net; web site www.westbytimes.com
Circulation: 2,000pd,; Sworn/Estimate/Non-Audited
Advertising rate: Open inch rate $8.24
Digital Platform - Mobile: Apple, Android
Digital Platform - Tablet: Apple iOS, Android, Windows 7
Pub...Chris Hardie
Adv. Mgr. .... Barb Formanek
Ed. ....Dorothy Jasperson
Mechanical Specifications: Type page 15 3/4 x 21.
Delivery Method: Mail, Racks
Areas Served: Vernon County

WINDSOR

DEFOREST TIMES-TRIBUNE (THUR)

6616 Lake Rd, Windsor, WI, 53598-9759, Dane, USA; gen tel (608) 846-5576; adv tel (608) 846-5576; ed tel (608) 846-5576; gen fax (608) 846-5757; adv fax (608) 846-5757; ed fax (608) 846-5757; disp adv e-mail lkanderson@hngnews.com; class adv e-mail spstar@hngnews.com; ed e-mail jkurtz@hngnews.com; web site www.deforestenews.com
Circulation: 2,825pd,; Sworn/Estimate/Non-Audited
Advertising rate: Open inch rate $13.45
Established: 1895
Group: Hometown News Group
Digital Platform - Mobile: Apple, Android
Digital Platform - Tablet: Apple iOS, Android, Windows 7
Pub.. Brian Knox
Circ. Mgr...............................Christine Benisch
Bus. Mgr...Chris Drake
Mgr Ed ....Jake Kurtz
Delivery Method: Mail, Newsstand, Racks
Areas Served: 53532, 53555, 53597, 53955

WINNECONNE

THE WINNECONNE NEWS (WED)

908 E Main St, Ste B, Winneconne, WI, 54986-9672, USA; gen tel (920) 582-4541; gen fax (920) 582-4417; disp adv e-mail monicaw@rogerspublishing.com; ed e-mail beckyladue@rogerspublishing.com
Established: 1953
Group: Rogers Printing Solutions
Ed. ....Becky LaDue
Proofreader.................................Mary Harper
Adv. Mgr. ....Kari Joas

WITTENBERG

THE WITTENBERG ENTERPRISE & BIRNAMWOOD NEWS (THUR)

600 S Webb St, Wittenberg, WI, 54499-9040, Shawano, USA; gen tel (715) 253-2737; adv tel (715) 253-2737; ed tel (715) 253-2737; gen fax (715) 253-3176; adv fax (715) 253-3176; ed fax (715) 253-3176; disp adv e-mail mnelson@wolfrivermedia.com; class adv e-mail mnelson@wolfrivermedia.com; ed e-mail mnelson@wolfrivermedia.com; web site www.wittenbergenterprise.com
Circulation: 1,100pd,; Sworn/Estimate/Non-Audited
Advertising rate: Open inch rate $5.00
Established: 1893
Group: Wolf River Media llc
Digital Platform - Mobile: Apple, Android
Digital Platform - Tablet: Apple iOS, Android, Windows 7
Pub./Ed. ....Miriam Nelson
Classified Mgr. ....Kimberly Timm
Mechanical Specifications: Type page 12 3/4 x 21 1/2; E - 6 cols, 2, 1/4 between; A - 6 cols, 2, 1/4 between; C - 6 cols, 2, 1/4 between. Equipment & Software: Hardware — IBM; Software — Microsoft/Windows 3.1, Microsoft/Windows 95.
Delivery Method: Mail, Newsstand
Areas Served: Shawano County

WYOMING

AFTON

STAR VALLEY INDEPENDENT (THUR)

360 S Washington St, Afton, WY, 83110, Lincoln, USA; gen tel (307)885-5727; adv tel (307)885-5727; ed tel (307)885-5727; gen fax (307)885-5742; adv fax (307)885-5742; ed fax (307)885-5742; disp adv e-mail sviad1@silverstar.com; class adv e-mail sviclassifieds@silverstar.com; ed e-mail svisarah@silverstar.com; web site www.starvalleyindependent.com
Circulation: 4,000pd,; Sworn/Estimate/Non-Audited
Advertising rate: Open inch rate $7.50
Established: 1902
Digital Platform - Mobile: Apple, Android
Digital Platform - Tablet: Apple iOS, Android
Pub.. Dan Dockstader
Managing Ed.................................Sarah Hale
Circ. Mgr...Paula Nield
Adv. Mgr. ....Josh Hendreson
Sports Ed...................................Dahl Erickson
Adv. Sales......................................Patty Taylor
Adv. Mgr. ....Josh Henderson
Delivery Method: Mail, Racks
Areas Served: Lincoln County

BUFFALO

BUFFALO BULLETIN (THUR)

58 N Lobban Ave, Buffalo, WY, 82834-1953, Johnson, USA; gen tel (307)684-2223; adv tel (307)684-2223; ed tel (307)684-2223; gen fax (307)684-7431; adv fax (307)684-7431; ed fax (307)684-7431; disp adv e-mail clayton@buffalobulletin.com; class adv e-mail clayton@buffalobulletin.com; ed e-mail jen@buffalobulletin.com; web site www.buffalobulletin.com
Circulation: 3,800pd,; USPS
Advertising rate: Open inch rate $24.00
Digital Platform - Mobile: Apple, Android
Digital Platform - Tablet: Apple iOS, Android, Windows 7
Office Mgr. .... Tammy Teigen
Pub.. Robert Hicks
News Ed. .... Jen Sieve-Hicks
Adv. Sales Rep.......................Clayton Maynard
Business Mgr.................................Evelyn Lack
Adv. Sales Rep..............................Shelley Gill
Delivery Method: Mail
Areas Served: Johnson County

CASPER

CASPER JOURNAL (WED)

170 Star Ln, Casper, WY, 82604-2883, Natrona, USA; gen tel (307)265-3870; adv tel (307)265-3870; ed tel (307)266-0516; gen fax (307)265-4616; adv fax (307)265-4616; ed fax (307)265-4616; disp adv e-mail publisher@casperjournal.com; class adv e-mail publisher@casperjournal.com; ed e-mail editor@casperjournal.com; web site www.casperjournal.com
Circulation: 600pd, 25,000fr; CVC
Advertising rate: Open inch rate $23.00
Established: 1978
Group: Lee Enterprises, Inc.
Digital Platform - Mobile: Apple, Android
Digital Platform - Tablet: Apple iOS, Android
Pub./Ed. ....Dale Bohren
Assistant Ed.......................... Gen Cotherman
Reporter .... Makayla Moore
Adv. Sales..................................Janet Johnson
Circ. Mgr.................................LeeAnn Crawley
Mechanical Specifications: Type page 10 1/2 x 16 2/3; E - 5 cols, 2, 1/16 between; A - 5 cols, 2, 1/16 between; C - 9 cols, 1 1/16, 1/16 between.Equipment & Software: Hardware — PC, APP/Mac; Presses — KP; Software — TCMS-In Design
Delivery Method: Mail, Carrier, Racks
Areas Served: 82601, 82604, 82609, 82605, 82636, 82644, 82643

CODY

THE CODY ENTERPRISE (TUES, THUR)

3101 Big Horn Ave, Cody, WY, 82414-9250, Park, USA; gen tel (307) 587-2231; adv tel (307) 587-2231; ed tel (307) 587-2231; gen fax (307) 587-5208; adv fax (307) 587-5208; ed fax (307) 587-5208; disp adv e-mail office@codyenterprise.com; class adv e-mail classified@codyenterprise.com; ed e-mail amber@codyenterprise.com; web site www.codyenterprise.com
Circulation: 7,050pd,; Sworn/Estimate/Non-Audited
Advertising rate: Open inch rate $18.72
Established: 1899
Digital Platform - Mobile: Apple, Android
Digital Platform - Tablet: Apple iOS, Android
Co-Pub.. Bob Kennedy
Publisher..................................John Malmberg
Prodn. Mgr. ....John Sides
Editor ....Vin Cappiello
Mechanical Specifications: Type page 11 1/2 x 21; E - 6 cols, 1 3/4, 1/6 between; A - 6 cols, 1 3/4, 1/6 between; C - 6 cols, 1 3/4, 1/6 between.Equipment & Software: ; Presses — G/Community.
Delivery Method: Mail, Newsstand, Racks
Areas Served: Cody and Powell in Park County (82414, 82435)

DOUGLAS

THE DOUGLAS BUDGET (WED)

310 E Center St, Douglas, WY, 82633-2541, Converse, USA; gen tel (307)358-2965; adv tel (307)358-2965; ed tel (307)358-2965; gen fax (307)358—2926; adv fax (307)358-2926; ed fax (307)358-2926; disp adv e-mail publisher@douglas-budget.com; class adv e-mail publisher@douglas-budget.com; ed e-mail publisher@douglas-budget.com; web site www.douglas-budget.com
Circulation: 3,908pd, 20fr; USPS
Advertising rate: Open inch rate $13.50
Established: 1886
Group: Sage Publishing
Digital Platform - Mobile: Apple, Android
Digital Platform - Tablet: Apple iOS, Android
Pub./Ed..Matt Adelman
Mechanical Specifications: Type page 11 1/2 x 21; E - 6 cols, 1 3/4, 1/6 between; A - 6 cols, 1 3/4, 1/6 between; C - 6 cols, 1 3/4, 1/6 between.Equipment & Software: Hardware — 2-APP/Mac Intel; Presses — 9-G/Community; Software — Adobe/Photoshop CS5, Adobe/InDesign CS5, Adobe/Illustrator CS5
Delivery Method: Mail, Newsstand, Carrier, Racks
Areas Served: Converse County, Wyoming; all zip codes

DUBOIS

DUBOIS FRONTIER (THUR)

8 C St, Dubois, WY, 82513, Fremont, USA; gen tel (307)455-2525; adv tel (307)455-2525; ed tel (307)455-2525; disp adv e-mail frontierads@wyoming.com; class adv e-mail frontierads@wyoming.com; ed e-mail duboisfrontier@wyoming.com; web site www.duboisfrontier.com
Circulation: 1,200pd,; Sworn/Estimate/Non-Audited
Advertising rate: Open inch rate $5.00
Established: 1927
Mng. Ed.................................... Christine Smith
Delivery Method: Mail, Racks
Areas Served: Dubois and surrounding communities of Fremont County

EVANSTON

UINTA COUNTY HERALD (TUES, FRI)

849 Front St, Ste 101, Evanston, WY, 82930-3475, Uinta, USA; gen tel (307)789-6560; adv tel (307)789-6560 ext. 102; ed tel (307)789-6560 ext. 110; gen fax (307)789-2700; adv fax (307)789-2700; ed fax (307)789-2700; disp adv e-mail bliechty@uintacountyherald.com; class adv e-mail mtesoro@uintacountyherald.com; ed e-mail editor@uintacountyherald.com; web site www.uintacountyherald.com

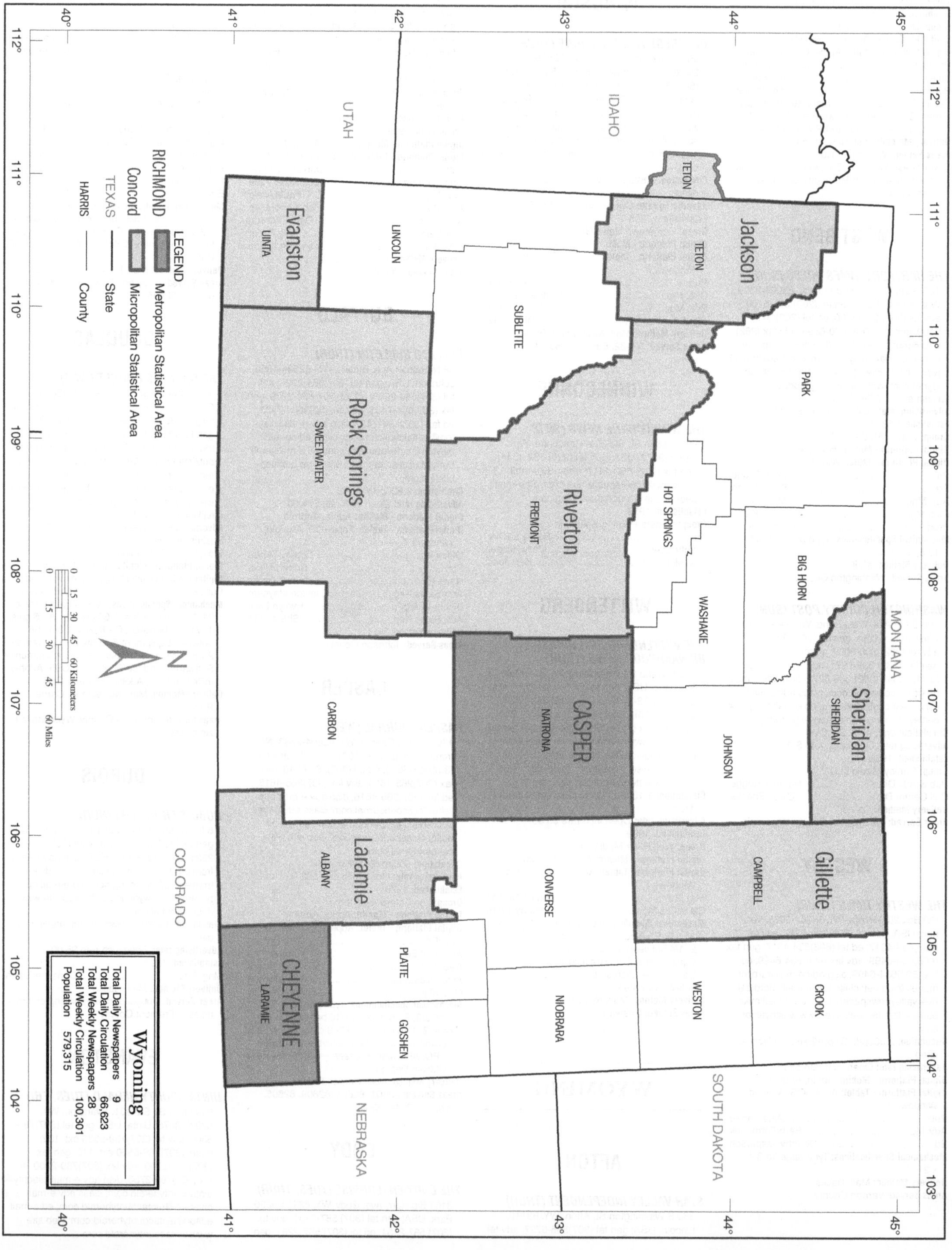
Wyoming
Total Daily Newspapers 9
Total Daily Circulation 66,623
Total Weekly Newspapers 28
Total Weekly Circulation 100,301
Population 579,315
LEGEND
RICHMOND Metropolitan Statistical Area
Concord Micropolitan Statistical Area
TEXAS State
HARRIS County
0 15 30 45 60 Kilometers
0 15 30 45 60 Miles
N
MONTANA
IDAHO
UTAH
COLORADO
NEBRASKA
SOUTH DAKOTA
Jackson
TETON
PARK
Sheridan
SHERIDAN
BIG HORN
Gillette
CAMPBELL
CROOK
WASHAKIE
HOT SPRINGS
JOHNSON
WESTON
SUBLETTE
Riverton
FREMONT
CASPER
NATRONA
CONVERSE
NIOBRARA
LINCOLN
Evanston
UINTA
Rock Springs
SWEETWATER
CARBON
Laramie
ALBANY
PLATTE
GOSHEN
CHEYENNE
LARAMIE

Circulation: 3,250pd, 73fr; Sworn/Estimate/Non-Audited
Advertising rate: Open inch rate $14.40
Established: 1937
Group: News Media Corp.
Digital Platform - Mobile: Apple, Android, Windows, Blackberry
Digital Platform - Tablet: Apple iOS, Android, Windows 7, Blackberry Tablet OS, Kindle, Nook, Kindle Fire
Pub. .... Mark Tesoro
Circ. Mgr. .... Jodi Jensen
Ed. .... Matt Roberts
Prodn. Mgr. .... Kae Ellis
Mechanical Specifications: Type page 13 x 21 1/2; E - 6 cols, 2, 1/6 between; A - 6 cols, 2, 1/6 between; C - 6 cols, 2, 1/6 between. Equipment & Software: Hardware — APP/Mac; Software — Adobe/PageMaker 5.0, Microsoft/Word 4.0, Multi-Ad/Creator 3.6, Microsoft/Excel 5.0.
Delivery Method: Mail, Newsstand, Racks
Areas Served: Uinta County

GREEN RIVER

GREEN RIVER STAR (WED)

445 Uinta Dr, Green River, WY, 82935-4815, Sweetwater, USA; gen tel (307)875-3103; adv tel (307)875-3103; ed tel (307)875-3103; disp adv e-mail sales1@greenriverstar.com; class adv e-mail sales1@greenriverstar.com; ed e-mail editor@greenriverstar.com; web site www.greenriverstar.com
Circulation: 3,200pd,; Sworn/Estimate/Non-Audited
Advertising rate: $10.50
Established: 1890
Publisher .... J. Louis Mullen
Advertising .... Sarah Wallace
Editor .... David Martin

GUERNSEY

GUERNSEY GAZETTE (TUES)

40 S Wyoming St, Guernsey, WY, 82214, Platte, USA; gen tel (307)836-2021; adv tel (307)322-2627; ed tel (307)836-2021; gen fax (307)836-2021; adv fax (307)836-2021; ed fax (307)836-2021; disp adv e-mail kcoburn@guernseygazette.com; class adv e-mail ggads@guernseygazette.com; ed e-mail ggeditor@guernseygazette.com; web site www.guernseygazette.com
Circulation: 550pd,; Sworn/Estimate/Non-Audited
Advertising rate: Open inch rate $10.99
Group: News Media Corp.
Digital Platform - Mobile: Apple, Android
Digital Platform - Tablet: Apple iOS, Android, Windows 7
Pub. .... Jeff Robertson
Gen. Mgr./Account Exec. .... Karry Coburn
Ed. .... Vicki Hood
Mechanical Specifications: 6 columns, 1.5" per column, 1 pica gutter. 9.75" x 13" printed areaEquipment & Software: Hardware — Macs
Delivery Method: Mail, Newsstand, Racks
Areas Served: Platte County

JACKSON

JACKSON HOLE NEWS&GUIDE (WED)

1225 Maple Way, Jackson, WY, 83001-8567, Teton, USA; gen tel (307) 733-2047; adv tel (307) 732 7070; ed tel (307) 732 7063; gen fax (307) 733-2138; adv fax (307) 733-2138; ed fax (307) 732-2138; disp adv e-mail adsales@jhnewsandguide.com; class adv e-mail classifieds@jhnewsandguide.com; ed e-mail editor@jhnewsandguide.com; web site www.jhnewsandguide.com - 392,200(views) 82,200(visitors)
Circulation: 6,835pd,; USPS
Advertising rate: Open inch rate $22.20
Established: 1970
Group: Teton Media Works, Inc.
Digital Platform - Mobile: Apple, Android
Digital Platform - Tablet: Apple iOS, Android
Publisher .... Kevin Olson
Adv. Dir. .... Adam Meyer
Director of Business Development .... Amy Golightly
Editor .... John Moses
Mechanical Specifications: Type page 10 1/6 x 15 5/6; E - 4 cols, 2 2/5, 1/6 between; A - 4 cols, 2 2/5, 1/6 between; C - 7 cols, between. Equipment & Software: Hardware — APP/Mac; Presses — 7-HI/V-15A; Software — QPS/QuarkXPress 4.1.
Delivery Method: Mail, Newsstand, Racks
Areas Served: 83001, 02, 014, 011, 012, 013, 025

KEMMERER

THE KEMMERER GAZETTE (THUR)

708 J C Penney Dr, Kemmerer, WY, 83101-2936, Lincoln, USA; gen tel (307)877-3347; adv tel (307)877-3347; ed tel (307)877-3347; gen fax (307)877-3736; adv fax (307)877-3736; ed fax (307)877-3736; disp adv e-mail advertising@kemmerergazette.com; class adv e-mail advertising@kemmerergazette.com; ed e-mail editor@kemmerergazette.com; web site www.kemmerergazette.com
Circulation: 1,650pd,; Sworn/Estimate/Non-Audited
Advertising rate: Open inch rate $6.90
Group: News Media Corp.
Digital Platform - Mobile: Apple, Android, Windows, Blackberry
Digital Platform - Tablet: Apple iOS, Android, Windows 7, Blackberry Tablet OS, Kindle, Nook, Kindle Fire
Pub. .... Mark Tesoro
Ed. .... Ryan O'Connell
Office Mgr. .... Rose Capellen
Adv. Mgr. .... Cortney Reed
Mechanical Specifications: Type page 13 x 21 1/4; E - 6 cols, 2, 1/8 between; A - 6 cols, 2, 1/8 between; C - 6 cols, 2, 1/8 between. Equipment & Software: Hardware — APP/Mac; Software — Adobe/PageMaker.
Delivery Method: Mail, Racks
Areas Served: Lincoln County

LANDER

LANDER JOURNAL (WED, SUN)

332 Main St, Lander, WY, 82520-3102, Fremont, USA; gen tel (307)332-2323; adv tel (307)332-2323; ed tel (307)332-2323; gen fax (307)332-9332; adv fax (307)332-9332; ed fax (307)332-9332; disp adv e-mail journal@wyoming.com; class adv e-mail journal@wyoming.com; ed e-mail newsdepartment@wyoming.com; web site www.landerjournal.net
Circulation: 4,475pd, 2,600fr; Sworn/Estimate/Non-Audited
Advertising rate: Open inch rate $8.00
Group: The Riverton Ranger, Inc.
Digital Platform - Mobile: Apple, Android
Digital Platform - Tablet: Apple iOS, Android, Windows 7
Pub. .... Steve Peck
Delivery Method: Mail, Racks
Areas Served: Fremont County

LINGLE

THE LINGLE GUIDE (MON)

228 Main St, Lingle, WY, 82223, Goshen, USA; gen tel (307)837-2255; adv tel (307)837-2255; ed tel (307)837-2255; gen fax (307)532-2283 ; adv fax (307)532-2283; ed fax (307)532-2283; disp adv e-mail calbers@lingleguide.com; class adv e-mail jgood@lingleguide.com; ed e-mail calbers@lingleguide.com; web site lingleguide.com
Group: News Media Corp.

LUSK

THE LUSK HERALD (WED)

227 S Main St, Lusk, WY, 82225, Niobrara, USA; gen tel (307)334-2867; adv tel (307)334-2867; ed tel (307)334-2867; gen fax (307)334-2514; adv fax (307)334-2514; ed fax (307)334-2514; disp adv e-mail lhads@luskherald.com; class adv e-mail lhads@luskherald.com; ed e-mail jeff@luskherald.com; web site www.luskherald.com
Circulation: 1,300pd,; Sworn/Estimate/Non-Audited
Advertising rate: Open inch rate $11.49
Established: 1886
Group: News Media Corp.
Digital Platform - Mobile: Apple, Android, Windows, Blackberry
Digital Platform - Tablet: Apple iOS, Android, Windows 7, Blackberry Tablet OS, Kindle, Nook, Kindle Fire
Pub. .... Jeff Robertson
Ed. .... Brandie Collins
Gen. Mgr. .... Rob Mortimore
Office Mgr. .... Tom Bartelt
Mechanical Specifications: Type page 9 3/4 x 13; E - 6 cols, 1 1/2, 1/6 between; A - 6 cols, 1 1/2, 1/6 between; C - 6 cols, 1 1/2, 1/6 between.Equipment & Software: Hardware — APP/Mac; Software — Multi Ad, Adobe Creative Suite
Delivery Method: Mail, Newsstand, Racks
Areas Served: Niobrara County

LYMAN

BRIDGER VALLEY PIONEER (FRI)

317 Bradshaw St # 2, Lyman, WY, 82937, Uinta, USA; gen tel (307)787-3229; adv tel (307)789-6560 ext. 103; ed tel (307)789-6560; gen fax (307)787-6795; adv fax (307)787-6795; ed fax (307)787-6795; disp adv e-mail ads@bridgervalleypioneer.com; class adv e-mail ads@bridgervalleypioneer.com; ed e-mail news@bridgervalleypioneer.com; web site www.bridgervalleypioneer.com
Circulation: 1,800pd,; Sworn/Estimate/Non-Audited
Advertising rate: Open inch rate $12.10
Group: News Media Corp.
Digital Platform - Mobile: Apple, Android
Digital Platform - Tablet: Apple iOS, Android, Windows 7, Blackberry Tablet OS, Kindle, Nook, Kindle Fire
Pub. .... Mark Tesoro
Ed. .... Virginia Giorgis
Adv. .... Jerilyn Case
Delivery Method: Mail, Racks
Areas Served: Uinta County

MOORCROFT

MOORCROFT LEADER (THUR)

304 N Riley Ave, Moorcroft, WY, 82721, Crook, USA; gen tel (307)756-3371; adv tel (307)756-3371; ed tel (307)756-3371; gen fax (307)756-9827; adv fax (307)756-3371; ed fax (307)756-3371; disp adv e-mail mlbooks@collinscom.net; class adv e-mail adslead@collinscom.net; ed e-mail mleader@collinscom.net; web site www.moorcroft-leader.com
Circulation: 1,200pd, 135fr; Sworn/Estimate/Non-Audited
Advertising rate: Open inch rate $4.75
Established: 1909
Group: Moorcroft Leader
Pub./Ed./Adv. Mgr. .... Margaret Bauer
Adv. Mgr. .... Melissa Paden
Reporter .... Grace Moore
Mechanical Specifications: Type page 10 x 13; E - 6 cols, 1 7/12, 1/6 between; A - 6 cols, 1 7/12, 1/6 between; C - 6 cols, 1 7/12, 1/6 between.Equipment & Software: Hardware — APP/Power Mac; Software — Adobe/PageMaker 6.0.
Delivery Method: Mail, Newsstand
Areas Served: Crook, Campbell, and Weston County

NEWCASTLE

NEWS LETTER JOURNAL (THUR)

14 W Main St, Newcastle, WY, 82701-2122, Weston, USA; gen tel (307)746-2777; adv tel (307)746-2777; ed tel (307)746-2777; gen fax (307)746-2660; adv fax (307)746-2660; ed fax (307)746-2660; disp adv e-mail sales@newslj.com; class adv e-mail office@newslj.com; ed e-mail editor@newslj.com; web site www.newslj.com
Circulation: 2,500pd, 50fr; Sworn/Estimate/Non-Audited
Advertising rate: Open inch rate $13.00
Established: 1890
Digital Platform - Mobile: Apple, Android
Digital Platform - Tablet: Apple iOS, Android
Assc. Pub./Ed. .... Bob Bonnar
Office Mgr. .... Becky Vodopich
Adv. Sales Mgr. .... Stacy Haggerty
Graphic Designer .... Stephanie Bonnar
Circ. Mgr. .... Kim Dean
Mechanical Specifications: Type page 13 1/4 x 21; A - 6 cols, 2 1/16, 1/6 between; C - 6 cols, 2 1/16, 1/6 between.Equipment & Software: Hardware — APP/Mac; Software — QPS/QuarkXPress, Adobe/Photoshop, Adobe/PageMaker.
Delivery Method: Mail, Newsstand, Racks
Areas Served: Weston County

PINE BLUFFS

PINE BLUFFS POST (THUR)

201 E 2nd St, Pine Bluffs, WY, 82082, Laramie, USA; gen tel (307)245-3763; adv tel (307)245-3763; ed tel (307)245-3763; gen fax (307)245-3325; adv fax (307)245-3325; ed fax (307)245-3325; disp adv e-mail dclark@pinebluffspost.com; class adv e-mail dclark@pinebluffspost.com; ed e-mail editor@pinebluffspost.com; web site www.pinebluffspost.com
Circulation: 1,100pd,; Sworn/Estimate/Non-Audited
Advertising rate: Open inch rate $7.50
Established: 1908
Group: Stevenson Newspapers
Digital Platform - Mobile: Apple, Android
Digital Platform - Tablet: Apple iOS, Android, Windows 7
Owner .... Gary W. Stevenson
Owner .... Sue Stevenson
Pub./Mng. Ed. .... Cynthia Shroyer
Gen. Mgr. .... Polly Taylor
Delivery Method: Mail, Newsstand, Racks
Areas Served: Laramie County, Northern Colorado and the Western Nebraska Panhandle

PINEDALE

SUBLETTE EXAMINER (THUR)

219 E Pine St, Ste 109, Pinedale, WY, 82941, Sublette, USA; gen tel (307)367-3203; adv tel (307)367-3203; ed tel (307)367-3203; gen fax (307)367-3209; adv fax (307)367-3209; ed fax (307)367-3209; disp adv e-mail spape@subletteexaminer.com; class adv e-mail spape@subletteexaminer.com; ed e-mail mtesoro@subletteexaminer.com; web site www.subletteexaminer.com
Group: News Media Corp.
Editor .... Megan Neher
Publisher .... Mark Tesoro
Gen. Mgr./Adv. Dir .... Sharon Paper

THE PINEDALE ROUNDUP (FRI)

219 E Pine St, Ste 116, Pinedale, WY, 82941, Sublette, USA; gen tel (307)367-2123; adv tel (307)367-2123; ed tel (307)367-2123; gen fax (307)367-6623; adv fax (307)367-6623; ed fax (307)367-6623; disp adv e-mail spape@pinedaleroundup.com; class adv e-mail spape@pinedaleroundup.com; ed e-mail mtesoro@uintacountyherald.com; web site www.pinedaleroundup.com
Circulation: 4,000pd,; Sworn/Estimate/Non-Audited

Advertising rate: Open inch rate $17.00
Established: 1904
Group: News Media Corp.
Digital Platform - Mobile: Apple, Android, Windows, Blackberry
Digital Platform - Tablet: Apple iOS, Android, Windows 7, Blackberry Tablet OS, Kindle, Nook, Kindle Fire
Ed. .... Megan Neher
General Mgr. .... Kara Losik
Mechanical Specifications: Type page 11 x 17; E - 4 cols, 2 5/12, 1/6 between; A - 4 cols, 2 5/12, 1/6 between; C - 6 cols, 1 7/12, 1/6 between.Equipment & Software: Hardware — APP/Mac; Software — QPS/QuarkXPress 3.32, Adobe/Photoshop 3.0, Macromedia/ Freehand 5.5.
Delivery Method: Mail, Newsstand, Racks
Areas Served: Sublette County

POWELL

THE POWELL TRIBUNE (TUES, THUR)

128 S Bent St, Powell, WY, 82435-2714, Park, USA; gen tel (307)754-2221; adv tel (307)754-2221; ed tel (307)754-2221; gen fax (307)754-4873; adv fax (307)754-4873; ed fax (307)754-4873; disp adv e-mail toby@powelltribune.com; class adv e-mail fawn@powelltribune.com; ed e-mail tom@powelltribune.com; web site www.powelltribune.com
Circulation: 4,000pd,; Sworn/Estimate/Non-Audited
Advertising rate: Open inch rate $12.00
Established: 1908
Digital Platform - Mobile: Apple, Android, Windows, Blackberry
Digital Platform - Tablet: Apple iOS, Android, Windows 7, Blackberry Tablet OS, Kindle, Nook, Kindle Fire
Pub. .... Dave Bonner
Adv. Mgr./Gen. Mgr. .... Toby Bonner
Mng. Ed. .... Tom Lawrence
Office Mgr. .... Beth Cunning
Delivery Method: Mail, Racks
Areas Served: Park County

RIVERTON

WIND RIVER NEWS (THUR)

421 E Main St, Riverton, WY, 82501-4438, Fremont, USA; gen tel (307)856-2244; adv tel (307)856-2244; ed tel (307)856-2244; gen fax (307)856-0189; adv fax (307)856-0189; ed fax (307)856-0189; disp adv e-mail rangerads@wyoming.com; class adv e-mail luanne@dailyranger.com; ed e-mail steve@dailyranger.com; web site www.dailyranger.com
Circulation: 3,500pd,; Sworn/Estimate/Non-Audited
Advertising rate: Open inch rate $5.50
Group: The Riverton Ranger, Inc.
Digital Platform - Mobile: Apple, Android
Digital Platform - Tablet: Apple iOS, Android, Windows 7
Pub./Ed. .... Steve Peck
Assistant Ed. .... Chris Peck
Circ. Mgr. .... Carl Manning
Delivery Method: Mail, Racks
Areas Served: Fremont County

ROZET

THE CAMPBELL COUNTY OBSERVER (FRI)

PO Box 222, Rozet, WY, 82727-0222, Campbell, USA; gen tel (307)670-8980; adv tel (307)670-8980; ed tel (307)670-8980; gen fax (307)670-9348; adv fax (307)670-9348; ed fax (307)670-9348; disp adv e-mail countycampbellobserver@gmail.com ; class adv e-mail countycampbellobserver@gmail.com; ed e-mail countycampbellobserver@gmail.com
Circulation: 2,000pd,; Sworn/Estimate/Non-Audited
Advertising rate: $10
Established: 2011
Group: Patriot Publishing
Owner/Publisher/Editor .... Nicholas De Laat
Owner/Manager .... Candice De Laat
Advertising Sales Manager .... Anne Peterson
Advertising Sales .... Dale Russell
Advertising Design .... Owen Clarke
Delivery Method: Mail, Newsstand
Areas Served: Gillette, Wright, Rozet and Recluse

SARATOGA

THE SARATOGA SUN (WED)

116 E Bridge St, Saratoga, WY, 82331, Carbon, USA; gen tel (307)326-8311; adv tel (307)326-8311; ed tel (307) 326-8311; gen fax (307)326-5108; adv fax (307)326-5108; ed fax (307) 326-5108; disp adv e-mail sunads@union-tel.com; class adv e-mail sunads@union-tel.com; ed e-mail saratogasun@netcommander.com; web site www.saratogasun.com
Circulation: 1,800pd, 20fr; Sworn/Estimate/Non-Audited
Advertising rate: Open inch rate $8.00
Established: 1888
Digital Platform - Mobile: Apple, Android
Digital Platform - Tablet: Apple iOS, Android
Pub./Owner .... Gary W. Stevenson
Ed. .... Joe Elder
Gen. Mgr. .... Liz Wood
Mechanical Specifications: Type page 10 1/2 x 14; E - 5 cols, 2, 1/8 between; A - 5 cols, 2, 1/8 between; C - 6 cols, 1 5/8, 1/8 between. Equipment & Software: Hardware — Mac/E Macs; Software — Adobe/PageMaker 7.0.
Delivery Method: Mail, Racks
Areas Served: Carbon County

SUNDANCE

THE SUNDANCE TIMES (THUR)

311 E Main St, Sundance, WY, 82729, Crook, USA; gen tel (307)283-3411; adv tel (307)283-3411; ed tel (307) 283-3411; gen fax (307)283-3332; adv fax (307)283-3332; ed fax (307) 283-3332; disp adv e-mail jeff@sundancetimes.com; class adv e-mail jeff@sundancetimes.com; ed e-mail web@sundancetimes.com; web site www.sundancetimes.com
Circulation: 1,800pd, 35fr; USPS
Advertising rate: Open inch rate $8.50
Established: 1884
Digital Platform - Mobile: Apple, Android, Windows, Blackberry
Digital Platform - Tablet: Apple iOS, Android, Windows 7, Blackberry Tablet OS
Adv. Mgr./Ed. .... Jeff Moberg
Mechanical Specifications: Type page 13 x 21.
Delivery Method: Mail, Racks
Areas Served: Crook County

THERMOPOLIS

THERMOPOLIS INDEPENDENT RECORD (THUR)

431 Broadway St, Thermopolis, WY, 82443-2715, Hot Springs, USA; gen tel (307)864-2328; adv tel (307)864-2328; ed tel (307)864-2328; gen fax (307)864-5711; adv fax (307)864-5711; ed fax (307)864-5711; disp adv e-mail ads@thermopir.com; class adv e-mail ads@thermopir.com; ed e-mail news@thermopir.com; web site www.thermopir.com
Circulation: 2,280pd,; Sworn/Estimate/Non-Audited
Advertising rate: $9.15
Established: 1901
Advertising Sales .... Amber Geis
Delivery Method: Mail, Newsstand, Racks

TORRINGTON

THE TORRINGTON TELEGRAM (WED, FRI)

2025 Main St, Torrington, WY, 82240-2708, Goshen, USA; gen tel (307)532-2184; adv tel (307)532-2184; ed tel (307)532-2184; gen fax (307)532-2283; adv fax (307)532-2283; ed fax (307)532-2283; disp adv e-mail rmort@torringtontelegram.com; class adv e-mail ttclass@torringtontelegram.com; ed e-mail tpearson@torringtontelegram.com; web site www.torringtontelegram.com
Circulation: 2,600pd, 70fr; Sworn/Estimate/Non-Audited
Advertising rate: Open inch rate $12.69
Established: 1907
Group: News Media Corp.
Digital Platform - Mobile: Apple, Android, Windows, Blackberry
Digital Platform - Tablet: Apple iOS, Android, Windows 7, Blackberry Tablet OS, Kindle, Nook, Kindle Fire
Pub. .... Jeff Robertson
Gen. Mgr./Adv. Mgr. .... Rob Mortimore
Office Mgr. .... Jean Good
Ed. .... Travis Pearson
Mechanical Specifications: 8 columns, 1.5" per column, 1 pica gutter, 13" x 21.5" page dimensionEquipment & Software: Hardware — Macs; Presses — Goss Community; Software — Multi Ad Creator, Adobe Creative Suite
Delivery Method: Mail, Newsstand, Carrier, Racks
Areas Served: Goshen County

WHEATLAND

THE PLATTE COUNTY RECORD-TIMES (WED)

1007 8th St, Wheatland, WY, 82201-2602, Platte, USA; gen tel (307)322-2627; adv tel (307)322-2627; ed tel (307)322-2627; gen fax (307)322-9612; adv fax (307)322-9612; ed fax (307)322-9612; disp adv e-mail kcoburn@pcrecordtimes.com; class adv e-mail amcdaniel@pcrecordtimes.com; ed e-mail pceditor@pcrecordtimes.com; web site www.pcrecordtimes.com
Circulation: 1,900pd,; Sworn/Estimate/Non-Audited
Advertising rate: Open inch rate $11.99
Established: 1960
Group: News Media Corp.
Digital Platform - Mobile: Apple, Android, Windows, Blackberry
Digital Platform - Tablet: Apple iOS, Android, Windows 7, Blackberry Tablet OS, Kindle, Nook, Kindle Fire
Pub. .... Jeff Robertson
Ed. .... Adam Louis
Office Mgr. .... Teri Cordingly
Adv. Mgr./Gen. Mgr. .... Karry Coburn
Advertising Rep. .... Amanda McDaniel
Mechanical Specifications: Type page 13 x 21; E - 8 cols, 1 1/2, between; A - 8 cols, 1 1/2, between; C - 8 cols, 1 1/2, between.
Delivery Method: Mail, Newsstand, Racks
Areas Served: Chugwater, Dwyer, Glendo, Guernsey, Hartville, Wheatland and all of Platte County

COMMUNITY NEWSPAPERS IN CANADA

ALBERTA

AIRDRIE

AIRDRIE CITY VIEW
(Thur)
#403-2903 Kingsview Blvd., Airdrie, AB, T4A 0C4, Canada; gen tel (403) 948-1885; gen fax (403) 948-2554; disp adv e-mail rsonghurst@airdrie.greatwest.ca; class adv e-mail classifieds@airdrie.greatwest.ca; ed e-mail achorney@airdrie.greatwest.ca; web site http://www.airdriecityview.com
Circulation: 557pd, 18,336fr; VAC
Advertising: Open inch rate $1.05.
Established: 2002.
Parent Co.:
Great West Newspapers LP
Pub....................................Cam Christianson
Ed ....Allison Chorney
Areas Served: Airdrie/Canada

AIRDRIE ECHO
(Wed)
112 - 1 Ave Ne, Airdrie, AB, T4B OR6, Canada, Canada; gen tel (403) 948-7280; gen fax (403) 912-2341; disp adv e-mail rmackintosh@postmedia.com; ed e-mail jchalmers@postmedia.com; web site www.airdrieecho.com
Circulation: 18,330fr; VAC
Advertising: Open inch rate $.65.
Established: 1975.
Parent Co.:
Postmedia Network Inc.
Quebecor Communications, Inc.
Pub....................................Ed Huculak
Ed. ....John Chalmers
Adv. Dir ....Roxanne Mackintosh
Mechanical Specifications: Type page 10 1/4 x 14; E - 6 cols, 1 1/2, 1/4 between; A - 6 cols, 1 1/2, 1/4 between; C - 6 cols, 1 1/2, 1/4 between.
Equipment & Software: ; Software — Microsoft/Word, Claris/Works.
Delivery Method: Carrier
Areas Served: Canada

ROCKY VIEW WEEKLY
(Tues)
#403 2903 Kingsview Blvd., Airdrie, AB, T4A 0C4, Canada, Canada; gen tel (403) 948-1885; gen fax (403) 948-2554; disp adv e-mail rsonghurst@airdrie.greatwest.ca; class adv e-mail rvwclassifieds@airdrie.greatwest.ca; ed e-mail achorney@airdrie.greatwest.ca; web site www.rockyviewweekly.com
Circulation: 457pd, 12,910fr; VAC
Advertising: Open inch rate $.99.
Established: 1970.
Parent Co.:
Glacier Media Group
Great West Newspapers LP
Rocky View Publishing
Pub....................................Cameron Christianson
Circ. Mgr....................................Lisa Gebruck
Ed ....Allison Chorney
Mechanical Specifications: Type page 10 1/4 x 15 1/2; E - 6 cols, 1 7/12, 1/6 between; A - 6 cols, 1 7/12, 1/6 between; C - 6 cols, 1 7/12, 1/6 between.
Equipment & Software: ; Presses — Tp; Software — QPS/QuarkXPress 4.0, Adobe/Illustrator 7.0, Adobe/Photoshop 5.5, Multi-Ad 4.0.
Delivery Method: Mail, Newsstand, Racks
Areas Served: Canada

ATHABASCA

THE ATHABASCA ADVOCATE
(Tues)
4917b 49th Street, Athabasca, AB, T9S 1C5, Athabasca County, Canada; gen tel (780) 675-9222; adv tel (780) 675-9222 ext. 24; ed tel (780) 675-9222; gen fax (780) 675-3143; disp adv e-mail production@athabasca.greatwest.ca ; ed e-mail advocate@athabasca.greatwest.ca; web site www.athabascaadvocate.com
Circulation: 41pd, 106fr; VAC
Advertising: Open inch rate $0.89.
Established: 1981.
Parent Co.:
Great West Newspapers LP
Ed. ....Vanessa Annand
Prod. Mgr. ....Meghan McIvor
Circ. Mgr....................................Mona Muzyka
Pub....................................Allendria Brunjes
Areas Served: Athabasca County

BANFF

BOW VALLEY CRAG & CANYON
(Wed)
201 Bear St., 2nd Fl., Banff, AB, T1L 1H2, Canada, Canada; gen tel (403) 762-2453; gen fax (403) 762-5274; disp adv e-mail rmackintosh@postmedia.com; ed e-mail russ.ullyot@sunmedia.ca; web site www.thecragandcanyon.ca
Circulation: 0pd, 8,537fr; CMCA
Advertising: Open inch rate $.80.
Established: 1900.
Parent Co.:
Postmedia Network Inc.
Quebecor Communications, Inc.
Pub ....Shawn Cornell
Ed ....Russ Ullyot
Adv. Dir....................................Roxanne Mackintosh
Mechanical Specifications: Type page 10 1/4 x 14; E - 6 cols, 1 7/12, between; A - 6 cols, 1 7/12, between; C - 6 cols, 1 7/12, between.
Equipment & Software: : Hardware — APP/Power Mac G4; Software — QPS/QuarkXPress 4.1, Microsoft/Word.
Delivery Method: Mail, Newsstand, Carrier, Racks
Areas Served: Canada

BARRHEAD

BARRHEAD LEADER
(Tues)
5015 51st St., Barrhead, AB, T7N 1A4, Bar-

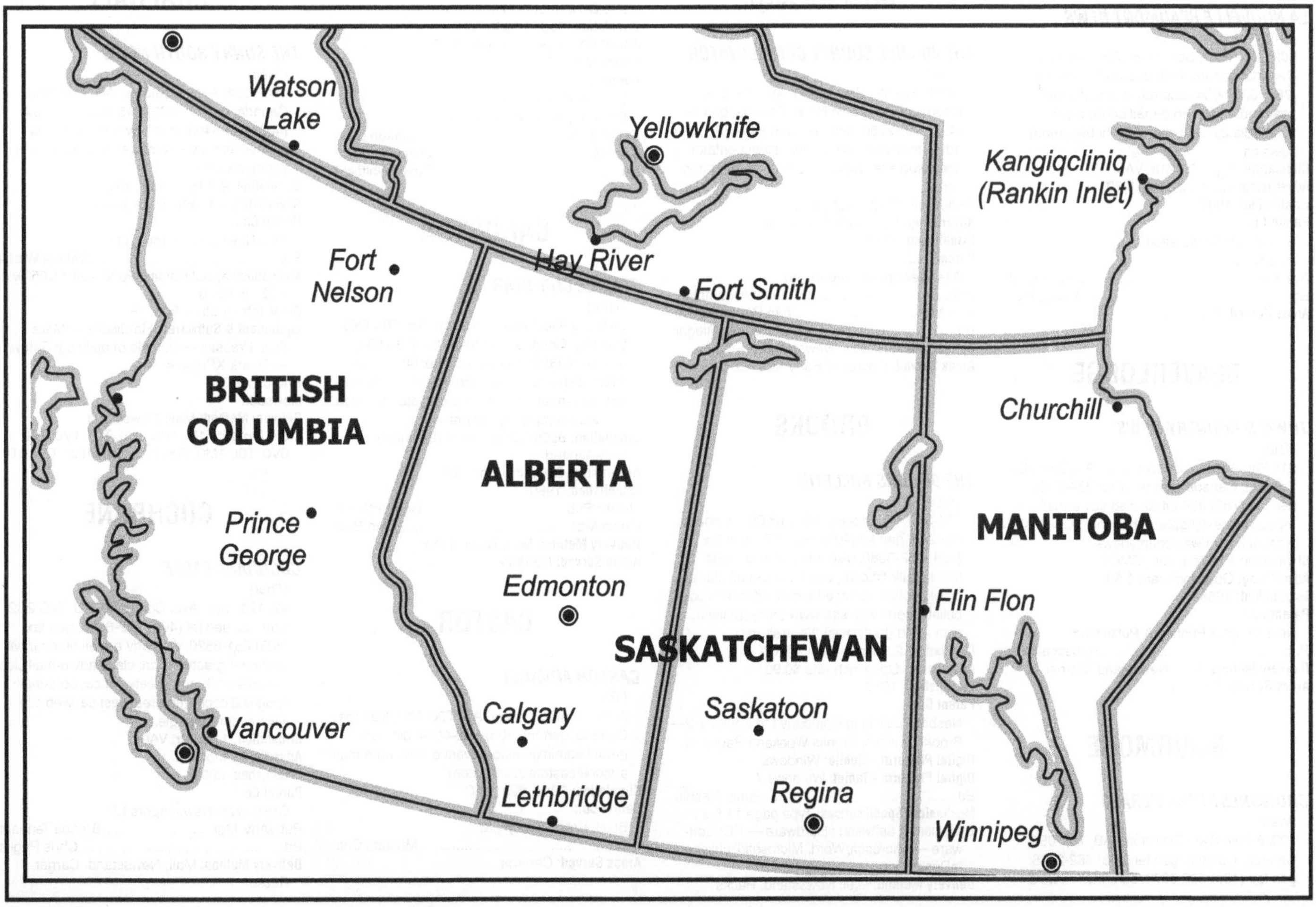

rhead, Canada; gen tel (780) 674-3823; gen fax (780) 674-6337; disp adv e-mail sales@barrhead.greatwest.ca; ed e-mail lleng@barrhead.greatwest.ca; web site www.barrheadleader.com
Circulation: 3,114pd, 3fr; VAC
Advertising: Open inch rate $87.00.
Established: 1927.
Parent Co.:
Glacier Media Group
Great West Newspapers LP
Pub .... Lynda Leng
Mechanical Specifications: Type page 10 1/3 x 15 1/3; E - 6 cols, 1 9/16, 1/6 between; A - 6 cols, 1 9/16, 1/6 between; C - 7 cols, 1 1/3, 1/6 between.
Delivery Method: Mail, Newsstand
Areas Served: Barrhead

BASSANO

THE BASSANO TIMES
(Tues)
402 First Ave., Bassano, AB, T0J 0B0, Canada, Canada; gen tel (403) 641-3636; adv tel (403) 641-3636; gen fax (403) 641-3952
Circulation: 503pd,; CMCA
Advertising: Open inch rate $.68.
Established: 1915.
Digital Platform - Mobile: Blackberry
Publisher/Advertising Manager .... Mary Lou Brooks
Mechanical Specifications: Type page 10 x 16; E - 6 cols, 1 1/2, 1/8 between; A - 6 cols, 1 1/2, 1/8 between; C - 6 cols, 1 1/2, 1/8 between.
Equipment & Software: : Hardware — IBM; Software — Microsoft/Windows.
Delivery Method: Mail, Newsstand
Areas Served: Canada

BEAUMONT

LA NOUVELLE BEAUMONT NEWS
(Fri)
5021b 52 Ave., Beaumont, AB, T4X 1E5, Canada; gen tel (780) 929-6632; gen fax (780) 929-6634; disp adv e-mail jfigeat@postmedia.com; ed e-mail bobby.roy@sunmedia.ca; web site www.thebeaumontnews.ca
Circulation: 11pd, 7,221fr; VAC
Advertising: Open inch rate $.82.
Established: 1987.
Parent Co.:
Sun Media Corporation
Post Media
Adv. Dir .... Jean Figeat
Ed .... Bobby Roy
Areas Served: Beaumont

BEAVERLODGE

TOWN & COUNTRY NEWS
(Thur)
916 2nd Avenue, Beaverlodge, AB, T0H 0C0, Canada, Canada; gen tel (780) 354-2980; gen fax (780) 354-2460; disp adv e-mail rebecca@nextchapterpublishing.ca; web site facebook.com/westcountynews
Circulation: 1,857pd, 20fr; CMCA
Advertising: Open inch rate $.66.
Established: 1956.
Parent Co.:
Next Chapter Printing & Publishing
Pub .... Rebecca Dika
Delivery Method: Mail, Newsstand, Carrier
Areas Served: Canada

BLAIRMORE

CROWSNEST PASS HERALD
(Wed)
12925 20th Ave., Blairmore, AB, T0K 0E0, Canada, Canada; gen tel (403) 562-2248; gen fax (403) 562-8379; ed e-mail news@passherald.ca; web site www.passherald.ca
Circulation: 1,361pd, 235fr; VAC
Advertising: Open inch rate $.75.
Established: 1930.
Pub .... Lisa Sygutek
Mechanical Specifications: Type page 10 1/4 x 16; E - 5 cols, 2, between; A - 5 cols, 2, between.
Equipment & Software: : Hardware — APP/Mac G3; Software — QPS/QuarkXPress.
Delivery Method: Mail, Racks
Areas Served: Canada

BONNYVILLE

BONNYVILLE NOUVELLE
(Tues)
5304 50th Ave., Bonnyville, AB, T9N 1Y4, Canada, Canada; gen tel (780) 826-3876; adv tel (780) 826-3876; gen fax (780) 826-7062; disp adv e-mail aclarke@bonnyville.greatwest.ca; ed e-mail koelschlagel@bonnyville.greatwest.ca; web site www.bonnyvillenouvelle.ca
Circulation: 626pd, 681fr; VAC
Advertising: Open inch rate $1.05.
Established: 1967.
Parent Co.:
Glacier Media Group
Great West Newspapers LP
Circ. Mgr .... Cindy Coates
Ed .... Kristen Oelschlagel
Pub .... Angie Hampshire
Mechanical Specifications: Type page 14 x 15 1/2; E - 7 cols, 1 3/5, 1/6 between; A - 6 cols, 1 1/3, 1/6 between; C - 6 cols, 1 1/3, 1/6 between.
Equipment & Software: : Hardware — APP/Mac; Presses — 3-HI; Software — Adobe/Photoshop, QPS/QuarkXPress.
Areas Served: Canada

BOW ISLAND

THE 40-MILE COUNTY COMMENTATOR
(Tues)
147-5 Ave. W., Bow Island, AB, T0K 0G0, County of Forty Mile No. 8, Canada; gen tel (403) 545-2258; gen fax (403) 545-6886; disp adv e-mail editor@bowislandcommentator.com; web site www.bowislandcommentator.com
Circulation: 426pd, 45fr; VAC
Advertising: Open inch rate $1.00.
Established: 1971.
Parent Co.:
Alta. Newspaper Group, Ltd
Pub .... Coleen Campbell
Adv. Mgr. .... Tom Conquergood
Ed. .... Jamie Rieger
Delivery Method: Mail, Newsstand
Areas Served: County of Forty Mile No. 8

BROOKS

THE BROOKS BULLETIN
(Tues)
124-3 St. W., Brooks, AB, T1R 0S3, Canada, Canada; gen tel (403) 362-5571; gen fax (403) 362-5080; disp adv e-mail diane@brooksbulletin.com; class adv e-mail diane@brooksbulletin.com; ed e-mail editor@brooksbulletin.com; web site www.brooksbulletin.com - 200,000(views) 330(visitors)
Circulation: 2,800pd, 188fr; CMCA
Advertising: Open inch rate $0.90.
Established: 1910.
Parent Co.:
Nesbitt Publishing Company Ltd.Editions: 2—Brooks Bulletin, Brooks Weekend Regional
Digital Platform - Mobile: Windows
Digital Platform - Tablet: Windows 7
Ed. .... Jamie Nesbitt
Mechanical Specifications: Type page 11.5 x 21.
Equipment & Software: : Hardware — PC; Software — Microsoft/Word, Microsoft/Publisher, InDesign
Delivery Method: Mail, Newsstand, Racks
Areas Served: Canada

CAMROSE

THE CAMROSE CANADIAN
(Thur)
4610 49th Ave., Camrose, AB, T4V 0M6, Camrose County, Canada; gen tel (780) 672-4421; adv tel (877) 786-8227; gen fax (780) 672-5323; disp adv e-mail ngoetz@postmedia.com; web site www.camrosecanadian.com
Circulation: 3,673pd, 15,292fr; VAC
Advertising: Open inch rate $.72.
Established: 1908.
Parent Co.:
Postmedia Network Inc.
Adv. Mgr. .... Dan Macpherson
Publisher .... Nick Goetz
Editor .... Trent Wilkie
Editor(online) .... Vince Burke
Publisher(online) .... Jim Clark
Mechanical Specifications: Type page 10 1/4 x 12 1/2; E - 8 cols, 1 3/16, 1/6 between; A - 8 cols, 1 3/16, 1/6 between; C - 8 cols, 1 1/4, 1/6 between.
Equipment & Software: : Hardware — APP/Mac; Presses — G; Software — QPS/QuarkXPress 4.1.
Areas Served: Camrose County

CANMORE

ROCKY MOUNTAIN OUTLOOK
(Thur)
Box 8610, Suite 201 - 1001. 6th Avenue, Canmore, AB, T1W 2V3, Canada; gen tel (403) 609-0220; gen fax (403)609-0221; disp adv e-mail clacroix@outlook.greatwest.ca; class adv e-mail jlyon@outlook.greatwest.ca; ed e-mail dwhitfield@rmoutlook.com; web site www.rmoutlook.com
Circulation: 0pd, 9,395fr; VAC
Advertising: Open inch rate $1.01.
Established: 2001.
Parent Co.:
Glacier Media Group
Great West Newspapers LP
Pub/Adv. Mgr .... Jason Lyon
Circ. Mgr .... Donna Browne
Ed .... Dave Whitfield

CARDSTON

TEMPLE CITY STAR
(Thur)
30-b 3rd Ave. West, Cardston, AB, T0K 0K0, Canada, Canada; gen tel (403) 653-4664; adv tel (403) 653-4664; gen fax (403) 653-3162; disp adv e-mail news@templecitystar.net; ed e-mail news@templecitystar.net; web site www.templecitystar.net
Circulation: 650pd, 50fr; Sworn/Estimate/Non-Audited
Advertising: Open inch rate $.81.
Established: 1980.
Owner/Pub .... Robert Smith
Office Mgr. .... Dan Burt
Delivery Method: Mail, Newsstand
Areas Served: Canada

CASTOR

CASTOR ADVANCE
(Thur)
5012 50 Ave., Castor, AB, T0C 0X0, Canada, Canada; gen tel (403) 882-4044; disp adv e-mail admin@castoradvance.com; ed e-mail editor@castoradvance.com
Circulation: 79pd, 22fr; VAC
Parent Co.:
Black Press Group Ltd.
Ed. .... Mustafa Eric
Areas Served: Canada

CHESTERMERE

THE CHESTERMERE ANCHOR CITY NEWS
(Thur)
P.o. Box 127, Chestermere, AB, T1X 1K8, Rocky View, Canada; gen tel (403) 774-1352; ed tel (403) 774-1322; gen fax (866) 552-0976; disp adv e-mail ads@theanchor.ca; class adv e-mail classifed@theanchor.ca; ed e-mail news@theanchor.ca; web site www.theanchor.ca
Circulation: 9pd, 7,923fr; VAC
Advertising: Open Line rate $0.90.
Established: 2001.
Mechanical Specifications: 10.34" Wide by 11.5" deep
Delivery Method: Newsstand, Carrier, Racks
Areas Served: Rocky View

CLARESHOLM

CLARESHOLM LOCAL PRESS
(Wed)
4913 2nd St. W., Claresholm, AB, T0L 0T0, Canada, Canada; gen tel (403) 625-4474; gen fax (403) 625-2828; disp adv e-mail info@claresholmlocalpress.ca; class adv e-mail roxanne@claresholmlocalpress.ca; ed e-mail rob@claresholmlocalpress.ca; web site www.claresholmlocalpress.ca
Circulation: 6pd, 16fr; VAC
Advertising: Open inch rate $.70.
Established: 1926.
Parent Co.:
EMS Press Ltd.
Owner/Pub .... Roxanne Thompson
Ed. .... Rob Vogt
Prod. Mgr. .... Amanda Zimmer
Areas Served: Canada

COALDALE

THE SUNNY SOUTH NEWS
(Tues)
1802 20th Ave., Coaldale, AB, T1M 1M2, Canada; gen tel (403) 345-3081; gen fax (403) 223-5408; disp adv e-mail office@sunnysouthnews.com; web site www.sunnysouthnews.com
Circulation: 2,263pd, 48fr; VAC
Advertising: 76 cents per agate line.
Parent Co.:
Alta. Newspaper Group, Ltd
Pub .... Valorie Wiebe
Mechanical Specifications: Page size 11.25" wide x 16.75" deep
6 col. tab - 1 col. = 9p6
Equipment & Software: : Hardware — Macs / PCs; Presses — outside of building; Software — Quark XPress 4
Photoshop 7
Newsedit
Delivery Method: Mail, Newsstand
Areas Served: T1M, T0K 2H0, T0K 1V0, T0L 0V0, T0L 1M0, T0K 2A0, T0K 1G0, T0K 0T0

COCHRANE

COCHRANE EAGLE
(Thur)
#2, 124 River Ave, Cochrane, AB, T4C 2C2, Canada; gen tel (403) 932-6588; gen fax (403) 851-6520; disp adv e-mail btennant@cochrane.greatwest.ca; class adv e-mail classifieds@cochrane.greatwest.ca; ed e-mail cpuglia@cochrane.greatwest.ca; web site www.cochraneeagle.com
Circulation: 11,631fr; VAC
Advertising: Modular.
Established: 2001.
Parent Co.:
Great West Newspapers LP
Pub./Adv. Mgr .... Brenda Tennant
Ed .... Chris Puglia
Delivery Method: Mail, Newsstand, Carrier, Racks

Areas Served: Cochrane/Rocky View County/ Alberta/
T4C 2C2

COCHRANE TIMES
(Wed)
Bay 8, 206 Fifth Ave. W., Cochrane, AB, T4C 1X3, Canada, Canada; gen tel (403) 932-3500; gen fax (403) 932-3935; disp adv e-mail roxanne.mackintosh@sunmedia.ca; class adv e-mail roxanne.mackintosh@sunmedia.ca; ed e-mail editor@cochranetimes.com; web site www.cochranetimes.com
Circulation: 1,374pd, 12,378fr; VAC
Advertising: Open inch rate $.72.
Established: 1985.
Parent Co.:
Postmedia Network Inc.
Quebecor Communications, Inc.
Pub....Shawn Cornell
Ed....Noel Edey
Adv Dir....Roxanne MacKintosh
Mechanical Specifications: Type page 10 1/4 x 12 1/4; E - 8 cols, 1 1/8, 3/16 between; A - 8 cols, 1 1/8, between; C - 8 cols, 1 1/8, between.
Equipment & Software: : Hardware — APP/Mac; Presses — G/Community; Software — QPS/QuarkXPress 3.3, Adobe/Photoshop 4.01, Adobe/Illustrator 7.01.
Areas Served: Canada

COLD LAKE

COLD LAKE SUN
(Tues)
5121 50 Ave, Cold Lake, AB, T9M 1P1, Canada; gen tel (780) 594-5881; gen fax (780) 594-2120; disp adv e-mail ljohnston@postmedia.com; ed e-mail plozinski@postmedia.com; web site www.coldlakesun.com
Circulation: 71pd, 7,179fr; VAC
Advertising: Open inch rate $.65.
Established: 1977.
Parent Co.:
Postmedia Network Inc.
Pub....Mary-Ann Kostiuk
Adv Mgr....Leanne Johnson
Ed....Peter Lozinski
Areas Served: Cold Lake, Alberta
T9M 1P1

THE COURIER
(Tues)
Bldg. 67 Centennial Bldg., Kingsway, Cold Lake, AB, T9M 2C5, Cold Lake, Canada; gen tel (780) 594-5206; ed tel (780) 840-8000 ext. 7854; gen fax (780) 594-2139; ed e-mail Jeff.Gaye@forces.gc.ca; web site www.thecouriernewspaper.ca
Circulation: 32pd, 1,995fr; VAC
Advertising: Open inch rate $1.07.Editions: 45—
Mgr....Connie Lavigne
Ed....Jeff Gaye
Admin....Angela Hetherington
Produc Coord....Alina Mallais
Mechanical Specifications: Type page 10 1/4 x 15.5; E - 6 cols, 1 1/2, between; A - 6 cols, 1 1/2, between; C - 6 cols, 1 1/2, between.
Equipment & Software: : Hardware — PC; Software — Microsoft/Office 97.
Acrobat 8.0, Adobe CS3
Delivery Method: Mail, Newsstand, Carrier
Areas Served: Cold Lake

CONSORT

THE CONSORT ENTERPRISE
(Wed)
5012 - 52st., Consort, AB, T0C 1B0, Canada, Canada; gen tel (403) 577-3337; adv tel (403) 577-3337; ed tel (403) 577-3337; gen fax (403) 577-3611; disp adv e-mail ads@consortenterprise.com; class adv e-mail ads@consortenterprise.com; ed e-mail editor@consortenterprise.com; web site www.consortenterprise.awna.com
Circulation: 2,935pd,; CMCA
Advertising: Open inch rate $.72.
Established: 1912.
Circ. Mgr./Adv. Mgr....Carol Bruha
Ed....David Bruha
Mechanical Specifications: Type page 10 x 16; E - 6 cols, 2, between; A - 6 cols, 2, between.
Delivery Method: Mail, Newsstand
Areas Served: Canada

CORONATION

EAST CENTRAL ALBERTA REVIEW
(Thur)
4923 Victoria Ave., Coronation, AB, T0C 1C0, Canada, Canada; gen tel (403) 578-4111; adv tel (403) 578-7120; gen fax (403) 578-2088; disp adv e-mail advertise@ECAreview.com; class adv e-mail admin@ECAreview.com; ed e-mail publisher@ECAreview.com; web site www.ecareview.com
Circulation: 90pd, 27,075fr; CMCA
Advertising: Open inch rate $12.25.
Established: 1911.
Digital Platform - Mobile: Apple
Pub....Joyce Webster
Office Mgr....Yvonne Thulien
Adv. Rep....Gayle Jaraway
Marketing Rep/Reporter PhotographerLisa Joy
Graphic Artist....Lisa Myers-Sortland
Mechanical Specifications: Type page 10 1/4 x 15 1/2; E - 6 cols, 1 1/2, between; A - 6 cols, 1 1/2, between; C - 6 cols, 1 1/2, between.
Equipment & Software: : Hardware — APP/Mac; Presses — web press, UV; Software — In-Design.
Delivery Method: Mail, Newsstand
Areas Served: Canada

DEVON

DEVON DISPATCH NEWS
(Fri)
4b Saskatchewan Drive, Devon, AB, T9G 1E7, Canada; gen tel (780) 987-3488; gen fax (780) 987-4431; disp adv e-mail jfigeat@postmedia.com; ed e-mail bobby.roy@sunmedia.ca; web site www.devondispatch.ca
Circulation: 2,021pd, 5,072fr; VAC
Advertising: Open line rate $0.82.
Established: 1976.
Parent Co.:
Postmedia Network Inc.
Pub....Susanne Holmlund
Ed....Bobby Roy
Adv. Dir....Jean Figeat
Areas Served: Devon, AB T9G 1E7, Canada

DRAYTON VALLEY

DRAYTON VALLEY WESTERN REVIEW
(Tues)
4905 52nd Ave., Drayton Valley, AB, T7A 1S3, Canada, Canada; gen tel (780) 542-5380; gen fax (780) 542-9200; disp adv e-mail theresa.hunt@sunmedia.ca; ed e-mail cweetman@postmedia.com; web site www.draytonvalleywesternreview.com
Circulation: 1,132pd, 5fr; VAC
Advertising: Open inch rate $0.72.
Established: 1966.
Parent Co.:
Postmedia Network Inc.
Quebecor Communications, Inc.
Pub....Susanne Holmlund
Adv. Dir....Pamela Allain
Ed....Cathy Weetman
Areas Served: Canada

DRUMHELLER

DRUMHELLER MAIL
(Wed)
515 Hwy 10 East, Drumheller, AB, T0J 0Y0, Canada, Canada; gen tel (403) 823-2580; gen fax (403) 823-3864; disp adv e-mail information@drumhellermail.com; ed e-mail bob@drumhellermail.com; web site www.drumhellermail.com
Circulation: 4,400pd, 0fr; CMCA
Advertising: Line rate - $1.12/line.
Established: 1911.
Pub....Ossie Sheddy
Mng. Ed....Bob Sheddy
Mechanical Specifications: Type page 12.4 x 21; E - 6 cols, 2 1/4, between; A - 6 cols, 2 1/4, between; C - 6 cols, 2 1/4, between.
Equipment & Software: ; Software — Creative Suite - Adobe
Delivery Method: Mail, Newsstand, Carrier, Racks
Areas Served: Canada

EDMONTON

EDMONTON EXAMINER
(Wed)
10006 101 St, Edmonton, AB, T5J 0S1, Canada; gen tel (780) 453-9001; adv tel (780) 444-5450; gen fax (780) 447-7333; disp adv e-mail rpaterson@postmedia.com; class adv e-mail bob.paterson@sunmedia.ca; ed e-mail dave.breakenridge@sunmedia.ca; web site www.edmontonexaminer.com
Circulation: 0pd, 131,000fr; CCAB
Advertising: Open inch rate $3.44 all zones.
Established: 1979.
Parent Co.:
Postmedia Network Inc.
Quebecor Communications, Inc.
Digital Platform - Mobile: Apple, Android, Windows
Digital Platform - Tablet: Apple iOS, Android, Windows 7, Blackberry Tablet OS, Kindle
Pub....John Caputo
Adv. Dir....Ted Dakin
Ed....Dave Breakenridge
Mechanical Specifications: Type page 10 1/4 x 12 1/2; E - 10 cols, between; A - 10 cols, between; C - 10 cols, between.
Equipment & Software: : Hardware — APP/Mac; Software — QPS/QuarkXPress 3.32, Adobe/Illustrator, Adobe/Photoshop.
Delivery Method: Carrier, Racks
Areas Served: Canada

LE FRANCO
(Thur)
8627-91 St., Rm 312, Edmonton, AB, T6C 3N1, Canada; gen tel (780) 465-6581; gen fax (780) 469-1129; disp adv e-mail commercial@lefranco.ab.ca; ed e-mail direction@lefranco.ab.ca; web site http://www.lefranco.ab.ca
Circulation: 3,206pd, 302fr; Sworn/Estimate/Non-Audited
Established: 1928.
Ed....Emma Hautecoeur
Delivery Method: Mail
Areas Served: Alberta

EDSON

EDSON LEADER
(Mon)
4820 3rd Ave., Edson, AB, T7E 1T8, Canada, Canada; gen tel (780) 723-3301; gen fax (780) 723-5171; disp adv e-mail pam.thesen@sunmedia.ca; ed e-mail ian.mcinnes@sunmedia.ca; web site www.edsonleader.com
Circulation: 3pd, 3,468fr; VAC
Advertising: Open inch rate $0.59.
Established: 1989.
Parent Co.:
Postmedia Network Inc.
Quebecor Communications, Inc.
Adv. Dir....Pamela Thesen
Pub....Janice Foisy
Ed....Ian McInnes
Equipment & Software: : Hardware — APP/Mac; Software — QPS/QuarkXPress.
Areas Served: Canada

THE WEEKLY ANCHOR
(Mon)
5040 3rd Ave., Edson, AB, T7E 1V2, Canada, Canada; gen tel (780) 723-5787; gen fax (780) 723-5725; disp adv e-mail anchorwk@telusplanet.net; class adv e-mail anchorwk@telusplanet.net; ed e-mail anchorwk@telusplanet.net; web site www.weeklyanchor.com
Circulation: 50pd, 6,025fr; CMCA
Advertising: Open inch rate $0.97.
Established: 1988.
Pub./Adv. Dir....Dana McArthur
Mechanical Specifications: Type page 15 1/2 x 15 5/9; E - 6 cols, between; A - 6 cols, between.
Delivery Method: Mail, Newsstand, Racks
Areas Served: Canada

ELK POINT

ELK POINT REVIEW
(Tues)
5022 - 49 Ave, Elk Point, AB, T0A 1A0, Canada, Canada; gen tel (780) 724-4087; gen fax (780) 645-2346; disp adv e-mail cgauvreau@greatwest.ca; ed e-mail vbrooker@stpaul.greatwest.ca; web site www.greatwest.ca
Circulation: 2,950pd, 0fr; VAC
Advertising: Open inch rate $0.69.
Established: 1963.
Parent Co.:
Glacier Media Group
Great West Newspapers LP
Pub./Adv. Mgr....Clare Gauvreau
Ed....Vicki Brooker
Prod....Marg Smith
Areas Served: Canada

FAIRVIEW

FAIRVIEW POST
(Wed)
10118-110 St., Fairview, AB, T0H 1L0, Canada; gen tel (780) 835-4925; gen fax (780) 835-4227; disp adv e-mail peter.meyerhoffer@sunmedia.ca; ed e-mail chris.eakin@sunmedia.ca; web site www.fairviewpost.com
Circulation: 119pd, 8fr; VAC
Advertising: Open inch rate $0.65.
Established: 1940.
Parent Co.:
Postmedia Network Inc.
Quebecor Communications, Inc.
Digital Platform - Mobile: Apple, Android, Blackberry
Digital Platform - Tablet: Apple iOS, Android, Blackberry Tablet OS, Kindle
Adv. Dir....Peter Meyerhoffer
Ed....Chris Eakin
Mechanical Specifications: 160 Lines
10 Columns
Page size: 10.33x11.43
Equipment & Software: : Hardware — APP/Mac G3; Software — QPS/QuarkXPress, Adobe/Photoshop 5.0, Adobe/Illustrator.
Delivery Method: Mail, Newsstand
Areas Served: T0H

FORT MACLEOD

THE MACLEOD GAZETTE
(Wed)
310 24th St., Fort Macleod, AB, T0L 0Z0, Municipal District of Willow Creek, Canada; gen tel (403) 553-3391; gen fax (403) 553-2961; disp adv e-mail tmgsales@telus.net; class adv e-mail tmgsales@telus.net; ed e-mail tmgedit@telus.net; web site www.fortmacleodgazette.com
Circulation: 1,150pd, 0fr; CMCA
Advertising: Open inch rate $0.76 per agate line.
Established: 1882.
Adv. Mgr....Emily McTighe
Circ. Mgr....Sharon Monical
Pub./Ed....Frank McTighe
Mechanical Specifications: Type page 10.25 x 15.5; E - 6 cols, 1 3/4, 1/6 between; A - 6 cols, 1 3/4, 1/6 between; C - 6 cols, 1.5, 1/6 between.
Equipment & Software: : Hardware — Mac, PC; Software — QuarkXPress 8.16, Adobe

Photoshop CS, Firefox, Thunderbird, Adobe Acrobat, Microsoft Word, Microsoft Excel, Microsoft Powerpoint, Simply Accounting.
Delivery Method: Mail, Newsstand
Areas Served: Municipal District of Willow Creek

FORT MCMURRAY

CONNECT

(Fri)
208, 9715 Main Street, Fort McMurray, AB, T9H 1T5, Canada; gen tel (780) 790-6627; gen fax (780) 714-6485; disp adv e-mail tim@starnews.ca; class adv e-mail tim@starnews.ca; ed e-mail dawn@starnews.ca; web site www.fortmacconnect.ca
Circulation: 19,992fr; VAC
Advertising: Open inch rate $1.15.
Established: 2002.
Parent Co.:
Star News Publishing Inc.
Publisher/Sales Manager ....Tim O'Rourke
Delivery Method: Mail, Newsstand, Racks
Areas Served: Fort McMurray/Regional Municipality of Wood Buffalo/Alberta/T9H 2C8

FORT SASKATCHEWAN

THE FORT SASKATCHEWAN RECORD

(Thur)
10404 99th Ave., 168a, Fort Saskatchewan, AB, T8L 3W2, Strathcona County, Canada; gen tel (780) 998-7070; gen fax (780) 998-5515; disp adv e-mail marie.keating@sunmedia.ca; ed e-mail ben.proulx@sunmedia.ca; web site www.fortsaskatchewanrecord.com
Circulation: 9pd, 8,806fr; VAC
Advertising: Open inch rate $0.71.
Established: 1922.
Parent Co.:
Postmedia Network Inc.
Digital Platform - Mobile: Apple, Android
Digital Platform - Tablet: Apple iOS, Android, Blackberry Tablet OS, Kindle
Sales Consultant ....MaryAnn Kochan
Pub...Jean Figeat
Advertising Consultant....... Krista Schroderous
Ed. ....Ben Proulx
Lindsay Morey
Mechanical Specifications: specs available on website
Equipment & Software: : Hardware — APP/Mac; Presses — N/A; Software — Adobe Creative Suite
Delivery Method: Mail, Carrier, Racks
Areas Served: Strathcona County

GRANDE CACHE

GRANDE CACHE MOUNTAINEER

(Thur)
1800 Pine Plaza, Grande Cache, AB, T0E 0Y0, Canada; gen tel (780) 827-3539; disp adv e-mail gcnews@telus.net; ed e-mail pamnews@telus.net; web site http://www.grandecachemountaineer.canic.ws/
Circulation: 1,060pd, 36fr; Sworn/Estimate/Non-Audited
Advertising: Open inch rate $0.70.
Established: 1970.
Pub./Ed./GM ....Pamela Brown
Sales...Lisa Gould
Delivery Method: Mail, Newsstand
Areas Served: Grande Cache Alberta

GRIMSHAW

BANNER POST

(Wed)
Po Box 686, Po Box 1010, Grimshaw, AB, T0H 1W0, Canada, Canada; gen tel (780) 836-3588; adv tel (780) 332-2215; gen fax (780) 836-2820; disp adv e-mail bannerpost@mrnews.ca; ed e-mail publisher@mrnews.ca; web site http://www.mrnews.ca/
Circulation: 0pd, 2fr; VAC
Advertising: Open inch rate $.75.
Established: 1965.
Parent Co.:
Mackenzie Report Inc.
Pub/Ed...Tom Mihaly
Ed ....Kristin Dyck
Office/Adv. Mgr ......Jillian Vandemark-Chomiak
Areas Served: Canada

HANNA

HANNA HERALD

(Wed)
113 - 1st Ave West, Hanna, AB, T0J 1P0, Canada; gen tel (403) 854-3366; gen fax (403) 854-3256; disp adv e-mail rmackintosh@postmedia.com; class adv e-mail deanne.cornell@sunmedia.ca; ed e-mail jackie.gold@sunmedia.ca; web site www.hannaherald.com
Circulation: 900pd, 0fr; CMCA
Advertising: Open inch rate $0.71.
Established: 1912.
Parent Co.:
Postmedia Network Inc.
Quebecor Communications, Inc.
Digital Platform - Mobile: Apple, Android, Windows
Digital Platform - Tablet: Apple iOS, Android, Windows 7, Blackberry Tablet OS, Kindle, Kindle Fire
Pub .... Shawn Cornell
Adv. Sales Rep.......................Deanne Cornell
Office Mgr. ....Krista Avery
Mng. Ed.......................................Jackie Gold
Delivery Method: Mail, Newsstand
Areas Served: Canada

HIGH LEVEL

THE ECHO-PIONEER

(Wed)
10006 - 97th St., High Level, AB, T0H 1Z0, Canada, Canada; gen tel (780) 926-2000; gen fax (780) 926-2001; disp adv e-mail echoads1@mrnews.ca; class adv e-mail echoads1@mrnews.ca; ed e-mail echonews2@mrnews.ca; web site www.mrnews.ca
Circulation:; Sworn/Estimate/Non-Audited
Established: 1976.
Parent Co.:
Mackenzie Report Inc.
Advertising.......................................Nikki Coles
Pub./Mng. Ed. ....Tom Mihaly
Office/Adv. ....Ann Bassett
Ed ....Matt Marcone
Advertising...................................Lacey Reid
Areas Served: Canada

THE MILE ZERO NEWS

(Wed)
10006-97 St., High Level, AB, T0H 1Z0, Canada; gen tel (780) 332-2215; gen fax (780) 926-2001; disp adv e-mail echo@mrnews.ca; web site www.mrnews.ca
Circulation: 0pd, 1,575fr; VAC
Advertising: Open inch rate $0.75.
Established: 1977.
Parent Co.:
Mackenzie Report Inc.
Office/Advertising ....Carmen Kratky
Pub...Tom Mihaly
Circ. Mgr.....................................Ann Bassett
Ed. ....Kristen Feddema
Adv. Sales ....Barb Schofield

HIGH PRAIRIE

SOUTH PEACE NEWS

(Wed)
4902 51st Ave., High Prairie, AB, T0G 1E0, Canada, Canada; gen tel (780) 523-4484; gen fax (780) 523-3039; disp adv e-mail southpeacenews@hotmail.com; class adv e-mail southpeacenews@hotmail.com; ed e-mail spn@cablecomet.com; web site www.southpeacenews.com
Circulation: 1,257pd, 0fr; CMCA
Advertising: Open inch rate $.85.
Pub...Mary Burgar
Ed. ....Chris Clegg
Mechanical Specifications: Type page 10 1/4 x 15 3/4.
Delivery Method: Mail, Newsstand
Areas Served: Canada

HIGH RIVER

THE HIGH RIVER TIMES

(Tues, Fri)
618 Centre St. S., High River, AB, T1V 1E9, Canada, Canada; gen tel (403) 652-2034; disp adv e-mail hmorgan@postmedia.com; class adv e-mail hmorgan@postmedia.com; ed e-mail krushworth@postmedia.com; web site www.highrivertimes.com
Circulation: 0pd, 6,406fr; VAC
Advertising: Open inch rate $0.70.
Established: 1905.
Parent Co.:
Postmedia Network Inc.
Admin./Office Mgr. ....Kaire Davis
Multimedia. Ed......................Kevin Rushworth
Reg. Adv. Dir. .... Roxanne Mackintosh
Advertising Manager...............Heather Morgan
Equipment & Software: : Hardware — APP/Mac
Delivery Method: Mail, Newsstand, Carrier
Areas Served: Canada

HINTON

THE HINTON PARKLANDER

(Mon)
387 Drinnan Way, Hinton, AB, T7V 2A3, Canada, Canada; gen tel (780) 865-3115; gen fax (780) 865-1252; class adv e-mail hintonparklander.classifieds@sunmedia.ca; ed e-mail eric.plummer@sunmedia.ca; web site www.hintonparklander.com
Circulation: 7pd, 3,720fr; VAC
Advertising: Open inch rate $0.61.
Established: 1955.
Parent Co.:
Postmedia Network Inc.
Digital Platform - Tablet: Apple iOS, Android, Windows 7, Blackberry Tablet OS, Kindle, Nook, Kindle Fire
Ed. .... Eric Plummer
Pub...Terry Thachuk
Nationals & Classified Booking...........Nathalie Lovoie-Murray
Mechanical Specifications: Type page 10 1/4 x 12 1/2; E - 8 cols, 1 13/16, 1/6 between; A - 8 cols, 1 13/16, 1/6 between; C - 8 cols, 1 13/16, 1/6 between.
Equipment & Software: : Hardware — APP/Mac; Software — Adobe InDesign CS3
Delivery Method: Mail, Newsstand, Carrier, Racks
Areas Served: Canada

THE HINTON VOICE

(Thur)
187 Pembina Ave., Hinton, AB, T7V 2B2, Canada; gen tel (890) 865-5688; gen fax (780) 865-5699; disp adv e-mail sales@hintonvoice.ca; web site www.hintonvoice.com
Circulation: 445fr; VAC
Pub...Tyler Waugh
Mktg. Specialist........................Sarah Burns
Prodn./Distrib. Mgr. ....Robin Garreck
Accounting.....................................Angie Still
Areas Served: Hinton

INNISFAIL

INNISFAIL PROVINCE

(Tues)
5036 - 48th St., Innisfail, AB, T4G 1M2, Canada, Canada; gen tel (403) 227-3477; gen fax (403) 227-3330; disp adv e-mail ddemers@innisfail.greatwest.ca; ed e-mail jbachusky@innisfail.greatwest.ca; web site www.innisfailprovince.ca
Circulation: 7pd, 8,240fr; VAC
Advertising: Open inch rate $0.94.
Established: 1905.
Parent Co.:
Glacier Media Group
Great West Newspapers LP
Pub/Adv. Mgr...............................Brent Spilak
Ed ....Johnnie Bachusky
Equipment & Software: : Hardware — PC, APP/Mac; Software — QPS/QuarkXPress 4.1, Adobe/Photoshop 5.5.
Areas Served: Canada

JASPER

THE FITZHUGH

(Thur)
626 Connaught Dr., Jasper, AB, T0E 1E0, Jasper, Canada; gen tel (780) 852-4888; gen fax (780) 852-4858; disp adv e-mail advertising@fitzhugh.ca; class adv e-mail advertising@fitzhugh.ca; ed e-mail editor@fitzhugh.ca; web site www.fitzhugh.ca
Circulation: 1,156pd, 3,359fr; VAC
Advertising: Open inch rate $0.95.
Established: 2005.
Parent Co.:
Jasper Media Group
Sales...Matt Figueira
Pub.......................................Jeremy Derksen
Prod. ....Mishelle Menzies
Ed. ....Nicole Veerman
Areas Served: Jasper

KILLAM

THE COMMUNITY PRESS

(Wed)
4919 - 50 St.,, Killam, AB, T0B 2L0, All of Flagstaff County, Alberta: Total municipalities covered: Bawlf, Daysland, Strome, Killam, Sedgewick, Lougheed, Hardisty, Amisk, Hughenden, Czar, Forestburg, Galahad, Heisler, Alliance, Canada; gen tel (780) 385-6693; adv tel (780-385-6693; gen fax (780) 385-3107; disp adv e-mail ads@thecommunitypress.com; class adv e-mail ads@thecommunitypress.com; ed e-mail news@thecommunitypress.com; web site www.thecommunitypress.com
Circulation: 2,000pd, 500fr; CMCA
Advertising: Open inch rate $.92.
Established: 1908.
Parent Co.:
Caribou Publishing
Editor ....Leslie Cholowsky
Publisher/Sales/Production Manager ....Eric Anderson
Sales..Jae Robbins
Production Manager ....Ally Anderson
Delivery Method: Mail, Newsstand, Racks
Areas Served: All of Flagstaff County, Alberta: Total municipalities covered: Bawlf, Daysland, Strome, Killam, Sedgewick, Lougheed, Hardisty, Amisk, Hughenden, Czar, Forestburg, Galahad, Heisler, Alliance

LAC LA BICHE

LAC LA BICHE POST

(Tues)
10211 101st St., Lac La Biche, AB, T0A 2C0, Canada; gen tel (780) 623-4221; gen fax (780) 623-4230; disp adv e-mail iwolstenholme@llb.greatwest.ca; ed e-mail rmckinley@llb.greatwest.ca; web site www.laclabichepost.com
Circulation: 1,123pd, 1fr; VAC
Advertising: Open inch rate $0.89.
Established: 1966.
Parent Co.:
Glacier Media Group
Great West Newspapers LP
Pub.....................................Robert McKinley
Sales Mgr......................... Iona Wolstenholme
Mechanical Specifications: all inserts must be folded to a letter -sized final size.

Delivery Method: Mail, Newsstand
Areas Served: T0A 2C0 T0A 2C1 T0A 2T0 T0A 1Z0
Edmonton, Calgary numerous

LACOMBE

LACOMBE GLOBE
(Thur)
5019-50 St., Lacombe, AB, T4L 1W8, Canada, Canada; gen tel (403) 782-3498; gen fax (403) 782-5850; disp adv e-mail ngoetz@postmedia.com; ed e-mail sswenson@postmedia.com; web site www.lacombeglobe.com
Circulation: 1,507pd, 8,604fr; VAC
Advertising: Open inch rate $0.58.
Established: 1900.
Parent Co.:
Postmedia Network Inc.
Quebecor Communications, Inc.
Adv. Dir .... Nick Goetz
Ed .... Sarah Swenson
Mechanical Specifications: Type page 13 x 21; E - 6 cols, 2 1/12, 1/6 between; A - 6 cols, 2 1/12, 1/6 between; C - 6 cols, 2 1/12, 1/6 between.
Equipment & Software: : Hardware — APP/Mac; Presses — Camrose; Software — QPS/QuarkXPress 5.0.
Areas Served: Canada

LAMONT

THE LAMONT LEADER
(Tues)
5038 50 Ave., Lamont, AB, T0B 2R0, Canada; gen tel (780) 895-2780; gen fax (780) 895-2705; disp adv e-mail lmtleader@gmail.com; ed e-mail lamontnews@gmail.com; web site lamontleader.com
Circulation: 0pd, 2,606fr; VAC
Advertising: Open inch rate $0.83.
Established: 2005.
Parent Co.:
Caribou Pub.
Pub............ Kerry Anderson
Ed. .... Michelle Pinon
Areas Served: Lamont, AB.

LEDUC

LEDUC REPRESENTATIVE
(Fri)
4504 61st Ave., Leduc, AB, T9E 3Z1, Canada, Canada; gen tel (780) 986-2271; gen fax (780) 986-6397; disp adv e-mail ngoetz@postmedia.com; ed e-mail bobby.roy@sunmedia.ca; web site www.leducrep.com
Circulation: 3,069pd, 16,449fr; VAC
Advertising: Open inch rate $0.87.
Established: 1905.
Parent Co.:
Postmedia Network Inc.
Quebecor Communications, Inc.
Pub............ Susanne Holmlund
Circ. Mgr............ Jan Eyre
Adv. Dir............ Nick Goetz
Ed .... Bobby Roy
Mechanical Specifications: Type page 10 1/4 x 15 3/4; E - 8 cols, 1/6 between; A - 8 cols, 1/6 between; C - 8 cols, 1/6 between.
Equipment & Software: : Hardware — APP/Mac; Presses — G/Community; Software — QPS/QuarkXPress 4.0, Adobe/Photoshop, Adobe/Acrobat.
Delivery Method: Mail, Newsstand, Carrier, Racks
Areas Served: Canada

LETHRBIDGE

LETHBRIDGE SUN TIMES
(Wed)
504 - 7th Street S, Lethrbidge, AB, T1J 2G8, Canada; gen tel (403) 328-4433; gen fax (403) 329-9355; ed e-mail ccampbell@abnewsgroup.com; web site www.lethsuntimes.com
Circulation: 1,274pd, 15,921fr; VAC
Parent Co.:
Alta. Newspaper Group, Ltd
Pub............ Coleen Campbell
Delivery Method: Carrier
Areas Served: City of Lethbridge

LLOYDMINSTER

LLOYDMINSTER MERIDIAN BOOSTER
(Wed)
5714 44th St., Lloydminster, AB, T9V 0B6, Canada, Canada; gen tel (780) 875-3362; adv tel (877) 786-8227; gen fax (780) 875-3423; disp adv e-mail ljohnston@postmedia.com; class adv e-mail meridianbooster.classifieds@sunmedia.ca; ed e-mail tweaver@postmedia.com; web site www.meridianbooster.com
Circulation: 2,653pd, 14,879fr; VAC
Advertising: Open inch rate $.98.
Established: 1954.
Parent Co.:
Postmedia Network Inc.
Quebecor Communications, Inc.
Pub............ Mary-Ann Kostiuk
Adv. Dir............ Leanne Johnson
Ed .... Taylor Weaver
Mechanical Specifications: Type page 11 1/2 x 16; E - 6 cols, 1 9/16, between; A - 6 cols, 1 9/16, between; C - 6 cols, 1 9/16, between.
Equipment & Software: : Hardware — APP/Mac; Presses — G/Community; Software — InDesign
Areas Served: Canada

MAGRATH

WESTWIND WEEKLY NEWS
(Thur)
74a South - 1st Street West, Box 9, Magrath, AB, T0K 1J0, Canada; gen tel (403) 758-6911; gen fax (403) 758-3661; disp adv e-mail sales@westwindweekly.com; web site www.westwindweekly.com
Circulation: 0pd, 51fr; VAC
Parent Co.:
Alta. Newspaper Group, Ltd
Pub............ Valorie Wiebe
Adv. Sales Consult............ Maggie Belisle
Office Admin. .... Joan Bly
Ed. .... J.W Schnarr
Delivery Method: Mail
Areas Served: towns of Magrath, Raymond and Stirling

MEDICINE HAT

PRAIRIE POST
(Fri)
3256 Dunmore Rd Se, Medicine Hat, AB, T1B 3R2, Canada; gen tel (403) 528-5769; gen fax (403) 528-2276; ed e-mail rdahlman@prairiepost.com; web site www.prairiepost.com
Circulation: 0pd, 12,562fr; VAC
Parent Co.:
Alberta Newspaper Group LP
Mng Ed. .... Ryan Dahlman
Areas Served: County of Newell, Cypress County, County of 40-Mile, Special Areas, City of Brooks, southwest Saskatchewan, City of Swift Current, M.D. of Acadia Valley

MILLET

LEDUC-WETASKIWIN PIPESTONE FLYER
(Thur)
5025 - 50 Street, Millet, AB, T0C 1Z0, Canada; gen tel (780) 387-5797; gen fax (780) 387-4397; disp adv e-mail sales1@pipestoneflyer.ca; ed e-mail editor@pipestoneflyer.ca; web site www.pipestoneflyer.ca
Circulation: 0pd, 16,935fr; VAC
Established: 1997.
Parent Co.:
Black Press Group Ltd.
Black Press, Prairie Division
Pub .... Michele Rosenthal
Ed .... Stu Salkeld
Delivery Method: Mail, Newsstand, Racks
Areas Served: City of Leduc, Leduc County, City of Wetaskiwin, Wetaskiwin County, Town of Millet, Pigeon Lake, Calmar, Thorsby, New Sarepta, Warburg, Winfield, Mulhurst Bay, Ma-Me-O Beach

MORINVILLE

THE FREE PRESS
(Tues)
10126 100 Ave., Morinville, AB, T8R 1R9, Sturgeon County, Canada; gen tel (780) 939-3309; adv tel (780) 939-3309; gen fax (780) 939-3093; disp adv e-mail morinville@shaw.ca; web site www.cowleynewspapers.com
Circulation: 55pd, 11,996fr; VAC
Advertising: Open inch rate $ 1.
Established: 1995.
Parent Co.:
W & E Cowley Publishing Ltd.
Pub............ Ed Cowley
Mechanical Specifications: Type page 10 1/4 x 15 1/2; E - 6 cols, 1 1/2, 1/12 between; A - 6 cols, 1 1/2, 1/12 between; C - 6 cols, 1 1/2, 1/12 between.
Equipment & Software: : Hardware — IBM; Software — QPS/QuarkXPress 5.0, Adobe/Photoshop 6.0, Adobe/Acrobat 5.0.
Areas Served: Sturgeon County

NANTON

THE NANTON NEWS
(Wed)
2019 20th Avenue, Nanton, AB, T0L 1R0, Canada, Canada; gen tel (403) 646-2023; gen fax (403) 646-2848; ed e-mail sheena.read@sunmedia.ca; web site www.nantonnews.com
Circulation: 592pd, 8fr; CMCA
Advertising: Open inch rate $0.48.
Established: 1903.
Parent Co.:
Postmedia Network Inc.
Pub............ Nancy Middleton
Circ. Mgr............ Donna Knowles
Group Pub............ Shawn Cornell
Circ. Mgr............ Lorelei Doell
Ed. .... Sheena Reed
Reg. Adv. Dir. .... Roxanne Mackintosh
Ed. .... Stephen Tipper
Areas Served: Canada

OKOTOKS

OKOTOKS WESTERN WHEEL
(Wed)
9 Mcrae St., Okotoks, AB, T1S 2A2, Canada; gen tel (403) 938-6397; gen fax (403) 938-2518; disp adv e-mail lplathan@okotoks.greatwest.ca; ed e-mail dpatterson@okotoks.greatwest.ca; web site www.westernwheel.com
Circulation: 91pd, 13,879fr; VAC
Advertising: Open inch rate $14.14.
Established: 1976.
Parent Co.:
Glacier Media Group
Great West Newspapers LP
Digital Platform - Mobile: Apple, Blackberry
Digital Platform - Tablet: Apple iOS, Blackberry Tablet OS
Ed .... Don Patterson
Pub .... Matt Rockley
Mechanical Specifications: Type page 10 1/4 x 15 1/4; E - 6 cols, 1 7/12, between; A - 6 cols, 1 7/12, between; C - 6 cols, 1 7/12, between.
Equipment & Software: : Hardware — APP/Mac; Software — QPS/QuarkXPress.
Delivery Method: Mail, Newsstand, Carrier, Racks
Areas Served: T0L 0A0,T0L 0H0, T0L 0J0,T0L 0K0,T0L 0P0,T0L 0X0,T0L 1H0,T0L 1K0,T0L 1R0,T0L 1W0,T0L 2A0,T0l 2T9,T0L 5G5,T1V and T1S.

OLDS

CARSTAIRS COURIER
(Tues)
5013 - 51 Street, Olds, AB, T4H 1P6, Canada, Canada; gen tel (403) 337-2806; adv tel (403) 337-2806; gen fax (403) 556-7515; ed e-mail dsingleton@olds.greatwest.ca; web site www.carstairscourier.ca
Circulation: 12pd, 3,289fr; CMCA
Advertising: Open inch rate $.83.
Established: 1982.
Parent Co.:
Glacier Media Group
Great West Newspapers LP
Ed .... Dan Singleton
Areas Served: Canada

MOUNTAIN VIEW GAZETTE
(Tues)
5013 - 51 St, Olds, AB, T4H 1P6, Canada; gen tel (403) 556-7510; gen fax (403) 556-7515; ed e-mail dsingleton@olds.greatwest.ca; web site www.mountainviewgazette.ca/
Circulation: 20,000fr; Sworn/Estimate/Non-Audited
Parent Co.:
Great West Newspapers LP
Grp. Pub./Gen. Mgr. .... Murray Elliott
Ed .... Dan Singleton

OLDS ALBERTAN
(Tues)
5013 51st St., Olds, AB, T4H 1P6, Canada; gen tel (403) 556-7510; gen fax (403) 556-7515; disp adv e-mail melliott@olds.greatwest.ca; ed e-mail dcollie@olds.greatwest.ca; web site www.oldsalbertan.ca
Circulation: 5pd, 6,933fr; VAC
Advertising: Open inch rate $.94.
Established: 1993.
Parent Co.:
Glacier Media Group
Great West Newspapers LP
Pub .... Murray Elliott
Ed .... Doug Collie

OYEN

OYEN ECHO
(Tues)
109 Sixth Ave. E., Oyen, AB, T0J 2J0, Special Area #3, Canada; gen tel (403) 664-3622; gen fax (403) 664-3622; disp adv e-mail oyenecho@telusplanet.net; class adv e-mail 88; ed e-mail oyenecho@telusplanet.net; web site www.oyenecho.ca
Circulation: 986pd, 22fr; VAC
Advertising: Agate $0.84.
Established: 1974.
Parent Co.:
Holmes Publishing Co. Ltd.
Digital Platform - Mobile: Apple
Pub............ Ronald E. Holmes
Ed. .... Diana Walker
Mechanical Specifications: Type page 10 1/4 x 16; E - 6 cols, 1 3/5, 1/6 between; A - 6 cols, 1 3/5, 1/6 between.
Equipment & Software: : Hardware — APP/Mac, APP/iMac, ADI/MicroScan; Software — QPS/QuarkXPress, Adobe/Photoshop, Adobe/Illustrator.
Delivery Method: Mail, Newsstand
Areas Served: Special Area #3
Note: we offer e-subs as well

PEACE RIVER

THE RECORD-GAZETTE

(Wed)
10002 100th St., Peace River, AB, T8S 1S6, Canada, Canada; gen tel (780) 624-2591; adv tel (877) 786-8227; gen fax (780) 624-8600; disp adv e-mail adsales@prrecordgazette.com; ed e-mail erin.steele@sunmedia.ca; web site www.prrecordgazette.com
Circulation: 0pd, 3fr; VAC
Advertising: Open inch rate $.68.
Established: 1914.
Parent Co.:
Postmedia Network Inc.
Mng. Ed............................ Kristjanna Grimmelt
reg. Adv. Dir..........................Peter Meyerhoffer
Sales (online)..................................Lori Czoba
City Ed.. Fred Rinne
Mechanical Specifications: Type page 13 x 21 1/4; E - 6 cols, 2 1/12, between; A - 6 cols, 2 1/12, between; C - 7 cols, 1 5/6, between.
Equipment & Software: : Hardware — APP/Mac; Software — QPS/QuarkXPress 3.31.
Areas Served: Canada

PINCHER CREEK

PINCHER CREEK ECHO

(Wed)
714 Main St., Pincher Creek, AB, T0K 1W0, Canada, Canada; gen tel (403) 627-3252; gen fax (403) 627-3949; disp adv e-mail rmackintosh@postmedia.com; ed e-mail cclow@postmedia.com; web site www.pinchercreekecho.com
Circulation: 1,077pd, 14fr; CMCA
Advertising: Open inch rate $.65.
Established: 1900.
Parent Co.:
Postmedia Network Inc.
Quebecor Communications, Inc.
Pub....................................... Nancy Middleton
Office Mgr................................Martha Goforth
Ed..Caitlin Clow
Adv. Dir .... Roxanne Mackintoch
Mechanical Specifications: Type page 10 1/4 x 15; E - 5 cols, 1 11/12, between; A - 6 cols, 1 1/2, between; C - 6 cols, 1 2/3, between.
Equipment & Software: : Hardware — APP/Mac.
Areas Served: Canada

PONOKA

PONOKA NEWS

(Wed)
5019-a 50th Ave., Ponoka, AB, T4J 1R6, Ponoka, Canada; gen tel (403) 783-3311; gen fax (403) 783-6300; disp adv e-mail judy.dick@ponokanews.com; class adv e-mail judy.dick@ponokanews.com; ed e-mail jeff.heyden-kaye@ponokanews.com; web site www.ponokanews.com
Circulation: 16pd, 5,856fr; CMCA
Advertising: Open column inch rate $13.09.
Established: 1954.
Parent Co.:
Black Press Group Ltd.Editions: 52— Ponoka News
Digital Platform - Mobile: Blackberry
Pres. ....Mary Kemmis
Mechanical Specifications: Type page 10.12" x 13"; 7 cols, column width 1.3" wide
Equipment & Software: ; Software — Adobe/PageMaker 7.0.
Delivery Method: Mail, Newsstand, Carrier, Racks
Areas Served: Ponoka

PROVOST

THE PROVOST NEWS

(Wed)
5111 50th St., Provost, AB, T0B 3S0, Provost M.D. No. 52, Canada; gen tel (780) 753-2564; gen fax (780) 753-6117; disp adv e-mail advertising@provostnews.ca; ed e-mail rcholmes@agt.net; web site www.provostnews.ca
Circulation: 1,300pd, 54fr; VAC
Advertising: Open inch rate $.82.
Established: 1910.
Parent Co.:
Holmes Publishing Co. Ltd.
Digital Platform - Mobile: Apple
Ed.......................................Richard C. Holmes
Delivery Method: Mail, Newsstand
Areas Served: Provost M.D. No. 52

RED DEER

CENTRAL ALBERTA LIFE

(Thur)
2950 Bremner Ave., Red Deer, AB, T4R 1M9, Canada, Canada; gen tel (403) 314-4373; gen fax (403) 342-4051; disp adv e-mail advertising@reddeeradvocate.com; class adv e-mail prausch@reddeeradvocate.com; ed e-mail editorial@reddeeradvocate.com; web site www.reddeeradvocate.com
Circulation: 33,301fr; Sworn/Estimate/Non-Audited
Advertising: Open line rate $1.26 .
Established: 1995.
Parent Co.:
Red Deer Advocate
Pub...Mary Kemmis
Mng Ed...................................... Crystal Rhyno
Adv. Mgr.....................................Wendy Moore
Circ. Mgr..Deb Reitmeie
Mechanical Specifications: Type page 10 x 12 7/8; A - 6 cols, 1 5/8, 1/6 between; C - 7 cols, 1 1/4, between.
Equipment & Software: : Hardware — APP/Mac; Software — QPS/QuarkXPress.
Areas Served: Canada

FRIDAY FORWARD

(Fri)
2950 Bremner Ave., Red Deer, AB, T4R 1M9, Canada, Canada; gen tel (403) 343-2400; adv tel (403) 314-4343; ed tel (403) 314-4325; gen fax (403) 342-4051; adv fax (403) 342-4051; ed fax (403) 341-6560; disp adv e-mail advertising@reddeeradvocate.com; class adv e-mail classified@reddeeradvocate.com; ed e-mail editorial@reddeeradvocate.com; web site www.reddeeradvocate.com
Circulation: 10,000pd,; AAM
Advertising: Open line rate $1.15 net.
Established: 1907.
Parent Co.:
Black Press Group Ltd.
Pub Red Deer Advocate; Pres Prarie/ East Kootenay Division Black PressMary Kemmis
Advt Mgr....................................Wendy Moore
Mng Ed...................................... Crystal Rhyno
National Rep & Major Acct AsstPatricia Rausch
Circulation Mgr.................... Debbie Reitmeier
Mechanical Specifications: Type page 10 x 12 7/8; A - 6 cols, 1 9/16, 1/6 between; C - 7 cols, 1 15/16, between.
Equipment & Software: : Hardware — APP/Mac; Software — QPS/QuarkXPress.
Delivery Method: Newsstand, Carrier
Areas Served: Canada

RED DEER EXPRESS

(Wed)
121 5301-43 St., Red Deer, AB, T4N 1C8, Canada, Canada; gen tel (403) 346-3356; adv tel (403) 625-4474; gen fax (403) 347-6620; disp adv e-mail publisher@reddeerexpress.com; class adv e-mail publisher@reddeerexpress.com; ed e-mail editor@reddeerexpress.com; web site www.reddeerexpress.com
Circulation: 0pd, 24,718fr; VAC
Advertising: Open inch rate $1.76.
Established: 1946.
Parent Co.:
Black Press Group Ltd.
Pub..Tracey Scheveers
Ed...Mark Weber
Equipment & Software: ; Software — QPS/QuarkXPress 4.1.
Areas Served: Canada

REDWATER

FARM 'N' FRIENDS

(Fri)
4720 50 Ave, Redwater, AB, T0A 2W0, Sturgeon , Canada; gen tel (780) 421-9715; gen fax (780) 942-2515; disp adv e-mail redwater@shaw.ca; class adv e-mail redwater@shaw.ca; ed e-mail redwater@shaw.ca; web site www.cowleynewspapers.com/farm-n-friends/
Circulation: 17,759fr; CMCA
Advertising: Open inch rate $1.
Established: 1999.
Parent Co.:
W & E Cowley Pub. Ltd.
Pub./Owner/Adv. Mgr./ Ed................Ed Cowley
Areas Served: Sturgeon

THE REVIEW

(Tues)
4720 50th Ave., Redwater, AB, T0A 2W0, Canada; gen tel (780) 942-2023; gen fax (780) 942-2515; disp adv e-mail redwater@shaw.ca; web site www.cowleynewspapers.com
Circulation: 4,405fr; VAC
Advertising: Open inch rate $1.
Established: 1989.
Parent Co.:
W & E Cowley Publishing Ltd.
Pub./Adv. Mgr./Owner......................Ed Cowley
Mechanical Specifications: Type page 10 1/3 x 15 2/5; E - 6 cols, 1 1/2, 1/6 between; A - 6 cols, 1 1/2, 1/6 between; C - 6 cols, 1 1/2, 1/6 between.
Equipment & Software: : Hardware — IBM; Software — QPS/QuarkXPress 5.0, Adobe/Photoshop 6.0, Adobe/Acrobat 5.0.

RIMBEY

RIMBEY REVIEW

(Tues)
5001-50 Ave. Main St., Rimbey, AB, T0C 2J0, Canada; gen tel (403) 843-4909; gen fax (403) 843-4907; disp adv e-mail sales@rimbeyreview.com; ed e-mail editor@rimbeyreview.com; web site www.rimbeyreview.com
Circulation: 7pd, 5,136fr; VAC
Advertising: Open inch rate $.93.
Established: 1997.
Parent Co.:
Black Press Group Ltd.
Pub.................................... Michele Rosenthal
Sales.......................................Connie Johnson
Ed...Treena Mielke
Delivery Method: Mail
Areas Served: t0c

ROCKY MOUNTAIN HOUSE

THE MOUNTAINEER

(Tues)
4814 49th St., Rocky Mountain House, AB, T4T 1S8, Canada; gen tel (403) 845-3334; gen fax (403) 845-5570; disp adv e-mail advertising@mountaineer.bz; class adv e-mail advertising@mountaineer.bz; ed e-mail editor@mountaineer.bz; web site www.mountaineer.bz
Circulation: 2,264pd, 53fr; VAC
Advertising: Open inch rate $.92.
Established: 1923.
Parent Co.:
Mountaineer Publishing Co.
Prodn. Mgr. ....Gail Krabben
Pub...Glen Mazza
Adv. Mgr...Penny Allen
Ed. .... Laura Button
Office Mgr. ....Bernie Visotto
Mechanical Specifications: Type page 11 5/8 x 21 1/4; E - 6 cols, 1 5/6, 1/6 between; A - 6 cols, 1 5/6, 1/6 between; C - 6 cols, 1 5/6, 1/6 between.
Equipment & Software: : Hardware — Microsoft/Windows 98; Software — Archetype/Corel Draw.

RYCROFT

RYCROFT CENTRAL PEACE SIGNAL

(Tues)
47011 50th St., Rycroft, AB, T0H 3A0, Canada, Canada; gen tel (780) 765-3604; gen fax (780) 785-2188; disp adv e-mail signalads@telus.net; class adv e-mail signalads@telus.net; ed e-mail signalnews@telus.net
Circulation: 2,633pd, 5fr; CMCA
Advertising: Open inch rate $.72.
Established: 1980.
Parent Co.:
847562 Alberta Ltd.
Pub/Advt Mgr.................................Dan Zahara
Circ. Mgr....................................... Carol Grover
Morgan Zahara
Mechanical Specifications: Type page 10 15/16 x 13; E - 6 cols, 1 7/12, 1/6 between; A - 6 cols, 1 7/12, 1/6 between; C - 6 cols, 1 7/12, 1/6 between.
Equipment & Software: : Hardware — IBM; Presses — G; Software — Adobe/PageMaker 6.5.
Delivery Method: Mail, Newsstand
Areas Served: Canada

SAINT PAUL

ST. PAUL JOURNAL

(Tues)
4813 50th Ave., Saint Paul, AB, T0A 3A0, Canada, Canada; gen tel (780) 645-3342; gen fax (780) 645-2346; disp adv e-mail rberlinguette@stpaul.greatwest.ca; ed e-mail jhuser@stpaul.greatwest.ca; web site www.spjournal.com
Circulation: 21pd, 460fr; VAC
Advertising: Open inch rate $.99.
Established: 1924.
Parent Co.:
Glacier Media Group
Great West Newspapers LP
Ed..Janice Huser
Pub...Janani Whitfield
Delivery Method: Mail, Newsstand
Areas Served: Canada

SHERWOOD PARK

SHERWOOD PARK/STRATHCONA COUNTY NEWS

(Fri)
168 Kaska Rd., 168 Kaska Road, Sherwood Park, AB, T8A 4G7, Strathcona, Canada; gen tel (780) 464-0033; adv tel (780) 464-0033 Ext 239; ed tel 780 464-0033; gen fax (780) 464-8512; disp adv e-mail jfigeat@postmedia.com; ed e-mail bproulx@postmedia.com; web site www.sherwoodparknews.com
Circulation: 1,702pd, 30,851fr; VAC
Advertising: Open inch rate $.96.
Established: 1976.
Parent Co.:
Postmedia Network Inc.
Division of Post Media
Digital Platform - Mobile: Apple, Android
Digital Platform - Tablet: Apple iOS, Android, Blackberry Tablet OS, Kindle
Adv. Dir...Jean Figeat
Circ. .... Dawn Zapatoski
Ed .... Ben Proulx
Mechanical Specifications: Type page 10.3125" x 11.5"; E & C - 10 cols, 1";
Equipment & Software: : Hardware — APP/Mac; Software — Indesign
Delivery Method: Carrier, Racks
Areas Served: Strathcona

SLAVE LAKE

LAKESIDE LEADER

(Wed)
103 Third Ave. Ne, Slave Lake, AB, T0G 2A0, Canada; gen tel (780) 849-4380; adv tel (780) 849-4380; gen fax (780) 849-3903;

ed e-mail lsleader@telusplanet.net; web site www.lakesideleader.com
Circulation: 3,672pd,; CMCA
Advertising: Open inch rate $.88.
Established: 1970.
Parent Co.:
South Peace News(High Prairie)
Pub.. Mary Burgar
Ed.. Joe McWilliams
Circulation Mgr/Primary Ad Contact..... Tammy Leslie
Delivery Method: Mail, Newsstand
Areas Served: Canada

SMOKY LAKE

SMOKY LAKE SIGNAL

(Wed)
4924 50 St., Smoky Lake, AB, T0A 3C0, Canada; gen tel (780) 656-4114; adv tel (780) 656-4114; ed tel 780-656-6530; gen fax (780) 656-4361; ed e-mail signal@smokylake.com; web site www.smokylake.com
Circulation: 355pd, 195fr; VAC
Advertising: Open inch rate $.75.
Established: 1978.
Parent Co.:
Smoky Lake Signal Press Ltd.
Ed/Pub/Owner.......................... Lorne Taylor
Areas Served: T0A 3C0

SPRUCE GROVE

THE GROVE EXAMINER

(Fri)
420 King Street, #1, Spruce Grove, AB, T7X 3B4, Canada, Canada; gen tel (780) 962-4257; adv tel (877) 786-8227; gen fax (780) 962-0658; disp adv e-mail matthew.maceachen@sunmedia.ca; class adv e-mail matthew.maceachen@sunmedia.ca; ed e-mail carsonm@bowesnet.com; web site www.sprucegroveexaminer.com
Circulation: 1,273pd, 11,471fr; VAC
Advertising: Open inch rate $.96.
Established: 1970.
Parent Co.:
Postmedia Network Inc.
Reg. Sales Mgr.................... Mary Ann Kostiuk
Prodn. Mgr.................................. Janet Stace
Pub.. Pamela Allain
Adv. Mgr......................... Matthew MacEachen
Ed.. Carson Mills
Areas Served: Canada

THE STONY PLAIN REPORTER

(Fri)
420 King Street, #1, Spruce Grove, AB, T7X 3B4, Canada, Canada; gen tel (780) 962-4257; adv tel (877) 786-8227; gen fax (780) 962-0658; disp adv e-mail matthew.maceachen@sunmedia.ca; class adv e-mail matthew.maceachen@sunmedia.ca; ed e-mail thomas.miller@sunmedia.ca; web site www.stonyplainreporter.com
Circulation: 1,643pd, 10,513fr; VAC
Advertising: Open inch rate $.96.
Established: 1945.
Parent Co.:
Postmedia Network Inc.
Circ. Mgr.............................. Mary-Ann Kostiuk
Ed.. Carson Mills
Prodn. Mgr.................................. Jim Myers
Pub.. Pamela Allain
CARDonline(10/31/14).............. Thomas Miller
Mechanical Specifications: Type page 10 1/4 x 15 3/4; E - 6 cols, 1 7/12, between; A - 6 cols, 1 7/12, between; C - 6 cols, 1 7/12, between.
Areas Served: Canada

ST. ALBERT

ST. ALBERT GAZETTE

(Wed, Sat)
340 Carelton Drive, St. Albert, AB, T8N 7L3, Canada, Canada; gen tel (780) 460-5500; ed tel (780) 460-5510; gen fax (780) 460-8220; disp adv e-mail advertising@stalbert.greatwest.ca; ed e-mail cmartindale@stalbert.greatwest.ca; web site www.stalbertgazette.com
Circulation: 1,652pd, 24,879fr; VAC
Advertising: Open inch rate $1.31.
Established: 1961.
Parent Co.:
Glacier Media Group
Great West Newspapers LP
Digital Platform - Mobile: Apple, Android, Blackberry
Digital Platform - Tablet: Apple iOS, Android, Kindle, Nook, Kindle Fire
Adv. Mgr.. Al Glaser
Pub.. Brian Bachynski
Ed.. Carolyn Martindale
Mechanical Specifications: Type page 9.45" x 15"; E - 6 cols, 2, 1/6 between; A - 6 cols, 2, 1/6 between; C - 7 cols, 1 3/8, 1/6 between.
Equipment & Software: : Hardware — APP/Mac; Presses — KBA Colora. ; Software — QPS/In Design
Delivery Method: Mail, Newsstand, Carrier, Racks
Areas Served: Canada

STETTLER

STETTLER INDEPENDENT

(Thur)
4810 50th St., Stettler, AB, T0C 2L0, Canada; gen tel (403) 742-2395; ed tel (403) 740-4431; gen fax (403) 742-8050; disp adv e-mail nicole.stratulate@stettlerindependent.com; class adv e-mail ddoell@stettlerindependent.com; ed e-mail editor@stettlerindependent.com; web site www.stettlerindependent.com
Circulation: 34pd, 33fr; VAC
Advertising: Open inch rate $.83.
Parent Co.:
Black Press Group Ltd.
Ad control.................................. Debbie Doell
Graphic artist.............................. Karen Fischer
reporter.............................. Landin Chambers
Equipment & Software: : Hardware — APP/Mac; Software — QPS/QuarkXPress.
Areas Served: Town of Stettler, County of Stettler, Big Valley, Erskine, Donalda, Gadsby, Botha, Buffalo Lake,

STRATHMORE

STRATHMORE STANDARD

(Wed)
Unit A-510 Hwy 1, Strathmore, AB, T1P 1M6, Canada, Canada; gen tel (403) 934-3021; gen fax (403) 934-5011; disp adv e-mail rmackintosh@postmedia.com; ed e-mail josh.chalmers@sunmedia.ca; web site www.strathmorestandard.com
Circulation: 3,679pd, 10,858fr; VAC
Advertising: Open inch rate $.78.
Established: 1909.
Parent Co.:
Postmedia Network Inc.
Quebecor Communications, Inc.
Ed.. Josh Chalmers
Adv. Dir.............................. Roxanne MacKintosh
Delivery Method: Mail, Newsstand, Carrier, Racks
Areas Served: Canada

STRATHMORE TIMES

(Fri)
123 2nd Avenue, Strathmore, AB, T1P 1K1, Canada; gen tel (403) 934-5589; gen fax (403) 934-5546; disp adv e-mail rose@strathmoretimes.com; class adv e-mail classifieds@strathmoretimes.com; ed e-mail miriam@strathmoretimes.com; web site www.strathmoretimes.com
Circulation: 11,937fr; VAC
Advertising: $.86.
Established: 2009.
Pub/Ed.. Mario Prusina
Adv Mgr.. Rose Hamrlik
Associate Editor.................. Miriam Ostermann
Delivery Method: Mail
Areas Served: Strathmore, Langdon, and all of Wheatland County

SUNDRE

SUNDRE ROUND-UP

(Tues)
103 2nd St. Nw, Sundre, AB, T0M 1X0, Canada, Canada; gen tel (403) 638-3577; gen fax (403) 638-3077; disp adv e-mail kcomfort@sundre.greatwest.ca; ed e-mail dsingleton@olds.greatwest.ca; web site www.sundreroundup.ca
Circulation: 879pd, 0fr; VAC
Advertising: Open inch rate $.89.
Established: 1961.
Parent Co.:
Glacier Media Group
Great West Newspapers LP
Pub.. Ray Lachambre
Ed.. Dan Singleton
Sales Mgr.................................. Kim Comfort
Mechanical Specifications: Type page 10 1/4 x 14 1/2; E - 6 cols, 1 11/20, between; A - 6 cols, 1 11/20, between; C - 6 cols, 1 11/20, between.
Equipment & Software: : Hardware — APP/Power Mac 7200; Software — QPS/QuarkXPress.
Areas Served: Canada

SWAN HILLS

GRIZZLY GAZETTE

(Tues)
5435 Plaza Ave., Swan Hills, AB, T0G 2C0, Canada; gen tel (780) 333-2100; gen fax (780) 333-2111; disp adv e-mail sgazette@telusplanet.net; class adv e-mail sgazette@telusplanet.net; ed e-mail sgazette@telusplanet.net; web site thegrizzlygazette.com
Circulation: 394pd, 135fr; CMCA
Advertising: $0.65 / agate line.
Established: 1977.
Gen. Mgr.................................. Phyllis Webster
Ed.. Carol Webster
Mechanical Specifications: Type page 10 1/4 x 12 1/2; E - 6 cols, 1 9/16, 1/8 between; A - 6 cols, 1 9/16, 1/8 between.
Equipment & Software: : Hardware — Apple Imac OS 10 snow leopard; Software — QuarkXPress 8
Delivery Method: Mail, Newsstand
Areas Served: Canada

SYLVAN LAKE

ECKVILLE ECHO

(Thur)
Suite 103 5020-50 A St., Sylvan Lake, AB, T4S 1R2, Canada; gen tel (403) 887-2331; gen fax (403) 887-2081; disp adv e-mail admin@sylvanlakenews.com; ed e-mail editor@sylvanlakenews.com
Circulation: 1,077pd, 2,466fr; VAC
Established: 1997.
Parent Co.:
Black Press Group Ltd.
Admin.................................. Cheryl Hyvonen
Pub.. Randy Holt
Ed.. Jenna Swan
Mechanical Specifications: 10.12 " x 13"
Delivery Method: Mail, Newsstand, Racks
Areas Served: t4s, t4n, rr1, rr4

SYLVAN LAKE NEWS

(Thur)
Suite 103, 5020-50a St.,, Sylvan Lake, AB, T4S 1R2, Canada, Canada; gen tel (403) 887-2331; adv tel (403) 887-2331; gen fax (403) 887-2081; disp adv e-mail sales@slyvanlakenews.com; ed e-mail editor@sylvanlakenews.com; web site www.sylvanlakenews.com
Circulation: 377pd, 7,715fr; VAC
Advertising: $15.12.
Established: 1935.
Parent Co.:
Black Press Group Ltd.
Admin.................................. Cheryl Hyvonen
Pub.. Randy Holt
Ed.. Jenna Swan
Equipment & Software: ; Software — QPS/QuarkXPress.
Delivery Method: Mail, Carrier, Racks
Areas Served: Canada

TABER

THE TABER TIMES

(Wed)
4822-53 St., Taber, AB, T1G 1W4, Canada, Canada; gen tel (403) 223-2266; gen fax (403) 223-1408; disp adv e-mail chrissales@tabertimes.com; web site www.tabertimes.com
Circulation: 54pd, 179fr; VAC
Advertising: Open inch rate $1.00.
Established: 1907.
Parent Co.:
Alta. Newspaper Group, Ltd
Pub.. Valorie Wiebe
Adv. Consult.......................... Christine Mykytiw
Adv. Consult.. Erin Lickiss
Ed.. Greg Price
Mechanical Specifications: Type page 11 1/2 x 21; E - 6 cols, 1 3/4, 1/4 between; A - 6 cols, 1 3/4, 1/4 between; C - 6 cols, 1 3/4, 1/4 between.
Equipment & Software: : Hardware — APP/Mac; Software — QPS/QuarkXPress 4.04, Adobe/Illustrator 7.0.1, Adobe/Photoshop 5.0.
Delivery Method: Mail, Newsstand, Carrier
Areas Served: Canada

THREE HILLS

THE THREE HILLS CAPITAL

(Wed)
411 Main St., Three Hills, AB, T0M 2A0, Canada, Canada; gen tel (403) 443-5133; gen fax (403) 443-7331; disp adv e-mail info@threehillscapital.com; class adv e-mail info@threehillscapital.com; ed e-mail info@threehillscapital.com; web site threehillscapital.com
Circulation: 1,029pd, 4fr; VAC
Established: 1916.
Adv. Mgr.............................. Theresa Shearlaw
Ed.. Timothy Shearlaw
Produ Mgr.................................. Jay Shearlaw
Delivery Method: Mail, Newsstand
Areas Served: Canada

TOFIELD

TOFIELD MERCURY

(Wed)
5312 50th St., Tofield, AB, T0B 4J0, Canada, Canada; gen tel (780) 662-4046; adv tel (780) 662-4046; gen fax (780) 662-3735; disp adv e-mail kamcjm@gmail.com; class adv e-mail kamcjm@gmail.com; ed e-mail tofmerc@telusplanet.net; web site www.tofieldmerc.com
Circulation: 1,400pd, 23fr; Sworn/Estimate/Non-Audited
Advertising: Open inch rate $.83.
Established: 1918.
Parent Co.:
Caribou Publishing
Pub/Advt Mgr.......................... Kerry Anderson
Mechanical Specifications: Type page 10 x 15 1/2; E - 5 cols, 1 5/6, between; A - 5 cols, 1 5/6, between.
Equipment & Software: : Hardware — IBM; Software — Archetype/Corel Draw 4.1, Adobe/PageMaker 5.0.
Delivery Method: Mail, Racks
Areas Served: Canada

VAUXHALL

VAUXHALL ADVANCE
(Thur)
516 2nd Ave. N., Vauxhall, AB, T0K 2K0, Canada; gen tel (403) 654-2122; gen fax (403) 654-4184; disp adv e-mail tabads@tabertimes.com; web site www.vauxhalladvance.com
Circulation: 0pd, 47fr; VAC
Advertising: Open inch rate $0.88.
Established: 1978.
Parent Co.:
Alta. Newspaper Group, Ltd
Ed. .... Greg Price
Pub. .... Valorie Wiebe
Office/Sales .... Shawna Wiestm
Mechanical Specifications: Type page 10 1/4 x 14 1/2; E - 6 cols, 1 5/8, 1/8 between; A - 6 cols, 1 5/8, 1/8 between; C - 6 cols, 1 5/8, 1/8 between.
Equipment & Software: : Hardware — APP/Macs; Software — QPS/QuarkXPress 4.04, Adobe/Illustrator 7.0.1, Adobe/Photoshop 5.0.
Delivery Method: Mail
Areas Served: Town of VAuxhall and hamlets of Hays and Enchant

VERMILION

VERMILION STANDARD
(Wed)
4917 50th Ave., Vermilion, AB, T9X 1A6, Canada; gen tel (780) 853-5344; adv tel (877) 786-8227; gen fax (780) 853-5203; disp adv e-mail ngoetz@postmedia.com; class adv e-mail ngoetz@postmedia.com; ed e-mail thermiston@postmedia.com; web site www.vermilionstandard.com
Circulation: 1,250pd, 3,972fr; VAC
Advertising: Open inch rate $.80.
Established: 1909.
Parent Co.:
Postmedia Network Inc.
Digital Platform - Mobile: Apple
Circulation .... Trina de Regt
Publisher .... Mary-Ann Kostiuk
Production and Circulation .... Pat Lavigne
Dir. of Adv. .... Nicki Goetz
Reg. Mng. Ed. ext.4 .... Taylor Hermiston
Delivery Method: Mail, Newsstand, Carrier, Racks
Areas Served: T9X

VERMILION VOICE
(Mon)
5006-50th Ave., Vermilion, AB, T9X 1A2, Canada; gen tel (780) 853-6305; gen fax (780) 853-5426; disp adv e-mail vermilionvoice@gmail.com; ed e-mail vermilionvoice@gmail.com; web site www.vermilionvoice.com
Circulation: 5,294fr; CMCA
Advertising: inch.
Established: 2004.
Pub .... Susan Chikie
Sales, reporter, newspaper layout .... Lorna Hamilton
Reporter and Sales .... Angela Mouley
Sales, reporter & graphics Shawna Chernichen
Graphics, website etc .... Amr Rezk
Delivery Method: Mail, Newsstand, Racks
Areas Served: Canada

VIKING

THE WEEKLY REVIEW
(Tues)
5208 50th Street, Viking, AB, T0B 4N0, Canada; gen tel (780) 336-3422; gen fax (780) 336-3223; disp adv e-mail vikingreview@gmail.com; ed e-mail vikingweeklyreview@gmail.com; web site www.weeklyreview.ca
Circulation: 0pd, 10fr; VAC
Advertising: Open inch rate $.83.
Established: 1977.
Parent Co.:
Caribou Publishing
Ed. .... Leslie Cholowsky
Pub. .... Eric Anderson
Owner .... Kerry Anderson
Areas Served: Beaver County, Viking, Alberta T0B 4N0

VULCAN

VULCAN ADVOCATE
(Wed)
112 - 3rd Ave. N, Vulcan, AB, T0L 2B0, Canada; gen tel (403) 485-2036; adv tel (877) 786-8227; gen fax (403) 485-6938; disp adv e-mail enid.fraser@sunmedia.ca; class adv e-mail enid.fraser@sunmedia.ca; ed e-mail stephen.tipper@sunmedia.ca; web site www.vulcanadvocate.com
Circulation: 1,032pd, 11fr; CMCA
Advertising: Open inch rate $.58.
Established: 1913.
Parent Co.:
Postmedia Network Inc.
Publisher .... Shawn Cornell
Editor .... Stephen Tipper
Reg. Dir. of Adv. .... Roxanne MacKintosh
Mechanical Specifications: Type page 10 1/4 x 15 1/2; E - 6 cols, 1 7/12, between; A - 6 cols, 1 7/12, between; C - 6 cols, 1 7/12, between.
Delivery Method: Mail, Newsstand

WABASCA

WABASCA FEVER
(Thur)
Box 519, Wabasca, AB, T0G 2K0, Canada; gen tel (780) 891-2108; gen fax (888) 318-555; disp adv e-mail wabascafever@shaw.ca; class adv e-mail wabascafever@shaw.ca; ed e-mail wabascafever@shaw.ca; web site http://www.slavelakewabascanewspapers.ca/wabasca_fever_newspaper.html
Circulation: 567pd, 172fr; VAC
Advertising: Open inch rate $0.98.
Established: 1998.
Parent Co.:
Thomas Alliance Inc.Patricia Thomas
Pub. .... Bruce Thomas
Delivery Method: Mail, Newsstand
Areas Served: Municipal District of Opportunity No. 17

WAINWRIGHT

WAINWRIGHT STAR EDGE
(Fri)
1027 3rd Ave, Wainwright, AB, T9W 1T6, MD of Wainwright, Canada; gen tel (780) 842-4465; adv tel (780) 842-4465 ext.112; gen fax (780) 842-2760; disp adv e-mail patrick@starnews.ca; class adv e-mail classifieds@starnews.ca; ed e-mail zak@starnews.ca; web site www.starnews.ca
Circulation: 0pd, 6,500fr; VAC
Advertising: Open inch rate $1.20.
Established: 2002.
Parent Co.:
Star News Inc.
Digital Platform - Mobile: Apple
Pub. .... Roger Holmes
Adv. Sales .... Patrick Moroz
Sales & Promo .... Sherry Shatz
Editor .... Zak McLachlan
Graphic Design Dept. Manager . Barb Tywoniuk
Mechanical Specifications: 8 Columns x 15.25" (10.25' x 15.25")
Delivery Method: Newsstand, Carrier, Racks
Areas Served: MD of Wainwright

WESTLOCK

THE WESTLOCK NEWS
(Tues)
9871 107th St., Westlock, AB, T7P 1R9, Canada, Canada; gen tel (780) 349-3033; gen fax (780) 349-3677; disp adv e-mail abaxandall@westlock.greatwest.ca; class adv e-mail abaxandall@westlock.greatwest.ca; ed e-mail dneuman@westlock.greatwest.ca; web site www.westlocknews.com
Circulation: 10pd, 5fr; VAC
Advertising: Open inch rate $0.89.
Established: 1901.
Parent Co.:
Glacier Media Group
Pub. .... George Blais
Circ. Mgr. .... Louise Strehlau
Ed. .... Olivia Bako
Adv. .... Connie Onyschuk
Adv. .... Joyce Weber
Delivery Method: Mail, Newsstand, Carrier
Areas Served: Canada

WETASKIWIN

WETASKIWIN TIMES
(Wed)
5013 51 St., Wetaskiwin, AB, T9A 1L4, Canada, Canada; gen tel (780) 352-2231; gen fax (780) 352-4333; disp adv e-mail pam.tremaine@sunmedia.ca; class adv e-mail pam.tremaine@sunmedia.ca; ed e-mail editor@sunmedia.ca; web site www.wetaskiwintimes.com
Circulation: 9,957fr; VAC
Advertising: Open inch rate $0.71.
Established: 1901.
Parent Co.:
Postmedia Network Inc.
Prodn. Mgr. .... Adam Roy
Pub. .... Nick Goetz
Office Mgr. .... Clara Mitchell
Adv. Mgr. .... Pam Tremaine
Ed. .... Sarah Swenson
Mechanical Specifications: Type page 10 1/4 x 12.5; E - 6 cols, 1 1/6, 1/8 between; A - 6 cols, 1 1/6, 1/8 between; C - 8 cols, 1 1/6, 1/8 between.
Equipment & Software: : Hardware — APP/Mac; Software — QPS/QuarkXPress, Adobe/Photoshop.
Areas Served: Canada

WHITECOURT

THE MAYERTHORPE FREELANCER
(Wed)
4732 - 50 Ave., Whitecourt, AB, T7S 1N7, Woodlands County, Canada; gen tel (780) 778-3977; gen fax (780) 778-6459; disp adv e-mail advertising@mayerthorpefreelancer.com; ed e-mail ann.harvey@sunmedia.ca; web site www.mayerthorpefreelancer.com
Circulation: 589pd, 7fr; CMCA
Advertising: Open inch rate $0.71.
Established: 1978.
Parent Co.:
Quebecor Communications, Inc.
Reg. Dir. of Adv. .... Pam Allain
Circ. Mgr. .... Candice Daniels
Ed. .... Christopher King
Mechanical Specifications: Type page 10 1/4 x 14; E - 8 cols, 1 3/16, 3/16 between; A - 8 cols, 1 3/16, 3/16 between; C - 8 cols, 1 3/16, 3/16 between.
Equipment & Software: : Hardware — APP/Power Mac 6100-80; Software — QPS/QuarkXPress 7.53.
Areas Served: Woodlands County

THE WHITECOURT STAR
(Wed)
4732 50th Ave., Whitecourt, AB, T7S 1N7, Canada; gen tel (780) 778-3977; gen fax (780) 778-6459; disp adv e-mail nikki.greening@sunmedia.ca; ed e-mail wcstar.editorial@sunmedia.ca; web site www.whitecourtstar.com
Circulation: 2,467pd, 113fr; VAC
Advertising: Open inch rate $0.74.
Established: 1961.
Parent Co.:
Postmedia Network Inc.
Digital Platform - Mobile: Apple
Pub. .... Pamela Allain
Sales .... Meghan Brown
Circ. .... Candice Daniels
Sales .... Nikki Greening
Front Office Classifieds .... Tracy McKinnon
Ed. .... Christopher King
Mechanical Specifications: Type page 10 1/4 x 16; E - 10 cols, 1 9/16, between; A - 10 cols, 1 9/16, between; C - 10 cols, 1 9/16, between.
Delivery Method: Mail, Newsstand, Carrier, Racks
Areas Served: T7S

COLD LAKE

BEAVER RIVER BANNER
(Wed)
4110 51 Ave, cold lake, AB, t9m 2a1, Canada, Canada; gen tel (780) 201-0623; web site www.beaverriverbanner.com
Circulation: 2,300fr; Sworn/Estimate/Non-Audited
Advertising: Open inch rate $.66.
Established: 1990.
Ed. .... Dan Brisebois
Mechanical Specifications: Type page 10 1/4 x 15 1/2; E - 6 cols, 1 3/5, 3/16 between; A - 6 cols, 1 3/5, 3/16 between; C - 6 cols, 1 3/5, 3/16 between.
Equipment & Software: : Hardware — PC ; Software — Archetype/Corel Draw x3, WordPerfect 8.0.
Delivery Method: Mail
Areas Served: Canada

BRITISH COLUMBIA

100 MILE HOUSE

100 MILE HOUSE FREE PRESS
(Thur)
3-536 Horse Lake Rd., Uptown Plaza, 100 Mile House, BC, V0K 2E0, Canada; gen tel (250) 395-2219; gen fax (250) 395-3939; disp adv e-mail publisher@100milefreepress.net; class adv e-mail classifieds@100milefreepress.net; ed e-mail newsroom@100milefreepress.net; web site www.100milefreepress.net
Circulation: 2,517pd, 4,115fr; VAC
Advertising: Open inch rate $13.02.
Established: 1960.
Parent Co.:
Black Press Group Ltd.
Publisher .... Martina Dopf
Sales .... Chris Nickless
Advertising Creative .... Kerri Mingo
Creative .... Debbie Theoret
Reporter .... Carole Rooney
Reception/Circulation .... Lori Brodie
Ed. .... Max Winkelman
Creative .... Evan Fentiman
Delivery Method: Mail, Newsstand, Carrier, Racks
Areas Served: South Cariboo

ABBOTSFORD

THE ABBOTSFORD NEWS
(Tues, Thur, Sat)
34375 Gladys Ave., Abbotsford, BC, V2S 2H5, Canada, Canada; gen tel (604) 853-1144; gen fax (604) 852-1641; disp adv e-mail donb@abbynews.com; ed e-mail newsroom@abbynews.com; web site www.abbynews.com
Circulation: 60pd, 38,927fr; AAM
Advertising: Open inch rate $2.52 (Tu, Sat); $2.18 (Th).
Established: 1922.
Parent Co.:
Black Press Group Ltd.

Circ. Mgr.................................... Kevin Hemery
Mng. Ed.................................... Andrew Holota
Pub.. Carly Ferguson
Adv Mgr.......................................Don Barbeau
Mechanical Specifications: Type page 12 1/2 x 21; E - 7 cols, 1 11/16, 11/12 between; A - 7 cols, 1 11/16, 11/12 between; C - 7 cols, 1 11/16, 11/12 between.
Equipment & Software: : Hardware — APP/Mac; Presses — G/Urbanite; Software — QPS/ QuarkXPress 4.1, Adobe/Photoshop 6.0, Adobe/Illustrator 9.0.
Areas Served: Canada

AGASSIZ

THE AGASSIZ-HARRISON OBSERVER

(Thur)
7167 Pioneer Ave, Agassiz, BC, V0M 1A0, Canada; gen tel (604) 796-4300 ; gen fax (604) 796-2081; disp adv e-mail ads@ahobserver.com; class adv e-mail tanya@blackpressused.ca; ed e-mail news@ahobserver.com; web site www.agassizharrisonobserver.com
Circulation: 590pd, 2,815fr; VAC
Advertising: Open inch rate $1.15.
Established: 1999.
Parent Co.:
Black Press Group Ltd.
Pub.. Carly Ferguson
Ed .... Erin Knutson
Class. Adv........................ Tanya Jeyachandran
Adv, Rep.............................. Christine Douglas
Areas Served: Agassiz, Harrison

ALDERGROVE

THE ALDERGROVE STAR

(Thur)
27118 Fraser Hwy., Aldergrove, BC, V4W 3P6, Canada, Canada; gen tel (604) 514-6770; gen fax (604) 856-5212; disp adv e-mail sales@aldergrovestar.com; ed e-mail newsroom@aldergrovestar.com; web site www.aldergrovestar.com
Circulation: 728pd, 6,469fr; VAC
Advertising: Open inch rate $0.97.
Established: 1957.
Parent Co.:
Black Press Group Ltd.
Adv. Sales Mgr.............................. Janice Reid
Ed. .... Kurt Langmann
Pub .... Lisa Farquharson
Delivery Method: Carrier, Racks
Areas Served: Canada

ARMSTRONG

OKANAGAN ADVERTISER

(Thur)
3400 Okanagan St., Armstrong, BC, V0E 1B0, Canada, Canada; gen tel (250) 546-3121; gen fax (250) 546-3636; web site OkanaganAdvertiser.com
Circulation: 4,000fr; Sworn/Estimate/Non-Audited
Advertising: Open inch rate $1.20.
Established: 1902.
Digital Platform - Mobile: Apple, Android, Windows, Blackberry
Digital Platform - Tablet: Apple iOS, Android, Windows 7, Blackberry Tablet OS, Kindle, Nook, Kindle Fire
Pub .... Will Hansma
Mechanical Specifications: Tabloid 1/4 Fold
Delivery Method: Mail, Newsstand, Racks
Areas Served: Canada

ASHCROFT

THE ASHCROFT-CACHE CREEK JOURNAL

(Thur)
120 4th Street, Ashcroft, BC, V0K 1A0, Canada, Canada; gen tel (250) 453-2261; ed tel (250) 453-2261; gen fax (250) 453-9625; disp adv e-mail publisher@accjournal.ca; ed e-mail editorial@accjournal.ca; web site https://www.ashcroftcachecreekjournal.com/
Circulation: 850pd, 87fr; CMCA
Advertising: Column inch $11.80.
Established: 1895.
Parent Co.:
Black Press Group Ltd.
Editor ....Barbara Roden
Salesperson.......................Christopher Roden
Mechanical Specifications: Type page 10 5/16 x 14 1/2; E - 6 cols, 1 7/12, between; A - 6 cols, 1 7/12, between; C - 6 cols, 1 7/12, between.
Equipment & Software: : Hardware — APP/Mac.
Delivery Method: Mail, Newsstand, Carrier
Areas Served: Canada

BARRIERE

BARRIERE STAR JOURNAL

(Thur)
1-4353 Conner Road, Barriere, BC, V0E 1E0, Canada, Canada; gen tel (250) 672-5611; gen fax (250) 672-9900; disp adv e-mail advertising@starjournal.net; class adv e-mail advertising@starjournal.net; ed e-mail news@starjournal.net; web site www.starjournal.net
Circulation: 2,043pd, 37fr; VAC
Established: 1999.
Parent Co.:
Black Press Group Ltd.
Ed. ....Jill Hayward
Adv./Office/Production ....Lisa Quiding
Delivery Method: Carrier
Areas Served: Canada

BOWEN ISLAND

BOWEN ISLAND UNDERCURRENT

(Fri)
102-495 Bowen Trunk Rd., Bowen Island, BC, V0N 1V0, Canada, Canada; gen tel (604) 947-2442; adv tel (604) 947-2442 ; ed tel (604) 947-2442; gen fax (604) 947-0148; disp adv e-mail ads@bowenislandundercurrent.com; class adv e-mail ads@bowenislandundercurrent.com; ed e-mail editor@bowenislandundercurrent.com; web site www.bowenislandundercurrent.com
Circulation: 73fr; VAC
Advertising: Open inch rate $0.40.
Established: 1972.
Parent Co.:
Glacier Media Group
Ed. ....Martha Perkins
Prodn. Mgr. ....Kaana Bjork
Adv. Sales .... Maureen Sawasy
Pub.. Peter Kvarnstrom
Mechanical Specifications: Type page 10 3/8 x 12 1/2; E - 6 cols, 1 11/18, between.
Equipment & Software: : Hardware — APP/Mac; Software — QPS/QuarkXPress 3.32.
Areas Served: Canada

BURNABY

BURNABY NOW

(Wed, Fri)
3430 Brighton Ave., Ste. 201a, Burnaby, BC, V5A 3H4, Canada; gen tel (604) 444-3451; adv tel (604) 444-3030; ed tel (604) 444-3007; gen fax (604) 444-3460; disp adv e-mail chendrix@burnabynow.com; ed e-mail ptracy@royalcityrecord.com; web site www.burnabynow.com
Circulation: 0pd, 43,574fr; CCAB
Advertising: Open inch rate $2.21.
Established: 1983.
Parent Co.:
Glacier Media Group
Pub...Lara Graham
Ed. .... Pat Tracy
Adv.. Cynthia Hendrix
Sports Ed.....................................Dan Olson
Mechanical Specifications: Type page 10 1/4 x 14; E - 6 cols, 1 9/16, 1/6 between; A - 6 cols, 1 9/16, 1/6 between; C - 7 cols, 1 3/8, 1/12 between.
Equipment & Software: : Hardware — APP/Mac.
Areas Served: Canada

THE RECORD

(Wed, Fri)
201a 3430 Brighton Ave., Burnaby, BC, V5A 3H4, Canada, Canada; gen tel (604) 444-3451; adv tel (604)444-3030; ed tel (604) 444-3007; gen fax (604) 444-3460; disp adv e-mail kgilmour@newwestrecord.ca; ed e-mail ptracy@newwestrecord.ca; web site www.royalcityrecord.com
Circulation: 0pd, 16,966fr; CCAB
Advertising: Open inch rate $15.82.
Established: 1981.
Parent Co.:
CanWest MediaWorks Publications, Inc.
Pub ....Lara Graham
Ed. .... Pat Tracy
Circ. Mgr .... Dale Dorsett
Areas Served: Canada

BURNS LAKE

BURNS LAKES DISTRICT NEWS

(Wed)
23 3rd Ave., Burns Lake, BC, V0J 1E0, Canada; gen tel (250) 692-7526; gen fax (250) 692-3685; disp adv e-mail advertising@ldnews.net; class adv e-mail advertising@ldnews.net; ed e-mail newsroom@ldnews.net; web site www.ldnews.net
Circulation: 1,181pd, 117fr; VAC
Advertising: Open inch rate $14.27 (per col. in.).
Established: 1986.
Parent Co.:
Black Press Group Ltd.
Adv. Mgr./Pub..........................Laura Blackwell
Prod. Mgr. .... Annamarie Douglas
front office .... Kim Piper
Editor .... Flavio Nienow
Delivery Method: Mail, Newsstand, Racks
Areas Served: v0j1e0 v0j1e1 v0j1e3 v0j 1e2

CAMPBELL RIVER

THE CAMPBELL RIVER COURIER-ISLANDER

(Wed, Fri)
104 - 250 Dogwood St, Campbell River, BC, V9W 5Z5, Campbell River, Canada; gen tel (250) 287-9227; gen fax (250) 287-8891; disp adv e-mail jacquie.duns@campbellrivermirror.com; class adv e-mail darceyw@campbellrivermirror.com; ed e-mail editor@campbellrivermirror.com; web site www.courierislander.com
Circulation: 0pd, 16,561fr; AAM
Advertising: Open inch rate $1.11 (Wed), $1.26 (Fri).
Established: 1945.
Pub ....David Hamilton
Ed ....Alistair Taylor
Circ. Mgr .... Kevin McKinnon
Mechanical Specifications: Type page 11 3/5 x 21 1/2; E - 10 cols, 1 1/10, 1/12 between; A - 10 cols, 1 1/10, 1/12 between; C - 10 cols, 1 1/10, 1/12 between.
Equipment & Software: : Hardware — APP/Mac; Software — QPS/QuarkXPress 4.1, Multi-Ad 4.1, Adobe/Illustrator 6.0, Adobe/Acrobat 4.0, Adobe/Photoshop 3.0.
Delivery Method: Mail, Newsstand, Carrier, Racks
Areas Served: Campbell River

THE CAMPBELL RIVER MIRROR

(Wed, Fri)
104-250 Dogwood St., Campbell River, BC, V9W 2X9, Canada, Canada; gen tel (250) 287-9227; ed tel (250) 287-9227; gen fax (250) 287-3238; ed e-mail editor@campbellrivermirror.com; web site www.campbellrivermirror.com
Circulation: 16,180pd,; AAM
Advertising: Open inch rate $1.46.
Established: 1971.
Parent Co.:
Black Press Group Ltd.
Ed. ....Alistair Taylor
Pub.......................................David Hamilton
Prod. .... Michelle Hueller
Circ. Mgr............................... Kevin McKinnon
Publisher.................................. Zena Williams
Publisher.............................. Artur Ciastkowski
Delivery Method: Mail, Newsstand, Carrier
Areas Served: Canada

CASTLEGAR

ROSSLAND NEWS

(Thur)
1810 8th Avenue, Unit 2, Castlegar, BC, V1N 2Y2, Canada; gen tel (250) 365 6497; disp adv e-mail sales@rosslandnews.com; ed e-mail newsroom@castlegarnews.com; web site www.rosslandnews.com
Circulation: 7pd, 1,063fr; VAC
Advertising: 7.14 Open Column Inch Rate.
Parent Co.:
Black Press Group Ltd.
Pub... Eric Lawson
Ed .... Jennifer Cowan
Delivery Method: Racks
Areas Served: Rossland

THE CASTLEGAR NEWS

(Thur)
Unit 2, 1810 8th Avenue, Castlegar, BC, V1N 2y2, Canada; gen tel (250) 365-6397; disp adv e-mail sales@castlegarnews.com; class adv e-mail sales@castlegarnews.com; ed e-mail newsroom@castlegarnews.com; web site www.castlegarnews.com
Circulation: 0pd, 6,442fr; VAC
Advertising: Open inch rate $12.09.
Established: 2004.
Parent Co.:
Black Press Group Ltd.
Pub... Eric Lawson
Delivery Method: Newsstand, Carrier, Racks
Areas Served: Castlegar

CHILLIWACK

CHILLIWACK TIMES

(Thur)
45951 Trethewey Ave., Chilliwack, BC, V2P 1K4, Canada; gen tel (604) 792-9117; gen fax (604) 792-9300; disp adv e-mail nbastaja@chilliwacktimes.com; ed e-mail kgoudswaard@chilliwacktimes.com; web site www.chilliwacktimes.com
Circulation: 27,605fr; AAM
Advertising: $2.09.
Established: 1984.Editions: 2—
Digital Platform - Mobile: Apple, Blackberry
Digital Platform - Tablet: Apple iOS, Blackberry Tablet OS
Ed. .... Ken Goudswaard
Pub... Jean Hincks
Mechanical Specifications: Type page 10 1/4 x 14; E - 6 cols, 1 9/16, 1/6 between; A - 6 cols, 1 9/16, 1/6 between; C - 7 cols, 1 5/16, between.
Equipment & Software: : Hardware — 8-APP/Mac G4; Software — Indesign CS2,Adobe/Photoshop 6, Adobe/Illustrator 9.
Delivery Method: Carrier, Racks
Areas Served: Canada

THE CHILLIWACK PROGRESS

(Wed, Fri)
45860 Spadina Ave., Chilliwack, BC, V2P 6H9, Canada, Canada; gen tel (604) 792-1931; gen fax (604) 792-4936; disp adv e-mail advertising@theprogress.com; ed e-mail editor@theprogress.com; web site www.theprogress.com
Circulation: 27,633pd,; AAM
Advertising: Open inch rate $2.12 (Wed), $2.15 (Fri).
Established: 1891.
Parent Co.:
Black Press Group Ltd.

Adv. Mgr. .... Kyle Williams
Circ. Mgr. .... Louise Meger
Ed. .... Greg Knill
Pub. .... Carly Ferguson
Mechanical Specifications: Type page 12 1/2 x 21 1/4; E - 7 cols, 1 11/16, 1/8 between; A - 7 cols, 1 11/16, 1/8 between; C - 7 cols, 1 11/16, 1/8 between.
Equipment & Software: : Hardware — APP/Mac; Presses — G/Urbanite; Software — QPS/QuarkXPress 3.3, Adobe/Illustrator 5.5, Adobe/Photoshop 2.5.
Delivery Method: Carrier
Areas Served: Canada

CLEARWATER

NORTH THOMPSON TIMES
(Thur)
74 Young Rd, Unit 14, Clearwater, BC, V0E 1N2, Canada; gen tel (250) 674-3343; gen fax (250) 674-3410; disp adv e-mail classifieds@clearwatertimes.com; ed e-mail newsroom@clearwatertimes.com; web site www.clearwatertimes.com
Circulation: 751pd, 20fr; CMCA
Advertising: Open inch rate $12.46.
Established: 1964.
Parent Co.:
Black Press Group Ltd.
Digital Platform - Mobile: Apple
Digital Platform - Tablet: Apple iOS
Ed. .... Keith McNeill
Admin Coord./Sales Rep .... Yevonne Cline
Pub .... Lorie Williston
Mechanical Specifications: Type page10x13.75"; E - 7 cols, 1 5/16, 1/8 between; A - 7 cols, 1 5/16, 1/8 between; C - 7cols, 1 5/16, 1/8 between.
Equipment & Software: : Hardware — APP/Mac, Mk; Software — Multi-Ad, Microsoft/Word. Indd,
Delivery Method: Mail
Areas Served: Canada

COURTENAY

COMOX VALLEY ECHO
(Fri)
407-e Fifth Street, Courtenay, BC, V9N 1J7, Canada, Canada; gen tel (250) 334-4722; gen fax (250) 334-3172; disp adv e-mail keith.currie@comoxvalleyecho.com; class adv e-mail debra.fowler@comoxvalleyecho.com; ed e-mail echo@comoxvalleyecho.com; web site www.comoxvalleyecho.com
Circulation: 50pd, 23,000fr; CCAB
Advertising: Open inch rate $19.10.
Established: 1994.
Digital Platform - Mobile: Apple, Android, Windows
Digital Platform - Tablet: Apple iOS, Android, Windows 7, Blackberry Tablet OS, Kindle
Publisher .... Keith Currie
Mng. Ed .... Debra Martin
Prodn. Mgr. .... Ryan Getz
Mechanical Specifications: Type page 10.5 x 21.5; E - 10 cols, 1 1/12, between; A - 10 cols, 1 1/12, between; C - 8 cols, 1 7/23, between.
Equipment & Software: : Hardware — APP/Mac; Presses — G/Community; Software — QPS/QuarkXPress 3.32, Adobe/Photoshop 6.0. Adobe creative Suite
Delivery Method: Mail, Newsstand, Carrier, Racks
Areas Served: Canada

COMOX VALLEY RECORD
(Tues, Thur)
765 Mcphee Ave., Courtenay, BC, V9N 2Z7, Canada; gen tel (250) 338-5811; gen fax (250) 338-5568; disp adv e-mail sales@comovalleyrecord.com; ed e-mail editor@comoxvalleyrecord.com; web site www.comoxvalleyrecord.com
Circulation: 21,741pd,; AAM
Advertising: Open inch rate $19.04.
Established: 1986.
Parent Co.:
Black Press Group Ltd.Liz Royer
Circ. Mgr. .... Terry Marshall
Ed. .... Terry Farrell
Prodn. Mgr. .... Susan Granberg
Pub .... Chrissie Bowker
Mechanical Specifications: Type page 10 1/4 x 14 1/2; E - 6 cols, 1 7/12, 1/6 between; A - 6 cols, 1 7/12, 1/6 between; C - 7 cols, 1 7/12, 1/6 between.
Equipment & Software: : Hardware — APP/Mac; Presses — G; Software — Multi-Ad/CAMS 3.6.3.
Delivery Method: Carrier
Areas Served: Canada

NORTH ISLAND MIDWEEK
(Wed)
765 Mcphee Ave, Courtenay, BC, V9N 2Z7, Canada, Canada; gen tel (250) 287-9227; gen fax (250) 287-3238; disp adv e-mail sueb@blackpress.ca; ed e-mail editor@comoxvalleyrecord.com; web site www.northislandmidweek.com
Circulation: 40pd, 37,030fr; CMCA
Advertising: Open inch rate $1.67.
Established: 1994.
Parent Co.:
Black Press Group Ltd.
Pub .... Chrissie Bowker
Ed .... Terry Farrell
Prod. Mgr. .... Susan Granberg
Circ Mgr. .... Terry Marshall
Delivery Method: Mail, Newsstand, Carrier
Areas Served: Canada

CRANBROOK

CRANBROOK DAILY TOWNSMAN
(Wed, Thur, Fri)
822 Cranbrook St. N., Cranbrook, BC, V1C 3R9, Canada; gen tel (250) 426-5201; adv tel (250) 426-5201; ed tel (250) 426-5201; gen fax (250) 426-5003; adv fax (250) 426-5003; ed fax (250) 426-5003; disp adv e-mail zena.williams@blackpress.ca; class adv e-mail zena.williams@blackpress.ca; ed e-mail barry.coulter@cranbrooktownsman.com; web site www.cranbrooktownsman.com
Circulation: 3,500pd,; CMCA
Advertising: Open inch rate $16.20/inch Tu/W/F.
Established: 1956.
Parent Co.:
Black Press Group Ltd.
Pub .... Zena Williams
Ed. .... Barry Coulter
Adv. Sales Mgr. .... Nicole Koran
Office Mgr. .... Jennifer Leiman
Mechanical Specifications: Type page 10.25 x 14.00
Delivery Method: Mail, Newsstand, Carrier, Racks
Areas Served: Cranbrook, Kimberley and surrounding areas

KOOTENAY ADVERTISER
(Thur)
1510-2nd St. N.,, Cranbrook, BC, V1C 3L2, Canada; gen tel (250) 489-3455; gen fax (250) 489-3743; disp adv e-mail advertising@kootenayadvertiser.com; ed e-mail editor@kootenayadvertiser.com; web site www.kootenayadvertiser.com
Circulation: 19,615fr; Sworn/Estimate/Non-Audited
Advertising: Open inch rate $1.78.
Established: 1972.
Parent Co.:
Black Press Group Ltd.
Prod. Mgr. .... Bridget Fix
Ed. .... Brian Coombs
Pub .... Zena Williams
Mechanical Specifications: Type page 10 1/4 x 14 1/2; E - 6 cols, 1 9/16, 1/6 between; A - 6 cols, 1 9/16, 1/6 between; C - 6 cols, 1 9/16, 1/6 between.
Equipment & Software: : Hardware — APP/Macs; Presses — WPC; Software — QPS/QuarkXPress.
Areas Served: Cranbrook, Kimberley, Invermere, Creston, Fernie

CRESTON

CRESTON VALLEY ADVANCE
(Thur)
1018 Canyon St., Creston, BC, V0B 1G0, Canada, Canada; gen tel (250) 428-2266; gen fax (250) 483-1909; disp adv e-mail advertising@crestonvalleyadvance.ca; ed e-mail editor@crestonvalleyadvance.ca; web site www.crestonvalleyadvance.ca
Circulation: 2pd, 9fr; VAC
Advertising: Open inch rate $9.80.
Established: 1948.
Parent Co.:
Torstar
Pub .... Lorne Eckersley
Circ. Mgr. .... Diane Audette
Ed. .... Brian Lorns
Sales Coord. .... Anita Horton
Ed. .... Brian Lawrence
Prod. Department .... Jacky Smith
Mechanical Specifications: Type page 10 1/4 x 16; E - 5 cols, 1 15/16, 1/8 between; A - 5 cols, 1 15/16, 1/8 between; C - 5 cols, 1 15/16, 1/8 between.
Areas Served: Canada

DAWSON CREEK

THE MIRROR
(Fri)
901-100th Ave., Dawson Creek, BC, V1G 1W2, Canada, Canada; gen tel (250) 782-4888; gen fax (250) 782-6300; disp adv e-mail jkmet@dcdn.ca; ed e-mail editor@dcdn.ca; web site http://www.dawsoncreekmirror.ca/
Circulation: 0pd, 7,457fr; Sworn/Estimate/Non-Audited
Advertising: Open inch rate $0.89.
Established: 1980.Editions: 52—
Reg. Mgr. .... William Julian
Assoc. Pub. .... Nicole Palfy
Ed .... Rob Brown
Circ Mgr .... Margot Owens
Mechanical Specifications: Type page 10 3/20 x 11 1/2; E - 6 cols, 1 1/2, 1/6 between; A - 6 cols, 1 1/2, 1/6 between; C - 7 cols, 1 3/10, between.
Equipment & Software: : Hardware — IBM; Software — WordPerfect 6.1, Archetype/Corel Draw.
Areas Served: Canada
Note: none

THE NORTHERN HORIZON
(Fri)
901 - 100th Ave, Dawson Creek, BC, V1G 1W2, Canada; gen tel (250) 782-4888; gen fax (250) 782-6300; disp adv e-mail jkmet@dcdn.ca; ed e-mail editor@dcdn.ca; web site http://www.northernhorizon.ca/
Parent Co.:
Glacier Media Group
Pub .... William Julian
Assoc. Pub. .... Nicole Palfy
Ed .... Rob Brown
Circ. Mgr .... Margot Owens

DELTA

DELTA OPTIMIST
(Wed, Fri)
5008-47a Avenue, Delta, BC, V4K 1T8, Canada; gen tel (604) 946-4451; gen fax (604) 946-5680; disp adv e-mail dhamilton@delta-optimist.com; ed e-mail editor@delta-optimist.com; web site www.delta-optimist.com
Circulation: 0pd, 17,050fr; CCAB
Advertising: Open inch rate $1.27.
Established: 1922.
Parent Co.:
Glacier Media Group
Gen Mgr .... Dave Hamilton
Ed. .... Ted Murphy
Pub .... Alvin Brouwer
Mechanical Specifications: Type page 10 1/4 x 14; E - 6 cols, 1 9/16, 1/6 between; A - 6 cols, 1 9/16, 1/6 between; C - 7 cols, 1 1/3, 1/12 between.
Equipment & Software: : Hardware — APP/Mac; Software — QPS/QuarkXPress.
Delivery Method: Carrier
Areas Served: Canada

DUNCAN

COWICHAN VALLEY CITIZEN
(Wed, Fri)
251 Jubilee Street, Duncan, BC, V9L 1W8, Canada, Canada; gen tel (250) 748-2666; gen fax (250) 748-1552; disp adv e-mail sskolos@cowichanvalleycitizen.com; class adv e-mail sskolos@cowichanvalleycitizen.com; ed e-mail news@cowichanvalleycitizen.com; web site www.cowichanvalleycitizen.com
Circulation: 21,135fr; CAC
Advertising: Open inch rate $1.24.
Established: 1986.
Parent Co.:
Torstar
Pub./Adv. Mgr. .... Shirley Skolos
Mng. Ed. .... Andrea Rondeau
Prod. Mgr. .... Alice Brownbridge
Circ. Mgr. .... Audette Lepage
Mechanical Specifications: Type page 10 1/4 x 13; A - 9 cols, 1 1/16, between; C - 7 cols, 1 5/8, between.
Equipment & Software: : Hardware — APP/Power Mac; Software — QPS/QuarkXPress 3.32, Adobe/Photoshop 4.0.
Areas Served: Canada

THE COWICHAN NEWS LEADER
(Wed, Fri)
251 Jubilee St, Duncan, BC, V9L 1W8, Canada, Canada; gen tel (250) 748-2666; gen fax (250) 746-8529; ed e-mail editor@cowichannewsleader.com; web site www.cowichannewsleader.com
Circulation: 0pd, 22,430fr; CMCA
Advertising: Open inch rate $1.64.
Established: 1905.
Circ. Mgr. .... Lara Stuart
Ed. .... John McKinley
Pub .... Shirley Skolos
Mechanical Specifications: Type page 12 x 21 1/2; E - 7 cols, 1 1/4, between; A - 7 cols, 1 1/4, between; C - 8 cols, 1 1/4, between.
Equipment & Software: : Hardware — APP/Mac; Software — Multi-Ad/Creator, QPS/QuarkXPress.
Delivery Method: Mail, Newsstand, Carrier, Racks
Areas Served: Canada

THE LAKE COWICHAN GAZETTE
(Wed)
251 Jubilee Street, Duncan, BC, V9L 1W8, Canada; gen tel (250) 748-2666; adv tel (250) 748-2666; disp adv e-mail warren.goulding@blackpress.ca; ed e-mail editor@lakecowichangazette.com; web site www.lakecowichangazette.com
Circulation: 430pd, 26fr; VAC
Advertising: Open inch rate $7.98 per col. inch.
Established: 1995.
Parent Co.:
Black Press Group Ltd.
Pub .... Waren Goulding
Classifieds .... Classified Ads
Ed .... Drew McLachlan
Delivery Method: Mail
Areas Served: Lake Cowichan

FERNIE

THE FREE PRESS
(Thur)
342 2nd Ave., Fernie, BC, V0B 1M0, Canada; gen tel (250) 423-4666; disp adv e-mail advertising@thefreepress.ca; ed e-mail editor@thefreepress.ca; web site www.thefreepress.ca
Circulation: 234pd, 5,643fr; VAC
Established: 1898.
Parent Co.:

Black Press Group Ltd.
Pub .... Andrea Horton
Ed ....Katie Smith
Adv ....Jennifer Cronin
Prod Mgr.................................Bonny McLardy
Mechanical Specifications: Type page 11 1/2 x 21 1/2; E - 10 cols, 1 1/6, between.
Equipment & Software: : Hardware — APP/Macs; Software — Adobe InDesign CS6, Multi-Ad.
Delivery Method: Carrier, Racks
Areas Served: VOB 1M0
VOB 1M2
VOB 1H0
VOB 2G0
VOB 1T0
VOB 1T4

FORT NELSON

THE FORT NELSON NEWS

(Wed)
4448 50th Ave., Ste. 3, P.o. Box 600, Fort Nelson, BC, V0C 1R0, Northern Rockies Regional District, Canada; gen tel (250) 774-2357; gen fax (250) 774-3612; disp adv e-mail ads@fnnews.ca; class adv e-mail ads@fnnews.ca; ed e-mail editorial@fortnelsonnews.ca; web site www.fortnelsonnews.ca
Circulation: 439pd, 665fr; VAC
Advertising: Open inch rate $.93.
Established: 1959.
Digital Platform - Mobile: Apple
Digital Platform - Tablet: Apple iOS
Ed & Pub .... Judith A. Kenyon
Mng. Ed...............................Alexandra Kenyon
reporter and photographer ....Kathy Smith
Mgr .... Abigail Neville
Mechanical Specifications: Type page 11 1/2 x 21 3/8; E - 10 cols, 1 1/16, between; A - 10 cols, between; C - 10 cols, between.
Equipment & Software: : Hardware — Macs; Presses — Glacier press in Dawson Creek; Software — In Design
Delivery Method: Mail, Newsstand, Carrier, Racks
Areas Served: Northern Rockies Regional District

FORT SAINT JOHN

NORTH PEACE EXPRESS

(Sun)
9916 98th St., Fort Saint John, BC, V1J 3T8, Canada; gen tel (250) 785-5631; gen fax (250) 785-3522; disp adv e-mail wj@ahnfsj.ca; ed e-mail editor@ahnfsj.ca
Circulation: 10,200fr; Sworn/Estimate/Non-Audited
Advertising: Open inch rate $1.76.
Established: 1942.
Pub .... William Julian
Circ. Mgr.................................. Debbie Oberlin
Mechanical Specifications: Type page 10 1/4 x 13; E - 5 cols, 2 1/12, 1/3 between; A - 5 cols, 2 1/12, 1/3 between; C - 5 cols, 2 1/12, 1/3 between.
Equipment & Software: : Hardware — APP/Mac; Software — QPS/QuarkXPress 3.2.

THE NORTHERNER

(Fri)
9916 98th St., Fort Saint John, BC, V1J 3T8, Canada; gen tel (250) 785-5631; gen fax (250) 785-3522; disp adv e-mail mhill@ahnfsj.ca; class adv e-mail rwallace@ahnfsj.ca; ed e-mail editor@ahnfsj.ca; web site www.thenortherner.ca
Circulation: 0pd, 8,657fr; Sworn/Estimate/Non-Audited
Advertising: Open inch rate $0.83.
Established: 1988.
Sales... Melody Hill
Pub... William Julian
Sales.. Ryan Wallace
Circ. .... Debbie Oberlin
Mechanical Specifications: Type page 10 1/4 x 12 3/4; E - 5 cols, 1 15/16, 3/16 between; A - 5 cols, 1 15/16, 3/16 between; C - 5 cols, 1 15/16, 3/16 between.
Equipment & Software: : Hardware — APP/Mac; Software — QPS/QuarkXPress 3.1.
Areas Served: V1J 2B2

FORT ST. JAMES

CALEDONIA COURIER

(Wed)
Box 1298, Fort St. James, BC, V0J 3A0, Canada; gen tel (250) 567-9258; gen fax (250) 567-2070; disp adv e-mail advertising@ominecaexpress.com; web site www.caledoniacourier.com
Circulation: 562pd, 31fr; VAC
Advertising: Open inch rate $0.81.
Established: 1972.
Parent Co.:
Black Press Group Ltd.
Pub./Sales Mgr............................. Pam Berger
Ed. .... Ruth Lloyd
Prod. .... Julia Beal
Prod. .... Wendy Haslam
Circ. .... Mariella Drogomatz
Mechanical Specifications: Type page 10 5/16 x 14 1/2; E - 6 cols, 1 9/16, 3/16 between; A - 6 cols, 1 9/16, 3/16 between; C - 6 cols, 1 9/16, 3/16 between.

GABRIOLA ISLAND

GABRIOLA SOUNDER

(Tues)
510 North Rd, Unit 1, Gabriola Island, BC, V0R 1X0, Canada; gen tel (250) 247-9337; adv tel (250) 247-9337; ed tel (250) 247-9337; gen fax (250) 247-8147; disp adv e-mail sarah@soundernew.com; class adv e-mail derek@soundernews.com; ed e-mail derek@soundernews.com; web site www.soundernews.com
Circulation: 50pd, 2,750fr; Sworn/Estimate/Non-Audited
Advertising: Open inch rate $0.65.
Established: 1989.
Parent Co.:
Gabriola Sounder Media Inc.
Pub.. Sarah Holmes
Ed./Sales/Prod. Mgr................ Derek Kilbourn
Delivery Method: Mail, Newsstand, Racks
Areas Served: Gabriola, and Mudge Island

GOLDEN

GOLDEN STAR

(Wed)
413a N. Ninth Ave., Golden, BC, V0H 1H0, Canada; gen tel (250) 344-5251; gen fax (250) 344-7344; disp adv e-mail advertising@thegoldenstar.net; class adv e-mail advertising@thegoldenstar.net; ed e-mail editor@thegoldenstar.net; web site www.thegoldenstar.net
Circulation: 502pd, 32fr; VAC
Advertising: Open inch rate $0.74.
Established: 1891.
Parent Co.:
Black Press Group Ltd.
Classified Mgr. .... Sue Hein
Pub.......................................Michele Lapointe
Ed. .... Jessica Schwitek
Mechanical Specifications: Type page 10 1/3 x 15 1/2; E - 6 cols, 1 1/2, 1/6 between; A - 6 cols, 1 1/2, 1/6 between; C - 6 cols, 1 1/2, 1/6 between.
Equipment & Software: : Hardware — APP/Mac; Presses — WPC; Software — Adobe/Photoshop, CreativeSuite
Areas Served: Golden

GRAND FORKS

THE GRAND FORKS GAZETTE

(Wed)
7255 Riverside Dr., Grand Forks, BC, V0H 1H0, Canada, Canada; gen tel (250) 442-2191; gen fax (250) 442-3336; disp adv e-mail advertising@grandforksgazette.ca; ed e-mail editor@grandforkscagazette.ca; web site grandforksgazette.ca
Circulation: 2,399pd, 12fr; VAC
Advertising: Open inch rate $8.20.
Established: 1897.
Parent Co.:
Black Press Group Ltd.
Prodn. Mgr. .... Della Mallette
Advertising .... Dyan Stoochnoff
Reporter ....Kathleen Saylors
Graphic Artist.......................... Dustin LaCroix
Circulation...........................Darlainea Redlack
Mechanical Specifications: Type page 10 x 15 1/2.
Delivery Method: Mail, Newsstand, Carrier
Areas Served: Canada

GREENWOOD

THE BOUNDARY CREEK TIMES

(Thur)
318 Copper St., Greenwood, BC, V0H 1J0, Canada, Canada; gen tel (250) 445-2233; disp adv e-mail dyan.stoochnoff@boundarycreektimes.com; web site boundarycreektimes.ca
Circulation: 471pd, 1fr; CMCA
Advertising: Open inch rate $.7.50 Cl.
Parent Co.:
Black Press Group Ltd.
Associate Publisher.............. Dyan Stoochnoff
Circulation...........................Darlainea Redlack
Reporter ....Kathleen Saylors
Mechanical Specifications: Type page 10 3/16 x 14 1/8; E - 5 cols, 1 7/16, 3/16 between; A - 5 cols, 1 7/16, 3/16 between; C - 5 cols, 1 7/16, 3/16 between.
Equipment & Software: : Hardware — IBM/486, Compaq; Software — Microsoft/Word, Microsoft/Works, Adobe/Pagemaker.
Delivery Method: Mail, Newsstand
Areas Served: Canada

HOPE

HOPE STANDARD

(Thur)
540 Wallace St., Hope, BC, V0X 1L0, Canada, Canada; gen tel (604) 869-2421; gen fax (604) 869-7351; disp adv e-mail sales@hopestandard.com; class adv e-mail classifieds@hopestandard.com; web site www.hopestandard.com
Circulation: 346pd, 0fr; VAC
Advertising: Open inch rate $1.11.
Established: 1959.
Parent Co.:
Torstar
Adv. Mgr................................. Patti Desjardins
Circ. Mgr............................... Janice McDonald
Pub... Carly Ferguson
Ed. ....X.Y. Zeng
Mechanical Specifications: Type page 10 3/8 x 14; E - 6 cols, 1 5/8, 1/8 between; A - 6 cols, 1 5/8, 1/8 between; C - 6 cols, 1 5/8, 1/8 between.
Areas Served: Canada

HOUSTON

HOUSTON TODAY

(Wed)
3232 Hwy 16 W., Houston, BC, V0J 1Z1, Canada, Canada; gen tel (250) 845-2890; gen fax (250) 847-2995; disp adv e-mail advertising@houston-today.com; web site www.houston-today.com
Circulation: 983pd, 305fr; VAC
Advertising: Open inch rate $1.02.
Parent Co.:
Torstar
Ed. .... Mary Ann Ruiter
Mng. Ed................................... Todd Hamilton
Reporter .... Jackie Lieuwen
Areas Served: Canada

INVERMERE

INVERMERE VALLEY ECHO

(Wed)
1008-8th Avenue, #8, Invermere, BC, V0A 1K0, n/a, Canada; gen tel (250) 341-6299; disp adv e-mail advertising@invermerevalleyecho.com; ed e-mail editor@invermerevalleyecho.com; web site www.invermerevalleyecho.com
Circulation: 488fr; VAC
Advertising: Open inch rate $7.
Established: 1956.
Parent Co.:
Torstar
Pub.. Dean Midyette
Ed. .... Nicole Trigg
Adv. Sales .... Amanda Nason
Delivery Method: Mail, Newsstand
Areas Served: n/a

THE COLUMBIA VALLEY PIONEER

(Fri)
#8, 1008-8th Avenue, Invermere, BC, V0A 1K0, Canada; gen tel (250) 341-6299; gen fax (855) 377-0312; disp adv e-mail ads@columbiavalleypioneer.com; class adv e-mail info@columbiavalleypioneer.com; ed e-mail news@columbiavalleypioneer.com; web site www.columbiavalleypioneer.com
Circulation: 499pd, 6,238fr; VAC
Established: 2004.
Parent Co.:
Misko Publishing
Reporter .... Steve Hubrecht
Advertising Sales...................... Dean Midyette
Graphic design
Emily Rawbon
Ed.
Nicole Trigg
Admin..................................... Amanda Murray
Reporter .... Eric Elliott
Delivery Method: Newsstand, Racks
Areas Served: Spillimacheen, Edgewater, Radium Hot Springs, Invermere, Panorama, Windermere, Fairmont Hot Springs, Canal Flats

KAMLOOPS

KAMLOOPS THIS WEEK

(Tues, Thur, Fri)
1365b Dalhousie Dr., Kamloops, BC, V2C 5P6, Canada; gen tel (250) 374-7467; ed tel (250) 374-7467; gen fax (250) 374-1033; disp adv e-mail sales@kamloopsthisweek.com; ed e-mail editor@kamloopsthisweek.com; web site www.kamloopsthisweek.com
Circulation: 0pd, 30,145fr; CCAB
Advertising: Open inch rate $1.62.
Established: 1988.
Parent Co.:
Thompson River Publications
Digital Platform - Mobile: BlackberryKelly Hall
Pub & Ed .... Chris Foulds
Delivery Method: Mail, Newsstand, Carrier, Racks
Areas Served: Canada

KELOWNA

KELOWNA CAPITAL NEWS

(Tues, Thur, Fri)
2495 Enterprise Way, Kelowna, BC, V1X 7K2, Canada, Canada; gen tel (250) 763-3212; adv tel (250) 763-3212; ed tel (250) 763-3212; gen fax (250) 862-5275; adv fax (250) 862-5275; ed fax (250) 862-5275; disp adv e-mail adsales@kelownacapnews.com; ed e-mail edit@kelownacapnews.com; web site www.kelownacapnews.com
Circulation: 43,046pd, 0fr; AAM
Advertising: Open inch rate $28.00.
Established: 1930.
Parent Co.:
Torstar
Pub. .... Karen Hill
Adv. Mgr.. Nigel Lark

Sales Mgr................................ Gary Jhonston
Circ. Mgr.................................Glenn Beaudry
Prodn. Mgr. ....Tessa Ringness
Mng. Ed.......................................Kevin Parnell
Mechanical Specifications: Type page 10 x 15; E - 6 cols, 1 31/60, 1/6 between; A - 6 cols, 1 31/60, 1/6 between; C - 6 cols, 1 31/60, 1/6 between.
Equipment & Software: : Hardware — APP/Mac; Presses — 8-G/Community; Software — QPS/QuarkXPress 4.11.
Delivery Method: Mail, Newsstand, Carrier, Racks
Areas Served: Canada

LAKE COUNTRY CALENDAR
(Wed)
2495 Enterprise Way, Kelowna, BC, V1X 7K2, Lake Country, Canada; gen tel (250) 763-3212; gen fax (250) 386-2624; disp adv e-mail ads4web@blackpress.ca; ed e-mail newsroom@lakecountrynews.net; web site www.lakecountrycalendar.net
Circulation: 306pd, 3,779fr; Sworn/Estimate/Non-Audited
Established: 2001.
Parent Co.:
Torstar
Ed. .... Barry Gerding
Trafficking Coordinator..........Jonathan Lawson
Online Editor.............................Kolby Solinsky
Director of Sales and Marketing .. Mark Walker
Areas Served: Lake Country

KEREMEOS

KEREMEOS REVIEW
(Thur)
605 7th Avenue, Keremeos, BC, V0X 1N0, Canada; gen tel (250) 499-2653; gen fax (250) 499-2645; disp adv e-mail publisher@keremeosreview.com; class adv e-mail publisher@keremeosreview.com; web site www.keremeosreview.com
Circulation: 889pd, 51fr; VAC
Advertising: Open inch rate $.73.
Established: 1998.
Parent Co.:
Torstar
Pub.. Don Kendall
Ed... Tara Bowie
Assoc. Pub..............................Andrea DeMeer
Adv. Rep....................................... Sandi Nolan
Areas Served: Keremeos

KIMBERLEY

THE KIMBERLEY DAILY BULLETIN
(Wed, Thur, Fri)
335 Spokane St., Kimberley, BC, V1A 1Y9, Canada; gen tel (250) 427-5333; adv tel (250) 427-5333; ed tel (250) 427-5333; gen fax (250) 427-5336; adv fax (250) 427-5336; ed fax (250) 427-5336; ed e-mail carolyn.grant@kimberleybulletin.com; web site www.kimberleybulletin.com
Circulation: 3,350pd, 3,350fr; CMCA
Advertising: Open inch rate $16.20/inch Tu/W/F.
Established: 1936.
Parent Co.:
Black Press Group Ltd.
Pub... Zena Williams
Ed. ....Carolyn Grant
Nicole Koran
Mechanical Specifications: Type page 10.25 x 14.00; E - 6 cols, 2 1/16, 1/8 between; A - 6 cols, 2 1/16, 1/8 between; C - 6 cols, 2 1/16, 1/8 between.
Delivery Method: Mail, Newsstand, Carrier
Areas Served: Cranbrook, Kimberley and surrounding areas

KITIMAT

NORTHERN SENTINEL - KITIMAT
(Wed)
626 Enterprise Ave., Kitimat, BC, V8C 2E4, Canada, Canada; gen tel (250) 632-6144; gen fax (250) 639-9373; disp adv e-mail advertising@northernsentinel.com; web site www.northernsentinel.com
Circulation: 439pd, 248fr; VAC
Advertising: Open inch rate $1.01.
Established: 1954.
Parent Co.:
Black Press Group Ltd.
Digital Platform - Mobile: Apple
Digital Platform - Tablet: Apple iOS
Publisher................................Louisa Genzale
Sarah Campbell
Editor/Reporter...............................Devyn Ens
Circulation.................................Johnsen Misty
Mechanical Specifications: Type page 10 1/4 x 14 1/2; E - 7 cols, 1 7/12, between; A - 7 cols, 1 7/12, between; C - 7 cols, 1 7/12, between.
Equipment & Software: ; Presses — WPC/Web Leader.
Delivery Method: Mail, Newsstand, Carrier, Racks
Areas Served: Canada

LADNER

SOUTH DELTA LEADER
(Fri) (Delta Leader, 30,000 - all of Delta, Monthly - last Friday of each monthly)
5008 47a Ave, Ladner, BC, V4K 1T8; gen tel (604) 948-3640 ; gen fax (604) 943-8619; disp adv e-mail dhamilton@delta-optimist.com; class adv e-mail classifieds@van.net; ed e-mail tmurphy@delta-optimist.com; web site www.southdeltaleader.com
Circulation: 0pd, 14,313fr; CCAB
Advertising: Open inch rate $1.26.
Established: 1999.
Digital Platform - Mobile: Apple, Blackberry
Digital Platform - Tablet: Apple iOS, Blackberry Tablet OS
Pub..Alvin Brouwer
Ed .... Ted Murphy
Gen Mgr/Adv. Sales................. Dave Hamilton
Delivery Method: Carrier, Racks
Areas Served: Canada

LADYSMITH

THE LADYSMITH CHRONICLE
(Tues)
940 Oyster Bay Drive, Ladysmith, BC, V9G 1A3, Canada, Canada; gen tel (250) 245-2277; adv tel (250) 245-2277; ed tel (250) 245-2277; gen fax (250) 245-2230; disp adv e-mail publisher@ladysmithchronicle.com; ed e-mail editor@ladysmithchronicle.com; web site www.ladysmithchronicle.com
Circulation: 1,348pd, 3,678fr; VAC
Advertising: Open inch rate $10.92.
Established: 1908.
Parent Co.:
Black Press Group Ltd.
Prodn. Mgr. .... Douglas Kent
Pub ....Teresa McKinley
Ed .... Craig Spence
Mechanical Specifications: Type page 10 1/4 x 14 1/2; E - 6 cols, 1 5/8, 3/16 between; A - 6 cols, 1 5/8, 3/16 between; C - 6 cols, 1 5/8, 3/16 between.
Equipment & Software: : Hardware — APP/Mac.
Delivery Method: Mail, Newsstand, Carrier, Racks
Areas Served: Canada

LANGLEY

LANGLEY ADVANCE
(Tues, Thur)
6375 202 St., Suite 112, Langley, BC, V2Y 1N1, Canada, Canada; gen tel (604) 534-8641; gen fax (604) 534-3383; disp adv e-mail peggy.obrien@langleyadvance.com; ed e-mail rhooper@langleyadvance.com; web site www.langleyadvance.com
Circulation: 0pd, 27,662fr; AAM
Advertising: Open inch rate $2.14.
Established: 1931.
Parent Co.:
Black Press Group Ltd.
Glacier Media Group
Pub .... Lisa Farquharson
Sales Mgr. ....Peggy O'Brien
Ed ....Roxanne Hooper
Mechanical Specifications: Type page 11 x 14; E - 6 cols, 1 9/16, between; A - 6 cols, 1 9/16, between; C - 7 cols, 1 3/8, between.
Equipment & Software: : Hardware — APP/Mac G4; Software — QPS/QuarkXPress 4.1, Adobe/Photoshop 5.02, Adobe/Illustrator 8.0.
Delivery Method: Carrier
Areas Served: Canada

LANGLEY TIMES
(Tues, Thur)
20258 Fraser Hwy., Langley, BC, V3A 4E6, Canada; gen tel (604) 533-4157; gen fax (604) 533-4623; disp adv e-mail admanager@langleytimes.com; ed e-mail newsroom@langleytimes.com; web site www.langleytimes.com
Circulation: 5,525pd, 45,363fr; CAC
Advertising: Open inch rate $2.02.
Established: 1982.
Parent Co.:
Black Press Group Ltd.
Sales Mgr ....Kelly Myers
Pub .... Lisa Farquharson
Ed ....Brenda Anderson
Delivery Method: Carrier
Areas Served: Canada

MAPLE RIDGE & PITT MEADOW TIMES
(Thur)
#112-6375 202nd St., Langley, BC, V2Y 1N1, Canada; gen tel (604) 463-2281; ed e-mail editorial@mrtimes.com; web site www.mrtimes.com
Circulation: 30,000fr; Sworn/Estimate/Non-Audited
Established: 1985.
Parent Co.:
Black Press Group Ltd.
Ed ....Roxanne Hooper
Mechanical Specifications: Type page 10 x 14; E - 6 cols, 1 2/3, 1/8 between; A - 6 cols, 1 2/3, 1/8 between; C - 7 cols, 1 2/5, 1/16 between.
Equipment & Software: : Hardware — 4-APP/iMac, 2-APP/Mac G4 (2000); Software — Adobe/Photoshop 5.5, QPS/QuarkXPress 4.0, Macromedia/Freehand 8.0, Adobe/Illustrator 5.5, Adobe/PageMaker 6.0, Microsoft/Word 2000, Microsoft/Excel 98, APP/Appleworks 5.
Delivery Method: Carrier
Areas Served: V4R, V2X, V2Y, V2W

LILLOOET

BRIDGE RIVER LILLOOET NEWS
(Wed)
979 Main St., Lillooet, BC, V0K 1V0, Canada, Canada; gen tel (250) 256-4219; adv tel (778) 773-4797; gen fax (250) 256-4210; adv fax (877) 765-6483; disp adv e-mail sales@lillooetnews.net; ed e-mail editor@lillooetnews.net; web site www.lillooetnews.net
Circulation: 1,709pd, 16fr; VAC
Advertising: Open inch rate $.76.
Established: 1934.
Parent Co.:
Glacier Media Group
Ed. ....Wendy Fraser
Publisher.............................Bruce MacLennan
Sales Associate............................ Eliza Payne
Mechanical Specifications: Type page 10 1/3 x 14; E - 6 cols, 1 3/5, between; A - 6 cols, 1 3/5, between.
Areas Served: Canada

MACKENZIE

THE TIMES
(Wed)
125-403 Mackenzie Blvd., Mackenzie, BC, V0J 2C0, Canada; gen tel (250) 997-6675; adv tel (250) 997-6675; ed tel (250) 997-6675; gen fax (250) 997-4747; adv fax (250) 997-4747; ed fax (250) 997-4747; disp adv e-mail ads@mackenzietimes.com; ed e-mail news@mackenzietimes.com; web site www.sterlingnews.com/Mackenzie
Circulation: 1,000pd,; Sworn/Estimate/Non-Audited
Advertising: Open inch rate $.86.
Established: 1999.
Pub/Ed... Jackie Benton
Adv Mgr ....Andrea Massicotte
Delivery Method: Mail, Newsstand, Carrier
Areas Served: VOJ 2CO

MAPLE RIDGE

THE MAPLE RIDGE NEWS
(Wed, Fri)
22611 Dewdney Trunk Road, Maple Ridge, BC, V2X 3K1, Canada; gen tel (604) 467-1122; adv tel (604) 476-2728; gen fax (604) 463-4741; disp adv e-mail ads@mapleridgenews.com; ed e-mail editor@mapleridgenews.com; web site www.mapleridgenews.com
Circulation: 30,365fr; AAM
Advertising: Open inch rate $1.77.
Established: 1978.
Parent Co.:
Black Press Group Ltd.
Ed. .... Michael Hall
Pub ....Lisa Prophet
Circ Mgr...Brian Yip
Mechanical Specifications: Type page 10 3/8 x 12 1/2; E - 6 cols, 1 5/8, 1/6 between; A - 6 cols, 1 5/8, 1/6 between; C - 6 cols, 1 5/8, 1/6 between.
Equipment & Software: : Hardware — APP/Mac; Software — QPS/QuarkXPress, Adobe/Photoshop.
Delivery Method: Carrier
Areas Served: Canada

MERRITT

MERRITT HERALD
(Thur)
2090 Granite Ave., Merritt, BC, V1K 1B8, Canada; gen tel (250) 378-4241; gen fax (250) 378-6818; disp adv e-mail sales2@merrittherald.com; class adv e-mail classifieds@merrittherald.com; ed e-mail newsroom@merrittherald.com; web site www.merrittherald.com
Circulation: 1,092pd, 5,589fr; VAC
Advertising: Open inch rate $.89.
Established: 1999.
Parent Co.:
Aberdeen Publishing
Merrit Newspapers
Pub... Theresa Arnold
Ed .... Cole Wagner
Office Mgr............................Kenneth Couture
Mechanical Specifications: Type page 10 5/16 x 14 1/2; E - 6 cols, 1 7/12, 1/6 between; A - 6 cols, 1 7/12, 1/6 between; C - 6 cols, 1 7/12, 1/6 between.
Areas Served: Merritt

MISSION

MISSION CITY RECORD
(Fri)
33047 1st Ave., Mission, BC, V2V 1G2, Mission - Abbotsford, Canada; gen tel (604) 826-6221; adv tel (800) 363-2232; gen fax (604) 826-8266; disp adv e-mail karen.murtagh@missioncityrecord.com; class adv e-mail adcontrol@missioncityrecord.com; ed e-mail kevin.mills@missioncityrecord.com; web site www.missioncityrecord.com
Circulation: 43pd, 11,038fr; AAM
Advertising: Open inch rate $1.61.
Established: 1908.
Parent Co.:
Black Press Group Ltd.

Pub .... Carly Ferguson
Ed .... Kevin Mills
Office Mgr. .... Krista Stobbe
Mechanical Specifications: Type page 10 3/8 x 12 7/8; E - 6 cols, 1 5/8, between; A - 6 cols, 1 5/8, between; C - 6 cols, 1 5/8, between.
Areas Served: Mission - Abbotsford

NAKUSP

ARROW LAKES NEWS

(Wed)
89 1st Avenue Northwest, Nakusp, BC, V0G 1R0, Canada, Canada; gen tel (250) 265-3841; disp adv e-mail sales@arrowlakesnews.com; ed e-mail newsroom@arrowlakesnews.com; web site www.arrowlakenews.com
Circulation: 585pd, 10fr; VAC
Advertising: Open inch rate $7.14.
Established: 1999.
Parent Co.:
Black Press Group Ltd.
Pub.......... Eric Lawson
Mechanical Specifications: Type page 10 1/4 x 14 1/4; E - 6 cols, 1 1/2, between; A - 6 cols, 1 1/2, between; C - 6 cols, 1 1/2, between.
Equipment & Software: : Hardware — APP/Mac; Software — Adobe/InDesign.
Delivery Method: Mail, Newsstand
Areas Served: Canada

NANAIMO

NANAIMO NEWS BULLETIN

(Mon, Fri, Sat)
777 Poplar St., Nanaimo, BC, V9S 2H7, Canada, Canada; gen tel (250) 753-3707; ed tel (250) 734-4621; gen fax (250) 753-0788; disp adv e-mail sueb@blackpress.ca; ed e-mail editor@nanaimobulletin.com; web site www.nanaimobulletin.com
Circulation: 32,454fr; AAM
Advertising: Open line rate $1.79.
Established: 1988.
Parent Co.:
Black Press Group Ltd.
Pub .... Sean McCue
Ed. .... Melissa Fryer
Prodn. Mgr. .... Darrell Summerfelt
Mechanical Specifications: Type page 10 1/4 x 14 1/2; A - 6 cols, 1 7/8, 1/8 between; C - 7 cols, 1 7/8, 1/8 between.
Equipment & Software: : Hardware — IBM, PC; Presses — G; Software — Adobe/Photoshop 7.0, QPS/QuarkXPress 4.0.
Areas Served: Canada

NELSON

NELSON STAR

(Wed, Fri)
91 Baker Street, Suite B, Nelson, BC, V1L 4G8, Canada; gen tel (877) 365-6397; disp adv e-mail advertising@nelsonstar.com; ed e-mail editor@nelsonstar.com; web site www.nelsonstar.com
Circulation: 0pd, 8,448fr; VAC
Advertising: $11.06.
Established: 2008.
Parent Co.:
Black Press Group Ltd.
Publisher.......... Eric Lawson
Delivery Method: Newsstand, Carrier, Racks
Areas Served: Nelson and surrounding areas, British Columbia

NEW WESTMINSTER

NEW WESTMINSTER RECORD

(Wed)
201a-3430 Brighton Ave, New Westminster, BC, V5A 3H4, Canada; gen tel (604) 444-6451; disp adv e-mail kgilmour@newwestrecord.ca; class adv e-mail mmacleod@newwestrecord.ca; ed e-mail ptracy@newwestrecord.ca; web site http://www.newwestrecord.ca/
Circulation: 0pd, 16,290fr; CCAB
Parent Co.:
Glacier Media Group
Pub .... Lara Graham
Ed .... Pat Tracy
Circ Mgr .... Dale Dorsett
Areas Served: Canada

NORTH VANCOUVER

NORTH SHORE NEWS

(Wed, Fri, Sun)
980 1st St. West, Unit 116, North Vancouver, BC, V7P 3N4, Canada, Canada; gen tel (604) 985-2131; adv tel (604) 985-2131; ed tel (604) 985-2131; disp adv e-mail display@nsnews.com; class adv e-mail classifieds@van.net; ed e-mail editor@nsnews.com; web site www.nsnews.com
Circulation: 0pd, 61,800fr; CCAB
Established: 1969.
Parent Co.:
Glacier Media Group
Digital Platform - Mobile: Apple
Pub .... Peter Kvarnstrom
Ed .... Layne Christensen
Dir, Sales & Marketing .... Vicki Magnison
Areas Served: Canada

NORTH/WEST SHORE OUTLOOK

(Thur)
116-980 West 1st Street, North Vancouver, BC, V7P 3N4, Canada; gen tel (604) 903-1000; disp adv e-mail vmagnison@nsnews.com; class adv e-mail classifieds@van.net; ed e-mail lchristensen@nsnews.com; web site www.northshoreoutlook.com
Circulation: 28,038fr; CMCA
Sales & Mktg. Dir. .... Vicki Magnison
Pub .... Peter Kvarnstrom
Circ. Mgr. .... Dale Dorsett
Ed .... Layne Christensen
Areas Served: Canada

OLIVER

OLIVER CHRONICLE

(Wed)
6379 Main Street, Oliver, BC, V0H 1T0, Canada, Canada; gen tel (250) 498-3711; gen fax (250) 498-3966; disp adv e-mail sales@oliverchronicle.com; ed e-mail editor@oliverchronicle.com; web site www.oliverchronicle.com
Circulation: 1,723pd, 0fr; VAC
Advertising: Open inch rate $.66.
Established: 1937.
Ed. .... Lyonel Doherty
Robert Doull
Pub .... Linda Bolton
Mechanical Specifications: Type page 14 1/4 x 21 1/2; E - 6 cols, 2 1/4, 3/16 between; A - 6 cols, 2 1/4, 3/16 between; C - 6 cols, 2 1/4, 3/16 between.
Equipment & Software: : Hardware — Mac; Software — All Mac software
Indesign
Delivery Method: Mail, Newsstand, Racks
Areas Served: Canada

OSOYOOS

OSOYOOS TIMES

(Wed)
8712 Main St., Osoyoos, BC, V0H 1V0, Canada, Canada; gen tel (250) 495-7225; gen fax (250) 495-6616; disp adv e-mail sales@osoyoostimes.com; ed e-mail editor@osoyoostimes.com; web site www.osoyoostimes.com
Circulation: 1,783pd, 0fr; VAC
Advertising: Open inch rate $.80.
Established: 1947.
Office Mgr. .... Jocelyn Merit
Adv. Mgr. .... Ken Baker
Ed .... Keith Lacey
Mng. Dir. .... Linda Bolton
Mechanical Specifications: Type page 10 1/4 x 14; E - 6 cols
Equipment & Software: : Hardware — PC; Software — InDesign
Archetype/Corel Draw, Archetype/PhotoShop CS5
Delivery Method: Mail, Newsstand
Areas Served: Osoyoos

PARKSVILLE

PARKSVILLE QUALICUM BEACH NEWS

(Tues, Fri)
1b/2a 1209 East Island Highway Parksville Heritage Centre, Parksville, BC, V9P 1R5, Canada, Canada; gen tel (250) 248-4341; gen fax (250) 248-4655; disp adv e-mail bboyd@pqbnews.com; class adv e-mail viads@bcclassified.com; ed e-mail editor@pqbnews.com; web site www.pqbnews.com
Circulation: 7pd, 16,386fr; AAM
Advertising: Open inch rate $1.40.
Established: 1982.
Parent Co.:
Black Press Group Ltd.
Pub.......... Peter McCully
Ed. .... John Harding
Sales Mgr. .... Brenda Boyd
Circ. Mgr. .... Michele Graham
Mechanical Specifications: Type page 10 1/4 x 14 1/2; E - 6 cols, 1 1/2, 1/4 between; A - 6 cols, 1 1/2, 1/4 between; C - 7 cols, 1 1/4, 3/8 between.
Equipment & Software: : Hardware — APP/Mac; Software — Multi-Ad/Creator 4.03.
Areas Served: Canada

THE OCEANSIDE STAR

(Thur)
166 E. Island Hwy., Parksville, BC, V9P 2G3, Canada; gen tel (250) 954-0600; gen fax (250) 954-0601; disp adv e-mail ads@oceansidestar.com; ed e-mail bwilford@oceansidestar.com; web site www2.canada.com/oceansidestar/index.html
Circulation: 0pd, 16,243fr; CMCA
Advertising: Open inch rate $1.21.
Parent Co.:
CanWest MediaWorks Publications, Inc.
Adv. Mgr. .... Coreen Greene
Circ. Mgr. .... Michael Kelly
Ed. .... Brian Wilford
Pub.......... Hugh Nicholson
Mechanical Specifications: Type page 10 7/16 x 12 1/2; E - 9 cols, 1 1/10, 1/12 between; A - 9 cols, 1 1/10, 1/12 between; C - 9 cols, 1 1/10, 1/12 between.
Equipment & Software: ; Presses — G/Community; Software — QPS/QuarkXPress 3.32, Adobe/Photoshop 4.0, Adobe/Illustrator.
Areas Served: Canada

PENTICTON

PENTICTON WESTERN NEWS

(Wed, Fri)
2250 Camrose St., Penticton, BC, V2A 8R1, Canada, Canada; gen tel (250) 492-3636; gen fax (250) 492-9843; disp adv e-mail larry@pentictonwesternnews.com; class adv e-mail classifieds@pentictonwesternnews.com; ed e-mail kpatton@pentictonwesternnews.com; web site www.pentictonwesternnews.com
Circulation: 22,146fr; AAM
Advertising: Open inch rate $1.26.
Parent Co.:
Black Press Group Ltd.
Circ. Mgr. .... Sue Kovacs
Pub .... Shannon Simpson
Sales Mgr. .... Larry Mercier
Ed .... Kristi Patton
Mechanical Specifications: Type page 10 1/3 x 14 1/2; E - 6 cols, 1 1/2, 1/6 between; A - 6 cols, 1 1/2, 1/6 between; C - 6 cols, 1 1/2, 1/6 between.
Equipment & Software: : Hardware — APP/Mac; Presses — G; Software — QPS/QuarkXPress 4.0, Adobe/Photoshop 4.0, Adobe/Illustrator 5.0.
Delivery Method: Newsstand, Carrier
Areas Served: Canada

PORT ALBERNI

ALBERNI VALLEY NEWS

(Tues, Thur)
4656 Margaret Street, Port Alberni, BC, V9Y 6H2, Canada; gen tel (250) 723-6399; gen fax (250) 723-6395; disp adv e-mail publisher@albernivalleynews.com; ed e-mail editor@albernivalleynews.com; web site www.albernivalleynews.com
Circulation: 9,025pd,; AAM
Advertising: Open line rate $1.31.
Established: 2006.
Parent Co.:
Black Press Group Ltd.
Publisher.......... Teresa Bird
Ed. .... Susan Quinn
Delivery Method: Carrier, Racks
Areas Served: Canada

PORT COQUITLAM

TRI CITY NEWS

(Wed, Fri)
118 - 1680 Broadway Street, Port Coquitlam, BC, V3C 2M8, Canada; gen tel (604) 525-6397; adv tel (604) 472-3020; ed tel (604) 472-3030; disp adv e-mail admanager@tricitynews.com; web site tricitynews.com
Circulation: 0pd, 52,297fr; Sworn/Estimate/Non-Audited
Parent Co.:
Glacier Media
Delivery Method: Carrier
Areas Served: Port Moody, Belcarra, Anmore, Port Coquitlam, Coquitlam

TRI-CITY NEWS

(Wed, Fri)
1680 Broadway Street, Unit 118, Port Coquitlam, BC, V3C 2M8, Tri-Cities, Canada; gen tel (604) 525-6397; disp adv e-mail byamaura@tricitynews.com; ed e-mail newsroom@tricitynews.com; web site www.tricitynews.com
Circulation: 0pd, 45,335fr; CCAB
Advertising: Open inch rate $29.68.
Established: 1985.
Parent Co.:
Black Press Group Ltd.
Glacier Media Group
Ed. .... Richard Dal Monte
Pub .... Shannon Mitchell
Adv. Dir. .... Bentley Yamaura
Circ Mgr .... Kim Yorston
Delivery Method: Carrier
Areas Served: Tri-Cities

PORT HARDY

NORTH ISLAND GAZETTE

(Wed)
#3-7053 Market St., Port Hardy, BC, V0N 2P0, Canada; gen tel (250) 949-6225; gen fax (250) 949-7655; disp adv e-mail sales@northislandgazette.com; class adv e-mail viads@bcclassified.com; ed e-mail publisher@northislandgazette.com; web site www.northislandgazette.com
Circulation: 1,065pd, 500fr; CMCA
Advertising: Open line rate $1.08.
Established: 1965.
Parent Co.:
Black Press Group Ltd.
Sales Rep .... Natasha Griffiths
Lisa Harrison
Lilian Meerveld
Tyson Whitney
Hanna Petersen
Mechanical Specifications: Type page 10 3/8 x 14.
Delivery Method: Mail, Newsstand, Carrier,

Racks
Areas Served: Canada

POWELL RIVER

POWELL RIVER PEAK

(Wed)
4400 Marine Ave., Powell River, BC, V8A 2K1, Powell River Regional District, Canada; gen tel (604) 485-5313; gen fax (604) 485-5007; disp adv e-mail sales@prpeak.com; class adv e-mail cindy@prpeak.com; ed e-mail publisher@prpeak.com; web site www.prpeak.com
Circulation: 2,084pd, 48fr; VAC
Advertising: Open inch rate $1.10.
Established: 1995.
Parent Co.:
Glacier Media GroupEditions: 2— The Powell River Peak and The Weekend Shopper
Circ. Dir. .... Michele Stewart
Pub/Ed .... Jason Schreuers
Sales .... Dot Campbell
Mechanical Specifications: Type page 10 1/4 x 13.8; E - 6 cols, 1 1/2, 1/8 between; A - 6 cols, 1 1/2, 1/8 between; C - 6 cols, 1 1/2, 1/8 between.
Equipment & Software: : Hardware — APP/Mac; Software — In Design CS4, Adobe/Photoshop CS4 Microsoft/Word 5.0, Aldus/Freehand.
Delivery Method: Mail, Newsstand, Carrier
Areas Served: Powell River Regional District
Note: Discover Powell River, annual tourism publication, available each year at end of March

PRINCETON

PRINCETON SIMILKAMEEN SPOTLIGHT

(Wed)
282 Bridge St., Princeton, BC, V0X 1W0, Canada; gen tel (250) 295-3535; gen fax (250) 295-7322; disp adv e-mail advertising@similkameenspotlight.com; ed e-mail editor@similkameenspotlight.com; web site www.similkameenspotlight.com
Circulation: 2,227pd, 43fr; VAC
Advertising: $8.86 per ci.
Established: 1948.
Parent Co.:
Black Press Group Ltd.Andrea Demeer
Ed/Assist. Pub .... Andrea DeMeer
Pub .... Don Kendall
Adv Mgr. .... Sandi Nolan
Mechanical Specifications: Type page 10 1/3 x 14; E - 6 cols, 1 9/16, between; A - 6 cols, 1 9/16, between; C - 6 cols, 1 9/16, between.
Equipment & Software: : Hardware — APP/Mac; Software — QPS/QuarkXPress 4.04.
Delivery Method: Mail, Racks

QUEEN CHARLOTTE

HAIDA GWAII OBSERVER

(Fri)
623 7th St., Queen Charlotte, BC, V0T 1S0, Canada; gen tel (250) 559-4680; adv tel (250) 559-4680; ed tel (250) 559-4680; gen fax (250) 559-8433; adv fax (250) 559-4680; ed fax (250) 559-4680; disp adv e-mail chris.williams@haidagwaiiobserver.com; ed e-mail observer@haidagwaii.ca; web site www.haidagwaiiobserver.com
Circulation: 963pd, 2fr; VAC
Advertising: Open line rate $1.45.
Established: 1969.
Pub./Ed. .... Todd Hamilton
Sales Mgr. .... Chris Williams
Mechanical Specifications: Type page 7 1/2 x 10; E - 3 cols, 2 1/2, between; A - 3 cols, 2 1/2, between.
Equipment & Software: ; Presses — AB Dick 360 x 2; Software — InDesign, Photoshop, MW Word, etc
Delivery Method: Mail, Newsstand
Areas Served: V0T 1S0, V0T 1T0, V0T 1R0, V0T 1Y0, V0T 1M0

QUESNEL

QUESNEL CARIBOO OBSERVER

(Wed, Fri)
188 Carson Ave., Quesnel, BC, V2J 2A8, Canada; gen tel (250) 992-2121; gen fax (250) 992-5229; disp adv e-mail advertising@quesnelobserver.com; class adv e-mail publisher@quesnelobserver.com; ed e-mail editor@quesnelobserver.com; web site www.quesnelobserver.com
Circulation: 984pd, 2,487fr; VAC
Advertising: Open inch rate $1.21.
Parent Co.:
Black Press Group Ltd.
Ed. .... Autumn McDonald
Pub/Sales Mgr. .... Tracey Roberts
Delivery Method: Mail, Racks
Areas Served: V2J

REVELSTOKE

REVELSTOKE REVIEW

(Wed)
518 2nd St., Revelstoke, BC, V0E 2S0, Canada, Canada; gen tel (250) 837-4667; gen fax (250) 837-2003; disp adv e-mail mavis@revelstoketimesreview.com; ed e-mail editor@revelstoketimesreview.com; web site www.revelstoketimesreview.com
Circulation: 770pd, 216fr; VAC
Advertising: Open inch rate $.85.
Established: 1898.
Parent Co.:
Black Press Group Ltd.
Digital Platform - Mobile: Apple
Digital Platform - Tablet: Apple iOS, Kindle
Pub./Adv Mgr .... Mavis Cann
Office Mgr. .... Fran Carlson
Ed .... Alex Cooper
Delivery Method: Mail, Newsstand, Carrier
Areas Served: Canada

RICHMOND

RICHMOND NEWS

(Thur)
#200-8211 Ackroyd Road, Richmond, BC, V6X 2C9, Canada; gen tel (604) 270-8031; gen fax (604) 270-2248; disp adv e-mail rakimow@richmond-news.com; class adv e-mail classifieds@van.net; ed e-mail eedmonds@richmond-news.com; web site www.richmond-news.com
Circulation: 0pd, 46,114fr; CCAB
Advertising: Open inch rate $2.29.
Established: 1979.
Parent Co.:
Glacier Media Group
CanWest MediaWorks Publications, Inc.
Pub .... Pierre Pelletier
Adv Dir .... Rob Akimow
Ed .... Eve Edmonds
Circ Mgr .... Kristene Murray
Mechanical Specifications: Type page 10 1/4 x 14; E - 6 cols, 1 9/16, between; A - 6 cols, 1 9/16, between; C - 7 cols, 1 5/16, between.
Delivery Method: Carrier
Areas Served: Canada

SALMON ARM

EAGLE VALLEY NEWS

(Wed)
171 Shuswap St. Nw, Salmon Arm, BC, V1E 4N7, Canada, Canada; gen tel (250) 832-2131; gen fax (250) 832-5140; disp adv e-mail advertising@saobserver.net; class adv e-mail classifieds@eaglevalleynews.com; ed e-mail newsroom@saobserver.net; web site www.eaglevalleynews.com
Circulation: 376pd, 12fr; CMCA
Advertising: Open inch rate $11.34.
Parent Co.:
Black Press Group Ltd.
Adv. Mgr. .... Rick Proznick
Ed. .... Tracy Hughes
Sales .... Laura Lavigne
Reporter/Columnist .... Lachlan Labere
Mechanical Specifications: Type page 10 1/4 x 14 1/2; E - 6 cols, 1 7/12, 1/6 between; A - 6 cols, 1 7/12, 1/6 between; C - 7 cols, 1 5/8, 1/6 between.
Equipment & Software: : Hardware — APP/Mac; Software — Adobe Indesign CS6 Version 8.0
Delivery Method: Mail, Newsstand
Areas Served: Canada

SALMON ARM OBSERVER

(Wed)
171 Shuswap St., Nw, Salmon Arm, BC, V1E 4N7, Canada, Canada; gen tel (250) 832-2131; gen fax (250) 832-5140; disp adv e-mail advertising@saobserver.net; class adv e-mail classifieds@saobserver.net; ed e-mail newsroom@saobserver.net; web site www.saobserver.net
Circulation: 1,951pd, 50fr; CMCA
Advertising: Open inch rate $18.48.
Established: 1907.
Parent Co.:
Black Press Group Ltd.
Pub .... Rick Proznick
Senior Ed. .... Tracy Hughes
Mechanical Specifications: Type page 10 5/16 x 14; E - 7 cols, 1 5/16, 3/16 between; A - 7 cols, 1 5/16, 3/16 between.
Equipment & Software: : Hardware — APP/Mac; Software — Indesign CS3 Ver. 5.0
Delivery Method: Mail, Newsstand
Areas Served: Canada

SHUSWAP MARKET NEWS

(Fri)
171 Shuswap St. Nw, Salmon Arm, BC, V1E 4N7, Canada, Canada; gen tel (250) 832-2131; gen fax (250) 832-5140; disp adv e-mail advertising@saobserver.net; class adv e-mail classifieds@saobserver.net; ed e-mail newsroom@saobserver.net; web site www.saobserver.net
Circulation: 0pd, 12,732fr; CMCA
Advertising: Open inch rate $18.48.
Established: 1907.
Parent Co.:
Black Press Group Ltd.
Pub .... Rick Proznick
Ed. .... Tracy Hughes
Mechanical Specifications: Type page 10 5/16 x 14; E - 7 cols, 1 9/16, 3/16 between; A - 7 cols, 1 9/16, 3/16 between; C - 7 cols, 1 9/16, 3/16 between.
Equipment & Software: : Hardware — APP/Mac; Software — Indesign CS6 Ver. 8.0
Delivery Method: Carrier, Racks
Areas Served: Canada

SALT SPRING ISLAND

GULF ISLANDS DRIFTWOOD

(Wed)
328 Lower Ganges Rd., Salt Spring Island, BC, V8K 2V3, Canada, Canada; gen tel (250) 537-9933; gen fax (250) 537-2613; disp adv e-mail sales@driftwoodgimedia.com; ed e-mail news@driftwoodgimedia.com; web site www.driftwoodgulfislandsmedia.com
Circulation: 2,300pd, 2,200fr; Sworn/Estimate/Non-Audited
Advertising: Open line rate $18.58.
Established: 1960.
Parent Co.:
Driftwood Publishing Ltd.
Digital Platform - Mobile: Apple, Android, Blackberry, Other
Digital Platform - Tablet: Apple iOS, Android, Blackberry Tablet OS, Other
Mng. Ed. .... Gail Sjuberg
Prodn. Mgr. .... Lorraine Sullivan
Publisher .... Amber Ogilvie
Equipment & Software: ; Presses — G
Delivery Method: Mail, Newsstand
Areas Served: Canada

SECHELT

COAST REPORTER

(Fri)
5485 Wharf Road, Sechelt, BC, V0N 3A0, Canada; gen tel (604) 885-4811; gen fax (604) 885-4818; disp adv e-mail pat@coastreporter.net; class adv e-mail classified@coastreporter.net; ed e-mail editor@coastreporter.net; web site www.coastreporter.net
Circulation: 31pd, 11,639fr; VAC
Advertising: Open line rate $1.20.
Parent Co.:
Glacier Media Group
Pub .... Peter Kvarnstrom
Circ. Mgr. .... Christine Wood
Ed./Assoc. Pub .... John Gleeson
Sales Mgr. .... Pat Paproski
Class. Supv. .... Shelley Alleyne
Areas Served: Sechelt, Gibsons

SIDNEY

THE PENINSULA NEWS REVIEW

(Wed, Fri)
102-9830 Second Street, Sidney, BC, V8L 3C6, Canada, Canada; gen tel (250) 656-1151; ed tel (250) 656-1151; gen fax (250) 656-5526; disp adv e-mail sales@peninsulanewsreview.com; ed e-mail editor@peninsulanewsreview.com; web site www.peninsulanewsreview.com
Circulation: 14,497fr; AAM
Advertising: Open inch rate $1.79.
Established: 1905.
Parent Co.:
Black Press Group Ltd.Steven Heywood
Dale Naftel
Chris R Cook
Hugo Wong
Rosemarie Bandura
Equipment & Software: : Hardware — Optiquest/Screens, Starmax/400; Software — QPS/QuarkXPress 3.32, Multi-Ad/Creator 3.7.
Delivery Method: Carrier
Areas Served: Canada

SMITHERS

THE SMITHERS INTERIOR NEWS

(Wed)
3764 Broadway, Smithers, BC, V0J 2N0, Canada, Canada; gen tel (250) 847-3266; gen fax (250) 847-2995; disp adv e-mail publisher@interior-news.com; ed e-mail editor@interior-news.com; web site www.interior-news.com
Circulation: 13pd, 152fr; VAC
Advertising: Open inch rate $1.31.
Established: 1907.
Parent Co.:
Black Press Group Ltd.
Pub/Sales Mgr .... Grant Harris
Ed .... Chris Gareau
Mechanical Specifications: Type page 12 1/8 x 21; E - 7 cols, 1 3/5, 1/6 between; A - 7 cols, 1 3/5, 1/6 between; C - 7 cols, 1 3/5, 1/6 between.
Equipment & Software: : Hardware — APP/Mac.
Areas Served: Canada

SOOKE

THE SOOKE NEWS MIRROR

(Wed)
#4 6631 Sooke Road, Sooke, BC, V9Z 0A3, District of Sooke, Canada; gen tel (250) 642-5752; adv tel (250) 642-5752; gen fax (250) 642-4767; disp adv e-mail sales@sookenewsmirror.com; ed e-mail editor@sookenewsmirror.com; web site www.sookenewsmirror.com
Circulation: 65pd, 5,660fr; AAM
Advertising: Open inch rate $.86.
Parent Co.:

Black Press Group Ltd.
publisher .... Rod Sluggett
editor .... Laird Kevin
Advertising Sales .... Kelvin Phair
Delivery Method: Mail, Newsstand, Carrier
Areas Served: District of Sooke

SQUAMISH

SQUAMISH CHIEF

(Thur)
38117 Second Avenue, Squamish, BC, V8B 0B9, Canada; gen tel (604) 892-9161 ; gen fax (604) 892-8483; disp adv e-mail ads@squamishchief.com; class adv e-mail jgibson@squamishchief.com; ed e-mail michaela@squamishchief.com; web site www.squamishchief.com
Circulation: 794fr; VAC
Parent Co.:
Glacier Media Group
Pub .... Darren Roberts
Ed .... Michaela Garstin
Mktg Coord. .... Tina Pisch
Sales & Mktg. Mgr .... Jennifer Gibson
Circ. Mgr .... Denise Conway
Areas Served: Squamish

SUMMERLAND

SUMMERLAND REVIEW

(Thur)
13226 Victoria Rd. N., Summerland, BC, V0H 1Z0, Canada; gen tel (250) 494-5406; gen fax (250) 494-5453; disp adv e-mail rob@summerlandreview.com; class adv e-mail class@summerlandreview.com; ed e-mail news@summerlandreview.com; web site www.summerlandreview.com
Circulation: 52pd, 21fr; VAC
Advertising: Open inch rate $.81.
Parent Co.:
Black Press Group Ltd.
Ed. .... John Arendt
Pub .... Shannon Simpson
Sales Mgr .... Rob Murphy
Class./Circ Mgr .... Nan Cogbill
Areas Served: Summerland

SURREY

CLOVERDALE REPORTER

(Wed)
17586 56a Ave., Surrey, BC, V3S 1G3, Canada; gen tel (604) 575-2400; adv tel (604) 575-2423; disp adv e-mail cynthia.dunsmore@cloverdalereporter.com; class adv e-mail bcclassifieds@blackpress.com; ed e-mail editor@cloverdalereporter.com; web site www.cloverdalereporter.com
Circulation: 0pd, 15,840fr; VAC
Established: 1996.
Parent Co.:
Black Press Group Ltd.
Sales Representative .... Cynthia Dunsmore
Ed. .... Sam Anderson
Reporter .... Grace Kennedy
Delivery Method: Carrier, Racks
Areas Served: Surrey, B.C. V3S 1G3

SURREY NOW-LEADER

(Wed, Fri)
102-5460 152nd St., Surrey, BC, V3S 5J9, Canada, Canada; gen tel (604) 572-0064; adv tel (604) 572-0064; ed tel (604)543-5816; gen fax (604) 575-2544; adv fax (604)572-7948; disp adv e-mail sueb@blackpress.ca; class adv e-mail sueb@blackpress.ca; ed e-mail beau.simpson@surreynowleader.com; web site www.surreynowleader.com
Circulation: 54,457fr; AAM
Advertising: Open inch rate $38.84.
Parent Co.:
Black Press Group Ltd.Editions: 2— 2 total Ã ££Ã ££Ã &-pound;Ã Â¯Ã £Ã Â¿Ã £Ã Â½ North Delta Leader (14,000); Surrey Leader (68,000);
Delivery Method: Carrier
Areas Served: Canada

THE NOW NEWSPAPER

(Tues, Thur)
102 - 5460 152 St, Surrey, BC, V3S 5J9, Canada, Canada; gen tel (604) 572-0064; gen fax (604) 572-6438; disp adv e-mail dal.hothi@thenownewspaper.com; class adv e-mail sarah.sigurdswon@thenownewspaper.com; ed e-mail bsimpson@thenownewspaper.com; web site www.thenownewspaper.com
Circulation: 177,757fr; CCAB
Advertising: $4.68.
Established: 1984.
Ed ....Beau Simpson
Pub .... Dwayne Weidendorf
Ad Control/Admin .... Sarah Sigurdson
Sales Mgr .... Dal Hothi
Delivery Method: Carrier
Areas Served: Canada

THE PEACE ARCH NEWS

(Wed, Fri)
200-2411 160 Street, Surrey, BC, V3S 0C8, Canada; gen tel (604) 531-1711; gen fax (604) 531-7977; ed e-mail editorial@peacearchnews.com; web site www.peacearchnews.com
Circulation: 37,141fr; AAM
Advertising: Open inch rate $23.68 column inch..
Parent Co.:
Black Press Group Ltd.
Ed. .... Lance Peverley
Mechanical Specifications: Type page 10 1/4 x 12 1/2; E - 6 cols, between; A - 6 cols, between; C - 6 cols, between.
Delivery Method: Carrier
Areas Served: Canada

TERRACE

THE TERRACE STANDARD

(Thur)
3210 Clinton St, Terrace, BC, V8G5R2, Canada, Canada; gen tel (250) 638-7283; gen fax (250) 638-8432; disp adv e-mail bwhusband@terracestandard.com; class adv e-mail classifieds@terracestandard.com; ed e-mail newsroom@terracestandard.com; web site www.terracestandard.com
Circulation: 7,729fr; VAC
Advertising: Open inch rate $1.31.
Established: 1969.
Parent Co.:
Black Press Group Ltd.
Editor .... Quinn Bender
Sales .... Bert Husband
Mechanical Specifications: Type page 12 1/16 x 21 1/2; E - 7 cols, 1 5/8, 1/8 between; A - 7 cols, 1 5/8, 1/8 between; C - 7 cols, 1 5/8, 1/8 between.
Equipment & Software: : Hardware — APP/Mac; Presses — G/Community; Software — Multi-Ad/Creator 4.0.
Areas Served: Canada

TUMBLER RIDGE

TUMBLER RIDGE NEWS

(Thur) (on line on Tuesdays)
230 Mains Street, Tumbler Ridge, BC, V0C 2W0, Canada; gen tel (250) 242-5343 ; gen fax (250) 242-5340; disp adv e-mail advertising@tumblerridgenews.com; ed e-mail editor@tumblerridgenews.com; web site www.tumblerridgenews.com - 12,000(views)
Circulation: 2pd, 1,179fr; VAC
Advertising: .67.
Established: 1997.
Digital Platform - Mobile: Windows
Owner .... Loraine Funk
Pub/Ed. .... Trent Ernst
Sales Mgr .... Lisa Allen
Mechanical Specifications: 10.25" x 16" - 8 columns Please email for rate sheet. We accept pdf, jpg, tif and word.
Equipment & Software: ; Software — adobe
Delivery Method: Mail, Newsstand, Carrier
Areas Served: Tumbler Ridge

UCLUELET

WESTERLY NEWS

(Wed)
102-1801 Bay Street, Ucluelet, BC, V0R 3A0, Canada; gen tel (250) 726-7029; gen fax (250) 726-4282; disp adv e-mail office@westerlynews.ca; ed e-mail andrew.bailey@westerlynews.ca; web site www.westerlynews.ca
Circulation: 7pd, 0fr; Sworn/Estimate/Non-Audited
Advertising: $8 a column inch (1.33" x 1") B&W .
Established: 1987.
Parent Co.:
Black Press Group Ltd.
Ed .... Andrew Bailey
Pub .... Peter McCully
Nora O'Malley
Delivery Method: Mail, Newsstand, Racks
Areas Served: V0R 3A0, V0R 2Z0

VALEMOUNT

THE VALLEY SENTINEL

(Thur)
1418 Bruce Place, Valemount, BC, V0E 2Z0, Canada; gen tel (250) 566-4425; gen fax (250) 566-4528; disp adv e-mail ads@valley-sentinel.com ; ed e-mail articles@valley-sentinel.com ; web site www.thevalleysentinel.com
Circulation: 385pd, 13fr; VAC
Advertising: Open inch rate $1.03.
Established: 1986.
Parent Co.:
Aberdeen Publishing
Digital Platform - Mobile: Apple
Ad Sales .... Deanna Mickelow
Pub .... Joshua Estabroks
Delivery Method: Mail
Areas Served: V0E, V0J

VANCOUVER

GEORGIA STRAIGHT

(Thur)
1635 West Broadway, Vancouver, BC, V6J 1W9, Canada; gen tel (604) 730-7000; gen fax (604) 730-7010; disp adv e-mail sales@straight.com; ed e-mail contact@straight.com; web site www.straight.com
Circulation: 25pd, 81,544fr; VAC
Advertising: Open inch rate $6.17.
Established: 1967.
Parent Co.:
Vancouver Free Press Publishing Corp.
Sales Director .... Tara Lalanne
Circulation Manager .... Dexter Vosper
IT Director .... Dennis Jangula
Editor .... Charlie Smith
Mechanical Specifications: Type page 10 3/16 x 15 1/2.
Delivery Method: Mail, Newsstand, Racks
Areas Served: Metro Vancouver, British Columbia

THE FALSE CREEK NEWS

(Fri)
661 A Market Hill, Vancouver, BC, V5Z 4B5, Canada; gen tel (604) 875-9626; gen fax (604) 875-0336; disp adv e-mail adsales@thefalsecreeknews.com; ed e-mail mail@thefalsecreeknews.com; web site www.thefalsecreeknews.com
Circulation: 25,000fr; Sworn/Estimate/Non-Audited
Advertising: Open inch rate $7.29.
Adv. Sales .... M. Juma
Mng. Ed. .... Stephen Bowell
Mechanical Specifications: Type page 7 1/2 x 9 1/2; E - 5 cols, 1 1/2, 1/8 between; A - 5 cols, 1 1/2, 1/8 between.

THE VANCOUVER COURIER

(Wed, Fri)
303 West 5th Ave, Vancouver, BC, V5Y 1J6, Canada, Canada; gen tel (604) 738-1411; gen fax (604) 731-1474; disp adv e-mail mbhatti@vancourier.com; ed e-mail mperkins@vancourier.com; web site www.vancourier.com
Circulation: 0pd, 92,575fr; CCAB
Advertising: Open inch rate $2.81.
Parent Co.:
Glacier Media Group
CanWest MediaWorks Publications, Inc.Editions: 2— 2 total ½ Eastside Edition (60,000); Westside Edition (59,000);
Pub .... Alvin Brouwer
Ed .... Martha Perkins
Mktg Dir .... Michelle Bhatti
Mechanical Specifications: Type page 10 x 15; E - 6 cols, between; A - 6 cols, between; C - 7 cols, between.
Equipment & Software: : Hardware — APP/Mac; Software — QPS/QuarkXPress, Adobe/Illustrator, Adobe/Photoshop.
Areas Served: Canada

THE WESTENDER

(Thur)
303 West 5th Ave, Vancouver, BC, V5Y 1J6, Canada; gen tel (604) 742-8686; disp adv e-mail matty@westender.com; ed e-mail editor@westender.com; web site http://www.westender.com/
Circulation: 0pd, 23,887fr; CCAB
Parent Co.:
Glacier Media Group
Pub .... Gail Nugent
Ed .... Kelsey Klassen
Circ Mgr .... Miguel Black
Areas Served: Canada

WE VANCOUVER WEEKLY

(Thur)
303 West 5th Ave, Vancouver, BC, V5Y 1J6, Canada; gen tel (604) 742-8686; adv tel (604) 742-8677; gen fax (604) 606-8687; disp adv e-mail matty@westender.com; ed e-mail editor@westender.com; web site www.wevancouver.com
Circulation: 0pd, 53,671fr; CMCA
Advertising: Open inch rate $38.92.
Pub .... Gail Nugent
Ed .... Kelsey Klassen
Circ. Mgr .... Miguel Black
Mechanical Specifications: Type page 10 3/8" wide x 14" tall
Equipment & Software: : Hardware — APP/Mac
Delivery Method: Newsstand, Carrier, Racks
Areas Served: All of Vancouver

VANDERHOOF

VANDERHOOF OMINECA EXPRESS

(Wed)
150 W. Columbia, Vanderhoof, BC, V0J 3A0, Canada; gen tel (250) 567-9258; gen fax (250) 567-2070; disp adv e-mail publisher@ominecaexpress.com; ed e-mail newsroom@ominecaexpress.com; web site www.ominecaexpress.com
Circulation: 998pd, 52fr; VAC
Advertising: Open inch rate $1.06.
Established: 1978.
Parent Co.:
Black Press Group Ltd.
Pub./Sales Mgr .... Pam Berger
Ed .... Vivian Chui
Office/Sales/Circ .... Denise Smith
Mechanical Specifications: Type page 10 5/16 x 14 1/2; E - 6 cols, 1 9/16, 3/16 between; A - 6 cols, 1 9/16, 3/16 between; C - 6 cols, 1 9/16, 3/16 between.
Areas Served: Vanderhoof

VERNON

THE MORNING STAR

(Wed, Fri, Sun)
4407 25th Ave., Vernon, BC, V1T 1P5, Canada; gen tel (250) 545-3322; gen fax (250) 542-1510; disp adv e-mail stephanie@vernonmorningstar.com; class adv e-mail Classifieds@vernonmorningstar.com; ed e-mail glenn@vernonmorningstar.com; web site www.vernonmorningstar.com
Circulation: 29,884pd,; AAM
Advertising: Open inch rate $1.75.
Established: 1988.
Parent Co.:
Torstar
Circ. Mgr....................... Tammy Stelmachowich
Mng. Ed..................................... Glenn Mitchell
Pub.. Ian Jensen
Class. Mgr................................ Carol Williment
Mechanical Specifications: Type page 10 5/16 x 14 1/2; E - 6 cols, 1 9/16, 1/4 between; A - 6 cols, 1 9/16, 1/4 between; C - 7 cols, 1 3/8, 3/16 between.
Equipment & Software: : Hardware — APP/Mac; Presses — 8-G/Community; Software — Multi-Ad, QPS/QuarkXPress.
Areas Served: Canada

VICTORIA

GOLDSTREAM GAZETTE

(Wed, Fri)
205-774 Goldstream Ave, Victoria, BC, V9B 2X3, Langford, Canada; gen tel (250) 478-9552; gen fax (250) 478-6545; disp adv e-mail publisher@goldstreamgazette.com; ed e-mail editor@goldstreamgazette.com; web site www.goldstreamgazette.com
Circulation: 17,546fr; AAM
Advertising: Open line rate $1.82.
Established: 1976.
Parent Co.:
Black Press Group Ltd.
Pub.. Penny Sakamoto
Circ. Mgr................................. Mellissa Mitchell
Pub.. Michelle Cabana
Delivery Method: Carrier
Areas Served: Langford

OAK BAY NEWS

(Wed, Fri)
207a-2187 Oak Bay Avenue, Victoria, BC, V8R 1G1, Canada; gen tel (250) 480-3251; adv tel (250) 480-3251; ed tel (250) 480-3260; disp adv e-mail jgairdner@blackpress.ca; class adv e-mail bcclassifieds@blackpress.ca; ed e-mail editor@oakbaynews.com; web site www.oakbaynews.com
Circulation: 0pd, 6,212fr; AAM
Advertising: Open inch rate $12.04.
Established: 1974.
Parent Co.:
Black Press Group Ltd.
Pub.. Janet Gairdner
Editor.......................... Christine van Reeuwyk
Prod... Lyn Quan
Advertising Consultant.................John Stewart
Multimedia Journalist....................... Keri Coles
Delivery Method: Carrier
Areas Served: Canada

SAANICH NEWS

(Wed, Fri)
104b-3550 Saanich Road, Victoria, BC, V8X 1X2, Canada; gen tel (250) 381-3484; gen fax (250) 386-2624; disp adv e-mail staylor@saanichnews.com; class adv e-mail rod.fraser@saanichnews.com; ed e-mail editor@saanichnews.com; web site www.saanichnews.com
Circulation: 31,240fr; AAM
Advertising: Open inch rate $1.99.
Parent Co.:
Black Press Group Ltd.
Sales... Rod Fraser
Pub.. Oliver Sommer
Ed .... Dan Ebenal
Circ Mgr... Miki Speirs
Sales.. Sarah Taylor
Areas Served: Canada

VICTORIA NEWS

(Wed, Fri)
818 Broughton St., Victoria, BC, V8W 1E4, Canada, Canada; gen tel (250) 381-3484; gen fax (250) 386-2624; ed e-mail editor@vicnews.com; web site http://www.vicnews.com/
Circulation: 24,517fr; AAM
Advertising: Open inch rate $1.95.
Parent Co.:
Black Press Group Ltd.
Group Pub............................ Penny Sakamoto
Pub .... Mike Cowan
Ed .... Pamela Roth
Mechanical Specifications: Type page 10 1/4 x 14 1/2; E - 5 cols, 1 1/2, 1/6 between; A - 6 cols, 1 1/2, 1/6 between; C - 8 cols, 1 1/4, 1/6 between.
Equipment & Software: : Hardware — APP/Mac; Software — QPS/QuarkXPress, Adobe/Photoshop, Multi-Ad.
Areas Served: Canada

WHISTLER

PIQUE NEWSMAGAZINE

(Thur)
103-1390 Alpha Lake Rd., Whistler, BC, V0N 1B1, Canada; gen tel (604) 938-0202; gen fax (604) 938-0201; disp adv e-mail susan@piquenewsmagazine.com; class adv e-mail traffic@piquenewsmagazine.com; ed e-mail edit@piquenewsmagazine.com; web site www.piquenewsmagazine.com
Circulation: 41pd, 10,997fr; VAC
Advertising: Open inch rate $1.20.
Established: 1994.
Parent Co.:
Glacier Media Group
Pique Publishing Inc.
Ed. .... Clare Ogilvie
Pub .... Sarah Strother
Sales Mgr .... Susan Hutchinson
Circ Mgr.. Katie Bechtel
Sales Coord........................... Jennifer Treptow
Mechanical Specifications: Type page 9 1/2 x 12 7/8; E - 4 cols, 2 1/4, 3/8 between; A - 4 cols, 2 1/4, 3/8 between; C - 5 cols, 1 3/4, 3/8 between.
Equipment & Software: : Hardware — APP/Mac; Presses — AG/Imagesetter; Software — QPS/QuarkXPress, Adobe/Photoshop, Adobe/Illustrator.

THE WHISTLER QUESTION

(Tues)
103-1390 Alpha Lake Rd, Whistler, BC, V0N 1B4, Canada, Canada; gen tel (604) 932-5131; gen fax (604) 932-2862; disp adv e-mail susan@piquenewsmagazine.com; class adv e-mail mail@piquenewsmagazine.com; ed e-mail editor@whistlerquestion.com; web site www.whistlerquestion.com
Circulation: 433pd, 5,762fr; VAC
Advertising: Open inch rate $1.00.
Established: 1976.
Parent Co.:
Glacier Media Group
Pres., WPLP .... Sarah Strother
Office/Class. Mgr .... Kathryn Bechtel
Ed .... Alyssa Noel
Sales Mgr .... Susan Hutchinson
Areas Served: Canada

WILLIAMS LAKE

THE WILLIAMS LAKE TRIBUNE

(Wed)
188 N. 1st Ave., Williams Lake, BC, V2G 1Y8, Canada, Canada; gen tel (250) 392-2331; gen fax (250) 392-7253; disp adv e-mail advertising@wltribune.com; class adv e-mail classifieds@wltribune.com; ed e-mail editor@wltribune.com; web site www.wltribune.com
Circulation: 1,109pd, 9,794fr; VAC
Advertising: Line rate $1.49.
Established: 1930.
Parent Co.:
Black Press Group Ltd.
Pub .... Kathy McLean
Ed .... Angie Mindus
Class. Mgr... Lynn Bolt
Delivery Method: Mail, Newsstand, Carrier, Racks
Areas Served: Canada

MANITOBA

ALTONA

THE RED RIVER VALLEY ECHO

(Thur)
67 2nd St., Altona, MB, R0G 0B0, Canada; gen tel (204) 324-5001; gen fax (204) 324-1402; disp adv e-mail Darcie.Morris@sunmedia.ca; ed e-mail winkler.news@sunmedia.ca; web site www.altonaecho.com
Circulation: 27pd, 4,427fr; VAC
Advertising: Open inch rate $1.10.
Established: 1941.
Parent Co.:
Postmedia Network Inc.
Quebecor Communications, Inc.
Ed. .... Greg Vandermeulen
Adv Dir. .... Darcie Morris
Mechanical Specifications: Type page 10 1/4 x 14; E - 6 cols, 1 3/5, between; A - 6 cols, 1 3/5, between; C - 8 cols, 1 7/12, between.
Equipment & Software: : Hardware — APP/Mac; Software — Indesign/QPS/QuarkXPress, Baseview/News Edit Pro.
Delivery Method: Carrier, Racks
Areas Served: Altona

BEAUSEJOUR

THE CLIPPER WEEKLY & LAC DU BONNET CLIPPER

(Thur)
27a-3rd Street South, Beausejour, MB, R0E 0C0, Canada; gen tel (204) 268-4700 ; gen fax (204) 268-3858 ; web site www.clipper.mb.ca
Circulation: 46pd, 12,340fr; VAC
Parent Co.:
Clipper Publishing Corp.Editions: 2— The Clipper Weekly and Lac du Bonnet Clipper
Digital Platform - Mobile: Apple, Android, Windows, Blackberry, Other
Digital Platform - Tablet: Apple iOS, Android, Windows 7, Blackberry Tablet OS, Nook, Other
Publisher.................................. Kim MacAulay
Editor .... Mark Buss
Delivery Method: Mail, Newsstand, Racks
Areas Served: R0E 0A0, R0E 0C0, R0E 1M0, R0E 0K0, R0E 0Z0, R0E 0R0, R0E 0T0, R0E 1A0, R0E 1Z0, R0E 0X0, R0E 0Y0, R0E 1A0, R0E 1J0, R0E 1L0, R0E 1M0, R0E 1R0, R0E 1T0, R0E 1V0, R0E 1X0, R0E 1Y0, R0E 1Z0, R0E 2A0, R0E 2B0, R0E 2G0

BOISSEVAIN

THE BOISSEVAIN RECORDER

(Fri)
425 South Railway Street, Boissevain, MB, R0K 0E0, Canada, Canada; gen tel (204) 534-6479; gen fax (204) 534-2977; disp adv e-mail ads@therecorder.ca; class adv e-mail mail@therecorder.ca; ed e-mail editor@therecorder.ca; web site www.therecorder.ca
Circulation: 3,863pd, 44fr; VAC
Advertising: $.50 per agate line.
Established: 1899.
Ed. .... Lorraine E. Houston
Mechanical Specifications: Type page 10 x 14; E - 6 cols, 1 3/5, 1/6 between; A - 6 cols, 1 3/5, 1/6 between; C - 6 cols, 1 3/5, 1/6 between.
Equipment & Software: : Hardware — APP/Mac; Presses — ABD/360; Software — Adobe/PageMaker 6.5.
Delivery Method: Mail, Newsstand
Areas Served: Canada

BRANDON

WESTMAN JOURNAL

(Thur)
315 College Avenue, Unit D, Brandon, MB, R7A 1E7, Canada; gen tel (204) 725-0209; gen fax (204) 725-3021; disp adv e-mail rthomson@wheatcityjournal.ca; class adv e-mail agrelowshi@wheatcityjournal.ca; ed e-mail newsroom@wheatcityjournal.ca; web site www.westmanjournal.com
Circulation: 13,500fr; VAC
Established: 2002.
Parent Co.:
Glacier Media GroupRick Thomson
Alida Grelowski
Adam Wilken
Jamie Polmateer
Wade Branston
Brian Aitkinson
Admin Asst....................................... Judy Cluff
Delivery Method: Carrier, Racks
Areas Served: Brandon, MB

CARBERRY

CARBERRY NEWS EXPRESS

(Mon)
34 Main St. W., Carberry, MB, R0K 0H0, Canada; gen tel (204) 834-2153; gen fax (204) 834-2714; disp adv e-mail ads@carberrynews.ca; ed e-mail kathy@carberrynews.ca; web site www.carberrynews.ca
Circulation: 593pd, 34fr; VAC
Advertising: Open inch rate $0.60.
Established: 1910.
Parent Co.:
FP Newspapers Inc.
Gen. Mgr. .... Kathy Carr
Eva Rutz
Mechanical Specifications: Type page 11 1/2 x 17; E - 5 cols, 1 7/8, 1/8 between; A - 6 cols, 1 5/8, 1/8 between; C - 6 cols, 1 5/8, 1/8 between.
Equipment & Software: : Hardware — APP/Mac; Presses — SLN, A-M/multi 11 x 17, HI/10 x 14; Software — QPS/QuarkXPress.
Delivery Method: Mail, Newsstand, Racks
Areas Served: Carberry, RM of North Cypress, Manitoba, Saskatchewan, Alberta, British Columbia, Ontario

CARMAN

THE VALLEY LEADER

(Thur)
4 - 1st St Sw, Carman, MB, R0G 0J0, Canada, Canada; gen tel (204) 745-2051; gen fax (204) 745-3976; disp adv e-mail Darcie.Morris@sunmedia.ca; ed e-mail winkler.news@sunmedia.ca; web site http://www.pembinatoday.ca/carmanvalleyleader
Circulation: 955pd, 3,872fr; VAC
Advertising: Open inch rate $1.10.
Established: 1896.
Parent Co.:
Postmedia Network Inc.
Quebecor Communications, Inc.
Adv Dir.. Darcie Morris
Ed .... Greg Vandermeulen
Mechanical Specifications: Type page 11 1/2 x 15; E - 6 cols, 1 1/2, 1/8 between; A - 6 cols, 1 1/2, 1/8 between; C - 8 cols, 1 3/16, 1/8 between.
Equipment & Software: : Hardware — APP/Mac; Software — QPS/QuarkXPress.
Areas Served: Canada

CARTWRIGHT

SOUTHERN MANITOBA REVIEW
(Thur)
B-635 Bowles St., Cartwright, MB, R0K 0L0, Canada; gen tel (204) 529-2342; gen fax (204) 529-2029; ed e-mail cartnews@mts.net; web site www.southernmanitobareview.com
Circulation: 790pd, 10fr; CMCA
Advertising: Open inch rate $.50.
Established: 1899.
Ed. .... Vicki Wallace
Mechanical Specifications: Type page 11 1/2 x 15 1/2; E - 6 cols, 1.6", 1/6 between; A - 6 cols, 1.6", 1/6 between; C - 6 cols, 1.6", 1/6 between.
Equipment & Software: : Hardware — IBM; Software — Adobe InDesign
Delivery Method: Mail
Areas Served: Canada

DAUPHIN

DAUPHIN HERALD
(Tues)
120 1st Ave. Ne, Dauphin, MB, R7N 1A5, Canada, Canada; gen tel (204) 638-4420; gen fax (204) 638-8760; disp adv e-mail bwright@mymts.net; class adv e-mail classifieds@dauphinherald.com; ed e-mail psbailey@mymts.net; web site www.dauphinherald.com
Circulation: 1,189pd, 59fr; VAC
Advertising: Open inch rate $1.06.
Established: 1916.
Pub./Owner .... Robert F. Gilroy
Adv. Mgr. .... Brent Wright
Circ. Mgr. .... Mandy Carderry
Ed. .... Shawn Bailey
Mechanical Specifications: Type page 10 1/4 x 16; E - 6 cols, 1 7/12, 1/8 between; A - 6 cols, 1 7/12, 1/8 between; C - 6 cols, 1 7/12, 1/8 between.
Equipment & Software: : Hardware — IBM; Presses — G/Community; Software — QPS/QuarkXPress 4.0, Adobe/Illustrator 8.0, Adobe/Photoshop 5.0, Adobe/Acrobat 5.0.
Delivery Method: Mail, Newsstand, Carrier, Racks
Areas Served: Canada

DELORAINE

THE DELORAINE TIMES AND STAR
(Fri)
122 Broadway, N., Deloraine, MB, R0M 0M0, Canada; gen tel (204) 747-2249; gen fax (204) 747-3999; disp adv e-mail ads.cpocket@mts.net; ed e-mail cpocket@mts.net; web site http://www.delorainetimes.ca
Circulation: 770pd, 57fr; VAC
Advertising: Open inch rate $.52.
Established: 1887.
Parent Co.:
Corner Pocket Publishing Ltd.
Glacier Media Group
Office Mgr. .... Judy Wells
Equipment & Software: : Hardware — APP/Mac; Software — Adobe/PageMaker, Adobe/Photoshop.
Delivery Method: Mail, Racks
Areas Served: R0M IL0, R0K 0E0, R0M 0M0, R0M 0X0, R0M IK0, R0M 2E0

EMERSON

THE SOUTHEAST JOURNAL
(Thur)
108 Church Street, Emerson, MB, R0A 0L0, Manitoba, Canada; gen tel (204) 373-2493; adv tel (204) 373-2493; ed tel (204) 373-2493; gen fax (204)-272-3492; disp adv e-mail sej@mts.net; class adv e-mail sej@mts.net; ed e-mail sej@mts.net; web site www.southeastjournal.ca
Circulation: 14pd, 3,500fr; VAC
Delivery Method: Mail
Areas Served: Manitoba

FLIN FLON

FLIN FLON REMINDER
(Wed, Fri)
14 North Ave., Flin Flon, MB, R8A 0T2, Canada; gen tel (204) 687-3454; gen fax (204) 687-4473; disp adv e-mail ads@thereminder.ca; class adv e-mail sales@thereminder.ca; ed e-mail news@thereminder.ca; web site www.thereminder.ca
Circulation: 12pd, 38fr; VAC
Advertising: Open inch rate $.65.
Established: 1946.
Parent Co.:
Glacier Media Group
Pub .... Valerie Durnin
Ed .... Jonathon Naylor
Office Admin .... Shannon Thompson
Areas Served: Flin Flon

GLENBORO

GAZETTE
(Tues)
702 Railway Ave., Glenboro, MB, R0K 0X0, Canada, Canada; gen tel (204) 827-2343; gen fax (204) 827-2207; disp adv e-mail gazette2@mts.net; ed e-mail gazette@mts.net; web site http://www.baldur-glenborogazette.ca/
Circulation: 1,557pd, 0fr; CMCA
Advertising: Open inch rate $5.10.
Mike Johnson
Travis JohnsonEd./Pub/Advs
Mechanical Specifications: Type page 12 x 15 1/2; E - 5 cols, 1 3/4, 1/4 between; A - 5 cols, 1 3/4, 1/4 between; C - 5 cols, 1 3/4, 1/4 between.
Equipment & Software: : Hardware — IBM.
Areas Served: Canada

GRANDVIEW

THE EXPONENT
(Tues)
414 Main St., Grandview, MB, R0L 0Y0, Canada; gen tel (204) 546-2555; gen fax (204) 546-3081; ed e-mail expos@mts.net; web site www.grandviewexponent.com
Circulation: 1,687pd, 27fr; VAC
Advertising: Open line rate $.54.
Established: 1901.
Ed. .... Clayton Chaloner
Mechanical Specifications: Type page 10 1/4 x 14 1/4; E - 6 cols, 1 7/12, 1/6 between; A - 6 cols, 1 7/12, 1/6 between; C - 6 cols, 1 7/12, 1/6 between.
Equipment & Software: ; Software — Microsoft/Windows XP Professional, Adobe/PageMaker 7.0.
Delivery Method: Mail, Newsstand
Areas Served: Rol oyo R0L 0X0 and others

KILLARNEY

KILLARNEY GUIDE
(Fri)
336 Park St., Killarney, MB, R0K 1G0, Canada; gen tel (204) 523-4611; gen fax (204) 523-4445; disp adv e-mail ads@killarneyguide.ca; ed e-mail news@killarneyguide.ca; web site http://new.killarneyguide.ca/
Circulation: 56pd, 134fr; VAC
Advertising: Open inch rate $.50.
Ed. .... Jay Struth
Adv. Mgr. .... Wendy Johnston
Circ Mgr .... Iris Krahn
Mechanical Specifications: Type page 15 x 14 1/2; E - 6 cols, 1 7/12, 3/4 between; A - 6 cols, 1 7/12, 3/4 between; C - 6 cols, 1 7/12, 3/4 between.
Equipment & Software: : Hardware — APP/Mac; Software — Adobe/PageMaker, Multi-Ad.
Areas Served: R0K 1G0 and many more

MANITOU

THE WESTERN CANADIAN
(Tues)
424 Ellis Ave. E., Manitou, MB, R0G 1G0, Canada, Canada; gen tel (204) 242-2555; gen fax (204) 242-3137; ed e-mail thewesterncanadian@gmail.com; web site http://www.thewesterncanadian.ca/
Circulation: 1,057pd, 0fr; VAC
Advertising: Open inch rate $.52.
Ed. .... Grant Howett
Mechanical Specifications: Type page 10 1/4 x 14; E - 5 cols, 2, 1/8 between; A - 5 cols, 2, 1/8 between; C - 5 cols, 2, 1/8 between.
Equipment & Software: : Hardware — IBM.
Areas Served: Canada

MELITA

MELITA NEW ERA
(Fri)
128 Main St., Melita, MB, R0M 1L0, Canada; gen tel (204) 522-3491; gen fax (204) 522-3648; disp adv e-mail ads.cpocket@mts.net; ed e-mail cpocket@mts.net; web site http://www.melitanewera.ca/
Circulation: 1,104pd, 0fr; CMCA
Advertising: Open inch rate $.52.
Established: 1916.
Parent Co.:
Glacier Media Group
Ed. .... Patty Lewis
Mechanical Specifications: Type page 10 1/4 x 14; E - 6 cols, 1 3/5, 1/16 between; A - 6 cols, 1 3/5, 1/16 between; C - 6 cols, 1 3/5, 1/16 between.
Equipment & Software: : Hardware — APP/Mac; Software — Multi-Ad/Creator.
Areas Served: Canada

MINNEDOSA

MINNEDOSA TRIBUNE
(Fri)
14 3rd Ave. Sw, Minnedosa, MB, R0J 1E0, Canada; gen tel (204) 867-3816; gen fax (204) 867-5171; disp adv e-mail adsales@minnedosatribune.com; class adv e-mail class@minnedosatribune.com; ed e-mail editor@minnedosatribune.com; web site www.minnedosatribune.com
Circulation: 456pd, 258fr; VAC
Advertising: Open inch rate $.65.
Established: 1883.
Pub./Ed .... Darryl Holyk
Adv .... Heather Horner
Office Mgr/Class. .... Georgia Kerluke
Mechanical Specifications: Type page 10 1/2 x 16; E - 6 cols, between; A - 6 cols, between; C - 6 cols, between.
Equipment & Software: : Hardware — IBM; Software — Adobe/PageMaker 6.5, Archetype/Corel Draw 8, Adobe/Photoshop 5.0.
Areas Served: Minnedosa

MORDEN

MORDEN TIMES
(Thur)
104 Eighth St., Morden, MB, R6M 1Y7, Canada, Canada; gen tel (204) 822-4421; gen fax (204) 822-4079; disp adv e-mail Darcie.Morris@sunmedia.ca; ed e-mail winkler.news@sunmedia.ca; web site www.mordentimes.com
Circulation: 4,924pd, 5,418fr; VAC
Advertising: Open inch rate $1.10.
Parent Co.:
Postmedia Network Inc.
Quebecor Communications, Inc.
Adv Dir .... Darcie Morris
Ed .... Greg Vandermeulen
Mechanical Specifications: Type page 10 5/16 x 14; E - 6 cols, 1 7/12, 1/6 between; A - 6 cols, 1 7/12, 1/6 between; C - 8 cols, 1 1/4, 1/12 between.
Equipment & Software: : Hardware — APP/Mac; Software — QPS/QuarkXPress.
Areas Served: Canada

NEEPAWA

NEEPAWA BANNER
(Fri)
243 Hamilton St., Neepawa, MB, R0J 1H0, Canada; gen tel (204) 476-3401; gen fax (204) 476-5073; ed e-mail nekwaddell@neepawabanner.com; web site www.neepawabanner.com
Circulation: 92pd, 8,179fr; VAC
Advertising: Open inch rate $1.00.
Established: 1989.
Pub/Ed. .... Ken Waddell
Mechanical Specifications: Type page 7 x 14; E - 8 cols, 1 7/8, 3/8 between; A - 6 cols, 1 5/8, 3/8 between; C - 6 cols, 1 5/8, 3/8 between.
Equipment & Software: : Hardware — APP/Power Mac; Software — Adobe/PageMaker 6.0, Microsoft/Word 5.0, Adobe/FileMaker Pro.
Areas Served: Neepawa

THE NEEPAWA BANNER AND PRESS
(Fri)
423 Hamilton St., Neepawa, MB, R0J 1H0, Canada; gen tel (204) 476-3401; gen fax (204) 476-5073; disp adv e-mail ads@neepawabanner.com; class adv e-mail print@neepawabanner.com; ed e-mail news@neepawabanner.com; web site www.neepawabanner.com
Circulation: 100pd, 8,200fr; VAC
Advertising: 1.01.
Established: 1896.
Parent Co.:
Neepawa Banner
Digital Platform - Mobile: Apple
Digital Platform - Tablet: Apple iOS
Ed .... Kate Atkinson
Mechanical Specifications: Type page 10 3/8 x 16; E - 6 cols, 1 9/16, 1/6 between; A - 6 cols, 1 9/16, 1/6 between; C - 6 cols, 1 9/16, 1/6 between.
Equipment & Software: : Hardware — APP/Mac; Software — QPS/QuarkXPress 5.0, Adobe/Adobe Photoshop 7.0.
Delivery Method: Mail, Newsstand, Racks
Areas Served: R0J

PILOT MOUND

THE SENTINEL COURIER
(Tues)
13 Railway St., Pilot Mound, MB, R0G 1P0, Canada; gen tel (204) 825-2772; gen fax (204) 825-2439; ed e-mail sentinel@mymts.net ; web site www.sentinelcourier.com
Circulation: 1,273pd, 31fr; VAC
Advertising: Open inch rate $.52.
Ed. .... Susan Peterson
Mechanical Specifications: Type page 10 1/2 x 14; E - 5 cols, 2, 1/4 between; A - 5 cols, 2, 1/4 between.
Equipment & Software: : Hardware — APP/Mac; Software — QPS/QuarkXPress.
Areas Served: Pilot Mound

PORTAGE LA PRAIRIE

CENTRAL PLAINS HERALD LEADER
(Thur)
1941 Saskatchewan Ave. W., Portage La Prairie, MB, R1N 0R7, Canada; gen tel (204) 857-3427; gen fax (204) 239-1270; disp adv e-mail daria.zmiyiwsky@sunmedia.ca; ed e-mail mickey.dumont@sunmedia.ca; web site http://www.portagedailygraphic.com/
Circulation: 4,551pd, 9,595fr; VAC

Advertising: Open inch rate $1.65.
Parent Co.:
Postmedia Network Inc.
Quebecor Communications, Inc.
Class./Circ. Mgr. .... Guey Fiset
Adv. Dir .... Daria Zmiyiwsky
Ed .... Mickey Dumont
Mechanical Specifications: Type page 14 x 22 3/4; E - 6 cols, 2 1/8, 1/8 between; A - 6 cols, 2 1/8, 1/8 between; C - 6 cols, 2 1/8, 1/8 between.
Equipment & Software: : Hardware — APP/Mac; Presses — G; Software — Adobe/Photoshop, Baseview/NewsEdit, Adobe/Typestyler, QPS/QuarkXPress.
Areas Served: Central Plains

RESTON

THE RESTON RECORDER

(Fri)
330 4th St., Reston, MB, R0M 1X0, Canada, Canada; gen tel (204) 877-3321; gen fax (204) 522-3648; ed e-mail recorder@mts.net; web site http://www.restonrecorder.ca/
Circulation: 116pd, 59fr; VAC
Advertising: Open inch rate $.52.
Parent Co.:
Glacier Media Group
Office Mgr. .... Dolores Caldwell
Pub/Ed. .... Patty Lewis
Mechanical Specifications: Type page 10 1/2 x 14; E - 6 cols, 1 3/5, 1/6 between; A - 6 cols, 1 3/5, 1/6 between; C - 6 cols, 1 3/5, 1/6 between.
Equipment & Software: : Hardware — APP/Mac; Software — Multi-Ad/Creator.
Areas Served: Canada

RIVERS

RIVERS BANNER GAZETTE-REPORTER

(Fri)
529 2nd Ave., Rivers, MB, R0K 1X0, Riverdale, Canada; gen tel (204) 328-7494; gen fax (204) 328-5212; ed e-mail kwaddell@neepawabanner.com; web site www.rivers-banner.com
Circulation: 93pd, 1,668fr; VAC
Advertising: Open inch rate $.77.
Established: 1993.
Parent Co.:
Neepawa Banner
Pub/Ed. .... Ken Waddell
Gen. Mgr. .... Sheila Runions
Mechanical Specifications: Type page 10 x 14; E - 2 cols, 3 1/4, 1/4 between; A - 6 cols, 1 5/8, 1/4 between; C - 8 cols, 1 5/8, 1/4 between.
Equipment & Software: : Hardware — iMac; Software — FileMaker Pro 6, Adobe inDesign CS4, Adobe Photoshop CS4, Adobe Bridge CS4, Adobe Acrobat 9 Pro, Open Office 3
Delivery Method: Mail
Areas Served: Riverdale

ROBLIN

THE ROBLIN REVIEW

(Tues)
119 First Ave. Nw, Roblin, MB, R0L 1P0, Canada; gen tel (204) 937-8377; gen fax (204) 937-8212; disp adv e-mail reviewads@mts.net; class adv e-mail reviewads@mts.net; ed e-mail rreview@mts.net; web site theroblinreview.com
Circulation: 50pd, 26fr; VAC
Advertising: Open inch rate $.59.
Established: 1913.
Circ. Mgr. .... Patricia Liske
Ed. .... Ed Doering
Production Mgr. .... Brent Wright
Ad. consultant .... Jackie Edel
Mechanical Specifications: Type page 11 1/4 x 17; E - 6 cols, 1 5/8, 2/16 between; A - 6 cols, 1 5/8, 2/16 between; C - 6 cols, 1 5/8, 1/8 between.
Equipment & Software: : Hardware — IBM; Software — QPS/QuarkXPress.
Delivery Method: Mail, Racks
Areas Served: Roblin, MB

RUSSELL

BANNER

(Tues)
455 Main St., Russell, MB, R0J 1W0, Canada; gen tel (204) 773-2069; gen fax (204) 773-2645; disp adv e-mail ads@russellbanner.com; ed e-mail editor@russellbanner.com; web site www.russellbanner.com
Circulation: 2,654pd, 19fr; VAC
Advertising: Open inch rate $.59.
Adv .... Jessica Ludwig
Circ .... Pauline Olarte
Ed .... Racheal Scratch
Mechanical Specifications: Type page 11 1/2 x 17; E - 5 cols, 2, between; A - 5 cols, 2, between; C - 5 cols, 2, between.
Equipment & Software: : Hardware — APP/Mac; Presses — ABD.
Areas Served: Russell and area

SAINT BONIFACE

LA LIBERTE

(Wed)
Po Box 190, Saint Boniface, MB, R2H 3B4, Canada; gen tel (204) 237-4823; gen fax (204) 231-1998; ed e-mail la-liberte@la-liberte.mb.ca; web site http://la-liberte.mb.ca/tag/saint-boniface
Circulation: 0pd, 12fr; VAC
Advertising: Open inch rate $1.69.
Established: 1913.
Dir/Ed. .... Sophie Gaulin
Assoc. Ed. .... Bernard Bocquel
Office Admin .... Roxanne Bouchard
Mechanical Specifications: Type page 10 3/8 x 15 3/8; E - 5 cols, 1 15/16, 1/6 between; A - 5 cols, 1 15/16, 1/6 between; C - 5 cols, 1 15/16, 1/6 between.
Equipment & Software: : Hardware — APP/Mac; Software — QPS/QuarkXPress 4.0.
Delivery Method: Mail, Carrier
Areas Served: Winnipeg/Manitoba/CAnada/ R2H Manitoba
Canada

SELKIRK

SELKIRK JOURNAL

(Thur)
366 Main St, Unit 300, Selkirk, MB, R1A 2J7, Canada; gen tel (204) 482-7402; gen fax (204) 482-3336; disp adv e-mail jbilsky@postmedia.com; ed e-mail bjones@postmedia.com; web site http://www.interlaketoday.ca/selkirkjournal
Circulation: 14,334fr; VAC
Advertising: Open inch rate $1.33.
Parent Co.:
Postmedia Network Inc.
Quebecor Communications, Inc.
Adv Dir .... Jenifer Bilsky
Ed .... Brook Jones
Mechanical Specifications: Type page 10 1/8 x 14; E - 6 cols, 1 7/12, 1/6 between; A - 6 cols, 1 7/12, 1/6 between; C - 6 cols, 1 7/12, 1/6 between.
Equipment & Software: : Hardware — APP/Mac; Presses — G/Urbanite; Software — QPS/QuarkXPress 4.0.
Areas Served: Selkirk

SHOAL LAKE

CROSSROADS THIS WEEK

(Fri)
353 Station Road, Shoal Lake, MB, R0J 1Z0, Canada, Canada; gen tel (204) 759-2644; adv tel (204) 759-2644; ed tel (204) 759-2644; gen fax (204) 759-2521; adv fax (204) 759-2521; ed fax (204) 759-2521; disp adv e-mail ctwdisplay@mymts.net; class adv e-mail ctwclassified@mymts.net; ed e-mail ctwnews@mymts.net; web site www.crossroadsthisweek.com
Circulation: 2,294pd, 25fr; VAC
Advertising: Open Inch Rate $13.16.
Established: 1977.
Parent Co.:
Nesbitt Publishing Ltd.
Advertising Manager .... Connie Kay
Classified/Accounting .... Michelle Genslorek
News Reporter .... Darrell Nesbitt
Publisher .... Ryan Nesbitt
News Reporter .... Marcie Harrison
Mechanical Specifications: Type page 10 5/16 x 14 1/4; E - 6 cols, 1 9/16, 1/6 between; A - 6 cols, 1 9/16, 1/6 between; C - 6 cols, 1 9/16, 1/6 between.
Equipment & Software: : Hardware — IMAC G5s; Software — Multi-Ad/Creator 8.0.2
Delivery Method: Mail, Newsstand
Areas Served: Canada

SOUTH MOUNTAIN PRESS

(Fri)
353 Station Road, Shoal Lake, MB, R0J 1Z0, Yellowhead, Canada; gen tel (204) 759-2644; adv tel (204) 759-2644; ed tel (204) 759-2644; gen fax (204) 759-2521; adv fax (204) 759-2521; ed fax (204) 759-2521; disp adv e-mail smpdisplay@mymts.net; class adv e-mail smpclassified@mymts.net; ed e-mail smpnews@mymts.net
Circulation: 46pd, 1,492fr; VAC
Advertising: 10.64.
Established: 2005.
Parent Co.:
Nesbitt Publishing Ltd.
Advertising .... Connie Kay
Editor .... Marcie Harrison
Classified/Accounting .... Michelle Gensiorek
Publisher .... Ryan Nesbitt
Reporter/Photographer .... Darrell Nesbitt
Delivery Method: Racks
Areas Served: Yellowhead

SOURIS

SOURIS PLAINDEALER

(Fri)
53 Crescent Ave. W., Souris, MB, R0K 2C0, Canada, Canada; gen tel (204) 483-2070; gen fax (204) 522-3648; ed e-mail spdealer@mts.net; web site http://www.sourisplaindealer.ca/
Circulation: 54fr; VAC
Advertising: Open inch rate $.52.
Parent Co.:
Glacier Media Group
Office Mgr. .... Darcy Semeschuk
Pub/Ed. .... Patti Lewis
Mechanical Specifications: Type page 10 x 14; E - 6 cols, 1 7/12, 1/6 between; A - 6 cols, 1 7/12, 1/6 between; C - 6 cols, 1 7/12, 1/6 between.
Equipment & Software: : Hardware — PC; Software — Adobe/PageMaker.
Areas Served: Canada

STEINBACH

THE CARILLON

(Thur)
377 Main St., Steinbach, MB, R5G 1A5, Canada, Canada; gen tel (204) 326-3421; gen fax (204) 326-4860; disp adv e-mail ads@thecarillon.com; class adv e-mail mgauthier@thecarillon.com; ed e-mail gburr@thecarillon.com; web site www.thecarillon.com
Circulation: 1,140pd, 234fr; VAC
Advertising: Open inch rate $1.45.
Pub/Gen. Mgr. .... Laurie Finley
Ed .... Grant Burr
Circ Mgr. .... Holly-Jaide Nickel
Mechanical Specifications: Type page 11 1/2 x 17; E - 5 cols, 2 1/6, between; A - 5 cols, 2 1/6, between; C - 5 cols, 2 1/6, between.
Equipment & Software: : Hardware — PC; Presses — ABD, 2-GTO, 1-Miller, 1-Komari; Software — Microsoft/Windows, NetWare.
Areas Served: Canada

STONEWALL

THE INTERLAKE SPECTATOR

(Thur)
3411 3rd Avenue South, Unit 3, Stonewall, MB, R0C 2Z0, Canada; gen tel (204) 467-2421; gen fax (204) 467-5967; disp adv e-mail jbilsky@postmedia.com; ed e-mail bjones@postmedia.com; web site http://www.interlaketoday.ca/interlakespectator
Circulation: 1,520pd, 10,780fr; VAC
Advertising: Open inch rate $1.28.
Parent Co.:
Postmedia Network Inc.
Quebecor Communications, Inc.
Adv Dir. .... Jenifer Bilsky
Ed .... Brook Jones
Areas Served: Stonewall

THE STONEWALL ARGUS & TEULON TIMES

(Thur)
3411 3rd Avenue South, Stonewall, MB, R0C 2Z0, Canada, Canada; gen tel (204) 467-2421; gen fax (204) 467-5967; disp adv e-mail jbilsky@postmedia.com; ed e-mail bjones@postmedia.com; web site http://www.interlaketoday.ca/stonewallargusteulontimes
Circulation: 1,219pd, 6,467fr; VAC
Advertising: Open inch rate $1.05.
Parent Co.:
Postmedia Network Inc.
Quebecor Communications, Inc.
Ed .... Brook Jones
Adv Dir .... Jenifer Bilsky
Mechanical Specifications: Type page 10 1/8 x 14; E - 6 cols, 1 7/12, 1/6 between; A - 6 cols, 1 7/12, 1/6 between; C - 6 cols, 1 7/12, 1/6 between.
Equipment & Software: : Hardware — APP/Mac; Presses — G/Urbanite; Software — QPS/QuarkXPress 4.0.
Areas Served: Canada

SWAN RIVER

SWAN VALLEY STAR & TIMES

(Tues)
704 Main St. E., Swan River, MB, R0L 1Z0, Canada; gen tel (204) 734-3858; gen fax (204) 734-4935; disp adv e-mail info@starandtimes.ca; class adv e-mail info@starandtimes.ca; ed e-mail editor@starandtimes.ca; web site www.starandtimes.ca
Circulation: 2,700pd, 0fr; CMCA
Advertising: Open agate line rate $.76.
Established: 1900.
Adv. Mgr., Publ., Gen. Mgr., Owner .... Brian T. Gilroy
Ed. .... Danielle Gordon-Broome
Mechanical Specifications: Type page 12 x 21; E - 6 cols, 2, 1/6 between; A - 6 cols, between; C - 6 cols, between.
Equipment & Software: : Hardware — IBM; Software — Adobe/PageMaker 6.0, Archetype/Corel Draw 6.0, QPS/QuarkXPress 4.0.
Delivery Method: Mail, Newsstand, Racks
Areas Served: Canada

THE PAS

OPASQUIA TIMES

(Wed, Fri)
352 Fischer Avenue, Box 750, The Pas, MB, R9A 1K8, Canada; gen tel (204) 623-3435; gen fax (204) 623-5601; disp adv e-mail opads@mymts.net; class adv e-mail opclass@mymts.net; ed e-mail opeditor@mymts.net; web site www.opasquiatimes.com
Circulation: 1,200pd, 0fr; VAC
Established: 1978.
Gen. Mgr. .... Jennifer Cook
Ed. .... Trent Allen
Areas Served: Opasquia

THOMPSON

THOMPSON CITIZEN/NICKEL BELT NEWS

(Fri)
141 Commercial Pl., Thompson, MB, R8N 1T1, Canada, Canada; gen tel (204) 677-4534; adv tel (204) 677-4534 ext 1; ed tel (204) 677-4534 ext 6; gen fax (204) 677-3681; disp adv e-mail ads@thompsoncitizen.net; ed e-mail editor@thompsoncitizen.net; web site www.thompsoncitizen.net
Circulation: 61pd, 6,000fr; Sworn/Estimate/Non-Audited
Advertising: Open inch rate $1.45 Nickel Belt News.
Established: 1961.
Parent Co.:
Glacier Media Group
Digital Platform - Mobile: Apple
Digital Platform - Tablet: Apple iOS
Gen. Mgr. .... Lynn Taylor
Ed. .... Ian Graham
Mechanical Specifications: Type page 9 1/2 x 15; A - 5 cols, 1 3/4, between; C - 1 cols, 1 3/4, between.
Delivery Method: Racks
Areas Served: Canada

TREHERNE

TIMES

(Mon)
194 Broadway St., Treherne, MB, R0G 2V0, Canada; gen tel (204) 723-2542; gen fax (204) 723-2754; ed e-mail trehernetimes@mts.net; web site www.trehernetimes.ca
Circulation: 842fr; VAC
Advertising: Open inch rate $.78.
Ed. .... Gary Lodwick
Areas Served: Treherne

VIRDEN

VIRDEN EMPIRE-ADVANCE

(Fri)
305 Nelson Street West, Virden, MB, R0M 2C0, Canada, Canada; gen tel (204) 748-3931; gen fax (204) 748-1816; disp adv e-mail virden@empireadvance.ca; ed e-mail manager@empireadvance.ca; web site http://www.empireadvance.ca/
Circulation: 27fr; VAC
Advertising: Open inch rate $.53.
Parent Co.:
Glacier Media Group
Gen Mgr .... Cheryl Rushing
Mechanical Specifications: Type page 10 1/4 x 15 3/4; E - 6 cols, 1 7/12, 1/6 between; A - 6 cols, 1 7/12, 1/6 between; C - 6 cols, 1 7/12, 1/6 between.
Equipment & Software: : Hardware — Pentium/PC; Software — Adobe/PageMaker 6.5, Archetype/Corel Draw 4.0, Adobe/Illustrator 7.0, Adobe/Acrobat 4.0.
Areas Served: Canada

WINKLER

WINKLER TIMES

(Thur)
583 Main St., Winkler, MB, R6W 4B3, Canada, Canada; gen tel (204) 325-4771; gen fax (204) 325-8646; disp adv e-mail Darcie.Morris@sunmedia.ca; ed e-mail winkler.news@sunmedia.ca; web site http://www.pembinatoday.ca/winklertimes
Circulation: 7,459fr; VAC
Advertising: Open inch rate $1.17.
Established: 1997.
Parent Co.:
Postmedia Network Inc.
Quebecor Communications, Inc.
Adv Dir .... Darcie Morris
Ed .... Greg Vandermeulen
Mechanical Specifications: Type page 10 5/6 x 14; E - 6 cols, 1 7/12, 1/6 between; A - 6 cols, 1 7/12, 1/6 between; C - 8 cols, 1 1/4, 1/12 between.
Equipment & Software: : Hardware — APP/Mac; Software — QPS/QuarkXPress.
Delivery Method: Mail, Carrier, Racks
Areas Served: Canada

WINNIPEG

THE HEADLINER

(Wed)
1355 Mountain Ave., Winnipeg, MB, R2X 3B6, Canada; gen tel (204) 697-7021; adv tel (204) 697-7021; ed tel (204) 697-7093; gen fax (204) 953-4300; disp adv e-mail sales@canstarnews.com; class adv e-mail classified@canstarnews.com; ed e-mail letters@canstarnews.com; web site www.canstarnews.com
Circulation: 43pd, 5,372fr; Sworn/Estimate/Non-Audited
Established: 1992.
Parent Co.:
Winnipeg Free Press
Managing Editor .... John Kendle
Sales Manager .... Barb Borden
Delivery Method: Carrier, Racks
Areas Served: Headingley, St. François Xavier, Cartier, Macdonald, Marquette, Rosser, Fannystelle, Portage la Prairie

THE HERALD

(Wed)
1355 Mountain Ave., Winnipeg, MB, R2X 3B6, Canada; gen tel (204) 697-7009; adv tel (204) 697-7021; gen fax (204) 953-4300; disp adv e-mail sales@canstarnews.com; ed e-mail letters@canstarnews.com; web site www.canstarnews.com
Circulation: 984pd, 43,869fr; VAC
Parent Co.:
Winnipeg Free Press
Digital Platform - Mobile: Other
Digital Platform - Tablet: Other
Natl. Sales Mgr .... Linda MacKenzie
Mng. Ed .... John Kendle
Darren Ridgley
Sales Mgr .... Barb Borden
Equipment & Software: : Hardware — APP/Mac; Software — QPS/QuarkXPress.
Delivery Method: Carrier
Areas Served: R2E, R2C, R2G, R2K, R2L, R3W

THE LANCE

(Wed)
1355 Mountain Ave., Winnipeg, MB, R2X 3B6, Canada; gen tel (204) 697-7009; adv tel (204) 697-7021; ed tel (204) 697-7093; gen fax (204) 953-4300; disp adv e-mail sales@canstarnews.com; class adv e-mail classifieds@canstarnews.com; ed e-mail letters@canstarnews.com; web site www.canstarnews.com
Circulation: 37,996fr; Sworn/Estimate/Non-Audited
Established: 1931.
Parent Co.:
Winnipeg Free Press
Digital Platform - Mobile: Other
Digital Platform - Tablet: Other
Managing Editor .... John Kendle
Deputy Editor .... Darren Ridgley
Executive Assistant .... Linda Mackenzie
Sales Manager .... Barb Borden
Equipment & Software: : Hardware — APP/Mac; Software — QPS/QuarkXPress.
Delivery Method: Carrier
Areas Served: R2H, R2J, R2M, R2N, R3X

THE METRO

(Wed)
1355 Mountain Ave., Winnipeg, MB, R2X 3B6, Canada; gen tel (204) 697-7009; gen fax (204) 953-4300; disp adv e-mail sales@canstarnews.com; ed e-mail letters@canstarnews.com; web site www.canstarnews.com
Circulation: 141pd, 36,979fr; VAC
Established: 1973.
Parent Co.:
Winnipeg Free Press
Digital Platform - Mobile: Other
Digital Platform - Tablet: Other
Mng. Ed .... John Kendle
Deputy Ed .... Darren Ridgley
Exec Asst .... Linda Mackenzie
Sales Mgr .... Barb Borden
Equipment & Software: : Hardware — APP/Mac
Delivery Method: Carrier
Areas Served: R2Y, R3E, R3G, R3J, R3K, R3R

THE SOU'WESTER

(Wed)
1355 Mountain Ave., Winnipeg, MB, R2X 3B6, Canada; gen tel (204) 697-7020; adv tel (204) 697-7021; gen fax (204) 953-4300; disp adv e-mail classifieds@canstarnews.com; ed e-mail letters@canstarnews.com; web site www.winnipegfreepress.com
Circulation: 0pd, 38,583fr; Sworn/Estimate/Non-Audited
Established: 2009.
Parent Co.:
Winnipeg Free Press
Managing Editor .... John Kendle
Sales Manager .... Barb Borden
Areas Served: Southwest Winnipeg

THE TIMES

(Wed)
1355 Mountain Ave., Winnipeg, MB, R2X 3B6, Canada; gen tel (204) 697-7009; adv tel (204) 697-7021; gen fax (204) 953-4300; disp adv e-mail sales@canstarnews.com; ed e-mail letters@canstarnews.com; web site www.canstarnews.com
Circulation: 20pd, 37,763fr; VAC
Parent Co.:
Winnipeg Free Press
Digital Platform - Mobile: Other
Digital Platform - Tablet: Other
Mng. Ed .... John Kendle
Darren Ridgley
Sales Mgr .... Barb Borden
Linda MacKenzie
Mechanical Specifications: Type page 10 1/4 x 16; E - 6 cols, 1 5/8, 3/16 between; A - 6 cols, 1 5/8, between; C - 8 cols, 1 3/16, 1/8 between.
Equipment & Software: : Hardware — APP/Mac; Software — QPS/QuarkXPress.
Delivery Method: Carrier
Areas Served: R2P, R2R, R2V, R2W, R2X

NEW BRUNSWICK

BATHURST

THE NORTHERN LIGHT

(Tues)
355 King Ave., Bathurst, NB, E2A 1P4, Canada, Canada; gen tel (506) 546-4491; gen fax (506) 546-1491; ed e-mail mulock.greg@thenorthernlight.ca; web site https://www.telegraphjournal.com/northern-light/
Circulation: 2,890pd, 12fr; VAC
Advertising: Open inch rate $1.41.
Parent Co.:
Brunswick News, Inc.
Ed. .... Greg Mulock
Mechanical Specifications: Type page 13 x 21 1/2; E - 6 cols, 2 1/12, 1/6 between; A - 6 cols, 2 1/12, 1/6 between; C - 9 cols, 1 1/3, 1/6 between.
Equipment & Software: : Hardware — APP/Mac, Mk; Presses — 4-G/Community; Software — QPS/QuarkXPress.
Areas Served: Canada

CAMPBELLTON

THE TRIBUNE

(Fri)
6 Shannon St., Campbellton, NB, E3N 3G9, Canada; gen tel (506) 753-4413; gen fax (506) 759-9595; ed e-mail tribune@tribunenb.ca; web site http://www.telegraph-journal.com/tribune/
Circulation: 2fr; VAC
Advertising: Open inch rate $.66.
Pub./Ed .... Peter Makintosh
Mechanical Specifications: Type page 12 7/8 x 21; E - 6 cols, 1/6 between; A - 6 cols, 1/6 between; C - 6 cols, 1/6 between.
Equipment & Software: : Hardware — IBM/Pentium; Software — QPS/QuarkXPress, Microsoft/Windows 95.
Areas Served: Campbellton

EDMUNDSTON

LE MADAWASKA

(Sat)
20 Rue Saint Francois, Edmundston, NB, E3V 1E3, Canada; gen tel (506) 735-5575; gen fax (506) 735-8086; ed e-mail mad-production@brunswicknews.com; web site https://www.telegraphjournal.com/le-mad-awaska/
Circulation: 2,561pd, 20fr; VAC
Advertising: Open inch rate $.53.
Parent Co.:
Brunswick News, Inc.
Pub .... Hermel Volpe
Mechanical Specifications: Type page 13 x 21; E - 6 cols, 2 1/8, between; A - 6 cols, 2 1/8, between.
Equipment & Software: : Hardware — APP/Power Mac G3, PC Power 266 mHz Risc Processor; Presses — 8-G/Community; Software — Adobe/PageMaker 6.01.
Areas Served: Edmundston

FREDERICTON

NORTHSIDE THIS WEEK

(Sat)
984 Prospect St., Fredericton, NB, E3B 5A2, Canada; gen tel (506) 452-6671; gen fax (506) 452-7405; ed e-mail shelley.wood@brunswicknews.com
Circulation: 9,950fr; Sworn/Estimate/Non-Audited
Advertising: Open inch rate $.60.
Parent Co.:
Brunswick News, Inc.
Pub./Ed .... Shelly Wood

GRAND FALLS

L' ETOILE CATARACTE

(Thur)
229 Broadway Blvd., Grand Falls, NB, E3Z 2K1, Canada; gen tel (506) 473-3083; gen fax (506) 473-3105; ed e-mail rickard.mark@victoriastar.ca; web site https://www.telegraphjournal.com/letoile/
Circulation: 0pd, 6,296fr; CMCA
Advertising: Open inch rate $.50.
Parent Co.:
Brunswick News, Inc.
Ed. English .... Mark Rickard
Ed., French .... Madeleine Leclerc
Mechanical Specifications: Type page 13 x 21 1/2; E - 6 cols, 2 1/16, 1/6 between; A - 6 cols, 2 1/16, 1/6 between; C - 6 cols, 2 1/16, 1/6 between.
Equipment & Software: : Hardware — APP/Macs; Presses — 5-HI/V-15; Software — Microsoft/Word.
Areas Served: Canada

VICTORIA COUNTY STAR

(Wed)
229 Broadway Blvd., Grand Falls, NB, E3Z 2K1, Canada; gen tel (506) 473-3083; gen fax (506) 473-3105; ed e-mail rickard.mark@victoriastar.ca; web site https://www.telegraphjournal.com/victoria-star/
Circulation: 2,175pd, 2fr; VAC
Advertising: Open inch rate $.65.
Established: 2003.

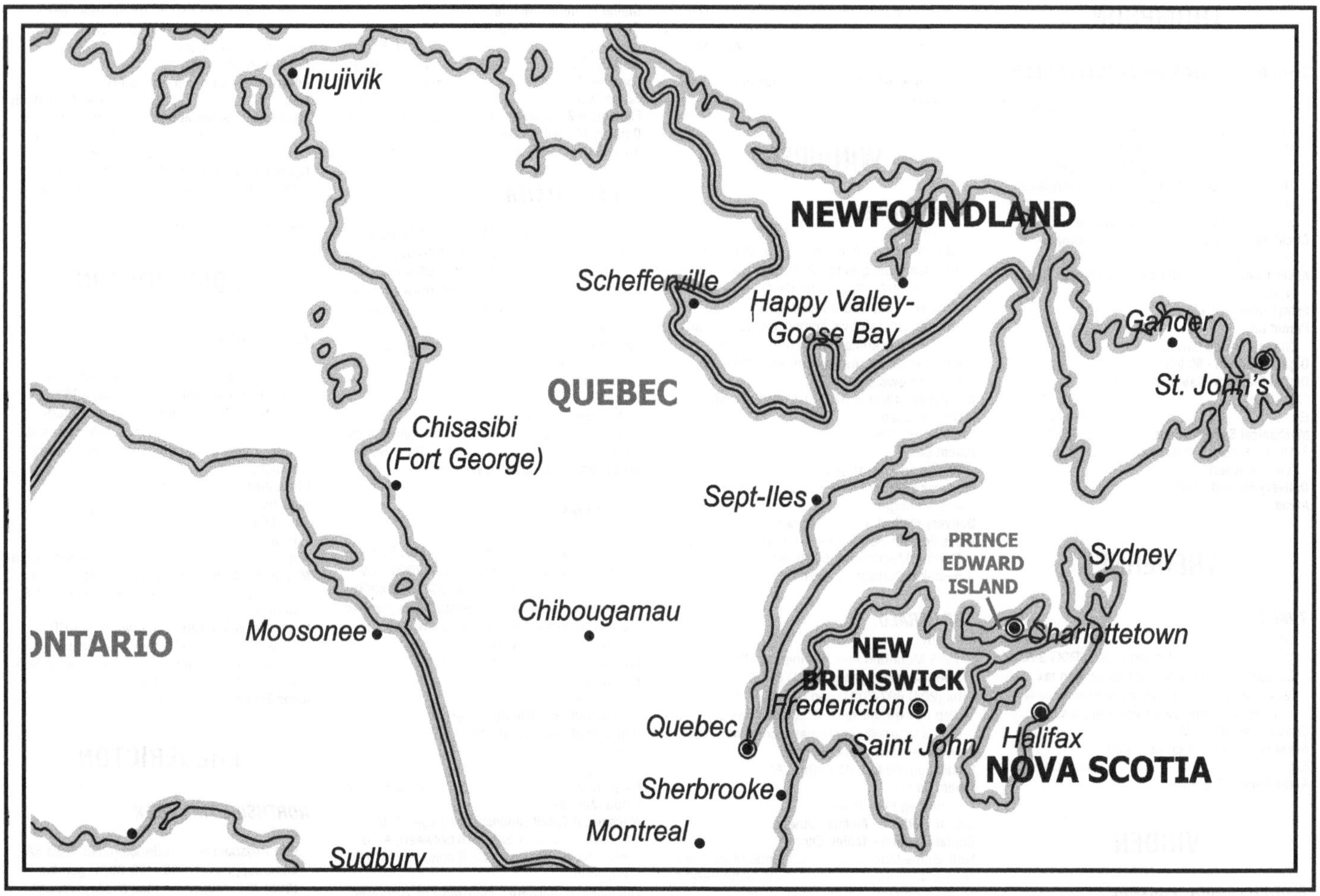

Parent Co.:
Brunswick News, Inc.
Ed., English ....Mark Rickard
Ed., French ....Madeleine Leclerc
Mechanical Specifications: Type page 11 1/2 x 21 1/2; E - 10 cols, 1/8 between; A - 10 cols, 1/8 between; C - 10 cols, 1/8 between.
Equipment & Software: : Hardware — APP/Mac; Software — QPS/QuarkXPress, Adobe/ Photoshop.
Areas Served: Grand Falls

HARTLAND

THE OBSERVER

(Wed)
941 Industrial Dr., Hartland, NB, E7P 2G8, Canada, Canada; gen tel (506) 375-4458; gen fax (506) 375-4281
Circulation: 2,569pd,; Sworn/Estimate/Non-Audited
Advertising: Open inch rate $7.28.
Established: 1909.
Gen. Mgr. ....Stewart Fairgrieve
Mechanical Specifications: Type page 12 x 21; E - 6 cols, 1 7/8, 1/8 between; A - 6 cols, 1 7/8, 1/8 between; C - 6 cols, 1 7/8, 1/8 between.
Equipment & Software: : Hardware — PC; Presses — HI; Software — QPS/QuarkXPress.
Areas Served: Canada

MIRAMICHI

MIRAMICHI LEADER

(Mon, Wed)
175 General Manson Way, Miramichi, NB, E1N 6K7, Canada; gen tel (506) 622-2600; gen fax (506) 622-6506; ed e-mail cook.nancy@miramichileader.com; web site https://www.telegraphjournal.com/miramichi-leader/
Circulation: 3,768pd, 13fr; CMCA
Advertising: Open inch rate $.99.
Parent Co.:
Brunswick News, Inc.
Pub..Nancy Cook
Circ. Mgr..................................Christine Savoy
Mechanical Specifications: Type page 10 9/16 x 16; E - 6 cols, 1 2/3, 1/8 between; A - 6 cols, 1 2/3, 1/8 between; C - 6 cols, 1 2/3, 1/4 between.
Equipment & Software: : Hardware — APP/Mac; Software — QPS/QuarkXPress 15.0, Adobe/ Photoshop 6.
Areas Served: Canada

OROMOCTO

THE OROMOCTO POST-GAZETTE

(Thur)
291 Restigouche Rd., Oromocto, NB, E2V 2H2, Canada; gen tel (506) 357-9813; gen fax (506) 452-7405; disp adv e-mail shelley.wood@brunswicknews.com; ed e-mail williams.kimberly@dailygleaner.com; web site www.brunswicknews.com
Circulation: 0pd, 12,844fr; CMCA
Advertising: Open inch rate $.74.
Parent Co.:
Brunswick News, Inc.
Adv. Mgr.......................................Shelly Wood
Pub/Ed................................Kimberly Williams
Mechanical Specifications: Type page 10 1/4 x 11 1/2; E - 6 cols, 1 3/5, 1/6 between; A - 9 cols, 1, between; C - 8 cols, 1, between.
Equipment & Software: : Hardware — PC, APP/ Mac; Presses — G; Software — QPS/ QuarkXPress, Adobe/PageMaker, Adobe/ Photoshop.
Areas Served: Canada

SACKVILLE

THE SACKVILLE TRIBUNE-POST

(Wed)
80 Main St., Sackville, NB, E4L 4A7, Canada; gen tel (506) 536-2500; gen fax (506) 536-4024; ed fax (506) 536-4024; ed e-mail sdoherty@sackvilletribunepost.com; web site www.sackvilletribunepost.com
Circulation: 2,150pd, 4fr; VAC
Advertising: Open inch rate $.76.
Established: 1902.
Parent Co.:
Transcontinental Media
Pub..Richard Russell
Ed. ....Scott Doherty
Circ/Class. Mgr ....Tanya Austin
Mechanical Specifications: Type page 12 x 21; E - 10 cols, 2, 1/4 between; A - 10 cols, 2, 1/4 between; C - 10 cols, 2, 1/4 between.
Equipment & Software: : Hardware — APP/Mac; Software — QPS/QuarkXPress.
Delivery Method: Mail, Newsstand
Areas Served: Sackville

SAINT JOHN

THE NEW FREEMAN

(Fri)
One Bayard Dr., Saint John, NB, E2L 3L5, Canada, Canada; gen tel (506) 653-6806; gen fax (506) 653-6818; ed e-mail tnf@nb.aibn.com; web site http://www.dioceseofsaintjohn.org/TNF.aspx
Circulation: 7,000pd,; Sworn/Estimate/Non-Audited
Advertising: Open inch rate $15.00.
Established: 1900.
Mng. Ed.....................................Margie Trafton
Mechanical Specifications: Type page 12 x ; E - 5 cols, 2, 1/4 between; A - 5 cols, 2, 1/4 between.
Equipment & Software: : Hardware — Seiko; Software — WordPerfect, Microsoft/Windows, Adobe/PageMaker.
Areas Served: Canada

SAINT STEPHEN

ST. CROIX COURIER

(Tues)
P.O. Box 250, 47 Milltown Boulevard, Saint Stephen, NB, E3L 2X2, Canada, Canada; gen tel (506) 466-3220; gen fax (506) 466-9950; disp adv e-mail cairns@stcroixcourier.ca; ed e-mail editor@stcroixcourier.ca; web site www.stcroixcourier.com
Circulation: 1,075pd, 40fr; VAC
Advertising: Open inch rate $.84.
Established: 1865.
Pub...Leith Orr
Gen. Mgr. ....Shelley McKeeman
Ed ....Krisi Marples
Mechanical Specifications: Type page 13 1/4 x 21; E - 6 cols, 2 1/16, 3/16 between; A - 6 cols, 2 1/16, 3/16 between; C - 6 cols, 2 1/16, 3/16 between.
Equipment & Software: : Hardware — APP/ Mac, COM.
Areas Served: Canada

SHEDIAC

LE MONITEUR ACADIEN

(Wed)
Cp 5191 817, West Boudreau, Shediac, NB, E4P 8T9, Canada; gen tel (506) 532-6680; gen fax (506) 532-6681; web site www.moniteuracadien.com

Circulation: 3,500pd, 500fr; Sworn/Estimate/ Non-Audited
Advertising: Open inch rate $1.15.
Ed. ....Gilles Hache
Mechanical Specifications: Type page 10 2/5 x 13 1/4; E - 5 cols, between; A - 5 cols, between; C - 5 cols, between.
Equipment & Software: : Hardware — APP/Mac; Software — QPS/QuarkXPress 3.3.
Delivery Method: Mail, Newsstand, Carrier
Areas Served: Westmorland county, Shediac, Dieppe, Cap-Pele, Memramcook

SUSSEX

THE KINGS COUNTY RECORD
(Tues)
593 Main St., Sussex, NB, E4E 7H5, Canada; gen tel (506) 433-1070; gen fax (506) 432-3532; ed e-mail craig.victoria@kingscorecord.com; web site https://www.telegraphjournal.com/kings-county-record/
Circulation: 0pd, 2fr; VAC
Advertising: Open inch rate $.54.
Parent Co.:
Brunswick News, Inc.
Pub./Ed.......................................Victoria Craig
Circ. Mgr.......................................Teresa Perry
Mechanical Specifications: Type page 13 x 21 1/2; E - 6 cols, 2 1/16, 3/16 between; A - 6 cols, 2 1/16, 3/16 between; C - 8 cols, 1 1/2, 3/16 between.
Equipment & Software: : Hardware — PC, APP/ Mac.
Areas Served: Sussex

WOODSTOCK

THE BUGLE-OBSERVER
(Tues, Fri)
110 Carleton St., Woodstock, NB, E7M 1E4, Canada; gen tel (506) 328-8863; gen fax (506) 328-3208; ed e-mail news@thebugle.ca; web site https://www.telegraphjournal.com/bugle-observer/
Circulation: 2,693pd, 56fr; CMCA
Advertising: Open inch rate $.50.
Established: 1976.
Parent Co.:
Brunswick News, Inc.
Gen Mgr.................................Peter Macingosh
Circ. Mgr.................................Edward Farrell
Equipment & Software: : Hardware — APP/Mac; Software — PBS.
Areas Served: Canada

NEW FOUNDLAND

CARBONEAR

THE COMPASS
(Tues)
176 Water St., Carbonear, NL, A1Y 1C3, Canada; gen tel (709) 596-6458; gen fax (709) 596-1700; ed e-mail editor@cbncompass.ca; web site www.cbncompass.ca
Circulation: 2,376pd, 0fr; VAC
Advertising: Open inch rate $1.00.
Parent Co.:
Transcontinental Media
Ed..Bill Bowman
Mechanical Specifications: Type page 12 x 22 1/2; E - 6 cols, 2, between; A - 6 cols, 2, between; C - 8 cols, 1 1/2, between.
Equipment & Software: : Hardware — APP/Mac, PC; Software — WordPerfect.
Areas Served: Carbonear

CLARENVILLE

THE PACKET
(Thur)
8 B Thomson St., Clarenville, NL, A5A 1Y9, Canada, Canada; gen tel (709) 466-2243; gen fax (709) 466-2717; ed e-mail editor@thepacket.ca; web site www.thepacket.ca
Circulation: 1,109pd, 0fr; VAC
Advertising: Open inch rate $1.00.
Parent Co.:
Transcontinental Media
Ed............................... Barbara Dean-Simmons
Mechanical Specifications: Type page 11 x 21; E - 6 cols, 1 11/16, 3/16 between; A - 6 cols, 1 11/16, 3/16 between; C - 8 cols, 1 1/4, 3/16 between.
Equipment & Software: : Hardware — APP/ Mac; Software — Microsoft/Word, APP/Mac System Link.
Areas Served: Canada

GANDER

THE GANDER BEACON
(Thur)
61 Elizabeth Dr., Gander, NL, A1V 1W8, Canada; gen tel (709) 256-4371; gen fax (709) 256-3826; web site www.ganderbeacon.ca
Circulation: 929pd, 0fr; VAC
Advertising: Open inch rate $.69.
Parent Co.:
Transcontinental Media
Gen. Mgr.....................................Kevin Higgins
Mechanical Specifications: Type page 12 x 21; E - 6 cols, 1 1/16, 1/6 between; A - 6 cols, 1 1/16, 1/6 between; C - 8 cols, 1 3/16, 1/6 between.
Equipment & Software: : Hardware — APP/Mac; Software — Microsoft/Word.
Areas Served: Gander

GRAND FALLS

THE ADVERTISER
(Thur)
Po Box 129, Grand Falls, NL, A2A 2J4, Canada; gen tel (709) 489-2162; gen fax (709) 489-4817; ed e-mail editor@advertisernl.ca; web site www.gfwadvertiser.ca
Circulation: 1,600pd, 0fr; VAC
Advertising: Open inch rate $1.00.
Parent Co.:
Transcontinental Media
Ed... Ron Ennis
Areas Served: Grand Falls

HAPPY VALLEY

THE LABRADORIAN
(Mon)
2 Hillcrest Rd., Happy Valley, NL, A0P 1E0, Canada; gen tel (709) 896-3341; adv tel (709) 896-3341; gen fax (709) 896-8781; disp adv e-mail sgallant@thelabradorian.ca; ed e-mail editor@thelabradorian.ca; web site www.thelabradorian.ca
Circulation: 2,009pd, 0fr; VAC
Advertising: Open inch rate $1.00.
Parent Co.:
Transcontinental Media
Adv ....Sharon Gallant
Mechanical Specifications: Type page 11 x 21 1/2; E - 6 cols, 1 3/4, 1/8 between; A - 6 cols, 1 3/4, 1/8 between; C - 8 cols, 1 1/2, between.
Equipment & Software: : Hardware — IBM; Software — WordPerfect 5.1, Adobe/PageMaker 4.0.
Areas Served: Happy Valley, Goose Bay

HARBOUR BRETON

HARBOUR BRETON COASTER
(Tues)
30-42 Canada Drive, Harbour Breton, NL, A0H 1P0, Canada; gen tel (709) 885-2378; gen fax (709) 885-2393; ed e-mail editor@thecoasterr.ca; web site www.thecoasterr.ca
Circulation: 1,283pd, 0fr; CMCA
Advertising: Open inch rate $.61.
Parent Co.:
Transcontinental Media
Ed. .... Clayton Hunt
Areas Served: Canada

LABRADOR CITY

THE AURORA
(Mon)
500 Vanier Ave., Labrador City, NL, A2V 2K7, Canada; gen tel (709) 944-2957; gen fax (709) 944-2958; ed e-mail mmurphy@optipress.ca; web site www.theaurora.ca
Circulation: 1,001pd,; VAC
Advertising: Open inch rate $.61.
Established: 1969.
Parent Co.:
Transcontinental Media
Pub.......................................Shawn Woodford
Ed. .... Michelle Stewart
Mechanical Specifications: Type page 10 1/4 x 16; E - 9 cols, 1 7/8, 1/8 between; A - 10 cols, 1/8 between; C - 8 cols, 1 1/8, 1/8 between.
Equipment & Software: : Hardware — APP/Mac; Software — QPS/QuarkXPress.
Areas Served: Canada

LEWISPORTE

THE PILOT
(Wed)
P151 Main St, Lewisporte, NL, A0G 3A0, Canada, Canada; gen tel (709) 535-6910; gen fax (709) 535-8640; disp adv e-mail pilotsales@optipress.ca; ed e-mail editor@pilotnl.ca; web site http://www.lportepilot.ca/
Circulation: 312pd, 0fr; VAC
Advertising: Open inch rate $1.00.
Parent Co.:
Transcontinental Media
Adv. Mgr.................................Joanne Chaffey
Ed. ....Karen Wells
Mechanical Specifications: Type page 13 x 21; E - 6 cols, 2, 1/2 between; A - 6 cols, 2, 1/2 between; C - 9 cols, 1 3/4, 1/4 between.
Equipment & Software: : Hardware — APP/iMac; Software — Microsoft/Word 5.0.
Areas Served: Canada

MARYSTOWN

THE SOUTHERN GAZETTE
(Tues)
Po Box 1116, Marystown, NL, A0E 2M0, Canada, Canada; gen tel (709) 279-3188; gen fax (709) 279-2628; ed e-mail editor@southerngazette.ca; web site www.southerngazette.ca
Circulation: 2,231pd, 0fr; VAC
Advertising: Open inch rate $1.00.
Parent Co.:
Transcontinental Media
Ed...George MacVicar
Mechanical Specifications: Type page 13 x 21 1/2; E - 6 cols, 2 1/12, between; A - 6 cols, 2 1/12, between; C - 9 cols, 1 1/12, between.
Equipment & Software: : Hardware — PC; Software — WordPerfect.
Areas Served: Canada

PORT AUX BASQUES

THE GULF NEWS
(Mon)
Po Box 1090, Port aux Basques, NL, A0M 1C0, Canada, Canada; gen tel (709) 695-3671; adv tel (709) 279-3188; gen fax (709) 695-7901; adv fax (709) 279-2628; disp adv e-mail wrose@thewesternstar.com; ed e-mail chantelle.macisaac@gulfnews.ca; web site www.gulfnews.ca
Circulation: 2,912pd, 0fr; VAC
Advertising: Open inch rate $1.00.
Parent Co.:
Transcontinental Media
Ed ....Chantelle Macisaac
Adv.. Wendy Rose
Areas Served: Canada

SAINT ANTHONY

NORTHERN PEN
(Mon)
10-12 North St., Saint Anthony, NL, A0K 4S0, Canada, Canada; gen tel (709) 454-2191; gen fax (709) 454-3718; disp adv e-mail kparsons@nothernpen.ca; ed e-mail arandell@nothernpen.ca; web site www.northernpen.ca
Circulation: 1,085pd, 0fr; VAC
Advertising: Open inch rate $1.00.
Established: 1980.
Parent Co.:
Transcontinental Media
Adv. Mgr....................................Kathy Parsons
Office/Circ Mgr..................... Frances Reardon
Ed .... Adam Randell
Mechanical Specifications: Type page 11 x 21 1/2; E - 6 cols, 1 3/4, between; A - 6 cols, 1 3/4, between; C - 8 cols, 1 1/2, between.
Equipment & Software: : Hardware — PC; Software — Adobe/PageMaker.
Areas Served: Canada

SPRINGDALE

THE NOR'WESTER
(Thur)
Po Box 28, Springdale, NL, A0J 1T0, Canada, Canada; gen tel (709) 673-3721; gen fax (709) 673-4171; ed e-mail editor@thenorwester.ca; web site www.thenorwester.ca
Circulation: 1,730pd, 0fr; VAC
Advertising: Open inch rate $1.00.
Parent Co.:
Transcontinental Media
Ed. ....Rudy Norman
Areas Served: Canada

ST. JOHN'S

LE GABOTEUR
(Bi-Mthly)
65 Ridge Road, St. John's, NL, A1B 4P5, Canada; gen tel (709) 753-9585; disp adv e-mail annonces@gaboteur.ca; ed e-mail redaction@gaboteur.ca; web site www.gaboteur.ca
Circulation: 850pd, 0fr; CMCA
Established: 1984.
Dir/Ed.................................. Jacinthe Tremblay
Delivery Method: Mail
Areas Served: Canada

STEPHENVILLE

THE GEORGIAN
(Mon)
43 Main St., 43 Main Street, Stephenville, NL, A2N 2Z4, Canada; gen tel (709) 643-4531; gen fax (709) 643-5041; ed e-mail editor@thegeorgian.ca; web site www.thegeorgian.ca
Circulation: 1,152pd, 0fr; CMCA
Advertising: Open inch rate $1.00.
Established: 1970.
Parent Co.:
Transcontinental Media
Ed. .... Christopher Vaughan

Delivery Method: Mail, Newsstand, Carrier, Racks
Areas Served: Canada

NOVA SCOTIA

AMHERST

AMHERST DAILY NEWS

(Fri)
147 S. Albion St., Amherst, NS, B4H 2X2, Canada; gen tel (902) 667-5102; ed tel (902) 661-5426; gen fax (902) 667-0419; disp adv e-mail gcoish@amherstdaily.com; ed e-mail darrell.cole@tc.tc; web site www.cumberlandnewsnow.com
Circulation: 4,057pd, 349fr; VAC
Advertising: Open inch rate $.76.
Established: 1893.
Parent Co.:
Transcontinental Media
Pub....Richard Russell
Ops. Mgr. ....Greg Landry
Adv. Mgr. ....Gladys Coish
Circ. Mgr. ....Chuck MacInnes
Sr. Ed. ....Darrell Cole
Mechanical Specifications: Type page 10.25 x 14; E - 6 cols, 2 1/16, 1/8 between; A - 6 cols, 2 1/16, 1/8 between; C - 6 cols, 2 1/16, 1/8 between.
Areas Served: Amherst, Nova Scotia

THE CITIZEN-RECORD

(Wed)
147 South Albion St., Amherst, NS, B4H 2X2, Canada; gen tel (902) 667-5102; gen fax (902) 667-0419; disp adv e-mail gcoish@amherstdaily.com; ed e-mail darrell.cole@tc.tc; web site www.cumberlandnewsnow.com
Circulation: 4,892pd, 504fr; VAC
Parent Co.:
Transcontinental Media
Digital Platform - Mobile: Apple, Android
Digital Platform - Tablet: Apple iOS, Android
Pub....Richard Russell
Adv. Mgr. ....Gladys Coish
Ed ....Darell Cole
Delivery Method: Mail, Newsstand, Carrier
Areas Served: B0H

ANTIGONISH

THE CASKET

(Wed)
88 College St., Antigonish, NS, B2G 1X7, Canada, Canada; gen tel (902) 863-4370; gen fax (902) 863-1943; disp adv e-mail brianlazzuri@thecasket.ca; class adv e-mail brianlazzuri@thecasket.ca; ed e-mail editor@thecasket.ca; web site www.thecasket.ca
Circulation: 27,000fr; Sworn/Estimate/Non-Audited
Advertising: Base line rate $.70/agate line NET.
Established: 1852.
Parent Co.:
SaltWire
Gen Mgr/Mng Ed/Adv Mgr....Brian Lazzuri
Mechanical Specifications: Type page 10 x 20; E - 6 cols, 2, between; A - 6 cols, 2, between; C - 6 cols, 2, between.
Equipment & Software: : Hardware — PCs; Software — In design
Delivery Method: Mail, Carrier, Racks
Areas Served: Canada

BASS RIVER

THE SHORELINE JOURNAL

(Wed, Mthly)
Box 41, Bass River, NS, B0M 1B0, Muncipality of County of Colchester, Canada; gen tel (902) 647-2968; adv tel (902)647-2968; ed tel (902) 647-2968; gen fax (902) 647-2194; adv fax (902) 647-2194; disp adv e-mail maurice@theshorelinejournal.com; ed e-mail maurice@theshorelinejournal.com; web site www.theshorelinejournal.com
Circulation: 1,363pd, 0fr; CMCA
Advertising: Base line rate $.70/agate line NET.
Established: 1994.Maurice Rees
Mechanical Specifications: The Shoreline Journal is an
offset tabloid. Image area is 10-1/4â x 15-5/8â . Column width is 1.5â with 6 columns per page. Line Screens. B&W 100, Colour 100 lines per inch.
Delivery Method: Mail, Newsstand
Areas Served: Muncipality of County of Colchester

BRIDGEWATER

LIGHTHOUSE NOW

(Thur)
353 York St., Bridgewater, NS, B4V 3K2, Canada; gen tel (902) 543-2457; adv tel (902) 543-1569; gen fax (902) 543-2228; disp adv e-mail daveda.savory@lighthousenow.ca; class adv e-mail tracy.williams@lighthousenow.ca; ed e-mail editorial@southshorenow.ca; web site https://lighthousenow.ca/
Circulation: 6,573pd, 26,963fr; VAC
Advertising: Open inch rate $1.24.
Pub ....Lynn Hennigar
Circ. Mgr....Laurenda Reeves
Emma Smith
Mechanical Specifications: Type page 10 5/16 x 16; E - 6 cols, 1 5/8, 1/6 between; A - 6 cols, 1 5/8, 1/6 between; C - 6 cols, 1 5/8, 1/6 between.
Equipment & Software: : Hardware — APP/Mac; Presses — 5-HI; Software — QPS/QuarkXPress, Adobe/Photoshop, Adobe/Acrobat.
Areas Served: Bridgewater

THE BULLETIN

(Tues)
353 York St., Bridgewater, NS, B4V 3K2, Canada, Canada; gen tel (902) 543-2457; gen fax (902) 543-2228; ed e-mail editorial@southshorenow.ca; web site https://lighthousenow.ca
Circulation: 7,030pd, 127fr; Sworn/Estimate/Non-Audited
Advertising: Open inch rate $1.24.
Established: 1888.
Pub ....Lynn Hennigar
Circ. Mgr....Laurenda Reeves
Emma Smith
Mechanical Specifications: Type page 10 5/16 x 16; E - 6 cols, 1 5/8, 1/6 between; A - 6 cols, 1 5/8, 1/6 between; C - 6 cols, 1 5/8, 1/6 between.
Equipment & Software: : Hardware — APP/Mac; Presses — 5-HI; Software — QPS/QuarkXPress, Adobe/Photoshop, Adobe/Acrobat, Adobe/Illustrator, Adobe/Dimensions, Adobe/Indesign.
Areas Served: Canada

COMEAUVILLE

LE COURRIER DE LA NOUVELLE-ECOSSE

(Fri)
795 Route 1, Comeauville, NS, B0W 2Z0, Canada, Canada; gen tel (902) 769-3078; gen fax (902) 769-3869; ed e-mail administration@lecourrier.com,; web site www.lecourrier.com
Circulation: 1,302pd, 5fr; ODC
Advertising: Open inch rate $1.05.
Established: 1937.
Prod. Mgr. ....Stephanie LeBlanc
Ed ....Francis Robichaud
Mechanical Specifications: Type page 11 x 13; E - 5 cols, 2, between; A - 5 cols, 2, between.
Equipment & Software: : Hardware — APP/Mac; Software — Adobe/InDesign, Microsoft/Word, Adobe/Photoshop, Adobe/Illustrator, Microsoft/Excel.
Areas Served: Canada

DIGBY

THE DIGBY COUNTY COURIER

(Thur)
124 Water St., Digby, NS, B0V 1A0, Canada; gen tel (902) 245-4715; gen fax (902) 245-6136; disp adv e-mail info@digbycourier.ca; ed e-mail editor@digbycourier.ca; web site www.digbycourier.ca
Circulation: 1,192pd, 0fr; CMCA
Advertising: Open inch rate $.75.
Established: 1874.
Parent Co.:
Transcontinental Media
Ed ....Dave Glenen
Mechanical Specifications: Type page 12 1/2 x 21; E - 7 cols, 1/8 between; A - 7 cols, 1/8 between; C - 7 cols, 1/8 between.
Equipment & Software: : Hardware — APP/Mac; Presses — G/5SC; Software — QPS/QuarkXPress.
Delivery Method: Mail, Newsstand
Areas Served: Canada

ENFIELD

ENFIELD WEEKLY PRESS

(Wed)
287 Highway 2, Enfield, NS, B2T 1C9, Canada; gen tel (902) 883-3181; gen fax (902) 883-3180; disp adv e-mail michelewhite@enfieldweeklypress.com; class adv e-mail admin@enfieldweeklypress.com; ed e-mail editor@enfieldweeklypress.com; web site www.enfieldweeklypress.com
Circulation: 10,914fr; VAC
Advertising: Open inch rate $.80.
Pub ....Leith Orr
Adv. Rep ....Michele White
Areas Served: Enfield

FALL RIVER LAKER

(Thur)
287 Highway 2, Enfield, NS, B2T 1C9; gen tel (902) 883-3181, Ext. 3 ; gen fax (902) 883-3180 ; disp adv e-mail michelewhite@enfieldweeklypress.com; class adv e-mail admin@enfieldweeklypress.com; ed e-mail editor@enfieldweeklypress.com; web site www.thelaker.ca
Circulation: 2,247pd, 7,703fr; VAC
Advertising: Open inch rate $.81.
Pub ....Leith Orr
Adv. Rep ....Michele White
Areas Served: Enfield

GREENWOOD

THE AURORA

(Mon)
Po Box 99, Greenwood, NS, B0P 1N0, Canada, Canada; gen tel (902) 765-1494; gen fax (902) 765-1717; disp adv e-mail auroramarketing@ns.aliantzinc.ca; ed e-mail auroraeditor@ns.aliantzinc.ca; web site www.auroranewspaper.com
Circulation: 5,900fr; Sworn/Estimate/Non-Audited
Advertising: Open inch rate.
Mgr. Ed. ....Sara Keddy
Admin Clerk....Dejah Roulston-Wilde
Adv ....Christianne Robichaud
Graphics designer ....Brian Graves
Mechanical Specifications: Type page 11 x 13; E - 6 cols, 1 5/8, 3/20 between; A - 6 cols, 1 5/8, 3/20 between.
Equipment & Software: : Hardware — IBM; Software — Adobe/PageMaker 6.5, Archetype/Corel Draw 5.0.
Delivery Method: Mail, Newsstand, Carrier, Racks
Areas Served: Canada

GUYSBOROUGH

GUYSBOROUGH JOURNAL

(Wed)
P.O. Box 210, Guysborough, NS, B0H 1N0, Canada; gen tel (902) 533-2851; gen fax (902) 533-2750; disp adv e-mail advertising@guysboroughjournal.ca; ed e-mail news@guysboroughjournal.ca; web site www.guysboroughjournal.com
Circulation: 6,890pd, 13fr; VAC
Advertising: Open inch rate $.71.
Pub ....Allan Murphy
Ed/Mgr/Pub....Hellen Murphy
Office/Circ. Mgr....Sharon Heighton
Areas Served: Guysborough

HALIFAX

BEDFORD - SACKVILLE WEEKLY NEWS

(Thur)
211 Horseshoe Lake Dr, Halifax, NS, B3S 0B9, Canada; gen tel (902) 426-2811; gen fax (902) 426-1170; disp adv e-mail sales@herald.ca; class adv e-mail classified@herald.ca; ed e-mail newsroom@herald.ca; web site http://thechronicleherald.ca/community/bedfordsackvilleobserver
Circulation: 29,302fr; CMCA
Digital Platform - Mobile: Apple
Digital Platform - Tablet: Apple iOS
Adv. Media Dir....Sheryl Grant
Mng. Ed....Kim Moar
Delivery Method: Mail, Newsstand
Areas Served: Canada

COLE HARBOUR WEEKLY

(Thur)
211 Horseshoe Lake Dr, Halifax, NS, B3S 0B9, Canada; gen tel (902) 426-2811; gen fax (902) 426-1170; disp adv e-mail sales@herald.ca; class adv e-mail classifieds@herald.ca; ed e-mail newsroom@herald.ca; web site www.thechronicleherald.ca
Circulation: 37,643fr; CMCA
Digital Platform - Mobile: Apple
Digital Platform - Tablet: Apple iOS
Pub....Fred Fiander
Adv. Media Dir....Sheryl Grant
Delivery Method: Mail, Newsstand
Areas Served: Canada

HALIFAX WEST-CLAYTON PARK WEEKLY NEWS

(Thur)
211 Horseshoe Lake Dr, Halifax, NS, B3S 0B9, Canada; gen tel (902) 421-5888; disp adv e-mail sgrant@herald.ca; class adv e-mail classified@herald.ca; ed e-mail newsroom@herald.ca; web site www.thechronicleherald.ca
Circulation: 37,145fr; CMCA
Digital Platform - Mobile: Apple
Digital Platform - Tablet: Apple iOS
Adv. Media Dir....Sheryl Grant
Mng. Ed....Kim Moar
Delivery Method: Mail, Newsstand
Areas Served: Canada

INVERNESS

THE INVERNESS ORAN

(Wed)
15767 Central Avenue, Inverness, NS, B0E 1N0, USA; gen tel (902) 258-2253; gen fax (902) 258-2632; ed e-mail editor@oran.ca; web site www.oran.ca
Circulation: 16pd, 54fr; VAC
Advertising: Open inch rate $.74.
Established: 1976.
Ed....Rankin MacDonald
Areas Served: Inverness

KENTVILLE

REGISTER

(Thur)
28 Aberdeen St, Suite 6, Kentville, NS, B4N 2N1, Canada; gen tel (902) 538-3189; gen fax (902) 681-0923; disp adv e-mail events@kentvilleadvertiser.ca; web site http://www.kingscountynews.ca/
Circulation: 3,392pd, 47fr; CMCA
Advertising: Open inch rate $.65.
Parent Co.:
Transcontinental Media
Pub....... Fred Fiander
Mechanical Specifications: Type page 12 1/2 x 21; E - 7 cols, 1/8 between; A - 7 cols, 1/8 between; C - 7 cols, 1/8 between.
Equipment & Software: : Hardware — APP/Mac; Presses — G/SSC; Software — QPS/QuarkXPress.
Areas Served: Canada

THE ADVERTISER

(Tues)
28 Aberdeen St, Suite 6, Kentville, NS, B4N 2N1, Canada, Canada; gen tel (902) 681-2121; gen fax (902) 681-0830; disp adv e-mail events@kentvilleadvertiser.ca; ed e-mail ffiander@thevanguard.ca; web site http://www.kingscountynews.ca/
Circulation: 3,189pd, 49fr; CMCA
Advertising: Open inch rate $1.05.
Parent Co.:
Transcontinental Media
Pub....... Fred Fiander
Mechanical Specifications: Type page 10 1/2 x 15 3/4; E - 6 cols, 1/4, 1/8 between; A - 6 cols, 1/8 between; C - 6 cols, 1/8 between.
Areas Served: Canada

LIVERPOOL

THE ADVANCE

(Tues)
271 Main St., Liverpool, NS, B0T 1K0, Canada; gen tel (902) 354-3441; gen fax (902) 354-2455; ed e-mail ffayander@thevanguard.ca; web site http://www.theadvance.ca/
Circulation: 1,573pd,; CMCA
Advertising: Open inch rate $.88.
Parent Co.:
Transcontinental Media
Pub....... Fred Fayander
Areas Served: Canada

MIDDLETON

MIRROR-EXAMINER

(Wed)
87 Commercial St., Middleton, NS, B0S 1P0, Canada; gen tel (902) 825-3457; gen fax (902) 825-6707; disp adv e-mail kentpub.ads@ns.sympatico.ca
Circulation: 3,101pd,; Sworn/Estimate/Non-Audited
Advertising: Open inch rate $.75.
Pub....... Garnet Austen
Adv. Mgr....... Wayne Smith
Ed. .... Lori Errington
Mechanical Specifications: Type page 12 1/2 x 21; E - 7 cols, 1/8 between; A - 7 cols, 1/8 between; C - 7 cols, 1/8 between.
Equipment & Software: : Hardware — APP/Mac; Presses — G/SSC; Software — QPS/QuarkXPress.

THE SPECTATOR

(Thur)
87 Commercial St., Middleton, NS, B0S 1P0, Canada; gen tel (902) 532-2219; gen fax (902) 825-6707; disp adv e-mail info@annapolisspectator.ca; ed e-mail editor@annapolisspectator.ca; web site www.annapoliscountyspectator.ca
Circulation: 2,048pd, 0fr; CMCA
Advertising: Open inch rate $.94.
Parent Co.:
Transcontinental Media
Pub....... Fred Fiander
Ed. .... Lawrence Powell
Mechanical Specifications: Type page 10 1/2 x 13; E - 6 cols, 1/8 between; A - 6 cols, 1/8 between; C - 6 cols, 1/8 between.
Equipment & Software: : Hardware — APP/Mac; Presses — G/SSC; Software — QPS/QuarkXPress.

PICTOU

THE PICTOU ADVOCATE

(Wed)
21 George St., Pictou, NS, B0K 1H0, Canada, Canada; gen tel (902) 485-8014; adv tel (902) 759-0716; gen fax (902) 752-4816; disp adv e-mail mark@pictouadvocate.com; ed e-mail editor@pictouadvocate.com; web site www.pictouadvocate.com
Circulation: 732pd, 4fr; VAC
Advertising: Open inch rate $.83.
Established: 1893.
Ed .... Jackie Jardine
Pub....... Leith Orr
Delivery Method: Mail
Areas Served: Canada

PORT HAWKESBURY

THE REPORTER

(Wed)
2 Maclean Court, Port Hawkesbury, NS, B9A 3K2, Canada; gen tel (902) 625-3300; gen fax (902) 625-1701; disp adv e-mail nicole-fawcett@porthawkesburyreporter.com; ed e-mail jake@porthawkesburyreporter.com; web site www.porthawkesburyreporter.com
Circulation: 87pd,; VAC
Pub .... Rick Cluett
Adv .... Nicole Fawcett
Areas Served: Port Hawkesbury

SHELBURNE

THE COAST GUARD

(Tues)
164 Water St., Shelburne, NS, B0T 1W0, Canada; gen tel (902) 875-3244; gen fax (902) 875-3454; disp adv e-mail info@thecoastguard.ca; ed e-mail ffaynder@transcontinental.ca; web site www.thecoastguard.ca
Circulation: 2,290pd, 0fr; CMCA
Advertising: Open inch rate $.98.
Parent Co.:
Transcontinental Media
Pub....... Fred Fayander
Mechanical Specifications: Type page 13 x 21; E - 6 cols, 2, between; A - 6 cols, 2, between; C - 6 cols, 2, between.
Equipment & Software: : Hardware — APP/Macs; Software — QPS/QuarkXPress.
Areas Served: Canada

TATAMAGOUCHE

THE LIGHT

(Wed)
Po Box 1000, Tatamagouche, NS, B0K 1V0, Canada; gen tel (902) 956-8099; disp adv e-mail kristinhirtle@tatamagouchelight.com; ed e-mail raissatetanish@tatamagouchelight.com; web site www.tatamagouchelight.com
Circulation: 2,497pd, 4,378fr; VAC
Pub .... Leith Orr
Areas Served: Tatamagouche

WINDSOR

HANTS JOURNAL

(Thur)
73 Gerrish St., Windsor, NS, B0N 2T0, Canada; gen tel (902) 798-8371; gen fax (902) 798-5451; web site www.hantsjournal.ca
Circulation: 2,233pd, 15fr; CMCA
Advertising: Open inch rate $.91.
Established: 1867.
Parent Co.:
Transcontinental Media
Sales. Mgr....... Ray Savage
Mechanical Specifications: Type page 9 2/3 x 21 1/2.
Areas Served: Canada

YARMOUTH

THE VANGUARD

(Tues)
2 Second St., Yarmouth, NS, B5A 4B1, Canada, Canada; gen tel (902) 742-7111; gen fax (902) 742-6527; disp adv e-mail fred.fiander@tc.tc; ed e-mail info@thevanguard.ca; web site www.thevanguard.ca
Circulation: 3,485pd, 52fr; CMCA
Advertising: Open inch rate $1.12.
Established: 1966.
Parent Co.:
Transcontinental Media
Pub .... Fred Fiander
Ed .... Fred Hatfield
Mechanical Specifications: Type page 13 x 21; E - 6 cols, 2, between; A - 6 cols, 2, between; C - 6 cols, 2, between.
Equipment & Software: : Hardware — APP/Macs; Software — QPS/QuarkXPress.
Areas Served: Canada

NORTHWEST TERRITORIES

FORT SMITH

NORTHERN JOURNAL

(Other)
207 Mcdougal Rd., Fort Smith, NT, X0E 0P0, Canada, Canada; gen tel (867) 872-3000; gen fax (867) 872-2754; disp adv e-mail admin@norj.ca; ed e-mail don@norj.ca; web site http://norj.ca/
Circulation: 3,660pd, 4,065fr; Sworn/Estimate/Non-Audited
Advertising: $100 per insert (online).
Established: 1978.
Parent Co.:
Cascade Publishing Ltd.
Mgr .... Sandra Jaque
Ed. .... Don Jaque
Mechanical Specifications: Type page 11 x 17; E - 5 cols, 1 7/8, 1/6 between; A - 6 cols, 1 7/12, 1/6 between; C - 6 cols, 1 7/12, 1/6 between.
Equipment & Software: : Hardware — PC; Software — Adobe/PageMaker 7.0, Adobe/Illustrator 9.0, Adobe/Photoshop 6.0.
Delivery Method: Carrier
Areas Served: Canada

HAY RIVER

THE HUB

(Wed)
8-4 Courtoreille St., Hay River, NT, X0E 1G2, Canada; gen tel (867) 874-6577; gen fax (867) 874-2679; disp adv e-mail ads@hayriverhub.com; ed e-mail web@hayriverhub.com; web site www.hayriverhub.com
Circulation: 1,996pd, 182fr; VAC
Advertising: Open inch rate $1.40.
Established: 1973.
Pub....... Chris Brodeur
Adv. Mgr....... Lehaina Andrews
Circ. Mgr....... Lorna Desilets
Mechanical Specifications: Type page 10 1/4 x 15 1/2; E - 6 cols, 1 3/5, 1/6 between; A - 6 cols, 1 3/5, 1/6 between; C - 6 cols, 1 3/5, 1/6 between.
Equipment & Software: : Hardware — APP/Mac G4, APP/iMac; Software — QPS/QuarkXPress 4.0, Multi-Ad/Creator 2.0, Adobe/Photoshop 5.5.
Areas Served: X0E 1G2, X0E 0P0, X0E 0M0, X0E 0N0, X1A 2P2, X0E 0L0

YELLOWKNIFE

DEH CHO DRUM

(Thur)
5108 50th St., Yellowknife, NT, X1A 2R1, Canada; gen tel (867) 873-4031; gen fax (867) 873-8507; disp adv e-mail advertising@nnsl.com; ed e-mail editorial@nnsl.com; web site http://www.nnsl.com/dehcho/dehcho.html
Circulation: 708fr; VAC
Advertising: Open inch rate $1.56.
Established: 1993.
Pub....... Jack Sigvaldason
Gen. Mgr. .... Michael Scott
Adv. Mgr. .... Petra Ehrke
Circ. Mgr. .... Debra Davis
Mng. Ed. .... Bruce Valpy
Mechanical Specifications: Type page 10 5/16 x 15 3/8; E - 6 cols, 1 9/16, 1/6 between; A - 6 cols, 1 9/16, 1/6 between; C - 6 cols, 1 9/16, 1/6 between.
Equipment & Software: : Hardware — PC, APP/Mac; Presses — ABD, GTO, Kora; Software — QPS/QuarkXPress 3.3, Adobe/Photoshop, Adobe/PageMaker, Adobe/Illustrator, Archetype/Corel Draw, Microsoft/Windows 95, Macromedia/Freehand, Netscape, Eudora.
Areas Served: Yellowknife

INUVIK DRUM

(Thur)
Po Box 2820, Yellowknife, NT, X1A 2R1, Canada; gen tel (867) 873-4031; gen fax (867) 873-8507; disp adv e-mail advertising@nnsl.com; ed e-mail editorial@nnsl.com; web site www.nnsl.com
Circulation: 201pd, 290fr; VAC
Advertising: Open inch rate $1.56.
Pub....... Jack Sigvaldason
Gen. Mgr. .... Michael Scott
Adv. Mgr. .... Petra Ehrke
Circ. Mgr. .... Debra Davis
Mng. Ed. .... Bruce Valpy
Mechanical Specifications: Type page 10 1/8 x 15 3/8; E - 6 cols, 1 7/12, 1/6 between; A - 6 cols, 1 7/12, 1/6 between; C - 6 cols, 1 7/12, 1/6 between.
Equipment & Software: : Hardware — PC, APP/Mac; Presses — ABD, GTO, Kora; Software — QPS/QuarkXPress 3.3, Adobe/Photoshop, Adobe/PageMaker, Macromedia/Freehand, Adobe/Illustrator, Microsoft/Windows 95, Archetype/Corel Draw, Netscape, Eudora.
Areas Served: Yellowknife

L'AQUILON

(Fri)
5102-51 Street, 2nd Floor, Yellowknife, NT, X1A 1S7, Canada; gen tel (867) 873-6603; gen fax (867) 873-6663; disp adv e-mail sandra@repco-media.ca; ed e-mail aquilon@internorth.com; web site www.aquilon.nt.ca
Circulation: 875fr; Sworn/Estimate/Non-Audited
Advertising: Open inch rate $1.56.
Established: 1986.
Ed. .... Alain Bessette
Mechanical Specifications: Type page 11 x 17; E -6 cols, 2, 1/6 between
Equipment & Software: : Hardware — APP/Mac; Software — InDesign-Photoshop-MS Word
Delivery Method: Mail, Racks
Areas Served: X1A
X0E
X0A

NEWS/NORTH

(Mon)
5108 50th St., Yellowknife, NT, X1A 2R1, Canada, Canada; gen tel (867) 873-4031; gen fax (867) 873-8507; disp adv e-mail advertising@nnsl.com; ed e-mail editorial@nnsl.com; web site www.nnsl.com

Circulation: 1,922pd, 2,167fr; VAC
Advertising: Open inch rate $2.03.
Pub....................................... Jack Sigvaldason
Gen. Mgr. .... Michael Scott
Adv. Mgr. .... Petra Ehrke
Circ. Mgr. .... Debra Davis
Ed. .... Bruce Valpy
Mechanical Specifications: Type page 10 5/8 x 15 3/8; E - 6 cols, 1 9/16, 1/6 between; A - 6 cols, 1 9/16, 1/6 between; C - 6 cols, 1 9/16, 1/6 between.
Equipment & Software: : Hardware — APP/Mac, PC; Presses — GTO, ABD, Kora; Software — QPS/QuarkXPress 3.3, Adobe/Photoshop, Adobe/PageMaker, Macromedia/Freehand, Adobe/Illustrator, Microsoft/Windows 95, Archetype/Corel Draw, Netscape, Eudora.
Areas Served: Canada

YELLOWKNIFER
(Wed, Fri)
5108 50th St., Yellowknife, NT, X1A 2R1, Canada; gen tel (867) 873-4031; gen fax (867) 873-8507; disp adv e-mail advertising@nnsl.com; ed e-mail editorial@nnsl.com; web site www.nnsl.com
Circulation: 2,077pd, 963fr; VAC
Advertising: Open inch rate $1.66.
Pub....................................... Jack Sigvaldason
Gen. Mgr. .... Michael Scott
Adv. .... Petra Ehrke
Circ. Mgr. .... Debra Davis
Mng. Ed. .... Bruce Valpy
Mechanical Specifications: Type page 10 5/16 x 15 3/8; E - 6 cols, 1 9/16, 1/6 between; A - 6 cols, 1 9/16, 1/6 between; C - 6 cols, 1 9/16, 1/6 between.
Equipment & Software: : Hardware — PC, APP/Mac; Presses — GTO, ABD, Kora; Software — QPS/QuarkXPress 3.3, Adobe/Photoshop, Adobe/PageMaker, Macromedia/Freehand, Adobe/Illustrator, Microsoft/Windows 95, Archetype/Corel Draw, Netscape, Eudora.
Areas Served: Yellowknife

NUNAVUT

IQALUIT

NUNATSIAQ NEWS
(Fri)
Po Box 8, Iqaluit, NU, X0A 0H0, Canada; gen tel (867) 979-5357; adv tel (800) 263-1452; gen fax (867) 979-4763; adv fax (800) 417-2474; disp adv e-mail ads@nunatsiaqonline.ca; ed e-mail editor@nunatsiaq.com; web site www.nunatsiaq.com
Circulation: 5,388fr; VAC
Advertising: Open inch rate $2.91.
Established: 1973.
Pub... Steven Roberts
Adv. Mgr. .... Bill McConkey
Ed. .... Jim Bell
Mechanical Specifications: Type page 10 5/16 x 13 3/4; E - 6 cols, 1 7/12, between; A - 6 cols, 1 7/12, between; C - 6 cols, 1 7/12, between.
Equipment & Software: : Hardware — APP/Mac; Software — QPS/QuarkXPress.
Areas Served: Nunavut

YELLOWKNIFE

KIVALLIQ NEWS
(Wed)
Po Box 2820, Yellowknife, NU, X1A 2R1, Canada; gen tel (867) 873-4031; gen fax (867) 873-8507; disp adv e-mail advertising@nnsl.com; ed e-mail editorial@nnsl.com; web site www.nnsl.com
Circulation: 935fr; VAC
Pub .... Jack Sigvaldason
Areas Served: Yellowknife

NUNAVUT NEWS/NORTH
(Mon)
Po Box 2820, Yellowknife, NU, X1A 2R1, Canada; gen tel (867) 873-4031; gen fax (867) 873-8507; disp adv e-mail advertising@nnsl.com; ed e-mail editorial@nnsl.com; web site www.nnsl.com
Circulation: 4,161fr; VAC
Pub .... Jack Sigvaldason
Gen Mgr. .... Michael Scott
Areas Served: Nunavut

ONTARIO

AILSA CRAIG

THE MIDDLESEX BANNER
(Wed)
175 Main St., Ailsa Craig, ON, N0M 1A0, Canada; gen tel (519) 293-1095; gen fax (519) 293-1095; web site www.banner.on.ca
Circulation: 736pd, 708fr; CMCA
Established: 1996.
Pub./Ed. .... Brad Harness
Areas Served: Canada

ALEXANDRIA

THE GLENGARRY NEWS
(Wed)
3 Main St., Alexandria, ON, K0C 1A0, Canada, Canada; gen tel (613) 525-2020; gen fax (613) 525-3824; web site www.glengarrynews.ca
Circulation: 1,075pd, 86fr; VAC
Advertising: Open inch rate $.82.
Established: 1892.
Adv. Mgr. .... Bonnie MacDonald
Mng. Ed. .... Steven Warburton
Sports Ed. .... Sean Bray
JT Grossmith
Mechanical Specifications: Type page 12 7/8 x 21; E - 7 cols, 1/6 between; A - 7 cols, 1/6 between; C - 7 cols, 1/6 between.
Equipment & Software: : Hardware — APP/Power Mac, PC; Software — Multi-Ad/Creator 4.0.1, QPS/QuarkXPress 3.32.
Delivery Method: Mail, Newsstand
Areas Served: Canada

ALLISTON

THE ALLISTON HERALD
(Thur)
169 Dufferin St. S, Unit 22, Alliston, ON, L9R 1E6, Canada; gen tel (705) 435-6228; gen fax (705) 435-3342; ed e-mail herald@simcoe.com; web site www.simcoe.com
Circulation: 3,076pd, 22,860fr; VAC
Advertising: Open inch rate $1.45.
Parent Co.:
Metroland Media Group Ltd.
Sales Mgr. .... Angela Makaroff
Equipment & Software: : Hardware — APP/Mac; Software — QPS/QuarkXPress, Aldus/PageMaker, Multi-Ad, Claris/Works.
Delivery Method: Carrier
Areas Served: L9R, L0G, L0N, L0L, L0M

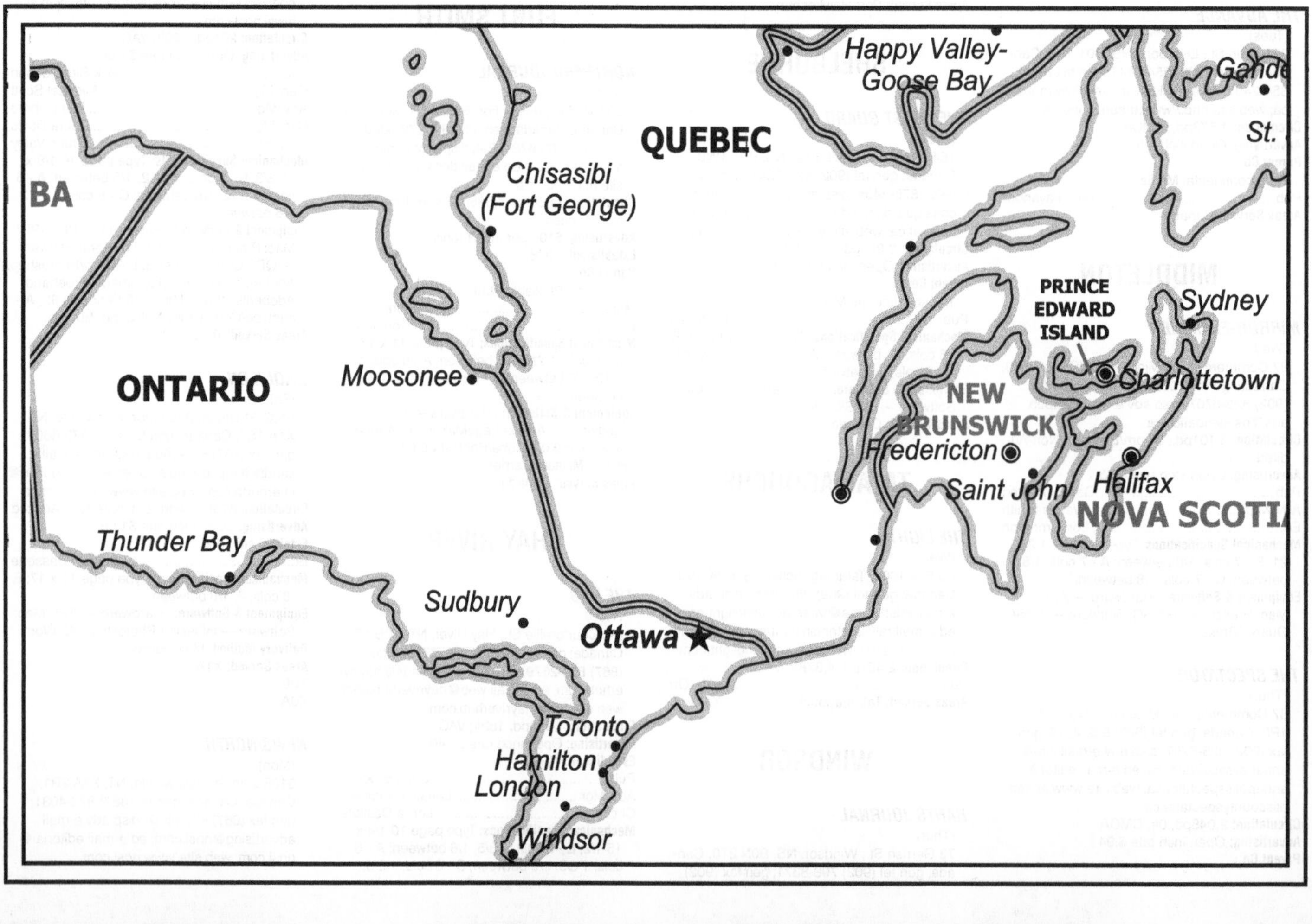

AMHERSTBURG

RIVER TOWN TIMES
(Wed)
67 Richmond Street, Amherstburg, ON, N9V 1G1, Canada; gen tel (519) 736-4175; gen fax (519) 736-5420; disp adv e-mail sales@rivertowntimes.com; ed e-mail mail@rivertowntimes.com; web site www.rivertowntimes.com
Circulation: 9,183fr; CMCA
Advertising: .95.
Established: 1995.
Ed. .... Ron Giofu
Mechanical Specifications: 10.25x14.75
Delivery Method: Carrier
Areas Served: Canada

ARNPRIOR

ARNPRIOR CHRONICLE GUIDE EMC
(Thur)
8 Mcgonigal St., Arnprior, ON, K7S 1L8, Canada; gen tel (613) 623-6571; disp adv e-mail leslie.osborne@metroland.com; class adv e-mail christine.jarrett@metroland.com; ed e-mail theresa.fritz@metroland.com; web site www.insideottawavalley.com
Circulation: 8,213fr; CMCA
Pub .... Mike Tracy
Ed .... Theresa Fritz
Areas Served: Canada

WEST CARLETON REVIEW
(Thur)
8 Mcgonigal St., Arnprior, ON, K7S 1L8, Canada; gen tel (613) 623-6571; disp adv e-mail leslie.osborne@metroland.com; web site www.insideottawavalley.com
Circulation: 7,099fr; CMCA
Parent Co.:
Metroland Media Group Ltd.Theresa Fritz
Mike Tracy

ASTRA

WING COMMANDER
(Fri)
Po Box 1000, Sta. Forces, Astra, ON, K0K 3W0, Canada; gen tel (613) 965-7248; adv tel (613) 392-2811; ed tel (613) 392-2811; gen fax (613) 965-7490; web site www.forces.gc.ca
Circulation: 3,000fr; Sworn/Estimate/Non-Audited
Advertising: Open inch rate $6.10.
Ed. in Chief .... Mark Peebles
Mng. Ed .... Andrea Steiner
Asst. Ed .... Amber Gooding
Mechanical Specifications: Type page 10 1/4 x 14 1/2; E - 6 cols, 1 57/100, between; A - 6 cols, 1 57/100, between; C - 6 cols, between.
Equipment & Software: : Hardware — PC; Software — QPS/QuarkXPress, WordPerfect, Archetype/Corel Draw.

ATIKOKAN

ATIKOKAN PROGRESS
(Mon)
109 Main St. E., Atikokan, ON, P0T 1C0, Canada; gen tel (807) 597-2731; gen fax (807) 597-6103; ed e-mail progress@nwon.com; web site www.atikokanprogress.ca
Circulation: 1,173pd, 38fr; VAC
Advertising: Open inch rate $0.67.
Established: 1950.
Circ. Mgr .... Eve Shine
Ed. .... Michael McKinnon
Mechanical Specifications: Type page 10 1/2 x 15; E - 5 cols, 1 11/12, 1/6 between; A - 5 cols, 1 11/12, 1/6 between; C - 5 cols, 1 1/2, 1/6 between.
Equipment & Software: : Hardware — PC; Software — Microsoft/Windows 95, Archetype/Corel Draw 5.0.
Delivery Method: Mail, Newsstand, Carrier
Areas Served: P0T1C0

AURORA

THE AURORA BANNER
(Thur, Sun)
250 Industrial Parkway N., Aurora, ON, L4G 4C3, Canada; gen tel (905) 727-0819; gen fax (905) 727-2909; disp adv e-mail lmcdonald@yrmg.com; ed e-mail tmcfadden@yrmg.com; web site www.yorkregion.com
Circulation: 16,087fr; CCAB
Parent Co.:
Metroland Media Group Ltd.
Managing Ed. .... Ted McFadden
Areas Served: Canada

THE AURORAN
(Thur)
15213 Yonge St Ste 8, Aurora, ON, L4G 1L8, Canada; gen tel (905) 727-3300; adv tel (416) 803-9940; gen fax (905) 727-2620; disp adv e-mail zach@lpcmedia.ca; class adv e-mail cynthia@auroran.com; ed e-mail brock@auroran.com; web site www.newspapers-online.com/auroran
Circulation: 15pd, 20,000fr; CMCA
Advertising: Open inch rate $8.00.
Established: 2000.
Parent Co.:
London Publishing
Digital Platform - Mobile: Apple, Android
Digital Platform - Tablet: Apple iOS, Android
Ed. .... Brock Weir
Prod. Mgr. .... Cynthia Proctor
Adv. Sales .... Diane Buchanan
Adv. Sales .... Zach Shoub
Delivery Method: Mail, Carrier, Racks
Areas Served: Canada

AYLMER

THE AYLMER EXPRESS
(Wed)
390 Talbot St. E., Aylmer, ON, N5H 2R9, Canada; gen tel (519) 773-3126; gen fax (519) 773-3147; disp adv e-mail advertise@aylmerexpress.ca; web site www.aylmerexpress.ca
Circulation: 13pd, 14fr; VAC
Advertising: Open inch rate $.69.
Adv. Mgr. .... Pam Morton
Circ. Mgr .... Wanda Kapogines
Ed. .... John Hueston
Prodn. Mgr. .... Karen Hueston
Mechanical Specifications: Type page 15 3/4 x 21.
Areas Served: Aylmer

AYR

AYR NEWS
(Wed)
40 Piper St., Ayr, ON, N0B 1E0, Canada; gen tel (519) 632-7432; gen fax (519) 632-7743; disp adv e-mail hall.ayrnews@gmail.com; web site www.ayrnews.ca
Circulation: 0fr; VAC
Advertising: Open inch rate $.77.
Established: 1854.
Circ. Mgr .... Heidi E. Ostner
Mechanical Specifications: Type page 13 x 21 1/2; E - 6 cols, 1 7/8, 1/8 between; A - 6 cols, 1 7/8, 1/8 between; C - 6 cols, 1 7/8, 1/8 between.
Equipment & Software: : Hardware — APP/Mac; Software — Adobe/PageMaker 6.5, Adobe/Photoshop 6.0, Corel Graphics 8.0.
Delivery Method: Mail, Newsstand
Areas Served: N0B 1E0

BANCROFT

BANCROFT THIS WEEK
(Fri)
254 Hastings St., Bancroft, ON, K0L 1C0, Canada; gen tel (613) 332-2002; gen fax (613) 332-1710; disp adv e-mail david.zilstra@gmail.com; class adv e-mail melissa@haliburtonpress.com; ed e-mail jenn@haliburtonpress.com; web site www.bancroftthisweek.com
Circulation: 8,962fr; CMCA
Pub/Adv Dir .... David Zilstra
Mng. Ed .... Jenn Watt
Sales Rep .... Melissa Armstong
Areas Served: Canada

THE BANCROFT TIMES
(Thur)
93 Hastings St. N., Bancroft, ON, K0L 1C0, Canada; gen tel (613) 332-2300; gen fax (613) 332-1894; web site www.thebancrofttimes.ca
Circulation:; VAC
Advertising: $8.56 per column inch/ $.61agate line.
Owner .... Dean Walker
Managing Ed .... Jenn Watt
Areas Served: ontario & provinces

BARRIE

INNISFIL JOURNAL
(Thur)
21 Patterson Rd., Barrie, ON, L4N 7W6, Canada; gen tel (705) 726-0573; gen fax (705) 726-9350; ed e-mail rvanderlinde@simcoe.com; web site www.simcoe.com
Circulation: 10,998fr; CMCA
Parent Co.:
Metroland Media Group Ltd.
Gen. Mgr. .... Elise Allaine
Areas Served: Canada

THE BARRIE ADVANCE
(Thur)
21 Patterson Rd., Barrie, ON, L4N 7W6, Canada; gen tel (705) 726-0573; gen fax (705) 726-9350; ed e-mail bareditor@simcoe.com; web site www.simcoe.com
Circulation: 4,288pd, 52,759fr; VAC
Advertising: Open inch rate $2.35.
Parent Co.:
Metroland Media Group Ltd.
Torstar
Adv. Dir .... Shaun Sauve
Distr. Mgr .... Heather Harris
Ian Proudfoot
Areas Served: Barrie

BARRY'S BAY

BARRY'S BAY THIS WEEK
(Wed)
19574 Opeongo Line, Barry's Bay, ON, K0J 1B0, Canada; gen tel (613) 756-2944; gen fax (613) 756-2994; disp adv e-mail michel@thevalleygazette.ca; class adv e-mail classified@thevalleygazette.ca; ed e-mail christine@thevalleygazette.ca; web site http://www.thevalleygazette.ca/node/3
Circulation: 1,292pd, 0fr; CMCA
Advertising: Open inch rate $.65.
Parent Co.:
Quebecor Communications, Inc.
Gen. Mgr. .... Pete Lapinskie
Owner/Pub/Adv .... Michel Lavigne
Ed .... Christine Hudder
Areas Served: Canada

BEETON

THE SCOPE OF INNISFIL
(Wed)
34 Main St. W, Beeton, ON, L0G 1A0, Canada; gen tel (905) 729-2287; gen fax (905) 729-2541; disp adv e-mail sales@innisfilscope.com; ed e-mail editor@innisfilscope.com; web site www.innisfilscope.com
Circulation: 100pd, 12,433fr; CMCA
Advertising: Open inch rate $1.05.
Established: 1968.
Parent Co.:
Simcoe-York Group
Adv. .... Alex Pozdrowski
Ed. .... Wendy Soloduik
Mechanical Specifications: Type page 10 1/2 x 15; E - 6 cols, 1 2/3, 1/6 between; A - 6 cols, 1 2/3, 1/6 between; C - 6 cols, 1 2/3, 1/6 between.
Equipment & Software: : Hardware — APP/Mac.
Areas Served: Canada

THE TIMES OF NEW TECUMSETH
(Thur)
34 Main St. W., Beeton, ON, L0G 1A0, Canada; gen tel (905) 729-2287; gen fax (905) 729-2541; ed e-mail editor.syp@rogers.com; web site www.newtectimes.com
Circulation: 2,230pd, 100fr; VAC
Advertising: Open inch rate $.81.
Established: 1974.
Parent Co.:
Simcoe-York Group
Ed. .... Wendy Soloduik
Production Mgr .... John Speziali
Annette Derraugh
Mechanical Specifications: Type page 10 1/2 x 15; E - 6 cols, 1 2/3, 1/6 between; A - 6 cols, 1 2/3, 1/6 between; C - 6 cols, 1 2/3, 1/6 between.
Equipment & Software: : Hardware — APP/Mac; Software — QPS/QuarkXPress.
Areas Served: L0G1A0, L0G1L0, L9R, LOG 1BO

TOTTENHAM TIMES
(Wed)
34 Main St. W., Beeton, ON, L0G 1A0, Canada, Canada; gen tel (905) 729-2287; gen fax (905) 729-2541; ed e-mail editor.syp@rogers.com; web site www.newtectimes.com
Circulation: 2,125pd, 75fr; Sworn/Estimate/Non-Audited
Advertising: Open inch rate $8.63.
Established: 1978.
Parent Co.:
Simcoe-York Group
Adv. Mgr. .... John Archibald
Prodn. Mgr. .... Kristen Haire
Mechanical Specifications: Type page 10 1/2 x 15; E - 6 cols, 1 2/3, 1/6 between; A - 6 cols, 1 2/3, 1/6 between; C - 6 cols, 1 2/3, 1/6 between.
Equipment & Software: : Hardware — APP/Mac; Software — QPS/QuarkXPress.
Areas Served: Canada

BELLEVILLE

BELLEVILLE NEWS
(Thur)
250 Sidney St., Belleville, ON, K8P 5E0, Canada; gen tel (613) 966-2034; adv tel (613) 966-2034 ext. 504; disp adv e-mail mhudgins@metroland.com; class adv e-mail slacroix@perfprint.ca; ed e-mail chris.malette@metroland.com; web site http://www.insidebelleville.com/belleville-on/
Parent Co.:
Metroland Media Group Ltd.
Circ Mgr .... Paul Mitchell
Ed .... Chris Malette
Adv .... Melissa Hudgin

BELLEVILLE NEWS EMC
(Thur)
244 Ashley St, Belleville, ON, K0K 2B0, Canada; gen tel (613) 966-2034; disp adv e-mail leslie.osborne@metroland.com; class adv e-mail abarr@metroland.com; ed e-mail theresa.fritz@metroland.com; web site www.insideottawavalley.com
Circulation: 22,549fr; CMCA
Established: 2010.
Parent Co.:

Metroland Media Group Ltd.
Pub....John Kearns
Circ Mgr....Chris Paveley
Ed....Theresa Fritz
Adv. Sales....Leslie Osborne
Delivery Method: Mail
Areas Served: Canada

CAMPBELLFORD/NORTHWEST NEWS EMC
(Thur)
244 Ashley St, Belleville, ON, K0K 2B0, Canada; gen tel (613) 966-2034; adv tel (613) 966-2034; ed tel (613) 966-2034 ext. 510; disp adv e-mail jkearns@theemc.ca; ed e-mail tbush@theemc.ca; web site www.insideottawavalley.com
Circulation: 11,630fr; CMCA
Established: 2010.
Pub....John Kearns
Mng. Ed....Terry Bush
Delivery Method: Mail
Areas Served: Canada

QUINTE WEST EMC
(Thur)
250 Sidney St., Belleville, ON, K8P 5E0, Canada; gen tel (613) 966-2034; web site www.insideottawavalley.com
Circulation: 23,089fr; CMCA
Parent Co.:
Metroland Media Group Ltd.
Pub....John Kearns
Community....Sharon LaCroix
Areas Served: Canada

STIRLING/NORTHEAST NEWS EMC
(Thur)
244 Ashley St., Belleville, ON, K0K 2B0, Canada; gen tel (613) 966-2034; adv tel (613) 966-2034; ed tel (613) 966-2034 ext. 510; disp adv e-mail jkearns@theemc.ca; ed e-mail tbush@theemc.ca; web site www.insideottawavalley.com
Circulation: 11,564fr; CMCA
Established: 2010.
Pub....John Kearns
Mng. Ed....Terry Bush
Delivery Method: Mail
Areas Served: Canada

THE COMMUNITY PRESS
(Thur)
199 Front St., Suite 118, Belleville, ON, K8N 5H5, Canada; gen tel (613) 395-3015; ed tel (613) 392-6501; gen fax (613) 395-2992; ed fax (613) 392-0505; disp adv e-mail gerry.drage@sunmedia.ca; class adv e-mail intelligencer.classifieds@sunmedia.ca; ed e-mail brice.mcvicar@sunmedia.ca; web site www.communitypress-online.com
Circulation: 46,476fr; CMCA
Advertising: Open inch rate $1.61.Editions: 2—2 total Ã ££Ã ££ Community Press/Belleville Edition; Community Press/Quiate West Edition;
Ed....Brice McVicar
Adv. Dir....Gerry Drage
Circ Mgr....Jason Hawley
Mechanical Specifications: Type page 10 1/4 x 15 1/4; E - 9 cols, 1 1/36, 1/8 between; A - 9 cols, 1 1/36, 1/8 between; C - 6 cols, 1 7/12, 1/8 between.
Equipment & Software: : Hardware — APP/Power Mac G4; Software — Adobe/InDesign 1.52, Adobe/Photoshop 6.0, Adobe/Illustrator 9.0, Creator 6.0, QPS/QuarkXPress 4.0.
Areas Served: Canada

BLENHEIM

BLENHEIM NEWS-TRIBUNE
(Wed)
62 Talbot St. W., Blenheim, ON, N0P 1A0, Canada, Canada; gen tel (519) 676-3321; adv tel (519) 676-5023; ed tel (519) 676-3321; gen fax (519) 676-3454; adv fax (519) 676-3454; ed e-mail pl.tribune@southkent.net; web site https://www.facebook.com/bleheimnewstribune/?ref=page_internal
Circulation: 1,927pd, 78fr; AAM
Advertising: Open inch rate $.49.
Established: 1884.
Ed....Pete Laurie
Prod Mgr....Dave Stepniak
Mechanical Specifications: Type page 10 1/4 x 16; E - 6 cols, 1 7/12, between.
Equipment & Software: : Hardware — MAC Compuiters; Presses — Thre AB DFicks; Software — Quark
InDesign
Photo SHop
llustrator
Delivery Method: Mail
Areas Served: Canada

BLYTH

NORTH HURON PUBLISHING INC.
(Thur)
413 Queen St., Po Box 429, Blyth, ON, N0M 1H0, Canada; gen tel (519) 523-4792; gen fax (519) 523-9140; web site www.northhuron.on.ca
Circulation: 1,772pd, 26fr; CMCA
Pub....Keith Roulston
Delivery Method: Mail, Racks
Areas Served: Canada

BOLTON

CALEDON CITIZEN
(Thur)
30 Martha St, Suite 205, Bolton, ON, L7E 5V1, Canada; gen tel (905) 857-6626; gen fax (905) 857-6363; disp adv e-mail erin@lpcmedia.ca; class adv e-mail heather@caledoncitizen.com; ed e-mail editor@caledoncitizen.com; web site www.caledoncitizen.com
Circulation: 12,240fr; CMCA
Advertising: Open inch rate $1.40.
Established: 1983.
Parent Co.:
Simcoe-York Group
Mng. Ed....Bill Rea
Pub....Alan Claridge
Office Mgr....Mary Speck
Mechanical Specifications: Type page 10 7/16 x 15; E - 6 cols, 1 5/8, between.
Equipment & Software: : Hardware — APP/Mac; Software — QPS/QuarkXPress 6.0.
Delivery Method: Mail, Carrier
Areas Served: Canada

CALEDON ENTERPRISE
(Tues, Thur)
12612 Hwy. 50 N., Bolton, ON, L7E 5T1, Canada; gen tel (905) 857-3433; gen fax (905) 857-5002; disp adv e-mail mcrake@caledonenterprise.com; class adv e-mail classifieds@metroland.com; ed e-mail rwilkinson@caledonenterprise.com; web site www.caledonenterprise.com
Circulation: 0pd, 17,530fr; CCAB
Advertising: Open inch rate $1.41.
Parent Co.:
Metroland Media Group Ltd.
Torstar
Circ Mgr....Sheila Ogram
Ed....Robyn Wilkinson
Adv. Rep....Melinda Crake
Areas Served: Canada

KING WEEKLY SENTINEL
(Thur)
30 Martha Streeet, Suite 205, Bolton, ON, L7E 5V1, Caledon, Canada; gen tel (905) 857-6626; gen fax (905) 857-6363; disp adv e-mail zach@lpcmedia.ca; class adv e-mail admin@caledoncitizen.com; ed e-mail editor@kingsentinel.com; web site www.kingsentinel.com
Circulation: 30pd, 10,200fr; Sworn/Estimate/Non-Audited
Advertising: Open line rate $.90.
Established: 1980.
Editor....Mark Pavilons
Mechanical Specifications: Type page 10 1/2 x 15; E - 6 cols, 1 13/20, 1/6 between; A - 6 cols, 1 13/20, 1/6 between; C - 6 cols, 1 13/20, 1/6 between.
Equipment & Software: : Hardware — APP/Mac; Software — QPS/QuarkXPress.
Delivery Method: Newsstand, Carrier, Racks
Areas Served: Caledon

BOTHWELL

OLD AUTOS
(Mon)
348 Main St., Bothwell, ON, N0P 1C0, Canada; gen tel (800) 461-3457; disp adv e-mail ads@oldautos.ca; class adv e-mail classifieds@oldautos.ca; ed e-mail info@oldautos.ca; web site www.oldautos.ca
Circulation: 14,643pd, 306fr; AAM
Established: 1987.
Publisher....Mary Jo DePelsmaeker
Delivery Method: Mail, Newsstand
Areas Served: Canada

BRACEBRIDGE

BRACEBRIDGE EXAMINER
(Thur)
34 Ep Lee Dr., Bracebridge, ON, P1L 1P9, Canada, Canada; gen tel (705) 645-8771; gen fax (705) 645-1718; disp adv e-mail mbradley@metroland.com; class adv e-mail classifieds@metroland.com; ed e-mail psteel@metrolandnorthmedia.com; web site www.bracebridgeexaminer.com
Circulation: 83pd, 8,171fr; CMCA
Advertising: Open inch rate $1.04.
Parent Co.:
Metroland Media Group Ltd.
Torstar
Adv. Mgr....Meriel Bradley
Ed....Pamela Steel
Circ Mgr....Andrew Allen
Mechanical Specifications: Type page 11 1/2 x 21 1/2; E - 6 cols, between; A - 6 cols, between; C - 6 cols, between.
Areas Served: Canada

WHAT'S UP MUSKOKA
(Wed)
Unit 12-440 Ecclestone Drive, Bracebridge, ON, P1L 1Z6, Muskoka, Canada; gen tel (705) 646-1314; gen fax (705) 645-6424; web site www.whatsupmuskoka.com
Circulation: 0pd, 26,000fr; CMCA
Advertising: Open inch rate $.67.
Established: 2008.
Parent Co.:
Postmedia Network Inc.
Quebecor Communications, Inc.
Mechanical Specifications: Type page 10 1/3 x 12 1/2; E - 6 cols, 1 1/2, between; A - 6 cols, 1 1/2, between; C - 6 cols, 1 1/2, between.
Delivery Method: Mail, Racks
Areas Served: Muskoka

MUSKOKA DISTRICT WEEKENDER
(Fri)
34 E. P. Lee Drive, Bracebridge, ON, P1L 1V2, Canada; gen tel (705) 645-8771; gen fax (705) 645-1718; disp adv e-mail ddickson@metrolandnorthmedia.com; web site www.muskokaregion.com
Circulation: 26,430fr; CMCA
Sales Coordinator....Coral Brush
Areas Served: Canada

THE MUSKOKAN
(Thur)
34 Ep Lee Dr., Bracebridge, ON, P1L 1P9, Canada; gen tel (705) 645-8771; gen fax (705) 645-1718; web site www.muskokan.com
Circulation: 24,000fr; Sworn/Estimate/Non-Audited
Advertising: Open inch rate $1.64.
Parent Co.:
Metroland Media Group Ltd.
Torstar
Adv. Sales Mgr....Paul Drummond
Editorial Coord....Jake Good
Prodn. Coord....Marianne Dawson

BRAMPTON

ACTION LONDON SARNIA
(Tues)
Professor's Lake Parkway, Brampton, ON, L6S 4P8, Canada; gen tel (800) 525-6752; ed e-mail info@lemetropolitain.com; web site www.laction.ca
Circulation: 1,907pd, 1,106fr; ODC
Ed....Denis Poirier
Sales Dir....Richard Caumartin

LE REGIONAL
(Wed)
99 Professors Lake Parkway, Brampton, ON, L6S 4P8, Canada; gen tel (905) 732-9666; gen fax (905) 790-9127; disp adv e-mail marketing@leregional.com; class adv e-mail marketing@leregional.com; ed e-mail info@leregional.cm; web site www.leregional.com
Circulation: 76pd, 4,164fr; CMCA
Established: 2000.Christiane Beaupre
Delivery Method: Mail, Racks
Areas Served: Canada

METROPOLITAIN (LE)
(Wed)
99 Professors Lake Pkwy, Brampton, ON, L6S 4P8, Canada; gen tel (905) 790-3229; gen fax (905) 790-9127; web site www.lemetropolitain.com
Circulation: 329pd, 8,028fr; CMCA
Ed....Denis Poirier
Areas Served: Canada

BRANTFORD

BRANT NEWS
(Thur)
111 Easton Rd., Brantford, ON, N3P 1J4, Canada; gen tel (519) 758-1157; gen fax (519) 753-3567; disp adv e-mail lbutler@brantnews.com; class adv e-mail classified@metrolandwest.com; ed e-mail sallen@brantnews.com; web site www.brantnews.com
Circulation: 0pd, 48,716fr; CCAB
Established: 2009.
Parent Co.:
Metroland Media Group Ltd.
Metroland Media
Circ Mgr....Linda Hill
Ed....Sean Allen
Adv Mgr....Loren Butlet
Areas Served: Canada

BROCKVILLE

ST. LAWRENCE NEWS
(Thur)
7712 Kent Blvd., Brockville, ON, K6V 7H6, Canada; gen tel (613) 498-0305; gen fax (613) 498-0307; web site www.emcstlawrence.ca
Circulation: 29,325fr; CMCA
Parent Co.:
Metroland Media Group Ltd.
Areas Served: Canada

THE RECORDER & TIMES
(Wed, Thur)
2479 Parkedale Avenue, Brockville, ON, K6V 3H2, Leeds & Grenville Counties, Canada; gen tel (613) 342-4441; adv tel (613) 342-4441 Ext. 500267; ed tel (613) 342-4441 Ext. 500107; gen fax (613) 342-4456; disp adv e-mail ksammon@postmedia.com; ed e-mail dgordanier@postmedia.com; web site www.recorder.ca
Circulation: 29,300fr; CMCA
Advertising: Open inch rate $1.07.
Established: 1997.

Parent Co.:
Post Media
Med. Sales Dir. .... Kerry Sammon
Mechanical Specifications: Type page 10 1/4 x 14 1/4; E - 6 cols, 1 5/8, 1/8 between; A - 6 cols, 1 5/8, 1/8 between; C - 7 cols, 1 1/3, 1/8 between.
Equipment & Software: : Hardware — APP/Mac.
Delivery Method: Newsstand, Carrier
Areas Served: Leeds & Grenville Counties

BURKS FALLS

ALMAGUIN NEWS

(Thur)
59 Ontario St., Burks Falls, ON, P0A 1C0, Canada; gen tel (705)382-9996; gen fax (705) 382-9997; disp adv e-mail advertising@almaguinnews.com; ed e-mail editor@almaguinnews.com; web site www.almaguinnews.com
Circulation: 2,230pd, 150fr; CMCA
Advertising: Open inch rate $.75.
Established: 1889.
Parent Co.:
Metroland Media Group Ltd.
Gen. Mgr. .... Bill Allen
Adv. Rep................................ Twila Armstrong
News Ed. .... Rob Learn
Mechanical Specifications: Type page 10 x 21 1/2"; E - 9 cols, 1 1/16, between; A - 9 cols, 1 3/8, between; C - 9 cols, 1 3/8, between.
Delivery Method: Mail, Newsstand
Areas Served: Canada

BURLINGTON

THE BURLINGTON POST

(Thur, Fri)
5040 Mainway, Unit 1, Burlington, ON, L7L 7G5, Canada, Canada; gen tel (905) 632-4444; gen fax (905) 632-9162; ed e-mail letters@burlingtonpost.com; web site www.burlingtonpost.com
Circulation: 40pd, 47,808fr; CCAB
Advertising: Open inch rate $8.90.
Established: 1965.
Parent Co.:
Metroland Media Group Ltd.
Torstar
Ed. in Chief .... Jill Davis
Mng. Ed.. Don Ford
Sports Ed....................................... Kevin Nagel
Advertising Director .... Debbi Koppejan
Equipment & Software: : Hardware — APP/Mac; Software — QPS/QuarkXPress, Microsoft/Word.
Delivery Method: Carrier
Areas Served: Canada

CALEDONIA

GLANBROOK GAZETTE

(Thur)
3 Sutherland St. W., Caledonia, ON, N3W 1C1, Canada; gen tel (905) 765-4441; gen fax (905) 765-3651; disp adv e-mail advertising@sachem.ca; web site www.sachem.ca
Circulation: 9,194fr; CMCA
Parent Co.:
Metroland Media Group Ltd.
Areas Served: Canada

THE GRAND RIVER SACHEM

(Thur)
3 Sutherland St. W., Caledonia, ON, N3W 1C1, Canada; gen tel (905) 765-4441; gen fax (905) 765-3651; disp adv e-mail advertising@sachem.ca; web site www.sachem.ca
Circulation: 77pd, 21,137fr; CMCA
Advertising: Open inch rate $.55.
Parent Co.:
Metroland Media Group Ltd.
Adv. Mgr....................................... Nancy Plank
Adv. Mgr., Classified .... Georgia Mete
Ed. .... Neil Dring
Mechanical Specifications: Type page 10 1/3 x 14; E - 6 cols, 1 3/5, between; A - 6 cols, 1 1/3, between.
Equipment & Software: : Hardware — APP/Mac.
Areas Served: Canada

CAMBRIDGE

CAMBRIDGE TIMES

(Tues, Thur)
475 Thompson Dr. Units 1-4, Cambridge, ON, N1T 2K7, Canada; gen tel (519) 623-7395; gen fax (519) 623-9155; disp adv e-mail tanderson@cambridgetimes.ca; class adv e-mail classified@metrolandwest.com; ed e-mail rvivian@cambridgetimes.ca; web site www.cambridgetimes.ca
Circulation: 31,628fr; CMCA
Advertising: Open inch rate $22.70.
Parent Co.:
Metroland Media Group Ltd.
Torstar
Pub .... Donna Luelo
Ed .... Richard Vivian
Prod/Circ. Mgr. .... Carron Woods
Adv. Mgr.. Ted Anderson
Mechanical Specifications: Type page 11 x 17; E - 6 cols, 2 1/20, between; A - 6 cols, 2 1/20, between; C - 6 cols, 2 1/20, between.
Equipment & Software: : Hardware — APP/Mac; Software — QPS/QuarkXPress, Adobe/Photoshop, Adobe/Illustrator.
Delivery Method: Carrier
Areas Served: Canada

CANNINGTON

BROCK CITIZEN

(Thur)
2d Cameron St. E., Cannington, ON, L0E 1E0, Canada; gen tel (705) 432-8842; gen fax (705) 432-2942; disp adv e-mail btrickett@mykawartha.com; class adv e-mail lmunro@mykawartha.com; ed e-mail ltuffin@mykawartha.com; web site http://www.mykawartha.com/brocktownship-on/
Circulation: 5,497fr; Sworn/Estimate/Non-Audited
Advertising: Open inch rate $.93.
Parent Co.:
Metroland Media Group Ltd.
Torstar
Ed .... Peter Bishop
Gen. Mgr. .... Mary Babcock
Mng. Ed.. Lois Tuffin
Office Mgr .... Kim Riel

CHATHAM

CHATHAM THIS WEEK

(Wed)
138 King Street West, Chatham, ON, N7M 1ES, Southwestern Ontario, Canada; gen tel (519) 351-7331; gen fax (519) 351-7774; ed e-mail peter.epp@sunmedia.ca; web site www.chathamthisweek.com
Circulation: 19,760fr; CMCA
Parent Co.:
Postmedia Network Inc.Dean Muharrem
Media Sales Mgr................... Aaron Rodrigues
Managing Ed.................................... Peter Epp
Office Mgr. .... Rachel Blain
Areas Served: Southwestern Ontario

COURIER PRESS

(Thur)
138 King Street West, Chatham, ON, N7M 1E3, Chatham Kent, Canada; gen tel (519) 354 2000; gen fax (519) 351 7774; web site www.wallaceburgcourierpress.com
Circulation: 8,914fr; CMCA
Advertising: Open inch rate $.62.
Established: 1967.
Parent Co.:
Postmedia Network Inc.
Sun Media
Pub... Dean Muharrem
Circ. Mgr.. Mary Dixon
Delivery Method: Carrier
Areas Served: Chatham Kent

CHESTERVILLE

THE CHESTERVILLE RECORD

(Wed)
7 King St., Chesterville, ON, K0C 1H0, Canada, Canada; gen tel (613) 448-2321; gen fax (613) 448-3260; disp adv e-mail news@chestervillerecord.com; ed e-mail editor@chestervillerecord.com; web site www.agrinewsinteractive.com
Circulation: 1,456pd, 2fr; CMCA
Advertising: Open inch rate $.67.
Established: 1894.
Pub.. Robin R. Morris
Ed. .... Nelson Zandbergen
Mechanical Specifications: Type page 13 x 21 1/2; E - 6 cols, 2, 1/6 between; A - 6 cols, 2, 1/6 between; C - 6 cols, 2, 1/6 between.
Equipment & Software: : Hardware — APP/Mac; Software — Multi-Ad/Creator 4.0, QPS/QuarkXPress 4.1, Adobe/Photoshop 5.5, Adobe/Illustrator 7.0.
Areas Served: Canada

THE CHESTERVILLE RECORD/THE VILLAGER

(Wed)
7 King St., Chesterville, ON, K0C 1H0, Canada; gen tel (613) 448-2321; gen fax (613) 448-3260; web site www.chestervillerecord.com; russellvillager.com
Circulation: 2,600pd,; CMCA
Advertising: Open inch rate $.58.
Established: 1984.
Editor .... Muriel Carruthers
Mechanical Specifications: Type page 10 3/8 x 13 7/8; E - 6 cols, 1 5/8, 3/16 between; A - 6 cols, 1 5/8, 3/16 between; C - 6 cols, 1 5/8, 3/16 between.
Equipment & Software: : Hardware — APP/Mac; Software — Multi-Ad, QPS/QuarkXPress 4.1, Adobe/Photoshop 5.0, Adobe/Illustrator 7.0, Microsoft/Word.
Areas Served: Canada

CLARENCE CREEK

AGRICOM

(Fri, Bi-Mthly) (bimonthly)
2474 Rue Champlain, Clarence Creek, ON, K0A1N0, Canada; gen tel (613) 488-2651; gen fax (613) 488-2541; disp adv e-mail pub@journalagricom.ca; ed e-mail redaction@journalagricom.ca; web site www.journalagricom.ca
Circulation: 900pd, 1,100fr; Sworn/Estimate/Non-Audited
Advertising: 1,36/agate line + 400$ for colors.
Established: 1983.
Ed .... Isabelle Lessard
Delivery Method: Mail
Areas Served: Province of Ontario

CLINTON

CLINTON NEWS-RECORD

(Wed)
53 Albert St., Clinton, ON, N0M 1L0, Canada, Canada; gen tel (519) 482-3443; gen fax (519) 482-7341; disp adv e-mail clinton.ads@bowesnet.com; ed e-mail clinton.news@bowesnet.com; web site www.clintonnewsrecord.com
Circulation: 1,029pd, 22fr; CMCA
Advertising: Open inch rate $.69.
Parent Co.:
Postmedia Network Inc.
Quebecor Communications, Inc.
Pub... Neil Clifford
Adv. Mgr...................................... John Bauman
Ed. .... Cheryl Heath
Mechanical Specifications: Type page 11 1/2 x 17; E - 6 cols, 1 3/4, between; A - 6 cols, 1 3/4, between; C - 6 cols, 1 3/4, between.
Equipment & Software: : Hardware — APP/Mac; Software — QPS/QuarkXPress.
Areas Served: Canada

COBOURG

NORTHUMBERLAND NEWS

(Thur)
884 Division St., Bldg. 2, Unit 212, Cobourg, ON, K9A 5V6, Canada; gen tel (905) 373-7355; gen fax (905) 373-4719; web site www.northumberlandnews.com
Circulation: 0pd, 22,394fr; CCAB
Advertising: Open inch rate $1.94.
Parent Co.:
Metroland Media Group Ltd.
Torstar
Pub.................................. Timothy J. Whittaker
Office Mgr. .... Lillian Hook
Circ. Mgr.................................... Abe Fakhourie
Ed. in Chief .... Joanne Burghardt
Mng. Ed.. Dwight Irwin
Areas Served: Canada

COCHRANE

COCHRANE TIMES-POST

(Thur)
143, Sixth Avenue, Cochrane, ON, P0L 1C0, Canada; gen tel (705) 272-3344; gen fax (705) 272-3434; disp adv e-mail wayne.major@sunmedia.ca; ed e-mail kevin.anderson@sunmedia.ca; web site www.cochranetimespost.ca
Circulation: 1,254pd,; CMCA
Advertising: $7.73.
Established: 1904.
Parent Co.:
Postmedia Network Inc.
Pub.. Wayne Major
Sales Representative, print & digital..... Chantal Carriere
Reporter .... Ashley Lewis
Delivery Method: Mail, Newsstand, Carrier
Areas Served: Canada

COLLINGWOOD

COLLINGWOOD CONNECTION

(Fri)
11 Ronell Crescent, Unit B, Collingwood, ON, L9Y 4J6, Canada; gen tel (705) 444-1875; adv tel (800) 387-0668; gen fax (705) 444-1876; ed e-mail editor@simcoe.com; web site www.simcoe.com
Circulation: 11,516fr; CMCA
Advertising: Open inch rate $1.45.
Parent Co.:
Metroland Media Group Ltd.
Torstar
Ed. .... Scott Woodhouse
Prod. Mgr. .... Stephen Hall
Prodn. Dir.................................... Kent Feagan
General Mgr..................................... Carol Lamb
Sales Mgr. .... Patsy McCarthy
Delivery Method: Carrier
Areas Served: Canada

THE ENTERPRISE-BULLETIN

(Fri)
77 Simcoe St., Collingwood, ON, L9Y 3Z4, Canada; gen tel (705) 445-4611; gen fax (705) 444-6477; ed e-mail editorial@theenterprisebulletin.com; web site www.theenterprisebulletin.com
Circulation: 295pd, 18,858fr; CMCA
Advertising: Open inch rate $.91.
Parent Co.:
Postmedia Network Inc.
Sunmedia
Quebecor Communications, Inc.
Pub... Doreen Sykes
Circ. Mgr.................................... April MacLean
Ed. .... J.T. McVeigh
Mechanical Specifications: Type page 11 1/2 x 21 1/2; E - 5 cols, 2 1/2, between; A - 10 cols, 1 1/6, between; C - 8 cols, 1 1/3, between.

Areas Served: Canada

CORNWALL

SEAWAY NEWS

(Thur)
501 Campbell Street, Unit 6, Cornwall, ON, K6H 6X5, Cornwall and SD&G, Canada; gen tel (613) 933-0014; gen fax (613) 933-0024; disp adv e-mail patrick.larose@tc.tc; class adv e-mail diane.merpaw@tc.tc; ed e-mail nicholas.seebruch@tc.tc; web site www.cornwallseawaynews.com
Circulation: 36,541fr; CMCA
Advertising: Open inch rate $1.67.
Established: 1985.
Parent Co.:
Transcontinental Media
General Manager/ Publisher.......... Rick Shaver
Production Coordinator............ Colleen Parette
Media Strategy Manager........... Patrick Larose
Mechanical Specifications: Type page 10 3/8 x 16; E - 9 cols, 1 1/16, 1/10 between; A - 9 cols, 1 1/16, 1/10 between; C - 8 cols, 1 1/16, 1/10 between.
Equipment & Software: : Hardware — APP/Power Mac; Software — QPS/QuarkXPress 3.2, Adobe/Illustrator 5.5, Adobe/Photoshop 3.0.
Delivery Method: Newsstand, Carrier
Areas Served: Cornwall and SD&G

CREEMORE

CREEMORE ECHO

(Fri)
3 Caroline St. W., Creemore, ON, L0M 1G0, Canada, Canada; gen tel (705) 466-9906; gen fax (705) 466-9908; web site www.creemore.com
Circulation: 450pd, 3,396fr; CMCA
Advertising: Open inch rate $.56.
Pub.. Sara Hershoff
Office Mgr............................... Georgi Denison
Ed... Trina Berlo
Areas Served: Canada

DEEP RIVER

THE NORTH RENFREW TIMES

(Wed)
21 Champlain St., Deep River, ON, K0J 1P0, Canada; gen tel (613) 584-4161; adv tel (613) 584-4161; ed tel (613) 584-4161; disp adv e-mail NRT@magma.ca; class adv e-mail NRT@magma.ca; ed e-mail NRT@magma.ca; web site www.northrenfrewtimes.net
Circulation: 1,661pd,; CMCA
Advertising: Open inch rate $6.58.
Established: 1956.
Digital Platform - Tablet: Other
Pub.. Kelly Lapping
Editor.. Terry Myers
Mechanical Specifications: Type page 10 3/8 x 14; A - 9 cols, 1, 0.167 between
Delivery Method: Mail, Newsstand
Areas Served: Canada

DELHI

DELHI NEWS-RECORD

(Wed)
237 Main St., Delhi, ON, N4B 2M4, Canada, Canada; gen tel (519) 582-2510; gen fax (519) 582-0627; ed e-mail deleditorial@bowesnet.com; web site www.delhinewsrecord.com
Circulation: 506pd,; CMCA
Advertising: Open inch rate $0.75.
Parent Co.:
Postmedia Network Inc.
Quebecor Communications, Inc.
Adv. Mgr.................................... Walter Keleer
Ed.. Kim Novak
Prodn. Mgr.................................. Wayne Ward

Pub... Ken Koyoma
Areas Served: Canada

DORCHESTER

THE SIGNPOST

(Wed)
15 Bridge St., Dorchester, ON, N0L 1G2, Thames Centre, Middlesex County, Canada; gen tel (519) 268-7337; adv tel (519) 268-7337; ed tel (519) 268-7337; gen fax (519) 268-3260; adv fax (519) 268-3260; ed fax (519) 268-3260; disp adv e-mail advertising@dorchestersignpost.com; class adv e-mail classifieds@dorchestersignpost.com; ed e-mail w.spence@on.aibn.com; web site www.dorchestersignpost.com
Circulation: 1,468pd,; CMCA
Advertising: $11.34 per column inch.
Established: 1959.
Pub. .... Fred Huxley
Gen. Mgr. .... Lyndsay Huxley
Ed. .... Wendy Spence
Delivery Method: Mail, Newsstand, Carrier
Areas Served: Thames Centre, Middlesex County

DRAYTON

THE COMMUNITY NEWS

(Fri)
41 Wellington St. N., Drayton, ON, N0G 1P0, Canada; gen tel (519) 638-3066; gen fax (519) 843-7606; ed e-mail editor@wellingtonadvertiser.com; web site www.wellingtonadvertiser.com
Circulation: 5pd, 5,152fr; CMCA
Advertising: Open inch rate $.47.
Pub.. William Adsett
Ed. .... Dave Adsett
Mechanical Specifications: Type page 10.25 x 15; E - 6 cols, 1 4/7, between; A - 6 cols, 1 4/7, between; C - 6 cols, 1 4/7, between.
Areas Served: Canada

DRYDEN

DRYDEN OBSERVER

(Wed)
32 Colonization Ave., Dryden, ON, P8N 2Y9, Canada; gen tel (807) 223-2390; adv tel (807) 223-2390 ext. 35; ed tel (807) 223-2390 ext. 34; gen fax (807) 223-2907; adv fax (807) 223-2907; disp adv e-mail lorie@drydenobserver.ca; ed e-mail chrism@drydenobserver.ca; web site www.drydenobserver.ca
Circulation: 2,023pd, 7fr; CMCA
Advertising: Open inch rate $.83.
Established: 1897.
Parent Co.:
Norwest Printing
Adv. Mgr. .... LORIE LUNDY
Circ. Mgr..................................... Sean Clarke
Ed. .... CHRIS MARCHAND
Reporter .... Michael Christianson
Prod.. Brian Kasaboski
Office manager.......................... Laurie Fisher
Mechanical Specifications: Type page 11 1/2 x 21 1/2; E - 6 cols, 1 3/4, between; A - 6 cols, 1 3/4, between; C - 6 cols, 1 3/4, between.
Equipment & Software: : Hardware — APP/Mac; Software — QPS/QuarkXPress 4.0.
Delivery Method: Mail, Carrier
Areas Served: Canada

DUNDALK

ADVANCE

(Wed)
260 Main St. E., Dundalk, ON, N0C 1B0, Southgate, Canada; gen tel (519) 923-2203; gen fax (519) 923-2747; disp adv e-mail dundalk.herald@gmail.com; ed e-mail dundalk.heraldnews@gmail.com
Circulation: 1,299pd,; Sworn/Estimate/Non-Audited
Advertising: Open inch rate $.70.
Established: 1881.
Parent Co.:
herald newspaper corp
Pub... Matthew Walls
Delivery Method: Mail, Newsstand
Areas Served: Southgate

HERALD

(Wed)
260 Main St. E., Dundalk, ON, N0C 1B0, Canada; gen tel (519) 923-2203; gen fax (519) 923-2747; disp adv e-mail dundalk.herald@gmail.com; ed e-mail dundalk.heraldnews@gmail.com; web site www.dundalkherald.ca
Circulation: 1,443pd,; CMCA
Advertising: Open inch rate $.70.
Established: 1881.
Pub... Matthew Walls
Adv. Mgr. .... Cathy Walls
Areas Served: Canada

DURHAM

THE DURHAM CHRONICLE

(Wed)
190 Elizabeth St. E., Durham, ON, N0G 1R0, Canada, Canada; gen tel (519) 369-2504; gen fax (519) 369-3560
Circulation: 1,196pd, 21fr; Sworn/Estimate/Non-Audited
Advertising: Open inch rate $.37.
Pub... Marie David
Gen. Mgr. .... Bev Stoddart
Ed. .... Christine Meingast
Mechanical Specifications: Type page 11 1/4 x 16 3/4; E - 5 cols, 2 1/5, between; A - 5 cols, 2 1/5, between; C - 9 cols, between.
Equipment & Software: : Hardware — APP/Mac; Software — QPS/QuarkXPress 4.0.
Areas Served: Canada

EGANVILLE

THE EGANVILLE LEADER

(Wed)
150 John St., P.o. Box 310, Eganville, ON, K0J 1T0, Canada; gen tel (613) 628-2332; gen fax (613) 628-3291; disp adv e-mail leaderads@nrtco.net; ed e-mail leader@nrtco.net; web site www.eganvilleleader.com
Circulation: 6,096pd,; CMCA
Advertising: Open inch rate $.70.
Established: 1902.
Circ. Mgr.................................. Carol Kutschke
Ed. .... Gerald J. Tracey
Mechanical Specifications: Type page 13 1/2 x 21; E - 8 cols, 1 3/5, between; A - 8 cols, 1 3/5, between; C - 8 cols, 1 3/5, between.
Equipment & Software: : Hardware — IBM; Software — QPS/QuarkXPress.
Delivery Method: Mail, Newsstand, Racks
Areas Served: Canada

ELLIOT LAKE

THE MID-NORTH MONITOR

(Thur)
14 Hillside Drive South, Elliot Lake, ON, P5A 1M6, Canada, Canada; gen tel (705) 869-0588; adv tel (705) 848 - 7195; gen fax (705) 869-0587; disp adv e-mail karsten.johansen@sunmedia.ca; ed e-mail kevin.mcsheffrey@sunmedia.ca; web site www.midnorthmonitor.com
Circulation: 949pd,; Sworn/Estimate/Non-Audited
Advertising: Open inch rate $.94.
Established: 1978.
Parent Co.:
Postmedia
Postmedia Network Inc.
Circ. Mgr. .... Lolene Patterson
Managing Editor .... Kevin McSheffrey
Mechanical Specifications: Type page 10 1/4 x 15 ; E - 9 cols, 1" , 1/8" between; A - 9 cols, 1", 1/8" between; C - 9 cols, 1", 1/8" between.
Equipment & Software: : Hardware — Mac; Software — InDesign
Delivery Method: Mail, Newsstand
Areas Served: Canada

ELMVALE

SPRINGWATER NEWS

(Thur, Other) (Bi-weekly)
9 Glenview Ave., Elmvale, ON, L0L 1P0, Canada; gen tel (705) 322-2249; adv tel (705) 322-2249; ed tel (705) 321 2653; gen fax (705) 322-8393; adv fax (705) 322-8393; disp adv e-mail springwaternews@rogers.com; class adv e-mail springwaternews@rogers.com; ed e-mail springwaternews@rogers.com; web site www.springwaternews.ca - 2,311,899(views) 197,164(visitors)
Circulation: 140pd, 18,750fr; Sworn/Estimate/Non-Audited
Advertising: 75 cents.
Established: 1998.Editions: 423— Springwater News
Digital Platform - Mobile: Android, Windows, Blackberry
Digital Platform - Tablet: Android, Windows 7, Other
Mechanical Specifications: Tabloid 11x17 24 pages - 12 in colour
Equipment & Software: ; Software — Adobe Creative Suite 5
Microsoft Suite
Delivery Method: Mail, Newsstand, Carrier, Racks
Areas Served: L0L in North Simcoe County
L9M near Penetanguishene
L4R around Midland
L0K Wyebridge
L4M and L4n around Barrie
Note: Does someone want to buy the paper?

EMBRUN

JOURNAL LE REFLET

(Mon)
793 Rue Notre Dame Rr 3 # 3,, Embrun, ON, K0A 1W1, Canada; gen tel (613) 443-2741; web site www.lereflet.qc.ca
Circulation: 29pd, 18,102fr; ODC
Gen. Dir. .... Roger Duplantie
Areas Served: Embrun, ON

ERIN

THE ERIN ADVOCATE

(Wed)
8 Thompson Crescent, Erin, ON, N0B 1T0, Canada; gen tel (519) 833-9603; gen fax (519) 833-9605
Circulation: 1,054pd,; CMCA
Advertising: Open inch rate $.51.
Established: 1880.
Parent Co.:
Metroland Media Group Ltd.
Torstar
Pub... Ken Nugent
Adv. Mgr...................................... Bill Anderson
Ed. .... Joan Murray
Mechanical Specifications: Type page 10 3/8 x 14; E - 6 cols, 1 5/8, between; A - 6 cols, 1 5/8, between; C - 6 cols, 1 5/8, between.
Equipment & Software: : Hardware — APP/Mac; Software — QPS/QuarkXPress, Adobe/Illustrator.
Areas Served: Canada

ESSEX

ESSEX FREE PRESS

(Thur)
16 Centre St., Essex, ON, N8M 1N9, Canada, Canada; gen tel (519) 776-4268; gen fax (519) 776-4014; web site www.sxfreepress.

com
Circulation: 9,925fr; CMCA
Advertising: Open inch rate $2.31.
Established: 1896.
Pub....Lauri Brett
Mechanical Specifications: Type page 10 x 15; E - 5 cols, 2, 1/6 between.
Equipment & Software: : Hardware — APP/Mac; Software — Abbott Systems/Ready, Set, Go 5, QPS/QuarkXPress 4.0.
Areas Served: Canada

ETOBICOKE

ETOBICOKE GUARDIAN

(Thur)
307 Humberline Dr., Etobicoke, ON, M9W 5V1, Canada; gen tel (416) 675-4390; gen fax (416) 675-9296; web site www.insidetoronto.ca
Circulation: 0pd, 67,985fr; CCAB
Advertising: Open inch rate $5.00.
Established: 1917.
Parent Co.:
Metroland Media Group Ltd.
Torstar
Gen. Mgr....Marg Middleton
Pub....Betty Carr
Adv. Mgr....Cor Coran
Asst. Dir., Dist....Lesley Duff
Mng. Ed....Grace Peacock
Dir., Prodn....Dave Barnett
Prodn. Mgr....Katherine Bernal
Areas Served: Canada

EXETER

TIMES ADVOCATE

(Wed)
356 Main St. S., Exeter, ON, N0M 1S6, Canada; gen tel (519) 235-1331; adv fax (519) 235-0766; disp adv e-mail sales@southhuron.com; ed e-mail snixon@southhuron.com; web site www.southhuron.com
Circulation: 2,158pd, 84fr; CMCA
Advertising: Open inch rate $.84.
Established: 1873.
Parent Co.:
Metroland Media Group Ltd.
Torstar
Manager....Deb Lord
Editor....Scott Nixon
Sales....Deborah Schillemore
Mechanical Specifications: Type page 10 1/2 x 16; E - 6 cols, 1 9/16, 3/16 between; A - 6 cols, 1 9/16, 3/16 between; C - 6 cols, 1 9/16, 3/16 between.
Equipment & Software: : Hardware — APP/Mac; Software — Abbott Systems/Ready, Set, Go, QPS/QuarkXPress.
Delivery Method: Mail
Areas Served: N0M

FERGUS

THE FERGUS-ELORA NEWS EXPRESS

(Wed)
204 St. Andrew St. W, Fergus, ON, N1M 1M7, Canada; gen tel (519) 843-1310; gen fax (519) 323-4548; disp adv e-mail ads@centrewellington.com; ed e-mail editor@centrewellington.com; web site www.southwesternontario.ca/ferguselora-on
Circulation: 100pd, 7,850fr; CMCA
Advertising: Open inch rate $.84.
Established: 1852.
Parent Co.:
Metroland Media Group Ltd.
Torstar
Ed....Shannon Burrows
Equipment & Software: : Hardware — APP/Mac; Software — Indesign
Areas Served: Canada

THE WELLINGTON ADVERTISER

(Fri)
905 Gartshore St., Fergus, ON, N1M 2W8, Canada; gen tel (519) 843-5410; gen fax (519) 843-7607; disp adv e-mail advertising@wellingtonadvertiser.com; ed e-mail editor@wellingtonadvertiser.com; web site www.wellingtonadvertiser.com
Circulation: 235pd, 39,898fr; VAC
Advertising: Open inch rate $1.25.
Established: 1967.
Pub....William Adsett
Circ. Mgr....Catherine Goss
Ed....Dave Adsett
Mechanical Specifications: E - 6 cols, 1 1/2, 1 2/3 between; A - 6 cols, 1 1/2, 1 2/3 between; C - 6 cols, 1 1/2, 1 2/3 between.
Delivery Method: Mail, Newsstand, Carrier, Racks
Areas Served: Fergus

FONTHILL

FONTHILL VOICE OF PELHAM

(Wed)
8-209 Highway 20 East, Fonthill, ON, L0S 1E0, Canada, Canada; gen tel (905) 892-8690; gen fax (905) 892-0823; disp adv e-mail advertising@thevoiceofpelham.ca; ed e-mail editor@thevoiceofpelham.ca; web site www.thevoiceofpelham.ca
Circulation: 6,782fr; CMCA
Advertising: Open inch rate $.71.
Established: 1997.
Office Mgr....Leslie Chiapetta
Ed....Nate Smelle
Pub....Dave Burket
Mechanical Specifications: Type page 10 1/4 x 15 2/3; E - 6 cols, 1 1/2, 1/8 between; A - 6 cols, 1 1/2, 1/8 between; C - 6 cols, 1 1/2, 1/8 between.
Equipment & Software: : Hardware — APP/Power Mac; Software — In Design, Photoshop
Areas Served: Canada

FOREST

FOREST STANDARD

(Thur)
1 King St. W., Forest, ON, N0N 1J0, Canada; gen tel (519) 786-5242; gen fax (519) 786-4884
Circulation: 1,848pd,; CMCA
Advertising: Open inch rate $.74.
Pub....Dale Hayter
Adv. Mgr....Gil De Schutter
Circ. Mgr....Mavis Sanger
Ed....Gord Whitehead
Mechanical Specifications: Type page 11 1/4 x 16; E - 6 cols, 1 1/2, 1/4 between; A - 6 cols, 1 1/2, 1/4 between.
Equipment & Software: : Hardware — APP/Mac; Software — Archetype/Corel Draw, Adobe/PageMaker, Adobe/Illustrator.
Areas Served: Canada

FORT ERIE

THE FORT ERIE TIMES

(Thur)
450 Garrison Rd., Unit 1, Fort Erie, ON, L2A 1N2, Canada; gen tel (905) 871-3100; adv tel (905) 871-3100 x202; ed tel (905) 871-3100 x207; gen fax (905) 871-5243; adv fax (905) 871-5243; ed fax (905) 871-5243; disp adv e-mail myra.robertson@sunmedia.ca; ed e-mail kris.dube@sunmedia.com; web site www.forterietimes.com
Circulation: 9pd, 12,454fr; CMCA
Advertising: Open inch rate $1.00.
Parent Co.:
Postmedia Network Inc.
Quebecor Communications, Inc.
Digital Platform - Mobile: Apple
Ed....Sarag Ferguson
Mechanical Specifications: Tabloid 10.4" W x 11.5" H
Delivery Method: Carrier
Areas Served: Canada

FORT FRANCES

FORT FRANCES TIMES

(Wed)
116 First St., Fort Frances, ON, P9A 3M7, Canada, Canada; gen tel (807) 274-5373; gen fax (807) 274-7286; disp adv e-mail ads@fortfrances.com; web site www.fortfrances.com
Circulation: 3,134pd, 130fr; CMCA
Advertising: Open inch rate $1.02.
Pub....James R. Cumming
Office Mgr....Linda Plumridge
Adv. Mgr....Debbie Ballare
Ed....Michael Behan
Prod. Mgr....Don Cumming
Mechanical Specifications: Type page 12 x 21 1/2; E - 6 cols, 2, 1/6 between; A - 6 cols, 2, 1/6 between.
Equipment & Software: : Hardware — APP/Mac; Presses — HI/Cottrell V-15A; Software — QPS/QuarkXPress 3.3.
Areas Served: Canada

FRASERVILLE

MILLBROOK TIMES

(Thur, Mthly)
1287 Larmer Line, Fraserville, ON, K0L 1V0, Cavan Monaghan Twp, Peterborough County, Canada; gen tel (705) 932-3001; gen fax (705) 932-8816; disp adv e-mail kgraham@nexicom.net; class adv e-mail thetimes@nexicom.net; ed e-mail thetimes@nexicom.net; web site http://themillbrooktimes.ca
Circulation: 100pd, 4,000fr; Sworn/Estimate/Non-Audited
Advertising: Open inch rate $.95.
Established: 1987.
Pub....Karen Graham
Mechanical Specifications: Type page 10 x ; E - 5 cols, 2, between; A - 5 cols, 2, between; C - 5 cols, 2, between.
Equipment & Software: : Hardware — PC.; Software — Adobe Creative Suite 5.5
Delivery Method: Mail, Newsstand
Areas Served: Cavan Monaghan Twp, Peterborough County

GEORGETOWN

INDEPENDENT & FREE PRESS

(Thur)
280 Guelph St., Unit 29, Georgetown, ON, L7G 4B1, Canada; gen tel (905) 873-0301; gen fax (905) 873-0398; web site www.independentfreepress.com
Circulation: 22,522fr; CCAB
Advertising: Open inch rate $1.98.
Parent Co.:
Metroland Media Group Ltd.
Torstar
Gen. Mgr....Steve Foreman
Circ. Mgr....Cindi Campbell
Circ. Mgr....Nancy Geissler
Mng. Ed....John McGhie
Publisher....Dana Robbins
Mechanical Specifications: Type page 11 1/2 x 14 3/4; E - 9 cols, between; A - 9 cols, between.
Equipment & Software: : Hardware — APP/Mac; Software — Baseview/NewsEdit, QPS/QuarkXPress.
Areas Served: Canada

GERALDTON

GERALDTON-LONGLAC TIMES STAR

(Wed)
401 Main St., Geraldton, ON, P0T 1M0, Canada; gen tel (807) 854-1919; gen fax (807) 854-1682; ed e-mail editor@thetimesstar.ca; web site www.thetimesstar.ca
Circulation: 642pd, 19fr; CMCA
Advertising: Open inch rate $.53.
Established: 1945.
Prodn. Mgr....Mike Goulet
Justin Saindon
Ed....Eric Pietsch
Mechanical Specifications: Type page 11 x 17; E - 5 cols, 1 14/15, 1/5 between; A - 5 cols, 1 14/15, 1/5 between; C - 5 cols, 1 14/15, 1/5 between.
Equipment & Software: : Hardware — PC; Software — QPS/QuarkXPress, Microsoft/Word, WordPerfect.
Areas Served: Canada

GLENCOE

TRANSCRIPT & FREE PRESS

(Thur)
243 Main St., Glencoe, ON, N0L 1M0, Canada; gen tel (519) 287-2615; gen fax (519) 287-2408
Circulation: 1,033pd,; CMCA
Advertising: Open inch rate $.74.
Circ. Mgr....Dale Hayder

GLOUCESTER

EXPRESS D'ORLEANS

(Wed)
Canotek Road Unit 30, Unit 30, Gloucester, ON, K1J 8R7, Canada; gen tel (613) 744-4800
Circulation: 10,742pd, 200fr; ODCMadeleine Joanisse
Areas Served: Gloucester, Ottawa, Ontario.

ORLEANS STAR

(Thur)
Po Box 46009, Gloucester, ON, K1J 9H7, Canada; gen tel (613) 323-2801; adv tel (613) 744-4800; web site www.orleansstar.ca
Circulation: 11pd, 42,989fr; CCAB
Areas Served: Canada

GODERICH

GODERICH SIGNAL-STAR

(Wed)
120 Huckins St. Industrial Park, Goderich, ON, N7A 3X8, Canada; gen tel (519) 524-2614; gen fax (519) 524-9175; web site www.goderichsignalstar.com
Circulation: 3,150pd, 18fr; CMCA
Advertising: $11.34.
Established: 1848.
Parent Co.:
Postmedia Network Inc.
Sales Mgr....John Bauman
Mechanical Specifications: Type page 11 1/4 x 21 1/4; E - 6 cols, 1 7/12, 1/6 between; A - 6 cols, 1 7/12, 1/6 between; C - 6 cols, 1 7/12, 1/6 between.
Equipment & Software: : Hardware — .; Presses — ; Software —
Areas Served: Canada

GORE BAY

MANITOULIN RECORDER

(Fri)
37 D Meredith St., Gore Bay, ON, P0P 1H0, Canada, Canada; gen tel (705) 282-2003; gen fax (705) 282-2432
Circulation: 997pd, 72fr; AAM
Advertising: Open inch rate $.88.
Established: 1908.
Pub....R.L. McCutcheon
Ed....Tom Sasvari
Prodn. Mgr....Al Ryan
Equipment & Software: : Hardware — 3-APP/Mac G3; Presses — G/Community; Software — QPS/QuarkXPress 3.32.
Areas Served: Canada

GRAND BEND

LAKESHORE ADVANCE
(Wed)
58 Ontario St. North, Grand Bend, ON, N0M 1T0, Canada; gen tel (519) 238-5383; gen fax (519) 238-5131; disp adv e-mail lakeshore.ads@sunmedia.ca; ed e-mail lakeshore.advance@sunmedia.ca; web site www.lakeshoreadvance.com
Circulation: 979pd, 13fr; CMCA
Advertising: 55Ã £££Ã &-pound;£Ã £Ã Â¢.
Parent Co.:
Quebecor
Adv. Dir. .... Neil Clifford
Mechanical Specifications: Page Size: 10.25" wide x 11.42" high
9 col x 160 ag
Delivery Method: Mail
Areas Served: Canada

GRAVENHURST

THE GRAVENHURST BANNER
(Thur)
140 Muskoka Rd. S., Gravenhurst, ON, P1P 1X2, Canada; gen tel (705) 687-6674; gen fax (705) 687-7213; web site www.muskokaregion.com/gravenhurst-on
Circulation: 96pd, 5,237fr; CMCA
Advertising: Open inch rate $.88.
Parent Co.:
Metroland Media Group Ltd.
Torstar
Gen. Mgr. .... Bill Allen
Adv. .... Jack Tynan
Areas Served: Canada

GRIMSBY

THE GRIMSBY LINCOLN NEWS
(Wed)
32 Main St. W., Grimsby, ON, L3M 1R4, Canada; gen tel (905) 945-8392; gen fax (905) 945-3916; web site www.thegrimsbylincolnnews.com
Circulation: 23,800fr; Sworn/Estimate/Non-Audited
Advertising: Open inch rate $1.96.
Parent Co.:
Metroland Media Group Ltd.
Torstar
Editorial Mgr............................. Mike Williscraft
Ed. ....Scott Rosts

GUELPH

GUELPH TRIBUNE
(Tues, Thur)
367 Woodlawn Rd. W., Unit 1, Guelph, ON, N1H 7K9, Canada, Canada; gen tel (519) 763-3333; gen fax (519) 763-4814; web site www.guelphtribune.ca
Circulation: 41,612fr; VAC
Advertising: Open inch rate $1.60.
Parent Co.:
Metroland Media Group Ltd.
Torstar
Pub...Peter Winkler
Sales Mgr.............................. Heather Dunbar
Ed. .... Doug Coxson
Areas Served: Canada

HAGERSVILLE

THE HALDIMAND PRESS
(Thur)
6 Parkview Rd., Hagersville, ON, N0A 1H0, Canada, Canada; gen tel (905) 768-3111; disp adv e-mail alana@haldimandpress.com; class adv e-mail design@haldimandpress.com; ed e-mail kaitlyn@haldimandpress.com; web site www.haldimandpress.com
Circulation: 3,073pd,; Sworn/Estimate/Non-Audited
Established: 1868.
Pub..Jillian Zynomirski
Publisher.......................................Kaitlyn Clark
Delivery Method: Mail, Newsstand
Areas Served: Canada

HALIBURTON

THE HIGHLANDER
(Thur)
195 Highland Street, The Village Barn, Haliburton, ON, K0M 1S0, Canada; gen tel (705) 457-2900; disp adv e-mail walt@haliburtonhighlander.ca; web site www.haliburtonhighlander.ca
Circulation: 8,062fr; CMCA
Established: 2011.
Pub... Bram Lebo
Delivery Method: Newsstand, Racks
Areas Served: Canada

HAMILTON

THE BAY OBSERVER
(Thur)
140 King Street East, Hamilton, ON, L8N 1B2, USA; gen tel (905) 522-6000; gen fax (905) 522-5838; web site www.bayobserver.ca
Circulation: 0pd, 28,246fr; CMCA
Pub...John Best
Areas Served: Canada

HANOVER

THE POST
(Thur)
413 18th Ave., Hanover, ON, N4N 3S5, Canada; gen tel (519) 364-2001; gen fax (519) 364-6950; disp adv e-mail janie.harrison@sunmedia.ca; class adv e-mail han.classifieds@sunmedia.ca; ed e-mail patrick.bales@sunmedia.ca; web site www.thepost.on.ca
Circulation: 84pd, 15,393fr; CMCA
Advertising: Open inch rate $0.90.
Established: 1880.
Parent Co.:
Postmedia Network Inc.
Quebecor Communications, Inc.
Digital Platform - Mobile: Apple
Gen. Mgr.......................................Marie David
Circ. Mgr... Rod Currie
Ed. .... Patrick Bales
Adv. Mgr................................... Kiera Merriam
Mechanical Specifications: Tabloid 9 col x 160 lines
Equipment & Software: : Hardware — APP/Mac; Software — QPS/QuarkXPress 4.0.
Indesign
Delivery Method: Carrier
Areas Served: Canada

HARROW

HARROW NEWS
(Tues)
5 King St., P.o. Box 310, Harrow, ON, N0R 1G0, Canada; gen tel (519) 738-2542; gen fax (519) 738-3874; disp adv e-mail harnews@mnsi.net; class adv e-mail harnews@mnsi.net; ed e-mail natalie@mdirect.net
Circulation: 1,221pd, 3fr; CMCA
Advertising: Open inch rate $.37.
Established: 1930.
Circ. Mgr.................................Natalie Koziana
Mechanical Specifications: Type page 10 1/4 x 15; E - 6 cols, 1 1/2, 3/8 between; A - 6 cols, 1 1/2, 3/8 between; C - 6 cols, 1 1/2, 3/8 between.
Delivery Method: Mail, Newsstand
Areas Served: Canada

HAWKESBURY

LE CARILLON
(Thur)
1100 Aberdeen St., Hawkesbury, ON, K6A 1K7, Canada, Canada; gen tel (613) 632-4155; adv tel (613) 632-4155; ed tel (613) 632-4155; gen fax (613) 632-6122; adv fax (613) 632-6383; ed fax (613) 632-6383; disp adv e-mail yvan.joly@eap.on.ca; nicole.pilon@eap.on.ca; ed e-mail nouvelles@eap.on.ca; web site www.lecarillon.ca
Circulation: 30pd, 15,000fr; Sworn/Estimate/Non-Audited
Advertising: Open inch rate $1.15.
Established: 1948.
Parent Co.:
Cie d'Edition Andre Paquette, Inc.
Pres. ....Bertrand Castonguay
Circ. Mgr.................................. Gilles Normand
Chief Ed.................................François Legault
Mechanical Specifications: Type page 10 1/2 x 14 1/4; E - 8 cols, 1/6 between; A - 8 cols, 1/6 between; C - 8 cols, 1/6 between.
Equipment & Software: : Hardware — APP/Mac; Software — Adobe/Photoshop 9, Adobe/Illustrator 9, QPS/QuarkXPress 4.1, Harris/V15, In-Design
Delivery Method: Carrier
Areas Served: Canada

LE/THE REGIONAL
(Thur)
124 Rue Principale E., Hawkesbury, ON, K6A 1A3, Canada; gen tel (613) 632-0112; gen fax (613) 632-0277; disp adv e-mail pub@le-regional.ca; ed e-mail news@le-regional.ca; web site www.le-regional.ca
Circulation: 34,484fr; Sworn/Estimate/Non-Audited
Advertising: $1.04 per line agate.
Established: 1995.Editions: 2— 2 total Ã &-pound;£ Le/The Regional-Hawkesbury, ON; Le/The Regional-Lachute, QC;
Owner .... Sylvain Roy
Mechanical Specifications: Type page 11.317" x 15"; E - 8 cols, 0.1292" between;
Equipment & Software: : Hardware — APP/Mac; Software — Adobe/Photoshop, Adobe, Indesign, Illustator etc
Delivery Method: Mail, Newsstand, Carrier, Racks
Areas Served: K6A 1A3

TRIBUNE EXPRESS
(Wed)
1100 Aberdeen, Hawkesbury, ON, K6A 1K7, Canada, Canada; gen tel (613) 632-4155; adv tel (613) 632-4155; ed tel (613) 632-4155; gen fax (613) 632-6122; adv fax (613) 632-6383; ed fax (613) 632-6383; disp adv e-mail yvan.joly@eap.on.ca; nicole.pilon@eap.on.ca; ed e-mail nouvelles@eap.on.ca; web site www.tribune-express.ca
Circulation: 11pd, 26,430fr; Sworn/Estimate/Non-Audited
Advertising: Open inch rate $1.30.
Established: 1984.
Parent Co.:
Cie d'Edition Andre Paquette, Inc.
President ....Bertrand Castonguay
Circ. Mgr.................................. Gilles Normand
Newspaper manager .... Yvan Joly
sales secretary, national, display... Nicole Pilon
Mechanical Specifications: Type page 10 1/2 x 14 1/4; E - 8 cols, 1/6 between; A - 8 cols, 1/6 between; C - 8 cols, 1/6 between.
Equipment & Software: : Hardware — APP/Mac, 8-HI/V15; Software — QPS/QuarkXPress 4.1, Adobe/Illustrator 9, Adobe/Photoshop 9, In-Design
Delivery Method: Carrier
Areas Served: Canada

HEARST

LE NORD
(Wed)
1004, Rue Prince., Hearst, ON, P0L 1N0, Hearst, Canada; gen tel (705) 372-1233; gen fax (705) 362-5954; disp adv e-mail lenordjournalpub@gmail.com; class adv e-mail lenordjournalpub@gmail.com; ed e-mail journalistenord@gmail.com; web site www.lenord.on.ca - 5,000(views)
Circulation: 1,409pd, 65fr; CMCA
Advertising: Open inch rate $1.24.
Established: 1976.
Parent Co.:
Lignes Agates Marketing
Digital Platform - Mobile: Apple
Ed. ....Omer Cantin
Gen. Mgr. ....Steve McInnis
Graphic Designer ....Karine Hebert
Mechanical Specifications: Type page 5col. X 175 MAL
Equipment & Software: : Hardware — APP/Mac; Software — Adobe/PageMaker 7.5, Adobe/Illustrator 7.0, Microsoft/Word 8.0, Adobe/Photoshop 5.0.
Delivery Method: Mail, Newsstand, Carrier
Areas Served: Hearst

HORNEPAYNE

JACKFISH JOURNAL
(Wed)
113 Herbert Ave., Hornepayne, ON, P0M 1Z0; gen tel (807) 868-2381; gen fax (807) 868-2673; web site www.hornepayne.com
Circulation: 200pd, 30fr; CMCA
Pub./Ed. .... Lisa Stewart
Areas Served: Canada

HUNTSVILLE

HUNTSVILLE FORESTER
(Thur)
11 Main St. W., Huntsville, ON, P1H 2C5, Canada; gen tel (705) 789-5541; gen fax (705) 789-9381; ed e-mail news@metrolandnorthmedia.com; web site www.huntsvilleforester.com
Circulation: 161pd, 9,177fr; CMCA
Advertising: Open inch rate $.87.
Established: 1877.
Parent Co.:
Metroland Media Group Ltd.
Torstar
Pub./Gen. Mgr.................................... Bill Allen
Adv. Mgr......................................Andrew Allen
News Ed............................Tamara De la Vega
Jack Tynan
Mechanical Specifications: Type page 10 1/4 x 15; E - 6 cols, 1 11/20, between; A - 6 cols, 1 11/20, between; C - 6 cols, 1 11/20, between.
Delivery Method: Mail, Newsstand, Racks
Areas Served: Canada

HUNTSVILLE/MUSKOKA ADVANCE
(Sun)
11 Main St. W, Huntsville, ON, P1H 2C5, Canada; gen tel (705) 789-5541; gen fax (705) 789-9381; web site www.huntsvilleforester.com
Circulation: 7,100pd, 23,038fr; Sworn/Estimate/Non-Audited
Advertising: Open inch rate $10.29.
Regl. Pub. ....Joe Anderson
Adv. Mgr.......................................Micheal Hill
Circ. Mgr..................................Brenda McGary
Ed. ....Bruce Hickey
Prodn. Mgr. ....Paula Ashby
Mechanical Specifications: Type page 10 1/4 x 15; E - 6 cols, 1 11/20, between; A - 6 cols, 1 11/20, between.

IGNACE

DRIFTWOOD ENTERPRISES
(Wed)
153 Balsam, Ignace, ON, P0T 1T0, Canada; gen tel (807) 934-6482
Circulation: 303pd,; CMCA
Established: 1978.
Areas Served: Canada

IROQUOIS FALLS A

THE ENTERPRISE

(Thur)
441 Main Street, Iroquois Falls A, ON, P0K 1G0, Canada; gen tel (705) 232-4081; gen fax (705) 232-4235; disp adv e-mail news@theenterprise.ca; class adv e-mail news@theenterprise.ca; ed e-mail editor@theenterprise.ca
Circulation: 1,607pd, 120fr; CMCA
Advertising: $0.45 per agate line.
Established: 1963.
Pub.. William C. Cavell
Adv. Mgr.................................... Tory Delaurier
Delivery Method: Mail
Areas Served: Canada

JOHNSTOWN

MANOTICK MESSENGER

(Thur)
3201 County Road 2., Johnstown, ON, ON K0E 1T0, Canada; gen tel (613) 692-6000; gen fax (616) 692-3758; disp adv e-mail advert@bellnet.ca; ed e-mail newsfile@bellnet.ca; web site www.manotickmessenger.on.ca
Circulation: 9,503fr; CMCA
Pub. ....Jeff Morris
Adv. Rep..................................Gary Coulombe
Areas Served: Canada

KAPUSKASING

THE NORTHERN TIMES

(Wed)
51 Riverside Dr, Kapuskasing, ON, P5N 1A7, Canada; gen tel (705) 335-2283 ext. 222; adv tel (705)-335-2283 ext. 230; ed tel (705)-335-2283 ext. 223; gen fax (705) 337-1222; adv fax (705) 337-1222; ed fax (705) 337-1222; disp adv e-mail wayne.major@sunmedia.ca; ed e-mail kevin.anderson@sunmedia.ca; web site www.kapuskasingtimes.com
Circulation: 1,784pd,; CMCA
Advertising: Open inch rate $8.82.
Established: 1961.
Parent Co.:
Postmedia Network Inc.
Quebecor Communications, Inc.
Digital Platform - Mobile: Apple, Blackberry
Digital Platform - Tablet: Apple iOS, Blackberry Tablet OS
Pub..Wayne Major
Senior Sales Representative.......Sylvie Genier
Managing Ed. ....Kevin Anderson
Mechanical Specifications: Type page 9 x 12.25; E - 9 cols, 1 1/5, 1/8 between; A - 9 cols, 1 1/5, 1/8 between; C - 9 cols, 1 1/5, 1/8 between.
Equipment & Software: : Hardware — APP/Mac; Software — InDesign3, Adobe/Illustrator 7.0, Adobe/Photoshop 4.0, Microsoft/Word 10.0.
Delivery Method: Mail, Newsstand, Carrier
Areas Served: Canada

THE WEEKENDER

(Thur)
51 Riverside Dr, Kapuskasing, ON, P5N 1A7, Canada; gen tel (705) 335-2283 ext. 222; adv tel (705) 335-2283 ext. 230; ed tel (705) 335-2283 ext. 223; gen fax (705) 337-1222; adv fax (705) 337-1222; ed fax (705) 337-1222; disp adv e-mail wayne.major@sunmedia.ca; ed e-mail kevin.anderson@sunmedia.ca; web site www.kapuskasingtimes.com
Circulation: 8,486fr; CMCA
Advertising: Open inch rate $8.82.
Established: 1961.
Parent Co.:
Postmedia Network Inc.
Quebecor Communications, Inc.
Digital Platform - Mobile: Apple, Blackberry
Digital Platform - Tablet: Apple iOS, Blackberry Tablet OS
Pub..Wayne Major
Senior Sales Representative.......Sylvie Genier
Managing Ed..........................Kevin Anderson
Mechanical Specifications: Type page 9 x 12.25; E - 9 cols, 1 1/5, 1/8 between; A - 9 cols, 1 1/5, 1/8 between; C - 9 cols, 1 1/5, 1/8 between.
Equipment & Software: : Hardware — APP/Mac; Software — InDesign3, Adobe/Illustrator 7.0, Adobe/Photoshop 4.0, Microsoft/Word 10.0.
Delivery Method: Mail, Newsstand, Carrier
Areas Served: P5N, P0L

KENORA

LAKE OF THE WOODS ENTERPRISE

(Thur)
33 Main St., Kenora, ON, P9N 3X7, Canada; gen tel (807) 468-5555; gen fax (807) 468-4318; web site www.lotwenterprise.com
Circulation: 122pd, 7,771fr; CMCA
Advertising: Open inch rate $1.12.
Established: 2003.
Parent Co.:
Postmedia Network Inc.
Adv. Mgr...Ted Weiss
Reg. Managing Ed. ....Reg Clayton
Mechanical Specifications: Type page 10 1/4 x 14 1/4; E - 6 cols, 1 9/16, 1/6 between; A - 6 cols, 1 9/16, 1/6 between; C - 6 cols, 1 9/16, 1/6 between.
Equipment & Software: : Hardware — APP/Mac; Software — Adobe InDesign, Adobe/Illustrator, Adobe/Photoshop.
Areas Served: Canada

KESWICK

THE GEORGINA ADVOCATE

(Thur)
184 Simcoe Ave., Keswick, ON, L4P 2H7, Canada; gen tel (905) 476-7753; gen fax (905) 476-5785; web site www.yorkregion.com
Circulation: 17,190fr; CMCA
Advertising: Open inch rate $1.56.
Parent Co.:
Metroland Media Group Ltd.
Torstar
Pub... Ian Proudfoot
Bus. Mgr.................................. Robert Lazurko
Adv. Mgr...Neil Moore
Ed. in Chief .... Debora Kelly
Ed. .... Tracy Kibble
Mechanical Specifications: Type page 10 3/8 x 14; E - 9 cols, 1 1/16, 1/8 between; A - 9 cols, 1 1/16, 1/8 between; C - 9 cols, 1 1/16, 1/8 between.
Equipment & Software: : Hardware — APP/Mac; Presses — KP; Software — QPS/QuarkXPress.
Areas Served: Canada

KINCARDINE

THE INDEPENDENT

(Wed)
840 Queen St., Kincardine, ON, N2Z 2Z4, Canada, Canada; gen tel (519) 396-3111; gen fax (519) 396-3899; web site www.independent.on.ca
Circulation: 1,906pd, 82fr; CMCA
Advertising: Open inch rate $.71.
Established: 1975.
Ed. ....Eric Howald
Mechanical Specifications: Type page 10 1/4 x 15 1/2; E - 6 cols, 1 9/16, 1/6 between; A - 6 cols, 1 3/4, 1/6 between; C - 6 cols, 1 3/4, 1/6 between.
Equipment & Software: : Hardware — PC; Software — Adobe/PageMaker 7.0.
Delivery Method: Mail, Newsstand
Areas Served: Canada

THE KINCARDINE NEWS

(Thur)
719 Queen St., Kincardine, ON, N2Z 1Z9, Canada, Canada; gen tel (519) 396-2963; gen fax (519) 396-6865; disp adv e-mail kincardine.sales@sunmedia.ca; ed e-mail kincardine.news@sunmedia.ca; web site www.kincardinenews.com
Circulation: 59pd, 5,787fr; Sworn/Estimate/Non-Audited
Parent Co.:
Postmedia Network Inc.
Digital Platform - Mobile: Apple, Android, Windows, Blackberry
Digital Platform - Tablet: Apple iOS, Android, Windows 7, Blackberry Tablet OS, Kindle, Nook, Kindle Fire
Ed. .... Troy Patterson
Mechanical Specifications: Tabloid 10.333 x 11.4288
Equipment & Software: : Hardware — APP/Mac; Software — QPS/QuarkXPress.
Delivery Method: Mail, Newsstand, Carrier, Racks
Areas Served: Canada

KINGSTON

FRONTENAC EMC

(Thur)
375 Select Drive Unit 14, Kingston, ON, K7M 8R1, Canada; gen tel (613) 546-8884; gen fax (613) 546-3607; web site www.emcfrontenac.ca
Circulation: 8,639fr; CMCA
Pub.. Duncan Weir
Areas Served: Canada

KINGSTON HERITAGE EMC

(Thur)
375 Select Dr., Kingston, ON, K7M 8R1, Canada; gen tel (613) 546-8885; disp adv e-mail kdillon@theheritageemc.ca; web site www.insideottawavalley.com
Circulation: 45,862fr; CMCA
Parent Co.:
Metroland Media Group Ltd.
Gen. Mgr. .... Donna Glasspoole
Sales Coordinator.................Kate Lawrenence
Areas Served: Canada

KINGSTON THIS WEEK

(Thur)
18 St. Remy Place, Kingston, ON, K7M 6C4, Canada; gen tel (613) 389-7400; gen fax (613) 389-7507; web site www.kingstonthisweek.com
Circulation: 48,840fr; CMCA
Advertising: Open inch rate $2.14.
Parent Co.:
Quebecor Communications, Inc.
Gen. Mgr.. Ron Drillen
Mng. Ed.. Tracy Weaver
News Ed. .... Lynn Rees Lambert
Photo Ed..Rob Mooy
Liza Nelson
Mechanical Specifications: Type page 10 3/8 x 12 4/7; E - 9 cols, 1 1/16, between; A - 9 cols, 1 1/16, between; C - 9 cols, 1 1/16, between.
Areas Served: Canada

THE FRONTENAC GAZETTE

(Thur)
375 Select Dr., Ste. 14, Kingston, ON, K7M 8R1, Canada; gen tel (613) 546-8885; gen fax (613) 546-3607; web site www.whatsonkingston.com
Circulation: 8,220fr; CMCA
Advertising: Open inch rate $.95.
Parent Co.:
Metroland Media Group Ltd.
Pub...Darryl Cembal
Areas Served: Canada

THE HERITAGE

(Thur)
375 Select Dr., Unit 14, Kingston, ON, K7M 8R1, Canada, Canada; gen tel (613) 546-8885; gen fax (613) 546-3607; web site www.kingstonregion.com/kingstonregion
Circulation: 12pd, 38,833fr; Sworn/Estimate/Non-Audited
Advertising: Open inch rate $1.76.
Ed. ....Darryl Cembal
Mechanical Specifications: Type page 10 1/4 x 15; E - 6 cols, 1 9/16, 1/6 between; A - 6 cols, 1 9/16, 1/6 between; C - 6 cols, 1 9/16, 1/6 between.
Equipment & Software: : Hardware — PC; Software — Adobe/PageMaker 6.5, Archetype/Corel Draw 2.0.
Areas Served: Canada

KINGSVILLE

THE KINGSVILLE REPORTER

(Tues)
17 Chestnut St., Kingsville, ON, N9Y 1J9, Canada, Canada; gen tel (519) 733-2211; gen fax (519) 733-6464; disp adv e-mail rsims@postmedia.com
Circulation: 1,107pd, 7fr; CMCA
Advertising: Open inch rate $.57.
Parent Co.:
Postmedia Network Inc.
Adv. Mgr...Rita Sims
News Ed. ....Nelson Santos
Reception .... Joyce Pearce
Associate News Editor................Steve I'Anson
Mechanical Specifications: Type page 10 1/4 x 15; E - 6 cols, 1 5/9, between; A - 6 cols, 1 5/9, between; C - 6 cols, 1 5/9, between.
Delivery Method: Mail, Newsstand
Areas Served: Canada

KIRKLAND LAKE

NORTHERN NEWS

(Mon, Wed, Fri)
Eight Duncan Ave., Kirkland Lake, ON, P2N 3L4, Canada; gen tel (705) 567-5321; gen fax (705) 567-6162; adv fax (705) 567-5377; ed fax (705) 567-6162; disp adv e-mail display@northernnews.ca; web site www.northernnews.ca
Circulation: 3,122pd,; Sworn/Estimate/Non-Audited
Advertising: Open inch rate $.57.
Parent Co.:
Postmedia Network Inc.
Quebecor Communications, Inc.
Circ. Mgr......................................Tony Howell
Managing Ed. ....Joe O'Grady
Sports Ed...................................Jeff Wilkinson
Adv. Dir...Lisa Wilson
Mechanical Specifications: Type page 13 x 21 1/2; E - 6 cols, 2 1/16, 1/8 between; A - 6 cols, 2 1/16, 1/8 between; C - 9 cols, 1 1/2, 1/8 between.

KITCHENER

KITCHENER POST

(Fri)
630 Riverbend Dr Unit 104, Unit 104, Kitchener, ON, N2K 3S2; gen tel (519) 579-7166; gen fax (519) 579-2029; web site www.kitchenerpost.ca
Circulation: 58,770fr; CMCA
Parent Co.:
Metroland Media Group Ltd.
Managing Ed................................ Bob Vrbanac
Areas Served: Canada

LAKEFIELD

LAKEFIELD HERALD

(Fri)
74 Bridge St., Lakefield, ON, K0L 2H0, Canada; gen tel (705) 652-6594 ; gen fax (705) 652-6912; disp adv e-mail ads@lakefieldherald.com; ed e-mail editor@lakefieldherald.com; web site www.lakefieldherald.com
Circulation: 937pd, 39fr; CMCA
Areas Served: Canada

LANARK

THE LANARK ERA

(Tues)
66 George St., Lanark, ON, K0G 1K0,

Lanark Highlands Township, Canada; gen tel (613) 259-2220; disp adv e-mail kristy.gibson@lanarkera.com; class adv e-mail lanarkera@primus.ca; ed e-mail gena.gibson@lanarkera.com; web site www.lanarkera.com
Circulation: 888pd, 27fr; CMCA
Advertising: $8.62 per column inch.
Established: 1895.
Ed./Owner....................................Gena Gibson
Equipment & Software: : Hardware — iMac computers; Presses — None; Software — Adobe InDesign, Adobe Photoshop, etc.
Delivery Method: Mail, Newsstand
Areas Served: Lanark Highlands Township

LEAMINGTON

WHEATLEY JOURNAL

(Wed)
194 Talbot Street E., Unit #5, Leamington, ON, N8H 1M2, Chatham-Kent, Canada; gen tel (519) 398-9098; gen fax (519) 398-8561
Circulation: 586pd, 11fr; CMCA
Advertising: Open inch rate $.48.
Established: 1895.
Parent Co.:
Southpoint Publishing Inc.
Pub...Jim Heyens
Delivery Method: Mail, Newsstand
Areas Served: Chatham-Kent

LINDSAY

KAWARTHA LAKES THIS WEEK

(Tues, Thur)
192 St. David St., Lindsay, ON, K9V 4Z4, Canada; gen tel (705) 324-8600; gen fax (705) 324-5694; disp adv e-mail mbabcock@mykawartha.com; ed e-mail mtully@mykawartha.com; web site www.mykawartha.com
Circulation: 0pd, 21,867fr; CCAB
Advertising: Open inch rate $2.20.
Parent Co.:
Metroland Media Group Ltd.
Torstar
Pub...Bruce Danford
Bus. Admin./Opns.......................Linda Suddes
Office Mgr...Kim Riel
Adv. Mgr....................................Shane Lockyer
Ed. in Chief.......................................Lois Tuffin
News Ed...Marcus Tully
Prodn. Mgr....................................Scott Prikker
Regl. Dist. Mgr................................Jeff Braund
Dir., Distr........................Tracy Magee-Graham
Mechanical Specifications: Type page 10 3/8 x 14; E - 9 cols, 1 1/18, 3/15 between; A - 9 cols, 1 1/18, 3/15 between; C - 9 cols, 1 1/18, 3/15 between.
Areas Served: Canada

LISTOWEL

THE LISTOWEL BANNER

(Wed)
185 Wallace Ave. N., Listowel, ON, N4W 1K8, Canada, Canada; gen tel (519) 291-1660; gen fax (519) 291-3771; disp adv e-mail ads@northperth.com; ed e-mail editor@northperth.com; web site www.northperth.com
Circulation: 1,881pd, 22fr; CMCA
Advertising: Open inch rate $.68.
Established: 1866.
Parent Co.:
Metroland Media Group Ltd.
Torstar
Gen. Mgr...Bill Huether
Adv. Mgr..Alicia Hunter
Circ. Mgr.................................Peggy Haasnoot
Ed..Pauline Kerr
Sports Ed.......................................Terry Bridge
Prodn. Mgr...........................Marie McKertcher
Areas Served: Canada

LITTLE CURRENT

MANITOULIN EXPOSITOR

(Wed)
1 Manitowaning Rd., Little Current, ON, P0P 1K0, Canada; gen tel (705) 368-2744; gen fax (705) 368-3822; disp adv e-mail sales@manitoulin.ca; ed e-mail editor@manitoulin.ca; web site www.manitoulin.ca
Circulation: 3,801pd, 178fr; AAM
Advertising: Open inch rate $.90.
Established: 1879.
Digital Platform - Mobile: Apple, Android, Windows, Blackberry
Digital Platform - Tablet: Apple iOS, Android, Windows 7
Pub....................................Rick L. McCutcheon
Gen. Mgr......................................Kerrene Tilson
Sales Mgr...Greg Lloyd
Production Manager................David Patterson
Alicia McCutcheon
Mechanical Specifications: Type page 10 1/4 x 16; E - 6 cols, 1 1/2, 1/8 between; A - 6 cols, 1 1/2, 1/8 between; C - 6 cols, 1 1/2, 1/8 between.
Equipment & Software: ; Presses — 5-Goss/Metro
Delivery Method: Mail, Newsstand
Areas Served: Canada

LONDON

ACTION (L')

(Wed)
920 Huron St., London, ON, N5Y 4K4, Canada; gen tel (519) 433-4130; gen fax (905) 790-9127; disp adv e-mail marketing@laction.ca; ed e-mail info@lemetropolitain.com; web site www.laction.ca
Circulation: 1,648pd, 812fr; CMCA
Ed...Denis Poirier
Sales Dir............................Richard Caumartin
Areas Served: Canada

LONDONER

(Thur)
1147 Gainsborough Road, London, ON, N6H 5L5, Canada; gen tel (519) 673-5005; gen fax (519) 673-4624; disp adv e-mail linda.leblanc@sunmedia.ca; ed e-mail don.biggs@sunmedia.ca; web site www.thelondoner.ca
Circulation: 140,111fr; CMCA
Advertising: $35.00.
Parent Co.:
Postmedia Network Inc.
Publisher...................................Linda LeBlanc
Delivery Method: Carrier
Areas Served: Canada

LUCKNOW

THE LUCKNOW SENTINEL

(Wed)
619 Campbell St., Lucknow, ON, N0G 2H0, Canada; gen tel (519) 528-2822; adv tel (519) 528-2822; ed tel (519) 528-2822; gen fax (519) 528-3529; adv fax (519) 528-3529; ed fax (519) 528-3529; disp adv e-mail lucksentads@bowesnet.com; ed e-mail lucksented@bowesnet.com; web site www.lucknowsentinel.com
Circulation: 1,037pd, 44fr; CMCA
Advertising: Open inch rate $.55.
Established: 1873.
Parent Co.:
Postmedia Network Inc.
Quebecor Communications, Inc.
Ed..Troy Patterson
Mechanical Specifications: Type page 10 .25 x 11.422; E - 9 cols, 1/16 " between columns
Equipment & Software: : Hardware — APP/Mac; Software — QPS/QuarkXPress 4.1.
Delivery Method: Mail, Newsstand
Areas Served: Canada

MANITOUWADGE

THE ECHO

(Wed)
105 Warbler, Manitouwadge, ON, P0T 2C0, Canada; gen tel (807) 228-2333; adv tel (807) 228-2317; disp adv e-mail manitouwadgeecho@gmail.com; ed e-mail news@theecho.ca; web site www.theecho.ca
Circulation: 346pd,; CMCA
Advertising: Open inch rate $.78.
Established: 1964.
Pub..B.J. Schermann
Prodn. Mgr..........................Scott Schermann
Mechanical Specifications: Type page 10 x 15 3/4; E - 5 cols, 1 3/4, 1/4 between; A - 5 cols, 1 3/4, 1/4 between.
Equipment & Software: : Hardware — IBM/ASP-133; Software — QPS/QuarkXPress.
Delivery Method: Mail, Newsstand
Areas Served: Canada

MARATHON

THE MARATHON MERCURY

(Tues)
91 Peninsula Rd., Marathon, ON, P0T 2E0, Canada; gen tel (805) 229-1520; gen fax (805) 229-1595
Circulation: 689pd, 13fr; CMCA
Advertising: Open inch rate $.85.
Established: 1948.
Adv. Mgr..............................Garry R. McInnes
Ed...P. Douglas Gale
Mechanical Specifications: Type page 10 1/4 x 15 7/8; E - 5 cols, 2, between; A - 5 cols, 2, between; C - 5 cols, 2, between.
Equipment & Software: : Hardware — APP/Mac LC 630, APP/Power Mac G4; Software — QPS/QuarkXPress 4.1, Multi-Ad/Creator 4.0.1, Adobe/Photoshop 5.0.
Areas Served: Canada

MARKHAM

MARKHAM ECONOMIST & SUN

(Thur)
50 Mcintosh Drive Unit 115, Markham, ON, L3R-9T3, Canada; gen tel (905) 943-6100; adv tel (905) 943-6100; ed tel (905) 943-6100; gen fax (905) 943-6129; adv fax (905) 943-6129; ed fax (905) 943-6129; disp adv e-mail abeswick@yrmg.com; ed e-mail boneill@yrmg.com; web site www.yorkregion.com
Circulation: 71,119fr; CMCA
Advertising: variable - modular.
Established: 1881.
Parent Co.:
Metroland Media Group Ltd.
Torstar
Pub...Ian Proudfoot
Ed..Bernie O'Neill
Gen. Mgr.....................................John Willems
Online Adv..................................Meriel Bradley
Equipment & Software: : Hardware — APP/Power Mac; Software — QPS/QuarkXPress, Multi-Ad.
Areas Served: Canada

THE RICHMOND HILL LIBERAL

(Thur)
50 Mcintosh Drive Unit 115, Markham, ON, L3R 9T3, Canada; gen tel (905) 943-6100; adv tel (905) 943-6095; gen fax (905) 943-6129; adv fax (905) 943-6129; disp adv e-mail abeswick@yrmg.com; class adv e-mail jkopacz@yrmg.com; ed e-mail mbeck@yrmg.com; web site www.yorkregion.com
Circulation: 0pd, 84,047fr; CCAB
Advertising: variable - modular.
Established: 1878.
Parent Co.:
Metroland Media Group Ltd.
Torstar
Pub...Ian Proudfoot
Bus. Mgr...................................Robert Lazurko
Retail Adv. Mgr...........................Anne Beswick
Ed. in Chief....................................Debora Kelly
Ed..Marney Beck
General Manager.........................John Willems
Areas Served: Canada

MARMORA

HAVELOCK CITIZEN

(Fri)
Po Box 239, Marmora, ON, K0K 2M0, Canada; gen tel (613) 962-2360; gen fax (613) 472-5026
Circulation: 35,000pd, 2,321fr; Sworn/Estimate/Non-Audited
Advertising: Open inch rate $36.00.
Parent Co.:
Shield Media
Ed...Nancy Derrer
Mechanical Specifications: Type page 10 1/4 x 15 3/4; E - 6 cols, 1 5/8, between; A - 6 cols, 1 5/8, between; C - 6 cols, 1 5/8, between.
Areas Served: KOL 1ZO, KOL 2ZO

MATTAWA

THE MATTAWA RECORDER

(Sun)
341 Mcconnell St., Mattawa, ON, P0H 1V0, Canada; gen tel (705) 744-5361; gen fax (866) 831-6626; disp adv e-mail recorder@bellnet.ca
Circulation: 1,100pd,; Sworn/Estimate/Non-Audited
Advertising: Open inch rate $.60.
Pub...Tom Edwards
Adv. Mgr...................................Heather Edwards
Mechanical Specifications: Type page 10 x 14; E - 5 cols, 2, 1/4 between; A - 5 cols, 2, 1/4 between.
Delivery Method: Mail, Newsstand
Areas Served: P0H 1V0

MEAFORD

BLUE MOUNTAINS COURIER-HERALD

(Wed)
24 Trowbridge St. West, Unit 6, Meaford, ON, N4L 1Y1, Canada; gen tel (519) 538-1421; gen fax (519) 538-5028; disp adv e-mail pamero@simcoe.com; ed e-mail lmartin@simcoe.com; web site www.simcoe.com
Circulation: 505pd,; CMCA
Ed...Lori Martin
Circ Mgr....................................Heather Harris
Adv Mgr....................................Pamela Amero
Areas Served: Canada

EXPRESS

(Wed)
24 Trowbridge St. W Unit 6, Meaford, ON, N4L 1Y1, Canada; gen tel (519) 538-1421; gen fax (519) 538-5028; web site www.meafordexpress.com
Circulation: 544pd, 96fr; CMCA
Advertising: Open inch rate $1.12.
Established: 1906.
Parent Co.:
Metroland Media
Metroland Media Group Ltd.
Ed..Scott Woodhouse
Adv...Pamela Amero
Community Events..............................Chris Fell
Mechanical Specifications: Type page 12 3/4 x 21; E - 6 cols, 2, 1/6 between; A - 6 cols, 2, 1/6 between; C - 6 cols, 2, 1/6 between.
Equipment & Software: : Hardware — APP/Mac; Software — Multi-Ad 2.81, Adobe/Photoshop 5.0, Adobe/Illustrator 5.0, QPS/QuarkXPress 3.31.
Areas Served: Canada

MIDLAND

THE MIRROR

(Thur)
488 Dominion Ave., Midland, ON, L4R 1P6, Canada; gen tel (705) 527-5500; gen fax (705) 527-5467; web site www.simcoe.com
Circulation: 1pd, 21,821fr; CMCA
Advertising: Open inch rate $2.22.
Parent Co.:
Metroland Media Group Ltd.
Torstar
Pub....Joe Anderson
Gen. Mgr.....Leigh Gate
Adv. Mgr.....Leigh Rourke
Circ. Mgr....Kyla Mosley
Ed.....Travis Mealing
Mng. Ed....Lori Martin
Mechanical Specifications: Type page 10 3/8 x 14; E - 9 cols, 1 1/16, 3/16 between; A - 9 cols, 1 1/16, 3/16 between; C - 9 cols, 1 1/16, 3/16 between.
Areas Served: Canada

MILDMAY

TOWN AND COUNTRY CRIER

(Thur)
100 Elora St., Mildmay, ON, N0G 2J0, Canada; gen tel (519) 367-2681; gen fax (519) 367-5417
Circulation: 1,211pd, 169fr; CMCA
Advertising: Open inch rate $.44.
Pub....John H. Hafermehl
Ed....Susan Bross
Mechanical Specifications: Type page 10 x 15 1/2; E - 5 cols, 2, 1/4 between; C - 4 cols, 2 1/2, 1/4 between.

MILTON

THE MILTON CANADIAN CHAMPION

(Tues, Thur)
555 Industrial Dr., Milton, ON, L9T 5E1, Canada, Canada; gen tel (905) 878-2341; gen fax (905) 876-2364; ed e-mail editorial@miltoncanadianchampion.com; web site www.miltoncanadianchampion.com
Circulation: 22pd, 31,158fr; CCAB
Advertising: Open inch rate $8.90.
Established: 1860.
Parent Co.:
Metroland Media Group Ltd.
Torstar
Digital Platform - Mobile: Apple, Android, Windows, Blackberry
Pub....Neil Oliver
Ed....Karen Miceli
News/Sports Ed....Steve LeBlanc
Prodn. Mgr....Tim Coles
Regional General Manager ....David Harvey
Director of Advertising....Katy Letourneau
Circ. Manager....Sarah McSweeney
Delivery Method: Carrier
Areas Served: Canada

MINDEN

THE MINDEN TIMES

(Thur)
2 Iga Rd., Unit 2, Minden, ON, K0M 2K0, Minden, Canada; gen tel (705) 286-1288; gen fax (705) 286-4768; disp adv e-mail jenniferm@haliburtonpress.com; class adv e-mail classifieds@mindentimes.ca; ed e-mail editor@mindentimes.ca; web site www.mindentimes.ca
Circulation: 1,076pd, 259fr; CMCA
Advertising: Open inch rate $.65.
Established: 1980.
Parent Co.:
White Pine Media
Ed....Jenn Watt
Sales....Jennifer McEathron
Circ., Classified....Debbie Comer
Equipment & Software: : Hardware — APP/Mac; Software — Adobe/PageMaker 4.0.
Delivery Method: Mail, Newsstand
Areas Served: Minden

MISSISSAUGA

AWAAZ PUNJABI

(Wed)
7015 Tranmere Dr. Suite #16, Mississauga, ON, L5S 1T7, Canada; gen tel (905)795-8282; adv tel (416) 899 8140; ed tel (905) 795-0639; gen fax (905) 795-9801; disp adv e-mail marketing@weeklyvoice.com; class adv e-mail admin@weeklyvoice.com; ed e-mail pnews@weeklyvoice.com; web site www.awaazpunjabi.com - 20,000(views) 15,000(visitors)
Circulation: 9,900fr; CMCA
Advertising: Request.
Established: 2000.
Digital Platform - Mobile: Windows
Digital Platform - Tablet: Windows 7Sudhir Anand
Delivery Method: Mail, Newsstand, Racks
Areas Served: Canada

BRAMPTON GUARDIAN

(Thur, Fri)
3145 Wolfedale Rd., Mississauga, ON, L5C 3A9, Canada; gen tel (905) 273-8111; gen fax (905) 454-4385; disp adv e-mail scott.hartman@thebramptonguardian.com; class adv e-mail classified@thebramptonguardian.com; ed e-mail plonergan@metroland.com; web site www.thebramptonguardian.com
Circulation: 0pd, 162,867fr; CCAB
Advertising: Open inch rate $4.37.
Parent Co.:
Metroland Media Group Ltd.
Torstar
Circ. Mgr....Dave Coleman
Pub....Dana Robbins
Gen Mgr....Bill Anderson
Ed....Patricia Lonergan
Mechanical Specifications: Type page 13 x 22 1/2; E - 10 cols, 1 1/16, between; A - 10 cols, 1 1/16, between; C - 10 cols, 1 1/16, between.
Equipment & Software: : Hardware — APP/Mac; Software — QPS/QuarkXPress, Adobe/Illustrator, WordPerfect.
Delivery Method: Carrier
Areas Served: Canada

MISSISSAUGA NEWS

(Thur, Fri)
3145 Wolfedale Road, Mississauga, ON, L5C 3A9, Canada`; gen tel (905) 273-8230; gen fax (905) 568-0181; ed e-mail tlanks@mississauga.net; web site www.mississauga.com
Circulation: 0pd, 129,215fr; CCAB
Advertising: Open inch rate $7.35.
Parent Co.:
Metroland Media Group Ltd.Editions: 2— The Booster (70,266); This Week (54,947)
Pub....Dana Robbins
Community News/Ed. ....Clark Kim
Areas Served: Canada

MITCHELL

THE MITCHELL ADVOCATE

(Wed)
42 Montreal St., Mitchell, ON, N0K 1N0, Canada; gen tel (519) 348-8431; gen fax (519) 348-8836; web site www.mitchelladvocate.com
Circulation: 1,790pd, 22fr; CMCA
Advertising: Open inch rate $.73.
Parent Co.:
Postmedia Network Inc.
Quebecor Communications, Inc.
Ed....Andy Bader
Adv. Mgr. ....Juanita Belfour
Mechanical Specifications: Type page 11 3/8 x 21 1/4; E - 6 cols, 1 3/4, between; A - 6 cols, 1 3/4, between; C - 6 cols, 1 3/4, between.
Equipment & Software: : Hardware — APP/Mac LC 475; Software — QPS/QuarkXPress, Adobe/Photoshop.
Areas Served: Canada

MORRISBURG

THE MORRISBURG LEADER

(Wed)
Hwy. 2, 31 Shopping Centre, 41 Main St., Morrisburg, ON, K0C 1X0, Canada; gen tel (613) 543-2987; gen fax (613) 543-3643; disp adv e-mail leaderads@vianet.ca; web site www.morrisburgleader.ca
Circulation: 1,774pd, 54fr; CMCA
Advertising: Open inch rate $.65.
Established: 1976.
Adv. Mgr....Mike Laurin
Circ. Mgr....Wanda Dawley
Ed....Sam Laurin
Mng. Ed....Bonnie McNairn
Prodn. Mgr....Terry Laurin
Mechanical Specifications: Type page 12 3/8 x 21 1/2; E - 6 cols, 1/6 between; A - 6 cols, 1/6 between; C - 6 cols, 1/6 between.
Areas Served: Canada

MOUNT FOREST

ARTHUR ENTERPRISE NEWS

(Wed)
277 Main St. S., Mount Forest, ON, N0G 2L0, North Wellington, Canada; gen tel (519) 323-1550; gen fax (519) 323-4548; disp adv e-mail phaasnoot@northperth.com; class adv e-mail classifieds@metroland.com; ed e-mail sburrows@metroland.com; web site http://www.southwesternontario.ca/arthur-on/
Circulation: 2,699pd, 0fr; VAC
Advertising: Open inch rate $.61.
Established: 1862.
Parent Co.:
Metroland Media Group Ltd.
Torstar
Digital Platform - Mobile: Apple, Android, Windows, Blackberry
Digital Platform - Tablet: Apple iOS, Android, Windows 7, Blackberry Tablet OS
Ed....Shannon Burrows
Adv....Peggy Haasnoot
Mechanical Specifications: Page 10.375"x11.5"
Delivery Method: Mail, Newsstand, Racks
Areas Served: North Wellington

THE MOUNT FOREST CONFEDERATE

(Wed)
277 Main St. S., Mount Forest, ON, N0G 2L0, Wellington County/ Grey County , Canada; gen tel (519) 323-1550; gen fax (519) 323-4548; disp adv e-mail klucas@mountforest.com ; ed e-mail editor@mountforest.com; web site www.mountforest.com
Circulation: 1,108pd,; CMCA
Advertising: Open inch rate $.59.
Established: 1865.
Parent Co.:
Metroland Media Group Ltd.
Circ. Mgr....Cathy Higdon
Ed....Lynne Turner
Prodn. Mgr....Cornelia Svela
Sales....Kim Lucas
Mechanical Specifications: Type page 12 3/4 x 21 1/4; E - 6 cols, 1 1/2, 1/6 between; A - 6 cols, 1 1/2, 1/6 between; C - 6 cols, 1 1/2, 1/6 between.
Equipment & Software: : Hardware — APP/Mac 7200; Software — QPS/QuarkXPress 3.32, Adobe/Photoshop 4.0.
Delivery Method: Mail, Newsstand
Areas Served: Wellington County/ Grey County

NAPANEE

NAPANEE GUIDE

(Thur)
2 Dairy Ave., Unit 11, Napanee, ON, K7R 3T1, Canada; gen tel (613) 354-6648; gen fax (613) 354-6708; disp adv e-mail david@napaneeguide.com; web site www.napaneeguide.com
Circulation: 14,962fr; CMCA
Parent Co.:
Postmedia Network Inc.
Quebecor Communications, Inc.
Group Adv. Dir....Liza Nelson
Distribution Supervisor ....Rob McLellan
Areas Served: Canada

THE NAPANEE BEAVER

(Thur)
72 Dundas St. E., Napanee, ON, K7R 1H9, Canada; gen tel (613) 354-6641; gen fax (613) 354-2622; web site www.napaneebeaver.com
Circulation: 15,698fr; CMCA
Advertising: Open inch rate $.54.
Established: 1870.
Digital Platform - Mobile: Apple
Pub....Jean M. Morrison
Bus. Mgr....Deb Mccann
Ed....Seth Duchene
Prodn. Mgr....Michelle Bowes
Scott Johnston
Mechanical Specifications: Type page 12 x 21 1/4.
Delivery Method: Carrier
Areas Served: Canada

NEW HAMBURG

NEW HAMBURG INDEPENDENT

(Wed)
77 Peel St., New Hamburg, ON, N3A 1E7, Township of Wilmot, Canada; gen tel (519) 662-1240; gen fax (519) 662-3521; disp adv e-mail kschattner@newhamburgindependent.ca; class adv e-mail classified@metrolandwest.com; ed e-mail editor@newhamburgindependent.ca; web site www.newhamburgindependent.ca
Circulation: 1,770pd,; CMCA
Advertising: Open inch rate $.69.
Established: 1878.
Parent Co.:
Metroland Media Group Ltd.
Torstar
Pub....Donna Luelo
Adv. Mgr....Heather Dunbar
Adv. Rep....Kyle Schattner
Ed....Scott Miller Cressman
Admin/Circulation....Leta Gastle
Reporter/photographer....Chris Thomson
Equipment & Software: : Hardware — APP/Mac; Software — QPS/QuarkXPress 3.32, Adobe/Illustrator 5.0, Adobe/Photoshop 3.0, Microsoft/Word 5.1a, Norton Utilities 3.21, Adobe/Streamline 3.0, Adobe/Acrobat 2.0.
Delivery Method: Mail, Newsstand, Carrier
Areas Served: Township of Wilmot

NEW LISKEARD

SPEAKER WEEKENDER

(Fri)
18 Wellington St., New Liskeard, ON, P0J 1P0, Canada; gen tel (705) 647-6791; gen fax (705) 647-9669; web site www.facebook.com/pages/Temiskaming-Speaker-Weekender/884448971667310
Circulation: 10,450fr; CMCA
Gen. Mgr. ....Lois Perry
Areas Served: Canada

TEMISKAMING SPEAKER

(Wed)
18 Wellington St. S., New Liskeard, ON, P0J 1P0, Canada; gen tel (705) 647-6791; gen fax (705) 647-9669; adv fax (705) 647-9669; ed e-mail editorial@northernontario.ca; web site www.northernontario.ca
Circulation: 3,021pd, 138fr; CMCA
Advertising: Open inch rate $1.07.
Established: 1906.Editions: Temiskaming Speaker & Temiskaming Speaker Weekender
Digital Platform - Mobile: Apple
Gen. Mgr. ....Lois Perry
Ed....Gordon Brock
Mechanical Specifications: Type page 13 x 21

1/4; E - 6 cols, 2 1/8, 1/8 between; A - 6 cols, 2 1/8, 1/8 between; C - 6 cols, 2 1/8, 1/8 between.
Equipment & Software: : Hardware — APP/Mac; Presses — G/Community; Software — QPS/QuarkXPress 3.1, Adobe/Illustrator 5.0, Multi-Ad/Creator.
Delivery Method: Mail, Newsstand, Carrier, Racks
Areas Served: Canada

NEWMARKET

BRADFORD & WEST GWILLIMBURY TOPIC
(Thur)
580b Steven Crt., Newmarket, ON, L3Y 4X1, Canada; gen tel (905) 775-1188; disp adv e-mail asmug@metroland.com; ed e-mail tmcfadden@yrmg.com; web site www.simcoe.com
Circulation: 10,538fr; CMCA
Parent Co.:
Metroland Media Group Ltd.
Adv Mgr .... Amanda Sung
Ed .... Ted McFadden
Areas Served: Canada

THE NEWMARKET ERA-BANNER
(Thur)
580b Steven Ct, Newmarket, ON, L3Y 4X1, Canada; gen tel (905) 773-7627; adv tel (416) 798-7284; gen fax (905) 853-5379; adv fax (905) 853-5379; ed fax (905) 853-5379; disp adv e-mail admin@erabanner.com; ed e-mail newsroom@erabanner.com; web site www.yorkregion.com
Circulation: 31pd, 15,946fr; VAC
Advertising: Open inch rate $2.96.
Parent Co.:
Metroland Media Group Ltd.
Torstar
Digital Platform - Mobile: Apple, Android
Digital Platform - Tablet: Apple iOS, Android
Pub.. Ian Proudfoot
Dir., Adv./Prodn./Distribution...... Gord Paolucci
Retail Sales Mgr......................... Dave Williams
Adv. Coord. .... Darlene Baker
Circ. Mgr.. Megan Pike
Distribution Coord.................. Teresa Mathison
Ed. in Chief .... Debora Kelly
Ed. .... Ted McFadden
Areas Served: Newmarket, Aurora, East Gwillimbury, and York region

NIPIGON

NIPIGON-RED ROCK GAZETTE
(Tues)
155b Railway Street, Nipigon, ON, P0T 2J0, Canada; gen tel (807) 887-3583; gen fax (807) 887-3720
Circulation: 486pd, 17fr; CMCA
Advertising: Open inch rate $0.86.
Circ. Mgr./Ed. .... Pamela Behun
Pub.. Blair Oborne
Delivery Method: Mail
Areas Served: Canada

OAKVILLE

OAKVILLE BEAVER
(Thur, Fri)
467 Speers Rd., Oakville, ON, L6K 3S4, Canada; gen tel (905) 845-3824; gen fax (905) 337-5568; ed e-mail editor@oakvillebeaver.com; web site www.oakvillebeaver.com
Circulation: 118pd, 53,175fr; CCAB
Advertising: Open inch rate $8.90.
Established: 1962.
Parent Co.:
Metroland Media Group Ltd.
Torstar
Pub.. Neil Oliver
Dir., Adv. .... Daniel Baird
Circ. Mgr............................. Sarah McSweeney
Ed. in Chief .... Jill Davis
Sports Ed....................................... Jon Kuiperij
Prodn. Mgr. .... Manuel Garcia
Ed. .... Angela Blackburn
Delivery Method: Carrier
Areas Served: Canada

OHSWEKEN

TURTLE ISLAND NEWS
(Wed)
Box 329, Ohsweken, ON, N0A 1M0, Canada; gen tel (519)445-0868; gen fax (519) 445-0865; disp adv e-mail sales@theturtleislandnews.com; web site www.theturtleislandnews.com
Circulation: 5,000fr; Sworn/Estimate/Non-Audited

ORANGEVILLE

ORANGEVILLE CITIZEN
(Thur)
10 First St., Orangeville, ON, L9W 2C4, Canada; gen tel (519) 941-2230; gen fax (519) 941-9361; web site www.citizen.on.ca
Circulation: 17,967fr; CMCA
Advertising: Open inch rate $.80.
Pub....................................... Alan M. Claridge
Ed. .... Thomas M. Claridge
Classifieds .... Carolyn Dennis
Equipment & Software: ; Software — Microsoft, QPS/QuarkXPress, Claris/Works.
Delivery Method: Mail, Newsstand, Carrier
Areas Served: Canada

THE ORANGEVILLE BANNER
(Tues, Thur)
37 Mill St., Orangeville, ON, L9W 2M4, Canada; gen tel (519) 941-1350; gen fax (519) 941-9600; web site www.orangevillebanner.com
Circulation: 85pd, 20,303fr; CCAB
Advertising: Open inch rate $1.61.
Established: 1893.
Parent Co.:
Metroland Media Group Ltd.
Torstar
Gen. Mgr. .... Gordon Brewerton
Prodn. Mgr. .... Janine Taylor
Mechanical Specifications: Type page 10 3/8 x 12 1/2; E - 10 cols, 1, 1/8 between; A - 10 cols, 1, 1/8 between; C - 10 cols, 1, 1/8 between.
Equipment & Software: : Hardware — APP/Mac 6500, APP/Mac G4; Software — QPS/QuarkXPress 5.0, Adobe/Photoshop 7.0, CS, Adobe/Illustrator 7.0, 10.0, CS.
Areas Served: Canada

ORILLIA

ORILLIA TODAY
(Thur)
25 Ontario St., Orillia, ON, L3V 6H1, Canada; gen tel (705) 329-2058; gen fax (705) 329-2059; web site www.orilliatoday.com
Circulation: 24,297fr; CMCA
Advertising: Open inch rate $2.22.
Established: 1991.
Parent Co.:
Metroland Media Group Ltd.
Torstar
Pub.. Joe Anderson
Gen. Mgr. .... Leigh Gate
Adv. Mgr..................................... Leigh Rourke
Mng. Ed.. Lori Martin
Community/News................. Martin Melbourne
Distr. Mgr...................................... Kyla Mosley
Areas Served: Canada

ORLEANS

WEEKLY JOURNAL
(Thur)
5300 Canotek Rd., Unit 30, Orleans, ON, K1J 8R7, Canada; gen tel (613) 744-4800; gen fax (613) 744-0866
Circulation: 47,000fr; Sworn/Estimate/Non-Audited
Advertising: Open inch rate $1.22.
Adv. Mgr. .... Terry Tyo
Ed. .... Patricia Lonergan
Prodn. Mgr. .... Sylvie Parsier
Mechanical Specifications: Type page 10 1/2 x 12 1/2; E - 8 cols, 1 1/6, 1/6 between; A - 8 cols, 1 1/6, 1/6 between; C - 8 cols, 1 1/6, 1/6 between.
Equipment & Software: : Hardware — APP/Power Mac 7200-90; Software — QPS/QuarkXPress 3.32, Macromedia/Freehand 5.0.

ORONO

WEEKLY TIMES
(Wed)
5310 Main St., Orono, ON, L0B 1M0, Canada; gen tel (905) 983-5301; gen fax (905) 983-5301
Circulation: 1,040pd,; CMCA
Advertising: Open inch rate $.44.
Ed. .... Marg Zwart
Mechanical Specifications: Type page 10 1/8 x 15 1/2; E - 2 cols, 3 15/16, 1/4 between.

OSHAWA

AJAX-PICKERING NEWS ADVERTISER
(Wed, Thur)
865 Farewell Ave., Oshawa, ON, L1H 7L5, Canada; gen tel (905) 579-4400; gen fax (905) 579-2238; disp adv e-mail dfletcher@durhamregion.com; ed e-mail jburghardt@durhamregion.com; web site www.durhamregion.com
Circulation: 0pd, 51,910fr; CCAB
Advertising: Open inch rate $3.86.
Parent Co.:
Metroland Media Group Ltd.
Torstar
Pub................................... Timothy J. Whittaker
Adv. Mgr. .... Duncan Fletcher
Circ. Mgr.................................. Abe Fackhourie
Ed. .... Joanne Burghardt
Mechanical Specifications: Type page 10 3/8 x 14; E - 9 cols, 1 1/16, between; A - 9 cols, 1 1/16, between; C - 9 cols, 1 1/16, between.
Equipment & Software: : Hardware — APP/Mac; Software — Multi-Ad, QPS/QuarkXPress, Adobe/Illustrator, Adobe/Photoshop.
Areas Served: Canada

CANADIAN STATESMAN
(Wed, Thur, Fri)
865 Farewell St., Oshawa, ON, L1H 7L5, Ontario , Canada; gen tel (905) 579-4400; adv tel (905) 215-0440; ed tel (905) 215-0462; gen fax (416) 523-6161; ed e-mail mjohnston@durhamregion.com; web site www.durhamregion.com
Circulation: 104,250pd,; Sworn/Estimate/Non-Audited
Advertising: Open inch rate $1.81.
Pub................................... Timothy J. Whittaker
Dir. Adv. .... Fred Eismont
Managing Ed.......................... Mike Johnston
Areas Served: Ontario

CLARINGTON THIS WEEK
(Wed)
865 Farewell St., Oshawa, ON, L1H 7L5, Canada; gen tel (905) 579-4400; gen fax (905) 579-2238; web site newsdurhamregion.com
Circulation: 24,150fr; Sworn/Estimate/Non-Audited
Advertising: Open inch rate $1.03.
Parent Co.:
Metroland Media Group Ltd.
Torstar
Pub.. Tim Whittaker
Office Mgr. .... Lillian Hook
Adv. Dir.. Fred Eismont
Ed. in Chief .... Joanne Burghardt
Mng. Ed....................................... Mike Johnston
Areas Served: Oshawa, Ontario, L1H 7L5

OSHAWA-WHITBY THIS WEEK
(Wed, Thur)
865 Farewell St., Oshawa, ON, L1H 7L5, Canada, Canada; gen tel (905) 579-4400; gen fax (905) 579-2238; adv fax (905) 579-6851; ed fax (905) 579-1809; web site www.durhamregion.com
Circulation: 0pd, 106,207fr; CCAB
Advertising: Open inch rate $5.54.
Parent Co.:
Metroland Media Group Ltd.
Torstar
Pub.................................. Timothy J. Whittaker
Office Mgr. .... Lillian Hook
Adv. Mgr...................................... Fred Eismont
Adv. Coord. .... Tina Jennings
Circ. Mgr.................................... Abe Fakhourie
Ed. in Chief .... Joanne Burghardt
Mng. Ed....................................... Mike Johnston
Copy Ed.. Tim Kelly
Entertainment Ed...................... Christy Chase
Photo Ed.............................. Walter Passarella
Regl. Ed. .... Judi Bobbitt
Sports Ed.................................... Brian Legree
Prodn. Mgr. .... Janice O'Neil
Mechanical Specifications: Type page 10 3/8 x 14; E - 9 cols, 1 1/16, between; A - 9 cols, 1 1/16, between; C - 9 cols, 1 1/16, between.
Equipment & Software: : Hardware — APP/Mac; Software — Multi-Ad, QPS/QuarkXPress, Adobe/Illustrator, Adobe/Photoshop.
Areas Served: Canada

OSHWEKEN

TEKAWENNAKE
(Wed)
Po Box 130, Oshweken, ON, N0A 1M0, Canada; gen tel (519) 753-0077; gen fax (519) 753-0011
Circulation: 2,500pd,; Sworn/Estimate/Non-Audited
Advertising: Open inch rate $.85.
Pub.. G. Scott Smith
Mechanical Specifications: Type page 10.25 x 13.25; E - 6 cols, 2, 1/8 between; A - 5 cols, 2, 1/8 between; C - 5 cols, 2, 1/8 between.
Equipment & Software: : Hardware — APP/Power Mac 7500-100; Software — QPS/QuarkXPress, Adobe/Photoshop, Adobe/Illustrator.
Delivery Method: Mail, Newsstand

OTTAWA

KANATA KOURIER-STANDARD EMC
(Thur)
57 Auriga Dr. Unit 103, Ottawa, ON, K2E 8B2, Canada; gen tel (613) 723-5970; gen fax (613)224-2265; web site www.insideottawavalley.com
Circulation: 28,642fr; CMCA
Advertising: Open inch rate $1.39.
Parent Co.:
Metroland Media Group Ltd.
Runge Newspapers, Inc.
Pub. .... Mike Tracy
Ed. .... Theresa Fritz
Mechanical Specifications: Type page 10 x 13 1/2; E - 6 cols, 1 9/16, 1/6 between; A - 6 cols, 1 9/16, 1/6 between; C - 6 cols, 1 9/16, 1/6 between.
Equipment & Software: : Hardware — 4-APP/Mac G4, MS/NT Server; Presses — G/Community; Software — QPS/QuarkXPress 4.1.
Areas Served: Canada

L'ORA DI OTTAWA
(Mon)
203 Louisa St., Ottawa, ON, K1R 6Y9, Ottawa Carleton, Canada; gen tel (613) 232-5689; gen fax (855) 596 8522; disp adv e-mail info@loradiottawa.ca; class adv e-mail info@loradiottawa.ca; ed e-mail info@loradiottawa.ca; web site loradiottawa.ca
Circulation: 1,111pd, 242fr; AAM
Advertising: Open inch rate $.57.
Established: 1968.

Managing Editor ....Paolo Siraco
Assistant Editor..........................Cynthia Nuzzi
Accounting..................................Olita Schultz
Client Services .... AnnaMaria Morrone
Mechanical Specifications: Type page 11-1/4" x 16.5"; E - 8 cols, 1.5", 1/4 between.
Equipment & Software: : Hardware — APP/Mac; Software — Adobe Suite
Delivery Method: Mail
Areas Served: Ottawa Carleton

MANOTICK NEWS EMC

(Thur)
57 Auriga Drive Unit 103, Ottawa, ON, K2E 8B2, Canada; gen tel (613) 723-5970; gen fax (613) 224-2265; disp adv e-mail mstoodley@theemc.ca; ed e-mail joe.morin@metroland.com; web site www.insideottawavalley.com
Circulation: 11,392fr; CMCA
Parent Co.:
Metroland Media Group Ltd.
Pub...Mike Tracy
Ed. ....Theresa Fritz
Areas Served: Canada

NEPEAN-BARRHAVEN NEWS EMC

(Thur)
57 Auriga Drive Unit 103, Ottawa, ON, K2E 8B2, Canada; gen tel (613) 723-5970; gen fax (613) 224-2265; ed e-mail Nevil.hunt@metroland.com; web site www.insideottawavalley.com
Circulation: 50,401fr; CMCA
Parent Co.:
Metroland Media Group Ltd.
Pub. ....Mike Tracy
Ed. ....Theresa Fritz
Areas Served: Canada

ORLEANS NEWS EMC

(Thur)
57 Auriga Drive Unit 103, Ottawa, ON, K2E 8B2, Canada; gen tel (613) 723-5970; disp adv e-mail dave.badham@metroland.com; web site www.insideottawavalley.com
Circulation: 42,273fr; CMCA
Parent Co.:
Metroland Media Group Ltd.
Pub. ....Mike Tracy
Ed. ....Theresa Fritz
Areas Served: Canada

OTTAWA EAST EMC

(Thur)
57 Auriga Drive Unit 103, Ottawa, ON, K2E 8B2, Canada; gen tel (613) 723-5970; gen fax (613) 224-2265; disp adv e-mail ghamilton@thenewsemc.ca; ed e-mail matthew.jay@metroland.com; web site www.insideottawavalley.com
Circulation: 36,519fr; CMCA
Parent Co.:
Metroland Media Group Ltd.
Ed. ....Theresa Fritz
Pub...Mike Tracy
Areas Served: Canada

OTTAWA SOUTH EMC

(Thur)
57 Auriga Drive Unit 103, Ottawa, ON, K2E 8B2, Canada; gen tel (613) 723-5970; gen fax (613) 224-2265; disp adv e-mail cmanor@theemc.ca; ed e-mail blair.edwards@metroland.com; web site www.insideottawavalley.com
Circulation: 41,820fr; CMCA
Parent Co.:
Metroland Media Group Ltd.
Pub. ....Mike Tracy
Ed. ....Theresa Fritz
Areas Served: Canada

OTTAWA WEST EMC

(Thur)
57 Auriga Drive Unit 103, Ottawa, ON, K2E 8B2, Canada; gen tel (613)723-5970; disp adv e-mail dave.pennett@metroland.com; web site www.insideottawavalley.com
Circulation: 35,247fr; CMCA
Parent Co.:
Metroland Media Group Ltd.
Pub...Mike Tracy
Ed. ....Theresa Fritz
Areas Served: Canada

THE HILL TIMES

(Mon, Wed)
69 Sparks St., Ottawa, ON, K1P 5A5, Canada; gen tel (613) 232-5952; gen fax (613) 232-9055; disp adv e-mail production@hilltimes.com; classified@hilltimes.com; web site www.hilltimes.com
Circulation: 3,614pd, 9,555fr; CMCA
Advertising: Open inch rate $6.54.
Established: 1989.
Digital Platform - Mobile: Apple, Android, Windows
Digital Platform - Tablet: Apple iOS, Android
Pub...Jim Creskey
Pub...Ross Dickson
Gen. Mgr. ....Andrew Morrow
Ed. ....Kate Malloy
Prod. Mgr. ....Benoit Deneault
Pub.............................. Anne Marie Creskey
Mechanical Specifications: Type page 10 3/8 x 13 1/2; E - 4 cols
Equipment & Software: : Hardware — APP/Mac; Software — Adobe/Indesign, Adobe/Illustrator, Adobe/Photoshop.
Delivery Method: Mail, Newsstand, Carrier, Racks
Areas Served: Canada

THE STAR

(Thur)
5300 Canotek Rd., Unit 30, Ottawa, ON, K1J 8R7, Canada; gen tel (613) 744-4800; gen fax (613) 744-0866; web site www.eastottawa.ca
Circulation: 45,439fr; CMCA
Advertising: Open inch rate $1.36.
Parent Co.:
Transcontinental Media
Pub...Michael Curram
Pub...Terry Tyo
Ed. ....Patricia Lonergan

THE STITTSVILLE NEWS

(Thur)
57 Auriga Drive Unit 103, Ottawa, ON, K2E 8B2, Canada; gen tel (613) 723-5970; disp adv e-mail jillmartin@theemc.ca; ed e-mail theresa.fritz@metroland.com; web site www.insideottawavalley.com
Circulation: 13,217fr; CMCA
Advertising: Open inch rate $.59.
Parent Co.:
Metroland Media Group Ltd.
Runge Newspapers, Inc.
Publisher..Mike Tracy

PALMERSTON

MINTO EXPRESS

(Wed)
171 William St., Palmerston, ON, N0G 2P0, Town of Minto, Canada; gen tel (519) 343-2440; gen fax (519) 343-2267; web site www.mintoexpress.com
Circulation: 476pd, 5fr; CMCA
Advertising: Open inch rate $.80.
Parent Co.:
Metroland Media Group Ltd.
Torstar
Gen. Mgr. ....Bill Heuther
Shannon Burrows
Delivery Method: Mail, Newsstand, Racks
Areas Served: Town of Minto

PARIS

PARIS STAR

(Thur)
3 Elm St., Unit 3, Paris, ON, N0E 1N0, Canada; gen tel (519) 756-2020; gen fax (519) 756-9470; disp adv e-mail ashley.demers@sunmedia.ca; ed e-mail parisedit@bowesnet.com; web site www.parisstaronline.com
Circulation: 4,877fr; CMCA
Advertising: Open inch rate $.72.
Established: 1850.
Parent Co.:
Postmedia Network Inc.
Quebecor Communications, Inc.
Pub..Ken Koyama
Ed. ....Michael Peeling
Mechanical Specifications: Type page 10 x 16; E - 5 cols, 2, 1/8 between; A - 5 cols, 2, 1/8 between; C - 6 cols, 1 3/4, 1/8 between.
Equipment & Software: : Hardware — APP/Mac; Software — QPS/QuarkXPress 3.31.
Areas Served: Canada

PARKHILL

THE PARKHILL GAZETTE

(Thur)
165 King St., Parkhill, ON, N0M 2K0, Canada; gen tel (519) 294-6264; gen fax (519) 294-6391
Circulation: 860pd,; CMCA
Advertising: Open inch rate $.74.
Adv. Mgr. ....Melaime Carter
Circ. Mgr.......................................Dale Hayter
Ed. ....Gord Whitehead
Areas Served: Canada

PARRY SOUND

PARRY SOUND BEACON STAR

(Fri)
67 James Street, Parry Sound, ON, P2A 2X4, Canada; gen tel (705) 746-2104; gen fax (705) 746-8369; disp adv e-mail cbarnes@metrolandnorthmedia.com; ed e-mail cpeck@metrolandnorthmedia.com; web site www.parrysound.com
Circulation: 7,433fr; CMCA
Parent Co.:
Metroland Media Group Ltd.
Regional Gen. Mgr. .... Shaun Sauve
Areas Served: Canada

PARRY SOUND NORTH STAR

(Wed)
67 James St., Parry Sound, ON, P2A 2X4, Canada, Canada; gen tel (705) 746-2104; gen fax (705) 746-8369; disp adv e-mail jheidman@metrolandnorthmedia.com; ed e-mail jtynan@metrolandnorthmedia.com; web site www.parrysound.com
Circulation: 2,081pd, 125fr; CMCA
Advertising: Open inch rate $1.09.
Established: 1874.
Parent Co.:
Metroland Media Group Ltd.
Reg'l Gen. Mgr..................................Bill Allen
Adv. Sales Mgr............ Janice Heidman Louch
Mng. Ed..Jack Tynan
Areas Served: Canada

PENETANGUISHENE

GOUT DE VIVRE

(Thur)
343 Lafontaine St. W., Penetanguishene, ON, L9M 1R3, Canada; gen tel (705) 533-3349; web site www.legoutdevivre.com
Circulation: 912pd, 0fr; CMCATherese Maheux
Areas Served: Canada

PETERBOROUGH

PETERBOROUGH THIS WEEK

(Wed, Fri)
884 Ford St., Peterborough, ON, K9J 5V4, Canada; gen tel (705) 749-3383; gen fax (705) 749-0074; ed e-mail prellinger@mykawartha.com; web site www.mykawartha.com
Circulation: 42,947fr; CCAB
Advertising: Open inch rate $3.02.
Parent Co.:
Metroland Media Group Ltd.
Torstar
Pub...Bruce Danford
Gen. Mgr.....................................Linda Sudes
Adv. Mgr. ....Adam Milligan
Reg'l Dir., Adv. ....Mary Babcock
Circ. Mgr.......................................Tracy Magee
Ed. in Chief.......................................Lois Tuffin
Special Pjcts. Ed........................Paul Relinger
News Ed. ....Mike Lacey
Prodn. Mgr. ....Scott Prikker
Mechanical Specifications: Type page 11 1/2 x 21 1/2; E - 10 cols, 1, between; A - 10 cols, 1, between.
Areas Served: Canada

PICTON

THE COUNTY WEEKLY NEWS

(Thur)
3-252 Main St., Picton, ON, K0K 2T0, Canada; gen tel (613) 476-4714; gen fax (613) 476-1281; ed e-mail chris.malette@sunmedia.ca; web site www.countyweeklynews.ca
Circulation: 11,591fr; CMCA
Parent Co.:
Postmedia Network Inc.
News Ed. ....Dave Vachon
Areas Served: Canada

THE PICTON GAZETTE

(Thur)
267 Main St., Picton, ON, K0K 2T0, Canada; gen tel (613) 476-3201; adv tel (613) 476-3201 ext. 105; ed tel (613) 476-3201 ext. 110; gen fax (613) 476-3464; disp adv e-mail advertise@pictongazette.com, gazetteclass@bellnet.ca; ed e-mail gazette@bellnet.ca; web site www.pictongazette.com
Circulation: 11,450fr; CMCA
Advertising: Open inch rate $.40.
Established: 1830.Editions: 1—
Pub.......................................Jean M. Morrison
Ed. ....Adam Bramburger
Prodn. Mgr. ....Michelle Bowes
Mechanical Specifications: Tabloid pages, 6 columns, 212 agates deep
Equipment & Software: ; Software — Quark XPress 9, Adobe Photoshop, Adobe Illustrator, Adobe InDesign, Adobe Acrobat, Word, TextEdit
Delivery Method: Carrier
Areas Served: Canada

PORT COLBORNE

IN PORT NEWS

(Wed)
228 E. Main St., Port Colborne, ON, L3K 1S4, Canada; gen tel (905) 732-2411; web site www.inportnews.ca
Circulation: 9,849fr; CMCA
Parent Co.:
Postmedia Network Inc.John Tobon
Julia Coles
Areas Served: Canada

PORT DOVER

PORT DOVER MAPLE LEAF

(Wed)
351 Main St., Port Dover, ON, N0A 1N0, Norfolk County, Canada; gen tel (519) 583-0112; disp adv e-mail ads@portdovermapleleaf.com; ed e-mail news@portdovermapleleaf.com; web site www.portdovermapleleaf.com
Circulation: 2,904pd, 15fr; Sworn/Estimate/Non-Audited
Advertising: Open inch rate $7.40.
Established: 1873.
Paul Morris
Stan MorrisEd.s
Mechanical Specifications: Type page 10 1/2 x 16; E - 5 cols, 2, 1/8 between; A - 10 cols, 1, 1/8 between; C - 10 cols, 1, 1/8 between.
Equipment & Software: : Hardware — PC; Soft-

ware — InDesign
Delivery Method: Mail, Newsstand, Racks
Areas Served: Norfolk County

PORT ELGIN

SHORELINE BEACON

(Tues)
694 Goderich St., Port Elgin, ON, N0H 2C0, Canada; gen tel (519) 832-9001; gen fax (519) 389-4793; web site www.shorelinebeacon.com
Circulation: 2,102pd, 15fr; CMCA
Advertising: Open inch rate $.69.
Established: unknown.
Parent Co.:
Postmedia Network Inc.
Quebecor Communications, Inc.
Gen. Mgr. .... Kiera Merriam
Mechanical Specifications: 10.33"w x 160 agates
Areas Served: Canada

PORT PERRY

THE PORT PERRY STAR

(Thur)
180 Mary St., Port Perry, ON, L9L 1C4, Canada; gen tel (905) 985-7383; gen fax (905) 985-3708; web site www.durhamregion.com
Circulation: 12,000pd, 125fr; Sworn/Estimate/Non-Audited
Advertising: Open inch rate $1.35.
Established: 1866.
Parent Co.:
Metroland Media Group Ltd.
Torstar
Pub... Tim Whittaker
Sales Mgr..................... Stephanie Isert-Kohek
Circ. Coordinator........................ Laurie Tromley
Mng. Ed...................................... Mike Johnston
Areas Served: Scugog Township, select areas in Brock, Little Britain, Pontypool

THE STANDARD NEWSPAPER

(Thur)
94a Water St., Port Perry, ON, L9L 1J2, Durham Region, Canada; gen tel (905) 985-6985; gen fax (905) 985-9253; disp adv e-mail standardnancy@powergate.ca; class adv e-mail office-standard@powergate.ca; ed e-mail standarddarryl@powergate.ca; web site www.thestandardnewspaper.ca - 6,000(views)
Circulation: 11,868fr; CMCA
Established: 2004.
Parent Co.:
Skyline Media
Digital Platform - Mobile: Apple, Android, Windows, Blackberry, Other
Digital Platform - Tablet: Apple iOS, Android, Windows 7, Blackberry Tablet OS, Kindle, Nook, Kindle Fire, Other
Gen. Mgr.................................. Colleen Green
Ed. .... Darryl Knight
Adv. Rep. .... Nancy Lister
Reporter .... Dan Cearns
Equipment & Software: : Hardware — Mac & PCs; Software — Adobe InDesign
Delivery Method: Mail, Newsstand, Carrier, Racks
Areas Served: Durham Region

PORT STANLEY

LAKE ERIE BEACON (OOB)

(Fri, Bi-Mthly) (Every second week)
204 A Carlow Road, Port Stanley, ON, N5L 1C5, Central Elgin, Canada; gen tel (519) 782-4563; adv tel (519) 782-4563; ed tel (519) 782-4563; gen fax (519) 782-4563; adv fax (519) 782-4563; ed fax (519) 782-4563; disp adv e-mail linda@lebeacon.ca ; class adv e-mail linda@lebeacon.ca ; ed e-mail andrew@lebeacon.ca; web site www.lebeacon.ca
Circulation: 7,000fr; CMCA
Advertising: Modular Rates.
Established: 2004.
Parent Co.:
Kettle Creek Publishing Ltd.
Digital Platform - Mobile: Apple, Other
Digital Platform - Tablet: Apple iOS, Other
Mechanical Specifications: TIFF, JPEG, PDF, MS Word, Quark Express
Equipment & Software: : Hardware — Apple Computers; Software — Quark Express
Adobe Illustrator & Photoshop
MS Office
Delivery Method: Mail, Newsstand
Areas Served: Central Elgin
Note: The Lake Erie Beacon is also E-mailed to 700+ recipients and is available on Facebook and on ISSUU.com

PRESCOTT

THE PRESCOTT JOURNAL

(Wed)
3201 County Rd. 2, Prescott, ON, K0E 1T0, Canada, Canada; gen tel (613) 925-4265; gen fax (613) 925-2837; disp adv e-mail adsales@prescottjournal.com; ed e-mail journal@stlawrenceprinting.on.ca; web site www.prescottjournal.com
Circulation: 1,123pd, 99fr; CMCA
Advertising: Open inch rate $10.36.
Established: 1891.
Pub... Beth Morris
Prodn. Mgr. .... Dave Flinn
Jamie Nurse
Mechanical Specifications: Type page 10.325" x 16"; 6 columns 1.125" wide x 220 agates
Equipment & Software: : Hardware — APP/Mac; Presses — 6-G/Community; Software — CS4
Delivery Method: Mail, Newsstand, Carrier
Areas Served: Canada

RAINY RIVER

RAINY RIVER RECORD

(Tues)
312 Third St., Rainy River, ON, P0W 1L0, Canada; gen tel (807) 852-3366; ed tel (807) 852-3337; gen fax (807) 852-4434; disp adv e-mail advertising@rainyriverrecord.com; ed e-mail editorial@rainyriverrecord.com; web site www.rainyriverrecord.com
Circulation: 609pd,; CMCA
Advertising: Open inch rate $.70.
Established: 1919.
Circ. Mgr.................................... Anne Mailloux
Sales.. Melissa Hudgin
Ed. .... Sharon LaCroix
Mechanical Specifications: Type page 10 1/2 x 15; E - 5 cols, 1 4/5, 2/9 between; A - 5 cols, 1 4/5, 2/9 between; C - 5 cols, 1 4/5, 2/9 between.
Equipment & Software: : Hardware — APP/Mac G3, APP/Mac G4; Software — QPS/QuarkXPress 4.04, Adobe/Photoshop 6.0.
Areas Served: Canada

RED LAKE

THE NORTHERN SUN NEWS

(Wed)
200 Howey Street, Red Lake, ON, P0V 2M0, Canada; gen tel (807) 727-2888; gen fax (807) 727-3961; disp adv e-mail pamela@thenorthernsun.com; ed e-mail lindsay@thenorthernsun.com; web site www.thenorthernsun.com
Circulation: 780pd,; CMCA
Gen Mgr. .... Kathy Coutts
Adv. Sales & Mrktg. .... Pamela O'Neill
Areas Served: Canada

RENFREW

THE RENFREW MERCURY EMC

(Thur)
35 Opeongo Rd. W., Renfrew, ON, K7V 2T2, Canada; gen tel (613) 432-3655; gen fax (613) 432-6689; ed e-mail rmedit@runge.net; web site www.insideottawavalley.com/renfrew-on
Circulation: 13,309fr; CMCA
Advertising: Open inch rate $.96.
Established: 1871.
Parent Co.:
Metroland Media Group Ltd.
Runge Newspapers, Inc.
Pub.. Mike Tracy
Ed. .... Theresa Fritz
Areas Served: Canada

RIDGETOWN

THE RIDGETOWN INDEPENDENT NEWS

(Wed)
1 Main St. W., Ridgetown, ON, N0P 2C0; gen tel (519) 674-5205; gen fax (519) 674-2573
Circulation: 1,674pd,; CMCA
Editor in Chief....................... Shelia Mcbrayne
Managing Editor .... Gordon Brown
Areas Served: Canada

ROCKLAND

ROCKLAND VISION

(Fri)
1315 Laurier St., Rockland, ON, K4K 1L5, Canada; gen tel (613) 446-6456; gen fax (613) 446-1381; disp adv e-mail paulo.casimiro@eap.on.ca; web site www.facebook.com/pg/Le-journal-Vision-newspaper-199878750108078/about/?ref=page_internal
Circulation: 23,297pd, 39fr; ODC
Advertising: Open inch rate $1.12.
Established: 1994.
Prodn. Mgr. .... Paulo Casimiro
Mechanical Specifications: Type page 10 1/2 x 14; E - 8 cols, 1 5/16, between; A - 8 cols, between; C - 8 cols, between.

SAINT CATHARINE'S

THOROLD NIAGARA NEWS

(Thur) (1)
10-1 St. Paul St., Saint Catharine's, ON, L2R 7L4, Canada; gen tel (905) 688-4332; gen fax (905) 688-6313; disp adv e-mail lauren.krause@sunmedia.ca; web site www.thoroldedition.ca
Circulation: 7,225fr; CMCA
Parent Co.:
Postmedia Network Inc.
Reporter .... Jeff Blay
Advertising .... Lauren Krause

SAINT THOMAS

ST. THOMAS/ELGIN WEEKLY NEWS

(Thur)
15 St. Catharine Street, Saint Thomas, ON, N5P 2V7, Canada; gen tel (519) 633-1640; gen fax (519) 633-0558; disp adv e-mail geoff@theweeklynews.ca; ed e-mail editor@theweeklynews.ca; web site www.theweeklynews.ca
Circulation: 30,393fr; CMCA
Advertising: Modular.
Parent Co.:
Metroland Media Group Ltd.
Office/Sales Manager....................... Geoff Rae
Delivery Method: Carrier
Areas Served: Canada

SARNIA

SARNIA & LAMBTON COUNTY THIS WEEK

(Wed)
140 Front St S, Sarnia, ON, N7t2M6, Lambton County, Canada; gen tel (519) 336-1100; adv tel (519) 336-1100; ed tel (519) 336-1100; gen fax (519) 336-1833; adv fax (519) 336-1833; ed fax (519) 336-1833; disp adv e-mail stw.sales@sunmedia.ca; ed e-mail stw.sales@sunmedia.ca; web site Www.sarniathisweek.ca
Circulation: 41,300fr; Sworn/Estimate/Non-Audited
Advertising: Open inch rate $1.27.
Established: 1993.
Parent Co.:
Postmedia Network Inc.
Marketing Manager.................... Chris Courtis
Mechanical Specifications: Type page 10 1/2 x 13 1/4; A - 9 cols, 1 1/6, 1/6 between; C - 9 cols, 1 1/6, 1/6 between.
Delivery Method: Carrier, Racks
Areas Served: N7S 5P1
Note: We are the only weekly community editorial paper & averages 48 pages. Our paper is also posted on our web site in it's entirety

SARNIA THIS WEEK

(Thur)
140 Front St. S, Sarnia, ON, N7T 7M8, Canada, Canada; gen tel (519) 336-1100; gen fax (519) 336-1833; ed e-mail production@sarniamedia.com; web site www.sarniathisweek.com
Circulation: 39,476fr; CMCA
Advertising: Open inch rate $1.18.
Parent Co.:
Quebecor Communications, Inc.
Pub.. Linda LeBlanc
Distribution Mgr. .... Penny Churchill
Areas Served: Canada

THE PETROLIA TOPIC

(Wed)
140 Front St. S, Sarnia, ON, N7T 7M8, Canada, Canada; gen tel (519) 336-1100 x2230; adv tel (519) 882-4798; ed tel (519) 336-1100 x2230; gen fax (519) 336-1833; adv fax (519) 882-4635; ed fax (519) 336-1833; ed e-mail reporter@petroliatopic.com; web site www.petroliatopic.com
Circulation: 1,309pd,; CMCA
Advertising: Open inch rate $.70.
Established: 1866.
Parent Co.:
Postmedia Network Inc.
Quebecor Communications, Inc.
Pub.. Linda LeBlanc
Delivery Method: Mail, Newsstand
Areas Served: Canada

SAULT SAINTE MARIE

SAULT STE. MARIE THIS WEEK

(Thur)
2 Towers St., Sault Sainte Marie, ON, P6A 2T9, Canada; gen tel (705) 949-6111; ed tel (705) 759-5825; gen fax (705) 942-8596; disp adv e-mail sste.advertising@sunmedia.ca; ed e-mail sandra.paul@sunmedia.ca; web site www.saultthisweek.com
Circulation: 31,122fr; CMCA
Advertising: Open inch rate $1.37.
Established: 1967.
Parent Co.:
Postmedia Network Inc.
Quebecor Communications, Inc.
Pub. .... Lou Maulucci
Ed. .... Sandra Paul
Mechanical Specifications: Type page 10 1/4 x 11 1/2; E - various, between; A - 9 cols, between; C - 9 cols, between.
Equipment & Software: : Hardware — APP/Mac; Software — InDesign, Macromedia/Free Hand 8.0.1, Multi-Ad 4.0.1.
Delivery Method: Newsstand, Carrier, Racks
Areas Served: Canada

SEAFORTH

THE HURON EXPOSITOR

(Wed)

8 Main St. S., Seaforth, ON, N0K 1W0, Canada; gen tel (519) 527-0240; gen fax (519) 527-2858; disp adv e-mail max.bickford@sunmedia.ca; class adv e-mail seaforth.classifieds@sunmedia.ca; ed e-mail seaforth.news@sunmedia.ca; web site www.seaforthhuronexpositor.com - 6,931(views) 4,892(visitors)
Circulation: 1,160pd, 22fr; CMCA
Advertising: Open inch rate $.68.
Established: 1860.
Parent Co.:
Postmedia Network Inc.
Quebecor Communications, Inc.
Pub.. Neil Clifford
Multi Media Journalist................Whitney South
Mechanical Specifications: Type page 11 1/4 x 11 3/8; E - 9 cols, 1 3/4, 1/8 between; @RecordBody:**Delivery Method:** Mail, Newsstand
Areas Served: Canada

SHARBOT LAKE

THE FRONTENAC NEWS
(Thur)
1095 Garrett St., Rear, Sharbot Lake, ON, K0H 2P0, Central Frontenac, Canada; gen tel (613) 279-3150 ; gen fax (613) 279-3172; disp adv e-mail info@frontenacnews.ca; class adv e-mail info@frontenacnews.ca; ed e-mail info@frontenacnews.ca; web site Frontenacnews.ca
Circulation: 9,135fr; Sworn/Estimate/Non-Audited
Advertising: 6 col. 10.50 col. inch.
Established: 1973.
Digital Platform - Mobile: Windows
Publisher/Editor.............................. Jeff Green
Designer/bookeeper .... Scott Cox
Delivery Method: Mail
Areas Served: Central Frontenac

SIMCOE

TIMES-REFORMER
(Tues)
50 Gilbertson Dr., Simcoe, ON, N3Y 4L2, Canada, Canada; gen tel (519) 426-3528; gen fax (519) 426-9255; web site www.simcoereformer.ca
Circulation: 1,411pd, 17,315fr; CMCA
Advertising: Open inch rate $1.20.
Parent Co.:
Postmedia Network Inc.
Quebecor Communications, Inc.
Adv. Mgr...Sue Downs
Ed. ....Kim Novak
Areas Served: Canada

SIOUX LOOKOUT

THE BULLETIN
(Wed)
40 Front St., Sioux Lookout, ON, P8T 1B9, Canada; gen tel (807) 737-3209; adv tel (807) 737-4207; gen fax (807) 737-3084; web site www.soiuxbulletin.com
Circulation: 4,472fr; CMCA
Advertising: Open inch rate $.69.
Ed. .... Dick MacKenzie
Mechanical Specifications: Type page 10 x 14.
Equipment & Software: : Hardware — PC; Software — Adobe/PageMaker 5.0, Archetype/Corel Draw.
Areas Served: Canada

WAWATAY NEWS
(Thur) (Every other thur)
16 5th Ave., Sioux Lookout, ON, P8T 1B7, Canada; gen tel (807) 737-2951; gen fax (807) 737-3224; web site www.wawataynews.ca
Circulation: 399pd, 5,618fr; CMCA
Advertising: Open inch rate $.83.
Established: 1974.
Reporter .... Rick Garrick
Mechanical Specifications: Type page 10 1/4 x 15 3/4; E - 6 cols, 1 9/16, 1/16 between; A - 6 cols, 1 9/16, 1/16 between; C - 6 cols, 1 9/16, 1/16 between.
Equipment & Software: : Hardware — APP/Mac, PC; Software — QPS/QuarkXPress 3.3, Adobe/Photoshop, Adobe/Illustrator.

SMITH FALLS

THE CARLETON PLACE-ALMONTE CANADIAN GAZETTE EMC
(Thur)
65 Lorne St., Smith Falls, ON, K7A 4T1, Canada; gen tel (613) 283-3182; disp adv e-mail ssinfield@perfprint.ca; ed e-mail akulp@perfprint.ca; web site www.insideottawavalley.com
Circulation: 12,071fr; CMCA
Advertising: Open inch rate $.75.
Parent Co.:
Metroland Media Group Ltd.
Group Pub.l................................ Duncan Weir
Reg. Ed. .... Ryland Coyne
Areas Served: Canada

THE PERTH COURIER EMC
(Thur)
65 Lorne St., Smith Falls, ON, K7A 4T1, Canada, Canada; gen tel (613) 283-3180; ed e-mail editor@perthcourier.com; web site www.insideottawavalley.com
Circulation: 11,641fr; CMCA
Advertising: Open inch rate $.87.
Established: 1834.
Parent Co.:
Metroland Media Group Ltd.
Pub. .... Duncan Weir
Ryland Coyne
Mechanical Specifications: Type page 13 1/4 x 21; E - 8 cols, 1 1/2, 1 7/8 between; A - 8 cols, 1 1/2, 1 7/8 between; C - 11 cols, 1 1/2, 1 1/6 between.
Areas Served: Canada

SMITHS FALLS

KEMPTVILLE ADVANCE EMC
(Thur)
65 Lorne St., Smiths Falls, ON, K7A 4T1, Canada; gen tel (613) 283-3181; disp adv e-mail liz.gray@metroland.com; ed e-mail joe.morin@metroland.com ; web site www.insideottawavalley.com
Circulation: 10,707fr; CMCA
Parent Co.:
Metroland Media Group Ltd.
Group Pub.................................. Duncan Weir
Ed. .... Kerry Sammon
Areas Served: Canada

SMITHS FALLS RECORD NEWS EMC
(Thur)
65 Lorne St., Smiths Falls, ON, K7A 4T1, Canada; gen tel (613) 283-3182; gen fax (613) 283-7480; web site www.insideottawavalley.com/smithsfalls-on
Circulation: 11,455fr; CMCA
Advertising: Open inch rate $.69.
Parent Co.:
Metroland Media Group Ltd.
Pub.. Duncan Weir
Circ. Mgr .... Jason Beck
Ed. .... Ryland Coyne
Areas Served: Canada

ST MARYS

ST. MARY'S JOURNAL ARGUS
(Wed)
11 Wellington St. N., St Marys, ON, N4X 1B7, Canada; gen tel (519) 284-2440; gen fax (519) 284-3650; disp adv e-mail ksteven@stmarys.com; class adv e-mail csmith@stmarys.com; ed e-mail sslater@stmarys.com; web site www.southwesternontario.ca
Circulation: 1,354pd, 110fr; CMCA
Advertising: Open inch rate $.72.
Parent Co.:
Metroland Media Group Ltd.
Torstar
Business Manager...................Anita McDonald
Sales Supervisor ....Stevens Kara
Advertising/Circulation................Colleen Smith
Equipment & Software: : Hardware — APP/Mac; Software — Adobe/Photoshop 3.0, Adobe/PageMaker 5.0, Multi-Ad/Creator 3.7.
Delivery Method: Mail
Areas Served: Canada

STONEY CREEK

ANCASTER NEWS
(Thur)
333 Arvin Ave., Stoney Creek, ON, L8E 2M6, Ancaster, Canada; gen tel (905) 523-5800; gen fax (905) 664-3319; disp adv e-mail hollyc@hamiltonnews.com; web site www.ancasternews.com
Circulation: 13,040fr; CMCA
Advertising: Open inch rate $2.24.
Established: 1967.
Parent Co.:
Metroland Media Group Ltd.
TorstarEditions: 52— Ancaster News
Digital Platform - Mobile: Apple, Android, Windows, Blackberry
Pub... Neil Oliver
Gen. Mgr. .... Jason Pehora
Office Mgr. .... Lorna Lester
News Ed. .... Debra Downey
Mng Ed .... Gordon Cameron
Dir of Advt...................................Holly Chriss
Mechanical Specifications: Full page is 10 columns x 161 agate lines; same as 10.375" x 11.5"
Delivery Method: Carrier
Areas Served: Ancaster

DUNDAS STAR NEWS
(Thur)
333 Arvin Ave., Stoney Creek, ON, L8E 2M6, Dundas, Canada; gen tel (905) 664-8800; gen fax (905) 664-3319; disp adv e-mail hollyc@hamiltonnews.com; ed e-mail editor@dundasstarnews.com; web site www.dundasstarnews.com
Circulation: 15,067fr; CMCA
Advertising: Open inch rate $2.24.
Established: 1883.
Parent Co.:
Metroland Media Group Ltd.
TorstarEditions: 52— Dundas Star News
Digital Platform - Mobile: Apple, Android, Windows, Blackberry
Pub... Neil Oliver
Gen. Mgr. .... Jason Pehora
Office Mgr. .... Lorna Lester
Ed .... Debra Downey
Produ Mgr. .... Mike Boyle
Mng Ed .... Gordon Cameron
Dir of Advt..................... Holly Christofilopoulos
Mechanical Specifications: 10 columns x 161 agate lines; same as 10.375" x 11.5"
Delivery Method: Carrier
Areas Served: Dundas

HAMILTON MOUNTAIN NEWS
(Thur)
333 Arvin Ave., Stoney Creek, ON, L8E 2M6, Hamilton, Canada; gen tel (905) 664-8800; gen fax (905) 664-3319; disp adv e-mail hollyc@hamiltonnews.com; ed e-mail gordbowes@hamiltonnews.com; web site www.hamiltonnews.com
Circulation: 49,984fr; CMCA
Advertising: Open inch rate $2.11.
Established: 1968.
Parent Co.:
Metroland Media Group Ltd.
Torstar Corp.Editions: 52— Hamilton News
Digital Platform - Mobile: Apple, Android, Windows, Blackberry
Gen. Mgr. .... Jason Pehora
Managing Editor .... Gordon Cameron
Director of Advertising .. Holly Christofilopoulos
Mechanical Specifications: Full page is 10 columns x 161 agate lines; same as 10.375" x 11.5"
Delivery Method: Carrier
Areas Served: Hamilton

STONEY CREEK NEWS
(Thur)
333 Arvin Ave., Stoney Creek, ON, L8E 2M6, Stoney Creek, Canada; gen tel (905) 664-8800; gen fax (905) 664-3319; disp adv e-mail editor@hamiltonmountainnews.com; ed e-mail editor@stoneycreeknews.com; web site www.stoneycreeknews.com
Circulation: 29,931fr; CMCA
Advertising: Open inch rate $1.79.
Established: 1948.
Parent Co.:
Metroland Media Group Ltd.
TorstarEditions: 52—
Digital Platform - Mobile: Apple, Android, Windows, Blackberry
Pub... Neil Oliver
Gen. Mgr. .... Jason Pehora
Ed. .... Michael Pearson
Mng Ed. .... Gordon Cameron
Produ Mgr. .... Mike Boyle
Adv. Dir......................... Holly Christofilopoulos
Mechanical Specifications: Full page is 10 columns x 161 agate lines; same as 10.375" x 11.5"
Delivery Method: Carrier
Areas Served: Stoney Creek

STRATFORD

STRATFORD GAZETTE
(Thur)
10 Downie St. Unit 207, Stratford, ON, N5A 7K4, Canada; gen tel (519) 271-8002; gen fax (519) 271-5636; disp adv e-mail jhaefling@stratfordgazette.com; class adv e-mail lcarter@stratfordgazette.com; ed e-mail news@stratfordgazette.com; web site www.southwesternontario.ca
Circulation: 19,855fr; CMCA
Parent Co.:
Metroland Media Group Ltd.
Front Office/Distribution ....Laura Carter
Sales Supervisor .... Julie Haefling
Business Manager..................Anita McDonald
Delivery Method: Mail, Carrier
Areas Served: Canada

STRATHROY

THE STRATHROY AGE DISPATCH
(Thur)
73 Front Street West, Strathroy, ON, N7G 1X6, Canada; gen tel (519) 245-2370; gen fax (519) 245-1647; web site www.strathroyagedispatch.com
Circulation: 1,480pd,; CMCA
Established: 1861.
Parent Co.:
Postmedia Network Inc.
Quebecor Communications, Inc.
Pub..Bev Ponton
Reg. Ed. .... Don Biggs
Equipment & Software: : Hardware — APP/Power Mac, APP/Mac G4; Software — QPS/QuarkXPress 7.5.
Delivery Method: Mail, Carrier, Racks
Areas Served: N7G, NOM, NON, NOL

SUDBURY

JOURNAL LE VOYAGEUR
(Wed)
336 Rue Pine, Suite 302, Sudbury, ON, P3C 1X8, Canada; gen tel (705) 673-3377; gen fax (705) 673-5854; web site www.lavoixdunord.ca
Circulation: 7,157pd, 1,342fr; CMCA
Advertising: Open inch rate $1.16.
Ed. in Chief .... Patrick Breton
Mechanical Specifications: Type page 10 1/4 x 14; E - 5 cols, 2, 1/6 between; A - 10 cols, 1/6 between; C - 10 cols, 1/6 between.
Equipment & Software: : Hardware — APP/Mac;

Software — Adobe/PageMaker 6.5, Claris/Work 4.0, Adobe/Illustrator 7.0, Multi-Ad/Creator 3.5.3, QPS/QuarkXPress.
Delivery Method: Mail, Carrier
Areas Served: Canada

NORTHERN LIFE
(Tues, Thur)
158 Elgin St., Sudbury, ON, P3E 3N5, Canada; gen tel (705) 673-5667; adv tel (705) 673-5667 Ext. 313; ed tel (705) 673-5667 Ext. 337; gen fax (705) 673-4652; disp adv e-mail classify@northernlife.ca; ed e-mail mgentili@sudbury.com; web site www.sudbury.com
Circulation: 5,381pd, 30,024fr; CCAB
Advertising: Open inch rate $2.40.
Established: 1970.
Pub....................................Abbas Homayed
Pres. ....Michael R. Atkins
Managing Ed..................................Mark Gentili
Mechanical Specifications: Type page 10 3/8 x 14; E - 9 cols, between; A - 9 cols, between; C - 9 cols, between.
Areas Served: Canada

TAVISTOCK

TAVISTOCK GAZETTE
(Wed)
119 Woodstock St. S., Tavistock, ON, N0B 2R0, Canada; gen tel (519) 655-2341; adv tel (519) 655-2341; ed tel (519) 655-2341; web site www.tavistock.on.ca
Circulation: 1,178pd, 2fr; CMCA
Advertising: Open inch rate $.67.
Established: 1895.Editions: 49—
Circulation Manager ....Sheri Gladding
Ed. ....William J. Gladding
Equipment & Software: : Hardware — Macintosh; Software — CS4
Delivery Method: Mail, Newsstand
Areas Served: Canada

TECUMSEH

SHORELINE WEEK
(Fri)
1614 Lesperance Rd., Tecumseh, ON, N8N 1X2, Canada; gen tel (519) 735-2080; gen fax (519) 735-2082
Circulation: 17,312fr; CMCA
Advertising: Open inch rate $1.04.
Parent Co.:
Postmedia Network Inc.
CanWest MediaWorks Publications, Inc.
Pub...Dave Calibaba
Mgr., Sales.................................Rusty Wright
Ed. ....William England
Mechanical Specifications: Type page 10 1/4 x 15 1/2; E - 6 cols, 1 1/2, 3/16 between; A - 6 cols, 1 7/10, between; C - 7 cols, 1 3/8, 1/4 between.
Equipment & Software: : Hardware — APP/Mac; Software — QPS/QuarkXPress 4.0.
Areas Served: Canada

THE LAKESHORE NEWS
(Thur)
1116 Lesperance Road, Tecumseh, ON, N8N 1X2, Canada, Canada; gen tel (519) 735-2080; gen fax (519) 735-2082; web site www.facebook.com/Lakeshore-News-285820481600683/?ref=page_internal
Circulation: 9,389fr; VAC
Advertising: Open inch rate $.70.
Established: 1948.
Parent Co.:
Postmedia Network Inc.
CanWest MediaWorks Publications, Inc.
Gen. Mgr. .... Dave Calibaba
Ed. .... Bill Harris
Mechanical Specifications: Type page 10 1/4 x 15; E - 6 cols, 1 9/16, between; A - 6 cols, 1 9/16, between; C - 6 cols, 1 5/16, between.
Equipment & Software: : Hardware — 3-APP/Mac; Software — QPS/QuarkXPress 3.32.
Areas Served: Canada

TERRACE BAY

TERRACE BAY SCHREIBER NEWS
(Tues)
25 Simcoe Plaza, Terrace Bay, ON, P0T 2W0, Canada; gen tel (807) 825-9425; gen fax (807) 825-9458
Circulation: 287pd, 21fr; CMCA
Advertising: Open inch rate $.86.
Reporter/Photographer...........Karen Schaeffer
Pub...Blair Oborne
Edior ....Pamela Behun
Areas Served: Canada

THAMESVILLE

HERALD
(Wed)
105 Elizabeth St, Box 580, Thamesville, ON, N0P 2K0, Canada; gen tel (519) 692-3825
Circulation: 594pd,; CMCA
Advertising: Open inch rate $.40.
Ed. .... Orval Schilbe
Mng. Ed....................................... May Schilbe
Areas Served: Canada

THOROLD

FORT ERIE POST
(Thur)
3300 Merrittville Hwy Unit 1b, Thorold, ON, L2V 4Y6, Canada; gen tel (905) 688-2444; web site www.niagarathisweek.com/fort-erie-on
Parent Co.:
Metroland Media Group Ltd.
Adv. .... Dave Hawkins
Areas Served: Thorold, Ontario

NIAGARA THIS WEEK
(Wed, Thur)
3300 Merrittville Hwy, Unit 1b, Thorold, ON, L2V 4Y6, Canada; gen tel (905) 688-2444; gen fax (905) 688-9272; web site www.niagarathisweek.com
Circulation: 0pd, 87,118fr; CCAB
Advertising: Open inch rate $3.21.
Parent Co.:
Metroland Media Group Ltd.
Torstar
Gen. Mgr. ....David Bos
Adv. Mgr. .... Debbi Koppejan
Editorial Dir. .... Mike Williscraft
Newspaper/Online Adv. .... Dave Hawkins
Areas Served: Canada

THUNDER BAY

THUNDER BAY SOURCE
(Thur)
87 N. Hill St., Thunder Bay, ON, P7A 5V6, Canada; gen tel (807) 346-2650; adv tel (807) 346-2510; gen fax (807) 345-9923; web site www.tbnewswatch.com
Circulation: 43,740fr; CMCA
Advertising: Open inch rate $1.68.
Established: 1976.
Parent Co.:
T.Bay Post Inc
Digital Platform - Mobile: Apple, Android, Windows
Mng. Ed...................................... Leith Dunick
Reporter ....Doug Diaczuk
Reporter .... Matt Vis
Content editor ....Nicole Dixon
Equipment & Software: : Hardware — CS; Software — QPS/QuarkXPress 8.1.6, Adobe/Acrobat 4.0, Adobe/Photoshop 6.0, Adobe/Illustrator 9.
Delivery Method: Carrier
Areas Served: P7A, P7B, P7C, P7E

TILBURY

THE TILBURY TIMES
(Tues)
40 Queen St. S., Tilbury, ON, N0P 2L0, Canada; gen tel (519) 682-0411; ed tel (519) 809-4347; gen fax (519) 682-3633; disp adv e-mail dbarnwell@tilburytimes.com; class adv e-mail dbarnwell@tilburytimes.com; ed e-mail gharvieux@tilburytimes.com
Circulation: 863pd, 50fr; CMCA
Advertising: Open inch rate $.65.
Established: 1883.
Parent Co.:
Postmedia Network Inc.
Pub... Bob Thwaites
Ed. ....Gerry Harvieux
Mechanical Specifications: Type page 10 1/4 x 15 1/2; E - 6 cols, 1 1/2, 3/16 between; A - 6 cols, 1 7/10, between; C - 7 cols, 1 3/8, 1/4 between.
Equipment & Software: : Hardware — APP/Mac; Software — QPS/QuarkXPress 4.0.
Areas Served: N0P, N0R

TILLSONBURG

THE TILLSONBURG NEWS
(Fri)
25 Townline Rd., Tillsonburg, ON, N4G 4H6, Canada; gen tel (519) 688-6397; adv tel (519) 688-4400; gen fax (519) 842-3511; web site www.tillsonburgnews.com
Circulation: 1,173pd,; CMCA
Advertising: Open inch rate $1.02.
Parent Co.:
Postmedia Network Inc.
Quebecor Communications, Inc.
Pub..Michael Walsh

TIMMINS

TIMMINS TIMES
(Thur)
815 Pine St. S., Timmins, ON, P4N 8S3, Canada, Canada; gen tel (705) 268-6252; gen fax (705) 268-2255; web site www.timminstimes.com
Circulation: 16,325fr; CMCA
Advertising: Open inch rate $.96.
Parent Co.:
Postmedia Network Inc.
Quebecor Communications, Inc.
Pub...Wayne Major
Ed. .... Len Gillis
Regional Managing Editor.......Kevin Anderson
Mechanical Specifications: Type page 10 x 14 1/4; E - 6 cols, 1 3/4, 1/8 between; A - 6 cols, 1 3/4, 1/8 between; C - 6 cols, 1 3/4, 1/8 between.
Equipment & Software: : Hardware — APP/Mac; Software — Adobe/PageMaker 6.0, QPS/QuarkXPress 4.0, Adobe/Illustrator 6.0, Adobe/Photoshop 4.0.
Areas Served: Canada

TOBERMORY

THE BRUCE PENINSULA PRESS
(Tues)
39 Legion St., Tobermory, ON, N0H 2R0, Canada; gen tel (519) 596-2658; gen fax (519) 596-8030; web site www.brucepeninsulapress.com
Circulation: 400pd, 2,235fr; CMCA
Pub. ....John Francis
Production Mgr./Signs ....Scott McFarlane
Editor ....Marianne Wood
Areas Served: Canada

TORONTO

ANGLICAN JOURNAL
(Mthly)
80 Hayden Street, Toronto, ON, M4Y 3G2, Canada; gen tel (416) 924-9199; adv tel (226) 664-0350; disp adv e-mail advertising@national.anglican.ca; ed e-mail editor@anglicanjournal.com; web site www.anglicanjournal.com
Circulation: 123,352pd, 1,200fr; Sworn/Estimate/Non-Audited
Established: 1875.
Delivery Method: Mail
Areas Served: Toronto, ON M4Y 32

ANNEX GUARDIAN
(Fri)
One River View Garden, Toronto, ON, M6S 4E4, Canada; gen tel (416) 493-4400; gen fax (416) 767-4880; disp adv e-mail salesinfo@insidetoronto.com; class adv e-mail classifieds@metroland.com; ed e-mail gbalogiannis@insidetoronto.com; web site www.insidetoronto.ca
Circulation: 55,500fr; Sworn/Estimate/Non-Audited
Advertising: Open inch rate $3.19.
Parent Co.:
Torstar
Ed ....Grace Peacock
Sales Dir..................................Meriel Bradley

BEACH-RIVERDALE MIRROR
(Thur)
100 Tempo Ave., Toronto, ON, M2H 2N8, Canada; gen tel (416) 493-4400; gen fax (416) 493-6190; disp adv e-mail salesinfo@insidetoronto.com; class adv e-mail classifieds@metroland.com; ed e-mail newsroom@insidetoronto.com; web site www.insidetoronto.ca
Circulation: 0pd, 22,241fr; CCAB
Parent Co.:
Metroland Media Group Ltd.
Torstar
Pub ....Betty Carr
Gen. Mgr. .... Marg Middleton
Adv. Rep ....Meriel Bradley
Areas Served: Canada

BLOOR WEST VILLAGER
(Thur)
2323 Bloor St. W, Toronto, ON, M6S 4W1, Canada; gen tel (416) 675-4390; gen fax (416) 767-4880; disp adv e-mail mbradley@metroland.com; ed e-mail gpeacock@insidetoronto.com; web site www.insidetoronto.com
Circulation: 0pd, 39,948fr; CCAB
Advertising: Open inch rate $3.19.
Parent Co.:
Metroland Media Group Ltd.
Torstar
Pub...Betty Carr
Adv. Dir...................................Meriel Bradley
Ed ....Grace Peacock
Areas Served: Canada

CITY CENTRE MIRROR
(Thur)
175 Gordon Baker Rd., Toronto, ON, M2H 2S6, Canada; gen tel (416) 774-2367; gen fax (416) 493-6190; disp adv e-mail mbradley@metroland.com; class adv e-mail classifieds@metroland.com; ed e-mail newsroom@insidetoronto.com; web site www.insidetoronto.com
Circulation: 0pd, 25,186fr; CCAB
Parent Co.:
Metroland Media Group Ltd.
Managing Ed. ....Antoine Tedesco
Areas Served: Canada

L'EXPRESS
(Tues)
17 Carlaw Ave., Toronto, ON, M4M 2R6, Canada; gen tel (416) 465-2107; gen fax (416) 465-3778; web site www.lexpress.to
Circulation: 20,000pd, 15,000fr; Sworn/Estimate/Non-Audited
Advertising: Open inch rate $6.27.
Pub...Jean Mazare
Adv. Mgr. ....Akli Iiu
Circ. Mgr............................ Marianne Santhan
Ed. ....Francois Bergeron
Areas Served: Toronto, ON

NORTH YORK MIRROR
(Thur)
100 Tempo Ave., Toronto, ON, M2H 2N8, Canada; gen tel (416) 493-4400; gen fax (416) 495-6629; disp adv e-mail sales@insidetoronto.com; web site www.insidetoronto.com
Circulation: 0pd, 92,500fr; CCAB
Advertising: Open inch rate $5.68.
Established: 1957.
Parent Co.:
Metroland Media Group Ltd.
TorstarEditions: 3— 3 total Ã £&-pound; Downsview (41,098); Willowdale (38,516); York Mills/Don Mills (22,386);
V.P. ....Betty Carr
Gen. Mgr. ....Marg Middleton
Sales Rep. ....Dmitry Borovik
Sales Rep. ....Angela Carruthers
Mng. Ed.....................................Paul Futhey
Dir. Adv. ....Stacey Allen
Mechanical Specifications: Type page 10 3/8 x 14; E - 9 cols, 1 1/16, between; A - 9 cols, 1 1/16, between; C - 9 cols, 1 1/16, between.
Equipment & Software: : Hardware — APP/Mac; Presses — G/Urbanite, G/Metroliner; Software — QPS/QuarkXPress 3.32.
Delivery Method: Carrier
Areas Served: Canada

THE BULLETIN - JOURNAL OF DOWNTOWN TORONTO
(Other) (Printed 4th Monday each month, in mail by next Thur.)
260 Adelaide St E Ste 121, Toronto, ON, M5A 1N1, Canada; gen tel (416) 929-0011; adv tel (416) 929-0011 ext. 5 ; ed tel (416) 929-0011 ext. 3; gen fax (416) 929-0011; adv fax (416) 929-0011; ed fax (416) 929-0011 ext. 3; disp adv e-mail sales@thebulletinca; class adv e-mail classified@thebulletin.ca; ed e-mail deareditor@thebulletin.ca; web site www.thebulletin.ca
Circulation: 49,822fr; CMCA
Advertising: $5.52/line grooss, $.4.69/line net.
Established: 1998.
Parent Co.:
Community Bulletin Newspaper Group, Inc.
Digital Platform - Mobile: Apple, Android
Digital Platform - Tablet: Apple iOS, Android, Blackberry Tablet OS, Kindle Fire
Pub...Paulette Touby
Ed...Frank Touby
Mng Ed. ....Anisa Lancione
Mechanical Specifications: Broadsheet on super-calendar glossy stock.
CMYK throughout.
Width x Height:
6 ea.columns with 5-3/8" gutters over 9.5" print width x 19" height
Folded for mail via Canada Post to 5" x 22"
In racks at 11" x 10.5"
Equipment & Software: ; Software — Quark Xpress
InDesign
PhotoShop
Delivery Method: Mail, Newsstand, Carrier, Racks
Areas Served: Canada
Note: The Bulletin covers editorially and is mailed free to all households and many businesses in a large area of Downtown Toronto which includes 14 distinct neighbourhoods.

THE PARKDALE VILLAGER
(Thur)
175 Gordon Baker Rd, Toronto, ON, M2H 2S6, Canada; gen tel (416) 493-4400; adv tel (416) 493-4400; ed tel (416) 774-2367; gen fax (416) 493-6190 ; adv fax (416) 493-6190 ; ed fax (416) 493-6190 ; disp adv e-mail atedesco@insidetoronto.com; ed e-mail atedesco@insidetoronto.com; web site www.parkdaleliberty.ca
Circulation: 24,917fr; CCAB
Parent Co.:
Metroland Media Group Ltd.
Digital Platform - Mobile: Apple, Android, Blackberry
Digital Platform - Tablet: Apple iOS, Android, Blackberry Tablet OS
Pub.. Ian Proudfoot
Mng. Ed...................................Antoine Tedesco
Delivery Method: Mail, Racks
Areas Served: Canada

THE SCARBOROUGH MIRROR
(Thur, Fri)
100 Tempo Ave., Toronto, ON, M2H 2N8, Canada, Canada; gen tel (416) 493-4400; gen fax (416) 495-6629; web site www.insidetoronto.com
Circulation: 120,532fr; CCAB
Advertising: Open inch rate $4.62.
Parent Co.:
Metroland Media Group Ltd.
TorstarEditions: 3— 3 total ½ East (35,049); North (32,217); South (42,734);
Vice Pres./Grp. Pub. ....Betty Carr
Gen. Mgr. ....Marg Middleton
Regl. Mgr., HR ....Kelly Atkinson
Dir., Bus. Admin. ....Bruce Espey
Regl. Dir, Adv. ....Tim Corcoran
Sales Rep. ....Kayland McCully
Sales Rep. ....Frank Li
Sales Rep. ....Shauna Paolucci
Sales Rep. ....Cathie Orban
Sales Rep. ....Leema Williams
Sales Rep. ....Michelle King
Mng. Ed.......................................Al Shackleton
Dir., Prodn....................................Dave Burnett
Prodn. Mgr. ....Katherine Bernal
Mechanical Specifications: Type page 10 3/8 x 14; E - 9 cols, 1 1/16, between; A - 9 cols, 1 1/16, between; C - 9 cols, 1 1/16, between.
Equipment & Software: : Hardware — APP/Mac; Presses — G/Urbanite, G/Metroliner; Software — QPS/QuarkXPress 3.32.
Areas Served: Canada

THE YORK GUARDIAN
(Thur)
100 Tempo Ave., Toronto, ON, M2H 2N8, Canada, Canada; gen tel (416) 493-4400; gen fax (416) 495-6629; web site www.insidetoronto.com
Circulation: 28,544fr; CCAB
Advertising: Open inch rate $1.56.
Parent Co.:
Metroland Media Group Ltd.
Torstar
Pub...Betty Carr
Gen. Mgr. ....Marg Middleton
Adv. Mgr. ....Tim Corcoran
Circ. Mgr.......................................Jaime Munoz
Mng. Ed...Paul Futhey
Mechanical Specifications: Type page 10 3/8 x 14; E - 9 cols, 1 1/16, between; A - 9 cols, 1 1/16, between; C - 9 cols, 1 1/16, between.
Equipment & Software: : Hardware — APP/Mac; Presses — G/Urbanite, G/Metroliner; Software — QPS/QuarkXPress 3.32.
Areas Served: Canada

TRENTON

THE COMMUNITY PRESS
(Thur)
41 Quinte St., Trenton, ON, K8V 5R3, Canada; gen tel (613) 395-3015; gen fax (613) 392-0505; ed e-mail editor@community-press-online.com; web site www.communitypress.ca
Circulation: 0pd, 45,644fr; CMCA
Advertising: Open inch rate $.94.
Pub...John Knowles
Gen. Mgr ....Chuck Parker
Mng. Ed...Ross Lees
News Ed. ....John Campbell
Mechanical Specifications: Type page 10 1/4 x 15; E - 9 cols, 1 1/36, 1/8 between; A - 9 cols, 1 1/36, 1/8 between; C - 6 cols, 1 7/12, 1/8 between.
Equipment & Software: : Hardware — APP/Mac G4; Software — Adobe/Photoshop 6.0, Creator 6.0, Adobe/InDesign 1.52, QPS/QuarkXPress 4.0, Adobe/Illustrator 9.0.
Areas Served: Canada

TRENTONIAN
(Thur)
41 Quinte St., Trenton, ON, K8V 5R3, Canada; gen tel (613) 392-6501; gen fax (613) 392-0505; disp adv e-mail advertising@trentonia.ca; ed e-mail newsroom@trentonian.ca; web site www.trentonian.ca
Circulation: 15,084fr; CMCA
Advertising: Open inch rate $1.06.
Parent Co.:
Postmedia Network Inc.
Quebecor Communications, Inc.
Pub...John Knowles
Adv. Mgr. ....Rachel Henry
Circ. Mgr...Tim Devine
Mng. Ed..Ross Lees
Prodn. Mgr. ....Sherin Tyson

TWEED

THE TWEED NEWS
(Wed)
242 Victoria St. N., Tweed, ON, K0K 3J0, Municpality of Tweed, Canada; gen tel (613) 478-2017; adv tel (613) 478-2699; ed tel (613) 478-2017; gen fax (613) 478-2749; adv fax (613) 478-2749; ed fax (613) 478-2749; disp adv e-mail info@thetweednews.ca; class adv e-mail info@thetweednews.ca; ed e-mail info@thetweednews.ca; web site www.thetweednews.ca
Circulation: 796pd, 42fr; CMCA
Advertising: $10.50 per column inch.
Established: 1887.
Circ. Mgr..............................Roseann Trudeau
Ed./Pub. ....Rodger Hanna
Mechanical Specifications: Type page 12 3/4 x 21; E - 6 cols, 2, 1/4 between; A - 6 cols, 2, 1/4 between; C - 6 cols, 2, 1/4 between.
Equipment & Software: : Hardware — APP/Mac; Software — QPS/QuarkXPress.
Delivery Method: Mail, Racks
Areas Served: Municpality of Tweed

UXBRIDGE

UXBRIDGE TIMES-JOURNAL
(Thur)
16 Bascom St., Uxbridge, ON, L9P 1J3, Canada; gen tel (905) 852-9141; gen fax (905) 852-9341; web site www.durhamregion.com
Circulation: 0pd, 8,825fr; CCAB
Advertising: Open inch rate $1.20.
Established: 1869.
Parent Co.:
Metroland Media Group Ltd.
Torstar
Pub...Tim Whittaker
Adv. Mgr. ....Judy Pirone
Ed. in Chief ....Joanne Burghardt
Ed. ....Judi Bobbitt
Areas Served: Canada

VANKLEEK HILL

THE REVIEW
(Wed)
76 Main St. E., Vankleek Hill, ON, K0B 1R0, Champlain Township, Canada; gen tel (613) 678-3327; gen fax (613) 937-2591; adv fax (613) 937-2591; ed fax (613) 937-2591; disp adv e-mail ads@thereview.ca; class adv e-mail classifieds@thereview.ca; ed e-mail editor@thereview.ca; web site www.thereview.ca
Circulation: 2,785pd, 727fr; CMCA
Advertising: Open inch rate $.74.
Established: 1893.
Classified Adv. Mgr................Irene Sensyzcyzn
Ed. ....Louise Sproule
Prodn. Mgr. ....Suzanne Tessier
Accounts......................................Diane Duval
Advertising Sales.............Shirley Shuberynski
Reporters/Photographer......Theresa Ketterling
Advertising Sales.........................Tara Kirkpatrick
Website Designer .... Sharon Graves-McRae
Graphic Designer.....................Dorothy Hodge
Mechanical Specifications: Type page 15 x 22 3/4; E - 8 cols, 1 1/2, 3/8 between; A - 8 cols, 1 1/2, 3/8 between; C - 8 cols, 1 1/2, 3/8 between.
Equipment & Software: : Hardware — PC; Software — InDesign, Photoshop, Word
Delivery Method: Mail, Newsstand
Areas Served: Champlain Township

VAUGHAN

VAUGHAN CITIZEN
(Thur)
8611 Weston Rd Unit 29, Vaughan, ON, L4L 9P1, Canada; gen tel (905) 264-8703; adv tel (905) 264-8703; ed tel (905) 264-8703; gen fax (905) 264-9453; adv fax (905) 264-9453; ed fax (905) 264-9453; disp adv e-mail gpaolucci@yrmg.com; ed e-mail dkelly@yrmg.com; web site www.yorkregion.com
Circulation: 57,814fr; CMCA
Parent Co.:
Metroland Media Group Ltd.
Digital Platform - Mobile: Apple, Android
Digital Platform - Tablet: Apple iOS, Android
Vice Pres./Reg. Pub................... Ian Proudfoot
Ed. in Chief .... Debora Kelly
Reg. Gen. Mgr.............................John Willems
Delivery Method: Mail, Racks
Areas Served: Maple, Woodbridge, Concord, and Kleinburg

VIRGIL

THE NIAGARA ADVANCE
(Thur)
1501 Niagara Stone Rd., Virgil, ON, L0S 1T0, Canada, Canada; gen tel (905) 468-3283; gen fax (905) 468-3137; web site www.niagaraadvance.ca
Circulation: 20pd, 7,610fr; CMCA
Advertising: Open inch rate $.98.
Established: 1917.
Parent Co.:
Postmedia Network Inc.
Quebecor Communications, Inc.
Pub...Tim Dundas
Ed. ....Penny Coles
Delivery Method: Carrier
Areas Served: Canada

WALKERTON

WALKERTON HERALD-TIMES
(Thur)
10 Victoria St. N., Walkerton, ON, N0G 2V0, Brockton, Canada; gen tel (519) 881-1600; gen fax (519) 881-0276; disp adv e-mail ads@walkerton.com; web site www.walkerton.com
Circulation: 1,296pd, 3fr; CMCA
Advertising: Open inch rate $.53.
Established: 1861.
Parent Co.:
Metroland Media Group Ltd.
Torstar
Adv. Sales Mgr.................................April Wells
Circ. Mgr.......................................Cathy Spitzig
Ed. ....John McPhee
Delivery Method: Mail, Newsstand
Areas Served: Brockton

WASAGA BEACH

THE WASAGA SUN
(Thur)
1456 Mosley St., Wasaga Beach, ON, L9Z 2B9, Canada; gen tel (705) 429-1688; gen fax (705) 422-2446; web site www.wasagasun.ca
Circulation: 8,168fr; CMCA
Advertising: Open inch rate $1.12.
Parent Co.:
Torstar
Adv. Mgr. ....Christine Brown
Pub..Joe Anderson
Gen. Mgr. ....Catherine Haller
Ed. ....Scott Woodhouse
Mng. Ed.....................................Craig Widdifield
Prodn. Mgr. ....Stephen Hall
Mechanical Specifications: Type page 11 1/2 x

21 1/2; E - 6 cols, 1 3/4, 1/6 between; A - 6 cols, 1 3/4, 1/6 between; C - 6 cols, 1 3/4, 1/6 between.

WATERDOWN

THE FLAMBOROUGH REVIEW

(Thur)
30 Main St. N., Waterdown, ON, L0R 2H0, Canada; gen tel (905) 689-2003; adv tel (905) 689-2003 ext. 272; ed tel (905) 689-2003 ext. 321; gen fax (905) 689-3110; disp adv e-mail tlindsay@burlingtonpost.com; ed e-mail editor@flamboroughreview.com; web site www.flamboroughreview.com
Circulation: 21pd, 13,999fr; CCAB
Advertising: Modualr Advertising Rates Available.
Established: 1918.
Parent Co.:
Metroland Media Group Ltd.
Torstar
Pub.......................... Neil Oliver
Adv. Mgr.......................... Ted Lindsay
Circ. Mgr.......................... Charlene Hall
Ed.......................... Brenda Jefferies
Advertising Director.......................... Debbi Koppejan
Equipment & Software: : Hardware — 7-APP/Mac; Software — QPS/QuarkXPress 4.0, Adobe/Photoshop 5.0, Adobe/Illustrator.
Delivery Method: Carrier
Areas Served: Canada

WATERLOO

WATERLOO CHRONICLE

(Thur)
279 Weber St. N., Ste. 20, Waterloo, ON, N2J 3H8, Canada; gen tel (519) 886-2830; gen fax (519) 886-9383; ed e-mail editorial@waterloochronicle.ca; web site www.waterloochronicle.ca
Circulation: 29,538fr; CMCA
Advertising: Open inch rate $1.18.
Parent Co.:
Metroland Media Group Ltd.
Torstar
Pub.......................... Peter Winkler
Adv. Mgr., Retail Sales.......................... Gerry Mattice
Ed.......................... Bob Vrbanac
Mechanical Specifications: Type page 10 5/16 x 14 1/4; E - 6 cols, 1 9/16, between; A - 6 cols, 1 9/16, between; C - 8 cols, between.
Equipment & Software: ; Software — QPS/QuarkXPress 4.1.

WATFORD

WATFORD GUIDE-ADVOCATE

(Thur)
5292 Nauvoo Rd., Watford, ON, N0M 2S0, Canada; gen tel (519) 876-2809; gen fax (519) 876-2322
Circulation: 1,919pd,; CMCA
Advertising: Open inch rate $.73.
Established: 1875.
Pub.......................... Dale Hayter
Adv. Mgr.......................... Gill Deschutter
Ed.......................... Stephanie Cattryse
Mechanical Specifications: Type page 10 x 16; E - 6 cols, 1 9/16, 1/8 between; A - 6 cols, 1 9/16, 1/8 between; C - 6 cols, 1 9/16, 1/8 between.
Equipment & Software: : Hardware — APP/Mac; Software — Adobe/PageMaker, Adobe/Photoshop, Adobe/Illustrator, Microsoft/Word.

WAWA

THE ALGOMA NEWS REVIEW

(Wed)
33 St. Marie St., Wawa, ON, P0S 1K0, Canada; gen tel (705) 856-2267; gen fax (705) 856-4952; ed e-mail editor@thealgomanews.ca; web site www.thealgomanews.ca
Circulation: 598pd, 33fr; CMCA
Advertising: Open inch rate $.58.
Established: 1964.
Ed.......................... Tammy Landry
Adv. Mgr.......................... Christel Gignac
Mechanical Specifications: Type page 10 1/4 x 16 1/4; E - 5 cols, 1 15/16, 3/16 between; A - 5 cols, 1 15/16, 3/16 between; C - 5 cols, 1 15/16, 3/16 between.
Equipment & Software: : Hardware — APP/Mac.
Areas Served: Canada

WEST LORNE

CHRONICLE

(Thur)
168 Main St., West Lorne, ON, N0L 2P0, Canada, Canada; gen tel (519) 768-2220; gen fax (519) 768-2221; web site www.thechronicle-online.com
Circulation: 100pd, 5,463fr; CMCA
Advertising: Open inch rate $.93.
Established: 1993.
Parent Co.:
Quebecor Communications, Inc.Bev Ponton
Reg. Managing Ed.......................... Ian McCallum
Mechanical Specifications: Type page 10 1/4 x 15; E - 5 cols, 2, 1/4 between; A - 5 cols, 2, 1/4 between; C - 5 cols, 2, 1/4 between.
Equipment & Software: : Hardware — APP/Mac; Software — Adobe/Illustrator, QPS/QuarkXPress, Adobe/PageMaker 6.5.
Areas Served: Canada

WESTPORT

RIDEAU VALLEY MIRROR

(Thur)
43 Bedfrod St., Westport, ON, K0G 1X0, Canada; gen tel (613) 273-8000; gen fax (613) 273-8001; disp adv e-mail advertising@review-mirror.com; ed e-mail newsroom@review-mirror.com; web site www.review-mirror.com
Circulation: 1,662pd, 57fr; CMCA
Advertising: Open inch rate $.65.
Adv. Mgr.......................... Bill Ritchie
Circ. Mgr.......................... Louise Haughton
Ed.......................... Howie Crichton
Areas Served: Canada

WHEATLEY

SOUTHPOINT SUN

(Wed)
14 Talbot Street West, Wheatley, ON, N0P 2P0, Canada; gen tel (519) 825-4541; gen fax (519) 825-4546; disp adv e-mail journal@mnsi.net; web site www.southpointsun.ca
Circulation: 10,579fr; CMCA
Pub.......................... Jim Heyens
Ed.......................... Sheila McBrayne
Areas Served: Canada

WIARTON

THE WIARTON ECHO

(Tues)
573 Berford St., Wiarton, ON, N0H 2T0, Canada, Canada; gen tel (519) 534-1560; adv tel (519) 534-1563; ed tel (519) 534-1560; gen fax (519) 534-4616; adv fax (519) 534-4616; ed fax (519) 534-4616; disp adv e-mail echoads@bowesnet.com; ed e-mail wiartonecho@bmts.com; web site www.wiartonecho.com
Circulation: 1,361pd, 6fr; CMCA
Advertising: Open inch rate $.65.
Established: 1879.
Parent Co.:
Postmedia Network Inc.
Quebecor Communications, Inc.
Ed.......................... Keith Gilbert
Equipment & Software: ; Software — QPS/QuarkXPress 4.0.
Areas Served: Canada

WILLOWDALE

THE EAST YORK MIRROR

(Thur)
10 Tempo Ave., Willowdale, ON, M2H 3S5, Canada; gen tel (413) 493-4400; gen fax (413) 495-6629; web site www.metroland.com
Circulation: 0pd, 34,643fr; CCAB
Advertising: Open inch rate $4.04.
Established: 1995.
Parent Co.:
Metroland Media Group Ltd.
Torstar
Pub.......................... Betty Carr
Gen. Mgr.......................... Marg Middleton
Adv. Dir.......................... Stacey Allen
Sales Rep.......................... Paris Quinn
Circ. Mgr.......................... Kim Buenting
Ed.......................... Deborah Bodine
Mng. Ed.......................... Alan Shackleton
Prodn. Mgr.......................... Katherine Bernal
Prodn. Dir.......................... Dave Barnett
Mechanical Specifications: Type page 10 3/8 x 14; E - 9 cols, 1 1/16, between; A - 9 cols, 1 1/16, between; C - 9 cols, 1 1/16, between.
Equipment & Software: : Hardware — APP/Mac; Presses — G/Urbanite, G/Metroliner; Software — QPS/QuarkXPress 3.32.
Areas Served: Canada

WINCHESTER

WINCHESTER PRESS

(Wed)
545 St. Lawrence St., Winchester, ON, K0C 2K0, Canada, Canada; gen tel (613) 774-2524; gen fax (613) 774-3967; disp adv e-mail advert@winchesterpress.on.ca; ed e-mail news@winchesterpress.on.ca; web site www.winchesterpress.on.ca
Circulation: 2,646pd, 342fr; CMCA
Advertising: Open line rate $0.79.
Established: 1888.
Owner/Pres.......................... Beth Morris
Adv. Mgr./Co. Pub.......................... Donna Rushford
Mechanical Specifications: Type page 13 x 21 1/2; E - 6 cols, 2 1/12, 3/4 between; A - 6 cols, 2 1/12, 3/4 between; C - 6 cols, 2 1/12, 3/4 between.
Equipment & Software: : Hardware — APP/Mac, PC; Software — Multi-Ad, WordPerfect, Word Star, QPS/QuarkXPress.
Delivery Method: Mail, Racks
Areas Served: Canada

WINDSOR

LE REMPART

(Wed)
7515 Forest Glade Dr., Windsor, ON, N8T 3P5, Canada, Canada; gen tel (519) 948-4139; gen fax (519) 948-0628; web site www.lerempart.ca
Circulation: 5,735pd, 802fr; CMCA
Advertising: Open inch rate $1.00.
Established: 1966.
Pub.......................... Dennis Poirier
Gen. Mgr.......................... Christiane Beaupre
Dir., sales.......................... Richard Caumartin
Mechanical Specifications: Type page 10 x 15 5/8; E - 5 cols, 2, 1/6 between; A - 5 cols, 2, 1/6 between.
Equipment & Software: : Hardware — IBM, Pentium/PC; Software — Aldus/PageMaker 6.5.
Areas Served: Canada

WINGHAM

THE WINGHAM ADVANCE-TIMES

(Wed)
11 Veterans Rd., Wingham, ON, N0G 2W0, Canada; gen tel (519) 357-2320; gen fax (519) 357-2900; ed e-mail pkerr@wingham.com; web site www.wingham.com
Circulation: 862pd,; CMCA
Advertising: Open inch rate $.59.
Parent Co.:
Metroland Media Group Ltd.
Torstar
Adv. Mgr.......................... Sandy Woodcock
Ed.......................... Bill Huether
Prodn. Mgr.......................... Dave Russell

WOODSTOCK

THE INGERSOLL TIMES

(Wed)
16 Brock Street, Woodstock, ON, N4S 3B4, Canada; gen tel (519) 537-2341; disp adv e-mail cwetton@postmedia.com; class adv e-mail hbrubacher@postmedia.com; ed e-mail jvandermeer@postmedia.com; web site www.ingersolltimes.com
Circulation: 500pd,; CMCA
Established: 1969.
Parent Co.:
Postmedia Network Inc.
Quebecor Communications, Inc.
Ed.......................... Jennifer Vandermeer
Group Dir., Media Sales.......................... Ian Dowding
Media sales.......................... Claire Wetton
Delivery Method: Mail, Newsstand, Carrier
Areas Served: Canada

THE NORWICH GAZETTE

(Wed)
16 Brock Street, Woodstock, ON, N4S 3B4, Canada; gen tel (519) 537-2341; disp adv e-mail tleake@postmedia.com; class adv e-mail hbrubacher@postmedia.com; ed e-mail jennifer.vandermeer@sunmedia.ca; web site www.norwichgazette.ca
Circulation: 822pd,; CMCA
Established: 1876.
Parent Co.:
Postmedia Network Inc.
Ed.......................... Jennifer Vandermeer
Group Director, Media Sales.......................... Ian Dowding
Media sales.......................... Tara Leake
Media sales.......................... John Macintosh
Classified sales.......................... Heidi Brubacher
Circ.......................... Beth Faulkner
Delivery Method: Mail, Newsstand
Areas Served: Canada

PRINCE EDWARD ISLAND

ALBERTON

WEST PRINCE GRAPHIC

(Wed)
4 Railway St., Alberton, PE, C0B 1B0, Canada; gen tel (902) 853-3320; gen fax (902) 853-3071; ed e-mail cindy@peicanada.com; web site www.peicanada.com
Circulation: 121pd, 5,733fr; CMCA
Advertising: Open inch rate $.70.
Established: 1980.
Pub.......................... Paul MacNeill
Adv. Mgr.......................... Jan MacNeill
Circ. Mgr.......................... Nicole Ford
Ed.......................... Cindy Chant
Mechanical Specifications: Type page 13 x 21 1/3.

MONTAGUE

ATLANTIC POST CALLS

(Fri)
567 Main Street, Montague, PE, C0A 1R0, Canada; gen tel (902) 838-2515; adv tel (902) 838-4392 Ext. 203; ed tel (902) 838-2515 x 201; gen fax (902) 838-4392; adv

fax (902) 838-4392; ed fax (902) 838-4392; disp adv e-mail jan@peicanada.com; ed e-mail paul@peicanada.com; web site www.peicanada.com
Circulation: 752pd, 625fr; CMCA
Established: 1979.Paul MacNeill
Jan MacNeill
Areas Served: Canada

THE EASTERN GRAPHIC
(Wed)
567 Main St., Montague, PE, C0A 1R0, Canada; gen tel (902) 838-2515; gen fax (902) 838-4392; ed e-mail editor@peicanada.com; web site www.peicanada.com
Circulation: 4,743pd, 196fr; CMCA
Advertising: Open inch rate $.85.
Pub....Paul MacNeill
Adv. Mgr....Jan MacNeill
Ed....Heather Moore
Prodn. Coord....Kim Madigan
Mechanical Specifications: Type page 13 x 21 1/2; E - 6 cols, 2, between; A - 6 cols, 2, between; C - 6 cols, 2, between.
Equipment & Software: : Hardware — APP/Mac; Software — QPS/QuarkXPress.
Areas Served: Canada

SUMMERSIDE

LA VOIX ACADIENNE
(Wed)
5, Ave Maris Stella, Summerside, PE, C1N 6M9, Canada; gen tel (902) 436-6005; gen fax (902) 888-3976; disp adv e-mail pub@lavoixacadienne.com; ed e-mail texte@lavoixacadienne.com; web site www.lavoix-acadienne.com
Circulation: 1,517pd, 20fr; ODC
Advertising: Open inch rate $1.15.
Established: 1976.
Dir. Gen....Marcia Enman
Ed....Jacinthe Laforest
Mechanical Specifications: Type page 10 1/4 x 12 1/2; E - 5 cols, between; A - 5 cols, between.
Equipment & Software: : Hardware — APP/Mac; Software — Microsoft/Word 98, Adobe/PageMaker 6.5, Macromedia/Freehand 9, Claris/FileMaker Pro 4.1, Adobe/Acrobat Reader 4.0, Adobe/Photoshop 6, Adobe/Illustrator 9.
Areas Served: all provinces of Canada

QUEBEC

ACTON VALE

LA PENSEE DE BAGOT
(Wed)
800 Roxton St., Acton Vale, QC, J0H 1A0, Canada; gen tel (450) 546-3271; gen fax (450) 546-3491; web site www.lapensee.qc.ca
Circulation: 0pd, 0fr; CCAB
Advertising: Open inch rate $.73.
Established: 1951.
Adv. Mgr....Michel Dorais
Adv. Rep....Robert Beauchemin
Adv. Rep....Jean-Francois Dorais
Ed....Benoit Chartier
Mechanical Specifications: Type page 11 1/2 x 15; E - 8 cols, 1 1/4, 1/6 between; A - 8 cols, 1 1/4, 1/6 between; C - 8 cols, 1 1/4, 1/6 between.
Equipment & Software: : Hardware — APP/Mac; Software — QPS/QuarkXPress.
Areas Served: Canada

ALMA

LE LAC ST. JEAN
(Wed)
100 St. Joseph St., Locale 01, Alma, QC, G8B 7A6, Canada; gen tel (418) 668-4545; gen fax (418) 668-8522; web site www.lelac-stjean.com
Circulation: 80pd, 23,534fr; CCAB
Advertising: Open inch rate $1.14.
Parent Co.:
Transcontinental Media
Gen. Mgr....Michelle Dupont
Areas Served: Canada

AMOS

CITOYEN DE L'HARRICANA
(Wed)
92 Rue Principale Sud, Amos, QC, J9T 2J6, Canada; gen tel (819)732-6531; gen fax (819) 732-3764; disp adv e-mail manon.poirier@quebecormedia.com; ed e-mail caroline.couture@quebecormedia.com; web site www.lechoabitibien.ca
Circulation: 19pd, 11,238fr; CCABCaroline Couture
Areas Served: Canada

AMQUI

L'AVANT-POSTE GASPESIEN
(Wed)
217 Leonidas Ave., Amqui, QC, G5J 2B8, Canada; gen tel (418) 629-3443; gen fax (418)562-4607; disp adv e-mail gaby.veilleux@hebdosquebecor.com; ed e-mail lucie-rose.levesque@hebdosquebecor.com; web site lavantposte.ca
Circulation: 22pd, 16,881fr; CCAB
Advertising: Open inch rate $.79.
Parent Co.:
Quebecor Communications, Inc.
Regl. Dir. Gen....Alain St-Amand
Dir. Gen....Francis Desrosiers
Ed....Lucy-Rose Levesque
Areas Served: Canada

ASBESTOS

LES ACTUALITES
(Wed)
572 1st Ave., Asbestos, QC, J1T 4R4, Canada; gen tel (819) 879-6681; gen fax (819) 879-2355; ed e-mail nathalie.hurdle@quebecormedia.com; web site journallesactualites.ca
Circulation: 4pd, 13,160fr; CCAB
Parent Co.:
Reseau Select/Select Network
Quebecor Communications, Inc.
Digital Platform - Mobile: Blackberry
Ã©ditrice....Carole Pellerin
Mechanical Specifications: Type page 10 1/8 x 11 13/16; E - 10 cols, 5/8 between; A - 10 cols, 5/8 between; C - 10 cols, 5/8 between.
Areas Served: Canada

BAIE COMEAU

MANIC
(Wed)
Rue De Bretagne, Baie Comeau, QC, G5C 1X5, Canada; gen tel (418) 589-9990
Circulation: 4pd, 14,765fr; CCABPaul Brisson
Areas Served: Canada

OBJECTIF PLEIN JOUR
(Wed)
625 Bvd., Lafleche, Ste. 309, Baie Comeau, QC, G5C 1C5, Canada; gen tel (418) 589-5900; gen fax (418) 589-8216; web site www.pleinjourdebaiecomeau.ca
Circulation: 16,435fr; Sworn/Estimate/Non-Audited
Advertising: Open inch rate $.75.
Parent Co.:
Quebecor Communications, Inc.Sebastien Rouillard

PLEIN JOUR DE BAIE COMEAU
(Wed)
625 Bvd., Lafleche, Ste. 309, Baie Comeau, QC, G5C 1C5, Canada; gen tel (418) 589-5900
Circulation: 4pd, 20,578fr; CCABSebastien Rouillard
Areas Served: Canada

PLEIN JOUR SUR MANICOUAGAN
(Wed)
625 Bvd., Lafleche, Ste. 309, Baie Comeau, QC, G5C 1C5, Canada; gen tel (418) 589-5900; gen fax (418) 589-8216; disp adv e-mail atelier.baiecomeau@hebdosquebecor.com; ed e-mail raphael.hovington@hebdosquebecor.com; web site www.pleinjourdebaiecomeau.ca
Circulation: 7pd, 15,628fr; BPA
Advertising: Open inch rate $.84.
Parent Co.:
Quebecor Communications, Inc.Sebastien Rouillard
Areas Served: Canada

BEAUPORT

BEAUPORT EXPRESS
(Fri)
710 Bouvier, Suite 107, Beauport, QC, G2J 1C2, Canada, Canada; gen tel (418) 628-7460; gen fax (418) 622-1511; web site www.beauportexpress.com
Circulation: 11pd, 28,463fr; CCAB
Advertising: Open inch rate $1.21.
Pub....Yvan Rancourt
Ed....Paul Lessard
Prodn. Mgr....Gilles Brault
Mechanical Specifications: Type page 10 x 11 3/4; C - 2 cols, 2, between.
Areas Served: Canada

BEAUPRE

AUTRE VOIX
(Wed)
Boulevard Ste-anne Bureau 101, Bureau 101, Beaupre, QC, G0A 1E0, Canada; gen tel (418) 827-1511
Circulation: 3pd, 13,297fr; CCABLilianne Laprise
Areas Served: Canada

BELOEIL

L'OEIL REGIONAL
(Sat)
393 Laurier Blvd., Beloeil, QC, J3G 4H6, Canada; gen tel (450) 467-1821; gen fax (450) 467-3087; disp adv e-mail publicite@oeilregional.com; ed e-mail redaction@oeilregional.com; web site www.oeilregional.com
Circulation: 8pd, 34,637fr; CCAB
Advertising: Open inch rate $1.02.
Parent Co.:
Reseau Select/Select Network
Les Hebdos MonteregiensSerge Landry
Mechanical Specifications: Type page 10 1/4 x 16 1/2; E - 8 cols, 1 1/6, 1/6 between; A - 8 cols, 1 1/6, 1/6 between; C - 8 cols, 1 1/6, 1/6 between.
Areas Served: Canada

BERTHIERVILLE

PUBLIQUIP
(Sun)
Rue Gilles Villeneuve, Berthierville, QC, J0K 1A0, Canada; gen tel (450) 836-3666
Circulation: 701pd, 50,494fr; ODCFrancoise Trepanier

BOUCHERVILLE

LA RELÃ¨VE
(Tues)
528 St. Charles St., Boucherville, QC, J4B 3M5, Canada; gen tel (450) 641-4844; adv tel (514) 926-2354; gen fax (450) 641-4849; disp adv e-mail c.desmarteau@videotron.ca; class adv e-mail classees@lareleve.qc.ca; ed e-mail lareleve@lareleve.qc.ca; web site www.lareleve.qc.ca
Circulation: 0pd, 58,800fr; Sworn/Estimate/Non-Audited
Advertising: Open inch rate $1.60.
Established: 1987.
Parent Co.:
Groupe MessierEditions: Boucherville / Longueuil Est
Ed. & Gen. Mgr....Charles Desmarteau
Mechanical Specifications: Type page 10 1/4" x 14 1/4".
Areas Served: J4B, J4M, J4N, J4G, J3E, J0L 2S0, J3X, J0L 1N0, J0L 2R0, J0L 1A0

LA SEIGNEURIE
(Wed)
391 Boul. De Mortagne, Boucherville, QC, J4B 3M5, Canada; gen tel (450) 641-4844; gen fax (450) 641-4849; disp adv e-mail lareleve@lareleve.qc.ca; ed e-mail redaction@la-seigneurie.qc.ca; web site www.la-seigneurie.qc.ca
Circulation: 33,856fr; Sworn/Estimate/Non-Audited
Advertising: Open inch rate $.84.
Parent Co.:
La RelÃ¨ve
Pub....Charles Desmarteau
Mechanical Specifications: Type page 10 1/4 x 17; E - 8 cols, between; A - 8 cols, between; C - 8 cols, between.
Equipment & Software: : Hardware — IBM.
Areas Served: Quebec

CAP AUX MEULES

LE RADAR
(Fri)
110 Chemin Gros Cap, Cap Aux Meules, QC, G4T 1R3, Canada; gen tel (418) 986-2345; gen fax (418) 986-6358; ed e-mail redacteur@leradar.qc.ca; web site www.leradar.qc.ca
Circulation: 2,079pd, 2,179fr; AAM
Advertising: Open inch rate $.58.
Parent Co.:
Reseau Select/Select Network
Adv. Mgr....Lucille Tremblay
Circ. Mgr....Francoise Decoste
Ed....Achilles Hubert
Equipment & Software: : Hardware — APP/Mac; Software — QPS/QuarkXPress 4.0.
Areas Served: Canada

CHAMBLY

CHAMBLY EXPRESS
(Tues)
C-1691, Boul Perigny, Chambly, QC, J3L 1X1, Canada; gen tel (450) 658-5559; gen fax (450) 658-1620; web site www.chambly-express.ca
Circulation: 27,037fr; CCAB
Areas Served: Canada

JOURNAL DE CHAMBLY
(Wed)
1685 Bourgogne Ave., Chambly, QC, J3L 4B3, Canada, Canada; gen tel (450) 658-6516; gen fax (450) 658-3785; web site www.journaldechambly.com
Circulation: 5pd, 27,471fr; CCAB
Advertising: Open inch rate $.95.
Parent Co.:
Reseau Select/Select Network
Les Hebdos Monteregiens
Mng. Ed....Daniel Noiseux

Mechanical Specifications: Type page 10 1/4 x 17.
Areas Served: Canada

CHATEAUGUAY

CHATEAUGUAY EXPRESS
(Wed)
69, Boul St-jean-baptiste, 2nd Floor, Chateauguay, QC, J6J 3H6, Canada; gen tel (450) 692-9111; gen fax (450) 692-9192; web site www.chateauguayexpress.ca
Circulation: 40,468fr; CCAB
Areas Served: Canada

LE SOLEIL DU MERCREDI
(Wed, Sat)
82 Salaberry Sud, Chateauguay, QC, J6J 4J6, Canada; gen tel (450) 692-8552; gen fax (450) 692-3460; web site www.montereigieweb.com
Circulation: 11pd, 34,473fr; CCAB
Advertising: Open inch rate $1.00.
Parent Co.:
Les Hebdos Monteregiens
Ed. .... Michel Auclair
Robert Fichaud
Prodn. Mgr. .... Jeanne D'Arc Germain
Areas Served: Canada

LE SOLEIL DU ST-LAURENT
(Wed, Sat)
82 Salaberry St. S., Chateauguay, QC, J6J 4J6, Canada; gen tel (450) 692-8552; gen fax (450) 692-3460; disp adv e-mail publicite@cybersoleil.com; ed e-mail redaction@cybersoleil.com; web site www.cybersoleil.com
Circulation: 32,750fr; Sworn/Estimate/Non-Audited
Advertising: Open inch rate $.97.
Parent Co.:
Les Hebdos Monteregiens
Adv. Rep. .... Diane Cadieux
Adv. Rep. .... Guylaine Mercier
Adv. Rep. .... Yolaine Dorais
Ed. .... Michel Thibault
Ed. .... Carole Gagne
Mechanical Specifications: Type page 11 x 17; E - 5 cols, 2, between; A - 8 cols, 2 1/2, between; C - 8 cols, between.
Equipment & Software: : Hardware — APP/Mac; Software — QPS/QuarkXPress, Adobe/Illustrator.

SOLEIL DU SAMEDI
(Sat)
Rue Salaberry Sud, Chateauguay, QC, J6J 4J6, Canada; gen tel (450) 692-8552
Circulation: 34pd, 31,092fr; CCABJeanne-d'Arc Germain
Areas Served: Canada

COATICOOK

LE PROGRES DE COATICOOK
(Wed)
72 Rue Child, Coaticook, QC, J1A 2B1, Canada; gen tel (819) 849-9846; gen fax (819) 849-1041; web site www.leprogres.net
Circulation: 77pd, 8,782fr; CCAB
Advertising: Open inch rate $0.83.
Parent Co.:
Reseau Select/Select Network
Ed. .... Monique Cote
Areas Served: Canada

COWANSVILLE

LE GUIDE DE COWANSVILLE
(Wed)
121 Rue Principale, Cowansville, QC, J2K 1J3, Canada; gen tel (450) 263-5288; gen fax (450) 263-9435; web site http://www.journalleguide.com/
Circulation: 6pd, 18,340fr; CCAB
Advertising: Open inch rate $.82.
Pub. .... Cathy Bernard
Sec. .... Louise Denicourt
Reg'l Ed. .... Caroline Rioux
Mechanical Specifications: Type page 11 1/4 x 15; C - 8 cols, 1 1/8, 1/8 between.
Areas Served: Canada

DELSON

LE REFLET
(Wed)
11 Rt. 132, Delson, QC, J5B 1G9, Canada; gen tel (450) 635-9146; gen fax (450) 635-4619; disp adv e-mail publicite@lereflet.qc.ca; web site www.lereflet.qc.ca
Circulation: 49,427fr; CCAB
Advertising: Open inch rate $.90.
Parent Co.:
Les Hebdos Monteregiens
Pub./Dir. .... Robert Fichaud
Sales Dir. .... Sandy Roy
Ed. .... Helene Gingras
Areas Served: Canada

DOLBEAU-MISTASSINI

LE NOUVELLES HEBDO
(Wed)
1741 Rue Des Pins, Dolbeau-Mistassini, QC, G8L 1J7, Canada; gen tel (418) 276-6211; adv tel (418) 276-6211; gen fax (418)276-6166; web site http://www.nouvelleshebdo.com/
Circulation: 55pd, 12,594fr; CCABMichel Aub&#65533;
Areas Served: Canada

DONNACONA

COURRIER DE PORTNEUF
(Wed)
276,rue Notre-dame, Donnacona, QC, G3M 1G7, Canada; gen tel (418) 285-0211; gen fax (418) 285-2441; ed e-mail denise.paquin@courrierdeportneuf.com; web site www.courrierdeportneuf.com
Circulation: 31pd, 34,944fr; CCAB
Established: 1982.
adjointe administrative .... Louise Latulippe
Delivery Method: Carrier
Areas Served: Canada

DORVAL

CITES NOUVELLES
(Wed)
455 Boulevard Fenelon, Bureau 303, Dorval, QC, H9S 5T8, Canada; gen tel (514) 636-7314; gen fax (514) 636-7317; web site www.citesnouvelles.com
Circulation: 4pd, 44,286fr; CCAB
Established: 1974.
Parent Co.:
Transcontinental Media
Publisher .... Denis Therrien
Sales Support Supervisor .... Joy-Ann Dempsey
Production manager .... Robert Bourcier
News Director .... Jean Nicolas Aubé
Delivery Method: Carrier, Racks
Areas Served: Canada

LACHINE MESSENGER
(Thur)
455 Boulevard Fenelon, Suite 303, Dorval, QC, H9S 5T8, Canada; gen tel (514) 636-7314; gen fax (514) 363-7315; web site www.messagerlachine.com
Circulation: 20,000fr; Sworn/Estimate/Non-Audited
Advertising: Open inch rate $1.22.
Pub. .... Patricia Ann Beaulieu
Adv. Mgr. .... Tina Lemelin
Ed. .... Robert Leduc

MAGAZINE DE L'ILE-DES-SOEURS
(Wed)
455 Boulevard Fenelon, Dorval, QC, H9S 5T8, Canada; gen tel (514) 636-7314
Circulation: 2pd, 8,226fr; CCABPatricia Ann Beaulieu
Areas Served: Canada

MESSAGER DE LACHINE / DORVAL
(Thur)
455 Boulevard Fenelon, Suite 303, Dorval, QC, H9S 5T8, Canada; gen tel (514) 636-7314; gen fax (514) 636-7315; web site http://www.messagerlachine.com
Circulation: 0pd, 24,993fr; CCABPatria Ann Beaulieu
Areas Served: Canada

MESSAGER DE VERDUN
(Thur)
455 Fenelon Suite 303, 303, Dorval, QC, H9S 5T8, Canada; gen tel (514) 636-7314; gen fax (514) 636-7317; web site www.messagerverdun.com
Circulation: 0pd, 23,936fr; CCABPatricia Ann Beaulieu
Areas Served: Canada

THE CHRONICLE
(Wed)
455 Boulevard Fenelon, Suite 303, Dorval, QC, H9S 5T8, Canada; gen tel (514) 636-7314; gen fax (514) 636-7317; adv fax (514) 636-7317; ed fax (514) 636-7317; web site www.westislandchronicle.com
Circulation: 5pd, 43,393fr; CMCA
Advertising: Open inch rate $1.69.
Established: 1925.
Parent Co.:
Transcontinental Media
General Manager .... Denis Therrien
Sales Support Supervisor .... Joy-Ann Dempsey
Production Manager .... Robert Bourcier
News Director .... Jean Nicolas Aubé
Mechanical Specifications: Type page 11 1/2 x 21 1/4; E - 5 cols, 2 3/16, 1/8 between; A - 10 cols, 1 1/16, 1/8 between; C - 10 cols, 1 1/16, 1/8 between.
Equipment & Software: : Hardware — APP/Mac G3.
Delivery Method: Carrier, Racks
Areas Served: Canada

DRUMMONDVILLE

JOURNAL L'IMPACT DE DRUMMONDVILLE
(Thur)
2345, Rue St-pierre, Drummondville, QC, J2C 5A7, Canada; gen tel (819) 445-7000; gen fax (819) 445-7001; web site www.limpact.ca
Circulation: 4pd, 46,173fr; CCAB
Ed. .... Jean Crepeau
Areas Served: Canada

L'EXPRESS
(Wed, Sun)
1050 Cormier St., Drummondville, QC, J2C 2N6, Canada; gen tel (819) 478-8171; gen fax (819) 478-4306; web site www.journalexpress.ca
Circulation: 11pd, 48,116fr; CCAB
Advertising: Open inch rate $1.26.
Parent Co.:
Transcontinental Media
Ed. .... Johanne Marceau
Areas Served: Canada

LA PAROLE
(Wed)
1050 Rue Cormier, Drummondville, QC, J2C 2N6, Canada, Canada; gen tel (819) 478-8171; gen fax (819) 393-0741; web site www.journalexpress.ca
Circulation: 46,000fr; Sworn/Estimate/Non-Audited
Advertising: Open inch rate $1.40.
Established: 1929.
Parent Co.:
Reseau Select/Select Network
Adv. Dir. .... Eyves Shabot
Ed. .... Johanne Marceau
Areas Served: Canada

EDMUNDSTON

INFO WEEK-END
(Wed)
322 Victoria St., Edmundston, QC, E3V 2H9, Canada; gen tel (506) 739-5083; disp adv e-mail pub@infoweekend.ca; web site journaux.apf.ca/infoweekend
Circulation: 21,550fr; CCAB
Advertising: Open line rate $.77.Michel Chalifour
Areas Served: Canada

EGAN SOUTH

LE GATINEAU
(Thur)
135-b, Highway 105, Egan South, QC, J9E 3A9, Canada; gen tel (819) 449-1725; gen fax (819) 449-5108; ed e-mail redaction@lagatineau.com; web site www.lagatineau.com
Circulation: 11,210fr; CCAB
Advertising: Open inch rate $.66.
Established: 1955.
Executive Director .... Denise Lacourcière
Mechanical Specifications: Type page 10 3/4 x 14 5/16.
Delivery Method: Carrier, Racks
Areas Served: Canada

FARNHAM

JOURNAL L'AVENIR & DES RIVIERES
(Wed)
221 Main St., Farnham, QC, J2N 1L5, Canada; gen tel (450) 293-3138; gen fax (450) 293-2093; web site www.laveniretdesrivieres.com
Circulation: 3pd, 11,442fr; CCAB
Gen. Mgr. .... Renel Bouchard
Pub. .... Elrsa Fournyer
Circ. Mgr. .... Charles Couture
Areas Served: Canada

L'AVENIR DE BROME MISSISQUOI, INC.
(Wed)
221 Rue Principale Est., Farnham, QC, J2N 1L5, Canada; gen tel (450) 293-3138; gen fax (450) 293-2093; ed e-mail cassandra.deblois@tc.tc; web site www.laveniretdesrivieres.com
Circulation: 34pd, 8,554fr; Sworn/Estimate/Non-Audited
Advertising: Open inch rate $.66.
Pub. .... Group le Canada Francais

FERMONT

LE TRAIT D'UNION DU NORD
(Mon) (Every other mon)
850 Place Daviault, Fermont, QC, G0G 1J0, Canada; gen tel (418) 287-3655; gen fax (418) 287-3874; disp adv e-mail publicite@journaltdn.ca; class adv e-mail publicite@journaltdn.ca; ed e-mail redaction@journaltdn.ca; web site www.journaltdn.ca
Circulation: 1,700fr; Sworn/Estimate/Non-Audited
Advertising: Open inch rate $.47.
Established: 1983.
Ed. .... Eric Cyr
Graphic & Adv. Consultant .... Lynda Raiche

FORESTVILLE

JOURNAL HAUTE COTE-NORD
(Wed)
100-31 Rte. 138, Forestville, QC, G0T 1E0, Canada, Canada; gen tel (418) 587-2090; gen fax (418) 587-6407; web site www.journalhautecotenord.com
Circulation: 20pd, 5,510fr; CCAB
Advertising: Open inch rate $.62.
Pub. .... Luc Brisson
Sec. ....Guylaine Boulianne
Mng. Ed. .... Shirley Kennedy
Mechanical Specifications: Type page 11 x 17; E - 8 cols, between; A - 8 cols, between.
Areas Served: Canada

GASPE

HAVRE
(Wed)
Rue Jacques Cartier, Gaspe, QC, G4X 1M9, Canada; gen tel (418) 368-3242
Circulation: 6pd, 8,207fr; CCABBernard Johnson
Areas Served: Canada

LE PHARILLON
(Wed)
144 Rue De Jacques-cartier, Gaspe, QC, G4X 1M9, Canada, Canada; gen tel (418) 368-3242; gen fax (418) 368-1705; disp adv e-mail gas.redaction@tc.tc; class adv e-mail gas.redaction@tc.tc; ed e-mail gas.redaction@tc.tc; web site www.lepharillon.ca
Circulation: 10pd, 8,720fr; CCAB
Advertising: Open inch rate $.89.
Parent Co.:
Reseau Select/Select Network
Quebecor Communications, Inc.
Gen. Mgr. .... Alain St-Amand
Mng. Ed. .... Bernard Johnson
Mechanical Specifications: Type page 12 1/2 x 11 1/2.
Areas Served: Canada

GATINEAU

LA REVUE DE GATINEAU
(Wed)
160 Hospital Rd., Ste. 30, Gatineau, QC, J8T 8J1, Canada, Canada; gen tel (819) 568-7736; gen fax (819) 568-8728; ed e-mail pascal.laplante@tc.tc; web site www.info07.com
Circulation: 8pd, 91,029fr; CCAB
Advertising: Open inch rate $2.36.
Parent Co.:
Transcontinental Media
Gen. Mgr. .... Jacques Blais
Ed. .... Martin Godcher
Mechanical Specifications: Type page 10 3/8 x 14 1/4; E - 8 cols, 1 1/8, between; A - 8 cols, 1 1/8, between; C - 8 cols, 1 1/8, between.
Equipment & Software: : Hardware — APP/Mac.
Areas Served: Canada

LE BULLETIN
(Wed)
435 Blvd Rue Principale, Gatineau, QC, J8L 2G8, Canada; gen tel (819) 986-5089; adv tel (819) 986-5089; ed tel (819) 986-5089; gen fax (819) 986-2073; adv fax (819) 986-2073; ed fax (819) 986-2073; disp adv e-mail yannick.boursier@tc.tc; ed e-mail yannick.boursier@tc.tc; web site www.lebulletin.net
Circulation: 20pd, 14,308fr; CCAB
Digital Platform - Mobile: Apple, Android
Digital Platform - Tablet: Apple iOS, Android
Pub./Ed. .... Yannick Boursier
Delivery Method: Mail, Racks
Areas Served: Canada

LE BULLETIN D'AYLMER
(Wed)
C-10 181 Principale St., (secteur Aylmer), Gatineau, QC, J9H 6A6, Canada; gen tel (819) 684-4755; gen fax (819) 684-6428; disp adv e-mail ventes.sales@bulletinaylmer.com; ed e-mail abawqp@videotron.ca; web site www.bulletinaylmer.com
Circulation: 181pd, 2,309fr; CMCA
Advertising: Open inch rate $0.890.
Established: 1971.
Prodn. Mgr. .... Charles Viau
Classifieds manager .... Nadia Paradis
Ed. .... Lily Ryan
Lynne Lavery
Mechanical Specifications: Type page 10 1/4 x 11; E - 6 cols, 1 5/8, between; A - 6 cols, 1 5/8, between; C - 9 cols, 1 1/5, between.
Equipment & Software: : Hardware — APP/Mac G4, APP/Power Mac G3; Software — QPS/QuarkXPress 5, Adobe/Photoshop 6, Adobe/Illustrator.
Delivery Method: Carrier
Areas Served: Canada

LE REGIONAL DE HULL
(Wed)
160, Boul. Hospital, Office 30, Gatineau, QC, J8T 8J1, Canada, Canada; gen tel (819) 776-1063; gen fax (819) 568-7544; web site www.info07.com
Circulation: 11,000fr; Sworn/Estimate/Non-Audited
Advertising: Open inch rate $.48.
Adv. Mgr. .... Dino Roberges
Ed. .... Jacques Blais
Areas Served: Canada

THE WEST-QUEBEC POST
(Fri)
C-10 181 Principale St., Secteur Aylmer, Gatineau, QC, J9H 6A6, Pontiac, Canada; gen tel (819) 684-4755; gen fax (819) 684-6428; disp adv e-mail ventes.sales@bulletinaylmer.com; ed e-mail abawqp@videotron.ca
Circulation: 761pd, 5,214fr; CMCA
Advertising: 72 cents per agate line, or $10.08 per column inch net.
Established: 1895.
Parent Co.:
9040-9681 Quebec Inc.
Publisher .... Fred Ryan
General Manager .... Lynne Lavery
Editor .... Lily Ryan
sales manager .... Sophia Ryan
Classified and subscription manager....... Nadia Paradis
Mechanical Specifications: Type page 10 2/5 x 11; E - 6 cols, 1 5/8, between; A - 6 cols, 1 5/8, between; Classifieds - 9 cols, 1 1/5, between.
Equipment & Software: : Hardware — Mac Intel with OSX10.6; Software — QuarkXpress 6.5 and 9; Adobe Creative Suite 2, 3, and 4 Office Suite 2008
Delivery Method: Mail, Newsstand, Carrier, Racks
Areas Served: Pontiac

WEEK-END OUTAOUAIS
(Sat)
160 Hospital Blvd., Ste. 30, Gatineau, QC, J8T 8J1, Canada; gen tel (819) 568-7736; gen fax (819) 568-7038; web site www.info07.com
Circulation: 90,000fr; Sworn/Estimate/Non-Audited
Pub./Gen. Mgr. .... Jacques Blais
Mechanical Specifications: Type page 10 3/8 x 14 1/4; E - 8 cols, 1 1/8, between; A - 8 cols, 1 1/8, between; C - 8 cols, 1 1/8, between.
Equipment & Software: : Hardware — APP/Mac.

GRANBY

GRANBY EXPRESS
(Wed)
398 Main St., Ste 5, Granby, QC, J2G 2W6, Canada; gen tel (450) 777-4515; gen fax (450) 777-4516; web site www.granbyexpress.com
Circulation: 3pd, 41,995fr; CCAB
Advertising: Open inch rate $.99.
Sales Coord. .... Nancy Corriveau
Mng. Ed. .... Maritime Chagnon
Reg'l Ed. .... Caroline Rioux
Mechanical Specifications: Type page 10 1/4 x 12 1/2; E - 8 cols, between; A - 8 cols, between; C - 8 cols, between.
Equipment & Software: : Hardware — IBM; Software — Microsoft/Word, Microsoft/Windows 95.
Areas Served: Canada

LA VOIX DE L'EST PLUS
(Wed)
76 Dufferin St., Granby, QC, J2G 9L4, Canada; gen tel (450) 375-4555; gen fax (450) 372-1308; ed fax (450) 777-4865; disp adv e-mail pub@lapresse.ca; ed e-mail redaction@lavoixdelest.qc.ca; web site www.cyberpresse.ca
Circulation: 8,965pd, 128fr; AAM
Advertising: Open inch rate $1.18.
Established: 1935.
Parent Co.:
Gesca Ltd.
Reseau Select/Select Network
Mng. Ed. .... Francois Beaudoin
Adv. Mgr. .... Daniel Touchette
Dir., Finance/Admin. .... Gilbert Arl
Adv. Mgr., Sales .... Daniel Touchet
Circ. Dir. .... Christian Malo
Ed. .... Guy Granger
News Ed. .... Haswa Budway
Sports Ed. .... Andre Bilodeau
Prodn. Mgr., Pre Press .... Claudette Ospiguy
Pub. .... Louisse Boisvert
Info. Mgr. .... Marc Gendron
Adv. Mgr. .... Martyne Lessard
Mechanical Specifications: Type page 10 1/4 x ; E - 10 cols, 1, 1/8 between; A - 10 cols, 1, 1/8 between; C - 10 cols, 1, 1/8 between.
Equipment & Software: : Hardware — APP/Mac.
Areas Served: Canada

HUDSON

HUDSON GAZETTE
(Wed)
397 Main Rd., Hudson, QC, J0P 1H0, Canada, Canada; gen tel (450) 458-5482; gen fax (450) 458-3337; web site www.hudsongazette.com
Circulation: 21,000fr; Sworn/Estimate/Non-Audited
Advertising: Open inch rate $.88.
Established: 1950.
Pub. .... Greg Jones
Circ. Mgr. .... Louise Craig
Ed. .... Jim Duff
Mechanical Specifications: Type page 10 7/8 x 14 1/8; E - 8 cols, 1 1/16, 1/6 between; A - 8 cols, 1 1/16, 1/6 between; C - 8 cols, 1 1/16, 1/6 between.
Equipment & Software: : Hardware — APP/Mac; Software — QPS/QuarkXPress.
Areas Served: Canada

HUNTINGDON

LES HEBDOS MONTEREGIENS
(Wed)
66 Chateauguay St., Huntingdon, QC, J0S 1H0, Canada; gen tel (450) 264-5364; gen fax (450) 264-9521; disp adv e-mail petitesannonces@gleaner-source.com; pub@gleaner-source.com; ed e-mail redaction@gleaner-source.com; web site www.monteregieweb.com
Circulation: 5,000pd, 91fr; Sworn/Estimate/Non-Audited
Advertising: Open inch rate $12.88.
Parent Co.:
Hebdos Quebec
Gen. Mgr. .... Andre Castagnier
Ed. .... Susanne J. Brown
Mechanical Specifications: Type page 10 1/4 x 16; E - 8 cols, 1 1/8, 1/8 between; A - 8 cols, 1 1/8, 1/8 between; C - 8 cols, 1 1/8, 1/8 between.
Equipment & Software: : Hardware — APP/Mac; Software — Microsoft/Word 5.1, QPS/QuarkXPress 3.3, Adobe/Photoshop 3.05.

JOLIETTE

ACTION MERCREDI
(Wed, Sun)
342, Beaudry Nord, Joliette, QC, J6E 6A6, Canada; gen tel (450) 759-3664; gen fax (450) 759-3190; web site www.laction.com
Circulation: 9pd, 51,680fr; CCABBenoit Bazinet Benoit Bazinet
Areas Served: Canada

L'ACTION
(Wed)
342 Beaudry N., Joliette, QC, J6E 6A6, Canada, Canada; gen tel (450) 759-3664; adv tel (450) 752-0447; ed tel (450) 759-3664; adv fax (450) 759-3190; ed fax (450) 759-3190; disp adv e-mail infolanaudiere@tc.tc; web site www.laction.com
Circulation: 19,450fr; CCAB
Advertising: Open inch rate $1.32.
Established: 1973.
Parent Co.:
Transcontinental Media
Sales Rep. .... Norman Harvey
Pub. .... Benoit Bazinet
Prodn. Mgr. .... Chantal Proulx
Pres. .... Natalie Lariviere
Mgr. .... Carole Bonin
Regl. Dir. .... Sebastien Nadeau
Sales Mgr. .... Harvey Norman
Ed. .... Andre Lafreniere
Ed. .... Francine Rainville
Prodn. Mgr. .... Chantal Troulx
Mechanical Specifications: Type page 10 1/2 x 14 1/2; E - 8 cols, between.
Equipment & Software: : Hardware — CD/Rom, DS, SyQuest 44, SyQuest 88, SyQuest 200; Software — QPS/QuarkXPress 3.32, Adobe/Illustrator 5.5, Adobe/Photoshop 3.05.
Areas Served: Canada

LE JOURNAL DE JOLIETTE
(Wed)
1075 Blvd Firestone 5e Etage, Joliette, QC, J6E 6X6, Canada; gen tel (450) 960-2424; adv tel (450) 960-2424; ed tel (450) 960-2424; gen fax (450) 960-2626; adv fax (450) 960-2626; ed fax (450) 960-2626; disp adv e-mail johanne.roussy2@quebecormedia.com; ed e-mail janique.duguay@quebecormedia.com; web site www.lejournaldejoliette.ca
Circulation: 60,740fr; CCAB
Advertising: Open inch rate $.96.
Established: 1992.
Parent Co.:
Quebecor Communications, Inc.
Digital Platform - Mobile: Apple, Android, Windows, Blackberry
Digital Platform - Tablet: Apple iOS, Android, Windows 7, Blackberry Tablet OS
Ed. .... Janique Duguay
Regional Director .... Patricia Beaulieu
Mechanical Specifications: Type page 14 1/4 x 10 1/4; E - 8 cols, 1 1/4, between; A - 8 cols, 1 1/4, between; C - 8 cols, 1 1/4, between.
Delivery Method: Mail, Racks
Areas Served: Canada

LE REGIONAL
(Wed)
342 Beaugry N. St., Joliette, QC, J6E 6A6, Canada; gen tel (450) 759-3664; gen fax (450) 759-9828; web site http://www.le-regional.ca/
Circulation: 64,096fr; ODC
Pub. .... Benoit Bazinet

KAHNAWAKE

THE EASTERN DOOR
(Fri)
P.o. Box 1170, Kahnawake, QC, J0L 1B0, Canada; gen tel (450) 635-3050; gen fax (450) 635-8479; web site www.easterndoor.com
Circulation: 1,020pd, 81fr; CMCA
Ed./Pub. .... Steve Bonspiel

Areas Served: Canada

KNOWLTON

BROME COUNTY NEWS

(Tues)
5 B Rue Victoria, Knowlton, QC, J0E 1V0, Canada; gen tel (450) 242-1188; gen fax (450) 243-5155
Circulation: 10,000fr; Sworn/Estimate/Non-Audited
Advertising: Open inch rate $1.08.
Parent Co.:
Alta. Newspaper Group, Ltd
Pub. .... Ken Wells
Ed. .... Sharon McCully
Prodn. Mgr. .... Richard Lessard
Equipment & Software: ; Software — QPS/QuarkXPress 6.1.
Areas Served: J0E 1V0

LA MALBAIE

HEBDO CHARLEVOISIEN

(Wed)
53, Rue John-nairne Ste. 100, La Malbaie, QC, G5A 1L8, La Malbaie, Canada; gen tel (418) 665-1299; gen fax (418) 453-3349; disp adv e-mail hebdo@charlevoix.net; web site www.charlevoixendirect.com
Circulation: 30pd, 14,487fr; CCABCharles Warren
Areas Served: La Malbaie

PLEIN JOUR DE CHARLEVOIX

(Fri)
249 Rue John Nairne, La Malbaie, QC, G58 1M4, Canada; gen tel (418) 665-6121; gen fax (418) 665-3105
Circulation: 15,438fr; Sworn/Estimate/Non-Audited
Advertising: Open inch rate $.56.
Parent Co.:
Quebecor Communications, Inc.
Mng. Ed. .... Richard Harley

LA TUQUE

L'ECHO DE LA TUQUE

(Wed)
324 St. Joseph St., La Tuque, QC, G9X 1L2, Canada; gen tel (819) 523-6141; gen fax (819) 523-6143; ed e-mail redaction_latuque@tc.tc; web site www.lechodelatuque.com
Circulation: 0pd, 6,406fr; CCAB
Advertising: Open inch rate $.80.
Parent Co.:
Reseau Select/Select Network
Transcontinental Media
Dir. .... Michele Scarpeno
Areas Served: Canada

LAC ETCHEMIN

LA VOIX DU SUD

(Wed)
1516 A. Rt. 277, Lac Etchemin, QC, G0R 1S0, Canada; gen tel (418) 625-7471; gen fax (418) 625-5200; disp adv e-mail caroline.gilbert@tc.tc; class adv e-mail caroline.gilbert@tc.tc; ed e-mail caroline.gilbert@tc.tc; web site www.lavoixdusud.com
Circulation: 14pd, 27,758fr; CCAB
Advertising: Open inch rate $.99.
Parent Co.:
Transcontinental Media
Ed. .... Caroline Gilbert
Prodn. Mgr. .... Rock Bizier
Areas Served: Canada

LAC MEGANTIC

L'ECHO DE FRONTENAC

(Fri)
5040 Blvd. Des Veterans, Lac Megantic, QC, G6B 2G5, Canada; gen tel (819) 583-1630; gen fax (819) 583-1124; web site www.echodefrontenac.com
Circulation: 3,709pd, 4,192fr; CCAB
Advertising: Open inch rate $.75.
Parent Co.:
Reseau Select/Select Network
Sales Dir. .... Michel Pilotte
Ed. .... Gaetan Poulin
Asst. Ed. .... Suzanne Poulin
Mng. Ed. .... Remi Tremblay
Mechanical Specifications: Type page 14 1/4 x 10 1/8; E - 5 cols, between; A - 8 cols, between; C - 8 cols, between.
Equipment & Software: : Hardware — APP/Mac.
Areas Served: Canada

LACHUTE

L'ARGENTEUIL

(Wed)
52 Main St., Lachute, QC, J8H 3A8, Canada, Canada; gen tel (450) 562-2494; gen fax (450) 562-1434; disp adv e-mail francois.leblanc@eap.on.ca; web site www.largenteuil.ca
Circulation: 39pd, 16,540fr; ODC
Advertising: Open inch rate $.98.
Parent Co.:
Reseau Select/Select Network
Cie d'Edition Andre Paquette, Inc.
Pres. .... Bertrand Castonguay
Dir. Gen. .... Roger Duplantie
Dir., Adv. .... Francois Leblanc
Circ. Mgr. .... Alain Morris
Ed. .... Robert Savard
Areas Served: Canada

LASALLE

LA VOIX POPULAIRE

(Thur)
420 La Fleur St., Lasalle, QC, H8R 3H6, Canada; gen tel (514) 363-5656; gen fax (514) 363-3895; web site www.lavoixpopulaire.com
Circulation: 4pd, 29,159fr; CCAB
Advertising: Open inch rate $1.06.
Parent Co.:
Transcontinental Media
Ed. .... Louis Mercier
Ed. In Chief. .... Yannick Pinel
Areas Served: Canada

MESSAGER DE LASALLE

(Thur)
420 Lafleur Ave, Suite 303, Lasalle, QC, H9S 5T8, Canada; gen tel (514) 636-7314
Circulation: 3pd, 32,736fr; CCABPatricia Ann Beaulieu
Areas Served: Canada

LAVAL

COURRIER-LAVAL

(Wed, Sat)
2700 Francis Hughes Ave., Ste. 200, Laval, QC, H7S 2B9, Canada; gen tel (450) 667-4360; gen fax (450) 667-0845; web site www.courrierlaval.com
Circulation: 8pd, 12,788fr; CCAB
Advertising: Open inch rate $2.27.
Established: 1945.
Parent Co.:
Transcontinental Media
Sales Dir. .... Janique Duguay
Regl. Dir. .... Rejean Monette
Ed. .... Claude Labelle
Prodn. Mgr. .... Martine Cotton
Mechanical Specifications: Type page 11 3/8 x 15; E - 8 cols, between; A - 8 cols, between.
Equipment & Software: : Hardware — APP/Mac.
Areas Served: Canada

L'HEBDO DE LAVAL

(Fri)
3221 Hwy. 440 W., Ste. 209, Laval, QC, H7P 5P2, Canada; gen tel (450) 681-4948; gen fax (450) 681-2824
Circulation: 84,860fr; Sworn/Estimate/Non-Audited
Advertising: Open inch rate $1.35.
Gen. Mgr. .... Marc Ouellette
Mng. Ed. .... Francois Forget

MISSIONS ETRANGERES

(Wed)
Place Juge-desnoyers, Laval, QC, H7G 1A5, Canada; gen tel (450) 667-4190
Circulation: 6,585pd, 5,647fr; ODCBertrand Roy

NOUVELLES PARC EXTENSION NEWS

(Fri) (Every other sat)
3860 Notre-dame Blvd., Suite 304, Laval, QC, H7V 1S1, Canada; gen tel (450) 978-9999; gen fax (450) 687-6330; disp adv e-mail sales@the-news.ca; ed e-mail editor@the-news.ca; web site www.px-news.com
Circulation: 0pd, 9,403fr; Sworn/Estimate/Non-Audited
Advertising: Open inch rate $15.00.
Established: 1993.
Co-Publisher .... George S. Guzmas
Prodn. Mgr. .... George Bakoyannis
Mechanical Specifications: Type page 10 1/4 x 14 1/4; E - 8 cols, 1 1/6, 1/6 between; A - 8 cols, 1 1/6, 1/6 between; C - 8 cols, 1 1/6, 1/6 between.
Equipment & Software: : Hardware — Pentium 4; Software — INDESIGN.
Delivery Method: Carrier, Racks
Areas Served: H3N

THE LAVAL NEWS

(Sat) (Every other Saturday)
3860 Notre-dame Blvd., Suite 304, Laval, QC, H7V 1S1, Canada; gen tel (450) 978-9999; gen fax (450) 687-6330; disp adv e-mail sales@the-news.ca; ed e-mail editor@the-news.ca; web site www.lavalnews.ca
Circulation: 27,982fr; CMCA
Advertising: Open inch rate $17.00.
Established: 1993.
Parent Co.:
Newsfirst Multi-Media
Digital Platform - Mobile: Apple, Android
Digital Platform - Tablet: Apple iOS, Android
Co-Publisher .... George S. Guzmas
Prodn. Mgr. .... George Bakoyannis
Mechanical Specifications: Type page 10 3/10 x 14 1/4; E - 8 cols, 1 1/6, 1/6 between; A - 8 cols, 1 1/6, 1/6 between; C - 8 cols, 1 1/6, 1/6 between.
Equipment & Software: ; Presses — G/486MFP 3.
Delivery Method: Carrier, Racks
Areas Served: Canada

THE NORTH SHORE NEWS

(Sat) (Every 2nd week (24 per year))
3860 Notre-dame Blvd., Suite 304, Laval, QC, H7V 1S1, Canada; gen tel (450) 978-9999; gen fax (450) 678-6330; disp adv e-mail gg@newsfirst.ca; ed e-mail editor@newsfirst.ca; web site www.ns-news.com
Circulation: 0pd, 16,353fr; CMCA
Advertising: 10.90.
Established: 2005.
Parent Co.:
Newsfirst Multimedia
Digital Platform - Tablet: Windows 7
Co-Pub .... George Guzmas
Mechanical Specifications: Tabloid
Equipment & Software: : Hardware — PC; Software — Adobe CS6
Delivery Method: Newsstand, Racks
Areas Served: Canada

LEVIS

JOURNAL DE LEVIS

(Wed)
580, Boul, Alphonse-desjardins, Levis, QC, G6V 6R8, Canada; gen tel (418) 833-3113; gen fax (418) 833-0890; web site www.journaldelevis.com
Circulation: 5pd, 68,595fr; CCABSandra Fontaine
Areas Served: Canada

JOURNAL LE PEUPLE

(Wed)
421 Dorimene Desjardins Rue, Levis, QC, G6V 8V6, Canada; gen tel (418) 833-9398; gen fax (418) 833-8177; web site http://www.hebdosregionaux.ca/chaudiere-appalaches/le-peuple-levis/
Circulation: 3pd, 68,451fr; CCAB
Advertising: Open inch rate $1.46.
Established: 1936.
Parent Co.:
Quebecor Communications, Inc.Paul Lessard
Mechanical Specifications: Type page 10 x 11 3/4; E - 5 cols, 2, between; A - 10 cols, 1, between; C - 5 cols, 2, between.
Equipment & Software: ; Software — Adobe/Illustrator.
Areas Served: Canada

PEUPLE DE LOTBINIERE

(Wed)
5790, Boul. Etienne-dallaire, Suite 103 B, Levis, QC, G6V 8V6, Canada, Canada; gen tel (418) 728-2131; gen fax (418) 728-4819; disp adv e-mail ventes.lotbiniere@hebdosquebecor.com; ed e-mail redaction.lotbiniere@hebdosquebecor.com; web site www.lepeuplelotbiniere.canoe.ca
Circulation: 1pd, 15,029fr; CCAB
Advertising: Open inch rate $0.96.
Parent Co.:
Quebecor Communications, Inc.
Adv. Rep. .... Lise Racette
Paul Lessard
Areas Served: Canada

LONGUEUIL

BROSSARD ECLAIR

(Wed)
267 St. Charles Ouest, Longueuil, QC, J4H 1E3, Canada; gen tel (450) 646-3333; gen fax (450) 674-0205; web site http://www.brossardeclair.ca/
Circulation: 32,482fr; CCAB
Advertising: Open inch rate $1.02.
Parent Co.:
Reseau Select/Select Network
Quebecor Communications, Inc.
Ed. .... Lucie Masse
Mechanical Specifications: Type page 10 1/2 x 14 1/2; E - 8 cols, between; C - 1 cols, between.
Areas Served: Canada

LE COURRIER DU SUD/SOUTH SHORE COURIER

(Wed)
267 Saint Charles W, Longueuil, QC, J4H 1E3, Canada, Canada; gen tel (450) 646-3333; adv tel (450) 646-3333; gen fax (450) 674-0205; disp adv e-mail journal@courrierdusud.com; ed e-mail editeur@courrierdusud.com; web site http://www.lecourrierdusud.ca/
Circulation: 145,800fr; CCAB
Advertising: Open inch rate $3.82.
Established: 1947.
Parent Co.:
Quebecor Communications, Inc.
Digital Platform - Mobile: Apple, Android, Windows, Blackberry
Digital Platform - Tablet: Apple iOS, Android, Windows 7, Blackberry Tablet OS
Pub. .... Lucie Masse
Ed. .... Jinette Claude Teron
Delivery Method: Mail, Racks
Areas Served: Canada

MAGAZINE DE SAINT LAMBERT

(Wed)
St Charles Ouest, Longueuil, QC, J4H 1E3,

Canada
Circulation: 0pd, 14,164fr; CCAB
Gen. Mgr. ....Lucie Masse
Areas Served: Canada

REVUE DE LA MACHINERIE AGRICOLE
(Tues)
468 Boul. Roland-therrien, Longueuil, QC, J4H 4E3, Canada; gen tel (450) 677-2556; gen fax (450) 677-4099; web site www.marevueagricole.com
Circulation: 1,300pd, 33,200fr; ODCMartyne Simard

LOUISEVILLE

L'ECHO DE MASKINONGE
(Wed)
43 Saint Louis, Louiseville, QC, J5V 2C7, Canada; gen tel (819) 228-5532; gen fax (819) 228-9379; adv fax (819) 228-5532; web site www.lechodemaskinonge.com
Circulation: 28pd, 13,907fr; CCAB
Advertising: Open inch rate $.71.
Established: 1921.
Parent Co.:
Transcontinental Media
Dir. ... AndrÃ ££££ Lamy
Sales Coord................................ Diane Beland
Areas Served: Canada

MAGOG

REFLET DU LAC
(Wed)
53 Rue Centre, Bureau 300, Magog, QC, J1X 5B6, Canada; gen tel (819) 843-3500; gen fax (819) 843-3085
Circulation: 0pd, 24,662fr; CCAB
CEO...Monique Cote
Areas Served: Canada

MANSFIELD

JOURNAL OF PONTIAC
(Other)
Unit 5, 289, Rue Principale, Mansfield, QC, J0X 1R0, Mansfield-et-Pontefract, Canada; gen tel (819) 683-3582; gen fax (819) 683-2977; disp adv e-mail journal@journalpontiac.com; class adv e-mail notice@journalpontiac.com; ed e-mail editor@journalpontiac.com; web site www.pontiacjournal.com
Circulation: 70pd, 9,302fr; Sworn/Estimate/Non-Audited
Advertising: $1.09 Gross Black and white + 25% process colour.
Established: 1987.
Parent Co.:
155106 Canada Inc.
Gen. Mgr. .... Lynne Lavery
Delivery Method: Mail, Newsstand, Carrier
Areas Served: Mansfield-et-Pontefract

MATANE

AVANT POSTE
(Wed)
305, Rue De La Gare, Following 107, Matane, QC, G4W 3J2, Canada; gen tel (418) 629-3443; gen fax (418) 562-4607; web site www.lavantposte.ca
Circulation: 6pd, 8,609fr; CCABJean Gagnon
Areas Served: Canada

LA VOIX GASPESIENNE
(Wed)
305 De La Gare St., Ste. 107, Matane, QC, G4W 3J2, Canada; gen tel (418) 562-4040; adv tel (418) 562-0666; ed tel (418) 562-0666; gen fax (418) 562-4607; web site http://www.lavantagegaspesien.com
Circulation: 13pd, 17,247fr; CCAB
Advertising: Open inch rate $.76.
Parent Co.:
Quebecor Communications, Inc.
(Ed.)... Jean Gagnon
Areas Served: Canada

VOIX DE LA MATANIE
(Wed)
Rue De La Gare, Matane, QC, G4W 3J2, Canada; gen tel (418) 562-4040; gen fax (418) 562-4607
Circulation: 11pd, 17,402fr; CCABJean Gagnon
Areas Served: Canada

MONT TREMBLANT

INFORMATION DU NORD SAINTE-AGATHE
(Thur)
1107 Rue De Saint Jovite, Mont Tremblant, QC, J8E 3J9, Canada; gen tel (819) 425-8658; gen fax (819) 425-7713; web site www.linformationdunordsainteagathe.ca
Circulation: 15,474pd, 26fr; Sworn/Estimate/Non-Audited
Advertising: Open inch rate $0.93.
Parent Co.:
Quebecor Communications, Inc.Johanne Regimbald
Mechanical Specifications: Type page 10 x 11 1/2; E - 10 cols, between.
Equipment & Software: : Hardware — APP/Mac; Software — QPS/QuarkXPress 4.1, Adobe/Photoshop 4.01, Adobe/Illustrator 6.0.

MONT-JOLI

LE INFORMATION
(Wed)
Rue Doucet, Mont-Joli, QC, G5H 1R6, Canada; gen tel (418) 775-4381
Circulation: 33pd, 9,867fr; CCABFrancis Desrosiers
Areas Served: Canada

MONT-LAURIER

JOURNAL LE CHOIX D'ANTOINE LABELLE
(Wed)
Boulevard A.-paquette, Mont-Laurier, QC, J9L1K5, Canada; gen tel (819) 623-3112
Circulation: 0pd, 17,000fr; CCABAndre Guillemette
Areas Served: Canada

JOURNAL LE COURANT DES HAUTES-LAURENTIDES
(Thur)
534, De La Madone, Mont-Laurier, QC, J9L 1S5, Canada; gen tel (819) 623-7374; gen fax (819) 623-7375; web site www.lecourant.ca
Circulation: 18,400fr; ODCSylvie Vaillancourt

MONT-TREMBLANT

INFORMATION DU NORD L'ANNONCIATION
(Thur)
1107, Rue De St-jovite, Mont-Tremblant, QC, J8E 3J9, Canada; gen tel (819) 425-8658; gen fax (819) 425-7713; web site www.hebdosquebecor.com
Circulation: 7,974pd, 15,500fr; Sworn/Estimate/Non-Audited
Advertising: Open inch rate $.49.
Established: 1980.
Parent Co.:
Quebecor Communications, Inc.
Ed. ....Josee Gauvin
Ã £££ditrice ...... Johanne Regimbald
Mechanical Specifications: Type page 10 x 11 1/2.
Equipment & Software: : Hardware — APP/Mac; Software — QPS/QuarkXPress 4.1, Adobe/Photoshop 4.01, Adobe/Illustrator 6.0.

INFORMATION DU NORD MONT TREMBLANT
(Wed)
1107 Rue De St. Jovite, Mont-Tremblant, QC, J8E 3J9, Canada, Canada; gen tel (819) 425-8658; gen fax (819) 425-7713; web site www.hebdosquebecor.com
Circulation: 4pd, 15,029fr; CCAB
Advertising: Open inch rate $.58.
Parent Co.:
Quebecor Communications, Inc.
Adv. Mgr....................................Michel Gareau
Johanne Regimbald
Mechanical Specifications: Type page 10 x .
Equipment & Software: ; Software — QPS/QuarkXPress 4.1, Adobe/Photoshop 4.01, Adobe/Illustrator 6.0.
Areas Served: Canada

INFORMATION DU NORD VALLEE DE LA ROUGE
(Wed)
Rue De St-jovite, Mont-Tremblant, QC, J8E 3J9, Canada; gen tel (819) 425-8658
Circulation: 2pd, 15,487fr; CCABJohanne Regimbald
Areas Served: Canada

POINT DE VUE LAURENTIDES
(Wed)
580 Rue De Saint Jovite Ste 201, Mont-Tremblant, QC, J8E 2Z9, Canada; gen tel (819) 425-7666; adv tel (819) 425-7666; ed tel (819) 425-7666; gen fax (819) 425-9111; adv fax (819) 425-9111; ed fax (819) 425-9111; disp adv e-mail infolaurentides@transcontinental.ca; ed e-mail infolaurentides@transcontinental.ca; web site www.pointdevuemonttremblant.com
Circulation: 31,760fr; CCAB
Digital Platform - Mobile: Apple, Android
Digital Platform - Tablet: Apple iOS, Android
Delivery Method: Mail, Racks
Areas Served: Canada

MONTMAGNY

L'OIE BLANCHE
(Wed)
70 Rue De L'anse, Montmagny, QC, G5V 1G8, Canada; gen tel (418) 248-8820; gen fax (418) 248-4033; web site www.oieblanc.com
Circulation: 17pd, 22,533fr; CCAB
Advertising: Open inch rate $.61.
Parent Co.:
Reseau Select/Select Network
Pub...Yannick Patelli
Mechanical Specifications: Type page 11 3/4 x 15.
Areas Served: Canada

LE PEUPLE COTE-SUD
(Wed)
80 Boul. Tache E., Montmagny, QC, G5V 3S7, Canada; gen tel (418) 248-0415; gen fax (418) 248-2377; web site www.camoe.ca
Circulation: 27pd, 20,852fr; CCAB
Advertising: Open inch rate $.51.
Established: 1900.
Parent Co.:
Quebecor Communications, Inc.
Pub.......................................Claueettne Tardis
Mechanical Specifications: Type page 10 1/4 x 11 3/4.
Areas Served: Canada

MONTREAL

ECHOS VEDETTES
(Sat)
465 Mcgill Ave., Montreal, QC, H2W 2H1, Canada, Canada; gen tel (514) 528-7111; gen fax (514) 528-7115
Circulation: 54,193pd, 875fr; Sworn/Estimate/Non-Audited
Gen. Mgr..............................Sylvie Bourgeault
Areas Served: Canada

FLAMBEAU
(Tues)
Boulevard Langelier Bureau 210, Bureau 210, Montreal, QC, H1P 3C6, Canada; gen tel (514) 899-5888
Circulation: 0pd, 56,194fr; CCABStephane Desjardins
Areas Served: Canada

GUIDE DE MONTREAL-NORD
(Tues)
Boulevard Langelier Bureau 210, Bureau 210, Montreal, QC, H1P 3C6, Canada; gen tel (514) 899-5888
Circulation: 0pd, 34,440fr; CCABYannick Pinel
Areas Served: Canada

INFORMATEUR DE RIVIERE DES PRAIRIES
(Tues)
Boulevard Langelier Bureau 210, Bureau 210, Montreal, QC, H1P 3C6, Canada; gen tel (514) 899-5888
Circulation: 20,917fr; CCABYannick Pinel
Areas Served: Canada

JOURNAL DE ROSEMONT / PETITE PATRIE
(Tues)
8770 Langelier Boulevard Bureau 210, Montreal, QC, H1P 3C6, Canada; gen tel (514) 899-5888; gen fax (514) 899-5001; web site www.journalderosemont.com
Circulation: 0pd, 59,344fr; CCABStephane Desjardins
Areas Served: Canada

JOURNAL DE ST MICHEL
(Sat)
Cp 50, Succ. St-michel, Montreal, QC, H2A 3L8, Canada; gen tel (514) 721-4911; gen fax (514) 374-4171; web site www.journaldestmichel.com
Circulation: 20pd, 24,035fr; ODCClaude Bricault

JOURNAL L'AVENIR DE L'EST
(Tues)
8770, Boulevard Langelier Bureau 210, Montreal, QC, H1P 3C6, Canada, Canada; gen tel (514) 899-5888; gen fax (514) 899-5001; web site http://www.avenirdelest.com
Circulation: 0pd, 27,818fr; CCAB
Advertising: Open inch rate $.75.
Ed. ....Paul Sauve
Areas Served: Canada

NOUVELLES HOCHELAGA MAISONNEUVE
(Tues)
Boulevard Langelier Bureau 210, Bureau 210, Montreal, QC, H1P 3C6, Canada; gen tel (514) 899-5888; web site www.nouvelleshochelagamaisonneuve.com
Circulation: 22,615fr; CCABStephane Desjardins
Areas Served: Canada

ORATOIRE
(Sat)
Chemin Queen Mary, Montreal, QC, H3V 1H6, Canada; gen tel (514) 733-8211
Circulation: 25,131pd, 4,346fr; ODCClaude Grou

PLATEAU
(Thur)
8770 Langelier Boulevard Bureau 210, Montreal, QC, H1P 3C6, Canada; gen tel (514) 899-5888; gen fax (514) 899-5001; web site www.leplateau.com
Circulation: 34,869fr; CCABStephane Desjardins
Areas Served: Canada

THE SUBURBAN WEST ISLAND
(Wed)
7575 Trans Canada Hwy, Suite 105, Montreal, QC, H4T 1V6; gen tel (514) 484-1107; gen fax (514) 484-9616; disp adv e-mail amanda@thesuburban.com; ed e-mail editor@thesuburban.com; web site www.westislandgazette.com
Circulation: 40,239fr; CMCA
Editor-in-chief .... Beryl Wajsman
Director of sales .... Amanda Lavigne

TOURISME PLUS
(Wed)
B.p. 7 Succ Ahuntsic, Succ. Ahuntsic, Montreal, QC, H3L 3N5, Canada; gen tel (514) 881-8583
Circulation: 123pd, 1,266fr; ODCMichel Villeneuve

TRANSCONTINENTAL MEDIAS
(Tues)
8770 Langelier, Suite 210, Montreal, QC, H1P 3C6, Canada; gen tel (514) 899-5888; adv fax (514) 899-5001; web site www.journalderosemont.com
Circulation: 36,024fr; Sworn/Estimate/Non-Audited
Advertising: Open inch rate $1.12.
Parent Co.:
Transcontinental Media
publisher .... Stephane Desjardins
Mechanical Specifications: Type page 10 x 14; E - 8 cols, 1 1/4, 1/8 between; A - 8 cols, 1 1/4, 1/8 between; C - 8 cols, 1 1/4, 1/8 between.
Equipment & Software: : Hardware — APP/Mac G3.
Delivery Method: Carrier, Racks

VERDUN MESSENGER
(Thur)
6239 Monk Blvd., Montreal, QC, H4E 3H8, Canada; gen tel (514) 768-1920; gen fax (514) 768-3306
Circulation: 3pd, 24,364fr; CCAB
Advertising: Open inch rate $.80.
Pub .... Lou Mercaer
Ed. .... Pierre Lussier
Areas Served: Canada

NAPIERVILLE

JOURNAL LE COUP D'OEIL
(Wed)
350 Saint Jacques St., Napierville, QC, J0J 1L0, Canada, Canada; gen tel (450) 245-3344; gen fax (450) 245-7419; web site www.coupdoeil.info
Circulation: 9pd, 15,602fr; CCAB
Advertising: Open inch rate $14.14.
Established: 1978.
Digital Platform - Mobile: Apple
Digital Platform - Tablet: Apple iOS
Circ. Mgr. .... Charles Couture
Mng. Ed .... Claude Trahan
Journalist .... Jacques LaRochelle
Areas Served: Canada

NATASHQUAN

LE PORTAGEUR
(Wed)
50, Chemin D'en-haut, Natashquan, QC, G0G 2E0, Canada; gen tel (418) 726-3736; gen fax (418) 726-3714
Circulation: 490fr; Sworn/Estimate/Non-Audited
Advertising: Open inch rate $.50.
Adv. Mgr. .... Cindy Carbonneau
Ed. .... Michel Richard
Mechanical Specifications: Type page 8 1/2 x 11; E - 3 cols, 2 1/2, 1/8 between; C - 3 cols, 2 1/2, 1/8 between.
Equipment & Software: : Hardware — PC; Software — Adobe/PageMaker 6.5.

NEW CARLISLE

SEA-COAST PUBLICATIONS INC./THE GASPE SPEC
(Wed)
128 Gerard D. Levesque, New Carlisle, QC, G0C 1Z0, Canada; gen tel (418) 752-5400; ed tel (418)752-5070; gen fax (418) 752-6932; web site www.gaspespec.com
Circulation: 2,309pd,; CMCA
Advertising: Open inch rate $.96.
Established: 1975.
Pub .... Sharon Renouf-Farrell
Gen. Mgr. .... Joan Sawyer Imhoff
Adv. Mgr. .... Robert Bradbury
News Ed. .... Gilles Gagne
Mechanical Specifications: Type page 10 1/4 x 15 1/2; E - 5 cols, 1 15/16, 1/8 between; A - 5 cols, 1 15/16, 1/8 between; C - 5 cols, 1 15/16, 1/8 between.
Equipment & Software: : Hardware — APP/Mac; Presses — WPC; Software — Adobe/PageMaker.
Delivery Method: Mail, Newsstand
Areas Served: Canada

NEW RICHMOND

L'ECHO DE LA BAIE
(Wed)
143 Boulevard Perron E, New Richmond, QC, G0C 2B0, Canada; gen tel (418) 392-5083; gen fax (418) 392-6605; ed e-mail redaction_latuque@tc.tc; web site lechodelabaie.canoe.ca
Circulation: 7pd, 18,364fr; CCAB
Advertising: Open inch rate $1.09.
Parent Co.:
Quebecor Communications, Inc.
Pub .... Bernard Johnson
Areas Served: Canada

NICOLET

COURRIER-SUD
(Wed)
3255 Rte Marie-victorin, Nicolet, QC, J3T 1X5, Canada; gen tel (819) 293-4551; gen fax (819) 293-8758; ed e-mail redaction_cs@transcontinental.ca; web site www.lecourriersud.com
Circulation: 52pd, 20,758fr; CCAB
Advertising: Open inch rate $.92.
Parent Co.:
Transcontinental Media
Sales Coord. .... Claire Knight
Ed. .... Nancy Allaire
Mechanical Specifications: Type page 10 x 12 3/4.
Areas Served: Canada

PIEDMONT

JOURNAL ACCES
(Sat)
Rue Principale, Piedmont, QC, J0R 1K0, Canada; gen tel (450) 227-7999; web site http://www.journalacces.qc.ca/
Circulation: 25,720fr; ODCJosee Pilotte

PLESSISVILLE

L'AVENIR DE L'ERABLE
(Wed)
1620 Saint-calixte St., Plessisville, QC, G6L 1P9, Canada; gen tel (819) 362-7049; gen fax (819) 362-2216; web site www.lavenirderable.com
Circulation: 9pd, 10,779fr; CCAB
Advertising: Open inch rate $.87.
Parent Co.:
Transcontinental Media
Dir., Sales .... Pierre Gaudet
Ed. .... Sylvia Cote
Ed. .... Ghislain Chauvette
Areas Served: Canada

QUEBEC

CHARLESBOURG EXPRESS
(Fri)
710 Bouvier, Suite 107, Quebec, QC, G2J 1C2, Canada; gen tel (418) 628-7460; gen fax (418)840-1207; web site www.quebechebdo.com
Circulation: 9pd, 27,178fr; CCAB
Advertising: Open inch rate $1.20.
Parent Co.:
Reseau Select/Select Network
Transcontinental Media
Gen. Mgr. .... Alain LePage
Ed. .... Lilianne Laprise
Areas Served: Canada

JOURNAL L'ACTUEL
(Fri)
710 Bouvier, Suite 107, Quebec, QC, G2J 1C2, Canada; gen tel (418) 628-7460; gen fax (418) 622-1511; web site www.lactuel.com
Circulation: 5pd, 57,753fr; CCAB
Advertising: Open inch rate $1.26.
Parent Co.:
Transcontinental Media
Ed. .... Lilianne Laprese
Dir. .... Alain LePage
Ed. .... Lilianne Laprise
Areas Served: Canada

L'APPEL
(Fri)
710 Rue Bouvier Bureau 107, Quebec, QC, G2J 1C2, Canada; gen tel (418) 628-7460; adv tel (418) 628-7460; ed tel (418) 628-7460; gen fax (418) 622-1511; adv fax (418) 622-1511; ed fax (418) 622-1511; disp adv e-mail redaction_quebec@tc.tc; ed e-mail redaction_quebec@tc.tc; web site www.lappel.com
Circulation: 10pd, 44,099fr; CCAB
Established: 1945.
Digital Platform - Mobile: Apple, Android
Digital Platform - Tablet: Apple iOS, Android
Reg. Gen. Mgr. .... Michel Chalifour
Delivery Method: Mail, Racks
Areas Served: Canada

QUEBEC CHRONICLE-TELEGRAPH
(Wed)
1040 Belvedere, Suite 218, Quebec, QC, G1S 3G3, Canada; gen tel (418) 650-1764; gen fax (418) 650-5172; disp adv e-mail production@qctonline.com; ed e-mail editor@qctonline.com; web site www.qctonline.com
Circulation: 907pd, 24fr; CMCA
Advertising: Open inch rate $1.35.
Established: 1764.
Circulation Manager .... Wendy Little
Editor and Publisher .... Stacie Stanton
Mechanical Specifications: Type page 10 1/3 x 13 7/8; E - 6 cols, 1 5/8, 3/16 between; A - 6 cols, 1 5/8, 3/16 between; C - 5 cols, 1 5/8, 3/16 between.
Equipment & Software: : Hardware — APP/Mac; Software — Microsoft/Word 5.1, Adobe/PageMaker 6.5, Adobe/Illustrator 8.0, Adobe/Photoshop 6.0.
Delivery Method: Mail, Newsstand
Areas Served: Canada

QUEBEC EXPRESS
(Fri)
710 Bouvier, Suite 107, Bureau 900, Quebec, QC, G2J 1C2, Canada; gen tel (418) 628-7460; gen fax (418) 622-1511
Circulation: 7pd, 28,899fr; CCAB
Pub./Ed. .... Lilianne Laprise
Areas Served: Canada

REPENTIGNY

ECHO DE REPENTIGNY
(Wed)
Notre-dame Apt A, Apt. A, Repentigny, QC, J6A 2T8, Canada; gen tel (450) 932-4782; gen fax (450) 932-4794; web site www.lechoderepentigny.ca
Circulation: 59,248fr; CCABMartin Gravel
Areas Served: Canada

HEBDO RIVE NORD
(Tues, Fri)
1004 Rue Notre-dame, Repentigny, QC, J5Y 1S9, Canada; gen tel (450) 581-5120; gen fax (450) 581-4515; web site www.hebdorivenord.com
Circulation: 6pd, 53,954fr; CCAB
Advertising: Open inch rate $1.11.
Parent Co.:
Transcontinental Media
Chief Ed. .... Yannick Boulanger
Regl. Mgr. .... Sebastien Nadeau
Sales Mgr. .... Stephane Joseph
Prodn. Mgr. .... Chantal Proulx
Equipment & Software: : Hardware — APP/Mac; Software — QPS/QuarkXPress, Adobe/Illustrator, Adobe/Photoshop, Aldus/Freehand.
Areas Served: Canada

L'ARTISAN
(Tues)
1004 Rue Nortre-dame, Repentigny, QC, J5Y 1S9, Canada; gen tel (450) 581-5120; gen fax (450) 581-4515; web site www.journallartisan.com
Circulation: 45,212fr; Sworn/Estimate/Non-Audited
Advertising: Open inch rate $1.07.
Parent Co.:
Transcontinental Media
Adv. Mgr. .... Stephane Joseph
Ed. .... Yannick Boulanger
Prodn. Mgr. .... Chantal Proulx
Equipment & Software: : Hardware — APP/Mac; Software — QPS/QuarkXPress, Adobe/Illustrator, Adobe/Photoshop, Aldus/Freehand.

RIMOUSKI

AVANTAGE VOTRE JOURNAL
(Wed)
183 St-germain Ouest, Rimouski, QC, G5L 4B8, Canada; gen tel (418) 722-0205; web site http://www.lavantage.qc.ca/
Circulation: 64pd, 43,009fr; CCABLucie Moisan
Areas Served: Canada

LE PROGRES-ECHO
(Sun)
217, Avenue LÃ©onidas Sud, Bureau 6-d, Rimouski, QC, G5L 2T5, Canada; gen tel (418) 721-1212; adv fax (418) 723-1855; ed fax (418) 722-4078; web site www.rimouskois.ca
Circulation: 4pd, 29,084fr; CCAB
Advertising: Open inch rate $1.02.
Parent Co.:
Quebecor Communications, Inc.
Pub .... Alain St. Amand
Ed. .... Ernie Wells
Mechanical Specifications: Type page 12 1/2 x 11 1/2; E - 10 cols, between; A - 10 cols, between; C - 10 cols, between.
Areas Served: Canada

LE RIMOUSKOIS
(Wed)
217 Leonidas Ave, Po Box 3217, Branch A, Rimouski, QC, G5L 9G6, Canada; gen tel (418) 721-1212; gen fax (418) 723-1855; adv fax (418) 723-1855; ed fax (418) 723-4078; web site www.rimouskois.ca
Circulation: 4pd, 29,084fr; CCAB
Advertising: Open inch rate $.82.
Parent Co.:
Quebecor Communications, Inc.
Pub .... Alain St. Amand
Ed. .... Ernie Wells
Mechanical Specifications: Type page 12 1/2 x

11 1/2; E - 10 cols, between; A - 10 cols, between.
Equipment & Software: ; Presses — WPC.
Areas Served: Canada

RIVIERE-DU-LOUP

INFO DIMANCHE
(Sun)
Rue Fraser, Riviere-du-Loup, QC, G5R 1C6, Canada; gen tel (418) 862-1911; gen fax (418) 862-6165; web site www.infodimanche.com
Circulation: 106pd, 31,754fr; CCABMichel Chalifour
Areas Served: Canada

L'INFORMATION
(Wed)
55-a Rue De L'hotel De Ville, Riviere-du-Loup, QC, G5R 1L4, Canada, Canada; gen tel (418) 775-4381; gen fax (418) 862-4387; web site www.linformation.ca
Circulation: 30pd, 9,311fr; BPA
Advertising: Open inch rate $.82.
Parent Co.:
Quebecor Communications, Inc.
Ed. .... Francis Desrosiers
Areas Served: Canada

LE SAINT-LAURENT PORTAGE
(Wed)
55-a, Rue De L'hotel De Ville, Riviere-du-Loup, QC, G5R 1L4, Canada; gen tel (418) 862-1774; gen fax (418) 862-4387; web site www.lesaintlaurentportage.ca
Circulation: 11pd, 34,286fr; CCAB
Advertising: Open inch rate $.89.
Parent Co.:
Quebecor Communications, Inc.
Mng. Ed...Gilles LeBel
Ed. .... Pierre Levesque
Mechanical Specifications: Type page 10 1/4 x 12.
Equipment & Software: : Hardware — APP/Mac; Software — QPS/QuarkXPress.
Areas Served: Canada

ROBERVAL

L'ETOILE DU LAC
(Wed)
797 Blvd. Saint Joseph, Ste. 101, Bureau 101, Roberval, QC, G8H 2L4, Canada; gen tel (418) 275-2911; gen fax (418) 275-2834; web site www.letoiledulac.com
Circulation: 95pd, 14,602fr; CCAB
Advertising: Open inch rate $1.06.
Established: 1915.
Parent Co.:
Transcontinental Media
Regional Publisher ....Michel Dupont
Ed. in Chief ....Daniel Migneault
Sales manager ....Claudia Turcotte
Publisher.........................Michel Aub&#65533;
Areas Served: Canada

ROUYN-NORANDA

ABITIBI EXPRESS ROUYN
(Tues)
438 Ave. Lariviere, Rouyn-Noranda, QC, J9X 4J1, Canada; gen tel (819) 797-6776; ed tel (819) 767-6776; gen fax (819) 797-4725; ed fax (819) 797-4725; web site http://www.abitibiouestrouynnoranda.ca
Circulation: 18pd, 29,398fr; CCAB
Areas Served: Canada

CITOYEN ROUYN NORANDA
(Wed)
1 Rue Du Terminus, Rouyn-Noranda, QC, J9X 3B5, Canada; gen tel (819) 762-4361 x 221; adv tel (819) 762-4361; ed tel (819) 279-7032; gen fax (819) 797-2450; disp adv e-mail stefan.baillargeon@tc.tc or marie-eve.bouchard@tc.tc; class adv e-mail vicky.aumond@tc.tc; ed e-mail joel.caya@tc.tc; web site lafrontiere.ca
Circulation: 17pd, 19,749fr; CCAB
Established: 1937.
General manager............................Joel Caya
Delivery Method: Mail, Newsstand, Carrier, Racks
Areas Served: Canada

SAGUENAY

LE COURRIER DU SAGUENAY
(Wed)
3635 Blvd Harvey Ste 201, Saguenay, QC, G7X 3B2, Canada; gen tel (418) 542-2442; adv tel (418) 542-2442; ed tel (418) 542-2442; gen fax (418) 542-5225; adv fax (418) 542-5225; ed fax (418) 542-5225; disp adv e-mail redaction.saguenay@tc.tc; ed e-mail redaction.saguenay@tc.tc; web site www.courrierdusaguenay.com
Circulation: 16pd, 72,964fr; CCAB
Digital Platform - Mobile: Apple, Android, Windows, Blackberry
Digital Platform - Tablet: Apple iOS, Android, Windows 7, Blackberry Tablet OS
Ed. ....Joan Sullivan
Delivery Method: Mail, Racks
Areas Served: Canada

SAINT ANDRE-AVELLIN

LA PETITE NATION
(Wed)
3 Ste.10, Principale St., Saint Andre-Avellin, QC, J0V 1W0, Canada, Canada; gen tel (819) 983-2725; gen fax (819) 983-6844; ed e-mail pascal.laplante@tc.tc; web site http://www.lapetitenation.com
Circulation: 19pd, 10,108fr; CCAB
Advertising: Open inch rate $.73.
Parent Co.:
Transcontinental Media
Ed. ....Eric Bernard
Areas Served: Canada

SAINT AUGUSTIN DE DESMAURES

NIC
(Wed)
Route 138 Ste 100, Suite 100, Saint Augustin de Desmaures, QC, G3A 2C6, Canada; gen tel (418) 908-3438
Circulation: 2,863pd, 268fr; ODCSophie Bouchard

SAINT BRUNO

LE JOURNAL DE ST-BRUNO
(Fri)
1507 Roberval, Saint Bruno, QC, J3V 3P8, Canada; gen tel (450) 653-3685; gen fax (450) 653-6967; ed e-mail pclair@versants.com; web site http://www.journaldest-bruno.qc.ca/
Circulation: 4pd, 18,900fr; CCAB
Advertising: Open inch rate $.89.
Parent Co.:
Les Hebdos Monteregiens
Ed. ....Philippe Clair
Prod. Mgr. ....Stéphanie Lambert
Mechanical Specifications: Type page 11 1/2 x 17.
Areas Served: Canada

SAINT EUSTACHE

EVEIL
(Sat)
Rue St-eustache, Saint Eustache, QC, J7R 2L2, Canada
Circulation: 0pd, 55,993fr; CCABSerge Langlois
Areas Served: Canada

LA CONCORDE
(Wed)
53 Rue St. Eustache, Saint Eustache, QC, J7R 2L2, Canada; gen tel (450) 472-3440; gen fax (450) 473-1629
Circulation: 52,172fr; CCAB
Advertising: Open inch rate $1.08.
Ed. .... Jean-Claude Langlois
Areas Served: Canada

LE GROUPE JCL INC.
(Sat)
53, Rue Saint-eustache, Saint Eustache, QC, J7R 2L2, Canada; gen tel (450) 472-3440; adv fax (450) 435-7968; ed fax (450) 435-0588; disp adv e-mail infojournaux@groupe-jcl.com; class adv e-mail infojournaux@groupejcl.com; ed e-mail infojournaux@groupejcl.com; web site www.leveil.com
Circulation: 60,000fr; Sworn/Estimate/Non-Audited
Advertising: Open inch rate $1.00.
Dir., Sales ....Louis Kemp
Circ. Mgr................................Norman Langlois
Ed. in Chief ....Claude Desjardins
Ed. .... Jean Claude Langlois
Sports Ed.................................Marco Brunelle
Dir., Prodn...........................Yves Bourbonnais
Dir., Dist. ....Serge Langlois

SAINT GEORGES

JOURNAL DE LA BEAUCE
(Fri)
11720 1re Rue, Bureau 2, Saint Georges, QC, G5Y 2C8, Canada; gen tel (418) 220-0222
Circulation: 32,653fr; ODCLyne Genest

L'ECLAIREUR-PROGRES/BEAUCE NOUVELLES
(Wed)
12625 1st Ave. E., Saint Georges, QC, G5Y 2E4, Canada; gen tel (418) 228-8858; gen fax (418) 228-0268; web site leclaireurprogres.canoe.ca
Circulation: 13pd, 38,115fr; CCAB
Advertising: Open inch rate $.86.
Parent Co.:
Quebecor Communications, Inc.
Gen. Mgr. .... Gilbert Bernier
Areas Served: Canada

PROGRES DE BELLECHASSE
(Wed)
98e Rue, Saint Georges, QC, G5Y 8G1, Canada; gen tel (418) 228-8858
Circulation: 0pd, 19,789fr; CCABGilbert Bernier
Areas Served: Canada

SAINT HUBERT

VALLEE DU RICHELIEU EXPRESS
(Wed)
4480 Chemin Chambly, Bureau 204, Saint Hubert, QC, J3Y 3M8, Canada; gen tel (450) 678-6187; adv tel (450) 678-6187; ed tel (450) 678-6187; disp adv e-mail valleedurichelieu@tc.tc; ed e-mail valleedurichelieu@tc.tc; web site www.valleedurichelieuexpress.ca
Circulation: 1pd, 34,751fr; CCAB
Digital Platform - Mobile: Apple, Android
Digital Platform - Tablet: Apple iOS, Android
Delivery Method: Mail, Racks
Areas Served: Canada

SAINT HYACINTHE

LE CLAIRON REGIONAL DE SAINT-HYACINTHE
(Tues)
655 Rue St. Anne, Saint Hyacinthe, QC, J2S 5G4, Canada; gen tel (450) 773-6028; adv tel (450) 771-0677; gen fax (450) 773-3115; web site www.leclarion.qc.ca
Circulation: 0pd, 0fr; CCAB
Advertising: Open inch rate $.94.
Established: 1912.
Pub. ....Benoit Chartier
Adv. Mgr. ....Guillaume Bedard
Adv. Mgr. ....Zea Bedard
Circ. Mgr..............................Claude Gaudreau
Mng. Ed.................................Martin Bourassa
Ed. .... Martin Bourrassa
Prodn. Mgr. ....Josee Cusson
Equipment & Software: : Hardware — APP/Mac; Software — QPS/QuarkXPress.
Areas Served: Canada

SAINT JEROME

JOURNAL LE NORD
(Wed)
393 Laurentides Blvd., Saint Jerome, QC, J7Z 4L9, Canada; gen tel (450) 438-8383; gen fax (450) 438-4174; ed e-mail editeur@journallenord.com; web site www.journallenord.com
Circulation: 9pd, 55,388fr; CCAB
Advertising: Open inch rate $1.08.
Established: 1986.
Pub...................................Francois LaFerriere
Ed. ....Mychel Lapointe
Mechanical Specifications: Type page 10 1/4 x 14 1/4; E - 8 cols, 1 1/6, 1/6 between.
Equipment & Software: : Hardware — APP/Mac; Presses — G/Urbanite; Software — QPS/QuarkXPress, Adobe/Photoshop, Adobe/Illustrator.
Areas Served: Canada

L'ECHO DU NORD
(Wed)
179 St. George St., Saint Jerome, QC, J7Z 4Z8, Canada; gen tel (450) 436-5381; gen fax (450) 436-5904; web site http://echosdunord.com/
Circulation: 391pd, 53,385fr; CCAB
Advertising: Open inch rate $.92.
Parent Co.:
Quebecor Communications, Inc.
Ed. ....Andre Guillemette
Prodn. Mgr. ....Jean-Paul Sauriol
Areas Served: Canada

LE MIRABEL
(Sat)
179 Rue St. Georges, Saint Jerome, QC, J7Z 4Z8, Canada, Canada; gen tel (450) 436-8200; gen fax (450) 436-8912; web site www.lemirabel.com
Circulation: 51,862fr; CCAB
Advertising: Open inch rate $1.04.
Established: 1974.
Parent Co.:
Quebecor Communications, Inc.
Pub. ....Marc Fradellin
Gen. Mgr. ....Andre Guillemette
Prodn. Dir. .... Christine Leonard
Areas Served: Canada

SAINT JULIE

INFORMATION DE STE JULIE
(Wed)
Rue Jules Choquet Local 2, Local 2, Saint Julie, QC, J3E 1W6, Canada; gen tel (450) 649-0719
Circulation: 3pd, 19,435fr; CCABSerge Landry
Areas Served: Canada

SAINT LAURENT

COURRIER-AHUNTSIC
(Fri)

1500 Jules Poitras Blvd., Saint Laurent, QC, H4N 1X7, Canada; gen tel (514) 855-1292; gen fax (514) 855-9916; web site www.courrierahuntsic.com; www.transcontinental-media.com
Circulation: 0pd, 32,391fr; CCAB
Advertising: Open inch rate $1.08.
Parent Co.:
Transcontinental Media
Gen. Mgr. .... Alain De Choiniere
Information Dir. .... Marilaine Bolduc-Jacob
Areas Served: Canada

EXPRESS D'OUTREMONT
(Thur)
Jules-poitras, Saint Laurent, QC, H4N 1X7, Canada; gen tel (514) 286-1066; gen fax (514) 286-9310; web site www.expressou-tremont.com
Circulation: 2pd, 19,654fr; CCABJean Aube
Areas Served: Canada

LE COURRIER BORDEAUX/CARTIERVILLE
(Fri)
1500 Jules Poitras Blvd., Saint Laurent, QC, H4N 1X7, Canada; gen tel (514) 855-1292; gen fax (514) 855-9916; web site www.trans-continental.com; www.courrierbc.com
Circulation: 4pd, 17,925fr; CCAB
Advertising: Open inch rate $.87.
Parent Co.:
Transcontinental Media
Ed. .... Alain De Choinire
Mechanical Specifications: Type page 11 3/8 x 15; E - 8 cols, between; A - 8 cols, between.
Equipment & Software: ; Software — APP/Mac.
Areas Served: Canada

PROGRES VILLERAY/ PARC EXTENSION
(Tues)
Jules-poitras, Saint Laurent, QC, H4N 1X7, Canada; gen tel (514) 270-8088
Circulation: 20,276fr; CCABJean Aube
Areas Served: Canada

SAINT-LAURENT NEWS
(Sun)
1500 Blvd. Jules Poitras, Saint Laurent, QC, H4N 1X7, Canada; gen tel (514) 855-1292; gen fax (514) 855-1855; disp adv e-mail petitesannonces@journalmetro.com; class adv e-mail petitesannonces@journalmetro.com; web site www.nouvellessaint-laurent.com
Circulation: 29,317fr; Sworn/Estimate/Non-Audited
Advertising: Open inch rate $1.00.
Parent Co.:
Transcontinental Media
Ed. .... Yannick Pinel
Mechanical Specifications: Type page 10 x 14 1/4; E - 4 cols, between; C - 8 cols, between.
Equipment & Software: ; Software — APP/Mac.

THE SUBURBAN EAST END EDITION
(Thur)
7575 Trans Canada Highway, Suite 105, Saint Laurent, QC, H4T 1V6, Canada; gen tel (514) 484-1107; gen fax (514) 484-9616; disp adv e-mail amanda@thesuburban.com; ed e-mail editor@thesuburban.com; web site www.thesuburban.com
Circulation: 26,746fr; CMCABeryl Wajsman

SAINT LEONARD

PROGRES SAINT-LEONARD
(Wed)
8770 Langelier Blvd. Ste. 210, Bureau 210, Saint Leonard, QC, H1P 3C6, Canada; gen tel (514) 899-5888; gen fax (514) 899-5001; web site www.progresstleonard.com
Circulation: 31,355fr; Sworn/Estimate/Non-Audited
Advertising: Open inch rate $1.07.
Parent Co.:
Transcontinental MediaYannick Pinel
Ed. .... Lucy Lecoures

SAINT LIN LAURENTIDES

EXPRESS MONTCALM
(Wed)
Rue Saint-isidore, Saint Lin Laurentides, QC, J5M 2V4, Canada; gen tel (450) 439-2525
Circulation: 20,004fr; CCABBenoit Bazinet
Areas Served: Canada

SAINT PASCAL

LE PLACOTEUX
(Wed)
491 Ave. D'anjou, Saint Pascal, QC, G0L 3Y0, Canada; gen tel (418) 492-2706; gen fax (418) 492-9706; web site www.leplaco-teux.com
Circulation: 75pd, 18,315fr; CCAB
Advertising: Open inch rate $.85.
Parent Co.:
Reseau Select/Select Network
Ed. .... Maurice Gagnon
Adv. Mgr. .... Raymond Freve
Areas Served: Canada

SAINT SAUVEUR-DES-MONTS

JOURNAL LE PAYS D'EN HAUT LA VALLEE
(Fri)
Rue De La Gare Bureau 104, Bureau 104, Saint Sauveur-des-Monts, QC, J0R 1R6, Canada; gen tel (450) 227-4646
Circulation: 50pd, 29,756fr; ODCAndre Guillemette

SAINT TITE

HEBDO MEKINAC DESCHENAUX
(Sat)
C.p. 4057, Saint Tite, QC, G0X 3H0, Canada; gen tel (819) 537-5111
Circulation: 13,540fr; ODCLena Sauvageau

SAINT-GEORGES

LE POINT
(Tues)
9085, Boul. Lacroix, Saint-Georges, QC, G5Y 2B4, Canada; gen tel (418) 695-2601; gen fax (418) 695-1391; web site www.lepoint.ca
Circulation: 47,878fr; CCAB
Advertising: Open inch rate $.66.
Parent Co.:
Quebecor Communications, Inc.
Pres. .... Claude Poulin
Mechanical Specifications: Type page 11 1/2 x 12 1/2; E - 5 cols, 1 7/8, 1/8 between; A - 5 cols, 1 7/8, 1/8 between; C - 5 cols, 1 7/8, 1/8 between.
Equipment & Software: : Hardware — APP/Mac Classic; Presses — WPC; Software — Microsoft/Word 4.0.
Areas Served: Canada

LE REVEIL
(Tues)
9085, Boul. Lacroix, Saint-Georges, QC, G5Y 2B4, Canada; gen tel (418) 695-2601; gen fax (418) 695-1391; web site lereveil.canoe.ca
Circulation: 0pd, 73,191fr; CCAB
Advertising: Open inch rate $.56.
Parent Co.:
Quebecor Communications, Inc.
Pub. .... Diane Audet
Prodn. Mgr. .... Andre Rousseau
Mechanical Specifications: Type page 10 1/4 x 11 3/4; E - 5 cols, 2, 1/8 between; A - 5 cols, 2, 1/8 between; C - 5 cols, 2, 1/8 between.
Areas Served: Canada

SAINTE ADELE

LE JOURNAL DES PAYS D'EN HAUT LE VALLEE
(Wed)
94 De La Gare St-saviour, Sainte Adele, QC, J8B 2P7, Canada; gen tel (450) 229-6664; gen fax (450) 227-8144; web site http://www.lejournaldespaysdenhautlavallee.ca/
Circulation: 30,057fr; CCAB
Advertising: Open inch rate $.73.
Parent Co.:
Quebecor Communications, Inc.
Pub. .... Mario Marois
Mechanical Specifications: Type page 11 1/2 x 12 3/4.
Areas Served: Canada

SAINTE JEAN SUR RICHELIEU

JOURNAL LE RICHELIEU
(Tues)
Rue Richelieu, Sainte Jean sur Richelieu, QC, J3B 6X3, Canada; gen tel (450) 347-0323
Circulation: 4pd, 42,273fr; CCABRenel Bouchard
Areas Served: Canada

L'ECHO DE ST-JEAN-SUR-RICHELIEU
(Wed)
81 Rue Richelieu Bureau 102 B, Sainte Jean sur Richelieu, QC, J3B 6X2, Canada; gen tel (450) 376-4646 ; adv tel (450) 376-4646; ed tel (450) 376-4646; gen fax (450) 376-4666 ; adv fax (450) 376-4666 ; ed fax (450) 376-4666 ; disp adv e-mail henri-paul.raymond@quebecormedia.com; ed e-mail daniel.noiseux@quebecormedia.com; web site www.lechodesaintjean.ca
Circulation: 55,426fr; CCAB
Digital Platform - Mobile: Apple, Android, Windows, Blackberry
Digital Platform - Tablet: Apple iOS, Android, Windows 7, Blackberry Tablet OS
Ed. .... Daniel Noiseux
Delivery Method: Mail, Racks
Areas Served: Canada

LE CANADA FRANCAIS
(Thur)
84 Rue Richelieu, Sainte Jean sur Richelieu, QC, J3B 6X3, Canada; gen tel (450) 347-0323; gen fax (450) 347-4539; ed e-mail web@tc.tc; web site www.canadafrancais.com
Circulation: 8,313pd, 8,313fr; AAM
Advertising: Open inch rate $.99.
Gen. Mgr. .... Renel Bouchard
Adv. Mgr. .... Charles Coutre
Circ. Mgr. .... Christian Marleau
Ed. .... Gilles Levesque
Ed. .... Robert Paradis
Mechanical Specifications: Type page 11 1/2 x 15; E - 8 cols, 1 1/16, 1/6 between; A - 8 cols, 1 1/6, 1/6 between; C - 8 cols, 1 1/6, 1/6 between.
Areas Served: Canada

SAINTE JULIE

L'INFORMATION
(Wed)
566 Jules Choquet St., Local 2, Sainte Julie, QC, J3E 1W6, Canada; gen tel (450) 649-0719; gen fax (450) 649-7748; disp adv e-mail l.bourdua@ infodeste-julie.qc.ca; ni.beausejour@ infodeste-julie.qc.ca; ed e-mail redaction@infodeste-julie.qc.ca; web site www.monsaintejulie.ca
Circulation: 1pd, 20,563fr; CCAB
Advertising: Open inch rate $.84.
Serge Landry
Ariane DesrochersEd.s
Mechanical Specifications: Type page 10 x 15; E - 8 cols, between; A - 8 cols, between; C - 8 cols, between.
Equipment & Software: : Hardware — IBM.
Areas Served: Canada

SAINTE MARIE-DE-BEAUCE

BEAUCE MEDIA
(Wed)
1147 Blvd. Vachon N., Sainte Marie-de-Beauce, QC, G6E 3B6, Canada; gen tel (418) 387-8000; gen fax (418) 387-4495; web site www.beaucemedia.ca
Circulation: 3pd, 25,092fr; CCAB
Parent Co.:
Quebecor Communications, Inc.Gilbert Bernier
Areas Served: Canada

EDITION BEAUCE NORD
(Wed)
691, Boul. Vachon Nord, Sainte Marie-de-Beauce, QC, G6E 1M3, Canada; gen tel (418) 387-1205
Circulation: 2pd, 24,833fr; CCABClaude Grondin
Areas Served: Canada

SAINTE THERESE

L'ECHO DE ST EUSTACHE
(Wed)
204 Blvd Labelle Ste 208, Sainte Therese, QC, J7E 2X7, Canada; gen tel (450) 818-7575; adv tel (450) 818-7575; ed tel (450) 818-7575; gen fax (450) 818-7582 ; adv fax (450) 818-7582 ; ed fax (450) 818-7582
Circulation: 57,641fr; CCAB
Digital Platform - Mobile: Apple, Android, Windows, Blackberry
Digital Platform - Tablet: Apple iOS, Android, Windows 7, Blackberry Tablet OS
Areas Served: Canada

LE COURRIER
(Wed)
190 Cure-labelle Blvd., Rm. 204, Sainte Therese, QC, J7E 2X5, Canada; gen tel (450) 434-4144; adv tel (866) 637-5236; gen fax (450) 434-3142; web site www.journalle-courrier.com
Circulation: 55,014fr; CCAB
Advertising: Open inch rate $1.12.
Established: 1973.
Pub./Ed. .... Louis Sauvageau
Mechanical Specifications: Type page 10 1/4 x 14 1/4; E - 8 cols, between; A - 8 cols, between.
Equipment & Software: : Hardware — APP/Mac.
Areas Served: Canada

LE NORD-INFO
(Sat)
50 B Rue Turgeon, Sainte Therese, QC, J7E 3H4, Canada; gen tel (450) 435-6537; gen fax (450) 435-0588
Circulation: 60,079fr; CCAB
Advertising: Open inch rate $1.08.
Gen. Mgr. .... Serge Langlois
Circ. Mgr. .... Norman Langlois
Ed. .... Jean Claude Langlois
Areas Served: Canada

VOIX DES MILLE ILES
(Wed)
Rue Turgeon, Sainte Therese, QC, J7E 3H4, Canada; gen tel (450) 435-6537; web site http://www.nordinfo.com/
Circulation: 65,177fr; CCABSerge Langlois
Areas Served: Canada

SALABERRY-DE-

VALLEYFIELD

LE JOURNAL SAINT-FRANCOIS

(Wed)

61 Jacques-cartier St., Salaberry-de-Valleyfield, QC, J6T 4R4, Canada; gen tel (450) 371-6222; gen fax (450) 371-7254; web site www.st-francois.com

Circulation: 36pd, 34,817fr; CCAB

Advertising: Open inch rate $.84.

Parent Co.:

Les Hebdos Monteregiens

Pub./Dir. .... Diane Dumont

Sales Dir. .... Stephane Brais

Ed. in Chief .... Denis Bourbonnais

Mechanical Specifications: Type page 11 1/2 x 15; E - 4 cols, 2 1/2, 1/6 between; C - 8 cols, 1 1/4, 1/6 between.

Areas Served: Canada

LE SOLEIL DU ST-LAURENT

(Sat)

20 Academy St., Salaberry-de-Valleyfield, QC, J6T 6M9, Canada; gen tel (450) 373-8555; gen fax (450) 373-8666; disp adv e-mail publicite@lesoleil.qc.ca; ed e-mail redaction@lesoleil.qc.ca; web site www.lesoleil.qc.ca

Circulation: 32,750fr; Sworn/Estimate/Non-Audited

Advertising: Open inch rate $.98.

Parent Co.:

Les Hebdos Monteregiens

Dir. .... Andre Mooney

Sales Dir. .... Pierre Montreuil

Adv. Rep. .... Diane Mayer

Adv. Rep. .... Serge Proulx

Adv. Rep. .... Jean-Pierre Tessier

Adv. Rep. .... Peter Rozon

Ed. .... Mario Pitre

Mechanical Specifications: Type page 10 1/4 x 17.

SOLEIL DE VALLEYFIELD

(Sat)

20 Rue De L'academie, Salaberry-de-Valleyfield, QC, J6T 2H8, Canada; gen tel (450) 373-8555; adv tel (450) 373-8555; ed tel (450) 373-8555; ed e-mail diane.dumont@quebecormedia.com; web site http://www.journalsaint-francois.ca

Circulation: 23pd, 35,953fr; CCAB

Pub. .... Andre Mooney

Delivery Method: Mail, Racks

Areas Served: Canada

VALLEYFIELD EXPRESS

(Thur)

720 Blvd Monseigneur-langlois Ste 100, Salaberry-de-Valleyfield, QC, J6S 5H7, Canada; gen tel (450) 371-7117; adv tel (450) 371-7117; ed tel (450) 371-7117; gen fax (450) 371-7611; adv fax (450) 371-7611; ed fax (450) 371-7611; disp adv e-mail redactionvalleyfieldexpress@tc.tc; ed e-mail redactionvalleyfieldexpress@tc.tc; web site www.valleyfieldexpress.ca

Circulation: 43,310fr; CCAB

Digital Platform - Mobile: Apple, Android

Digital Platform - Tablet: Apple iOS, Android

Pub. .... RÃ©seau MontÃ©rÃ©gie

Delivery Method: Mail, Racks

Areas Served: Canada

SEPT-ILES

LE PORT CARTOIS

(Wed)

365 Laure Blvd., Sept-Iles, QC, G4R 1X2, Canada; gen tel (418) 962-4100; gen fax (418) 962-0439; web site www.hebdosquebecor.com

Circulation: 6pd, 19,072fr; CCAB

Advertising: Open inch rate $.55.

Parent Co.:

Quebecor Communications, Inc.

Adv. Mgr. .... Isabelle Chiasson

Ed. .... Catherine Martin

Areas Served: Canada

NORD COTIER

(Wed)

Boulevard Laure, Sept-Iles, QC, G4R 1Y2, Canada; gen tel (418) 960-2090

Circulation: 23pd, 19,095fr; CCABGino Levesque

Areas Served: Canada

NORDEST PLUS

(Wed)

365 Boul. Laure, Sept-Iles, QC, G4R 1X2, Canada; gen tel (418) 962-4100; gen fax (418) 962-0439; disp adv e-mail atelier.septiles@hebdosquebecor.com; ed e-mail redaction.septiles @ hebdosquebecor.com; web site www.hebdosquebecor.com

Circulation: 13,999fr; Sworn/Estimate/Non-Audited

Advertising: Open inch rate $.67.

Dir. .... Isabelle Chiasson

Mng. Ed. .... Mario Thibeault

SHAWINIGAN

HEBDO DU ST. MAURICE

(Wed)

2102 Champlain Ave., Shawinigan, QC, G9N 6T8, Canada, Canada; gen tel (819) 537-5111; adv tel (866) 637-5236; gen fax (819) 537-5471; web site www.lhebdodustmaurice.com

Circulation: 24pd, 36,640fr; CCAB

Advertising: Open inch rate $1.15.

Parent Co.:

Transcontinental Media

Pub. .... Michel Matteau

Lena Sauvageau

Adv. Mgr. .... Gilles Guay

Ed./Dir., Information .... Bernard Lepage

Mechanical Specifications: Type page 11 1/4 x 13 1/2; E - 10 cols, 1, 1/6 between; A - 10 cols, 1, 1/6 between; C - 10 cols, 1, 1/6 between.

Areas Served: Canada

L'ECHO DE SHAWINIGAN

(Wed)

795 Blvd 5e Rue Local 101, Shawinigan, QC, G9N 1G2, Canada; gen tel (819) 731-0327; adv tel (819) 731-0327; ed tel (819) 731-0327; gen fax (819) 731-0328; adv fax (819) 731-0328 ; ed fax (819) 731-0328; disp adv e-mail serge.buchanan@quebecormedia.com; ed e-mail hugues.carpentier@quebecormedia.com; web site www.lechodeshawinigan.ca

Circulation: 37,369fr; CCAB

Digital Platform - Mobile: Apple, Android, Windows, Blackberry

Digital Platform - Tablet: Apple iOS, Android, Windows 7, Blackberry Tablet OS

Ed. .... Hugues Carpentier

Delivery Method: Mail, Racks

Areas Served: Canada

L'HEBDO MEKINAC/DES CHENAUX

(Wed)

Cp 490, Shawinigan, QC, G9N 6T8, Canada; gen tel (819) 537-5111; gen fax (819) 537-5471; web site www.lhebdomekinacdeschenaux.com

Circulation: 13,540pd, 0fr; Sworn/Estimate/Non-Audited

Parent Co.:

Transcontinental Media

Pub. .... Michel Matteau

Dir., Information .... Bernard Lepage

Ed. .... Gilles Guay

Mechanical Specifications: Type page 11 1/4 x 13 1/2; E - 10 cols, 1, 1/8 between; A - 10 cols, 1, 1/8 between; C - 10 cols, 1, 1/8 between.

SHAWVILLE

THE EQUITY

(Wed)

133 Center St., Shawville, QC, J0X 2Y0, Canada; gen tel (819) 647-2204; gen fax (819) 647-2206; disp adv e-mail kathy@theequity.ca; class adv e-mail news@theequity.ca; ed e-mail news@theequity.ca; web site www.theequity.ca

Circulation: 2,835pd,; CMCA

Advertising: Open inch rate $9.66 (Or $0.69 per agate line).

Established: 1883.

Parent Co.:

Pontiac Printshop Ltd.

Pub. .... Charles Dickson

Mechanical Specifications: Type page 13 1/2 x 21; E - 5 cols, 2 3/8, 1/8 between; A - 8 cols, 1 1/2, 1/8 between; C - 8 cols, 1 1/2, 1/8 between.

Equipment & Software: ; Presses — WPC/Full Process; Software — QPS/QuarkXPress 4.0.

Delivery Method: Mail, Newsstand

Areas Served: Canada

SHERBROOKE

JOURNAL DE MAGOG

(Wed)

Galt Ouest, Sherbrooke, QC, J1K 2V8, Canada; gen tel (819) 575-7575

Circulation: 28,000fr; CCABSarah Beaulieu

Areas Served: Canada

JOURNAL DE SHERBROOKE

(Wed)

Rue Galt Ouest, Sherbrooke, QC, J1K 2V8, Canada; gen tel (819) 575-7575

Circulation: 63,500fr; CCABSarah Beaulieu

Areas Served: Canada

NOUVELLE DE SHERBROOKE

(Sun)

Rue Roy, Sherbrooke, QC, J1K 2X8, Canada; gen tel (819) 566-8022

Circulation: 51,200fr; ODCAndre Custeau

SOREL

JOURNAL LA VOIX

(Fri)

58 Charlotte St., Sorel, QC, J3P 1G3, Canada, Canada; gen tel (450) 743-8466; gen fax (450) 742-8567; disp adv e-mail publicite@journallavoix.net; ed e-mail redaction@journallavoix.net; web site www.journallavoix.net; monteregieweb.com

Circulation: 29,562fr; CCAB

Advertising: Open inch rate $1.00.

Established: 1960.

Parent Co.:

Les Hebdos Monteregiens

Adv. Rep. .... Parise Bergeron

Adv. Rep. .... Anne-Marie Nadeau

Ed. .... Joey Olivier

Ed. .... Johanne Berthiaume

Mechanical Specifications: Type page 15 x 17.

Areas Served: Canada

SOREL-TRACY

LES 2 RIVES

(Tues)

77 George St., Sorel-Tracy, QC, J3P 1C2, Canada; gen tel (450) 742-9408; gen fax (450) 742-2493; web site www.les2rives.com

Circulation: 1pd, 29,562fr; CCAB

Advertising: Open inch rate $1.00.

Parent Co.:

Les Hebdos Monteregiens

Gen. Mgr. .... Marcel Rainville

Ed. .... Louise Gregoire Racicot

Mechanical Specifications: Type page 10 1/4 x 17.

Areas Served: Canada

SOREL-TRACY EXPRESS

(Tues)

100 Rue Plante, Sorel-Tracy, QC, J3P 7P5, Canada; gen tel (450) 746-0886; adv tel (450) 746-0886; ed tel (450) 746-0886; gen fax (450) 746-0801; adv fax (450) 746-0801; ed fax (450) 746-0801; disp adv e-mail sorel-tracyexpress@tc.tc; ed e-mail sorel-tracyexpress@tc.tc; web site www.sorel-tracy-express.ca

Circulation: 31,018fr; CCAB

Digital Platform - Mobile: Apple, Android

Digital Platform - Tablet: Apple iOS, Android

Pres. .... Claude Poulin

Delivery Method: Mail, Racks

Areas Served: Canada

STANSTEAD

THE STANSTEAD JOURNAL

(Wed)

620 Dufferin, Stanstead, QC, J0B 3E0, Memphremagog, Canada; gen tel (819) 876-7514; disp adv e-mail ads@stanstead-journal.com; ed e-mail communique@stanstead-journal.com; web site www.stanstead-journal.com

Circulation: 1,625pd,; AAM

Advertising: Open inch rate $1.05.

Established: 1845.

Parent Co.:

Stanstead Journal Publishing

Digital Platform - Mobile: Apple, Android, Windows

Digital Platform - Tablet: Apple iOS, Android, Windows 7, Other

Sales Mgr. .... Jean-Yves Durocher

Prodn. Mgr. .... Mylene Piche

Delivery Method: Mail, Newsstand, Carrier, Racks

Areas Served: Memphremagog

TERREBONNE

LA REVUE DE TERREBONNE

(Wed)

231 Sainte-marie St., Terrebonne, QC, J6W 3E4, Lanaudiere, Canada; gen tel (450) 964-4444; gen fax (450) 471-1023; disp adv e-mail ventes@larevue.qc.ca; class adv e-mail petitesannonces@larevue.qc.ca; ed e-mail redaction@larevue.qc.ca; web site www.larevue.qc.ca

Circulation: 10pd, 55,990fr; Sworn/Estimate/Non-Audited

Advertising: Open inch rate $1.70 each agate line.

Established: 1959.

Parent Co.:

Guide Rouge

Le Trait d'Union

Digital Platform - Mobile: Apple, Android, Windows, Blackberry

Digital Platform - Tablet: Apple iOS, Android, Windows 7, Blackberry Tablet OS

Pub./Pres./CEO .... Gilles Bordonado

News Dir .... Veronick Talbot

Mktg Dir .... Daniel Soucy

Sales Coord .... Lise Bourdages

Areas Served: Lanaudiere

LE TRAIT D'UNION

(Wed)

231, Rue Sainte-marie, Terrebonne, QC, J6W 3E4, Canada; gen tel (450) 964-4444; gen fax (450) 471-1023; class adv e-mail petitesannonces@larevue.qc.ca; ed e-mail redaction@larevue.qc.ca; web site www.letraitdunion.com

Circulation: 10pd, 49,990fr; ODC

Advertising: Open inch rate $1.34.

Established: 1976.

Parent Co.:

La Revue de Terrebonne

Président .... Gilles Bordonado

Rédactrice en chef .... Véronick Talbot

Coordonnatrice aux ventes ...... Lise Bourdages

Delivery Method: Newsstand, Carrier, Racks

Areas Served: Terrebonne

Mascouche

THETFORD MINES

COURRIER FRONTENAC
(Wed)
Boulevard Frontenac Est Cp 789, C.p. 789, Thetford Mines, QC, G6G 5V3, Canada; gen tel (418) 338-5181
Circulation: 15pd, 22,826fr; CCABLucyl Lachance
Areas Served: Canada

TROIS-RIVIERES

L'ECHO DE TROIS-RIVIERES
(Wed)
3625 Blvd Du Chanoine-moreau, Trois-Rivieres, QC, G8Y 5N6, Canada; gen tel (819) 371-4823 ; adv tel (819) 371-4823 ; ed tel (819) 371-4823 ; gen fax (819) 371-4804; adv fax (819) 371-4804; ed fax (819) 371-4804; disp adv e-mail jocelyn.ouellet@quebecormedia.com; ed e-mail serge.buchanan@quebecormedia.com; web site www.lechodetroisrivieres.ca
Circulation: 68,580fr; CCAB
Digital Platform - Mobile: Apple, Android, Windows, Blackberry
Digital Platform - Tablet: Apple iOS, Android, Windows 7, Blackberry Tablet OS
Ed. .... Serge Buchanan
Delivery Method: Mail, Racks
Areas Served: Canada

L'HEBDO JOURNAL
(Wed)
525 Barkoff St., Ste. 205, Bureau 205, Trois-Rivieres, QC, G8T 2A5, Canada; gen tel (819) 379-1490; adv tel (866) 637-5236; gen fax (819) 379-0705; disp adv e-mail publicite.hj@transcontinental.ca; ed e-mail redaction.hj@transcontinental.ca; web site www.lhebdojournal.com
Circulation: 30pd, 60,411fr; CCAB
Advertising: Open inch rate $1.24.
Established: 1967.
Parent Co.:
Transcontinental Media
Sales Mgr. .... Alain Bernard
Pub. .... Sylviane Lussier
Ed. .... Emilie Valley
Areas Served: Canada

VAL D'OR

ABITIBI EXPRESS VAL D'OR
(Tues)
1834 3rd Ave. 2nd Floor, Val d'Or, QC, J9P 7A9, Canada; gen tel (819) 874-2151; web site www.abitibiexpress.ca
Circulation: 22pd, 31,088fr; CCAB
Areas Served: Canada

LE CITOYEN DE LA VALLEE DE L'OR
(Wed)
1462 Rue De La Quebecoise, Val d'Or, QC, J9P 5H4, Canada; gen tel (819) 874-4545; gen fax (819) 874-4547; web site http://www.lechoabitibien.ca/
Circulation: 36pd, 19,883fr; CCAB
Advertising: Open inch rate $1.38.
Parent Co.:
Quebecor Communications, Inc.
Gen. Mgr. .... Endre Renaud
Adv. Mgr. .... Carroline Couture
Mng. Ed. .... Louis Lavoie
Areas Served: Canada

VAUDREUIL-DORION

ETOILE DE L'OUTAOUAIS ST LAURENT
(Sat)
Avenue St-charles, Vaudreuil-Dorion, QC, J7V 2N4, Canada; gen tel (450) 455-6111
Circulation: 28pd, 56,711fr; ODCAngele Marcoux Prevost

JOURNAL PREMIERE EDITION
(Sat)
469 St. Charles Ave., Vaudreuil-Dorion, QC, J7V 2N4, Canada; gen tel (450) 455-7955; adv tel (450) 455-1050; gen fax (450) 455-3028; adv fax (450) 455-1050; web site www.journalpremiereedition.com
Circulation: 7pd, 61,880fr; CCAB
Areas Served: Canada

VICTORIAVILLE

L'ECHO DE VICTORIAVILLE
(Wed)
106 Blvd Bois-francs Nord, Victoriaville, QC, G6P 1E7, Canada; gen tel (819) 604-6686 ; adv tel (819) 604-6686 ; ed tel (819) 604-6686 ; gen fax (819) 604-6398 ; adv fax (819) 604-6398; ed fax (819) 604-6398; disp adv e-mail alain.saint-amand@quebecormedia.com; ed e-mail jean.crepeau@quebecormedia.com; web site www.lechodevictoriaville.ca
Circulation: 42,844fr; CCAB
Digital Platform - Mobile: Apple, Android, Windows, Blackberry
Digital Platform - Tablet: Apple iOS, Android, Windows 7, Blackberry Tablet OS
Ed. .... Jean Crepeau
Delivery Method: Mail, Racks
Areas Served: Canada

LA NOUVELLE
(Sun)
43 Notre Dame St. E., Cp 130, Victoriaville, QC, G6P 3Z4, Canada; gen tel (819) 758-6211; gen fax (819) 758-2759; web site www.lanouvelle.net
Circulation: 44,008fr; Sworn/Estimate/Non-Audited
Advertising: Open inch rate $1.18.
Parent Co.:
Transcontinental Media
Sales Dir. .... Pierre Gaudet
Pub. .... Michel Gauthier
Director de l'information...... Ghislain Chauvette
Mng. Ed. .... Sylvie Cote
Prodn. Mgr. .... Danielle Deveault

NOUVELLE UNION
(Wed, Fri)
Rue Notre-dame Est, Victoriaville, QC, G6P 3Z4, Canada; gen tel (819) 758-6211
Circulation: 13pd, 38,872fr; CCABLucie Lecours
Areas Served: Canada

VILLE-MARIE

LE JOURNAL TEMISCAMIEN
(Wed)
22 Rue Ste-anne, Ville-Marie, QC, J9V 2B7, Canada; gen tel (819) 622-1313; gen fax (819) 622-1333
Circulation: 8,500fr; Sworn/Estimate/Non-Audited
Advertising: Open inch rate $.64.
Ed. .... Lionel Lacasse

WAKEFIELD

THE LOW DOWN TO HULL AND BACK NEWS
(Wed)
815 Riverside Drive, Wakefield, QC, J0X 3G0, La Pêche, Quebec, Canada; gen tel (819) 459-2222; adv tel (613) 241-6767; ed tel (819) 459-2222; gen fax (819) 459-3831; disp adv e-mail lowdowndavid1@gmail.com; class adv e-mail classifieds@lowdownonline.com; ed e-mail general@lowdownonline.com; web site www.lowdownonline.com
Circulation: 2,531pd,; CMCA
Advertising: $8 per column inch.
Established: 1973.
Digital Platform - Mobile: Apple, Android, Windows, Blackberry
Digital Platform - Tablet: Apple iOS, Blackberry Tablet OS
General Manager.......... Liette Robert
Admin. Asst. .... Heather Hopewell
Pub./Owner .... Nikki Mantell
Circ. Mgr. .... Agnes McMillan
Ed. .... Melanie Scott
Reporter .... Ben Bulmer
Reporter .... NIcole McCormick
Mechanical Specifications: 5 columns

10.4" wide x 15.25"

300 dpi for ads
Delivery Method: Mail, Newsstand, Racks
Areas Served: La Pêche, Quebec

WEST MILL

THE MONITOR
(Thur)
345 Victoria, Ste. 508, West Mill, QC, H3Z 2M6, Canada; gen tel (514) 484-5610; gen fax (514) 484-6028; web site www.themonitor.ca
Circulation: 35,164fr; Sworn/Estimate/Non-Audited
Advertising: Open inch rate $1.44.
Ed. .... Yannick Pinel
Ed. in Chief .... Toula Foscolos
Mechanical Specifications: Type page 10 1/8 x 14 1/8; E - 8 cols, 2, 1/16 between; A - 8 cols, 2, 1/16 between; C - 8 cols, 1 1/8, 1/16 between.
Equipment & Software: : Hardware — APP/Power Mac; Software — QPS/QuarkXPress 4.0, Adobe/Photoshop 4.01, Adobe/Illustrator 6.0.

WESTMOUNT

THE WESTMOUNT EXAMINER
(Thur)
245 Victoria Street, Suite 210, Westmount, QC, H3Z 2M6, Canada; gen tel (514) 484-5610; adv tel (514) 484-5610; ed tel 514-484-5610; gen fax (514) 484-6028; disp adv e-mail marie-france.paquette@tc.tc; web site www.westmountexaminer.com
Circulation: 2pd, 9,282fr; CMCA
Advertising: Open inch rate $1.21.
Established: 1935.
Parent Co.:
Transcontinental Media
Digital Platform - Mobile: Apple
Digital Platform - Tablet: Apple iOS
Assistant publisher ...... Marie-France Paquette
Publisher.......... Patricia-Ann Beaulieu
Media Consultant.......... Harvey Aisthental
Mechanical Specifications: Type page 11 3/8 x 15; E - 8 cols, 1 1/6, 1/6 between; A - 8 cols, 1 1/6, 1/6 between; C - 8 cols, 1 1/6, 1/6 between.
Equipment & Software: : Hardware — APP/Mac; Software — QPS/QuarkXPress, Adobe/Photoshop 5.5, Adobe/Illustrator.
Delivery Method: Newsstand, Carrier, Racks
Areas Served: H3Y, H3Z

THE WESTMOUNT INDEPENDENT
(Tues)
310 Victoria Bldg. # 105, Westmount, QC, H3Z 2M9, Canada; adv tel (514) 223-3567; ed tel (514) 223-3578; gen fax (514) 935-9241; disp adv e-mail advertising@westmountindependent.com; web site www.westmountindependent.com
Circulation: 15,057fr; CMCA
Pub .... David Price
Advt Consultant .... Arleen Candiotti
Areas Served: Westmount, Quebec

WINDSOR

ETINCELLE
(Wed)
193 Rue Saint-georges, Windsor, QC, J1S 1J7, Canada; gen tel (819) 845-2705; gen fax (819) 845-5520; web site www.letincelle.qc.ca
Circulation: 36pd, 10,515fr; CCAB
Advertising: Open inch rate $.69.
Established: 1970.
Ed. in Chief .... Ralph Cote
Genevieve Gray
Ed. .... Claude Frenette
Mechanical Specifications: Type page 10 x 15; E - 8 cols, between; C - 8 cols, between.
Delivery Method: Carrier
Areas Served: Canada

SASKATCHEWAN

ASSINIBOIA

ASSINIBOIA TIMES
(Fri)
410 1st Ave. E., Assiniboia, SK, S0H 0B0, Canada, Canada; gen tel (306) 642-5901; gen fax (306) 642-4519; ed e-mail joyce@assiniboiatimes.ca
Circulation: 212pd, 2,937fr; CMCA
Advertising: Open inch rate $.95.
Parent Co.:
Prairie Newspaper Group
Glacier Media Group
Editor .... Joyce Simard
General Manager.......... Kevin Rasmussen
Mechanical Specifications: Type page 10 1/2 x 15; E - 6 cols, 1 7/12, between; A - 6 cols, 1 7/12, between; C - 6 cols, 1 7/12, between.
Equipment & Software: : Hardware — 5-PC; Software — WordPerfect.
Areas Served: Canada

BIGGAR

THE INDEPENDENT
(Thur)
102 3 Ave W, Biggar, SK, S0K 0M0, Canada, Canada; gen tel (306) 948-3344; gen fax (306) 948-2133
Circulation: 1,310pd, 538fr; CMCA
Advertising: Open inch rate $.71.
Pub. .... Margaret Hasein
Gen. Mgr. .... Daryl Hasein
Adv. Mgr. .... Urla Tyler
Ed. .... Kevin Bratigan
Mechanical Specifications: Type page 11 x 17; E - 6 cols, 1 1/2, 1/6 between; A - 6 cols, 1 1/2, 1/6 between; C - 6 cols, 1 1/2, 1/6 between.
Equipment & Software: : Hardware — APP/Mac; Software — Adobe/PageMaker 6.0.
Areas Served: Canada

CANORA

CANORA COURIER
(Wed)
123 First Ave. E., Canora, SK, S0A 0L0, Canada; gen tel (306) 563-5131; gen fax (306) 563-6144; disp adv e-mail sales.canoracourier@sasktel.net; class adv e-mail office.canoracourier@sasktel.net; ed e-mail canoracourier@sasktel.net; web site canoracourier.com
Circulation: 1,136pd, 9fr; CMCA
Advertising: Open inch rate $.78.
Parent Co.:
Glacier Media Group
Pub .... Ken Lewchuk
Mechanical Specifications: Type page 10 1/4 x 15 1/2; E - 6 cols, 1 2/3, between; A - 6 cols, 1 2/3, between; C - 6 cols, 1 2/3, between.
Equipment & Software: : Hardware — 10-PC; Software — In design
Delivery Method: Mail, Newsstand
Areas Served: Canada

PREECEVILLE PROGRESS
(Thur)

123 First Ave. E., Canora, SK, S0A 0L0, Canada; gen tel (306) 563-5131; gen fax (306) 563-6144; disp adv e-mail sales.canoracourier@sasktel.net; class adv e-mail office.canoracourier@sasktel.net; ed e-mail canoracourier@sasktel.net; web site http://www.preecevilleprogress.com/
Circulation: 971pd, 4fr; CMCA
Advertising: Open inch rate $.76.
Parent Co.:
Canora Courier
Glacier Media GroupKen Lewchuk
Mechanical Specifications: Type page 10 1/4 x 15 1/2; E - 6 cols, 1 2/3, between; A - 6 cols, 1 2/3, between; C - 6 cols, 1 2/3, between.
Equipment & Software: : Hardware — 10-PC; Presses — 3-KP/News King; Software — Archetype/Corel Draw, WordPerfect, Ventura.
Areas Served: Canada

THE KAMSACK TIMES
(Thur)
123 First Ave. E., Canora, SK, S0A 0L0, Canada; gen tel (306) 563-5131; adv tel (306) 563-5131; ed tel (306) 542-2626; gen fax (306) 563-6144; disp adv e-mail k.lewchuk@sasktel.net; class adv e-mail office.canoracourier@sasktel.net; ed e-mail kamsacktimes@sasktel.net; web site kamsacktimes.com
Circulation: 1,100pd, 5fr; CMCA
Advertising: Open inch rate $.81.
Parent Co.:
Canora Courier
Glacier Media Group
Publisher....................................Ken Lewchuk
Mechanical Specifications: Type page 10 1/4 x 15 1/2; E - 6 cols, 1 2/3, between; A - 6 cols, 1 2/3, between; C - 6 cols, 1 2/3, between.
Equipment & Software: : Hardware — 10-PC; Presses — 3-KP/News King; Software — Archetype/Corel Draw, WordPerfect, Ventura.
Delivery Method: Mail, Newsstand
Areas Served: Canada

CARLYLE

CARLYLE OBSERVER
(Fri)
132 Main St., Carlyle, SK, S0C 0R0, Canada; gen tel (306) 453-2525; gen fax (306) 453-2938; web site www.carlyleobserver.com
Circulation: 113pd, 2,877fr; CMCA
Advertising: Open inch rate $.91.
Established: 1936.
Parent Co.:
Glacier Media Group
Pub...Cindy Moffett
Mechanical Specifications: Type page 11 x 17; E - 5 cols, 2, between; A - 5 cols, 2, between; C - 6 cols, 1 1/2, between.
Equipment & Software: : Hardware — 4-PC; Presses — 2-ABD.
Areas Served: Canada

CARNDUFF

GAZETTE-POST NEWS
(Fri)
106 Broadway, Carnduff, SK, S0C 0S0, Canada; gen tel (306) 482-3252; gen fax (306) 482-3373
Circulation: 1,006pd,; CMCA
Advertising: Open inch rate $.74.
Established: 1899.
Pub...Bruce Shwanke
Mechanical Specifications: Type page 10 x 21; E - 6 cols, 1 1/2, between; A - 6 cols, 1 1/2, between; C - 6 cols, 1 1/2, between.
Equipment & Software: : Hardware — 2-APP/Mac; Software — QPS/QuarkXPress 4.0, QPS/QuarkXPress 4.1.
Areas Served: Canada

CORONACH

TRIANGLE NEWS
(Mon)
118 Centre St., Coronach, SK, S0H 0Z0, Canada; gen tel (306) 267-3381; web site www.trianglenews.sk.ca
Circulation: 339pd, 336fr; CMCA
Advertising: Open inch rate $.77.
Parent Co.:
Transcontinental
Delivery Method: Mail, Newsstand
Areas Served: S0H - 0B0, 0Z0, 1B0, 2J0, 2W0, 3R0, 4K0, 4Lo, S0C 0Ko

CRAIK

CRAIK WEEKLY NEWS
(Mon)
221 Third St., Box 360, Craik, SK, S0G 0V0, R.M. of Craik No. 222, Canada; gen tel (306) 734-2313; gen fax (306) 734-2789; disp adv e-mail craiknews@sasktel.net
Circulation: 880pd,; Sworn/Estimate/Non-Audited
Advertising: Open inch rate $.51.
Established: 1908.
Ed. .... Harve Friedel
Mechanical Specifications: Type page 10 1/4 x 15; E - 6 cols, 1 17/30, 1/6 between; A - 6 cols, 1 17/30, 1/6 between; C - 6 cols, 1 17/30, 1/6 between.
Equipment & Software: : Hardware — PC; Software — INDESIGN CS4
Delivery Method: Mail
Areas Served: R.M. of Craik No. 222

CUT KNIFE

HIGHWAY 40 COURIER
(Wed)
200 Steele St., Cut Knife, SK, S0M 0N0, Canada; gen tel (306) 398-4901; gen fax (306) 398-4909
Circulation: 440pd, 13fr; CMCA
Advertising: Open inch rate $.52.
Established: 1959.Editions: 49— Highway 40 Courier
Publisher/Editor .... Lorie Gibson
Mechanical Specifications: Type page 10 1/2 x 15 1/2; E - 6 cols, 1 5/8, 3/16 between; A - 6 cols, 1 5/8, 3/16 between; C - 6 cols, 1 5/8, 3/16 between.
Equipment & Software: : Hardware — iMac 2.5 ghz /Laserjet 4050N, Ricoh; Presses — Located off site - North Battleford Publishing; Software — Adobe/InDesign CS3, Photoshop CS3, MicrosoftWord 2011.
Delivery Method: Mail, Newsstand
Areas Served: Canada

DAVIDSON

DAVIDSON LEADER
(Mon)
205 Washington St., Davidson, SK, S0G 1A0, Canada; gen tel (306) 567-2047; gen fax (306) 567-2900; web site www.leaderonline.ca
Circulation: 1,238pd, 44fr; CMCA
Advertising: Open inch rate $.65.
Established: 1904.
Parent Co.:
Davidson Publishing Ltd.
Publisher..................................... Tara De Ryk
Mechanical Specifications: Type page 10 1/4 x 15 3/4; E - 5 cols, 1 29/30, 1/6 between; A - 5 cols, 1 29/30, 1/6 between; C - 5 cols, 1 29/30, 1/6 between.
Equipment & Software: : Hardware — 4-APP/Mac; Software — Adobe Creative Suite
Delivery Method: Mail, Newsstand
Areas Served: Canada

ESTERHAZY

THE ESTERHAZY MINER-JOURNAL
(Mon)
606 Veterans Ave., Esterhazy, SK, S0A 0X0, Canada; gen tel (306) 745-6669; gen fax (306) 745-2699; web site www.minerjournal.com
Circulation: 1,334pd, 0fr; CMCA
Advertising: Open inch rate $.71.
Established: 1907.
Adv. Mgr. ....Brenda Matchett
Ed. ....Helen Solmes
Mechanical Specifications: Type page 10 1/4 x 16; E - 5 cols, 1 11/12, between; A - 5 cols, 1 11/12, between; C - 5 cols, 1 11/12, between.
Equipment & Software: : Hardware — APP/Mac; Software — Adobe/PageMaker 5.0.
Areas Served: Canada

ESTEVAN

ESTEVAN MERCURY
(Wed)
68 Souris Ave N., Estevan, SK, S4A 2M3, Canada; gen tel (306) 634-2654; gen fax (306) 634-3934; disp adv e-mail adsales@estevanmercury.ca; ed e-mail editor@estevanmercury.ca; web site www.estevanmercury.ca
Circulation: 269pd, 5,015fr; AAM
Advertising: $12.30.
Established: 1903.
Parent Co.:
Glacier Media Group
Digital Platform - Mobile: Apple, Android, Windows, Blackberry
Digital Platform - Tablet: Apple iOS, Android, Windows 7, Blackberry Tablet OS, Kindle, Nook, Kindle Fire
Pub... Rick Sadick
Prod. Mgr. .... Jihyun Choi
Ed. ....Norm Park
Mechanical Specifications: Please call
Delivery Method: Mail, Newsstand, Carrier, Racks
Areas Served: Canada

SOUTHEAST LIFESTYLES
(Thur)
300 Kensington Avenue, Estevan, SK, S4A 2A7, Canada; gen tel (306) 634-5112; gen fax (306) 634-2588; web site http://www.sasklifestyles.com/
Circulation: 18pd, 6,585fr; CMCA
Advertising: Open inch rate $1.19.
Established: 1999.
Parent Co.:
Glacier Media Group
Digital Platform - Mobile: Apple, Android, Windows, Blackberry, Other
Digital Platform - Tablet: Apple iOS, Android, Windows 7, Blackberry Tablet OS, Kindle, Nook, Kindle Fire, Other
Pub... Rick Sadick
Ed. ....Norm Park
Mechanical Specifications: Please Call
Delivery Method: Mail, Newsstand, Carrier, Racks
Areas Served: Canada

ESTON

ESTON-ELROSE PRESS REVIEW
(Tues)
108 W. Main St., Eston, SK, S0L 1A0, Canada; gen tel (306) 962-3221; gen fax (306) 962-4445
Circulation: 753pd,; CMCA
Advertising: Open inch rate $9.38.
Parent Co.:
Jamac Publishing
Pub..Stewart Crump
Adv. Mgr. ....Barry Malindine
Ed. ....Tim Crump
Equipment & Software: : Hardware — 3-APP/Mac.
Areas Served: Canada

FOAM LAKE

FOAM LAKE REVIEW
(Mon)
325 Main St., Foam Lake, SK, S0A 1A0, Canada; gen tel (306) 272-3262; gen fax (306) 272-4521; web site www.foamlakereview.com
Circulation: 1,123pd, 3fr; CMCA
Advertising: Open inch rate $.70.
Ed. ....Bob Johnson
Equipment & Software: : Hardware — APP/Mac; Presses — ABD/375, Cord/C4 sheet fit, HI/Letter Press 11x15; Software — QPS/QuarkXPress, Adobe/PageMaker, Adobe/Typestyler.
Areas Served: Canada

FORT QU'APPELLE

FORT QU'APPELLE TIMES
(Tues)
141 Broadway St. W., Fort Qu'Appelle, SK, S0G 1S0, Canada; gen tel (306) 332-5526; gen fax (306) 332-5414
Circulation: 837pd,; CMCA
Advertising: Open inch rate $.86.
Established: 1951.
Pub...Sandra Huber
Adv. Mgr. ....Cassandra Archer
Ed. ....Linda Aspinall
Mechanical Specifications: Type page 10 1/4 x 16; E - 6 cols, 2, between; A - 6 cols, 2, between; C - 6 cols, 2, between.
Equipment & Software: : Hardware — APP/Mac; Software — QPS/QuarkXPress 4.1.
Delivery Method: Mail, Newsstand
Areas Served: Canada

GRAVELBOURG

GRAVELBOURG TRIBUNE
(Mon)
611 Main St., Gravelbourg, SK, S0H 1X0, R.M of Gravelbourg, Canada; gen tel (306) 648-3479; adv tel (306) 648-3479; ed tel (306) 648-3479; gen fax (306) 648-2520; adv fax (306) 648-2520; disp adv e-mail trib.ads@sasktel.net; class adv e-mail (306) 648-3479; ed e-mail trib.editorial@sasktel.net; web site http://gravelbourgtribune.wixsite.com/tribune
Circulation: 875pd, 30fr; CMCA
Advertising: Open inch rate $.59.
Established: 1986.
Digital Platform - Mobile: Apple
Digital Platform - Tablet: Other
Ed ....Paul Boisvert
Mechanical Specifications: Type page 10 1/4 x 15 1/2; E - 5 cols, 1 7/8, between; A - 5 cols, 1 7/8, between; C - 5 cols, 1 7/8, between.
Equipment & Software: : Hardware — APP/Mac; Presses — ABD/360, KP; Software — Quark Express/Photoshop/Microsoft Word
Delivery Method: Mail, Newsstand
Areas Served: R.M of Gravelbourg

GRENFELL

BROADVIEW EXPRESS
(Mon)
813 Desmond St., Grenfell, SK, S0G 2B0, Canada; gen tel (306) 697-2722; adv tel (306) 697-2722; gen fax (306) 697-2689; adv fax (306) 697-2689; disp adv e-mail sunnews@sasktel.net; ed e-mail sunnews@sasktel.net; web site www.grenfellsun.sk.ca
Circulation: 266pd, 158fr; CMCA
Advertising: Open inch rate $.68.
Established: 1965.
Parent Co.:
Transcontinental Media
Circ. Mgr. .... Suzette Stone
Sales Associate .... Mariann Hughes
Mechanical Specifications: Type page 10 1/8 x 15 1/2; E - 6 cols, 1 1/2, between; A - 6 cols,

1 1/2, between; C - 6 cols, 1 1/2, between.
Equipment & Software: : Hardware — 4-PC; Presses — ABD; Software — Adobe/PageMaker, QPS/QuarkXPress.
Delivery Method: Mail, Newsstand
Areas Served: Canada

GRENFELL SUN
(Mon)
813 Desmond St., Grenfell, SK, S0G 2B0, Canada; gen tel (306) 697-2722; gen fax (306) 697-2689; disp adv e-mail sunnews@sasktel.net; ed e-mail sunnews@sasktel.net; web site grenfellsun.sk.ca
Circulation: 710pd, 128fr; CMCA
Advertising: Open inch rate $.73.
Established: 1892.
Parent Co.:
Transcontinental Media
Office Manager............................ Sarah Pacio
Mechanical Specifications: Type page 10 1/8 x 15 1/2; E - 6 cols, 1 1/2, between; A - 6 cols, 1 1/2, between; C - 6 cols, 1 1/2, between.
Equipment & Software: : Hardware — 4-PC; Software — Adobe/PageMaker, QPS/QuarkXPress.
Delivery Method: Mail, Newsstand
Areas Served: Canada

GULL LAKE

ADVANCE SOUTHWEST (FORMERLY GULL LAKE ADVANCE)
(Mon)
1462 Conrad Ave., Gull Lake, SK, S0N 1A0, Canada; gen tel (306) 672-3373; adv tel (306) 741-2448; disp adv e-mail sales@advancesouthwest.com; ed e-mail kate@advancesouthwest.com; web site www.advancesouthwest.com
Circulation: 600pd, 7,900fr; Sworn/Estimate/Non-Audited
Advertising: Open inch rate $1.12.
Established: 1909.
Parent Co.:
Winquist Ventures Ltd.
Pub ....Kate Winquist
Delivery Method: Mail, Carrier
Areas Served: Southwest Saskatchewan
Postal Codes: S0N, S9H, S0G

HERBERT

THE HERALD
(Tues)
716 Herbert Ave., Herbert, SK, S0H 2A0, Canada, Canada; gen tel (306) 784-2422; gen fax (306) 784-3246; disp adv e-mail herbertherald@sasktel.net; class adv e-mail herbertherald@sasktel.net; ed e-mail herbertherald@sasktel.net
Circulation: 1,442pd, 5fr; CMCA
Advertising: Open inch rate $.70.
Established: 1911.
Digital Platform - Mobile: Apple
Ed. ....Rhonda J. Ens
Mechanical Specifications: Type page 10 1/4 x 15; E - 6 cols, 1 5/8, 1/4 between; A - 6 cols, 1 5/8, 1/4 between; C - 6 cols, 1 5/8, 1/4 between.
Equipment & Software: : Hardware — APP/Mac; Software — Microsoft/Word, QPS/QuarkXPress, WriteNow.
Delivery Method: Mail, Newsstand
Areas Served: Canada

HUDSON BAY

HUDSON BAY POST-REVIEW
(Thur)
20 Railway Ave., Hudson Bay, SK, S0E 0Y0, Canada, Canada; gen tel (306) 865-2771; gen fax (306) 865-2340; disp adv e-mail post-review3@sasktel.net
Circulation: 910pd, 27fr; CMCA
Advertising: Open inch rate $.90.
Established: 1950.
Mgr.. Sherry Pilon
Mechanical Specifications: Type page 10.25 x 15 1/2; E - 6 cols, 1 1/2, 1/3 between; A - 6 cols, 1 1/2, 1/3 between; C - 6 cols, 1 1/2, 1/3 between.
Delivery Method: Mail, Newsstand
Areas Served: Canada

HUMBOLDT

EAST CENTRAL TRADER
(Fri)
535 Main Street, Humboldt, SK, S0K 2A0, Canada; gen tel (306) 682-2561; gen fax (306) 682-3322; disp adv e-mail sford@humboldtjournal.ca; ed e-mail cmcrae@humboldtjournal.ca; web site www.humboldtjournal.ca
Circulation: 5pd, 5,443fr; CMCA
Ed. .... Becky Zimmer
Group Publisher..................... Brent Fitzpatrick
Areas Served: Canada

THE HUMBOLDT JOURNAL
(Wed)
535 Main St., Humboldt, SK, S0K 2A0, Canada; gen tel (306) 682-2561; gen fax (306) 682-3322; disp adv e-mail sford@humboldtjournal.ca; ed e-mail cmcrae@humboldtjournal.ca; web site www.humboldtjournal.ca
Circulation: 1,765pd, 29fr; CMCA
Advertising: Open inch rate $.1.05.
Established: 1905.
Parent Co.:
Glacier Media Group
Ed. .... Becky Zimmer
Mechanical Specifications: Type page Tabloid 11x17
Column size 1.583 inches
Delivery Method: Mail, Newsstand, Carrier, Racks
Areas Served: Canada

INDIAN HEAD

INDIAN HEAD-WOLSELEY NEWS
(Thur)
508 Grand Ave., Indian Head, SK, S0G 2K0, Canada; gen tel (306) 695-3565; gen fax (306) 695-3448
Circulation: 938pd, 20fr; CMCA
Advertising: Open inch rate $.74.
Pub.. Jodi Gendron
Circ. Mgr.................................... Kerri McCabe
Ed. .... Marcel Gendron
Mechanical Specifications: Type page 10 1/4 x 15.
Equipment & Software: : Hardware — IBM; Software — QPS/QuarkXPress 4.1, Adobe/PageMaker 6.5.
Areas Served: Canada

ITUNA

THE ITUNA NEWS
(Mon)
214 1st Avenue N.e., Ituna, SK, S0A 1N0, Canada; gen tel (306) 795-2412; gen fax (306) 795-3621; web site www.ituna.ca
Circulation: 578pd, 1fr; CMCA
Advertising: Open inch rate $.54.
Prodn. Mgr. .... Bob Johnson
Ed
Heidi Spilchuk
Areas Served: Canada

KINDERSLEY

KINDERSLEY CLARION
(Wed)
919 Main St., Kindersley, SK, S0L 1S0, Kindersley, Canada; gen tel (306) 463-4611; gen fax (306) 463-6505; disp adv e-mail ads.jamac@gmail.com; class adv e-mail classifieds.jamac@gmail.com; ed e-mail editor.jamac@gmail.com; web site theclarion.ca
Circulation: 1,238pd,; Sworn/Estimate/Non-Audited
Advertising: Open inch rate $.87.
Parent Co.:
Jamac Publishing
Pub...Stewart Crump
Ed. ....Kevin Mcbain
Salesperson................................ Laurie Kelly
Mechanical Specifications: Type page 13 4/5 x 21 2/5; E - 7 cols, between; A - 7 cols, between; C - 8 cols, between.
Equipment & Software: : Hardware — APP/Mac; Presses — G/Community; Software — QPS/QuarkXPress, Baseview.
Areas Served: Kindersley

LEADER NEWS
(Wed)
919 Main St., Kindersley, SK, S0L 1S0, Canada, Canada; gen tel (306) 463-4611; gen fax (306) 463-6505; disp adv e-mail editor.jamac@gmail.com
Circulation: 710pd,; CMCA
Advertising: Open inch rate $.67.
Parent Co.:
Jamac Publishing
Pub...Stewart Crump
Adv. Mgr. .... Barry Malindine
Ed. .... Kevin McBain
Equipment & Software: : Hardware — APP/Mac; Presses — G/Community; Software — QPS/QuarkXPress, Baseview.
Areas Served: Canada

WEST CENTRAL CROSSROADS
(Fri)
919 Main St., Kindersley, SK, S0L 1S0, Canada; gen tel (306) 463-4611; gen fax (306) 463-6505
Circulation: 15,160fr; CMCA
Advertising: Open inch rate $1.36.
Parent Co.:
Jamac Publishing
Pub...Stewart Crump
Ed. .... Tim Crump
Equipment & Software: : Hardware — APP/Mac; Presses — G/Community; Software — QPS/QuarkXPress, Baseview.

KIPLING

KIPLING CITIZEN
(Fri)
#4 - 207 - 6th Avenue, Kipling, SK, S0G 2S0, Canada; gen tel (306) 736-2535; adv tel (306) 736-2535; ed tel (306) 736-2535; gen fax (306) 736-8445; adv fax (306) 736-8445; ed fax (306) 736-8445; disp adv e-mail thecitizen@sasktel.net; class adv e-mail thecitizen@sasktel.net; ed e-mail thecitizen@sasktel.net
Circulation: 730pd, 13fr; CMCA
Advertising: $9.10 col inch.
Established: 1936.
Parent Co.:
Glacier Media Group
Gen. Mgr. .... Laura Kish
Reporter .... Connie Schwalm
Sales Representative .... Sean Choo-Foo
Mechanical Specifications: Type page 9.83 x 15.7; 6 cols, .15 between columns
Equipment & Software: : Hardware — 3-PC; Software — Aldus/PageMaker 6.5, Microsoft/Works,
Adobe InDesign CS3, Adobe Photoshop CS3, Open Office, WordPerfect
Delivery Method: Mail, Newsstand
Areas Served: Canada

LA RONGE

THE NORTHERNER
(Thur)
715 La Ronge Ave., La Ronge, SK, S0J 1L0, Canada, Canada; gen tel (306) 425-3344; gen fax (306) 425-2827; disp adv e-mail ads.northerner@sasktel.net; class adv e-mail ads.northerner@sasktel.net; ed e-mail northerner@sasktel.net
Circulation: 198pd, 136fr; CMCA
Advertising: Open inch rate $.61.
Established: 1975.
Office Mgr./Circ...................... Debra Parkinson
Mechanical Specifications: Type page 10.25 x 15.75; E - 6 cols, 1 11/12, 1/6 between; A - 6 cols, 1 11/12, 1/6 between; C - 6 cols, 1 11/12, 1/6 between.
Equipment & Software: : Hardware — 3-APP/Mac; Software — CS3
Delivery Method: Mail, Newsstand
Areas Served: Canada

LANGENBURG

LANGENBURG FOUR-TOWN JOURNAL
(Wed)
102 Carl Ave., Langenburg, SK, S0A 2A0, Canada; gen tel (306) 743-2617; gen fax (316) 743-2299
Circulation: 1,199pd,; CMCA
Advertising: Open inch rate $.68.
Editor/Publisher ....Bill Johnston
Areas Served: Canada

LANIGAN

LANIGAN ADVISOR
(Mon)
42 Main Street, Lanigan, SK, S0K 2M0, Canada; gen tel (306) 365-2010; gen fax (306) 365-3388
Circulation: 828pd, 15fr; CMCA
Publisher/Editor ....Linda Mallett
Areas Served: Canada

LLOYDMINSTER

LLOYDMINSTER SOURCE
(Tues, Thur)
5921-50th Ave, Lloydminster, SK, S9V 1W5, Canada; gen tel (306) 825-5111; gen fax (306) 825-5147; ed e-mail colin@lloydminstersource.com
Circulation: 13,889fr; CMCA
Publisher..................................... Reid Keebaugh
Mng. Ed. .... Mike D'Armour
Prod. Mgr. ....Karrie Chang
Areas Served: Canada

LUMSDEN

WATERFRONT PRESS
(Thur)
635 James St. N., Lumsden, SK, S0G 3C0, Canada; gen tel (306) 731-3143; gen fax (306) 731-2277
Circulation: 167pd, 3,993fr; CMCA
Advertising: Open inch rate $.99.
Jacqueline Chouinard
Lucien ChouinardEd.s
Mechanical Specifications: Type page 10 x 15 1/4; E - 5 cols, 2, between; A - 5 cols, 2, between; C - 5 cols, 2, between.
Equipment & Software: : Hardware — PC; Software — Adobe/PageMaker, Corel/Photo Paint, Quickbooks.
Areas Served: S0G 0H0, S0G 0W0, S0G 3C0, S0G 3C0, S0G 4L0, S0G 4P0

MACKLIN

MACKLIN MIRROR
(Wed)
4701 Herald St., Macklin, SK, S0L 2C0, Canada; gen tel (306) 753-2424; gen fax (306) 753-2432; disp adv e-mail macklin.jamac@gmail.com; ed e-mail stacey.jamac@gmail.com
Circulation: 638pd, 33fr; CMCA
Advertising: Open inch rate $.68.

Established: 1977.
Parent Co.:
Jamac PublishingEditions: 1,000— Macklin Mirror

Editor/Publisher .... Delilah Reschny
Reporter .... Stacey Lavallie
Mechanical Specifications: 10.25" X 16" high
Equipment & Software: : Hardware — Mac OSX ; Software — Adobe InDesign CS4, Adobe Acrobat Pro, Acrobat Distiller, Adobe Photoshop CS4
Delivery Method: Mail, Newsstand, Racks
Areas Served: Canada

MAPLE CREEK

MAPLE CREEK & SOUTHWEST ADVANCE TIMES
(Tues)
116 Harder Street, Maple Creek, SK, S0N 1N0, Canada; gen tel (306) 662-2100; gen fax (306) 662-5005; disp adv e-mail ads@maplecreeknews.com; ed e-mail editorial@maplecreeknews.com; web site www.maplecreeknews.com
Circulation: 1,506pd, 76fr; CMCA
Parent Co.:
Alta. Newspaper Group, Ltd
Manager .... Angela Litke
Advertising Sales .... Della Fournier
Areas Served: Canada

THE MAPLE CREEK NEWS
(Thur)
116 Harder St., Maple Creek, SK, S0N 1N0, Canada; gen tel (306) 662-2133; gen fax (306) 662-5005; disp adv e-mail ads@maplecreeknews.com; ed e-mail editorial@maplecreeknews.com; web site www.maplecreeknews.com
Circulation: 1,514pd,; CMCA
Advertising: Open inch rate $.80.
Established: 1902.
Parent Co.:
Alta. Newspaper Group, Ltd
Ad Sales .... Deb Ridley
Office/Circulation Manager .... Megan Chamney
Mechanical Specifications: Type page 13 x 21 1/2; E - 6 cols, 2, 1/6 between; A - 6 cols, 2, 1/6 between; C - 6 cols, 2, 1/6 between.
Equipment & Software: : Hardware — 4-APP/Mac; Software — QPS/QuarkXPress 4.1.
Areas Served: Canada

MEADOW LAKE

NORTHERN PRIDE
(Thur)
219 Centre Street, Meadow Lake, SK, S9X 1Z4, Canada; gen tel (306) 236-5353; disp adv e-mail pride.terry@sasktel.net; class adv e-mail pride.terry@sasktel.net; ed e-mail pride.terry@sasktel.net; web site www.northernprideml.com
Circulation: 1,638pd, 4,283fr; CMCA
Advertising: $1.15 Agate line.
Established: 1993.
Pub .... Terry Villeneuve
Delivery Method: Mail, Newsstand, Carrier, Racks
Areas Served: Canada

MELFORT

NORTH EAST SUN
(Fri)
901 Main St., Melfort, SK, S0E 1A0, Canada; gen tel (306) 752-5737; gen fax (306) 752-5358; disp adv e-mail cassie.johnson@sunmedia.ca; ed e-mail greg.wiseman@sunmedia.ca; web site www.melfortjournal.com
Circulation: 21,761fr; CMCAKen Sorensen
Areas Served: Canada

THE MELFORT JOURNAL
(Tues)
901 Main St., Melfort, SK, S0E 1A0, Canada; gen tel (306) 752-5737; gen fax (306) 752-5358; web site www.melfortjournal.com
Circulation: 1,132pd,; CMCA
Advertising: Open inch rate $.90.
Parent Co.:
Postmedia Network Inc.
Quebecor Communications, Inc.
Pub .... Ken Sorensen
Equipment & Software: ; Software — Microsoft, QPS/QuarkXPress.
Areas Served: Canada

MELVILLE

THE MELVILLE ADVANCE
(Fri)
218 3rd Ave. W., Melville, SK, S0A 2P0, Stanley, Canada; gen tel (306) 728-5448; gen fax (306) 728-4004; disp adv e-mail sales@grasslandsnews.ca; class adv e-mail contact@grasslandsnews.ca; ed e-mail editor@grasslandsnews.ca; web site www.melvilleadvance.com
Circulation: 1,679pd, 17fr; CMCA
Advertising: Open inch rate $.70.
Established: 1928.
Parent Co.:
Grasslands News GroupGeorge Brown
Group Publisher .... Chris Ashfield
Mechanical Specifications: Type page 10 1/8 x 15 3/4; E - 6 cols, 2 1/4, 1/4 between; A - 6 cols, 2 1/4, 1/4 between; C - 6 cols, 2 1/4, 1/4 between.
Equipment & Software: ; Presses — Itek/960
Delivery Method: Mail, Newsstand
Areas Served: Stanley

MOOSE JAW

FYI
(Wed)
44 Fairford St W., Moose Jaw, SK, S6H 1V1, Canada; gen tel (306) 692-6441; ed e-mail editorial@mjtimes.sk.ca; web site www.mjtimes.sk.ca
Circulation: 24,086fr; CMCA
Areas Served: Canada

MOOSOMIN

WORLD-SPECTATOR
(Mon)
714 Main Street, Moosomin, SK, S0G 3N0, Canada; gen tel (306) 435-2445; gen fax (306) 435-3969; web site www.world-spectator.com
Circulation: 3,609pd,; CMCA
Advertising: Open inch rate $.93.
Established: 1884.
Ed. .... Kevin Weedmark
Mechanical Specifications: Type page 10 x 16 1/2; E - 6 cols, 1/6 between; A - 6 cols, 1/6 between; C - 6 cols, 1/6 between.
Equipment & Software: : Hardware — 6-APP/Mac; Software — QPS/QuarkXPress 3.32.
Delivery Method: Mail, Newsstand
Areas Served: Moosomin, Rocanville, Wapella, Wawota, Redvers, Maryfield, Spy Hill, Tantallon, Elkhorn, St Lazare

MUENSTER

ORDER OF ST. BENEDICT
(Wed)
100 College Dr., Muenster, SK, S0K 2Y0, Canada; gen tel (306) 682-1772; gen fax (306) 682-5285; disp adv e-mail pm.ads@stpeterspress.ca; ed e-mail pm.canadian@stpeterspress.ca; web site www.prairiemessenger.ca
Circulation: 4,300pd,; CMCA
Advertising: Open inch rate $13.95.
Established: 1904.
Adv. Mgr. .... Gail Kleefeld
Ed. .... Peter Novecosky
Assoc. Ed. .... Maureen Weber
Assoc. Ed. .... Don Ward
Layout Artist .... Lucille Stewart
Mechanical Specifications: Type page 10 1/8 x 15; E - 5 cols, 2, 1/6 between; A - 5 cols, 2, 1/6 between; C - 5 cols, 2, 1/6 between.
Equipment & Software: : Hardware — APP/Power Mac; Presses — 4-G/Community, HI; Software — QPS/QuarkXPress 8.15.
Delivery Method: Mail
Areas Served: Canada

NIPAWIN

NIPAWIN JOURNAL
(Wed)
117 1st Ave., Nipawin, SK, S0E 1E0, Canada; gen tel (306) 862-4618; gen fax (306) 862-4566; ed e-mail greg.wiseman@sunmedia.ca; web site www.nipawinjournal.com
Circulation: 1,093pd,; CMCA
Advertising: Open inch rate $.95.
Parent Co.:
Postmedia Network Inc.
Quebecor Communications, Inc.
Gen. Mgr. .... Ken Sorenson
Managing Ed. .... Greg Wiseman
Mechanical Specifications: Type page 10 5/8 x 14 3/4; E - 6 cols, 1 1/2, 1/4 between; A - 6 cols, 1 1/2, 1/4 between; C - 6 cols, 1 1/2, 1/4 between.
Equipment & Software: : Hardware — 6-APP/Mac; Presses — 4-G/Community.
Areas Served: Canada

NOKOMIS

LAST MOUNTAIN TIMES
(Tues)
103 1st Ave. W., Nokomis, SK, S0G 3R0, RM Wreford, Canada; gen tel (306) 528-2020; adv tel (306) 528-2020; ed tel (306) 528-2020; gen fax (306) 528-2090; disp adv e-mail editor@lastmountaintimes.ca; class adv e-mail editor@lastmountaintimes.ca; ed e-mail editor@lastmountaintimes.ca; web site www.lastmountaintimes.ca
Circulation: 850pd, 40fr; Sworn/Estimate/Non-Audited
Advertising: Open inch rate $0.78.
Established: 1908.
Parent Co.:
Last Mountain Times
Owner/Pub Ed .... Dave Degenstien
Mechanical Specifications: Type page 10 1/4 x 15 3/4; E - 5 cols, 1 29/30, 1/6 between; A - 5 cols, 1 29/30, 1/6 between; C - 5 cols, 1 29/30, 1/6 between.
Equipment & Software: : Hardware — 4 - PCs; Software — Adobe InDesign CS6
Delivery Method: Mail, Newsstand
Areas Served: RM Wreford
Note: Printed off-site by contracted printer

NORTH BATTLEFORD

BATTLEFORDS NEWS-OPTIMIST
(Tues)
892 104th St., North Battleford, SK, S9A 1M9, Canada; gen tel (306) 445-7261; gen fax (306) 445-3223; ed e-mail newsoptimist.news@sasktel.net; web site www.newsoptimist.ca
Circulation: 2,288fr; CMCA
Advertising: Open inch rate $1.03.
Parent Co.:
Glacier Media Group
Ed. .... Becky Doig
Mechanical Specifications: Type page 11 1/4 x 15 2/3; E - 6 cols, 1 1/2, 1/6 between; A - 6 cols, 1 1/2, 1/6 between; C - 6 cols, 1 7/12, 1/6 between.
Equipment & Software: : Hardware — APP/Mac; Presses — G/Community; Software — QPS/QuarkXPress 3.3, Adobe/PageMaker 5.0, Multi-Ad/Creator 3.5, Adobe/Photoshop 2.0.
Areas Served: Canada

REGIONAL OPTIMIST
(Thur)
892-104th Street, North Battleford, SK, S9A 3E6, Canada; gen tel (306) 445-7261; gen fax (306) 445-3223; ed e-mail newsoptimist.news@sasktel.net; web site www.newsoptimist.ca
Circulation: 13,514fr; CMCA
Ed .... Becky Doig
Areas Served: Canada

OUTLOOK

THE OUTLOOK
(Thur)
108 Saskatchewan Ave. E, Outlook, SK, S0L 2N0, Canada, Canada; gen tel (306) 867-8262; gen fax (306) 867-9556
Circulation: 1,208pd, 49fr; CMCA
Advertising: Open inch rate $.78.
Established: 1909.
Parent Co.:
Glacier Media Group
General Manager .... Delwyn Luedtke
Mechanical Specifications: Type page 10 1/4 x 14 1/2; E - 5 cols, 1/6 between; A - 6 cols, 1/6 between;
Equipment & Software: : Hardware — APP/Mac; Presses — G/Community; Software — Adobe/CS6
Delivery Method: Mail, Newsstand
Areas Served: Canada

OXBOW

THE OXBOW HERALD
(Mon)
Po Box 420, Oxbow, SK, S0C 2B0, Canada; gen tel (306) 483-2323; gen fax (306) 483-5258; disp adv e-mail lorena@oxbowherald.sk.ca; ed e-mail liz@oxbowherald.sk.ca; web site www.SaskNewsNow.com
Circulation: 908pd,; CMCA
Advertising: Open inch rate $.82.
Parent Co.:
Transcontinental Media
Advertising Manger .... Lorena Wolensky
Editor .... Lizz Bottrell
Reporter .... Marilyn Johnson
Mechanical Specifications: Type page 10 1/2 x 14 1/2; E - 5 cols, 2, 1/6 between; A - 5 cols, 2, 1/6 between; C - 5 cols, 2, 1/6 between.
Delivery Method: Mail, Racks
Areas Served: Canada

RADVILLE

RADVILLE DEEP SOUTH STAR
(Thur)
#1-420 Floren St., Radville, SK, S0C 2G0, Canada, Canada; gen tel (306) 869-2202; gen fax (306) 869-2533; disp adv e-mail circulation@rdstar.sk.ca; web site www.rdstar.sk.ca
Circulation: 624pd,; CMCA
Advertising: $.75 per agate line net gross.
Parent Co.:
Transcontinental Media
Pub. .... Roger Holmes
Areas Served: Canada

REGINA

EAU VIVE (L')
(Thur)
210-1440 9th Ave N, Regina, SK, S4R 8B1, Canada; gen tel (306) 347-0481; gen fax (306) 565-3450; web site http://nonprofits.accesscomm.ca/leauvive/web/
Circulation: 1,046pd,; CMCA
Publisher .... Jean-Pierre Picard
Administrative Assistant .... Angeline Feumba

Areas Served: Canada

ROSETOWN

THE ROSETOWN EAGLE

(Mon)
114 2nd Ave. W., Rosetown, SK, S0L 2V0, Canada, Canada; gen tel (306) 882-4348; adv tel (306) 882-4348; ed tel (306) 882-4348; gen fax (306) 882-4204; disp adv e-mail ads.eagle@gmail.com; class adv e-mail frontdesk.eagle@gmail.com; ed e-mail editor.eagle@gmail.com
Circulation: 1,562pd, 57fr; CMCA
Advertising: Open inch rate $10.50.
Established: 1909.
Owner/publisher .... Stewart Crump
Simone Gaudet
Ads .... Loretta Torrence
David McIver
Mechanical Specifications: Type page 12 x 20 1/2; E - 6 cols, 1 5/8, 1/4 between; A - 6 cols, 1 5/8, 1/4 between; C - 6 cols, 1 5/8, 1/4 between.
Equipment & Software: : Hardware — 5-APP/Mac; Software — Aldus/PageMaker.
Delivery Method: Mail, Newsstand
Areas Served: Canada

SHAUNAVON

THE SHAUNAVON STANDARD

(Tues)
346 Centre St., Shaunavon, SK, S0N 2M0, Canada, Canada; gen tel (306) 297-4144; gen fax (306) 297-3357; disp adv e-mail jgregoire@theshaunavonstandard.com; ed e-mail standard@theshaunavonstandard.com
Circulation: 916pd,; CMCA
Advertising: Open inch rate $.69.
Established: 1913.
Parent Co.:
Alta. Newspaper Group, Ltd
Ed. .... Paul MacNeil
Adv. Sales .... Joanne Gregoire
Mechanical Specifications: Type page 11 1/2 x 17; E - 5 cols, 2, 1/4 between; A - 5 cols, 2, 1/4 between; C - 5 cols, 2, 1/4 between.
Equipment & Software: : Hardware — 4-APP/Mac; Software — Multi-Ad, Adobe/PageMaker.
Areas Served: Canada

SHELLBROOK

SHELLBROOK CHRONICLE

(Fri)
46 Main St., Shellbrook, SK, S0J 2E0, Canada, Canada; gen tel (306) 747-2442; gen fax (306) 747-3000; disp adv e-mail chads@sbchron.com; web site http://shellbrookchronicle.com/
Circulation: 155pd, 3,484fr; CMCA
Advertising: Open inch rate $13.32.
Established: 1912.
Pub.. C.J. Pepper
Mechanical Specifications: Type page 10 1/4 x 15; E - 6 cols, 1 7/12, 1/6 between; A - 6 cols, 1 7/12, 1/6 between; C - 6 cols, 1 7/12, 1/6 between.
Equipment & Software: : Hardware — 6-PC; Software — QPS/QuarkXPress, Microsoft/Paintbrush, Archetype/Corel Draw, Microsoft/Windows 95, Adobe/Acrobat, Adobe/Illustrator.
Areas Served: Canada

SPIRITWOOD HERALD

(Fri)
46 Main St., Shellbrook, SK, S0J 2E0, Canada, Canada; gen tel (306) 747-2442; gen fax (306) 747-3000; disp adv e-mail chads@sbchron.com; web site www.spiritwoodherald.com
Circulation: 52pd, 2,435fr; Sworn/Estimate/Non-Audited
Advertising: $13.65/col inch.
Publisher................................. Clark J Pepper
Mechanical Specifications: Type page 10 1/4 x 15; E - 6 cols, 1 7/12, 1/6 between; A - 6 cols, 1 7/12, 1/6 between; C - 6 cols, 1 7/12, 1/6 between.
Equipment & Software: : Hardware — 6-PC; Software — QPS/QuarkXPress, Microsoft/Paintbrush, Archetype/Corel Draw, Microsoft/Windows 95, Adobe/Acrobat, Adobe/Illustrator.
Delivery Method: Mail, Newsstand, Racks
Areas Served: S0J 0L0, S0M 0Y0, S0M 0Z0, S0J 1N0, S0M 1S0, S0M 1W0, S0J 1V0, S0J 2G0, S0J 2M0

SWIFT CURRENT

PRAIRIE POST

(Fri)
600 Chaplin Street East, Swift Current, SK, S9H 1J3, Canada; gen tel (306) 773-8260; adv tel (306) 773-8260; ed tel (306) 773-8260; gen fax (306) 773-0504; adv fax (306) 773-0504; ed fax (306) 773-0504; disp adv e-mail ktumback@prairiepost.com; ed e-mail mliebenberg@prairiepost.com; web site http://www.prairiepost.com
Circulation: 17,814fr; CMCA
Director of Sales and Marketing .... Doug Evjen
Advertising................................ Stacey Powell
Areas Served: Canada

THE SOUTHWEST BOOSTER

(Thur)
30 4th Ave. Nw, Swift Current, SK, S9H 3X4, Canada, Canada; gen tel (306) 773-9321; gen fax (306) 773-9136; disp adv e-mail boosterads@swbooster.com; web site www.swbooster.com
Circulation: 16,985fr; CMCA
Advertising: Open inch rate $1.29.
Established: 1969.
Parent Co.:
Transcontinental Media
Pub... Bob Watson
Adv. Mgr. .... Mark Soper
Circ. Mgr... Ken Mattice
Mng. Ed.................................. Scott Anderson
Prodn. Mgr. .... George Driscoll
Mechanical Specifications: Type page 10 3/8 x 15 5/8; E - 6 cols, 1 15/16, 3/16 between; A - 6 cols, 1 15/16, 3/16 between; C - 6 cols, 1 15/16, 3/16 between.
Equipment & Software: : Hardware — APP/Power Mac 7.5.5, QMS/Laser Printer 860, Avantra Image Setter; Presses — 3-KP; Software — QPS/QuarkXPress 6.0, Macromedia/Freehand 8, Adobe/Photoshop 4.0, Adobe/Illustrator 5.5, Adobe/InDesign.
Areas Served: Canada

TISDALE

PARKLAND REVIEW

(Fri)
1004-102 Ave., Tisdale, SK, S0E 1T0, Canada, Canada; gen tel (306) 873-4515; gen fax (306) 873-4712; disp adv e-mail adsrecorder@sakstel.net; ed e-mail newsrecorder@sakstel.net
Circulation: 11,625fr; CMCA
Advertising: Open inch rate $1.26.
Parent Co.:
Glacier Media Group
Adv. Mgr. .... August Grandguillar
Ed. .... Brent Fitzpatrick
Prodn. Mgr. .... Gord Anderson
Adv. Mgr.. Dan Sully
Delivery Method: Mail
Areas Served: Canada

THE TISDALE RECORDER

(Wed)
1004 102nd Ave., Tisdale, SK, S0E 1T0, Canada, Canada; gen tel (306) 873-4515; gen fax (306) 873-4712; disp adv e-mail newsrecorder3@sasktel.net; ed e-mail newsrecorder@sasktel.net
Circulation: 669pd, 25fr; CMCA
Advertising: Open inch rate $1.03.
Parent Co.:
Glacier Media Group
Pub... Brent Fitzpatrick
Ed. .... James Tarrant
Ad. .... August Grandguillot
Areas Served: Canada

UNITY

UNITY-WILKIE PRESS-HERALD

(Fri)
310 Main St., Unity, SK, S0K 4L0, Canada, Canada; gen tel (306) 228-2267; gen fax (306) 228-2767; disp adv e-mail ads.northwest.herald@sasktel.net; ed e-mail northwest.herald@sasktel.net; web site http://unitystories.com/press-herald/
Circulation: 1,400pd, 0fr; Sworn/Estimate/Non-Audited
Advertising: Open inch rate $.54.
Parent Co.:
Prairie Newspaper Group
Ed. .... Helena Long
Office Manager .... Jackie Boser
ad designer .... Tim Holtorf
Mechanical Specifications: Type page 10 1/12 x 16; E - 5 cols, 1 11/12, 1/6 between; A - 5 cols, 1 11/12, 1/6 between; C - 5 cols, 1 11/12, 1/6 between.
Equipment & Software: : Hardware — 4-APP/Mac; Presses — ABD/9480; Software — Adobe/Photoshop, Adobe/PageMaker, WordPerfect 2.0.
Delivery Method: Mail, Newsstand
Areas Served: Canada

WEYBURN

WEYBURN THIS WEEK

(Fri)
115 2nd St Ne, WEYBURN, SK, S4H0T7, Canada, Canada; gen tel (306) 842-3900; gen fax (306) 842-2515; web site www.weyburnthisweek.com
Circulation: 3pd, 5,546fr; CMCA
Advertising: Open inch rate $.95.
Parent Co.:
Glacier Media Group
Pub.. Rick Major
Mechanical Specifications: Type page 10 1/2 x 15; E - 6 cols, 1 7/12, 1/6 between; A - 6 cols, 1 7/12, 1/6 between; C - 6 cols, 1 7/12, 1/6 between.
Equipment & Software: : Hardware — APP/Power Mac 7300-180; Software — Adobe/PageMaker 6.5, Adobe/Illustrator 7.0, Adobe/Photoshop 4.0.
Areas Served: Canada

WADENA

WADENA NEWS

(Mon)
102 First St Ne, Wadena, SK, S0A 4J0, Canada, Canada; gen tel (306) 338-2231; gen fax (306) 338-3421; web site http://wadenanews.ca/
Circulation: 1,913pd, 79fr; CMCA
Advertising: Open inch rate $10.08.
Established: 1908.
Pub... Alison Squires
Mechanical Specifications: Type page 10 1/3 x 15 1/2; E - 5 cols, 1 14/15, 1/6 between; A - 5 cols, 1 14/15, 1/6 between; C - 5 cols, 1 14/15, 1/6 between.
Equipment & Software: : Hardware — MAC
Delivery Method: Mail, Newsstand
Areas Served: Canada

WAKAW

THE WAKAW RECORDER

(Wed)
224 First St. S., Wakaw, SK, S0K 4P0, Canada, Canada; gen tel (306) 233-4325; gen fax (306) 233-4386
Circulation: 1,375pd, 14fr; CMCA
Advertising: agate line 0.55.
Ed. .... Dwayne Biccum
Delivery Method: Mail
Areas Served: Canada

WARMAN

CLARK'S CROSSING GAZETTE

(Thur)
109 Klassen Street West, 109 Klassen Street West, Warman, SK, S0K 4S0, Corman Park, Canada; gen tel (306) 668-0575; gen fax (306) 668-3997; disp adv e-mail ads@ccgazette.ca; class adv e-mail ads@ccgazette.ca; ed e-mail editor@ccgazette.ca; web site http://www.ccgazette.ca - 5,000(views) 1,400(visitors)
Circulation: 15pd, 16,500fr; Sworn/Estimate/Non-Audited
Advertising: $15.94.
Established: 2008.
Parent Co.:
JENSON PUBLISHING
Publisher..................................... Terry Jenson
Mechanical Specifications: 6 col. x 212 lines page
Tabloid
Equipment & Software: : Hardware — Macintosh OS; Presses — Ultraviolet Web Offset; Software — Adobe CS5.5
Delivery Method: Mail, Newsstand, Carrier, Racks
Areas Served: Corman Park

WATROUS

THE WATROUS MANITOU

(Mon)
309 Main St., Watrous, SK, S0K 4T0, Canada, Canada; gen tel (306) 946-3343; gen fax (306) 946-2026; web site www.thewatrousmanitou.com
Circulation: 1,387pd, 21fr; CMCA
Advertising: Open inch rate $9.66.
Established: 1933.
Mechanical Specifications: Type page 10 1/4 x 15 3/4; E - 6 cols, 1 15/16, 3/16 between; A - 6 cols, 1 15/16, 3/16 between
Equipment & Software: : Hardware — Mac platform; Software — Adobe/InDesign
Delivery Method: Mail
Areas Served: Canada

WATSON

NAICAM NEWS

(Fri)
100-102 Main St., Watson, SK, S0K 4V0, Canada, Canada; gen tel (306) 287-4388; gen fax (306) 287-3308
Circulation: 396pd,; Sworn/Estimate/Non-Audited
Advertising: Open inch rate $.72.
Pub./Gen. Mgr. .... Karen Mitchell
Mechanical Specifications: Type page 10 1/4 x 15 3/4; E - 5 cols, 1 29/30, between; A - 5 cols, 1 29/30, between; C - 5 cols, 1 29/30, between.
Equipment & Software: : Hardware — APP/Mac; Software — Adobe/PageMaker 5.0.
Areas Served: Canada

WEYBURN

WEYBURN REVIEW

(Wed)
904 East Ave., Weyburn, SK, S4H 2Y8, Canada, Canada; gen tel (306) 842-7487; gen fax (306) 842-0282; web site www.weyburnreview.com
Circulation: 2,189pd, 59fr; CMCA
Advertising: Open inch rate $1.14.

Established: 1909.
Parent Co.:
Glacier Media Group
Digital Platform - Mobile: Apple, Android, Windows, Blackberry
Digital Platform - Tablet: Apple iOS, Android, Windows 7, Blackberry Tablet OS
Pub...Rick Major
Mng. Ed..Patricia Ward
Mechanical Specifications: 5 (9.67") column broadsheet x 278 lines deep.
11 picas per column.
Equipment & Software: : Hardware — APP/Mac; Presses — G/Community, lk; Software — InDesign 5.5
Delivery Method: Mail, Newsstand, Carrier
Areas Served: Canada

WHITEWOOD

THE WHITEWOOD HERALD

(Fri)
708 S. Railway St., Whitewood, SK, S0G 5C0, Canada, Canada; gen tel (306) 735-2230; gen fax (306) 735-2899; disp adv e-mail ads@whitewoodherald.com; class adv e-mail contact@whitewoodherald.com; ed e-mail herald@whitewoodherald.com; web site www.whitewoodherald.sk.ca
Circulation: 667pd, 88fr; CMCA
Advertising: Open inch rate $.62.
Pub...Chris Ashfield
Mechanical Specifications: Type page 10 1/4 x 16; E - 5 cols, 1 7/8, 3/16 between; A - 5 cols, 1 7/8, 3/16 between; C - 5 cols, 1 7/8, 3/16 between.
Equipment & Software: : Hardware — 2-APP/Mac; Software — QPS/QuarkXPress, Adobe/Streamline, Adobe/Illustrator, Adobe/Acrobat, Adobe/Photoshop.
Delivery Method: Mail, Newsstand
Areas Served: Canada

WYNYARD

THE ADVANCE/GAZETTE

(Mon)
301 Bosworth St., Wynyard, SK, S0A 4T0, Canada, Canada; gen tel (306) 554-2224; gen fax (306) 554-3226
Circulation: 1,211pd, 18fr; CMCA
Advertising: Open inch rate $.75.
Ed. ....Bob Johnson
Mechanical Specifications: Type page 12 x 17; E - 5 cols, 2, between; A - 5 cols, 2, between; C - 5 cols, 2, between.
Equipment & Software: : Hardware — 4-PC; Software — Microsoft/Access, Archetype/Corel Draw.
Areas Served: Canada

YORKTON

YORKTON THIS WEEK

(Wed)
20 3rd Ave. N., YORKTON, SK, S3N 2X3, Canada, Canada; gen tel (306) 782-2465; gen fax (306) 786-1898; disp adv e-mail classifieds@yorktonthisweek.com; ed e-mail editorial@yorktonthisweek.com; web site www.yorktonthisweek.com
Circulation: 2,777pd, 59fr; Sworn/Estimate/Non-Audited
Advertising: Open inch rate $1.51.
Parent Co.:
Glacier Media Group
Publisher....................................Jim Ambrose
Prodn. Mgr. ....Debbie Barr
Equipment & Software: : Hardware — 9-APP/Mac
Delivery Method: Newsstand, Carrier
Areas Served: Canada

YUKON TERRITORY

WHITEHORSE

YUKON NEWS

(Wed, Fri)
211 Wood St., Whitehorse, YT, Y1A 2E4, Canada; gen tel (867) 667-6285; adv tel (867) 667-6283; ed tel (867) 667-6285; gen fax (867) 668-3755; adv fax (867) 668-3755; ed fax (867) 668-3755; disp adv e-mail mthomas@yukon-news.com; class adv e-mail wordads@yukon-news.com; ed e-mail editor@yukon-news.com; web site www.yukon-news.com
Circulation: 1,729pd, 2,537fr; AAM
Advertising: Open line rate $1.38.
Established: 1960.
Parent Co.:
Black Press Ltd.
Digital Platform - Mobile: Apple, Android, Windows, Blackberry
Digital Platform - Tablet: Apple iOS, Android, Windows 7, Blackberry Tablet OS, Kindle, Nook, Kindle Fire
Publisher.....................................Mike Thomas
Mechanical Specifications: Type page 11 1/2 x 15 1/2; E - 5 cols, 1 11/12, 1/6 between; A - 5 cols, 1 11/12, 1/6 between; C - 5 cols, 1 11/12, 1/6 between.
Equipment & Software: : Hardware — APP/Macs, APP/iMac; Presses — 6-G/Community; Software — Adobe CS3
Delivery Method: Mail, Newsstand, Racks
Areas Served: Canada

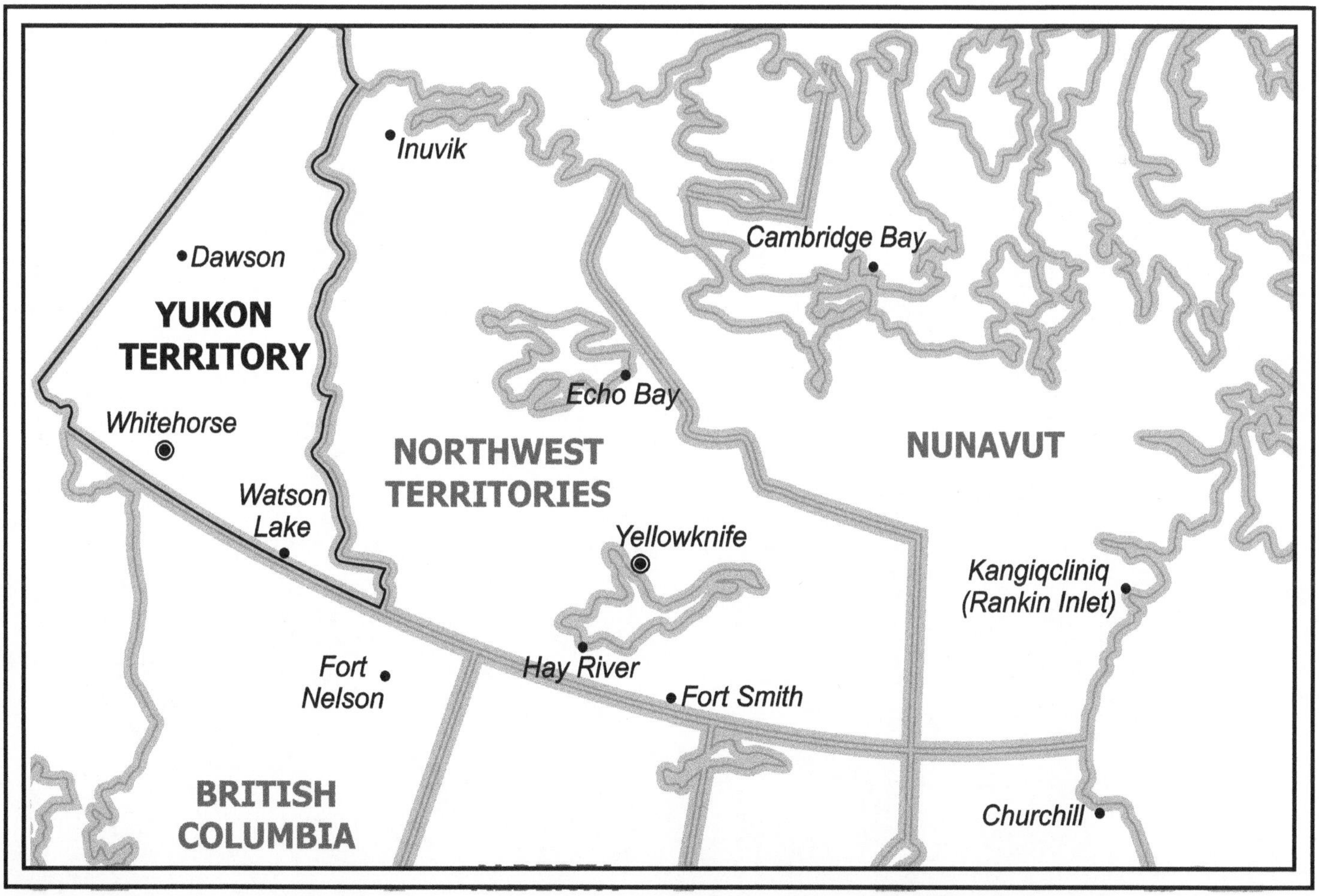

Section II

Shopper and TMC Publications Published in the United States and Canada

United States

Alabama 2
Arizona 2
Arkansas 3
California 3
Colorado 5
Connecticut 6
Delaware 6
Florida 7
Georgia 8
Idaho 10
Illinois 11
Indiana 14
Iowa 17
Kansas 22
Kentucky 23
Louisiana 24
Maine 25
Maryland 25
Massachusetts 25
Michigan 26
Minnesota 31
Mississippi 36
Missouri 36
Montana 38
Nebraska 39
New Hampshire 41
New Jersey 41
New Mexico 41
New York 42
North Carolina 49
North Dakota 51
Ohio 51
Oklahoma 54
Oregon 55
Pennsylvania 56
Rhode Island 59
South Carolina 60
South Dakota 60
Tennessee 61
Texas 63
Utah 66
Vermont 67
Virginia 67
Washington 67
West Virginia 68
Wisconsin 69
Wyoming 75

Canada

Alberta 75
British Columbia 76
Nova Scotia 76
Ontario 76
Quebec 78
Saskatchewan 78

SHOPPER/TMC PUBLICATIONS IN THE U.S.

ALABAMA

ALBERTVILLE

THE SHOPPER
(Tues)
PO Box 1729, Albertville, AL, 35950-0028, USA; tel (256) 840-3000; fax (256) 840-2987
Circulation: 13,600fr; Sworn/Estimate/Non-Audited
Advertising: Open inch rate $4.10
Pub. .... Ben Shurett

ENTERPRISE

DALEVILLE SUN-COURIER
(Wed)
628A Glover Ave, Enterprise, AL, 36330-2014, USA; tel (334) 393-2969; fax (334) 393-2987; e-mail news@southeastsun.com; web site www.southeastsun.com
Circulation: 37pd,6,056fr; CVC
Advertising: Open inch rate $15.60
Established: 1986
Adv. Mgr. .... Russell Quattlebaum
Ed. .... Kim Lewis
Co-pub. .... Caroline Quattlebaum
Circ. Mgr .... Janet Corneil
Prod. Mgr .... Slayton Shaw
Mechanical Specifications: Type page 9.9"x20"; 6 cols
Equipment: Hardware — APP; Software — Indesign/CS.
Delivery Method: Newsstand, Carrier, Racks
Zip Codes Served: 36322, 36362, 36352

QST PUBLICATIONS-(CONSOLIDATED)
(Wed)
628A Glover Ave, Enterprise, AL, 36330-2014, USA; tel (334) 393-2969; fax (334) 393-2987; e-mail publisher@southeastsun.com; adv e-mail sales@southeastsun.com; ed e-mail news@southeastsun.com; web site www.southeastsun.com
Circulation: 388pd,20,875fr; CVC
Established: 1982
Co-publisher .... Russell Quattlebaum
Circulation Manager .... Janet Corneil
Co-publisher .... Caroline Quattlebaum
Delivery Method: Mail, Carrier, Racks

SOUTHEAST SUN
(Wed)
628A Glover Ave, Enterprise, AL, 36330-2014, USA; tel (334) 393-2969; fax (334) 393-2987; e-mail publisher@southeastsun.com; web site www.southeastsun.com
Circulation: 294pd,14,365fr; CVC
Advertising: Open inch rate $15.60
Established: 1982
Adv. Mgr. .... Russell Quattlebaum
Mng. Ed .... Kay Kirkland
Opns. Mgr. .... Caroline Quattlebaum
Circ. Mgr .... Janet Corneil
Prod. Mgr .... Slayton Shaw
Mechanical Specifications: Type page 9.9" x 20"; 6 cols
Delivery Method: Racks
Zip Codes Served: 36331, 36330, 36351, 36318, 36316

FORT PAYNE

SAND MOUNTAIN SHOPPER'S GUIDE
(Tues)
811 Greenhill Blvd NW, Fort Payne, AL, 35967, USA; tel (256) 845-2550; fax (256) 845-7459; adv e-mail advertising@times-journal.com ; ed e-mail news@times-journal.com ; web site www.times-journal.com
Circulation: 12,500fr; CAC
Advertising: Open inch rate $9.75
Established: 1900
Group: Southern Newspapers Inc.
Publisher .... Tricia Dunne
Delivery Method: Mail
Zip Codes Served: 35967,35968,35971,35978,35986,35988,35989,35984

GADSDEN

TIMES2
(Wed)
401 Locust St, Gadsden, AL, 35901-3737, USA; tel (256) 549-2000; adv tel (256) 549-2077; ed tel (256) 549-2049; fax (256) 549-2013; adv fax (256) 549-2013; ed fax (256) 549-2105; e-mail glen.porter@gadsdentimes.com; adv e-mail david.bragg@gadsdentimes.com; ed e-mail news@gadsdentimes.com; web site www.gadsdentimes.com
Circulation: 19,000fr; Sworn/Estimate/Non-Audited
Advertising: Open inch rate $10.00
Established: 2005
Group: GateHouse Media, Inc.
Digital Platform - Mobile: Apple, Android, Windows, Blackberry
Digital Platform - Tablet: Apple iOS, Android, Windows 7, Blackberry Tablet OS, Kindle, Nook, Kindle Fire
Pub. .... Glen Porter
Circ. Mgr. .... John Chapman
Sales Mgr. .... David Bragg
Mechanical Specifications: Type page 12 x 21 1/2; E - 6 cols, 1 13/16, between; A - 6 cols, 1 13/16, between; C - 9 cols, 1 13/16, between.
Equipment: ; Software — QPS/QuarkXPress.
Delivery Method: Mail, Carrier, Racks
Zip Codes Served: 35901, 35903, 35904, 35905, 35906, 35907, 35954, 35956

LUVERNE

BONUS EXPRESS
(Wed)
118 S Forest Ave, Luverne, AL, 36049-1502, USA; tel (334) 335-3541; fax (334) 371-7104; web site www.greenvilleadvocate.com
Circulation: 6,500fr; Sworn/Estimate/Non-Audited
Advertising: Open inch rate $6.75
Pub. .... Ed Darling
Bus. Mgr. .... Tammy Faulk

MOBILE

AMERICAN CLASSIFIEDS - MOBILE
(Thur)
PO Box 91329, Mobile, AL, 36691-1329, USA; tel (251) 344-5454; fax (251) 344-5743; e-mail mobile@americanclassifies.com; web site www.americanclassifieds.com
Circulation: 0pd,24,330fr; CVC
Advertising: Open inch rate $16.65
Established: 1989
Digital Platform - Mobile: Windows
Digital Platform - Tablet: Windows 7
Publisher .... Tom Carter
Mechanical Specifications: Type page 10"x16"; 1 col.x 1.2"; 8 col. page
Delivery Method: Racks
Zip Codes Served: 36507,36509,36521,36525,36526,36527,36528,36532,36535,36541,36544,36551,36560,36567,36571,36572,36575,36578,36580,36582,36587,36602,36603,36604,36605,36606,36607,36609,36610,36611,36612,36618,36619,36693,36695.

MONTGOMERY

BULLETIN BOARD
(Thur)
425 Molton St, Montgomery, AL, 36104-3523, USA; tel (334) 272-1225; fax (334) 271-2143; adv e-mail ads@thebulletinboard.com; web site www.thebulletinboard.com
Circulation: 17,250pd,300fr; Sworn/Estimate/Non-Audited
Advertising: Open inch rate $13.25
Group: Gannett
Gen. Mgr. .... French Salter
Mechanical Specifications: Type page 7 1/2 x 10; A - 3 cols, 2 1/2, 1/6 between; C - 3 cols, 2 1/2, 1/6 between.
Equipment: Hardware — APP/Super Mac; Software — QPS/QuarkXPress 3.32.

PELHAM

AMERICAN CLASSIFIEDS - BIRMINGHAM
(Thur)
250 Yeager Pkwy, Pelham, AL, 35124-1800, USA; web site www.americanclassifieds.com
Circulation: 0pd,33,538fr; CVC
Advertising: Open inch rate $29.00Brian Merrill
Mechanical Specifications: Type page 10" x 16"; 8 cols
Delivery Method: Racks
Zip Codes Served: BIRMINGHAM, AL MSA

ARIZONA

COTTONWOOD

KUDOS
(Wed)
116 S Main St, Cottonwood, AZ, 86326-3909, USA; tel (928) 634-2241; fax (928) 634-2312; e-mail pmiller@verdenews.com; adv e-mail pmiller@verdenews.com; web site www.verdenews.com
Circulation: 11,499fr; VAC
Established: 1947
Group: Western News&Info, Inc.
Publisher .... Pam Miller
Editor .... Dan Engler
Delivery Method: Mail
Zip Codes Served: Yavapai County

SMART SHOPPER
(Wed)
116 S Main St, Cottonwood, AZ, 86326-3909, USA; tel (928) 634-2241; fax (928) 634-2312; e-mail pmiller@verdenews.com; adv e-mail pmiller@verdenews.com; web site www.verdenews.com
Circulation: 18,077fr; VAC
Established: 1947
Group: Western News&Info, Inc.
Publisher .... Pam Miller
Editor .... Dan Engler
Delivery Method: Mail
Zip Codes Served: Yavapai County

GLOBE

GILE COUNTY ADVANTAGE
(Tues)
298 N Pine St, Globe, AZ, 85501-2516, USA; tel (928) 425-7121; fax (928) 425-7001; web site www.silverbelt.com
Circulation: 3,700fr; Sworn/Estimate/Non-Audited
Advertising: Open inch rate $7.00
Pub. .... Marc Marian
Ed. .... Andrea Marcandi

LAKE HAVASU CITY

RIVER EXTRA
(Sun)
2225 Acoma Blvd W, Lake Havasu City, AZ, 86403-2907, USA; tel (928) 453-4237; fax (928) 855-2637; adv fax (928) 855-9892; e-mail sales@havasunews.com; adv e-mail ads@havasunews.com; web site www.havasunews.com
Circulation: 6,445fr; VAC
Advertising: Open inch rate $21.38
Group: Western News&Info, Inc.
Pub. .... Michael E. Quinn
Ed. .... Becky Maxedon
Prodn. Mgr. .... Kelly Parks
Mechanical Specifications: Type page 11 5/8 x 21; E - 6 cols, 1 13/16, between; A - 6 cols, 1 13/16, between; C - 6 cols, 1 13/16, between.
Zip Codes Served: 86403, 86404, 86406

SMART BUYER
(Tues)
2225 Acoma Blvd W, Lake Havasu City, AZ, 86403-2907, USA; tel (928) 453-4237; adv tel (928) 855-2197; fax (928) 855-2637; adv fax (928) 855-9892; e-mail sales@havasunews.com; adv e-mail ads@havasunews.com; web site www.havasunews.com
Circulation: 0pd,27,044fr; VAC
Advertising: Open inch rate $21.38
Group: Western News&Info, Inc.
Pub. .... Michael E. Quinn
Ed. .... Becky Maxedon
Mechanical Specifications: Type page 11 5/8 x 21; E - 6 cols, 1 13/16, between; A - 6 cols, 1 13/16, between; C - 6 cols, 1 13/16, between.
Zip Codes Served: 86403, 86404, 86406

PRESCOTT

SMART SHOPPER
(Wed)
1958 Commerce Center Cir, Prescott, AZ, 86301-4454, USA; tel (928) 445-3333; fax (928) 445-4756; web site www.dcourier.com
Circulation: 53,061fr; VAC
Group: Western News&Info, Inc.
Executive Editor .... Tim Wiederaenders
Prodn. Dir. .... Gary Brinkman
Publisher/CEO .... Kelly Soldwedel
Advertising Director .... Joe Mickelson

SMART SHOPPER ASH FORK
(Wed)
1958 Commerce Center Cir, Prescott, AZ, 86301-4454, USA; tel (928) 445-3333; adv tel (928) 445-3333; fax (928) 445-4756; adv fax (928) 445-4756; web site www.dcourier.com

Circulation: 1,052fr; VAC
Group: Western News&Info, Inc.
Executive Editor................Tim Wiederaenders
Prodn. Dir.................................Gary Brinkman
Publisher/CEO.........................Kelly Soldwedel
Advertising Director...................Joe Mickelson
Delivery Method: Mail
Zip Codes Served: Ash Fork

SIERRA VISTA

SIERRA VISTA HERALD - SUNDAY BRAVO SHOPPER

(Sun) (Special Thanksgiving Day issue)
102 Fab Ave, Sierra Vista, AZ, 85635-1741, USA; tel (520) 458-9440; adv tel (520) 515-4630; ed tel (520) 515-4610; fax (520) 459-0120; e-mail becky.bjork@svherald.com; adv e-mail becky.bjork@svherald.com; ed e-mail eric.petermann@svherald.com; web site www.svherald.com
Circulation: 10,372pd,8,854fr; VAC
Advertising: Open inch rate $15.25
Established: 1955
Group: Wick Communications
Digital Platform - Mobile: Apple, Windows
Digital Platform - Tablet: Apple iOS, Windows 7
Co-Chrmn.....................................Robert Wick
Pub. ....Philip Vega
Adv. Dir..Becky Bjork
Dir., Mktg. ....Patricia Wick
Circ. Mgr................................Jeremy Feldman
Sports Ed...................................Matt Hickman
Data Processing Mgr.................Joan Hancock
IT Mgr...Don Judd
Prodn. Mgr., Composing........Rebecca Jackson
Prodn. Foreman, Press/CameraRhett Hartgrove
Managing Editor.......................Eric Petermann
Mechanical Specifications: Type page 9 89/100 x 21; E - 6 cols, 1 56/100, 5/6 between; A - 6 cols, 1 56/100, 5/6 between; C - 9 cols, 1, 58/100 between.
Equipment: ; Presses — 15-unit Goss Community
Delivery Method: Mail, Newsstand, Carrier, Racks
Zip Codes Served: 85635, 85650, 85615, 85616, 85636, 85603
Note: Advertisements in the Sierra Vista Herald (mS) are automatically included in the Bisbee Daily Review (mS).

SUN CITY

GLENDALE-PEORIA TODAY

(Fri)
10102 W Santa Fe Dr, Sun City, AZ, 85351-3106, USA; tel (623) 977-8351; fax (623) 876-2555; e-mail jjoseph@yourwestvalley.com; web site www.yourwestvalley.com
Circulation: 18,840pd,1fr; CAC
Group: Independent Newsmedia Inc. Usa
Editor.......................................Dan McCarthy

SURPRISE TODAY

(Wed)
10102 W Santa Fe Dr, Sun City, AZ, 85351-3106, USA; tel (623) 977-8351; adv tel (623) 876-2572; ed tel (623) 876-2534; fax (623) 876-3698; e-mail pbruns@yourwestvalley.com; ed e-mail dmccarthy@yourwestvalley.com; web site www.yourwestvalley.com
Circulation: 1pd,32,294fr; CAC
Advertising: Open inch rate $21.25
Established: 1996
Group: Independent Newsmedia Inc. Usa
Pub. ....Marji Ranes
Exec. Ed...................................Dan McCarthy
Dir, Nat'l Accts. ....Tom Legg
Mechanical Specifications: Type page 10" x 12.75"; 6 cols
Delivery Method: Carrier, Racks
Zip Codes Served: 85351

TUCSON

BUYER'S EDGE

(Wed)
4850 S Park Ave, Tucson, AZ, 85714-1637, USA; tel (520) 573-4395

DANDY DIME CLASSIFIEDS

(Fri)
4500 E Speedway Blvd, Ste 72-73, Tucson, AZ, 85712-5303, USA; tel (800) 575-4574; fax (520) 327-4900; web site www.dandydime.com
Circulation: 25,000fr; Sworn/Estimate/Non-Audited
Advertising: Open inch rate $30.00
Established: 1973Editions: 2— 2 total; Dandy Dime Classifieds-North;
Gen. Mgr. ....Ross Elmore
Mechanical Specifications: Type page 10 1/4 x 16; A - 8 cols, 1 1/4, 1/8 between; C - 8 cols, 1 1/4, 1/8 between.
Equipment: Hardware — APP/Power Macs, HP/Vectra VL; Software — Multi-Ad/Creator, Adobe/Photoshop, SUN/Suntype, QPS/QuarkXPress, Microsoft/Windows 95.
Zip Codes Served: 85732

TUCSON SHOPPER - WEEK B

(Fri)
1861 W Grant Rd, Tucson, AZ, 85745-1223, USA; web site www.newtucsonshopper.com
Circulation: 30,875fr; CVC
Advertising: $86.00 (smallest modular rate)
Established: 1980Dave Fredricks
Mechanical Specifications: Type page 7.5" x 10"; 4 cols
Delivery Method: Newsstand, Racks
Zip Codes Served: TUCSON, AZ

WICKENBURG

SHOPPER NEWS

(Wed)
179 N Washington, Wickenburg, AZ, 85358, USA; tel (928) 684-7218

ARKANSAS

CROSSETT

ASHLEY COUNTY SHOPPER GUIDE

(Mon)
106 E 2nd Ave, Crossett, AR, 71635-2902, USA; tel (870) 364-5186; fax (870) 364-2116; e-mail ad@ashleynewsobserver.com
Circulation: 11,157fr; Sworn/Estimate/Non-Audited
Advertising: Open inch rate $6.50
Pub. ....Barney White
Adv. Mgr..Pat Tullos

DUMAS

DELTA ADVERTISER

(Mon)
136 E Waterman St, Dumas, AR, 71639-2227, USA; tel (870) 382-4925; fax (870) 382-6421
Circulation: 5,537fr; Sworn/Estimate/Non-Audited
Advertising: Open inch rate $8.05
Pub. ....Terry G. Hawkins
Equipment: ; Presses — HI/Cottrell V-15; Software — QPS/QuarkXPress 4.1.

FORREST CITY

EAST ARKANSAS ADVERTISER

(Wed)
222 N Izard St, Forrest City, AR, 72335-3324, USA; tel (870) 633-3131; fax (870) 633-0599; e-mail fctimes@thnews.com; adv e-mail addept@thnews.com; ed e-mail tamjohns@thnews.com; web site thnews.com
Circulation: 16,200fr; Sworn/Estimate/Non-Audited
Advertising: Open inch rate $13.76
Established: 1978
Pub. ....Weston McCollum Lewey
Pub. ....Bonner McCollum
Circ. Mgr................................Ronnie Barnett
Mng. Ed................................Tamara Johnson
ad sales ....Tammy Long
Mechanical Specifications: edit page 6 x 21: 1 col 1.833, 2 col 3.792, 3 col 5.75, 4 col 7.708, 5 col 9.667, 6 col 11.625; class 9x21: 1.181, 2.487, 3.793, 5.099, 6.405, 7.711, 9.017, 10.323, 11.625
Equipment: Hardware — Mac OS X v10.6.8, ECRM MAKO NEWS CTP; Presses — 7-G/Community; Software — QPS/QuarkXPress 6.52, Multi-Ad/Creator 7.0.6, Adobe/Photoshop cs2 v 9.0.2, Illustrator cs2 12.0.1, Adobe/Acrobat 7 Pro v 7.1.0
Delivery Method: Mail, Newsstand, Carrier, Racks
Zip Codes Served: 72336

FORT SMITH

RIVER VALLEY ADVERTISER

(Wed)
3600 Wheeler Ave, Fort Smith, AR, 72901-6621, USA; tel (479) 785-7711

HOT SPRINGS

THRIFTY NICKEL WANT ADS

(Thur)
670 Ouachita Ave, Hot Springs, AR, 71901-3920, USA; tel (501) 623-4404; fax (501) 623-2454; e-mail hstn@swbell.net
Circulation: 30,000fr; Sworn/Estimate/Non-Audited
Advertising: Open inch rate $6.00
Pub. ....Danny Encow
Zip Codes Served: 71913

JASPER

THE NEWTON COUNTY TIMES

(Wed)
101 CHURCH$8.25 Per Col Inch St, Jasper, AR, 72641, USA; tel (870) 446-2645; adv tel (870) 741-2325; fax (870) 446-6286; e-mail NewtonCoTimes <news@newtoncountytimes.com>; web site www.newtoncountytimes.com
Circulation: 1,872pd,100fr; CVC
Advertising: $8.25 per column inch
Established: 1917
Group: Phillips Media Group LLC
Community Publishers, Inc.
Digital Platform - Tablet: Apple iOS
Publisher...Jim Perry
Editor..Jeff Dezort
Advertising Manager................Todd Edwards
Mechanical Specifications: Type page 10.25" x 20.5"; 6 cols
Equipment: Hardware — APP/Mac; Software — Adobe/PageMaker, Microsoft/Word, QPS/QuarkXPress.
Delivery Method: Racks

SILOAM SPRINGS

NEIGHBOR SHOPPER

(Tues)
101 N Mount Olive St, Siloam Springs, AR, 72761-3156, USA; tel (479) 524-5144; fax (479) 273-7777; web site http://hl.nwaonline.com/
Circulation: 11,600fr; Sworn/Estimate/Non-Audited
Advertising: Open inch rate $6.53
Pub. ....John Dilmore
Adv. Mgr..Jim Quillen
Circ. Mgr....................................George Loftus
Mechanical Specifications: Type page 13 x 21 1/4; A - 6 cols, between; C - 9 cols, between.
Equipment: Hardware — APP/Mac; Presses — G; Software — Baseview.
Zip Codes Served: 72712

CALIFORNIA

AUBURN

AUBURN TRADER

(Thur)
1030 High St, Auburn, CA, 95603-4707, USA; tel (530) 888-7653; fax (530) 268-3326; e-mail auburntrader@goldcountrymedia.com; adv e-mail toddf@goldcountrymedia.com; web site www.auburntrader.com
Circulation: 15,000fr; Sworn/Estimate/Non-Audited
Advertising: modular
Established: 1981
Group: Brehm Communications, Inc.
CEO...Jeremy Burke
Delivery Method: Mail, Racks
Zip Codes Served: 95603 95604
Note: Penny Power Publications Inc. is owned by Brehm Communications Inc. Through it's subsidiaries, Auburn Journal, Inc., Democrat Co., Gull Communications, Hi-Desert Publishing Co., Inc., News West Publishing Company Inc., Penny Power Publications Inc., Placer Community Newspapers

COVERSTORY

(Wed)
1030 High St, Auburn, CA, 95603-4707, USA; tel (530) 885-5656; fax (530) 887-1231; e-mail auburnjournal@goldcountrymedia.com; web site www.auburnjournal.com
Circulation: 11,250fr; Sworn/Estimate/Non-Audited
Advertising: Open inch rate $4.00
Established: 1872Editions: 2— 2 total; Auburn Journal CoverStory (11,286); Colfax CoverStory (3,685);
Pub. ....Tony Hazarian
Gen. Mgr., Print Div.......................Jim Easterly
Adv. Mgr...Jim Therma
Internet Sales/Mktg. Mgr..............Kady Guyton
Circ. Dir..Gary John
Exec. Ed...Deric Rothe
Sr. Ed. ....Tom Taylor
IT Mgr...Daniel Eggen
Prodn. Mgr., Adv............................Susan Morin
Mechanical Specifications: Type page 11 1/16 x 21; E - 6 cols, 1 13/16, 1/8 between; A - 6 cols, 1 13/16, 1/8 between; C - 9 cols, 1 1/8, 1/8 between.
Equipment: Hardware — PC, APP/Mac; Presses — G; Software — APT.
Zip Codes Served: 95604, 95602, 95603

BLYTHE

DESERT SHOPPER

(Thur)
153 S Broadway, Blythe, CA, 92225-2501,

USA; tel (760) 922-3181; fax (760) 922-3184; adv e-mail advertising@pvvt.com; ed e-mail mbachman@pvvt.com; web site www.pvvt.com
Circulation:6,877fr; VAC
Established: 1925
Group: Western News&Info, Inc.
Publisher....................................... Debbie Hoel
Adv. Rep... Jill Madsen
Mng. Ed...................................... Jaclyn Randall

CANYON COUNTRY

SANTA CLARITA GAZETTE & FREE CLASSIFIEDS

(Fri)
27261 Camp Plenty Rd, Canyon Country, CA, 91351-2634, USA; web site www.santaclaritafree.com
Circulation: 114pd,8,594fr; CVC
Advertising: $75.00 (smallest modular rate)
Established: 1998Doug Sutton
Mechanical Specifications: Type page 10.75" x 17"; 6 cols
Delivery Method: Newsstand, Racks
Zip Codes Served: LOS ANGELES—RIVERSIDE—ORANGE COUNTY, CA

EUREKA

ON THE MARKET (EVERY OTHER SAT)

930 6th St, Eureka, CA, 95501-1112, USA; tel (707) 441-0500; fax (707) 441-0568; e-mail realestate@times-standard.com; web site www.times-standard.com
Circulation: 20,135pd,270fr; Sworn/Estimate/Non-Audited
Advertising: Open inch rate $14.61
Pub. .... Dianna Crow
Adv. Dir.................................. Shonnie Bradbury
System Admin. .... Ron Maloney
Prodn. Mgr. .... Jason Kennedy
Mechanical Specifications: Type page 9 7/8 x 11 1/2; E - 5 cols, 1 7/8, 3/16 between; A - 5 cols, 1 7/8, 3/16 between.
Equipment: Hardware — IBM; Presses — G/Urbanite; Software — Adobe/Photoshop 6.0, Adobe/PageMaker.
Zip Codes Served: 95440, 95501, 95503, 95511, 95519, 95521, 95524, 95525, 95526, 95527, 95528, 95536, 95537, 95540, 95542, 95546, 95547, 95549, 95551, 95552, 95553, 95554, 95559, 95560, 95562, 95563, 95564, 95565, 95569, 95570, 95571, 95573, 95595

GALT

GALT SHOPPER

(Wed)
604 N Lincoln Way, Galt, CA, 95632-8601, USA; tel (209) 745-1551; adv tel (209) 745-1551; fax (209) 745-4492; adv fax (209) 745-4492; e-mail advertising@herburger.net; adv e-mail classified@herburger.net; ed e-mail editor_galtherald@herburger.net; web site www.galtheraldonline.com
Circulation:6,743fr; VAC
Advertising: Open inch rate $9.25
Group: Herburger Publications, Inc.
Pub. .... David Herburger
Adv. Mgr.. Jim O'Donnell
Mng. Ed................................ Bonnie Rodriguez
Delivery Method: Mail
Zip Codes Served: 95632

GRIDLEY

THE GRIDLEY SHOPPING NEWS

(Wed)
650 Kentucky St, Gridley, CA, 95948-2118, USA; tel (530) 846-3661; fax (530) 846-4519; e-mail gherald@gridleyherald.com; ed e-mail publisher@gridleyherald.com; web site www.gridleyherald.com
Circulation:5,500fr; Sworn/Estimate/Non-Audited
Advertising: Open inch rate $12.00
Group: GateHouse Media, Inc.
Ed. .... Lisa Van De Hey
Circ. Mgr.............................. Rachel Marubashi
Mechanical Specifications: Type page 13 x 21; E - 6 cols, 2, 1/8 between; A - 6 cols, 2, 1/8 between; C - 9 cols, 1/8 between.
Delivery Method: Carrier

LAKEPORT

LAKE COUNTY'S PENNY SAVER

(Wed)
2150 S Main St, Lakeport, CA, 95453-5620, USA; tel (707) 263-5636; adv tel (707) 263-5636; e-mail advertising@record-bee.com ; adv e-mail advertising@record-bee.com ; web site http://www.hometown-shopper.com/eedition/
Circulation:15,500fr; Sworn/Estimate/Non-Audited
Advertising: Open inch rate $5.38
Group: Digital First Media
Delivery Method: Newsstand, Racks

LODI

SENTINEL EXPRESS

(Wed)
125 N Church St, Lodi, CA, 95240-2102, USA; tel (209) 369-2761; ed tel (209) 369-7035; fax (209) 369-1084; ed fax (209) 369-6706; e-mail news@lodinews.com; adv e-mail ads@lodinews.com; ed e-mail news@lodinews.com; web site www.lodinews.com
Circulation:10,014fr; Sworn/Estimate/Non-Audited
Advertising: Open inch rate 6/47 (plus pick-up in Lodi News-Sentinel
Established: 2010
Group: Lodi News-Sentinel
Pub. .... Marty Weybret
Ed. .... Richard Hanner
Ad Director .... Tracy Kelley
Mechanical Specifications: Type page 13 x 21 1/2; E - 6 cols, 2 1/16, 1/8 between; A - 6 cols, 2 1/16, 1/8 between; C - 8 cols, 1 7/16, 1/8 between.
Equipment: Hardware — APP/Mac G3; Presses — 12-G/Community; Software — Multi-Ad/Creator 4.01.
Delivery Method: Carrier
Zip Codes Served: 95240, 95242, 95258
Note: This is a TMC product printed in combination with the Lodi News-Sentinel

MANTECA

BULLETIN EXTRA

(Fri)
531 E Yosemite Ave, Manteca, CA, 95336-5806, USA; tel (209) 249-3500; fax (209) 249-3559; adv fax (209) 249-3559; adv e-mail ads@mantecabulletin.com; web site www.mantecabulletin.com
Circulation:16,518fr; Sworn/Estimate/Non-Audited
Advertising: Open inch rate $19.48
Group: Morris Newspaper Group of California
Advertising Director..................... Chuck Higgs
Delivery Method: Carrier
Zip Codes Served: 95336, 95337, 95366, 95330, 95231

MOUNT SHASTA

VOICE OF THE MOUNTAIN

(Wed)
924 N Mount Shasta Blvd, Mount Shasta, CA, 96067-8700, USA; tel (530) 926-5214; fax (530) 926-4166; e-mail news@mtshatanews.com; web site www.mtshastanews.com
Circulation:5,000fr; Sworn/Estimate/Non-Audited
Advertising: Open inch rate $11.00
Established: 1954
Pub. .... Genny Axtman
Office Mgr. .... Linda Bonebrake
Circ. Mgr................................ Dave Reynolds
Ed. .... Steve Gerace
Equipment: Hardware — APP/Mac OS 9.2; Presses — Goss/Community; Software — QPS/QuarkXPress 4.11.

OJAI

OJAI VALLEY SHOPPER

(Wed, Fri)
408 Bryant Cir, Ste A, Ojai, CA, 93023-4210, USA; tel (805) 646-1476; fax (805) 646-4281; web site www.ojaivalleynews.com
Circulation:12,000fr; Sworn/Estimate/Non-Audited
Advertising: Open inch rate $11.65
Established: 1891
Gen. Mgr. .... Jodie Miller
Mng. Ed.................................... Lenny Roberts
Ed. .... Bret Bradigan
Zip Codes Served: 93024

ONTARIO

NUESTRA GENTE

(Thur)
1511 W Holt Blvd, Ste J, Ontario, CA, 91762-3658, USA; tel (909) 460-2555; fax (909) 460-2558; ed e-mail editor@nuestra-gente.com; web site www.nuestra-gente.com
Circulation:88,000fr; Sworn/Estimate/Non-Audited
Advertising: Open inch rate $36.00
Established: 1996
Zip Codes Served: San Bernadino County

OROVILLE

THE DIGGER & SHOPPER NEWS

(Tues)
PO Box 5006, 2057 Mitchell Ave., Oroville, CA, 95966-0006, USA; tel (530) 533-2170; fax (530) 533-2181; e-mail suzanne@diggernews.com; adv e-mail dave@diggernews.com; ed e-mail pat@diggernews.com; web site www.diggernews.com
Circulation: 324pd,15,139fr; CVC
Advertising: $17.15
Established: 1977
Publisher....................................... David Miller
Delivery Method: Mail, Newsstand, Racks
Zip Codes Served: 95965, 95966, 95968, 95916

PALM DESERT

WHITE SHEET

(Tues)
73400 Highway 111, Palm Desert, CA, 92260-3908, USA; tel (760) 346-0601; fax (760) 352-0936; web site www.greenandwhitesheet.com
Circulation:40,000fr; Sworn/Estimate/Non-Audited
Advertising: Open inch rate $12.36
Pub. .... Hal J. Paradis
Mechanical Specifications: Type page 10 x 10; E - 6 cols, 1 7/12, 1/8 between; A - 6 cols, 1 7/12, 1/8 between; C - 6 cols, 1 7/12, 1/8 between.
Equipment: Hardware — PCs, Gateway; Software — Microsoft/Windows.
Zip Codes Served: 92260

PALMDALE

ANTELOPE VALLEY PRESS EXPRESS

(Sat)
37404 Sierra Hwy, Palmdale, CA, 93550-9343, USA; tel (661) 273-2700; adv tel (661) 273-2700; fax (661) 947-4870; adv fax (661)947-4870; e-mail email@avpress.com; adv e-mail msherwood@avpress.com; ed e-mail editor@avpress.com; web site www.avpress.com
Circulation:35,091fr; VAC
Advertising: Open inch rate $13.50
Established: 1915
Group: Antelope Valley Newspapers Inc
Vice Pres./Gen. Mgr.................... Cherie Bryant
Pub. .... William Markham
Mng. Ed................................. Charles Bostwick
Mechanical Specifications: Type page 13 x 21 1/2; E - 6 cols, 2 1/30, 1/6 between; A - 6 cols, 2 1/16, 1/6 between; C - 9 cols, 1 3/8, between.
Equipment: Hardware — MPS; Presses — Goss
Delivery Method: Carrier, Racks
Zip Codes Served: 93534,93535,93536,93550,93551,93552,93591,93543

RAMONA

RAMONA SENTINEL

(Thur)
850 Main St, Ste 106, Ramona, CA, 92065-1968, USA; tel (760) 789-1350; adv tel (760) 789-1350; ed tel (760) 789-1350; fax (760) 789-4057; adv fax (760) 789-4057; ed fax (760) 789-4057; e-mail admin@ramonasentinel.com; adv e-mail admin@ramonasentinel.com; web site www.ramonasentinel.com
Circulation: 13,166pd,; AAM
Advertising: Open inch rate $19.05
Established: 1862
Group: Union-Tribune Community Press
Digital Platform - Mobile: Apple, Android, Windows, Blackberry
Digital Platform - Tablet: Apple iOS, Android, Windows 7, Nook, Kindle Fire
Ed. .... Maureen Robertson
Gen Mgr.................................. Tina Tamburino
VP of Sales..................................... Don Parks
Mechanical Specifications: 6 Column 10.33" x 12.25"
Delivery Method: Carrier, Racks
Zip Codes Served: 92065

REDLANDS

GREEN SHEET

(Thur)
721 Nevada St, Ste 207, Redlands, CA, 92373-8051, USA; tel (800) 678-4237; fax (760) 346-3597; e-mail cch-greensheet@worldnet.att.net; web site www.greenandwhitesheet.com
Circulation:75,000fr; Sworn/Estimate/Non-Audited
Advertising: Open inch rate $28.01Editions: 4— 4 total; Green Sheet-Redlands (18,500); Green Sheet-Riverside (16,500); Green Sheet-San Bernardino (17,500); Green Sheet-West San Bernardino (22,500);
Pub. .... Hal J. Paradis
Gen. Mgr. .... Chuck Holcomb
Mechanical Specifications: Type page 10 x 10; E - 6 cols, 1 7/12, 1/8 between; A - 6 cols, 1 7/12, 1/8 between; C - 6 cols, 1 7/12, 1/8 between.
Equipment: Hardware — PCs, Gateway; Software — Microsoft/Windows.
Zip Codes Served: 92261

REEDLEY

HERALD ADVERTISER

(Tues)
1130 G St, Reedley, CA, 93654-3004, USA;

tel (559) 638-2244; fax (559) 638-5021; e-mail reedleyexponent@yahoo.com; web site www.reedleyexponent.com
Circulation:14,285fr; Sworn/Estimate/Non-Audited
Advertising: Open inch rate $11.50
Pub. .... Fred Hall
Mktg. Dir.................. Cheri Williams
Mng. Ed.................. Cheryl Lingo
Zip Codes Served: 93657

SAN FRANCISCO

THE ADVERTISER
(Thur)
132 10th St, San Francisco, CA, 94103-2605, USA; tel (415) 861-8370; fax (415) 861-0521; e-mail info@sfadvertiser.com; web site www.sfadvertiser.com
Circulation:52,000fr; Sworn/Estimate/Non-Audited
Tom Lee
Wilbur LeePub.s
Mechanical Specifications: Type page 10 1/4 x 16 1/2.
Equipment: Hardware — APP/Mac, IBM/PC; Presses — WPC/Web Leader; Software — Microsoft/Word 5.1A, QPS/QuarkXPress, Adobe/Photoshop.

SANTA CLARITA

SCV EXPRESS
(Fri, Sun)
24000 Creekside Rd, Santa Clarita, CA, 91355-1726, USA; tel (661) 259-1234; fax (661) 254-8068; web site www.the-signal.com
Circulation:100,571fr; Sworn/Estimate/Non-Audited
Advertising: Open inch rate $25.60
Pub. .... Jay Horn
Ed. .... Laila Little John

SANTA CRUZ

SANTA CRUZ GOOD TIMES
(Thur)
1205 Pacific Ave, Ste 301, Santa Cruz, CA, 95060-3936, USA; tel (831) 458-1100; fax (831) 458-1295; e-mail letters@gtweekly.com; web site www.gtweekly.com
Circulation: 4pd,34,777fr; CVC
Advertising: $168.00 (smallest modular rate)
Established: 1975
Group: C-VILLE Holdings LLC
Mainstreet Media Group, LLC
Digital Platform - Mobile: Apple, Android, Windows, Blackberry, Other
Digital Platform - Tablet: Apple iOS, Android, Blackberry Tablet OS, Kindle, Kindle Fire
Circ. Mgr.................. Pamela Pollard
Ed. .... Greg Archer
Prodn. Mgr. .... Josh Becker
Publisher.................. Jeff Mitchell
Pub. Mgr .... Phyllis Pfeiffer
Adv. Mgr.................. Don Parks
Circ. Mgr .... Christina Clayton
Mechanical Specifications: Type page 9.4" x 11.5"; 5 cols
Equipment: Hardware — APP/Mac; Software — QPS/QuarkXPress 3.31, Adobe/Photoshop 3.0, Adobe/Illustrator 6.0.
Delivery Method: Newsstand, Racks

TAFT

BARGAIN HUNTER
(Tues)
800 Center St, Taft, CA, 93268-3129, USA; tel (661) 763-3171; fax (661) 763-5638; ed e-mail editor@bak.rr.com; web site www.taftmidwaydriller.com
Circulation:4,000fr; Sworn/Estimate/Non-Audited
Advertising: Open inch rate $10.00
Group: GateHouse Media, Inc.
Pub. .... John Watkins
Circ. Mgr.................. Melissa Robertson
Ed. .... Doug Keeler

TURLOCK

THE JOURNAL SHOPPING NEWS
(Sat)
138 S Center St, Turlock, CA, 95380-4508, USA; tel (209) 634-9141; adv tel (209) 634-9141; ed tel (209) 634-9141; fax (209) 632-8813; adv fax (209) 632-8813; ed fax (209) 632-8813; e-mail adinfo@turlockjournal.com; adv e-mail classifieds@turlockjournal.com; ed e-mail news@turlockjournal.com; web site www.turlockjournal.com
Circulation: 6,030pd,14,500fr; Sworn/Estimate/Non-Audited
Advertising: Open inch rate $13.91
Established: 1904
Pub. .... Hank Veen
Ed. .... Kristina Hacker
Adv. Sales.................. Victoria Batesole
Sales Mgr.................. Taylor Phillips
Mechanical Specifications: Type page 13 x 21 1/2; E - 6 cols, 2 1/16, 1/8 between; A - 6 cols, 2 1/16, 1/8 between; C - 9 cols, 1 5/16, 1/8 between.
Equipment: Hardware — 2-APP/Power Mac, 1-APP/Mac IIci, APP/Mac G4; Presses — 8-G/Community; Software — Adobe/PageMaker 6.5, QPS/QuarkExpress 3.04, Adobe/Photoshop 5.0, Baseview/NewsEdit Pro, Adobe/Illustrator, Multi-Ad/Creator.
Zip Codes Served: 95380, 95381, 95382, 95315, 95324, 95316, 95326, 95328

UKIAH

HOMETOWN SHOPPER
(Tues)
212 W Mill St, Ukiah, CA, 95482-5474, USA; tel (707) 462-1573; fax (707) 462-3550; e-mail willbutler@hometown-shopper.com; web site www.hometown-shopper.com
Circulation:43,357fr; Sworn/Estimate/Non-Audited
Advertising: Frequency discount available
Established: 1989
Group: Media News Group
Digital First Media
Digital Platform - Mobile: Apple, Android
Gen. Mgr. .... Will Butler
Prodn. Mgr.................. Patsy Jordan
Mechanical Specifications: Type
Full page 8 column x 11" = 10"x11"
Half page vertical 8 column x 5.458" = 10"x5.458"
Half page horizontal 4 column x 11" = 4.958" x 11"
Quarter page Vertical 2 column x 11" = 2.431" x 11"
Quarter page horizontal 4 column x 5.458"
Equipment: Hardware — APP/Mac.; Software — Ad Base
Delivery Method: Mail
Zip Codes Served: 95482
Note: Printed at the Paradise Post Chico Calif. a sister paper.

VICTORVILLE

REVIEW
(Tues)
13891 Park Ave, Victorville, CA, 92392-2435, USA; tel (760) 241-7744; adv tel (760) 951-6288; fax (760) 241-1860; adv fax (760) 955-5376; e-mail vvnews@link.freedom.com; web site www.highdesert.com
Circulation:26,600fr; Sworn/Estimate/Non-Audited
Advertising: Open inch rate $15.02Editions: 2—2 total; Preview-Barstow (5,600); Preview-Victor Valley (34,000);
Pub. .... Stephan Wingert
Circ. Mgr.................. Jackie Parsons
Ed. .... Don Holland
Prodn. Mgr. .... Harry Pontius
Mechanical Specifications: Type page 13 x 21 1/2; E - 6 cols, 2 1/16, 1/8 between; A - 6 cols, 2 1/16, 1/8 between; C - 9 cols, 1 1/3, 1/8 between.
Equipment: Hardware — Dewar; Presses — 10-G/Urbanite; Software — Baseview.
Zip Codes Served: 92392

VISALIA

AMERICAN CLASSIFIEDS - VISALIA
(Thur)
1516 W Mineral King Ave, Visalia, CA, 93291-5819, USA; web site www.americanclassifiedsvisalia.com
Circulation: 0pd,26,235fr; CVC
Advertising: Open inch rate $10.00
Established: 1986Glen Christensen
Mechanical Specifications: Type page 10.25" x 15.70"; 8 cols
Delivery Method: Newsstand, Carrier, Racks
Zip Codes Served: VISALIA—TULARE—PORTERVILLE, CA

WOODLAND HILLS

VALLEY VANTAGE
(Thur)
23009 Ventura Blvd, Woodland Hills, CA, 91364-1107, USA; tel (818) 223-9545; fax (818) 223-9552; e-mail wnrcnews@instanet.com; web site www.valleynewsgroup.com
Circulation:20,000fr; Sworn/Estimate/Non-Audited
Advertising: Open inch rate $25.00
Pub. /Ed. .... Kathleen Sterling
Zip Codes Served: 91364, 91365, 91367, 91302, 91356

YUCAIPA

CENTURY GROUP NEWSPAPERS
(Fri)
35154 Yucaipa Blvd, Yucaipa, CA, 92399-4339, USA; tel (909) 797-9101; fax (909) 797-0502; e-mail tbush@centurygroup.com; web site www.centurygroup.com
Circulation: 5,278pd,65,861fr; CVC
President / CEO / Pub. .... Toebe Bush
Owner.................. Gerald A. Bean

COLORADO

BRIGHTON

ADAM COUNTY ADVERTISER
(Wed)
PO Box 646, Brighton, CO, 80601-0646, USA; tel (303) 659-2522; fax (303) 659-2901; web site www.metrowestfyi.com
Circulation: 21,000pd,; Sworn/Estimate/Non-Audited
Pub. .... Allen Messick

BURLINGTON

THE PLAINSDEALER
(Thur)
202 S 14th St, Burlington, CO, 80807-2322, USA; tel (719) 346-5381; adv tel (719) 346-5381; ed tel (719) 346-5381; fax (719) 346-5514; adv fax (719) 346-5514; ed fax (719) 346-5514; e-mail brecord@plainstel.com; adv e-mail brecordadverting@plainstel.com; ed e-mail brecordeditor@plainstel.com
Circulation: 3,100pd,3,350fr; Sworn/Estimate/Non-Audited
Advertising: Open inch rate $11.00
Digital Platform - Mobile: Windows
Pub. .... Rol Hudler
Advt Dir.................. Shannon Floyd
Equipment: Hardware — APP/Mac; Presses — 4-KP/News King; Software — QPS/QuarkXPress, Adobe/Photoshop.
Delivery Method: Mail

COLORADO SPRINGS

AMERICAN CLASSIFIEDS - COLORADO SPRINGS
(Thur)
PO Box 9738, Colorado Springs, CO, 80932-0738, USA; web site www.thenickel.com
Circulation:23,997fr; CVC
Advertising: Open inch rate $10.00
Established: 1971Karen Christensen
Mechanical Specifications: Type page 10.5" x 15"; 8 cols
Delivery Method: Mail, Carrier, Racks
Zip Codes Served: Colorado Springs, CO

ESTES PARK

ESTES INSIDE & OUT
(Fri)
351 Moraine Ave, Unit B, Estes Park, CO, 80517-8056, USA; tel (970) 586-3356 ; fax (970) 586-9532; e-mail tgcirculation@eptrail.com; adv e-mail tgcirculation@eptrail.com; ed e-mail srowan@eptrail.com; web site www.eptrail.com
Circulation:2,900fr; Sworn/Estimate/Non-Audited
Advertising: $11.50
Established: 1921
Group: Prairie Mountain Publishing
Digital Platform - Mobile: Apple, Android, Windows, Blackberry
Digital Platform - Tablet: Apple iOS, Android, Windows 7, Blackberry Tablet OS, Kindle, Nook, Kindle Fire
Delivery Method: Mail, Newsstand, Racks

FORT COLLINS

AMERICAN CLASSIFIEDS - FORT COLLINS / GREELEY / DENVER
(Thur)
1229 E Mulberry St, Fort Collins, CO, 80524-3513, USA; web site www.frontrangeads.com
Circulation: 0pd,36,664fr; CVCShelia Skinner

COLORADO CONNECTION
(Wed, Sat)
1300 Riverside Ave, Fort Collins, CO, 80524-4353, USA; tel (970) 493-6397; fax (970) 224-7726; web site www.coloradoan.com
Circulation:24,500fr; Sworn/Estimate/Non-Audited
Advertising: Open inch rate $20.75
Group: Gannett
Pub. .... Kim Roegner
Circ. Mgr.................. Cathy Jack-Romero
Exec. Ed.................. Bob Moore
Mechanical Specifications: Type page 11 5/8 x 21 1/2; E - 6 cols, 1 5/6, 1/8 between; A - 6 cols, 1 5/6, 1/8 between; C - 10 cols, 1 3/32, 3/32 between.
Equipment: Hardware — IBM/AS 400; Presses — G/Urbanite; Software — ACT/APT.
Zip Codes Served: 80524, 80521, 80525, 80526, 80528

GRAND JUNCTION

THE NICKEL
(Wed)
1635 N 1st St, Grand Junction, CO, 81501-2124, USA; tel (970) 242-5555; fax (970) 245-9250; e-mail doug.freed@nickads.com; web site www.nickads.com
Circulation:26,000fr; Sworn/Estimate/Non-Audited
Advertising: Open inch rate $8.00
Group: Cox Media Group
Gen. Mgr. .... Doug Freed
Sales Mgr. .... Kari Fowler
Dist. Mgr. .... Sharon Sale
Prodn. Mgr. .... Randy Raisch
Mechanical Specifications: Type page 10 1/8 x 11 7/8; A - 7 cols, 1 3/8, 1/6 between; C - 7 cols, 1 3/8, 1/6 between.
Equipment: Hardware — APP/Power Macs; Software — QPS/QuarkXPress, Baseview/Classflow, Adobe/Illustrator, Adobe/Photoshop.
Zip Codes Served: 81413, 81416, 81501, 81503, 81504, 81505, 81506, 81520, 81521, 81526, 81601, 81624, 81635, 81643, 81646, 81650, 81652

MONTE VISTA

SLV LIFESTYLES
(Wed)
835 1st Ave, Monte Vista, CO, 81144-1474, USA; tel (719) 852-3531; fax (719) 852-3387; adv e-mail jfapublisher@gmail.com; ed e-mail MonteVistaNews@gmail.com
Circulation:18,000fr; Sworn/Estimate/Non-Audited
Advertising: Open inch rate $24.75
Group: Valley Publishing, Inc.
Pub. .... Jennifer Alonzo
Sales Mgr. .... Stacy Turner
Prodn. Mgr. .... Elli Bone

PAONIA

HIGH COUNTRY SHOPPER
(Wed)
231 Grand Ave, Paonia, CO, 81428, USA; tel (970) 527-4576; fax (970) 527-6191; e-mail info@highcountryshopper.com; adv e-mail display@highcountryshopper.com; ed e-mail content@highcountryshopper.com; web site www.highcountryshopper.com
Circulation:17,500fr; Sworn/Estimate/Non-Audited
Advertising: Open inch rate $6.50 black/white
Established: 1978
Group: Medrano Holdings LLCEditions: 1—High Country Shopper
Digital Platform - Mobile: Apple, Android, Windows, Blackberry
Digital Platform - Tablet: Apple iOS, Android, Windows 7, Blackberry Tablet OS, Kindle, Nook, Kindle Fire
Office Manager .... Rita Olin
Production Manager .... Tina Walker
Mechanical Specifications: Type page 10 1/4 x 15; A - 6 cols, 1 1/2, 1/4 between; C - 6 cols, 1 1/2, 1/4 between.
Equipment: Hardware — APP/Mac; Software — InDesign
Delivery Method: Mail, Racks
Zip Codes Served: 81428, 81425, 81416, 81410, 81414, 81418,81413, 81415, 81419
Note: We are a direct mail publication.

PUEBLO

AMERICAN CLASSIFIEDS - PUEBLO
(Thur) (Rack Display Sign)
811 W 4th St, Pueblo, CO, 81003-2393, USA; tel (719) 544-4752; web site www.acpueblo.com
Circulation:20,991fr; CVC
Established: 1975
Pres. .... Ernie Montano
Delivery Method: Racks
Zip Codes Served: 81001, 81003, 81004, 81005, 81006, 81007, 81008, 81019, 81022, 81025, 81039, 81052, 81054, 81055, 81058, 81063, 81067, 81069, 81050, 81101, 81089, 81082, 81212, 81120, 81123, 81133, 81140, 811044, 81201, 81211, 81222, 81223, 81226, 81233, 81240, 81242, 81252, 81253

PUEBLO WEST

PUEBLO WEST VIEW
(Thur)
215 S Purcell Blvd, Pueblo West, CO, 81007-5083, USA; tel (719) 547-9606; fax (719) 547-4380; e-mail comments@pueblowestview.com; web site www.pueblowestview.com
Circulation:15,000fr; Sworn/Estimate/Non-Audited
Advertising: Open inch rate $12.45
Established: 1996
Pub. .... Robert H. Rawlings
Adv. Dir. .... Lou Braden
Mechanical Specifications: Type page 13 x 21 1/2; E - 6 cols, 2 1/16, 1/8 between; A - 6 cols, 2 1/16, 1/8 between; C - 6 cols, 2 1/16, 1/8 between.
Equipment: Hardware — APP/Mac; Presses — MAN/Uniset.
Zip Codes Served: 81007

WOODLAND PARK

COURIER EXTRA
(Wed)
1200 Highway 24, Woodland Park, CO, 80863-9229, USA; tel (719) 687-3006; fax (719) 687-3009; web site coloradocommunitynewspapers.com
Circulation:10,911fr; CVC
Advertising: Open inch rate $9.41
Sales Mgr. .... Asa Cole
Mechanical Specifications: Type page 11 1/2 x 21; E - 6 cols, between; A - 6 cols, between; C - 6 cols, between.
Equipment: Hardware — APP/Macs; Presses — 10-G/Community; Software — QPS/QuarkXPress.

CONNECTICUT

BROOKFIELD

YANKEE PENNYSAVER
(Thur)
246 Federal Rd, Commons Ste D-15, Brookfield, CT, 06804, USA; tel (203) 775-9122; fax (203) 775-9623; e-mail steven@ctpennysaver.com; adv e-mail ads@ctpennysaver.com; ed e-mail susan@ctpennysaver.com; web site www.ctpennysaver.com
Circulation:95,397fr; Sworn/Estimate/Non-Audited
Advertising: Open inch rate $20.10
Established: 1994Editions: 9— 9 total; Ridgefield Paper-Ridgefield CT (10,500); Yankee Pennysaver-Bethel/Newtown (15,522); Yankee Pennysaver-Brewster/Carmel/Pawling (2,900); Yankee Pennysaver-Danbury (15,430); Yankee Pennysaver-Danbury/Brookfield (18,538); Yankee Pennysaver-Monroe/Ea
Digital Platform - Mobile: Apple, Android
Digital Platform - Tablet: Apple iOS, Android
Susan K. Blumenthal
Steven SilverPub.s
Mechanical Specifications: Type page 6 3/4 x 9 3/4; E - 2 cols, 3, between; A - 2 cols, 3, between; C - 2 cols, 3, between.
Equipment: Hardware — APP/Power Mac; Software — QPS/QuarkXPress.
Delivery Method: Mail
Zip Codes Served: 06755, 06757, 06776, 06784, 06785, 06793, 06794, 06804, 06810, 06811, 06877, 06790, 06468, 06482, 06470
Note: We publish Legal Notices, Probate and Foreclosures. We accept tobacco & firearms ads.

GUILFORD

SHORE LINE SHOPPER
(Sat)
PO Box 349, Guilford, CT, 06437-0349, USA; tel (203) 453-2711; fax (203) 453-4152; e-mail jcompton@journalregister.com; web site www.journalregister.com
Circulation:20,530fr; Sworn/Estimate/Non-Audited
Advertising: Open inch rate $5.23Editions: 2—2 total; Shore Line Shopper-East (8,927); Shore Line Shopper-West (11,603);
Pub. .... John Shields
Adv. Mgr. .... Peter Johnson
Mechanical Specifications: Type page 10 1/4 x 16; E - 4 cols, 2 1/2, 1/6 between; A - 6 cols, 1 5/8, 1/6 between; C - 6 cols, 1 5/8, 1/6 between.
Equipment: Hardware — APP/Mac; Software — Multi-Ad/Creator.
Zip Codes Served: 8608

SOUTHINGTON

STEP SAVER
(Fri)
213 Spring St, Southington, CT, 06489-1542, USA; tel (860) 628-9438; fax (860) 621-1841; e-mail sales@stepsaver.com; info@stepsaver.com; circulation@stepsaver.com; web site www.stepsaver.com
Circulation:43,000fr; Sworn/Estimate/Non-Audited
Advertising: Open inch rate $30.30Editions: 4—4 total; Step Saver-Bristol (25,226); Step Saver-Cheshire (9,754); Step Saver-Plainville/Farmington (12,372); Step Saver-Southington (16,893);
Prodn. Mgr. .... Kevin Smalley
Mechanical Specifications: Type page 10 1/2 x 15; E - 6 cols, between; A - 6 cols, between.
Equipment: Hardware — 21-APP/Mac; Presses — 9-G/Community SSC, G/Community SSC 4 color; Software — QPS/QuarkXPress.
Zip Codes Served: 6489

TORRINGTON

BETTER LIVING
(Fri)
190 Water St, Torrington, CT, 06790-5325, USA; tel (860) 489-3121; fax (860) 489-6790; ed e-mail editor@registercitizen.com; web site www.registercitizen.com
Circulation:16,000fr; Sworn/Estimate/Non-Audited
Advertising: Open inch rate $6.19
Pub. .... Wes Rowe
Prodn. Mgr. .... Peter Robustelli
Mechanical Specifications: Type page 12 x 21 1/2; E - 6 cols, 1 7/8, between; A - 6 cols, 1 7/8, between; C - 9 cols, 1 1/4, between.
Zip Codes Served: 6790

THE GOOD NEWS ABOUT TORRINGTON
PO Box 58, Torrington, CT, 06790-0058, USA; tel (860) 489-3121; fax (860) 489-6790

TRUMBULL

BARGAIN NEWS LLC
(Thur)
30 Nutmeg Dr, Trumbull, CT, 06611-5453, USA; tel (203) 377-3000; fax (203) 377-2632; web site www.bargainnews.com
Circulation: 33,000pd,500fr; Sworn/Estimate/Non-Audited
Advertising: Open inch rate $12.75
Pub. .... John F. Roy
Gen. Mgr. .... Carol Leach
Mechanical Specifications: Type page 10 x 15; A - 5 cols, 2, between; C - 5 cols, 2, 1/6 between.
Equipment: Hardware — PCs, APP/Macs.

VERNON

HEBRON COLUMBIA
(Fri)
130 Old Town Rd, Vernon, CT, 06066-2322, USA; tel (860) 875-3366; fax (860) 875-2089; web site www.remindernews.com
Circulation:26,577fr; Sworn/Estimate/Non-Audited
Advertising: Open inch rate $6.50
Pub. .... Ken Hovland
Gen. Mgr. .... George Cunningham
Adv. Mgr. .... Doug Fabian
Circ. Mgr. .... Frian Smith
Zip Codes Served: 6226

WATERTOWN

TOWN TIMES
(Wed, Thur, Sun)
449 Main St, Watertown, CT, 06795-2628, USA; tel (860) 274-8851; fax (860) 945-3116; e-mail voicespub@earthlink.net; towntimes@earthlink.net; ed e-mail jtaylor@towntimesnews.com; web site http://www.primepublishers.com/towntimesnews/
Circulation: 23,114pd,; CAC
Advertising: Open inch rate $15.35
Gen. Mgr. .... Annette Linster
Adv. Mgr. .... Rudy Mazurosky
Circ. Mgr. .... Walter K. Mazurosky
Ed. .... James Taylor
Prodn. Mgr. .... Kurt Mazurosky
Mechanical Specifications: Type page 10 x 15; E - 5 cols, 2, 1/2 between; A - 5 cols, 2, 1/2 between; C - 5 cols, 2, 1/2 between.
Equipment: Hardware — APP/Mac, PC; Software — QPS/QuarkXPress, Brainworks.

DELAWARE

DOVER

INDEPENDENT NEWSMEDIA INC. USA
110 Galaxy Dr, Dover, DE, 19901-9262, USA; tel (302) 674-3600; fax (877) 377-2424; e-mail newsroom@newszap.com; web site www.newszap.com
Circulation: 1,580pd,1,939fr; CAC
Established: 1953
Chrmn. of the Bd./CEO .... Joe Smyth
Corp. Pres. .... Tamra Brittingham
Pres., Opns. .... Ed Dulin
Vice Pres., Adv. .... Darel LaPrade
Dir., Research/Devel. .... Chris Engel
Exec. Asst. .... Sheila Clendaniel
Pub. .... Greg Tock
Note: Independent Newspapers Inc. owns three daily newspapers and 25 weekly publications.

FLORIDA

BONIFAY

HOLMES COUNTY ADVERTISER

(Wed)
112 E Virginia Ave, Bonifay, FL, 32425-2327, USA; tel (850) 547-2270; fax (850) 547-9200; e-mail holmescoadvertiser@wseca.net; web site www.chipleypaper.com
Circulation:4,200fr; Sworn/Estimate/Non-Audited
Advertising: Open inch rate $4.00
Pub. .... Gary Woodham
Adv. Mgr. .... Michelle Pate
Circ. Mgr. .... Terri Tomkiewicz
Ed. .... Kathy Foster
Prodn. Mgr. .... Kim McDonald
Zip Codes Served: 32425

BUNNELL

FLAGLER PENNYSAVER

(Wed)
2729 E Moody Blvd, Bunnell, FL, 32110-5963, USA; tel (386) 437-5971; fax (386) 437-2232; e-mail flagleri@psavers.com; web site www.floridapennysavers.com
Circulation:36,966fr; CVC
Advertising: Open inch rate $10.80
Group: News-Journal Corp.
Pub. .... Leonard A. Marsh
Bus. Mgr. .... Kelli Hull
Sales Supvr. .... Pat Waterman
Circ. Mgr. .... Jan Ridell
Sales Mgr .... James Drummond

CAPE CORAL

LEE COUNTY SHOPPER

(Wed)
2510 Del Prado Blvd S, Cape Coral, FL, 33904-5750, USA; tel (239) 574-1110; adv tel (239) 574-1110; ed tel (239) 574-1110; fax (239) 573-2318; adv fax (239) 574-3403; ed fax (239) 574-5693; adv e-mail jkonig@breezenewspapers.com; ed e-mail news@breezenewspapers.com; web site www.leecountyshopper.com
Circulation: 4pd,61,362fr; CVC
Advertising: Open inch rate $40.00
Established: 1961
Group: Ogden Newspapers Inc.
Circ. Mgr. .... Barbarra Smith
Prodn. Mgr. .... David Warren
Publisher .... Scott Blonde
Commerical Print Manager .... Renee Brown
Advertising Director .... Jim Konig
Mechanical Specifications: Type page 10 5/16 x 16; E - 6 cols, 1 2/3, 1/6 between; A - 6 cols, 1 2/3, 1/6 between; C - 6 cols, 1 2/3, 1/6 between.
Equipment: Hardware — APP/Macs; Presses — DGM 430 4/Cold Set Towers 1/UV Tower; Software — Multi-Ad/Creator 8.04, QPS/QuarkXPress 8
Delivery Method: Mail, Newsstand, Carrier, Racks
Zip Codes Served: 33904, 33901, 33903, 33905, 33907, 33908,33909, 33912,33913, 33914, 33916, 33917,33919, 33920,33924, 33931, 33936,33966, 33971,33972,33974,33976, 33990, 33991, 33993

SANIBEL - CAPTIVA SHOPPER'S GUIDE

(Mthly)
2510 Del Prado Blvd S, Cape Coral, FL, 33904-5750, USA; web site www.breezenewspapers.com
Circulation: 1pd,4,843fr; CVC
Advertising: N/A
Group: Ogden Newspapers Inc.Scott Blonde

CLERMONT

SUMTER SHOPPER

(Wed)
637 8th St, Clermont, FL, 34711-2159, USA; tel (352) 748-2424; fax (352) 567-5640; web site sumtercountyshopper.com
Circulation:22,000fr; Sworn/Estimate/Non-Audited
Advertising: Open inch rate $8.86
Group: Independent Publications Inc
Sun Publications of Fla.
Pub. .... Linda Briody
Zip Codes Served: 34731

DELAND

WEST VOLUSIA PENNYSAVER

(Wed)
1422 N Woodland Blvd, Deland, FL, 32720-2260, USA; tel (386) 736-2880; adv tel (800) 218-2186; fax (386) 736-3587; e-mail wvpsoa@psavers.com; web site www.floridapennysavers.com
Circulation:55,620fr; CVC
Advertising: Open inch rate $15.75
Established: 1971
Group: Halifax Media
News-Journal Corp.Editions: 2— 2 total; West Volusia Pennysaver-North (19,000 sat. 19,000 wed.);
Display Sales Manager .... Linda Sherwood
Gen. Mgr. .... Kelli Hull
Circ. Mgr. .... Jon Riddell
Circ. Supvr. .... Evan Baldwin
Mechanical Specifications: Type page 9 7/8 x 11 1/2; A - 7 cols, 1 5/16, 1/6 between; C - 7 cols, 1 5/16, 1/6 between.
Equipment: Hardware — APP/Power Mac, APP/Mac G4; Software — Multi-Ad Creator 6.5, Adobe/Photoshop 6, QPS/QuarkXPress 4.02, Adobe/Illustrator 9.0.
Delivery Method: Carrier, Racks
Zip Codes Served: 32723, 32180, 32190, 32130, 32720, 32724, 32725, 32738, 32713, 32706

DESTIN

LOG EXTRA

(Wed)
1225 Airport Rd, Destin, FL, 32541-2909, USA; tel (850) 837-2828; fax (850) 654-5982; e-mail thelog@link.freedom.com; web site www.destin.com
Circulation:4,200fr; Sworn/Estimate/Non-Audited
Advertising: Open inch rate $4.50
Pub. .... Rick Thomason
Adv. Mgr. .... Tom Stephens
Circ. Mgr. .... Mark Hurt
Ed. .... Jim Wagner

FORT LAUDERDALE

TEENLINK

(Thur)
500 E Broward Blvd, Fort Lauderdale, FL, 33394-3000, USA; ed tel (954) 574-5316; ed e-mail jjhon@sfteenlink.com; web site http://www.sun-sentinel.com/teenlink/
Circulation:66,773fr; CVCLisa Goodlin

FORT WALTON BEACH

THRIFTY NICKEL - FT. WALTON BEACH

(Thur)
151 Mary Esther Blvd Suite 202, Fort Walton Beach, FL, 32548, USA; tel (850) 243-6771; fax (850) 664-0865; e-mail steveroot@pensacola.com; adv e-mail steveroot@pensacola.com; web site www.FWBthriftynickel.com
Circulation:11,709fr; CVC
Advertising: Open inch rate $5.00 - $10.50
Established: 1980
Group: Thrifty Nickel Publications, LlcEditions: 1—
Digital Platform - Mobile: Apple, Android, Windows, Blackberry, Other
Digital Platform - Tablet: Apple iOS, Android, Windows 7, Blackberry Tablet OS, Kindle, Nook, Kindle Fire, Other
Publisher .... Steve Root
Mechanical Specifications: 8 Columns x 16" = 1 page
1 column = 7,6 picas
2 columns = 15,6 picas
Equipment: Hardware — IBM; Software — coreldraw ver 8, pagemaker 5
Delivery Method: Racks
Zip Codes Served: 32433, 32434, 32439, 32531, 32536, 32541, 32542, 32544, 32547, 32548, 32549, 32550, 32564, 32566, 32567, 32569, 32578, 32579, 36420, 35467

KISSIMMEE

OSCEOLA NEWS-GAZETTE

(Thur, Sat) (2x Wkly)
108 Church St, Kissimmee, FL, 34741-5055, USA; tel (407) 846-7600; adv tel (407) 846-7600; ed tel (407) 846-7600; fax (407) 846-8516; e-mail mplocha@osceolanews-gazette.com; adv e-mail bberry@osceolanewsgazette.com; ed e-mail bmcbride@osceolanewsgazette.com; web site www.aroundosceola.com
Circulation: 561pd,40,126fr; CVC
Advertising: Open inch rate $22.25
Established: 1891
Circ. Mgr. .... Kathy Beckham
Internet Systems Mgr. .... Randy Sorenson
Publisher .... Matt Plocha
Editor .... Brian McBride
Production Manager .... Angelique Prioe
Accounting .... Pam Bikowicz
Mechanical Specifications: 6 col. x 16" - 96" page
1 Column: 1.54"
2 Column: 3.23"
3 Column: 4.92"
4 Column: 6.61"
5 Column: 8.30"
6 Column: 10.00"
Equipment: Hardware — APP/Mac; Presses — 9-G; Software — In Design, QPS/QuarkXPress 4.1, Adobe/Photoshop 6.0, Adobe/Illustrator 9.0, Macromedia/Freehand 7.0, Adobe/Acrobat 4.0.
Delivery Method: Mail, Newsstand, Carrier, Racks
Zip Codes Served: 34741, 34743, 34744, 34746, 34758, 34759, 34771, 34769, 34772, 34747

LAKELAND

POLK VOICE

300 W Lime St, Lakeland, FL, 33815-4649, USA; tel (863) 802-7452

MELBOURNE

THRIFTY NICKEL - MERRITT ISLAND

(Thur)
2525 Aurora Rd, Ste 102, Melbourne, FL, 32935-2833, USA; web site www.thriftynickelcfl.com
Circulation: 0pd,14,975fr; CVC
Advertising: CP
Established: 1982Joey Laurino
Mechanical Specifications: Type page 10.5" x 15.5"; 8 cols
Delivery Method: Mail, Carrier, Racks

MIAMI

HERALD VALUES

(Thur)
1 Herald Plz, Miami, FL, 33132-1609, USA; tel (305) 350-2111; adv tel (305) 376-3315; web site www.miamiherald.com
Circulation: 0pd,787,390fr; VAC
Group: The McClatchy Company
Pres./Pub. .... David A. Landsberg
Vice Pres., Finance/CFO .... Greg Curling
Vice Pres./Broward Bus. Mgr. .... Donna Dickey
Vice Pres./CFO .... Susan A. Rosenthal
Vice Pres., Targeted Publications .... Dory Trinka
Vice Pres., HR/Asst. to Pub. .... Elissa Vanaver
Gen. Mgr., MiamiHerald.com .... Raul Lopez
Adv. Dir., Classified .... Patricia Royal
Adv. Dir., Local .... David Jost
Adv. Dir., Nat'l .... Matthew Fine
Interactive Sales Mgr. .... Jackie Kaplan
Vice Pres., Mktg./Bus. Devel. .... Willard Soper
Circ. Vice Pres. .... Bernie Kosanke
Vice Pres./Exec. Ed. Aminda Marques Gonzalez
Dir., Int'l Edition .... Tony Espetia
Mng. Ed., Multimedia .... Rick Hirsch
Mng. Ed., News .... Dave Wilson
Asst. Mng. Ed., Broward .... Pat Andrews
Dir., Photography .... Luis Rios

MOUNT DORA

TRIANGLE NEWS LEADER

(Thur)
4645 N Highway 19A, Mount Dora, FL, 32757-2039, USA; tel (352) 589-8811; fax (352) 357-3202; adv e-mail classified@sunpubfl.com; web site www.trianglenews-leader.com
Circulation:28,061fr; CVC
Advertising: Open inch rate $11.81
Group: Independent Publications Inc
Lakeway Publishers, Inc.
Sun Publications of Fla.
Office Mgr. .... Marion Witt
Gen. Mgr. .... Donna Covert
Adv. Dir. .... Ann Yager
Circ. Mgr. .... Randi Weeks
Prodn. Mgr. .... Val Neeley
Prod. Mgr .... Dawn Hendry
Zip Codes Served: 32757

NEW SMYRNA BEACH

NEW SMYRNA PENNYSAVER

(Wed)
223 Canal St, New Smyrna Beach, FL, 32168-7089, USA; web site www.floridapennysavers.com
Circulation:27,035fr; CVC
Advertising: Open inch rate $12.70Bill Offill

ORMOND BEACH

DAYTONA PENNYSAVER

(Wed)
454 S Yonge St, Ormond Beach, FL, 32174-7501, USA; tel (386) 677-4262; adv tel (386) 676-3100; fax (386) 677-6608; e-mail daytona.pennysaver@psavers.com; web site www.floridapennysavers.com
Circulation:66,186fr; CVC
Advertising: Open inch rate $19.65
Established: 1981
Group: News-Journal Corp.
Gen. Mgr. .... Kelli Hull
Display Gen. Sales Mgr. .... Toni Maddux
Classified Gen. Sales Mgr. .... Mary Morrissey
Circ. Mgr. .... Jon Riddell
Asst. Circ. Supvr. .... Aaron Fleury
Zip Codes Served: 32174

VOLUSIA PENNYSAVER, INC.

(Wed, Thur, Sat)

454 S Yonge St, Ormond Beach, FL, 32174-7501, USA; tel (386) 677-4262; fax (386) 677-6608; e-mail clarissa.williams@psavers.com; web site www.floridapennysavers.com
Circulation:112,300fr; Sworn/Estimate/Non-Audited
Advertising: Rate Card by Request
Established: 1971
Group General Manager ...... Clarissa Williams
Pub./Gen. Mgr. ...... Leonard A. Marsh
Gen. Mgr. ...... Kelli Hull
Gen. Sales Mgr. ...... Toni Maddux
Gen. Sales Mgr. ...... Mary Morrissey
Circ. Mgr. ...... Jon Riddell
Sales Mgr ...... Daniele Lowe
Delivery Method: Mail, Carrier, Racks

PALATKA

ST. JOHN'S PENNYSAVER
(Thur)
930 S State Road 19, Palatka, FL, 32177-9306, USA; tel (386) 681-2788; adv tel (386) 328-4649; e-mail daniele.lowe@psavers.com; web site www.floridapennysavers.com
Circulation:15,426fr; Sworn/Estimate/Non-AuditedClarissa Williams

PANAMA CITY

THRIFTY NICKEL PUBLICATIONS, LLC
(Thur)
1522 Chestnut Ave, Panama City, FL, 32405-2576, USA; tel (850) 747-1155; fax (850) 784-0677; e-mail classifiedstnol@gmail.com; web site http://panamacity.thriftynickel.com/
Circulation:20,975fr; CVC
Advertising: Open inch rate $11.00
Established: 1987
Owner/Gen. Mgr. ...... Stephen White
Mechanical Specifications: Type page 10 9/16 x 16"; A - 8 cols, 1 1/4, 1/12 between; C - 8 cols, 1 1/4, 1/12 between.
Equipment: Hardware — Pentium/PC 360, PC 486, PC 133; Presses — G/Community; Software — InDesign, Photoshop, Adobe Illustrator
Delivery Method: Racks
Zip Codes Served: 32405

THE ADVERTISER
(Thur)
2905 E Highway 98, Panama City, FL, 32401-5429, USA; tel (850) 785-7355; fax (850) 785-1509; e-mail pcadvertiser@bellsouth.net
Circulation:20,000fr; Sworn/Estimate/Non-Audited
Advertising: Open inch rate $8.00
Established: 1983
Pub. ...... Pamela Howell
Adv. Mgr. ...... Michelle Skipper
Mechanical Specifications: Type page 10 1/4 x 15 2/5.
Equipment: Hardware — 6-APP/Mac; Software — Adobe/Photoshop 3.0, Adobe/PageMaker 6.0.

PENSACOLA

THRIFTY NICKEL - PENSACOLA
(Thur)
225 N Pace Blvd, Pensacola, FL, 32505-7915, USA; tel (850) 469-9712; fax (850) 469-9718; e-mail steveroot@pensacola.com; web site www.ThriftyNickelPensacola.com
Circulation:37,129fr; CVC
Advertising: Open inch rate $5.66 - $12.00
Established: 1885
Group: Thrifty Nickel Publications, LlcEditions: 1—
Digital Platform - Mobile: Apple, Android, Windows, Blackberry, Other
Digital Platform - Tablet: Apple iOS, Android, Windows 7, Blackberry Tablet OS, Kindle, Nook, Kindle Fire, Other
General Manager ...... Steve Root
Mechanical Specifications: Type page 10.75" x 16"; 8 cols
Equipment: Hardware — IBM
Delivery Method: Mail, Carrier, Racks
Zip Codes Served: 32505, 32507, 32504, 32506

STUART

FLASHES SHOPPING GUIDE
(Wed)
5675 SE Grouper Ave, Stuart, FL, 34997-3103, USA; tel (772) 287-0650; ed tel (772) 219-2741; fax (772) 283-5090; e-mail flashesreceptionist@theflashes.com; adv e-mail sales@theflashes.com; ed e-mail classifieds@theflashes.com; goodneighbor@theflashes.com; communityevents@theflashes.com; web site www.theflashes.com
Circulation:60,000fr; Sworn/Estimate/Non-Audited
Advertising: Open inch rate $15.20
Established: 1951Editions: 3— 3 total; Central Flashes Shopping Guide (20,000); North Flashes Shopping Guide (20,000); South Flashes Shopping Guide (20,000);
Pub. ...... Kevin Hawken
Adv. Mgr. ...... Gary Dean
Equipment: Hardware — APP/Mac, DTI, APP/Mac LaserWriter; Software — Synaptic.
Zip Codes Served: 34944

TALLAHASSEE

AMERICAN CLASSIFIEDS - TALLAHASSEE
(Thur)
2441 Monticello Dr, Tallahassee, FL, 32303-4761, USA; web site www.americanclassifieds.com
Circulation: 0pd,23,886fr; CVC
Advertising: Open inch rate $12.00Larrie Jemison
Mechanical Specifications: Type page 10.5" x 16"; 8 cols
Delivery Method: Racks

TAMPA

THE FLYER, INC.
(Wed)
201 Kelsey Ln, Ste A, Tampa, FL, 33619-4310, USA; tel (813) 626-9430; adv tel (813) 626-9430; web site www.theflyer.com
Circulation:1,600,000fr; CVC
Established: 1977Editions: 73—
Digital Platform - Mobile: Apple, Android, Windows
Digital Platform - Tablet: Apple iOS
Mechanical Specifications: Type page 6.25" x 9.25"; 4 cols
Equipment: Hardware — Mac, PCs, iPADs; Presses — Goss Community, Didde; Software — CS 6
Delivery Method: Mail

VENICE

THE SUN SHOPPER
(Fri)
200 E Venice Ave, Venice, FL, 34285-1941, USA; tel (941) 207-1000; fax (941) 484-8460; web site www.venicegondolier.com
Circulation:18,000fr; Sworn/Estimate/Non-Audited
Advertising: Open inch rate $22.00Editions: 2— 2 total; Englewood/West Port; Venice;
Pub. ...... Bob Vedder
Adv. Mgr. ...... Lang Capasso
Circ. Mgr. ...... Karen Gardner
Ed. ...... Bob Mudge
Prodn. Mgr. ...... James King
Mechanical Specifications: Type page 13 x 21; E - 6 cols, 2 1/16, 5/16 between; A - 6 cols, 2 1/16, 5/16 between; C - 9 cols, 1 3/8, 1/8 between.
Equipment: Hardware — APP/Mac; Presses — HI/V-15A; Software — Multi-Ad/Creator 4.01, Baseview, QPS/QuarkXPress 3.32, Adobe/Photoshop 5.0.
Zip Codes Served: 34285

WEST PALM BEACH

FLORIDA PENNYSAVER
(Thur)
2751 S Dixie Hwy, West Palm Beach, FL, 33405-1233, USA; tel (561) 820-4777; fax (561) 820-4594; e-mail info@flapennysaver.com; web site www.flapennysaver.com
Circulation:36,300fr; Sworn/Estimate/Non-Audited
Advertising: Open inch rate $109.78
Group: Cox Media GroupEditions: 22— 22 total; El Pennysaver (10,000); Florida Pennysaver-SW West Palm Beach (17,100); Florida Pennysaver-East Boynton Beach (17,600); Florida Pennysaver-East Delray Beach (19,800); Florida Pennysaver-East Boca Raton (21,800); Florida Pennysaver-East Jupiter
Gen. Mgr. ...... Joyce Sullivan
Classified Mgr. ...... Janet Taylor Fisher
Display Mgr. ...... Glen Muench
Adv. Sales Mgr. ...... Jackie Ceaseretti
Zip Codes Served: 33416

WINTER HAVEN

ADVERTISER OF POLK COUNTY
(Wed)
1122 5th St SW, Winter Haven, FL, 33880-3725, USA; tel (863) 299-2201; fax (863) 299-5672; e-mail advpaper@aol.com; web site www.theadvertiser.com
Circulation:37,000fr; Sworn/Estimate/Non-Audited
Advertising: Open inch rate $6.50
Pub. ...... Larry A. Knowles
Co Pub. ...... Cindy Yates
Mechanical Specifications: Type page 10 1/4 x 17.
Equipment: Hardware — APP/Mac; Software — First Class.
Zip Codes Served: 33880

LAKE WALES SHOPPER
(Wed)
455 6th St NW, Winter Haven, FL, 33881-4061, USA; tel (863) 401-6900; adv tel (863) 802-7473; ed tel (863) 802-7504; fax (863) 401-6999; e-mail news@newschief.com; adv e-mail legals@newschief.com; ed e-mail lynne.maddox@theledger.com; web site www.newschief.com
Circulation:16,710fr; Sworn/Estimate/Non-Audited
Advertising: Open inch rate $10.00
Mng. Ed. ...... Joe Braddy
Mechanical Specifications: Type page 10 3/16 x 16; E - 8 cols, 1 1/8, 1/8 between; A - 8 cols, 1 1/8, 1/8 between; C - 8 cols, 1 1/8, 1/8 between.
Equipment: Hardware — APP/Mac; Presses — G/Urbanite, HI/V-15D; Software — QPS/QuarkXPress.
Zip Codes Served: 33853

ZEPHYRHILLS

PASCO SHOPPER
(Wed)
5739 Gall Blvd, Zephyrhills, FL, 33542-3453, USA; tel (352) 567-5639; fax (352) 567-5640; e-mail info@pasconews.com; web site www.pascoshoppingguide.com
Circulation:31,050fr; Sworn/Estimate/Non-Audited
Advertising: Open inch rate $14.20
Group: Independent Publications Inc
Sun Publications of Fla.Editions: 3— 3 total; Pasco News (15,000); Wesley Chapel Connection (4,000); Zephyrhills Sun (19,000);
Pub. ...... Ann Licate
Mechanical Specifications: Type page 9 5/8 x 16; E - 5 cols, 1 7/8, 1/8 between; A - 5 cols, 1 7/8, 1/8 between; C - 5 cols, 1 7/8, between.
Equipment: Hardware — APP/Power Mac; Presses — KP, 8-WPC/Web Leader; Software — Adobe/PageMaker, Adobe/Photoshop, QPS/QuarkXPress.
Zip Codes Served: 33524, 33525, 33535, 33537, 33540, 33541, 33543, 33544, 33574, 33576, 34602

GEORGIA

AMERICUS

THE AMERICUS SHOPPER
(Tues)
1403 Felder St, Americus, GA, 31709-5362, USA; tel (229) 924-9000; fax (229) 928-2977; web site http://www.sumtercountychamber.com/
Circulation:17,000fr; Sworn/Estimate/Non-Audited
Advertising: Open inch rate $5.00
Pub. ...... Joel Ward

BAINBRIDGE

POST-SEARCHLIGHT EXTRA
(Wed, Sat)
301 N Crawford St, Bainbridge, GA, 39817-3612, USA; tel (229) 246-2827; fax (229) 246-7665; e-mail publisher@e-postprint.com; web site www.thepostsearchlight.com
Circulation:34,000fr; Sworn/Estimate/Non-Audited
Advertising: Open inch rate $13.30
Established: 1907
Group: Boone Newspapers, Inc.
Adv. Mgr. ...... Jeff Findley
Asst. Adv. Mgr. ...... Tameka Thomas
Circ. Mgr. ...... Teshiki Parrish
Mng. Ed. ...... Carol Heard
Sports Ed. ...... Joe Crine
Mechanical Specifications: Type page 13 x 21 1/2; E - 6 cols, 2 1/3, 1/8 between; A - 6 cols, 2 1/3, 1/8 between; C - 6 cols, 2 1/3, 1/8 between.
Equipment: Hardware — APP/Mac; Presses — G/Community; Software — QPS/QuarkXPress, Adobe/Photoshop.
Zip Codes Served: 31717

CANTON

CHEROKEE TRIBUNE PLUS
(Wed)
521 E Main St, Canton, GA, 30114-2805, USA; tel (770) 795-5000; fax (770) 479-3505; web site www.cherokeetribune.com
Circulation:10,000fr; CAC
Advertising: Open inch rate $18.00
Group: Times-Journal, Inc.
Pub. ...... Otis A. Brumby
Vice Pres. Sales/Mktg. ...... Wade Stephens
Adv. Mgr. ...... Kim Fowler
Circ. Dir. ...... Matt Heck
Ed. ...... Barbara Jacoby
Sports Ed. ...... John Bednarowski
Zip Codes Served: 30061

COLUMBUS

THRIFTY NICKEL - COLUMBUS
(Thur)
4425 Holly Ave, Columbus, GA, 31904-6525, USA; tel (706) 571-3463; adv tel (706) 571-3463; fax (706) 327-8075; adv fax (706) 327-8075; e-mail columbus@peachads.com; adv e-mail charlie@peachads.com; web site www.columbusthriftynickel.com
Circulation:32,352fr; CVC
Established: 1990
Digital Platform - Mobile: Apple
Digital Platform - Tablet: Apple iOSRandy Eiland
Delivery Method: Racks

CONYERS

MIKE'S SHOPPER
(Mthly)
2274 Salem Rd SE, Ste 106-232, Conyers, GA, 30013-2097, USA; tel (770) 388-0438; fax (770) 922-3338; e-mail Info@mikesshoppers.com
Circulation:25,450fr; Sworn/Estimate/Non-Audited
Advertising: Open inch rate $7.50
Pub. .... Thad Doug
Mechanical Specifications: Type page 6 x 16; A - 6 cols, 1 1/2, between; C - 6 cols, 1 1/2, between.
Equipment: Hardware — COM/7700-4400, APP/Mac IIsi; Software — QPS/QuarkXPress 4.0.
Zip Codes Served: 30013

CORDELE

BUYERS GUIDE
(Tues)
306 W 13th Ave, Cordele, GA, 31015-2348, USA; tel (229) 273-2277; fax (229) 273-7239; web site www.cordeledispatch.com
Circulation:12,500fr; Sworn/Estimate/Non-Audited
Advertising: Open inch rate $5.42
Adv. Mgr. .... Chris Mann
News Ed. .... Peggy King
Composing Mgr. .... Betty Ruis
Mechanical Specifications: Type page 13 x 21 1/2; E - 6 cols, 2 1/8, between; A - 6 cols, 2 1/8, between; C - 9 cols, 2 1/8, between.
Zip Codes Served: 31015

COVINGTON

THE COVINGTON NEWS
(Tues)
1166 Usher St NW, Covington, GA, 30014-2451, USA; tel (770) 787-6397; fax (770) 786-6451; e-mail circulation@covnews.com; web site www.covnews.com
Circulation:43,500fr; Sworn/Estimate/Non-Audited
Advertising: Open inch rate $7.50
Pub. .... Charles H. Morris
Circ. Mgr. .... Bill Herbert
Mechanical Specifications: Type page 6 x 16; A - 6 cols, 1 1/2, between; C - 6 cols, 1 1/2, between.
Equipment: Hardware — APP/Mac G4; Software — QPS/QuarkXPress 4.0, Adobe/Photoshop, Baseview.
Zip Codes Served: 30014, 30016, 30025, 30054, 30055, 30262, 30070, 30012, 30013, 30094

DOUGLAS

DOUGLAS SHOPPER
(Tues)
404 Peterson Ave N, Douglas, GA, 31533-4916, USA; tel (912) 384-9112; adv tel (912) 384-1980; fax (912) 384-4220; e-mail Graphics@YourDouglasShopper.com; adv e-mail Sales@YourDouglasShopper.com; web site www.yourdouglasshopper.com
Circulation:20,760fr; Sworn/Estimate/Non-Audited
Advertising: Open inch rate $6.25
Office Mgr. .... Sharon Mart
Mechanical Specifications: Type page 10 1/4 x 15; E - 6 cols, 1 1/2, between; A - 6 cols, 1 1/2, between; C - 6 cols, 1 1/2, between.
Equipment: Hardware — APP/Power Macs; Presses — 5-KP; Software — Multi-Ad/Creator, QPS/QuarkXPress.
Zip Codes Served: 31533

EATONTON

THE EATONTON MESSENGER
(Thur)
100 N Jefferson Ave, Eatonton, GA, 31024-1020, USA; tel (706) 485-3501; fax (706) 485-4166; e-mail msgr@msgr.com; ed e-mail editor@msgr.com; web site msgr.com
Circulation: 5,500pd,; USPS
Advertising: Open inch rate $9.
Established: 1968
Group: Smith Communications, IncEditions: Total circulation 18,500
Associate Editor .... Lynn Hobbs
Pub .... Mark Smith , Sr.
Mechanical Specifications: six columns-13x21-column-1.8 inches
Equipment: Hardware — HP/ScanJet, HP/LaserJet 5p; Presses — !8 unit Urbanite- double out- 90% color pages; Software — Microsoft/Windows 6.1.
Delivery Method: Mail, Newsstand, Carrier, Racks
Zip Codes Served: 31024, 31061

FITZGERALD

BEN HILL IRWIN WILCOX SHOPPER
(Tues)
602 S Grant St, Fitzgerald, GA, 31750-3314, USA; tel (229) 423-6684; fax (229) 423-3785; e-mail bhiwshopper@windstream.net; web site bhiwshopper.com
Circulation:16,600fr; Sworn/Estimate/Non-Audited
Advertising: Open inch rate $6.00
Established: 1982
Adv. Mgr. .... Terry Hulsey
Circ. Mgr. .... Randy Hulsey
Mechanical Specifications: Type page 6 x 15; E - 6 cols, 1 1/2, between; A - 6 cols, 1 1/2, between; C - 6 cols, 1 1/2, between.
Equipment: Hardware — IBM; Software — Adobe/PageMaker.
Delivery Method: Mail
Zip Codes Served: 31750, 31774,31798, 31001,31071,31072, 31079,31783

GRIFFIN

TOWN & COUNTRY SHOPPER
(Sun)
1422 Georgia Highway 16 W, Griffin, GA, 30223-2054, USA; tel (770) 467-8888; fax (763) 389-1728; e-mail pueproduction@ecm-inc.com; web site www.ecm-inc.com
Circulation:16,611fr; CVC
Advertising: Open inch rate $8.80
Established: 1976
Group: Adams Publishing Group, LLC
Pub. .... Julian L. Andersen
Adv. Mgr. .... Timothy Enger
Mechanical Specifications: Type page 9 9/16 x 15; E - 6 cols, 1 5/6, 1/4 between; A - 5 cols, 1 5/6, 1/4 between; C - 6 cols, 1 1/2, 1/4 between.
Equipment: Hardware — APP/Mac; Software — QPS/QuarkXPress 3.32.
Zip Codes Served: 55371

HINESVILLE

BARROW COUNTY NEWS
(Wed)
125 S Main St, Hinesville, GA, 31313-3217, USA; tel (912) 876-0156; fax (912) 368-6329; web site www.coastalcourier.com
Circulation:13,000fr; Sworn/Estimate/Non-Audited
Advertising: Open inch rate $8.60
Group: Morris Multimedia, Inc.
Pub. .... Mark Griffin
Adv. Rep. .... Lillian McKnight
Debbie Burgamy
Mechanical Specifications: Type page 10 1/4 x 13; A - 6 cols, 1 9/16, 1/6 between.

TRI-COUNTY PENNYSAVER
(Wed)
123 S Main St, Hinesville, GA, 31313-3217, USA; tel (912) 876-0156; fax (912) 368-6329; web site www.coastalcourier.com
Circulation:20,872fr; Sworn/Estimate/Non-Audited
Advertising: Open inch rate $12.30
Group: Morris Multimedia, Inc.
Pub. .... Marshall Griffin
Gen. Mgr. .... Kathryn Fox
Adv. Rep. .... Lillian McKnight
Exec. Ed. .... Patrick Donahue
Mng. Ed. .... Pat Watkins
Prodn. Mgr. .... Leslie Miller
Mechanical Specifications: Type page 10 1/4 x 13; E - 6 cols, 2, between; A - 6 cols, 2, between.
Zip Codes Served: 31313

LA FAYETTE

WALKER COUNTY PLUS
(Tues)
102 N Main St, La Fayette, GA, 30728-2418, USA; tel (706) 638-1859; fax (706) 638-7045; e-mail walkercountymessenger@walkermessenger.com; web site www.walkermessenger.com
Circulation:15,350fr; Sworn/Estimate/Non-Audited
Advertising: Open inch rate $7.49
Established: 1877
Group: Rome News-Tribune
Pub. .... Don Stilwell
Office Mgr./Classifieds/Legals Rebekah Rollins
Adv. Rep. .... Alycia Edgeman
Ed. .... Becky McDaniel
Sports Ed. .... Scott Herpst
Editorial Asst. .... Kristi Sellers
Mechanical Specifications: Type page 13 x 21 1/4; E - 6 cols, 2 1/16, 1/8 between; A - 6 cols, 2 1/16, 1/8 between; C - 9 cols, 1 3/8, 1/8 between.
Equipment: ; Presses — 8-G/Community.
Zip Codes Served: 30728, 30707, 30739, 30741

LAGRANGE

LA GRANGE SHOPPER
(Wed)
105 Ashton St, Lagrange, GA, 30240-3111, USA; tel (706) 884-7311; fax (706) 884-8712; web site www.lagrangenews.com
Circulation:14,800fr; Sworn/Estimate/Non-Audited
Advertising: Open inch rate $11.75
Established: 1983
Group: Boone Newsmedia, LLC
Pub. .... Lynn McLamb
Bus./Office Mgr. .... Judy Phillips
Ed. .... Daniel Baker
Mechanical Specifications: Type page 11 5/8 x 21 1/2; E - 6 cols, 1 5/6, between; A - 6 cols, 1 5/6, between; C - 9 cols, 1 5/24, between.
Equipment: Hardware — APP/Mac; Presses — G; Software — Baseview.
Zip Codes Served: 30230, 30217, 30222, 31822, 31833, 36274

MARIETTA

THRIFTY NICKEL - MARIETTA NORTH
(Thur)
1468 Roswell Rd, Marietta, GA, 30062-3670, USA; tel (770) 971-8333; fax (770) 578-1673; e-mail office@atlantathriftynickel.com; web site www.atlantathriftynickel.com
Circulation:19,021fr; CVC
Advertising: Open inch rate $15.00
Established: 1984
Group: WantAds of Idaho Falls, Inc.
Publisher .... Amy Hollingshead
Mechanical Specifications: Eight (8) columns x 15.5-inch column depth
Equipment: ; Software — InDesign
Delivery Method: Racks
Zip Codes Served: All north metro counties

THRIFTY NICKEL - SOUTH METRO
(Thur)
1468 Roswell Rd, Marietta, GA, 30062-3670, USA; tel (770) 971-8333; fax (770) 578-1673; e-mail office@atlantathriftynickel.com; web site www.atlantathriftynickel.com
Circulation:17,134fr; CVC
Advertising: Open inch rate $15.00
Established: 1984
Group: WantAds of Idaho Falls, Inc.Amy Hollingshead
Mechanical Specifications: Eight (8) columns x 15.5" depth
Delivery Method: Racks
Zip Codes Served: all south metro atlanta

SAVANNAH

SAVANNAH PENNYSAVER
(Wed)
1464 E Victory Dr, Savannah, GA, 31404-4108, USA; tel (912) 238-2040; adv fax (912) 944-0010; e-mail savpennysaver@savpennysaver.com; adv e-mail sales@savpennysaver.com; classifieds@savpennysaver.com; ed e-mail circulation@savpennysaver.com; web site www.savannahpennysaver.com
Circulation: 65,363pd,; AAM
Advertising: Open inch rate $19.51
Group: Morris Multimedia, Inc.Editions: 3— 3 total; Coastal Empire Pennysaver-Islands/Southeast (27,060); Coastal Empire Pennysaver-Southside/Midtown (28,160); Coastal Empire Pennysaver-Westside/Downtown (23,940);
Pub. .... Av Rocker
Pub. .... Chris Grissin
Contact .... Joe McGlamery
Circ. Mgr. .... Robert Foy
Mechanical Specifications: Type page 10 1/4 x 13; E - 6 cols, 1 5/8, 1/8 between; A - 6 cols, 1 5/8, 1/8 between.
Equipment: Hardware — APP/Mac; Presses — 12-G; Software — QPS/QuarkXPress 3.31.
Zip Codes Served: 31401, 31404, 31405, 31406, 31407, 31408, 31410, 31411, 31412, 31419, 31302, 31322, 31324, 31326, 31328

THOMSON

DOLLAR SAVER
(Wed)
101 Church St, Thomson, GA, 30824-2613, USA; tel (706) 595-1601; fax (706) 597-8974; e-mail composing@mcduffieprogress.com; ed e-mail classifieds@mcduffieprogress.com; web site www.mcduffieprogress.com
Circulation:15,000fr; Sworn/Estimate/Non-Audited
Advertising: Open inch rate $9.00
Pub .... Dick Mitchell
Adv. Mgr. .... Tim Phillips
Ed. .... Justin Schuver
Equipment: Hardware — APP/Mac; Presses — 10-KP; Software — QPS/QuarkXPress, Baseview.
Zip Codes Served: 30824

TIFTON

TIFTON SHOPPER
(Tues)
211 Tift Ave N, Tifton, GA, 31794-4463, USA; tel (229) 382-4321; fax (229) 387-7322; web site www.tiftongazette.com
Circulation:15,661fr; Sworn/Estimate/Non-Audited
Advertising: Open inch rate $6.85
Pub. .... Frank Sayles
Adv. Mgr. .... Lisa Beckham
Circ. Mgr. .... Rachel Wainwright
Mng. Ed. .... Flo Rankin
Sports Ed. .... Kyle Dean
Mechanical Specifications: Type page 6 x 13; E - 6 cols, 1 9/16, 1/6 between; A - 6 cols, 1 9/16, 1/6 between; C - 6 cols, 1 9/16, 1/6 between.
Equipment: Hardware — APP/Mac LC III, APP/Mac Quadra 650, APP/Mac 8500; Software — Custom Hypercard, Claris/Macdraw Pro, Adobe/PageMaker, Multi-Ad/Creator, Adobe/Illustrator, Adobe/Photoshop.
Zip Codes Served: 31620

VIDALIA

ADVANTAGE
(Mon)
PO Box 669, Vidalia, GA, 30475-0669, USA; tel (912) 537-3131; fax (912) 537-4899; e-mail theadvance@bellsouth.net
Circulation:23,000fr; Sworn/Estimate/Non-Audited
Advertising: Open inch rate $7.50
Group: Advance Publications, Inc.
Adv. Mgr. .... Daniel Ford
Ed. .... William F. Ledford
Zip Codes Served: 30474

WARNER ROBINS

WARNER ROBINS BUYERS GUIDE
(Wed)
1553 Watson Blvd, Warner Robins, GA, 31093-3449, USA; tel (478) 744-4200; fax (478) 329-1591; web site www.american.com
Circulation:24,325fr; Sworn/Estimate/Non-Audited
Advertising: Open inch rate $9.75
Pub. .... T.J. Browning
Ed. .... David Cranshaw
Mechanical Specifications: Type page 10 1/2 x 16; E - 6 cols, 1 9/16, between; A - 6 cols, 1 9/16, between; C - 6 cols, 1 9/16, between.
Equipment: Hardware — APP/Mac; Presses — G/Rockwell, 8-G/Community; Software — Macromedia/Freehand, QPS/QuarkXPress, Adobe/Illustrator.
Zip Codes Served: 31088

WAYCROSS

WAYCROSS SHOPPER
(Tues)
540 Plant Ave, Waycross, GA, 31501-3510, USA; tel (912) 285-8539; fax (912) 283-5231; e-mail info@thewaycrossshopper.com; web site www.thewaycrossshopper.com
Circulation:28,268fr; CVC
Advertising: Open inch rate $8.00
Established: 1981
Pub. .... Al Joiner
Adv. .... Louise Carter
Circ. .... Lori McGill
Mechanical Specifications: Type page 10.25" x 14"; 6 cols
Equipment: Hardware — APP/Mac; Presses — 5-G; Software — Multi-Ad/Creator.
Delivery Method: Racks
Zip Codes Served: 31501, 31502, 31503, 31516, 31542, 31550, 31552, 31553, 31557

WINDER

BARROW NEWS-JOURNAL
(Wed)
77 E May St, Winder, GA, 30680-1951, USA; tel (770) 867-6397; adv tel (706) 367-5233; ed tel (706) 367-5233; fax (706) 367-8056; adv fax (706) 621-4118; ed fax (706) 367-8056; e-mail ads@mainstreetnews.com; adv e-mail scott@mainstreetnews.com; ed e-mail mike@mainstreetnews.com; web site www.barrownewsjournal.com
Circulation: 4,500pd,0fr; Sworn/Estimate/Non-Audited
Advertising: Open inch rate $7.00
Established: 1893
Group: MainStreet Newspapers, Inc.
Digital Platform - Mobile: Apple, Android
Digital Platform - Tablet: Apple iOS, Android
Scott Buffington
Mike BuffingtonCo-Publishers
Mechanical Specifications: 6 column broadsheet format
(ROP, Legal and Classified Pages)
1column .... 1.5625 inches
2 columns .... 3.25 inches
3 columns .... 4.9375 inches
4 columns .... 6.625 inches
5columns .... 8.3125 inches
6 columns .... 10.0 inches
Full column depth is 21 inches
Equipment: Hardware — Mac; Presses — Goss Community; Software — Adobe Creative Suite
Delivery Method: Mail, Newsstand, Racks
Zip Codes Served: 30680, 30011, 30666, 30620

IDAHO

BLACKFOOT

BINGHAM COUNTY BARGAINS
(Wed)
34 N Ash St, Blackfoot, ID, 83221-2101, USA; tel (208) 785-1100; fax (208) 785-4239; e-mail mnews@cableone.net
Circulation: 0pd,4,250fr; Sworn/Estimate/Non-Audited
Advertising: Open inch rate $8.00
Group: Horizon Publications Inc.
Pub. .... Leonard C. Martin
Adv. Mgr. .... Wayne Ingram
Circ. Mgr. .... Joe Kimbro
Press Foreman .... Kelly Koontz
Mechanical Specifications: Type page 10.16x 21 1/2; E - 6 cols, 1.6", 1/6 between columns
Equipment: Hardware — Macs; Presses — 6-KP; Software — Indesign
Delivery Method: Newsstand, Carrier
Zip Codes Served: 83203, 83210, 83215, 83218, 83221, 83236, 83256 and 83262.

BOISE

AMERICAN CLASSIFIEDS - BOISE
(Thur)
3612 W Overland Rd, Boise, ID, 83705-6034, USA; web site www.americanclassifieds.com
Circulation:32,632fr; CVCDoug Bourkland

BURLEY

WEEKLY MAILER
(Tues)
221 W Main St, Burley, ID, 83318-1616, USA; tel (208) 678-6643; adv tel (208) 678-6643; fax (208) 678-6375; adv fax (208) 678-6375; e-mail jay@theweeklymailer.com; adv e-mail jay@theweeklymailer.com; ed e-mail News@theweeklymailer; web site www.minicassia.com
Circulation:15,675fr; Sworn/Estimate/Non-Audited
Advertising: Open inch rate $16.00
Established: 1995
Group: Sierra Marketing
Digital Platform - Mobile: Windows
Pub. .... Jay Lenkersdorfer
Circ. Mgr. .... Paul Lyons
Mechanical Specifications: 11 pica column, one pica gutter, 5 columns wide by 11 inches tall.
Delivery Method: Mail
Zip Codes Served: 83318, 83350, 83336, 83343, 83347, 83311, 83312, 83323, 83342, 83346, 83350

COEUR D ALENE

NICKELS WORTH
(Thur)
107 N 5th St, Coeur D Alene, ID, 83814-2708, USA; tel (208) 667-0651; fax (208) 765-6969; adv e-mail ads@nickelsworth.com; web site www.nickelsworth.com
Circulation: 13pd,31,471fr; CVC
Advertising: Open inch rate $10.70
Established: 1972
Ed. .... Chrissy Johnson
Distribution Mgr. .... Tim Rostkoski
Mechanical Specifications: Type page 10 x 15; A - 6 cols, 1 7/12, 1/6 between; C - 6 cols, 1 7/12, 1/6 between.
Zip Codes Served: 83816

GRANGEVILLE

THE SHOPPER
(Tues)
900 W Main St, Pob 690, Grangeville, ID, 83530-5192, USA; tel (208) 983-1200; fax (208) 983-1336; adv e-mail amcnab@idahocountyfreepress.com; web site www.idahocountyfreepress.com
Circulation:10,425fr; CVC
Advertising: $12.40 (combo with Free Press)
Established: 1981
Digital Platform - Mobile: Android
Digital Platform - Tablet: Windows 7Andrew McNab
Mechanical Specifications: 10-in X 20-in; 6-cols; 1.562-col
Delivery Method: Mail, Racks
Zip Codes Served: 83530;83522;83526 ;83523;83548;83555;83525;83536; 83539;83539;83552;83539; 83543; 83542; 83850; 83547; 83549; 83554

IDAHO FALLS

THRIFTY NICKEL WANT ADS
(Thur)
444 E Elva St, P.O. Box 1705, Idaho Falls, ID, 83401-2652, USA; tel (208) 529-9360; fax (208) 529-9491; e-mail photo@tnwa.org; web site www.idahofalls.tnol.com
Circulation:3,995fr; CVC
Advertising: Open inch rate $12.00
Established: 1978
Group: WantAds of Idaho Falls, Inc.
Digital Platform - Mobile: Apple, Android
Gen. Mgr. .... David Marlowe
Adv. Mgr. .... Sherri Griffen
Mechanical Specifications: Quarter Fold
Delivery Method: Newsstand, Racks
Zip Codes Served: 83403

LEWISTON

MONEYSAVER-LEWIS CLARK EDITION
(Thur)
626 Thain Rd, Lewiston, ID, 83501-5742, USA; tel (208) 746-0483; fax (208) 746-8507; adv e-mail ads@lcmoneysaver.com; web site www.lcmoneysaver.com
Circulation:37,274fr; CVC
Advertising: Open inch rate $12.65
Established: 1973
Group: Eagle Newspapers, Inc.
Publication Mgr. .... Diane Johnson
Circ. Mgr. .... Ron Carroll
Mechanical Specifications: Type page 10 1/12 x 15 1/2; E - 7 cols, 1 5/6, 1/6 between; A - 7 cols, 1 5/6, 1/6 between.
Equipment: Hardware — PCs, QMS/Laser Printer; Software — QPS/QuarkXPress 5.0, Adobe/PageMaker 6.5, Archetype/Corel Draw 6.5.
Zip Codes Served: 83501, 83520, 83522, 83523, 83524, 83525, 83526, 83530, 83533, 83534, 83535, 83536, 83536, 83537, 83538, 83539, 83540, 83541, 83543, 83544, 83545, 83546, 83551, 83552, 83553, 83554, 83555, 83806, 83823, 83825, 83827, 83834, 83836, 83843, 83855, 83857, 838

MONEYSAVER-PALOUSE EDITION
(Thur)
626 Thain Rd, Lewiston, ID, 83501-5742, USA; tel (208) 882-2595; fax (208) 883-4420; e-mail palouse@moneysav.com; web site www.palousemoneysaver.com
Circulation:5,834fr; CVC
Advertising: Open inch rate $6.50
Group: Eagle Newspapers, Inc.
Mgr. .... Diane Johnson
Mechanical Specifications: Type page 10 1/2 x 15 1/2; A - 7 cols, 1 5/6, 1/6 between; C - 7 cols, 1 5/6, 1/6 between.
Equipment: Hardware — PCs, QMS/Laser Printer, Illustrator; Software — QPS/QuarkXPress, Adobe/PageMaker, Archetype/Corel Draw.
Zip Codes Served: 83843, 99163

MOUNTAIN HOME

FAMILY LINE
(Tues)
195 S Third East St, Mountain Home, ID, 83647, USA; tel (208) 587-3331; fax (208) 587-9205; e-mail bfincher@mountainhome-news.com; web site www.mountainhome-news.com
Circulation:6,000fr; Sworn/Estimate/Non-Audited
Advertising: 7.35
Mechanical Specifications: 10.75" x 13"
Delivery Method: Mail, Racks
Zip Codes Served: 83647

NAMPA

IDAHO PRESS
(Wed)
1618 N Midland Blvd, Nampa, ID, 83651-1751, USA; tel (208) 467-9251; fax (208) 467-1863; ed e-mail op-ed@idahopress.com; web site www.idahopress.com
Circulation:35,000fr; Sworn/Estimate/Non-Audited
Group: Pioneer Newspapers Inc
Media Sales Rep. .... Angela Sammons
Circ. Dir. .... Ron Tincher
Ed. .... Vickie Schaffeld Holbrook
IT Dir. .... Joe Hansen
Prodn. Dir. .... Roger Stowell
Publisher .... Matt Davison
Equipment: Hardware — APP/Mac, PC; Presses — G/Community; Software — QPS/QuarkXPress 4.1.
Zip Codes Served: 83651

POCATELLO

PORTNEUF VALLEY TRADER
(Wed)
305 S Arthur Ave, Pocatello, ID, 83204-3306, USA; tel (208) 232-4161; fax (208) 233-8007;

web site www.journalnet.com
Circulation:16,800fr; Sworn/Estimate/Non-Audited
Advertising: Open inch rate $6.00
Pub. .... Bill Kunerth
Adv. Dir. .... Matt Petrie
Adv. Asst. .... Mikkel McBride
Circ. Dir .... Nathan Slater
Mng. Ed. .... Ian Fennell
Dir., IT Services .... Justin Smith
Mechanical Specifications: Type page 11 2/3 x 20 1/2; A - 6 cols, 1 4/5, 1/7 between; C - 9 cols, 1 1/6, 1/5 between.
Equipment: Hardware — APP/Mac; Presses — G/Urbanite; Software — QPS/QuarkXPress.
Zip Codes Served: 83204

TWIN FALLS

SOOPER ADS
(Thur)
453 Main Ave E, Twin Falls, ID, 83301-6422, USA; web site www.sooperads.com
Circulation:11,444fr; CVCRichard Borah

ILLINOIS

ALEDO

TOWN CRIER
PO Box 309, Aledo, IL, 61231-0309, USA; tel (800) 582-4373

AUBURN

SOUTH COUNTY EXPRESS
(Thur)
110 N 5th St, Auburn, IL, 62615-1449, USA; tel (217) 438-6155; fax (217) 438-6156; e-mail southco@royell.org; web site www.southcountypublications.com
Circulation:10,073fr; Sworn/Estimate/Non-Audited
Advertising: Open inch rate $6.00
Group: South County Publications
Pub. .... Joseph Michelich
Adv. Mgr. .... Connie Michelich
Mechanical Specifications: Type page 10 3/16 x 15 1/2; A - 5 cols, 1 7/8, between.
Zip Codes Served: 62615, 62530, 62558, 62629, 62536, 62661

BEARDSTOWN

STAR-GAZETTE EXTRA
(Mon, Thur)
1210 Wall St, Beardstown, IL, 62618-2327, USA; tel (217) 323-1010; adv tel same; ed tel (217) 323-1010; fax (217) 323-1644; ed fax (217) 323-1644; e-mail sgbusiness@casscomm.com; adv e-mail melissa.clements@casscomm.com; ed e-mail editor@casscomm.com; web site www.beardstownnewspapers.com
Circulation: 2,233pd,11,800fr; Sworn/Estimate/Non-Audited
Advertising: please inquire
Established: 1842
Group: Delphos Herald, Inc.
Digital Platform - Mobile: Apple, Android, Windows
Digital Platform - Tablet: Apple iOS, Android, Windows 7
General Manager .... Melissa Clements
Mechanical Specifications: please inquire
Delivery Method: Mail, Newsstand, Racks
Zip Codes Served: 62618

BELLEVILLE

COMMAND POST
(Fri)
120 S Illinois St, Belleville, IL, 62220-2130, USA; tel (618) 234-1000; fax (618) 235-0556; adv e-mail classified@bnd.com; obits@bnd.com; ed e-mail newsroom@bnd.com; web site www.bnd.com
Circulation:44,000fr; Sworn/Estimate/Non-Audited
Advertising: Open inch rate $15.96
Established: 1858
Group Manager .... Todd Eschman
Adv. Dir. .... Melissa Mason
Sales Mgr. .... Marsha Hopkins
Circ. Dir. .... John Grove
Ed. .... Jeffry Couch
Mechanical Specifications: Type page 10 x 11 1/2; A - 5 cols, 2 1/16, 1/8 between; C - 8 cols, 1 1/4, 1/8 between.
Equipment: Hardware — DEC/VAX, APP/Macs, PCs; Presses — G/Urbanite.
Delivery Method: Mail, Racks
Zip Codes Served: 62220

BELVIDERE

BOONE COUNTY SHOPPER
(Thur)
112 Leonard Ct, Belvidere, IL, 61008-3613, USA; tel (815) 544-2166; fax (815) 544-5558; e-mail info@boonecountyshopper.com; web site www.boonecountyshopper.com
Circulation: 0pd,20,639fr; CVC
Advertising: Open inch rate $16.75
Established: 1957
Pres./Gen. Mgr. .... Edward Branom
Sales Mgr. .... Matthew Branom
Mechanical Specifications: Type page 10 3/8 x 15; A - 6 cols, 1 5/8, 1/8 between.
Equipment: Hardware — APP/Mac G3, APP/Mac G4; Software — Multi-Ad/Creator 4.0.2, Photoshop
Delivery Method: Mail
Zip Codes Served: 61008 61011 61065 61038 61012

CANTON

FULTON COUNTY SHOPPER
(Mon)
53 W Elm St, Canton, IL, 61520-2511, USA; tel (309) 647-5100; fax (309) 647-4665; ed e-mail kharris@cantondailyledger.com; web site www.cantondailyledger.com
Circulation:17,000fr; Sworn/Estimate/Non-Audited
Advertising: Open inch rate $9.30
Group: GateHouse Media, Inc.
Circ. Mgr. .... Rick Bybee
Publisher .... Carla Spotser

CARBONDALE

AT HOME WITH FLIPSIDE
(Thur)
710 N Illinois Ave, Carbondale, IL, 62901-1283, USA; tel (618) 529-5454; fax (618) 457-2935; e-mail news@thesouthern.com; web site www.thesouthern.com
Circulation:36,500fr; Sworn/Estimate/Non-Audited
Advertising: Open inch rate $10.50
Pub. .... Bob Williams
Nat'l Acct. Exec. .... Brian Flath
Ed. .... Gary Metro
Mng. Ed. .... Mark Fitton
Sports Ed. .... Les Winkeler
MIS Mgr. .... David Fiedler
Prodn. Mgr. .... Bill Brasher
Opns. Mgr. .... Abby Hatfield
Zip Codes Served: 62901, 62918, 62959, 62948, 62966

CARLINVILLE

ENQUIRER EXPRESS
(Mon)
125 E Main St, Carlinville, IL, 62626-1726, USA; tel (217) 854-2534; fax (217) 854-2535; e-mail enquirer@dtnspeed.net
Circulation:15,000fr; Sworn/Estimate/Non-Audited
Advertising: Open inch rate $6.30
Cir.Mgr .... Eric Berlin
Ed. .... Jay Hendrids
Mechanical Specifications: Type page 10 x 15 1/2; A - 5 cols, 2, between.
Zip Codes Served: 62626

CARMI

THE MONEY STRETCHER WHITE COUNTY
(Tues)
323 E Main St, Carmi, IL, 62821-1810, USA; tel (618) 382-4176; fax (618) 384-2163; e-mail tknox@carmitimes.com; adv e-mail ctrout@carmitimes.com; web site www.carmitimes.com
Circulation:8,200fr; Sworn/Estimate/Non-Audited
Advertising: Open inch rate $8.80
Established: 2012
Group: GateHouse Media, Inc.
General Manager, Content .... Tammy Knox
Delivery Method: Mail
Zip Codes Served: 62821, 62835, 62887, 62820, 62869, 62827, 62867, 62871, 62844

CARROLLTON

GREENE COUNTY SHOPPER
(Mon)
428 N Main St, Carrollton, IL, 62016-1146, USA; tel (217) 942-3626; fax (217) 942-3699; e-mail gazette@midwest.net
Circulation:11,613fr; Sworn/Estimate/Non-Audited
Advertising: Open inch rate $6.99
Adv. Mgr. .... Sheryl Cook
Prodn. Mgr. .... Albert Scott
Mechanical Specifications: Type page 10 1/4 x 16; E - 5 cols, 2, between; A - 5 cols, 2, between.
Equipment: Hardware — APP/Power Mac.
Zip Codes Served: 62016

JERSEY COUNTY SHOPPER
(Mon)
428 N Main St, Carrollton, IL, 62016-1146, USA; tel (618) 498-4413; fax (217) 942-3699; e-mail gazette@midwest.net
Circulation:15,097fr; Sworn/Estimate/Non-Audited
Advertising: Open inch rate $6.99
Adv. Mgr. .... Sheryl Cook
Prodn. Mgr. .... Albert Scott
Mechanical Specifications: Type page 10 1/4 x 16; E - 5 cols, 2, between; A - 5 cols, 2, between.
Equipment: Hardware — APP/Power Mac.
Zip Codes Served: 62016

CENTRALIA

CRIER/SCHROL,RLC CLOCKTOWEER
(Wed) (weekly)
232 E Broadway, Centralia, IL, 62801-3251, USA; tel (618) 532-5604; adv tel same; ed tel (618) 532-5604; fax (618) 532-5919; adv fax same; ed fax (618) 532-5919; e-mail dnichols@moringsentinel.com; adv e-mail same; ed e-mail luanne Dreoge; web site www.morningsentinel.com
Circulation:8,000fr; Sworn/Estimate/Non-Audited
Advertising: Open inch rate $10.78
Established: 1965
Group: Centralia Press Ltd.Editions: 3— Rend Lake Clock tower 2300, Crier 2400 The Schrol 2200
Pub. .... John Perrine
Bus. Office Mgr. .... Julie Copple
Adv. Mgr. .... Dan Nichols
circulation manager .... Ray Albert
Advertising Manager .... Debbie Elling
editor .... luAnn Droege
Equipment: Hardware — 227 mueller; Presses — Urbanite
Delivery Method: Mail, Newsstand
Zip Codes Served: 62801 62881
Note: Single buy goes into all tmc targeted publications. TMC's are addressed and mailed to non Sentinel and
Salem Times Commoner customers

THE SHOPPERS WEEKLY PAPERS
(Wed)
301 E Broadway, Centralia, IL, 62801-3252, USA; tel (618) 533-7283; fax (618) 533-7284; e-mail info@theshoppersweekly.com; adv e-mail ads@theshoppersweekly.com; ed e-mail info@theshoppersweekly.com; web site www.theshoppersweekly.com
Circulation:25,500fr; Sworn/Estimate/Non-Audited
Advertising: Open inch rate $14.00
Established: 1988Editions: 2— 2 total; The Shopper's Weekly Mt. Vernon / Benton Paper (10,500); The Shopper's Weekly Centralia / Salem Paper (15,000);
General Manager .... John Stuehmeier
Display Adv. .... Rhonda Hatcher
Publisher .... Cathy Stuehmeier
Prodn. Mgr. .... Scott Pinkowski
Mechanical Specifications: Type page 10 1/4 x 14; A - 6 cols, 1 2/3".
Delivery Method: Mail, Carrier, Racks
Zip Codes Served: 62801, 62881, 62864, 62812 & 20 others

CHAMPAIGN

AMERICAN CLASSIFIEDS
(Thur)
61 E University Ave, Champaign, IL, 61820-4109, USA; tel (217) 356-4804; fax (217) 356-4970; e-mail champaign@americanclassifieds.com; web site www.americanclassifieds.com
Circulation: 0pd,27,478fr; CVC
Advertising: Open inch rate $11.35
Pub. .... Denny Merrifield
Prodn. Mgr. .... Pam Hardwick
Zip Codes Served: 61820

CHICAGO

INSIDE BOOSTER
(Wed)
6221 N Clark St, Chicago, IL, 60660-1207, USA; tel (773) 465-9700; fax (773) 465-9800; e-mail insidepublicationschicago@gmail.com; adv e-mail inside1958@gmail.com; ed e-mail insidepublicationschicago@gmail.com; web site www.insideonline.com
Circulation: 18pd,8,433fr; CVC
Advertising: $25
Established: 1906Editions: 52— News-Star, Inside-Booster & Skyline
Digital Platform - Tablet: Apple iOS, Android, Windows 7, Kindle, Nook, Kindle Fire
publisher .... Ron Roenigk
Mechanical Specifications: 10.25" x 15.75" / 5 Columns
Equipment: Hardware — iMac; Presses — none; Software — CS4
Delivery Method: Mail, Newsstand, Carrier, Racks
Zip Codes Served: 60618, 60613, 60647, 60657, 60614, 60622, 60610, 60611, 60625, 60640

INSIDE-BOOSTER
(Wed) (Bi-weekly)
6221 N Clark St, Chicago, IL, 60660-1207, USA; tel (773) 465-9700; adv tel (773) 465-9700; ed tel (773) 465-9700; fax (773) 465-9800; adv fax (773) 465-9800; ed fax (773) 465-9800; e-mail insidepublicationschicago@gmail.com; adv e-mail inside1958@gmail.com; ed e-mail insidepublicationschicago@gmail.com; web site www.insideonline.com
Circulation: 18pd,8,433fr; CVC
Advertising: $22.00
Established: 1906Editions: Skyline, News-Star and Inside-Booster
Publisher....Ron Roenigk
Mechanical Specifications: page size 10.25" wide x 15.75" tall
Equipment: Hardware — iMac; Presses — none; Software — CS4
Delivery Method: Mail, Newsstand, Carrier, Racks
Zip Codes Served: 60610, 60611, 60613, 60614, 60618, 60622, 60625, 60626, 60640, 60657, 60660
Note: In Jan. 2013 we purchased Skyline newspaper

SKYLINE
(Wed)
6221 N Clark St, Chicago, IL, 60660-1207, USA; tel (773) 465-9700; fax (773) 465-9800; e-mail insidepublicationschicago@gmail.com; adv e-mail inside1958@gmail.com; ed e-mail insidepublicationschicago@gmail.com; web site www.insideonline.com
Circulation: 18pd,6,812fr; CVC
Advertising: $22.00
Established: 1906Editions: 52— News-Star, Inside-Booster & Skyline
Digital Platform - Mobile: Apple
Digital Platform - Tablet: Apple iOS, Android, Windows 7, Kindle, Nook, Kindle Fire
Pub....Ron Roenigk
Mechanical Specifications: 10.25" x 15.75" / 5 Columns
Equipment: Hardware — iMac; Presses — none; Software — CS4
Delivery Method: Mail, Newsstand, Carrier, Racks
Zip Codes Served: 60602, 60603, 60604, 60605, 60607, 60610, 60611, 60614, 60654

CRYSTAL LAKE

NORTHWEST CITIZEN SHOPPER
(Wed)
7717 S Rte 31, Crystal Lake, IL, 60014, USA; tel (815) 459-4040; adv tel (815) 455-4800; ed tel (815) 459-4122; fax (815) 477-4960; adv fax (815) 477-8898; web site www.nwherald.com
Circulation: 4,500pd,44,818fr; Sworn/Estimate/Non-Audited
Advertising: Open inch rate $7.15Editions: 3— 3 total; Shopper's Service-North (9,653); Shopper's Service-South (22,735); Shopper's Service-West (16,930);
Pub./COO....John Rung
Vice Pres./Adv. Dir....Scott Rosenburgh
Adv. Mgr....Chris Rutherford
Vice Pres./Mkt. Devel....J.Tom Shaw
Mktg. Dir....Brent Maring
Circ. Dir....Kara Hansen
Ed....Dan McCaleb
Vice Pres./Exec. Ed....Chris Krug
Features Ed....Scott Helmchen
Sports Ed....Eric Olson
Mechanical Specifications: Type page 10 5/8 x 13; A - 5 cols, 2, 1/8 between; C - 7 cols, 1 1/4, 1/8 between.
Equipment: Hardware — APP/Mac G3, AU/Oman Production System; Presses — 10-G/Urbanite; Software — QPS/QuarkXPress, Adobe/Photoshop, Adobe/Illustrator.

DECATUR

HERALD NEWS REVIEW
(Mon)
601 E William St, Decatur, IL, 62523-1142, USA; tel (219) 429-5151; e-mail http://herald-review.com/; ed e-mail news@thenews-dispatch.com; web site http://herald-review.com/
Circulation:20,000fr; Sworn/Estimate/Non-Audited
Advertising: Open inch rate $10.00
Circ. Mgr....Julie McKiel
Sports Ed....Adam Parkhouse
Publisher....Bill Hackney
Pub....Patrick Kellar
Adv. Dir....Isis Cains
Exec. Ed....Chris Schable
Mng. Ed....David Hawk
Mechanical Specifications: Broadsheet format 10.125" wide by 20.75" deep
Delivery Method: Carrier
Zip Codes Served: 46360

PRAIRIE SHOPPER
(Wed)
601 E William St, Decatur, IL, 62523-1142, USA; tel (217) 421-8940; fax (217) 421-6942
Circulation:25,000fr; Sworn/Estimate/Non-Audited
Advertising: Open inch rate $12.59
Circ. Mgr....John Knieriem
Ed....Gary Sawyer
Prodn. Mgr....Don Whitman
Mechanical Specifications: Type page 10 x 13; E - 6 cols, 1 2/3, between; A - 6 cols, 1 2/3, between.
Equipment: Hardware — APP/Mac; Software — Adobe/PageMaker 6.0, QPS/QuarkXPress, Adobe/Photoshop, Multi-Ad/Creator.
Zip Codes Served: 62523

DEKALB

THE MIDWEEK
(Wed)
1586 Barber Greene Rd, Dekalb, IL, 60115-7900, USA; tel (815) 756-4841; ed tel (815) 787-7861; fax (815) 756-2079; adv e-mail obits@daily-chronicle.com; ed e-mail news@daily-chronicle.com; web site www.daily-chronicle.com
Circulation:28,500fr; Sworn/Estimate/Non-Audited
Group: Shaw Media
Pub....Don Bricker
Advertising Director....Karen Pletsch
Dana Herra
Zip Codes Served: 60115, 60178, 60135, 60112, 60145, 60146, 60150

DURAND

VOLUNTEER PLUS
(Wed)
109 E Oak St, Durand, IL, 61024-8000, USA; tel (815) 248-4407; fax (815) 248-9176; e-mail volunteer@stateline-isp.com
Circulation:5,100fr; Sworn/Estimate/Non-Audited
Advertising: Open inch rate $9.50
Pub....Curt Stalheim
Adv. Mgr....C.J. Gregg
Circ. Mgr....Cheryl Bradt
Mechanical Specifications: Type page 10 x 16; A - 6 cols, 1 7/12, between; C - 6 cols, 1 7/12, between.
Equipment: ; Software — Microsoft/Windows 95, Adobe/PageMaker 6.5.

EFFINGHAM

CROSSROADS SUPERSAVER
(Wed)
201 N Banker St, Effingham, IL, 62401-2304, USA; tel (217) 347-7151; adv tel (217) 347-7151; fax (217) 342-9315; adv fax (217) 342-9315; e-mail advertising@effinghamdailynews.com; adv e-mail advertising@effinghamdailynews.com; ed e-mail news@effinghamdailynews.com; web site www.effinghamdailynews.com
Circulation:10,000fr; Sworn/Estimate/Non-Audited
Established: 1980
Group: CNHI, LLC
Circ. Mgr....Todd Buenker
Equipment: Hardware —
Delivery Method: Mail, Carrier
Zip Codes Served: 62401, 62467, 62411, 62414, 62424, 62426, 62838, 62443, 62445, 62461, 62473, 62839, 62434, 62858, 62428, 62436, 62447, 62468, 62418,62426, 62458, 62880, 62432, 62448, 62459, 62475, 62479, 62480,62481, 62854, 62422, 62431, 62444, 62462, 62463, 62465, 61957

EUREKA

WOODFORD STAR
(Mon)
1926 S Main St, Eureka, IL, 61530-1666, USA; tel (309) 467-3314; adv tel (309) 467-3314 Ext. 203; ed tel (309) 467-3314 Ext. 209; fax (309) 467-4563; e-mail mbarra@mtco.com; adv e-mail hbowman@mtco.com; ed e-mail mcdowell@mtco.com; web site woodcojo.com
Circulation:16,200fr; Sworn/Estimate/Non-Audited
Advertising: Open inch rate $13.31
Established: 1980
Dir....Mark Barra
Gen. Mgr....Barry Winterland
Mechanical Specifications: Type page 11 5/8 x 21; E - 6 cols, 1 3/4, between; A - 6 cols, 1 3/4, 3/16 between; C - 9 cols, 1 3/16, 1/8 between.
Equipment: Hardware — APP/Mac; Software — Photshop
Indesign
Delivery Method: Mail
Zip Codes Served: 61530

FREEPORT

FREEPORT SHOPPING NEWS
(Wed) (Weekly)
1705 S Galena Ave, Freeport, IL, 61032-2519, USA; tel (815) 235-4106; adv tel (815) 235-4106; e-mail freeportshopnews@themonroetimes.com; adv e-mail lhughes@themonroetimes.com
Circulation:21,221fr; CVC
Advertising: Open inch rate $26.23
Established: 1970
Sales Mgr....Laura Hughes
Prodn. Mgr....Jaimie Tran
Gen. Mgr....Carl Hearing
Mechanical Specifications: Type page 10 3/8 x 16 3/4; A - 6 cols, 1 5/8, between.
Delivery Method: Mail, Carrier
Zip Codes Served: 61032, 61013, 61018, 61019, 61048, 61070, 61027, 61044, 61062, 61085, 61030, 61046, 61078, 61007, 61039, 61067

GALATIA

MONEY STRETCHER
(Tues)
109 N Main Cross St, Galatia, IL, 62935-1224, USA; tel (618) 268-6291; fax (618) 268-4325; e-mail mspaper@mychoice.net; mspaper@clearwave.com; web site www.galatiamoneystretcher.com
Circulation:27,780fr; Sworn/Estimate/Non-Audited
Advertising: Open inch rate $15.00
Group: GateHouse Media, Inc.
Pub....James D. Bond
Adv. Mgr....Janette Bond
Mechanical Specifications: Type page 9 3/4 x 14 1/2; E - 6 cols, 1 1/2, 1/6 between; A - 6 cols, 1 1/2, 1/6 between; C - 6 cols, 1 1/2, 1/6 between.
Equipment: Hardware — APP/Power Mac 7200/90, Microtek/Scanmaker E6, QMS/Laserwriter 860, APP/Mac Quadra 630; Software — Multi-Ad/Creator 4.0, Adobe/Photoshop 4.0.

GALVA

WROVA WEEKLY SHOPPER
(Wed)
348 Front St, Galva, IL, 61434-1365, USA; tel (309) 932-2103; fax (309) 932-3282; e-mail galvinnews@mchsi.com; web site www.galvanews.com
Circulation:2,245fr; Sworn/Estimate/Non-Audited
Advertising: Open inch rate $3.70
Pub....Donald Cooper
Adv. Mgr....Kelly Duke
Ed....Doug Boock

GREENVILLE

BOND AND FAYETTE COUNTY SHOPPER
(Mon)
201 N 3rd St, Greenville, IL, 62246-1003, USA; tel (618) 664-4566; adv tel (618) 664-4566; fax (618) 664-4567
Circulation:20,200fr; Sworn/Estimate/Non-Audited
Advertising: Open inch rate $9.25
Gen. Mgr....Steve Holt
Ed....Terri Holt
Mechanical Specifications: Type page 9 1/2 x 16.
Equipment: Hardware — APP/Mac; Software — Adobe/PageMaker, Multi-Ad/Creator.
Zip Codes Served: 62246

HIGHLAND

SHOPPER'S REVIEW
(Tues)
1200 12th St, Highland, IL, 62249-1909, USA; tel (618) 654-4459; fax (618) 654-9702; adv e-mail shoppersreview@charter.net; web site www.theshoppersreview.com
Circulation: 133pd,18,476fr; CVC
Advertising: Open inch rate $9.75
Established: 1984
Owner/Publisher....Jeff Stratton
Delivery Method: Mail, Newsstand
Zip Codes Served: 62201, 62216, 62230, 62245, 62249, 62061, 62074, 62273, 62275, 62281, 62293

HILLSBORO

M & M JOURNAL
(Mon)
431 S Main St, Hillsboro, IL, 62049-1433, USA; tel (217) 532-3933; fax (217) 532-3632; e-mail thejournal-news@consolidated.net; adv e-mail advertisejn@consolidated.net
Circulation:21,350fr; Sworn/Estimate/Non-Audited
Advertising: Open inch rate $4.00
Established: 1974
Publisher....John M. Galer
Mechanical Specifications: Type page 13 x 21 1/2; E - 9 cols, 1 3/10, 1/6 between; A - 9 cols, 1 3/10, 1/6 between; C - 9 cols, 1 3/10, 1/6 between.

Equipment: Hardware — APP/Mac; Presses — Nine Unit News King; Software — Adobe/PageMaker, QPS/QuarkXPress, Adobe/Photoshop, Adobe/Illustrator.
Delivery Method: Mail
Zip Codes Served: 62049 62056 62075 62560 62626 62640 62690 and others

HOFFMAN ESTATES

DOLLAR WISE
(Wed)
2500 W Higgins Rd, Ste 350, Hoffman Estates, IL, 60169-7207, USA; tel (630) 894-0934; fax (630) 894-0953
Circulation:236,580fr; CVC
Advertising: Open inch rate $50.00
Ed. .... Dino Thanos

HOOPESTON

THE EXTRA
(Wed) (Friday TMC)
308 E Main St, Hoopeston, IL, 60942-1505, USA; tel (217) 283-5111; adv tel (217) 283-5111 ; ed tel (217) 283-5111; fax (217) 283-5846; adv fax (217) 283-5846 ; ed fax (217) 283-5846; adv e-mail chronads@frontier.com; ed e-mail chronreporter@frontier.com; web site http://www.newsbug.info/hoopeston_chronicle/
Circulation: 724pd,7,726fr; Sworn/Estimate/Non-Audited
Advertising: Open inch rate $10.35
Established: 1872
Group: Community Media GroupEditions: 52— Reporter .... Jordan Crook
Mechanical Specifications: Type page 10 1/4 x ; E - 6 cols, between; A - 6 cols, between; C - 6 cols, between.
Equipment: ; Presses — KP.
Delivery Method: Mail
Zip Codes Served: 60942

LA SALLE

ILLINOIS VALLEY SHOPPER
(Wed)
426 2nd St, La Salle, IL, 61301-2334, USA; tel (815) 223-3200; adv tel (815) 220-6945; ed tel (815) 220-6940; fax (815) 223-2543; e-mail sales@newstrib.com; support@newstrib.com; adv e-mail vpsales@newstrib.com; ed e-mail ntnews@newstrib.com; web site www.newstrib.com
Circulation:15,000fr; Sworn/Estimate/Non-Audited
Advertising: Open inch rate $8.00
Established: 1970
Group: NEWSTRIBUNE
Pub. .... Joyce McCullough
Adv. .... Scott Stravrakas
Ed. .... Linda Kleczewski
Pre Press Mgr. .... Joseph Zokal
Circ. Mgr. .... Mike Miller
Mailroom Mgr. .... Fort Miller
Mechanical Specifications: Type page 13 x 21 1/2; E - 6 cols, 2 1/2, 1/3 between; A - 6 cols, 2 1/2, 1/3 between; C - 9 cols, 1 1/10, 1/3 between.
Equipment: Hardware — APP/Mac, PC; Presses — G/Urbanite; Software — QPS/QuarkXPress, APT, Adobe/Illustrator, Adobe/Photoshop.
Delivery Method: Carrier, Racks
Zip Codes Served: LaSalle, Bureau & Putnam counties

LANARK

PRAIRIE ADVOCATE
(Wed)
446 S Broad St, Lanark, IL, 61046-1245, USA; tel (815) 493-2560; fax (815) 493-2561; e-mail pa@pacc-news.com; web site www.pacc-news.com
Circulation: 1,994pd,14,342fr; CVC
Advertising: Open inch rate $14.80
Established: 1937
Circ. Mgr. .... Elizabeth Lang
Ed. .... Thomas Kocal
Sports Ed. .... Craig Lang
Marketing Rep .... Andrew Williamson
Executive .... Lynn Kocal
Mechanical Specifications: Type page 10 1/5 x 16; E - 5 cols, 2, 1/9 between; A - 5 cols, 2, 1/9 between; C - 5 cols, 2, 1/9 between.
Zip Codes Served: 61046, 61078, 61062, 61051, 61014, 61053, 61074, 61285, 61081, 61041, 61030, 61064, 52070

LINCOLN

LOGAN COUNTY SHOPPER
(Wed)
2201 Woodlawn Rd, Ste 350, Lincoln, IL, 62656-9645, USA; tel (217) 732-2101; fax (217) 732-7039; e-mail courier@lincolncourier.com; web site www.lincolncourier.com
Circulation:6,200fr; Sworn/Estimate/Non-Audited
Advertising: Open inch rate $5.59
Group: GateHouse Media, Inc.
Pub. .... Michele Long
Adv. Mgr. .... Jody Roberts
Circ. Mgr. .... Diana Wagner
News Ed. .... Dan Tackett
Sports Ed. .... Justin Tierney
Website Mgr. .... Lisa Whitson
Mechanical Specifications: Type page 13 x 21 1/4; E - 6 cols, 2, 1/8 between; A - 6 cols, 2, 1/8 between; C - 9 cols, 1 3/8, between.
Equipment: Hardware — Dewar; Presses — G/Community.
Zip Codes Served: 62656

MENDOTA

MENDOTA SHOPPING GUIDE
(Wed)
1313 Lakewood Dr, Mendota, IL, 61342-1097, USA; tel (815) 539-9800; fax (815) 539-7477; e-mail msg1@tsf.net
Circulation:11,500fr; Sworn/Estimate/Non-Audited
Advertising: Open inch rate $7.40
Ed. .... Thomas G. Merkel
Zip Codes Served: 61342

MOLINE

AD EXTRA
(Wed)
1720 5th Ave, Moline, IL, 61265-7907, USA; tel (309) 764-4344; adv tel (309) 757-5019; ed tel (309) 757-4990; fax (309) 797-0311; adv fax (309) 797-0321; ed fax (309) 757-4992; e-mail info@qconline.com; adv e-mail advertising@qconline.com; web site www.qconline.com
Circulation: 0pd,28,000fr; Sworn/Estimate/Non-Audited
Advertising: Open inch rate $19.79
Group: Lee Enterprises, Inc.
MM AD DIR .... Kelly Johannes
Mechanical Specifications: Type page 10.50" x 19.50"; 6 columns 1.56"
Delivery Method: Mail
Zip Codes Served: 61230, 61231, 61412, 61413, 61232, 61233, 61234, 61235, 61236, 61238, 61239, 61241, 61240, 61241, 61242, 61244, 61284, 61250, 61434, 61254, 61256, 61257, 61258, 61259, 61260, 61442, 61443, 61453, 61261, 61262, 61263, 61264, 61344, 61265, 61462, 61272, 61465, 61468, 61273, 61274, 61275, 61276, 61277, 61278, 61279, 61201, 61476, 61281, 61282, 61283, 61284, 61486, 61490, 52722, 52801, 52802, 52803, 52804, 52806, 52807

MONMOUTH

PENNYSAVER
(Wed)
400 S Main St, Monmouth, IL, 61462-2164, USA; tel (309) 734-3176; fax (309) 734-7649; e-mail generalmanager@reviewatlas.com; web site www.reviewatlas.com
Circulation:14,350fr; CVC
Advertising: Open inch rate $9.25
Group: GateHouse Media, Inc.
Gen. Mgr. .... Tony Scott
Bus. Mgr. .... Cheryl Free
Adv. Mgr. .... Wendy Todd
Circ. Mgr. .... Dave Spence
Ed. .... Matt Hutton
Sports Ed. .... Marty Touchette
Website Mgr. .... Ken Exum
Mechanical Specifications: Type page 10 1/4 x 16; E - 6 cols, between; A - 6 cols, between; C - 6 cols, between.
Equipment: Hardware — APP/Power Mac G4, APP/Power Mac G3; Presses — 7-G/Community; Software — QPS/QuarkXPress, Multi-Ad/Creator, Adobe/Photoshop.
Zip Codes Served: 61462, 61473, 61469, 61447, 61453

OAK BROOK

SHOPLOCAL
(Tues, Sat)
2000 York Rd, Oak Brook, IL, 60523-8820, USA; tel (630) 368-4100; fax (630) 368-4194
Circulation:4,600,000fr; Sworn/Estimate/Non-Audited
Ed. .... Susan Jacobs
Mechanical Specifications: Type page 9 1/2 x 13.
Equipment: ; Presses — G/Metroliner.
Zip Codes Served: 60611

OLNEY

THE ADVANTAGE
(Sat)
206 S Whittle Ave, Olney, IL, 62450-2251, USA; tel (618) 393-2931; fax (618) 392-2953; web site www.olneydailymail.com
Circulation:3,300fr; Sworn/Estimate/Non-Audited
Advertising: Open inch rate $18.13
Group: GateHouse Media, Inc.
Pub. .... Ray McGrew
Adv. Mgr. .... Cristy Gaiter
Circ. Mgr. .... Joseph Gardner
Ed. .... Mark Allen
Sports Ed. .... Justin Hatten
Prodn. Mgr. .... Tony Childers
Mechanical Specifications: Type page 12 x 21 1/2; E - 6 cols, 1 7/8, 1/3 between; A - 6 cols, 1 7/8, 1/3 between; C - 8 cols, 1 3/8, 1/3 between.
Equipment: ; Presses — G.
Zip Codes Served: 62450

PEKIN

TAZEWELL COUNTY SHOPPER
(Wed)
20 S 4th St, Pekin, IL, 61554-4203, USA; tel (309) 346-1111; adv fax (309) 346-9815; ed fax (309) 346-1446; adv e-mail advertise@pekintimes.com; ed e-mail editor@pekintimes.com; web site www.pekintimes.com
Circulation:11,000fr; Sworn/Estimate/Non-Audited
Advertising: Open inch rate $4.50
Group: GateHouse Media, Inc.
Pub. .... Gregg Ratliff
Adv. Mgr. .... Michelle Holder
Circ. Mgr. .... Anthony Moreno
Ed. .... Michelle Teheux
Mechanical Specifications: Type page 11 1/2 x 21 1/2; E - 6 cols, 1 3/4, between; A - 6 cols, between; C - 9 cols, 1 1/8, between.
Zip Codes Served: 61555

PEORIA

AMERICAN CLASSIFIEDS - PEORIA
(Thur)
7501 N University St, Ste 2, Peoria, IL, 61614-1222, USA; web site http://centralil.tnol.com/
Circulation:12,617fr; CVCLori Lushina

PONTIAC

LIVINGSTON SHOPPING NEWS
(Wed)
318 N Main St, Pontiac, IL, 61764-1930, USA; tel (815) 842-1153; adv tel (815) 842-1153; ed tel (815) 842-1153; fax (815) 842-4388; adv fax (815) 842-4388; ed fax (815) 842-4388; e-mail lstiles@pontiacdailyleader.com; adv e-mail lstiles@pontiacdailyleader.com; ed e-mail ldreditor@mchsi.com; web site www.pontiacdailyleader.com
Circulation:17,500fr; Sworn/Estimate/Non-Audited
Advertising: 8.25
Group: GateHouse Media, Inc.
Creative Designer .... Darlene Miller
Advertising Executive .... Judy Sweitzer
Adv Executive
Matt Studinger
Delivery Method: Mail, Carrier
Zip Codes Served: 61764, 60420, 60460, 60916, 60920, 60921, 60929, 60934, 60946, 61319, 61333, 61726, 61739, 61740, 61741, 61743, 61744, 61769, 61773, 61775

PRINCETON

ILLINOIS VALLEY SHOPPING NEWS
(Wed)
316 S Main St, Princeton, IL, 61356-2023, USA; tel (815) 875-4461; fax (815) 875-1235; e-mail news@bcrnews.com
Circulation: 7,000pd,13,000fr; Sworn/Estimate/Non-Audited
Advertising: Open inch rate $8.30
Pub. .... Sam Fisher
Adv. Mgr. .... Sandy Pistole
Circ. Mgr. .... Jelss Vanderly
Mng. Ed. .... Tom Martin
Mechanical Specifications: Type page 13 x 21 1/2; E - 6 cols, 2, 1/4 between; A - 6 cols, 2, 1/4 between; C - 9 cols, 1 1/4, 1/4 between.
Equipment: Hardware — APP/Mac; Software — QPS/QuarkXPress 4.0, Adobe/Photoshop 4.0, Microsoft/Works 4.0, Adobe/Illustrator 6.0.

RANTOUL

RANTOUL PRESS
(Wed)
1332 Harmon Dr, Rantoul, IL, 61866-3310, USA; tel (217) 892-9613; adv tel (217) 840-8704; fax (217) 892-2313; e-mail tevans@news-gazette.com; adv e-mail tevans@news-gazette.com; ed e-mail tevans@news-gazettecom; web site rantoulpress.com
Circulation: 3,000pd,6,700fr; USPS
Advertising: $16.25
Established: 1875
Group: News-Gazette, Inc.Editions: 1— Rantoul Press - 6,700
President .... John Foreman
General Manager .... Tim Evans
Publisher .... John Reed
Mechanical Specifications: 21 inches tall
Widths:

1c 1.5694"
2c 3.3056"
3c 5.0417"
4c 6.7778"
5c 8.5139"
6c 10.25"
Equipment: Hardware — APP/Mac; Software — InDesign
Delivery Method: Mail, Newsstand, Carrier, Racks
Zip Codes Served: 61866, 61878,61865, 61862, 60949, 60957, 61847, 61843, 61840, 61812
Note: This is a total market coverage publication that is voluntary pay

ROCKFORD

THE STAR SHOPPER
(Thur)
99 E State St, Rockford, IL, 61104-1009, USA; tel (815) 987-1200; fax (815) 961-5833; web site www.rrstar.com
Circulation:51,700fr; Sworn/Estimate/Non-Audited
Advertising: Open inch rate $12.34
Group: GateHouse Media, Inc.
Pub. .... Scott Bowers
Gen. Mgr. .... Tom Lasley
Adv. Dir. .... Michele Massoth
Mkt. Devel. Dir. .... Thomas G. Lasley
Circ. Mgr. .... Michael Prazma
Exec. Ed. .... Linda Grist Cunningham
Mng. Ed. .... Jeff Gauger
Sports Ed. .... Randy Ruef
Prodn. Dir. .... Kris Smith
Prodn. Mgr. .... Carey Sydow
Mechanical Specifications: Type page 11 5/8 x 21 1/2; E - 6 cols, 1 5/6, 1/8 between; A - 6 cols, 1 5/6, 1/8 between; C - 10 cols, 1 1/8, 7/16 between.
Equipment: Hardware — Tandem; Presses — 8-H/Colormatic; Software — SII, QPS/QuarkXPress 4.11, 2-Multi-Ad/Creator 1.61.
Zip Codes Served: 61104, 61101, 61012, 16038, 61065, 61008, 61072, 61073, 61080, 61101, 61103, 61107, 61108, 61109, 61111, 61114, 61115

ROCKTON

THE HERALD
(Wed)
1107 N Blackhawk Blvd, Rockton, IL, 61072-1500, USA; tel (815) 877-4044; fax (815) 654-4857; e-mail info@rvpublishing.com
Circulation:6,245fr; Sworn/Estimate/Non-Audited
Advertising: Open inch rate $8.00
Group: Rock Valley Publishing LLC
Pub. .... Peter Cruger
Gen. Mgr. .... Randall Johnson
Ed. .... Mike Ruggles
Mechanical Specifications: Type page 10 1/8 x 16; E - 4 cols, between; A - 4 cols, between; C - 6 cols, between.
Equipment: ; Presses — G/Community.
Delivery Method: Mail
Zip Codes Served: 61072

SOUTH HOLLAND

THE SHOPPER
(Wed)
924 E 162nd St, South Holland, IL, 60473-2442, USA; tel (708) 333-5901; fax (708) 333-9630; e-mail general@myshopper.biz; web site www.myshopper.biz
Circulation:26,160fr; CVC
Advertising: Open inch rate $3.07 - $4.59
Established: 1957Editions: 5— 6 total The Shopper-Dolton/Calumet City (11,000); The Shopper-Lansing (8,800); The Shopper-Dyer/St. John (10,500); The Shopper-South Holland/Thornton (7,300);
Pub. .... Arlo Kallemeyn
Circ. Mgr. .... Dave Kallemeyn
Prodn. Mgr. .... Eileen Curley
Mechanical Specifications: Type page 10 1/4 x 16.
Equipment: Hardware — APP/Mac; Presses — G/Suburban; Software — Adobe/InDesign, Adobe/Photoshop, Adobe/Illustrator.
Delivery Method: Mail, Carrier, Racks
Zip Codes Served: 60473, 60419, 60827, 60438, 46311, 46373, 60409

SPRINGFIELD

SPRINGFIELD ADVERTISER
(Wed)
1 Copley Plz, Springfield, IL, 62701-1927, USA; tel (217) 788-1300; adv tel (217) 788-1360; ed tel (217) 788-1513; fax (217) 788-1551; e-mail sjrweb@sj-r.com; adv e-mail advertise@sj-r.com; ed e-mail sports@sj-r.com; sjr@sj-r.com; web site www.sj-r.com
Circulation:64,000fr; Sworn/Estimate/Non-Audited
Advertising: Open inch rate $10.55
Group: GateHouse Media, Inc.
Director of Operations .... Mike Kreppert
Adv. Dir. .... Gary Tyler
Adv. Mgr. .... Jen Barkus
Circ. Mgr. .... Robert Titone
Asst. Circ. Mgr. .... Shan Bailey
Exec. Ed. .... Jon Broadbooks
Mng. Ed. .... Erin Orr
Features Ed. .... Brien Murphy
Sports Ed. .... Jim Ruppert
Mechanical Specifications: Type page 13 x 21 1/4; E - 6 cols, 1 5/6, 1/8 between; A - 6 cols, 1 5/6, 1/8 between; C - 9 cols, 1 1/4, between.
Equipment: ; Presses — 9-G/Metro.
Delivery Method: Mail

SPRINGFIELD SHOPPER
(Thur)
1 Copley Plz, Springfield, IL, 62701-1927, USA; tel (217) 788-1330; fax (217) 788-1372; adv e-mail katherine.rotherham@sj-r.com
Circulation:22,000fr; Sworn/Estimate/Non-Audited
Advertising: Open inch rate $12.50
Established: 1975
Group: GateHouse Media, Inc.
Manager .... Angela Stewart
Multi-Media Sales Representative..... Katherine Rotherham
Equipment: Hardware — APP/Mac, APP/Mac G4; Presses — G/Community; Software — QPS/QuarkXPress 4.0, Multi-Ad/Creator, Baseview.
Delivery Method: Racks

VANDALIA

THE LEADER-UNION PUBLISHING CO.
(Mon)
229 S 5th St, Vandalia, IL, 62471-2703, USA; tel (618) 283-3374; fax (618) 283-0977; web site www.leaderunion.com
Circulation:11,600fr; Sworn/Estimate/Non-Audited
Advertising: Open inch rate $10.00
Group: Landmark Communications, Inc.
Pub. .... Dave Bell
Office Mgr. .... Lovetta Lockart
Adv. Mgr. .... Peggy Schulze
Circ. Mgr. .... Susie Pontious
Mng. Ed. .... Rich Bauer
Prodn. Mgr. .... Mike Rosenkoetter
Advertising Sales Rep .... Bridget Lash
Mechanical Specifications: Type page 13 x 21 1/2; A - 6 cols, 2 1/16, 1/8 between.
Delivery Method: Mail
Zip Codes Served: 62471

VIRDEN

GOLD NUGGET EXPRESS
(Mon, Wed)
169 W Jackson St, Virden, IL, 62690-1269, USA; tel (217) 965-3355; fax (217) 965-4512; e-mail nj1655@aol.com; adv e-mail nj1655@aol.com; ed e-mail nj1655@aol.com
Circulation:8,588fr; Sworn/Estimate/Non-Audited
Advertising: Open inch rate $5.00
Established: 1985
Gen. Mgr. .... Nathan Jones
Circ. Mgr. .... Julie Westerhausen

WATERLOO

REPUBLIC-TIMES SHOPPER
(Mon)
114 N Main St, Waterloo, IL, 62298-1201, USA; tel (618) 939-3814; fax (618) 939-3815; e-mail trsales2@htc.net
Circulation:12,000fr; Sworn/Estimate/Non-Audited
Advertising: Open inch rate $9.10
Established: 1870
Pub. .... Kermit Constantine
Gen. Mgr. / Ed. .... Lynn Venhaus
Circ. Coord. .... Amber Vogel
Adv. Sales .... Chandra Moffitt
Mechanical Specifications: Type page 11 1/2 x 21 1/2; E - 6 cols, between; A - 6 cols, between; C - 10 cols, between.
Zip Codes Served: 62298

WEST FRANKFORT

SI TRADER
(Fri)
111 S Emma St, West Frankfort, IL, 62896-2729, USA; tel (618) 937-2850; fax (618) 937-2177; web site www.sitraders.com
Circulation: 36,000pd,; Sworn/Estimate/Non-Audited
Advertising: Open inch rate $12.00
Group: GateHouse Media, Inc.
Pub. .... Lynn Kidd
Circ. Mgr .... Feather Little
Equipment: Hardware — APP/Mac, Kk; Presses — G/Community; Software — OPS, Multi-Ad/Creator, Synaptic.

WILMINGTON

PRAIRIE SHOPPER
(Mon)
111 S Water St, Wilmington, IL, 60481-1373, USA; tel (815) 476-7966; fax (815) 476-7002; e-mail fpnads@cbcast.com; adv e-mail fpnads@cbcast.com; ed e-mail fpnnews@cbcast.com
Circulation:17,900fr; Sworn/Estimate/Non-Audited
Advertising: Open inch rate $13.00
Established: 1976
Group: Free Press Newspapers
Publisher .... Eric Fisher
Mechanical Specifications: Type page 11.1 x 20.5; E - 6 cols, 1.75, 1/6 between; A - 6 cols, 1 7/12, 1/6 between.
Equipment: Hardware — Mac; Software — Adobe/PageMaker 6.0, Adobe/Photoshop 3.02., Quark
Delivery Method: Mail
Zip Codes Served: 60481, 60408, 60416, 60407, 60421 60424, 60444, 60450, 60961, 60474
Note: Door-to-door mail delivery to every household in 16 communities

YORKVILLE

FOX VALLEY SHOPPING NEWS
(Wed)
110 E Countryside Pkwy, Ste C, Yorkville, IL, 60560-1814, USA; tel (630) 553-7431; fax (630) 553-0310
Circulation:35,500fr; Sworn/Estimate/Non-Audited
Advertising: Open inch rate $12.50
Zip Codes Served: 60560

ZION

BARGAINEER
(Mon)
2711 Sheridan Rd, Ste 202, Zion, IL, 60099-2650, USA; tel (847) 746-9000; fax (847) 746-9150; e-mail zion@kenoshanews.com; web site www.zion-bentonnews.com
Circulation:25,000fr; Sworn/Estimate/Non-Audited
Advertising: Open inch rate $11.00Editions: 3— 3 total; Bargaineer-Gurnee; Bargaineer-Waukegan; Bargaineer-Zion;
Adv. Mgr. .... Frank M. Misureli
Circ. Mgr. .... Tony Decesaro
Ed. .... Mona Shannon
Zip Codes Served: 60099

INDIANA

ANDERSON

MADISON COUNTY DIRECT
(Wed)
1133 Jackson St, Anderson, IN, 46016-1433, USA; tel (765) 622-1212; fax (765) 640-4815; e-mail newsroom@heraldbulletin.com; ed e-mail letters@heraldbulletin.com; web site www.theheraldbulletin.com
Circulation:19,000fr; Sworn/Estimate/Non-Audited
Advertising: Open inch rate $8.35
Group: Community Newspaper Holdings, Inc.
Pub. .... Henry Bird
Adv. Mgr. .... Mark Elliott
Circ. Mgr. .... Amy Winters
Ed. .... Steve Dick
Sports Ed. .... Rick Teverbaugh
Equipment: Hardware — CText; Presses — G/Urbanite.
Zip Codes Served: 46016

ANGOLA

SMART SHOPPER
(Tues)
45 S Public Sq, Angola, IN, 46703-1926, USA; tel (260) 665-3117; fax (260) 665-2322; e-mail circulation@kpcnews.net; web site www.fwdailynews.com
Circulation:46,000fr; Sworn/Estimate/Non-Audited
Advertising: Open inch rate $7.45
Group: KPC Media Group, Inc.Editions: 4— 4 total; Smart Shopper - DeKalb; Smart Shopper - La Grange; Smart Shopper - Noble; Smart Shopper - Steuben;
Pres./CEO .... Terry Housholder
Adv. Dir. .... Karen Bloom
Circ. Dir. .... Bruce Hakala
Ed. .... Mike Marturello
Mechanical Specifications: Type page 13 x 21 1/2; E - 6 cols, 2 1/16, 1/8 between; A - 6 cols, 2 1/16, 1/8 between; C - 9 cols, 1 3/8, 1/16 between.
Equipment: Hardware — PC, APP/Mac; Presses — G/Community; Software — QPS/QuarkX-

Press 4.0, Multi-Ad.

ATTICA

MESSENGER
(Tues)
113 S Perry St, Attica, IN, 47918-1349, USA; tel (765) 762-2411; fax (765) 762-1547; adv e-mail atticasales@sbcglobal.net; ed e-mail atticaeditor@sbcglobal.net
Circulation:13,578fr; Sworn/Estimate/Non-Audited
Advertising: Open inch rate $21.40
Group: Community Media Group
Adv. Mgr./ Gen. Mgr. .... Greg Willhite
Office Mgr............................ Roberta Hembree
Ed .... Gretchen Stone
Mechanical Specifications: Type page 11 1/2 x 21; E - 6 cols, 1 9/16, 1/6 between; A - 6 cols, 1 9/16, 1/6 between; C - 6 cols, 1 9/16, 1/6 between.
Equipment: Hardware — APP/Mac; Presses — KP; Software — QPS.
Delivery Method: Mail
Zip Codes Served: 47918

BLOOMINGTON

ADD SHEET
(Wed)
2620 N Walnut St, Ste 300, Bloomington, IN, 47404-2008, USA; tel (812) 339-4000; fax (812) 339-4515
Circulation:25,000fr; Sworn/Estimate/Non-Audited
Jan R. Grossmann
Larry GrossmannPub.s
Zip Codes Served: 47401, 47408, 47429, 65201, 65202, 65203, 65211, 65212, 65215, 65216, 65217, 65218

COLUMBIA CITY

POST AND MAIL SHOPPING NEWS
(Tues) (Tuesday plus repeat in daily Monday thru Saturday as 2-edition combo rate)
927 W Connexion Way, Columbia City, IN, 46725-1031, USA; tel (260) 244-5153; fax (260) 244-7598; e-mail publisher@thepostandmail.com; web site www.thepostandmail.com
Circulation: 3,450pd,9,987fr; Sworn/Estimate/Non-Audited
Advertising: 17.90 2-edition combo rate
Established: 1988
Group: Horizon Publications Inc.
Publisher/Advertising Mgr......... Cindy Stockton
Mechanical Specifications: Broadsheet column width 6 column 10.5"
Delivery Method: Newsstand, Carrier, Racks
Zip Codes Served: 46725, 46764, 46787, 46723

COLUMBUS

REPUBLIC EXTRA
(Wed)
2980 N National Rd, Ste A, Columbus, IN, 47201-3234, USA; tel (812) 372-7811; e-mail advertise@therepublic.com; web site www.therepublic.com
Circulation:11,600fr; Sworn/Estimate/Non-Audited
Group: AIM Media Indiana
Digital Platform - Mobile: Apple, Android, Windows, Other
Digital Platform - Tablet: Apple iOS, Android, Windows 7, Kindle, Nook, Kindle Fire, Other
Pub./Adv. Dir. .... Chuck Wells
Mechanical Specifications: Type page 13 x 21 1/2; E - 6 cols, 2 1/6, between; A - 6 cols, 2 1/6, between; C - 9 cols, 1 5/16, between.
Zip Codes Served: 47201

CONNERSVILLE

SHOPPER STOPPER
(Mon)
PO Box 287, 406 N. Central Ave., Connersville, IN, 47331-0287, USA; tel (765) 825-0581; fax (765) 825-4599; e-mail newsexaminer@newsexaminer.com; web site www.newsexaminer.com
Circulation:6,200fr; Sworn/Estimate/Non-Audited
Advertising: Open inch rate $10.20
Gen. Mgr. .... Kelly Pierce
Mechanical Specifications: Type page 11 5/8 x 21 1/4; E - 6 cols, 1 2/3, 13/16 between; A - 6 cols, 1 2/3, 13/16 between; C - 9 cols, 1 1/4, 1/25 between.
Delivery Method: Carrier
Zip Codes Served: 47331

CORYDON

SHOPPER
(Mon)
301 N Capitol Ave, Corydon, IN, 47112-1140, USA; tel (812) 738-2211; fax (812) 738-1909; e-mail ads@corydondemocrat.com; web site www.corydondemocrat.com
Circulation:16,601fr; Sworn/Estimate/Non-Audited
Advertising: Open inch rate $10.75
Pres./Pub. .... Jonathan O'Bannon
Adv. Sales Rep. .... Kelly Green
Ed. .... Jo Ann Spieth-Saylor
Dir., Opns. .... Karen Hanger
Mechanical Specifications: Type page 13 x 21 1/4; E - 6 cols, 2 1/16, between; A - 6 cols, 2 1/16, between; C - 8 cols, 1 1/2, between.
Equipment: Hardware — APP/Macs; Presses — 4-G/Community; Software — QPS/QuarkXPress 5.1, Adobe/Photoshop 5.0, Freehand 8.

DECATUR

BERNE SHOPPING NEWS
(Tues)
141 S 2nd St, Decatur, IN, 46733-1664, USA; tel (260) 724-2121; adv fax (260) 724-7981; e-mail dailydemo@decaturdailydemocrat.com; adv e-mail advertising@decaturdailydemocrat.com; ed e-mail editorial@decaturdailydemocrat.com; web site www.decaturdailydemocrat.com
Circulation: 5,000pd,; Sworn/Estimate/Non-Audited
Advertising: Open inch rate $12 .54
Established: 1857
Group: Horizon Publications Inc.
Pub. .... Ronald Storey
Bus. Mgr. .... Jennifer Kaerh
Adv. Mgr., Classified .... Ita Mari Long
Circ. Mgr. .... Ryan Green
Mng. Ed. .... Robert W. Shraluka
Features Ed. .... J. Swygart
Lifestyle Ed. .... Kristen Baron
Sports Ed. .... James Hopkins
Mechanical Specifications: Type page 13 x 21 1/2; E - 6 cols, 2 1/8, 1/8 between; A - 6 cols, 2 1/8, 1/8 between; C - 6 cols, 2 1/8, 1/8 between.
Delivery Method: Newsstand, Carrier, Racks

EVANSVILLE

AMERICAN CLASSIFIEDS
(Thur)
999 N Congress Ave, Evansville, IN, 47715-2469, USA; tel (812) 428-8484; fax (812) 428-8482; web site http://evansville.tnol.com/
Circulation:26,000fr; Sworn/Estimate/Non-Audited
Advertising: Open inch rate $7.00Editions: 4— 4 total; Carmi American Classifieds; Evansville American Classifieds; Henderson American Classifieds; Princeton American Classifieds;
Circ. Mgr. .... Judy Smith
Ed. .... James Hall
Prodn. Mgr. .... Kristy Kerley
Mechanical Specifications: Type page 10 1/4 x 15; E - 8 cols, 1 3/16, 1/8 between; A - 8 cols, 1 3/16, 1/8 between; C - 8 cols, 1 3/16, 1/8 between.
Equipment: Hardware — 9-APP/Power Mac, APP/Mac G3, APP/Mac G4; Software — Adobe/PageMaker 6.0.
Zip Codes Served: 47711

THRIFTY NICKEL - EVANSVILLE
(Thur)
999 N Congress Ave, Evansville, IN, 47715-2469, USA; tel (812) 428-8484; adv tel (812) 428-8484; fax (812) 428-8482; adv fax (812 428-8482; e-mail americanclassifieds@sigecom.net; adv e-mail americanclassifieds@sigecom.net; web site evansvillethriftynickel.com
Circulation:21,129fr; CVC
Advertising: Open inch rate $13.32
Established: 1981
Digital Platform - Mobile: Apple, Android, Blackberry
Digital Platform - Tablet: Apple iOS, Android, Blackberry Tablet OS, Kindle, Kindle FireJim Hall
Mechanical Specifications: Full page image 101/2 wide x 17 tall
Delivery Method: Racks
Zip Codes Served: 42420, 47601, 47620, 47630, 47670, 47708, 47710, 47712, 47714, 47715, 47720

FISHERS

LOCAL LIVING
(Thur)
13095 Publishers Dr, Fishers, IN, 46038-8826, USA; tel (317) 444-4444; adv tel (317) 444-4444; ed tel (317) 444-4444; fax (317) 444-7500; adv fax (317) 444-7500; ed fax (317) 444-6600; web site www.indystar.com/noblesville
Established: 1888/1870
Group: Gannett

GOSHEN

EXTRA
(Mon)
114 S Main St, Goshen, IN, 46526-3702, USA; tel (574) 533-2151; fax (574) 533-0839; e-mail news@goshennews.com; circulation@goshennews.com; bus.office@goshennews.com; ed e-mail classifieds@goshennews.com; web site www.goshennews.com
Circulation:14,200fr; Sworn/Estimate/Non-Audited
Advertising: Open inch rate $6.30
Pub. .... Jim Kroemer
Circ. Mgr. .... Rick Carlson
Ed. .... Michael Wanbaugh
Mechanical Specifications: Type page 13 x 21 1/2; E - 6 cols, 2 1/16, 1/12 between; A - 6 cols, 2 1/16, 1/12 between; C - 8 cols, 1 1/2, 1/12 between.
Zip Codes Served: 46526

HUNTINGTON

HUNTINGTON COUNTY TAB
(Mon, Thur)
1670 Etna Ave, Huntington, IN, 46750-4132, USA; tel (260) 356-1107; fax (260) 356-1177; e-mail tabnewsroom@comcast.net; adv e-mail tabads@comcast.net; ed e-mail tabnewsroom@comcast.net; web site www.huntingtoncountytab.com
Circulation: 300pd,30,220fr; CVC
Advertising: Open inch rate $8.37
Established: 1985
Adv. Mgr. .... Russ Grindle
Mng. Ed. .... Scott Trauner
Circ. Mgr .... Jim Broderick
Mechanical Specifications: Type page 10 1/4 x 15 1/4; E - 7 cols, 1 3/8, between; A - 7 cols, 1 3/8, between; C - 7 cols, 1 3/8, between.
Equipment: Hardware — iMAC; Software — Multi-Ad Creator
Microsoft Word
Quark
Delivery Method: Carrier
Zip Codes Served: 46750, 46702, 46713, 46770, 46783, 46792, 46799

INDIANAPOLIS

AMERICAN CLASSIFIEDS
(Thur)
359 E Thompson Rd, Indianapolis, IN, 46227-1624, USA; tel (317) 782-8111; adv tel (317) 782-8111; fax (317) 782-0882; adv fax (317) 782-0882; e-mail christina.indy@americanclassifieds.com; adv e-mail christina.indy@americanclassifieds.com; web site www.americanclassifieds.com
Circulation:24,711fr; CVC
Advertising: Open inch rate $9.00
Established: 1987
Ed. .... Dal Dhanjal
Prodn. Mgr. .... Kevin Harris
Christina Miller
Equipment: Hardware — APP/Macs; Software — Adobe/PageMaker.
Delivery Method: Racks
Zip Codes Served: 7 Counties

SPEEDWAY TOWN PRESS
(Wed)
1538 Main St, Indianapolis, IN, 46224-6527, USA; tel (317) 241-4345; fax (317) 241-4386; e-mail thepress@in-motion.net
Circulation:9,000fr; Sworn/Estimate/Non-Audited
Advertising: Open inch rate $11.50 net
Established: 1956
Gen. Mgr. .... Barbara Pericins
Adv. Mgr. .... Shirley Nelson
Ed. .... Beth Sullivan
Mechanical Specifications: Type page 10 3/8 x 16; E - 7 cols, 1 3/8, 1/8 between; A - 7 cols, 1 3/8, 1/8 between.
Delivery Method: Carrier, Racks
Zip Codes Served: 46224, 46222, 46241, 46214

THE PRESS SPEEDWAY TOWN PRESS-WESTSIDE MESSENGER
(Wed)
1432 Main St, Indianapolis, IN, 46224-6526, USA; tel (317) 241-4345; fax (317) 241-4386; e-mail thepress@sbcglobal.net
Circulation:4,500fr; Sworn/Estimate/Non-Audited
Advertising: Open inch rate $12.
Digital Platform - Mobile: Apple
Owner/Pub .... Shirley Nelson
Mechanical Specifications: Type page 10 3/8 x 16; E - 7 cols, 1 3/8, 1/8 between; A - 7 cols, 1 3/8, 1/8 between.
Delivery Method: Newsstand, Carrier, Racks
Zip Codes Served: 46224

KENDALLVILLE

SMART SHOPPER
(Tues)
102 N Main St, Kendallville, IN, 46755-1714, USA; tel (260) 347-0400; fax (260) 347-7281; e-mail circulation@kpcnews.net; web site www.kpcnews.com
Circulation:46,250fr; Sworn/Estimate/Non-Audited
Advertising: Open inch rate $6.75
Group: KPC Media Group, Inc.
CEO .... Terry Housholder
Production Manager .... Gary Crager

Chief Operating Officer.................... Terry Ward
Mechanical Specifications: Type page 11 1/2 x 21 1/2; E - 6 cols, 2 1/32, 5/32 between; A - 6 cols, 2 1/32, 5/32 between; C - 9 cols, 2 1/32, 5/32 between.
Equipment: Hardware — APP/Mac; Software — QPS/QuarkXPress, Adobe/Photoshop.
Zip Codes Served: 46755, 46703, 46706, 46767

KENTLAND

INDIANA SPIRIT
(Tues)
305 E Graham St, Kentland, IN, 47951-1235, USA; tel (219) 474-5531; fax (219) 474-5354; e-mail editor@sugardog.com
Circulation:53,105fr; Sworn/Estimate/Non-Audited
Advertising: Open inch rate $11.00
Group: Community Media Group
Adv. Mgr.................................... Tony Bulington
Pres. .... Don Hurd
Circ. Mgr.. Betty Long
Mechanical Specifications: Type page 10 1/4 x 14; E - 6 cols, between; A - 6 cols, between; C - 6 cols, between.
Equipment: ; Presses — KP.
Zip Codes Served: 47951

LAGRANGE

COUNTIAN
(Mon)
410 E 100 S, Lagrange, IN, 46761-8867, USA; tel (260) 463-2166; fax (260) 463-2734; e-mail publisher@lagrangepublishing.com; adv e-mail advertising@lagrangepublishing.com; ed e-mail editor@lagrangepublishing.com; sports@lagrangepublishing.com; web site www.lagrangepublishing.com
Circulation: 5,200pd,5,000fr; Sworn/Estimate/Non-Audited
Advertising: Open inch rate $9.90
Established: 1856
Group: LaGrange Publishing Co.
Digital Platform - Mobile: Windows
Pub. .... William Connelly
Prodn. Mgr. ....Allen Connelly
Mechanical Specifications: Type page broadsheet - 11x21.5" - six 1.73" columns
Equipment: Hardware — PCs; Presses — KP/News King; Software — Microsoft/Windows 7 3.11, WordPerfect 6.1, Adobe/PageMaker 6.0.
Delivery Method: Mail, Newsstand
Zip Codes Served:
46761,46746,46795,46565,46571,

LAWRENCEBURG

THE MARKET PLACE
(Mon)
126 W High St, Lawrenceburg, IN, 47025-1908, USA; tel (812) 537-0063; adv tel (812) 537-0063; ed tel (513) 367-4582; fax (812) 537-5576; ed e-mail community@register-publications.com; web site www.thedcregister.com/
Circulation:17,000fr; Sworn/Estimate/Non-Audited
Advertising: Open inch rate $18.00
Group: Delphos Herald, Inc.
Pub. .... Tom Brooker
Ed. ....Erika Schmidt Russell

MARION

THE CURRENT BARGAIN
(Mon)
610 S Adams St, Marion, IN, 46953-2041, USA; tel (765) 664-5111; adv tel (765) 664-5112; fax (765) 668-4256; e-mail ctreport@indy.rr.com; web site www.chronicle-tribune.com
Circulation:13,000fr; Sworn/Estimate/Non-Audited
Advertising: Open inch rate $14.31
Established: 1867
Group: Paxton Media Group, LLC
IT Manager................................. Brent Folkner
Publisher...................................... Linda Kelsay
Advertising Director...................... Stan Howard
Mechanical Specifications: Type page 12 5/8 x 21 1/2; E - 6 cols, 2, 1/8 between; A - 6 cols, 2, 1/8 between; C - 9 cols, 2, 1/8 between.
Equipment: ; Presses — G/Urbanite; Software — Multi-Ad/Creator, Adobe.
Delivery Method: Racks
Zip Codes Served: 46953

MONTICELLO

THE NEWS REMINDER
(Mon)
114 S Main St, Monticello, IN, 47960-2328, USA; tel (574) 583-5121; fax (574) 583-4241; e-mail adclerk@thehj.com; adv e-mail Martin.vanee@sbcglobal.net; ed e-mail martin.vanee@sbcglobal.net; web site www.news-bug.info
Circulation:15,870fr; Sworn/Estimate/Non-Audited
Advertising: Open inch rate $18.95
Established: 1977
Group: Community Media Group
VP... Marty VanEe
Mechanical Specifications: Type page 10 7/16 x 16; E - 5 cols, 2, 1/6 between; A - 5 cols, 2, 1/6 between; C - 7 cols, 1 5/16, 1/6 between.
Equipment: Hardware — PC
Mac; Presses — Harris; Software — Mediaspan
Delivery Method: Mail, Racks
Zip Codes Served: 47960, 46923, 47923, 47995, 47980, 47959, 47946, 46913, 46920, 46929, 46917, 46977, 46916

MOUNT VERNON

POSEY ADVANTAGE
231 Main St, Mount Vernon, IN, 47620-1839, USA; tel (812) 838-4811

NASHVILLE

MARKETPLACE
(Wed)
147 E Main St, Nashville, IN, 47448-7008, USA; tel (812) 988-2221; fax (812) 988-6502; e-mail newsroom@bcdemocrat.com; adv e-mail ads@bcdemocrat.com; web site www.browncountyindiana.com
Circulation: 4,500pd,1,500fr; Sworn/Estimate/Non-Audited
Advertising: Open inch rate $7.00
Established: 1870
Owner/ Pub.......................................Jeff Brown
Adv. Mgr..................................Keith L. Fleener
Ed. ....Sara Clifford
Mechanical Specifications: Type page 13 x 21; A - 6 cols, 2, 1/6 between; C - 6 cols, 2, 1/6 between.
Equipment: Hardware — APP/Power Mac; Software — QPS/QuarkXPress 4.1, Multi-Ad/Creator 4.1, Adobe/Photoshop 5.5, APP/Apple Works 5.0.

OSSIAN

SUNRISER NEWS
(Tues)
PO Box 365, Ossian, IN, 46777-0365, USA; tel (260) 622-4108; fax (260) 622-6439; e-mail ossianj@adamswells.com; web site www.sunrisernews.com
Circulation:12,242fr; Sworn/Estimate/Non-Audited
Advertising: Open inch rate $6.00
Pub. ....Doug Brown
Mechanical Specifications: 23" web
Delivery Method: Mail, Newsstand
Zip Codes Served: 46714

PAOLI

ORANGE COUNTIAN
(Wed)
131 S Court St, Paoli, IN, 47454-1323, USA; tel (812) 723-2572; fax (812) 723-2592; e-mail ocpinc@ocpnews.com
Circulation:11,887fr; Sworn/Estimate/Non-Audited
Advertising: Open inch rate $6.25
Pub. .... Arthur Hampton
Adv. Mgr................................Melissa Hampton
Ed. .... Dennis Ellis
Mechanical Specifications: Type page 13 x 21; E - 6 cols, between; A - 6 cols, between.
Equipment: Hardware — APP/Mac; Software — QPS/QuarkXPress, Multi-Ad/Creator.
Delivery Method: Mail
Zip Codes Served: 47454-47452-47432-47469-47118-47140-47527-47125

PEKIN

GREEN BANNER PUBLICATIONS, INC.
(Wed)
490 E State Road 60, Pekin, IN, 47165-7928, USA; tel (812) 967-3176; fax (812) 967-3194; e-mail sales@gbpnews.com; web site www.gbpnews.com
Circulation: 0pd,62,293fr; CVC
Established: 1933
Pub. ....Joe Green
Note: Green Banner Publications owns five community newspapers and they also provide complete distribution and printing services.

PLYMOUTH

THE SHOPPER
(Sun)
214 N Michigan St, Plymouth, IN, 46563-2135, USA; tel (574) 936-3101; fax (574) 936-3844; adv fax (574) 936-7491; ed fax (574) 936-3844; e-mail news@thepilotnews.com; adv e-mail ads@thepilotnews.com; ed e-mail pilot@thepilotnews.com; web site www.thepilotnews.com
Circulation: 6,227pd,; Sworn/Estimate/Non-Audited
Advertising: Open inch rate $11.75
Established: 1851
Group: Heritage Publications (2003) Inc.
Pub. .... Rick A. Kreps
Gen. Mgr..Jerry Bingle
Adv. Mgr., Mktg......................... Cindy Stockton
Mng. Ed.................................Lois Tomaszewski
Sports Ed................................James Costello
Prodn. Foreman, Composing . Greg Hildebrand
Mechanical Specifications: Type page 13 x 21 1/2; E - 6 cols, 2 1/16, 1/8 between; A - 6 cols, 2 1/16, 1/8 between; C - 10 cols, 1 3/8, 1/16 between.

PORTLAND

THE CIRCULATOR
(Mon, Tues, Wed, Thur, Fri, Sat)
309 W. Main St., Portland, IN, 47371-3149, USA; tel (260) 726-8141; fax (260) 726-8143; adv e-mail cr.ads@comcast.net; ed e-mail cr.news@comcast.net; web site www.thecr.com
Circulation:11,500fr; Sworn/Estimate/Non-Audited
Advertising: Open inch rate $10.80
Digital Platform - Mobile: Apple
Adv. Mgr.......................................Jeanne Lutz
Ed. .... John Ronald
Prodn. Mgr. ....Brian Dodds
Mechanical Specifications: 11"x21"
Delivery Method: Mail, Newsstand, Carrier, Racks
Zip Codes Served: 47371, 47320, 47326, 47336, 47369,47373,47380'47381,46711,46740 , 45846

PRINCETON

GIBSON COUNTY TODAY
(Mon)
100 N Gibson St, Princeton, IN, 47670-1855, USA; tel (812) 385-2525; fax (812) 386-6199; web site www.pdclarion.com
Circulation:5,600fr; Sworn/Estimate/Non-Audited
Advertising: Open inch rate $7.44
Group: Brehm Communications, Inc.
Pub. .... Gary Blackburn

WABASH AND EDWARDS TODAY
(Thur)
100 N Gibson St, Princeton, IN, 47670-1855, USA; tel (812) 385-2525; fax (812) 386-6199
Group: Brehm Communications, Inc.
Ed. .... Andrea Howe

RICHMOND

COMMUNITY PRESS
(Wed, Sun)
PO Box 308, Richmond, IN, 47375-0308, USA; tel (317) 962-1575; fax (317) 966-6377
Circulation:11,018fr; Sworn/Estimate/Non-Audited
Pub. .... Kevin Lashbrook
Zip Codes Served: 47375

WEEKLY ITEM
(Wed)
1175 N A St, Richmond, IN, 47374-3226, USA; tel (765) 962-1575; adv tel (765) 973-4442 ; ed tel (765) 973-4489; fax (765) 973-4556; adv e-mail rdking@gannett.com; ed e-mail gfallon@gannett.com; web site www.pal-item.com
Circulation:25,000fr; Sworn/Estimate/Non-Audited
Advertising: Open inch rate $5.50
Group: Gannett
Mechanical Specifications: Type page 11 5/8 x 21; E - 6 cols, 1 5/6, between; A - 6 cols, 1 5/6, between; C - 9 cols, 1 3/4, between.
Equipment: Hardware — APP/Mac; Software — InDesign
Delivery Method: Carrier
Zip Codes Served: 47374

ROCHESTER

SHOPPING GUIDE NEWS
(Wed)
617 Main St, Rochester, IN, 46975-1319, USA; tel (574) 223-5417; fax (574) 223-8330; e-mail shoppingguide@rtcol.com; web site www.the-papers.com
Circulation: 0pd,8,759fr; CVC
Advertising: Open inch rate $10.45
Established: 2010
Group: The Papers Incorporated
Owner.................................... Ron Vaumgartner
Adv. Mgr.. Kip Schumm
Circ. Mgr..................................... Elaine Pearson
Mechanical Specifications: Type page 10 1/4 x 15; E - 6 cols, 1 9/16, between; A - 6 cols, 1 9/16, between.
Equipment: Hardware — 3-APP/Mac; Software — Multi-Ad/CAMS, QPS/QuarkXPress, Multi-Ad/Creator 4.0, Multi-Ad/Creator2, Claris/Works.
Zip Codes Served: 46975

ROCKPORT

LINCOLN'S COUNTRY SHOPPER
(Tues)
541 Main St, Rockport, IN, 47635-1429, USA; tel (866) 379-5400; fax (812) 649-9197; e-mail advertising@perrycountynews.com; adv e-mail advertising@perrycountynews.com; ed e-mail editor@spencercountyjournal.com; web site www.spencercountyjournal.com
Circulation:9,600fr; Sworn/Estimate/Non-Audited
Advertising: Open inch rate $13.40
Established: 1970
Group: Landmark Communications, Inc.
Ed. .... Vince Luecke
Pub. .... Dave Eldridge
Mechanical Specifications: STANDARD COLUMN WIDTHS
ROP and Classified
1 column=1.64 inches
2 columns=3.39 inches
3 columns=5.14 inches
4 columns=6.88 inches
5 columns=8.63 inches
6 columns=10.38 inches
Total Print Area
10.38 inches wide by 21.5 inches deep
Equipment: Hardware — Apple; Presses — Goss Community; Software — Adobe CS, MS Office
Delivery Method: Mail, Racks
Zip Codes Served: 47635, 47556, 47617, 47634, 47615, 47611, 47550, 47531, 47536, 47537, 47577, 47579, 47552, 47523, 47637, 47532, 47541

SHELBYVILLE

THE EXTRA
(Thur)
123 E Washington St, Shelbyville, IN, 46176-1463, USA; tel (317) 398-6631; adv tel (317) 398-1264; ed tel (317) 398-1277; fax (317) 398-0194; e-mail shelbynews@shelbynews.com; adv e-mail rhonda@shelbynews.com; ed e-mail pgable@shelbynews.com; web site www.shelbynews.com
Circulation:4,500fr; Sworn/Estimate/Non-Audited
Advertising: Open inch rate $4.50
Established: 1982
Adv. Mgr. .... Jody Street
Ed. .... Tom Albert
Mechanical Specifications: Type page 13 x 21 1/2; E - 6 cols, 2 1/16, 1/6 between; A - 6 cols, 2 1/16, 1/6 between; C - 6 cols, 2 1/16, 1/6 between.
Equipment: Hardware — CNI; Presses — G; Software — Baseview/Managing Editor.
Zip Codes Served: 46176

SOUTH BEND

MARKET PLACE
(Mon)
225 W Colfax Ave, South Bend, IN, 46601-1606, USA; tel (574) 235-6389; fax (574) 236-1765; adv e-mail ads@sbtinfo.com
Circulation:65,700fr; Sworn/Estimate/Non-Audited
Advertising: Open inch rate $10.70
Established: 1872Editions: 3— 3 total; Marshall Star Watch (5,400); Metro Star Watch (43,300); Michigan Star Watch (11,700);
Pub. .... David Ray
Gen. Mgr. .... Steve Funk
Adv. Mgr. .... Carol Smith
Circ. Mgr. .... Kevin Shaw
Mng. Ed. .... Ed Semmler
Mechanical Specifications: Type page 13 x 21; E - 6 cols, 2 1/16, between; A - 6 cols, 2 1/16, between; C - 10 cols, 1 3/16, between.
Zip Codes Served: 46626

TELL CITY

LINCOLNLAND SHOPPING GUIDE
(Wed)
537 Main St, Tell City, IN, 47586-2210, USA; tel (812) 547-3424; fax (812) 547-2847; e-mail editor@perrycountynews.com; adv e-mail advertising@perrycountynews.com; ed e-mail editor@perrycountynews.com; web site www.perrycountynews.com
Circulation:8,200fr; Sworn/Estimate/Non-Audited
Advertising: $10.05
Established: 1970
Group: Landmark Communications, Inc.
Adv. Mgr. .... Cindy Dauby
Circ. Mgr. .... Joyce Dauby
Ed. .... Vince Luecke
Pub. .... Dave Eldridge
Mechanical Specifications: STANDARD COLUMN WIDTHS
ROP and Classified
1 column=1.64 inches
2 columns=3.39 inches
3 columns=5.14 inches
4 columns=6.88 inches
5 columns=8.63 inches
6 columns=10.38 inches
Total Print Area
10.38 inches wide by 21.5 inches deep
Equipment: Hardware — Apple; Presses — Goss Community; Software — Adobe CS, MS Office
Delivery Method: Mail, Racks
Zip Codes Served: 47586, 47520, 47551, 47514, 47525, 47574, 47576, 47588, 47515, 47550, 47531, 47536, 42348, 42351

TERRE HAUTE

HOMETOWN
(Mon)
222 S 7th St, Terre Haute, IN, 47807-3601, USA; tel (812) 231-4200; fax (812) 231-4348; web site www.tribstar.com
Circulation:19,000fr; Sworn/Estimate/Non-Audited
Advertising: Open inch rate $5.00
Group: Community Newspaper Holdings, Inc.
Pub. .... B.J. Riley
Adv. Dir. .... John Mcclure
Circ. Dir. .... Courtney Zellars
Mechanical Specifications: Type page 6 x 21.
Equipment: Hardware — APP/Mac; Software — QPS/QuarkXPress.
Zip Codes Served: 47807

VERSAILLES

SPOTLIGHT-ADVERTISER
(Mon)
115 S Washington St, Versailles, IN, 47042-8016, USA; tel (812) 689-6364; fax (812) 689-6508; ed e-mail publication@ripleynews.com; web site www.ripleynews.com
Circulation:13,500fr; Sworn/Estimate/Non-Audited
Advertising: Open inch rate $7.00
Pub. .... Linda Chandler
Pres. .... Gene Demaree
Ed. .... Wanda English Burnett
Mechanical Specifications: Type page 13 x 21; E - 6 cols, 2, between; A - 6 cols, 2, between; C - 8 cols, 1 1/2, between.
Equipment: Hardware — APP/Macs; Presses — 4-KP; Software — Microsoft/Word, Adobe/PageMaker, Adobe/Illustrator 88.
Zip Codes Served: 47042

WABASH

THE PAPER
(Wed)
606 N State Road 13, Wabash, IN, 46992-7735, USA; tel (260) 563-8326; fax (260) 563-2863; e-mail accounting@thepaperofwabash.com; adv e-mail ads@thepaperofwabash.com; ed e-mail news@thepaperofwabash.com; web site www.thepaperofwabash.com
Circulation: 200pd,16,569fr; CVC
Advertising: Open inch rate $7.05
Established: 1977
Digital Platform - Mobile: Apple, Android, Windows, Blackberry, Other
OWNER, PUB.
Wayne W. Rees
Gen. Mgr. .... Michael W. Rees
Sales Rep. .... Julie Frieden
Sales Rep. .... Barb Keffaber
Circ. Mgr. .... Teresa Guy
Ed. .... Brent Swan
Opns. Mgr. .... Sam Frieden
Prodn. Mgr. .... Mike Plummer
Eric Stearley
Circ. Mgr .... Julie Schnepp
Mechanical Specifications: Type page 10 1/4 x 15; E - 7 cols, 1 3/16, between; A - 7 cols, 1 3/16, between; C - 7 cols, 1 3/16, between.
Equipment: Hardware — APP/Mac; Presses — 8-G/Community, 2-G/Community with folders; Software — QPS/QuarkXPress.
Delivery Method: Mail, Newsstand, Carrier
Zip Codes Served: 45951, 46702, 46713, 46926, 46940, 46941, 46943, 46946, 46952, 46962, 46974, 46984, 46990, 46992

WINAMAC

THE INDEPENDENT
(Sat)
114 W Main St, Winamac, IN, 46996-1208, USA; tel (574) 946-6628; fax (574) 946-7471; e-mail admin@pulaskijournal.com; adv e-mail ford@pulaskijournal.com; ed e-mail news@pulaskijournal.com; web site www.pulaskijournal.com
Circulation:9,800fr; USPS
Advertising: Open inch rate $7.25
Established: 1977
Publisher/Owner .... John Haley
Mng. Ed. .... Kari Beth Stout
Advertising Director .... Christine Ford
Mechanical Specifications: Full Page 10.25" (6 columns) x 15.75"
1 Column - 1.569"
2 Column - 3.306"
3 Column - 5.042"
4 Column - 6.778
5 Column - 8.514
Equipment: Hardware — 2011 iMac; Software — inDesign
Delivery Method: Mail, Newsstand, Racks
Zip Codes Served: 46996, 46985, 46968, 46960, 46939, 47957, 47946, 46534, 46945

IOWA

ALGONA

THE REMINDER
(Tues)
14 E Nebraska St, Algona, IA, 50511-2630, USA; web site www.algona.com
Circulation:13,300fr; CVCKate Thompson

AMES

STORY COUNTY ADVERTISER
(Wed)
317 5th St, Ames, IA, 50010-6101, USA; tel (515) 232-2160; fax (515) 232-2364; e-mail results@amesadvertiser.com; news@amestrib.com; ed e-mail letters@amestrib.com; web site www.amestrib.com
Circulation:23,558fr; CVC
Advertising: Open inch rate $19.41
Group: Iowa Newspapers, Inc.
Pub. .... John Goossen
Dir., Adv. .... John Greving
Dir., Circ. .... Dan Cronin
Dir., Prodn. .... Don Roof
Mechanical Specifications: Type page 10 1/2 x 13; E - 8 cols, 1 3/8, between; A - 8 cols, 1 3/8, between; C - 8 cols, 1 3/8, between.
Equipment: Hardware — APP/Macs; Presses — 4-G/Urbanite; Software — QPS/QuarkXPress.
Zip Codes Served: 50010, 50014

ANAMOSA

JOURNAL-EUREKA AND TOWN CRIER
(Tues, Thur)
405 E Main St, P.O. Box 108, Anamosa, IA, 52205-1866, USA; tel (319) 462-3511; fax (319) 462-4540; e-mail Admin@AnamosaJE.com; adv e-mail Advertising@anamosaje.com; ed e-mail Editorial@anamosaje.com; web site Journal-Eureka.com
Circulation: 2,150pd,11,218fr; Sworn/Estimate/Non-Audited
Advertising: Open inch rate $10
Established: 1855
Group: Anamosa Publications
Publisher .... W. James Johnson
Mechanical Specifications: Type page 6 x 21; E - 6 cols, 1.5 inches, 1 pica between; A - 6 cols, 1.5 inches, 1 pica between.
Equipment: Hardware — APP/Mac.; Software — Word, Adobe Creative Suite
Delivery Method: Mail
Zip Codes Served: 52205, 52212, 52214, 52252, 52305, 52306, 52310, 52312, 52320, 52321, 52323, 52219, 52336, 52362,

ATLANTIC

SOUTHWEST IOWA SHOPPER
(Tues)
PO Box 230, Atlantic, IA, 50022-0230, USA; web site www.atlanticnewstelegraph.com
Circulation:13,374fr; CVCConnie Collins

AUBURN

TRI-COUNTY SPECIAL
(Wed)
PO Box 106, Auburn, IA, 51433-0106, USA
Circulation:8,132fr; CVCGary D. Dudley

BELMOND

REMINDER
(Wed)
PO Box 263, Belmond, IA, 50421-0263, USA; web site www.printingservicesinc.net
Circulation:9,413fr; CVC
Advertising: Open inch rate $7.30JONI WORDEN

BLOOMFIELD

TRI-COUNTY SHOPPER
(Wed)
PO Box 168, Bloomfield, IA, 52537-0168, USA; web site tri-countyshopper.com
Circulation: 0pd,11,746fr; CVC
Advertising: Open inch rate $8.00Jeri Lyn Rupe

BOONE

BOONE COUNTY SHOPPING NEWS
(Wed)

2136 Mamie Eisenhower Ave, 2136 Mamie Eisenhower Ave, Boone, IA, 50036-4437, USA; web site www.newsrepublican.com
Circulation:11,318fr; CVCClaudia Lovin

BURLINGTON

HAWK EYE SHOPPER
(Tues)
800 S Main St, Burlington, IA, 52601-5870, USA; tel (319) 754-8461; fax (319) 754-6824; adv e-mail advertising@thehawkeye.com; web site www.thehawkeye.com
Circulation: 14,457pd,; VAC
Advertising: Open inch rate $4.65
HR Mgr. .... Jan Jaeger
Adv. Mgr. .... Janet Stottmeister
Circ. Mgr. .... Tom Seivert
Ed. .... Steve Delaney
Mng. Ed. .... Dale Alison
Systems Mgr. .... Tony Miller
Prodn. Mgr. .... Steve Deggendorf
Mechanical Specifications: Type page 10 3/4 x 13 1/2; A - 5 cols, 1/8 between; C - 5 cols, 1/8 between.
Equipment: Hardware — APP/Macs; Presses — G/Urbanite.
Zip Codes Served: 52601

CARROLL

CARROLL TODAY
(Tues)
PO Box 593, Carroll, IA, 51401-0593, USA; tel (712) 792-2179; fax (712) 792-2309; e-mail ldndesign@thewebunwired.com
Circulation:19,000fr; Sworn/Estimate/Non-Audited
Advertising: Open inch rate $4.95
Pub. .... Lucas Knowles
Delivery Method: Mail

SMART SHOPPER
(Tues)
220 W 7th St, Carroll, IA, 51401-2317, USA; tel (712) 792-2179; fax (712) 792-2309
Circulation:13,701fr; CVC
Advertising: Open inch rate $6.00
Pub. .... Lucas Knowles

TIMES HERALD ADVERTISER
(Tues)
508 N Court St, Carroll, IA, 51401-2747, USA; tel (712) 792-3573; fax (712) 792-5218; e-mail general@carrollspaper.com; ed e-mail newspaper@carrollspaper.com; web site www.carrollspaper.com
Circulation:23,700fr; Sworn/Estimate/Non-Audited
Advertising: Open inch rate $8.00
Pub. .... James Wilson
Gen. Mgr. .... Ann Wilson
Adv. Mgr. .... Tom Burns
Circ. Mgr. .... Daniel Haberl
Prodn. Mgr. .... Beckham Miller
Mechanical Specifications: Type page 12 15/16 x 21; E - 8 cols, 1 1/2, 1/6 between; A - 8 cols, 1 1/2, 1/6 between; C - 8 cols, 1 1/2, 1/6 between.
Zip Codes Served: 51401

CEDAR RAPIDS

PENNY SAVER
(Wed)
500 3rd Ave SE, Cedar Rapids, IA, 52401-1608, USA; tel (319) 398-8222; fax (319) 398-5848; web site www.pennysaverguide.com
Circulation:82,659fr; CVC
Advertising: Open inch rate $20.00
Adv.Dir .... Chris Edwards
Prodn. Mgr. .... Audrey Wheeler
Mechanical Specifications: Type page 9 1/4 x 11 5/8; E - 5 cols, 1 11/16, 1/8 between; A - 5 cols, 1 11/16, 1/8 between; C - 7 cols, 1 1/4, 1/8 between.
Equipment: Hardware — APP/Mac; Presses — G/Community.
Zip Codes Served: 52401

TIDBITS OF LINN COUNTY
(Tues)
5001 1st Ave SE, Ste 105 PMB 162, Cedar Rapids, IA, 52402-3251, USA; tel (319) 360-3936; e-mail russ@tidbitpapers.com; web site www.tidbitpapers.com
Circulation:12,980fr; CVC
Advertising: $150 (smallest modular rate)
Established: 2005Russ Swart
Delivery Method: Mail, Racks

CENTERVILLE

AD EXPRESS
(Wed)
201 N 13th St, Centerville, IA, 52544-1748, USA; tel (641) 856-6336; fax (641) 856-8118; e-mail iowegianad@mchsi.com; web site www.dailyiowegian.com
Circulation: 580pd,11,343fr; CVC
Advertising: Open inch rate $8.00
Group: Community Newspaper Holdings, Inc.
Publisher .... Becky Maxwell
Ed. .... Michael Schaffer
Mechanical Specifications: Type page 13 x 21 1/2; E - 6 cols, between; A - 6 cols, between; C - 6 cols, between.
Equipment: Hardware — APP/Mac; Presses — G/Community.
Zip Codes Served: 52544

CHARITON

CHARITON SHOPPER'S GUIDE
(Tues, Thur)
815 Braden Ave, Chariton, IA, 50049-1742, USA; tel (641) 774-2137; fax (641) 774-2139; e-mail charnews@charitonleader.com; web site www.charitonleader.com
Circulation:4,000fr; Sworn/Estimate/Non-Audited
Advertising: Open inch rate $7.20
Ed. .... David A. Paxton

CHARLES CITY

NORTHEAST IOWA SHOPPER
(Tues)
801 Riverside Dr, Charles City, IA, 50616-2248, USA; tel (641) 228-3211; fax (641) 228-2641; adv e-mail joelg@charlescitypress.com; ed e-mail editor@charlescitypress.com; web site www.charlescitypress.com
Circulation:16,306fr; CVC
Advertising: Open inch rate $17.63
Established: 1963
Group: Enterprise Media Inc
Pub. .... Christopher Hall Hall
Adv. Mgr. .... Joel Gray
Equipment: Hardware — APP/Mac; Presses — 13-G/Community; Software — QPS/QuarkXPress, Multi-Ad.
Delivery Method: Mail, Newsstand, Carrier, Racks
Zip Codes Served: 50616, 50435, 50471, 50468, 50653, 50658, 50636, 50619, 50628, 50461, 50466, 50460, 50603, 50645, 50659

THE EXTRA
(Thur)
801 Riverside Dr, Charles City, IA, 50616-2248, USA; tel (641) 228-3211; fax (641) 228-2641; adv e-mail ads@charlescitypress.com; web site www.ncppub.com
Circulation:2,264fr; CVC
Advertising: Open inch rate $8.95
Group: GateHouse Media, Inc.
Pub. .... Gene Hall
Gen. Mgr. .... Joel Gray
Pub. .... Lisa Miller
Adv. Mgr. .... Lois Kuehl
Circ. Mgr .... Tasha Lange

CHEROKEE

AREA ADVERTISER
(Tues)
111 S 2nd St, Cherokee, IA, 51012-1839, USA; tel (712) 225-5111; fax (712) 225-2910; e-mail editor@ctimes.biz; web site www.chronicletimes.com
Circulation:10,000fr; Sworn/Estimate/Non-Audited
Advertising: Open inch rate $10.50
Pub. .... Paul Struck
Adv. Mgr. .... Troy Valentine
Circ. Mgr. .... Patrice Martin
Mng. Ed. .... Ken Ross
Zip Codes Served: 51012

CRESCO

CRESCO SHOPPER
(Tues)
116 2nd Ave SE, Cresco, IA, 52136-1838, USA; tel (563) 547-2025; adv tel (563) 547-2025; fax (563) 547-3831; e-mail shopper@iowatelecom.net; adv e-mail shopper1@iowatelecom.net
Circulation:13,551fr; Sworn/Estimate/Non-Audited
Advertising: Open inch rate $9.00
Established: 1965
Digital Platform - Mobile: Apple
Adv. Mgr./Co-Owner .... Peggy Loveless
Ed. .... John Loveless
Equipment: Hardware — Apple G-4's & G-5's; Presses — 2-KP/News King; Software — Adobe/PageMaker & Adobe Creative Suite/InDesign
Delivery Method: Mail
Zip Codes Served: 50455, 50466, 50603, 50628, 50659, 50661, 52101, 52130, 52131, 52132, 52134, 52136, 52144, 52150, 52154, 52155, 52163, 52165, 52171, 55939, 55951, 55965, 55977

CRESTON

SOUTHWEST IOWA ADVERTISER
(Wed)
503 W Adams St, Creston, IA, 50801-3112, USA; tel (641) 782-2141; fax (641) 782-6628; e-mail publisher@crestonnews.com; office@crestonnews.com; news@crestonnews.com; web site www.crestonnews.com
Circulation:8,195fr; CVC
Advertising: Open inch rate $11.63
Group: Shaw Media
Pub. .... Rich Paulsen
Adv.Mgr. .... Craig Mittag
Circ. Mgr. .... Ron Bernard
Mng. Ed .... Stephani Finley
Prodn. Mgr. .... Kevin Lindley
Mechanical Specifications: Type page 13 x 21 1/2; A - 6 cols, 2, 1/6 between; C - 9 cols, 1 5/16, 1/6 between.
Equipment: Hardware — APP/Mac; Presses — 7-G/Community; Software — QPS/QuarkXPress.
Zip Codes Served: 50801

DAVENPORT

THRIFTY NICKEL
(Thur)
500 E 3rd St, Davenport, IA, 52801-1708, USA; tel (563) 333-2601; fax (563) 333-2666; e-mail qcnickel@qcthriftynickel.com; web site www.qcthriftynickel.com
Circulation:7,521fr; CVC
Advertising: Open inch rate $17.00
Established: 1982
Pub. .... Karla Pinner
Mechanical Specifications: Type page 10 1/4 x 16; A - 7 cols, 1 1/3, 1/6 between; C - 7 cols, 1 1/3, 1/6 between.
Equipment: Hardware — APP/Power Mac, Umax/Scanners, HP/4MV Printer; Software — QPS/QuarkXPress 3.32, Adobe/Photoshop 4.0, Adobe/Illustrator, Multi-Ad/CAMS 3.32.
Zip Codes Served: 61244, 61265, 61282, 61201, 61264

DENISON

CRAWFORD COUNTY ADVISOR
(Wed)
1410 Broadway, Denison, IA, 51442-2053, USA; e-mail greg.wehle@bulletinreview.com; adv e-mail greg.wehle@bulletinreview.com; web site www.dbrnews.com
Circulation:10,807fr; CVC
Advertising: Open inch rate $7.75
Established: 1934Greg Wehle
Mechanical Specifications: Type page 10.25" x 21.5"; 6 cols
Delivery Method: Mail, Racks

DUBUQUE

DUBUQUE ADVERTISER
(Wed)
2966 John F Kennedy Rd, Dubuque, IA, 52002-1049, USA; web site www.dbadvertiser.com
Circulation:36,109fr; Sworn/Estimate/Non-AuditedRandall Aird
President .... Greg Birkett

DYERSVILLE

EASTERN IOWA SHOPPING NEWS
(Tues)
223 1st Ave E, Dyersville, IA, 52040-1202, USA; tel (563) 875-7131; fax (563) 875-2279; e-mail easternshopnews@wcinet.com; web site www.wcinet.com; www.dyersvillecommercial.com
Circulation: 43pd,20,137fr; CVC
Advertising: 12.25
Established: 1978
Group: Woodward Communications, Inc.
Publisher/General Manager .... Mary Ungs-Sogaard
Managing Editor .... Beth Lutgen
Director of Prepress Production .... Kari Voss
Mechanical Specifications:
Equipment: Hardware —
Delivery Method: Mail
Zip Codes Served:

EAGLE GROVE

WRIGHT COUNTY SHOPPER'S GUIDE
(Wed)
PO Box 6, Eagle Grove, IA, 50533-0006, USA; tel (515) 448-4745; fax (515) 448-3182; e-mail egeagle@goldfieldaccess.net
Circulation:2,800fr; Sworn/Estimate/Non-Audited
Advertising: Open inch rate $4.80
Pub. .... Ryan Harvey
Adv. Mgr. .... Leigh Banwell
Circ. Mgr. .... Regina Lesher
Ed. .... Kim Demory
Mechanical Specifications: Type page 14 x 21; E - 6 cols, 2 1/8, 1/6 between; A - 6 cols, 2 1/8, 1/6 between.
Equipment: Hardware — APP/Mac.; Software — Microsoft/Word, Adobe/PageMaker, QPS/QuarkXPress, Adobe/Photoshop.
Zip Codes Served: 50533

ELDRIDGE

EASTERN IOWA BIZZZY BEE

(Wed)
214 N 2nd St, Eldridge, IA, 52748-1208, USA; tel (563) 285-8111; adv tel (563) 285-8111; ed tel (563) 285-8111; fax (563) 285-8114; e-mail btubbs@northscottpress.com; adv e-mail jmartens@northscottpress.com; web site www.northscottpress.com
Circulation: 18,000pd,; Sworn/Estimate/Non-Audited
Advertising: Open inch rate $11.00
Established: 1968
Group: North Scott Press, Inc.
Digital Platform - Mobile: Apple
Pub.. William F. Tubbs
Mng. Ed.................................... Scott Campbell
Advertising Mgr ....Jeff Martens
Mechanical Specifications: Type page 10 3/8 x 16; E - 4 cols, 2 1/2, between; A - 4 cols, 2 1/2, between; C - 6 cols, 1 3/4, between.
Equipment: Hardware — APP/Mac; Software — Adobe/InDesign
Photoshop
Microsoft World
Delivery Method: Mail, Racks
Zip Codes Served: Scott, Clinton, Jackson, Jones and Cedar counties.
Note: The Eastern Iowa Bizzzy Bee is a common section with five newspapers: Eldridge North Scott Press, DeWitt Observer, Maquoketa Sentinel-Press, Anamosa Journal, Tipton Conservative.

FOREST CITY

THE WINNEBAGO

(Tues)
PO Box 350, Forest City, IA, 50436-0350, USA; web site www.winnebagoshopper.com
Circulation:9,794fr; Sworn/Estimate/Non-AuditedHoward Query

FORT DODGE

CONSUMER NEWS

(Wed)
713 Central Ave, Fort Dodge, IA, 50501-3813, USA; tel (515) 576-6721; fax (515) 573-2136; e-mail cnews@fdconsumernews.com; web site www.ftdodgeconsumernews.com
Circulation:17,523fr; CVC
Advertising: Open inch rate $13.05
Established: 1970
Group: Ogden Newspapers Inc.Editions: 1— Consumer News (17,750;
Adv. Mgr..............................Charlene Peterson
Mechanical Specifications: Type page 10 3/8 x 10.5; E - 6 cols, 1 5/8, 1/8 between; A - 6 cols, 1 5/8, 1/8 between; C - 6 cols, 1 5/8, 1/8 between.
Equipment: Hardware — APP/Mac G4; Presses — Offset; Software — Multi-Ad/Creator 4.0.4.
Delivery Method: Mail, Carrier, Racks
Zip Codes Served: 50501, 50516,50040, 50132, 5021, 50246, 50249, 50518, 50523, 50524, 50530, 50532, 50543, 50544, 5055, 50566, 50569, 50594, 50548, 50529

MESSENGER EXTRA

(Wed)
713 Central Ave, Fort Dodge, IA, 50501-3813, USA; tel (515) 573-2141; adv tel (515) 573-2141 ext. 416; ed tel (515) 573-2141 ext 465; fax (515) 573-2148; adv e-mail cbargfrede@messengernews.net; ed e-mail jcurtis@messengernews.net; web site www.messengernews.net
Circulation:15,065fr; Sworn/Estimate/Non-Audited
Advertising: 14.70
Established: 1856
Group: The Nutting Company, Inc.
Pub...................................... Terry Christensen
Office Mgr........................... Melissa Wendland
Adv. Mgr...................................Cory Bargfrede
Circ. Mgr.................................. Grant Gibbons
City Ed... Bill Shea
Mechanical Specifications: Type page 11 x 21 1/2; E - 6 cols, 1 3/4, 1/16 between; A - 6 cols, 1 3/4, 1/16 between; C - 9 cols, 1 1/4, 1/16 between.
Equipment: Hardware — HP LaserJet 5500n Printer, HP 5550n Printer, Epson V330 Scanner; Presses — 14-G, Press Drive - 2 Fin/100 hp; Software — Multi-Ad/Creator 8, Adobe
Delivery Method: Mail, Carrier
Zip Codes Served: 50501, 50518, 50524, 50533, 50557, 50569, 50574

GRINNELL

GRINNELL PENNYSAVER

(Wed)
925 Broad St, Grinnell, IA, 50112-2047, USA; tel (641) 236-5611; fax (641) 236-0625
Circulation:14,635fr; Sworn/Estimate/Non-Audited
Advertising: Open inch rate $11.0
Group: Gannett
Gen. Mgr.................................Diane Goodlow
Adv. Mgr.. Jill Brown
Mechanical Specifications: Type page 10 1/4 x 14; A - 6 cols, 1 1/2, 1/16 between; C - 6 cols, 1 1/2, 1/16 between.
Equipment: Hardware — APP/Mac.
Zip Codes Served: 50112

HARLAN

PENNYSAVER

(Tues) (weekly)
1114 7th St, Harlan, IA, 51537-1338, USA; tel (712) 755-3111; fax (712) 755-3324; e-mail news2@harlanonline.com; web site www.harlanonline.com
Circulation:8,900fr; Sworn/Estimate/Non-Audited
Advertising: Open inch rate $8.75
Established: 1971
Pub.. Alan Mores
Pub...Steven Mores
Adv. Mgr.. Mike Kolbe
Ed..Robert Bjoin
Mechanical Specifications: Type page 14 3/4 x 21 1/2; A - 6 cols, 2 1/4, 1/6 between.
Equipment: Hardware — APP/Mac, APP/Mac LaserWriter II, APP/Power Mac 7500; Presses — 10-G/Community; Software — Multi-Ad/Creator 4.0, Adobe/PageMaker 6.0.
Delivery Method: Mail, Newsstand, Racks
Zip Codes Served: 51442, 51446, 51454, 51521, 51527, 51530, 51531, 51536, 51537, 51543, 51553, 51559, 51562, 51565, 51570

HAWARDEN

AREA WIDE AD-VERTISER

(Wed)
926 Avenue F, Hawarden, IA, 51023-2275, USA; tel (712) 551-1051; fax (712) 551-1057; e-mail independent@longlines.com
Circulation:6,685fr; CVC
Advertising: Open inch rate $8.50
Established: 1970Bruce Odson
Mechanical Specifications: 6 column full-page 10" x 14.5"
Equipment: ; Software — Creative Suite
Delivery Method: Mail
Zip Codes Served: 51023, 51027, 51001, 57001, 57004, 51062, 57025

IDA GROVE

REMINDER

(Tues)
210 2nd St, Ida Grove, IA, 51445-1403, USA; tel (712) 364-3131; fax (712) 364-3010; web site www.idacountycourier.com
Circulation:6,100fr; Sworn/Estimate/Non-Audited
Advertising: Open inch rate $7.90
Pub.. Roger D. Rector
Bus. Mgr....................................... Amy Forbes
Mechanical Specifications: Type page 11 1/2 x 21; A - 6 cols, 1 13/16, 1/8 between; C - 6 cols, 1 13/16, 1/8 between.
Equipment: Hardware — APP/Mac; Software — InDesign 2.02.

INDIANOLA

EXTRA

(Tues)
112 N Howard St, Indianola, IA, 50125-2510, USA; tel (515) 961-2511; fax (515) 961-4833; web site www.indianolarecordherald.com
Circulation:10,467fr; Sworn/Estimate/Non-Audited
Advertising: Open inch rate $13.70
Group: Gannett
Pub. .... Amy Duncan
Ed..Adam Wilson
Mechanical Specifications: Type page 13 x 21; E - 6 cols, 2, 1/6 between; A - 6 cols, 2, 1/6 between; C - 10 cols, 1 3/16, 1/6 between.
Zip Codes Served: 50125

IOWA CITY

ADD SHEET

(Wed)
1725 N Dodge St, Iowa City, IA, 52245-9589, USA; tel (319) 337-3181; fax (319) 339-7342; e-mail customerservice@press-citizen.com; web site www.press-citizen.com
Circulation:24,000fr; Sworn/Estimate/Non-Audited
Advertising: Open inch rate $7.95
Group: Gannett
Pub.......................... Susan Patterson Frank
Circ. Mgr...................................... Jean Suckow
Mng. Ed..Jim Lewers
Prodn. Mgr. .... Amy Sparby
Mechanical Specifications: Type page 11 5/8 x 21 1/4; A - 6 cols, 1 4/5, 2/5 between; C - 9 cols, 1 3/5, 2/5 between.
Zip Codes Served: 52245

IOWA FALLS

TIMES-CITIZEN

(Wed, Sat)
406 Stevens St, Iowa Falls, IA, 50126-2214, USA; tel (641) 648-2521; fax (641) 648-4606; e-mail tcc@iafalls.com; web site www.times-citizen.com
Circulation:34,000fr; Sworn/Estimate/Non-Audited
Advertising: Open inch rate $6.55
Pub....................................... Mark H. Hamilton
Gen. Mgr..Jo Martin
Circ. Mgr.................................. Susan Duncan
Mechanical Specifications: Type page 6 x 21; A - 6 cols, between; C - 6 cols, between.
Equipment: Hardware — APP/Power Macs, CD-ROMs, Scanners, Image Setter; Software — QPS/QuarkXPress 3.2, Adobe/PageMaker 6.0, Adobe/Illustrator 6.5.
Zip Codes Served: 50126

KNOXVILLE

MARION COUNTY REMINDER

(Tues)
122 E Robinson St, Knoxville, IA, 50138-2329, USA; tel (641) 842-2155; fax (641) 842-2929; e-mail class@journalexpress.net; adv e-mail advertising@journalexpress.net; ed e-mail editor@journalexpress.net; web site www.journalexpress.net
Circulation:20,615fr; CVC
Advertising: Open inch rate $10.00
Group: Community Newspaper Holdings, Inc.
Digital Platform - Mobile: Apple, Android, Windows
Digital Platform - Tablet: Apple iOS, Android, Windows 7, Blackberry Tablet OS, Kindle, Nook, Kindle Fire
Pub...................................... Rebecca Maxwell
Marketing Consultant .... Beth Adamcik
Marketing Consultant .... Susan Martin
Head Expeditor.......................... Amanda Heck
Cashier..Kelly Binns
Publisher.................................. Becky Maxwell
Mechanical Specifications: 6 Col.
1 Column 1.583 - 9p6
2 Columns 3.292 - 19p9
3 Columns 5 - 30p
4 Columns 6.708 - 40p3
5 Columns 8.417 - 50p6
6 Columns 10.125 - 60p9
Tab Sizes
Ad Lengths
1 Inch 6 picas
2 Inches 12 picas
3 Inches 18 picas
4 Inches 24 picas
5 Inches 30 picas
6 Inches 36 picas
7 Inches 42 picas
8 Inches 48 picas
9 Inches 54 picas
10 Inches 60 picas
11 Inches 66 picas
12 Inches 72 picas
13 Inches 78 picas
14 Inches 84 picas
15 Inches 90 picas
16 Inches 96 picas
17 Inches 102 picas
18 Inches 108 picas
19 Inches 114 picas
20 Inches 120 picas
Full Page 60p x 58p6 (10 x 9.776)
1/2 Page Vertical 30p x 58p6 (5 x 9.776)
1/2 Page Horizontal 60p x 29p3 10 x 4.888)
1/4 Page 30p x 29p3 (5 x 4.888)
1/8 Page 30p x 14p6 (5 x 2.444)
Equipment: ; Software — Adobe/Illustrator CS5, QuarkXPress 3.31, Adobe/Photoshop CS5, Adobe InDesign CS5, Quark XPress 9.3
Delivery Method: Mail, Carrier, Racks
Zip Codes Served: 50138, 50219, 50214, 50232, 50143, 50049, 50062, 50163, 50225, 50057, 50118, 50170, 50272, 50150, 50044/50016, 50119, 50265, 50119/50265

LE MARS

SHOPPERS GUIDE

(Wed)
41 1st Ave NE, Le Mars, IA, 51031-3535, USA; tel (712) 546-7031; fax (712) 546-7035; e-mail sentinel@lemarscomm.net; web site www.lemarssentinel.com
Circulation:7,000fr; Sworn/Estimate/Non-Audited
Advertising: Open inch rate $14.55
Established: 1857
Group: Rust Communications
Pub...Tom Stangl
Adv.......................................David Copenhaver
Circ. Mgr.................................. Christine Pape
Mktg. Dir.. Monte Jost
Ed..................................Magdalene Landegent
Prodn. Mgr. .... Don Luksan
Mechanical Specifications: Type page 13 x 21 1/2.
Equipment: Hardware — APP/Mac; Presses — 6-G/Community; Software — Claris/Works 5.0, Multi-Ad/Creator, QPS/QuarkXPress, Microsoft/Publisher.
Zip Codes Served: 51031

MAQUOKETA

THE SHOPPER
(Wed)
108 N Main St, Maquoketa, IA, 52060-2201, USA; tel (563) 652-6803; fax (563) 652-3406
Circulation:12,996fr; CVC
Advertising: Open inch rate $4.75
Adv. Mgr. .... Judy Van Hecke

MARENGO

IOWA COUNTY ADVERTISER
(Wed)
100 W Main St, Marengo, IA, 52301-4705, USA; tel (319) 642-5506; fax (319) 642-5509
Circulation: 3,979pd,6,309fr; CVC
Advertising: Open inch rate $5.00
Pub. .... Diane Godlow
Sales Mgr. .... John Rotter
Circ. Mgr. .... Audrey Yardley
Mechanical Specifications: Type page 6 x 14; E - 6 cols, 2 1/3, 1/6 between; A - 9 cols, 1 2/3, 1/6 between.
Equipment: Hardware — APP/Mac; Presses — 8-KP/News King 2000; Software — Adobe/Photoshop, Adobe/PageMaker, QPS/QuarkXPress, Microsoft.

MARSHALLTOWN

PENNYSAVER
(Wed, Sat)
507 E Anson St, Marshalltown, IA, 50158-3317, USA; tel (641) 752-6630; fax (641) 752-7073; e-mail ps@marshalltownpennysaver.com; web site www.marshalltownpennysaver.com
Circulation:30,000fr; Sworn/Estimate/Non-Audited
Advertising: Open inch rate $13.75
Group: Ogden Newspapers Inc.
Pub. .... Mike Schlesinger
Marketing Director .... Denise Kemp
Mechanical Specifications: Type page 10 1/4 x 16; E - 7 cols, 1 1/4, 3/16 between; A - 7 cols, 1 1/4, 3/16 between; C - 7 cols, 1 1/4, 3/16 between.
Equipment: ; Presses — G/Community; Software — Multi-Ad/Creator 4.0, Adobe/Photoshop.
Zip Codes Served: 50158

MASON CITY

THE MASON CITY SHOPPER
(Tues)
300 N Washington Ave, Mason City, IA, 50401-3222, USA; tel (641) 421-0500; fax (641) 421-0592; e-mail classads@globegazette.com; web site www.masoncityshopper.com
Circulation:23,016fr; CVC
Advertising: Open inch rate $10.00Howard Query
Sales Rep. .... Linda Hawk
Mechanical Specifications: Type page 10 1/2 x 16; E - 5 cols, 1 11/12, 3/16 between; A - 5 cols, 1 15/16, 3/16 between; C - 5 cols, 1 15/16, 3/16 between.
Equipment: Hardware — APP/Mac 7100; Software — Multi-Ad/Creator 3.6.2, QPS/QuarkXPress.
Zip Codes Served: 50401

MONTICELLO

MONTICELLO SHOPPERS' GUIDE
(Wed)
111 E Grand St, Monticello, IA, 52310-1688, USA; tel (319) 465-3555; fax (319) 465-4611; e-mail mexpress@n-connect.net; web site www.monticelloexpress.com
Circulation:10,200fr; Sworn/Estimate/Non-Audited
Advertising: Open inch rate $9.20
Co-Pub. .... Dan Goodyear
Adv. Mgr. .... Mark Spensley
Prodn. Mgr. .... Jill Brokaw
Ed. .... Kim Brooks
Mechanical Specifications: Type page 10 1/4 x 16; E - 6 cols, 1 9/16, 1/6 between; A - 6 cols, 1 9/16, 1/6 between; C - 6 cols, 1 9/16, 1/6 between.
Equipment: Hardware — 12-APP/Power Mac; Software — Microsoft/Word, Adobe/Photoshop, Adobe/PageMaker 6.5.
Zip Codes Served: 52310

MOUNT VERNON

THE SUNLIGHT
(Thur)
108 1st St SW, Mount Vernon, IA, 52314-4706, USA; tel (319) 895-6216; fax (319) 895-6217; e-mail news@mtvernonlisbonsun.com; adv e-mail advertising@mtvernonlisbonsun.com; web site www.mtvernonlisbonsun.com
Circulation:3,350fr; Sworn/Estimate/Non-Audited
Advertising: Open inch rate $7.00
Established: 1975
Adv. Mgr. .... Rich Eskelsen
Circ. Mgr. .... Valerie Burkhart-Fisher
Ed. .... Jake Krob
Mechanical Specifications: Type page 13 x 21 1/2; E - 6 cols, 2, 1/6 between; A - 6 cols, 2, 1/6 between; C - 8 cols, 1 1/2, 1/6 between.
Equipment: Hardware — APP/Mac; Software — QPS/QuarkXPress, APP/AppleWorks, 2-Multi-Ad/Creator, Adobe/Photoshop.
Zip Codes Served: 52314

MT PLEASANT

MT. PLEASANT SHOPPER
(Tues)
215 W Monroe St, Mt Pleasant, IA, 52641-2110, USA; tel (319) 385-3131; adv tel (319) 385-3131; ed tel (319) 385-3131; fax (319) 385-8048; adv fax (319) 385-8048; ed fax (319) 385-8048; e-mail pub@mpnews.net; adv e-mail adv@mpnews.net; ed e-mail news@mpnews.net; web site www.mpnews.net
Circulation:11,622fr; CVC
Advertising: Open inch rate $9.70
Established: 1890
Group: Inland Media Company, Inc.
Publisher/Ad Director .... Bill Gray
Mechanical Specifications: Type page 10 1/4 x 16; A - 6 cols, 1 1/2, 1/6 between; C - 6 cols, 1 1/2, 1/6 between.
Equipment: Hardware — APP/Mac; Presses — 4-G/Community; Software — Photoshop; InDesign
Delivery Method: Carrier, Racks
Zip Codes Served: 52641, 52644, 52645, 52646, 52647, 52648, 52649, 52651, 52652, 52653, 52654, 52656, 52659

MUSCATINE

THE POST
(Wed)
301 E 3rd St, Muscatine, IA, 52761-4116, USA; tel (563) 263-2331; fax (563) 262-8042; e-mail sales@muscatinepost.com; web site www.muscatinejournal.com
Circulation: 811pd,; AAM
Advertising: Open inch rate $8.00
Pub. .... Bob Blackman
Adv. Mgr. .... Jaime Bryant
Circ. Mgr. .... Tom McCoy
News Ed. .... Rusty Schrader
Mechanical Specifications: Type page 10 3/4 x 16; E - 7 cols, 1 5/12, 1/12 between; A - 7 cols, 1 5/12, 1/12 between; C - 7 cols, 1 5/12, 1/12 between.
Equipment: Hardware — APP/Mac Quadra 650, APP/Mac Performa 6300CD; Software — QPS/QuarkXPress, Multi-Ad/Creator.
Zip Codes Served: 52761

NEW HAMPTON

NEW HAMPTON SHOPPER
(Tues)
10 N Chestnut Ave, New Hampton, IA, 50659-1349, USA; tel (641) 394-2111; fax (641) 394-2113; e-mail nhtribune@mchsi.com; web site www.newhamptontribune.com
Circulation:20,000fr; Sworn/Estimate/Non-Audited
Advertising: Open inch rate $3.80
Pub. .... Matt Bryant
Pub. .... Dan Feuling
Adv. Mgr. .... Amannda Pemble
Circ. Mgr. .... Ruth Walden
Mechanical Specifications: Type page 15 1/8 x 21 1/2; A - 9 cols, 1 9/16, between; C - 9 cols, 1 9/16, between.

NEWTON

JASPER COUNTY ADVERTISER
(Wed)
200 1st Ave E, Newton, IA, 50208-3716, USA; web site www.newtondailynews.com
Circulation:15,012fr; CVC
Advertising: Open inch rate $13.77
Group: Shaw MediaDan Goetz

OELWEIN

SHOPPER'S REMINDER
(Mon)
25 1st St SE, Oelwein, IA, 50662-2306, USA; tel (319) 283-4524; fax (319) 283-3268
Circulation:20,280fr; CVC
Advertising: Open inch rate $16.71
Group: Community Media Group
Adv. Mgr. .... Tracy Cummings
Circ. Mgr. .... Sue Hosto
Editor .... David DeZur
Zip Codes Served: 50662

ORANGE CITY

AD-VISOR
(Tues)
113 Central Ave SE, Orange City, IA, 51041-1738, USA; tel (712) 737-4266; adv tel same; ed tel (712) 737-4266; fax (712) 737-3896; adv fax same; ed fax (712) 737-3896; e-mail pluimpub@orangecitycomm.net; adv e-mail same; ed e-mail same; web site siouxcountynews.com
Circulation:8,878fr; CVC
Advertising: Open inch rate $7.25
Established: 1951Editions: 52— Ad-Visor
Pres. .... Robert Hulstein
Adv. Mgr. .... Dennis Den Hartog
Circ. Mgr. .... Amy Rassel
Ed. .... Doug Calsbeek
Mng. Ed. .... Dale H. Pluim
Prodn. Mgr. .... El Top
Mechanical Specifications: Broadsheet page 8 col. wide x 21.5 tall
Equipment: Hardware — APP/Mac; Presses — Heidelburg MOZP-Heidelburg Quick Master-# unit Harris V15 web- 2 Color AB Dick
Delivery Method: Mail, Carrier
Zip Codes Served: 51041

OSAGE

TOWN & COUNTRY SHOPPER
(Wed)
112 N 6th St, Osage, IA, 50461-1202, USA; tel (641) 732-3721; fax (641) 732-5689; e-mail mcpress@mcpress.com; ed e-mail editor@mcpress.com; web site www.mcpress.com
Circulation:6,500fr; Sworn/Estimate/Non-Audited
Advertising: Open inch rate $7.50
Pub. .... Dave Stanley
Adv. Sales Mgr. .... Kelly Kuper
Ed. .... David Namanny
Mechanical Specifications: Type page 14 x 21 1/2; E - 6 cols, 2, 1/6 between; A - 6 cols, 2, 1/6 between; C - 6 cols, 2, 1/6 between.
Equipment: Hardware — APP/Power Mac; Presses — KP/News King; Software — Adobe/PageMaker.
Zip Codes Served: 50461

OSCEOLA

THE ADVERTISER
(Tues)
111 E Washington St, Osceola, IA, 50213-1244, USA; web site www.osceolaiowa.com
Circulation: 65pd,11,265fr; CVCRich Paulsen

OSKALOOSA

OSKALOOSA SHOPPER
(Wed)
1901 A Ave W, Oskaloosa, IA, 52577-1962, USA; tel (641) 672-2581; adv tel (641) 672-2581 ext. 413; ed tel (641) 672-2581 ext. 425; fax (641) 672-2294; adv fax (641) 673-8226; ed fax (641) 672-1264; e-mail debve@oskyherald.com; adv e-mail debve@oskyherald.com; ed e-mail oskynews@oskyherald.com; web site www.oskaloosa.com
Circulation:16,973fr; CVC
Advertising: $11.55 pci
Established: 1960
Group: Community Newspaper Holdings, Inc.
Digital Platform - Mobile: Android
Digital Platform - Tablet: Apple iOS, Android, Kindle, Nook, Kindle Fire
PUblisher .... Deb Van Engelenhoven
Mechanical Specifications: 6 col. x 21 inches (10.2125" x 21")
Delivery Method: Mail, Carrier, Racks
Zip Codes Served: 52577, 50207, 50027, 52543, 52553, 52561, 50143, 52586, 52595, 50136, 52591, 50256, 52355, 50268, 50104, 52563, 52566, 50138, 50150, 50219, 50242, 50255, 52222, 50171, 50044, 50116

PELLA

TOWN CRIER
(Wed)
810 E 1st St, Pella, IA, 50219-1529, USA; tel (641) 628-1130; fax (641) 628-2826; web site www.towncriernews.com
Circulation:12,000fr; Sworn/Estimate/Non-Audited
Advertising: Open inch rate $5.00
Pub. .... Keith Aldrich
Pub. .... Logan Andeweg
Adv. Mgr. .... Dede Doschadis
Circ. Mgr. .... Wilma Brouwer
Mechanical Specifications: Type page 16 x 21 1/2; A - 9 cols, 1 11/16, 1/8 between; C - 9 cols, 1 11/16, 1/8 between.
Equipment: Hardware — AM/Desktop.
Zip Codes Served: 50219

PERRY

CHIEFLAND SHOPPER
(Tues)
1323 2nd St, Perry, IA, 50220-1511, USA; tel (515) 465-4666; fax (515) 465-3087; e-mail publisher@theperrychief.com; adv e-mail

ads@theperrychief.com; ed e-mail news@theperrychief.com; web site www.theperrychief.com
Circulation: 12,500fr; Sworn/Estimate/Non-Audited
Advertising: Open inch rate $9.30
Established: 1874
Publisher.................................. Patricia Snyder
Adv. Mgr.............................. Linda Schumacher
Prodn. Mgr............................ Donald Thomas
Managing Editor........................... Laura Pieper
Mechanical Specifications: Type page 14 7/8 x 21; E - 8 cols, 1 3/4, between; A - 8 cols, 1 5/6, between; C - 8 cols, 1 5/6, between.
Equipment: Hardware — Dell Studio XPS 9100 (6); Software — Adobe CS 5.5
Delivery Method: Mail, Carrier
Zip Codes Served: 50220 50003 50026 50029 50039 50059 50063 50066 50070 50107 50109 50115 50129 50146 50156 50167 50216 50233 50235 50276 50277

POCAHONTAS

POCAHONTAS COUNTY ADVERTISER
(Tues)
218 N Main St, Pocahontas, IA, 50574-1605, USA; tel (712) 335-3553; fax (712) 335-3856; e-mail publisher@pokyrd.com; adv e-mail ads@pokyrd.com; ed e-mail editor@pokyrd.com
Circulation: 5,820fr; Sworn/Estimate/Non-Audited
Advertising: Open inch rate $7.17
Owner/Publisher/Editor.................... Chris Vrba
Equipment: Hardware — APP/Power Mac; Software — Adobe/InDesign, Microsoft/Word.
Delivery Method: Mail, Newsstand, Carrier, Racks
Zip Codes Served: 50574, 50581, 50510, 50515, 50527, 50540, 50541, 50546, 50554, 50562, 50563, 50565, 50568, 50571, 50576, 50575, 50593, 51366

ROCK RAPIDS

THE NORTHWEST IOWA EXTRA
(Thur)
310 1st Ave, Rock Rapids, IA, 51246-1506, USA; tel (712) 472-2525; adv tel (712) 472-2525; ed tel (712) 472-2525; fax (712) 472-3414; adv fax (712) 472-3414; ed fax (712) 472-3414; e-mail lmiller@ncppub.com; adv e-mail lkuehl@ncppub.com; ed e-mail jjensen@ncppub.com; web site www.ncppub.com
Circulation: 1,712fr; CVC
Advertising: Open inch rate $10.44
Group: New Century Press
Digital Platform - Mobile: Apple, Android, Windows, Blackberry
Digital Platform - Tablet: Apple iOS, Android, Windows 7, Blackberry Tablet OS, Kindle, Nook, Kindle Fire
Pub./COO..................................... Jim Hensley
Ed.. Jessica Jensen
Gen. Mgr.. Lisa Miller
Mechanical Specifications: Type page 11 5/8 x 21 1/2; E - 6 cols, 1 13/16, 1/6 between; A - 6 cols, 1 13/16, 1/6 between; C - 6 cols, 1 13/16, 1/6 between.
Equipment: ; Software — QPS/QuarkXPress 4.0.
Delivery Method: Mail, Newsstand
Zip Codes Served: 51246

ROCKWELL CITY

CALHOUN COUNTY REMINDER
(Tues)
515 4th St, Rockwell City, IA, 50579-1901, USA; tel (712) 297-8931; fax (712) 297-7193; adv e-mail ads@calhouncontyreminder.com; web site www.calhouncountyreminder.com
Circulation: 6,061fr; CVC
Advertising: Open inch rate $5.00
Adv. Mgr.................................. Gary D. Dudley
Circ. Mgr.................................. Janet Anderson
Prodn. Mgr............................. Robert Johnson
Mechanical Specifications: Type page 6 x 16; E - 6 cols, 1 1/2, between; A - 6 cols, 1 1/2, between.
Equipment: Hardware — APP/Mac; Presses — G; Software — Adobe/PageMaker.
Zip Codes Served: 50579

SHELDON

THE GOLDEN SHOPPER
(Tues)
227 Nineth St, Sheldon, IA, 51201, USA; tel (712) 324-5347; fax (712) 324-2345; e-mail pww@iowainformation.com; adv e-mail ads@iowainformation.com; ed e-mail editor@iowainformation.com; web site www.nwestiowa.com
Circulation: 16,448fr; CVC
Advertising: Open inch rate $8.82
Established: 1962
Group: Iowa Information, Inc.
Digital Platform - Mobile: Apple
Pres.. Jeff Wagner
Adv. Mgr................................ Peter W. Wagner
Ed.. Jeff Grant
Prodn. Mgr.................................. Dawn Groen
Mechanical Specifications: Type page 12 7/8 x 21 1/2; E - 6 cols, 2, 1/6 between; A - 6 cols, 2, 1/6 between; C - 6 cols, 2, 1/6 between.
Equipment: Hardware — Most current Mac's, direct to plate ; Presses — SIX MERCURY FOUR-HIGH PRESSES AND SPLICERS CONNECTED TO TWO FOLDERS
Delivery Method: Mail, Newsstand, Carrier, Racks
Zip Codes Served: 51003, 51041, 51046, 51201, 51231, 51232, 51234, 51237, 51238, 51243, 51244, 51248, 51249, 51250, 51346, 51349, 51350, 51237, 51022, 51245

SHENANDOAH

WEEKLY TIMES
(Mon)
617 W Sheridan Ave, Shenandoah, IA, 51601-1707, USA; tel (712) 246-3097; fax (712) 246-3099; e-mail ads@valleynewstoday.com; ed e-mail editorial@valleynewstoday.com; web site southwestiowanews.com
Circulation: 22,847fr; CVC
Advertising: Open inch rate $22.15
Established: 1882
Pub... Barbara Trimble
Adv.. Mark Anderson
Circ. Mgr................................ Kimberly Kellison
Ed.. Kevin Slater
Mechanical Specifications: Type page 11.832" x 21"; 7 cols
Delivery Method: Mail, Racks

SIOUX CENTER

SIOUX CENTER SHOPPER
(Tues)
67 3rd St NE, Sioux Center, IA, 51250-1834, USA; tel (712) 722-0511; fax (712) 722-0507; e-mail ads@siouxcenternews.com
Circulation: 12,500fr; Sworn/Estimate/Non-Audited
Advertising: Open inch rate $6.45
Ed.. Scott Beernink
Prodn. Mgr......................... Denise VanderBroek
Equipment: Hardware — APP/Mac; Software — OSystem 9, Adobe/PageMaker 6.5, QPS/QuarkXPress 4.1, Macromedia/Freehand 9, Adobe/Illustrator 9, Adobe/Photoshop 6.0.
Zip Codes Served: 51250

SIOUX CITY

SHOPPER'S GUIDE
(Wed)
515 Pavonia St, Sioux City, IA, 51101-2245, USA; tel (712) 224-6277; fax (712) 255-7301; e-mail steve.griffith@lee.net
Circulation: 49,550fr; Sworn/Estimate/Non-Audited
Advertising: Open inch rate $15.00
Established: 1985
Gen. Mgr..................................... Steve Griffith
Mechanical Specifications: Type Page 9.889" x 10"
6 column format
1 column 1.556" wide
Equipment: Hardware — Gateway; Software — APT/Falcon
Delivery Method: Carrier, Racks
Zip Codes Served: 51101, 51102, 51103, 51104, 51105, 51108, 51109, 51054, 50117, 51024, 51030, 51039, 68776, 68030, 68741, 57049, 57025, 57038

SPENCER

THE NORTHWEST IOWA SHOPPER WEEKEND
(Sat)
310 E Milwaukee St, Spencer, IA, 51301-4569, USA; tel (712) 262-6610; fax (712) 262-3044; e-mail advertising@spencerdailyreporter.com; web site www.spencerdailyreporter.com
Circulation: 18,000fr; Sworn/Estimate/Non-Audited
Advertising: Open inch rate $11.75
Pub.. Paula Buenger
Ed.. Randy Cauthron
Mechanical Specifications: Type page 13 x 21 1/2; E - 6 cols, 2, between; A - 6 cols, 2, between; C - 6 cols, 2, between.
Equipment: Hardware — APP/Mac; Presses — 11-G/community.
Zip Codes Served: 57301

STORM LAKE

ADVERTISING GUIDE
(Tues)
527 Cayuga St, Storm Lake, IA, 50588-2319, USA; tel (712) 732-3130; fax (712) 732-3152; e-mail info@stormlakepilottribune.com; sledt@ncn.net; web site www.stormlakepilottribune.com
Circulation: 15,575fr; CVC
Advertising: Open inch rate $7.45
Pub.. Paula Buenger
Adv. Mgr................................ Janelle Madison
Prodn. Mgr.................................... Tim Marlow
Mechanical Specifications: Type page 13 4/5 x 21 1/2; E - 8 cols, 1 7/12, 1/6 between; A - 8 cols, 1 7/12, 1/6 between; C - 8 cols, 1 7/12, 1/6 between.
Equipment: Hardware — APP/Mac; Presses — 4-G/Community.
Zip Codes Served: 50510, 50535, 50540, 50554, 50565, 50567, 50568, 50574, 50575, 50576, 50583, 50585, 50588, 50592, 50593, 51002, 51005, 51020, 51025, 51033, 51047, 51053, 51431, 51445, 51450, 51458, 51466

STORM LAKE PILOT TRIBUNE
(Tues, Thur, Sat)
527 Cayuga St, PO Box 1187, Storm Lake, IA, 50588-2319, USA; tel (712) 732-3130; fax (712) 732-3152; e-mail info@stormlakepilottribune.com; adv e-mail kari@stormlakepilottribune.com; ed e-mail dlarsen@stormlakepilottribune.com; web site www.stormlakepilottribune.com
Circulation: 2,000pd,15,690fr; Sworn/Estimate/Non-Audited
Advertising: Open inch rate $11.50
Established: 1840
Digital Platform - Mobile: Apple, Android, Windows
Digital Platform - Tablet: Apple iOS, Android, Windows 7, Kindle Fire
Gen. Mgr........................... Kari Vander Woude
Adv. Mgr...................................... Jason Lindsay
Pub.. Paula Buenger
Mechanical Specifications: Type page 10 x 21 1/2; E - 6 cols, 1 9/16, 2/16 between;
Equipment: Hardware — ctp Presteligence; Presses — G/Community.
Delivery Method: Mail, Newsstand, Racks
Zip Codes Served: 50588, 51002, 51005, 50535, 50540, 51020, 51025, 50554, 51033, 50565, 50568, 51047, 50576, 51053, 50585, 50592, 50593,

STUART

5 X 80 BULLETIN
(Tues, Bi-Mthly)
119 NW 2nd St, Stuart, IA, 50250-7704, USA; tel (515) 523-1010; fax (515) 523-2825; e-mail ads@thestuartherald,com; adv e-mail ads@thestuartherlad.com; ed e-mail news@thestuartherald.com; web site www.stuartia.com
Circulation: 9,500fr; Sworn/Estimate/Non-Audited
Advertising: Open inch rate $7.75
Established: 1871
Digital Platform - Mobile: Apple
Digital Platform - Tablet: Apple iOS
Owner...................................... Kristy Lonsdale
Delivery Method: Mail, Newsstand
Zip Codes Served: 50250,50002,50003,50048,50070,50072,50849,50115,50029,50115,50146,50164,50216,50233,50273

TAMA

TAMA COUNTY SHOPPER
(Wed)
220 W 3rd St, Tama, IA, 52339-2308, USA; tel (641) 484-2841; fax (641) 484-5705; adv e-mail nsund@tamatoledonews.com; ed e-mail editor@tamatoledonews.com; web site www.tamatoledonews.com
Circulation: 12fr; Sworn/Estimate/Non-Audited
Advertising: Open inch rate $12.46
Group: Ogden Newspapers Inc.
Pub........................... D. Michael Schlessinger
Adv. Mgr....................................... Nancy Sund
Ed.. John Speer
Mechanical Specifications: Type page 10 x 21 1/2; A - 6 cols, 1 2/5, between; C - 6 cols, 1 2/5, between.
Delivery Method: Mail, Racks
Zip Codes Served: 52339, 52342, 52215, 50675, 52217, 50635, 52208, 52224, 50173, 50632

VINTON

VINTON LIVEWIRE
(Wed)
108 E 5th St, Vinton, IA, 52349-1759, USA; tel (319) 472-3303; fax (319) 472-4811; adv e-mail ads@vintonnewspapers.com; web site www.vintonnewspapers.com or www.vintonlivewire.com
Circulation: 11,518fr; Sworn/Estimate/Non-Audited
Advertising: Open inch rate $9.75 thru Dec. 31, 2017
Established: 1957
Group: Community Media Group
Gen. Mgr.................................. Mona Garwood
Mechanical Specifications: Page Size 10 1/4 x 14; 6 col. format; 1 col = 1.6"
Delivery Method: Mail, Carrier
Zip Codes Served: 52349, 52210, 52229, 52313, 52332, 52345, 52213, 52352, 52206, 52209, 52224, 52249, 52315, 50651, 52346

WASHINGTON

WASHINGTON COUNTY SHOPPERS GUIDE
(Tues)
111 N Marion Ave, Washington, IA, 52353-1728, USA; tel (319) 653-2191; fax (319) 653-7524; e-mail pub@washjrnl.com; news@washjrnl.com; web site washjrnl.com
Circulation:11,451fr; CVC
Advertising: Open inch rate $12.34
Group: Inland Media Company, Inc.
Inland Newspaper Machinery LLC
Publisher.. Matt Bryant
Pres. ....Darwin Sherman
News Ed. .... John Butters
Mechanical Specifications: Type page 10 5/8 x 16; A - 6 cols, 1 7/12, 1/6 between; C - 6 cols, 1 7/12, 1/6 between.
Equipment: Hardware — APP/Mac; Presses — 4-HI/V-15A; Software — Adobe/PageMaker 5.2, Microsoft/Word 6.0, QPS/QuarkXPress 3.1.1, Adobe/Photoshop 3.0, Claris 4.0, Multi-Ad/Creator 3.3.7.
Delivery Method: Carrier

WATERLOO

CEDAR VALLEY SAVER
(Thur, Bi-Mthly)
3641 Kimball Ave, Waterloo, IA, 50702-5757, USA; tel (319) 232-4500; fax (319) 232-4500; e-mail brian@cvsaver.com; adv e-mail ton@cvsaver.com; web site www.cvsaver.com
Circulation:37,832fr; Sworn/Estimate/Non-Audited
Advertising: $21 / col. in.
Established: 2004
Pub. .... Brian Lewis
Mechanical Specifications: Tabloid - 11.25" x 17"
Equipment: Hardware — Macs & PCs; Presses — N/A; Software — N/A
Zip Codes Served: 50701, 50702, 50703

INSIDER
(Tues)
501 Commercial St, Waterloo, IA, 50701-5413, USA; tel (319) 291-1400; fax (319) 291-2069; adv e-mail woo.ads@wcfcourier.com; web site www.wcfcourier.com
Circulation: 8,574pd,786fr; AAM
Advertising: $14.00Editions: 3— 3 total; Insider-Cedar Falls (21,000); Insider-E. Waterloo (21,200); Insider-W. Waterloo (19,300);
Pub. .... David Braton
Adv. Dir...................................... Sharon Jordan
Ed. .... Nancy Newhoff
Adv. Mgr... Tara Sieble
Circ. Mgr .... Scott Kinter
Mechanical Specifications: Type page 6 x 13; E - 4 cols, 1 7/12, between; A - 4 cols, 1 7/12, between.
Equipment: Hardware — APP/Mac; Presses — HI; Software — Baseview/Class Act II.
Zip Codes Served: 50613

WAVERLY

BREMER-BUTLER SUPER SHOPPER
(Tues)
311 W Bremer Ave, Waverly, IA, 50677-3144, USA; tel (319) 352-3334; fax (319) 352-5135; e-mail news@waverlynewspapers.com; circ@waverlynewspapers.com; web site communitynewspapergroup.com
Circulation:7,942fr; Sworn/Estimate/Non-Audited
Advertising: Open inch rate $7.30
Group: Community Media Group
Digital Platform - Mobile: Apple
Digital Platform - Tablet: Apple iOS
Pub. .... Deb Weigel
Adv. Mgr... Michael Izer
Anelia Dimitrova
Sports Ed... Pat Racette
Delivery Method: Mail
Zip Codes Served: 50677, 50602, 50619, 50622, 50636, 50647, 50666, 50668, 50670, 50674, 50676, 50658, 50645, 50613

WEST POINT

BONNY BUYER
(Wed)
403 Avenue D, West Point, IA, 52656-9391, USA; tel (319) 837-6232; fax (319) 837-6913; e-mail buyer@iowatelecom.net; bbclassifieds@gmail.com; web site www.bonnybuyer.net
Circulation:22,058fr; CVC
Advertising: Open inch rate $9.50
Group: Community Media Group
Pub. ....Lucinda Ward

KANSAS

ABILENE

CENTRAL MARKETPLACE
(Wed)
303 N Broadway St, Abilene, KS, 67410-2616, USA; tel (785) 263-1000; fax (785) 263-1645; e-mail publisher@abilene-rc.com; news@abilene-rc.com; web site www.abilene-rc.com
Circulation:5,300fr; Sworn/Estimate/Non-Audited
Advertising: Open inch rate $6.50
Adv. Mgr... Julie Patton
Circ. Mgr............................ Daniel Vandenburg
Ed. .... Dave Bergmeier
Sports Ed... Chris Orr
Mechanical Specifications: Type page 13 x 21 1/2; E - 6 cols, 2, between; A - 6 cols, 2, between; C - 6 cols, 2, between.
Equipment: Hardware — APP/Mac; Presses — G/Community; Software — Adobe/PageMaker 6.0, Claris/Works 4.0.
Zip Codes Served: 67410

ASHLAND

THE CLARK COUNTY CLIPPER
(Thur)
705 Main St, Ashland, KS, 67831, USA; tel (620) 635-2312; fax (620) 635-2643; e-mail minneola_record@hotmail.com
Circulation: 1,260pd,; Sworn/Estimate/Non-Audited
Advertising: Open inch rate $4.00
Ed. .... Amber Woodruff

CANEY

GOOD NEWS
(Wed)
124 N State St, Caney, KS, 67333-1334, USA; tel (620) 879-5460; fax (620) 879-2264; ed e-mail editor@goodnewspress.com; web site www.goodnewspress.com
Circulation:42,000fr; Sworn/Estimate/Non-Audited
Advertising: Open inch rate $15.96Editions: 6— 6 total; Bartlesville Good News (8,330); Caney/Sedan Good News (3,510); Coffeyville Good News (9,965); Independence Good News (7,690); Neodesha/Cherrydale Good News (4,885); Parsons Good News (7,409);
Adv. Dir... Penny Coy
Adv. Mgr.................................. Kirk Clinkscales
Circ. Mgr... Carol Powell
Ed. .... June Freisberg
Prodn. Mgr. .... Sherry Owen
Mechanical Specifications: Type page 10 1/8 x 14; E - 6 cols, 1 1/8, 1/8 between; A - 3 cols, 3 1/4, 1/8 between.
Equipment: Hardware — 20-APP/Mac; Software — Adobe/Photoshop 4.0, Adobe/PageMaker 6.5.
Zip Codes Served: 67333

CLAY CENTER

CLAY CENTER SAVER
(Tues)
805 5th St, Clay Center, KS, 67432-2502, USA; tel (785) 632-2127; fax (785) 632-6526; e-mail dispatch@claycenter.com
Circulation:4,012fr; Sworn/Estimate/Non-Audited
Advertising: Open inch rate $6.90
Pub. .... Harry E. Valentine

COLBY

COUNTRY ADVOCATE
(Wed)
155 W 5th St, Colby, KS, 67701-2312, USA; tel (785) 462-3963; adv tel (785) 462-3963; ed tel (785) 462-3963; fax (785) 462-7749; adv fax (785) 462-7749; e-mail colby.editor@nwkansas.com; adv e-mail sfriedlander@nwkansas.com; ed e-mail colby.editor@nwkansas.com; web site www.nwkansas.com
Circulation:25,000fr; Sworn/Estimate/Non-Audited
Advertising: Open inch rate $13.95
Established: 1932
Group: Haynes Publishing Co.
Pub. .... Sharon Friedlander
Sales/artist.............................. Kathryn Ballard
Circ. Mgr....................................... Sheila Smith
Mechanical Specifications: Type page 10 1/8 x 21 1/2; E - 6 cols, 2, 1/8 between; A -6 cols, 2, 1/8 between.
Equipment: Hardware — APP/Mac; Presses — HI
Delivery Method: Mail, Newsstand, Carrier, Racks
Zip Codes Served: 67700-99,80900-99

CONCORDIA

ADVERTISER
(Tues)
PO Box 309, Concordia, KS, 66901-0309, USA; tel (785) 243-2424; fax (785) 243-4407; e-mail bladeempire@nckn.com; web site www.bladeempire.com
Circulation:11,000fr; Sworn/Estimate/Non-Audited
Advertising: Open inch rate $8.20
Established: 1902
Group: Concordia Blade-Empire Publishing Co.
Digital Platform - Mobile: Apple
Digital Platform - Tablet: Apple iOS
Class. Adv. Mgr...................... Denise Lahodny
Ed. .... Brad Lowell
Prodn. Mgr. .... Jim Lowell
Advertising Mgr .... Lowell Jay
Equipment: Hardware — macs
ctp; Presses — 4 unit News King; Software — Creator
Delivery Method: Mail, Newsstand, Carrier, Racks
Zip Codes Served: 66901

DODGE CITY

THE SHOPPER'S WEEKLY
(Wed)
705 N 2nd Ave, Dodge City, KS, 67801-4410, USA; tel (620) 225-4151; fax (620) 225-4154
Circulation:23,000fr; Sworn/Estimate/Non-Audited
Advertising: Open inch rate $6.75
Adv. Mgr...................................... Darrel Adams
Prodn. Mgr. .... Edward O'Neal
Mechanical Specifications: Type page 10 x 12 3/4; A - 6 cols, 1 7/12, 1/6 between; C - 6 cols, 1 7/12, 1/6 between.
Equipment: Hardware — APP/Mac; Presses — G/Community; Software — Adobe/PageMaker.

EMPORIA

THE SHOPPER
(Tues)
718 Commercial St, Emporia, KS, 66801, USA; tel (620) 343-1303; fax (620) 343-9257
Circulation:20,855fr; Sworn/Estimate/Non-Audited
Advertising: Open inch rate $9.98
Established: 1972
Pub. .... Yvonne Pool
Mechanical Specifications: Type page 10 1/4 x 15; E - 6 cols, 1 9/16, 3/16 between; A - 6 cols, 1 7/12, 1/6 between; C - 6 cols, 1 7/12, 1/6 between.
Zip Codes Served: 66801, 66835, 66833, 66854, 66865, 66868, 66864, 66846, 66845, 66850, 66869, 66856, 66839, 66523, 66860, 66852, 66871, 66510

FORT SCOTT

COUNTRYSIDE
(Wed)
12 E Wall St, Fort Scott, KS, 66701-1423, USA; tel (620) 223-1460; fax (620) 233-1469; ed e-mail editor@fstribune.com
Circulation:5,900fr; Sworn/Estimate/Non-Audited
Advertising: Open inch rate $5.75
Pub. .... Julie Righter
Adv. Mgr...................................... Laurie Harter
Circ. Mgr..................................... Debbie Swaic
Ed. .... Scott Munuzum
Mechanical Specifications: Type page 11 3/8 x 13; E - 4 cols, 2 1/3, 1/3 between; A - 4 cols, 2 1/3, 1/3 between; C - 7 cols, 1 1/3, 1/3 between.
Equipment: Hardware — APP/Mac Power; Presses — G/Community; Software — Abbott Systems/Ready, Set, Go, QPS/QuarkXPress.

GARDEN CITY

SHOPMATE
(Tues)
310 N 7th St, Garden City, KS, 67846-5521, USA; tel (620) 275-8500; fax (620) 275-5165; adv e-mail advertising@gctelegram.com; web site www.gctelegram.com
Circulation:13,600fr; Sworn/Estimate/Non-Audited
Advertising: Open inch rate $9.26
Ed. .... Dena Sattler
Prodn. Mgr. .... Jerry Naab
Mechanical Specifications: Type page 13 1/4 x 21 1/2; E - 6 cols, 2 1/10, 1/6 between; A - 6 cols, 2 1/10, 1/6 between; C - 8 cols, 2 1/10, 1/6 between.
Equipment: ; Presses — G/Community.

HAYS

THE HAYS DAILY NEWS EXTRA
(Wed)
507 Main St, Hays, KS, 67601-4228, USA; tel (785) 628-1081; fax (785) 628-8186; adv e-mail advertising@dailynews.net; ed e-mail newsroom@dailynews.net; web site www.hdnews.net
Circulation:10,000fr; Sworn/Estimate/Non-Audited
Advertising: Open inch rate $5.00
Established: 1929
Group: GateHouse Media, Inc.

Adv. Dir. .... Mary Karst
Circ. Mgr. .... Robert Wiegel
Ed. .... Olaf Frandsen
Mechanical Specifications: Type page 10.2917 x 21 1/2; E - 6 cols, 1.6111 3/16 between; A - 6 cols, 1.6111, 3/16 between; C - 8 cols, 1.1892, 3/16 between.
Equipment: Hardware — APP/Mac; Presses — 10-G/Community; Software — QPS/QuarkXPress, Freedom, Multi-Ad/Creator. Indesign
Delivery Method: Mail, Carrier
Zip Codes Served: multiple

HUMBOLDT

HUMBOLDT UNION

909 Bridge St, Humboldt, KS, 66748-1833, USA; tel (620) 473-3801; fax (620) 473-3858

HUTCHINSON

THE BEE

(Thur)
300 W 2nd Ave, Hutchinson, KS, 67501-5211, USA; tel (620) 694-5700; fax (620) 662-4186; e-mail classifieds@hutchnews.com; adv e-mail advertising@hutchnews.com; ed e-mail newsrelease@hutchnews.com; web site http://www.hutchnews.com/the_buzz
Circulation: 8,800pd,10,200fr; Sworn/Estimate/Non-Audited
Advertising: Open inch rate $8.65
Group: GateHouse Media, Inc.Editions: 18,000—
Digital Platform - Mobile: Apple, Android, Windows, Blackberry
Digital Platform - Tablet: Apple iOS, Android, Windows 7, Blackberry Tablet OS, Kindle, Kindle Fire
Mkt Solutions Mgr. .... Anita Stuckey
Mechanical Specifications: Type page 10 1/2 x 21 1/2; E - 6 cols, 1 15/16, 3/16 between
Equipment: Hardware — 80-PC, 2-V/5300, 1-III/3850; Presses — Goss Urbanite; Software — Adobe/Illustrator 9.0, Adobe/Photoshop 6.0, Multi-Ad/Creator 3.8, QPS/QuarkXPress 4.0, Microsoft/Word 7.0.
Delivery Method: Newsstand, Carrier, Racks
Zip Codes Served: 67501, 67502, 67505, 67570 and 67561

IOLA

IOLA-REGISTER SHOPPER

(Tues)
302 S Washington Ave, Iola, KS, 66749-3255, USA; tel (620) 365-2111; fax (620) 365-6289; e-mail iolaregister@ir.kscoxmail.com; web site www.iolaregister.com
Circulation:9,850fr; Sworn/Estimate/Non-Audited
Advertising: Open inch rate $8.00
Adv. Mgr. .... Mark Hastings
Ed. .... Susan Lynn
Assoc. Ed. .... Emerson Lynn
Mechanical Specifications: Type page 13 x 21 1/2.
Equipment: Hardware — APP/Mac; Software — Multi-Ad/Creator II 4.0, QPS/QuarkXPress 4.1.

KANSAS CITY

WYANDOTTE COUNTY SHOPPER

(Wed)
7735 Washington Ave, Kansas City, KS, 66112-2444, USA; tel (913) 371-4300; fax (913) 342-8620; web site www.kckansan.com
Circulation:5,000fr; Sworn/Estimate/Non-Audited
Advertising: Open inch rate $8.85
Group: GateHouse Media, Inc.
Gen. Mgr. .... Drew Savage
Mechanical Specifications: Type page 13 x 21 1/2; E - 6 cols, 2 1/16, between; A - 6 cols, 2 1/16, between; C - 9 cols, 1 1/4, between.
Zip Codes Served: 66101

LEAVENWORTH

CHRONICLE SHOPPER

(Wed)
422 Seneca St, Leavenworth, KS, 66048-1910, USA; tel (913) 682-0305; fax (913) 682-1114; adv e-mail kfrey@leavenworthtimes.com; ed e-mail mrountree@leavenworthtimes.com; web site http://www.leavenworthtimes.com/
Circulation:20,840fr; Sworn/Estimate/Non-Audited
Advertising: Open inch rate $10.50
Established: 1903
Group: GateHouse Media, Inc.
Pub. .... Steve Curd
Mechanical Specifications: Type page 10 1/4 x 16; E - 5 cols, 2, between; A - 5 cols, 2, between; C - 5 cols, 2, between.
Zip Codes Served: 66048, 66043, 66027, 66020, 66007, 66086

CHRONICLE SHOPPER OF LEAVENWORTH

505 Cherokee St, Leavenworth, KS, 66048-2625, USA; tel (800) 521-1447

LIBERAL

SHOPPER'S WEEKLY

(Mon)
16 S Kansas Ave, Liberal, KS, 67901-3732, USA; tel (620) 624-2541; fax (620) 624-0735; web site www.swdtimes.com
Circulation:30,000fr; Sworn/Estimate/Non-Audited
Advertising: Open inch rate $9.50
Established: 1984
Pub. .... Larry Reynolds
Mechanical Specifications: Type page 9 3/4 x 12 1/2; A - 6 cols, 1 1/2, 1/8 between; C - 6 cols, 1 1/2, 1/8 between.
Equipment: Hardware — APP/Mac; Presses — Atlas/Web Leader with Quad; Software — QPS/QuarkXPress 4.0.
Zip Codes Served: 67905, 73942, 67950, 67951, 67864, 67870, 67877, 67880, 73932, 73444, 73450

MULVANE

BANDWAGON

(Tues)
204 W Main St, Mulvane, KS, 67110-1765, USA; tel (316) 777-4233
Circulation:5,600fr; Sworn/Estimate/Non-Audited
Advertising: Open inch rate $8.90
Adv. Mgr. .... Tracy Spencer
Ed. .... Michael Robinson
Mechanical Specifications: Type page 14 1/2 x 21 1/2; E - 6 cols, 2 1/4, between; A - 6 cols, between.
Zip Codes Served: 67110

NEWTON

BUYER'S EDGE OF SOUTH CENTRAL KANSAS

(Mthly)
706 N Main St, Newton, KS, 67114-1830, USA; tel (316) 281-7899; adv tel (316) 281-7899; ed tel (316) 281-7899; e-mail editor@harveycountynow.com; adv e-mail bruce@harveycountynow.com; ed e-mail editor@hillsborofreepress.com; web site www.buyersedgeks.com
Circulation:20,246fr; Sworn/Estimate/Non-Audited
Advertising: Open inch rate $11.50
Established: 2005
Group: Kansas Publishing Ventures
Digital Platform - Mobile: Apple, Android, Windows, Blackberry
Digital Platform - Tablet: Apple iOS, Android, Windows 7, Blackberry Tablet OS, Kindle, Nook, Kindle Fire
Founding Publisher .... Joel Klaassen
Ed. .... Don Ratzlaff
Adv. Mgr. .... Natalie Hoffman
Circ. Mgr. .... Nicole Suderman
Prod. Mgr. .... Kevin Hower
Marketing Dude (sales manager) .... Bruce Behymer
Owner and Publisher .... Joey Young
Mechanical Specifications: 6 col x 21
Equipment: Hardware — Mac; Software — Quark
CS5
FotoFusion
Delivery Method: Mail, Newsstand, Carrier, Racks
Zip Codes Served: 67114 TMC racked in many other locations

PRATT

SUNFLOWER SHOPPER'S GUIDE

(Wed)
320 S Main St, Pratt, KS, 67124-2706, USA; tel (620) 672-5511; fax (620) 672-5514; adv e-mail admanager@pratttribune.com; ed e-mail editor@pratttribune.com; web site www.pratttribune.com
Circulation:5,500fr; Sworn/Estimate/Non-Audited
Advertising: Open inch rate $7.00
Group: GateHouse Media, Inc.Editions: 1—
Publisher .... Randy Mitchell
Advertising Manager .... Lucas Wiegert
Mechanical Specifications: Type page 13 x 21; E - 6 cols, 2 1/16, 1/8 between; A - 6 cols, 2 1/16, 1/8 between; C - 6 cols, 2 1/16, 1/8 between.
Delivery Method: Carrier, Racks
Zip Codes Served: 67124

SALINA

BUYER'S GUIDE

(Wed)
1118 W Cloud St, Salina, KS, 67401-7063, USA; tel (785) 823-7290; fax (785) 823-3176; e-mail info@buyersguide4u.com; adv e-mail ads@guide.kscoxmail.com; web site www.buyersguide4u.com
Circulation:22,278fr; CVC
Advertising: Open inch rate $12.00
Established: 1970
General Manager .... Michelle Burton
Production .... Denise Goddard
Direct Mail .... Jim Furgison
Production .... Dawn Schnepf
Clerical .... Krystal Illingsworth
Direct Mail .... Dick Carpenter
Direct Mail .... Barb Fetter
Equipment: Hardware — PC / Macs; Software — InDesign CS4, Photoshop CS4, Illustrator CS3, Microsoft Office 10
Delivery Method: Mail, Newsstand, Carrier, Racks
Zip Codes Served: 674

WINFIELD

THE LEADER

(Mthly)
201 E 9th Ave, Winfield, KS, 67156-2817, USA; tel (620) 221-1050; fax (620) 221-1101; e-mail subscribe@winfieldcourier.com; adv e-mail classified@winfieldcourier.com; advertising@winfieldcourier.com; ed e-mail courier@winfieldcourier.com; web site www.winfieldcourier.com
Circulation:14,100fr; Sworn/Estimate/Non-Audited
Group: Seaton Group
Pub. .... Lloyd Craig
Adv. Dir. .... Marsha Wesseler
Circ. Mgr. .... Wes Townsley
Ed. .... Frederick D. Seaton
Mng. Ed. .... Roy Graber
Mechanical Specifications: Type page 10 x 13; A - 4 cols, 2 1/2, between; C - 4 cols, 2 1/2, between.
Equipment: Hardware — APP/Mac; Presses — G/Community; Software — Adobe/PageMaker, Multi-Ad/Creator.

KENTUCKY

BOWLING GREEN

COUNTRY PEDDLER

(Wed)
PO Box 492, Bowling Green, KY, 42102-0492, USA; web site www.countrypeddlerbg.com
Circulation:25,475fr; CVC
Advertising: Open inch rate $14.77 - $19.19
Established: 1971
Group: News PublishingBelinda Saltzman
Prod. Mgr. .... Trish Crawford

CARROLLTON

RIVER CITY TRADING POST

(Mon)
122 6th St, Carrollton, KY, 41008-1009, USA; tel (502) 732-4261; fax (502) 732-0453; adv e-mail demoads@bellsouth.net; circulation@mycarrollnews.com; web site www.mycarrollnews.com; www.lcni.com
Circulation:9,900fr; Sworn/Estimate/Non-Audited
Advertising: Open inch rate $9.18
Group: Landmark Communications, Inc.
Office Mgr. .... Doris Miller
Pub. .... Jeff Moore
Adv. Sales .... Deborah Garrett
Circ. Mgr. .... Carla Kidwell
Special Sections Ed. .... Phyllis McLaughlin
Asst. Ed. .... Joan Wright
Mechanical Specifications: Type page 10 x 14; E - 5 cols, 2, 1/8 between; A - 5 cols, between; C - 5 cols, between.
Zip Codes Served: 41008

CYNTHIANA

HARRISON SHOPPER

(Mon)
302 Webster Ave, Cynthiana, KY, 41031-1647, USA; tel (859) 234-1035; adv tel (859) 234-1035; fax (859) 234-8096; adv e-mail ads@cynthianademocrat.com; web site www.cynthianademocrat.com; www.theharrison-shopper.com
Circulation:16,050fr; USPS
Advertising: Open inch rate $11.79
Established: 1971
Group: Landmark Media Enterprises, LLC
Pub. .... George Jacobs
Adv. Mgr. .... Patricia Jenkins
Delivery Method: Mail, Carrier
Zip Codes Served: 41031,41010,41064,41040,41004,40348,40311,40370

EMINENCE

HENRY COUNTY LOCAL
(Mon)
1378 Eminence Rd, Eminence, KY, 40019, USA; tel (502) 845-2858; fax (502) 845-2921; web site www.hclocal.com
Circulation:7,146fr; Sworn/Estimate/Non-Audited
Advertising: Open inch rate $5.29
Gen. Mgr. .... Melissa Blankenship
Circ. Mgr. .... Marty DeWitt
Mechanical Specifications: Type page 13 x 21 1/2; E - 6 cols, 2, 1/6 between; A - 6 cols, 2, 1/6 between; C - 8 cols, 1 1/2, 1/6 between.
Equipment: Hardware — APP/Mac; Presses — G/Community; Software — QPS/QuarkXPress 3.32, Multi-Ad/Creator 4.0.
Zip Codes Served: 40050

FALMOUTH

THE SHOPPER'S OUTLOOK (FREE SHOPPER)
(Tues)
210 Main St, Falmouth, KY, 41040-1223, USA; tel (859) 654-3332; adv tel (859) 654-3333; fax (859) 654-4365; e-mail news@falmouthoutlook.com; adv e-mail ads@falmouthoutlook.com; ed e-mail news@falmouthoutlook.com; web site www.falmouthoutlook.com
Circulation: 9,209pd,9,096fr; USPS
Advertising: Open inch rate $19.56
Established: 1986
Group: Delphos Herald, Inc.Editions: 33— The Shopper's Outlook
Digital Platform - Mobile: Apple, Android, Windows, Blackberry, Other
Digital Platform - Tablet: Apple iOS, Android, Windows 7, Blackberry Tablet OS, Kindle, Nook, Kindle Fire, Other
News editor
Jackie Vaughn
Advertising and Graphics Coordinator ... Jessie Beckett
Publisher .... Neal Belcher
Typesetter .... Tammy Wessel
Receptionist/Bookkeeper .... Kathy Randolph
Mechanical Specifications: Type page 9.89 x 21.25
1 col- 1.56
2 col. 3.22
3 col 4.89
4 col 6.56
5 col. 8.22
6 col. 9.89
Equipment: Hardware — APP/Mac; Software — Microsoft/Word2010, Adobe/PhotoshopCS5 InDesign
Delivery Method: Mail, Newsstand
Zip Codes Served: 41040, 41006, 41043, 41033, 41001

FRANKFORT

BUYER'S GUIDE
(Wed)
1216 Wilkinson Blvd, Frankfort, KY, 40601-1243, USA; tel (502) 227-4556; fax (502) 227-2831; web site www.state-journal.com
Circulation:3,800fr; Sworn/Estimate/Non-Audited
Advertising: Open inch rate $11.50
Group: Frankfort Publishing Co.
Pub. .... Ann Dix Maenza
Adv. Dir. .... Lloyd Lynch
Ed. .... Carleton L. West
Mechanical Specifications: Type page 10 x 13; E - 5 cols, 1 13/16, 1/4 between; A - 5 cols, 1 13/16, 1/4 between; C - 6 cols, 1 1/2, 1/4 between.

FULTON

FULTON SHOPPER
(Wed)
304 E State Line St, Fulton, KY, 42041-1600, USA; tel (270) 472-1121; fax (270) 472-1129; e-mail leadernews@bellsouth.net; adv e-mail leaderads@bellsouth.net
Circulation:9,000fr; Sworn/Estimate/Non-Audited
Advertising: Open inch rate $9.00
Pub. .... Dennis Richardson
Mechanical Specifications: Type page 13 x 21 1/2; E - 6 cols, 2, 1/5 between; A - 6 cols, 2, 1/5 between; C - 6 cols, 2, 1/5 between.
Zip Codes Served: 42041, 38257, 42050, 42031, 42085, 42088, 42070, 42032, 42021, 38261, 38271, 38237, 38226

GEORGETOWN

THE SCOTT SHOPPER
(Tues)
1481 Cherry Blossom Way, Georgetown, KY, 40324-8953, USA; tel (502) 863-1111; fax (502) 863-6296; e-mail news@news-graphic.com; adv e-mail advertising@news-graphic.com; web site www.news-graphic.com
Circulation:15,700fr; Sworn/Estimate/Non-Audited
Advertising: Open inch rate $10.00
Pres./Pub. .... Mike Scogin
Adv. Dir. .... Sabra Oller
Ed. .... Andrea Giusti
Prodn. Mgr. .... Paula Willis

LA GRANGE

MARKETPLACE
(Mon)
204 S 1st Ave, La Grange, KY, 40031-1204, USA; tel (502) 222-7183; adv tel (877) 822-4237; fax (502) 222-7194; e-mail oldhamnews@ntr.net; news@oldhamera.com; generalmanager@oldhamera.com; ed e-mail editor@oldhamera.com; circulation@oldhamera.com; web site www.oldhamera.com
Circulation:27,500fr; Sworn/Estimate/Non-Audited
Advertising: Open inch rate $9.73
Group: Landmark Communications, Inc.
Gen. Mgr. .... Melissa Blankenship
Circ. Mgr. .... Mabel Parrish
Ed. .... Jacquelyn Stoess-Hack
Equipment: ; Presses — WPC/Web Leader; Software — Multi-Ad/Creator, QPS/QuarkXPress 3.2.
Zip Codes Served: 40031, 40068, 40055, 40070, 40006, 40245, 40014, 40045, 40026, 40059, 40077, 40010, 40241

MAYSVILLE

THE ADVERTISER
(Mon)
120 Limestone St, Maysville, KY, 41056-1284, USA; tel (606) 564-9091; fax (606) 564-6893; web site www.maysville-online.com
Circulation:22,839fr; CVC
Advertising: Open inch rate $13.12
Established: 1972
Pub. .... Robert L. Hendrickson
Adv. Mgr. .... Patty Moore
Circ. Mgr. .... Marsha Fritz
Mng. Ed. .... Mary Ann Kearns
News Ed. .... Marla Toncray
Zip Codes Served: 41056

MIDDLESBORO

CUMBERLAND TRADING POST
(Thur)
120 N 11th St, Middlesboro, KY, 40965-1024, USA; tel (606) 248-1010; fax (606) 248-7614; adv e-mail advertising@middlesborodailynews.com; ed e-mail editor@middlesborodailynews.com; sports@middlesborodailynews.com; web site www.cumberlandtradingpost.com; www.middlesborodailynews.com
Circulation:14,000fr; Sworn/Estimate/Non-Audited
Advertising: Open inch rate $6.12
Pub. .... Cynthia Orr
Adv. Mgr. .... Pat Cheek
Mng. Ed. .... Brandy Calvert
Circ. Mgr. .... Lisa Gray
Correspondent .... C.J. Harte
Sports Ed. .... Jay Compton
Lifestyle Ed. .... Donna Greene

MOREHEAD

SHOPPING NEWS
(Thur)
722 W 1st St, Morehead, KY, 40351-1404, USA; tel (606) 784-4116; fax (606) 784-7337; web site www.themoreheadnews.com
Circulation:20,566fr; Sworn/Estimate/Non-Audited
Advertising: Open inch rate $8.90
Pub. .... Rob McCullough
Adv. Mgr. .... Dan Duncan
Mng. Ed. .... Stephanie Ockerman

MOUNT STERLING

THE ADVERTISER
(Mon)
219 Midland Trl, Mount Sterling, KY, 40353-9070, USA; tel (859) 498-2222; fax (859) 498-2228; adv e-mail advertising@msadvocate.com; ed e-mail news@msadvocate.com; sports@msadvocate.com; classified@msadvocate.com; web site www.msadvocate.com
Circulation:19,968fr; Sworn/Estimate/Non-Audited
Advertising: Open inch rate $8.45
Pub. .... Matt Hall
Adv. Mgr. .... Sharon Manning
Equipment: Hardware — APP/Mac; Presses — G/Community; Software — Adobe/PageMaker 6.5, QPS/QuarkXPress 4.0.
Zip Codes Served: 40353

OWENSBORO

THRIFTY NICKEL - OWENSBORO
(Thur)
629 E 21st St, Owensboro, KY, 42303-3814, USA; web site www.americanclassifieds.com
Circulation:16,087fr; Sworn/Estimate/Non-AuditedJohnna O'Bryan

PARIS

THE CITIZEN-ADVERTISER
(Mon)
123 W 8th St, Paris, KY, 40361-1343, USA; tel (859) 987-1870; fax (859) 987-3729; e-mail citadinc@bellsouth.net
Circulation:10,815fr; Sworn/Estimate/Non-Audited
Advertising: Open inch rate $6.65
Adv. Mgr. .... Beverly Brannon
Ed. .... James Brannon
Prodn. Mgr. .... Rebecca Lawyer
Mechanical Specifications: Type page 13 x 21; E - 6 cols, 2, between; A - 6 cols, between.
Zip Codes Served: 40361

PIKEVILLE

THE MOUNTAIN BARGAIN HUNTER
(Fri)
129 Caroline Ave, Pikeville, KY, 41501-1101, USA; tel (606) 437-4054; fax (606) 437-4246; ed e-mail sports@news-expressky.com; web site www.news-expressky.com
Circulation:23,000fr; Sworn/Estimate/Non-Audited
Advertising: Open inch rate $4.25
Pub. .... Jeff Vanderbeck
Adv. Dir. .... Mike Davis
Circ. Mgr. .... Lisa Moore
Ed. .... Jerry Boggs
Sports Ed. .... Randy White
Prodn. Mgr. .... Tina Gayheart

SHELBYVILLE

SENTINEL NEWS PLUS
(Mon)
703 Taylorsville Rd, Shelbyville, KY, 40065-9125, USA; tel (502) 633-2526; fax (502) 633-2618; web site www.sentinelnews.com
Circulation:19,232fr; Sworn/Estimate/Non-Audited
Advertising: Open inch rate $13.40
Group: Landmark Communications, Inc.
Landmark Community Newspapers, LLC
Pub. .... Kerry Johnson
Adv. Mgr. .... Neal Kimbell
Adv. Mgr. .... Dan Barry
Classified Adv. .... Vanessa Riddell
Ed. .... Steve Doyle
Sports Ed. .... Laura Clark
Webmaster .... Todd Stephenson
Mechanical Specifications: Type page 11 5/8 x 21 1/2; E - 6 cols, 1 5/6, 1/8 between; A - 6 cols, 1 5/6, 1/8 between; C - 8 cols, between.
Zip Codes Served: 40066

SHEPHERDSVILLE

PIONEER NEWS
(Mon, Wed)
455 N Buckman St, Shepherdsville, KY, 40165-5902, USA; tel (502) 543-2288; fax (502) 955-9704; e-mail editor@pioneernews.net; adv e-mail editor@pioneernews.net; ed e-mail editor@pioneernews.net; subscriptions@pioneernews.net; web site www.pioneernews.net
Circulation: 7,000pd,23,000fr; Sworn/Estimate/Non-Audited
Advertising: Open inch rate $13.46
Adv. Sales Rep. .... Nancy Gray
Adv. Sales Rep. .... Laura Felts
Ed. .... Thomas J. Barr
Sports Ed. .... Mike Farner
Mechanical Specifications: Type page 13 x 21 1/2; E - 6 cols, 2 1/16, between; A - 6 cols, 2 1/16, between; C - 8 cols, 1 1/2, between.
Equipment: Hardware — APP/Mac; Presses — KP; Software — Microsoft/Word.
Delivery Method: Mail
Zip Codes Served: 40165, 40229, 40047, 40150,

LOUISIANA

ALEXANDRIA

AMERICAN CLASSIFIEDS - ALEXANDRIA
(Thur)
2052 Rapides Ave, Alexandria, LA, 71301-6635, USA; web site www.americanclassifieds.com
Circulation: 0pd,25,105fr; CVC
Advertising: Open inch rate $20.00

Established: 1983
Group: American Classifieds (OOB)Orkke Clifton
Circ. Mgr. .... Dan Smith
Prod. Mgr. .... Kathy Gardner

BREAUX BRIDGE

BREAUX BRIDGE MARKETPLACE
1011 Berard St, Breaux Bridge, LA, 70517-4810, USA; tel (337) 332-1621

COUSHATTA

COUSHATTA CITIZEN SHOPPER
(Thur)
1904 Ringgold Ave, Coushatta, LA, 71019-9089, USA; tel (318) 932-4201; fax (888) 820-4160; e-mail news@coushattacitizen.com; adv e-mail news@coushattacitizen.com; ed e-mail news@coushattacitizen.com
Circulation: 3,200pd,3,900fr; Sworn/Estimate/Non-Audited
Advertising: Open inch rate $4.73
Established: 1871
Group: Natchitoches Times Newspapers
Ed/Adv Rep .... Bruce Watkins
Pub. .... Lovan Thomas
Adv. Mgr. .... Jennifer Moseley
Ed. .... Mary James
Mechanical Specifications: Type page 12 x 21; E - 6 cols, 2 1/3, between; A - 6 cols, 2 1/3, between.
Equipment: Hardware — APP/Mac.
Delivery Method: Mail
Zip Codes Served: 71019

HOMER

ADVERTISER
(Tues)
604 N Main St, Homer, LA, 71040-3806, USA; tel (318) 927-3721; fax (318) 927-3721; web site 1990
Circulation:8,233fr; Sworn/Estimate/Non-Audited
Advertising: Open inch rate $5.35
Established: 1924
Group: Natchitoches Times Newspapers
Ed. .... Jackie Roberts
Mechanical Specifications: 6 Columns Per Page, 21 Inches Deep,
1 Pica between columns.

1 column	12.5 picas	..........2-in.
2 columns	25.5 picas	4.25 in.
3 columns	39.0 picas	6.45 in.
4 columns	52.0 picas	8.66 in.
5 columns	65.0 picas	10.75 in.
6 columns	78.0 picas	13 in.

Delivery Method: Mail, Racks
Zip Codes Served: 71040, 71038, 71003, 71079, 71048, 71072 and 71740.

HOUMA

THE WEEKLY WANT ADS
(Thur)
6160 W Park Ave, Houma, LA, 70364-1700, USA; web site www.houmaweekly.com
Circulation:25,701fr; CVC
Advertising: $63.00 (smallest modular rate)
Established: 1987
Pub. .... Brian Rushing
Adv. Mgr. .... Marian Long
Circ. Mgr .... Brooke Adams
Prod. Mgr .... Gavin Stevens
Mechanical Specifications: Type page 10.25" x 13.75"; 7 cols
Delivery Method: Mail, Racks

LAFAYETTE

QUIK QUARTER CLASSIFIEDS - ACADIANA
(Thur)
1100 Bertrand Dr, Lafayette, LA, 70506-4110, USA; web site www.QQclassifieds.com
Circulation:40,975fr; CVCANGIE SAVOIE

QUIK QUARTER CLASSIFIEDS - TECHE
(Thur)
1100 Bertrand Dr, Lafayette, LA, 70506-4110, USA; web site www.QQclassifieds.com
Circulation:19,230fr; CVCANGIE SAVOIE

RAYNE

TRIBUNE PLUS
(Wed)
108 N Adams Ave, Rayne, LA, 70578-5918, USA; tel (337) 334-3186; fax (337) 334-8474; e-mail raynenews@cox-internet.com
Circulation:5,703fr; Sworn/Estimate/Non-Audited
Advertising: Open inch rate $6.60
Pub. .... Milo Nickel
Adv. Mgr. .... Josie Henry
Mng. Ed. .... Paul Kedinger
Zip Codes Served: 70578

SHREVEPORT

AMERICAN CLASSIFIEDS - SHREVEPORT
(Thur)
5910 Hearne Ave, Shreveport, LA, 71108-3802, USA; web site www.americanclassifieds.com
Circulation:45,698fr; CVC
Advertising: Open inch rate $8.00
Established: 1982Michael Ledet
Mechanical Specifications: Type page 10" x 17.25"; 8 cols
Delivery Method: Mail, Racks

SLIDELL

BARGAINS PLUS!
(Thur)
155 Robert St, Slidell, LA, 70458-3647, USA; tel (985) 649-9515; adv tel (985) 649-1007; fax (985) 649-9518; e-mail bargainsplus-now@gmail.com; adv e-mail bargains@bellsouth.net; ed e-mail mrcartoonmap@gmail.com; web site www.bargainsplusnow.com
Circulation:22,275fr; CVC
Advertising: Open inch rate $15.00
Established: 1991
Pub. .... Tony Onellion
Delivery Method: Racks

SULPHUR

FORT FOLK GUARDIAN
(Fri)
714 E Napoleon St, Sulphur, LA, 70663-3402, USA; tel (337) 527-7075; fax (337) 527-7059; e-mail swdailyadvertising@yahoo.com; web site www.sulphurdailynews.com
Circulation:13,000fr; Sworn/Estimate/Non-Audited
Advertising: Open inch rate $14.75
Group: GateHouse Media, Inc.
Pub. .... Suzzane Paveto

MAINE

PORTLAND

SAVING SOURCE
(Fri)
390 Congress St, Portland, ME, 04101-3514, USA; tel (207) 791-6650; adv tel (207) 791-6100; fax (207) 791-6920; e-mail communitynews@pressherald.com; web site www.pressherald.com
Circulation:140,000fr; Sworn/Estimate/Non-Audited
Pub. .... Richard L. Connor
Adv. Mgr. .... Michelle Lester
Exec. Ed. .... Scott Wasser
Mechanical Specifications: Type page 13 x 20 3/4.

MARYLAND

ABERDEEN

THE BARGAINER
(Mon)
214 W Bel Air Ave, Aberdeen, MD, 21001-2421, USA; tel (410) 642-2233; adv tel (410) 398-3311; fax (410) 272-4208; web site www.thebargaineeronline.com
Circulation:37,000fr; Sworn/Estimate/Non-Audited
Advertising: Open inch rate $43.00
Group: Adams Publishing Group, LLC
Gen. Mgr. .... Todd Frederick
Adv. Mgr. .... Harry Porter
Mechanical Specifications: Type page 10 1/4 x 13 1/2; A - 6 cols, 1 1/2, between.
Equipment: Hardware — IBM/PC, APP/Mac.
Zip Codes Served: 21001

GERMANTOWN

THE MERCHANDISER MAGAZINE
(Mthly)
12900 Cloverleaf Center Dr, Ste A, Germantown, MD, 20874-9177, USA; tel (240) 912-3200; adv tel (800) 936-6121; fax (240) 686-1340; e-mail support@merchmag.com.com; adv e-mail adexperts@merchmag.com; web site www.merchmag.com
Circulation:1,122,000fr; USPS
Established: 1982Editions: 48—
CEO/Publisher .... Matthew L. Griswold
Mechanical Specifications: Type page 9 3/4 x 11 3/4; E - 2 cols, between; A - 2 cols, between.
Equipment: Hardware — 25-APP/Mac G4, APP/Mac G5; Presses — None; Software — Adobe/Indesign 6.0.
Delivery Method: Mail
Zip Codes Served: Washington DC MSA

HAGERSTOWN

HERALD-MAIL EXPRESS
(Wed)
100 Summit Ave, Hagerstown, MD, 21740-5509, USA; tel (301) 733-5123; fax (301) 739-7518; e-mail news@herald-mail.com; ed e-mail lifestyle@herald-mail.com; web site www.herald-mail.com
Circulation:27,000fr; Sworn/Estimate/Non-Audited
Advertising: Open inch rate $9.00
Group: Schurz Communications Inc
Circ. Dir. .... Brian Tedrick
Exec. Ed. .... Jake Womer
Ed. .... John League
Opns. Dir. .... Brian Sease
Zip Codes Served: 21740

HANOVER

MARYLAND PENNYSAVER
(Wed)
1342 Charwood Rd, Hanover, MD, 21076-3113, USA; web site www.pennysaverwired.com
Circulation:840,992fr; CVCChris Shertzer

WESTMINSTER

MASON-DIXON MARKETPLACE
(Wed)
201 Railroad Ave, Westminster, MD, 21157-4823, USA; tel (410) 848-4400; fax (410) 857-1176
Circulation:39,000fr; Sworn/Estimate/Non-Audited
Advertising: Open inch rate $7.55
Group: Landmark Communications, Inc.
Pub. .... Patricia Richardson
Advertising Director .... Erin Hahn
Zip Codes Served: 21157

MASSACHUSETTS

BOSTON

CITY SHOPPER
(Wed) (Weekly)
160 Commonwealth Ave, Boston, MA, 02116-2707, USA; tel (617) 262-2489; fax (617) 424-9227; e-mail production@cityshopperonline.com; web site www.cityshopperonline.com
Circulation:40,000fr; Sworn/Estimate/Non-Audited
Advertising: Open inch rate $70.00
Office Mgr. .... Ann Marie LeMiere
Adv. Mgr. .... Barry N. Franklin
Art Dir. .... Raymond Sin
Adv. Sales .... Linita Droster
Brad Hinrichs
Mechanical Specifications: Type page 7 1/2 x 10; A - 2 cols, between; C - 2 cols, between.
Delivery Method: Carrier, Racks

CLINTON

ITEM EXTRA
(Fri)
156 Church St, Clinton, MA, 01510-2563, USA; tel (978) 368-0176; fax (978) 368-1151
Circulation:6,100fr; Sworn/Estimate/Non-Audited
Advertising: Open inch rate $11.50
Pub. .... Gary Hutner
Adv. Mgr. .... Ronald Chapdelaine
Mechanical Specifications: Type page 11 5/8 x 21; E - 6 cols, 2 1/16, 1/8 between; A - 6 cols, 2 1/16, 1/8 between.
Zip Codes Served: 1510

CONCORD

ACTION UNLIMITED
(Sat)
100 Domino Dr, # 1, Concord, MA, 01742-2817, USA; web site www.actionunlimited.com
Circulation:103,892fr; CVC

Advertising: $12.00-$60.00
Publisher.....Carol Toomey
Adv. Mgr.....Pam Kaplan
Circ. Mgr.....Joe Toomey
Prod. Mgr.....Karl Meyer

FALL RIVER

CLASSIFIED PLUS
(Fri)
207 Pocasset St, Fall River, MA, 02721-1532, USA; tel (508) 676-8211; fax (508) 676-2588; e-mail news@heraldnews.com; web site www.heraldnews.com
Circulation:5,000fr; Sworn/Estimate/Non-Audited
Advertising: Open inch rate $8.25
Group: GateHouse Media, Inc.
Pub.....Dan Goodrich
Adv. Mgr.....Doug Palmacci
Circ. Mgr.....John Rose
Ed.....Karen Hupp
Mng. Ed.....Lisa Herren
Prodn. Mgr.....Michael Niland
Mechanical Specifications: Type page 10 1/2 x 12; C - 7 cols, 1 7/16, 1/4 between.
Equipment: Hardware — IBM/PC, APP/Mac, MON; Presses — G/Urbanite; Software — Dewar/View, Multi-Ad/Creator, INSI, QPS/QuarkXPress, Adobe/Photoshop.
Zip Codes Served: 2722

FALMOUTH

CAPE COD SHOPPER
50 Depot Ave, Falmouth, MA, 02540-2302, USA; tel (508) 548-4700; fax (508) 540-8407
Ed.....Pamela Kokmeyer
Ad. Director.....Sean Randall

GREAT BARRINGTON

SHOPPER'S GUIDE
(Wed)
141 West Ave, Great Barrington, MA, 01230-1811, USA; tel (413) 528-0095; adv tel (413) 528-0095; ed tel (413) 528-0095; fax (413) 528-4805; e-mail andy@shoppersguideinc.com; adv e-mail andy@shoppersguideinc.com; ed e-mail andy@shoppersguideinc.com; web site www.shoppersguide-inc.com
Circulation:24,000fr; Sworn/Estimate/Non-Audited
Advertising: Open inch rate $9.00
Established: 1968
Digital Platform - Mobile: Apple, Android, Windows
Digital Platform - Tablet: Apple iOS, Android, Kindle, Kindle Fire
Pub.....Eunice Raifstanger
Gen. Mgr.....Robin Hare
Marketing and Sales.....Andrew Hare
Mechanical Specifications: Type page 10 3/8 x 16; A - 6 cols, 1 5/8, between.
Equipment: Hardware — IBM; Software — Adobe
Delivery Method: Mail, Racks
Zip Codes Served: 1230

PALMER

BUY LINE
(Fri)
24 Water St, Palmer, MA, 01069-1885, USA; tel (413) 967-3505; fax (413) 289-1977; adv e-mail ads@turley.com; web site www.turley.com
Circulation:22,000fr; Sworn/Estimate/Non-Audited
Advertising: Open inch rate $11.00
Pub.....Patrick H. Turley
Adv. Mgr.....Beth Baker
Zip Codes Served: 1082

SHOPPING GUIDE
(Tues)
24 Water St, Palmer, MA, 01069-1885, USA; tel (413) 283-8393; adv tel (800) 824-6548; fax (413) 289-1977; adv e-mail ads@turley.com; web site www.turley.com
Circulation:12,794fr; Sworn/Estimate/Non-Audited
Advertising: Open inch rate $10.50
Group: Turley Publications, Inc.
Pub.....Patrick H. Turley
Adv. Mgr.....Beth Baker
Zip Codes Served: 1069

WEBSTER

SMART SHOPPER
(Wed)
75B Main St, Webster, MA, 01570-2206, USA; web site www.smartshopperad.com
Circulation:21,720fr; CVCCheri MacKinney

THE YANKEE XPRESS
(Fri, Mthly) (Four times a month)
168 Gore Rd, Webster, MA, 01570-6814, USA; tel (508) 943-8784; adv tel (508) 943-8784; fax (508) 943-8129; adv fax (508) 943-8129; e-mail news@theyankeexpress.com; adv e-mail ads@theyankeexpress.com; ed e-mail news@theyankeexpress.com; web site www.theankeexpress.com
Circulation:68,510fr; Sworn/Estimate/Non-Audited
Advertising: Open inch rate $10.00
Established: 1975Editions: 4— TheYankeeXpress-SouthCounty, 21,722; TheYankeeXpressRoutes 12-20, 19,773; BlackstoneValleyXpress-South edition 18,935; BlackstoneValleyXpress-North edition 21,288
Digital Platform - Mobile: Apple, Android, Windows
Digital Platform - Tablet: Apple iOS, Android, Windows 7
Publisher.....Barbara Van Reed
Production Manager.....Sally Patterson
Mechanical Specifications: Tabloid, page size 11" wide by 15" high.
Delivery Method: Mail, Racks
Zip Codes Served: 01501, 01507, 01508, 01509, 01516, 01519, 01525, 01526, 01527, 01534, 01536, 01537, 01538, 01540, 01560, 01568, 01569, 01570, 01571, 01588, 01590, 01756
Note: We publish four times a month, each week mailed to a different group of towns, with some overlap (Webster and Oxford).

WESTBOROUGH

HEADLINERS
(Fri)
27 Otis St, Westborough, MA, 01581-3349, USA; tel (508) 871-1900; fax (508) 871-1998
Circulation:1,200,000fr; Sworn/Estimate/Non-Audited
Zip Codes Served: 1843

WESTFIELD

PENNYSAVER
(Sun)
62 School St, Westfield, MA, 01085-2835, USA; tel (413) 562-4181; adv e-mail sales@thewestfieldnewsgroup.com; web site www.thewestfieldnews.com
Circulation:30,000fr; Sworn/Estimate/Non-Audited
Advertising: Open inch rate $19.00
Group: The Westfield News Group LLC
Digital Platform - Mobile: Apple, Android, Windows, Blackberry
Digital Platform - Tablet: Apple iOS, Android, Windows 7, Blackberry Tablet OS, Kindle, Nook, Kindle Fire
President/Owner.....Patrick Berry
Delivery Method: Newsstand, Carrier
Zip Codes Served: 01085, 01077, 01030, 01001, 01089, 01034, 01008, 01073, 01060, 01027, 01013, 01020, 01040, 06035, 06070, 06078, 01103, 01104, 01105, 01108

MICHIGAN

ADRIAN

ACCESS SHOPPERS' GUIDE
(Mon)
133 N Winter St, Adrian, MI, 49221-2042, USA; tel (517) 265-5111; adv tel (517) 265-5111; ed tel (517) 265-5111; fax (517) 265-3030; adv fax (517) 265-3030; ed fax (517) 263-4132; e-mail customerservice@accessshoppersguide.com; adv e-mail kinclan@telegramadvertising.com; web site www.accessshoppersguide.com
Circulation:22,046fr; CVC
Advertising: Open inch rate $13.25
Established: 1977
Group: GateHouse Media, Inc.
Digital Platform - Mobile: Apple, Android, Windows, Blackberry
Digital Platform - Tablet: Apple iOS, Android, Windows 7, Blackberry Tablet OS, Kindle, Nook, Kindle Fire
President and Publisher.....Rob Young
Mechanical Specifications: Type page 10.25" x 11"; 8 cols
Equipment: ; Presses — Goss Community - Tensor and Monograph 4-High
Delivery Method: Mail, Carrier, Racks
Zip Codes Served: 49220, 49221, 49228, 49229, 49230, 49235, 49236, 49238, 49,247, 49248, 43533, 49253, 49256, 49265, 49256, 49268, 49271, 49276, 49279, 49286, 49287, 49289

ALLEGAN

FLASHES PUBLISHERS
(Sun)
595 Jenner Dr, Allegan, MI, 49010-1516, USA; tel (269) 673-1658; adv tel (616) 672-2141; fax (269) 673-4761; e-mail ; adv e-mail clarissa.mcdonald@flashespublishers.com; web site www.flashespublishers.com
Circulation:52,500fr; Sworn/Estimate/Non-Audited
Advertising: Open inch rate $32 for all 5 publications
Established: 1934
Group: GateHouse Media, Inc.Editions: 5— 5 total - Allegan Flashes Shopping Guide (16,010); MyLakeshore (7520), MyZeeland (10,720), Holland North (9220), Holland South (8955)
Prodn. Mgr.....Gerard Raab
Mechanical Specifications:
Equipment: Hardware — AG/Imagesetter, APP/Mac Network; Presses — G/Community, DEV/Horizon; Software — QPS/QuarkXPress, Adobe/Photoshop, Adobe/PageMaker, Adobe/Illustrator.
Delivery Method: Carrier
Zip Codes Served: 49010, 49055, 49328, 49344, 49311, 49348, 49450, 39408, 49453, 49406, 49419, 49408, 49090, 49423, 49424, 49464

ALMA

ALMA REMINDER
(Sun)
311 E Superior St, Alma, MI, 48801-1832, USA; tel (989) 463-6071; fax (989) 463-3338; web site www.morningstarpublishing.com
Circulation:17,470fr; CVC
Advertising: Open inch rate $6.30-19.00
Established: 1950
Director of Sales & Marketing.....Tammy Fisher
Pub.....Jim O'Rourke
Circ. Mgr.....Christine Fox
Prod. Mgr.....Ron Martin
Mechanical Specifications: Type page: 9.75 x 16; 6 col
Delivery Method: Carrier
Zip Codes Served: 48801, 48847, 48880, 48877, 48806, 48811, 48807, 48832, 48856, 48871, 48875, 48883, 48889, 48891, 48862

MID MICHIGAN BUYER'S GUIDE
(Sun)
311 E Superior St, Alma, MI, 48801-1832, USA; tel (989) 779-6000
Circulation: 0pd,64,720fr; Sworn/Estimate/Non-Audited
Advertising: Open inch rate $16.25
Group: Digital First Media
Advertising Sales Manager.....Tammy Fisher
Adv. Mgr.....Bettie Watson
Ed.....Kathy Palon
Equipment: Hardware — PC; Software — Mk/Newscrafters.
Delivery Method: Carrier
Zip Codes Served: 48612, 48615, 48617, 48618, 48622, 48624, 48625, 48629, 48630, 48632, 48651, 48653, 48656, 48662, 48801, 48806, 48807, 48811, 48818, 48832, 48847, 48856, 48858, 48871, 48877, 48878, 48880, 48883, 48889, 48891, 48893, 49310, 49340, 49667

THE EDMORE ADVERTISER
(Sun)
311 E Superior St, Alma, MI, 48801-1832, USA; tel (989) 463-6071; fax (989) 463-3338; web site www.michigannewspapers.net
Circulation:11,495fr; Sworn/Estimate/Non-Audited
Advertising: Open inch rate $8.60
Pub.....Al Frattura
Gen. Mgr.....Tammi Fischer
Mechanical Specifications: Type page 9 3/4 x 16; A - 6 cols, 1 1/2, 1/8 between; C - 6 cols, 1 1/2, 1/8 between.
Equipment: Hardware — APP/Macs; Presses — 14-G/Community; Software — QPS/QuarkXPress.
Zip Codes Served: 49305, 49310, 49320, 49322, 48829, 48632, 48620, 49338, 49336, 49340, 48877, 49342, 48886, 48888, 49346, 49347, 48891, 48893

ALPENA

ALPENA STAR
(Sun)
431 N Ripley Blvd, Alpena, MI, 49707-3014, USA; tel (989) 356-2121; fax (989) 354-8275; web site www.morningstarpublishing.com
Circulation:24,564fr; CVC
Advertising: Open inch rate $6.30-19.00
Established: 1950
Group: Digital First Media
Adv. Mgr.....Tom Greene
Adv. Mgr.....Rebecca Saddler
Prodn. Mgr.....Jerry Stahl
Pub.....Jim O'Rourke
Adv. Mgr.....Tammy Fisher
Circ. Mgr.....Christine Fox
Prod. Mgr.....Ron Martin
Mechanical Specifications: Type page 9 3/4 x 16; A - 6 cols, 1 5/8, 1/8 between; C - 6 cols, 1 5/8, 1/8 between.
Equipment: Hardware — APP/Mac, PC; Presses — 9-G/Community; Software — QPS/QuarkXPress.
Zip Codes Served: 49735, 48721, 48740, 48742, 48762, 49707, 49744, 49746, 49747, 49753, 49766, 49776

PRESQUE ISLE STAR
(Sun)
431 N Ripley Blvd, Alpena, MI, 49707-3014, USA; tel (989) 356-2121; fax (989) 354-8275; e-mail alpena@michigannewspapers.com; web site www.morningstarpublishing.com
Circulation:5,607fr; CVC

Advertising: Open inch rate $6.30
Established: 1950
Gen. Mgr. ....Tom Greene
Mechanical Specifications: Type page 9 3/4 x 16; A - 6 cols, 1 5/8, 1/8 between; C - 6 cols, 1 5/8, 1/8 between.
Equipment: Hardware — APP/Mac, PC; Presses — 9-G/Community; Software — QPS/QuarkXPress.

BANGOR

REMINDER SHOPPING GUIDE
(Sun)
416 Railroad St, Bangor, MI, 49013-1366, USA; tel (269) 427-7474; fax (269) 427-5286; e-mail reminder@lotusnet.com
Circulation: 11pd,13,193fr; Sworn/Estimate/Non-Audited
Advertising: Open inch rate $7.50
Pub. ....Kim Montoy
Mechanical Specifications: Type page 10 19/100 x 16.

BATTLE CREEK

BATTLE CREEK SHOPPER NEWS
(Thur)
1001 Columbia Ave E, Battle Creek, MI, 49014-4401, USA; tel (269) 965-3955; adv tel (269) 965-3955; ed tel (269) 965-3955; fax (269) 968-8586; adv fax (269) 968-8586; ed fax (269) 968-8586; e-mail Shopperads@J-adgraphics.com; adv e-mail shopperads@j-adgraphics.com; ed e-mail shopper@j-adgraphics.com; web site www.thebattlecreekshopper.com
Circulation: 28pd,48,047fr; CVC
Advertising: Open inch rate $12.30
Established: 1967
Group: J-Ad GraphicsEditions: 1— 8 other sister publications
Digital Platform - Mobile: Android
Digital Platform - Tablet: Apple iOS
Pub. ....Fred Jacobs
Adv. Mgr. ....Donna Hazel
Circ. Mgr....................................Marlene Adkins
Ed. ....Shelley Sulser
Mechanical Specifications: Type page 10 1/2 x 16; 6 cols
Equipment: Hardware — APP/Mac, COM, Mk; Presses — 17-units Heidelbery Mercury; Software — QPS/QuarkXPress, Adobe/Photoshop, Mk, Baseview/Class Act.
Delivery Method: Carrier
Zip Codes Served: 49011, 49012, 49015, 49017, 49020, 49033, 49034, 49051, 49053, 49094

BIG RAPIDS

PIONEER EAST SHOPPER
(Mon)
115 N Michigan Ave, Big Rapids, MI, 49307-1401, USA; web site www.pioneergroup.com
Circulation:6,469fr; CVC
Advertising: Open inch rate $12.50 - $16.25
Established: 1862John Norton
Mechanical Specifications: Type page: 10 x 15.5; 5 col

RIVER VALLEY SHOPPER
(Mon)
115 N Michigan Ave, Big Rapids, MI, 49307-1401, USA; web site www.pioneergroup.com
Circulation:25,360fr; CVC
Advertising: Open inch rate $12.50 - $16.25
Established: 1862John Norton
Mechanical Specifications: Type page: 10 x 15.5; 5 col

TRI-COUNTY SHOPPERS GUIDE
(Mon)
115 N Michigan Ave, Big Rapids, MI, 49307-1401, USA; tel (231) 796-4831; fax (231) 796-1152; e-mail advertising@pioneergroup.net; web site www.pioneergroup.com
Circulation:17,841fr; CVC
Advertising: Open inch rate $12.50 - $16.25
Established: 1862
Group: Pioneer Group
Pub. ....John Norton
Adv. Mgr. ....Sharon Frederick
Circ. Mgr.......................................Candy Allan
Mechanical Specifications: Type page 10 x 15 1/2; A - 5 cols, 1 3/8, 1/2 between.
Zip Codes Served: 49307

WEST SHORE SHOPPER
(Mon)
115 N Michigan Ave, Big Rapids, MI, 49307-1401, USA; web site www.pioneergroup.com
Circulation:11,995fr; CVC
Advertising: Open inch rate $12.50 - $16.25
Established: 1862John Norton
Mechanical Specifications: Type page: 10 x 15.5; 5 col

BRECKENRIDGE

SAGINAW VALLEY SHOPPER
(Mon)
221 E Saginaw St, Breckenridge, MI, 48615-2511, USA; tel (989) 799-3200; fax (989) 842-5203; e-mail comp@svshopper.com
Circulation:11,600fr; Sworn/Estimate/Non-Audited
Advertising: Open inch rate $4.30
Circ. Mgr.....................................Edward Belles
Mechanical Specifications: Type page 10 1/4 x 16.
Equipment: Hardware — APP/Mac; Software — Multi-Ad/CAMS.
Zip Codes Served: 48615

BRIGHTON

MARKETEER
(Sat, Mthly)
110 E North St, Brighton, MI, 48116-1528, USA; tel (810) 227-1575; adv tel (810) 227-1575; fax (810) 227-8189; adv fax (810) 227-8189; e-mail ads@georgemosesco.com; adv e-mail gmoses@georgemosesco.com; ed e-mail gmoses@georgemosesco.com; web site www.marketeer.ws
Circulation:70,911fr; CVC
Advertising: Open inch rate $24.75
Established: 1974Editions: 2— The Marketeer - Eastern Edition (23,654); The Marketeer - Livingston (47,257)
Digital Platform - Mobile: Apple, Android, Windows
Digital Platform - Tablet: Apple iOS, Android, Windows 7, Blackberry Tablet OS
Publisher, CFO .... Melanie Moses
Publisher, President, Advertising Director......... George J. Moses
Production Manager / Art Director...... Kathleen Smolinski
Mechanical Specifications: Type page 6 x 9 3/4.
Equipment: Hardware — IBM; Presses — 13-G/Suburban; Software — Microsoft/Windows, Adobe/InDesign, Adobe/Photoshop, Adobe/Illustrator.
Delivery Method: Mail
Zip Codes Served: 48116,48114, 48843, 48855, 48139, 48169, 48143, 48189, 48178, 48165, 48353

CARO

SHOPPER'S ADVANTAGE
(Mon)
344 N State St, Caro, MI, 48723-1538, USA; tel (989) 673-3181; fax (989) 673-5662
Circulation:19,538fr; CVC
Advertising: Open inch rate $7.00
Pub. ....Tim Murphy
Circ. Mgr...Ven Stark
Mechanical Specifications: Type page 10 5/16 x 16; A - 7 cols, 1 15/16, 1/8 between; C - 7 cols, 1 15/16, 1/8 between.
Equipment: Hardware — APP/Mac; Presses — 6-G/Community, 8-G/Web Community; Software — Multi-Ad/Creator, Adobe/PageMaker.
Zip Codes Served: 48723

SHOPPERS ADVANTAGE
(Mon)
PO Box 106, Caro, MI, 48723-0106, USA; web site www.tcadvertiser.com
Circulation:23,370fr; CVC
Advertising: Open inch rate $10.00
Established: 1869Tim Murphy
Mechanical Specifications: Type page 10.25" x 11.5"; 7 cols
Delivery Method: Mail, Racks

CHARLOTTE

FLASHES ADVERTISING & NEWS
(Sat)
241 S Cochran Ave, Charlotte, MI, 48813-1584, USA; tel (517) 663-2361; adv tel (517) 543-1099 ext 225; ed tel (517) 543-1099 ext 224; fax (517) 543-1993; adv fax (517) 543-1993; ed fax (517) 543-1993; e-mail cgwing@county-journal.com; adv e-mail cgwing@county-journal.com; ed e-mail tsilvas@county-journal.com; web site http://www.theflashesnews.com/
Circulation: 15pd,11,358fr; CVC
Advertising: Open inch rate $8.15
Established: 1945
Group: The County Journal
Pub./Sales/Owner.....................Cindy Gaedert
Circ. Mgr ....Travis Silvas
Mechanical Specifications: Type page 10 1/4 x 16; E - 6 cols, 1 9/16, between; A - 6 cols, 1 9/16, between.
Equipment: Hardware — Mac Mini; Presses — ABD/360, ATF/Davidson 641; Software — Indesign
Delivery Method: Carrier
Zip Codes Served: 48827, 48821, 49264, 48854,

THE COUNTY JOURNAL
(Sat)
241 S Cochran Ave, Charlotte, MI, 48813-1584, USA; tel (517) 543-1099; fax (517) 543-1993; e-mail cgwing@county-journal.com; adv e-mail cgwing@county-journal.com; ed e-mail tsilvas@county-journal.com; web site www.county-journal.com
Circulation: 19pd,20,211fr; CVC
Advertising: Open inch rate $9.40
Established: 2006
Group: Flashes Advertising & News
Owner, Pub. & Sales.................Cindy Gaedert
Circ. Mgr.......................................Travis Silvas
Mechanical Specifications: Type page: 10.25 x 16; 6 col
Equipment: ; Software — Mac Minie
Delivery Method: Carrier
Zip Codes Served: 48813, 49076, 49021, 49096, 48876, 48890, 48861, 48827, 48821

CHEBOYGAN

SHOPPERS FAIR
(Sat)
308 N Main St, Cheboygan, MI, 49721-1545, USA; tel (231) 627-7144; fax (231) 627-5331; e-mail news@cheboygannews.com; web site www.cheboygannews.com
Circulation:15,500fr; Sworn/Estimate/Non-Audited
Advertising: Open inch rate $11.00
Group: GateHouse Media, Inc.
Pub. ....Gary Lamburg
Adv. Mgr. ....Nancy Kidder
Prodn. Mgr. .... Jerry Pond
Mechanical Specifications: Type page 10 x 15 1/4; E - 5 cols, 1 7/8, 3/16 between; A - 5 cols, 1 7/8, 3/16 between; C - 5 cols, 1 7/8, 3/16 between.
Zip Codes Served: 49721

STRAITS AREA STAR
(Sun)
222 N Main St, Cheboygan, MI, 49721-1640, USA; tel (231) 627-3151; fax (231) 627-6244; e-mail cheboygan@michigannewspapers.com
Circulation:12,271fr; Sworn/Estimate/Non-Audited
Advertising: Open inch rate $8.00
Gen. Mgr. ....Dan McDonald
Mechanical Specifications: Type page 10 3/8 x 16; E - 4 cols, 2 1/2, 1/8 between; A - 6 cols, 1 5/8, 1/8 between; C - 6 cols, 1 5/8, 1/8 between.
Equipment: Hardware — APP/Mac, PC; Presses — 9-G/Community; Software — QPS/QuarkXPress.
Zip Codes Served: 49735

CLARKSTON

PENNY STRETCHER
(Wed)
5 S Main St, Clarkston, MI, 48346-1597, USA; tel (248) 625-3370; fax (248) 625-0706; e-mail ClarkstonNews@gmail.com; adv e-mail Don@ShermanPublications.org; ed e-mail ClarkstonNews@gmail.com; web site ClarkstonNews.com
Circulation: 0pd,15,907fr; CVC
Advertising: Open inch rate $14.64
Established: 1981
Group: Sherman Publications, Inc.
Digital Platform - Mobile: Android, Windows
Digital Platform - Tablet: Android, Windows 7
Pub ....Don Rush
Mechanical Specifications: Type page 10 x 11; E - 8 cols, between.
Equipment: Hardware — windows; Presses — offset; Software — adobe
Delivery Method: Mail
Zip Codes Served: 48346, 48348, 48350
Note: Ads which appear in The Penny Stretcher automatically are inserted into the paid community newspaper, The Clarkston News. Circulation 2,500 and are posted on our website ClarkstonNews.com as a pdf section.

COLDWATER

SHOPPERS GUIDE
(Wed)
57 S Monroe St, Coldwater, MI, 49036-1928, USA; tel (517) 279-9764; fax (517) 278-8597
Circulation:22,079fr; Sworn/Estimate/Non-Audited
Advertising: Open inch rate $5.50
Pub. ....Harold Shultz

CONCORD

THE SALESMAN
(Sun)
102 N Main St, PO Box 205, Concord, MI, 49237-9647, USA; tel (517) 524-8540; e-mail ads@salesmanpublications.com; web site www.salesmanpublications.com
Circulation: 0pd,52,745fr; CVC
Advertising: Open inch rate $26.10
Established: 1948Bettie Watson
Mechanical Specifications: Type page: 10.5 x 16; 6 col
Delivery Method: Mail, Carrier

ESCANABA

UP ACTION NEWS
(Sun)
600 Ludington St, Escanaba, MI, 49829-3830, USA; tel (906) 789-9122; fax (906) 789-

5600; e-mail advertising@upaction.com
Circulation:19,900fr; Sworn/Estimate/Non-Audited
Advertising: Open inch rate $15.55
Established: 1979
Group: Ogden Newspapers Inc.
Gen. Mgr. .... Terrie Belongie
Circ. Mgr. .... Dennis Bowen
Pub. .... Dan McDonald
Mechanical Specifications: Type page 10 1/8 x 16; E - 5 cols, 1 11/12, 1/6 between; A - 5 cols, 1 11/12, 1/6 between; C - 5 cols, 1 11/12, 1/6 between.
Equipment: Hardware — Mk; Software — QPS/QuarkXPress, Multi-Ad 4.0.
Delivery Method: Mail, Carrier, Racks
Zip Codes Served: 49829

FREMONT

HI-LITES SHOPPERS GUIDE
(Sun)
1212 Locust St, Fremont, MI, 49412-1825, USA; tel (231) 924-0630; fax (231) 924-5580; e-mail ads@hi-lites.net; web site www.hi-lites.net
Circulation:21,121fr; CVC
Advertising: Open inch rate $6.75
Established: 1947
Pub. .... B. Jon Sovinski
Circ. Mgr. .... Tom Kowalski
Mechanical Specifications: Type page 10.375" x 16"; 6 cols
Equipment: Hardware — 9-APP/Mac, Screen 3050 Imagesetter; Presses — 6-G/Community; Software — QPS/QuarkXPress, Adobe/PageMaker, Adobe/Illustrator.
Delivery Method: Mail, Carrier, Racks
Zip Codes Served: 49412

GAYLORD

MARKETPLACE UPNORTH
(Sat)
2058 S Otsego Ave, Gaylord, MI, 49735-9422, USA; tel (989) 732-1111; fax (989) 732-3490; e-mail pub@gaylordheraldtimes.com; web site www.gaylordheraldtimes.com
Circulation:12,000fr; Sworn/Estimate/Non-Audited
Advertising: Open inch rate $10.20
Adv. Mgr., Sales/Mktg. .... Kim Ballerd
Ed. .... Cathy Landry
Mechanical Specifications: Type page 11 5/8 x 21 1/2; E - 6 cols, 2 1/12, between; A - 6 cols, 2 1/12, between; C - 6 cols, 2 1/12, between.
Equipment: Hardware — APP/Mac.
Zip Codes Served: 49735

GLADWIN

GLADWIN BUYERS GUIDE
(Sun)
317 W Cedar Ave, Gladwin, MI, 48624-2021, USA; tel (989) 426-9351; fax (989) 426-0551; web site www.morningstarpublishing.com
Circulation:12,475fr; CVC
Advertising: Open inch rate $6.30-19.00
Established: 1950
Adv. Mgr. .... Marlene Bennett
Pub. .... Jim O'Rourke
Adv. Mgr. .... Tammy Fisher
Circ. Mgr .... Christine Fox
Prod. Mgr .... Ron Martin
Mechanical Specifications: Type page: 9.75 x 16; 6 col
Equipment: Hardware — APP/Mac; Presses — 14-G/Community; Software — MK/Newscrafter, QPS/QuarkXPress.

GOBLES

MICHIGAN PRINTING/VAN BUREN

COUNTY ADVERTISER
(Mon)
205 S State St, Gobles, MI, 49055-9405, USA; tel (269) 628-5122; fax (269) 628-5198; e-mail abcadvertiser@yahoo.com; web site vbcadvertiser.com
Circulation:7,000fr; Sworn/Estimate/Non-Audited
Advertising: Open inch rate $6.40
Established: 1945
Pub. .... Pam Harris
Mechanical Specifications: Type page 10 1/2 x 15 3/4; E - 6 cols, 1, between.

GREENVILLE

BUY LINE
(Mon)
109 N Lafayette St, Greenville, MI, 48838-1853, USA; tel (616) 754-9301; fax (616) 754-8559; web site www.thedailynews.cc
Circulation:36,236fr; Sworn/Estimate/Non-Audited
Advertising: Open inch rate $9.99Editions: 3—3 total; Buy Line-Central (16,286); Buy Line-North (5,177); Buy Line-South (16,131);
Ed. .... Robert Stafford
Adv. Mgr. .... Mike Buckner
Circ. Mgr. .... Carol Pettengill
Prodn. Mgr. .... Christopher Hunter
Zip Codes Served: 48838

HILLSDALE

TIP-OFF SHOPPING GUIDE
(Mon)
33 McCollum St, Hillsdale, MI, 49242-1630, USA; tel (517) 437-7351; fax (517) 437-3963; e-mail tipoff@tipoffonline.com; adv e-mail tipoff@tipoffonline.com; web site www.tipoffonline.com
Circulation:17,600fr; Sworn/Estimate/Non-Audited
Advertising: Open inch rate $8.20
Established: 1968
Group: GateHouse Media, Inc.Editions: 17,600—
Prodn. Mgr. .... Laura Lamb
general manager .... Dave Ferro
Mechanical Specifications: Type page 10 1/8 x 11; A - 6 cols, 1 5/8, between; C - 6 cols, 1 5/8, between.
Equipment: Hardware — APP/Mac
Delivery Method: Carrier
Zip Codes Served: Hillsdale Co. and Surrounding Areas

HOWARD CITY

RIVER VALLEY NEWS SHOPPER
(Mon)
491 W Shaw St, Howard City, MI, 49329-9401, USA; tel (231) 937-4740; fax (231) 937-4048; e-mail rvshopper@pioneergroup.net; web site www.rivervalleyshopper.com
Circulation:22,800fr; Sworn/Estimate/Non-Audited
Advertising: Open inch rate $13.75
Group: Pioneer Group
Pub. .... John Norton
Sales Mgr. .... Sharon Frederick
Mechanical Specifications: Type page 10 x 16; A - 5 cols, 1 7/8, 1/8 between; C - 5 cols, 1 7/8, 1/8 between.
Zip Codes Served: 49337, 49349, 49303, 49326, 49347, 49322, 49330, 49327, 49319, 49343, 49339, 49329, 49336

HOWELL

GREEN SHEET
(Sun)
323 E Grand River Ave, Howell, MI, 48843-2322, USA; tel (517) 548-2000; fax (517) 548-3005; web site www.greensheetclassifieds.com
Circulation:56,305fr; AAM
Advertising: Open inch rate $10.20
Pub. .... Richard Perlberg
Retail Adv. Mgr. .... John Utter
Circ. Mgr. .... Mary Scott
Ed. .... Mike Malott
Retail Adv. Mgr .... Lisa Vernon
Zip Codes Served: 48844

HUDSON

BI-COUNTY HERALD
(Tues)
115 S Church St, Hudson, MI, 49247-1301, USA; tel (517) 448-2201; adv tel (517) 448-8271; ed tel (517) 448-8271; fax (517) 448-2201; adv fax (517) 448-8271; ed fax (517) 448-8271; e-mail geri.monahan@gmail.com; adv e-mail geri.monahan@gmail.com; ed e-mail geri.monahan@gmail.com
Circulation:12,241fr; Sworn/Estimate/Non-Audited
Advertising: Open inch rate $6.00
Pub. .... John W. Monahan
Karen Downing
Geri Monahan
Mechanical Specifications: 8 columns - each column 1.5 with 1/8" cutter
Delivery Method: Mail
Zip Codes Served: 49247

IRON MOUNTAIN

ADVERTISER
(Tues)
421 S Stephenson Ave, Iron Mountain, MI, 49801-3454, USA; tel (906) 774-3708; fax (906) 774-1088; e-mail khicks@ironmountainadvertiser.com; adv e-mail advertiser@ironmountainadvertiser.com
Circulation:20,600fr; Sworn/Estimate/Non-Audited
Advertising: Open rate-local $17.50, National rate-$19.55
Established: 1975
Group: Ogden Newspapers Inc.
Digital Platform - Mobile: Windows
Gen Mgr. .... Karen Hicks
Mechanical Specifications: Type page 10 1/4 x 16; E - 6 cols, 1 1/2, between; A - 6 cols, 1 1/2, 1/6 between.
Equipment: Hardware — APP/Mac; Software — QPS/QuarkXPress.
Delivery Method: Carrier
Zip Codes Served: 49801, 49807, 49815, 49831, 49834, 49847, 49852, 49870, 49874, 49876, 49877, 49879, 49881, 49882, 49902, 49903, 49915, 49920, 49927, 49935, 49964, 54102, 54103, 54119, 54120, 54121, 54125, 54151, 54156

IRONWOOD

NORTH COUNTRY SUN
(Mon)
216 E Aurora St, Ironwood, MI, 49938-2164, USA; tel (906) 932-3530; fax (906) 932-3074; e-mail evergreen@charterinternet.com; web site www.northcountrysun.com
Circulation:15,705fr; CVC
Advertising: Open inch rate $8.95
Pub. .... Gary A. La Pean
Adv. Mgr. .... Richard Barringer
Mechanical Specifications: Type page 10 1/2 x 16 1/2; E - 6 cols, 1 1/2, between; A - 6 cols, 1 1/2, between.
Equipment: Hardware — APP/Mac; Presses — 8-G.
Zip Codes Served: 49938

RANGE SOURCE
(Sat)
118 E McLeod Ave, Ironwood, MI, 49938-2120, USA; tel (906) 932-2211; fax (906) 932-5358; e-mail news@yourdailyglobe.com; adv e-mail classifieds@yourdailyglobe.com; ed e-mail news@yourdailyglobe.com; web site www.yourdailyglobe.com
Circulation: 0pd,12,000fr; Sworn/Estimate/Non-Audited
Advertising: Open inch rate $12.00
publisher .... Sue Mizell
Mechanical Specifications: 6 col x 21.5
1 col - 2.028"
2 col - 4.222"
3 col - 6.417"
4 col - 8.611"
5 col - 10.806"
6 col - 13.00"
Equipment: Hardware — APP/Mac; Presses — Goss Community; Software — QPS/QuarkXPress
Delivery Method: Mail, Racks
Zip Codes Served: 49938, 49911, 49968, 54534, 54547, 54550

KALKASKA

STAR PENNYSTRETCHER
(Sun)
318 N Cedar St, Kalkaska, MI, 49646-8424, USA; tel (231) 533-8523; fax (231) 533-6803
Circulation:9,230fr; Sworn/Estimate/Non-Audited
Advertising: Open inch rate $8.05
Pub. .... Al Frattura
Ed. .... Hadley Robinson
Prodn. Mgr. .... Mary Hansen
Mechanical Specifications: Type page 10 x 16.

LANSING

CHARLOTTE SHOPPING GUIDE
(Sun)
120 E Lenawee St, Lansing, MI, 48919-1000, USA; tel (517) 541-2531; fax (517) 543-3677; web site www.lsj.com
Circulation:11,100fr; AAM
Advertising: Open inch rate $15.00
Established: 1856
Group: Lansing Community Newspapers
Pub. .... Brian Priester
Adv. Mgr. .... Stacia King
Circ. Mgr. .... Linda Argue
Prod. Mgr. .... Jack Conaboy
Circ. Mgr .... Mark Conover
Mechanical Specifications: Type page: 10 x 10; 6 col

THE SOURCE SAMPLER
(Thur, Sat, Sun)
120 E Lenawee St, Lansing, MI, 48919-1000, USA; tel (517) 377-1000; fax (517) 377-1284; adv e-mail classifieds@lsj.com; web site www.lsj.com
Circulation:332,725fr; Sworn/Estimate/Non-Audited
Advertising: Open inch rate $6.35
Group: GannettEditions: 2—2 total; City; State;
Adv. Dir. .... Stacia King
Exec. Ed. .... Mickey Hirten
Mng. Ed. .... Stephanie Angel
Mechanical Specifications: Type page 13 x 22; E - 6 cols, 2 1/16, 3/16 between; A - 6 cols, 2 1/16, 3/16 between; C - 10 cols, 1 3/16, 1/16 between.
Equipment: Hardware — APP/Mac 6/82, DTI/Classified 4.2.3, 2-III/3850, 2-III/3850, DTI/Editorial 5.2; Presses — TKS; Software — Multi-Ad/Creator 6.0, Adobe/Photoshop 6.0, Adobe/PageMaker 6.5, QPS/QuarkXPress 4.0.
Zip Codes Served: 48919

LOWELL

LOWELL BUYERS GUIDE
(Sat)
PO Box 128, Lowell, MI, 49331-0128, USA; tel (616) 897-9555; fax (616) 897-4809; e-mail ledger@lowellbuyersguide.com; web site www.lowellbuyersguide.com
Circulation: 0pd,14,203fr; CVC
Advertising: Open inch rate $6.93
Established: 1954
Gen. Mgr. .... Jon Jacob
Mechanical Specifications: Type page 10.375" x 16"; 6 cols
Delivery Method: Racks

LUDINGTON

LUDINGTON SHOPPER'S EDITION
(Sun)
202 N Rath Ave, Ludington, MI, 49431-1663, USA; tel (269) 845-5181; fax (231) 843-4011; e-mail ldn@ludingtondailynews.com; adv e-mail rmcgrew@cmgms.com; ed e-mail editor@ludingtondailynews.com; web site www.ludingtondailynews.com
Circulation:9,410fr; Sworn/Estimate/Non-Audited
Advertising: Open inch rate $17.17
Established: 1867
Group: Community Media Group
Digital Platform - Mobile: Apple
Digital Platform - Tablet: Apple iOS
GM Shoreline Media
VP Community Media Group........ Ray McGrew
Editor .... Patti Klevorn
Circulation Manager .... Kellie Shilander
Mechanical Specifications: Type page 13 x 21 1/2; E - 6 cols, 2 1/16, between; A - 6 cols, 2 1/16, between; C - 6 cols, 2 1/16, between.
Equipment: Hardware — APP/Mac; Presses — 12 unit Goss Community; Software — Adobe/Photoshop, Adobe/InDesign, Adobe/Illustrator.
Delivery Method: Carrier, Racks
Zip Codes Served: 49431, 49454, 49405, 49660, 49410, 49411, 49304, 49402, 49644

MANISTEE

WEST SHORE SHOPPER'S GUIDE
(Sun)
75 Maple St, Manistee, MI, 49660-1554, USA; tel (231) 723-3592; fax (231) 723-4733; e-mail advocate@pioneergroup.com; web site www.pioneergroup.com
Circulation:14,293fr; CVC
Advertising: Open inch rate $11.50
Group: Pioneer Group
Pub. / Gen. Mgr. .... Marilyn Barker
Circ. Mgr. .... Aaron DeKuiper
Mng. Ed. .... David Barber
Equipment: Hardware — APP/Mac G3; Presses — HI/V-15A; Software — QPS/QuarkXPress 4.04.
Zip Codes Served: 49660

MANISTIQUE

THE ADVISOR
(Mon)
311 Oak St, Manistique, MI, 49854-1409, USA; tel (906) 341-2424; fax (906) 341-8062; e-mail advisor@chartermi.net
Circulation: 10pd,8,660fr; CVC
Advertising: Open inch rate $5.00
Established: 1948
Jack Ozanich
Paul OzanichPub.s
Mechanical Specifications: Type page: 10.25 x 16; 6 col

MARQUETTE

ACTION SHOPPER
(Wed)
249 W Washington St, Marquette, MI, 49855-4321, USA; tel (906) 228-8920; fax (906) 228-5777
Circulation: 1pd,26,000fr; Sworn/Estimate/Non-Audited
Advertising: Open inch rate $12.00
Established: 1972
Group: Ogden Newspapers Inc.
Pub. .... Adam Berger
Mechanical Specifications: Type page 10 1/4 x 14 1/2; E - 7 cols, 1/6 between; A - 7 cols, 1/6 between; C - 7 cols, 1/6 between.
Zip Codes Served: 49855, 49849, 49866

MIDLAND

MIDLAND BUYERS GUIDE
(Sun)
614 Haley St, Midland, MI, 48640-5310, USA; tel (989) 631-0660; fax (989) 631-1752; web site www.21stcenturynewspapers.com
Circulation:22,200fr; Sworn/Estimate/Non-Audited
Advertising: Open inch rate $13.55
Gen. Mgr. .... Don Negus

MOUNT PLEASANT

CLARE COUNTY BUYER'S GUIDE
(Sun)
PO Box 447, Mount Pleasant, MI, 48804-0447, USA; tel (989) 779-6079; adv tel (989) 779-6079; ed tel (989) 779-6079; fax (989) 779-6171; adv fax (989) 779-6171; ed fax (989) 779-6171; e-mail cturner@michigannewspapers.com; adv e-mail classifieds@michigannewspapers.com; ed e-mail news@michigannewspapers.com; web site www.morningstarpublishing.com
Circulation:11,405fr; CVC
Advertising: Open inch rate $6.30-19.00
Established: 1950
Digital Platform - Mobile: Apple, Android, Windows, Blackberry
Digital Platform - Tablet: Apple iOS, Android, Windows 7, Blackberry Tablet OS
Pub. .... Jim O'Rourke
Ed. .... Al Frattura
Mktg. Dir. .... Tammy Fisher
Adv. Mgr. .... Don Megus
Circ. Mgr .... Christine Fox
Prod. Mgr .... Ron Martin
Mechanical Specifications: Type page: 9.75 x 16; 6 col
Equipment: Hardware — APP/Mac; Presses — 14-G/Community; Software — MK/Newscrafter, QPS/QuarkXPress.
Delivery Method: Mail
Zip Codes Served: Clare County

MT. PLEASANT BUYERS GUIDE
(Sun)
711 W Pickard St, Mount Pleasant, MI, 48858-1585, USA; tel (989) 779-6000; fax (989) 779-6050; web site www.morningstarpublishing.com
Circulation:23,280fr; CVC
Advertising: Open inch rate $6.30-19.00
Established: 1950
Pub. .... Al Frattura
Mktg. Dir. .... Tammy Fisher
Circ. Mgr. .... Christine Fox
Pub. .... Jim O'Rourke
Prod. Mgr .... Ron Martin
Mechanical Specifications: Type page: 9.75 x 16; 6 col
Equipment: Hardware — APP/Mac; Presses — 14-G/Community; Software — Mk/Newscrafters, QPS/QuarkXPress.
Delivery Method: Carrier, Racks
Zip Codes Served: 48858

MUNISING

ALGER COUNTY SHOPPER
(Mon)
132 E Superior St, Munising, MI, 49862-1122, USA; tel (906) 387-3282; adv tel (906) 387-3282; ed tel (906) 387-3282; fax (906) 387-4054; e-mail munisingnews@jamadots.com; adv e-mail munisingnews@jamadots.com; ed e-mail munisingnews@jamadots.com
Circulation:5,000fr; Sworn/Estimate/Non-Audited
Advertising: Open inch rate $7.50
Established: 1989
Group: Peterson Publishing, Inc
Adv. Mgr. .... Willie J. Peterson
Mechanical Specifications: Type page 10 1/4 x 15; E - 6 cols, 1 1/2, 1/6 between; A - 6 cols, 1 1/2, 1/6 between.
Delivery Method: Mail
Zip Codes Served: 49862, 49816, 49825, 49891, 49878, 49826, 49806, 49822, 49839, 49854, 49883, 49884, 49845

MUSKEGON

BUYERS' GUIDE
(Thur)
1781 5th St, Muskegon, MI, 49441-2694, USA; tel (231) 722-3784; fax (231) 728-7192
Circulation:23,000fr; Sworn/Estimate/Non-Audited
Advertising: Open inch rate $7.00
Pub. .... Dale A. Bush
Ed. .... Barbara Berry
Mechanical Specifications: Type page 10 1/2 x 16; E - 6 cols, between; A - 6 cols, 1 5/8, 1/8 between.
Equipment: Hardware — COM; Presses — KP/Color King, Hamada, ATF/Chief; Software — Microsoft/Publisher 98.
Zip Codes Served: 49441

NEW BALTIMORE

ADVISER & SOURCE
(Sun)
51180 Bedford St, New Baltimore, MI, 48047-2533, USA; tel (586) 716-8100; adv tel (586) 716-8107 ext. 600; ed tel (586) 323-8145; fax (586) 716-8533; adv e-mail ads@advisorsource.com; ed e-mail jody.mcveigh@advisorsource.com; web site www.source-newspapers.com
Circulation:44,000fr; Sworn/Estimate/Non-Audited
Advertising: Open inch rate $39.35
Pub. .... Jeffrey Parra
Gen. Mgr. .... Chris Troszak
Circ. Dir. .... Jared Waterstone
Ed. .... Jody McVeigh
Assoc. Ed. .... Don Chamberlain
Prodn. Dir. .... Donna Bassett
Mechanical Specifications: Type page 13 x 21 1/2; E - 6 cols, 2 1/16, 1/8 between; A - 6 cols, 2 1/16, 1/8 between; C - 9 cols, 1 3/8, 1/8 between.
Equipment: Hardware — APP/Mac, Kk/Photo scanner, HP/Laser Printer, AU/APS100 Rips, AU/Imagesetters 108; Presses — G/Cosmo; Software — Multi-Ad/Creator 4.0, QPS/QuarkXPress 3.31, Adobe/Photoshop 3.0, Microsoft/Windows NT.

NILES

THE LEADER
(Mon)
217 N 4th St, Niles, MI, 49120-2301, USA; tel (269) 683-2100; fax (269) 683-2175; adv e-mail advertising@leaderpub.com; web site www.leaderpub.com
Circulation:36,589fr; CVC
Advertising: Open inch rate $19.50
Established: 1971
Group: Boone Newspapers, Inc.Editions: 2— 2 total; Leader-East (20,000); Leader-West (24,000);
Adv. Mgr. .... Bryan Clapper
Mechanical Specifications: Type page 9 3/4 x 14; E - 6 cols, 1 1/2, between; A - 6 cols, 1 1/2, between; C - 6 cols, 1 1/2, between.
Equipment: Hardware — APP/Mac; Presses — KP/News King; Software — QPS/QuarkXPress 4.0.
Zip Codes Served: 49047, 49120

ORTONVILLE

ORTONVILLE CITIZEN
(Mon)
12 South St, Ortonville, MI, 48462-7717, USA; tel (248) 627-4332; web site www.thecitizenonline.com
Circulation:11,542fr; Sworn/Estimate/Non-Audited
Advertising: Open inch rate $11.14
Established: 1995
Group: sherman publications
Pub .... Jim Sherman
Adv. Mgr. .... Jackie Nowicki
Circ. Mgr .... Luan Offer
Prod. Mgr .... Susan Speed
editor .... david fleet
Mechanical Specifications: Type page: 10 x 11; 8 col
Delivery Method: Mail

OTSEGO

COMMUNITY SHOPPERS GUIDE
(Sat)
PO Box 168, Otsego, MI, 49078-0168, USA; tel (269) 694-9431; fax (269) 694-9145; e-mail shoppersguide@sbcglobal.net; adv e-mail shoppersguide@sbcglobal.net; ed e-mail shoppersguide@sbcglobal.net; web site www.communityshoppersguide.net
Circulation:13,215fr; CVC
Advertising: Open inch rate $15.00
Established: 1945
Digital Platform - Mobile: Apple, Android, Windows, Blackberry
Digital Platform - Tablet: Apple iOS, Android, Windows 7, Blackberry Tablet OS, Kindle, Nook, Kindle FireMarty Bennett
Mechanical Specifications: Type page 10.37" x 16"; 4 cols
Delivery Method: Carrier, Racks
Zip Codes Served: 49009,49004, 49046, 49055, 49070, 49078, 49080

SHOPPERS GUIDE
(Sat)
117 N Farmer St, Otsego, MI, 49078-1147, USA; tel (269) 694-9431; fax (269) 694-9145; e-mail shoppersguide@sbcglobal.net; web site www.communityshoppersguide.net
Circulation:13,215fr; Sworn/Estimate/Non-Audited
Advertising: Open inch rate $14.18
Established: 1945
Ed. .... Martins Bennett
Mechanical Specifications: Type page 10 1/4 x 12 3/4; E - 4 cols, 2 3/8, between; A - 4 cols, 2 3/8, between.
Equipment: Hardware — APP/Macs.
Delivery Method: Mail, Carrier
Zip Codes Served: 49078, 49080, 49070, 49009, 49004, 49046

OWOSSO

DURAND INDEPENDENT
(Sun)
1907 W M-21, Owosso, MI, 48867, USA; tel (989) 723-1118; fax (989) 725-1834; e-mail indysales@owossoindependent.com; adv

e-mail Jean@owossoindependent.com; ed e-mail News@owossoindependent.com; web site www.owossoindependent.com
Circulation:9,100fr; Sworn/Estimate/Non-Audited
Advertising: Open inch rate $11.25
Established: 1968
Pub. .... Michael Flores
Ed. .... William Constine
Adv. Mgr. .... Jean Yanna
Mechanical Specifications: Type page 10 x 15; A - 6 cols, between; C - 6 cols, between.
Equipment: Hardware — APP/Power Macs; Software — QPS/QuarkXPress, Adobe/Photoshop, Adobe/Illustrator.
Zip Codes Served: 48414

THE PERRY INDEPENDENT
(Sun)
1907 W M-21, Owosso, MI, 48867, USA; tel (989) 723-1118; fax (989) 725-1834; e-mail indysales@chartermi.net; web site www.owossoindependent.com
Circulation:6,800fr; Sworn/Estimate/Non-Audited
Advertising: Open inch rate $8.30
Pub. .... Michael Flores
Adv. Mgr. .... Paul Constine
Ed. .... Bill Constine
Mechanical Specifications: Type page 10 x 16; E - 6 cols, between; A - 6 cols, between; C - 6 cols, between.
Equipment: Hardware — APP/Power Macs; Software — QPS/QuarkXPress, Adobe/Photoshop, Adobe/Illustrator.

OXFORD

AD-VERTISER
(Wed)
666 S Lapeer Rd, Oxford, MI, 48371-5034, USA; tel (248) 628-4801; fax (248) 628-9750; e-mail shermanpub@aol.com; web site www.theoxfordleader.com
Circulation:25,974fr; CVC
Advertising: Open inch rate $14.08
Established: 1961
Group: Sherman Publications, Inc.
Pub. .... Jim Sherman
Adv. Mgr. .... Eric Lewis
Mechanical Specifications: Type page 10 x 11; E - 8 cols, between.
Delivery Method: Mail
Zip Codes Served: 48371

PAW PAW

PAW PAW FLASHES
(Mon)
32280 E Red Arrow Hwy, Paw Paw, MI, 49079-8764, USA; tel (269) 657-3072; adv tel (269) 657-5080; fax (269) 657-5723; e-mail vineyardpress@vineyardpress.biz; adv e-mail ads@vineyardpress.biz; ed e-mail courieredi-torial@vineyardpress.biz; web site http://www.pawpawcourierleader.com/
Circulation:17,500fr; Sworn/Estimate/Non-Audited
Advertising: Open inch rate $8.00
Established: 1936
Group: Vineyard Press, Inc.
General Manager .... Steven Racette
Delivery Method: Mail, Newsstand, Carrier, Racks
Zip Codes Served: 49079

PETOSKEY

NORTHERN MICHIGAN REVIEW
(Sat)
319 State St, Petoskey, MI, 49770-2746, USA; tel (231) 347-2544; fax (231) 347-6833; e-mail petoskeynews@petoskeynews.com; web site www.petoskeynews.com
Circulation:35,000fr; Sworn/Estimate/Non-Audited
Advertising: Open inch rate $30.08
Pub. .... Doug Caldwell
Adv. Mgr. .... Christy Bur
Mktg. Mgr. .... Dena Sydow
Circ. Mgr. .... Carl Redder
Prodn. Mgr. .... Dennis Collins
Mechanical Specifications: Type page 11 5/8 x 21; E - 6 cols, 1 13/16, between; A - 6 cols, 1 13/16, between; C - 6 cols, 1 13/16, between.
Equipment: Hardware — APP/Mac; Presses — G/Community; Software — QPS/QuarkXPress 4.11.
Zip Codes Served: 49770

PONTIAC

GREATER DETROIT ADS
(Sun)
48 W Huron St, Pontiac, MI, 48342-2101, USA; tel (248) 322-2199; adv tel (248) 322-2199; ed tel (248) 322-2199; e-mail rparr@mlive.com; adv e-mail cplaxton@mlive.com; ed e-mail kfrick@mlive.com
Circulation: 0pd,114,110fr; CAC
Adv. Vice Pres. .... Charity Plaxton
Pub. .... Jim O'Rourke
Delivery Method: Mail, Carrier
Zip Codes Served: Oakland County

PORT HURON

BLUE WATER SHOPPER
(Mon)
911 Military St, Port Huron, MI, 48060-5414, USA; tel (810) 985-7171; fax (810) 989-6294; web site www.thetimesherald.com
Circulation:58,000fr; Sworn/Estimate/Non-Audited
Advertising: Open inch rate $12.70
Established: 1982
Group: Gannett
General Manager/Director of Advertising....Lori Driscoll
Pub. .... Brian Priester
Distribution Director .... Brian Gavin
Equipment: ; Software — QPS/QuarkXPress, Adobe/Illustrator, Adobe/PageMaker.
Delivery Method: Carrier
Zip Codes Served: 48060

SANDUSKY

SANILAC BUYER'S GUIDE
(Fri)
72 S Elk St, Sandusky, MI, 48471, USA; tel (810) 648-4000; adv tel (810) 648-4000; ed tel (810) 648-4000; fax (810) 648-4526; adv fax (810) 648-4526; ed fax (810) 648-4526; e-mail scneditor@mihomepaper.com; adv e-mail jvanderpoel@mihomepaper.com; ed e-mail elevine@mihomepaper.com; web site http://sanilaccountynews.mihomepaper.com
Circulation:17,929fr; CVC
Advertising: Modular ad format, $12.00 pci equivalent
Established: 1969
Group: JAMS Media
Digital Platform - Mobile: Apple
Digital Platform - Tablet: Apple iOS
Circ. Mgr. .... Michele Dicus
Prodn. Mgr. .... Betty Pagel
Pub. .... Jane Vanderpoel
Mechanical Specifications: Tabloid: 9.5" X 10" in 4 column format
Equipment: Hardware — COM, APP/Mac; Software — Claris/Works, Multi-Ad/CAMS, Claris/FileMaker Pro, Adobe/PageMaker, QuarkX; Great Plains.
Delivery Method: Mail
Zip Codes Served: 48401, 48410, 48416, 48419, 48422, 48426, 48427, 48434, 48450, 48453, 48454, 48456, 48465, 48466, 48469, 48471, 48472

SANILAC BUYERS GUIDE
(Fri)
65 S Elk St, Sandusky, MI, 48471-1337, USA; tel (810) 648-4000; fax (810) 648-4526; e-mail info@mihomepaper.com; adv e-mail sales@mihomepaper.com; ed e-mail elevine@mihomepaper.com; web site www.mihomepaper.com
Circulation: 50pd,18,490fr; CVC
Advertising: Modular Display Rates
Established: 1969
Group: JAMS Media
Digital Platform - Mobile: Apple
Digital Platform - Tablet: Apple iOS
Mechanical Specifications: Type page: 9.5 x 10; 4 col
Delivery Method: Mail
Zip Codes Served: 48401, 48410, 48416, 48419, 48422, 48426, 48427, 48494, 48450, 48458, 48454, 48456, 48465, 48466, 48469, 48471, 48472

SARANAC

IONIA COUNTY SHOPPERS GUIDE
(Sat)
13 N Bridge St, Saranac, MI, 48881-5122, USA; tel (616) 642-9411; fax (616) 642-6040; web site www.ioniacountyshoppersguide.com
Circulation:16,500fr; CVC
Advertising: Open inch rate $8.03
Established: 1968
Pub. .... John R. Brown
Gen. Mgr. .... Carol Benjamin
Adv. Sales .... Sue Nystrom
Mechanical Specifications: Type page 10.375" x 16; 6 cols
Delivery Method: Mail, Carrier, Racks
Zip Codes Served: Saranac, MI

SAULT SAINTE MARIE

TRI-COUNTY BUYER'S GUIDE
(Sun)
109 Arlington St, Sault Sainte Marie, MI, 49783-1901, USA; tel (906) 632-2235; fax (906) 632-1222; e-mail ensales@sooeveningnews.com; web site www.sooeveningnews.com
Circulation:18,741fr; Sworn/Estimate/Non-Audited
Advertising: Open inch rate $17.40
Group: GateHouse Media, Inc.
Adv. Mgr. .... Howard Kaiser
Circ. Mgr. .... Mike Ferraro
Ed. .... Ken Filkins
Zip Codes Served: 49783

STURGIS

GATEWAY SHOPPERS GUIDE
(Tues)
201 N Clay St, Sturgis, MI, 49091-1453, USA; tel (269) 651-2944; fax (269) 651-8855; e-mail info@thegatewayshopper.com; web site www.thegatewayshopper.com
Circulation:24,000fr; Sworn/Estimate/Non-Audited
Advertising: Open inch rate $9.12
Established: 1952
Group: GateHouse Media, Inc.Editions: 2— 2 total; Indiana Gateway Shoppers Guide (10,437); Michigan Gateway Shoppers Guide (15,000);
Pub. .... Dan Tollefson
Mechanical Specifications: Type page 10.58 x 16
Delivery Method: Carrier
Zip Codes Served: 49091, 49028, 49030, 49032, 49040, 49042, 49075, 49099, 46746, 46761, 46776, 46795, 46784, 46565, 46571

TAWAS CITY

NORTHEASTERN SHOPPER NORTH
(Sun)
129 North St E, Tawas City, MI, 48763-9294, USA; tel (989) 362-6111; adv tel (989) 362-6111; ed tel (989) 362-6111; fax (989) 362-7080; adv fax (989) 362-7080; ed fax (989) 362-7080; web site www.morningstar-publishing.com
Circulation:20,360fr; CVC
Advertising: Open inch rate $6.30-19.00
Established: 1954
Pub. .... Jim Rourke
Adv. Mgr. .... Tammy Fisher
Circ. Mgr. .... Christine Fox
Prod. Mgr. .... Ron Martin
Adv. Mgr. .... Thomas R. Greene
Mechanical Specifications: Type page: 9.75 x 16; 6 col
Zip Codes Served: Iosco County and parts of Alcona, Arenac and Ogemaw Counties

NORTHEASTERN SHOPPER SOUTH
(Sun)
129 North St E, Tawas City, MI, 48763-9294, USA; tel (989) 362-6111; adv tel (989) 362-6111; ed tel (989) 362-6111; fax (989) 362-7080; adv fax (989) 362-7080; ed fax (989) 362-7080; web site www.morningstar-publishing.com
Circulation:11,989fr; CVC
Advertising: Open inch rate $6.30-19.00
Established: 1954
Group: Morning Star Publishing Company
Pub. .... Jim Rourke
Adv. Mgr. .... Tammy Fisher
Circ. Mgr. .... Christine Fox
Prod. Mgr. .... Ron Martin
Mechanical Specifications: Type page: 9.75 x 16; 6 col
Zip Codes Served: Iosco County and parts of Alcona, Arenac and Ogemaw Counties

THREE RIVERS

HOMETOWN GAZETTE
57 N Main St, Three Rivers, MI, 49093-1531, USA; tel (269) 273-3290

PENNY SAVER
(Sun)
124 N Main St, Three Rivers, MI, 49093-1522, USA; tel (269) 279-7488; fax (269) 279-6007; e-mail news@threeriversnews.com; info@threeriversnews.com; web site www.threeriversnews.com
Circulation:14,675fr; CVC
Advertising: Open inch rate $6.50
Established: 1984
Digital Platform - Mobile: Apple, Android
Digital Platform - Tablet: Apple iOS, Android
Pub. .... Richard L. Milliman
Mechanical Specifications: Type page: 10 x 11.5; 5 col
Delivery Method: Carrier
Zip Codes Served: 49093, 49042,49072,49099,49091,49061,49067,49073

TRAVERSE CITY

GRAND TRAVERSE INSIDER
(Sun)
415 Cass St, Traverse City, MI, 49684-2589, USA; tel (231) 486-0072; fax (231) 486-2203; adv e-mail jroddy@michigannewspapers.com; ed e-mail dlein@michigannewspapers.com; web site http://www.morningstarpublishing.com/grand_traverse_insider/
Circulation:41,875fr; CVC
Advertising: Open inch rate $6.30-19.00
Established: 1950
Group: Morning StarAl Frattura
Pub. .... Jim O'Rourke
Adv. Mgr. .... Tammy Fisher

Circ. Mgr .... Christine Fox
Prod. Mgr .... Ron Martin
Mechanical Specifications: Type page: 9.75 x 16; 6 col

NORTH COAST
(Sat)
120 W Front St, Traverse City, MI, 49684-2202, USA; tel (231) 946-2000; adv tel (231) 933-1465; ed tel (231) 933-1472; fax (231) 946-8273; adv fax (231) 946-0340; ed fax (231) 946-8632; adv e-mail lbacon@record-eagle.com; web site www.record-eagle.com
Circulation:19,400fr; Sworn/Estimate/Non-Audited
Advertising: $4.00 including color
Established: 1858
Group: CNHI, LLC
Publisher .... Paul Heidbreder
Mechanical Specifications: Type page 11 x 21
Equipment: Hardware — IBM; Presses — TKS; Software — QPS/QuarkXPress 3.3.
Delivery Method: Newsstand, Carrier, Racks
Zip Codes Served: 49684, 49686, 49620, 49680, 49621, 49629, 49633, 49637, 49643, 49649, 49650, 49651, 49654, 49653, 49670, 49676, 49682, 49683, 49690

VASSAR

CASS RIVER TRADER
(Mon)
5881 Frankenmuth Rd, Vassar, MI, 48768-9401, USA; tel (989) 823-8651; fax (989) 823-2531; adv e-mail ryan@northernmichigan.com; ed e-mail ryan@northernmichigan.com; web site www.cassrivertrader.com
Circulation: 4pd,18,497fr; CVC
Advertising: Open inch rate $5.95
Established: 1967
Digital Platform - Mobile: Apple, Android, Blackberry
Digital Platform - Tablet: Apple iOS, Android, Blackberry Tablet OS
Gen. Mgr. .... Ryan Bilbey
Mechanical Specifications: Type page 10 3/8 x 15; E - 6 cols, between; A - 6 cols, 1 5/8, 1/8 between; C - 6 cols, 1 5/8, 1/8 between.
Equipment: Hardware — APP/Mac; Software — QPS/QuarkXPress 2015
Delivery Method: Mail, Carrier, Racks
Zip Codes Served: 48768, 48415, 48722, 48435, 48734, 48746, 48757, 48758, 48744, 48769, 48760, 48601, 48736, 48723

WARREN

C & G NEWSPAPERS
(Wed)
13650 E 11 Mile Rd, Warren, MI, 48089-1422, USA; tel (586) 498-8000; ed tel (586) 498-1042; fax (586) 498-9631; adv e-mail classified@candgnews.com; ed e-mail mail@candgnews.com; web site www.candgnews.com
Circulation:614,210fr; CVC
Adv. Mgr. .... Elaine Myers
Ed. .... John Carlisle
Editorial Dir. .... Gregg Demers
Adv. Dir. .... Jeff Demers

MINNESOTA

ALBERT LEA

FREEBORN COUNTY SHOPPER
(Tues)
110 W Pearl St, Albert Lea, MN, 56007-2645, USA; tel (507) 373-1310; fax (507) 373-4253; web site www.freeborncountyshopper.com
Circulation:16,579fr; CVC
Advertising: Open inch rate $17.01
Established: 1974
Group: Boone Newspapers, Inc.
Gen. Mgr. .... Julia Thompson
Sales Mgr. .... Janna LeHocky Arbic
Mechanical Specifications: Type page 10 1/8 x 12.75; E - 4 cols, 2 3/8, between; A - 4 cols, 2 3/8, between.
Equipment: Hardware — APP/Mac.
Zip Codes Served: 56007

TRIBUNE SHOPPING NEWS
(Sun)
808 W Front St, Albert Lea, MN, 56007-1947, USA; tel (507) 373-1411; fax (507) 373-0333; adv e-mail advertising@albertleatribune.com; web site www.albertleatribune.com
Circulation:6,500fr; Sworn/Estimate/Non-Audited
Advertising: Open inch rate $6.00
Group: Boone Newspapers, Inc.
Pub. .... Scott Schmeltzer
Adv. Mgr. .... Crystal Miller
Circ. Mgr. .... Jim Gold
Mng. Ed. .... Tim Engstrom
Mechanical Specifications: Type page 13 x 21 1/2; E - 6 cols, between; A - 6 cols, between; C - 9 cols, between.
Equipment: Hardware — APP/Mac; Software — QPS/QuarkXPress 3.2.

ALEXANDRIA

LAKELAND SHOPPING GUIDE
(Sun)
225 7th Ave E, Alexandria, MN, 56308-1831, USA; tel (320) 763-3133; adv tel (320) 763-3133; ed tel (320) 763-3133; fax (320) 763-3258; e-mail echo@echopress.com; adv e-mail echo@echopress.com; ed e-mail echo@echopress.com; web site www.echopress.com
Circulation: 0pd,23,598fr; VAC
Advertising: Open inch rate $16.50
Group: Forum Communications Co.
Adv. Mgr. .... Jody Hanson
Circ. Mgr. .... Lynn Mounsdon
Ed. .... Jeff Beach
Mechanical Specifications: 6 col x 21" page SAU
Delivery Method: Carrier
Zip Codes Served: 56308 plus 30 mil radius

ANNANDALE

ADVANTAGE
(Sun)
PO Box D, Annandale, MN, 55302-0079, USA; tel (320) 274-3052; fax (320) 274-2301; adv e-mail ads@annandaleadvocate.com
Circulation:7,250fr; Sworn/Estimate/Non-Audited
Advertising: Open inch rate $8.15
Pub. .... Steven Prinsen
Zip Codes Served: 55302

AURORA

EAST RANGE SHOPPER
(Mon)
96 Main St N, Aurora, MN, 55705-1364, USA; tel (218) 229-2245; fax (218) 229-2766
Circulation:6,000fr; Sworn/Estimate/Non-Audited
Advertising: Open inch rate $4.00Roger Johnston
Gail Johnston
Mechanical Specifications: Type page 6 x 13; A - 6 cols, 1 7/12, between.
Equipment: Hardware — APP/Power Mac 7600-132, Epson/Scanner; Presses — ABD/360; Software — QPS/QuarkXPress 3.3.2.
Delivery Method: Mail, Carrier
Zip Codes Served: 55705, 55750, 55708, 55735, 55741, 55763

AUSTIN

MOWER COUNTY SHOPPER
(Tues)
3405 W Oakland Ave, Austin, MN, 55912-5501, USA; tel (507) 437-7731; fax (507) 437-7733; e-mail shopper@smig.net; web site www.mowercountyshopper.com
Circulation:17,866fr; CVC
Advertising: N/A
Established: 1964
Group: Boone Newspapers, Inc.
Gen. Mgr. .... Matt Stay
Acct. Rep. .... Nolan Christensen
Circ. Mgr. .... Nancy Prizler
Mechanical Specifications: Type page: 10.125 x 13; 4 col
Equipment: Hardware — APP/Mac.

BEMIDJI

BUYLINE
(Sat)
1320 Neilson Ave SE, Bemidji, MN, 56601-5406, USA; tel (218) 333-9200; adv tel (218) 333-9778; ed tel (218) 333-9774; fax (218) 333-9819; adv fax (218) 333-9819; ed fax (218) 333-9819; e-mail service@bemidjipioneer.com; adv e-mail advertising@bemidjipioneer.com; ed e-mail news@bemidjipioneer.com; web site www.bemidjipioneer.com
Circulation:12,188fr; VAC
Advertising: Open inch rate $11.00
Group: Forum Communications Company
Digital Platform - Mobile: Apple, Android
Digital Platform - Tablet: Apple iOS, Android
Pub. .... Dennis Doeden
Advertising Director .... Todd Keute
Mechanical Specifications: Type page 10.676" x 21 1/2; E - 6 cols, 1/6 between; A - 6 cols, 1/6 between; C - 9 cols, 1/6 between.
Equipment: Hardware — PC
Delivery Method: Mail, Racks
Zip Codes Served: 56601 56621 56676 56678 56630 56663 56647 56683 56661 56650 56633

BLUE EARTH

TOWN CRIER SHOPPER
(Mon)
125 N Main St, Blue Earth, MN, 56013-1960, USA; tel (507) 526-7324; fax (507) 526-4080; e-mail lnauman@faribaultcountyregister.com; adv e-mail lnauman@faribaultcountyregister.com; ed e-mail chunt@faribaultcountyregister.com; web site www.faribaultcountyregister.com
Circulation: 2,600pd,6,700fr; Sworn/Estimate/Non-Audited
Advertising: Open inch rate $10.20
Established: 1979
Group: Ogden Newspapers Inc.
Pub./Gen. Mgr. .... Lori Nauman
Equipment: Hardware — Mac
Delivery Method: Mail, Newsstand, Carrier
Zip Codes Served: 56013 56098 56023 56025 56047 56039 56010 56090 56027 56033 56014 56097 56051 56058 50424 50451 50556

BRAINERD

ECHOLAND - PIPER SHOPPER
(Fri)
506 James St, Brainerd, MN, 56401-2942, USA; tel (218) 829-4705; adv tel (218) 855-5895; ed tel (218) 855-5894; fax (218) 829-7735; e-mail susie.alters@brainerddispatch.com; adv e-mail advertising@brainerddispatch.com; ed e-mail readeropinion@brainerddispatch.com; web site www.pineandlakes.com
Circulation:28,502fr; CVC
Advertising: $10.30
Established: 1975
Group: Forum Communications Co.
Digital Platform - Mobile: Apple, Android, Windows, Blackberry, Other
Digital Platform - Tablet: Apple iOS, Android, Windows 7, Blackberry Tablet OS, Kindle, Nook, Kindle Fire, Other
Publisher .... Pete Mohs
Advertising Director .... Susie Alters
Mechanical Specifications: Type page: 10.75" (6 col) x 21"
Delivery Method: Mail, Newsstand, Carrier, Racks
Zip Codes Served: 56401, 56425, 56449, 56442, 56465, 56468, 56472, 56474, 56448, 56447, 56441, 56431, 56455, 56450, 56444, 56364, 56466, 56479, 56345, 56473, 56452, 56655, 56484, 56662, 56435, 56472, 56435, 56474, 56442, 56465, 56425, 56468

ECHOLAND SHOPPER
(Fri)
506 James St, Brainerd, MN, 56401-2942, USA; tel (218) 829-4705; adv tel (218) 855-5895; ed tel (218) 855-5894; fax (218) 829-7735; adv fax (218) 829-7735; e-mail news@pequotlakesecho.com; adv e-mail advertising@brainerddispatch.com; ed e-mail nancy.vogt@pineandlakes.com; web site www.pineandlakes.com
Circulation:33,864fr; CVC
Advertising: Open inch rate $10.30
Group: Forum Communications Company
Digital Platform - Mobile: Apple, Android, Windows, Blackberry, Other
Digital Platform - Tablet: Apple iOS, Android, Windows 7, Blackberry Tablet OS, Kindle, Nook, Kindle Fire, Other
Pub. .... Pete Mohs
Editor .... Nancy Vogt
Advertising Director .... Susie Alters
Mechanical Specifications: 6 col (10.75") x 21"
Equipment: Hardware — APP/Mac; Presses — Kodak Transetters; Software — Preps by Kodak
Delivery Method: Mail, Newsstand, Carrier, Racks
Zip Codes Served: 56401, 56425, 56449, 56442, 56465, 56468, 56472, 56474, 56448, 56447, 56441, 56431, 56455, 56450, 56444, 56364, 56466, 56479, 56345, 56473, 56452, 56655, 56484, 56662, 56435

BUFFALO

THE DRUMMER
(Sun)
108 Central Ave, Buffalo, MN, 55313-1521, USA; tel (763) 682-1221; fax (763) 682-5458; e-mail thedrummer@ibm.net; business@thedrummer.com; adv e-mail ads@thedrummer.com; ed e-mail edd@thedrummer.com; web site www.thedrummer.com
Circulation:60,000fr; Sworn/Estimate/Non-Audited
Advertising: Open inch rate $17.75
Established: 1971Editions: 2— 2 total; Drummer (18,338); Drummer-Wright County (28,902);
Pub. .... James P. McDonnell
Ed. .... Jean E. McDonnell
Prodn. Mgr. .... Tom McDonnell
Mechanical Specifications: Type page 13 x 21 1/2; E - 8 cols, 1 1/2, 5/36 between; A - 8 cols, 1 1/2, 5/36 between; C - 8 cols, 1 1/2, 5/36 between.
Zip Codes Served: 55313

CAMBRIDGE

SCOTSMAN
(Sun)
234 Main St S, Cambridge, MN, 55008-1611,

USA; tel (763) 689-1981; fax (763) 689-4372; e-mail print.cambridge@ecm-inc.com; web site www.hometownsource.com
Circulation: 10pd,46,393fr; CAC
Advertising: Open inch rate $23.30
Established: 1964
Group: Lee & Steel, Inc.
Adams Publishing Group, LLCEditions: 7— 7 total; Braham/Rush City (5,700); Chisago (8,400); Kanabec (8,000); North Anoka (11,200); Pine (10,500); Rum River (10,000); Star Zone (17,400);
Pub. .... Julian Anderson
Gen. Mgr. .... Jeff Andres
Mechanical Specifications: Type page 10 x 15; E - 6 cols, 1 3/4, between; A - 6 cols, 1 3/4, between.
Zip Codes Served: 55008

CANNON FALLS

CANNON SHOPPER
(Mon)
120 4th St S, Cannon Falls, MN, 55009-2433, USA; tel (507) 263-3991; fax (507) 263-2300; e-mail beacon@cannonfalls.com; web site www.cannonfalls.com
Circulation:9,064fr; Sworn/Estimate/Non-Audited
Advertising: Open inch rate $7.15
Adv. Mgr. .... David Templin
Ed. .... G. Richard Dalton
Prodn. Mgr. .... Pal Flaten
Mechanical Specifications: Type page 14 x 21 1/2; E - 6 cols, 2, 1/30 between; A - 6 cols, 2, 1/30 between.
Zip Codes Served: 55009

COON RAPIDS

ANOKA COUNTY SHOPPER
(Wed)
4101 Coon Rapids Blvd NW, Coon Rapids, MN, 55433-2525, USA; tel (763) 421-4444; ed tel (763) 712-3514; fax (763) 421-4315; ed e-mail editor.anokaunion@ecm-inc.com; web site www.abcnewspapers.com
Circulation:48,617fr; CAC
Advertising: Open inch rate $21.95
Established: 1976
Group: Adams Publishing Group, LLCEditions: 2— 2 total; Anoka County Shopper-East (31,751);
Gen. Mgr. .... Eric Olson
Adv. Mgr. .... Mike Johnson
Ed. .... Peter Bodley
Online Servs. Dir. .... Howard Burke
Prodn. Mgr. .... Dave Soucy
Adv. Dir/Gen. Mgr .... Tom Murray
Mechanical Specifications: Type page 11 x 21; E - 6 cols, 1 3/4, 1/8 between; A - 6 cols, 1 3/4, 1/8 between; C - 8 cols, 1 1/2, 1/8 between.
Equipment: Hardware — 2-APP/Power Mac G5; Software — InDesign CS.
Zip Codes Served: 55433

DEER RIVER

DEERPATH SHOPPER
(Mon)
15 1st St NE, Deer River, MN, 56636-8769, USA; tel (218) 246-8533; fax (218) 246-8540; e-mail drpub@paulbunyan.net
Circulation:6,000fr; Sworn/Estimate/Non-Audited
Advertising: Open inch rate $3.97
Ed. .... Robert Barnacle
Zip Codes Served: 56636

ELK RIVER

STAR NEWS
(Sat)
506 Freeport Ave NW, Ste A, Elk River, MN, 55330-4755, USA; tel (763) 441-3500; adv tel (763) 241-3650; fax (763) 441-6401; e-mail print.elkriver@ecm-inc.com; adv e-mail class@ecm-inc.com; ed e-mail editor.erstarnews@ecm-inc.com; web site www.erstarnews.com
Circulation: 155pd,20,209fr; CAC
Advertising: Open inch rate $22.28
Established: 1872
Group: Adams Publishing Group, LLC
Ed. .... Jim Boyle
Assoc. Ed. .... Joni Astrup
Sports Reporter .... Eric Oslund
Advertising Sales Rep .... Nicole Vadner
Advertising Sales Rep .... Tradie Wivoda
Multimedia Sales Dir .... Liz Moscatelli
Prodn. Mgr. .... Andy Lawson
Adv. Dir .... Marlys Ellingson
Pub. .... Marge Winkleman
Gen. Mgr. .... Jeff Andres
Mechanical Specifications: Type page: 10 x 21; 6 col
Equipment: Hardware — APP/Mac.
Zip Codes Served: 55330

ELY

NORTH COUNTRY SAVER
(Sat)
15 E Chapman St, Ely, MN, 55731-1227, USA; tel (218) 365-3141; fax (218) 365-3142; e-mail elyecho@aol.com; adv e-mail ads@elyecho.com; web site www.elyecho.com
Circulation: 4,400pd,4,100fr; Sworn/Estimate/Non-Audited
Advertising: Open inch rate $9.50
Established: 1980
Group: Milestones, Inc.
Digital Platform - Mobile: Apple, Android, Windows
Digital Platform - Tablet: Apple iOS, Android, Windows 7, Blackberry Tablet OS, Kindle, Nook, Kindle Fire
Pub. .... Anne Swenson
Adv. Mgr. .... Nick Wognum
Advertising Supervisor .... Lisa Vidal-Sainio
Mechanical Specifications: Type page 9.6x10; E - 6 cols, 1.46, 1/4 between
Equipment: Hardware — APP/Mac, ; Software — Indesign, Photoshop
Delivery Method: Mail, Newsstand, Racks
Zip Codes Served: 55731, 55706, 55732, 55607, 55782, 55790, 55796

FAIRMONT

FAIRMONT PHOTO PRESS
(Wed)
112 E 1st St, Fairmont, MN, 56031-2807, USA; tel (507) 238-9456; fax (507) 238-9457; e-mail jeff@fairmontphotopress.com; adv e-mail ads@fairmontphotopress.com; ed e-mail editor@fairmontphotopress.com; web site www.fairmontphotopress.com
Circulation: 36pd,11,896fr; CVC
Advertising: Open inch rate $12.10
Established: 1963
Digital Platform - Mobile: Apple
Digital Platform - Tablet: Apple iOS
Adv./Sales. .... Randy Chirpich
Ed./Circ. .... Sherman L. Kumba
Pressman .... Larry Day
Mgr. .... Jeff Hagen
Graphics Designer .... Samantha Hillmer
Graphics Designer .... Becky Glazier
Customer service .... Tari Stradtman
Mechanical Specifications: Type page 11 x 16; E - 6 cols, 1 11/16, 1/8 between; A - 6 cols, 1 11/16, 1/8 between; C - 6 cols, 1 11/16, 1/8 between.
Equipment: Hardware — 8-MAC OS 10.1; Presses — Chief/15, Digital Impressia; Software — Adobe/PageMaker 6.5, Creative Suite, MAC InDesign CS5.5, Adobe Photoshop CS5.1, Adobe Illustrator CS5.1
Delivery Method: Mail, Carrier
Zip Codes Served: 56031,56171,56121,56127,56181,56176,56027,56039,56047,56075,56088,50514,50531,50590,50578

FARIBAULT

FARIBAULT AREA SHOPPER
(Sat)
514 Central Ave N, Faribault, MN, 55021-4304, USA; tel (507) 333-3100; adv tel (507) 333-3120; fax (507) 333-3102; adv e-mail amccann@faribault.com; ed e-mail srook@faribault.com; web site www.faribault.com
Circulation:7,396fr; Sworn/Estimate/Non-Audited
Advertising: Open inch rate $20.10
Established: 1978
Group: Adams Publishing Group, LLC
Pub. .... Sam Gett
Mechanical Specifications: Type page 11 5/8 x 21 1/2; E - 6 cols, 1 5/6, between; A - 6 cols, 1 5/6, between; C - 6 cols, 1 5/6, between.
Delivery Method: Carrier
Zip Codes Served: 56052, 55021, 55069, 55946, 55052, 55049, 55053, 55019, 55087

FERGUS FALLS

THE MIDWEEK, INC.
(Sun)
831 E Vasa Ave, Fergus Falls, MN, 56537-3064, USA; tel (218) 739-3308; fax (218) 739-5424; e-mail midweek@themidweek.com; web site www.themidweek.com
Circulation:36,350fr; CVC
Advertising: Open inch rate $11.45
Pub. .... Richard Anderson
Advt.Mgr .... Jim Tederson
Circ. Mgr. .... Sean Bell
Mechanical Specifications: Type page 6 x 16.
Equipment: Hardware — APP/Mac; Presses — G.
Zip Codes Served: 56537

THIS WEEK'S SHOPPING NEWS
(Sun) (Thanksgiving Edition)
831 E Vasa Ave, Fergus Falls, MN, 56537-3064, USA; tel (218) 739-3308; fax (218) 739-5424; e-mail results@themidweekpublications.com; adv e-mail results@themidweekpublications.com; web site www.themidweek.com
Circulation:19,553fr; CVC
Advertising: Open inch rate $15.25
Established: 1978
Digital Platform - Mobile: Apple, Android, Windows, Blackberry
Digital Platform - Tablet: Apple iOS, Android, Windows 7, Blackberry Tablet OS, Kindle, Nook, Kindle FireRichard Anderson
Sales Manager .... Jon Anderson
Production Manager .... Paula Grunewald
Mechanical Specifications: Type page: 10.33 x 16; 6 col
Equipment: Hardware — Mac
Delivery Method: Mail, Carrier, Racks
Zip Codes Served: 56309 56324 56515 56524 56528 56531 56533 56534 56537 56543 56551 56567 56571 56572 56573 56576 56579 56586 56587 56588 56590

WEEKENDER
(Fri)
914 E Channing Ave, Fergus Falls, MN, 56537-3738, USA; tel (218) 736-7511; fax (218) 736-5919; web site www.fergusfallsjournal.com
Circulation:4,200fr; Sworn/Estimate/Non-Audited
Advertising: Open inch rate $10.25
Group: Boone Newspapers, Inc.
Pub./Pres. .... David Churchill
Gen. Mgr. .... Joel Myhre
Circ. Mgr. .... Connie Knapp
Mechanical Specifications: Type page 12 15/16 x 21 1/2; E - 6 cols, 2, 1/6 between; A - 6 cols, 2, 1/6 between; C - 9 cols, 1 5/16, 1/12 between.
Equipment: Hardware — APP/Mac; Software — Adobe/PageMaker 6.5, Aldus, QPS/QuarkXPress 3.32, Adobe/Photoshop 3.0, Macromedia/Freehand 7.0.

FOREST LAKE

ST. CROIX VALLEY PEACH
(Sun)
146 Lake St N, Ste 125, Forest Lake, MN, 55025-2109, USA; tel (651) 464-4601; fax (651) 464-4605; web site www.hometownsource.com
Circulation:27,004fr; CAC
Advertising: Open inch rate $13.60
Established: 1954
Group: Adams Publishing Group, LLC
Pres. .... Julian L. Anderson
Gen Mgr. .... Jeff Andres
Mgr. .... Steve Rajtar
Adv. Mgr. .... Carol Lehnen
Ed. .... Cliff Buchan
Adv. Dir. .... Jerry Gloe
Mechanical Specifications: Type page 10 2/5 x 15; A - 6 cols, 1 3/5, 1/6 between; C - 6 cols, 1 3/5, 1/6 between.
Equipment: Hardware — APP/Mac; Presses — 8-HI; Software — QPS/QuarkXPress, Adobe/Illustrator, Adobe/Photoshop.
Zip Codes Served: 54009, 54020, 54024, 55002, 55005, 55012, 55013, 55014, 55025, 55038, 55045, 55047, 55056, 55073, 55074, 55079, 55084, 55092, 55304

FULDA

MURRAY COUNTY ADVANTAGE
(Mon)
PO Box 439, 118 N St. Paul Ave, Fulda, MN, 56131-0439, USA; tel (507) 425-2303; adv tel (507) 425-2303; ed tel (507) 425-2303; fax (507) 425-2501; adv fax (507) 425-2501; ed fax (507) 425-2501; e-mail text@fuldafreepress.net; adv e-mail ads@fuldafreepress.net; ed e-mail jerry@fuldafreepress.net; web site www.fuldafreepress.net
Circulation:7,947fr; CVC
Advertising: $7.20
Established: 1881
Digital Platform - Mobile: Apple
Digital Platform - Tablet: Apple iOS
Publisher .... Gerald D. Johnson
Mechanical Specifications: Eight columns 15x21.5 inches
Delivery Method: Mail
Zip Codes Served: 56131,56172,56114,56115,56119,56122,56123,
56128,56141,56151,56153,56155,56170,56175,56180,56183,56185,56186

GLENCOE

THE GLENCOE ADVERTISER
(Sun)
716 10th St E, Glencoe, MN, 55336-2212, USA; tel (320) 864-5518; fax (320) 864-5510; ed e-mail chronicle@glencoenews.com; web site www.glencoenews.com
Circulation:13,500fr; Sworn/Estimate/Non-Audited
Advertising: Open inch rate $9.85
Pub. .... William C. Ramige
Adv. Mgr. .... Sue Colden
Circ. Mgr. .... Trisha Karelf
Mng. Ed. .... Rich Glennie
Mechanical Specifications: Type page 13 x 21 1/2; A - 6 cols, between.
Zip Codes Served: 55336

GRAND RAPIDS

HERALD-REVIEW/MANNEY'S SHOPPER

(Wed, Sun)
301 NW 1st Ave, Grand Rapids, MN, 55744-2704, USA; tel (218) 326-6623; fax (218) 326-6627; e-mail graps@mx3.com; adv e-mail subscriptions@grandrapidsmn.com; web site www.grandrapidsmn.com
Circulation: 14,300pd,22,700fr; Sworn/Estimate/Non-Audited
Established: 1896
Editor....................Britta Arendt
Advertising Director....................Mark Roy
Publisher....................Todd Keute
Mechanical Specifications: Type page 10 5/8 x 16; E - 5 cols, 2, 1/8 between; A - 5 cols, 2, 1/8 between.
Equipment: Hardware — APP/Mac; Presses — KP; Software — Adobe/Typestyler, MultiAd/AdCreator, Adobe/Photoshop, QPS/QuarkXPress.
Delivery Method: Mail, Newsstand, Carrier
Zip Codes Served: 55744

HALSTAD

THE SHOPPER

(Mon)
301 3rd Ave W, Halstad, MN, 56548-4027, USA; tel (218) 456-2133; fax (218) 456-2567; e-mail shopdiv@rrv.net; adv e-mail publisher@rrv.net
Circulation:23,342fr; CVC
Advertising: Open inch rate $13.95
Established: 1975
Group: GateHouse Media, Inc.Don Forney
Pub....................Don Forney
Circ. Mgr....................Karen Rauser
Mechanical Specifications: Type page: 11.7 x 21.5; 6 col
Delivery Method: Mail, Carrier, Racks
Zip Codes Served: 56548

HASTINGS

TRADE WINDS SHOPPING GUIDE

(Sun)
745 Spiral Blvd, Hastings, MN, 55033-3651, USA; tel (651) 437-6153; fax (651) 437-5911; e-mail news@hastingsstargazette.com; web site www.hastingsstargazette.com
Circulation:15,000fr; Sworn/Estimate/Non-Audited
Advertising: Open inch rate $12.00
Pub....................Steven R. Messick
Adv. Mgr....................Chad Richardson
Equipment: Hardware — APP/Mac; Software — QPS/QuarkXPress 4.0.
Zip Codes Served: 55033

HIBBING

MANNEY'S SHOPPER

(Sun)
2142 1st Ave, Hibbing, MN, 55746-3759, USA; tel (218) 263-8357; fax (213) 263-9201; web site www.manneys.com
Circulation: 3pd,14,925fr; Sworn/Estimate/Non-Audited
Advertising: Open inch rate $16.44Editions: 3— 3 total; Manney's Shopper-Grand Rapids Area (18,250); Manney's Shopper-Hibbing Area (15,605); Manney's Shopper-Virginia Area (19,771);
Gen. Mgr....................Mark Roy
Zone Mgr....................Brian Palokangas
Circ. Dir....................Ida Meyer
Mechanical Specifications: Type page 11 5/8 x 21 1/2; E - 6 cols, 1 7/8, 1/10 between; A - 6 cols, 1 7/8, 1/10 between.
Equipment: Hardware — APP/Mac; Presses — 8-HI; Software — QPS/QuarkXPress.
Zip Codes Served: 54880, 55616, 55720, 55744, 55746, 55792

HUTCHINSON

HUTCHINSON LEADER AND LEADER SHOPPER

(Wed, Sun)
170 Shady Ridge Rd NW Ste 100, Suite 100, Hutchinson, MN, 55350-1454, USA; tel (320) 587-5000; fax (320) 587-6104; e-mail true@hutchinsonleader.com; adv e-mail warden@hutchinsonleader.com; ed e-mail hanneman@hutchinsonleader.com; web site http://www.crowrivermedia.com/hutchinson-leader
Circulation:1,992fr; CAC
Advertising: Open inch rate $11.59
Established: 1880
Group: Red Wing Publishing Co.
Pub....................Brent Schacherer
Adv. Mgr....................Kevin True
Ed....................Doug Hanneman
Mechanical Specifications: Type page 13 x 21 1/2; E - 6 cols, 1.715" 1/8 between; A - 6 cols, 1.715, 1/8 between; C - 6 cols, 1.715, 1/8 between.
Equipment: Hardware — APP/Power Macs; Presses — G/Community; Software — Multi-Ad/Creator, QPS/QuarkXPress.
Delivery Method: Mail, Newsstand, Carrier
Zip Codes Served: 56228, 55350, 55336, 55321, 55324, 55325, 55336, 55342, 55354, 55355, 55381, 55385, 55395, 55396, 55312, 55314

ISLE

BARGAIN HUNTER

(Sat)
PO Box 26, Isle, MN, 56342-0026, USA; tel (320) 676-3123; adv tel (218) 927-3761; ed tel (218) 927-3761; fax (320) 676-8450; adv fax (218) 927-3763; ed fax (218) 927-3763; e-mail rbouley@millelacsmessenger.com; adv e-mail rbouley@millelacsmessenger.com; ed e-mail news@millelacsmessenger.com; web site www.millelacsmessenger.com
Circulation:21,481fr; CVC
Advertising: Open inch rate $16.72
Established: 1987
Group: Adams Publishing Group, LLC
Digital Platform - Mobile: Apple, Android, Windows, Blackberry
Digital Platform - Tablet: Apple iOS, Android, Windows 7, Blackberry Tablet OS, Kindle, Nook, Kindle Fire
Operations Manager....................RoxAnne Bouley
Circulation Manager....................Sharon Dotzler
Mechanical Specifications: Type page 10 x 21; E - 7 cols, 1.389, 1/8 between; A - 7 cols, 1.389, 1/8 between; C - 7 cols, 1.389, 1/8 between.
Equipment: Hardware — Macs; Software — Adobe and Quark
Delivery Method: Mail, Newsstand, Racks
Zip Codes Served: 56431, 55748, 56350, 55760, 56469, 55787, 55752, 55798, 56401, 56441, 56444, 56447, 56450, 56455, 56342, 56386, 56359, 56338

JACKSON

JACKSON COUNTY LIVEWIRE

(Sun)
310 2nd St, Jackson, MN, 56143-1640, USA; tel (507) 847-3771; fax (507) 847-5822; e-mail info@livewireprinting.com; web site www.livewireprinting.com
Circulation: 5pd,10,344fr; CVC
Advertising: Open inch rate $10.25
Established: 1929
Pub....................Justin R. Lessman
Mechanical Specifications: Type page 9 3/4 x 15; E - 6 cols, 1 1/2, 1/8 between; A - 6 cols, 1 1/2, 1/8 between; C - 6 cols, 1 1/2, 1/8 between.
Equipment: Hardware — PC; Presses — 7-G; Software — Adobe/PageMaker.
Zip Codes Served: 56143, 56160, 56111, 56127, 56171, 56176, 56181, 51334, 51360, 51363, 56101, 56101, 56137, 56161

KENYON

KENYON AREA SHOPPER

(Sat)
638 2nd St, Kenyon, MN, 55946-1334, USA; web site www.thekenyonleader.com
Circulation:2,132fr; CVC
Advertising: Open inch rate $9.75
Established: 2007
Reporter....................Kevin Anderson
Mechanical Specifications: Type page: 10.389 x 21.5; 6 col
Zip Codes Served: 55946
Note: We no longer have a separate shopper.

LAKE CITY

LAKE CITY SHOPPER

(Tues)
111 S 8th St, Lake City, MN, 55041-1666, USA; tel (651) 345-3316; fax (651) 345-4200; e-mail graphic@rconnect.com; adv e-mail ads@lakecitygraphic.com; ed e-mail news@lakecitygraphic.com; web site www.lakecitygraphic.com
Circulation:7,800fr; Sworn/Estimate/Non-Audited
Advertising: Open inch rate $9.90
Established: 1959
Group: Lake City Printing Co.
Digital Platform - Mobile: Apple, Android, Windows, Blackberry, Other
Digital Platform - Tablet: Apple iOS, Android, Windows 7, Blackberry Tablet OS, Kindle, Nook, Kindle Fire, Other
Pub....................Terry Schumacher
Adv. Mgr....................Dean Schumacher
editor....................Andrew Eggenberger
Mechanical Specifications: 6 column 10.625 x 21
Delivery Method: Mail, Carrier, Racks
Zip Codes Served: 55041

LINDSTROM

SEARCH SHOPPER

(Thur, Sun)
12631 Lake Blvd, Lindstrom, MN, 55045-9344, USA; tel (651) 257-5115; fax (651) 257-5500; e-mail chisago@citlink.net; web site www.chisagocountypress.com
Circulation: 3,500pd,16,000fr; Sworn/Estimate/Non-Audited
Advertising: Open inch rate $11.37
Established: 1898
Digital Platform - Mobile: Apple
Pub....................Matt Silver
Prodn. Mgr....................Laure Peterson
Ed....................Denise Martin
Mechanical Specifications: Type page 10 x 21; E - 6 cols, 2 1/3, 1/6 between; A - 6 cols, 2 1/3, 1/6 between; C - 6 cols, 2 1/3, 1/6 between.
Equipment: Hardware — APP/Mac; Software — QPS/QuarkXPress 8.5
Delivery Method: Mail, Newsstand, Carrier, Racks
Zip Codes Served: 55045, 55013, 55012, 55056, 55074, 55079, 55092, 55085, 55084, 55002, 55073

LUVERNE

LUVERNE ANNOUNCER

(Sun)
117 W Main St, Luverne, MN, 56156-1843, USA; tel (507) 283-2333; fax (507) 283-2335; e-mail rick@star-herald.com; adv e-mail sales@star-herald.com; ed e-mail editor@star-herald.com; web site www.star-herald.com
Circulation: 3pd,9,135fr; CVC
Advertising: Open inch rate $10.10
Established: 1931
Digital Platform - Mobile: Apple
Digital Platform - Tablet: Apple iOS
Adv. Mgr....................Rick Peterson
Ed....................Lori Ehde
Mechanical Specifications: Type page: 12.5 x 21; 6 col
Equipment: Hardware — APP/Mac.
Delivery Method: Mail, Carrier, Racks
Zip Codes Served: 56156

MADELIA

PURE GOLD

(Mthly)
112 W Main St, Madelia, MN, 56062-1440, USA; tel (507) 642-3636; fax (507) 642-3535; e-mail mikek@madtelco.net
Circulation:15,000fr; Sworn/Estimate/Non-Audited
Advertising: Open inch rate $7.95
Established: 1999
Group: Prairie Publishing, Inc
Ed....................Mike Koob
Mechanical Specifications: Type page 10 x 15; E - 6 cols, between; A - 6 cols, between.
Delivery Method: Mail
Zip Codes Served: 560

MANKATO

HOME MAGAZINE

(Tues)
1400 Madison Ave Ste 610, Madison East Center, Mankato, MN, 56001-5488, USA; tel (507) 387-7953; fax (507) 387-4775; e-mail homemag@homemagonline.com; web site www.homemagonline.com
Circulation: 10pd,37,502fr; CVC
Advertising: Open inch rate $24.30
Established: 1971
Creative Servs. Mgr....................Kay Brandt
Sales Mgr....................MaryKay Degrood
Circ. Mgr....................Robin Stenzel
Ed....................Kelly Anderson
Mechanical Specifications: Type page 10 1/2 x 15; A - 6 cols, 1 2/3, 1/12 between; C - 6 cols, 1 2/3, 1/12 between.
Equipment: Hardware — APP/Mac G4; Software — Multi-Ad/Creator 6, QPS/QuarkXPress, Adobe/PageMaker, Macromedia/Freehand, Adobe/Typestyler.
Zip Codes Served: 56001, 56010, 56017, 56024, 56028, 56034, 56037, 56048, 56050, 56055, 56057, 56058, 56062, 56063, 56065, 56068, 56074, 56077, 56078, 56080, 56082, 56090, 56091, 56093, 56097

MARSHALL

INDEPENDENT SHOPPER'S REVIEW

(Tues, Wed) (Tues/Wed - Mail/Carrier)
508 W Main St, Marshall, MN, 56258-1317, USA; tel (507) 537-1551; fax (507) 537-1557; e-mail independent@marshallindependent.com; adv e-mail tbrandl@marshallindependent.com; ed e-mail phpeterson@marshallindependent.com; web site none
Circulation: 0pd,12,599fr; Sworn/Estimate/Non-Audited
Advertising: Open inch rate - pick up rate -$3.60 per column inch (local rates) - pick up when running first in Independent
Established: 1874
Group: Ogden Newspapers Inc.
Pub....................Russell D. Labat
Creative Servs. Mgr....................Deb Johnson
Adv. Mgr....................Tara Brandl
Ed....................Per Peterson
Circu Mgr....................Rob Purrington
Mechanical Specifications: Type page 6 x 21 1/2; E - 6 cols, 1.583", C - 9 cols, 1.022".

Equipment: ; Presses — Printed at the House of Print, Madelia, MN; Software — QPS/QuarkXPress 8, Multi-Ad/Creator 6.0.5, Adobe/Photoshop 6.0, Adobe/Illustrator 10.0.
Delivery Method: Mail, Carrier, Racks
Zip Codes Served: 56258,56263,56239,56157, 56264,56229,56175,56132,56115,56169,56 291,56264,

MINNEAPOLIS

STAR TRIBUNE BUYER'S EDGE

(Mon)
425 Portland Ave, Minneapolis, MN, 55488-1511, USA; tel (612) 673-4510; fax (612) 673-4359
Advertising: Open inch rate $9.45
Adv. Mgr. .... Michelle Casserly
Ed. .... John Ewoldt
Mng. Ed. .... Susan Hopper

MONTEVIDEO

MONTEVIDEO STAR ADVISOR

(Mon)
PO Box 99, Montevideo, MN, 56265-0099, USA; web site www.montenews.com
Circulation: 11,412fr; CVC
Advertising: Open inch rate $9.75
Established: 1929Kurt Dahl
Mechanical Specifications: Type page: 10.25 x 13.75; 6 col

MONTICELLO

MONTICELLO SHOPPER

(Sun)
116 E River St, Monticello, MN, 55362-9390, USA; tel (763) 295-3131; fax (763) 295-3080; e-mail monticellotimes@monticellotimes.com; web site www.monticellotimes.com
Circulation: 26,800fr; Sworn/Estimate/Non-Audited
Advertising: Open inch rate $15.35
Group: American Community Newspapers LLC
Pub. .... Bruce Treichler
Adv. Mgr. .... Terry Sweet
Mechanical Specifications: Type page 13 x 21 1/2; E - 6 cols, 2, 1/4 between; A - 6 cols, 2, 1/4 between.
Equipment: Hardware — APP/Mac; Software — QPS/QuarkXPress.
Zip Codes Served: 55362, 55308, 55309, 55301, 55320, 55358, 55330, 55320, 55319, 55398, 55376

MOOSE LAKE

EVERGREEN SHOPPER

(Mon)
308 Elm Ave, Moose Lake, MN, 55767-7706, USA; tel (218) 485-4406; fax (218) 485-0237; e-mail evergreen@ml-star-gazette.com; web site www.ml-star-gazette.com
Circulation: 18,500fr; Sworn/Estimate/Non-Audited
Advertising: Open inch rate $8.00
Established: 1895
Mechanical Specifications: Type page 10 1/2 x 15.
Equipment: Hardware — APP/Macs; Software — Adobe/PageMaker 6.0.
Zip Codes Served: 55767

NEW LONDON

LAKES AREA REVIEW

(Sat)
106 Norwood St SW, New London, MN, 56273-8520, USA; tel (320) 354-2945; fax (320) 354-6300; e-mail lakesareareview@tds.net; adv e-mail reviewsales@tds.net
Circulation: 145pd,6,335fr; CVC
Advertising: Open inch rate $12.35
Established: 1899
Group: Village Ink Ltd.
PUBLISHER .... Theodore ALMEN
Mechanical Specifications: Type page 6 5/8 x 21 1/2; E - 6 cols, 2, 1/8" between; A - 6 cols, 2, 1/8 between; C - 6 cols, 2, 1/8 between.
Equipment: Hardware — 5-APP/iMac; Software — QPS/QuarkXPress 8.0, Adobe/Photoshop 7.0, Adobe/Acrobat 5.0, Adobe/Illustrator 8.0.
Delivery Method: Mail, Newsstand
Zip Codes Served: 56288, 56273, 56201, 56312, 56279, 56289

NEW ULM

NEW ULM SHOPPER/POST REVIEW

(Tues)
514 3rd St N, New Ulm, MN, 56073-1704, USA; tel (507) 359-2091; fax (507) 359-7362; e-mail bfense@nujournal.com; adv e-mail Nushopper@nujournal.com; web site www.nujournal.com
Circulation: 16,500pd,; Sworn/Estimate/Non-Audited
Advertising: Open inch rate $5.60
Group: Ogden Newspapers Inc.
Pub. .... Bruce Fenske
Adv. Mgr. .... Becky Tykwinski
Mechanical Specifications: Type page 6 x 21 1/4; E - 5 cols, 2 1/6, 1/6 between; A - 5 cols, 2 1/16, 1/6 between; C - 5 cols, 2 1/16, 1/6 between.
Delivery Method: Mail, Carrier, Racks
Zip Codes Served: 56073, 56021, 55332, 55334, 55335, 56041, 56054,, 56062, 56266, 56074, 56085, 56087, 55346

NORTHFIELD

NORTHFIELD WEEKENDER

(Sat)
115 5th St W, Northfield, MN, 55057-2007, USA; tel (507) 645-1107; adv tel (507) 645-1110; fax (507) 645-6005; adv e-mail chjellming@northfieldnews.com; web site www.northfieldnews.com
Circulation: 9,464fr; Sworn/Estimate/Non-Audited
Advertising: Open inch rate $21.00
Established: 1978
Group: Adams Publishing Group, LLC
Pub .... Chad Hjellming
Mechanical Specifications: Type page 11 5/8 x 21 1/2; E - 6 cols, 1 5/6, between; A - 6 cols, 1 5/6, between; C - 6 cols, 1 5/6, between.
Delivery Method: Mail, Carrier
Zip Codes Served: 55057, 55019, 55009, 55031, 55088, 55046, 55018, 55065

OWATONNA

OWATONNA AREA SHOPPER

(Sat)
135 W Pearl St, Owatonna, MN, 55060-2316, USA; tel (507) 451-2840; adv tel (507) 444-2389; ed tel (507) 444-2389; fax (507) 444-2382; ed fax (507) 451-6020; adv e-mail gbergerson@owatonna.com; ed e-mail jjackson@owatonna.com; web site www.owatonna.com
Circulation: 7,255fr; Sworn/Estimate/Non-Audited
Advertising: Open inch rate $20.25
Established: 1978
Group: Adams Publishing Group, LLC
Digital Platform - Mobile: Other
Digital Platform - Tablet: Other
Circ. Mgr. .... Carol Harvey
Ad Dir. .... Ginny Bergerson
Publisher .... Tom Murray
Mechanical Specifications: Type page 11 5/8 x 21 1/2; E - 6 cols, 1 5/6, between; A - 6 cols, 1 5/6, between; C - 6 cols, 1 5/6, between.
Equipment: Hardware — pc'S; Presses — GOSS; Software — Adobe/InDesign.
Delivery Method: Carrier
Zip Codes Served: 55060, 56046, 55985, 55924, 55917, 56026, 55927

PARK RAPIDS

PARK RAPIDS ENTERPRISE EXPRESS

(Sat)
203 Henrietta Ave N, Park Rapids, MN, 56470-2617, USA; tel (218) 732-3364; fax (218) 732-8757; e-mail aerickson@parkrapidsenterprise.com; web site www.parkrapidsenterprise.com
Circulation: 8,599fr; VAC
Group: Forum Communications Co.
Publisher .... Rory Palm
Adv. Mgr. .... Candy Parks
Sports Editor .... Vance Carlson
Editor .... Anna Erickson
Equipment: Hardware — PCs; Software — QuarkXPress 8, Adobe Photoshop

PAYNESVILLE

CENTRAL MINNESOTA LAKES AREA SHOPPER

(Sun)
211 Washburne Ave, Paynesville, MN, 56362-1642, USA; tel (320) 243-3772; fax (320) 243-4492; adv e-mail ads@paynesvillepress.com; ed e-mail editor@paynesvillepress.com; web site www.paynesvillearea.com
Circulation: 105pd,9,053fr; CVC
Advertising: $8.50
Established: 1887Michael Jacobson
Delivery Method: Carrier, Racks
Zip Codes Served: 56362
55329
56368
56273
56312

PIPESTONE

FREE STAR SHOPPER

(Mon)
115 2nd St NE, Pipestone, MN, 56164-1956, USA; tel (507) 825-3333; adv tel (507) 825-3333; ed tel (507) 825-3333; fax (507) 825-2168; adv fax (507) 825-2168; ed fax (507) 825-2168; e-mail pipepub@pipestonestar.com; adv e-mail pipepub@pipestonestar.com; ed e-mail editor@pipestonestar.com; web site www.pipestonestar.com
Circulation: 3pd,10,807fr; CVC
Advertising: $10.80
Established: 1976
Group: Pipestone Publishing Co., Inc.
Digital Platform - Mobile: Apple, Android
Digital Platform - Tablet: Apple iOS, Android
Pub. .... John C. Draper
Adv. Mgr. .... Paul Lorang
Circ. Mgr. .... Glenda Carstensen
Mechanical Specifications: Type page 15 1/8 x 21 1/2; E - 7 cols, 2 1/16, 1/8 between; A - 7 cols, 2 1/16, 1/8 between; C - 7 cols, 2 1/16, 1/8 between.
Equipment: Hardware — MAC OSX; Presses — Contract-outsource; Software — InDesign Suite
Delivery Method: Mail, Newsstand, Carrier, Racks
Zip Codes Served: 56164, 56122,56128, 56134, 56139, 56140, 56144, 56149, 56151, 56170, 56178, 56186, 57024, 57026, 57028, 57030, 57065

RED WING

EAGLE EXTRA

(Sat)
2760 N Service Dr, Red Wing, MN, 55066-1985, USA; tel (651) 388-8235; adv tel (651) 301-7854; fax (651) 388-3404; adv e-mail advertising@republican-egle.com; web site www.republican-eagle.com
Circulation: 14,327fr; USPS
Advertising: Open inch rate $13.77
Pub. .... Steve Messick
Ed. .... Anne Jacobson
Advertising Director .... Phil Frebault
Mechanical Specifications: Type page 13 x 21 1/2; E - 6 cols, 2 1/16, 1/8 between; A - 6 cols, 2 1/16, 1/8 between; C - 8 cols, 1 1/2, 1/8 between.
Delivery Method: Mail
Zip Codes Served: 55066

HIAWATHA VALLEY SHOPPER

(Sat)
PO Box 324, Red Wing, MN, 55066-0324, USA; tel (715) 792-2880; fax (715) 273-4769; e-mail info@helmerprinting.com; web site www.helmerprinting.com
Circulation: 10pd,9,219fr; CVC
Advertising: Open inch rate $18.83
Group: Helmer Printing, Inc.
Adv. Mgr. .... Mark Helmer
Circ. Mgr. .... Steve Block
Ed. .... Scott P. Helmer
Prodn. Mgr. .... John Vogland
Mechanical Specifications: Type page 10 1/4 x 14; E - 5 cols, 2, 1/72 between; A - 5 cols, 2, 1/72 between; C - 5 cols, 2, 1/72 between.
Equipment: Hardware — APP/Mac, PC; Presses — G/Community; Software — Claris/FileMaker Pro, QPS/QuarkXPress, Adobe/Illustrator, Adobe/Photoshop.
Zip Codes Served: 55066

REDWOOD FALLS

REDWOOD FALLS LIVEWIRE

(Mon, Thur)
219 S Washington St, Redwood Falls, MN, 56283-1700, USA; tel (507) 637-2929; fax (507) 637-3175; web site www.redwoodfalls-gazette.com
Circulation: 6,200fr; Sworn/Estimate/Non-Audited
Advertising: Open inch rate $8.00
Group: GateHouse Media, Inc.
Pub. .... Pat Schmidt
Circ. Mgr. .... Barb Cole
Ed. .... Troy Krause
Prodn. Mgr. .... Peggy Kipfer

ROCHESTER

THE ROCHESTER SHOPPER

(Tues)
18 1st Ave SE, Rochester, MN, 55904-3722, USA; tel (507) 285-7600; fax (507) 285-7666; adv e-mail addesign@postbulletin.com
Circulation: 18,000fr; Sworn/Estimate/Non-Audited
Advertising: Open inch rate $8.80Editions: 1—1 total; Austin Edition;
Adv. Mgr. .... Audrey Groteboer
Circ. Mgr. .... William Lisser
Ed. .... Randy Chapman
Prodn. Mgr. .... Jeff Lansing
Zip Codes Served: 55903

ROSEAU

BORDERLINE

(Sun)
106 Center St W, Roseau, MN, 56751-1417, USA; tel (218) 463-1521; fax (218) 463-1530;

e-mail rtr@mncable.net
Circulation:5,000fr; Sworn/Estimate/Non-Audited
Advertising: Open inch rate $25.00
Pub. .... Jody Driscoll
Zip Codes Served: 56751

SAINT CLOUD

THE SHOPPING NEWS
(Tues)
3000 7th St N, Saint Cloud, MN, 56303-3108, USA; tel (320) 259-3600; fax (320) 252-8773; web site www.sctimes.com
Circulation:47,500fr; Sworn/Estimate/Non-Audited
Group: Gannett
Gen. Mgr. .... Julie Schlagheck
Mechanical Specifications: Type page 10 x 15; A - 4 cols, between; C - 4 cols, between.
Equipment: Hardware — APP/Mac; Software — Baseview, Adobe/Photoshop.
Zip Codes Served: 56302

SAINT PETER

MINNESOTA RIVER VALLEY SHOPPER
(Sun)
311 S Minnesota Ave, Saint Peter, MN, 56082-2523, USA; tel (507) 931-4520; fax (507) 931-4522; web site www.stpeterherald.com
Circulation:11,241fr; CAC
Advertising: Open inch rate $15.50
Established: 1978
Group: Adams Publishing Group, LLC
Adv. Mgr. .... Kathleen Davies
Ed. .... Ed Lee
Mechanical Specifications: Type page 11 5/8 x 21 1/2; E - 6 cols, 1 5/6, between; A - 6 cols, 1 5/6, between; C - 6 cols, 1 5/6, between.
Zip Codes Served: 56082, 56058, 56057, 56044, 56050, 56017

SAUK CENTRE

DAIRYLAND PEACH
(Sun)
601 Sinclair Lewis Ave, Sauk Centre, MN, 56378-4884, USA; tel (320) 352-6569; fax (320) 352-6181; e-mail print.saukcentre@ecm-inc.com; web site www.dailylandpeach.com
Circulation:26,236fr; CAC
Advertising: Open inch rate $10.90
Established: 1967
Group: Adams Publishing Group, LLC
Gen. Mgr. .... Tom West
Classified Mgr. .... Karen Banal
Circ. Mgr. .... Brian McCoy
Prodn. Mgr. .... Annette Gruber
Adv. Dir. .... Carmen Meyer
Mechanical Specifications: Type page 10.3889 x 15; A - 6 cols, 1.5, between; C - 6 cols, 1.5, between.
Equipment: Hardware — COM; Software — QPS/QuarkXPress.
Zip Codes Served: 56378

MID-MINNESOTA SHOPPER
(Sun)
522 Sinclair Lewis Ave, Sauk Centre, MN, 56378-1246, USA; web site www.saukherald.com
Circulation: 579pd,14,478fr; CVC
Advertising: Open inch rate $8.97
Established: 1867Dave Simpkins
Mechanical Specifications: Type page: 10 x 14.75; 6 col

SLAYTON

MURRAY COUNTY WHEEL/HERALD
(Mon)
2734 Broadway Ave, Slayton, MN, 56172-1314, USA; tel (507) 836-8726; fax (507) 836-8942; e-mail wheelherald@gmail.com; adv e-mail wheelherald@gmail.com; ed e-mail wheelherald@gmail.com
Circulation:6,850fr; CVC
Advertising: Open inch rate $8.10
Established: 1972
Adv. Mgr. .... Randy Beers
Business Manager .... Katie Beers
Mechanical Specifications: Type page: 15 x 21.5; 8 col
Delivery Method: Mail
Zip Codes Served: 56172, 56114, 56115, 56122, 56123, 56131, 56132, 56151, 56141, 56151, 56155, 56170, 56175, 56183, 56185, 56186

SLEEPY EYE

BROWN COUNTY REMINDER
(Mon)
119 Main St E, Sleepy Eye, MN, 56085-1352, USA; tel (507) 794-3511; adv tel (507) 794-3511; ed tel (507) 794-3511; fax (507) 794-5031; e-mail ddurheim@stjamesnews.com; adv e-mail ddurheim@stjamesnews.com; ed e-mail ddurheim@stjamesnews.com; web site www.sleepyeyenews.com
Circulation:7,385fr; CVC
Advertising: Open inch rate $9.00
Group: GateHouse Media, Inc.
General Manager .... Duane "Doc" Durheim
Delivery Method: Mail, Carrier

SPRING VALLEY

BLUFF COUNTRY READER
(Mon)
112 N Broadway St, Spring Valley, MN, 55975-1224, USA; tel (507) 346-7365; fax (507) 346-7366; e-mail info@bluffcountry-news.com; adv e-mail ads@bluffcountrynews.com; ed e-mail news@bluffcountrynews.com; web site www.bluffcountryreader.com
Circulation: 48pd,18,748fr; CVC
Advertising: Open inch rate $11.25
Established: 1999
Group: Bluff Country Newspaper Group
Bluffs Country Newspaper GroupEditions: 1—
Pub. .... David Phillips
Circ. Mgr. .... Debby Groth
Ed. .... Melissa Vander Plas
Mechanical Specifications: Type page 10.22 x 15; E - 5 cols, 1 15/16, 1/6 between; A - 5 cols, 1 15/16, between; C - 5 cols, 1 15/16, between.
Equipment: Hardware — APP/Mac; Software — Adobe Creative Cloud - InDesign, etc.
Delivery Method: Mail, Newsstand, Racks
Zip Codes Served: 55975, 55990, 55936, 55961, 55967, 52134, 55951, 55926, 55933, 55923, 55934, 55935, 55949, 52155, 55962, 55965, 55939, 55922, 55954, 52101, 55974, 55931, 52140, 55921, 55943, 55971

STAPLES

SUNDAY SQUARE SHOOTER
(Sun)
224 4th St NE, Staples, MN, 56479-2428, USA; tel (218) 894-1112; fax (218) 894-3570; e-mail info@staplesworld.com
Circulation:9,500fr; Sworn/Estimate/Non-Audited
Advertising: Open inch rate $10.75
Established: 1890
Gen. Mgr. .... Brenda Halvorson
Adv. Mgr. .... Gary Mueller
Ed. .... Tom Crawford
Mechanical Specifications: Type page 13 x 21 1/2; E - 6 cols, 2, 1/16 between; A - 6 cols, 2, 1/16 between; C - 6 cols, 2, 1/16 between.
Equipment: Hardware — APP/Macs; Software — QPS/QuarkXPress 4.0, Adobe/Photoshop 5.0.
Zip Codes Served: 56479, 56466, 56473, 56481

TYLER

SOUTHWESTERN PEACH
(Wed)
151 N Tyler St, Tyler, MN, 56178-1160, USA; tel (507) 247-5502; fax (507) 247-5502; e-mail tribute@tylertribute.com
Circulation:3,000fr; Sworn/Estimate/Non-Audited
Advertising: Open inch rate $8.00
Established: 1972
Pub. .... William Clark
Pub. .... Diane Clark
Ed. .... Robert Wolfington
Mechanical Specifications: Type page 10 x 15; E - 6 cols, 1 1/2, 1/8 between; A - 6 cols, 1 1/2, 1/8 between; C - 6 cols, 1 1/2, 1/8 between.
Equipment: ; Presses — G/Community.

VIRGINIA

NORTHLAND SHOPPER
(Sun)
704 S 7th Ave, Virginia, MN, 55792-3086, USA; tel (218) 741-5544; fax (218) 741-1005; ed e-mail bhanna@mesabidailynews.net; web site www.virginiamn.com
Circulation: 12,155pd,8,500fr; CAC
Advertising: Open inch rate $3.10
Gen. Mgr. .... Shelly Lindbeurg
Adv. Mgr. .... Christopher Knight
Ed. .... William Hanna
Prodn. Mgr. .... Jeff Asbach
Mechanical Specifications: Type page 13 x 21 1/2; E - 6 cols, 1 5/6, between; A - 6 cols, 1 5/6, between; C - 9 cols, 1 5/6, between.
Equipment: Hardware — APP/Mac; Presses — G/UR; Software — Baseview.
Zip Codes Served: 55792

WACONIA

THE GOLD MINER
(Sat)
8 S Elm St, Waconia, MN, 55387-1412, USA; tel (952) 442-4414; adv tel (952) 442-4414; ed tel (952) 442-4414; fax (952) 442-6815; adv fax (952) 442-6815; ed fax (952) 442-6815; e-mail kristi.pexa@ecm-inc.com; adv e-mail norma.carstensen@ecm-inc.com; ed e-mail todd.moen@ecm-inc.com; web site www.lakerpioneer.com)
Circulation: 15,284pd,; CAC
Advertising: Open inch rate $19.50
Digital Platform - Mobile: Apple, Android
Digital Platform - Tablet: Apple iOS, Android
Mng. Ed. .... Todd Moen
Adv. Mgr. .... Kristi Pexa
Gen. Mgr. .... Mark Weber
Delivery Method: Mail
Zip Codes Served: Hennepin County

WALKER

CO-PILOT
(Sat)
408 Minnesota Ave, Walker, MN, 56484-2293, USA; tel (218) 547-1000; fax (218) 547-3000; e-mail pilotads@pilotindependent.com; web site www.walkermn.com
Circulation:10,000fr; Sworn/Estimate/Non-Audited
Advertising: Open inch rate $7.90
Established: 1897
Group: Adams Publishing Group, LLC
Ed. .... Dean Morrill
Genera Manager .... Terri Firestine
Mechanical Specifications: Type page 11 3/5 x 21 1/2; E - 6 cols, 1 4/5, 1/8 between; A - 6 cols, 1 4/5, 1/8 between.
Equipment: Hardware — APP/Power Mac 7200, Centris 650, APP/Mac G3; Software — InDesign, Multi-Ad/Creator.
Delivery Method: Mail

WASECA

WASECA AREA SHOPPER
(Tues)
213 2nd St NW, Waseca, MN, 56093-2401, USA; tel (507) 835-3380; fax (507) 835-3435; e-mail jfrazier@wasecacountynews.com; web site www.wasecacountynews.com
Circulation:8,384fr; CAC
Advertising: Open inch rate $15.70
Group: Adams Publishing Group, LLC
Publisher .... Julie Frazier
Mechanical Specifications: Type page 11 5/8 x 21 1/2; E - 6 cols, 1 5/6, between; A - 6 cols, 1 5/6, between; C - 6 cols, 1 5/6, between.
Delivery Method: Carrier
Zip Codes Served: 56093, 56048, 56096, 56072, 56078, 56091

WILLMAR

SUNDAY REMINDER
(Sun)
PO Box 839, Willmar, MN, 56201-0839, USA; tel (320) 235-1150; fax (320) 235-6769; e-mail feedback@wctrib.com; web site www.wctrib.com
Circulation: 0pd,28,434fr; VAC
Advertising: Open inch rate $7.40
Group: Forum Communications Co.
Pub. .... Steve Ammermann
Adv. Mgr. .... Jan Queenan
Circ. Mgr. .... Mark Herman
Mng. Ed. .... Kelly Boldan
Mechanical Specifications: Type page 10 1/4 x 13; E - 5 cols, 2, 1/12 between; A - 5 cols, 2, 1/12 between; C - 6 cols, 1 1/2, 11/72 between.
Equipment: Hardware — SIA; Presses — 8-G/Community; Software — Dewar/Sys IV.
Zip Codes Served: 56201

WINDOM

THE SHOPPER
(Sat)
260 10th St, Windom, MN, 56101-1411, USA; web site www.windomnews.com
Circulation:8,795fr; CVC
Advertising: Open inch rate $10.50
Established: 1969Trevor Slette
Mechanical Specifications: Type page: 11.3 x 21.6; 6 col

WINDOM SHOPPER
(Mon)
260 10th St, Windom, MN, 56101-1411, USA; tel (507) 831-3455; fax (507) 831-3740; e-mail citizen@windomnews.com; web site www.windomnews.com
Circulation:9,000fr; Sworn/Estimate/Non-Audited
Advertising: Open inch rate $8.00
Pub. .... Trevor Slette
Adv. Mgr. .... Linda A. Bramstedt
Ed. .... Rahn Larson
Mechanical Specifications: Type page 13 x 21 1/2; E - 6 cols, 2, between; A - 6 cols, 2, 1/6 between; C - 9 cols, 1 5/16, 1/6 between.
Equipment: Hardware — Pentium/PC; Software — Adobe/PageMaker 5.0, Archetype/Corel Draw 5.0, Microsoft/Word.
Zip Codes Served: 56019, 56083, 56101, 56118, 56120, 56126, 56137, 56143, 56145, 56150, 56152, 56159, 56160, 56161, 56174, 56183, 56187

WINSTED

HERALD JOURNAL CLASSIFIEDS & GOING OUT
(Fri)
PO Box 129, Winsted, MN, 55395-0129, USA; tel (320) 485-2535; fax (320) 485-2878; e-mail hj@heraldjournal.com; adv e-mail ads@heraldjournal.com; web site www.herald-journal.com
Circulation: 6,700pd,2,483fr; Sworn/Estimate/Non-Audited
Advertising: Open inch rate $9.75
Established: 1989
Group: Herald Journal Publishing, Inc.
Gen. Mgr. .... Dale Kovar
Mechanical Specifications: Type page 15 x 21 1/2; E - 6 cols, 2, between; A - 6 cols, 2, between.
Equipment: Hardware — APP/Mac; Software — InDesign, Adobe/Photoshop.
Delivery Method: Mail, Racks
Zip Codes Served: 53349, 55395, 55354, 55367, 55360, 55388, 55328, 55359, 55390, 55321, 55325

WORTHINGTON

THE BULLETIN
(Tues)
300 11th St, Worthington, MN, 56187-2451, USA; tel (507) 376-9711; fax (507) 376-5202; adv e-mail dgadvertisers@dglobe.com; web site www.dglobe.com
Circulation:10,433fr; VAC
Advertising: Open inch rate $11.00
Group: Forum Communications Co.
Pub. .... Joni Harms
Shopper Mgr. .... Doreen Milstead
Circ. Mgr. .... Denise Erwin
Prodn. Mgr. .... Rob Muck
Zip Codes Served: 56187

ZUMBROTA

GRIMSRUD PUBLISHER
(Wed)
225 S Main St, Zumbrota, MN, 55992-1698, USA; tel (507) 732-7617; fax (507) 732-7619; e-mail news@zumbrota.com; web site www.zumbrota.com
Circulation: 3,239pd,9,137fr; Sworn/Estimate/Non-Audited
Publisher .... Peter Grimsrud
Ed. .... Matt Grimsrud
Equipment: Hardware — APP/Mac; Software — Adobe/PageMaker 6.0.
Zip Codes Served: 55992

MISSISSIPPI

GRENADA

GRENADA LAKE HERALD
(Wed)
50 Corporate Row, Grenada, MS, 38901-2823, USA; tel (662) 226-4321; fax (662) 226-8310; e-mail dailystar@grenadastar.com; circulation@grenadastar.com; web site www.grenadastar.com
Circulation:8,000fr; Sworn/Estimate/Non-Audited
Advertising: Open inch rate $9.50
Established: 1955
Pub. .... Joseph Lee
Adv. Mgr. .... Nusete Mcdhail
Ed. .... Ninette Laster
Prodn. Mgr. .... Fred Adams
Mechanical Specifications: Type page 11 1/2 x 21 1/2; E - 6 cols, 1 3/4, 1/8 between; A - 6 cols, 1 3/4, 1/8 between; C - 6 cols, 1 3/4, 1/8 between.
Equipment: Hardware — Gateway/2000, APP/Power Mac, PixelCraft/Flatbed 1200 dpi Scanner, APP/Mac Quicktake 100 Digital Camera, ECR/Scriptsetter VRL 36 Imagesetter, Xante/Acell-a-Writer 8200 Laser Printer; Presses — KP/Press King; Software — Adobe/PageMaker 5.0, QPS/Q
Zip Codes Served: 38901

GULFPORT

PENNY PINCHER WANT ADS
(Thur)
15029 Dedeaux Rd, Gulfport, MS, 39503-3283, USA; tel (228) 832-8118; fax (228) 832-2548; e-mail ads@pennypinchergulfport.com; adv e-mail graphics@pennypinchergulfport.com; web site www.pennypinchergulfport.com
Circulation:40,000fr; Sworn/Estimate/Non-Audited
Advertising: Open inch rate $6.00
Established: 1987
Digital Platform - Mobile: Apple
Digital Platform - Tablet: Apple iOS
Gen. Mgr. .... Donna Chiasson
Circ. Mgr. .... Rex Chiasson
Mechanical Specifications: Type page 10 1/4 x 13 3/4; A - 6 cols, 1 1/2, 1/4 between; C - 6 cols, 1 1/2, 1/4 between.
Equipment: Hardware — APP/Mac; Software — Adobe/PageMaker 5.0.
Delivery Method: Racks

HATTIESBURG

IMPACT OF HATTIESBURG
(Wed)
219 S 40th Ave, Ste E, Hattiesburg, MS, 39402-1623, USA; tel (601) 264-8181; fax (601) 264-8398; adv e-mail kevin@impact-ads.com; ed e-mail news@hattiesburgimpact.com; web site www.impactads.com
Circulation:65,887fr; CVC
Advertising: Open inch rate $20.00
Established: 1991
Pub. .... Ronnie L. Buckley
Adv. Mgr. .... Bob Barger
Circ. Mgr .... Ellen Paul
General Manager .... Kevin Williamson
Mechanical Specifications: 10.25 x 17.00
Delivery Method: Mail
Zip Codes Served: 39401, 39402, 39465, 39475, 39482, 39428, 39479, 39119

HOUSTON

THE SHOPPER PLUS
(Tues)
225 E Madison St, Houston, MS, 38851-2320, USA; tel (662) 456-3771; fax (662) 456-5202; e-mail news@chickasaw360.com; adv e-mail advertising@chickasaw360.com; web site www.chickasaw360.com
Circulation:14,000fr; Sworn/Estimate/Non-Audited
Advertising: Open inch rate $8.50
Mng Ed .... Lisa Boyles
Office Mgr. .... Teresa Nichols
Adv Mgr .... Lori Smith

LOUISVILLE

LOUISVILLE SHOPPER'S GUIDE
(Tues)
233 N Court Ave, Louisville, MS, 39339-2648, USA; tel (662) 773-6241; fax (662) 773-6242; e-mail newsroom@winstoncountyjournal.com; web site www.winstoncountyjournal.com
Circulation:7,100fr; Sworn/Estimate/Non-Audited
Advertising: Open inch rate $10.00
Circ. Mgr. .... Brenda Perry
Ed. .... Joseph McCain

MERIDIAN

IMPACT OF LAUREL
(Wed, Sun)
902 14th St, Meridian, MS, 39301-4455, USA; tel (601) 649-1129; fax (601) 649-0424; web site http://impact360.ms/
Circulation:33,351fr; CVC
Advertising: Open inch rate $17.00
Established: 1976
Pub. .... Ronnie L. Buckley
Gen. Mgr. .... Kevin Williamson
Circ. Mgr. .... Jerry Clark
Adv. Mgr. .... Bob Barger
Circ. Mgr .... Ellen Paul
Mechanical Specifications: Type page 10.25 x 17.00; E - 6 cols, 1 1/2, 1/4 between; A - 6 cols, 1 1/2, 1/4 between.
Equipment: Hardware — APP/Macs; Software — DTI/Ad-Builder.
Delivery Method: Mail, Carrier
Zip Codes Served: 39441

NATCHEZ

MISS-LOU BUYERS GUIDE
(Wed)
503 N Canal St, Natchez, MS, 39120-2902, USA; tel (601) 442-9101; fax (601) 442-7315; web site www.natchezdemocrat.com
Circulation:7,500fr; Sworn/Estimate/Non-Audited
Group: Boone Newspapers, Inc.
Pub. .... Kevin Cooper
Circ. Mgr. .... Sam King
Prodn. Mgr. .... Johnnie Griffin
Mechanical Specifications: Type page 11 x 21 1/2; E - 6 cols, 1 5/6, 1/6 between; A - 6 cols, 2 5/6, 1/6 between; C - 10 cols, 1 5/8, 1/6 between.
Delivery Method: Newsstand, Carrier
Zip Codes Served: 39120

NEW ALBANY

GAZETTE GUIDE
(Wed)
713 Carter Ave, New Albany, MS, 38652-3310, USA; tel (662) 534-6321; fax (662) 534-6355; e-mail wayne.mitchell@journalinc.com; adv e-mail advertising@newalbanygazette.com; web site www.newalbanygazette.com
Circulation: 0pd,12,000fr; USPS
Advertising: Open inch rate $14.15 combo with paid Gazette paper
Group: Journal Inc.
Pub. .... T. Wayne Mitchell
Mechanical Specifications: Type page 11 x 20.5; E - 6 cols, 2, 1/6 between; A - 6 cols, 2, 1/6 between; C - 6cols, 1 1/2, 1/6 between.
Equipment: Hardware — APP/Macs; Software — Adobe/InDesign CS3; Adobe Photoshop CS3
Delivery Method: Mail
Zip Codes Served: 38652

MISSOURI

ADRIAN

STAR LITE SHOPPERS GUIDE
(Wed)
39 E Main St, Adrian, MO, 64720-8201, USA; tel (816) 297-2100; e-mail adrianjournal@usa.net; web site www.adrianjournal.com
Circulation:5,500fr; Sworn/Estimate/Non-Audited
Advertising: Open inch rate $6.85
Ed. .... Stephen M. Oldfield
Mechanical Specifications: Type page 14 x 21; E - 6 cols, 2, 1/6 between; A - 6 cols, 2, 1/6 between; C - 6 cols, 2, 1/6 between.
Zip Codes Served: 64720

ALBANY

GENTRY COUNTY SHOPPER
(Tues)
106 W Clay St, Albany, MO, 64402-1602, USA; tel (660) 726-3901; fax (660) 726-3367; e-mail gcs@albanymo.net; publisher@maryvilledailyforum.com
Circulation:8,500fr; Sworn/Estimate/Non-Audited
Advertising: Open inch rate $6.00
Group: GateHouse Media, Inc.
Pub. .... Mike Herring

AURORA

BIG AA SHOPPER
(Wed)
33 W Olive St, Aurora, MO, 65605-1430, USA; tel (417) 678-2115; e-mail new@auroraadvertiser.net; adv e-mail admanager@auroraadvertiser.net; web site auroraadvertiser.net
Circulation:8,000fr; Sworn/Estimate/Non-Audited
Advertising: Open inch rate $5.50
Group: GateHouse Media, Inc.
Pub. .... Judy Dingman
Ad Manager .... Paul Ward
Mechanical Specifications: Type page 10 x 21 1/2; E - 6 cols, 1.56, 1/6 between;
Equipment: Hardware — PCs; Presses — KP/News King; Software — Adobe/PageMaker 5.0.
Zip Codes Served: 65605

BETHANY

PONY EXPRESS
(Tues)
PO Box 351, Bethany, MO, 64424-0351, USA; tel (660) 425-6325; fax (660) 425-3441; e-mail rclipper@grm.net; web site www.republicanclipper.com
Circulation:13,000fr; Sworn/Estimate/Non-Audited
Advertising: Open inch rate $8.35
Adv. Mgr. .... Kathy Conger
Ed. .... Philip G. Conger
Mechanical Specifications: Type page 10 x 16; E - 7 cols, 1 1/3, 1/6 between; A - 7 cols, 1 1/3, 1/6 between.
Equipment: Hardware — 3-APP/Power Mac, APP/Mac G3, APP/Mac G4; Software — Adobe/PageMaker 6.0.
Zip Codes Served: 64424

CAMERON

CAMERON SHOPPER
(Tues)
403 E Evergreen St, Cameron, MO, 64429-2096, USA; tel (816) 632-6543; fax (816) 632-4508; ed e-mail editor@mycameronnews.com; web site www.mycameronnews .com
Circulation:15,000fr; Sworn/Estimate/Non-Audited
Advertising: Open inch rate $8.15
Digital Platform - Mobile: Apple
Digital Platform - Tablet: Apple iOS
Prodn. Dir. .... Jeff King
Publisher .... Wally Gallian
Editor .... Chris Johnson
CFO .... Debbie Wiedmier

Mechanical Specifications: Type page 10 1/4 x 16; A - 6 cols, 1 1/2, 1/6 between; C - 6 cols, 1 1/2, 1/6 between.
Equipment: Hardware — APP/Macs; Presses — G/Community; Software — QPS/QuarkX-Press.
Zip Codes Served: 64429

CAPE GIRARDEAU

SOUTHEAST MISSOURIAN PLUS
(Wed)
301 Broadway St, Cape Girardeau, MO, 63701-7330, USA; tel (573) 388-3680; adv tel (573) 388-2751; fax (573) 335-2712; adv fax (573) 339-0815; e-mail 301cape@semissourian.com; web site www.semissourian.com
Circulation: 10,930pd,194fr; CAC
Advertising: Open inch rate $16.00
Group: Rust Communications
Pub. .... Jon Rust
Adv. Dir. .... Donna Denson
Circ. Dir. .... Mark Kneer
Ed. .... Robert Miller
Prodn. Mgr. .... Steve Rose
Mechanical Specifications: Type page 11 5/8 x 21 1/2; A - 6 cols, 1 5/6, 1/8 between; C - 9 cols, 1 3/16, 1/8 between.
Equipment: Hardware — 50-APP/Mac, 40-IBM/AT Class DOS; Presses — 6-WPC/Web Leader (1 Quad Color), 4-WPC/Web Leader; Software — QPS/QuarkXPress, Baseview/NewsEdit, Adobe/Photoshop, Adobe/Illustrator.
Zip Codes Served: 63701, 63755, 63775

COLE CAMP

BENTON COUNTY SHOPPER
(Wed)
PO Box 280, Cole Camp, MO, 65325-0280, USA; tel (660) 668-4418; fax (660) 647-2121; e-mail news@ovpinc.com
Circulation:8,820fr; Sworn/Estimate/Non-Audited
Advertising: Open inch rate $4.65
Ed. .... Frank Mercer
Zip Codes Served: 65325

COLUMBIA

THE ADD SHEET!
(Wed)
302 Campusview Dr, Ste 104, Columbia, MO, 65201-7507, USA; tel (573) 875-4000; fax (573) 875-4003; e-mail contact@addsheet.com; web site www.addsheet.com
Circulation:26,026fr; CVC
Advertising: Open inch rate $7.00
Established: 1969
Jamie Canine
Jake SheaferPub.s
Mechanical Specifications: Type page 7 3/4 x 10 3/4; A - 2 cols, 3 7/12, 1/6 between.
Equipment: Hardware — PDF; Software — Adobe/Photoshop 6.0, QPS/QuarkXPress 4.0, Multi-Ad 4.0, Adobe/Illustrator 7.0, Macromedia/Freehand 9.0.
Zip Codes Served: 65201, 65202, 65203, 65211, 65212, 65215, 65216, 65217, 65218, 65299, 65010, 65279

EL DORADO SPRINGS

CEDAR COUNTY BUYERS GUIDE
(Wed)
105 S Main St, El Dorado Springs, MO, 64744-1123, USA; tel (417) 876-2500; fax (417) 876-5986; e-mail thestar@socket.net
Circulation:7,000fr; Sworn/Estimate/Non-Audited
Advertising: Open inch rate $4.50
Established: 1979
Pub. .... Patsy Brownlee
Gen. Mgr. .... Mae McNeece

EXCELSIOR SPRINGS

TOWN & COUNTRY LEADER
(Wed)
417 S Thompson Ave, Excelsior Springs, MO, 64024-2129, USA; tel (816) 637-6155; fax (816) 637-8411; e-mail publisher@leader-press.com; adv e-mail wanda@leaderpress.com; ed e-mail editor@leaderpress.com; web site www.excelsiorspringsstandard.com
Circulation:20,000fr; Sworn/Estimate/Non-Audited
Advertising: Open inch rate $9.90
Established: 1892
Group: Excelsior Publishing Company
Digital Platform - Mobile: Apple, Android, Windows
Digital Platform - Tablet: Apple iOS, Android, Windows 7, Blackberry Tablet OS, Kindle, Nook, Kindle Fire
Sales Manager .... Wanda Rowe
Circulation Manager .... Dave Copeland
Managing Editor .... Eric Copeland
Publisher, Editor .... Brian Rice
Production Manager .... Liz Johnson
Equipment: Hardware — Apple platform/iMac Intel; Presses — 6-G/Community; Software — Adobe CS 5.5, MS Office
Delivery Method: Carrier, Racks
Zip Codes Served: 64024, 64060, 64085, 64089,64068, 64072, 64077, 64017, 64084, 64062, 64048, 64465, 64671

HIGGINSVILLE

THE LAFAYETTE COUNTY SHOPPER
(Tues)
3002 Highway 13 Blvd, Higginsville, MO, 64037-1870, USA; tel (660) 584-3611; fax (660) 584-7966
Circulation:10,000fr; Sworn/Estimate/Non-Audited
Advertising: Open inch rate $6.50
Group: Main Street Media, Inc.
Pub. .... Frank W. Mercer
Adv. Mgr. .... Beverly Mackie
Mechanical Specifications: Type page 13 x 21 1/2.
Equipment: Hardware — APP/Mac; Software — Adobe/PageMaker, Adobe/Typestyler.

IRONTON

MOUNTAIN ECHO X-TRA
(Wed)
110 N Main St, Ironton, MO, 63650-1108, USA; tel (573) 546-3917; fax (573) 546-3919
Circulation:6,700fr; Sworn/Estimate/Non-Audited
Advertising: Open inch rate $5.25
Pub. .... Judith Schaaf-Wheeler
Mechanical Specifications: Type page 11 1/2 x 21 1/2; E - 6 cols, 1 5/6, 1/10 between; A - 6 cols, 2 1/8, between; C - 6 cols, 2 1/8, between.
Equipment: Hardware — APP/Power Macs, APP/Mac G4; Software — QPS/QuarkX-Press, Multi-Ad/Creator.
Zip Codes Served: 63650

JOPLIN

BIG NICKEL
(Thur)
2916 E 20th St, Joplin, MO, 64804-1215, USA; tel (417) 624-4100; fax (417) 624-8503; adv e-mail classified@bignickel.com; web site www.bignickel.com
Circulation:50,000fr; Sworn/Estimate/Non-Audited
Advertising: Open inch rate $13.50
Group: GateHouse Media, Inc.Editions: 2— 2 total; Big Nickel-Northern; Big Nickel-Southern;
Gen. Mgr. .... Chuck Elliott
Classified Mgr./Dist. Mgr. .... Jerry Snider
Mechanical Specifications: Type page 11 3/8 x 16; E - 6 cols, 1 9/16, 1/8 between; A - 6 cols, 1 9/16, 1/8 between; C - 6 cols, 1 9/16, 1/8 between.
Equipment: Hardware — APP/Power Macs; Software — QPS/QuarkXPress.

KANSAS CITY

AMERICAN CLASSIFIEDS
(Thur)
12103 E 43rd St, Kansas City, MO, 64133-2060, USA; tel (816) 356-8790; web site www.americanclassifiedskc.com
Circulation:250,000fr; Sworn/Estimate/Non-AuditedEditions: 3— 3 total; American Classifieds-East (200,000); American Classifieds-Kansas (120,000); American Classifieds-North (90,000);
Gen. Mgr. .... Debbie Hall

THRIFTY NICKEL - KANSAS CITY - KANSAS
(Thur)
12103 E 43rd St, Kansas City, MO, 64133-2060, USA; web site www.kcnickel.com
Circulation:12,033fr; CVC
Advertising: Open inch rate $15.00
Established: 1978Debbie Hall
Mechanical Specifications: Type page: 10.5 x 16; 8 col

KENNETT

DAILY DUNKLIN DEMOCRAT EXTRA
(Wed)
203 1st St, Kennett, MO, 63857-2052, USA; tel (573) 888-4505; fax (573) 888-5114; web site www.dddnews.com
Circulation:6,242fr; CAC
Advertising: Open inch rate $12.20
Group: Rust Communications
Pub. .... Bud Hunt
Office Mgr. .... Debbie Wright
Adv. Mgr. .... Terri Coleman
Clrc. Mgr. .... Randy Hindmon
News Ed. .... Diana Coronado
Mechanical Specifications: Type page 13 x 21 1/2; E - 6 cols, 2 1/16, 1/16 between; A - 6 cols, 2 1/16, 1/16 between; C - 9 cols, 1 3/16, 1/16 between.
Equipment: Hardware — APP/Mac, PC; Presses — 8-G/Community; Software — Novell 4.1, Multi-Ad/Creator, Macromedia/Freehand, Adobe/PageMaker, QPS/QuarkXPress.
Zip Codes Served: 63857

KIRKSVILLE

KIRKSVILLE CRIER
(Wed)
110 E McPherson St, Kirksville, MO, 63501-3506, USA; tel (660) 665-4663; fax (660) 665-2608; e-mail kvdaily@sbcglobal.net; web site www.kirksvilledailyexpress.com
Circulation:22,500fr; Sworn/Estimate/Non-Audited
Advertising: Open inch rate $10.00
Established: 1988
Pub. .... Larry Freels
Adv. Dir. .... George Wriedt
Composition Mgr. .... Kathy Veatch
Circ. Mgr. .... Steve Montgomery
Mechanical Specifications: Type page 13 x 21; E - 6 cols, 2, 1/8 between; A - 6 cols, 2, 1/8 between; C - 6 cols, 2, 1/8 between.
Equipment: Hardware — APP/Mac; Software — QPS/QuarkXPress 3.32, Adobe/PageMaker 6.0.
Delivery Method: Carrier
Zip Codes Served: 63501

LEES SUMMIT

LEE'S SUMMIT ADVERTISING EXTRA
(Wed)
415 SE Douglas St, Lees Summit, MO, 64063-4246, USA; tel (816) 524-2345; adv tel (816) 282-7003; ed tel (816) 282-7001; fax (816) 524-5136; e-mail shernandez@lsjournal.com; adv e-mail mleonard@lsjournal.com; ed e-mail jbeaudoin@lsjournal.com; web site www.lsjournal.com
Circulation:5,000fr; VAC
Advertising: Open inch rate $15.00
Established: 1881
Group: Lee's Summit Journal
Publisher, Editor .... Maria Martin
Circ. Mgr. .... John McCall
Advertising Sales Manager ... Sonja Hernandez
Mechanical Specifications: Type page 13 x 21; E - 6 cols, 2 1/16, 1/8 between; A - 6 cols, 2 1/16, 1/8 between; C - 9 cols, 1 3/4, 1/8 between.
Equipment: Hardware — PC; Software — QPS/QuarkXPress 3.1, Adobe/Photoshop 3.0.

MARSHALL

SALINE COUNTY CITIZEN
(Wed)
121 N Lafayette Ave, Marshall, MO, 65340-1747, USA; tel (660) 886-2233; fax (660) 886-8544; web site www.marshallnews.com
Circulation:8,200fr; Sworn/Estimate/Non-Audited
Advertising: Open inch rate $8.49
Pub. .... Shelley Arth
Adv. Mgr. .... Mike Davis
Circ. Mgr. .... Pat Morrow
Ed. .... Eric Crump
Equipment: Hardware — 2-APP/Mac G3, 1-APP/Mac G4; Software — 4-Adobe/Photoshop 5.1, QPS/QuarkXPress 4.1.
Zip Codes Served: 65340

MARSHFIELD

THE EDGE
(Wed)
225 N Clay St, Marshfield, MO, 65706-1652, USA; tel (417) 468-2013; fax (417) 859-7930; e-mail news@marshfieldmail.com; web site www.marshfieldmail.com
Circulation:19,400fr; Sworn/Estimate/Non-Audited
Advertising: Open inch rate $7.75
Pub. .... Dave Berry
Adv. Mgr. .... Debra Chapman
Ed. .... Mark Lile
Mechanical Specifications: Type page 12 7/8 x 21; E - 6 cols, 2, between; A - 6 cols, 2, between.
Zip Codes Served: 65706

MARYVILLE

MARYVILLE PENNY PRESS
(Tues)
111 E Jenkins St, Maryville, MO, 64468-2318, USA; tel (660) 562-2424; fax (660) 562-2823; e-mail mdform@asde.net; web site www.maryvilledailyforum.com
Circulation:15,000fr; Sworn/Estimate/Non-Audited
Advertising: Open inch rate $10.50
Group: GateHouse Media, Inc.
Pub. .... Phil Cobb

NEVADA

NEVADA NEWS
(Wed)
131 S Cedar St, Nevada, MO, 64772-3309, USA; tel (417) 667-3344; adv tel (417) 667-3344; fax (417) 667-7475; web site www.nevadadailymail.com
Circulation:17,900fr; Sworn/Estimate/Non-Audited
Advertising: Open inch rate $5.95
Pub. .... Julie Simpson
Delivery Method: Mail, Carrier, Racks
Zip Codes Served: 64772

OSCEOLA

ST. CLAIR COUNTY BUYER'S GUIDE
(Wed)
3rd & Pine St, Osceola, MO, 64776, USA; tel (417) 646-2211; fax (417) 646-8015
Circulation:4,100fr; Sworn/Estimate/Non-Audited
Advertising: Open inch rate $5.00
Adv. Mgr................................Michael Crawford
Zip Codes Served: 64776

OWENSVILLE

EAST CENTRAL AD MART
(Tues)
106 E Washington Ave, Owensville, MO, 65066-1316, USA; tel (573) 437-2323; fax (573) 437-3033; e-mail wardpub@fidnet.com
Circulation:6,792fr; Sworn/Estimate/Non-Audited
Advertising: Open inch rate $5.00
Adv. Mgr.................................. Dennis Warden
Mechanical Specifications: Type page 12 1/2 x 21 1/2; E - 6 cols, 1 15/16, 1/8 between; A - 6 cols, 1 15/16, 1/8 between; C - 6 cols, 1 15/16, 1/8 between.
Equipment: Hardware — APP/Mac Centris 610, APP/Power Mac 6100, APP/Power Mac 6200, APP/iMac; Software — Adobe/PageMaker 6.5.
Zip Codes Served: 65066

PERRYVILLE

THE REPUBLIC-MONITOR SHOPPING GUIDE
(Wed)
10 W St Maries St, Perryville, MO, 63775, USA; tel (573) 547-4567; fax (573) 547-1643; web site www.perryvillenews.com
Circulation:6,000fr; Sworn/Estimate/Non-Audited
Advertising: Open inch rate $7.00
Established: 1889
Pub. .... Kate Martin
Mechanical Specifications: Type page 13 x 21; E - 6 cols, 1 7/8, 1/6 between; A - 6 cols, 1 7/8, 1/6 between; C - 9 cols, 1 3/16, 1/6 between.
Zip Codes Served: 63775

RICHMOND

TOWN & COUNTRY LEADER EAST
(Wed)
204 W North Main St, Richmond, MO, 64085-1610, USA; tel (816) 776-5454; fax (816) 470-6397; adv e-mail ads@richmond-dailynews.com
Circulation:8,950fr; Sworn/Estimate/Non-Audited
Advertising: Open inch rate $7.00
Mechanical Specifications: Type page 9.75 x 15; E - 6 cols, 1.5, 1/8 between; A - 6 cols, 1.5, 1/8 between.
Equipment: Hardware — 3-APP/Mac LC, APP/Power Mac 7200, 2-APP/Mac Performa, 4-APP/Power Mac 63; Presses — 5-G/Community; Software — QPS/Indesign CS5.5
Zip Codes Served: 64085

SAINT PETERS

THRIFTY NICKEL WANT ADS - ST. LOUIS
(Thur)
4139 Mexico Rd, Saint Peters, MO, 63376-6410, USA; web site www.americanclassifieds.com
Circulation: 0pd,45,051fr; CVC
Advertising: Open inch rate $17.00
Established: 1983Gerald McPeek
Mechanical Specifications: Type page: 10.5 x 16; 8 col

SEDALIA

FREE PLAINSMAN
(Wed)
700 S Massachusetts Ave, Sedalia, MO, 65301-4548, USA; tel (660) 826-1000; adv tel (660) 826-1000 Ext 230; ed tel 6608262413 Ext 223; fax (660) 826-2413; e-mail advertising@sedaliademocrat.com; adv e-mail advertising@sedaliademocrat.com; web site www.freeplainsman.com
Circulation:13,785fr; Sworn/Estimate/Non-Audited
Advertising: $14.14 pci
Pub. .... Frank Lyon
Adv. Mgr................................ Denise McMillen
Circ. Mgr................................Howard Cochran
Prodn. Mgr.................................. Allen Cooper
Mechanical Specifications: 8 col (10") x 21.5" maximum size. Col sizes: 1(1.1"), 2(2.38"), 3(3.65"), 4(4.92"), 5(6.19"), 6(7.46"), 7(8.73")
Equipment: Hardware — APP/Mac; Presses — 10-G; Software — Baseview.
Delivery Method: Carrier, Racks

SEYMOUR

WEBSTER COUNTY ADVERTISER
(Wed)
221 S Commercial St, Seymour, MO, 65746-8743, USA; tel (417) 935-2257; fax (417) 935-2487; ed e-mail citizen@webstercountycitizen.com; web site http://www.webstercountycitizen.com/
Circulation:; Sworn/Estimate/Non-Audited
Advertising: Open inch rate $4.50
Ed. .... Dan Wehmer
Prodn. Mgr. .... Beverly Hannum
Mechanical Specifications: Type page 13 x 21; E - 6 cols, 2, 1/6 between; A - 6 cols, 2, 1/6 between; C - 6 cols, 2, 1/6 between.
Equipment: Hardware — APP/Mac; Presses — 8-G/Community; Software — Adobe/PageMaker 6.0.

SPRINGFIELD

PENNYPOWER SHOPPING NEWS
(Tues)
651 N Boonville Ave, Springfield, MO, 65806-1005, USA; tel (417) 836-1100; fax (417) 836-1147
Circulation:145,000fr; Sworn/Estimate/Non-Audited
Advertising: Open inch rate $8.75
Group: GannettEditions: 8— 8 total; Pennypower Shopping News-Northeastern Edition (16,850);
Circ. Mgr.. Sam Barnard
Mechanical Specifications: Type page 6 1/4 x 10.
Equipment: Hardware — APP/Mac G3; Software — QPS/QuarkXPress.
Zip Codes Served: 65804

WASHINGTON

WASHINGTON MISSOURIAN/ MISSOURIAN PUBLISHING CO
(Wed, Sat)
14 W Main St, Washington, MO, 63090-2518, USA; tel (636) 239-7701; adv tel (636) 390-3008; ed tel (636) 239-7701; fax (636) 239-0915; adv fax (636) 390-5608; ed fax (636) 239-0915; e-mail washnews@emissourian.com; adv e-mail ads@emissourian.com; ed e-mail washnews@emissourian.com; web site www.emissourian.com
Circulation: 16,000pd,7,325fr; Sworn/Estimate/Non-Audited
Advertising: $13.00 National Rate
Established: 1937
Group: Missourian Publishing Company
Digital Platform - Mobile: Apple, Android, Windows, Blackberry
Digital Platform - Tablet: Apple iOS, Android, Windows 7, Blackberry Tablet OS, Kindle, Nook, Kindle Fire
Gen. Mgr.................................William L. Miller
Adv. Dir.................................Jane Haberberger
Managing Editor ....Ed Pruneau
MultiMedia Sales Director ....Terry O'Neill
Mechanical Specifications: Type page 12 1/2 x 21 1/2; E - 6 cols, 1 7/8, 3/16 between; A - 6 cols, 1 7/8, 3/16 between; C - 6 cols, 1 7/8, 3/16 between.
Equipment: Hardware — APP/Mac; Presses — G/Urbanite.
Delivery Method: Mail, Carrier, Racks
Zip Codes Served: 63090, 63001, 63015, 63025, 63069, 63089, 63014, 63068, 65041, 65066, 63341, 63332, 63342, 63357, 63084, 63013, 63037, 63056, 63091, 63077, 63041, 63060, 63061, 63072, 63080, 63383, 63390

MONTANA

BOZEMAN

MINI NICKEL CLASSIFIEDS
(Thur)
1910 N 22nd Ave, Bozeman, MT, 59718-7031, USA; tel (406) 548-3353; fax (406) 585-8542; e-mail classifieds@mininickel.com; web site www.mininickel.com
Circulation:21,000fr; Sworn/Estimate/Non-Audited
Group: Lee Enterprises, Inc.
Manager ....J'Aime Wisner
Equipment: Hardware — APP/Macs
Delivery Method: Racks

MINI NICKLE CLASSIFIEDS
(Thur)
3810 Valley Commons Dr, Ste 6, Bozeman, MT, 59718-6477, USA; tel (406) 586-8241; fax (406) 585-8542; e-mail classified@mininickel.com; web site www.mininickel.com
Circulation:25,742fr; CVC
Advertising: Open inch rate $11.55
Gen. Mgr....................................Kathy Turgeon
Mechanical Specifications: Type page 10 1/4 x 16; E - 7 cols, 1 5/16, 1/16 between.
Equipment: Hardware — APP/Mac 7200, APP/Mac 6400, CD-ROM, Zip Drive 100; Software — Multi-Ad/Creator 4.0, Adobe/Photoshop 4.0, Adobe/PageMaker 4.2, Claris/Works 3.0.

PENNY PINCHER
(Wed)
2820 W College St, Bozeman, MT, 59718-3925, USA; tel (406) 587-4491; fax (406) 587-7995; ed e-mail citydesk@dailychronicle.com; web site www.dailychronicle.com
Circulation:15,000fr; Sworn/Estimate/Non-Audited
Advertising: Open inch rate $4.59
Pub. ....Stephanie Pressly
Circ. Mgr.. Bill Fedrick
Prodn. Mgr. ....Ed Renaud
Mechanical Specifications: Type page 10 13/16 x 13; E - 5 cols, between; A - 5 cols, between.
Equipment: Hardware — 16-DGM/400; Software — Baseview/AdManager Pro-Classifieds.
Zip Codes Served: 59771, 59218, 59715

TIDBITS OF THE NORTH METRO
(Other) (Published and distributed every 2 weeks)
880 Matheson Way, Bozeman, MT, 59715-3221, USA; adv tel (763) 218-0033; ed tel (763) 218-0033; e-mail DEAN@REALBITS.COM; adv e-mail SALES@REALBITS.COM; ed e-mail DEAN@REALBITS.COM; web site www.tidbitstwincities.com
Circulation:23,000fr; CVC
Advertising: 41.66
Established: 1996
Group: DBA Falcon Prince Publishing, Falcon Prince Inc.Editions: 5— ANOKA E. 5000/ ANOKA WEST 4600 / N RAMSEY 4200 / SHERBURNE 4100/ NW HENNEPIN 4100
Digital Platform - Mobile: Android, Windows, Blackberry, Other
Digital Platform - Tablet: Android, Windows 7
OWNER PUBLISHER ....Dean Prince
Mechanical Specifications: 2 INCH COLUMNS FULL PAGE SPACE IS 10X12
Equipment: Hardware — PC; Presses — web; Software — Adobe
Delivery Method: Racks
Zip Codes Served: 55011,55014,55109,55110,55112,55113,55117,55125,55127,55301,55403,55304,55309,55311,55316,55330,55362,55369,55374,55376,55398,55421,55427,55428,55429,55432,55433, 55434,55443,55444,55445,55448,55449,

GREAT FALLS

CONSUMERS PRESS
(Thur)
205 River Dr S, Great Falls, MT, 59405-1854, USA; tel (406) 761-2406; fax (406) 791-1436; web site www.consumerspress.com
Circulation: 40pd,33,000fr; CVC
Advertising: Open inch rate $9.95
Group: Gannett
Gen. Mgr...................................... Grant Bebee
Mechanical Specifications: Type page 11 1/2 x 17; A - 7 cols, 1 5/16, 1/6 between; C - 7 cols, 1 5/16, 1/6 between.
Equipment: Hardware — APP/Power Mac; Software — QPS/QuarkXPress 3.32.

HAVRE

THE HI-LINE SHOPPER
(Tues, Wed)
119 2nd St, Havre, MT, 59501-3507, USA; tel (406) 265-6795; fax (406) 265-6798; e-mail hdn@havredailynews.com; web site www.havredailynews.com
Circulation:7,200fr; Sworn/Estimate/Non-Audited
Advertising: Shopper Only $5.50 pci
Pub./Adv. Mgr................................Stacy Mantle
Prodn. Dir..................................Scot Anderson
Circ. Mgr.....................................Leeds Jodene
Mechanical Specifications: Type page 12 1/2 x 21 1/2; E - 6 cols, 2, 1/8 between; A - 6 cols, 2, 1/8 between; C - 9 cols, 1 1/4, 1/8 between.
Equipment: Hardware — APP/Mac; Presses — G/Community; Software — QPS/QuarkXPress, Adobe/Illustrator, Macromedia/Freehand, Adobe/Typestyler.
Delivery Method: Carrier, Racks
Zip Codes Served: 59538, 59526, 59527, 59522, 59520, 59521, 59523, 59545, 59501

JORDAN

TRADEWIND

(Mon)
PO Box 303, Jordan, MT, 59337-0303, USA; tel (406) 557-2337; fax (406) 557-6284; e-mail tradewind@midrivers.com
Circulation:3,770fr; Sworn/Estimate/Non-Audited
Advertising: Open inch rate $8.00
Pub. .... Janet F. Guptill

LIVINGSTON

PARK COUNTY SUPER SHOPPER

(Tues)
401 S Main St, Livingston, MT, 59047-3418, USA; tel (406) 222-2000; adv tel (800) 345-8412; ed tel (800) 345-8412; fax (406) 222-8580; adv fax (406) 222-8580; ed fax (406) 222-8580; e-mail news@livingstonenterprise.com; adv e-mail jdurfey@livent.net; ed e-mail news@livent.net; web site www.livingstonenterprise.com
Circulation:4,050fr; Sworn/Estimate/Non-Audited
Advertising: No display advertising space available
Established: 1883
Group: Yellowstone Communications
Digital Platform - Mobile: Apple, Android, Windows, Blackberry
Digital Platform - Tablet: Apple iOS, Android, Windows 7, Blackberry Tablet OS, Kindle, Nook, Kindle Fire
Pub. .... John Sullivan
Adv. Mgr. .... Jim Durfey
Circ. Mgr. .... David Campbell
Mechanical Specifications: Type page 10" x 15.5"; E - 4 cols, 2 1/14, 1/6 between; A - 4 cols, 2 1/14, 1/6 between;
Equipment: Hardware — APP/Power Mac Computer to plate; Presses — G/Community; Software — Indesign
Delivery Method: Mail
Zip Codes Served: 59047,59018, 59030, 59082, 59086, 59020,59027, 59065, 59081, 82190
Note: Printed once for 3 months

MISSOULA

THE MESSENGER

(Wed)
500 S Higgins Ave, Missoula, MT, 59801-2736, USA; tel (406) 721-2460; fax (406) 721-6139; e-mail messenger@missoulian.com; web site www.montanamessenger.com
Circulation:35,035fr; Sworn/Estimate/Non-Audited
Advertising: Open inch rate $8.00
Pub. .... John Vanstrydonck
Mechanical Specifications: Type page 10 1/2 x 16; E - 8 cols, 1 1/8, 1/6 between; A - 8 cols, 1 1/8, 1/6 between; C - 8 cols, 1 1/8, 1/6 between.

PLENTYWOOD

THE GREETER

(Tues)
108 N Main St, Plentywood, MT, 59254-1816, USA; tel (406) 765-1733; fax (406) 765-2106; e-mail thegreeter@aol.com; adv e-mail advertising@mygreeter.com; web site www.mygreeter.com
Circulation:3,000fr; Sworn/Estimate/Non-Audited
Advertising: Open inch rate $10.00
Established: 1986
Pub. .... Richard Rice
Mechanical Specifications: Type page 10 3/4 x 13; E - 5 cols, 2 1/16, between; A - 5 cols, 2 1/16, between; C - 5 cols, 2 1/16, between.
Equipment: Hardware — 2-APP/MacG4, 3-APP/iMac; Presses — ABD; Software — Adobe/PageMaker.
Delivery Method: Mail, Newsstand, Carrier, Racks
Zip Codes Served: 59254

POLSON

ADVERTISER

(Wed)
49488 US Highway 93, Polson, MT, 59860-2160, USA; tel (406) 883-4343; fax (406) 883-4349; e-mail mail@leaderadvertiser.com; web site www.leaderadvertiser.com
Circulation:25,000fr; Sworn/Estimate/Non-Audited
Advertising: Open inch rate $7.92
Group: Hagadone Corporation
Pub. .... Dan Drewrey
Ed. .... Jenna Cerderberg
Zip Codes Served: 59864

NEBRASKA

ALBION

THE ADVISOR

(Tues)
1112 W State St, Albion, NE, 68620-1362, USA; tel (402) 395-9965; fax (402) 395-9969; e-mail advisor@frontiernet.net; adv e-mail debcon@frontiernet.net; web site www.theadvisorne.com
Circulation:21,192fr; CVC
Advertising: Open inch rate $9.90
Established: 1997
Gen. Mgr. .... Debra J. Condreay
Mechanical Specifications: Type page 10 5/16 x 16; A - 7 cols, between.
Equipment: Hardware — APP/Mac G4, APP/Mac 4400; Software — Indesign, Adobe/Photoshop 5.5, Adobe/Illustrator 7.0.1, Baseview.
Delivery Method: Mail, Carrier, Racks
Zip Codes Served: 68620,68622,68623,68627,68628,68636,68637,68638,68640,68642,68644,68647,68652,68655,68660,68663,68665,68713,687,25,68726,686734,68735,68742,68756,68758,68763,68766,68780,68815,68816,68826,68842,68859,68862,68864,68875,

ALLIANCE

T-H PLUS

(Wed)
114 E 4th St, Alliance, NE, 69301-3402, USA; tel (308) 762-3060; fax (308) 762-3063; e-mail athnews@alliancetimes.com; web site www.alliancetimes.com
Circulation:3,000fr; Sworn/Estimate/Non-Audited
Advertising: Open inch rate $4.00
Established: 1989
Prodn. Mgr. .... Mark Sherlock
Mng. Editor .... John E. Weare
Gen. Mgr. .... Aaron Wade
Pub .... Tom Shaal
Mechanical Specifications: Type page 11 1/2 x 21 1/2; E - 6 cols, 1 4/5, 1/6 between; A - 6 cols, 1 4/5, 1/6 between; C - 7 cols, 1 1/2, 1/6 between.
Equipment: Hardware — APP/Mac; Presses — G.
Zip Codes Served: 69301

BLAIR

THE CLIPPER

(Tues)
138 N 16th St, Blair, NE, 68008-1633, USA; tel (402) 426-2121; adv tel (402) 426-2121; ed tel (402) 426-2121; fax (402) 426-2227; adv fax (402) 426-2227; ed fax (402) 426-2227; e-mail lhansen@enterprisepub.com; adv e-mail lhansen@enterprisepub.com; ed e-mail editor@enterprisepub.com; web site www.enterprisepub.biz
Circulation:8,400fr; USPS
Advertising: Open inch rate $15.50
Group: Enterprise Publishing Co.
Publisher .... Mark Rhoades
Sales Mgr. .... Lynette Hansen
Managing Editor .... Katie Rohman
Art Director .... Jen Stolz
Mechanical Specifications: 1 col. = 1.83"
2 col. = 3.79"
3 col. = 5.75"
4 col. = 7.71"
5 col. = 9.55"
6 col. = 11.625"
Equipment: ; Presses — HI/V-15.
Delivery Method: Mail
Zip Codes Served: 68008, 68029, 68002, 68034, 68023, 68068, 68061, 68044, 68007, 68025

BROKEN BOW

CUSTER COUNTY CHIEF/XTRA

(Mon)
305 S 10th Ave, Broken Bow, NE, 68822-2019, USA; tel (308) 872-2471; fax (308) 872-2415; e-mail chiefads@custercountychief.com; adv e-mail chiefads@custercountychief.com; web site www.custercountychief.com
Circulation:8,299fr; Sworn/Estimate/Non-Audited
Advertising: Open inch rate $8.00
Group: Heritage Publications (2003) Inc.
Pub. .... Bill Parsons
Adv.Rep .... Roxannie Payne
Prodn. Supvr. .... Dian Fransen
Delivery Method: Mail

COLUMBUS

COLUMBUS AREA CHOICE

(Tues)
PO Box 648, Columbus, NE, 68602-0648, USA; tel (402) 564-2741; adv tel (402) 563-7522; fax (402) 563-7564
Circulation:23,283fr; CVC
Advertising: Open inch rate $9.10
Adv. Mgr. .... Pam Hannah
Pub. .... Bill Vobejda
Mechanical Specifications: Type page 10 5/16 x 16; E - 7 cols, 1 1/3, between; A - 7 cols, 1 1/3, 1/4 between; C - 7 cols, 1 1/3, between.
Equipment: Hardware — APP/Mac; Software — QPS/QuarkXPress, Multi-Ad/Creator.
Zip Codes Served: 68001, 68014, 68036, 68601, 68620, 68624, 68626, 68629, 68631, 68632, 68634, 68640, 68642, 68643, 68644, 68647, 68650, 68651, 68653, 68657, 68658, 68660, 68661, 68662, 68663

TELEGRAM ADVANTAGE

(Tues)
1254 27th Ave, Columbus, NE, 68601-5656, USA; tel (402) 564-2741; fax (402) 563-7500; e-mail sports@columbustelegram.com; web site www.columbustelegram.com
Circulation:14,000fr; Sworn/Estimate/Non-Audited
Advertising: Open inch rate $15.98
Circ. Mgr. .... Greg Pehrson
Ed. .... James Dean
Prodn. Mgr. .... Jerry Gaver
Pub. .... Jim Dean
Mechanical Specifications: Type page 12 x 21 1/2; E - 6 cols, 2, 1/6 between; A - 6 cols, 2, 1/6 between; C - 9 cols, 1 1/8, 1/8 between.
Equipment: Hardware — APP/Mac; Presses — HI/V-15A; Software — QPS/QuarkXPress, Adobe/Photoshop, Baseview.
Zip Codes Served: 68601

FREMONT

FREMONT AREA SHOPPER

(Wed) (Weeily)
135 N Main St, Fremont, NE, 68025-5673, USA; tel (402) 721-5000; adv tel (402) 941-1426; fax (402) 721-8047; e-mail advetising@fremonttribune.com; adv e-mail julie.veskerna@lee.net; ed e-mail fremont.newsroom@lee.net; web site www.fremonttribune.com
Circulation:18,636fr; Sworn/Estimate/Non-Audited
Advertising: Open inch rate $10.00
Established: 2002
Group: Lee Enterprises, Inc.
Pub. .... Vincent Laboy
Advertising Team Leader .... Julie Veskerna
Mechanical Specifications: Type page 10.25 x 21; E - 6 cols, 1 1/4, 1/8 between; A - 9 cols, 1 1/4, 1/8 between; C - 9 cols, 1 1/4, 1/8 between.
Equipment: Hardware — APP/Mac; Presses — Goss Community; Software — Microsoft/Word.
Delivery Method: Mail
Zip Codes Served: 68025, 68031, 68036, 68038, 68040, 68648, 68649

GRAND ISLAND

AD/VENTURE

(Thur)
422 W 1st St, Grand Island, NE, 68801-5802, USA; tel (308) 382-1000; fax (308) 382-8129; e-mail editor@theindependent.com; web site www.theindependent.com
Circulation:25,000fr; Sworn/Estimate/Non-Audited
Advertising: Open inch rate $17.00
Pub. .... Robert Krecklow
Adv. Mgr. .... Jeff Barr
Circ. Mgr. .... Chris Smith
Ed. .... Bill Dunn
Prodn. Mgr. .... Dennis Kraus
Zip Codes Served: 68802

HARTINGTON

HARTINGTON SHOPPER

(Wed)
213 N Broadway Ave, Hartington, NE, 68739-4619, USA
Circulation: 130pd,7,145fr; CVC
Advertising: Open inch rate $9.15
Established: 1960Tom Schieffer
Mechanical Specifications: Type page: 10.25 x 16; 6 col

HASTINGS

ENCORE

(Wed)
908 W 2nd St, Hastings, NE, 68901-5063, USA; tel (402) 462-2131; fax (402) 461-4657; e-mail tribune@hastingstribune.com; web site www.hastingstribune.com
Circulation:7,000fr; Sworn/Estimate/Non-Audited
Advertising: Open inch rate $9.84
Group: Seaton Group
Pub. .... Donald R. Seaton
Bus. Mgr. .... Don Kissler
Adv. Mgr. .... Wanda Williams
Circ. Mgr. .... Galen Quick
Mng. Ed. .... Darran Fowler
Prodn. Mgr. .... Scott Carstensen
Mechanical Specifications: Type page 11 1/2 x 21; E - 6 cols, 1 3/4, 1/8 between; A - 6 cols, 1 3/4, 1/8 between; C - 8 cols, 1 1/3, 1/16 between.
Equipment: Hardware — APP/Mac; Presses — G/Urbanite; Software — Baseview, QPS/QuarkXPress 4.0.
Zip Codes Served: 68901

HEBRON

THE ADVISOR (1ST & 3RD MON)
341 Lincoln Ave, Hebron, NE, 68370-1525, USA; tel (402) 768-6980; fax (402) 768-6984
Circulation:6,600fr; Sworn/Estimate/Non-Audited
Advertising: Open inch rate $5.75
Pub. .... Lori Werner

HOLDREGE

HOLDREGE SHOPPING NEWS
(Tues)
418 Garfield St, Holdrege, NE, 68949-2219, USA; tel (308) 995-4441; fax (308) 995-5992; e-mail holdregecitizennews@yahoo.com
Circulation:5,700fr; Sworn/Estimate/Non-Audited
Advertising: Open inch rate $4.30
Pub. .... Robert D. King
Adv. Mgr. .... Barbara Penrod
Ed. .... Tunney Price
Prodn. Mgr. .... Dan Jordan
Zip Codes Served: 68949

KEARNEY

SHOPPING LINK
(Tues)
13 E 22nd St, Kearney, NE, 68847-5404, USA; tel (308) 237-2152; adv tel (308) 233-9790; fax (308) 233-9736; ed fax (308) 233-9745; ed e-mail news@kearneyhub.com; letters@kearneyhub.com; web site www.kearneyhub.com
Circulation:5,600fr; Sworn/Estimate/Non-Audited
Advertising: Open inch rate $8.00
Established: 1888
Adv. Mgr. .... Lori Guthard
Circ. Mgr. .... Cathy Headlee
Mng. Ed. .... Michael Konz
Mechanical Specifications: Type page 11 5/8 x 21; E - 6 cols, 1 4/5, 1/8 between; A - 6 cols, 1 4/5, 1/8 between; C - 9 cols, 1 1/5, 1/8 between.
Equipment: Hardware — PC; Presses — 13-G/Community; Software — Microsoft/Windows 98, Microsoft/NT, QPS/QuarkXPress 4.04, Adobe/Photoshop 5.0, Microsoft/Windows 2000.
Delivery Method: Carrier
Zip Codes Served: 68847

LEXINGTON

PEOPLE PLUS
(Wed)
114 W 5th St, Lexington, NE, 68850-1903, USA; tel (308) 324-5511; fax (308) 324-5240; adv e-mail ads@lexch.com; ed e-mail news@lexch.com; web site www.lexch.com
Circulation:8,200fr; Sworn/Estimate/Non-Audited
Advertising: Open inch rate $10.69
Pub. .... Terrie L. Baker
Cir. Mng. .... Leona Buhlmann
Equipment: Hardware — IBM/PC; Software — Microsoft/Word, QPS/QuarkXPress.
Zip Codes Served: 68850

LINCOLN

AMERICAN CLASSIFIEDS - LINCOLN
(Thur)
1240 N 48th St, Lincoln, NE, 68504-3178, USA; web site www.americanclassifieds.com
Circulation:20,497fr; CVC
Advertising: Open inch rate $996.00
Established: 1977Otis Seals
Mechanical Specifications: Type page: 10.5 x 15.75; 8 col

MCCOOK

BIG NICKEL
(Fri)
W First and E Sts, McCook, NE, 69001, USA; tel (308) 345-4500; fax (308) 345-7881; e-mail sskiles@ocsmccook.com; adv e-mail adsales1@mccookgazette.com; ed e-mail editor@mccookgazette.com; web site www.mccookgazette.com
Circulation:4,000fr; Sworn/Estimate/Non-Audited
Advertising: Open inch rate $4.00
Group: Rust Communications
Pub. .... Shary Skiles
Mechanical Specifications: Page size - 11" wide x 22.667" tall
print area - 10.125" wide x 21"tall
1 col = 1.5483"
2 col = 3.2636"
3 col = 4.9789"
4 col = 6.6942"
5 col - 8.4094"
6 col = 10.1247"
Equipment: Hardware — APP/Mac; Presses — Goss Suburban; Software — InDesign
Delivery Method: Newsstand, Carrier, Racks
Zip Codes Served: 69001, 67730, 67739, 67749, 68922, 68926, 68948, 69001, 69020, 69021, 69022, 69024, 69025, 69026, 69032, 69033, 69034, 69038, 69040, 69043, 69044, 69045, 69046

NEBRASKA CITY

PENNY PRESS 1
(Mon)
823 Central Ave, Nebraska City, NE, 68410-2408, USA; tel (402) 873-3334; fax (402) 873-5436; adv e-mail kkaufman@ncnewspress.com; ed e-mail editor@ncnewspress.com; web site www.ncnewspress.com
Circulation: 7pd,19,632fr; CVC
Advertising: Open inch rate $18.48
Established: 1854
Group: GateHouse Media, Inc.Kathy Kaufman
Mechanical Specifications: 1.5 inch column width, 6 col. broadsheet on 22" paper
Delivery Method: Mail, Newsstand
Zip Codes Served: 68410,68446, 68346, 68448, 51640

NORFOLK

DAILY NEWS PLUS
(Wed)
525 W Norfolk Ave, Norfolk, NE, 68701-5236, USA; tel (402) 371-1020; fax (402) 371-5802; ed fax (402) 644-2080; e-mail ndnews@norfolkdailynews.com; ed e-mail editor@norfolkdailynews.com; web site www.norfolkdailynews.com
Circulation:32,000fr; Sworn/Estimate/Non-Audited
Advertising: Open inch rate $26.25
Pub. .... Jerry Huse
Gen. Mgr. .... Les Mann
Adv. Mgr. .... Larry Bartscher
Ed. .... Kent Warneke
Prodn. Mgr. .... Mike Jones
Equipment: Hardware — APP/Mac; Presses — G/Urbanite; Software — Multi-Ad/Creator.
Zip Codes Served: 68701

NORFOLK AREA SHOPPER
(Wed)
404 W Norfolk Ave, Norfolk, NE, 68701-5235, USA; tel (402) 379-4100; fax (402) 379-1289; adv e-mail ads@norfolkareashopper.com; web site www.norfolkareashopper.com
Circulation:26,859fr; CVC
Advertising: Open inch rate $ 10.90
Established: 1988
Adv. Mgr. .... Julie Hermsen
Mechanical Specifications: Type page 10 5/16 x 16; E - 7 cols, 1 1/3, between; A - 7 cols, 1 1/3, between.
Equipment: Hardware — APP/Mac; Software — Adobe/PageMaker, QPS/QuarkXPress, Multi-Ad, Adobe/Photoshop.
Delivery Method: Mail, Carrier, Racks
Zip Codes Served: 68636, 68641, 68642, 68644, 68652, 68701, 68715, 68717, 68718, 68720, 68723, 68726, 68727, 68729, 68735, 68737, 68738, 68739, 68740, 68745, 68747, 68748, 68752, 68756, 68758, 68761, 68764, 68765, 68767, 68768, 68769, 68771, 68779, 68781, 68786, 68787, 687

OMAHA

AMERICAN CLASSIFIEDS
(Thur)
4060 Vinton St, Omaha, NE, 68105-3862, USA; tel (402) 342-4426; fax (402) 342-2706; web site www.americanclassifieds.com
Circulation:23,283fr; CVC
Advertising: Open inch rate $11.45
Established: 2000Editions: 2— 2 total; American Classifieds-Council Bluffs; American Classifieds-Omaha;
President/Publisher .... Kathy Napora
Prodn. Mgr. .... Kim Kelsey
Mechanical Specifications: Type page 9.9 x 21.5; A - 6 cols, 1 1/6, 1/6 between; C - 8 cols, 1 1/6, 1/6 between.
Equipment: Hardware — APP/Mac; Software — QPS/QuarkXPress, Adobe/Photoshop.

SEWARD

SEWARD COUNTY CONNECTION
(Thur)
129 S 6th St, Seward, NE, 68434-2003, USA; tel (402) 643-3676; fax (402) 643-6774; web site www.sewardindependent.com
Circulation:3,800fr; Sworn/Estimate/Non-Audited
Advertising: Open inch rate $8.75
Group: Enterprise Publishing Co.
Pub. .... Mark Rhoades
Gen. Mgr. .... Kevin L. Zadina
Circ. Mgr. .... Tammy Leff
Prodn. Mgr. .... Patti Danbom
Mechanical Specifications: Type page 15 x 22; E - 6 cols, 2 1/30, 1/6 between; A - 6 cols, 2 1/30, 1/6 between; C - 6 cols, 2 1/30, 1/6 between.
Equipment: Hardware — APP/Macs; Software — Adobe/PageMaker.
Zip Codes Served: 68434

SYRACUSE

PENNY PRESS
(Mon)
123 W 17th St, Syracuse, NE, 68446, USA; tel (402) 269-2135; fax (402) 269-2392; web site www.ncnewspress.com
Circulation:18,500fr; Sworn/Estimate/Non-Audited
Advertising: Open inch rate 15.75
Established: 1975
Group: GateHouse Media, Inc.
Publications Director .... Kathy Kaufman
Circ. Mgr. .... Janet Entler
Prodn. Mgr. .... Diane Bechtold
Production Director .... Dick Little
Zip Codes Served: 68446+

WAHOO

MARKET WEEKLY
(Wed)
564 N Broadway St, Wahoo, NE, 68066-1653, USA; tel (402) 443-4162; fax (402) 443-4459; adv e-mail advertising@wahoonewspaper.com; circulation@wahoonewspaper.com; classifieds@wahoonewspaper.com; ed e-mail news@wahoonewspaper.com; web site www.wahoo-ashland-waverly.com
Circulation:14,745fr; Sworn/Estimate/Non-Audited
Advertising: Open inch rate $13.40 pci
Group: BH Media Group
Advertising Manager .... Candi Puren
General Mgr Central Weeklies Group .... Amy McKay
Delivery Method: Mail, Carrier, Racks
Zip Codes Served: 68066, 68003, 68015, 68017, 68065, 68070, 68462, 68336, 68366, 68347, 68349, 68033, 68042, 68041, 68040, 68648, 68050, 68073, 68304, 68428

WAYNE

MORNING SHOPPER
(Mon)
114 Main St, Wayne, NE, 68787-1940, USA; web site www.wayneherald.com
Circulation:8,979fr; Sworn/Estimate/Non-AuditedKevin Peterson

WEST POINT

ELKHORN VALLEY SHOPPER
(Wed)
134 E Grove St, West Point, NE, 68788-1823, USA; tel (402) 372-2412; fax (402) 372-3530; e-mail wpnews@cableone.net; adv e-mail wpnewsadv@cableone.net; ed e-mail wpnewseditor@cableone.net; web site www.wpnews.com
Circulation: 18pd,9,132fr; CVC
Advertising: Open inch rate $12.45
Pub. .... Tom Kelly
Circ. Mgr. .... Colleen Ernesti
Mng. Ed. .... Willis Mahannah
Equipment: Hardware — 5-Power PC, APP/LaserWriter 16-600, 2-HP/ScanJet, HP/LaserJet 4MV, 2-HP/LaserJet II, 7-Compaq; Presses — ABD/360, ABD/375, HI, 3-WPC/Web Leader; Software — Caere/OmniPage Pro 7.0, Adobe/PageMaker 6.0, Adobe/Photoshop 3.0, Claris/MacWrite, Multi
Zip Codes Served: 68788-0040

YORK

ADVANTAGE
(Tues)
327 N Platte Ave, York, NE, 68467-3547, USA; tel (402) 362-4478; fax (402) 362-6748; e-mail news@yorknewstimes.com; adv e-mail kathy.larson@yorknewstimes.com; ed e-mail news@yorknewstimes.com; web site www.yorknewstimes.com
Circulation:15,601fr; Sworn/Estimate/Non-Audited
Advertising: Open inch rate $17.50
Group: BH Media Group
Pub. .... Greg Awtry
Adv. Mgr. .... Kathy Larson
Mechanical Specifications: Type page 11 5/8 x 21 1/2; E - 6 cols, 1 4/5, 1/8 between; A - 6 cols, 1 4/5, 1/8 between; C - 6 cols, 1 4/5, 1/8 between.
Equipment: Hardware — APP/PC; Presses — 6-KP; Software — QPS/QuarkXPress, InDesign
Delivery Method: Mail, Carrier, Racks
Zip Codes Served: 68467, 68316, 68319, 68351, 68354, 68359, 68365, 68367, 68371, 68401, 68406, 68416, 68434, 68436, 68444, 68453, 68456, 68460, 68666, 68818, 68843, 68979

NEW HAMPSHIRE

KEENE

MONADNOCK SHOPPER NEWS

(Wed)
445 West St, Keene, NH, 03431-2448, USA; tel (603) 352-5250; fax (603) 357-9351; e-mail ads@shoppernews.com; adv e-mail sales@shoppernews.com; ed e-mail editorial@shoppernews.com; web site www.shoppernews.com
Circulation: 9pd,42,415fr; CVC
Advertising: Open inch rate $18.68
Adv. Mgr. .... Mitchell G. Shakour
Ed. .... Michelle Green
Mechanical Specifications: Type page 10 3/8 x 16; E - 7 cols, 1 3/8, between; A - 7 cols, 1 3/8, between; C - 7 cols, 1 3/8, between.
Equipment: Hardware — APP/Mac; Presses — WPC/Web Leader; Software — Adobe/PageMaker, Adobe/Photoshop.
Zip Codes Served: 3431

NEW LONDON

THE RADIO SHOPPER

(Tues)
PO Box 2295, New London, NH, 03257-2295, USA; web site www.wntk.com
Circulation:7,365fr; Sworn/Estimate/Non-AuditedRobert Vinikoor

PLYMOUTH

THE PENNYSAVER

(Tues)
607 Tenney Mountain Hwy, Village Sq, Ste 137, Plymouth, NH, 3264, USA; tel (603) 536-3160; fax (603) 536-8150; e-mail advertising@pennysavernh.com; web site www.pennysavernh.com
Circulation:16,441fr; CVC
Advertising: Open inch rate $6.00
Established: 1971
Pub. .... Thomas D. Walrath
Adv. Mgr. .... David W. Walrath
Circ. Mgr. .... Steve Benner
Mechanical Specifications: Type page: 10.125 x 16; 6 col
Equipment: Hardware — APP/Mac; Software — Multi Ad/Creator.

NEW JERSEY

BAYONNE

HUDSON REPORTER ASSOCIATES, LP

(Wed, Sun)
447 Broadway, 447 Broadway, Bayonne, NJ, 07002-3623, USA; tel (201) 798-7800; fax (201) 798-0018; e-mail dunger@hudsonreporter.com; web site 447 Broadway
Circulation: 45,808pd,0fr; CAC
Established: 1983
Co-Pub./Gen. Mgr. .... Lucha Malato
Co-Pub./Adv. Dir. .... David S. Unger
Note: Hudson Reporter Inc. also publishes five speacialty publications; the Secaucus Guidebook, Phone Hoboken, Phone Med, All About Horses and the Gateway Guide.

CHERRY HILL

NEWSPAPER MEDIA GROUP

(Tues, Fri)
2 Executive Campus, Ste 400, Cherry Hill, NJ, 08002-4102, USA; tel (856) 779-3800; fax (609) 921-2714; adv fax (609) 921-2714; ed fax (609) 924-3842; e-mail feedback@centraljerseycom; adv e-mail gmclassified@gmnews.com; ed e-mail ahuston@centraljersey.com; web site www.newspapermediagroup.com
Circulation: 348pd,128,939fr; CVC
Advertising: Open inch rate Tues $23.22; Fri. $26.82
Established: 1786
Ed. .... Aubrey Huston
Exec. Ed. .... Donna Kenyon
Mechanical Specifications: Full page depth 21" 1/8" between
1 col 1.625"
2 col 3.360"
3 col 5.097"
4 col 6.833"
5 col 8.570"
6 col 10.305"
Equipment: Hardware — PCs, HP, Sun/Sparc; Presses — G Community; Software — HI/Pagination, HI/Editorial, Dewar/Classified, CJ/Circulation.
Delivery Method: Mail, Newsstand
Zip Codes Served: 08540, 08550, 08502, 08536, 08558, 08542

NEWTON

SHOPPER'S GUIDE

(Sat)
2 Spring St, Newton, NJ, 07860-2077, USA; tel (973) 383-1500; fax (973) 383-9284; adv e-mail adcomp@njherald.com; ed e-mail newsroom@njherald.com; business@njherald.com; web site www.njherald.com
Circulation:39,115fr; Sworn/Estimate/Non-Audited
Advertising: Open inch rate $24.76
Exec. Ed. .... Bruce Comlinson
Adv. Dir. .... Trish Hruby
Adv.Dir. .... Mitch Mayer
Circ. Dir. .... Mike Lawson
Mechanical Specifications: Type page 13 x 21 1/2; E - 6 cols, 2 5/8, 1/8 between; A - 6 cols, 2 5/8, 1/8 between; C - 9 cols, 1 2/5, 1/16 between.
Equipment: Hardware — 4-APP/Power Mac G4, 1-APP/iMac; Presses — 8-G/Urbanite U1050; Software — QPS/QuarkXPress, Multi-Ad/Creator 1.6.2, Baseview.
Zip Codes Served: 7860

TURNERSVILLE

TODAY'S SHOPPER

(Wed) (BI-Weekly)
PO Box 1110, Turnersville, NJ, 08012-0880, USA; tel (856) 228-9852; fax (856) 228-6445; adv e-mail gary@todaysshopper.net; web site www.todaysshopper.net
Circulation:81,600fr; CVC
Established: 1994
Digital Platform - Mobile: Android
Digital Platform - Tablet: Apple iOS
Publisher .... Gary Becker
Delivery Method: Mail
Zip Codes Served: 08080,08032,08012,08094,08081,08028,08071,08062

VINELAND

BRIDGETON JOURNAL

891 E Oak Rd, Vineland, NJ, 08360-2311, USA; tel (856) 451-1775

WOODLAND PARK

NORTH JERSEY DEALS

(Fri)
1 Garret Mountain Plz, Woodland Park, NJ, 07424-3320, USA; tel (973) 569-7000; adv tel (973) 569-7000; ed tel (973) 569-7000; fax (973) 569-7129; adv fax (973) 569-7129; ed fax (973) 569-7129; e-mail friedmanj@northjersey.com; adv e-mail friedmanj@northjersey.com; web site www.northjersey.com
Circulation: 0pd,75,032fr; CAC
Established: 2003
Group: North Jersey Media Group Inc.
VP/Pub. .... Janice Friedman
VP/Pub. .... Michael Lawson
Pres. .... Stephen A Borg
Delivery Method: Mail
Zip Codes Served: Passaic County

NEW MEXICO

ALBUQUERQUE

NEW MEXICO MARKETPLACE

(Mthly)
4308 Carlisle Blvd NE, Ste 103, Albuquerque, NM, 87107-4849, USA; tel (505)888-0500; adv tel (505)888-0500; fax (505)888-1078; adv fax (505)888-1078; e-mail info@nmmarketplace.com; adv e-mail classifieds@nmmarketplace.com; ed e-mail patrick@nmmarketplace.com; web site nmmarketplace.com
Circulation:; VAC
Established: 1986
Zip Codes Served: 87199

DEMING

THE SOUTHWEST COPPER SHOPPER

(Wed)
219 E Maple St, Deming, NM, 88030-4267, USA; tel (575) 546-2611; fax (575) 546-8116
Circulation:7,000fr; Sworn/Estimate/Non-Audited
Advertising: Open inch rate $12.00
Group: Gannett
Adv. Mgr. .... Monica Gutierres
Circ. Mgr. .... Janet Mattice
Ed. .... Joshua Byers
Mechanical Specifications: Type page 10 1/8 x 15 3/4; E - 5 cols, 1 15/16, 3/16 between; C - 8 cols, 1 5/6, between.
Equipment: ; Presses — G/Community.
Zip Codes Served: 88030

FARMINGTON

AMERICAN CLASSIFIEDS - FARMINGTON - FOUR CORNERS

(Thur)
928 E Main St, Ste C, Farmington, NM, 87401-2700, USA; tel (505) 564-2535; e-mail 4corners@AmClass.us; adv e-mail Allen@AmClass.us; web site www.AmClass.us
Circulation:29,421fr; CVC
Advertising: Open inch rate $13.86
Established: 1985
Group: Want Ads of Farmington, Inc.
Digital Platform - Mobile: Apple, Android
Digital Platform - Tablet: Apple iOS, Android
Pres. .... Robert Elmore
Sales Mgr. .... Allen Elmore
Mechanical Specifications: 1 column .... 1-1/4 inches (1.25) 2 columns .... 2-9/16 inches (2.5625) 3 columns .... 3-7/8 inches (3.875) 4 columns .... 5-3/16 inches (5.1875) 5 columns .... 6-1/2 inches (6.5) 6 columns .... 7-13/16 inches (7.8125) 7 columns .... 9-1/8 inches (9.125) 8 columns .... 10-1/2 inches (10.5) Full Page Size .... 8 columns x 16 inches
Equipment: Hardware — Mac; Software — Adobe
Delivery Method: Racks
Zip Codes Served: Various - See CVC Audit

FOUR CORNERS AMERICAN CLASSIFIEDS (THRIFTY NICKEL)

(Thur)
928 E Main St, Ste C, Farmington, NM, 87401-2700, USA; tel (505) 564-2535; adv tel (505) 564-2535; fax (505) 326-3025; adv fax (505) 326-3025; e-mail Allen@AmClass.us; adv e-mail Allen@AmClass.us; web site www.AmClass.us
Circulation:29,000fr; CVC
Advertising: 13.86
Established: 1985
Digital Platform - Mobile: Apple, Android
Digital Platform - Tablet: Apple iOS, Android
President .... Robert Elmore
Sales Manager .... Allen Elmore
Circ. Mgr. .... Spencer Elmore
Mechanical Specifications: 1 column, 2 columns, 3 columns, 4 columns, 5 columns, 6 columns, 7 columns, 8 columns. Full Page Size, 8 columns x 16 inches
Equipment: Hardware — Apple/Mac; Software — Adobe
Delivery Method: Racks
Zip Codes Served: Various, see CVC Audit

SAN JUAN SUN

(Wed)
201 N Allen Ave, Farmington, NM, 87401-6212, USA; tel (505) 325-4545; fax (505) 564-4630; e-mail obits@daily-times.com; web site www.daily-times.com
Circulation:21,500fr; Sworn/Estimate/Non-Audited
Group: Gannett
Pub. .... Sammy M. Lopez
Mechanical Specifications: Type page 11 7/8 x 21 1/2; E - 6 cols, 1 5/6, 1/6 between; A - 6 cols, 1 5/6, 1/6 between; C - 9 cols, 1 1/6, 1/6 between.
Equipment: Hardware — APP/Mac; Presses — 6-G/Urbanite; Software — Baseview.
Zip Codes Served: 87401

GRANTS

BEACON MID-WEEK

(Tues, Fri)
523 W Santa Fe Ave, Grants, NM, 87020-2535, USA; tel (505) 287-4411; fax (505) 287-7822; e-mail ccbeacon@starband.net; classifieds@cibolabeacon.com; adv e-mail advertising@cibolabeacon.com; ed e-mail editor@cibolabeacon.com; web site www.cibolabeacon.com
Circulation: 8,800pd,5,600fr; Sworn/Estimate/Non-Audited
Advertising: Open inch rate $6.95
Established: 1945
Adv. Mgr. .... Sylvia Gonzales
Circ. Mgr. .... Pam Lujan
Ed. .... Donald Jaramillo
Equipment: Hardware — APP/Mac, PC; Presses — HI/V-15A; Software — Adobe/PageMaker, QPS/QuarkXPress, Adobe/Photoshop, Microsoft/Word.
Zip Codes Served: 87020, 87021

LAS CRUCES

AMERICAN CLASSIFIEDS - LAS CRUCES

(Thur)
580 S Valley Dr, Ste 100, Las Cruces, NM, 88005-2700, USA; web site www.americanclassifieds.com
Circulation:26,218fr; VAC
Advertising: Open inch rate $15.00Marla Honeycutt

NEW YORK

ALBANY

PENNYSAVER/MONEYSAVER/ ADVERTISER

(Thur)
645 Albany Shaker Rd, Albany, NY, 12211-1158, USA; tel (518) 454-5501; fax (518) 454-5542; e-mail ads@crwnewspapers.com
Circulation: 187,000fr; Sworn/Estimate/Non-Audited
Established: 1960
Pub....Charles Hug
Mechanical Specifications: Type page 9 3/4 x 10; 6 cols, 1 1/2" per column
Delivery Method: Mail
Zip Codes Served: 12822, 12833, 12835, 12846, 12850, 12859, 12878, 12831, 12866, 12863, 12020, 12151, 12065, 12170, 12118, 12188, 12047, 12110, 12189, 12211, 12302, 12148, 12027, 12019, 12180, 12052, 12061, 12198, 12144, 12140, 12018, 12196, 12153, 12123, 12062, 12063, 12033, 12054, 12159, 12205

ALBION

LAKE COUNTRY PENNYSAVER

(Sun)
170 N Main St, Albion, NY, 14411-1063, USA; tel (585) 589-5641; fax (585) 589-1239; adv e-mail ads@lakecountrymedia.com; web site www.lakecountrypennysaver.com
Circulation: 10pd,20,325fr; VAC
Advertising: Open inch rate $12.72
Established: 1947Editions: 1—
Pub....Karen Sawicz
Ed....Gary Hill
Mechanical Specifications: Type page 10 3/8 x 16; E - 6 cols, 1 5/8, 3/16 between; A - 6 cols, 1 5/8, 3/16 between; C - 6 cols, 1 5/8, 3/16 between.
Equipment: Hardware — APP/Mac; Presses — Hamada/2 Color; Software — Adobe Creative Suite
Delivery Method: Mail, Newsstand, Carrier, Racks
Zip Codes Served: 14411, 14012, 14058, 14098, 14103, 14105, 14429, 14442, 14452, 14470, 14473, 14476, 14477, 14479, 14508, 14571

ARCADE

ARCADE PENNYSAVER

(Sun)
277 Main St, Arcade, NY, 14009-1212, USA; tel (716) 496-7291; adv tel (716) 870-9675; fax (585) 492-5474; adv e-mail kevino@pennysavers.com; web site http://pennysavers.com
Circulation: 11,185fr; CVC
Advertising: Open inch rate $8.11
Established: 1939Gerry Grabowski
Pub....Gary Durawa
Ad. Mgr....Judy Beckwith
Circ. Mgr....Bill Marshall
Mechanical Specifications: Type page: 10.25 x 16; 6 col

AVON

GENESEE VALLEY PENNY SAVER - BATAVIA

(Fri)
PO Box 340, Avon, NY, 14414-0340, USA; web site www.gvpennysaver.com
Circulation: 16,300fr; VAC
Advertising: Open inch rate $11.25
Established: 1948Steve Harrison
Mechanical Specifications: Type page: 7.667 x 11; 4 col

GENESEE VALLEY PENNY SAVER - DANSVILLE WAYLAND

(Fri)
PO Box 340, Avon, NY, 14414-0340, USA; e-mail steveharrison@gvpennysaver.com; adv e-mail dariareitknecht@gvpennysaver.com; ed e-mail steveharrison@gvpennysaver.com; web site www.gvpennysaver.com
Circulation: 0pd,9,052fr; VAC
Advertising: Open inch rate $11.25
Established: 1948Steve Harrison
Mechanical Specifications: Type page: 7.667 x 11; 4 col

GENESEE VALLEY PENNY SAVER - EASTWAY

(Fri)
PO Box 340, Avon, NY, 14414-0340, USA; web site www.gvpennysaver.com
Circulation: 16,169fr; VAC
Advertising: Open inch rate $11.25
Established: 1948Steve Harrison
Mechanical Specifications: Type page: 7.667 x 11; 4 col

GENESEE VALLEY PENNY SAVER - FAIRPORT

(Fri)
PO Box 340, Avon, NY, 14414-0340, USA; web site www.gvpennysaver.com
Circulation: 16,404fr; VAC
Advertising: Open inch rate $11.25
Established: 1948Steve Harrison
Mechanical Specifications: Type page: 7.667 x 11; 4 col

GENESEE VALLEY PENNY SAVER - LIVINGSTON

(Fri)
PO Box 340, Avon, NY, 14414-0340, USA; web site www.gvpennysaver.com
Circulation: 13,322fr; VAC
Advertising: Open inch rate $11.25
Established: 1948Steve Harrison
Mechanical Specifications: Type page: 7.667 x 11; 4 col

GENESEE VALLEY PENNY SAVER - OATKA

(Fri)
PO Box 340, Avon, NY, 14414-0340, USA; e-mail steveharrison@gvpennysaver.com; adv e-mail dariareitknecht@gvpennysaver.com; ed e-mail steveharrison@gvpennysaver.com; web site www.gvpennysaver.com
Circulation: 14,572fr; VAC
Advertising: Open inch rate $11.25
Established: 1948Steve Harrison
Mechanical Specifications: Type page: 7.667 x 11; 4 col

GENESEE VALLEY PENNY SAVER - PITTSFORD / E ROCHESTER

(Fri)
PO Box 340, Avon, NY, 14414-0340, USA; web site www.gvpennysaver.com
Circulation: 11,666fr; VAC
Advertising: Open inch rate $11.25
Established: 1948Steve Harrison
Mechanical Specifications: Type page: 7.667 x 11; 4 col

GENESEE VALLEY PENNY SAVER - RUSH / HENRIETTA

(Fri)
PO Box 340, Avon, NY, 14414-0340, USA; web site www.gvpennysaver.com
Circulation: 15,382fr; VAC
Advertising: Open inch rate $11.25
Established: 1948Steve Harrison
Mechanical Specifications: Type page: 7.667 x 11; 4 col

GENESEE VALLEY PENNY SAVER - TRI-COUNTY ADVERTISER

(Fri)
PO Box 340, Avon, NY, 14414-0340, USA; web site tricountyadvertiser.org
Circulation: 14,882fr; VAC
Advertising: Open inch rate $11.25
Established: 1948Steve Harrison
Mechanical Specifications: Type page: 7.667 x 11; 4 col

GENESEE VALLEY PENNY SAVER - WEBSTER - ONTARIO - WALWORTH

(Fri)
PO Box 340, Avon, NY, 14414-0340, USA; fax (585) 226-3390; adv fax (585) 226-3390; ed fax (585) 226-3390; e-mail steveharrison@gvpennysaver.com; adv e-mail dariareitknecht@gvpennysaver.com; ed e-mail steveharrison@gvpennysaver.com; web site www.gvpennysaver.com
Circulation: 0pd,17,216fr; VAC
Advertising: Open inch rate $11.25
Established: 1948
Pub./Pres....Steve Harrison
Mechanical Specifications: Type page: 7.667 x 11; 4 col

GENESEE VALLEY PENNYSAVER

(Sat)
1471 Rte 15, Avon, NY, 14414, USA; tel (585) 226-8111; fax (585) 226-3390; e-mail mail@gvpennysaver.com; web site www.gvpennysaver.com
Circulation: 171,677fr; CVC
Advertising: Open inch rate $11.25
Established: 1948Editions: 9— 9 total; Genesee Valley Penny Saver-Eastway (16,527); Genesee Valley Penny Saver-Genesee (18,320); Genesee Valley Penny Saver-Fairport/Perinton (18,758); Genesee Valley Penny Saver-Livingston (14,544); Genesee Valley Penny Saver-Tri-County (13,492); Gene
Vice Pres....Kim Dougherty
Circ. Mgr....Shari L. Rapone
Ed....J. Stephen Harrison
Controller....Kathy Hammond
Advertising Director....Daria Reitknecht
Mechanical Specifications: Type page: 7.667 x 11; 4 col
Equipment: Hardware — APP/Mac; Presses — 2-WPC/Web Leader; Software — Multi-Ad/Creator 4.0, QPS/QuarkXPress 4.0.
Delivery Method: Mail, Carrier, Racks
Zip Codes Served: 14003, 14005, 14013, 14020, 14036, 14040, 14054, 14056, 14058, 14125, 14143, 14414, 14416, 14422, 14423, 14424, 14425, 14428, 14431, 14435, 14443, 14454, 14462, 14466, 14467, 14469, 14471, 14472, 14475, 14480, 14481, 14482, 14485, 14486, 14487, 14506, 145

BATAVIA

DRUMMER PENNYSAVER

(Sun)
2 Apollo Dr, Batavia, NY, 14020-3002, USA; tel (585) 344-2055; fax (585) 344-2050; web site www.drummerpennysaver.com
Circulation: 23,015fr; CVC
Advertising: Open inch rate $9.65
Adv Mgr....Sheila Mitchell
Circ. Mgr....Christine Smith
Ed....Mark Gracyzk
Prodn. Mgr....Dan Zwierzynski
Mechanical Specifications: Type page 10 1/3 x 16.
Zip Codes Served: 14021

BOHEMIA

CARRIER NEWS

(Thur)
2950 Veterans Memorial Hwy, Bohemia, NY, 11716-1037, USA; tel (631) 698-8400; fax (631) 580-7748; e-mail production@lipennysaver.com; web site www.lipennysaver.com
Circulation: 4,084fr; Sworn/Estimate/Non-Audited
Pub./ Pres....Richard Megenedy
Adv. Mgr....Ron Rudolph
Circ. Mgr....Jennifer Goodman
Mechanical Specifications: Type page 6 3/8 x 9 7/8; A - 2 cols, 1 1/2, between; C - 4 cols, 1 1/2, between.
Equipment: Hardware — Optiquest/2000; Software — QPS/QuarkXPress.

BROCKPORT

TRI-COUNTY ADVERTISER

(Sun)
15 Main St, Brockport, NY, 14420-1901, USA; tel (585) 637-5100; fax (585) 637-0111; e-mail www.gvpennysaver.com
Circulation: 15,950fr; CVC
Advertising: Open inch rate $7.28
Ed....Sally A. Cottrell
Mechanical Specifications: Type page 10 1/4 x 16; E - 6 cols, 1 5/16, between; A - 6 cols, between.
Equipment: Hardware — APP/Macs; Presses — WPC/Web Leader; Software — QPS/QuarkXPress 4.0, Adobe/Photoshop 5.2, Multi-Ad-Creator 3.6.2.
Zip Codes Served: 14420

BRONX

THE BRONX PENNY PINCHER

(Thur)
3797 E Tremont Ave, Bronx, NY, 10465-2457, USA; tel (718) 828-1104; fax (718) 828-7974; e-mail bxpp@aol.com; adv e-mail bxpp@aol.com; ed e-mail bxpp@aol.com; web site www.bronxpennypincher.com
Circulation: 0pd,78,375fr; VAC
Advertising: Modular Rate $65.00
Established: 1978Editions: Throgs Neck, 23,100, Morris Park, 16,200, Castle Hill, 16025, Pelham Pkwy. North, 15050, Parkchester, 8025
Digital Platform - Mobile: Apple, Android, Windows, Blackberry
Digital Platform - Tablet: Apple iOS, Android, Windows 7, Blackberry Tablet OS
Pub./Gen. Mgr....Barbara Perrone
Delivery Method: Mail
Zip Codes Served: Bronx County

BROOKLYN

THE LOCAL MERCHANTEER

(Mthly)
599 Manhattan Ave, Brooklyn, NY, 11222-2078, USA; tel (718) 383-1077; fax (718) 389-7912; e-mail merchanteer@aol.com
Circulation: 8,000fr; Sworn/Estimate/Non-Audited
Heather Branch
John Haines
Robert HainesEd.s

BUFFALO

ALDEN METRO SOURCE

(Sat)
75 Boxwood Ln, Buffalo, NY, 14227-2707, USA; tel (716) 668-5223; adv tel (716) 668-5223; ed tel (716) 668-5223 ext. 8007; fax (716) 668-4526; adv fax (716) 668-4526; ed fax (716) 668-4526; e-mail dguastaferro@metrowny.com; adv e-mail jbeckwith@metrowny.com; ed e-mail mondesko@metrowny.com; web site www.metrowny.com
Circulation: 4,784fr; CVC
Advertising: Open inch rate $8.11
Established: 1968
Group: Metro Group, Inc.
Pub....Denny Guastaferro
Adv. Mgr....Judy Beckwith
Ed....Matthew Ondesko

Pub./Prod. Mgr............................ Gary Durawa
Circ. Mgr.. Bill Marshall
Mechanical Specifications: Type page: 10 x 12.8; 6 col
Delivery Method: Mail
Zip Codes Served: 14001, 14004, 14102

AMHERST / GETZVILLE SMART SHOPPER
(Sat)
75 Boxwood Ln, Buffalo, NY, 14227-2707, USA; tel (716) 668-5223; adv tel (716) 668-5223; ed tel (716) 668-5223 ext. 8007; fax (716) 668-4526; adv fax (716) 668-4526; ed fax (716) 668-4526; e-mail dguastaferro@metrowny.com; adv e-mail jbeckwith@metrowny.com; ed e-mail mondesko@metrowny.com; web site www.metrowny.com
Circulation:14,421fr; CVC
Advertising: Open inch rate $8.11
Established: 1968
Group: Metro Group, Inc.
Pub.................................... Denny Guastaferro
Adv. Mgr.....................................Judy Beckwith
Ed..Matthew Ondesko
Pub./Prod. Mgr............................ Gary Durawa
Circ. Mgr.. Bill Marshall
Mechanical Specifications: Type page: 10 x 12.8; 6 col
Delivery Method: Mail
Zip Codes Served: Eerie County

CLARENCE METRO SOURCE
(Sat)
75 Boxwood Ln, Buffalo, NY, 14227-2707, USA; tel (716) 668-5223; adv tel (716) 668-5223; ed tel (716) 668-5223 ext. 8007; fax (716) 668-4526; adv fax (716) 668-4526; ed fax (716) 668-4526; e-mail dguastaferro@metrowny.com; adv e-mail jbeckwith@metrowny.com; ed e-mail mondesko@metrowny.com; web site www.metrowny.com
Circulation:8,765fr; CVC
Advertising: Open inch rate $8.11
Established: 1968
Group: Metro Group, Inc.
Pub.................................... Denny Guastaferro
Adv. Mgr.....................................Judy Beckwith
Ed..Matthew Ondesko
Pub... Gary Durawa
Circ. Mgr.. Bill Marshall
Mechanical Specifications: Type page: 10 x 12.8; 6 col
Delivery Method: Mail
Zip Codes Served: Eerie County

DEPEW METRO SOURCE
(Sat)
75 Boxwood Ln, Buffalo, NY, 14227-2707, USA; tel (716) 668-5223; adv tel (716) 668-5223; ed tel (716) 668-5223 ext. 8007; fax (716) 668-4526; adv fax (716) 668-4526; ed fax (716) 668-4526; e-mail dguastaferro@metrowny.com; adv e-mail jbeckwith@metrowny.com; ed e-mail mondesko@metrowny.com; web site www.metrowny.com
Circulation:7,084fr; CVC
Advertising: Open inch rate $8.11
Established: 1968
Group: Metro Group, Inc.
Pub.................................... Denny Guastaferro
Adv. Mgr.....................................Judy Beckwith
Ed..Matthew Ondesko
Pub... Gary Durawa
Circ. Mgr.. Bill Marshall
Mechanical Specifications: Type page: 10 x 12.8; 6 col
Delivery Method: Mail
Zip Codes Served: Eerie County

EGGERTSVILLE / SNYDER SMART SHOPPER
(Sat)
75 Boxwood Ln, Buffalo, NY, 14227-2707, USA; tel (716) 668-5223; adv tel (716) 668-5223; ed tel (716) 668-5223 ext. 8007; fax (716) 668-4526; adv fax (716) 668-4526; ed fax (716) 668-4526; e-mail dguastaferro@metrowny.com; adv e-mail jbeckwith@metrowny.com; ed e-mail mondesko@metrowny.com; web site www.metrowny.com
Circulation:11,056fr; CVC
Advertising: Open inch rate $8.11
Established: 1968
Group: Metro Group, Inc.
Pub.................................... Denny Guastaferro
Adv. Mgr.....................................Judy Beckwith
Ed..Matthew Ondesko
Pub... Gary Durawa
Circ. Mgr.. Bill Marshall
Mechanical Specifications: Type page: 10 x 12.8; 6 col
Delivery Method: Mail
Zip Codes Served: Eerie County

KENMORE / TONAWANDA SOURCE
(Sat)
75 Boxwood Ln, Buffalo, NY, 14227-2707, USA; tel (716) 668-5223; adv tel (716) 668-5223; ed tel (716) 668-5223 ext. 8007; fax (716) 668-4526; adv fax (716) 668-4526; ed fax (716) 668-4526; e-mail dguastaferro@metrowny.com; adv e-mail jbeckwith@metrowny.com; ed e-mail mondesko@metrowny.com; web site www.metrowny.com
Circulation:13,519fr; CVC
Advertising: Open inch rate $8.11
Established: 1968
Group: Metro Group, Inc.
Pub.................................... Denny Guastaferro
Adv. Mgr.....................................Judy Beckwith
Ed..Matthew Ondesko
Pub... Gary Durawa
Circ. Mgr.. Bill Marshall
Mechanical Specifications: Type page: 10 x 12.8; 6 col
Delivery Method: Mail
Zip Codes Served: Eerie County

LANCASTER SOURCE
(Sat)
75 Boxwood Ln, Buffalo, NY, 14227-2707, USA; tel (716) 668-5223; adv tel (716) 668-5223; ed tel (716) 668-5223 ext. 8007; fax (716) 668-4526; adv fax (716) 668-4526; ed fax (716) 668-4526; e-mail dguastaferro@metrowny.com; adv e-mail jbeckwith@metrowny.com; ed e-mail mondesko@metrowny.com; web site www.metrowny.com
Circulation:13,466fr; CVC
Advertising: Open inch rate $8.11
Established: 1968
Group: Metro Group, Inc.
Pub.................................... Denny Guastaferro
Adv. Mgr.....................................Judy Beckwith
Ed..Matthew Ondesko
Pub... Gary Durawa
Circ. Mgr.. Bill Marshall
Mechanical Specifications: Type page: 10 x 12.8; 6 col
Delivery Method: Mail
Zip Codes Served: Eerie County

LEWISTON / YOUNGSTOWN METRO RETAILER
(Sat)
75 Boxwood Ln, Buffalo, NY, 14227-2707, USA
Circulation:7,302fr; Sworn/Estimate/Non-AuditedDenny Guastaferro

LOCKPORT METRO RETAILER
(Sat)
75 Boxwood Ln, Buffalo, NY, 14227-2707, USA; web site www.metrowny.com
Circulation:30,420fr; CVC
Established: 1968Denny Guastaferro
Mechanical Specifications: Type page: 10 x 12.8; 6 col

LOCKPORT RETAILER
(Sat) (Weekly)
75 Boxwood Ln, Buffalo, NY, 14227-2707, USA; tel (716) 434-4055; ed tel (716) 668-5223; fax (716) 438-1394; e-mail dbutton@metrowny.com; adv e-mail jbeckwith@metrowny.com; ed e-mail mondesko@metrowny.com; web site www.metrowny.com
Circulation:29,148fr; CVC
Advertising: Open inch rate $14.51
Established: 19
Group: Metro Group, Inc.
Strategic Publications, LLCEditions: 1— Lockport Retailer - 30,420 circ.
Digital Platform - Mobile: Apple, Android, Windows
Digital Platform - Tablet: Apple iOS, Android, Windows 7
Adv. Mgr.....................................Judy Beckwith
Pub... Gary Durawa
Circ. Mgr.. Bill Marshall
Mechanical Specifications: Page Size 10 3/4" x 14"
Equipment: ; Presses — Harris Vis; Software — Adobe In-Design
Delivery Method: Carrier
Zip Codes Served: 14012, 14028, 14067, 14094, 14105, 14108, 14120, 14126, 14131, 14132, 14172
Note: Lockport Retailers is one of 24 weekly community newspapers that is published by the Metro Group, Inc.

NORTH BUFFALO SMART SHOPPER
(Sat)
75 Boxwood Ln, Buffalo, NY, 14227-2707, USA; tel (716) 668-5223; adv tel (716) 668-5223; ed tel (716) 668-5223 ext. 8007; fax (716) 668-4526; adv fax (716) 668-4526; ed fax (716) 668-4526; e-mail dguastaferro@metrowny.com; adv e-mail jbeckwith@metrowny.com; ed e-mail mondesko@metrowny.com; web site www.metrowny.com
Circulation:10,149fr; CVC
Advertising: Open inch rate $8.11
Established: 1968
Group: Metro Group, Inc.
Pub.................................... Denny Guastaferro
Adv. Mgr.....................................Judy Beckwith
Ed..Matthew Ondesko
Pub... Gary Durawa
Circ. Mgr.. Bill Marshall
Mechanical Specifications: Type page: 10 x 12.8; 6 col
Delivery Method: Mail
Zip Codes Served: 14001, 14004, 14102

NORTH CHEEKTOWAGA SOURCE
(Sat)
75 Boxwood Ln, Buffalo, NY, 14227-2707, USA; tel (716) 668-5223; adv tel (716) 668-5223; ed tel (716) 668-5223 ext. 8007; fax (716) 668-4526; adv fax (716) 668-4526; ed fax (716) 668-4526; e-mail dguastaferro@metrowny.com; adv e-mail jbeckwith@metrowny.com; ed e-mail mondesko@metrowny.com; web site www.metrowny.com
Circulation:16,458fr; CVC
Advertising: Open inch rate $8.11
Established: 1968
Group: Metro Group, Inc.
Pub.................................... Denny Guastaferro
Adv. Mgr.....................................Judy Beckwith
Ed..Matthew Ondesko
Pub... Gary Durawa
Circ. Mgr.. Bill Marshall
Mechanical Specifications: Type page: 10 x 12.8; 6 col
Delivery Method: Mail
Zip Codes Served: Eerie County

NORTH TONAWANDA SOURCE
(Sat)
75 Boxwood Ln, Buffalo, NY, 14227-2707, USA; tel (716) 668-5223; adv tel (716) 668-5223; ed tel (716) 668-5223 ext. 8007; fax (716) 668-4526; adv fax (716) 668-4526; ed fax (716) 668-4526; e-mail dguastaferro@metrowny.com; adv e-mail jbeckwith@metrowny.com; ed e-mail mondesko@metrowny.com; web site www.metrowny.com
Circulation:17,618fr; CVC
Advertising: Open inch rate $8.11
Established: 1968
Group: Metro Group, Inc.
Pub.................................... Denny Guastaferro
Adv. Mgr.....................................Judy Beckwith
Ed..Matthew Ondesko
Pub... Gary Durawa
Circ. Mgr.. Bill Marshall
Mechanical Specifications: Type page: 10 x 12.8; 6 col
Delivery Method: Mail
Zip Codes Served: Eerie County

RIVERSIDE REVIEW
(Wed)
215 Military Rd, Buffalo, NY, 14207-2631, USA; tel (716) 877-8400; fax (716) 877-8742; web site www.buffaloreview.com
Circulation:14,000fr; Sworn/Estimate/Non-Audited
Advertising: Open inch rate $8.75
Ed..Richard Mack
Zip Codes Served: 14207

SOUTH BUFFALO METRO SOURCE
(Sat)
75 Boxwood Ln, Buffalo, NY, 14227-2707, USA; tel (716) 668-5223; adv tel (716) 668-5223; ed tel (716) 668-5223 ext. 8007; fax (716) 668-4526; adv fax (716) 668-4526; ed fax (716) 668-4526; e-mail dguastaferro@metrowny.com; adv e-mail jbeckwith@metrowny.com; ed e-mail mondesko@metrowny.com; web site www.metrowny.com
Circulation:14,328fr; CVC
Advertising: Open inch rate $8.11
Established: 1968
Group: Metro Group, Inc.
Pub.................................... Denny Guastaferro
Adv. Mgr.....................................Judy Beckwith
Ed..Matthew Ondesko
Pub... Gary Durawa
Circ. Mgr.. Bill Marshall
Mechanical Specifications: Type page: 10 x 12.8; 6 col
Delivery Method: Mail
Zip Codes Served: Eerie County

SOUTH CHEEKTOWAGA SOURCE
(Sat)
75 Boxwood Ln, Buffalo, NY, 14227-2707, USA; tel (716) 668-5223; adv tel (716) 668-5223; ed tel (716) 668-5223 ext. 8007; fax (716) 668-4526; adv fax (716) 668-4526; ed fax (716) 668-4526; e-mail dguastaferro@metrowny.com; adv e-mail jbeckwith@metrowny.com; ed e-mail mondesko@metrowny.com; web site www.metrowny.com
Circulation:16,730fr; CVC
Advertising: Open inch rate $8.11
Established: 1968
Group: Metro Group, Inc.
Pub.................................... Denny Guastaferro
Adv. Mgr.....................................Judy Beckwith
Ed..Matthew Ondesko
Pub... Gary Durawa
Circ. Mgr.. Bill Marshall
Mechanical Specifications: Type page: 10 x 12.8; 6 col
Delivery Method: Mail
Zip Codes Served: Eerie County

TONAWANDA SOURCE
(Sat)
75 Boxwood Ln, Buffalo, NY, 14227-2707, USA; web site www.metrowny.com
Circulation:10,538fr; CVC
Established: 1968Denny Guastaferro
Managing Editor...................Matthew Ondesko
Pub... Gary Durawa
Adv. Mgr.....................................Judy Beckwith
Circ. Mgr.. Bill Marshall
Mechanical Specifications: Type page: 10 x 12.8; 6 col

WILLIAMSVILLE SMART SHOPPER
(Sat)
75 Boxwood Ln, Buffalo, NY, 14227-2707, USA; tel (716) 668-5223; adv tel (716) 668-5223; ed tel (716) 668-5223 ext. 8007; fax (716) 668-4526; adv fax (716) 668-4526; ed fax (716) 668-4526; e-mail dguastaferro@metrowny.com; adv e-mail jbeckwith@metrowny.com; ed e-mail mondesko@metrowny.com; web site www.metrowny.com
Circulation: 0pd,9,100fr; CVC
Advertising: Open inch rate $8.11

Established: 1968
Group: Metro Group, Inc.
Pub. .... Denny Guastaferro
Adv. Mgr. .... Judy Beckwith
Ed. .... Matthew Ondesko
Pub. .... Gary Durawa
Circ. Mgr .... Bill Marshall
Mechanical Specifications: Type page: 10 x 12.8; 6 col
Delivery Method: Mail
Zip Codes Served: Erie County

CANANDAIGUA

AD GROUP - LYONS SHOPPING GUIDE

(Wed)
73 Buffalo St, Canandaigua, NY, 14424-1001, USA; tel (585) 394-0770; adv tel 585-394-0770 ext. 217; ed tel (585) 394-0770 ext.264; adv e-mail bkesel@messengerpostmedia.com; ed e-mail smccrory@messengerpostmedia.com; web site www.MPNnow.com
Circulation:6,099fr; Sworn/Estimate/Non-AuditedBrian Doane

AD GROUP - NEWARK PENNYSAVER

(Fri)
73 Buffalo St, Canandaigua, NY, 14424-1001, USA; tel (585) 394-0770; adv tel 585-337-4217; ed tel 585-337-4276; adv e-mail bkesel@messengerpostmedia.com; ed e-mail bdoane@messengerpostmedia.com
Circulation: 0pd,5,979fr; CVC
Advertising: Open inch rate $5.35 - $8.03
Established: 1936
Pres./Pub .... Brian Doane
Mechanical Specifications: Type page: 10.25 x 16; 6 col

AD GROUP - SODUS PENNYSAVER

(Tues)
73 Buffalo St, Canandaigua, NY, 14424-1001, USA; tel (585) 394-0770; adv tel 585-394-0770 ext. 217; ed tel (585) 394-0770 ext.264; adv e-mail bkesel@messengerpostmedia.com; ed e-mail smccrory@messengerpostmedia.com; web site www.MPNnow.com
Circulation:8,023fr; Sworn/Estimate/Non-AuditedBrian Doane

COMMUNITY NEWS

(Thur)
73 Buffalo St, Canandaigua, NY, 14424-1001, USA; tel (585) 381-3300; fax (585) 381-8618; adv e-mail classifieds@messengerpostmedia.com; web site www.mpnnow.com
Circulation:160,000fr; Sworn/Estimate/Non-Audited
Advertising: Open inch rate $8.50
Group: GateHouse Media, Inc.
Pub. .... Kathy Hammond
Adv. Mgr. .... Jerry Grundman
Zip Codes Served: 14450

GENESEE VALLEY PENNY SAVER - CANANDAIGUA

(Fri)
202 S Main St, Canandaigua, NY, 14424-2115, USA; tel (585) 393-1111; fax (585) 393-1823; e-mail can@gvpennysaver.com; web site www.gvpennysaver.com
Circulation:16,350fr; VAC
Advertising: Open inch rate $11.25
Established: 1948
Digital Platform - Mobile: Apple, Android
Digital Platform - Tablet: Apple iOS
President .... Steve Harrison
Mechanical Specifications: Type page: 7.667 x 11; 4 col
Delivery Method: Mail
Zip Codes Served: 14424, 14469, 14471, 14560, 14512, 14507, 14512, 14873

LYONS CLYDE SAVANNAH SHOPPER

(Fri)
73 Buffalo St, Canandaigua, NY, 14424-1001, USA; web site www.MPNnow.com
Circulation: 0pd,5,549fr; CVC
Advertising: Open inch rate $5.35 - $8.03
Established: 1936
Group: AD Group WC Incorporated
Pub. .... Brian Doane
Adv. Mgr. .... Beth Kesel
Circ. Mgr. .... Cathy Buksar
Mechanical Specifications: Type page: 10.25 x 16; 6 col
Zip Codes Served: Ontario County

SODUS WILLIAMSON PENNYSAVER

(Fri)
73 Buffalo St, Canandaigua, NY, 14424-1001, USA; e-mail rprocida@messengerpostmedia.com; adv e-mail bkesel@messengerpostmedia.com; ed e-mail cathyb@messengerpostmedia.com; web site www.MPNnow.com
Circulation: 0pd,9,337fr; VAC
Advertising: Open inch rate $5.35 - $8.03
Established: 1936
Group: AD Group WC Incorporated
Pub. .... Brian Doane
Adv. Mgr. .... Beth Kesel
Circ. Mgr. .... Cathy Buksar
Mechanical Specifications: Type page: 10.25 x 16; 6 col
Delivery Method: Mail
Zip Codes Served: Ontario County

TIMESAVER

(Fri)
73 Buffalo St, Canandaigua, NY, 14424-1001, USA; tel (585) 394-0770; adv tel (585) 394-0770; ed tel (585) 394-0770; e-mail rprocida@messengerpostmedia.com; adv e-mail bkesel@messengerpostmedia.com; ed e-mail bdoane@messengerpostmedia.com
Circulation: 0pd,10,714fr; CVC
Advertising: Open inch rate $5.35 - $8.03
Established: 1957
Group: AD Group WC Incorporated
Pres./Pub. .... Brian Doane
Adv. Mgr. .... Beth Kesel
Mechanical Specifications: Type page: 10.25 x 16; 6 col
Delivery Method: Mail
Zip Codes Served: Ontario County

CARLE PLACE

MARKET PLACE PUBLICATIONS

(Thur)
234 Silverlake Blvd, Carle Place, NY, 11514-1644, USA; tel (516) 997-7909; fax (516) 997-7906; e-mail info@marketplacepublications.com; adv e-mail jeanette@marketplacepublications.com; ed e-mail events@marketplacepublications.com; web site www.marketplacepublications.com
Circulation:30,500fr; Sworn/Estimate/Non-Audited
Established: 1987Editions: 4— 4 total covering New Hyde Park, Garden City Park, Herricks, Manhasset Hills, Floral Park,Mineola, Carle Place, Williston Park, East Williston
Digital Platform - Mobile: Apple, Android, Windows, Blackberry
Digital Platform - Tablet: Apple iOS, Android, Windows 7, Blackberry Tablet OS, Kindle, Nook, Kindle Fire
Publ. .... Jeanette Frisina
Mechanical Specifications: Type page 9 3/4 x 13; E - 4 cols, 2 5/8, 3/8 between; A - 4 cols, 2 5/8, 3/8 between; C - 5 cols, 1 3/4, 1/4 between.
Equipment: Hardware — APP/Mac; Software — Adobe/PageMaker, Indesign
Delivery Method: Mail, Carrier
Zip Codes Served: 11001, 11514, 11040, 11426, 11507, 11596, 11577, 11501, 11514, 11004, 11590, 11010, 11530, 11003, 11580, 11552, 11565
Note: We also mail inserts and hand deliver door hangers.

CHEEKTOWAGA

METRO COMMUNITY NEWS

(Sat)
75 Boxwood Ln, Cheektowaga, NY, 14227-2707, USA; tel (716) 668-5223; fax (716) 668-4526; e-mail info@metrowny.com; web site www.metrowny.com
Circulation:279,152fr; Sworn/Estimate/Non-AuditedEditions: 25— 25 total; Alden (5,767); Am-Ton (15,202); Amherst/Getzville (16,605); Cheektowaga Harlem/Genesee (11,339); Cheektowaga Union/Genesee (9,602); Clarence (8,359); Depew (8,149); Grand Island (6,066); Kenmore/Tonawanda (13,958); Lancaster (11,038); Lewiston/
Pub. .... Gerard Grabowski
Ed. .... Lorne Marshall
Dist. Mgr. .... Bill Marshall
Mechanical Specifications: Type page 10 x 15; E - 6 cols, 1 1/2, between; A - 6 cols, 1 1/2, between; C - 8 cols, 1 1/8, between.
Equipment: ; Presses — 20-HI/NC25.
Zip Codes Served: 14227

CHESTER

ORANGE COUNTY MARKETPLACE, LTD.

(Fri) (Weekly)
69 Brookside Ave, Ste 208, Chester, NY, 10918-1308, USA; tel (845) 469-4000; fax (845) 469-3901; e-mail marketplacetoday09@gmail.com; adv e-mail marketplacetodayads@gmail.com; web site themarketplacetoday.com
Circulation:83,612fr; CAC
Established: 1984
Group: Orange County Marketplace, Ltd. Editions: 5— Monroe-15,500 -Warwick/Goshen-18,960-Newburgh-14,450-New Windsor/Cornwalls-18,353-Middletown-18,929
Pub. .... Howard Kaplan
CFO .... Steven Herman
Mechanical Specifications: Type page 10 x 9.4; E - 3 cols, 3 1/2, between; A - 3 cols, 3 1/2, between; C - 3 cols, 3 1/2, between.
Equipment: Hardware — APP/Mac G5; Software — QPS/QuarkXPress.
Delivery Method: Mail
Zip Codes Served: 10910,10917,10926,10930,10950,10975,10979,10987,10953,12518,12520,12553,12575,12577,12550,10940,10941,10918,10924,10981,10912,10921,10990,10969
Note: 100% mailed distribution by zip code to Orange County,N.Y.

CLIFTON PARK

CAPITAL REGION WEEKLY NEWSPAPER GROUP

(Thur)
PO Box 1450, Clifton Park, NY, 12065-0806, USA; web site www.crwnewspapers.com
Circulation: 0pd,171,388fr; VAC
Advertising: Open inch rate $15.56 - $75.60
Established: 1950Patrick J. Smith
Mechanical Specifications: Type page: 9.75 x 11; 6 col

CLIFTON SPRINGS

THE MERCHANDISER

(Thur)
70 Stephens St, P.O. Box 642, Clifton Springs, NY, 14432-1051, USA; tel (315) 462-6411; fax (315) 462-7627; e-mail mail@themerchandiser.net; adv e-mail mail@themerchandiser.net; ed e-mail n/a; web site www.themerchandiser.net
Circulation: 20pd,15,040fr; VAC
Advertising: Open inch rate $8.00
Established: 1945Editions: 1—
Digital Platform - Mobile: Android, Windows
Digital Platform - Tablet: Android, Windows 7
Pres .... Cheryl Tears
Mechanical Specifications: Type page: 7.25 x 10; 4 col
Equipment: ; Software — CS6
Delivery Method: Mail
Zip Codes Served: 14432 14532 14548 14526 14504 14561 14547 14518 14537 14513

COBLESKILL

MY SHOPPER

(Sun)
2403 State Route 7 Ste 4, E.Side Village Mall, Cobleskill, NY, 12043-5740, USA; tel (518) 234-8215; fax (518) 234-8520; adv e-mail classifieds@myshopperonline.com; web site www.pennysaveronline.com
Circulation: 8pd,27,354fr; CVC
Advertising: Open inch rate $9.90
Established: 1987
Group: Snyder CommunicationsEditions: 2— 2 total; My Shopper-Mohawk Valley (11,775); My Shopper-Schoharie Valley (15,616);
Pub. .... Richard Snyder
Gen. Mgr. .... Rick Brightman
Mechanical Specifications: Type page 10 3/4 x 16; E - 6 cols, 1 5/8, 1/4 between; A - 6 cols, 1 5/8, 1/4 between; C - 6 cols, 1 5/8, 1/4 between.
Equipment: Hardware — APP/Power Mac; Software — Multi-Ad/Creator, Adobe/Photoshop.
Zip Codes Served: 12043

MY SHOPPER - MOHAWK VALLEY

(Sun)
2403 State Route 7, Ste 4, Cobleskill, NY, 12043-5740, USA; web site www.myshopper-online.com
Circulation: 2pd,11,573fr; VAC
Advertising: Open inch rate $10.00
Established: 1995Richard Snyder
Mechanical Specifications: Type page: 10.75 x 16; 6 col

MY SHOPPER - SCHOHARIE EDITION

(Sun)
2403 State Route 7, Ste 4, Cobleskill, NY, 12043-5740, USA; web site www.myshopper-online.com
Circulation: 2pd,14,769fr; VAC
Advertising: Open inch rate $11.45
Established: 1987Richard Snyder
Mechanical Specifications: Type page: 10.75 x 16; 6 col

CORNING

CORNING LEADER

(Sat)
34 W Pulteney St, Corning, NY, 14830-2211, USA; tel (607) 936-4651; adv tel (607) 936-4651; ed tel (607) 936-4651; fax (607) 796-0319; ed e-mail sdupree@the-leader.com; web site http://www.the-leader.com/
Circulation:17,778fr; Sworn/Estimate/Non-Audited
Advertising: Open inch rate $18.00
Group: New York Newspaper Advertising Service, Inc.
GateHouse Media, Inc.
Adv. Mgr. .... Sue Jackson

HORSEHEADS SHOPPER

(Sat)
34 W Pulteney St, Corning, NY, 14830-2211, USA; tel (607) 936-4651; adv tel (607) 936-4651; ed tel (607) 936-4651; fax (607) 936-9939; adv fax (607) 962-0782; ed fax (607) 936-9939; e-mail fbenson@the-leader.com; adv e-mail amingos@the-leader.com; ed e-mail sdupree@the-leader.com; web site www.e-zshopper.com
Circulation: 0pd,21,300fr; CVC
Advertising: Open inch rate $16.50
Established: 1972
Group: GateHouse Media, Inc.

Pub. .... Phil Husick
Circ. Dir. .... Elmer Kuehner
Mng. Ed. .... Joe Dunning
Features Ed. .... Derek Ek
Online Ed. .... Stella DuPree
Sports Ed. .... Shawn Vargo
Prodn. Foreman, Pressroom .... Jim Jones
Adv. Mgr. .... Adam Mingos
Mechanical Specifications: Type page 11 5/8 x 21 1/2; E - 6 cols, 1 5/6, 1/8 between; A - 6 cols, 1 5/6, 1/8 between; C - 9 cols, 1 3/16, 1/8 between.
Delivery Method: Mail, Carrier

CORTLAND

CONSUMER NEWS

(Mon)
110 Main St, Cortland, NY, 13045-6600, USA; tel (607) 756-5665; adv tel (607) 756-5665; ed tel (607) 756-5665; fax (607) 756-4758; adv fax (607) 756-4758; ed fax (607) 756-4758; adv e-mail manderson@cortlandstandard.net; ed e-mail news@cortlandstandard.net; web site www.cortlandstandard.net
Circulation:10,254fr; Sworn/Estimate/Non-Audited
Advertising: Open inch rate 17.34
Adv. Mgr. .... Mike Anderson
Circ. Mgr. .... Guy Ussery
Exec. Ed. .... Sherwood Chapman
Pres. .... Kevin R. Howe
Man. Ed. .... Kevin Conlon
Publisher .... Evan Geibel
Press foreman .... Raymond Marsh
Mechanical Specifications: Type page: 11 5/8 x 21.5; Columns: 1 3/4, 1/8 between
Delivery Method: Mail
Zip Codes Served: 13045, 13040, 13052, 13053, 13068, 13073, 13092, 13803, 13101, 13159

DELHI

COUNTY SHOPPER

(Fri)
97 Main St, Ste 5, Delhi, NY, 13753-1231, USA; tel (607) 746-2178; fax (607) 746-6272; e-mail shopper@dckr.com; web site www.dckr.com
Circulation:21,787fr; CVC
Advertising: Open inch rate $10.60
Established: 1966
Vice Pres. .... Kim Shepard
Adv. Mgr. .... Randy Shepard
Circ. Mgr. .... Karen Graves
Ed. .... Shirley Pyne Decker
Prodn. Mgr. .... Ralph Schoonebeek
Mechanical Specifications: Type page 10.3125 x 16; E - 6 cols, 1 9/16, 1/8 between; A - 6 cols, 1 9/16, 1/8 between; C - 6 cols, 1 5/8, 1/8 between.
Equipment: Hardware — APP/Mac; Software — Adobe/PageMaker 6.5, Claris/FileMaker Pro.
Zip Codes Served: 13753, 13731, 13739, 13740, 13750, 13751, 13860

COUNTY SHOPPER - CATSKILL PARK

(Fri)
97 Main St, Ste 5, Delhi, NY, 13753-1231, USA; web site www.countyshopperonline.com
Circulation: 0pd,3,994fr; VAC
Advertising: Open inch rate $12.30
Established: 1966Randy Shepard
Mechanical Specifications: Type page: 10.3125 x 16; 6 col

COUNTY SHOPPER - DELAWARE

(Fri)
97 Main St, Ste 5, Delhi, NY, 13753-1231, USA; web site www.countyshopperonline.com
Circulation: 0pd,15,799fr; VAC
Advertising: Open inch rate $12.30
Established: 1966Randy Shepard
Mechanical Specifications: Type page: 10.3125 x 16; 6 col

EAST ROCHESTER

THE SHOPPING BAG ADVERTISER

(Wed)
201 Main St, East Rochester, NY, 14445-1703, USA; web site www.rochesteradvertiser.com
Circulation:205,402fr; Sworn/Estimate/Non-AuditedPeter J. Stahlbrodt

EDGEWOOD

PENNYSAVER NEWS

(Thur)
1 Rodeo Dr, Edgewood, NY, 11717-8318, USA; tel (631) 698-8400; fax (631) 580-7749; e-mail production@lipennysaver.com; web site www.lipennysaver.com
Circulation:220,000fr; Sworn/Estimate/Non-Audited
Advertising: Open inch rate $10.50
Established: 1958Editions: 35— 35 total; Pennysaver-Bay Shore/Brightwaters (15,950); Pennysaver-Bayport/Blue Point (4,734); Pennysaver-Bellport/E Patchogue (8,974); Pennysaver-Brentwood/Bay Shore W. (15,655); Pennysaver-Centereach/Lake Grove (11,448); PennySaver-Central Islip/Islandia
Circ. Mgr. .... Jennifer Goodman
Ed. .... Richard Megenedy
Prodn. Mgr. .... Brenda Colonna
Mechanical Specifications: Type page 6 3/8 x 9 7/8; C - 4 cols, 1 1/2, between.
Equipment: Hardware — Optiquest; Software — QPS/QuarkXPress.

ELMA

PENNYSAVER

(Sun)
6091 Seneca St, Bldg C, Elma, NY, 14059-9807, USA; tel (716) 714-5620; fax (716) 714-5621; e-mail sales@rwpennysaver.com; sales@wnyps.com; web site www.wnyps.com
Circulation:7,766fr; VAC
Advertising: Open inch rate $57.85Editions: 5— 5 total Akron/Corfu Pennysaver (7,983); Attica Pennysaver (7,079); East Aurora/Elma Pennysaver (16,256); Orchard Park Pennysaver (12,285); West Seneca Pennysaver (19,741);
GNL Manager .... John Rozeski
Prod. Manager/IT .... Robert Rozeski
Accounting Manager .... Cheryl Kawalski
Equipment: Hardware — Mac; Software — Freehand,Indesign.
Zip Codes Served: 14127

ELMSFORD

PENNYSAVER

(Wed)
85 Executive Blvd, Elmsford, NY, 10523-1326, USA; tel (914) 592-5222; fax (914) 220-5454; e-mail info@nysaver.com; web site http://pennysavernow.com
Circulation:188,350fr; Sworn/Estimate/Non-Audited
Established: 1969Editions: 16— Ardsley/Hartsdale Shoppers Guide (13,300); Bronxville/Eastchester/Tuckahoe Pennysaver (11,350); Greenwich (CT)/Byram (NY) Pennysaver (10,700); Larchmont/Mamaroneck Pennysaver (12,500); Mount Vernon/Fleetwood Pennysaver (12,200); New Rochelle/Pe
Pub. .... Larry Ross Weinberger
Adv. Mgr. .... Stacie Boering
Circ. Mgr. .... Ed Levitt
Prodn. Mgr. .... Robin Lloyd
Mechanical Specifications: Type page 7 x 9 5/8.
Equipment: Hardware — 30-APP/Mac; Software — QPS/QuarkXPress 3.32.

FARMINGDALE

SOUTH BAY'S NEIGHBOR

(Wed)
565 Broadhollow Rd, Ste 3, Farmingdale, NY, 11735-4826, USA; tel (631) 226-2636; adv tel (631) 226-2636; ed tel (631) 226-2636; fax (631) 226-2680; adv fax (631) 226-2680; ed fax (631) 226-2680; e-mail jsantana@theneighbornewspapers.com; adv e-mail jlambert@theneighbornewspapers.com; ed e-mail jlambert@theneighbornewspapers.com; web site www.theneighbornewspapers.com
Circulation: 23pd,138,594fr; VAC
Advertising: N/A
Established: 1953
Group: Long Island Media Group LLCEditions: 7— 7 total: Babylon/W. Babylon South Bay's Newspaper (18,696); Lindenhurst,Copiague,Amityville (23,871); Deer Park/N. Babylon/Dix Hill South Bay's Newspaper (18,485); Farmingdale South Bay's Newspaper (12,388); Massapequa E./Massapequa Park South Bay's News
Digital Platform - Mobile: Apple, Android, Windows, Blackberry
Digital Platform - Tablet: Apple iOS, Android, Windows 7, Blackberry Tablet OS
Pub./Adv. Dir. .... Jeff Lambert
Ed. .... Jamie Ryan
Mechanical Specifications: Type page 9.875 x 11; 7 col
Equipment: Hardware — APP/Mac; Presses — 6-KP; Software — Multi-Ad/Creator 6.5, Microsoft/Word 5.0, Adobe/Photoshop 5.0, QPS/QuarkXPress 3.2.
Delivery Method: Mail
Zip Codes Served: 11701, 11702, 11703, 11704, 11726, 11729, 11746, 11757, 11758, 11762, 11795, 11783, 11795, 11783, 11735, 11762, 11758

THE NEIGHBOR NEWSPAPERS

(Wed)
565 Broadhollow Rd, Ste 3, Farmingdale, NY, 11735-4826, USA; tel (631) 226-2636; adv tel (631) 226-2636; ed tel (631) 226-2636; fax (631) 226-2680; adv fax (631) 226-2680; ed fax (631) 226-2680; e-mail jsantana@theneighbornewspapers.com; adv e-mail jlambert@theneighbornewspapers.com; ed e-mail jlambert@theneighbornewspapers.com; web site www.theneighbornewspapers.com
Circulation: 0pd,42,975fr; VAC
Advertising: N/A
Established: 1953
Group: Long Island Media Group LLC
Digital Platform - Mobile: Apple, Android, Windows, Blackberry
Digital Platform - Tablet: Apple iOS, Android, Windows 7, Blackberry Tablet OS
Pub./Adv. Dir. .... Jeff Lambert
Ed. .... Jamie Ryan
Mechanical Specifications: Type page 9.875 x 11; 7 col
Equipment: Hardware — APP/Mac; Presses — 6-KP; Software — Multi-Ad/Creator 6.5, Microsoft/Word 5.0, Adobe/Photoshop 5.0, QPS/QuarkXPress 3.2.
Delivery Method: Mail
Zip Codes Served: 11701, 11702, 11703, 11704, 11726, 11729, 11746, 11757, 11758, 11762, 11795, 11783, 11795, 11783, 11735, 11762, 11758

FREDONIA

DUNKIRK/FREDONIA/WESTFIELD PENNYSAVER

(Sun)
276 W Main St, Fredonia, NY, 14063-2234, USA; tel (716) 679-1500; fax (716) 672-2626
Circulation:5,619fr; CVC
Advertising: Open inch rate $6.50
Established: 1965
Pub. .... Thomas K. Webb
Adv. Mgr. .... Mark Coyle
Mechanical Specifications: Type page 10 1/8 x 16; A - 6 cols, 1 1/2, between.
Delivery Method: Carrier
Zip Codes Served: 14048, 14063, 14787, 14718, 14874, 14752, 14716, 14769, 14757, 14782, 14723

FREDONIA PENNYSAVER

(Sun)
PO Box 493, Fredonia, NY, 14063-0493, USA; web site www.fredoniapennysaver.com
Circulation:18,708fr; CVC
Advertising: Open inch rate $6.70
Established: 1965Tom Webb
Mechanical Specifications: Type page: 10.125 x 16; 6 col

THE SILVER CREEK PENNYSAVER

(Sun)
276 W Main St, Fredonia, NY, 14063-2234, USA; tel (716) 679-1500; fax (716) 672-2626; web site www.fredoniapennysaver.com
Circulation:5,590fr; CVC
Advertising: Open inch rate $6.70
Established: 1965
Pub. .... Thomas K. Webb
Adv. Mgr. .... Mark Coyle
Mechanical Specifications: Type page 10 1/8 x 16; A - 6 cols, 1 1/2, between.
Zip Codes Served: 14136, 14063, 14081, 14135, 14138

FREEVILLE

SUBURBAN CORTLAND-ITHACA SHOPPER

(Tues)
9 Main St, Freeville, NY, 13068-9599, USA; tel (607) 844-9119; fax (607) 844-3381; e-mail fshopper@twcny.rr.com
Circulation:24,737fr; CVC
Advertising: Open inch rate $8.05
Established: 1949
Circ. Mgr. .... Michael Down
Mechanical Specifications: Type page 10 1/4 x 16; E - 6 cols, 1 1/2, between; A - 6 cols, 1 1/2, between.
Equipment: Hardware — V, APP/Mac; Presses — G; Software — QPS/QuarkXPress 4.0.
Zip Codes Served: 13068, 13073, 13053, 14817, 13092, 13801, 13835, 13726, 14850, 13045, 13077, 13071, 13077

FULTON

THE PATRIOT ADVERTISER

(Sun)
67 S 2nd St, Fulton, NY, 13069-1725, USA; tel (315) 598-6397; ed e-mail editor@fultonvalleynews.com; web site http://valleynewsonline.com/
Circulation:6,778fr; CVCJohn Badoud

GARDEN CITY

PRIMETIME

(Fri)
2 Endo Blvd, Garden City, NY, 11530-6707, USA; tel (516) 569-4000; fax (516) 569-4942; adv fax (516) 766-4283; adv e-mail rglickman@liherald.com; web site www.liprimetime.com
Circulation:102,138fr; VAC
Established: 1987
Group: Richner Communications, Inc.Editions: 10— Baldwin/Baldwin Harbor PrimeTime (11,202); Cedarhurst/Lawrence PrimeTime (10,337); Franklin Square PrimeTime (7789); Hewlett/Woodmere PrimeTime (14,765); Lynbrook/East Rockaway PrimeTime (12,431); Oceanside/Island Park PrimeTime (14,070) Rockville Centre Primetime (10,498), Valley Stream Primetime (12,284), Malverne/W. Hempstead Primetime (10,719), Elmont Primetime (10,594)

Pub. .... Clifford Richner
Pub. .... Stuart Richner
Adv. Mgr. .... Rhonda Glickman
Vice Pres., Opns. .... Michael Bologna
Adv. Manager PrimeTime Xpress.... Lori Berger
Mechanical Specifications: Type page 6 3/16 x 9 7/8; E - 2 cols, 3 1/16, 1/6 between; A - 2 cols, 3 1/16, 1/6 between; C - 4 cols, 1 9/16, 1/6 between.
Equipment: Hardware — APP/Mac; Presses — 8-G/Community; Software — QPS/QuarkXPress.
Delivery Method: Mail
Zip Codes Served: 11509, 11516, 11696, 11559, 11691, 11557, 11581, 11598, 11518, 11563, 11570, 11558, 11572, 11510, 11580, 11010, 11565, 11552, 11003

GRAND ISLAND

GRAND ISLAND PENNYSAVER

(Tues)
1859 Whitehaven Rd, Grand Island, NY, 14072-1803, USA; tel (716) 773-7676; fax (716) 773-7190; e-mail skip@wnypapers.com; adv e-mail grandislandsales@wnypapers.com; ed e-mail dispatch@wnypapers.com; web site www.wnypapers.com
Circulation:6,800fr; Sworn/Estimate/Non-Audited
Advertising: Open inch rate $13.96
Established: 1944
Digital Platform - Mobile: Windows
Publisher and CEO.................. Skip Mazenauer
Ed. .... Larry Austin
Mng. Ed... Terry Duffy
Prodn. Mgr. .... Wendy Juzwicki
Mechanical Specifications: Type page 10 3/4 x 13; E - 5 cols, 2, 1/8 between; A - 5 cols, 2, 1/8 between; C - 5 cols, 2, 1/8 between.
Equipment: Hardware — 90-APP/PowerMac 7200, UMax/Astra 610 Scanner, Umax/Astra 1220S Scanner, HP/LaserJet 5000 Printer; Software — QPS/QuarkXPress 5.0, Adobe/Photoshop 3.0, Adobe/Illustrator 5.0.
Delivery Method: Carrier
Zip Codes Served: 14072

GRANVILLE

MANCHESTER NEWSPAPERS, INC.

(Fri)
14 E Main St, Granville, NY, 12832-1334, USA; tel (518) 642-1234; fax (518) 642-1344; e-mail publisher@manchesternewspapers.com; web site www.manchesternewspapers.com
Circulation: 0pd,49,317fr; CVC
Established: 1875
Pres. .... John MacArthur Manchester
Exec. Vice Pres....................... Lisa Manchester

HAMBURG

HAMBURG PENNYSAVER

(Sun)
141 Buffalo St, Hamburg, NY, 14075-5010, USA; tel (716) 649-4413; fax (716) 649-6374; web site http://www.pennysavers.com/index.php
Circulation:24,447fr; CVC
Advertising: Open inch rate $8.11
Established: 1939Gerry Grabowski
Pub. .... Gary Durawa
Ad. Mgr .... Judy Beckwith
Circ. Mgr .... Bill Marshall
Mechanical Specifications: Type page: 10.25 x 16; 6 col

PENNYSAVER

(Sun)
141 Buffalo St, Hamburg, NY, 14075-5010, USA; tel (716) 649-4413; fax (716) 649-6374; ed e-mail meyerdan@thesunnews.net
Circulation:26,000fr; Sworn/Estimate/Non-Audited
Advertising: Open inch rate $8.26Editions: 7—7 total; Allegany-Olean Pennysaver (11,157); Arcade Pennysaver (12,893); Blasdell-Lackawanna Pennysaver (13,499); Cuba-Franklinville Pennysaver (8,502); Gowanda Pennysaver (11,658); Hamburg Pennysaver (25,456); Springville Pennysaver (10,467);
Pub. .... Gerry Grabowski
Prodn. Mgr. .... Michael Hanes
Mechanical Specifications: Type page 10 1/4 x 16; A - 7 cols, 1 3/8, 1/8 between; C - 7 cols, 1 3/8, 1/8 between.
Equipment: Hardware — APP/Mac; Presses — 7-HI; Software — Custom, Adobe/Photoshop, FireWorks 2.0, QPS/QuarkXPress, Adobe/InDesign.
Zip Codes Served: 14075, 14141

HAMMONDSPORT

NEW YORK STATE'S SOUTHERN TIER SHOPPER

(Tues)
1 Myrtle Ave, Hammondsport, NY, 14840-9596, USA; tel (607) 569-2622; adv tel (607) 569-2522; fax (607) 569-2624; adv fax (607) 569-2624; e-mail ads@the-shopper.com; adv e-mail ads@the-shopper.com; web site www.the-shopper.com
Circulation:22,788fr; CVC
Advertising: Open inch rate $7.00
Established: 1954
Digital Platform - Mobile: Apple, Android
Digital Platform - Tablet: Apple iOS, Android
Pub. .... Rita Butters
Mechanical Specifications: Type page 10 7/8 x 16; A - 7 cols, 1 3/8, 1/8 between.
Delivery Method: Mail
Zip Codes Served: 14807, 14809, 14810, 14815, 14819, 14820, 14821, 14823, 14826, 14827, 14840, 14843, 14856, 14870, 14873, 14874, 14879

HICKSVILLE

PENNYSAVER/TOWN CRIER

(Thur)
325 Duffy Ave, Hicksville, NY, 11801-3644, USA; tel (516) 942-8400; fax (516) 942-3730; e-mail production@lipennysaver.com; web site www.lipennysaver.com
Circulation:325,000fr; Sworn/Estimate/Non-AuditedEditions: 15— 15 total; Babylon-West Islip Town Crier (27,836); Bellmore-Merrick Town Crier (24,650); Deer Park-North Babylon Town Crier (16,030); East Meadow Town Crier (12,739); Farmingdale-Bethpage Pennysaver (20,364); Hicksville Town Crier (14,417); Huntington/Col
Office Mgr. .... Albert Dicroce
Ed. .... Bob Sussi
Equipment: Hardware — APP/Mac; Presses — 10-KP/Color King.

HORNELL

PENNESAVERPLUS

(Sun)
85 Canisteo St, Hornell, NY, 14843-1544, USA; tel (607) 324-1425; adv tel (607) 324-1425; ed tel (607) 324-1425; fax (607) 324-1753; e-mail kellyschecter@eveningtribune.com; adv e-mail kellyschecter@eveningtribune.com; ed e-mail editor@eveningtribune.com; web site www.dansvilleonline.com
Circulation:34,000fr; CVC
Advertising: Open inch rate $8.50
Group: GateHouse Media, Inc.
Regional Advertising Director..... Kelly Schecter
Regional Publisher .... Rick Emanuel
General Manager - Wellsville .... Oak Duke
General Manager .... Les Bowen
Mechanical Specifications: Type page 10 3/8 x 16; A - 6 cols, 1 3/8, between.
Equipment: Hardware — Mac; Software — Mulit Ad Creator, Quark XPress,
Delivery Method: Carrier
Zip Codes Served: 14802, 14803, 14707, 14708, 14804, 14806, 14709, 14807, 14808, 14810, 14711, 14813, 14714, 14715, 14819, 14822, 14717, 14823, 14029, 14826, 14727, 14836, 14437, 14735, 14739, 14839, 14545, 14727, 14843, 14744, 14745, 14855, 14754, 14512, 14808, 14517, 14529, 14877, 14774, 14776, 14777, 14880, 14462, 14727, 14560, 14884, 14885, 14572, 14560, 14895, 14897, 14898, 16923, 16948
Note: Hornell-Canisteo PenneSaver, on August 26th merged with the Allegany County PennySaver and Dansville-Wayland PennySaver to create PenneSaverPlus

HORSEHEADS

THE SHOPPER

(Sat)
57 S Carroll St, Horseheads, NY, 14845-2766, USA; tel (607) 796-2800; fax (607) 796-0319; e-mail info@e-zshopper.com; web site www.e-zshopper.com
Circulation:27,000fr; CVC
Advertising: Open inch rate $15.25
Group: GateHouse Media, Inc.
Pub. .... Denny Bruen
Mechanical Specifications: Type page 10 3/8 x 16; E - 8 cols, 1 1/8, between; A - 8 cols, 1 1/8, between.
Equipment: Hardware — APP/Mac; Software — Adobe/PageMaker, Microsoft/Word.
Zip Codes Served: 14814, 14816, 14830, 14838, 14845, 14861, 14864, 14871, 14872, 14894, 14901, 14903, 14904, 14905, 16925, 16936

INTERLAKEN

TRI-VILLAGE PENNYSAVER

(Fri)
8372 Geneva St, Interlaken, NY, 14847-9625, USA; tel 607-532-4320; fax (607) 532-9557; e-mail eseamon@tsweeklygroup.com; adv e-mail treynolds@tsweeklygroup.com; web site http://trivillagepennysaver.com
Circulation: 5pd,20,000fr; Sworn/Estimate/Non-Audited
Advertising: Open inch rate $12.00
Established: 1949Editions: 2— 2 total; Ithaca Pennysaver (29,097); Tri-Village Pennysaver (7,076);
Gen. Mgr. .... Dave Barry
Mechanical Specifications: Type page 10 1/4 x 16; E - 6 cols, 1 5/8, between; A - 6 cols, 1 5/8, between; C - 6 cols, 1 5/8, between.
Equipment: Hardware — Desk Top, APP/Mac; Software — Adobe/PageMaker.
Zip Codes Served: 14847

LE ROY

LEROY PENNYSAVER

(Sun)
1 Church St, Le Roy, NY, 14482-1017, USA; tel (585) 768-2201; fax (585) 768-6334; e-mail editor@leroyny.com; web site www.leroyny.com
Circulation:7,700fr; Sworn/Estimate/Non-Audited
Advertising: Open inch rate $9.91
Pub. .... David J. Grayson
Mechanical Specifications: Type page 7 7/8 x 11; A - 4 cols, 1 3/4, between.

LIBERTY

CATSKILL SHOPPER - EASTERN SULLIVAN COUNTY

(Fri)
5512 State Route 55, Liberty, NY, 12754-2830, USA; tel (845) 292-0500; adv tel (845) 292-0500; ed tel (845) 292-0500; fax (845) 292-0585; adv fax (845) 292-0585; ed fax (845) 292-0585; e-mail gm@catskillshopper-online.com; adv e-mail catskillshopper@hvc.rr.com; ed e-mail cs-editorial@hvc.rr.com; web site www.catskillshopperonline.com
Circulation:20,680fr; CVC
Advertising: Open inch rate $24.47
Established: 1967
Group: GateHouse Media, Inc.Editions: 3— 3 total; Catskill Shopper-Eastern Sullivan County; Catskill Shopper-Ulster County; Catskill Shopper-Western Sullivan County
Pub./Gen. Mgr. .... Helen Diehl
Mechanical Specifications: Type page 10 3/8 x 16; E - 7 cols, 1 3/8, between; A - 7 cols, 1 3/8, between; C - 7 cols, 1 3/8, between.
Delivery Method: Mail
Zip Codes Served: Eastern Sullivan County

CATSKILL SHOPPER - ULSTER COUNTY

(Fri)
5512 State Route 55, Liberty, NY, 12754-2830, USA; tel (845) 292-0500; adv tel (845) 292-0500; ed tel (845) 292-0500; fax (845) 292-0585; adv fax (845) 292-0585; ed fax (845) 292-0585; e-mail gm@catskillshopper-online.com; adv e-mail catskillshopper@hvc.rr.com; ed e-mail cs-editorial@hvc.rr.com; web site www.catskillshopperonline.com
Circulation:7,037fr; CVC
Advertising: Open inch rate $11.76
Established: 1967
Group: GateHouse Media, Inc.Editions: 3— 3 total; Catskill Shopper-Eastern Sullivan County; Catskill Shopper-Ulster County; Catskill Shopper-Western Sullivan County
Pub./Gen. Mgr. .... Helen Diehl
Mechanical Specifications: Type page 10 3/8 x 16; E - 7 cols, 1 3/8, between; A - 7 cols, 1 3/8, between; C - 7 cols, 1 3/8, between.
Delivery Method: Mail
Zip Codes Served: Ulster County

MELVILLE

NEWSDAY HOMETOWN SHOPPER

(Thur)
235 Pinelawn Rd, Melville, NY, 11747-4226, USA; tel (631) 843-2500; ed tel (631) 843-2024; fax (631) 843-2160; ed fax (631) 843-2614; e-mail promotions@newsday.com; adv e-mail promotions@newsday.com; ed e-mail localeditorial@newsday.com; web site www.hometownshopperli.com
Circulation: 190,399pd,761,594fr; AAM
Advertising: call for rates
Established: 1954Editions: 79—
Local Mktg Sales Project Mgr James Rosenfeld
VP Local Retail Sales............... Denise Fulham
Ed .... Barbara Fisher
Delivery Method: Mail, Carrier

THIS WEEK PENNYSAVER

(Sat)
25 Deshon Dr, Melville, NY, 11747-4207, USA; web site www.starcpg.com
Circulation:836,778fr; CVC
Established: 1976David Kniffin
Mechanical Specifications: Type page: 6.25 x 9.875; 2 col

NANUET

PENNYSAVER

(Thur)
233 W Route 59, Nanuet, NY, 10954-2218, USA; tel (845) 627-3600; fax (845) 627-8730; e-mail info@nysaver.com; web site www.nysaver.com
Circulation:99,300fr; Sworn/Estimate/Non-AuditedEditions: 7— 7 total; Central Rockland Pennysaver (9,950); Clarkstown East Pennysaver (12,900); Clarkstown West Pennysaver (13,000); East Ramapo Pennysaver (12,700);

North Rockland Pennysaver (12,500); Orangetown Pennysaver (13,600); West Ramapo Pennysaver (11,200);
CEO/Pub.................................... Darwin Oordt
Pres. .... Herbert Solomon
Circ. Mgr..Ed Levitt
Prodn. Mgr.................................Robin Lloyd
Mechanical Specifications: Type page 7 x 9 5/8.
Equipment: Hardware — 30-APP/Mac; Software — QPS/QuarkXPress 3.32.

NORWICH

NORWICH PENNYSAVER
(Tues)
18-20 Mechanic St, Norwich, NY, 13815-1437, USA; web site www.pennysaveronline.com
Circulation: 17pd,16,608fr; VAC
Advertising: Open inch rate $11.95
Established: 1949
Publisher.................................Richard Snyder
Brad Dick
Mechanical Specifications: Type page: 10.75 x 16; 6 col

SIDNEY PENNYSAVER
(Tues)
18-20 Mechanic St, Norwich, NY, 13815-1437, USA; tel (607) 334-4714; fax (607) 337-3003; e-mail info@pennysaver.com; web site www.pennysaveronline.com
Circulation: 231pd,11,044fr; VAC
Advertising: Open inch rate $10.00
Established: 1949
Group: Snyder CommunicationsEditions: 2— 2 total; Norwich Pennysaver (17,230); Sidney Pennysaver (11,595);
Pub. ....Richard Snyder
Adv. Mgr.. Russ Foote
Circ. Mgr..Brad Dick
Mechanical Specifications: Type page 10 3/4 x 16; A - 6 cols, 1 5/8, 1/8 between; C - 6 cols, 1 5/8, 1/8 between.
Equipment: Hardware — APP/Mac; Presses — G/Community; Software — Multi-Ad/Creator 4.03.
Zip Codes Served: 13815

WHARTON VALLEY PENNYSAVER
(Tues)
PO Box 111, Norwich, NY, 13815-0111, USA; tel (607) 334-4714; adv tel (607) 334-4714; ed tel (607) 334-4714; fax (607) 336-7318; adv fax (607) 336-7318; ed fax (607) 336-7318; e-mail info@pennysaveronline.com; adv e-mail rfoote@pennysaveronline.com; ed e-mail production@pennysaveronline.com; web site www.pennysaveronline.com
Circulation: 5pd,4,670fr; VAC
Advertising: Open inch rate $5.40
Group: Snyder Communications
Pub. ....Richard Snyder
Mng. Ed./Adv. Mgr........................... Russ Foote
Gen. Mgr.................................. Rick Brightman
Circ. Mgr..Brad Dick
Delivery Method: Mail
Zip Codes Served: Wharton Valley

ONEIDA

ONEIDA-MADISON PENNYSAVER
(Sun)
130 Broad St, Oneida, NY, 13421-1684, USA; tel (315) 363-5100; fax (315) 363-9832; ed fax (315) 363-0416; e-mail advertising@oneidadispatch.com; adv e-mail advertising@oneidadispatch.com; ed e-mail newsroom@oneidadispatch.com; web site www.oneidadispatch.com
Circulation:22,275fr; Sworn/Estimate/Non-Audited
Advertising: $10.99
Established: 1984
Group: Digital First Media
Gen. Mgr./Adv. Dir.........................Karen Alvord
Mechanical Specifications: 1 co. = 1.392"
2 col. 2.921"
3 col - 4.451"
4 col 5.981"
5 col 7.51"
6 col 9.04"
Delivery Method: Carrier
Zip Codes Served: 13421, 13032, 13163, 13037, 13163, 13035, 13054, 13157, 13162, 13308, 13478, 13082, 13316, 13408, 13409, 13134, 13476, 13478, 13461

PENNYSAVER
(Sun)
208 Lenox Ave, Oneida, NY, 13421-1628, USA; tel (315) 697-2969; fax (315) 363-3119; e-mail newsroom@oneidadispatch.com; adv e-mail advertising@oneidadispatch.com; web site www.oneidadailydispatch.com
Circulation: 7pd,22,252fr; CVC
Advertising: Open inch rate $8.84
Pub. ....Philip Austin
Adv. Dir... Karen Albert
Circ. Mgr...Mark Albert
Ed. ....Kurt Wanfried
Prodn. Mgr. .... Robert Bennett
Mechanical Specifications: Type page 10 3/8 x 16; E - 6 cols, 1 5/8, between; A - 6 cols, 1 5/8, between; C - 6 cols, 1 5/8, between.
Equipment: Hardware — APP/Mac IIsi, APP/Super Mac, APP/Mac IIvx; Software — QPS/QuarkXPress, Multi-Ad/Creator, Appleshare 3.0.
Zip Codes Served: 13421

ORCHARD PARK

RW PUBLICATIONS - AKRON / CORFU PENNYSAVER
(Sun)
3770 Transit Rd, Orchard Park, NY, 14127-2053, USA; web site www.wnyps.com
Circulation: 0pd,7,870fr; CVC
Advertising: Open inch rate $11.10
Established: 1961John Rozeski
Mechanical Specifications: Type page: 10.25 x 16; 6 col

RW PUBLICATIONS - ATTICA PENNYSAVER
(Sun)
3770 Transit Rd, Orchard Park, NY, 14127-2053, USA; web site www.wnyps.com
Circulation: 0pd,6,752fr; VAC
Advertising: Open inch rate $10.90
Established: 1961John Rozeski
Mechanical Specifications: Type page: 10.25 x 16; 6 col

RW PUBLICATIONS - EAST AURORA / ELMA PENNYSAVER
(Sun)
3770 Transit Rd, 3770 Transit Rd, Orchard Park, NY, 14127-2053, USA; web site www.wnyps.com
Circulation: 0pd,15,737fr; VAC
Advertising: Open inch rate $14.80
Established: 1961John Rozeski
Mechanical Specifications: Type page: 10.25 x 16; 6 col

RW PUBLICATIONS - ORCHARD PARK PENNYSAVER
(Sun)
3770 Transit Rd, Orchard Park, NY, 14127-2053, USA; web site www.wnyps.com
Circulation: 0pd,11,886fr; VAC
Advertising: Open inch rate $13.60
Established: 1961John Rozeski
Mechanical Specifications: Type page: 10.25 x 16; 6 col

RW PUBLICATIONS - WEST SENECA PENNYSAVER
(Sun)
3770 Transit Rd, Orchard Park, NY, 14127-2053, USA; web site www.wnyps.com
Circulation: 0pd,20,108fr; VAC
Advertising: Open inch rate $16.15
Established: 1961John Rozeski
Mechanical Specifications: Type page: 10.25 x 16; 6 col

OVID

SENECA COUNTY AREA SHOPPER
(Wed)
1885 State Route 96A, Ovid, NY, 14521-9712, USA
Circulation: 0pd,11,317fr; VAC
Advertising: Open inch rate $8.00
Established: 2005Bridgette Goodman
Mechanical Specifications: Type page: 10.25 x 16; 6 col

OWEGO

OWEGO PENNYSAVER
(Sun)
181-183 Front St, Ste 2, Owego, NY, 13827-1592, USA; tel (607) 687-2434; fax (607) 687-6858; e-mail opennysaver@stny.rr.com; web site www.owegopennysaver.com
Circulation:20,000fr; Sworn/Estimate/Non-Audited
Advertising: Open inch rate $13.61
Gen. Mgr...David Barry
Ed. .... Wendy Post
Mechanical Specifications: Type page 10 1/4 x 13; E - 6 cols, 1 1/2, 1/4 between; A - 4 cols, 2 1/2, 1/4 between; C - 8 cols, 1 1/4, between.
Equipment: Hardware — APP/Mac G3, APP/Mac-7300; Software — Multi-Ad 4.03, QPS/QuarkXPress 4.1, ALS 2.0, Adobe/Photoshop 5.5, Adobe/Image Ready 2.0, Adobe/GoLive 5.0, Adobe/Acrobat 4.0, Adobe/Illustrator 8.0.
Zip Codes Served: 13827

OZONE PARK

PENNYSAVER
(Fri)
10814 Crossbay Blvd, Ozone Park, NY, 11417-1521, USA; tel (718) 843-5878; fax (718) 843-2975; e-mail ads2sell@aol.com; web site www.queenspennysaver.com
Circulation:9,950fr; CVC
Adv. Mgr........................Debbie Ann Schneider
Ed. .... Linda Burke

PENN YAN

CHRONICLE AD-VISER
(Wed, Sun)
138 Main St, Penn Yan, NY, 14527-1219, USA; tel (315) 536-4422; fax (315) 536-0682; e-mail news@chronicle-express.com; web site www.chronicle-express.com
Circulation: 3,200pd,12,654fr; Sworn/Estimate/Non-Audited
Advertising: Open inch rate $14.50
Group: GateHouse Media, Inc.
Pub. ....Karen Morris
Circ. Mgr...Bob Corey
Ed.................................Gwenn Chamberlain
Prodn. Mgr. ....Genny Hillman
Zip Codes Served: 14527, 14815, 14418, 14441, 14837, 14842, 14878, 14840, 14478, 14857, 14415, 14887, 14891, 14893

PERRY

PERRY SHOPPER
(Sat, Sun)
75 Main St S, Perry, NY, 14530-1523, USA; tel (585) 237-2212; fax (585) 237-2211; e-mail ads@perryshopper.com; web site www.perryshopper.com
Circulation:7,250fr; CVC
Advertising: Open inch rate $14.38
Established: 1965
Pub. .... Christine Kennedy
Office Mgr. ....Kimmie Wolcott
Mechanical Specifications: Type page 7 1/2 x 11; E - 4 cols, 1 3/4, between; A - 4 cols, 1 3/4, between.
Equipment: Hardware — APP/Mac G4, APP/Mac G3; Software — Adobe/PageMaker 6.5.
Delivery Method: Mail, Newsstand, Carrier
Zip Codes Served: 1453014550,14427,14525,

PLATTSBURGH

PENNYSAVER
(Thur)
177 Margaret St, Plattsburgh, NY, 12901-1837, USA; tel (518) 563-0100; fax (518) 562-0303; e-mail mail@adkpennysaver.com; web site www.adkpennysaver.com
Circulation:30,000fr; Sworn/Estimate/Non-Audited
Advertising: Open inch rate $7.90Editions: 4— 4 total; Pennysaver-Main (15,000); Pennysaver-Northern (3,000); Pennysaver-Southern (6,000); Pennysaver-Tri Lakes (6,000);
Adv. Mgr...................................Carol Van Hise
Circ. Mgr.. Mark Rigby
Mechanical Specifications: Type page 10 1/4 x 16; A - 6 cols, 1 7/16, between; C - 6 cols, 1 7/16, between.
Equipment: Hardware — APP/Mac; Software — Adobe/PageMaker 6.5.

PRESS EXTRA
(Sat)
170 Margaret St, Plattsburgh, NY, 12901-1838, USA; tel (518) 561-2300; fax (518) 561-3362; e-mail news@pressrepublican.com; adv e-mail classifieds@pressrepublican.com; legalads@pressrepublican.com; ed e-mail letters@pressrepublican.com; web site www.pressrepublican.com
Circulation:16,000fr; Sworn/Estimate/Non-Audited
Advertising: Open inch rate $13.00
Group: CNHI
Mktg. Dir......................................George Rock
Publisher.. Brad Bailey
Mechanical Specifications: Type page 13 x 21 1/2; E - 6 cols, 2 1/4, between; A - 6 cols, between; C - 9 cols, between.
Zip Codes Served: 12901

RED CREEK

SHOPPER
(Mon)
6784 Main St, Red Creek, NY, 13143, USA; tel (315) 754-6229; fax (315) 754-6431; adv e-mail advertising@wayuga.com
Circulation:17,686fr; CVC
Advertising: Open inch rate $6.10
Pub. ....Angelo Palermo
Adv. Mgr.....................................Charles Palermo
Mechanical Specifications: Type page 10 1/4 x 16; E - 6 cols, 1 5/8, between; A - 6 cols, between.
Equipment: Hardware — APP/Macs, IBM; Presses — WPC/Web Leader; Software — Multi-Ad/Creator.
Zip Codes Served: 14590

THE WAYUGA SHOPPER
(Mon)
PO Box 199, Red Creek, NY, 13143-0199, USA; web site www.wayuga.com
Circulation:21,372fr; VAC
Established: 1965Angelo Palermo
Mechanical Specifications: Type page: 10.326 x 16; 6 col

RICHFIELD SPRINGS

HALL OF FAME PENNYSAVER
(Sun)
3178 US Highway 20, Richfield Springs, NY, 13439-2808, USA; tel (315) 858-1730; fax (315) 858-2988; e-mail production@pennysaveronline.com ; info@pennysaveronline.com; web site www.pennysaveronline.com
Circulation:18,597fr; CVC
Advertising: Open inch rate $9.10
Group: Snyder Communications
Gen. Mgr. .... Rick Brightman
Circ. Mgr. .... Betty Garner
Ed. .... Richard Snyder

ONEONTA-COOPERSTOWN PENNYSAVER
(Thur)
3178 US Highway 20, Richfield Springs, NY, 13439-2808, USA; web site www.pennysaveronline.com
Circulation: 0pd,10,012fr; VAC
Advertising: Open inch rate $10.05
Established: 1954Richard` Snyder
Mechanical Specifications: Type page: 11.25 x 16; 6 col

PENNYSAVER
(Thur)
3178 US Highway 20, Richfield Springs, NY, 13439-2808, USA; web site www.pennysaveronline.com
Circulation: 2pd,18,597fr; CVC
Established: 1954Richard Snyder
Mechanical Specifications: Type page: 11.25 x 16; 6 col

TURNPIKE PENNYSAVER
(Thur)
3178 US Highway 20, Richfield Springs, NY, 13439-2808, USA; web site www.pennysaveronline.com
Circulation: 2pd,7,096fr; VAC
Advertising: Open inch rate $9.40
Established: 1954Richard Snyder
Mechanical Specifications: Type page: 11.25 x 16; 6 col

ROUND LAKE

THE PENNYSAVER
(Thur)
2037 Route 9, Round Lake, NY, 12151-1701, USA; tel (518) 877-7160; fax (518) 877-7824
Circulation:173,000fr; Sworn/Estimate/Non-Audited
Advertising: Open inch rate $23.35
Group: Hearst Communications, Inc.
Pub. .... Patrick J. Smith

SPRINGVILLE

SPRINGVILLE PENNYSAVER
(Fri)
49 E Main St, Springville, NY, 14141-1245, USA; tel (716) 592-2818; fax (716) 592-3948; web site http://www.pennysavers.com/index.php
Circulation:9,768fr; Sworn/Estimate/Non-AuditedGerry Grabowski

STATEN ISLAND

STATEN ISLAND PENNYSAVER
(Thur)
101 Tyrellan Ave, Ste 420, Staten Island, NY, 10309-2651, USA; tel (718) 966-1200; fax (718) 966-7775; e-mail info@siregister.com; web site www.siregister.com
Circulation:150,000fr; Sworn/Estimate/Non-Audited
Advertising: Open inch rate $39.00
Pub. .... Dan McDonough
Adv. Dir. .... Antionette Zuest
Mechanical Specifications: Type page 10 1/4 x 14; E - 5 cols, 2, 1/6 between; A - 5 cols, 2, 1/6 between; C - 7 cols, 1 7/16, between.
Equipment: Hardware — APP/Macs; Software — QPS/QuarkXPress.
Zip Codes Served: 10305

SYOSSET

NORTH SHORE TODAY
(Wed)
6851 Jericho Tpke, Syosset, NY, 11791-4494, USA; tel (516) 496-4300; fax (516) 496-9898; e-mail nstoday@aol.com; web site www.northshoretoday.com
Circulation:147,903fr; CAC
Established: 1984Editions: 15— 15 total; North Shore Today-Commack (10,758); North Shore Today-Dix Hills/Melville (15,863); North Shore Today-East Northport (10,847); North Shore Today-Glen Cove (10,179); North Shore Today-Glen Head (8,095); North Shore Today-Great Neck (14,580); Nort
Pub. .... Mark Schlau
Assoc. Pub. .... Ross Bergrin
Gen. Mgr. .... Vincent Gerbasio
Ed. .... Mark Schalu
Mechanical Specifications: Type page 6 1/4 x 9 7/8; E - 2 cols, 3 1/6, 1/8 between; A - 2 cols, 3 1/6, 1/8 between; C - 2 cols, 3 1/6, 1/8 between.
Equipment: Hardware — APP/Mac; Software — Adobe/PageMaker 6.5, Macromedia/Freehand 7.0, QPS/QuarkXPress 4.04.
Zip Codes Served: 11577, 11576, 11596, 11568, 11507, 11030, 11040, 11050, 11020, 11021, 11023, 11024, 11791, 11797, 11803, 11804, 11753, 11801, 11743, 11724, 11721, 11746, 11740, 11747, 11545, 11547, 11579, 11542, 11771, 11732, 11765, 11709, 11560, 11768, 11731, 11725, 115

SYRACUSE

EAGLE NEWSPAPERS
(Wed, Thur)
2501 James St, Ste 100, Syracuse, NY, 13206-2996, USA; tel (315) 434-8889; fax (315) 434-8883; e-mail newsroom@eaglenewsonline.com; adv e-mail cfarley@eaglenewsonline.com; ed e-mail newsroom@eaglenewsonline.com; web site www.eaglenewsonline.com
Circulation: 326pd,17,711fr; CVC
Pres./Pub. .... David Tyler

PENNYSAVER/PENNYWISE
(Tues)
750 W Genesee St, Syracuse, NY, 13204-2306, USA; tel (315) 685-7000; fax (315) 685-3772; e-mail dchubb@axcess.net
Circulation:120,126fr; Sworn/Estimate/Non-AuditedEditions: 10— 10 total; Auburn Pennysaver (18,439); Cortland (10,449); FM-Zone 1 (13,353); FM-Zone 2 (14,438); Geneva (10,248); Moravia (9,142); Pennywise (9,121); Seneca Falls (10,901); Skaneateles/Marcellus Pennysaver (8,505); Town & Country (14,530);
Gen. Mgr. .... Mike Grandstaff
Adv. Mgr. .... Victor Ianno
Circ. Mgr. .... David Spearing
Prodn. Mgr. .... Jack Jensen
Mechanical Specifications: Type page 10 3/8 x 13; E - 6 cols, 1 7/8, 5/16 between; A - 6 cols, 1 7/8, 5/16 between; C - 6 cols, 1 7/8, 5/16 between.
Equipment: Hardware — APP/Mac; Presses — 12-G/Community w/folders; Software — QPS/QuarkXPress, Multi-Ad/Creator.

SCOTSMAN COMMUNITY PUBLICATION
(Sun)
750 W Genesee St, Syracuse, NY, 13204-2306, USA; tel (315) 472-7825; fax (315) 478-1434; e-mail pennysaver@scotsmanpress.com; adv e-mail classifieds@cnypennysaver.com; ed e-mail editorial@scotsmanpress.com; web site www.scotsmanonline.com
Circulation:260,000fr; Sworn/Estimate/Non-Audited
Advertising: Open inch rate $12.29
Established: 1954Editions: 24— 24 total; SCP-Auburn (19,235); SCP-Baldwinsville (12,862); SCP-Bellevue/Geddes (10,363); SCP-Camillus/Solvay (19,096); SCP-City Edition (5,388); SCP-Court/Butternut (8,485); SCP-Courtland (9,426); SCP-East Syracuse/Minoa (10,457); SCP-Eastwood (8,308); S
Pub. .... A. Loren Colburn
Assoc. Pub. .... Thomas C. Cuskey
Circ. Mgr. .... David Spearing
Ed. .... Deb Lum
Mechanical Specifications: Type page 10 5/16 x 13; E - 6 cols, 1 5/8, 1/8 between; A - 6 cols, 1 5/8, 1/8 between; C - 6 cols, 1 5/8, 1/8 between.
Zip Codes Served: 13221

SCOTSMAN PENNYSAVER - BALDWINSVILLE
(Sun)
750 W Genesee St, Syracuse, NY, 13204-2306, USA; web site www.scotsmanonline.com
Circulation:14,172fr; CVCJohn Badoud

SCOTSMAN PENNYSAVER - LIVERPOOL
(Sun)
750 W Genesee St, Syracuse, NY, 13204-2306, USA; web site www.scotsmanonline.com
Circulation:21,323fr; CVCJohn Badoud

SCOTSMAN PENNYSAVER - PENNYWISE
(Sun)
750 W Genesee St, Syracuse, NY, 13204-2306, USA; web site www.scotsmanonline.com
Circulation:9,400fr; CVCJohn Badoud

SCOTSMAN PENNYSAVER - SKANEATELES
(Sun)
750 W Genesee St, Syracuse, NY, 13204-2306, USA; web site www.scotsmanonline.com
Circulation:6,876fr; CVCJohn Badoud

SCOTSMAN PENNYSAVER - SW SYRACUSE EDITION
(Sun)
750 W Genesee St, Syracuse, NY, 13204-2306, USA; web site www.scotsmanonline.com
Circulation:15,963fr; CVCJohn Badoud

UTICA

UTICA PENNYSAVER
(Thur)
221 Oriskany St E, Utica, NY, 13501-1201, USA; web site www.uticaod.com/pennysaver
Circulation: 0pd,35,704fr; CVC
Advertising: Open inch rate $25.25
Established: 2006Donna Donovan
Mechanical Specifications: Type page: 10.12 x 10.75; 6 col

WARSAW

WARSAW PENNY SAVER
(Sat)
72 N Main St, Warsaw, NY, 14569-1329, USA; tel (585) 786-8161; fax (585) 786-5159; web site www.warsawpennysaver.com
Circulation:9,087fr; VAC
Advertising: Open inch rate $10.50
Established: 1965
Display Adv. Mgr. .... Gail Herman
Prodn. Mgr. .... Christine Kennedy-Till
Mechanical Specifications: Type page 7 1/2 x 11; A - 4 cols, 1 7/8, between.

WATERTOWN

JEFFERSON COUNTY PENNYSAVER
(Fri)
260 Washington St, Watertown, NY, 13601-4669, USA; tel (315) 782-0400; fax (315) 661-2524; e-mail pennysaver@wdt.net; web site www.watertowndailytimes.com; www.jeffpennysaver.com
Circulation:18,481fr; CVC
Advertising: Open inch rate $14.45
Group: Johnson Newspaper Corp.
Pub. .... John B. Johnson
Adv. Mgr. .... Barb Peck
Adv. Sales Mgr. .... Laurie Denesha
Dir., Info Servs. .... Tom Kitto
Mechanical Specifications: Type page 10 x 12 3/4; A - 5 cols, between.
Equipment: ; Software — PBS Informatel/AdPlus.

NORTHERN NEW YORK PENNYSAVER
(Fri)
260 Washington St, Watertown, NY, 13601-4669, USA; tel (315) 782-1000; adv tel (315) 661-2326; fax (315) 661-2522; adv fax (315) 661-2522; adv e-mail ccampany@wdt.net
Circulation: 0pd,7,306fr; VAC
Advertising: Open inch rate $9.69
Established: 1976
Group: Northern New York Newspapers
Advertising Director .... Karen Romeo
Mechanical Specifications: Type page: 11.75 x 20.5; 9 col
Delivery Method: Carrier, Racks
Zip Codes Served: will send as an attachment

WATKINS GLEN

HI LITES
(Mon)
217 N Franklin St, Watkins Glen, NY, 14891-1201, USA; web site www.hilites.net
Circulation:8,975fr; VAC
Advertising: Open inch rate $9.05
Established: 1952Bridgette Goodman
Mechanical Specifications: Type page: 10.375 x 15.75; 7 col

WELLSVILLE

ALLEGANY COUNTY PENNYSAVER
(Sun)
159 N Main St, Wellsville, NY, 14895-1149, USA; tel (585) 593-5300; fax (585) 593-5303; e-mail publisher@wellsvilledaily.com; ed e-mail editor@wellsvilledaily.com; web site www.wellsvilledaily.com
Circulation:18,000fr; CVC
Advertising: Open inch rate $12.15
Group: GateHouse Media, Inc.
Adv. Mgr. .... Oak Duke
Circ. Mgr. .... Robert Polley
Ed. .... John Anderson
Zip Codes Served: 14895

WESTFIELD

QUALITY GUIDE
(Sat)
39 E Main St, Westfield, NY, 14787-1303, USA; tel (716) 326-3163; fax (716) 326-3165; adv e-mail ads@westfieldrepublican.com; web site www.westfieldrepublican.com
Circulation:10,312fr; Sworn/Estimate/Non-Audited
Advertising: Modular Rate Sheet
Group: Ogden Newspapers Inc.

General Manager ....Jim Saxton
Inside Sales............................. Peggy Stravato
Mechanical Specifications: Type page 10 9/16 x 11 1/2; E - 6 cols, 1 21/32, between; A - 6 cols, 1 21/32, between.
Zip Codes Served: 14787, 14757, 14775, 14781, 14716, 14769, 14736 & 16428

WHITE PLAINS

LOHUD EXPRESS
(Thur)
1 Gannett Dr, White Plains, NY, 10604-3402, USA; tel (914) 694-9300; fax (914) 694-5018; e-mail customerservice@lohud.com; web site www.lohud.com
Circulation:272,000fr; Sworn/Estimate/Non-Audited
Advertising: Open inch rate $32.50
Pub. .... Michael J. Fisch
Circ. Dir.......................................Elaine Kersch
Ed. ....Henry Freeman

WILLIAMSVILLE

BEE GROUP NEWSPAPERS
5564 Main St, Williamsville, NY, 14221-5410, USA; tel (716) 632-4700; fax (716) 633-8601; e-mail tmeaser@beenews.com; adv e-mail salesdept@beenews.com; web site www.beenews.com
Established: 1879
Group: Bee Group Newspapers
Pres./Pub. .... Trey Measer
David Sherman

YORKTOWN HEIGHTS

PENNYSAVER
(Wed)
1520 Front St, Yorktown Heights, NY, 10598-4638, USA; tel (914) 962-3871; fax (914) 962-4820; adv fax (914) 962-5123; web site www.nypennysaver.com
Circulation:176,091fr; CVC
Established: 1958Editions: 10— 10 total: Mt. Kisco Book-18,102; Carmel Book-16,227; Brewster Book-13,230; Yorktown-25,112 Central Westchester-26,387; Southern Westchester-15,189; Peekskill-22,904; Fishkill-12,221; Wappingers-13,242; Hopewell-13,447
Owner/Pub....................................Carla Chase
Circ. Mgr.. Gary Olsen
Vice President & COO.............Dave Fitzmorris
Mechanical Specifications: Type page 7 1/4 x 9 3/4; E - 4 cols, 2, 3/16 between; A - 4 cols, 2, between.
Equipment: Hardware — AT; Presses — 6-HI, 7-HI; Software — AT.
Delivery Method: Mail, Newsstand, Racks
Zip Codes Served: 10598,10589,10547,10527,10501,10505,10587,10540,10517, 10588,10535,10541,10542,10512,12563,10509,6812,10560, 10519,10549,10536,10507,10506,10576,10590,10518,10597, 10526,10578,6831,10562,10520,10510,10546,10570,10514, 10594,10532,10504,10591,10522,10533,10603,10523,10595, 10566,10567,10548,10511,10596,10524,10579,10537,12524, 12508,10516,12512,12527,12533,12582,12570,12564,12531, 12522,12594,12590,12537,

YORKTOWN PENNYSAVER - BREWSTER - NEW FAIRFIELD
(Wed)
1520 Front St, Yorktown Heights, NY, 10598-4638, USA; web site www.chasemediagroup.com
Circulation:13,379fr; VAC
Established: 1958Carla Chase
Mechanical Specifications: Type page: 7.5 x 9.75; 4 col

YORKTOWN PENNYSAVER - CARMEL
(Wed)
1520 Front St, Yorktown Heights, NY, 10598-4638, USA; web site www.chasemediagroup.com
Circulation:15,621fr; VAC
Established: 1958Carla Chase
Mechanical Specifications: Type page: 7.5 x 9.75; 4 col

YORKTOWN PENNYSAVER - CROTON - OSSINING
(Wed)
1520 Front St, Yorktown Heights, NY, 10598-4638, USA; web site www.chasemediagroup.com
Circulation:25,187fr; VAC
Established: 1958Carla Chase
Mechanical Specifications: Type page: 7.5 x 9.75; 4 col

YORKTOWN PENNYSAVER - FISHKILL
(Wed)
1520 Front St, Yorktown Heights, NY, 10598-4638, USA; web site www.chasemediagroup.com
Circulation:11,569fr; VAC
Established: 1958Carla Chase
Mechanical Specifications: Type page: 7.5 x 9.75; 4 col

YORKTOWN PENNYSAVER - HOPEWELL
(Wed)
1520 Front St, Yorktown Heights, NY, 10598-4638, USA; web site www.chasemediagroup.com
Circulation:12,336fr; VAC
Established: 1958Carla Chase
Mechanical Specifications: Type page: 7.5 x 9.75; 4 col

YORKTOWN PENNYSAVER - MAHOPAC
(Wed)
1520 Front St, Yorktown Heights, NY, 10598-4638, USA; web site www.chasemediagroup.com
Circulation: 0pd,15,621fr; VAC
Established: 1958Carla Chase
Mechanical Specifications: Type page: 7.5 x 9.75; 4 col

YORKTOWN PENNYSAVER - MT. KISCO - KATONAH
(Wed)
1520 Front St, Yorktown Heights, NY, 10598-4638, USA; web site www.chasemediagroup.com
Circulation:16,934fr; VAC
Established: 1958Carla Chase
Mechanical Specifications: Type page: 7.5 x 9.75; 4 col

YORKTOWN PENNYSAVER - N WHITE
(Wed)
1520 Front St, Yorktown Heights, NY, 10598-4638, USA; web site www.chasemediagroup.com
Circulation:16,085fr; CVC
Established: 1958Carla Chase
Mechanical Specifications: Type page: 7.5 x 9.75; 4 col

YORKTOWN PENNYSAVER - PAWLING
(Wed)
1520 Front St, Yorktown Heights, NY, 10598-4638, USA; web site www.chasemediagroup.com
Circulation:12,336fr; VAC
Established: 1958Carla Chase
Mechanical Specifications: Type page: 7.5 x 9.75; 4 col

YORKTOWN PENNYSAVER - PEEKSKILL
(Wed)
1520 Front St, Yorktown Heights, NY, 10598-4638, USA; web site www.chasemediagroup.com
Circulation:23,248fr; VAC
Established: 1958Carla Chase
Mechanical Specifications: Type page: 7.5 x 9.75; 4 col

YORKTOWN PENNYSAVER - PLEASANTVILLE
(Wed)
1520 Front St, Yorktown Heights, NY, 10598-4638, USA; web site www.chasemediagroup.com
Circulation:25,187fr; VAC
Established: 1958Carla Chase
Mechanical Specifications: Type page: 7.5 x 9.75; 4 col

YORKTOWN PENNYSAVER - PUTNAM VALLEY
(Wed)
1520 Front St, Yorktown Heights, NY, 10598-4638, USA; web site www.chasemediagroup.com
Circulation:23,248fr; VAC
Established: 1958Carla Chase
Mechanical Specifications: Type page: 7.5 x 9.75; 4 col

YORKTOWN PENNYSAVER - TARRYTOWN
(Wed)
1520 Front St, Yorktown Heights, NY, 10598-4638, USA; web site www.chasemediagroup.com
Circulation:14,786fr; VAC
Established: 1958Carla Chase
Mechanical Specifications: Type page: 7.5 x 9.75; 4 col

YORKTOWN PENNYSAVER - WAPPINGERS
(Wed)
1520 Front St, Yorktown Heights, NY, 10598-4638, USA; web site www.chasemediagroup.com
Circulation:13,227fr; VAC
Established: 1958Carla Chase
Mechanical Specifications: Type page: 7.5 x 9.75; 4 col

YORKTOWN PENNYSAVER - YORKTOWN SOMERS
(Wed)
1520 Front St, Yorktown Heights, NY, 10598-4638, USA; tel (914) 962-3871; web site www.chasemediagroup.com
Circulation:25,838fr; VAC
Established: 1958
Digital Platform - Mobile: Apple, Android, Windows
Digital Platform - Tablet: Windows 7Carla Chase
Mechanical Specifications: Type page: 7.5 x 9.75; 4 col
Delivery Method: Mail

NORTH CAROLINA

AHOSKIE

THE ROANOKE-CHOWAN'S SHOPPER WEEKLY
(Thur)
801 Parker Ave E, Ahoskie, NC, 27910-3641, USA; tel (252) 332-2123; fax (252) 332-3940; web site www.roanoke-chowannewsherald.com
Circulation:5,000fr; Sworn/Estimate/Non-Audited
Advertising: Open inch rate $9.98
Group: Boone Newspapers, Inc.
Ed. .... Calvin Bryant

ALBEMARLE

ADVANTAGE
(Sun)
237 W North St, Albemarle, NC, 28001-3923, USA; tel (704) 982-2121; fax (704) 982-8736; e-mail snapnews@vnet.net; web site www.thesnaponline.com
Circulation:10,000fr; Sworn/Estimate/Non-Audited
Advertising: Open inch rate $8.80
Established: 1880
Pub. ....Sandy Selvy
Adv. Mgr.................................... Manda Harkey
Circ. Mgr...Lena Dean
Ed. ....Jim Lisk
Prodn. Mgr. ....Ryan Starnes
Mechanical Specifications: Type page 11 5/8 x 21 1/2; E - 6 cols, 1 13/16, between; A - 6 cols, 1 13/16, between; C - 6 cols, 1 13/16, between.
Equipment: Hardware — APP/Mac; Presses — G/Community; Software — QPS/QuarkXPress 4.2, Adobe/PageMaker 6.5.
Zip Codes Served: 28002

ASHEVILLE

IWANNA
(Tues)
291 Sweeten Creek Rd, Asheville, NC, 28803-1527, USA; tel (828) 274-8888; fax (828) 274-8533; e-mail sales@iwanna.com; web site www.iwanna.com
Circulation: 17,651pd,4,100fr; CVC
Advertising: Open inch rate $18.00
Established: 1976
Circ. Mgr......................................Mark Graham
Prodn. Mgr. .... Lisa Gallagher
Advertising Manager ....Patricia Betts
Mechanical Specifications: Type page 10 1/4 x 13; A - 4 cols, 2 3/8, 1/4 between; C - 4 cols, 2 3/8, 1/4 between.
Equipment: Hardware — APP/Macs; Presses — 10-G/Community; Software — Adobe/InDesign 2.0.
Delivery Method: Racks
Zip Codes Served: 28813

CHARLOTTE

PENNY SAVER
(Wed)
3419 Selwyn Farms Ln, Charlotte, NC, 28209-4030, USA; tel (704) 527-7079; fax (704) 525-2446; e-mail info@todayspennysaver.com; web site www.carolinapennysaver.com
Circulation:31,500fr; Sworn/Estimate/Non-Audited
Established: 1985Editions: 3— 3 total; Penny Saver-Charlotte (15,000); Penny Saver-Lake Norman (7,000); Penny Saver-Rock Hill (9,500);
Pub. ....Charles Sosnick
Prodn. Mgr. .... Don Wells
Mechanical Specifications: Type page 9 3/4 x 12 13/16; E - 6 cols, 1 1/2, 1/6 between; A - 6 cols, 1 1/2, 1/6 between; C - 6 cols, 1 1/2, 1/6 between.
Equipment: Hardware — PC; Software — Adobe/PageMaker.
Zip Codes Served: 28105, 28134, 28203, 28205, 28209, 28210, 28211, 28212, 28213, 28215, 28217, 28226, 28270, 28273, 28277

ELKIN

YADKIN VALLEY ADVERTISER
(Wed)
214 E Main St, Elkin, NC, 28621-3431, USA; tel (336) 835-1513; fax (336) 835-8742; e-mail editor@elkintribune.com; web site www.elkintribune.com

Circulation: 19,000fr; Sworn/Estimate/Non-Audited
Advertising: Open inch rate $6.99
Group: Civitas Media, LLC-OOB
Gen. Mgr. .... Peter J. Cook
Circ. .... Kathy Groce
Ed. .... Cliff Clark
Mng. Ed. .... Steve Steiner
Sports. Ed. .... Eric Lusk
Adv. Mgr. .... Wanda Walls
Adv. Mgr. .... Nicholas Elmes
Mechanical Specifications: Type page 11 9/16 x 21 1/2; A - 6 cols, 1 3/4, between; C - 6 cols, 1 1/3, between.
Equipment: Hardware — APP/Mac; Software — QPS/QuarkXpress 6.0.
Zip Codes Served: 28621

FAYETTEVILLE

CAROLINA TRADER AUTOS
(Wed, Bi-Mthly)
458 Whitfield St, Fayetteville, NC, 28306-1614, USA; tel (910) 433-2229; fax (910) 323-0845; e-mail trader-ads-sale@carolinatrader.com; web site www.carolina-trader.com
Circulation: 17,500fr; Sworn/Estimate/Non-Audited
Group: Fayetteville Publishing Co.
Pub. .... Charles Broadwell
Adv. Mgr. .... Mona Bass
Mechanical Specifications: Type page 10 x 13.
Equipment: Hardware — IBM; Software — Adobe/PageMaker, QPS/QuarkXPress, Archetype/Corel Draw.

FRANKLIN

MACON COUNTY NEWS
(Thur)
107 Highlands Rd, Franklin, NC, 28734-2709, USA; tel (828) 369-6767; ed tel (828)369-6767; fax (828) 369-2700; e-mail maconcountynews@gmail.com; ed e-mail editor@maconnews.com; web site www.maconnews.com
Circulation: 200pd,12,500fr; Sworn/Estimate/Non-Audited
Advertising: Open inch rate $7.40
Established: 1983
Ed. .... Teresa Tabor
Adv. Dir. .... Betsey Gooder
Mechanical Specifications: Call for information, please.
Equipment: Hardware — MAC; Software — Photoshop, Quark Xpress, Adobe Illustrator, etc.
Delivery Method: Mail, Newsstand, Racks
Zip Codes Served: 28725, 28734, 28741, 28763, 28779

GARNER

SOUTHSIDE SHOPPER
(Thur)
PO Box 449, Garner, NC, 27529-0449, USA; tel (919) 772-9002; fax (919) 772-4172; e-mail sshopper@sshopper.com; web site www.sshopper.com
Circulation: 0pd,22,356fr; CVC
Advertising: Open inch rate $14.00
Established: 1977
Pub. .... David W. Mundy
Circulation Mgr. .... Tim Hunt
Sales Mgr. .... Greg Byars
Office Mgr. .... Becky Mundy
Mechanical Specifications: Type page 10 1/4 x 15; E - 6 cols, 1 1/2, between; A - 6 cols, 1 1/2, between.
Equipment: Hardware — APP/Mac, PC; Presses — 8-G/Community, WPC; Software — Support, QPS/QuarkXPress.
Zip Codes Served: 27529

GREENSBORO

AMERICAN CLASSIFIEDS - GREENSBORO
(Thur)
5214 W Market St, Greensboro, NC, 27409-2616, USA; web site www.americanclassifieds.com
Circulation: 32,975fr; Sworn/Estimate/Non-AuditedDan Leasure

THE CLIPPER
(Wed)
200 E Market St, Greensboro, NC, 27401-2910, USA; tel (910) 373-7000; adv tel (336) 373-7360; ed tel (336) 373-7051; fax (910) 373-7137; adv e-mail keeley.duckworth@News-Record.com; ed e-mail jeff.gauger@News-Record.com; web site http://www.greensboro.com/
Circulation: 79,848fr; VAC
Pub. .... Van King
Adv. Mgr. .... Judy Nance
Circ. Mgr. .... David Berrier
Ed. .... Pat Yack
Prodn. Mgr. .... David Reno
Mechanical Specifications: Type page 10 3/4 x 13; E - 5 cols, 2, between; A - 5 cols, 2, between.
Equipment: ; Presses — G/Metro.
Zip Codes Served: 27420

HENDERSON

TRI-COUNTY SHOPPER
(Wed)
PO Box 908, Henderson, NC, 27536-0908, USA; tel (252) 436-2700; fax (252) 430-0125
Circulation: 19,000fr; Sworn/Estimate/Non-Audited
Advertising: Open inch rate $11.12
Adv. Dir. .... Deborah Tuck
Prodn. Mgr. .... Chris Burwell

HENDERSONVILLE

TOWN TOOTER
(Thur)
1625 Four Seasons Blvd, Ste 161, Hendersonville, NC, 28792-2857, USA; tel (828) 692-7550; fax (828) 692-7336; e-mail towntooter@towntooter.com; web site www.towntooter.com
Circulation: 18,186fr; CVC
Advertising: Open inch rate $11.00
Established: 1994
Gen. Mgr. .... Jeffrey Mueller
Mechanical Specifications: Type page 10 1/2 x 13; E - 6 cols, 1 5/8, 3/16 between; A - 6 cols, 1 5/8, 3/16 between; C - 6 cols, 1 5/8, 3/16 between.
Equipment: Hardware — IBM; Software — Microsoft/Windows.
Zip Codes Served: 28704, 28710, 28712, 28720, 28722, 28729, 28732, 28739, 28792, 28793, 28801, 28803, 28805, 28806, 28727, 28731

HICKORY

IWANNA
(Thur)
961 11th Avenue Blvd SE, Hickory, NC, 28602-4348, USA; tel (828) 328-5296; fax (828) 328-5296; web site www.iwanna.com
Circulation: 17,800pd,1,000fr; Sworn/Estimate/Non-Audited
Advertising: Open inch rate $12.00
Pub. .... Dean DeBord
Pub. .... John DeBord
Gen. Mgr. .... Derek DeBord
Mechanical Specifications: Type page 10 1/4 x 12 3/4; A - 4 cols, 2 3/8, 1/4 between; C - 4 cols, 2 3/8, 1/4 between.
Equipment: Hardware — APP/Mac; Software — Adobe/PageMaker 6.5.

POW
(Fri)
1100 Park Pl, Hickory, NC, 28601, USA; tel (828) 322-4510; adv tel (828) 322-4510; ed tel (828) 322-4510; fax (828) 322-8439; adv fax (828) 267-0294; ed fax (828) 324-8179; e-mail advertising@hickoryrecord.com; adv e-mail advertising@hickoryrecord.com; ed e-mail news@hickoryrecord.com; web site www.hickoryrecord.com
Circulation: 15,260pd,; CAC
Advertising: Open inch rate $28.00
Group: BH Media Group
Pub. .... Eric Millsaps
Reg. Pub. .... Tim Dearman
Mng. Ed. .... John Miller
Adv. Dir. .... Cathy Fagan
Circ. Dir. .... David Eggers
Prodn. Mgr. .... Jim Lillagore
Bus. Ed. .... John Dayberry
City Ed. .... Patrick Jean
Lifestyle Ed. .... Josh LaFontaine
News Ed. .... Michelle L. Bloomfield
Opinion Page Ed. .... Larry Clark
Sports Ed. .... Chris Hobbs
Adv. Dir. .... Jason Propst
Mechanical Specifications: Type page 13 x 21; E - 6 cols, 2 1/16, 1/8 between; A - 6 cols, 2 1/16, 1/8 between; C - 8 cols, 1 3/4, 1/16 between.
Delivery Method: Mail
Zip Codes Served: Catawba County

LAURINBURG

COMMUNITY NEWS ADVERTISER
(Wed)
211 W Cronly St, Laurinburg, NC, 28352-3637, USA; tel (910) 277-3541; ed tel (910) 277-3540; fax (910) 276-3815; web site www.laurinburgexchange.com
Circulation: 14,200fr; Sworn/Estimate/Non-Audited
Advertising: Open inch rate $9.30
Group: Champion Media
Pub. .... Denny Koenders
Circ. Mgr. .... Jerry Mims
Ed. .... Scott Witten

NEW BERN

THE SHOPPER
(Wed)
3200 Wellons Blvd, New Bern, NC, 28562-5234, USA; tel (252) 633-1153; fax (252) 633-2663; web site www.encshopper.com
Circulation: 19,075fr; CVC
Advertising: Open inch rate $12.00
Established: 1971
Group: Times Media GroupEditions: 2— The Shopper-Havelock/Cherry Point (7,950); The Shopper-New Bern (23,550);
Pub. .... Nancy Eckard
Circ. Mgr. .... Betty Stonestreet
Prodn. Mgr. .... Christi Lane
Adv. Sales .... CeCelia Stallings
Adv. Sales .... Jim Davidson
Mechanical Specifications: Type page 10.373 x 10.082; E - 9 cols, 1 9/16, 3/8 between; A - 6 cols, 1 9/16, between.
Equipment: Hardware — 2-APP/iMac, APP/Mac G4, APP/Mac G3.
Zip Codes Served: 28560, 28561, 28562, 28532, 28570, 28586

THE SHOPPER - HAVELOCK / CHERRY POINT
(Wed)
PO Box 12407, New Bern, NC, 28561-2407, USA; web site www.encshopper.com
Circulation: 0pd,5,000fr; CVC
Advertising: N/A
Established: 1971Nancy Eckard
Mechanical Specifications: Type page: 10.373 x 10.082; 9 col

THE SHOPPER - NEW BERN
(Wed)
PO Box 12407, New Bern, NC, 28561-2407, USA; web site www.encshopper.com
Circulation: 0pd,14,150fr; CVC
Advertising: N/A
Established: 1971Nancy Eckard
Mechanical Specifications: Type page: 10.373 x 10.082; 9 col

ROANOKE RAPIDS

THE REVUE
(Wed)
PO Box 520, Roanoke Rapids, NC, 27870-0520, USA; tel (252) 537-2505; fax (252) 537-2314; e-mail herald@rrdailyherald.com; web site www.rrdailyherald.com
Circulation: 7,287fr; Sworn/Estimate/Non-Audited
Advertising: Open inch rate $3.32
Pub. .... Titus Workman
Bus. Mgr. .... Linda Smith
Circ. Mgr. .... Carol Moseley
Mng. Ed. .... John Moeur
News Ed. .... Kris Smith
Adv. Dir. .... Linda Foster
Prodn. Mgr. .... David Hager
Mechanical Specifications: Type page 13 x 21 1/2; E - 6 cols, between; A - 6 cols, between; C - 9 cols, between.
Equipment: Hardware — APP/Mac; Presses — 7-Web Atlas; Software — Baseview, QPS/QuarkXPress, Multi-Ad/Creator.
Zip Codes Served: 27870

SHALLOTTE

BRUNSWICK COUNTY NEWS
(Thur)
129 Forest Dr, Shallotte, NC, 28470-4455, USA; tel (910) 754-8662; e-mail news@brunswick-nc.net
Circulation: 6,000fr; Sworn/Estimate/Non-Audited
Advertising: Open inch rate $4.55
Ed. .... Rachel Miller
Zip Codes Served: 28459; 28429; 28268; 29470

SHELBY

SHELBY SHOPPER & INFO
(Thur)
503 N Lafayette St, Shelby, NC, 28150-4426, USA; tel (704) 484-1047; adv tel (704) 484-1047; fax (704) 484-1067; adv fax (704) 484-1067; e-mail news@shelbyinfo.com; adv e-mail advertising@shelbyinfo.com; classified@shelbyinfo.com; ed e-mail news@shelbyinfo.com; web site www.shelbyinfo.com
Circulation: 28,000fr; CVC
Advertising: Open inch rate $16.00
Established: 1984
Group: Community First Media, Inc.
Digital Platform - Mobile: Apple
Digital Platform - Tablet: Apple iOS
Advertising Manager .... Mike Marlow
Prodn. Mgr. .... Greg Ledford
Circ. Mgr .... Les Wood
Prod. Mgr .... Carolyn Henwood
Mechanical Specifications: Type page 10 1/3 x 15; E - 6 cols, 1 5/8, between; A - 6 cols, 1 5/8, between; C - 6 cols, 1 5/8, between.
Equipment: Hardware — 1-APP/Power Mac 7100, 1-APP/Mac IIci; Software — Adobe/InDesign
Delivery Method: Racks
Zip Codes Served: 28017, 28019, 28020, 28021, 28024, 28038, 28040, 28042, 28043, 28052, 28086, 28090, 28150, 28151, 28152, 28169, 28168, 28016, 29702, 29018, 28073, 28089, 28114, 28136, 28150, 28152

WILMINGTON

AD PAK
(Wed)
210 Old Dairy Rd, Ste A2, Wilmington, NC, 28405-4448, USA; tel (910) 791-0688; adv tel (910) 791-0688; ed tel (910) 791-0688; fax (910) 791-9534; adv fax (910) 791-9534; ed fax (910) 791-9534; adv e-mail jeff@adpakweekly.com; ed e-mail susie@adpakweekly.com; web site www.adpakdeals.com
Circulation: 10,000fr; Sworn/Estimate/Non-Audited
Advertising: Open inch rate $8.00
Established: 1976
Group: H&P Media LLC
Partner .... Jeff Phenicie
Prodn. Mgr. .... Susie Riddle
Mechanical Specifications: Type page 10 1/4 x 13; E - 6 cols, 1 5/8, between; A - 6 cols, 1 5/8, between; C - 6 cols, 1 5/8, between.
Equipment: Hardware — APP/Mac 6-4, APP/IMac; Software — QPS/QuarkXPress 4.0.
Delivery Method: Carrier, Racks
Zip Codes Served: 28401, 28403, 28405, 28409, 28411, 28412, 28480, 28428, 28449, 28429, 28425, 28457, 28451, 28461

WINSTON SALEM

THRIFTY NICKEL - WINSTON-SALEM
(Thur)
505 Peters Creek Pkwy, Winston Salem, NC, 27101-4930, USA; tel (336) 773-1595; fax (336) 773-1597; web site http://thriftynickelusa.com/
Circulation: 0pd,16,528fr; CVC
Advertising: Open inch rate $15.00
Established: 1982Jim Noonan
Mechanical Specifications: Type page: 10.4 x 16; 7 col

THRIFTY NICKEL WANT ADS
(Thur)
1427 Peters Creek Pkwy, Winston Salem, NC, 27103-4636, USA; tel (336) 773-1595; fax (336) 773-1597; e-mail thriftynickel@emadisonriver.com; web site www.wsthriftynickel.com
Circulation: 22,373fr; CVC
Advertising: Open inch rate $12.00
Gen. Mgr. .... Carol Young
Adv. Mgr. .... James Noonan
Circ. Mgr. .... Becky Douglas
Prodn. Mgr. .... Shelby Powell
Zip Codes Served: 27127

NORTH DAKOTA

BISMARCK

FINDER
(Wed)
707 E Front Ave, Bismarck, ND, 58504-5646, USA; tel (701) 250-8210; fax (701) 223-4240; e-mail legals@bismarcktribune.com; web site www.bismarcktribune.com; www.finderads.com
Circulation: 40,000fr; Sworn/Estimate/Non-Audited
Advertising: Open inch rate $16.70
Pub. .... Brian Kroshus
Adv. Dir. .... Kristin Wilson
Sales Mgr. .... Nancy Janssen
Circ. Mgr. .... Ken Bohl
Mechanical Specifications: Type page 10 1/2 x 15; E - 7 cols, 1 1/3, 1/6 between; A - 7 cols, 1 1/3, 1/6 between; C - 7 cols, 1 1/3, 1/6 between.
Equipment: Hardware — APP/Mac; Presses — HI; Software — Multi-Ad/Creator 5.0.
Zip Codes Served: 58554

BOWMAN

THE FINDER
(Wed)
18 S Main St, Bowman, ND, 58623-4012, USA; tel (701) 523-5623; fax (701) 523-3441; e-mail finder@ndsupernet.com
Circulation: 11,500fr; Sworn/Estimate/Non-Audited
Advertising: Open inch rate $7.35
Prodn. Mgr. .... Kevin Cummings
Mechanical Specifications: Type page 10 x 16; E - 6 cols, between; A - 6 cols, between.
Zip Codes Served: 58623

DICKINSON

PENNYSAVER
(Thur)
131 E Villard St, Dickinson, ND, 58601-5246, USA; tel (701) 225-1374; fax (701) 225-8914; e-mail pennysaver@ndsupernet.com
Circulation: 8,900fr; Sworn/Estimate/Non-Audited
Advertising: Open inch rate $5.00
Group: Lee Enterprises, Inc.
Adv. Mgr. .... Irene Schafer
Mechanical Specifications: Type page 10 1/2 x 15; A - 7 cols, 1 1/3, between.
Equipment: Hardware — APP/Mac; Presses — 4-HI/single wide offset; Software — Multi-Ad/Creator 4.01.
Delivery Method: Racks
Zip Codes Served: 58601

FARGO

THE METRO WEEKLY
(Wed)
101 5th St N, Fargo, ND, 58102-4826, USA; tel (701) 451-5774; fax (701) 241-5497; ed e-mail lstoneburner@forumcomm.com
Circulation: 35,000fr; CVC
Advertising: Open inch rate $12.00
Established: 1969
Group: Forum Communications Co.
Pub. .... Dennis Winskowski
Circ. Mgr. .... Ilene Munter
Ed. .... Karen Huber
Mechanical Specifications: Type page 10 9/16 x 16 1/2; E - 7 cols, 1 3/8, 1/12 between; A - 7 cols, 1 3/8, between.
Equipment: Hardware — PC; Presses — 9-G.
Zip Codes Served: 58078

JAMESTOWN

PRAIRIE POST
(Tues)
PO Box 1760, Jamestown, ND, 58402-1760, USA; tel (701) 952-2796; adv fax (701) 952-0025; e-mail js@jamestownsun.com; web site www.jamestownsun.com
Circulation: 17,000fr; Sworn/Estimate/Non-Audited
Advertising: Open inch rate $11.09
Pub. .... Bruce Henke
Adv. Mgr. .... Gene Keller
Circ. Mgr. .... Jeremy Feldman
Ed. .... Kathy Steiner
Prodn. Mgr. .... Tina Olson
Zip Codes Served: 58401

MINOT

THE TRADING POST
(Tues)
301 4th St SE, Minot, ND, 58701-4066, USA; tel (701) 857-1900; adv tel (701) 857-1963; ed tel (701) 857-1959; fax (701) 857-1907; adv fax (701) 857-1907; e-mail mdnews@minotdailynews.com; adv e-mail jhart@minotdailynews.com
Circulation: 15,000fr; Sworn/Estimate/Non-Audited
Group: Ogden Newspapers Inc.
Adv. Dir. .... Jim Hart
Publisher .... Dan McDonald
Mechanical Specifications: Type page 13 x 21 1/2; E - 6 cols, 1 5/6, 1/6 between; A - 6 cols, 1 5/6, 1/6 between; C - 9 cols, 1 1/3, 1/12 between.
Equipment: ; Presses — 8-G/Urbanite.
Delivery Method: Mail, Newsstand, Racks
Zip Codes Served: 58318, 58329, 58341, 58368, 58384, 58531, 58540, 58575, 58576, 58701, 58703, 58704, 58718, 58725, 58740, 58746, 58752, 58756, 58759, 58763, 58770, 58771, 58784, 58785, 58788, 58790, 58852, 58801, 58849

WAHPETON

SOUTHERN VALLEY SHOPPER
(Mon)
601 Dakota Ave, Wahpeton, ND, 58075-4325, USA; tel (701) 642-8585; fax (701) 642-1501; e-mail ads@wahpetondailynews.com; adv e-mail ads@wahpetondailynews.com; ed e-mail editor@wahpetondailynews.com; web site www.wahpetondailynews.com
Circulation: 13,700fr; Sworn/Estimate/Non-Audited
Advertising: Open inch rate $7.10
Pub. .... Ken Harty
Advt Mgr .... Tara Klostreich
Mechanical Specifications: Email ads@wahpetondailynews.com for specs.
Equipment: Hardware — APP/Mac; Presses — G/Community; Software — InDesign CS5, Adobe/Photoshop 5.0, Baseview/News Edit Pro.
Delivery Method: Mail, Newsstand, Carrier, Racks
Zip Codes Served: 58075, 56520, 58001, 58017, 58018, 58030, 58032, 58040, 58041, 58043, 58053, 58058, 58061, 58060, 58067, 58075, 58077, 58081, 56536, 56296, 56522, 56543, 56553, 56579, 56594, 57224, 57225, 57260, 57570

OHIO

ALLIANCE

MR. THRIFTY
(Thur, Fri)
40 S Linden Ave, Alliance, OH, 44601-2447, USA; tel (330) 821-1200; fax (330) 821-8258; e-mail reviewads@alliancelink.com; web site www.the-review.com
Circulation: 49,284fr; Sworn/Estimate/Non-Audited
Advertising: Open inch rate $22.00Editions: 5— 5 total; Mr. Thrifty 5 (8,035); Mr. Thrifty-4 (14,497); Mr. Thrifty-1 (16,848); Mr. Thrifty-3 (8,636); Mr. Thrifty-2 (16,652);
Pub. .... Charles Dix
Adv. Mgr. .... Jeff Kaplan
Circ. Mgr. .... Ken Pagani
Mng. Ed. .... Sarah Gold
Mechanical Specifications: Type page 13 x 20 1/2; A - 6 cols, 20 1/2, between; C - 6 cols, 20 1/2, between.
Zip Codes Served: 44601, 44641, 44685, 44632, 44615

BELLEVUE

GAZETTE EXTRA
(Mon)
250 Castalia St, Ste E, Bellevue, OH, 44811-1200, USA; tel (419) 483-4190; adv tel (419) 483-4190; fax (419) 483-3737; adv fax (419) 483-3737; adv e-mail sales@gazettepublishingco.com; ed e-mail news@gazettepublishingco.com; web site www.thebellevuegazette.com
Circulation: 7,100fr; Sworn/Estimate/Non-Audited
Advertising: $12.45
Established: 1865
Group: Ohio Community Media, LLCEditions: The Bellevue Gazette
Editor .... Becky Brooks
Equipment: ; Presses — Corporate press
Delivery Method: Mail, Carrier
Zip Codes Served: 44811

BRYAN

THE COUNTYLINE
(Sun)
127 S Walnut St, Bryan, OH, 43506-1718, USA; tel (419) 636-1111; fax (419) 636-8937; e-mail cl@bryantimes.com; web site www.bryantimes.com
Advertising: Open inch rate $10.76
Established: 1963
Mechanical Specifications: Type page 10 3/4 x 13; E - 5 cols, 2 1/4, 1/6 between; A - 5 cols, 2 1/4, 1/6 between; C - 5 cols, 2 1/4, 1/6 between.

CAMBRIDGE

GUERNSEY NOBLE ADVERTISER
(Sun)
61234 Southgate Rd, Cambridge, OH, 43725-8945, USA; tel (740) 432-7077; adv tel (740) 439-2680; fax (740) 439-7072; e-mail advertiser@jadeinc.com; web site www.theadvertiser.net
Circulation: 15,259fr; Sworn/Estimate/Non-Audited
Established: 1987
Gen. Mgr. .... Cindy Pollock
Mechanical Specifications: Type page 10 x 12 1/2; E - 4 cols, 2 3/8, between; A - 4 cols, 2 3/8, between; C - 4 cols, 2 3/8, between.
Zip Codes Served: 43722, 43723, 43725, 43732, 43733, 43741, 43749, 43750, 43755, 43762, 43768, 43772, 43773, 43778, 43780

JEFFERSONIAN ADVANTAGE
(Sun)
831 Wheeling Ave, Cambridge, OH, 43725-2316, USA; tel (740) 439-3531; adv tel (740) 439-3532; fax (740) 439-3533; e-mail sports@daily-jeff.com; web site www.daily-jeff.com
Circulation: 9,098fr; CVC
Advertising: Open inch rate $3.00
Established: 1885
Publisher .... Andrew S. Dix
Adv. Mgr. .... Edward Archibald
Accounting .... Joyce Yontz
Circ. Mgr. .... Chris Cryder
General Manager .... John Kridelbaugh
Mechanical Specifications: Type page 13 x 21 1/2; A - 6 cols, 2 1/16, 1/12 between; C - 9 cols, 1 3/8, 1/18 between.
Equipment: Hardware — APP/Macs, Mk; Presses — G/Community; Software — QPS/QuarkXPress, Multi-Ad, Adobe/Photoshop, Baseview.
Zip Codes Served: 43725
Note: Jeffersonian Co. LLC owns The Daily Jeffersonian in Cambridge, OH. Jeffersonian Co. LLC is part of Dix Communications which is owned by the Wooster Republican Printing Co. Through it's subsidiaries, Alliance Publishing Co. LLC, Ashland Publishing Co. LL

CARROLL

LANCASTER/FAIRFIELD ADVERTISER
(Sun)
3675 Dolson Ct, Carroll, OH, 43112-9721, USA; tel (740) 681-4333; fax (740) 654-5617; e-mail ohioclassified@nncogannett.com; web site www.centralohio.com
Circulation:201,749fr; Sworn/Estimate/Non-Audited
Group: GannettEditions: 8— 8 total; Coshocton County Advertiser (14,500); Hocking Valley Advertiser (10,073); Lancaster/Fairfield Advertiser (35,572); Newark/Licking Advertiser (37,176); Perry County Advertiser (13,800); Pickaway County Advertiser (20,240); Ross County Advertiser
Adv. Mgr. .... Rick Szabrak

CELINA

THE STANDARD SHOPPING NEWS
(Tues)
123 E Market St, PO Box 140, Celina, OH, 45822-1730, USA; tel (419) 586-2371; adv tel (419) 586-2371; ed tel (419) 586-2371; fax (419) 586-6271; adv fax (419) 586-2371; ed fax (419) 586-2371; e-mail fsnyder@dailystandard.com; adv e-mail production@dailystandard.com;; ed e-mail newsroom@dailystandard.com; web site www.dailystandard.com
Circulation:2,700fr; Sworn/Estimate/Non-Audited
Advertising: Open inch rate $2.00
Pub. .... Frank Snyder
Circ. Mgr. .... Diane Buening
Prodn. Mgr. .... Lawrence Smelser
Mechanical Specifications: Type page 13 x 21; E - 6 cols, 2 1/8, between; A - 6 cols, 2 1/8, between; C - 6 cols, 1 1/8, between.
Equipment: ; Presses — Goss
Delivery Method: Mail
Zip Codes Served: 45822, 45826, 45828, 45846, 45860, 45862, 45882, 45883

CHILLICOTHE

ROSS COUNTY ADVERTISER
(Sun)
50 W Main St, Chillicothe, OH, 45601-3103, USA; tel (740) 772-2111; fax (740) 772-9501; web site www.centralohio.com/advertiser
Circulation:24,883fr; Sworn/Estimate/Non-Audited
Group: Gannett
Gen. Mgr. .... Mike Throne

CIRCLEVILLE

PICKAWAY COUNTY ADVERTISER
(Sun)
123 W Main St, Circleville, OH, 43113-1619, USA; tel (740) 477-3386; fax (740) 474-9750; e-mail pickaway@jcpgroup.com; web site www.centralohio.com/advertiser
Circulation:18,000fr; Sworn/Estimate/Non-Audited
Advertising: Open inch rate $36.00
Group: Gannett
Sales Mgr. .... Cris Clark

CLEVELAND

SUN NEWSPAPERS
(Thur)
5510 Cloverleaf Pkwy, Cleveland, OH, 44125-4815, USA; tel (216) 986-2600; fax (216) 986-2401; e-mail sun@sunnews.com; web site www.sunnews.com
Circulation: 52,097pd,39,319fr; AAM
Pres./CEO .... Keith Mathis
Classified Mgr. .... Donna Krause
Circ. Mgr. .... Cathy McBride
Exec. Ed. .... Linda Kinsey
Mgr. Online News .... Bob Palmer

COLUMBUS

OUTLOOK
(Sat)
815 N High St, Ste G, Columbus, OH, 43215-6425, USA; tel (614) 268-8525; adv tel (212) 242-6863; ed tel (614) 268-8525 x7#; fax (614) 261-8200; ed e-mail bvitale@outlook-media.com; web site http://outlookcolumbus.com/
Circulation:10,242fr; Sworn/Estimate/Non-Audited
Advertising: Open inch rate $21.40
Group: Gannett
Pub. .... Cindy George Bealer
Adv. Mgr. .... Bill Anliker
Ed. .... Jill Nevels-Haun
Mechanical Specifications: Type page 13 x 21 1/2; E - 6 cols, 2 1/16, between; A - 6 cols, 2 1/16, between; C - 9 cols, 1 7/8, between.
Equipment: Hardware — APP/Mac; Presses — G; Software — Baseview, QPS/QuarkXPress 8.6.

COSHOCTON

COSHOCTON COUNTY ADVERTISER
(Sun)
550 Main St, Coshocton, OH, 43812-1612, USA; tel (740) 295-3435; fax (740) 623-0618; e-mail coshoctonadv@nncogannett.com; web site www.centralohio.com/advertiser
Circulation:11,000fr; Sworn/Estimate/Non-Audited
Group: Gannett
Adv. Mgr. .... Michael Block
Mechanical Specifications: Type page 10 x 11 1/4; E - 4 cols, 2 3/8, 1/8 between; A - 4 cols, 2 3/8, 1/8 between; C - 8 cols, between.
Zip Codes Served: 43812, 43844, 43824, 43811

COVINGTON

COUNTRY LIVING
(Mon, Mthly)
395 S High St, Covington, OH, 45318-1121, USA; tel (937) 473-2028; fax (937) 473-2500; e-mail arenspub@gmail.com; adv e-mail arenspub@gmail.com; web site www.arenspub.com
Circulation: 15,900pd,17,000fr; Sworn/Estimate/Non-Audited
Advertising: Open inch rate $19.34
Established: 1954
Digital Platform - Mobile: Apple
Adv. Mgr. .... Gary L. Godfrey
Mechanical Specifications: 4 columns x 10 inches or 7.250 inches x 10 inches
Each column is 1.750 inches
Equipment: Hardware — APP/Mac.
Delivery Method: Mail, Carrier, Racks
Zip Codes Served: 45318

PENNY SAVER
(Mon)
395 S High St, Covington, OH, 45318-1121, USA; tel (937) 473-2028; fax (937) 473-3299; e-mail production@woh.rr.com; web site www.arenspub.com
Circulation: 3pd,11,748fr; CVC
Advertising: Open inch rate $10.23
Adv. Mgr. .... Gary L. Godfrey
Equipment: Hardware — APP/Mac; Software — QPS/QuarkXPress, Adobe/PageMaker, Multi-Ad/Creator.
Zip Codes Served: 45302, 45306, 45318, 45333, 45351, 45363, 45388, 45822, 45826, 45845, 45860, 45865, 45869, 45871

STILLWATER VALLEY ADVERTISER
(Wed)
395 S High St, Covington, OH, 45318-1121, USA; tel (937) 473-2028; fax (937) 473-2500; e-mail arenspub@gmail.com; web site www.arenspub.com
Circulation: 123pd,10,776fr; Sworn/Estimate/Non-Audited
Advertising: Open inch rate $11.90
Established: 1954
Digital Platform - Mobile: Apple
Digital Platform - Tablet: Apple iOS
Publisher .... Gary L. Godfrey
Mechanical Specifications: 6 x 16 Tabl; 10 1/4 x 16
Equipment: Hardware — APP/Mac; Software — QPS/QuarkXPress, Adobe/PageMaker, Multi-Ad/Creator.
Delivery Method: Mail, Newsstand, Carrier
Zip Codes Served: 45308, 45318, 45328, 45337, 45339, 45359, 45361, 45383

DEFIANCE

CRESCENT EXTRA
(Fri)
624 W 2nd St, Defiance, OH, 43512-2105, USA; tel (419) 784-5441; fax (419) 784-1492; adv e-mail cnads@crescent-news.com; ed e-mail crescent@crescent-news.com; web site www.crescent-news.com
Circulation:9,500fr; USPS
Advertising: Open inch rate $5.00
Group: Adams Publishing Group, LLC
Publisher .... Mark Ryan
Mng. Ed. .... Dennis Van Scoder
Circulation Mgr. .... Greg Meyers
Mechanical Specifications: Type page 8.75 x 10.25; E - 5 cols, 1/6 between; A - 5 cols, 1/6 between; C - 7 cols, 1/6 between.
Equipment: Hardware — APP/Mac; Presses — ; Software — Adobe/Photoshop, InDesign
Delivery Method: Mail
Zip Codes Served: 43512, 43545

DELPHOS

THE DART
(Mon)
405 N Main St, Delphos, OH, 45833-1577, USA; tel (419) 695-0015; fax (419) 695-4675; ed fax (419) 692-7704; web site www.delphosherald.com
Circulation:4,000fr; Sworn/Estimate/Non-Audited
Advertising: Open inch rate $10.00
Pub. .... Murray Cohen
Gen. Mgr. .... Ray Geary
Zip Codes Served: 45833

ELYRIA

COVERSTORY
(Wed)
225 East Ave, Elyria, OH, 44035-5634, USA; tel (440) 329-7000; fax (440) 329-7272; e-mail ect@ohio.net
Circulation:30,000fr; Sworn/Estimate/Non-Audited
Advertising: Open inch rate $7.45
Pub. .... Arthur Hudnutt
Gen. Mgr. .... Cooper Hudnutt
Adv. Mgr. .... Tom Meecha
Circ. Mgr. .... Gary Cozart
Prodn. Mgr. .... Bill McCartney
Mechanical Specifications: Type page 13 x 22 1/4; E - 6 cols, 2 1/16, 1/8 between; A - 6 cols, 2 1/16, 1/8 between; C - 9 cols, 1 3/8, 1/8 between.
Equipment: ; Presses — G/Metro.
Zip Codes Served: 44035

FREMONT

OTTAWA COUNTY OUTLOOK
(Sat)
1800 E State St, Ste B, Fremont, OH, 43420-4083, USA; tel (419) 334 1059; fax (419) 332-9750; e-mail pcnewsdesk@gannett.com
Circulation:7,000fr; Sworn/Estimate/Non-Audited
Advertising: Open inch rate $10.66
Group: Gannett
Reporter .... Jon Stinchcomb
Mechanical Specifications: Type page 13 x 21 1/2; A - 6 cols, 2 1/16, between; C - 9 cols, 1 3/8, between.
Zip Codes Served: 43452

GALION

WEEKLY AD-VISOR
(Sat)
366 Portland Way N, Galion, OH, 44833-1633, USA; tel (419) 468-1117; fax (419) 468-7255
Circulation: 4,000pd,12,500fr; Sworn/Estimate/Non-Audited
Advertising: Open inch rate $7.20
Pub. .... Vicki Taylor
Circ. Mgr. .... Yvonne Hawes
Ed. .... Cindi Shroyer
Mechanical Specifications: Type page 10 x 20 1/2; E - 6 cols, 1 13/16, 1/8 between; A - 6 cols, 1 13/16, 1/8 between; C - 9 cols, 1 3/16, 1/8 between.
Equipment: Hardware — APP/Mac; Presses — 22-G/Community; Software — QPS/QuarkXPress, Baseview.
Zip Codes Served: 44833

HAMILTON

JOURNAL-NEWS EXTRA
(Mon)
228 Court St, Hamilton, OH, 45011-2820, USA; tel (513) 863-8200; ed tel (513) 863-8200; fax (513) 896-9489; web site www.journal-news.com
Circulation:27,000fr; Sworn/Estimate/Non-Audited
Advertising: Open inch rate $9.85Editions: 2— 2 total; Journal-News EXTRA (17,000); Oxford EXTRA (10,000);
Pub. .... Ann Haffman
Circ. Mgr. .... Mike Stevens
Mechanical Specifications: Type page 13 x 21 1/2; E - 6 cols, 2 1/16, 1/8 between; A - 6 cols, 2 1/16, 1/8 between; C - 10 cols, 1 3/16, 1/8 between.
Zip Codes Served: 45011

HARRISON

MARKET PLACE
(Mon)
307 Harrison Ave, Harrison, OH, 45030-1331, USA; tel (812) 537-0063; fax (513) 367-4593
Circulation: 5,643pd,17,000fr; Sworn/Estimate/Non-Audited
Advertising: Open inch rate $29.50
Pub. .... Joe Awad
Circ. Mgr. .... Dawn Waders
Zip Codes Served: 45030

KENT

THE ADVANTAGE
(Sat)
1050 W Main St, Kent, OH, 44240-2006, USA; tel (330) 541-9400; adv tel (330) 541-9400; ed tel (330) 541-9400; fax (330) 296-2698; adv fax (330) 296-2698; ed fax (330) 296-2698; web site www.recordpub.com

Circulation:9,600fr; Sworn/Estimate/Non-Audited
Advertising: Open inch rate $13.96
Established: 1975
Digital Platform - Mobile: Apple
Digital Platform - Tablet: Apple iOS
Pub. .... David Dix
General Manager
Ron Waite
Marketing Director ....Harry Newman
Mechanical Specifications: Type page 10 3/8 x 21; E - 6 cols, 1 7/8, between; A - 5 cols, 1 7/8, between; C - 5 cols, 1 7/8, between.
Equipment: Hardware — APP/Macs; Presses — Koenig&Bauer; Software — Adobe
Delivery Method: Mail
Zip Codes Served: 44240

LANCASTER

HOCKING VALLEY ADVERTISER
(Sun)
138 W Chestnut St, Lancaster, OH, 43130-4308, USA; tel (740) 654-1321; fax (740) 681-4505; web site www.theadvertiser.net
Circulation:8,000fr; Sworn/Estimate/Non-Audited
Group: Gannett
Ad Manager......................................Dan Nase

LEWIS CENTER

THE BAG
(Sun)
7801 N Central Dr, Lewis Center, OH, 43035-9407, USA; tel (740) 548-2100; adv tel (614) 461-5500; ed tel (740) 548-2100; fax (740) 928-2892; adv fax (740) 928-2892; ed fax (740) 928-2892; e-mail shauck@thisweeknews.com; adv e-mail rkeller@dispatch.com; ed e-mail shauck@thisweeknews.com; web site www.thebag.com
Circulation:811,248fr; CAC
Advertising: Open inch rate $53.00
Gen. Mgr. .... Rebecca Keller
Sr. Web. Producer.................... Stefanie Hauck
Delivery Method: Mail, Carrier
Zip Codes Served: Franklin, Delaware, Fairfield, Hocking, Licking,
Muskinghum, Madison, Marion, Morrow, Perry, Pickaway, Reliable, Ross, and Union

LIMA

THE MARKETPLACE
(Mon)
3515 Elida Rd, Lima, OH, 45807-1538, USA; tel (419) 223-1010; adv tel (419) 993-2040; ed tel (419) 993-2060; fax (419) 229-0426; adv fax (419) 221-2884; ed fax (419) 229-2926; e-mail info@limanews.com; adv e-mail classifieds@limanews.com; ed e-mail limanews@limanews.com; web site www.limanews.com
Circulation:31,000fr; Sworn/Estimate/Non-Audited
Advertising: $10.30
Established: 1994
Group: Civitas Media, LLC-OOB
Mechanical Specifications: Type page 9.88" x 21"; E - 6 cols, 1.5425", .125" between; A - 6 cols, 1.5425", .125" between; C - 6 cols, 1.5425", .125" between.
Equipment: Hardware — PC 486, PC 386; Presses — 6-MAN/Lithoflex; Software — MediaSpan AMP, PMP
Delivery Method: Carrier
Zip Codes Served: 45801, 45804, 45805, 45806, 45807, 45875, 45844, 45876, 45853, 45830, 45893, 45833, 45817, 45808, 45887, 45850, 45854, 45895, 45819, 45888

LORAIN

EXPRESS LINE
(Fri)
1657 Broadway, Lorain, OH, 44052-3439, USA; tel (440) 245-6901; fax (440) 245-5637; ed e-mail letters@morningjournal.com; web site www.morningjournal.com
Circulation:24,000fr; Sworn/Estimate/Non-Audited
Advertising: Open inch rate $10.10
Pub. .... Jeffery Suderok
Adv. Mgr.................................. Ronald D. Beal
Circ. Dir.. Tony Ort
Mechanical Specifications: Type page 12 x 21 1/4; E - 6 cols, between; A - 6 cols, between; C - 9 cols, between.
Equipment: Hardware — 16-APP/Mac, 29-SII/Dakota C-10; Presses — 12-G/Urbanite; Software — Adobe/Photoshop 3.0.5, QPS/QuarkXPress 3.3.2.
Zip Codes Served: 44052

MARION

MARION COUNTY SHOPPER'S COMPASS
(Sun)
909 Pole Lane Rd, Marion, OH, 43302-8524, USA; tel (740) 383-3199; adv tel (740) 383-3199; ed tel (740) 383-3199; fax (740) 383-3299; adv fax (740) 383-3299; ed fax (740) 383-3299; e-mail office@marionshopperscompass.com; adv e-mail maria@marionshopperscompass.com; ed e-mail office@marionshopperscompass.com; web site www.marionshopperscompass.com
Circulation: 0pd,25,863fr; CVC
Advertising: Open inch rate $9.20
Established: 1998
Pub./Gen. Mgr...............................Julia Walsh
Adv. Mgr.......................... Maria Castricone
Delivery Method: Mail
Zip Codes Served: Marion County

MILLERSBURG

THE BARGAIN HUNTER - HOLMES
(Mon)
7368 County Road 623, Millersburg, OH, 44654-9256, USA; tel (330) 674-2300; fax (888) 769-3960; ed e-mail kvalentini@alonovus.com; web site www.alonovus.com
Circulation: 45pd,20,698fr; Sworn/Estimate/Non-Audited
Advertising: Open inch rate $11.99
Established: 1973
Group: AloNovus Corp.
Pres... Michael Mast
Fulfillment Mgr................................Dan Price
Circulation Mgr .... Rick Festi
Editor .... Kyle Valentini
Delivery Method: Mail, Carrier, Racks
Zip Codes Served: 43804, 44610, 44611, 44624, 44627, 44633, 44637, 44638, 44654, 44661, 44681, 44687, 44690

THE BARGAIN HUNTER - TUSCARAWAS
(Mon)
7368 County Road 623, Millersburg, OH, 44654-9256, USA; tel (330) 674-2300; fax (888) 769-3960; ed e-mail kvalentini@alonovus.com; web site www.alonovus.com
Circulation: 0pd,17,604fr; Sworn/Estimate/Non-Audited
Advertising: Open inch rate $11.99
Established: 1973
Group: AloNovus Corp.
Pres... Michael Mast
Fulfillment Mgr................................Dan Price
Ed .... Kyle Valentini
Circulation Mgr .... Rick Festi
Delivery Method: Carrier, Racks
Zip Codes Served: 44622, 44663

THE BARGAIN HUNTER - WAYNE
(Mon)
7368 County Road 623, Millersburg, OH, 44654-9256, USA; tel (330) 674-2300; fax (868) 708-3960; ed e-mail kvalentini@alonovus.com; web site www.alonovus.com
Circulation: 0pd,13,718fr; Sworn/Estimate/Non-Audited
Advertising: Open inch rate $11.99
Established: 1973
Group: AloNovus Corp.
Pres .... Michael Mast
Fulfillment Mgr................................Dan Price
Editor .... Kyle Valentini
Delivery Method: Mail, Carrier, Racks
Zip Codes Served: 44691, 44667, 44676, 44618, 44606, 44676, 44627

TUSCARAWAS BARGAIN HUNTER
(Mon, Fri)
7368 County Road 623, Millersburg, OH, 44654-9256, USA; tel (330) 674-2300; fax (330) 674-2461; ed e-mail kvalentini@alonovus.com; web site www.alonovus.com
Circulation:17,604fr; Sworn/Estimate/Non-Audited
Advertising: Modular
Established: 1973
Group: AloNovus Corp.
Pres .... Michael Mast
Sales Mgr .... Clint Alguire
Circ. Mgr.. Rick Festi
Ed .... Kyle Valentini
Delivery Method: Carrier, Racks
Zip Codes Served: 44622, 44663

MOUNT GILEAD

MORROW COUNTY SHOPPER'S COMPASS
(Mon)
114 Iberia St, Mount Gilead, OH, 43338-1263, USA; tel (419) 947-9234; adv tel (419) 947-9234; ed tel (419) 947-9234; fax (419) 947-1030; adv fax (419) 947-1030; ed fax (419) 947-1030; e-mail scompass@yahoo.com; adv e-mail scompass@yahoo.com; ed e-mail scompass@yahoo.com; web site www.shopperscompass.net
Circulation: 0pd,13,275fr; CVC
Advertising: Open inch rate $5.69
Established: 1969
Pub./Gen. Mgr................................. Jim Walsh
Delivery Method: Mail
Zip Codes Served: Morrow County

MOUNT VERNON

SHOPPER'S MART
(Sun)
18 E Vine St, Mount Vernon, OH, 43050-3226, USA; tel (740) 397-5333; fax (740) 397-1321; e-mail admin@mountvernonnews.com; sports@mountvernonnews.com; web site www.mountvernonnews.com
Circulation:28,000fr; Sworn/Estimate/Non-Audited
Established: 1983
Pub. ....Kay Culbertson
Adv. Mgr....................................T. Corby Wise
Prodn. Mgr.............................Dean Hammons
Equipment: ; Presses — G/Urbanite.
Zip Codes Served: 43050

NAPOLEON

SPOTLITE
(Mon)
595 E Riverview Ave, Napoleon, OH, 43545-1865, USA; tel (419) 592-5055; fax (419) 592-9778; e-mail nwsignal@bright.net; web site www.northwestsignal.net
Circulation:8,500fr; Sworn/Estimate/Non-Audited
Advertising: Open inch rate $8.00

Adv. Mgr..................................... Sally Heaston
Circ. Mgr.....................................John L. Kuser
Ed. .... Brian Koeller
Prodn. Mgr. ....James K. Kuser
Zip Codes Served: 43545

NEW LEXINGTON

TRIBUNE SHOPPING NEWS
(Sun)
399 Lincoln Park Dr, New Lexington, OH, 43764-1078, USA; tel (740) 342-4121; fax (740) 342-4131
Circulation:15,250fr; Sworn/Estimate/Non-Audited
Advertising: Open inch rate $17.15
Adv. Mgr....................................David Shubert
Ed. .... Deb Hutmire
Mechanical Specifications: Type page 13 x 21 1/2; E - 9 cols, 15/16 between; A - 9 cols, 15/16 between.
Zip Codes Served: 43764

NEWARK

NEWARK-LICKING ADVERTISER
(Sat)
22 N 1st St, Newark, OH, 43055-5608, USA; tel (740) 328-8533; fax (740) 328-8582; web site www.theadvertiser.net
Circulation:11,000fr; Sworn/Estimate/Non-Audited
Advertising: Open inch rate $10.00
Group: Gannett
Adv. Mgr...................................... Randy Green
Zip Codes Served: 43055, 43056,

PAULDING

WEEKLY REMINDER
(Mon)
113 S Williams St, Paulding, OH, 45879-1429, USA; tel (419) 399-4015; fax (419) 399-4030; e-mail progress@progressnewspaper.org; adv e-mail dnutter@progressnewspaper.org; web site www.progressnewspaper.org
Circulation:8,200fr; USPS
Advertising: Open inch rate $9.50
Established: 1875
Group: Delphos Herald, Inc.Editions: 52—
Pub. .... Doug Nutter
Mechanical Specifications: 10.5" wide by 21.3" high
Delivery Method: Mail
Zip Codes Served: 45879 45813 45880 45821 45873 45849 45851 45861 45886 45855

PORTSMOUTH

FOCUS
(Sun)
637 6th St, Portsmouth, OH, 45662-3924, USA; tel (740) 353-3101; fax (740) 353-7280; e-mail dtimes@zoomnet.net; web site www.portsmouth-dailytimes.com
Circulation:16,100fr; Sworn/Estimate/Non-Audited
Pub. ....Jim Freeland
Adv. Mgr... Sue Pelfrey
Circ. Mgr.................................... Louanen Blair
Mng. Ed..Art Kuhn
Mechanical Specifications: Type page 13 x 21 1/2; E - 6 cols, 2 1/16, 1/5 between; A - 6 cols, 2 1/16, 1/5 between; C - 9 cols, between.
Equipment: Hardware — APP/Mac; Presses — G/Community; Software — QPS/QuarkXPress, Adobe/Photoshop.

RITTMAN

TRADING POST
(Sun)
PO Box 45, Rittman, OH, 44270-0045, USA; tel (330) 925-3040; fax (330) 927-6890; web site www.tradingpostnewspapers.com
Circulation:65,000fr; Sworn/Estimate/Non-Audited
Advertising: Open inch rate $25.00
Established: 1975Editions: 3— 3 total; Trading Post-East (23,768); Trading Post-Norton (4,300); Trading Post-West (12,796);
Pub. ....Bruce M. Trogdon
Ed. .... Mike Trogdon
Mechanical Specifications: Type page 10 5/16 x 16; E - 8 cols, 1 1/4, between; A - 8 cols, 1 1/4, between.
Equipment: Hardware — APP/Mac G4; Software — QPS/QuarkXPress, Vision Data Classified, Adobe/Photoshop, Multi-Ad/Creator, Baseview/Managing Editor, Class Force.
Zip Codes Served: 44214, 44215, 44217, 44230, 44235, 44251, 44254, 44270, 44273, 44275, 44276, 44281, 44274, 44287, 44645, 44866, 44880, 44203, 44256

SANDUSKY

TSR EXPRESS
(Sun)
314 W Market St, Sandusky, OH, 44870-2410, USA; tel (419) 625-5500; adv tel (419) 625-5500; ed tel (419) 625-5500; fax (419) 625-7211; adv fax (419) 625-1137; ed fax (419) 625-3007; adv e-mail Bobrapp@tandemnetwork.com; ed e-mail mattwesterhold@sanduskyregister.com; web site www.sanduskyregister.com
Circulation:12,249fr; Sworn/Estimate/Non-Audited
Advertising: Open inch rate $5.72
Adv. Dir......................................Mark A. Yocum
Circ. Mgr..William Ney
Pub. ....Tim Parkinson
Mechanical Specifications: Type page 13 x 21 1/2; E - 6 cols, 2, 1/4 between; A - 6 cols, 2, 1/4 between; C - 9 cols, 1 1/3, 1/6 between.
Equipment: Hardware — APP/Mac; Software — Baseview.
Delivery Method: Carrier
Zip Codes Served: 44870, 44839, 44824

SPRINGFIELD

TRI-COUNTY SHOPPERS NEWS
(Sun)
202 N Limestone St, Springfield, OH, 45503-4246, USA; tel (937) 325-7041; fax (937) 328-0321
Circulation:66,425fr; Sworn/Estimate/Non-Audited
Pub. ....Steve Sidlo
Adv. Mgr....................................... Steve Roche
Media Consultant .... Eric Sirons
Zip Codes Served: 45502

SWANTON

THE KEY SHOPPERS' NEWS, INC.
(Tues)
2961 US Highway 20A, P.O. Box 35, Swanton, OH, 43558-9709, USA; tel (419) 826-1010; adv tel (419) 826-1010; fax (419) 826-3655; adv fax (419) 826-3655; e-mail keyshoppersnews@embarqmail.com
Circulation:24,084fr; CVC
Advertising: Open inch rate $12.00
Established: 1972Editions: 1—
Founder .... Robert R. Self
Pres. .... Hazel Wood
Circulation Manager .... Dave Mann
Mechanical Specifications: Type page 10 1/8 x 16.
Equipment: Hardware — PC's; Software — DTI/Ad-Builder.
Delivery Method: Carrier
Zip Codes Served: 43558

VAN WERT

WEST CENTRAL OHIO SHOPPING GUIDE
(Sun)
700 Fox Rd, Van Wert, OH, 45891-2441, USA; tel (419) 238-2285; fax (419) 238-0447; e-mail info@timesbulletin.com; web site www.timesbulletin.com
Circulation:14,200fr; Sworn/Estimate/Non-Audited
Group: Delphos Herald, Inc.
Publisher..Kirk Dougal
Mechanical Specifications: Type page 13 x 21 1/2; E - 6 cols, 1 13/16, 3/16 between; A - 6 cols, 1 13/16, 3/16 between; C - 8 cols, 1 3/8, 1/8 between.
Equipment: Hardware — APP/Macs; Presses — G/Community; Software — QPS/QuarkXPress, Baseview/Class Act.
Zip Codes Served: 45891

WILLARD

SHOPPER'S HELPER
(Tues)
211 S Myrtle Ave, Willard, OH, 44890-1407, USA; tel (419) 752-3854; fax (419) 933-2031; e-mail globe@sdgnewsgroup.com; web site http://www.sdgnewsgroup.com/
Circulation:13,234fr; Sworn/Estimate/Non-Audited
Pub. .... Scott Gove
Adv. Mgr...................................... Karla Souslin
Circ. Mgr.. Sally Roth
Ed. .... Jane Ernsberger
Delivery Method: Mail
Zip Codes Served: 44837, 44890, 44807, 44855, 44865, 44878, 44847, 44887, 44854

WILLOUGHBY

CHATTER
(Thur)
7085 Mentor Ave, Willoughby, OH, 44094-7948, USA; tel (440) 954-7159; fax (440) 951-0917; adv e-mail publisher@news-herald.com; ed e-mail editor@news-herald.com; web site www.news-herald.com
Circulation:5,159fr; AAM
Advertising: Open inch rate $20.10
Circ. Mgr...............................Josephine Camino
Ed. ....Tricia Ambrose
Prodn. Mgr. ....Brian McCloskey
Mechanical Specifications: Type page 13 x 21; E - 6 cols, 2 1/16, 1/8 between; A - 6 cols, 2 1/6, 1/8 between; C - 8 cols, 1 5/8, 1/16 between.
Equipment: Hardware — APP/Mac G3/233, APP/Mac 4400-200; Presses — 7-G/Metroliner, 2-G/3:2; Software — Baseview/IQUE (313).
Zip Codes Served: 44094

WOODSFIELD

MONROE COUNTY SENTINEL
(Mon)
103 E Court St, Woodsfield, OH, 43793-1110, USA; tel (740) 472-0734; fax (740) 472-0735; e-mail monroecountybeacon@sbcglobal.net; web site www.mcbeacon.com
Circulation:7,450fr; Sworn/Estimate/Non-Audited
Advertising: Open inch rate $13.25
Group: Delphos Herald, Inc.
Mechanical Specifications: Type page 13 x 21; E - 6 cols, 1 3/4, between; A - 6 cols, 1 7/8, between; C - 8 cols, 1 1/2, between.

XENIA

BEAVERCREEK NEWS-CURRENT EXTRA
(Wed)
1836 W Park Sq, Xenia, OH, 45385-2668, USA; tel (937) 372-4444; fax (937) 294-2981; ed e-mail membs@civitasmedia.com; web site http://beavercreeknewscurrent.com/
Circulation:18,000fr; Sworn/Estimate/Non-Audited
Advertising: Open inch rate $12.00Diane Chiddister

GREENE COUNTY SHOPPER
(Thur)
30 S Detroit St, Xenia, OH, 45385-3502, USA; tel (937) 372-4444; fax (937) 372-3385; e-mail info@brownpublishing.com; web site www.brownpublishing.com
Circulation:3,500fr; Sworn/Estimate/Non-Audited
Advertising: Open inch rate $8.00
Pub. .... Mike Savage
Adv. Mgr.............................. Barb Van de Ventor
Circ. Mgr......................................Gina Riefstahl

OKLAHOMA

EL RENO

EL RENO TRIBUNE
(Wed, Sat)
102 E Wade St, El Reno, OK, 73036-2742, USA; tel (405) 262-5180; fax (405) 262-3541; e-mail rdyer@elrenotribune.com; adv e-mail ethompson@elrenotribune.com; ed e-mail sdyer@elrenotribune.com ; web site www.ertribune.com
Circulation: 4,200pd,5,500fr; Sworn/Estimate/Non-Audited
Advertising: $5
Established: 1934
Digital Platform - Mobile: Windows
Digital Platform - Tablet: Windows 7
Pub. .... Ray T. Dyer
Pub. .... Sean E. Dyer
Adv. Mgr...Erin Dyer
Circ. Mgr... Mark Lyle
Ed. .... Brett Jones
Equipment: ; Presses — Harris V-30
Delivery Method: Mail, Racks
Zip Codes Served: 73036

ENID

SHOPPER'S EDGE
(Fri)
122 W Owen K Garriott Rd, Enid, OK, 73701-5618, USA; tel (580) 233-1722; fax (580) 233-3764; adv e-mail classified@theshoppersedge.net; web site www.theshoppersedge.net
Circulation:24,500fr; Sworn/Estimate/Non-Audited
Advertising: Open inch rate $8.25
Group: Community Newspaper Holdings, Inc.
Pub. ....Lisa Bland-Selix
Mechanical Specifications: Type page 10 x 13.
Zip Codes Served: 73702

LAWTON

AMERICAN CLASSIFIEDS
(Thur)
1811 NW Cache Rd, Lawton, OK, 73507-4519, USA; tel (580) 357-5311; fax (508) 357-0271; e-mail americanclassified@swbell.net; web site www.americanclassifieds.com
Circulation:30,000fr; Sworn/Estimate/Non-Audited
Advertising: Open inch rate $7.68

LINDSAY

SHOPPER NEWS NOTE
(Wed)
318 S Main St, Lindsay, OK, 73052-5636, USA; tel (405) 756-3169; fax (405) 756-8609; e-mail theshopper@valornet.com
Circulation: 42pd,6,203fr; Sworn/Estimate/Non-Audited
Advertising: Open inch rate $6.58
Established: 1981
Vice-Pres./Publisher....................Holly Belknap
Gen. Mgr.................................William Belknap
Mechanical Specifications: Type page 11.75 x 21.5; E - 6 cols, 1.8192, 1/8 between; A - 6 cols, 1.8192, 1/8 between; C - 6 cols, 1.8192, 1/8 between.
Equipment: Hardware — 5-APP/Mac.
Delivery Method: Mail
Zip Codes Served: 73002, 73010, 73011, 73031, 73052, 73057, 73433, 73434

MIAMI

MIAMI NEWS-RECORD
(Tues, Wed, Fri) (TMC on Wednesday)
14 1st Ave NW, Miami, OK, 74354-6224, USA; tel (918) 542-5533; fax (918) 542-1903; adv e-mail advertising@miaminewsrecord.com; classifieds@miaminewsrecord.com; ed e-mail news@miaminewsrecord.com; web site www.miamiok.com
Circulation: 3,100pd,1,500fr; Sworn/Estimate/Non-Audited
Advertising: Open inch rate $10.44
Established: 1908
Group: GateHouse Media, Inc.Editions: Miami News-Record 3100, Northeast Oklahoma Trading Post 1500
Digital Platform - Mobile: Apple
Digital Platform - Tablet: Apple iOS
Publisher...................................Cheryl Franklin
Managing Editor ....Dorothy Ballard
Sports Editor.......................................Jim Ellis
Equipment: Hardware — Apple; Presses — Outsourced; Software — TownNews TCMS, SaxoTech
Delivery Method: Mail, Newsstand, Racks
Zip Codes Served: 74354, 74355, 74343, 74331, 74358, 74339, 74363, 74370

NEWCASTLE

EARLY BIRD EXPRESS
(Wed)
120 NE 2nd St, Ste 102, Newcastle, OK, 73065-4185, USA; tel (405) 387-5277; fax (405) 387-9863; adv e-mail ads@newcastlepacer.com; classifieds@newcastlepacer.com; ed e-mail editor@newcastlepacer.com; news@newcastlepacer.com; web site www.newcastlepacer.com
Circulation:14,841fr; Sworn/Estimate/Non-Audited
Advertising: Open inch rate $10.65
Pub. ....Robin Wilson
Adv. Dir..Kim Noe
Mng. Ed................................ Victoria Middleton
Zip Codes Served: 73065

OKLAHOMA CITY

BUYER'S EDGE
9000 Broadway Ext, Oklahoma City, OK, 73114-3708, USA; tel (405) 475-3575

POTEAU

MINI PENNY
(Wed)
804 N Broadway St, Poteau, OK, 74953-3503, USA; tel (918) 647-3188; fax (918) 647-8198; e-mail publisher@poteaudailynews.com; adv e-mail addirector@poteaudailynews.com; ed e-mail editor@poteaudailynews.com; web site www.poteaudailynews.com
Circulation:5,100fr; Sworn/Estimate/Non-Audited
Advertising: Open inch rate $8.50
Established: 1886
Group: Heritage Publications (2003) Inc.
General Manager/Circulation Director......David McKimmey
Mechanical Specifications: broadsheet
Delivery Method: Racks

THE SHOPPER'S GUIDE
(Wed)
804 N Broadway St, Poteau, OK, 74953-3503, USA; tel (918) 647-3188; fax (918) 647-8198; e-mail publisher@poteaudailynews.com; adv e-mail addirector@poteaudailynews.com; ed e-mail editor@poteaudailynews.com; web site www.poteaudailynews.com
Circulation:7,200fr; Sworn/Estimate/Non-Audited
Advertising: Open inch rate $8.50
Established: 1886
Group: Heritage Publications (2003) Inc.
Pub... Kim McConnell
Mechanical Specifications: 23 inch tabloid
Delivery Method: Carrier, Racks
Zip Codes Served: 74901 74902 74930 74932 74937 74940 74951 74953 74956 74959 74941 74571 74949 74947 74944 74943 74942 74935 74577 74549 74563 74955 74402—03 74948

THE SHOPPERS GUIDE
(Wed)
804 N Broadway St, Poteau, OK, 74953-3503, USA; tel (918) 647-3188; fax (918) 647-8198; adv e-mail publisher@poteaudailynews.com; ed e-mail editor@poteaudailynews.com; web site www.poteaudailynews.com
Circulation:8,500fr; Sworn/Estimate/Non-Audited
Advertising: Open inch rate $2.00
Group: Horizon Publications Inc.
General Manager/Circulation Director......David McKimmey
Mechanical Specifications: Type page 9 7/8 x 13; E - 6 cols, 1 1/2, 1/6 between; A - 6 cols, 1 1/2, 1/6 between; C - 6 cols, 1 1/2, 1/6 between.
Equipment: Hardware — APP/Macs; Presses — KP/News King; Software — InDesign
Delivery Method: Carrier, Racks
Zip Codes Served: 74902, 74930, 74932, 74937, 74940, 74951, 74953, 74956, 74959, 74966, 74939, 74571, 74947, 74942, 74577

TULSA

AMERICAN CLASSIFIEDS
(Thur)
2626 S Sheridan Rd, Ste 100, Tulsa, OK, 74129-1031, USA; tel (918) 836-0707; fax (918) 836-0719; e-mail tulsa.americanclassifieds@yahoo.com; web site www.americanclassifieds.com
Circulation:35,000fr; Sworn/Estimate/Non-Audited
Advertising: Open inch rate $7.00
Pub. .... Linda Enlow

TULSA PENNYSAVER
(Thur)
8545 E 41st St, Tulsa, OK, 74145-3305, USA; tel (918) 663-1414
Circulation:35,000fr; Sworn/Estimate/Non-Audited
Advertising: Open inch rate $8.35
Established: 1965
Pub. .... Mike Brown
Gen. Mgr. ....Charles Cagle
Opns. Dir. .... Bill Roberts

OREGON

BEND

CENTRAL OREGON NICKEL ADS
(Thur)
1777 SW Chandler Ave, Bend, OR, 97702-3200, USA; tel (541) 382-0977; fax (541) 382-5250; adv e-mail ads@conickelads.com; web site www.conickelads.com
Circulation: 0pd,10,000fr; VAC
Advertising: Open inch rate $7.00
Established: 1985
Group: Western Communications, Inc.
Sales Specialist ....Debbie Coffman
Tonya McKiernan
Equipment: Hardware — APP/Mac G3.
Delivery Method: Newsstand, Racks
Zip Codes Served: 97701

COOS BAY

SOUTH COAST SHOPPER
(Thur)
PO Box 1440, Coos Bay, OR, 97420-0399, USA; tel (541) 269-0310; adv tel (541) 269-9034; fax (541) 269-2675; adv fax (541) 269-2675; e-mail shopper@scod.com; web site www.southcoastshopper.com
Circulation: 4pd,18,380fr; CVC
Advertising: Open inch rate $30.00
Established: 1982
Sales Mgr...................................... Ron Mitchell
Ed. .... Cliff Chambers
Zip Codes Served: 97420

HERMISTON

THE NICKEL WANT AD NEWSPAPER
(Thur)
1055 N 1st St, Hermiston, OR, 97838-1338, USA; web site www.thenickelonline.com
Circulation: 0pd,16,023fr; VAC
Advertising: Open inch rate $6.85Tiffany Rieg

KLAMATH FALLS

THE NICKEL
(Thur)
2051 Radcliffe Ave, Klamath Falls, OR, 97601-3303, USA; tel (541) 883-2292; fax (541) 882-7716; e-mail classified@klamathfallsnickel.com; sales@klamathfallsnickel.com; web site www.klamathfallsnickel.com
Circulation:19,500fr; Sworn/Estimate/Non-Audited
Advertising: Open inch rate $5.75
Group: Adams Publishing Group, LLC
Gen. Mgr. .... Roz Brooks
Adv. Mgr. .... Anita Moore

LA GRANDE

THE NICKEL - LA GRANDE
(Thur)
1112 1/2 Adams Ave, La Grande, OR, 97850-2699, USA; web site www.lagrandenickel.com
Circulation:13,982fr; CVCSusy McBride

LAKE OSWEGO

BEST BITES & BUYS
(Mthly)
6972 Montauk Cir, Lake Oswego, OR, 97035-7826, USA; tel (503) 598-3468; fax (503) 684-0619; e-mail mike@bestpublications.net; web site www.bestpublications.net
Circulation:10,000fr; USPS
Advertising: Open column inch (21 per page) rate $80.00
Established: 1994
Digital Platform - Mobile: Apple, Android
Publisher.......................... Michael R. Olmstead
Prodn. Mgr. .... Micheal R. Olmstead
Mechanical Specifications: Type page 8x10 1/2; A - 2 cols, 1/4 between.
Equipment: Hardware — PC; Software — Corel Draw X5, Microsoft/Windows 7, Adobe/Photoshop CS.
Delivery Method: Mail
Zip Codes Served: 97062

MEDFORD

MEDFORD NICKEL
(Thur)
111 N Fir St, Medford, OR, 97501-2772, USA; tel (541) 776-4422; adv tel (541) 776-4422; ed tel (541) 776-4422; fax (541) 776-4390; adv fax (541) 776-4390; ed fax (541) 776-4390; e-mail gsingletary@mailtribune.com; adv e-mail dderose@mailtribune.com; ed e-mail mkrueger@mailtribune.com; web site www.medfordnickel.com
Circulation: 0pd,25,800fr; VAC
Advertising: Open inch rate $8.24
Established: 1982
Group: Dow Jones Local Media Group
Pub./Gen. Mgr......................... Grady Singletary
Delivery Method: Mail, Racks
Zip Codes Served: Jackson County

NEWBERG

VALLEY CLASSIFIEDS
(Wed)
500 E Hancock St, Newberg, OR, 97132-2898, USA; tel (503) 538-2181; fax (503) 538-1632; e-mail thegraphic@eaglenewspapers.com
Circulation:5,500fr; Sworn/Estimate/Non-Audited
Advertising: Open inch rate $8.45
Established: 1888
Pub. .... Allen Herriges
Adv. Mgr. .... Monty Gant
Ed. .... Gary Allen
Zip Codes Served: 97132

ONTARIO

TREASURE VALLEY REMINDER
(Thur)
1160 SW 4th St, Ontario, OR, 97914-4365, USA; tel (541) 889-5387; adv tel (541) 889-5387; fax (541) 889-3347; adv fax (541) 889-3347; e-mail Johnd@argusobserver.com; adv e-mail N/A; web site www.argusobserver.com
Circulation: 0pd,16,340fr; VAC
Advertising: Open inch rate $2.80 Only pickup from Argus Observer Only
Established: 1897
Group: Wick Communications
Pub. .... John Dillon
Mechanical Specifications: Type page 10 x 21 1/2; E - 6 cols, between; A - 6 cols, between; C - 9 cols, between.
Equipment: ; Presses — G/Community.
Delivery Method: Carrier
Zip Codes Served: 97914, 97913, 97918, 97901, 97907, 83661, 83619, 83655, 83672, 83612 and 83660.

PORTLAND

NICKEL ADS - CENTRAL PORTLAND
(Fri)
12151 NE Halsey St, Ste 105, Portland, OR, 97220-2042, USA; web site www.nickelads.com
Circulation:30,434fr; CACGina Alford

NICKEL ADS - EAST PORTLAND
(Thur)
12151 NE Halsey St, Ste 105, Portland, OR, 97220-2042, USA; web site www.nickelads.com
Circulation:26,260fr; Sworn/Estimate/Non-AuditedGina Alford

NICKEL ADS - MID VALLEY
(Fri)
12151 NE Halsey St, Ste 105, Portland, OR, 97220-2042, USA; web site www.nickelads.com
Circulation:24,868fr; CACGina Alford

NICKEL ADS - WEST PORTLAND
(Thur)
12151 NE Halsey St, Ste 105, Portland, OR, 97220-2042, USA; web site www.nickelads.com
Circulation:21,684fr; Sworn/Estimate/Non-AuditedGina Alford

NICKEL ADS PORTLAND, OREGON
(Fri)
6605 SE Lake Rd, Portland, OR, 97222-2161, USA; tel (971) 204-7759; adv tel (971) 204-7759; fax (503) 620-3433; adv fax (503) 620-3433; e-mail istanton@pamplinmedia.com; adv e-mail istanton@commnewspapers.com; web site www.community-classifieds.com
Circulation:80,000fr; Sworn/Estimate/Non-Audited
Advertising: Open inch rate $12.85
Established: 1967
Group: Pamplin Media/ Community NewspapersEditions: 1— Nickel Ads-Nickel Ads-E. Portland (80,000);
Sr. commercial Sales Rep........... Ilene Stanton
Mechanical Specifications: Type page: full page: 10.25x10.25
Equipment: Hardware — APP/Mac; Presses — G, Dauphin, Ryobi; Software — Multi-Ad/Creator 4.0, QPS/QuarkXPress 4.0, Adobe/Photoshop 5.5, Adobe/Illustrator 9.0.
Delivery Method: Racks
Zip Codes Served: Portland Metro area

ROSEBURG

UMPQUA SHOPPER
(Tues)
345 NE Winchester St, Roseburg, OR, 97470-3328, USA; tel (541) 672-3321; adv tel (541) 957-4226; ed tel (541) 957-4210; fax (541) 957-5925; e-mail nrsupport@nrtoday.com; adv e-mail classifieds@nrtoday.com; ed e-mail creed@nrtoday.com; web site www.nrtoday.com
Circulation:33,000fr; Sworn/Estimate/Non-Audited
Advertising: Open inch rate $18.53Editions: 3— 3 total; Umpqua Shopper-Central (9,247); Umpqua Shopper-North (8,539); Umpqua Shopper-South (8,807);
Pub. .... Mark Raymond
Zip Codes Served: 97479

TILLAMOOK

TILLAMOOK COUNTY SHOPPER LLC
(Tues)
1011 Main Ave, Tillamook, OR, 97141-3817, USA; tel (503) 842-7116; fax (503) 842-7116;

e-mail shopper1@gorge.net
Circulation:14,500fr; Sworn/Estimate/Non-Audited
Advertising: Open inch rate $5.50
Established: 2000
Pub. ....Jim Pittman
Mechanical Specifications: Type page 11 1/2 x 17; A - 6 cols, 1 5/8, 1/8 between; C - 6 cols, 1 5/8, 1/8 between.
Equipment: Hardware — 3-IBM/PC; Software — Adobe CS4
Zip Codes Served: 97141, 97130, 97131, 97147, 97136, 97118, 97107, 97134, 97108, 97122, 97112, 97135, 97149

PENNSYLVANIA

BENSALEM

NORTHEAST TIMES
(Wed)
3412 Progress Dr, Ste C, Bensalem, PA, 19020-5817, USA; tel (215) 354-3000; adv tel (215) 354-3000; ed tel (215) 354-3030; fax (215) 244-1406; adv fax (215) 244-1406; ed fax (215) 244-1406; e-mail asanzick@bsmphilly.com; adv e-mail asanzick@bsmphilly.com; ed e-mail pronews@bsmphilly.com; web site northeasttimes.com
Circulation:100,000fr; Sworn/Estimate/Non-Audited
Established: 1934
Group: Broad Street Media
Advertising Representative .... Alice Sanzick
Mechanical Specifications: Tab size (10" x 10")
Delivery Method: Carrier
Zip Codes Served: 19115,19152,19111,19149,19116,19135,19136,19152,19154,19114, 19124

BLOOMSBURG

AROUND THE HOUSE
(Sat)
3185 Lackawanna Ave, Bloomsburg, PA, 17815-3329, USA; tel (570) 784-2121; adv tel (570) 387-1234 ext 1216; ed tel (570) 387-1234 ext 1301; fax (570) 784-9226; adv fax (570) 416-0220; ed fax (570) 784-9226; adv e-mail adv@pressenterprise.net; ed e-mail news@pressenterprise.net; web site www.pressenterpriseonline.com
Circulation:23,246fr; Sworn/Estimate/Non-Audited
Advertising: Open inch rate $20.10
Pub. ....Brandon R. Eyerly
Adv. Dir.................................Sandra J. Sterner
Circ. Mgr.....................................Don Whitmire
Ed. ....Jim Sachetti
Mng. Ed.....................................Dean Kashner
Prodn. Mgr. ....Bill Bason
Mechanical Specifications: Type page 11 5/8 x 21 1/2; E - 6 cols, 1 13/16, 1/8 between; A - 6 cols, 1 13/16, 1/8 between; C - 9 cols, 1 1/8, 1/8 between.
Equipment: Hardware — APP/Macs; Presses — G, HI, Tensor; Software — Multi-Ad/Creator 3.8.1.
Delivery Method: Mail
Zip Codes Served: 17815, 17821, 18603, 17814, 17820, 17824, 17856, 17859,17868, 17868, 18631, 18635, 18655, 18660

BRADFORD

BRADFORD ERA
(Mon)
43 Main St, Bradford, PA, 16701-2019, USA; tel (814) 368-3173; fax (814) 362-6510; e-mail info@bradfordera.com; ed e-mail news@bradfordera.com; web site www.bradfordera.com
Circulation: 8,476pd,43fr; VAC
Advertising: Open inch rate $13.32
Group: Community Media Group
Adv. Mgr...Jill Henry
Ed. ....John H. Satterwhite
Mng. Ed.......................Marty Robacker Wilder
Prodn. Mgr. ....Linda Cardamone
Mechanical Specifications: Type page 13 x 21; E - 6 cols, 2 1/18, 1/6 between; A - 6 cols, 2 1/18, 1/6 between; C - 9 cols, 1 1/9, 1/12 between.
Equipment: Hardware — 8-APP/Macs; Presses — HI/V-15D; Software — C-Text, Multi-Ad/Creator 4.0.1, Adobe/Photoshop 4.0, Adobe/Illustrator 6.0, QPS/QuarkXPress 3.3.

CHAMBERSBURG

THE FRANKLIN SHOPPER
(Wed)
25 Penncraft Ave, Fl 4, Chambersburg, PA, 17201-5600, USA; tel (717) 263-0359; fax (717) 263-1314; e-mail manager@franklinshopper.com; adv e-mail ads@franklinshopper.com; distribution@franklinshopper.com; web site www.franklinshopper.com
Circulation: 0pd,55,297fr; VAC
Advertising: Open inch rate $20.12 Full Circulation
Established: 1984
Group: Blue Ridge Publishing Co.Editions: 4—4 total; Franklin Shopper-Central (24,258); Franklin Shopper-Northern (7,711); Franklin Shopper-Southern (13,045); Franklin Shopper-Washington Co. (MD) (10,500);
Digital Platform - Mobile: Apple
Pub. .... Margaret Booth-Ehle
Office Mgr. ....Shirley Paylor
General Manager ....Rick Heckman
Art Dir...Mark Hartman
Dist. Mgr................................ Beverly McClure
Business Manager.....................Teresa Straley
Sales Manager ....Carol Dibiase
Mechanical Specifications: Type page 10 x 16; E - 6 cols, 1 3/8, 3/16 between; A - 6 cols, 1 3/8, 3/16 between; C - 6 cols, 1 3/8, 3/16 between.
Equipment: Hardware — Mac Platform computers; Software — Multi-Ad/Creator 2.0,MediaSpan, QPS/QuarkXPress, Adobe/Illustrator.
Delivery Method: Carrier, Racks
Zip Codes Served: 17201, 17210, 17211, 17212, 17214, 17217, 17219, 17220, 17221, 17222, 17224, 17225, 17231, 17232, 17235, 17236, 17240, 17241, 17244, 17246, 17247, 17250, 17251, 17252, 17254, 17256, 17261, 17263, 17265, 17266, 17268, 17270, 17275

COCHRANTON

AREA SHOPPER
(Sat)
4177 Rt 19, Cochranton, PA, 16314, USA; tel (814) 425-7272; fax (814) 425-7311; e-mail lwilson@theareashopper.com; web site www.theareashopper.com
Circulation:80,000fr; Sworn/Estimate/Non-Audited
Advertising: Open inch rate $12.90
Established: 1847Editions: 2— 2 total; North Area Shopper; South Area Shopper;
Ed. ....Simon Miller
Prodn. Mgr. ....Brian Miller
Zip Codes Served: 16406

COOPERSBURG

PENNY POWER
(Wed)
202 S 3rd St, Coopersburg, PA, 18036-2150, USA; tel (610) 282-4808; fax (610) 282-1932; e-mail sales@pennypowerads.com; web site www.pennypowerads.com
Circulation: 0pd,71,963fr; CVC
Advertising: Open inch rate $32.35
Established: 1981
Digital Platform - Mobile: Windows
Pub. ....Cecile Brogan
Adv. Mgr. ....Patricia Young
Patricia Holzer
Circulation/Preprint Manager......Dan Krochmal
Mechanical Specifications: Type page 10 5/16 x 16; E - 6 cols, 1 1/2, between; A - 6 cols, 1 1/2, between.
Equipment: ; Software — Adobe/Acrobat, Multi Ad Creator, QPS/QuarkXPress, Adobe/Photoshop
AdMax
Windows 10
Delivery Method: Mail
Zip Codes Served: 18036, 18060, 18015, 18055, 18034, 18081, 18972, 18921, 18920, 18953, 18077, 18039, 18930, 18942, 18951, 18981, 18968, 18935, 18955, 18970, 18947, 18949, 18950, 18910, 18916, 18923, 18902, 18944, 18927, 18962, 18911, 18960, 18917, 18964, 18969

EAST STROUDSBURG

THE POCONO SHOPPER
(Wed)
96 S Courtland St, East Stroudsburg, PA, 18301-2827, USA; tel (570) 421-4800; fax (570) 421-4255; e-mail pshopper@ptd.net; web site www.poconoshopper.com
Circulation: 9,014pd,187fr; AAM
Advertising: Open inch rate $12.96
Group: Times-Shamrock CommunicationsEditions: 2— 2 total; Pocono Shopper-North; Pocono Shopper-South;
Gen. Mgr. ....Kevin Brislin
Zip Codes Served: 18301

EBENSBURG

PENNYSAVER
(Wed)
437 S Center St, Ste 2, Ebensburg, PA, 15931-1972, USA; tel (814) 472-8600; fax (814) 472-9292; web site www.tradersguide.com
Circulation:8,000fr; Sworn/Estimate/Non-Audited
Advertising: Open inch rate $8.25
Established: 1983
Group: Target Media Partners
Ed. ....Susan Shank
Prodn. Mgr. ....Cathy Hayduk
Mechanical Specifications: Type page 10 3/8 x 13; E - 6 cols, 1 5/8, between; A - 6 cols, 1 5/8, between.
Zip Codes Served: 15900,16600,15500,15700

TRADERS GUIDE
(Wed)
437 S Center St, Ebensburg, PA, 15931-1972, USA; tel (814) 472-8600; adv tel (814) 472-8600; fax (814) 472-9292; e-mail sue@tradersguide.com; adv e-mail sue@tradersguide.com; web site http://www.tradersguide.com
Circulation: 5,000pd,250fr; Sworn/Estimate/Non-Audited
Advertising: Open inch rate $8.50
Established: 1983
Group: Target Mediap Partners
Ed. ....Susan J. Shank
Prodn ....Cathy Haytuk
Circulation Manager .... Michael Moyer
Mechanical Specifications: Type page 10 3/8 x 13; E - 6 cols, 1 1/2, between; A - 6 cols, 1 1/2, between.
Equipment: Hardware — 5-APP/Mac, 12-PCs; Software — Multi-Ad/Creator 3.8, Ad-Force.
Delivery Method: Mail, Newsstand, Racks
Zip Codes Served: 159,166,155,157

ELLWOOD CITY

THIS WEEK
(Sat)
501 Lawrence Ave, Ellwood City, PA, 16117-1927, USA; tel (724) 758-5573; fax (724) 758-2410; e-mail ecledger@hotmail.com; web site http://www.ellwoodcityledger.com/
Circulation:5,000fr; Sworn/Estimate/Non-Audited
Pub. ....Alan Buncher
Circ. Mgr................................Crete Crawford
Mechanical Specifications: Type page 13 x 21 1/2; E - 6 cols, 2 1/12, 1/8 between; A - 6 cols, 2 1/12, 1/8 between; C - 6 cols, 2 1/12, 1/8 between.
Equipment: Hardware — PC, APP/Mac; Presses — G/Community; Software — MS/Word, Baseview.

ERIE

ERIE PENNY SAVER
(Mthly)
3723 Elmwood Ave, Erie, PA, 16508-2473, USA; e-mail pennysavererie@gmail.com
Circulation: 0pd,68,778fr; CVC
Advertising: N/A
Established: 1993
Pub./Gen. Mgr.................................Jeff Hayden
Delivery Method: Mail, Carrier
Zip Codes Served: Erie County

EVERETT

SHOPPER'S GUIDE
(Sat, Sun)
6 E Main St, Everett, PA, 15537-1256, USA; tel (814) 653-1151; fax (814) 652-9544; e-mail shopperguide@embarqmail.com
Circulation: 69pd,23,548fr; Sworn/Estimate/Non-Audited
Advertising: Open inch rate $11.50Editions: 2—2 total; Weekly Guide-North (11,144); Weekly Guide-South (18,356);
Digital Platform - Mobile: Apple
Publisher...................................Joseph Beegle
Ed. ....Holly Claycomb
Mechanical Specifications: Type page 10 5/8 x 13; E - 6 cols, 1 1/2, 1/8 between; A - 6 cols, 1 1/2, 1/8 between; C - 6 cols, 1 1/2, 1/8 between.
Equipment: Hardware — APP/Mac; Presses — G/Urbanite; Software — QPS/QuarkXPress.
Zip Codes Served: 16602

FORT WASHINGTON

MONTGOMERY NEWSPAPERS
(Sun)
290 Commerce Dr, Fort Washington, PA, 19034-2400, USA; tel (215) 542-0200; fax (215) 643-9475; adv e-mail classifieds@montgomerynews.com; web site www.montgomerynews.com
Circulation: 8,113pd,784fr; CAC
Established: 1896
Pub. ....Elizabeth Wilson
Circ. Mgr......................................John Maguire
Note: Montgomery Newspapers also owns one twice-yearly, two quarterly and seven monthly publications.

GROVE CITY

MARKET GUIDE
(Wed, Sat)
201 Erie St, Ste A, Grove City, PA, 16127-1659, USA; tel (724) 458-5010; fax (724) 458-1609; adv e-mail alliednews@gmail.com; web site www.alliednews.com
Circulation:10,000fr; USPS

Advertising: Open inch rate $16.91
Established: 1869
Group: CNHI
Publisher....................................... Sharon Sorg
Delivery Method: Mail, Newsstand, Carrier, Racks
Zip Codes Served: 16127

HAMBURG

EAST PENN VALLEY MERCHANDISER

(Wed)
6 N 3rd St, Hamburg, PA, 19526-1502, USA; tel (610) 562-2267; adv tel (610) 562-2267; fax (610) 562-2770; adv fax (610) 562-2770; e-mail George@windsorpress.com; adv e-mail DIsplay@windsorpress.com; web site www.windsorpress.com
Circulation: 27pd,40,454fr; CVC
Advertising: Open inch rate $9.26
Established: 1958
Digital Platform - Mobile: Apple
Circ. Mgr................................ David Wisniewski
Prodn. Mgr............................ George T. Mitten
Display Advertising Manager. Bonnie Schaeffer
Assistant Display Advertising Manager.......Lori Kleinsmith
Mechanical Specifications: Type page 10 x 16; A - 6 cols, 1 5/8, between; C - 6 cols, 1 5/8, between.
Equipment: Hardware — APP/Power Mac, APP/Mac; Presses — None; Software — Multi-Ad/CAMS, QPS/QuarkXPress.
Delivery Method: Mail, Carrier, Racks
Zip Codes Served: 18011, 18031, 18049, 18051, 18062, 18066, 18087, 18106, 19510, 19511, 19522, 19526, 19529, 19530, 19534, 19536, 19539, 19547, 19560, 19562

NORTHERN BERKS MERCHANDISER

(Wed)
6 N 3rd St, Hamburg, PA, 19526-1502, USA; tel (610) 562-2267; adv tel (610) 562-2267; fax (610) 562-2770; adv fax (610) 562-2770; e-mail George@windsorpress.com; adv e-mail DIsplay@windsorpress.com; web site www.windsorpress.com
Circulation: 14pd,310,242fr; CVC
Advertising: Open inch rate $9.26
Established: 1958Editions: n/a
Digital Platform - Mobile: Apple
Dist. Mgr................................ David Wisniewski
Prodn. Mgr............................ George T. Mitten
Display Advertising Manager. Bonnie Schaeffer
Assistant Display Advertising Manager.......Lori Kleinsmith
Mechanical Specifications: Type page 10 x 16; A - 6 cols, 1 5/8, between; C - 6 cols, 1 5/8, between.
Equipment: Hardware — APP/Mac, APP/Power Mac; Presses — 6-HI/V-15D; Software — QPS/QuarkXPress, VisionData
Delivery Method: Mail, Carrier, Racks
Zip Codes Served: 19526, 18011, 18031, 18049, 18051, 18062, 18066, 18087, 18106, 19510, 19511, 19522, 19526, 19529, 19530, 19534, 19536, 19539, 19547, 19560, 19562

HUGHESVILLE

EAST LYCOMING SHOPPER

(Mon)
1025 Route 405 Hwy, Hughesville, PA, 17737-9069, USA; tel (570) 584-2134; fax (570) 584-5399; e-mail shopper@elsnonline.com; adv e-mail shopper@elsnonline.com; ed e-mail shopper@elsnonline.com; web site www.elsnonline.com
Circulation:18,500fr; Sworn/Estimate/Non-Audited
Advertising: Open inch rate $8.25
Established: 1957
Group: Ogden Newspapers Inc.
General Manager .... Sharon Dapp
Mechanical Specifications: Type page 10 x 10; E - 5 cols, 1.58, between; A - 6 cols, between; C - 8 cols, between.

Delivery Method: Carrier, Racks
Zip Codes Served: 17737, 17754, 17756, 17752, 17777

KITTANNING

HORSE TRADER

(Tues)
380 State Route 28 and 66, Kittanning, PA, 16201-3808, USA; tel (724) 543-6290; fax (724) 543-2379; e-mail info@shophorsetrader.com; graphics@shophorsetrader.com; web site www.shophorsetraderweekly.com
Circulation: 0pd,55,840fr; VAC
Advertising: Open inch rate $12.12
Established: 1979
Pub. .... Barry W. Crytzer
Gen. Mgr. .... Sylvia Crytzer
Mechanical Specifications: Type page 10 1/4 x 16; E - 6 cols, between.
Equipment: Hardware — APP/Mac; Software — Adobe/PageMaker 6.0, Adobe/Photoshop 4.0, Multi-Ad/Creator, QPS/QuarkXPress.

LEBANON

KAPP - DAUPHIN / SCHUYLKILL AREA MERCHANDISER

(Wed)
100 E Cumberland St, Lebanon, PA, 17042-5400, USA; web site www.themerchandiser.com
Circulation: 0pd,18,287fr; VAC
Advertising: Open inch rate $8.80
Established: 1976Valerie Stokes

KAPP - GETTYSBURG AREA MERCHANDISER

(Wed)
100 E Cumberland St, Lebanon, PA, 17042-5400, USA; web site www.themerchandiser.com
Circulation: 0pd,23,175fr; VAC
Advertising: N/A
Established: 1975Valerie Stokes

KAPP - GREATER READING MERCHANDISER EASTERN EDITION

(Wed)
100 E Cumberland St, Lebanon, PA, 17042-5400, USA; web site www.themerchandiser.com
Circulation: 0pd,24,297fr; VAC
Advertising: Open inch rate $14.80
Established: 1971Valerie Stokes

KAPP - GREATER READING MERCHANDISER NORTHERN EDITION

(Wed)
100 E Cumberland St, Lebanon, PA, 17042-5400, USA; web site www.themerchandiser.com
Circulation: 0pd,29,353fr; Sworn/Estimate/Non-Audited
Advertising: Open inch rate $14.80
Established: 1971Valerie Stokes

KAPP - GREATER READING MERCHANDISER WESTERN EDITION

(Wed)
100 E Cumberland St, Lebanon, PA, 17042-5400, USA; web site www.themerchandiser.com
Circulation: 0pd,36,244fr; VAC
Advertising: Open inch rate $16.00
Established: 1971Valerie Stokes

KAPP - HAMPSTEAD/MANCHESTER AREA MERCHANDISER

(Wed)
100 E Cumberland St, Lebanon, PA, 17042-5400, USA; web site www.themerchandiser.com
Circulation: 0pd,13,845fr; VAC
Advertising: Open inch rate $6.40

Established: 2006Valerie Stokes

KAPP - HANOVER AREA MERCHANDISER

(Wed)
100 E Cumberland St, Lebanon, PA, 17042-5400, USA; web site www.themerchandiser.com
Circulation: 0pd,38,155fr; VAC
Advertising: Open inch rate $12.30
Established: 1974Valerie Stokes

KAPP - HERSHEY AREA MERCHANDISER

(Wed)
100 E Cumberland St, Lebanon, PA, 17042-5400, USA; web site www.themerchandiser.com
Circulation: 0pd,23,975fr; VAC
Advertising: Open inch rate $10.25
Established: 1968Valerie Stokes

KAPP - LEBANON VALLEY AREA MERCHANDISER

(Wed)
100 E Cumberland St, Lebanon, PA, 17042-5400, USA; web site www.themerchandiser.com
Circulation: 0pd,37,907fr; VAC
Advertising: Open inch rate $16.60
Established: 1954Valerie Stokes

KAPP - MYERSTOWN AREA MERCHANDISER

(Wed)
100 E Cumberland St, Lebanon, PA, 17042-5400, USA; web site www.themerchandiser.com
Circulation: 0pd,19,586fr; VAC
Advertising: Open inch rate $11.90
Established: 1948Valerie Stokes

KAPP - NORTHERN ADAMS / YORK AREA MERCHANDISER

(Wed)
100 E Cumberland St, Lebanon, PA, 17042-5400, USA; web site www.themerchandiser.com
Circulation: 0pd,24,154fr; VAC
Advertising: Open inch rate $6.40 - $16.00Valerie Stokes

MERCHANDISER

(Mon, Tues, Wed)
100 E Cumberland St, Lebanon, PA, 17042-5400, USA; tel (717) 273-8127; fax (717) 273-0420; e-mail sales@themerchandiser.com; frontdesk@themerchandiser.com; web site www.themerchandiser.com
Circulation:599,028fr; Sworn/Estimate/Non-Audited
Established: 1950Editions: 11— 10 total; Dauphin/Schuylkill Merchandiser (17,521); Gettysburg Merchandiser (22,014); Greater Reading Merchandiser-Zone 1 (30,150); Greater Reading Merchandiser-Zone 2 (38,247); Greater Reading Merchandiser-Zone 3 (30,699); Hanover Merchandiser (42,175);
Gen. Mgr. .... Valerie Stokes
Adv. Mgr. .... James Snyder
Circ. Mgr. .... Joanne Walkinshaw
Prodn. Mgr. .... Gary Shiner
Sales Manager .... Randy Miller
Mechanical Specifications: Type page 10 1/4 x 16.
Equipment: Hardware — APP/Mac; Software — Vision Data/Classified, InDesign
Delivery Method: Carrier
Zip Codes Served: 17042

THE PALM

(Wed)
718 Poplar St, Lebanon, PA, 17042-6755, USA; tel (717) 272-5611; fax (717) 274-1608; e-mail citydesk@ldnews.com; adv e-mail advertising@ldnews.com; ed e-mail citydesk@ldnews.com; web site www.ldnews.com
Circulation:22,100fr; Sworn/Estimate/Non-Audited
Advertising: Open inch rate $9.00

Publisher... Scott Downs
Advertising Manager .... Rich Canazaro
Circulation Manager .... Joe Clark
Delivery Method: Newsstand, Carrier, Racks

LEWISBURG

THE VALLEY TRADER

(Tues, Wed) (Bi-Weekly)
PO Box 392, Lewisburg, PA, 17837-0392, USA; tel (570) 524-0962; adv tel (570) 809-9000; fax (570) 523-7070; adv fax (570) 523-7070; e-mail thevalleytrader@yahoo.com; adv e-mail thevalleytrader@yahoo.com; web site www.thevalleytrader.com
Circulation: 14,227pd,7,773fr; Sworn/Estimate/Non-Audited
Advertising: Open inch rate $13.00
Established: 1980Editions: 1—
Digital Platform - Mobile: Apple
Digital Platform - Tablet: Apple iOS
Owner and Founder..................... Max Oberdorf
Mechanical Specifications: Type page 9.25 x 12; E - 6 cols, 1 1/4, 1/6 between; A - 6 cols, 1 1/2, 1/6 between; C - 6 cols, 1 1/2, 1/6 between.
Equipment: Hardware — 3-APP/Power Mac G4's, 1-iMac 24", 1 Apple PowerBook Pro; Software — Multi-Ad/Creator 8.41, Adobe Creative Suite 5.5, Microsoft Office, others
Delivery Method: Mail, Racks
Zip Codes Served: 17837, 17870, 17844, 17701, 17801, 17847, 17815, 17821,17872,17821,18603,17737,17777
Note: We do all ads in Full Color at No Extra charge as other paper do. We are now doing editorial in every issue with local writers doing columns

MANSFIELD

PENNY-SAVER

(Fri)
193A N Main St, Mansfield, PA, 16933-1311, USA; tel (570) 662-3277; adv tel (607) 765-0018; fax (570) 662-7676; e-mail adcopy@ptd.net; adv e-mail darlenebeers18@gmail.com; web site www.mansfieldpennysaver.com
Circulation:17,500fr; Sworn/Estimate/Non-Audited
Advertising: Open inch rate $6.63
Established: 1947Editions: 17,500—
Gen. Sales Mgr. .... Darlene Beers
Mechanical Specifications: Each full page is 80". 5 colx18"h Color is available. Reaching loyal readers every week with proven results.
Delivery Method: Mail, Racks
Zip Codes Served: 16933, 16929, 16940, 16930, 16932, 16939, 16938, 16901, 16917, 16912, 16935, 16946, 17765, 16911, 16920,16936,14830,14845,14858, 14870,14870, 14901, 15478, 16921, 16922, 16925, 16947, 16950, 17724, 17771
Note: 4 - Seasonal guides published (Spring, Summer, Fall, Winter/Holiday) See our website for more information

MEADVILLE

BRAVO EXTRA

(Mon)
947 Federal Ct, Meadville, PA, 16335-3234, USA; tel (814) 724-6370; fax (814) 724-8755; e-mail tribune@meadvilletribune.com; web site www.meadvilletribune.com
Circulation:6,500fr; Sworn/Estimate/Non-Audited
Group: Community Newspaper Holdings, Inc.
Pub. .... Jeanne Moore-Yount
Adv. Mgr. .... Helen Powers
Ed. .... Pat Bywater
Prodn. Dir. .... Chris Wade
Zip Codes Served: 16335

MECHANICSBURG

GUIDE NEWS
(Wed)
800 W Church Rd, Mechanicsburg, PA, 17055-3179, USA; tel (717) 766-0211 ext 2312; adv tel (717) 766-0211 ext 2400; ed tel (717) 766-0211 ext 2400; fax (717) 691-5796; e-mail guideads@frycomm.com troy@frycomm.com; adv e-mail guideads@frycomm.com; ed e-mail guideads@frycomm.com; web site www.theguideonlinepa.com
Circulation:141,500fr; USPS
Advertising: Open inch rate $10.35
Established: 1936
Group: Fry Communications, Inc.Editions: 6— West Shore, Mechanicsburg,Carlisle,Perry County,Harrisburg,Dillsburg
Digital Platform - Mobile: Windows
General Manager .... Troy Williams
Delivery Method: Mail
Zip Codes Served: 17011,17025,17043,17070,17093,17011,17055,17050,17027,17072,17007,17013,17015,17065,17081,17241,17266,17324,17006,17020,17024,17037,17040,17047,17053,17068,17074,17090,17028,17109,17111,17112,17019

MOUNT JOY

CHESTER COUNTY COMMUNITY COURIER
(Wed)
1425 W Main St, Mount Joy, PA, 17552-9589, USA; tel (717) 492-2514; adv tel (717) 492-2514; fax (717) 492-2584; e-mail jhemperly@engleonline.com; adv e-mail jhemperly@engleonline.com; ed e-mail news@engleonline.com; web site www.engleonline.com
Circulation: 0pd,89,636fr; CVC
Advertising: Open inch rate $46.30
Established: 1988
Group: Engle Printing & Publishing Co., Inc. Editions: 4— 4 total Community Courier-Downingtown/Exton (51,479); Oxford CC 15,311, Octorara Community Courier 7,660; Community Courier-Morgantown/Honey Brook (15,200);
Circ. Mgr. .... Mark Malloy
VP Operations .... Jeremy Engle
Sales Manager .... John Hemperly
Mechanical Specifications: Type page 10 3/8 x 16; E - 6 cols, 1 5/8, between; A - 6 cols, 1 5/8, between; C - 6 cols, 1 5/8, between.
Equipment: Hardware — APP/Mac; Presses — Yes
Operate our own printing plant; Software — QPS/QuarkXPress 4.0, Adobe/Illustrator 8.0, Adobe/Photoshop 7.0, Adobe/InDesign.
Delivery Method: Mail
Zip Codes Served: 19316, 19425, 19320, 19335, 19341, 19343, 19353, 19354, 19358, 19367, 19369, 19372, 19480, 19376, 19442, 19460, 19508, 19520, 19344, 19543, 19371, 19523, 19310, 19330, 19352, 19363, 19370, 17509, 17527, 19362, 19365, 19390, 19442, 19358, 19508, 19520,
Note: Free Community Weekly paper home delivered by the US Post Office. Average 30% local Editorial space.

ENGLE PRINTING & PUBLISHING CO., INC.
(Wed)
1425 W Main St, Mount Joy, PA, 17552-9589, USA; tel (717) 492-2514; fax (717) 492-2584; e-mail jhemperly@engleonline.com; adv e-mail classifieds@engleonline.com; sales@engleonline.com; ed e-mail newsdept@engleonline.com; web site www.engleonline.com
Circulation: 0pd,444,397fr; CVC
Established: 1955
Adv. Mgr. .... John Hemperly
Note: Local Weekly Free Saturation Distribution. 28 Editions reaching over 438,000 Homes. Delivered each week(100% by the US Post Office)
30% local editorial.
Competitive Preprint rates. Sub-Zip Code distribution available

HERSHEY COMMUNITY COURIER
(Wed)
1425 W Main St, Mount Joy, PA, 17552-9589, USA; tel (717) 492-2514; adv tel (717) 492-2514; ed tel (717) 892-6018; fax (717) 492-2584; ed fax (717) 892-6024; e-mail jhemperly@engleonline.com; adv e-mail jhemperly@engleonline.com; ed e-mail news@engleonline.com
Circulation: 0pd,28,490fr; CVC
Advertising: 18.40
Established: 1954
Group: Engle Printing & Publishing Co., Inc. Editions: 1— Hershey Community Courier 28,267
General Sales Manager .... John Hemperly
Mechanical Specifications: Type page 10 3/8 x 13; E - 6 cols, 1 3/8, between; A - 6 cols, 1 3/8, between; C - 6 cols, 1 3/8, between.
Equipment: Hardware — APP/Mac; Presses — YES. In house coldset web presses plus glossy printing via UV light; Software — QPS/QuarkXPress 4.0, Adobe/Illustrator 8.0, Adobe/Photoshop 7.0, Adobe/InDesign.
Delivery Method: Mail
Zip Codes Served: 17003, 17010, 17033, 17036, 17078, 17022
Note: Saturation delivery via US Post Office. 30% Local News content. Ask about our competitive Preprint rates

MERCHANDISER-LANCASTER COUNTY
(Wed)
1425 W Main St, Mount Joy, PA, 17552-9589, USA; tel (717) 492-2514; fax (717) 492-2584; e-mail jhemperly@engleonline.com; adv e-mail jhemperly@engleonline.com
Circulation: 0pd,84,510fr; CVC
Advertising: 66.50
Established: 1959
Group: Engle Printing & Publishing Co., Inc. Editions: 7— Elizabethtown 12732, donegal 9551; Manheim Central 10757, Warwick 13327, Hempfield 18999,manheim township 14238, Columbia 4513
General Sales Manager .... John Hemperly
Circ. Mgr. .... Mark Malloy
Prodn. Mgr. .... Jeremy Engle
Mechanical Specifications: Type page 10 3/8 x 16; E - 6 cols, 1 5/8, between; A - 6 cols, 1 5/8, between; C - 6 cols, 1 5/8, between.
Equipment: Hardware — APP/Mac; Presses — Yes. printed on in-house coldset web press; Software — QPS/QuarkXPress 4.0, Adobe/Illustrator 8.0, Adobe/Photoshop 7.0, Adobe/InDesign.
Delivery Method: Mail
Zip Codes Served: 17512, 17022, 17041, 17547, 17550, 17552, 17570, 17521, 17543, 17564, 17545, 17520, 17601, 17603, 17538, 17554, 17575, 17607, 17606, 17312, 17317, 17406, 17368, 17545, 17601, 17603
Note: Free Community paper. 100% home delivery by US Post Office. Average 30% local editorial content.

PENNYSAVER
(Wed)
1425 W Main St, Mount Joy, PA, 17552-9589, USA; tel (717) 492-2514; adv tel (717) 492-2514; ed tel (717) 892-6018; fax (717) 492-2584; ed fax (717) 892-6024; e-mail jhemperly@engleonline.com; ed e-mail news@engleonline.com; web site www.engleonline.com
Circulation: 0pd,31,410fr; CVC
Advertising: $33.78
Established: 1963
Group: Engle Printing & Publishing Co., Inc.Editions: 3— Conestoga Valley 13288; Pequea Valley 7061; garden Spot 11,061
Circ. Mgr. .... Mark Malloy
Sales Manager .... John Hemperly
Advertising Sales Manager .... Greg March
Mechanical Specifications: Type page 10 3/8 x 13; E - 6 cols, 1 5/8, between; A - 6 cols, 1 5/8, between; C - 6 cols, 1 5/8, between.
Equipment: Hardware — APP/Mac; Presses — Yes. In - house coldset web presses plus glossy printing via UV ; Software — QPS/QuarkXPress 4.0, Adobe/Illustrator 8.0, Adobe/Photoshop 7.0, Adobe/InDesign.
Delivery Method: Mail
Zip Codes Served: 17501, 17505, 17506, 17507, 17508, 17517, 17519, 17522, 17527, 17528, 17501, 17505, 17506, 17507, 17508, 17517, 17519, 17522, 17527, 17528, 17529, 17534, 17535, 17540, 17549, 17555, 17557, 17562, 17569, 17572, 17576, 17578, 17580, 17581, 17585, 17601, 17602, 19540
Note: Free Community Weekly paper home delivered by the US Post Office. Average 30% local Editorial space. Ask about our competitive preprint rates.

SHOPPER
(Wed)
PO Box 500, Mount Joy, PA, 17552-0500, USA; tel (717) 653-1833; fax (717) 653-6165; e-mail sales@engleonline.com
Circulation:106,726fr; Sworn/Estimate/Non-Audited
Advertising: Open inch rate $45.00
Established: 1958Editions: 19— 4 total; Camp Hill Shopper (32,661); East Shore Shopper (28,487); Mechanicsburg Shopper (34,472); Middletown Area Shopper (10,424);
Pres./Pub. .... Charles A. Engle
Circ. Mgr. .... Mark Malloy
Prodn. Mgr. .... Jeremy Engle
Mechanical Specifications: Type page 10 3/8 x 16; E - 6 cols, 1 3/8, between; A - 6 cols, 1 3/8, between; C - 6 cols, 1 3/8, between.
Equipment: Hardware — APP/Mac; Presses — GOSS,TENSOR; Software — QPS/QuarkXPress 4.0, Adobe/Illustrator 8.0, Adobe/Photoshop 7.0, Adobe/InDesign.
Delivery Method: Mail, Carrier
Zip Codes Served: 17011, 17319, 17043, 17339, 17070, 17008, 17019, 17027, 17055, 17072, 17323, 17057, 17112, 17109, 17110, 17111, 17003, 17010, 17033, 17036, 17078, 17057, 17112, 17109, 17111

MOUNTVILLE

SAVVY SHOPPER
3708 Hempland Rd, Mountville, PA, 17554-1542, USA; tel (800) 360-2547; fax (717) 569-5101

NEW CASTLE

WEEKLY BARGAIN BULLETIN
(Fri)
1576 Sunrise Dr, New Castle, PA, 16105-5340, USA; tel (724) 654-5529; adv tel (724) 654-4557; adv e-mail ads@weeklybargainbulletin.com; web site www.wbblive.com
Circulation: 0pd,20,950fr; VAC
Advertising: Open inch rate $7.50
Established: 1972
Adv. Mgr. .... Frank W. Hutchison
Ed. .... Karen Hutchison
Mechanical Specifications: Type page 10 x 16; E - 7 cols, 1 3/8, 1/16 between; A - 7 cols, 1 3/8, 1/16 between; C - 7 cols, 1 3/8, 1/16 between.
Equipment: Hardware — APP/Mac; Software — Adobe/PageMaker.
Zip Codes Served: 15010, 16101, 16102, 16105, 16112, 16116, 16117, 16132, 16140, 16142, 16156, 16157, 16160

OIL CITY

ADVERTISER
(Sat)
1510 W 1st St, Oil City, PA, 16301-3211, USA; tel (814) 676-7444; fax (814) 677-8351; web site www.thederrick.com
Circulation:11,543fr; Sworn/Estimate/Non-Audited
Advertising: Open inch rate $6.25
Zip Codes Served: 16301

PENNSBURG

UPPER PERK SHOPPER'S GUIDE
(Mon, Sat)
878 Main St, Pennsburg, PA, 18073-1602, USA; tel (215) 679-4133; fax (215) 679-5490; e-mail upshopper@comcast.net
Circulation: 0pd,22,000fr; USPS
Advertising: Open inch rate $11.25
Established: 1979Editions: 1—
Digital Platform - Mobile: Apple
Digital Platform - Tablet: Apple iOS
Pub. .... Paul M. Verna
Mechanical Specifications: Type page 6 x 16.
Equipment: Hardware — APP/Mac, Dataproducts/LZR; Presses — none; Software — Multi-Ad/.; InDesign
Delivery Method: Mail, Carrier, Racks
Zip Codes Served: 18073,18041,18054,18056,18070,18074,18076,18092,18935, 18951 Partial,18968,19472,19503,19504,19525

PITTSBURGH

PENNYSAVER
(Thur, Sun)
460 Rodi Rd, Pittsburgh, PA, 15235-4547, USA; tel (412) 871-2345; fax (412) 243-2843; web site www.pittsburghpennysaver.com
Circulation: 0pd,506,754fr; VAC
Advertising: Open inch rate $11.00Editions: 73— Aliquippa/Monaca/South Heights/Crescent Pennysaver (15,393); Ambridge/Baden/Conway PennySaver (8,869); Belle/Vernon PennySaver (7,100); Bellevue PennySaver (10,126); Bethel Pk./Library/Finleyville/Gastonville/Courtney/Elrama Pennysaver (11,852)
Gen. Mgr. .... Dean Deluca
Richard Scaife
Mechanical Specifications: Type page 7 1/2 x 10.
Equipment: Hardware — PC, COM, APP/Mac; Software — Graphix/Adtaker, Multi-Ad, Adobe/Illustrator.
Zip Codes Served: 15235

RIDGWAY

SHOP RIGHT
(Mon)
325 Main St, Ste A, Ridgway, PA, 15853-8019, USA; tel (814) 773-3161; ed tel (814) 773-3151; fax (814) 776-1086; ed e-mail ridgwayrecord@shop-right.com; web site www.ridgwayrecord.com
Circulation: 2,656pd,; Sworn/Estimate/Non-Audited
Advertising: Open inch rate $7.75
Group: Heritage Publications (2003) Inc.
Pub. .... Darlene Coder
Bus. Mgr. .... Karen Kilhoffer
Circ.Mgr. .... Brandon Laiphner
Prodn. .... Mike Tucker
Editor .... Joseph Bell
Adv. Dir. .... Krista Zameroski
Ed. .... Brent Addleman
Mechanical Specifications: Type page 11 31/50 x 21 1/2; E - 6 cols, 1 3/4, 1/8 between; A - 6 cols, 1 3/4, 1/8 between; C - 8 cols, 1 9/25, 1/8 between.
Delivery Method: Mail, Newsstand, Carrier, Racks

SAINT MARYS

DAILY PRESS
(Wed)
245 Brusselles St, Saint Marys, PA, 15857-1501, USA; tel (814) 781-1596; fax (814) 834-7473; e-mail smnews@smdailypress.com;

adv e-mail circulation@smdailypress.com; classifieds@smdailypress.com; dailypress-adv@alltel.net; ed e-mail editor3@zitomedia.net; publisher3@zitomedia.net; web site www.smdailypress.com
Circulation: 4,723pd,3,700fr; Sworn/Estimate/Non-Audited
Advertising: Open inch rate $7.75
Established: 1910
Group: Heritage Publications (2003) Inc.
Pub. .... Darlene Coder
Ed. .... Brent Addleman
Mechanical Specifications: Type page 13 x 21 1/2; E - 6 cols, 1 13/16, 1/6 between; A - 6 cols, 1 13/16, 1/6 between; C - 8 cols, 1 3/8, between.
Equipment: Hardware — APP/Mac; Software — Baseview.
Zip Codes Served: 15852, 15821, 15827, 15831, 15834, 15841, 15845, 15846, 15833, 15868, 15870

SCRANTON

THE VALLEY ADVANTAGE
(Fri)
149 Penn Ave, Scranton, PA, 18503-2055, USA; tel (570) 348-9185; fax (570) 207-3448; e-mail advantage@timesshamrock.com; web site www.thevalleyadvantage.com
Circulation: 20,000pd,; Sworn/Estimate/Non-Audited
Advertising: Open inch rate $8.00
Group: Times-Shamrock CommunicationsEditions: 2— 2 total; Ad Vantage-Down Valley; Ad Vantage-Mid & Upper Valley;
Adv. Mgr. .... Tim Holmes
Ed. .... Christopher Cornell
Mechanical Specifications: Type page 10 x 13; E - 4 cols, 2 1/2, between; A - 4 cols, 2 1/2, between; C - 8 cols, 1 1/4, between.
Equipment: Hardware — APP/Mac Plus; Software — Adobe/PageMaker.

SMITHMILL

AD BARGAIN
(Wed)
1787 Viola Pike, # RT453, Smithmill, PA, 16680, USA; tel (814) 378-7079; fax (814) 378-7598; e-mail adbargain@comcast.net
Circulation:17,000fr; Sworn/Estimate/Non-Audited
Advertising: Open inch rate $7.35
Established: 1981Jan Daye
Ed. .... Jeanette L. Daye
Equipment: Hardware — APP/Mac; Software — Adobe.
Zip Codes Served: 16680

SOUTH WILLIAMSPORT

WEBB WEEKLY
(Tues) (Weekly)
280 Kane St, Ste 2, South Williamsport, PA, 17702-7166, USA; tel (570) 326-9322; adv tel (570) 326-9322; ed tel (570) 326-9322; e-mail LAndrews@webbweekly.com; adv e-mail LAndrews@webbweekly.com; ed e-mail webbnews@webbweekly.com; web site webbweekly.com
Circulation:58,000fr; Sworn/Estimate/Non-Audited
Established: 1998
Digital Platform - Mobile: Apple, Android, Windows, Blackberry
Digital Platform - Tablet: Apple iOS, Android, Windows 7, Blackberry Tablet OS, Kindle, Nook, Kindle Fire
Delivery Method: Mail
Zip Codes Served: Lycoming County, PA
Clinton County, PA
Sullivan County, PA

STATE COLLEGE

THE BARGAIN SHEET
(Thur)
1001 University Dr, State College, PA, 16801-6600, USA; tel (814) 237-1900; fax (814) 237-4036; e-mail bsheet@vicon.net; web site http://www.bargainsheet.net/
Circulation: 0pd,28,585fr; CVC
Advertising: Open inch rate $10.55
Gen. Mgr. .... James Bair
John Cooke
Zip Codes Served: 16801

STROUDSBURG

POCONO RECORD PLUS
(Sat)
511 Lenox St, Stroudsburg, PA, 18360-1516, USA; tel (570) 420-4372; adv tel (570) 420-4378; fax (570) 424-2625; adv e-mail advertising@poconorecord.com; ed e-mail letters@poconorecord.com; web site www.poconorecord.com
Circulation:18,157fr; Sworn/Estimate/Non-Audited
Group: GateHouse Media, Inc.
Pres. .... Joe Vanderhoof
Associate Pub and Adv. Dir. .... Brad Bailey
Zip Codes Served: 18360

TROY

TROY PENNYSAVER
(Tues)
29 Canton St, Troy, PA, 16947, USA; tel (570) 297-4158; adv tel (888) 400-2329; fax (570) 297-4150; e-mail troyads@tsweeklygroup.com; adv e-mail troyads@tsweeklygroup.com; web site www.troypennysaver.com
Circulation: 123pd,12,175fr; Sworn/Estimate/Non-Audited
General Manager .... Dave Barry
Mechanical Specifications: Type page 10 1/4 x 13.
Delivery Method: Mail, Newsstand, Carrier, Racks
Zip Codes Served: 16947

TUNKHANNOCK

MULLIGAN TOWN & COUNTRY SHOPPER - N WAYNE COUNTY
(Fri)
312 Mile Rd, Tunkhannock, PA, 18657-7007, USA; web site www.mulliganprinting.com
Circulation: 0pd,19,039fr; CVC
Established: 1986Charles J. Mulligan

MULLIGAN'S PENNY$AVER - WYOMING COUNTY
(Wed)
110 E Harrison St, Tunkhannock, PA, 18657-1140, USA; tel (570) 836-5204; adv e-mail met@mulliganprinting.com; web site www.mulliganprinting.com
Circulation: 2pd,21,091fr; VAC
Advertising: N/A
Established: 1976Charles J. Mulligan

MULLIGAN'S SHOPPER - LACKAUANNA COUNTY
(Wed)
110 E Harrison St, Tunkhannock, PA, 18657-1140, USA; tel (570) 836-5204; adv tel (570) 996-4719; web site www.mulliganprinting.com
Circulation:18,829fr; Sworn/Estimate/Non-AuditedCharles J. Mulligan

MULLIGAN'S SHOPPING GUIDE - SUSQUEHANNA COUNTY
(Wed)
110 E Harrison St, Tunkhannock, PA, 18657-1140, USA; web site www.mulliganprinting.com
Circulation: 2pd,25,909fr; VAC
Advertising: N/A
Established: 1978Charles J. Mulligan

WARREN

WARREN COUNTY GUIDE
(Mon)
315 2nd Ave, Ste 312, Warren, PA, 16365-2433, USA; tel (814) 726-3400; fax (814) 726-3688
Circulation:17,000fr; Sworn/Estimate/Non-Audited
Advertising: Open inch rate $11.00
Pub. .... Robert J. Williams
Mechanical Specifications: Type page 12 7/8 x 21 1/2; E - 6 cols, 2, 1/6 between; A - 6 cols, 2, 1/6 between.
Equipment: Hardware — APP/Power Mac; Presses — G/Community; Software — Multi-Ad/Creator 4.2.
Zip Codes Served: 16365

WEST CHESTER

WEST CHESTER VOICE
(Wed)
250 N Bradford Ave, West Chester, PA, 19382-1912, USA; tel (610) 430-1187; fax (610) 430-1190; e-mail advertising@dailylocal.com; web site www.dailylocal.com
Circulation:20,000fr; Sworn/Estimate/Non-Audited
Advertising: Open inch rate $12.12
Pub. .... Shelly Menan
Circ. Dir. .... Christopher Smith
Ed. .... Andy Hachatorian
Mechanical Specifications: Type page 12 x 21 1/2; E - 6 cols, 1 7/8, between; A - 6 cols, 1 7/8, between; C - 10 cols, 1 1/4, between.
Equipment: Hardware — Pentium/PC 200; Presses — G/Urbanite; Software — CNI.
Zip Codes Served: 19382

WILKES BARRE

NEPA SHOPPER
(Fri)
15 N Main St, Wilkes Barre, PA, 18701-2604, USA; tel (570) 829-7101; fax (717) 829-2002; e-mail tlnews@timesleader.com; adv e-mail classifieds@timesleader.com; circ@timesleader.com; web site www.timesleader.com
Circulation:51,023fr; Sworn/Estimate/Non-Audited
Advertising: Open inch rate $6.13
Vice Pres., Classified Adv. .... Michelle Lester
Vice Pres., Circ. .... Dick DeHaven
Ed. .... Richard L. Connor
Mechanical Specifications: Type page 13 x 21 3/4; E - 6 cols, 2 1/8, 3/16 between; A - 6 cols, 2 1/6, 3/16 between; C - 9 cols, 1 11/32, 1/16 between.
Equipment: ; Presses — MAN/Geo.
Zip Codes Served: 18711

RHODE ISLAND

BRISTOL

EAST BAY NEWSPAPERS
(Other)
1 Bradford St, Bristol, RI, 02809-1906, USA; tel (401) 253-6000; adv tel (401) 253-1000; fax (401) 253-6055; e-mail bristol@eastbaynewspapers.com; adv e-mail classifieds@eastbaynewspapers.com; web site www.eastbayri.com
Circulation: 11,545pd,12,487fr; CVC
Established: 1837
Pub./ Adv. Mgr. .... Matthew D. Hayes
Gen. Mgr. .... Lisa Carro
Advertising Dir. .... Toni Nuttall
Ed. .... Jim McGaw
Mng. Ed. .... Scott Pickering
Prodn. Mgr. .... Jock Hayes
MANAGING DIRECTOR, ONE BRADFORD .... Dichiappari Kirsten

COVENTRY

THE REMINDER
(Tues)
1049 Main St, Coventry, RI, 02816-5706, USA; tel (401) 821-2216; adv tel (401) 821-2216; ed tel (401) 821-2216; fax (401) 821-0397; adv fax (401) 821-0397; ed fax (401) 821-0397; e-mail rireminder@aol.com; adv e-mail rireminder@aol.com; ed e-mail rireminder@aol.com; web site www.rireminder.com
Circulation: 0pd,28,697fr; CVC
Advertising: Open inch rate $12.00
Established: 1954
Pub./Adv. Mgr. .... Peter Stevens
Ed. .... Amey Tilley
Equipment: Hardware — APP/Mac, SUN/Suntype; Software — QPS/QuarkXPress.
Delivery Method: Mail
Zip Codes Served: 02816, 02817, 02822, 02825, 02831, 02893

WAKEFIELD

SOUTHERN RHODE ISLAND NEWSPAPERS
(Thur)
187 Main St, Wakefield, RI, 02879-3504, USA; tel (401) 789-9744; fax (401) 789-1550; web site www.ricentral.com
Circulation: 1,920pd,264fr; CAC
Publisher .... Nanci Batson
Note: Southern Rhode Island Newspapers is owned by RISN (Rhode Island Suburban Newspapers) Operations.

WARWICK

PENNYSAVER
(Sat)
1944 Warwick Ave, Warwick, RI, 02889-2448, USA; tel (401) 732-3100; adv tel (401) 732-3100; ed tel (401) 732-3100; fax (401) 732-3110; e-mail richardf@rhodybeat.com; adv e-mail richardf@rhodybeat.com
Circulation:12,000fr; Sworn/Estimate/Non-Audited
Advertising: Open inch rate $9.64
Established: 1975
Group: Beacon Communications, Inc
Pub. .... John I. Howell
Gen. Mgr. .... Richard G. Fleischer
Equipment: Hardware — PC; Software — In-Design
Delivery Method: Racks
Zip Codes Served: 02889,886,888,818,905,910,920

WOONSOCKET

CUMBERLAND LINCOLN NEIGHBORS
(Wed)
75 Main St, Woonsocket, RI, 02895-4312, USA; tel (401) 762-3000; adv tel (401) 767-8505; ed tel (401) 767-8550; fax (401) 765-2834; adv fax (401) 767-8509; e-mail news@woonsocketcall.com; ed e-mail publisher@

woonsocketcall.com; web site www.woonsocketcall.com
Circulation:17,000fr; Sworn/Estimate/Non-Audited
Advertising: Open inch rate $12.00
Group: Rhode Island Media Group
Pub. ....Barry M. Mechanic
Mng. Ed.................................Daniel Trafford
Mechanical Specifications: Type page 12 x 21 1/2; E - 6 cols, 1 7/8, between; A - 6 cols, 1 7/8, between; C - 9 cols, 1 1/4, between.

WOONSOCKET NEIGHBOUR
(Fri)
75 Main St, Woonsocket, RI, 02895-4312, USA; tel (401) 762-3000; fax (401) 765-2834; e-mail notices@woonsocketcall.com; web site www.woonsocketcall.com
Circulation:16,000fr; Sworn/Estimate/Non-Audited
Advertising: Open inch rate $16.00
Pub. .... Barry Mechanic
Mechanical Specifications: Type page 12 x 21 1/2; E - 6 cols, 1 7/8, between; A - 6 cols, 1 7/8, between; C - 9 cols, 1 1/4, between.
Equipment: ; Presses — G/Urbanite.

SOUTH CAROLINA

CAMDEN

KERSHAW CO. EXTRA
(Wed)
909 W Dekalb St, Camden, SC, 29020-4259, USA; tel (803) 432-6157; fax (803) 432-7609; web site www.chronicle-independent.com
Circulation:11,000fr; Sworn/Estimate/Non-Audited
Advertising: Open inch rate $11.70
Pub. .... Mike Michner
Adv. Mgr................................ Betsy Greenway

CHERAW

CHESTERFIELD COUNTY SHOPPER
(Wed)
25 Chesterfield Hwy, Cheraw, SC, 29520-3101, USA; tel (843) 537-2791; fax (843) 537-1912; e-mail countysh@bellsouth.net; adv e-mail advertising@chesterfieldcountyshopper.com; circulation@florencenewsjournal.com; ed e-mail publisher@florencenewsjournal.com; web site chesterfieldcountyshopper.com
Circulation: 0pd,13,568fr; CVC
Advertising: Open inch rate $9.00
Gen. Mgr.......................................David Linton
Adv. Mgr.....................................Carol Grooms
Mechanical Specifications: Type page 10 5/12 x 16; E - 6 cols, 1 2/3, between; A - 6 cols, 1 2/3, between.
Equipment: Hardware — APP/Macs; Software — QPS/QuarkXPress 3.31, Baseview/Class Manager, Baseview/Display Manager.

CONWAY

HORRY NEWS & SHOPPER
(Tues)
2510 Main St, Conway, SC, 29526-3365, USA; tel (843) 602-3784; adv tel (843) 602-3784; ed tel (843) 602-3784; fax (843) 602-3784; adv fax (843) 602-3784; ed fax (843) 602-3784; e-mail stephen.robertson@MyHorryNews.com; adv e-mail swrobertson10@gmail.com; ed e-mail swrobertson10@gmail.com; web site www.MyHorryNews.com
Circulation:32,500fr; Sworn/Estimate/Non-Audited
Advertising: Open inch rate $11.00
Established: 1985
Group: Horry IndependentEditions: 1—
Digital Platform - Mobile: Apple, Android, Windows, Blackberry
Digital Platform - Tablet: Apple iOS, Android, Windows 7, Blackberry Tablet OS
Pub. .... Stephen Robertson
Production Mgr. .... Becky Stevens
Mechanical Specifications: 6 cols x 12 height or 72 col. inches.
Equipment: Hardware — Apple/Mac; Software — Quark Xpress, Adobe products.
Delivery Method: Mail, Newsstand, Carrier, Racks
Zip Codes Served: 29526, 29527, 29544, 29511, 29569, 29568, 29545, 29577, 29582

GREENVILLE

IWANNA
(Tues)
25 Airpark Ct, Greenville, SC, 29607-6188, USA; tel (864) 232-8585; adv tel (864) 233-1400; fax (864) 232-8585; web site www.iwanna.com
Circulation: 24,000pd,; Sworn/Estimate/Non-Audited
Advertising: Open inch rate $10.50
Established: 1988
Group: Fayetteville Publishing Co.
Circ. Mgr......................................Mark Grahan
Prodn. Mgr. ....David Denton
Contact ....Rod Duckett
Mechanical Specifications: Type page 10 1/4 x 13; A - 4 cols, 2 3/8, 1/4 between; C - 4 cols, 2 3/8, 1/4 between.
Equipment: Hardware — APP/Mac; Software — Adobe/PageMaker 6.5, Adobe/Illustrator, Adobe/Photoshop 4.0.
Zip Codes Served: 29606

HARTSVILLE

THE HARTSVILLE NEWS JOURNAL
(Wed)
416 W Carolina Ave, Hartsville, SC, 29550-4524, USA; tel (843) 332-0858; fax (843) 332-7368; e-mail newsjournal@sc.rr.com; adv e-mail advertising@hartsvillenewsjournal.com; circulation@florencenewsjournal.com; classifieds@hartsvillenewsjournal.com; circulation@florencenewsjournal.com; ed e-mail editor@hartsvillenewsjournal.com; publisher@florencenewsjournal.com; web site www.hartsvillenewsjournal.com
Circulation: 4pd,14,618fr; CVC
Advertising: Open inch rate $9.00
Established: 1974
Group: Swartz Media, LLC
Pub. ....Don Swartz
Classified Adv. Mgr. ....Connie Gainey
Prodn. Mgr. ....Beth Strett
Advertising.............................Scarlett Caddell
Circ. Mgr...John Truett
Mechanical Specifications: Type page 13 x 21; E - 6 cols, 2 1/16, 1/6 between; A - 6 cols, 2 1/16, 1/6 between; C - 9 cols, 1 7/16, 1/60 between.
Equipment: Hardware — APP/Mac; Software — QPS/QuarkXPress, Adobe/Photoshop, Microsoft/Word.

LORIS

THE LORIS SCENE
(Wed)
PO Box 309, Loris, SC, 29569-0309, USA; tel (843) 756-1447; fax (843) 756-7800; e-mail lsnews@sccoast.com; web site www.lorissc.com
Circulation: 2,000pd,; Sworn/Estimate/Non-Audited
Advertising: Open inch rate $5.10
Adv. Mgr....................................Annette Norris
Ed. ....Steve Robertson
Mechanical Specifications: Type page 10 x 16; E - 6 cols, 1 1/2, 1/5 between; A - 6 cols, 1 1/2, 1/5 between; C - 6 cols, 1 1/2, 1/5 between.
Equipment: Hardware — APP/Mac; Software — Adobe/PageMaker, Adobe/Photoshop, Microsoft.

NORTH CHARLESTON

SHOPPER
(Wed)
PO Box 40635, North Charleston, SC, 29423-0635, USA; tel (843) 552-6826; fax (843) 552-0228; e-mail lgemmett@aol.com; adv e-mail lgemmett@aol.com; web site www.shopperads.com
Circulation:21,000fr; Sworn/Estimate/Non-Audited
Advertising: Open inch rate $13.75
Established: 1993
Adv. Mgr...........................Lynn Kutz-Gemmett
Ed. ....Richard P. Gemmett
Mechanical Specifications: Type page 10 1/4 x 13; E - 6 cols, 1 9/16, 1/4 between; A - 6 cols, between; C - 6 cols, between.
Equipment: Hardware — APP/Mac, IBM; Software — QPS/QuarkXPress.
Delivery Method: Racks
Zip Codes Served: 4 counties

SENECA

GOLDEN CORNER SHOPPER
(Mon)
210 W North 1st St, Seneca, SC, 29678-3250, USA; tel (864) 882-2375; fax (864) 882-2381; web site www.upstatetoday.com
Circulation:34,979fr; Sworn/Estimate/Non-Audited
Advertising: Open inch rate $10.00
General Manager .... Hal Welch
Press Mgr.......................................Mike Watts
Editor .... John Hadaworth
Mechanical Specifications: Type page 10 1/8 x 12.
Equipment: Hardware — APP/Macs; Presses — 14 — Goss Urbanite; Software — QPS/QuarkXPress 3.3, Multi-Ad/Creator, Microsoft/Word.
Zip Codes Served: 29642, 29640, 29671, 29657

WALTERBORO

THE SHOPPER
(Wed)
228 E Washington St, Walterboro, SC, 29488-3918, USA; tel (843) 549-2586; fax (843) 549-2446; e-mail thepress@lowcountry.com; adv e-mail pressads@lowcountry.com
Circulation:19,686fr; Sworn/Estimate/Non-Audited
Advertising: Open inch rate $11.50
Established: 1992
Adv. Mgr. .... Hal Welch
Cir. Mgr..Tanny Hiott
Ed. ....Taylor Smith
Prodn. Mgr. ....Katrena McCall
Mechanical Specifications: Type page 10 1/4 x 16; E - 5 cols, 2 11/12, between; A - 5 cols, 2 11/12, between.
Equipment: Hardware — APP/Mac; Software — Adobe/Photoshop 4.0, QPS/QuarkXPress 4.0.
Zip Codes Served: 29488, 29475, 29481, 29493, 29446, 29452, 29435, 29474, 29929, 29082, 29433

SOUTH DAKOTA

ABERDEEN

MIDLAND SHOPPER
(Wed, Sun)
214 N Main St, Aberdeen, SD, 57401-3464, USA; tel (605) 226-3222; fax (605) 225-5021; e-mail mail.midlandpress@midconetwork.com
Circulation:52,310fr; Sworn/Estimate/Non-Audited
Advertising: Open inch rate $9.88
Established: 1979
Prodn. Mgr. .... Kristi Jacobson
Mechanical Specifications: Type page 10 1/2 x 15 3/4; E - 6 cols, 1 5/8, between; A - 6 cols, 1 5/8, between; C - 6 cols, 1 5/8, between.
Equipment: Hardware — APP/Mac Classic, APP/Mac Centris 610, APP/Power Mac G3; Presses — KP/News King; Software — Claris/MacWrite, Adobe/PageMaker, Microsoft/Works, Macromedia/Freehand, Adobe/Photoshop Microsoft/Word.
Zip Codes Served: 57401, 57421, 57424, 57426, 57427, 57428, 57219, 57430, 57432, 57433, 57434, 57435, 57439, 57440, 57441, 57445, 57446, 57448, 57449, 57451, 57422, 57429, 57437, 57438, 57452, 57454, 57456, 57457, 57460, 57461, 57601, 57465, 57466, 57467, 57468, 57469, 574

BROOKINGS

PROFILE
(Tues)
312 5th St, Brookings, SD, 57006-1924, USA; tel (605) 692-6271; fax (605) 692-2979; e-mail registerdesign@brookingsregister.com; helpdesk@newsmediacorp.com; sports@brookingsregister.com; adv e-mail registeradvertising@brookingsregister.com; web site www.brookingsregister.com
Circulation:15,000fr; Sworn/Estimate/Non-Audited
Advertising: Open inch rate $11.07Editions: 2— 2 total; Ag ProFile (8,000); City ProFile (3,000);
Adv. Dir...............................William McMacken
Mechanical Specifications: Type page 13 x 21 1/2; E - 6 cols, between; A - 6 cols, between; C - 6 cols, between.
Equipment: ; Presses — G/Community.
Zip Codes Served: 57006

TOWN & COUNTRY SHOPPER
(Tues)
609 5th Ave, Brookings, SD, 57006-1428, USA; tel (605) 692-9311; fax (605) 692-6750; e-mail shopper@brookings.net
Circulation:16,000fr; Sworn/Estimate/Non-Audited
Advertising: Open inch rate $6.00
Gen. Mgr. ....Dianne K. Ammann
Circ. Mgr...................................Larry Ammann
Equipment: Hardware — APP/Mac; Software — QPS/QuarkXPress, Adobe/PageMaker.

CUSTER

WESTERN TRADER
(Wed)
522 Mount Rushmore Rd, Custer, SD, 57730-1930, USA; tel (605) 673-2217; adv tel (605) 673-2217; ed tel (605) 673-2217; fax (605) 673-3321; adv fax (605) 673-3321; ed fax (605) 673-3321; e-mail custerchronicle@gwtc.net & custernews@gwtc.net; adv e-mail custerads@gwtc.net; ed e-mail custerchronicle@gwtc.net & custernews@gwtc.net; web site www.custercountychronicle.com

Circulation: 2,415pd,240fr; Sworn/Estimate/Non-Audited
Advertising: Open inch rate $9.75
Established: 1880
Group: Southern Hills Publishing
Digital Platform - Mobile: Apple, Android, Windows, Blackberry, Other
Digital Platform - Tablet: Apple iOS, Android, Windows 7, Blackberry Tablet OS, Kindle, Nook, Kindle Fire, Other
Pub. .... Charles W. Najacht
Gen. Mgr. .... Jason Ferguson
Ed. .... Norma G. Najacht
Mechanical Specifications: Type page 13 x 21 1/2; E - 6 cols, 1.562" each
Equipment: Hardware — iMacs; Software — QuarkXPress 2015
Delivery Method: Mail, Newsstand, Racks
Zip Codes Served: 57730 and surrounding area in all of Custer County

HURON

PAY DAY

(Wed)
49 3rd St SE, Huron, SD, 57350-2015, USA; tel (605) 353-6401; adv tel (605) 353-7414; fax (605) 353-7457; adv fax (605) 353-7450; e-mail mededmail@aol.com; adv e-mail mdavis@plainsman.com; web site www.plainsman.com
Circulation:15,000fr; Sworn/Estimate/Non-Audited
Advertising: Open inch rate $15.50
Established: 2001
Digital Platform - Mobile: Apple
Pub .... Mark Davis
Mechanical Specifications: Tab. 9.9" x 12"
Delivery Method: Mail, Carrier
Zip Codes Served: 57350

MILBANK

THE VALLEY SHOPPER

(Mon)
203 S 3rd St, Milbank, SD, 57252-1908, USA; tel (605) 432-1000; fax (605) 432-1004; e-mail midpub@midlandpublishing.com; web site www.midlandpublishing.com
Circulation:16,649fr; Sworn/Estimate/Non-Audited
Co-Owner/Pub. .... Michael Sipe
Co-Owner .... Betty Sipe
Prodn. Mgr. .... Tammy Teske
Brandon Sipe
Nick Sipe
Madisen Sipe
Jennifer Wanorick
Jeannie Trevett
Zip Codes Served: 57252

MITCHELL

THE ADVISOR ADVANTAGE

(Wed)
120 S Lawler St, Mitchell, SD, 57301-3443, USA; tel (605) 996-5514; fax (605) 996-5020; e-mail dailynews@mitchellrepublic.com; web site www.mitchellrepublic.com
Circulation:17,372fr; VAC
Advertising: Open inch rate $8.65Kim Sinkie
Pub. .... Korrie Wenzel
Adv. Mgr. .... Kevin Flemmer
Circ. Mgr. .... Jon Louder
Mechanical Specifications: Type page 10 3/4 x 13; A - 5 cols, 2 1/16, between; C - 7 cols, 1 5/16, between.
Equipment: Hardware — APP/Mac IIci, APP/Mac, APP/Mac IIsi, APP/Mac 7100; Presses — 7-G/Community; Software — Adobe/PageMaker, Multi-Ad/Creator, QPS/QuarkXPress.

MOBRIDGE

MONDAY REMINDER

(Mon)
1413 E Grand Xing, Mobridge, SD, 57601-2905, USA; tel (605) 845-3646; fax (605) 845-7659; e-mail office@mobridgetribune.com; adv e-mail ads@mobridgetribune.com; ed e-mail news@mobridgetribune.com; web site www.mobridgetribune.com
Circulation:6,200fr; Sworn/Estimate/Non-Audited
Advertising: Open inch rate $12.30
Established: 1951
Group: Bridge City Publishing, Inc.
Digital Platform - Mobile: Apple, Android, Windows
Digital Platform - Tablet: Apple iOS, Windows 7
Pub .... Larry Atkinson
Ed .... Catherine Zerr
Gen Mgr. .... Linda Meyer
Sales Mgr .... Risa Fryling
ASI/Printing Manager .... Arden Nelson
Mechanical Specifications: Type page 10 3/4 x 16; E - 5 cols, 2 1/16, between; A - 5 cols, 2 1/16, between.
Equipment: Hardware — APP/Macs; Presses — 6-G/Community; Software — Adobe CC 2017
Delivery Method: Mail, Newsstand, Carrier
Zip Codes Served: 57601, 57648, 57632, 57423, 57646, 57631, 57472, 57420, 57452, 57428, 58538, 57641, 57642, 57643, 57658, 57639, 57657, 57661, 57630, 57656, 57628, 57633, 57450

PIERRE

REMINDER PLUS

(Wed) (Weekly)
333 W Dakota Ave, Pierre, SD, 57501-4512, USA; tel (605) 224-7301; fax (605) 224-9210; e-mail news@capjournal.com; adv e-mail sales@capjournal.com; ed e-mail publisher@capjournal.com; web site www.capjournal.com
Circulation:20,550fr; Sworn/Estimate/Non-Audited
Advertising: Open inch rate $18.50
Established: 1881
Group: Wick Communications
Pub. .... Steve Baker
Adv. Dir. .... Tim Craig
Mechanical Specifications: Type page 14 x 21 1/2; E - 8 cols, between; A - 8 cols, 1 1/2, 1/6 between; C - 8 cols, 1 1/2, 1/6 between.
Equipment: Hardware — PC; Presses — 7 unit G/Community; Software — Adobe cs 5.5
Delivery Method: Mail, Carrier, Racks
Zip Codes Served: 57501 .... Pierre 57532
Fort Pierre 57345 .... Highmore 57564
Onida 57536 .... Harrold 57522
Blunt 57371 .... Ree Heights 57520
Agar 57537 .... Hayes 57540
Holobird 57553 .... Milesville 57548
Lower Brule 57568 .... Presho 57339
Fort Thompson 57544 .... Kennebec 57569
Reliance 57576 .... Vivian 57625
Eagle Butte 57442 .... Gettysburg 57623
Dupree 57450 .... Hoven 57652
Ridgeview 57475 .... Tolstoy 57636
Lantry 57455 .... Lebanon 57420
Akaska 57622 .... Cherry Creek 57647
Parade 57567 .... Phillip 57543
Kadoka 57579 .... White River 57559
Murdo 57552 .... Midland 57560
Norris 57531 .... Draper 57585
Wood 57534 .... Hamill 57521
Belvedere 57541 .... Ideal 57584
Witten 57562 .... Okaton

SIOUX FALLS

AD VENTURE CLASSIFIEDS

(Wed) (monthly)
622 S Minnesota Ave, Ste 200, Sioux Falls, SD, 57104-4877, USA; tel (605) 332-0421; fax (605) 330-0513; adv e-mail ads@michelscom.com; web site www.adventure-online.com
Circulation: 28pd,8,508fr; VAC
Established: 2001
Group: J&C Publications
Digital Platform - Mobile: Apple
General Manager .... Lloyd Uthe
Delivery Method: Racks
Zip Codes Served: 57101-10

SIOUX FALLS SHOPPING NEWS

(Wed)
4005 S Western Ave, Sioux Falls, SD, 57105-6514, USA; tel (605) 339-3633; adv tel (605) 275-6373; ed tel (605) 274-2650; fax (605) 335-6873; adv fax (605) 334-2953; e-mail info@siouxfallsshoppingnews.com; sales@sfshoppingnews.com; adv e-mail ads@sfshoppingnews.com; web site www.sfshoppingnews.com
Circulation: 0pd,87,804fr; CVC
Advertising: Open inch rate $28.00
Established: 1939Editions: sioux falls shopping news.com
Digital Platform - Mobile: Windows
Digital Platform - Tablet: Windows 7
ceo/ president .... Lesnar K A
sales manager .... cathy crisp
Mechanical Specifications: Type page 10 1/4 x 16; E - 6 cols, 1 9/16, between; A - 6 cols, 1 9/16, between.
Equipment: Hardware — APP/Mac, PC; Presses — 16-G/Community 4 high; Software — Adobe/PageMaker, QPS/QuarkXPress, Multi-Ad/Creator, Adobe/Photoshop.
Delivery Method: Mail, Carrier, Racks

SPEARFISH

WEEKLY PROSPECTOR

(Tues)
315 Seaton Cir, Spearfish, SD, 57783-3212, USA; tel (605) 642-2761; fax (605) 642-9060; e-mail news@bhpioneer.com; sports@bhpioneer.com; adv e-mail classifieds@bhpioneer.com; dru@bhpioneer.com; ed e-mail news@bhpioneer.com; web site www.bhpioneer.com
Circulation:21,386fr; Sworn/Estimate/Non-Audited
Advertising: Open inch rate $13.75
Established: 1976
Digital Platform - Mobile: Android
Digital Platform - Tablet: Android
Pub. .... Letitia Lister
Adv. Mgr. .... Dru Thomas
Ed. .... Mark Watson
Mechanical Specifications: 7col x 13.5" column width 1.403"
Equipment: ; Presses — Goss; Software — Apple
Delivery Method: Mail, Carrier, Racks
Zip Codes Served: 57783, 57754,57732, 57779,57793,57779,57717,57760,57762,57788,57785,57758,57765,57792,57787,57748,57626,57720,57724,57776,82714,82711,82720,82712,82729,82721,82740,59316,59332,59311,59341,57701,57702,57703

VERMILLION

THE BROADCASTER

(Tues)
201 W Cherry St, Vermillion, SD, 57069-1109, USA; tel (605) 624-4429; fax (605) 624-2696; adv e-mail compads@plaintalk.net; web site www.vermillionsd.com
Circulation:10,775fr; VAC
Advertising: Open inch rate $6.00
Owner/Pub. .... Gary Wood
Mechanical Specifications: Type page 11 x 16; E - 6 cols, 1 1/2, between; A - 6 cols, 1 1/2, between.
Equipment: Hardware — APP/Power Mac, APP/Mac; Presses — 5-KP; Software — Adobe/PageMaker, Multi-Ad/Creator, Adobe/Photoshop.
Zip Codes Served: 57069

WAGNER

WAGNER ANNOUNCER

(Wed)
209 S Main Ave, Wagner, SD, 57380-1727, USA; tel (605) 384-5616; fax (605) 384-5955; e-mail announcer@hcinet.net; web site www.announceronline .com
Circulation:6,400fr; Sworn/Estimate/Non-Audited
Advertising: Open inch rate $5.25
Mng. Ed. .... Monica Wepking

WATERTOWN

COTEAU SHOPPER

(Sun)
120 3rd Ave NW, Watertown, SD, 57201-2311, USA; tel (605) 882-1358; fax (605) 882-1152; e-mail advertise@coteaushopper.com; adv e-mail advertise@coteaushopper.com; ed e-mail advertise@coteaushopper.com; web site www.coteaushopper.com
Circulation: 11pd,25,577fr; VAC
Advertising: Open inch rate $22.00
Established: 1979
Pub. .... Mark Roby
Mktg. Mgr. .... Tim Oviatt
Circ. Mgr. .... Paul Reinschmidt
Prodn. Mgr. .... Dan Sumner
Mechanical Specifications: Type page 13 x 21 1/2; E - 8 cols, 1 1/2, 1/8 between; A - 8 cols, 1 1/2, 1/8 between.
Equipment: Hardware — APP/Mac; Presses — HI/Cottrell; Software — QPS/QuarkXPress 3.3, QPS/QuarkXPress 4.0.
Delivery Method: Mail, Newsstand, Carrier
Zip Codes Served: 57201 and many many more

YANKTON

MISSOURI VALLEY SHOPPER

(Tues)
319 Walnut St, Yankton, SD, 57078-4344, USA; tel (605) 665-5884; fax (605) 665-0288; e-mail mvcompads@yankton.net; web site www.missourivalleyshopper.com
Circulation:22,288fr; CVC
Advertising: Open inch rate $12.07
Ed. .... Gary Wood
Mechanical Specifications: Type page 10 x 16; E - 6 cols, 1 1/2, between; A - 6 cols, 1 1/2, between.
Equipment: Hardware — APP/Mac IIsi, APP/Power Mac 6100, APP/Mac SE, APP/Power Mac 7200; Presses — 6-KP; Software — Adobe/PageMaker, Multi-Ad/Creator, Adobe/Photoshop.
Zip Codes Served: 57078

TENNESSEE

ASHLAND CITY

CHEATHAM COUNTY MONEY SAVER

(Wed)
202 N Main St, Ste A, Ashland City, TN, 37015-1318, USA; tel (615) 792-4230; fax (615) 792-3671; e-mail actimes@mtcngroup.com; web site www.tennessean.com
Circulation:8,300fr; Sworn/Estimate/Non-Audited
Advertising: Open inch rate $3.48
Established: 1981
Group: Gannett
The Tennessean

TN Media
Gen. Mgr. .... Shirley Bradley
Delivery Method: Mail
Zip Codes Served: 37015, 37146, 37035

CLARKSVILLE

PEDDLER

(Thur)
2012 Wilma Rudolph Blvd, Clarksville, TN, 37040-6620, USA; tel (931) 552-1160; fax (931) 552-1777; adv e-mail ads@e-peddler.com; web site www.e-peddler.com
Circulation:30,000fr; Sworn/Estimate/Non-Audited
Advertising: Open inch rate $7.00
Adv. Mgr. .... William Crouch
Circ. Mgr. .... Kenneth Griffin
Prodn. Mgr. .... Julie Epps
Equipment: Hardware — APP/Mac.
Zip Codes Served: 37040

COOKEVILLE

THE PEDDLER

(Thur)
420 N Washington Ave, Ste 7, Cookeville, TN, 38501-2678, USA; tel (931) 526-5910; adv tel (931) 526-5910; fax (931) 528-9735; adv fax (931) 528-9735; e-mail peddler38501@yahoo.com; adv e-mail peddler38501@gmail.com; ed e-mail peddler38501@gmail.com; web site www.thepeddlertn.com
Circulation:18,000fr; Sworn/Estimate/Non-Audited
Established: 1977
owner/publisher .... Timothy Sneed
Mechanical Specifications: Type page 10 1/2 x 12 3/4; E - 6 cols, 1 2/3, between; A - 6 cols, 1 2/3, between.
Delivery Method: Racks
Zip Codes Served: numerous

DAYTON

SUNRISE EDITION

(Wed, Sun)
3687 Rhea County Hwy, Dayton, TN, 37321-5819, USA; tel (423) 775-6111; fax (423) 775-8218; e-mail news@rheaheraldnews.com; web site rheaheraldnews.com
Circulation: 11,800pd,8,000fr; Sworn/Estimate/Non-Audited
Advertising: Open inch rate $10.76
Established: 1898
Circ. Mgr. .... Lynne Spivey
Publisher .... Sara Locke
Managing Editor .... Reed Johnson
Mechanical Specifications: Type page 11 5/8 x 21; E - 6 cols, 1 27/32, between; A - 6 cols, 1 27/32, between; C - 9 cols, 1 3/16, between.
Equipment: Hardware — APP/Mac G3, APP/Mac G4; Software — Adobe InDesign CS3
Zip Codes Served: 37321, 37381, 37338, 37337, 37332

DICKSON

DICKSON SHOPPER

(Tues)
104 Church St, Dickson, TN, 37055-1826, USA; tel (615) 446-2811; fax (615) 446-4608; web site www.tennessean.com
Circulation:19,800fr; Sworn/Estimate/Non-Audited
Advertising: Open inch rate $8.30
Group: Gannett
The Tennessean
TN Media
Gen. Mgr. .... Becky Moran
Mechanical Specifications: Type page 10 1/4 x 11 1/2; E - 6 cols, 1 1/2, between; A - 6 cols, 1 1/2, between; C - 6 cols, 1 1/2, between.
Zip Codes Served: 37056

FAYETTEVILLE

EXCHANGE

(Wed)
408 Main Ave S, Fayetteville, TN, 37334-3446, USA; tel (931) 433-9737; fax (931) 433-0053; adv e-mail katie@exchange-inc.com; web site www.exchange-inc.com
Circulation: 7pd,76,355fr; CVC
Advertising: Open inch rate $12.50
Established: 1979
Pub. .... Will Thomas
Office Mgr. .... Judy Flint
Adv. Mgr. .... Mary Ann Marsh
Circ. Mgr. .... Greta Painter
Prodn. Mgr. .... Melissa Hyde
Mechanical Specifications: Type page 10 1/4 x 16; E - 6 cols, 1 9/16, 3/16 between; A - 6 cols, 1 9/16, 3/16 between; C - 6 cols, 1 9/16, 3/16 between.
Equipment: Hardware — APP/Mac; Presses — 3-Web Press; Software — Adobe/PageMaker, Adobe/Photoshop, First Class/Ad Manager.
Delivery Method: Mail
Zip Codes Served: 35750, 37144, 37328, 37334, 37335, 37348, 37359, 38449, 38488, 37324, 37355

EXCHANGE - LINCOLN CO./FAYETTEVILLE

(Wed)
408 Main Ave S, Fayetteville, TN, 37334-3446, USA; tel (931) 433-9737; adv tel (931) 968-1144; ed tel (931) 455-1360; fax (931) 433-0053; adv fax (931) 433-0053; ed fax (931) 433-0053; e-mail production@exchange-inc.com; adv e-mail katie@exchange-inc.com; ed e-mail greta@exchange-inc.com; web site www.exchange-onthe.net
Circulation: 5pd,15,073fr; VAC
Advertising: Open inch rate $14.77 - $19.19
Established: 1979
Pub. .... Will Thomas
Delivery Method: Mail

EXCHANGE - MADISON COUNTY

(Wed)
408 Main Ave S, Fayetteville, TN, 37334-3446, USA; tel (931) 433-9737; adv tel (931) 968-1144; ed tel (931) 455-1360; fax (931) 433-0053; adv fax (931) 433-0053; ed fax (931) 433-0053; e-mail production@exchange-inc.com; adv e-mail katie@exchange-inc.com; ed e-mail greta@exchange-inc.com; web site www.exchange-onthe.net
Circulation: 0pd,12,702fr; VAC
Advertising: Open inch rate $14.77 - $19.19
Established: 1979
Pub. .... Will Thomas
Delivery Method: Mail

EXCHANGE - MANCHESTER (FORMERLY COFFEE COUNTY SHOPPER)

(Wed)
408 Main Ave S, Fayetteville, TN, 37334-3446, USA; web site www.exchangeonthe.net
Circulation: 0pd,14,884fr; VAC
Advertising: Open inch rate $14.77 - $19.19
Established: 1974Will Thomas

EXCHANGE - TULLAHOMA

(Wed)
408 Main Ave S, Fayetteville, TN, 37334-3446, USA; web site www.exchangeonthe.net
Circulation: 1pd,12,153fr; VAC
Advertising: Open inch rate $14.77 - $19.19
Established: 2003
CEO .... Will Thomas

EXCHANGE - WINCHESTER

(Wed)
408 Main Ave S, Fayetteville, TN, 37334-3446, USA; web site www.exchangeonthe.net
Circulation: 0pd,14,691fr; VAC
Advertising: Open inch rate $14.77 - $19.19Will Thomas

GALLATIN

THE SUMNER COUNTY SHOPPER

(Wed)
1 Examiner Ct, Gallatin, TN, 37066-7111, USA; tel (615) 452-2561; fax (615) 452-9110; e-mail gnenews@mtcngroup.com; web site www.gallatinnewsexaminer.com
Circulation:23,000fr; Sworn/Estimate/Non-Audited
Advertising: Open inch rate $15.50
Group: Gannett
The Tennessean
TN Media
General Manager .... Mike Towle
Mechanical Specifications: Type page 13 1/8 x 21 1/2; E - 6 cols, 2 1/16, 1/8 between; A - 6 cols, 2 1/16, 1/8 between; C - 10 cols, 1 1/4, 1/8 between.
Equipment: Hardware — APP/Mac, Hyphen Pelbox Typesetter, Umax/Powerlock Pro Scanner; Presses — WPC/Web Leader offset; Software — Multi-Ad/Creator, QPS/QuarkXPress, Adobe/Photoshop.
Zip Codes Served: 37066

HARROGATE

TRI-STATE CONNECTION

(Fri)
6988 Cumberland Gap Pkwy, Harrogate, TN, 37752-8230, USA; web site www.thetsconnection.com
Circulation: 0pd,4,417fr; VAC
Established: 2004Lynn Earls

JEFFERSON CITY

STANDARD BANNER PLUS

(Tues)
122 W Old Andrew Johnson Hwy, Jefferson City, TN, 37760-1945, USA; tel (865) 475-2081; adv tel (865) 471-9268; fax (865) 475-8539; e-mail info@standardbanner.com; plus@standardbanner.com; news@standardbanner.com; adv e-mail displayads@standardbanner.com; classifieds@standardbanner.com; web site www.standardbanner.com
Circulation:3,000fr; Sworn/Estimate/Non-Audited
Advertising: Open inch rate $8.25
Established: 1956
Adv. Mgr. .... Shane Cook
Circ. Mgr. .... Karen Trolinger
Mng. Ed. .... Dale Gentry
Prodn. Mgr. .... Paul Young
Mechanical Specifications: Type page 13 x 21; E - 6 cols, 2 1/16, between; A - 6 cols, 2 1/16, between; C - 6 cols, 2 1/16, between.
Equipment: Hardware — APP/Power Macs, PCs; Presses — KP; Software — Adobe/PageMaker 6.0.
Zip Codes Served: 37760, 37725, 37877, 37890, 37820, 37861

KINGSTON

THE SHOPPER

(Tues)
204 Franklin St, Kingston, TN, 37763-2625, USA; tel (865) 376-3481; fax (865) 376-1945; web site www.roanecounty.com
Circulation:17,550fr; Sworn/Estimate/Non-Audited
Advertising: Open inch rate $5.50
Group: Landmark Communications, Inc.
Pub. .... Johnny Teglas
Office Mgr. .... Tiffeney Yeary
Adv. Mgr. .... Kevin Kile
Ed. .... Terri Likens
Mechanical Specifications: Type page 13 x 21; E - 6 cols, 2 1/16, 1/8 between; A - 6 cols, 2 1/16, 1/8 between; C - 6 cols, 2 1/16, 1/8 between.
Zip Codes Served: 37763

KNOXVILLE

AMERICAN CLASSIFIEDS

(Thur)
10420 Kingston Pike, Knoxville, TN, 37922-3191, USA; tel (865) 249-7061; fax (865) 531-3493; e-mail placeads@americanclassifiedknoxville.com; web site www.americanclassifiedsknoxville.com
Circulation:24,696fr; Sworn/Estimate/Non-Audited
Advertising: Open inch rate $14.00
Patty Baker
Ben pattersonCo-Owners
Mechanical Specifications: Type page 10 3/8 x 16; E - 8 cols, 1 1/4, 1/16 between; A - 8 cols, 1 1/4, 1/16 between.
Equipment: Hardware — IBM; Software — Adobe/PageMaker 6.5, Adobe/Photoshop 4.0.
Zip Codes Served: 37110, 37617, 37682, 37705, 37714, 37715, 37760, 37774, 37930, 38261, 38281, 38502, 38506, 38573

HALLS SHOPPER NEWS

(Mon)
4509 Doris Cir, Knoxville, TN, 37918-5808, USA; tel (865) 922-4136; fax (865) 922-5275; e-mail news@hallsnews.com; web site www.shoppernewsnow.com
Circulation:93,880fr; Sworn/Estimate/Non-Audited
Advertising: Open inch rate $10.00
Established: 1961
Adv. Sales Mgr. .... Patty Fecco
Adv. Sales .... Darlene Kinsey Hutchison
Ed. .... Sandra L. Clark
Mechanical Specifications: Type page 10 4/5 x 13; E - 5 cols, 2 1/16, 3/16 between; A - 5 cols, 2 1/16, 3/16 between; C - 5 cols, 2 1/16, 3/16 between.
Equipment: Hardware — APP/Mac, PC; Software — Adobe/PageMaker 6.5.
Zip Codes Served: 37928

MANCHESTER

THE SHOPPER

(Wed)
105 W High St, Manchester, TN, 37355-1697, USA; tel (931) 728-3273; fax (931) 723-9158; e-mail production@totalgraphics.net; web site www.totalgraphics.net
Circulation:20,820fr; Sworn/Estimate/Non-Audited
Advertising: Open inch rate $10.25
Pub. .... Will Thomas
Sales. Mgr. .... Mary Marsh
Zip Codes Served: 37355

PARIS

PEDDLER ADVANTAGE

(Thur)
512 N Market St, Paris, TN, 38242-3415, USA; web site www.peddlerads.com
Circulation: 0pd,15,748fr; VAC
Advertising: Open inch rate $8.50
Established: 1985Gary Benton

THE PEDDLER/ADVANTAGE

(Wed)
512 N Market St, Paris, TN, 38242-3415, USA; tel (731) 644-9595; fax (731) 644-9970; e-mail peddlerads@bellsouth.net
Circulation:20,436fr; Sworn/Estimate/Non-Audited
Advertising: Open inch rate $6.70
Adv. Mgr. .... Gary Benton

Zip Codes Served: 38242, 38320, 37058, 37061, 42071, 38237, 38201, 38221

SOUTH PITTSBURG

SEQUATCHIE VALLEY PURCHASE
(Wed)
307 1/2 Elm Ave, South Pittsburg, TN, 37380-1337, USA; tel (423) 837-6312; adv tel (423) 837-6312; ed tel (423) 837-6312; fax (423) 837-8715; e-mail mcnews@marioncountynews.net; adv e-mail classifiedworks@marioncountynews.net; ed e-mail classifiedworks@marioncountynews.net; web site www.marioncountynews.net
Circulation:8,600fr; USPS
Advertising: Open inch rate $6.50
Pub. .... Melissa Brown
Managing Ed. .... Kathie Tierney
Composer .... Christy Sacks
Zip Codes Served: 37380

TALBOTT

THE SMOKY MOUNTAIN TRADER
(Thur)
6158 W Andrew Johnson Hwy, Talbott, TN, 37877-8603, USA; tel (423) 587-1700; fax (423) 587-2906; web site www.thesmtrader.com
Circulation: 0pd,8,971fr; CVC
Advertising: Open inch rate $12.75
Established: 1987
Pub. .... Lynn Earls
Circ. Mgr .... Kent Hatmaker
Mechanical Specifications: Type page 10 x 12 1/2.
Equipment: Hardware — APP/Mac, IBM; Software — Adobe/PageMaker, Archetype/Corel Draw.
Zip Codes Served: 37708, 37711, 37713, 37722, 37725, 37743, 37760, 37810, 37813, 37814, 37818, 37820, 37821, 37861, 37862, 37877, 37890, 37892

WAVERLY

SHOPPER'S GUIDE
(Wed)
302A W Main St, Waverly, TN, 37185-1513, USA; tel (931) 296-7705; fax (931) 296-5156; e-mail newsdemocrat@bellsouth.net
Circulation:9,500fr; Sworn/Estimate/Non-Audited
Advertising: Open inch rate $5.25
Established: 1976
Pub. .... Bill Ridings
Mechanical Specifications: Type page 10 1/4 x 13; A - 6 cols, 2, 1/6 between; C - 6 cols, 2, 1/6 between.
Equipment: Hardware — APP/Mac; Software — Adobe/PageMaker, Microsoft/Word.
Zip Codes Served: 37185

WHITE HOUSE

BARGAIN BROWSER
(Tues)
101 Highland Dr, Hwy 31, White House, TN, 37188, USA; tel (615) 672-3555; fax (615) 672-5971; e-mail sales@bargainbrowser.com; web site www.bargainbrowser.com
Circulation: 4pd,22,500fr; Sworn/Estimate/Non-Audited
Advertising: Open inch rate $7.48
Pub. .... W. Douglas Lee
Adv. Mgr. .... Mandy Christenson
Circ. Mgr. .... Drew Christenson
Ed. .... Barbara Lee
Mechanical Specifications: Type page 10 3/8 x 14; E - 6 cols, 1 5/8, 1/8 between; A - 6 cols, 1 5/8, 1/8 between.
Equipment: Hardware — APP/Mac; Software — Adobe/PageMaker, Adobe/Photoshop, Adobe/Illustrator.
Zip Codes Served: 37188

TEXAS

ABILENE

AMERICAN CLASSIFIEDS
(Thur)
2903 N 3rd St, Abilene, TX, 79603-7116, USA; tel (325) 673-4521; fax (325) 673-4525; e-mail americanclassifieds@abilene.com; web site www.abileneads.net
Circulation: 0pd,25,490fr; VAC
Advertising: Open inch rate $10.00
Established: 1981
Owner .... Karla Hutchinson
Circ. Mgr. .... Tom Netherlin
Equipment: Hardware — 2-APP/Mac G3, 2-APP/Mac Perfoma 6300 CD, APP/Mac 6100/60, APP/Mac 8500/180, Scanners; Software — Adobe/PageMaker 6.5, Adobe/Photoshop, Adobe/Illustrator, QPS/QuarkXPress, Marcromedia/Freehand.
Zip Codes Served: 79603

AMARILLO

AMERICAN CLASSIFIEDS
(Thur)
1612 S Washington St, Amarillo, TX, 79102-2662, USA; tel (806) 376-8663; fax (806) 376-5219; e-mail amarillo@americanclassifieds.com; web site www.americanclassifieds.com
Circulation: 0pd,26,378fr; VAC
Advertising: Open inch rate $7.00
Established: 1981
Gen. Mgr. .... Debby Burnett
Adv. Mgr. .... Christine Spring
Circ. Mgr. .... Ryan Putman
Prodn. Mgr. .... Christine Hasenaver

ATHENS

THE STAR
(Thur)
201 S Prairieville St, Athens, TX, 75751-2541, USA; tel (903) 675-5626; fax (903) 675-9450; e-mail news2@athensreview.com; adv e-mail addirector@athensreview.com; ed e-mail sportseditor@athensreview.com; editor@athensreview.com; web site www.athensreview.com
Circulation:8,550fr; Sworn/Estimate/Non-Audited
Advertising: Open inch rate $5.00
Group: Community Newspaper Holdings, Inc.
Pub. .... Linge Svehlak
Adv. Dir. .... Andi Green
Circ. Mgr. .... Ginger McDaniel
Sports Ed. .... Jayson Larson
Mechanical Specifications: Type page 11 3/4 x 21 1/2; E - 6 cols, between; A - 6 cols, between; C - 8 cols, between.
Equipment: Hardware — APP/Macs; Presses — HI/Cottrell V-15A; Software — Baseview, QPS/QuarkXPress.
Zip Codes Served: 75751

ATLANTA

CASS COUNTY SHOPPER
(Wed)
PO Box 1188, Atlanta, TX, 75551-1188, USA; tel (903) 796-7133; fax (903) 796-3294; e-mail production@casscountynow.com; adv e-mail advertising@casscountynow.com; ed e-mail news@casscountynow.com; web site www.casscountynow.com
Circulation:7,000fr; Sworn/Estimate/Non-Audited
Advertising: 7.95
Established: 1879
Group: Northeast Texas Publishing
Digital Platform - Mobile: Apple, Windows
Publisher .... Austin Lewter
Delivery Method: Mail, Newsstand, Carrier, Racks
Zip Codes Served: 75551, 75555, 75556, 75560, 75572, 75563, 75566

BEAUMONT

AMERICAN CLASSIFIEDS - BEAUMONT
(Thur)
2678 Calder St, Beaumont, TX, 77702-1917, USA; web site www.americanclassifieds.com
Circulation:43,986fr; CVCMarla Honeycutt

BOWIE

MONTAGUE COUNTY SHOPPER
(Thur)
1300 E Wise St, Bowie, TX, 76230-4521, USA; tel (940) 872-6186; fax (940) 872-3559; web site www.morgan.net
Circulation:15,000fr; Sworn/Estimate/Non-Audited
Advertising: Open inch rate $6.00
Pub. .... Carol Johnson
Mechanical Specifications: Type page 10 1/4 x 16.
Equipment: Hardware — APP/Mac, PC; Presses — 10-HI/V-15A; Software — Adobe/PhotoMaker, Adobe/PageMaker.
Zip Codes Served: 76228, 76230, 76239, 76251, 76255, 76261, 76265, 76270

BRENHAM

BANNER EXTRA
(Thur)
2430 S Chappell Hill St, Brenham, TX, 77833-6098, USA; tel (979) 836-7956; fax (979) 830-8577; e-mail circ@brenhambanner.com; adv e-mail classified@brenhambanner.com; ed e-mail edit@brenhambanner.com; web site www.brenhambanner.com
Circulation: 6,500pd,13,185fr; Sworn/Estimate/Non-Audited
Advertising: Open inch rate $7.78Editions: 1—1 total; Home Improvement;
Gen. Mgr. .... Danny Hukel
Retail Adv. Mgr. .... Helen Nowicki
Ed. .... Michael Mueck
Printing Supvr. .... Clem Krolczyk
Mechanical Specifications: Type page 10 1/8 x 13; E - 5 cols, 2 1/8, between; C - 7 cols, 1 1/4, between.
Equipment: Hardware — APP/Mac; Presses — WPC/Web Leader; Software — Baseview.
Zip Codes Served: 77833

BROWNSVILLE

BARGAIN BOOK
(Wed)
1300 Wildrose Ln, Brownsville, TX, 78520-8600, USA; tel (956) 546-5113; fax (956) 546-0903; adv e-mail adcopy@bargainbook.cc; web site http://www.valleybargainbook.com/classifieds/
Circulation: 0pd,144,976fr; CVC
Advertising: Open inch rate $66.45
Established: 1978Editions: 4— 4 total; Bargain Book-Central (22,323); Bargain Book-Laredo (55,085); Bargain Book-North (39,335); Bargain Book-South (50,039);
Gen. Mgr. .... Linda Medrano
Circ. Mgr. .... Marco Alvardo
Prodn. Mgr. .... Craig Virnig
Mechanical Specifications: Type page 10 1/2 x 16; E - 6 cols, 1 5/8, between; A - 6 cols, 1 5/8, between; C - 6 cols, 1 5/8, between.
Equipment: Hardware — APP/Mac; Presses — 13-HI; Software — Adobe/PageMaker 6.0, QPS/QuarkXPress 3.2, Adobe/Photoshop 3.1, Macromedia/Freehand 5.0, Adobe/Illustrator 5.0.

BARGAIN BOOK - CENTRAL
(Wed)
1300 Wildrose Ln, Brownsville, TX, 78520-8600, USA; web site www.valleybargainbook.com
Circulation: 0pd,23,204fr; VAC
Advertising: Open inch rate $15.00
Established: 1981Dennis Wade

BARGAIN BOOK - SOUTH
(Wed)
1300 Wildrose Ln, Brownsville, TX, 78520-8600, USA; web site www.valleybargainbook.com
Circulation: 0pd,23,204fr; VAC
Advertising: Open inch rate $21.00
Established: 1978Dennis Wade

BROWNWOOD

THE BROWN COUNTY POST
(Tues)
700 Carnegie St, Brownwood, TX, 76801-7040, USA; tel (325) 646-2541; fax (325) 646-6835; e-mail news@brownwoodbulletin.com; adv e-mail ads@brownwoodbulletin.com; web site www.brownwoodbulletin.com
Circulation:9,700fr; Sworn/Estimate/Non-Audited
Advertising: Open inch rate $6.50
Established: 1900
Pub. .... Robert Brincefield
Assoc. Pub. .... Bill Crist
Mktg. Mgr. .... Juliette Lemond
Mechanical Specifications: Type page 13 x 21 1/2; E - 6 cols, 2, between; A - 6 cols, 2, between; C - 10 cols, 1 1/5, between.
Equipment: Hardware — APP/Macs; Presses — 7-G/Community; Software — Baseview/Editorial, Baseview/Classified.
Zip Codes Served: 76801

BRYAN

AMERICAN CLASSIFIEDS
(Thur)
923 S Texas Ave, Bryan, TX, 77803-4554, USA; tel (979) 822-7899; fax (979) 822-9098; web site http://bryancollegestation.tnol.com
Circulation: 0pd,27,388fr; VAC
Advertising: Open inch rate $8.00
Established: 1988
Pub. .... Pat Niles
Pub. .... Steve Niles
Adv. Sales Mgr. .... Candace Hollis

CARTHAGE

PANOLA SHOPPER
(Wed, Sat)
109 W Panola St, Carthage, TX, 75633-2631, USA; tel (903) 693-7888; fax (903) 693-5857; e-mail news@panolawatchman.com; web site www.panolawatchman.com
Circulation:10,000fr; Sworn/Estimate/Non-Audited
Advertising: Open inch rate $7.95
Established: 1871
Pub. .... Bill Holder
Adv. Mgr. .... Lanette Jeans
Sports Ed. .... Travis Curry

CENTER

THE MERCHANDISER

(Tues)
137 San Augustine St, Center, TX, 75935-3951, USA; tel (936) 598-3377; fax (936) 598-6394
Circulation:7,000fr; Sworn/Estimate/Non-Audited
Advertising: Open inch rate $7.85
Established: 1972
Publisher....JoAnna Martin
Mechanical Specifications: Type page 13 x 21 1/2; E - 6 cols, between; A - 6 cols, between; C - 9 cols, between.
Delivery Method: Carrier, Racks
Zip Codes Served: 75935

CLEVELAND

EASTEX ADVOCATE

(Wed)
106 W Hanson St, Cleveland, TX, 77327-4406, USA; tel (281) 592-2626; web site www.hcnonline.com
Circulation: 0pd,8,726fr; CVC
Advertising: Open inch rate $9.88
Group: Times Media GroupDianne Brady

EASTEX SHOPPER

(Wed)
PO Box 1628, Cleveland, TX, 77328-1628, USA; tel (281) 592-2626; fax (281) 592-2629; e-mail clevelandadvocate@hcnonline.com; web site www.clevelandadvocate.com
Circulation:15,000fr; Sworn/Estimate/Non-Audited
Advertising: Open inch rate $8.55
Established: 1965
Adv. Mgr....Diane Brady
Ed....Vanesa Brashier
Graphic Artist....Janet Sterns
Mechanical Specifications: Type page 11 5/8 x 21 1/2; E - 6 cols, 2, between; A - 6 cols, 2, between; C - 10 cols, 1 1/10, between.
Zip Codes Served: 77327

CLUTE

BUYER'S EXPRESS

(Wed)
720 S Main St, Clute, TX, 77531-5411, USA; tel (979) 265-7411; fax (979) 265-9052; e-mail news@thefacts.com; web site www.thefacts.com
Circulation:14,000fr; Sworn/Estimate/Non-Audited
Advertising: Open inch rate $4.50
Pub....Bill Cornwell
Gen. Mgr....Judy Starnes
Retail Mgr....Deana Lesco
Circ. Mgr....Glenn Blount
Mng. Ed....Yvonne Mintz
Prodn. Mgr....Frankie Ramirez
Equipment: Hardware — APP/Mac; Software — QPS/QuarkXPress, Microsoft/Word.

CORPUS CHRISTI

AD SACK

(Fri)
2660 S Padre Island Dr, Corpus Christi, TX, 78415-1806, USA; tel (361) 854-0137; adv tel (361) 854-0137; ed tel n/a; fax (361) 854-2439; adv fax (361) 854-2439; ed fax n/a; e-mail adsack@adsack.com; adv e-mail eortiz@adsack.com; ed e-mail n/a; web site www.adsack.com
Circulation: 0pd,44,975fr; VAC
Advertising: Open inch rate $26.00
Established: 1971
Group: GateHouse Media, Inc.
General Manager....Elda Ortiz
Mechanical Specifications: 1 col. = 1.68"
2 cols. = 3.44"
3 cols. = 5.20"
4 cols. = 6.97"
5 cols. = 8.74"
6 cols. = 10.50"
Each page = 10.50" x 15.75" deep
Delivery Method: Racks
Zip Codes Served: 78401, 78402, 78404, 78405, 78407, 78408, 78409, 78410, 78411, 78412, 78413, 78414, 78415, 78416, 78417, 78418, 78330, 78332, 78336, 78339, 78102, 78343, 78351, 78358, 78022, 78359, 78362, 78363, 78370, 78372, 78373, 78374, 78377, 78379, 78380, 78382, 78384, 78383, 78387, 78389, 78390, 78071, 78393

AMERICAN CLASSIFIEDS

(Thur)
1308 Airline Rd, Corpus Christi, TX, 78412-3910, USA; tel (361) 980-0008; fax (361) 980-1088; web site http://cc.tnol.com
Circulation:45,000fr; Sworn/Estimate/Non-Audited
Advertising: Open inch rate $13.00
Established: 1996
Pub....Galen Niles
Adv. Mgr....Judy Carson

CORSICANA

STAR SHOPPER

(Wed)
PO Box 622, Corsicana, TX, 75151-9006, USA; tel (903) 872-3931; adv tel (877) 670-3400; fax (903) 872-6878; e-mail dailysun@corsicanadailysun.com; web site www.corsicanadailysun.com
Circulation: 4,500pd,12,992fr; Sworn/Estimate/Non-Audited
Advertising: Open inch rate $8.68
Group: Community Newspaper Holdings, Inc.
Pub....Raymond Linex
Circ. Mgr....David Smith
Ed....Bob Belcher
Mechanical Specifications: Type page 13 x 21 1/2; E - 6 cols, 2 1/16, 1/4 between.
Equipment: Hardware — APP/Mac; Presses — 5-G/Urbanite; Software — Baseview/NewsEdit, QPS/QuarkXPress.
Zip Codes Served: 75151

DALLAS

GREENSHEET

(Wed, Thur, Fri)
7929 Brookriver Dr, Ste 350, Dallas, TX, 75247-6922, USA; tel (214) 853-6088; fax (214) 853-6003; ed e-mail marketing@thegreensheet.com; web site http://dallas.thegreensheet.com/
Circulation:31,608fr; VAC
Advertising: Open inch rate $12.50
Established: 1970Editions: 20— Arlington Grand Prairie (thur) 15570; Austin (thur) 49038; Dallas City (fri) 29725; Dallas East (fri) 33933; Dallas North (fri) 23363; Dallas South (fri) 38760; East (fri) 35126; Greater Fort Worth (thur) 33509; Innerloop (fri) 30268; North (fri) 40975; Northeast Tarrant County (thur) 10015; Northwest (fri) 29390; South (thur) 24933; Southeast (fri) 33032; Southwest (fri) 29538; Suburban North (fri) 29339; Suburban Northwest (fri) 36861; Suburban Southeast (fri) 27355; Suburban Southwest (fri) 34444; West (fri) 26124
Digital Platform - Mobile: Apple, Android, Windows, Blackberry
Digital Platform - Tablet: Apple iOS, Android, Windows 7, Blackberry Tablet OS, Kindle, Nook, Kindle Fire
Pub....Kathleen Douglass
Prodn. Mgr....Ted Stiles
Dirk Van Slyke
Mechanical Specifications: Type page 10 1/4 x 14; E - 6 cols, 1 2/3, 1/6 between; A - 6 cols, 1 2/3, 1/6 between; C - 6 cols, 1 2/3, 1/6 between.
Equipment: Hardware — 90-Compaq/486DX2 Pentium workstation, 18-APP/Power Mac 8100, 2-IBM/RS 6000; Presses — 10-HI/V-15D; Software — Multi-Ad/Creator 4.0, Macromedia/Freehand 5.5, Adobe/Photoshop 3.0, Sysdeco/R5CLSPAG Pagination, Cascade/Imageflow, Cascade/Dataflow,
Delivery Method: Racks
Zip Codes Served: 75235

LA SUBASTA DE DALLAS

(Thur)
1555 W Mockingbird Ln, Ste 212, Dallas, TX, 75235-5080, USA; tel (214) 951-9500; adv tel (713) 777-1010; fax (214) 951-9400; e-mail customerservice@lasubasta.com ; adv e-mail sales@lasubasta.com; web site www.lasubasta.com
Circulation:57,137fr; VAC
Sales Manager....Eduardo Perez

DENISON

THE HERALD DEMOCRAT SHOPPER BRYAN COUNTY

(Wed)
331 W Woodard St, Denison, TX, 75020-3136, USA; tel (903) 465-1400; fax (903) 465-1453
Circulation:; Sworn/Estimate/Non-Audited
Advertising: Open inch rate $12.85
Established: 1977
Circ. Mgr....Richard White
Prodn. Mgr....Teresa Redd
Mechanical Specifications: Type page 11 3/8 x 16; A - 6 cols, 1 2/3, 1/6 between; C - 6 cols, 1 2/3, 1/6 between.
Equipment: Hardware — APP/Mac; Presses — 8-HI/V-15D; Software — Adobe/PageMaker, Adobe/Photoshop, QPS/QuarkXPress, Multi-Ad/CAMS.

THE HERALD DEMOCRAT SHOPPER COLLIN COUNTY

(Wed)
331 W Woodard St, Denison, TX, 75020-3136, USA; tel (903) 465-1400; fax (903) 465-1453
Circulation:; Sworn/Estimate/Non-Audited
Advertising: Open inch rate $12.85
Established: 1977
Circ. Mgr....Richard White
Prodn. Mgr....Teresa Redd
Mechanical Specifications: Type page 11 3/8 x 16; A - 6 cols, 1 2/3, 1/6 between; C - 6 cols, 1 2/3, 1/6 between.
Equipment: Hardware — APP/Mac; Presses — 8-HI/V-15D; Software — Adobe/PageMaker, Adobe/Photoshop, QPS/QuarkXPress, Multi-Ad/CAMS.

THE HERALD DEMOCRAT SHOPPER COOKE COUNTY

(Wed)
331 W. Woodard St., Denison, TX, 75020-3136, USA; tel (903) 465-7171; fax (903) 465-1453
Circulation: 0pd,0fr; Sworn/Estimate/Non-Audited
Circ. Mgr....Richard White
Prodn. Mgr....Teresa Redd
Mechanical Specifications: Type page 11 3/8 x 16; A - 6 cols, 1 2/3, 1/6 between; C - 6 cols, 1 2/3, 1/6 between.
Equipment: Hardware — APP/Mac; Presses — 8-HI/V-15D; Software — Adobe/PageMaker, Adobe/Photoshop, QPS/QuarkXPress, Multi-Ad/CAMS.
Zip Codes Served: 76240,76272,76238,76263,76252,76253,76250

THE HERALD DEMOCRAT SHOPPER GRAYSON COUNTY

(Wed)
331 W Woodard St, Denison, TX, 75020-3136, USA; tel (903) 465-7171; fax (903) 465-1453; web site http://heralddemocrat.com/herald-democrat-shopper
Circulation:53,000fr; Sworn/Estimate/Non-Audited
Advertising: Open inch rate $23.00
Established: 1968
Gen. Mgr....Richard White
Mechanical Specifications: Type page 10 3/4 x 16; A - 6 cols, 1 2/3, between.
Equipment: Hardware — APP/Mac; Presses — 8-HI/V-15P, 8-HI/V-15D; Software — Adobe/PageMaker, Adobe/Photoshop, QPS/QuarkXPress, Multi-Ad/CAMS.
Zip Codes Served: 73432, 73439, 73440, 73446, 73447, 73449, 73450, 73455, 73460, 73461, 74530, 74701, 74720, 74721, 74723, 74726, 74729, 74730, 74731, 74733, 74741, 74747, 74748, 74753, 74836, 74856, 75020, 75058, 75076, 75090, 75092, 75095, 75414, 75459, 75479, 75489, 754

THE HERALD DEMOCRAT SHOPPER MARSHALL-JOHNSTON COUNTY

(Wed)
331 W Woodard St, Denison, TX, 75020-3136, USA; tel (903) 465-1400; adv tel (903) 465-1400; fax (903) 465-1453; adv fax (903) 464-1453; e-mail rwhite@heralddemocrat.com; adv e-mail rwhite@heralddemocrat.com
Circulation: 0pd,50,000fr; Sworn/Estimate/Non-AuditedEditions: 0— 0
Circ. Mgr....Richard White
Prodn. Mgr....Teresa Redd
Mechanical Specifications: Type page 11 3/8 x 16; A - 6 cols, 1 2/3, 1/6 between; C - 6 cols, 1 2/3, 1/6 between.
Equipment: Hardware — APP/Mac; Presses — 8-HI/V-15D; Software — Adobe/PageMaker, Adobe/Photoshop, QPS/QuarkXPress, Multi-Ad/CAMS.
Zip Codes Served: 73460, 73455, 73450, 73439, 73440, 73449

THE SHOPPER

(Wed)
331 W Woodard St, Denison, TX, 75020-3136, USA; tel (903) 465-1400; fax (903) 465-1453; e-mail rwhite@heralddemocrat.com
Circulation:52,000fr; Sworn/Estimate/Non-Audited
Advertising: Open inch rate $10.54
Adv. Mgr....Richard White
Mechanical Specifications: Type page 11 3/8 x 16; A - 6 cols, 1 2/3, 1/6 between; C - 6 cols, 1 2/3, 1/6 between.
Equipment: Hardware — APP/Mac; Presses — 8-HI/V-15A, 8-HI/V-15D; Software — Adobe/PageMaker, Adobe/Photoshop, QPS/QuarkXPress, Multi-Ad/CAMS.
Zip Codes Served: 75090, 75092, 76233, 76245, 76264, 76278, 76270, 75076, 75058, 76273, 75020, 75021, 75489, 75414, 75459, 75495, 75491, 75479

FORT WORTH

WEDGWOOD SHOPPING NEWS

(Wed) (every two weeks)
6001 Granbury Rd, Fort Worth, TX, 76133-2719, USA; tel (817) 292-2260; fax (817) 292-9692; e-mail wsn@mesh.net
Circulation:25,000fr; Sworn/Estimate/Non-Audited
Established: 1963
Publisher....Carla Duke
Prodn. Mgr....Karen Scott
Editor....Kay Pirtle
Sales Person....Linda Sosa
Mechanical Specifications: Type page 10 1/4 x 13 1/4.
Equipment: ; Software — Adobe/PageMaker.
Delivery Method: Mail, Racks
Zip Codes Served: 76133

GEORGETOWN

SAN GABRIEL WEEKLY
(Thur)
707 S Main St, Georgetown, TX, 78626-5700, USA; tel (512) 930-4824; adv e-mail ads@wilcosun.com; ed e-mail editor@wilcosun.com; web site wilcosun.com
Circulation:12,000fr; Sworn/Estimate/Non-Audited
Advertising: Open inch rate $11.00
Established: 1981
Pub. .... Clark Thurmond
Mechanical Specifications: Type page 13 x 21; E - 6 cols, 2, between; A - 6 cols, 2, between.
Equipment: Hardware — APP/Macs, IBM/PCs; Presses — Goss Community
Delivery Method: Mail
Zip Codes Served: 78627, 78626, 78628, 78633

GRAHAM

LAKE COUNTRY SHOPPER
(Thur)
620 Oak St, Graham, TX, 76450-3040, USA; tel (940) 549-7800; fax (940) 549-4364; e-mail publisher@grahamleader.com; adv e-mail advmgr@grahamleader.com; ed e-mail editor@grahamleader.com; web site www.grahamleader.com
Circulation:8,050fr; Sworn/Estimate/Non-Audited
Advertising: Open inch rate $9.35
Established: 1876
Group: Moser Community Media, LLCEditions: Final - 8,050
Vice President / Group Publisher
Graham Newspapers, Inc. .... Robb Krecklow
Advertising Manager .... Trish Shifflett
Publisher... Tyler Patton
Mechanical Specifications: Page size: 12.5 inches x 22.5 inches
Image area: 11 inches x 20.5 inches
6 Column width:
1 col = 1.75 inches
2 col = 3.75 inches
3 col = 5.6875 inches
4 col = 7.625 inches
5 col = 9.5625 inches
6 col = 11.5 inches
Equipment: Hardware — Apple:
I-Mac
Mac Mini; Presses — 9-unit Web Leader; Software — Adobe Creative Suite
Delivery Method: Mail, Newsstand, Racks
Zip Codes Served: 76450, 76374, 76372, 76427, 76491, 76483
Note: Non-duplicated coverage in CZ 76450

GREENVILLE

HUNT COUNTY SHOPPER
(Wed)
3617 Wesley St, Greenville, TX, 75401-9008, USA; tel (903) 455-5254; fax (903) 455-3297; e-mail hcshop@swbell.net; web site shophuntcounty.com
Circulation: 0pd,30,433fr; VAC
Advertising: Open inch rate $6.50
Established: 1965
Ed. .... Warren Hope
Mechanical Specifications: Type page 10 3/8 x 15; E - 6 cols, 1 5/8, between; A - 6 cols, 1 5/8, between; C - 6 cols, 1 5/8, between.
Equipment: Hardware — IBM, APP/Mac; Software — Adobe/PageMaker.
Zip Codes Served: 75401

HARLINGEN

BARGAIN BOOK - NORTH
(Wed)
1126 S Commerce St, Harlingen, TX, 78550-7707, USA; web site www.valleybargainbook.com
Circulation: 0pd,39,568fr; VAC
Advertising: Open inch rate $21.00
Established: 1981Dennis Wade

HEARNE

ROBERTSON COUNTY BOOSTER
(Wed)
120 W 3rd St, Hearne, TX, 77859-2502, USA; tel (979) 279-3411; fax (979) 279-5401; e-mail news@robconews.com; web site www.robconews.com
Circulation:2,500fr; Sworn/Estimate/Non-Audited
Advertising: Open inch rate $1.00
Gen. Mgr. .... John Melvin

HOUSTON

VOICE OF ASIA
(Fri)
6200 Highway 6 S, Ste 225, Houston, TX, 77083-1539, USA; web site www.voiceofasiaonline.com
Circulation: 0pd,9,900fr; VAC
Advertising: Open inch rate $25.00
Established: 1987
Publisher.................................. Koshy Thomas

HUMBLE

HOMETOWN SHOPPER
(Fri)
19123 Player Park Dr, Humble, TX, 77346-6149, USA; tel (281) 540-6680; fax (281) 548-0899; e-mail hometown_shopper@comcast.net; web site www.hometownshopper.us
Circulation:13,500fr; Sworn/Estimate/Non-Audited
Advertising: Open inch rate $9.00
Established: 1990
Office Mgr. .... Mary Conrad
owner.. Geneva Robuck
Mechanical Specifications: Type page 10 5/16 x 13; E - 6 cols, 1 9/16, between; A - 6 cols, 1 9/16, between; C - 6 cols, 1 9/16, between.
Delivery Method: Newsstand, Racks

KAUFMAN

KAUFMAN SHOPPER
PO Box 460, Kaufman, TX, 75142-0460, USA; web site www.hartmannews.com
Circulation:8,400fr; CVCMichael Gresham

SHOPPING GUIDE
(Tues)
PO Box 460, Kaufman, TX, 75142-0460, USA; tel (972) 932-2171; fax (972) 932-2172; e-mail sales@kaufmanherald.com; adv e-mail circulation@kaufmanherald.com; web site www.kaufmanherald.com
Circulation:8,400fr; Sworn/Estimate/Non-Audited
Advertising: Open inch rate $10.15
Retail Adv. .... Monica Lewis
Ed. .... Michael Gresham
Equipment: Hardware — APP/Macs; Software — QPS/QuarkXPress.
Zip Codes Served: 75142

LAREDO

BARGAIN BOOK - LAREDO
(Wed)
3100 State Highway 359, Laredo, TX, 78043-4115, USA; web site www.laredosbargainbook.com
Circulation: 0pd,31,377fr; VAC
Advertising: Open inch rate $14.00
Established: 1998Dennis Wade

LONGVIEW

AMERICAN CLASSIFIEDS
(Thur)
506 N 2nd St, Longview, TX, 75601-6438, USA; tel (903) 758-6900; fax (903) 758-8181; e-mail longview@americanclassifieds.com; web site www.tnol.com
Circulation: 0pd,44,408fr; CVC
Advertising: Open inch rate $8.00
Established: 1985
Adv. Mgr. .... Gary Krell
Prodn. Mgr. .... Tracy Krell
Mechanical Specifications: Type page 10 2/5 x 16 1/4; A - 8 cols, 1 1/5, between; C - 8 cols, 1 1/5, between.
Equipment: Hardware — APP/Macs, PCs; Software — Adobe/PageMaker 6.5, Adobe/Photoshop 5.0.
Zip Codes Served: 75455, 75456, 75494, 75601, 75602, 75603, 75604, 75605, 75630, 75631, 75633, 75636, 75638, 75640, 75644, 75647, 75650, 75651, 75652, 75656, 75657, 75662, 75668, 75670, 75684, 75686, 75691, 75693, 75755, 75765, 75935, 75974

LUBBOCK

THRIFTY NICKEL - LUBBOCK
(Thur)
3845 50th St, Lubbock, TX, 79413-3807, USA; tel (806) 793-2500; fax (806) 793-2501; e-mail randy@lubbocktnol.com; adv e-mail traci@lubbocktnol.com; web site www.thriftynickellubbock.com
Circulation: 0pd,35,189fr; CVC
Advertising: Open inch rate $13.75
Established: 1983
Digital Platform - Mobile: Apple
Digital Platform - Tablet: Apple iOSRandy Eiland
Delivery Method: Racks

MCKINNEY

PENNY SAVER SHOPPING GUIDE
1650 W Virginia St, Ste 202, McKinney, TX, 75069-7703, USA; tel (972) 542-6282

MINERAL WELLS

MINERAL WELLS INDEX
(Wed, Sat)
300 SE 1st St, Mineral Wells, TX, 76067-5331, USA; tel (940) 325-4465; adv tel (940) 325-4465; ed tel (940) 325-4465; fax (940) 325-2020; e-mail publisher@mineralwellsindex.com; adv e-mail mgray@mineralwellsindex.com; ed e-mail editor@mineralwellsindex.com; web site www.mineralwellsindex.com
Circulation:13,555fr; Sworn/Estimate/Non-Audited
Advertising: Open inch rate $10.00
Established: 1900
Group: Community Newspaper Holdings, Inc.
Mng. Ed. .... David May
Equipment: Hardware — n/a; Presses — n/a; Software — n/a
Delivery Method: Mail, Racks

ODESSA

THRIFTY NICKEL WANT ADS
(Thur)
2611 Golder Ave, Odessa, TX, 79761-1101, USA; tel (432) 333-4184; adv tel (432) 634-7120; fax (432) 333-1517; adv fax (432) 333-1517; e-mail thrifty@ourthritynickel.com; adv e-mail jayw@ourthriftynickel.com; ed e-mail gailengelgau@gmail.com; web site www.ourthriftynickel.com
Circulation: 0pd,29,283fr; VAC
Advertising: Open inch rate $6.00
Established: 1980
Digital Platform - Mobile: Apple, Android, Windows, Blackberry
Digital Platform - Tablet: Apple iOS, Android, Windows 7, Blackberry Tablet OS, Kindle, Kindle Fire, Other
Publisher...................................... Gail Engelgau
Mechanical Specifications: 10.58" X 16"
Delivery Method: Racks
Zip Codes Served: 76246,79701,79703,79705.79706.79714.79720.79721.79731.79735.79741.79743,79745.79752.79756.79761.79762.79763.79764.79765.79766.79782.

ORANGE

SMART SHOPPER
(Wed)
200 W Front St, Orange, TX, 77630-5812, USA; tel (409) 883-3571; fax (409) 883-6342; ed e-mail editorial@orangeleader.com; web site www.orangeleader.com
Circulation:24,844fr; CVC
Advertising: Open inch rate $21.58
Pub. .... Eric Bauer
Adv. Dir. .... Kim Dwyer
Ed. .... Richard Nelson
Zip Codes Served: 70668, 77611, 776142, 77614, 77626, 77630, 77632, 77662

PARIS

DOLLARSAVER SHOPPER
(Wed)
101 Lamar Ave, Paris, TX, 75460-4218, USA; tel (903) 784-3328; fax (903) 785-0265; e-mail dollarsaver@1starnet.com; web site www.dollarsavershopper.com
Circulation:36,950fr; CVC
Advertising: Open inch rate $12.55
Established: 1982
Pub. .... Roger C. Hooper
Prodn. Mgr. .... Sean Norton
Mechanical Specifications: Type page 10 7/8 x 16; A - 6 cols, 1 2/3, 1/6 between.
Zip Codes Served: 74562, 74728, 74735, 74743, 74745, 74756, 74759, 74764, 74765, 74766, 75411, 75412, 75416, 75417, 75421, 75423, 75425, 75426, 75428, 75432, 75434, 75435, 75436, 75446, 75449, 75455, 75457, 75460, 75462, 75468, 75469, 75470, 75473, 75477, 75482, 75486, 754

RED OAK

GOLD SHEET SHOPPER
(Sat)
421 N Interstate 35 Rd, Red Oak, TX, 75154-4243, USA; tel (972) 617-6397; fax (972) 617-6223; e-mail alangell@ix.netcom.com
Circulation:5,000fr; Sworn/Estimate/Non-Audited
Advertising: Open inch rate $4.85
Ed. .... Alan Gell
Equipment: Hardware — PC; Software — Adobe/PageMaker.

RIVER OAKS

AMERICAN CLASSIFIEDS
(Thur)
2609 Jacksboro Hwy, River Oaks, TX, 76114-2242, USA; tel 682-703-2626; fax 682-703-2631; web site http://fortworth.tx.tnol.com/
Circulation: 0pd,15,810fr; VAC
Advertising: Open inch rate $8.50
Established: 1982Editions: 4— 4 total; American Classifieds-Arlington; American Classi-

fieds-Bedford; American Classifieds-Denton; American Classifieds-Fort Worth;
Pub. .... Jason McBride

AMERICAN CLASSIFIEDS - FORT WORTH-ARLINGTON
(Thur)
2609 Jacksboro Hwy, River Oaks, TX, 76114-2242, USA; web site www.americanclassifieds.com
Circulation: 0pd,15,073fr; CVC
Advertising: Open inch rate $8.50
Established: 1982Victor Verstraete

SAN ANGELO

AMERICAN CLASSIFIEDS
(Thur)
15 N Tyler St, San Angelo, TX, 76901-3105, USA; tel (325) 944-7653; fax (325) 944-0387; e-mail sanangelo@thriftynickelads.com; web site www.angeloads.com
Circulation: 0pd,20,990fr; VAC
Advertising: Open inch rate $9.00
Established: 1983
Adv. Mgr. .... Stacie Squier
Ed. .... Pat Houston-Logan
Mechanical Specifications: Type page 10 1/2 x 15 1/2; A - 8 cols, 1 1/4, between; C - 8 cols, 1 1/4, between.
Equipment: Hardware — APP/Mac G4, APP/iMac; Software — QPS/QuarkXPress 4.1, Adobe/Illustrator 9.0, Adobe/Photoshop 6.0.

SAN ANTONIO

THRIFTY NICKEL
(Thur)
9258 Culebra Rd, Ste 115, San Antonio, TX, 78251-2872, USA; tel (210) 824-7554; fax (210) 824-3004; adv e-mail rbeanland@tnolsa.com; web site www.tnolsa.com
Circulation:20,000fr; Sworn/Estimate/Non-Audited
Advertising: Open inch rate $12.00
Established: 1983Editions: 1— San Antonio 20M
Digital Platform - Mobile: Apple, Android
Digital Platform - Tablet: Android, Kindle
Publisher.......................................Robert Funk
Office Administrator................. Rusty Beanland
Mechanical Specifications: Type page 10 1/2 x 16; A - 8 cols, 1 1/4, 2/25 between; C - 8 cols, 1 1/4, 2/25 between.
Equipment: Hardware — APP/Mac; Software — QPS/QuarkXPress 6.0, Macromedia/Freehand 5.0, Macos 7.5.3,. Pongrass Pagination, In Design
Delivery Method: Racks
Zip Codes Served: 78201 thru 78298 plus 78006

STEPHENVILLE

CROSS TIMBERS TRADING POST
(Wed)
590 E South Loop, Stephenville, TX, 76401-5310, USA; tel (254) 965-3124; fax (254) 965-4269; e-mail news@empiretribune.com; web site www.empiretribune.com
Circulation:11,650fr; Sworn/Estimate/Non-Audited
Advertising: Open inch rate $11.20
Pub. .... Rochelle Sidham
Adv. Mgr. .... Judy Terry
Ed. .... Sara Vanden Berge
Equipment: ; Software — QPS/QuarkXPress 3.2.

SWEETWATER

NOLAN COUNTY SHOPPER
(Tues)
112 W 3rd St, Sweetwater, TX, 79556-4430, USA; tel (325) 236-6677; fax (325) 235-4967; e-mail publisher@sweetwaterreporter.com; adv e-mail advertising@sweetwaterreporter.com; ed e-mail editor@sweetwaterreporter.com; web site www.sweetwaterreporter.com
Circulation: 2,500pd,3,500fr; Sworn/Estimate/Non-Audited
Advertising: Open inch rate $11.80
Established: 1881
Group: Heritage Publications (2003) Inc.
Pub. .... Sharon Friedlander
Bus. Mgr.................................. Danica Hickson
Adv. Sales Mgr. .... Brenda Morales
Adv. Sales Mgr. .... Justin Ramirez
Composing Mgr. .... Pablo Rodriguez
Prodn. Mgr., Pressroom .... Bleu Reyes
General Manager / Ad Director Zela Armstrong
Mechanical Specifications: Type page 12 x 21 1/2; E - 6 cols, 2 1/16, 1/8 between; A - 6 cols, 2 1/16, 1/8 between; C - 8 cols, 1 1/2, 1/8 between.
Delivery Method: Mail, Carrier, Racks

TEMPLE

AMERICAN CLASSIFIEDS
(Thur)
2905 W Adams Ave, Temple, TX, 76504-2862, USA; tel (254) 771-2777; fax (254) 771-2231; web site www.tnol.com
Circulation: 0pd,22,313fr; VAC
Advertising: Open inch rate $29.00
Established: 1985
Pub. .... BJ Minor
Mechanical Specifications: Type page 10 1/2 x 16; A - 8 cols, 1 1/4, 1/8 between; C - 8 cols, 1 1/4, 1/8 between.
Equipment: Hardware — APP/Mac; Software — QPS/QuarkXPress.

TERRELL

TERRELL TRIBUNE UPDATE
(Sun) (Free distribution shopper)
150 9th St, Terrell, TX, 75160-3061, USA; tel (972) 563-6476; adv tel (972) 563-6476; ed tel (972) 563-6476; fax (972) 563-0340; adv fax (972) 563-6476; ed fax (972) 563-6476; e-mail publisher@terrelltribune.com; adv e-mail selswick@terrelltribune.com; ed e-mail editor@terrelltribune.com; web site www.terrelltribune.com
Circulation: 1,600pd,11,500fr; Sworn/Estimate/Non-Audited
Advertising: Open inch rate $11.00
Established: 1898
Digital Platform - Mobile: Apple, Android, Windows, Blackberry, Other
Publisher...................................... Mike Elswick
Advertising Director............Stephanie Elswick
Managing Editor .... Todd Jorgenson
Mechanical Specifications: Broadsheet
Delivery Method: Mail, Carrier
Zip Codes Served: 75160, 75161

TEXARKANA

AMERICAN CLASSIFIEDS
(Thur)
2402 Summerhill Rd, Texarkana, TX, 75501-3571, USA; tel (903) 794-0996; fax (903) 792-2199; e-mail amaclasstxk@gmail.com; adv e-mail tnick101@aol.com; web site www.Texarkanaamclass.com
Circulation: 0pd,26,587fr; CVC
Advertising: Open inch rate $9.50
Established: 1981
Digital Platform - Mobile: Windows
Publisher................................ Dennis Skinner
Delivery Method: Racks
Zip Codes Served: 71701-71770, 71801-71866, 71944, 71971, 71973, 72064, 73045, 74501-74745, 75501-75574, 78537

TYLER

AMERICAN CLASSIFIEDS - TYLER
(Thur)
1211 W Southwest Loop 323, Tyler, TX, 75701-9344, USA; tel (903) 597-2516; fax (903) 597-8726; web site http://tyler.tx.tnol.com/
Circulation:30,633fr; CVCLarry Morris

VICTORIA

AMERICAN CLASSIFIEDS
(Thur)
2708 N Ben Wilson St, Victoria, TX, 77901-5729, USA; tel (361) 575-6400; fax (361) 575-6427; web site www.americanclassifieds.com
Circulation: 0pd,15,992fr; VAC
Advertising: Open inch rate $11.00
Established: 1996
Ed. .... Kevin Kalich
Prodn. Mgr. .... Rhonda Kalich
Mechanical Specifications: Type page 11 1/2 x 17 1/4; A - 8 cols, 1 1/4, 1/8 between; C - 8 cols, 1 1/4, 1/8 between.
Equipment: Hardware — 2-APP/Mac G3, 2-APP/Mac G4, 1-APP/Mac Star Max 4000/160; Presses — HI/Cold Webb; Software — Adobe/Photoshop 5.5, Adobe/PageMaker 6.5, Adobe/Illustrator 8.0.

WACO

AMERICAN CLASSIFIEDS
(Thur)
3901 W Waco Dr, Waco, TX, 76710-7107, USA; tel (254) 752-0334; fax (254) 752-0339; web site www.americanclassifieds.com
Circulation: 0pd,29,786fr; VAC
Advertising: Open inch rate $11.00
Established: 1982
Pub. .... Carol Treese
Adv. Mgr. .... Rusty Baker
Mechanical Specifications: Type page 10 1/2 x 16; A - 8 cols, 1 1/4, 1/8 between; C - 8 cols, 1 1/4, 1/8 between.
Equipment: Hardware — APP/Mac G3; Software — QPS/QuarkXPress, Adobe/Photoshop.

WAXAHACHIE

ELLIS COUNTY TRADING POST
(Wed)
200 W Marvin Ave, Waxahachie, TX, 75165-3040, USA; tel (972) 937-3310; fax (972) 937-1139; e-mail sbrooks@waxahachietx.com; adv e-mail jhenderson@waxahachietx.com; ed e-mail nwhite@waxahachietx.com; web site www.waxahachietx.com
Circulation:26,500fr; Sworn/Estimate/Non-Audited
Advertising: Open inch rate $25.00
Group: GateHouse Media, Inc.
Publisher..................................... Scott Brooks
Delivery Method: Newsstand, Carrier, Racks

WEATHERFORD

PARKER COUNTY SHOPPER
(Tues)
512 Palo Pinto St, Weatherford, TX, 76086-4128, USA; tel (817) 594-7447; adv tel (817) 598-0857; fax (817) 594-9734; web site www.weatherforddemocrat.com
Circulation:30,000fr; Sworn/Estimate/Non-Audited
Advertising: Open inch rate $12.50
Group: Community Newspaper Holdings, Inc.
Pub. .... Steve Boggs
Adv. Mgr. .... Renae Alexander
Ed. .... Phil Riddle
Mechanical Specifications: Type page 10 1/2 x 13; A - 6 cols, 1 2/3, between.
Zip Codes Served: 76086

WICHITA FALLS

AMERICAN CLASSIFIEDS - WICHITA FALLS
(Thur)
2912 Buchanan St, Wichita Falls, TX, 76308-1760, USA; tel (940) 691-2200; fax (940) 691-4411; e-mail Amclasswf@gmail.com; web site www.WichitaFallsAmericanClassifieds.com
Circulation: 0pd,15,291fr; VAC
Advertising: Open inch rate $7.00
Established: 1996
Digital Platform - Mobile: Apple, Android, Windows
Digital Platform - Tablet: Apple iOS, Windows 7, Blackberry Tablet OS
Pub .... Duke Singer
Mechanical Specifications: 8 column x 16 inches 7.5 picas per column
6 picas per inch
Delivery Method: Racks
Zip Codes Served: 15 counties see CVS audit

UTAH

LOGAN

QUALITY BUYS
(Tues)
75 W 300 N, Logan, UT, 84321-3971, USA; tel (435) 752-2121; fax (435) 753-6642; web site www.hjnews.com
Circulation:15,900fr; Sworn/Estimate/Non-Audited
Advertising: Open inch rate $6.25
Pub. .... Bruce K. Smith
Adv. Dir. .... Shawn Brady
Circ. Dir. .... Russ Davis
Managing Ed. .... Charles McCollum
Mechanical Specifications: Type page 12 1/2 x 20 1/2; E - 6 cols, 1 13/16, 1/8 between; A - 6 cols, 1 13/16, 1/8 between; C - 9 cols, 1 13/16, 1/8 between.
Equipment: Hardware — APP/Mac; Presses — 16-Dauphin/35; Software — QPS/QuarkXPress 3.2, Baseview.
Zip Codes Served: 84028, 84038, 84305, 84308, 84318, 84319, 84320, 84325, 84326, 84327, 84328, 84332, 84333, 84335, 84338, 84339, 84341, 83228, 83232, 83237, 83263, 83286

MOUNT PLEASANT

PYRAMID SHOPPER
(Wed)
49 W Main St, Mount Pleasant, UT, 84647-1327, USA; tel (435) 462-2134; fax (435) 462-2459; e-mail pyramid@avpro.com
Circulation:8,600fr; Sworn/Estimate/Non-Audited
Advertising: Open inch rate $7.00
Pub. .... Rona Rahlf
Mng. Ed. .... Cheryl Brewer
Zip Codes Served: 84647

OREM

THRIFTY NICKEL - UTAH
(Thur)
1407 N State St, Orem, UT, 84057-2545, USA; tel (801) 796-8401; adv tel (801) 796-8401; ed tel (801) 796-8401; fax (801) 796-8395; adv fax (801) 796-8395; ed fax (801) 796-8395; e-mail nickelnorm@hotmail.

com; adv e-mail nickelnorm@hotmail.com; ed e-mail nickelnorm@hotmail.com; web site www.thriftynickelutah.com
Circulation:13,000fr; Sworn/Estimate/Non-Audited
Advertising: Open inch rate $15.00
Established: 1992
Group: American Classifieds / Thrifty NickelEditions: 1—
Digital Platform - Mobile: Apple, Android, Windows
Digital Platform - Tablet: Apple iOS, Android, Windows 7
Pub./Ed./Adv. Dir. .... Norm Wilkinson
Mechanical Specifications: Type page 10 1/4 x 16; A - 8 cols, 1 1/4, 1/6 between; C - 8 cols, 1 1/4, 1/6 between.
Equipment: Hardware — Windows; Software — QPS/QuarkXPress, Adobe/Photoshop, Adobe/Illustrator, Corel,
Delivery Method: Racks
Zip Codes Served: 84003, 84004, 84032, 84042, 84043, 84057, 84058, 84062, 84066, 84078, 84097, 84501, 84634, 84601, 84602, 84603, 84604, 84605, 84606, 84648, 84660, 84663, 84701, 84021

RICHFIELD

THE RICHFIELD SHOPPER
(Wed)
65 W Center St, Richfield, UT, 84701-2546, USA; tel (435) 896-5476; fax (435) 896-8123; adv e-mail reaperad@richfieldreaper.com; class@richfieldreaper.com; web site www.richfieldreaper.com
Circulation:7,300fr; Sworn/Estimate/Non-Audited
Established: 1998
Pub. .... Chuck Hawley
Office Mgr. .... Cherry Niemeyer
Ed. .... Sandy Phillips
Prodn. Mgr. .... Roger Barney
Adv. Mgr. .... Roxanne Waybrant
Equipment: Hardware — APP/Mac; Presses — G/Community; Software — InDesign and Microsoft Word.
Zip Codes Served: 84701

VERMONT

BURLINGTON

BUYERS' DIGEST
(Wed)
191 College St, Burlington, VT, 05401-8589, USA; tel (800) 639-7011; fax (802) 862-5622; ed e-mail mtownsend@burlingtonfreepress.com; web site www.buyersdigest.com
Circulation:30,000fr; Sworn/Estimate/Non-Audited
Advertising: Open inch rate $9.24
Group: GannettEditions: 4— 4 total; Buyer's Digest-Central; Buyer's Digest-North; Buyer's Guide-Motor Digest; Buyer's Guide-North Country;
Pres./Pub. .... Bradley I. Robertson
Mechanical Specifications: Type page 10 1/4 x 13 3/4; A - 4 cols, 2 1/2, between; C - 8 cols, 1 1/4, between.
Zip Codes Served: 5454

CHITTENDEN COUNTY ADVERTISER
(Thur)
191 College St, Burlington, VT, 05401-8589, USA; tel (802) 863-3441; fax (802) 862-5622; e-mail sports@bfp.burlingtonfreepress.com; adv e-mail letters@bfp.burlingtonfreepress.com; legals@bfp.burlingtonfreepress.com; web site www.burlingtonfreepress.com
Circulation:33,700fr; Sworn/Estimate/Non-Audited
Advertising: Open inch rate $23.75
Group: Gannett
Pub. .... Brad Robertson

FRANKLIN-GRAND ISLE COUNTY ADVERTISER
(Fri)
191 College St, Burlington, VT, 05401-8589, USA; tel (802) 863-3441; fax (802) 862-5622; ed e-mail mtownsend@burlingtonfreepress.com
Circulation:18,000fr; Sworn/Estimate/Non-Audited
Advertising: Open inch rate $9.95
Group: Gannett
Pub. .... Brad Robertson

LAMOILLE COUNTY ADVERTISER
(Fri)
191 College St, Burlington, VT, 05401-8589, USA; tel (802) 863-3441; fax (802) 862-5622
Circulation:11,700fr; Sworn/Estimate/Non-Audited
Advertising: Open inch rate $9.95
Group: Gannett
Pres./Pub. .... Brad Robertson

SAINT ALBANS

EXTRA
(Sat)
281 N Main St, Saint Albans, VT, 05478-2503, USA; tel (802) 524-9771; fax (802) 527-1948; e-mail news@samessenger.com; sports@samessenger.com; web site www.samessenger.com
Circulation:21,000fr; Sworn/Estimate/Non-Audited
Advertising: Open inch rate $10.10
Pub. .... Emerson Lynn
Circ. Mgr. .... Tammy Jo Sellers
Mng. Ed. .... Gary Rutkowski
Prodn. Mgr. .... Jeremy Read
Zip Codes Served: 5478

VIRGINIA

BEDFORD

BEDFORD BULLET
(Mon)
233 W Depot St, Bedford, VA, 24523-1935, USA; tel (540) 586-8612; fax (540) 586-0834; e-mail news@bedfordbulletin.com; sports@bedfordbulletin.com; adv e-mail advertising@bedfordbulletin.com; ed e-mail news@bedfordbulletin.com; web site www.bedfordbulletin.com
Circulation:19,700fr; Sworn/Estimate/Non-Audited
Advertising: Open inch rate $14.22
Established: 1983
Group: Landmark Media Enterprises, LLC Landmark Communications, Inc.
Pub. .... Jay Bondurant
Bus. Mgr. .... Gale Wasson
Ed. .... Tom Wilmoth
Mechanical Specifications: Tabloid 6 column (9.885") X 10"
Equipment: Hardware — APP/Macs; Software — Indesign CS
Delivery Method: Mail
Zip Codes Served: 24523;24122;24174;24095;24121;24104;24556;24526

DANVILLE

PIEDMONT SHOPPER
(Thur)
3157 Westover Dr, Danville, VA, 24541-5449, USA; tel (434) 822-1800; fax (434) 822-2400; web site www.piedmontshopper.com
Circulation: 0pd,24,975fr; VAC
Advertising: Open inch rate $12.00
Established: 2001
Digital Platform - Mobile: Apple
Digital Platform - Tablet: Apple iOS
Pub. .... Kathy Crumpton
Delivery Method: Racks

GALAX

GAZETTE PLUS
(Wed)
108 W Stuart Dr, Galax, VA, 24333-2114, USA; tel (276) 236-5178; fax (276) 236-0756; e-mail news@galaxgazette.com; adv e-mail ads@galaxgazette.com; classifieds@galaxgazette.com; circulation@galaxgazette.com; web site www.galaxgazette.com
Circulation:6,175fr; Sworn/Estimate/Non-Audited
Advertising: Open inch rate $9.52
Established: 1982
Group: Landmark Community Newspapers, LLC
Pub. .... Chuck Burress
Adv. Mgr. .... Randy Kegley
Ed. .... Brian Funk
Circulation Manager .... Tammy Manning
Equipment: Hardware — APP/Mac
Delivery Method: Mail
Zip Codes Served: 24333, 24343, 24348, 24381

INDEPENDENCE

DECLARATION
(Mthly)
578 D Gwynn Shopping Ctr, Independence, VA, 24348, USA; tel (276) 773-2222; fax (276) 773-2287; e-mail lchambers@valink.com; ed e-mail editor@independencedeclaration.com.; web site www.independencedeclaration.com
Circulation:2,400fr; Sworn/Estimate/Non-Audited
Advertising: Open inch rate $7.00
Established: 1980
Group: Landmark Community Newspapers, LLC
Adv. Mgr. .... Linda S. Litz
Circ. Mgr. .... Amy Adkins
Ed. .... Larry Chambers
Mechanical Specifications: Type page 13 x 21 1/2; E - 6 cols, 2, 1/8 between; A - 6 cols, 2, 1/8 between; C - 6 cols, 2, 1/8 between.
Equipment: Hardware — APP/Macs; Software — QPS/QuarkXPress, Microsoft/Word.
Zip Codes Served: 24333, 24348

SPRINGFIELD

THE BUYER'S GUIDE (EVERY OTHER WED)
6200 Rolling Rd, Unit 2276, Springfield, VA, 22152-8012, USA; tel (703) 505-2087; fax (703) 866-3994; web site www.bguide.net
Circulation:100,000fr; Sworn/Estimate/Non-Audited
Advertising: Open inch rate $19.50
Established: 1977Editions: 3— 3 total; The Buyer's Guide-Alexandria/Mount Vernon; The Buyer's Guide-Fairfax/Annandale; The Buyer's Guide-Springfield/Burke;
Ed. .... Julie C. Moore
Mechanical Specifications: Type page 9 5/6 x 13; E - 4 cols, 2 1/3, 1/6 between; A - 4 cols, 2 1/3, 1/6 between; C - 8 cols, 1 1/6, 3/4 between.
Equipment: Hardware — APP/Mac G4, MS/NT Server; Software — QPS/QuarkXPress 4.11, Adobe/Photoshop 5.5.
Zip Codes Served: 22308, 22309, 22310, 22315, 22060, 22079, 22150, 22151, 22152, 22153, 22041, 22003, 22015, 22039, 22030, 22031, 22032

SUFFOLK

TIDEWATER SHOPPER
(Thur)
130 S Saratoga St, Suffolk, VA, 23434-5323, USA; tel (757) 539-0733; web site www.suffolknewsherald.com
Circulation:20,000fr; Sworn/Estimate/Non-Audited
Advertising: Open inch rate $10.15
Established: 1873
Adv. Mgr. .... Earl Jones
Ed. .... Andy Prutsok
Zip Codes Served: 23434

WINCHESTER

BYRD NEWSPAPERS
2 N Kent St, Winchester, VA, 22601-5038, USA; tel (540) 667-3200
Group: Ogden Newspapers Inc.

WYTHEVILLE

ENTERPRISE BUYERS CATALOGUE
(Fri)
460 W Main St, Wytheville, VA, 24382-2207, USA; tel (276) 228-6611; fax (276) 228-7260; web site www.wythenews.com
Circulation:8,200fr; Sworn/Estimate/Non-Audited
Advertising: Open inch rate $6.25
Pub. .... Sam Cooper
Adv. Dir. .... Barbara Sewell
Circ. Dir. .... Sonny Corpus
Ed. .... Mark Sage
Mng. Ed. .... Jeff Simmons
Mechanical Specifications: Type page 13 x 21; E - 6 cols, 1/4 between; A - 6 cols, 1/4 between; C - 9 cols, 1/8 between.
Equipment: ; Presses — HI.
Zip Codes Served: 24382

WASHINGTON

ANACORTES

FIDALGO THIS WEEK
(Tues)
901 6th St, Anacortes, WA, 98221-1716, USA; tel (360) 293-3122; ed tel (360) 293-3122 x1040; fax (360) 293-5000; e-mail feedback@goanacortes.com; adv e-mail adservices@skagitpublishing.com; ed e-mail jdarnton@goanacortes.com; web site www.goanacortes.com
Circulation:6,809fr; Sworn/Estimate/Non-Audited
Advertising: Open inch rate $4.00 plus Anacortes American
Group: Skagit Publishing
Publisher .... Jack Darnton
News Ed. .... Elaine Walker
Delivery Method: Carrier

CAMAS

AT YOUR LEISURE
(Tues)
425 NE 4th Ave, Camas, WA, 98607-2129, USA; tel (360) 834-2141; fax (360) 834-3423; web site www.camaspostrecord.com
Circulation:6,000fr; Sworn/Estimate/Non-Audited
Advertising: Open inch rate $7.50
Adv. Mgr. .... Michael Gallagher
Circ. Mgr. .... Shelly Atwell

Ed. ....Heather Acheson
Mechanical Specifications: Type page 13 x 21; E - 6 cols, 2 1/16, 1/8 between; A - 6 cols, 2 1/16, 1/8 between; C - 9 cols, 1 1/4, 1/8 between.
Equipment: Hardware — APP/Macs; Presses — WPC/Web Leader; Software — QPS/QuarkXPress, Claris/MacWrite.
Zip Codes Served: 98607

CENTRALIA

ETC!
(Wed)
321 N Pearl St, Centralia, WA, 98531-4323, USA; tel (360) 807-8203; fax (360) 807-8258; web site www.chronline.com
Circulation:10,000fr; Sworn/Estimate/Non-Audited
Advertising: Open inch rate $18.98
Pub. ....Christine Fosset
Mktg. Mgr. ....Christine Fossett
Exec. Ed.....................................Michael Wagar
Mechanical Specifications: Type page 13 x 21 1/2; E - 6 cols, 2, 1/6 between; A - 6 cols, 2, between; C - 8 cols, 1 1/2, between.
Equipment: Hardware — APP/Macs; Presses — G/Community; Software — Multi-Ad/Creator, QPS/QuarkXPress.
Zip Codes Served: 98531

COUPEVILLE

THE WHIDBEY CLASSIFIEDS
(Wed)
107 S Main St, Ste E101, Coupeville, WA, 98239-3569, USA; tel (360) 675-6611; ed tel (360) 675-6611; fax (360) 679-2695; ed e-mail publisher@whidbeynewstimes.com; editor@whidbeynewstimes.com; web site www.whidbeynewstimes.com
Circulation:7,500fr; Sworn/Estimate/Non-Audited
Advertising: Open inch rate $18.10Editions: 2— 2 total; Whidbey Hot Sheet-North (5,294); Whidbey Hot Sheet-South (2,486);
Pub. ....Marcia Van Dyke
Adv. Mgr..Terry Tinker
Ed. ....Jim Larsen
Zip Codes Served: 98277

FERNDALE

WHATCOM COUNTY SHOPPER
(Wed)
2004 Main St, Ferndale, WA, 98248-9468, USA; tel (360) 384-1411; fax (360) 384-1417; e-mail news@ferndalerecordjournal.com; web site www.ferndalerecordjournal.com
Circulation:4,600fr; Sworn/Estimate/Non-Audited
Advertising: Open inch rate $15.40
Adv. Mgr..................................Kimberly Winjum
Mechanical Specifications: Type page 13 x 21; E - 6 cols, 2 1/16, 1/8 between; A - 6 cols, 2 1/16, 1/8 between; C - 8 cols, 1 1/2, 1/8 between.
Zip Codes Served: 98248

GRAND COULEE

STAR BUYER'S GUIDE
(Wed)
PO Box 150, Grand Coulee, WA, 99133-0150, USA; tel (509) 633-1350; fax (509) 633-3828; e-mail star@grandcoulee.com; web site www.grandcoulee.com
Circulation:4,800fr; Sworn/Estimate/Non-Audited
Advertising: Open inch rate $8.50
Ed. ....Scott W. Hunter
Reporter ....Roger S. Lucas
Prodn. Coord.................................Gwen Hilson
Zip Codes Served: 99133

KELSO

THE NICKEL-KELSO
(Thur)
1510 Grade St, Kelso, WA, 98626-3003, USA; web site www.thenickel.net
Circulation:20,065fr; VACDave Bragg

KENNEWICK

NICKEL NIK / BUYLINE - TRI CITIES
(Fri)
3321 W Kennewick Ave, Ste 190, Kennewick, WA, 99336-2968, USA; tel (509) 783-5555; adv tel (509) 783-5555; fax (509) 783-4203; adv fax (509) 783-4203; e-mail KristenB@TMPNW.com; adv e-mail KristenB@TMPNW.com; web site www.recycler.com
Circulation:12,536fr; CVC
Advertising: Open inch rate $10.00
Established: 1999
Group: Target Media Partners
Digital Platform - Mobile: Other
Digital Platform - Tablet: Other
Regional Manager......................Kristen Bryant
Mechanical Specifications: Type page: 10.5 x 15; 7 col
Delivery Method: Racks

THE GIANT NICKEL
(Thur)
4812 W Clearwater Ave, Kennewick, WA, 99336-2119, USA; tel (509) 783-5455; fax (509) 783-3402; e-mail terri@giantnickel.com; adv e-mail terri@giantnickel.com; web site www.giantnickel.com
Circulation: 0pd,30,287fr; CVC
Advertising: Open inch rate $9.50
Established: 1971
Group: Tevada Publishing, Inc
Gen. Mgr. .... Terri Drake
Mechanical Specifications: Type page 10 2/5 x 14; A - 7 cols, 1 2/5, 1/8 between; C - 7 cols, 1 2/5, 1/8 between.
Delivery Method: Racks
Zip Codes Served: 98923, 98926, 98932, 98935, 98936, 98937, 98942, 98944, 98948, 98951, 98952, 98953, 99301, 99320, 99323, 99324, 99326, 99336, 99337, 99343, 99344, 99352, 99353, 99354, 99360, 99362

MOSES LAKE

NICKEL SAVER
(Thur)
715 W 3rd Ave, Moses Lake, WA, 98837-2006, USA; tel (509) 765-5681; fax (509) 766-9977; web site nickelsaver.recycler.com
Circulation:14,765fr; CVC
Advertising: Open inch rate $12.00
Prodn. Mgr. .... Sue Tebow
Mechanical Specifications: Type page 9 3/4 x 15; E - 7 cols, 1 1/4, 1/6 between; A - 7 cols, 1 1/4, 1/6 between.
Equipment: ; Software — QPS/QuarkXPress 3.32.
Zip Codes Served: 98837

POULSBO

SOUND PUBLISHING, INC.
19351 8th Ave NE, Ste 106, Poulsbo, WA, 98370-8710, USA; tel (360) 394-5800; fax (360) 394-5841; e-mail marketing@soundpublishing.com; web site www.soundpublishing.com; www.bainbridgereview.com
Circulation: 13,394pd,309,003fr; CAC
Established: 1988
Vice Pres. ....Lori Maxim
CFO ....David Theobald
Pub. ....Chris Allen-Hoch
President ....Gloria Fletcher
Director, National and Regional Sales....Barrett Stephen
Kurt Ploudre
Note: Sound Publishing Inc. is Printing, Publishing and Distribution Company. Sound Publishing is a division of Canadian-based Black Press Ltd.

SPOKANE

NICKEL NIK - SPOKANE
(Fri)
2103 N Division St, Spokane, WA, 99207-2262, USA; tel (509) 328-5555; adv tel (509) 328-5555; e-mail KristenB@TMPNW.com; adv e-mail KristenB@TMPNW.com; web site www.recycler.com
Circulation:18,490fr; CVC
Advertising: Open inch rate $12.00
Established: 1956
Group: Target Media Partners
Digital Platform - Mobile: Other
Digital Platform - Tablet: Other
Regional Manager......................Kristen Bryant
Mechanical Specifications: Type page: 10.25 x 16; 7 col
Delivery Method: Racks

THE EXCHANGE
(Thur)
304 W 3rd Ave, Spokane, WA, 99201-4314, USA; web site www.nickel-wantads.com
Circulation:31,654fr; VACBarbara Powers

STANWOOD

STANWOOD CAMANO ADVERTISER
(Tues)
9005 271st St NW, Stanwood, WA, 98292-5998, USA; tel (360) 629-2155; fax (360) 629-4211; e-mail frontdesk@scnews.com; adv e-mail classifieds@scnews.com; ed e-mail newsroom@scnews.com; web site www.scnews.com
Circulation: 3,900pd,14,400fr; Sworn/Estimate/Non-Audited
Advertising: Open inch rate $17.80
Established: 1891
Group: Pioneer Newspapers Inc
Digital Platform - Mobile: Apple
Digital Platform - Tablet: Apple iOS, Kindle, Nook, Kindle Fire
Editor/general manager................. Kelly Ruhoff
Delivery Method: Mail, Newsstand, Racks
Zip Codes Served: 98292

WALLA WALLA

BUYLINE
(Fri)
2200 Melrose St, Ste 1, Walla Walla, WA, 99362-1556, USA; tel (509) 783-5555; fax (509) 529-7057; web site buylineads.recycler.com
Circulation:22,500fr; Sworn/Estimate/Non-Audited
Advertising: Open inch rate $9.10
Established: 1971
Gen. Mgr. .... Susan Salaver
Mechanical Specifications: Type page 9 3/4 x 14; A - 7 cols, 1 1/4, 3/8 between; C - 7 cols, 1 1/4, 3/8 between.
Equipment: Hardware — IBM, APP/Mac; Software — SUN/Suntype, QPS/QuarkXPress 4.1, Adobe/Illustrator 8.0, Adobe/Photoshop 5.0, Adobe/Acrobat 4.0.
Zip Codes Served: 99362, 99324, 97862, 99348, 99360, 99361, 99328, 97813, 97886, 99323, 99329, 97801, 97838, 97882

TIDBITS OF THE BLUE MOUNTAIN REGION
(Tues)
PO Box 2722, Walla Walla, WA, 99362-0335, USA; web site www.tidbitsfun.com
Circulation:4,975fr; CVC
Advertising: Open inch rate $12.17
Established: 1996Mark Driver
Mechanical Specifications: Type page: 10 x 15.35; 3 columns

WENATCHEE

NCW NICKEL ADS
(Thur)
201 N Mission St, Wenatchee, WA, 98801-2003, USA; tel (509) 662-1405; adv tel (509) 662-1405; fax (509) 664-6644; adv fax (509) 664-6644; e-mail KristenB@NCWNickelads.com; adv e-mail 509-664-6644; web site www.recycler.com
Circulation:19,511fr; CVC
Advertising: 12.00
Established: 1976
Group: Target Media Partners
Digital Platform - Mobile: Other
Digital Platform - Tablet: Other
Regional Manager......................Kristen Bryant
Mechanical Specifications: 9.75' wide x 14.50' tall
Delivery Method: Racks
Zip Codes Served: 98801,98802,98816,98841,98848,98826,98815,98856

YELM

NISQUALLY VALLEY SHOPPER
(Wed)
118 Prairie Park St, Yelm, WA, 98597, USA; tel (360) 458-2681; fax (360) 458-5741; e-mail yelmnews@yelmonline.com; adv e-mail advertise@yelmonline.com; class@yelmonline.com; web site www.yelmonline.com
Circulation:21,000fr; Sworn/Estimate/Non-Audited
Advertising: Open inch rate $17.80
Established: 1922
Adv. Mgr. .... Angie Evans
Ed. ....Keven R. Graves
Mechanical Specifications: Type page 11 1/2 x 21 1/2; E - 6 cols, 3 3/4, 1/8 between; A - 6 cols, 3 3/4, 1/8 between; C - 8 cols, 1 1/3, 1/8 between.
Equipment: Hardware — APP/Macs; Software — QPS/QuarkXPress 4.1, Adobe/Acrobat 4.0, Multi-Ad/Creator 2 1.6.1.
Zip Codes Served: 98597, 98576, 98580, 98589, 98558, 98328

WEST VIRGINIA

GRAFTON

TAYLOR COUNTY VALUE GUIDE
(Sat)
914 W Main St, Grafton, WV, 26354-1028, USA; tel (304) 265-3333; fax (304) 265-3342
Circulation:5,900fr; Sworn/Estimate/Non-Audited
Group: News Media Corp.
Pub. ....Jean Ellerman
Zip Codes Served: 26201

KEYSER

TODAY'S SHOPPER
(Sat)
21 Shamrock Dr, Keyser, WV, 26726-6012, USA; tel (304) 788-3333; fax (304) 788-3398; adv e-mail advertising@newsroom.info; ed e-mail lbeavers@newstribune.info; newsroom@newstribune.info; web site www.newstribune.info

Circulation:12,800fr; USPS
Advertising: Open inch rate $9.06
Established: 1912
Group: GateHouse Media, Inc.
Ed. .... Liz Beavers
Pub. .... Kelly Miller
Mechanical Specifications: 6 column, 1.5" each
Delivery Method: Mail
Zip Codes Served: 26726

MARTINSBURG

BUYER'S GUIDE
(Tues)
415 Wilson St, Martinsburg, WV, 25401-3023, USA; tel (304) 267-9983; fax (304) 263-7106; e-mail tom@yourbg.com; adv e-mail ads@yourbg.com; graphics@yourbg.com; web site www.yourbg.com
Circulation: 0pd,36,244fr; VAC
Advertising: Open inch rate $20.00
Established: 1982Editions: Buyers Guide -37,835
Digital Platform - Mobile: Apple, Android
Digital Platform - Tablet: Apple iOS
Pub. .... Thomas J. Aird
Adv. Mgr. .... David Aird
Mechanical Specifications: Type page 10 1/4 x 14; A - 7 cols, between; 1 5/12, 1/12 between.
Equipment: Hardware — APPLE; Software — Creator - Photoshop - acrobat
Delivery Method: Carrier
Zip Codes Served: 25401, 25411, 25414, 25419, 25420, 25425, 25427, 25428, 25430, 25438, 25440, 25442, 25443, 25446

MOUNDSVILLE

GREEN TAB
(Sun)
605 Court Ave, Moundsville, WV, 26041-2139, USA; tel (304) 845-4050; fax (304) 845-4312; adv e-mail advertising@greentab.com; web site greentab.com
Circulation: 0pd,15,828fr; VAC
Advertising: Open inch rate $15.10
Established: 1961
Group: Ogden Newspapers Inc.Editions: 3— Northern, 11,462; Marshall, 16,269; Wetzel, 13,919
Publisher.. Brian Clutter
Distribution Manager .... Vince Johnson
Mechanical Specifications: Type page 10" x 10"; 6 columns
1.5" column
Equipment: Hardware — APP/Mac IIci, APP/Mac; Software — Adobe/Photoshop, Adobe/PageMaker, Multi-Ad/Creator, Adobe/Illustrator.
Delivery Method: Mail, Carrier, Racks
Zip Codes Served: 26041, 26155, 26003 are the main cities

RIPLEY

THE STAR-HERALD
(Sat)
305 Church St N, Ripley, WV, 25271-1205, USA; tel (304) 372-4222; fax (304) 372-5544; e-mail publisher@jacksonnewspapers.com; adv e-mail circ@jacksonnewspapers.com; web site www.jacksonnewspapers.com
Circulation:13,000fr; Sworn/Estimate/Non-Audited
Advertising: Open inch rate $7.00
Group: GateHouse Media, Inc.
Sales Rep. .... Tina Mandrake
Circ. Mgr. .... Cathy Beegle
News Ed. .... Gregory Matics
Zip Codes Served: 26164

WISCONSIN

ABBOTSFORD

CENTRAL WISCONSIN SHOPPER
(Tues)
103 W Spruce St, Abbotsford, WI, 54405-9734, USA; tel (715) 223-2342; fax (715) 223-3505; e-mail tpprint@pcpros.net; tp@tpprinting.com; rr@tpprinting.com; web site www.centralwinews.com
Circulation:18,300fr; Sworn/Estimate/Non-Audited
Advertising: Open inch rate $8.25
Established: 1981
Pub. .... Carol O'Leary
Circ. Mgr. .... Jane Kroeplin
Prodn. Mgr. .... Kevin Flink
Mechanical Specifications: Type page 10 1/3 x 14; A - 6 cols, 1 9/16, 1/8 between; C - 6 cols, 1 9/16, 1/8 between.
Equipment: Hardware — 9-APP/Mac G3, 8-APP/Mac G4; Presses — KP; Software — Multi-Ad/Creator 2, QPS/QuarkXPress.
Zip Codes Served: 54405, 54421, 54425, 54460, 54422, 54437, 54426, 54411, 54448, 54484, 54446, 54498

ANTIGO

JOURNAL EXPRESS
(Mon)
612 Superior St, Antigo, WI, 54409-2049, USA; tel (715) 623-4191; fax (715) 623-4193; e-mail adj@dwave.net; web site www.antigodailyjournal.com
Circulation:5,610fr; Sworn/Estimate/Non-Audited
Group: Berner Bros. Publishing Co., Inc.
Digital Platform - Mobile: Apple
Pub, Ed .... Fred Berner
Mechanical Specifications: Type page 11.625 x 21; E - 6 cols, 2 1/6, 1/8 between; A - 6 cols, 2 1/6, 1/8 between
Equipment: Hardware — APP/Macs; Presses — G/Community.; Software — QuarkXpress
Delivery Method: Mail
Zip Codes Served: 54409, 54418, 54414, 54424, 54428, 54463, 54430, 54465, 54485, 54491, 54408, 54462, 54435, 54566, 54149, 54541, 54175, 54138, 54452 54464

THE ANTIGO AREA SHOPPER
(Tues)
616 5th Ave, Antigo, WI, 54409-2223, USA; tel (715) 623-5081; adv tel (715) 623-5081; ed tel (715) 623-5081; fax (715) 623-5032; adv fax (715) 623-5032; ed fax (715) 623-5032; e-mail info@theshopperwi.com; adv e-mail shaughn@advertisewis.com; ed e-mail mckenzie@advertisewis.com; web site www.theshopperwi.com
Circulation: 0pd,12,418fr; CVC
Advertising: Open inch rate $7.00
Established: 2011
Group: Gannett
Pub./Gen. Mgr. .... McKenzie Glenetske
Adv. Mgr. .... Shaughn Novy
Mechanical Specifications: Type page 10 3/8 x 12 1/2; E - 4 cols, 1/2 between; A - 4 cols, 1/2 between; C - 4 cols, 1/2 between.
Equipment: Hardware — APP/Mac; Software — QPS/QuarkXPress, Adobe/Photoshop.
Delivery Method: Mail
Zip Codes Served: 54409, 54418, 54424, 54428, 54430, 54462, 54464, 54465, 54485, 54491, 54408, 54414, 54435, 54450, 54138, 54149, 54175, 54566, 54463, 54501

APPLETON

APPLETON FOX CITIES BARGAIN BULLETIN
(Wed)
306 W Washington St, Appleton, WI, 54911-5452, USA
Circulation:58,819fr; CVC
Advertising: Open inch rate $20.74
Established: 1964Amy Leitzke
Mechanical Specifications: Type page: 9.375 x 10.75; 6 col

ASHLAND

EVERGREEN COUNTRY SHOPPER
(Mon)
417 9th Ave W, Ashland, WI, 54806-1324, USA; tel (715) 682-8131; fax (715) 682-6400; e-mail ads@evergreencountryshopper.com; web site www.evergreencountryshopper.com
Circulation: 0pd,13,684fr; CVC
Advertising: Open inch rate $9.00
Established: 1974Editions: 2— Evergreen Country Shopper 13,930; Evergreen County Shopper Zone 2 - 10,408
Owner/Pub. .... Gary A. LaPean
District Mgr. .... Richard Barringer
Circ. Mgr. .... Dean Olsen
Prodn. Mgr. .... Jeanne Oksiuta
Hunter Tyler
Mechanical Specifications: Type page 10 1/2 x 16 1/2; E - 6 cols, 1 1/2, between; A - 6 cols, 1 1/2, between.
Equipment: ; Presses — 8-Goss.
Delivery Method: Mail, Carrier
Zip Codes Served: 54806

BALDWIN

BALDWIN SHOPPER
(Sun)
PO Box 214, Baldwin, WI, 54002-0214, USA; tel (715) 273-4601; fax (715) 273-4769; e-mail infor@helmerprinting.com; web site www.helmerprinting.com
Circulation: 2pd,7,567fr; Sworn/Estimate/Non-Audited
Advertising: Open inch rate $15.83
Established: 1940
Group: Helmer Printing, Inc.
Adv. Mgr. .... Mark Helmer
Circ. Mgr. .... Steve Block
Ed. .... Scott Helmer
Prodn. Mgr. .... Scott A. Helmer
Equipment: Hardware — APP/Mac; Presses — G/Community.
Zip Codes Served: 54002

BEAVER DAM

BEAVER DAM - TRI COUNTY
(Wed)
805 Park Ave, Beaver Dam, WI, 53916-2205, USA; web site www.capitalnewspapers.com
Circulation:17,805fr; VAC
Advertising: Open inch rate $18.98James Kelsh

MONDAY MARKETEER
(Mon)
805 Park Ave, Beaver Dam, WI, 53916-2205, USA; web site www.capitalnewspapers.com
Circulation:10,578fr; VAC
Advertising: Open inch rate $13.75Scott Zeinemann

MONDAY-MINI
(Mon)
805 Park Ave, Beaver Dam, WI, 53916-2205, USA; tel (920) 887-0321; fax (920) 887-8790; web site www.wiscnews.com
Circulation:19,320fr; Sworn/Estimate/Non-Audited
Advertising: Open inch rate $11.10
Group: Capital Newspapers
Pub. .... James Kelsh
Adv. Mgr. .... Scott Zienemann
Circ. Dir. .... Teresa Klinger
Ed. .... Aaron Holbrook
Mechanical Specifications: Type page 10 1/8 x 15; E - 5 cols, 2, between; A - 5 cols, 2, between; C - 7 cols, 1 1/3, between.
Equipment: Hardware — APP/Power Mac G3; Software — Adworks 4.19, QPS/QuarkXPress 3.31.
Zip Codes Served: 53916

SHOPPERS VIEW
(Mon)
805 Park Ave, Beaver Dam, WI, 53916-2205, USA; web site www.capitalnewspapers.com
Circulation:7,110fr; VAC
Advertising: Open inch rate $12.47Scott Zeinemann

TRI-COUNTY
(Wed)
805 Park Ave, Beaver Dam, WI, 53916-2205, USA; tel (920) 887-0321; fax (920) 887-8790; e-mail customerservice@madison.com; web site www.capitalnewspapers.com
Circulation:29,480fr; Sworn/Estimate/Non-Audited
Advertising: Open inch rate $20.63
Group: Capital Newspapers
Pub. .... James Kelsh
Adv. Mgr. .... Scott Zienemann
Circ. Dir. .... Teresa Klinger
Equipment: Hardware — APP/Power Mac G3; Software — Adworks 4.19, QPS/QuarkXPress 3.31.
Zip Codes Served: 53916

BELDENVILLE

FREE PRESS
(Sun)
N 6402 790 St, Beldenville, WI, 54003, USA; tel (800) 533-1635; fax (715) 273-4769; e-mail info@helmerprinting.com; web site www.helmerprinting.com
Circulation: 3pd,13,363fr; CVC
Advertising: Open inch rate $18.50
Established: 1940
Group: Helmer Printing, Inc.
Pub. .... Scott Helmer
Adv. Mgr. .... Mark Helmer
Circ. Mgr. .... Steve Block
Prodn. Mgr. .... John Vogland
Mechanical Specifications: Type page 10 1/4 x 14; E - 5 cols, 2, 1/72 between; A - 5 cols, 2, 1/72 between; C - 5 cols, 2, 1/72 between.
Equipment: Hardware — APP/Macs, PCs; Presses — G/Community; Software — Claris/FileMaker Pro, QPS/QuarkXPress, Adobe/Illustrator, Adobe/Photoshop.
Zip Codes Served: 55033

HIAWATHA VALLEY SHOPPER
(Sun)
N6402 790th St, Beldenville, WI, 54003-4704, USA; tel (715) 273-4601; fax (715) 273-4769; e-mail info@helmerprinting.com; web site www.helmerprinting.com
Circulation: 3pd,8,759fr; VAC
Advertising: Open inch rate $24.81
Established: 1940
Group: Helmer Printing, Inc.
Adv. Mgr. .... Mark Helmer
Mechanical Specifications: Type page: 10.875 x 14; 5 col
Equipment: Hardware — APP/Mac.
Zip Codes Served: 54003

SHOPPER
(Sun)
N6402 790th St, Beldenville, WI, 54003-4704, USA; tel (715) 273-4601; fax (715) 273-4769; e-mail info@helmerprinting.com; web site www.helmerprinting.com
Circulation: 17pd,7,872fr; Sworn/Estimate/

Non-Audited
Advertising: Open inch rate $18.15
Established: 1940
Group: Helmer Printing, Inc.
Pub. .... Scott Helmer
Adv. Mgr. .... Mark Helmer
Mechanical Specifications: Type page 10 1/4 x 14; E - 5 cols, 2, 1/72 between; A - 5 cols, 2, 1/72 between; C - 5 cols, 2, 1/72 between.
Equipment: Hardware — APP/Mac; Presses — 4-G/Community; Software — QPS/QuarkXPress, Adobe/Illustrator, Adobe/Photoshop.
Zip Codes Served: 54011

THE BALDWIN SHOPPER
(Sun)
PO Box 40, Beldenville, WI, 54003-0040, USA; web site www.helmerprinting.com
Circulation: 0pd,5,327fr; VAC
Advertising: Open inch rate $24.81
Established: 1955Mark Helmer
Mechanical Specifications: Type page: 10.875 x 14; 5 col

THE ELLSWORTH SHOPPER
(Sun)
PO Box 40, Beldenville, WI, 54003-0040, USA; web site www.helmerprinting.com
Circulation: 3pd,7,240fr; VAC
Advertising: Open inch rate $24.81
Established: 1955Mark Helmer
Mechanical Specifications: Type page: 10.875 x 14; 5 col

THE HASTINGS FREE PRESS
(Sun)
PO Box 40, Beldenville, WI, 54003-0040, USA; web site www.helmerprinting.com
Circulation: 1pd,14,001fr; VAC
Advertising: Open inch rate $24.81
Established: 1955Mark Helmer
Mechanical Specifications: Type page: 10.875 x 14; 5 col

THE HUDSON FREE PRESS
(Sun)
PO Box 40, Beldenville, WI, 54003-0040, USA; web site www.helmerprinting.com
Circulation: 1pd,7,530fr; VAC
Advertising: Open inch rate $24.81
Established: 1955Mark Helmer
Mechanical Specifications: Type page: 10.875 x 14; 5 col

THE MISS-CROIX SHOPPER
(Sun)
PO Box 40, Beldenville, WI, 54003-0040, USA; web site www.helmerprinting.com
Circulation:2,985fr; VAC
Advertising: Open inch rate $24.81
Established: 1955Mark Helmer
Mechanical Specifications: Type page: 10.875 x 14; 5 col

THE RIVER FALLS SHOPPER
(Sun)
PO Box 40, Beldenville, WI, 54003-0040, USA; web site www.helmerprinting.com
Circulation: 1pd,6,314fr; VAC
Advertising: Open inch rate $24.81Mark Helmer
Mechanical Specifications: Type page: 10.875 x 14; 5 col

BELOIT

MY STATELINE SHOPPER
(Wed)
149 State St, Beloit, WI, 53511-6251, USA; tel (608) 365-8811; fax (608) 365-1420; adv fax (608) 365-0728; e-mail news@beloitdailynews.com; adv e-mail advertising@beloitdailynews.com; web site www.beloitdailynews.com
Circulation:11,500fr; USPS
Advertising: $6 pci
Group: Hagadone Corporation
Pub. .... Kent D. Eymann
Asst. Adv. Dir. .... Todd Colling
Ed. .... William Barth
News Ed. .... Clint Wolf
Mechanical Specifications: Type page 11 5/8 x 21 1/2; E - 6 cols, 1 5/6, 1/8 between; A - 6 cols, 1 5/6, 1/8 between; C - 8 cols, 1 1/3, 1/8 between.
Equipment: ; Presses — 6-G/Urbanite.
Delivery Method: Carrier, Racks
Zip Codes Served: 53511

BLACK EARTH

SAUK CITY SATELLITE SHOPPER
(Wed)
1126 Mills St, Black Earth, WI, 53515-9419, USA; tel (608)767-3655; adv tel (608)767-3655; ed tel (608)767-3655; fax (608)767-2222; adv fax (608)767-2222; ed fax (608)767-2222; e-mail marc@newspubinc.com; adv e-mail classifieds@newpubinc.com; ed e-mail nsa@newspubinc.com; web site www.wisad.com
Circulation:15,987fr; Sworn/Estimate/Non-Audited
Pub. .... Mike Carignan

BLACK RIVER FALLS

ARROW SHOPPER
(Tues)
409 E Main St, Black River Falls, WI, 54615-1460, USA; tel (715) 284-4304; adv tel (715) 284-4304; ed tel (715) 284-4304; fax (715) 284-4634; adv fax (715) 284-4634; ed fax (715) 284-4634; e-mail kathy@bannerjournal.com; adv e-mail kathy@bannerjournal.com; web site www.arrowshopper.com
Circulation: 0pd,20,723fr; VAC
Advertising: Open inch rate $11.00
Established: 1965
Digital Platform - Mobile: Apple
Digital Platform - Tablet: Apple iOS
Gen Mgr. .... Kathy Potter
Mechanical Specifications: 1 col. - 1.597" 4 col. - 6.785"
2 col. - 3.326" 5 col. - 8.514"
3 col. - 5.056" 6 co. - 10.243"
Zip Codes Served: 54612, 54616, 54738, 54627, 54630, 54747, 54758, 54770, 54661, 54773, 54622, 54629, 54635, 54642, 54659, 54644

BLACK RIVER FALLS SHOPPER
(Tues)
409 E Main St, Black River Falls, WI, 54615-1460, USA; tel (715) 284-4304; adv tel (715) 284-4304; ed tel (715) 284-4304; fax (715) 284-4634; adv fax (715) 284-4634; ed fax (715) 284-4634; e-mail kathy@bannerjournal.com; adv e-mail kathy@bannerjournal.com; ed e-mail news@bannerjournal.com; web site http://www.blackrivercountry.net/
Circulation: 25pd,18,300fr; USPS
Advertising: 11.00
Digital Platform - Mobile: Apple
Digital Platform - Tablet: Apple iOS
Gen. Mgr. .... Kathy Potter
Mechanical Specifications: 1 col. - 1.597" 4 col. - 6.785"
2 col. - 3.326" 5 col. - 8.514"
3 col. - 5.056" 6 co. - 10.243"
Delivery Method: Mail
Zip Codes Served: 54615, 54754, 54611, 54643, 54635, 54642, 54659, 54456, 54466, 54746, 54741, 54446, 54437, 54436, 54493, 54420, 54460, 54498

SHOPPER
(Tues)
409 E Main St, Black River Falls, WI, 54615-1460, USA; tel (715) 284-4304; fax (715) 284-4634; web site http://www.blackrivercountry.net/banner-journal-shopper/
Circulation:18,400fr; USPS
Advertising: Open inch rate $10.00
Pub. .... Daniel Witte
Ed. .... Jodee Brooke
Prodn. Mgr. .... Kathy Potter
Delivery Method: Mail, Racks
Zip Codes Served: 54615, 54754, 54611, 54643, 54635, 54642, 54659, 54456, 54466, 54746, 54741, 54446, 54437, 54436, 54493, 54420, 54460, 54498

BRILLION

BRILLION LAKE TO LAKE SHOPPER
(Tues)
425 W Ryan St, Brillion, WI, 54110-1037, USA; tel (920) 756-2131; adv tel (920) 756-2222; fax (920) 756-2701; e-mail info@zanderpressinc.com; adv e-mail publications@zanderpressinc.com; ed e-mail editor@thebrillionnews.com; web site www.mybrillionnews.com
Circulation:10,663fr; VAC
Advertising: Open inch rate $10.46
Established: 1957
Digital Platform - Mobile: Windows
Digital Platform - Tablet: Windows 7Beth Wenzel
Mechanical Specifications: Type page: 9 3/4 x 16; 6 Columns
Delivery Method: Mail, Carrier, Racks
Zip Codes Served: 54110, 54230, 54126, 54123, 53014, 54129, 54160, 54169, 53088, 54188

LAKE TO LAKE SHOPPER
(Tues)
425 W Ryan St, Brillion, WI, 54110-1037, USA; tel (920) 756-2222; fax (920) 756-2701; adv e-mail kris@zanderpressinc.com; ed e-mail editor@thebrillionnews.com; web site www.thebrillionnews.com
Circulation: 0pd,9,340fr; Sworn/Estimate/Non-Audited
Advertising: Open inch rate $9.45
Established: 1957
Group: Zander Press Inc.
Digital Platform - Mobile: Apple, Android
Digital Platform - Tablet: Apple iOS, Android
Circ. Mgr. .... Kris Bastian
Prodn. Mgr. .... Beth Wenzel
Mechanical Specifications: Type page 9.75 x 16; E - 6 cols, 1 1/2, 1/8 between; A - 6 cols, 1 1/2, 1/8 between; C - 6 cols, 1 1/2, 1/8 between.
Equipment: Hardware — iMac; Software — InDesign cloud
Delivery Method: Mail, Newsstand, Carrier
Zip Codes Served: 54110, 54230, 54129, 54123, 54160, 53014, 54207, 54247, 54126, 54130, 54169, 54130, 54952

BURLINGTON

ILLINOIS HI-LITER
(Wed)
700 N Pine St, Burlington, WI, 53105-1472, USA; tel (262) 763-3511; adv tel (262) 763-2575; fax (262) 539-4240; adv fax (262) 763-0996; e-mail cjensen@rvpublishing.com; adv e-mail adsales@hiliter.com; ed e-mail cjensen@rvpublishing.com
Circulation: 0pd,15,723fr; VAC
Advertising: Open inch rate $9.00
Established: 1957
Owner .... Peter Cruger
Pub. .... Jack Cruger
Sales Mgr. .... Rory Fraley
Mechanical Specifications: Type page 10 1/2 x 16; E - 6 cols, 1 5/8, between; A - 6 cols, 1 5/8, between; C - 6 cols, 1 5/8, between.
Equipment: Hardware — APP/Mac, CreoScitex Dolev 800; Presses — G/Suburban; Software — QPS/QuarkXPress 4.0, Adobe/Illustrator 8.0, Adobe/Photoshop 5.5.
Delivery Method: Mail
Zip Codes Served: 53105, 53120, 53147, 53185, 53182, 53168, 53139, 53128, 53121, 53181, 53167

WISCONSIN HI-LITER
(Wed)
700 N Pine St, Burlington, WI, 53105-1472, USA; tel (262) 763-3511; adv tel (262) 763-2575; fax (262) 539-4240; adv fax (262) 763-0996; e-mail cjensen@rvpublishing.com; adv e-mail adsales@hiliter.com; ed e-mail cjensen@rvpublishing.com
Circulation:35,754fr; VAC
Advertising: Open inch rate $9.00
Established: 1957
Owner .... Peter Cruger
Pub. .... Jack Cruger
Sales Mgr. .... Rory Fraley
Mechanical Specifications: Type page 10 1/2 x 16; E - 6 cols, 1 5/8, between; A - 6 cols, 1 5/8, between; C - 6 cols, 1 5/8, between.
Equipment: Hardware — APP/Mac, CreoScitex Dolev 800; Presses — G/Suburban; Software — QPS/QuarkXPress 4.0, Adobe/Illustrator 8.0, Adobe/Photoshop 5.5.
Delivery Method: Mail
Zip Codes Served: 53105, 53120, 53147, 53185, 53182, 53168, 53139, 53128, 53121, 53181, 53167

CEDARBURG

OZAUKEE COUNTY GUIDE
(Wed)
W61N306 Washington Ave, Ste L1, Cedarburg, WI, 53012-2451, USA; tel (262) 375-5100; web site www.gmtoday.com
Circulation: 0pd,28,087fr; VAC
Advertising: Open inch rate $16.50
Established: 1955
Group: Conley Media LLCPhil Paige
Mechanical Specifications: Type page: 10.6 x 10.5; 6 col

CHIPPEWA FALLS

ADVERTISER
(Sun)
321 Frenette Dr, Chippewa Falls, WI, 54729-3372, USA; tel (715) 723-5515; adv tel (866) 477-0648; fax (715) 723-9644; e-mail production@chippewa.com; ed e-mail publisher@chippewa.com; web site www.chippewa.com
Circulation:8,000fr; Sworn/Estimate/Non-Audited
Advertising: Open inch rate $13.14
Pub. .... Mark Baker
Circ. Mgr. .... Kim Spaeth
Prodn. Mgr. .... Joe Webb
Mechanical Specifications: Type page 12 1/2 x 21 1/2; A - 6 cols, 13/16, between; C - 6 cols, 3/16 between.
Equipment: Hardware — APP/Power Macs, Pre Press/Panther Pro; Presses — G/Community; Software — QPS/QuarkXPress, Adobe/Photoshop, Multi-Ad/Creator.
Zip Codes Served: 54729

DUNN COUNTY BIG BUCK
(Sat)
321 Frenette Dr, Chippewa Falls, WI, 54729-3372, USA; tel (715) 723-5515; fax (715) 723-9644; adv e-mail paul.pehler@lee.net; ed e-mail editor@chippewa.com; web site www.dunnconnect.com
Circulation:25,089fr; Sworn/Estimate/Non-Audited
Advertising: Open inch rate $13.19
Group: Lee Enterprises, Inc.
Digital Platform - Mobile: Apple, Android, Windows
Digital Platform - Tablet: Apple iOS, Android, Windows 7
Ed. .... Barb Lyon
Advertising Director .... Paul Pehler
Mechanical Specifications: Page: 9.889" x 21.5" 1 co: 1.556"
Equipment: Hardware — APP/Mac.
Delivery Method: Mail
Zip Codes Served: 54103, 54027, 54721, 54725, 54730, 54733, 54734, 54736, 54739, 54740,

54749, 54750, 54751, 54763, 54767, 54772

YOUR FAMILY SHOPPER

(Sat)
321 Frenette Dr, Chippewa Falls, WI, 54729-3372, USA; tel (715) 723-5515; fax (715) 723-9644; e-mail production@chippewa.com; ed e-mail publisher@chippewa.com; web site www.chippewa.com
Circulation:32,942fr; Sworn/Estimate/Non-Audited
Advertising: Open inch rate $13.34
Pub. .... Mark Baker
Adv. Mgr. .... Patrick Milliren
Circ. Mgr. .... Dave Porter
Ed. .... Ross Evavold
Prodn. Mgr. .... Joe Webb
Equipment: Hardware — APP/Mac; Software — Adobe/PageMaker, QPS/QuarkXPress.
Zip Codes Served: 54729

CLINTONVILLE

CLINTONVILLE SHOPPER'S GUIDE

(Tues)
17 9th St, Clintonville, WI, 54929-1535, USA; tel (715) 823-3107; fax (715) 823-1364
Circulation: 0pd,9,604fr; CVC
Advertising: Open inch rate $22.80
Group: Multi Media Channels
Digital Platform - Mobile: Apple, Android
Digital Platform - Tablet: Apple iOS, Android
Account Executive .... Jeff Hoffman
Mechanical Specifications: Type page 10 5/16 x 17 7/16; E - 4 cols, between; A - 4 cols, between.
Zip Codes Served: 54929, 54486,54948, 54978, 54166, 54107, 54950, 54922' 54949.

COLUMBUS

SHOPPING REMINDER

(Mon)
Beaver Dam, Columbus, WI, 53925, USA; tel (920) 623-3160; fax (920) 623-9383
Circulation:4,145fr; VAC
Advertising: Open inch rate $11.22
Group: Capital Newspapers
Pub. .... James Kelsh
Adv. Mgr. .... Scott Zeinemann
Mechanical Specifications: Type page 10 1/9 x 15 1/4; E - 6 cols, between; A - 6 cols, between.
Zip Codes Served: 53925

CUBA CITY

CUBA CITY ROUND UP SHOPPER

223 S Main St, Cuba City, WI, 53807-1543, USA; tel (608) 744-2107

ROUND-UP SHOPPER

(Mon)
223 S Main St, Cuba City, WI, 53807-1543, USA; tel (608) 744-2107; fax (608) 744-2108; e-mail tcpnews@pcii.net
Circulation:6,630fr; Sworn/Estimate/Non-Audited
Advertising: Open inch rate $5.00 pc.
Established: 1894
Group: Morris Multimedia, Inc.
Pub. .... John Ingebritsen
Adv. Mgr. .... Brian Muldoon
Ed. .... Stephanie Schroeder
Mechanical Specifications: Type page 10 1/2 x 15 3/4; A - 6 cols, 1 5/8, 3/16 between; C - 6 cols, 1 5/8, 3/16 between.
Equipment: Hardware — APP/Power Mac; Software — Adobe/Indesign, Microsoft/ Word 5.1a.
Delivery Method: Mail
Zip Codes Served: 53807

DELAVAN

WEEKEND HI-LITER

(Sat)
1102 Ann St, Delavan, WI, 53115-1938, USA; tel (262) 728-3411; fax (262) 725-7702; web site www.standardpress.com
Circulation:18,183fr; VAC
Advertising: Open inch rate $9.00
Established: 2007Cyndi Jensen
Mechanical Specifications: Type page: 10 1/2 x 16; 6 Columns
Delivery Method: Newsstand, Carrier, Racks

EAGLE RIVER

NORTH WOODS TRADER

(Wed)
425 W Mill St, Eagle River, WI, 54521-8002, USA; tel (715) 479-4421; fax (715) 479-6242; e-mail erpub@nnex.net; adv e-mail kurtk@vcnewsreview.com; ed e-mail garyr@vcnews-review.com; web site http://www.vilascountynewsreview.com/
Circulation:17,500fr; Sworn/Estimate/Non-Audited
Advertising: Open inch rate $14.90
Established: 1886
Group: Delphos Herald, Inc.
Publisher .... Kurt Krueger
Circulation Manager .... Liz Schmidt
Mechanical Specifications: Type page 11 x 21 1/8; E - 6 cols, 1 11/16, between; A - 6 cols, 1 11/16, between.
Delivery Method: Mail, Newsstand
Zip Codes Served: 54521, 54562, 54558, 54540, 54519, 54554, 54560, 49935

EAU CLAIRE

ENTERTAINMENT SPOTLIGHT SAVER

(Tues)
701 S Farwell St, Eau Claire, WI, 54701-3831, USA; tel (715) 833-9200; fax (715) 833-9244; web site www.leadertelegram.com
Circulation:23,000fr; Sworn/Estimate/Non-Audited
Advertising: Open inch rate $7.60
Pub. .... Pieter Graaskamp
Sales Dir. .... Dan Graaskamp
Circ. Dir. .... Mike Carlson
Ed. .... Don Huebscher
Prodn. Mgr. .... Steve Svihovec
Mechanical Specifications: Type page 13 x 21; E - 6 cols, 2 1/16, between; A - 6 cols, 2 1/16, between; C - 9 cols, 1 3/8, between.
Equipment: ; Presses — Dauphin.
Zip Codes Served: 54702

EDGERTON

EDGERTON REPORTER

(Wed)
21 N Henry St, Edgerton, WI, 53534-1859, USA; tel (608) 884-3367; fax (608) 884-8187; e-mail ereport@ticon.net
Circulation: 2,900pd,2,600fr; USPS
Advertising: Open inch rate $12.00
Established: 1874
Publisher and Editor .... Diane Everson
Delivery Method: Mail, Newsstand
Zip Codes Served: 53534

ELKHORN

WALWORTH COUNTY SHOPPER ADVERTISER

(Wed, Sun)
220B Commerce Ct, Elkhorn, WI, 53121-4371, USA; tel (262) 728-3424; adv tel (262) 728-3424; ed tel (262) 728-3424; fax (262) 728-5479; adv fax (262) 728-5479; ed fax (262) 728-5473; e-mail smaenner@communityshoppers.com; adv e-mail advertise@communityshoppers.com; ed e-mail newsdesk@communityshoppers.com; web site www.communityshoppers.com
Circulation: 0pd,39,009fr; CVC
Advertising: Open inch rate $20.40
Established: 1926
Group: The Gazette - gazettextra.com
Digital Platform - Mobile: Apple, Android, Windows
Digital Platform - Tablet: Apple iOS, Android, Windows 7, Blackberry Tablet OS
General Manager .... Scott Maenner
Sales Operations Manager......... Heidi Springer
Mechanical Specifications: Type page: 9.25" x 12.5"
Delivery Method: Carrier, Racks
Zip Codes Served: 53115, 53121, 53190, 53156, 53120, 53105, 53128, 53157, 53147, 53148, 53191, 53125, 53184, 53114, 53585

FORT ATKINSON

UNION EXTRA

(Wed)
28 Milwaukee Ave W, Fort Atkinson, WI, 53538-2018, USA; tel (920) 563-5553; fax (920) 563-2329; e-mail dailyunion@dailyunion.com; adv e-mail rgrindstaff@dailyunion.com; ed e-mail cspangler@dailyunion.com; web site www.dailyunion.com
Circulation:18,475fr; Sworn/Estimate/Non-Audited
Advertising: Open inch rate $11.40
Established: 1870
Group: W. D. Hoard & Sons CompanyEditions: 1—
Pub. .... Brian V. Knox
Advertising/Business Manager Robb Grindstaff
Mechanical Specifications: Type page 11.125x19.5; A - 6 cols, 1.75, .125 between; C - 8 cols, 1.281, .125 between.
Equipment: Hardware — APP/Mac, PC; Software — InDesign, QPS/QuarkXPress, Adobe/PageMaker 6.5, Adobe/Illustrator 8.0, Adobe/Photoshop 5.5, Delta Graph Pro 3.5.2, MS/Word 7.0, Corel/Word Perfect 8.0, Corel/ Quattro Pro 8.0., Pre1, AdForce
Delivery Method: Mail, Newsstand, Carrier, Racks
Zip Codes Served: 53538; 53549; 53038;53137;53178;53551,53523

FREDERIC

ADVERTISER

(Sat)
PO Box 490, Frederic, WI, 54837-0490, USA; tel (715) 327-4236; fax (715) 327-4870; e-mail addept@centurytel.net
Circulation:95,000fr; Sworn/Estimate/Non-Audited
Advertising: Open inch rate $7.50Editions: 5— 5 total; Indian Head Advertiser (20,617); Tri-County North Advertiser (16,769); Tri-County South Advertiser (20,181); Wild Rivers North Advertiser (20,434); Wild Rivers South Advertiser (20,670);
Pub. .... Douglas Panek
Circ. Mgr. .... Carolyn Foltz
Circ. Mgr. .... Letty McDonough
Ed. .... Gary B. King
Mechanical Specifications: Type page 6 x 16.
Equipment: Hardware — COM/8600, APP/Mac, HI; Presses — 7-HI/V-15A.
Zip Codes Served: 54837

INDIANHEAD ADVERTISER

(Mon, Sat)
303 Wisconsin Ave N, Frederic, WI, 54837-9048, USA; tel (715) 327-4236; adv tel (715) 327-4236; ed tel (715) 327-4236; fax (715) 327-4870; adv fax (715) 327-4870; ed fax (715) 327-4236; e-mail ICCPAONLINE@CENTURYTEL.NET; adv e-mail ICCPAONLINE@CENTURYTEL.NET; ed e-mail editor@leaderregister.com; web site www.iccpaonline.com
Circulation:19,335fr; Sworn/Estimate/Non-Audited
Advertising: Open inch rate $8.35
Established: 1933
Digital Platform - Mobile: Apple, Android, Windows, Blackberry
Digital Platform - Tablet: Apple iOS, Android, Windows 7, Blackberry Tablet OS, Kindle, Nook, Kindle FireDoug Panek
Mechanical Specifications: 6 col by 16" Each column is 1.65" wide
Delivery Method: Mail
Zip Codes Served: 54006,54830,54837,54840,54853,54858,54810,54872,54893,55037,55072,55073,55074,55012,55045,

INTER-COUNTY COOP

(Sat)
303 Wisconsin Ave N, Frederic, WI, 54837-9048, USA; web site www.yellowpaperads.com
Circulation:96,629fr; CVCDoug Panek

TRI-COUNTY NORTH ADVERTISER

(Sat)
303 Wisconsin Ave N, Frederic, WI, 54837-9048, USA; web site www.yellowpaperads.com
Circulation:19,474fr; VAC
Advertising: Open inch rate $8.35Doug Panek

TRI-COUNTY SOUTH ADVERTISER

(Sat)
303 Wisconsin Ave N, Frederic, WI, 54837-9048, USA; web site www.yellowpaperads.com
Circulation:17,763fr; VAC
Advertising: Open inch rate $8.35Douglas Panek

WILD RIVERS NORTH ADVERTISER

(Mon, Sat)
303 Wisconsin Ave N, Frederic, WI, 54837-9048, USA; tel (715) 327-4235; adv tel (715) 327-4236; fax (715) 327-4870; adv fax (715) 327-4870; e-mail iccpaonline@centurytel.net; adv e-mail iccpaonline@centurytel.net; ed e-mail editor@leaderregister.com; web site iccpaonline.com
Circulation: 0pd,18,984fr; VAC
Advertising: Open inch rate $8.35
Established: 1933
Digital Platform - Mobile: Apple, Android, Windows, Blackberry
Digital Platform - Tablet: Apple iOS, Android, Windows 7, Blackberry Tablet OS, Kindle, Nook, Kindle Fire
Mgr. .... Douglas Panek
Mechanical Specifications: 6 column by 16" tab format columns are 1.65" wide
Delivery Method: Mail
Zip Codes Served: 54801,54817,54821,54828,54838,54843,54859,54870,54871,54875,54876,54888,54890, 54870,54888

HARTFORD

HARTFORD BOOSTER

(Tues)
31 W Sumner St, Hartford, WI, 53027-1430, USA; tel (262) 673-2900; fax (262) 673-2907; e-mail ads@booster-ads.com; adv e-mail ads@booster-ads.com; ed e-mail lh@booster-ads.com; web site www.booster-ads.com
Circulation: 0pd,20,077fr; VAC
Advertising: Open inch rate $7.80
Established: 1938
Group: The Booster, Inc
Publisher .... Linda Hauser
Pres. .... Mark Hauser
Prodn. Mgr. .... Laura Hamm
Circulation .... Judy Lesmeister
Mechanical Specifications: Type page 10 x 16; E - 6 cols, 1 5/8, 1/6 between; A - 6 cols, 1 5/8, 1/6 between; C - 6 cols, 1 5/8, 1/6 between.
Equipment: Hardware — Mac; Software — Ado-

be Creative Suite
Delivery Method: Carrier
Zip Codes Served: 53027, 53002, 53034, 53035, 53059, 53076, 53078, 53086, 53039, 53050, 53091, 53095, 53033

WEST BEND BOOSTER
(Tues)
31 W Sumner St, Hartford, WI, 53027-1430, USA; tel (262) 673-2900; fax (262) 673-2907; e-mail ads@booster-ads.com; adv e-mail ads@booster-ads.com; ed e-mail lh@booster-ads.com; web site www.booster-ads.com
Circulation: 0pd,28,873fr; VAC
Advertising: Open inch rate $8.72
Established: 1980
Group: The Booster, Inc
Pub. .... Linda Hauser
President .... Mark Hauer
Mechanical Specifications: column 1.59", print area 10 1/8" x 16" 61p0x96p0
Equipment: Hardware — Macs; Presses — na; Software — Adobe Creative suite
Delivery Method: Carrier
Zip Codes Served: 53090, 53095, 53002, 53010, 53012, 53037, 53040, 53086

HARTLAND

LAKE COUNTRY BUYERS GUIDE
(Mon)
440 Cardinal Ln, Hartland, WI, 53029-2331, USA; tel (262) 367-3272; fax (262) 367-7414; e-mail lakenews@jcpgroup.com; web site www.livinglakecountry.com
Circulation:17,318fr; Sworn/Estimate/Non-Audited
Advertising: Open inch rate $17.49
Pub. .... Gary Jasiek
Ed. .... Scott Petersen
Zip Codes Served: 53066

KENOSHA

BARGAINEER
(Mon) (mailed for Wed delivery)
5800 7th Ave, Kenosha, WI, 53140-4131, USA; tel (262) 657-1000; adv tel (262) 656-6231; adv fax (262) 651-5101; adv e-mail ads@kenoshanews.com; ed e-mail newsroom@kenoshanews.com
Circulation: 0pd,34,000fr; Sworn/Estimate/Non-Audited
Established: 2014Editions: 1— 1
Pub. .... Ken Dowdell
Adv. Dir. .... Ed Gambardella
Mechanical Specifications: 10.875" x 20"
Equipment: Hardware — PC; Presses — off-site; Software — InDesign
Delivery Method: Mail
Zip Codes Served: 53140, 53142, 53143, 53144, 53168, 53104,53158

KIEL

TEMPO
(Tues)
606 Fremont St, Kiel, WI, 53042-1321, USA; tel (920) 894-2828; adv tel (920) 894-2828; fax (920) 894-2161; e-mail graphics@deltapublications.com; circulation@deltapublications.com; adv e-mail joe@deltapublications.com; web site www.deltapublications.com
Circulation: 0pd,20,410fr; VAC
Advertising: Open inch rate $12.28
Established: 1987
Group: Delta Publications, Inc.
Pub. .... Mike E. Mathes
Office Mgr. .... Sharon Meyer
Vice Pres., Sales .... Joe Mathes
Ed. .... Mark Sherry
Prodn. Mgr. .... Klaudia Schnell
Mechanical Specifications: Type page 9 1/3 x 15; 6 col
Equipment: Hardware — APP/Mac.
Delivery Method: Mail, Carrier

LA CROSSE

BUYERS EXPRESS
(Tues)
1523 Rose St, La Crosse, WI, 54603-2227, USA; tel (608) 791-7171; fax (800) 745-7105; e-mail thebuyersexpress@centurytel.net; web site www.thebuyersexpress.com
Circulation:40,000fr; Sworn/Estimate/Non-Audited
Advertising: Open inch rate $7.00
Adv. Mgr. .... Daniel J. Stumpf
Zip Codes Served: 54603

LA CROSSE FOXXY SHOPPER
(Mon)
401 3rd St N, La Crosse, WI, 54601-3267, USA; tel (608) 785- 7355; adv tel (800) 262-2400; fax (608) 791-8238; adv fax (608) 791-8238; e-mail lisa.faulkner@lee.net; adv e-mail ads@lacrossetribune.com; ed e-mail dan.petersen@lee.net; web site www.lacrosse-foxxy.com
Circulation: 1pd,20,448fr; CVC
Advertising: Open inch rate $14.68
Established: 1975
Group: Lee Enterprises, Inc.Editions: 3— Tri-County Foxxy Shopper East - 3 Paid, 12,463 Free; Tri-County Foxxy Shopper South - 3 Paid, 13,420 Free; Tri-County Foxxy Shopper West - 6 Paid, 11,839 Free.
Pub. .... Rusty Cunningham
Adv. Mgr. .... Lisa Faulkner
Circ. Mgr. .... Robin Noth
Prodn. Mgr. .... Sew Thomson
Mechanical Specifications: Type page 11 10/16 x 21 1/2; A - 6 cols, 1 13/16, 1/8 between; C - 6 cols, 1 13/16, 1/8 between.
Equipment: Hardware — APP/Mac, SyQuest/ Exterior Drive 200MB; Software — QPS/ QuarkXPress 3.12, Adobe/Photoshop 3.0.
Delivery Method: Mail, Carrier
Zip Codes Served: 53950, 54618, 54638, 54649, 54660, 54666, 54670, 54603, 54614, 54653, 54656, 54669, 54619, 54621, 54623, 54632, 54639, 54651, 54652, 54658, 54664, 54665, 54667

TRI-COUNTY FOXXY SHOPPER
(Mon)
401 3rd St N, La Crosse, WI, 54601-3267, USA; tel (608) 785- 7355; adv tel (800) 262-2400; fax (608) 791-8238; adv fax (608) 791-8238; e-mail lisa.faulkner@lee.net; adv e-mail ads@lacrossetribune.com; ed e-mail dan.petersen@lee.net; web site www.lacrosse-foxxy.com
Circulation: 4pd,12,414fr; VAC
Advertising: Open inch rate $14.68
Established: 1975
Group: Lee Enterprises, Inc.Editions: 3— Tri-County Foxxy Shopper East - 3 Paid, 12,463 Free; Tri-County Foxxy Shopper South - 3 Paid, 13,420 Free; Tri-County Foxxy Shopper West - 6 Paid, 11,839 Free.
Pub. .... Rusty Cunningham
Adv. Mgr. .... Lisa Faulkner
Circ. Mgr. .... Robin Noth
Pdn. Mgr .... Sew Thomson
Mechanical Specifications: Type page 11 10/16 x 21 1/2; A - 6 cols, 1 13/16, 1/8 between; C - 6 cols, 1 13/16, 1/8 between.
Equipment: Hardware — APP/Mac, SyQuest/ Exterior Drive 200MB; Software — QPS/ QuarkXPress 3.12, Adobe/Photoshop 3.0.
Delivery Method: Mail, Carrier
Zip Codes Served: 53950, 54618, 54638, 54649, 54660, 54666, 54670, 54603, 54614, 54653, 54656, 54669, 54619, 54621, 54623, 54632, 54639, 54651, 54652, 54658, 54664, 54665, 54667
Note: Averaged totals for East, South, West editions

WINONA FOXXY SHOPPER
(Sat)
401 3rd St N, La Crosse, WI, 54601-3267, USA; web site www.rivervalleynewspapers.com
Circulation:7,709fr; CVC
Advertising: Open inch rate $14.68
Established: 1975Chris Hardie
Mechanical Specifications: Type page: 9.889 x 21.5; 6 col

LANCASTER

REMINDER SHOPPER
(Mon)
208 W Cherry St, Lancaster, WI, 53813-1629, USA; tel (608) 723-2151; fax (608) 723-7272
Circulation:16,000fr; Sworn/Estimate/Non-Audited
Group: Morris Multimedia, Inc.
Pub. .... John Ingebritsen
Mechanical Specifications: Type page 10 3/4 x 16.
Equipment: Hardware — APP/Macs; Presses — HI/V-16.
Zip Codes Served: 53813

LODI

THE LODI SHOPPER
(Tues)
146 S Main St, Lodi, WI, 53555-1119, USA; tel (608) 592-3261; fax (608) 592-3866; e-mail lodient@hometownnewsgroup.com
Circulation:24,000fr; Sworn/Estimate/Non-Audited
Advertising: Open inch rate $11.52
Gen. Mgr. .... Jeniffer Setterly
Zip Codes Served: 53555

MADISON

COVERSTORY
(Sun)
1901 Fish Hatchery Rd, Madison, WI, 53713-1248, USA; tel (608) 252-6269; fax (608) 252-6333
Circulation:43,080fr; Sworn/Estimate/Non-Audited
Advertising: Open inch rate $12.00Editions: 3— 3 total; CoverStory-East (15,505); CoverStory-South (17,575); CoverStory-West (10,000);
Pub. .... Phil Blake
Pub. .... Clayton Frink
Gen. Mgr. .... Jeannine Koncar
Adv. Mgr. .... Jeff Schroeter
Circ. Mgr. .... Steve Swails
Mechanical Specifications: Type page 13 x 21 1/2; E - 6 cols, 2, 1/8 between; A - 6 cols, 2, 1/8 between; C - 10 cols, 1 1/4, 1/6 between.
Equipment: Hardware — HI; Presses — G.
Zip Codes Served: 53713

SHOPPER STOPPER
1901 Fish Hatchery Rd, Madison, WI, 53713-1248, USA; tel (608) 252-6200

MARINETTE

EAGLE HERALD SUNDAY
(Sun)
1809 Dunlap Ave, Marinette, WI, 54143-1706, USA; tel (715) 735-6611; fax (715) 735-7580; adv e-mail khofer@eagleherald.com; ed e-mail dkitkowski@eagleherald.com; web site ehextra.com
Circulation:32,620fr; Sworn/Estimate/Non-Audited
Advertising: Open inch rate $8.55
Vice Pres. .... Dan White
Adv. Dir. .... James Hofer
Ed. .... Terri Lescelius
Mechanical Specifications: Type page 13 x 21 1/2; E - 6 cols, 2 1/16, 1/8 between; A - 6 cols, 2 1/16, 1/8 between; C - 6 cols, 2 1/16, 1/8 between.
Equipment: Hardware — APP/Mac; Presses — 6-G/Urbanite, 4-G/Community.
Zip Codes Served: 54143

MARSHFIELD

MARSHFIELD HUB CITY TIMES AND BUYERS' GUIDE
(Wed)
214 W 5th St, Ste B, Marshfield, WI, 54449-2718, USA; tel (715) 344-4700; adv tel (715) 344-4700; ed tel (715) 344-4700; fax (715) 344-5117; adv fax (715) 344-5117; ed fax (715) 344-5117; e-mail dwood@mmclocal.com; adv e-mail dwood@mmclocal.com; ed e-mail kleonhardt@mmclocal.com; web site www.mmclocal.com
Circulation: 0pd,21,151fr; CVC
Advertising: Open inch rate $24.25
Established: 1970
Group: Multi Media Channels
Pub./Gen. Mgr. .... Dave Wood
Mechanical Specifications: Type page: 9.75 x 11"; 6 col
Delivery Method: Mail, Carrier
Zip Codes Served: Wood County

MAUSTON

BADGERLAND VALUES JUNEAU COUNTY
(Wed)
201 E State St, Mauston, WI, 53948-1346, USA; tel (608) 847-7744; fax (608) 847-4867
Circulation:12,870fr; VAC
Advertising: Open inch rate $16.60
Pub. .... George Althoff
Mechanical Specifications: Type page 10 3/8 x 17; E - 6 cols, 1 5/8, between; A - 6 cols, 1 5/8, between; C - 6 cols, 1 5/8, between.
Zip Codes Served: 53948

MEDFORD

THE SHOPPER
(Tues)
116 Wisconsin Ave, Medford, WI, 54451-1749, USA; tel (715) 748-2626; fax (715) 748-2699; e-mail starnews@centralwinews.com; adv e-mail Snads@centralwinews.com; web site www.centralwinews.com/starnews
Circulation:11,800fr; USPS
Advertising: Open inch rate $8.25
Established: 1983
Group: Central Wisconsin Publications Inc.
Pub. .... Carol O'Leary
Adv. Mgr. .... Kris O'Leary
Mechanical Specifications: Type page 10 1/3 x 14; A - 6 cols, 1 7/12, 1/12 between; C - 6 cols, 1 7/12, 1/12 between.
Equipment: Hardware — APP/Mac; Software — InDesign.
Delivery Method: Mail, Racks
Zip Codes Served: 54451, 54470, 54480, 54433

MENOMONIE

DUNN COUNTY REMINDER
(Wed)
710 Main St E, Menomonie, WI, 54751-2615, USA; tel (715) 235-3411; adv tel (866) 477-0648; fax (715) 235-0936; web site www.dunnconnect.com
Circulation:23,150fr; Sworn/Estimate/Non-Audited
Advertising: Open inch rate $11.30
Adv. Mgr. .... Denny Bodoh
Ed. .... Barb Lyon
Mechanical Specifications: Type page 10 x 16; A - 6 cols, 1 5/8, between; C - 6 cols, 1 5/8, between.
Equipment: Hardware — APP/Mac; Software — Multi-Ad/Creator 3.0.1, QPS/QuarkXPress

3.1.
Zip Codes Served: 54751

MERRILL

WAUSAU TIMES / BUYERS' GUIDE
(Tues)
807 E 1st St, Merrill, WI, 54452-2412, USA; tel (715) 536-7121; adv tel (715) 536-7121; ed tel (715) 536-7121; fax (715) 539-3686; adv fax (715) 539-3686; ed fax (715) 539-3686; e-mail tschreiber@mmclocal.com; adv e-mail tsopata@mmclocal.com; ed e-mail clueck@mmclocal.com ; web site www.wausautimes.com
Circulation: 0pd,25,450fr; VAC
Advertising: Open inch rate $28.30
Established: 1975
Group: Brown County Publishing, MMC llc.
Digital Platform - Mobile: Windows
Digital Platform - Tablet: Windows 7
Gen. Mgr. .... Tim Schreiber
Ed. .... Colin Lueck
Pub. .... Patrick J. Wood
Lead Sales .... Todd Sopata
Mechanical Specifications: Type page 9 3/4 x 11; E - 6 cols, 2 13/40, 1/4 between; A - 4 cols, 2 13/40, 1/4 between; C - 8 cols, 1 1/2, 1/4 between.
Equipment: Hardware — PC's; Presses — KP/News King, HI/Sheet-fed pressBr; Software — Adobe/PageMaker 5.0.
Delivery Method: Newsstand, Carrier, Racks
Zip Codes Served: Marathon County WI

MIDDLETON

MIDDLETON WEST SIDE SHOPPER
(Wed)
7505 Hubbard Ave, Ste 100, Middleton, WI, 53562-3132, USA; ed e-mail mgeieger@newspubinc.com; web site www.newspubinc.com
Circulation:12,786fr; Sworn/Estimate/Non-AuditedMarlene Shiffman

MONROE

MONROE SHOPPING NEWS
(Wed)
1065 4th Ave W, Monroe, WI, 53566-1318, USA; tel (608) 328-4202; adv tel (608) 328-4202; ed tel (608 328-4202; e-mail mjohnson@themonroetimes.net; adv e-mail lhughes@themonroetimes.com; ed e-mail editor@themonroetimes.com; web site www.mymonroeshoppingnews.com
Circulation: 0pd,19,433fr; Sworn/Estimate/Non-Audited
Advertising: 17.85 per inch rate
Established: 1984
Group: Morris Multi Media
Adv. Mgr. .... Laura Hughes
Publisher...................................... Matt Johnson
Mechanical Specifications: Type page 10 3/8 x 16 3/4; E - 6 cols, 1 5/8, between; A - 6 cols, 1 5/8, between.
Equipment: Hardware — PC; Software — InDesign, Ad Force
Delivery Method: Mail, Racks
Zip Codes Served: 53566, 53522, 53550, 53520, 53502, 53570, 53574, 61050, 61060, 61087, 61089, 53541, 53587, 53599, 53504, 53516

STATELINE BUYERS'GUIDE
(Sat) (Weekly)
1065 4th Ave W, Monroe, WI, 53566-1318, USA; tel (608) 328-4202; adv tel (608) 328-4202 ; ed tel (608) 328-4202; adv e-mail lhughes@themonroetimes.com; ed e-mail editor@themonroetimes.com; web site www.themonroetimes.com
Circulation: 0pd,5,589fr; Sworn/Estimate/Non-Audited
Advertising: Open inch rate $23.26
Pub. .... Carl Hearing
Adv. Dir... Laura Hughes
Mechanical Specifications: Type page 11.125x 20; E - 6 cols, 2 1/30, 1/6 between; A - 6 cols, 2 1/30, 1/6 between; C - 9 cols, 1 2/5, 1/12 between.
Equipment: Hardware — 2-APP/Power Mac, APP/Power Mac, APP/Power Mac, 4-APP/Power Mac; Software — Multi-Ad/Creator 4.01, QPS/QuarkXPress 3.32, Adobe/Photoshop 3.0.
Delivery Method: Carrier
Zip Codes Served: 53566, 53522

MOUNT HOREB

MT. HOREB TOWN AND COUNTRY SHOPPER
(Wed)
118 E Main St, Mount Horeb, WI, 53572-2138, USA; web site www.newspubinc.com
Circulation:9,211fr; Sworn/Estimate/Non-AuditedMarlene Schiffman

MUKWONAGO

LIVING - KETTLE MORAINE SUNDAY
(Sun)
111 N Rochester St, Ste 3, Mukwonago, WI, 53149-1309, USA; tel (262) 368-2966; adv tel (262) 368-2968; ed tel (262) 368-2970; fax (262) 368-2967; adv fax (262) 368-2967; ed fax (262) 368-2967; e-mail mukpubs@jcpgroup.com; adv e-mail shall@jcpgroup.com; ed e-mail csbauer@jcpgroup.com; web site themukwonagochief.com
Circulation: 9,812pd,; Sworn/Estimate/Non-Audited
Advertising: Open inch rate $14.30
Group: Gannett
Lake County Publications
Gen. Mgr. .... Sue Hall

MUKWONAGO PUBLICATIONS
(Wed)
111 N Rochester St, Ste 3, Mukwonago, WI, 53149-1309, USA; tel (262) 368-2966; fax (262) 368-2967; e-mail mukpubs@jcpgroup.com; web site www.livinglakecountry.com
Circulation: 2,230pd,; AAM
Group: Gannett
Pub. .... Steve Lyles
Ed. in Chief. .... Scott Peterson
Mechanical Specifications: column width 1.729", 5 columns wide by 11" tall.
Delivery Method: Mail, Carrier, Racks
Zip Codes Served: 53149

NEILLSVILLE

THE SHOPPER
(Tues)
614 Hewett St, Neillsville, WI, 54456-1529, USA; tel (715) 743-2600; adv tel (715) 284-4304; ed tel (715) 743-2600; fax (715) 743-5460; adv fax (715) 284-4634; ed fax (715) 743-5460; e-mail kathy@bannerjournal.com; adv e-mail kathy@bannerjournal.com; ed e-mail pressnews@tds.net
Circulation: 25pd,18,300fr; USPS
Advertising: Open inch rate $11.00
Digital Platform - Mobile: Apple
Digital Platform - Tablet: Apple iOS
Pub. .... Daniel Witte
Prodn. Mgr. .... Kathy Potter
Mechanical Specifications: 1 col. - 1.597" 4 col. - 6.785"
2 col. - 3.326" 5 col. - 8.514"
3 col. - 5.056" 6 col. 10.243"
Equipment: Hardware — APP/Macs; Software — Abobe Systems/Quark, Microsoft/Word.
Zip Codes Served: 54615, 54754, 54611, 54643, 54635, 54642, 54659, 54456, 54466, 54746, 54741, 54446, 54437, 54436, 54493, 54420, 54460, 54498

NEW GLARUS

NEW GLARUS SUGAR RIVER SHOPPER
(Wed)
109 5th Avenue, Unit A, New Glarus, WI, 53574, USA; web site www.newspubinc.com
Circulation:8,684fr; Sworn/Estimate/Non-AuditedJohn Donaldson

NEW LONDON

NEW LONDON BUYERS' GUIDE
(Mon)
301 S Pearl St, New London, WI, 54961-1489, USA; web site www.newlondoninfo.com
Circulation:14,952fr; CVC
Advertising: Open inch rate $22.80

OCONTO

FOREST COUNTY BEACON
(Mon)
648 Brazeau Ave, Oconto, WI, 54153-1946, USA; tel (920) 834-4242; fax (920) 834-4878
Circulation:4,000fr; Sworn/Estimate/Non-Audited
Advertising: Open inch rate $6.25
Group: Gannett
Mechanical Specifications: Type page 10 x 21.5
Equipment: Hardware — APP/Macs.
Zip Codes Served: 54153

LAKES/FOREST BEACON
(Mon)
PO Box 200, 648 Brazeau Ave, Oconto, WI, 54153-0200, USA; tel (920) 834-4242; adv tel (920)676-0495; ed tel (920) 834-4242; fax (920) 834-4878; e-mail OCR-Adsmbx@gannett.com; adv e-mail ccolton@gannett.com; ed e-mail editorial@goocontocounty.com; web site www.ocontocountyreporter.com
Circulation:7,000fr; Sworn/Estimate/Non-Audited
Advertising: Open rate $7.75
Group: Gannett
Advertising Executive ....Corey Colton
News Clerk .... Judy Nowak
Mechanical Specifications: Type page 10 x 20.
Equipment: Hardware — pc.
Delivery Method: Mail, Racks
Zip Codes Served: 54153, 54124,54174,54149,54175,54138,54566,54541,54114,54104,54125

OCONTO COUNTY BEACON
(Sun)
PO Box 200, Oconto, WI, 54153-0200, USA; tel (920) 834-4242; adv tel (920) 676-0495; ed tel (920) 834-4242; fax (920) 834-4878; e-mail OCR-Adsmbx@gannett.com; adv e-mail ccolton@gannett.com; ed e-mail jmnowak@gannett.com
Circulation:8,635fr; Sworn/Estimate/Non-Audited
Advertising: Open inch rate $7.75
Group: Gannett
Advertising Executive ....Corey Colton
Mechanical Specifications: Type page 12 1/2 x 21.
Equipment: Hardware — APP/Macs., PC
Delivery Method: Mail, Racks
Zip Codes Served: 54153,54139,54141,54101,54154

OCONTO FALLS

BONUS
(Sun)
107 S Main St, Oconto Falls, WI, 54154-1436, USA; tel (920) 848-3427; fax (920) 848-3430
Circulation:16,458fr; Sworn/Estimate/Non-Audited
Advertising: Open inch rate $8.14
Adv. Mgr..Kevin Jacobs
Mechanical Specifications: Type page 10 1/2 x 16 1/2; E - 6 cols, 1 5/8, between; A - 6 cols, 1 5/8, between.
Equipment: Hardware — APP/Mac Quadra 650, APP/Power Mac 7100; Software — QPS/QuarkXPress.
Zip Codes Served: 54154

OSHKOSH

COMMUNITY SNAPSHOT
(Mon, Wed)
224 State St, Oshkosh, WI, 54901-4839, USA; tel (920) 235-7700; fax (920) 235-1316; e-mail oshkoshnews@thenorthwestern.com; web site www.thenorthwestern.com
Circulation:35,600fr; Sworn/Estimate/Non-Audited
Advertising: Open inch rate $5.95
Group: Gannett
Gen. Mgr. .... Stewart Rickmond
Adv. Dir.. Lisa O'Halloran
Exec. Ed.............................. Stewart Rieckman
Zip Codes Served: 54901

OSHKOSH BUYERS GUIDE
(Fri)
2075 S Washburn St, Oshkosh, WI, 54904-8946, USA; web site www.oshkoshinfo.com
Circulation: 1pd,22,937fr; Sworn/Estimate/Non-AuditedMaureen Bryden

PLATTEVILLE

GRANT, IOWA, LAFAYETTE SHOPPING NEWS
(Tues)
11 Means Dr, Platteville, WI, 53818-3829, USA; tel (608) 348-2374; fax (608) 348-3388; e-mail plattevilleshopnews@wcinet.com; web site www.shoppingnewspapers.com
Circulation: 56pd,30,300fr; Sworn/Estimate/Non-Audited
Advertising: Open inch rate $17.80
Established: 1950
Group: Woodward Communications, Inc.
Distribution Manager ....Shelley Brown
Regional Publisher .... Borkowski Lee
Director of Pre-Press Production........Kari Voss
Mechanical Specifications: Type page 10 3/8 x 16 1/2; A - 6 cols, 1 5/8, 1/8 between.
Delivery Method: Carrier

PORTAGE

BADGERLAND VALUES COLUMBIA COUNTY
(Wed)
PO Box 470, Portage, WI, 53901-0470, USA; web site www.capitalnewspapers.com
Circulation:15,198fr; Sworn/Estimate/Non-Audited
Advertising: Open inch rate $16.60
Established: 2001
Group: Lee Enterprises, Inc.Editions: 3— Shopper Stopper Columbia: 16,839 Free; Shopper Stopper Sauk: 16,292 Free; Shopper Stopper Extra Sauk: 15,131 Free.
GM.. Jon Denk
Mechanical Specifications: Type page: 9.8889 x 21.5; 6 col
Delivery Method: Carrier, Racks

SHOPPER STOPPER
(Wed)
1640 La Dawn Dr, Portage, WI, 53901-8822, USA; tel (608) 493-2291; fax (608) 745-3530; e-mail sales@shopperstopper.com; web site www.shopstop.net
Circulation: 221pd,128,800fr; Sworn/Estimate/Non-Audited
Advertising: Open inch rate $27.06

Group: Capital NewspapersEditions: 6— 6 total; Shopper Stopper-Baraboo/Dells/Reedsburg (20,979); Shopper Stopper-Columbia/Marquette County (22,219); Shopper Stopper-Juneau County Supplement (18,671); Shopper Stopper-Lake Wisconsin (22,539); Shopper Stopper-Northeastern Dane (20,856); Shopper
Pub. .... George Althoff
Mechanical Specifications: Type page 10 7/16 x 17; E - 7 cols, 1 3/8, between; A - 7 cols, 1 3/8, between.
Equipment: ; Presses — 6-HI/V-22; Software — QPS/QuarkXPress.
Zip Codes Served: 53561

PRAIRIE DU CHIEN

WISCONSIN-IOWA SHOPPING NEWS

(Tues)
405 N Marquette Rd, Prairie Du Chien, WI, 53821-1205, USA; tel (608) 326-2457; fax (608) 326-6621; e-mail prairieshopnews@wcinet.com; web site www.shoppingnewspapers.com
Circulation: 20pd,17,100fr; CVC
Advertising: Open inch rate $11.00
Established: 1977
Group: Woodward Communications, Inc.
Regional Publisher .... Lee Borkowski
Sales Manager .... Tina Sander
Mechanical Specifications: Type Page: 10 1/4 x 16 1/2; 6 Columns
Delivery Method: Mail

RHINELANDER

HODAG BUYER'S GUIDE

(Wed)
24 W Rives St, Rhinelander, WI, 54501-3164, USA; tel (715) 369-3331; adv tel (715) 369-3331; ed tel (715) 369-3331; fax (715) 369-4859; adv fax (715) 369-4859; ed fax (715) 369-4859; e-mail pdaniels@mmclocal.com; adv e-mail hodagads@mmclocal.com; ed e-mail starjournal@mmclocal.com; web site www.rhinelanderinfo.com
Circulation: 1pd,15,949fr; CVC
Advertising: Open inch rate $22.65
Established: 1977
Group: Multi Media Channels LLC
Digital Platform - Mobile: Apple, Android, Windows, Blackberry
Digital Platform - Tablet: Apple iOS, Android, Windows 7, Blackberry Tablet OS
Gen. Mgr. .... Peter Daniels
Circ. Mgr...................................... Cathy Oelrich
Mechanical Specifications: Type page: 9.75 x 11; 6 col
Delivery Method: Carrier, Racks
Zip Codes Served: 54501, 54487, 54529, 54548, 54568, 54531, 54562, 54539, 54463, 54558, 54520, 54521

NORTHWOODS SUPER SHOPPER

(Sat)
232 S Courtney St, Stop 14, Rhinelander, WI, 54501-3319, USA; tel (715) 365-6397; adv tel (715) 365-6397; ed tel (262) 306-5043; fax (715) 365-6367; adv fax (715) 365-6367; ed fax (715) 365-6367; e-mail news@rhinelanderdailynews.com; adv e-mail advertising@rivernewsonline.com; ed e-mail news@rivernewsonline.com; web site www.rivernewsonline.com
Circulation: 0pd,29,508fr; CVC
Advertising: Open inch rate $7.25
Established: 2010
Pub./Ed.. Gregg Walker
Assoc. Ed............................. Heather Schaefer
Classifieds/Adv. Dir. .... Jan Juedes
Gen. Mgr. .... Wendi Ell
Circ. Mgr. .... Corey Richter
Sports Ed.................................... Jeremy Mayo
Subscriptions .... Susan Taves
Mechanical Specifications: Type page 11 5/8 x 21 1/2; E - 6 cols, 1 5/6, 1/8 between; A - 6 cols, 1 5/6, 1/8 between; C - 6 cols, 1 5/6, 1/8 between.
Delivery Method: Mail
Zip Codes Served: Oneida County

RICE LAKE

THE EARLY BIRD

(Sat)
28 S Main St, Rice Lake, WI, 54868-2269, USA; tel (715) 234-2121; adv tel (715) 234-2121; ed tel (715) 234-2121; fax (715) 234-5232; adv fax (715) 234-5232; ed fax (715) 234-5232; e-mail publish1@chronotype.com; adv e-mail advertising@chronotype.com; ed e-mail newsroom@chronotype.com; web site www.ricelakeonline.com
Circulation: 2pd,28,963fr; VAC
Advertising: Open inch rate $14.95
Established: 1978
Group: Adams Publishing Group, LLCEditions: 52—
Publisher.............................. Warren Dorrance
Mechanical Specifications: Type page: 9.889 x 20.75; 6 col
Equipment: Hardware — Mac; Software — CS3, AdWorks
Delivery Method: Newsstand, Carrier
Zip Codes Served: 54805, 54813, 54812, 54817, 54818, 54819, 54822, 54728, 54004, 54828, 54829, 54733, 54835, 54841, 54843, 54845, 54744, 54848, 54857, 54757, 54862, 54762, 54867, 54868, 54763, 54870, 65871, 54801, 54875, 54876, 54888, 54889, 54895, 54896

RICHLAND CENTER

RICHLAND CENTER SHOPPING NEWS

(Tues)
272 N Main St, Richland Center, WI, 53581-2239, USA; tel (608) 647-2911; fax (608) 647-7238; e-mail rcentershopnews@wcinet.com; web site www.shoppingnewspapers.com
Circulation: 6pd,13,100fr; CVC
Advertising: Open inch rate $10.15
Established: 1932
Group: Woodward Communications, Inc.
General Manager .... Lee Borkowski
Prod. Mgr./Sales Team Lead .... Jodi Peterson
Mechanical Specifications: Type Page: 10.4 x 16.5; 6 Columns
Delivery Method: Carrier

RIVER FALLS

HOT SHEET SHOPPER

(Sun)
2815 Prairie Dr, P.O. Box 25, River Falls, WI, 54022-5211, USA; tel (715) 386-9333; adv tel (715) 426-1052; fax (715) 386-9891; e-mail hso@rivertowns.net; ed e-mail hsoeditor@rivertowns.net; web site www.hudsonstarobserver.com
Circulation:22,150fr; Sworn/Estimate/Non-Audited
Advertising: Open inch rate $10.98
Established: 1854
Publisher.................................... Steve Dzubay
Adv. Mgr. .... Mary Beth Kremer
Ed. .... Douglas W. Stohlberg
Prodn. Mgr. .... Rebecca LaMar
Mechanical Specifications: Type page 13 x 21 1/2; E - 6 cols, 1 13/16, 1/8 between; A - 6 cols, 1 13/16, 1/5 between; C - 8 cols, 1 3/8, 1/8 between.
Equipment: Hardware — PC; Presses — G; Software — QPS/QuarkXPress.
Zip Codes Served: 54016

SEYMOUR

ADVERTISER COMMUNITY NEWS

(Mon)
800 E Factory St, P.O. Box 100, Seymour, WI, 54165-1210, USA; tel (920) 833-0420; fax (920) 833-0423; e-mail sey.prod@adcommnews.com; adv e-mail ken.h@adcommnews.com; ed e-mail keith.s@adcommnews.com; web site www.advertiser-communitynews.com
Circulation: 121pd,8,940fr; CVC
Advertising: Open inch rate $.11.75
Established: 2009
Group: K & M Community Papers LLC
Circ. Mgr...................................... Ken Hodgden
Mechanical Specifications: Type page 9.75 x 13.75
Delivery Method: Mail, Newsstand, Carrier
Zip Codes Served: 54165, 54106, 54170, 54152, 54155, 54162,54131,54107
Note: we are a free community news paper 9100 circulation covering north east outagamie county wisconsin

SHEBOYGAN

THE SHEBOYGAN SUN

(Thur)
708 Erie Ave, # A, Sheboygan, WI, 53081-4060, USA; tel (920) 803-9945; adv tel (920) 803-9945; ed tel (920) 803-9945; fax (920) 803-9946; adv fax (920) 803-9945; ed fax (920) 803-9945; e-mail thesun@sheboygansun.com; adv e-mail ads@sheboygansun.com; ed e-mail gdillon@sheboygansun.com; web site www.sheboygansun.com
Circulation: 0pd,48,978fr; VAC
Advertising: Open inch rate $18.98
Established: 1999
Group: Walton Publishing, LLC
Publisher... Greg Dillon
Mike Walton
Mechanical Specifications: 1 column - 1.487"
2 column - 3.139"
3 column - 4.79"
4 column - 6.44"
5 column - 8.097"
6 column - 9.75"
double truck - 20.5"
page size: 96 column inches - 6 columns x 16"
Delivery Method: Mail
Zip Codes Served: 53001, 53011, 53013, 53020, 53023, 53026, 53031, 53044, 53070, 53073, 53075, 53081, 53083, 53085, 53093
Note: 100% direct mail distribution.

THE SHORELINE CHRONICLE

(Wed)
632 Center Ave, Sheboygan, WI, 53081-4621, USA; tel (920)457-7711; adv tel (920)457-7711; ed tel (920)457-7711; e-mail ljohnson2@gannett.com; adv e-mail ljohnson2@gannett.com; ed e-mail Leah.Ulatowski@gannettwisconsin.com; web site www.sheboyganpress.com
Circulation: 12,080pd,24,438fr; VAC
Advertising: Open inch rate $14.03

STEVENS POINT

STEVENS POINT BUYERS' GUIDE/CITY TIMES

(Wed)
73 Sunset Blvd, Stevens Point, WI, 54481-2378, USA; tel (715) 344-4700; adv tel (715) 344-4700; ed tel (715) 344-4700; fax (715) 344-4700; adv fax (715) 344-4700; ed fax (715) 344-4700; e-mail publisher@mmclocal.com; adv e-mail publisher@mmclocal.com; ed e-mail bmakuski@mmclocal.com; web site www.SPCityTimes.com
Circulation: 0pd,21,133fr; CVC
Advertising: Open inch rate $25.60
Established: 1970
Group: Multi Media Channels
Digital Platform - Mobile: Apple, Android, Windows
Pub./Gen. Mgr. .... Dave Wood
Mechanical Specifications: Type page: 9.75 x 11"; 6 col
Delivery Method: Mail, Newsstand, Carrier
Zip Codes Served: Stevens Point

STRUM

THE AD-DELITE

(Tues)
15 5th Ave, Strum, WI, 54770, USA; tel (715) 695-3401; fax (715) 695-3322; adv e-mail addelite@triwest.net; web site www.ad-delite.com
Circulation: 14pd,15,653fr; CVC
Advertising: Open inch rate $10.55
Established: 1967
Digital Platform - Mobile: Apple, Android
Digital Platform - Tablet: Apple iOS, AndroidRenee Preston
Mechanical Specifications: Type page: 10 1/2 x 16; 6 Columns
Delivery Method: Mail, Racks
Zip Codes Served: 54755,54764,54743,54747,54738,54770,54758,54741,54760,54722,54742,54773,54701

VERONA

GREAT DANE SHOPPING NEWS

(Wed)
133 Enterprise Dr, Verona, WI, 53593-9122, USA; tel (608) 845-9559; fax (608) 845-9550; e-mail ungcomposing@wcinet.com; web site www.wcinet.com
Circulation:31,407fr; CVC
Advertising: Open inch rate $12.80
Established: 1998
Group: Woodward Communications, Inc.
Regional Publisher .... Lee Borkowski
Sales Mgr .... Neumeister Kathy
Mechanical Specifications: Type page 10 3/8 x 16; E - 4 cols, between; A - 6 cols, 1 5/8, 1/8 between; C - 6 cols, 1 5/8, 1/8 between.
Equipment: Hardware — APP/Mac, 6-APP/Mac G4; Software — QPS/QuarkXPress 3.3, Adobe/Acrobat, Adobe/Illustrator.
Delivery Method: Mail
Zip Codes Served: 53589, 53521, 53534, 53536, 53575, 53593, 53711

WATERTOWN

JEFFERSON COUNTY LIVING

(Fri)
W4540 Linmar Ln, Watertown, WI, 53094-8505, USA; tel (920) 674-2679; adv tel (920) 674-2679; ed tel (920) 674-2679; fax (920) 674-6322; adv fax (920) 674-6322; ed fax (920) 674-6322; e-mail kkrause@jcpgroup.com; adv e-mail shall@jrn.com; ed e-mail mrosenau@jrn.com; web site www.jcpgroup.com
Circulation: 0pd,30,515fr; VAC
Advertising: Open inch rate $29.70
Pub./Gen. Mgr. .... Sue Hall
Delivery Method: Mail
Zip Codes Served: Jefferson County

LIVING JEFFERSON COUNTY ADVERTISER-NORTH

(Fri)
W4540 Linmar Ln, Watertown, WI, 53094-8505, USA; tel (920) 674-2679; adv tel (920) 674-2679; ed tel (920) 674-2679; fax (920) 674-6322; adv fax (920) 674-6322; ed fax (920) 674-6322; e-mail kkrause@jcpgroup.com; adv e-mail shall@jrn.com; ed e-mail mrosenau@jrn.com; web site www.jcpgroup.com
Circulation:9,111fr; CVC
Pub./Gen. Mgr. .... Sue Hall
Delivery Method: Mail
Zip Codes Served: Northern Jefferson County

LIVING JEFFERSON COUNTY

ADVERTISER-SOUTH
(Fri)
W4540 Linmar Ln, Watertown, WI, 53094-8505, USA; tel (920) 674-2679; adv tel (920) 674-2679; ed tel (920) 674-2679; fax (920) 674-6322; adv fax (920) 674-6322; ed fax (920) 674-6322; e-mail kkrause@jcpgroup.com; adv e-mail shall@jrn.com; ed e-mail mrosenau@jrn.com; web site www.jcpgroup.com
Circulation:22,584fr; CVC
Pub./Gen. Mgr.................................Sue Hall
Delivery Method: Mail
Zip Codes Served: Southern Jefferson County

WAUKESHA

LAKE COUNTRY SUNDAY POST
(Sun)
801 N Barstow St, Waukesha, WI, 53186-4801, USA; web site www.gmtoday.com
Circulation:16,344fr; CVC
Advertising: Open inch rate $8.30Bill Yorth

WAUSAU

WAUSAU BUYERS GUIDE
(Tues)
106 E Wausau Ave, Wausau, WI, 54403-3372, USA; tel (715) 842-4424; fax (715) 842-5989; e-mail wausaubg@jcpgroup.com; web site www.wausauinfo.com
Circulation: 0pd,18,377fr; CVC
Advertising: Open inch rate $23.75
Group: Gannett
Circ. Mgr.......................................Dan Daniels
Mechanical Specifications: Type page 10 1/3 x 12 1/2; A - 5 cols, between.
Zip Codes Served: 54401, 54402, 54403, 54474, 54416, 54455, 54411, 54426, 54448, 54440, 54471

WEST BEND

WEEKEND POST
(Fri)
100 S 6th Ave, West Bend, WI, 53095-3309, USA; tel (262) 306-5000; adv tel (262)306-5079; ed tel (262)306-5043; fax (262)338-5271; adv fax (262)338-5271; ed fax (262)338-1984; e-mail customerservice_ls@conleynet.com; adv e-mail hrogge@conleynet.com; ed e-mail jmcbride@conleynet.com; web site www.gmtoday.com
Circulation: 0pd,46,000fr; CVC
Advertising: Open inch rate $15.88
Established: 1950
Publisher.................................Heather Rogge
Circulation Dierector.....................Kim Dietrich
Equipment: ; Presses — own; Software — Adobe/Photoshop 6.0, Multi-Ad/Creator 6.5, QPS/QuarkXPress.
Delivery Method: Carrier
Zip Codes Served: 53090, 53095, 53060, 53002, 53037, 53086, 53027, 53040, 53076, 53033, 53022, 53017, 53010, 53075

WYOMING

CHEYENNE

TRADER'S SHOPPER'S GUIDE
(Fri)
2021 Warren Ave, Cheyenne, WY, 82001-3725, USA; tel (307)634-8895; adv tel (307)634-8895; ed tel (307)634-8895; e-mail info@wyotraders.com; adv e-mail info@wyotraders.com; ed e-mail info@wyotraders.com; web site www.wyotraders.com
Circulation:21,745fr; CVC
Pub. ....Patrick Rice

SHERIDAN

THE COUNTRY BOUNTY
(Tues)
303 S Main St, Ste 201, Sheridan, WY, 82801-4815, USA; web site www.sheridanmedia.com
Circulation: 0pd,17,977fr; VAC
Advertising: Open inch rate $8.50
Established: 1974Bob Grammens
Mechanical Specifications: Type page: 10.13 x 12.56; 6 Columns
Equipment: ; Software — Multi-Ad/CAMS

SHOPPER/TMC PUBLICATIONS IN CANADA

ALBERTA

CAMROSE

THE CAMROSE BOOSTER
(Tues)
4925 48th St., Camrose, AB, T4V 1L7, Camrose, Flagstaff and Beaver, Canada; tel (780) 672-3142; fax (780) 672-2518; e-mail ads@camrosebooster.com; adv e-mail ads@camrosebooster.com; ed e-mail news@camrosebooster.com; web site www.camrosebooster.com
Circulation: 12pd, 13,030fr; CVC
Advertising: Open inch rate $15.02 (National)
Established: 1952
Publisher.....................................Blain Fowler
Comptroller............................Don Hutchinson
Associate Publisher / Sales Manager.... Ronald Pilger
Sales Rep.......................................Jeff Fowler
Sales Rep.....................................Mike Ploner
Circ. Mgr.......................................Leanne Taje
Production Manager......................Kirby Fowler
Art Director.....................................Pat Horton
Mechanical Specifications: Type page 9.45 x 15 ; 5 cols
Delivery Method: Mail, Carrier, Racks
Postal Codes Served: All T4V postal codes plus T0B's

EDMONTON

FLYER FORCE
(Thur)
5637 70 Street Nw, Edmonton, AB, T6B 3P6, Canada; tel (780)436-8050
Circulation:; Sworn/Estimate/Non-Audited

FALHER

SMOKY RIVER EXPRESS
(Wed)
217 Main St. W., Falher, AB, T0H 1M0, Canada, Canada; tel (780) 837-2585; fax (780) 837-2102; e-mail srexpres@telus.net; adv e-mail srexpres@telus.net; ed e-mail sreeditor@telus.net; web site www.smokyriverexpress.com
Circulation: 2,021pd,; CMCA
Advertising: Open inch rate $.88
Established: 1967
Circ. Mgr.......................................Mary Burgar
Mechanical Specifications: Type page 10.33 x 15.5
Equipment:; Software — Microsoft/Windows 95.
Delivery Method: Mail, Newsstand
Postal Codes Served: T0H 1M0

FORT SASKATCHEWAN

THE FORT SASKATCHEWAN RECORD
(Thur)
10404 99th Ave., 168a, Fort Saskatchewan, AB, T8L 3W2, Strathcona County, Canada; tel (780) 998-7070; fax (780) 998-5515; e-mail fortrecord.news@sunmedia.ca; adv e-mail marie.keating@sunmedia.ca; ed e-mail ben.proulx@sunmedia.ca; web site www.fortsaskatchewanrecord.com
Circulation: 9pd, 8,806fr; VAC
Advertising: Open inch rate $0.71
Established: 1922
Group: Postmedia Network Inc.
Sales Consultant..................MaryAnn Kochan
Pub. ....Jean Figeat
Advertising Consultant.......Krista Schroderous
Ed. ....Ben Proulx
Lindsay Morey
Mechanical Specifications: specs available on website
Equipment: Hardware — APP/Mac; Presses — N/A; Software — Adobe Creative Suite
Delivery Method: Mail, Carrier, Racks
Postal Codes Served: Strathcona County

IRRICANA

WHEEL & DEAL
(Mon)
Po Box 40, Irricana, AB, T0M 1B0, Canada; tel (204) 954-1400; ed tel (403) 697-4703; fax (403) 935-4981; e-mail deal@wheel-deal.com; web site www.albertafarmexpress.ca
Circulation: 281pd, 71,900fr; Sworn/Estimate/Non-Audited
Advertising: Open inch rate $1.90
Established: 1969
Group: Great West Newspapers LP
Pub. ....Will Berboven
Pub. ....Bob Willcox
Assoc. Pub...................................John Morriss
Adv. Mgr.....................................Donna Berting
Circ. Mgr...Linda Tityk
Mechanical Specifications: Type page 10 1/4 x 13; A - 6 cols, 1 1/2, 1/6 between; C - 7 cols, 1/6 between.
Postal Codes Served: T0M 1B0

LETHBRIDGE

THE LETHBRIDGE SHOPPER
(Sat)
12th Street B North, 234A, Lethbridge, AB, T1H 2K7, Canada, Canada; tel (403) 527-5777; fax (403) 526-7352; e-mail ethurlbeck@shoppergroup.com; adv e-mail ethurlbeck@shoppergroup.com; ed e-mail ethurlbeck@shoppergroup.com; web site www.shoppergroup.com
Circulation: 33,176fr; CVC
Advertising: $71.40 (smallest modular rate)
Established: 1976
Group: Alta. Newspaper Group, Ltd
Ed. ....Ron Heizelman
Adv. Mgr..............................Edward Thurlbeck
Mechanical Specifications: Type page 10.25 x 16; 6 cols
Delivery Method: Carrier
Postal Codes Served: T1A, T1B, T1C

THE SOUTHERN SUN TIMES
(Wed)
504 7th St., S., Lethbridge, AB, T1J 2H1, Canada; tel (403) 328-4411; fax (403) 320-7539
Advertising: Open inch rate $.95
Group: Alta. Newspaper Group, Ltd
Gen. Mgr.......................................Bob Carey
Postal Codes Served: T1H 2J1

MEDICINE HAT

THE MEDICINE HAT SHOPPER
(Sat)
922 Allowance Ave. Se, Medicine Hat, AB, T1A 3G7, Canada, Canada; tel (403) 527-5777; fax (403) 526-7352; e-mail ethurlbeck@shoppergroup.com; adv e-mail ethurlbeck@shoppergroup.com; web site www.shoppergroup.com
Circulation: 26,089fr; CVC
Advertising: $71.40 (smallest modular rate)
Established: 1976
Group: Alta. Newspaper Group, Ltd
Sales Manager....................Edward Thurlbeck
Ed. ....Ron Heizelman
Mechanical Specifications: Type page 10.25 x 16; 6 cols
Delivery Method: Carrier
Postal Codes Served: T1A,T1B,T1C

PONOKA

THE BASHAW STAR
(Wed)
5019a Chipman Ave., Ponoka, AB, T4J 1R6, Bashaw, Canada; tel (403) 783-3311; fax (403) 783 6300; e-mail manager@bashawstar.com
Circulation: 216pd, 15fr; CMCA
Advertising: Open inch rate $.61
Group: Black Press Group Ltd.
Ed. ....Mustafa Eric
Mechanical Specifications: Type page 10 1/8 x 13; E - 7 cols, 1 1/12, 3/16 between; A - 7 cols, 1 1/12, 3/16 between; C - 8 cols, 3/16

between.
Equipment: Hardware — APP/Mac; Software — QPS/QuarkXPress.

VEGREVILLE

VEGREVILLE NEWS ADVERTISER
(Wed)
5110 50th St., Vegreville, AB, T9C 1R9, Canada; tel (780) 632-2861; fax (780) 632-7981; adv e-mail ads@newsadvertiser.com; ed e-mail editor@newsadvertiser.com; web site www.newsadvertiser.com
Circulation: 50pd, 11,241fr; Sworn/Estimate/Non-Audited
Advertising: Open inch rate $15.26
Established: 1950Editions: 1 - News Advertiser (11241), News Advertiser Insider (6000)
Gen. Mgr. .... Arthur Beaudette
Ed. .... Dan Beaudette
Mechanical Specifications: Type page 10.25" x 15.5"; 6 cols
Equipment:; Presses — Digitala and small offset; Software — Adobe Creative Cloud, CorelDRAW, Windows 10, Xerox FreeFlow
Delivery Method: Mail, Carrier, Racks
Postal Codes Served: T9C 1R9 T0B 0C0 T0B 0K0 T0b 0P0 T0B 0R0 T0B 0W0 T0B 1C0 T0B 1S0 T0B 2B0 T0B 2C0 T0B 2G0 T0B 2R0 T0B 2S0 T0B 2W0 T0B 3B0 T0B 3H0 T0B 3K0 T0B 3T0 T0B 4A0 T0A 3C0 T0B 4B0 T0B 4J0 T0B 4K0 all of T9C T0B 4N0 T0B 4R0 T0B 4S0

BRITISH COLUMBIA

BURNABY

BUY & SELL
(Thur)
4664 Lougheed Hwy., Ste. W020, Burnaby, BC, V5C 5T5, Canada; tel (604) 540-4455; adv tel (604) 280-1000; fax (604) 540-6451; web site www.buysell.com
Circulation: 42,005fr; Sworn/Estimate/Non-Audited
Established: 1971Editions: 3 - 3 total; BC Interior; Frazer Valley; Greater Vancouver;
Prodn. Mgr. .... Zac Goodman
Postal Codes Served: V6X 2C9

CRANBROOK

KOOTENAY ADVERTISER
(Mon, Fri)
1510 Second St., N., Cranbrook, BC, V1C 3L2, Cranbrook, Canada; tel (250) 489-3455; e-mail distribution@kootenayadvertiser.com; adv e-mail advertising@kootenayadvertiser.com; ed e-mail editor@kootenayadvertiser.com; web site www.kootenayadvertiser.com
Circulation: 21,000fr; Sworn/Estimate/Non-Audited
Advertising: 20.72 column inch
Established: 1972
Prodn. Mgr. .... Bridget Fix
Mechanical Specifications: Type page 10 1/4 x 14 1/2; 7 cols,
Delivery Method: Newsstand, Carrier, Racks
Postal Codes Served: V0A, V0B, V1A, V1C

GRAND FORKS

WEST KOOTENAY ADVERTISER
(Thur)
7255 Riverside Dr., Grand Forks, BC, V0H 1H0, Boundary, Canada; tel (250) 442-2191; fax (866) 897-0678; e-mail publisher@grandforksgazette.ca; classifieds@grandforksgazette.ca; circulation@grandforksgazette.ca; production@grandforksgazette.ca; accounting@grandforksgazette.ca; adv e-mail sales@grandforksgazette.ca; ed e-mail editor@grandforksgazette.ca; web site www.grandforksgazette.ca
Circulation: 4,000fr; Sworn/Estimate/Non-Audited
Advertising: Open inch rate $.88
Group: Black Press
Circ. Mgr. .... Darlainea Redlack
Mechanical Specifications: Type page 10 1/4 x 15 1/2; E - 5 cols, 2, 1/16 between; A - 5 cols, 2, 1/16 between; C - 5 cols, 2, 1/16 between.
Postal Codes Served: v0h1h0-v0h1h9, V0H 1E0-v0h 1E3, v0h1j0,v0h1m0,v0h 1yo, v0h 1b0, v0h 2b0

KASLO

PENNYWISE
(Tues)
Po Box 430, Kaslo, BC, V0G 1M0, Canada; tel (250) 353-2602; fax (250) 353-7444; e-mail info@pennywiseads.com; web site www.pennywiseads.com
Circulation: 27,000fr; Sworn/Estimate/Non-Audited
Advertising: Open inch rate $.75Editions: 4 - 4 total; Castlegar/Slocan Valley Pennywise; Kootenay Lake Pennywise; Nelson Pennywise; Trail/Beaver Valley/Salmo Pennywise;
Pub. .... Patricia Axen-Rotch
Adv. Mgr. .... Julie Wilson
Ed. .... Tania Seafoot

PENNYWISE - CASTLEGAR / SLOCAN VALLEY
(Tues)
Po Box 430, Kaslo, BC, V0G 1M0, Canada; web site www.pennywiseads.com
Circulation: 8,515fr; CVC
Advertising: $60.12 (smallest modular rate)
Established: 1975Patty Axenroth
Mechanical Specifications: Type page 6.75" x 9.7"; 2 cols
Delivery Method: Racks
Postal Codes Served: Kalso BC

PENNYWISE - KOOTENAY LAKE
(Tues)
Po Box 430, Kaslo, BC, V0G 1M0, Canada; web site www.pennywiseads.com
Circulation: 3,505fr; CVC
Advertising: $60.12 (smallest modular rate)
Established: 1975Patty Axenroth
Mechanical Specifications: Type page 6.75" x 9.7"; 2 cols
Delivery Method: Racks
Postal Codes Served: Kalso, BC

PENNYWISE - NELSON
(Tues)
Po Box 430, Kaslo, BC, V0G 1M0, Canada; web site www.pennywiseads.com
Circulation: 0pd, 5,661fr; CVC
Advertising: $60.12 (smallest modular rate)
Established: 1975Patty Axenroth
Mechanical Specifications: Type page 6.75" x 9.7"; 2 cols
Delivery Method: Racks
Postal Codes Served: Kalso, BC

PENNYWISE - TRAIL / BEAVER VALLEY / SALMO
(Tues)
Po Box 43, Kaslo, BC, V0G 1M0, Canada; web site www.pennywiseads.com
Circulation: 0pd, 8,607fr; CVC
Advertising: $60.12 (smallest modular rate)
Established: 1975Patty Axenroth
Mechanical Specifications: Type page 6.75" x 9.7"; 2 cols
Delivery Method: Racks
Postal Codes Served: Kalso, BC

SALMON ARM

LAKESHORE NEWS
(Fri)
161 Hudson Ave., Salmon Arm, BC, V1E 4N8, Canada; tel (250) 832-9461; fax (250) 832-5246; e-mail lsn@lakeshorenews.bc.ca; web site lakeshorenews.bc.ca
Circulation: 0pd, 13,745fr; Sworn/Estimate/Non-Audited
Group: Black Press Group Ltd.

SURREY

THE LINK
(Sat)
#203 -12732 80th Avenue, Surrey, BC, V3W 3A7, BC, Canada; tel (604) 880-3463; adv tel (604) 880-3463; ed tel (608) 880-3463; fax (604) 591-2113; e-mail editorpd@hotmail.com; adv e-mail editorpd@hotmail.com; ed e-mail editorpd@hotmail.com; web site www.thelinkpaper.ca
Circulation: 20,000fr; Sworn/Estimate/Non-Audited
Advertising: Open inch rate $12.00
Established: 1972
Group: South Asian Link Publications
Ed. .... Paul Dhillon
Mechanical Specifications: Type page 10 1/4 x 14 3/4; E - 6 cols, 1 7/12, 1/6 between; A - 6 cols, 1 1/3, 1/6 between.
Delivery Method: Mail, Newsstand, Carrier, Racks

NOVA SCOTIA

TRURO

WEEKEND READ
(Fri)
6 Louise St., Truro, NS, B2N 5C3, Canada; tel (902) 893-9405; fax (902) 895-6104; e-mail news@trurodaily.com; web site www.trurodaily.com
Circulation: 20,479fr; Sworn/Estimate/Non-Audited
Advertising: Open inch rate $1.06
Pub. .... Richard Russell
Ed. .... Carl Fleming
Postal Codes Served: B2N 5C3

ONTARIO

ARNPRIOR

ARNPRIOR CHRONICLE WEEKENDER
(Fri)
116 John St. N., Arnprior, ON, K7S 2N6, Canada; tel (613) 623-6571; fax (613) 623-7518; e-mail acgedit@runge.net; web site www.runge.net
Circulation: 6,500fr; Sworn/Estimate/Non-Audited
Advertising: Open inch rate $7.14
Pub. .... Chris McWebb
Gen. Mgr. .... Derek Walter
Postal Codes Served: K7S 2N6

BARRIE

SUPER SHOPPER, BUY, TRADE & SELL
(Thur)
122 Commerce Park Dr., Unit D, Barrie, ON, L4N 8W8, Canada; tel (705) 722-7777; adv tel (705) 726-6015; fax (705) 726-7645; web site www.buysell.com
Circulation: 12,699pd, 1,200fr; Sworn/Estimate/Non-Audited
Established: 1977
Circ. Mgr. .... Mike Gritzan
Mechanical Specifications: Type page 7 1/8 x 10 1/4; C - 4 cols, 1 3/4, 1/27 between.
Postal Codes Served: L4N 2M2

BEETON

THE WOODBRIDGE ADVERTISER
(Thur)
2 Main St. W., Beeton, ON, LOG 1AO, Canada; tel (905) 729-4501; fax (905) 729-3961; e-mail wa@csolve.net; web site www.ontariosauctionpaper.com
Circulation: 2,000pd,; Sworn/Estimate/Non-Audited
Advertising: Open inch rate $11.10
Ed. .... Karl Mallette
Editorial Mgr. .... Tina Dedels
Postal Codes Served: L0N 1P0

BELLEVILLE

SHOPPER'S MARKET
(Thur)
365 N. Front St., Belleville, ON, K8P 5E6, Canada; tel (613) 962-3422; adv tel (866) 541-6757; fax (613) 962-0543; adv fax (866) 757-0227; e-mail readerads@cogeco.net; adv e-mail placeit@classifiedextra.ca; advertise@canoe.quebecor.com; web site shoppersmarket.classifiedextra.ca
Circulation: 50,000fr; Sworn/Estimate/Non-Audited
Advertising: Open inch rate $1.28
Adv. Mgr. .... Charles Parker
Nat'l Dir., Sales .... Martin Courchesne
Mechanical Specifications: Type page 10 1/4 x 12 3/10; A - 6 cols, 1 5/8, 3/16 between.
Postal Codes Served: K8N 5A5

BRANTFORD

BRANTFORD PENNYSAVER
(Fri)
61 Dalkeith Dr., Unit 5, Brantford, ON, N3P 1M1, Canada; tel (519) 756-0076; fax (519) 756-9034; e-mail classifieds@brantfordpennysaver.com; web site www.brantfordpennysaver.com
Advertising: Open inch rate $1.26
Pub. .... Andrea Demeer
Adv. Mgr. .... Alan Burns
Circ. Mgr. .... Adrian Trombetta
Prodn. Mgr. .... Trudy Loslo
Mechanical Specifications: Type page 10 1/4 x 11 1/4; E - 6 cols, 1 1/2, between.
Postal Codes Served: N3P 1M1

BRIGHTON

THE BRIGHTON INDEPENDENT
(Thur)
21 Meade St, Brighton, ON, K0K 1H0, Canada, Canada; tel (613) 475-0255; adv tel (613) 475-0255 X 214; ed tel (613) 966-2034; fax (613) 475-4546; e-mail jkearns@metroland.com; adv e-mail jkearns@metroland.com; ed e-mail tbush@metroland.com; web site www.metroland.com
Circulation: 7,816fr; CMCA
Advertising: Open inch rate $1.33

Established: 1973
Group: Metroland Media Group Ltd.
Circ. Mgr. .... Benita Stansel
Publisher .... John Kearns
Delivery Method: Carrier, Racks
Postal Codes Served: K0k 1h0, K8v, K0k 1L0, K0l 1L0, K0k is0

BURKS FALLS

OMEGA FORESTER
(Fri)
59 Ontario St., Burks Falls, ON, P0A 1C0, Canada; tel (705) 382-3943; fax (705) 382-3440; e-mail anews@onlink.net; web site www.almaguinnews.com
Advertising: Open inch rate $9.00
Sales Mgr. .... Doug Pincoee
Postal Codes Served: P0A 1C0

CAMBRIDGE

HOMEFINDERS
(Fri)
26 Ainslie St. S., Cambridge, ON, N1R 3K1, Canada; tel (519) 621-3820
Pub. .... Verne Shaull
Adv. Mgr. .... Trudy Mouat

CHATHAM

CHATHAM PENNYSAVER
(Fri)
930 Richmond St., Chatham, ON, N7M 5J5, Canada; tel (519) 351-4362; adv tel (866) 541-6757; fax (519) 351-2452; e-mail chathampennysaver@bowesnet.com; adv e-mail placeit@classifiedextra.ca; web site www.chathampennysaver.com
Circulation: 38,914fr; Sworn/Estimate/Non-Audited
Pub./Gen. Mgr. .... Dean Muharrem
Office Mgr. .... Melissa Steele
Sales Mgr. .... Tracey Weaver-Curran
Supervisor .... Martin Steele
Mechanical Specifications: Type page 10 1/4 x 12; E - 7 cols, between; A - 7 cols, between; C - 7 cols, between.
Postal Codes Served: N7M 5J5

PENNYSAVER
(Thur)
138 King Street West, Chatham, ON, N7M 1E3, Chatham Kent, Canada; tel (519) 354 2000; fax (519) 351 7774; e-mail shawn.steveley@sunmedia.ca
Circulation: 39,878fr; CCAB
Advertising: Open inch rate $1.69
Group: Postmedia Network Inc.Editions: 6 -
Sales Manager .... Shawn Steveley
Rep .... Michelle Owcher
rep .... Cam Innes
Postal Codes Served: N7L, N7M, N8A, NOP

CORNWALL

STANDARD-FREEHOLDER COMPLIMENTARY
(Fri)
1150 Montreal Road, Cornwall, ON, K6H 1E2, Canada; tel (613) 933-3160; adv tel (613) 933-3160 x246; ed tel (613) 933-3160 X 225; fax (613) 933-7521; adv fax (613) 933-7521; e-mail ads@standard-freeholder.com; adv e-mail ads@standard-freeholder.com; placeit@classifiedextra.ca; adman@standard-freeholder.com; ed e-mail news@standard-freeholder.com; web site www.standard-freeholder.com
Circulation: 10,739pd, 21,066fr; Sworn/Estimate/Non-Audited
Group: Quebecor Communications, Inc.
Pub./Gen. Mgr. .... Milton Ellis
Adv. Mgr. .... Peter Padbury
Circulation Sales And Inserts .... Tony Joubert
Mechanical Specifications: Type page 11 1/2 x 21 1/2; E - 10 cols, 1 1/10, between; A - 10 cols, 1 1/10, between; C - 10 cols, 1 1/10, between.

DURHAM

THE DURHAM CHRONICLE
(Wed)
190 Elizabeth St. E., Durham, ON, N0G 1R0, Canada, Canada; tel (519) 369-2504; fax (519) 369-3560; e-mail themarkdale-standard@bmts.com
Circulation: 1,196pd, 21fr; Sworn/Estimate/Non-Audited
Advertising: Open inch rate $.37
Pub. .... Marie David
Gen. Mgr. .... Bev Stoddart
Ed. .... Christine Meingast
Mechanical Specifications: Type page 11 1/4 x 16 3/4; E - 5 cols, 2 1/5, between; A - 5 cols, 2 1/5, between; C - 9 cols, between.
Equipment: Hardware — APP/Mac; Software — QPS/QuarkXPress 4.0.
Postal Codes Served: Canada

ELLIOT LAKE

MARKETPLACE
(Thur)
14 Hillside Dr. S., Elliot Lake, ON, P5A 1M6, Canada; tel (705) 848-7195; fax (705) 848-0249; e-mail karsten.johansen@sunmedia.ca; adv e-mail karsten.johansen@sunmedia.ca; ed e-mail kevin.mcsheffrey@sunmedia.ca; web site www.elliotlakestandard.ca
Circulation: 3,817pd, 8,000fr; CMCA
Advertising: Open inch rate $9.80
Established: 1956
Group: Sunmedia
Circ. Mgr. .... Lolene Patterson
Managing Editor .... Kevin McSheffrey
General Manager .... Karsten Johansen
Mechanical Specifications: Page size - 10.25" wide X 15' tall, 9 column
Delivery Method: Mail, Newsstand, Carrier, Racks

FORT ERIE

FORT ERIE SHOPPING TIMES
(Wed)
450 Garrison Rd., Unit 1, Fort Erie, ON, L2A 1N2, Canada; tel (905) 871-3100; fax (905) 871-5243; e-mail feeditor@cogeco.net; ed e-mail editorial@forterietimes.com; web site www.forterietimes.ca
Circulation: 11,800fr; Sworn/Estimate/Non-Audited
Advertising: Open inch rate $.44
Group: Postmedia Network Inc.
Quebecor Communications, Inc.
Pub. .... Tim Dundas
Adv. Mgr. .... Myra Robertson
Circ. Mgr. .... Petrina Istok
Postal Codes Served: L2A 5Y2

GANANOQUE

THE REPORTER
(Thur)
79 King St. E., Gananoque, ON, K7G 1E8, Canada, Canada; tel (613) 382-2156; fax (613) 382-3010; e-mail reporter@tipgananoque.com; web site www.gananoquereporter.com
Circulation: 14pd, 6,421fr; CMCA
Advertising: Open inch rate $.82
Established: 1860
Group: Postmedia Network Inc.
Quebecor Communications, Inc.
Ed. .... Anne Craig
Mechanical Specifications: Type page 12 x 21 1/2; E - 7 cols, 1 9/16, 1/6 between; A - 7 cols, 1 9/16, 1/6 between; C - 7 cols, 1 9/16, 1/6 between.
Equipment: Hardware — APP/Mac, PC; Software — QPS/QuarkXPress 4.1, Adobe/Illustrator 10.0, Adobe/Photoshop 7.0.

GODERICH

FOCUS
(Fri)
120 Huckins St., Goderich, ON, N7A 4B6, Canada; tel (519) 524-2614; fax (519) 524-9175; ed e-mail focus@bowesnet.com; web site www.focusnewsmagazine.com
Circulation: 20,150fr; Sworn/Estimate/Non-Audited
Advertising: Open inch rate $1.08
Pub. .... Dave Sykes
Adv. Mgr. .... Kevin Shrier
Mechanical Specifications: Type page 10 3/8 x 14 7/8; E - 6 cols, 1 7/12, 1/2 between; A - 6 cols, 1 7/12, 1/2 between; C - 6 cols, 1 7/12, 1/2 between.
Postal Codes Served: N7A 4B6

GUELPH

GUELPH PENNYSAVER
(Fri)
86 Dawson Rd., Guelph, ON, N1H 1A8, Canada; tel (519) 823-5070; fax (519) 894-5401; e-mail g-pennysaver@on.albn.com
Circulation: 47,000fr; Sworn/Estimate/Non-Audited
Advertising: Open inch rate $1.52
Gen. Mgr. .... Andrea Demeer
Postal Codes Served: N1H 1A8

KITCHENER

PENNYSAVER
(Thur)
685 Wabanaki Dr., Kitchener, ON, N2C 2G3, Canada; tel (519) 894-1411; fax (519) 894-5401; e-mail classifieds@kitchenerpennysaver.com; web site www.k-wreview.ca
Circulation: 95,000fr; Sworn/Estimate/Non-Audited
Advertising: Open inch rate $2.54Editions: 2 - 2 total; Cambridge Pennysaver (30,000); Kitchener Pennysaver (90,000);
Pub./Gen. Mgr. .... Andrea Demeer
Display Sales Mgr. .... Kelly Polito
Classified Sales Mgr. .... Kathy Dowling
Postal Codes Served: N2C 2G3

LEAMINGTON

LEAMINGTON SHOPPER
(Fri)
75 Oak St., Leamington, ON, N8H 2B2, Canada; tel (519) 326-4434; fax (519) 326-2171; adv e-mail shopper@wincom.net; web site www.leamingtonpostandshopper.com
Circulation: 17,400fr; Sworn/Estimate/Non-Audited
Advertising: Open inch rate $1.02
Established: 1971
Pub. .... Donald Gage
Adv. Mgr. .... Linda Gage
Mechanical Specifications: Type page 10 2/5 x 14; E - 9 cols, 1 1/16, 1/8 between; A - 9 cols, 1 1/16, 1/8 between.
Delivery Method: Carrier
Postal Codes Served: N8H 2X8
Note: We recently added news content and changed the name from Leamington Shopper to Tri-Town News serving the communities of Kingsville , Leamington & Wheatley

LONDON

PENNYSAVER
(Fri)
369 York St., London, ON, N6A 4G1, Canada; tel (519) 685-2020; adv tel (519) 667-5472; fax (519) 649-0908; adv fax (519) 667-4573; e-mail newsdesk@lfpress.com; adv e-mail pennyreaderads@londonpennysaver.com; web site www.lfpress.com; www.londonpennysaver.com
Circulation: 159,000fr; Sworn/Estimate/Non-Audited
Advertising: Open inch rate $3.17
Gen. Mgr. .... Cathy Forster
Sales Rep. .... Nick Hawkins
Circ. Mgr. .... Tracey Spence
Postal Codes Served: N5Z 3L1

NAPANEE

FRIDAY REGIONAL BEAVER
(Fri)
72 Dundas St. E., Napanee, ON, K7R 1H9, Canada; tel (613) 354-6641; fax (613) 354-2622; e-mail beaver@bellnet.ca; web site www.napaneebeaver.com
Advertising: Open inch rate $.70
Established: 1870
Pub. .... Jean Morrison
Mechanical Specifications: Type page 10 5/16 x 15 1/4; E - 6 cols, 1 9/16, 1/6 between; A - 6 cols, 1 9/16, 1/6 between; C - 6 cols, 1 9/16, 1/6 between.

NIAGARA FALLS

NIAGARA SHOPPING NEWS
(Wed, Fri)
4949 Victoria Ave., Niagara Falls, ON, L2E 4C7, Canada; tel (905) 357-2440; adv tel (877) 786-8227; fax (905) 357-1620; e-mail niagaraclassifieds@cogeco.net; web site www.ospreymedia.ca; www.niagarashoppingnews.ca
Circulation: 29,250fr; Sworn/Estimate/Non-Audited
Advertising: Open inch rate $.68
Group: Quebecor Communications, Inc.
Pub. .... Tim Dundas
Postal Codes Served: L2E 4C7

OAKVILLE

SHOPPING NEWS
(Wed)
2526 Speers, Unit 11, Oakville, ON, L6L 5M2, Canada; tel (905) 827-2244; fax (905) 827-9950; ed e-mail editorial@oakvilletoday.ca; web site www.metroland.com
Circulation: 49,800fr; Sworn/Estimate/Non-Audited
Advertising: Open inch rate $1.84
Group: Torstar
Gen. Mgr. .... Lars Melander
Adv. Mgr. .... Ian Holryd
Mechanical Specifications: Type page 10 7/16 x 14 1/4; E - 8 cols, 1 3/16, 1/8 between; A - 8 cols, 1 3/16, 1/8 between; C - 8 cols, 1 3/16, 1/8 between.
Postal Codes Served: L6C 5T7

OTTAWA

SMART SHOPPER
(Thur)
6 Antares Dr., Ottawa, ON, K1G 5H7, Canada; tel (613) 733-4099; fax (613) 733-7107; adv e-mail classads@ott.sunpub.com; web site www.ottawasmartshopper.ca
Circulation: 166,000fr; Sworn/Estimate/Non-Audited

Advertising: Open inch rate $2.22
CEO..Pierre Peladeau
Adv. Mgr................................ Shane Patacairk
Circ. Mgr..Marty Holski
Mechanical Specifications: Type page 10 1/4 x 11 1/2; A - 6 cols, 1 5/8, between.
Postal Codes Served: K2E 7J6

PARIS

PARIS STAR
(Thur)
3 Elm St., Unit 3, Paris, ON, N0E 1N0, Canada; tel (519) 756-2020; fax (519) 756-9470; e-mail brex.cservice@sunmedia.ca; adv e-mail ashley.demers@sunmedia.ca; ed e-mail parisedit@bowesnet.com; web site www.parisstaronline.com
Circulation: 4,877fr; CMCA
Advertising: Open inch rate $.72
Established: 1850
Group: Postmedia Network Inc.
Quebecor Communications, Inc.
Pub. .... Ken Koyama
Ed. .... Michael Peeling
Mechanical Specifications: Type page 10 x 16; E - 5 cols, 2, 1/8 between; A - 5 cols, 2, 1/8 between; C - 6 cols, 1 3/4, 1/8 between.
Equipment: Hardware — APP/Mac; Software — QPS/QuarkXPress 3.31.
Postal Codes Served: Canada

PETERBOROUGH

THE EXAMINER
(Fri)
730 The Kingsway, Peterborough, ON, K9J 8L4, Canada; tel (705) 745-4641; fax (705) 743-4581; e-mail newsroom@peterboroughexaminer.com; web site www.peterboroughexaminer.com
Circulation: 49,000fr; Sworn/Estimate/Non-Audited
Advertising: Open inch rate $1.35
Established: 1847
Group: Quebecor Communications, Inc.
Pub. ....Darren Murphy
Dir., Sales/Mktg. .... Barb Weightman
Adv. Dir.................................. Bob Doornenbal
Mng. Ed..E. N. Arnold
Prodn. Mgr. .... Terry Keating

SAINT CATHERINE'S

ST. CATHERINES SHOPPING NEWS
(Wed)
140 Welland Ave., Unit 1, Saint Catharine's, ON, L2R 2N6, Canada; tel (905) 688-4332; fax (905) 688-6313
Circulation: 50,000fr; Sworn/Estimate/Non-Audited
Advertising: Open inch rate $.73
Group: Quebecor Communications, Inc.
Pub. .... Timothy Dundas
Adv. Mgr.......................................Jamie Mowat
Postal Codes Served: L2R 2N6

SAINT THOMAS

ELGIN COUNTY MARKET
(Thur)
16 Hincks St., Saint Thomas, ON, N5R 5Z2, Canada; tel (519) 631-3782; fax (519) 631-3759; e-mail classified@elgincountymarket.com; web site www.elgincountymarket.com
Circulation: 32,000fr; Sworn/Estimate/Non-Audited
Advertising: Open inch rate $.81
Group: Postmedia Network Inc.
Gen. Mgr. .... Bev Ponton
Postal Codes Served: N5P 1H4

STRATHROY

AGE DISPATCH FOCUS
(Wed)
8 Front St. E., Strathroy, ON, N7G 1Y4, Canada; tel (519) 245-2370; fax (519) 245-1647; e-mail agedispatch@strathroyonline.com; web site www.strathroyagedispatch.com
Circulation: 5,000fr; Sworn/Estimate/Non-Audited
Advertising: Open inch rate $1.12
Established: 1861
Group: Postmedia Network Inc.
Quebecor Communications, Inc.
Pub. .... Linda Leblanc
Adv. Mgr...............................Denise Armstrong
Circ. Mgr....................................... Cheryl Klaver
Mechanical Specifications: Type page 10 1/4 x 13; E - 8 cols, 1 3/16, 1/6 between; A - 9 cols, 1 3/16, 1/6 between; C - 8 cols, 1 3/16, 1/6 between.
Postal Codes Served: N7G 1Y4

SUDBURY

ENTERTAINMENT
(Thur)
33 Mackenzie St., Sudbury, ON, P3C 4Y1, Canada; tel (705) 674-5271; fax (705) 674-6834; ed e-mail editorial@thesudburystar.com; web site www.thesudburystar.com
Circulation: 40,000fr; Sworn/Estimate/Non-Audited
Pub. .... Bruce Cowan
Circ. Mgr.................................... David Paquette
Prodn. Mgr. .... Merle Smith
Mechanical Specifications: Type page 13 x 22; E - 6 cols, between; A - 6 cols, between; C - 6 cols, between.
Postal Codes Served: P3C 4Y1

TILLSONBURG

LAKE SHORE SHOPPER
(Fri)
25 Townline Rd., Tillsonburg, ON, N4G 4H6, Canada; tel (519) 688-1177; fax (519) 688-9353; web site www.theshopper.ca
Circulation: 40,434fr; Sworn/Estimate/Non-Audited
Advertising: Open inch rate $.96
Group: Postmedia Network Inc.
Quebecor Communications, Inc.
Pub. .... Michael Walsh
Adv. Mgr.................................... David Hopkins
Circ. Mgr.. Joan Tewes
Prodn. Mgr. .... Sharon Craig
Mechanical Specifications: Type page 10 3/8 x 15; A - 9 cols, 1 9/16, between.

WASAGA BEACH

THE STAYNER SUN
(Thur)
1456 Mosley St., Wasaga Beach, ON, L9Z 2B9, Canada, Canada; tel (705) 428-2638; fax (705) 422-2446; e-mail sunnews@simcoe.com; web site www.staynersun.ca
Circulation: 4,088fr; CMCA
Advertising: Open inch rate $1.12
Group: Metroland Media Group Ltd.
Torstar
Pub. .... Joe Anderson
Gen. Mgr................................Catherine Haller
Bus. Mgr... Mary Ellis
Adv. Dir... Shaun Sauve
Adv. Mgr...................................... Wendy Sherk
Ed. .... Scott Woodhouse
Prodn. Mgr. .... Stephen Hall
Mechanical Specifications: Type page 11 1/2 x 21 1/2; E - 10 cols, 1 1/16, 3/32 between; A - 10 cols, 1 1/16, 3/32 between; C - 10 cols, 1 1/16, 3/32 between.
Equipment: Hardware — APP/Mac; Software — QPS/QuarkXPress 3.32.

WELLAND

WELLAND SHOPPING NEWS
(Wed)
440 Niagara St., Unit 7, Welland, ON, L3C 1L5, Canada; tel (905) 735-9222; fax (905) 735-9224; e-mail nsncirculation@niagaracommunitynewspapers.com; wsnclassified@wellandshoppingnews.com; web site www.wellandshoppingnews.ca
Circulation: 22,900fr; Sworn/Estimate/Non-Audited
Advertising: Open inch rate $.55
Group: Quebecor Communications, Inc.
Gen. Mgr. .... Timothy Dundas
Adv. Mgr..................................Amanda Houser
Mechanical Specifications: Type page 10 3/8 x 16 3/4; E - 6 cols, 1 5/8, 1/8 between; A - 6 cols, 1 5/8, 1/8 between.
Postal Codes Served: L3B 3W5

WINDSOR

WINDSOR SMART SHOPPER
(Thur)
4525 Rhodes Dr., Unit 400, Windsor, ON, NEW 5R8, Canada; tel (519) 966-4500; fax (519) 966-3660; e-mail design@windsorpennysaver.com; delivery@windsorpennysaver.com; sales@windsorpennysaver.com; adv e-mail placeit@classifiedextra.cam; web site www.windsorpennysaver.com
Circulation: 119,000fr; Sworn/Estimate/Non-Audited
Advertising: Open inch rate $2.41
Pub. .... Shannon Ricker
Sales Mgr .... Ed Donovan
Postal Codes Served: N8T 1R1

WOODSTOCK

OXFORD SHOPPING NEWS/REVIEW
(Tues, Thur)
16 Brock St., Woodstock, ON, N4S 3V4, Canada; tel (519) 537-6657; fax (519) 537-8542; adv e-mail osnclassifieds@bowesnet.com; web site www.oxfordshoppingnews.com
Circulation: 35,000fr; Sworn/Estimate/Non-Audited
Advertising: Open inch rate $.81
Group: Postmedia Network Inc.
Quebecor Communications, Inc.
Pub. .... Andrea Demeer
Sales Mgr............................... Rosaline Bruyns

QUEBEC

CHATEAUGUAY

LE SOLEIL DU MERCREDI
(Wed, Sat)
82 Salaberry Sud, Chateauguay, QC, J6J 4J6, Canada; tel (450) 692-8552; fax (450) 692-3460; e-mail info@linformation.net; web site www.monteregieweb.com
Circulation: 11pd, 34,473fr; CCAB
Advertising: Open inch rate $1.00
Group: Les Hebdos Monteregiens
Ed. .... Michel Auclair
Robert Fichaud
Prodn. Mgr. ....Jeanne D'Arc Germain
Postal Codes Served: Canada

SAINT JEAN

LE GROUP CANADA FRANCAIS
(Wed)
84 Rue Richelieu, Saint Jean, QC, J3B 6X3, Canada; tel (450) 347-0323; fax (450) 347-4539; web site www.canadafrancais.com
Circulation: 18,500fr; Sworn/Estimate/Non-Audited
Advertising: Open inch rate $1.69
Circ. Mgr..................................Renel Bouchard
Ed. ....Robert Paradis
Postal Codes Served: J3B 6X3

SASKATCHEWAN

ESTEVAN

TRADER EXPRESS
(Fri)
68 Souris Ave. N., Estevan, SK, S4A 2A6, Canada; tel (306) 634-2654; fax (306) 634-3934; e-mail mercury_merc1@sasktel.net; classifieds@estevanmercury.ca; adv e-mail adsales@estevanmercury.ca; ed e-mail editor@estevanmercury.ca; sports@estevanmercury.ca; web site www.estevanmercury.ca
Circulation: 6,046fr; Sworn/Estimate/Non-Audited
Advertising: Open inch rate $.88
Pub. ....Peter Ng
Adv. Mgr...................................... Janice Boyle
Circ. Mgr... Kim Schoff
Mechanical Specifications: Type page 11 1/2 x 13; A - 5 cols, 2, between; C - 5 cols, 2, between.
Postal Codes Served: S4A 2A6

NORTH BATTLEFORD

ADVERTISER-POST
(Fri)
892-104 St., North Battleford, SK, S9A 3E6, Canada; tel (306) 445-7261; fax (306) 445-3223; e-mail battlefords.publishing@sasktel.net
Circulation: 16,000fr; Sworn/Estimate/Non-Audited
Advertising: Open inch rate $1.03
Pub. .... Alana Schweitzer
Circ. Mgr.....................................Gary Wouters
Ed. .... Becky Doig
Prodn. Mgr. .... Claude Paradis
Mechanical Specifications: Type page 10 1/4 x 15 2/3; E - 5 cols, 1 11/12, 1/6 between; A - 5 cols, 1 11/12, 1/6 between; C - 6 cols, 1 7/12, 1/6 between.
Postal Codes Served: S9A 3E6

PRINCE ALBERT

PRINCE ALBERT SHOPPER
(Mon)
Po Box 1930, Prince Albert, SK, S6V 6J9, Canada; tel (306) 763-8461; fax (306) 763-1856; e-mail pashopper@sasktel.net; web site www.princealbertshopper.com
Circulation: 20,000fr; Sworn/Estimate/Non-Audited
Advertising: Open inch rate $.76
Adv. Mgr. .... Jerry Paskiw
Mechanical Specifications: Type page 10 3/4 x 16.
Postal Codes Served: 26V 6J9

SHELLBROOK

SHOPPER CHRONICLE

(Fri)
44 Main St., Shellbrook, SK, S0J 2E0, Canada; tel (306) 747-2442; fax (306) 747-3000; e-mail chnews@shellbrookchronicle.com
Circulation: 4,587fr; Sworn/Estimate/Non-Audited
Advertising: Open inch rate $13.72
Pub. .... C.J. Pepper
Ed. .... Brad Dupuis
Mechanical Specifications: Type page 10 1/4 x 15; E - 6 cols, 1 7/12, 1/6 between; A - 6 cols, 1 7/12, 1/6 between; C - 6 cols, 1 7/12, 1/6 between.

TISDALE

PARKLAND REVIEW

(Fri)
1004-102 Ave., Tisdale, SK, S0E 1T0, Canada; tel (306) 873-4515; fax (306) 873-4712; e-mail recorderoffice@sasktel.net; adv e-mail adsrecorder@sakstel.net; ed e-mail newsrecorder@sakstel.net
Circulation: 11,625fr; CMCA
Advertising: Open inch rate $1.26
Group: Glacier Media Group
Adv. Mgr. .... August Grandguillar
Ed. .... Brent Fitzpatrick
Prodn. Mgr. .... Gord Anderson
Adv. Mgr. .... Dan Sully
Delivery Method: Mail
Postal Codes Served: Canada

WEYBURN

WEYBURN & AREA BOOSTER

(Sat) (Delivered Friday and Saturday)
904 East Ave., Weyburn, SK, S4H 2K4, Canada; tel (306) 842-7487; fax (306) 842-0282; e-mail production@weyburnreview.com; web site www.weyburnreview.com
Circulation: 6,280fr; Sworn/Estimate/Non-Audited
Advertising: Open inch rate $15.96
Group: Priaire Newspaper GroupEditions: 52 -
Pub. .... Darryl D. Ward
Ed. .... Patricia A. Ward
Mechanical Specifications: 5 column tabloid 9.67" x 15.75"
Equipment: Hardware — Mac platform; Software — Indesign, Photoshop
Delivery Method: Newsstand, Carrier, Racks
Postal Codes Served: S4H 2K4

YORKTON

THE MARKETPLACE

(Fri)
20 Third Ave., Yorkton, SK, S3N 2X3, Canada; tel (306) 782-2465; fax (306) 786-1898; e-mail publisher@yorktonthisweek.com; web site www.yorktonthisweek.com
Circulation: 20,000fr; Sworn/Estimate/Non-Audited
Advertising: Open inch rate $13.86
Circ. Mgr. .... Jim Kinaschuk
Publisher .... Jim Ambrose
Prodn. Mgr. .... Debbie Barr
Mechanical Specifications: Type page 13 1/2 x 16; E - 5 cols, 2 1/12, 1/6 between; A - 5 cols, 2 1/12, 1/6 between; C - 5 cols, 2 1/12, 1/6 between.
Delivery Method: Newsstand, Carrier, Racks
Postal Codes Served: S3N, SOA, SOE, ROJ, SOG, ROM

YORKTON NEWS REVIEW

(Thur)
18 1st Ave. N, Yorkton, SK, S3N 1J4, Canada, Canada; tel (306) 783-7355; fax (306) 782-9138; e-mail ads@yorktonnews.com; adv e-mail kenchyz@yorktonnews.com; ed e-mail editorial@yorktonnews.com; web site www.yorktonnews.com
Circulation: 6,797fr; CMCA
Advertising: Open inch rate $14.70
Established: 21
Group: Glacier Media Group
Adv. Mgr. .... Ken Chyz
Ed. .... Shannon Deveau
Prodn. Mgr. .... Carol Melnechenko
Mechanical Specifications: Type page 9.875 x 15 1/2; E - 6 cols, 1.5, 1/6 between; A - 6 cols, 1.5, 1/6 between; C - 6 cols, 1.5, 1/6 between.
Equipment: Hardware — APP/Mac; Software — Adobe, QPS/QuarkXPress. In Design
Delivery Method: Newsstand, Carrier, Racks
Postal Codes Served: S3N

Section III

Specialty and Niche Publications

Alternative Newspaper in the United States 2
Black Newspapers in the United States........................ 12
Schools and Departments of Journalism 23
Schools and Departments of Journalism - Foreign............. 51
College and University Newspapers............................ 53
Ethnic Newspapers in the United States........................ 99
Gay and Lesbian Newspapers in the United States............ 108
Hispanic Newspapers in the United States..................... 110
Jewish Newspapers in the United States....................... 121
Military Newspapers in the United States 127
Religious Newspapers in the United States 133
Alternative Newspapers in Canada 141
Ethnic Newspapers in Canada 142

Niche

Parenting Publications in the United States 145
Real Estate Publications in the United States 151
Senior Publications in the United States 154

ALTERNATIVE NEWSPAPER IN THE UNITED STATES

ALABAMA

BIRMINGHAM

BIRMINGHAM WEEKLY
(Wed)
2014 6th Ave N, Birmingham, AL, 35203-2702, Jefferson, USA; tel (205) 939-4030; fax (205) 212-1005; web site www.bhamweekly.com

ALASKA

ANCHORAGE

ANCHORAGE PRESS
(Thur)
540 E 5th Ave, Anchorage, AK, 99501-2636, Anchorage, USA; tel (907) 561-7737; fax (907) 561-7777; e-mail contact@anchoragepress.com; adv e-mail steve.abeln@anchoragepress.com; ed e-maileditor@anchoragepress.com; web site www.anchoragepress.com
Circulation: 20,000fr; Sworn/Estimate/Non-Audited
Advertising: Open inch rate $24.00
Established: 1992
Group: Wick Communications
Editor....................Brendan Kelley-Hellenthal
Publisher....................Steve Abeln
Pub....................Kari Slight
Sales Mgr./Adv. Mgr....................Jill Tillion
Ed....................Krestia DeGeorge
Mechanical Specifications: Type page 9 3/4 x 15; E - 6 cols, 1 1/2, 1/16 between; A - 6 cols, 1 1/2, 1/16 between.

ARIZONA

PHOENIX

NEW TIMES
(Thur)
1201 E Jefferson St, Phoenix, AZ, 85034-2300, Maricopa, USA; tel (602) 271-0040; adv tel (602) 258-1073; adv fax (602) 495-9954; e-mail marketing@newtimes.com; adv e-mail andrew.meister@newtimes.com; ed e-mailamy.silverman@newtimes.com; web site www.phoenixnewtimes.com
Circulation: 0pd, 65,000fr; AAM
Advertising: Open inch rate $34.00
Established: 1970
Group: Voice Media Group
Digital Platform - Mobile: Apple, Android, Windows
Digital Platform - Tablet: Apple iOS, Android, Windows 7, Kindle, Kindle Fire
Publisher....................Kurtis Barton
Associate Publisher....................Jennifer Meister
Circ. Mgr....................Eloy Vigil
Editor....................Rick Barrs
Mng. Editor....................Amy Silverman
Mechanical Specifications: Ad dimensions based on column inch
Delivery Method: Racks
Zip Codes Served: Valley Wide

TUCSON

TUCSON WEEKLY
(Thur)
7225 N Mona Lisa Rd, Ste 125, Tucson, AZ, 85741-2581, Pima, USA; tel (520) 797-4384; adv tel (520) 797-4384; ed tel (520) 797-4384; fax (520) 575-8891; adv fax (520) 575-8891; ed fax (520) 575-8891; e-mail tucsoneditor@tucsonlocalmedia.com; adv e-mail Casey@tucsonlocalmedia.com; ed e-mailTucsonEditor@tucsonlocalmedia.com; web site www.tucsonweekly.com
Circulation: 38,500fr; VAC
Group: Tucson Local Media, LLC
Pres/Pub....................Jason Joseph
Gen Mgr....................Jaime Hood
Ad. Dir....................Casey Anderson
News Ed....................Jim Nintzel
Prod. Mgr....................Chalo Grubb
Circ. Mgr. / Special Events Mgr. Laura Horvath
Mechanical Specifications: Type page 10" x 11"
Delivery Method: Racks
Zip Codes Served: Tucson Metro

ARKANSAS

FAYETTEVILLE

THE FREE WEEKLY
(Thur)
212 N East Ave, Fayetteville, AR, 72701-5225, Washington, USA; tel (479) 571-6419; adv tel (479) 571-6431; fax (479) 442-1714; e-mail rdavis@nwaonline.com; adv e-mail sporter@nwaonline.com; web site www.freeweekly.com
Circulation: 197pd, 8,000fr; Sworn/Estimate/Non-Audited
Advertising: Open inch rate $9.00
Established: 1994
Group: Northwest Arkansas Newspapers LLC WEHCO Media, Inc.
Adv. Dir....................Kent Eikenberry
Classified Adv. Mgr....................Jim Mears
Display Adv. Mgr....................Gareth Hollis
Circ. Dir....................Keith Sanford
General manager....................Susan Porter
Publisher....................Rusty Turner

CALIFORNIA

CHICO

CHICO NEWS & REVIEW
(Thur)
353 E 2nd St, Chico, CA, 95928-5469, Butte, USA; tel (530) 894-2300; fax (530) 892-1111; e-mail alecb@newsreview.com; adv e-mail alecb@newsreview.com; ed e-mailchicoeditor@newsreview.com; web site www.newsreview.com/chico/
Circulation: 40,441fr; CVC
Advertising: N/A
Established: 1977
Group: Chico Community Publishing Inc.
Digital Platform - Tablet: Other
Pres....................Jeff Vonkaenel
General Manager....................Alec Binyon
Circ. Mgr....................Mark Schuttenberg
Editor....................Melissa Daugherty
Prodn. Mgr....................Tina Flynn
Mechanical Specifications: Type page 10" x 11.5"; 5 cols
Equipment: Hardware — APP/Mac, PC, nice cameras, cheap cameras, voice recording devices, pens, paper, bicycles, etc.; Presses — We print on one of the finest presses in the State in Paradise, CA (Paradise Post Printing); Software — QPS/QuarkXPress 4.0, InDesign, Microsoft/Word 5.1, Libre Office Suite, Adobe/Illustrator, Adobe/PageMaker, Macromedia/Freehand.
Delivery Method: Racks
Zip Codes Served: 95928, 95926, 95965, 95969, 95973, 96080, 95929, 95966, 95954, 96021, 95988, 95948, 95963, 96055, 95951, 95968, 95938, 95953, 95917, 95974, 96035, 95913, 95925
Note: The Chico News & Review is a growing newspaper in terms of year over year print ad revenue and circulation. We don't syndicate content and we are almost entirely supported by our community's vibrant and healthy local businesses. We win multiple CNPA awards every year (California Newspaper Publishers Association) against metro weeklies. In Chico, we've out-circulated the competing daily paper since the late 1980's.

CULVER CITY

LA WEEKLY
(Thur)
3861 Sepulveda Blvd, Culver City, CA, 90230-4605, Los Angeles, USA; tel (310) 574-7100; adv tel (310) 574-7379; adv fax (310) 574-7495; adv e-mail sales@laweekly.com; ed e-maileditor@laweekly.com; web site www.laweekly.com
Circulation: 65,128fr; AAM
Established: 1978
Group: Semanal Media
Editor....................Drex Heikes
Delivery Method: Racks

FOUNTAIN VALLEY

OC WEEKLY
(Thur)
18475 Bandilier Cir, Fountain Valley, CA, 92708-7000, Orange, USA; tel (714) 550-5900; fax (714) 550-5908; e-mail letters@ocweekly.com; web site www.ocweekly.com
Circulation: 22pd, 64,111fr; AAM
Group: Duncan McIntosh Co., Inc.
Pres./CEO....................Duncan Mcintosh
Adv. Dir....................Scott Mabry
Ed....................Gustavo Arellano
Mng. Ed....................Nick Schou
Sales Dir....................Ryan Whipple
Mechanical Specifications: Type page 10 x 13; E - 4 cols, 2 5/16, between; A - 4 cols, 2 5/16, between.

HERMOSA BEACH

EASY READER
(Thur)
PO Box 427, 832 Hermosa Ave, Hermosa Beach, CA, 90254-0427, Los Angeles, USA; tel (310) 372-4611; fax (424) 212-6708; e-mail easyreader@easyreader.info; adv e-mail classifiedads@easyreader.info; displayads@easyreader.info; ed e-mailnews@easyreader.info; web site http://www.easyreadernews.com/
Circulation: 27,684pd,; AAM
Advertising: Open inch rate $20.00
Established: 1970
Group: C-VILLE Holdings LLC
Adv. Mgr....................Kevin Cody
Dispaly Sales....................Amy Berg
Display Sales....................Erin McCoy
Classifieds....................Tami Quattrone
Arts/Entertainment Ed....................Bondo Wyszpolski
News Ed....................Mark McDermott
Prodn. Dir....................Graciela Huerta
Richard Budman
Mechanical Specifications: Type page 10 1/2 x 11 1/2; E - 4 cols, 2 1/4, 1/6 between; A - 4 cols, 2 1/4, 1/6 between; C - 7 cols, 1 1/4, 1/6 between.
Equipment: Hardware — PC, APP/Mac; Software — Microsoft/Word, QPS/QuarkXPress.
Delivery Method: Mail, Newsstand, Carrier, Racks
Zip Codes Served: 90254, 90266, 90277, 90288, 90245. 90272, 90274
Note: Easy Reader is the largest circulation, weekly newspaper serving the South Bay area of Los Angeles.

LOS ANGELES

CIPS MARKETING GROUP, INC.
(Wed, Sun)
13110 Avalon Blvd, Los Angeles, CA, 90061-2738, Los Angeles, USA; tel (310) 769-6900; fax (310) 538-1170; web site www.cipsmarketing.com
Circulation: 578,512pd,; CAC
Established: 1962Jennifer Fawkes
President & CEO....................Manuel Collazo

ENTERTAINMENT TODAY INC
(Fri)
12021 Wilshire Blvd, Ste 398, Los Angeles, CA, 90025-1206, Los Angeles, USA; tel (213) 387-2060; adv tel (213) 387-2060; ed tel (213) 387-2060; fax (310) 526-6891; adv fax (310) 526-6891; ed fax (310) 526-6891; e-mail editor@entertainmenttoday.net; adv e-mail ad@entertainmenttoday.net; ed e-maileditor@entertainmenttoday.net; web site www.entertainmenttoday.net
Circulation: 210,000fr; Sworn/Estimate/Non-Audited
Advertising: Open inch rate $62.00
Established: 1967Editions: 2— Entertainment Today-Los Angeles (155,000);
Digital Platform - Mobile: Apple, Android, Windows, Blackberry
Digital Platform - Tablet: Apple iOS, Android, Windows 7, Blackberry Tablet OS, Kindle, Nook, Kindle Fire
Pub....................Katz Ueno
Mechanical Specifications: Type page 10 1/2 x 12 3/4; E - 5 cols, 2 1/16, 1/8 between; A - 5 cols, 2 1/16, 1/8 between; C - 6 cols, 1 5/8, 1/8 between.
Equipment: Hardware — APP/Mac Performas, Pentium 4, IBM; Software — Adobe/PageMaker 6.5, Adobe/Photoshop 5.5, Adobe/Illustrator, QPS/QuarkXPress, Archetype/Corel Draw 8.0, Adobe/InDesign 2.0.
Zip Codes Served: 91506

OAKLAND

EAST BAY EXPRESS
(Wed)
620 3rd St, Oakland, CA, 94607-3551, Alameda, USA; tel (510) 879-3700; fax (510) 879-3794; e-mail info@eastbayexpress.com; web site www.eastbayexpress.com
Circulation: 50,000fr; Sworn/Estimate/Non-Audited
Advertising: Open inch rate $20.30
Established: 1978
Pub....................Jody Colley
Mktg./Promo. Mgr....................Terry Furry

Circ. Mgr.................................... Nate Elpenrich
Mng. Ed.................................... Kathleen Wentz
Ed. .... Nick Miller
Mechanical Specifications: Type page 10 3/16 x 16; E - 5 cols, 1 7/8, 1/6 between; A - 5 cols, 1 7/8, 1/6 between; C - 5 cols, 1 7/8, 1/6 between.

PALM SPRINGS

DESERT POST WEEKLY

(Thur)
750 N Gene Autry Trl, Palm Springs, CA, 92262-5463, Riverside, USA; tel (760) 322-8889; web site www.desertsun.com
Circulation:; Sworn/Estimate/Non-Audited
Advertising: Open inch rate $13.85
Group: C-VILLE Holdings LLC
Advertising .... Kim Renstrom
Mechanical Specifications: Type page 9 13/20 x 12; E - 5 cols, between; A - 5 cols, between.

PALO ALTO

PALO ALTO WEEKLY

(Fri)
450 Cambridge Ave, Palo Alto, CA, 94306-1507, Santa Clara, USA; tel (650) 326-8210; fax (650) 326-3928; e-mail editor@paweekly.com; adv e-mail ads@paweekly.com; ed e-maileditor@paweekly.com; web site www.paloaltoonline.com
Circulation: 33,500pd, 19,349fr; Sworn/Estimate/Non-Audited
Advertising: Open inch rate $43.65
Established: 1979
Group: C-VILLE Holdings LLCEditions: 1— Palo Alto (33,000);
Digital Platform - Mobile: Apple, Android
Pub..Bill Johnson
Mechanical Specifications: Type page 10 x 13.
Equipment: ; Presses — SLN.
Delivery Method: Mail, Newsstand
Zip Codes Served: 94301, 94025, 94022

SACRAMENTO

SACRAMENTO NEWS & REVIEW

(Thur)
1124 Del Paso Blvd, Sacramento, CA, 95815-3607, Sacramento, USA; tel (916) 498-1234; adv tel (916) 498-1234; ed tel (916) 498-1234; fax (916) 498-7910; adv fax (916) 498-7910; ed fax (916) 498-7910; e-mail sacdofi@newsreview.com; adv e-mail snradinfo@newsreview.com; ed e-mailsactonewstips@newsreview.com; web site https://www.newsreview.com/sacramento
Circulation: 64,463fr; CVC
Advertising: Open inch rate $50.00
Established: 1989
Group: Chico Community Publishing, Inc.
Distribution Mgr ....Greg Erwin
President ....Jeff von Kaenel
Chief Operating Officer.......Deborah Redmond
Sales Manager ....Michael Gelbman
Design Manager ....Chris Terrazas
Mechanical Specifications: Full page 10" x 10.5", 5 column and 8 column formats available
Equipment: ; Software — Adobe Creative Suite 5.5 (Bridge, Illustrator, InDesign, Photoshop)
Delivery Method: Mail, Newsstand, Racks
Zip Codes Served: 95602, 95603, 95605, 95608, 95610, 95616, 95618, 95619, 95621, 95624, 95626, 95628, 95630, 95648, 95650, 95652, 95655, 95658, 95660, 95661, 95662, 95663, 95667, 95670, 95673, 95677, 95678, 95682, 95691, 95693, 95695, 95742, 95746, 95747, 95757, 95758, 95762, 95765, 95776, 95811, 95814, 95815, 95816, 95817, 95818, 95819, 95820, 95821, 95822, 95823, 95824, 95825, 95826, 95827, 95828, 95829, 95831, 95832, 95833, 95834, 95835, 95837, 95838, 95841, 95842, 95843, 95864, 95945, 95949, 95959.
Note: Chico Community Publishing, Inc is the parent company of Sacramento News & Review (SN&R), Chico News & Review (CN&R), Reno News & Review (RN&R) and N&R Publications

SAN DIEGO

SAN DIEGO CITY BEAT

(Wed)
3047 University Ave, Ste 202, San Diego, CA, 92104-3039, San Diego, USA; tel (619) 281-7526; fax (619) 281-5273; e-mail editor@sdcitybeat.com; web site www.sdcitybeat.com

SAN DIEGO READER

(Thur)
2323 Broadway, Ste 200, San Diego, CA, 92102-1950, San Diego, USA; tel (619) 235-3000; fax (619) 231-0489; e-mail info@sdreader.com; web site www.sandiegoreader.com
Circulation: 0pd, 77,417fr; VAC
Advertising: Open inch rate $100.40Editions: 130,000— 1
Publisher and editor.......................Jim Holman
Gen. Mgr. .... Howard Rosen
Adv. Mgr. .... Linda Flounders
Prodn. Mgr. .... Sandy Matthews
Mechanical Specifications: Type page 10 1/4 x 13; E - 6 cols, 1 1/2, 1/4 between; A - 6 cols, 1 1/2, 1/4 between; C - 6 cols, 1 1/2, 1/4 between.
Equipment: Hardware — APP/Mac; Software — QPS/QuarkXPress 4.04, Adobe/Acrobat 4.0.

SAN FRANCISCO

SF WEEKLY

(Thur)
835 Market St Ste 550, Suite 550, San Francisco, CA, 94103-1906, San Francisco, USA; tel (415) 359-2600; fax (415) 541-9096; e-mail mailbox@sfweekly.com; web site www.sfweekly.com
Circulation: 68,992fr; VAC
Advertising: Open inch rate $39.00
Group: San Francisco Media Company
Digital Platform - Mobile: Apple, Android
Digital Platform - Tablet: Apple iOS, AndroidChanning Joseph
Peter Lawrence Kane
Jessie Schiewe
Mechanical Specifications: Type page 10 x 12 3/8; E - 4 cols, 2 2/5, 1/6 between; A - 4 cols, 2 3/8, 1/6 between; C - 8 cols, 1 1/16, between.
Equipment: ; Presses — Offset.
Delivery Method: Newsstand, Racks

SAN JOSE

METRO

(Wed)
550 S 1st St, San Jose, CA, 95113-2806, Santa Clara, USA; tel (408) 200-1300; fax (408) 271-3521; adv fax (408) 298-6992; ed fax (408) 298-0602; e-mail letters@metronews.com; web site www.metroactive.com
Circulation: 77,715fr; VAC
Advertising: Open inch rate $38.00Editions: 1— Metro Santa Cruz (38,000);
Pub... Dan Pulcrano
Circ. Dir. .... Jorge Lopez
Arts Ed..Michael Gant
Design Dir. .... Kara Brown
Mechanical Specifications: Type page 10 3/4 x 13 11/16; E - 4 cols, 2 5/16, 1/4 between; A - 4 cols, 2 5/16, 1/4 between; C - 8 cols, 1 1/4, between.

SAN LUIS OBISPO

NEW TIMES

(Thur)
1010 Marsh St, San Luis Obispo, CA, 93401-3630, San Luis Obispo, USA; tel (805) 546-8208; fax (805) 546-8641; e-mail bob@newtimesslo.com; adv e-mail advertsing@newtimesslo.com; ed e-maileditorial@newtimesslo.com; web site www.newtimesslo.com
Circulation: 10pd, 34,978fr; VAC
Advertising: Full page $1237
Established: 1986
Digital Platform - Mobile: Apple, Android
Digital Platform - Tablet: Apple iOS, Android
Publisher...................................... Bob Rucker
Arts Dir... Alex Zuniga
Mechanical Specifications: Type page 10 1/4 x 12.75; E - 4 cols, 2 3/8, between; A - 4 cols, 2 3/8, between; C - 8 cols, 1 1/8, between.
Equipment: Hardware — APP/Mac; Presses — News Press Santa Barbara; Software — QPS/QuarkXPress.
Delivery Method: Racks
Zip Codes Served: 93402, 93405, 93476, 93401, 93422, 93446, 93453, 93451, 93485, 93420, 93448, 93433, 93424, 93448, 93445, 93444, 93428, 93442, 93430, 93452, 93402

SAN PEDRO

RANDOM LENGTHS NEWS

(Thur) (Every Other Thursday)
PO Box 731, San Pedro, CA, 90733-0731, Los Angeles, USA; tel (310) 519-1442; adv tel (310) 519-1442; fax (310) 832-1000; adv fax (310) 832-1000; e-mail editor@randomlengthsnews.com; adv e-mail reads@randomlengthnews.com; web site www.randomlengthsnews.com
Circulation: 5,000pd, 22,000fr; Sworn/Estimate/Non-Audited
Advertising: $15.50
Established: 1979
Group: Allen Publications
Digital Platform - Mobile: Android
Digital Platform - Tablet: Apple iOS, Android, Kindle
Pub.................................James Preston Allen
Delivery Method: Mail, Newsstand, Racks
Zip Codes Served: 90731, 90732, 90733, 90275, 90274, 90744, 90745, 90717, 90710, 90806

RANDOM LENGTHS/HARBOR INDEPENDENT NEWS

(Thur) (Every other Thur)
1300 S Pacific Ave, San Pedro, CA, 90731-4108, Los Angeles, USA; tel (310) 519-1442; adv tel (310) 561-7811; ed tel (310) 519-1016; fax (310) 832-1000; e-mail editor@randomlengthsnews.com; adv e-mail rlnsales@randomlengthsnews.com; ed e-mailreporter@randomlengthsnews.com; web site www.randomlengthsnews.com
Circulation: 1,000pd, 22,500fr; Sworn/Estimate/Non-Audited
Advertising: Open inch rate $15.50
Established: 1979
Digital Platform - Mobile: Apple, Android, Windows
Digital Platform - Tablet: Apple iOS, Android, Windows 7
Pub.................................James Preston Allen
Gen. Mgr. .... S.K. Matsumiya
Mechanical Specifications: Type page 10 1/4 x 12 3/4; E - 5 cols, 2 5/12, between; A - 5 cols, 2 5/12, between; C - 7 cols, 1 3/8, 1/16 between.
Equipment: Hardware — APP/Mac; Presses — WPC/Offset; Software — Adobe/PageMaker 6.0.
Delivery Method: Mail, Newsstand, Racks
Zip Codes Served: 90731, 90732, 90733, 90744, 90745, 90710, 90717, 90274, 90275, 90802-13

SAN RAFAEL

PACIFIC SUN

(Fri)
835 4th St, Ste B, San Rafael, CA, 94901-3260, Marin, USA; tel (415) 485-6700; fax (415) 485-6226; e-mail letters@pacificsun.com; web site www.pacificsun.com
Circulation:; Sworn/Estimate/Non-Audited
Advertising: Open inch rate $30.58
Established: 1963
Group: C-VILLE Holdings LLC
Pub.. Sam Chapman
Mechanical Specifications: Type page 10 3/16 x 13 5/16; E - 4 cols, between; A - 4 cols, between; C - 8 cols, between.
Equipment: Hardware — APP/Mac; Software — QPS/QuarkXPress, Adobe/PageMaker, Adobe/Illustrator.

SANTA BARBARA

SANTA BARBARA INDEPENDENT

(Thur) (online daily)
12 E Figueroa St, Santa Barbara, CA, 93101-2709, Santa Barbara, USA; tel (805) 965-5205; fax (805) 965-5518; e-mail admin@independent.com; sales@independent.com; adv e-mail sales@independent.com; ed e-mailnews@independent.com, arts@independent.com,lisitngs@independent.com; web site www.independent.com
Circulation: 0pd, 39,097fr; VAC
Advertising: Open inch rate $30.00
Established: 1985
Group: C-VILLE Holdings LLC
Editor in chief.................... Marianne Partridge
Sarah Sinclair
Publisher.................................... Brandi Rivera
Mechanical Specifications: Type page 9 13/16 x 12 5/8; E - 5 cols, 1 13/16, between; A - 5 cols, 1 13/16, between; C - 7 cols, 1 5/16, between.
Equipment: Hardware — APP/Mac, PC; Software — QPS/QuarkXPress, Adobe/Photoshop.
Delivery Method: Newsstand, Racks
Zip Codes Served: 93067, 93013, 93108, 93103, 93105, 93101, 93109, 93110, 93111, 93117, 93460, 93463, 93441, 93427, 93436

SANTA CRUZ

METRO SANTA CRUZ

(Wed)
115 Cooper St, Santa Cruz, CA, 95060-4526, Santa Cruz, USA; tel (831) 457-9000; adv tel (831) 457-8500; fax (831) 457-5828; web site www.metroactive.com
Circulation: 77,715fr; VAC
Advertising: Open inch rate $14.28
Pub.. Debra Whizan
Ed. ....Tracy Hukill
Mechanical Specifications: Type page 10 x 12 3/4; E - 4 cols, between; A - 4 cols, between; C - 8 cols, between.

SANTA MARIA

THE SANTA MARIA SUN

(Thur)
2540 Skyway Dr, Santa Maria, CA, 93455-1514, Santa Barbara, USA; tel (805) 347-1968; fax (805) 347-9889; e-mail krosa@santamariasun.com; adv e-mail krosa@santamariasun.com; ed e-mailjpayne@newtimesslo.com; web site www.santamariasun.com
Circulation: 10pd, 18,000fr; VAC
Advertising: $1033 full page
Established: 200
Digital Platform - Mobile: Apple, Android
Digital Platform - Tablet: Apple iOS, Android, Kindle

Publisher....................................... Bob Rucker
Arts Dir.. Alex Zuniga
Equipment: Hardware — APP/Mac; Presses — News Press Santa Barbara; Software — QPS/QuarkXPress.
Delivery Method: Racks
Zip Codes Served: 93455, 93454, 93434,93444, 92436, 93437, 93440, 93427, 93463, 93460, 934401

SANTA ROSA

NORTH BAY BOHEMIAN

(Wed)
847 5th St, Santa Rosa, CA, 95404-4526, Sonoma, USA; tel (707) 527-1200; fax (707) 527-1288; e-mail sales@bohemian.com; web site www.bohemian.com
Circulation: 25,000fr; Sworn/Estimate/Non-Audited
Pub.......................... Rosemary Mackay Olson
Adv. Dir.. Lisa Santos
Mechanical Specifications: Full Page 9"wide x 10" high, 300 dpi
Delivery Method: Racks
Zip Codes Served: Sonoma, Napa and Marin Counties.

SEASIDE

MONTEREY COUNTY WEEKLY

(Thur)
668 Williams Ave, Seaside, CA, 93955-5736, Monterey, USA; tel (831) 394-5656; fax (831) 394-2909; e-mail mail@mcweekly.com; ed e-mailletters@mcweekly.com; web site www.montereycountyweekly.com
Circulation: 0pd, 35,975fr; CVC
Advertising: Open inch rate $18.20
Established: 1988
Publisher.................................. Erik Cushman
Circ. Mgr..................................... Cecilia Traver
Exec. Ed. & CEO.......................... Bradley Zeve
Prodn. Mgr. .... Karen Loutzenheiser
Editor .... Mary Duan
Managing Editor .... Mark Anderson
Ed. .... Paul Wilmer
Walter Ryce
Editorial Department
Adam Joseph
Mechanical Specifications: Type page 10 x 12 7/8; E - 4 cols, 2 5/16, 1/3 between.
Equipment: Hardware — APP/Mac G4; Software — QPS/QuarkXPress 4.1, Adobe/Photoshop 4.0.

COLORADO

BOULDER

BOULDER WEEKLY

(Thur)
690 S Lashley Ln, Boulder, CO, 80305-5920, Boulder, USA; tel (303) 494-5511; adv tel (303) 494-5511 x109; fax (303) 494-2585; e-mail info@boulderweekly.com; adv e-mail franzan@boulderweekly.com; ed e-maileditorial@boulderweekly.com; web site www.boulderweekly.com
Circulation: 25,000fr; Sworn/Estimate/Non-Audited
Advertising: $11.72
Established: 1993
Digital Platform - Mobile: Apple, Android
Digital Platform - Tablet: Apple iOS, Android, Windows 7, Kindle
Pub... Stewart Sallo
Associate Publisher................. Fran Zankowski
Mechanical Specifications: Full page: 9.5 x 12.5
3/4 page 7.085 x 12.336
3/4 page 9.5 x 9.2
2/3 page 9.5 x 8.178
Mini Page 7.085 x 9.2
1/2 vert 4.667 x 12.336
1/2 horizontal 9.5 x 6.076
1/4 standard 4.667 x 6.076
1/4 vert 2.25 x 12.336
1/4 horizontal 9.5 x2.953
1/6 standard 4.667 x 3.996
1/6 vert 2.25 x 8.178
1/8 vert 2.25 x 6.076
1/8 horizontal 4.667 x 2.953
1/12 vert 2.25 x 3.996
1/12 horizontal 4.667 x 1.919
1/16 2.25 x2.953
Delivery Method: Newsstand, Racks
Zip Codes Served: 80302, 80303, 80304, 80305, 80301, 80027, 80026, 80516, 80501, 80466

COLORADO SPRINGS

COLORADO SPRINGS INDEPENDENT

(Thur)
235 S Nevada Ave, Colorado Springs, CO, 80903-1906, El Paso, USA; tel (719) 577-4545; fax (719) 577-4107; e-mail letters@csindy.com; web site www.csindy.com
Circulation: 1,500pd, 36,000fr; Sworn/Estimate/Non-Audited
Established: 1993
Pub.. John Weiss
Adv. Mgr.. Teri Homick
Adv. Mgr., Classified .... Carrie Simison-Bitz
Mng. Ed.. Kirk Woundy
Art Dir.. Kathy Conarro
Mechanical Specifications: Type page 10 1/16 x 12 3/4; E - 4 cols, 2 3/8, 2/10 between; A - 4 cols, 2 3/8, 1/5 between; C - 8 cols, 1 1/10, 1/6 between.
Equipment: Hardware — APP/iMac, APP/Mac G4; Presses — 10-G/Community; Software — QPS/QuarkXPress 4.11, Adobe/Photoshop 6, Adobe/Illustrator 9.

DENVER

DENVER WESTWORD

(Thur)
969 N Broadway, Denver, CO, 80203-2705, Denver, USA; tel (303) 296-7744; fax (303) 296-5416; e-mail retail@westword.com; web site www.westword.com
Circulation: 732pd, 55,000fr; Sworn/Estimate/Non-Audited
Advertising: Open inch rate $37.25
Group: Voice Media Group
Digital Platform - Mobile: Apple, Android
Digital Platform - Tablet: Apple iOS, Android
Publisher.. Scott Tobias
Assoc. Pub.............................. Tracy Kontrelos
Circ. Mgr..................................... Curt Sanders
Prodn. Mgr. .... Michael Wilson

CONNECTICUT

HARTFORD

HARTFORD ADVOCATE

(Thur)
121 Wawarme Ave, Hartford, CT, 06114-1507, Hartford, USA; tel (203) 382-9666; fax (203) 382-9657; ed e-maileditor@fairfieldweekly.com; web site www.fairfieldweekly.com
Circulation: 31,570fr; VAC
Established: 1978
Pub.. Joshua Mamis
Ed. .... Nick Keppler
Adv. Dir.................................... Susan Leighton
Circ. Mgr.................................. Bryan Mcenery
Prodn. Mgr. .... Peter Uus
Mechanical Specifications: Type page 10 x 11 1/2; E - 5 cols, 1 15/16, between; A - 5 cols, 1 15/16, between; C - 8 cols, between.
Equipment: Hardware — APP/Mac; Software — Microsoft/Word, Microsoft/Excel.

HARTFORD COURANT

(Thur)
285 Broad St, Hartford, CT, 06115-3785, Hartford, USA; tel (860) 241-6200; ed tel 860-520-6941; fax (203) 382-9657; ed e-mailletters@courant.com; web site www.ctnow.com
Circulation: 31,839fr; VAC
Established: 1978
Pub.. Joshua Mamis
Ed. .... Nick Keppler
Adv. Dir.................................... Susan Leighton
Circ. Mgr.................................. Bryan Mcenery
Prodn. Mgr. .... Peter Uus
Mechanical Specifications: Type page 10 x 11 1/2; E - 5 cols, 1 15/16, between; A - 5 cols, 1 15/16, between; C - 8 cols, between.
Equipment: Hardware — APP/Mac; Software — Microsoft/Word, Microsoft/Excel.

NEW HAVEN

NEW HAVEN ADVOCATE

(Wed)
900 Chapel St, Ste 1100, New Haven, CT, 06510-2810, New Haven, USA; tel (203) 789-0010; fax (203) 787-1418; ed e-maileditor@newhavenadvocate.com; web site www.newhavenadvocate.com
Circulation: 16pd, 40,000fr; Sworn/Estimate/Non-Audited
Group: C-VILLE Holdings LLC
Pub.. Joshua Mamis
Adv. Dir.................................... Susan Leighton
Circ. Mgr.................................. Brian McEnery
Mng. Ed...................................... John Adamian
Mechanical Specifications: Type page 10 1/4 x 12 3/4; E - 5 cols, 1 15/16, between; A - 5 cols, 1 15/16, between.
Equipment: ; Software — QPS/QuarkXPress, Adobe/Photoshop.

DISTRICT OF COLUMBIA

WASHINGTON

WASHINGTON CITY PAPER

(Thur)
1400 I St NW, Ste 900, Washington, DC, 20005-6527, District Of Columbia, USA; tel (202) 332-2100; fax (202) 332-8500; e-mail mail@washingtoncitypaper.com; web site www.washingtoncitypaper.com
Circulation: 0pd, 53,450fr; VAC
Advertising: Open inch rate $47.37
Pub.. Amy Austin
Circ. Mgr.. Matt Curry
Ed. .... Erik Wemple
Eric Norwood
Mechanical Specifications: Type page 10 13/16 x 13 3/4; E - 5 cols, 2 1/16, 1/8 between; A - 5 cols, 2 1/16, 1/8 between; C - 5 cols, 2 1/16, 1/8 between.
Equipment: Hardware — APP/Mac, PC

FLORIDA

MIAMI

MIAMI NEW TIMES

(Thur)
2800 Biscayne Blvd, Ste 100, Miami, FL, 33137-4554, Miami-Dade, USA; tel (305) 576-8000; adv fax (305) 571-7677; e-mail editorial@miami-newtimes.com; ed e-mailchuck.striouse@miaminewtimes.com; web site www.miaminewtimes.com
Circulation: 40,000fr; Sworn/Estimate/Non-Audited
Established: 1987
Digital Platform - Tablet: Apple iOS, Windows 7, Blackberry Tablet OS, Kindle Fire
Mng. Ed.................................... Chuck Strouse
Prodn. Mgr. .... Mike Lugo
Publisher.................................... Adam Simon
Russell Breiter
Mechanical Specifications: Type page 10 x 12 7/8; E - 8 cols, between; A - 8 cols, between.

NEW TIMES BROWARD-PALM BEACH

PO Box 011591, Miami, FL, 33101-1591, USA; web site www.browardpalmbeach.com
Established: 1997
Group: Voice Media Group
Ed. .... Chuck Strouse

ORLANDO

ORLANDO WEEKLY

(Wed)
16 W Pine St, Orlando, FL, 32801-2612, Orange, USA; tel (407) 377-0400; adv tel (407) 377-0415; ed tel (407) 377-0400 ext. 232; fax (407) 377-0420; e-mail graham@orlandoweekly.com; ed e-mailjyoung@orlandoweekly.com; web site www.orlandoweekly.com
Circulation: 0pd, 25,000fr; Sworn/Estimate/Non-Audited
Advertising: Open inch rate $41.00
Established: 1990
Group: Euclid Media Group
Digital Platform - Mobile: Apple, Android, Windows, Other
Digital Platform - Tablet: Apple iOS, Android, Windows 7
Pub... Graham Jarrett
Reg'l. Pub.............................. Michael Wagner
Ed. in Cheif .... Jessica Bryce Young
Cal. Ed. .... Thad McCollum
Web Ed.. Colin Wolfe
Staff Writer.......................... Monivette Cordeiro
Art Dir.................................. Melissa McHenry
Mechanical Specifications: Type page 10 x 10
Equipment: Hardware — APP/Mac
Delivery Method: Racks

TAMARAC

EASTSIDER

(Thur)
6501 Nob Hill Rd, Tamarac, FL, 33321-6422, Broward, USA; tel (954) 429-1207; fax (954) 698-9062; e-mail bwebd@tribune.com; web site www.forumpub.com
Circulation:; Sworn/Estimate/Non-Audited
Adv. Mgr..................................... Olga Carmier
Circ. Mgr. .... Ed Wilder
Exec. Ed... Pam Doto
Prodn. Mgr. .... Stewart Cady

TAMPA

CREATIVE LOAFING

(Wed)
1911 N 13th St, Ste W200, Tampa, FL, 33605-3652, Hillsborough, USA; tel (813) 739-4800; adv tel (813) 739-4815; fax (813) 739-4801; adv e-mail chris.madalena@creativeloafing.com; ed e-maildavid.warner@creativeloafing.com; web site tampa.creativeloafing.com
Circulation: 50,000fr; VAC
Advertising: 70.00
Established: 1987
Group: Womack Newspapers, inc
Mechanical Specifications: Type page 10x10.625; E - 4 cols, 2.406, between; A - 4 cols, 2.406, between; C - 6 cols, 1 7/16, between.
Equipment: Hardware — APP/Mac; Software — QPS/QuarkXPress 3.0.
Delivery Method: Newsstand, Racks
Zip Codes Served: 33510, 33511, 33594, 33602,

33603, 33604, 33605, 33606, 33607, 33609, 33610, 33611, 33612, 33613, 33614, 33615, 33616, 33617, 33618, 33619, 33620, 33624, 33625, 33626, 33629, 33634, 33635, 33684, 33701, 33702, 33703, 33704, 33705, 33706, 33707, 33708, 33709, 33710, 33711, 33712, 33713, 33714, 33716, 33755, 33756, 33759, 33760, 33761, 33762, 33763, 33764, 33765, 33767, 33770, 33771, 33772, 33773, 33774, 33776, 33777, 33778, 33781, 33782, 33785, 34660, 34677, 34681, 34683, 34684, 34685, 34695, 34698

GEORGIA

ATHENS

FLAGPOLE MAGAZINE

(Tues)
112 Foundry St, Athens, GA, 30601-2672, Clarke, USA; tel (706) 549-9523; fax (706) 548-8981; e-mail mail@flagpole.com; web site www.flagpole.com

Circulation: 13,658fr; CVC
Group: C-VILLE Holdings LLC
Adv. Mgr. .... Alicia Nickles
Mng. Ed. .... Christina Cotter
Ed. .... Pete McCommons
Prodn. Dir. .... Larry Tenner
Mechanical Specifications: Type page 13 x 10.
Equipment: Hardware — APP/Mac; Software — QPS/QuarkXPress 3.31, Macromedia/ Freehand 5.0, Adobe/Photoshop 3.01.

ATLANTA

CREATIVE LOAFING ATLANTA

(Thur) (Weekly)
231 18th St NW, Ste 8150, Atlanta, GA, 30363-1116, Fulton, USA; tel (404) 688-5623; adv tel (404) 688-5623; fax (404) 522-1532; adv fax (404) 614-3599; web site www.clatl.com

Circulation: 80,000fr; VAC
Advertising: Open inch rate $81.77
Established: 1972
Group: Womack Newspapers, incEditions: 52—
Digital Platform - Mobile: Apple
Publisher .... Sharry Smith
Editor in Chief .... Eric Celeste
Advertising Director .... Eric Moran
Marketing and Promotions Director Leigh Anne Anderson
Equipment: Hardware — APP/Mac, PC; Software — QPS/QuarkXPress, Adobe/ Photoshop.
Delivery Method: Newsstand, Racks
Zip Codes Served: available upon request

HAWAII

WAILUKU

MAUI TIME WEEKLY

(Thur)
16 S Market St, Ste 2K, Wailuku, HI, 96793-2201, Maui, USA; tel (808) 244-0777; fax (808) 244-0446; e-mail editor@mauitime.com; web site www.mauitime.com

Circulation: 18,000fr; Sworn/Estimate/Non-Audited
Established: 1997
Delivery Method: Racks

IDAHO

BOISE

BOISE WEEKLY

(Wed)
523 W Broad St, Boise, ID, 83702-7642, Ada, USA; tel (208) 344-2055; fax (208) 342-4733; e-mail info@boiseweekly.com; web site www.boiseweekly.com

Circulation: 35,000fr; Sworn/Estimate/Non-Audited
Established: 1992
Group: C-VILLE Holdings LLC
Circ. Dir. .... Stan Jackson
Pub. .... Sally Freeman
Mechanical Specifications: Type page 9 5/8 x 12 1/2; E - 4 cols, 1/8 between; A - 4 cols, between; C - 6 cols, between.
Equipment: Hardware — APP/Macs; Software — Adobe/Illustrator 6.0, Microsoft/Word, QPS/QuarkXPress 4.0, Adobe/Photoshop 4.0, Macromedia/Freehand 8.

ILLINOIS

CHICAGO

READER

(Thur)
11 E Illinois St, Chicago, IL, 60611-5652, Cook, USA; tel (312) 828-0350; fax (312) 828-0305; ed fax (312)828-9926; e-mail mail@chicagoreader.com; web site www.chicagoreader.com

Circulation: 329pd, 100,000fr; Sworn/Estimate/ Non-Audited
Advertising: Open inch rate $76.25
Established: 1971
Assoc. Pub. .... Steve Timble
Pub. .... James Warren
Adv. Mgr. .... Brett Murphy
Circ. Mgr. .... Perry A. Kim
Ed. .... Alison TRUE
Mng. Ed. .... Kiki Yablon
Mechanical Specifications: Type page 10 x 16; E - 5 cols, 1 7/8, 1/6 between; A - 5 cols, 1 7/8, 1/6 between; C - 5 cols, 1 7/8, 1/6 between.
Equipment: Hardware — APP/Mac; Software — QPS/QuarkXPress, Adobe/Photoshop.

SPRINGFIELD

ILLINOIS TIMES

(Thur)
1240 S 6th St, Springfield, IL, 62703-2408, Sangamon, USA; tel (217) 753-2226; fax (217) 753-2281; e-mail swhalen@illinoistimes.com; web site www.illinoistimes.com

Circulation: 19pd, 27,951fr; CVC
Advertising: Modular Rates: 1/8 P $295 1/4 P $575 1/2 P $900 Full $1645
Established: 1975
Group: C-VILLE Holdings LLC
Circ. Mgr. .... Brenda Matheis
Assoc. Pub. .... Lisa Ellis
Mechanical Specifications: Type page 10 1/4 x 11 1/2; E - 4 cols, 2 3/8, 3/16 between; A - 4 cols, 2 3/8, 3/16 between; C - 6 cols, 1 1/2, 3/16 between.
Equipment: Hardware — APP/Mac.
Zip Codes Served: 62701, 62702, 62703, 62704, 62706, 62707, 62563, 62568, 62650, 62629, 62675, 62684

INDIANA

INDIANAPOLIS

NUVO

(Wed)
3951 N Meridian St, Ste 200, Indianapolis, IN, 46208-4078, Marion, USA; tel (317) 254-2400; fax (317) 254-2405; e-mail nuvo@nuvo.net; adv e-mail advertising@nuvo.net; ed e-maileditors@nuvo.net; web site www.nuvo.net

Circulation: 0pd, 24,920fr; CVC
Advertising: Open inch rate $30.00
Established: 1990
Digital Platform - Mobile: Apple, Android, Windows, Blackberry, Other
Digital Platform - Tablet: Apple iOS, Android, Windows 7, Blackberry Tablet OS, Kindle, Nook, Kindle Fire, Other
Ed./Pub. .... Kevin McKinney
Circ. Mgr. .... Kathy Flahavin
Ed. .... Kat Coplen
Sales Mgr. .... Dave Searle
Mechanical Specifications: Type page 10 3/8 x 11 5/8; E - 5 cols, 1 7/8, 1/8 between; A - 4 cols, 2 1/2, 1/8 between; C - 8 cols, 1 1/4, 1/16 between.
Equipment: Hardware — APP/Mac; Software — Microsoft/Word 15.3
CS5 (InDesign, Photoshop,Illustrator, etc.)
Excel 11.6
Claris/FileMakerPro 15.0
AdForce 5.1.3.2
Delivery Method: Mail, Newsstand, Racks
Zip Codes Served: 46032 46033 46037 46038 46055 46060 46062 46074 46077 46107 46113 46123 46131 46142 46143 46168 46201 46202 46203 46204 46205 46208 46214 46216 46217 46218 46219 46220 46221 46222 46224 46225 46226 46227 46228 46229 46231 46234 46235 46236 46237 46239 46240 46241 46250 46254 46256 46260 46268 46278 46280 47405 47406

IOWA

JOHNSTON

CITYVIEW

(Wed, Mthly)
5619 NW 86th St, Ste 600, Johnston, IA, 50131-2955, Polk, USA; tel (515) 953-4822; adv tel (515) 953-4822, ext. 303; ed tel (515) 953-4822 ext. 305; fax (515) 953-1394; adv fax (515) 953-1394; ed fax (515) 953-1394; e-mail editor@dmcityview.com; adv e-mail dan.juffer@dmcityview.com; ed e-maileditor@dmcityview.com; web site www.dmcityview.com

Circulation: 0pd, 30,000fr; Sworn/Estimate/ Non-Audited
Advertising: modular, call for details
Established: 1992
Group: Big Green Umbrella MediaEditions: 1—
Digital Platform - Mobile: Apple
Digital Platform - Tablet: Apple iOS
Publisher .... Shane Goodman
Art Director .... Celeste Jones
Equipment: Hardware — Apple; Software — Adobe products, Newsware
Delivery Method: Mail, Racks

KENTUCKY

BOWLING GREEN

BOWLING GREEN PARENT

(Bi-Mthly) (5 times per year)
1881 Mount Victor Ln, Bowling Green, KY, 42103-9043, Warren, USA; tel (270) 535-1519; adv tel (270) 535-1519; e-mail info@bgparent.com; adv e-mail info@bgparent.com; ed e-mailinfo@bgparent.com; web site www.bgparent.com

Circulation: 10,000fr; Sworn/Estimate/Non-Audited
Established: 2010
Group: JS Publishing
Digital Platform - Mobile: Apple, Android, Windows, Blackberry
Digital Platform - Tablet: Apple iOS, Android, Windows 7, Blackberry Tablet OS
Owner & Publisher .... Jennifer Simpson
Delivery Method: Racks
Zip Codes Served: 42101, 42102, 42103, 42104, 42164, 42134, 42141, 42127

LOUISVILLE

LEO WEEKLEY

(Wed)
607 W Main St, Ste 01, Louisville, KY, 40202-2991, Jefferson, USA; tel (502) 895-9770; fax (502) 895-9779; e-mail leo@leoweekly.com; adv e-mail dbrennan@leoweekly.com; ed e-mailleo@leoweekly.com; web site www.leoweekly.com

Circulation: 25,125fr; CVC
Established: 1990
Digital Platform - Mobile: Apple, Android, Windows, Blackberry, Other
Digital Platform - Tablet: Apple iOS, Android, Windows 7, Blackberry Tablet OS, Kindle, Nook, Kindle Fire, Other

LOUISVILLE ECCENTRIC OBSERVER (LEO)

(Wed)
301 E Main St, Ste 201, Louisville, KY, 40202-1247, Jefferson, USA; tel (502) 895-9770; adv tel 502-895-9770 x 208; ed tel 502-895-9770 x 204; fax (502) 895-9779; adv fax (502) 895-9779; e-mail leo@leoweekly.com; adv e-mail advertising@leoweekly.com; ed e-mailskelley@leoweekly.com; web site www.leoweekly.com

Circulation: 24,045fr; VAC
Advertising: Open inch rate $32.00
Established: 1990
Group: Womack Newspapers, incEditions: 52—
Publisher .... David Brennan
Editor .... Sarah Kelley
Mechanical Specifications: Full Page: 9.5" W x 9.75" T
1/2H page: 9.5" W x 4.7917" T
1/2V page: 4.667" W x 9.75" T
1/4V page: 2.25" W x 9.75" T
1/4S page: 4.667" W x 4.7917" T
1/8V page: 2.25" W x 4.7917" T
1/8H page: 4.667" W x 2.3125" T
1/16 page: 2.25" W x 2.3125" T
Equipment: Hardware — MAC; Presses — Gannett Printing
Louisville, KY; Software — InDesign 2.0
Delivery Method: Racks
Zip Codes Served: 40202 40207 40204 40205 47130 40206 47150 40222 40217 40241 40203
40243 40220 40208 40258 40216 40292 47129
40291 40272 40214 40299 40213 40059 40219 40215 40031 40211 40245 47172 40218 40165 40014 40209 40223 40212 40242 47112 47161 40228 47119 40229

PIKEVILLE

MEDICAL LEADER
(Wed)
116 Main St, Pikeville, KY, 41501-1144, Pike, USA; tel (606) 218-4509; fax (606) 218-4825; web site www.medicalleader.org

LOUISIANA

LAFAYETTE

IND MONTHLY
(Mthly)
551 Jefferson St, Lafayette, LA, 70501-6905, Lafayette, USA; tel (337) 988-4607; fax (337) 983-0150; e-mail indbox@theind.com; adv e-mail druek@theind.com; ed e-mailwalterp@theind.com; web site www.theind.com
Circulation: 12,500fr; Sworn/Estimate/Non-Audited
Established: 2003

LOUISIANA MEDICAL NEWS
(Mthly)
600 Guilbeau Rd, Ste A, Lafayette, LA, 70506-8405, Lafayette, USA; tel (337) 235-5455; adv tel (337) 235-5455; fax (337) 232-2959; adv fax (337) 232-2959; e-mail editor@louisianamedicalnews.com; adv e-mail scott@louisianamedicalnews.com; ed e-maileditor@louisianamedicalnews.com; web site www.louisianamedicalnews.com
Circulation: 1,200pd, 12,000fr; USPS
Advertising: upon request
Established: 2004
Group: Louisiana Medical News LLC
Digital Platform - Mobile: Apple, Android, Windows
Digital Platform - Tablet: Apple iOS, Android, Windows 7
Mechanical Specifications: Acceptable Software Applications:
Indesign CS3; High Res PDFs; All typefaces must be Adobe Type 1
Acceptable Types of Media:
Macintosh System OSX Compatible; e-mail; or upload (Please contact design@southcomm.com for instructions.)
4/C Digital Ad Submission: 4-color photographs should be saved in CMYK modes as Photoshop eps files in binary format with no transfer functions or custom halftone screens used.
B/W Digital Ad Submission:
B/W photographs should be saved in grayscale mode with a resolution of at least 170 dpi. Line art must be at least 300 dpi.
PDF Specification:
In Distiller, use standard Adobe Pdf preset PDF/X-1a:2001.
Ad Submission:
PDFs and/or materials to create ads with should be sent directly to your sales representative.
AD PRODUCTION: Medical News Inc, reserves the right to add a surcharge of $250 for advertisement production, which includes two rounds of revisions. After two proofs, an additional fee of $50 per revision will be added. These charges may be adjusted or waived. For more information, please contact the Market Publisher.
Any Production Questions
design@southcomm.com
Delivery Method: Mail
Zip Codes Served: 70001-71497

TIMES OF ACADIANA
(Wed)
1100 Bertrand Dr, Lafayette, LA, 70506-4110, Lafayette, USA; tel (337) 289-6300; fax (337) 261-2630; e-mail timesedit@timesofacadiana.com; events@timesofacadiana.com; web site www.timesofacadiana.com
Circulation: 36,000fr; Sworn/Estimate/Non-Audited
Group: C-VILLE Holdings LLC
Pub. .... Ted Power
Adv. Mgr. .... Chris Messa
Mng. Ed. .... Lisa Faust
Prodn. Mgr. .... Melissa Herbert
Mechanical Specifications: Type page 9 13/16 x 12 13/16; E - 4 cols, 2 5/16, 1 between; A - 4 cols, 2 5/16, between; C - 4 cols, 2 5/16, 1 between.
Equipment: Hardware — APP/Mac; Software — Adobe/Photoshop, Adobe/Illustrator, QPS/QuarkXPress.
Zip Codes Served: 70502

NEW ORLEANS

GAMBIT
(Tues)
3923 Bienville St, New Orleans, LA, 70119-5102, Orleans, USA; tel (504) 486-5900; adv tel (504) 483-3150; ed tel (504) 483-3105; fax (504) 483-3159; adv fax (504) 483-3159; ed fax (866) 473-7199; e-mail response@gambitweekly.com; adv e-mail sandys@gambitweekly.com; ed e-mailresponse@gambitweekly.com; web site www.bestofneworleans.com
Circulation: 15pd, 37,438fr; VAC
Established: 1981
Digital Platform - Mobile: Apple, Android, Windows, Blackberry
Digital Platform - Tablet: Apple iOS, Android, Windows 7
Publisher .... Jeanne Foster
Advertising Director .... Sandy Stein
Production Director .... Dora Sison
Editor .... Kevin Allman
Managing Editor .... Kandace Graves
Mechanical Specifications: Type page 10 3/8 x 12 13/16; E - 4 cols, 2 3/8, between; A - 4 cols, 2 3/8, between.
Equipment: Hardware — APP/Mac, PC; Software — Adobe/Photoshop/ InDesign
Delivery Method: Racks
Zip Codes Served: 80 different zip codes throughout Louisiana and other states.

MAINE

BANGOR

THE MAINE EDGE
(Wed)
1 Cumberland Pl, Ste 204, Bangor, ME, 04401-5090, Penobscot, USA; tel (207) 942-2901; fax (207) 942-5602; e-mail info@themaineedge.com; adv e-mail advertising@themaineedge.com; ed e-maileditorial@themaineedge.com; web site www.themaineedge.com
Circulation: 18,500fr; Sworn/Estimate/Non-Audited
Advertising: 24.00
Established: 2006
Group: Edge Media GroupEditions: 1—
Digital Platform - Mobile: Android
Digital Platform - Tablet: Android
Ed. .... Allen Adams
Adv./Ops. Mgr. .... Matthew Fern
Pub. .... Michael Fern
Mechanical Specifications: Format Page 10.055: x 13"; 4 cols, 2.42", 1/8" between A-6 cols, 1.5717", 1.8" between C-8 cols, 1.1475", 1.8" between.
Equipment: Hardware — PC, Canon, Scanner, Software - Adobe CC; Software — Adobe CC
Delivery Method: Racks
Zip Codes Served: 04401, 04412, 04416, 04427, 04429, 04444. 04450, 04456, 04468, 04469, 04472, 04473, 04605, 04974, 04915, 04981

MARYLAND

BALTIMORE

CITY PAPER
(Wed)
812 Park Ave, Baltimore, MD, 21201-4807, Baltimore City, USA; tel (410) 523-2300; adv tel (410) 523-2300; ed tel (410) 523-2300; fax (410) 523-1154; adv fax (410) 523-2222; ed fax (410) 523-1154; e-mail dfarley@citypaper.com; adv e-mail jmarsh@citypaper.com; ed e-maillgardner@citypaper.com; web site www.citypaper.com
Circulation: 80,000fr; Sworn/Estimate/Non-Audited
Advertising: Open inch rate $43.90
Established: 1977
Pub. .... Don Farley
Adv. Mgr. .... Jennifer Marsh
Circ. Mgr. .... Christine Grabowski
Ed. .... Lee Gardener
Mechanical Specifications: Type page 10 x 12 1/2; E - 4 cols, 2 3/16, 1/6 between; A - 4 cols, 2 3/16, 1/6 between; C - 6 cols, 1 1/2, 1/6 between.
Equipment: Hardware — APP/Mac; Software — QPS/QuarkXPress, Adobe/Photoshop, Adobe/Illustrator.

MASSACHUSETTS

BOSTON

BOSTON'S WEEKLY DIG
(Wed)
242 E Berkeley St, Ste 2, Boston, MA, 02118-2797, Suffolk, USA; tel (617) 426-8942; fax (617) 426-8944; web site www.weeklydig.com
Circulation:; Sworn/Estimate/Non-Audited
Established: 1999
Pres. .... Jeff Lawrence
Gen. Mgr. .... Amanda Nicholson
Advisor .... Joseph B. Darby
Sales Mgr. .... Alex Lapplin
Ed. .... Jim Stanton
Mng. Ed. .... Laura Dargus
Arts/Music Ed. .... David Day
News/Features Ed. .... Cara Bayles

THE IMPROPER BOSTONIAN MAGAZINE
(Wed) (Every other Mon)
142 Berkeley St, Ste 3, Boston, MA, 02116-5143, Suffolk, USA; tel (617) 859-1400; fax (617) 859-1446; adv e-mail advertising@improper.com; web site www.improper.com
Circulation: 556pd, 82,727fr; Sworn/Estimate/Non-Audited
Established: 1991
Pub. .... Wendy Semonian
Office Mgr. .... Gretchen Bastrom
Mktg. Dir. .... Stacey Shane
Mng. Ed. .... Andrew Rimas
Prodn. Dir. .... Melinda Pattulo
Mechanical Specifications: Type page 9 1/4 x 11; E - 4 cols, 2 3/16, 1/8 between; A - 4 cols, 2, 1/8 between; C - 6 cols, 1 3/8, 1/8 between.
Equipment: ; Software — QPS/QuarkXPress 4.0, Adobe/Photoshop.

NORTHAMPTON

VALLEY ADVOCATE
(Thur)
115 Conz St, Northampton, MA, 01060-4444, Hampshire, USA; tel (413) 529-2840; fax (413) 529-2844; ed e-maileditor@valleyadvocate.com; listings@valleyadvocate.com; web site www.valleyadvocate.com
Circulation: 26,297fr; VAC
Group: Newspapers of New England
H.S. Gere & Sons
Pres. .... Aaron Julian
Adv. Dir. .... Patty Desroches
Circ. Mgr. .... Darrell Hendrick
Ed. in Chief .... Tom Vannah
Mng. Ed. .... Mark Roessler
Listings. Ed. .... Tom Sturm
Mechanical Specifications: Type page 10 3/16 x 12 9/16; E - 5 cols, 1 5/16, 1/8 between; A - 5 cols, 1 7/8, 3/16 between; C - 8 cols, 1 1/8, 1/8 between.
Equipment: ; Software — QPS/QuarkXPress.

WORCESTER

WORCESTER MAGAZINE
(Thur)
72 Shrewsbury St, Worcester, MA, 01604-4625, Worcester, USA; tel (978) 728-4302; adv tel (978) 728-4302; ed tel (978) 728-4302; fax (978) 534-6004; adv fax (978) 534-6004; ed fax (978) 534-6004; e-mail editor@worcestermag.com; adv e-mail sales@worcestermagazine.com; ed e-maileditor@worcestermag.com; web site www.worcestermag.com
Circulation: 22,877fr; CVC
Advertising: N/A
Established: 1976
Digital Platform - Mobile: Apple, Android, Blackberry
Digital Platform - Tablet: Apple iOS, Android, Blackberry Tablet OS
Pub. .... Kathy Real
Ed. .... Brittany Durgin
Sales Mgr. .... Helen Linnehan
Prod. Mgr. .... Don Cloutier
Mechanical Specifications: Four (4) columns x 10.75 inch column depth
; 9.5 wide x 10.75 depth (modular format)
Delivery Method: Mail, Newsstand, Racks
Zip Codes Served: Central Massachusetts

MICHIGAN

CHARLOTTE

THE COUNTY JOURNAL
(Sat)
241 S Cochran Ave, Charlotte, MI, 48813-1584, Eaton, USA; tel (517) 543-1099; fax (517) 543-1993; e-mail cgwing@county-journal.com; adv e-mail cgwing@county-journal.com; ed e-mailtsilvas@county-journal.com; web site www.county-journal.com
Circulation: 19pd, 20,211fr; CVC
Advertising: Open inch rate $9.40
Established: 2006
Group: Flashes Advertising & News
Owner, Pub. & Sales .... Cindy Gaedert
Circ. Mgr. .... Travis Silvas
Mechanical Specifications: Type page: 10.25 x 16; 6 col
Equipment: ; Software — Mac Minie
Delivery Method: Carrier
Zip Codes Served: 48813, 49076, 49021, 49096, 48876, 48890, 48861, 48827, 48821

FERNDALE

METRO TIMES
(Wed)
1200 Woodward Hts, Ferndale, MI, 48220-1427, Oakland, USA; tel (313) 961-4060; ed tel (313) 961-6598; fax (313) 964-4849; e-mail adsales@metrotimes.com; ed e-mailmjackman@metrotimes.com; web site www.metrotimes.com
Circulation: 18pd, 38,215fr; VAC
Advertising: Open inch rate $39.34

Established: 1980
Pub. .... Chris Keating
Sr. Acct. Exec. .... Jim Nutter
Circ. Mgr. .... Annie O'Brien
Ed. .... Vince Grzegorek
Mechanical Specifications: Type page 10 1/8 x 12 3/4; E - 6 cols, 1 3/8, between; A - 6 cols, 1 3/8, between; C - 6 cols, 1 3/8, between.

LANSING

CITY PULSE
(Wed)
1905 E Michigan Ave, Lansing, MI, 48912-2828, Ingham, USA; tel (517) 371-5600; fax (517) 999-6061; e-mail publisher@lansingcitypulse.com; web site www.lansingcitypulse.com

MINNESOTA

MINNEAPOLIS

CITY PAGES
(Wed)
800 N 1st St, Ste 300, Minneapolis, MN, 55401-1387, Hennepin, USA; tel (612) 372-3700; fax (612) 372-3737; e-mail adinfo@citypages.com; web site www.citypages.com
Circulation: 112,025fr; Sworn/Estimate/Non-Audited
Advertising: Open inch rate $61.00
Circ. Mgr. .... Tom Imberston
Ed. in Chief .... Kevin Hoffman
Mng. Ed. .... Matt Smith
Prodn. Mgr. .... Doug Snow
Editor .... Mary Erickson
Mechanical Specifications: Type page 4 x 12.375; E - 4 cols, 2 2/5, 1/6 between; A - 6 cols, 1 9/16, 1/6 between; C - 8 cols, 1 3/16, 1/6 between.
Equipment: ; Software — QPS/QuarkXPress, Macromedia/Freehand, Adobe/Photoshop, Adobe/PageMaker.

MISSOURI

KANSAS CITY

THE PITCH
(Wed)
1701 Main St, Kansas City, MO, 64108-1368, Jackson, USA; tel (816) 561-6061; adv tel (816) 218-6702; ed tel (816) 756-0502; fax (816) 960-1538; e-mail pitch@pitch.com; web site www.pitch.com
Circulation: 42,500fr; Sworn/Estimate/Non-Audited
Advertising: Open inch rate $33.00
Established: 1980
Group: Womack Newspapers, inc
Circulation Director .... Mike Ryan
Production Manager .... Christina Riddle
Accounts Receivable .... Jodi Waldsmith
Editor .... Scott Wilson
Managing Editor .... Justin Kendall
Art Director .... Allysen Peck
Pub. .... Amy Malarski
Mechanical Specifications: Type page 10 3/4 x 11; E - 4 cols, 2 3/8, 1/8 between; A - 8 cols, 1 1/8, 1/8 between; C - 8 cols, 1 1/8, 1/8 between.
Equipment: Hardware — APP/Mac; Presses — G/Suburban; Software — QPS/QuarkXPress 4.0.
Delivery Method: Newsstand
Zip Codes Served: Kansas City DMA

SAINT LOUIS

THE RIVERFRONT TIMES
(Thur)
308 N 21st St, Saint Louis, MO, 63103-1642, Saint Louis City, USA; tel (314) 754-5966; adv tel (314) 754-5932; ed tel (314) 754-6404; fax (314) 754-5955; adv fax (314) 754-6449; ed fax (314) 754-6416; e-mail Letters@riverfronttimes.com; adv e-mail kyle.ingram@riverfronttimes.com; web site www.riverfronttimes.com
Circulation: 297pd, 55,000fr; Sworn/Estimate/Non-Audited
Advertising: Open inch rate $57.62
Established: 1977
Group: Euclid Media Group
Digital Platform - Mobile: Apple, Android, Windows, Blackberry, Other
Digital Platform - Tablet: Apple iOS, Android, Windows 7, Blackberry Tablet OS, Kindle, Nook, Kindle Fire, Other
Circ. Mgr. .... Kevin Powers
Editor in Chief .... Sarah Fenske
Publisher .... Chris Keating
Mechanical Specifications: Type page 9.72 x 10.75
Equipment: Hardware — APP/Mac
Delivery Method: Mail, Racks

MONTANA

MISSOULA

MISSOULA INDEPENDENT
(Thur)
317 S Orange St, Missoula, MT, 59801-1810, Missoula, USA; tel (406) 543-6609; fax (406) 543-4367; e-mail indy@missoulanews.com; web site www.missoulanews.com
Circulation: 18pd, 14,012fr; Sworn/Estimate/Non-Audited
Established: 1991
Group: Lee Enterprises, Inc.
Digital Platform - Mobile: Apple
Digital Platform - Tablet: Apple iOS
Prodn. Dir. .... Joe Weston
Editor .... Brad Tyer
General Manager .... Andy Sutcliffe
Mechanical Specifications: Type page 10 3/4 x 13 1/2; E - 5 cols, 2 1/60, 1/6 between; A - 5 cols, 2 1/60, 1/6 between; C - 7 cols, 1 2/5, 1/6 between.
Equipment: Hardware — APP/Mac; Software — QPS/QuarkXPress.
Zip Codes Served: 59801

NEBRASKA

OMAHA

THE READER
(Mthly)
PO Box 7360, 2314 M Street, Omaha, NE, 68107-0360, Douglas, USA; tel (402) 341-7323; adv tel (402) 341-7323; ed tel (402) 341-7323; fax (402) 341-6967; adv fax (402) 341-6967; e-mail help@thereader.com; adv e-mail buildyourbusiness@thereader.com; ed e-mailjohnh@thereader.com; web site www.thereader.com
Circulation: 210pd, 35,000fr; CVC
Advertising: Open inch rate $28.00
Established: 1991
Digital Platform - Mobile: Other
Digital Platform - Tablet: Other
Publisher .... John Heaston
Prodn. Mgr. .... Eric Stoakes
Mechanical Specifications: Image Area 10 x 10 ; 4 cols
Equipment: Hardware — APP/Mac; Software — Adobe Creative Suite, Microsoft Office Suite
Delivery Method: Mail, Racks
Zip Codes Served: 51501,51503,68147,68005,68022,68046,68102,68105,68106,68107,68108,68110,68111,68112,68114,68116,98117,68118,68123,68124,68127,68128,68130,68131,68132,68134,68135,68137,68144,68154,68508

NEVADA

HENDERSON

LAS VEGAS WEEKLY
(Thur)
2360 Corporate Cir, Fl 4, Henderson, NV, 89074-7740, Clark, USA; tel (702) 990-2400; fax (702) 990-2424; e-mail lasvegasweekly@lasvegasweekly.com; web site http://www.lasvegasweekly.com
Circulation: 0pd, 65,029fr; VAC
Advertising: N/A
Established: 1996
Group: C-VILLE Holdings LLC
Pub. .... Bruce Spotleson
Sales Mgr. .... Lani Dorlack
Circ. Mgr. .... Ron Gannon
Ed. .... Hermando Amaya
Mechanical Specifications: Type page 10 1/2 x 13 1/2; E - 4 cols, 2 1/16, between; A - 5 cols, 2 1/16, between; C - 8 cols, between.
Equipment: ; Software — QPS/QuarkXPress, Claris/FileMaker Pro.

RENO

RENO NEWS & REVIEW
(Thur)
708 N Center St, Reno, NV, 89501-1159, Washoe, USA; tel (775) 324-4440; fax (775) 324-4572; e-mail reno@newsreview.com; web site www.newsreview.com
Circulation: 0pd, 28,552fr; VAC
Advertising: Open inch rate $65.00
Group: C-VILLE Holdings LLC
CEO .... Jeff von Kaenel
Gen. Mgr. .... John Murphy
Sales Mgr. .... Martin Flynn
Distr. Mgr. .... Karen Brooke
Ed. .... Brian Burghart
Mechanical Specifications: Type page 10 13/16 x 13 1/8; E - 5 cols, 2 1/6, between; A - 5 cols, 2 1/6, between; C - 6 cols, 1 3/4, between.
Equipment: Hardware — APP/Mac; Software — QPS/QuarkXPress 3.3, Adobe/Illustrator 5.5.
Zip Codes Served: 89503

NEW HAMPSHIRE

MANCHESTER

THE HIPPO
(Thur)
49 Hollis St, Manchester, NH, 03101-1239, Hillsborough, USA; tel (603) 625-1855; adv tel (603) 625-1855; ed tel (603) 625-1855; e-mail news@hippopress.com; adv e-mail sales@hippopress.com; ed e-mailnews@hippopress.com; web site www.hippopress.com
Circulation: 41,180fr; Sworn/Estimate/Non-Audited
Advertising: N/A
Established: 2001
Digital Platform - Mobile: Apple, Android
Digital Platform - Tablet: Apple iOS
Publisher .... Jody Reese
Circulation .... Doug Ladd
Mechanical Specifications: Type page: 10.25 x 11.25; 4 col
Delivery Method: Newsstand, Racks
Zip Codes Served: 01879, 01830, 01830, 03275, 03031, 03811, 03032, 03110, 03220, 03303, 03304, 03033, 03238, 03301, 03303, 03038, 03042, 03234, 03235, 03249, 03045, 03841, 03049, 03106, 03051, 03246, 03052, 03053, 03307, 03101, 03102, 03103, 03104, 03106, 03109, 03253, 03054, 03055, 03060, 03062, 03063, 03064, 03070, 03256, 03276, 03261, 03076, 03263, 03065, 03077, 03079, 03885, 03276, 03281, 03086, 03087, 03289
Note: We're more of a weekly magazine than an alt paper. Our coverage includes lots of information about food, arts and entertainment. Feel free to request copies or visit our website for more information.

NEW JERSEY

ELMWOOD PARK

CBA INDUSTRIES
(Wed)
669 River Dr, Ste 404, Elmwood Park, NJ, 07407-1361, Bergen, USA; tel (201) 587-1717; fax (201) 414-5201; e-mail tjcastello@cbaol.com
Circulation: 955,095fr; CAC
Established: 1962
Chrmn. .... Harold Matzner
Pres. .... Barry Schiro
Market Mapping Specialist .... Tom Castello
Executive VP .... Eva Kohn
Midwest Regional Sales Representative .. Nikki Schultz
Senior VP, Marketing .... Nick Passariello
Senior VP, Sales .... John Durante
VP, Sales .... Tim Brahney

PLEASANTVILLE

ATLANTIC CITY WEEKLY
(Thur)
1000 W Washington Ave, Pleasantville, NJ, 08232-3861, Atlantic, USA; tel (609) 646-4848; fax (609) 272-7378; e-mail advertising@acweekly.com; adv e-mail classified@acweekly.com; ed e-maileditorial@acweekly.com; web site atlanticcityweekly.com
Circulation: 44pd, 34,170fr; VAC
Advertising: Full - $1250; 1/2 - $668; 1/4 - $370
Established: 1974
Group: BH Media Group
Ed. .... Jeff Schwachter
Delivery Method: Mail, Newsstand, Racks

NEW MEXICO

ALBUQUERQUE

WEEKLY ALIBI
(Wed)
217 Sierra Dr SE, Albuquerque, NM, 87108-2714, Bernalillo, USA; tel (505) 346-0660; fax (505) 256-9651; e-mail letters@alibi.com; adv e-mail tierna@alibi.com; ed e-maileditorial@alibi.com; web site www.alibi.com
Circulation: 0pd, 32,814fr; VAC
Established: 1994
Group: NuCity Publications
Digital Platform - Mobile: Apple, Android, Windows, Blackberry
Digital Platform - Tablet: Apple iOS, Android, Windows 7, Blackberry Tablet OS
Sales Dir. .... John Hankinson
Circ. Mgr. .... Darrell Sparks
interim publisher .... Jesse Schultz
Owner .... Christopher Johnson
Managing Editor .... Devin O'Leary

Mechanical Specifications: Type page 10 x 13; E - 4 cols, 2 7/16, between; A - 4 cols, 2 7/8, between; C - 8 cols, between.
Equipment: Hardware — APP/Mac
Delivery Method: Racks
Zip Codes Served: 87048, 87114, 87113, 87122, 87120, 87107, 87109, 87111, 87104, 87110, 87112, 87120, 87121, 87106, 87108, 87116, 87123, 87117

NEW YORK

ALBANY

METROLAND
(Thur)
419 Madison Ave, Albany, NY, 12210-1767, Albany, USA; tel (518) 463-2500; fax (518) 463-3712; e-mail metroland@metroland.net; web site www.metroland.net
Circulation: 40,000fr; Sworn/Estimate/Non-Audited
Group: C-VILLE Holdings LLC
Pub....................Stephen Leon
Art Dir....................John Bracchi
Mechanical Specifications: Type page 10 x 12 3/4; E - 4 cols, 2 1/4, 1/6 between; A - 4 cols, 2 1/4, 1/6 between; C - 8 cols, 1 1/8, 1/6 between.

BUFFALO

ART VOICE
(Thur)
810 Main St, Buffalo, NY, 14202-1501, Erie, USA; tel (716) 881-6604 ; fax (716) 881-6682; e-mail advertise@artvoice.com; adv e-mail classifieds@artvoice.com; ed e-maileditorial@artvoice.com; web site www.artvoice.com
Circulation: 55,350pd,; Sworn/Estimate/Non-Audited
Advertising: Open inch rate $65.00 (Inserts)
Group: Kahnsama Publication
Digital Platform - Mobile: Apple, Android, Windows, Blackberry
Digital Platform - Tablet: Apple iOS, Android, Windows 7, Blackberry Tablet OS
Adv. Dir....................Judy Sperry
Pub....................Jamie Moses
Mechanical Specifications: Type page 10 x 11.5, 4 cols
Delivery Method: Mail, Newsstand, Racks
Zip Codes Served: Lewiston, Lockport, Niagara Falls, North Tonawanda, Grand Island, Tonawanda, Amherst, Clarence, Buffalo, Cheektowaga, Lancaster, alden, West Seneca, Elma, East Aurora, Orchard Part, Hamburg, Angola, Springville, Derby, Dunkirk, Fredonia, Silvercreek, and West Falls

ARTVOICE
(Thur)
810812 Main St, Buffalo, NY, 14202-4006, Erie, USA; tel (716) 881-6604; adv tel (716) 881-6604; ed tel (716) 881-6604; fax (716) 881-6682 ; e-mail editorial@artvoice.com; adv e-mail jamie@artvoice.com; ed e-mailjamie@artvoice.com; web site www.artvoice.com
Circulation: 55,000fr; Sworn/Estimate/Non-Audited
Established: 1990
Managing editor....................Buck Quigley
Delivery Method: Racks
Zip Codes Served: Buffalo-Niagara region

ITHACA

ITHACA TIMES
(Wed)
109-111 N Cayuga St, Ithaca, NY, 14851, Tompkins, USA; tel (607) 277-7000; fax (607) 277-1012; ed e-maileditor@ithacatimes.com; web site www.ithacatimes.com
Circulation: 19,700fr; Sworn/Estimate/Non-Audited
Established: 1972
Group: Newski Inc
Digital Platform - Mobile: Apple
Digital Platform - Tablet: Apple iOS
Pub....................James Bilinski
Editor....................Nick Reynolds
Mechanical Specifications: sold by page fraction
Zip Codes Served: 14850, 14851, 14853

NEW YORK

NEW YORK PRESS
(Wed)
79 Madison Ave, Fl 16, New York, NY, 10016-7807, New York, USA; tel (212) 268-8600; fax (212) 268-0502; adv e-mail advertising@nypress.com; web site www.nypress.com
Circulation: 97pd, 116,000fr; Sworn/Estimate/Non-Audited
Advertising: Open inch rate $60.00
Pres....................Tom Allon
Pub....................Alex Schweitzer
Circ. Mgr....................John Baxter
Ed....................Jerry Portwood
Mechanical Specifications: Type page 10 x 12 7/8; E - 6 cols, 1 1/2, 3/16 between; A - 6 cols, 1 1/2, 3/16 between; C - 7 cols, 1 1/4, 3/16 between.
Equipment: Hardware — APP/Mac; Software — QPS/QuarkXPress, Adobe/PageMaker.

THE VILLAGE VOICE
(Wed)
80 Maiden Ln, Rm 2105, New York, NY, 10038-4893, New York, USA; tel (212) 475-3300; fax (212) 475-8944; e-mail ads@villagevoice.com; web site http://www.villagevoice.com/
Circulation: 260,000fr; Sworn/Estimate/Non-Audited
Group: Reading Eagle Company
Pub....................Michael Cohen
Assoc. Pub....................Christa Dwyer Ryan
Mktg./Promos. Dir....................Sean Pierce
Circ. Dir....................Julian Suardi
Ed....................Tony Ortega
Mng. Ed....................Deborah Kolben

PLATTSBURGH

LAKE CHAMPLAIN WEEKLY
(Wed)
4701 State Route 9, Plattsburgh, NY, 12901-6036, Clinton, USA; tel (518) 563-1414; adv tel (518) 563-1414; ed tel (518) 563-1414; fax (518) 563-7060; adv fax (518) 563-7060; ed fax (518) 563-7060; e-mail advertising@studleyprinting.com; adv e-mail advertising@studleyprinting.com; ed e-maileditor@studleyprinting.com; web site www.lakechamplainweekly.com
Circulation: 12,000fr; Sworn/Estimate/Non-Audited
Advertising: 12.00
Established: 2000
Group: Studley Printing & Publishing, Inc. Editions: 3— Northern HGL-7,200; Northern Exploring-10,000, Northern Bride-3500
Digital Platform - Mobile: Apple, Android, Windows, Blackberry
Digital Platform - Tablet: Apple iOS, Android, Windows 7, Blackberry Tablet OS, Kindle, Nook, Kindle Fire, Other
William Studley
Bridgette StudleyPublishers
Mechanical Specifications: 1 column width-1.537"; 2 column width-3.229"; 3 column width-4.922"; 4 column width-6.615"; 5 column width-8.307:' 6 column width-10" Page height is 11.625"
Equipment: ; Presses — 5 Color ADAST Digital Press, 4 color Ryobi Digital Press, 2 Color Ryobi press, Xerox Digital press, Roland wide format press; Software — Creative Suite Cloud
Delivery Method: Newsstand, Racks
Zip Codes Served: all of 129 zip code and 12883

ROCHESTER

CITY NEWSPAPER
(Wed)
250 N Goodman St, Rochester, NY, 14607-1100, Monroe, USA; tel (585) 244-3329; adv tel 585-244-3329 x20; ed tel 585-244-3329 x25; fax (585) 244-1126; adv fax (585) 244-1126; ed fax (585) 244-1126; e-mail info@rochester-citynews.com; adv e-mail ads@rochester-citynews.com; ed e-mailthemail@rochester-citynews.com; web site www.rochestercitynewspaper.com
Circulation: 31pd, 32,197fr; VAC
Advertising: Modular rates (please inquire)
Established: 1971
Digital Platform - Mobile: Other
Digital Platform - Tablet: Other
co-publisher....................William Towler
New Business Director....................Betsy Matthews
co-publisher/Editor....................Mary Anna Towler
Production Manager....................Ryan Williamson
Arts & Entertainment Editor....................Jake Clapp
Mechanical Specifications: Print area 9.9"w x 11.6"h.
Equipment: Hardware — PC; Presses — none; Software — Adobe InDesign, Adobe/Photoshop, Adobe/Acrobat, Adobe/Illustrator
Delivery Method: Mail, Racks
Zip Codes Served: Rochester metro

SYRACUSE

SYRACUSE NEW TIMES
(Wed)
1415 W Genesee St, Syracuse, NY, 13204-2119, Onondaga, USA; tel (315) 422-7011; fax (315) 422-1721; web site www.syracusenewtimes.com
Circulation: 5pd, 34,810fr; VAC
Advertising: N/A
Established: 1969
Group: All Times Publishing
Managing Editor
Bill DeLapp
Owner and publisher....................Bill Brod
Editor-in-chief....................Bill DeLapp
Photographer....................Michael Davis
Mechanical Specifications: Type page 9.32 x 10.62; E - 4 cols, 2 1/16, 1/16 between; A - 5 cols, 2 1/16, 1/16 between; C - 7 cols, 1 1/2, 1/16 between.

NORTH CAROLINA

ASHEVILLE

MOUNTAIN XPRESS
(Wed)
2 Wall St, Asheville, NC, 28801-2721, Buncombe, USA; tel (828) 251-1333; fax (828) 251-1311; e-mail xpress@mountainx.com; web site www.mountainx.com
Circulation: 9pd, 28,385fr; CVC
Advertising: Open inch rate $23.50
Established: 1994
Pub....................Jeff Fobes
Office Mgr....................Patty Levesque
Arts & Entertainment/Managing EditorRebecca Sulock
Techn. Mgr....................Stefan Colosimo
Distribution Manager....................Jeff Tallman
Art & Design Manager....................Carrie Lare
News/Managing Editor....................Margaret Williams
Advertising Manager....................Susan Hutchinson
Webmaster....................Kyle Kirkpatrick
Mechanical Specifications: Type page 10 1/4 x 12 3/4; E - 4 cols, 2 7/16, 1/8 between; A - 4 cols, 2 7/16, 1/8 between; C - 6 cols, 1 1/2, 1/5 between.
Equipment: Hardware — APP/Mac; Software — InDesign
Zip Codes Served: 28700 through 28999

BOONE

THE WATAUGA MOUNTAIN TIMES
(Wed, Thur)
474 Industrial Park Dr, Boone, NC, 28607-3937, Watauga, USA; tel (828) 264-3612; fax (828) 262-0282; e-mail charlie.price@mountaintimes.com; adv e-mail classifieds@mountaintimes.com; ed e-mailnewpaper@mountaintimes.com; web site mountaintimes.com/home
Circulation: 0pd, 12,739fr; CVC
Advertising: Open inch rate $30.24
Established: 1978
Group: Adams Publishing Group, LLCEditions: 3— 3 total; Ashe Mountain Times; Avery Mountain Times; Watauga Mountain Times;
Digital Platform - Mobile: Apple, Android
Digital Platform - Tablet: Apple iOS, Android
Circ. Mgr....................Andy Ganiey
Gene Fowler
Adv. Dir....................Charlie Price
Ed....................Tom Mayer
Lead Features Editor....................Brad Miller
Mechanical Specifications: Type page 10 1/2 x 13; E - 6 cols, 1 9/16, 1/6 between; A - 6 cols, 1 9/16, 1/6 between; C - 6 cols, 1 9/16, 1/6 between.
Equipment: Hardware — PC; Presses — Goss; Software — Adobe/PageMaker.
Delivery Method: Newsstand
Zip Codes Served: Watauga and Ashe
28604....................Banner Elk
N/A....................1915
28607....................Boone
N/A....................8080
28605....................Blowing Rock
N/A....................1165
28608....................Boone
N/A....................40
28698....................Zionville
N/A....................300
28615....................Creston
....................780
28617....................Crumpler
....................808
28626....................Fleetwood
....................1024
28631....................Grassy Creek
....................291
28643....................Lansing
....................1278
28684....................Todd
....................785
28693....................Warrensville
....................493
28692....................Vilas
N/A....................340
28619....................Beech Mtn
N/A....................300
37683....................Mountain City
N/A....................160
28679....................Sugar Grove
N/A....................180
37691....................Trade
N/A....................120
28657....................Newland
N/A....................160
Non Alloc....................0
TOTAL CIRC....................18219
28604....................Banner Elk
N/A....................1915
28607....................Boone
N/A....................8080
28605....................Blowing Rock
N/A....................1165
28608....................Boone
N/A....................40
28698....................Zionville
N/A....................300
28615....................Creston

.... 780
28617 .... Crumpler
.... 808
28626 .... Fleetwood
.... 1024
28631 .... Grassy Creek
.... 291
28643 .... Lansing
.... 1278
28684 .... Todd
.... 785
28693 .... Warrensville
.... 493
28692 .... Vilas
N/A 340
28619 .... Beech Mtn
N/A 300
37683 .... Mountain City
N/A 160
28679 .... Sugar Grove
N/A 180
37691 .... Trade
N/A 120
28657 .... Newland
N/A 160
Non Alloc 0
TOTAL CIRC 18219
28604 .... Banner Elk
N/A 1915
28607 .... Boone
N/A 8080
28605 .... Blowing Rock
N/A 1165
28608 .... Boone
N/A 40
28698 .... Zionville
N/A 300
28615 .... Creston
.... 780
28617 .... Crumpler
.... 808
28626 .... Fleetwood
.... 1024
28631 .... Grassy Creek
.... 291
28643 .... Lansing
.... 1278
28684 .... Todd
.... 785
28693 .... Warrensville
.... 493
28692 .... Vilas
N/A 340
28619 .... Beech Mtn
N/A 300
37683 .... Mountain City
N/A 160
28679 .... Sugar Grove
N/A 180
37691 .... Trade
N/A 120
28657 .... Newland
N/A 160
Non Alloc 0
TOTAL CIRC 18219

CHARLOTTE

CREATIVE LOAFING CHARLOTTE

(Wed)
1000 NC Music Factory Blvd, Apt C2, Charlotte, NC, 28206-6010, Mecklenburg, USA; tel (704) 522-8334; fax (704) 522-8088; e-mail Publisher@yesweekly.com; web site http://clclt.com/
Circulation: 40,000fr; Sworn/Estimate/Non-Audited
Advertising: 25
Established: 1987
Group: Womack Newspapers, inc
Delivery Method: Newsstand, Racks
Zip Codes Served: Charlotte, NC

DURHAM

THE INDEPENDENT WEEKLY

(Wed)
302 E Pettigrew St, Ste 3A, Durham, NC, 27701-3712, Durham, USA; tel (919) 286-1972; fax (919) 286-4274; e-mail swatson@indyweek.com; web site www.indyweek.com
Circulation: 53,806fr; VAC
Established: 1983
Group: C-VILLE Holdings LLC
Pub. .... Sioux Watson
Adv. Mgr. .... Gloria Wyly Mock
Circ. Mgr. .... Robert VanVeld
Ed. .... Lisa Sorg
Prodn. Mgr. .... Maria Shain
Mechanical Specifications: Type page 9 7/8 x 11 1/2; E - 4 cols, 2 3/8, 3/16 between; A - 4 cols, 2 3/8, between; C - 6 cols, 1 1/2, 3/16 between.
Equipment: Hardware — 2-APP/Mac G3, 2-APP/Mac G4; Software — QPS/QuarkXPress 3.32, Adobe/Photoshop 3.0, Macromedia/Freehand 5.5.
Zip Codes Served: 27514, 27516, 27510, 27278, 27312, 27701, 27707, 27712, 27560, 27709, 27713, 27609, 27601, 27610, 27511, 27545, 27520, 27526, 27502

GREENSBORO

YES! WEEKLY

(Wed)
5500 Adams Farm Ln, Ste 204, Greensboro, NC, 27407-7059, Guilford, USA; tel (336) 316-1231 ; adv tel (336) 316-1231; ed tel (336) 316-1231; fax (336) 316-1930; e-mail publisher@yesweekly.com; adv e-mail publisher@yesweekly.com; ed e-mailpublisher@yesweekly.com; web site www.yesweekly.com
Circulation: 20,000fr; Sworn/Estimate/Non-Audited
Advertising: Moduler
Established: 2005
Group: Womack Newspapers, Inc
Digital Platform - Mobile: Apple, Android
Digital Platform - Tablet: Apple iOS, Android
Pub. .... Charles Womack
News Ed. .... Katie Murawski
Mechanical Specifications: 9.9 x 10.2 tall
Delivery Method: Newsstand, Carrier, Racks

OHIO

CINCINNATI

CINCINNATI CITYBEAT

(Wed)
811 Race St, Fl 5, Cincinnati, OH, 45202-2042, Hamilton, USA; tel (513) 665-4700; fax (513) 665-4369; e-mail letters@citybeat.com; ed e-maileditor@citybeat.com; web site www.citybeat.com
Circulation: 13pd, 30,000fr; Sworn/Estimate/Non-Audited
Advertising: Open inch rate $30.00
Established: 1994
Group: Womack Newspapers, inc
Digital Platform - Mobile: Apple
Publisher .... Dan Bockrath
Circ. Mgr. .... Steve Ferguson
Editor .... Danny Cross
Creative Director .... Rebecca Sylvester
Director of Sales and Marketing ... Chuck Davis
Equipment: Hardware — APP/Mac; Software — Adobe/Photoshop, Macromedia/Freehand, QPS/QuarkXPress, Adobe/PageMaker.
Delivery Method: Carrier, Racks
Zip Codes Served: 45202

COLUMBUS

ALIVE

(Thur)
62 E Broad St, Columbus, OH, 43215-3500, Franklin, USA; tel (614) 221-2449; fax (614) 461-8746; e-mail alive@alivewired.com; web site www.columbusalive.com
Circulation: 34,937fr; CAC
Advertising: Open inch rate $32.81
Established: 1983
Group: New Media Investment Group
Pub. .... Katie Wolse-Lloyd
Circ. Mgr. .... Cindy Bailey
Content Director .... Brian Lindamood
Prodn. Mgr. .... Gretchen Zimmer
Adv. Dir. .... Amy Bishop
Mechanical Specifications: Type page 10 1/8 x 12 1/2; E - 4 cols, 2 3/8, 1/6 between; A - 4 cols, 2 3/8, 1/6 between; C - 8 cols, 1 3/16, between.
Equipment: Hardware — APP/Mac; Software — QPS/QuarkXPress 4.0, Adobe/Photoshop 4.0.

DAYTON

DAYTON CITY PAPER

(Tues)
126 N Main St, Ste 240, Dayton, OH, 45402-1766, Montgomery, USA; tel (937) 222-8855; adv tel (937) 222-8855 x 603; ed tel (937) 222-8855 x 604; e-mail contactus@daytoncitypaper.com; adv e-mail advertising@daytoncitypaper.com; ed e-maileditor@daytoncitypaper.com; web site www.daytoncitypaper.com
Circulation: 20,120fr; Sworn/Estimate/Non-Audited
Established: 2003
Group: Dayton City Media
CEO, Dayton City Media .... Paul Noah
Publisher .... Wanda Esken
Delivery Method: Carrier, Racks
Zip Codes Served: Entire metro Dayton Ohio region

TOLEDO

THE TOLEDO CITY PAPER

(Wed)
1120 Adams St, Toledo, OH, 43604-5509, Lucas, USA; tel (419) 244-9859; fax (419) 244-9871; e-mail editor@toledocitypaper.com; web site www.toledocitypaper.com
Circulation: 0pd, 38,029fr; VAC
Advertising: CP
Established: 1997
Group: Adams Street Publishing Co.
Publisher .... Collette Jacobs
Adv. Dir. .... Mark Jacobs
Mechanical Specifications: Type page 9 1/2 x 11 7/8; E - 4 cols, 2 1/8, 1/4 between; A - 4 cols, 2 1/8, 3/8 between; C - 5 cols, 1 3/4, 3/16 between.
Equipment: Hardware — APP/Mac; Software — QPS/QuarkXPress 3.30, Adobe/Photoshop 3.0, Adobe/Illustrator.
Delivery Method: Racks
Zip Codes Served: 43609, 43610, 43611, 43612, 43613, 43614, 43615, 43602, 43603, 43604, 43605, 43606, 43607, 43608, 43537, 43402, 43460, 43522, 43528, 43542, 43617, 43618, 43551, 43558, 43560, 43566, 43571, 43616, 43619, 43620, 43623, 43624

OKLAHOMA

OKLAHOMA CITY

OKLAHOMA GAZETTE

(Wed)
3701 N Shartel Ave, Oklahoma City, OK, 73118-7102, Oklahoma, USA; tel (405) 605-6789; fax (405) 528-4600; adv e-mail advertising@tierramediagroup.com; web site www.okgazette.com
Circulation: 0pd, 36,082fr; VAC
Advertising: Open inch rate $58
Established: 1979
Group: Tierra Media Group
Pub .... Bill Bleakley
Associate Pub. .... James Bengfort
Mechanical Specifications: Type page 10.25 x 12.25
Advertising - 4 columns, 2.2" wide with 1/8" between
Classifeds - 6 columns, 1.5" wide with 1/16" between
Delivery Method: Racks

TULSA

THE TULSA VOICE

(Wed, Mthly)
1603 S Boulder Ave, Tulsa, OK, 74119-4407, Tulsa, USA; tel (918)585-9924; fax (918)585-9926; web site thetulsavoice.com
Circulation: 28,747fr; VAC
Digital Platform - Mobile: Apple, Windows
Delivery Method: Newsstand

OREGON

EUGENE

EUGENE WEEKLY

(Thur) (Online several days a week.)
1251 Lincoln St, Eugene, OR, 97401-3418, Lane, USA; tel (541) 484-0519; adv tel (541) 484-0519; ed tel (541) 484-0519; fax (541) 484-4044; e-mail office@eugeneweekly.com; adv e-mail camilla.h.mortensen@gmail.com; ed e-mailcamilla.h.mortensen@gmail.com; web site www.eugeneweekly.com
Circulation: 10pd, 34,518fr; VAC
Established: 1982
Group: What's Happening Inc.
Digital Platform - Mobile: Apple, Android
Digital Platform - Tablet: Apple iOS, Android
Ed. .... Camilla Mortensen
Director of Advertising .... Rob Weiss
Mechanical Specifications: Type page 10 1/4 x 12 9/16; E - 4 cols, 2 3/8, 1/4 between; A - 4 cols, 2 3/8, 1/4 between; C - 6 cols, 1 1/2, 1/4 between.
Delivery Method: Mail, Newsstand, Carrier, Racks
Zip Codes Served: 97401, 97402, 97405, 97424, 97477, 97448

PORTLAND

WILLAMETTE WEEK

(Wed) (Wednesday)
2220 NW Quimby St, Portland, OR, 97210-2624, Multnomah, USA; tel (503) 243-2122; adv tel (503) 223-1500; fax (503) 243-1115; adv fax (503) 223-0388; adv e-mail imyers@wweek.com; ed e-mailMzusman@wweek.com; web site www.wweek.com
Circulation: 100pd, 70,000fr; Sworn/Estimate/Non-Audited
Advertising: Open inch rate $45.02
Established: 1974
Group: City of Roses Newspaper Company
City of Roses Newspaper Company
Digital Platform - Mobile: Apple, Android
Digital Platform - Tablet: Apple iOS, Android
Publisher .... Mark Zusman
Associate Publisher .... Jane Smith
Mechanical Specifications: Type page 9 3/4 x 13 1/8; E - 5 cols, 1 4/5, 1/8 between; A - 5 cols, 1 4/5, 1/8 between; C - 6 cols, 1 1/2, 1/8 between.
Equipment: Hardware — APP/Mac, Umax/Scanners, Xante/Accel-a-Writer, Tektronic/Phaser 740 Color Printer, Apple/Laserwriter 8500; Presses — Tensor/1400 Horizon; Software — Creative Suite, Adobe/Photoshop 4.0, Adobe/Illustrator 8.0.
Delivery Method: Newsstand, Racks

Zip Codes Served: 97201-97245

PENNSYLVANIA

COLUMBIA

BUSINESSWOMAN
(Wed)
3912 Abel Dr, Columbia, PA, 17512-9031, Lancaster, USA; tel (717) 285-1350; fax (717) 285-1360; e-mail danderson@onlinepub.com; web site www.businesswomanpa.com

PHILADELPHIA

PHILADELPHIA WEEKLY
(Wed)
1500 Sansom St, Fl 3, Philadelphia, PA, 19102-2800, Philadelphia, USA; tel (215) 563-7400; fax (215) 563-6799; ed fax (215) 563-0620; e-mail mail@philaweekly.com; web site www.philadelphiaweekly.com
Circulation: 9pd, 69,414fr; VAC
Advertising: Open inch rate $67.00
Established: 1981
Pub.. Roseann Oleyn
Mktg. Mgr. .... Lauren Reilly
Circ. Mgr..Cyril Metz
Ed. ....Adamma Ince
Mechanical Specifications: Type page 10 x 11 5/8; E - 6 cols, 1 1/2, between; A - 6 cols, 1 1/2, between.
Equipment: Hardware — APP/Mac; Software — QPS/QuarkXPress.

PITTSBURGH

PITTSBURGH CITY PAPER
(Wed)
650 Smithfield St, Ste 2200, Pittsburgh, PA, 15222-3925, Allegheny, USA; tel (412) 316-3342; fax (412) 316-3388; e-mail info@pghcitypaper.com; web site www.pghcitypaper.com
Circulation: 60,627fr; VAC
Group: Eagle Media
Pub...................................... Michael Frischling
Mktg. Dir.................................. Traci Schneider
Circ. Mgr..Jim Lavrinc
Ed. ....Chris Potter
Opns. Dir..................................Kevin Shepherd
Art Dir...................................Lisa Cunningham
Mechanical Specifications: Type page 10 1/4 x 12 3/4; E - 4 cols, 2 3/8, between; A - 4 cols, 2 3/8, between.
Equipment: Hardware — IBM; Software — Adobe/Photoshop 5.0, Adobe/PageMaker 7.0.

WILKES BARRE

WEEKENDER
(Wed)
15 N Main St, Wilkes Barre, PA, 18701-2690, Luzerne, USA; tel (570) 829-7100; fax (570) 831-7375; adv fax (570) 829-2002; e-mail weekender@theweekender.com; web site www.theweekender.com
Circulation: 41,000fr; AAM
Advertising: Open inch rate $18.45
Group: Civitas Media, LLC-OOB
Gen. Mgr. .... Rachel Hugh
Ed. ....Mike Lello
Mechanical Specifications: Type page 10 1/4 x 12 3/4; E - 5 cols, 2, 1/6 between; A - 5 cols, 2, 1/6 between; C - 8 cols, 1 1/4, 1/6 between.
Equipment: Hardware — APP/Mac; Presses — MAN/Geoman; Software — QPS/QuarkXPress 3.32, Adobe/Photoshop 5.0.

RHODE ISLAND

PAWTUCKET

MOTIF MAGAZINE
(Bi-Mthly)
65 Blackstone Ave, Pawtucket, RI, 02860-1068, Providence, USA; tel (401)312+3305; e-mail news@motifri.com; adv e-mail getout@motifri.com; web site motifri.com
Circulation: 24,328fr; VAC
Delivery Method: Newsstand
Zip Codes Served: 02860

PROVIDENCE

PROVIDENCE PHOENIX
(Thur)
150 Chestnut St, Providence, RI, 02903-4645, Providence, USA; tel (401) 273-6397; fax (401) 351-1399; e-mail lpapineau@phx.com; web site www.providencephoenix.com
Circulation: 68,000fr; Sworn/Estimate/Non-Audited
Advertising: Open inch rate $40.25
Group: C-VILLE Holdings LLC
Associate Publisher.....................Steve Brown
Pub................................... Stephen M. Mindich
Circ. Mgr....................................James Dorgan
Ed. ....Peter Kadzis
Mng. Ed......................................Lou Papineau
Prodn. Mgr. .... Stacey Congdon
Mechanical Specifications: Type page 10 x 14; E - 6 cols, 1 1/2, between; A - 6 cols, 1 1/2, between.
Equipment: Hardware — APP/Mac; Software — QPS/QuarkXPress.

SOUTH CAROLINA

CHARLESTON

THE CHARLESTON CITY PAPER
(Wed)
1316 Rutledge Ave, Charleston, SC, 29403-3050, Charleston, USA; tel (843) 577-5304; e-mail editor@charlestoncitypaper.com; adv e-mail Sales@charlestoncitypaper.com; web site www.charlestoncitypaper.com
Circulation: 35,000fr; Sworn/Estimate/Non-Audited
Advertising: $40.
Established: 1998
Digital Platform - Mobile: Apple, Android
Digital Platform - Tablet: Apple iOS, Android
Pub..Noel Mermer
Adv. Dir...Blair Barna
Arts Ed..Scott Suchy
Mechanical Specifications: Type page 9.5 x 10 3/4; E - 4 cols, 2 1/8, 1/8 between; A - 4 cols, 2 1/8, 1/3 between; C - 6 cols, between.
Equipment: Hardware — APP/Mac; Software — QPS/QuarkXPress 4.0, Adobe/Photoshop 5.0, Adobe/Illustrator 8.0.
Delivery Method: Newsstand, Racks

COLUMBIA

FREE TIMES
(Wed)
1534 Main St, Columbia, SC, 29201-2808, Richland, USA; tel (803) 765-0707; fax (803) 765-0727; e-mail publisher@free-times.com; adv e-mail ads@free-times.com; ed e-maileditor@free-times.com; web site www.free-times.com
Circulation: 0pd, 30,753fr; Sworn/Estimate/Non-Audited
Advertising: N/A
Established: 1987
Group: Evening Post Publishing Company
Digital Platform - Mobile: Apple, Android
Digital Platform - Tablet: Apple iOS, Android
Prodn. Mgr. .... Lisa Heinz
Executive Editor..............................Eva Moore
Publisher & Advertising Director............Chase Heatherly
Mechanical Specifications: Type page 10 x 11 1/4; E - 4 cols, 2 1/3, 1/6 between; A - 6 cols, 1 1/2, 1/6 between; C - 8 cols, 1 1/12, between.
Equipment: Hardware — APP/Mac; Software — Adobe/Photoshop 6.0, Macromedia/Freehand 10, QPS/QuarkXPress 4.1, Claris/FileMaker 4.1, Multi-Ad/CAMS 4.34.
Delivery Method: Newsstand, Racks
Zip Codes Served: 29169-29172, 29033, 29036, 29201-29212, 29223

TENNESSEE

KNOXVILLE

METRO PULSE
(Thur)
602 S Gay St, Fl 2, Knoxville, TN, 37902-1605, Knox, USA; tel (865) 522-5399; adv tel (865) 342-6070; ed tel (865) 342-6068; fax (865) 522-2955; adv e-mail sales@metropulse.com; ed e-maileditor@metropulse.com; web site www.metropulse.com
Circulation: 30,000fr; Sworn/Estimate/Non-Audited
Advertising: modular rates apply
Established: 1991
Group: E. W. Scripps Co.
Digital Platform - Mobile: Apple, Android
Digital Platform - Tablet: Apple iOS, Android, Kindle
Dir. of Sales .... Kevin Pack
Ed. ....Coury Turczyn
Mechanical Specifications: Type page 9 3/4 x 12 1/2; E - 4 cols, 2 1/8, 3/8 between; A - 4 cols, 2 1/8, 3/8 between; C - 8 cols, 1, 1/8 between.
Equipment: Hardware — Apple/Mac; Presses — Very large ones.; Software — InDesign/InCopy, Illustrator, Photoshop
Delivery Method: Racks
Zip Codes Served: 37902, 37912, 37920, 37921, 37927, 37922, 37923, 37919, 37916, 37918, 37909, 37931, 37934, 37849, 37801, 37830, 37771

MEMPHIS

MEMPHIS FLYER
(Thur)
65 Union Ave, Ste 200, Memphis, TN, 38103-5131, Shelby, USA; tel (901) 521-9000; fax (901) 521-0129; e-mail memflyken2@aol.com; adv e-mail jrushing@memphisflyer.com; ed e-mailbruce@memphisflyer.cpm; web site www.memphisflyer.com
Circulation: 0pd, 44,300fr; Sworn/Estimate/Non-Audited
Advertising: N/A
Established: 1989
Group: Contemporary Media, Inc.
Digital Platform - Mobile: Apple
Digital Platform - Tablet: Apple iOS
Pub..Kenneth Neill
Adv. Dir.................................. Jeffrey Goldberg
Circ. Mgr...................................Robbie French
Ed. .... Bruce Van Wyngarden
Mng. Ed...Susan Ellis
Prodn. Mgr...............................Cheryl S. Bader
Equipment: Hardware — APP/Mac; Software — InCopy
Delivery Method: Racks
Zip Codes Served: 381xx

NASHVILLE

NASHVILLE SCENE
(Thur)
210 12th Ave S, Ste 100, Nashville, TN, 37203-4046, Davidson, USA; tel (615) 844-5503; fax (615) 244-8578; e-mail sales@nashvillescene.com; web site www.nashvillescene.com
Circulation: 12pd, 42,659fr; VAC
Advertising: Open inch rate $38.35
Group: C-VILLE Holdings LLC
Pub.. Mike Smith
Assoc. Pub......................... Susan Torregrossa
Mktg. Dir.......................................Carla Holder
Circ. Mgr.................................. Casey Sanders
Ed. .... Jim Ridley
Art Dir......................................Elizabeth Jones
Mechanical Specifications: Type page 9 3/4 x 12 3/8; E - 4 cols, 2 1/4, 1/4 between; A - 4 cols, 2 1/4, 1/4 between.
Equipment: Hardware — APP/Mac; Presses — G/Urbanite; Software — QPS.

TEXAS

AUSTIN

AUSTIN CHRONICLE
(Thur)
4112 Speedway, Austin, TX, 78751-4630, Travis, USA; tel (512) 454-5766; adv tel (512) 454-5766; ed tel (512) 454-5766; fax (512) 458-6910; e-mail mail@austinchronicle.com; adv e-mail sales@austinchronicle.com; ed e-mailkjones@austinchronicle.com; web site www.austinchronicle.com
Circulation: 74pd, 65,932fr; VAC
Advertising: Open inch rate $60.00
Established: 1981
Pub.. Nick Barbaro
Circ. Mgr....................................... Dan Hardick
Ed. ....Louis Black
Listings Ed........................... James Renovitch
Film Ed .... Marjorie Baumgarten
Sales Dir .... Cassidy Frazier
Ed .... Kimberley Jones
Mechanical Specifications: Type page 10 x 12 1/2; E - 4 cols, 2 3/8, between; A - 4 cols, 2 3/8, between; C - 8 cols, 1 1/8, between.
Equipment: Hardware — APP/Mac; Software — InDesign
Delivery Method: Racks
Zip Codes Served: 78601-78759

THE TEXAS OBSERVER
(Wed) (Every other Fri)
307 W 7th St, Austin, TX, 78701-2917, Travis, USA; tel (800) 939-6620; fax (512) 474-1175; e-mail observer@texasobserver.org; web site www.texasobserver.org
Circulation: 9,500pd,; Sworn/Estimate/Non-Audited
Established: 1954
Exec. Pub.....................................Carlton Carl
Pub.....................................Charlotte McCann
Assoc. Pub.....................................Julia Austin
Assoc. Ed.......................................Dave Mann
Ed...Bob Moser
Art Dir..Leah Ball
Publisher..................................... Piper Nelson
Mechanical Specifications: Type page 8 1/2 x 11.

DALLAS

DALLAS OBSERVER
(Thur)
3800 Maple Ave, Ste 700, Dallas, TX, 75219-4072, Dallas, USA; tel (214) 757-9000; fax (214) 757-8590; web site www.dallasobserver.com
Circulation: 90,200fr; Sworn/Estimate/Non-Audited

Advertising: Open inch rate $44.38
Group: Voice Media Group
Pub....... Amy Jones
Retail Sales Mgr....... Stephanie Riggs
Classified Dir....... Jennifer Brown
Circ. Dir....... Carlos Garcia
Ed....... Mark Donald
Mng. Ed....... Patrick Williams
Prod. Mgr....... Crystal Betts
Mechanical Specifications: Type page 10 x 12 1/2.

FORT WORTH

FORT WORTH WEEKLY
(Wed)
3311 Hamilton Ave, Fort Worth, TX, 76107-1877, Tarrant, USA; tel (817) 321-9700; adv tel (817) 321-9700; ed tel (817) 321-9700; fax (817) 321-9733; adv fax (817) 321-9733; ed fax (817) 321-9575; e-mail Michael.Newquist@fwweekly.com; adv e-mail Brian.Martin@fwweekly.com; ed e-mailGayle.Reaves@fwweekly.com; web site www.fwweekly.com
Circulation: 23,064fr; VAC
Advertising: Open inch rate $18.25
Established: 1994
Digital Platform - Mobile: Apple, Android, Windows, Blackberry
Digital Platform - Tablet: Apple iOS, Android, Windows 7, Blackberry Tablet OS
Ed....... Gayle Reaves
Adv. Dir....... Michael Newquist
Classified Adv. Dir....... Brian Martin
Eric Griffey
Delivery Method: Mail, Racks
Zip Codes Served: Tarrant County

HOUSTON

HOUSTON PRESS
(Thur)
1621 Milam St, Ste 100, Houston, TX, 77002-8059, Harris, USA; tel (713) 280-2400; adv tel (713) 280-2451; ed tel (713) 280-2480; fax (713) 280-2496; adv fax (713) 280-2444; e-mail letters@houstonpress.com; adv e-mail Danielle.Dalati@houstonpress.com; web site www.houstonpress.com
Circulation: 85,000pd,; Sworn/Estimate/Non-Audited
Established: 1989
Group: Village Voice Media
Pub....... Stuart Folb
Adv. Mgr....... Danielle Dalati
Ed....... Margaret Downing
Mng. Ed....... Catherine Matusow
Art Dir....... Monica Fuentes
Production Manager....... Daniel Ortega
Marketing Director....... Brenna Croom
Online Director....... Michael McCormick
Delivery Method: Newsstand, Racks

SAN ANTONIO

SAN ANTONIO CURRENT
(Wed)
915 Dallas St, San Antonio, TX, 78215-1433, Bexar, USA; tel (210) 227-0044; fax (210) 227-7755; web site www.sacurrent.com
Circulation: 19,378fr; VAC
Advertising: Open inch rate $9.25
Established: 1986
Publisher....... Michael Wagner
Advertising Director....... Greg Harman
Mechanical Specifications: Type page 10 x 12 1/2; E - 4 cols, 2 1/4, 1/20 between; A - 4 cols, 2 1/4, 1/20 between; C - 8 cols, 1 1/5, 1/20 between.
Equipment: Hardware — APP/Mac, PC; Software — QPS/QuarkXPress, Adobe/PageMaker, Microsoft/Word, Microsoft/Excel, Wordperfect, Lotus, Multi-Ad/CAMS, Quickbook, Eudora.
Delivery Method: Newsstand

UTAH

SALT LAKE CITY

SALT LAKE CITY WEEKLY
(Thur)
248 S Main St, Salt Lake City, UT, 84101-2001, Salt Lake, USA; tel (801) 575-7003; fax (801) 575-6106; e-mail comments@cityweekly.net; web site www.cityweekly.net
Circulation: 46,467fr; VAC
Advertising: Open inch rate $40.00
Established: 1984
Pub....... John Saltas
Retail Sales Mgr....... Doug Kruithof
Ed....... Dylan Woolf Harris
Mechanical Specifications: Type page 10 x 13; E - 4 cols, 2 1/8, 1/8 between; A - 8 cols, 1 1/16, 1/8 between; C - 8 cols, 1 1/16, between.
Equipment: Hardware — APP/Mac, PCs; Software — QPS/QuarkXPress 3.3, Adobe/Photoshop, Microsoft/Word.
Delivery Method: Racks
Zip Codes Served: 84101, 84102, 84103, 84104, 84105, 84106, 84107, 84108, 84109, 84110, 84111, 84112, 84113, 84114, 84115, 84116, 84117, 84118, 84119, 84120, 84121, 84122, 84123, 84124, 84125, 84126, 84127, 84128, 84130, 84131, 84132, 84133, 84134, 84135, 84136, 84137, 84138, 84139, 84140, 84141, 84142, 84143, 84144, 84145, 84147, 84148, 84150, 84151, 84152, 84153, 84157, 84158, 84165, 84170, 84171, 84180, 84184, 84185, 84189, 84190, 84199

VERMONT

BURLINGTON

SEVEN DAYS
(Wed)
255 S Champlain St, Burlington, VT, 05401-4881, Chittenden, USA; tel (802) 864-5684; fax (802) 865-1015; e-mail pamela@sevendaysvt.com; adv e-mail sales@sevendaysvt.com; ed e-mailpamela@sevendaysvt.com (arts); matthew@sevendaysvt.com (news); web site www.sevendaysvt.com
Circulation: 8pd, 35,975fr; CVC
Advertising: Modular rates
Established: 1995
Digital Platform - Mobile: Apple, Android
Digital Platform - Tablet: Apple iOS, Android
Assoc. Pub./Ed....... Pamela Polston
Sales Dir./Assoc. Pub....... Colby Roberts
Pub./Ed....... Paula Routly
Creative Dir./Assoc. Pub....... Don Eggert
Assoc. Pub....... Cathy Resmer
Marketing Dir....... Corey Grenier
Classifieds & personals manager Ashley Cleare
Prodn. Mgr....... John James
Bus. Mgr....... Cheryl Brownell
Calendar Ed....... Kristen Ravin
Political Ed....... Paul Heintz
Mechanical Specifications: Type page 9.625 x 11.25; E - 4 cols, 2.3
Equipment: Hardware — APP/Mac; Software — QPS/QuarkXPress.
Delivery Method: Newsstand, Carrier, Racks
Zip Codes Served: 05001, 05031, 05041, 05047, 05060, 05061, 05091, 05401, 05403, 05404, 05405, 05408, 05439, 05441, 05443, 05444, 05445, 05446, 05450, 05451, 05452, 05454, 05456, 05458, 05461, 05462, 05463, 05464, 05465, 05466, 05468, 05469, 05470, 05471, 05472, 05473, 05474, 05477, 05478, 05479, 05482, 05486, 05487, 05489, 05491, 05494, 05495, 05602, 05640, 05461, 05648, 05651, 05655, 05656, 05658, 05660, 05661, 05663, 05667, 05671, 05673, 05674, 05676, 05701, 05733, 05734, 05735, 05740, 05743, 05753, 05760, 05766, 05770, 05819, 05826, 05828, 05843, 05873,

VIRGINIA

CHARLOTTESVILLE

C-VILLE WEEKLY
(Wed)
308 E Main St, Charlottesville, VA, 22902-5234, Charlottesville City, USA; tel (434) 817-2749; adv tel (434) 817-2749 ext. 36; ed tel (434) 817-2749 ext. 20; fax (434) 817-2758; adv fax (434) 817-2758; ed fax (434) 817-2758; e-mail advertising@c-ville.com; adv e-mail classifieds@c-ville.com; ed e-maileditor@c-ville.com; web site www.c-ville.com
Circulation: 0pd, 22,673fr; VAC
Advertising: 1/8 Pg $280.00; 1/4 Pg $400.00; 3/8 Pg $510.00
Established: 1988
Group: C-VILLE Holdings LLC
Digital Platform - Mobile: Apple, Android, Windows, Blackberry
Digital Platform - Tablet: Apple iOS, Android, Windows 7, Blackberry Tablet OS, Kindle, Nook, Kindle Fire
Advt Mgr....... Erica Gentile
Ed....... Giles Morris
Pub....... Aimee Andrews
Circ. Mgr....... Miguel Coredine
Equipment: Hardware — APP/Mac; Software — QPS/QuarkXPress, Adobe/Photoshop.
Delivery Method: Mail, Newsstand, Racks
Zip Codes Served: Albemarle County

THE HOOK
(Thur)
100 2nd St NW, Charlottesville, VA, 22902-5193, Charlottesville City, USA; web site www.readthehook.com
Circulation: 18,999fr; Sworn/Estimate/Non-Audited
Editor....... Hawes Spencer
Circulation....... Anna Harrison

LYNCHBURG

THE BURG
(Fri)
101 Wyndale Dr, Lynchburg, VA, 24501-6710, Lynchburg City, USA; tel (434) 385-5525; web site http://www.newsadvance.com/the_burg/
Group: BH Media Group
Adv. Dir....... Jason McBride

RICHMOND

STYLE WEEKLY
(Wed)
1313 E Main St, Apt 103, Richmond, VA, 23219-3600, Richmond City, USA; tel (804) 358-0825; fax (804) 358-1079; e-mail info@styleweekly.com; web site www.styleweekly.com
Circulation: 13pd, 30,680fr; VAC
Established: 1982
Group: C-VILLE Holdings LLC
Publisher....... Lori Waran
Editor....... Jason Roop
Mechanical Specifications: Type page 9 7/8 x 13; E - 4 cols, between; A - 4 cols, between.
Equipment: Hardware — IBM; Software — Microsoft/Windows, Aldus/Freehand, Adobe/Photoshop, Adobe/Indesign.

WASHINGTON

SEATTLE

SEATTLE WEEKLY
(Wed)
307 3rd Ave S, Ste 200, Seattle, WA, 98104-2687, King, USA; tel (206) 623-0500; adv tel (206) 623-0500; ed tel (206) 623-0500; fax (206) 467-4338; e-mail news@seattleweekly.com; adv e-mail Advertising@Seattleweekly.com; web site www.seattleweekly.com
Circulation: 66pd, 45,000fr; Sworn/Estimate/Non-Audited
Established: 1976
Group: Sound Publishing
Digital Platform - Mobile: Apple, Android, Windows, Other
Digital Platform - Tablet: Apple iOS, Android, Windows 7, Kindle Fire, Other
Circ. Mgr....... Jay Kraus
Ed. in Chief....... Mark Baumgarten
Ad Director....... Sara Dellinger
Mechanical Specifications: Type page 11 1/4 x 13 5/8; E - 4 cols, 2 5/16, 1/8 between; A - 4 cols, 2 5/16, 1/8 between; C - 4 cols, 2 5/16, 1/8 between.
Equipment: Hardware — PC, Pentium 120, Novell, APP/Mac; Software — Microsoft/Word.
Delivery Method: Mail, Newsstand, Racks

THE STRANGER
(Wed) (Bi-weekly (every other week on Wednesdays))
1535 11th Ave, Ste 300, Seattle, WA, 98122-3933, King, USA; tel (206) 323-7101; adv tel (206) 323-7101; ed tel (206) 323-7101; fax (206) 323-7203; adv fax (206) 325-4865; ed fax (206) 323-7203; e-mail press@thestranger.com; adv e-mail adinfo@thestranger.com; ed e-maileditor@thestranger.com; web site www.thestranger.com
Circulation: 47pd, 50,891fr; VAC
Advertising: Open inch rate $50.00
Established: 1991
Group: Index Newspapers LLC
Digital Platform - Mobile: Apple, Android, Windows, Blackberry
Digital Platform - Tablet: Apple iOS, Android, Windows 7, Blackberry Tablet OS, Kindle, Nook, Kindle Fire
Publisher....... Tim Keck
Gen. Mgr....... Laurie Saito
Mng. Ed....... Christopher Frizzelle
Ed....... Dan Savage
Prodn. Mgr....... Erica Tarrant
Delivery Method: Mail, Racks
Zip Codes Served: 98199 98109 98119 98121 98101 98104 98134 98108 98112 98102 98122 98144 98118 98105 98195 98115 98125 98155 98103 98117 98133 98177 98107 98106 98116 98126 98136 98106 98146 98166 98028 98072 98011 98052 98033 98034 98004 98005 98006 98007 98027 98040 98108 98168 98188 98198 98178 98055 98056 98057 98030 98032 98003 98023 98422

SPOKANE

THE PACIFIC NORTHWEST INLANDER
(Thur)
1227 W Summit Pkwy, Spokane, WA, 99201-7003, Spokane, USA; tel (509) 325-0634; fax (509) 325-0638; e-mail info@inlander.com; adv e-mail sales@inlander.com; ed e-maileditor@inlander.com; web site www.inlander.com
Circulation: 50pd, 52,000fr; Sworn/Estimate/Non-Audited
Established: 1993
Digital Platform - Mobile: Apple, Android, Windows

Digital Platform - Tablet: Apple iOS
Owner-Publisher........................Ted McGregor
Distribution Manager.................Trevor Rendall
Owner-Publisher...................Ted S. McGregor
Prodn. Mgr. ....Wayne Hunt
Editor...Jacob Fries
Equipment: Hardware — APP/Mac; Software — Adobe/PageMaker/InDesign
Delivery Method: Mail, Racks
Zip Codes Served: 83814, 83822, 83835, 83843, 83852, 83854, 83855, 83856, 83857, 83858, 83860, 83861, 83864, 83869, 83870, 83876, 99001, 99003, 99004, 99005, 99006, 99009, 99011, 99016, 99019, 99021, 99022, 99027, 99030, 99036, 99037, 99163, 99201, 99202, 99203, 99204, 99205, 99206, 99207, 99208, 99212, 99216, 99217, 99218, 99223, 99224

WISCONSIN

MADISON

ISTHMUS

(Thur)
101 King St, Madison, WI, 53703-3313, Dane, USA; tel (608) 251-5627; fax (608) 251-2165; e-mail edit@isthmus.com; web site www.thedailypage.com
Circulation: 72pd, 37,536fr; VAC
Advertising: Open inch rate $41.29
Established: 1976
Group: Isthmus Publishing Co., Inc.
Digital Platform - Mobile: Android
Pub.......................................Vincent P. O'Hern
Dir., Admin...................................Kathy Bailey
Circ. Mgr....................................Tom Dehlinger
Ed. ....Dean Robins
Prodn. Mgr. ....Ellen Meany
Advertising Manager...................Chad Hopper
Mechanical Specifications: Type page 10 x 12 1/2; E - 4 cols, 2 1/4, 1/4 between; A - 4 cols, 2 1/4, 1/4 between; C - 6 cols, 1 1/2, 1/4 between.
Equipment: Hardware — PC, APP/Mac; Presses — no presses; Software — QPS/QuarkXPress, Adobe/Photoshop.
Delivery Method: Mail, Racks
Zip Codes Served: 53703 through 53719
Note: We also produce the original Annual Manual in August and a number of other supplements including Dining.

MILWAUKEE

SHEPHERD EXPRESS WEEKLY NEWS

(Wed)
207 E Buffalo St, Ste 410, Milwaukee, WI, 53202-5712, Milwaukee, USA; tel (414) 276-2222; fax (414) 276-3312; e-mail postmaster@shepherd-express.com; web site www.expressmilwaukee.com
Circulation: 15pd, 57,410fr; VAC
Circ. Mgr...............................Joseph Porubcan
Ed. ....Louis Fortis
Mechanical Specifications: Type page 10 x 12 1/2; E - 4 cols, between; A - 4 cols, between.

WAUSAU

CITY PAGES

(Thur)
300 N 3rd St, Ste 200, Wausau, WI, 54403-5400, Marathon, USA; tel (715) 845-5171; adv tel (715) 845-5171; ed tel (715) 845-5171; fax (715) 845-5887; adv fax (715) 848-5887; ed fax (715) 848-5887; e-mail tammy@thecitypages.com; adv e-mail advertising@thecitypages.com; ed e-mailtammy@thecitypages.com; web site thecitypages.com
Circulation: 8pd, 17,021fr; VAC
Advertising: Open inch rate $24.33
Established: 1993
Digital Platform - Mobile: Apple, Android, Windows, Blackberry
Digital Platform - Tablet: Apple iOS, Android, Windows 7, Blackberry Tablet OS, Kindle, Nook, Kindle Fire
Ed/Pub.................................Tammy Stezenski
Administrative assistant............Kayla Zastrow
Mechanical Specifications: Type page 10 x 12; E - 4 cols, 2 3/8, between; A - 4 cols, 2 3/8, between.
Equipment: Hardware — APP/Mac; Software — Adobe package, including InDesign, Photoshop, Illustrator. Office: Word, Excel,
Delivery Method: Mail, Newsstand, Racks
Zip Codes Served: 54401, 54402, 54403, 54476, 54440, 54455, 54448, 54474, 54481, 54492
Note: Three magazine supplements:
Summer magazine, 18K circa
'Program' year-round guide early Sept., 19K+
Holiday/winter magazine 18K week before Thanksgiving

WYOMING

JACKSON

JH WEEKLY

(Wed)
567 W Broadway Ave, Jackson, WY, 83001-8641, Teton, USA; tel (307) 732-0299; adv tel (307) 732-0299; ed tel (308) 732-0299; fax (307) 732-0996; e-mail publisher@planetjh.com; adv e-mail sales@planetjh.com; ed e-maileditor@planetjh.com; web site www.jhweekly.com
Circulation: 8,000fr; Sworn/Estimate/Non-Audited
Established: 2002
Delivery Method: Newsstand, Racks
Zip Codes Served: 83001,83002,83014,83025, 83455

BLACK NEWSPAPERS IN THE UNITED STATES

ALABAMA

BIRMINGHAM

BIRMINGHAM TIMES

(Thur)
115 3rd Ave W, Birmingham, AL, 35204-4114, Jefferson, USA; tel (205) 251-5158; fax (205) 323-2294; e-mail info@birminghamtimes.com; web site www.thebirminghamtimes.com
Circulation:; VAC
Advertising: Open inch rate $14.47
Established: 1964
Pub..James E. Lewis
Gen. Mgr. ....Mary Jo Robinson
Adv. Mgr...Doug Jones
Circ. Mgr...................................Phillip Eldridge
Ed. ....Cheryle Eldridge
Mechanical Specifications: Type page 13 x 21; E - 6 cols, 2 1/16, 1/8 between; A - 6 cols, 2 1/16, 1/8 between; C - 10 cols, 1, 1/4 between.
Equipment: Hardware — APP/Mac, PC; Presses — HI; Software — QPS/QuarkXPress 3.31, Adobe/Illustrator, Adobe/Photoshop.

EUTAW

GREENE COUNTY DEMOCRAT

(Wed)
206 Prairie Ave, Eutaw, AL, 35462-1174, Greene, USA; tel (205) 372-3373; adv tel (334) 372-3373; ed tel (334) 372-3373; fax (205) 372-2243; adv tel (334) 372-2243; ed tel (334) 372-2243; e-mail jzippert@aol.com; adv e-mail Jzippert@aol.com; ed e-mail jzippert@aol.com; web site www.greenecodemocrat.com
Circulation: 4,000pd, 300fr; USPS
Advertising: Open inch rate $10.00
Established: 1890
Digital Platform - Mobile: Apple
Digital Platform - Tablet: Apple iOS
Co-Pub.......................................Carol Zippert
Circ. Mgr...............................Barbara Amerson
Ed. ....John Zippert
Mechanical Specifications: Type page 13 x 29 1/2; E - 6 cols, 2 1/16, 1/8 between; A - 6 cols, 2 1/16, 1/8 between; C - 6 cols, 2 1/16, 1/8 between.
Equipment: Hardware — APP/Mac; Software — QPS/QuarkXPress 2.0.
Delivery Method: Mail, Racks
Zip Codes Served: 35460 to 35470

HUNTSVILLE

SPEAKIN' OUT WEEKLY

(Wed)
101 Oakwood Ave NE, Huntsville, AL, 35811-1960, Madison, USA; tel (256) 551-1020; fax (256) 551-0607; e-mail WSmoth3193@aol.com; web site www.speakinoutweeklynews.com
Circulation: 26,000pd, 1,000fr; Sworn/Estimate/Non-Audited
Advertising: Open inch rate $19.84 local; $34.00 National
Established: 1980
Digital Platform - Mobile: Apple, Windows
Digital Platform - Tablet: Apple iOS, Windows 7
Assoc. Pub........Jemeana Smothers-Roberson
Ed. ....William Smothers
Mechanical Specifications: Type page 10.25" by 21"
Equipment: Hardware — APP/Mac; Software — Adobe/PageMaker 6.5.
Delivery Method: Mail, Newsstand
Zip Codes Served: 35810 35811 35816 35806 35601 35801 35758
Note: Published since 1980

MOBILE

MOBILE BEACON AND ALABAMA CITIZEN

(Wed)
2311 Costarides St, Mobile, AL, 36617-2442, Mobile, USA; tel (251) 479-0629; fax (251) 479-0610; e-mail mobilebeaconinc@bellsouth.net
Circulation: 7,000pd, 20fr; Sworn/Estimate/Non-Audited
Advertising: Open inch rate $18.95
Ed. ....Cleretta T. Blackmon

MONTGOMERY

MONTGOMERY/TUSKEGEE TIMES

(Thur)
525 Augusta Ave, Montgomery, AL, 36111-1315, Montgomery, USA; tel (334) 280-2444; fax (334) 280-2454; e-mail adixon711@aol.com
Advertising: Open inch rate $16.54
Gen. Mgr. ....Almaria Dixon Smith
Circ. Mgr....................................Daryl Watkins
Ed. ....Rev. Al Dixon
Mng. Ed..................................Alphonso Dixon
Prodn. Mgr. ....Alverene Butler

CALIFORNIA

BAKERSFIELD

BAKERSFIELD NEWS OBSERVER

(Wed)
1219 20th St, Bakersfield, CA, 93301-4611, Kern, USA; tel (661) 324-9466; fax (661) 324-9472; e-mail observernews@gmail.com; adv e-mail observeradvertising@gmail.com; ed e-mail jamesluckey@thenewsobserver.net; web site theobservergroup.com
Circulation: 40,000fr; Sworn/Estimate/Non-Audited
Advertising: Open inch rate $32.00
Established: 1977
Owner..Ellen Coley
Pub & Mng Partner.....................Joseph Coley
Circ. Mgr....................................James Luckey
Ed. ....James Coley
Prodn. Mgr. ....Jon Williams
Owner...Jon Coley
Mechanical Specifications: Type page 13 x 21; E - 6 cols, 2, 1/4 between; A - 6 cols, 2, 1/4 between; C - 10 cols, 1 1/2, 1/4 between.
Equipment: Hardware — Imac; Software — Adobe CS5, MS Office 2010
Delivery Method: Newsstand, Carrier, Racks
Zip Codes Served: 93301, 93304, 93305, 93306, 93307, 93309, 93312, 93313, 93314

EAST RANCHO DOMINGUEZ

COMPTON BULLETIN

(Wed)
800 E Compton Blvd, East Rancho Dominguez, CA, 90221-3302, Los Angeles, USA; tel (310) 635-6776; fax (310) 635-4045; e-mail news@thecomptonbulletin.com; adv e-mail ads@thecomptonbulletin.com; ed e-mail news@thecomptonbulletin.com; web site www.thecomptonbulletin.com
Circulation: 32,516pd, 42,484fr; Sworn/Estimate/Non-Audited
Advertising: Open inch rate $45.00
Pub....................................Lisa Grace-Kellogg
Ed. ....Allison Eaton

FRESNO

THE CALIFORNIA ADVOCATE

(Fri)

1555 E St, Fresno, CA, 93706-2005, Fresno, USA; tel (559) 268-0941; fax (559) 268-0943; e-mail newsroom@caladvocate.com; web site www.caladvocate.com
Circulation: 33,013pd,; Sworn/Estimate/Non-Audited
Advertising: Open inch rate $39.50
Pub.. Mark Kimber
Ed. ....Pauline Kimber
Mechanical Specifications: Type page 13 x 21; E - 6 cols, 2, 1/3 between.
Zip Codes Served: 93706, 93705, 93721, 93612, 93613, 93637, 93638, 92320, 93662, 93277, 93245, 95340

LOS ANGELES

LA WATTS TIMES
(Thur)
3540 Wilshire Blvd, PH 3, Los Angeles, CA, 90010-2357, Los Angeles, USA; tel (213) 251-5700; fax (213) 251-5720; e-mail LAWATTSNUS@AOL.COM; adv e-mail advertising@lawattstimes.com; ed e-mail editorial@lawattstimes.com; web site www.lawattstimes.com
Circulation: 450pd, 25,000fr; Sworn/Estimate/Non-Audited
Advertising: Open inch rate $58.24
Pub... Melanie Polk
Bus. Mgr...................................Vincent Martin
Adv. Dir....................................Willa Robinson
Mng. Ed....................................... Sam Richard
Dist. Mgr...................................Issac Mctyiere
Mechanical Specifications: Type page 10 x 16; E - 5 cols, 2, 1/8 between; A - 5 cols, 2, 1/8 between; C - 5 cols, 2, 1/8 between.

LOS ANGELES SENTINEL
(Thur)
3800 Crenshaw Blvd, Los Angeles, CA, 90008-1813, Los Angeles, USA; tel (323) 299-3800; fax (323) 299-9896; e-mail geninfo@lasentinel.net; web site www.losangelessentinel.net
Circulation: 30,675fr; CVC
Advertising: Open inch rate $25.00
Pub.. Danny Bakewell
Ed. .... Ken Miller
Mechanical Specifications: Type page 13 x 21 1/2; E - 6 cols, 2 1/16, 1/8 between; A - 6 cols, 2 1/16, 1/8 between; C - 10 cols, between.
Equipment: Hardware — APP/Mac, IBM/486; Software — Microsoft/Word, QPS/QuarkXPress, Adobe/PageMaker, Adobe/Photoshop.

OUR WEEKLY
(Thur)
8732 S Western Ave, Los Angeles, CA, 90047-3326, Los Angeles, USA; web site www.ourweekly.com
Circulation: 0pd, 49,975fr; CVC
Advertising: N/A
Established: 2004
Publisher.. Natalie Cole
Advertising Manager...................... David Miller
Circulation Manager .... Arnold Cole

WAVE COMMUNITY NEWSPAPER
(Thur)
1730 W Olympic Blvd, Ste 500, Los Angeles, CA, 90015-1008, Los Angeles, USA; tel (323) 556-5720; adv tel 323-556-5720 ext.245; fax (213) 835-0584; adv tel 213-835-0584; e-mail dwanlass@wavepublication.com; adv e-mail rbush@wavepublication.com; web site www.wavenewspapers.com
Circulation: 150,000fr; AAM
Advertising: Open inch rate $150.00
Established: 1912Editions: 9— Culver City; East; Northeast; West; West Hollywood, Hollywood
Digital Platform - Mobile: Blackberry
Digital Platform - Tablet: Windows 7
Pub... Pluria Marshall
Ed. .... Andre Herndon
Mng. Ed......................................Don Wanlass
Sr. VP Sales &Marketing..............Robert Bush
Mechanical Specifications: Type page 13 x 21 1/2; E - 6 cols, 2 1/16, 1/8 between; A - 6 cols, 2 1/16, 1/8 between; C - 10 cols, between.
Equipment: Hardware — APP/Mac.
Delivery Method: Newsstand, Carrier, Racks
Zip Codes Served: Greater Los Angels
Note: African American, Hispanic, Gay and General Market Papers

OAKLAND

OAKLAND POST
(Fri, Sat)
405 14th St, Ste 1215, Oakland, CA, 94612-2707, Alameda, USA; tel (510) 287-8200; adv tel (510) 287-8220; fax (510) 287-8247; adv e-mail ads@postnewsgroup.net; web site www.postnewsgroup.com
Circulation: 0pd, 15,790fr; VAC
Advertising: Open inch rate $50.00
Established: 1963
Group: Post News Group
Pub.. Paul Cobbs
Chief Operating Officer............Maxine Ussery
Production Manager...................... Jack Naidu
Associate Editor...................Ashley Chambers
Associate Editor.................... Taison Kwamilele
Editor ....Kenneth Epstein
Mechanical Specifications: Type page 12 3/4 x 21 1/2; C - 9 cols, 1 3/8, between.
Delivery Method: Carrier

RICHMOND POST
(Fri, Sat)
405 14th St, Ste 1215, Oakland, CA, 94612-2707, Alameda, USA; tel (510) 287-8200; adv tel (510) 287-8220; fax (510) 287-8247; adv e-mail ads@postnewsgroup.net; web site www.postnewsgroup.com
Circulation: 0pd, 2,903fr; VAC
Advertising: Open inch rate $50.00
Established: 1963
Group: Post News Group
Pub.. Paul Cobbs
Chief Operating Officer............Maxine Ussery
Production Manager...................... Jack Naidu
Associate Editor...................Ashley Chambers
Associate Editor.................... Taison Kwamilele
Editor ....Kenneth Epstein
Mechanical Specifications: Type page 12 3/4 x 21 1/2; C - 9 cols, 1 3/8, between.
Delivery Method: Carrier

PASADENA

PASADENA JOURNAL-NEWS
(Thur)
1541 N Lake Ave, Ste A, Pasadena, CA, 91104-2375, Los Angeles, USA; tel (626) 798-3972; fax (626) 798-3282; e-mail pasjour@pacbell.net; web site www.pasadenajournal.com
Circulation: 7,500pd,; Sworn/Estimate/Non-Audited
Advertising: Open inch rate $18.00
Co-Pub.....................................Joe C. Hopkins
Ed. ....Ruthie Hopkins
Webmaster .... Harmony Coburn
Mechanical Specifications: Type page 10 x 15; E - 5 cols, 1 3/4, between; A - 5 cols, 1 3/4, between; C - 5 cols, 1 3/4, between.
Zip Codes Served: 91001, 91101, 91105, 91105, 91107, 91107, 91109, 91706, 91730, 91184, 91342, 91745, 91765, 91770, 91775, 91792, 91104, 91103, 91106, 91102, 91108, 91702, 91710, 91737, 91201, 91740, 91763, 91766, 91773, 91790, 91801

RIVERSIDE

BLACK VOICE NEWS
(Thur)
4290 Brockton Ave, Riverside, CA, 92501-3447, Riverside, USA; tel (951) 682-6070; fax (951) 276-0877; e-mail cherylbrown@blackvoicenews.com; web site www.blackvoicenews.com
Circulation: 10,000pd, 1,810fr; CVC
Advertising: Open inch rate $24.50
Established: 1972
Co-Pub...................................Cheryl R. Brown
Co-Pub.................................... Hardy L. Brown
Circ. Mgr..Lee Ragin
Mechanical Specifications: Type page 13 x 21; E - 6 cols, 2, 1/6 between; C - 8 cols, 1 3/4, 1/6 between.
Equipment: Hardware — APP/Mac; Software — QPS/QuarkXPress.

SACRAMENTO

OBSERVER GROUP
(Fri)
2330 Alhambra Blvd, Sacramento, CA, 95817-1121, Sacramento, USA; tel (916) 452-4781; fax (916) 452-7744; e-mail circulation@sacobserver.com; web site www.sacobserver.com
Circulation: 50,000pd, 100fr; Sworn/Estimate/Non-Audited
Advertising: Open inch rate $47.50
Pub... William H. Lee
Circ. Mgr....................................... Joe Stinson
Prodn. Mgr. ....Larry Lee
Mechanical Specifications: Type page 12 15/16 x 21; E - 6 cols, between; A - 6 cols, between.

SAN BERNARDINO

PRECINCT REPORTER
(Thur)
670 N Arrowhead Ave, Ste B, San Bernardino, CA, 92401-1102, San Bernardino, USA; tel (909) 889-0597; fax (909) 889-1706; e-mail news@precinctreporter.com; adv e-mail sales@precinctreporter.com; web site www.precinctreporter.com
Circulation:; Sworn/Estimate/Non-Audited
Advertising: Open inch rate $35.00
Established: 1965
Ed. ....Brian Townsend
Mechanical Specifications: 10 x 21
Delivery Method: Newsstand, Carrier, Racks

SAN DIEGO

SAN DIEGO VOICE & VIEWPOINT
(Thur)
3619 College Ave, San Diego, CA, 92115-7041, San Diego, USA; tel (619) 266-2233; fax (619) 266-0533; e-mail voiceandviewpoint@gmail.com; web site www.sdvoice.com
Circulation: 25,000pd,; Sworn/Estimate/Non-Audited
Advertising: Open inch rate $26.00
Ed. ....John Warren
Mng. Ed..........................Gerri Adams-Warren

SAN FRANCISCO

CALIFORNIA VOICE
(Sun)
1791 Bancroft Ave, San Francisco, CA, 94124-2644, San Francisco, USA; tel (415) 671-1000; fax (415) 671-1005; e-mail sunmedia97@aol.com; web site www.sunreporter.com
Circulation: 38,840pd,; CVC
Advertising: Open inch rate $23.00
Pub................................Amelia Ashley-Ward

METRO REPORTER
(Tues)
1791 Bancroft Ave, San Francisco, CA, 94124-2644, San Francisco, USA; tel (415) 671-1000; fax (415) 671-1005; e-mail sundoc97@aol.com; sunmedia97@aol.com; web site www.sunreporter.com
Circulation: 111,013fr; CVC
Advertising: Open inch rate $65.00Editions: 7— Metro Reporter-Berkley (8,947); Metro Reporter-Oakland (32,650); Metro Reporter-Richmond (10,595); Metro Reporter-San Francisco (24,113); Metro Reporter-San Joaquin (10,011); Metro Reporter-San Jose/Peninsula (17,410); Metro Reporter-Vallejo (7,
Circ. Mgr.. Lovie Ward
Ed. ....Amelia Ashley-Ward
Mechanical Specifications: Type page 13 x 21; E - 6 cols, 2 1/16, between; A - 6 cols, 2 1/16, between; C - 6 cols, 2 1/16, between.

SAN FRANCISCO BAY VIEW
(Mthly)
4917 3rd St, San Francisco, CA, 94124-2309, San Francisco, USA; tel (415) 671-0789; adv tel (415) 671-0789; ed tel (415) 671-0789; fax (415) 671-0789; e-mail editor@sfbayview.com; adv e-mail editor@sfbayview.com; ed e-mail editor@sfbayview.com; web site www.sfbayview.com
Circulation: 700pd, 20,000fr; Sworn/Estimate/Non-Audited
Advertising: Open inch rate $15.00
Established: 1976
Digital Platform - Mobile: Windows
Digital Platform - Tablet: Windows 7
Pub.. Willie Ratcliff
Ed. ....Mary Ratcliff
Mechanical Specifications: Type page 12.5 x 22.5; E - 6 cols, 2", 1/6 between; A - 6 cols, 2", 1/6 between; C - 6 cols, 2", 1/6 between.
Equipment: Hardware — 3-Pentium/MMXs, 2-APP/Power Mac G5; Software — Adobe/InDesign.
Delivery Method: Mail, Newsstand, Racks
Zip Codes Served: 94102, 94103, 94107, 94112, 94115, 94117, 94124, 94132, 94134, 94577, 94601, 94603, 94605, 94607, 94609, 94610, 94612, 94619, 94621, 94702, 94703, 94704, 94705, 94710

SUN REPORTER
(Thur)
11286 Fillmore St, San Francisco, CA, 94115, San Francisco, USA; tel (415) 671-1000; fax (415) 671-1005; e-mail sunmedia97@aol.com; web site No Website
Circulation: 20,000pd, 5,000fr; Sworn/Estimate/Non-Audited
Advertising: Open inch rate $63.00
Established: 1949
Ed. ....Amelia Ashley-Ward
Ed. ....Amelia Ashley Ward
Mktg./Adv. Mgr. .... Roslyn Gillis
Mechanical Specifications: Type page 11 x 14; E - 5 cols, 2 1/16, between; A - 5 cols, 2 1/16, between; C - 5 cols, 2 1/16, between.
Zip Codes Served: 94124

VICTORVILLE

THE SAN BERNARDINO AMERICAN NEWS
(Thur)
14537 Anacapa Rd, Ste 24, Victorville, CA, 92392-2705, San Bernardino, USA; tel (909) 889-7677; adv tel (909) 889-7677; ed tel (909) 889-7677; fax (909) 889-2882; adv tel (909) 889-2882; ed tel (909) 889-2882; e-mail msbamericannews@gmail.com; adv e-mail sbamericannews@gmail.com; ed e-mail samerisam1@earthlink.net; web site sbnews.us
Circulation: 10,000pd,; Sworn/Estimate/Non-Audited
Advertising: Open inch rate $23.90
Established: 1969
Group: Don Roberto Group Inc
Digital Platform - Mobile: Apple, Windows, Blackberry
Digital Platform - Tablet: Apple iOS, Windows 7, Blackberry Tablet OS

Pub.. Mary Harris
Co-Pub.. Clifton Harris
Delivery Method: Mail, Carrier
Zip Codes Served: 92405, 92410-11, 92335-6, 92346, 92324,92392-4, 92301, 92345, 92307, 92311,91730, 92570, 92552, 92521, 92392, 92395, 91737, 92572,

COLORADO

DENVER

DENVER WEEKLY NEWS

(Thur)
2937 Welton St, Denver, CO, 80205-3021, Denver, USA; tel (303) 292-5158; fax (303) 292-5344; e-mail dwnews2@yahoo.com
Advertising: Open inch rate $30.00
Ed. ....Lenora Alexander

CONNECTICUT

NEW HAVEN

INNER-CITY NEWS

(Mon)
50 Fitch St, Ste 2, New Haven, CT, 06515-1366, New Haven, USA; tel (203) 387-0354; adv tel 203 387-0354; ed tel 203 387-0354; fax (203) 387-2684; adv tel (203) 387-2684; ed tel (203) 387-2684; e-mail jthomas@penfieldcomm.com; adv e-mail jthomas@penfieldcomm.com; ed e-mail jthomas@penfieldcomm.com
Circulation: 25,000fr; Sworn/Estimate/Non-Audited
Advertising: Open inch rate $55.00
Established: 1990
Digital Platform - Mobile: Apple
Digital Platform - Tablet: Apple iOS
CEO.. John Thomas
Mechanical Specifications: Type page 9 3/4 x 13 5/8; E - 4 cols, 2 5/6, between; A - 4 cols, 2 5/6, between; C - 8 cols, 1 5/6, between.
Delivery Method: Newsstand, Racks
Zip Codes Served: 6515

DISTRICT OF COLUMBIA

WASHINGTON

DISTRICT CHRONICLES

(Thur)
525 NW Bryant St, Washington, DC, 20059-1005, District Of Columbia, USA; tel 202-806-9401; adv tel 202-806-9401; ed tel 202-806-9401; e-mail lkaggwa@howard.edu; adv e-mail lkaggwa@howard.edu; ed e-mail lkaggwa@howard.edu; web site www.districtchronicles.com
Circulation: 9,975fr; Sworn/Estimate/Non-Audited
Advertising: $20
Established: 2001
Publisher............................ Lawrence Kaggwa
Mechanical Specifications: 1.94"

WASHINGTON AFRO-AMERICAN

(Fri)
1917 Benning Rd NE, Washington, DC, 20002-4723, District Of Columbia, USA; tel (202) 332-0080; fax (877) 570-9297; e-mail editor@afro.com; web site www.afro.com
Circulation: 5,463pd, 649fr; AAM
Advertising: Open inch rate $46.56
Established: 1892
Digital Platform - Mobile: Apple, Android
Pub.. John J. Oliver
Circ. Mgr.................................. Edgar Brookins
Prodn. Mgr. .... Denise Dorsey
Mechanical Specifications: Type page 13 x 21; E - 6 cols, 2, 1/8 between; A - 6 cols, 2, between; C - 9 cols, 1, 1/8 between.
Equipment: Hardware — APP/Mac; Software — QPS/QuarkXPress, AP Adsend.
Delivery Method: Mail, Newsstand, Racks

WASHINGTON INFORMER

(Thur)
3117 Martin Luther King Jr Ave SE, Washington, DC, 20032-1537, District Of Columbia, USA; tel (202) 561-4100; adv tel (202) 888-6835; ed tel (202) 561-4100; fax (202) 888-6835; adv tel (202) 888-6835; e-mail news@washingtoninformer.com; adv e-mail rburke@washingtoninformer.com; ed e-mail news@washingtoninformer.com; web site www.washingtoninformer.com
Circulation: 188pd, 15,512fr; CVC
Advertising: Open inch rate $47.10
Established: 1964Editions: 52—
Digital Platform - Mobile: Apple, Android, Windows, Blackberry
Digital Platform - Tablet: Apple iOS, Android, Windows 7, Blackberry Tablet OS, Kindle, Nook, Kindle Fire
Director of Advertising..................... Ron Burke
Publisher........................ Denise Rolark Barnes
circulation manager................. Angie Johnson
Editor.. Kevin McNeir
Mechanical Specifications: 1 column 1.75"
2 columns 3.625"
3 columns 5.625"
4 columns 7.562"
5 columns 9.5"
Page Depth 12.375
Total Inches Per Page 61.875"
Equipment: Hardware — APP/Mac, IBM; Software — Microsoft/Word, InDesign, Adobe/Photoshop.
Delivery Method: Mail, Carrier, Racks
Zip Codes Served: 20001- 22314
Note: ABOUT THE WASHINGTON INFORMER
The Washington Informer Newspaper Co. Inc. is a multi-media company founded on October 16, 1964 by Dr Calvin Rolark, and established to report on news directly impacting African Americans in the District of Columbia and surrounding suburbs of Maryand and Virginia. The editorial content focuses on positive news, that educates, informs and empowers those members of the community who have historically been disenfranchised and ignored by local mainstream media. The Washington Informer reaches over 50,000 readers each week through our award winning newspaper print edition; a weekly average of 50,000 page views through our award winning website; 7,500 weekly subscribers through our weekly email newsletter, and growing numbers through our social media platforms including Twitter, Facebook, Instagram and LinkedIn. The Washington Informer is the official sponsor of the Annual Washington Informer Spelling Bee and African American Heritage Tour. The company recently launched WI Bridge, a monthly publication for the Washington area's thriving millenneal community, and a podcast studio is currently under construction.

WASHINGTON SUN

(Thur)
830 Kennedy St NW, Washington, DC, 20011-2948, District Of Columbia, USA; tel (202) 882-1021; fax (202) 882-9817; e-mail thewashingtonsun@aol.com
Circulation: 55,000pd,; Sworn/Estimate/Non-Audited
Ed. .... Stephen Cooke
Mng. Ed... Mae Lynn
Mechanical Specifications: Type page 13 x 21 1/2; E - 6 cols, 2 1/16, 1/8 between; A - 6 cols, 2 1/16, 1/8 between.
Equipment: Hardware — IBM, PC.

FLORIDA

FORT LAUDERDALE

SOUTH FLORIDA TIMES

(Fri)
3020 NE 32nd Ave, Ste 200, Fort Lauderdale, FL, 33308-7233, Broward, USA; tel (954) 356-9360; fax (954) 356-9395; adv e-mail advertising@sfltimes.com; web site www.sfltimes.com
Circulation: 20,000pd,; Sworn/Estimate/Non-Audited
Advertising: Open inch rate $21.18
Pub.................................. Robert Beatty, Esq.
Ed. .... Brad Bennett
Mechanical Specifications: Type page 13 x 21; E - 6 cols, 2 1/16, 1/8 between; A - 6 cols, 2 1/16, 1/8 between.
Equipment: Hardware — PC, APP/Mac; Software — Adobe/PageMaker 6.0, Microsoft/Word 7.0.

WESTSIDE GAZETTE

(Thur)
545 NW 7th Ter, Fort Lauderdale, FL, 33311-8140, Broward, USA; tel (954) 525-1489; fax (954) 525-1861; e-mail wgazette@bellsouth.net; web site www.thewestsidegazette.com
Circulation: 30,000pd,; Sworn/Estimate/Non-Audited
Advertising: Open inch rate $31.91
Pub.. Bobby Henry
Adv. Mgr. .... Charles Moseley
Circ. Mgr................................ Elizabeth Miller
Ed. .... Pamela Lewis
Mechanical Specifications: Type page 13 x 21 1/2; E - 6 cols, 2 1/16, 1/8 between; A - 6 cols, 2 1/16, 1/8 between.

FORT MYERS

COMMUNITY VOICE

(Thur)
3046 Lafayette St, Fort Myers, FL, 33916-4324, Lee, USA; tel (239) 337-4444; fax (239) 334-8289; e-mail commuvoice@aol.com
Circulation: 12,000fr; Sworn/Estimate/Non-Audited
Advertising: Open inch rate $15.00
Established: 1987
Ed. .... Corey F. Weaver
Mechanical Specifications: Type page 10 5/6 x 12; E - 6 cols, 1 9/16, between; A - 6 cols, 1 9/16, between.
Equipment: Hardware — PC, IBM/Compatibles; Software — Windows `95.

JACKSONVILLE

FLORIDA STAR

(Sat)
PO Box 40629, Jacksonville, FL, 32203-0629, Duval, USA; tel (904) 766-8834; fax (904) 765-1673; e-mail info@thefloridastar.com; adv e-mail ad@thefloridastar.com; ed e-mail clara@thefloridastar.com; web site www.thefloridastar.com
Circulation: 35,000pd,; Sworn/Estimate/Non-Audited
Advertising: Open inch rate $15.00
Established: 1951
Group: SCC Communications-The Florida Star Newspaper, The Georgia Star Newspaper
Digital Platform - Mobile: Apple, Windows
Digital Platform - Tablet: Apple iOS, Windows 7, Blackberry Tablet OS, Kindle
Owner/Editor-in-Chief........... Clara McLaughlin
Mechanical Specifications: Type page 13 x 21 1/2; E - 6 cols, 2 1/16, 1/8 between; A - 6 cols, 2 1/16, 1/8 between; C - 6 cols, 2 1/16, 1/8 between.
Equipment: Hardware — PC.
Delivery Method: Mail, Newsstand, Carrier, Racks

JACKSONVILLE FREE PRESS

(Thur)
1122 Edgewood Ave W, Jacksonville, FL, 32208-3419, Duval, USA; tel (904) 634-1993; fax (904) 765-3803; e-mail jfreepress@aol.com; web site www.jacksonvillefreepress.com
Circulation: 43,500pd,; Sworn/Estimate/Non-Audited
Advertising: Open inch rate $30.50
Established: 1986
Digital Platform - Mobile: Windows
Digital Platform - Tablet: Windows 7
Adv. Mgr.................................. Brenda Burwell
Ed. .... Sylvia Perry
Editor .... Lynette Jones
Editorial Director.................. Reggie Fullwood
Community Relations .... Charles Griggs
Mechanical Specifications: Type page 13 x 21 1/2; A - 6 cols, 2 1/8, 1/8 between.
Delivery Method: Mail, Newsstand
Zip Codes Served: All throughout Duval County, Florida

MIAMI

THE MIAMI TIMES

(Wed)
900 NW 54th St, Miami, FL, 33127-1818, Miami-Dade, USA; tel 305-694-6210; adv tel (305) 693-7093; fax 305-757-5770; adv tel (305) 694-6215; adv e-mail advertising@miamitimesonline.com; ed e-mail editorial@miamitimesonline.com; web site www.miamitimesonline.com
Circulation: 15,660pd, 0fr; VAC
Advertising: Open inch rate $56.75
Established: 1923
Digital Platform - Mobile: Apple, Android
Digital Platform - Tablet: Apple iOS, Android
Pub...................................... Rachel J. Reeves
Assistant To The Publisher .... Karen Franklin
VP Business Development..... Garth B. Reeves
Executive Editor....................... Carolyn Guniss
Operation Manager............ Lorraine Cammock
Mechanical Specifications: 1 Column = 2"
2 Columns = 4.167"
3 Columns = 6.3"
4 Columns = 8.45"
5 Columns = 10.625"
6 Columns = 12.75"
Full Page 12.75 x 20.75 (124.5 inches)
Junior Page 10.625 x 18 (90 inches)
Half Page 12.75 x 10.5 (63 inches)
Strip Ad 12.75 x 4 (24 inches)
Eighth Page 8.45 x 4 (16 inches)
Equipment: Hardware — APP/Mac, IBM; Software — MediaSpann/SmartPublisher/News 2 Edit.
Delivery Method: Mail, Newsstand
Zip Codes Served: 33009 33056, 33010 33125, 33012 33126, 33013 33127, 33014 33128, 33015 33130, 33016 33132, 33018 33133, 33020 33134, 33021 33135, 33023 33136, 33024 33137, 33025 33138, 33026 33139, 33030 33140, 33031 33141, 33032 33141, 33033 33142, 33034 33143, 33050 33144, 33054 33145, 33055 33146, 33147, 33149, 33150, 33153, 33154, 33155, 33156, 33157, 33159, 33160, 33161, 33162, 33163, 33165, 33166, 33167, 33168, 33169, 33170, 33172, 33173, 33174, 33175, 33176, 33177, 33179, 33180, 33181, 33182, 33183, 33184, 33185, 33186, 33189, 33193, 33196, 33247, 33302, 33309, 33311, 33312, 33313, 33314, 33317

ORLANDO

THE ORLANDO TIMES

(Thur)
4403 Vineland Rd Ste B5, Quorum Center, Orlando, FL, 32811-7362, Orange, USA; tel (407) 841-3052; adv tel (407) 849-0434; fax (407) 849-0434; e-mail calvincollinsjr@aol.

com; adv e-mail calvincollinsjr@aol.com; web site www.orlando-times.com
Circulation: 7,289pd, 3,111fr; Sworn/Estimate/Non-Audited
Advertising: Open inch rate $19.00
Established: 1976
Pres./Pub. ....Dr. Calvin Collins
Adv. Mgr. ....Kevin T. Collins
Prodn. Mgr. ....Lottie H. Collins
Mechanical Specifications: Type page 10 x 21; E - 6 cols, between; A - 6 cols, between; C - 6 cols, between.
Equipment: Hardware — IBM; Software — Microsoft/Word.
Delivery Method: Mail, Newsstand, Carrier, Racks

PENSACOLA

NEW AMERICAN WEEKLY

(Thur)
619 N De Villiers St, Pensacola, FL, 32501-3817, Escambia, USA; tel (850) 432-8410; fax (850) 434-5023; e-mail napressweekly@aol.com
Circulation: 34,800pd, 2,905fr; Sworn/Estimate/Non-Audited
Advertising: Open inch rate $44.80
Pub...Angelina LeRoy
Adv. Mgr. ....Wallace LeRoy
Ed. ....Kelli Pogue
Mechanical Specifications: Type page 13 x 21 1/2; E - 6 cols, 2 1/16, 1/8 between; A - 6 cols, 2 1/16, 1/8 between.
Equipment: Hardware — IBM.

PENSACOLA VOICE

(Thur)
213 E Yonge St, Pensacola, FL, 32503-3766, Escambia, USA; tel (850) 434-6963; fax (850) 469-8745; e-mail info@pensacolavoice.com; jmiles@pensacolavoice.com; adv e-mail ads@pensacolavoice.com; web site www.pensacolavoice.com
Circulation: 37,500pd,; Sworn/Estimate/Non-Audited
Advertising: Open inch rate $23.10
Established: 1967
Ed. ....Jacqueline Miles
Mechanical Specifications: Type page 13 x 21 1/2; E - 6 cols, between; A - 6 cols, between; C - 6 cols, between.
Equipment: Hardware — APP/Mac; Software — Baseview/NewsEdit, QPS/QuarkXPress.
Delivery Method: Mail, Newsstand, Carrier, Racks

SAINT PETERSBURG

WEEKLY CHALLENGER

(Thur)
2500 Martin Luther King St S, Ste F, Saint Petersburg, FL, 33705-3554, Pinellas, USA; tel (727) 896-2922; fax (727) 823-2568; e-mail editor@theweeklychallenger.com; web site www.theweeklychallenger.com
Circulation: 552pd, 4,511fr; VAC
Advertising: Open inch rate $18.00
Pub..Ephel Johnson
Adv. Mgr. ....Dianne Speithes
Graphic Artist.......................Lorraine Bellinger
Mechanical Specifications: Type page 13 3/4 x 21; E - 8 cols, 1 1/2, 1/4 between; A - 8 cols, 1 1/2, 1/4 between; C - 8 cols, 1 1/2, 1/4 between.
Equipment: Hardware — APP/Mac.

TALLAHASSEE

CAPITAL OUTLOOK

(Thur)
1363 E Tennessee St, Tallahassee, FL, 32308-5107, Leon, USA; tel (850) 877-0105; adv tel (850) 877-0105; ed tel (859) 877-0105; fax (850) 877-5110; adv tel (850) 877-5110; ed tel (850) 877-5110; e-mail info@capitaloutlook.com; adv e-mail advertising@capitaloutlook.com; ed e-mail pressreleases@capitaloutlook.com; web site www.capitaloutlook.com
Circulation: 1,000pd,; Sworn/Estimate/Non-Audited
Advertising: Open inch rate $33.00
Established: 1975
Group: LIVE Communications, Inc.
General Manager................Taralisha Sanders
Delivery Method: Mail, Racks
Zip Codes Served: Multiple

TAMPA

DAYTONA TIMES

(Thur) (on-line daily)
PO Box 48857, Tampa, FL, 33646-0124, Hillsborough, USA; tel (813) 319-0961; fax (813) 628-0713; e-mail sales@flcourier.com; adv e-mail sales@flcourier.com; web site www.daytonatimes.com
Circulation: 15,000fr; Sworn/Estimate/Non-Audited
Advertising: Open inch rate $33.60
Established: 1977
Digital Platform - Mobile: Apple, Android, Windows
Digital Platform - Tablet: Apple iOS, Android, Other
Circ. Mgr.....................................Glenn Cherry
Ed. ....Charles W. Cherry
Mechanical Specifications: 6C x 20" 1C =1.66"
Equipment: Hardware — APP/Mac; Software — Adobe/PageMaker.
Delivery Method: Mail, Newsstand, Racks
Zip Codes Served: 32116,32117, 32118, 32119, 32122, 32114, 32115, 32120, 32121, 32124, 32125, 32126, 32198

FLORIDA SENTINEL-BULLETIN

(Tues, Wed, Thur, Fri)
2207 E 21st Ave, Tampa, FL, 33605-2043, Hillsborough, USA; tel (813) 248-1921; fax (813) 248-4507; ed e-mail ghayes@flsentinel.com; web site www.flsentinel.com
Circulation: 49,892pd, 126fr; Sworn/Estimate/Non-Audited
Advertising: Open inch rate $14.00
Pub.............................. S. Kay Andrews Wells
Adv. Dir......................................Betty Dawkins
Ed. ....Gwen Hayes
Mechanical Specifications: Type page 10 x 15; E - 5 cols, 2, between; A - 5 cols, 2, between; C - 5 cols, 2, between.
Equipment: Hardware — APP/Mac, Mk; Presses — HI/V-150.; Software — Presses; HI/V-150.

GEORGIA

ALBANY

ALBANY SOUTHWEST GEORGIAN

(Wed)
311 S Jackson St, Ste A, Albany, GA, 31701-0689, Dougherty, USA; tel (229) 436-2156; fax (229) 435-6860; e-mail aswgeorgian@gmail.com
Circulation:; Sworn/Estimate/Non-Audited
Advertising: Open inch rate $17.05
Established: 1938
Publisher..G Searles
Mechanical Specifications: Full page: 21x10.833,Half page: 10x10.833, 1/4 page:10x5.333
Equipment: Hardware — IBM; Software — Adobe/PageMaker.
Delivery Method: Mail, Carrier, Racks
Zip Codes Served: 31701,31705,31707,31709, 39813,31730,39840,39842,39846,31779,31791,31793

ATLANTA

ATLANTA DAILY WORLD

(Thur) (daily online)
3485 N Desert Dr, Ste 2109, Atlanta, GA, 30344-8125, Fulton, USA; tel 404-761-1114; adv tel 678-515-2053; fax 404-761-1164; e-mail publisher@atlantadailyworld.com; adwnews@atlantadailyworld.com; adv e-mail advertising@atlantadailyworld.com; ed e-mail adwnews@atlantadailyworld.com; web site www.atlantadailyworld.com
Circulation: 0pd, 3,836fr; VAC
Advertising: Open inch rate $53.38
Established: 1928
Group: Real Times Media, Inc.
Digital Platform - Mobile: Apple
Digital Platform - Tablet: Apple iOS, Android, Windows 7, Blackberry Tablet OS, Kindle, Nook, Kindle Fire
Pub...Alexis Scott
Adv. Dir..................................Michelle Gipson
Mng. Ed.........................Maria Odum-Hinmon
Prodn. Mgr. ....Wendell Scott
Mechanical Specifications: Type page 10.5 X 13; E - 6 cols, 2, 1/8 between; A - 6 cols, 2, 1/8 between; C - 8 cols, 1 1/2, 1/16 between.
Delivery Method: Mail, Newsstand, Carrier, Racks

THE ATLANTA INQUIRER

(Thur)
947 Martin Luther King Jr Dr NW, Atlanta, GA, 30314-2947, Fulton, USA; tel (404) 523-6086; fax (404) 523-6088; e-mail news@atlinq.com; adv e-mail ads@atlinq.com; ed e-mail news@atlinq.com; web site www.atlinq.com
Circulation: 0pd, 0fr; Sworn/Estimate/Non-Audited
Advertising: Open inch rate $30.80
Established: 1960
Adv. Mgr...........................Sallie Pope Howard
Circ. Mgr...................................Herbert Linsey
Ed. ....John B. Smith
Prodn. Mgr. ....Kimberly Bryant
Mechanical Specifications: Type page 11 1/2 x 21 1/2; E - 6 cols, 2 1/16, between; A - 6 cols, 2 1/16, between; C - 6 cols, 2 1/16, between.
Equipment: Hardware — APP/Mac.
Zip Codes Served: 30001, 30181, 30265, 30333, 30453, 31208

THE ATLANTA VOICE

(Thur) (Electronic Edition)
633 Pryor St SW, Atlanta, GA, 30312-2738, Fulton, USA; tel (404) 524-6426; adv tel (404) 524-6426 x 15; ed tel (404) 524-6426 x 13; fax (404) 523-7853; e-mail info@theatlantavoice.com; adv e-mail ads@theatlantavoice.com; web site www.theatlantavoice.com
Circulation: 228pd, 24,480fr; CAC
Advertising: Open inch rate $65.17
Established: 1966
Group: Voice News Network
Digital Platform - Mobile: Apple, Blackberry
Digital Platform - Tablet: Apple iOS, Kindle
Pub...Janis L. Ware
Editor ....James A. Washington
Sales Asst...April Ivey
Ed. in Chief..........................Stan Washington
Mechanical Specifications: Type page 10 x 13 1/2; A - 6 cols, 1 1/2, 1/4 between; C - 6 cols, 1 1/2, 1/4 between.
Delivery Method: Mail, Newsstand, Racks

AUGUSTA

THE METRO COURIER

(Thur)
314 Walton Way, Augusta, GA, 30901-2436, Richmond, USA; tel (706) 724-6556; fax (706) 722-7104; e-mail metrocourier@comcast.net
Circulation: 29,010pd,; Sworn/Estimate/Non-Audited
Advertising: Open inch rate $16.50
Ed. ....Barbara A. Gordon
Mechanical Specifications: Type page 13 x 21; E - 6 cols, 2, 1/5 between; A - 6 cols, 2, 1/5 between; C - 6 cols, 2, 1/5 between.
Equipment: Hardware — APP/Mac IIsi; Software — Microsoft/Word, Adobe/PageMaker.

COLUMBUS

THE COLUMBUS TIMES

(Wed)
2230 Buena Vista Rd, Columbus, GA, 31906-3111, Muscogee, USA; tel (706) 324-2404; fax (706) 596-0657; e-mail columbustimes@knology.net; web site www.columbustimes.com
Circulation: 10,000pd,; Sworn/Estimate/Non-Audited
Advertising: Open inch rate $15.00
Pub.............................Ophelia Devore-Mitchell
Mng. Ed...........................Helmut Gertjegerdes
News Ed. ....Carol Gertjegerdes
Mechanical Specifications: Type page 13 x 21 1/2; E - 6 cols, 2 1/16, between; A - 6 cols, 2 1/16, between; C - 6 cols, 2 1/16, between.
Equipment: Hardware — APP/Mac; Software — Adobe/Photoshop, QPS/QuarkXPress.

DECATUR

THE CHAMPION

(Thur)
114 New St, Ste E, Decatur, GA, 30030-5356, Dekalb, USA; tel (404) 373-7779; fax (404) 373-7721; e-mail JohnH@dekalbchamp.com; adv e-mail JohnH@dekalbchamp.com; ed e-mail Kathy@dekalbchamp.com; web site www.championnewspaper.com
Circulation: 645pd, 58fr; CVC
Advertising: Open inch rate $30.20
Pub...........................Carolyn Jernigan-Glenn
COO/Gen. Mgr. ....John Hewitt
Ed. ....Kathy Mitchell
Mng. Ed................................Gale Horton Gay
Prodn. Mgr. ....Kemesha Hunt
Classic/Web Designer..............Travis Hutchins
Mechanical Specifications: Type page 10 1/4 x 14 1/4; E - 5 cols, 2, 3/16 between; A - 5 cols, 2, 3/16 between; C - 7 cols, 1 5/16, 3/16 between.
Equipment: Hardware — PC; Software — Adobe/PageMaker 5.0.
Delivery Method: Mail, Newsstand, Racks

SAVANNAH

SAVANNAH HERALD

(Wed) (Weekly)
2135 Rowland Ave, Ste B, Savannah, GA, 31404-4453, Chatham, USA; tel (912) 356-0025; fax (912) 356-0028; e-mail news@savannahherald.net; adv e-mail sales@savannahherald.net; ed e-mail news@savannahherald.net; web site www.savannahherald.net
Circulation: 12,500fr; Sworn/Estimate/Non-Audited
Advertising: Open inch rate $12.00
Digital Platform - Mobile: Apple
Digital Platform - Tablet: Apple iOS
Publisher...............................Kenneth Adams
Co-Publisher...........................Khristi Chisholm
Mechanical Specifications: Type page 10.5 x 20; E - 6 cols, between; A - 6 cols, between; C - 6 cols, between.
Equipment: Hardware — APP/Mac; Software — Adobe/InDesign CC
Delivery Method: Newsstand, Racks

THE SAVANNAH TRIBUNE

(Wed)
PO Box 2066, Savannah, GA, 31402-2066, Chatham, USA; tel (912) 233-6128; fax (912)

233-6140; e-mail sharon@savannahtribune.com; web site www.savannahtribune.com
Circulation: 15,000fr; Sworn/Estimate/Non-Audited
Advertising: Open inch rate $14.00
Established: 1875
Gen. Mgr.................................... Marius Davis
Adv. Mgr....................................... Tanya Milton
Ed.. Shirley James
Mechanical Specifications: Type page 11 5/8 x 21 1/2; E - 6 cols, 1 5/6, 1/8 between; A - 6 cols, 1 5/6, 1/8 between; C - 6 cols, 1 5/6, 1/8 between.
Equipment: Hardware — MAC; Presses — Outsourced; Software — QPS 5.0.
Zip Codes Served: 31401, 31404, 31405, 31406, 31419, 31411, 31410, 31314, 31409, 31415, 31408, 31407

UNION CITY

ATLANTA-NEWS LEADER
(Fri)
4405 Mall Blvd, Ste 521, Union City, GA, 30291-2083, Fulton, USA; tel (770) 969-7711; fax (770) 969-7811; e-mail atlmet@bellsouth.net
Circulation: 5,000pd, 30,000fr; Sworn/Estimate/Non-Audited
Advertising: Open inch rate $11.29
Gen. Mgr.................................... Esther Edans
Adv. Mgr................................ Creed W. Pannell
Ed.. Nicole Robinson
Assoc. Ed..................................... Carla Harper
Mechanical Specifications: Type page 13 x 21 1/2; E - 6 cols, 2 1/4, between; A - 6 cols, 2 1/4, between; C - 6 cols, 2 1/4, 1/8 between.
Equipment: Hardware — APP/Mac; Software — Adobe.

THE ATLANTA METRO
(Fri)
4405 Mall Blvd, Ste 521, Union City, GA, 30291-2083, Fulton, USA; tel (770) 969-7711; fax (770) 969-7811; e-mail atlmet@bellsouth.net
Circulation: 5,000pd, 30,000fr; Sworn/Estimate/Non-Audited
Circ. Mgr.................................. Willie Robinson
Ed.. Creed W. Pannell
Assoc. Ed..................................... Carla Harper
Mechanical Specifications: Type page 10 3/20 x 14 1/4; E - 4 cols, 2 1/8, 3/16 between; C - 4 cols, 2 1/8, 3/16 between.
Equipment: Hardware — APP/Power Mac 6500, APP/Mac Quadra 840; Software — Adobe/PageMaker 6.0, QPS/QuarkXPress 3.3.

ILLINOIS

CHICAGO

CHICAGO CRUSADER
(Thur)
6429 S Martin Luther King Dr, Chicago, IL, 60637, Cook, USA; tel (773) 752-2500; adv tel (773) 752-2500; ed tel (773) 752-2500; fax (773) 752-2817; adv tel (773) 752-2817; ed tel (773) 752-2817; e-mail crusaderil@aol.com; adv e-mail achicagocrusader@aol.com; ed e-mail crusaderil@aol.com; web site www.chicagocrusader.com
Circulation: 90,661pd,; Sworn/Estimate/Non-Audited
Advertising: Open inch rate $68.12
Established: 1940
Digital Platform - Mobile: Apple, Android, Windows, Blackberry
Digital Platform - Tablet: Apple iOS, Android, Windows 7, Blackberry Tablet OS, Kindle Fire
Adv. Dir....................................... John L. Smith
Ed...................................... Dorothy R. Leavell
Ed.. Erick Johnson
Mechanical Specifications: Call (773) 752-2500
Equipment: Hardware — APP/Mac; Software — Adobe CS6 Suite, Microsoft Office, QPS/QuarkXPress.
Delivery Method: Mail, Newsstand
Zip Codes Served: Call (773) 752-2500 for complete list

CHICAGO DEFENDER
(Wed)
4445 S Dr Martin Luther King Dr, Chicago, IL, 60653, Cook, USA; tel (312) 225-2400; adv tel (312) 225-2400; ed tel (312) 225-2400; fax (312) 225-5659; adv tel (312) 225-9231; ed tel (312) 225-9231; ed e-mail editorial@chicagodefender.com; web site www.chicagodefender.com
Circulation: 3,178pd, 7,907fr; VAC
Advertising: Open inch rate $97.59
Established: 1905
Group: Real Times Media, Inc.
Pres./COO........................... Michael A. House
Exec. Ed....................................... Shari Noland
Adv. Sr. Acct. Exec...... Leanne Muller-Wharton
Managing Editor .... Kathy Chaney
CFO, Dir. of Fin & Bus Op................. Carol Bell
Mechanical Specifications: Type page 10 13/16 x 13; E - 5 cols, 2 1/16, 1/8 between; A - 5 cols, 2 1/16, 1/8 between; C - 5 cols, 2 1/16, 1/8 between.
Equipment: Hardware — APP/Mac.
Delivery Method: Mail, Newsstand, Racks

HYDE PARK CITIZEN
(Wed)
806 E 78th St, Chicago, IL, 60619-2937, Cook, USA; tel (773) 783-1251; fax (773) 783-1301
Circulation: 20,418fr; CVC
Advertising: Open inch rate $106.76
Pub.. William Garth
Adv. Mgr...................................... Janice Garth

N'DIGO
(Thur)
1006 S Michigan Ave, Ste 200, Chicago, IL, 60605-2209, Cook, USA; tel (312) 822-0202; adv tel 312 264 6272; fax 312 431 8893; adv tel 312 431 8893; e-mail admin@ndigo.com; adv e-mail hhartman@ndigo.com; ed e-mail dsmallwood@ndigo.com; web site www.ndigo.com
Circulation: 130,000fr; Sworn/Estimate/Non-Audited
Advertising: Open inch rate $89.44
Established: 1989
Digital Platform - Mobile: Apple
Digital Platform - Tablet: Apple iOS
Pub................................. Hermene D. Hartman
Editor .... David Smallwood
Administrator .... Sylvester Cosby
Business Development.............. Walter Aikens
Mechanical Specifications: Type page 10 1/8 x 12 1/2; E - 5 cols, 2 1/4, between; A - 4 cols, 2 1/2, between; C - 5 cols, 2, between.
Equipment: Hardware — APP/Mac; Software — QPS/QuarkXPress.
Delivery Method: Racks
Zip Codes Served: 60610, 60611, 60612, 60613, 60614, 60615, 60616, 60617, 60618, 60619, 60620, 60621, 60622, 60623, 60624, 60625, 60626, 60627, 60628, 60629, 60631, 60632, 60634, 60636, 60637, 60639, 60640, 60642, 60643, 60644, 60645, 60647, 60649, 60651, 60652, 60653, 606

NEW METRO NEWS
(Thur)
501 E 32nd St, Apt 501, Chicago, IL, 60616-4016, Cook, USA; tel (312) 791-0880
Advertising: Open inch rate $20.20
Ed... Nathaniel Clay
Prodn. Mgr................................ John Dunham
Mechanical Specifications: Type page 12 x 21; E - 6 cols, 2, 1/16 between.

SOUTH SUBURBAN CITIZEN
(Wed)
806 E 78th St, Chicago, IL, 60619-2937, Cook, USA; tel (773) 783-1251; fax (773) 783-1301; e-mail citizen_newsroom@yahoo.com; web site www.thechicagocitizen.com
Circulation: 20,355fr; CVC
Advertising: Open inch rate $106.76
Pub.. William Garth
Adv. Mgr...................................... Janice Garth

SOUTHEND CITIZEN
(Wed)
806 E 78th St, Chicago, IL, 60619-2937, Cook, USA; tel (773) 783-1251; fax (773) 783-1301; web site www.thechicagocitizen.com
Circulation: 30,130fr; CVC
Advertising: Open inch rate $129.17
Pub.. William Garth
Adv. Mgr...................................... Janice Garth

EAST SAINT LOUIS

EAST ST. LOUIS MONITOR
(Thur)
1501 State St, East Saint Louis, IL, 62205-2011, Saint Clair, USA; tel (618) 271-0468; fax (618) 271-8443
Circulation: 8,800pd,; Sworn/Estimate/Non-Audited
Advertising: Open inch rate $14.60
Adv. Mgr................................ George Laktzian
Circ. Mgr..................................... Ahmad Saae
Ed... Anne Jordan
Prodn. Mgr............................... Frazier Garner
Mechanical Specifications: Type page 12 x 21 1/2; E - 6 cols, 2, between.
Equipment: Hardware — COM/8000; Software — Typesetter S.N. 1252.

INDIANA

FORT WAYNE

FROST ILLUSTRATED
(Wed)
3121 S Calhoun St, Fort Wayne, IN, 46807-1901, Allen, USA; tel (260) 745-0552; e-mail news@frostillustrated.com; adv e-mail fwfrostads@gmail.com; ed e-mail fwfrostnews@gmail.com; web site www.frostillustrated.com
Circulation: 1,380pd, 39fr; CVC
Advertising: Open inch rate $19.00
Established: 1968
Digital Platform - Mobile: Apple, Android, Windows, Blackberry
Digital Platform - Tablet: Apple iOS, Android, Windows 7, Blackberry Tablet OS
Pub.. Edward N. Smith
Managing Ed....................... Michael Patterson
Layout & Production Manager..... Andy Kurzen
Mechanical Specifications: Type page 10 2/5 x 16; E - 5 cols, between; A - 5 cols, between; C - 8 cols, between.
Equipment: Hardware — APP/Mac; Software — Adobe/InDesign, Photoshop
Delivery Method: Mail, Newsstand, Racks
Zip Codes Served: 46801, 46802, 46803, 46804, 45805, 46806, 46807, 46808, 46809, 46815, 46816, 46818, 46819, 46825, 46835

GARY

GARY CRUSADER
(Thur)
1549 Broadway, Gary, IN, 46407-2240, Lake, USA; tel (219) 885-4357; fax (219) 883-3317; e-mail crusaderil@aol.com; web site www.crusaderil.com
Circulation: 44,000pd,; Sworn/Estimate/Non-Audited
Advertising: Open inch rate $32.53
Ed...................................... Dorothy R. Leavell
Mng. Ed.................................... David Denson
Prodn. Mgr.................................... John Smith
Mechanical Specifications: Type page 10 x 14; E - 5 cols, between; A - 5 cols, between; C - 6 cols, between.
Equipment: Hardware — APP/Mac; Software — Adobe/PageMaker.

INDIANAPOLIS

INDIANA HERALD
(Fri)
2170 N Illinois St, Indianapolis, IN, 46202-1334, Marion, USA; tel (317) 923-8291; fax (317) 923-8292; e-mail herald1@earthlink.net; adv e-mail indyherald@earthlink.net; ed e-mail herald1@earthlink.net; web site www.indianaherald.com.
Circulation: 15,000pd,; Sworn/Estimate/Non-Audited
Advertising: Open inch rate $17.00
Established: 1958
Adv. Mgr.............................. Bernice Matheson
Ed.. Mary B. Tandy
Mechanical Specifications: Type page 10.125 x 21 1/2; E -
Equipment: Hardware — PC.
Delivery Method: Mail, Newsstand, Racks
Zip Codes Served: 462

INDIANAPOLIS RECORDER
(Fri)
2901 N Tacoma Ave, Indianapolis, IN, 46218-2737, Marion, USA; tel (317) 924-5143; fax (317) 924-5148; e-mail newsroom@indyrecorder.com; web site www.indianapolisrecorder.com
Circulation: 6,358pd, 5,257fr; CVC
Advertising: Open inch rate $33.00
Owner/Chrmn........................ William G. Mays
Pub... Carolene Mays
Circ. Mgr...................................... Angie Kuhn
Ed...................................... Shannon Williams
Prodn. Mgr.................................. Jeana Lewis
Mechanical Specifications: Type page 13 x 21; E - 6 cols, between; A - 6 cols, between; C - 9 cols, between.
Equipment: Hardware — APP/Mac.

KANSAS

WICHITA

THE COMMUNITY VOICE
(Thur) (Every other Thurs)
2918 E Douglas Ave, Wichita, KS, 67214-4709, Sedgwick, USA; tel (316) 681-1155; e-mail press@tcvpub.com; adv e-mail adcopy@tcvpub.com; ed e-mail press@tcvpub.com; web site tcvpub.com
Circulation: 10,892fr; CVC
Established: 1993
Editor-in-Chief.......................... Bonita Gooch
Mechanical Specifications: Tabloid. 9.90"W X 10.25"H
Equipment: Hardware — I; Software — Indesign, Photoshop
Delivery Method: Mail, Newsstand
Zip Codes Served: 67214, 67219, 67220, 67226, 67203, 67208, 67206 major service area

KENTUCKY

LOUISVILLE

THE LOUISVILLE DEFENDER
(Thur)
1720 Dixie Hwy, Louisville, KY, 40210-2314, Jefferson, USA; tel (502) 772-2591; fax (502) 775-8655; e-mail loudefender@aol.com
Circulation: 2,615pd, 73fr; Sworn/Estimate/

Non-Audited
Advertising: Open inch rate $14.60
Adv. Mgr. .... Clarence Leslie
Circ. Mgr. .... Marie Brown
Ed. .... Yvonne Coleman
Mechanical Specifications: Type page 13 x 21 1/2; E - 6 cols, between; A - 6 cols, between; C - 8 cols, between.
Equipment: Hardware — APP/Mac.

LOUISIANA

ALEXANDRIA

ALEXANDRIA NEWS WEEKLY

(Thur)
1746 Mason St, Alexandria, LA, 71301-6242, Rapides, USA; tel (318) 443-7664; adv tel (318) 487-1827; e-mail anwnews@bellsouth.net
Circulation: 10,000pd,; Sworn/Estimate/Non-Audited
Advertising: Open inch rate $15.00
Adv. Mgr. .... Leon Coleman
Ed. .... Alice Coleman
Mechanical Specifications: Type page 14 x 21; E - 6 cols, between; A - 6 cols, between; C - 9 cols, between.
Equipment: Hardware — PC; Software — WordPerfect 6.1.

MONROE

MONROE FREE PRESS

(Thur)
216 Collier St, Monroe, LA, 71201-7202, Ouachita, USA; tel (318) 388-1310; fax (318) 388-2911; e-mail rooseveltwright@prodigy.net; web site www.monroefreepress.com
Circulation: 15,000pd,; Sworn/Estimate/Non-Audited
Advertising: Open inch rate $10.00
Ed. .... Roosevelt Wright
Mechanical Specifications: Type page 13 x 21; E - 6 cols, 2 1/16, 1/8 between; A - 6 cols, 2 1/16, 1/8 between; C - 6 cols, 2 1/16, 1/8 between.
Equipment: Hardware — IBM; Software — Adobe/PageMaker 6.0.

NEW ORLEANS

LOUISIANA WEEKLY

(Mon)
2215 Pelopidas St, New Orleans, LA, 70122-4957, Orleans, USA; tel (504) 282-3705; fax (504) 282-3773; e-mail info@louisianaweekly.com; web site www.louisianaweekly.com
Circulation: 8,300pd, 1,700fr; Sworn/Estimate/Non-Audited
Advertising: Open inch rate $19.41
Mktg. Mgr. .... Chris Hall
Circ. Mgr. .... Jim Hall
Exec. Ed. .... Renette Dejoie-Hall
Ed. .... Edmund W. Lewis
Webmaster .... David T. Baker
Mechanical Specifications: Type page 13 x 21 1/2; E - 6 cols, 2 1/8, between; A - 6 cols, 2 1/8, between; C - 8 cols, 1 1/2, between.
Equipment: Hardware — APP/PowerMac; Presses — WPC/Web Leader; Software — QPS/QuarkXPress 4.1, MS/Word, Corel/WordPerfect, Adobe/Photoshop 5.5.

NEW ORLEANS DATA NEWS WEEKLY

(Sat)
3501 Napoleon Ave, New Orleans, LA, 70125-4843, Orleans, USA; tel (504) 821-7421; fax (504) 821-7622; e-mail datanewsad@bellsouth.net; ed e-mail datanewseditor@bellsouth.net; web site www.ladatanews.com
Circulation: 0pd, 19,976fr; CVC
Advertising: Open inch rate $74.12
Established: 1967
Group: New Orleans Data News Weekly
Digital Platform - Tablet: Apple iOS, Windows 7, Blackberry Tablet OS
Pub. .... Terry B. Jones
Circ. Mgr. .... Chric Mercadel
Mechanical Specifications: Type page 10 3/4 x 14; E - 5 cols, between; A - 5 cols, between.
Equipment: Hardware — APP/Mac; Software — Adobe/Photoshop 5.0, InDesign
Delivery Method: Racks

SHREVEPORT

SHREVEPORT SUN

(Thur)
2224 Jewella Ave, Shreveport, LA, 71109-2410, Caddo, USA; tel (318) 631-6222; fax (318) 635-2822; e-mail sunweekly@aol.com; adv e-mail sunweeklyads@aol.com; web site www.sunweeklynews.com
Circulation: 5,000pd,; Sworn/Estimate/Non-Audited
Advertising: Open inch rate $11.76
Established: 1920
Ed. .... Sonya C. Landry
Advt Mgr .... Larry Rogers
Circulation Mgr .... Brenda Demming
Mechanical Specifications: Type page 13 x 21 1/2; E - 6 cols, 2 1/16, 1/8 between; A - 6 cols, 2 1/16, 1/8 between; C - 10 cols, between.
Equipment: Hardware — APP/Mac, IBM; Software — Adobe/PageMaker 4.2, Microsoft/Word, Quicken.
Delivery Method: Mail, Newsstand, Racks

MARYLAND

BALTIMORE

AFRO-AMERICAN

(Sat)
2519 N Charles St, Baltimore, MD, 21218-4602, Baltimore City, USA; tel 410-554-8200; web site www.afro.com
Circulation: 724pd,; Sworn/Estimate/Non-Audited

EVERY WEDNESDAY

(Wed)
2519 N Charles St, Baltimore, MD, 21218-4602, Baltimore City, USA; tel (410) 554-8200; fax (410) 554-8150; web site www.afro.com
Advertising: Open inch rate $25.00
Pub. .... John J. Oliver
Adv. Mgr. .... Susan Warshaw
Ed. .... Dorothy Boulware

PRINCE GEORGE'S COUNTY TIMES

(Fri)
2513 N Charles St, Baltimore, MD, 21218-4602, Baltimore City, USA; tel (410) 366-3900; fax (410) 243-1627; e-mail btimes@btimes.com; web site www.btimes.com
Advertising: Open inch rate $20.04
Adv. Sales Mgr. .... Donnie Manuel
Mng. Ed. .... Joy Bramble
Prodn. Mgr. .... Freddie Howard

THE AFRO AMERICAN NEWSPAPER-BALTIMORE

(Sat)
2519 N Charles St, Baltimore, MD, 21218-4602, Baltimore City, USA; tel (410) 554-8200; fax (877) 570-9297; e-mail adafro@afro.com; web site www.afro.com
Circulation: 5,234pd, 261fr; AAM
Advertising: Open inch rate $40.49
Pub. .... John J. Oliver
Adv. Mgr. .... Susan Warshaw
Circ. Mgr. .... Sammy Graham
Mng. Ed. .... Tiffaney Ginyard
Adv. Dir. .... Lenora Howze
Mechanical Specifications: Type page 13 x 21; E - 6 cols, 2, 1/8 between; A - 6 cols, 2, 1/8 between; C - 9 cols, 1 1/2, between.
Equipment: Hardware — PC, APP/Mac; Software — QPS/QuarkXPress, Adobe/Photoshop.

THE AFRO AMERICAN NEWSPAPER-WASHINGTON

(Sat)
2519 N Charles St, Baltimore, MD, 21218-4602, Baltimore City, USA; tel (410) 554-8200; fax (877) 570-9297; e-mail adafro@afro.com; web site www.afro.com
Advertising: Open inch rate $46.56
Pub. .... John J. Oliver
Adv. Mgr. .... Susan Warshaw

THE ANNAPOLIS TIMES

(Sat)
2513 N Charles St, Baltimore, MD, 21218-4602, Baltimore City, USA; tel (410) 366-3900; fax (410) 243-1627; e-mail btimes@btimes.com; web site www.btimes.com
Circulation: 3,975fr; CVC
Advertising: N/A
Established: 1986
Pub. .... Joy Bramble
Circ. Mgr .... Ida Neal
Delivery Method: Carrier, Racks

THE BALTIMORE TIMES

(Sat)
2513 N Charles St, Baltimore, MD, 21218-4602, Baltimore City, USA; tel (410) 366-3900; fax (410) 243-1627; e-mail btimes@btimes.com; adv e-mail ads@btimes.com; ed e-mail kreevie@btimes.com; web site www.baltimoretimes-online.com
Circulation: 19,975fr; CVC
Advertising: N/A
Established: 1986
Digital Platform - Mobile: Apple
Digital Platform - Tablet: Apple iOS
Pub. .... Joy Bramble
Sales Mgr. .... Donnie Manuel
Mng. Ed. .... Dena Wane
Prodn. Mgr. .... Freddie Howard
Circ. Mgr .... Ida Neal
Mechanical Specifications: Type page 10 x 13; E - 5 cols, 1 19/20, between; A - 5 cols, 1 19/20, between; C - 5 cols, 1 19/20, between.
Equipment: Hardware — PC, APP/Mac; Software — QPS/QuarkXPress, cs5.5
Delivery Method: Carrier, Racks

MASSACHUSETTS

DORCHESTER

BAY STATE BANNER

(Thur)
1100 Washington St, Dorchester, MA, 02124-5520, Suffolk, USA; tel (617) 261-4600; web site http://www.baystatebanner.com/
Circulation: 27,388fr; CAC
Established: 1965Yawu Miller

MICHIGAN

DETROIT

MICHIGAN CHRONICLE

(Wed)
479 Ledyard St, Detroit, MI, 48201-2641, Wayne, USA; tel (313) 963-8100; fax (313) 963-8788; e-mail chronicle4@aol.com; web site www.michronicleonline.com
Circulation: 20,910pd, 1,321fr; CVC
Advertising: Open inch rate $39.64
Established: 1936
Group: Real Times, Inc.
COO .... Karen A. Love
Pub. .... Samuel Logan
Mng. Ed. .... Cornelius Fortune
Prodn. Mgr. .... Raymond Allen
Mechanical Specifications: Type page 11 5/8 x 21 1/4; E - 6 cols, 1 5/6, 1/8 between; A - 6 cols, 1 5/6, 1/8 between; C - 9 cols, 1 3/16, between.
Equipment: Hardware — APP/Mac, IBM; Software — QPS/QuarkXPress.

MICHIGAN CITIZEN

(Thur)
1055 Trumbull St, Detroit, MI, 48216-1938, Wayne, USA; tel (313) 963-8282; fax (313) 963-8285; e-mail editor@michigancitizen.com; web site www.michigancitizen.com
Circulation: 58,000pd,; Sworn/Estimate/Non-Audited
Advertising: Open inch rate $33.11
Established: 1978
Pub. .... Catherine Kelly
Circ. Mgr. .... Staria Shegog
Ed. .... Teresa Kelly
Mechanical Specifications: Type page 13 x 21; E - 6 cols, 2 1/16, 1/8 between; A - 6 cols, 2 1/16, 1/8 between; C - 9 cols, 1 3/4, 1/8 between.
Equipment: Hardware — PC.

ECORSE

TELEGRAM

(Thur)
PO Box 29085, Ecorse, MI, 48229-0085, Wayne, USA; tel (313) 928-2955; fax (313) 928-3014; e-mail telegram@telegramnews.net; web site www.telegramnews.net
Circulation: 35,000pd,; Sworn/Estimate/Non-Audited
Advertising: Open inch rate $20.50
Adv. Dir. .... Gina Wilson

GRAND RAPIDS

THE GRAND RAPIDS TIMES

(Fri)
2016 Eastern Ave SE, Grand Rapids, MI, 49507-3235, Kent, USA; tel (616) 245-8737; fax (616) 245-1026; e-mail staff@grtimes.com; web site www.grtimes.com
Circulation: 6,000pd,; Sworn/Estimate/Non-Audited
Advertising: Open inch rate $17.00
Ed. .... Patricia Pulliam
Mechanical Specifications: Type page 10 x 15; E - 5 cols, between; A - 5 cols, between.
Equipment: Hardware — APP/Power Mac; Software — Adobe/PageMaker.

MINNESOTA

MINNEAPOLIS

INSIGHT NEWS

(Mon)
1815 Bryant Ave N, Minneapolis, MN, 55411-3212, Hennepin, USA; tel (612) 588-1313; fax (612)588-2031; e-mail info@insightnews.com; adv e-mail selene@insightnews.com; ed e-mail al@insightnews.com; web site www.insightnews.com
Circulation: 65pd, 34,835fr; CAC
Advertising: Open inch rate $69.84
Established: 1976
Group: McFarlane Media Interests, Inc.
Publisher .... Batala McFarlane

Circ. Mgr.............................. Jamal Mohammed
President ....Al McFarlane
Prodn. Mgr. .... Patricia Weaver
Delivery Method: Newsstand, Racks
Zip Codes Served: Minneapolis and St. Paul Metro Area

MINNESOTA SPOKESMAN-RECORDER

(Thur)
3744 4th Ave S, P.O. Box 8558, Minneapolis, MN, 55409-1327, Hennepin, USA; tel (612) 827-4021; adv tel 612-827-4021; ed tel 612-827-4021; fax (612) 827-0577; adv tel 612-827-0577; ed tel 612-827-0577; e-mail display@spokesman-recorder.com; adv e-mail display@spokesman-recorder.com; ed e-mail jfreeman@spokesman-recorder.com; web site www.spokesman-recorder.com
Circulation: 9,800pd, 50,000fr; Sworn/Estimate/Non-Audited
Advertising: Open inch rate $55.46
Established: 1934
CEO/Pub.................................. Tracey Williams
Adv. Acct. Exec ....Raymond Boyd
Adv. Mgr......................................James Stroud
Mechanical Specifications: Type page 6 x 21 1/4; E - 6 cols, 2 1/16, 1/8 between; A - 6 cols, 2 1/16, 1/8 between; C - 6 cols, 2 1/16, 1/8 between.
Equipment: Hardware — APP/Mac, IBM.
Delivery Method: Mail, Newsstand, Carrier, Racks

MISSISSIPPI

JACKSON

JACKSON ADVOCATE

(Thur)
100 W Hamilton St, Jackson, MS, 39202-3237, Hinds, USA; tel (601) 948-4122; fax (601) 948-4125; e-mail jadvocat@aol.com; web site www.jacksonadvocate.com
Circulation: 17,000pd,; Sworn/Estimate/Non-Audited
Advertising: Open inch rate $22.00
Established: 1938
Adv. Mgr.......................................Alice Tisdale
Mechanical Specifications: Type page 13 x 21.

MISSISSIPPI LINK

(Thur)
2659 Livingston Rd, Jackson, MS, 39213-6926, Hinds, USA; tel (601) 896-0084; adv tel (601) 368-8481; ed tel (601) 896-0084; fax (601) 896-0091; e-mail publisher@mississippilink.com; adv e-mail jlinkads@bellsouth.net; ed e-mail editor@mississippilink.com; web site www.mississippilink.com
Circulation: 17,000pd, 150fr; Sworn/Estimate/Non-Audited
Advertising: Open inch rate $18.00
Established: 1993
Pub... Jackie Hampton
Ed. .... Ayesha Mustafaa
Mechanical Specifications: 6 columns (11.625") X 21"
Delivery Method: Mail, Newsstand, Carrier, Racks

MISSOURI

KANSAS CITY

KANSAS CITY GLOBE

(Thur)
615 E 29th St, Kansas City, MO, 64109-1110, Jackson, USA; tel (816) 531-5253; fax (816) 531-5256; e-mail kcglobe@swbell.net; web site www.thekcglobe.com
Circulation: 10,500pd,; Sworn/Estimate/Non-Audited
Advertising: Open inch rate $15.80
Ed. .... Marion Jordon
Prodn. Mgr. ....Denise Jordon
Mechanical Specifications: Type page 13 x 21; E - 6 cols, 2 1/16, 1/8 between; A - 6 cols, 2 1/16, 1/8 between.
Equipment: Hardware — IBM; Software — Adobe/PageMaker.

THE CALL

(Fri)
1715 E 18th St, Kansas City, MO, 64108-1611, Jackson, USA; tel (816) 842-3804; adv tel (816) 842-3804; ed tel (816) 842-3804; fax (816) 842-4420; adv tel (816) 842-4420; ed tel (816) 842-4420; e-mail kccallnews@hotmail.com; web site www.kccall.com
Circulation: 16,456pd,; AAM
Advertising: Open inch rate $15.00
Digital Platform - Mobile: Apple, Windows
Digital Platform - Tablet: Apple iOS, Windows 7
Pub.. Donna Stewart
Circ. Mgr...................................... Barbara Way
Mng. Ed.................................Donna F. Stewart
Mechanical Specifications: Type page 13 x 21; E - 6 cols, between; A - 6 cols, between; C - 8 cols, between.
Delivery Method: Mail, Newsstand, Carrier, Racks

SAINT LOUIS

ST. LOUIS AMERICAN

(Thur)
2315 Pine St, Saint Louis, MO, 63103-2218, Saint Louis City, United States; tel (314) 533-8000; fax (314) 533-2332; e-mail kjones@stlamerican.com; web site www.stlamerican.com
Circulation: 87pd, 66,993fr; CAC
Advertising: Open inch rate $51.50
Established: 1928
Digital Platform - Mobile: Apple, Android, Windows
Digital Platform - Tablet: Apple iOS, Android, Windows 7
Pub... Donald Suggs
COO/Adv. Dir. ....Kevin Jones
Prodn. Mgr. .... Mike Terhaar
Mechanical Specifications: Type page 12 x 21; E - 6 cols, between; A - 6 cols, between; C - 10 cols, between.
Equipment: Hardware — IBM; Software — Microsoft/Office, Adobe/PageMaker, QPS/QuarkXPress, Archetype/Corel Draw.
Delivery Method: Newsstand, Racks
Zip Codes Served: 74 different throughout St. Louis

ST. LOUIS ARGUS

(Thur)
4595 Dr Martin Luther King Dr, Saint Louis, MO, 63113-2332, Saint Louis City, USA; tel (314) 531-1323; fax (314) 531-1324; e-mail media@stlouisargus.com; web site www.stlouisargus.com
Circulation: 33,000fr; Sworn/Estimate/Non-Audited
Advertising: Open inch rate $21.68
Pub... Eddie Hasaan
Office Mgr. .... Judith McDuffie
Ed. .... Erick Wilson
Mechanical Specifications: Type page 13 1/8 x 21; E - 6 cols, 2 1/16, between; A - 6 cols, 2 1/16, between; C - 6 cols, 2 1/16, between.

ST. LOUIS EVENING WHIRL

(Mon)
PO Box 8055, Saint Louis, MO, 63156-8055, Saint Louis City, USA; tel (678) 778-2616; adv tel N/A; fax N/A; adv tel N/A; e-mail tpcwhirl@aol.com; adv e-mail tpcwhirl@aol.com; ed e-mail tpcwhirl@aol.com; web site www.thewhirlonline.com
Circulation: 50,500pd,; Sworn/Estimate/Non-Audited
Advertising: Open inch rate $30.00
Established: 1938
Pub .... Barry R. Thomas
Ed. ....Anthony L. Sanders
Mechanical Specifications: Type page 12 1/2 x 21 1/2; E - 7 cols, 1 5/8, 3/16 between; A - 7 cols, 1 5/8, 3/16 between; C - 9 cols, 1 1/4, 1/8 between.
Equipment: Hardware — IBM; Software — Adobe/PageMaker 6.5, WinFax.
Delivery Method: Mail, Newsstand

NEVADA

LAS VEGAS

LAS VEGAS SENTINEL-VOICE

(Thur)
900 E Charleston Blvd, Las Vegas, NV, 89104-1554, Clark, USA; tel (702) 380-8100; fax (702) 380-8102; e-mail lvsentinelvoice@earthlink.net
Circulation: 6,500fr; Sworn/Estimate/Non-Audited
Advertising: Open inch rate $17.00
Assoc. Pub............................. Kathi Overstreet
Ed. ....Ramon Savoy
Mechanical Specifications: Type page 10 1/4 x 14; E - 6 cols, 1 5/8, between; A - 6 cols, 1 5/8, between; C - 6 cols, 1 5/8, between.
Equipment: Hardware — APP/Mac, IBM; Software — Adobe/PageMaker, Microsoft/Word.

NEW JERSEY

TRENTON

NUBIAN NEWS

(Mthly)
324 S Broad St, Trenton, NJ, 08608-2500, Mercer, USA; tel (609) 656-0950; fax (609) 858-2785
Circulation: 10,000pd,; Sworn/Estimate/Non-Audited
Advertising: Open inch rate $30.00
Gen. Mgr. .... Art Tolbert
Adv. Mgr.......................... Kamau Kujichagulia
Circ. Mgr.. Paul Teel
Mng. Ed.....................................Cheryl Wilson
Mechanical Specifications: Type page 11 x 17; E - 4 cols, 2 1/3, 1/6 between.
Zip Codes Served: 8618

NEW YORK

BROOKLYN

AFRO TIMES

(Thur)
1195 Atlantic Ave, Brooklyn, NY, 11216-2709, Kings, USA; tel (718) 636-9119; fax (718) 857-9115; e-mail challengegroup@yahoo.com
Circulation: 57,004pd,; Sworn/Estimate/Non-Audited
Advertising: Open inch rate $66.65
Pub.................................... Thomas H. Watkins
Adv. Mgr...................................... Ariana Perez
Mng. Ed..Janel Gross

OUR TIME PRESS

(Thur)
679 Lafayette Ave, Brooklyn, NY, 11216-1009, Kings, USA; tel (718) 599-6828; fax (718) 599-6825; ed e-mail editors@ourtimepress.com; web site www.ourtimepress.com
Circulation: 20,000fr; Sworn/Estimate/Non-Audited
Advertising: Open inch rate $54.00
Established: 1995
David Mark Greaves
Bernice Elizabeth GreenEd.s
Mechanical Specifications: Type page 10 x 15; E - 4 cols, 2 3/8, 1/6 between; A - 4 cols, 2 3/8, 1/6 between; C - 5 cols, 1 7/8, 1/6 between.
Delivery Method: Mail, Carrier, Racks
Zip Codes Served: 11201, 11205, 11207, 11212, 11213, 11216, 11217, 11221, 11225, 11233, 11238

THE NEW AMERICAN

(Thur)
1195 Atlantic Ave, Brooklyn, NY, 11216-2709, Kings, USA; tel (718) 636-9119; fax (718) 857-9115; e-mail challengegroup@yahoo.com; newamerican@hotmail.com
Circulation: 60,137pd,; Sworn/Estimate/Non-Audited
Advertising: Open inch rate $66.65
Pub.................................... Thomas H. Watkins
Adv. Mgr...................................... Ariana Perez
Mng. Ed.............................. Tatianna Singleton

BUFFALO

BUFFALO CRITERION

(Sat)
623-625 William St, Buffalo, NY, 14206, Erie, USA; tel (716) 882-9570; fax (716) 882-9570; e-mail criterion@apollo3.com; web site www.buffalocriterion.com
Circulation: 10,000pd,; Sworn/Estimate/Non-Audited
Advertising: Open inch rate $13.50
Pub.................................. Evelyn Merriweather
Adv. Mgr.......................................Pat Ferguson
Ed. ....Frances J. Merriweather
Prodn. Mgr. .... Evelyn Ferguson
Mechanical Specifications: Type page 10.5 x 21; E - 6 cols, 2 1/16, 1/8 between; A - 6 cols, 2 1/16, 1/8 between; C - 8 cols, between.
Equipment: Hardware — PC.

CHALLENGER COMMUNITY NEWS CORP.

(Wed)
140 Linwood Ave, Apt C12, Buffalo, NY, 14209-2022, Erie, USA; tel (716) 881-1051; fax (716) 881-1053; e-mail editor@thechallengernews.com; adv e-mail advertising@thechallengernews.com; ed e-mail editor@thechallengernews.com; web site www.challengercn.com
Circulation: 12,500pd,; Sworn/Estimate/Non-Audited
Advertising: Open inch rate $19.00
Established: 1963
Ed. .... Barbara Banks
Mechanical Specifications: Type page 10 x 14; E - 5 cols, between; A - 5 cols, between; C - 5 cols, between.
Equipment: Hardware — Apple; Software — Adobe/Photoshop, /Indesign
Delivery Method: Mail, Newsstand, Racks

NEW YORK

BLACK STAR NEWS

(Thur)
32 Broadway, Ste 511, New York, NY, 10004-1665, New York, USA; tel (646) 261-7566; adv tel (212) 422-2352; ed tel (646) 261-7566; e-mail advertise@blackstarnews.com; adv e-mail advertise@blackstarnews.com; ed e-mail Milton@blackstarnews.com; web site www.blackstarnews.com
Established: 1977
Digital Platform - Mobile: Apple, Android
Digital Platform - Tablet: Apple iOS, Android
Pub./Ed.-in-Chief ....Milton Allimadi
Assistant Web Ed................Neanda Salvaterra
Delivery Method: Mail, Racks
Zip Codes Served: New York County

NEW YORK AMSTERDAM NEWS
(Thur)
2340 Frederick Douglass Blvd, New York, NY, 10027-3619, New York, USA; tel (212) 932-7400; adv tel (212) 932-7498; ed tel 212-932-7465; adv tel 212 932-7497; ed tel (212) 932-7467; e-mail info@amsterdamnews.com; adv e-mail penda.howell@amsterdamnews.com; web site www.amsterdamnews.com
Circulation: 6,295pd, 1,254fr; AAM
Advertising: Open inch rate $62.39
Established: 1909
Digital Platform - Mobile: Apple, Android, Windows
Digital Platform - Tablet: Apple iOS, Android
Publisher / Editor in Chief............ Elinor Tatum
Vice President, Advertising, Sales, Partnerships........................... Penda Howell
Editor....................................... Nayaba Arinde
Mechanical Specifications: 1 column......1.342"
2 columns.....2.833"
3 columns.....4.313"
4 columns.....5.788"
6 columns.....8.75"
12 columns...18.5"
Gutter space vertically and horizontally is .125"
Page depth is 11.5"
Delivery Method: Mail, Newsstand
Zip Codes Served: New York, NY

NEW YORK BEACON
(Fri)
237 W 37th St, Rm 201, New York, NY, 10018-6958, New York, USA; tel (212) 213-8585; fax (212) 213-6291; e-mail newyorkbeacon@yahoo.com; web site www.newyorkbeacon.net
Circulation: 71,750pd, 12,722fr; Sworn/Estimate/Non-Audited
Advertising: Open inch rate $62.14
Adv. Dir.. Miatta Smith
Ed. in Chief.................................. Walter Smith
Mng. Ed... Willie Egyir
Mechanical Specifications: Type page 10 x 14; E - 2 cols, 2, between; A - 5 cols, 2, between; C - 5 cols, between.
Delivery Method: Newsstand
Zip Codes Served: 212, 718, 646, 916' 915

NORTH CAROLINA

CHARLOTTE

CHARLOTTE POST
(Thur)
1531 Camden Rd, Charlotte, NC, 28203-4753, Mecklenburg, USA; tel (704) 376-0496; fax (704) 342-2160; e-mail publisher@thecharlottepost.com; web site www.thecharlottepost.com
Circulation: 20,400pd,; Sworn/Estimate/Non-Audited
Advertising: Open inch rate $30.00
Established: 1975
Pub...................................... Gerald O. Johnson
Gen. Mgr..................................... Bob Johnson
Bus. Mgr... Betty Potts
Ed.. Herb White
Mechanical Specifications: Type page 13 1/4 x 22; E - 6 cols, 2, 1/4 between; A - 6 cols, 2, 1/4 between; C - 9 cols, 1 1/2, 1/8 between.
Equipment: Hardware — APP/Power Mac G4; Software — QPS/QuarkXPress 4.1, Adobe/Photoshop 6.00, Adobe/Illustrator 6.0, Macromedia/Freehand 10.00, Caere/OmniPage Pro 8.0, Adobe/Acrobat.

THE STAR OF ZION
(Mthly)
PO Box 26770, Charlotte, NC, 28221-6770, Mecklenburg, USA; tel (704) 599-4630; fax (704) 688-2556; e-mail sozbusiness@yahoo.com; adv e-mail sozbusiness@yahoo.com; ed e-mail sozbusiness@yahoo.com; web site thestarofzion.com
Circulation: 8,500pd, 1,000fr; Sworn/Estimate/Non-Audited
Advertising: Open inch rate $12.00
Established: 1876
Group: Star of Zion Newspaper
Editor and Publisher...................... Addie Lisby
Mechanical Specifications: Type page 9 1/2 x 12; E - 2 cols, 2, between.
Delivery Method: Mail
Zip Codes Served: 28262,37914,37915,30331, 30311, 28269 28221

DURHAM

THE CAROLINA TIMES
(Thur)
923 Old Fayetteville St, Durham, NC, 27701-3914, Durham, USA; tel (919) 682-2913; fax (919) 688-8434; e-mail thecarolinatimes@cs.com; adv e-mail adstct@cs.com; ed e-mail thecarolinatimes@cs.com
Circulation: 6,100pd,; USPS
Advertising: Open inch rate $14.75
Established: 1927
Pub................................Kenneth W. Edmonds
Mechanical Specifications: Type page 10.75 x 21; E - 6 cols, 2 1/16, 1/8 between; A - 6 cols, 2 1/16, 1/8 between; C - 6 cols, 2 1/16, 1/8 between.
Equipment: Hardware — IBM.
Delivery Method: Mail, Newsstand, Racks
Zip Codes Served: 27701, 27702, 27703, 27704, 27705, 27708, 27709, 27710, 27712, 27713, 27715, 27717, 27722; 27514, 27516, 27517;, 27601, 27601, 27603, 27604, 27605, 27606, 27607, 27608, 27610, 27611, 27612

THE TRIANGLE TRIBUNE
(Sun)
115 Market St, Ste 360G, Durham, NC, 27701-3252, Durham, USA; tel (919) 688-9408; adv tel (919) 688-9086; fax (919) 688-2740; e-mail editor@triangletribune.com; adv e-mail linda.lanel@triangletribune.com; web site www.triangletribune.com
Circulation: 1,713fr; Sworn/Estimate/Non-Audited
Advertising: Open inch rate $15.00
Established: 1997
Group: The Charlotte Post Publshing
Digital Platform - Mobile: Other
Digital Platform - Tablet: Other
CEO/Pub.................................Gerald Johnson
Ed. ....Bonitta Best
Mechanical Specifications: Type page 11 5/8 x 21; E - 6 cols, 1 5/6, between; A - 6 cols, 1 5/6, between; C - 9 cols, 1 3/20, between.
Equipment: Hardware — APP/Mac; Software — QPS/QuarkXPress 9.5.4, Adobe/Acrobat 10.0, Adobe/Photoshop.
Delivery Method: Mail, Newsstand, Carrier
Zip Codes Served: 27701, 27713, 27610

GREENSBORO

CAROLINA PEACEMAKER
(Thur)
807 Summit Ave, Greensboro, NC, 27405-7833, Guilford, USA; tel (336) 274-6210; fax (336) 273-5103; adv e-mail ads@carolinapeacemaker.com; ed e-mail editor@carolinapeacemaker.com; web site www.carolinapeacemaker.com
Circulation: 9,100pd,; Sworn/Estimate/Non-Audited
Advertising: Open inch rate $30.00
Established: 1967
Pub...........................John Marshall Kilimanjaro
Adv. Mgr.......................... C. Vickie Kilimanjaro
Ed.....................................Afraque Kilimanjaro
Mechanical Specifications: Type page 11 x 20 3/4; E - 6 cols, 1 7/8, 1/4 between; A - 6 cols, between; C - 10 cols, between.
Equipment: Hardware — APP/Mac; Software — QPS/QuarkXPress.
Delivery Method: Mail, Racks

RALEIGH

THE CAROLINIAN
(Thur) (Thur`Every other Mon)
519 S Blount St, Raleigh, NC, 27601-1827, Wake, USA; tel (919) 834-5558; fax (919) 832-3243; e-mail thecarolinian@bellsouth.net; web site www.raleighcarolinian.info
Circulation: 15,202pd,; Sworn/Estimate/Non-Audited
Advertising: Open inch rate $22.00
Pub.. Paul R. Jervay
Adv. Mgr....................................... Paul Jervay
Circ. Mgr.................................Andrew Alston
Ed. ....Evelyn Jervay
Mechanical Specifications: Type page 13 x 21; E - 6 cols, 2 1/16, 1/8 between; A - 6 cols, 2 1/16, 1/8 between; C - 6 cols, 2 1/16, 1/8 between.
Equipment: Hardware — APP/Mac, IBM.

STATESVILLE

COUNTY NEWS
(Wed)
211 S Center St, Statesville, NC, 28677-5873, Iredell, USA; tel (704) 873-1054; fax (704) 873-1054; e-mail publisher@countynews4you.com
Circulation: 7,500pd,; Sworn/Estimate/Non-Audited
Advertising: Open inch rate $35.00
Pub... Fran Farrer
Mechanical Specifications: Type page 13 x 21 1/2; E - 6 cols, 2 1/12, 1/8 between; A - 6 cols, 2 1/12, 1/8 between; C - 6 cols, 2 1/12, 1/8 between.

WILMINGTON

GREATER DIVERSITY NEWS
(Thur)
272 N Front St, Ste 406, Wilmington, NC, 28401-4078, New Hanover, USA; tel (910) 762-1337; fax (910) 763-6304; web site www.greaterdiversity.com
Circulation: 2,500pd, 2,500fr; Sworn/Estimate/Non-Audited
Advertising: Open inch rate $15.60
Kathy Grear
Peter GrearPub.s
Mechanical Specifications: Type page 13 x 21 1/2; E - 6 cols, 2, 1/6 between; A - 6 cols, 2, 1/6 between; C - 6 cols, 2, 1/6 between.
Equipment: Hardware — APP/Mac, Dataproducts/LZR 1580; Software — QPS/QuarkXPress 3.32.

WILMINGTON JOURNAL
(Thur)
412 S 7th St, Wilmington, NC, 28401-5214, New Hanover, USA; tel (910) 762-5502; fax (910) 343-1334; e-mail wilmjourn@aol.com; web site www.wilmingtonjournal.com
Circulation: 10,120pd, 880fr; Sworn/Estimate/Non-Audited
Advertising: Open inch rate $32.00
Office Mgr......................Shawn Jervay Thatch
Adv. Exec.......................................Robin Allen
Circ. Mgr................................ Edward Crumdy
Pub./Ed....................Mary Alice Jervay Thatch
Mechanical Specifications: Type page 13 x 21; E - 6 cols, 2 1/16, 1/8 between; A - 6 cols, 2 1/16, 1/8 between.
Equipment: Hardware — IBM; Software — Adobe/PageMaker, QPS/QuarkXPress, Windows 95.

WINSTON SALEM

THE CHRONICLE
(Thur)
617 N Liberty St, Winston Salem, NC, 27101-2912, Forsyth, USA; tel (336) 723-8428; fax (336) 723-9173; e-mail news@wschronicle.com; adv e-mail adv@wschronicle.com; web site www.wschronicle.com
Circulation: 10,000pd,; Sworn/Estimate/Non-Audited
Advertising: Open inch rate $28.50
Established: 1974
Co-Founder/Pub. ....Ernest H. Pitt
Co-Founder.......................Ndubisi Egemonye
Gen. Mgr...Elaine Pitt
Mechanical Specifications: Type page 13 x 21; E - 6 cols, 2 1/8, 1/8 between; A - 6 cols, 2 1/8, 1/8 between; C - 9 cols, 1 1/4, 1/8 between.
Equipment: Hardware — APP/Power Mac; Software — QPS/QuarkXPress 3.21.

OHIO

CINCINNATI

CINCINNATI HERALD
(Thur)
354 Hearne Ave, Cincinnati, OH, 45229-2818, Hamilton, USA; tel (513) 961-3331; fax (513) 961-0304; e-mail jmkearney@mail.com; web site www.thecincinnatiherald.com
Circulation: 16,000pd,; Sworn/Estimate/Non-Audited
Advertising: Open inch rate $27.83
Pub...................................Jan Michele Kearney
Adv. Mgr..Walter White
Ed. in Chief.......................................Dan Yount
Prodn. Mgr. .... Wade Lacey
Mechanical Specifications: Type page 13 x 21; E - 6 cols, 2 1/16, 1/8 between; A - 6 cols, 2 1/16, 1/8 between; C - 10 cols, between.
Equipment: Hardware — APP/Mac; Software — Microsoft/Word, QPS/QuarkXPress.

COLUMBUS

KING MEDIA ENTERPRISES
(Wed)
750 E Long St, Ste 3000, Columbus, OH, 43203-1874, Franklin, USA; tel (614) 224-8123; fax (216) 451-0404; e-mail info@call-post.com; adv e-mail advertising@call-post.com; classifieds@call-post.com; web site www.cleveland.com
Advertising: Open inch rate $25.88Editions: 2— Call and Post-Cincinnati; Call and Post-Cleveland;
Vice Pres., Mktg./Adv..................Douglas Rice
Circ. Mgr....................................Carl Matthews
Mng. Ed... Gil Price
Vice Pres., Opns......................... Cheri Daniels
Mechanical Specifications: Type page 13 x 21; E - 6 cols, between; A - 6 cols, between; C - 6 cols, between.
Equipment: Hardware — IBM; Software — Archetype/Corel Draw, Ventura/Publisher.

TOLEDO

THE TOLEDO JOURNAL
(Wed)
3021 Douglas Rd, Toledo, OH, 43606-3504, Lucas, USA; tel (419) 472-4521; fax (419) 472-1604; e-mail toledo411@aol.com; toljour@aol.com; web site www.thetoledojournal.com
Circulation: 12pd, 11,397fr; CVC
Advertising: Open inch rate $28.65
Established: 1975
Pub.. Sandra S. Stewart
Circulation Manager..............Myron A. Stewart
Production Manager.........................Jeff Willis
Mechanical Specifications: Type page 10 1/4 x 16; E - 6 cols, 1, 1/8 between; A - 6 cols, 1, between.
Equipment: Hardware — APP/Mac; Software — Adobe/Photoshop.

Zip Codes Served: 43602, 43611, 43620, 43560

YOUNGSTOWN

THE BUCKEYE REVIEW
(Tues)
1201 Belmont Ave, Youngstown, OH, 44504-1101, Mahoning, USA; tel (330) 743-2250; fax (330) 746-2340; e-mail buckeyereview@yahoo.com
Circulation: 5,250fr; Sworn/Estimate/Non-Audited
Advertising: Open inch rate $21.50
Established: 1927
Ed. .... Mike McNair

OKLAHOMA

OKLAHOMA CITY

BLACK CHRONICLE
(Thur)
1528 NE 23rd St, Oklahoma City, OK, 73111-3260, Oklahoma, USA; tel (405) 424-4695; fax (405) 424-6708; e-mail alisdsey@blackchronicle.com; web site www.blackchronicle.com
Circulation: 30,000pd,; Sworn/Estimate/Non-Audited
Advertising: Open inch rate $16.44
Adv. Rep. .... T.C. Brown
Ed. .... Russell M. Perry
Mng. Ed. .... Albert J. Lindsey
Mechanical Specifications: Type page 14 1/2 x 21 1/2; E - 8 cols, 1 2/3, between; A - 8 cols, 1 2/3, between; C - 8 cols, 1 2/3, between.
Equipment: Hardware — APP/Mac; Software — Adobe/PageMaker.

TULSA

THE OKLAHOMA EAGLE
(Fri)
624 E Archer St, Tulsa, OK, 74120-1000, Tulsa, USA; tel (918) 582-7124; fax (918) 582-8905; e-mail editor@theoklahomaeagle.net
Circulation: 5,000pd,; Sworn/Estimate/Non-Audited
Advertising: Open inch rate $17.02
Pub. .... James O. Goodwin
Mechanical Specifications: Type page 13 x 21; A - 6 cols, 2 1/16, between.

OREGON

PORTLAND

PORTLAND OBSERVER
(Wed)
4747 NE M L King Blvd, Portland, OR, 97211-3398, Multnomah, USA; tel (503) 288-0033; fax (503) 288-0015; e-mail news@portlandobserver.com; web site www.portlandobserver.com
Circulation: 7,000pd, 30,000fr; Sworn/Estimate/Non-Audited
Advertising: Open inch rate $24.75
Adv. Mgr. .... Charles Washington
Circ. Mgr. .... Mark Washington
Ed. .... Mike Leighton
Prodn. Mgr. .... Paul Newfeldt
Mechanical Specifications: Type page 13 x 21; E - 6 cols, 2 1/16, 1/8 between; A - 6 cols, 2 1/16, 1/8 between; C - 6 cols, between.
Equipment: Hardware — IBM; Software — Microsoft/Word 6.5.

THE SKANNER
(Thur) (Every other Thurs)
415 N Killingsworth St, Portland, OR, 97217-2440, Multnomah, USA; tel (503) 285-5555; fax (503) 285-3400; e-mail info@theskanner.com; adver@theskanner.com; web site www.theskanner.com
Circulation: 10,500pd,; Sworn/Estimate/Non-Audited
Advertising: Open inch rate $69.50
Pub. .... Bernie Foster
Circ. Mgr. .... Jerry Foster
Ed. .... Bobbie Dore Foster
Prodn. Mgr. .... David Kidd
Mechanical Specifications: Type page 10 1/2 x 16; E - 6 cols, 1 5/8, between; A - 6 cols, 1 5/8, between.

PENNSYLVANIA

PHILADELPHIA

PHILADELPHIA SUNDAY SUN
(Sun)
6661 Germantown Ave, Ste 63, Philadelphia, PA, 19119-2251, Philadelphia, USA; tel (215) 848-7864; fax (215) 848-7893; e-mail sundaysunads@yahoo.com; ed e-mail taesun@philasun.com; web site www.philasun.com
Circulation: 20,000pd,; Sworn/Estimate/Non-Audited
Advertising: Open inch rate $25.89
Established: 1992
Digital Platform - Mobile: Apple, Android, Windows, Blackberry
Digital Platform - Tablet: Apple iOS, Android, Windows 7, Blackberry Tablet OS, Kindle, Nook, Kindle Fire
Mng. Ed. .... Teresa Emerson
Adv. .... Tera Moyet
Mechanical Specifications: Type page 10 1/4 x 14; E - 5 cols, 1 7/8, 1/6 between; A - 5 cols, 1 7/8, 1/6 between; C - 5 cols, 1 7/8, 1/6 between.
Equipment: Hardware — IBM/486; Software — AMI/Pro, QPS/QuarkXPress, Microsoft/Windows 98.
Delivery Method: Mail, Newsstand, Carrier, Racks
Zip Codes Served: Philadelphia County

PHILADELPHIA TRIBUNE
(Tues, Fri, Sun)
520 S 16th St, # 26, Philadelphia, PA, 19146-1565, Philadelphia, USA; tel (215) 893-4050; fax (215) 735-3612; e-mail info@phila-tribune.com; web site http://www.phillytrib.com/
Circulation: 2,964pd, 9,421fr; CAC
Advertising: Open inch rate $95.95
Mktg. Dir. .... Al Thomas
Circ. Mgr. .... Michael Levere
CEO Pres. .... Robert W. Bogle
Mng. Ed. .... Irv Randolph

SCOOP USA
(Fri)
PO Box 14013, Philadelphia, PA, 19122-0013, Philadelphia, USA; tel 215 309-3139; fax 267 534-2943; adv e-mail advscoop@aol.com; ed e-mail edscoopusa@aol.com; web site www.scoopusanewspaper.com
Circulation: 32,000fr; Sworn/Estimate/Non-Audited
Advertising: Open inch rate $22.00
Established: 1960
Digital Platform - Mobile: Apple
Digital Platform - Tablet: Apple iOS
Publisher .... Sherri Darden
editor/publisher .... R. Sonny Driver
Mechanical Specifications: Type page 10 x 16; E - 6 cols, 1 1/2, 3/16 between.
Equipment: Hardware — 3-APP/Mac, APP/Scanner, HP/Printer; Software — Adobe/Photoshop, QPS/QuarkXPress 3.31.
Delivery Method: Mail, Newsstand, Carrier, Racks
Zip Codes Served: 191.. / 081.. / 190..

PITTSBURGH

NEW PITTSBURGH COURIER
(Wed)
315 E Carson St, Pittsburgh, PA, 15219-1202, Allegheny, USA; tel (412) 481-8302; adv tel (313) 963-8100; fax (412) 481-1360; e-mail webmaster@newpittsburghcourier.com; adv e-mail ads@newpittsburghcourier.com; ed e-mail newsroom@newpittsburghcourier.com; web site www.newpittsburghcourieronline.com
Circulation: 2,014pd, 593fr; CVC
Advertising: Open inch rate $27.31
Established: 1910
Group: Real Times Media, Inc.Editions: 1—
Digital Platform - Mobile: Apple, Android, Windows
Digital Platform - Tablet: Apple iOS, Android, Windows 7, Blackberry Tablet OS, Kindle, Nook, Kindle Fire
Asst. to Pub. .... Stephan Broadus
Adv. Mgr. .... Eric Gaines
Circ. Mgr. .... Jeff Marion
Editor & Publisher .... Rod Doss
Managing Editor .... Ulish Carter
Mechanical Specifications: Type page Broadsheet 10.625 x 20 1/2; E - 6 cols, 1.667, 1/8 between
Equipment: Hardware — APP/Mac; Software — QPS/QuarkXPress.
Delivery Method: Mail, Newsstand, Carrier, Racks

RHODE ISLAND

PROVIDENCE

THE PROVIDENCE AMERICAN
(Mthly)
PO Box 5859, Providence, RI, 02903-0859, Providence, USA; tel (401) 475-6480; fax (401) 475-6254; web site The Providence American
Circulation: 11,000fr; Sworn/Estimate/Non-Audited
Advertising: Open inch rate $20.00
Pub. .... Peter C. Wills
Mechanical Specifications: Type page 10 x 16; E - 4 cols, 1 1/2, between; A - 6 cols, between; C - 6 cols, between.
Equipment: Hardware — APP/Mac; Software — Adobe/PageMaker.

SOUTH CAROLINA

CHARLESTON

CHARLESTON CHRONICLE
(Wed)
1111 King St, Charleston, SC, 29403-3761, Charleston, USA; tel (843) 723-2785; fax (843) 577-6099; e-mail chaschron@aol.com
Circulation: 6,000pd,; Sworn/Estimate/Non-Audited
Advertising: Open inch rate $13.00
Adv. Mgr. .... Tolbert Small
Ed. .... Jim French
Mechanical Specifications: Type page 13 x 21; E - 6 cols, 2 1/16, 1/8 between; A - 6 cols, 2 1/16, 1/8 between; C - 6 cols, 2 1/16, 1/8 between.
Equipment: Hardware — APP/Power Mac 6100; Software — QPS/QuarkXPress.

COLUMBIA

BLACK NEWS
(Thur)
1310 Harden St, Columbia, SC, 29204-1820, Richland, USA; tel (803) 799-5252; fax (803) 799-7709; e-mail scbnews@aol.com; web site www.scblacknews.com
Circulation: 75,000pd,; Sworn/Estimate/Non-Audited
Advertising: Open inch rate $36.91
Pres./CEO/Pub. .... Isaac Washington
Gen. Mgr. .... Clannie Washington
Adv. Mgr. .... Melvin Hart
Circ. Mgr. .... Benjamin Jackson
Prodn.Mgr. .... Wendy Brinker
Asst. Bus. Mgr. .... Ruth Carlton
Mechanical Specifications: Type page 13 x 21 1/2; E - 6 cols, 2 1/16, 1/8 between; A - 6 cols, 2 1/16, 1/8 between; C - 9 cols, between.

CAROLINA PANORAMA
(Thur)
2346 Two Notch Rd, Ste A, Columbia, SC, 29204-2279, Richland, USA; tel (803) 256-4015; fax (803) 256-6732; e-mail cpanorama@aol.com; adv e-mail Ads@CarolinaPanorama.com; ed e-mail News@CarolinaPanorama.com; web site www.carolinapanorama.com
Circulation: 15,000fr; Sworn/Estimate/Non-Audited
Advertising: Open inch rate $15.00
Established: 1986
Group: MBD Media, LLC
Digital Platform - Mobile: Apple, Android, Windows, Blackberry
Digital Platform - Tablet: Apple iOS, Android, Kindle, Kindle Fire
Pub. .... Nate Abraham Jr.
Mechanical Specifications: Type page 11 x 21 1/2; E - 6 cols, 2 1/16, 1/8 between; A - 6 cols, 2 1/16, 1/8 between; C - 10 cols, between.
Equipment: Hardware — APP/Mac; Software — Adobe/InDesign
Delivery Method: Newsstand, Racks
Zip Codes Served: 29016, 29033, 29044, 29052, 29053, 29063, 29072, 29115, 29118, 29130, 29135, 29169, 29172, 29180, 29201, 29203, 29204, 29205, 29209, 29210, 29212, 29223, 29229

TENNESSEE

MEMPHIS

TRI STATE DEFENDER
(Thur)
203 Beale St, Ste 200, Memphis, TN, 38103-3727, Shelby, USA; tel (901) 523-1818; fax (901) 578-5037; ed e-mail editorial@tri-statedefender.com; web site www.tri-statedefenderonline.com
Circulation: 524pd, 3,709fr; Sworn/Estimate/Non-Audited
Advertising: Open inch rate $23.00
Associate Publisher/Exec. Ed. Karanja Ajanaku
Mechanical Specifications: Type page 13 x 21; E - 6 cols, 2 1/16, 1/8 between; A - 6 cols, 2 1/16, 1/8 between; C - 9 cols, 1 5/16, between.
Equipment: Hardware — APP/Mac; Software — QPS/QuarkXPress.

NASHVILLE

CHATTANOOGA COURIER
(Thur)
805 Bradford Ave, Nashville, TN, 37204-2105, Davidson, USA; tel (615) 292-9150; fax (615) 292-9056; e-mail npnews@comcast.

net; web site www.pridepublishinggroup.net
Circulation: 24,000pd,; Sworn/Estimate/Non-Audited
Advertising: Open inch rate $24.00
Pub.. Meekahl Davis
Circ. Mgr.......................................Scott Davies
Ed. ....Geraldine D. Heath
Mechanical Specifications: Type page 13 1/4 x 21 1/2; E - 6 cols, 2 1/8, between; A - 6 cols, 2 1/8, between; C - 6 cols, 2 1/8, between.
Equipment: Hardware — Software QPS/QuarkXPress.; Software — QPS/QuarkXPress.

MURFREESBORO VISION
(Thur)
805 Bradford Ave, Nashville, TN, 37204-2105, Davidson, USA; tel (615) 292-9150; fax (615) 292-9056; e-mail npnews@comcast.net; web site www.pridepublishinggroup.net
Circulation: 16,000pd,; Sworn/Estimate/Non-Audited
Advertising: Open inch rate $21.00
Pub.. Meekahl Davis
Circ. Mgr.......................................Scotty Davis
Mng. Ed..................................Geraldine Heath
Mechanical Specifications: Type page 13 1/4 x 21 1/2; E - 6 cols, 2 1/8, between; A - 6 cols, 2 1/8, between; C - 6 cols, 2 1/8, between.
Equipment: Hardware — Software QPS/QuarkXPress.; Software — QPS/QuarkXPress.

NASHVILLE PRIDE
(Fri)
805 Bradford Ave, Nashville, TN, 37204-2105, Davidson, USA; tel (615) 292-9150; fax (615) 292-9056; e-mail npnews@comcast.net; web site www.pridepublishinggroup.com
Circulation: 42,000pd,; Sworn/Estimate/Non-Audited
Advertising: Open inch rate $32.50
Pub.. Meekahl Davis
Adv. Mgr.......................................Scott Davis
Mng. Ed..................................Geraldine Heath
Prodn. Mgr. ....James Lewis
Mechanical Specifications: Type page 13 x 21; E - 6 cols, between; A - 6 cols, between; C - 6 cols, between.
Equipment: Hardware — APP/Mac; Software — QPS/QuarkXPress.

TENNESSEE TRIBUNE
(Thur)
1501 Jefferson St, Nashville, TN, 37208-3016, Davidson, USA; tel (615) 321 3268; adv tel (615) 321 3268; ed tel 615 509 3181; fax 1-866 694 7534 ; adv tel (866) 694-7534; e-mail tennesseetribunenews@aol.com; adv e-mail sales1501@aol.com; ed e-mail tennesseetribunenews@aol.com; web site www.tntribune.com
Circulation: 1,200pd, 24,450fr; CVC
Advertising: Open inch rate $36.00
Established: 1970
Digital Platform - Mobile: Apple
Digital Platform - Tablet: Apple iOS
Pub.................................. Rosetta Miller Perry
Assoc. Pub..............................William Miller III
Assoc. Pub.............................. Wanda Benson
VP Advert....................................James Artis
Mechanical Specifications: Type page 13 x 20 1/4; E - 6 cols, 2 1/6, between; A - 6 cols, between.
Equipment: Hardware — APP/Mac; Software — QPS/QuarkXPress.
Delivery Method: Mail, Newsstand, Carrier, Racks
Zip Codes Served: Nashville, Jackson, Memphis, Chattanooga, Knoxville

THE ENLIGHTENER
(Wed)
625 Main St, Nashville, TN, 37206-3603, Davidson, USA; tel (615) 292-9150; fax (615) 292-9056; e-mail npnews@comcast.net; web site www.pridepublishinggroup.net
Circulation: 26,700pd,; Sworn/Estimate/Non-Audited
Advertising: Open inch rate $28.00
Pub.. Meekahl Davis
Mng. Ed..Lisa Pate
Mechanical Specifications: Type page 13 1/4 x 21 1/2; E - 6 cols, 2 1/8, between; A - 6 cols, 2 1/8, between; C - 6 cols, 2 1/8, between.
Equipment: Hardware — Software; QPS/QuarkXPress.; Software — QPS/QuarkXPress.

TEXAS

AUSTIN

NOKOA-THE OBSERVER
(Thur)
PO Box 1131, Austin, TX, 78767-1131, Travis, USA; tel (512) 499-8713; fax (512) 499-8740; e-mail akwasievans@gmail.com; web site www.nokoatheobserver.com
Circulation: 0pd, 4,336fr; CVC
Advertising: Open inch rate $35.00
Established: 1987
Ed. ....Akwasi Evans
Mechanical Specifications: Type page 13 x 21; E - 6 cols, 2, 1/8 between; A - 6 cols, 2, 1/8 between; C - 6 cols, 2, 1/8 between.
Equipment: Hardware — APP/Mac; Software — Adobe/PageMaker 6.0, Microsoft/Word 5.1.

THE VILLAGER
(Fri)
4132 E 12th St, Austin, TX, 78721-1905, Travis, USA; tel (512) 476-0082; adv tel (512) 476-0082; ed tel (512) 476-0082; fax (512) 476-0179; adv tel (512) 476-0179; ed tel (512) 476-0179; e-mail vil3202@aol.com; adv e-mail vil3202@aol.com; ed e-mail vil3202@aol.com; web site www.austinvillager.com
Circulation: 0pd, 5,975fr; CVC
Advertising: Open inch rate $20.00
Established: 1973
Digital Platform - Mobile: Blackberry
Ed./Pub... T.L. Wyatt
Mechanical Specifications: Type page 11.25 x 21; E - 6 cols, 1.75 between; A - 6 cols, 2, 1/8 between; C - 6 cols, 2, 1/8 between.
Equipment: Hardware — APP/Mac.
Delivery Method: Racks
Zip Codes Served: 78701, 78702, 78704, 78721, 78723, 78744, 78741, 78751, 786

DALLAS

DALLAS EXAMINER
(Thur)
1516 Corinth St, Dallas, TX, 75215-2113, Dallas, USA; tel (214) 428-3446; fax (214) 428-3451; ed e-mail editorial@ @dallasexaminer.com; web site www.dallasexaminer.com
Circulation: 1,280pd, 10,000fr; Sworn/Estimate/Non-Audited
Advertising: Open inch rate $36.00
Pub..Mollie Finch Belt
Adv. Mgr....................................James C. Belt
Mechanical Specifications: Type page 13 x 21; E - 6 cols, 2 1/16, 1/8 between; A - 6 cols, 2 1/16, 1/8 between.
Equipment: Hardware — APP/Mac; Software — QPS/QuarkXPress.

DALLAS POST TRIBUNE
(Thur)
2726 S Beckley Ave, Dallas, TX, 75224-2938, Dallas, USA; tel (214) 946-7678; fax (214) 946-7680; e-mail posttrib@airmail.net; web site www.dallaspost.com
Circulation: 378pd, 1,734fr; VAC
Advertising: Open inch rate $35.00
Established: 1947
Publisher....................................Theodore Lee
Mng. Ed....................................... Dorothy Lee
Advertising Manager..........Veronica Zambrano
Circulation Manager .... Elster Coleman
Production Manager ....Chloe Buckley
Mechanical Specifications: Type page 13 x 21; E - 6 cols, 2 1/16, 1/8 between; A - 6 cols, 2 1/16, 1/8 between; C - 6 cols, 2 1/16, 1/8 between.
Equipment: Hardware — APP/Mac.

DALLAS WEEKLY
(Thur)
3101 Martin Luther King Jr Blvd, Dallas, TX, 75215-2415, Dallas, USA; tel (214) 428-8958; fax (214) 428-2807; web site www.dallasweekly.com
Circulation: 10pd, 4,890fr; CAC
Advertising: Open inch rate $39.18
Pub....................................James Washington
Ed. in chief............................Gordon Jackson
Mechanical Specifications: Type page 9 7/8 x 12; A - 6 cols, 1 9/16, between; C - 6 cols, 1 9/16, between.

GARLAND JOURNAL NEWS
(Other) (1st & 15th of the month)
320 S R L Thornton Fwy, Ste 220, Dallas, TX, 75203-1804, Dallas, USA; tel (214) 941-0110; e-mail publisher@texasmetronews.com; adv e-mail sales@texasmetronews.com; ed e-mail editorial@texasmetronews.com; web site www.garlandjournalnews.com
Circulation: 0pd, 1,990fr; VAC
Advertising: CP
Established: 1994
Digital Platform - Mobile: Apple, Android
Digital Platform - Tablet: Apple iOS, Android
Pub./Gen. Mgr.............................Cheryl Smith
Advertising Manger.......................BJ Fullylove
Circulation Manger ....K Davis
Delivery Method: Mail, Racks
Zip Codes Served: Dallas County
Tarrant County
Ellis County
Denton County
Wise County
Hunt County
Collin County

TEXAS METRO NEWS
(Other) (Bi-Weekly (1st and 15th each month))
320 S R L Thornton Fwy, Ste 220, Dallas, TX, 75203-1804, Dallas, USA; tel (214) 941-0110; adv tel (214) 941-0110; e-mail publisher@texasmetronews.com; adv e-mail sales@texasmetronews.com; ed e-mail editorial@texasmetronews.com; web site www.texasmetronews.com
Circulation: 0pd, 1,988fr; VAC
Advertising: CP
Established: 1994
Digital Platform - Mobile: Apple, Android
Digital Platform - Tablet: Apple iOS, Android
Pub./Gen. Mgr.............................Cheryl Smith
Advertising Manager.....................BJ Fullylove
Circulation Manager ....K Davis
Delivery Method: Mail, Newsstand, Carrier, Racks
Zip Codes Served: Dallas County
Tarrant County
Ellis County
Denton County
Wise County
Hunt County
Collin County

THE DALLAS EXAMINER
(Thur)
400 S Zang Blvd Ste 1022, P.O. Box 3720, Dallas, TX, 75208-6609, Dallas, USA; tel 2149413100; adv tel 2149413100; ed tel 2149413100; fax 214-941-3117; adv tel 214-941-3117; ed tel 214-941-3117; e-mail mbelt@dallasexaminer.com; adv e-mail mbelt@dallasexaminer.com; ed e-mail mbelt@dallasexaminer.com; web site www.dallasexaminer.com
Circulation: 895pd, 9,076fr; VAC
Advertising: Open inch rate $36.00
Established: 1986
Digital Platform - Mobile: Apple
Digital Platform - Tablet: Windows 7
Publisher...Mollie Belt
Robyn Jimenez
Delivery Method: Mail, Newsstand, Racks

FARMERSVILLE

THE POWER PAGES NEWS
(Mthly)
313 S Hamilton St, Farmersville, TX, 75442-2518, Collin, USA; tel (972) 784-6648 ; adv tel (972) 784-6648 ; ed tel (972) 784-6648 ; e-mail ppages2@sbcglobal.net; adv e-mail ppages2@sbcglobal.net; ed e-mail ppages2@sbcglobal.net; web site www.powerpagesnews.com
Circulation: 0pd, 875fr; VAC
Advertising: N/A
Established: 1995
Digital Platform - Mobile: Apple, Android, Windows, Blackberry
Digital Platform - Tablet: Apple iOS, Android, Windows 7, Blackberry Tablet OS, Kindle
Advertising Manager.......................Hattie Kelly
Publisher.......................................Sandra Kelly
Production Manager ....Scott B. Kelly
Circulation Manager ....Vickie Brooks
Delivery Method: Mail, Racks
Zip Codes Served: 75442

HOUSTON

AFRICAN AMERICAN NEWS & ISSUES
(Wed)
6130 Wheatley St, Houston, TX, 77091-3947, Harris, USA; tel (713) 692-1892; fax (713) 692-1183; e-mail news@aframnews.com; web site www.aframnews.com
Circulation: 2,228pd, 312,818fr; Sworn/Estimate/Non-Audited
Advertising: Open inch rate $225.00
Established: 1996Editions: 3— Central Southwest; Gulf Coast; Metroplex North;
Pub...............................Roy Douglas Malonson
Gen. Mgr.......................Shirley Ann Malonson
Mechanical Specifications: Type page 11 5/8 x 21.
Equipment: Hardware — IBM; Software — Adobe/PageMaker, Adobe/Photoshop.

FORWARD TIMES
(Thur)
4411 Almeda Rd, Houston, TX, 77004-4901, Harris, USA; tel (713) 526-4727; fax (713) 526-3170; e-mail forwardtimes@forwardtimes.com; web site www.forwardtimes.com
Circulation: 64,580pd,; Sworn/Estimate/Non-Audited
Advertising: Open inch rate $28.60
Assoc. Pub...................Karen Carter Richards
Adv. Mgr.................................Henrietta Smith
Ed. ....Lenora Carter
Prodn. Mgr. ....Shirley Daughery
Mechanical Specifications: Type page 13 x 21 1/2; E - 6 cols, 2 1/16, 1/8 between; A - 6 cols, 2 1/16, 1/8 between; C - 6 cols, 2 1/16, 1/8 between.
Equipment: Hardware — IBM; Software — Archetype/Corel Draw, Microsoft/Windows 3.1.

HOUSTON DEFENDER MEDIA GROUP, FORMERLY HOUSTON DEFENDER
(Thur)
12401 S Post Oak Rd, Houston, TX, 77045-2020, Harris, USA; tel (713) 663-6996; fax (713) 663-7116; e-mail news@defendermediagroup.com; adv e-mail ads@defendermediagroup.com; ed e-mail news@defendermediagroup.com; web site www.defendernetwork.com
Circulation: 41pd,; CAC
Advertising: Open inch rate $35.00
Established: 1930
Digital Platform - Mobile: Apple, Android

Pub. & CEO ....Sonceria Messiah-Jiles
Ed. ....Von Jiles
Adv. & Marketing Dir. ....Selma Dodson Tyler
Print Ed.................................Marilyn Marshall
Online Ed.......................ReShonda Billingsley
Multi-media Mgr. ....LaGloria Wheatfall
Mechanical Specifications: Type page Tabloid - 10.75" x 14"; Full Page: 9.75" x 13"; Half Page (h) 9.75 x 6.5"; Half Page (v) 5.78" x 11"; Qtr: 5.78" x 5.65"
Equipment: Hardware — APP/Mac.
Delivery Method: Mail, Newsstand, Racks
Zip Codes Served: Houston Metro

HOUSTON METRO WEEKENDER

(Fri)
4411 Almeda Rd, Houston, TX, 77004-4901, Harris, USA; tel (713) 526-4727; fax (713) 526-3170; e-mail fowardtimes@forwardtimes.com; web site www.forwardtimes.com
Circulation: 75,000fr; Sworn/Estimate/Non-Audited
Advertising: Open inch rate $36.60
Assoc. Pub.....................Karen Carter Richard
Adv. Dir........................Henrietta Smith-Wilson
Mng. Ed......................................Lenora Carter
Prodn. Mgr. ....Shirley Daugherty
Mechanical Specifications: Type page 13 x 21 1/2; E - 6 cols, 2 1/16, 1/8 between; A - 6 cols, 2 1/16, 1/8 between; C - 6 cols, 2 1/16, 1/8 between.
Equipment: Hardware — IBM; Software — Archetype/Corel Draw, Microsoft/Windows 3.1.

HOUSTON SUN

(Fri)
1520 Isabella St, Houston, TX, 77004-4042, Harris, USA; web site www.houstonsun.com
Circulation: 9,925fr; Sworn/Estimate/Non-AuditedDorris Ellis

LONGVIEW

EAST TEXAS REVIEW

(Thur)
517 S Mobberly Ave, Longview, TX, 75602-1827, Gregg, USA; web site www.easttexasreview.com
Circulation: 0pd, 3,980fr; VAC
Advertising: Open inch rate $19.64
Established: 1995
Publisher/General Manager.............Joycelyne Fadojutimi
Advertising Manager.................LaDana Moore
Circulation Manager ....Teddy LaRose
Production Manager................Teresa Shearer

LUBBOCK

SOUTHWEST DIGEST

(Thur)
902 E 28th St, Lubbock, TX, 79404-1718, Lubbock, USA; tel (806) 762-3612; fax (806) 762-4605; e-mail swdigest@sbcglobal.net; web site www.southwestdigest.com
Circulation: 800pd, 4,000fr; Sworn/Estimate/Non-Audited
Advertising: Open inch rate $15.00
Ed. .... T.J. Patterson
Mechanical Specifications: Type page 13 x 21; E - 6 cols, 2 1/16, 1/8 between; A - 6 cols, 2 1/16, 1/8 between; C - 6 cols, 2 1/16, 1/8 between.
Delivery Method: Mail, Newsstand, Racks
Zip Codes Served: 79401, 79403, 79404, 79413, 79414, 79423, 79424

PLANO

NORTH DALLAS GAZETTE

(Thur)
3401 Custer Rd, Ste 169, Plano, TX, 75023-7546, Collin, USA; tel (972) 516-4191; fax (972) 509-9058; e-mail publisher@northdallasgazette.com; web site www.northdallasgazette.com
Circulation: 8pd, 9,967fr; VAC
Advertising: N/A
Established: 1991
Pub.................................... Thurman R. Jones
Ed. .... Ruth Ferguson
Mechanical Specifications: Type page 12 1/2 x 20 1/2; E - 6 cols, 2, between; A - 6 cols, 2, between; C - 6 cols, 2, between.
Equipment: Hardware — APP/Macs; Software — QPS/QuarkXPress.
Zip Codes Served: 75023, 75149, 75201, 75040, 75080, 75069, 75002, 75006, 75098

RUSK

TEXAS INFORMER

(Mthly)
PO Box 332, 941 Loop 343, Rusk, TX, 75785-0332, Cherokee, USA; tel (903) 683-5743; adv tel 903 721 3112; ed tel 903 721-3112; fax (903) 683-1577; adv tel 903 683-1577; ed tel 903-683-1577; e-mail info@texasinformer.com; adv e-mail info@texasinformer.com; ed e-mail informernews08@aol.com; web site www.texasinformer.com
Circulation: 0pd, 2,500fr; Sworn/Estimate/Non-Audited
Advertising: CP
Established: 1995Editions: 12— January-December
Digital Platform - Mobile: Apple, Android, Windows, Blackberry
Digital Platform - Tablet: Apple iOS, Android, Windows 7, Blackberry Tablet OS
Pub./Ed.
Maxine Session - Co-Publisher/ Editor
Walater Session -Co-PublisherMaxine Session
Mechanical Specifications: Three (3) columns x 13-inch column depth.
Full page: 10.5" wide x 13" depth.
Local: $2,000.00 Full page - $250.00 1/8 page
National: $2,000.00 Full page - $250.00 1/8 page
Insert Open Rate: $100. per thousand
Classified Rate: 15.00 for first 10 words
Volume, frequency, contract, color and other rates may be available from publisher.
Equipment; Software — Adobe Endesign
Delivery Method: Mail, Racks
Zip Codes Served: Cherokee County
Jacksonville, Tx. - 75766
Rusk, TX. - 75785
Alto, TX. - 75925
Anderson County
Palestine - 75801
Houston County
Crockett, TX. - 75835
Angelina County
Lufkin, TX. - 75901
Rusk County
Henderson, TX. - 75652

SAN ANTONIO

SAN ANTONIO OBSERVER

(Wed)
3427 Belgium Ln, San Antonio, TX, 78219-2501, Bexar, USA; tel (210) 212-6397; fax (210) 271-0441; e-mail taylor2039@aol.com
Circulation: 60pd, 16,051fr; Sworn/Estimate/Non-Audited
Advertising: Open inch rate $40.00
Pres. ....Lanell Taylor
Adv. Mgr. ....Sherry Logan
Prodn. Mgr. ....Gus Lopez
Mechanical Specifications: Type page 10 1/4 x 11 1/4; E - 4 cols, between.

THE SAN ANTONIO OBSERVER

(Wed)
3427 Belgium Ln, San Antonio, TX, 78219-2501, Bexar, USA; web site www.saobserver.com
Circulation: 22pd, 2,934fr; VAC
Advertising: Open inch rate $60.00
Established: 1995Fabby Ali
Publisher...................................... Sherry Logan
Advertising Manager......................Waseem Ali
Production Manager ....Charles Jones

THE SAN ANTONIO REGISTER

(Wed)
3427 Belgium Ln, San Antonio, TX, 78219-2501, Bexar, USA; web site www.saregister.com
Circulation: 0pd, 9,486fr; CVC
Advertising: Open inch rate $60.00
Established: 1931Sherry Logan

THE TYMES

(Wed)
3427 Belgium Ln, San Antonio, TX, 78219-2501, Bexar, USA; tel 2102229220; adv tel 2102229220; ed tel 2102229220; e-mail Wsmali@aol.com; adv e-mail Wsmali@aol.com; ed e-mail Wsmali@aol.com; web site www.tha-tymes.com
Circulation: 10,000fr; CVC
Advertising: $60 per column inch
Established: 2002
Digital Platform - Mobile: Apple, Android
Digital Platform - Tablet: Apple iOS, Android
President/CEO..............................Waseem Ali
Mechanical Specifications: 10.25x9.75
Delivery Method: Mail, Newsstand, Racks

VIRGINIA

NORFOLK

JOURNAL AND GUIDE

(Thur)
974 Norfolk Sq, Norfolk, VA, 23502-3212, Norfolk City, USA; tel (757) 543-6531; fax (757) 543-7620; e-mail njguide@gmail.com
Circulation: 15,000pd,; Sworn/Estimate/Non-Audited
Advertising: Open inch rate $18.45
Pub.................................... Brenda H. Andrews
Circ. Mgr.................................. Michael Brooks
Prodn. Mgr. .... David Todd
Mechanical Specifications: Type page 13 x 21; E - 6 cols, between; A - 6 cols, between.
Equipment: Hardware — APP/Mac.

RICHMOND

RICHMOND FREE PRESS

(Thur)
422 E Franklin St, Fl 2, Richmond, VA, 23219-2226, Richmond City, USA; tel (804) 644-0496; adv tel (804) 643-5436; ed tel (804) 643-7519; e-mail news@richmondfreepress.com; adv e-mail advertising@richmondfreepress.com; web site www.richmondfreepress.com
Circulation: 69pd, 31,259fr; VAC
Advertising: Open inch rate $28.35
Established: 1991
Group: Paradigm Communications, Inc.
Pres./Pub. .... Jean Patterson Boone
Prodn. Mgr. .... April A. Coleman
Mechanical Specifications: Printed page area: 11" wide x 21" deep • 126 column inchest
6 Column Width
Display Measurements
COLUMN SIZE
1 column 1.698"
2 columns 3.558"
3 columns 5.418"
4 columns 7.278"
5 columns 9.138"
6 columns 11"
8 Column Width Legal/
Classified Measurements
COLUMN SIZE
1 column 1.223"
2 columns 2.625"
3 columns 4.02"
4 columns 5.417"
5 columns 6.813"
6 columns 8.2"
7 columns 9.593"
8 columns 11"
Equipment: Hardware — APP/Mac; Software — Creative Suite 3; Dreamweaver 4
Delivery Method: Newsstand, Racks
Zip Codes Served: 23219, 23220, 23223, 23224, 23227, 23225, 23230, 23803, 23221, 23231, 23235, 23228, 23234, 23150, 23113, 23060, 23294, 23229, 23005, 23233

THE VOICE

(Wed)
205 E Clay St, Richmond, VA, 23219-1325, Richmond City, USA; tel (804) 644-9060; fax (804) 644-5617; e-mail info@voicenewspaper.com; adv e-mail ads@voicenewspaper.com; ed e-mail editor@voicenewspaper.com; web site www.voicenewspaper.com
Circulation: 100pd, 25,000fr; CVC
Advertising: Open inch rate $24
Established: 1985
Group: Southside Voice, Inc.Editions: 1— The VOICE
Digital Platform - Mobile: Apple, Android, Windows, Blackberry
Digital Platform - Tablet: Apple iOS, Android, Windows 7, Blackberry Tablet OS, Kindle, Nook, Kindle Fire
Ed. ....Algeree Johnson
Executive Manager.................. Marlene Jones
Mechanical Specifications: Type page 10.20 x 11.25; E - 4 cols, 2.375" between; A - 4 cols, 2 1/4, 1/4 between; C - 6 cols, 1 1/2, between.
Equipment: Hardware — APP/Mac; Software — Adobe InDesign, Illustator, PhotoShop, Microsoft Office
Delivery Method: Racks
Zip Codes Served: 23219, 23235, 23228, 23223, 23220, 23806, 23040, 23139, 23002, 23911, 23922, 23930, 23824, 23901, 23942, 23966, 23944, 23947, 23111,

ROANOKE

THE ROANOKE TRIBUNE

(Thur)
2318 Melrose Ave NW, Roanoke, VA, 24017-3906, Roanoke City, USA; tel (540) 343-0326; fax (540) 343-7366; e-mail trib@rt.roacoxmail.com; web site www.theroanoketribune.org
Circulation: 6,000pd,; Sworn/Estimate/Non-Audited
Advertising: Open inch rate $7.20
Ed. ....Claudia A. Whitworth
Assoc. Ed.. Stan Hale
Mechanical Specifications: Type page 13 x 21; E - 6 cols, 2 1/8, between; A - 6 cols, 2 1/8, between; C - 6 cols, 2 1/8, between.
Equipment: Hardware — APP/Mac; Software — Adobe/PageMaker.

WASHINGTON

SEATTLE

FACTS NEWS

(Wed)
2765 E Cherry St, Seattle, WA, 98122-4900, King, USA; tel (206) 324-0552; fax (206) 324-1007; e-mail seattlefacts@yahoo.com
Circulation: 100,000pd,; Sworn/Estimate/Non-Audited
Advertising: Open inch rate $22.50
Pub.. Dennis Beaver
Adv. Mgr.....................................Marla Beaver

Ed. .... Lavonne Marla
Mechanical Specifications: Type page 9 x 17 1/2; E - 8 cols, between; A - 8 cols, between.
Equipment: Hardware — APP/Mac; Software — Abbott Systems/Ready, Set, Go.

SEATTLE MEDIUM
(Wed)
2600 S Jackson St, Seattle, WA, 98144-2402, King, USA; tel (206) 323-3070; fax (206) 322-6518; e-mail mediumnews@aol.com; web site www.seattlemedium.com
Circulation: 13,500pd,; Sworn/Estimate/Non-Audited
Advertising: Open inch rate $34.00
Co-Pub.................................. Chris B. Bennett
Co-Pub.. Joan Owens
Gen. Mgr. .... Prisilla Hailey

TACOMA TRUE-CITIZEN
(Thur)
2600 S Jackson St, Seattle, WA, 98144-2402, King, USA; tel (206) 323-3070; fax (206) 322-6518; e-mail mediumnews@aol.com; web site www.seattlemedium.com
Circulation: 13,500pd,; Sworn/Estimate/Non-Audited
Advertising: Open inch rate $25.00
Co-Pub.................................. Chris B. Bennett
Co-Pub.. Joan Owens
Gen. Mgr. .... Pricilla Hailey
Mechanical Specifications: Type page 13 x 21; E - 6 cols, 2 1/16, 1/8 between; A - 6 cols, 2 1/16, 1/8 between; C - 10 cols, 1 1/4, between.
Equipment: Hardware — IBM.

WISCONSIN

GLENDALE

MILWAUKEE COURIER
(Sat)
6310 N Port Washington Rd, Glendale, WI, 53217-4300, Milwaukee, USA; tel (414) 449-4860; fax (414) 906-5383; e-mail milwaukeecourier@aol.com; web site milwaukeecourieronline.com
Circulation: 60,000pd, 60,000fr; Sworn/Estimate/Non-Audited
Advertising: Open inch rate $18.00
Gen. Mgr. .... Sandra Robinson
Circ. Mgr................................ Robert Robinson
Mechanical Specifications: Type page 13 x 21; E - 6 cols, 2, 1/4 between; A - 6 cols, 2, 1/4 between; C - 9 cols, 1 1/4, between.

MILWAUKEE

MILWAUKEE COMMUNITY JOURNAL
(Wed, Fri)
3612 N Martin Luther King Dr, Milwaukee, WI, 53212-4134, Milwaukee, USA; tel (414) 265-5300; fax (414) 265-6647; adv e-mail advertising@communityjournal.net; ed e-mail editorial@communityjournal.net; web site www.communityjournal.net
Circulation: 75,000fr; Sworn/Estimate/Non-Audited
Advertising: Open inch rate $37.00
Pub....................................... Patricia O. Pattillo
Adv. Mgr. .... Colleen Newsom
Circ. Mgr................................. Robert Thomas
Ed. .... Thomas Mitchell
PRODN. MGR.
Teretha Mallard
Mechanical Specifications: Type page 13 x 21 1/2; E - 6 cols, 2, 1/8 between; A - 6 cols, 2, 1/8 between; C - 8 cols, 1 2/3, 1/8 between.
Equipment: Hardware — APP/Mac; Software — QPS/QuarkXPress, Microsoft/Word.

THE MILWAUKEE COURIER
(Sat)
2003 W Capitol Dr, Milwaukee, WI, 53206-1939, Milwaukee, USA; tel (414) 449-4860; fax (414) 585-9101; e-mail milwaukeecourier@aol.com; web site www.milwaukeecourier.com
Circulation: 40,000fr; Sworn/Estimate/Non-Audited
Advertising: Open inch rate $21.63
Established: 1964
Group: Milwaukee Courier Inc
Digital Platform - Mobile: Apple, Android, Windows, Blackberry
Digital Platform - Tablet: Apple iOS, Android, Windows 7, Blackberry Tablet OS, Kindle, Nook, Kindle Fire
Pub .... Jerrel Jones
Mechanical Specifications: Type page full page 10"x18", half page horizontal 10"x9" half page vertical 4.9375"x18", quarter page 4.9375"x9"
Delivery Method: Newsstand, Carrier, Racks

SCHOOLS AND DEPARTMENTS OF JOURNALISM

ALABAMA

ALABAMA STATE UNIV. — 915 S Jackson St, Montgomery, AL, 36104-5716, USA (334) 229-4419; fax (334) 229-4934; e-mail ayoleke@aol.com; web site www.thehornettribune.com
Prof./Chair — David Okeowo
Bryan Weaver
Prof. — E.K. Daufin
Julian K. Johnson
Assoc. Prof./Dir., Forensics — Tracy Banks
James B. Lucy
Assoc. Prof. — Elizabeth Fitts
Asst. Prof. — Richard Emmanuel
Instr. — James Adams
Instr. — Coke Ellington
Instr. — Valerie Heard
Instr. — Jonathan Himsel
Instr. — John Moore
Instr. — Walter Murphy
Instr. — Larry Owens
AFFILIATIONS: ASJMC, SEJC, NCA, PRCA, NABJ, SSCA
DEGREES:BA
DEPARTMENTS: Department of Communications, 1984
FACILITIES: TV Studio, Radio Lab, Radio Station, Computer Labs
SEQUENCES: Print Journalism, Radio/Television, Public Relations and Speech Communication

AUBURN UNIVERSITY — 217 Tichenor Hall, Auburn, AL, 36849-5211 (334) 844-2727; fax (334) 844-4573; web site media.cla.auburn.edu/cmjn
Chair/Assoc. Prof. — Mary Helen Brown
Prof. — Susan Brinson
Prof. — George Plasketes
Prof. — Ed Williams
Prof. — J. Emmett Winn
Assoc. Prof. — Brigitta Brunner
Assoc. Prof. — Nan Fairley
Assoc. Prof. — Margaret Fitch-Hauser
Assoc. Prof. — SeiHill Kim
Assoc. Prof. — Judy Sheppard
Assoc. Prof. — David Sutton
Assoc. Prof. — Debra Worthington
Asst. Prof. — Robert Agne
Asst. Prof. — Jennifer Wood Adams
Asst. Prof. — John Carvalho
Asst. Prof. — Kristen Hoerl
Asst. Prof. — Hollie Lavenstein
Asst. Prof. — Chris Walker
Asst. Prof. — Kevin Smith
Asst. Prof. — Norman Youngblood
AFFILIATIONS: PRCA, SPJ
DEGREES:BA, MA
DEPARTMENTS: Department of Communication and Journalism, 1936 (Journalism Major offered before 1974 by English Dept.)
FACILITIES: AM/FM, CN, ETV, JN, PRA, VDT
SEQUENCES: Journalism, Communication, Radio/Television/Film, Public Relations; Grad. Studies in Communication

JACKSONVILLE STATE UNIVERSITY — 700 Pelham Rd. N., Jacksonville, AL, 36265-1602 (256) 782-5300; fax (256) 782-8175; e-mail kharbor@jsu.edu; web site www.jsu.edu/depart/edprof/comm
Chair/Prof. — Kingsley O. Harbor
Prof. — Augustine Ihator
Asst. Prof./Internship Coord. — Jerry Chandler
Asst. Prof. — Jeffrey Hedrick
Part-time Fac./Mgr., Stud. Media — Mike Stedham
Adj. Fac. — Pamela Hill
Adj. Fac. — Laura Tutor
Adj. Fac. — Mickey Shadrix
William Meehan
AFFILIATIONS: BEA, SPJ, PRSA, RTNDA, ASJMC, CMA
DEGREES:BA- Communication; minor in Communication (ACEJMC - accredited communication program)
DEPARTMENTS: Department of Communication
FACILITIES: Macintosh computer lab, FM radio station, Two TV studios, Four Digital editing bays, Smart classrooms, affiliated TV station WJXS
SEQUENCES: Concentrations: Broadcasting, Print Journalism, Public Relations

SAMFORD UNIVERSITY — Dept. of Journalism & Mass Communication, Birmingham, AL, 35229 (205) 726-2465; fax (205) 726-2586; e-mail rnankney@samford.edu
Chair — Bernie Ankney
AFFILIATIONS: AAF, KTA, Nate. Broadcasting Society, PRSSA
DEGREES:BA
DEPARTMENTS: Department of Journalism and Mass Communication, 1985
FACILITIES: AP, FM, CN, DR, VDT
SEQUENCES: Broadcast, News/Editorial, Public Relations, Advertising

SPRING HILL COLLEGE — 4000 Dauphin St, Mobile, AL, 36608-1780, USA (251) 380-3850; fax (251) 460-2185; e-mail shcmedia@shc.edu; sbabington@shc.edu; web site http://newswire.shc.edu/Stuart Babington
Integrated Multimedia Center (IMC) Operations Mgr and Student Media adviser — J.L. Stevens II
DEGREES:BA
DEPARTMENTS: Department of Communication Arts, 1971
SEQUENCES: BA with Concentrations: Integrated Communication (Advertising and Public Relations), Journalism and Electronic Media (Video/Audio Production in Digital Formats)

TROY STATE UNIVERSITY — 101 Wallace Hall, Troy, AL, 36082 (334) 670-3289; fax (334) 670-3707; e-mail info@jschool.troyst.edu
Dir. — Steven Padgett
DEPARTMENTS: Hall School of Journalism
SEQUENCES: Journalism Program: Professionally oriented programs to prepare students for entry-level positions in advertising, public relations, print and broadcast journalism

UNIVERSITY OF ALABAMA — 490 Phifer Hall Ste. 490, Corner Colonial Dr., Univ. Blvd., Tuscaloosa, AL, 35487-0172 (205) 348-5520; fax (205) 348-3836; e-mail chammond@ua.edu
Dean — Loy Singleton
Prof./Dir., School of Library & Information Studies — Elizabeth Aversa
Prof./Chair, Adv./PR — Bruce Berger
Prof. — Rick Bragg
Prof./Reagan Chair, Assoc. Dean, Grad. Studies — Jennings Bryant
Prof. — Jeremy Butler
Phifer Prof. — Matthew Bunker
Prof. — Karen J. Cartee
Prof./Chair, Telecommunication/Film — Gary Copeland
Bristol-EBSCO Prof. — Margaret Dalton
Prof./Dir., Institute for Comm. & Information Research — William Evans
Prof. — William Gonzenbach
Prof. — Tom Harris
Prof. — Marsha Houston
Prof. — Steven Miller
Prof. — Yorgo Pasadeos
Prof./Phifer Prof. — Joseph Phelps
Prof. — David Sloan
Assoc. Prof./Chair, Commun. Studies — Beth Bennett
Assoc. Prof. — Kimberly Bissell
AFFILIATIONS: ACES, NABJ, NPPA, SPJ
DEGREES:BA, MA, MLIS, PhD
DEPARTMENTS: College of Communication and Information Sciences, 1927
FACILITIES: AP, CN, DR, ETV, JM, JN, FM, VDT
SEQUENCES: Advertising and Public Relations, Communication Studies, Journalism, School of Library and Information Studies, Telecommunication and Film

UNIVERSITY OF SOUTH ALABAMA — 1000 University Commons, Mobile, AL, 36688 (251) 380-2800; fax (251) 380-2850; e-mail glwilson@usouthal.edu
Prof./Chair — Gerald L. Wilson
Prof. — Donald K. Wright
Assoc. Prof. — James L. Aucoin
Assoc. Prof. — Steven C. Rockwell
Assoc. Prof. — Richard Ward
Asst. Prof. — James F. Carstens
Asst. Prof. — Melva Kearney
Asst. Prof. — Patricia Mark
Asst. Prof. — Jeanne McPherson
Asst. Prof. — James M. Rosene
Instr. — Genevieve Dardeau
Instr. — April Dupree Taylor
Instr. — Heather Terry
Lectr. — Jerold Aust
Lectr. — Carolyn Combs
Lectr. — Dre Comiskey
Lectr. — Jill Haynes
Lectr. — Kelly Kendall
Lectr. — Maureen Maclay
Lectr. — Jennifer Penry
DEGREES:BA, MA
DEPARTMENTS: Department of Communication, 1964
FACILITIES: CATV, CCTV, CN, ComN,

ComR, JN, PRA, VDT
SEQUENCES: Communication Technology, Interpersonal Communication and Rhetoric, Organizational Communication, Print and Broadcast Journalism, Public Relations and Advertising, Radio/TV/Film

ALASKA

UNIVERSITY OF ALASKA ANCHORAGE — 3211 Providence Dr., Anchorage, AK, 99508 (907) 786-4180; fax (907) 786-4190; e-mail journalism@jpc.alaska.edu; web site www.jpc.uaa.alaska.edu
Chair — Fred Pearce
AFFILIATIONS: AAF, PRSSA
DEGREES:BA
DEPARTMENTS: Department of Journalism and Public Communication, 1976
SEQUENCES: Journalism (convergent program includes print, broadcasting, magazine, web), Public Relations & Advertising, Telecommunications and Information Technology, Graphics and Design

UNIVERSITY OF ALASKA AT FAIRBANKS — PO Box 756120, Fairbanks, AK, 99775 (907) 474-7761; fax (907) 474-6326; e-mail fyjnb@uaf.edu
Chair — Charles Mason
AFFILIATIONS: SPJ, KAM
DEPARTMENTS: Department of Journalism, 1966
FACILITIES: Two radio stations, a TV station, campus newspaper, computer writing lab, audio/video editing labs, online production lab, darkroom facilities, multimedia labs
SEQUENCES: Journalism Program: The ACEJMC-accredited department offers four sequences: News/editorial, broadcasting, photojournalism and multimedia

ARIZONA

ARIZONA STATE UNIVERSITY — 555 N. Central Ave., Tempe, AZ, 85004-1248 (602) 496-3867; fax (602) 496-7041; e-mail cronkiteinfol@asu.edu
Dean — Christopher Callahan
Prof. — John E. Craft
Prof./Knight Chair in Journ. — Stephen K. Doig
Prof. — Donald G. Godfrey
Prof./Dir., Media Research Program — Bruce D. Merrill
Prof. — Edward J. Sylvester
Prof. — George Watson
Assoc. Prof. — Craig Allen
Assoc. Prof. — Marianne Barrett
Class Manager — Sharon Bramlett-Solomon
Assoc. Prof. — Mary-Lou Galician
Assoc. Prof. — Fran Matera
Assoc. Prof./Dir., Grad. Studies — Joseph A. Russomanno
Assoc. Prof. — Dennis Russell
Asst. Prof. — Dina Gavrilos
Asst. Prof. — Carol Schwalbe
Asst. Prof. — William Silcock
Asst. Prof. — Xu Wu
Clinical Prof. — Bruce D. Itule
Clinical Prof./Assoc. Dir. — Frederic A. Leigh
AFFILIATIONS: AMJ, NPPA, NATAS, PRSSA, RTNDA, SPJ, WICI
DEGREES:BA, MMC
DEPARTMENTS: Walter Cronkite School of Journalism and Mass Communication, 1957
FACILITIES: AP, FM, CAT, CCTV, CN, ComN, ComTV, DR, ETV, PRA, VDT
SEQUENCES: Journalism, Media Management, Media Production, Strategic Media & Public Relations, Media Analysis & Criticism

NORTHERN ARIZONA UNIVERSITY — PO Box 5619, Flagstaff, AZ, 86011-5619 (928) 523-2232; fax (928) 523-1505; e-mail school.communication@nau.edu; web site www.comm.nau.edu
Dir. — Tom Knights
AFFILIATIONS: AAF, AER, AZ Newspapers Assn., NPPA, PAD, PRSSA, RMCPA, SCA, SPJ, SWECJMC, WICI, WSCA, BEA
DEPARTMENTS: School of Communnication, 1966
SEQUENCES: Communication Program: The School of Communication offers degrees in advertising, electronic media, journalism, merchandising, photography, public relations, speech communication and visual communication. Sequences offered within these disciplines includ

UNIVERSITY OF ARIZONA — 845 N. Park Ave., Tucson, AZ, 85721-0158 (520) 621-7556; fax (520) 621-7557; e-mail journal@email.arizona.edu; web site www.journalism.arizona.edu
Head/Soldwedel Family Prof./Prof. — Jacqueline E. Sharkey
Prof. — Terry Wimmer
Prof. — Bruce Itule
Assoc. Prof. — Shahira Fahmy
Assoc. Prof. Emer. — William F. Greer
Assoc. Prof. — Alan Weisman
Assoc. Prof. — Maggy Zanger
Asst. Prof. — David Cuillier
Asst. Prof. — Celeste Gonzalez de Bustamante
Asst. Prof. — Kevin R. Kemper
Asst. Prof. — Susan Knight
Asst. Prof. — Linda Lumsden
Asst. Prof. — Jeannine Relly
Asst. Prof. — Jay Rochlin
Asst. Prof. — Kim Newton
Instr. — Steve Auslander
Instr. — Rhonda Bodfield Bloom
Instr. — Mark Evans
Instr. — Tom Beal
Instr. — Cathalena Burch
AFFILIATIONS: SPJ, AZ Newspaper Assn, KTA, Nat'l Assn of Hispanic Journalists, Native American Journalists Assn
DEGREES:BA, MA
DEPARTMENTS: Department of Journalism, 1951
FACILITIES: CN, CATV, ETV, ComN, ComTV, JN (The Tombstone Epitaph, El Independiente, AZ Cat's Eye, Border Beat, The Cat Scan)
SEQUENCES: News-Editorial

ARKANSAS

ARKANSAS STATE UNIVERSITY — 114 Cooley Dr., Rm. 331, Jonesboro, AR, 72401 (870) 972-2468; fax (870) 972-3856; web site comm.astate.edu
Dean/Prof. — Russell E. Shain
Chair, RTV/Prof. — Osabuohien Amienyi
Chair, Commun. Studies/Prof. — Tom Baglan
Prof. — Gilbert L. Fowler
Prof. — Mary Jackson-Pitts
Assoc. Prof. — Lillie Fears
Assoc. Prof./Chair, Journ. — Joel T. Gambill
Assoc. Prof. — Jack Zibluk
Asst. Prof. — Carey Byars
Asst. Prof. — Holly Byars
Asst. Prof. — Linda Clark
Asst. Prof. — Sandra Combs
Asst. Prof. — Robert Franklin
Asst. Prof. — Myleea Hill
Asst. Prof. — Matt Ramsey
Asst. Prof. — Mathew Thatcher
Asst. Prof. — Marcilene Thompson-Hayes
Asst. Prof. — Lily Zeng
Instr. — Alex Brown
Instr. — Michael B. Doyle
AFFILIATIONS: AAF, NBS/AER, KTA, PRSSA, SPJ, AWC, ABC, BEA, NPPA, NABJ, Arkansas Press Association, Arkansas Broadcasters Association
DEGREES:BS- Journalism, Radio-TV, Graphic Communications; BA-Communication Studies; BSE- Speech & Theatre; MSMC- Journalism, Radio-TV; MA-Speech & Theatre
DEPARTMENTS: College of Communications, 1936
FACILITIES: AP, FM, CATV, CN, DR, JR, VDT, NPR, AdA, JN, PRA
SEQUENCES: Radio-TV Dept.- Broadcast Journalism, Audio-Video Production, New Media, Electronic Media Sales & Promotion; Journalism Dept.- News-Editorial, Advertising, Public Relations, Photojournalism, Graphic Communications; Communications Studies Dept

ARKANSAS TECH UNIVERSITY — T-1, 1209 N. Fargo Ave., Russellville, AR, 72801 (479) 964-0890; fax (479) 964-0899; e-mail dvocate@atu.edu
Head/Prof. — Donna R. Vocate
Assoc. Prof. — Seok Kang
Assoc. Prof. — Hanna Norton
Asst. Prof. — Warren Byrd
Asst. Prof. — Anthony Caton
Asst. Prof. — Tommy Mumert
Instr. — Russ Hancock
DEGREES:BA, MA
DEPARTMENTS: Department of Speech, Theatre and Journalism
FACILITIES: ETV, FM, CN, VDT, CCTV, DR
SEQUENCES: Print Journalism, Broadcast Journalism, Public Relations and Multi-media Journalism

HARDING UNIVERSITY — Reynolds Center, 501 S. Burks Blvd., Searcy, AR, 72143 (501) 279-4445; fax (501) 279-4605; e-mail communication@harding.edu
Dean/Prof. — Michael L. James
Prof. — Jack R. Shock
Prof. — Steven Frye
Assoc. Prof. — Kelly Elander
Assoc. Prof. — Dutch Hoggatt
Asst. Prof. — Jim Miller
Asst. Prof. — Steve Shaner
Instr. — Jeremy Beauchamp
Instr. — Bob Ritchie
Adj. — Mark Prior
AFFILIATIONS: ABEA, AER, BEA, RTNDA
DEGREES:BA, BS
DEPARTMENTS: Department of Communication, 1983
FACILITIES: TV studio, Cable TV Channel, FM Radio, 95.3Mhz KHVU, AM Radio 1660, KHCA
SEQUENCES: Advertising, Print Journalism, Public Relations, Interactive Media, Broadcast Journalism, Electronic Media Production

HENDERSON STATE UNIVERSITY — 1100 Henderson St., Arkadelphia, AR, 71999-0001 (870) 230-5182; fax (870) 230-5144; e-mail taylorm@hsu.edu
Chair — Michael Miller
Dir., Print Journalism — Michael Ray Taylor
DEGREES:BA
DEPARTMENTS: Communication and Theatre Arts Department, 1989
SEQUENCES: News-Editorial, Mass Media, PR, Communication, Theater

JOHN BROWN UNIV. — 2000 W University St, Siloam Springs, AR, 72761-2112, USA (479) 524-7255; fax (479) 524-7394; e-mail advocate@jbu.edu; web site advoacte.jbu.edu
Chair — Carey Byars
Gary Warner
Grace Pennington
Anna Mulder
DEGREES:BS
DEPARTMENTS: Department of Communication, Division of Communication and Fine Arts, 1983
SEQUENCES: Journalism Program: A full program leading to a BS in Journalism, Broadcasting or PR

UNIVERSITY OF ARKANSAS — 116 Kimpel Hall, Fayetteville, AR, 72701 (479) 575-3601; fax (479) 575-4314; e-mail pwatkins@uark.edu; web site www.uark.edu/depts/jourinfo/public_html/
Chair/Assoc. Prof. — Patsy Watkins
Prof. — Dale Carpenter
Prof. — Larry Foley
Prof. — Hoyt Purvis
Prof. — Jan LeBlanc Wicks
Assoc. Prof. — Gerald Jordan
Assoc. Prof. — Phyllis Miller
Assoc. Prof. — Louise Montgomery
Assoc. Prof. — Rick Stockdell
Asst. Prof. — Ignatius Fosu
Instr. — Eric Gorder
Instr. — Kim Martin
Instr. — Katherine Shurlds
Prof. Emer. — Roy Reed
AFFILIATIONS: AAF, PRSSA, SPJ, UAABJ
DEGREES:BA, MA
DEPARTMENTS: Walter J. Lemke Department of Journalism, 1930
FACILITIES: AP, FM, CATV, CN, ComN, ComR, ComTV, JM, VDT
SEQUENCES: News/Magazine, Advertising/Public Relations, Broadcasting

UNIVERSITY OF ARKANSAS AT LITTLE ROCK — 2801 S. University, Little Rock, AR, 72204 (501) 569-3250; fax (501) 569-8371; web site www.ualr.edu
Dir./Assoc. Prof. — Jamie Byrne
Prof. — David M. Guerra
Prof. — Bruce L. Plopper
Assoc. Prof. — Jeanne Rollberg
Assoc. Prof. — Gregory Stefaniak
Asst. Prof. — Tim Edwards
Asst. Prof. — Mark Giese
Asst. Prof. — Carlton Rhodes
Asst. Prof. — Kristie A. Swain
Instr. — David Weekley
Part-time Lectr. — Ron Breeding
Part-time Lectr. — Frank Fellone
Part-time Lectr. — Ben Fry
Part-time Lectr. — John Paul Jones
Part-time Lectr. — Dixie Martin
Part-time Lectr. — Robert Pest
Part-time Lectr. — J.J. Thompson
Part-time Lectr. — Wally Tucker
Part-time Lectr. — Theresa Wallent
Fac. Emer. — Edward Jay Friedlander
AFFILIATIONS: KTA, NABJ, NBS-AERho, PRSSA, SPJ
DEGREES:BA, MA
DEPARTMENTS: School of Mass Communication, 1971
FACILITIES: AM/FM, AP, CATV, CN, ComN, ComR, ComTV, DR, JM, PRA, VDT, departmental statewide news service
SEQUENCES: Radio/TV/Film, News-Editorial, Broadcast Journalism, Professional and Technical Writing, Public Relations

UNIVERSITY OF CENTRAL ARKANSAS — Dept. of Speech, Theatre & Mass Commun., Conway, AR, 72035 (501) 450-3162; fax (501) 450-3296; e-mail bobw@mail.uca.edu
Chair — Bob Willenbrink
AFFILIATIONS: AER
DEGREES:BA, BS
DEPARTMENTS: Department of Speech, Theater and Mass Communication, 1943
SEQUENCES: Mass Communication Program: BA and BS degrees with emphasis in Telecommunications or Journalism. Courses offered in magazine/newspaper writing, photography, TV/radio production, desktop publishing/video, media theory/ethics/law

CALIFORNIA

BIOLA UNIVERSITY — 13800 Biola Ave, La Mirada, CA, 90639-0002, USA (562) 906-4569; fax (562) 906-4515; e-mail lily.park@biola.edu; web site chimes.biola.edu
Chair/Prof. — Michael A. Longinow
Advertising Manager — Sarah Sjoberg

Prof. — J. Douglas Tarpley
Assoc. Prof. — Michael Bower
Asst. Prof. — Tamara Welter
Instr. — James Hirsen
Instr. — Chi-Chung Keung
Instr. — Mark Landsbaum
Instr. — Greg Schneider
Instr. — Melissa Nunnally
AFFILIATIONS: PRSA, PRSSA
DEGREES:BA
DEPARTMENTS: Department of Journalism, 2007
FACILITIES: AP, CN, JM, PRA, VDT
SEQUENCES: Print, Broadcast, Public Relations, Visual

CALIFORNIA LUTHERAN UNIVERSITY — 60 W Olsen Rd, Thousand Oaks, CA, 91360-2700, USA (805) 493-3366; fax (805) 493-3479; e-mail kelley@robles.callutheran.eduColleen Cason
Chair — Sharon Docter
Jonathan Culmer
Margaret Nolan
DEGREES:BA
DEPARTMENTS: Department of Communication Arts, 1981
SEQUENCES: Journalism Program: The Communication Arts Department offers a BA in Communication Arts along with concentrations in journalism, advertising/public relations and media production. The department also offers a BA in marketing communication in conjunction

CALIFORNIA POLYTECHNIC STATE UNIVERSTIY — Journalism Dept., San Luis Obispo, CA, 93407 (805) 756-2508; fax (805) 756-5744; e-mail gmramos@calpoly.edu
Chair/Prof. — George Ramos
Prof. — Nishan Havandjian
Prof. — Patrick Munroe
Prof. — Teresa Allen
Prof. — John Soares
Assoc. Prof. — Douglas J. Swanson
Full-time Lectr. — Brady Teufel
AFFILIATIONS: ACT, SPJ, PRSSA, California Newspaper Publishers Assn., Radio and Television News Directors Assn., California collegiate Media Assn.
DEGREES:BS
DEPARTMENTS: Journalism Department, 1953
FACILITIES: AP, FM, ComN, ComR, ComTV, DR, JN, VDT
SEQUENCES: Specializations: Agricultural Journalism, Broadcast Journalism, News-Editorial, Public Relations

CALIFORNIA STATE POLYTECHNIC UNIVERSITY, POMONA — 3801 W. Temple Ave., Pomona, CA, 91768-4007 (909) 869-3520; fax (909) 869-4823; e-mail rakallan@csupomona.edu
Chair — Richard A. Kallan
Debra Shea
AFFILIATIONS: ASJSA, PRSSA, SPJ, WICI
DEGREES:BS
DEPARTMENTS: Communication Department, 1968
SEQUENCES: Journalism Program: BS program with options in Journalism, Public Relations, and Communication Studies

CALIFORNIA STATE UNIVERSITY, CHICO — Tehama Hall, Chico, CA, 95929-0145 (530) 898-4015; fax (530) 898-4345
Dean — Phyllis Fernlund
AFFILIATIONS: SPJ, IABC, Forensics, Designers in Progress, Digital Filmmakers Guild, Catapult Design, Graphic Arts Technical Organization, Instructional Technology Society
DEGREES:BA, BS, MA, MS
DEPARTMENTS: College of Communication and Education, 1969
FACILITIES: AP, AdA, UPI, NPR-FM, CCTV, DR, EVT, JM, PRA, JN, VDT
SEQUENCES: Department of Communication Design: Media Arts, Graphic Design, Information and Communication Systems, Instructional Technology. Department of Communication Arts and Sciences: Human Communication, Organizational Communication. Department of Journalism

CALIFORNIA STATE UNIVERSITY, DOMINGUEZ HILLS — 1000 E. Victoria, Carson, CA, 90747 (310) 243-3313; fax (310) 243-3779; e-mail ewhetmore@csudh.edu
Chair — Edward Whetmore
AFFILIATIONS: PRSSA, SPJ
DEGREES:BA
DEPARTMENTS: Communications Department, 1973
SEQUENCES: Communication Program: Offers BA degree in Communications, options in Mass Communications, Electronic Media Production, Public Relations; also minor in Advertising, certificate in Telecommunications

CALIFORNIA STATE UNIVERSITY, FRESNO — 225 E. San Ramon Ave., M/S MF 10, Fresno, CA, 93740-8029 (559) 278-2087; fax (559) 278-4995; e-mail sallyan@csufresno.edu
Chair — Donald M. Priest
General Manager — Rich Marshall
AFFILIATIONS: ADS, NPPA, SPJ
DEGREES:BA, MA
DEPARTMENTS: Department of Mass Communication and Journalism, 1952
FACILITIES: AP, AM, FM, AdA, CN, ComTV, DR, JN, PRA, VDT

CALIFORNIA STATE UNIVERSITY, FULLERTON — PO Box 6846, Fullerton, CA, 92834-6846 (714) 278-3517; fax (714) 278-2209; web site communications.fullerton.edu
Chair/Prof. — Anthony R. Fellow
Prof. — Jeff Brody
Prof./Coord., Photocommunications — David DeVries
Prof. — Cynthia King
Prof. — Paul Lester
Prof. — Coral Ohl
Prof./Dean — Rick Pullen
Prof. — Anthony Rimmer
Prof./Early Ret. Prog. — Shay Sayre
Prof. — Edgar Trotter
Prof./Vice Chair, Grad. Coord. — Diane Witmer
Prof./Assoc. Dean — Fred Zandpour
Assoc. Prof. — Olan Farnall
Assoc. Prof./Early Ret. Prog. — Carolyn Johnson
Assoc. Prof./Coord., Advertising — Kuen-Hee Ju-Pak
Assoc. Prof. — Dean Kazoleas
Assoc. Prof. — Nancy Snow
Assoc. Prof./Coord., Journalism — Andi Stein
Asst. Prof. — Carol Ames
Asst. Prof. — Assaf Avni
AFFILIATIONS: AAF, BEA, IABC, KTA, NPPA, PRSSA, SPJ
DEGREES:BA, MA- Communications
DEPARTMENTS: Department of Communications, 1961
FACILITIES: AdA, CCTV, ComN, ComTV, DR, JM, JN, PRA, VDT, CATV
SEQUENCES: Concentrations: Advertising, Entertainment Studies, Journalism, Photo-Communications, Public Relations

CALIFORNIA STATE UNIVERSITY, HAYWARD — 25800 Carlos Bee Blvd., Hayward, CA, 94542 (510) 885-3292; fax (510) 885-4099; e-mail jhammerb@csuhayward.edu
Interim Chair — John Hammerback
DEPARTMENTS: Department of Mass Communication, 1973
SEQUENCES: Mass Communication, with options in Advertising, Broadcasting, Journalism, Photo-communication and Public Relations; Minor in Mass Communication, a Mass Communication Option in the Liberal Studies Major, and a Mass Communication emphasis in the waiver pro

CALIFORNIA STATE UNIVERSITY, LONG BEACH — 1250 Bellflower Blvd., Long Beach, CA, 90840-4601 (562) 985-4981; fax (562) 985-5300
Interim Chair/Assoc. Prof. — Raul Reis
Prof. — William Babcock
Prof. — William Mulligan
Prof. — Emma Phillingane
Asst. Prof. — Christopher Burnett
Asst. Prof. — Jennifer Fleming
Asst. Prof. — Heloiza Herscovitz
Asst. Prof. — Christopher Karadjov
Asst. Prof. — Carla Yarbrough
Lectr. — Judith Frutig
Lectr. — Barbara Kingsley
Part-time Fac. — Amara Aguilar
Part-time Fac. — Lee Brown
Part-time Fac. — John Canalis
Part-time Fac. — Henrietta Charles
Part-time Fac. — Monica Edwards
Part-time Fac. — David Ferrell
Part-time Fac. — Daniel Garvey
Part-time Fac. — Greg Hardesty
Part-time Fac. — Cees Kendall
AFFILIATIONS: KTA, PRSSA, SPJ
DEGREES:BA- Journalism
DEPARTMENTS: Department of Journalism, 1966
FACILITIES: AP, CAW, FM, DR, JM, JN, VDT
SEQUENCES: Broadcast, Online, Print, Photojournalism, Public Relations

CALIFORNIA STATE UNIVERSITY, LOS ANGELES — Music 104, 5151 State University Dr., Los Angeles, CA, 90032 (323) 343-4200; fax (323) 343-6467
DEPARTMENTS: Department of Communication Studies, 1965
SEQUENCES: Communication Program: Sequences in Public Relations, Professional Communication and Broadcast Journalism

CALIFORNIA STATE UNIVERSITY, NORTHRIDGE — 18111 Nordhoff St, Northridge, CA, 91330-0001, USA (818) 677-3135; fax (818) 677-3438; web site www.csun.edu
Chair/Prof. — Kent Kirkton
Melissa Lalum
Prof. — Susan Henry
Jody Holcomb
Prof. — Maureen Rubin
Assoc. Prof. — Rick Marks
Editor — Loren Townsley
Asst. Prof. — Jose Luis Benavides
Asst. Prof. — David Blumenkrantz
Asst. Prof. — Linda Bowen
Asst. Prof. — Jim Hill
Asst. Prof. — Melissa Wall
Lectr. — Lori Baker-Schena
Prof. Emer. — Jerry Jacobs
Prof. Emer. — DeWayne Johnson
Prof. Emer. — Lawrence Schneider
Part-time Fac. — Scott Brown
Part-time Fac. — Henrietta Charles
Part-time Fac. — Jeffrey Duclos
Part-time Fac. — Barbara Eisenstock
Part-time Fac. — Mariel Garza
Part-time Fac. — Keith Goldstein
Part-time Fac. — Lincoln Harrison
AFFILIATIONS: KTA, PRSSA, SPJ, RTNDA, California Chicano News Media Assn
DEGREES:BA, MA
DEPARTMENTS: Department of Journalism, 1958
FACILITIES: CNN, AP, UPI, FM, ComTV, ComN, ComR, DR, JM, JN, PRA, VDT
SEQUENCES: News Editorial

CALIFORNIA STATE UNIVERSITY, SACRAMENTO — 6000 J St., Sacramento, CA, 95819-6070 (916) 278-5340; e-mail valsmith@saclink.csus.edu
Chair — Val Smith
AFFILIATIONS: SPJ
DEGREES:BA- Journalism, Government/Journalism
DEPARTMENTS: Communication Studies/Journalism, 1947
FACILITIES: AdA, CATV, CN, ComN, ComR, ComTV, DR, JM, JN, PRA, VDT (IBM and Macintosh labs)
SEQUENCES: News-Editorial, Government Journalism

HUMBOLDT STATE UNIVERSITY — 1 Harpst St., Arcata, CA, 95521 (707) 826-4775; fax (707) 826-4770; e-mail mcmaster@humboldt.edu
Chair/Prof. — Mark Larson
Prof. — Craig Klein
Assoc. Prof. — George Estrada
Asst. Prof. — Marcy Burstiner
Asst. Prof. — Vicky Sama
DEGREES:BA
DEPARTMENTS: Department of Journalism and Mass Communication, 1960
FACILITIES: FM, ComN, JM, JN, PRA, VDT, AM
SEQUENCES: News-Editorial, Public Relations, Broadcast News, Media Studies

MENLO COLLEGE — 1000 El Camino Real, Atherton, CA, 94027-4300, USA; tel (1) (650) 543-3786; e-mail pr@menlo.edu; web site www.menlo.edu
Dean of Enrollment Management — Priscila de Souza
AFFILIATIONS: WSCUC
DEGREES:B.A., B.S.
DEPARTMENTS: Business marketing
FACILITIES: Residential living, athletics facilities, student dining, classroom buildings, student union
SEQUENCES: 4-year program, with general Education classes focused primarily in first 2 years.

PACIFIC UNION COLLEGE — Communication Dept., Angwin, CA, 94508 (707) 965-6437; fax (707) 965-6624; web site www.puc.edu/Departments/Communication
Chair — Jennifer Wareham Best
DEPARTMENTS: Communication Department, 1945
SEQUENCES: Journalism Program: Emphases in newspaper, magazine, broadcasting public relations for local, regional and national media. Includes internships, practicums. Majors in Journalism, Public Relations, Communication, International Communication and Speech Pa

PEPPERDINE UNIVERSITY — Communication Div., Malibu, CA, 90263 (310) 456-4211; fax (310) 456-3083; e-mail robert.chandler@pepperdine.edu
Chair — Robert C. Chandler
AFFILIATIONS: AAF, AERho, PRSSA, SPJ, WICI
DEGREES:BA, MA
DEPARTMENTS: Communication Division, 1972
FACILITIES: AdA, AP, FM, CCTV, CATV, ComN, ComTV, JN, JM, DR, PRA, VDT
SEQUENCES: Majors: Advertising, Journalism (News Editorial), Public Relations, Telecommunications

POINT LOMA NAZARENE UNIV. — 3900 Lomaland Dr, San Diego, CA, 92106-2810, USA (619) 849-2444; fax (619) 849-7009; e-mail news@pointweekly.com; sports@pointweekly.com; advertising@pointweekly.com; web site www.pointweekly.comStephanie Gant
Journalism Dir. — Dean Nelson
Coco Jones
Nathan Scharn
AFFILIATIONS: SPJ chapter, annual Writer's Symposium By The Sea
DEPARTMENTS: Journalism and Mass Communications majors
SEQUENCES: Majors: Journalism, Broadcast Journalism, Media Communication

SAINT MARY'S COLLEGE OF CALIFORNIA — Dept. of Communications, Moraga, CA,

94575 (510) 631-4000; fax (510) 631-0938
Chair — Michael A. Russo
DEPARTMENTS: Department of Communications, 1987
SEQUENCES: Journalism Program: A comprehensive Liberal Arts program including communications theory and practice in audio, video and print media

SAN DIEGO STATE UNIVERSITY — 5500 Campanile Dr., San Diego, CA, 92182-4561 (619) 594-5450; fax (619) 594-6246; e-mail jmsdesk@mail.sdsu.edu
Dir./Prof. — Diane Borden
Prof. — Joel Davis
Prof. — David Dozier
Prof. — Bill Eadie
Prof. — Barbara Mueller
Prof. — Tim Wulfemeyer
Assoc. Prof. — Bey-Ling Sha
Assoc. Prof. — Mei Zhong
Asst. Prof. — Noah Arceneaux
Asst. Prof. — Amy Schmitz Weiss
Lectr. — Valerie Barker
Man. Ed. — Lora Cicalo
Lectr. — Rebecca Coates Nee
Lectr. — David Coddon
Lectr./Van Deerlin Prof. of Commun. & Pub. Policy — John Eger
Lectr. — David Feldman
Lectr. — Chad Harris
Lectr. — Martin Kruming
Lectr. — Lanie Lockwood
Lectr. — Jim McBride
AFFILIATIONS: AAF, BEA, KTA, PRSSA, RTNDA, SPJ
DEGREES:BA- Communication, Journalism; MA- Communication
DEPARTMENTS: School of Journalism and Media Studies, 1951
FACILITIES: AdA, CATV, ComN, ComR, ComTV, ETV, AM, FM, PRA, VDT
SEQUENCES: BA Journalism and Communication with emphasis in Advertising, Public Relations, Specialization in Media Studies; MA Communication with specialization in Mass Communication and Media Studies

SAN FRANCISCO STATE UNIVERSITY — 1600 Holloway Ave, San Francisco, CA, 94132-1722, USA (415) 338-1689; fax (415) 338-2084; e-mail jour@sfsu.edu; web site www.journalism.sfsu.edu
Dept. Chair/Assoc. Prof. — Venise Wagner
Assoc. Dept. Chair/Prof. — Jon Funabiki
Dottie Katzeff
Prof. — John Burks
Barbara Landes
Nathan Codd
Prof. — Yvonne Daley
Prof. — Kenneth Kobre
Prof. — Erna R. Smith
Assoc. Prof. — Rachele Kanigel
Assoc. Prof. — Austin Long-Scott
Asst. Prof./Dir., Ctr. for Integration/Improvement of Journalism — Cristina Azocar
Asst. Prof. — Yumi Wilson
Prof. Emer. — John T. Johnson
Prof. Emer. — B.H. Liebes
Prof. Emer. — Betty Medsger
Prof. Emer. — Leonard Sellers
Prof. Emer. — Jerrold Werthimer
Lectr. — Harriet Chiang
Lectr. — Roland DeWolk
Lectr. — Jesse Garnier
Lectr. — David Greene
Lectr. — Sibylla Herbrich
DEGREES:BA, Interdisciplinary master's degree
DEPARTMENTS: Department of Journalism, 1961
FACILITIES: Writing, Online, Digital Labs
SEQUENCES: Majors: Print and Online Journalism, Photojournalism. Minor: Journalism

SAN JOSE STATE UNIVERSITY — One Washington Sq., San Jose, CA, 95192-0055 (408) 924-3240; fax (408) 924-3229; e-mail jmcinfo@casa.sjsu.edu; web site www.jmcweb.sjsu.edu
Dir./Prof. — William Briggs
Prof. — Cecelia Baldwin
Prof. — Harvey Gotliffe
Prof. — Clyde Lawrence
Prof. — Diana Stover
Prof./Coord., Grad. Studies — William Tillinghast
Prof. — Dennis Wilcox
Assoc. Prof. — Richard Craig
Assoc. Prof. — Scott Fosdick
Assoc. Prof. — Tim Hendrick
Assoc. Prof. — Kathleen Martinelli
Assoc. Prof. — Robert Rucker
Asst. Prof. — Lilly Buchwitz
Asst. Prof. — Michael Cheers
Lectr. — George Coakley
Lectr. — Chris DiSalvo
Lectr. — Stephen Eckstone
Lectr. — Mack Lundstrom
Lectr. — Cynthia McCune
Lectr. — Dona Nichols
AFFILIATIONS: AAF, KTA, NPPA, PRSSA, SPJ
DEGREES:BS- Advertising, Journalism, Public Relations; MS- Mass Communications
DEPARTMENTS: School of Journalism and Mass Communications, 1934
FACILITIES: AP, FM, AdA, CCTV, ComTV, DR, JN, PRA, VDT
SEQUENCES: Broadcast News, Magazine, Photojournalism, Reporting/Editing

SANTA CLARA UNIVERSITY — 500 El Camino Real, Arts and Sciences Bldg., #229, Santa Clara, CA, 95053 (408) 554-5498; fax (408) 554-4913
Head — Stephen Lee
DEGREES:BA
DEPARTMENTS: Department of Communication
SEQUENCES: Journalism Program: Department offers BA in Communication. Emphases in Mass Communication, Interpersonal Communication, Print, Online, Television Journalism, Video Production, New Technologies and Global Communication. Courses include newswriting, editin

STANFORD UNIVERSITY — McClatchy Hall, Stanford, CA, 94305-2050 (650) 723-1941; fax (650) 725-2472; e-mail comm-inforequest@lists.stanford.edu; web site communication.stanford.edu
Chair/Prof. — James Fishkin
Prof. — Theodore L. Glasser
Chandler Prof. — Shanto Iyengar
Frederic O. Glover Prof. — Jon Krosnick
Prof. — Clifford I. Nass
Edwards Prof. — Byron Reeves
Asst. Prof. — Jeremy Bailenson
Asst. Prof. — Fred Turner
Vstg. Prof. — Joel Brinkley
Vstg. Prof. — Glenn Frankel
Vstg. Prof. — Ann Grimes
Vstg. Prof. — Beth Noveck
Vstg. Prof. — Robert Luskin
Lectr. — John Markoff
Lectr. — Howard Rheingold
Lectr. — James Wheaton
Lectr. — Gregg Zachary
Courtesy Appointments — Jan Krawitz
Courtesy Appointments — Lawrence Lessig
Courtesy Appointments — Walter Powell
DEGREES:BA, MA, PhD
DEPARTMENTS: Department of Communication
FACILITIES: FM, RNA, CCTV, CN, ComN, ComTV, VDT
SEQUENCES: BA- Communication; MA- Journalism, Documentary Film/Video; PhD- Communication Research; John S. Knight Fellowship Program

UNIVERSITY OF CALIFORNIA AT BERKELEY — North Gate Hall, UC, Berkeley, CA, 94720 (510) 642-3383; fax (501) 643-9136
DEGREES:MJ
DEPARTMENTS: Graduate School of Journalism, 1968 (as school)
SEQUENCES: News-Editorial, Radio News, Television News, Photogaphy, Documentary Film, New Media, Magazine Writing

UNIVERSITY OF SAN FRANCISCO — 2130 Fulton St., San Francisco, CA, 94117-1080 (415) 422-6680; fax (415) 422-5680; e-mail goodwina@usfca.edu
Chair — Andrew Goodwin
DEPARTMENTS: Department of Media Studies, Journalism emphasis, 1974
SEQUENCES: Journalism Program: Liberal arts media studies program with professional sequence in print journalism and in electronic media. Emphases: Media & Society, Journalism, Electronic Media

UNIVERSITY OF SOUTHERN CALIFORNIA — 3502 Watt Way, ASC 325, Los Angeles, CA, 90089-0281 (213) 740-3914; fax (213) 740-8624; e-mail ascquery@usc.edu; web site www.annenberg.usc.edu
Dir./Annenberg Family Chair in Commun. Leadership/Univ. Prof. — Geneva Overholser
Wallis Annenberg Chair in Journalism and Democracy/Prof. — Jay T. Harris
Knight Chair in Media and Religion/Assoc. Prof. — Diane Winston
Prof./Dean, Annenberg School for Communication — Geoffrey Cowan
Prof. — K.C. Cole
Prof. — Ed Cray
Prof. — Felix Gutierrez
Prof. — Bryce Nelson
Prof. — Michael Parks
Prof. — Joe Saltzman
Prof. — Philip Seib
Prof. — Roberto Suro
Prof., Professional Practice/Assoc. Dir. — Patricia Dean
Prof., Professional Practice — Gerald Swerling
Assoc. Prof. — William Celis
Assoc. Prof. — Jonathan Kotler
Assoc. Prof. — Josh Kun
Assoc. Prof. — Judy Muller
Assoc. Prof. — Larry Pryor
Assoc. Prof. — Sandy Tolan
AFFILIATIONS: PRSSA, RTNDA
DEGREES:BA, MA
DEPARTMENTS: School of Journalism, USC Annenberg School for Communication, 1928
FACILITIES: AP, AM, CATV, CN, ComN, ComTV, PRA
SEQUENCES: BA/MA- Journalism (emphases in Print Journalism, Broadcast Journalism, Online Journalism); MA - Strategic Public Relations, Specialized Journalism (emphases in The Arts)

UNIVERSITY OF THE PACIFIC — 3601 Pacific Ave., Stockton, CA, 95211 (209) 946-2505; fax (209) 946-2694; e-mail qdong@uop.edu
Chair — Qingwen Dong
DEGREES:BA, MA
DEPARTMENTS: Department of Communication
SEQUENCES: Communication Program offers BA in Communication with an emphasis on one of three tracks: Communication Studies, Public Relations and Organizational Communication, and Media Studies. MA degree offered with concentration in Communication Theory, Interper

COLORADO

COLORADO STATE UNIVERSITY — C-225 Clark Bldg. 1785 Campus Delivery, Colorado State University, Fort Collins, CO, 80523 (970) 491-6310; fax (970) 491-2908; e-mail gluft@lamar.colostate.edu; web site www.colostate.edu/depts/tj
Prof./Chair — Gregory Luft
Prof. — Kirk Hallahan
Prof. — Marilee Long
Prof. — Garrett O'Keefe
Prof. — Donna Rouner
Prof./Dir., Center for Writing and Communication Technology — Donald Zimmerman
Assoc. Prof. — Cindy Christen
Assoc. Prof. — Kris Kodrich
Assoc. Prof. — James Landers
Assoc. Prof. — Patrick Plaisance
Assoc. Prof./Adv., Information Science and Technology prog. — Peter Seel
Assoc. Prof. — Jamie Switzer
Assoc. Prof./Grad. Program Coord. — Craig Trumbo
Asst. Prof. — Joseph Champ
Asst. Prof. — Jangyul Kim
Asst. Prof. — Minjeong Kim
Asst. Prof. — Rosa Martey
Asst. Prof. — Jonna Pearson
Instr. — Jeff Browne
Instr. — Chryss Cada
AFFILIATIONS: NPPA, PRSSA, SPJ, KTA
DEGREES:BA, MS, PhD
DEPARTMENTS: Department of Journalism and Technical Communication, 1968
FACILITIES: FM, CATV, CCTV, CN, ComN, PRA, VDT
SEQUENCES: Computer-Mediated Communication, News-Editorial, Public Relations, Specialized/Technical Communication, Television News and Video Communication

COLORADO STATE UNIVERSITY, PUEBLO — 2200 Bonforte Blvd., AM-117, Pueblo, CO, 81001-4901 (719) 549-2835; fax (719) 549-2120; e-mail jen.mullen@colostate-pueblo.edu; web site http://chass.colostate-pueblo.edu/mccnm/
Chair — Jennifer Mullen
DEPARTMENTS: Department of Mass Communications and Center for New Media
FACILITIES: KTSC-FM, KTSC-RMPBS
SEQUENCES: Communications Program: Integrated umbrella program provides emphases in Integrated Communication, Electronic Media and Journalism

MESA STATE COLLEGE — PO Box 2647, Grand Junction, CO, 81502 (970) 248-1287; fax (970) 248-1199; e-mail bevers@mesastate.edu; web site www.mesastate.edu/masscomm
Dir. — Byron Evers
DEGREES:BA
DEPARTMENTS: Mass Communications Department, 1981
SEQUENCES: Mass Communications Program: The department offers a Mass Communications bachelor's degree with concentrations in Media News-Editorial, Broadcast Production; Public Relations/Advertising; Print Media

METROPOLITAN STATE COLLEGE OF DENVER — PO Box 173362, Denver, CO, 80217-3362 (303) 556-3485; fax (301) 556-3013; e-mail hurleyd@mscd.edu
Chair — Deborah C. Hurley
DEPARTMENTS: Department of Journalism, 1987
SEQUENCES: Journalism Program: The Journalism Dept. has three sequences: news/editorial, photojournalism and public relations. The department uses a hands-on approach to teach reporting and editing. All faculty are current or former reporters/editors. The depart

UNIVERSITY OF COLORADO — Armory Bldg. 116, 1151 University Ave. 478 UCB, Boulder, CO, 80309-0478 (303) 492-5007; fax (303) 492-0969; e-mail sjmcdean@colorado.edu
Prof./Dean — Paul S. Voakes
Prof./Assoc. Dean/Dir. Graduate Studies — Andrew Calabrese
Prof./Dir., Ctr. for Media, Religion/Culture — Stewart M. Hoover

Prof./James E. de Castro Chair in Global Media Studies — Bella Mody
Prof./UNESCO Chair in Int'l Journalism Educ. — Marguerite J. Moritz
Prof. — Michael Tracey
Prof. — Robert Trager
Assoc. Prof./Co-Dir., Ctr. for Environmental Journalism — Len Ackland
Assoc. Prof./Head, Media Studies seq. — Shu-Ling Berggreen
Assoc. Prof. — Michael McDevitt
Assoc. Prof. — Polly McLean
Assoc. Prof. — Janice Peck
Assoc. Prof. — Brett Robbs
Assoc. Prof./Head, Adv. Seq. — David Slayden
Assoc. Prof. — Jan Whitt
Assoc. Prof./Co-Dir., Ctr. for Environmental Journalism/Head, News-Editorial seq. — Tom Yulsman
Asst. Prof./Assoc. Dir., Ctr. for Environmental Journalism — Deserai Crow
Asst. Prof. — Nabil Echchaibi
Asst. Prof. — Kendra Gale
Asst. Prof. — Lee Hood
AFFILIATIONS: AAF, KTA, SPJ, WICI
DEGREES:BS JR, MA, PhD
DEPARTMENTS: School of Journalism and Mass Communication, 1922
FACILITIES: AdA, AM, AP, CATV, ComN, ComR, ComTV, DR, JN, PRA, VDT
SEQUENCES: Advertising, Electronic Media (Broadcast News & Broadcast Production/Management), Media Studies, News-Editorial

UNIVERSITY OF DENVER — 2490 S. Gaylord St., Denver, CO, 80208 (303) 871-3976; fax (303) 871-4949; e-mail mcom@du.edu; web site www.du.edu/mcom
Assoc. Prof./Chair — Diane Waldman
Assoc. Prof./Dir., Mass Commun. Grad. Studies — Renee Botta
Assoc. Prof./Dir., Communication Undergrad. Studies — Rodney Buxton
Assoc. Prof./Dir., Estlow Int'l. Ctr. Journalism/New Media — Lynn Clark
Assoc. Prof. — Tony Gault
Assoc. Prof./Dir., Digital Media Studies Grad. prog. — Trace Reddell
Assoc. Prof./Dir., Int'l & Intercultural Communication Grad. prog. — Margie Thompson
Asst. Prof. — Christof Demont-Heinrich
Asst. Prof./Dir., Internships — Catherine A. Grieve
Asst. Prof. — Nadia Kaneva
Asst. Prof. — Sheila Schroeder
Asst. Prof. — Derigan Silver
Lectr. — Bill Depper
Lectr. — Elizabeth Henry
Lectr./Fac. Advisor to the Clarion — Ania Savage
Lectr. — Steve Scully
Prof. Emer. — Noel Jordan
Prof. Emer. — Harold Mendelsohn
DEGREES:BA, MA, MS
DEPARTMENTS: Department of Mass Communications and Journalism Studies, 1956
FACILITIES: AdA, CN, CCTV, PRA, VDT, ComN
SEQUENCES: Undergraduate: The department offers a BA in Communication with emphasis areas in General Communication, Communication Management, Culture and Communication, Film and Video Production, Interpersonal Communication; BA - Journalism Studies, Digital Media St

UNIVERSITY OF NORTHERN COLORADO — Dept. of Journalism, Greeley, CO, 80639 (970) 351-2726; fax (970) 351-2983
Prof./Chair — Charles Ingold
Endowed Prof. — Alice Klement
Assoc. Prof. — Wayne Melanson
Asst. Prof. — Lynn Klyde-Silverstein
Asst. Prof. — Lee Anne Peck
AFFILIATIONS: SPJ
DEGREES:BA
DEPARTMENTS: Department of Journalism and Mass Communications, 1970
FACILITIES: CN, CATV, 24 VDTs and 3 printers in news lab
SEQUENCES: Public Relations and Advertising Media, News-Editorial, Telecommunications

CONNECTICUT

CENTRAL CONNECTICUT STATE UNIV. — 1615 Stanley St, New Britain, CT, 06050-2439, USA (860) 832-3744; fax (860) 832-3747; e-mail ccsurecorder@gmail.com; ccsurecorder.ads@gmail.com; web site www.centralrecorder.com
Coord. — Vivian B. Martin
Melissa Traynor
Michael Walsh
Christopher Boulay
Christina LoBello
Adv. Mgr. — Kelsey
DEPARTMENTS: Department of English, 1984 (minor), 2009 (major)
SEQUENCES: A 40-credit program in which students may focus on print or broadcast; all students receive multimedia training.

FAIRFIELD UNIVERSITY — English Dept., N. Benson Rd., Fairfield, CT, 6824 (203) 254-4000; fax (203) 254-4131; e-mail jsimon@mail.fairfield.edu
Chair/Fac. — James Simon
Fac. — Jack Cavanaugh
Fac. — Marcy Mangels
Fac. — Jean Santopatre
Fac. — Fran Silverman
DEGREES:BA
SEQUENCES: Journalism within English major; stand-alone minor

QUINNIPIAC UNIVERSITY — 275 Mount Carmel Ave, Hamden, CT, 06518-1905, USA 8608301017; e-mail editor@quchronicle.com; web site www.quinnipiac.edu; quchronicle.com
Editor-in-Chief — David Friedlander
DEPARTMENTS: School of Communications, Ed McMahon Center, 1993

SOUTHERN CONNECTICUT STATE UNIVERSITY — 501 Crescent St. Morrill 202, New Haven, CT, 6515 (203) 392-5800; fax (203) 392-5809; e-mail harrisf1@southernct.edu
Chair — Frank Harris
AFFILIATIONS: SPJ
DEGREES:BA, BS
DEPARTMENTS: Journalism Department, 1976
FACILITIES: AM, AdA, AP, CATV, CCTV, CN, ComN, ComR, ComTV, DR, PRA, VDT
SEQUENCES: News-Editorial, Magazine, Broadcast, Public Relations

UNIVERSITY OF BRIDGEPORT — Dept. of Mass Commun., Bridgeport, CT, 6601 (203) 576-4705; e-mail carvethr@csusys.ctstateu.edu
Chair — Rod Carveth
AFFILIATIONS: AAF, IABC, SPJ, WICI
DEPARTMENTS: Department of Mass Communication, 1948
SEQUENCES: Journalism Program: The department offers sequences in news-editorial, advertising, and communication studies

UNIVERSITY OF CONNECTICUT — Journalism Dept., 337 Mansfield Rd., Storrs, CT, 06269-1129 (860) 486-4222; fax (860) 486-3294; e-mail jouadm01@unconnvm.uconn.edu; web site www.journalism.uconn.edu
Prof./Head — Maureen Croteau
Prof. — Wayne Worcester
Assoc. Prof. — Marcel Dufresne
Assoc. Prof. — Timothy Kenny
Asst. Prof. — Robert Wyss
Lectr. — Claire Bessette
Lectr. — Bob Hamilton
Lectr. — Douglas Hardy
Lectr. — Terese Karmel
Lectr. — Jonathan Lender
Lectr. — Gail MacDonald
Lectr. — Jon Sandberg
Lectr. — Julie Sprengelmeyer
Lectr. — Greg Stone
AFFILIATIONS: New England Newspaper Assn.
DEGREES:BA
DEPARTMENTS: Journalism Department, 1948
FACILITIES: AP, CN, ComN, ComTV, PRA, AM, FM, JN, VDT
SEQUENCES: News-Editorial

UNIVERSITY OF HARTFORD — 200 Bloomfield Ave., West Hartford, CT, 06117-1599 (860) 768-4633; fax (860) 768-4096; e-mail kelly@hartford.edu
Dir. — Lynne Kelly
DEGREES:BA, MA
DEPARTMENTS: School of Communication, 1956
SEQUENCES: Journalism Program: Offers BA and MA in Communication with emphasis in Journalism, Media, Advertising, Public Relations, Human Communication Studies, Integrated Communication

DELAWARE

UNIVERSITY OF DELAWARE — Journalism Program, Newark, DE, 19716 (302) 451-2361
DEPARTMENTS: Journalism Program
SEQUENCES: Journalism Program: Offers 21 hours of news writing, magazine writing and copy editing-layout courses, as well as extensive internship program with newspapers, magazines, electronic media and public relations offices

DISTRICT OF COLUMBIA

AMERICAN UNIVERSITY — 4400 Massachusetts Ave. NW, Washington, DC, 20016 (202) 885-2060; fax (202) 885-2099; web site www.soc.american.edu
Prof./Dean — Larry Kirkman
Prof. — Patricia Aufderheide
Prof. — Kathryn Montgomery
Prof. — Jack Orwant
Prof. — Chris Simpson
Prof. — Rodger Streitmatter
Assoc. Prof. — Randall Blair
Assoc. Prof. — W. Joseph Campbell
Assoc. Prof. — Wendell Cochran
Assoc. Prof. — Barbara Diggs-Brown
Assoc. Prof. — John Doolittle
Assoc. Prof. — John Douglass
Assoc. Prof. — Charlene Gilbert
Assoc. Prof. — Jane Hall
Assoc. Prof. — Jill Olmsted
Assoc. Prof. — Rick Rockwell
Assoc. Prof. — Richard Stack
Assoc. Prof. — Leonard Steinhorn
Assoc. Prof. — Wendy Swallow
Assoc. Prof. — John Watson
AFFILIATIONS: KTA, NATAS, PRSSA, SPJ, WICI
DEGREES:BA, BS, MA, MFA
DEPARTMENTS: School of Communication, 1966
FACILITIES: AP, AM, FM, CCTV, ComN, ComR, ComTV, DR, MM, PRA, VDT
SEQUENCES: Programs: Broadcast Journalism; Print Journalism; Public Communication; Film and Media Arts; Communication, Legal Institutions, Economics, and Government; Foreign Language and Communication Media; Multimedia Design and Development; Graduate Journalism and

CATHOLIC UNIVERSITY SCHOOL OF LAW — Institute for Communications Law Studies, Washington, DC, 20064 (202) 319-6295; fax (202) 319-4459
Dir. — Marin Scordato
DEPARTMENTS: Institute for Communications Law Studies
SEQUENCES: Communications Program: Specialized legal training in communications law for JD degree candidates with journalism or telecommunications backgrounds

GEORGE WASHINGTON UNIVERSITY — 805 21st St. NW, Ste. 400, Washington, DC, 20052 (202) 994-6227; fax (202) 994-5806; e-mail smpa@gwu.edu; web site www.gwu.edu/~smpa
AFFILIATIONS: Policomm Society, SPJ
DEGREES:BA, MA
DEPARTMENTS: Bachelor of Arts in Journalism, Political Communication, and Electronic Media; Master of Arts in Media and Public Affairs (School of Media and Public Affairs), 1947
FACILITIES: AM/FM, CCTV, CN, VDT, ETV, ComN, Internet, Center for Survey Research

HOWARD UNIVERSITY — 525 Bryant St. NW, Washington, DC, 20059 (202) 806-7690; fax (202) 232-8305; web site www.soc.howard.edu
Grad. Prof./Dean — Jannette L. Dates
Prof. (LWOP) — Noma Anderson
Prof. — Anju Chaudhary
Prof. — Abraham Ford
Prof. — Haile Gerima
Prof. — Barbara Hines
Prof. — Lawrence Kaggwa
Prof. — Judi Moore Latta
Prof. — Abbas Malek
Prof. — Robert L. Nwanko
Prof. — Joan C. Payne
Prof. — Ronald C. Pearlman
Grad. Prof. — William H. Starosta
Grad. Prof. (LWOP)/Vice Provost — Orlando L. Taylor
Prof. — Clint C. Wilson
Prof. — Richard Wright
Assoc. Prof. — S. Torriano Berry
Assoc. Prof. — Debra A. Busacco
Assoc. Prof. — Alonzo Crawford
Assoc. Prof. — Melbourne S. Cummings
AFFILIATIONS: SPJ, NABJ, PRSSA, AAF, BCCA, BEA
DEGREES:BA- Communication and Culture, Journalism, R/TV/F; BS- Communication Sciences and Disorders; MA- Communication and Culture; MS- Communication Sciences and Disorders; MFA- Film; PhD- Communication and Culture, Communication Sciences and Disorders
DEPARTMENTS: School of Communications, 1971
FACILITIES: AM, AdA, RNA, FM, CN, ComN, ComR, CCTV, ETV, JN, PRA, VDT
SEQUENCES: Print/On-line Journalism, Broadcast News, Advertising/Public Relations, Film Audio Production, Television Production, Telecommunications Management, Legal Communication, Speech Communication, Speech-Language Pathology and Audiology

FLORIDA

EDWARD WATERS COLLEGE — Mass Communications Program, Jacksonville, FL, 32218 (904) 366-2502
Coord. — Emmanuel C. Alozie
DEGREES:BA
DEPARTMENTS: Mass Communications Program, 1982/83
SEQUENCES: Radio/TV, Journalism

FLAGLER COLLEGE — Communication Dept., 74 King St., Saint Augustine, FL, 32085-1027 (904) 819-6247; fax (904) 826-3471;

e-mail halcombt@flagler.edu
Chair/Assoc. Prof. — Tracy Halcomb
Assoc. Prof. — Jim Gilmore
Asst. Prof. — James Pickett
Asst. Prof. — Nadia Reardon
Asst. Prof. — Helena Sarkio
Asst. Prof. — Rosemary Tutt
Instr. — Rob Armstrong
Instr. — Dan McCook
Instr. — Victor Ostrowidzki
Instr. — Barry Sand
DEGREES:BA- Communication
DEPARTMENTS: Communication Department, 1989
FACILITIES: FM, CATV, CCTV, CN, DR, PRA, VDT
SEQUENCES: Journalism, Broadcasting, Public Relations

FLORIDA A&M UNIVERSITY — 510 Orr Dr., Ste. 4003, School of Journalism & Graphic Communication Bldg., Tallahassee, FL, 32307-4800 (850) 599-3379; fax (850) 561-2399; e-mail james.hawkins@famu.edu
Dean — James E. Hawkins
Prof./Dir., Grad. Studies — Michael E. Abrams
Prof. — F. Todd Bertolaet
Prof./Dir., Div. of Journalism — Dorothy Bland
Prof. — Vincent Blyden
Prof. — LaRae Donnellan
Prof. — Gerald O. Grow
Prof./Assoc. Dean./Dir., Div. of Graphic Communication — Arvid Mukes
Prof./Knight Chair — Joe Ritchie
Prof. — Kay Wilder
Prof. — Gale Workman
Assoc. Prof. — Bettye Grable
Assoc. Prof. — Joseph Ippolito
Assoc. Prof. — Kenneth Jones
Asst. Prof./Vstg. Dir., Career Devel. Servs. — Yanela Gordon
Asst. Prof./Dir., H.S./Community College Rel. — M. Diane Hall
Asst. Prof. — Gina Kinchlow
Asst. Prof. — Andrew Skerritt
Asst. Prof. — Valerie White
Instr./Mgr., FAMU-TV 20 — Ernest Jones
AFFILIATIONS: BCCA, KTA, EPT, SPJ, PRSSA, NABJ, Florida Pubic Relations Assn., Graphic Arts Education Assn., American Assn. of University Printers, Graphic Arts Technical Foundation, ACEJMC, ACCGC
DEGREES:BSJ, BS- Public Relations, Graphic Communication, Graphic Design; MS- Journalism
DEPARTMENTS: School of Journalism and Graphic Communication, 1974
FACILITIES: FM Radio, Educational Access Television, Student PR Agency, Eleven Computer Labs, Digital Photo Lab, B&W and Color Processing
SEQUENCES: Newspaper Journalism, Magazine Production, Broadcast Journalism, Public Relations, Printing Management, Photography, Graphic Design

FLORIDA INTERNATIONAL UNIVERSITY — Biscayne Bay Campus, 3000 NE 151st St., North Miami, FL, 33181 (305) 919-5625; fax (305) 919-5203; e-mail kopenhav@fiu.edu; web site http://jmc.fiu.edu
Prof. — Frederick Blevens
Assoc. Prof. — Margo Berman
Assoc. Prof. — Mario Diament
Assoc. Prof./Interim Chair, Dept. of Journ./Broadcasting — Teresa Ponte
Assoc. Prof. — Neil Reisner
Assoc. Prof./Interim Assoc. Dean — Allan Richards
Assoc. Prof. — Lorna Veraldi
Assoc. Prof. — Mercedes Vigon
Asst. Prof. — Lynn Farber
Asst. Prof./Coord., Spanish-language Journ. Master's Prog. — Lilliam Martinez-Bustos
Asst. Prof. — Elizabeth Marsh
Asst. Prof. — Michael Scott Sheerin
Lillian Lodge Kopenhaver
David Park
Moses Shumow
Juliet Pinto
Ted Gutsche
Kathy Fitspatrick
Kurt Wise
Yu Liu
Weirui Wang
Maria Elena Villar
Sigal Segev
AFFILIATIONS: PRSSA, AAF AWC, SPJ, KTA, AdFed
DEGREES:BS, MS
DEPARTMENTS: School of Journalism and Mass Communication, 1978
FACILITIES: VDT, ComN, Graphics Lab, EDIT, ENG, TV Studio, CATV, 6 computer labs
SEQUENCES: Tracks: Undergraduate-Advertising, Journalism, Public Relations, Multimedia; Broadcasting; Graduate-Integrated Marketing Communications: Advertising and Public Relations, Spanish-language Journalism, Student Media Advising, Spanish/English-language Journalism

FLORIDA SOUTHERN COLLEGE — 111 Lake Hollingsworth Dr, Lakeland, FL, 33801-5607, USA (863) 680-4168; fax (863) 680-6244; web site www.fscsouthern.com
Chair — Russell Barclay
Michael Trice
Laura Howell
DEGREES:BA, BS
DEPARTMENTS: Department of Communication
SEQUENCES: Journalism Program: BA and BS in Communication with concentrations in Advertising, Journalism, and Public Relations

JACKSONVILLE UNIVERSITY — Dept. of Mass Communication Studies, Jacksonville, FL, 32211 (904) 744-3950
Dir. — Dennis Stouse
AFFILIATIONS: SCJ, Florida Public Relations Assn.
DEPARTMENTS: Department of Mass Communication Studies
FACILITIES: Weekly newspaper, college magazine, yearbook, radio station, cable television access, national film studies journal
SEQUENCES: Journalism Program: JU's program blends the arts and sciences with a skills-oriented communications curriculum. Sequences available are Newspaper/Magazine, PR/Advertising, Radio/TV/Film. Many internship opportunities are available including a summer int

KAPLAN UNIVERSITY — 6301 Kaplan University Ave., Fort Lauderdale, FL, 33309 (954) 515-4015; fax (888) 887-6494; e-mail Cstevenson@kaplan.edu; web site www.kaplan.edu
Academic. Prog. Dir. — Carolyn N. Stephenson
DEGREES:AS, BS
DEPARTMENTS: College of Arts and Sciences, Department of Communications
SEQUENCES: Communication Programs: The University offers an online BS in Communication degree with emphasis areas in technical writing and organizational communication. The degree program provides an interdisciplinary approach that combines both theory and applicati

UNIVERSITY OF CENTRAL FLORIDA — 4000 Central Florida Blvd., Orlando, FL, 32816-1344 (407) 823-2681; fax (407) 823-6360; web site communication.cos.ucf.edu
Prof. — Mary Alice Shaver
Prof./Head, Adv./PR — Robert Davis
Prof./Head, Journalism — Fred Fedler
Prof./Grad. Dir. — Burt Pryor
Prof. — Ron Smith
Assoc. Prof./Head, Radio/TV — George Bagley
Assoc. Prof./Head, I/O — Jeff Butler
Assoc. Prof. — Denise DeLorme
Assoc. Prof. — W. Joe Hall
Assoc. Prof. — Jose Maunez
Assoc. Prof. — Maria Cristina Santana
Asst. Prof. — Kimiko Akita
Asst. Prof. — Tim Brown
Asst. Prof. — Steve Collins
Asst. Prof. — Gene Costain
Asst. Prof. — Sally Hastings
Asst. Prof. — Jim Katt
Asst. Prof. — Rick Kenney
Asst. Prof. — Sam Lawrence
Asst. Prof. — John Malala
AFFILIATIONS: AAF, BEA, FPRA, KTA, NPPA, NABJ, NAHJ, RTNDA, SPJ
DEPARTMENTS: Nicholson School of Communication, 1964
SEQUENCES: Advertising/Public Relations, Interpersonal Communication, Journalism, Organizational Communication, Radio/Television; MA- track in Mass Communication, track in Interpersonal Communication

UNIVERSITY OF FLORIDA — 2096 Weimer, Gainesville, FL, 32611-8400 (352) 392-0466; fax (352) 392-3919; web site www.jou.ufl.edu
Dean/Prof. — John Wright
Prof./Interim Assoc. Dean, UF Grad. School/UF Research Foundation Prof. — Laurence B. Alexander
Prof./Joseph L. Brechner Eminent Scholar/Dir., Marion Brechner Citizen Access Proj. — Bill F. Chamberlin
Prof./Assoc. Dean, Research/AI and Effie Flanagan Prof. in Journalism & Communications — Sylvia Chan-Olmsted
Prof./Co-Dir., Documentary Institute — Sandra Dickson
Prof. — Julie Dodd
Prof. — Mary Ann Ferguson
Prof./Sr. Assoc. Dean/AI and Effie Flanagan Prof. in Journalism and Communications — Linda Childers Hon
Dean Emerita/Prof. — Terry Hynes
Prof. — Lynda Lee Kaid
Prof./UF Res. Foundation Prof. — John Kaplan
Prof. — Kathleen Kelly
Prof./Knight Chair in Journalism Technologies and the Democratic Process — Melinda (Mindy) McAdams
Prof./Chair, Dept. of Journalism — William McKeen
Prof. — Jon D. Morris
Prof./Chair, Dept. of Telecommunication — David Ostroff
Prof./Co-Dir., Documentary Institute — Churchill Roberts
Prof./Asst. Dean, Student Servs. — Jon A. Roosenraad
Prof./Chair, Dept. of Adv. — John C. Sutherland
Prof./Assoc. Dean, Grad. Studies/Research/AI and Effie Flanagan Prof. in Journalism & Communication — Debbie Treise
AFFILIATIONS: AAF, NBS/AER, BEA, KTA, PRSSA, SPJ, Florida Press Assn., Florida Public Relations Assn., Florida Assn. of Broadcasters, Florida Magazine Assn
DEGREES:BS- Advertising, Journalism, Public Relations, Telecommunication; MA- Mass Communication, Advertising Management; PhD- Mass Communication; Joint MAMC-JD; Joint PhD-JD
DEPARTMENTS: College of Journalism and Communications, 1925
FACILITIES: AP, UPI, AM, FM, AdA, CATV, CCTV, CN, CcomN, ComR, ETV, HDTV, PRA, VDT

UNIVERSITY OF MIAMI — 5202 University Dr., Coral Gables, FL, 33124 (305) 284-2265; fax (305) 284-3648; e-mail sgrogg@miami.edu
Dean — Sam L. Grogg
Prof. — Stanley Harrison
Prof. — Anthony Allegro
Prof. — Stephen Bowles
Prof. — Bruce Garrison
Prof. — Paul Lazarus
Prof. — Edward Pfister
Prof. — William Rothman
Prof. — Michael Salwen
Prof. — Mitchell Shapiro
Prof./Prog. Dir., PR — Don Stacks
Prof. — Thomas Steinfatt
Assoc. Prof. — Grace Barnes
Assoc. Prof./Prog. Dir., Vis Comm. — Marie-Helene Bourgoignie-Robert
Assoc. Prof./Vice Dean — Sanjeev Chatterjee
Assoc. Prof./Prog. Dir., Broadcast — Paul Driscoll
Assoc. Prof. — Michel Dupagne
Assoc. Prof. — Leonardo Ferreira
Assoc. Prof. — Lisa Gottlieb
Assoc. Prof./Vice Dean, External Affairs/Advancement — Robert Hosmon
AFFILIATIONS: AAF, AER, BEA, NATAS, SPJ, PRSSA, 4-A Ad Club, WICI, RTNDA, Florida Assn. of Broadcasters
DEGREES:BSC, BFA, MA, MFA, PhD
DEPARTMENTS: School of Communication, 1985
FACILITIES: AP, FM, CN, CATV, ComN, ComR, ComTV, DR, AdA, PRA, VDT
SEQUENCES: Majors: Advertising, Public Relations, Broadcasting, Broadcast Journalism, Media Management, Journalism, Visual Communication, Motion Pictures, Communication Studies

UNIVERSITY OF NORTH FLORIDA — 4567 St. Johns Bluff Rd. S., Jacksonville, FL, 32224-2645 (904) 620-2651; fax (904) 620-2652; e-mail opatters@unf.edu; web site www.unf.edu/coas/cva
Chair — Oscar Patterson
AFFILIATIONS: PRSSA, AdFed
DEGREES:BA, BS, BFA
DEPARTMENTS: Department of Communications and Visual Arts, 1987
FACILITIES: CATV, CCTV, CN, ComN, DR, PRA, AdA
SEQUENCES: Mass Communications: Advertising, Broadcasting, Journalism, Public Relations; Visual Arts: Graphic Design (portfolio review required), Photography, Studio Arts, Art History

UNIVERSITY OF SOUTH FLORIDA — 4202 E. Fowler Ave., CIS 1040, Tampa, FL, 33620-7800 (813) 974-2591; fax (813) 974-2592; e-mail mcom@cas.usf.edu
Prof./Dir. — Edward Jay Friedlander
Assoc. Prof. — Dan Bagley
Assoc. Prof. — Kim Golombisky
Assoc. Prof./Grad. Dir. — Kenneth Killebrew
Assoc. Prof. — Larry Leslie
Assoc. Prof./Head, Adv. seq./Zimmerman Adv. Prog. Prof. — Scott Liu
Assoc. Prof./Head, Journalism seq. — Randy Miller
Asst. Prof. — Kelli Burns
Asst. Prof. — Roxanne Watson
Asst. Prof./Head, PR seq. — Kelly Page Werder
Asst. Prof. — Rick Wilber
Instr. — Bob Batchelor
Instr./Head, Tele. seq. — Marie Curkan-Flanagan
Instr. — Rebecca Hagen
Instr. — Charles O'Brien
Instr. — Kristin Arnold Ruyle
Vstg. Instr. — Liisa Hyvarinen Temple
Advisor — Kalah Mueller
Advisor — Denise Nicholas
Adj. Fac. — Neil Vicino
AFFILIATIONS: FBA, FPA, FSNE, AAF, KTA, PRSSA, RTNDA, SPJ
DEGREES:BA, MA
DEPARTMENTS: School of Mass Communications, 1970
FACILITIES: AM/FM, AdA, CCTV, CN, ComN, DR, ETV, PRA, computer and graphics labs
SEQUENCES: Advertising, Journalism (magazine, news-editorial), Public Relations, Telecommunications (broadcast news, broadcast production)

UNIVERSITY OF SOUTH FLORIDA ST.

PETERSBURG — 140 7th Ave. S, FCT 204, Saint Petersburg, FL, 33701-5016 (727) 873-4850; fax (727) 873-4034
Dir./Assoc. Prof. — Robert Dardenne
Prof./Grad. Dir. — Deni Elliott
Prof. — G. Michael Killenberg
Prof. — Tony Silvia
Assoc. Prof. — Mark J. Walters
Asst. Prof. — Xiaopeng (Paul) Wang
Adj. Fac. — Cheryl Koski
Adj. Fac. — Beth Reynolds
Adj. Fac. — Andrew Skerritt
Adj. Fac. — Deborah Wolfe
DEGREES:BA, MA
DEPARTMENTS: Dept. of Journalism and Media Studies, 1992
FACILITIES: Apple computer lab
SEQUENCES: Journalism and Media Studies: Student chosen focuses include reporting, feature writing, editing, visualdDigital communication

UNIVERSITY OF WEST FLORIDA — 11000 University Pkwy., Bldg. 36, Pensacola, FL, 32514 (850) 474-2874; fax (850) 474-3153; e-mail bswain@uwf.edu
Chair — Bruce Swain
AFFILIATIONS: BEA, PRSSA, FPRA, AAF
DEGREES:BA, MA
DEPARTMENTS: Communication Arts, 1967
FACILITIES: AdA, CCTV, ComN, ComTV, FM, JN, PRA, VDT
SEQUENCES: Journalism (broadcast and print), Advertising, Public Relations, Radio/Television/Film, Organizational Communication, Graduate Program in Health Communication Leadership

GEORGIA

BERRY COLLEGE — 2277 Martha Berry Hwy., Mount Berry, GA, 30149-0299 (706) 233-4089; fax (706) 802-6738; e-mail bfrank@berry.edu
Chair — Robert L. Frank
DEGREES:BA
DEPARTMENTS: Department of Communication, 1986
FACILITIES: CATV, CCTV, ComN, DR, JM, PRA, VDT
SEQUENCES: Journalism, Public Relations, Visual Communication

BRENAU UNIVERSITY — One Centennial Cir., Gainesville, GA, 30501 (770) 538-4743; fax (770) 538-4558; e-mail sblakley@lib.brenau.edu
Chair — Stewart Blakley
DEPARTMENTS: School of Business and Mass Communication, Department of Mass Communication
SEQUENCES: Mass Media Program: Two-year BA degree program in Journalism, Electronic Media, Public Relations and Corporate Communications follows the lower-division Liberal Arts core curriculum

CLARK ATLANTA UNIVERSITY — 223 James P. Brawley Dr., SW, Atlanta, GA, 30314 (440) 880-8304; e-mail olafjames@earthlink.net
Chair — James McJunkins
DEGREES:BA- Mass Media Arts
DEPARTMENTS: Department of Mass Media Arts , 1977
SEQUENCES: Journalism, Public Relations, Radio/TV/Film

GEORGIA COLLEGE & STATE UNIVERSITY — Campus Box 32, Milledgeville, GA, 31061 (478) 445-8260; fax (478) 445-2364; e-mail maryjean.land@gcsu.edu
Chair/Prof. — Mary Jean Land
Prof. — Ginger Carter Miller
Asst. Prof. — Macon McGinley
Asst. Prof. — Stephen Price
Instr. — Angela Criscoe
Instr. — Pate McMichael
Advisor — Hope Buchanan
DEGREES:BA- Mass Communication
DEPARTMENTS: English Speech and Journalism, Mass Communication Program, 1984
FACILITIES: Digital Media, Graphics Lab, Digital TV Studio, Student Operated Radio Station
SEQUENCES: Print Advertising, Public Relations, Telecommunications

GEORGIA SOUTHERN UNIVERSITY — Dept. of Communication Arts, Statesboro, GA, 30460 (912) 681-5138; fax (912) 681-0822; e-mail hfulmer@gasou.edu
Program Head — Ernest T. Wyatt
DEGREES:BS
DEPARTMENTS: Journalism Program in Department of Communication Arts
SEQUENCES: Journalism Program: A BS degree program of practical news-editorial orientation. Curriculum emphasizes liberal arts. Internships optional. Journalism is one of five disciplines in Communication Arts. Others are Broadcasting (Radio-TV-Film), Public Re

GEORGIA STATE UNIVERSITY — 1027 One Park Pl. S, Atlanta, GA, 30303 (404) 651-3200; fax (404) 651-1409; e-mail jouckw@langate.gsu.edu
Chair — Carol Winkler
AFFILIATIONS: SPJ, PRSSA, WICI
DEGREES:BA, MA
DEPARTMENTS: Department of Communication, 1963
FACILITIES: AP, FM, CCTV, CN
SEQUENCES: Print, Broadcast, Public Relations, Film/Video, Speech, Theatre

KENNESAW STATE UNIVERSITY — 1000 Chastain Rd., Box 2207, Kennesaw, GA, 30144 (770) 423-6298; fax (770) 423-6740; e-mail bwassmut@kennesaw.edu
Chair/Prof. — Birgit Wassmuth
Prof. — Deanna Womack
Prof. — Chuck Aust
Assoc. Prof. — Charles Mayo
Assoc. Prof./Eminent Scholar/Robert D. Fowler Distinguished Chair — Leonard Witt
Asst. Prof. — Audrey Allison
Asst. Prof. — Philip Aust
Asst. Prof. — Joshua Azriel
Asst. Prof. — Barbara Gainey
Asst. Prof. — May Gao
Asst. Prof. — Amber Hutchins
Asst. Prof. — Heeman Kim
Asst. Prof. — Georgios Triantis
Instr. — Emily Holler
Instr. — Jan Phillips
Lectr. — Stephen J. McNeill
Prof. Emer. — Jeffrey Anderson
AFFILIATIONS: ASJMC, NCA, PRSSA
DEGREES:BS
DEPARTMENTS: Department of Communication, 1991
FACILITIES: AM/FM, CN, ComN, Digital Media Lab, JM, NYTS
SEQUENCES: Journalism and Citizen Media, Organizational Communication, Media Studies, Public Relations

MERCER UNIVERSITY AT MACON — 1400 Coleman Ave., Macon, GA, 31207-0001 (912) 752-2979; e-mail jottshall_cm@mercer.edu
Broadcast/Film — Cynthia Gottshall
DEPARTMENTS: Communication and Theatre Arts Department, 1976
SEQUENCES: Communication Program: Administered by Communication and Theatre Arts Departments. Students may emphasize print journalism or broadcasting and film

TOCCOA FALLS COLLEGE — School of Communication, Toccoa Falls, GA, 30598 (706) 886-7299; fax (706) 886-6412; e-mail comm@tfc.edu
Dir. — Jerry Fliger
DEGREES:BA, BS
DEPARTMENTS: School of Communication
SEQUENCES: Communication Program: Sequences in Broadcasting, Interpersonal/Organizational, Journalism

UNIVERSITY OF GEORGIA — 120 Hooper St., Athens, GA, 30602-3018 (706) 542-1704; fax (706) 542-2183; web site www.grady.uga.edu
Dean/ Prof. — E. Culpepper Clark
Prof./Sr. Assoc. Dean — Alison Alexander
Prof./Dir., Cox Ctr. — Lee Becker
Prof./Interim Head, Telecomm. Dept. — Joseph R. Domnick
Prof./Dir., Cox Inst. — Conrad C. Fink
Prof./Dir., Ctr. Health & Risk Commun. — Vicki S. Freimuth
Carter Prof. — John F. Greenman
Prof./Head, Adv./PR Dept. — Karen W. King
Prof. — Bruce Klopfenstein
Prof. — Dean M. Krugman
Prof./Assoc. Dean — Jeffrey K. Springston
Prof. — Ruth Ann Lariscy
Prof. — William Lee
Prof./Head, Journalism Dept. — Kent Middleton
Prof./Peabody Awards Dir. — Horace Newcomb
Prof. — John Soloski
Prof. — Spencer F. Tinkham
Prof. — Leonard N. Reid
Prof. — Scott Shamp
Prof./Knight Chair — Patricia Thomas
AFFILIATIONS: AD Club, NABJ, PRSSA, NPPA, UGAzine, Magazine Club, Di Gamma Kappa, Georgia Gameday, IABC
DEGREES:ABJ (BA in Journalism and Mass Communication), MA, PhD
DEPARTMENTS: Henry W. Grady College of Journalism and Mass Communication, 1915
FACILITIES: AP, FM, CCTV, CN, ComN, DR, JM, PRA, VDT, Microwave uplink, Satellite downlink
SEQUENCES: Departments: Advertising & Public Relations, Journalism, Telecommunications

VALDOSTA STATE UNIVERSITY — 1500 N. Patterson, Dept. Of Communication Arts, Valdosta, GA, 31698-0001 (229) 333-5820; fax (229) 293-6182; e-mail ccates@valdosta.edu
Head — Carl Cates
DEPARTMENTS: Department of Communication Arts
SEQUENCES: The Department of Communication Arts is a multidisciplinary department with the academic disciplines of Speech Communication, Inter-cultural Communication, Organizational Communication, Public Relations, Theatre, Dance, Mass Media, and Broadcast Journalis

HAWAII

CHAMINADE, UNIVERSITY OF HONOLULU — Dept. of Communication, Honolulu, HI, 96816-1578 (808) 735-4711; fax (808) 739-8328; e-mail cbieberl@chaminade.edu
Dir. — Clifford Bieberly
AFFILIATIONS: NCA
DEGREES:BA
DEPARTMENTS: Department of Communication, 1985
SEQUENCES: Mass Communication, Marketing Communication

HAWAII PACIFIC UNIVERSITY — 1136 Union Mall, Suite 208, Honolulu, HI, 96813 (808) 544-0825; fax (808) 544-0835; e-mail editor@kalamalama.com; web site http://hpulamalama.com/wp/
Dean/Prof. — Steven Combs
Prof. — John Hart
Assoc. Prof. — John Barnum
Assoc. Prof. — Peter Britos
Assoc. Prof. — James Whitfield
Asst. Prof. — Brian Cannon
Asst. Prof. — Matt George
Asst. Prof. — Serena Hashimoto
Asst. Prof. — Lowell Douglas Ing
Asst. Prof. — Anne Kennedy
Asst. Prof. — Laurence LeDoux
Asst. Prof. — Penny Smith
Asst. Prof. — Yanjun Zhao
Instr. — Dale Burke
Instr. — Katherine Clark
Instr. — Thomas Dowd
Instr. — Rose Helens-Hart
Instr. — Marianne Luken
Instr. — Malia Smith
Instr. — Lewis Trusty
DEGREES:BA, BS, MA/COM
DEPARTMENTS: College of Communication

UNIVERSITY OF HAWAII AT MANOA — 2550 Campus Rd., Honolulu, HI, 96822 (808) 956-8881; fax (808) 956-5396; e-mail jour@hawaii.edu
Chair/Assoc. Prof. — Gerald Kato
Prof. — Thomas J. Brislin
Prof. — Beverly Deepe Keever
Assoc. Prof. — Ann Auman
Asst. Prof. — Jonathan Lillie
AFFILIATIONS: KTA, PRSSA, SPJ
DEGREES:BA
DEPARTMENTS: School of Communications, 1963
FACILITIES: AP, FM, CN, ComN, ComR, ComTV, DR, PRS, VDT
SEQUENCES: Multiple Media Platforms: Print, Broadcast, Online & other new media formats.

IDAHO

BOISE STATE UNIV. — 1910 University Dr, Boise, ID, 83725-0001, USA (208) 426-6300; fax (208) 426-3884; e-mail mcox@boisestate.edu; web site www.arbiteronline.comBrad Arendt
Chrmn. — V. Marvin Cox
Steve Lyons
Dwight Murphy
Shannon Morgan
DEGREES:BA- Mass Communication/Journalism; MA- Communication
DEPARTMENTS: Department of Communication
SEQUENCES: Mass Communication/Journalism Emphasis, Communication/English, Journalism Emphasis: The department offers courses in media studies, reporting and news writing, magazine writing, visual communication, audio and video production, new communication technolo

IDAHO STATE UNIVERSITY — Campus Box 8009, Pocatello, ID, 83709; tel (1) 208 (208) 282-2247; fax (208) 282-2258; e-mail bgchief@isu.edu; web site isubengal.com

UNIVERSITY OF IDAHO — PO Box 443178, Moscow, ID, 84844-3178 (208) 885-6458; fax (208) 885-6450; e-mail jamm@uidaho.edu
Dir./Assoc. Prof. — Kenton Bird
Prof. — Sandra Haarsager
Assoc. Prof. — Mark Secrist
Asst. Prof. — Patricia Hart
Asst. Prof. — Rebecca Tallent
Lectr. — H. James Clark
Lectr. — Sue Hinz
Fac. — Denise Bennett
Fac. — Glenn Mosley
Fac. — Vicki Rishling
Prof. Emer. — Bert Cross
Prof. Emer. — Peter Haggart
Prof. Emer. — Tom Jenness
Prof. Emer. — Paul Miles
Prof. Emer. — Jane Pritchett
AFFILIATIONS: SPJ, Ad Club, PR Club, NAJA
DEGREES:BA, BS
DEPARTMENTS: School of Journalism and Mass Media, 2003

FACILITIES: FM, CN, ETV, ComN, VDT
SEQUENCES: Advertising, Journalism, Public Relations, Radio-TV-Digital Media Production

ILLINOIS

AUGUSTANA COLLEGE — 639 38th St, Rock Island, IL, 61201-2210, USA (309) 794-3460; fax (309) 794-3460; e-mail observer@augustana.edu; web site www.augustana.eduCarolyn Yaschur
Advisor — David Schwartz
DEGREES:BA
DEPARTMENTS: Department of Communication Studies
SEQUENCES: Majors: Communication Studies, Multimedia Journalism and Mass Communication

BRADLEY UNIVERSITY — Dept. of Communication, Peoria, IL, 61625 (309) 677-2354; fax (309) 677-3446; e-mail pfg@bradley.edu
Chair/Prof. — Paul Gullifor
Prof. — Bob Jacobs
Prof. — Ali Zohoori
Assoc. Prof. — Olatunji Dare
Assoc. Prof. — Chris Kasch
Assoc. Prof. — Ron Koperski
Assoc. Prof. — Ed Lamoureux
Assoc. Prof. — Gregory Pitts
Asst. Prof. — Stephen Banning
Asst. Prof. — Maha Bashri
Asst. Prof. — Elena Gabor
Asst. Prof. — Sara Netzley
Asst. Prof. — Margaret Young
Lectr. — Laura Garfinkel
Lectr. — B.J. Lawrence
Lectr. — Linda Strasma
Instr. — Jan Frazier
Instr./Asst. Dir., Forensics — Tyler Billman
Dir., Forensics — Dan Smith
Prof. Emer. — E. Neal Claussen
AFFILIATIONS: AAF, PRSSA, SPJ, WICI
DEGREES:BA, BS
DEPARTMENTS: Department of Communication, 1947
FACILITIES: CCTV, FM, CN, ETV, DR, VDT
SEQUENCES: Advertising, Electronic Media, Journalism, Organizational Communications, Public Relations

COLUMBIA COLLEGE CHICAGO — 600 S. Michigan Ave., Chicago, IL, 60605-1996 (312) 369-7687; fax (312) 369-8059; e-mail brice@colum.edu
Acting Chair — Barry Rice
DEPARTMENTS: Department of Journalism
SEQUENCES: Undergraduate majors in News Reporting and Writing, Magazine, Broadcast Journalism (Radio & TV), Reporting on Health, Science & Environment. Undergraduate minor in Publication Production. Graduate program (MA) in Public Affairs Reporting

DEPAUL UNIVERSITY — 2320 N. Kenmore Ave., Chicago, IL, 60614 (773) 325-7585; fax (773) 325-7584; e-mail bspeciche@depaul.edu
Chair — Barbara L. Speicher
DEGREES:BA, MA
DEPARTMENTS: Department of Communication
SEQUENCES: Undergraduate course offerings in Public Relations and Advertising, Radio Television & Film, Journalism, Social & Political Discourse, Relational Group & Organizational Communication. Graduate coursework in Corporate Communication, Multicultural Communic

EASTERN ILLINOIS UNIVERSITY — 600 Lincoln Ave., 2521 Buzzard Hall, Charleston, IL, 61920-3099 (217) 581-6003; fax (217) 581-7188; e-mail journal@eiu.edu
Chair/Prof. — James Tidwell
Prof. — Brian Poulter
Prof. — L.R. Hyder
Prof./Dir., Stud. Pubs. — John Ryan
Assoc. Prof./Advisor, Minority Newspaper — Joe Gisondi
Assoc. Prof./Advisor, PRSSA — Terry Johnson
Assoc. Prof./Advisor, Yearbook — Sally Turner
Asst. Prof./Advisor, Broadcast — Janice Collins
Asst. Prof. — Eunseong Kim
Asst. Prof./Advisor, Newspaper — Lola McElwee
Asst. Prof./Advisor, Online — Bryan Murley
Instr. — Wanda Brandon
Instr. — Dan Hagen
Instr. — John Johnson
Instr. — Doug Lawhead
Instr. — Elizabeth Viall
AFFILIATIONS: KTA, NABJ, PRSSA, SCJ, WICI, SPJ, CMA
DEGREES:BA
DEPARTMENTS: Department of Journalism, 1975
FACILITIES: AP, FM, CN, ComN, DR, ETV, JM , PRA, VDT, HS (sponsors high school press assn., hosts state high school journalism assn.), hosts state community college press assn., headquarters Mid-America Press Institute
SEQUENCES: Journalism Major. Journalism, Public Relations Minors. Concentrations: Writing and Reporting, Editing, Design, Photojournalism, Public Relations, New and Emerging Media, Broadcast News

GOVERNORS STATE UNIV. — 1 University Pkwy, E2543, University Park, IL, 60484-3165, USA (708) 534-4517; fax (708) 534-7895; e-mail phoenix@govst.edu; web site www.gsuphoenix.com
Faculty Advisor — Debbie James
Emeritus Professor — Michael Purdy
AFFILIATIONS: Arts and Sciences
DEGREES:BA, MA
DEPARTMENTS: Department of Communications
FACILITIES: VDT
SEQUENCES: BA - Film/Video Production, Journalism, Multi Media Production, Public Relations, Speech; MA - Communication Studies, Human Performance and Training, Media Communications.

ILLINOIS COLLEGE — 1101 West College Ave., Jacksonville, IL, 62650 (217) 245-3000
Chair, English — Jim Kerbaugh
Chair, Communications/Theatre — Peter Verkruyse
DEPARTMENTS: Journalism, 1970
SEQUENCES: Journalism Program: Students interested in a career in journalism may major in Communications or English. The college offers writing and communication courses and various internships. Local newspapers also employ students

ILLINOIS STATE UNIVERSITY — Campus Box 4480, Normal, IL, 61790-4480 (309) 438-3671; fax (309) 438-3048; e-mail communication@ilstu.edu
Exec. Dir. — Larry W. Long
DEGREES:BA, BS, MA, MS
DEPARTMENTS: School of Communication
FACILITIES: Television and two radio stations, daily newspaper, computer labs and digital photography facilities
SEQUENCES: Majors in Communication Studies and Communication Studies Education, Journalism, Mass Communication, and Public Relations. Concentrations in news editorial writing, broadcast journalism, visual communication, radio, television, interactive media, graphics

LOYOLA UNIVERSITY OF CHICAGO — Lake Shore Campus, Loyola Hall, 1110 W. Loyola Ave., Chicago, IL, 60626 (773) 508-3730; fax (773) 508-8821; e-mail cmun@luc.edu
Chair — Bren A.O. Murphy
DEPARTMENTS: Department of Communication, 1968
SEQUENCES: Journalism Program: Within an integrated communication curriculum, offers participatory learning in journalism as well as administrative and critical analyses of mass communication

NORTHERN ILLINOIS UNIVERSITY — Dept. of Communication, DeKalb, IL, 60115 (815) 753-1563; fax (815) 753-7109; e-mail jchown@niu.edu; web site www.niu.edu/comm
Acting Chair — Jeff Chown
Assoc. Prof. — Orayb Najjar
Assoc. Prof. — Craig Seymour
Asst. Prof./Journ. Area Coord. — Bill Cassidy
Asst. Prof. — Sabryna Cornish
Asst. Prof. — Induk Kim
Asst. Prof. — Thomas Oates
Instr. — Jason Akst
Supportive Professional Staff/Gen. Mgr., Broadcast News — Allen May
Supportive Professional Staff/News Dir. — Alex Wiertelak
AFFILIATIONS: KTA, PRSSA, NABJ, SPJ, WICI
DEGREES:BA, BS, MA (Journalism area participates in the department's graduate program)
DEPARTMENTS: Department of Communication, Journalism Area, 1959
FACILITIES: AP, AM, CATV, CCTV, CN, DR, FM, PRA, VDT
SEQUENCES: Journalism: Students select courses in news-editorial, broadcast news, photojournalism and public relations

NORTHWESTERN UNIVERSITY — 1845 Sheridan Rd, Evanston, IL, 60208-0815, USA (847) 467-1882; fax (847) 491-5565
Dean — John Lavine
Prof. — David Abrahamson
Prof. — Martin Block
Prof. — Jack Doppelt
Prof. — Loren Ghiglione
Prof. — Alec Klein
Prof. — Donna Leff
Prof. — Frank Mulhern
Prof. — Jon Petrovich
Prof. — David Protess
Prof. — Don Schultz
Prof. — Ellen Shearer
Assoc. Prof. — Clarke Caywood
Assoc. Prof. — Mary Coffman
Assoc. Prof. — Tom Collinger
Assoc. Prof. — Doug Foster
Assoc. Prof. — Jeremy Gilbert
Assoc. Prof. — Rich Gordon
Assoc. Prof. — John Greening
Assoc. Prof. — Ava Greenwell
DEGREES:BSJ, MSJ, MSIMC
FACILITIES: JM, AP

ROOSEVELT UNIVERSITY — 18 S. Michigan Ave., Chicago, IL, 60605 (312) 281-3337; fax (312) 281-3231; e-mail comm@roosevelt.edu
Chair — Linda Jones
DEPARTMENTS: Department of Communication
SEQUENCES: Journalism Program: Journalism, public relations, integrated communications (advertising). Grad. studies in journalism and integrated marketing communications. Campuses downtown and suburbs. All faculty professionals in their fields

SOUTHERN ILLINOIS UNIVERSITY CARBONDALE — 1100 Lincoln Dr., Carbondale, IL, 62901-6606 (618) 453-4308; fax (618) 453-7714; e-mail mcma@siu.edu
Prof./Dean — Gary P. Kolb
Prof. — William Babcock
Prof./Dir. Global media Research Ctr. — John Downing
Prof. — John Hochheimer
Interim Chair, Radio- Television/Prof. — Phylis Johnson
Prof. — Dennis T. Lowry
Prof. — Eileen Meehan
Assoc. Prof. — Lilly A. Boruszkowski
Assoc. Prof. — Lisa Brooten
Assoc. Prof. — Susan Felleman
Assoc. Prof./Dir., Journ. — William Freivogel
Assoc. Prof. — Katherine Frith
Assoc. Prof. — Walter B. Jaehnig
Assoc. Prof. — Jyotsna Kapur
Assoc. Prof. — Fern Logan
Assoc. Prof. — Daniel Overturf
Assoc. Prof. — Jake Podber
Assoc. Prof. — Jyotika Ramaprasad
Assoc. Prof./Interim Dir., Grad. Studies — Jan Peterson Roddy
Assoc. Prof. — R. William Rowley
AFFILIATIONS: AAF, BEA, BICA, ITVA, KTA, NABJ, NAEB, NBS, SINBA, SCJ, SIRIS, SPE, UFVA, WICI
DEGREES:BA- Cinema & Photography, Radio-Television; BS- Journalism; MA- Mass Communication and Media Arts with concentrations in Interactive Multimedia, Media Management, Media Theory and Research, Professional Media Practice, and Telecommunication; MFA- Mass Com
DEPARTMENTS: College of Mass Communication and Media Arts, 1993
FACILITIES: AdA, UPI, ComN, CCTV, ETV, JN, VDT
SEQUENCES: Cinema & Photography (cinema production, cinema studies, fine arts photography, professional photography), Journalism (advertising/IMC, news editorial, photojournalism), Radio-Television (management and sales, news, video/audio production)

SOUTHERN ILLINOIS UNIVERSITY EDWARDSVILLE — Dept. of Mass Communications, Edwardsville, IL, 62026-1775 (618) 650-2230; fax (618) 650-3716; e-mail rdonald@siue.edu; web site www.siue.edu/MASSCOMM
Assoc. Prof./Chair — Patrick Murphy
Prof. — Ralph R. Donald
Prof. — Riley Maynard
Assoc. Prof./Dir., Grad. Studies — Gary Hicks
Asst. Prof. — Bala Baptiste
Asst. Prof. — Judy Landers
Instr. — Elza Ibroscheva
Instr. — Michael Montgomery
Instr. — Zixue Tai
Instr. — Kimberly Wilmot Voss
Prof. Emer. — John A. Regnell
Prof. Emer. — John R. Rider
Prof. Emer. — Jack Shaheen
Prof. Emer. — William G. Ward
Assoc. Prof. Emer. — Nora Baker
Assoc. Prof. Emer. — Barbara Regnell
AFFILIATIONS: SPJ, AAF, MCAI
DEGREES:BA, BS, MS
DEPARTMENTS: Department of Mass Communications, 1969
FACILITIES: FM, AdA, CCTV, CN, ComN, ComTV, DR, JM, VDT, ComR, CNN News Source, AP
SEQUENCES: Television and Radio, Corporate and Institutional Media, Media Advertising and Print and Electronic Journalism

UNIVERSITY OF ILLINOIS — 810 S. Wright St., 119 Gregory Hall/MC-462, Urbana, IL, 61801 (217) 333-2350; fax (217) 333-9882; e-mail ccomm@uiuc.edu; web site www.comm.uiuc.edu
Sleeman Prof./Dean — Ronald E. Yates
Prof. — William F. Brewer
Prof. — Angharad N. Valdivia
Prof./Dir., Institute for Comm. Research/Sandage — Clifford G. Christians
Prof. — C.L. Cole
Prof./Swanlund Chair — Leon D. Dash
Prof. — Matthew C. Ehrlich
Prof./College Scholar — Norman K. Denzin
Knight Chair Prof. — Brant Houston
Prof./Head, Journ. — Walter G. Harrington
Prof. — Steve J. Helle
Prof. — Louis W. Liebovich

Prof./Dir., Grad. Studies, Inst. of Comm. Research/College Scholar — John C. Nerone
Prof. — Kent A. Ono
Prof./Head, Adv. — Jan Slater
Assoc. Dean, Research/Assoc. Prof. — Amy J. Aidman
Assoc. Prof. — Christopher D. Benson
Assoc. Prof. — Nancy J. Benson
Assoc. Prof. — William E. Berry
Assoc. Prof. — Jay M. Rosenstein
AFFILIATIONS: ACT, AAF, ADS, AHJ, KTA, NABJ, SPJ
DEGREES:BS, MS, PhD
DEPARTMENTS: College of Communications, 1927
FACILITIES: AdA, AP, AM/FM, CATV, ComN, DR, CN, VDT, ETV
SEQUENCES: Advertising, Broadcast Journalism, News-Editorial Journalism, Media Studies

UNIVERSITY OF ILLINOIS-CHICAGO —
1007 W. Harrison St., MC132, Chicago, IL, 60607-7137 (312) 996-3187; fax (312) 413-2125; e-mail comm@uic.edu
Head — Zizi Papacharissi
DEPARTMENTS: Department of Communication
SEQUENCES: The Department of Communication provides undergraduate students with a broad liberal education that covers communication from the personal through the international levels and builds responsible citizenship. Students gain depth in understanding communicat

UNIVERSITY OF ST. FRANCIS — 500
Wilcox St., Joliet, IL, 60435 (815) 740-5064; fax (815) 740-4285; e-mail trosner@stfrancis.edu
Chair — Terre Layng Rosner
DEPARTMENTS: Mass Communication Department, 1976
SEQUENCES: Mass Communication Program: Concentrations in Broadcasting, Public Relations/Advertising/Journalism, Media Arts. Internships in all areas

WESTERN ILLINOIS UNIVERSITY — 1
University Cir., Macomb, IL, 61455 (309) 298-1948; e-mail y-tang@wiu.edu; web site http://www.wiu.edu/cofac/bcj/
Asst Prof
Dir of Journalism — Yong Tang
Assoc. Prof./Advisor, WAF — Teresa Simmons
AFFILIATIONS: College of Fine Arts and Communication
DEGREES:BA- Journalism BA-Broadcasting
DEPARTMENTS: Department of Broadcasting & Journalism
FACILITIES: Computer and electronic class rooms, digital photography class room
SEQUENCES: Journalism Concentrations: News-Editorial, PR and Advertising. Opportunities: Internships in newspaper, public relations, and advertising firms Broadcasting Concentrations: Sports broadcasting, broadcasting production and broadcasting performance

INDIANA

ANDERSON UNIVERSITY — 1100 E. Fifth
St., Anderson, IN, 46012 (765) 641-4340
Chair — Donald G. Boggs
AFFILIATIONS: SCJ, ICVM
DEPARTMENTS: Department of Communication, 1977
SEQUENCES: Journalism Program: Forty-five hour Mass Communication major with specializations in Journalism, Broadcast Journalism, Broadcast Production and Public Relations

BALL STATE UNIVERSITY — Art and
Journalism Bldg. 300, Muncie, IN, 47306 (765) 285-6000; fax (765) 285-6002; e-mail bsujourn@bsu.edu; web site www.bsu.edu/journalism
Prof./Dean — Roger Lavery
Prof./Chair — Marilyn Weaver
Prof. — Mark Masse
Prof./Coord., Mag. — David Sumner
Assoc. Prof. — Robert Gustafson
Assoc. Prof. — Alfredo Marin-Carle
Assoc. Prof./Coord., PR — Robert Pritchard
Asst. Prof./Coord., Journ. Graphics — Jennifer George-Palilonis
Asst. Prof./Coord. Advertising — Michael Hanley
Asst. Prof. — Kenneth Heinen
Asst. Prof. — Tendayi Kumbula
Asst. Prof. — Becky McDonald
Asst. Prof./Coord., Photojournalism — Thomas Price
Asst. Prof./Coord., News-Editorial — Mary Spillman
Asst. Prof. — Dustin Supa
Asst. Prof./Asst. Chair/Curricular Advising/ Grad. Advisor — Daniel Waechter
Instr. — Pamela Farmen
Instr./Coord. Secondary Education — Brian Hayes
Instr./Mng. Ed., NewsLink — Sy Jenkins
Instr. — David Kitchell
Pam Gard
AFFILIATIONS: AAF, JEA, NABJ, NPPA, PRSSA, SND, SPJ
DEGREES:BA, BS, MA
DEPARTMENTS: College of Communication, Information and Media, Department of Journalism
FACILITIES: AdA, AP, AM/FM, CATV, CCTV, JM, JN, ComN, DR, ETC, PRA, VDT
SEQUENCES: Majors: Advertising, Journalism (Journalism Graphics, Magazine, News-Editorial, Photojournalism), Public Relations, Secondary Education

BUTLER UNIV. — 4600 Sunset Ave,
Indianapolis, IN, 46208-3443, USA (317) 940-9358; fax (317) 940-9713; e-mail mweiteka@butler.edu; web site dawgnet.butler.edu
Dir. — Kwadwo Anokwa
Charles St. Cyr
Lauren Fisher
Meg Shaw
DEPARTMENTS: Eugene S. Pulliam School of Journalism
SEQUENCES: Journalism Program: The journalism major has course sequences in news-editorial, public relations, and integrated communication: public relations and advertising. The department also coordinates an interdisciplinary major in public and corporate commun

CALUMET COLLEGE OF ST. JOSEPH —
2400 New York Ave, Whiting, IN, 46394-2146, USA (219) 473-4322; fax (219) 473-4219; web site www.ccsj.edu
PD — Dawn Muhammad
Daren Jasienlecki
Mark Cassello
DEGREES:BA- Communication Arts with journalism emphasis
DEPARTMENTS: Division of Communication and Fine Arts
SEQUENCES: Journalism Program: News-Editorial sequence

DEPAUW UNIVERSITY — 609 S. Locust
Street, Greencastle, IN, 46135-00037 (765) 658-4495; fax (765) 658-4499; e-mail jeffmccall@depauw.edu
Professor of media studies — Jeffrey M. McCall
DEPARTMENTS: Department of English and Department of Communication Arts and Sciences
FACILITIES: Pulliam Center for Contemporary Media
SEQUENCES: Mass Communication Program: Coursework offered in news writing and editing, magazine writing, broadcast journalism, media law, media criticism and organizational communication

FRANKLIN COLLEGE — 501 E. Monroe St.,
Franklin, IN, 46131 (317) 738-8200; fax (317) 738-8234; e-mail bbridges@franklincollege.edu; web site psj.franklincollege.edu
Dir. — Ray Begovich
AFFILIATIONS: SPJ
DEGREES:BA
DEPARTMENTS: Pulliam School of Journalism, 1940
FACILITIES: AdA, AP, FM, DR, JM, JN, PRA, VDT
SEQUENCES: News/Editorial, Advertising/ Public Relations, Broadcast Journalism, Secondary-School Teaching, Visual Communications

GOSHEN COLLEGE — Dept. of
Communication, 1700 South Main St., Goshen, IN, 46526-4798 (574) 535-7450; fax (574) 535-7660; e-mail dstoltzfus@goshen.edu; web site www.goshen.edu
Prof. — Duane Stoltzfus
DEPARTMENTS: Department of Communication
SEQUENCES: Majors in broadcasting, communication, journalism and public relations.

INDIANA STATE UNIVERSITY — Dept.
of Communication, Terre Haute, IN, 47809 (812) 237-3221; fax (812) 237-3217; e-mail mbuchholz@isugw.indstate.edu
Prof. — Paul D. Hightower
Assoc. Prof. — Michael O. Buchholz
AFFILIATIONS: SPJ
DEGREES:BA, BS
DEPARTMENTS: Department of Communication, 1952
FACILITIES: AP, FM, CCTV, JN, DR, VDT
SEQUENCES: News/Editorial, Photojournalism and Magazine Writing

INDIANA UNIVERSITY — Bloomington
Campus, Ernie Pyle Hall, Rm. 200, 940 E. Seventh St., Bloomington, IN, 47405 (812) 855-9247; fax (812) 855-0901; web site journalism.iupui.edu
Dean/Prof. — Bradley Hamm
Prof. — John E. Dvorak
Prof. — Shannon Martin
Prof. — David P. Nord
Prof./Roy W. Howard Research Prof. — David H. Weaver
Assoc. Prof. — David E. Boeyink
Assoc. Prof./Assoc. Dean, Undergrad. Studies — Bonnie J. Brownlee
Assoc. Prof. — Claude H. Cookman
Assoc. Prof. — Jon P. Dilts
Assoc. Prof. — Michael R. Evans
Assoc. Prof. — Tony Fargo
Assoc. Prof. — Owen V. Johnson
Assoc. Prof. — Jim Kelly
Assoc. Prof. — Radhika Parameswaran
Assoc. Prof. — Steven L. Raymer
Assoc. Prof./Assoc. Dean, Grad. Studies — Amy L. Reynolds
Assoc. Prof. — S. Holly Stocking
Asst. Prof. — Mike Conway
Asst. Prof. — Lessa Hatley Major
Asst. Prof. — Emily Metzgar
AFFILIATIONS: NPPA, PRSSA, SPJ, WICI
DEPARTMENTS: School of Journalism, 1911

INDIANA UNIVERSITY — Indianapolis
Campus, 535 W. Michigan St., Indianapolis, IN, 46202 (317) 278-5320; fax (317) 278-5321; e-mail dperkins@foi.iupui.edu; web site www.journalism.iupui.edu
Prof./Exec. Assoc. Dean — James W. Brown
Prof. — Jonas Bjork
Prof. — Sherry Ricchiardi
Asst. Prof. — Pamela Laucella
Lectr. — Robert Dittmer
Adj. Prof./Pub., The Sagamore — Maggie Balough Hillery
Adj. Prof./Pub. Emer., The Sagamore — Patrick McKeand
Prof. Emer. — Shirley Quate
DEGREES:BAJ, MA Prof., MA Res., PhD
FACILITIES: AP, AM, FM, CATV, CCTV, CN, DR, ETV, JM, VDT
SEQUENCES: News-Editorial, Broadcast News, Photojournalism, Advertising, PR, Magazine, Media Management, Journalism Education

INDIANA WESLEYAN UNIVERSITY — 4201
S Washington St, Marion, IN, 46953-4974, USA (765) 677-1818; fax (765) 677-1755; e-mail amy.smelser@indwes.edu; web site https://www.indwes.edu/undergraduate/majors/division-of-communication-and-theatre/
Ed. — Amy Smelser
Instructor — Amy Smelser
DEGREES:BS in Journalism, BS in Media Communication
DEPARTMENTS: Division of Communication and Theatre
FACILITIES: Online university newspaper (The Sojourn), Online community newspaper (GrantCOnnected.net), television station, radio station and theatre guild
SEQUENCES: Communication Program: Majors in Communication Studies, Journalism, Media Communication, Public Relations and Theatre. Integrated theory and practical application program

PURDUE UNIVERSITY/BRIAN LAMB SCHOOL OF COMMUNICATION — 100
N. University St., West Lafayette, IN, 47907-2098, USA; tel (01) (765) 494-3429; fax (765) 496-1394; web site www.cla.purdue.edu/communication
AFFILIATIONS: College of Liberal Arts
SEQUENCES: Undergraduate majors Mass Communication and Public Relations. Courses in Journalism. MA and PhD programs in Public Relations and Mass Communication.

SAINT MARY-OF-THE-WOODS COLLEGE
— Hulman Hall, Rm. 011, Saint Mary-of-the-Woods, IN, 47876 (812) 535-5132; fax (812) 535-5228; e-mail nmayfield@smwc.edu
Chair — Nancy Pieters Mayfield
DEPARTMENTS: Department of English, Journalism & Languages
SEQUENCES: Journalism Program: Stresses professional preparation of women in journalism in a liberal arts context. Classrooom and External Degree formats. News/Editorial/Computer Layout and Design

TAYLOR UNIVERSITY — 236 West Reade
Avenue, Upland, IN, 46989-1001, USA (765) 998-5590; e-mail dnhensley@taylor.edu; web site www.taylor.edu
Director, Professional Writing major — Dennis E. Hensley
Instructor in Professional Writing — Linda Taylor
AFFILIATIONS: Taylor University
DEGREES:Bachelor of Science in Communication
DEPARTMENTS: Department of Communication
FACILITIES: Second Floor, Nussbaum Hall, Taylor University

UNIVERSITY OF EVANSVILLE — 1800
Lincoln Ave., Evansville, IN, 47722 (812) 488-2341; fax (812) 488-2717; e-mail dt4@evansville.edu; web site www.evansville.edu
Prof./Chair — Mark L. Shifflet
Prof. — Hope Bock
Prof. — Michael J. Stankey
Prof. — T. Dean Thomlison
Instr. — Lori Smith
DEGREES:BA, BS
DEPARTMENTS: Department of Communication, 1955
FACILITIES: FM, AP, CN, DR, VDT
SEQUENCES: Advertising, Public Relations/ Media Writing, Video Production, Online Media Development

UNIVERSITY OF INDIANAPOLIS — 1400 E. Hanna Ave., Indianapolis, IN, 46227 (317) 788-3280; fax (317) 788-3490; e-mail catchings@uindy.edu; web site www.communication.uindy.edu
Chair — Billy Catchings
DEPARTMENTS: Department of Communication, 1985
SEQUENCES: Communication Program: Program includes skills and theory courses in journalism, electronic media, and public relations in a liberal arts Methodist-affiliated university, biweekly newspaper, radio station, television channel, and public relations agency.

UNIVERSITY OF NOTRE DAME — Dept. of American Studies, Notre Dame, IN, 46556 (219) 631-7316; fax (219) 631-4268; e-mail al.astudiel.l@nd.edu
Dir., John W. Gallivan Program in Journalism, Ethics & Democracy — Robert Schmuhl
DEPARTMENTS: Department of American Studies
SEQUENCES: Journalism Program: Students take courses on journalism and the media, as well as writing courses, within the context of American Studies, or they participate in the John W. Gallivan Program in Journalism, Ethics and Democracy, a five-course concentratio

UNIVERSITY OF SOUTHERN INDIANA — 8600 University Blvd., Evansville, IN, 47712-3596 (812) 461-5220; fax (812) 465-7152; e-mail wrinks@usi.edu; web site www.usi.edu/libarts/comm
Chair/Assoc. Prof. — J. Wayne Rinks
Prof. — Karen H. Bonnell
Prof. — Gael L. Cooper
Assoc. Prof. — Leigh Anne Howard
Assoc. Prof. — Chad R. Tew
Asst. Prof. — David N. Black
Asst. Prof. — Wesley T. Durham
Asst. Prof. — Yoon-Joo Lee
Asst. Prof. — John K. Saliba
Asst. Prof. — Robert E. West
Instr. — Karen S. Braselton
Instr. — Erin Gibson
Instr. — Robert W. Jeffers
Instr. — John M. Morris
Instr. — Mary B. Reese
Prof. Emer. — Seymour Brodsky
Prof. Emer. — Dal M. Herring
Prof. Emer. — Helen R. Sands
Prof. Emer. — Mary A. Schroeder
Prof. Emer. — Kenneth G. Vance
AFFILIATIONS: SPJ, AAF, PRSSA
DEGREES:BA, BS
DEPARTMENTS: Department of Communications, 1985
FACILITIES: AP, AdA, AM, CCTV, CN, ComN, ComTV, DR, JN, PRA, VDT
SEQUENCES: Majors: Public Relations and Advertising (sequence in each), Journalism (print journalism and online journalism), Communication Studies (speech), Radio and Television (R-TV production and broadcast journalism)

VALPARAISO UNIVERSITY — 1809 Chapel Dr, Valparaiso, IN, 46383-4517, USA (219) 464-5271; fax (219) 464-6742; e-mail douglas.kocher@valpo.edu; web site www.valpo.edu/torch
Chair — Douglas J. Kocher
Jason Paupore
Andy Simmons
Luis Fifuentes
Kathryn Kattalia
DEPARTMENTS: Department of Communication
SEQUENCES: Communication Program: Five majors: Communication Law, New Media-Journalism, Public and Corporate Communication, Public Relations, Television-Radio. Practical experience stressed; internship required; co-op education available

JOURNALISM PROGRAM, VINCENNES UNIVERSITY — 1002 N 1st St, Vincennes, IN, 47591-1504, USA (812) 888-4551; fax (812) 888-5531; e-mail trailblazer@vinu.edu
Jrnlism Asst. Professor — Emily Taylor
DEPARTMENTS: The Journalism Program
SEQUENCES: Journalism Program: Newspaper-oriented curriculum with two sequences, news-editorial and print media advertising. Five lecture courses, production laboratories for each sequence, and two inter-departmental photography courses.

IOWA

CLARKE COLLEGE — 1550 Clarke Dr, Dubuque, IA, 52001-3117, USA (563) 588-6335; fax (563) 588-6789; e-mail abdul.sinno@clarke.eduDiana Russo
Chair — Abdul Karim Sinno
Sarah Bradford
DEPARTMENTS: Communication Department
SEQUENCES: Journalism Program: Communication Major: print journalism, advertising and PR multimedia

DRAKE UNIVERSITY — 2507 University Ave., Des Moines, IA, 50311 (515) 271-2838; fax (515) 271-2798; e-mail charles.edwards@drake.edu; web site www.drake.edu/journalism
Dean — Charles Edwards
Prof. — Todd Evans
Prof. — John Lytle
Prof./Assoc. Dean — Patricia Prijatel
Assoc. Prof. — Janet Hill Keefer
Assoc. Prof. — Ronda Menke
Assoc. Prof. — Lee Jolliffe
Assoc. Prof. — Gary Wade
Assoc. Prof./Asst. Dean — David Wright
Asst. Prof. — Koji Fuse
Asst. Prof. — Dorothy Pisarski
Asst. Prof. — Angela Renkoski
Asst. Prof. — Kathleen Richardson
Asst. Prof. — Jill Van Wyke
Prof. Emer. — William F. Francois
Prof. Emer. — Barry M. Foskit
Prof. Emer. — Henry Milam
Prof. Emer. — Joe R. Patrick
Prof. Emer. — Herbert Strentz
Prof. Emer. — Louis J. Wolter
AFFILIATIONS: AAF, KTA, PRSSA, SPJ
DEGREES:BA
DEPARTMENTS: School of Journalism and Mass Communication, 1920
FACILITIES: AdA, CATV, CCTV, CN, ComN, ComR, ComTV, JM, PRA, VDT, WEBJ
SEQUENCES: Advertising (Creative Track and Management Track), Electronic Media (Radio and TV Production and Broadcast News), Magazines, News/Internet, Public Relations

GRAND VIEW COLLEGE — 1331 Grandview Ave., Des Moines, IA, 50316 (515) 263-2931; fax (515) 263-2990; e-mail wschaefer@gvc.edu; web site www.gvc.edu/academics/comm
Chair — William Schaefer
DEGREES:BA
DEPARTMENTS: Communication Department, 1974
SEQUENCES: Journalism Program: GVC has around 120 majors earning BA degrees in Mass Communication, Journalism, Broadcast and Graphic Journalism

IOWA STATE UNIVERSITY OF SCIENCE AND TECHNOLOGY — 101 Hamilton Hall, Ames, IA, 50011-1180 (515) 294-4342; fax (515) 294-5108; e-mail greenlee@iastate.edu
Dir. — Michael Bugeja
Prof. — Eric Abbott
Prof. — Thomas Beell
Prof. — Jane W. Peterson
Prof. — Kim Smith
Prof. — Lulu Rodriguez
Assoc. Prof. — Joel Geske
Assoc. Prof. — Barbara Mack
Assoc. Prof. — Marcia Prior-Miller
Asst. Prof. — Jeff Blevins
Asst. Prof. — David Bulla
Asst. Prof. — Dennis Chamberlin
Asst. Prof. — Michael Dahlstrom
Asst. Prof. — Daniela Dimitrova
Asst. Prof. — Jacob Groshek
Asst. Prof. — Chad Harms
Asst. Prof. — Suman Lee
Asst. Prof. — Jay Newell
Asst. Prof. — Sela Sar
Sr. Lectr. — Erin Wilgenbusch
AFFILIATIONS: KTA, PBK, PKP, PRSA, PRSSA, SPJ, BEA, RTNDA, IBNA, NPPA, AAA, ACR, ICA, IABC
DEGREES:BA, BS, MS
DEPARTMENTS: Greenlee School of Journalism and Communication, 1905
FACILITIES: AP, AdA, AM/FM, ETV-Channel 18 cable, CN, ComN, BTA, PRA, Integrated Multimedia Suite, Audio and Editing Bays, Focus Group Rooms, JM, VDT
SEQUENCES: Majors: Advertising, Journalism and Mass Communication

UNIVERSITY OF IOWA — 100 Adler Journalism Bldg., Rm. E305, Iowa City, IA, 52242-2004 (319) 335-3486; fax (319) 335-3502; e-mail journalism-admin@uiowa.edu; web site www.uiowa.edu/jmc
Interim Dir. — Marc Armstrong
Prof. — Kay Amert
Prof. — Dan Berkowitz
Prof. — Stephen Bloom
Prof./Dir. — Pamela J. Creedon
Prof. — Judy Polumbaum
Prof. — Carolyn Stewart Dyer
Assoc. Prof. — Julie Andsager
Assoc. Prof. — Stephen Berry
Assoc. Prof. — Venise Berry
Assoc. Prof./Coord., Iowa Ctr. for Commun. Study/Advisor, Journal of Communication Inquiry — Meenakshi Gigi Durham
Assoc. Prof. — Lyombe(Leo) Eko
Assoc. Prof. — John Kimmich Javier
Assoc. Prof. — Donald McLeese
Assoc. Prof. — Jane Singer
Asst. Prof. — John Bennett
Asst. Prof. — Stacey Cone
Asst. Prof. — Frank Durham
Asst. Prof. — Sujatha Sosale
George H. Gallup Lectr. — Ann Haugland
AFFILIATIONS: KTA, PRSSA, SPJ, NABJ, RTNDA, Ed On Campus
DEGREES:BA, BS, MA, PhD
DEPARTMENTS: School of Journalism and Mass Communication, 1924
FACILITIES: AP, AM, FM, CATV, CCTV, CN, DR, JM, VDT

UNIVERSITY OF NORTHERN IOWA — Communications Studies Dept., 326 Lang, Cedar Falls, IA, 50614-01397 (319) 273-2217; fax (319) 273-7356; e-mail john.fritch@uni.edu
Dept. Chair — John Fritch
AFFILIATIONS: BEA, PRSSA
DEPARTMENTS: Communications Studies Department
SEQUENCES: Undergrad.: Communication Studies, Electronic Media, Public Relations. Grad.: Communication Education, Mass Communication, Organizational Communication/Human Resources, Performance Studies, Public Relations, General Communication Studies. Journalism Minor

KANSAS

BAKER UNIVERSITY — PO Box 65, Baldwin City, KS, 66006-0065, USA (913) 594-6451; fax (913) 594-3570; e-mail bayha@harvey.bakeru.edu; web site www.thebakerorange.comGwyn Mellinger
Chair — Ann Rosenthal
Dave Bostwick
Chris Smith
DEPARTMENTS: Department of Communication and Theatre Arts, 1976
SEQUENCES: Journalism Program: Program is news-editorial oriented, emphasizing writing, editing, reporting and production skills. Mass Communication Program: Program is theory and production oriented, emphasizing radio and television production and post productio

FORT HAYS STATE UNIVERSITY — 600 Park St., Hays, KS, 67601, U.S.A. (785) 628-4018; fax (785) 628-4075; e-mail lhunting@fhsu.edu; web site www.fhsu.edu
Dir. — Linn Ann Huntington
Dr. — Qing Jiang Yao
Dr. — Hsin-Yen Yang
DEPARTMENTS: Department of Communication Studies, Area of Journalism
SEQUENCES: Journalism Program: Coursework in journalism, mass communications, public relations, advertising, photography, desktop publishing and other journalism-related areas.

KANSAS STATE UNIVERSITY — 105 Kedzie Hall, Manhattan, KS, 66506-1501 (785) 532-6890; fax (785) 532-5484; e-mail journalism@ksu.edu; web site jmc.ksu.edu
Prof./Dir. — Angela Powers
Prof. — William J. Adams
Prof./Head, PR seq. — Todd Simon
Assoc. Prof. — Soontae An
Assoc. Prof./Ross Beach Chair — Louise Benjamin
Assoc. Prof./Head, Journalism Digital Media Sequence — Bonnie Bressers
Assoc. Prof. — Joye Gordon
Assoc. Prof. — Thomas Gould
Assoc. Prof./Assoc. Dir., Research/Grad. Studies — Hyun-Seung Jin
Assoc. Prof./Head, Adv. Seq. — R. Charles Pearce
Assoc. Prof./Assoc. Dir., Undergrad. Studies — J. Steven Smethers
Asst. Prof. — Kimetris Baltrip
Asst. Prof./R.M. Seaton Professinal Chair — Fred Brock
Asst. Prof. — Gloria Freeland
Asst. Prof. — Ginger Loggins
Asst. Prof. — Sam Mwangi
Asst. Prof. — Nancy Muturi
Asst. Prof./Dir., Student Publications Inc./Exec. Dir., Journalism Educ. Assn. — Linda Puntney
Asst. Prof. — Seong-Hun Yun
Instr. — Stacy Neumann
AFFILIATIONS: AAF, ACT, NABJ, PRSSA, SCJ, SJEA, SND, SPJ
DEPARTMENTS: A.Q. Miller School of Journalism and Mass Communications, 1910
FACILITIES: AM/FM, AP, CATV, CN, JM, PRA, VDT
SEQUENCES: Advertising, Digital Media, Journalism, Public Relations

PITTSBURG STATE UNIVERSITY — 1701 S. Broadway, 417 Grubbs Hall, Pittsburg, KS, 66762 (620) 235-4716; fax (620) 235-4686; e-mail jscott@pittstate.edu
Chair — Peter K. Hamilton
DEPARTMENTS: Department of Communication
SEQUENCES: Communication Program: A Communication major with tracks in Advertising, Broadcasting, Communication Education, News Editorial, Photojournalism, Public Relations, and Theatre (BA/BSEd degree). MA in Communication offered with specialized emphasis in app

UNIVERSITY OF KANSAS — 1435 Jayhawk Blvd., 200 Stauffer-Flint Hall, Lawrence, KS, 66045-7575 (785) 864-4755; fax (785) 864-4396; e-mail jschool@ku.edu; web site www.journalism.ku.edu
Assoc. Prof./Dean — Ann M. Brill
Prof./Knight Chair on the News, Leadership/Community — Pam Fine
Prof. — Ted Frederickson
Prof. — James K. Gentry

Prof. — David D. Perlmutter
Prof./Accrediting Coun. — Susanne Shaw
Assoc. Prof. — Robert Basow
Assoc. Prof./Chair, Strategic Commun. — Timothy Bengtson
Assoc. Prof. — John Broholm
Assoc. Prof./Assoc. Dean — David Guth
Assoc. Prof. — Carol Holstead
Assoc. Prof. — Linda Lee
Assoc. Prof. — Tien-Tsung Lee
Assoc. Prof. — Charles Marsh
Assoc. Prof. — Max Utsler
Assoc. Prof./Interim Dir., Grad. Program — Tom Volek
Assoc. Prof./Chair, News Information — Mike Williams
Asst. Prof. — Barbara Barnett
Asst. Prof. — Mugur V. Geana
Asst. Prof. — Crystal Lumpkins
AFFILIATIONS: AAF, PRSSA, KTA, Journalism Multicultural Scholars Program
DEGREES:BS, MS
DEPARTMENTS: William Allen White School of Journalism and Mass Communications, 1911 (Dept.), 1944 (School)
FACILITIES: AdA, AP, CN, ETV, JM, PRA, VDT
SEQUENCES: News and Information (print, broadcast news, magazine, online); Strategic Communications (advertising, public relations, marketing, management)

WASHBURN UNIVERSITY — 316 Henderson Learning Resources Ctr., 1700 SW College Ave., Topeka, KS, 66621 (785) 670-1836; fax (785) 670-1234; e-mail massmedia@washburn.edu; web site www.morforu.wikidot.com
Chair/Fellow PRSA/Prof. — Dr. Barbara DeSanto
Prof. — Frank Chorba
Prof. — Charles Cranston
Asst. Prof. — Kathy Menzie
Asst. Prof. — Maria Raicheva-Stover
Lectr. — Regina Cassell
DEPARTMENTS: Mass Media Department
SEQUENCES: Mass Media: Major concentrations include broadcasting, film & video, media writing & publishing, advertising and public relations

WICHITA STATE UNIVERSITY — Elliott School of Communication, Wichita, KS, 67260-0031 (316) 978-3185; fax (316) 978-3006; e-mail susan.huxman@wichita.edu
Assoc. Prof./Dir. — Susan Huxman
Prof. — Philip Gaunt
Prof. — Sharon Iorio
Prof. — Vernon Keel
Assoc. Prof. — Les Anderson
Assoc. Prof. — Rick Armstrong
Assoc. Prof. — Dan Close
Assoc. Prof. — Patricia Dooley
Assoc. Prof. — Kevin Hager
Assoc. Prof. — Keith Williamson
Asst. Prof. — Michael Boyle
Asst. Prof. — Jeff Jarman
Asst. Prof. — Amy Lauters
Asst. Prof. — Greg Stene
Asst. Prof. — Mike Wood
Instr. — Nancy Fisher
Instr. — Kevin Keplar
Instr. — Connie Morris
Sr. Fellow — Randy Brown
Professional-in-Residence — Al Higdon
AFFILIATIONS: SPJ, AAF
DEGREES:BA, MA
DEPARTMENTS: Elliott School of Communication, 1927/1989
FACILITIES: DR, CATV, CN, FM, ComN, ComTV, ADA, PRA, VDT
SEQUENCES: Strategic Communication, Broadcast Journalism, Electronic Media, Integrated Marketing Communications, Print Journalism

KENTUCKY

ASBURY COLLEGE — 1 Macklem Dr, Wilmore, KY, 40390-1152, USA (859) 858-3511; fax (859) 858-3921; e-mail mlonginow@asbury.edu; web site collegian.asbury.eduDeanna Morono
Chair — James R. Owens
Kayla Dubois
Zack Klemme
Morgan Schutters
DEPARTMENTS: Department of Communication Arts, 1983
FACILITIES: Independent student newspaper with web edition, yearbook, literary magazine, campus-wide radio stations, cable TV covering surrounding county, Media 100, web page production, recording studio, special-interest magazines, internships in print and electroni
SEQUENCES: Journalism Program: Three sequences: News-Editorial, Public Relations, Magazine & Publishing; Literary Journalism. Media Communications Program: Five sequences: Performance, Production, Film Studies, Multimedia. Applied Communications Program: Five sequ

EASTERN KENTUCKY UNIVERSITY — Combs Building, Room 326, Richmond, KY, 40475-3102 (859) 622-1881; fax (859) 622-2354; e-mail reggie.beehner@eku.edu; web site http://www.easternprogress.com/
Adviser, Eastern Progress — Reggie Beehner

MOREHEAD STATE UNIVERSITY — BR 115-A, Dept. of Communication & Theatre, Morehead, KY, 40351 (606) 783-5312; fax (606) 783-2457; e-mail j.atkins@moreheadstate.edu; web site www.trailblazeronline.net
Chair — Robert Willenbrink
Journalism Coord. — Joan Atkins
DEPARTMENTS: Journalism Area, Department of Communication and Theatre
FACILITIES: Wireless technology available in all labs and teaching facilities. Student practicum and work opportunities available via univerity-owned NPR affiliate radio station, student-produced cable TV news programs and a weekly student newspaper
SEQUENCES: Journalism Program: Undergraduate program in Journalism with both print and broadcast emphases. Other departmental majors include Advertising/Public Relations, Electronic Media Production, Organizational/Interpersonal Communication and Theatre. Master

MURRAY STATE UNIVERSITY — 114 Wilson Hall, Murray, KY, 42071-3311 (809) 762-2387; fax (270) 809-2390; e-mail journalism@murraystate.edu; web site www.themurraystatenews.com
Prof./Interim Chair — Allen White
Prof. — John Dillon
Prof. — Roger Haney
Prof./Grad. Coord. — Bob Lochte
Prof. — Jeanne S. Scafella
Assoc. Prof. — Ann Landini
Assoc. Prof. — Debbie Owens
Assoc. Prof. — Celia Wall
Sr. Lectr. — Bob Valentine
Sr. Lectr. — Gill Welsch
Lectr. — Joe Hedges
Lectr. — Jeremy McKeel
Lectr. — Robin B. Orvino-Proulx
Adj. — Darryl Armstrong
Adj. — Janett Blythe
Adj. — Victoria Daughrity
Adj. — Kate Lochte
Adj. — Jeff Prater
Adj. — Ann Thrower
Adj. — Mark Welch
AFFILIATIONS: SCJ, NBS-AERho, AAF, PRSSA
DEGREES:BS, BA, MS, MA
DEPARTMENTS: Department of Journalism and Mass Communications, 1975
FACILITIES: AdA, AP, FM, CATV, DR, ETV, JN, PRA, VDT
SEQUENCES: Majors: Journalism, Advertising, Public Relations, Electronic Media

NORTHERN KENTUCKY UNIVERSITY — 134 Landrum Academic Center, Nunn Dr., Highland Heights, KY, 41099 (859) 572-5435; fax (859) 572-6187; e-mail ragsdale@nku.edu
Chair — Gaut Ragsdale
AFFILIATIONS: AAF, BEA, PRSSA
DEGREES:BA
DEPARTMENTS: Communications Department, 1972
FACILITIES: AM/FM, CATV, CCTV, CN, ComN, ComTV, DR, PRA, VDT
SEQUENCES: Journalism Sequences: Advertising, General Editorial, Public Relations, Photojournalism. Radio/Television Sequences: Business, Engineering, Programming. Speech Communication Sequences: Organizational Communication, Rhetorical Theory, Speech/Theatre A

UNIVERSITY OF KENTUCKY — 107 Grehan Bldg., Lexington, KY, 40506-0042 (859) 257-1730; fax (859) 323-3168; e-mail amy.jarvis@uky.edu
Prof./Dir. — Beth E. Barnes
Prof. — Richard Labunski
Prof. — Thomas Lindlof
Assoc. Prof. — Chike Anyaegbunam
Assoc. Prof. — Dennis Altman
Assoc. Prof. — Jim Hertog
Assoc. Prof. — Elizabeth Scoobie Ryan
Assoc. Prof. — Leland Buck Ryan
Assoc. Prof. — Scott Whitlow
Asst. Prof. — Deborah Chung
Asst. Prof. — John Clark
Asst. Prof. — Mel Coffee
Asst. Prof. — Al Cross
Asst. Prof. — Alyssa Eckman
Asst. Prof. — Michael Farrell
Asst. Prof. — Phillip Hutchison
Asst. Prof. — Bobi Ivanov
Asst. Prof. — Yung Soo Kim
Asst. Prof. — Zixue Tai
Asst. Prof. — Kathleen Kakie Urch
AFFILIATIONS: AAF, NABJ, PRSSA, SPJ
DEGREES:BA, BS, College-wide MA, PhD-Communication
DEPARTMENTS: School of Journalism and Telecommunications, 1914
FACILITIES: AdA, AM/FM, AP, CN, DR, VDT
SEQUENCES: Integrated Strategic Communications, Journalism and Telecommunications

UNIVERSITY OF LOUISVILLE — Dept. of Communication, 310 Strickler Hall, Louisville, KY, 40292 (502) 852-6976; fax (502) 852-8166; e-mail al@Louisville.edu; web site comm.louisville.edu
Chair — Al Futrell
DEGREES:B.S. B.A. M.S.
DEPARTMENTS: Department of Communication, 1971
FACILITIES: Newspaper, studio, media labs, Nikon school locker
SEQUENCES: Communication Program: Bachelor's degree with major in Communication and concentrations in Communication Studies, Advertising and Public Relations, and Media (Print, Broadcast and Digital)

WESTERN KENTUCKY UNIVERSITY — 1660 Normal St, Western Kentucky University, Bowling Green, KY, 42101-3536, USA (270) 745-2653; e-mail carrie.pratt@wku.edu; web site www.wkuherald.com
Operations Mgr — Sherry West
Herald Adviser, Multiplatform News Adviser — Carrie Pratt
Office Associate — Tracy Newton
Advt Adviser and Sales Mgr — Will Hoagland
Dir of Student Publications — Chuck Clark
Talisman adviser — Sam Oldenburg
AFFILIATIONS: CMA, ACP, KPA, KIPA
DEGREES:BA
DEPARTMENTS: School of Journalism & Broadcasting, 1999
FACILITIES: AdA, AP, CCTV, CN, DR, ETV, FM, PRA, VDT
SEQUENCES: Programs: Advertising, Broadcasting, Mass Communication, News-Editorial, Photojournalism, PR, Film

LOUISIANA

GRAMBLING STATE UNIVERSITY — PO Box 45, Grambling, LA, 71245 (318) 274-2403; fax (318) 274-3194; e-mail edum@gram.edu
Acting Head — Martin O. Edu
AFFILIATIONS: PRSSA, NABJ, NBS, SND, WICI
DEGREES:BA, MA- Mass Communication
DEPARTMENTS: Department of Mass Communication, 1988
FACILITIES: FM, AP, CATV, DR, JN, VDT
SEQUENCES: News-Editorial, Public Relations, Visual Communication, Broadcasting

LOUISIANA STATE UNIVERSITY — 211 Journalism Bldg., Baton Rouge, LA, 70803-7202 (225) 578-2336; fax (225) 578-2125; web site www.manship.lsu.edu
Prof./Dean — John M. Hamilton
Prof. — Timothy Cook
Prof. — Louis A. Day
Prof. — Ronald G. Garay
Prof. — Robert K. Goidel
Prof. — Ralph Izard
Prof. — Laura Lindsay
Prof. — Richard A. Nelson
Assoc. Prof. — Jinx Broussard
Assoc. Prof./Assoc. Dean — Margaret H. DeFleur
Assoc. Prof./Assoc. Dean — David D. Kurpius
Assoc. Prof. — Eileen Meehan
Assoc. Prof./Assoc. Dean — Anne Osborne
Assoc. Prof. — Jay L. Perkins
Assoc. Prof. — Judith Sylvester
Assoc. Prof. — Denis Wu
Asst. Prof. — Lori Boyer
Asst. Prof. — Ketan Chitnis
Asst. Prof. — Emily Erickson
Asst. Prof. — Craig Freeman
AFFILIATIONS: ABC, AAF, SPJ, KTA, PRSSA
DEGREES:BMC, MMC, PhD
DEPARTMENTS: Manship School of Mass Communication, 1925
FACILITIES: AdA, CCTV, FM, CN, ComN, ComTV, DR, PRA
SEQUENCES: Advertising, Journalism, Political Communication, Public Relations

LOUISIANA STATE UNIVERSITY IN SHREVEPORT — Branson Hall, Rm. 330, Shreveport, LA, 71115 (318) 797-5375; fax (318) 797-5132; e-mail jnolan@lsus.edu
Chair — Jack Nolan
DEGREES:BA
DEPARTMENTS: Department of Communications
FACILITIES: Writing, desktop publishing labs
SEQUENCES: Mass Communications (Journalism), Mass Communications (Public Relations), Speech, Speech Pathology

LOUISIANA TECH UNIVERSITY — 152 Keeny, Ruston, LA, 71272-0045 (318) 257-4427; fax (318) 257-4558; e-mail blick@latech.edu; web site eb.journ.latech.edu
Head — Thomas Edward Blick
DEGREES:BA
DEPARTMENTS: Journalism Department, 1928
FACILITIES: FM, AdA, ComN, ComR, DR, JN, VDT
SEQUENCES: News-Editorial

LOYOLA UNIVERSITY NEW ORLEANS — 6363 St. Charles Ave., Box 201, New Orleans, LA, 70118 (504) 865-3430; fax (504) 865-2333; e-mail cfbolner@loyno.edu; web site www.loyno.edu/communications
Chair/Assoc. Prof. — Teri K. Henley
Prof. — A.L. Lorenz
Assoc. Prof. — S.L. Alexander
Assoc. Prof. — William M. Hammel
Assoc. Prof./Dir., Grad. Prog. — David M. Myers
Assoc. Prof. — Leslie G. Parr
Assoc. Prof. — J. Cathy Rogers
Asst. Prof. — Debra A. Woodfork
Instr. — Lisa C. Martin
Instr. — Trish O'Kane
Loyola University Chair for Environmental Communications — Robert A. Thomas
AFFILIATIONS: AAF, BEA, KTA, SPJ, PRSSA, RTNDA
DEGREES:BA, MA
DEPARTMENTS: Department of Communications, 1937
FACILITIES: AdA, AP, CCTV, CN, ComN, ComTV, DR, JN, PRA, VDT
SEQUENCES: Advertising, Broadcast Journalism, Broadcast Production, Communications Studies, Film Studies, Photojournalism, Print Journalism, Public Relations

MCNEESE STATE UNIVERSITY — PO Box 90335, Lake Charles, LA, 70609 (337) 475-5290; fax (337) 475-5291; e-mail hover@mcneese.edu
Head/Prof. — Henry Overduin
Prof. — Leonard Barchak
Assoc. Prof. — Carrie Chrisco
Assoc. Prof., Speech Prog. — Larry Vinson
Asst. Prof. — Patrick Roddy
Asst. Prof. — Tracy Standley
Asst. Prof., Speech Prog. — Davey Stephens
Instr., Speech Prog. — Robert Markstrom
Instr., Speech Prog. — Amy Veuleman
Editor Emer., American Press/Journalist-in-Residence — Jim Beam
AFFILIATIONS: PRSSA
DEGREES:BS, BA
DEPARTMENTS: Department of Mass Communication, 1990
FACILITIES: Broadcast Studios (TV and Radio), and Control Room, two computer labs, including multi-media production, CD and DVD; five editing suites, cable radio station
SEQUENCES: Journalism, Radio/TV, Public Relations, General Communication, Speech Education, Professional Sales Communication

NICHOLLS STATE UNIVERSITY — PO Box 2031, Thibodaux, LA, 70310 (985) 448-4586; fax (985) 448-4577; e-mail james.stewart@nicholls.edu; web site www.nicholls.edu/maco
Head/Assoc. Prof. — James L. Stewart
Prof. — Lloyd Chiasson
Assoc. Prof. — Rickey Duet
Asst. Prof. — Andy Simoncelli
Instr. — Lance Arnold
Instr. — Nicky Boudreaux
Instr. — Felicia Harry
Prof. Emer. — Alfred Delahaye
DEGREES:BA
DEPARTMENTS: Department of Mass Communication, 1957
FACILITIES: AdA, FM, CATV, CN, ComN, ComTV, PRA, VDT
SEQUENCES: Broadcast Journalism, Print Journalism, Public Relations

NORTHWESTERN STATE UNIVERSITY OF LOUISIANA — 103 John S. Kyser Hall, Natchitoches, LA, 71497 (318) 357-4425; fax (318) 357-4434; e-mail journalism@nsula.edu; web site www.liberalarts.nsula.edu/journalism
Dept. Head/Assoc. Prof. — Paula F. Furr
Prof. — Hesham Mesbah
Assoc. Prof. — Mary Brocato
Asst. Prof. — William Broussard
Asst. Prof. — Jung Lim
Asst. Prof. — Jerry Pierce
Asst. Prof. — Jarrett Reeves
Dir./Producer NSU 22 — David Antilley
Wise Endowed Chair — Raymond Strother
Prof. Emer. — Thomas Whitehead
Broadcast Technician — Michael Lofton
Admin. Asst. — Marie Hall
DEGREES:BA, major and minor available
DEPARTMENTS: Department of Journalism, 1948
SEQUENCES: Public Relations, News Editorial, Broadcast

SOUTHEASTERN LOUISIANA UNIVERSITY — 344 D. Vickers Hall, Sycamore St., SLU 10451, Hammond, LA, 70402 (504) 549-2105; fax (504) 549-5014; e-mail fcom1157@selu.edu
Head/Assoc. Prof. — Karen Fontenot
Prof. — Joe Mirando
Prof. — William Parrill
Prof. — T. Win Welford
Prof. — Jack Wellman
Assoc. Prof. — Lynn Wellmann
Asst. Prof. — Frances Brandau-Brown
Asst. Prof. — Joe Burns
Instr. — Mike Applin
Instr. — Terri Miller-Drufner
DEGREES:BA
DEPARTMENTS: Department of Communication & Theatre, 2000
FACILITIES: ComN, FM
SEQUENCES: Mass Communication and Journalism, Organizational Communication, Journalism Education

SOUTHERN UNIVERSITY AND A&M COLLEGE — 220 Stewart Hall, Baton Rouge, LA, 70813 (225) 771-5790; fax (225) 771-4943; e-mail mahmoud_braima@cxs.subr.edu
Head — Mahmoud Braima
DEGREES:BA, MA- Mass Communication
DEPARTMENTS: Department of Mass Communications, 1978
FACILITIES: AP, CCTV
SEQUENCES: Areas: Journalism, Broadcast, Public Relations

UNIVERSITY OF LOUISIANA AT LAFAYETTE — Rm. 107, Burke-Hawthorne Hall, Hebrard Blvd., Lafayette, LA, 70503 (337) 482-6103; fax (337) 482-6104; web site comm.louisiana.edu
Dept. Head/Assoc. Prof. — Bette J. Kauffman
Assoc. Prof. — Jeffrey M. Gibson
Asst. Prof. — Tae-hyun Kim
Asst. Prof. — Robert E. Lewis
Asst. Prof. — Joel R. Willer
Instr. — Jarrett Reeves
Part-time Adj. Fac — Mark Simmons
AFFILIATIONS: AF, ACA, PRSSA, SPJ, SCM, SNPA, LPA, NCS, ICE, PIMS, LBEA, NAB, NAMJ, ASJMC, Hearst Awards program
DEGREES:BA, MS
DEPARTMENTS: Department of Communication, 1981
FACILITIES: AM/FM, CATV, CCTV, ComN, DR, ETV, VDT
SEQUENCES: Interpersonal/Organizational Communication, Mass Communication (Advertising, Broadcasting or Journalism seq.) and Public Relations

UNIVERSITY OF LOUISIANA AT MONROE — Dept. of Communication, Monroe, LA, 71209-0322 (318) 342-1406; fax (318) 342-1422; e-mail kauffman@ulm.edu
Dept. Head/Assoc. Prof. — Bette J. Kauffman
Assoc. Prof. — Jeffrey M. Gibson
Asst. Prof. — Tae-hyun Kim
Asst. Prof. — Robert E. Lewis
Asst. Prof. — Joel R. Willer
Instr. — Jarrett Reeves
Part-time Adj. Fac. — Mark Simmons
AFFILIATIONS: KTA, PRAL, PRSSA, SPJ
DEGREES:BA, MA
DEPARTMENTS: Department of Communication, 1955
FACILITIES: AP, CCTV, CN, ComN, ComR, ComTV, DR, FM (2), PRA, VDT
SEQUENCES: Journalism, Public Relations, Management and Marketing, Media Production

UNIVERSITY OF NEW ORLEANS — 127 Liberal Arts Bldg., New Orleans, LA, 70148 (504) 286-6273; fax (504) 286-6378 (student newspaper); e-mail english@uno.edu
Chair — Peter Schock
DEPARTMENTS: Journalism Area, English Department
SEQUENCES: Journalism Program: Three-person journalism faculty offers coursework and minor in print journalism

XAVIER UNIVERSITY OF LOUISIANA — 909 S. Jefferson Davis Pkwy., New Orleans, LA, 70125 (504) 520-5092; fax (504) 520-7919; e-mail jmelcher@xula.edu
PD — Joe Melcher
DEPARTMENTS: Department of Communications, 1982
SEQUENCES: Communications Program: Undergraduate liberal arts based program; Public Relations, Radio, TV or Print emphases available; houses student newspaper, Xavier Herald

MAINE

UNIVERSITY OF MAINE — Dept. of Communication & Journalism, Orono, ME, 04469-5724 (207) 581-1283; fax (207) 581-1286; e-mail john@maine.edu
Chair/Prof. — John C. Sherblom
Prof. — Kristin M. Langellier
Assoc. Prof. — Paul Grosswiler
Assoc. Prof. — Kathryn Olmstead
Assoc. Prof. — Eric E. Peterson
Assoc. Prof. — Claire F. Sullivan
Asst. Prof. — Lyombe Eko
Asst. Prof. — Shannon Martin
Asst. Prof. — Michael McCauley
Asst. Prof. — Nathan Stormer
Asst. Prof. — Natalia Tolstikova
Instr. — Katherine Heidinger
Instr. — Ann James Joles
Instr. — Margaret Nagle
Instr. — Marie Tessier
Prof. Emer. — Arthur Guesman
Prof. Emer. — Alan Miller
AFFILIATIONS: AAF, BEA, SPJ
DEGREES:BA
DEPARTMENTS: Department of Communication and Journalism, 1948
FACILITIES: AP, CCTV, CN, ETV, FM, VDT
SEQUENCES: News-Editorial, Advertising, Mass Communication, Broadcast Journalism

MARYLAND

BOWIE STATE UNIVERSITY — 14000 Jericho Park Rd.,, Bowie, MD, 20715-9465 (301) 860-3700; fax (301) 860-3728; e-mail conwumechili@bowiestate.edu
Chair — Dr. Chuka Onwumechili
DEPARTMENTS: Department of Communications, 1978
SEQUENCES: Mass Communication Program: Prepares students for careers in News, Broadcasting, PR, Advertising and Telecommunications

DEFENSE INFORMATION SCHOOL — 6500 Mapes Rd., Ft. George G. Meade, MD, 20755-5620 (301) 677-2173; e-mail webmeisters@dinfos.osd.mil; web site www.dinfos.osd.mil
Chief, Pub. Affairs Dept. — Lt. Col. R. Steven Murray
SEQUENCES: The Defense Information School has a long-standing tradition of producing outstanding Public Affairs and Visual Information personnel for the Dept. of Defense

GOUCHER COLLEGE — 1021 Dulaney Valley Rd., Baltimore, MD, 21204 (410) 337-6200; fax (410) 337-6085; e-mail communications@goucher.edu
Dir. — Patsy Sims
DEGREES:MFA
DEPARTMENTS: MFA in Creative Nonfiction, 1998
SEQUENCES: Program Offers: students are encouraged to pursue specific interests in television and film studies, radio and television production, print and radio and television journalism, photography, advertising and public relations, human communication and media r

HOOD COLLEGE — 401 Rosemont Ave, Frederick, MD, 21701-8524, USA (301) 696-3641; fax (301) 696-3578; e-mail weinberg@hood.eduRita Davis
Dir./Prof. of Journalism — Al Weinberg
DEGREES:BA
DEPARTMENTS: Communication Arts Program
SEQUENCES: Communication Program: BA in communication arts offered. Program requires a core of basic courses and then divides into the journalism track, emphasizing print or broadcast, and the public relations track

LOYOLA COLLEGE — 4501 N. Charles St., Baltimore, MD, 21210-2601 (410) 617-2528; fax (410) 617-2198; e-mail eking@loyola.edu
Chair — Russell Cook
Journ. — Andrew Ciofalo
Adv./PR — Neil Alperstein
Journ./PR — Elliot King
TV-Radio — Michael Braden
Graphics — Diana Samet
DEGREES:BA
DEPARTMENTS: Department of Communication
SEQUENCES: Communications Program: BA, professional program: Journalism, Advertising/Public Relations, TV-Radio, Digital Media, Creative Writing. Internships, international study, graphics, computer lab. Majors: 400.

TOWSON UNIVERSITY — 8000 York Rd., Towson, MD, 21252 (410) 704-3431; fax (410) 704-3656; e-mail cflippen@towson.edu
Chair — Charles Flippen
DEGREES:BA, BS, MA
DEPARTMENTS: Mass Communication and Communication Studies Department
SEQUENCES: Mass Communication Program: 1100 BA, BS and MA students (20 full-time and 50 part-time faculty). Tracks in Journalism and New Media, Advertising and Strategic Public Relations and Integrated Communication. Certificates in Broadcast Journalism and Interd

UNIVERSITY OF MARYLAND — 1117 Journalism Bldg., College Park, MD, 20742 (301) 405-2383 (Dean's Office); fax (301) 314-9166
Interim Dean/Prof./Richard Eaton Chair in Broadcast — Lee Thornton
Assoc. Dean/Dir., Undergrad. Studies — Olive Reid
Acting Assoc. Dean — Steve Crane
Asst. Dean — Marchelle Payne-Gassaway
Asst. Dean — Frank Quine
Asst. Dean/Dir., Bus. Administration — Linda Ringer
Asst. Dean — Sheila Young
Prof. — David Broder
Prof. — Reese Cleghorn
Prof./Merrill Chair in Journalism — Jon Franklin
Prof./Knight Chair in Journalism — Haynes Johnson
Prof. — Eugene L. Roberts
Prof. — Linda Steiner
Prof. — Carl Sessions Stepp
Assoc. Prof. — Ira Chinoy
Assoc. Prof. — Christopher Hanson

Assoc. Prof. — John Newhagen
Assoc. Prof. — Susan Moeller
Assoc. Prof. — Eric Zanot
Asst. Prof. — Ron Yaros
AFFILIATIONS: KTA, SPJ, NABJ, RTNDA
DEGREES:BA, MJ, MA, PhD
DEPARTMENTS: Philip Merrill College of Journalism, 1947
FACILITIES: AP, AMCFbA, AdA, CATV, CCTV, CN, ConiN, Comit, ComTV, DR, ETV, JM, PRA, VDT
SEQUENCES: The college has a core journalism curriculum, rather than sequences, with emphasis on print, broadcast, and online journalism and specializations in public affairs, business-finance and science environmental journalism

UNIVERSITY OF MARYLAND — 2130A Skinner Hall, College Park, MD, 20742-7635 (301) 405-8077; fax (301) 314-9471
Chair/Prof., Pub. Rel./Feminist Scholarship — Elizabeth Toth
Prof., Commun./Research Methods/ Cognition/Persuasion — Edward L. Fink
Prof., History of Rhetoric/Textual Criticism — Robert N. Gaines
Prof., Contemporary Rhetorical Theory & Criticism/Social Change — James F. Klumpp
Prof./Dir., Grad. Studies/Political Commun./ Rhetorical, Feminist & Media Criticism — Shawn J. Parry-Giles
Prof., Listening/Commun. Mgmt./Commun. Educ. — Andrew D. Wolvin
Assoc. Prof., Pub. Rel./Health Commun./ Feminist Scholarship — Linda Aldoory
Assoc. Prof., Intercultural Commun./ Persuasion, Negotiation & Conflict — Deborah A. Cai
Assoc. Prof., Argumentation/Interpersonal Commun. — Dale Hample
Assoc. Prof., Social Influence/Persuasion/ Compliance Gaining — Monique Mitchell Turner
Assoc. Prof., Rhetoric & Political Culture/ Legal Commun. — Trevor Parry-Giles
Assoc. Prof., Feminist & Rhetorical Criticism/ Political Commun./Pub. Address — Mari Boor Tonn
Research Prof., Political Campaign Commun. — Kathleen E. Kendall
Asst. Prof., Middle Eastern Media/Pub. Rel. — Sahar Mohamed Khamis
Asst. Prof., Intercultural Commun./ Organizational Commun., Negotiation & Conflict — Meina Liu
Asst. Prof., Rhetoric/Religion/Feminist Theory — Kristy Maddux
Asst. Prof., Persuasion & Social Influence/ Health Commun. — Xiaoli Nan
Asst. Prof., Feminist & Rhetorical Criticism/ Religious Commun. — Nneka Ifeoma Ofulue
Asst. Prof., Persuasion/Social Influence — Torsten Reimer
Vstg. Asst. Prof., Commun. Theory/Mass Media — Brecken Chinn Swartz
DEPARTMENTS: Department of Communication, 1998

MASSACHUSETTS

BOSTON UNIVERSITY — 640 Commonwealth Ave., Boston, MA, 2215 (617) 353-3450; fax (617) 353-3405; e-mail com@bu.edu
Dean — Thomas E. Fiedler
AFFILIATIONS: PRSSA, SPJ, WICI, B/PAA, BEA
DEPARTMENTS: College of Communication, 1947
SEQUENCES: Communication Programs: Undergraduate: Film and Television, Communication (Mass Communication, Advertising and Public Relations), Journalism (News Editorial, Magazine, Photojournalism, Broadcast Journalism). Graduate: Broadcast Journalism, Business and Ec

EMERSON COLLEGE — 120 Boylston St., Boston, MA, 2116 (617) 824-8354; fax (617) 824-8569
Dean — Stuart J. Sigman
AFFILIATIONS: SPJ, BEA, AER, NATAS, RTNDA
DEGREES:BA, BFA, BS, MA
DEPARTMENTS: School of Communication, 1997
FACILITIES: FM, AP, UPI, TV Studios, VDT, CATV, CN, ComN, ComTV, DR
SEQUENCES: Video, Film, Audio, Print and Broadcast Journalism, Integrated Marketing Communication, Advertising, Public Relations

HAMPSHIRE COLLEGE — School of Communications & Cognitive Science, Amherst, MA, 1002 (413) 549-4600
Dean — Richard Muller
DEPARTMENTS: School of Communications and Cognitive Science
SEQUENCES: Journalism Program: Interdisciplinary program in communication study; TV and print journalism; mass communication emphasis on liberal arts background

NORTHEASTERN UNIVERSITY — 360 Huntington Ave., 102 Lake Hall, Boston, MA, 02115-5000 (617) 373-3236; fax (617) 373-8773; e-mail s.burgard@neu.edu
Dir./Assoc. Prof — Stephen Burgard
Prof. — Nicholas Daniloff
Assoc. Prof. — Belle Adler
Assoc. Prof. — Charles Fountain
Assoc. Prof. — William Kirtz
Assoc. Prof. — Laurel Leff
Assoc. Prof. — James Ross
Assoc. Prof. — Alan Schroeder
Asst. Prof — Elizabeth Matson
Asst. Prof./Coord., Cooperative Educ. Placement — Kellianne Murphy
Lectr. — Carlene Hempel
Lectr. — Gladys McKie
Lectr. — Lincoln McKie
Vstg. Prof. — Daniel Kennedy
Part-time Fac. — David Abel
Part-time Fac. — Dana Barbuto
Part-time Fac. — Michael Blanding
Part-time Fac. — James Chiavelli
Part-time Fac. — Allan Coukell
Part-time Fac. — Paul Della Valle
Dir. — Jonathan Kauffman
AFFILIATIONS: PRSSA, KTA, New England Press Assn.
DEGREES:BA, MA
DEPARTMENTS: School of Journalism
FACILITIES: CATV, CN, AdA, ComN, ComR, ComTV, DR, PRA, VDT, FM

SIMMONS COLLEGE — Dept. of Communications, Boston, MA, 2115 (617) 521-2838; fax (617) 521-3199; e-mail jcorcoran@bmsvax.simmons.edu
DEPARTMENTS: Department of Communications
SEQUENCES: Journalism Program: Writing for news media. Reporting, features, interviews, editorials, reviews. Emphasis is on the practical, with students encouraged to supplement classroom experience and instruction through work on campus publications and supervise

STONEHILL COLLEGE — 320 Washington St., Easton, MA, 2537 (508) 565-1116; fax (508) 565-1565; e-mail dwomack@stonehill.edu
Chair — Israel Khyri Abraham
DEGREES:BA
DEPARTMENTS: Department of Communication & Theatre Arts, 1983
SEQUENCES: BA in communication; minor in journalism. Emphasizes impact of media on society & theory and research. Required courses in media systems, media theory and electronic media industries.

SUFFOLK UNIVERSITY — 41 Temple St., Boston, MA, 2114 (617) 573-8236; fax (617) 742-6982; e-mail rrosenth@suffolk.edu
Chair — Dr. Robert Rosenthal
DEPARTMENTS: Department of Communication and Journalism
FACILITIES: HD Television Studio, Media Lab, Dark Room, Journalism Computer Lab
SEQUENCES: Journalism Programs: Print Journalism, Broadcast Journalism, Media Studies, Public Relations, Film, Communication Studies, Advertising, Organizational Communication.

UNIVERSITY OF MASSACHUSETTS — 108 Bartlett Hall, Amherst, MA, 01003-0520 (413) 545-1376; fax (413) 545-3880; e-mail klist@journ.umass.edu
Dir. — Karen List
AFFILIATIONS: KTA
DEGREES:BA
DEPARTMENTS: Journalism Department, 1971
FACILITIES: FM, AP, CN, DR, VDT
SEQUENCES: News-Ed., Non-Fiction Writing

MICHIGAN

ALMA COLLEGE — 614 W Superior St, Alma, MI, 48801-1504, USA (989) 463-7161; fax (989) 463-7161; e-mail almanian@alma.edu; almanianopinion@yahoo.com; almanian@hotmail.com; web site students.alma.edu/organizations/almanianRobert Vivian
Brendan Guilford
Olga Wrobel
DEPARTMENTS: Communication program
SEQUENCES: Communication program: Communication majors investigate the way messages and media influence individuals, groups, and societies through rigorous coursework and a required internship.

CALVIN COLLEGE — 3201 Burton SE, Grand Rapids, MI, 49546 (616) 526-6283; fax (616) 526-6601; e-mail bytw@calvin.edu
Chair, Dept. of Commun. Arts & Sciences — Randall Bytwerk
Prof., Dept. of English — Don Hettinga
DEPARTMENTS: Department of Communication Arts and Sciences; Department of English (Journalism minor)
SEQUENCES: Communication Programs: BA degree with liberal-arts emphases in mass media and film. Department of English (Journalism minor): Interdisciplinary liberal-arts program with strong writing component

CENTRAL MICHIGAN UNIVERSITY — 454 Moore Hall, Mount Pleasant, MI, 48859 (989) 774-3196; fax (989) 774-7114; e-mail jrndept@cmich.edu
Chair/Prof. — Maria B. Marron
Prof. — John Hartman
Prof. — Dennis Jeffers
Prof. — John Palen
Prof. — Alice Tait
Prof. — Jiafei Yin
Assoc. Prof. — Carole Eberly
Assoc. Prof. — Elliott Parker
Full-time Assoc. Prof. — Jim Wojcik
Asst. Prof. — Tim Boudreau
Asst. Prof. — Yun Jung Choi
Asst. Prof. — Jong Hyuk Lee
Asst. Prof. — David London
Full-time Asst. Prof. — Ken McDonald
Full-time Asst. Prof. — Kent Miller
Part-time Asst. Prof. — Ed Hutchison
Part-time Asst. Prof. — Ron Marmarelli
Instr. — Tereza Dean
Instr. — Steve Jessmore
Instr. — Dawn Paine
Editor & Publisher — Cynthia Gall
AFFILIATIONS: AAF, PRSSA, SPJ, CPPA
DEGREES:BA, BS
DEPARTMENTS: Department of Journalism, 1959
FACILITIES: AP, CATV, CN, DR, ETV, FM
SEQUENCES: Advertising, News-Editorial, Photojournalism, Public Relations

EASTERN MICHIGAN UNIVERSITY — 612 Pray Harrold, Ypsilanti, MI, 48197-4210 (734) 487-4220; fax (734) 483-9744; e-mail carol.schlagheck@emich.edu
Head — Laura George
Journ. Program Coord. — Carol Schlagheck
DEPARTMENTS: Department of English Language and Literature
SEQUENCES: Journalism Program: Offers a major and minor in Journalism and an interdisciplinary major in Public Relations. Journalism courses cover news/feature writing, copyediting, editorial procedures of layout and design, history of journalism, law and Web journa

GRAND VALLEY STATE UNIVERSITY — 1 Campus Dr., Allendale, MI, 49401-9401 (616) 331-3668; fax (616) 331-2700; e-mail barkod@gvsu.edu; web site www.gvsu.edu
Dir. — Alex Nesterenko
DEGREES:BA, BS, MS
DEPARTMENTS: School of Communications
FACILITIES: WGVU-TV (PBS station) and WGVU-FM (NPR station)
SEQUENCES: Journalism Program: BA, BS degrees offered in Journalism, Advertising/PR, Photography, Broadcasting, Film/Video, Communication Studies, Theatre, and Health Communication. MS degree offered in Communication Management

MADONNA UNIVERSITY — 36600 Schoolcraft, Livonia, MI, 48150 (734) 432-5559; fax (734) 432-5393; e-mail nhaldane@madonna.edu; web site www.madonna.edu
Dir. — Neal Haldane
DEPARTMENTS: Journalism-Public Relations Program, 1947
SEQUENCES: Journalism Program: Program is broadly based to include aspects of newspaper, magazine, publicity, graphics, television, photography and advertising production. Video Communications: Aimed at those interested in writing, producing and directing for sing

MICHIGAN STATE UNIVERSITY — College of Communication Arts & Sciences, East Lansing, MI, 48824-1212 (517) 355-3410; fax (517) 432-1244; web site www.cas.msu.edu
Prof./Dir., School of Journalism — Jane Briggs-Bunting
Prof./Dean Brandt Chair, PR — Charles T. Salmon
Prof./Chair, Dept. of Commun. — Charles K. Atkin
Prof./Co-Dir., Quello Ctr. — Johannes M. Bauer
Prof./Dir., MIND Lab — Frank Biocca
Prof. — Howard S. Bossen
Prof. — Franklin Boster
Prof. — Mary Bresnahan
Prof. — Sue Carter
Prof./Chair, Dept. of Adv., PR and Retailing — Richard Cole
Prof./Dir., Media/Information Studies Doctoral Prog. — Lucinda D. Davenport
Prof./Dir., Knight Ctr. — Jim Detjen
Prof. — William A. Donohue
Prof. — Frederick G. Fico
Prof. — Linda Good
Prof. — Carrie J. Heeter
Prof. — Patricia Huddleston
Prof. — Stephen R. Lacy
Prof. — Robert J. Larose
Prof. — Tim Levine
AFFILIATIONS: IABC, KTA, SND, SPJ, WICI, PRSSA
DEGREES:BA- Advertising, Communication, Communicative Sciences and Disorders, Media Arts & Technology, Journalism, Telecommunication; Information Studies and Media; BS in Media & Communication Technology, Retailing; MA- Advertising, Communication, Communicative S

DEPARTMENTS: College of Communication Arts and Sciences, 1955
FACILITIES: AP, AM, FM, CCTV, ComN, CN, DR, ETV, VDT, Knight Center for Environmental Journalism, Quello Center for Telecommunication Management and Law, Health and Risk Communication Center, Games for Entertainment and Learning (GEL) Lab, Digital Media Arts and Tech

OAKLAND UNIVERSITY — Journalism Program, Rochester, MI, 48309-4401 (248) 370-4121; fax (248) 370-4208; e-mail shreve@oakland.edu; web site www.oakland.edu/rcj/jrn
Co-Dir. — Holly Shreve-Gilbert
DEPARTMENTS: Journalism Program, 1978
SEQUENCES: Journalism Program: Professional approach, designed to educate and train reporters, with emphases on print, new media, web, public relations, broadcast and advertising. Mandatory internship. Scholarships available

UNIVERSITY OF DETROIT MERCY — 4001 W. McNichols, Detroit, MI, 48219-0900 (313) 993-1698; fax (313) 993-1166; e-mail bolzbj@udmercy.edu
Chair — Barbara J. Bolz
DEPARTMENTS: Communication Studies Department, 1956
SEQUENCES: Journalism Program: One of the most popular majors of the university, the department has opportunities in electronic broadcasting, communication, public relations/advertising and journalism

UNIVERSITY OF MICHIGAN — Dept. of Communication Studies, Ann Arbor, MI, 48109-1285 (734) 764-0420; fax (734) 764-3288; e-mail comm.studies.dept@umich.edu
Chair — Michael Traugott
Dir., Interdepartmental PhD Prog. — Susan Douglas
AFFILIATIONS: WICI, NABJ
DEGREES:BA, PhD
DEPARTMENTS: Department of Communication Studies, 1926
FACILITIES: AM/FM, AP, CCTV, CN, VDT
SEQUENCES: BA- Communication Studies; PhD (interdepartmental)- Mass Communication

WAYNE STATE UNIVERSITY — Dept. of Communication, Detroit, MI, 48201 (313) 577-2627; fax (313) 577-6300; e-mail aa5200@wayne.edu
Dir. — Benjamin Burns
AFFILIATIONS: SPJ
DEGREES:BA- Major in Journalism
DEPARTMENTS: Journalism Program, Department of Communication, 1948

WESTERN MICHIGAN UNIVERSITY — 1903 W. Michigan St., Kalamazoo, MI, 49008-3805 (269) 387-3148; fax (269) 387-3990; e-mail richard.junger@wmich.edu
Prog. Dir. — Dr. Richard Junger
DEGREES:BA
DEPARTMENTS: Department of Communication and Journalism, 1976
SEQUENCES: Broadcast, News-Editorial, Magazine

MINNESOTA

BEMIDJI STATE UNIVERSITY — 1500 Birchmont Dr., NE, Bemidji, MN, 56601-2699 (218) 755-3358; fax (218) 755-4369; e-mail LMengelkock@bemidjistate.edu
Chair — Louise Mengelkoch
DEGREES:BS
DEPARTMENTS: Department of Mass Communication
SEQUENCES: Mass Communication Program: Offers BS in Mass Communication, with concentrations in print, public relations and broadcast media

MINNESOTA STATE UNIVERSITY MANKATO — 136 Nelson Hall, Mankato, MN, 56001 (507) 389-6417; fax (507) 389-5525; e-mail mass-communications@msus.edu
Chair/Prof. — Charles Lewis
Prof. — Marshel Rossow
Assoc. Prof. — Ellen M. Mrja
Assoc. Prof. — Jane McConnell
Asst. Prof. — John Gaterud
Adj. Fac. — Scott Roemhildt
Adj. Fac. — Shelly Schultz
Adj. Fac. — Pete Steiner
Adj. Fac. — John Cross
Adj. Fac. — Dale Ericson
Adj. Fac. — Carlienne Frisch
Adj. Fac. — Rachael Hanel
Adj. Fac. — Bob McConnell
Adj. Fac. — Joe Tougas
Adj. Fac. — Tim Krohn
Adj. Fac. — Michael Larson
Prof. Emer. — Gladys B. Olson
AFFILIATIONS: SPJ
DEGREES:BA, BS
DEPARTMENTS: Mass Communications Department, 1968
FACILITIES: CN, DR, FM, VDT
SEQUENCES: Journalism, Media Studies and Public Relations

MINNESOTA STATE UNIVERSITY, MOOREHEAD — Mass Communications Dept., Moorhead, MN, 56563 (218) 477-2855; fax (218) 477-4333; e-mail strandm@mnstate.edu
Chair/Prof. — Mark Strand
Prof. — C.T. Hanson
Prof. — Martin Grindeland
Prof. — Wayne Gudmundson
Prof. — Shelton Gunaratne
Assoc. Prof. — William B. Hall
Assoc. Prof. — Dan Johnson
Assoc. Prof. — Camilla Wilson
Asst. Prof. — Jody Mattern
Asst. Prof. — Aaron Quanbeck
Asst. Prof. — Reggie Radniecki
Instr. — Mark Anthony
Instr. — David Arntson
Instr. — Marv Bossart
Instr. — David Christy
Instr. — Liz Conmy
Instr. — Nancy Edmonds Hanson
Instr. — David Howland
Instr. — Jason Hummel
Instr. — Kerstin Kealy
AFFILIATIONS: AAF, PRSSA, SPJ
DEGREES:BS, BA
DEPARTMENTS: Mass Communications Department, 1967
FACILITIES: AP, AM, AdA, CATV, CCTV, CN, ComN, ComR, ComTV, DR, PRA, VDT
SEQUENCES: Advertising, Broadcast Journalism, Photojournalism, Print Journalism, PR, dual major in English/Mass Communications, Integrated Advertising/PR, Online Journalism

ST. CLOUD STATE UNIVERSITY — 720 4th Ave. S, Saint Cloud, MN, 56301-4498 (320) 308-3293; fax (320) 654-5337; e-mail comm@stcloudstate.edu; web site www.stcloudstate.edu/comm/index.html
Chair/Prof. — Roya Akhavan-Majid
Prof./Grad. Prog. Dir. — Niaz Ahmed
Prof. — Marjorie Fish
Prof. — Mark Mills
Prof. — Peter Przytula
Prof./Coord., News Editorial — Michael Vadnie
Assoc. Prof. — Lisa Heinrich
Assoc. Prof./Coord., Broadcast — Gregory Martin
Assoc. Prof./Coord., PR — Gretchen Tiberghien
Asst. Prof. — Marie Dick
Asst. Prof. — Mark Eden
Asst. Prof. — Bill Huntzicker
Asst. Prof. — Ilia Rodriguez
Asst. Prof./Coord., Adv. — Roger Rudolph
Adj. Prof. — Hon. Bernard Bolan
Adj. Prof. — Michael Larson
Adj. Prof. — Mike Knaak
Adj. Prof. — Paul Middlestaedt
Adj. Prof. — Michael Porter
Prof. Emer. — E. Scott Bryce
AFFILIATIONS: AAF, Minn. Newspaper Assoc., PRSSA, SPJ
DEGREES:BS, MS
DEPARTMENTS: Department of Mass Communications, 1972
FACILITIES: AdA, AP, FM, CATV, CN, ComN, DR, PRA, VUT, JN
SEQUENCES: Advertising, Broadcast, News Editorial, Public Relations

ST. MARY'S UNIVERSITY OF MINNESOTA — 700 Terrace Heights, Winona, MN, 55987 (507) 457-1502; fax (507) 457-1633; e-mail dbeckman@smumn.edu
Coord. — Dean Beckman
DEPARTMENTS: Media Communications Program, Department of Social Science.
SEQUENCES: Offers majors in Public Relations, Journalism and Electronic Publishing and minors in Public Relations, Journalism and Electronic Publishing

UNIVERSITY OF MINNESOTA — 111 Murphy Hall, 206 Church St. SE, Minneapolis, MN, 55455-0418 (612) 625-1338; fax (612) 626-8251; e-mail sjmc@umn.edu
Dir./Assoc. Prof. — Albert R. Tims
Prof. — Tsan-Kuo Chang
Prof./Mithun Land Grant Chair in Adv. — John Eighmey
Prof. — Ronald Faber
Prof./Dir., Minnesota Journalism Ctr. — Kathleen Hansen
Silha Prof./Dir., Silha Ctr. — Jane Kirtley
Prof./Cowles Chair — Dan Sullivan
Prof./Dir., Undergrad. Studies — Daniel B. Wackman
Assoc. Prof. — Kenneth Doyle
Assoc. Prof. — Chris Ison
Assoc. Prof. — Mark Pedelty
Assoc. Prof. — Dona Schwartz
Assoc. Prof. — Gary Schwitzer
Assoc. Prof./Dir., Grad. Studies — Brian Southwell
Assoc. Prof./John and Elizabeth Bates Cowles Prof., Journ., Diversity and Equality — Catherine Squires
Asst. Prof. — Miranda Brady
Asst. Prof. — Giovanna Dell'Orto
Asst. Prof. — Jisu Huh
Asst. Prof. — Kathy Roberts Forde
Asst. Prof. — Amy Sanders
AFFILIATIONS: AAF, KTA, NABJ, PRISM, PRSSA, SPJ
DEGREES:BA, MA, PhD
DEPARTMENTS: School of Journalism and Mass Communication, 1924
FACILITIES: AP, CCTV, CN, JM, AM/FM, AdA, VDT, ComN, PRA

UNIVERSITY OF ST. THOMAS — Dept. of Journalism & Mass Communication, Saint Paul, MN, 55105 (612) 962-5250; fax (612) 962-6360; e-mail kebunton@stthomas.edu
Chair/Prof. — Kris Bunton
Prof. — Thomas B. Connery
Prof. — John Cragan
Prof. — Robert L. Craig
Prof. — Mark Neuzil
Prof. — Kevin Sauter
Assoc. Prof. — Bernard Armada
Assoc. Prof. — Carol Bruess
Assoc. Prof. — Mike O'Donnell
Assoc. Prof. — Debra Petersen
Assoc. Prof. — Tim Scully
Asst. Prof. — Betsy Anderson
Asst. Prof. — Craig Bryan
Asst. Prof. — Dina Gavrilos
Asst. Prof. — Stephanie Gelarneault
Asst. Prof. — John Purdy
Asst. Prof. — Ellen Riordan
Asst. Prof. — Wendy Wyatt
Part-time Instr. — Mark Anfinson
Part-time Instr. — Bruce Benidt
AFFILIATIONS: SPJ, PRSSA, Ad Fed
DEGREES:BA
DEPARTMENTS: Department of Communication & Journalism, 1958
FACILITIES: AM, CATV, CCTV, CN, ComN, DR, PRA, VDT
SEQUENCES: Advertising, Broadcasting, News-Editorial, Communication Studies, Public Relations, Media Studies

WINONA STATE UNIVERSITY — Dept. of Mass Communication, Winona, MN, 55987 (507) 457-5474; fax (507) 457-5155; e-mail mscmdept@winona.edu
Chair — Cindy Killion
AFFILIATIONS: AERO, IABC, SCJ, AAF
DEGREES:BA
DEPARTMENTS: Department of Mass Communication, 1981
FACILITIES: AP, FM, CATV, CN, ComN, DR, ETV, JN, VDT
SEQUENCES: Advertising, Broadcast, Journalism, Photojournalism, Public Relations

MISSISSIPPI

ALCORN STATE UNIVERSITY — 1000 ASU Dr., #269, Alcorn State, MS, 39096-7500 (601) 877-6613; fax (601) 877-2213
Chair — Sherlynn Byrd
Prof./Title III Activity Dir./Gen. Mgr., ASU Cable-TV/WPRL-FM — Shafiquir Rahman
Asst. Prof. — Duanne Byrge
Instr./Newsletter Advisor — Terrence Nimor
Instr./Video Supvr./Internship Coord. — Robert Waller
Instr./News Dir., WPRL-FM — Angela Boykin
AFFILIATIONS: ACA, BCCA, PBS-ALSS
DEGREES:BA
DEPARTMENTS: Department of Communications, 1990
FACILITIES: FM, Video production editing facilities, satellite TVRO, electronic newsroom/layout design lab, public access cable channel, TV13
SEQUENCES: Print, Broadcast

DEPARTMENT OF MASS COMMUNICATIONS, RUST COLLEGE — 150 Rust Avenue, Holly Springs, MS, 38635 (662) 252-8000; fax (662) 252-8869; e-mail dmoyo@rustcollege.edu
Department Chair — Debayo R. Moyo
AFFILIATIONS: Rust College
DEGREES:B.A.
DEPARTMENTS: Department of Mass Communications, 1981
FACILITIES: WURC-FM 88.1; RC-TV2; The Rustorian
SEQUENCES: Journalism Programs: Broadcast Journalism (Television/Radio), Print Journalism (Newspaper/Magazine)

JACKSON STATE UNIVERSITY — 1230 Raymond Rd., Jackson, MS, 39217-0990 (601) 979-2151; fax (601) 979-5800; e-mail dwight.e.brooks@jsums.edu; web site www.jsums.edu/jsumasscom/
Chair/Prof. — Dwight Brooks
Assoc. Prof. — Olorundare E. Aworuwa
Assoc. Prof. — Joseph Clive Enos
Asst. Prof. — Li-Jing Chang
Asst. Prof./Coord., Adv. — Andrea Dilworth
Asst. Prof. — Ayana Haaruun
Asst. Prof. — Teresa Taylor
Instr./Dir., Programs — Sunny Smith
Adj. Instr. — Gail H. M. Brown
Adj. Instr. — Riva Brown
Adj. Instr. — Elaina Jackson
Adj. Instr. — Dathan Thigpen
Admin. Asst. — Aly Ash
Sec. — Regina Clay
DEPARTMENTS: Department of Mass Communications
SEQUENCES: Mass Communications: seeks to educate student who can take their place in the leadership of mass communications industries and provide support for the mission of Jackson State University through a cooperative relationship

with local media, businesses, in

MISSISSIPPI STATE UNIVERSITY — 130 McComas Hall, Mississippi State, MS, 39762 (662) 325-3320; fax (662) 325-3210; e-mail jforde@comm.msstate.edu; web site www.comm.msstate.edu
Assoc. Prof./Head — John Forde
DEPARTMENTS: Department of Communication
SEQUENCES: Journalism Program: Offers major in Communication with concentrations in broadcasting, communication studies, journalism, public relations, theatre

MISSISSIPPI UNIVERSITY FOR WOMEN — 1100 College Street, MUW - 1619, Columbus, MS, 39701-5800 (662) 329-7354; fax (662) 329-7250; e-mail mhatton@muw.edu
Chair/Assoc. Prof., Commun. — Martin L. Hatton
DEGREES:BS/BA
DEPARTMENTS: Department of Communication
SEQUENCES: Communication Division: Offers B.S./B.A. in new media convergence

MISSISSIPPI VALLEY STATE UNIV. — 14000 Highway 82 W, Itta Bena, MS, 38941-1400, USA (662) 254-3458; fax (622) 254-6704; e-mail deltadevilsgazettefacad@gmail.com; web site deltadevilsgazette.com
Asst. Prof. — Esin C. Turk
Asst. Prof./Dir., Forensics — Samuel Osunde
Carolyn Gordon
Mr. — Zainul Abedin
DEGREES:BA- Mass Communication, Speech Communication
DEPARTMENTS: Department of Mass Communications, 1994
FACILITIES: Macintosh computer lab; digital photo lab, performing arts theatre; FM radio station, television studio, radio studio(all state-of-the-art)
SEQUENCES: Broadcasting, Journalism, Public Relations, Speech Communication

TOUGALOO COLLEGE — 500 W County Line Rd, Tougaloo, MS, 39174-9700, USA (601) 977-6159; fax (601) 977-6160; e-mail cwhite@tougaloo.eduTeresa Fulgham
Dir. Journ. Program — Colleen White
SEQUENCES: Journalism Program: Course offerings represent a solid foundation in journalistic study in keeping with a liberal arts education. The college newspaper is The Harambee

UNIVERSITY OF MISSISSIPPI — 331 Farley Hall, University, MS, 38677-1848 (662) 915-7146; fax (662) 915-7765; e-mail jebaker@olemiss.edu; web site www.olemiss.edu/depts/Journalism
Prof./Hederman Lectr. — Samir A. Husni
Assoc. Prof. — Jeanni Atkins
Assoc. Prof./Head, Print seq. — Joe Atkins
Assoc. Prof./Grad. Coord. — Carmen Manning-Miller
Assoc. Prof./Talbert Lectr. — Burnis Morris
Asst. Prof. — Ken Boutwell
Asst. Prof./Student Media Dir. — Ralph Braseth
Asst. Prof. — Flora Caldwell
Asst. Prof. — D. Michael Cheers
Asst. Prof. — Charles Raiteri
Asst. Prof./Head, Broadcast seq. — Brad Schultz
Asst. Prof. — Melanie Stone
Asst. Prof. — Kathleen Woodruff Wickham
Instr./Dir., MS Scholastic Press — Robin Street
Prof. Emer. — Jack Bass
Prof. Emer. — Jere Hoar
AFFILIATIONS: AAF, KTA, NABJ, RTNDA, SPJ
DEGREES:BA, MA
DEPARTMENTS: Department of Journalism, 1947
FACILITIES: AP, CATV, CN, FM, VDT
SEQUENCES: Print, Radio/TV (PR, magazine emphases available)

UNIVERSITY OF SOUTHERM MISSISSIPPI — Box 5121, Hattiesburg, MS, 39406-5121 (601) 266-4258; fax (601) 266-6473; e-mail journalism@usm.edu; web site www.usm.edu/mcj
Dir./Prof. School of Mass Commun. and Journ. — Christopher P. Campbell
Prof. — David R. Davies
Prof. — S.M. Mazharul Haque
Prof. — S. Dixon McDowell
Asst. Prof. — Phillip Gentile
Asst. Prof. — Cheryl Jenkins
Asst. Prof. — Keith F. Johnson
Asst. Prof. — Kim LeDuff
Asst. Prof. — Mary Lou Sheffer
Asst. Prof. — Jae-Hwa Shin
Asst. Prof. — Fei Xue
Professor of Practice — Stephen Coleman
Professor of Practice — Gina Gayle
Professor of Practice — Joey Goodsell
Instr./Publication Mgr. — Maggie Williams
Prof. Emer. — Ed Wheeler
Prof. Emer. — Gene Wiggins
Photojournalist-in-Residence — Clarence Williams
AFFILIATIONS: AAF, NABJ, NPPA, PRSSA, SPJ
DEGREES:BA- Advertising, Journalism, Radio-Television-Film; MA, MS- Communication with Mass Communication Emphasis; MS- Public Relations; PhD- Communication with Mass Communication emphasis
DEPARTMENTS: School of Mass Communication and Journalism, 2001
FACILITIES: AdA, AP, CCTV, DR, FM, JN, PRA, VDT
SEQUENCES: Emphasis Areas: Advertising; Journalism (News/Editorial, News/Editorial with Photojournalism Concentration, Public Relations); Radio, Television, and Film (Broadcast Journalism, Film, Radio/Television Production)

MISSOURI

COLLEGE OF THE OZARKS — Dept. of Mass Communication, Point Lookout, MO, 65726 (417) 690-3458; e-mail schroeder@cofo.edu
Contact — Jared Schroeder
DEGREES:BA, BS
DEPARTMENTS: Department of Mass Communication
SEQUENCES: Emphases in Journalism, Video Production and Radio/Sound Production.

CULVER-STOCKTON COLLEGE — 1 College Hl, Canton, MO, 63435-1257, USA (573) 231-6371; fax (573) 231-6611; e-mail swiegenstein@culver.edu; web site www.culver.eduJoy Daggs
Journalism/PR Head — Steve Wiegenstein
Interpersonal Head — Bob Paige
DEPARTMENTS: Communication Department
SEQUENCES: Communication Program: A general communication education in a liberal arts setting. Students may choose among three interdisciplinary tracks: interpersonal communication, journalism, and public relations

EVANGEL UNIVERSITY — 1111 N Glenstone Ave, Springfield, MO, 65802-2125, USA (417) 865-2815; e-mail evangellance@gmail.com; web site http://www.evangellance.comMelinda Booze
DEPARTMENTS: Department of Communication (with an emphasis in either journalism, communication studies, or electronic media)
SEQUENCES: Journalism Program: Includes a major, minor and concentration in the field; a secondary education major is also offered.

LINCOLN UNIVERSITY — Dept. of Humanities, MSC03 2240, Jefferson City, MO, 65102 (573) 681-5280; fax (573) 681-5438; e-mail govangd@lincolnu.edu
Dept. Head/Assoc. Prof. — Don Govang
Asst. Prof. — Ted Jacobs
Asst. Prof. — Art Fulcher
Part-time Fac. — Leslie Cross
Part-time Fac. — Tom Cwynar
DEGREES:BA, BS
DEPARTMENTS: Department of Humanities, Fine Arts and Journalism Program, 1942

LINDENWOOD UNIVERSITY — 209 S. Kingshighway St., Saint Charles, MO, 63301 (314) 949-4835; fax (314) 949-4910; e-mail jwilson@lindenwood.edu
Dean — Jim Wilson
DEPARTMENTS: Communications Division, 1948
SEQUENCES: Journalism Program: Majors offered in Corporate Communication and Mass Communication (emphases in Radio/TV, PR, Multimedia, Journalism, Industrial Communication, Sports Information, or Communication Management Sales)

MARYVILLE UNIVERSITY — 13550 Conway Rd., Saint Louis, MO, 63141 (314) 529-9473; fax (314) 542-9085; e-mail gboy@maryville.edu
PhD — Gerald Boyer
DEPARTMENTS: Communications Program
SEQUENCES: Communications Program: Students specialize in one of three areas offered through courses and/or internships: Public Communication, Business/Marketing Communication, or Broadcasting

MISSOURI SOUTHERN UNIVERSITY — 3950 Newman Rd, Joplin, MO, 64801-1512, USA (417) 625-9823; fax (417) 625-9585; e-mail chart@mssu.edu; web site www.thechartonline.com
Head — J.R. Moorman
Chad Stebbins
T.R. Hanrahan
Alexandra Nicolas
DEPARTMENTS: Department of Communications, 1980
SEQUENCES: Communications Program: Offers majors with options in mass communications, public relations, speech communication, and international communication. The department publishes a weekly student newspaper and student magazine and operates a cable television s

MISSOURI STATE UNIVERSITY — 901 S. National Ave., Springfield, MO, 65804 (417) 836-5218; fax (417) 836-4637; e-mail mjf@missouristate.edu
Head/Prof. — Karen Buzzard
Prof. — Arlen Diamond
Prof. — Thomas Dickson
Prof. — Mark Paxton
Prof. — Joel Persky
Assoc. Prof. — Mark Biggs
Assoc. Prof. — Jaime Bihlmeyer
Assoc. Prof. — Weiyan Wang
Assoc. Prof. — Timothy White
Asst. Prof. — Andrew Cline
Asst. Prof. — Deborah Larson
Asst. Prof. — Mary Jane Pardue
Instr. — Cheryl Hellmann
Lectr. — Jack Dimond
AFFILIATIONS: AER, AWC, IABC, PR Club
DEGREES:BA, BS
DEPARTMENTS: Department of Media, Journalism and Film, 1971
FACILITIES: FM, CN, ComN, ComTV, DR, PRA, VDT
SEQUENCES: Journalism (Print and Broadcast); Film Studies, Media Operations, Media Production, Digital Film Production, Screenwriting and Electronic Arts.

MISSOURI WESTERN STATE COLLEGE — SS/C 208, Saint Joseph, MO, 64507 (816) 271-4310; fax (816) 271-4543; e-mail klr9015@griffon.mwsc.edu
Chair — Ken Rosenauer
DEGREES:BA
DEPARTMENTS: Department of English, Foreign Languages, and Journalism, 1973
SEQUENCES: Journalism Program: Offers a journalism minor and three BAs in English, with emphases in public realations, writing, and technical communications. Produce a weekly newspaper, a yearbook and an annual literary publication.

NORTHWEST MISSOURI STATE UNIVERSITY — 800 University Dr., Wells Hall #237, Maryville, MO, 64468-6001 (660) 562-1361; fax (660) 562-1947; e-mail jerryd@mail.nwmissouri.edu
Chair — Jerry Donnelly
DEPARTMENTS: Department of Mass Communication
SEQUENCES: Journalism Program: Programs in Mass Media, Broadcast Journalism, Media Advertising, Public Relations and Print Journalism

SAINT LOUIS UNIVERSITY — 3733 W. Pine Blvd., Xavier Hall 300, Saint Louis, MO, 63108 (314) 977-3191; fax (314) 977-3195; e-mail commdept@slu.edu
Chair/Prof. — Kathleen Farrell
Prof. — Rob Anderson
Prof./Ed., Boulevard Magazine — Richard Burgin
Prof./Dir., Political Journ. — Avis Meyer
Prof. — William Tyler
Assoc. Prof. — Liese Hutchison
Assoc. Prof. — Robert Krizek
Assoc. Prof. — Karla Scott
Assoc. Prof. — Paaige Turner
Asst. Prof. — Angela Beattie
Asst. Prof. — Matt Carlson
Asst. Prof. — Dan Kozlowski
Asst. Prof. — Jennifer Ohs
Asst. Prof. — Elizabeth Richard
Asst. Prof. — Gary Seibert
Asst. Prof. — Robert Stahl
Asst. Prof. — April Trees
AFFILIATIONS: AAF
DEGREES:BA, MA, MA (Research)
DEPARTMENTS: Department of Communication, 1976
FACILITIES: AdA, CN, VDT
SEQUENCES: Communication Professions, Communication Technology

SOUTHEAST MISSOURI STATE UNIVERSITY — Dept. of Mass Communication, Cape Girardeau, MO, 63701-2750 (573) 651-2241; fax (573) 651-5967; e-mail masscomm@semo.edu
Prof. — Tamara Baldwin
Prof. — James Dufek
Prof. — Susan Gonders
Prof. — Bruce Mims
Prof. — Mike Weatherson
Assoc. Prof. — Larry Underberg
Assoc. Prof. — Glen Williams
Asst. Prof. — Karie Hollerbach
Asst. Prof. — Fred Jones
Asst. Prof. — Don Jung
Asst. Prof. — Roy Keller
Instr. — Karen Kight
Instr. — Cindie Jeter-Yanow
Instr. — Roger Stout
Instr. — Jennifer Summary
Instr. — Roseanna Whitlow
Instr. — Tamara Zellers-Buck
Adj. Fac. — Brooke Clubbs
Adj. Fac. — Kara Cracraft
Adj. Fac. — Ellen Dillon
AFFILIATIONS: AAF, PRSSA, SPJ, MCA-I/ITVA, NBS, Missouri Broadcasters Assn., Missouri Press Assn
DEGREES:BA, BS
DEPARTMENTS: Department of Mass Communication, 1983
FACILITIES: FM, CATV, CCTV, DR, JM, JN
SEQUENCES: Advertising, Communication Studies, Corporate Communication, Journalism, Media Studies, PR, Radio,

Speech Education, Video Production

STEPHENS COLLEGE — 1200 E. Broadway, Columbia, MO, 65215 (573) 876-7133; fax (314) 876-7248; e-mail johnb@stephens.edu
Chair — John S. Blakemore
AFFILIATIONS: APR
DEPARTMENTS: Mass Communication Department (TV-Radio-Journalism-Public Relations)
SEQUENCES: Journalism Program: Mass Communication major with choice of three emphases: Broadcast Media Production, Journalism or Public Relations. Mass Communication minors in Broadcast Media Production, Journalism, Public Relations

TRUMAN STATE UNIVERSITY — Communication Dept., Kirksville, MO, 63501 (660) 785-4481; fax (660) 785-7486; e-mail heinz@truman.edu
Contact — Heinz D. Woehlk
AFFILIATIONS: IABC, SPJ
DEGREES:BA
DEPARTMENTS: Language and Literature Division, 1974
FACILITIES: AP, CCTV, CN, ComN, ComR, ComTV, DR, PRA, VDT
SEQUENCES: Journalism, Speech Comm.

UNIVERSITY OF CENTRAL MISSOURI — Dept. of Communication, Warrensburg, MO, 64093 (660) 543-4840; fax (660) 543-8006; e-mail fair@umco.edu
Chair — Charles Fair
AFFILIATIONS: BEA, PRSSA, SPJ, Missouri Broadcasters Assoc., Missouri Press Assoc., UFVA.
DEGREES:BA, BS, BSE (teacher certification), MA
DEPARTMENTS: Department of Communication
FACILITIES: FM, CATV, ComN, ComR, CornTV, DR, ETV, JM, JN, PRA, VDT, Digital TV.
SEQUENCES: Mass Communication, Broadcasting and Film, Public Relations, Print Journalism (News Editorial)

UNIVERSITY OF MISSOURI — School of Journalism, Columbia, MO, 65211 (573) 882-6686; fax (573) 884-8989
Dean/Prof. — Dean Mills
Prof./Knight Chair in Editing — Jacqui Banaszynski
Prof./Harte Chair in Innovation — Judy Bolch
Prof./Assoc. Dean, Undergrad. Studies and Admin. — Brian Brooks
Prof./Maxine Wilson Gregory Chair in Journ. Research — Glen Cameron
Prof. — Brant Houston
Prof. — Stuart Loory
Prof. — Daryl Moen
Prof. — Geneva Overholser
Prof. — Byron Scott
Prof. — Zoe Smith
Prof. — Martha Steffens
Prof. — James Sterling
Prof./Assoc. Dean, Grad. Studies/Research — Esther Thorson
Prof. — Wayne Wanta
Prof. — Steve Weinberg
Prof. — Lee Wilkins
Prof. — Betty Winfield
Assoc. Prof. — Clyde Bentley
Assoc. Prof. — Mary Kay Blakely
AFFILIATIONS: AAF, BEA, IABC, KAM, KTA, PRSSA, SPJ
DEGREES:BJ, MA, PhD
DEPARTMENTS: School of Journalism, 1908
FACILITIES: AdA, AM/FM, AP, ComN, Corn TV, DR, ETV, JM, VDT
SEQUENCES: Advertising, Broadcast News, Magazine, News-Editorial, Photojournalism

UNIVERSITY OF MISSOURI-KANSAS CITY — 202 Haag Hall, 5120 Rockhill Rd., Kansas City, MO, 64110 (816) 235-1337; fax (816) 235-5539; e-mail com-s@umkc.edu
Chair/Assoc. Prof. — Carol Koehler
Prof. — Michael R. Neer
Prof. — Robert Unger
Assoc. Prof. — G.Thomas Poe
Assoc. Prof. — Peter Morello
Assoc. Prof. — Greg Gutenko
Asst. Prof. — Caitlin Horsmon
Asst. Prof. — Michael McDonald
Instr., Radio — Angela Elam
Instr. — Linda H. Kurz
Instr. — Judith K. McCoromick
Prof. Emer. — Gaylord Marr
Prof. Emer. — Gregory D. Black
Prof. Emer. — Joan E. Aitken
Prof. Emer. — Larry G. Ehrlich
Prof. Emer. — Robin League
AFFILIATIONS: SCA, PRSA
DEGREES:BA
DEPARTMENTS: Department of Communication Studies, 1972
FACILITIES: AM/FM, CN, DR, AdA, PRA
SEQUENCES: Communication Studies program offers emphasis in Journalism and Mass Communication, Interpersonal and Public Communication or Film and Media Arts

UNIVERSITY OF MISSOURI-ST. LOUIS — 1 University Blvd., 235 GSB, Saint Louis, MO, 63121 (314) 516-5496; fax (314) 516-5816; e-mail murraymd@umsl.edu
UM Board of Curators' Distinguished Prof. — Michael D. Murray
DEPARTMENTS: Mass Communication, 1982
SEQUENCES: Journalism Program: Undergraduate degree (BS in Media Studies). Minor in Public Affairs Reporting

WEBSTER UNIV. — 470 E Lockwood Ave, Saint Louis, MO, 63119-3141, USA (314) 961-2660; fax (314) 968-7059; e-mail wujournal@gmail.com; web site www.webujournal.com
Journ. Seq. — Don Corrigan
Kelly Kendall
DEPARTMENTS: Department of Journalism/ Media Communications Department, 1977
SEQUENCES: Journalism Program: Department is heavy on print/community newspaper orientation. Media program offers photojournalism, audio recording, video production, radio, and cable television access. Also offers media courses on Vienna and Leiden campuses. Grad

MONTANA

THE UNIVERSITY OF MONTANA — 32 Campus Dr., Missoula, MT, 59812-0648 (406) 243-4001; e-mail peggy.kuhr@umontana.edu; web site www.umt.edu/journalism
Dean — Peggy Kuhr
Prof. — Carol Van Valkenburg
Prof. — Dennis Swibold
Prof. — Clem Work
Assoc. Prof. — Ray Ekness
Assoc. Prof. — Keith Graham
Assoc. Prof. — Denise Dowling
Asst. Prof. — Ray Fanning
Asst. Prof. — Jeremy Lurgio
Asst. Prof. — Nadia White
Prof. Emer. — Nathaniel Blumberg
Prof. Emer. — Charles Hood
Prof. Emer. — Greg MacDonald
Prof. Emer. — Robert McGiffert
Prof. Emer. — Bill Knowles
Prof. Emer. — Jerry E. Brown
Prof. Emer. — Sharon Barrett
Adj. Instr. — Printer Bowler
Adj. Instr. — Gus Chambers
Adj. Instr. — Jeff Hull
DEGREES:BA, MA
DEPARTMENTS: School of Journalism, 1914
FACILITIES: AM/FM, AP, CCTV, CN, ComN, COMTV, DR, ETV, JM, VDT
SEQUENCES: Print, Photojournalism/ Multi-media, Broadcast News, Broadcast Production

NEBRASKA

CREIGHTON UNIV. — 2500 California Plz, Omaha, NE, 68178-0133, USA (402) 280-4058; fax (402) 280-1494; e-mail emw@creighton.edu; web site www.creightonian.comMelissa Hillebrand
Chair/Prof. — Eileen M. Wirth
Prof./Charles and Mary Heider Endowed Jesuit Chair — Father Don Doll
Kelly Fitzgerald
Assoc. Prof. — Timothy S. Guthrie
Assoc. Prof. — Jeffrey Maciejewski
Assoc. Prof. — Carol Zuegner
Asst. Prof. — Kristoffer Boyle
Asst. Prof. — Joel Davies
Asst. Prof. — Charles Heider
Asst. Prof. — Mary Heider
Lectr. — Andrew Hughes
Lectr. — Kathleen Hughes
Lectr. — Richard Janda
Lectr. — Kathryn Larson
Lectr. — Brian Norton
Lectr. — Wendy Wiseman
Lectr. — Angela Zegers
AFFILIATIONS: AAF, AER, PRSSA, SPJ
DEGREES:BA, BS
DEPARTMENTS: Department of Journalism and Mass Communication, 1924
FACILITIES: AdA, CN, ComN, ComR, ComTV, DR, PRA, VDT
SEQUENCES: News, Photojournalism, Public Relations, Advertising, Digital/New Media, Graphic Design

HASTINGS COLLEGE — 710 N. Turner, Hastings, NE, 68901 (402) 461-7460; fax (402) 461-7442
Chair — Jack Kramer
DEPARTMENTS: Department of Communication Arts/Business and Economics
SEQUENCES: Journalism Program: Communication Arts major with four possible emphases: advertising and public relations, broadcast journalism, print journalism and new media

UNIVERSITY OF NEBRASKA AT OMAHA — Arts & Sciences Hall 108, 6001 Dodge St., Omaha, NE, 68182-0012 (402) 554-2600; fax (204) 554-3836; e-mail jlipschultz@mail.unomaha.edu
Dean/Prof. — Gail F. Baker
Dir./Prof. — Jeremy Harris Lipschultz
Prof./Asst. Dir. — Shereen Bingham
Grad. Chair/Assoc. Prof. — Barbara Pickering
Prof. — Robert Carlson
Reilly Prof./Basic Course Dir. — Karen Dwyer
Prof./Asst. Dean — Michael Hilt
Prof./Sr. Vice Chancellor — Terry Hynes
Prof./Kayser Prof. — Bruce Johansen
Prof. — Marshall Prisbell
Prof. — Michael Sherer
Prof./Grad. Dean/Assoc. Vice Chancellor — Deborah Smith-Howell
Assoc. Prof. — Chris Allen
Assoc. Prof. — Teresa Lamsam
Assoc. Prof. — David Ogden
Assoc. Prof./Internship Coord. — Hugh Reilly
Assoc. Prof. — Randall Rose
Assoc. Prof./Media Writing Coord. — Sherrie Wilson
Asst. Prof. — Ana Cruz
Asst. Prof./GM, UNO TV & KVNO-FM — Robert Franklin
AFFILIATIONS: Ad Club, ASTD, BEA, KTA, NBS, PRSSA, Studies in Media & Information Literacy Education (SIMILE), SPJ
DEGREES:BAC, BSC, MA
DEPARTMENTS: School of Communication 2004, College of Communication, Fine Arts and Media 2005
FACILITIES: FM, AdA, CATV, CN, ComN, ComR, ComTV, DR, ETV, PRA, VDT
SEQUENCES: Broadcasting (News or New Media), Journalism (News-Editorial or Public Relations/Advertising or Media Studies), Speech Communication, Communication (MA)

UNIVERSITY OF NEBRASKA-KEARNEY — Mitchell Ctr. 146, Kearney, NE, 68849 (308) 865-8249; fax (308) 865-1537; e-mail lawsong@unk.edu
Chair — George Lawson
DEPARTMENTS: Department of Communication
SEQUENCES: Broadcast Program: Specialization offered in Broadcasting. Journalism Program: Specializations offered in News-Editorial, Advertising, Public Relations, Sports Communication, Mass Media and Multimedia. Speech Program: Specializations offered in Speec

UNIVERSITY OF NEBRASKA-LINCOLN — 200 Centennial Mall N., 147 Andersen Hall, Lincoln, NE, 68588-0443 (402) 472-3041; fax (402) 472-8597; e-mail wnorton1@unl.edu
Dean/Prof. — Will Norton
Prof. — Charlyne Berens
Prof. — Laurie Thomas Lee
Prof. — Nancy Mitchell
Prof. — Jan Poley
Prof. — James Randall
Prof. — Jerry Renaud
Prof./Assoc. Dean — Linda Shipley
Prof. — Joe Starita
Prof. — Larry Walklin
Prof. — John Wunder
Assoc. Prof. — Tim Anderson
Assoc. Prof. — John Bender
Assoc. Prof. — Susan Burzynski Bullard
Assoc. Prof. — Carla Kimbrough
Assoc. Prof. — Frauke Hachtmann
Assoc. Prof. — Barney McCoy
Assoc. Prof. — Mary Kay Quinlan
Assoc. Prof. — Bruce Thorson
Vstg. Assoc. Prof. — Ruth Brown
AFFILIATIONS: AAF, AER, APME, ASNE, KTA, NAB, NBA, NPA, PRSSA, SPJ
DEGREES:BJ, MA
DEPARTMENTS: College of Journalism and Mass Communications, 1917
FACILITIES: AP, AM/FM, CCTV, CN, CATV, DR, JM, JN, VDT
SEQUENCES: Majors: Advertising, Broadcasting, News-Editorial

NEVADA

UNIVERSITY OF NEVADA, LAS VEGAS — 4505 S Maryland Pkwy, # 2011, Las Vegas, NV, 89154-9900, USA (702) 895-2028; fax (702) 895-1515; e-mail chief.freepress@unlv.edu; web site www.unlvfreepress.com
Adviser — Rick Velotta
Editor-in-Chief — Bianca Cseke
Managing Editor — Blaze Lovell
Director of Marketing & Sales — Nicole Gallego
AFFILIATIONS: College of Urban Affairs
DEGREES:BA, MA.
DEPARTMENTS: Hank Greenspun School of Journalism and Media Studies, 1976. IABC, SPJ.
FACILITIES: AdA, KUNV Radio (NPR), CN, RPA, VDT, computerized writing labs (Mac & PC), TV studios, cable channel
SEQUENCES: Areas of Concentration: Broadcast Journalism, Print Journalism, Integrated Marketing Communications (IMC), Media Studies.

UNIVERSITY OF NEVADA-RENO — Mail Stop 310, Reno, NV, 89557-0310 (775) 784-6531; fax (775) 784-6656; e-mail journalism@nevada.edu; web site journalism.unr.edu
Dean — Jerry Ceppos
Prof./Endowed Chair — Larry Dailey
Prof./Endowed Chair — Ed Lenert
Prof. — Jake Highton
Prof. — Saundra Keyes

Prof. — Warren Lerude
Prof. — Bourne Morris
Assoc. Prof. — Howard Goldbaum
Assoc. Prof./Grad. Studies Dir. — Donica Mensing
Assoc. Prof. — David Ryfe
Asst. Prof. — Bob Felten
Asst. Prof. — Todd Felts
Lectr. — Deidre Pike
Prof. Emer. — Theodore Conover
Prof. Emer. — James Ellis
Prof. Emer. — Joseph Howland
Adm. Fac. — Kristin Burgarello
Adm. Fac/Dir., Devel./Coord., Recruiting/ Retention — Paul Mitchell
AFFILIATIONS: AAF, BEA, SPJ, KTA, RTNDA, PRSSA
DEGREES:BA, MA
DEPARTMENTS: Donald W. Reynolds School Journalism, 1921
FACILITIES: FM, AdA, CATV, CN, ComN, ComTV, JM, PRA, VDT
SEQUENCES: Emphases: Print and Online Journalism, Broadcast Journalism, Advertising, Public Relations, Integrated Marketing Communications, Interactive Environmental MA. Program.

NEW HAMPSHIRE

KEENE STATE COLLEGE OF THE UNIVERSITY SYSTEM OF NEW HAMPSHIRE — 229 Main St., Keene, NH, 03435-1402 (603) 358-2724; fax (603) 358-2138
Prof. — Rose Kundanis
Assoc. Prof. — David Payson
Asst. Prof. — Marianne Salcetti
Asst. Prof. — Mark Timney
Staff. — Craig Brandon
DEGREES:BA
DEPARTMENTS: Journalism Major (in Division of Arts and Humanities), 1975.
FACILITIES: AP, FM, CCTV, CN, ComN, DR, JM, VDT
SEQUENCES: Journalism with courses in print and broadcast journalism

SOUTHERN NEW HAMPSHIRE UNIVERSITY — 2500 N. River Rd., 3100 Cleburne St., Manchester, NH, 03106-1045 (603) 668-2211; fax (603) 645-9779; e-mail a.kubilius@snhu.edu
Chair — Ausra Kubilius
DEGREES:BA
DEPARTMENTS: Department of Communications.
SEQUENCES: Communication major with sequences in journalism, public relations, video producation. Also majors in digital media and graphic design. Emphasis on liberal arts and internships

UNIVERSITY OF NEW HAMPSHIRE — 104 Hamilton Smith Hall, Durham, NH, 3824, USA (603) 862-0251; fax (603) 862-3563; e-mail lcm@cisunix.unh.edu
Dir. — Lisa Miller
DEGREES:Bachelor's in English/Journalism. Graduate degree offered: master's in nonfiction writing.
DEPARTMENTS: English/Journalism major
SEQUENCES: Undergraduate Journalism Program: Newswriting, feature writing, editing, magazine writing taught and internships supervised by journalists on English Department faculty

NEW JERSEY

FAIRLEIGH DICKINSON UNIVERSITY — School of Commun. Arts, Teaneck, NJ, 7666 (201) 692-2415; fax (201) 692-2081
Dir. — Bernard F. Dick
DEGREES:BA, MA
DEPARTMENTS: School of Communication Arts, 1973
SEQUENCES: Communication Program: BA Sequences- Advertising/Public Relations, Journalism, Film and Television; MA- Corporate and Organizational Communication

RIDER UNIVERSITY — Dept. of Communications, Lawrenceville, NJ, 8648 (609) 896-5089; fax (609) 895-5772; e-mail schwartzh@enigma.rider.edu
Chair — Howard Schwartz
AFFILIATIONS: SPJ
DEPARTMENTS: Department of Communications, 1934.
FACILITIES: VDT, FM, AP, Microcomputer, SPJ, RTV
SEQUENCES: Journalism Program: News-editorial, PR; emphasis on internships; multi-media

ROWAN UNIV. — 201 Mullica Hill Rd, Glassboro, NJ, 08028-1700, USA (856) 256-4713; fax (856) 256-4929; e-mail communication@rowan.edu; web site www.thewhitonline.com
Prof. — Don Bagin
Kathryn Quigley
Prof. — R. Michael Donovan
Prof. — Anthony Fulginiti
Prof. — Richard Grupenhoff
Prof. — Kenneth Kaleta
Prof. — Janice Rowan
Prof. — Edward Streb
Assoc. Prof. — Julia Chang
Assoc. Prof. — Cynthia Corison
Assoc. Prof. — Edgar Eckhardt
Assoc. Prof. — Suzanne Fitzgerald
Assoc. Prof. — Carl Hausman
Assoc. Prof. — Martin Itzkowitz
Assoc. Prof. — Frances Johnson
Assoc. Prof. — Diane Penrod
Assoc. Prof. — Donald Stoll
Assoc. Prof. — Sanford Tweedie
Asst. Prof. — Kenneth Albone
Asst. Prof. — Lorin Arnold
AFFILIATIONS: Advertising Club, PRSSA
DEGREES:BA, MA, MA (Masters in Writing, Masters in Public Relations)
DEPARTMENTS: College of Communication, 1996
FACILITIES: CCTV, CN, FM Radio, JM, VDT
SEQUENCES: Advertising, Journalism, Radio/TV/Film, Public Relations, Communication Studies, Writing Arts

RUTGERS UNIVERSITY — 4 Huntington St., New Brunswick, NJ, 8903 (732) 932-7500; fax (732) 932-1523; e-mail jpavlik@rutgers.edu
Chair/Prof. — John Pavlik
Prof. — Robert Kubey
Prof. — Linda Steiner
Assoc. Prof. — Montague Kern
Assoc. Prof. — William Solomon
Assoc. Prof. — Barbara Straus Reed
Asst. Prof. — Jack Bratich
Asst. Prof. — David Greenberg
Asst. Prof. — Susan Keith
Asst. Prof. — Deepa Kumar
Asst. Prof. — Regina Marchi
Instr. — Steven Miller
Prof. Emer. — Jerome Aumente
Prof. Emer. — Roger Cohen
Prof. Emer. — Thomas B. Hartmann
University Prof. — Richard Heffner
Adj. Fac. — Guy Baehr
Adj. Fac. — Tom Cafferty
Adj. Fac. — Nat Clymer
Adj. Fac. — Benjamin Davis
AFFILIATIONS: SCILS
DEGREES:BA
DEPARTMENTS: Department of Journalism and Mass Media Studies, 1925
FACILITIES: FM, CN, ComN, VDT, ETV, AdA
SEQUENCES: News-Editorial, Broadcast Journalism, Mass Media and Government, Media Studies

RUTGERS UNIVERSITY-NEWARK — Hill Hall Room 501, Newark, NJ, 7102 (973) 353-5279; fax (973) 353-1450; e-mail engnwk@andromeda.Rutgers.edu
Chair. — Virginia Tiger
DEPARTMENTS: Rutgers Newark English Department, 1975

SETON HALL UNIVERSITY — 400 S. Orange Ave., South Orange, NJ, 7079 (973) 761-9474; e-mail readerpe@shu.edu
Chair. — Peter Reader
DEGREES:BA
DEPARTMENTS: Department of Communicaton
SEQUENCES: Journalism Program: BA program with News/Editorial sequence. Courses in broadcasting, print graphics, computer graphics and public relations

WILLIAM PATERSON UNIVERSITY — Hobart Hall, 300 Pompton Rd., Wayne, NJ, 7470 (973) 720-2150; fax (973) 720-2483; e-mail leej67@upunj.edu
Chair. — Joann Lee
DEPARTMENTS: Communication Department.

NEW MEXICO

EASTERN NEW MEXICO UNIVERSITY — Dept. of Communicative Arts & Sciences, Portales, NM, 88130 (505) 562-2130; fax (505) 562-2847; e-mail janet.roehl@enmu.edu; web site www.unm.ed/~cjdept
DEPARTMENTS: Department of Communicative Arts and Sciences, 1972
SEQUENCES: Journalism Program: Offers a major and a minor degree in journalism. Stresses reporting, editing, visual communication, online communication, and law and ethics

NEW MEXICO HIGHLANDS UNIVERSITY — Dept. of English, Speech & Journalism, Box 9000, Las Vegas, NM, 87701 (505) 425-7511; fax (505) 454-3389; e-mail linderpeter@nmhu.edu
Chair — Peter Linder
DEPARTMENTS: Department of English, Speech and Journalism of the Humanities Div.
SEQUENCES: Journalism Program: Offers major course work with emphasis on news-editorial

NEW MEXICO STATE UNIVERSITY — Dept. 3J, Box 30001, Las Cruces, NM, 88003-8001 (505) 646-1034; fax (505) 646-1255; e-mail nanhowel@nmsu.edu
Interim Head — Anne Hubbell
Prof. — J. Sean McCleneghan
Assoc. Prof. — Hwiman Chung
Asst. Prof. — Bruce Berman
Asst. Prof. — Mary Lamonica
Asst. Prof. — Roger Mellen
Asst. Prof. — Frank Thayer
College Fac. — Pam Porter
Instr. — Ralph Escandon
Instr. — Colin Gromatazky
Instr. — Carrie Hamblen
Instr. — J.D. Jarvis
Instr. — Bob Nosbisch
Instr. — Michael Olson
Instr. — Hugo Perez
Instr. — Ronald Salak
Instr. — Charles Scholz
Instr. — Ricardo Trujillo
Instr. — Krista West
Instr. — Gary Worth
AFFILIATIONS: NAB, BEA, NPR, PBS, NPPA, NMPA, AAF, NMBA, SPJ
DEGREES:BA
DEPARTMENTS: Department of Journalism and Mass Communications, 1963
FACILITIES: AP, NPR-FM, PBS-TV, CN, ComN, DR, VDT
SEQUENCES: Concentrations: Advertising, Broadcasting, News-Editorial, Photojournalism, Public Relations

UNIVERSITY OF NEW MEXICO — Dept. of Communication & Journalism, Albuquerque, NM, 87131-0001 (505) 277-5305; fax (505) 277-4206; e-mail cjdept@unm.edu
Chair — John Oetzel
AFFILIATIONS: SPJ
DEGREES:BA
DEPARTMENTS: Department of Communication and Journalism, 1948
FACILITIES: CN, ComN, ComR, ComTV, DR, VDT, FM, ETV, AdA, AP
SEQUENCES: Broadcast Journalism, Print Journalism, PR, Advertising

NEW YORK

BUFFALO STATE COLLEGE — 1300 Elmwood Ave., Bishop 210, Buffalo, NY, 14222 (716) 878-6008; fax (716) 878-4697; e-mail smithrd@buffalostate.edu; web site www.buffalostate.edu/communication
Chair — Ronald D. Smith
AFFILIATIONS: PRSSA, SPJ
DEGREES:BA
DEPARTMENTS: Department of Communication, 1975
FACILITIES: FM, AdA, CCTV, CN, ComN, ComTV, PRA, VDT
SEQUENCES: Journalism (print/online news and broadcast news); Broadcasting (television production and radio production); Public Communication (public relations and advertising); Communication Studies

CANISIUS COLLEGE — 2001 Main St, Buffalo, NY, 14208-1035, USA (716) 888-2115; fax (716) 888-3118; e-mail Irwin@canisius.edu
Professor of Communications — Barbara Irwin
Eric Koehler
Jennifer Gorczynski
Marisa Loffredo
DEGREES:BS, BA
DEPARTMENTS: Department of Communication Studies
SEQUENCES: Communication Studies: Sequences in Journalism and Media Studies, Advertising and Public Relations and Interpersonal and Organization Communication. Digital Media Arts featuring graphic design and interactive multimedia

COLUMBIA UNIVERSITY — 2950 Broadway, Mail Code 3800, New York, NY, 10027 (212) 854-8608; fax (212) 854-2352; e-mail admissions@journalism.columbia.edu; web site www.journalism.columbia.edu
Prof. — Helen Benedict
Prof. — Ann Cooper
Prof. — Sheila Coronel
Prof. — Tom Edsall
Prof. — Samuel G. Freedman
Prof. — Todd Gitlin
Prof. — Ari Goldman
Prof. — David Klatell
Prof. — Nicholas Lemann
Prof. — Sylvia Nasar
Prof. — Stephen Isaacs
Prof./Dir., Nat'l Arts Journalism Prog. — Michael Janeway
Prof. — Victor Navasky
Prof. — Michael Schudson
Prof. — James B. Stewart
Prof. — Michael Shapiro
Prof. — Alexander Stille
Prof. — Richard Wald
Prof. — Jonathan Weiner
Assoc. Prof. — John Dinges
AFFILIATIONS: NABJ, SAJA, SPJ
DEGREES:MSJ, MAJ, PhD
DEPARTMENTS: Graduate School of Journalism, 1912
FACILITIES: AP, JM, JN, CCTV, VDT
SEQUENCES: Newspaper Journalism, Broadcast Journalism, Magazine Journalism,

New Media

CORNELL UNIVERSITY — 337 Kennedy Hall, Ithaca, NY, 14853-4203 (607) 255-2601; fax (607) 254-1322; e-mail dyd1@cornell.edu
Chair — Geraldine K. Gay
AFFILIATIONS: PRSSA, WICI
DEGREES:BS, MS, PHD
DEPARTMENTS: Department of Communication, 1945
SEQUENCES: Communication Program: Comprehensive communication program with emphases in communication in the life sciences, communication planning and evaluation, and communication & technology at the undergraduate level, with social psychology of communication, uses

CUNY GRADUATE SCHOOL OF JOURNALISM — 230 W. 41st St., 4th Fl., New York, NY, 10036 (646) 758-7800; fax (646) 758-7809; web site journalism.cuny.edu
Dean — Stephen Shepard
DEGREES:MA
DEPARTMENTS: School of Journalism, 2006
SEQUENCES: The only publicly funded graduate school of journalism in the northeastern U.S., it offers a three-semester Master of Arts program that equips students to work in multi-media newsrooms and to report in the specialty areas. The Master of Arts degree in jo

FORDHAM UNIVERSITY — Rose Hill Campus, Bronx, NY, 10458 (718) 817-4863; fax (718) 817-4868; e-mail paullevinson1@cs.com
Chair — Paul Levinson
DEPARTMENTS: Department of Communications and Media Studies
SEQUENCES: Journalism Program: A comprehensive Liberal Arts program including communications theory and practice, leading to undergraduate and graduate degrees (MA)

HOFSTRA UNIVERSITY — 111 Hofstra University, Hempstead, NY, 11549-1000 (516) 463-4873; fax (516) 463-4866; e-mail jrnbmk@hofstra.edu
Chair — Barbara Kelly
AFFILIATIONS: SPJ, NABJ, RTNDA
DEGREES:BA, MA.
DEPARTMENTS: School of Communication, Department of Journalism, Media Studies and Public Relations, 1995
SEQUENCES: Print Journalism, Broadcast Journalism, Public Relations, Mass Media Studies

IONA COLLEGE — 715 North Ave., New Rochelle, NY, 10801-1890 (914) 633-2230; fax (914) 637-2797; e-mail masscom@iona.edu
Chair/Asst. Prof./Undergrad. Coord. — Orly Schachar
Prof. — John Darretta
Prof. — George Thottam
Assoc. Prof. — Nancy-Jo Johnson
Asst. Prof. — Mike McDermott
Asst. Prof. — Ann Rodriguez
Asst. Prof. — Ray Smith
Asst. Prof. — Susan Vaughn
Instr. — Virginia Hill
Instr. — Natalie Ryder
Adj. Fac. — Ivette Allen
Adj. Fac. — Tom Callahan
Adj. Fac. — Bill Corbett
Adj. Fac. — Nancy Cutler
Adj. Fac. — Jim Eggensperger
Adj. Fac. — Minaz Fazal
Adj. Fac. — Marybeth Kissane
Adj. Fac. — Woody Klein
Adj. Fac. — Nancy Kriz
Adj. Fac. — Drew Kulakovich
AFFILIATIONS: AAF, PRSSA, SPJ
DEGREES:BA, BS, MA, MSJ
DEPARTMENTS: Department of Mass Communication
FACILITIES: Film/Video Tape Library, Film Theater, Radio Labs, Ad&PR Library, Television Studio, Video Studio, Journalism Lab
SEQUENCES: Journalism, Advertising, Public Relations, TV and Video

ITHACA COLLEGE — Roy H. Park School of Communications, Ithaca, NY, 14850 (607) 274-1021; fax (607) 274-1108; web site www.ithaca.edu
Dean/Prof. — Diane Lynch
Prof./Park Distinguished Chair — Jo Ann Caplin
Prof./Park Distinguished Chair — Christopher Harper
Prof. — Diane Gayeski
Prof./Grad. Prog. Chair — Sandra Herndon
Prof. — Steven Skopik
Prof. — Wenmouth Williams
Prof. — Patricia Zimmermann
Assoc. Prof. — Ben Crane
Assoc. Prof. — Raymond Gozzi
Assoc. Prof. — John Hochheimer
Assoc. Prof./Cinema & Photography Chair — Janice Levy
Assoc. Prof. — Gina Marchetti
Assoc. Prof./Television/Radio Chair — Sharon Mazzarella
Assoc. Prof. — Barbara Morgenstern
Assoc. Prof. — Megan Roberts
Assoc. Prof. — John Rosenbaum
Assoc. Prof./Organizational Communication, Learning, and Design Chair — Gordon Rowland
Assoc. Prof. — Steven Seidman
Assoc. Prof. — Madelyn Williams
DEGREES:BS, BA, BFA, MS
DEPARTMENTS: Roy H. Park School of Communications, 1948
FACILITIES: Text & Graphics lab, Media Research lab, Multi-Media lab, Interactive Media lab, film sound stage, two television studios, still photography studio, color and B&W print photography developing and processing lab, three studios for analog and digital audio
SEQUENCES: TV-Radio, Journalism, Organizational Communication/ Learning & Design, Integrated Marketing Communications, Cinema & Photography, Film, Photography & Visual Arts

LONG ISLAND UNIVERSITY - THE BROOKLYN CAMPUS — 1 University Plz., Brooklyn, NY, 11201-5372 (718) 488-1534 Kalman Siegel Newslab; fax (718) 246-6365; e-mail ralph.engelman@liu.edu
Dept. Chair — Ralph Engelman
AFFILIATIONS: KTA, SPJ, George Polk Awards
DEGREES:BA
DEPARTMENTS: Department of Journalism, 1945
FACILITIES: AM/FM, AdA, CATV, ComN, ComTV, ETV, PRA, DR, CCTV, CN, VDT
SEQUENCES: Newspaper, Advertising, Magazine, New Media, Public Relations, Radio-Television News, Video Journalism

MARIST COLLEGE — 3399 North Rd., Poughkeepsie, NY, 12601 (845) 575-3650; fax (845) 575-3645; e-mail subir.sengupta@marist.edu
Dean/Prof. — John Ritschdorff
Assoc. Prof. — James Fahey
Assoc. Prof. — Laura Linder
Assoc. Prof./Asst. Dean — Subir Sengupta
Assoc. Prof. — Mark Van Dyke
Assoc. Prof. — Paula Willoquet
Asst. Prof. — Missy Alexander
Asst. Prof. — Cochece Davis
Asst. Prof. — Sue Lawrence
Asst. Prof. — James Maritato
Asst. Prof. — Carol Pauli
Asst. Prof. — Joe Ross
Asst. Prof. — Shannon Roper
Asst. Prof. — Keith Strudler
Instr. — Jeff Bass
Instr. — Marcia Christ
Instr. — Dennis Conway
Instr. — Keith Hamel
Instr. — Brett Phares
Dir., Internship Prog. — Gerald McNulty
AFFILIATIONS: AAF, BEA, NATAS, PRSSA, SPJ, NCA
DEGREES:BA
DEPARTMENTS: School of Communication and the Arts, 1980
FACILITIES: AdA, FM, CATV, CCTV, CN, DR, VDT
SEQUENCES: Advertising, Communication Studies, Gaming/Interactive Media, Public Relations/Organizational Communication, Radio/Television/Film, Sports Communication

NEW YORK UNIVERSITY — 10 Washington Pl., 5th Fl., New York, NY, 10003 (212) 998-7980; fax (212) 995-4148; web site www.nyu.edu/gsas/dept/journal
Chair — Jay Rosen
AFFILIATIONS: PRSSA, SPJ
DEGREES:BA, MA
DEPARTMENTS: Department of Journalism and Mass Communication, 1909
FACILITIES: AP, FM, CCTV, CN, DR, broadcast studios and editing facilities, computer labs, news service, desktop publishing, student magazine
SEQUENCES: Newspaper, Magazine, Broadcast News, Public Relations, Media Criticism

NIAGARA UNIVERSITY — 338 Dunleavy Hall, Niagara University, NY, 14109 (716) 286-8460; e-mail barner@niagara.edu; web site www.niagara.edu/communication
Chair/Assoc. Prof. — Mark R. Barner
Assoc. Prof. — Brian M. Murphy
Asst. Prof. — Randy Nichols
Asst. Prof. — Mary Sterpka-King
AFFILIATIONS: ASJMC, ICA
DEGREES:BA
DEPARTMENTS: Communication Studies Program, 1973
FACILITIES: CCTV, CN, DR
SEQUENCES: Print Journalism, Mass Communication, Broadcasting

PACE UNIVERSITY (PLEASANTVILLE) — 861 Bedford Rd., Pleasantville, NY, 10570 (914) 773-3790; e-mail rklaeger@pace.edu
Chair — Robert Klaeger
DEGREES:BA
DEPARTMENTS: Department of Communications, 1975
SEQUENCES: Special sequences in Print Journalism, Broadcast Journalism; Journalism major and minor

ROCHESTER INSTITUTE OF TECHNOLOGY — 92 Lomb Memorial Dr., Rochester, NY, 14623-5604 (585) 475-6649; fax (585) 475-7732; e-mail cmvgpt@rit.edu
Chair — Bruce Austin
DEGREES:BS, MS
DEPARTMENTS: Department of Communication 2006
SEQUENCES: B.S. degree-Professional & Technical Communication; B.S. degree-Advertising & Public Relations; M.S. degree-Communication & Media Technologies.

ST. BONAVENTURE UNIVERSITY — 3261 W. State Rd., Saint Bonaventure, NY, 14778-2289 (716) 375-2520; fax (716) 375-2588; e-mail jmc@sbu.edu
Dean — Lee Coppola
Assoc. Prof. — John Hanchette
Assoc. Prof. — Christopher Mackowski
Assoc. Prof./Coord., Print — Denny Wilkins
Asst. Prof. — Pauline Hoffmann
Asst. Prof. — Carole McNall
Asst. Prof./Coord., PR/Adv. — Bro. Basil Valente
Lectr. — Patrick Vecchio
Lectr./Coord., Broadcast — Paul Wieland
Vstg. Prof. — Breea Willingham
Broadcast Journalism Lab Supvr. — Mary Beth Garvin
Dir., IMC Grad. Prog. — Kathleen Mason
Adj. Fac. — John Bartimole
Adj. Fac. — Robert Carr
Adj. Fac. — John Eberth
Adj. Fac. — James Eckstrom
Adj. Fac. — Jean Trevarton Ehman
Adj. Fac. — Donald Gilliland
Adj. Fac./PhotoJournalism — Darrell Gronemeier
Adj. Fac. — Kelly Hendrix
AFFILIATIONS: AAF, BEA, KTA, PRSA, RTNDA, SPJ
DEGREES:BA, MA
DEPARTMENTS: Russell J. Jandoli School of Journalism and Mass Communication, 1949
FACILITIES: AM/FM, CATV, CCTV, CN, ComN, ComR, ETV, JM, PRA, VDT
SEQUENCES: News-Editorial, Broadcasting, PR-Advertising

ST. JOHN FISHER COLLEGE — 3690 East Ave, Rochester, NY, 14618-3537, USA (585) 385-8360; fax (585) 385-7311; e-mail cardinalcourier@sjfc.edu; web site www.cardinalcourieronline.com
Chair/Prof. — Lauren Vicker
Media Adviser — Marie Villa
DEPARTMENTS: Communication/ Journalism, 1975
FACILITIES: Campus newspaper, TV Club, PR and Ad Clubs
SEQUENCES: A writing-based program in a liberal arts environment. Concentrations offered in Advertising, Broadcasting/ Telecommunications, Print Journalism, Production, and Public Relations, as well as a programs which combine two or more concentrations. Campus newsp

STATE UNIVERSITY OF NEW YORK AT ALBANY — 1400 Washington Ave., Albany, NY, 12222 (518) 442-4884; e-mail nroberts@albany.edu; web site www.albany.edu/journalism
Prof./Dir., Journ. Prog. — Nancy L. Roberts
DEPARTMENTS: Department of English, 1973
SEQUENCES: Journalism Program: BA in Journalism with active internship program in new media, print, radio, television, public relations/advocacy communications, book publishing, and more. 4 Fulltime faculty, 20 part-time Professional Media Lecturers.

STONY BROOK UNIVERSITY — SUNY 3384 Melville Library N4004, Stony Brook, NY, 11790-3384 (631) 632-7403; fax (631) 632-7550; e-mail journalism@stonybrook.edu
Dean — Howard Schneider
DEPARTMENTS: School of Journalism, 2006
SEQUENCES: Stony Brook University's new School of Journalism is the first and only undergraduate school of journalism in New York State's public university system. With a focus on the high-tech future of the media, its mission is to train the next generation of TV c

SUNY COLLEGE AT NEW PALTZ — Coykendall Science Bldg., New Paltz, NY, 12561 (845) 257-3450; fax (845) 257-3461; e-mail commedia@newpaltz.edu
Chair — Pat Sullivan
DEPARTMENTS: Communication and Media Department
FACILITIES: WNPC-TV, AM/FM, Graphics Lab, Avid editing and ProTools, TV studios
SEQUENCES: Journalism Program with wide range of practical and theoretical courses. Requires an internship. Electronic Media Production and Media Management Programs with advanced television and radio production courses

SYRACUSE UNIVERSITY — 215 University Pl., Syracuse, NY, 13244-2100 (315) 443-2301; fax (315) 443-3946; e-mail newhouse@syr.edu
Dean — Lorraine Branham
Prof. — Stanley R. Alten
Prof. — Richard L. Breyer
Prof. — George A. Comstock

Prof. — Elizabeth L. Flocke
Prof. — William A. Glavin
Prof. — Charlotte Grimes
Prof. — Sharon R. Hollenback
Prof. — John P. Jones
Prof. — Lawrence Mason
Prof. — Peter K. Moller
Prof. — David M. Rubin
Prof. — Maria P. Russell
Prof. — Nancy W. Sharp
Prof. — Pamela J. Shoemaker
Prof. — Robert J. Thompson
Prof. — Jay B. Wright
Assoc. Prof. — Hubert Brown
Assoc. Prof. — Melissa Chessher
Assoc. Prof. — Fiona Chew
AFFILIATIONS: KTA, NATAS, NPPA, PRSSA, SPJ, WICI
DEGREES:BS, MA, MS, PhD
DEPARTMENTS: S.I. Newhouse School of Public Communications, 1934
FACILITIES: FM, CCTV, VDT, DR, PRA, ComN, CN, AP
SEQUENCES: Undergraduate: Advertising, Arts Journalism, Broadcast Journalism, Communications, Magazine, Newspaper, Photography/Graphics/Interactive Media, Public Relations, Television/Radio/Film. Graduate: Advertising, Broadcast Journalism, Magazine, Media Studies,

THE EMPIRE STATE TRIBUNE — 56 Broadway, Fl 5, New York, NY, 10004-1613, USA 212-659-0742; e-mail estribune@tkc.edu; web site www.empirestatetribune.com
Assistant Affiliate Professor of Journalism — Clemente Lisi

UTICA COLLEGE OF SYRACUSE UNIVERSITY — 1600 Burrstone Rd., Utica, NY, 13502 (315) 792-3241; fax (315) 792-3173; e-mail cfriend@utica.edu
Dir./Prof. — Cecilia Friend
AFFILIATIONS: PRSSA, ACP
DEGREES:BA, BS
DEPARTMENTS: Department of Communication
FACILITIES: Internet, CN, ComN, ComR, DR, FM, PRSSA, ACP
SEQUENCES: Communication Arts, Journalism, Public Relations, Public Relations-Journalism

NORTH CAROLINA

APPALACHIAN STATE UNIVERSITY — PO Box 32039, Boone, NC, 28608 (828) 262-2405; fax (828) 262-2543; e-mail townsws@appstate.edu
Chair — Stuart Towns
DEGREES:BS
DEPARTMENTS: Department of Communication
SEQUENCES: Journalism Program: Offered as major in the communication program, along with majors in electronic media/broadcasting, advertising, organizatonal/public communication, and public relations

CAMPBELL UNIVERSITY — 180 Main St., Buies Creek, NC, 27506 (910) 893-1520; fax (910) 893-1924; e-mail smithm@campbell.edu
Chair — Michael R. Smith
Fellow Chair — Archie K. Davis
DEGREES:BA
DEPARTMENTS: Department of Mass Communication, 1991
FACILITIES: Mass Communication: Department offers BA degrees in Broadcast, Journalism, Public Relations and Advertising. Facilities include FM radio station, desktop publishing/graphic design computer labs, radio and television studios, photography labs, and ENG equi
SEQUENCES: Broadcast Journalism, Public Relations and Advertising

EAST CAROLINA UNIVERSITY — 102 Joyner E., Greenville, NC, 27858-4353 (252) 328-4227; fax (252) 328-1509; e-mail keyesa@mail.ecu.edu
Dir. — Tim Hudson
DEGREES:MA, BS
DEPARTMENTS: School of Communication, Journalism Major, Public Relations Major, Media Production Major, Communication Studies Major, Media Studies Major
FACILITIES: VDT, CN, non-linear editing, cable newscasts
SEQUENCES: Offers programs that lead to a BS in Communication with major concentration in journalism, public relations, media production, communication studies or media studies. MA in Communication studies

ELON UNIVERSITY — McEwen Communications Bldg., Campus Box 2850, Elon, NC, 27244 (336) 278-5724; fax (336) 278-5734; e-mail communications@elon.edu; web site www.elon.edu/communications
Dean/Prof. — Paul Parsons
Prof./Fletcher Chair/Grad. Dir. — David Copeland
Assoc. Prof. — Janna Anderson
Assoc. Prof. — Brooke Barnett
Assoc. Dean/Assoc. Prof. — Constance Book
Assoc. Prof. — Vic Costello
Assoc. Prof. — Michael Frontani
Assoc. Prof. — Jessica Gisclair
Assoc. Prof./Dept. Chair — Don Grady
Assoc. Prof. — Anthony Hatcher
Assoc. Prof. — Byung Lee
Assoc. Prof. — Harlen Makemson
Assoc. Prof. — Tom Nelson
Assoc. Prof. — George Padgett
Assoc. Prof./Pulitzer Prize winner — Michael Skube
Assoc. Prof. — Frances Ward-Johnson
Asst. Prof. — Lee Bush
Asst. Prof. — Ken Calhoun
Asst. Prof. — Ocek Eke
Asst. Prof. — Amanda Gallagher
AFFILIATIONS: SPJ, RTNDA, PRSSA, Cinelon, E Pluribus Unum, Lambda Pi Eta
DEGREES:BA, MA
DEPARTMENTS: School of Communications, 2000
FACILITIES: FM, AP, CCTV, CN, DR, ETV, VDT
SEQUENCES: Journalism, Strategic Communications, Media Arts & Entertainment, Communication Science

HIGH POINT UNIV. — 1 University Pkwy, High Point, NC, 27268-0002, USA (800) 345-6993; fax (336) 841-4513; e-mail news@highpoint.edu; web site www.highpoint.eduBobby Hayes
Dir./Prof. — Wilfrid Tremblay
Prof. — Kate Fowkes
Assoc. Prof. — Judy Isaksen
Assoc. Prof. — John Luecke
Asst. Prof. — Nahed Eltantawy
Asst. Prof. — Jim Goodman
Asst. Prof. — Brad Lambert
Asst. Prof. — Jim Trammell
Asst. Prof. — Gerald Voorhees
Lectr. — Kristina Bell
Opns. Mgr. — Don Moore
Video Producer — Martin Yount
Admin. Asst. — Michelle Devlin
AFFILIATIONS: Lambda Pi Eta
DEGREES:BA
DEPARTMENTS: The Nido R. Qubein School of Communication
FACILITIES: Internet Radio, CCTV, Advertising/PR Agency, Game Design Studio, Student Newspaper, Television Production Studios, Multi-track Audio Recording Studio, Editing Suites, Computer Labs, Theatre-screening Room
SEQUENCES: Electronic Media Production, Games and Interactive Media Design, Journalism, Media and Popular Culture Studies, Strategic Communication.

JOHNSON C. SMITH UNIVERSITY — 100 Beatties Ford Rd., Charlotte, NC, 28216 (704) 378-1096; fax (704) 378-3539; e-mail klharris@jcsu.edu
Interim Dept. Chair — Kandace L. Harris
DEPARTMENTS: Department of Communication Arts
FACILITIES: Journalism, Graphic Design, and Audio/Video Production Labs
SEQUENCES: Communication Arts Program: Offers a B.A. degree to develop students who are trained in Media Production, Journalism, Public Relations or Marketing Communications.

LENOIR-RHYNE COLLEGE — School of Communication and Literature, Hickory, NC, 28603 (828) 328-7164; fax (828) 328-7163; e-mail Richter@lrc.edu
Chair — William Richter
DEGREES:BA
DEPARTMENTS: School of Communication and Literature
FACILITIES: FM, CCTV, CN, DR, VDT
SEQUENCES: Communication Program: Offers mass comm., journalism, television, speech, law, internship, PR and integrated liberal arts courses leading to an BA in Communication

NORTH CAROLINA A&T STATE UNIVERSITY — 1601 E. Market St., A322 New General Classroom Bldg., Greensboro, NC, 27411 (336) 334-7900; fax (336) 334-7770
Chair — Humphrey A. Regis
Prof. — Kevin Keenan
Prof. — Tamrat Mereba
Assoc. Prof. — Linda Florence Callahan
Assoc. Prof. — Rita Lauria
Assoc. Prof. — Teresa Jo Styles
Asst. Prof. — Nagatha Tonkins
Asst. Prof. — Anthony Welborne
Asst. Prof. — Sheila Whitley
Asst. Prof. — Gail Wiggins
Adj. Asst. Prof. — Kimberly Moore
Instr. — Emily Burch-Harris
Instr. — Bruce Clark
Instr. — Allen Johnson
Instr. — Jacqueline Jones
Instr. — Alexis Nyandwi
Instr. — Willis Smith
Instr. — Brian Tomlin
Instr. — Mary Vanderlinden
Instr. — Frances Ward Johnson
DEGREES:BS- Journalism and Mass Communication with a concentration in one of the above sequences
DEPARTMENTS: Department of Journalism and Mass Communication, 1986
FACILITIES: Journalism and Mass Communication Computer Lab, Journalism Newspaper Lab, Television Studio, Radio Station
SEQUENCES: Electronic Media and Journalism, Broadcast Production, Media Management, Print Journalism and Public Relations

NORTH CAROLINA CENTRAL UNIV. — 1801 Fayetteville St, Durham, NC, 27707-3129, USA (919) 530-7116; fax (919) 530-7991; e-mail campusecho@nccu.edu; web site www.campusecho.comDr. Bruce DePyssler
Associate Professor — Thomas Evans
Carlton Koonce
DEGREES:BA
DEPARTMENTS: Department of English & Mass Communication, 2003
FACILITIES: CCTV, CN, VDT
SEQUENCES: Mass communication with concentrations in journalism, broadcast, or communication studies

UNIVERSITY OF NORTH CAROLINA — School of Journalism & Mass Communication, Campus Box 3365, UNC-CH, 117 Carroll Hall, Chapel Hill, NC, 27514 (919) 962-1204; fax (919) 962-0620; e-mail jean_folkerts@unc.edu; web site www.jomc.unc.edu
Dean/Alumni Distinguished Prof. — Jean Folkerts
Prof./Knight Chair in Journ. and Digital Media Economics — Penelope Muse Abernathy
Prof./James L. Knight — Jane Delano Brown
Dean Emer./John Thomas Kerr Distinguished Prof. — Richard R. Cole
Prof./Assoc. Dean for Grad. Studies — Anne Johnston
Glaxo Wellcome Distinguished Prof. of Medical Journalism — Thomas R. Linden
Prof./Richard Cole Eminent Prof. — Daniel Riffe
Kenan Prof. — Donald L. Shaw
Prof. — Richard Simpson
Prof./Sr. Assoc. Dean — Dulcie Straughan
Distinguished Prof. in Sports Commun. — John Sweeney
Prof. — Charles A. Tuggle
James Howard & Hallie McLean Parker Distinguished Prof. — Ruth Walden
Walter Spearman Prof. — Jan Yopp
Prof. — Xinshu Zhao
Assoc. Prof. — Deb Aikat
Assoc. Prof. — Lois Boynton
Assoc. Prof. — George W. Cloud
Assoc. Prof. — Pat Davison
Assoc. Prof. — Frank Fee
AFFILIATIONS: AAF, IABC, KTA, SPJ, NPPA, ENAC, SND, PRSSA
DEGREES:BA, MA, PhD
DEPARTMENTS: School of Journalism and Mass Communication, 1950
FACILITIES: AP, CCTV, ComTV, CN, DR, ETV, JM, JN, VDT
SEQUENCES: Advertising, Electronic Communication, News-Editorial, Public Relations, Visual Communication

UNIVERSITY OF NORTH CAROLINA AT PEMBROKE — Box 1510, Pembroke, NC, 28372-1510 (910) 522-5723; fax (910) 522-5795; e-mail masscomm@uncp.edu
Chair — Jamie Litty
DEPARTMENTS: Department of Mass Communications, 1983
SEQUENCES: Department of Mass Communications: Join the most diverse student body in the UNC system, where we offer majors and minors in broadcasting, journalism, public relations, and media integration.

UNIVERSITY OF NORTH CAROLINA-ASHEVILLE — 1 University Heights, CPO 2120, Asheville, NC, 28804 (828) 232-5027; fax (828) 232-2421; e-mail west@unca.edu
Chair — Mark D. West
DEPARTMENTS: Department of Mass Communication, 1980
SEQUENCES: Mass Communication Program: A Liberal Arts program focusing on the functions of print and electronic media in society. The program emphasizes clear writing, critical thinking and creative visual production

WINGATE UNIVERSITY — Communication Studies, Wingate, NC, 28174 (704) 233-8188; fax (704) 233-8192; e-mail coon@wingate.edu
Chair — Jim Coon
DEPARTMENTS: Communication Studies
SEQUENCES: Journalism Program: Interdisciplinary, focusing on communication theories and techniques. Emphases in journalism, public relations, speech communication, broadcast journalism and media arts

WINSTON-SALEM STATE UNIVERSITY — 601 Martin Luther King Jr. Dr., 314 Hall-Patterson Bldg., Winston-Salem, NC, 27110 (336) 750-2320; fax (336) 750-2100; e-mail jeterph@wssu.edu
Chair/Prof. — Phillip Jeter
Prof. — Lorna D. Cobb
Assoc. Prof. — Brian C. Blount
Assoc. Prof. — Marilyn Roseboro
Assoc. Prof. — Abhijit Sen
Asst. Prof. — Laine Goldman
Asst. Prof. — Doug C. Osman
Asst. Prof. — Valerie S. Saddler

Instr. — Elvin Jenkins
Staff — Marcia Bonner
Staff — Ben Donnelly
Staff — Jerome Hancock
Staff — Monica Melton
Staff — Hollie Stevenson-Parrish
Staff — Darlene Vinson
Staff — Harvest R. Williams
Part-time Staff — Larry Bell
Part-time Staff — Grady Crosby
Part-time Staff — Nicole Ferguson
Part-time Staff — Bonnie Weymouth
DEGREES:BA
DEPARTMENTS: Department of Mass Communications
SEQUENCES: Mass Communications with a choice of either Journalism or Electronic Media learning tracks prepare students for careers in journalism and broadcasting. Students gain real world experience working in the department-run WSNC 90.5 FM National Public Radio st

NORTH DAKOTA

NORTH DAKOTA STATE UNIVERSITY — Box 5075, Minard 321, Fargo, ND, 58105-5075 (701) 231-7705; fax (701) 231-7784; e-mail paul.nelson.1@ndsu.edu
Prof./Head — Paul E. Nelson
AFFILIATIONS: PRSSA, SPJ
DEPARTMENTS: Department of Communication
SEQUENCES: Mass Communication Program: Concentrations in Journalism, Public Relations, Advertising, Broadcasting, Mass Communication Technologies and Web Design.

UNIVERSITY OF NORTH DAKOTA — PO Box 7169, Grand Forks, ND, 58202 (701) 777-2159; fax (701) 777-3090; e-mail scomm@und.nodak.edu
Dir. — Stephen Rendahl
Prof. — Richard Fiordo
Prof. — James Hikins
Prof. — Lana Rakow
Assoc. Prof. — Lucy Ganje
Assoc. Prof. — Victoria Holden
Assoc. Prof. — Michael Nitz
Assoc. Prof. — Richard Shafer
Instr. — Mary Haslerud Opp
Prof. Emer. — Raymond Fischer
AFFILIATIONS: AAF, KTA, PRSSA, SPJ
DEGREES:BA, BS Ed, MA, MS Ed, PhD
DEPARTMENTS: School of Communication
FACILITIES: AM, FM, CATV, CCTV, CN, ComN, ComTV, DR, ETV, JN, VDT
SEQUENCES: Communication

OHIO

BOWLING GREEN STATE UNIVERSITY — 302 West Hall, Bowling Green, OH, 43403 (419) 372-8349; fax (419) 372-0202; e-mail rfirsdo@bgnet.bgsu.edu; web site www.bgsu.edu/departments/journalism
Chair/Assoc. Prof. — Terry Rentner
Prof. — J. Oliver Boyd-Barrett
Assoc. Prof. — Nancy Brendlinger
Assoc. Prof. — Catherine Cassara
Assoc. Prof. — James Foust
Assoc. Prof. — Melissa Spirek
Asst. Prof. — Katherine Bradshaw
Asst. Prof. — Victoria Smith Ekstrand
Instr. — Efrem Graham
Instr. — Julie Hagenbuch
Instr. — Kelly Taylor
Prof. Emer. — James Bissland
Prof. Emer. — Joseph Delporto
Prof. Emer. — Harold Fisher
Prof. Emer. — James Gordon
Prof. Emer. — F. Dennis Hale
Prof. Emer. — John Huffman
Prof. Emer. — Laurence Jankowski
Prof. Emer. — Raymond Laakaniemi
AFFILIATIONS: KTA, PRSSA, Radio-TV News Assn., SND, SPJ, NABJ
DEGREES:BS- Journalism; MA, PhD- Communication Studies
DEPARTMENTS: Department of Journalism, 1941
FACILITIES: AP, AM, FM, CCTV, CN, CNN, DR, ETV, JM, PRA, VDT, Media 100
SEQUENCES: Broadcast, Public Relations, Print

CLEVELAND STATE UNIVERSITY — 2121 Euclid Ave., Cleveland, OH, 44115-2214 (216) 687-4630; fax (216) 687-5435; e-mail j.lee@csuohio.edu; web site www.csuohio.edu/com
School Dir. — Richard Perloff
Div. Dir. — Jae-won Lee
AFFILIATIONS: SPJ, PRSSA, AAF
DEGREES:BA- Journalism and Promotional Communication, Master of Applied Communication- Theory and methodology
DEPARTMENTS: School of Communication 1972, 2004
FACILITIES: FM, CATV, CCTV, JN (The Cleveland Stater), VDT (writing labs, television studio, digital editing suites, audio production rooms, screening rooms, satellite downlink), CATI (Computer-Assisted Telephone Interviewing) Lab.
SEQUENCES: Journalism, Public Relations, Advertising

FRANCISCAN UNIVERSITY OF STEUBENVILLE — G-8 Egan Hall, 1235 University Blvd., Steubenville, OH, 43952 (740) 283-3771; fax (740) 283-6452; e-mail wlewis@franciscan.edu
Chair — Wayne Lewis
DEGREES:BA
DEPARTMENTS: Communication Arts Department
SEQUENCES: Communication Program: BA degree in Mass Communications with concentrations in Journalism and Radio/TV

JOHN CARROLL UNIVERSITY — 1 John Carroll Blvd, University Heights, OH, 44118-4538, USA (216) 397-1711; fax (216) 397-1729; e-mail jcunews@gmail.com; web site www.jcunews.com
Chair/Assoc. Prof. — Mary Ann Flannery
Robert T. Noll
Prof. — Jacqueline J. Schmidt
Katie Sheridan
Bob Seeholzer
Prof. — Alan Stephenson
Assoc. Prof. — Mary Beadle
Tim Ertle
Asst. Prof. — Margaret Algren
Asst. Prof. — Richard Hendrickson
Asst. Prof. — Robert Prisco
Instr. — Bob Noll
Instr. — David Reese
Part-time Instr. — Fred Buchstein
Part-time Instr. — Mark Eden
Part-time Instr. — Bill Nichols
DEGREES:BA, MA- Media Management
DEPARTMENTS: Department of Communications
FACILITIES: Electronic newsroom, television studio, editing booths, screening rooms, audio production booth, satellite downlink, graphics laboratory. Department members advise student newspaper, FM radio station, TV-news

MARIETTA COLLEGE — 215 5th St, Marietta, OH, 45750-4033, USA (740) 376-4848; fax (740) 376-4807; e-mail mac@Marietta.edu; web site www.marcolian.com/
Chair — Jack L. Hillwig
AFFILIATIONS: AER, SCJ
DEGREES:BA
DEPARTMENTS: Mass Media Department, 1975
SEQUENCES: Journalism Program: Department offers majors in Advertising/Public Relations, Corporate Communications, Journalism and Radio/Television

OHIO STATE UNIVERSITY — 3016 Derby Hall, 154 N. Oval Mall, Columbus, OH, 43210-1339 (614) 292-3400; fax (614) 292-2055; e-mail glynn.14@osu.edu
Dir./Prof. — Carroll J. Glynn
Prof. — Donald Cegala
Prof. — Brenda Dervin
Prof. — Daniel McDonald
Prof. — Michael Slater
Assoc. Prof. — Stephen Acker
Assoc. Prof. — Prabu David
Assoc. Prof. — John Dimmick
Assoc. Prof. — William Eveland
Assoc. Prof. — Lance Holbert
Assoc. Prof. — Susan Kline
Assoc. Prof. — Gerald Kosicki
Assoc. Prof. — Emily Moyer-Gus
Assoc. Prof. — Amy Nathanson
Assoc. Prof. — Felecia Ross
Assoc. Prof. — Thomas Schwartz
Assoc. Prof. — Laura Stafford
Assoc. Prof. — Sharon West
Asst. Prof. — Osei Appiah
Assoc. Prof. — Kelly Garrett
AFFILIATIONS: AAMA, KTA, PRSSA, SPJ
DEGREES:BAJ, BA, MA, PhD
DEPARTMENTS: School of Journalism, 1914; School of Journalism and Communication, 1997; School of Comunication, 2004
FACILITIES: AP, ETV, IN, VDT, PRA
SEQUENCES: BA- Public Affairs; BA- Strategic Communication, Communication Technology, Communication Analysis and practice.

OHIO UNIVERSITY — Scripps Hall 105, Court St. & Park Pl., Athens, OH, 45701 (740) 593-2590; fax (740) 593-2592; e-mail info@scrippsjschool.org; web site scrippsjschool.org
Dir./Assoc. Prof. — Thomas Hodson
Prof./Assoc. Dir., Grad. Studies/Research — Joseph Bernt
Prof. — Anne Cooper-Chen
Prof. — Marilyn Greenwald
Prof./Assoc. Dir. — Robert Stewart
Prof. — Patrick Washburn
Prof. — Patricia Westfall
Assoc. Prof. — Bojinka Bishop
Assoc. Prof. — Hong Cheng
Assoc. Prof./Dir. Studies, Honors Tutorial College — Bernhard Debatin
Assoc. Prof. — Sandra Haggerty
Assoc. Prof. — Ronald Pittman
Assoc. Prof. — Mary Rogus
Asst. Prof. — Patricia Cambridge
Asst. Prof. — Aimee Edmondson
Asst. Prof. — Cary Frith
Asst. Prof. — Ellen Gerl
Asst. Prof. — Michelle Honald
Asst. Prof./Dir., Inst. for Int'l Journalism — Yusuf Kalyango
Asst. Prof. — Bill Reader
AFFILIATIONS: AAF, AWC, BSCC, KTA, OJSS, PRSSA, RTNDA, SPJ
DEGREES:BSJ, MSJ, PhD
DEPARTMENTS: E. W. Scripps School of Journalism, 1924
FACILITIES: AP, NYTS, UPI, AM, FM, AdA, CATV, Bloomberg Terminal, CCTV, CN, CNN, ComN, ComR, DR, ETV, JM, PRA, VDT
SEQUENCES: Advertising, Broadcast News, Magazine, Newswriting and Editing, Online Journalism, Public Relations

OHIO WESLEYAN UNIVERSITY — Dept. of Journalism, Delaware, OH, 43015 (740) 368-3650; fax (740) 368-3649; e-mail tregan@cc.owu.edu
Chair/Prof. — Trace Regan
Assoc. Prof. — Paul Kostyu
Lectr. — Richard McClure
Lectr. — Jim Underwood
Vstg. Asst. Prof. — Afi-Odelia Scruggs
DEGREES:BA
DEPARTMENTS: Department of Journalism, 1945
FACILITIES: AP, FM, CATV, CN, VDT
SEQUENCES: News-Editorial

OTTERBEIN COLLEGE — 1 Otterbein College, Westerville, OH, 43081 (614) 823-3380; fax (614) 823-3367; e-mail dwootton@otterbein.edu
Chair — Susan Millsap
AFFILIATIONS: PRSSA
DEGREES:BA
DEPARTMENTS: Department of Communication
FACILITIES: CN, FM, CATV, DR, VDT
SEQUENCES: Journalism Program: BA program in news-editorial sequence. Interdisciplinary BA in PR and in Broadcasting. Courses in media writing, news writing, broadcast production, public relations, desktop publishing, advanced reporting, media ethics and regulatio

UNIVERSITY OF AKRON — School of Communication, Akron, OH, 44325-1003 (330) 972-7600; fax (330) 972-8045; e-mail dbturner@uakron.edu; web site www.uakron.edu/schlcomm
Dir. — Dudley B. Turner
DEPARTMENTS: School of Communication
SEQUENCES: Journalism Program: Twenty journalism and public relations courses plus internships are part of the Mass Media-Communication degree

UNIVERSITY OF CINCINNATI — Div. of Electronic Media, Cincinnati, OH, 45221-0003 (513) 556-9488; fax (513) 556-0202; e-mail wolframk@uc.edu
Chair — Manfred K. Wolfram
Journalism Coord. — Marjorie Fox
DEPARTMENTS: Division of Electronic Media
FACILITIES: NewsKing automated newsroom, digital cameras and editing systems
SEQUENCES: Journalism Program: Degree is in Electronic Media; students may concentrate in electronic journalism. Journalism courses offered are Introduction to Broadcast Journalism, Broadcast News Writing, and Uptown, a class dedicated to production of the campus t

UNIVERSITY OF DAYTON — 300 College Park, Dayton, OH, 45469-1410 (917) 229-2028; fax (937) 000-0000; e-mail Donald.yoder@notes.udayton.edu
Chair — Donald D. Yoder
DEPARTMENTS: Department of Communication
SEQUENCES: Journalism Program: Undergraduate concentration areas include news-editorial, broadcasting, PR and communication management. Largest department at university

UNIVERSITY OF FINDLAY — 1000 N. Main St., Findlay, OH, 45840 (419) 434-4445; fax (419) 434-4616; e-mail stevens@findlay.edu; web site www.findlay.edu/academics/info/colleges.htm
Dir. — Dennis Stevens
DEGREES:BA
DEPARTMENTS: Communication Department
SEQUENCES: Communiction Program: BA degree in Digital Media, Health Communication, Interpersonal Communication, Journalism and Public Relations

UNIVERSITY OF TOLEDO — 2801 W. Bancroft St., University Hall, Rm. 4600, Toledo, OH, 43606-3390 (419) 530-2005; fax (419) 530-4771; e-mail jbenjam@utnet.utoledo.edu
Chair — Jim Benjamin
AFFILIATIONS: PRSSA, SPJ
DEGREES:BA
DEPARTMENTS: Department of Communication, 1945
SEQUENCES: Communication Program: Offers BA in communication with concentrations in journalism, broadcasting,

and public relations. Journalism concentration combines professional skills approach (writing, reporting, editing) with liberal-arts approach (law, history

WRIGHT STATE UNIVERSITY — Dept. of Communication, Dayton, OH, 45435 (937) 775-2145; fax (973) 775-2146; e-mail james.sayer@wright.edu
Chair — James Sayer
Melanie Reach
DEPARTMENTS: Department of Communication, 1966
SEQUENCES: Journalism Program: Offers coursework and experience in broadcast and print journalism, public realtions and visual communication

XAVIER UNIVERSITY — 3800 Victory Pkwy., Cincinnati, OH, 45207-5171 (513) 745-3087; fax (513) 745-3705; e-mail desilva@Xavier.edu
Chair — Indra De Silva
DEGREES:BA
DEPARTMENTS: Communication Arts Department
SEQUENCES: Communication Program: Multi-track program with 36 hour majors in Public Relations, Advertising, Electronic Media and Organizational Communication leading to a BA in Communication Arts

YOUNGSTOWN STATE UNIVERSITY — 1 University Plz., Youngstown, OH, 44555-3415 (330) 941-1467; e-mail journalism@cc.ysu.edu
Dir., Journalism — Alyssa Lenhoff
Chair, English — Gary Salvner
DEPARTMENTS: Department of English
SEQUENCES: Journalism Program: Offers a Journalism major through writing courses and lab experience in newspaper journalism. Students complete hands-on internships in newsrooms and are assisted with the process of landing first journalism jobs

OKLAHOMA

EAST CENTRAL UNIVERSITY (OKLAHOMA) — 1100 E. 14th St., Ada, OK, 74820-6999 (580) 559-5485; fax (580) 332-1623; e-mail bgrnst@ecok.edu
Chair — Robert Greenstreet
DEPARTMENTS: Communication Department
SEQUENCES: Journalism Program: Major in Mass Communication. Concentration in Electronic and Print Media, and Advertising/Public Relations

NORTHEASTERN STATE UNIVERSITY (OKLAHOMA) — Dept. of Mass Communications, Tahlequah, OK, 74464 (918) 456-5511; e-mail osborne@cherokee@nsuok.ed
Chair — Rodney Osborne
DEPARTMENTS: Department of Mass Communications
SEQUENCES: Mass Communications Program: Approximately 250 students, half are majors. Courses offered in all areas of print, broadcast, public relations, advertising and photography

OKLAHOMA BAPTIST UNIVERSITY — 500 W. University, Box 61308, Shawnee, OK, 74804 (405) 878-2236; fax (405) 878-8701; e-mail roger.hadley@okbu.edu; web site www.okbu.edu/jour_pr.htm
Chair — Roger Hadley
DEGREES:BA
DEPARTMENTS: Journalism and Public Relations Department
SEQUENCES: Journalism Program: Offers BA degree in Journalism (news-editorial sequence) as well as BA in Public Relations (general). Minors: Journalism; Public Relations.

OKLAHOMA CHRISTIAN UNIVERSITY — 2501 E. Memorial Rd., Edmond, OK, 73103 (405) 425-5521; fax (405) 425-5614; e-mail philip.patterson@oc.edu
Chair — Larry Jurney
DEGREES:BA
DEPARTMENTS: Department of Communication, 1970
SEQUENCES: Communication Program: BA degrees in journalism, advertising/public relations, radio/TV and multimedia.

OKLAHOMA CITY UNIVERSITY — 2501 N. Blackwelder, Oklahoma City, OK, 73106 (405) 521-5252; fax (405) 521-5928; e-mail kharmon@okcu.edu
Chair — Karlie Harmon
DEPARTMENTS: Department of Mass Communications
SEQUENCES: Mass Communications Program: Multi-track system with sequences of study in Advertising, Broadcast, Public Relations, Print

OKLAHOMA STATE UNIVERSITY — 206 Paul Miller Bldg., Stillwater, OK, 74078-0195 (405) 744-6354; fax (405) 744-7104; e-mail melissa.powers@okstate.edu
Dir. — Derina Holtzhausen
Assoc. Prof. — Brooks Garner
Assoc. Prof. — Jack Hodgson
Assoc. Prof. — Stan Ketterer
Assoc. Prof. — Tom Weir
Assoc. Prof. — Jami Fullerton
Assoc. Prof. — Lori McKinnon
Assoc. Prof. — Joey Senat
Assoc. Prof. — Mike Sowell
Asst. Prof. — Bobbi K. Hooper
Asst. Prof. — Roy Kelsey
Asst. Prof. — Marc Krein
Asst. Prof. — Sheree Martin
Asst. Prof. — John McGuire
Asst. Prof. — Ray Murray
Vstg. Asst. Prof. — Ken Graham
Vstg. Asst. Prof. — Bill Handy
Vstg. Asst. Prof. — Harry Hix
Vstg. Asst. Prof. — Scott Lambert
Vstg. Asst. Prof. — Gina Noble
AFFILIATIONS: ACT, AAF, AER, DTA, PRSSA, SPJ, WAC
DEGREES:BS, BA, MS
DEPARTMENTS: School of Journalism and Broadcasting, 1927
FACILITIES: AP, FM, CATV, CBS, CCTV, CN, CNN News Source, ComN, ComR, DR, ETV, JN, PRA, Mac labs
SEQUENCES: Specializations: Advertising, News-Editorial, Public Relations, Broadcast, Sports Media

SOUTHERN NAZARENE UNIV. — 6729 NW 39th Expy, Bethany, OK, 73008-2605, USA (405) 491-6382; fax (405) 491-6378; e-mail echo@snu.edu; web site echo.snu.edu
Speech Commun. Dept. — Pam Broyles
Yearbook — Marcia Feisal
Newspaper — Jim Wilcox
Graphic Design — Andrew Baker
Broadcasting — Les Dart
DEGREES:Mass Communication Degree
SEQUENCES: Journalism Program: : A Liberal Arts degree offered in cooperation with the departments of Speech Communication and English.

UNIVERSITY OF CENTRAL OKLAHOMA — Mass Communication Dept., Edmond, OK, 73034 (405) 974-5303; fax (405) 974-5125; e-mail tclark@ucok.edu
Chair — Terry M. Clark
DEGREES:BA
DEPARTMENTS: Mass Communication Department
SEQUENCES: BA degree with emphasis in advertising, broadcasting, corporate communication, interpersonal communication, general journalism, photography, public relations

UNIVERSITY OF OKLAHOMA — 395 W. Lindsey St., Norman, OK, 73019-4021 (405) 325-2721; fax (405) 325-7565; e-mail jfoote@ou.edu; web site jmc.ou.edu
Dean/Prof. — Joe Foote
Prof. — Jim Avery
Prof. — Fred Beard
Prof. — Deborah Chester
Prof. — J. Madison Davis
Prof. — Peter Gross
Prof. — Linda P. Morton
Prof. — Charles C. Self
Assoc. Prof. — Meta Carstarphen
Assoc. Prof. — David Craig
Assoc. Prof. — Peter Gade
Assoc. Prof. — Timothy Hudson
Assoc. Prof. — Misha Nedeljkovich
Asst. Prof. — Ralph Beliveau
Asst. Prof. — Matthew Cecil
Asst. Prof. — Robert Kerr
Asst. Prof. — Ken McMillen
Asst. Prof. — Jennifer Tiernan
Asst. Prof. — Katerina Tsetura
Asst. Prof. — Christa Ward
AFFILIATIONS: AAF, KTA, NABJ, PRSSA, SPJ, AWC, OUCB, NAJA, NAHJ, AAJA
DEGREES:BAJ, MA, MPW
DEPARTMENTS: Gaylord College of Journalism and Mass Communication, 1913
FACILITIES: AP, FM, CATV, CN, CommR, DR, JM, PRA, VDT
SEQUENCES: Advertising, Journalism, Professional Writing, Public Relations, Broadcasting and Electronic Media

UNIVERSITY OF TULSA — 600 S. College, Tulsa, OK, 74104 (918) 631-3805; fax (918) 631-3809; e-mail john-coward@utulsa.edu
Chair — John Coward
DEGREES:BA
DEPARTMENTS: Faculty of Communication
FACILITIES: CN, CATV, FM, Computer lab
SEQUENCES: Mass Communication Emphasis: The Communication Department offers a five-course communication core followed by electives in journalism, video production, media studies and public relations. Part of a comprehensive Communication major

OREGON

LINFIELD COLLEGE — 900 SE Baker St., McMinnville, OR, 97128-6894 (503) 883-2291; fax (503) 883-2360; e-mail bthomps@linfield.edu
Chair — Brad Thompson
DEGREES:BA
DEPARTMENTS: Department of Communication
SEQUENCES: Mass Communication Program: Offers mass communication major and media studies minor that emphasize liberal arts, writing, information gathering and visual communication skills in four tracks: public relations, print, electronic, and media studies. Interns

SOUTHERN OREGON UNIVERSITY — 1250 Siskiyou Blvd., Ashland, OR, 97520 (541) 552-6424; fax (541) 552-8446; e-mail pittman@sou.edu
Chair — Garth Pittman
DEPARTMENTS: Department of Communication
SEQUENCES: Concentrations in Journalism and/or Media Studies. Journalism emphasizes news editorial & photojournalism; strong practicum/internship program

UNIVERSITY OF OREGON — 1222 E. 13th Ave. #300, University of Oregon, Eugene, OR, 97403 (541) 346-5511; e-mail letters@dailyemerald.com; web site http://www.dailyemerald.com/
Dean — Timothy W. Gleason
Prof. — Thomas H. Bivins
Prof. — Patricia A. Curtin
Prof. — Charles F. Frazer
Prof. — Lauren Kessler
Prof. — Duncan L. McDonald
Prof. — Deborah K. Morrison
Prof./Assoc. Dean, Undergrad. Studies — Julianne H. Newton
Prof. — Jon Palfreman
Prof./Sr. Assoc. Dean/Dir., Turnbull Ctr. — Alan G. Stavitsky
Prof./Assoc. Dean, Grad. Studies/Research — H. Leslie Steeves
Prof. — James Upshaw
Prof. — Janet Wasko
Prof. — Kyu Ho Youm
Assoc. Prof. — Carol Ann Bassett
Assoc. Prof. — Carl R. Bybee
Assoc. Prof. — Scott R. Maier
Assoc. Prof. — Ann K. Maxwell
Assoc. Prof. — Debra Merskin
Assoc. Prof. — Daniel Miller
AFFILIATIONS: KTA, Ad Club, PRSSA, SPJ, NABJ
DEGREES:BA, BS, MA, MS, PhD
DEPARTMENTS: School of Journalism and Communication, 1912
FACILITIES: AP, AM, FM, CDTV, CN, DR, ETC, VDT
SEQUENCES: Advertising, Communications Studies, Journalism, News-Editorial, Electronic Media, Magazine, Public Relations

UNIVERSITY OF PORTLAND — 5000 N. Willamette Blvd., Portland, OR, 97203-5798 (503) 283-7229; fax (503) 283-7399; e-mail gayle@uofport.edu
Chair — Barbara Mae Gayle
DEGREES:BA, BS, MA, MS
DEPARTMENTS: Department of Communication Studies
SEQUENCES: Communication Program: BA Degree. Offers broad preparation for graduate study or professional careers. Organizational Communication Program: BS degree. For students seeking careers in organizational communication, public relations or personnel. Offere

PENNSYLVANIA

BLOOMSBURG UNIVERSITY - THE VOICE — Dept. of Mass Communications, Bloomsburg, PA, 17815 (717) 389-4633; fax (570) 389-3983; e-mail voiceeditor@huskies.bloomu.edu
Chair — Dana Ulloth
DEGREES:BA
DEPARTMENTS: Department of Mass Communications, 1985
FACILITIES: Television studios, Radio Station, Magazine, Newspaper
SEQUENCES: Mass Communication, Journalism, Public Relations/Advertising, Telecommunications

CABRINI UNIVERSITY LOQUITUR — 610 King of Prussia Rd, Radnor, PA, 19087-3623, USA; tel (1) (610) 902-8360; fax (610) 902-8285; e-mail loquitur@cabrini.edu; web site www.theloquitur.com
Chair — Jerome Zurek
EIC — Angelina Miller
AFFILIATIONS: SCJ
DEGREES:BA
DEPARTMENTS: Department of Communications, 1973
FACILITIES: AdA, CATV, CCTV, CN, ComN, ComTV, DR, JM, PRA, VDT, ComR, FM
SEQUENCES: Journalism & Writing; Video, Radio, Photography & Convergence; Integrated Marketing Communication

DUQUESNE UNIVERSITY — 600 Forbes Ave., Pittsburgh, PA, 15282 (412) 396-6460; fax (412) 396-4792; e-mail arnett@duq.edu
Chair/Prof. — Ronald C. Arnett
Assoc. Prof. — Patricia Arneson

Assoc. Prof. — Robert V. Bellamy
Assoc. Prof. — D. Clark Edwards
Assoc. Prof. — Janie M.H. Fritz
Assoc. Prof. — Margaret Patterson
Assoc. Prof. — Richard H. Thames
Assoc. Prof. — Francis Thornton
Assoc. Prof. — Calvin Troup
Asst. Prof. — Michael J. Dillon
Asst. Prof. — Roy Joseph
Asst. Prof. — Kathleen Roberts
Asst. Prof. — Joseph Sora
Instr. — S. Alyssa Groom
Prof. Emer. — Eva Robotti
AFFILIATIONS: KTA, PRSSA, SPJ
DEGREES:BA, MA, PhD
DEPARTMENTS: Department of Communication and Rhetorical Studies, 1948
SEQUENCES: Major: Communication Studies (Corporate Communication/ Interpersonal Public Relations, Integrated Marketing Communication, Management Communication, Information Management in Organizations, Media Organizations, Rhetoric and Argumentation and Self-Designed

ELIZABETHTOWN COLLEGE — Dept. of Communications, Elizabethtown, PA, 17022 (717) 361-1262; fax (717) 361-1180; e-mail GILLISTL@etown.edu
Chair/Assoc. Prof. — Tamara L. Gillis
Prof. — Robert C. Moore
Assoc. Prof. — Hans-Erik Wennberg
Assoc. Prof./Dir., Broadcasting — Randy K. Yoder
Instr. — David Donovan
Lectr./Dir., Stud. Pubs. — Kirsten Johnson
Adj. Instr. — John Feeser
Adj. Instr. — William M. Sloane
Adj. Instr — Stephen Trapnell
AFFILIATIONS: BEA, IABC, SCJ, IRTS, IBS, CMA
DEGREES:BA
DEPARTMENTS: Department of Communications, 1975
FACILITIES: FM, AdA, CATV, CCTV, CN, ComN, DR, JN, JM, PRA, VDT
SEQUENCES: Marketing Communications, Public Relations, Mass Communication (Radio, TV, Journalism), Honors (self-designed)

INDIANA UNIVERSITY OF PENNSYLVANIA — Dept. of Journalism, Indiana, PA, 15705 (412) 357-4411; fax (412) 357-7845; e-mail jn-dept@grove.iup.edu
Chair — Stanford G. Mukasa
David Loomis
DEPARTMENTS: Department of Journalism
SEQUENCES: Journalism Program: Practical approach, interdisciplinary program (with internships) for careers in news-editorial and public relations

LA SALLE UNIVERSITY — 1900 W. Olney Ave., Philadelphia, PA, 19141-1199 (215) 951-1844; fax (215) 951-5043; e-mail texter@lasalle.edu; web site www.lasalle.edu/academ/commun/home.htm
Chair — Lynne Texter
DEPARTMENTS: Department of Communication, 1985
SEQUENCES: Communication Program: The program provides a core of courses then invites students to complete a track in journalism, mass communication, public relations, or communication management. Master Degree Program in Professional Communication: Michael Smith, D

LEHIGH UNIV. — 33 Coppee Dr, Bethlehem, PA, 18015-3165, USA (610) 758-4454; fax (610) 758-6198; e-mail bw@lehigh.edu; web site www.thebrownandwhite.com
Head — Wally Trimble
Julie Stewart
Ed. in Chief — Jack Lule
DEPARTMENTS: Department of Journalism and Communication
SEQUENCES: Journalism Program: Undergraduate degree programs in journalism and science writing; minors in journalism, science writing and communication. The program emphasizes writing, research, communication technology and global studies. It has offered coursewo

LINCOLN UNIVERSITY OF THE COMMONWEALTH OF PENNSYLVANIA — 1570 Baltimore Pike, Lincoln University, PA, 19352 (484) 365-8145; fax (484) 365-8156; web site www.thelincolnianonline.com
Prof./Dir. — Serajul Bhuiyan
DEPARTMENTS: Department of English and Mass Communications
SEQUENCES: English Communications: The English Communications Major prepares students for careers in mass media. The major exposes students to common elements (familiarity with English, American, and African American literature; knowledge of media principles and pra

LOCK HAVEN UNIVERSITY — Dept. of Communication Media, Lock Haven, PA, 17745-2390 (570) 484-2376; fax (570) 484-2436; e-mail kkline@lhup.edu
Chair — Karen E. Kline
DEPARTMENTS: Communication Media Program, Department of Communication
SEQUENCES: Program offers professional training qualifying students for entry level positions in the mass media. Students can select one of three concentrations: print journalism, broadcast media or public relations and advertising

LYCOMING COLLEGE — 700 College Pl., Williamsport, PA, 17701 (570) 321-4297; fax (570) 321-4389; e-mail wild@lycoming.edu
Chair — Fredric M. Wild
DEPARTMENTS: Department of Communication, 1976
SEQUENCES: Communication Major: The program emphasizes the liberal arts through an interdisciplinary core and professional tracks in public relations and corporate communication, electronic media, and reporting and media writing

MILLERSVILLE UNIVERSITY — PO Box 1002, Millersville, PA, 17551-0302 (717) 872-3233; fax (717) 871-2051; e-mail bill.dorman@millersville.edu
Chair — Bill Dorman
DEPARTMENTS: Department of Communication and Theatre

POINT PARK UNIVERSITY — Dept. of Journalism & Mass Communication, Pittsburgh, PA, 15222-1984 (412) 392-4730; fax (412) 392-3917; e-mail hfallon@pointpark.edu; web site www.pointpark.edu
Chair/Prof. — Helen Fallon
Prof./Dir., Grad. Prog. — Dane S. Claussen
Prof. — David J. Fabilli
Prof. — Robert O'Gara
Assoc. Prof. — William R. Moushey
Asst. Prof. — Heather Starr Fiedler
Asst. Prof./Broadcaster-in-Residence — Jan Getz
Asst. Prof. — Steven M. Hallock
Asst. Prof. — Anthony Moretti
Asst. Prof. — Christopher Rolinson
Vstg. Prof. — Johan Yssel
AFFILIATIONS: Ad Club, SPJ, PRSSA, CSB (College Students in Broadcasting - AWRT affiliation)
DEGREES:AA, BA, BFA, BS, MA
DEPARTMENTS: Department of Journalism and Mass Communication, 1960
FACILITIES: AdA, CCTV, CN, ComN, ComTV, DR, FM, JM, JN, PRA, UPI, VDT
SEQUENCES: Advertising and Public Relations, Broadcasting (Radio and TV), Print, Public Relations, Journalism and Mass Communication, Photojournalism, Photography, Digital Media, Integrated Marketing Communication

SAINT JOSEPH'S UNIVERSITY — 5600 City Ave., Philadelphia, PA, 19131-1395 (610) 660-1884; fax (610) 660-3235; e-mail jparker@sju.edu
Chair — Jo Alyson Parker
DEPARTMENTS: Department of English
SEQUENCES: English Program: Designed to acquaint students with many forms of literary expression, to deepen their sensibilities and enrich their lives. Clear judgment and concise communication are a goal of every course. Students choose a concentration in literatur

SHIPPENSBURG UNIVERSITY/ COMMUNICATION/JOURNALISM DEPARTMENT — 1871 Old Main Dr., Shippensburg, PA, 17257 (717) 477-1521; fax (717) 477-4013; e-mail commjour@ship.edu; web site webspace.ship.edu/commjour
Chair/Prof./electronic media — Edward J. Carlin
Assoc. Prof./print& online media — Michael W. Drager
Asst. Prof./public relations — Carrie Sipes
Asst. Prof./print & online media — Stephanie Anderson Witmer
Asst. Prof./print & online media — Kyle Heim
Assit. Prof./electronic media — James Lohrey
Asst. Prof./public relations — Jamila Cupid
Instr. — Amy Williams
DEGREES:BA- Communications/Journalism; MS- Communication Studies
DEPARTMENTS: Communications/ Journalism Department
FACILITIES: DR, CCTV, CN, ComN, PRA, VDT, AM/FM, AP
SEQUENCES: Electronic Media, Print Media, Public Relations

SUSQUEHANNA UNIVERSITY — 514 University Ave., Selinsgrove, PA, 17870-1164 (570) 372-4355; fax (570) 372-2757; e-mail augustin@susqu.edu
Chair — Larry D. Augustine
DEPARTMENTS: Department of Communications, 1966
SEQUENCES: Program includes Broadcasting, Communications Studies, Corporate Communications, Journalism, Mass Communications, Public Relations, Secondary Education and Speech Communication

TEMPLE UNIVERSITY — 2020 N. 13th St., Philadelphia, PA, 19122-6080 (215) 204-7433; fax (215) 204-1974; e-mail news@temple-news.com; web site www.temple.edu/journalism
Chair/Assoc. Prof. — Andrew Mendelson
Prof. — Thomas Eveslage
Prof./Dir., MJ Prog./Dir., Photojournalism seq. — Edward Trayes
Assoc. Prof. — Christopher Harper
Assoc. Prof. — Carolyn Kitch
Assoc. Prof./Dir., Broadcast Journ. seq. — Karen M. Turner
Assoc. Prof./Dir., News-Ed. seq. — Linn Washington
Assoc. Prof. — Fabienne Darling-Wolf
Asst. Prof. — Shenid Bhayroo
Asst. Prof. — Susan Jacobson
Asst. Prof. — George Miller
Asst. Prof./Internship Dir. — Maida Odom
Asst. Prof./Dir., Mag. seq. — Larry Stains
Asst. Prof. — Francesca Viola
AFFILIATIONS: KTA, SPJ, NABJ, RTNDA, ED2010
DEGREES:BA, MJ, PhD
DEPARTMENTS: Department of Journalism, 1927
FACILITIES: FM, CN, JM, DR, VDT
SEQUENCES: Broadcast Journalism, Magazine, Mass Media Photography, News-Editorial

THE PENNSYLVANIA STATE UNIVERSITY — 201 Carnegie Bldg., University Park, PA, 16802 (814) 863-1484; fax (814) 863-8044; web site www.psu.edu/dept/comm
Dean/Prof./Co-Dir., Sports Journ. Ctr. — Douglas Anderson
Foster Prof., Writing/Editing — Tony Barbieri
Curley Prof. First Amendment Studies/Co-Dir., PA First Amendment Ctr. — Clay Calvert
Prof./Assoc. Vice Pres./Sr. Assoc. Dean, Undergrad. Educ. — Jeremy Cohen
Prof./Distinguished Professional-in-Residence/Co-Dir., Sports Journ. Ctr. — John J. Curley
Prof./Pioneers Chair, Telecommunications — Robert M. Frieden
Prof./Knight Chair in Sports Journalism and Society and dir., Curley Sports Journalism Ctr. — Malcolm Moran
Prof./Assoc. Dean, Grad. Studies/Research/ Dir., Page Ctr. for Integrity in Public Com. — John S. Nichols
Prof./Co-Dir., Media Effects Lab — Mary Beth Oliver
Distinguished Prof./Dir., Washington Prog./ Co-Dir., PA First Amendment Ctr. — Robert D. Richards
Prof./Co-Dir., Media Effects Lab — S. Shyam Sundar
Prof./Palmer Chair, Telecommunications & Law/Co-Dir., Institute for Information Policy — Richard D. Taylor
Assoc. Prof./Dept. Head, Adv./PR — Robert A. Baukus
Assoc. Prof. — Ronald V. Bettig
Assoc. Prof./Dir., Int'l Programs — Barbara O. Bird
Assoc. Prof. — Lyn E. Elliot
Assoc. Prof. — Russell Frank
Assoc. Prof. — Jeanne L. Hall
Assoc. Prof. — Martin E. Halstuk
Assoc. Prof./Dir., Editing Excellence Ctr./ Assoc. Dir., Sports Journ. Ctr. — Marie C. Hardin
AFFILIATIONS: AAF, KTA, NABJ, SPJ, WICT, NAMIC, PSAJD, AHANA, PRSSA, PSAF, RTNDA, SFO
DEGREES:BA - Advertising, Public Relations, Film-Video, Journalism, Media Studies, Telecommunications; MA - Media Studies, Telecommunications Studies; PhD - Mass Communications
DEPARTMENTS: College of Communications, 1930
FACILITIES: AM/FM, AP, CCTV, CN, ComMedia, ComRadio, ETV, VDT
SEQUENCES: Majors: Advertising/Public Relations, Film and Video, Journalism, Media Studies, Telecommunications

THE PENNSYLVANIA STATE UNIVERSITY, ALTOONA COLLEGE — 3000 Ivyside Park, Altoona, PA, 16601 (814) 949-5769; fax (814) 949-5774
Coord. — Bob Trumpbour
DEGREES:BA
DEPARTMENTS: Communications Program
SEQUENCES: An integrated program that balances theory and hands-on production, the major is designed to give students the experience to become versatile media practitioners with a curriculum that explores the implications of the transition to digital technologies an

UNIVERSITY OF PENNSYLVANIA — Annenberg School for Communication, Philadelphia, PA, 19104-6220 (215) 898-7041; fax (215) 898-2024; e-mail admin@pobox.asc.upenn.edu
DEPARTMENTS: Program in Communication
SEQUENCES: Communication Program: Graduate program in Media Criticism, Mass Communication Research, Health and Development Communication, Political Communication

UNIVERSITY OF PITTSBURGH — 526 Cathedral of Learning, Pittsburgh, PA, 15260 (412) 624-6536; fax (412) 624-6639; e-mail patsy1@pitt.edu
Coord. — Patsy Sims
DEPARTMENTS: Department of English,

Non-Fiction Writing (newspaper or magazine)
SEQUENCES: Journalism Program: Undergraduate writing major in Newspaper and Magazine tracts; MFA in Creative Non-Fiction

URSINUS COLLEGE — Dept. of Media & Communication Studies, Collegeville, PA, 19426-1000 (610) 409-3603; fax (610) 409-3733; e-mail jmiller@ursinus.edu
Chair — Jay K. Miller
DEPARTMENTS: Department of Media and Communication Studies, 1987
SEQUENCES: The Media and Communication Studies Department offers an interdisciplinary course of study in which students examine the aesthetic, cultural, economic, legal, political and ethical implications of communication in society. Based in the liberal arts and d

YORK COLLEGE OF PENNSYLVANIA — MAC Ctr., Country Club Rd., York, PA, 17405-7199 (717) 815-1354; fax (717) 849-1602; e-mail bfurio@ycp.edu
Chair — Brian Furio
AFFILIATIONS: PRSSA
DEGREES:BA
DEPARTMENTS: Division of Communication
FACILITIES: PRA, CN, AM/FM, DR, TV production center
SEQUENCES: Majors in Public Relations and Mass Communication

PUERTO RICO

UNIVERSITY OF PUERTO RICO — PO Box 21880, UPR Sta., San Juan, PR, 931 (787) 764-0000; fax (787) 763-5390; web site copu.upr.clu.edu
Dir. — Eliseo Colon Zayas
DEGREES:BA, MA
DEPARTMENTS: School of Communication
SEQUENCES: Communication Programs: BA with majors in Journalism, Advertising and Public Relations and Audiovisual Communications. MA with majors in Theory and Research and Journalism

UNIVERSITY OF THE SACRED HEART — PO Box 12383, San Juan, PR, 00914-0383 (787) 728-1515; fax (787) 268-8874; e-mail cgarcia@sagrado.edu; web site www.sagrado.edu
Dir. — Carmen Sara Garcia
DEGREES:BA, MA
DEPARTMENTS: Department of Communication, 1981
SEQUENCES: BAC- Communication: major in Advertising, Journalism, Telecommunications, Photography, Radio Production, Marketing, Visual Arts and General Communications; Associated Degrees in Photography, and Radio Production; MAC- Communications: major in Public Rela

RHODE ISLAND

UNIVERSITY OF RHODE ISLAND — Dept. of Journalism, Kingston, RI, 2881 (401) 874-2195; fax (401) 874-4450; e-mail lllevin@uri.edu; web site www.uri.edu/artsci/Jor
Chair — Linda Lotridge Levin
AFFILIATIONS: RTNDA, SPJ
DEGREES:BA
DEPARTMENTS: Department of Journalism, 1960
FACILITIES: VDT, AM, FM, CCTV, CN, ComN, DR, ComR, ComTV, PRA
SEQUENCES: News-Editorial, Broadcast Journalism, Public Relations

SOUTH CAROLINA

BENEDICT COLLEGE — 1600 Harden St, Columbia, SC, 29204-1058, USA (803) 705-4645; fax (803) 253-5065; web site www.benedict.edu
Chair — Carolyn Drakeford
Momo Rogers
DEGREES:B.A. in Mass Communication
DEPARTMENTS: Media Arts Department
SEQUENCES: Mass Communication Program: offers two concentrations to students choosing the major. The print concentration prepares students who wish to pursue career opportunities in publication, writing, and related fields, while the broadcast concentration prepare

CLAFLIN UNIVERSITY — 400 Magnolia St., Orangeburg, SC, 29115-4498 (803) 535-5769; e-mail cgooch@claflin.edu
Chair/Prof. — Cheryl R. Gooch
Prof. — Lynette Lashley
Asst. Prof. — Preston Blakely
Asst. Prof. — Julian Williams
Instr. — Gary Dawkins
Journalist-in-Residence — Lee Harter
Prodn. Specialist — Ameen Hall
Video Studio Dir. — Michael Fiarwell
DEGREES:BA
DEPARTMENTS: Department of Mass Communications, 1997
FACILITIES: Modern television studio in which students produce several television shows; all digital student-run radio station; all-digital off-line editing system. In future, it will add an all-digital comprehensive media lab
SEQUENCES: Offers courses that prepare students for careers in broadcast journalism, print journalism, public relations and electronic production. The Mass Communications concentration courses develop students' competence and skills in broadcast journalism, print jo

COLLEGE OF CHARLESTON — 66 George St, Charleston, SC, 29424-0001, USA (843) 953-7017; fax (843) 953-7037; e-mail mcgeeb@cofc.edu; web site www.cofc.edu/communication
Chair — Brian McGee
Katie Orlando
DEGREES:BA, MA
DEPARTMENTS: Department of Communication, 1994
SEQUENCES: Communication Department: The bachelor of arts degree in communication has three concentrations: media studies (converged media, including reporting and other media functions); corporate and organizational communication (public relations, training and dev

FRANCIS MARION UNIVERSITY — PO Box 100547, Florence, SC, 29501-0547 (843) 661-1605; fax (843) 661-1547; e-mail dstewart@fmarion.edu
Chair — Don Stewart
DEPARTMENTS: Department of Mass Communication
SEQUENCES: Mass Communication major: Requires admission based on GPA. Provides students guidance and encouragement to develop communication skills needed to begin careers in journalism, public relations and allied professions. The major includes a core curriculum of

UNIVERSITY OF SOUTH CAROLINA — School of Journalism and Mass Communications, Columbia, SC, 29208 (803) 777-3244; fax (803) 777-4103; web site www.jour.sc.edu
Dir./Prof. — Carol J. Pardun
Prof./Dean, College of Mass Commun. and Information Studies — Charles Bierbauer
Prof. — Shirley Staples Carter
Prof. — Lowndes F. Stephens
Assoc. Prof./Chair, Print and Broadcast Journ. Seq. — Kenneth Campbell
Assoc. Prof./Assoc. Dir., Grad. Studies — Erik L. Collins
Assoc. Prof. — Bonnie L. Drewniany
Assoc. Prof. — Sonya F. Duhe
Assoc. Prof. — Augie Grant
Assoc. Prof. — Cecile S. Holmes
Assoc. Prof./Int'l Studies Coord. — Keith Kenney
Assoc. Prof. — Bruce E. Konkle
Assoc. Prof./Chair, Vis. Comm. seq. — Vance L. Kornegay
Assoc. Prof. — Richard Moore
Assoc. Prof./Chair, Adv./PR Seq. — Ran Wei
Assoc. Prof. — Thomas Weir
Assoc. Prof. — Ernest L. Wiggins
Asst. Prof. — Glenda Alvarado
Asst. Prof. — John Besley
Asst. Prof. — Tom Klipstine
AFFILIATIONS: AAF, AER, KTA, NABJ, PRSSA, SND, SPJ
DEGREES:BA, MA, MMC, PhD.
DEPARTMENTS: School of Journalism and Mass Communication, 2002 (formerly College of Journalism and Mass Communications, 1923)
FACILITIES: AP, AM, FM, AdA, CCTV, ETV, JN, VDT
SEQUENCES: Programs of Study: Advertising, Electronic Journalism, Print Journalism, Public Relations, Visual Communications

UNIVERSITY OF SOUTH CAROLINA UPSTATE — 800 University Way, Spartanburg, SC, 29303 (864) 503-5844; fax (864) 503-5814; e-mail cugochukwu@uscupstate.edu
Chair — Rachelle Prioleau
DEGREES:BA
DEPARTMENTS: Fine Arts and Communication Studies
SEQUENCES: Fine Arts and Communication Studies program offers a BA in Communications which examines communication processes in interpersonal, small group and public settings and within organizations, in cultures and in the mass media

UNIVERSITY OF SOUTH CAROLINA, AIKEN — 471 University Pkwy., Aiken, SC, 29801 (803) 641-3481; fax (803) 641-3461; e-mail williamh@usca.edu
Chair — William Harpine
DEGREES:BA
DEPARTMENTS: Department of Communications, 1998
SEQUENCES: BA in Communications, which examines communication processes in interpersonal, small group and public settings and within organizations, in cultures and in the mass media

WINTHROP UNIVERSITY — Dept. of Mass Communication, Rock Hill, SC, 29733-0001 (803) 323-2121; fax (803) 323-2464; e-mail clickw@winthrop.edu
Chair/Prof. — J. William Click
Part-time Prof. — William A. Fisher
Assoc. Prof. — Haney Howell
Assoc. Prof. — Marilyn S. Sarow
Assoc. Prof. — Lawrence C. Timbs
Asst. Prof. — Padmini Patwardhan
Asst. Prof. — Guy Reel
Instr. — Mark Nortz
Part-time Instr. — Bonnye Stuart
AFFILIATIONS: RTNDAC (Radio Television News Directors Assn of the Carolinas), KTA, SPJ, AWIC
DEGREES:BA, BS
DEPARTMENTS: Department of Mass Communication, 1925
FACILITIES: CCTV, CN, VDT
SEQUENCES: Broadcasting, Journalism, Integrated Marketing Communication

SOUTH DAKOTA

BLACK HILLS STATE UNIVERSITY — College of Arts & Sciences, 1200 University St., Unit 9003, Spearfish, SD, 57799-9003 (605) 642-6420; fax (605) 642-6762; e-mail marycatonrosser@bhsu.edu
Asst. Prof., Mass Commun. — Mary Caton-Rosser
DEGREES:BS, BA
DEPARTMENTS: College of Arts and Sciences
SEQUENCES: Journalism Program: Four-year undergraduate degree program in mass commmunications with emphases in print journalism, computer publishing, multi-media, photography, public relations or telecommunications

MOUNT MARTY COLLEGE — Journalism/Public Relations Program, Yankton, SD, 57078 (605) 668-1506
Dir. — Jerry W. Wilson
DEPARTMENTS: Journalism/Public Relations Program
SEQUENCES: BA in Journalism/Public Relations with two emphases, built upon core communications courses, a solid liberal arts background, and extensive applied experience.

SOUTH DAKOTA STATE UNIVERSITY — Rotunda Ln., Brookings, SD, 57007-0596 (605) 688-4171; fax (605) 688-5034; e-mail mary.arnold@sdstate.edu
Head — Mary Peterson Arnold
Prof. — John E. Getz
Prof. — Lyle D. Olson
Prof. — Mary Arnold
Assoc. Prof. — Doris J. Giago
Assoc. Prof. — Dennis Hinde
Assoc. Prof. — Roxanne Neuberger Lucchesi
Assoc. Prof. — James L. Paulson
Asst. Prof. — Matthew Cecil
Instr. — Frank A. Klock
Part-time Instr. — Jennifer Tiernan
Prof. Emer. — Richard W. Lee
Prof. Emer. — Mary J. Perpich
AFFILIATIONS: AAF, ACT, KTA
DEGREES:BS, BA, MS
DEPARTMENTS: Department of Journalism and Mass Communication, 1924
FACILITIES: AP, CCTV, CN, ComN, ComR, DR, ETV, JN, VDT
SEQUENCES: News-Editorial, Advertising, Broadcast Journalism, Agricultural Journalism

UNIVERSITY OF SOUTH DAKOTA — 414 E. Clark St., Vermillion, SD, 57069 (605) 677-5477; fax (605) 677-4250; e-mail troberts@usd.edu; web site www.usd.edu/cfa/MassComm/mcom.html
Chair — Terry Robertson
AFFILIATIONS: AAF, PRSSA, SPJ, AIGA
DEGREES:BA, BS, MA
DEPARTMENTS: Department of Mass Communication, 1915
SEQUENCES: Programs: Advertising, Electronic Media, Journalism, Public Relations, Visual Communication

TENNESSEE

AUSTIN PEAY STATE UNIVERSITY — Dept. of Communication & Theatre, Clarksville, TN, 37044 (931) 221-7378; fax (931) 221-7265; e-mail gotcherm@apsu.edu
Chair — Mike Gotcher
DEGREES:BA, BS, MA
DEPARTMENTS: Department of Communication and Theatre
FACILITIES: AM, CN, TV studio, campus magazine, cable TV channel
SEQUENCES: Broadcast Media, Public

Relations, Print and Web Journalism, Radio-TV, Corporate Communication, Media Technologies, Theatre, Theatre Education; online MA- Corporate Communication

BELMONT UNIV. — 1900 Belmont Blvd, Nashville, TN, 37212-3758, USA (615) 460-6000; fax (615) 460-5532; e-mail vision@mail.belmont.edu; web site www.belmontvision.com; www.belmont.eduLinda Quigley
Chair — Thom Storey
Karen Bennett
Bethany Brinton
Lance Conzett
AFFILIATIONS: PRSSA
DEGREES:BA, BS
DEPARTMENTS: Department of Media Studies, 1986
SEQUENCES: Audio Video Production, Journalism, Mass Communication, Public Relations, Video Production.

CHRISTIAN BROTHERS UNIVERSITY — Dept. of Communication and Performing Arts, Memphis, TN, 38104 (901) 722-0386; fax (901) 722-0494
Head — Joseph Ajami
DEGREES:BA
DEPARTMENTS: Journalism Option (in Department of Communication and Performing Arts), 1986
FACILITIES: AdA, CN, ComN, ComTV, DR, VDT

EAST TENNESSEE STATE UNIVERSITY — PO Box 70667, Johnson City, TN, 37614 (423) 439-4491; fax (423) 439-7540; e-mail Robertsc@etsu.edu
Chair — Charles Roberts
DEGREES:BA, BS
DEPARTMENTS: Department of Communication, 1968
SEQUENCES: Communication Program: Offers a BS/BA with a major in mass communications with four division options: advertising, broadcasting (sequences in management, news and production/performance), journalism and public relations

LIPSCOMB UNIVERSITY — Dept. of Communication, Nashville, TN, 37204-3951 (615) 279-6072; fax (615) 269-1834
Chair/Assoc. Prof. — James F. McCollum
AFFILIATIONS: SPJ, PRSSA
DEPARTMENTS: Department of Communication, 1950
FACILITIES: WZLU-LPFM
SEQUENCES: Concentrations in journalism, mass communication, oral communication and public relations

MIDDLE TENNESSEE STATE UNIVERSITY — MTSU Box 51, Murfreesboro, TN, 37132 (615) 898-2813; fax (615) 898-5682; e-mail lmccann@mtsu.edu
Dean/Prof. — Roy L. Moore
Assoc. Dean/Prof. — John Omachonu
Dir., Devel. — Steven.J Barnes
Academic Advisor. — Sarah Jackson
Academic Advisor. — Hattie Traylor
Prof. — Edd Applegate
Prof. — David P. Badger
Prof. — Richard Barnet
Prof. — Marc Barr
Prof. — John Bodle
Prof. — Larry Burriss
Prof. — Cosette Collier
Prof. — David Eason
Prof. — Paul Fischer
Prof. — Christopher R. Harris
Prof./Chair, Dept. of Recording Industry — Christian Haseleu
Prof. — John Hill
Prof. — Thomas Hutchison
Prof. — Tom Jimison
Prof. — Edward M. Kimbrell
AFFILIATIONS: AM, AER, MCAI, RTNDA, KT, NABJ, PRSSA, SPJ
DEGREES:BS, MFA, MS
DEPARTMENTS: College of Mass Communication, 1972
FACILITIES: AP, EM, CATV. CN, CNN, ComR, DDR, VDT, digital imaging lab, digital animation lab, photography lab, internet electronic newsroom
SEQUENCES: Departments: Electronic Media Communication, School of Journalism, Recording Industry; Graduate Studies- Mass Communication, Recording Industry, Office of Communication Research, Seigenthaler Chair of First Amendment Studies

MILLIGAN COLLEGE — PO Box 500, Milligan College, TN, 37682 (423) 461-8994; fax (423) 461-8965; e-mail sjdahlman@milligan.edu; web site www.milligan.edu
Chair — Simon J. Dahlman
DEGREES:BA, BS
DEPARTMENTS: Communications Area, 1988
SEQUENCES: A communications major with 36 semester hours leads to BA or BS degree. Five emphases available: broadcasting, digital media, film studies, journalism, and public relations

TENNESSEE TECHNOLOGICAL UNIVERSITY — Journalism Dept., 1 William L. Jones Dr., Cookeville, TN, 38505-0001 (931) 372-3060; fax (931) 372-6225; e-mail ehutch@tntech.edu
Dir. — Earl R. Hutchison
DEPARTMENTS: Department of English and Communication, Communication/Journalism

THE UNIVERSITY OF TENNESSEE — 1345 Circle Park Dr., 302 Communications-UEB, Knoxville, TN, 37996-0332 (865) 974-3031; fax (865) 974-3896; e-mail cci@utk.edu; web site cci.utk.edu
Dean/Prof. — Michael Wirth
Prof. — Paul G. Ashdown
Prof. — Benjamin J. Bates
Prof. — Dorothy A. Bowles
Prof. — Charles E. Caudill
Prof. — John E. Haley
Prof. — Roxanne Hovland
Prof. — Mariea G. Hoy
Prof./Chair, Excellence-Journ. — Mark E. Littmann
Prof. — Barbara A. Moore
Prof. — Margaret A. Morrison
Prof./Dir., Internationalization/Outreach — Norman R. Swan
Prof./Dir., School of Adv. & PR — Ronald Taylor
Prof. — Dwight L. Teeter
Assoc. Prof. — Lisa T. Fall
Assoc. Prof. — Daniel J. Foley
Assoc. Prof. — Mark D. Harmon
Assoc. Prof. — Robert B. Heller
Assoc. Prof. — Barbara K. Kaye
Assoc. Prof. — Catherine A. Luther
AFFILIATIONS: AAF, NBS/AER, KTA, PRSSA, SPJ
DEGREES:BS, MS, PHD in Communication and Information
DEPARTMENTS: College of Communication and Information, 2002; College of Communications, 1969; School of Journalism, 1947
FACILITIES: FM, AdA, CN, ComN, ComR, ComTV, CATV, PRA, VDT, JM
SEQUENCES: Advertising, Public Relations, Journalism and Electronic Media

UNIVERSITY OF MEMPHIS — Journalism Dept., Memphis, TN, 38152 (901) 678-2401; fax (901) 678-4287; e-mail jredmond@memphis.edu
Chair/Prof. — David Arant
Prof. — E.W. Bill Brody
Prof./Grad. Coord./Head, PR — Rick Fischer
Prof. — Elinor Grusin
Prof. — Dan Lattimore
Prof. — Jim Redmond
Assoc. Prof. — Ronald Spielberger
Assoc. Prof. — Art Terry
Assoc. Prof./Asst. Chair — Sandra Utt
Asst. Prof. — Joe Hayden
Asst. Prof. — Cynthia Hopson
Asst. Prof. — Candy Justice
Asst. Prof. — Lurene Kelley
Asst. Prof. — Jin Yang
Instr. — Norm Hays
Instr. — Olivia Miller
Instr. — Robert Willis
Prof. Emer. — John DeMott
Prof. Emer. — John Lee
Prof. Emer. — Herbert Williams
AFFILIATIONS: AAF, KTA, NABJ, PRSSA, SPJ
DEGREES:BA, MA
DEPARTMENTS: Journalism Department, 1956
FACILITIES: FM, AdA, CATV, CN, ComN, ComR, ComTV, DR, ETV, JN, VDT, PRA
SEQUENCES: Advertising, Broadcast News, News-Editorial, Public Relations, Internet Journalism

UNIVERSITY OF TENNESSEE AT CHATTANOOGA — Communication Dept., Chattanooga, TN, 37403-2598 (423) 425-4400; fax (423) 425-4695
Interim Head/Assoc. Prof./Luther Masingill
Prof. — Betsy B. Alderman
Prof./West Chair of Excellence in Commun. — David B. Sachsman
Head/Frank McDonald Prof. — S. Kittrell Rushing
Assoc. Prof. — Rebekah Bromley
Assoc. Prof. — ELizabeth Gailey
Asst. Prof. — Charlene Simmons
Lectr. — Felicia McGhee-Hilt
Part-time Instr./Dir., WUTC/Jazz 88 — John McCormack
Part-time Instr. — Chris Willis
Part-time Instr. — Deborah Luhrs
Prof. Emer. — Peter K. Pringle
AFFILIATIONS: SPJ, BEA, PRSSA, AAF, NABJ, ASJMC
DEGREES:BA
DEPARTMENTS: Communication Department, 1978; Accredited ACEJMC, 1996
FACILITIES: FM, AdA, CCTV, CN, ComN, PRA, VDT, AP, CATV
SEQUENCES: Communication

UNIVERSITY OF TENNESSEE AT MARTIN — Dept. of Communications, 305 Gooch Hall, Martin, TN, 38238 (731) 881-7546; fax (731) 881-7550; e-mail Rnanney@utm.edu
Chair — Robert Nanney
AFFILIATIONS: Newspaper, SPJ, PRSSA, Broadcasting Guild, NABJ, WIC, VisComm Society, yearbook
DEGREES:BA, BS
DEPARTMENTS: Department of Communications, 1971
FACILITIES: AM/FM, DR, JN, CableTV, TV, AP, VDT, Audio/Video editing lab
SEQUENCES: Broadcasting, News Editorial, PR, Visual Communication

---

TEXAS

ABILENE CHRISTIAN UNIVERSITY — Journalism & Mass Communication Dept., Abilene, TX, 79699 (325) 674-2296; fax (325) 674-2139; e-mail cheryl.bacon@jmc.acu.edu
Chair/Prof. — Cheryl M. Bacon
Prof./Dir., Electronic Media — Larry Bradshaw
Assoc. Prof./Dir., Journ. — Merlin Mann
Instr. — Dave Hogan
Instr. — J.R. Kessler
Instr. — Susan Lewis
Instr./Dir., Photojourn. — Cade White
Prof. Emer. — Charles H. Marler
AFFILIATIONS: AAF, KTA, PRSSA, SPJ
DEGREES:BS
DEPARTMENTS: Journalism and Mass Communication Department, 1969
FACILITIES: AP, AM/FM, AdA, CATV, LPTV, ComN, ComTV, DR, ETV, JN, PRA, VDT, Lexis/Nexis
SEQUENCES: Integrated Marketing Communication, Journalism, Electronic Media

ANGELO STATE UNIVERSITY — Dept. of Communications, Drama & Journalism, San Angelo, TX, 76909 (915) 942-2031; fax (915) 942-2078; e-mail jack.eli@angelo.edu
Prof./Head — Jack C. Eli
AFFILIATIONS: AAF, TIPA, TJEC
DEPARTMENTS: Department of Communications, Drama and Journalism, 1965
SEQUENCES: Journalism Program: Offers courses in news editorial, advertising/public relations and broadcasting

BAYLOR UNIVERSITY — Dept. of Journalism, 1 Bear Plaza #97330, Waco, TX, 76798-7353 (254) 710-3261; fax (254) 710-3363; web site www.baylorlariat.com
Chair/Assoc. Prof. — Clark Baker
Prof. — Mike Blackman
Prof. — Sara Stone
Assoc. Prof. — Robert Darden
Assoc. Prof. — Douglas Ferdon
Asst. Prof. — Mia Moody
Instr. — Sharon Bracken
Instr. — Cassy Burleson
Instr. — Allin Means
Instr. — Brad Owens
Instr. — Maxey Parrish
Instr. — Carol Perry
Instr. — Amanda Sturgill
Instr. — Kevin Tankersley
AFFILIATIONS: KTA, NABJ, PRSSA, SPJ
DEGREES:BA, MA, MIJ
DEPARTMENTS: Department of Journalism, 1927
FACILITIES: AP, FM, DR, JM, JN, PRA, VDT, CCTV
SEQUENCES: News-Editorial, Public Relations, International Journalism, Photojournalism

BAYLOR UNIVERSITY — 1 Bear Pl, Unit 97330, Waco, TX, 76798-7330, USA (254) 710-3407; fax (254) 710-1714; e-mail lariat@baylor.edu; web site www.baylorlariat.com
Dir., Mktg. Information — Paul Carr
Advertising Sales and Marketing Manager — Jamile Yglecias
Asst. Media Adviser — Julie Freeman
AFFILIATIONS: Baylor University
DEGREES:B.A., M.A., M.I.J.
DEPARTMENTS: Newspaper; Yearbook; Magazine; Website; Broadcast;

HARDIN-SIMMONS UNIVERSITY — Dept. of Communication, Abilene, TX, 79698 (915) 670-1414; fax (915) 670-1409; e-mail dbaergen.comm@hsutx.edu; web site www.hsutx.edu/academics/LiberalArts/communication
Chair — Darrel Baergen
DEPARTMENTS: Department of Communication
SEQUENCES: Journalism Program: Twenty-eight hours in Journalism/Public Relations and forty-five hours in Broadcasting/Visual Communication

HOUSTON BAPTIST UNIVERSITY — Dept. of Communications, Houston, TX, 77074-3298 (281) 649-3520; fax (281) 649-3246; e-mail srsnyder@hbu.edu
Chair/Assoc. Prof./Photography — Steven R. Snyder
Prof. — James S. Taylor
Assoc. Prof./Advisor, Collegian — Alice Rowlands
Asst. Prof./PR — Laura B. Ashley
Instr./Program Mgr., Instructional TV — Clay Porter
Instr./Opns. Mgr., Instructional TV — Isaac Simpson
Adj. Prof. — Vivian Camacho
Adj. Prof. — Don Kobos

DEGREES:BA, BS
DEPARTMENTS: Department of Communications, 1979
FACILITIES: TV studio, Newspaper lab, DR
SEQUENCES: Newswriting/Reporting, TV Production, Advertising/PR, Photojournalism/ Photography

LAMAR UNIVERSITY-BEAUMONT — Box 10050, Beaumont, TX, 77710 (409) 880-8153; fax (409) 880-8760; e-mail commdept@hal.lamar.edu
Chair — Patrick Harrigan
DEGREES:BS
DEPARTMENTS: Department of Communication
SEQUENCES: Communicaton Program: The department offers a broad-based major in communication with concentrations in corporate communication studies, media/ broadcast and film studies, journalism studies, and advertising studies

MIDWESTERN STATE UNIVERSITY — B110 Fain Fine Arts Ctr., Wichita Falls, TX, 76308 (940) 397-4391; fax (940) 397-4909; e-mail jim.sernoe@mwsu.edu
Chair/Assoc. Prof. — Jim Sernoe
Asst. Prof./Advisor, Campus Watch — Jim Gorham
Asst. Prof. — Sandra Grant
Asst. Prof. — Liz Minden
Asst. Prof./Advisor, The Wichitan — Randy Pruitt
Adj. Fac. — Judy Braddy
Adj. Fac. — Kory Dorman
Adj. Fac. — Roma Prassel
Adj. Fac. — Donnie Kirk
Adj. Fac. — Pam Morgan
Prof. Emer. — June Kable
Assoc. Prof. Emer. — Dencil R. Taylor
AFFILIATIONS: ACP, ASJMC, BEA, CBI, CMA, PRSA, SWEJMC, SWJC, TIPA
DEGREES:BA
DEPARTMENTS: Mass Communication Department, 1985
FACILITIES: TV studios, visual arts lab, Macintosh labs, Newspaper lab

PRAIRIE VIEW A&M UNIVERSITY — PO Box 0156, Prairie View, TX, 77446-0156 (409) 857-4511; fax (409) 857-2309; e-mail dejun_liu@pvamu.edu
Head — Dejun Liu
AFFILIATIONS: ACA, NAB, NABJ, AAF, NCA, SPJ, SSCA, TSCA
DEGREES:BA
DEPARTMENTS: Department of Communications, 1974
SEQUENCES: Journalism Program: The department, a part of the College of Arts and Sciences, offers a BA in Communications with a core of courses from all areas of the department (journalism, RATV, speech). Students then select the remainder of their major courses in

SAM HOUSTON STATE UNIVERSITY — 1804 Ave J, Huntsville, TX, 77341-0001, USA (936) 294-1341; fax (936) 294-1888
Chair/Prof. — Janet A. Bridges
Philip J. Warner Chair in Journ. — Michael L. Blackman
Philip J. Warner Chair in Journ. — Mickey Herskowitz
Assoc. Prof. — Tony R. DeMars
Assoc. Prof. — Anthony Friedmann
Assoc. Prof. — Hugh S. Fullerton
Assoc. Prof. — Christopher White
Asst. Prof. — Rene Qun Chen
Asst. Prof. — Wanda Reyes Velazquez
Instr. — Ruth M. Pate
Lectr. — Richard O. Kosuowei
Lectr. — Mel Strait
Lectr. — Patsy K. Ziegler
AFFILIATIONS: AAF, NBS, PRSSA, 3MG, TABS, NABJ
DEGREES:BA
DEPARTMENTS: Department of Mass Communication
FACILITIES: CTV, FM-Radio, newspaper, yearbook
SEQUENCES: Broadcast Journalism, Broadcast Production, Media Sales & Management, Print Journalism, Public Relations

SOUTHERN METHODIST UNIVERSITY — 3300 Dyer St., Umphrey Lee Ctr., Rm. 280, Dallas, TX, 75205 (214) 768-2775; fax (214) 768-3307; e-mail stratton@mail.sum.edu
Administrator — Judy Stratton
AFFILIATIONS: KTA, Press Club of Dallas, SPJ, Texas Assn. of Broadcast Educators, RTNDA
DEGREES:BA
DEPARTMENTS: Division of Journalism, Meadows School of the Arts
SEQUENCES: Journalism (News-Editorial and Broadcast Journalism)

STEPHEN F. AUSTIN STATE UNIVERSITY — Dept. of Communication, Nacogdoches, TX, 75962 (936) 468-4001; fax (936) 468-1331; e-mail wmouton@sfasu.edu
Interim Chair — Wanda Mouton
DEPARTMENTS: Department of Communication
SEQUENCES: Journalism Program: Broadcasting and journalism, with journalism courses grouped into news-editorial, photojournalism, advertising, and public relations emphases; also has a speech division

TEXAS A&M UNIVERSITY — 4234 Tamu, College Station, TX, 77843-0001, USA (979) 458-1802; fax (979) 845-6594; e-mail r-sumpter@tamu.edu; jourminor@tamu.edu
Dir., Journ. Studies/Assoc. Prof., Commun. — Randall S. Sumpter
Program Asst. — Roberto Farias
Sr. Lectr. — Edward L. Walraven
Lectr. — Dale A. Rice
SEQUENCES: Journalism Education Program: Offers an interdisciplinary minor in journalism emphasizing skills courses and frequent interaction with news professionals

TEXAS A&M UNIVERSITY — 107 Scoates Hall, College Station, TX, 77843-0001, USA (979) 862-3003; fax (979) 845-6296; e-mail dj-king@tamu.edu
Program Coord. — Deborah Dunsford
DEPARTMENTS: Department of Agricultural Leadership, Education, and Communications
SEQUENCES: Agricultural Communications/ Agricultural Journalism: Program focuses on the exchange of accurate information about the agricultural and natural resources industries through the most effective and efficient channels available using appropriate communicati

TEXAS A&M UNIVERSITY-COMMERCE — 2600 Neal St., Commerce, TX, 75429-3011 (903) 886-5229; fax (903) 468-3250; web site www.tamu-commerce.edu
Head/Prof. — John Hanners
Prof. — Lamar W. Bridges
Prof. — Robert Sanders
Assoc. Prof. — Gary Burton
Assoc. Prof. — John Mark Dempsey
Asst. Prof. — John Bellotti
Asst. prof. — Carrie Lee Klypchak
Asst. Prof. — Michael G. Knight
Instr. — James T. Anderson
Instr./Publications Advisor — Fred Stewart
Prof. Emer. — Georgia Anne Bomar
Prof. Emer. — Anthony J. Buckley
Prof. Emer. — Otha C. Spencer
DEGREES:BA, BS, MA, MS
DEPARTMENTS: Mass Media, Communication, and Theatre Department (formerly Journalism and Printing and Communication and Theater), 2001
FACILITIES: ComN, PRA, VDT, JN, Instructional Printing Facilities, Hdq. Texas Intercollegiate Press Association & Hall of Fame, AM/FM, CATV, ETV.
SEQUENCES: Journalism (majors in News-Editorial, Public Relations, Journalism/ Agricultural Sciences, Journalism/ Economics (double majors)), and Teaching emphases, Radio Television, Radio/ Television/Agricultural Sciences, Speech Communication and Teaching Emphases, T

TEXAS A&M UNIVERSITY-KINGSVILLE — 700 University Blvd., MSC 178, Kingsville, TX, 78363 (361) 593-3401; fax (361) 593-3402; e-mail william.alnor@tamuk.edu
Journalism Dir. — William M. Alnor
AFFILIATIONS: SWECJMC, UIL, TIPA
DEGREES:BA- Communication
DEPARTMENTS: Journalism/Department of Communications and Theater Arts
SEQUENCES: News-Editorial, Radio-TV

TEXAS A&M UNIVERSITY-TEXARKANA — 2600 N. Robison Rd., Texarkana, TX, 75505-5518 (903) 223-3169; fax (903) 223-3120
DEGREES:BS
DEPARTMENTS: Mass Communications and Journalism Department, 2002
SEQUENCES: Mass Communication and Journalism Program: Offers BS in Mass Communications. Graduates of their program are prepared for careers in the field of Journalism, Corporate Communication and Promotional Communication.

TEXAS CHRISTIAN UNIVERSITY — Dept. of Journalism, Fort Worth, TX, 76129 (817) 257-7425; fax (817) 257-7322; e-mail journalism@tcu.edu
Dir./Prof. — Tommy G. Thomason
Prof./Grad. Advisor, Ad/PR — Douglas Ann Newsom
Prof./Grad. Advisor, News, Chair, Div., Journalism — Suzanne Huffman
Prof. — William T. Slater
Assoc. Prof. — Amiso George
Assoc. Prof./Chair, Div., Ad/PR — Julie O'Neil
Assoc. Prof. — Maggie Thomas
Assoc. Prof. — John Tisdale
Asst. Prof. — Stacy Landreth-Grau
Asst. Prof. — Daxton Stewart
Asst. Prof. — Larry Lauer
Asst. Prof. — Janice Wood
Instr. — Steve Levering
Adj. Fac. — Geoff Campell
Adj. Fac. — Dave Ferman
Adj. Fac. — Claudia Butts
Adj. Fac. — Linda Campbell
Adj. Fac. — Carmen Goldthwaite
Adj. Fac. — Kent Chapline
Adj. Fac. — Mark Horvit
John Lumpkin
AFFILIATIONS: AAF, KTA, NABJ, PRSSA, SPJ
DEGREES:BA, BS, MS (Journalism and Ad/PR).
DEPARTMENTS: Schieffer School of Journalism, 1927
FACILITIES: AP, AM, FM, Ad/PR A, ComN, DR, JM, JN, VDT, Photolab, CATV
SEQUENCES: BA- News-Editorial, International Communication; BS- News-Editorial, Broadcast Journalism, PR/ Advertising; Teaching Certification; MS- Journalism Ad/PR

TEXAS LUTHERAN UNIV. — 1000 W Court St, Seguin, TX, 78155-5978, USA (830) 372-8073; fax (830) 372-8074; e-mail lonestarlutheran@tlu.edu; web site www.lslonline.netRobin Bisha
Chair — Steven S. Vrooman
Kristi Quiros
Emmalee Drummond
Naomi Urquiza
DEPARTMENTS: Department of English and Communication Studies
SEQUENCES: Communication Studies Program: Introduces students to the fundamental principles of human communication, as well as to the study of a variety of the historical and cultural forms such communication takes. Through participation with the student publicatio

TEXAS SOUTHERN UNIVERSITY — Dept. of Communications, Houston, TX, 77004 (713) 313-7214; fax (713) 313-7529; e-mail moore_sw@tsu.edu
Chair — Shirley Moore
DEPARTMENTS: Department of Communications, 1947
SEQUENCES: Journalism Program: The program offers bachelor's and master's degrees with concentrations in News/ Editorial, Advertising/PR and Broadcast Journalism

TEXAS STATE UNIVERSITY-SAN MARCOS — 601 University Dr., San Marcos, TX, 78666-4616 (512) 245-2656; fax (512) 245-7649; e-mail bergen@txstate.edu; web site www.masscomm.txstate.edu
Prof./Dir. — Lori Bergen
Prof. — Tom Grimes
Prof./Coord., Gen. Mass Comm. — Kate Pierce
Prof./Assoc. Dir., Grad. Studies — Sandhya Rao
Prof. — Bruce Smith
Prof. — Federico Subervi
Assoc. Profs./Coord., Electronic Media — Tim England
Assoc. Prof./Assoc. dean — Laurie Fluker
Assoc. Prof./Assoc. Dir. RRHEC — Judy Oskam
Assoc. Prof./Coord., PR — Frank Walsh
Assoc. Prof. — Susan Weill
Asst. Prof. — Gilbert Martinez
Asst. Prof.(Spring 2008) — Alexander Muk
Asst. Prof. — Ray Niekamp
Asst. Prof. — Cindy Royal
Lectr./Dir., Student Pubs — Bob Bajackson
Lectr. — Larry Carlson
Lectr. — Cunhyeong Ci
Lectr./Coord., Print — Kym Fox
Lectr./Coord., Ad — Jody Gibson
AFFILIATIONS: AAF, Ad Club, KTA, PRSSA, RTNDA, SPJ
DEGREES:BA, MA
DEPARTMENTS: School of Journalism and Mass Communication, 1947
FACILITIES: AdA, AP, CN, CNN, FM, ETV, JM, JN, PRA, VDT
SEQUENCES: Advertising, Electronic Media, General Mass Communication, Print Journalism, Public Relations

TEXAS TECH UNIVERSITY — University & Broadway, Lubbock, TX, 79409-3082 (806) 742-3385; fax (806) 742-1085; web site www.depts.ttu.edu/masscom
Dean/Prof. — Jerry C. Hudson
Prof./Associate Dean of Faculty — Dennis A. Harp
Prof./Marshall and Sharleen Formby Regents
Prof. — Tom Johnson
Prof./Chair, Dept. of Advertising — Don Jugenheimer
Prof./Associate Dean for graduate studies — Michael Parkinson
Prof./Morris Professor and chair, Dept. of Journalism — Randy Reddick
Prof./Hutcheson Professional — Karl Wolfshohl
Assoc. Prof./Chair, Dept. of Public Relations — Coy Callison
Assoc. Prof./Chair, Dept. Electronic Media — Todd Chambers
Assoc. Prof./Associate dean of students — William F. Dean
Assoc. Prof. — Jimmie Reeves
Assoc. Prof. — Roger C. Saathoff
Assoc. Prof. — Elizabeth Watts
Assoc. Prof./Regents professor of Hispanic and International Communication — Kent Wilkinson
Asst. Prof. — Shannon Bichard
Asst. Prof. — Lori Boyer
Asst. Prof. — Samuel Bradley
Asst. Prof. — Glenn Cummins

Asst. Prof. — Maria Fontenot
Asst. Prof. — Mandy Gallagher
AFFILIATIONS: AAF, KTA, PRSSA, SPJ, WICI
DEGREES:BA, MA, PhD
DEPARTMENTS: College of Mass Communications
FACILITIES: AP, FM, AdA, CN, DR, ETV, JM, JN, PRA, VDT
SEQUENCES: Advertising, Electronic Media and Communications, Journalism, PR

TEXAS WESLEYAN UNIVERSITY — Dept. of Mass Communication, 1201 Wesleyan St., Fort Worth, TX, 76105 (817) 531-4927; fax (817) 531-6585; e-mail msewell@txwes.edu
Chair — Michael Sewell
DEPARTMENTS: Department of Mass Communication
SEQUENCES: Journalism Program: Undergraduate programs in three emphases: Ad/PR, Journalism and Radio-TV

TRINITY UNIVERSITY — Dept. of Communication, San Antonio, TX, 78212-7200 (210) 999-8113; fax (210) 999-8355; e-mail wchrist@trinity.edu
Chair/Prof. — William G. Christ
Prof. — Sammye L. Johnson
Prof. — Robert Huesca
Assoc. Prof. — Jennifer Henderson
Asst. Prof. — Aaron Delwiche
Asst. Prof. — Patrick Keating
Instr./Opns. Mgr., Comm. Ctr. — James Bynum
Instr./Opns. Mgr. — Matt Fleeger
Instr./Dir., Underwriting — Dianah McGreehan
Instr./Dir., Devl. — Kate Rawley
Instr./Dir., Music/Chief Announcer — Aaron Prado
Instr./Sta. Mgr. — Alfredo Cruz
AFFILIATIONS: NCA, ICA, BEA
DEGREES:BA
DEPARTMENTS: Department of Communication, 1930
FACILITIES: FM, CATV, CCTV, ComN, ComTV, DR, VDT

UNIVERSITY OF HOUSTON — 4800 Calhoun Rd., Houston, TX, 77204-3002 (713) 743-2873; fax (713) 743-2876; e-mail bolson@uh.edu
Dir./Assoc. Prof. — Beth Olson
Prof. — William Douglas
Prof. — William Hawes
Prof. — Garth Jowett
Prof. — Mike Ryan
Assoc. Prof. — Martha Haun
Assoc. Prof. — Jaesub Lee
Assoc. Prof. — Jim Query
Assoc. Prof. — Fred Schiff
Asst. Prof. — Michael Berryhill
Asst. Prof. — Lan Ni
Asst. Prof. — Damion Waymer
Clinical Prof. — David McHam
Clinical Asst. Prof. — Deborah Bridges
Clinical Asst. Prof. — Suzanne Buck
Clinical Asst. Prof. — Craig Crowe
Clinical Asst. Prof. — Julie Fix
Clinical Asst. Prof. — Keith Houk
Clinical Asst. Prof. — Randy Polk
AFFILIATIONS: AAF, AWC, BEA, NABJ, PRSSA, SPJ
DEGREES:BA, MA
DEPARTMENTS: Journalism Program, 1963; Jack J. Valenti School of Communication, 1978
FACILITIES: TV, CCTV, CN, ComN, ComTV, ETV, VDT
SEQUENCES: Concentrations: Health Communication, Journalism, Media Production, Media Studies, Public Relations/Advertising, Organizational/Corporate Communication, Interpersonal Communication

UNIVERSITY OF NORTH TEXAS — PO Box 311460, Denton, TX, 76203-1460 (940) 565-2205; fax (940) 565-2370; e-mail zavoina@unt.edu
Chair/Assoc. Prof./Coord., Photo seq. — Susan Zavoina
Prof./Coord., Photo seq. — Richard Wells
Prof. — Roy K. Busby
Assoc. Prof. — Jim Albright
Assoc. Prof./Coord., Adv. seq. — Sheri Broyles
Assoc. Prof./Dir., Grad. Prog. — Mitchell Land
Asst. Prof. — Daechun An
Asst. Prof./NT Daily Advisor — Tracy Everbach
Asst. Prof./Coord., Broadcast-News seq. — Eric Gormly
Asst. Prof. — Jacque Lambiase
Asst. Prof./Coord., News-Editorial seq. — James Mueller
Prof. Emer. — Jim Rogers
Prof. Emer. — Reg Westmoreland
AFFILIATIONS: AAF, DTA, NABJ, NAHJ, PRSSA, SPJ, NPPA, IABC
DEGREES:BA, MA, MJ
DEPARTMENTS: Department of Journalism, 1945. Mayborn Graduate Institute of Journalism
FACILITIES: AP, DR, JM, JN, FM, VDT, PRA, ADA
SEQUENCES: News Writing-Editorial, Advertising, Public Relations, Photojournalism, Broadcast News

UNIVERSITY OF TEXAS AT ARLINGTON — 700 W. Greek Row Dr., Arlington, TX, 76019 (817) 272-2163; fax (817) 272-2732; e-mail commdept@uta.edu
Chair/Assoc. Prof. — Charla Markham Shaw
Prof. — Earl R. Andresen
Assoc. Prof. — Thomas Christie
Assoc. Prof. — Tom Ingram
Asst. Prof. — Camille Broadway
Asst. Prof. — Karishma Chatterjee
Asst. Prof. — Andrew Clark
Asst. Prof. — Glenn Hubbard
Asst. Prof. — Chyng-Yang Jang
Asst. Prof. — Sasha Grant
Asst. Prof. — Eronini Megwa
Asst. Prof. — Ivana Segvic Boudreaux
Asst. Prof. — Chunke Su
Asst. Prof. — Shelley Wigley
Specialist — Rudy Bechtel
AFFILIATIONS: AAF, KTA, PRSSA, SPJ
DEGREES:BA, MA
DEPARTMENTS: Department of Communication, 1972
FACILITIES: AdA, AP, CATV, ComN, ComR, ComTV, DN, DR, PRA, VDT
SEQUENCES: Advertising, News-Editorial, Broadcast, News and Public Affairs, Public Relations and Communication Technology, Communication Studies

UNIVERSITY OF TEXAS AT AUSTIN — School of Journalism, Austin, TX, 78712 (512) 471-1845; fax (512) 471-7979; e-mail jou@journalism.utexas.edu
Dir. — Tracy Dahlby
Prof. — Rosental Alves
Prof. — Lorraine Branham
Prof. — Dennis Darling
Prof. — Maxwell E. McCombs
Prof. — Marvin Olasky
Prof. — Stephen D. Reese
Prof. — Russell G. Todd
Assoc. Prof. — Gene Burd
Assoc. Prof. — Renita Coleman
Assoc. Prof. — Mercedes L. De Uriarte
Assoc. Prof./Grad. Advisor — Don Heider
Assoc. Prof. — Robert Jensen
Assoc. Prof. — Dominic Lasorsa
Assoc. Prof. — Paula Poindexter
Assoc. Prof. — Maggie Rivas-Rodriguez
Assoc. Prof. — George Sylvie
Asst. Prof. — Donna DeCesare
Asst. Prof. — Dustin Harp
Asst. Prof. — Mark Tremayne
AFFILIATIONS: KTA, SPJ, NABJ, NAAJA, AIC, Magazine Club
DEGREES:BJ, MA, PhD
DEPARTMENTS: School of Journalism, 1914
FACILITIES: AP, AM, CCTV, CN, ComN, ComR, ComTV, DR, ETV, FM, JM, NYTS, PRA
SEQUENCES: Broadcast News, Print Journalism, Photojournalism, Multi-media Journalism

UNIVERSITY OF TEXAS AT BROWNSVILLE — Gorgas Hall, 80 Fort Brown, Brownsville, TX, 78520-4993 (956) 882-8851; fax (956) 882-7064; e-mail john.a.cook@utb.edu
Program Coord. — John Cook

UNIVERSITY OF TEXAS AT EL PASO — 500 W. University Ave., El Paso, TX, 79968-0550 (915) 747-6285; fax (915) 747-5236; e-mail com@utep.edu; web site www.utep.edu/com/
Chair/Dir., Sam Donaldson Ctr. for Commun. Studies — Patricia Witherspoon
Assoc. Dir., Sam Donaldson Ctr. for Commun. Studies — Zita Arocha
DEGREES:BA, MA- Communication
DEPARTMENTS: Department of Communication; Sam Donaldson Ctr. for Communication Studies
SEQUENCES: Communication, Electronic Media, Media Advertising, Print Media, Public Relations, Organizational Communication/Public Relations

UNIVERSITY OF TEXAS OF THE PERMIAN BASIN — Faculty of Communication, 4901 E. University, Odessa, TX, 79762 (432) 552-2323; fax (432) 552-2374; e-mail mcgavin_l@utpb.edu
Area Coord. — Jon Paulson
DEPARTMENTS: Communication Program
SEQUENCES: Journalism Program: Emphasizes preparation for professional work in radio, TV or print media

UNIVERSITY OF TEXAS-PAN AMERICAN — 1201 University Dr., Edinburg, TX, 78541 (956) 381-3583; fax (956) 381-2685; e-mail ghanem@panam.edu
Chair — Salma Ghanem
DEPARTMENTS: Department of Communication

WEST TEXAS A&M UNIVERSITY — Dept. of Art, Communication and Theatre, Canyon, TX, 79016 (806) 651-2411; fax (806) 651-2818; e-mail dwohlfarth@mail.wtamu.edu
DEGREES:BA, BS
DEPARTMENTS: Department of Art, Communication, and Theatre
SEQUENCES: Mass Communications: Well-rounded program leading to BA or BS in Mass Communications with any one of the following emphases: print media, broadcasting or advertising/PR

UTAH

BRIGHAM YOUNG UNIVERSITY — 360 BRMB, Provo, UT, 84602 (801) 422-2997; fax (801) 422-0160; e-mail comms_secretary@byu.edu
Chair — Bradley Rawlins
Prof. — Edward E. Adams
Prof. — R. John Hughes
Prof. — Steven R. Thomsen
Prof. — Laurie J. Wilson
Assoc. Prof. — Sherry L. Baker
Assoc. Prof. — Mark A. Callister
Assoc. Prof. — Larrie E. Gale
Assoc. Prof. — Douglas R. McKinlay
Assoc. Prof. — Russell H. Mouritsen
Assoc. Prof. — Allen W. Palmer
Assoc. Prof. — Kenneth D. Plowman
Assoc. Prof./Assoc. Chair, Grad. Studies — Kevin L. Stoker
Assoc. Prof. — Robert I. Wakefield
Asst. Prof. — Joel Campbell
Asst. Prof. — Edward L. Carter
Asst. Prof. — Dale Cressman
Asst. Prof. — Christopher Cutri
Asst. Prof. — L. Kevin Kelly
Asst. Prof. — Quint B. Randle
AFFILIATIONS: AAF, ABA, AEJMC, AJHA, APPE, ASJMC, ASNE, BEA, ICA, IIQM, IPRR, IAMCR, IABC, IABD, KTA, LASA, NAB, POPAI, PRSA, RTNDA, SPJ, SPM, NNA, SWECJMC, UPA
DEGREES:BA, MA
DEPARTMENTS: Department of Communications, 1933
FACILITIES: AP, NPR wire, AM/FM, AdA, CATV, CCTV, ComN, ComR, ComTV, DR, ETV, JN, PRA, VDT
SEQUENCES: Curriculum Areas: Communications Studies, Advertising, Print and Broadcast Journalism, Public Relations. Programs/Centers: International Media Studies, Communications Research

SOUTHERN UTAH UNIVERSITY — 351 W. University Blvd., Centrum 213, Cedar City, UT, 84720 (435) 586-7861; fax (435) 865-8352; e-mail smith_jo@suu.edu
Chair — Jon Smith
DEGREES:BA, BS, MA
DEPARTMENTS: Department of Communication
FACILITIES: AdA, AP, ComTV, CN, DR, ETV, FM, VDT
SEQUENCES: Curriculum Areas: Advertising, Broadcasting, Interpersonal Communication, Journalism and Public Relations

UNIVERSITY OF UTAH — 255 S. Central Campus Dr., Rm. 2400, Salt Lake City, UT, 84112-0491 (801) 581-6888; fax (801) 585-6255; e-mail duignan@admin.comm.utah.edu
Chair — Ann Darling
AFFILIATIONS: AER, KTA, PRSSA, SPJ, WICI, UAF
DEGREES:BS, BA, MS, MA, PhD (in Communication, not Mass Communication)
DEPARTMENTS: Department of Communication, 1948
FACILITIES: AM, FM, CCTV, ETV
SEQUENCES: PR, Electronic Journalism, News-Ed, Communication Technology.

UTAH STATE UNIVERSITY — Dept. of Journalism & Communication, Logan, UT, 84322-4605 (435) 797-3292; fax (435) 797-3973; e-mail jcom@aggiemail.usu.edu; mike.sweeney@usu.edu; web site www.usu.edu/journalism; www.hardnewscafe.usu.edu
Prof./Grad. Coord. — Edward C. Pease
Assoc. Prof. — Cathy Ferrand Bullock
Assoc. Prof. — Penny Byrne
Assoc. Prof. — Brenda Cooper
Asst. Prof. — Nancy M. Williams
Lectr. — Dean Byrne
Lectr. — R. Troy Oldham
Lectr. — Preston Parker
Adj. Instr. — Ron Boam
Adj. Instr. — Cami Boehme
Adj. Instr. — Jane Koerner
Adj. Instr. — Shane Krebs
Adj. Instr. — Tim Vitale
Adj. Instr. — Jay Wamsley
Adj. Instr. — Friend Weller
AFFILIATIONS: ASJMC, BEA, PNNA, PRSSA, SPJ
DEGREES:BA, BS
DEPARTMENTS: Department of Journalism and Communication
FACILITIES: CATV, CCTV, CN, ComN, ComTV, DR, ETV, PRA, VDT
SEQUENCES: Concentrations: Broadcasting/Electronic Media, Print Journalism, Public Relations/Corporate Communications

WEBER STATE UNIVERSITY — Dept. of Communication, Ogden, UT, 84408-1605 (801) 626-6426; fax (801) 626-7975; e-mail jjosephson@weber.edu
Chair — Randolph J. Scott
DEPARTMENTS: Department of Communication
SEQUENCES: Journalism Program: Separate emphases in Journalism, Public

Relations and Electronic Media leading to bachelor's degrees

VERMONT

ST. MICHAEL'S COLLEGE — Winooski Park, Colchester, VT, 5439 (802) 654-2257; fax (802) 654-2560; e-mail ksultze@smcvt.edu; web site academics.smcvt.edu/journalism
Chair/Assoc. Prof. — Kimberly Sultze
Prof. — David T.Z. Mindich
Assoc. Prof. — Jon Hyde
Asst. Prof. — Traci Griffith
Asst. Prof. — Jerry Swope
Instr. — Donna Atwater
Instr. — Paul Beique
Instr. — Bob Davis
Instr. — Mike Donoghue
Instr. — Kevin Kelley
Instr. — Kerry Litchfield
Instr. — Nick Monsarrat
Instr. — Marybeth Christie Redmond
Instr. — Matt Powers
Instr. — Shay Totten
Instr. — Sarah Tuff
Assoc. Prof. Emer. — Gifford Hart
AFFILIATIONS: New England Press Assn., Vermont Press Assn.
DEGREES:BA
DEPARTMENTS: Department of Journalism and Mass Communication, 1974
FACILITIES: AM/FM, ComN, ComTV, DR, JN, PRA, VDT, AdA, electronic newsroom, digital video cameras and editing, desktop publishing system, Web page production, video editing, FM, radio production lab, internships in print and broadcast media, Web design, politics, pub
SEQUENCES: News-Editorial, Broadcast Journalism, New Media

VIRGINIA

EMORY AND HENRY COLLEGE — PO Box 947, Garnand Dr., Emory, VA, 24327 (276) 944-6822; fax (276) 944-6934; e-mail tkeller@ehc.edu
Chair — Teresa Keller
DEPARTMENTS: Department of Mass Communications, 1975
SEQUENCES: Program: For students considering careers in print journalism, broadcasting, graphic design, advertising, public relations, web journalism and web design. Strong liberal arts emphasis

GEORGETOWN UNIVERSITY — 3101 Wilson Blvd., Ste. 200, Arlington, VA, 22201 (202) 687-7000; fax (703) 812-9324
Assoc. Dean — Denise Li
DEGREES:MPS-Journalism
DEPARTMENTS: School of Continuing Studies
SEQUENCES: Program fuses traditional journalism and new media, offering three tracks: Advocacy/Immersion Journalism, Cultural Journalism and International/Political Journalism.

HAMPTON UNIVERSITY — 546 E. Queen St., Hampton, VA, 23668 (757) 727-5405; fax (757) 728-6011
Dean — Tony Brown
AFFILIATIONS: AAF, KTA, NABJ, PRSSA
DEGREES:BA
DEPARTMENTS: Scripps Howard School of Journalism & Communications, 1967
FACILITIES: AP, FM, CATV, CN, ComN, DR, ETV, VDT
SEQUENCES: Broadcast Journalism; Public Relations, Advertising; Print Journalism, Electronic Media Production

JAMES MADISON UNIVERSITY — MSC # 2104, Harrisonburg, VA, 22807 (540) 568-7007; fax (540) 568-7026; e-mail anderssd@jmu.edu; web site smad.jmu.edu
Dir./Prof. — Steve Anderson
Asst. Dir./Prof. — Dietrich Maune
Prof. — Dona Gilliam
Prof. — Rustin Greene
Prof. — George Johnson
Prof. — Marilou Johnson
Prof. — Alex Leidholdt
Prof. — Roger Soenksen
Prof. — Charles Turner
Prof. — John Woody
Assoc. Prof. — John Guiniven
Assoc. Prof. — Joe Hinshaw
Assoc. Prof. — Tom McHardy
Assoc. Prof. — Tom O'Connor
Assoc. Prof. — Kevin Reynolds
Assoc. Prof. — Dave Wendelken
Asst. Prof. — Mike Grundmann
Asst. Prof. — Kathy Hughes
Asst. Prof. — Nancy Nusser
DEGREES:BA, BS
DEPARTMENTS: School of Media Arts and Design
FACILITIES: High-definition Video Production Studio and Post-Production Lab, Interactive Media Lab, Magazine Lab, Writing Lab, Resource Center
SEQUENCES: Programs: Concentrations in Corporate Communication, Digital Video and Cinema, Interactive Journalism

LIBERTY UNIV. — 1971 University Blvd, Lynchburg, VA, 24515-0002, USA (434) 582-2128; fax (434) 582-2420; e-mail advertising@liberty.edu; web site www.liberty.edu/champion
Dean, School of Commun. — William Gribbin
Debra Huff
Jr. Assoc. Dean — Cecil V. Kramer
Benjamin Lesley
Chrmn. — William Mullen
Amanda Sullivan
DEGREES:BS, MA
DEPARTMENTS: Department of Communication Studies, 1994
FACILITIES: The Department sponsors a student newspaper (The Liberty Champion), student radio station (C-91, The Light), Yearbook (Selah), drama and debate teams.
SEQUENCES: BS in Communication Studies: Communication Studies majors complete 42 hours including 12 core hours and 30 hours of concentration in one of the following areas: Speech Communication, Broadcasting, Journalism, or Advertising/Public Relations. Minors are

LYNCHBURG COLLEGE — 1501 Lakeside Dr, Lynchburg, VA, 24501-3113, USA (434) 544-8301; fax (804) 544-8661; e-mail critograph@lynchburg.edu; web site www.critograph.com
Editor-in-Chief — Rachad Davis
Dena/Prof., Journ. — Heywood Greenberg
Copy Desk Chief — Wayne Garret
DEPARTMENTS: School of Communication & Arts, 1983
SEQUENCES: Journalism Program: Offers print, broadcast, mass communication and speech commuunication. Students produce cable video programs and weekly newspaper. Emphasis on experiential education as well as theory

MARY BALDWIN COLLEGE — Communication Dept., Staunton, VA, 24401 (504) 887-7112; fax (540) 887-7040; e-mail bdorries@mbc.edu
Chair — Bruce Dorries
DEPARTMENTS: Communication Department
FACILITIES: Independent student newspaper, TV station, year book
SEQUENCES: A generalist, liberal arts-based Communication program that combines mass communication course work and human communication classes with emphasis on community service learning projects

MARYMOUNT UNIV. — 2807 N Glebe Rd, Arlington, VA, 22207-4224, USA (703) 522-5600; fax (703) 284-3817; e-mail banner@marymount.edu; web site www.marymount.edu
Mass Commun. Coord. — Paul Byers
Vincent Stovall
Mass Commun. Coord. — Ralph Frasca
DEPARTMENTS: Department of Communication & Graphic Design, 1973
SEQUENCES: Mass Communication Program: Offers BA with concentrations in Print Journalism, Broadcasting and Visual Communication. Program combines professional-skills approach (writing, editing, internships) with liberal-arts approach (history, law, theory)

NORFOLK STATE UNIVERSITY — 700 Park Ave., Norfolk, VA, 23504 (757) 823-8331; fax (757) 823-9119; e-mail wgbrockington@nsu.edu
Chair/Assoc. Prof. — Wanda Brockington
Prof./Grad. Coord. — Stan Tickton
Assoc. Prof. — Paula Briggs
Asst. Prof. — Cathy Jackson
Asst. Prof. — Marcia Taylor
Instr. — Steve Opfer
Adj. Fac. — Battinto Batts
Adj. Fac. — Carl Daniels
Adj. Fac. — Jen'Nein T. Ferrell
Adj. Fac. — Kimberly Payne
Adj. Fac. — Marquita Smith
Spartan Echo
AFFILIATIONS: NABJ, PRSSA, AER
DEGREES:BA, BS, MA
DEPARTMENTS: Department of Mass Communications and Journalism, 1994 (formerly Department of Journalism, 1975, and Department of Mass Communication, 1975)
FACILITIES: AM/FM, AdA, CATV, CCTV, CN, ComN, ComTV, PRA, VDT
SEQUENCES: General Broadcasting, General Journalism

RADFORD UNIVERSITY — 200 Jefferson St., Campus PO Box 6932, Radford, VA, 24142 (540) 831-5282; fax (540) 831-5883
Dir. — Lynn Zoch
AFFILIATIONS: AER, IABC, SCJ
DEGREES:BS, BA- Journalism; MS-Corporate PR
DEPARTMENTS: Department of Communication, 1968; School of Communication, 2008
FACILITIES: FM, CATV, CCTV, CN, ComN, VDT
SEQUENCES: News-Editorial, PR

REGENT UNIVERSITY — 1000 Regent University Dr., Virginia Beach, VA, 23464-9800 (757) 226-4237; fax (757) 226-4275
Chair — Mark Menga
DEGREES:MA- Journalism; PhD- Journalism and Communication
DEPARTMENTS: School of Journalism
SEQUENCES: Journalism Program: MA in Journalism with sequences in news-editorial, broadcast journalism, public relations, magazine, professional writing and journalism education.

UNIVERSITY OF RICHMOND — Journalism Dept., Richmond, VA, 23173 (804) 289-8323; fax (804) 287-6052; e-mail snash@richmond.edu
Journ. Chair — Steve Nash
DEPARTMENTS: Major and Minor in Journalism
FACILITIES: AP, FM, CN, DR
SEQUENCES: Journalism Department: Emphases on news gathering and news writing. Has broad liberal arts requirements

VIRGINIA COMMONWEALTH UNIVERSITY — 901 W. Main St., Richmond, VA, 23284-2034 (804) 828-2660; fax (804) 828-9175; web site www.has.vcu.edu/mac
Dir./Prof. — Judy VanSlyke Turk
Assoc. Prof./Assoc. Dir. — June Nicholson
Asst. Dir., Devel. — Michael Hughes
Asst. Dir., Student Services/Scholastic Journ. — Carol Mawyer
Prof. — Thomas Donohue
Assoc. Prof. — Tim Bajkiewicz
Assoc. Prof. — Bonnie Newman Davis
Assoc. prof. — Ernest F. Martin
Assoc. Prof. — Jeff South
Assoc. Prof. — Clarence Thomas
Assoc. Prof. — Debora Wenger
Asst. Prof. — Pieter Blikslager
Asst. Prof. — Bridget Camden
Asst. Prof. — Soo Yeon Hong
Asst. Prof. — Yan Jin
Asst. Prof. — Suzanne Lysak
Asst. Prof. — Marcus Messner
Asst. Prof. — William Oglesby
Asst. Prof. — Scott Sherman
Asst. Prof. — Will Sims
AFFILIATIONS: KTA, NABJ, PRSSA, RTNDA, SPJ
DEGREES:BS, MS, Interdisciplinary Ph.D
DEPARTMENTS: School of Mass Communications, 1950
FACILITIES: AP, AM, FM, CN, VDT
SEQUENCES: Undergraduate: Advertising (Strategy Concentration, Creative Concentration); Journalism (Broadcast Concentration, Print Concentration); Public Relations. Graduate: Advertising Master of Science Program (Adcenter); Multi-Media Journalism Master of Science

VIRGINIA POLYTECHNIC INSTITUTE AND STATE UNIVERSITY — Dept. of Communication, 121 Shanks Hall, Blacksburg, VA, 24061-0311 (540) 231-7136; fax (540) 231-9817; e-mail rhollowa@vt.edu; web site www.comm.vt.edu
Head — Rachel L. Holloway
DEGREES:BA, MA
DEPARTMENTS: Department of Communication, 1980
FACILITIES: FM, CAJV, CCTV, CN, ComN, ComJV, DR, EJV, PRA, VDT
SEQUENCES: Speech, Print Journalism, Broadcasting, PR, Film

VIRGINIA UNION UNIV. — 1500 N Lombardy St, Richmond, VA, 23220-1711, USA (804) 257-5655; fax (804) 257-5818
Dept. Chair — Gloria D. Brogdon
Peter S. Tahsoh
DEGREES:BA
DEPARTMENTS: Department of Mass Communications, 1976
FACILITIES: Campus radio station, multimedia lab, digital editing lab, campus television studio
SEQUENCES: Journalism Department: Offers Broadcast and News-Editorial sequences with internship programs in local news media

WASHINGTON AND LEE UNIVERSITY — Dept. of Journalism & Mass Commun., Lexington, VA, 24450 (540) 458-8432; fax (540) 458-8845; e-mail journalism@wlu.edu
Head/Prof. — Brian E. Richardson
Prof. — Robert J. deMaria
Prof. — Pamela K. Luecke
Prof. — Hampden H. Smith
Prof. — Edward Wasserman
Assoc. Prof. — Claudette Guzan Artwick
Asst. Prof. — Adedayo Abah
Asst. Prof. — Doug Cumming
Prof. Emer. — Louis W. Hodges
Prof. Emer. — John K. Jennings
AFFILIATIONS: SPJ
DEGREES:BA
DEPARTMENTS: Department of Journalism and Mass Communications, 1925
FACILITIES: AP, FM, CATV, CCTV, CN, VDT
SEQUENCES: Electronic Prof., Print Prof., Comm., Business Journalism

WASHINGTON

CENTRAL WASHINGTON UNIVERSITY — Dept. of Communication, Ellensburg, WA, 98926 (509) 963-1066; fax (509) 963-1060; web site www.cwu.edu/~comm
Chair — Corwin King
P A Mauton Hartwig
DEPARTMENTS: Department of Communication, 1947
SEQUENCES: Journalism Major: The Journalism major includes specializations in print, online and broadcast journalism. A separate major is offered in Public Relations and Communication Studies

EASTERN WASHINGTON UNIVERSITY — 705 W. 1st Ave., Spokane, WA, 98201-3900 (509) 623-4347; fax (509) 623-4238; e-mail steve.blewett@mailserver.ewu.edu
Dir./Prof. — Steve Blewett
DEGREES:BA, BS
DEPARTMENTS: Journalism Program, 1950
SEQUENCES: Journalism Program: Offers a BA in News-Editorial with student-designed second concentration emphasis; BS in Public Relations; BA in Electronic Publishing, emphasis on Web design and intranet applications. All tracks stress strong professional community

GONZAGA UNIVERSITY — Dept. of Communication Arts, Spokane, WA, 99258 (509) 328-4220
Dir. — Michael Kirkhorn
DEGREES:BA
DEPARTMENTS: Department of Communication Arts/Journalism Program
SEQUENCES: Journalism Program: BA combines historical, legal, ethical and theoretical perspectives with strong writing and editing component and professional practice and criticism. Special emphasis on sports and environmental reporting and reporting on religion, a

PACIFIC LUTHERAN UNIVERSITY — Dept. of Communication & Theatre, Tacoma, WA, 98447 (206) 535-7762; fax (206) 536-5063
Chair — Michael Bartanen
Area Head — Clifford Rowe
DEPARTMENTS: Department of Communication & Theatre (Journalism emphasis), 1980
SEQUENCES: Journalism Program: PLU offers strong liberal arts education combined with technical training in journalism and broadcasting

SEATTLE UNIVERSITY — 900 Broadway, Seattle, WA, 98122 (206) 296-5340; fax (206) 296-5409; e-mail damhsoir@seattleu.edu
Chair — Gary Atkins
DEPARTMENTS: Communication Department
SEQUENCES: Journalism Program: News-Ed. Seeks to produce graduates who can become responsible professionals in journalism or undertake specialized graduate study. Communication Studies: Liberal arts study of communication, including speech, interpersonal and organ

UNIVERSITY OF WASHINGTON — Box 353740, 102 Communications, Seattle, WA, 98195-3740 (206) 543-2660; fax (206) 616-3762; e-mail kolsen@u.washington.edu
Chair — Gerald J. Baldasty
AFFILIATIONS: SPJ, AWC
DEGREES:BA, MA, MC, PhD
DEPARTMENTS: Department of Communication, 1907
SEQUENCES: Journalism, Communication and Culture, Communication Technology and Society, International Communication, Social Interaction, Political Communication, Rhetoric and Critical Studies

WALLA WALLA COLLEGE — 204 S College Ave, College Place, WA, 99324-1139, USA (509) 527-2971; fax (509) 527-2674; e-mail comm@wwc.eduRoss Brown
Chair — Pamela Harris
DEGREES:BA
DEPARTMENTS: Communications Department, 1988
SEQUENCES: Communication Program: BA in Mass Communication with concentrations in Journalism and Public Relations, Media (includes broadcasting, video/audio production, performance)

WASHINGTON STATE UNIVERSITY — Edward R. Murrow School of Communication, Pullman, WA, 99164-2520 (509) 335-1556; fax (509) 335-1555; e-mail communication@wsu.edu; web site communication.wsu.edu
Interim Dir./Prof. — Erica Austin
Prof. — E. Lincoln James
Prof./Cable 8 News Exec. Producer — Glenn Johnson
Prof./Head, PR seq. — Bruce Pinkleton
Prof. — Joey Reagan
Prof. — Patricia Sias
Prof. — Alexis S. Tan
Assoc. Prof. — Rick Busselle
Assoc. Prof. — David Demers
Assoc. Prof./Head, Comm. Studies seq. — Jolanta Drzewiecka
Assoc. Prof./Assoc. Dir., Undergrad. Studies — John Irby
Assoc. Prof. — Betsy Krueger
Assoc. Prof./Assoc. Dir., Opns. and Budget — Michael Salvador
Assoc. Prof./Exec. Dir., Northwest Access — Susan Ross
Assoc. Prof./Head, Journ. seq. — Elizabeth Blanks Hindman
Asst. Prof. — Douglas Blanks Hindman
Asst. Prof. — Stacey Hust
Asst. Prof. — Moon Lee
Asst. Prof. — Todd Norton
Asst. Prof./Dir., Murrow Symposium/Cable 8 Productions — Marvin Marcelo
AFFILIATIONS: AERho, PRSSA, Ad Club, AWIC, SPJ, IABC, RTNDA
DEGREES:BA, MA, PhD- Communication
DEPARTMENTS: The Edward R. Murrow School of Communication, 1964
FACILITIES: AAF, AM, FM, CATV, CN, FDT, DR, ETV, AP, CCTV, ComN, Research Labs/Centers: Consortium for Communication and Decision Making; Laboratory for the Study of Communication, Emotions and Cognition; Access Northwest; Western Journal of Black Studies
SEQUENCES: Advertising, Broadcasting, Journalism, Public Relations, Communication Studies, Media Law, Applied Intercultural Comm, Organizational Comm

WESTERN WASHINGTON UNIVERSITY — 516 High St., CF 251, Bellingham, WA, 98225-9161 (360) 650-3252; fax (360) 650-2848; e-mail marissa.doiron@wwu.edu; web site www.ac.wwu.edu/~journal
Chair/Assoc. Prof. — Shearlean Duke
Assoc. Prof. — Carolyn Dale
Assoc. Prof. — Brad Howard
Assoc. Prof. — Tim Pilgrim
Asst. Prof. — John Harris
Asst. Prof. — Jennifer Keller
Asst. Prof. — Peggy Watt
Lectr. — Stephen Howie
Lectr. — Carolyn Nielsen-Thompson
AFFILIATIONS: SPJ
DEGREES:BA- Journalism (News-Editorial), Journalism-Public Relations and Visual Journalism; Joint degree- Environmental Journalism
DEPARTMENTS: Department of Journalism, 1967
FACILITIES: FM, CATV, CCTV, CN, ComN, ComR, ComTV, DR, ETV, JM, PRA, VDT
SEQUENCES: News-Editorial, Public Relations, Visual Journalism, Environmental Journalism

WHITWORTH UNIVERSITY — Dept. of Communication Studies, Spokane, WA, 99251 (509) 777-4739; fax (509) 777-4512; e-mail gwhitehouse@whitworth.edu
Chair — Virginia Whitehouse
DEPARTMENTS: Department of Communication Studies, 1946
SEQUENCES: Communication Studies: The Communication Studies department offers majors in journalism and mass communication, speech communication and communication

WEST VIRGINIA

BETHANY COLLEGE — Morlan Hall, Bethany, WV, 26032 (304) 829-7716; fax (304) 829-7161; e-mail psutherl@bethanywv.edu
Chair/Assoc. Prof. — Patrick J. Sutherland
Vstg. Prof./Dir., Stud. Pubs. Ctr. — Michael King
Asst. Prof. — Steve Cohen
Asst. Prof. — Jay Libby
Adj. Prof. — Keri Brown
Adj. Prof. — Jim Forbes
AFFILIATIONS: SPJ, WICI, PRSSA, NBS
DEGREES:BA
DEPARTMENTS: Department of Communication, 1965
FACILITIES: CATV, JM, JN, VDT, PRA, AdA, FM, AP, DR
SEQUENCES: Advertising, Documentary Studies, Electronic Media, Graphics, Print, Public Relations

MARSHALL UNIVERSITY — 1 John Marshall Dr., Huntington, WV, 25755-2622 (304) 696-2360; fax (304) 696-2732; e-mail sojmc@marshall.edu
Dean/Prof. — Corley F. Dennison
Prof. — Charles G. Bailey
Prof. — Burnis Morris
Assoc. Prof. — Janet L. Dooley
Assoc. Prof. — Rebecca J. Johnson
Assoc. Prof. — Marc Seamon
Asst. Prof. — Allyson B. Goodman
Asst. Prof. — Dan W. Hollis
Asst. Prof. — Marilyn H. McClure
Asst. Prof. — Maryl Neff
Asst. Prof. — Joan E. Price
Asst. Prof. — Ruth Sullivan
Instr. — Sean Stewart
Part-time Instr. — Bill Bissett
Part-time Instr. — Sandy Savage
AFFILIATIONS: AAF, NBS, NABJ, PRSSA, SPJ
DEGREES:BA, MAJ
DEPARTMENTS: W. Page Pitt School of Journalism and Mass Communications, 1926
FACILITIES: AP, FM, CATV, CCTV, DR, JN, PRA, VDT
SEQUENCES: Advertising, Broadcast Journalism, Journalism Education, Online Journalism, Print Journalism, Public Relations, Radio-Television

WEST VIRGINIA UNIVERSITY — 1511 University Ave., Morgantown, WV, 26506-6010 (304) 293-3505; fax (304) 293-3072; e-mail pireed@mail.wvu.edu; web site journalism.wvu.edu
Dean/Prof. — Maryanne Reed
Associate Professor — John Temple
Assoc. Prof. — Joel Beeson
Assoc. Dean/Assoc. Prof./Widmeyer Comm. Professorship in PR — Diana Knott Martinelli
Asst. Prof. — Robert Britten
Asst. Prof. — Rita Colistra
Associate Professor — Sang (Sammy) Lee
Director of Graduate Studies/Associate Professor — Stephen Urbanski
Teaching Assistant Professor — Cathy Mezera
Prof. Emer. — Paul A. Atkins
Prof. Emer. — John H. Boyer
Prof. Emer. — Charles F. Cremer
Prof. Emer. — Robert M. Ours
Prof. Emer./Dean Emer. — Guy H. Stewart
Assistant Professor — Hongmin Ahn
Assistant Professor — Alison Bass
Assistant Professor — Dana Coester
Teaching Assistant Professor — Emily Corio
Teaching Associate Professor — Gina Martino Dahlia
Harrison/Omnicom Chair, Visiting Assistant Professor — Jim Ebel
Teaching Assistant Professor — April Johnston
Lecturer — Mary Kay McFarland
Director of Online Programs — Chad Mezera
Teaching Assistant Professor — Elizabeth Oppe
Shott Chair in Journalism, Asst. Prof. — Lois Raimondo
Teaching Assistant Professor — Tom Stewart
Assistant Dean, Student Services — Oliver Street
Assoc. Prof. — Ivan Pinnell
Asst. Prof. — Sara Magee
Asst. Prof. — Bonnie Stewart
Ogden Newspapers Vstg. Prof. — George Esper
Lectr. — Richard Bebout
Lectr. — Jaine Boyles
AFFILIATIONS: AAF, BEA, KTA, PRSSA, DIMA, RTNDA, SPJ
DEGREES:BSJ, MSJ
DEPARTMENTS: Perley Isaac Reed School of Journalism, 1939
FACILITIES: AdA, AM/FM, AP, CN, ComTV, ETV, JN, PRA, VDT
SEQUENCES: Advertising, Print Journalism, Television Journalism, Visual Journalism, Public Relations, Strategic Communications, IMC Graduate Program (Online Only), General Journalism Graduate Program

WISCONSIN

MARQUETTE UNIVERSITY — 1131 W. Wisconsin Ave., Milwaukee, WI, 53223-2313 (414) 288-7133; fax (414) 288-5227; e-mail coc@marquette.edu
Interim Dean/William R. Burleigh and E.W. Scripps Prof. — Lynn H. Turner
Prof. — Claire Badaracco
Prof./Nieman Prof., Journ. — Bonnie S. Brennen
Prof. — Robert J. Griffin
Prof./Gretchen and Cyril Colnik Chair — Lawrence C. Soley
Assoc. Prof. — Daradirek Ekachai
Assoc. Prof. — John A. Grams
Assoc. Prof./Chair, Broadcast/Electronic Commun. — Michael Havice
Assoc. Prof. — James V. Pokrywczynski
Assoc. Prof. — James F. Scotton
Assoc. Prof. — Karen L. Slattery
Assoc. Prof./Chair, Journ. — William J. Thorn
Assoc. Prof./Chair, Adv./PR — Joyce M. Wolburg
Assoc. Prof. — Ana C. Garner
Asst. Prof. — Kati Tusinski Berg
Asst. Prof. — Sumana Chattopadhyay
Asst. Prof./Nieman Prof. Emer. — Richard Leonard
Asst. Prof. — Erik F. Ugland
Asst. Prof. — Jean M. Grow
Professional-in-Residence — Linda Menck
AFFILIATIONS: AAF, BEA, IABC, KTA, NABJ, PRSSA, SPJ
DEGREES:BA, MA
DEPARTMENTS: J. William and Mary Diederich College of Communication, 2005 ; College of Communication, 1988; College of Journalism, 1912
FACILITIES: AdA, AM, AP, CCTV, CN, DR, JM, JN, VDT
SEQUENCES: Advertising, Broadcasting and Electronic Communication, Journalism, Public Relations

UNIVERSITY OF WISCONSIN-EAU CLAIRE — Dept. of Communication & Journalism, Eau Claire, WI, 54702 (715) 836-2528; fax (715)

836-3820; e-mail bakerda@uwec.edu
Interim Chair — David Baker
Prof. — Terry L. Chmielewski
Prof. — Judy Sims
Prof. — W. Robert Sampson
Assoc. Prof. — Edward Frederick
Assoc. Prof. — Jan Larson
Asst. Prof. — Arlyn Anderson
Asst. Prof. — Martha Fay
Asst. Prof. — Ellen Mahaffy
Asst. Prof. — Michael Dorsher
Asst. Prof. — Jeanie Geurink
Asst. Prof. — Won Yong Jang
Asst. Prof. — Jack Kapfer
Asst. Prof. — Nichole Schultz
Sr. Lectr./Dir., Forensics — Karen Morris
Sr. Lectr. — Kelly Jo Wright
Part-time Fac. — Rachel Woodward
Part-time Fac. — Elizabeth Danko Chmielewski
Part-time Fac. — Mary Beth Doud
Part-time Fac. — Janet Driever
AFFILIATIONS: AAF, ABC, BEA, IABC, KTA, NCA, PRSSA, SPJ, WI Broadcasters Assn., WI Newspaper Assn.
DEGREES:BA, BS in Communication, Journalism or Mass Communication
DEPARTMENTS: Department of Communication and Journalism, 1953
FACILITIES: FM, CATV, CCTV, CN, DR, VDT
SEQUENCES: Advertising, Broadcast Journalism, Organizational Communication, Print Journalism, Public Communication, Public Relations

UNIVERSITY OF WISCONSIN-LA CROSSE — 346 Center for the Arts, La Crosse, WI, 54601 (608) 785-8519; fax (608) 785-6719; e-mail rodrick.rich@uwlax.edu; web site perth.uwlax.edu/commstudies
Chair — Richard Rodrick
DEGREES:BA, BS in Communication Studies; minor in Communication Studies
DEPARTMENTS: Communication Studies, 1964
SEQUENCES: Program Emphasis: Public Relations and Organizational Communication, Telecommunications, Persuasion, and Interpersonal Communication

UNIVERSITY OF WISCONSIN-MADISON — 821 University Ave., Madison, WI, 53706-1497 (608) 262-3691; fax (608) 262-1361; web site www.journalism.wisc.edu
Dir./Prof. — James L. Baughman
Prof. — Deborah L. Blum
Prof./Chair, Frank Thayer Ctr. — Robert E. Drechsel
Evjue-Bascom Prof. — Sharon Dunwoody
Prof. — Jo Ellen Fair
Prof. — Lew Friedland
Prof. — Douglas M. McLeod
Prof. — Jack W. Mitchell
Maier-Bascom Prof. — Dhavan Shah
Prof. — Hemant Shah
Prof. — Stephen L. Vaughn
James E. Burgess Prof. — Stephen J. A. Ward
Assoc. Prof. — Gregory J. Downey
Asst. Prof. — Dominique Brossard
Instructional Staff — Kathleen B. Culver
Instructional Staff — Pat Hastings
Instructional Staff — Debora Pierce
Instructional Staff — Steve Walters
Prof. Emer. — Raymond Anderson
Prof. Emer. — William B. Blankenburg
AFFILIATIONS: AAF, PRSSA, SPJ, WICI
DEGREES:BA, BS, MA, PhD
DEPARTMENTS: School of Journalism and Mass Communication, 1905
SEQUENCES: Journalism, Strategic Communication

UNIVERSITY OF WISCONSIN-MADISON — 440 Henry Mall, Madison, WI, 53706-1563 (608) 262-1464; fax (608) 265-3042; e-mail lifescicomm@cals.wisc.edu; web site www.wisc.edu/lsc
Chair/Prof. — Jacqueline C. Bush Hitchon
Prof. — Marion R. Brown
Prof. — Albert C. Gunther
Prof. — Alan B. Knox
Prof. — Larry R. Meiller
Prof. — Garrett J. O'Keefe
Prof. — Suzanne Pingree
Assoc. Prof. — Shiela I. Reaves
Assoc. Prof. — Robin Shepard
Asst. Prof. — Calvin D. Brutus
Asst. Prof. — Patricia A. Loew
Adj. Assoc. Prof. — Jacob G. Stockinger
Lectr. — Michael J. Flaherty
Lectr. — B. Wolfgang Hoffmann
Lectr. — Brian D. Howell
Lectr. — Susan Lampert-Smith
Lectr. — William Ronald Seely
Lectr. — Mary Ellen Spoerke
Prof. Emer. — Fritz A. Albert
Prof. Emer. — Margaret Andreasen
AFFILIATIONS: NAMA, SPJ
DEGREES:BS, MS, PhD
DEPARTMENTS: Department of Life Sciences Communication, 1908
FACILITIES: AdA, AM/FM, CN, ComN, ComTV, DR, ETV, PRA, VDT
SEQUENCES: Integrated Marketing Communication, Science and Technology Reporting in Agriculture/Natural Resources/Environment, Health/Biological Sciences, Family/Consumer Sciences

UNIVERSITY OF WISCONSIN-MILWAUKEE / DEPARTMENT OF JOURNALISM, ADVERTISING, AND MEDIA STUDIES (JAMS) — 3210 N Maryland Ave, Bolton Hall, 510B, Milwaukee, WI, 53211-3164, USA; tel (+1) (414) 229-4436; fax (414) 229-2411; e-mail jams-email@uwm.edu; web site jams.uwm.edu
Professor and Director of Graduate Studies — David Allen
Assistant Professor — Xiaoxia Cao
Senior Lecturer — Jane Hampden Daley
Lecturer — Jackie Leonard-Tackett
Associate Professor — Elana Levine
Senior Lecturer — Jessica McBride
Associate Professor and Department Chair — Michael Newman
Associate Professor and Director of Undergraduate Studies — Richard Popp
Professor — David Pritchard
Senior Lecturer — Joette Rockow
Professor — Jeffery Smith
Senior Lecturer — Marc Tasman
Lecturer — Eric Lohman
Lecturer — Rachael Jurek
Associate Lecturer — Jessie Garcia Marble
Academic Department Associate — Anna Kupiecki
Digital Media Specialist — Jeff Loomis
AFFILIATIONS: PRSSA, SPJ, AdClub, and campus advertising, broadcasting, and minority journalist organizations.
DEGREES:BA, MA
DEPARTMENTS: Department of Journalism, Advertising, and Media Studies, Department of Journalism and Mass Communication, 1950
FACILITIES: AdA, AM/FM, AP, CATV, CCTV, CN, ComN, ComTV, JN, PRA, VDT
SEQUENCES: Journalism, Advertising, Media Studies

UNIVERSITY OF WISCONSIN-OSHKOSH — 800 Algoma Blvd., Oshkosh, WI, 54901-8696 (414) 424-1042; fax (414) 424-7146; e-mail journalism@uwosh.edu; web site www.uwosh.edu/journalism
Chair/Prof. — Mike Cowling
Prof. — Julie K. Henderson
Assoc. Prof. — Timothy R. Gleason
Assoc. Prof. — Miles B. Maguire
Asst. Prof. — Elizabeth Crisp Crawford
AFFILIATIONS: AAF, KTA, PRSSA, SPJ, Wisconsin Newspaper Assn.
DEPARTMENTS: Department of Journalism, 1966
SEQUENCES: News-Editorial, Ad/PR

UNIVERSITY OF WISCONSIN-RIVER FALLS — 410 S 3rd St, 310 North Hall, River Falls, WI, 54022-5010, USA; tel (1) (715) 425-3169; fax (715) 425-0658; e-mail journalism@uwrf.edu; web site uwrfvoice.com
Advisor — Andris Straumanis
Chair — Sandra Ellis
DEGREES:BS/BA
DEPARTMENTS: Department of Communication and Media Studies
SEQUENCES: Journalism Program: The Department of Communication and Media Studies offers a bachelor's degree in journalism that includes courses in broadcast, print and online production. Facilities include a student-run radio station and a weekly newspaper.

UNIVERSITY OF WISCONSIN-STEVENS POINT — Div. of Communication, Stevens Point, WI, 54481 (715) 346-3409; fax (715) 346-4769
Assoc. Dean/Head — Richard Ilkka
DEPARTMENTS: Division of Communication, 1968
SEQUENCES: Communication Program: Broad-based major in Communication with emphases in Interpersonal, Organizational, Mass Communication, Public Relations/Advertising, Individually Planned.

UNIVERSITY OF WISCONSIN-WHITEWATER — 800 W. Main St., Whitewater, WI, 53190 (262) 472-1034; fax (262) 472-1419; e-mail voglbaus@uww.edu
Contact — Sally Vogl-Bauer
DEPARTMENTS: Department of Communication
SEQUENCES: Communication Department: Offers comprehensive programs in Advertising, Electronic Media, Public Relations, Print and Broadcast Journalism. Majors and minors offered in College of Arts and Communication

WYOMING

UNIVERSITY OF WYOMING — Dept. of Communication & Journalism, Laramie, WY, 82071-3904 (307) 766-6277; fax (307) 766-3812; e-mail klsmith@uwyo.edu; web site www.uwyo.edu/comm/index.htm
Chair — Ken Smith
AFFILIATIONS: AAF, SPJ, SCJ, Wyoming Press Assn., Wyoming Assn. of Broadcasters
DEGREES:BA, BS, MA
DEPARTMENTS: Department of Communication and Journalism, 1948
FACILITIES: AdA, CATV, CN, ComN, DESK, DR, EDIT, JN, PRA, VID, VDT
SEQUENCES: General Communication Studies, Advertising, Print Journalism, PR

SCHOOLS AND DEPARTMENTS OF JOURNALISM - FOREIGN

AUSTRALIA

BOND UNIVERSITY — Communication & Media Studies, Gold Coast, 4229, Australia; tel (61) 7 5595 2516; fax 5595 2540; e-mail mpearson@staff.bond.edu.au
Prof. — Mark Pearson
AFFILIATIONS: Journalism Education Assn
DEGREES:BA, BJ, BComm
DEPARTMENTS: Communication and Media Studies, 1990
SEQUENCES: Programs: Two-year (six-semester) program leading to BJ, BA or BComm with major in journalism, foreign correspondence, television reporting or sports reporting. Course Master of Journalism, Master of Communication - one year

CHARLES STUART UNIVERSITY — Panorama Ave., Bathurst, 2795, Australia; tel (61) 2 6338 4539; fax 6338 4409; e-mail tomwatson@csu.edu.au
Assoc. Prof./Head of School — Tom Watson
AFFILIATIONS: Journalism Education Assn., PR Institute of Australia, Int'l Advertising Assoc
DEGREES:Graduate Certificate and Diploma, BA, MA, MA (Hons), PhD
DEPARTMENTS: School of Communication, 1974
SEQUENCES: Programs: Print and Broadcast Journalism, Sport & Recreation/Journalism, PR and Organizational Communication, Advertising, Advertising/Marketing (2004), Commercial Radio Management, Cultural Performance, Theatre/Media

JSCHOOL: JOURNALISM EDUCATION & TRAINING — 82 Ann St., Brisbane, 4000, Australia; tel (61) 7 3137 0080; fax 3036 6148; e-mail director@jschool.com.au
Prof. — John Henningham
DEPARTMENTS: Diploma of Journalism, 2002
SEQUENCES: Programs: One-year intensive vocational program in journalism, with practical journalism training integrated with courses in politics, social institutions, humanities and news media theory

UNIVERSITY OF CANBERRA — Kirinari St., Bruce, 2601, Australia; tel (61) 2 6201 2475; fax 6201 2630; e-mail rwb@comedu.canberra.edu.au; web site www.canberra.edu.au
Prof. — Kerry Green
AFFILIATIONS: Journalism Education Assn., PR Institute of Australia, Advertising Federation of Australia, Int'l Advertising Assn
DEGREES:B. Comm, M. Comm, PhD
DEPARTMENTS: School of Professional Communication
SEQUENCES: Programs: Print and Broadcast Journalism, PR, Advertising & Marketing Comm

UNIVERSITY OF QUEENSLAND — Journalism Dept., Brisbane, 4072, Australia; tel (61) 7 3365 3088; fax 3365 1377; e-mail journ@uq.edu.au
Acting Head of School — Michael Bromley
DEPARTMENTS: Journalism, 1921
SEQUENCES: Journalism Program: A three-year program leading to a BJ or a BA with single major or double major in Journalism and Mass Communication. Fourth

year honors program. Coursework Master of Journalism (MJ) - 1.5 years. Graduate Diploma in Journalism (GDJ) -1

UNIVERSITY OF SOUTHERN QUEENSLAND — Journalism Program, Toowoomba, 4350, Australia; tel (61) 76 312 100; fax 312 598; e-mail S97571@DDSCU.DDIAE.OZ.AU
DEGREES:BA
SEQUENCES: Journalism Program: Three-year course leading to a BA with double major in journalism. All journalism units, except those for advanced broadcast, are available to external students

UNIVERSITY OF WESTERN SYDNEY — School of Communication, Design & Media, Penrith South DC, 1797, Australia; tel (61) 2 9852 5422; fax 9852 5424; e-mail commarts@uws.edu.au; web site www.uws.edu.au/communication_arts
DEPARTMENTS: Communication, journalism, PR, media production 1985, contemporary arts, design 1989; School of Communication, Design & Media 2000, School of Communication Arts 2005. The University has six campuses across Western Sydney, with all Communication Arts cou
FACILITIES: AM/FM, CN, ComN, DR, JM, PRA, VDT
SEQUENCES: Three and four-year program for B.Communication in Journalism, Public Relations, Advertising, Media Production. Three and four-year programs for B.Design, B.Music, B.Performance, B.Contemporary Art; one-year full-time coursework Master of Professional

AUSTRIA

UNIVERSITY OF SALZBURG — PO Box 505, A-5010 Salzburg, Austria; tel (43) 662 8044 4150; fax 804 4413; e-mail FABRIS@EDVZ.SBG.AC.AT
Chair — Hans H. Fabris
AFFILIATIONS: OeGPuK, DGPuK, IAMCR
DEGREES:MA, PhD
DEPARTMENTS: Department of Journalism and Communications, 1968
SEQUENCES: Offers a MA and PhD with sequences in journalism, PR and AV media

CANADA

CARLETON UNIVERSITY — 1125 Colonel By Dr., Ottawa, ON, K1S 5B6, Canada (613) 520-7404; fax (613) 520-6690; e-mail karim_karim@carleton.ca; web site www.carleton.ca/sjc
Dir./Assoc. Prof. — Karim Karim
Prof. — G. Stuart Adam
Prof. — Michael Dorland
Prof. — Michele Martin
Assoc. Prof. — Elly Alboim
Assoc. Prof. — Paul Attallah
Assoc. Prof. — Andrew Cohen
Assoc. Prof. — Christopher Dornan
Assoc. Prof. — Ross Eaman
Assoc. Prof. — Barbara Freeman
Assoc. Prof. — Sheryl Hamilton
Assoc. Prof. — Peter Johansen
Assoc. Prof. — Catherine McKercher
Assoc. Prof. — Mary McGuire
Assoc. Prof. — Kathryn O'Hara
Assoc. Prof. — Klaus Pohle
Assoc. Prof. — Eileen Saunders
Assoc. Prof. — Lois Sweet
Assoc. Prof. — Chris Waddell
Assoc. Prof. — Dwayne Winseck
DEGREES:BJ, BA, MJ, MA, PhD
DEPARTMENTS: School of Journalism and Communication, 1945
FACILITIES: AM/FM, CATV, CCTV, CN, ComN, ComR, CP, DR, JN, VDT

CONCORDIA UNIVERSITY — 7141 Sherbrooke St. W., Montreal, QC, H4B 1R6, Canada (514) 848-2424; fax (514) 848-2473; e-mail gashmj8590@yahoo.ca; web site artsandscience.concordia.ca/journalism
DEPARTMENTS: Communication Studies Department, 1965; Journalism Department, 1975
SEQUENCES: Journalism Program: Oriented toward professional training within an academic framework. Offers three-year undergraduate and one-year graduate programs in broadcasting and print. Communication Studies Program: Offers BA, MA and PhD level programs in mass

RYERSON UNIVERSITY — 350 Victoria St., Toronto, ON, M5B 2K3, Canada (416) 979-5319; fax (416) 979-5216; e-mail secretary@journalism.ryerson.ca; web site www.ryerson.ca/journalism
Chair/Assoc. Prof. — Paul Knox
Assoc. Prof. — Gene Allen
Assoc. Prof. — Marsha Barber
Assoc. Prof. — Lynn Cunningham
Assoc. Prof. — Don Gibb
Assoc. Prof. — Abby Goodrum
Assoc. Prof. — Suanne Kelman
Assoc. Prof. — John Miller
Assoc. Prof. — Ann Rauhala
Assoc. Prof. — Ivor Shapiro
Assoc. Prof. — Joyce Smith
Asst. Prof. — Jagg Carr-Locke
Asst. Prof. — April Lindgren
Asst. Prof. — Janice Neil
Asst. Prof. — Robert Ortega
Asst. Prof. — Bill Reynolds
Asst. Prof. — Vinita Srivastava
DEGREES:BJ, MJ
DEPARTMENTS: School of Journalism, 1948
FACILITIES: CP, RNA, CCTV, ComN, JM, JN, VDT, news website and online portals
SEQUENCES: Journalism Program: Four-year BJ emphasizes early exposure to practical news-gathering and includes liberal studies, a wide selection of specialized and critical-issues courses, internships and capstone newsroom activities. Professional MJ includes two-ye

ST. CLAIR COLLEGE OF APPLIED ARTS AND TECHNOLOGY — Journalism Dept., Windsor, ON, N9A 6S4, Canada (519) 966-1656; fax (519) 966-2737
Coord. — Susan MacKenzie
DEPARTMENTS: Journalism Department
SEQUENCES: Journalism Program: Three-year print journalism (writing, editing, photography) and one-year diploma course for university graduates

UNIVERSITY OF BRITISH COLUMBIA — 6388 Crescent Rd., Vancouver, BC, V6T 1Z2, Canada (604) 822-6688; fax (604) 822-6707; e-mail dlogan@interchange.ubc.ca; web site www.journalism.ubc.ca
Dir./Prof. — Donna Logan
Assoc. Prof. — Stephen Ward
Asst. Prof. — Mary Lynn Young
Instr. — Claude Adams
Instr. — David Beers
Vstg. Prof. — Peter C. Newman
Grad. Advisor — Sim Lee
DEGREES:MJ
DEPARTMENTS: School of Journalism, 1998

UNIVERSITY OF CALGARY — 2500 University Dr. NW, Social Sciences 320, Calgary, AB, T2N 1N4, Canada (403) 282-6716; fax (403) 282-6716; e-mail dtaras@ucalgary.ca
DEGREES:MA
DEPARTMENTS: Communication Studies Program, 1982
SEQUENCES: Communication Program: Graduate program (only) offering masters in Communication Studies (course-based) and MA in Communications. Specialties: Organizational Communications, Law and Communications Policy, Intercultural Communications, Gender and New Info

UNIVERSITY OF KING'S COLLEGE — 6350 Coburg Rd., Halifax, NS, B3H 2A1, Canada (902) 422-1271; fax (902) 423-3357; e-mail kim.kierans@ukings.ns.ca
Dir. — Kim Kierans
DEPARTMENTS: School of Journalism
SEQUENCES: Journalism Program: A four-year program leading to a Bachelor of Journalism (Honors) and a one-year program for students with a previous degree leading to a Bachelor of Journalism. Also offers combined honors degrees in journalism and arts and humanities

UNIVERSITY OF REGINA — Ad Hum Bldg., Rm. 105, 3737 Wascana Pkwy, Regina, SK, S4S OA2, Canada (306) 585-4420; fax (306) 585-4867; e-mail journalism@uregina.ca; web site www.uregina.ca/arts/journalism
DEGREES:BA
DEPARTMENTS: School of Journalism, 1980
SEQUENCES: Journalism Program: A four-year program leading to a BA in Journalism or a two-year degree for students with a previous degree leading to a Bachelor of Journalism

UNIVERSITY OF WESTERN ONTARIO — North Campus Bldg., Rm. 240, 1151 Richmond St., London, ON, N6A 5B7, Canada (519) 661-3542; fax (519) 661-3506; e-mail journalism@uwo.ca; web site www.fims.uwo.ca
Dean — Thomas Carmichael
Assoc. Dean — Nick Dyer-Witheford
Prof. — David Spencer
Assoc. Prof. — Tim Blackmore
Assoc. Prof. — James Compton
Assoc. Prof. — Keir Keightley
Assoc. Prof. — Daniel Robinson
Assoc. Prof. — Romayne Smith Fullerton
Lectr./Journ. Program Coord. — Paul Benedetti
Lectr. — Mary Doyle
Lectr. — Meredith Levine
Lectr. — Cliff Lonsdale
Prof. Emer. — Ken Bambrick
Prof. Emer. — Peter Desbarats
Prof. Emer. — Judith Knelman
Prof. Emer. — Michael Nolan
DEGREES:MA
DEPARTMENTS: Faculty of Information and Media Studies
FACILITIES: CCTV, CP, RNA, VDT
SEQUENCES: The Faculty offers a one year, three-term graduate program leading to a Master of Arts degree in Journalism. The curriculum stresses a balance of academic and practical courses and offers a solid grounding in the tools and practices of print, broadcast an

UNIVERSITY OF WINDSOR — Communication Studies, Windsor, ON, N9B 3P4, Canada (519) 253-3000; fax (519) 971-3642; e-mail goldman@uwindsor.ca; vanzet@uwindsor.ca
Chair — Irvin Goldman
DEPARTMENTS: Communication Studies, 1969
SEQUENCES: Communication Program: Media production processes, communication policy, political economy of communication, media studies, and communication theory and research at undergraduate level

CHILE

PONTIFICIA UNIVERSIDAD CATOLICA DE CHILE — School of Journalism, Alameda 340, Santiago, Chile; tel (56) 2 354 2016; fax 354 2054; e-mail mgronemeyer@puc.cl; web site www.per.puc.cl
Dir. — Maria-Elena Gronemeyer
DEGREES:Licentiate in Journalism; professional title in Journalism
DEPARTMENTS: School of Journalism, 2004

UNIACC UNIVERSITY — Av. Salvador 1200, Santiago, Chile; tel (56) 2 274 6699; fax 204 3116
Dir. — Andres Guiloff
DEPARTMENTS: Facultad de Communicacion, 1991

EGYPT

THE AMERICAN UNIVERSITY IN CAIRO — 113 Kasr el Aini St., Cairo, 1511, Egypt; tel (20) 2 797 6202; fax 795 7565; e-mail h_amin@aucegypt.edu; web site www.aucegypt.edu
Chair/Prof. — Hussein Amin
DEGREES:BA, MA
DEPARTMENTS: Department of Journalism and Mass Communication, 1937
FACILITIES: CN, DR, CCTV, RNA, VDT
SEQUENCES: Journalism, Broadcast Journalism, and Integrated Marketing Communication

FINLAND

UNIVERSITY OF TAMPERE — Kalevantie 4,, Dept. of Journalism and Mass Communication, Tampere, 33014, Finland; tel (358) 3 3551 6243; fax 3551 6248; e-mail tiedotusopin.laitos@uta.fi; web site www.uta.fi/laitokset/tiedotus/index1.html
Head/Prof. — Taisto Hujanen
Prof. — Risto Kunelius
Prof. — Heikki Luostarinen
Prof. — Kaarle Nordenstreng
Prof. — Pertti Suhonen
Lectr. (i.a.) — Ari Heinonen
Lectr. (.i.a.) — Jyrki Jyrkiainen
Lectr. (i.a.) — Kaarina Melakoski
Lectr. (i.a.) — Inari Teinila
Lectr. (i.a.) — Hannu Vanhanen
DEGREES:BA, MA PhD
DEPARTMENTS: Department of Journalism and Mass Communication
FACILITIES: Newsroom laboratory, FM radio station, journalism research and development centre
SEQUENCES: Journalism Program: Originating from an undergraduate program established in Helsinki in 1925, today includes BA, MA and PhD studies within the Faculty of Social Sciences. Sequences in print journalism, photojournalism, radio journalism, television journ

FRANCE

UNIVERSITE PANTHEON-ASSAS (PARIS II) — Institut Francais de Presse, Sciences de L'Information, 92 rue d'Assas, Paris, France; tel (33) 1 4441 5793; fax 4441 5949; e-mail ifp@u-paris2.fr
Chair — Nadine Toussaint Desmoulins
DEGREES:MA, PhD
SEQUENCES: Journalism Program: For third-year (BA) students, at MA and PhD levels

GERMANY

CATHOLIC UNIVERSITY — School of Journalism, Eichstaett-Ingolstadt, Ostenstr. 25, Eichstaett, 85072, Germany; tel (49) 8421 93-1555; fax 93-1786; e-mail klaus-dieter.altmeppen@ku-eichstaett.de; web site www.journalistik-eichstaett.de
Chair — Klaus-Dieter Altmeppen
DEPARTMENTS: School of Journalism

UNIVERSITY FOR MUSIC AND THEATER HANNOVER — Expo-Plaza 12, Hannover, D-30539, Germany; tel (49) 511 310 0497; fax 310 0400; e-mail info@hmt-hannover.de; web site www.ijk.hmt-hannover.de
Chair — Helmut Scheres
DEGREES:BA, MA
DEPARTMENTS: Department of Journalism and Communication Research, 1985
FACILITIES: AM/FM, CCTV, VDT, media library

MALAYSIA

UNIVERSITI KEBANGSAAN MALAYSIA (NATIONAL UNIVERSITY OF MALAYSIA) — Dept. of Communication, 43600 UKM Bangi, Malaysia; tel (60) 3 829 2456; fax 825 6484
Dept. Head — Samsudin Abdul Rahim
DEGREES:BA, MA, PhD
DEPARTMENTS: Department of Communication, Faculty of Social Sciences & Humanities, 1976
SEQUENCES: PR, Journalism, Film, Adv., Dev. Comm., Broadcasting

NETHERLANDS

UNIVERSITY OF AMSTERDAM — Dept. of Communication, Kloveniersburgwal 48, Amsterdam, 1012CX, Netherlands; tel (31) 20 525 2230; fax 525 3681
DEPARTMENTS: Department of Communication

QATAR

NORTHWESTERN UNIVERSITY IN QATAR — Texas A&M University Bldg.,, 1st Fl., Ste. 225, Doha, Qatar; tel (974) 4230300; e-mail nu-qadmissions@northwestern.edu; web site www.qatar.northwestern.edu/default.aspx
Dean — John Margolis
Sr. Assoc. Dean — Richard Roth
DEGREES:BS
SEQUENCES: Journalism Program: Offers concentrations including print, broadcast and multimedia leading to a BS in Journalism awarded by Northwestern's Medill School of Journalism. Communication Program: With curricular offerings in the areas of communication theor

SINGAPORE

NANYANG TECHNOLOGICAL UNIVERSITY — 31 Nanyang Link, Singapore, 637718, Singapore; tel (65) 6790 6109; fax 6791 5214; web site www.ntu.edu.sg/sci
Dean — Ang Peng Hwa
DEPARTMENTS: School of Communication and Information
FACILITIES: Campus newspaper, computer and multimedia labs, TV studios
SEQUENCES: Communication Studies Program: Honors degree programme with four sequences: Journalism, PR and Advertising, Broadcasting and Research. Facilities include campus newspaper, computer and multimedia labs, TV studios. Mandatory internship.

SOUTH AFRICA

POTCHEFSTROOM UNIVERSITY — Private Bag X6001, 2520 Potchefstroom, South Africa; tel (27) 18 299 1642; fax 299 1651; e-mail komasdeb@puknet.ac.za
Head — Arnold S. De Beer
DEGREES:BA, MA, PhD
DEPARTMENTS: Department of Communication
SEQUENCES: Communication Program: A three/four year program in mass communication (print and broadcasting media), corporate communication (advertising and public relations), and interpersonal communication (intercultural, development, organizational, speech communic

UNITED ARAB EMIRATES

THE AMERICAN UNIVERSITY OF SHARJAH — PO Box 26666, Sharjah, United Arab Emirates; tel (971) 6 515 2872; e-mail mhashem@aus.edu; web site www.aus.edu
Chair/Prof. — Mahboub Hashem
DEGREES:BA- Mass Communication
DEPARTMENTS: Department of Mass Communication, 1937
SEQUENCES: Mass Communication Program: Department of Mass Communication is fully accredited in both the UAE and USA. MCM majors study a variety of mass media-related subjects including advertising, communications theory, media production, public relations and journa

ZAYED UNIVERSITY — Academic City, Al Ruwayyah, United Arab Emirates; tel (971) 4 402 1111; fax 402 1016; e-mail kenneth.starck@zu.ac.ae; web site www.zu.ac.ae
Dean — Kenneth Starck
Administrative Officer — Andrea Juhasz
Prof. — Badran Badran
Prof. — Lyall Crawford
Prof./Asst. Dean, Abu Dhabi — Kent Sidel
Prof./Asst. Dean, Dubai — Ron Wolfe
Prof. — Sevil Sonmez
Assoc. Prof. — Nancy Beth Jackson
Assoc. Prof. — James Piecowye
Assoc. Prof. — Lena Jayyusi
Assoc. Prof. — Adel Jendli
Assoc. Prof. — Alma Kadragic
Assoc. Prof. — Sheena Westwood
Assoc. Prof. — Peyman Pejman
Asst. Prof. — Philip Cass
Asst. Prof. — Matt Dyck
Asst. Prof. — Gaelle Duthler
Asst. Prof. — Will McCarthy
Asst. Prof. — Nadia Rahman
Asst. Prof. — Alia Yunis
AFFILIATIONS: ASJMC, BEA, ICA
DEGREES:BS
DEPARTMENTS: College of Communication and Media Sciences, 1999
SEQUENCES: Film and Broadcast Media, Magazine and Multi-Media Journalism, Public Relations and Advertising

UNITED KINGDOM

CITY UNIVERSITY, LONDON — Northampton Sq., London, EC1V 0AB, United Kingdom; tel (44) 20 7040 8221; fax 7040 8594; e-mail journalism@city.ac.uk; web site www.city.ac.uk/journalism
Dept. Head — Rod Allen
DEGREES:BA, MA
DEPARTMENTS: Department of Journalism, 1976
SEQUENCES: Courses: BA in Journalism and a Social Science, BA in Journalism and Contemporary History; Postgraduate Diplomas in Newspaper, Periodical; Television Current Affairs and Broadcast Journalism; MA in Publishing Studies, MA/MSc in Electronic Publishing, MA i

LONDON COLLEGE OF PRINTING AND DISTRIBUTIVE TRADES — Elephant and Castle, London, SE1 6SB, United Kingdom; tel (44) 71 735 9100; fax 587 5297
SEQUENCES: Journalism Program: The college offers various courses in journalism including a Postgraduate Diploma in Radio Journalism

UNIVERSITIES OF STRATHCLYDE/ GLASGOW CALEDONIAN — Scotttish Centre for Journalism Studies, Strathclyde University, Glasgow, G1 1XH, United Kingdom; tel (44) 41 553 4166; fax 552 3493; e-mail gordon.j.smith@strath.ac.uk
Course Dir. — Jennifer McKay
DEGREES:Postgraduate Diploma in Journalism Studies; M.Litt in Journalism Studies, M.Litt in Journalism Research
DEPARTMENTS: Scottish Centre for Journalism Studies, 1993
SEQUENCES: Print Journalism, Broadcasting, Law, Government, Shorthand, Information Management, Journalism and Society

UNIVERSITY OF WALES, CARDIFF — Bute Bldg., King Edward VII Ave., Cardiff, CF10 3NB, United Kingdom; tel (44) 29 2087 4041; fax 2023 8832; e-mail Jomec@cardiff.ac.uk
Head of School — John Tulloch
DEGREES:BA, Diploma, MA, MPhil, PhD
DEPARTMENTS: School of Journalism, Media and Cultural Studies
SEQUENCES: BA in Journalism, Film & Broadcasting; Diploma Journalism Studies, Diploma Public & Media Relations; MA Journalism Studies, MA European Journalism, MA in International Journalism, MA in International PR, MA in Political Communication

UNIVERSITY OF WESTMINSTER — Watford Rd., Northwick Park, Harrow, HA1 3TP, United Kingdom; tel (44) 207 911 5000
DEPARTMENTS: School of Communication and Creative Industries

COLLEGE AND UNIVERSITY NEWSPAPERS

ALABAMA

ALABAMA A&M UNIV.: MAROON & WHITE — 4900 Meridian St. , Normal, AL, 35762, USA; tel (256) 372-5385; fax (256) 372-8795
Diane Anderson
Format: Tabloid

ALABAMA STATE UNIV.: HORNET TRIBUNE — PO Box 271, Montgomery, AL, 36101-0271, USA; tel (334) 229-4419; fax (334) 229-4934; e-mail: ayoleke@aol.com; web site: www.thehornettribune.com
Prof./Chair — David Okeowo
Bryan Weaver
Prof. — E.K. Daufin
Julian K. Johnson
Assoc. Prof./Dir., Forensics — Tracy Banks
James B. Lucy
Assoc. Prof. — Elizabeth Fitts
Asst. Prof. — Richard Emmanuel
Instr. — James Adams
Instr. — Coke Ellington
Instr. — Valerie Heard
Instr. — Jonathan Himsel
Instr. — John Moore
Instr. — Walter Murphy
Instr. — Larry Owens
Format: Broadsheet

ATHENS STATE UNIV.: ATHENIAN — 300 N Beaty St, Athens, AL, 35611-1999, USA; tel (256) 233-8169; fax (256) 233-8128; e-mail: the.athenian@athens.edu.
Tena Bullington
Aletha Pardue
Format: Tabloid

AUBURN UNIV.: AUMNIBUS — PO Box 244023, Montgomery, AL, 36124-4023, USA; tel (334) 244-3662; fax (334) 244-3131; e-mail: aumnibuseditor@yahoo.com; web site: aumnews.squarespace.com
Taylor Manning
Christine Kneidter
Amber Acker
Format: Broadsheet

AUBURN UNIV.: AUBURN PLAINSMEN — 255 Duncan Dr Ste 1111, Auburn University, AL, 36849-0001, USA; tel (334) 844-9021; fax (334) 844-9114; e-mail: news@theplainsman.com; adv email: advertising@theplainsman.com; web site: www.theplainsman.com
Jennifer Adams
Tom Hopf
Lindsey Davidson
Rod Guajardo
Format: Broadsheet

BIRMINGHAM-SOUTHERN COLLEGE: HILLTOP NEWS — 900 Arkadelphia Rd # 549014, Birmingham, AL, 35254-0002, USA; tel (205) 226-7706; e-mail: hilltop@bsc.edu; web site: www.bsc.edu
Peter Donahue
Kimmie Farris
Kimmie Sarris
Yuan Gong
Adv. Mgr. — Glorious
Format: Tabloid

HUNTINGDON COLLEGE: GARGOYLE — 1500 E Fairview Ave, Montgomery, AL, 36106-2148, USA; tel (314) 833-4354; fax (334) 264-2951; e-mail: gargoyle@huntingdon.edu
Jackie Trimble
Matthew Adams
Beth Woodfin
Format: Tabloid

JACKSONVILLE STATE UNIV.: CHANTICLEER — 700 Pelham Rd N Rm 180, Jacksonville, AL, 36265-1602, USA; tel (256) 782-8192; fax (256) 782-5645; e-mail: chantyeditor@gmail.com; web site: www.thechanticleeronline.com
Mike Stedham
Zach Childree
Ryan Rutledge

Format: Tabloid

JAMES FAULKNER STATE CMTY. COLLEGE — 1900 S US Highway 31, Bay Minette, AL, 36507-2698, USA; tel (251) 580-2100
Margaret Strickland

JOHN C. CALHOUN STATE CMTY. COLLEGE: COLLEGE DAZE — PO Box 2216, Decatur, AL, 35609-2216, USA; tel (256) 306-2500
Robin Philip
Format: Tabloid

OAKWOOD COLLEGE: SPREADING OAK — 7000 Adventist Blvd NW, Huntsville, AL, 35896-0003, USA; tel (256) 726-7000; e-mail: oakspread@yahoo.com; web site: www.oakwood.edu
Michael Vance
Format: Broadsheet

SAMFORD UNIV.: SAMFORD CRIMSON — Su # 292269, Birmingham, AL, 35229-0001, USA; tel (205) 726-2466; fax (205) 726-2586; e-mail: crimson@samford.edu; web site: www.samfordcrimson.com
Jon Clemmensen
Format: Tabloid

SPRING HILL COLLEGE: SPRINGHILLIAN — 4000 Dauphin St, Mobile, AL, 36608-1791, USA; tel (251) 380-3850; fax (251) 460-2185; e-mail: shcmedia@shc.edu; sbabington@shc.edu; adv email: hillian@stumail.shc.edu; ed email: hillian@stumail.shc.edu; web site: http://newswire.shc.edu/
Stuart Babington
Integrated Multimedia Center (IMC) Operations Mgr and Student Media adviser — J.L. Stevens II
Published: Thur
Digital Edition Available?: Y
Digital Platform - Mobile: Apple, Android, Windows
Price: Free
Format: Tabloid

STILLMAN COLLEGE: TIGER'S PAW — PO Box 1430, Tuscaloosa, AL, 35403-1430, USA; tel (205) 349-4240
Format: Tabloid

TROY UNIVERSITY: THE TROPOLITAN — Hall School of Journalism and Communication, Troy, AL, 36082-0001, USA; tel (334) 670-3583; fax (334) 670-3707; e-mail: sstewart71298@troy.edu; adv email: sstewart71298@troy.edu; ed email: sstewart71298@troy.edu; web site: www.tropnews.com; www.troy.edu
Advisor — Steve Stewart
Published: Thur Certain home sports game days
Digital Edition Available?: Y
Format: Broadsheet

UNIV. OF ALABAMA: CRIMSON WHITE — PO Box 870170, Tuscaloosa, AL, 35487-0170, USA; tel (205) 348-7845; fax (205) 348-8036; e-mail: news@cw.ua.edu; web site: www.cw.ua.eduEst. 1894
Drew Gunn
Corey Craft
Amanda Peterson
Format: Broadsheet

UNIV. OF ALABAMA AT BIRMINGHAM: KALEIDOSCOPE — 1110 12th Street South, Birmingham, AL, 35205, USA; tel (205) 934-3354; fax (205) 934-8050; e-mail: masutton@uab.edu; adv email: ads@insideuab.com; web site: studentmedia.uab.eduEst. 1967
Amy Kilpatrick
Ed. in Chief — Daniel Twieg
Bill Neville
Director — Marie Sutton
Published: TuesCirc.(fr.) 6,000
Digital Edition Available?: Y
Digital Platform - Mobile: Apple, Android
Digital Platform - Tablet: Apple iOS, Android
Insert rate: $75 per 1,000
Price: Free
Format: Broadsheet

UNIV. OF ALABAMA HUNTSVILLE: THE CHARGER TIMES — 301 Sparkman Drive, Huntsville, AL, 35899-0001, USA; e-mail: chargertimes@uah.edu; adv email: ctlayout@uah.edu; ed email: cteditor@uah.edu; web site: chargertimes.com ; chargertimes.net ; chargertimes.uah.edu
Editor-in-Chief — Morgan Blair
Managing Editor — Amy Dunham
Published: Tues, Fri
Digital Edition Available?: N
Format: News Site

UNIV. OF MONTEVALLO: ALABAMIAN — 75 College Dr, Montevallo, AL, 35115, USA; tel (205) 665-6222; fax (205) 665-6232; e-mail: alabamian@montevallo.edu; web site: http://www.thealabamian.com/
Adviser — Tiffany Bunt
Editor — Reed Strength
Business Manager — Stephanie Howe
Published: Bi-Mthly
Digital Edition Available?: Y
Format: Broadsheet

UNIV. OF NORTH ALABAMA: THE FLOR-ALA — One Harrison Plaza, UNA Box 5300, Florence, AL, 35632, USA; tel (256) 765-4364; e-mail: editor@florala.net; web site: www.florala.netEst. 1830
Student Media Advisor — Scott Morris
Published: Thur, Other biweekly
Digital Edition Available?: Y
Insert rate: N/A
Price: Free
Format: Tabloid

UNIV. OF WEST ALABAMA: THE LIFE — 100 US-11, Livingston, AL, 35470, USA; tel (205) 652-3892; fax (205) 652-3586; web site: www.uwa.edu/thelife
Betsy Compton
Format: Tabloid

UNIVERSITY OF SOUTH ALABAMA: THE VANGUARD — 336 Alpha Hall South, Mobile, AL, 36688-0001, USA; tel (251)460-6442; fax (251) 414-8293; web site: www.usavanguard.comEst. 1963
Editor-in-Chief — Cassie Fambro
Adviser — Aucoin J
Managing Editor — Alanna Whitaker
Published: MonCirc.(fr.) 2,000
Digital Edition Available?: Y
Digital Platform - Mobile: Other
Format: Tabloid

ALASKA

ALASKA PACIFIC UNIV.: APU JOURNAL — 4101 University Dr Ste 19, Anchorage, AK, 99508-4625, USA; tel (907) 564-8297; fax (907) 564-8236; e-mail: journal@alaskapacific.edu
Rosanne Pagano
Michelle Coles
Format: Tabloid

UNIV. OF ALASKA ANCHORAGE: THE NORTHERN LIGHT — 3211 Providence Dr., Campus Ctr. 215, Anchorage, AK, 99508-4614, USA; tel (907) 786-1434; fax (907) 786-1331; adv email: ads@thenorthernlight.org; ed email: editor@thenorthernlight.org; web site: www.thenorthernlight.orgEst. 1988
Paola Banchero
Mariya Proskuryakova
Executive Editor — Shana Roberson
Format: Tabloid

UNIV. OF ALASKA FAIRBANKS: THE SUN STAR — PO Box 756640, Fairbanks, AK, 99775-6640, USA; tel (907) 474-6039; fax (907) 474-5508; e-mail: fystar@uaf.edu; web site: www.uafsunstar.com
Editor-in-Chief — Chavis Lakeidra
Manager Advertising
Published: Tues
Digital Edition Available?: Y
Digital Platform - Mobile: Apple, Android, Windows, Blackberry
Digital Platform - Tablet: Apple iOS, Android, Windows 7, Blackberry Tablet OS, Kindle, Nook, Kindle Fire
Format: Broadsheet

UNIV. OF ALASKA SOUTHEAST: WHALESONG — 11120 Glacier Hwy, Juneau, AK, 99801-8699, USA; tel (907) 796-6434; fax (907) 796-6399; e-mail: uas.whalesong@gmail.com; whalesong@uas.alaska.edu; web site: www.uas.alaska.edu/whalesongEst. 1981
Jeremy Hsieh
Taylor Murph
Randi Spary
Hollis Kitchin
Format: Tabloid

ARIZONA

ARIZONA STATE UNIV.: STATE PRESS — PO Box 871502, Tempe, AZ, 85287-1502, USA; tel (480) 965-7572; fax (480) 965-8484; e-mail: state.press@asu.edu; web site: www.statepress.com
Jason Manning
Tosh Stuart
Leo Gonzalez
Format: Tabloid

EMBRY-RIDDLE AERO UNIV.: HORIZONS — 3700 Willow Creek Road, Prescott, AZ, 86301, USA; tel (928) 777-3891; e-mail: prnews@erau.edu; web site: www.erau.edu/
Alan Malnar
Gen Mgr. — Katie
Format: Tabloid

GLENDALE CMTY. COLLEGE: THE VOICE — 6000 W Olive Ave, Glendale, AZ, 85302-3090, USA; tel (623) 845-3820; fax (623) 845-3072; e-mail: ads@gccvoice.com; web site: www.gccvoice.com
Mike Mullins
Eric Carroll
Michelle Tabatabai-Shab
Format: Tabloid

MESA COMMUNITY COLLEGE: MESA LEGEND — 1833 W Southern Ave, Mesa, AZ, 85202-4866, USA; tel (480) 461-7270; fax (480) 461-7334; e-mail: jackm@mesacc.edu; web site: www.mesalegend.comEst. 1962
Advisor — Jack Mullins
Published: Bi-MthlyCirc.(fr.) 5,000
Digital Edition Available?: Y
Insert rate: $75 per 1,000
Price: $0.0
Format: Tabloid (small format)

NORTHERN ARIZONA UNIV.: LUMBERJACK — PO Box 6000, Flagstaff, AZ, 86011-0180, USA; tel (928) 523-4921; fax (928) 523-9313; e-mail: lumberjack@nau.edu; web site: www.jackcentral.com
Ace Mcmillin
Gary Sundt
Joshua Garcia
Jesica Demarco
Format: Tabloid

PARADISE VALLEY CMTY. COLLEGE: PUMA PRESS — 18401 N 32nd St, Phoenix, AZ, 85032-1200, USA; tel (602) 787-6772; fax (602) 787-7285; e-mail: pumapress@pvmail.maricopa.edu; adv email: judy.galbraith@paradisevalley.edu; ed email: judy.galbraith@paradisevalley.edu; web site: http://nevalleynews.org/Est. 1991
Judy Galbraith
Published: MthlyCirc.(fr.) 2,000
Digital Edition Available?: Y
Digital Platform - Mobile: Apple
Insert rate: $200.
Price: Free
Format: Tabloid
Note: Paradise Valley Community College is converged online media with Scottsdale Community College to form the Northeast Valley News.

PIMA COMMUNITY COLLEGE: AZTEC PRESS — 2202 W. Anklam Rd., Tucson, AZ, 85709-0001, USA; tel (520) 206-6800; fax (520) 206-6834; e-mail: aztec_press@pima.edu; adv email: aztecpress_ad@pima.edu; web site: aztecpressonline.comEst. 1970
Business manager — Andrew Paxton
Published: Bi-MthlyCirc. (pd.) 0 (fr.) 5,000
Digital Edition Available?: Y
Price: Free
Format: Tabloid

THUNDERBIRD SCHOOL OF GLOBAL MGMT.: DAS TOR — 1 Global Pl, Glendale, AZ, 85306-3216, USA; tel (602) 978-7000; fax (602) 978-7971; e-mail: dastor@thunderbird.edu; web site: www.thunderbird.edu
Sailaja Kattubadi
Format: Tabloid

UNIV. OF ARIZONA: ARIZONA DAILY WILDCAT — 615 N. Park Ave., Ste. 101, Tucson, AZ, 85719-5094, USA; tel (520) 621-8659; fax (520) 626-8303; e-mail: display@wildcat.arizona.edu; ed email: editor@wildcat.arizona.edu; web site: www.wildcat.arizona.eduEst. 1899
Mark Woodhams
Asst. Dir. — Brett Fera
Published: Mon, Tues, Wed, Thur, Fri
Digital Edition Available?: Y
Digital Platform - Mobile: Apple, Android
Digital Platform - Tablet: Apple iOS, Android
Format: Tabloid

WEST NEWS — 4701 W Thunderbird Rd # 117, Glendale, AZ, 85306-4900, USA; tel 602-543-8575Est. 2010
Editor-in-chief — Robert Gehl
Price: Free
Format: Tabloid

YAVAPAI COLLEGE: THE ROUGH WRITER — 1100 E Sheldon St Bldg 3-118, Prescott, AZ, 86301-3297, USA; fax (928) 717-7678; e-mail: roughwriter.yc.edu; adv email: ycwriters@yahoo.com; web site: http://roughwriter.yc.edu/
Colette Strassburg
Brandon Ross
Elizabeth Zieche
Insert rate: ycwriters@yahoo.com
Format: Tabloid

ARKANSAS

ARKANSAS STATE UNIV.: THE HERALD — PO Box 1930, State University, AR, 72467-1930, USA; tel (870) 972-3076; fax (870) 972-3339; e-mail: herald@astate.edu; adv email: herald@astate.edu; ed email: herald@astate.edu; web site: www.asuherald.comEst. 1921
Advisor — Bonnie Thrasher
Editor — Lindsey Blakely
Advertising Manager — Jana Waters
Published: Mon, ThurCirc.(fr.) 5,000
Digital Edition Available?: Y
Insert rate: None
Price: Free
Format: Broadsheet

ARKANSAS TECH. UNIV.: ARKA TECH
— 1815 Coliseum Drive, Russellville, AR, 72801-7400, USA; tel (479) 968-0284; fax (479) 964-0889; e-mail: arkatech@atu.edu; adv email: arkatech.ads@atu.edu; web site: www.arkatechnews.comEst. 1923
Tommy Mumert
Published: ThurCirc.(fr.) 2,100
Digital Edition Available?: Y
Insert rate: $100 per thousand
Format: Broadsheet

ARKANSAS TRAVELER: ARKANSAS TRAVELER — 119 Kimpel Hall, Fayetteville, AR, 72701, USA; tel (479) 575-3406; fax (479) 575-3306; e-mail: traveler@uark.edu; web site: http://www.uatrav.com/
Editor-in-Chief — Saba Naseem
Format: Broadsheet

HARDING UNIV.: BISON — PO Box 11192, Searcy, AR, 72149-0001, USA; tel (501) 279-4139; fax (501) 279-4127; e-mail: thebison@harding.edu; web site: thebison.harding.edu
Jermy Beauchamp
Advisor — Jermy
Format: Tabloid

HENDERSON STATE UNIV.: HENDERSON ORACLE — PO Box 7693, Arkadelphia, AR, 71999-7693, USA; tel (870) 230-5221; fax (870) 230-5549; e-mail: oracle@hsu.edu; adv email: oracleads@hsu.edu; web site: www.hsuoracle.comEst. 1910
Advisor — Steve Listopad
Published: MonCirc.(fr.) 2,000
Digital Edition Available?: Y
Format: Tabloid

HENDRIX COLLEGE: THE PROFILE — 1600 Washington Ave., Conway, AR, 72032, USA; tel (501) 329-6811; e-mail: proed@hendrix.edu; web site: www.theprofileonline.com
Alice Hines
Format: Tabloid

JOHN BROWN UNIV.: THREEFOLD ADVOCATE — 2000 W University St, Siloam Springs, AR, 72761-2121, USA; tel (479) 524-7255; fax (479) 524-7394; e-mail: advocate@jbu.edu; web site: advoacte.jbu.edu
Chair — Carey Byars
Gary Warner
Grace Pennington
Anna Mulder
Format: Tabloid

LYON COLLEGE — PO Box 2317, Batesville, AR, 72503-2317, USA; tel (870) 698-4288; fax (870) 698-4622; e-mail: highlander@lyon.edu
Gavin Johannsen

OUACHITA BAPTIST UNIV.: SIGNAL — Obu # 3759, Arkadelphia, AR, 71998-0001, USA; tel (870) 245-5210; fax (870) 245-5209; e-mail: Signal@obu.edu; adv email: Signal@obu.edu; ed email: Signal@obu.edu; web site: www.obusignal.com
Jeff Root
Published: Thur
Digital Edition Available?: Y
Format: broadsheet
Note: Online Edition: signalonline@obu.edu

PHILANDER SMITH COLLEGE: PANTHER — 900 W Daisy L Gatson Bates Dr, Little Rock, AR, 72202-3717, USA; tel (501) 370-5354; e-mail: jcheffen@philander.edu
Jimmy Cheffen
Format: Magazine

SOUTHERN ARKANSAS UNIV.: THE BRAY — P.O. Box 1400, Magnolia, AR, 71753-71753, USA; tel (870) 235-4269; fax (870) 235-5005; e-mail: saubrayeditors@yahoo.com; ed email: brayeditor@yahoo.com; web site: www.saumag.edu
John Cary
Wes Dowdy
Terri Richardson
Jamal Brown
Format: Broadsheet

THE FORUM, UNIVERSITY OF ARKANSAS AT LITTLE ROCK: UALR FORUM — 2801 S University Ave Dsc 201J, Little Rock, AR, 72204-1000, USA; tel (501) 569-3319; fax (501) 569-3209; adv email: adman@ualr.edu; ed email: editor@ualr.edu; web site: ualr.edu/forum
Sonny Rhodes
Exec. Ed. — Jacob Ellerbee
Published: Bi-MthlyCirc.(fr.) 2,500
Digital Edition Available?: Y
Format: Broadsheet

UNIVERSITY OF ARKANSAS AT PINE BLUFF: THE ARKANSAWYER — 1200 N. University Dr., Pine Bluff, AR, 71601, USA; tel (870) 575-8427; e-mail: arkansawyer@uapb.edu; adv email: arkansawyer@uapb.edu; ed email: arkansawyer@uapb.eduEst. 1921
Editor — Alicia Dorn
Published: Other Bi-weeklyCirc.(fr.) 1,000
Digital Edition Available?: N
Insert rate: $100
Price: Free
Format: Tabloid
Note: Advertising color positions available. All ads sold by contract by the semester or the year.

UNIVERSITY OF CENTRAL ARKANSAS: THE ECHO — PO Box 5038, Conway, AR, 72035-0001, USA; tel 501-499-9822; e-mail: ucaechoeditor@gmail.com; adv email: echonewspaperads@gmail.com; web site: www.ucaecho.net
David Keith
editor — Jordan Johnson
business manager — Hayley Trejo
Published: WedCirc.(fr.) 2,500
Digital Edition Available?: Y
Format: Broadsheet

WESTARK CMTY. COLLEGE: LION'S PRIDE — PO Box 3649, Fort Smith, AR, 72913-3649, USA; tel (501) 788-7261
Format: Magazine

CALIFORNIA

ALLIANT INTERNATIONAL UNIV.: ENVOY — 5130 E Clinton Way, Fresno, CA, 93727-2014, USA; tel (559) 456-2777; fax (858) 635-4853; e-mail: envoy@alliant.edu; envoy.alliant@gmail.com
Miles Beauchamp
Alexandria Proff
Format: Broadsheet

AMERICAN RIVER COLLEGE: AMERICAN RIVER CURRENT — 4700 College Oak Dr, Sacramento, CA, 95841-4286, USA; tel (916) 484-8653; fax (916) 484-8668; e-mail: current@arc.losrios.edu; web site: www.americanrivercurrent.com
Jill Wagner
Carol Hartman
Andrew Clementi
Format: Tabloid

ANTELOPE VALLEY COLLEGE: EXAMINER — 3041 W Avenue K, Lancaster, CA, 93536-5426, USA; tel (661) 722-6496; fax (661) 943-5573; web site: www.avc.edu
Charles Hood
Format: Tabloid

BAKERSFIELD COLLEGE: THE RENAGADE RIP — 1801 Panorama Dr, Bakersfield, CA, 93305-1299, USA; tel (661) 395-4324; fax (661) 395-4027; e-mail: ripmail@bakersfieldcollege.edu; adv email: daedward@bakersfieldcollege.edu; web site: www.therip.comEst. 1929
Advisor — Danny Edwards
Published: bi-weekly (once every two weeks on Wednesdays)Circ.(fr.) 3,000
Digital Edition Available?: Y
Price: Free
Format: Broadsheet

BIOLA UNIVERSITY: THE CHIMES — 13800 Biola Ave, La Mirada, CA, 90639-0001, USA; tel (562) 906-4569; fax (562) 906-4515; e-mail: lily.park@biola.edu; adv email: chimes.advertising@biola.edu; web site: chimes.biola.edu
Chair/Prof. — Michael A. Longinow
Advertising Manager — Sarah Sjoberg
Prof. — J. Douglas Tarpley
Assoc. Prof. — Michael Bower
Asst. Prof. — Tamara Welter
Instr. — James Hirsen
Instr. — Chi-Chung Keung
Instr. — Mark Landsbaum
Instr. — Greg Schneider
Instr. — Melissa Nunnally
Published: Thur
Digital Edition Available?: N
Format: Broadsheet

CALIFORNIA BAPTIST COLLEGE: BANNER — 8432 Magnolia Ave, Riverside, CA, 92504-3297, USA; tel (951) 343-4401; fax (951) 351-1808; e-mail: banner@calbaptist.edu
Mary Ann Pearson
Amanda Tredinnick
Kendall Dewitt
Format: Tabloid

CALIFORNIA INST. OF TECHNOLOGY: CALIFORNIA TECH NEWSPAPER — Caltech MSC 40-58, Pasadena, CA, mpearson@calbaptist.edu, USA; tel (626) 395-6154; e-mail: business@caltech.edu; web site: tech.caltech.edu
Vi Tran
Format: Tabloid

CALIFORNIA LUTHERAN UNIVERSITY: THE ECHO — 60 W Olsen Rd # 4200, Thousand Oaks, CA, 91360-2787, USA; tel (805) 493-3366; fax (805) 493-3479; e-mail: kelley@robles.callutheran.edu; ed email: echo@clunet.edu
Colleen Cason
Chair — Sharon Docter
Jonathan Culmer
Margaret Nolan
Insert rate: x
Format: Tabloid

CALIFORNIA POLYTECHNIC STATE UNIV.: MUSTANG NEWS — 1 Grand Ave, San Luis Obispo, CA, 93407-9000, USA; tel (805) 756-2537; fax (805) 756-6784; e-mail: editor@mustangnews.net; adv email: advertising@mustangnews.net; web site: www.mustangnews.netEst. 1916
GM — Paul Bittick
Published: Mon, ThurCirc.(fr.) 6,000
Digital Edition Available?: Y
Digital Platform - Mobile: Apple, Android
Digital Platform - Tablet: Apple iOS, Android
Format: Broadsheet

CALIFORNIA STATE UNIV.: UNIVERSITY TIMES — 5151 State University Dr # KH-C3098, Los Angeles, CA, 90032-4226, USA; tel (323) 343-4215; fax (323) 343-5337; e-mail: universitytimes@yahoo.com; adv email: jmunson@cslanet.calstatela.edu; ed email: universitytimes@yahoo.com; web site: www.calstatela.eduEst. 1947
Business, Advt. Mgr. — Jim Munson
Insert rate: $8/CPM
Price: Free
Format: Tabloid

CALIFORNIA STATE UNIV.: COLLEGIAN — 5201 N Maple Ave MS SA42, Fresno, CA, 93740-0001, USA; tel (559) 278-5735; fax (559) 278-2679; e-mail: collegian@csufresno.edu; web site: www.csufresno.edu/collegian
Jefferson Beavers
Virginia Sellars-Erxleben
Brian Maxey
Format: Tabloid

CALIFORNIA STATE UNIV.: ORION — Chico Dept. of Journalism, Chico, CA, 95926, USA; tel (530) 898-4237; fax (530) 898-4799; adv email: advertising@theorion.com; web site: www.theorion.com
David Waddell
Gillian Leeds
Jennifer Siino
Mike North
Format: Tabloid

CALIFORNIA STATE UNIV.: COYOTE CHRONICLE — 5500 University Pkwy, San Bernardino, CA, 92407-2318, USA; tel (909) 537-5289; fax (909)-537-7072; e-mail: sbchron@csusb.edu; web site: www.coyotechronicle.com
Jim Smart
Linda Sand
Ken Dillard
Format: Tabloid

CALIFORNIA STATE UNIV. DOMINGUEZ: CSUDH BULLETIN — 1000 E Victoria St Dept Sac, Carson, CA, 90747-0001, USA; tel (310) 243-2312; fax (310) 217-6935; e-mail: bulletin@csudh.edu; adv email: Advertise@csudh.edu; web site: www.csudh.edu/bulletin/
Catherine Risling
Marjan Khorashadi-Zadeh
Karen Mossiah
Published: Wed Bi-Weekly
Digital Edition Available?: N
Format: Tabloid

CALIFORNIA STATE UNIV. LONG BEACH: DAILY FORTY-NINER — 1250 Bellflower Blvd, Long Beach, CA, 90840-4601, USA; tel (562) 985-8001; fax (562) 985-1740; adv email: beverly.munson@csulb.edu; ed email: eicd49er@gmail.com; web site: www.daily49er.comEst. 1949
Beverly Munson
Barbara Kingsley-Wilson
Published: Mon, Tues, Wed, ThurCirc.(fr.) 6,000
Format: Tabloid

CALIFORNIA STATE UNIV., FULLERTON: DAILY TITAN — College Park Bldg., 2600 E. Nutwood Ave., Ste. 660, Fullerton, CA, 92831-3110, USA; tel (657) 278-4411; fax (657) 278-2702; adv email: ads@dailytitan.com; ed email: editorinchief@dailytitan.com; web site: www.dailytitan.comEst. 1960
Bus. Mgr. — Robert Sage
Published: Mon, Tues, Wed, ThurCirc.(fr.) 6,000
Digital Edition Available?: Y
Digital Platform - Mobile: Apple, Android
Digital Platform - Tablet: Apple iOS, Android
Insert rate: $55 CPM
Format: Broadsheet

CALIFORNIA STATE UNIVERSITY, BAKERSFIELD: THE RUNNER — 9001 Stockdale Hwy., Bakersfield, CA, 93311-1022, USA; tel (661) 654-2165; e-mail: runner@csub.edu; web site: http://therunneronline.comEst. 1974
Lecturer and Adviser to the Runner Student Media Center — Jennifer Burger
Published: Wed Back-to-School issue - 1st Day of Fall
Digital Edition Available?: Y
Digital Platform - Mobile: Apple, Android
Digital Platform - Tablet: Apple iOS, Android
Insert rate: $.10 per copy (up to 2,000)
Price: Free
Format: Broadsheet

CALIFORNIA STATE UNIVERSITY, EAST BAY.: THE PIONEER — 25800 Carlos Bee Blvd, Hayward, CA, 94542-3001, USA; tel (510) 885-3292; fax (510) 885-4099; adv email: pioneer.advertising@csueastbay.edu; ed email: pioneernewspaper@sueastbay.edu; web site: http://thepioneeronline.com/
Published: ThurCirc.(fr.) 10,000
Digital Edition Available?: Y
Format: Tabloid

CALIFORNIA STATE UNIVERSITY, NORTHRIDGE: SUNDIAL — 18111 Nordhoff St, Northridge, CA, 91330-8200, USA; tel (818) 677-3135; fax (818) 677-3438; adv email: ads@sundial.csun.edu; ed email: editor@csun.edu; web site: www.csun.eduEst. 1957
Chair/Prof. — Kent Kirkton
Melissa Lalum
Prof. — Susan Henry
Jody Holcomb
Prof. — Maureen Rubin
Assoc. Prof. — Rick Marks
Editor — Loren Townsley
Asst. Prof. — Jose Luis Benavides
Asst. Prof. — David Blumenkrantz
Asst. Prof. — Linda Bowen
Asst. Prof. — Jim Hill
Asst. Prof. — Melissa Wall
Lectr. — Lori Baker-Schena
Prof. Emer. — Jerry Jacobs
Prof. Emer. — DeWayne Johnson
Prof. Emer. — Lawrence Schneider
Part-time Fac. — Scott Brown
Part-time Fac. — Henrietta Charles
Part-time Fac. — Jeffrey Duclos
Part-time Fac. — Barbara Eisenstock
Part-time Fac. — Mariel Garza
Part-time Fac. — Keith Goldstein
Part-time Fac. — Lincoln Harrison
Published: Mon, Tues, Wed, ThurCirc.(fr.) 6,000
Digital Edition Available?: Y
Digital Platform - Mobile: Apple, Android
Digital Platform - Tablet: Apple iOS, Android
Format: Tabloid

CALIFORNIA STATE UNIVERSITY, SAN MARCOS: THE COUGAR CHRONICLE — 333 S Twin Oaks Valley Rd, San Marcos, CA, 92096-0001, USA; tel (760) 750-6099; fax (760) 750-3345; e-mail: csusm.chronicle@gmail.com; ed email: csusm.chronicle@gmail.com; web site: www.csusmchronicle.comEst. 1992
Advisor — Pam Kragen
Co-Editor-in-Chief, Editor of Design — Morgan Hall
Co-Editor-in-Chief — Kristin Melody
Advertising Manager — Rogers Jaffarian
Published: WedCirc. (pd.) 0 (fr.) 1,500
Digital Edition Available?: N
Price: Free
Format: Tabloid

CALIFORNIA STATE UNIVERSITY, STANISLAUS: THE SIGNAL — 1 University Cir, Turlock, CA, 95382-3200, USA; tel (209) 667-3411; fax (209) 667-3868; e-mail: sstevens2@csustan.edu; web site: www.csusignal.com
Format: Tabloid

CERRITOS COLLEGE: TALON MARKS — 11110 Alondra Blvd, Norwalk, CA, 90650-6298, USA; tel (562) 860-2451; fax (562) 467-5044; e-mail: editor@talonmarks.com; web site: www.talonmarks.com
Rich Cameron
Elieth Koulzons
Rick Gomez
Joey Berumen
News Ed. — Joey
Arts Ed. — Megan
Format: Broadsheet

CHABOT COLLEGE: SPECTATOR — 25555 Hesperian Blvd Ste 1635, Hayward, CA, 94545-2400, USA; tel (510) 723-7082; fax (510) 723-6919; e-mail: chabot_spectator@hotmail.com; web site: www.chabotspectator.com
Jeannie Wakeland
Format: Tabloid

CHAFFEY COLLEGE: THE BREEZE — 5885 Haven Ave., Rancho Cucamonga, CA, 91737, USA; tel (909) 652-6934; e-mail: thebreeze@chaffey.edu; adv email: michelle.dowd@chaffey.edu; web site: www.thebreezeonline.com
Adviser — Michelle Dowd
Published: Mon, Bi-MthlyCirc.(fr.) 3,000
Format: Tabloid

CHAPMAN UNIV.: THE PANTHER — 1 University Dr, Orange, CA, 92866-1005, USA; tel (714) 997-6870; fax (714) 744-7898; e-mail: panthernewspaper@gmail.com; web site: www.thepantheronline.com; www.chapman.edu/panthernewspaper
Amber Gonzales
Martin Syjuco
Michelle Thomas
Jillian Freitas
Business Mgr. — Jennifer
Dir., Art — Kim
Format: Tabloid

CITRUS COLLEGE: THE CLARION — 1000 W Foothill Blvd, Glendora, CA, 91741-1899, USA; tel (626) 914-8586; fax (626) 914-8797; e-mail: ccclarion@hotmail.com; web site: www.theclarion online.com
Margaret O'Neill
Emily Rios
Format: Tabloid

CITY COLLEGE OF SAN FRANCISCO: THE GUARDSMAN — 50 Phelan Ave # V67, San Francisco, CA, 94112-1898, USA; tel (415) 239-3446; fax (415) 239-3884; e-mail: email@theguardsman.com; adv email: advertising@theguardsman.com; ed email: editor@theguardsman.com; web site: www.theguardsman.comEst. 1935
Juan Gonzales
Published: Wed Bi-WeeklyCirc.(fr.) 7,000
Digital Edition Available?: Y
Price: Free
Format: Tabloid
Note: Also available on Pulse and Issuu.com/theguardsman.com

CLAREMONT COLLEGES — 175 E 8th St, Claremont, CA, 91711-3956, USA; tel (909) 621-8000; fax (909) 607-7825
Keith Koyano
Format: Broadsheet

CLAREMONT MCKENNA COLLEGE: FORUM — Heggblade Ctr., 500 E. 9th St., Claremont, CA, 91711, USA; tel (909) 607-6709; fax (909) 607-9489
Adam Sivitz
Format: Broadsheet

COLLEGE OF MARIN: ECHO-TIMES — 835 College Ave, Kentfield, CA, 94904-2590, USA; tel (415) 485-9690; fax (415) 485-0135; e-mail: echotimes@marin.cc.ca.us; web site: www.theechotimes.com
Elisa Forsgren
William Kennedy
Yukie Sano
Format: Tabloid

COLLEGE OF SAN MATEO: THE SAN MATEAN — 1700 W Hillsdale Blvd, San Mateo, CA, 94402-3784, USA; tel (650) 574-6330; e-mail: sanmatean@smccd.edu; web site: www.sanmatean.comEst. 1928
Ed Remitz
Margeret Baum
Sharon Ho
Laura Babbitt
Format: Broadsheet

COLLEGE OF THE CANYONS — 26455 Rockwell Canyon Rd, Santa Clarita, CA, 91355-1899, USA; tel (661) 259-7800; fax (661) 362-3043
Jim Ruebsamen

COLLEGE OF THE DESERT: THE CHAPARRAL — 43500 Monterey Ave, Palm Desert, CA, 92260-9399, USA; tel (760) 776-7244; fax (760) 862-1338; e-mail: chaparral@collegeofthedesert.edu; web site: www.thechaparral.com
Aaron White
Edward Grofer
Sarah Wilson
Format: Broadsheet

COLLEGE OF THE SEQUOIAS: CAMPUS — 915 S Mooney Blvd, Visalia, CA, 93277-2234, USA; tel (559) 730-3844; fax (559) 730-3991; e-mail: campusnews@cos.edu; adv email: campusads@cos.edu; ed email: campusnews@cos.edu; web site: www.coscampusonline.comEst. 1933
Digital Platform - Mobile: Apple, Android
Format: Broadsheet

CONTRA COSTA COLLEGE: ACCENT ADVOCATE — 2600 Mission Bell Dr, San Pablo, CA, 94806-3195, USA; tel (510) 235-7800; fax (510) 235-6397; e-mail: advocate@contracosta.edu; web site: www.contracosta.edu; www.accentadvocate.com
Paul DeBlot
Holly Pablo
Sam Attal
Format: Broadsheet

COSUMNES RIVER COLLEGE: CONSUMNES CONNECTION — 8401 Center Pkwy, Sacramento, CA, 95823-5799, USA; tel (916) 691-7471; fax (916) 688-7181; web site: www.crcconnection.com
Yvette Lessard
Erin Bates
Bhavisha Patel
Lehsee Gausi
Format: Tabloid

CUESTA COLLEGE: CUESTONIAN — PO Box 8106, San Luis Obispo, CA, 93403-8106, USA; tel (805) 546-3286; fax (805) 546-3904; e-mail: cuestonian@cuesta.edu; web site: www.cuestonian.cuesta.edu; www.cuesta.edu
Patrick Howe
Mary Mc Corkle
Sarah Clifford
Bethany Fraker
Format: Tabloid

CUYAMACA COLLEGE: COYOTE EXPRESS — 900 Rancho San Diego Pkwy Bldg G-109, El Cajon, CA, 92019-4369, USA; tel (619) 660-4000; fax (619) 660-4399; web site: www.cuyamaca.edu/coyoteexpressEst. 1977
Seth Slater
Mary Graham
Format: Tabloid

CYPRESS COLLEGE CHRONICLE: CYCHRON.COM & DIVERGENCE MAGAZINE — 9200 Valley View St., Cypress, CA, 90630-5805, USA; tel 714-484-7267; fax (714) 484-7466; e-mail: rmercer@cypresscollege.edu; web site: www.cychron.comEst. 1966
Robert Mercer
Published: MthlyCirc.(fr.) 4,000
Digital Edition Available?: Y
Digital Platform - Mobile: Apple, Android, Windows
Format: Online and Print Magazine
Note: Hosted on WordPress software on own server

DE ANZA COLLEGE: LA VOZ — 21250 Stevens Creek Blvd Rm L-41, Cupertino, CA, 95014-5797, USA; tel (408) 864-5626; e-mail: lavoz@fhda.edu; adv email: lavozadvertising@gmail.com; ed email: lavoz@fhda.edu; web site: www.lavozdeanza.comEst. 1967
Journalism Chair — Cecilia Deck
Published: Mon, Bi-Mthly 16 issues from late September to mid-JuneCirc.(fr.) 2,200
Digital Edition Available?: Y
Digital Platform - Mobile: Apple
Digital Platform - Tablet: Apple iOS
Insert rate: TBA
Price: Free
Format: Tabloid
Note: Student newspaper for De Anza College, Cupertino, CA

DIABLO VALLEY COLLEGE: INQUIRER — 321 Golf Club Rd, Pleasant Hill, CA, 94523-1544, USA; tel (925) 685-1230; fax (925) 681-3045; e-mail: inquirer@dvc.edu; web site: www.dvc.edu/journalism
Ann Stenmark
Ashley Pittson
Catharine Ahr
Ed. — Barbara
Format: Broadsheet

DOMINICAN COLLEGE: HABIT — 50 Acacia Ave, San Rafael, CA, 94901-2298, USA; tel (415) 485-3204; fax (415) 485-3205; web site: www.dominican.edu
Melva Bealf
Format: Tabloid

EAST LOS ANGELES COLLEGE: CAMPUS NEWS — 1301 Avenida Cesar Chavez, Monterey Park, CA, 91754-6001, USA; tel (323) 265-8821; fax (323) 415-4190; e-mail: Elaccampusnews@gmail.com; adv email: jonfanie@yahoo.com; ed email: elaccampusnews@gmail.com; web site: elaccampusnews.comEst. 1945
Advisor — Jean Stapleton
Co-Adviser — Sylvia Rico-Sanchez
Published: Wed, Other Not
Published in summer or January. Weekly during school year. Circ.(fr.) 4,800
Digital Edition Available?: Y
Format: Broadsheet

EL CAMINO COLLEGE: THE UNION — 16007 Crenshaw Blvd., Torrance, CA, 90506, USA; tel (310) 660-3328; fax (310) 660-6092; e-mail: elcounionads000@yahoo.com; adv email: elcounionads000@yahoo.com; ed email: eccunion@gmail.com; web site: eccunion.comEst. 1946
Adv. Mgr. — Jack Mulkey
Adviser — Kate McLaughlin
Adviser — Stefanie Frith
Photo Adviser — Gary Kohatsu
Published: Bi-Mthly Twice per month Circ.(fr.) 5,000
Digital Edition Available?: Y
Insert rate: N/A
Format: Broadsheet

EVERGREEN VALLEY COLLEGE: EVERGREEN FLYER — 3095 Yerba Buena Rd, San Jose, CA, 95135-1598, USA; tel (408) 274-7900
Format: Broadsheet

FOOTHILL COLLEGE: FOOTHILL SENTINEL — 12345 S El Monte Rd, Los Altos Hills, CA, 94022-4597, USA; tel (650) 949-7372; fax (650) 949-7375; web site: www.foothillsentinel.org
Drew Dara Abrams
Format: Tabloid

FRESNO CITY COLLEGE: RAMPAGE — 1101 E University Ave, Fresno, CA, 93741-0002, USA; tel (559) 442-8262; fax (559) 265-5783; e-mail: rampage-news@fresnocitycollege.edu; web site: www.fresnocitycollegerampage.com
Dypnpa Ugwu-Oju
Leah Edward
Ramiro Gudino
Format: Tabloid

FULLER THEOLOGICAL SEMINARY: SEMI — 135 N Oakland Ave, Pasadena, CA, 91182-0002, USA; tel (626) 584-5430; fax (626) 304-3730
Carmen Valdez
Eugene Suen
Ben Cassil
Insert rate: semi-ads@dept.fuller.edu
Format: Magazine

FULLERTON COLLEGE: THE HORNET — 321 E Chapman Ave, Fullerton, CA, 92832-2095, USA; tel (714) 992-7154; fax (714) 447-4097; e-mail: hornet@fullcoll.edu; web site: www.fullcoll.eduEst. 1922
Advisor — Jay Seidel
Published: Wed
Digital Edition Available?: N
Format: Tabloid

GAVILAN COLLEGE: GAVILAN PRESS — 5055 Santa Teresa Blvd, Gilroy, CA, 95020-9599, USA; tel (408) 848-4837; fax (408) 848-4801
Faculty Advisor — Esmeralda Montenegro
Published: Bi-MthlyCirc. (pd.) 0 (fr.) 0
Digital Edition Available?: Y
Price: FREE
Format: Online only
Note: This publication is in transition. More information will be available when the fall semester begins.

GLENDALE CMTY. COLLEGE: EL VAQUERO — 1500 N Verdugo Rd Rm AD212, Glendale, CA, 91208-2809, USA; tel (818) 551-5214; fax (818) 551-5278; web site: www.elvaq.com
Michael Moreau
Jeff Smith
Format: Tabloid

GOLDEN GATE UNIV.: CAMPUS CURRENTS — 536 Mission St, San Francisco, CA, 94105-2968, USA; tel (415) 442-7871; fax (415) 442-7896; e-mail: campuscurrent@gguol.ggu.edu; web site: www.ggu.edu
Brian Louie
Ambrose Tse
Format: Tabloid

GOLDEN WEST COLLEGE: THE WESTERN SUN — 15744 Goldenwest St Rm 138, Huntington Beach, CA, 92647-3103, USA; tel (714) 895-8786; fax (714) 895-8795; e-mail: twsatgwc@aol.com; adv email: gwckcumper@yahoo.com; web site: www.westernsun.us; www.goldenwestcollege.edu/westernsunEst. 1966
Advisor — Jim Tortolano
Katie Cumper
Lanace Tonelli
Opal McClain
Sports Ed. — Fernando
Published: Bi-MthlyCirc.(fr.) 15,000
Digital Edition Available?: Y
Format: Tabloid
Note: Westernsun.us (website)

GROSSMONT COLLEGE: SUMMIT — 8800 Grossmont College Dr, El Cajon, CA, 92020-1798, USA; e-mail: summit@gcccd.edu; web site: gcsummit.com
Published: Mthly
Format: Tabloid

HASTINGS COLLEGE OF LAW — 200 McAllister St, San Francisco, CA, 94102-4978, USA; tel (415) 565-4786; fax (707) 313-0161
John Hendrickson

HUMBOLDT STATE UNIV.: LUMBERJACK — 1 Harpst Street, Arcata, CA, 95521-8299, USA; tel (707) 826-3271; e-mail: thejack@humboldt.edu; web site: www.thejackonline.org
Marcy Burstiner
Sara Wilmot
Format: Tabloid

JOHN F. KENNEDY UNIVERSITY — 100 Ellinwood Way, Pleasant Hill, CA, 94523-4817, USA; tel 925.969.3584; fax 925.969.3136; web site: www.jfku.edu

LANEY COLLEGE: LANEY TOWER — 900 Fallon St # 160, Oakland, CA, 94607-4893, USA; tel (510) 464-3460; fax (510) 834-3452; e-mail: laneytower@peralta.edu; web site: www.laneytower.com
Burt Dragin
Scott Strain
Felix Solomon
Published: Thur Every other week
Digital Edition Available?: Y
Format: Tabloid

LASSEN CMTY. COLLEGE: THE LASSEN COUGAR — PO Box 3000, Susanville, CA, 96130-3000, USA; tel (530) 251-8821; fax (530) 251-8839; e-mail: trougar@lassen.cc.ca.us; web site: www.lassencougar.com; www.lassen.cc.ca.us
Andrew Owen
Format: Tabloid

LOMA LINDA UNIV.: TODAY — Anderson St Burden Hall 11041, Loma Linda, CA, 92350-0001, USA; tel (909) 558-4526; fax (909) 558-4181; web site: www.llu.edu/news/today
Format: Tabloid

LONG BEACH CITY COLLEGE: VIKING — 4901 E Carson St Mail Drop Y-16, Long Beach, CA, 90808-1780, USA; tel (562) 938-4284; fax (562) 938-4948; e-mail: vikingnews@lbcc.edu; web site: www.lbccvikingnews.comEst. 1927
Patrick McKean
Kori Filipek
Michel Simmons
Format: Tabloid

LOS ANGELES CITY COLLEGE: COLLEGIAN — 855 N Vermont Ave, Los Angeles, CA, 90029-3588, USA; tel (323) 953-4000; web site: wwwa.lacitycollege.edu
Rhonda Guess
Format: Broadsheet

LOS ANGELES HARBOR COLLEGE: RANDON LENGTHS NEWS — PO Box 731, San Pedro, CA, 90733-0731, USA; tel (310) 519-1016; fax (310) 832-1000; adv email: rlnsales@randomlengthsnews.com; ed email: editor@randomlengthsnews.com; web site: www.randomlengthsnews.comEst. 1979
James Preston Allen
Paul Rosenberg
Mng Ed — Terelle Jerricks
Published: Thur, Bi-Mthly
Digital Edition Available?: Y
Digital Platform - Mobile: Apple, Android, Windows
Digital Platform - Tablet: Apple iOS, Android, Windows 7
Insert rate: see rate card at randomlengthsnews.com
Format: Tabloid

LOS ANGELES PIERCE COLLEGE: ROUNDUP — 6201 Winnetka Ave # 8212, Woodland Hills, CA, 91371-0001, USA; tel (818) 719-6483; fax (818) 719-6447; e-mail: newsroom.roundupnews@gmail.com; adv email: baileyjd@piercecollege.edu; ed email: newsroom.roundupnews@gmail.com; web site: www.theroundupnews.comEst. 1949
Jill Connelly
Julie Bailey
Adviser to the Roundup newspaper — Stefanie Frith
Published: WedCirc.(fr.) 5,000
Insert rate: No inserts accepted
Price: Free on campus
Format: Broadsheet

LOS ANGELES VALLEY COLLEGE: VALLEY STAR — 5800 Fulton Ave, Valley Glen, CA, 91401-4062, USA; tel (818) 947-2576; fax (818) 947-2610; e-mail: valleystar@lavalleystar.com; web site: www.lavalleystar.com
Rod Lyons
Bill Dauber
Sarah Knowles
Lucas Thompson
Format: Broadsheet

LOS MEDANOS COLLEGE: EXPERIENCE — 2700 E Leland Rd, Pittsburg, CA, 94565-5197, USA; tel (925) 439-2181; fax (925) 427-1599; web site: www.losmedanos.eduEst. 1974
Cindy McGrath
Format: Broadsheet

LOYOLA MARYMOUNT UNIV.: LOS ANGELES LOYOLAN — 1 Lmu Dr Ste 8470, Los Angeles, CA, 90045-2682, USA; tel (310) 338-7509; fax (310) 338-7887; e-mail: loyolan@lmu.edu; editor@theloyolan.com; web site: www.laloyolan.com
Tom Nelson
Gil Searano
Samantha Eisner
Jose Martinez
Heather Chong
Emily
Laura
Format: Tabloid

MENDOCINO COLLEGE — 1000 Hensley Creek Rd, Ukiah, CA, 95482-3017, USA; tel (707) 468-3096; fax (707) 468-3120
Debra Wallace
Format: Tabloid

MENLO COLLEGE: MENLO OAK — 1000 El Camino Real, Atherton, CA, 94027-4301, USA; tel (650) 543-3786; e-mail: pr@menlo.edu; web site: www.menlo.edu
Dean of Enrollment Management — Priscila de Souza
Format: Tabloid

MILLS COLLEGE: THE CAMPANIL — 157 Rothwell Ctr., 5000 MacArthur Blvd., Oakland, CA, 94613, USA; tel (510) 430-2246; fax (510) 430-3176; e-mail: eic@thecampanil.com; adv email: ads@thecampanil.com; web site: www.thecampanil.com
Sarah Pollock
Jennifer Courtney
Rashida Harmon
Morgan Ross
Opinion Ed. — Nicole
Features Ed. — Anna Belle
Format: Tabloid

MIRACOSTA COLLEGE: CHARIOT — 1 Barnard Dr Rm 3441, Oceanside, CA, 92056-3820, USA; tel (760) 757-2121; fax (760) 757-8209; e-mail: www.mccechariot.com
Meghan Sills
Insert rate: mccchariot@yahoo.com
Format: Tabloid

MODESTO JUNIOR COLLEGE: PIRATES' LOG — 435 College Ave, Modesto, CA, 95350-5800, USA; tel (209) 575-6223; fax (209) 575-6612; web site: www.pirateslog.org
Laura Paull
Format: Broadsheet

MOORPARK COLLEGE: STUDENT VOICE — 7075 Campus Rd., Moorpark, CA, 93021-1605, USA; tel (805) 378-1552; fax (805) 378-1438; e-mail: studentvoice@vcccd.edu; web site: www.studentvoiceonline.com
Joanna Miller
Format: Broadsheet

NOTRE DAME DE NAMUR UNIVERSITY: ARGONAUT — 1500 Ralston Ave, Belmont, CA, 94002-1997, USA; tel (650) 508-3500; fax (650) 508-3487; e-mail: argonaut@ndnu.edu; web site: www.theargonaut.net
Danielle Russo
Victor Gonzales
Format: Tabloid

OCCIDENTAL COLLEGE: THE OCCIDENTAL WEEKLY — 1600 Campus Rd # M-40, Los Angeles, CA, 90041-3314, USA; tel (323) 259-2886; fax (323) 341-4982; e-mail: weekly@oxy.edu; web site: www.oxyweekly.comEst. 1893
Riley Hooper
Ben Dalgetty
Ashly Burch
Marty Cramer
Bus. Mgr. — Elana
Adv. Mgr. — Tucker
Format: Tabloid

OHLONE COLLEGE: MONITOR — PO Box 3909, Fremont, CA, 94539-0390, USA; tel (510) 659-6074; fax (510) 659-6076; e-mail: monitor@ohlone.edu; monitor@ohlone.cc.ca.us; web site: www.ohlonemonitoronline.com
Adviser — Rob Dennis
Published: Nine times per semester
Digital Edition Available?: Y
Format: Tabloid

ORANGE COAST COLLEGE: COAST REPORT — 2701 Fairview Rd, Costa Mesa, CA, 92626-5561, USA; tel (714) 432-5561; fax (714) 432-5978; adv email: coastreportads@yahoo.com; ed email: editor@coastreportonline.com; coastreport@yahoo.com; web site: www.coastreportonline.comEst. 1948
Cathy Werblin
Format: Broadsheet

OXNARD COLLEGE — 4000 S Rose Ave, Oxnard, CA, 93033-6699, USA; tel (805) 986-5836; fax (805) 986-5806

PACIFIC UNION COLLEGE: C TWO — 1 Angwin Ave, Angwin, CA, 94508-9797, USA; tel (707) 965-6747; fax (707) 965-7123; e-mail: cc@puc.edu; web site: c2.puc.edu
Tammy McGuire
Peter Katz
Format: Broadsheet

PALOMAR COLLEGE: TELESCOPE — 1140 W Mission Rd Rm CH-7, San Marcos, CA, 92069-1487, USA; tel (760) 744-1150; fax (760) 744-8123; e-mail: telescopead@palomar.edu; web site: www.the-telescope.comEst. 1946
Erin Hiro
Sara Burbidge
Kelley Foyt
Format: Tabloid

PASADENA CITY COLLEGE: COURIER — 1570 E Colorado Blvd Rm T110-A, Pasadena, CA, 91106-2041, USA; tel (626) 585-7130; fax (626) 585-7971; e-mail: pasadenacourier@yahoo.com; adv email: courierads@yahoo.com; web site: www.pcccourier.com
Warren Swil
John Avery
Barbara Beaser
Format: Tabloid

PEPPERDINE UNIV.: GRAPHIC — 24255 Pacific Coast Hwy, Malibu, CA, 90263-3999, USA; tel (310) 506-4318; fax (310) 506-4411; adv email: graphicadvertising@pepperdine.edu; web site: www.pepperdine-graphic.com
Elizabeth Smith
Amanda Gordon
Ryan Hagen
Format: Broadsheet

POINT LOMA NAZARENE UNIV.: THE POINT WEEKLY — 3900 Lomaland Dr, San Diego, CA, 92106-2899, USA; tel (619) 849-2444; fax (619) 849-7009; e-mail: news@pointweekly.com; sports@pointweekly.com; advertising@pointweekly.com; web site: www.

pointweekly.com
Stephanie Gant
Journalism Dir. — Dean Nelson
Coco Jones
Nathan Scharn
Format: Tabloid

POMONA COLLEGE: STUDENT LIFE — Smith Campus Ctr., Claremont, CA, 91711-7003, USA; tel (909) 607-6709; e-mail: info@tsl.pomona.edu; adv email: business@tsl.pomona.edu; ed email: editor@tsl.pomona.edu; web site: www.tsl.pomona.eduEst. 1889
Ian Gallogly
Business Manager — Adam Belzberg
Editor-in-Chief — Jeff Zalesin
Published: FriCirc. (pd.) 50 (fr.) 2,000
Digital Edition Available?: Y
Format: Broadsheet

RANDY VANDERMEY: RANDY VANDERMEY — 132 Walnut Lane, Santa Barbara, CA, 93111, (805) 683-1115; tel 8056831115;8054034251cell; fax 8056831115;8054034251cell; e-mail: vanderme@westmont.edu; adv email: horizon@westmont.edu; ed email: horizon@westmont.edu; web site: http://horizon.westmont.edu/pages/contactEst. c. 1945
Advisor — Randy VanderMey
Editor-in-Chief — M<itchell MacMahon
Published: TuesCirc. (pd.) 300 (fr.) 800
Digital Edition Available?: Y
Digital Platform - Mobile: Apple
Digital Platform - Tablet: Apple iOS
Format: Tabloid

RIO HONDO COLLEGE: EL PAISANO — 3600 Workman Mill Rd, Whittier, CA, 90601-1699, USA; tel (562) 908-3453; fax (562) 463-4641; e-mail: elpaisano@riohondo.edu; web site: www.elpaisanonewspaper.com
John Francis
Mary Cowan
Salomon Baeza
James Tapparo
Exec. Dir. — Kathy
Format: Broadsheet

RIVERSIDE CMTY. COLLEGE: VIEWPOINTS — 4800 Magnolia Ave, Riverside, CA, 92506-1201, USA; tel (951) 222-8488; fax (951) 328-3505; e-mail: viewpoints@rcc.edu; web site: www.viewpointsonline.org
Allan Lovelace
Stephanie Holland
Chanelle Williams
Vanessa Soto
Photo Ed. — Lauren
Format: Tabloid

SACRAMENTO CITY COLLEGE: EXPRESS — 3835 Freeport Blvd, Sacramento, CA, 95822-1386, USA; tel (916) 558-2562; fax (916) 558-2282; e-mail: express@scc.losrios.edu; web site: www.scc.losrios.edu/express
Dianne Heimer
Hannah Ucol
Cecilio Padilla
Format: Broadsheet

SACRAMENTO STATE: THE STATE HORNET — 6000 J Street, Sacramento, CA, 95819, USA; tel 9162786584; e-mail: editor@statehornet.com; adv email: ads@statehornet.com; ed email: editor@statehornet.com; web site: 6000 J StreetEst. 1949
Faculty Adviser — Stu VanAirsdale
Published: Wed
Digital Edition Available?: Y
Format: Tabloid

SADDLEBACK COLLEGE: LARIAT, USA — tel (626) 815-6000; e-mail: clause@apu.edu; adv email: tim.posada@gmail.com; ed email: tim.posada@gmail.com; web site: www.lariatnews.comEst. 1967
Advisor — Tim Posada
Published: Wed
Digital Edition Available?: Y
Digital Platform - Mobile: Apple, Android, Windows, Blackberry, Other
Digital Platform - Tablet: Apple iOS, Android, Windows 7, Blackberry Tablet OS, Kindle, Nook, Kindle Fire, Other
Format: Tabloid

SAINT MARY'S COLLEGE OF CALIFORNIA: THE COLLEGIAN — P.O. Box 4407, Moraga, CA, 94575-4407, USA; tel (925) 631-4279; e-mail: staff@stmaryscollegian.com; adv email: collegianads@gmail.com; web site: www.stmaryscollegian.comEst. 1903
Advisor — Shawny Anderson
Co-Editor-in-Chief — Charlie Guese
Co-Editor-in-Chief — Sara DeSantis
Michael Bruer
Published: TuesCirc. (pd.) 0 (fr.) 1,000
Digital Edition Available?: Y
Insert rate: $10.00 per column inch ($8.25 for local)
Price: Free
Format: Tabloid

SAN BERNARDINO VALLEY COLLEGE: ARROWHEAD — 701 S Mount Vernon Ave, San Bernardino, CA, 92410-2798, USA; tel (909) 888-1996; fax (909) 381-4604; web site: www.sbvcarrowhead.com
Gary Kellam
Format: Tabloid

SAN DIEGO CITY COLLEGE: CITY TIMES — 1313 Park Blvd Rm T-316, San Diego, CA, 92101-4787, USA; tel (619) 388-4026; fax (619) 388-3814; e-mail: citytimes@gmail.com; adv email: ads.citytimes@gmail.com; web site: www.sdcitytimes.com
Roman Koenig
Vanessa Gomez
Format: Tabloid

SAN DIEGO MESA COLLEGE: MESA PRESS — 7250 Mesa College Dr, San Diego, CA, 92111-4999, USA; tel (619) 388-2630; fax (619) 388-2836; e-mail: mesa.press@gmail.com; web site: www.mesapress.comEst. 1966
Janna Braun
Format: Tabloid

SAN DIEGO MIRAMAR COLLEGE: THE SAGE — 10440 Black Mountain Rd, San Diego, CA, 92126-2999, USA; tel (619) 388-7800; fax (619)-388-7900; web site: www.sdmiramar.edu
Leslie Klipper
Sandy Treivasan
Format: Tabloid

SAN DIEGO STATE UNIV.: DAILY AZTEC — EBA-2, San Diego, CA, 92182-0001, USA; tel (619) 594-1804; fax (619) 594-1804; e-mail: daads@mail.sdsu.edu; web site: 2259 Birds NestEst. 1913
Andrew Dyer
Published: WedCirc.(fr.) 5,000
Format: Tabloid

SAN FRANCISCO STATE UNIVERSITY: GOLDEN GATE EXPRESS — 1600 Holloway Ave # 4200, San Francisco, CA, 94132-1740, USA; tel (415) 338-1689; fax (415) 338-2084; e-mail: jour@sfsu.edu; web site: www.journalism.sfsu.eduEst. 1934
Dept. Chair/Assoc. Prof. — Venise Wagner
Assoc. Dept. Chair/Prof. — Jon Funabiki
Dottie Katzeff
Prof. — John Burks
Barbara Landes
Nathan Codd
Prof. — Yvonne Daley
Prof. — Kenneth Kobre
Prof. — Erna R. Smith
Assoc. Prof. — Rachele Kanigel
Assoc. Prof. — Austin Long-Scott
Asst. Prof./Dir., Ctr. for Integration/ Improvement of Journalism — Cristina Azocar
Asst. Prof. — Yumi Wilson
Prof. Emer. — John T. Johnson
Prof. Emer. — B.H. Liebes
Prof. Emer. — Betty Medsger
Prof. Emer. — Leonard Sellers
Prof. Emer. — Jerrold Werthimer
Lectr. — Harriet Chiang
Lectr. — Roland DeWolk
Lectr. — Jesse Garnier
Lectr. — David Greene
Lectr. — Sibylla Herbrich
Format: Tabloid

SAN JOAQUIN DELTA COLLEGE: THE COLLEGIAN — 5151 Pacific Ave Shima 203, Stockton, CA, 95207-6370, USA; tel (209) 954-5156; fax (209) 954-5288; e-mail: deltacollegian@gmail.com; web site: www.deltacollegian.com
Bill Davis
Junifer Mamsaang
Format: Tabloid

SAN JOSE CITY COLLEGE: TIMES — 2100 Moorpark Ave, San Jose, CA, 95128-2799, USA; tel (408) 298-2181; fax (408) 288-6331; e-mail: thesjcctimes@hotmail.com; web site: www.sjcc.edu
Format: Tabloid

SAN JOSE STATE UNIV.: SPARTAN DAILY — 1 Washington Sq, San Jose, CA, 95112-3613, USA; tel (408) 924-3281; fax (408) 924-3282; e-mail: spartandaily@casa.sjsu.edu; adv email: spartandailyads@casa.sjsu.edu; web site: www.thespartandaily.com
Richard Craig
Timothy Hendrick
Jenny Ngo
Joey Akeley
Format: Tabloid

SANTA ANA COLLEGE: EL DON — 1530 W 17th St, Santa Ana, CA, 92706-3398, USA; tel (714) 564-5617; fax (714) 564-0821; e-mail: eldonbusiness@sac.edu; web site: www.eldononline.org
Charles Little
Allene Symons
Format: Tabloid

SANTA BARBARA CITY COLLEGE: CHANNELS — 721 Cliff Dr Rm 123, Santa Barbara, CA, 93109-2394, USA; tel (805) 965-0581; fax (805) 730-3079; e-mail: channels@sbcc.edu; web site: www.thechannelsonline.com
Patricia Stark
Format: Tabloid

SANTA CLARA UNIVERSITY: THE SANTA CLARA — 500 El Camino Real # 3190, Santa Clara, CA, 95053-0001, USA; tel (408) 554-4849; e-mail: news@thesantaclara.com; adv email: advertising@thesantaclara.com; ed email: editor@thesantaclara.com; letters@thesantaclara.com; news@thesantaclara.com; web site: www.thesantaclara.comEst. 1922
Sophie Mattson
Published: ThurCirc.(fr.) 1,100
Digital Edition Available?: Y
Digital Platform - Mobile: Other
Format: Tabloid

SANTA MONICA COLLEGE: CORSAIR — 1900 Pico Blvd # 303, Santa Monica, CA, 90405-1644, USA; tel (310) 434-4340; fax (310) 434-3648; e-mail: corsair.editorinchief@gmail.com; adv email: blaize_ashanti@smc.edu; ed email: corsair.editorinchief@gmail.com; web site: www.thecorsaironline.comEst. 1929
Saul Rubin
Price: Free
Format: Tabloid

SANTA ROSA JUNIOR COLLEGE: THE OAK LEAF — 1501 Mendocino Ave., Santa Rosa, CA, 95401-4332, USA; tel (707) 527-4401; e-mail: abelden@santarosa.edu; adv email: oakleaf-ads@santarosa.edu; ed email: abelden@santarosa.edu; web site: www.santarosa.eduEst. 1928
Ann Belden
Format: Tabloid

SHASTA COLLEGE: THE LANCE — PO Box 496006, Redding, CA, 96049-6006, USA; tel (530) 242-7729; fax (530) 225-3925; e-mail: editorial@sclance.com; web site: www.sclance.com
Craig Harrington
Format: Broadsheet

SIERRA COLLEGE: OUTLOOK — 5000 Rocklin Rd, Rocklin, CA, 95677-3397, USA; tel (916) 789-2699; fax (916) 789-2854
Kelly Kukis
Format: Tabloid

SOLANO COMMUNITY COLLEGE: TEMPEST — 4000 Suisun Valley Rd, Fairfield, CA, 94534-3197, USA; tel (707) 864-7000; fax (707) 864-0361; e-mail: tempest@solano.edu; adv email: samanda.dorger@solano.edu; ed email: tempest@solano.edu; web site: www.solanotempest.net
Journalism Adviser — Samanda Dorger
Published: Bi-MthlyCirc.(fr.) 1,500
Digital Edition Available?: Y
Digital Platform - Mobile: Apple, Android, Windows, Blackberry, Other
Digital Platform - Tablet: Apple iOS, Android, Windows 7, Blackberry Tablet OS
Price: Free
Format: Tabloid

SONOMA STATE UNIVERSITY: SONOMA STATE STAR — 1801 E Cotati Ave Salazar Hall 1053, Rohnert Park, CA, 94928-3613, USA; tel (707) 664-2776; fax (707) 664-4262; e-mail: star@sonoma.edu; adv email: sonomastatestar@gmail.com; ed email: star@sonoma.edu; web site: www.sonomastatestar.comEst. 1979
Editor-in-Chief — Dylan Sirdofsky
Advertising Manager — Amanda Saiki
Faculty Advisor — Paul Gullixson
Published: Tues
Digital Edition Available?: Y
Format: Tabloid

SOUTHERN CALIFORNIA UNIV. OF HEALTH SCIENCES — 16200 Amber Valley Dr, Whittier, CA, 90604-4051, USA; tel (562) 947-8755; fax (562) 902-3321
Pam Roosevelt

SOUTHWESTERN COLLEGE: THE SUN — 900 Otay Lakes Rd, Chula Vista, CA, 91910-7297, USA; tel (619) 482-6368; fax (619) 482-6513; e-mail: southwestern_sun@yahoo.com; web site: www.southwesterncollegesun.com
Max Branfcomb
Format: Broadsheet

STANFORD UNIV.: STANFORD DAILY — 456 Panama Mall, Stanford, CA, 94305-5294, USA; tel (650) 721-5803; fax (650) 725-1329; e-mail: eic@stanforddaily.com; web site: www.stanforddaily.com
Jason Shen
Mary Liz McCurdy
Devin Banerjee
Kamil Dada
Sr. Mng. Ed. — Eric
Format: Broadsheet

THE POLY POST — 3801 W Temple Ave Bldg 1, Pomona, CA, 91768-2557, USA; tel (909) 869-5483; fax (909) 869-3533; e-mail: advisor@thepolypost.com; adv email: advertise@thepolypost.com; web site: www.thepolypost.com
Doug Spoon
Amanda Newfield
Aaron Castrejon

Linda Perez
Format: Broadsheet

UNIV. OF CALIFORNIA BUS. SCHOOL: HAAS WEEK — Cheit Hall Rm 138, Berkeley, CA, 94720-0001, USA; tel (510) 642-7480; fax (510) 643-8764
Joe Moss
Insert rate: haasweek@haas.berkeley.edu
Format: Tabloid

UNIV. OF CALIFORNIA GRAD. SCHOOL OF MGMT.: THE ANDERSON EXCHANGE — 110 Westwood Plz, Rm D216, Los Angeles, CA, 90095-0001, USA; tel (310) 825-6488; fax (310) 206-3981; e-mail: exchange@anderson.ucla.edu; web site: andersonexchange.collegepublisher.com
Steve Gilison
Daniel Gelsi
Julie Lacouture
Format: Magazine

UNIV. OF CALIFORNIA IRVINE: THE NEW UNIVERSITY — 3100 Gateway Cmns Fl 3, Irvine, CA, 92697-0001, USA; tel (949) 824-8788; fax (949) 824-4828; e-mail: eic@newuniversity.org; adv email: admanager@newu.uci.edu; ed email: eic@newuniversity.org; web site: www.newuniversity.org
David Lumb
Sandy RoseCirc. (pd.) 0 (fr.) 8,000
Format: Tabloid

UNIV. OF CALIFORNIA SCHOOL OF LAW: KING HALL ADVOCATE — 400 Mrak Hall Dr, Davis, CA, 95616-5203, USA; tel (530) 752-0243
Heather Melton
Format: Tabloid

UNIV. OF CALIFORNIA, BERKELEY: THE DAILY CALIFORNIAN — 2483 Hearst Avenue Berkeley, CA 94709, Berkeley, CA, 94701-1949, USA; tel (510) 548-8300; fax (510) 849-2803; e-mail: dailycal@dailycal.org; dailycalifornian@dailycal.org; adv email: advertising@dailycal.org; ed email: editor@dailycal.org; web site: www.dailycal.orgEst. 1871
Editor in Chief and President — Karim Doumar
Published: Mon, Tues, Thur, FriCirc. (pd.) 10,000
Digital Edition Available?: Y
Format: Broadsheet

UNIV. OF CALIFORNIA, RIVERSIDE: HIGHLANDER — 101 Highlander Union Bldg., Riverside, CA, 92521-0001, USA; tel (951) 827-3617; fax (951) 827-7049; e-mail: editorinchief@highlandernews.org; adv email: highlanderads@ucr.edu; ed email: editorinchief@highlandernews.org; web site: www.highlandernews.orgEst. 1956
EIC — Chris LoCascio
Mgr Ed — Kevin Keckeisen
News Ed — Sandy Van
Erin Mahoney
A&E Ed. — Emily Wells
Sports Ed. — Kendall Petersen
Photo Ed. — Brian Tuttle
EIC — Myles Andrews-Duve
Published: TuesCirc.(fr.) 4,000
Digital Edition Available?: Y
Insert rate: 600.00
Format: Tabloid

UNIV. OF CALIFORNIA, SANTA BARBARA: DAILY NEXUS — PO Box 13402, Santa Barbara, CA, 93107-3402, USA; tel (805) 893-3828; e-mail: production@dailynexus.com; adv email: LINDA.MEYER@SA.UCSB.EDU; ed email: EIC@DAILYNEXUS.COM; web site: www.dailynexus.com
Adv. Mgr. — Linda Meyer
Published: ThurCirc.(fr.) 4,000
Digital Edition Available?: Y
Digital Platform - Mobile: Apple, Android, Windows, Blackberry, Other
Digital Platform - Tablet: Apple iOS, Android, Windows 7, Blackberry Tablet OS, Kindle, Nook, Kindle Fire, Other
Format: Tabloid

UNIV. OF CALIFORNIA-BERKELEY LAW SCHOOL — 215 Boalt Hall, Berkeley, CA, 94720-0001, USA; tel (510) 642-6483; fax (510) 642-9893
Joshua Rider
Format: Tabloid

UNIV. OF REDLANDS: BULLDOG WEEKLY — PO Box 3080, Redlands, CA, 92373-0999, USA; tel (909) 748-8880
Jessie Stapleton
Format: Broadsheet

UNIV. OF SAN DIEGO: THE USD VISTA — 5998 Alcala Park Frnt, San Diego, CA, 92110-2492, USA; tel (619) 260-4714; fax (619) 260-4807; web site: www.uofsdmedia.com
EIC — Brooklyn Dippo
Associate Ed — Sarah Brewington
Mgr Ed — Diego Luna
Published: Thur
Digital Edition Available?: Y
Format: Tabloid

UNIV. OF SAN DIEGO SCHOOL OF LAW: MOTIONS — 5998 Alcala Park, San Diego, CA, 92110-8001, USA; tel (619) 260-4600; fax (619) 260-4753; e-mail: motions@sandiego.edu; web site: www.sandiego.edu/motions
Damien Schiff
Format: Tabloid

UNIV. OF SAN FRANCISCO: FOGHORN — 2130 Fulton St, San Francisco, CA, 94117-1050, USA; fax (415) 422-2751; e-mail: foghorn_ads@yahoo.com; adv email: advertising@sffoghorn.info; web site: foghorn.usfca.edu/
Theresa Moore
Laura Plantholt
Nicholas Muhkar
Chelsea Sterling
Sports Ed. — Matt
Adv. Mgr. — Mark
Bus. Mgr. — Erika
Format: Broadsheet

UNIV. OF SAN FRANCISCO LAW SCHOOL: DAVIES FORUM — 2130 Fulton St, San Francisco, CA, 94117-1050, USA; tel (415) 422-6586; fax (415) 666-6433; e-mail: theforumusf@gmail.com
Ed. — Andie Vallee
Format: Tabloid

UNIV. OF SOUTHERN CALIFORNIA: DAILY TROGAN — 404 Student Un, Los Angeles, CA, 90089-0001, USA; tel (213) 740-2707; fax (213) 740-5666; e-mail: dtrojan@usc.edu; ed email: editor@dailytorjan.com; web site: www.dailytrojan.com
Mona Cravens
Scott A. Smith
David Khalaf
Sheri Brundage
Format: Tabloid

UNIV. OF THE PACIFIC — 3601 Pacific Ave, Stockton, CA, 95211-0197, USA; tel (209) 946-2115; fax (209) 946-2195; adv email: pacificanads@pacific.edu; ed email: pacificannews@pacific.edu; pacificaneditors@pacific.edu; pacificanlifestyles@pacific.edu; pacificansports@pacific.edu; web site: www.thepacificanonline.com
Dave Frederickson
Ruben Moreno
Devon Blount
Andrew Mitchell
Format: Tabloid

UNIVERSITY OF CALIFORNIA SAN DIEGO: THE GUARDIAN — 9500 Gilman Dr Dept 316, La Jolla, CA, 92093-0316, USA; tel (858) 534-3466; fax (858) 534-7691; adv email: ads@ucsdguardian.org; ed email: managing@ucsdguardian.org; web site: www.ucsdguardian.orgEst. 1967
Editor in Chief — Laira Martin
Published: Mon, Thur
Digital Edition Available?: Y
Price: Free
Format: Tabloid

UNIVERSITY OF CALIFORNIA, DAVIS: THE CALIFORNIA AGGIE — 25 Lower Freeborn Hall, 1 Shields Ave. , Davis, CA, 95616-5270, USA; tel (530) 752-9887; adv email: admanager@theaggie.org; ed email: editor@theaggie.org; web site: www.theaggie.orgEst. 1915
Editor-in-Chief — Bryan Sykes
New Media Manager — Chiara Alves
Managing Editor — Emily Stack
Campus Editor — Hannah Holzer
City Editor — Kaelyn Tuermer-Lee
Features Editor — Gillian Allen
Opinion Editor — Taryn DeOilers
Sports Editor — Veronica Vargo
Science Editor — Harnoor Gill
Arts and Culture Editor — Ally Overbay
Photo Director — Brian Landry
Copy Chief — Olivia Rockeman
Copy Chief — Maxine Mulvey
Design Director — Christie Neo
Layout Director — Amy Ye
Business Development Manager — Laurie Pederson
Distribution Manager — Bianca Atunez
Published: Thur
Digital Edition Available?: Y
Format: Broadsheet

UNIVERSITY OF CALIFORNIA, LOS ANGELES: THE DAILY BRUIN — 308 Westwood Plaza, Los Angeles, CA, 90095-8355, USA; tel (310) 825-9898; fax (310) 206-0906; adv email: ads@media.ucla.edu; ed email: editor@media.ucla.edu; web site: www.dailybruin.comEst. 1919
Bus. Mgr. — Jeremy Wildman
Media Advisor — Abigail Goldman
Student Media Dir — Doria Deen
Editor in chief — Mackenzie Possee
Published: Mon, Tues, Wed, Thur, Fri
Digital Edition Available?: Y
Price: Free
Format: Broadsheet

UNIVERSITY OF CALIFORNIA, SAN FRANCISCO: SYNAPSE — 108 W Millberry Un, San Francisco, CA, 94143-0001, USA; tel (415) 476-2211; fax (415) 502-4537; e-mail: synapse@ucsf.edu; adv email: synapse@ucsf.edu; web site: synapse.ucsf.edu
Managing Editor — Steven Chin
Published: Thur
Digital Edition Available?: Y
Digital Platform - Mobile: Apple, Android, Windows, Blackberry, Other
Digital Platform - Tablet: Apple iOS, Android, Windows 7, Blackberry Tablet OS, Kindle, Nook, Kindle Fire, Other
Format: Tabloid

UNIVERSITY OF LA VERNE: CAMPUS TIMES — 1950 3rd St, La Verne, CA, 91750-4401, USA; tel (909) 593-3511; fax (909) 392-2706; e-mail: ctimes@laverne.edu; adv email: ctimesad@laverne.edu; ed email: ctimes@laverne.edu; web site: www.laverne.edu/campus-timesEst. 1919
Elizabeth Zwerling
Jennifer Lemus Fernandez
Kevin Garrity
Eric Borer
Published: FriCirc.(fr.) 2,000
Format: Tabloid

VANGUARD UNIV.: VAGUARD VOICE — 55 Fair Dr, Costa Mesa, CA, 92626-6597, USA; tel (714) 662-5203; fax (714) 966-5482; e-mail: thevoice@vanguard.edu; web site: www.vanguard.edu
Kristy Eudy
Hannah Petrak
Format: Broadsheet

VENTURA COLLEGE — 4667 Telegraph Rd, Ventura, CA, 93003-3899, USA; tel (805) 654-6400; fax (805) 654-6466; web site: www.venturacollegepress.com
C. Weinstock

WEST VALLEY COLLEGE: NORSEMAN — 14000 Fruitvale Ave, Saratoga, CA, 95070-5698, USA; tel (408) 867-2200; fax (408) 741-4040; web site: www.westvalley.edu
Janine Gerzanics
Format: Tabloid

WHITTIER COLLEGE: QUAKER CAMPUS — PO Box 634, Whittier, CA, 90608-0634, USA; tel (562) 907-4254; fax (562) 945-5301; e-mail: qc@whittier.edu; web site: http://www.thequakercampus.org/Est. 1914
EIC, Mgr Ed — justin dennis
matther anson
Published: Thur
Digital Edition Available?: Y
Format: Tabloid

COLORADO

ARAPAHOE CMTY. COLLEGE: ARAPAHOE FREE PRESS — 5900 S Santa Fe Dr, Littleton, CO, 80120-1801, USA; tel (303) 797-5666; fax (303) 797-5650
Chris Ransick
Reem Al-Omari
Format: Tabloid

COLORADO CHRISTIAN UNIV.: VERITAS — 8787 W Alameda Ave, Lakewood, CO, 80226-2824, USA; tel (303) 202-0100; fax (303) 963-3001; e-mail: cougartrax@ccu.edu; web site: http://luke.ccu.edu/; www.ccu.edu
Jim McCormick
Daniel Cohrs
Format: Magazine

COLORADO COLLEGE: THE CATALYST — 1028 N. Weber St., Colorado Springs, CO, 80903, USA; tel (719) 389-6000; fax (719) 389-6962; e-mail: catalyst@coloradocollege.edu; web site: www.coloradocollege.edu
Jackson Solway
Alex Kronman
Format: Tabloid

COLORADO MESA UNIVERSITY: CRITERION — PO Box 2647, Grand Junction, CO, 81502-2647, USA; tel (970) 248-1570; fax (970) 248-1708; web site: www.thecrite.comEst. 1934
Eric Sandstrom
Jamie Banks

COLORADO SCHOOL OF MINES: MINES OREDIGGER — 1600 Maple St, Golden, CO, 80401-6114, USA; tel (303) 384-2188; fax (303) 273-3931; e-mail: oredig@mines.edu; web site: www.oredigger.net
Managing Editor — Emily McNair
Editor-in-Chief — Lucy Orsi
Design Editor — Taylor Polodna
Webmaster — Connor McDonald
Copy Editor — Arnaud Filliat
Faculty Advisor — Karen Gilbert
Editor-in-Chief — Deborah Good
Published: Mon
Digital Edition Available?: Y
Price: Free
Format: Tabloid

COLORADO STATE UNIV.: ROCKY MOUNTAIN COLLEGIAN — PO Box 13, Fort Collins, CO, 80522-0013, USA; tel (970)

491-1146; fax (970) 491-1690; e-mail: editor@collegian.com; web site: www.collegian.com
Holly Wolcott
Virginia Singarayar
Madeline Novey
Matt Minich
Sports Ed. — Matt L.
Adv. Mgr. — Kim
Format: Broadsheet

COLORADO STATE UNIV. ENGINEERING COLLEGE — PO Box 13, Fort Collins, CO, 80522-0013, USA; tel (970) 491-1686; fax (970) 491-1690; web site: www.collegian.com
Brandon Lowrey

COLORADO STATE UNIVERSITY-PUEBLO: CSU-PUEBLO TODAY — 2200 Bonforte Blvd Bcc 103P, Pueblo, CO, 81001-4901, USA; tel 719-549-2847; fax 719-549-2977; e-mail: leticia.steffen@csupueblo.edu; web site: www.csupueblotoday.com
Advisor — Leticia L. Steffen
Savana Charter
Published: once per semester (fall and spring)
Circ.(fr.) 3,000
Digital Edition Available?: Y

FRONT RANGE CMTY. COLLEGE: FRONT PAGE — 3645 W 112th Ave, Westminster, CO, 80031-2199, USA; tel (303) 404-5314; fax (303) 404-5199; e-mail: frontpage@frontrange.com; web site: www.frontrange.edu
John Heisel
Stephanie Munger
Jon Strungis
Format: Tabloid

FT. LEWIS COLLEGE: INDEPENDENT — 1000 Rim Dr # 252, Durango, CO, 81301-3911, USA; tel (970) 247-7405; fax (970) 247-7487; e-mail: independent@fortlewis.edu; web site: www.flcindependent.com
Leslie Blood
Kayala Andersen
Format: Tabloid

METROPOLITAN STATE COLLEGE: THE METROPOLITAN — PO Box 173362, Denver, CO, 80217-3362, USA; tel (303) 556-2507; fax (303) 556-3421; web site: themet.metrostudentmedia.com; www.mscd.edu/themetEst. 1979
Dianne Harrison Miller
Dominic Graziano
Format: Tabloid

MORGAN CMTY. COLLEGE: STUDENT VIEW — 920 Barlow Rd, Fort Morgan, CO, 80701-4371, USA; tel (970) 542-3170; fax (970) 867-3084
Jennifer Lankford
Format: Magazine

NORTHEASTERN JUNIOR COLLEGE: PLAINSMAN PATHWAYS — 100 College Ave, Sterling, CO, 80751-2399, USA; tel (970) 521-6796
Ian Storey
Patrick Kelling
Format: Tabloid

PIKES PEAK CMTY. COLLEGE: PIKES PEAK NEWS — 5675 S Academy Blvd # C12, Colorado Springs, CO, 80906-5422, USA; tel (719) 502-2000; fax (719) 579-3015; web site: www.ppcc.edu
Linda McGowan
Sonia Gonzales
Format: Tabloid

REGIS UNIV.: HIGHLANDER — 3333 Regis Blvd, Denver, CO, 80221-1099, USA; tel (303) 964-5391; fax (303) 964-5530; web site: www.regishighlander.com
Mary Beth Callie
Maricor Coquia
Format: Tabloid

TRINIDAD STATE JUNIOR COLLEGE: TROJAN TRIBUNE — 600 Prospect St # 182, Trinidad, CO, 81082-2356, USA; tel (719) 846-5011; fax (719) 846-5667
Charlene Duran
Format: Tabloid

UNIV. OF COLORADO: ADVOCATE — PO Box 173364, Denver, CO, 80217-3364, USA; tel (303) 556-2535; fax (303) 556-3679; adv email: advertising@ucdadvocate.com; ed email: editorinchief@ucdadvocate.com; web site: www.ucdadvocate.comEst. 1984
Editor in Chief — Madilyn Bates
Office Coordinator — Isra Yousif
Published: Wed
Digital Edition Available?: Y
Price: Free
Format: Tabloid

UNIV. OF COLORADO: THE SCRIBE — 1420 Austin Bluffs Pkwy, Colorado Springs, CO, 80918-3908, USA; tel (719) 262-3658; fax (719) 262-3600; e-mail: scribe@uccs.edu; web site: www.uccs.edu/scribe
Paul Fair
Format: Tabloid

UNIV. OF DENVER: THE CLARION — 2199 S University Blvd, Denver, CO, 80210-4700, USA; tel (303) 871-3131; fax (303) 871-2568; e-mail: duclarion@du.edu; web site: www.duclarion.com
Arianna Ranahosseini
Format: Tabloid

UNIV. OF NORTHERN COLORADO: THE MIRROR — 823 16th St, Greeley, CO, 80631-5617, USA; tel (970) 392-9270; fax (970) 392-9025; e-mail: info@uncmirror.com; adv email: ads@uncmirror.com; ed email: editor@uncmirror.com; web site: www.uncmirror.comEst. 1919
Kurt Hinkle
Josh Espinoza
Eric Heinz
Jordan Freemyer
Adv. Mgr. — Corey
Adv. Prodn. Mgr. — Lauren
Published: MonCirc.(fr.) 4,000
Digital Edition Available?: Y
Digital Platform - Mobile: Android
Digital Platform - Tablet: Android
Insert rate: $40/1,000
Price: $8/column inch
Format: Tabloid

US AIR FORCE ACADEMY: ACADEMY SPIRIT — 2304 Cadet Dr., Ste. 3100, Colorado Springs, CO, 80904-5016, USA; tel (719) 333-7731; fax (719) 333-4094
Kim Karda
Format: Tabloid

WESTERN STATE COLLEGE: TOP O' THE WORLD — 103 College Ctr, Gunnison, CO, 81231-0001, USA; tel 970-943-2138; fax 970-943-2702; e-mail: top@western.edu; adv email: topworld.ads@gmail.com; web site: www.western.edu/academics/communicationtheatre/top-o-the-worldEst. 1921
Format: Tabloid

CONNECTICUT

CENTRAL CONNECTICUT STATE UNIV.: THE RECORDER — 1615 Stanley St, New Britain, CT, 06050-2439, USA; tel (860) 832-3744; fax (860) 832-3747; e-mail: ccsurecorder@gmail.com; ccsurecorder.ads@gmail.com; web site: www.centralrecorder.com
Coord. — Vivian B. Martin
Melissa Traynor
Michael Walsh
Christopher Boulay
Christina LoBello
Adv. Mgr. — Kelsey
Format: Tabloid

CONNECTICUT COLLEGE: COLLEGE VOICE — PO Box 4970, New London, CT, 06320-4196, USA; tel (860) 439-2841; fax (860) 439-2843; e-mail: ccvoice@conncoll.edu; contact@thecollegevoice.org; web site: thecollegevoice.org
Justin O'Shea
Benjamin Eagle
Claire Gould
CR Baker
Format: Tabloid

EASTERN CONNECTICUT STATE UNIV.: CAMPUS LANTERN — 83 Windham St., 103 Student Ctr., Willimantic, CT, 06226-2211, USA; tel (860) 465-4445; fax (860) 465-4685; e-mail: general@campuslantern.org; lantern@stu.easternct.edu; web site: www.campuslantern.org
Edmond Chibeau
Daniel McCue
Christine Smith
Michael Rouleau
A&E Ed. — Andrew
Sports Ed. — Zach
Opinion Ed. — Jacquelyn
Format: Tabloid

FAIRFIELD UNIV.: MIRROR — PO Box AA, Fairfield, CT, 06824, USA; tel (203) 254-4000; fax (203) 254-4162; adv email: advertising@fairfieldmirror.com; web site: www.fairfieldmirror.com
Faculty adviser — Lei Xie
Published: WedCirc.(fr.) 3,500
Digital Edition Available?: Y
Format: Tabloid

MANCHESTER COMMUNITY COLLEGE: LIVE WIRE — 60 Bidwell Street, Manchester, CT, 06045-1046, USA; tel (860) 512-3290; e-mail: livewire@manchestercc.edu; web site: www.livewiremcc.orgEst. 1979
Stephania Davis
Published: Every six weeksCirc.(fr.) 4,000
Digital Edition Available?: Y
Price: Free
Format: Tabloid

NAUGATUCK VALLEY COMMUNITY COLLEGE: TAMARACK — 750 Chase Pkwy, Waterbury, CT, 06708-3089, USA; tel (203) 575-8040; fax (203) 596-8721; e-mail: nvcc@nvcc.commnet.edu; web site: www.nvcc.commnet.edu
Faculty Advisor — Steve Parlato
Editor-in-Chief — Chelsea Clow
Published: Mthly
Digital Edition Available?: Y
Format: Tabloid

QUINNIPIAC COLLEGE SCHOOL OF LAW: THE CHRONICLE — 275 Mount Carmel Ave, Hamden, CT, 06518-1908, USA; tel (203) 582-8358; fax (203) 582-5203; e-mail: thequchronicle@gmail.com; web site: www.quchronicle.com
Andrew Fletcher
Joe Pelletier
Format: Tabloid

QUINNIPIAC UNIVERSITY: THE QUINNIPIAC CHRONICLE — 275 Mount Carmel Ave, Hamden, CT, 06518-1908, USA; tel 8608301017; e-mail: editor@quchronicle.com; web site: www.quinnipiac.edu; quchronicle.com
Editor-in-Chief — David Friedlander
Format: Tabloid

SACRED HEART UNIV.: SPECTRUM — 5151 Park Ave, Fairfield, CT, 06825-1000, USA; tel (203) 371-7966; fax (203) 371-7828; e-mail: spectrum@sacredheart.edu; adv email: spectrum-advertising@sacredheart.edu; web site: www.shuspectrum.wordpress.com
Joanne Kabak
Lauren Sampson
Carli-Rae Panny
Kate Poole
Format: Tabloid

SOUTHERN CONNECTICUT STATE UNIV.: SOUTHERN NEWS — 501 Crescent St # 58, New Haven, CT, 06515-1330, USA; tel (203) 392-5804; fax (203) 392-6927; e-mail: snews@southernct.edu; web site: snews.southernct.edu
Frank Harris
Format: Tabloid

TRINITY COLLEGE: TRINITY TRIPOD — 300 Summit St Ste 1, Hartford, CT, 06106-3186, USA; tel (860) 297-2584; fax (860) 297-5361; e-mail: tripod@trincoll.edu; web site: https://commons.trincoll.edu/tripod/Est. 1904
Published: Tues
Digital Edition Available?: Y
Format: Tabloid

UNIV. OF BRIDGEPORT: THE SCRIBE — 244 University Ave, Bridgeport, CT, 06604-7775, USA; tel (203) 576-4382; fax (203) 576-4493; e-mail: scribe@bridgeport.edu; web site: www.thescribeonline.com
Richard Unger
Sharon Loh
Format: Tabloid

UNIV. OF CONNECTICUT: THE DAILY CAMPUS — 11 Dog Ln, Storrs, CT, 06268-2206, USA; tel (860) 486-3407; fax (860) 486-4388; e-mail: advertising@dailycampus.com; web site: www.dailycampus.com
Valerie Nezvesky
Christopher Duray
Format: Broadsheet

UNIV. OF HARTFORD: INFORMER — 200 Bloomfield Ave Rm 158, West Hartford, CT, 06117-1545, USA; tel (860) 768-4723; fax (860) 768-4728; e-mail: informer@hartford.edu; web site: www.hartfordinformer.com
Jonathan Whitson
Melissa O' Brien
Format: Tabloid

UNIV. OF NEW HAVEN: CHARGER BULLETIN — 300 Boston Post Rd, West Haven, CT, 06516-1999, USA; tel (203) 932-7182; fax (203) 931-6037; e-mail: chargerbulletin@newhaven.edu; web site: www.chargerbulletin.comEst. 1938
Zack Rosen
Erin Ennis
Sara McGuire
Michelle Blydenburg
Distribution Mgr. — Charles
Liana Teixeira
Elizabeth Field
Published: Wed
Format: Tabloid

WESLEYAN UNIVERSITY: WESLEYAN ARGUS — 45 Wyllys Ave, Middletown, CT, 06459-3211, USA; tel (860) 685-6902; fax (860) 685-3411; e-mail: argus@wesleyan.edu; adv email: argusads@wesleyan.edu; web site: www.wesleyanargus.com
— Natasha Nurjadin
— Aaron Stagoff-BelfortEditor-in-Chiefs
Published: Tues, Fri

WESTERN CONNECTICUT STATE UNIV.: ECHO — 181 White St, Danbury, CT, 06810-6855, USA; tel (203) 837-8706; fax (203) 837-8709; e-mail: wcsuecho@gmail.com; adv email: wcsuechoads@gmail.com; web site: http://wcsuecho.com/news/
John Birks
Todd Passan
Sarah Menichelli
Jessylyn Foley
Format: Tabloid

YALE UNIV.: YALE DAILY NEWS — PO Box 209007, New Haven, CT, 06520-9007, USA; tel (203) 432-2400; fax (203) 432-7425; e-mail: ydn@yale.edu; ydn@yaledailynews.com; adv email: business@yaledailynews.com; web site: www.yaledailynews.com
Jason Chen
Katherine Kavaler
Thomas Kaplan
Format: Broadsheet

YALE UNIV. LAW SCHOOL: THE YALE LAW JOURNAL — PO Box 208215, New Haven, CT, 06520-8215, USA; fax (203) 432-1666
Nicola Williams
Insert rate: nicola.williams@yale.edu
Format: Tabloid

DELAWARE

DELAWARE STATE UNIV.: HORNET — 1200 N Dupont Hwy, Dover, DE, 19901-2276, USA; tel (302) 857-6290; web site: www.desu.edu
Advisor — Marcia Taylor
EIC — Synquette Wilks
Published: Mthly
Format: Tabloid

THE REVIEW: THE REVIEW — 325 Academy St Rm 250, Newark, DE, 19716-6185, USA; tel (302) 831-1397; fax (302) 831-1396; e-mail: business@udreview.com; adv email: ads@udreview.com; ed email: editor@udreview.com; thereview.editorial@gmail.com; web site: www.udreview.comEst. 1882
Editor-in-Chief — Kerry Bowden
Format: Broadsheet

WIDENER UNIV. SCHOOL OF LAW: WIDENER LAW FORUM (OOB) — PO Box 7474, Wilmington, DE, 19803-0474, USA; tel (302) 477-2100; fax (302) 478-3495; e-mail: widenerlawforum@yahoo.com
Doretta McGinnis
Christopher Balala
Harry Matt Taylor
Format: Tabloid

DISTRICT OF COLUMBIA

AMERICAN UNIV.: THE EAGLE — 4400 Massachusetts Ave NW, Washington, DC, 20016-8003, USA; tel (202) 885-1414; fax (202) 885-1428; e-mail: editor@theeagleonline.com; web site: www.theeagleonline.com
Jen Calantone
Charlie Szold
Andrew Tomlinson
Caitlin E. Moore
Photo Ed. — Kelsey
Format: Broadsheet

CATHOLIC UNIV. OF AMERICA: THE TOWER — 127 Pryzbyla Ctr, Washington, DC, 20064-0001, USA; tel (202) 319-5779; fax (202) 319-6675; web site: www.cuatower.com
William McQuillen
Ben Newell
Format: Broadsheet

GALLAUDET UNIVERSITY: BUFF AND BLUE — PO Box 2334, Washington, DC, 20013-2334, USA; tel (202) 651-5000; fax (202) 651-5916; e-mail: ursabuffinblue@gmail.comursabuffinblue; web site: www.gallaudet.edu
Mary Lott
Format: Tabloid

GEORGE WASHINGTON UNIV.: GW HATCHET — 2140 G St NW, Washington, DC, 20052-0072, USA; tel (202) 994-7080; fax (202) 994-1309; e-mail: news@gwhatchet.comgwhatchet; adv email: ads@gwhatchet.comgwhatchet; web site: www.gwhatchet.comEst. 1904
Howard Marshall
Arron Elkins
Alex Byers
Beyers
Format: Broadsheet

GEORGE WASHINGTON UNIV. LAW SCHOOL: NOTE BENE — 2008 H St NW Bsmt, Washington, DC, 20052-0026, USA; tel (202) 994-6261; e-mail: notabene@law.gwu.edu; web site: http://notabene.gwsba.com
Sarah Valerio
Katie Earnest
Format: Tabloid

GEORGETOWN UNIV. LAW CENTER: GEORGETOWN LAW WEEKLY — 600 New Jersey Ave NW, Washington, DC, 20001-2075, USA; tel (202) 662-9357; fax (202) 662-9491
Brett Marston
Format: Tabloid

GEORGETOWN UNIVERSITY: THE HOYA — PO Box 571065, Washington, DC, 20057-1065, USA; tel (202) 687-3947; fax (202) 687-2741; e-mail: gm@thehoya.com; adv email: sales@thehoya.com; ed email: editor@thehoya.com; web site: www.thehoya.comEst. 1920
Roshan Vora
Michelle Lee
Kaphryn Devincenzo
Eamon O' connor
Mng. Ed. — Kathryn
General Manager — Mary Nancy Walter
Published: Tues, FriCirc.(fr.) 6,500
Digital Edition Available?: Y
Digital Platform - Mobile: Apple, Android
Price: see rate cards at www.thehoya.com/advertise
Format: Broadsheet

HOWARD UNIV.: HILLTOP — 816 Easley St Apt 805, Silver Spring, MD, 20910-4581, USA; tel (202) 806-4749; fax (202) 328-1681; e-mail: bussinessoffice@thehilltoponline.com; web site: www.thehilltoponline.com
Kevin Reed
Vanessa Rozier
Format: Broadsheet

MCDONOUGH BUS. SCHOOL/ GEORGETOWN UNIV.: GEORGETOWN GLOBE — 3520 Prospect St NW Ste 215, Washington, DC, 20007-2631, USA; tel (202) 678-0268; fax (202) 678-0268; e-mail: mba-globe@msb.edu; web site: www.georgetownglobe.com
Brenna Fleener
Format: Tabloid

FLORIDA

BARRY UNIV.: BARRY BUCCANEER — 11300 NE 2nd Ave, Miami Shores, FL, 33161-6695, USA; tel (305) 899-3093; fax (305) 899-4744; e-mail: buccaneer@mail.barry.edu; web site: http://student.barry.edu/buccaneer
Susannah Nesmith
Amor Tagan
Samantha Stanton
Format: Tabloid

BETHUNE-COOKMAN COLLEGE: VOICE OF THE WILDCATS — 640 Dr. Mary McLeod Bethune Blvd., Daytona Beach, FL, 32114, USA; tel (386) 481-2000; fax (386) 481-2701; e-mail: voiceofthewildcats@gmail.edu; adv email: voiceofthewildcats@gmail.com; ed email: voiceofthewildcates@gmail.com; web site: voiceofthewildcats.wordpress.com; www.cookman.eduEst. 1904
Ed — Petra Merrick
Layout/Paginator — Jamie Cobb
Sports Ed — Timothy White
Columnist — Augustinas Navickas
Technology Writer — Andres Whipple Girbes
Published: Mthly UniverCity MagazineCirc. (fr.) 1,000
Digital Edition Available?: Y
Price: Free
Format: Tabloid

CENTRAL FLORIDA CMTY. COLLEGE: PATRIOT PRESS — 3001 SW College Rd., Ocala, FL, 34474, USA; tel (352) 873-5800; fax (352) 291-4450; e-mail: patpress@cf.edu; web site: patpress.cf.edu; www.cfcc.cc.fl.us
Rob Marino
Format: Tabloid

DAYTONA STATE COLLEGE: IN MOTION — 1200 W International Speedway Blvd, Daytona Beach, FL, 32114-2817, USA; tel (386) 506-3268; fax (386) 506-3155; e-mail: inmotion@daytonastate.edu; adv email: inmotion@daytonastate.edu; ed email: inmotion@daytonastate.edu; web site: www.daytonastateinmotion.comEst. 1991
Advisor — Elena Jarvis
Published: MthlyCirc.(fr.) 10,002,000
Digital Edition Available?: Y
Digital Platform - Mobile: Other
Insert rate: we do not accept inserts
Price: free for first copy, 50 cents for additional copies
Format: Tabloid

EMBRY-RIDDLE AERONAUTICAL UNIVERSITY: AVION NEWSPAPER — 600 S Clyde Morris Blvd, Daytona Beach, FL, 32114-3900, USA; tel (386) 226-6049; e-mail: theavion@gmail.com; adv email: avionadvertising@gmail.com; web site: www.theavion.comEst. 1969
Advisor — Jessica Searcy
Published: TuesCirc.(fr.) 2,000
Digital Edition Available?: Y
Format: Tabloid

FLAGLER COLLEGE: GARGOYLE — PO Box 1027, Saint Augustine, FL, 32085-1027, USA; tel (904) 819-6333; fax (904) 826-3224; e-mail: gargoyle@flagler.edu; web site: gargoyle.flagler.eduEst. 1968
Brain Thomson

FLORIDA A&M UNIV.: FAMUAN — 510 Orr Dr Ste 3081, Tallahassee, FL, 32307-0001, USA; tel (850) 599-3159; fax (850) 561-2570; e-mail: thefamuanec@gmail.com; adv email: famuanads@hotmail.com; web site: www.thefamuan.com
Andrew Skeritt
Erica Butler
Format: Broadsheet

FLORIDA ATLANTIC UNIV.: UNIVERSITY PRESS — 777 Glades Rd, Boca Raton, FL, 33431-6496, USA; tel (561) 297-2960; fax (561) 297-2106; e-mail: upress@fau.edu; web site: www.upressonline.com
Michael Koretzky
Devin Desjarlais
Karla Bowsher
Lindsey Voltoline
Format: Tabloid

FLORIDA INSTITUTE OF TECHNOLOGY: THE CRIMSON — 150 W University Blvd Ofc, Melbourne, FL, 32901-6975, USA; tel (321) 674-8024; fax (321) 674-8017; e-mail: crimson@fit.edu; ed email: crimson@fit.edu; web site: http://crimson@fit.eduEst. 1967
Adviser — Ted Petersen
Editor-in-Chief — Drew Lacy
Format: Tabloid

FLORIDA INTERNATIONAL UNIV.: BEACON — University Park Campus, 11200 SW 8th St., Graham Ctr., Ste. 210, Miami, FL, 33174-2516, USA; tel (305) 348-6993; fax (305) 348-2712; e-mail: beacon@fiu.edu; web site: fiusm.com
Robert jaross
Tatiana Cantillo
Chris Necuze
Jessica Maya
Format: Broadsheet

FLORIDA MEMORIAL COLLEGE: THE LION'S TALE — 15800 NW 42nd Ave., Miami Gardens , FL, 33054, USA; tel (305) 626-3103; fax (305) 626-3102; e-mail: lionstal@fmuniv.edu; web site: www.fmuniv.edu
Nathanael Paul
Format: Broadsheet

FLORIDA SOUTHERN COLLEGE: SOUTHERN — 111 Lake Hollingsworth Dr, Lakeland, FL, 33801-5698, USA; tel (863) 680-4168; fax (863) 680-6244; web site: www.fscsouthern.com
Chair — Russell Barclay
Michael Trice
Laura Howell
Format: Tabloid

FLORIDA STATE COLLEGE AT JACKSONVILLE: THE CAMPUS VOICE — 101 State St W Rm C103, Jacksonville, FL, 32202-3099, USA; tel (904) 633-8283; fax (904) 632-3279; e-mail: campusvoice@fscj.edu; web site: www.campusvoiceonline.com
Zak Gragg
Editor-in-Chief — Jocelyn Rhoten
Published: Bi-Mthly
Digital Edition Available?: Y
Format: Tabloid

FSVIEW & FLORIDA FLAMBEAU: FSVIEW & FLORIDA FLAMBEAU — 277 N Magnolia Dr, Tallahassee, FL, 32301-2664, USA; tel 850-561-1600; fax 850-574-6578; e-mail: @tallahassee.com; adv email: eleporin@tallahassee.com; ed email: eleporin@tallahassee.com; web site: www.fsunews.comEst. 1915
General Manager — Eliza LePorin
Content Supervisor — Justin Dyke
Editor-in-Chief — Bailey Shertizinger
Chris Lewis
Liz Cox
Arriale Douglas
Format: Tabloid

HILLSBOROUGH CMTY. COLLEGE: HAWKEYE — 2112 N. 15th Street , Ybor City, FL, 33605, USA; tel (813) 227-7048; fax (813) 253-7760; web site: www.hccfl.edu
Valerie Zell
Insert rate: vzell@hccfl.edu
Format: Tabloid

JACKSONVILLE UNIV.: NAVIGATOR — 2800 University Blvd N, Jacksonville, FL, 32211-3394, USA; tel (904) 256-7526; fax (904) 256-7684; e-mail: navigator@jacksonville.edu; web site: navigator.ju.edu
Peter Moberg
Jean Sils
Renae Ingram
Format: Tabloid

LAKE SUMTER CMTY. COLLEGE: ANGLER — 9501 US Highway 441, Leesburg, FL, 34788-3950, USA; tel (352) 323-3629; fax (352) 435-5023; e-mail: anglern@lscc.edu; angler4always@yahoo.com; web site: www.lscc.edu
Heather Elmatti
Gina Mussatti
Format: Tabloid

LYNN UNIV.: THE I PULSE — 3601 N Military Trl, Boca Raton, FL, 33431-5598, USA;

tel (561) 237-7463; fax (561) 237-7097; e-mail: advertise@lynnipulse.org; web site: www.lynnipulse.org
Stefani Powers
Format: Tabloid

MIAMI DADE COLLEGE: THE REPORTER — 11380 NW 27th Ave., Rm. 4209, Miami, FL, 33167, USA; tel (305) 237-1255; e-mail: mbarco@mdc.edu; adv email: thereporteradvertising@gmail.com; web site: http://www.mdc.edu/main/thereporter/archive/vol02-02/Est. 2010
Advisor — Manolo Barco
Published: Bi-MthlyCirc.(fr.) 10,250
Format: Tabloid

NOVA SOUTHEASTERN UNIV.: THE CURRENT — 3301 College Ave Modular 4, Davie, FL, 33314-7721, USA; tel (954) 262-8455; fax (954) 262-8456; e-mail: thecurrent@nova.edu; nsnews@nova.edu; adv email: thecurrentad@nova.edu; web site: www.nsucurrent.com
Fiona Banton
Format: Tabloid

PALM BEACH ATLANTIC UNIVERSITY: BEACON — PO Box 24708, West Palm Beach, FL, 33416-4708, USA; tel (561) 803-2566; fax (561) 803-2577; e-mail: beacon@pba.edu; web site: readmybeacon.com
Advisor/Exec. Ed. — John Sizemore
Format: Tabloid

PALM BEACH CMTY. COLLEGE: BEACHCOMBER — 4200 S Congress Ave, Lake Worth, FL, 33461-4796, USA; tel (561) 862-4327; fax (561) 439-8210; e-mail: beachcomber@pbcc.edu.campus
Pam Jarret
Format: Broadsheet

PENSACOLA JUNIOR COLLEGE: CORSAIR — 1000 College Blvd Bldg 96, Pensacola, FL, 32504-8910, USA; tel (850) 484-1458; fax (850) 484-1149; e-mail: corsair@pjc.edu; web site: www.ecorsair.comEst. 1949
Christina Drain
Audrey Davis
Rose Jansen
Format: Tabloid

POLK CMTY. COLLEGE — 999 Avenue H NE, Winter Haven, FL, 33881-4256, USA; tel (863) 297-1000; fax (863) 297-1037
Patrick Jones

SAINT LEO UNIVERSITY: THE LIONS' PRIDE — 33701 State Road 52, Saint Leo, FL, 33574-9701, USA; tel (352) 588-7424; fax (352) 588-8300; e-mail: thelionspridenewspaper@gmail.com; adv email: thelionspridenewspaper@gmail.com; ed email: thelionspridenewspaper@gmail.com; web site: https://prideonlinedotnet.wordpress.com/
Valerie Kasper
Editor-in-Chief — Cassidy Whitaker
Published: Fri
Digital Edition Available?: Y
Digital Platform - Mobile: Apple, Android, Windows, Blackberry
Digital Platform - Tablet: Apple iOS, Android, Windows 7, Blackberry Tablet OS
Format: Tabloid

SOUTHEASTERN UNIVERSITY: SOUTHEASTERN TIMES — 1000 Longfellow Blvd, Lakeland, FL, 33801-6034, USA; tel (863) 667-5000; fax (863) 667-5200; e-mail: thetimes@seuniversity.edu; web site: www.seuniversity.edu
Chad Neuman
Format: Tabloid

SOUTHEASTERN UNIVERSRITY: SEU TIMES — 1000 Longfellow Blvd, Lakeland, FL, 33801-6034, USA; tel 8005008760; web site: www.seu.edu
Published: Mthly

ST. THOMAS UNIV.: SENTINEL — 16401 NW 37th Ave, Opa Locka, FL, 33054-6313, USA; tel (305) 628-6674; fax (305) 443-1210; e-mail: basic@stu.edu; web site: www.stu.edu
Sharon Brehm
Format: Tabloid

STETSON UNIV.: THE REPORTER — 421 N Woodland Blvd, Deland, FL, 32720, USA; tel (386)-822-7100; fax (904) 822-7233; adv email: advertising@stetson.edu; ed email: reporter@stetson.edu; web site: www.stetsonreporter.com
Andrew Davis
Joseph O'Brien
Jason Rickner
Format: Broadsheet

TALLAHASSEE CMTY. COLLEGE: TALON — 444 Appleyard Dr, Tallahassee, FL, 32304-2895, USA; tel (850) 201-8035; fax (850) 201-8427; e-mail: talon@tcc.fl.edu; adv email: talon@tcc.fl.edu; ed email: talon@tcc.fl.edu; web site: www.thetcctalon.comEst. 1968
Advisor — Dana Peck
Published: Bi-MthlyCirc.(fr.) 3,000
Price: Free
Format: Broadsheet

THE CURRENT - ECKERD COLLEGE — 4200 54th Ave S, Saint Petersburg, FL, 33711-4700, USA; tel 610 4317931; fax 610 4317931; e-mail: thecurrent@eckerd.edu; adv email: currentads@eckerd.edu; ed email: danielsa1@mac.com; web site: www.theonlinecurrent.comEst. 2009
Editor-in-Chief — Ashley Daniels
Managing Editor — Max Martinez
Price: Free
Format: Bi-weekly Newspaper

THE SANDSPUR: SANDSPUR — 1000 Holt Ave # 2742, Winter Park, FL, 32789-4499, USA; tel (407) 646-2696; adv email: advertising@thesandspur.org; ed email: staff@thesandspur.org; web site: www.thesandspur.orgEst. 1894
Published: ThurCirc. (pd.) 0 (fr.) 1,200
Digital Edition Available?: Y
Digital Platform - Mobile: Apple, Android, Windows
Digital Platform - Tablet: Apple iOS, Android
Format: Newspaper

UNIV. OF CENTRAL FLORIDA: CENTRAL FLORIDA FUTURE — 11825 High Tech Ave. Ste. 100, Orlando, FL, 32817, USA; tel (407) 447-4555; fax (407) 447-4556; e-mail: sales@ucfnews.com; web site: www.centralfloridafuture.comEst. 1968
Heissam Jebailey
Brian Linden
Trisha Irwin
Ray Bush
Format: Broadsheet

UNIV. OF FLORIDA: INDEPENDENT FL ALLIGATOR — PO Box 14257, Gainesville, FL, 32604-2257, USA; tel (352) 376-4458; fax (352) 376-4556; e-mail: advertising@alligator.org; ed email: editor@alligator.org; web site: www.alligator.org
Chelsea Keenan
Format: Tabloid

UNIV. OF MIAMI: MIAMI HURRICANE — 1330 Miller Road, Suite 200, Coral Gables, FL, 33146-2322, USA; tel (305) 284-4401; fax (305) 284-4404; e-mail: editor@themiamihurricane.com; adv email: tara@themiamihurricane.com; ed email: editor@themiamihurricane.com; web site: www.themiamihurricane.comEst. 1929
Sr. Advisor — Bob Radziewicz
Published: Mon, ThurCirc.(fr.) 10,000
Digital Edition Available?: Y
Price: Free
Format: Tabloid

UNIV. OF MIAMI SCHOOL OF LAW: RES IPSA LOQUITUR — 1311 Miller Rd, Coral Gables, FL, 33146-2300, USA; tel (305) 284-2339; fax (305) 284-3554; e-mail: resipsa@law.miami.edu; web site: www.law.miami.edu
Jennifer C. Pratt-Garces
Alex Britell
Format: Tabloid

UNIV. OF NORTH FLORIDA: SPINNAKER — 1 U N F Drive, Jacksonville, FL, 32224, USA; tel (904) 620-2727; fax (904) 620-3924; e-mail: spinsads@unf.edu; web site: www.espinnaker.comEst. 1977
Adina Daar
Format: Tabloid

UNIV. OF SOUTH FLORIDA: ORACLE — 4202 E Fowler Ave Svc 2, Tampa, FL, 33620-9951, USA; tel (813) 974-5190; fax (813) 974-4887; adv email: ads@usforacle.com; ed email: oraccleeditor@gmail.com; web site: www.usforacle.comEst. 1966
Jay Lawrence
Ed. in chief — Anastasia Dawson
Jimmy Geurts
Published: Mon, ThurCirc.(fr.) 8,000
Digital Edition Available?: Y
Format: Tabloid

UNIV. OF TAMPA: THE MINARET — 401 W Kennedy Blvd, Tampa, FL, 33606-1490, USA; tel (813) 257-3636; fax (813) 253-6207; e-mail: minaret@ut.edu; ut.minaret@gmail.com; web site: www.theminaretonline.com
Stephanie Tripp
Zoe LeCain
Charlie Hambos
Kyle Bennett
Format: Tabloid

UNIV. OF WEST FLORIDA: VOYAGER — 11000 University Pkwy Comm Arts 36, Pensacola, FL, 32514-5732, USA; tel (850) 474-2193; e-mail: mdp17@students.uwf.edu
Format: Broadsheet

VALENCIA CMTY. COLLEGE: VALENCIA VOICE — 1800 S Kirkman Rd, Orlando, FL, 32811-2302, USA; tel (407) 582-1572
Ken Carpenter
Format: Tabloid

GEORGIA

ABRAHAM BALDWIN AGRI COLLEGE: STALLION — 2802 Moore Hwy, Tifton, GA, 31793-5698, USA; fax (229) 391-4978; e-mail: stallion@stallion.abac.edu; web site: www.thestalliononline.com
Eric Cash
Format: Tabloid

AGNES SCOTT COLLEGE: THE PROFILE — 141 E College Ave, Decatur, GA, 30030-3797, USA; tel (404) 471-6000
Jeniffer Owen
Josie Hoilman
Format: Tabloid

ARMSTRONG ATLANTIC STATE UNIV.: INKWELL — Memorial College Ctr., 11935 Abercorn St., Rm. 202, Savannah, GA, 31419-1909, USA; tel (912) 344-3252; fax (912) 344-3475; e-mail: inkwellnews@gmail.com; web site: www.theinkwellonline.com
Tony Morris
Kristin Alonso
Format: Broadsheet

ATLANTA UNIVERSITY CENTER: THE AUC DIGEST — PO Box 3191, Atlanta, GA, 30302-3191, USA; tel (404) 523-6136; e-mail: aucdigestmail@aol.com; web site: www.aucdigest.comEst. 1973
Lo Jelks
Published: Thur
Digital Edition Available?: Y
Insert rate: $125 per thousand
Price: Free publication
Format: Tabloid

AUGUSTA STATE UNIV.: TE BELL RINGER — 2500 Walton Way, Augusta, GA, 30904-2200, USA; tel (706) 737-1600; fax (706) 729-2247; e-mail: bellringerproduction@gmail.com; web site: www.asubellringer.com
Advisor — Matthew Bosisio
Kara Mauldin
Stacie Cooper
Dee Taylor
Format: Broadsheet

BERRY COLLEGE: CAMPUS CARRIER — 2277 Martha Berry Hwy NW, Mount Berry, GA, 30149-9707, USA; tel (706) 238-7871; fax (706) 238-5846; e-mail: campus_carrier@berry.edu
Kevin Kleine
Jeanne Mathews
Rick Woodall
Format: Tabloid

BRENAU UNIV.: ALCHEMIST — 500 Washington St SE, Gainesville, GA, 30501-3628, USA; tel (770) 538-4762; fax (770) 538-4558; e-mail: alchemist@brenau.edu
Nathan R. Goss
Format: Tabloid

CLARK ATLANTA UNIV.: CAU PANTHER — PO Box 1523, Atlanta, GA, 30301-1523, USA; tel (404) 880-6219; e-mail: caunews05@yahoo.com
Advisor — James McJunkins
Format: Tabloid

CLAYTON STATE UNIV.: THE BENT TREE — 2000 Clayton State Blvd, Morrow, GA, 30260-1250, USA; tel (678) 466-5436; fax (678) 466-5470; e-mail: info@thebenttree.org; web site: www.thebenttree.org
Randy Clark
Sunitha Caton
Published: Mthly
Format: Tabloid

COLUMBUS STATE UNIV.: SABER — 4225 University Ave, Columbus, GA, 31907-5645, USA; tel (706) 562-1494; fax (706) 568-2434; e-mail: csusaber@yahoo.com; csusaber@gmail.com; saber@colstate.edu; web site: thesaber.wixsite.com/thesaberEst. 1958
Linda Reynold
Published: Other
Digital Edition Available?: Y
Format: Broadsheet

COVENANT COLLEGE: BAGPIPE — 14049 Scenic Hwy, Lookout Mountain, GA, 30750-4100, USA; tel (706) 820-1560; fax (706) 820-0672; e-mail: bagpipe@covenant.edu; web site: www.bagpipeonline.com
Cliff Foreman
Kaitlin Fender
Format: Tabloid

DARTON COLLEGE: CAVALIER ATTITUDE — 2400 Gillionville Rd, Albany, GA, 31707-3098, USA; tel (229) 317-6808
Roger Marietta
Format: Tabloid

EMORY UNIV.: THE EMORY WHEEL — P.O. Box W, Atlanta, GA, 30322-1006, USA; tel (404) 727-0279; e-mail: emorywheelexec@gmail.com; ed email: emorywheelexec@gmail.com; web site: www.emorywheel.comEst. 1919
Ed. — Priyanka Krishnamurthy

Exec. Ed. — Sonam Vashi
Managing Ed. — Lizzie Howell
Published: Tues, Fri
Digital Edition Available?: Y
Digital Platform - Mobile: Apple, Android, Windows
Digital Platform - Tablet: Apple iOS
Price: Free
Format: Broadsheet

FT. VALLEY STATE UNIV.: PEACHITE — 121 Huntington Chase Cir, Warner Robins, GA, 31088-2675, USA; tel (478) 825-6910; fax (478) 825-6140; e-mail: peachite@fvsu.edu.
Valerie White
Mick-Aela Nobles
Format: Broadsheet

GAINESVILLE COLLEGE: THE COMPASS — PO Box 1358, Gainesville, GA, 30503-1358, USA; tel (678) 717-3820; fax (678) 717-3832; e-mail: compass@gsc.edu; adv email: compass@gsc.edu; ed email: compass@gsc.edu; web site: www.gsccompass.org
Merrill Morris
Editor in Chief — Audrey Williams
Associate Editor — Brent VanFleet
Published: MthlyCirc.(fr.) 1,000
Digital Edition Available?: Y
Digital Platform - Mobile: Apple, Android, Windows
Format: Tabloid

GEORGIA COLLEGE & STATE UNIV.: COLLONNADE — 231 W. Hancock St., Milledgeville, GA, 31061 , USA; tel (478) 445-4511; fax (478) 445-2559; e-mail: colonnade@gcsu.edu; web site: www.gcsunade.com
Macon McGinley
Claire Dykes
Amanda Boddy
Elise Colcord
Format: Broadsheet

GEORGIA HEALTH SCIENCES UNIVERSITY (FORMERLY MEDICAL COLLEGE OF GEORGIA): THE CONNECTION — 1120 15th St, Augusta, GA, 30912-0004, USA; fax (706) 721-6397; ed email: smcgowen@georgiahealth.edu; web site: http://connection.georgiahealth.edu/
Communications Coordinator
Editor, The Connection (formerly the Beeper) — Stacey Hudson
Sharron Walls
Price: Free
Format: Tabloid

GEORGIA HIGHLANDS COLLEGE: SIX MILE POST — 3175 Cedartown Highway, Rome, GA, 30161, USA; tel (706) 295-6361; fax (706) 295-6610; e-mail: 6mpost@highlands.edu; adv email: ads6MP@student.highlands.edu; web site: www.sixmilepost.com
Kristie Kemper
Nick Godfrey
Format: Tabloid

GEORGIA INST. OF TECHNOLOGY: THE TECHNIQUE — 353 Ferst Dr Rm 137, Atlanta, GA, 30332-0001, USA; tel (404) 894-2830; fax (404) 894-1650; e-mail: editor@technique.gatech.edu; web site: www.nique.net
Mac Pitts
Emily Chambers
Jonathan Saethang
Hahnming Lee
Format: Tabloid

GEORGIA PERIMETER COLLEGE: THE COLLEGIAN — 555 N Indian Creek Dr, Clarkston, GA, 30021-2361, USA; tel (678)-891-3381; fax (404) 298-3882; e-mail: gpccollegian@gmail.com; web site: www.gpc.eduEst. 1986
Bus. Mgr. — Alice Murray
Nathan Guest
Insert rate: studnews@gpc.edu
Format: Tabloid

GEORGIA SOUTHERN UNIV.: THE GEORGE-ANNE — PO Box 8001, Statesboro, GA, 30460-1000, USA; tel (912) 478-5246; fax (912) 478-7113; e-mail: gaeditor@georgiasouthern.edu; adv email: ads1@georgiasouthern.edu; web site: Georgia Southern University GSU Student Media Box 8001Est. 1927
Exec. Ed. — Jozsef Papp
Published: Tues, Thur
Digital Edition Available?: Y
Insert rate: kcallaway@georgiasouthern.edu
Format: Tabloid

GEORGIA SOUTHWESTERN STATE UNIV.: SOU'WESTER — 800 Georgia Southwestern State University Dr., Americus, GA, 31709, USA; tel (229) 931-2003; fax (229) 931-2059; e-mail: gswpaper@yahoo.com; gswpaper@canes.gsw.edu; web site: www.gsw.edu
Josh Curtin
Emily Immke
Sidney Davis
Format: Tabloid

GEORGIA STATE UNIV.: SIGNAL — Ste. 200 University Ctr., 44 Courtland St., Atlanta, GA, 30303-3011, USA; tel (404) 413-1620; fax (404) 413-1622; e-mail: signaladvertisingco@gmail.com; web site: www.georgiastatesignal.comEst. 1933
Advisor — Bryce McNeil
Zac Gunter
Elijah Sarkesian
Beau Torres
Adv. Mgr. — Ona
Published: Tues (Fall & Spring with Incept issue) Circ.(fr.) 5,000
Digital Edition Available?: N
Format: Tabloid
Note: (application in development)

KENNESAW STATE UNIVERSITY: THE SENTINEL — 395 Cobb Ave NW, Kennesaw, GA, 30144-5588, USA; tel (470) 578-5470; fax (470) 578-9165; e-mail: sentinel@ksumedia.com; adv email: marketingmgr@ksumedia.com; ed email: eic@ksusentinel.com; web site: www.ksusentinel.comEst. 1967
Ed Bonza
Published: TuesCirc.(fr.) 5,000
Digital Edition Available?: Y
Digital Platform - Mobile: Apple, Android
Digital Platform - Tablet: Apple iOS, Android
Insert rate: $90/m
Format: Tabloid

LAGRANGE COLLEGE: THE HILLTOP NEWS — 601 Broad St # 1165, Lagrange, GA, 30240-2955, USA; tel (706) 880-8020; fax (706) 880-8920; e-mail: hilltopnews@laagrange.edu
Advisor — John Tures
Kate Bush
Chris Nylund
Format: Tabloid

MACON STATE COLLEGE: MACONSTATEMENT — 100 College Station Dr, Macon, GA, 31206-5145, USA; tel (478) 471-2700; fax (478) 757-2626; e-mail: mscmatrix@maconstate.edu; statement@maconstate.edu; web site: www.maconstatement.com
Ray Lightner
Glen Stone
Format: Tabloid

MERCER UNIV.: MECER CLUSTER — PO Box 72728, Macon, GA, 31207-5272, USA; tel (478) 301-2871; fax (478) 301-2977
Lee Greenway
Format: Tabloid

MOREHOUSE COLLEGE: MAROON TIGER — 830 Westview Dr SW, Atlanta, GA, 30314-3776, USA; tel (404) 681-2800; e-mail: mtiger@morehouse.edu; web site: www.morehouse.edu/themaroontiger/
Ed. in Chief — Edward T. Mitchell
Donovan Ramsey
Format: Tabloid

NORTH GEORGIA COLLEGE: THE VOICE — PO Box 5432, Dahlonega, GA, 30597-0001, USA; tel (706) 864-1468; fax (706) 864-1485; e-mail: voice@ngcsu.edu; web site: www.ngcsu.edu/voice
Debbie Martin
Format: Tabloid

OGLETHORPE UNIVERSITY: THE STORMY PETREL — 4484 Peachtree Rd. NE, Atlanta, GA, 30319, USA; tel (404) 364-8425; fax (404) 364-8442; e-mail: stormypetrel@oglethorpe.edu; web site: 3443 Somerset Trace
Ed. — Tali Schroeder
Published: Mthly
Format: Tabloid

SAVANNAH COLLEGE OF ART/DESIGN: THE CHRONICLE — PO Box 3146, Savannah, GA, 31402-3146, USA; tel (912) 525-5500; fax (912) 525-5506; e-mail: district@scad.edu; web site: www.scaddistrict.com
Aisha Michael
Format: Broadsheet

SHORTER COLLEGE: PERISCOPE — 315 Shorter Ave SW, Rome, GA, 30165-4267, USA; tel (706) 233-7208; fax (706) 236-1515; e-mail: the_periscope@hotmail.com; web site: www.theperiscope.org
Ashley Ottinger
Format: Tabloid

STATE UNIV. OF WEST GEORGIA: WEST GEORGIAN — 1601 Maple St, Carrollton, GA, 30118-0002, USA; tel (678) 839-5000; web site: www.westga.edu
Stephanie Smith
Format: Broadsheet

THOMAS COLLEGE: THE TALON — 1501 Millpond Rd, Thomasville, GA, 31792-7636, USA; tel (229) 226-1621; fax (229) 226-1653
Charity Nixon
Format: Magazine

TOCCOA FALLS COLLEGE: THE TALON — 107 Kincaid Dr, Toccoa Falls, GA, 30598-9602, USA; tel (706) 886-7299; fax (706) 886-0210; e-mail: talon@tfc.edu; web site: www.tfc.edu
Christine Brubaker
Format: Tabloid

UNIV. OF GEORGIA: THE RED AND BLACK — 540 Baxter St, Athens, GA, 30605-1106, USA; tel (706) 433-3000; fax (706) 433-3033; e-mail: news@randb.com; web site: www.redandblack.com
Ed Morales
General Manager — Natalie McClure
Digital Edition Available?: Y
Digital Platform - Mobile: Apple, Android
Digital Platform - Tablet: Apple iOS, Android
Format: Broadsheet

VALDOSTA STATE UNIV.: SPECTATOR — 1500 N Patterson St, Valdosta, GA, 31698-0001, USA; tel (229) 333-5686; fax (229) 249-2618; e-mail: spec@valdosta.edu; web site: www.vsuspectator.com
Pat Miller
John Pickworth
Editor In Chief — Desiree Thompson
Format: Broadsheet

WESLEYAN COLLEGE: PIONEER — 4760 Forsyth Rd, Macon, GA, 31210-4462, USA; tel (478) 757-5100; fax (478) 757-4027; e-mail: pioneer@wesleyancollege.edu; web site: www.wesleyancollege.edu
Dana Amihere
Format: Tabloid

HAWAII

BRIGHAM YOUNG UNIV.: KE'ALAKA'I — 55-220 Kulanui St Ste 1, Laie, HI, 96762-1266, USA; tel (808) 675-3696; fax (808) 675-3491; web site: kealakai.byuh.edu
Leeann Lambert
Karen Hemenway
Format: Tabloid

CHAMINADE UNIV.: SILVERSWORD — 3140 Waialae Ave, Honolulu, HI, 96816-1578, USA; tel (808) 739-4636; fax (808) 735-4891; e-mail: cuhpress@chaminade.edu; web site: www.cuhnews.com; www.chaminade.edu
Ashlee Duenas
Format: Tabloid

HAWAII PACIFIC UNIVERSITY: KALAMALAMA — 1154 Fort Street Mall Ste 312, Honolulu, HI, 96813-2712, USA; tel (808) 544-9379; fax (808) 566-2418; e-mail: kalamalama@hpu.edu; web site: http://www.hpu.edu/kalamalamaonline/index.htmlEst. 1992
Dayna Kalakau
Student Editor — Susanne Haala
Copy Editor — Nicole Kato
Associate Editor — Kara Jernigan
Faculty Editor — John Windrow
Photo Editor — Riana Stellburg
Sports Editor — Emily Tall
Social Media Tech — David Chow
Format: Tabloid

HONOLULU CMTY. COLLEGE UNIV. OF HAWAII: KA LA — 874 Dillingham Blvd, Honolulu, HI, 96817-4598, USA; tel (808) 845-9211; fax (808) 847-9876; e-mail: hcckala@gmail.com; web site: www.thekala.netEst. 1963
Adviser, Asst Professor of Journalism — Michael Leidemann
Published: MthlyCirc.(fr.) 900
Format: Tabloid

KAPIOLANI CMTY. COLLEGE: KAPI'O — 4303 Diamond Head Rd, Honolulu, HI, 96816-4496, USA; tel (808) 734-9166; fax (808) 734-9287; e-mail: kapio@hawaii.edu; web site: www.kapiolani.hawaii.edu/
Catherine E. Toth
Janell Nakahara
Format: Tabloid

LEEWARD CMTY. COLLEGE — 96-045 Ala Ike St # SC-216, Pearl City, HI, 96782-3366, USA; tel (808) 455-0603; fax (808) 455-0471; web site: emedia.leeward.hawaii.edu/kamanao/
Margaret Yasuhara

UNIV. OF HAWAII HILO: KE KALAHEA — 200 W. Kawili St., Campus Ctr. 215, Hilo, HI, 96720-4091, USA; tel (808) 974-7504; fax (808) 974-7782; e-mail: kalahea@hawaii.edu; web site: www.uhh.hawaii.edu/news/kekalahea
Marc Burba
Roxanne Yamane
Format: Tabloid

UNIVERSITY OF HAWAII MANOA: KA LEO O HAWAII — 2445 Campus Rd., Honolulu, HI, 96822-2216, USA; tel (808) 956-7043; fax (808) 956-9962; e-mail: editor@kaleo.org; adv email: advertising@kaleo.org; ed email: editor@kaleo.org; web site: www.kaleo.orgEst. 1922
Ed. Advisor — Jay Hartwell
Dir — Sandy Matsui
Published: Mon every two weeksCirc.(fr.) 10,000
Digital Edition Available?: Y
Digital Platform - Mobile: Apple, Android
Format: Tabloid

IDAHO

BOISE STATE UNIV.: ARBITER — 1910 University Dr, Boise, ID, 83725-0002, USA; tel (208) 426-6300; fax (208) 426-3884; e-mail: mcox@boisestate.edu; web site: www.arbiteronline.com
Brad Arendt
Chrmn. — V. Marvin Cox
Steve Lyons
Dwight Murphy
Shannon Morgan
Format: Broadsheet

BRIGHAM YOUNG UNIV. IDAHO: SCROLL — Spori Bldg # 114B, Rexburg, ID, 83460-0001, USA; tel (208) 496-2411; fax (208) 496-2911; e-mail: scrolleditor@byui.edu; web site: www.byui.edu/scroll; www.byuicomm.net
Jeff Hochstrasser
John Thompson
Advisor — Ryan Hales
Format: Tabloid

COLLEGE OF IDAHO: COYOTE — PO Box 52, Caldwell, ID, 83606-0052, USA; tel (208) 459-5509; fax (208) 459-5849; web site: www.collegeofidaho.edu/media/phonebooks/default.asp?dpt=COYN
Pres. — Danielle Blenker
Nicole Watson
Debbie Swanson
Colleen Smith
Price: Free
Format: Magazine

IDAHO STATE UNIV.: THE BENGAL — PO Box 8009, Pocatello, ID, 83209-0001, USA; tel (208) 282-4812; fax (208) 282-5301; e-mail: bgads@isu.edu; web site: www.isubengal.com
Jerry Miller
Clay Nelson
Format: Tabloid

LEWIS-CLARK STATE COLLEGE: PATHFINDER — 500 8th Avenue, Lewiston, ID, 83501, USA; tel (208) 792-2470; fax (208) 792-2082; e-mail: thepathfinder@lcmail.lcsc.edu; adv email: pathfinderbusmgr@lcmail.lcsc.edu; web site: www.lcsc.edu/pathfinder/
Bryce Kammers
Kaylee Brewster
Aaron Waits
Business Manager — Ryan Grether
Published: WedCirc. (pd.) 0 (fr.) 1,000
Digital Edition Available?: Y
Format: Tabloid

NORTH IDAHO COLLEGE: THE SENTINEL — North Idaho College Receiving Department (c/o Geoff Carr), Coeur D Alene, ID, 83814-2199, USA; tel (208) 769-3388; fax (208) 769-3361; e-mail: sentinel@nic.edu; web site: www.nicsentinel.com
Advisor — Geoff Carr
Published: Tri-weeklyCirc. (pd.) 3,000 (fr.) 3,000
Insert rate: $500
Price: Free
Format: Broadsheet

NORTHWEST NAZARENE UNIV.: CRUSADER — 623 Holly St, Nampa, ID, 83686-5897, USA; tel (208) 467-8656; fax (208) 467-8468; e-mail: crusader@nnu.edu
Amber Ford
Format: Tabloid

UNIV. OF IDAHO: ARGONAUT — 301 Student Un, Moscow, ID, 83844-0001, USA; tel (208) 885-7825; fax (208) 885-2222; e-mail: argonaut@uidaho.edu; web site: www.uiargonaut.com
Shawn O'Neal
Hannah Liter
Greg Connolly
Format: Broadsheet

ILLINOIS

AUGUSTANA COLLEGE: OBSERVER — 639 38th St, Rock Island, IL, 61201-2296, USA; tel (309) 794-3460; fax (309) 794-3460; e-mail: observer@augustana.edu; web site: www.augustana.edu
Carolyn Yaschur
Advisor — David Schwartz
Format: Tabloid

BENEDICTINE UNIV.: THE CANDOR — 5700 College Rd, Lisle, IL, 60532-0900, USA; tel (630) 829-6446; fax (630) 960-1126; e-mail: thecandor@yahoo.com; web site: www.thecandor.com
Chris Birks
Published: Wed
Digital Edition Available?: Y
Note: Digital only - 5000 views a month

BLACK HAWK COLLEGE: CHIEFTAIN — 6600 34th Ave Bldg 4, Moline, IL, 61265-5899, USA; tel (309) 796-5477; fax (309) 792-5976; e-mail: chieftain@bhc.edu
Tory Becht
Thomas Cross
David Craig
Format: Tabloid

BRADLEY UNIVERSITY: BRADLEY SCOUT — 1501 W Bradley Ave, Peoria, IL, 61625-0003, USA; tel (309) 676-7611; fax (309) 677-2609; e-mail: bradleyscout@gmail.com; adv email: bradleyscout@gmail.com; ed email: bradleyscout@gmail.com; web site: www.bradleyscout.comEst. 1898
Ed. — Sam Pallini
Managing Ed. — Kristin Kreher
Adv. Mgr. — Travis Kelso
Published: FriCirc.(fr.) 4,000
Format: Tabloid

CARL SANDBURG COLLEGE — 140 S Prairie St, Galesburg, IL, 61401-4605, USA; tel (309) 344-2518; fax (309) 342-5171

CHICAGO KENT COLLEGE OF LAW — 565 W Adams St Fl 2, Chicago, IL, 60661-3652, USA; tel (312) 906-5016; fax (312) 906-5280; e-mail: comment@kentlaw.edu; web site: http://www.kentlaw.edu/student_orgs/commentator

COLLEGE OF DUPAGE: THE COURIER — 425 Fawell Blvd., Glen Ellyn, IL, 60137-6599, USA; tel (630) 942-2113; fax (630) 942-3747; ed email: editor@cod.edu; web site: www.codcourier.orgEst. 1967
Editor-in-chief — Nick Davison
Published: Wed
Insert rate: $750 per insert
Format: Tabloid

COLLEGE OF LAKE COUNTY: CHRONICLE — 19351 W Washington St, Grayslake, IL, 60030-1198, USA; tel (847) 543-2057; web site: www.clcillinois.edu/activities/chronicle.asp
John Kupetz
Nathan Caldwell
Format: Tabloid

COLUMBIA COLLEGE — 600 S Michigan Ave Fl 5, Chicago, IL, 60605-1996, USA; tel 312-369-8903; ed email: jlyon@colum.edu; web site: www.columbiachronicle.comEst. 1965
Faculty advisor — Jeff Lyon
Price: Free
Format: Tabloid

COLUMBIA COLLEGE CHICAGO: COLUMBIA CHRONICLE — 33 E Congress Pkwy Ste 224, Chicago, IL, 60605-1237, USA; tel 312-369-8955; fax (312)369-8430; e-mail: chronicle@colum.edu; adv email: crichert@colum.edu; ed email: chronicle@colum.edu; web site: www.columbiachronicle.comEst. 1978
General Manager — Chris Richert
Published: MonCirc.(fr.) 6,000
Digital Edition Available?: Y
Insert rate: $85 per 1,000 inserts - 3K min
Format: Tabloid

CONCORDIA UNIV.: SPECTATOR — 7400 Augusta Street, River Forest, IL, 60305-1499, USA; tel (708) 209-3191; fax (708) 209-3176; adv email: spectator@cuchicago.edu; web site: www.cuchicago.edu/student_life/spectator
Melissa Williams
Benjamin Parviz
Kathryn Klement
Format: Tabloid

DEPAUL UNIVERSITY: THE DEPAULIA — 14 E. Jackson Blvd., Chicago, IL, 60604, USA; tel (312) 362-7644; e-mail: eic@depauliaonline.com; adv email: business@depauliaonline.com; ed email: eic@depauliaonline.com; web site: www.depauliaonline.comEst. 1923
Marla Krause
Published: MonCirc.(fr.) 5,000
Digital Edition Available?: Y
Digital Platform - Mobile: Apple, Android
Digital Platform - Tablet: Apple iOS, Android
Insert rate: see online media kit
Price: Free
Format: Tabloid

DEVRY UNIVERSITY: HARD COPY — 3300 N. Campbell Ave., Campus Life Ctr., Chicago, IL, 60618, USA; tel (773) 697-2089; fax (773) 697-2706; e-mail: dvu.chi.hardcopy@gmail.com
Joe Onorio
Marvin Cespedes
Format: Tabloid

DOMINICAN UNIV.: DOMINICAN STAR — 7900 Division St, River Forest, IL, 60305-1066, USA; tel (708) 524-6800; fax (708) 524-5900; e-mail: domadmis@dom.edu
Marie Simpson
Format: Tabloid

EASTERN ILLINOIS UNIV.: DAILY EASTERN NEWS — 600 Lincoln Ave., Charleston, IL, 61920, USA; tel (217) 581-2812; fax (217) 581-2923; e-mail: DENeic@gmail.com; DENnewsdesk@gmail.com; DENNews.com@gmail.com; web site: http://www.dailyeasternnews.com/
Taylor Angelo
Lola Burnham
Emily Steele
Chris Lee
Mng. Ed. — Collin
Format: Tabloid

ELGIN COMMUNITY COLLEGE: THE OBSERVER — 1700 Spartan Dr, Elgin, IL, 60123-7193, USA; tel (847) 697-1000; fax (847) 888-7352; e-mail: elgincollegeobserver@yahoo.com; adv email: elgincollegeobserver@yahoo.com; ed email: observereditorinchief@gmail.com; web site: www.elgin.eduEst. 1951
Faculty Advisor — Lori Clark
Editor-in-Chief — Michelle Pain
Managing Editor — Fernando Chang
Published: Bi-weeklyCirc. (pd.) 1,000
Digital Edition Available?: N
Price: Free
Format: Tabloid

ELMHURST COLLEGE: LEADER — 190 S Prospect Ave, Elmhurst, IL, 60126-3296, USA; tel (630)617-3320; e-mail: leadernewsec@gmail.com; adv email: advertising@ecleader.org; ed email: leadernewsec@gmail.com; web site: ecleader.org
Ron Wiginton
Aaron Schroeder
Eric Lutz
Editor-in-Chief — Haleema Shah
Published: Tues
Published bi-weekly
Digital Edition Available?: Y
Format: Tabloid

GOVERNORS STATE UNIV.: PHOENIX — 1 University Pkwy., University Park, IL, 60484-3165, USA; tel (708) 534-4517; fax (708) 534-7895; e-mail: phoenix@govst.edu; web site: www.gsuphoenix.com
Faculty Advisor — Debbie James
Emeritus Professor — Michael Purdy
Published: Wed First and third Wednesdays
Price: Free
Format: Tabloid

GREENVILLE COLLEGE: PAPYRUS — 315 E College Ave, Greenville, IL, 62246-1145, USA; tel (618) 664-2800; fax (618) 664-1373; e-mail: papyrus@greenville.edu; web site: www.greenville.edu
Susan Chism
Format: Tabloid

HAROLD WASHINGTON COLLEGE: HERALD — 30 E Lake St Rm 635, Chicago, IL, 60601-2449, USA; tel (312) 553-3141; fax (312) 553-5647; e-mail: hwc_heraldnews@ccc.edu; web site: www.theheraldhwc.comEst. 1979
Faculty Advisor — Molly Turner
Price: Free
Format: Tabloid

HIGHLAND CMTY. COLLEGE: HIGHLAND CHRONICLE — 2998 W Pearl City Rd, Freeport, IL, 61032-9341, USA; tel (815) 235-6121; fax (815) 235-6130; e-mail: highland.chronicle@highland.edu
Sam Tucibat
Format: Tabloid

ILLINOIS COLLEGE: RAMBLER — 1101 W College Ave, Jacksonville, IL, 62650-2299, USA; tel (217) 245-3030; fax (217) 245-3056; e-mail: rambler@ic.edu; web site: www.ic.edu
John S. Rush
Laurel Berkel
Format: Tabloid

ILLINOIS INST. OF TECHNOLOGY: TECH NEWS — Herman Union Bldg., 3201 S. State St., Rm. 221, Chicago, IL, 60616, USA; tel (312) 567-3085; e-mail: technews@iit.edu
Aanchal Taneja
Brian Wolber
Lory Mishra
Format: Tabloid

ILLINOIS STATE UNIVERSITY: THE VIDETTE — 100 North University Street, Normal, IL, 61761, USA; tel (309) 438-7685; fax (309) 438-5211; e-mail: vidette@ilstu.edu; adv email: vidette@ilstu.edu; ed email: vidette@ilstu.edu; web site: www.videtteonline.comEst. 1888
John Plevka
Brooke Goodwin
Amy Gorczowski
Ed. — Kristi Demonbreun
Format: Tabloid

ILLINOIS WESLEYAN UNIVERSITY: THE ARGUS — 104 University Ave, Bloomington, IL, 61701-1798, USA; tel (309) 556-3117; fax (309) 556-3977; e-mail: argus@iwu.edu; web site: www.blogs.iwu.edu/argus
James Plath
Published: Fri
Format: Broadsheet

JOHN A. LOGAN COLLEGE: VOLUNTEER — 700 Logan College Dr, Carterville, IL, 62918-2501, USA; tel (618) 985-2828; fax (618) 985-4654; e-mail: volunteernews@jalc.edu
Matt Garrison
Tara Fasol
Format: Tabloid

JOLIET JUNIOR COLLEGE: BLAZER — 1215 Houbolt Rd, Joliet, IL, 60431-8800, USA; tel (815) 280-2313; fax (815) 280-6730; e-mail: blazermail@jjc.edu; adv email: blazermail@jjc.edu; ed email: blazermail@jjc.edu; web site: www.jjc.edu/blazer
Advisor — Robert Marcink
Published: Other Our frequency is tri-weekly, or 5 times per semester.Circ.(fr.) 2,000
Digital Edition Available?: Y
Digital Platform - Mobile: Windows, Blackberry
Digital Platform - Tablet: Windows 7
Insert rate: $350
Price: Free
Format: Tabloid

KASKASKIA COLLEGE: THE SCROLL — 27210 College Rd, Centralia, IL, 62801-7878, USA; tel (618) 545-3000; fax (618) 532-2365; web site: scroll.kaskaskia.edu
Dale Hill
Nathan Wilkins
Sue Hardebeck
Digital Edition Available?: Y
Format: Tabloid

KELLOGG GRAD. SCHOOL OF MGMT.: MERGER MONTHLY — 2001 Sheridan Rd, Evanston, IL, 60208-0814, USA; tel (847) 491-3924; fax (847) 467-6173
Nick Slater
Format: Tabloid

KENNEDY-KING COLLEGE: THE GATE — Chicago, IL, 60621, USA; tel (773) 602-5179; fax (773) 602-5521; e-mail: editor@thegatenewspaper.com; adv email: editor@thegatenewspaper.com; web site: www.thegatenewspaper.comEst. 2010
Editor — Adriana Maria Cardona-Maguigad
Published: Bi-MthlyCirc.(fr.) 13,000
Digital Edition Available?: Y
Insert rate: We have reasonable prices on all our ads sizes.
Format: print and online

KISHWAUKEE COLLEGE: KALEIDOSCOPE — 21193 Malta Rd, Malta, IL, 60150-9699, USA; tel (815) 825-2086; fax (815) 825-2072; e-mail: kscope@kishwaukeecollege.edu; web site: www.kishkscope.com
Melissa Blake
John Myers
Andrew Hallgren
Nelle Smith
Instructor — John
Ed. In Chief — Marissa Skonie
Format: Tabloid

KNOX COLLEGE: THE KNOX STUDENT — 2 E South St Knox College K-240, Galesburg, IL, 61401-4999, USA; tel (646) 784-4367; fax (309) 341-7081; e-mail: tks@knox.edu; adv email: tksmarketing@knox.edu; web site: KNOX COLLEGE BOX 2 E SOUTH STEst. 1878
Tom Martin
Co-Editor-in-Chief — Jonathan Schrag
Co-Editor-in-Chief — Lillie Chamberlin
Published: Thur
Digital Edition Available?: N
Format: Tabloid

LAKE FOREST COLLEGE: STENTOR — 555 N Sheridan Rd, Lake Forest, IL, 60045-2399, USA; tel (847) 735-5215; fax (847) 735-6298; e-mail: stentor@lakeforest.edu; web site: www.thestentor.com
Heather Brown
Annie Cooper
Nate Butala
Format: Tabloid

LAKE LAND COLLEGE: THE NAVIGATOR — 5001 Lake Land Blvd, Mattoon, IL, 61938-9366, USA; tel (217) 234-5269; fax (217) 234-5390; e-mail: studentpublications@lakeland.cc.il.us; web site: www.navigatornews.org
Dir of Student Life — Valerie Lynch
Published: Mthly
Digital Edition Available?: N
Format: Tabloid

LEWIS AND CLARK CMTY. COLLEGE: THE BRIDGE — 5800 Godfrey Rd, Godfrey, IL, 62035-2466, USA; tel (618) 468-6042; fax (618) 468-6055; e-mail: bridge@lc.edu
Lori Artis
Anthony Lanham
Format: Tabloid

LEWIS UNIV.: THE FLYER — 1 University Pkwy, Romeoville, IL, 60446-1832, USA; tel (815) 836-5196; e-mail: lewisflyernews@gmail.com; web site: www.thelewisflyer.com
Lisa O'Toole
Adam Olszeski
Format: Tabloid

LINCOLN LAND CMTY. COLLEGE: LAMP — 5250 Shepherd Rd, Springfield, IL, 62703-5408, USA; tel (217) 786-2318; fax (217) 786-2340; web site: www.llcc.edu
Brenda Protz
Format: Tabloid

LOYOLA UNIV.: THE LOYOLA PHOENIX — 6525 N Sheridan Rd Ste 1, Chicago, IL, 60626-5386, USA; tel (773) 508-7120; fax (773) 508-7121; e-mail: phoenixbusiness@luc.edu; web site: www.loyolaphoenix.com
Kimberly Boonjathai
Leeann Maton
Format: Tabloid

LOYOLA UNIV. LAW SCHOOL — 33 N Dearborn St, Chicago, IL, 60602-3102, USA; tel (312) 346-3191; fax (312) 915-7201
Sam Puleo
Format: Tabloid

MALCOLM X COLLEGE: MALCOLM X-PRESS — 1900 W Van Buren St Rm 2218, Chicago, IL, 60612-3145, USA; tel (312) 850-7462; fax (312) 850-7323
Cynthia-Val Chapman
Beth Lewis
Price: Free
Format: Tabloid

MCHENRY COUNTY COLLEGE: TARTAN — 8900 US Highway 14, Crystal Lake, IL, 60012-2761, USA; tel (815) 455-8571; fax ; e-mail: tartan@mchenry.edu; web site: www.mchenry.edu; www.mcctartan.net
Advisor — Toni Countryman
Published: MthlyCirc.(fr.) 2,000
Digital Edition Available?: N
Format: Tabloid

MCKENDREE UNIVERSITY: MCKENDREE REVIEW — 701 College Rd, Lebanon, IL, 62254-1291, USA; tel (618) 537-6821; fax (618) 537-2377; e-mail: mckreview@mckendree.edu; web site: lance.mckendree.edu/review/
Gabe Shapiro
Editor in Chief — Sarah Adams
Associate Editor — Chris Moore
Web/Design Editor — Kevin Schaefer
Theresa Schmidt
Format: Tabloid

MILLIKIN UNIV.: DECATURIAN — 1184 W Main St, Decatur, IL, 62522-2084, USA; tel (217) 425-4626; fax (217) 425-1687; e-mail: decaturian@millikin.edu; web site: www.thedeconline.com
Priscilla Marie Meddaugh
Caitlin Hennessy
Lauren Krage
Format: Tabloid

MONMOUTH COLLEGE: THE COURIER — 700 E Broadway, Monmouth, IL, 61462-1998, USA; tel (309) 457-3456; fax (309) 457-2363; e-mail: courier@monm.edu; web site: www.monm.edu/courier
Michelle Nutting
Lucas Pauley
Format: Tabloid

MORAINE VALLEY CMTY. COLLEGE: GLACIER — 9000 W. College Pkwy., Palos Hills, IL, 60465-0937, USA; tel (708) 608-4177; fax (708) 974-0790; e-mail: glacier@morainevalley.edu; web site: www.mvccglacier.com
Stacey Reichard
William Lukitsch
Rob Peto
Frank Florez
Published: Bi-Wkly
Digital Edition Available?: Y
Digital Platform - Mobile: Apple
Digital Platform - Tablet: Apple iOS
Format: Tabloid

MORTON COLLEGE: COLLEGIAN — 3801 S Central Ave Rm 328-C, Cicero, IL, 60804-4398, USA; tel (708) 656-8000; fax (708) 656-3924; e-mail: collegian@morton.edu; web site: www.morton.edu
Rose Dimesio
Format: Tabloid

NATIONAL COLLEGE OF CHIROPRACTIC: ALUMNUS — 200 E. Roosevelt Rd, Lombard, IL, 60148-4539, USA; tel (630) 889-6628; fax (630) 889-6554
Frank Sutter
Published: MthlyCirc.(fr.) 5,000
Digital Edition Available?: Y
Digital Platform - Mobile: Other
Digital Platform - Tablet: Other
Format: Magazine

NORTH CENTRAL COLLEGE: NCC CHRONICLE — 31 N Loomis St, Naperville, IL, 60540, USA; tel (630) 637-5422; fax (630) 637-5441; e-mail: chronicle@noctrl.edu; web site: orgs.noctrl.edu/chronicle
Nancy Kirby
Format: Tabloid

NORTH PARK UNIV.: NORTH PARK PRESS — 3225 W Foster Ave, Chicago, IL, 60625-4895, USA; tel (773) 649-2816; e-mail: northparkpress@gmail.com; web site: www.northparkpress.com
Casey Smagala
Editor-In-Chief — Erin Hegarty
Staff Advisory — Kristie Vuocolo
Online Editor — Hannah Williams
Price: Free
Format: Tabloid

NORTHEASTERN ILLINOIS UNIVERSITY: INDEPENDENT — 5500 N Saint Louis Ave Rm E049, Chicago, IL, 60625-4699, USA; tel (773) 442-4577; fax (773) 442-4579; e-mail: neiuindependent@gmail.com; adv email: neiuadvertising@yahoo.com; web site: www.neiuindependent.orgEst. 1961
Editor-in-Chief — Jacklyn Nowotnik
Managing Editor — Matthew Greenberg
Published: Tues, Bi-Mthly
Digital Edition Available?: Y
Digital Platform - Mobile: Apple, Android, Windows
Digital Platform - Tablet: Apple iOS, Android, Windows 7
Insert rate: Call for quote
Price: Free
Format: Tabloid

NORTHERN ILLINOIS UNIV.: NORTHERN STAR — Northern Illinois University, Campus Life Building, Suite 130, Dekalb, IL, 60115, USA; tel (815) 753-4239; fax (815) 753-0708; e-mail: editor@northernstar.info; adv email: ads@northernstar.info; ed email: editor@northernstar.info; web site: www.northernstar.infoEst. 1899
Jim Killam
Maria Krull
Justin Weaver
Price: Free
Format: Tabloid

NORTHWESTERN UNIV. SCHOOL OF LAW — 357 E Chicago Ave, Chicago, IL, 60611-3069, USA; tel (312) 503-4714
Unknown Unknown

NORTHWESTERN UNIVERSITY — 1845 Sheridan Rd, Evanston, IL, 60208-0815, USA; tel (847) 467-1882; fax (847) 491-5565
Dean — John Lavine
Prof. — David Abrahamson
Prof. — Martin Block
Prof. — Jack Doppelt
Prof. — Loren Ghiglione
Prof. — Alec Klein
Prof. — Donna Leff
Prof. — Frank Mulhern
Prof. — Jon Petrovich
Prof. — David Protess
Prof. — Don Schultz
Prof. — Ellen Shearer
Assoc. Prof. — Clarke Caywood
Assoc. Prof. — Mary Coffman
Assoc. Prof. — Tom Collinger
Assoc. Prof. — Doug Foster
Assoc. Prof. — Jeremy Gilbert
Assoc. Prof. — Rich Gordon
Assoc. Prof. — John Greening
Assoc. Prof. — Ava Greenwell

NORTHWESTERN UNIVERSITY: THE DAILY NORTHWESTERN — 1999 Campus Dr, Evanston, IL, 60208-2532, USA; tel (847) 491-3222; fax (847) 491-9905; e-mail: eic@dailynorthwestern.com; adv email: spc-compshop@northwestern.edu; web site: www.dailynorthwestern.comEst. 1881
Published: Mon, Tues, Wed, Thur, Fri
Digital Edition Available?: Y
Format: Tabloid

OAKTON CMTY. COLLEGE: THE OCCURRENCE — 1600 E Golf Rd, Des Plaines, IL, 60016-1268, USA; tel (847) 635-1678; fax (847) 635-2610; e-mail: occurrence@oakton.edu
Sue Fox
Format: Tabloid

OLIVET NAZARENE UNIV.: GLIMMERGLASS — PO Box 592, Bourbonnais, IL, 60914-0592, USA; tel (815) 939-5315; fax (815) 928-5549; ed email: glimmerglass@olivet.eduEst. 1941
Jay Martinson
Published: Tues
Digital Edition Available?: Y
Digital Platform - Mobile: Apple, Android, Windows, Blackberry
Digital Platform - Tablet: Apple iOS, Android, Windows 7, Blackberry Tablet OS
Format: Online Publication

PARKLAND COLLEGE: PROSPECTUS NEWS — 2400 W Bradley Ave Rm X-155, Champaign, IL, 61821-1899, USA; tel (217) 351-2216; e-mail: prospectus@parkland.edu; adv email: prospectusads@parkland.edu; ed email: prospectus.editor@gmail.com; web site: www.prospectusnews.comEst. 1969
John Eby
Sean Herman
Published: WedCirc.(fr.) 1,000
Digital Edition Available?: Y
Digital Platform - Mobile: Other
Format: Tabloid

PRAIRIE STATE COLLEGE: STUDENT REVIEW — 202 S Halsted St Rm 1260, Chicago Heights, IL, 60411-8226, USA; tel (708) 709-3910; fax (708) 755-2587; e-mail: psc_student_review@yahoo.com; web site: www.prairiestate.edu/studentreview
Helen Manley
Nike Atewologun
Sam Williams

Format: Tabloid

PRINCIPIA COLLEGE: PRINCIPIA PILOT
— 1 Maybeck Pl, Elsah, IL, 62028-9799, USA; tel (618) 374-5415; fax (618) 374-5122; e-mail: principia.pilot@gmail.com; web site: www.prin.edu; www.principiapilot.orgEst. 1944
Craig Savoye
David Miller
Katie Ward
Ben Chernivsky
Format: Tabloid

QUINCY UNIV.: THE FALCON — 1800 College Ave, Quincy, IL, 62301-2699, USA; tel (217) 228-5275; fax (217) 228-5473; e-mail: qufalcon@gmail.com; web site: http://www.quincy.edu/information/publications-a-media/the-falconEst. 1929
Advisor — David Adam
Chair of Fine Arts & Communication — Barbara Schleppenbach
Published: Mthly
Digital Edition Available?: Y
Format: Tabloid

REND LAKE COLLEGE — 468 N Ken Gray Pkwy, Ina, IL, 62846-2408, USA; tel (618) 437-5321
Michael Peeples

RICHLAND CMTY. COLLEGE: COMMUNICATUR — 1 College Park, Decatur, IL, 62521-8513, USA; tel (217) 875-7211; fax (217) 875-6961; e-mail: comm@richland.edu; communicatur@richland.edu; web site: www.richland.edu
Marlise McDaniel
Todd Houser
Tina Cooper
Format: Tabloid

ROBERT MORRIS COLLEGE: EAGLE — 401 S State St Fl 2, Chicago, IL, 60605-1225, USA; tel (312) 935-6876; fax (312) 935-6880; e-mail: eaglenews@robertmorris.edu; eagle@robertmorris.edu
Cherie Meador
Matt Kirouac
Format: Tabloid

ROCK VALLEY COLLEGE: VALLEY FORGE — 3301 N Mulford Rd, Rockford, IL, 61114-5699, USA; tel (815) 921-7821; fax (815) 921-3333
Frank Coffman
Format: Tabloid

ROOSEVELT UNIV.: TORCH — 430 S Michigan Ave, Chicago, IL, 60605-1394, USA; tel (312) 281-3246; fax (312) 341-3732; e-mail: torchcu@roosevelt.edu; web site: www.rooseveltorch.com
Billy Montgomery
Mallory Blazetic
Format: Tabloid

SAINT XAVIER UNIVERSITY: THE XAVIERITE — 3700 W 103rd St, Chicago, IL, 60655-3199, USA; tel (773) 298-3380; fax (773) 298-3381; e-mail: thexavierite@yahoo.com; adv email: thexavierite@yahoo.com; ed email: thexavierite@yahoo.com; web site: www.thexavierite.comEst. 1935
Asst. Dir — Peter Kreten
Format: Tabloid

SCHOOL OF THE ART INSTITUTE: F NEWSMAGAZINE — 112 S Michigan Ave, Chicago, IL, 60603-6105, USA; tel (312) 345-3838; fax (312) 345-3839; e-mail: fadvertising@saic.edu; ed email: editors@fnewsmagazine.com; web site: www.fnewsmagazine.com
Paul Elitzik
Rachel Oginni
Natalie Edwards
Format: Tabloid

SOUTHERN ILLINOIS UNIV.: DAILY EGYPTIAN — Communications Bldg, 1100 Lincoln Dr, Carbondale, IL, 62901, USA; tel (618) 536-3311; fax (618) 453-3248; e-mail: deadvert@siu.edu; web site: www.siude.comEst. 1916
Eric J. Fidler
Jerry Bush
Sherri Killion
Andrea Zimmerman
Ed. in Chief — Diana
Features Ed. — Derek
Photo Ed. — Edyta
Sports Ed. — Stile
Webmaster — Ashley
Format: Tabloid

SOUTHERN ILLINOIS UNIVERSITY EDWARDSVILLE: THE ALESTLE — One Hairpin Drive, Morris University Ctr, Rm 2022, Edwardsville, IL, 62026, USA; tel (618) 650-3528; fax (618) 650-3514; adv email: advertising@alestlelive.com; ed email: editor@alestlelive.com; web site: www.alestlelive.comEst. 1959
Advisor — Tammy Merrett
Published: Tues, Thur Tuesdays online exclusivelyCirc.(fr.) 3,500
Digital Edition Available?: N
Digital Platform - Mobile: Apple, Android
Digital Platform - Tablet: Apple iOS, Android
Insert rate: varies
Price: Varies
Format: Tabloid-16"

TRINITY CHRISTIAN COLLEGE: COURIER — 6601 W College Dr, Palos Heights, IL, 60463-0929, USA; tel (708) 239-4715; fax (708) 385-5665; e-mail: www.trnty.edu
Whitney Dickison
Format: Tabloid

TRINITY INTERNATIONAL UNIV.: TRINITY DIGEST — 2065 Half Day Rd # T-2922, Deerfield, IL, 60015-1241, USA; tel (847) 317-8155; fax (847) 317-8142
Erika Sjogren
Format: Tabloid

TRITON COLLEGE: FIFTH AVENUE JOURNAL — 2000 5th Ave, River Grove, IL, 60171-1995, USA; tel (708) 456-0300; web site: www.triton.edu
Dawn Unger
Format: Tabloid

UNIV. OF CHICAGO: CHICAGO MAROON — 1212 E 59th St Lowr Level, Chicago, IL, 60637-1604, USA; tel (773) 702-1403; fax (773) 702-3032; e-mail: editor@chicagomaroon.com; adv email: ads@chicagomaroon.com; web site: www.chicagomaroon.comEst. 1892
Editor-in-Chief — Rebecca Guterman
Editor-in-Chief — Sam Levine
Managing Editor — Emily Wang
Published: Tues, Fri
Digital Edition Available?: Y

UNIV. OF CHICAGO LAW SCHOOL: THE PHOENIX — 1111 E 60th St, Chicago, IL, 60637-2786, USA; tel (773) 702-3164; fax (773) 834-4332; e-mail: phoenix@law.uchicago.edu; web site: www.law.uchicago.edu Est. 1901
William Weaver
Lisa Alvarez
Format: Tabloid

UNIV. OF ILLINOIS: DAILY ILLINI — 512 E Green St, Champaign, IL, 61820-5720, USA; tel (217) 337-8300; fax (217) 337-8303; adv email: adsales@illinimedia.com; ed email: news@illinimedia.com; web site: www.dailyillini.comEst. 1871
Advisor — Lilyan Levant
Adv. Dir. — Nancy Elliott
Ed. in Chief — Darshan Patel
Ad Director — Travis Truitt
Published: Mon, Tues, Wed, ThurCirc.(fr.) 10,000
Digital Edition Available?: Y
Digital Platform - Mobile: Apple, Android, Windows, Blackberry
Digital Platform - Tablet: Apple iOS, Android, Windows 7, Blackberry Tablet OS, Kindle, Nook, Kindle Fire
Format: Broadsheet

UNIV. OF ILLINOIS AT CHICAGO: THE CHICAGO MAROON — 1001 W Van Buren St, Chicago, IL, 60607-2900, USA; tel (312) 421-0480; fax (312) 421-0491; e-mail: chicagomaroon@gmail.com; web site: www.chicagoflame.comEst. 1988
Darryl Brehm
Kate Lee
Format: Tabloid

UNIV. OF ILLINOIS/SPRINGFIELD: THE JOURNAL — 1 University Plz, Springfield, IL, 62703-5407, USA; tel (217) 206-6397; fax (217) 206-6048; e-mail: journal@uis.edu; adv email: journalmgr@uis.edu; ed email: journal@uis.edu; web site: www.uisjournal.comEst. 1985
Faculty Advisor — Debra Landis
EIC — Marc Cox
Published: Wed Back-to-school edition in July/ mailed to newly enrolled students and circulatedCirc.(fr.) 3,000
Digital Edition Available?: Y
Insert rate: $300 for 3,000 ad inserts
Price: Free
Format: Tabloid
Note: www.uisjournal.com
Web provider: Student Newspapers Online

UNIV. OF ST. FRANCIS: ENCOUNTER — 500 Wilcox St, Joliet, IL, 60435-6188, USA; tel (815) 740-3816; fax (815) 740-4285; e-mail: encounter@stfrancis.edu; web site: http://usfencounter.stfrancis.edu
Brien McHugh
Editor in Chief — Mike Clinton
Asst. Editor in Chief — Thaschara VanDyke
Published: MthlyCirc.(fr.) 500
Digital Edition Available?: Y
Format: Tabloid

UNIVERSITY OF CHICAGO BOOTH SCHOOL OF BUSINESS: CHICAGO BUSINESS — 5807 S Woodlawn Ave # C26A, Chicago, IL, 60637-1610, USA; tel (773) 702-1234; fax (773) 834-0628; e-mail: chibusmag@gmail.com; adv email: chibusmag@gmail.com; ed email: chibusmag@gmail.com; web site: www.chibus.com
— Christopher Laws
— Elizabeth OatesEditor in Chiefs
Published: BiweeklyCirc.(fr.) 1,000
Digital Edition Available?: N
Format: Tabloid

WAUBONSEE CMTY. COLLEGE: INSIGHT — Rt. 47 at Waubonsee Dr., Sugar Grove, IL, 60554, USA; tel (630) 466-2555; fax (630) 466-9102; e-mail: insight@waubonsee.edu; web site: www.waubonsee.edu
Gary Clarke
DJ Terek
Format: Tabloid

WESTERN ILLINOIS UNIVERSITY: WESTERN COURIER — 1 University Cir, Macomb, IL, 61455-1390, USA; tel (309) 298-1876; fax (309) 298-2309; e-mail: westerncourier@wiu.edu; micour@wiu.edu; adv email: westerncourier@gmail.com; ed email: micour@wiu.edu; web site: www.westerncourier.comEst. 1905
Editor-in-Chief — Nick Ebelhack
Advertising Manager — Rachel Nelson
Published: Mon, Wed, FriCirc.(fr.) 4,500
Digital Edition Available?: Y
Insert rate: $100 per 1000
Price: Free
Format: Tabloid

WHEATON COLLEGE: THE WHEATON RECORD — 501 College Ave., Wheaton, IL, 60187, USA; tel (630) 752-5077; e-mail: the.record@my.wheaton.edu; adv email: ads.wheatonrecord@gmail.com; ed email: the.record@wheaton.edu; web site: http://www.wheatonrecord.com/Est. 1876
— Philip Kline
— Alycia Vander VegtCo-editor in chiefs
Published: Thur
Digital Edition Available?: Y
Digital Platform - Mobile: Apple, Android
Digital Platform - Tablet: Android, Kindle
Price: $35 per year
Format: Tabloid

WILBUR WRIGHT COLLEGE: THE WRIGHT TIMES — 4300 N Narragansett Ave, Chicago, IL, 60634-1500, USA; tel (773) 481-8555; fax (773) 481-8555; e-mail: web.wrighttimes@yahoo.com; web site: www.wrighttimes.net; wright.ccc.edu
Terrence Doherty
Juan Pintor
Format: Tabloid

WILLIAM RAINEY HARPER COLLEGE: THE HARBINGER — 1200 W Algonquin Rd, Palatine, IL, 60067-7398, USA; tel (847) 925-6460; fax (847) 925-6033; e-mail: harperharbinger@gmail.com; web site: www.harpercollege.edu
Kent McDill
Format: Broadsheet

INDIANA

ANDERSON UNIV.: ANDERSONIAN — 1100 E 5th St, Anderson, IN, 46012-3495, USA; tel (765) 641-4341; fax (765) 641-3851; e-mail: andersonian@anderson.edu; web site: www.anderson.edu/andersonian/
David Baird
Kayla Dunkman
Tarah Novak
Stacy Wood
Format: Tabloid

BALL STATE UNIVERSITY: BALL STATE DAILY NEWS — AJ 276, Muncie, IN, 47306-0001, USA; tel (765) 285-8218; e-mail: editor@bsudailynews.com; web site: www.bsudailynews.comEst. 1922
Publications Adviser — Lisa Renze-Rhodes
Published: WedCirc.(fr.) 10,000
Digital Edition Available?: Y
Format: Tabloid

BETHEL COLLEGE: BETHEL BEACON — 1001 Bethel Cir, Mishawaka, IN, 46545-5591, USA; tel (574) 257-2672; fax (574) 257-2583; e-mail: beacon@bethelcollege.edu; web site: www.bethelcollege.edu/studentlife/media/beacon/
Tim Ceravolo
Amanda Armstrong
Format: Tabloid

BUTLER UNIV.: BUTLER COLLEGIAN — 4600 Sunset Ave # 112, Indianapolis, IN, 46208-3487, USA; tel (317) 940-9358; fax (317) 940-9713; e-mail: mweiteka@butler.edu; adv email: advertising@butler.edu; web site: dawgnet.butler.edu
Dir. — Kwadwo Anokwa
Charles St. Cyr
Lauren Fisher
Meg Shaw
Format: Tabloid

CALUMET COLLEGE OF ST. JOSEPH: THE SHAVINGS — 2400 New York Ave, Whiting, IN, 46394-2195, USA; tel (219) 473-4322; fax (219) 473-4219; web site: www.ccsj.edu
PD — Dawn Muhammad
Daren Jasieniecki

Mark Cassello
Published: Bi-Mthly
Digital Edition Available?: N
Format: Tabloid

DEPAUW UNIV.: DEPAUW — 609 S Locust St, Greencastle, IN, 46135-2047, USA; tel (765) 658-5972; fax (765) 658-5991; web site: www.thedepauw.com
Lili Wright
Samuel Autman
Jonathan Batuello
Alex Turco
Macy Ayers
Format: Tabloid

EARLHAM COLLEGE: EARLHAM WORD — PO Box 273, Richmond, IN, 47375-0273, USA; tel (765) 983-1569; fax (765) 983-1641; web site: ecword.org
Maria Salvador
Marisa Keller
Format: Broadsheet

FRANKLIN COLLEGE: FRANKLIN — 101 Branigin Blvd, Franklin, IN, 46131-2623, USA; tel (317) 738-8191; fax (317) 738-8234; e-mail: thefranklin@franklincollege.edu; web site: www.thefranklinonline.com
Katie Coffin
Format: Broadsheet

GOSHEN COLLEGE — 1700 S Main St, Goshen, IN, 46526-4794, USA; tel (574) 535-7745; fax (574) 535-7660; e-mail: record@goshen.edu; web site: record.goshen.edu
Duane Stoltzfus
Marlys Weaver

HANOVER COLLEGE: TRIANGLE — PO Box 890, Hanover, IN, 47243-0890, USA; tel (812) 866-7073; fax (812) 866-7077; e-mail: triangle@hanover.edu; web site: www.hanovertriangle.com
Kay Stokes
Melisa Cole
Format: Tabloid

INDIANA STATE UNIV.: INDIANA STATESMAN — 716 Hulman Memorial Student Un, Terre Haute, IN, 47809-0001, USA; tel (812) 237-7629; fax (812) 237-7629; web site: www.indianastatesman.com
Heidi Staggs
Caitlin Hancock
Daniel Greenwell
Format: Broadsheet

INDIANA UNIV.: INDIANA DAILY STUDENT — 940 E 7th St Rm 120, Bloomington, IN, 47405-7108, USA; tel (812) 855-0763; fax (812) 855-8009; e-mail: ids@indiana.edu; web site: www.idsnews.com
Susan McGlocklin
Published: Mon, Tues, Wed, Thur, Fri
Digital Edition Available?: Y
Digital Platform - Mobile: Apple, Android
Format: Broadsheet

INDIANA UNIV.: CORRESPONDENT — PO Box 9003, Kokomo, IN, 46904-9003, USA; tel (765) 455-9280; fax (765) 455-9537; e-mail: paper@iuk.edu; web site: www.kokomocorrespondent.com
David Brewster
Alyx Arnett
Johnathan Grant
Format: Tabloid

INDIANA UNIV.: PREFACE — PO Box 7111, South Bend, IN, 46634-7111, USA; tel (574) 520-4878; fax (574) 237-4599; web site: www.iusb.edu
Beth Stutsman
Format: Broadsheet

INDIANA UNIV. EAST: HOWLER — 2325 Chester Blvd, Richmond, IN, 47374-1289, USA; tel (765) 973-8255; fax (765) 973-8388; e-mail: howler@iue.edu; web site: www.iue.edu
Belinda Wyss
Rob Zinkan
Format: Tabloid

INDIANA UNIV. KELLEY SCHOOL OF BUS. — 1309 E 10th St, Bloomington, IN, 47405-5308, USA; tel (812) 855-8100; fax (812) 855-9039
Chris Hildreth
Format: Tabloid

INDIANA UNIV. NORTHWEST: NORTHWEST PHOENIX — 3400 Broadway, Moraine 110, Gary, IN, 46408-1101, USA; tel (219) 980-6795; fax (219) 980-6948; e-mail: phoenixn@iun.edu; web site: www.iun.edu/~phoenixn
Scott Fulk
Don Sjoerdsma
Format: Tabloid

INDIANA UNIV. SOUTHEAST: HORIZON — 4201 Grant Line Rd, New Albany, IN, 47150-6405, USA; tel (812) 941-2253; e-mail: horizon@ius.edu; web site: iushorizon.com
Adviser — Adam Maksl
Published: Mon Every two weeksCirc.(fr.) 2,000
Digital Edition Available?: Y
Price: Free
Format: Tabloid

INDIANA WESLEYAN UNIVERSITY: ARGOSY — 4201 S Washington St, Marion, IN, 46953-4974, USA; tel (765) 677-1818; fax (765) 677-1755; e-mail: amy.smelser@indwes.edu; web site: https://www.indwes.edu/undergraduate/majors/division-of-communication-and-theatre/
Ed. — Amy Smelser
Instructor — Amy Smelser
Format: Tabloid

INDIANA-PURDUE UNIV. — 2101 E Coliseum Blvd Ste 100, Fort Wayne, IN, 46805-1499, USA; tel (260) 481-6583; fax (260) 481-6045; e-mail: publisher@ipfwcommunicator.org; adv email: ads@ipfwcommunicator.org; web site: www.ipfwcommunicator.org
Matt cClure
Kristin Conley
Aaron Greene
Format: Broadsheet

MANCHESTER COLLEGE: OAK LEAVES — 604 E College Ave # 11, North Manchester, IN, 46962-1232, USA; tel (260) 982-5317; fax (260) 982-5043; web site: www.manchester.edu/OSD/OakLeaves/index.htm
Katherine Ings
Adam King
Cyndel Taylor
Format: Tabloid

MARIAN COLLEGE: KNIGHT TIMES — 3200 Cold Spring Rd, Indianapolis, IN, 46222-1997, USA; tel (317) 955-6397; fax (317) 955-6448; web site: www.marian.edu
Gay Lynn Crossley
Sarah Kreicker
Format: Tabloid

PURDUE UNIV. NORTH CENTRAL: THE VOICE — 1401 S. U.S. 421, Westville, IN, 46391-9542, USA; tel (219) 785-5213; fax (219) 785-5544; e-mail: spectator@pnc.edu; ed email: thevoice@pnc.edu; web site: www.pnc.edu
Suzanne Webber
Lyndsie Daikhi
Format: Tabloid

PURDUE UNIVERSITY CALUMET: THE CHRONICLE — 2200 169th St, Hammond, IN, 46323-2068, USA; tel (219) 989-2547; fax (219) 989-2770; e-mail: pucchronicle@gmail.com; adv email: chronicle.businessmanager@gmail.com; ed email: pucchronicle@gmail.com; web site: pucchronicle.comEst. 1982
Editor-in-Chief — Jessica Gerlich
Sports Editor — William Koester
Entertainment Editor — Michelle Mullins
Business Manager — Dante Vidal Silguero
Photo Editor — Morgan Walker
Production Manager — Samantha Gonzalez
Published: Mon
Digital Edition Available?: Y
Format: Tabloid

ROSE-HULMAN INST. OF TECHNOLOGY: THE ROSE THORN — 5500 Wabash Ave # CM5037, Terre Haute, IN, 47803-3920, USA; tel (812) 877-8255; e-mail: thorn@rose-hulman.edu; adv email: thorn-biz@rose-hulman.edu; web site: http://thorn.rose-hulman.edu/
Advisor — Thomas Adams
Business Manager — Marcus Willerscheidt
Editor-in-Chief — Katrina Brandenburg
Published: FriCirc. (pd.) 0 (fr.) 1,000
Digital Edition Available?: Y
Insert rate: $250
Price: $0
Format: Tabloid

ST. JOSEPH'S COLLEGE: OBSERVER — PO Box 870, Rensselaer, IN, 47978-0870, USA; tel (219) 866-6224
Charles Kerlin
Mike Koscielny
Format: Tabloid

TAYLOR UNIV.: THE ECHO — 236 W. Reade Ave, Upland, IN, 46989, USA; tel (765) 998-5359; e-mail: echo@taylor.edu
Faculty Advisor — Alan Blanchard
Published: Fri
Digital Edition Available?: Y

TAYLOR UNIV.: ECHO — 236 W. Reade Ave., Upland, IN, 46989-1001, USA; tel (765) 998-5359; e-mail: echo@taylor.edu; adv email: echoads@taylor.edu; web site: http://theechonews.com/Est. 1913
Ed. in Chief — Donna Downs
Faculty Adviser — Alan Blanchard
Published: Fri
Digital Edition Available?: Y
Price: Free
Format: Broadsheet

THE PURDUE EXPONENT: THE PURDUE EXPONENT — PO Box 2506, West Lafayette, IN, 47996-2506, USA; tel (765) 743-1111; fax (765) 743-6087; e-mail: help@purdueexponent.org; adv email: advertising@purdueexponent.org; web site: www.purdueexponent.orgEst. 1889
Pub. — Patirck Kuhnle
Prodn. Dir. — Ingraham Vancel
Advertising director — Mindy Coddington
Published: Mon, Tues, Wed, Thur, Fri M Th during summerCirc.(fr.) 12,000
Digital Edition Available?: Y
Digital Platform - Mobile: Apple, Android
Digital Platform - Tablet: Apple iOS, Android
Insert rate: $95/M
Format: Broadsheet

UNIV. OF EVANSVILLE: CRESCENT MAGAZINE — 1800 Lincoln Ave, Evansville, IN, 47714-1506, USA; tel (812) 488-2846; fax (812) 488-2224; e-mail: crescentmagazine@evansville.edu; adv email: crescentadvertising@evansville.edu; ed email: crescentmagazine@evansville.eduEst. 2009
Writing Director — Amy Reinhart
Marketing & Sales Director — Rebecca Kish
Published: Thur, MthlyCirc.(fr.) 1,700
Digital Edition Available?: N
Insert rate: $300 for 1700 insertions
Price: $2.50
Format: assorted
Note: We no longer offer a weekly newspaper. We switched format in fall 2009. We are now a monthly magazine.

UNIV. OF INDIANAPOLIS: THE REFLECTOR — 1400 E Hanna Ave, Indianapolis, IN, 46227-3697, USA; tel (317) 788-3269; fax (317) 788-3490; e-mail: reflector@uindy.edu; web site: www.reflector.uindy.edu
Jeanne Criswell
JP Sinclair
Adrian Kendrick
Samantha Cotten
Format: Broadsheet

UNIV. OF NOTRE DAME: THE OBSERVER — PO Box 779, Notre Dame, IN, 46556-0779, USA; tel (574) 631-7471; fax (574) 631-6927; e-mail: observad@nd.edu; web site: www.ndsmcobserver.com
Theresa Bea
Mary Claire Rodriguez
Jenn Metz
Bill Brink
Format: Tabloid

UNIV. OF NOTRE DAME ENGINEERING SCHOOL — 257 Cushing Hall, Notre Dame, IN, 46556, USA; tel (574) 631-5530; fax (574) 631-8007; e-mail: techrev@nd.edu; web site: www.nd.edu
Cathy Pieronek
Brandon Chynowegh

UNIV. OF SOUTHERN INDIANA: SHIELD — 8600 University Blvd, Evansville, IN, 47712-3590, USA; tel (812) 464 8600; fax (812) 465-1632; e-mail: sheild@usi.edu; adv email: shieldads@gmail.com; ed email: shieldpix@gmail.com; web site: www.usishield.com; www.usi.edu
Jon Webb
Format: Tabloid

VALPARAISO UNIVERSITY: THE TORCH — 1809 Chapel Dr, Valparaiso, IN, 46383-4517, USA; tel (219) 464-5271; fax (219) 464-6742; e-mail: douglas.kocher@valpo.edu; web site: www.valpo.edu/torch
Chair — Douglas J. Kocher
Jason Paupore
Andy Simmons
Luis Fifuentes
Kathryn Kattalia
Format: Tabloid

JOURNALISM PROGRAM, VINCENNES UNIVERSITY: TRAILBLAZER — 1002 N 1st St, Vincennes, IN, 47591-1500, USA; tel (812) 888-4551; fax (812) 888-5531; e-mail: trailblazer@vinu.edu
Jrnlism Asst. Professor — Emily Taylor
Format: Tabloid

IOWA

BUENA VISTA UNIV.: TACK — 610 W 4th St, Storm Lake, IA, 50588-1798, USA; tel (712) 749-1247; e-mail: ucbvu@bvu.edu
Jamii Claiborne
Carly Evans
Lindsey Marean
Format: Tabloid

CENTRAL COLLEGE: THE CENTRAL RAY — 812 University, Pella, IA, 50219, USA; tel (877) 462-3687; fax (515) 628-5316; e-mail: theray@central.edu; ed email: carmane@central.edu; web site: www.central.edu
Emily Betz
Format: Tabloid

CLARKE COLLEGE: COURIER — 1550 Clarke Dr, Dubuque, IA, 52001-3198, USA; tel (563) 588-6335; fax (563) 588-6789; e-mail:

abdul.sinno@clarke.edu
Diana Russo
Chair — Abdul Karim Sinno
Sarah Bradford
Format: Tabloid

COE COLLEGE: COE COSMOS — 1220 1st Ave NE # 1, Cedar Rapids, IA, 52402-5092, USA; tel (319) 399-8646; fax (319) 399-8667; e-mail: cosmos@coe.edu; web site: www.coe.eduEst. 1889
Susanne Gubanc
Published: Fri
Digital Edition Available?: N
Format: Tabloid

CORNELL COLLEGE: THE CORNELLIAN — 600 First St SW, Mount Vernon, IA, 52314, USA; tel (319) 895-4430; fax (319) 895-5264; e-mail: cornellian@cornellcollege.edu; web site: www.thecornellian.com
Format: Broadsheet

DES MOINES AREA CMTY. COLLEGE: THE CHRONICLE — 2006 S Ankeny Blvd Bldg 2, Ankeny, IA, 50023-8995, USA; tel (515) 965-6425; fax (515) 433-5033; e-mail: chronicle@dmacc.edu; web site: www.campuschronicle.net
Julie Roosa
Julie Cahill
Kelsey Edwards
Format: Tabloid

DRAKE UNIV.: TIMES-DELPHIC — 2507 Univ., Ave. 124N Meredith Hall, Des Moines, IA, 50311-4516, USA; tel (515) 271-3867; fax (515) 271-2798; e-mail: times.delphic@drake.edu; web site: www.timesdelphic.com
Jill Van Wyke
Caleb Bailey
Matt Vasilogambros
Format: Broadsheet

GRACELAND COLLEGE: GRACELAND TOWER — 1 University Pl, Lamoni, IA, 50140-1684, USA; tel (641) 784-5000; fax (641) 784-5480; e-mail: tower@graceland.edu; web site: www.graceland.edu
Nicky Kerr
Format: Tabloid

GRAND VIEW UNIVERSITY: THE GRAND VIEWS — Cowles Communication Ctr., 1331 Grandview Ave., Des Moines, IA, 50316-1453, USA; tel (515) 263-2806; fax (515) 263-2990; e-mail: grandviews@grandview.edu; web site: www.thegrandviews.com; www.grandview.eduEst. 1949
Mark Siebert
Editor — Stephanie Ivankovich
Published: Fri
Digital Edition Available?: Y
Price: Free
Format: Tabloid

GRINNELL COLLEGE: SCARLET & BLACK — P.O. Box 5886, Grinnell, IA, 50112-3128, USA; tel (641) 269-3325; fax (641) 269-4888; e-mail: newspapr@grinnell.edu; web site: www.thesandb.com
Published: Fri
Digital Platform - Mobile: Apple, Android
Format: Broadsheet

IOWA CENTRAL CMTY. COLLEGE: COLLEGIAN — 330 Avenue M, Fort Dodge, IA, 50501-5739, USA; tel (515) 576-0099; fax (515) 576-7724; e-mail: mcintyre@iowacentral.com; web site: http://www.iccc.cc.ia.us/collegian/staff.htm
Bill McIntyre
Ian Schmit
Format: Tabloid

IOWA LAKES CMTY. COLLEGE: SPINDRIFT — 300 S 18th St, Estherville, IA, 51334-2721, USA; tel (712) 362-2604; fax (712) 362-8363; e-mail: pbuchholz@iowalakes.edu; info@iowalakes.edu; web site: www.iowalakes.edu
Pam Bushholz
Format: Broadsheet

IOWA STATE DAILY — 108 Hamilton Hall, Ames, IA, 50011-1181, USA; tel (515) 294-4120; fax (515) 294-4119; e-mail: ads@iowastatedaily.com; adv email: ads@iowastatedaily.com; ed email: editor@iowastatedaily.com; web site: www.iowastatedaily.comEst. 1890
Gen. Mgr. — Laura Widmer
Ed. Advisor — Mark Witherspoon
Ed. — Stephen Koenigsfeld
Published: Mon, Tues, Wed, Thur, Fri
Digital Platform - Mobile: Apple, Android
Digital Platform - Tablet: Apple iOS, Android

IOWA STATE UNIVERSITY: IOWA STATE DAILY — 2420 Lincoln Way, Suite 205, Ames, IA, 50014, USA; tel (515) 294-4120; fax (515) 294-4119; e-mail: spoon@iowastatedaily.com; adv email: sara.brown@iowastatedaily.com; ed email: news@iowastatedaily.com; web site: www.iowastatedaily.comEst. 1890
Advisor — Mark Witherspoon
General Manager of the Iowa State Daily Media Group — Lawrence Cunningham
Business Manager — Janey Nicholas
Operations manager — Sarah Lefebre
Advertising manager — Sara Brown
Editor in chief — Emily Barske
Published: Mon, Tues, Wed, Thur, FriCirc.(fr.) 12,500
Digital Edition Available?: Y
Digital Platform - Mobile: Apple, Android
Price: 40 cents per issue after the first free issue
Format: Broadsheet

IOWA WESLEYAN COLLEGE: WESLEYAN COURIER — 601 N Main St, Mount Pleasant, IA, 52641-1398, USA; tel (319) 385-8021; fax (319) 385-6363; web site: www.iwc.edu
Format: Broadsheet

IOWA WESTERN CMTY. COLLEGE: THE ROVER — 2700 College Rd, Council Bluffs, IA, 51503-1057, USA; tel (712) 325-3200; web site: iwccrover.wordpress.com
Camille Steed
Format: Tabloid

KIRKWOOD COMMUNITY COLLEGE: COMMUNIQUE — 6301 Kirkwood Blvd. SW , Cedar Rapids, IA, 52404 , USA; tel (319) 398-5444; fax (319) 398-7141; e-mail: communique@kirkwood edu.; web site: www.kirkwoodstudentmedia.com
Sarah Baker
Publisher — Rose Kodet
Published: six times each semester
Digital Edition Available?: Y
Format: Broadsheet

LORAS COLLEGE: LORIAN — 1450 Alta Vista St, Dubuque, IA, 52001-4399, USA; tel (563) 588-7954; fax (563) 588-7339; e-mail: lorian@loras.edu; adv email: lorian@loras.edu; ed email: lorian@loras.edu; web site: myduhawk.comEst. 1913
Advisor — Timothy Manning
Anna Sweeney
Co-Exec. Ed. — Cassandra Busch
Published: ThurCirc.(fr.) 1,600
Digital Edition Available?: Y
Insert rate: $200
Price: Free
Format: Tabloid

MAHARISHI UNIV. OF MGMT.: THE REVIEW — 1000 N 4th St # 694, Fairfield, IA, 52557-0002, USA; tel (641) 472-0778; e-mail: jkarpen@mum.edu; adv email: jkarpen@mum.edu; ed email: jkarpen@mum.edu; web site: https://www.mum.edu/the-review/recent-issues/Est. 1985
Jim Karpen
Published: every two weeksCirc.(fr.) 1,000
Digital Edition Available?: N
Insert rate: $200
Format: Newsletter

MT. MERCY COLLEGE: MT. MERCY TIMES — 1330 Elmhurst Dr NE, Cedar Rapids, IA, 52402-4797, USA; tel (319) 363-1323; fax (319) 366-0893; e-mail: mmctimes@mtmercy.edu; web site: times.mtmercy.edu
Joe Sheller
Mellette Maurice
Brian Heinemann
Format: Tabloid

MUSCATINE CMTY. COLLEGE: CALUMET — 152 Colorado St, Muscatine, IA, 52761-5396, USA; tel (563) 288-6053; fax (563) 264-6074
Kristina Koch
Format: Tabloid

NORTH IOWA AREA CMTY. COLLEGE: LOGOS — 500 College Drive , Mason City, IA, 50401, USA; tel (641) 422-4304; fax (641) 422-4280; e-mail: peterpau@niacc.edu; web site: www.niacc.edu/logos
Paul Peterson
Emily Knoop
Collie Wood
Format: Tabloid

NORTHWESTERN COLLEGE: BEACON — 101 7th St SW, Orange City, IA, 51041-1996, USA; tel (712) 707-7043; fax (712) 707-7345; e-mail: beacon@nwciowa.edu; web site: beacon.nwciowa.edu
Carl Vandermeulen
Kim Eason
Format: Tabloid

PALMER COLLEGE OF CHIROPRACTIC: BEACON — 1000 Brady St., Davenport, IA, 52803, USA; tel (563) 884-5686; fax (563) 884-5719; e-mail: beacon@palmer.edu; web site: www.palmerbeacon.com
Ramneek Bhogal
Stephanie O'Neill
Stewart McMillan
Format: Broadsheet

SIMPSON COLLEGE: SIMPSONIAN — 701 N C St, Indianola, IA, 50125-1202, USA; tel (515) 961-1738; fax (515) 961-1350; e-mail: thesimp@simpson.edu; web site: www.thesimpsonian.com
Emily Schettler
Format: Tabloid

UNIV. OF DUBUQUE: THE BELLTOWER — 2000 University Ave # 6, Dubuque, IA, 52001-5050, USA; tel (563) 589-3369; fax (319) 589-3419
Laura Steinbeck
Format: Tabloid

UNIV. OF IOWA: DAILY IOWAN — 104 West Washington St , Iowa City, IA, 52240, USA; tel (319) 335-5791; fax (319) 335-6297; e-mail: daily-iowan@uiowa.edu; web site: www.dailyiowan.com
William Casey
Debra Plath
Pete Recker
Format: Broadsheet

UNIV. OF NORTHERN IOWA: NORTHERN IOWAN — L011 Maucker Un, Cedar Falls, IA, 50614-0001, USA; tel (319) 273-2157; fax (319) 273-5931; e-mail: northern-iowan@uni.edu; web site: www.northerniowan.com
Michele Smith
Dana Klesner
Seth Hadenfelt
Alex Johansen
Circ. — Jeremy
Exec. Ed. — Nikki
News Ed. — Larissa
Prodn. — Anna
Published: Mon, ThurCirc.(fr.) 5,000
Digital Edition Available?: Y
Digital Platform - Mobile: Apple, Android
Digital Platform - Tablet: Apple iOS, Android
Insert rate: $75 per thousand
Format: Tabloid
Note: App is the Northern Iowan Facebook and Twitter let us know if you want price sheet and publication schedule

WALDORF COLLEGE: LOBBYIST — 106 S 6th St, Forest City, IA, 50436-1797, USA; tel (641) 585-2450; fax (641) 582-8194; e-mail: lobbyist@waldorf.edu; web site: lobbyist.waldorf.edu
David Damm
Sarah Soy
Caitlin Leitzen
Matt Knutson
Format: Tabloid

WARTBURG COLLEGE: WARTBURG TRUMPET — 100 Wartburg Blvd, Waverly, IA, 50677-2200, USA; tel (319) 352-8289; fax (319) 352-8242; e-mail: trumpet@wartburg.edu; web site: www.wartburg.edu/trumpet
Cliff Brockmen
Luke Shanno
Jackie Albrecht
Format: Tabloid

WILLIAM PENN UNIV.: CHRONICLE — 201 Trueblood Ave., Oskaloosa, IA, 52577, USA; tel (641) 673-2170; adv email: chronicle@wmpenn.edu
Published: Mthly

KANSAS

BAKER UNIVERSITY: BAKER ORANGE — PO Box 65, Baldwin City, KS, 66006-0065, USA; tel (913) 594-6451; fax (913) 594-3570; e-mail: bayha@harvey.bakeru.edu; web site: www.thebakerorange.com
Gwyn Mellinger
Chair — Ann Rosenthal
Dave Bostwick
Chris Smith
Format: Broadsheet

BARTON COUNTY CMTY. COLLEGE: INTERROBANG — 245 NE 30 Rd, Great Bend, KS, 67530-9107, USA; tel (620) 792-9239; fax 6207861157; web site: www.bartonccc.eduEst. 1969
Yvonda Acker
Published: Bi-weekly Print; Weekly Online
Format: Tabloid

BENEDICTINE COLLEGE: CIRCUIT — 1020 N 2nd St, Atchison, KS, 66002-1499, USA; tel (913) 360-7390; fax (913) 367-6102; e-mail: circuit@benedictine.edu; web site: www.bccircuit.com
Kevin Page
Format: Tabloid

BETHANY COLLEGE — PO Box 184, Lindsborg, KS, 67456-0184, USA; tel (785) 227-8234; fax (785) 227-2004
Joel Wiede

BETHEL COLLEGE: COLLEGIAN — 300 E 27th St, North Newton, KS, 67117-1716, USA; tel (316) 284-5271; fax (316) 284-5286; e-mail: collegian@bethelks.edu; adv email: collegian@bethelks.edu; ed email: collegian@bethelks.edu; web site: www.bethelks.edu/collegian
Advisor — Christine Crouse-Dick
Price: $17.00 per year
Format: Tabloid

BUTLER COUNTY CMTY. COLLEGE: THE LANTERN — 901 S Haverhill Rd, El Dorado, KS, 67042-3225, USA; tel (316) 322-3170; fax (316) 322-3109; e-mail: lantern@butlercc.edu; web site: www.lanternonline.com; www.butlercc.edu
Melissa Roberts
Format: Broadsheet

COFFEYVILLE CMTY. COLLEGE: NA — 400 W. 11th , Coffeyville, KS, 67337, USA; tel (316) 252-7137

COLBY CMTY. COLLEGE: TROJAN EXPRESS — 1255 S Range Ave, Colby, KS, 67701-4099, USA; tel (785) 462-3984; fax (785) 460-4699; web site: www.freewebs.com/trojanexpress
Trent Rose
Format: Tabloid

COWLEY COUNTY CMTY. COLLEGE: COWLEY PRESS — 125 S 2nd St, Arkansas City, KS, 67005-2662, USA; tel (620) 441-5287; fax (620) 441-5377; e-mail: editor@cowleypress.com; web site: www.cowleypress.com
Meg Smith
Alyssa Campbell
Richard Gould
Format: Tabloid

FT. HAYS STATE UNIV.: UNIVERSITY LEADER — 600 Park St Picken 104, Hays, KS, 67601-4009, USA; tel (785) 628-3478; fax (785) 628-4004; web site: www.fhsu.edu
Gretchen Fields
Format: Broadsheet

JOHNSON COUNTY CMTY. COLLEGE: CAMPUS LEDGER — 12345 College Blvd # 7, Overland Park, KS, 66210-1283, USA; tel (913) 469-8500; fax (913) 469-2577; web site: www.campusledger.com
Anne Christiansen-Bullers
Matt Galloway
Format: Tabloid

KANSAS CITY CMTY. COLLEGE: THE BLUE DEVIL'S — 7250 State Ave, Kansas City, KS, 66112-3003, USA; tel (913) 334-1100; fax (913) 288-7617; web site: kckcc.edu
Bryan Whitehead
Format: Tabloid

KANSAS WESLEYAN UNIV.: ADVANCE — 100 E Claflin Ave Ste 87, Salina, KS, 67401-6100, USA; tel (785) 827-5541; fax (785) 827-0927
Jack Morris
Format: Tabloid

MCPHERSON COLLEGE: SPECTATOR — PO Box 1402, McPherson, KS, 67460-1402, USA; tel (620) 242-0449; fax (620) 241-8443; web site: spectator.mcpherson.edu
Adviser — Adam Pracht
Editor-in-Chief — Shannon Williams
Format: Broadsheet

MIDAMERICA NAZARENE UNIVERSITY: THE TRAILBLAZER — 2030 E. College Way, Olathe, KS, 66062, USA; tel (913) 971-3289; fax (913) 971-3421; adv email: ehodgson@mnu.edu; ed email: tb-edit@mnu.edu; web site: www.trailblazer.mnubox.comEst. 1967
Editor-in-Chief — Sarah Glass
Managing Editor — Molly Farnsworth
Section Editor — Christina Wilkins
Faculty Advisor — Melinda Smith
Format: Tabloid

NEWMAN UNIVERSITY - THE VANTAGE: VANTAGE — 3100 W McCormick St, Wichita, KS, 67213-2008, USA; tel (316) 942-4291; fax (316) 942-4483; e-mail: vantage@newmanu.edu
Editor — Kristen McCurdy
Format: Tabloid

PRATT CMTY. COLLEGE — 348 NE Hwy. 61, Pratt, KS, 67124, USA; tel (316) 672-5641; fax (316) 672-5641

STUDENT PUBLICATIONS INC. — 103 Kedzie Hall, Manhattan, KS, 66506-1505, USA; tel (785) 532-6555; fax (785) 532-6236; e-mail: news@spub.ksu.edu; adv email: adsales@spub.ksu.edu; classifieds@spub.ksu.edu; web site: www.kstatecollegian.comEst. 1896
Steve Wolgast
Ed. — Tim Schrag
Format: Student Newspaper

TABOR COLLEGE: THE TABOR VIEW — 400 S. Jefferson St., Hillsboro, KS, 67063-1753, USA; tel (620) 947-3121; fax (620) 947-2607; e-mail: theview@tabor.edu; adv email: theview@tabor.edu; ed email: theview@tabor.edu; web site: https://www.facebook.com/TaborView?ref=hl
Advisor — Sara Jo Waldron
Editor-in-Chief — Jared Janzen
Sara Sigley
Heather Deckert
Published: Mthly
Digital Edition Available?: Y
Format: Tabloid

THE UNIVERSITY DAILY KANSAN: THE UNIVERSITY DAILY KANSAN — 1000 Sunnyside Ave, Lawrence, KS, 66045-7599, USA; tel (785) 864-4724; fax (785) 864-5261; e-mail: editor@kansan.com; adv email: adsales@kansan.com; ed email: editor@kansan.com; web site: www.kansan.comEst. 1904
Gen. Mgr./News Advisor — Malcolm Gibson
Sales and Marketing Adviser — Jon Schlitt
Published: Mon, Tues, Wed, Thur Weekly in summer (June/July)Circ. (pd.) 11,000
Digital Edition Available?: Y
Digital Platform - Mobile: Android
Digital Platform - Tablet: Apple iOS, Android
Format: Broadsheet

UNIV. OF KANSAS ENGINEERING SCHOOL: KANSAS ENGINEER — 4010 Learned Hall, Lawrence, KS, 66045-7526, USA; tel (785) 864-8853
Mary Jane Dunlap
Jill Hummels
Format: Magazine

WASHBURN UNIV.: WASHBURN REVIEW — 1700 SW College Ave, Topeka, KS, 66621-1101, USA; tel (785) 670-2506; fax (785) 670-1035; e-mail: review@washburn.edu; web site: www.washburnreview.org
Nicole Stejskal
Format: Broadsheet

WICHITA STATE UNIV.: THE SUNFLOWER — 1845 Fairmount St, Wichita, KS, 67260-0001, USA; tel (316) 978-3456; fax (316) 978-3778; ed email: editor@thesunflower.com; sports.editor@thesunflower.com; web site: www.thesunflower.com
Ronda Voorhis
Candice Tullis
Scott Elpers
Jorge M. De Hoyos
Format: Broadsheet

KENTUCKY

ASBURY COLLEGE: THE ASBURY COLLEGIAN — 1 Macklem Dr, Wilmore, KY, 40390-1198, USA; tel (859) 858-3511; fax (859) 858-3921; e-mail: mlonginow@asbury.edu; web site: collegian.asbury.edu
Deanna Morono
Chair — James R. Owens
Kayla Dubois
Zack Klemme
Morgan Schutters
Format: Broadsheet

BELLARMINE COLLEGE: CONCORD — 2001 Newburg Rd, Louisville, KY, 40205-0671, USA; tel (502) 452-8157; e-mail: theconcard@bellarmine.edu; web site: www.theconcordonline.com
Erika Osborne
Format: Broadsheet

BEREA COLLEGE: PINNACLE — 2150 Cpo, Berea, KY, 40404-0001, USA; tel (859) 985-3208; fax (859) 985-3914; e-mail: pinnacle@berea.edu; web site: www.bereacollegepinnacle.com
Chris Lakes
Kwadwo Juantuah
Format: Tabloid

CAMPBELLSVILLE UNIVERSITY: CAMPUS TIMES — 1 University Dr., Campbellsville, KY, 42718, USA; tel (270) 789-5035; fax (270)789-5145; web site: www.campbellsville.edu/campus-times
Published: Monthly when school is in sessionCirc.(fr.) 2,000
Digital Edition Available?: N
Digital Platform - Mobile: Apple

CENTRE COLLEGE: CENTR COLLEGE CENTO — 600 W Walnut St, Danville, KY, 40422-1394, USA; tel (859) 238-5350; e-mail: cento@centre.edu; adv email: business@centre.edu; ed email: ed-in-chief@centre.eduEst. 1888
Tess Simon
Katy Meyer
Amy Senders
Format: Broadsheet

EASTERN KENTUCKY UNIV.: THE EASTERN PROGRESS — 521 Lancaster Ave, Richmond, KY, 40475-3102, USA; tel (859) 622-1881; fax (859) 622-2354; e-mail: progress@eku.edu; adv email: progressads@eku.edu; web site: www.easternprogress.comEst. 1922
Reggie Beehner
Kristie Hamon
Gina Portwood
Park Greer
Published: Thur During semestersCirc.(fr.) 8,000
Format: Broadsheet

GEORGETOWN COLLEGE: GEORGETONIAN — 400 E College St Ste 1 # 280, Georgetown, KY, 40324-1628, USA; fax (502) 863-8150
Whitley Arens
Format: Tabloid

HENDERSON CMTY. COLLEGE — 2660 S Green St, Henderson, KY, 42420-4699, USA; tel (270) 827-1867Est. 1978
Scott Taylor

KENTUCKY STATE UNIV.: THOROBRED NEWS — 400 E Main St, Frankfort, KY, 40601-2355, USA; tel (502) 597-5915; fax (502) 597-5927; web site: http://www.ksuthorobreds.com/
Sepricia White
Terri McCray
Cornell Ferrill
Format: Tabloid

KENTUCKY WESLEYAN COLLEGE: PANOGRAM — 3000 Frederica St, Owensboro, KY, 42301-6055, USA; tel (270) 852-3596; fax (270) 852-3597; e-mail: panogram@kwc.edu
Randall Vogt
General Editor — Devyn Lott
Published: Bi-Mthly
Format: Tabloid

MOREHEAD STATE UNIV.: TRAIL BLAZER — 150 University Blvd, Morehead, KY, 40351, USA; tel (606) 783-2697; fax (606) 783-9113; e-mail: editor@trailblazeronline.net; web site: www.trailblazeronline.net
Joan Atkins
Format: Broadsheet

MURRAY STATE UNIV.: MURRAY STATE NEWS — 111 Wilson Hall, Murray, KY, 42071-3311, USA; tel (270) 809-6877; fax (270) 809-3175; e-mail: news@murraystate.edu; web site: www.thenews.org
Mia Walters
Format: Broadsheet

NORTHERN KENTUCKY UNIV.: NORTHERNER — University Ctr Rm 335, Newport, KY, 41099-0001, USA; tel (859) 572-5772; fax (859) 572-5772; e-mail: northerner@nku.edu; web site: www.thenortherner.com
Drew Laskey
Format: Broadsheet

UNIV. OF KENTUCKY: KENTUCKY KERNEL — Grehan Journalism Bldg Rm 26, Lexington, KY, 40506-0001, USA; tel (859) 257-2872; fax (859) 323-1906; e-mail: features@kykernel.com; adv email: news@kykernel.com; web site: www.kykernel.com
Chris Poore
Kenny Colston
Format: Broadsheet

UNIVERSITY OF LOUISVILLE: LOUISVILLE CARDINAL — Houehens Bldg, Ste LL07, Louisville, KY, 40292-0001, USA; fax (502) 852-0700; adv email: advertising@louisvillecardinal.com; ed email: editor@louisvillecardinal.com; web site: www.louisvillecardinal.comEst. 1926
Editor-in-Chief — Simon Isham
Adviser — Ralph Merkel
Published: TuesCirc.(fr.) 8,000
Digital Edition Available?: Y
Digital Platform - Mobile: Apple, Android, Windows, Blackberry, Other
Digital Platform - Tablet: Apple iOS, Android, Windows 7, Blackberry Tablet OS, Kindle, Nook, Kindle Fire, Other
Price: Free
Format: Tabloid

UNIVERSITY OF THE CUMBERLANDS — 6191 College Station Dr, Williamsburg, KY, 40769-1372, USA; tel 606.539.4172; e-mail: thepatriot@ucumberlands.edu; web site: www.thepatriot.ucumberlands.ed

WESTERN KENTUCKY UNIVERSITY: COLLEGE HEIGHTS HERALD — 1906 College Heights Blvd # 11084, Bowling Green, KY, 42101-1084, USA; tel (270) 745-2653; e-mail: carrie.pratt@wku.edu; adv email: william.hoagland@wku.edu; ed email: herald.editor@wku.edu; web site: www.wkuherald.comEst. 1925
Operations Mgr — Sherry West
Herald Adviser, Multiplatform News Adviser — Carrie Pratt
Office Associate — Tracy Newton
Advt Adviser and Sales Mgr — Will Hoagland
Dir of Student Publications — Chuck Clark
Talisman adviser — Sam Oldenburg
Published: Tues, Thur Topper Extra sports section
Published on home football daysCirc.(fr.) 7,000
Digital Edition Available?: Y
Digital Platform - Mobile: Other
Digital Platform - Tablet: Other
Insert rate: Call for information
Price: Call for information
Format: Broadsheet

LOUISIANA

BOSSIER PARISH CMTY. COLLEGE: KALEIDOSCOPE — 6220 E Texas St, Bossier City, LA, 71111-6922, USA; tel (318) 678-6000; fax X; e-mail: kaleidoscope@bpcc.edu; web site: www.bpcc.edu
Candice Gibson
Cathy Hammel
Format: Tabloid

CENTENARY COLLEGE: CONGLOMERATE — PO Box 41188, Shreveport, LA, 71134-1188, USA; tel (318) 792-5136; e-mail: paper@centenary.edu; web site: www.centenary.edu/life/congo
Mark Gruettner
Roxie Smith
Format: Tabloid

DELGADO COMMUNITY COLLEGE: DELGADO DOLPHIN — 615 City Park Ave, New Orleans, LA, 70119-4399, USA; tel (504) 671-6008; fax (504) 483-1953; e-mail: thedolphin29@gmail.com; web site: www.dcc.edu
Susan Hague
J.C. Romero
Format: Tabloid

DILLARD UNIV.: COURTBOUILLON — 2601 Gentilly Blvd, New Orleans, LA, 70122-3097, USA; tel (504) 283-8822; fax (504) 816-4107; web site: www.dillard.edu
Format: Tabloid

GRAMBLING STATE UNIVERSITY: GRAMBLINITE — 403 Main St, Grambling, LA, 71245-2761, USA; tel (318) 247-3331; fax (318) 274-3194; e-mail: mediarelations@gram.edu; web site: www.thegramblinite.com
Interim Director of University Communications, Marketing, and Media Relations — Mitzi LaSalle
Published: Thur
Digital Edition Available?: Y
Digital Platform - Mobile: Windows
Format: Broadsheet

LOUISIANA COLLEGE: WILDCAT — 1140 College Dr Dept English, Pineville, LA, 71359-1000, USA; tel (318) 487-7011; fax (318) 487-7310; e-mail: wildcat@lacollege.edu
Jessie Redd
Format: Tabloid

LOUISIANA STATE UNIV. — 1800 Hwy. 71 S., Alexandria, LA, 71302, USA; tel (318) 767-2602; e-mail: sentrynews@lsua.edu
Elizabeth Beard
Nancy Borden
Trayce Snow
Format: Tabloid

LOUISIANA STATE UNIV.: ALMAGEST — 1 University Pl No 344, Shreveport, LA, 71115-2301, USA; tel (318) 797-5328; fax (318) 797-5328; adv email: almagest@lsus.edu; web site: www.thealmagest.com
Rose-Marie Lillian
Karen Wissing
Format: Tabloid

LOUISIANA STATE UNIVERSITY: THE DAILY REVEILLE — Of Student Media B-39 Hodges Hall Ofc, Baton Rouge, LA, 70803-0001, USA; tel (225) 578-4810; fax (225) 578-1698; e-mail: editor@lsureveille.com; adv email: national@tigers.lsu.edu; ed email: editor@lsureveille.com; web site: www.lsureveille.comEst. 1887
Nicholas Persac
Kyle Whitfield
Kodi Wilson
Editor in Chief — Andrea Gallo
Editor in Chief — Balkom Taylor
Editor-in-Chief — Chandler Rome
Published: Mon, Tues, Wed, Thur, Fri
Digital Edition Available?: Y
Digital Platform - Mobile: Apple, Android
Digital Platform - Tablet: Apple iOS, Android
Price: First copy is free, 25 cents per copy after
Format: Tabloid

LOYOLA UNIVERSITY NEW ORLEANS: THE MAROON — 6363 Saint Charles Ave, New Orleans, LA, 70118-6195, USA; tel (504) 865-3535; fax (504) 865-3534; e-mail: maroon@loyno.edu; adv email: ads@loyno.edu; web site: www.loyolamaroon.comEst. 1923
Advisor — Michael Giusti
Published: FriCirc.(fr.) 2,750
Digital Edition Available?: Y
Digital Platform - Mobile: Apple, Android
Digital Platform - Tablet: Apple iOS, Android
Format: Tabloid

MCNEESE STATE UNIV.: CONTRABAND — PO Box 91375, Lake Charles, LA, 70609-0001, USA; tel (337) 475-5646; fax (337) 475-5259; e-mail: contraband@mcneese.edu; msucontraband@gmail.com; web site: www.msucontraband.com
Candace Townsend
Robert Teal
Sarah Puckett
Format: Tabloid

NICHOLLS STATE UNIV.: THE NICHOLLS WORTH — PO Box 2010, Thibodaux, LA, 70310-0001, USA; tel (985) 448-4259; fax (985) 448-4267; web site: www.thenichollsworth.com
Stephen Hartmann
Format: Tabloid

NORTHWESTERN STATE UNIVERSITY: THE CURRENT SAUCE — The Current Sauce, Natchitoches, LA, 71497, USA; tel (318) 357-5456; e-mail: thecurrentsauce@gmail.com; adv email: thecurrentsauce@gmail.com; ed email: thecurrentsauce@gmail.com; web site: www.nsulastudentmedia.comEst. 1914
Editor-in-Chief — Alec Horton
Associate Editor — Jordan Reich
Managing Editor — Christina Arrechavala
Photo Editor — Valentina Perez
PR Manager — Elisabeth Perez
Assistant PR Manager — Chloe' Romano
Ad Sales Representative — Julia Towry
Designer — Sarah Hill
Administrative Assistant — Maygin Chesson
Published: WedCirc.(fr.) 1,000
Digital Edition Available?: N
Digital Platform - Mobile: Apple
Digital Platform - Tablet: Apple iOS
Price: Free
Format: Broadsheet

SOUTHEASTERN LOUISIANA UNIV.: LION'S ROAR — Slu 10877, Hammond, LA, 70402-0001, USA; tel (985) 549-3731; fax (985) 549-3842; e-mail: lionsroar@selu.edu; web site: www.selu.edu/lionsroarEst. 1929
Lee Lind
Don Aime
Format: Broadsheet

SOUTHERN UNIV. A&M COLLEGE: SOUTHERN DIGEST — PO Box 10180, Baton Rouge, LA, 70813-0180, USA; tel (225) 771-2230; fax (225) 771-3253; e-mail: editor@southerndigest.com; web site: www.southerndigest.comEst. 1928
Stephanie Cain
Derick Hackett
Christopher Jones
Fran Hoskins
Format: Tabloid

SOUTHERN UNIVERSITY: THE SOUTHERN DIGEST — PO Box 10180, Baton Rouge, LA, 70813-0180, USA; tel (225) 771-2231; fax (225) 771-5840; e-mail: digest@subr.edu; adv email: camelia_gardner@subr.edu; ed email: fredrick_batiste@subr.edu; web site: www.southerndigest.comEst. 1926
Student Media Director — Heather Freeman
Advertising/Business Manager — Camelia Jackson
Publications Assistant/Advisor — Fredrick Batiste
Published: Tues, ThurCirc.(fr.) 4,000
Digital Edition Available?: Y
Insert rate: Please call
Price: 0
Format: Tabloid

TULANE UNIVERSITY: HULLABALOO — Lavin-Bernick Center G06, New Orleans, LA, 70118, USA; tel (504) 865-5657; e-mail: hull@tulane.edu; adv email: hullabaloo.advertising@gmail.com; web site: www.thehullabaloo.comEst. 1902
Senior Business Manager — Brooke Rhea
Editor In-Chief — Lily Milwit
Published: Thur Homecoming Magazine and Spring MagazineCirc.(fr.) 4,000
Digital Edition Available?: Y
Format: Tabloid

UNIV. OF LOUISIANA AT LAFAYETTE THE VERMILION: THE VERMILION — PO Box 44813, Lafayette, LA, 70504-0001, USA; tel (337) 482-6110; fax (337) 482-6959; e-mail: vermadvertising@gmail.com; adv email: vermadvertising@gmail.com; ed email: hollyhoooot@gmail.com; web site: thevermilion.comEst. 1904
Business Manager — Thomas Schumacher
Published: Wed Aug, Sept, Oct, Nov
Insert rate: $50 per 1000
Format: Tabloid

UNIV. OF LOUISIANA AT MONROE: THE HAWKEYE — 700 University Ave, Monroe, LA, 71209, USA; tel (318) 342-5454; e-mail: ulmhawkeye@gmail.com; adv email: ulmhawkeyead@gmail.com; ed email: ulmhawkeye@gmail.com; web site: www.ulmhawkeye.comEst. 1934
Editor in Chief — Ethan Dennis
Advertising Director — Clarence Nash, Jr.
Published: Mon
Digital Edition Available?: Y
Insert rate: $150 per 1000
Format: newspaper tabloid

UNIVERSITY OF NEW ORLEANS: DRIFTWOOD — 2000 Lakeshore Dr # UC252, New Orleans, LA, 70148-0001, USA; tel (504) 280-6378; fax (504) 280-6010; e-mail: driftwood@uno.edu; web site: driftwood.uno.edu
Editor in Chief — Edie Talley
Format: Tabloid

XAVIER UNIV. OF LOUISIANA: XAVIER HERALD — 1 Drexel Drive, Box 299, New Orleans, LA, 70125-1098, USA; tel (504) 520-5092; fax (504) 520-7919; adv email: herald@xula.edu; web site: www.xula.edu; www.xulaherald.comEst. 1925
Advisor — Melinda Shelton
Published: Bi-MthlyCirc.(fr.) 2,000
Digital Edition Available?: N
Format: Tabloid
Note: online version; printed edition 6x per semester; 2,000 each printing

MAINE

BATES COLLEGE: BATES STUDENT — 2 Andrews Rd, Lewiston, ME, 04240-6028, USA; tel (207) 795-7494; e-mail: thebatesstudent@hotmail.com; web site: www.batesstudent.com
Regina Tavani
Zoe Rosenthal
Format: Tabloid

BOWDOIN COLLEGE: BOWDOIN ORIENT — 6200 College Sta, Brunswick, ME, 04011-8462, USA; tel (207) 725-3300; fax (207) 725-3975; e-mail: orient@bowdoin.edu; adv email: orientads@bowdoin.edu; web site: orient.bowdoin.edu/orient
Zoe Lescaze
Lizzy Tarr
Will Jacob
Gemma Leghorn
Format: Tabloid

COLBY COLLEGE: COLBY ECHO — 4600 Mayflower Hill Dr., Waterville, ME, 04901, USA; tel (207) 859-4000; fax (207) 872-3555; e-mail: echo@colbyecho.com; web site: www.colbyecho.com
Peter Rummel
Kira Novak
Elisabeth Ponsot
Format: Broadsheet

HUSSON COLLEGE: SPECTATOR — 1 College Cir, Bangor, ME, 04401-2999, USA; tel (207) 941-7700; fax (207) 941-7190
Josh Scroggins

UNIV. OF MAINE: UNIVERSITY TIMES — PO Box 417, Presque Isle, ME, 04769, USA; tel (207) 768-9400; e-mail: utimes@maine.edu
Tara White
Format: Broadsheet

UNIVERSITY OF MAINE: THE MAINE CAMPUS — Memorial Union, University of Maine, Orono, ME, 04469-5748, USA; tel (207) 581-1273; e-mail: info@mainecampus.com; adv email: ads@mainecampus.com; ed email: eic@mainecampus.com; web site: www.mainecampus.comEst. 1875
Ed. in Chief — Jordan Houdeshell
Bus. Mgr. — Elliott Simpson
Published: MonCirc.(fr.) 1,500
Digital Edition Available?: Y
Format: Newsprint

UNIVERSITY OF SOUTHERN MAINE: THE FREE PRESS, USM STUDENT COMMUNITY NEWSPAPER — PO Box 9300, Portland, ME, 04104-9300, USA; tel (207) 780-4084; fax N/A; e-mail: editor@usmfreepress.org; adv email: ads@usmfreepress.org; ed email: editor@usmfreepress.org; web site: www.usmfreepress.orgEst. 1972
Business Manager — Lucille Siegler
Published: Mon 11 issues per semester plus Summer orientation issuesCirc.(fr.) 2,800
Digital Edition Available?: Y
Insert rate: N- $100 for full run
Price: Free
Format: Flat Tabloid

MARYLAND

ANNE ARUNDEL CMTY. COLLEGE CAMPUS CURRENT: CAMPUS CURRENT — 101 College Pkwy Hum 206, Arnold, MD, 21012-1857, USA; tel (410) 777-2803; fax (410) 777-2021; e-mail: campuscurrent@aacc.edu; web site: www.campus-current.com
Advisor — Sheri Venema
Published: Bi-MthlyCirc.(fr.) 2,500
Format: Tabloid

BOWIE STATE UNIV.: THE SPECTRUM — 14000 Jericho Park Rd Rm 260, Bowie, MD, 20715-3319, USA; tel (301) 860-3729; fax (301) 860-3714
Rex Martin
Kristina Rowley
Jocelyn Jones
Format: Tabloid

CMTY. COLLEGE OF BALTIMORE CITY ESSEX: MONTAGE — 7201 Rossville Blvd Rm 116, Baltimore, MD, 21237-3855, USA; tel

(443) 840-1576; fax (410) 780-6209
Jeremy Caplan
Corey States
Insert rate: montage@ccbcmd.edu
Format: Broadsheet

COLLEGE OF SOUTHERN MARYLAND — PO Box 910, La Plata, MD, 20646-0910, USA; tel (301) 934-2251; fax (301) 934-7680; e-mail: hawkeye@csmd.edu
Ed. — Karen Smith-Hupp

COLUMBIA UNION COLLEGE: COLUMBIA JOURNAL — 7600 Flower Ave, Takoma Park, MD, 20912-7794, USA; tel (301) 891-4118; e-mail: cj@cuc.edu
Athina Lavinos
Jaclyn Wile
Heidi Lohr
Format: Tabloid

GOUCHER COLLEGE: THE QUINDECIM — 1021 Dulaney Valley Rd, Towson, MD, 21204-2780, USA; tel (410) 337-6322; fax (410) 337-6434; e-mail: quin@goucher.edu; askhd@goucher.edu; web site: www.thequindecim.com
Matt Simon
Lori Shull
Ben Spangler
Format: Tabloid

HOOD COLLEGE — 401 Rosemont Ave, Frederick, MD, 21701-8575, USA; tel (301) 696-3641; fax (301) 696-3578; e-mail: weinberg@hood.edu
Rita Davis
Dir./Prof. of Journalism — Al Weinberg

HOWARD CMTY. COLLEGE: HCC TIMES — 10901 Little Patuxent Pkwy, Columbia, MD, 21044-3197, USA; tel (410) 772-4937; fax (410) 772-4280; e-mail: newspaper@howardcc.edu; web site: www.howardcc.edu
Advertising Manager — Michelle Plummer
Published: Bi-Mthly
Digital Edition Available?: Y
Price: Free
Format: Tabloid

LOYOLA COLLEGE: GREYHOUND — 4501 N Charles St Bellarmine Hall 1, Baltimore, MD, 21210-2694, USA; tel (410) 617-2282; fax (410) 617-2982; e-mail: greyhoundads@loyola.edu; web site: www.loyolagreyhound.com
Joe Morelli
Kat Kienle
Format: Tabloid

MCDANIEL COLLEGE: THE MCDANIEL FREE PRESS — 2 College Hill, Westminster, MD, 21157-4390, USA; tel (410) 751-8600; fax (410) 857-2729; e-mail: freepress@mcdaniel.edu; web site: mcdanielfreepress.com
— Sarah Hull
— Daniel Valentin-MoralesCo-Editor-In-Chiefs
Published: Mthly
Digital Edition Available?: Y
Price: 0
Format: Tabloid

MONTGOMERY COLLEGE: THE MONTGOMERY ADVOCATE — 51 Mannakee St, Rockville, MD, 20850-1199, USA; tel (240) 567-7176; fax (240) 567-5091; e-mail: info@mcadvocate.com; adv email: info@mcadvocate.com; ed email: editor@mcadvocate.com; web site: http://mcadvocate.comEst. 1957
Steve Thurston
Digital Edition Available?: Y
Format: Tabloid
Note: We are online only. We do not publish a paper.

MONTGOMERY COLLEGE: EXCALIBUR — 7600 Takoma Ave., Commons Rm. 202, Takoma Park, MD, 20912, USA; tel (240) 567-1490; fax (301) 650-1334; e-mail: excaliburnewspaper@montgomerycollege.edu
Angela Clubb
Format: Tabloid

MONTGOMERY COLLEGE GERMANTOWN: THE GLOBE — 20200 Observation Dr, Germantown, MD, 20876-4098, USA; tel (240) 567-7840; fax (240) 567-7843; e-mail: theglobe@montgomerycollege.edu; web site: www.montgomerycollege.edu
Dave Anthony
Format: Tabloid

MOUNT ST. MARY'S UNIV.: THE MOUNTAIN ECHO — 16300 Old Emmitsburg Rd, Emmitsburg, MD, 21727-7700, USA; tel (301) 447-5246; fax (301) 447-5755; e-mail: echo@msmary.edu; web site: www.themountainecho.com
Sheldon Shealer
Allison Doherty
Format: Tabloid

NOTRE DAME OF MARYLAND UNIVERSITY: COLUMNS — 4701 N. Charles St., Baltimore, MD, 21210-2476, USA; tel (410) 532-5580; fax (410) 532-5796; e-mail: Columns@ndm.edu; adv email: Columns@ndm.edu; ed email: Columns@ndm.edu; web site: www.ndmcolumns.com
Editor-in-Chief — Mariel Guerrero
Lead Writer/ Managing Editor — Marguerite Linz
Digital Edition Available?: Y
Format: Tabloid

PRINCE GEORGES CMTY. COLLEGE: OWL — 301 Largo Rd, Largo, MD, 20774-2109, USA; tel (301) 336-6000; fax (301) 808-0960; e-mail: theowlnewspaper@hotmail.com; web site: www.pgcc.edu
Patrick Peterson
Malcolm Beech
Abelaja Obajimi
Format: Tabloid

SALISBURY UNIV.: FLYER — PO Box 3183, Salisbury, MD, 21802-3183, USA; tel (410) 543-6191; fax (410) 677-5359; e-mail: flyer@salisbury.edu; web site: www.suflyerblog.blogspot.com
Leslie Pusey
Vanessa Junkin
Format: Tabloid

ST. JOHNS COLLEGE: GADFLY — 60 College Ave, Annapolis, MD, 21401-1655, USA; tel (410) 263-2212
Ian McCracken
Format: Magazine

ST. MARY'S COLLEGE OF MARYLAND: THE POINT NEWS — 18952 E Fisher's Road, Saint Mary's City, MD, 20686, USA; tel (240) 895-4213; fax (240) 895-4445; e-mail: pointnews@smcm.edu; web site: www.smcm.edu/PointNews
Justin Perry
Matt Molek
Format: Tabloid

STEVENSON UNIVERSITY: THE VILLAGER — 1525 Greenspring Valley Rd, Stevenson, MD, 21153-0641, USA; tel (443) 394-9781; e-mail: suvillager@gmail.com; web site: stevensonvillager.comEst. 2016 online
Chip Rouse
Published: Thur every Thursday onlineCirc. (pd.) 0
Digital Edition Available?: Y
Digital Platform - Mobile: Apple, Android
Digital Platform - Tablet: Apple iOS, Android
Price: Free
Format: online

THE BOTTOM LINE: THE BOTTOM LINE — Lane Center 217 , Frostburg, MD, 21532-2303, USA; tel (301) 687-4326; fax (301) 687-3054; e-mail: thebottomline@frostburg.edu; tblonline@gmail.comthebottomline; web site: www.thebottomlineonline.orgEst. 1948
Dustin Davis
Editor-in-Chief — Marina Byerly
Manging Editor — Michelle Giambruno
Business Manager — Marissa Nedved
Insert rate: $115 per 1,300
Price: Free
Format: Broadsheet

THE JOHNS HOPKINS NEWS-LETTER: NEWS-LETTER — 3400 N Charles St, Baltimore, MD, 21218-2680, USA; tel (410) 516-4228; e-mail: chiefs@jhunewsletter.com; business@jhunewsletter.com; adv email: business@jhunewsletter.com; web site: www.jhunewsletter.comEst. 1896
Marie Cushing
Leah Maniero
Published: Thur
Format: Broadsheet

TOWSON UNIV.: TOWERLIGHT — 8000 York Rd University Un Rm 309, Towson, MD, 21252-0001, USA; tel (410) 704-2288; fax (410) 704-3862; e-mail: towerlight@towson.edu; adv email: towerlightads@yahoo.com; ed email: towerlighteditor@gmail.com; towerlightnews@gmail.com; towerlightsports@gmail.com; towerlightarts@gmail.com; web site: www.thetowerlight.com
Mike Raymond
Ashley Rabe
Daniel Gross
Format: Tabloid

UNIV. OF MARYLAND BALTIMORE: UMB VOICE — PO Box 600, Parkton, MD, 21120-0600, USA; tel (410) 706-7820; fax (410) 343-3371
Susie Flaherty
Clare Banks
Format: Tabloid

UNIV. OF MARYLAND BALTIMORE COUNTY: RETRIEVER WEEKLY — Uc 214, 1000 Hilltop Cir, Baltimore, MD, 21250-0001, USA; tel (410) 455-1260; fax (410) 455-1265; e-mail: eic@retrieverweekly.com; web site: www.retrieverweekly.com
Christopher Corbett
Nimit Bhatt
Gaby Arevalo
Format: Tabloid

UNIVERSITY OF MARYLAND: DIAMONDBACK — 3136 S Campus Dining Hall, College Park, MD, 20742-8401, USA; tel (301) 314-8000; fax (301) 314-8358; e-mail: diamondbackeditor@gmail.com; adv email: dbkadvertising@gmail.com; ed email: newsumdbk@gmail.com; web site: dbknews.comEst. 1909
Ed. in chief — Mina Haq
Published: Thur
Digital Edition Available?: Y
Format: Broadsheet

US NAVAL ACADEMY: TRIDENT — 121 Blake Rd, Annapolis, MD, 21402-1300, USA; tel (410) 293-1536; fax (410) 293-3133; web site: www.dcmilitary.com
Jessica Clark
Martha Thorn
Format: Tabloid

MASSACHUSETTS

AMERICAN INTERNATIONAL COLLEGE: YELLOW JACKET — 1000 State St # 4, Springfield, MA, 01109-3151, USA; tel (413) 205-3265; fax (413) 205-3955; ed email: yellowjacket@aic.edu
Will Hughes
Brian Steele
Format: Tabloid

AMHERST COLLEGE: AMHERST STUDENT — AC#1912, Keefe Campus Center, Amherst, MA, 01002-5000, USA; tel (413) 206-9319; e-mail: astudent@amherst.edu; adv email: astudent@amherst.edu; web site: amherststudent.amherst.edu
Publisher — Christopher Friend
Published: WedCirc.(fr.) 1,600
Digital Edition Available?: Y
Format: Tabloid

ASSUMPTION COLLEGE: LE PROVOCATEUR — 500 Salisbury St, Worcester, MA, 01609-1296, USA; tel (508) 767-7155; fax (508) 799-4401; e-mail: provoc@assumption.edu; web site: www.leprovoc.com
Sara Swillo
Greg Sebastiao
Format: Tabloid

BABSON COLLEGE: BABSON FREE PRESS — 231 Forest St., Babson Park, MA, 02457, USA; tel (781) 239-5541; fax (781) 239-5554; e-mail: freepress@babson.edu; adv email: babsonfreep@babson.edu; web site: www.babsonfreep.com
Anthony Micale
Insert rate: n.edu
Format: Tabloid

BECKER COLLEGE — 61 Sever St, Worcester, MA, 01609-2195, USA; tel (508) 791-9241; fax (508) 831-7505; e-mail: info@becker.edu

BENTLEY UNIVERSITY: THE VANGUARD — MA, USA; tel (781) 891-2921; fax (781) 891-2574; e-mail: ga_vanguard@bentley.edu; web site: www.bentleyvanguard.com; www.bentleyvanguardonline.com
Maria Dilorenzo
Sindhu Palaniappan
Greg Kokino
Published: Thur
Format: Tabloid

BOSTON COLLEGE: THE HEIGHTS — McElroy Commons 113, 140 Commonwealth Ave., Chestnut Hill, MA, 02467-3800, USA; tel (617) 552-2221; fax (617) 552-1753; adv email: ads@bcheights.com; web site: www.bcheights.com
Dave Givler
Matt DeLuca
Format: Broadsheet

BOSTON UNIV.: THE DAILY FREE PRESS — 648 Beacon St, Boston, MA, 02215-2013, USA; tel (617) 236-4433; fax (617) 236-4414; e-mail: editor@dailyfreepress.com; adv email: ads@dailyfreepress.com; web site: www.dailyfreepress.comEst. 1970
Ed. — Kyle Plantz
Managing Ed. — Felicia Gans
Published: Mon, Tues, Wed, Thur Online for summer, breaking content.Circ.(fr.) 5,000
Digital Edition Available?: Y
Price: Free
Format: Tabloid

BRANDEIS UNIVERSITY: THE JUSTICE — 415 South St MS 214, Waltham, MA, 02453-2728, USA; tel (781) 736-3750; fax (781) 736-3756; e-mail: editor@thejustice.org; adv email: ads@thejustice.org; web site: www.thejustice.orgEst. 1949
Published: Tues
Digital Edition Available?: Y
Format: Tabloid

BRIDGEWATER STATE COLLEGE: COMMENT — Rondileau Campus Ctr Rm 103A, Bridgewater, MA, 02325-0001, USA; tel (508) 531-1719; fax (508) 531-6181; e-mail: comment@bridgew.edu; web site: www.

bsccomment.com
Justin McCauley
Monica Monteiro
Format: Tabloid

BRISTOL CMTY. COLLEGE: OBSERVER — 777 Elsbree St, Fall River, MA, 02720-7399, USA; tel (508) 678-2811; fax (508) 676-7146; e-mail: observer@bristolcc.edu; web site: www.bristolcc.edu/Students/observer/index.cfm
Alex Potter
Format: Tabloid

CAPE COD CMTY. COLLEGE: MAIN SHEET — 2240 Iyannough Rd, West Barnstable, MA, 02668, USA; tel (508) 362-2131; fax (508) 375-4116; e-mail: info@capecod.edu; web site: www.capecod.eduEst. 1961
James Kershner
Format: Tabloid

CLARK UNIVERSITY: THE SCARLET — 950 Main St # B-13, Worcester, MA, 01610-1400, USA; tel (508) 793-7508; fax (508) 793-8813; e-mail: scarlet@clarku.edu; web site: www.clarku.edu
Editor-In-Chief — Jeremy Levine
Published: ThurCirc.(fr.) 700
Digital Edition Available?: Y
Format: Tabloid

COLLEGE OF THE HOLY CROSS: CRUSADER — 1 COLLEGE ST, WORCESTER, MA, 01610-2395, USA; tel (508) 293-1283; fax (508) 793-3823; e-mail: crusader@g.holycross.edu; adv email: crusaderadvertising@gmail.com; web site: www.thehccrusader.com
Steve Vineberg
Co-Editor-in-Chief — Sara Bovat
Co-Editor-in-Chief — Emily Vyse
Published: Fri
Digital Edition Available?: Y
Format: Tabloid

DEAN COLLEGE — 99 Main St, Franklin, MA, 02038-1994, USA; tel (508) 541-1630; fax (508) 541-1946

EASTERN NAZARENE COLLEGE: VERITAS — 23 E Elm Ave, Quincy, MA, 02170-2999, USA; tel (617) 745-3000; fax (617) 745-3490; web site: www1.enc.edu
Erica Scott Mcgrath
Emily Prugh
Format: Tabloid

ELMS COLLEGE: ELMS COLLEGE — 291 Springfield St, Chicopee, MA, 01013-2839, USA; tel (413) 594-2761; web site: www.elms.edu
James Gallant
Format: Magazine

EMERSON COLLEGE: BERKELEY BEACON — 150 Boylston St, Boston, MA, 02116-4608, USA; tel (617) 824-8687; fax (617) 824-8908; e-mail: berkeley_beacon@emerson.edu; web site: www.berkeleybeacon.com
Ric Kahn
Matt Byrne
Paddy Shea
Format: Tabloid

EMMANUEL COLLEGE: CURRENT FOCUS — 400 Fenway, Boston, MA, 02115-5798, USA; tel (617) 735-9715; e-mail: editors@emmanuel.edu
Anne Tyson
Format: Tabloid

ENDICOTT COLLEGE: OBSERVER — 376 Hale St., Callahan Ctr., Beverly, MA, 01915-2096, USA; tel (978) 232-2050; fax (978) 232-3003; e-mail: observer@mail.endicott.edu; web site: www.endicott.edu
Abigail Bottome
Format: Tabloid

FITCHBURG STATE COLLEGE: THE POINT — 160 Pearl St, Fitchburg, MA, 01420-2697, USA; tel (978) 665-3647; e-mail: pointstorybudget@yahoo.com; web site: www.thepointfsc.com; www.fsc.edu
Doris Schmidt
John McGinn
Format: Tabloid

FRAMINGHAM STATE UNIVERSITY - THE GATEPOST: THE GATEPOST — McCarthy Center 410, Framingham, MA, 01702-2499, USA; tel (508) 626-4605; fax (508) 626-4097; e-mail: gatepost@framingham.edu; adv email: gatepost@framingham.edu; ed email: gatepost@framingham.edu; web site: www.fsugatepost.comEst. 1930
Desmond McCarthy
Advisor — Meredith O'Brien-Weiss
Administrative Assistant — Robin KurKomelis
Editor-in-Chief — Kerrin Murray
Associate Editor — Joe Kourieh
Associate Editor — Karin Radoc
Published: Fri
Digital Edition Available?: Y
Format: Tabloid

GORDON COLLEGE: TARTAN — 255 Grapevine Rd, Wenham, MA, 01984-1899, USA; tel (978) 927-2306; fax (978) 524-3300; e-mail: tartan@gordon.edu
Eric Convey
Format: Tabloid

HAMPSHIRE COLLEGE: THE CLIMAX — 893 West St, Amherst, MA, 01002-3359, USA; tel (413) 549-4600; fax (413) 559-5664; e-mail: hampshireclimax@ gmail.com; web site: climax.hampshire.edu
Nicki Feldman
Format: Tabloid

HARVARD BUSINESS SCHOOL: HARBUS NEWS — USA; tel (617) 495-6528; fax (617) 495-8619; e-mail: general@harbus.org; web site: www.harbus.org
Matthew Grayson
Joanne Knight
Format: Tabloid

HARVARD LAW SCHOOL: HARVARD LAW RECORD — Harvard Law Record, Harvard Law School, Cambridge, MA, 02138-9984, USA; tel (617) 297-3590; fax (617) 495-8547; e-mail: record@law.harvard.edu; web site: www.hlrecord.org
Matt Hutchins
Chris Szabla
Rebecca Agule
Mark Samburg
Format: Tabloid

HARVARD UNIV.: HARVARD CRIMSON — 14 Plympton St, Cambridge, MA, 02138-6606, USA; tel (617) 576-6600; fax (617) 576-7860; e-mail: ads@thecrimson.com; web site: www.thecrimson.com
Peter F. Zhu
Julian L. Bouma
Format: Broadsheet

HARVARD UNIV./JFK SCHOOL OF GOV'T — 30 Jfk St, Cambridge, MA, 02138-4902, USA; tel (617) 495-5969
Stephanie Geosits

HOLYOKE CMTY. COLLEGE: THE PHOENIX — 303 Homestead Ave, Holyoke, MA, 01040-1099, USA; tel (413) 538-7000; fax (413) 552-2045
Fred Cooksey
Format: Magazine

LASELL COLLEGE: 1851 — 1844 Commonwealth Ave, Auburndale, MA, 02466-2716, USA; tel (617) 243-2000; fax (617) 243-2480; e-mail: newspaper@lasell.edu
Marie C. Franklin
Michelle McNickle
Briana Nestor
Format: Magazine

LESLEY UNIVERSITY: LESLEY CHRONICLE — 47 Oxford St, Cambridge, MA, 02138-1972, USA; tel (617) 349-8501; fax (617) 349-8558; web site: www.chronicle.com
Gabriella Montell
Format: Tabloid

MASSACHUSETTS COLLEGE OF LIBERAL ARTS: THE BEACON — 375 Church St Rm 111, North Adams, MA, 01247-4124, USA; tel (413) 662-5535; fax (413) 662-5010; e-mail: beacon@mcla.edu; web site: www.mclabeacon.com
Jennifer Augur
Published: WedCirc.(fr.) 1,000
Digital Edition Available?: Y
Price: Free
Format: Tabloid

MASSACHUSETTS COLLEGE OF PHARMACY: DISPENSER — 179 Longwood Ave, Boston, MA, 02115-5896, USA; tel (617) 732-2800; web site: www.mcphs.edu
Stephany Orphan
Format: Tabloid

MASSACHUSETTS INST. OF TECHNOLOGY: THE TECH — 84 Massachusetts Ave Ste 483, Cambridge, MA, 02139-4300, USA; tel (617) 253 1541; fax (617) 258-8226; e-mail: general@tech.mit.edu; letters@the-tech.mit.edu; adv email: ads@tech.mit.edu; web site: thetech.comEst. 1881
Chrmn. — Aislyn Schalck
Ed. in Chief — Jessica Pourian
Chairman — Karleigh Moore
Published: ThurCirc.(fr.) 8,100
Digital Edition Available?: Y
Price: $0.00
Format: Tabloid

MERRIMACK COLLEGE: BEACON — 315 Turnpike St, North Andover, MA, 01845-5800, USA; tel (978) 837-5000; fax (978) 837-5004; web site: www.merrimack.edu
Russ Mayer
Michael Salvucci
Format: Tabloid

MIDDLESEX CMTY. COLLEGE: CAMPUS REPORT — 591 Springs Rd, Bedford, MA, 01730-1197, USA; tel (781) 280-3769; fax (781) 275-4396
Sarah Screaux
Format: Tabloid

MOUNT HOLYOKE COLLEGE: MOUNT HOLYOKE NEWS — 9007 Blanchard Campus Center, South Hadley, MA, 01075-1423, USA; tel (413) 538-2269; fax (413) 538-2476; e-mail: mhnews@mtholyoke.edu; web site: http://mountholyokenews.org/Est. 1917
Publisher — Linda Valencia Xu
Editor-in-Chief — Geena Molinaro
Published: Thur
Format: Tabloid

MOUNT IDA COLLEGE: VOICE — 777 Dedham St, Newton Center, MA, 02459-3310, USA; tel (617) 928-4754; fax (617) 928-4766
Melissa Constantine
Matt Caldwell
Jen Barrett
Format: Tabloid

NEW ENGLAND SCHOOL OF LAW: DUE PROCESS — 154 Stuart St, Boston, MA, 02116-5687, USA; tel (617) 451-0010; fax (617) 422-7224; e-mail: dueprocess@nesl.edu; adv email: dueprocess@nesl.edu; ed email: dueprocess@nesl.edu; web site: https://www.nesl.edu/students/stuorg_dp.cfmEst. 2012
Rebecca Castaneda
Tara Cho
Kelly Lavari
Editor-in-Chief — Joe Sciabica
Assistant Editor-In-Chief — Emily White
Published: Other Due Process publishes five (5) regular issues, and one (1) end of year commemorative yearbook.
Digital Edition Available?: Y
Digital Platform - Mobile: Windows
Digital Platform - Tablet: Windows 7
Format: Tabloid

NICHOLS COLLEGE: N/A — PO Box 5000, Dudley, MA, 01571-5000, USA; tel (508) 213-1560; fax (508) 943-5354; e-mail: admissions@nichols.edu; web site: www.nichols.edu/Est. 1815
Assistant Director of Admissions / International Students Counselor — Emily Reardon
Price: $42,440
Format: Business

NORTHEASTERN UNIVERSITY: THE HUNTINGTON NEWS — 295 Huntington Ave Ste 208, Boston, MA, 02115-4433, USA; tel (857) 362-7325; fax (857) 362-7326; e-mail: editor@huntnewsnu.com; adv email: advertise@huntnewsnu.com; ed email: editorial@huntnewsnu.com; web site: www.HuntNewsNU.comEst. 1926
Editor in chief — Colin Young
Published: Thur
Price: Free
Format: Broadsheet

NORTHERN ESSEX COMMUNITY COLLEGE: OBSERVER — 100 Elliott St., Haverhill, MA, 01830-2399, USA; tel (978) 556-3633; e-mail: observer@necc.mass.edu; web site: 100 Elliott StreetEst. 1962
Adv. Mgr. — Amy Callahan
Published: Bi-Mthly
Digital Edition Available?: Y
Format: Tabloid

QUINSIGAMOND CMTY. COLLEGE: OPEN DOOR — 670 W Boylston St, Worcester, MA, 01606-2092, USA; tel (508) 854-4285; fax (508) 852-6943; e-mail: opendoor@qcc.mass.edu
Pat Bisha-Valencia
Published: Mthly
Digital Edition Available?: Y
Format: Tabloid

SALEM STATE COLLEGE: THE SALEM STATE LOG — 352 Lafayette St., Ellison Campus Ctr., Salem, MA, 01970-5348, USA; tel (978) 542-6448; fax (978) 542-2077; e-mail: thelog@ssclog.com; web site: www.salemstate.edu/log
Peggy Dillon
Format: Tabloid

SIMMONS COLLEGE: THE SIMMONS VOICE — 300 The Fenway, Boston, MA, 02115-5820, USA; tel (617) 521-2442; fax (617) 521-3148; e-mail: voice@simmons.edu; web site: www.thesimmonsvoice.com
Adviser — James Corcoran
Advisor
Editor
— Sarah Kinney
Published: ThurCirc.(fr.) 1,500
Digital Edition Available?: N
Format: Tabloid

SMITH COLLEGE: SOPHIAN — Capen Anx, Northampton, MA, 01063-0001, USA; tel (413) 585-4971; fax (413) 585-2075; e-mail: sophian@smith.edu; web site: www.smithsophian.comEst. 1911
EIC — Hira Humayun
Published: Thur
Digital Edition Available?: Y
Format: Tabloid

SPRINGFIELD COLLEGE: THE STUDENT — 263 Alden St, Springfield, MA, 01109-3788, USA; tel (413) 748-3000; fax (413) 748-3473; e-mail: activities@spfldcol.edu; web site: www.spsldcol.edu
Claire Wright
Evin Giglio
Format: Tabloid

STONEHILL COLLEGE: SUMMIT — 320 Washington St # 1974, North Easton, MA, 02357-0001, USA; tel (508) 565-1000; fax (508) 565-1794
Matt Gorman
Format: Tabloid

SUFFOLK UNIV.: SUFFOLK JOURNAL — 41 Temple St Rm 428, Boston, MA, 02114-4241, USA; tel (617) 573-8323; fax (617) 994-6400; e-mail: suffolkjournal@gmail.com; web site: www.suffolkjournal.net; www.suffolk.edu Est. 1940
Bruce Butterfield
Melissa Hanson
Jeremy Hayes
Published: Wed
Digital Edition Available?: Y
Price: $0.00
Format: Tabloid

SUFFOLK UNIV. LAW SCHOOL: DICTA — 120 Tremont St, Boston, MA, 02108-4977, USA; tel (617) 305-3011; fax (617) 573-8706
Format: Tabloid

TUFTS UNIV.: THE TUFTS DAILY — PO Box 53018, Medford, MA, 02153-0018, USA; tel (617) 627-3090; fax (617) 627-3910; web site: www.tuftsdaily.com
Giovanni Russonello
Format: Tabloid

UNIV. OF MASSACHUSETTS: DAILY COLLEGIAN — USA; tel (413) 545-3500; fax (413) 545-3699; ed email: editor@dailycollegian.com; web site: www.dailycollegian.com; www.umass.edu
Alyssa Creamer
Format: Tabloid

UNIV. OF MASSACHUSETTS: MASS MEDIA — 100 Morrissey Blvd, Boston, MA, 02125-3393, USA; tel (617) 287-7992; fax (617) 287-7897; e-mail: editor@umassmedia.com; web site: www.umassmedia.com Est. 1966
Donna Neal
Caleb Nelson
Format: Broadsheet

UNIV. OF MASSACHUSETTS: THE TORCH — 285 Old Westport Rd., Campus Ctr., 2nd Fl., North Dartmouth, MA, 02747-2300, USA; tel (508) 999-8158; fax (508) 999-8128; e-mail: torch@umassd.edu; adv email: TorchAds@umassd.edu; web site: www.umasstorch.com
Jason Jones
Chris Donovan
Megan Gauthier
Format: Broadsheet

UNIV. OF MASSACHUSETTS LOWELL CONNECTOR: CONNECTOR — 71 Wilder St Ste 6, Lowell, MA, 01854-3096, USA; tel (978) 934-5001; fax (978) 934-3072; e-mail: connector@uml.edu; web site: www.uml.edu/connector Est. 1924
Ruben Sanca
Format: Tabloid

WELLESLEY COLLEGE: THE WELLESLEY NEWS — 106 Central St, Wellesley, MA, 02481-8210, USA; tel (781) 283-2689; fax (781) 431-7520; e-mail: thewellesleynews@gmail.com; adv email: thewellesleynews@gmail.com; ed email: thewellesleynews@gmail.com; web site: www.thewellesleynews.com Est. 1901
Managing Editor — Alice Liang
Editor-in-Chief — Stephanie Yeh
Published: Wed
Digital Edition Available?: Y
Format: Tabloid

WESTERN NEW ENGLAND COLLEGE: WESTERNER — 1215 Wilbraham Rd, Springfield, MA, 01119-2684, USA; tel (413) 782-1580; fax (413) 796-2008
Wayne Barr
Format: Tabloid

WESTFIELD STATE UNIVERSITY: THE WESTFIELD VOICE — 577 Western Avenue, Westfield, MA, 01085, USA; tel (413) 572-5431; fax (413) 572-5477; e-mail: thevoice@westfield.ma.edu; adv email: thevoiceadvertisement@gmail.com Est. 1946
Editor-in-Chief — Joshua Clark
Editor-in-Chief — Andrew Burke
Managing Editor — Emily Hanshaw
Assistant Managing Editor — Matthew Carlin
Published: Fri
Digital Edition Available?: Y
Price: Free
Format: Tabloid

WILLIAMS COLLEGE: WILLIAMS RECORD — 39 Chapin Hall Dr., Williamstown, MA, 01267, USA; tel (413) 597-2289; fax (413) 597-2450; e-mail: williamsrecordeic@gmail.com; adv email: williamsrecordadvertising@gmail.com; ed email: williamsrecordeic@gmail.com; web site: www.williamsrecord.com Est. 1887
Editor-in-Chief — Rachel Scharf
Ed. In Chief — Matthew Borin
Published: Wed Circ. (fr.) 2,000
Digital Edition Available?: Y
Price: $45/semester
Format: Broadsheet

WORCESTER POLYTECHNIC INSTITUTE: TECH NEWS — 100 Institute Rd, Worcester, MA, 01609-2280, USA; tel (508) 831-5464; fax (508) 831-5721; e-mail: technews@wpi.edu; adv email: ads@wpi.edu; web site: www.wpi.edu/News/TechNews
Michelle Ephraim
Format: Tabloid

WORCESTER STATE COLLEGE: STUDENT VOICE — 486 Chandler St # G-209, Worcester, MA, 01602-2861, USA; tel (508) 929-8589; fax (508) 756-8210; e-mail: studentvoice@worcester.edu
Elizabeth Bidinger
Format: Tabloid

MICHIGAN

ALBION COLLEGE: ALBION PLEIAD — 611 E. Porter St., Albion, MI, 49224, USA; tel (517) 629-1315; fax (517) 629-0509; e-mail: pleiad@albion.edu; adv email: pleiad@albion.edu; ed email: pleiad@albion.edu; web site: www.albionpleiad.com Est. 1883
Glenn Deutsch
Mng. Ed. — Steve Markowski
Mng. Ed. — Beau Brockett, Jr.
Features Editor — Katie Boni
Andrew Wittland
Opinions editor — Morgan Garmo
Published: Mon, Wed, Fri
Digital Edition Available?: Y
Digital Platform - Mobile: Other
Digital Platform - Tablet: Other
Format: Online News Publication
Note: Publishes three days a week online and three times a school semester in print.

ALMA COLLEGE: ALMANIAN — 614 W Superior St, Alma, MI, 48801-1599, USA; tel (989) 463-7161; fax (989) 463-7161; e-mail: almanian@alma.edu; almanianopinion@yahoo.com; almanian@hotmail.com; adv email: almanianadvert@yahoo.com; web site: students.alma.edu/organizations/almanian
Robert Vivian
Brendan Guilford
Olga Wrobel
Format: Tabloid

ANDREWS UNIV.: STUDENT MOVEMENT — 5 Student Ctr, Berrien Springs, MI, 49104-0001, USA; tel (269) 471-3385; fax (269) 471-3524; e-mail: smeditor@andrews.edu; web site: www.andrews.edu/sm
Ashleigh Burtnett
Michele Krpalek
Stephanie Smart
Format: Tabloid

AQUINAS COLLEGE: THE SAINT — 1607 Robinson Rd SE, Grand Rapids, MI, 49506-1799, USA; tel (616) 632-2975; fax (616) 732-4487; e-mail: saint.editors@aquinas.edu; adv email: saint.business@aquinas.edu; ed email: saint.editors@aquinas.edu; web site: www.aquinas.edu/thesaint Est. 1980
Dan Brooks
Editor in Chief — Matt Kuczynski
Published: Bi-Mthly Circ. (fr.) 1,000
Digital Edition Available?: Y
Insert rate: $200
Price: Free
Format: Tabloid

CALVIN COLLEGE: CHIMES — 3201 Burton St., Student Commons, Grand Rapids, MI, 49546-4301, USA; tel (616) 819-0011; fax (616) 957-8551; e-mail: chimes@calvin.edu; web site: http://clubs.calvin.edu/chimes
Lauren DeHaan
Emma Slager
Published: Fri
Digital Edition Available?: Y
Format: Tabloid

CENTRAL MICHIGAN UNIVERSITY: CENTRAL MICHIGAN LIFE — 436 Moore Hall, Mount Pleasant, MI, 48859-0001, USA; tel (989) 774-3493; fax (989) 774-7805; e-mail: advertising@cm-life.com; adv email: advertising@cm-life.com; ed email: editor@cm-life.com; web site: www.cm-life.com Est. 1919
Advisor — Kathy Simon
Director, Student Publications — David Clark
Editor, 2013-2014 — Catey Traylor
Advertising Manager, 2013-2014 — Julie Bushart
Published: Mon, Wed, Fri Circ. (pd.) 150 (fr.) 10,000
Digital Edition Available?: Y
Digital Platform - Mobile: Apple, Android
Digital Platform - Tablet: Apple iOS
Insert rate: $55/single sheet
Price: Free
Format: Broadsheet

DELTA COLLEGE: DELTA COLLEGIATE — 1961 Delta Rd # H, University Center, MI, 48710-1002, USA; tel (989) 686-9000; e-mail: collegiate@delta.edu; info@delta.edu; web site: www.delta.edu/collegiate
Kathie Bachleda
Megan Tobias
Format: Tabloid

EASTERN MICHIGAN UNIVERSITY: THE EASTERN ECHO — 228 King Hall, Ypsilanti, MI, 48197-2239, USA; tel (734) 487-1026; fax (734) 487-6702; e-mail: editor@easternecho.com; adv email: brian.peterson24@gmail.com; ed email: editor@easternecho.com; web site: www.easternecho.com Est. 1881
Sydney Smith
Published: Mon, Thur
Digital Edition Available?: Y
Price: Free
Format: Broadsheet

FERRIS STATE TORCH.: THE TORCH — 401 South St, Big Rapids, MI, 49307-2744, USA; tel (231) 591-5946; fax (231) 591-3617; e-mail: torchads@ferris.edu; ed email: torch@ferris.edu; web site: www.fsutorch.com Est. 1931
Steve Fox
Laura Anger
Published: Wed Circ. (fr.) 4,300
Digital Edition Available?: Y
Insert rate: $60/k
Format: Tabloid

GRAND RAPIDS CMTY. COLLEGE: COLLEGIATE — 143 Bostwick Ave NE, Grand Rapids, MI, 49503-3201, USA; tel (616) 234-4157; fax (616) 234-4158; e-mail: grcc_collegiate@yahoo.com; web site: www.thecollegiatelive.com
Format: Tabloid

GRAND VALLEY STATE UNIV.: THE GRAND VALLEY LANTHORN — 1 Campus Dr, 0051 Kirkhof Center, Grand Valley State University, Allendale, MI, 49401, USA; tel (616) 331-2460; fax (616) 331-2465; e-mail: lanthorn@gvsu.edu; adv email: advertising@lanthorn.com; ed email: editorial@lanthorn.com; web site: www.lanthorn.com Est. 1964
Business Manager — Shelby Carter
Editor-and-Chief — Emily Doran
Advertising Manager — Ian Borthwick
Published: Mon, Thur
Digital Edition Available?: Y
Format: Broadsheet

HENRY FORD CMTY. COLLEGE: MIRROR NEWS — 5101 Evergreen Rd # C-117, Dearborn, MI, 48128-2407, USA; tel (313) 845-9639; fax (313) 845-9876; e-mail: mirrorbm@hfcc.edu; web site: www.hfccmirror.com
Cassandra Fluker
Joshua Gillis
Format: Tabloid

HILLSDALE COLLEGE: COLLEGIAN — 33 E College St, Hillsdale, MI, 49242-1298, USA; tel (517) 437-7341; fax (517) 437-3293; e-mail: collegian@hillsdale.edu; web site: www.hillsdale.edu
Ingrid Jacques
Format: Tabloid

HOPE COLLEGE: ANCHOR — P.O. Box 9000, Holland, MI, 49422-9000, USA; tel (616) 395-7877; fax (616) 395-7183; e-mail: anchor@hope.edu; adv email: anchorads@hope.edu; web site: anchor.hope.edu Est. 1887
Rosie Jahng
Co-Editor-in-Chief — Amanda Long
Co-Editor-in-Chief — James Champane Patterson
Emily West
Format: Tabloid

JACKSON CMTY. COLLEGE: PHOENIX — 2111 Emmons Rd, Jackson, MI, 49201-8399, USA; tel (517) 787-0800; fax (517) 787-8663; e-mail: phoenix@jccmi.edu; web site: www.jccmi.edu
Karessa E. Weir
Format: Tabloid

KALAMAZOO COLLEGE: INDEX — 1200 Academy St Ofc, Kalamazoo, MI, 49006-3295, USA; tel (269) 337-7000; fax (269) 337-7216; web site: www.kzoo.edu
Brian Ditez
Format: Tabloid

LAKE SUPERIOR STATE UNIV.: COMPASS — 650 W Easterday Ave, Sault Sainte Marie, MI, 49783-1626, USA; tel (906) 635-2551; fax (906) 635-7510; e-mail: compass@lssu.edu; adv email: compass@lssu.edu; ed email: compass@lssu.edu; web site: compass.lssu.edu Est. 1946
Editor In Chief — Asher Stephenson
Published: Mthly
Digital Edition Available?: N
Digital Platform - Mobile: Windows

Format: Tabloid

LANSING CMTY. COLLEGE: THE LOOKOUT — Mail Code 1170, Lansing, MI, 48933, USA; tel (517) 483-1291; fax (517) 483-1290; e-mail: hookl@lcc.edu; adv email: hookl@lcc.edu; ed email: hookl@lcc.edu; web site: www.lcc.edu/lookoutEst. 1959
Advisor — Larry Hook
Published: Bi-Mthly
Digital Edition Available?: Y
Insert rate: N/A
Price: Free

MICHIGAN TECHNOLOGICAL UNIV.: MICHIGAN TECH — MUB 106 1400 Townsend Dr, Houghton, MI, 49931, USA; tel (906) 487-2404; fax (906) 487-3125; web site: www.mtulode.com
Kara W. Sokol
Kayla R. Herrera
Format: Broadsheet

MOTT CMTY. COLLEGE: MCC POST — 1401 E Court St, Flint, MI, 48503-2090, USA; tel (810) 762-5616; fax (810) 762-5646
Steve Bossey
Format: Tabloid

NORTHERN MICHIGAN UNIVIVERSITY: THE NORTH WIND — 1401 Presque Isle Ave, Marquette, MI, 49855-5301, USA; tel (906) 227-2545; fax (906) 227-2449; e-mail: northwind@gmail.com; adv email: hkasberg@nmu.edu ; web site: www.thenorthwindonline.comEst. 1972
Advisor — Kristy Basolo
Published: Thur
Digital Edition Available?: Y
Format: Tabloid

NORTHWESTERN MICHIGAN COLLEGE: WHITE PINE PRESS — 1701 E Front St, Traverse City, MI, 49686-3061, USA; tel (231) 995-1173; fax (231) 995-1952; e-mail: whitepinepress@gmail.com; web site: www.whitepinepress.org
Michael Anderson
Nora Stone
Jacob Bailey
Format: Tabloid

OAKLAND UNIV.: OAKLAND POST — 61 Oakland Ctr, Rochester, MI, 48309-4409, USA; tel (248) 370-4268; fax (248) 370-4264; e-mail: editor@oaklandpostonline.com; web site: www.oaklandpostonline.comEst. 1957
Holly Gilbert
Business Manager — Don Ritenburgh
Published: Tues
Digital Edition Available?: Y
Digital Platform - Mobile: Apple
Format: Tabloid

OLIVET COLLEGE: ECHO — 320 S. Main St., Olivet, MI, 49076-9456, USA; tel (269) 749-7622; e-mail: echo@olivetcollege.edu; adv email: echo@olivetcollege.edu; ed email: echo@olivetcollege.edu; web site: www.ocecho.comEst. 1888
Joanne Williams
Editor — Brian Freiberger
Published: Fri, Bi-Mthly Every other Friday during academic yearCirc.(fr.) 1,100
Digital Edition Available?: Y
Price: N/A
Format: Tabloid

ROCHESTER COLLEGE: THE SHIELD — 800 W Avon Rd, Rochester Hills, MI, 48307-2704, USA; tel (248) 218-2030; fax (248) 218-2045; e-mail: theshield@rc.edu; web site: www.rcshield.com
Liz Fulton
Chelsea Hackel
Published: Bi-MthlyCirc.(fr.) 550
Digital Edition Available?: Y
Price: $0
Format: Magazine/Online

SAGINAW VALLEY STATE UNIV.: THE VALLEY VANGUARD — 125 Curtiss Hall, 7400 Bay Rd, University Center, MI, 48710-0001, USA; tel (989) 964-4248; e-mail: vanguard@svsu.edu; web site: www.thevalleyvanguard.com
Sara Kitchen
Format: Tabloid

SCHOOLCRAFT COLLEGE: THE CONNECTION — 18600 Haggerty Rd Rm W169, Livonia, MI, 48152-2696, USA; tel (734) 462-4422; fax (734) 462-4554; e-mail: sao@schoolcraft.edu; web site: www.schoolcraft.edu; sao.schoolcraft.edu
Jeffrey Petts
Kathy Hansen
Ryan Russell
Format: Tabloid

SOUTHWESTERN MICHIGAN COLLEGE: THE SOUTHWESTER — 58900 Cherry Grove Rd, Dowagiac, MI, 49047-9726, USA; tel (269) 782-1457; fax (269) 782-1446; e-mail: swester@swmich.edu; ed email: swester@swmich.edu; web site: http://southwester.swmich.edu/Est. 1968
Senior Writer and Coordinator of Media Relations — John Eby
Digital Edition Available?: Y
Digital Platform - Mobile: Apple, Android, Windows, Blackberry
Digital Platform - Tablet: Apple iOS, Android, Windows 7, Blackberry Tablet OS, Kindle, Nook, Kindle Fire
Price: Free
Format: digital only southwester.swmich.edu
Note: We no longer offer a journalism program so the newspaper became a college publication rather than a student publication and discontinued a printed product at the beginning of 2014. It's updated as new content becomes available.

SPRING ARBOR UNIV.: CRUSADER — 106 E Main St Ste A28, Spring Arbor, MI, 49283-9701, USA; tel (517) 523-3616; fax (517) 750-2108
Eric Platt
Format: Tabloid

ST. CLAIR COUNTY COMMUNITY COLLEGE: ERIE SQUARE GAZETTE — 323 Erie St # 5015, Port Huron, MI, 48060-3812, USA; tel (810) 989-5733; fax (810) 984-4730; e-mail: eriesquaregazette@gmail.com; adv email: esgadvertising@gmail.com; web site: www.esgonline.orgEst. 1931
John Lusk
Editor-in-Chief — Erick Fredendall
Published: Bi-weekly
Digital Edition Available?: Y
Digital Platform - Mobile: Other
Format: Tabloid

THE STATE NEWS/MICHIGAN STATE UNIVERSITY: STATE NEWS — 435 E Grand River Ave, East Lansing, MI, 48823-4456, USA; tel (517) 295-1680; e-mail: feedback@statenews.com; adv email: advertising@statenews.com; ed email: editorinchief@statenews.com; web site: www.statenews.comEst. 1909
Advisor — Omar Sofradzija
Gen. Mgr. — Marty Sturgeon
Webmaster — Mike Joseph
Creative Adviser — Travis Ricks
Published: Thur Digital-only during summer semester at MSUCirc.(fr.) 7,500
Digital Edition Available?: Y
Digital Platform - Mobile: Apple, Android, Windows, Blackberry, Other
Digital Platform - Tablet: Apple iOS, Android, Windows 7, Blackberry Tablet OS, Kindle, Nook, Kindle Fire, Other
Format: Tabloid
Note: The State News/statenews.com is the independent student-run newspaper/news Web site at Michigan State University. It is a private non-profit entity spun off from the school in 1972.

UNIV. OF MICHIGAN: THE MICHIGAN TIMES — 303 E Kearsley St, Flint, MI, 48502-1907, USA; tel (810) 762-3475; fax (810) 762-3023; e-mail: mtimes@hotmail.com; web site: www.themichigantimes.com
Joseph Patterson
Jennifer Profitt
Format: Tabloid

UNIV. OF MICHIGAN: MICHIGAN DAILY — 420 Maynard St, Ann Arbor, MI, 48109-1327, USA; tel (734) 763-2459; fax (734) 764-4275; e-mail: news@michigandaily.com; tmdbusiness@gmail.com; web site: www.michigandaily.com
Jacob Smilovitz
Matt Aaronson
Dan Newman
Format: Broadsheet

UNIV. OF MICHIGAN BUS. SCHOOL: MONROE STREET — 701 Tappan Ave Ste 766, Ann Arbor, MI, 48109-1234, USA; tel (734) 764-2074; fax (734) 763-6450; adv email: msj.office@gmail.com; ed email: msj.editor@gmail.com; web site: www.themsj.com
Robyn Katzman
Maggie Sadowski
Format: Tabloid

UNIVERSITY OF MICHIGAN-DEARBORN: MICHIGAN JOURNAL — 4901 Evergreen Rd Ste 2130, Dearborn, MI, 48128-2406, USA; tel (313) 593-5428; fax (313) 593-5594; e-mail: themichiganj@gmail.com; web site: www.michiganjournal.orgEst. 1971
Tim Kiska
Editor-in-Chief — Ricky Lindsay
Advertising Manager — Kaitlynn Riley
Published: Tues
Digital Edition Available?: Y
Format: Broadsheet

WASHTENAW COMMUNITY COLLEGE: THE WASHTENAW VOICE — Ann Arbor, MI, 48105, USA; tel (734) 677-5125; fax (734) 677-5126; e-mail: thewasntehawvoice@gmail.com; adv email: ealliston@wccnet.edu; ed email: kgave@wccnet.edu; web site: www.washtenawvoice.comEst. 1967
Advisor — Keith Gave
Adv. Mgr. — Becky Alliston
Ed. — Natalie Wright
Published: Bi-MthlyCirc.(fr.) 5,000
Digital Edition Available?: Y
Digital Platform - Mobile: Apple, Android, Windows
Digital Platform - Tablet: Apple iOS, Android, Windows 7
Price: Free
Format: Broadsheet

WAYNE STATE UNIV.: THE SOUTH END — 5221 Gullen Mall, Student Center Bldg., Ste. 101, Detroit, MI, 48202, USA; tel (313) 577-8067; fax (313) 993-8108; e-mail: dv7262@wayne.edu; ed email: tseletters@gmail.com; web site: www.thesouthendnews.com
Carolyn Chin
Format: Broadsheet

WESTERN MICHIGAN UNIV.: WESTERN HERALD — 1517 Faunce Student Servs. Bldg., Kalamazoo, MI, 49008-5363, USA; tel (269) 387-2110; fax (269) 387-3820; e-mail: herald-general-manager@wmich.edu; adv email: herald-advertising@wmich.edu; ed email: herald-editor@wmich.edu; web site: www.westernherald.comEst. 1916
Editor-in-chief — Meghan Chandler
General Manager — Richard Junger
Published: Bi-MthlyCirc.(fr.) 10,000
Digital Edition Available?: Y
Digital Platform - Mobile: Apple, Android, Windows, Blackberry
Digital Platform - Tablet: Apple iOS, Android, Windows 7, Kindle, Nook, Kindle Fire
Insert rate: $300
Format: Tabloid
Note: $150 online display ad

MINNESOTA

AUGSBURG COLLEGE: AUGSBURG ECHO — 2211 Riverside Ave, Minneapolis, MN, 55454-1351, USA; tel (612) 330-1018; fax (612) 330-1649; adv email: echo@augsburg.edu; web site: www.augsburg.edu/organizations/descriptions/echo.html
Adviser — Boyd Koehler
Editor-in-chief — Jenny Pinther
Format: Tabloid

BEMIDJI STATE UNIV.: NORTHERN STUDENT — PO Box 58, Bemidji, MN, 56619-0058, USA; tel (218) 755-2001; fax (218) 755-2913; e-mail: northernstudent@yahoo.com; web site: www.northernstudent.comEst. 1926
Robby Robinson
Published: WedCirc. (pd.) 111 (fr.) 3,000
Digital Edition Available?: Y
Digital Platform - Mobile: Windows
Price: Free
Format: Tabloid

BETHEL COLLEGE: CLARION — 3900 Bethel Dr Ste 1504, Saint Paul, MN, 55112-6999, USA; tel (651) 635-8643; fax (651) 635-8650; e-mail: bethelclarion@gmail.com
Marie Wisner
Format: Tabloid

CARLETON COLLEGE: THE CARLETONIAN — 1 N College St, Northfield, MN, 55057-4044, USA; fax (507) 222-4000; e-mail: carletonian@carleton.edu; web site: www.carleton.edu/carletonian
James McMenimen
Vivyan Tran
Emily Howell
Format: Broadsheet

COLLEGE OF ST. SCHOLASTICA: CABLE — 1200 Kenwood Ave, Duluth, MN, 55811-4199, USA; tel (218) 723-6187; fax (218) 723-6290; e-mail: cable1@css.edu; web site: www.css.edu
Joe Wicklund
Print Corp
Kirby Montgomery
Format: Tabloid

CONCORDIA COLLEGE: CONCORDIAN — PO Box 104, Moorhead, MN, 56561-0104, USA; tel (218) 299-3826; fax (218) 299-4313; e-mail: concord@cord.edu; cordadd@cord.edu; adv email: cordadd@cord.edu; ed email: concord@cord.edu; web site: www.theconcordian.orgEst. 1920
Cathy McMullen
Terence Tang
Suzanne Maanum
Published: ThurCirc.(fr.) 2,000
Digital Edition Available?: Y
Digital Platform - Mobile: Apple, Android, Windows
Digital Platform - Tablet: Apple iOS, Android, Windows 7, Kindle Fire
Format: Broadsheet

CONCORDIA UNIV. AT ST. PAUL: SWORD — 275 Syndicate St N, Saint Paul, MN, 55104-5436, USA; tel (651) 641-8221; fax (651) 659-0207; e-mail: sword@csp.edu; web site: www.csp.edu/sword
Eric Dregni
Helena Woodruff
Rachel Kuhnle
Format: Tabloid

CROWN COLLEGE: THE STORM CHASER — 8700 College View Dr, Saint Bonifacius, MN, 55375-9001, USA; tel (952) 446-4100; fax (952) 446-4149; web site: www.crown.edu
William Allen
Format: Magazine

FERGUS FALLS CMTY. COLLEGE — 1414 College Way, Fergus Falls, MN, 56537-1009, USA; tel (877) 450-3322; fax (218) 736-1510
Angela Schroeder

GUSTAVUS ADOLPHUS COLLEGE: GUSTAVIAN WEEKLY — 800 W College Ave, Saint Peter, MN, 56082-1498, USA; tel (507) 933-7636; fax (507) 933-7633; e-mail: weekly@gac.edu; web site: www.gustavus.edu/weeklyEst. 1891
David Kogler
Victoria Clark
Jacob Seamans
Editor In Chief 2013-14 — Chelsea Johnson
Editor-in-Chief — Caroline Probst
Published: Fri
Digital Edition Available?: Y
Format: Tabloid

HAMLINE UNIV.: ORACLE — 1536 Hewitt Ave, Saint Paul, MN, 55104-1284, USA; tel (651) 523-2268; fax (651) 523-3144; e-mail: oracle@hamline.edu; web site: www.hamlineoracle.comEst. 1888
David Hudson
Editor-in-Chief — Stolz Catherine
Published: WedCirc.(fr.) 600
Digital Edition Available?: Y
Format: Tabloid

INVER HILLS CMTY. COLLEGE — 2500 80th St E Ste A, Inver Grove Heights, MN, 55076-3224, USA; tel (651) 450-8563; fax (651) 450-8679
Dave Page

MACALESTER COLLEGE: MAC WEEKLY — 1600 Grand Ave, Saint Paul, MN, 55105-1899, USA; tel (651) 696-6212; fax (651) 696-6685; e-mail: macweekly@macalester.edu; web site: www.themacweekly.com
Tom Poulos
Zac Farber
Matt Day
Format: Tabloid

MINNEAPOLIS CMTY. & TECH. COLLEGE: CITY COLLEGE NEWS — 1501 Hennepin Ave, Minneapolis, MN, 55403-1710, USA; tel (612) 659-6796; fax (612) 659-6825; web site: www.citycollegenews.com
Ben Lathrop
Andrea Johnson
Format: Tabloid

MINNESOTA STATE UNIV. MANKATO: REPORTER — Centennial Student Union 293, Mankato, MN, 56001, USA; tel (507) 389-1776; fax (507) 389-5812; e-mail: reporter-editor@mnsu.edu; adv email: reporter-ad@mnsu.edu; web site: www.msureporter.com
Anne Schuelke
Nicole Smith
Higginbotham
Advertising Sales Manager — Shelly Christ
Format: Tabloid

MINNESOTA STATE UNIV. MOORHEAD: THE ADVOCATE — PO Box 306, Moorhead, MN, 56561-0306, USA; tel (218)477-2552; fax (218) 477-4662; e-mail: advocate@mnstate.edu; web site: www.mnstate.edu/advocate
Kristi Monson
Format: Tabloid

NORMANDALE COMMUNITY COLLEGE: THE LIONS ROAR — 9700 France Ave S, Bloomington, MN, 55431-4399, USA; tel (952) 358-8129; e-mail: lionsroar@normandale.edu; web site: www.lionsroar.infoEst. 1969
Advisor — Mark Plenke
Format: Tabloid

NORTH CENTRAL UNIV.: THE NORTHERNER — 910 Elliot Ave, Minneapolis, MN, 55404-1391, USA; tel (612) 343-4495; fax (612) 343-4780; web site: www.ncunortherner.com
Reuben David
Format: Tabloid

NORTHLAND CMTY. & TECH. COLLEGE: NORTHERN LIGHT — 1101 Highway 1 E, Thief River Falls, MN, 56701-2528, USA; tel (218) 683-8801; fax (218) 683-8980; web site: www.northlandcollege.edu
Adam Paulson
Elizabeth Perfecto
Format: Tabloid

RIDGEWATER COLLEGE: RIDGEWATER REVIEW — 2101 15th Ave NW, Willmar, MN, 56201-3096, USA; tel (320) 222-5200; fax (320) 231-6602; e-mail: info@ridgewater.edu; web site: www.ridgewater.edu
Gregg Aamot
Format: Broadsheet

SOUTHWEST STATE UNIV.: THE SPUR — Bellows Academic 246, Marshall, MN, 56258, USA; tel (507) 537-6228; fax (507) 537-7359; e-mail: smsuspur@yahoo.com; smsuspur@gmail.com; web site: www.smsuspur.net
Jessica Boeve
Jason Zahn
McMellan Legaspi
Format: Broadsheet

ST. CLOUD STATE UNIV.: UNIVERSITY CHRONICLE — 720 4th Ave S, Saint Cloud, MN, 56301-4498, USA; tel (320) 308-4086; e-mail: editor@universitychronicle.net; adv email: advertising@universitychronicle.net; ed email: editor@universitychronicle.net; web site: www.universitychronicle.netEst. 1924
Sandesh Malla
Ashley Kalkbrenner
Tiffany Krupke
Jason Tham
Kamana Karki
Published: Mon
Digital Edition Available?: Y
Price: Free
Format: Tabloid

ST. JOHNS UNIV.: RECORD — PO Box 2000, Collegeville, MN, 56321-2000, USA; tel (320) 363-2540; fax (320) 363-2061; e-mail: record@csbsju.edu; web site: www.users.csbsju.edu/record
Kate Kompas
Format: Tabloid

ST. MARYS UNIV. OF MINNESOTA: CARDINAL — 700 Terrace Hts Ste 37, Winona, MN, 55987-1321, USA; tel (507) 457-1497; fax (507) 457-6967; web site: www.smumn.edu
Bob Conover
Format: Tabloid

ST. OLAF COLLEGE: MANITOU MESSENGER — 1520 Saint Olaf Ave, Northfield, MN, 55057-1099, USA; tel (507) 786-3275; fax (507) 786-3650; e-mail: manitoumessenger@stolaf.edu.com; adv email: mess-advertise@stolaf.edu; ed email: mess-exec@stolaf.edu; web site: www.manitoumessenger.com
Bridget Dinter
Format: Broadsheet

UNIV. OF MINNESOTA: MINNESOTA DAILY — 2221 University Ave SE Ste 450, Minneapolis, MN, 55414-3077, USA; tel (612) 627-4080; fax (612) 435-5865; e-mail: news@mndaily.com; web site: www.mndaily.com
Holly Miller
Format: Tabloid

UNIV. OF MINNESOTA: UNIVERSITY REGISTER — 600 East Fourth Street, Morris, MN, 56267, USA; tel (320) 589-6078; fax (320) 589-6079; e-mail: register@mrs.umn.eduEst. 1987
Ingrid Luisa Avenda
Joy Heysse
Eli Mayfield
Format: Broadsheet

UNIV. OF MINNESOTA DULUTH: UMD STATESMAN — 118 Kirby Ctr., 10 University Dr., Duluth, MN, 55812-2403, USA; tel (218) 726-8154; fax (218) 726-8276; e-mail: statesman@d.umn.edu; web site: www.umdstatesman.com
Lisa Hansen
Format: Tabloid

UNIV. OF MINNESOTA INST. OF TECH: MINNESOTA TECHNOLOG — 207 Church St SE Lind Hall 5, Minneapolis, MN, 55455-0134, USA; tel (612) 624-9816; fax (612) 626-0261; e-mail: technolog@itdean.umn.edu; web site: technolog.it.umn.edu/technolog
Paul Sorenson
Nate Johnson
Michelle Walter
Format: Magazine

UNIVERSITY OF NORTHWESTERN: THE NORTHWESTERN EXAMINER — 3003 Snelling Ave N, Saint Paul, MN, 55113, USA; tel (651) 631-5100; fax (651) 651-5124; e-mail: examiner@unwsp.edu; adv email: examinerads@unwsp.edu; web site: http://www.unwexaminer.com/about/
Doug Trouten
Published: Bi-Mthly
Digital Edition Available?: Y
Format: Tabloid

WILLIAM MITCHELL COLLEGE OF LAW: OPINION — 875 Summit Ave, Saint Paul, MN, 55105-3076, USA; e-mail: theopinion@wmitchell.edu
Lucas Hjelle
Format: Tabloid

WINONA STATE UNIV.: WINONAN — 175 W Mark St, Winona, MN, 55987, USA; tel (507) 457-5119; e-mail: winonan@winona.edu; web site: www.winona.edu/winonan
Jenna Cameron
Ed. in Chief — Alyx Minor
Editor-in-chief — Julia Sand
Published: Wed
Digital Edition Available?: Y
Insert rate: jccamero5034@winona.edu
Format: Broadsheet

MISSISSIPPI

ALCORN STATE UNIV.: CAMPUS CHRONICLE — 1000 Alcorn Dr Ste 269, Lorman, MS, 39096-7500, USA; tel (601) 877-6557; fax (601) 877-2213; e-mail: tnimox@lorman.alcorn.edu; web site: www.alcornchronicle.com
Toni Terrett
Larry Sanders
Erica L. Turner
Format: Tabloid

BELHAVEN COLLEGE: QUARTER TONE — 1500 Peachtree St, Jackson, MS, 39202-1789, USA; tel (601) 968-8702
Don Hubele
Format: Magazine

BULLDOG BEAT — PO Box 1068, Starkville, MS, 39760-1068, USA; tel (662) 323-1642; fax (662) 323-6586; e-mail: sdnads@bellsouth.net; adv email: sdnads@bellsouth.net; ed email: sdneditor@bellsouth.net; web site: www.starkvilledailynews.comEst. 1875
Pub. — Don Norman
Bus. Mgr. — Mona Howell
Circ. Mgr. — Byron Norman
Creative Dir. — Larry Bost
Educ. Ed. — Shea Staskowski
Online Ed. — Brian Hawkins
Published: Mon, Tues, Wed, Thur, Fri, Sat, SunCirc. (pd.) 7,071
Digital Platform - Mobile: Apple, Android, Windows
Digital Platform - Tablet: Apple iOS, Android, Windows 7
Price: 10.00/mo; 86.00/yr.
Note: For detailed production information, see West Point Daily Times Leader.

COPIAH-LINCOLN CMTY. COLLEGE: THE WOLF TALES — PO Box 649, Wesson, MS, 39191-0649, USA; tel (601) 643-8354; fax (601) 643-8226; web site: www.colin.edu
Mary Warren
Format: Broadsheet

DELTA STATE UNIV.: DELTA STATEMENT — 1003 W Sunflower Rd, Cleveland, MS, 38733-0002, USA; tel (662) 846-4715; fax (662) 846-4737; e-mail: statemnt@deltastate.edu; web site: www.deltastate.edu
Patricia Roberts
Kaitlyn Mize
Ashley Robertson
Format: Broadsheet

HINDS CMTY. COLLEGE: HINSONIAN — PO Box 1100, Raymond, MS, 39154-1100, USA; tel (601) 857-3323; web site: www.hindscc.edu
Cathy Hayden
Format: Tabloid

HOLMES CMTY. COLLEGE: GROWL — PO Box 369, Goodman, MS, 39079-0369, USA; tel (662) 472-2312; fax (662) 472-0012; web site: www.holmescc.edu
District Director of Communications — Steve Diffey
Published: Twice a senester
Digital Edition Available?: N
Format: Broadsheet

ITAWAMBA CMTY. COLLEGE: CHIEFTAIN — 602 W. Hill St., Fulton, MS, 38843-1022, USA; tel (662) 862-8244; e-mail: dsthomas@iccms.edu; ed email: dsthomas@iccms.edu; web site: www.iccms.edu
Dir., PR — Donna Thomas
Published: Three times each semester
Digital Edition Available?: Y
Format: Broadsheet

JACKSON STATE UNIVERSITY: THE BLUE & WHITE FLASH — PO Box 18449, Jackson, MS, 39217-0001, USA; tel (601) 979-2167; fax (601) 979-2876; e-mail: theflash@jsums.edu; adv email: shannon.d.tatum@jsums.edu; ed email: theflash@jsums.edu; web site: www.thejsuflash.com
Publications Coordinator/Ad Manager — Shannon Tatum
Published: ThurCirc.(fr.) 3,000
Digital Edition Available?: Y
Insert rate: $150 per 1000
Price: Free
Format: Broadsheet

JONES COUNTY JUNIOR COLLEGE: RADIONIAN — 900 S Court St, Ellisville, MS, 39437-3999, USA; tel (601) 477-4084; fax (601) 477-4191; e-mail: radionian@jcjc.edu; adv email: radionian@jcjc.edu; ed email: radionian@jcjc.edu; web site: www.jcjc.eduEst. 1927
Newspaper Adviser — Kelly Atwood

Published: Mthly
Digital Edition Available?: Y
Format: Broadsheet

MILLSAPS COLLEGE: PURPLE & WHITE — PO Box 150847, Jackson, MS, 39210-0001, USA; tel (601) 974-1211; fax (601) 974-1229
Woody Woodrick
Kate Royals
Kathleen Morrison
Format: Tabloid

MISSISSIPPI COLLEGE: MISSISSIPPI COLLEGIAN — 200 W College St, Clinton, MS, 39058-0001, USA; tel (601) 925-3462; fax (601) 925-3804; web site: news.mc.edu/~collegian/
Tim Nicholas
Gabriel Winston
Terra Kirkland
Format: Tabloid

MISSISSIPPI STATE UNIV.: THE REFLECTOR — PO Box 5407, Mississippi State, MS, 39762-5407, USA; tel (662) 325-2374; fax (662) 325-8985; e-mail: editor@reflector.msstate.edu; adv email: advertise@reflector.msstate.edu; web site: www.reflector-online.comEst. 1884
Julia Langford
Published: Tues, FriCirc.(fr.) 10,000
Digital Edition Available?: Y
Format: Broadsheet

MISSISSIPPI UNIV. FOR WOMEN: SPECTATOR — 1100 College St, Columbus, MS, 39701-5802, USA; tel (662) 329-7268; fax (662) 329-7269; e-mail: spectator@muw.edu; web site: www.muw.edu/spectator
Sarah Wilson
Juna'uh Allgood
Format: Tabloid

MISSISSIPPI VALLEY STATE UNIV.: DELTA DEVILS' GAZETTE — 14000 Highway 82 W, Itta Bena, MS, 38941-1401, USA; tel (662) 254-3458; fax (622) 254-6704; e-mail: deltadevilsgazettefacad@gmail.com; adv email: ehmcclary@mvsu.edu; ed email: deltadevilsgazettefacad@gmail.com; web site: deltadevilsgazette.com
Asst. Prof. — Esin C. Turk
Asst. Prof./Dir., Forensics — Samuel Osunde
Carolyn Gordon
Mr. — Zainul Abedin
Published: three per semester Circ.(fr.) 2,000
Digital Edition Available?: N
Price: Free on Campus, Mail Cost if Delivered
Format: Tabloid

NORTHEAST MISSISSIPPI COMMUNITY COLLEGE: THE BEACON — MS, USA; tel (662) 720-7304; fax (662) 720-7216; e-mail: beacon@nemcc.edu; adv email: beacon@nemcc.edu; ed email: beacon@nemcc.eduEst. 1949
Tony Finch
Advisor — Michael H Miller
Published: Other Two times each semesterCirc.(fr.) 3,000
Digital Edition Available?: Y
Price: Free
Format: Broadsheet

NORTHWEST MISSISSIPPI CMTY. COLLEGE: RANGER ROCKET — PO Box 7039, Senatobia, MS, 38668, USA; tel (662) 562-3276; fax (662) 562-3499; e-mail: rangerrocket1@northwestms.edu; web site: www.northwestms.eduEst. 1927
Ranate Ferreira
Chris Creasy
Format: Broadsheet

PEARL RIVER COMMNITY COLLEGE: THE DRAWL — 101 Highway 11 N, Poplarville, MS, 39470-2201, USA; tel (601) 403-1312; e-mail: cabadie@prcc.edu; adv email: cabadie@prcc.edu; ed email: cabadie@prcc.edu; web site: www.prcc.eduEst. 1909
Chuck Adadie
Published: MthlyCirc.(fr.) 2,000
Digital Edition Available?: Y
Price: Free
Format: Broad sheet

RUST COLLEGE: THE RUSTORIAN — 150 Rust Ave, Holly Springs, MS, 38635-2328, USA; tel (662) 252-8000 ext. 4553; fax (662) 252-8869; e-mail: rustorian_@hotmail.com; adv email: rustorian_@hotmail.com; web site: www.rustorian.com
Debayo Moyo
Published: Mthly
Digital Edition Available?: Y
Price: Free
Format: Tabloid

THE UNIVERSITY OF MISSISSIPPI: THE DAILY MISSISSIPPIAN — 201 Bishop Hall, Oxford , MS, 38677, USA; tel (662) 915-5503; fax (662) 915-5703; e-mail: studentmedia@olemiss.edu; ed email: dmeditor@gmail.com; web site: www.thedmonline.comEst. 1911
Ed. — Lacey Russell
Dir. of Student Media/Faculty Adviser — Patricia Thompson
Published: Mon, Tues, Wed, Thur, FriCirc.(fr.) 12,000
Digital Edition Available?: Y
Digital Platform - Mobile: Apple, Android
Format: Tall Tabloid

TOUGALOO COLLEGE: HARAMBEE — 500 W County Line Rd, Tougaloo, MS, 39174-9700, USA; tel (601) 977-6159; fax (601) 977-6160; e-mail: cwhite@tougaloo.edu
Teressa Fulgham
Dir. Journ. Program — Colleen White
Format: Tabloid

UNIV. OF SOUTHERN MISSISSIPPI: STUDENT PRINTZ — PO Box 5121, Hattiesburg, MS, 39406-0001, USA; tel (601) 266-4288; fax (601) 266-6473; e-mail: printz@usm.edu; ed email: printzeditors@gmail.com; web site: www.studentprintz.comEst. 1927
News Content Adviser — Chuck Cook
Published: WedCirc.(fr.) 1,700
Digital Edition Available?: Y
Format: Tabloid

WOOD COLLEGE — Weber Dr., Mathiston, MS, 39752, USA; tel (662) 263-5352
Jeanna Graves

MISSOURI

AVILA UNIVERSITY: THE TALON — 11901 Wornall Rd, Kansas City, MO, 64145-1007, USA; tel (816) 942-8400; fax (816) 501-2459; e-mail: talon@mail.avila.edu; web site: www.thetalon-online.com
Joe Snorgrass
Format: Tabloid

CROWDER COLLEGE: THE SENTRY — 601 Laclede Ave, Neosho, MO, 64850-9165, USA; tel (417) 451-3223; fax (417) 451-4280; e-mail: sentry@crowder.edu; web site: www.crowder.edu
Leona Bailey
Fabian Oechsle
Format: Broadsheet

CULVER-STOCKTON COLLEGE: THE MEGAPHONE — 1 College Hl, Canton, MO, 63435-1299, USA; tel (573) 231-6371; fax (573) 231-6611; e-mail: swiegenstein@culver.edu; web site: www.culver.eduEst. 1853
Joy Daggs
Journalism/PR Head — Steve Wiegenstein
Interpersonal Head — Bob Paige
Format: Broadsheet

DRURY COLLEGE: MIRROR — 900 N Benton Ave, Springfield, MO, 65802-3791, USA; tel (417) 873-7879; fax (417) 873-7897; e-mail: mirror@drurymirror.com; web site: www.drurymirror.com
Cristina Gilstrap
Jeromy Layman
Mallory Noelke
Format: Tabloid

EVANGEL UNIVERSITY: THE LANCE — 1111 N. Glenstone Ave., Springfield, MO, 65802-2125, USA; tel (417) 865-2815; e-mail: evangellance@gmail.com; ed email: evangellance@gmail.com; web site: http://www.evangellance.comEst. 1955
Melinda Booze
Published: Fri, Bi-MthlyCirc.(fr.) 1,500
Digital Edition Available?: Y
Format: Tabloid

FONTBONNE COLLEGE: FRONTBANNER — 6800 Wydown Blvd, Clayton, MO, 63105-3098, USA; tel (314) 889-1477; fax (314) 889-1451
Jason Sommer
Sara Lubbes
Format: Tabloid

LINCOLN UNIV.: LINCOLN CLARION — Elliff Hall, Rm. 208, Jefferson City, MO, 65102, USA; tel (573) 681-5446; fax (573) 681-5438; web site: www.lincolnu.edu
Advisor — Yusuf Kalyango
Format: Tabloid

LONGVIEW CMTY. COLLEGE: LONGVIEW CURRENT — 500 SW Longview Rd, Lees Summit, MO, 64081-2100, USA; tel (816) 672-2308; fax (816) 672-2025; e-mail: current@mcckc.edu; web site: www.longviewcurrent.com
Pat Sparks
Format: Tabloid

MISSOURI SOUTHERN UNIVERSITY: THE CHART — 3950 Newman Rd, Joplin, MO, 64801-1595, USA; tel (417) 625-9823; fax (417) 625-9585; e-mail: chart@mssu.edu; web site: www.thechartonline.comEst. 1939
Head — J.R. Moorman
Chad Stebbins
T.R. Hanrahan
Alexandra Nicolas
Format: Broadsheet

MISSOURI STATE UNIV.: THE STANDARD — 901 S National Ave, Springfield, MO, 65897-0001, USA; tel (417) 836-5272; fax (417) 836-6738; e-mail: standard@missouristate.edu; web site: www.the-standard.org
Jess Rollins
Format: Broadsheet

MISSOURI UNIV. OF SCIENCE & TECHNOLOGY: MISSOURI MINER — Missouri S&T , Rolla, MO, 65401-0249, USA; tel (573) 341-4312; fax (573) 341-4235; e-mail: miner@mst.edu; web site: mominer.mst.edu
Fred Ekstam
Frank Sauer
Sarah Richmond
Andrea Unnerstall
News Ed. — Jacob
Format: Tabloid

MISSOURI VALLEY COLLEGE: THE DELTA — 500 E. College St., Marshall, MO, 65340-3109, USA; tel (660) 831-4214; e-mail: postc@moval.edu; adv email: postc@moval.edu; web site: www.mvcdelta.com
Chris Post
Digital Edition Available?: Y
Format: Tabloid

MISSOURI WESTERN STATE UNIVERSITY: GRIFFON NEWS — 4525 Downs Dr Eder 221, Saint Joseph, MO, 64507-2246, USA; tel (816) 271-4412; fax (816) 271-4543; e-mail: bergland@missouriwestern.edu; web site: www.thegriffonnews.comEst. 1924
Robert Bergland
Published: ThurCirc.(fr.) 2,500
Digital Edition Available?: Y
Insert rate: $7/c.i.
Format: Broadsheet

NORTHWEST MISSOURI STATE UNIV.: NORTHWEST MISSOURIAN — 800 University Dr., Wells 4, Maryville, MO, 64468-6001, USA; tel (660) 562-1635; fax (660) 562-1521; e-mail: northwestmissourian@gmail.com; web site: www.nwmissourinews.comEst. 1914
Advisor — Steven Chappell
Editor-in-Chief — Brandon Zenner
Published: Thur
Digital Edition Available?: Y
Digital Platform - Mobile: Apple, Android, Windows
Format: Broadsheet

ROCKHURST UNIV.: THE SENTINEL — 1100 Rockhurst Rd, Kansas City, MO, 64110-2561, USA; tel (816) 501-4051; fax (816) 501-4290; e-mail: sentinel@rockhurst.edu; web site: www.rockhurstsentinel.com
Brian Roewe
Format: Magazine

SOUTHEAST MISSOURI STATE UNIV.: CAPAHA ARROW — 1 University Plz MS 2225, Cape Girardeau, MO, 63701-4710, USA; tel (573) 651-2540; fax (573) 651-2825; ed email: thearrow.news@gmail.com; web site: www.capahaarrow.com
Sam Blackwell
Erin Mustain
Ben Marxer
Format: Tabloid

SOUTHWEST BAPTIST UNIV.: THE OMNIBUS — 1600 University Ave, Bolivar, MO, 65613-2597, USA; tel (417) 328-1833; fax (417) 328-1579; e-mail: info@omnibusonline.com; web site: www.omnibusonline.com
Jessica Oliver
Nicole Heitman

ST. LOUIS CMTY. COLLEGE FLORISSANT VALLEY: THE FORUM — 3400 Pershall Rd, Saint Louis, MO, 63135-1408, USA; tel (314) 513-4454; e-mail: fvfoumeditor@stlcc.edu; ed email: fvforumeditor@stlcc.eduEst. 1963
Renee Thomas-Woods
Stephan Curry
Joshua Schoenhoff
Published: Mthly
Digital Edition Available?: N
Format: Tabloid
Note: Forum Newspaper blog address: fvforumflo.blogspot.com

ST. LOUIS CMTY. COLLEGE FOREST PARK: THE SCENE — 5600 Oakland Ave, Saint Louis, MO, 63110-1393, USA; tel (314) 644-9140; e-mail: the_scene_fp@yahoo.com
Format: Tabloid

ST. LOUIS CMTY. COLLEGE MERAMEC: THE MONTAGE — 11333 Big Bend Rd, Kirkwood, MO, 63122-5799, USA; tel (314) 984-7955; fax (314) 984-7947; e-mail: meramecmontage@gmail.com; web site: www.meramecmontage.comEst. 1962
Shannon Philpott-Sanders
Published: Other bi-weekly
Digital Edition Available?: Y
Digital Platform - Mobile: Other
Digital Platform - Tablet: Other
Format: Tabloid

ST. LOUIS UNIV.: UNIVERSITY NEWS — 20 N Grand Blvd Ste 354, Saint Louis, MO, 63103-2005, USA; tel (314) 977-2812; fax (314) 977-7177; e-mail: unews.slu@gmail.com; web site: www.unewsonline.com
Jason L. Young

Peter Zagotta
Kat Patke
Format: Broadsheet

STEPHENS COLLEGE: STEPHENS LIFE — 1200 E Broadway, Campus Box 2014, Columbia, MO, 65215-0001, USA; tel (573) 876-7133; e-mail: stephenslifemagazine@gmail.com; web site: http://www.stephens.edu/stephenslife
Kathy Vogt
Stephens Life Adviser — Josh Nichol-Caddy
Digital Edition Available?: Y
Format: Tabloid

TRUMAN STATE UNIV. — Barnett Hall News Ctr. 1200, 100 E. Normal St., Kirksville, MO, 63501-4200, USA; tel (660) 785-4449; fax (660) 785-7601; e-mail: indexads@truman.edu; web site: www.trumanindex.com
Don Krause
Blake Toppmeyer
Jessica Rapp
Stephanie Hall

UNIV. OF MISSOURI: CURRENT — 1 University Blvd, Saint Louis, MO, 63121-4400, USA; tel (314) 516-5174; fax (314) 516-6811; e-mail: thecurrent@umsl.edu; web site: www.thecurrentonline.com
Charlotte Petty
Dan Pryor
Advisor — Ryan Krull
Published: MonCirc.(fr.) 5,000
Digital Edition Available?: Y
Digital Platform - Mobile: Apple, Android, Windows, Other
Digital Platform - Tablet: Apple iOS, Android, Other
Format: Broadsheet

UNIV. OF MISSOURI: UNIVERSITY NEWS — 5327 Holmes St, Kansas City, MO, 64110-2437, USA; tel (816) 235-1393; fax (816) 235-6514; web site: www.unews.com
BJ Allen
Stefanie Crabtree
Hilary Hedges
Format: Tabloid

UNIV. OF MISSOURI: THE MANEATER NEWSPAPER — G210 MU Student Center, Columbia, MO, 65211, USA; tel (573) 882-5500; adv email: advertising@themaneater.com; ed email: editors@themaneater.com; web site: www.themaneater.comEst. 1955
Becky Diehl
Published: WedCirc.(fr.) 5,000
Digital Edition Available?: Y
Insert rate: $65 per 1,000 - 1 page insert
Format: Tabloid

UNIVERSITY OF CENTRAL MISSOURI: THE MULESKINNER — Martin 136, University of Central Missouri, Warrensburg, MO, 64093, USA; tel (660) 543-4050; fax (660) 543-8663; e-mail: muleskinner@ucmo.edu; adv email: muleskinnerads@ucmo.edu; web site: www.digitalburg.comEst. 1906
Adviser — Matt Bird-Meyer
Managing Editor — Jacque Flanagan
Published: Thur digitalburg.comCirc.(fr.) 3,000
Digital Edition Available?: Y
Digital Platform - Mobile: Apple, Android
Digital Platform - Tablet: Apple iOS, Android
Format: tabloid

WASHINGTON UNIV.: STUDENT LIFE — 1 Brookings Dr., Saint Louis, MO, 63130-4862, USA; tel (314) 935-4240; fax (314) 935-5938; adv email: advertising@studlife.com; ed email: editor@studlife.com; web site: www.studlife.comEst. 1878
General Manager — Raymond Bush
Published: Mon, ThurCirc.(fr.) 4,000
Insert rate: $345.00
Format: Broadsheet

WEBSTER UNIV.: THE JOURNAL — 470 E Lockwood Ave, Saint Louis, MO, 63119-3194, USA; tel (314) 961-2660; fax (314) 968-7059; e-mail: wujournal@gmail.com; ed email: editor@webujournal.com; web site: www.webujournal.com
Journ. Seq. — Don Corrigan
Kelly Kendall
Published: Wed
Digital Edition Available?: Y
Digital Platform - Mobile: Apple, Android
Digital Platform - Tablet: Apple iOS, Android
Format: Broadsheet

WESTMINSTER COLLEGE: THE COLUMNS — 501 Westminster Ave, Fulton, MO, 65251-1299, USA; tel (573) 592-5000; fax (573) 642-2699; web site: www.westminster-mo.edu
Debra Brenegan
Sarah Blackmon
Aassan Sipra
Format: Tabloid

WILLIAM JEWELL COLLEGE: HILLTOP MONITOR — 500 College Hl # 1016, Liberty, MO, 64068-1896, USA; tel (816) 781-7700; e-mail: monitor@william.jewell.edu; web site: www.thehilltopmonitor.com
Samantha Sanders
Jessie Newman
Trista Turley
Format: Tabloid

MONTANA

CARROLL COLLEGE: PROSPECTOR — 1601 N Benton Ave, Helena, MT, 59625-2826, USA; tel (406) 447-4300; fax (406) 447-4533; web site: www.carroll.edu
Brent Northup
Format: Tabloid

FLATHEAD VALLEY CMTY. COLLEGE OUT OF BUSINESS: MERCURY — 777 Grandview Dr, Kalispell, MT, 59901-2622, USA; tel (406) 756-3907; e-mail: mercury@fvcc.edu
Lowell Jaeger
Format: Tabloid

MONTANA STATE UNIV. BOZEMAN: EXPONENT — P.O. Box 174140, Bozeman, MT, 59717, USA; tel (406) 994-3976; fax (406) 994-2253
Amanda Larrinaga
Format: Tabloid

MONTANA STATE UNIV. NORTHERN: NORTHERN LIGHT — PO Box 7751, Havre, MT, 59501-7751, USA; tel (406) 265-4112; fax (406) 265-3777; web site: www.msun.edu
Lori Renfeld
Format: Tabloid

MONTANA TECH. UNIV.: TECHNORAT — 1300 W Park St, Butte, MT, 59701-8932, USA; tel (406) 496-4241; fax (406) 496-4702; e-mail: technocrat@mtech.edu
Patrick Munday
Format: Tabloid

ROCKY MOUNTAIN COLLEGE: TOP OF THE ROCK — 1511 Poly Dr, Billings, MT, 59102-1796, USA; tel (406) 657-1093; fax (406) 259-9751
Wilbur Wood
Format: Magazine

UNIV. OF GREAT FALLS — 1301 20th St S, Great Falls, MT, 59405-4996, USA; tel (406) 791-5231; fax (406) 791-5220
Jerry Habets

UNIVERSITY OF MONTANA: MONTANA KAIMIN — Don Anderson Hall Ste 207, Missoula, MT, 59812-0001, USA; tel (406) 243-6541; fax (406) 243-5475; e-mail: kaiminads@gmail.com; adv email: kaiminads@gmail.com; ed email: editor@montanakaimin.com; web site: http://www.montanakaimin.comEst. 1898
Office manager — Ruth Johnson
Advisor — Nadia White
Editor — Amy Sisk
Business manager — Nick McKinney
Published: Tues, Wed, Thur, Fri
Published online daily, updated as news breaksCirc.(fr.) 4,000
Digital Edition Available?: N
Price: Free
Format: Tabloid

NEBRASKA

CHADRON STATE COLLEGE: THE EAGLE — 1000 Main St # 235, Chadron, NE, 69337-2690, USA; tel (308) 432-6303; e-mail: editor@csceagle.com; adv email: ads@csceagle.com; ed email: opinion@csceagle.com; web site: www.csceagle.comEst. 1920
Advisor — Michael D. Kennedy
Mgr Ed — Jordyn Hulinsky
Opinion Ed — Janelle Kesterson
Advt Dir — Angie Webb
Sports Ed — Preston Goehring
Lifestyles Ed — Justine Stone
News Ed — Melanie Nelson
Published: ThurCirc.(fr.) 4,000
Digital Edition Available?: Y
Insert rate: $113
Format: Tabloid

CONCORDIA UNIVERSITY-NEBRASKA: THE SOWER — 800 N Columbia Ave Ste 1, Seward, NE, 68434-1599, USA; tel 703-434-0355; e-mail: sower@cune.org; web site: www.cunesower.com
Adviser — Ellen Beck
Published: Mthly Website updated throughout the weekCirc. (pd.) 0 (fr.) 1,300
Insert rate: $75
Price: Free
Format: Broadsheet

CREIGHTON UNIV.: CREIGHTONIAN — 2500 California Plz, Omaha, NE, 68178-0002, USA; tel (402) 280-4058; fax (402) 280-1494; e-mail: emw@creighton.edu; web site: www.creightonian.com
Melissa Hillebrand
Chair/Prof. — Eileen M. Wirth
Prof./Charles and Mary Heider Endowed Jesuit Chair — Father Don Doll
Kelly Fitzgerald
Assoc. Prof. — Timothy S. Guthrie
Assoc. Prof. — Jeffrey Maciejewski
Assoc. Prof. — Carol Zuegner
Asst. Prof. — Kristoffer Boyle
Asst. Prof. — Joel Davies
Asst. Prof. — Charles Heider
Asst. Prof. — Mary Heider
Lectr. — Andrew Hughes
Lectr. — Kathleen Hughes
Lectr. — Richard Janda
Lectr. — Kathryn Larson
Lectr. — Brian Norton
Lectr. — Wendy Wiseman
Lectr. — Angela Zegers
Format: Tabloid

DOANE COLLEGE: THE DOANE OWL — 1014 Boswell Ave Ste 289, Crete, NE, 68333-2440, USA; fax (402) 826-8269; e-mail: www.doaneline.com; adv email: owl@doane.edu
David Swartzlander
Bob Kenny
Insert rate: david.swartzlander@doane.edu
Format: Broadsheet

HASTINGS COLLEGE: COLLEGIAN — 710 N Turner Ave, Hastings, NE, 68901-7696, USA; tel (402) 461-7399; fax (402) 461-7442
Alicia O'Donnell
Lauren Lee
Format: Broadsheet

NEBRASKA WESLEYAN UNIV.: REVEILLE — 5000 Saint Paul Ave Smb 1221, Lincoln, NE, 68504-2760, USA; tel (402) 465-2352; fax (402) 465-2179; e-mail: reveille@nebrwesleyan.edu; web site: www.thereveillenwu.com
Jim Schaffer
Editor — Hannah Tangeman
Published: Bi-Mthly
Digital Edition Available?: Y
Insert rate: x
Format: Tabloid

NORTHEAST CMTY. COLLEGE: VIEWPOINT — PO Box 469, Norfolk, NE, 68702-0469, USA; tel (402) 844-7352; web site: www.neaccviewpoint.com
Jason Elznic
Format: Tabloid

PERU STATE COLLEGE: PERU STATE TIMES — PO Box 10, Peru, NE, 68421-0010, USA; tel (402) 872-2260; fax (402) 872-2302; e-mail: psctimes@yahoo.com
Savannah Wenzel
Format: Tabloid

UNIV. OF NEBRASKA: ANTELOPE — Mitchel Ctr. 156, Kearney, NE, 68847, USA; tel (308) 865-8487; fax (308) 865-1537; adv email: antelopeads@unk.edu
Tereca M Diffenderfer
Format: Broadsheet

UNIV. OF NEBRASKA AT OMAHA: GATEWAY — 6001 Dodge St Unit 116, Omaha, NE, 68182-1107, USA; tel (402) 554-2470; fax (402) 554-2735; ed email: jloza@unomaha.edu; web site: www.unogateway.comEst. 1913
Josie Loza
Cody Willmer
Kate O'Dell
Published: TuesCirc.(fr.) 2,500
Insert rate: $50/1000
Price: Free
Format: Tabloid

UNIV. OF NEBRASKA-LINCOLN: DAILY NEBRASKAN — P.O. Box 880448, Lincoln, NE, 68588-0448, USA; tel (402) 472-2588; e-mail: dn@unl.edu; adv email: dn@unl.edu; ed email: news@dailynebraskan.com; web site: DailyNebraskan.comEst. 1901
Daniel Shattil
Director of Sales and Marketing — David Thiemann
Published: MthlyCirc.(fr.) 4,500
Digital Edition Available?: Y
Digital Platform - Mobile: Apple, Android
Digital Platform - Tablet: Apple iOS, Android
Insert rate: n/a
Price: Free
Format: Magazine

WAYNE STATE COLLEGE: WAYNE STATER — 1111 Main St, Wayne, NE, 68787-1172, USA; tel (402) 375-7324; fax (402) 375-7204; e-mail: wstater@wsc.edu; web site: wildcat.wsc.edu/stater/
Max McElwain
Skylar Osovski
Katelynn Wolfe
Format: Tabloid

WESTERN NEBRASKA COMMUNITY COLLEGE: SPECTATOR — 1601 E 27th St, Scottsbluff, NE, 69361-1899, USA; tel (308) 635-6058; e-mail: spectator@wncc.edu
Adv. Mgr. — Mark Rein
Jay Grote
Digital Edition Available?: Y
Digital Platform - Mobile: Other
Price: Free
Format: Online Only — www.wnccspectator.com

NEVADA

CMTY. COLLEGE OF SOUTHERN NEVADA — 3200 E Cheyenne Ave # J2A, North Las Vegas, NV, 89030-4228, USA; tel (702) 651-4339; fax (702) 643-6427; e-mail: coyotepressonline@yahoo.com
Arnold Vell

UNIV. OF NEVADA: THE NEVADA SAGEBRUSH — Mill Stop 58, Reno, NV, 89557-0001, USA; tel (775) 784-4033; fax (775) 784-1952; ed email: editor@nevadasagebrush.com; web site: www.nevadasagebrush.com
Amy Koeckes
Jessica Fryman
Format: Tabloid

UNIVERSITY OF NEVADA, LAS VEGAS: SCARLET & GRAY FREE PRESS — PO Box 2011, Las Vegas, NV, 89125-2011, USA; e-mail: chief.freepress@unlv.edu; adv email: marketing.freepress@unlv.edu; ed email: managing.freepress@unlv.edu; web site: www.unlvfreepress.comEst. 1955
Editor-in-Chief — Bianca Cseke
Business Manager — Kathy Schreiber
Adviser — Rick Velotta
Managing Editor — Blaze Lovell
Director of Marketing & Sales — Nicole Gallego
Published: MonCirc.(fr.) 3,800
Digital Edition Available?: Y
Insert rate: N/A
Format: Tabloid

UNIVERSITY OF NEVADA, LAS VEGAS: UNLV SCARLET & GRAY FREE PRESS — 4505 S Maryland Pkwy , Las Vegas, NV, 89154-9900, USA; tel (702) 895-2028; fax (702) 895-1515; e-mail: chief.freepress@unlv.edu; adv email: marketing.freepress@unlv.edu; ed email: managing.freepress@unlv.edu; web site: www.unlvfreepress.comEst. 1955
Adviser — Rick Velotta
Editor-in-Chief — Bianca Cseke
Managing Editor — Blaze Lovell
Director of Marketing & Sales — Nicole Gallego
Published: MonCirc. (pd.) 0 (fr.) 3,800
Digital Edition Available?: Y
Insert rate: N/A
Price: Free
Format: Tabloid

NEW HAMPSHIRE

DARTMOUTH COLLEGE: THE DARTMOUTH — 6175 Robinson Hall, Hanover, NH, 03755-3507, USA; tel (603) 646-2600; fax (603) 646-3443; e-mail: publisher@dartmouth.com; thedartmouth@dartmouth.edu; web site: www.thedartmouth.comEst. 1799
Ray Lu
Pub. — Phil Rasansky
Format: Tabloid

FRANKLIN PIERCE COLLEGE: PIERCE ARROW — 40 University Dr, Rindge, NH, 03461-5045, USA; tel (603) 899-4170; fax (603) 899-1077; web site: http://www.franklinpierce.edu/
Kristen Nevious
Tony Catinella
Robin Michael
Format: Broadsheet

NEW ENGLAND COLLEGE: NEW ENGLANDER — 98 Bridge St, Henniker, NH, 03242-3292, USA; tel (603) 428-2000; fax (603) 428-7230; web site: www.nec.edu
William Homestead
Format: Magazine

PLYMOUTH STATE COLLEGE: CLOCK — HUB Ste. A9, Plymouth, NH, 03264, USA; tel (603) 535-2947; fax (603) 535-2729; ed email: editor@clock.plymouth.edu; web site: www.theclockonline.com
Joe Mealey
Meghan Plumpton
Samantha Kenney
Format: Tabloid

SOUTHERN NEW HAMPSHIRE UNIV.: THE PENMEN PRESS — 2500 N River Rd # 1084, Manchester, NH, 03106-1018, USA; e-mail: Penmenpress@snhu.edu; adv email: Penmenpress@snhu.edu; web site: PenmenPress.com
Jon Boroshok
Published: Bi-Mthly
Digital Edition Available?: Y
Digital Platform - Mobile: Apple, Android, Windows, Blackberry
Format: Tabloid

ST. ANSELM COLLEGE: ST. ANSELM CRIER — PO Box 1719, Manchester, NH, 03102, USA; tel (603) 641-7016; fax (603) 222-4289; e-mail: crier@anslem.edu; web site: www.saintanselmcrier.com
Jerome Day
Format: Tabloid

THE NEW HAMPSHIRE: NEW HAMPSHIRE — Memorial Union Bldg., Rm. 132, 83 Main St., Durham, NH, 03824-2538, USA; tel (603) 862-1323; fax (603) 862-1920; e-mail: tnh.news@unh.edu; adv email: tnh.advertising@unh.edu; ed email: tnh.editor@unh.edu; web site: www.tnhdigital.comEst. 1911
Advisor — Julie Pond
Published: Mon, ThurCirc.(fr.) 4,000
Digital Edition Available?: Y
Digital Platform - Mobile: Apple, Android
Insert rate: $130/1000
Format: Tabloid

UNIVERSITY OF NEW HAMPSHIRE — 104 Hamilton Smith Hall, Durham, NH, 3824, USA; tel (603) 862-0251; fax (603) 862-3563; e-mail: lcm@cisunix.unh.edu
Dir. — Lisa Miller

NEW JERSEY

ATLANTIC CAPE CMTY. COLLEGE: ATLANTIC REVIEW — 5100 Black Horse Pike, Mays Landing, NJ, 08330-2699, USA; tel (609) 343-5109; fax (609) 343-5030; ed email: atlanticcapereview9@gmail.com
Marge Nocito
Jerry Carcache
Anne Kemp
Format: Tabloid

BROOKDALE CMTY. COLLEGE: STALL — 765 Newman Springs Rd, Lincroft, NJ, 07738-1599, USA; tel (732) 224-2266; fax (732) 450-1591; e-mail: stallbcc@gmail.com; ed email: stall@brookdalecc.edu
Debbie Mura
Published: Mon, Other six times a semester
Digital Edition Available?: N
Format: Broadsheet

CAMDEN COUNTY COLLEGE: CAMPUS PRESS — PO Box 200, Blackwood, NJ, 08012-0200, USA; tel (856) 227-7200; fax (856) 227-3541; e-mail: campuspress@camdencc.edu; web site: www.camdencc.edu/campuspress
Format: Tabloid

CENTENARY COLLEGE: THE QUILL — 400 Jefferson St Ste 1, Hackettstown, NJ, 07840-2184, USA; tel (908) 852-1400 x2243; e-mail: levd@centenarycollege.edu; adv email: levd@centenarycollege.edu; web site: www.centenarycollege.eduEst. 1991
Advisor — Deborah Lev
Published: MthlyCirc.(fr.) 1,600
Digital Edition Available?: Y
Price: Free
Format: Tabloid

COLLEGE OF ST. ELIZABETH: THE STATION — 2 Convent Rd, Morristown, NJ, 07960-6989, USA; tel (973) 290-4242; fax (973) 290-4389; e-mail: thestation@cse.edu
Kristene Both
Format: Tabloid

COUNTY COLLEGE OF MORRIS: YOUNGTOWN EDITION — 214 Center Grove Rd Rm Scc, Randolph, NJ, 07869-2007, USA; tel (973) 328-5224; fax (973) 361-4031; e-mail: theyoungtownedition@yahoo.com
Matthew Ayres
Frank Blaha
Format: Tabloid

DREW UNIV.: THE ACRON — PO Box 802, Madison, NJ, 07940-0802, USA; tel (973) 408-4207; fax (973) 408-3887; e-mail: acorn@drew.edu; web site: www.drewacorn.com
David A.M. Wilensky
Sheryl Mccabe
Format: Tabloid

ESSEX COUNTY COLLEGE: ESSEX COUNTY COLLEGE — 303 University Ave, Newark, NJ, 07102-1798, USA; tel (973) 877-3559; fax (973) 877-3488
Kyle Miller
Advisor — Nessie Hill
Format: Tabloid

FAIRLEIGH DICKINSON UNIV.: EQUINOX — 1000 River Rd, Teaneck, NJ, 07666-1914, USA; tel (201) 692-2046; fax (201) 692-2376; e-mail: equinoxfdu@gmail.com; web site: https://fduequinox.wordpress.com/
Bruno Battistoli
Sarah Latson
Kayla Hastrup
Miruna Seitan
Lorena Chouza
Melissa Hartz
Published: Thur
Digital Edition Available?: N
Format: Tabloid

GLOUCESTER COUNTY COLLEGE: GAZETTE — 1400 Tanyard Rd, Sewell, NJ, 08080-4249, USA; tel (856) 468-5000; fax (856) 464-9153; e-mail: gazette@gccnj.edu
Advisor — Brooke Hoffman
Keesha Patterson
Insert rate: NA
Format: Tabloid

KEAN UNIV.: THE TOWER — 1000 Morris Ave Ste 1, Union, NJ, 07083-7131, USA; tel (908) 737-0468; fax (908) 737-0465; e-mail: thetower@kean.edu; web site: www.kean.edu/~thetower
Pat Winters Lauro
Eileen Ruf
Jillian Johnson
Emannuel Urenea
Format: Tabloid

MIDDLESEX COUNTY COLLEGE: QUO VADIS — 2600 Woodbridge Ave, Edison, NJ, 08837-3675, USA; tel (732) 548-6000; fax (732) 906-4167; e-mail: quovadis_newspaper@hotmail.com
Melissa Edwards
Format: Tabloid

MONMOUTH UNIVERSITY: THE OUTLOOK — 400 Cedar Ave Rm 260, West Long Branch, NJ, 07764-1804, USA; tel (732) 571-3481; e-mail: outlook@monmouth.edu; adv email: outlookads@monmouth.edu; web site: outlook.monmouth.eduEst. 1933
Professor of Journalism — John Morano
Office Coordinator — Sandra Brown
Published: WedCirc.(fr.) 5,000
Digital Edition Available?: Y
Price: Free
Format: Tabloid

MONTCLAIR STATE UNIV.: MONTCLARION — USA; tel (973) 655-5230; fax (973) 655-7804; e-mail: montclarioneditor@gmail.com; web site: www.themontclarion.org
Kristen Bryfogle
Kulsoom Rizvi
Nelson DePasquale
Format: Broadsheet

NEW JERSEY CITY UNIV.: GOTHIC — 2039 Kennedy Blvd., GSUB 305, Jersey City, NJ, 07305-1596, USA; tel (201) 200-3575; web site: www.njcu.edu
James Broderick
Erica Molina
Marlen Gonzalez
Format: Tabloid

NEW JERSEY INST. OF TECHNOLOGY: THE VECTOR — 150 Bleeker St, Newark, NJ, 07103-3902, USA; tel (973) 596-5416; fax (973) 596-3613; e-mail: news@njitvector.com; adv email: ads@njitvector.com; web site: www.njitvector.com
Melissa Silderstang
Format: Tabloid

OCEAN COUNTY COLLEGE: VIKING NEWS — PO Box 2001, Toms River, NJ, 08754-2001, USA; tel (732) 255-0481; fax None; e-mail: vnews@ocean.edu; web site: NoneEst. 1965
None
Published: Irregularly
Digital Edition Available?: N
Price: Free
Format: Tabloid

PRINCETON UNIVERSITY: THE DAILY PRINCETONIAN — PO Box 469, Princeton, NJ, 08542-0469, USA; tel (609) 258-3632; e-mail: eic@dailyprincetonian.com; adv email: bm@dailyprincetonian.com; ed email: eic@dailyprincetonian.com; web site: www.dailyprincetonian.comEst. 1876
Editor in Chief — Marcelo Rochabrun
Published: Mon, Tues, Wed, Thur, Fri
Format: Broadsheet

RICHARD STOCKTON COLLEGE: ARGO — 101 Vera King Farris Dr, Galloway, NJ, 08205-9441, USA; tel (609) 652-4296; fax (609) 748-5565; adv email: argoadvertising@yahoo.com
Craig Stambaugh
Lina Wayman
Format: Tabloid

ROWAN UNIV.: WHIT — 201 Mullica Hill Rd, Glassboro, NJ, 08028-1702, USA; tel (856) 256-4713; fax (856) 256-4929; e-mail: communication@rowan.edu; web site: www.thewhitonline.com
Prof. — Don Bagin
Kathryn Quigley
Prof. — R. Michael Donovan
Prof. — Anthony Fulginiti
Prof. — Richard Grupenhoff
Prof. — Kenneth Kaleta
Prof. — Janice Rowan
Prof. — Edward Streb
Assoc. Prof. — Julia Chang
Assoc. Prof. — Cynthia Corison
Assoc. Prof. — Edgar Eckhardt
Assoc. Prof. — Suzanne Fitzgerald
Assoc. Prof. — Carl Hausman
Assoc. Prof. — Martin Itzkowitz
Assoc. Prof. — Frances Johnson
Assoc. Prof. — Diane Penrod
Assoc. Prof. — Donald Stoll
Assoc. Prof. — Sanford Tweedie
Asst. Prof. — Kenneth Albone
Asst. Prof. — Lorin Arnold

Format: Tabloid

RUTGERS UNIV.: DAILY TARGUM — 126 College Ave Ste 431, New Brunswick, NJ, 08901-1166, USA; tel (732) 932-7051; fax (732) 932-0079; e-mail: news@dailytargum.com; web site: www.dailytargum.com
John Clyde
Format: Tabloid

RUTGERS UNIV.: RUTGERS CLEANER — 326 Penn St, Camden, NJ, 08102-1412, USA; tel (856) 225-6304; fax (856) 225-6579; e-mail: gleaner@camden.rutgers.edu; web site: gleaner.camden.rutgers.edu
Joe Capuzzo
Format: Tabloid

RUTGERS UNIV.: OBSERVER — 350 Martin Luther King Jr Blvd, Newark, NJ, 07102-1801, USA; tel (973) 353-5023; fax (973) 353-1333; e-mail: observercopy@gmail.com; web site: www.rutgersobserver.com
Executive Editor — Dina Sayedahmed
Format: Tabloid

RUTGERS UNIV. SCHOOL OF ENVIRONMENTAL & BIOLOGICAL SCIENCES: GREEN PRINT — 88 Lipman Dr, New Brunswick, NJ, 08901-8525, USA; tel (732) 932-3000; fax (732) 932-8526
Kathryn E. Barry
Format: Tabloid

SETON HALL UNIVERSITY: THE SETONIAN — 400 S. Orange Ave., Student Ctr., Rm. 224, South Orange, NJ, 07079, USA; tel (732) 925-7647; fax (973) 761-7943; e-mail: Thesetonian@gmail.com; web site: www.thesetonian.comEst. 1924
Amy Nyberg
Brian Wisowaty
Published: Thur
Digital Edition Available?: Y
Digital Platform - Mobile: Apple, Android
Format: Tabloid

ST. PETERS COLLEGE: PAUW WOW — 2641 John F Kennedy Blvd, Jersey City, NJ, 07306-5997, USA; tel (201) 938-1254; fax (201) 938-1254; e-mail: pauwwow@hotmail.com; adv email: ads@pauwwow.com; web site: pauwwow.com
Paul Almonte
Frank DeMichele
Rozen Pradhan
Format: Tabloid

STEVENS INSTITUTE OF TECHNOLOGY: THE STUTE — USA; tel (201) 216-3404; e-mail: stute@stevens.edu; adv email: stuteads@stevens.edu; ed email: eboard@thestute.com; web site: www.thestute.comEst. 1904
Ed. — Joseph Brosnan
Published: Fri
Digital Edition Available?: Y
Format: Tabloid

THE COLLEGE OF NEW JERSEY: THE SIGNAL — PO Box 7718, Ewing, NJ, 08628-0718, USA; tel (609) 771-2499; fax (609) 771-3433; e-mail: signal@tcnj.edu; adv email: signalad@tcnj.edu; web site: tcnjsignal.netEst. 1885
Emilie Lounsberry
Published: Wed
Digital Edition Available?: Y
Format: Tabloid

THE RIDER NEWS / RIDER UNIVERSITY — 2083 Lawrenceville Rd, Lawrenceville, NJ, 08648-3099, USA; tel (609) 896-5256; fax (609) 895-5696; e-mail: ridernews@rider.edu; web site: www.theridernews.comEst. 1930
Co-Adviser — Dianne Garyantes
Format: Tabloid

UNION COUNTY COLLEGE: SCROLL — 1033 Springfield Ave, Cranford, NJ, 07016-1598, USA; tel (908) 709-7000; web site: www.ucc.edu
Vice Pres. — John R. Farrell
Format: Tabloid

WILLIAM PATERSON UNIV.: THE BEACON — 300 Pompton Rd # SC329A, Wayne, NJ, 07470-2103, USA; tel (973) 720-3265; fax (973) 720-2093; e-mail: wpubeacon@hotmail.com; web site: www.wpubeacon.com
Jeff Wakemen
Tim Kauffeld
Robin Mulder
Format: Tabloid

NEW MEXICO

EASTERN NEW MEXICO UNIV.: THE CHASE — Station 27, Portales, NM, 88130-7400, USA; tel (575) 562-2757; fax (575) 562-2847; web site: https://www.enmuthechaseonline.com/
Advisor — Abigail Pino
Advisor
(dept. chair, associate prof of communication, graduate coordinator) — Patricia Dobson
Published: Mon
Digital Edition Available?: Y
Format: Broadsheet

NEW MEXICO DAILY LOBO — 1 University of New Mexico MS 3, Albuquerque, NM, 87131-0001, USA; tel (505) 277-7527; fax (505) 277-6228; e-mail: advertising@dailylobo.com; adv email: advertising@dailylobo.com; ed email: news@dailylobo.com; web site: www.dailylobo.com Est. 1895
Ed. in Chief — Jyllian Roach
Managing Ed. — JR Oppenheim
News Ed. — Jonathan Baca
News Ed. — Daniel Montano
Photo Ed. — Sergio Jimenez
Asst. Photo Ed. — William Aranda
Culture Ed. — Stephen Montoya
Asst. Culture Ed. — Tomas Lujan
Sports Ed. — Thomas Romero-Salas
Design Dir. — Jonathan Gamboa
Design Dir. — Sarah Lynas
Copy Chief — Craig Dubyk
Copy Ed. — Leanne Lucero
Ad. Mgr. — Zach Pavlik
Sales Mgr. — Sammy Chumpolpakdee
Class. Mgr. — Hannah Dowdy-Sue
News Ed. — David Lynch
Photo Ed. — Nick Fojud
Web Ed. — Veronica Munoz
Published: Mon, Tues, Wed, Thur, Fri, Sat

NEW MEXICO INST. OF MINING & TECHNOLOGY: PAYDIRT — 801 Leroy Pl, Socorro, NM, 87801-4750, USA; tel (575) 835-5525; fax (505) 835-6364; e-mail: paydirt@nmt.edu; paydirt-editor@nmt.edu; paydirt-ads@nmt.edu
Roger Renteria
Rachel Armstrong
Format: Tabloid

NEW MEXICO STATE UNIV.: ROUND UP — PO Box 30001, Las Cruces, NM, 88003-8001, USA; tel (575) 646-6397; fax (575) 646-5557; e-mail: roundup@nmsu.edu; web site: www.roundupnews.com
Jeff Hand
Jon Blazak
Format: Tabloid

UNIV. OF NEW MEXICO: NEW MEXICO DAILY LOBO — 1 University of New Mexico MS 3, Albuquerque, NM, 87131-0001, USA; tel (505) 277-5656; fax (505) 277-7530; e-mail: advertising@dailylobo.com; adv email: advertising@dailylobo.com; ed email: editorinchief@dailylobo.com; web site: www.dailylobo.comEst. 1895
Jim Fisher
Published: Mon, Tues, Wed, Thur, FriCirc.(fr.) 9,000
Digital Edition Available?: Y
Digital Platform - Mobile: Apple, Android
Digital Platform - Tablet: Apple iOS
Insert rate: $900
Price: Free
Format: Tabloid

NEW YORK

ALBANY COLLEGE OF PHARMACY: MORTAR AND PESTLE — 106 New Scotland Ave, Albany, NY, 12208-3492, USA; tel (518) 445-7200; fax (518) 445-7202
Jennie O'Rourke
Format: Tabloid

ALFRED UNIV.: FIAT LUX — Powell Campus Ctr., Alfred, NY, 14802, USA; tel (607) 871-2192; fax (607) 871-3797; e-mail: fiatlux@alfred.edu; web site: www.thefiatlux.com/
Robyn Goodman
Nadine Titus
Thomas Fleming
Format: Tabloid

BARD COLLEGE: BARD OBSERVER — PO Box 5000, Annandale, NY, 12504-5000, USA; tel (845) 758-7131; fax (845) 758-4294; e-mail: observer@bard.edu; web site: observer.bard.edu/index.shtml
Becca Rom Frank
Lilian Robinson
Christine Gehringer
Format: Tabloid

BARNARD COLLEGE: BARNARD BULLETIN — 3009 Broadway Frnt 1, New York, NY, 10027-6598, USA; tel (212) 854-5262; fax (212) 854-6220; e-mail: bulletinedboard@gmail.com; backcover@barnardbulletin.com; web site: barnardbulletin.com
Iffat Kabeer
Alison Hodgson
Meagan McElroy
Format: Magazine

BARUCH COLLEGE/CUNY: THE TICKER — 1 Bernard Baruch Way Ste 3-290, New York, NY, 10010-5585, USA; tel (646) 312-4712; fax (646) 312-4711; web site: www.theticker.org
Carl Aylman
Jhaneel Lockhart
Format: Tabloid

BOROUGH OF MANHATTAN CMTY. COLLEGE: VOICE OF THE VOICELESS — 199 Chambers St Rm S-207, New York, NY, 10007-1044, USA; tel (212) 220-8000; web site: www.bmcc.cuny.edu
Dr. Juliet Emanuel
Format: Tabloid

BRONX CMTY. COLLEGE: THE COMMUNICATOR — W. 181st St. & University Ave., Bronx, NY, 10453-2895, USA; tel (718) 289-5445; fax (718) 289-6324; e-mail: communicator@bcc.cuny.edu; web site: www.bcc.cuny.edu
Advisor — Andrew Rowan
Format: Tabloid

BROOME CMTY. COLLEGE — PO Box 1017, Binghamton, NY, 13902-1017, USA; tel (607) 778-5110
Bill Frobe

CANISIUS COLLEGE: THE GRIFFIN — 2001 Main St, Buffalo, NY, 14208-1098, USA; tel (716) 888-2115; fax (716) 888-3118; e-mail: Irwin@canisius.edu
Professor of Communications — Barbara Irwin
Eric Koehler
Jennifer Gorczynski
Marisa Loffredo
Format: Tabloid

CARDOZO SCHOOL OF LAW/YESHIVA — 55 5th Ave Fl 6, New York, NY, 10003-4301, USA; tel (212) 790-0283; fax (212) 790-0345; e-mail: cardozoinsider@att.net
Heela Justin

CAYUGA COMMUNITY COLLEGE: CAYUGA COLLEGIAN — 197 Franklin St, Auburn, NY, 13021-3011, USA; tel (315) 255-1743; fax (315) 255-2117; e-mail: cayugacollegian@gmail.comEst. 1954
Mary Gelling Merrit
Published: ON ANNOUNCED SCHEDULECirc. (fr.) 1,000
Digital Edition Available?: Y
Digital Platform - Tablet: Other
Price: Free
Format: Broadsheet

CITY COLLEGE OF NEW YORK: CAMPUS — Rm. 1-119, North Academic Center Bldg., 160 Convent Ave., New York, NY, 10031, USA; tel (212) 650-8177; fax (212) 650-8197; e-mail: ccnycampus@gmail.com; web site: www.ccnycampus.com
Linda Villarosa
Tania Bhuiyan
Format: Tabloid

CLARKSON UNIV.: INTEGRATOR — PO Box 8710, Potsdam, NY, 13699-0001, USA; tel (315) 265-9050; fax (315) 268-7661; e-mail: integrat@clarkson.edu; web site: www.clarksonintegrator.com
Mary Konecnik
Robert Trerice
Format: Tabloid

COLGATE UNIV.: COLGATE MAROON-NEWS — Student Union, Hamilton, NY, 13346, USA; tel (315) 228-7744; fax (315) 228-6839; e-mail: maroonnews@colgate.edu; adv email: ads.maroonnews@gmail.com; ed email: colgatemaroonnews@gmail.com; web site: thecolgatemaroonnews.comEst. 1868
Ed. — Matthew Knowles
Ed. — Luke Currim
Exec. Ed. — Amanda Golden
Published: ThurCirc.(fr.) 1,600
Digital Edition Available?: Y
Price: Free
Format: Tabloid

COLLEGE OF MT. ST. VINCENT: THE MOUNT TIMES — The Mount Times, Bronx, NY, 10471-1093, USA; tel (718) 405-3471; e-mail: mountimes@mountsaintvincent.edu; ed email: nquaranto.student@mountsaintvincent.eduEst. 1980
EIC — Nicole Quaranto
Co-EIC — Micheal Stephens-Emerson
Published: Bi-Mthly
Digital Edition Available?: N
Format: Tabloid

COLLEGE OF NEW ROCHELLE: TATLER — 29 Castle Pl Ste 1, New Rochelle, NY, 10805-2339, USA; tel (914) 654-5207; fax (914) 654-5866; e-mail: tatler@cnr.edu
Elizabeth Brinkman
Format: Tabloid

COLLEGE OF ST. ROSE: CHRONICLE — 432 Western Ave, Albany, NY, 12203-1490, USA; tel (518) 454-5151; fax (518) 454-2001; e-mail: chronicle@strose.edu; web site: www.strosechronicle.com
Cailin Brown
Execu Ed — Josh Heller
Mng Ed — Jonas Miller

Published: Tues
Price: Free
Format: Broadsheet

COLLEGE OF STATEN ISLAND: THE BANNER — 2800 Victory Blvd, Staten Island, NY, 10314-6600, USA; tel (718) 982-3056; fax (718) 982-3087; web site: www.csi.cuny.edu
Philip Masciantonio
Format: Tabloid

COLUMBIA UNIV.: COLUMBIA DAILY SPECTATOR — 2875 Broadway Ste 3, New York, NY, 10025-7847, USA; tel (212) 854-9550; fax (212) 854-9553; e-mail: info@columbiaspectator.com; spectator@columbia.edu; web site: www.columbiaspectator.com
Akhil Mehta
Ben Cotton
Thomas Rhiel
Andrew Hitti
Dir., Fin — Oscar
Dir. — Yipeng
Format: Broadsheet

COLUMBIA UNIV. BUS. SCHOOL — 3022 Broadway Rm 242, New York, NY, 10027-6945, USA; tel (212) 854-8396; fax (212) 854-7557
Matt Wong
Format: Broadsheet

COLUMBIA UNIV. LAW SCHOOL — 435 W 116th St, New York, NY, 10027-7237, USA; tel (212) 854-5833; fax (212) 854-1229; e-mail: jar2045@columbia.edu
Matthew Dean
Format: Broadsheet

COOPER UNION: COOPER PIONEER — 30 Cooper Sq Fl 3, New York, NY, 10003-7120, USA; tel (212) 353-4133; fax (212) 353-4343; ed email: Cooperpioneer@gmail.com
Bill McAllister
Format: Tabloid

CORNELL LAW SCHOOL — Myron Taylor Hall, Ithaca, NY, 14853, USA; tel (607) 255-0565
Rick Silverman
Format: Tabloid

CORNELL UNIV. ECONOMICS SCHOOL: THE VISIBLE — Cornell Dept. of Economics, Uris Hall, 4th Fl., Ithaca, NY, 14850, USA; tel (607) 255-8501; web site: www.rso.cornell.edu/ces
Rabia Muqaddam
Format: Magazine

CORNING CMTY. COLLEGE: THE CRIER — 1 Academic Dr, Corning, NY, 14830-3299, USA; tel (607) 962-9339; fax (607) 962-9008; e-mail: criernewspaper@yahoo.com
Paul McNaney
Format: Tabloid

CULINARY INSTITUTE OF AMERICA: LA PAPILLOTE — 1946 Campus Dr, Hyde Park, NY, 12538-1499, USA; tel (845) 452-1412; fax (845) 451-1093; e-mail: lapapillote@culinary.edu; web site: www.ciachef.eduEst. 1979
David Whalen
Published: Fri, Mthly
Digital Edition Available?: Y
Price: Free
Format: Tabloid

CUNY SCHOOL OF LAW: CUNY MATTERS — 2 Court Sq, Long Island City, NY, 11101-4356, USA; tel (718) 340-4222; web site: www.law.cuny.edu

CUNY SCHOOLS — 250 Bedford Park Blvd W, Bronx, NY, 10468-1527, USA; tel (718) 960-4966; fax (718) 960-7848; e-mail: lehmanmeridian@gmail.com
Michael Sullivan
Format: Tabloid

CUNY/BROOKLYN COLLEGE: THE KINGSMAN — 2900 Bedford Ave, Brooklyn, NY, 11210-2850, USA; tel (718) 951-5000; fax (718) 434-0875; e-mail: Dylc23@gmail.com; adv email: kingsman.buisness@; ed email: Dylc23@gmail.com; web site: http://kingsmanbc.com
Paul Moses
Published: Tues
Digital Edition Available?: Y
Digital Platform - Mobile: Apple
Digital Platform - Tablet: Apple iOS
Insert rate: N/A
Price: Free
Format: Tabloid

DOWLING COLLEGE: LIONS VOICE — 150 Idle Hour Blvd, Oakdale, NY, 11769-1999, USA; tel (631) 244-3000; fax (631) 244-3028; web site: lionsvoice.dowling.edu
Laura Pope Robbins
Derek Stevens
Format: Tabloid

DUTCHESS CMTY. COLLEGE: DUTCHESS CHRONICLE — 53 Pendell Rd, Poughkeepsie, NY, 12601-1595, USA; tel (845) 431-8000; fax (845) 431-8989; e-mail: communityrelations@sunydutchess.edu; Helpdesk@sunydutchess.edu; web site: www.sunydutchess.edu
Kevin Lang
Format: Tabloid

ELMIRA COLLEGE: OCTAGON — 1 Park Pl, Elmira, NY, 14901-2099, USA; tel (607) 735-1800; e-mail: octagon@elmira.edu; admissions@elmira.edu; web site: www.elmira.edu
David Williams
Jolene Carr
Format: Tabloid

FASHION INST. OF TECHNOLOGY: W27 — 227 W 27th St Ste A727, New York, NY, 10001-5902, USA; tel (212) 217-7999; fax (212) 217-7144; e-mail: w27newspaper@gmail.com; web site: www.fitnyc.edu
Richard Baleschrino
Format: Tabloid

FORDHAM UNIV.: THE RAM — 441 E. Fordham Rd., Sta. 37, Box B, Bronx, NY, 10458, USA; tel (718) 817-4379; fax (718) 817-4319; e-mail: theram@fordham.edu; web site: www.theramonline.com
Beth Knobel
Amanda Fiscina
Abigail Forget
Format: Tabloid

FORDHAM UNIV. LINCOLN CENTER: OBSERVER — 140 W. 62nd St., Rm. G-32, New York, NY, 10023-7414, USA; tel (212) 636-6280; fax (212) 636-7047; e-mail: fordhamobserver@gmail.com; adv email: fordhamobserveradvertising@gmail.com; web site: www.fordhamobserver.com
Elizabeth Stone
Ashley WennersHerron
Published: Other
Format: Tabloid

HAMILTON COLLEGE: SPECTATOR — 198 College Hill Rd, Clinton, NY, 13323-1295, USA; tel (315) 859-4011; fax (315) 859-4563
Erin W. Hoener
Insert rate: spec@hamilton.edu
Format: Tabloid

HARTWICK COLLEGE — c/o Daily Star, PO Box 250, Oneonta, NY, 13820, USA; tel (607) 432-1000; fax (607) 432-5847; e-mail: breeves@thedailystar.com; hilltops@hartwick.edu
Bill Reeves
Danielle Peloquin
Format: Tabloid

HILBERT COLLEGE: THE H-FILES — 5200 S Park Ave, Hamburg, NY, 14075-1597, USA; tel (716) 649-7900; fax (716) 649-0702; e-mail: info@hilbert.edu; web site: www.hilbert.edu
Charles A. S. Ernst
Published: 3 months in fall & spring
Digital Edition Available?: N
Format: Tabloid

HOBART & WILLIAM SMITH COLLEGE: HERALD — 300 Pulteney St, Geneva, NY, 14456-3382, USA; tel (315) 781-3857; e-mail: herald@hws.edu
Charlie Wilson
Belinda Littlefield
Format: Tabloid

HOFSTRA UNIV.: THE CHRONICLE — 200 Hofstra Univ., Rm. 203 Student Ctr., Hempstead, NY, 11550-1022, USA; tel (516) 463-6965; fax (516) 463-6977; web site: www.hofstrachronicle.com
Peter Goodman
Published: Tues
Digital Edition Available?: Y
Format: Tabloid

HOFSTRA UNIVERSITY: THE HOFSTRA CHRONICLE — 200 Hofstra University, Student Ctr., Room 203, Hempstead, NY, 11550, USA; tel (516) 463-6921; e-mail: hofstrachronicle@gmail.com; adv email: thechronicle.business@gmail.com; web site: www.thehofstrachronicle.comEst. 1935
Business Manager — Jake Nussbaum
Published: ThurCirc.(fr.) 3,000
Digital Edition Available?: Y
Format: Tabloid

HOUGHTON COLLEGE: HOUGHTON STAR — 1 Willard Ave Cpo 378, Houghton, NY, 14744-8732, USA; tel (585) 567-9500; fax (585) 567-9570; e-mail: star@houghton.edu; web site: www.houghtonstar.com
Joel Vanderweele
Format: Broadsheet

HUDSON VALLEY CMTY. COLLEGE: THE HUDSONIAN — 80 Vandenburgh Ave, Troy, NY, 12180-6037, USA; tel (518) 629-7187; fax (518) 629-7496; e-mail: hudnews@yahoo.com; web site: www.hvcc.edu
Mat Cantore
Nicole Monsees
Format: Tabloid

HUNTER COLLEGE/CUNY: HUNTER ENVOY — 695 Park Ave Rm 211, New York, NY, 10065-5024, USA; tel (212) 772-4251; fax (212) 772-5539; web site: www.thehunterenvoy.com
Joe Ireland
Format: Tabloid

IONA COLLEGE: THE IONIAN — 715 North Ave., LaPenta Student Union, 2nd Fl., New Rochelle, NY, 10801-1830, USA; tel (914) 633-2370; e-mail: ionian@iona.edu; web site: www.iona.edu
Hugh Short
James Hurley
Alana Rome
Heather Nannery
Format: Tabloid

ITHACA COLLEGE: ITHACAN — 269 Park Hall, Ithaca, NY, 14850-7258, USA; tel (607) 274-3208; fax (607) 274-1376; e-mail: ithacan@ithaca.edu; adv email: ithacanads@ithaca.edu; web site: www.theithacan.org
Michael Serino
Kira Maddox
Rachel Wolfgang
Advertising Sales Manager — Lawrence Hamacher
Published: ThurCirc.(fr.) 4,000
Digital Edition Available?: Y
Insert rate: $150 per 1000 issues (minimum 4000)
Format: Tabloid

JEFFERSON CMTY. COLLEGE: CANNON — 1220 Coffeen St, Watertown, NY, 13601-1897, USA; tel (315) 786-2200; fax (315) 788-0716; web site: www.sunyjefferson.edu
Andrea Pedrick
Danielle Sacca
Rachel Hunter
Format: Tabloid

JEWISH STUDENT PRESS SERVICE: NEW VOICES — 114 W 26th St Rm 1004, New York, NY, 10001-6812, USA; tel (212) 675-1168; fax (212) 929-3459; web site: www.newvoices.orgEst. 1970
Ben Sales
Format: Magazine

JOHN JAY COLLEGE OF CRIMINAL JUSTICE: THE JOHN JAY TIMES — 524 W 59th St, New York, NY, 10019-1007, USA; tel (212) 237-8308; fax (212) 237-8036
Babafunmilayo Oke
Format: Tabloid

KEUKA COLLEGE: KEUKONIAN — Office of Commun., Keuka Park, NY, 14478, USA; tel (315) 279-5231; fax (315) 279-5281; web site: www.keukonian.keuka.edu
Christen Smith
Kilee Brown
Chelsea DeGroote
Format: Tabloid

KINGSBOROUGH CMTY. COLLEGE: SCEPTER — 2001 Oriental Blvd # M230, Brooklyn, NY, 11235-2333, USA; tel (718) 368-5603; fax (718) 368-4833; e-mail: scepter@kingsborough.edu; web site: www.kbcc.cuny.edu/aboutKCC/Scepter
Kim Gill
Format: Tabloid

THE DOLPHIN — 1419 Salt Springs Rd, Syracuse, NY, 13214-1302, USA; tel (315) 445-4542; e-mail: dolphin@lemoyne.edu; adv email: dolphin@lemoyne.edu; ed email: dolphin@lemoyne.edu; web site: http://www.lemoyne.edu/DOING/CLUBS/TheDolphin/tabid/1959/Default.aspx
Co-Executive Editor — Ashley Casey
Amy Dieffenbacher
Price: Free
Format: Tabloid

LEHMAN COLLEGE: MERIDIAN — 250 Bedford Park Blvd W Rm 108, Bronx, NY, 10468-1589, USA; tel (718) 960-4966; fax (718) 960-8075; e-mail: lehmanmeridian@gmail.com; web site: www.lcmeridian.com
Jennifer Mackenzie
Alisia Cordero
Sidra Lackey
Published: Mthly
Digital Edition Available?: Y
Format: Tabloid

LONG ISLAND UNIV.: SEAWANHAKA — 1 University Plz Rm S305, Brooklyn, NY, 11201-5301, USA; tel (718) 488-1591; fax (718) 780-4182; e-mail: seawanhakapress@yahoo.com; web site: seawanhakapress.blogspot.com
Hal Bock
Ian Smith
Christina Long
Format: Tabloid

LONG ISLAND UNIV./C.W.POST: PIONEER — Hillwood Commons, Rm. 199, 720 Northern Blvd. (25A), Brookville, NY, 11548, USA; tel (516) 299-2619; fax (516) 299-2617; e-mail: pioneer@cwpost.liu.eduEst. 1954
Valerie Kellogg
Daniel Schrafel

Lisa Martens
Format: Tabloid

MANHATTAN COLLEGE: QUADRANGLE — 4513 Manhattan College Pkwy, Riverdale, NY, 10471, USA; tel (718) 862-7270; e-mail: thequad@manhatten.edu; web site: www.mcquadrangle.org
Jonathan Stone
Dom Delgardo
Brian O'Connor
Format: Tabloid

MANHATTANVILLE COLLEGE: TOUCHSTONE — 2900 Purchase St, Purchase, NY, 10577-2132, USA; tel (914) 323-5498; e-mail: touchstone@mville.edu; web site: http://mvilletouchstone.com/
Dana Schildkraut
Format: Tabloid

MARIST COLLEGE: CIRCLE — Lowell Thomas Communications Building Room 135-Mac Lab, Poughkeepsie, NY, 12601-1387, USA; tel (845) 575-3000; e-mail: writethecircle@hotmail.com; web site: www.maristcircle.com
Margeaux Lippman
Kaitlyn Smith
Matthew Spillane
Format: Tabloid

MEDAILLE COLLEGE: PERSPECTIVE — 18 Agassiz Cir, Buffalo, NY, 14214-2695, USA; tel (716) 884-3281; fax (716) 884-0291; web site: www.medailleperspective.com
Lisa Murphy
Megan Fitzgerald
Format: Tabloid

MEDGAR EVERS COLLEGE OF CUNY: ADAFI — 1637 Bedford Ave Rm S-304, Brooklyn, NY, 11225-2001, USA; tel (718) 270-6436; e-mail: adafi@mec.cuny.edu; student-club@mec.cuny.edu; web site: www.adafi.org
Robin Regina Ford
Luc Josaphat
Samantha Sylvester
Format: Tabloid

MERCY COLLEGE: THE IMPACT — 555 Broadway Frnt, Dobbs Ferry, NY, 10522-1189, USA; tel (914) 674-7422; fax (914) 674-7433; e-mail: mercyimpactnews@hotmail.com; web site: www.theimpactnews.com
Michael Perrota
Format: Tabloid

MONROE CMTY. COLLEGE: MONROE DOCTRINE — 1000 E Henrietta Rd, Rochester, NY, 14623-5780, USA; tel (585) 292-2540; e-mail: monroedoctrine@me.com; web site: www.monroedoctrine.orgEst. 1963
Lori Moses
Published: Other bi-weeklyCirc.(fr.) 3,500
Insert rate: n/a
Price: Free
Format: tabloid
Note: www.monroedoctrine.org

MORRISVILLE STATE COLLEGE: THE CHIMES — Journalism Dept., Morrisville, NY, 13408, USA; tel (315) 684-6041; fax (315) 684-6247; e-mail: chimes@morrisville.edu; adv email: mcdowebl@morrisville.edu; web site: thechimes.morrisville.edu
Brian McDowell
Format: Tabloid

MT. ST. MARY COLLEGE: CLARION — 330 Powell Ave, Newburgh, NY, 12550-3494, USA; tel (845) 569-3100; fax (845) 561-6762
Vince Begley
Nathan Rosenblum
Format: Tabloid

NASSAU CMTY. COLLEGE: VIGNETTE — College Ctr., 1 Education Dr., Garden City, NY, 11530-6793, USA; tel (516) 222-7071; fax (516) 572-3566; e-mail: informationservices@ncc.edu; vignetters@yahoo.com
Richard Conway
Format: Tabloid

NAZARETH COLLEGE OF ROCHESTER: GLEANER — 4245 East Ave, Rochester, NY, 14618-3790, USA; tel (585) 389-2525; fax (585) 586-2452
Halinka Spencer
Format: Tabloid

NEW YORK INSTITUTE OF TECHNOLOGY: CAMPUS SLATE — Northern Boulevard PO Box 8000, Old Westbury, NY, 11568, USA; tel (516) 686-7646; fax (516) 626-1290; e-mail: slate@nyit.edu; adv email: slate@nyit.edu; web site: www.campusslate.comEst. 1966
John Hanc
Editor in Chief — John Santamaria
Managing Editor — Kyle Reitan
Format: Tabloid

NEW YORK INSTITUTE OF TECHNOLOGY: NYIT CHRONICLE — 1849 Broadway Rm 212, New York, NY, 10023-7602, USA; tel (212) 261-1693; e-mail: chronicle@nyit.edu
William Lawrence
Format: Tabloid

NEW YORK LAW SCHOOL: THE DENOVO — 57 Worth St Rm L2, New York, NY, 10013-2926, USA; tel (212) 431-2100
Sally Harding
Format: Tabloid

NEW YORK METRO COMMUNITY COLLEGES: CAMPUS NEWS — 39 County Route 70, Greenwich, NY, 12834, USA; tel (518) 879 0965; fax (518) 507 6782; e-mail: editor@campus-news.org; adv email: advertising@campus-news.org; ed email: editor@campus-news.org; web site: www.campus-news.orgEst. 2010
Darren Johnson
Published: Mthly, Bi-MthlyCirc.(fr.) 10,000
Digital Edition Available?: Y
Price: Free
Format: Tabloid
Note: Community College Campus News hits 37 2-year colleges in the Northeast; mostly in the New York Metro region.

NEW YORK UNIV.: WASHINGTON SQUARE NEWS — 7 E 12th St Ste 800, New York, NY, 10003-4475, USA; tel (212) 998-4300; fax (212) 995-3790; web site: www.nyunews.com
David Cosgrove
Julia McCarthy
Eric Platt
Rachael Smith
Format: Tabloid

NEW YORK UNIVERSITY SCHOOL OF LAW: THE COMMENTATOR — 40 Washington Sq S Rm 110, New York, NY, 10012-1005, USA; tel (212) 998-0564; fax (212) 995-4032; e-mail: Law.commentator@nyu.edu; adv email: Law.commentator@nyu.edu; ed email: Law.commentator@nyu.edu; web site: www.law.nyu.edu/studentorganizations/thecommentatorEst. 1966
Naeem Crawford-Muhammad
Andrew S. Gehring
Robert Gerrity
Ana Namaki
Digital Edition Available?: Y
Digital Platform - Mobile: Apple, Android, Blackberry, Other
Digital Platform - Tablet: Apple iOS, Android, Blackberry Tablet OS, Kindle, Kindle Fire, Other
Format: Tabloid

NIAGARA COUNTY CMTY. COLLEGE: SPIRIT — 3111 Saunders Settlement Rd Ste 1, Sanborn, NY, 14132-9460, USA; tel (716) 614-6259; fax (716) 614-6264; e-mail: spirit@niagaracc.suny.edu
Amanda Pucci
Format: Tabloid

NIAGARA UNIV.: THE NIAGRA INDEX — Gallagher Ctr., Niagara University, NY, 14109-1919, USA; tel (716) 286-8512; fax (716) 286-8542; e-mail: theniagaraindex@yahoo.com
Bill Wolcott
Mary Colleen Mahoney
Marissa Christman
Format: Tabloid

NYACK COLLEGE: NYACK FORUM — 1 S Boulevard, Nyack, NY, 10960-3698, USA; tel (845) 358-1710; e-mail: wnyk@nyack.edu; forum@nyack.edu; web site: www.nyack.edu
Charles Beach
Format: Tabloid

NYU STERN SCHOOL OF BUS. — 44 W 4th St Mec 6-130, New York, NY, 10012-1106, USA; tel (212) 995-4432; fax (212) 995-4606; e-mail: opportun@stern.nyu.edu; helpdesk@stern.nyu.edu; web site: www.sternopportunity.com
Jeremy Carrine
Deborah Garcia
Rakesh Duggal
Format: Tabloid

ONONDAGA CMTY. COLLEGE: OVERVIEW — Rt. 173, Student Ctr. G100, Syracuse, NY, 13215, USA; tel (315) 498-2278; fax (315) 498-2001
Patti Orty
Format: Tabloid

ORANGE COUNTY CMTY. COLLEGE — 115 South St, Middletown, NY, 10940-6404, USA; tel (845) 341-4240; fax (845) 341-4238

PACE UNIV.: THE PACE PRESS — 41 Park Row Rm 902, New York, NY, 10038-1508, USA; tel (212) 346-1553; fax (212) 346-1265; e-mail: editor@pacepress.org; web site: www.pacepress.org
Mark McSherry
Format: Tabloid

PACE UNIV.: PACE CHRONICLE — 861 Bedford Rd., Pleasantville, NY, 10570-2799, USA; e-mail: pacechronicle@pace.edu
Katherine Fink
Published: Wed
Digital Edition Available?: Y
Format: Broadsheet

PACE UNIV. LAW SCHOOL: HEARSAY — 78 N Broadway, White Plains, NY, 10603-3710, USA; tel (914) 422-4205; e-mail: hearsay@law.case.edu; web site: www.law.pace.edu
Angela D'agostino
Format: Tabloid

POLYTECHNIC INSTITUTE OF NYU: THE POLYTECHNIC REPORTER — 6 Metrotech Ctr, Brooklyn, NY, 11201-3840, USA; tel (718) 260-3600; web site: www.poly.edu
Lowell Scheiner
Robert Griffin
William Modeste Jr.
Cheryl Mcnear
Format: Tabloid

PRATT INSTITUTE: THE PRATTLER — 200 Willoughby Ave, Brooklyn, NY, 11205, USA; tel 7186363600; e-mail: theprattler@gmail.com; ed email: theprattler@gmail.com; web site: www.prattleronline.comEst. 1940
Emily Oldenquist
Published: Other
Digital Edition Available?: Y
Format: Tabloid

QUEENS COLLEGE/CUNY: THE KNIGHT NEWS — 6530 Kissena Blvd, Flushing, NY, 11367-1597, USA; tel (718) 997-5000; e-mail: info@theknightnews.com; web site: www.theknightnews.com
Gerry Solomon
Editor-in-Chief — Will Sammon
Editor-In-Chief — Andrea Hardalo
Published: Tues
Digital Edition Available?: Y
Digital Platform - Mobile: Other
Format: Tabloid

QUEENSBOROUGH CMTY. COLLEGE: QUEENSBOROUGH COMMUNIQUE — 22205 56th Ave, Bayside, NY, 11364-1432, USA; tel (718) 631-6262; fax (718) 631-6637; web site: www.qcc.cuny.edu
Andrew Levy
Format: Tabloid

RENSSELAER POLYTECHNIC INST.: POLYTECHNIC — Rensselaer Union, Troy, NY, 12180-3590, USA; tel (518) 276-6000; fax (518) 276-8728; e-mail: poly@rpi.edu; business@poly.rpi.edu; adv email: notices@poly.rpi.edu; ed email: editor@poly.rpi.edu; news@poly.rpi.edu; edop@poly.rpi.edu; edop@poly.rpi.edu; sports@poly.rpi.edu; photo@poly.rpi.edu; notices@poly.rpi.edu; web site: www.poly.rpi.edu
Richard Hartt
Format: Tabloid

ROBERTS WESLEYAN COLLEGE: BEACON — 2301 Westside Dr Ofc, Rochester, NY, 14624-1997, USA; tel (585) 594-6385; fax (585) 594-6567; e-mail: beacon@roberts.edu
Editor-In-Chief — Taylor Plourde
Assistant Editor — Elisabeth Lindke
Layout Editor — Derick Trost
Published: Mthly
Digital Edition Available?: N
Format: Tabloid

ROCHESTER INST. OF TECHNOLOGY: REPORTER MAGAZINE — 37 Lomb Memorial Dr, Rochester, NY, 14623-5602, USA; tel (585) 475-2213; fax (585) 475-2214; e-mail: reporter@rit.edu; web site: www.reportermag.com
Rudy Pugliese
Andy Rees
Format: Tabloid

ROCKLAND CMTY. COLLEGE: OUTLOOK STUDENT PRESS — 145 College Rd, Suffern, NY, 10901-3699, USA; tel (845) 574-4389; e-mail: outlookpress@gmail.com; web site: www.sunyrockland.edu
Format: Tabloid

RUSSELL SAGE COLLEGE: QUILL — 65 1st St, Troy, NY, 12180-4003, USA; tel 518-244-2016; e-mail: perkip@sage.edu; adv email: perkip@sage.edu; ed email: perkip@sage.edu; web site: www.thequillrsc.comEst. 1950s
Penny Perkins
Format: Tabloid

SCHOOL OF VISUAL ARTS: VISUAL OPINION — 209 E 23rd St, New York, NY, 10010-3994, USA; tel (212) 592-2280; fax (212) 725-3587
Tina Crayton
Jane Resnick
Format: Magazine

SIENA COLLEGE: THE PROMETHEAN — 515 Loudon Rd., Student Union, Loudonville, NY, 12211-1459, USA; tel (518) 783-2330; fax (518) 786-5053; e-mail: newspaper@siena.edu; adv email: newspaper@siena.edu; ed email: newspaper@siena.edu; web site: www.siena.eduEst. 1937
Editor-in-Chief — Emily Radigan
Published: Fri
Published biweeklyCirc. (pd.) 0 (fr.) 500

Digital Edition Available?: N
Format: Broadsheet

SOUTHAMPTON COLLEGE — 239 Montauk Hwy, Southampton, NY, 11968-4198, USA; tel (631) 287-8239; fax (631) 287-5147
Diane Prescott

ST. BONAVENTURE UNIV.: THE BONA VENTURE — PO Box X, Saint Bonaventure, NY, 14778-2303, USA; tel (716) 375-2227; fax (716) 375-2252; e-mail: bonavent@sbu.edu; web site: www.thebv.org
Faculty Advisor — Carole McNall
Editor in Chief — Samantha Berkhead
Managing Editor — Kevin Rogers
Format: Broadsheet

ST. FRANCIS COLLEGE: VOICE — 180 Remsen St, Brooklyn, NY, 11201-4398, USA; tel (718) 522-2300; fax (718) 522-1274; e-mail: sscvoice@gmail.com
Emily Horowitz
Kevin Korber
Format: Tabloid

ST. JOHN FISHER COLLEGE: THE CARDINAL COURIER — 3690 East Ave, Rochester, NY, 14618-3537, USA; tel (585) 385-8360; fax (585) 385-7311; e-mail: cardinalcourier@sjfc.edu; adv email: mvilla@sjfc.edu; ed email: eem00114@sjfc.edu; web site: www.cardinalcourieronline.comEst. 2002
Chair/Prof. — Lauren Vicker
Media Adviser — Marie Villa
Published: Bi-Mthly
Digital Edition Available?: Y
Digital Platform - Mobile: Apple, Android
Digital Platform - Tablet: Apple iOS, Android, Blackberry Tablet OS, Kindle, Kindle Fire
Format: Tabloid

ST. JOHN'S UNIVERSITY: THE TORCH — 8000 Utopia Pkwy, Jamaica, NY, 11439-9000, USA; tel (718) 990-6756; fax (718) 990-5849; adv email: torchads@gmail.com; ed email: torchnews@gmail.com; web site: www.torchonline.com
Editor-in-Chief — Michael Cunniff
Published: WedCirc.(fr.) 3,000
Insert rate: varies — ask for rate sheet
Price: Free
Format: Tabloid

ST. JOHNS UNIV.: STORM FRONT — 300 Howard Ave, Staten Island, NY, 10301-4496, USA; tel (718) 390-4500; fax (718) 447-0941; e-mail: siadmhelp@stjohns.edu; web site: www.stjohns.edu
Crista Camerlengl
Format: Tabloid

ST. JOSEPHS COLLEGE — 155 W Roe Blvd, Patchogue, NY, 11772-2399, USA; tel (631) 447-3200; fax (631) 654-1782; e-mail: talon.li@student.sjcny.edu
Erin Bailey

ST. LAWRENCE UNIV.: HILL NEWS — 23 Romoda Dr, Canton, NY, 13617-1501, USA; tel (315) 229-5139; e-mail: hillnews@stlawu.edu; web site: www.blogs.stlawu.edu/thehillnews
Juri Kittler
Rachel Barman
Format: Tabloid

ST. THOMAS AQUINAS COLLEGE: THE THOMA — 125 Route 340, Sparkill, NY, 10976-1050, USA; tel (845) 398-4075; fax (845) 359-8136; e-mail: thoma@yahoo.com; thoma@stac.edu; web site: www.stac.edu
Kathleen Giroux
Format: Tabloid

STERN COLLEGE FOR WOMEN: THE OBERSVER — 245 Lexington Ave, New York, NY, 10016-4699, USA; tel (212) 340-7715; fax (212) 340-7773; e-mail: scwobserver@gmail.com; web site: www.yuobserver.com
Format: Tabloid

SUNY COLLEGE AT GENESEO: THE LAMRON — 10 Macvittie Cir # 42, Geneseo, NY, 14454-1427, USA; tel (585) 245-5896; fax (585) 245-5284; e-mail: lamron@geneseo.edu; adv email: lamronad@geneseo.edu; web site: www.thelamron.comEst. 1922
Advisor — Maddy Smith
Maria Lima
Tom Wilder
Published: ThurCirc.(fr.) 3,000
Digital Edition Available?: Y
Digital Platform - Mobile: Apple, Android
Format: Tabloid

SUNY COLLEGE OF TECHNOLOGY/ CANTON — 34 Cornell Dr Ofc, Canton, NY, 13617-1037, USA; tel (315) 386-7315; fax (315) 386-7962; e-mail: quinells@canton.edu
Scott Quinell
Format: Tabloid

SUNY COLLEGE OF TECHNOLOGY/DELHI: CAMPUS VOICE — 222 Farrell Center, Delhi, NY, 13753, USA; tel (607) 746-4270; fax (607) 746-4323; e-mail: campusvoice@delhi.edu; adv email: campusvoice@delhi.edu; ed email: campusvoice@delhi.edu; web site: http://www.delhi.edu/campus-life/activities/campus-voice/index.php
Advisor — Christina Viafore
Published: Mthly
Digital Edition Available?: Y
Format: Tabloid

SUNY COLLEGE OF TECHNOLOGY/ FARMINGDALE: RAMBLER — Melville Rd., Roosevelt Hall, Farmingdale, NY, 11735, USA; tel (631) 420-2611; fax (631) 420-2692; e-mail: rambler@farmingdale.edu
Jeff Borga
Format: Tabloid

SUNY COLLEGE/BUFFALO: RECORD — 1300 Elmwood Ave., Student Union 414, Buffalo, NY, 14222, USA; tel (716) 878-4531; fax (716) 878-4532; e-mail: bscrecord@gmail.com; adv email: pignatelli.record@live.com; ed email: bscrecord@gmail.com; web site: www.bscrecord.comEst. 1913
Managing Editor — Brandon Schlager
Executive Editor — Mike Meiler
Opinion Editor — Brian Alexander
News Editor — Michael Canfield
Sports Editor — Tom Gallagher
Culture Editor — Jennifer Waters
Published: WedCirc.(fr.) 1,500
Digital Edition Available?: N
Format: Tabloid

SUNY COLLEGE/CORTLAND: DRAGON CHRONICLE — PO Box 2000, Cortland, NY, 13045-0900, USA; tel (607) 753-2803; e-mail: dragonchronicle@cortland.edu; web site: www.cortland.edu
Format: Tabloid

SUNY COLLEGE/NEW PALTZ: THE NEW PALTZ ORACLE — Rm. 417, Student Union Bldg., 1 Hawk Dr., New Paltz, NY, 12561, USA; tel (845) 257-3030; fax (845) 257-3031; e-mail: oracle@hawkmail.newpaltz.edu; web site: http://oracle.newpaltz.edu
Melisa Goldman
Emma Boddors
Editor-in-Chief — Andrew Wyrich
Published: Thur
Digital Edition Available?: Y
Format: Tabloid

SUNY COLLEGE/OLD WESTBURY: THE CATALYST — PO Box 210, Old Westbury, NY, 11568-0210, USA; tel (516) 876-3000; e-mail: owcatalyst@gmail.com
Alicia Grant
Format: Broadsheet

SUNY COLLEGE/ONEONTA: STATE TIMES — Ravine Pkwy., Oneonta, NY, 13820, USA; tel (607) 436-2492; fax (607) 436-2002
Janet Day
Juliette Price
Format: Tabloid

SUNY COLLEGE/OSWEGO: OSWEGONIAN — 139A Campus Ctr., Oswego, NY, 13126, USA; tel (315) 312-3600; fax (315) 312-3542; e-mail: gonian@oswego.edu; info@oswegonian.com; adv email: advertising@oswegonian.com; web site: www.oswegonian.comEst. 1935
Arvin Diddi
Editor-in-Chief — Adam Wolfe
Format: Broadsheet

SUNY INST. OF TECHNOLOGY UTICA/ ROME: FACTORY TIMES — PO Box 3050, Utica, NY, 13504-3050, USA; tel (315) 792-7426; fax (315) 734-4198; e-mail: factorytimes@gmail.com
Patricia Murphy
Mark Ziobro
Format: Magazine

SUNY PLATTSBURGH: CARDINAL POINTS — 101 Broad St, Plattsburgh, NY, 12901-2637, USA; tel (518) 564-2174; fax (518) 564-6397; e-mail: cp@cardinalpointsonline.com; adv email: advertising@cardinalpointsonline.com; ed email: cp@cardinalpointsonline.com; web site: www.cardinalpointsonline.comEst. 1969
Shawn Murphy
Bus Mgr — Maureen Provost
Published: FriCirc. (pd.) 1,700 (fr.) 1,300
Digital Edition Available?: Y
Digital Platform - Mobile: Other
Insert rate: no inserts accepted
Price: free on and off campus
Format: Broadsheet

SUNY SULLIVAN: PROJECTOR — 112 College Rd, Loch Sheldrake, NY, 12759-5721, USA; tel (845) 434-5750; fax (914) 434-4806; web site: www.sunysullivan.edu
Kathleen Birkett
Published: Mon
Format: newsletter

SUNY/ALBANY: ALBANY STUDENT PRESS — 353 Broadway, Albany, NY, 12246-2915, USA; tel (518) 442-5666; fax (518) 442-5664; e-mail: asp_online@hotmail.com; web site: www.albanystudentpress.org
Brett Longo
Ted Bean
Jon Campbell
Format: Broadsheet

SUNY/BINGHAMTON: PIPE DREAM — PO Box 6000, Binghamton, NY, 13902-6000, USA; tel (607) 777-2515; fax (607) 777-2600; ed email: editor@bupipedream.com; web site: www.bupipedream.com
Shinsuke Kawano
Ashley Tarr
Chris Carpenter
Melissa Bykofsky
Photo Ed. — Teressa
Opinion Ed. — Marina
Format: Tabloid

SUNY/BUFFALO: THE SPECTRUM — 132 Student Un, Buffalo, NY, 14260-2100, USA; tel (716) 645-2152; fax (716) 645-2766; e-mail: spectrum@buffalo.edu; web site: www.ubspectrum.com
Debbie Smith
Steven Marth
Format: Tabloid

SUNY/STONY BROOK: STATESMAN — PO Box 1530, Stony Brook, NY, 11790-0609, USA; tel (631) 632-6480; fax (631) 632-9128; e-mail: advertise@sbstatesman.org; web site: www.sbstatesman.com
Frank D'alessandro
Bradley Donaldson
Format: Tabloid

SYRACUSE UNIVERSITY: THE DAILY ORANGE — 744 Ostrom Ave, Syracuse, NY, 13210-2942, USA; tel (315) 443-2314; fax (315) 443-3689; e-mail: ads@dailyorange.com; adv email: ads@dailyorange.com; ed email: editor@dailyorange.com; web site: www.dailyorange.comEst. 1903
Advisor/Gen. Mgr. — Peter Waack
Published: Mon, Tues, Wed, Thur, FriCirc. (pd.) 5 (fr.) 6,000
Digital Edition Available?: Y
Digital Platform - Mobile: Apple, Android, Windows, Blackberry, Other
Digital Platform - Tablet: Apple iOS, Android, Windows 7, Blackberry Tablet OS, Kindle, Nook, Kindle Fire, Other
Insert rate: $60 per 1000
Price: Free
Format: Tabloid
Note: Voted the #1 college paper in 2012 by The Society of Professional Journalists. Voted #1 College Newspaper Website in 2013 by Editor and Publisher.

THE COLLEGE AT BROCKPORT, SUNY: THE STYLUS — 350 New Campus Dr, Brockport, NY, 14420-2914, USA; tel (585) 395-2230; e-mail: stylus@brockport.edu; web site: www.brockportstylus.orgEst. 1914
Editor-in-Chief — Alyssa Daley
Executive Editor — Kristina Livingston
Managing Editor — Victoria Martinez
Campus Talk Editor — Breonnah Colon
News Editor — Lou Venditti
Lifestyles Editor — Alexandra Weaver
Sports Editor — Panagiotis Argitis
Published: Wed
Digital Edition Available?: Y
Format: Tabloid

THE CORNELL DAILY SUN — 139 W State St, Ithaca, NY, 14850-5427, USA; tel (607) 273-3606; fax (607) 273-0746; e-mail: letters@cornelldailysun.com; web site: www.cornellsun.comEst. 1880
Editor in Chief — Ben Gitlin
Managing Editor — Michael Linhorst
Associate Editor — Dani Neuharth-Keusch
Web Editor — Rahul Kishore
Business Manager — Chloe Gatta
Advertising Manager — Helene Beauchemin
Justin wheeler
Keenan Weatherford
Michael J. Stratford
Sophia Qasir
Format: Tabloid

THE EMPIRE STATE TRIBUNE — USA; tel 212-659-0742; e-mail: estribune@tkc.edu; adv email: estribune@tkc.edu; ed email: estribune@tkc.edu; web site: www.empirestatetribune.comEst. 2005
Assistant Affiliate Professor of Journalism — Clemente Lisi
Published: MonCirc.(fr.) 100
Digital Platform - Mobile: Apple, Android, Windows, Blackberry
Digital Platform - Tablet: Apple iOS

THE SKIDMORE NEWS — 815 N Broadway, Saratoga Springs, NY, 12866-1632, USA; tel (518) 580-5000; fax (518) 580-5188; e-mail: skidnews@skidmore.edu; web site: www.skidmorenews.comEst. 1925
Savannah Grier
Format: Tabloid

TOURO COLLEGE JACOB D. FUCHSBERG LAW CENTER: THE RESTATEMENT — 225 Eastview Dr, Central Islip, NY, 11722-4539, USA; tel (631) 761-7000; fax (631) 761-7009;

web site: www.tourolaw.edu
Patti Desrochers
Format: Tabloid

UNION COLLEGE CONCORDIENSIS: CONCORDIENSIS — 807 Union St., Schenectady, NY, 12308, USA; tel (518) 388-7128; e-mail: concordy@gmail.com; adv email: advertising@concordy.com; web site: http://www.concordy.com/Est. 1877
Ed. in Chief — Ajay Major
Format: Tabloid

UNIV. OF ROCHESTER: CAMPUS TIMES — CPU 277086 Campus Post Office, Rochester, NY, 14627, USA; tel (585) 275-5942; fax (585) 273-5303; e-mail: ctads@mail.rochester.edu; ed email: editor@campustimes.org; web site: www.campustimes.org
Dan Wasserman
Liz Bremer
Dana Hilfinger
Format: Tabloid

UNIVERSITY AT BUFFALO SCHOOL OF LAW: LAW LINKS — 410 O'Brian Hall, Amherst, NY, 14260-1100, USA; tel (716) 645-3176; fax (716) 645-5940; e-mail: lmueller@buffalo.edu; ed email: lmueller@buffalo.edu; web site: www.law.buffalo.eduEst. 2000
Webmaster — Kristina Lively
Published: MthlyCirc.(fr.) 12,000
Digital Edition Available?: Y
Digital Platform - Mobile: Apple, Android, Windows, Blackberry, Other
Digital Platform - Tablet: Apple iOS, Android, Windows 7, Blackberry Tablet OS, Kindle, Kindle Fire, Other
Price: Free
Format: Digital
Note: This is a HTML-formatted email

UTICA COLLEGE: TANGERINE — 1600 Burrstone Rd Hubbard 55, Utica, NY, 13502-4892, USA; tel (315) 792-3065; fax (315) 792-3173; web site: www.uctangerine.comEst. 1946
Editor-in-Chief — Christopher Cooper
Jonathan Monsiletto
Format: Tabloid

VASSAR COLLEGE: THE MISCELLANY NEWS — 124 Raymond Ave # 149, Poughkeepsie, NY, 12604-0002, USA; tel (845) 437-5349; fax (845) 437-5348; e-mail: misc@vassar.edu; web site: http://miscellanynews.org/
Editor-in-Chief — Talya Phelps
Published: Wed
Format: Tabloid

WADE WALLERSTEIN: THE PHOENIX — 1 Mead Way, Bronxville, NY, 10708-5999, USA; tel (973) 856-2617; fax (973) 856-2617; e-mail: phoenix@gm.slc.edu; phoenix@slc.edu; adv email: phoenix@gm.slc.edu; ed email: wwallerstein@gm.slc.edu; web site: sarahlawrencephoenix.com
Editor-in-Chief — Wade Wallerstein
Digital Edition Available?: Y
Price: Free
Format: Tabloid

WAGNER COLLEGE: WAGNERIAN — 1 Campus Rd, Staten Island, NY, 10301-4495, USA; tel (718) 390-3110; e-mail: wagnerian@wagner.edu
Published: Wed Bi-Weekly
Digital Edition Available?: N
Format: Tabloid

WATS, SIMON GRAD. SCHOOL OF BUS. — Schlegel Hall, University of Rochester, Rochester, NY, 14627, USA; tel (585) 275-9287; e-mail: wats@simon.rochester.edu
Acting Managing Editor — Natalie Antal
Assignment Editor — Vincent Pelletier
Durba Ray
Price: 0.00
Format: Magazine

WESTCHESTER CMTY. COLLEGE: THE VIKING NEWS — 75 Grasslands Rd, Valhalla, NY, 10595-1550, USA; tel (914) 606-6600; e-mail: thevikingnewswcc@hotmail.com; web site: www.sunywcc.edu
Craig Padawer
Format: Tabloid

YESHIVA UNIV.: COMMENTATOR — 500 W 185th St Ste 416, New York, NY, 10033-3201, USA; tel (212) 795-4308; fax (212) 928-8637; e-mail: news@yucommentator.com; web site: www.yucommentator.com
Michael Cinnamon
Simeon Botwinick
Isaac Silverstein
Format: Tabloid

YORK COLLEGE OF CUNY: PANDORA'S BOX — 9420 Guy R Brewer Blvd, Jamaica, NY, 11451-0002, USA; tel (718) 262-2529; fax (718) 262-5234; e-mail: pandora@york.cuny.edu; adv email: pandora@york.cuny.edu; ed email: pandora@york.cuny.edu; web site: http://pbwire.cunycampuswire.com/Est. 1967
William Hughes
Published: MthlyCirc. (pd.) 0 (fr.) 3,000
Digital Edition Available?: Y
Price: Free
Format: Tabloid

NORTH CAROLINA

APPALACHIAN STATE UNIV.: THE APPALACHIAN — Asu # 9025, Boone, NC, 28608-0002, USA; tel (828) 262-6149; fax (828) 262-6502; e-mail: theapp@appstate.edu; web site: www.theapp.appstate.edu
Jon LaFontaine
Format: Broadsheet

BARTON COLLEGE: COLLEGIATE — PO Box 5000, Wilson, NC, 27893-7000, USA; tel (252) 399-6370; fax (252) 399-6572
Rick Stewart
Brittaney Rosencrance
Format: Tabloid

BELMONT ABBEY COLLEGE: CRUSADER — 100 Belmont Mount Holly Rd, Belmont, NC, 28012-1802, USA; e-mail: albenthall@bac.edu; adv email: cathycomeau@bac.edu; ed email: anthonygwyatt@abbey.bac.edu; web site: www.thecrusaderonline.com
Published: Mthly
Digital Edition Available?: Y
Price: Free

BENNETT COLLEGE: BENNETT BANNER — 900 E Washington St, Greensboro, NC, 27401-3298, USA; tel (336) 517-2305; fax (336) 517-2303; e-mail: banner@bennett.edu; web site: www.bennettbanner.com
Yvonne Welbon
Insert rate: ywelbon@bennett.edu
Format: Tabloid

BREVARD COLLEGE: CLARION — 1 Brevard Dr., Brevard, NC, 28712, USA; tel (828) 883-8292; e-mail: clarion@brevard.edu; adv email: clarion@brevard.edu; ed email: clarion@brevard.edu; web site: www.brevard.edu/clarionEst. 1935
Advisor — John Padgett
Editor in Chief, 2013-2014 — Althea Dunn
Published: Fri August-May (no summer publication)Circ. (pd.) 0 (fr.) 300
Digital Edition Available?: Y
Price: Free
Format: Tabloid

CAMPBELL UNIV.: CAMPBELL TIMES — PO Box 130, Buies Creek, NC, 27506-0130, USA; tel (910) 893-1200; fax (910) 893-1924; web site: www.campbell.edu
Michael Smith
editor — Courtney Schultz
Published: Bi-Mthly
Digital Edition Available?: Y
Digital Platform - Mobile: Android
Format: Broadsheet

CATAWBA COLLEGE — 2300 W Innes St, Salisbury, NC, 28144-2488, USA; tel (704) 637-4257; web site: www.catawba.edu
Cyndy Allison

DAVIDSON COLLEGE: DAVIDSONIAN — PO Box 7182, Davidson, NC, 28035-7182, USA; e-mail: davidsonian@davidson.edu; adv email: davidsonian@davidson.edu; web site: www.davidsonian.comEst. 1914
Laura Chuckray
Caroline Queen
Lyla Halsted
Published: Wed
Digital Edition Available?: Y
Price: $45/ yearly subscription
Format: Newspaper
Note: Website www.davidsonian.com

DUKE UNIV. FUQUA BUS. SCHOOL: FUQUA TIMES — PO Box 90120, Durham, NC, 27708-0120, USA; tel (919) 660-7700; fax (919) 684-2818; e-mail: fuquatimes@gmail.com; web site: www.axml.net/fuquatimes
Mary Murphy
Format: Magazine

DUKE UNIVERSITY: THE CHRONICLE — PO Box 90858, Durham, NC, 27708-0858, USA; tel (919) 684-8111; fax (919) 668-1247; web site: dukechronicle.com
Editor — Yeshwanth Kandamalla
Published: Mon, Tues, Wed, Thur, FriCirc.(fr.) 12,000
Digital Edition Available?: Y
Format: Tabloid

ELIZABETH CITY STATE UNIV.: COMPASS — 1704 Weeksville Rd, Elizabeth City, NC, 27909, USA; tel (252) 335-3343; fax (252) 335-3795
Kip Branch
Format: Tabloid

ELON UNIVERSITY: PENDULUM — 7012 Campus Box, Elon, NC, 27244-2062, USA; tel (336) 278-7247; fax (336) 278-7426; e-mail: pendulum@elon.edu; adv email: pendulum@elon.edu; web site: elonpendulum.com
Advisor — Colin Donohue
Ed. in Chief — Andie Diemer
Pam Richter
Anna Johnson
Format: Tabloid

FAYETTEVILLE STATE UNIV.: BRONCOS' VOICE — 1200 Murchison Rd, Fayetteville, NC, 28301-4298, USA; tel (910) 672-2210; fax (910) 672-1964; web site: www.fsuvoice.com
Valonda Calloway
Nathalie Rivera
L'Asia Brown
Format: Tabloid

GREENSBORO COLLEGE: THE COLLEGIAN — 815 W Market St, Greensboro, NC, 27401-1875, USA; tel (336) 272-7102; fax (336) 271-6634
Advisor — L. Wayne Johns
Format: Tabloid

GUILFORD COLLEGE: GUILFORDIAN — 5800 W Friendly Ave, Greensboro, NC, 27410-4173, USA; tel (336) 316-2306; web site: www.guilfordian.com
Jeff Jeske
Format: Tabloid

HIGH POINT UNIV.: CAMPUS CHRONICLE — 833 Montlieu Ave, High Point, NC, 27262-4260, USA; tel (800) 345-6993; fax (336) 841-4513; e-mail: news@highpoint.edu; web site: www.highpoint.edu
Bobby Hayes
Dir./Prof. — Wilfrid Tremblay
Prof. — Kate Fowkes
Assoc. Prof. — Judy Isaksen
Assoc. Prof. — John Luecke
Asst. Prof. — Nahed Eltantawy
Asst. Prof. — Jim Goodman
Asst. Prof. — Brad Lambert
Asst. Prof. — Jim Trammell
Asst. Prof. — Gerald Voorhees
Lectr. — Kristina Bell
Opns. Mgr. — Don Moore
Video Producer — Martin Yount
Admin. Asst. — Michelle Devlin
Format: Tabloid

LENOIR-RHYNE UNIVERSITY: THE RHYNEAN — P.O. 7341, Hickory, NC, 28603, USA; tel (828) 328-7176; e-mail: harrisl@lr.edu; adv email: harrisl@lr.edu; ed email: richard.gould@lr.edu; web site: http://therhynean.wordpress.com/
Published: Mthly
Digital Edition Available?: Y
Format: Broad sheet

MEREDITH COLLEGE: MEREDITH HERLAD — 3800 Hillsborough St, Raleigh, NC, 27607-5298, USA; tel (919) 760-8600; e-mail: herald@meredith.edu
Suzanne Britt
Format: Tabloid

METHODIST UNIVERSITY: SMALLTALK — 5400 Ramsey St, Fayetteville, NC, 28311-1420, USA; tel (910) 630-7292; fax (910) 630-7253; e-mail: dmunoz@methodist.edu; web site: www.smalltalkmu.com
Director of Student Life — Doris Munoz
Published: Bi-MthlyCirc.(fr.) 2,400
Digital Edition Available?: N
Price: free to students
Format: magazine

NORTH CAROLINA A&T STATE UNIV.: REGISTER — PO Box E25, Greensboro, NC, 27411-0001, USA; tel (336) 334-7700; fax (336) 334-7173; e-mail: theatregister@gmail.com; web site: www.ncatregister.com
Emiley Burch Harris
Dexter R. Mullins
Format: Broadsheet

NORTH CAROLINA CENTRAL UNIV.: CAMPUS ECHO — 1801 Fayetteville St, Durham, NC, 27707-3129, USA; tel (919) 530-7116; fax (919) 530-7991; e-mail: campusecho@nccu.edu; web site: www.campusecho.com
Dr. Bruce DePyssler
Associate Professor — Thomas Evans
Carlton Koonce
Format: Broadsheet

NORTH CAROLINA STATE UNIV.: TECHNICIAN — 323 Witherspoon Student Ctr Ncsu Campus Box 7318, Raleigh, NC, 27695-0001, USA; tel (919) 515-2411; fax (919) 515-5133; e-mail: editor@technicianonline.com; adv email: advertising@technicianonline.com; web site: www.technicianonline.comEst. 1923
Advisor — Bradley Wilson
Russell Witham
Format: Broadsheet

PEACE COLLEGE: PEACE TIMES — 15 E Peace St, Raleigh, NC, 27604-1194, USA; tel (919) 508-2214; fax (919) 508-2326; web site: peace.edu
John Hill
Format: Tabloid

PFEIFFER UNIV.: FALCON'S EYE — PO Box 960, Misenheimer, NC, 28109-0960, USA; tel (704) 463-1360; fax (704) 463-1363; web

site: www.pfeiffer.edu
Charisse Levine
Format: Magazine

QUEENS UNIVERSITY OF CHARLOTTE: QUEENS CHRONICLE — Msc # 892, Charlotte, NC, 28274-0001, USA; tel (704) 337-2220; fax (704) 337-2503; e-mail: quoc.chronicle@gmail.com; web site: www.queens-chronicle.com
Editor-in-Chief — Dustin Saunders
Published: Bi-Mthly
Format: Tabloid

SALEM COLLEGE: SALEMITE — 601 S Church St, Winston Salem, NC, 27101-5376, USA; tel (336) 917-5113; fax (336) 917-5117; web site: www.thesalemite.com
Sarah Boyenger
Susan Smith
Format: Tabloid

THE DAILY TAR HEEL — 151 E Rosemary St, Chapel Hill, NC, 27514-3539, USA; tel (919) 962-1163; e-mail: sales@dailytarheel.com; adv email: sales@dailytarheel.com; ed email: dth@dailytarheel.com; web site: dailytarheel.comEst. 1893
Managing Ed. — Elise Young

THE DUKE CHRONICLE — 301 Flowers, Durham, NC, 27708-0001, USA; tel 919-684-2663 ; fax 919-684-4696; e-mail: advertising@chronicle.duke.edu; adv email: advertising@chronicle.duke.edu; ed email: chronicleletters@duke.edu; web site: http://www.dukechronicle.comEst. 1905

THE EAST CAROLINIAN — Self Help Bldg. ECU, Greenville, NC, 27858, USA; tel (252) 328-9238; fax (252) 328-9143; adv email: ads@theeastcarolinian.com; ed email: editor@theeastcarolinian.com; web site: www.theeastcarolinian.comEst. 1925
Advisor — Paul Isom
Editor — Caitlin Hale
Katelyn Crouse
Insert rate: $80/1,000
Format: Broadsheet

UNIV. OF NORTH CAROLINA: PINE NEEDLE — PO Box 1510, Pembroke, NC, 28372-1510, USA; tel (910) 521-6204; fax (910) 522-5795; e-mail: pineneedle@uncp.edu; web site: www.uncp.edu/pineneedle
Judy Curtis
Jodie Johnson
Wade Allen
Format: Tabloid

UNIV. OF NORTH CAROLINA: THE SEAHAWK — 601 S College Rd, Wilmington, NC, 28403-3201, USA; tel (910) 962-3229; e-mail: seahawk.news@uncw.edu; ed email: seahawk.editor@gmail.com; web site: www.theseahawk.orgEst. 1948
Autumn Beam
Lisa Huynh
Bethany Bestwina
Format: Tabloid

UNIV. OF NORTH CAROLINA: THE BLUE BANNER — 1 University Heights, Asheville, NC, 28804-3251, USA; fax (828) 251-6591; e-mail: www.thebluebanner.net; adv email: banner@unca.edu
Michael Gouge
Anna Kiser
Sam Hunt
Insert rate: mgouge@unca.edu
Format: Tabloid

UNIV. OF NORTH CAROLINA: CAROLINIAN — Uncg # N1, Greensboro, NC, 27412-0001, USA; tel (336) 334-5752; fax (336) 334-3518; e-mail: the_carolinian@hotmail.com; web site: www.carolinianonline.com
Y-Phuc Ayun
Casey Mann
John Boschini
Format: Broadsheet

UNIV. OF NORTH CAROLINA - THE DAILY TAR HEEL: THE DAILY TAR HEEL — 151 E Rosemary St, Chapel Hill, NC, 27514-3539, USA; tel (919) 962-1163; fax (919) 962-1609; adv email: ads@unc.edu; ed email: dth@dailytarheel.com; web site: www.dailytarheel.comEst. 1893
Erica Perel
Megan Mcginity
Published: Mon, Tues, Wed, Thur, FriCirc.(fr.) 17,000
Digital Edition Available?: Y
Digital Platform - Mobile: Apple, Android
Format: Broadsheet

UNIV. OF NORTH CAROLINA AT CHARLOTTE: NINER TIMES — 9201 University City Blvd, Charlotte, NC, 28223-1000, USA; fax (704) 687-3253; e-mail: www.nineronline.com; adv email: smpads@uncc.edu; ed email: editor@ninertimes.com; web site: www.ninertimes.com
Ed. in Chief — Christine Litchfield
EIC — Hunter Heilman
Published: TuesCirc.(fr.) 7,000
Digital Edition Available?: Y
Insert rate: uteditor@uncc.edu
Format: Broadsheet

UNIV. OF NORTH CAROLINA LAW SCHOOL — 3380 Vanhecke-Wettach Hall, Chapel Hill, NC, 27599-0001, USA; tel (919) 962-6200
Format: Broadsheet

WAKE FOREST UNIV.: OLD GOLD & BLACK — PO Box 7569, Winston Salem, NC, 27109-6240, USA; tel (336) 758-5279; fax (336) 758-4561; e-mail: ogb@wfu.edu; web site: www.oldgoldandblack.com
Wayne King
Tyler Kellner
Mariclaire Hicks
Format: Broadsheet

WESTERN CAROLINA UNIV.: THE WESTERN CAROLINIAN — 109A Old Student Union, Cullowhee, NC, 28723, USA; tel (828) 227-2694; fax (828) 227-7201; e-mail: jcaudell@westerncarolinian.com; adv email: jcaudell@westerncarolinian.com; ed email: amenz@westerncarolinian.com; web site: www.westerncarolinian.comEst. 1933
Ed. in Chief — Justin Caudell
Editor-in-Chief — Alexa Menz
Published: Bi-MthlyCirc. (pd.) 100 (fr.) 5,000
Digital Edition Available?: Y
Digital Platform - Mobile: Apple, Android, Windows
Digital Platform - Tablet: Apple iOS, Android, Windows 7
Format: Broadsheet

WINGATE UNIV.: WEEKLY TRIANGLE — PO Box 2, Wingate, NC, 28174-0002, USA; tel (704) 233-8163; fax (704) 233-8285
Keith Cannon
Brittany Ruffner
Format: Tabloid

WINSTON-SALEM STATE UNIV.: THE NEWS ARGUS — 103 Old Nursing, Winston Salem, NC, 27110-0001, USA; tel 3367502327; fax 3367508704; e-mail: thenewsargus@gmail.com; adv email: thenewsargus@gmail.com; ed email: thenewsargus@gmail.com; web site: www.thenewsargus.comEst. 1960
Advisor — Lona D. Cobb
Published: Mon, Bi-Mthly
Digital Edition Available?: Y
Digital Platform - Mobile: Windows
Insert rate: $100
Price: Free
Format: Tabloid

NORTH DAKOTA

BISMARCK STATE COLLEGE: MYSTCIAN — 1500 Edwards Ave, Bismarck, ND, 58501-1299, USA; tel (701) 224-5467; fax (701) 224-5529; e-mail: editor@mystician.org; web site: www.mystician.orgEst. 1939
Advisor — Karen Bauer
Published: Mthly
Digital Edition Available?: Y
Digital Platform - Mobile: Apple, Android, Windows, Blackberry, Other
Digital Platform - Tablet: Apple iOS, Android, Windows 7, Blackberry Tablet OS, Kindle, Nook, Kindle Fire, Other
Price: free publication
Format: news magazine
Note: We also have a news video broadcast: MystiCast
and Internet radio: The MYX

JAMESTOWN COLLEGE: COLLEGIAN — 6086 College Ln, Jamestown, ND, 58405-0001, USA; tel (701) 252-3467; fax (701) 253-4318; web site: www.jc.edu
Steve Listopad
Richard Schmit
Format: Tabloid

MINOT STATE UNIV.: RED AND GREEN — 500 University Ave W, Minot, ND, 58707-0002, USA; tel (701) 858-3000; e-mail: redgreen@minotstateu.edu; web site: www.minotstateu.edu
Bryce Berginski
Format: Tabloid

NORTH DAKOTA STATE COLLEGE OF SCIENCE — c/o Daily News, PO Box 760, Wahpeton, ND, 58074-0760, USA; tel (701) 642-8585; fax (701) 642-6068
Pam Marquart

NORTH DAKOTA STATE UNIV.: THE SPECTRUM — P.O. Box 6050, Fargo, ND, 58108-6050, USA; tel (701) 231-8929; fax (701) 231-9402; e-mail: ad.manager@ndsuspectrum.com; adv email: ad.manager@ndsuspectrum.com; ed email: editor@ndsuspectrum.com; web site: www.ndsuspectrum.comEst. 1896
Andrew Pritchard
Published: Mon, ThurCirc.(fr.) 7,000
Digital Edition Available?: Y
Format: Broadsheet

UNIV. OF NORTH DAKOTA: THE DAKOTA STUDENT — University of North Dakota Memorial Union, Grand Forks, ND, 58201, USA; tel (701) 777-2677; fax (701) 777-3137; e-mail: dakotastudentmedia@gmail.com; adv email: und.dakotastudent@email.und.edu; web site: www.dakotastudent.comEst. 1888
Editor-in-Chief — Carrie Sandstrom
Sales and Marketing Coordinator — Melissa Bakke
Managing/Opinion Editor — Adam Christianson
Features Editor — Kelsi Ward
News Editor — Larry Philbin
Sports Editor — Elizabeth Erickson
Multimedia Editor — Jaye Millspaugh
Photo Editor — Keisuke Yoshimura
Published: Tues, Fri
Digital Edition Available?: Y
Price: Free
Format: Tabloid

VALLEY CITY STATE UNIV. — Box 1431, VCSC Student Ctr., Valley City, ND, 58072, USA; tel (701) 845-7722

OHIO

ASHLAND UNIV.: COLLEGIAN — 401 College Ave, Ashland, OH, 44805-3799, USA; tel (419) 289-4142; fax (419) 289-5604; e-mail: collegian@ashland.edu; web site: www.ashland.edu/collegian
Katie Ryder
Format: Broadsheet

BALDWIN-WALLACE COLLEGE: EXPONENT — 275 Eastland Rd, Berea, OH, 44017-2088, USA; tel (440) 826-2900; fax (440) 826-8581; e-mail: exponent@bw.edu
Peter Kerlin
Gerrie
Format: Tabloid

BLUFFTON COLLEGE: WITMASUM — 1 University Dr, Bluffton, OH, 45817-2104, USA; tel (419) 358-3000; fax (419) 358-3356; e-mail: witmarsum@bluffton.edu; web site: www.witmarsum.org
Colin Lasu
Cyrus Weigand
Bethany Rayle
Format: Tabloid

BOWLING GREEN STATE UNIV.: THE BG NEWS — 100 Kuhlin Center, Bowling Green, OH, 43403-0001, USA; tel (419) 372-0328; fax (419) 372-0202; e-mail: thenews@bgnews.com; adv email: twhitma@bgsu.edu; ed email: thenews@bgnews.com; web site: www.bgviews.comEst. 1920
Director of Student Media — Robert Bortel
Hannah Finnerty
Holly Shively
Published: Mon, ThurCirc.(fr.) 4,500
Digital Edition Available?: Y
Digital Platform - Mobile: Apple, Android, Windows, Blackberry, Other
Digital Platform - Tablet: Apple iOS, Android, Windows 7, Blackberry Tablet OS, Kindle, Nook, Kindle Fire, Other
Insert rate: 70 per thousand
Price: Free
Format: tabloid

BOWLING GREEN STATE UNIVERSITY: THE BG NEWS — 204 W Hall, Bowling Green, OH, 43403-0001, USA; tel (419) 372-2607; e-mail: thenews@bgnews.com

CAPITAL UNIV.: CHIMES — 1 College and Main, Columbus, OH, 43209-2394, USA; tel (614) 236-6567; fax (614) 236-6948; e-mail: chimes@capital.edu; web site: cuchimes.comEst. 1926
Kelly Messinger
Published: ThurCirc.(fr.) 1,200
Insert rate: $130.00
Format: Tabloid

CAPITAL UNIV. LAW SCHOOL: RES IPSA LOQUITUR — 303 E Broad St, Columbus, OH, 43215-3200, USA; tel (614) 236-6011; fax (614) 445-7125; e-mail: resipsa@law.capital.edu
Susan Gilles
Sharon Simpson
Amanda Tuttle
Format: Magazine

CASE WESTERN RESERVE UNIV.: OBSERVER — 11111 Euclid Ave Rm A09, Cleveland, OH, 44106-1715, USA; tel (216) 368-6949; fax (216) 368-2914; web site: www.cwruobserver.com
Tricia Schellenbach
Bruce Douglas
Bryan Bourgeois
Format: Tabloid

CEDARVILLE UNIV.: CEDARS — 251 N Main St, Cedarville, OH, 45314-8564, USA; tel (937) 766-3298; fax (937) 766-3456; e-mail: cedars@cedarville.edu; adv email: jgilbert@cedarville.edu; web site: http://cedars.

cedarville.edu/
Faculty adviser — Jeff Gilbert
Published: MthlyCirc.(fr.) 1,200
Digital Edition Available?: Y

CENTRAL STATE UNIV.: GOLD TORCH — PO Box 1004, Wilberforce, OH, 45384-1004, USA; tel (937) 376-6095; fax (937) 376-6530; e-mail: info@centralstate.edu; web site: www.centralstate.edu
Mike Gormley
Format: Tabloid

CLEVELAND STATE UNIV.: CAULDRON — 2121 Euclid Ave, Cleveland, OH, 44115-2226, USA; tel (216) 687-2270; fax (216) 687-5155; e-mail: cauldroneditors@gmail.com; adv email: cauldronadverts@gmail.com; web site: www.csucauldron.com
Dan Lenhart
Editor-in-Chief — Samah Assad
Published: Tues
Digital Edition Available?: Y
Format: Tabloid

COLLEGE OF WOOSTER: WOOSTER VOICE — Box C-1387, Wooster, OH, 44691-2393, USA; tel (330) 263-2598; fax (330) 263-2596; e-mail: voice@wooster.edu; adv email: nisles@wooster.edu; ed email: voice@wooster.edu; web site: thewoostervoice.com
Travis Marmon
Ian Benson
Published: Tues
Digital Edition Available?: Y
Format: Tabloid

DENISON UNIV.: THE DENISONIAN — 100 W College St, Granville, OH, 43023, USA; tel (740) 587-6378; fax (740) 587-6767; e-mail: denisonian@denison.edu; web site: www.denisonian.com
Alan Miller
Format: Tabloid

FRANCISCAN UNIVERSITY OF STEUBENVILLE: THE TROUBADOUR — 1235 University Blvd, Steubenville, OH, 43952-1796, USA; tel (740) 284-5014; fax (740) 284-5452; e-mail: troub@franciscan.edu; web site: www.troubonline.com
Chris Pagano
Elizabeth Wong
Emily Lahr
Format: Tabloid

FRANKLIN UNIVERSITY: N/A — 201 S Grant Ave, Columbus, OH, 43215-5399, USA; tel (614) 797-4700; fax (614) 224-4025; adv email: N/A; ed email: N/A; web site: www.franklin.eduEst. 1902
Ed. — Sherry Mercurio
Insert rate: N/A
Price: N/A
Format: PDF
Note: This is an internal newsletter only. Outside content or ads are not permitted.

HEIDELBERG UNIVERSITY: KILIKILIK — 310 E. Market St., Tiffin, OH, 44883-2462, USA; tel (419) 448-2180Est. 1894
Visiting Assistant Professor of Communication — Mary Garrison
Digital Edition Available?: N
Format: News magazine
Note: We are in the process of rebuilding and investigating the possibility of going to an online format in addition to rebooting the print edition into a monthly.

HIRAM COLLEGE: THE ADVANCE — PO Box 67, Hiram, OH, 44234-0067, USA; tel (330) 569-5203; fax (330) 569-5479; e-mail: advance@hiram.edu
Christopher Benek
Format: Tabloid

JOHN CARROLL UNIVERSITY: CARROLL NEWS — 1 John Carroll Blvd, Cleveland, OH, 44118-4582, USA; tel (216) 397-1711; fax (216) 397-1729; e-mail: jcunews@gmail.com; adv email: jcunews@gmail.com; ed email: jcunews@gmail.com; web site: www.jcunews.comEst. 1925
Chair/Assoc. Prof. — Mary Ann Flannery
Robert T. Noll
Prof. — Jacqueline J. Schmidt
Katie Sheridan
Bob Seeholzer
Prof. — Alan Stephenson
Assoc. Prof. — Mary Beadle
Tim Ertle
Asst. Prof. — Margaret Algren
Asst. Prof. — Richard Hendrickson
Asst. Prof. — Robert Prisco
Instr. — Bob Noll
Instr. — David Reese
Part-time Instr. — Fred Buchstein
Part-time Instr. — Mark Eden
Part-time Instr. — Bill Nichols
Published: ThurCirc.(fr.) 1,600
Digital Edition Available?: Y
Digital Platform - Mobile: Other
Digital Platform - Tablet: Other
Price: Free
Format: Tabloid

KENT STATE UNIV.: DAILY KENT STATER — 201 Franklin Hall Rm 205, Kent, OH, 44242-0001, USA; tel (330) 672-0887; fax (330) 672-4880; e-mail: dksads@gmail.com; web site: www.kent.edu
Carl Schierhorn
Lori Cantor
Tami Bongiorni
Format: Broadsheet

KENYON COLLEGE: KENYON COLLEGIAN — PO Box 832, Gambier, OH, 43022-0832, USA; tel (740) 427-5338; fax (740) 427-5339; e-mail: collegian@kenyon.edu; web site: www.kenyoncollegian.com
Sarah Queller
Format: Tabloid

LAKELAND CMTY. COLLEGE: THE LAKELANDER — 7700 Clocktower Dr, Kirtland, OH, 44094-5198, USA; tel (440) 953-7264; e-mail: lakelander@lakelandcc.edu; web site: www.lakelandcc.edu
Susan Zimmerman
Format: Tabloid

LORAIN COUNTY CMTY. COLLEGE: COLLEGIAN — 1005 Abbe Rd N, Elyria, OH, 44035-1692, USA; tel (440) 366-4037; fax (440) 365-6519; e-mail: lcccstories@lorainccc.edu; colegian@lorainccc.edu; web site: www.collegianonline.org
Advisor — Cliff Anthony
Published: Bi-Mthly
Digital Edition Available?: Y
Digital Platform - Mobile: Other
Insert rate: $400 full page
Price: Free
Format: Tabloid

MALONE COLLEGE: AVISO — 2600 Cleveland Ave NW, Canton, OH, 44709-3308, USA; tel (330) 471-8212; fax (330) 454-6977; web site: www.theaviso.orgEst. 1958
David Dixon
Format: Tabloid

MALONE UNIVERSITY: AVISO AVW — 2600 Cleveland Ave NW, Canton, OH, 44709-3897, USA; tel 330-471-8277; web site: http://theaviso.org/

MARIETTA COLLEGE: MARCOLIAN — 215 5th St Dept 32, Marietta, OH, 45750-4071, USA; tel (740) 376-4555; fax (740) 376-4807; e-mail: marc@marietta.edu; web site: www.marcolian.com
Jessie Schmac
Jamie Tidd
Amy Bitely
Format: Broadsheet

MARIETTA COLLEGE: THE MARCOLIAN — 215 5th St Dept 32, Marietta, OH, 45750-4071, USA; tel (740) 376-4848; fax (740) 376-4807; e-mail: mac@Marietta.edu; web site: www.marcolian.com/
Chair — Jack L. Hillwig

MIAMI UNIV.: MIAMI STUDENT — 4200 N University Blvd, Middletown, OH, 45042-3497, USA; tel (513) 727-3200; fax (513) 727-3223; e-mail: miamistudent@gmail.com; miamistudent@muohio.edu; web site: www.mid.muohio.edu/orgs/hawkseye/
Catherine Couretas
John Heyda
Format: Broadsheet

MOUNT ST. JOSEPH UNIVERSITY: DATELINE — 5701 Delhi Rd, Cincinnati, OH, 45233-1670, USA; tel (513) 244-4200; web site: www.msj.edu
Elizabeth Barkley
Published: Mthly
Digital Edition Available?: Y
Digital Platform - Tablet: Windows 7
Format: online only

MT. UNION COLLEGE: DYNAMO — 1972 Clark Ave, Alliance, OH, 44601-3993, USA; tel (330) 823-2884; fax (330) 821-0425; e-mail: dynamo@muc.edu; web site: www.mucdynamo.com
Len Cooper
Format: Broadsheet

MUSKINGUM COLLEGE: BLACK AND MAGENTA — 163 Stormont St, New Concord, OH, 43762, USA; tel (740) 826-8296; fax (740) 826-8404; web site: www.bandmonline.com
Vivian Wagner
Josh Chaney
Format: Tabloid

OBERLIN COLLEGE: OBERLIN REVIEW — 135 W Lorain St # 90, Oberlin, OH, 44074-1053, USA; tel (440) 775-8123; fax (440) 775-6733; e-mail: advertisements@oberlinreview.org; web site: www.oberlin.edu
Daniel Dudley
Talia Chicherio
Caitlin Duke
Piper Niehaus
Format: Tabloid

OHIO NORTHERN UNIV.: NORTHERN REVIEW — 525 S Main St, Ada, OH, 45810, USA; tel (419) 772-2409; fax (419) 772-1880; e-mail: northern-review@onu.edu; web site: https://nr.onu.edu
Bill O'Connell
Nick Dutro
Published: Mon, Tues, Wed, Thur, Fri, Sat, Sun
Digital Edition Available?: Y
Format: Tabloid

OHIO STATE UNIV.: OHIO STATE LANTERN — 242 W 18th Ave Rm 211, Columbus, OH, 43210-1107, USA; tel (614) 292-2031; fax (614) 292-5240; e-mail: lantern@osu.edu; ed email: lanternnewsroom@gmail.com; web site: www.thelantern.comEst. 1881
Tom O'Hara
John Milliken
Kevin Bruffy
Format: Broadsheet

OHIO STATE UNIV. COLLEGE OF ENGINEERING: OHIO STATE ENGINEER — 2070 Neil Ave, Columbus, OH, 43210-1278, USA; tel (614) 292-7931; fax (614) 688-3805; web site: www.engineering.osu.edu
Edward McCaul
Format: Magazine

OHIO STATE UNIV. COLLEGE OF LAW — 55 W 12th Ave, Columbus, OH, 43210-1391, USA; tel (614) 292-2631

OHIO STATE UNIVERSITY: THE LANTERN — 242 W 18th Ave, Columbus, OH, 43210-1107, USA; tel 614-292-5721; fax 614-292-3722; web site: www.thelantern.com

OHIO UNIV.: THE POST — 325 Baker University Center, Athens, OH, 45701, USA; tel (740) 593-4011; fax (740) 593-0561; e-mail: posteditorial@ohiou.edu; web site: www.thepost.ohiou.edu
Ashley Lutz
Dave Hendricks
Ryan Dunn
Natalie Debruin
Sports Ed. — Joe
Advertising Admin. — Robert
Format: Broadsheet

OHIO WESLEYAN UNIVERSITY: TRANSCRIPT — 61 S Sandusky St Rm 106, Delaware, OH, 43015-2398, USA; tel (740) 368-2911; fax (740) 368-3649; e-mail: owunews@owu.edu; adv email: owunews@owu.edu; ed email: owunews@owu.edu; web site: transcript.owu.eduEst. 1867
Media Adviser — Jo Ingles
Published: ThurCirc. (pd.) 5 (fr.) 1,000
Digital Edition Available?: Y
Insert rate: http://transcript.owu.edu/advertisingInformation.html
Price: Free to students
Format: Broadsheet

OTTERBEIN UNIVERSITY: OTTERBEIN360.COM — Communication Department, Westerville, OH, 43081, USA; tel (614) 823 1159; e-mail: adviser@otterbein360.com; adv email: sales@otterbein360.com; web site: www.otterbein360.comEst. 1880
Advisor — Hillary Warren
Published: Mon, Tues, Wed, Thur, Fri, Sat, Sun
Digital Edition Available?: Y
Note: The Tan and Cardinal Newspaper has become a daily website, otterbein360.com, and a quarterly magazine, T&C.

SHAWNEE STATE UNIV.: UNIVERSITY CHRONICLE — 940 2nd St, Portsmouth, OH, 45662-4347, USA; tel (740) 351-3278; fax (740) 351-3566; e-mail: chronicle@shawnee.edu; web site: www.shawnee.edu/pub/chrn
Terry Hapney
Format: Broadsheet

SINCLAIR COMMUNITY COLLEGE: THE CLARION — 444 W 3rd St Rm 6314, Dayton, OH, 45402-1421, USA; tel (937) 512-2744; fax (937) 512-4590; e-mail: clarion@sinclair.edu; adv email: clarion@sinclair.edu; ed email: clarion@sinclair.edu; web site: www.sinclairclarion.comEst. 1977
Exec Ed — Gabrielle Sharp
Mng Ed — Barton Kleen
Associate Ed — Laina Yost
Advt Rep — Susan Day
Published: TuesCirc.(fr.) 4,000
Digital Edition Available?: N
Price: Free
Format: Tabloid

STARK STATE COLLEGE OF TECHNOLOGY: STUDENT INFORMER — 6200 Frank Ave NW, North Canton, OH, 44720-7299, USA; tel (330) 494-6170; fax (330) 497-6313; e-mail: studentinformer@starkstate.edu; web site: www.starkstate.edu/studentinformer
Format: Tabloid

THE NEWS RECORD — PO Box 210135, Cincinnati, OH, 45221-0135, USA; tel (513) 556-5900; fax (513) 556-5922; e-mail: newsrecordbiz@gmail.com; chief.newsrecord@gmail.com; ed email: chief.newsrecord@gmail.

com; web site: www.newsrecord.orgEst. 1880
Editor-in-chief — Ariel Cheung
Kristy Conlin
Format: Broadsheet

THE UNIVERSITY OF AKRON: THE BUCHTELITE — 302 Buchtel Common, Akron, OH, 44325-4206, USA; tel 330-972-7919; fax 330-972-7810; e-mail: adviser@buchtelite.com; adv email: business-manager@buchtelite.com; ed email: editor-in-chief@buchtelite.com; web site: buchtelite.comEst. 1889
Business Manager — Adam Bernhard
Editor-in-Chief — Zaina Salem
Published: Tues, ThurCirc.(fr.) 2,700
Digital Edition Available?: Y
Digital Platform - Mobile: Apple, Android
Digital Platform - Tablet: Apple iOS, Android
Format: Broadsheet

THE UNIVERSITY OF FINDLAY: THE PULSE — 1000 N Main St, Findlay, OH, 45840-3653, USA; tel (419) 434-5892; e-mail: pulse@findlay.edu; adv email: pulse@findlay.edu; ed email: pulse@findlay.edu; web site: www.findlay.edu/pulseEst. 1986 (as the Pulse)
Pulse Editor — Olivia Wile
Published: FriCirc.(fr.) 1,000
Digital Edition Available?: Y
Insert rate: $150 per press run
Price: Free
Format: tab
Note: We have a digital platform.

UNIV. OF AKRON: BUCHTELITE — 303 Carroll St Student Un Rm 51, Akron, OH, 44325-0001, USA; tel (330) 972-5475; fax (330) 972-7810; e-mail: adviser@buchtelite.com; ed email: editor@buchtelite.com; web site: www.buchtelite.com
Maryanne Bailey-Porter
Kevin Curwin
Allison Strouse
Format: Broadsheet

UNIV. OF DAYTON: FLYER NEWS — 232 Kennedy Union, Dayton, OH, 45469-0626, USA; tel (937) 229-3226; fax (937) 229-3893; e-mail: news@flyernews.com; adv email: advertising@flyernews.com; ed email: fn.editor@udayton.edu; web site: www.flyernews.com
Advisor — Frazier Smith
Co-Advisor — Amy Lopez-Matthews
Ed. — CC Hutten
Mng. Ed. — Matthew Worsham
Mng. Ed. — Meredith Whelchel
Print-Ed. — Julia Hall
Published: Tues B-Weekly (Daily online)Circ. (fr.) 3,000
Digital Edition Available?: Y
Price: Free
Format: Tabloid
Note: Flyer News now has a print editor in chief and an online editor in chief. This is the second year for this set up.

UNIV. OF DAYTON LAW SCHOOL — 300 College Park, Dayton, OH, 45469-0002, USA; tel (937) 229-3211
Jennifer Tate

UNIV. OF RIO GRANDE: SIGNALS — 218 N College Ave, Rio Grande, OH, 45674-3131, USA; tel (740) 245-7521; fax (740) 245-7239; e-mail: signals@rio.edu
Nick Claussen
Format: Tabloid

UNIVERSITY OF CINCINNATI: THE NEWS RECORD — PO Box 210135, Cincinnati, OH, 45221-0135, USA; tel (513) 556-5912; fax (513) 556 5922; web site: www.newsrecord.org

UNIVERSITY OF TOLEDO: THE INDEPENDENT COLLEGIAN — 2801 W Bancroft St, Toledo, OH, 43606-3390, USA; tel (419) 530-7788; fax (419) 530-7770; e-mail: editor@independentcollegian.com; adv email: sales@independentcollegian.com; ed email: editor@independentcollegian.com; web site: www.independentcollegian.comEst. 1919
Chairman of the board of trustees — J.R. Hoppenjans
Adviser — Erik Gable
Editor-in-Chief — Danielle Gamble
Published: WedCirc.(fr.) 8,000
Digital Edition Available?: Y
Digital Platform - Mobile: Other
Digital Platform - Tablet: Other
Insert rate: $55 per 1000/min-4000
Format: Broadsheet

WILBERFORCE UNIV.: MIRROR — PO Box 1001, Wilberforce, OH, 45384-1001, USA; tel (937) 376-2911; fax (937) 708-5793; e-mail: tmorah@wilberforce.edu; web site: www.wilberforce.edu
Tanya Morah
Courtney Wiggins
Format: Tabloid

WILMINGTON COLLEGE: WITNESS — 1870 Quaker Way, Wilmington, OH, 45177-2499, USA; tel (937) 382-6661; fax (937) 382-7077; web site: www2.wilmington.edu; www.wilmington.edu
Coreen Cockerill
Clair Green
Format: Tabloid

WITTENBERG UNIVERSITY: WITTENBERG TORCH — PO Box 720, Springfield, OH, 45501-0720, USA; tel 512.968.4648; e-mail: torch_editors@wittenberg.edu; web site: www.thewittenbergtorch.com
D'Arcy Fallon
Maggie McKune
Tara Osborne
Published: Wed
Digital Edition Available?: N
Format: Tabloid

WRIGHT STATE UNIV.: THE GUARDIAN — 14 Stud Ent Union 3640 Colonel Glenn Hwy, Dayton, OH, 45435-0001, USA; tel (937) 775-5534; fax (937) 775-5535; adv email: advertising@theguardianonline.com; ed email: editorial@theguardianonline.com; web site: www.theguardianonline.com
Tiffany Johnson
Format: Tabloid

XAVIER UNIV.: XAVIER NEWSWIRE — 3800 Victory Pkwy Dept 156, Cincinnati, OH, 45207-8010, USA; tel (513) 745-3607; fax (513) 745-2898; web site: www.xavier.edu/newswire
Kathryn Rosenbaum
Andrew Chestnut
Meghan Berneking
Format: Tabloid

YOUNGSTOWN STATE UNIV.: JAMBAR — 1 University Plz, Youngstown, OH, 44555-0002, USA; tel (330) 941-1991; fax (330) 941-2322; e-mail: thejambar@gmail.com; web site: www.thejambar.comEst. 1931
Mary Beth Earnheardt
Editor in Chief — Joshua Stipanovich
Chelsea Pflugh
Adam Rogers
Format: Broadsheet

YOUNGSTOWN STATE UNIVERSITY: THE JAMBAR — 1 University Plz, Youngstown, OH, 44555-0002, USA; tel (330) 941-3095; fax (330) 941-2322; web site: www.thejambar.com

OKLAHOMA

BARTLESVILLE WESLEYAN COLLEGE — 2201 Silver Lake Rd, Bartlesville, OK, 74006-6299, USA; tel (918) 335-6200; web site: www.okwu.edu

CAMERON UNIV.: COLLEGIAN — 2800 W Gore Blvd, Lawton, OK, 73505-6377, USA; tel (580) 581-2259; e-mail: collegian@cameron.edu
Christopher Keller
Format: Tabloid

CARL ALBERT STATE COLLEGE: VIKING BANNER — 1507 S McKenna St, Poteau, OK, 74953-5207, USA; tel (918) 647-1200; fax (918) 647-1266
Marcus Blair
Format: Tabloid

EAST CENTRAL UNIVERSITY: THE JOURNAL — 1100 E 14th St, Ada, OK, 74820-6915, USA; tel (580) 559-5250; fax (580) 559-5251; e-mail: journal@ecok.edu; ecujournal@me.com; web site: www.ecujournal.com
Cathie Harding
Melissa Hubble
Jonnathon Hicks
Format: Tabloid

LANGSTON UNIV.: GAZETTE — Sanford Hall Rm. 308W, Langston, OK, 73050, USA; tel (405) 466-3245; e-mail: lugazette@yahoo.com; web site: www.lugazette.com
Chaz Kyser
Format: Tabloid

NORTHEASTERN OKLAHOMA A&M COLLEGE — PO Box 3988, Miami, OK, 74354, USA; tel (918) 542-8441
Rebecca Kirk
Format: Tabloid

NORTHERN OKLAHOMA COLLEGE: THE MAVERICK — PO Box 310, Tonkawa, OK, 74653-0310, USA; tel (580) 628-6444; fax (580) 628-6209; web site: www.north-ok.edu
Jeremy Stillwell
Format: Tabloid

NORTHWESTERN OKLAHOMA STATE UNIV.: NORTHWESTERN NEWS — 709 Oklahoma Blvd, Alva, OK, 73717-2749, USA; tel (580) 327-8479; fax (580) 327-8127; e-mail: nwnewsroom@hotmail.com; nwnews@nwosu.edu; adv email: nwnewsroom@hotmail.com; ed email: nwnewsroom@hotmail.com; web site: www.nwosu.edu/northwestern-news or www.rangerpulse.comEst. 1897
Melanie Wilderman
Published: ThurCirc. (pd.) 200 (fr.) 1,400
Digital Edition Available?: Y
Digital Platform - Tablet: Kindle
Price: $12 per year mailed, free on campus
Format: Tabloid
Note: Northwestern News and rangerpulse.com are sister publications, but rangerpulse.com does carry content from both the newspaper and original content.

OKLAHOMA BAPTIST UNIV.: THE BISON — 500 W University St Ste 61704, Shawnee, OK, 74804-2522, USA; tel (405) 878-2128; fax (405) 878-2113; e-mail: Holly.easttom@okbu.edu; adv email: Holly.easttom@okbu.edu; web site: www.okbu.eduEst. 1942
Holly Easttom
Andrew Adams
Published: WedCirc. (pd.) 22 (fr.) 1,800
Digital Edition Available?: Y
Digital Platform - Mobile: Apple, Android
Digital Platform - Tablet: Other
Insert rate: None
Price: $10 a semester
Format: Broadsheet

OKLAHOMA CHRISTIAN UNIV.: THE TALON — PO Box 11000, Oklahoma City, OK, 73136-1100, USA; tel (405) 425-5538; fax (405) 425-5351; ed email: talon.letter@oc.edu
Philip Patterson
Kimberlee Rhodes
Will Kooi
Format: Tabloid

OKLAHOMA CITY COMMUNITY COLLEGE: PIONEER — 7777 S May Ave, Oklahoma City, OK, 73159-4499, USA; tel (405) 682-1611; e-mail: editor@occc.edu; adv email: matthew.s.carter@occc.edu; ed email: editor@occc.edu; web site: pioineer.occc.eduEst. 1978
M Scott Carter
Published: FriCirc.(fr.) 2,500
Digital Edition Available?: Y
Price: Free distribution on campus
Format: Tabloid

OKLAHOMA CITY UNIVERSITY: CAMPUS — 2501 N Blackwelder Ave Rm 117, Oklahoma City, OK, 73106-1493, USA; tel (405) 208-6068; fax (405) 208-6069; e-mail: stupub@okcu.edu; web site: www.mediaocu.comEst. 1907
Advisor — Kenna Griffin
Price: Free
Format: Tabloid

OKLAHOMA PANHANDLE STATE UNIV.: COLLEGIAN — PO Box 430, Goodwell, OK, 73939-0430, USA; tel (580) 349-2611; fax (580) 349-1350; e-mail: collegian@opsu.edu; web site: www.opsu.edu
Lora Hays
Samuel Moore
Format: Broadsheet

OKLAHOMA STATE UNIV.: DAILY O'COLLEGIAN — 106 Paul Miller, Stillwater, OK, 74078-4050, USA; tel (405) 744-6365; fax (405) 744-7936; ed email: editor@ocolly.com; web site: www.ocolly.com
Barbara Allen
Emily Holman
Format: Broadsheet

ORAL ROBERTS UNIV.: ORACLE — 7777 S Lewis Ave Lrc 175, Tulsa, OK, 74171-0001, USA; tel (918) 495-7080; fax (918) 495-6345; e-mail: oracle@oru.edu; adv email: oracleads@oru.edu; web site: www.oruoracle.comEst. 1965
Advisor — Kevin Armstrong
Published: Fri, Bi-MthlyCirc. (pd.) 0 (fr.) 3,500
Digital Edition Available?: Y
Insert rate: $175 for 2,000 preprinted inserts
Price: Free
Format: Tabloid
Note: Website only

SOUTHEASTERN OKLAHOMA STATE UNIV.: THE SOUTHEASTERN — 425 W University Blvd., Durant, OK, 74701-0609, USA; tel (580) 745-2944; fax (580) 745-7475; e-mail: campuspages@gmail.com; web site: www.thesoutheastern.com
Adviser — Tascha Bond
Managing Editor — Kourtney Kaufman
Published: Mthly Website updated weekly. Newspaper
Published monthly. Magazine released once a year.
Digital Edition Available?: Y
Digital Platform - Mobile: Apple, Android
Digital Platform - Tablet: Apple iOS, Android
Format: Newspaper/Online/Magazine

SOUTHERN NAZARENE UNIV.: THE ECHO — 6729 NW 39th Expy, Bethany, OK, 73008-2694, USA; tel (405) 491-6382; fax (405) 491-6378; e-mail: echo@snu.edu; adv email: grwillia@mail.snu.edu; ed email: kirarobe@mail.snu.edu; web site: echo.snu.edu
Speech Commun. Dept. — Pam Broyles
Yearbook — Marcia Feisal
Newspaper — Jim Wilcox
Graphic Design — Andrew Baker
Broadcasting — Les Dart
Published: Fri
Digital Edition Available?: Y
Format: Online

ST. GREGORY'S COLLEGE — 1900 W MacArthur St, Shawnee, OK, 74804-2499, USA; tel (405) 878-5100; fax (405) 878-5198
Andrew Sneider

THE VISTA: THE VISTA — 100 N University Dr, Edmond, OK, 73034-5207, USA; tel (405) 974-5123; fax (405) 974-3839; e-mail: vistamedia@yahoo.com; ed email: vista1903@gmail.com; web site: www.uco360.comEst. 1903
Teddy Burch
Nelson Solomon
Format: Broadsheet

TULSA CMTY. COLLEGE: TCC CONNECTION — 909 S Boston Ave Rm G-31, Tulsa, OK, 74119-2011, USA; tel (918) 595-7388; fax (918) 595-7308
Jerry Goodwin
Eric Bruce
Format: Tabloid

UNIV. OF OKLAHOMA: OKLAHOMA DAILY — 860 Van Vleet Rm 149A, Norman, OK, 73019-2035, USA; tel (405) 325-2521; fax (405) 325-5160; e-mail: dailynews@ou.edu; studentmedia@ou.edu; web site: www.oudaily.com; www.ou.edu
Judy Robinson
Jamie Hughes
Caitlin Harrison
Michelle Gray
Format: Broadsheet

UNIV. OF SCIENCE & ARTS OF OKLAHOMA: TREND — 1727 W Alabama Ave, Chickasha, OK, 73018-5371, USA; tel (405) 224-3140; fax (405) 521-6244; web site: www.trend.usao.edu
Faculty Advisor & Professor of Communication — J. C. Casey
Published: Other Ongoing (post several times a week)
Digital Edition Available?: Y
Digital Platform - Mobile: Other
Format: Online

UNIV. OF TULSA: COLLEGIAN — 800 Tucker Dr, Tulsa, OK, 74104-9700, USA; tel (918) 631-2259; fax (918) 631-2885; e-mail: collegian@utulsa.edu; web site: www.utulsa.edu/collegian/
Kendra Blevins
Editor-in-Chief — J.Christopher Proctor
Business and Advertising Manager — Elizabeth Cohen
Published: MonCirc.(fr.) 2,500
Digital Edition Available?: N
Format: Broadsheet
Note: Please contact Elizabeth Cohen about advertising by email at collegian@utulsa.edu or elizabeth-cohen@utulsa.edu

OREGON

CENTRAL OREGON COMMUNITY COLLEGE: BROADSIDE — 2600 NW College Way, Bend, OR, 97701-5933, USA; tel (541) 383-7252; fax (541) 383-7284; e-mail: broadsidemail@cocc.edu; web site: broadside.cocc.edu
advisor — Leon Pantenburg
Published: Bi-Mthly
Price: free
Format: Tabloid

CHEMEKETA CMTY. COLLEGE: CHEMEKETA COURIER — PO Box 14007, Salem, OR, 97309-7070, USA; tel (503) 399-5000; fax (503) 399-2519; e-mail: courier@chemeketa.edu; adv email: careeradvertising@yahoo.com; web site: www.chemeketa.edu/collegelife/newspaper/index.html
William Florence
Gale Hann
Russell Vineyard
Format: Tabloid

CLACKAMAS CMTY. COLLEGE: CLACKAMAS PRINT — 19600 Molalla Ave, Oregon City, OR, 97045-7998, USA; tel (503) 657-6958; fax (503) 650-7350; e-mail: chiefed@clackamus.edu
Melissa Jones
Kayla Berge
John Hurlburg
Format: Tabloid

EASTERN OREGON UNIV.: THE VOICE — 1 University Blvd Hoke 320, La Grande, OR, 97850-2807, USA; tel (541) 962-3386; fax (541) 962-3706; e-mail: thevoice@eou.edu; web site: www.eou.edu/thevoice
Kyle Janssen
Taylor Stanely Pawley
Format: Tabloid

LANE CMTY. COLLEGE: TORCH — 4000 East 30th Ave. Center Building, Room 008, Eugene, OR, 97405-0640, USA; tel (541) 463-5881; fax (541) 463-3993; e-mail: torch@lanecc.edu; web site: www.lcctorch.com
Dorothy Wearne
Lana Boles
James Anderson
Format: Tabloid

LEWIS & CLARK COLLEGE: PIONEER LOG — 0615 SW Palatine Hill Rd, Portland, OR, 97219-7879, USA; tel (503) 768-7146; fax (503) 768-7130; e-mail: piolog@lclark.edu; adv email: ads.piolog@gmail.com; ed email: piolog@gmail.com; web site: www.piolog.comEst. 1947
Editor-in-Chief — Caleb Diehl
Published: FriCirc.(fr.) 1,200
Digital Edition Available?: Y
Price: Free
Format: Tabloid

LINFIELD COLLEGE: LINFIELD REVIEW — 900 SE Baker St Ste A518, McMinnville, OR, 97128-6894, USA; tel (503) 883-2200; e-mail: review@linfield.edu; web site: www.linfield.edu/linfield-review
William Lingle
Dominic Baez
Format: Tabloid

LINN-BENTON CMTY. COLLEGE: COMMUTER — 6500 Pacific Blvd SW, Albany, OR, 97321-3774, USA; tel (541) 917-4451; fax (541) 917-4454; e-mail: commuter@linnbenton.edu; web site: www.commuter.linnbenton.edu
Rob Priewe
Frank Warren
Ryan henson Henson
Format: Tabloid

MT. HOOD CMTY. COLLEGE: ADVOCATE — 26000 SE Stark St, Gresham, OR, 97030-3300, USA; tel (503) 491-7250; fax (503) 491-6064; e-mail: advocatt@mhcc.edu
EIC — Ivy Davis
Advisor — Dan Ernst
Published: Fri
Format: Tabloid

OREGON INSTITUTE OF TECHNOLOGY: THE EDGE — 3201 Campus Dr # CU111C, Klamath Falls, OR, 97601-8801, USA; tel (541) 885-1371; fax (541) 885-1024; e-mail: edge@oit.edu
Steve Matthies
Format: Tabloid

OREGON STATE UNIV.: DAILY BAROMETER — 118 Memorial Un E, Corvallis, OR, 97331-8592, USA; tel (541) 737-3374; fax (541) 737-4999; web site: www.dailybarometer.com
Brandon Southward
Taryn Luna
Gail Cole
Candice Ruud
Format: Tabloid

PACIFIC UNIV.: PACIFIC INDEX — 2043 College Way, Forest Grove, OR, 97116, USA; tel (503) 352-2855; e-mail: index@pacificu.edu; ed email: karissa@pacindex.com; web site: www.pacindex.comEst. 1897
Adviser — Dave Cassady
Managing editor — Karrisa George
Web edition editor — Kathleen Rohde
Published: Bi-MthlyCirc.(fr.) 1,200
Digital Edition Available?: Y
Insert rate: $200
Format: Tabloid

PORTLAND CMTY. COLLEGE — PO Box 19000, Portland, OR, 97280-0990, USA; tel (503) 977-4184; fax (503) 977-4956; e-mail: tsteffen@pcc.eduEst. 1963
Tami Steffenhagen
Format: Broadsheet

PORTLAND STATE UNIV.: THE VANGAURD — PO Box 751, Portland, OR, 97207-0751, USA; tel (503) 725-5691; fax (503) 725-5860; e-mail: vanguardadvertising@gmail.com; web site: www.dailyvanguard.comEst. 1948
Judson Randall
Matthew Kirtley
Sarah J. Christensen
Format: Tabloid

REED COLLEGE: QUEST — 3203 SE Woodstock Blvd, Portland, OR, 97202-8199, USA; tel (503) 777-7707; fax (503) 788-6657; e-mail: quest@reed.edu
Format: Tabloid

SOUTHERN OREGON UNIV.: SISKIYOU — Stevenson Union, Rm. 336, 1250 Siskiyou Blvd., Ashland, OR, 97520-5001, USA; tel (541) 552-6307; fax (541) 552-6440; e-mail: siskiyou@students.sou.edu; web site: www.sou.edu/su/siskiyou
Karen Finnegan
Dwight Melton
Format: Tabloid

SOUTHWESTERN OREGON CMTY. COLLEGE: SOUTHWESTER — 1988 Newman Ave., Coos Bay, OR, 97420-2956, USA; tel (541) 888-7442
Bridget Hildreth
Format: Tabloid

THE BEACON/ UNIV. OF PORTLAND: THE BEACON — 5000 N Willamette Blvd, Portland, OR, 97203-5798, USA; tel (503) 943-7376; fax (503) 943-7833; e-mail: beacon@up.edu; adv email: beaconads@up.edu; web site: www.upbeacon.comEst. 1935
Nancy Copic
Published: We are now digital only!!!
Digital Edition Available?: Y
Format: ONLINE and mobile only

UMPQUA CMTY. COLLEGE: MAINSTREAM — PO Box 967, Roseburg, OR, 97470-0226, USA; tel (541) 440-4687; fax (541) 677-3214; e-mail: uccmainstream@yahoo.com; web site: www.mainstreamonline.org
Melinda Benton
Format: Tabloid

UNIV. OF OREGON: OREGON DAILY EMERALD — PO Box 3159, Eugene, OR, 97403-0159, USA; tel (541) 346-5511; fax (541) 346-5821; e-mail: news@dailyemerald.com; ed email: editor@dailyemerald.com; web site: www.dailyemerald.com
Allie Grasgreen
Emily E. Smith
Ivar Vong
Format: Tabloid

WESTERN OREGON UNIV.: WESTERN JOURNAL — 345 Monmouth Ave N, Monmouth, OR, 97361-1371, USA; tel (503) 838-9697; fax (503) 838-8616
Marissa Hufstader
Format: Magazine

WILLAMETTE UNIV.: COLLEGIAN — 900 State St, Salem, OR, 97301-3931, USA; tel (503) 370-6053; e-mail: collegian-exec@willamette.edu; adv email: collegian-ads@willamette.edu; web site: www.willamettecollegian.com
Advisor — Avery Bento
Bus. Mgr. — James Hoodecheck
Ed. in Chief — Gianni Marabella
Published: Bi-Mthly
Digital Edition Available?: N
Format: Tabloid

PENNSYLVANIA

ALBRIGHT COLLEGE: ALBRIGHTIAN — P.O. Box 15234, Reading, PA, 19612, USA; tel (610) 921-7558; e-mail: albrightian@albright.edu; web site: www.albright.edu/albrightian
Jon Bekken
Editor-in-chief — Sarah Timmons
Assistant Editor-in-Chief — Megan Homsher
Published: Bi-Mthly
Digital Edition Available?: Y
Digital Platform - Mobile: Apple, Android, Windows
Digital Platform - Tablet: Other
Format: Tabloid

ALLEGHENY COLLEGE: CAMPUS — PO Box 12, Meadville, PA, 16335-0012, USA; tel (814) 332-2754; fax (814) 724-6834; e-mail: thecampus1@gmail.com; web site: www.alleghenycampus.com
Penny Schaefer
Kristin Baldwin
Format: Broadsheet

ALVERNIA UNIVERSITY: THE ALVERNIAN — 400 Saint Bernardine St, Reading, PA, 19607-1737, USA; tel (610) 568-1557; e-mail: ryan.lange@alvernia.edu; web site: http://www.alvernia.edu/alvernian
Faculty Advisor — Ryan Lange
Published: MthlyCirc.(fr.) 700
Digital Edition Available?: N
Price: Free
Format: Tabloid

ARCADIA UNIV.: THE TOWER — 450 S Easton Rd, Glenside, PA, 19038-3295, USA; tel (215) 572-4082; fax (215) 881-8781; web site: www.arcadia.edu; www.thetoweronline.com
Michele Cain
Format: Tabloid

BLOOMSBURG UNIV.: VOICE — 400 E. Second St., Bloomsburg, PA, 17815, USA; tel (570) 389-4457; fax (570) 389-3905; web site: www.bloomu.edu/voice/index.php
Mary Bernath
Zach Sands
Joe Arleth
Format: Broadsheet

BRYN MAWR-HAVERFORD COLLEGE: BI COLLEGE NEWS — 101 N Merion Ave, Bryn Mawr, PA, 19010-2899, USA; tel (610) 526-5000; fax (610) 526-7479; e-mail: biconews@haverford.edu; web site: www.biconews.com
Eurie Kim
Sam Kaplan
Dave Merrell
Format: Tabloid

BUCKNELL UNIV.: BUCKNELLIAN — PO Box C-3952, Lewsiburg, PA, 17837-9988, USA; tel (570) 577-1520; fax (570) 577-1176; adv email: bucknellianads@bucknell.edu; web site:

http://bucknellian.blogs.bucknell.edu/Est. 1896
James F. Lee
Winnie Warner
Editor in Chief — Ben Kaufman
Published: FriCirc. (pd.) 550 (fr.) 4,000
Format: Broadsheet

BUCKNELL UNIV. COLLEGE OF ENGINEERING — 701 Moore Ave, Lewisburg, PA, 17837-2010, USA; tel (570) 577-1520; e-mail: bucknellian@bucknell.edu; web site: www.bucknell.edu/bucknellian
James Lee
Lily Beauvilliers
Format: Broadsheet

BUCKS COUNTY CMTY. COLLEGE: CENTURION — 275 Swamp Rd, Newtown, PA, 18940-9677, USA; tel (215) 968-8379; fax (215) 968-8271; e-mail: buckscenturion@gmail.com; adv email: orders@mymediamate.com; ed email: buckscenturion@gmail.com; web site: www.bucks-news.comEst. 1964
Tony Rogers
Published: ThurCirc.(fr.) 2,000
Price: Free
Format: Tabloid

BUTLER COUNTY CMTY. COLLEGE: CUBE — PO Box 1203, Butler, PA, 16003-1203, USA; tel (724) 287-8711; fax (724) 285-6047; e-mail: cube.stass@bc3.edu; web site: www.bc3.edu
David Moser
Patrick Reddick
Format: Tabloid

CABRINI UNIVERSITY LOQUITUR: LOQUITUR — 610 King of Prussia Rd, Radnor, PA, 19087-3698, USA; tel (610) 902-8360; fax (610) 902-8285; e-mail: loquitur@cabrini.edu; adv email: loquitur@cabrini.edu; ed email: loquitur@cabrini.edu; web site: www.theloquitur.comEst. 1959
Chair — Jerome Zurek
EIC — Angelina Miller
Published: Thur, Bi-MthlyCirc.(fr.) 1,400
Digital Edition Available?: Y
Digital Platform - Mobile: Apple, Android
Digital Platform - Tablet: Apple iOS, Android
Insert rate: 0
Price: 0
Format: Tabloid and online

CARNEGIE MELLON UNIV.: THE TARTAN — Box 119, Pittsburgh, PA, 15213, USA; tel (412) 268-2111; fax (412) 268-1596; e-mail: contact@tartan.org; adv email: advertising@thetartan.org; web site: www.thetartan.org
Published: MonCirc.(fr.) 6,000
Format: Broadsheet

CEDAR CREST COLLEGE: CRESTIAD — 100 College Dr, Allentown, PA, 18104-6196, USA; tel (610) 437-4471; fax (610) 437-5955; e-mail: crestiad@cedarcrest.edu; web site: www.cedarcrest.edu/crestiadEst. 1932
Elizabeth Ortiz
Price: feww
Format: Tabloid

CHEYNEY UNIV. OF PENNSYLVANIA: OFF THE RECORD — 1837 University Cir, Cheyney, PA, 19319-1019, USA; tel (610) 399-2121
Advisor — Owens Gwen
Digital Edition Available?: Y
Note: Online version
Published once a semester.

CLARION UNIV. OF PENNSYLVANIA: CLARION CALL — 270 Gemmell Student Ctr., Clarion, PA, 16214, USA; tel (814) 393-2000; fax (814) 393-2557; e-mail: call@clarion.edu; web site: www.clarioncallnews.com
Laurie Miller
Elizabeth Presutti
Luke Hampton
Format: Broadsheet

CMTY. COLLEGE ALLEGHENY COUNTY: ALLEGHENY VIEW — Office of Student Life, Pittsburgh, PA, USA; tel (412) 237-2543; fax (412) 237-6548; web site: www.ccac.edu
Christine McQuaide
Format: Tabloid

CMTY. COLLEGE ALLEGHENY COUNTY SOUTH: FORUM — 1750 Clairton Rd # Rt, West Mifflin, PA, 15122-3029, USA; tel (412) 469-6352; fax (412) 469-4333; web site: www.ccac.edu
Aaron Kindeall
Format: Broadsheet

CMTY. COLLEGE OF ALLEGHENY COUNTY BOYCE: BOYCE COLLEGIAN — 595 Beatty Rd, Monroeville, PA, 15146-1348, USA; tel (724) 325-6730; fax (724) 325-6799
Peggy Roche
Format: Tabloid

COMMUNITY COLLEGE OF ALLEGHENY: NORTH CAMPUS VOICE — 8701 Perry Hwy, Rm 2003 B, Pittsburgh, PA, 15237, USA; tel 412-369-4156; e-mail: rbeighey@ccac.edu; web site: ccac.edu

COMMUNITY COLLEGE OF ALLEGHENY:THE FORUM — 1750 Clourton Rd Rt 885, West Mifflin, PA, 15122, USA; tel 412-469-6352; fax 412-469-4333; web site: http://www.ccac.edu

COMMUNITY COLLEGE OF PHILADELPHIA: VANGUARD — 1700 Spring Garden St., Philadelphia, PA, 19130-3936, USA; tel (215) 751-8200; fax (215) 972-6201; web site: www.thestudentvanguard.comEst. 1964
Faculty Advisor — Randy LoBasso
Editor-In-Chief — Michael Castaneda
Associate Editor — Rachel Byrd
Managing Editor — Imzadi Davis
Business Manager — Devonte Gillespie
Published: Bi-Mthly
Digital Edition Available?: Y
Format: Tabloid

DELAWARE VALLEY COLLEGE: RAM PAGES — 700 E Butler Ave, Doylestown, PA, 18901-2698, USA; tel (215) 489-2345; fax (215) 230-2966; e-mail: rampages@delval.edu; web site: www.delvalrampages.com
James O'Connor
Format: Tabloid

DESALES UNIV.: THE MINSTREL — 2755 Station Ave, Center Valley, PA, 18034-9568, USA; tel (610) 282-1100; fax (610) 282-3798; e-mail: minstrel.desales@gmail.com; web site: www.desalesminstrel.org
Editor-in-Chief — Kellie Dietrich
Published: Bi-Mthly
Digital Edition Available?: Y
Price: Free
Format: Newspaper

DICKINSON COLLEGE: DICKINSONIAN — PO Box 1773, Carlisle, PA, 17013-2896, USA; tel (717) 254-8434; fax (717) 254-8430; e-mail: dsonian@dickinson.edu; web site: www.dickinson.edu/dickinsonian
Alec Johnson
Eddie Small
Format: Broadsheet

DREXEL UNIV.: THE TRIANGLE — 3141 Chestnut St, Philadelphia, PA, 19104-2875, USA; tel (215) 895-2585; web site: www.thetriangle.orgEst. 1926
EIC — David Stephenson
Mng Ed — Keith Hobin
Staff Mgr — Laura DiSanto
EIC — Alexandra Jones
Gina Vitale
Published: Fri
Insert rate: editor@thetriangle.org
Price: Free
Format: Broadsheet

DUQUESNE UNIVERSITY: THE DUQUESNE DUKE — 600 Forbes Ave, Pittsburgh, PA, 15282-0001, USA; tel (412) 396-6629; e-mail: theduke@duq.edu; adv email: dukeads@yahoo.com; web site: www.duqsm.comEst. 1925
Bobby Kerlik
Ed. in Chief — Jess Eagle
Brian Tierney
Matt Noonan
News Ed. — Shawn
Advertising Mgr. — Mickey
Published: Thur
Digital Edition Available?: Y
Format: Tabloid

EAST STROUDSBURG UNIV.: STROUD COURIER — 200 Prospect Street, East Stroudsburg, PA, 18301, USA; tel (570) 422-3295; fax (570) 422-3053; e-mail: stroudcourier@yahoo.com; web site: www.stroudcourier.com
Ryan Doyle
Stephanie Snyder
Format: Broadsheet

EASTERN UNIVERSITY:THE WALTONIAN — 1300 Eagle Rd, St Davids, PA, 19087, USA; tel 610-341-1710; fax 610-225-5255; e-mail: wtonline@eastern.edu; web site: www.waltonian.com

EDINBORO UNIV. OF PENNSYLVANIA: SPECTATOR — 119 San Antonio Hall, Edinboro, PA, 16444-0001, USA; tel (814) 732-2266; fax (814) 732-2270; e-mail: eupspectator1@yahoo.com; web site: www.eupspectator.com
Josh Tysiachney
Carli Hoehn
Britney Kemp
Canuron Ferranti
Format: Tabloid

ELIZABETHTOWN COLLEGE: ETOWNIAN — 1 Alpha Dr, Elizabethtown, PA, 17022-2297, USA; tel (717) 361-1132; fax (717) 361-1207; e-mail: editor@etown.edu; adv email: etownianads@etown.edu; ed email: editor@etown.edu; web site: www.etownian.com
EIC — Aileen Ida
Published: Thur
Digital Edition Available?: Y
Format: Broadsheet

FRANKLIN & MARSHALL COLLEGE: COLLEGE REPORTER — PO Box 3003, Lancaster, PA, 17604-3003, USA; tel (717) 291-4095; fax (717) 291-3886; adv email: reporterads@fandm.edu; ed email: reporter@fandm.edu; web site: thediplomat.fandm.edu
Justin Quinn
Patrick Bernard
Christian Wedekind
Format: Tabloid

GANNON UNIV.: GANNON KNIGHT — 109 University Sq # 2142, Erie, PA, 16541-0002, USA; tel (814) 871-7294; fax (814) 871-7208; e-mail: gannonknight@gannon.edu; web site: www.gannon.edu
Frank Garland
Format: Tabloid

GENEVA COLLEGE: CABINET — 3200 College Ave, Beaver Falls, PA, 15010-3599, USA; tel (724) 847-6605; fax (724) 847-6772; e-mail: cabinet.editor@gmail.comcabinet; web site: www.geneva.edu
Tom Copeland
Format: Tabloid

GETTYSBURG COLLEGE: GETTYSBURGIAN — PO Box 434, Gettysburg, PA, 17325, USA; tel (717) 337-6449; fax (717) 337-6463; web site: www.thegettysburgian.com
Joel Berg
Sean Parke
Format: Broadsheet

GROVE CITY COLLEGE: COLLEGIAN — 100 Campus Dr, Grove City, PA, 16127-2104, USA; tel (724) 458-2193; fax (724) 458-2167; e-mail: collegian@gcc.eduEst. 1891
Adviser — Nick Hildebrand
Editor-in_Chief — Karen Postupac
Managing Editor
— James Sutherland
Published: FriCirc.(fr.) 1,500
Digital Edition Available?: N
Price: Free
Format: Tabloid
Note: The Collegian is produced by students and
Published by Grove City College.

HOLY FAMILY COLLEGE: TRI-LITE — 9801 Frankford Ave, Philadelphia, PA, 19114, USA; tel (215) 637-5321; fax (215) 824-2438; web site: www.tri-liteonline.com
Laura Wkovitz
Format: Tabloid

INDIANA UNIV. OF PENNSYLVANIA: PENN — 319 Pratt Dr, Indiana, PA, 15701-2954, USA; tel (724) 357-1306; fax (724) 357-0127; adv email: the-penn@iup.edu; web site: www.thepenn.org
Joe Lawley
Heather Blake
Branden Oakes
Format: Tabloid

JUNIATA COLLEGE: NO STUDENT NEWSPAPER — 1700 Moore St, Huntingdon, PA, 16652-2196, USA; tel (814) 641-3000; web site: www.juniatian.com
Published: Bi-Mthly
Digital Edition Available?: N
Format: Tabloid

LA ROCHE COLLEGE: COURIER — 9000 Babcock Blvd, Pittsburgh, PA, 15237-5898, USA; tel (412) 536-1147; fax (412) 536-1067; e-mail: courier@laroche.edu; web site: www.larochecourier.com
Ed Stankowski
Rebecca Jeskey
Maggie Kelly
Format: Broadsheet

LA SALLE UNIV.: LA SALLE COLLEGIAN — 1900 W Olney Ave # 417, Philadelphia, PA, 19141-1108, USA; tel (215) 951-1000; fax (215) 763-9686; e-mail: collegian@lasalle.edu; web site: www.lasalle.edu/collegian
Robert O'Brien
Olivia Biagi
Format: Tabloid

LAFAYETTE COLLEGE: THE LAFAYETTE — Farinon Center Box 9470, Easton, PA, 18042, USA; tel (610) 330-5354; fax (610) 330-5724; e-mail: thelafayette@gmail.com; web site: www.lafayettestudentnews.com
EIC — William Gordon
Mgr Ed — Ian Morse
Format: Broadsheet

LEBANON VALLEY COLLEGE: LA VIE COLLEGIENNE — 101 N College Ave, Annville, PA, 17003-1400, USA; tel (717) 867-6169; e-mail: lavic@lvc.edu; web site: lavieonline.lvc.edu
Bob Vicic
Jake King
Katie Zwiebel
Format: Tabloid

LEHIGH UNIV.: BROWN & WHITE — 33 Coppee Dr, Bethlehem, PA, 18015-3165, USA; tel (610) 758-4454; fax (610) 758-6198;

e-mail: bw@lehigh.edu; web site: www.thebrownandwhite.com
Head — Wally Trimble
Julie Stewart
Ed. in Chief — Jack Lule
Format: Tabloid

LINCOLN UNIV.: LINCOLNIAN — 1570 Baltimore Pike, Lincoln University, PA, 19352-9141, USA; tel (484) 365-7524; fax (610) 932-1256; web site: www.thelincolnianonline.com
Eric Watson
Format: Tabloid

LOCK HAVEN UNIV. OF PENNSYLVANIA: EAGLE EYE — USA; tel (570) 484-2334; e-mail: lhueagleye@yahoo.com; web site: www.lhueagleye.com
Joe Stender
Jamie Kessinger
Format: Broadsheet

LUZERNE COUNTY CMTY. COLLEGE: OUTLOOK — 1333 S Prospect St, Nanticoke, PA, 18634-3899, USA; tel (570) 740-0638; fax (570) 740-0605
Brett Bonanny
Format: Tabloid

LYCOMING COLLEGE: LYCOURIER — 700 College Place, Williamsport, PA, 17701-5192, USA; tel (570) 321-4315; e-mail: lycourier@lycoming.edu; adv email: lycourier@lycoming.edu; ed email: lycourier@lycoming.edu; web site: http://lycourier.lycoming.edu
Advisor — Dave Heemer
Editor-in-Chief — Jordyn Hotchkiss
Published: Other BI-Wkly on ThursdaysCirc. (fr.) 800
Digital Edition Available?: N
Format: Broadsheet

MANSFIELD UNIV. OF PENNSYLVANIA: FLASHLIGHT — PO Box 1, Mansfield, PA, 16933-0001, USA; tel (570) 662-4986; fax (570) 662-4386; e-mail: flashlit@mnsfld.edu
Daniel Mason
Format: Tabloid

MARYWOOD UNIVERSITY: THE WOOD WORD — 2300 Adams Ave, Scranton, PA, 18509-1598, USA; tel (570) 348-6211; fax (570) 961-4768; e-mail: thewoodword@m.marywood.edu; web site: www.thewoodword.org
Ann Williams
Advisor — Lindsey Wotanis
Published: Mthly
Digital Edition Available?: N
Format: Tabloid

MERCYHURST UNIVERSITY: MERCIAD — 501 E 38th St, Erie, PA, 16546-0002, USA; tel (814) 824-2376; fax ; e-mail: editormerciad@mercyhurst.edu; adv email: admerciad@mercyhurst.edu; ed email: opinionmerciad@mercyhurst.edu; web site: merciad.mercyhurst.eduEst. 1929
Bill Welch
Published: WedCirc.(fr.) 1,200
Digital Edition Available?: Y
Insert rate: $100
Price: Free
Format: Broadsheet

MESSIAH COLLEGE: SWINGING BRIDGE — PO Box 3043, Mechanicsburg, PA, 17055, USA; tel (717) 796-5095; fax (717) 796-5249; e-mail: theswingingbridge@messiah.edu; adv email: theswingingbridge@messiah.edu; ed email: theswingingbridge@messiah.edu; web site: www.messiahsb.com
Professor of Communications — Ed Arke
Price: Free
Format: Tabloid

MILLERSVILLE UNIV. OF PENNSYLVANIA: THE SNAPPER — PO Box 1002, Millersville, PA, 17551-0302, USA; tel (717) 871-2102; fax (717) 872-3515; e-mail: snapper@marauder.millersville.edu; web site: thesnapper.com
Gene Ellis
Bradley Giuranna
Ashley Palm
Format: Broadsheet

MISERICORDIA UNIVERSITY: THE HIGHLANDER — 301 Lake St, Dallas, PA, 18612-7752, USA; tel (570) 674-6737; fax (570) 674-6751; e-mail: highland@misericordia.edu; web site: www.highlandernews.net
Published: Bi-Monthly
Format: Broadsheet

MONTGOMERY COUNTY CMTY. COLLEGE — 340 Dekalb Pike, Blue Bell, PA, 19422-1400, USA; tel (215) 619-7306; fax (215) 619-7191
Brian Brendlinger

MORAVIAN COLLEGE: THE COMENIAN — 1200 Main St, Bethlehem, PA, 18018-6650, USA; tel (610) 625-7509; fax (610) 866-1682; e-mail: comenian@moravian.edu; web site: comenian.org
Mark Harris
Kelly Grab
Carli Timpson
Published: Mthly
Digital Edition Available?: Y
Digital Platform - Mobile: Apple, Android, Windows, Blackberry
Digital Platform - Tablet: Apple iOS, Android, Windows 7, Blackberry Tablet OS, Kindle, Nook, Kindle Fire, Other
Format: Tabloid

MUHLENBERG COLLEGE: THE MUHLENBERG WEEKLY — 2400 W. Chew Street, Allentown, PA, 18104, USA; tel (484) 664-3195; e-mail: weeklyeditor@gmail.com; web site: www.muhlenbergweekly.comEst. 1883
Editor in Chief — Gregory Kantor
Published: Thur
Format: Tabloid

NORTHAMPTON CMTY. COLLEGE: THE COMMUTER — 3835 Green Pond Rd, Bethlehem, PA, 18020-7599, USA; tel (610) 861-5372; fax (610) 332-6163; e-mail: thecommuter@northampton.edu; adv email: thecommuter@northampton.edu; ed email: thecommuter@northampton.edu; web site: www.ncccommuter.org
Advisor — Rob Hays
Published: MthlyCirc. (pd.) 0 (fr.) 2,000
Digital Edition Available?: Y
Insert rate: n/a
Price: Free
Format: Tabloid
Note: Website under development; operational fall 2012

PENN STATE NEW KENSINGTON:COMMUNICATIONS DEPT — 3550 Seventh St rd, New Kensington, PA, 15068, USA; tel 724-334-6713; e-mail: aka11@psu.edu; web site: http://nk.psu.edu

PENN STATE UNIV.: THE DAILY COLLEGIAN — 123 S Burrowes St Ste 200, State College, PA, 16801-3882, USA; tel (814) 865-2531; fax (814) 865-3848; e-mail: collegian@psu.edu; adv email: mycollegianrep@gmail.com; web site: www.collegian.psu.edu
Opns. Mgr. — Wayne Lowman
Published: Mon, Tues, Wed, Thur, Fri
Digital Edition Available?: Y
Digital Platform - Mobile: Apple, Android
Digital Platform - Tablet: Apple iOS, Android
Format: Tabloid

PENN STATE UNIV.: LION'S ROAR — 1600 Woodland Rd, Abington, PA, 19001-3990, USA; tel (215) 881-7507; fax (215) 881-7660; e-mail: fdq1@psu.edu; web site: www.abington.psu.edu
Ed. — Frank Quattrone
Insert rate: fdq1@psu.edu
Format: Tabloid

PENN STATE UNIV.: HIGHACRES COLLEGIAN — 76 University Dr, Hazleton, PA, 18202-1291, USA; tel (570) 450-3131; fax (570) 450-3182
April Snyder
Format: Tabloid

PENN STATE UNIV.: MCKEESPORT COLLEGIAN — 4000 University Dr, White Oak, PA, 15131-7644, USA; tel (412) 675-9143
Kathleen Taylor Brown
Monica Michna
Format: Tabloid

PENN STATE UNIV.: THE BEHREND BEACON — 4701 College Dr, Erie, PA, 16563-4117, USA; tel (814) 898-6488; fax (814) 898-6019; e-mail: www.pserie.psu.edu
Editor in Chief — Sarah Veslany
Published: Tues
Format: Broadsheet

PENN STATE UNIV. — 200 University Dr, Schuylkill Haven, PA, 17972-2208, USA; tel (570) 385-6000
Wes Loder
Format: Broadsheet

PENN STATE UNIV.: ALTOONA COLLEGIATE REVIEW — Raymond Smith Bldg., Altoona, PA, 16601, USA; tel (814) 940-4658; fax (814) 949-5007
Savannah Straub
Margaret Moses
Format: Tabloid

PENN STATE UNIV. DELAWARE COUNTY: LION'S EYE — 25 Yearsley Mill Rd, Media, PA, 19063-5596, USA; tel (610) 892-1200; fax (610) 892-1357; e-mail: kab4@psu.edu
Karrie Bowen
Format: Tabloid

PENN STATE UNIV. HARRISBURG: CAPITAL TIMES — 777 W Harrisburg Pike # E-126, Middletown, PA, 17057-4846, USA; tel (717) 948-6440; fax (717) 948-6724; e-mail: captimes@psu.edu
Patrick Burrows
James Speed
Jenna Denoyelles
Format: Tabloid

PENN STATE UNIVERSITY: COLLEGE OF COMMUNICATIONS — 201 Carnegie Bldg, University Park, PA, 16802, USA; tel 814-863-1484; fax 814-863-8044; web site: http://comm.psu.edu

PHILADELPHIA NEIGHBORHOODS — 1515 Market St First Floor, Philadelphia, PA, 19102, USA; tel 315-729-9020; e-mail: charper@temple.edu; web site: www.philadelphianeighborhoods.com

POINT PARK COLLEGE: GLOBE — PO Box 627, Pittsburgh, PA, 15222, USA; tel (412) 392-4740; fax (412) 392-3902; e-mail: theglobeadvertising@gmail.com; ed email: szullo@pointpark.edu; web site: www.pointparkglobe.com
Steve Hallock
Sara Zullo
Format: Tabloid

READING AREA CMTY. COLLEGE: FRONT STREET JOURNAL — PO Box 1706, Reading, PA, 19603-1706, USA; tel (610) 607-6212; fax (610) 375-8255; web site: racc.edu
Melissa Kushner
Format: Broadsheet

ROBERT MORRIS UNIVERSITY : THE SENTRY: RMU SENTRY MEDIA — 6001 University Blvd, Moon Township, PA, 15108, USA; tel 412-397-6826; fax 412-397-2436; e-mail: sentrynews@mail.rmu.edu; adv email: sentrynewsads@mail.rmu.edu; ed email: sentrynews@mail.rmu.edu ; web site: www.rmusentrymedia.comEst. 2006
Published: Online only Circ.(fr.) 500
Digital Edition Available?: Y
Digital Platform - Mobile: Apple, Android
Digital Platform - Tablet: Apple iOS, Android

SAINT VINCENT COLLEGE: THE REVIEW — 300 Fraser Purchase Rd, Latrobe, PA, 15650-2690, USA; tel (724) 539-9761; e-mail: review.stvincent@gmail.com; ed email: bridget.fertal@stvincent.edu; web site: http://www.stvincentreview.com/
Dennis McDaniel
Editor-in-Chief — Bridget Fertal
Business Manager — Cheyenne Dunbar
Published: Wed
Digital Edition Available?: Y
Price: Free
Format: Tabloid

SETON HILL UNIVERSITY: SETONIAN — PO Box 343K, Greensburg, PA, 15601-1599, USA; tel (724) 830-4791; fax (724) 830-4611; e-mail: setonian@gmail.com; web site: www.setonhill.edu
Editor-in-Chief — Olivia Goudy
Published: Mthly
Format: Tabloid

SHIPPENSBURG UNIVERSITY:THE SLATE — Shippensburg University, Shippensburg, PA, 17257, USA; tel 717-477-1778; fax 717-477-4022; e-mail: slate@ship.edu; web site: www.theslateonline.com
Michael Drager

SLIPPERY ROCK UNIV.: THE ROCKET — 220 Eisenberg Classroom Bldg., Slipper Rock, PA, 16057, USA; tel (724) 738-2643; fax (724) 738-4896; e-mail: rocket.letters@sru.edu; web site: www.theonlinerocket.com
Joseph Harry
Josh Rizzo
Format: Broadsheet

ST. FRANCIS UNIV.: TROUBADOUR — PO Box 600, Loretto, PA, 15940-0600, USA; tel (814) 472-3038; fax (814) 472-3358
Dean Allison
Andrew Maloney
Format: Tabloid

ST. JOSEPHS UNIV.: HAWK — 5600 City Ave., 314 Campion Ctr., Philadelphia, PA, 19131-1395, USA; tel (610) 660-1079; fax (610) 660-1089; e-mail: thehawk@sju.edu; web site: www.sjuhawknews.com
Dr. Jenny Spinner
Karrin Randle
Katy Yavorek
Format: Tabloid

SUSQUEHANNA UNIV.: THE QUILL — CA Box 18, Selinsgrove, PA, 17870, USA; tel (570) 374-4298; fax (570) 372-2745; e-mail: suquill@susqu.edu; web site: www.suquill.comEst. 1896
Catherine Hastings
Published: FriCirc.(fr.) 2,200
Digital Edition Available?: N
Format: tabloid

SWARTHMORE COLLEGE: PHOENIX — 500 College Ave Ste 2, Swarthmore, PA, 19081-1390, USA; tel (610) 328-8000; fax (208) 439-9864; e-mail: phoenix@swarthmore.edu; web site: www.swarthmorephoenix.com
Mara Revkin
Format: Tabloid

TEMPLE UNIVERSITY: THE TEMPLE NEWS — 1755 N 13th St, Philadelphia, PA,

19122-6011, USA; tel 215-204-6737; fax 215-204-1663; e-mail: editor@temple-news.com; adv email: advertising@temple-news.com; web site: www.temple-news.comEst. 1921
John Di Carlo
Published: Tues Daily onlineCirc.(fr.) 5,000
Digital Edition Available?: Y
Digital Platform - Mobile: Apple, Android, Windows, Blackberry
Digital Platform - Tablet: Apple iOS, Android, Windows 7, Blackberry Tablet OS, Kindle, Nook
Price: Free
Format: Broadsheet

TEPPER SCHOOL OF BUSINESS AT CARNEGIE MELLON UNIVERSITY: ROBBER BARONS — 5000 Forbes Ave, Pittsburgh, PA, 15213-3815, USA; tel (412) 268-2269; e-mail: jywong@tepper.cmu.edu; adv email: robberbaronstepper@gmail.com; web site: http://tepper.campusgroups.com/rbp/about/
Tyson Bauer
Published: Thur
Digital Edition Available?: N
Format: Magazine
Note: No Advertisements Being Accepted for 2012-2013 School Year

THE BEHREND BEACON — Penn State University-Erie The Behrend College, Erie, PA, 16563, USA; tel 814-898-6488; e-mail: editor@psu.edu; web site: www.thebehrendbeacon.com

THE DAILY PENNSYLVANIAN: THE DAILY PENNSYLVANIAN — 4015 Walnut St. 2nd Fl, Philadelphia, PA, 19104-6198, USA; tel (215) 422-4640; fax (215) 422-4646; e-mail: advertising@theDP.com; adv email: advertising@theDP.com; web site: www.theDP.comEst. 1885
Eric Jacobs
Published: Mon, ThurCirc.(fr.) 6,000
Digital Edition Available?: Y
Insert rate: Contact us
Price: Contact us
Format: Broadsheet

THE FOURTH ESTATE — Harrisburg Area Community College, Harrisburg, PA, 17110, USA; tel 717-780-2582; e-mail: 4estate@hacc.edu

THE JOUST — 1 Neumann Dr, Aston, PA, 19014, USA; tel 610-358-4570; fax 610-361-5314; e-mail: glassj@neumann.edu; web site: www.neumann.edu

THE KEY — Keystone College, La Plume, PA, 18440, USA; tel 570-945-8449

THIEL COLLEGE — 75 College Ave, Greenville, PA, 16125-2181, USA; tel (724)589-2416; e-mail: newspaper@thiel.edu; web site: www.thiel.edu/thielensian
James Raykie
Alivia Lapcevich
Format: Tabloid

UNIV. OF PENNSYLVANIA ENGINEERING SCHOOL: PENNSYLVANIA TRIANGLE — 220 S 33rd St Rm 107, Philadelphia, PA, 19104-6315, USA; tel (215) 898-1444; fax (801) 469-4487; e-mail: triangle@seas.upenn.edu; web site: www.seas.upenn.edu/~triangle/
Mark Smyda
Bezhou Feng
Format: Magazine

UNIV. OF PENNSYLVANIA LAW SCHOOL — 3400 Chestnut St Ste 1, Philadelphia, PA, 19104-6204, USA; tel (215) 898-7483; fax (215) 573-2025
Doug Rennie
Format: Broadsheet

UNIV. OF PITTSBURGH: THE PITT NEWS — USA; tel (412) 648-7980; fax (412) 648-8491; e-mail: pittnews@pittnews.com; web site: www.pittnews.com
Harry Kloman
Ashwini Sivaganesh
John Hamilton
Victor Powell
Published: Mon, Tues, Wed, Thur, Fri
Digital Edition Available?: Y
Digital Platform - Mobile: Apple, Android, Windows
Digital Platform - Tablet: Apple iOS, Android, Windows 7
Format: Tabloid

UNIV. OF PITTSBURGH: ADVOCATE — 147 Student Union, 450 School House Rd., Johnstown, PA, 15904-1200, USA; tel (814) 269-7470; e-mail: joo10@pitt.edu; web site: www.upjadvocate.com
Leland Wood
Michael Cuccaro
Jon O' Connel
Ryan Brown
Format: Tabloid

UNIV. OF PITTSBURGH AT BRADFORD: SOURCE — 300 Campus Dr, Bradford, PA, 16701-2898, USA; tel (814) 362-7682; fax (814) 362-7518; e-mail: source@pitt.edu; adv email: tfjz@atlanticbb.net; ed email: tfjz@atlanticbb.net
Tim Ziaukas
Digital Edition Available?: N
Format: Tabloid

UNIV. OF PITTSBURGH/GREENSBURG: THE INSIDER — USA; tel (724) 836-7481; fax (724) 836-9888; e-mail: upginsider@gmail.com; web site: www.upginsider.com
Lori Jakiela
Format: Tabloid

UNIV. OF SCRANTON: AQUINAS — 800 Linden St, Scranton, PA, 18510, USA; tel (570) 941-7464; fax (570) 941-4836; e-mail: aquinas@scranton.edu; web site: academic.scranton.edu/organization/aquinas
Scott Walsh
Format: Tabloid

UNIV. OF THE SCIENCES IN PHILADELPHIA: THE USP — 600 S 43rd St, Philadelphia, PA, 19104-4495, USA; tel (215) 596-8800; web site: www.usp.edu
Miriam Gilbert
Leeann Tan
Meghan Baker
Format: Tabloid

URSINUS COLLEGE: GRIZZLY — PO Box 1000, Collegeville, PA, 19426-1000, USA; tel (610) 409-2448; e-mail: grizzly@ursinus.edu
Rebecca Jaroff
Format: Tabloid

VALLEY FORGE MILITARY COLLEGE — 1001 Eagle Rd, Wayne, PA, 19087-3695, USA; tel (610) 989-1403
Charles A. McGeorge

VILLANOVA UNIV.: THE VILLANOVIAN — 800 E Lancaster Ave, Villanova, PA, 19085-1478, USA; tel (610) 519-7207; fax (610) 519-5666; e-mail: business@villanovan.com; web site: www.villanovan.com
Jessica Ramey
Jody Ross
Tom Mogan
Tim Richer
Ed. in Chief — Laura
Format: Tabloid

WASHINGTON & JEFFERSON COLLEGE: THE RED & BLACK — 60 S Lincoln St, Washington, PA, 15301-4801, USA; tel (724) 222-4400; fax (724) 223-6534; e-mail: redandblackstaff@jay.washjeff.edu; web site: www.washjeff.eduEst. 1909
Dale Lolley
Published: Thur
Digital Edition Available?: N
Format: Tabloid
Note: Currently developing a website to host The Red&Black online.

WAYNESBURG UNIVERSITY:THE YELLOW JACKET: YELLOW JACKET — 51 West College St., Waynesburg, PA, 15370, USA; tel 724-627-8191; e-mail: jacket@waynesburg.edu

WEST CHESTER UNIVERSITY: THE QUAD — 253 Sykes Union, West Chester, PA, 19383-0001, USA; tel (610) 436-2375; fax (610) 436-3280; e-mail: quad@wcupa.edu; adv email: quadadvertising@wcupa.edu; ed email: quadeic@wcupa.edu; web site: www.wcuquad.comEst. 1934
Philip Thompsen
EIC — Samantha Mineroff
Published: MonCirc.(fr.) 2,500
Digital Edition Available?: Y
Digital Platform - Mobile: Apple, Android, Other
Digital Platform - Tablet: Apple iOS, Android, Other
Price: Free
Format: Tabloid

WESTMINSTER COLLEGE: WESTMINSTER HOLCAD — 319 S Market St, New Wilmington, PA, 16172-0001, USA; tel (724) 946-7224; e-mail: holcad@westminister.edu; web site: www.theholcad.com
Shannon Richtor
Format: Broadsheet

WHARTON SCHOOL OF GRAD. BUS.: WHARTON JOURNAL — 3730 Walnut St, Philadelphia, PA, 19104-3615, USA; tel (215) 898-3200; fax (215) 898-1200; e-mail: journal@wharton.upenn.edu; web site: www.whartonjournal.com
Mark Hanson
Anix Vyas
Gareth Keane
Format: Tabloid

WILKES UNIV.: BEACON — 130 S. River St., Conyngham Ctr., Office 101, Wilkes-Barre, PA, 18701, USA; tel (570) 408-5903; fax (570) 408-5902; e-mail: wilkesbeacon@wilkes.edu; web site: www.wilkesbeacon.com
Andrea Frantz
Michele Flannery
Nicole Frail
Format: Tabloid

WILSON COLLEGE: WILSON BILLBOARD — 1015 Philadelphia Ave, Chambersburg, PA, 17201-1285, USA; tel (717) 264-4141; fax (717) 264-1578
Aimee-Marie Dorsten
Format: Tabloid

YORK COLLEGE OF PENNSYLVANIA: THE SPARTAN — 441 Country Club Rd, York, PA, 17403-3651, USA; tel (717) 815-1312; e-mail: spartan@ycp.edu; web site: spartan.ycp.edu
Advisor — Steven Brikowski
Digital Edition Available?: Y
Format: Tabloid

RHODE ISLAND

BROWN UNIV./RHODE ISLAND SCHOOL OF DESIGN: COLLEGE HILL INDEPENDENT — PO Box 1930, Providence, RI, 02912-1930, USA; tel (401) 863-2008; e-mail: independent@brown.edu; theindyads@gmail.com; web site: www.theindy.org
Emily Segal
Alex Verdolini
Format: Tabloid

BRYANT COLLEGE: THE ARCHWAY — 1150 Douglas Pike Ste 1, Smithfield, RI, 02917-1290, USA; tel (401) 232-6028; fax (401) 232-6710; e-mail: archway@byrant.edu; web site: www.bryantarchway.com
Meagan Sage
Tracey Gant
John Crisafulli
Format: Tabloid

JOHNSON & WALES UNIV.: CAMPUS HERALD — 8 Abbott Park Pl, Providence, RI, 02903-3775, USA; tel (401) 598-1000; fax (401) 598-1171; e-mail: campusherald@jwu.edu; web site: www.jwu.edu
Michael Berger
Jessica Long
Catlin Benoit
Samantha Krivorit
Format: Tabloid

PROVIDENCE COLLEGE: THE COWL — 549 River Ave, Providence, RI, 02918-0001, USA; tel (401) 865-2214; fax (401) 865-1202; e-mail: cowl@providence.edu; web site: www.providence.edu
Richard F. Kless
Format: Tabloid

RHODE ISLAND COLLEGE: THE ANCHOR — Student Union Plz., 600 Mt. Pleasant Ave., Providence, RI, 02908-1940, USA; tel (401) 456-8544; fax (401) 456-8792; e-mail: news@anchorweb.org; web site: www.anchorweb.org
Rudy Cheeks
Ashley Dalton
Kameron Stualting
Format: Tabloid

ROGER WILLIAMS UNIV.: HAWKS JOURNAL — 1 Old Ferry Rd, Bristol, RI, 02809-2921, USA; tel (401) 254-3229; fax (401) 254-3355; e-mail: hawksherald@gmail.com; web site: www.hawksherald.com
Ben Whitmore
Advisor — Adrianne Mukiria
Adrianne Henderson
Format: Tabloid

THE BROWN DAILY HERALD: THE BROWN DAILY HERALD — PO Box 2538, Providence, RI, 02906-0538, USA; tel (401) 351-3260; fax (401) 351-9297; e-mail: herald@browndailyherald.com; adv email: advertising@browndailyherald.com; web site: www.browndailyherald.comEst. 1891
Lauren Aratani
Published: Mon, Tues, Wed, Thur, Fri
Digital Edition Available?: Y
Format: Tabloid

UNIV. OF RHODE ISLAND: GOOD 5 CENT CIGAR — 125 Memorial Union, 50 Lower College Rd., Kingston, RI, 02881, USA; tel (401) 874-2914; fax (401) 874-5607; e-mail: uricigar@gmail.com; web site: www.ramcigar.com
Lindsay Lorenz
Format: Tabloid

SOUTH CAROLINA

BENEDICT COLLEGE: BENEDICT TIGER — 1600 Harden St, Columbia, SC, 29204-1086, USA; tel (803) 705-4645; fax (803) 253-5065; web site: www.benedict.edu
Chair — Carolyn Drakeford
Momo Rogers
Format: Tabloid

BOB JONES UNIVERSITY: THE COLLEGIAN — 1700 Wade Hampton Blvd, Greenville, SC, 29614-0001, USA; tel (864) 370-1800; fax (864) 770-1307; e-mail: bsolomon@bju.edu; ed email: editor@bju.edu; web site: http://www.collegianonline.com/

Est. 1987
David Lovegrove
Betty Solomon
Joanne Kappel
Campus Media Supervisor — Larry Stofer
Published: Fri
Digital Edition Available?: Y
Insert rate: Free
Price: Free
Format: Tabloid

CLAFLIN UNIVERSITY: PANTHER — 400 Magnolia Street, Orangeburg, SC, 29115, USA; web site: claflin.edu/the-panther
Lee Harter
Published: Other print once per semester
Format: Tabloid

CLEMSON UNIV.: TIGER — 315 Hendrix Ctr, Clemson, SC, 29634-0001, USA; tel (864) 656-2150; fax (864) 656-4772; web site: www.thetigernews.com
Patrich Neal
Cory Bowers
Ashley Chris
Format: Tabloid

COASTAL CAROLINA UNIV.: CHANTICLEAR — PO Box 261954, Conway, SC, 29528-6054, USA; tel (843) 349-2330; fax (843) 349-2743; e-mail: chanticleer@coastal.edu; web site: www.coastal.educhanticleer
Issac Bailey
Kyle Drapeau
Clarie Arambulla
Format: Tabloid

COKER COLLEGE: PERISCOPE — 300 E College Ave, Hartsville, SC, 29550-3797, USA; tel (843) 383-8000; fax (843) 383-8047
Dick Puffer
Lance Player
Format: Tabloid

COLLEGE OF CHARLESTON: GEORGE STREET OBSERVER — 66 George St, Charleston, SC, 29424-0001, USA; tel (843) 953-7017; fax (843) 953-7037; e-mail: mcgeeb@cofc.edu; web site: www.cofc.edu/communication
Chair — Brian McGee
Katie Orlando
Format: Broadsheet

CONVERSE COLLEGE: CONVERSATIONILIST — 580 E Main St, Spartanburg, SC, 29302-0006, USA; tel (864) 596-9000; e-mail: admissions@converse.edu
Whitney Fisher
Format: Tabloid

FRANCIS MARION UNIVERSITY: THE PATRIOT — PO Box 100547, Florence, SC, 29502-0547, USA; tel (843) 661-1350; fax (843) 661-1373; e-mail: patriotnews@hotmail.com; adv email: patriotads@hotmail.com; web site: www.patriotnewsonline.com
David Sacash
Published: Bi-Mthly
Digital Edition Available?: Y
Format: Broadsheet

FURMAN UNIV.: PALADIN — PO Box 28584, Greenville, SC, 29613-0001, USA; e-mail: paladin@furman.edu; web site: www.furmannewsaper.com
Tyler Sines
Evan Bohnenblust
Jessica Lopez
Published: Bi-Mthly
Format: Broadsheet

LANDER UNIV.: FORUM — 320 Stanley Ave, Greenwood, SC, 29649-2099, USA; tel (864) 388-8000; fax (864) 388-8890; web site: www.lander.edu
Robert Stevenson
Format: Broadsheet

MEDICAL UNIV. OF SOUTH CAROLINA: MEDICAL UNIVERSIRTY OF SOUTH CAROLINA — PO Box 12110, Charleston, SC, 29422-2110, USA; tel (843) 792-4107; fax (843) 849-0214; e-mail: catalyst@musc.edu; web site: www.musc.edu/catalyst
Kim Draughn
Format: Tabloid

NEWBERRY COLLEGE: SCARLET & GRAY — 2100 College St, Newberry, SC, 29108-2197, USA; tel (803) 276-5010; fax (803) 321-5269; web site: www.newberry.edu
Jodie Peeler
Format: Broadsheet

PRESBYTERIAN COLLEGE: BLUE STOCKING — 503 S Broad St, Clinton, SC, 29325-2998, USA; tel (864) 833-8488; e-mail: pcbluestocking@gmail.comEst. 1927
Justin Brent
Co-Editor — Rachel Miles
Co-Editor — Ashleigh Bethea
Published: Mthly
Digital Edition Available?: Y
Format: Tabloid and online

SOUTH CAROLINA STATE UNIV.: THE COLLEGIAN — 300 College St NE, Orangeburg, SC, 29117-0002, USA; tel (803) 536-7237; fax (803) 536-7131; web site: http://www.thescsucollegian.com/
Rolondo Davis
Format: Broadsheet

THE JOHNSONIAN — 104 Digiorgio Campus Center Winthrop University, Rock Hill, SC, 29733-0001, USA; tel (803) 323-3419; fax (803) 323-3698; e-mail: thejohnsonian@yahoo.com; ed email: editors@mytjnow.com; web site: www.mytjnow.com
Faculty Adviser — Guy Reel
Format: Broadsheet

UNIV. OF SOUTH CAROLINA: CAROLINIAN — 800 University Way Clc 112, Spartanburg, SC, 29303-4932, USA; tel (864) 503-5138; fax (864) 503-5100; e-mail: carolinian@uscupstate.edu; web site: www.sc.edu/carolinian/
Chioma Ugochukwu
India Brown
Format: Tabloid

UNIV. OF SOUTH CAROLINA: THE DAILY GAMECOCK — 1400 Greene St, Columbia, SC, 29225-4002, USA; tel (803) 777-5064; fax (803) 777-6482; ed email: gamecockeditor@sc.edu; web site: www.dailygamecock.com
Scott Lindenberg
Erik Collins
Amanda Davis
Calli Burnett
Format: Broadsheet

UNIV. OF SOUTH CAROLINA: PACER TIMES — 471 University Pkwy, Aiken, SC, 29801-6399, USA; tel (803) 648-6851; fax (803) 641-3494; web site: www.pacertimes.com
Israel Butler
Format: Tabloid

SOUTH DAKOTA

AUGUSTANA UNIVERSITY: AUGUSTANA MIRROR — 2001 S Summit Ave, Sioux Falls, SD, 57197-0002, USA; tel (605) 274-4423; fax (605) 274-5288; e-mail: augustanamirror@gmail.com; web site: www.augiemirror.comEst. 1909
Advisor — Jeffrey Miller
Published: FriCirc.(fr.) 1,000
Digital Edition Available?: Y
Format: Tabloid

BLACK HILLS STATE UNIV.: JACKET JOURNAL — 1200 University St, Spearfish, SD, 57799-0002, USA; tel (605) 642-6389; fax (605) 642-6119; e-mail: jacketjournal@bhsu.edu; web site: www.bhsu.edu/jacketjournal1
Mary Caton-Rosser
Shelby Cihak
Kendra Bertsch
Format: Tabloid

DAKOTA STATE UNIV.: TROJAN TIMES — 820 N Washington Ave, Madison, SD, 57042-1799, USA; tel (605) 256-5278; fax (605) 256-5021; e-mail: times@dsu.edu; web site: www.clubs.dsu.edu/trojantimes
Justin Blessinger
Jenny Grabinger
Samantha Moulton
Format: Tabloid

MT. MARTY COLLEGE: MODERATOR — 1105 W 8th St Ste 564, Yankton, SD, 57078-3725, USA; tel (605) 668-1293; fax (605) 668-1508; e-mail: moderator@mtmc.edu; web site: www.mtmc.edu/student/moderator
Jill Paulson
Lauren Donlin
Alicia Pick
Format: Tabloid

NORTHERN STATE UNIV.: NORTHERN EXPONENT — 1200 S. Jay St., Student Ctr., Rm. 201, Aberdeen, SD, 57401, USA; tel (605) 626-2534; fax (605) 626-2559; e-mail: stupub@northern.edu; web site: www.nsuexponent.com
Tracy Rasmussen
Published: Mthly
Digital Edition Available?: Y
Price: Free
Format: Tabloid

SOUTH DAKOTA SCHOOL OF MINES & TECHNOLOGY: THE AURUM — 501 E Saint Joseph St, Rapid City, SD, 57701-3995, USA; e-mail: aurum.sdsmt@gmail.com; adv email: aurum.sdsmt@gmail.com; ed email: aurum.sdsmt@gmail.comEst. 1900
Business Manager — Daniel Cerfus
Secretary — Quinn del Val
Cuisiner Columnist — Robin Jerman
EIC — Dan Eitreim
Published: MthlyCirc.(fr.) 2,000
Digital Edition Available?: N
Format: Broadsheet

UNIV. OF SIOUX FALLS: VESSEL — 1101 W 22nd St, Sioux Falls, SD, 57105-1699, USA; tel (605) 331-6776; fax (605) 331-6692
Tiffany Leach
Janet Davison
Format: Magazine

UNIV. OF SOUTH DAKOTA: VOLANTE — 555 N Dakota St, Vermillion, SD, 57069-2300, USA; tel (605) 677-5494; fax (605) 677-5105; e-mail: volante@usd.edu; volanteonline@gmail.com; web site: www.volanteonline.com
Format: Broadsheet

TENNESSEE

AUSTIN PEAY STATE UNIV.: ALL STATE — PO Box 4634, Clarksville, TN, 37044-0001, USA; tel (931) 221-7376; fax (931) 221-7377; e-mail: theallstate@apsu.edu; adv email: allstateads@apsu.edu; web site: www.theallstate.org; www.apsu.edu
Tabitha Gillaland
Nicole June
Patrick Armstrong
Format: Broadsheet

BELMONT UNIV.: BELMONT VISION — 1900 Belmont Blvd, Nashville, TN, 37212-3757, USA; tel (615) 460-6000; fax (615) 460-5532; e-mail: vision@mail.belmont.edu; web site: www.belmontvision.com; www.belmont.edu
Linda Quigley
Chair — Thom Storey
Karen Bennett
Bethany Brinton
Lance Conzett
Format: Tabloid

BRYAN COLLEGE: TRIANGLE — Box 7807, Dayton, TN, 37321, USA; tel (423) 775-7285; fax (423) 775-7330; e-mail: triangle@bryan.edu; info@bryan.edu; web site: www.bryan.edu/7229; www.bryan.edu
John Carpenter
Allison McLean
Format: Tabloid

CARSON-NEWMAN UNIVERSITY: ORANGE & BLUE — 1646 Russell Ave, Jefferson City, TN, 37760, USA; tel (865) 471-3434; fax (865) 471-3416; e-mail: oandb@cn.edu; web site: www.orangeandblueonline.com; www.cn.edu
Glenn Cragwall
Format: Tabloid

CHATTANOOGA STATE TECH. CMTY. COLLEGE: COMMUNICATOR — Paul Starnes Ctr., Rm. S-260, 4501 Amnicola Hwy., Chattanooga, TN, 37406, USA; tel (423) 697-2471; fax (423) 697-4758; e-mail: communicator.editor@gmail.com
Betty A. Proctor
Keith Burkhalter
Format: Tabloid

CLEVELAND STATE CMTY. COLLEGE: THE CHEROKEE SIGNAL — PO Box 3570, Cleveland, TN, 37320-3570, USA; tel (423) 472-7141; fax (423) 478-6255; e-mail: tbartolo@clevelandstatecc.edu; web site: www.clevelandstatecc.edu
Adv. Mgr. — Tony Bartolo
Priscilla Simms
Format: Broadsheet

CUMBERLAND UNIV.: CUMBERLAND CHRONICLE — 1 Cumberland Sq., Lebanon, TN, 37087-3408, USA; tel (615) 444-2562; fax (615) 444-2569; e-mail: cumberlandchronicle@gmail.com; web site: www.cumberland.edu
Michael Rex
Published: Mon, Bi-Mthly
Digital Edition Available?: Y
Format: Tabloid

EAST TENNESSEE STATE UNIV.: EAST TENNESSEAN — PO Box 70688, Johnson City, TN, 37614-1709, USA; tel (423) 439-6170; fax (423) 439-8407; e-mail: etnews@etsu.edu; web site: www.easttennessean.com
Martha Milner
Candy Naff
Format: Tabloid

FISK UNIV.: FISK FORUM — Humanities Div., 1000 17th Ave. N., Nashville, TN, 37208-3045, USA; tel (615) 329-8500; fax (615) 329-8714; web site: www.fisk.edu
Karen Taylor
Keen West
Format: Tabloid

FREED-HARDEMAN UNIV.: BELL TOWER — 158 E Main St, Henderson, TN, 38340-2398, USA; fax (731) 989-6000; e-mail: belltower@fhu.edu; web site: www.fhu.edu
Derrick Spradlin
Eddie Eaton
Format: Tabloid

KING COLLEGE: KAYSEEAN — 1350 King College Rd, Bristol, TN, 37620-2649, USA; tel (423) 652-4829; fax (423) 968-4456
Katie Vandebrake
Format: Tabloid

LEE UNIV.: THE LEE CLARION — 1120 N Ocoee St, Cleveland, TN, 37311-4475, USA; tel (423) 614-8489; fax (423) 614-8341; e-mail: news@leeclarion.com; web site: www.leeclarion.com
Kevin Trowbridge
Michelle Bouman
Format: Broadsheet

LEMOYNE-OWEN COLLEGE: MAGICIAN — 807 Walker Ave, Memphis, TN, 38126-6595, USA; tel (901) 435-1309; fax (901) 435-1349; e-mail: magican@loc.edu; web site: www.locmagicianonline.com
Lydia Lay
Format: Tabloid

LIPSCOMB UNIV.: BABBLER — 1 University Park Dr, Nashville, TN, 37204-3956, USA; tel (615) 966-6604; fax (615) 966-6605; e-mail: babbler@lipscomb.edu; adv email: babbleradvertising@lipscomb.edu; web site: babbler.lipscomb.edu
Jimmy McCollum
Michael Gilbert
Kaitie McDermott
Format: Broadsheet

MARYVILLE COLLEGE: HIGHLAND ECHO — 502 E Lamar Alexander Pkwy, Maryville, TN, 37804-5919, USA; tel (865) 981-8241; e-mail: highland.echo@gmail.com; web site: echo.maryvillecollege.edu
Kim Trevathan
Format: Tabloid

MIDDLE TENNESSEE STATE UNIV.: SIDELINES — 1301 East Main Street, Box 36, Murfreesboro, TN, 37132-0001, USA; tel (615) 904-8357; fax (615) 494-7648; e-mail: editor@mtsusidelines.com; adv email: editor@mtsusidelines.com ; ed email: editor@mtsusidelines.com; web site: www.mtsusidelines.comEst. 1925
Editor-in-chief — Meagan White
Managing Editor — Dylan Aycock
News Editor — Sarah Taylor
Lifestyles Editor — Rhiannon Gilbert
Assistant Lifestyles Editor — Ethan Clark
Sports Editor — Michael Ward
Assistant Sports Editor — Connor Ulrey
Multimedia Editor — Grant Massey
Chief Videographer — Darian Lindsay
Photography Editor — Austin Lewis
Design Editor — Anna Claire Farmer
Design Editor — Justin Morales
Assistant News Editor — Savannah Hazlewood
Published: MthlyCirc.(fr.) 4,000
Digital Edition Available?: Y
Digital Platform - Mobile: Apple
Digital Platform - Tablet: Apple iOS
Format: Tabloid
Note:

MILLIGAN COLLEGE: STAMPEDE — PO Box 500, Milligan College, TN, 37682-0500, USA; tel (423) 461-8995; fax (423) 461-8965; e-mail: stampede@milligan.edu; web site: www.milliganstampede.comEst. 1866
Jim Dahlman
Kalee Nagel
Format: Tabloid

RHODES COLLEGE: THE SOU'WESTER — PO Box 3010, Memphis, TN, 38173-0010, USA; tel (901) 843-3885; fax (901) 843-3576; e-mail: Souwester souwester@rhodes.edu; web site: www.thesouwester.org
John Blaisdell
Format: Tabloid

SOUTHWEST TENNESSEE CMTY. COLLEGE: THE SOUTHWEST SOURCE — 5983 Macon Cv, Memphis, TN, 38134-7693, USA; tel (901) 333-4196; fax (901) 333-4995; e-mail: pworthy@southwest.tn.edu; adv email: cherron@southwest.tn.edu; web site: southwest.tn.edu/clubsEst. 2000
Phoenix Worthy
Coorindator — Connie Herron
Digital Edition Available?: N
Digital Platform - Mobile: Apple, Windows
Digital Platform - Tablet: Windows 7
Format: Tabloid
Note: We have not selected an Editor for 2013-2014 for the Southwest Source. We will by August 15, 2013

TENNESSEE TECHNOLOGICAL UNIV.: ORACLE — PO Box 5072, Cookeville, TN, 38505-0001, USA; tel (931) 372-3060; fax (931) 372-6225; e-mail: oracle@tntech.edu; adv email: ttuoracleads@gmail.com; ed email: oracle@tntech.edu; web site: www.tntechoracle.comEst. 1924
Advisor / Assistant Professor — Jon Ezell
Published: Fri Weekly during Fall and Spring semestersCirc.(fr.) 3,000
Digital Edition Available?: Y
Price: Free in single copy
Format: Broadsheet

TRUE NORTH CUSTOM PUBLISHING — 5600 Brainerd Rd Ste 1, Chattanooga, TN, 37411-5373, USA; tel 423.266.3234; web site: http://www.truenorthcustom.com
Ed. — Emily Young
Tim Lale
Katie Hammond
Alison Quiring
Opinion Ed. — Stephanie

TUSCULUM COLLEGE: PIONEER FRONTIER — PO Box 5098, Greeneville, TN, 37743-0001, USA; tel (423) 636-7300; fax (423) 638-7166; web site: www.tusculum.edu
Barth Cox
Format: Tabloid

UNION UNIV.: CARDINAL & CREAM — 1050 Union University Dr Dept Jenningshall, Jackson, TN, 38305-3656, USA; tel (731) 668-1818; fax (731) 661-5243; web site: www.cardinalandcream.info
Michael Chute
Gray Coyner
Andrea Turner
Format: Tabloid

UNIV. OF MEMPHIS: THE DAILY HELMSMAN — 113 Meeman Journalism Bldg, Memphis, TN, 38152-3290, USA; tel (901) 678-5474; fax (901) 678-0882; adv email: rlwillis@memphis.edu; web site: www.dailyhelmsman.com
Bus. Mgr. — Bob Willis
Published: Tues, Wed, Thur, FriCirc.(fr.) 6,500
Digital Edition Available?: Y
Insert rate: $75 per 1,000
Format: Tabloid

UNIV. OF TENNESSEE CHATTANOOGA: UNIVERSITY ECHO — 615 McCallie Ave, Chattanooga, TN, 37403-2504, USA; tel (423) 425-4298; fax (423) 425-8100; e-mail: echo@utcecho.com; web site: www.utcecho.com
Holly Cowart
Alexa Branblet
Paige Gabriel
Kate Bissinger
Features Ed. — Hayley
News Ed. — Rachel
Sports Ed. — Michael
Format: Tabloid

UNIV. OF TENNESSEE MARTIN: PACER TIMES — 314 Gooch Hall, Martin, TN, 38238-0001, USA; tel (731) 881-7780; fax (731) 881-7791; e-mail: pacer@ut.utm.edu; web site: www.utmpacer.com
Tomi McCutchen Parrish
Josh Lemons
Spencer Taylor
Format: Broadsheet

UNIV. OF THE SOUTH: SEWANEE PURPLE — 735 University Ave, Sewanee, TN, 37383-1000, USA; tel (931) 598-1204; e-mail: spurple@sewanee.edu; web site: www.sewaneepurple.com
Virginia Craighll
Format: Tabloid

UT DAILY BEACON (UNIVERSITY OF TENNESSEE): THE DAILY BEACON — 11 Communications Bldg., Knoxville, TN, 37996-0314, USA; tel (865) 974-5206; fax (865) 974-5569; e-mail: editorinchief@utdailybeacon.com; adv email: beaconads@utk.edu; ed email: letters@utdailybeacon.com; web site: utdailybeacon.comEst. 1906
Dir. of Student Media — Jerry Bush
Published: Mon, Thur Special issues (See Rate Card above)Circ.(fr.) 6,000
Digital Edition Available?: Y
Digital Platform - Mobile: Apple, Android, Windows, Blackberry, Other
Digital Platform - Tablet: Apple iOS, Android, Windows 7, Blackberry Tablet OS, Kindle, Nook, Kindle Fire, Other
Insert rate:
Price: Free on campus
Format: Tabloid
Note: Call for advertising details

VANDERBILT UNIV.: THE VANDERBILT HUSTLER — 2301 Vanderbilt Place Vu Sta B351504, Nashville, TN, 37235-0001, USA; tel (615) 322-4705; fax (615) 343-4969; e-mail: advertising@vanderbilthustler.com; ed email: editor@vanderbilthustler.com; web site: www.insidevandy.com
Chris Carroll
George Fischer
Carolyn Fischer
Hannah Twillman
Format: Broadsheet

VOLUNTEER STATE CMTY. COLLEGE: THE SETTLER — 1480 Nashville Pike, Gallatin, TN, 37066-3148, USA; tel (615) 452-8600; fax (615) 230-3481; e-mail: thesettler@allstate.edu; web site: www.settleronline.com
Clay Scott
Amy Webb
Format: Tabloid

WALTERS STATE CMTY. COLLEGE — 500 S Davy Crockett Pkwy, Morristown, TN, 37813-6899, USA; tel (423) 585-6816
Dianna Pearson

TEXAS

ABILENE CHRISTIAN UNIV.: OPTIMIST — PO Box 27892, Abilene, TX, 79699-0001, USA; fax (325) 674-2463; e-mail: christi.stark@acu.edu; web site: www.acuoptimist.com
Colter Hettich
Format: Broadsheet

AMARILLO COLLEGE: THE RANGER — PO Box 447, Amarillo, TX, 79178-0001, USA; tel (806) 371-5283; fax (806) 371-5398; e-mail: therangereditor@gmail.com; adv email: jlgibson@actx.edu; ed email: therangereditor@gmail.com; web site: www.acranger.comEst. 1930
Student Media Adviser
Matney Mass Media Program Coord — Jill Gibson
Student Media Coord — Maddisun Fowler
Published: Thur biweeklyCirc.(fr.) 2,500
Digital Edition Available?: Y
Insert rate: $250
Price: Free
Format: Broadsheet

ANGELINA COLLEGE: THE PACER — PO Box 1768, Lufkin, TX, 75902-1768, USA; tel (936) 633-5288; e-mail: lstapleton@angelina.eduEst. 1968
Advisor — Libby Stapleton
Published: Bi-MthlyCirc.(fr.) 1,500
Digital Edition Available?: N
Format: Broadsheet

ANGELO STATE UNIV.: RAM PAGE — PO Box 10895, San Angelo, TX, 76909-0001, USA; tel (325) 942-2040; e-mail: rampage@angelo.edu; web site: www.asurampage.com
Leah Cooper
Format: Broadsheet

AUSTIN COLLEGE: OBSERVER — 900 N Grand Ave Ste 6J, Sherman, TX, 75090-4400, USA; tel (903) 813-2296; fax (903) 813-2339; e-mail: observer@austincollege.edu
Felecia Garvin
Lauren Chiodo
Format: Tabloid

BAYLOR UNIVERSITY: THE BAYLOR LARIAT — 1 Bear Pl Unit 97330, Waco, TX, 76798-7330, USA; tel (254) 710-3407; fax (254) 710-1714; e-mail: lariat@baylor.edu; adv email: Lariat_Ads@baylor.edu; ed email: Lariat-Letters@baylor.edu; web site: www.baylorlariat.comEst. 1900
Dir., Mktg. Information — Paul Carr
Advertising Sales and Marketing Manager — Jamile Yglecias
Asst. Media Adviser — Julie Freeman
Published: Tues, Wed, Thur, FriCirc.(fr.) 4,000
Digital Edition Available?: Y
Digital Platform - Mobile: Apple, Android
Digital Platform - Tablet: Apple iOS, Android
Insert rate: (254) 710-3407
Price: (254) 710-3407
Format: Broadsheet

BROOKHAVEN COLLEGE: THE COURIER — 3939 Valley View Ln, Farmers Branch, TX, 75244-4997, USA; tel (972) 860-4700; fax (972) 860-4142; e-mail: bhc2110@dcccd.edu; web site: www.brookhavencourier.com; www.brookhavencollege.edu
Wendy Moore
Daniel Rodrigue
Format: Broadsheet

CENTRAL TEXAS COLLEGE — 6200 W Central Texas Expy, Killeen, TX, 76549-1272, USA; tel (254) 526-1755; fax (254) 526-1126

DEL MAR COLLEGE FOGHORN: FOGHORN — 101 Baldwin Blvd # HC210, Corpus Christi, TX, 78404-3805, USA; tel 361/698-1390; fax (361/698-2153; e-mail: editor@delmar.edu; adv email: rmuilenburg@delmar.edu; ed email: editor@delmar.edu; web site: www.foghornnews.comEst. 1935
Advisor — Robert Muilenburg
Donna Strong
Published: Tues, Bi-Mthly Tuesday every two weeks; no issues in summerCirc.(fr.) 2,500
Insert rate: $300 for 2500
Price: 0
Format: Broadsheet

EASTFIELD COLLEGE: EASTFIELD ET CETERA — 3737 Motley Dr, Mesquite, TX, 75150-2099, USA; tel (972) 860-7130; fax (972) 860-7040; e-mail: etc4640@dcccd.edu; web site: www.eastfieldnews.comEst. 1970
Sabine Winter
Format: Tabloid

EL PASO CMTY. COLLEGE: EL CONQUISTADOR — PO Box 20500, El Paso, TX, 79998-0500, USA; tel (915) 831-2500; fax (915) 831-2155; e-mail: tejanotribune@eppcc.edu
Steve Escajeda
Joe Old
Format: Tabloid

HARDIN-SIMMONS UNIV.: THE BRAND — 2200 Hickory St, Abilene, TX, 79601-2345,

USA; tel (325) 670-1438; fax (325) 677-8351; e-mail: brand@hsutx.edu; adv email: brandadv@hsutx.edu; web site: www.hsutx.edu
Adriel Wong
Format: Tabloid

HOUSTON BAPTIST UNIV.: COLLEGIAN — 7502 Fondren Rd, Houston, TX, 77074-3298, USA; tel (281) 649-3670; fax (281) 649-3246; e-mail: thecollegian@hbucollegian.com; adv email: ads@hbucollegian.com; web site: www.hbucollegian.comEst. 1963
Faculty Adviser — Jeffrey Wilkinson
Editor in Chief — Katie Brown
Advertising Manager — Tabatha Trapp
Published: Bi-Mthly
Digital Edition Available?: Y
Format: Collegian

HUSTON TILLOTSON COLLEGE — 900 Chicon St, Austin, TX, 78702-9997, USA; tel (512) 505-3000

KILGORE COLLEGE: FLARE — 1100 Broadway Blvd, Kilgore, TX, 75662-3299, USA; tel (903) 983-8194; fax (903) 983-8193; e-mail: kc_flare@yahoo.com; web site: www.theflareonline.com
Betty Craddock
christian Keit
Format: Broadsheet

LAMAR UNIV.: UNIVERSITY PRESS — PO Box 10055, Beaumont, TX, 77710-0055, USA; tel (409) 880-8102; fax (409) 880-8735; e-mail: advertising@lamaruniversitypress.com; web site: www.lamaruniversitypress.com
Andy Coughlan
Linda Barrett
Published: Thur end of semester special editions, seasonal editions
Digital Edition Available?: Y
Digital Platform - Mobile: Apple, Android
Digital Platform - Tablet: Apple iOS, Android
Format: Broadsheet

LETOURNEAU UNIV.: YELLOWJACKET — PO Box 7001, Longview, TX, 75607-7001, USA; tel (800) 759-8811; fax (903) 236-3129
Format: Broadsheet

MCLENNAN CMTY. COLLEGE — 1400 College Dr, Waco, TX, 76708-1499, USA; tel (254) 299-8524; fax (254) 299-8568

MCMURRY UNIV. — Box 277, McMurry Sta., Abilene, TX, 79697, USA; tel (325) 793-3800; fax (325) 793-4679

MIDLAND COLLEGE: EL PAISANO — 3600 N Garfield St, Midland, TX, 79705-6397, USA; tel (432) 685-4768; fax (432) 685-4769; e-mail: studentpublications@midland.edu; web site: www.midland.edu; www.midlandcollegepress.com
Karen Lenier
Format: Broadsheet

MIDWESTERN STATE UNIVERSITY: THE WICHITAN — 3410 Taft Blvd, Wichita Falls, TX, 76307-0014, USA; tel (940) 397-4704; e-mail: wichitan@mwsu.edu; adv email: wichitan@mwsu.edu; ed email: wichitan@mwsu.edu; web site: http://thewichitan.com/ Est. 1935
Advisor — Bradley Wilson
Published: WedCirc.(fr.) 1,000
Digital Edition Available?: Y
Format: Tabloid

NORTH LAKE COLLEGE: NEWS-REGISTER — 5001 N MacArthur Blvd Rm A-234, Irving, TX, 75038-3804, USA; tel (972) 273-3057; fax (972) 273-3441; e-mail: nnr7420@dcccd.edu; web site: www.newsregisteronline.com
Kathleen Stockmier
Editor-in-Chief — Grant V. Ziegler
Photography Editor — Joanna Mikolajczak
Published: Mthly
Format: Broadsheet

NORTHEAST TEXAS CMTY. COLLEGE: THE EAGLE — PO Box 1307, Mount Pleasant, TX, 75456-9991, USA; tel (903) 434-8232; fax (903) 572-6712; e-mail: eagle@ntcc.edu; web site: www.ntcc.edu
Mandy Smith
Daniel Lockler
Format: Broadsheet

OUR LADY OF THE LAKE UNIV.: LAKE FRONT — 411 SW 24th St Ste 105, San Antonio, TX, 78207-4617, USA; tel (210) 434-6711; fax (210) 436-0824; e-mail: lakefront@lake.ollusa.edu; lakefrontads@lake.ollusa.edu; web site: lakefront.ollusa.edu
Kay O'Donnell
Tessa Benavides
Format: Tabloid

PALO ALTO COLLEGE: THE PULSE — 1400 W Villaret Blvd, San Antonio, TX, 78224-2499, USA; tel (210) 486-3880; fax (210) 486-9271; e-mail: pac-info@alamo.edu; web site: alamo.edu/pacEst. 1983
Published: Bi-Mthly
Digital Edition Available?: Y

PANOLA COLLEGE: THE PONY EXPRESS — 1109 W Panola St, Carthage, TX, 75633-2397, USA; tel (903) 693-2079; fax (903) 693-5588; web site: www.panola.edu
Teresa Beasley
Format: Broadsheet

PARIS JUNIOR COLLEGE: THE BAT — 2400 Clarksville St, Paris, TX, 75460-6298, USA; tel (903) 785-7661; fax (903) 782-0370; web site: www.parisjc.edu
Sharon Dennehy
Format: Tabloid

PAUL QUINN COLLEGE — 3837 Simpson Stuart Rd, Dallas, TX, 75241-4398, USA; tel (214) 302-3600

PRAIRIE VIEW A&M UNIV.: PANTHER — PO Box 519, Prairie View, TX, 77446-0519, USA; tel (936) 261-1353; fax (936) 261-1365; e-mail: panther@pvamu.edu; web site: www.pvpanther.com
Lewis Smith
Whitney Harris
Format: Broadsheet

RICE UNIV.: RICE THRESHER — 6100 Main St., MS-524, Houston, TX, 77251-1892, USA; tel (713) 348-4801; e-mail: thresher@rice.edu; web site: www.ricethresher.org
Advisor — Kelley Callaway
Format: Tabloid

RICHLAND COLLEGE: CHRONICLE — 12800 Abrams Rd., Dallas, TX, 75243-2199, USA; tel (972) 238-6079; fax (972) 238-6037; adv email: advertise@dcccd.edu; web site: www.richlandchronicle.com
Published: Tues Weekly on TuesdayCirc.(fr.) 3,000
Digital Edition Available?: N
Format: Tabloid

SAM HOUSTON STATE UNIVERSITY — PO Box 2207SHSU, Huntsville, TX, 77341-0001, USA; tel (936) 294-1341; fax (936) 294-1888
Chair/Prof. — Janet A. Bridges
Philip J. Warner Chair in Journ. — Michael L. Blackman
Philip J. Warner Chair in Journ. — Mickey Herskowitz
Assoc. Prof. — Tony R. DeMars
Assoc. Prof. — Anthony Friedmann
Assoc. Prof. — Hugh S. Fullerton
Assoc. Prof. — Christopher White
Asst. Prof. — Rene Qun Chen
Asst. Prof. — Wanda Reyes Velazquez
Instr. — Ruth M. Pate
Lectr. — Richard O. Kosuowei
Lectr. — Mel Strait
Lectr. — Patsy K. Ziegler

SAM HOUSTON STATE UNIVERSITY: THE HOUSTONIAN — PO Box 2178, Huntsville, TX, 77341-0001, USA; tel (936) 294-1505; fax (936) 294-1888; e-mail: pcm009@shsu.edu; adv email: advertise@houstonianonline.com; ed email: eic@houstonianonline.com; web site: www.houstonianonline.comEst. 1913
Business Manager — Paty Mason
Faculty Advisor — Dr. Marcus Funk
Advertising Manager — Carlos Medina
Published: Wed Orientation Edition, Student GuideCirc.(fr.) 2,500
Digital Edition Available?: Y
Digital Platform - Mobile: Apple, Android
Insert rate: $150/1000
Price: Free
Format: Broadsheet

SAN ANTONIO COLLEGE: THA RANGER — 1300 San Pedro Ave, San Antonio, TX, 78212-4299, USA; tel (210) 486-1765; fax (210) 486-9239; e-mail: sac-ranger@alamo.edu; web site: www.theranger.orgEst. 1926
Advisor — Marianne Odom
Insert rate: NA
Price: Free
Format: Tabloid

SAN JACINTO COLLEGE: SAN JACINTO TIMES — 8060 Spencer Hwy, Pasadena, TX, 77505-5998, USA; tel (281) 478-2752; fax (281) 478-2703; e-mail: rsaldivar88@yahoo.com; web site: www.sanjacintotimes.com
Fred F. Faour
Format: Tabloid

SOUTH PLAINS COLLEGE: PLAINSMAN PRESS — PO Box 46, Levelland, TX, 79336-0046, USA; tel (806) 894-9611; fax (806) 894-5274; e-mail: ppress@southplainscollege.edu ; web site: http://www.southplainscollege.edu/ppress/News.html
Advisor — Charles Ehrenfeld
Jayme Wheeler
Published: Bi-weekly
Digital Edition Available?: Y
Price: Free
Format: Broadsheet

SOUTHERN METHODIST UNIV.: SMU CAMPUS WEEKLY — 3140 Dyer St Ste 315, Dallas, TX, 75205-1977, USA; tel (214) 768-4555; fax (214) 768-4573; adv email: dcads@smu.edu; web site: www.smudailycampus.comEst. 1915
Exec. Dir./Editorial Advisor — Jay Miller
Dyann Slosar
Int. Exec. Dir. — Candace Barnhill
Published: ThurCirc.(fr.) 3,000
Price: Free
Format: Broadsheet

SOUTHWEST TEXAS JUNIOR COLLEGE: SOUTHWEST TEXAN — 2401 Garner Field Rd, Uvalde, TX, 78801-6221, USA; tel (830) 591-7350; fax (830) 591-4185; web site: www.swtjc.net
Terrie Wilson
Format: Broadsheet

SOUTHWESTERN ADVENTIST UNIV.: SOUTHWESTERNER — 100 W Hillcrest St, Keene, TX, 76059-1922, USA; tel (817) 645-3921; fax (817) 202-6790; e-mail: southwesterner@swau.edu; web site: southwesterner.swau.eduEst. 1958
Ed. — Glen Robinson
Associate Editor — Julena Allen
Sierra Hernandez
Digital Edition Available?: Y
Format: Online only

ST. EDWARDS UNIV.: HILLTOP VIEWS — PO Box 1033, Austin, TX, 78767-1033, USA; tel (512) 448-8426; fax (512) 428-1084; e-mail: hilltopviewsonline@gmail.com; adv email: hilltopviewsads@gmail.com; ed email: hilltopviewseditors@gmail.com; web site: hilltopviewsonline.com
Editor-In-Chief — Andrea Guzman
Editor-In-Chief — Gabrielle Wilkosz
Managing Editor — Amanda Gonzalez
Published: Wed
Digital Edition Available?: Y

ST. MARY'S UNIV. OF SAN ANTONIO: RATTLER — 1 Camino Santa Maria, San Antonio, TX, 78228, USA; tel (210) 436-3401; fax (210) 431-4307; e-mail: rattlernews@stmarytx.edu; web site: http://www.stmurattlernews.com/home/
Patrica R. Garcia
Leo Reyes
Sarah Mills
Format: Broadsheet

STEPHEN F. AUSTIN UNIV.: THE PINE LOG — PO Box 13049, Sfa Station, Nacogdoches, TX, 75962-0001, USA; tel (936) 468-4703; fax (936) 468-1016; e-mail: pinelog@sfasu.edu; web site: www.thepinelog.comEst. 1924
Pat Spence
Editor in Cheif — Mark Rhoudes
Format: Broadsheet

SUL ROSS STATE UNIV.: SKYLINE — PO Box C112, Alpine, TX, 79832-0001, USA; tel (432) 837-8011; fax (432) 837-8664; e-mail: skyline@sulross.edu; web site: ^www.sulross.edu
Student Publications Advisor — Cheryl Zinsmeyer
Format: Tabloid

TARLETON STATE UNIVERSITY: JTAC NEWS — Box T-0440, Stephenville, TX, 76402, USA; tel (254) 968-9056; fax (254) 968-9709; e-mail: jtac@tarleton.edu; adv email: jtac_ads@tarleton.edu; ed email: jtac@tarleton.edu; web site: www.jtacnews.comEst. 1919
Dir. — Caleb Chapman
Published: WedCirc.(fr.) 1,000
Digital Edition Available?: Y
Digital Platform - Mobile: Apple, Android, Windows, Blackberry
Digital Platform - Tablet: Apple iOS, Android, Windows 7, Blackberry Tablet OS, Kindle, Nook, Kindle Fire
Format: Tabloid

TARRANT COUNTY COLLEGE: THE COLLEGIAN — 828 W Harwood Rd Cab 1124A, Hurst, TX, 76054-3219, USA; tel (817) 515-6391; fax (817) 515-6767; ed email: tcceditor@lycos.com; web site: www.tccd.net/collegian
Eddye Gallagher
Chris Webb
Format: Broadsheet

TEXARKANA COLLEGE: TC NEWS — 2500 N Robison Rd, Texarkana, TX, 75599-0001, USA; tel (903) 838-4541; fax (903) 832-5030; web site: www.tc.cc.tx.us; www.texarkanacollege.edu
Jean Cotten
Caitlin Williams
Format: Broadsheet

TEXAS A&M UNIV.: BATTALION — the Grove Bldg 8901, 215 Limar St, College Station, TX, 77843-0001, USA; tel (979) 845-3313; fax (979) 845-2647; e-mail: editor@thebatt.com; adv email: battads@thebatt.com; web site: www.thebatt.com
Cheri Shipman
Amanda Casanova
Format: Broadsheet

TEXAS A&M UNIV. COMMERCE: EAST TEXAN — PO Box 4104, Commerce, TX, 75429-4104, USA; tel (903) 886-5985; fax (903) 468-3128; e-mail: theeasttexan@gmail.com; web site: www.theeasttexan.comEst. 1915
Fac. Advisor — Fred Stewart
Published: Bi-MthlyCirc.(fr.) 1,000
Digital Edition Available?: Y
Insert rate: $300
Format: Broadsheet
Note: www.issuu.com/tamuc.easttexan tamuceasttexan.com

TEXAS A&M UNIV. CORPUS CHRISTI: ISLAND WAVES — 6300 Ocean Dr, Corpus Christi, TX, 78412-5599, USA; tel (361) 825-7024; fax (361) 825-3931; adv email: islandwaves.ads@tamucc.edu; ed email: editor-in-chief.islandwaves@tamucc.edu; web site: islandwaves.tamucc.edu; www.tamucc.edu
Rob Boscamp
Brittnye Screws
Format: Tabloid

TEXAS A&M UNIV. GALVESTON: THE NAUTILUS — PO Box 1675, Galveston, TX, 77553-1675, USA; tel (409) 740-4420; fax (409) 740-4775; e-mail: nautilus@tamug.edu; web site: www.tamug.edu/stuact/Nautilusmain.htm
Kayce Peirce
Format: Tabloid

TEXAS A&M UNIV. KINGSVILLE: SOUTH TEXAN — MSC 123, TX, 78363, USA; tel (361) 593-2111; fax (361) 593-4046; e-mail: thesouthtexan@yahoo.com; web site: www.tamek.edu/southtexan
Advisor — Manuel Flores
Jaime Gonzalez
Amanda Marcum
Format: Broadsheet

TEXAS A&M UNIVERSITY — 107 Scoates Hall, College Station, TX, 77843-0001, USA; tel (979) 862-3003; fax (979) 845-6296; e-mail: dj-king@tamu.edu
Program Coord. — Deborah Dunsford

TEXAS A&M UNIVERSITY — 4234 Tamu, College Station, TX, 77843-0001, USA; tel (979) 458-1802; fax (979) 845-6594; e-mail: r-sumpter@tamu.edu; journminor@tamu.edu
Dir., Journ. Studies/Assoc. Prof., Commun. — Randall S. Sumpter
Program Asst. — Roberto Farias
Sr. Lectr. — Edward L. Walraven
Lectr. — Dale A. Rice

TEXAS CHRISTIAN UNIVERSITY: TCU SKIFF — TCU Box 298050, Fort Worth, TX, 76129-0001, USA; tel (817) 257-7428; fax (817) 257-7133; e-mail: 360@tcu360.com; adv email: ads@tcu360.com; ed email: 360@tcu360.com; web site: www.tcu360.comEst. 1902
Manager of Student Media Sales and Marketing — Leah Griffin
Assistant Professor of Professional Practice — Jean Marie Brown
Published: Thur IMAGE MagazineCirc. (pd.) 0 (fr.) 2,000
Digital Edition Available?: Y
Format: Tabloid
Note: TCU360.com has a mobile website that works on all mobile and tablet platforms but does not have native apps for any of the above platforms.

TEXAS LUTHERAN UNIV.: LONE STAR LUTHERAN — 1000 W Court St, Seguin, TX, 78155-9996, USA; tel (830) 372-8073; fax (830) 372-8074; e-mail: lonestarlutheran@tlu.edu; web site: www.lslonline.net
Robin Bisha
Chair — Steven S. Vrooman
Kristi Quiros
Emmalee Drummond
Naomi Urquiza
Format: Broadsheet

TEXAS SOUTHERN UNIV.: THE TSU HERALD — 3100 Cleburne Ave., Student Ctr., Houston, TX, 77004-4501, USA; tel (713) 313-1976; fax (713) 313-4453; web site: www.tsu.edu
Alice Rogers
Format: Tabloid

TEXAS STATE UNIV.: THE UNIVERSITY STAR — 601 University Dr Bldg Trinity, San Marcos, TX, 78666-4684, USA; tel (512) 245-3487; fax (512) 245-3708; e-mail: stareditor@txstate.edu; adv email: starad1@txstate.edu; ed email: stareditor@txstate.edu; web site: www.universitystar.comEst. 1911
Advisor — Bob Bajackson
Published: Mon, Wed, Thur
Digital Edition Available?: Y
Digital Platform - Mobile: Apple, Android
Insert rate: $80
Format: Broadsheet

TEXAS STUDENT MEDIA: THE DAILY TEXAN — PO Box D, Austin, TX, 78713-8904, USA; tel (512) 471-4591; fax (512) 471-2952; web site: www.dailytexanonline.comEst. 1900
Advisor — Doug Warren
Published: Mon, Tues, Wed, Thur, FriCirc.(fr.) 13,000
Digital Edition Available?: Y
Digital Platform - Mobile: Apple
Format: Broadsheet

TEXAS TECH UNIVERSITY: THE DAILY TOREADOR — Box 43081, Lubbock, TX, 79409-3081, USA; tel (806) 742-3388; fax (806) 742-2434; e-mail: dailytoreador@ttu.edu; adv email: dawn.zuerker@ttu.edu; ed email: editor@dailytoreador.com; web site: www.dailytoreador.comEst. 1925
Student Media Dir. — Susan Peterson
Asst. Dir./Adv. Mgr. — Dawn Zuerker
Asst. Dir./Editorial/Broadcasting Advisor — Sheri Lewis
Asst Dir/Media Advisor — Andrea Watson
Kristi Deitiker
Amie Ward
Published: Mon, Thur Summer semesters: once per week
Digital Edition Available?: Y
Format: Broadsheet

TEXAS WOMAN'S UNIV.: LASSO — PO Box 425828, Denton, TX, 76204-5828, USA; tel (940) 898-2191; fax (940) 898-2188; e-mail: twu_lasso@yahoo.com; web site: www.twu.edu/lasso
Alejandro Barrientos
Luis Rendon
Advisor — Rhonda Ross
Format: Tabloid

THE BATTALION — 1111 Tamu, College Station, TX, 77843-0001, USA; tel 979-845-3313; fax 979-845-2647; e-mail: editor@thebatt.com; web site: http://thebatt.com/Est. 1893
Published: Mon, Tues, Wed, Thur, Fri

THE RAMBLER: RAMBLER — 1201 Wesleyan St, Fort Worth, TX, 76105-1536, USA; tel (817) 531-7552; fax (817) 531-4878; e-mail: twurambler@yahoo.com; adv email: rambleradvertising@yahoo.com; ed email: twurambler@yahoo.com; web site: www.therambler.orgEst. 1917
Kelli Lamers
Ashely Oldham
Tiara Nugent
Martin Garcia
Student Media Director — Kay Colley
Published: Biweekly print; weekly onlineCirc. (fr.) 1,200
Insert rate: $100
Format: Broadsheet

TRINITY UNIV.: TRINITONIAN — 1 Trinity Pl, San Antonio, TX, 78212-7201, USA; tel (210) 999-8555; fax (210) 999-7034; e-mail: trinitonian-adv@trinity.edu; web site: www.trinitonian.com
Kathryn Martin
Jordan Krueger
Format: Tabloid

TRINITY VALLEY CMTY. COLLEGE: TVCC NEWS-JOURNAL — 100 Cardinal St, Athens, TX, 75751-3243, USA; tel (903) 675-6302; fax (903) 675-6316; e-mail: journalstaff@tvcc.edu; web site: www.tvccnewsjournal.comEst. 1972
Danny Teague
Judy Greenlee
Melisa Boon
Media Instructor/Adviser — Deidre Jones
Format: Tabloid

TYLER JUNIOR COLLEGE: THE APACHE POW WOW — 1400 E Devine St # 204, Tyler, TX, 75701-2207, USA; tel (903) 510-2335; fax (903) 510-3246; web site: www.tjcnewspaper.com
Laura Krantz
Format: Broadsheet

UNIV. OF DALLAS: UNIVERSITY NEWS — 1845 E Northgate Dr # 732, Irving, TX, 75062-4736, USA; tel (972) 721-4070; fax (972) 721-4136; e-mail: udnews1@yahoo.com; web site: www.udallasnews.comEst. 1993
Raymond Wilkerson
Format: Tabloid

UNIV. OF HOUSTON: THE DAILY COUGAR — 7 Uc Satellite Student Publications, Houston, TX, 77204-0001, USA; tel (713) 743-5350; fax (713) 743-5384; e-mail: news@thedailycougar.com; adv email: ads@thedailycougar.com; web site: www.thedailycougar.com
Ronnie Turner
Matthew Keever
Hiba Adi
Patricia Estrada
Opinion Ed. — Alan
Format: Tabloid

UNIV. OF HOUSTON CLEAR LAKE: THE SIGNAL — 2700 Bay Area Blvd, Houston, TX, 77058-1002, USA; tel (281) 283-2569; fax (281) 283-2569; e-mail: thesignal@uhcl.edu; web site: uhclthesignal.com/wordpress; prtl.uhcl.edu/thesignal
Taleen Washington
Lindsay Humphrey
Matt Griesmyer
Format: Tabloid

UNIV. OF HOUSTON DOWNTOWN: DATELINE — 1 Main St, Houston, TX, 77002-1014, USA; tel (713) 221-8569; fax (713) 221-8119; e-mail: datelinedowntownhtx@gmail.com; adv email: editor@dateline-downtown.com; ed email: editor@dateline-downtown.com; web site: 2103 Hickory Trail PlaceEst. 1973
Associate Prof. — Joe Sample
Published: Mon bi-weekly
Digital Edition Available?: Y
Digital Platform - Mobile: Apple, Android
Digital Platform - Tablet: Apple iOS, Android
Insert rate: Free
Price: Free
Format: Tabloid
Note: Multi-Platform Advertising Available (social media, podcast, print)

UNIV. OF MARY HARDIN-BAYLOR: BELLS — 900 College St # 8012, Belton, TX, 76513-2578, USA; tel (254) 295-4598; web site: thebells.umhb.edu
Crystal Donahue
Format: Broadsheet

UNIV. OF NORTH TEXAS: NORTH TEXAS DAILY — 225 S Ave B, GAB Room 117, Denton, TX, 76201, USA; tel (940) 565-2851; fax (940) 565-3573; e-mail: editor@ntdaily.com; web site: www.ntdaily.com
Allie Durham
Kerry Solan
Courtney Roberts
Format: Broadsheet

UNIV. OF ST. THOMAS: THE SUMMA — 3800 Montrose Blvd, Houston, TX, 77006-4626, USA; tel (713) 525-3579; fax (713) 525-2159
Michelle Gautreau
Format: Broadsheet

UNIV. OF TEXAS: PAISANO — 14545 Roadrunner Way, San Antonio, TX, 78249-1515, USA; tel (210) 690-9301; fax (210) 690-3423; e-mail: paisanoeditor@sbcglobal.net; web site: www.Paisano-online.com
Rachel Hill
Format: Broadsheet

UNIV. OF TEXAS AT TYLER: PATRIOT TALON — 3900 University Blvd, Tyler, TX, 75799-0001, USA; tel (903) 565-7131; adv email: ads@patriottalon.com; ed email: editor@patriottalon.com; web site: www.patriottalon.comEst. 1976
Adviser — Lorri Allen
Editor in Chief — Nathan Wright
Published: Bi-MthlyCirc.(fr.) 2,000
Digital Edition Available?: Y
Digital Platform - Mobile: Apple, Android, Windows, Blackberry
Price: Free
Format: Broadsheet

UNIV. OF TEXAS COLLEGE OF BUS. — CBA 3.328 A, Austin, TX, 78712, USA; tel (512) 708-9357
Sunio Varghese
Format: Broadsheet

UNIV. OF TEXAS COLLEGE OF ENGINEERING: VECTOR — 301 E. Dean Keeton St. C2100, Austin, TX, 78712-2100, USA; tel (512) 471-3003; fax (512) 471-4304; e-mail: vector.ut@gmail.com; web site: www.engr.utexas.edu
An Nguyen
Format: Tabloid

UNIV. OF TEXAS DALLAS: UTD MERCURY — PO Box 830688, Richardson, TX, 75083-0688, USA; tel (972) 883-2286; fax (972) 883-2772; e-mail: mercury@utdallas.edu; adv email: ads@mercury.utdallas.edu; web site: www.utdmercury.comEst. 1980
James Wooley
Lauren Buell
Format: Broadsheet

UNIV. OF TEXAS EL PASO: THE PROSPECTOR — 105 Union East, El Paso, TX, 79968-0622, USA; tel (915) 747-5161; fax (915) 747-8031; e-mail: studentpublications@utep.edu; adv email: prospectorads@utep.edu; ed email: theprospector1@gmail.com; web site: www.theprospectordaily.comEst. 1914
Dir — Kathleen Flores
Asst. Adv. Dir. — Veronica Gonzalez
Published: Tues www.theprospectordaily.comCirc. (pd.) 0 (fr.) 5,000
Digital Edition Available?: Y
Digital Platform - Mobile: Apple, Android
Digital Platform - Tablet: Apple iOS, Android
Price: Free
Format: Tabloid

UNIV. OF TEXAS PAN AMERICAN: PAN AMERICAN — 1201 W. University Dr., Edinburg, TX, 78539, USA; tel (956) 381-2541; fax (956) 316-7122; e-mail: spubs@utpa.edu; web site: www.panamericanonline.com
Gregory M. Selber
Mariel Cantu
Brian Silva

Format: Tabloid

UNIV. OF TEXAS PERMIAN BASIN: MESA JOURNAL — 4901 E University Blvd Rm MB2215A, Odessa, TX, 79762-8122, USA; tel (432) 552-2659; fax (432) 552-3654; e-mail: mesajournal@utpb.edu; web site: mesajournalnews.comEst. 1975
Advisor — myra Salcedo
Published: Mon, Tues, Wed, Thur, SatCirc.(fr.) 6,000
Digital Edition Available?: Y
Digital Platform - Mobile: Apple, Android
Format: Online

UNIVERSITY OF TEXAS AT ARLINGTON: THE SHORTHORN — P.O. Box 19038, Arlington, TX, 76019-0001, USA; tel (817) 272-3188; fax (817) 272-5009; e-mail: editor.shorthorn@uta.edu; adv email: ads.shorthorn@uta.edu; ed email: editor.shorthorn@uta.edu; calendar.shorthorn@uta.edu; web site: www.theshorthorn.comEst. 1919
Brian Schopf
Tammy Skrehart
Production Mgr. — Adam Drew
Dir. of Student Pubs. — Beth Francesco
Newsroom advisor — Laurie Fox
Bus Mgr — Lori Doskocil
Published: Wed Daily online
Digital Edition Available?: Y
Digital Platform - Mobile: Apple, Android, Windows, Blackberry, Other
Format: Broadsheet
Note: Daily e-newsletter subscription available; creative agency started 2016.

UNIVERSITY OF TEXAS AT BROWNSVILLE: THE COLLEGIAN — 1 West University Boulevard, Brownsville, TX, 78520-4956, USA; tel (956) 882-5143; fax (956) 882-5176; e-mail: collegian@utb.edu; adv email: collegian.advertising@utb.edu; ed email: collegian@utb.edu; web site: utbcollegian.com
Advisor — Azenett Cornejo
Editor — Cleiri Quezada
Published: MonCirc.(fr.) 4,000
Digital Edition Available?: Y
Price: Free
Format: Tabloid

UNIVERSITY OF THE INCARNATE WORD: LOGOS — 4301 Broadway, CPO 494, San Antonio, TX, 78209-6318, USA; tel (210) 829-3964; fax (210) 283-5005; e-mail: mercer@uiwtx.edu; adv email: mercer@uiwtx.edu; ed email: mercer@uiwtx.edu; web site: www.uiw.edu/logosEst. 1935
Advisor — Michael L. Mercer
Published: Mthly
Digital Edition Available?: Y
Digital Platform - Mobile: Other
Digital Platform - Tablet: Other
Format: Broadsheet
Note: Interactive website is http://www.uiwlogos.org

WAYLAND BAPTIST UNIV.: TRAIL BLAZER — 1900 W 7th St # 1272, Plainview, TX, 79072-6900, USA; tel (806) 291-1088; fax (806) 291-1980; e-mail: trailblazer@wbu.edu; web site: www.wbu.eduEst. 1950
Steven Long
Published: Bi-Mthly Bi-WeeklyCirc. (pd.) 100 (fr.) 1,500
Digital Edition Available?: Y
Digital Platform - Mobile: Other
Digital Platform - Tablet: Other
Insert rate: $8.00 PCI
Format: Broadsheet

WEST TEXAS A&M UNIV.: PRAIRIE — PO Box 60747, Canyon, TX, 79016-0001, USA; tel (806) 651-2410; fax (806) 651-2818; e-mail: bleschper@mail.wtamu.edu; theprairiemail@yahoo.com; web site: www.theprairieonline.com; www.theprairienews.com
Christaan Eayrs
Joe Dowd
Kayla Goodman
Format: Tabloid

WILEY COLLEGE: WILDCAT PROWLER — 711 Wiley Ave, Marshall, TX, 75670-5151, USA; tel (903) 923-2400
Format: Tabloid

UTAH

BRIGHAM YOUNG UNIVERSITY: DAILY UNIVERSE — 152 BRMB, Provo, UT, 84602-3701, USA; tel (801) 422-2957; e-mail: dureceptionist@gmail.com; adv email: ellen_hernandez@byu.edu; ed email: universe.ideas@gmail.com; web site: universe.byu.edu
Director — Steve Fidel
Published: Tues
Digital Edition Available?: Y
Digital Platform - Mobile: Apple, Android
Digital Platform - Tablet: Apple iOS, Android
Format: Broadsheet

DIXIE STATE COLLEGE: DIXIE SUN — 225 S. 700 E. JEN, Saint George, UT, 84770, USA; tel (435) 652-7818; fax (435) 656-4019; e-mail: dixiesun@dixie.edu; adv email: dixiesunads@dixie.edu; ed email: dixiesun@dixie.edu; web site: www.dixiesunlink.com
Rhiannon Bent
Taylor Forbes
Rachel Tanner
Format: Broadsheet

SNOW COLLEGE: SNOWDRIFT NEWSPAPER — 150 College Ave, Ephraim, UT, 84627-1299, USA; tel (435) 283-7385; e-mail: snowdrift@snow.edu; web site: www.snow.edu/snowdrift
Greg Dart
Justin Albee
Kelly Peterson
Format: Broadsheet

SOUTHERN UTAH UNIV.: UNIVERSITY JOURNAL — 351 W University Blvd, Cedar City, UT, 84720-2415, USA; tel (435) 865-8226; e-mail: journal@suu.edu; adv email: Gholdston@suuews.com; ed email: journal@suu.edu; web site: www.suunews.comEst. 1937
John Gholdston
Published: Mon, ThurCirc.(fr.) 2,000
Digital Edition Available?: Y
Insert rate: $250.
Price: First copy free/$.25 succeeding
Format: Broadsheet

UNIV. OF UTAH: DAILY UTAH CHRONICLE — 200 Central Campus Dr Rm 234, Salt Lake City, UT, 84112-9110, USA; tel (801) 581-2788; fax (801) 581-6882; ed email: news@chronicle.utah.edu; press@chronicle.utah.edu; web site: www.dailyutahchronicle.com
Rachel Hanson
Michael Mcfall
Format: Tabloid

UTAH STATE UNIV.: UTAH STATESMAN — PO Box 1249, Logan, UT, 84322-0001, USA; tel (435) 797-6397; fax (435) 797-1760; e-mail: statesmanoffice@aggiemail.com; web site: www.utahstatesman.comEst. 1902
Jay Wamsley
Format: Broadsheet

UTAH STATE UNIVERSITY EASTERN: EAGLE — 451 N. 400 E. St., Price, UT, 84501-3315, USA; tel (435) 613-5123; e-mail: Susan.polster@usu.edu; web site: Usueagle.comEst. 1937
Adviser — Susan Polster
Published: Thur, OtherCirc.(fr.) 1,000
Digital Edition Available?: Y
Digital Platform - Mobile: Apple, Android, Blackberry, Other
Digital Platform - Tablet: Apple iOS, Android, Blackberry Tablet OS, Kindle, Kindle Fire, Other
Insert rate: 10 cents each per 1,000
Format: Broadsheet

UTAH VALLEY UNIVERSITY: UVU REVIEW — 800 W University Pkwy # Mt, Orem, UT, 84058-6703, USA; tel (801) 863-8688; fax (801) 863-8601; adv email: robbina@uvu.edu; web site: www.uvureview.com
Bus. Mgr. — Robbin Anthony
Brent Sumner
Published: Mon
Price: Free
Format: Broadsheet

WEBER STATE UNIV.: THE SIGNPOST — 3910 West Campus Drive Dept 2110, Ogden, UT, 84408-2110, USA; tel (801) 626-7526; fax (801) 626-7401; e-mail: thesignpost@weber.edu; adv email: signpostads@weber.edu; ed email: gedwards@weber.edu; web site: www.wsusignpost.comEst. 1937
Advt Mgr — Shelley Hart
Office Mgr
— Georgia Edwards
Signpost Adviser — Jean Norman
Published: Mon, Thur 8 issues (once a week) during the summer semesterCirc.(fr.) 2,000
Digital Edition Available?: Y
Digital Platform - Mobile: Apple, Android
Price: Free
Format: Tabloid
Note: signpost.mywebermedia.com MyWeberMedia app on iTunes and Android

WESTMINSTER COLLEGE: THE FORUM — 1840 S 1300 E, Salt Lake City, UT, 84105-3697, USA; tel (801) 832-2320; fax (801) 466-6916; e-mail: forum@wesminstercollege.edu; ed email: forumeditor@westminstercollege.edu; web site: www.forumfortnightly.com
Ann Green
Fred Fogo
Kimberly Zarkin
Format: Tabloid

VERMONT

BENNINGTON COLLEGE: THE BENNINGTON FREE PRESS — 1 College Dr, Bennington, VT, 05201-6004, USA; tel (802) 442-5401; fax (802) 442-6164
Veronica Jorgensen
Format: Magazine

JOHNSON STATE COLLEGE: BASEMENT MEDICINE — 337 College Hl, Johnson, VT, 05656-9898, USA; tel (802) 635-1357; web site: www.jsc.edu
Nathan Burgess
Format: Tabloid

LYNDON STATE COLLEGE: CRITIC — PO Box 919, Lyndonville, VT, 05851-0919, USA; tel (802) 626-6413; e-mail: critic@lyndonstate.edu; web site: www.lyndonstate.edu/critic
Benjamin Holbrook
Format: Tabloid

MIDDLEBURY COLLEGE: MIDDLEBURY CAMPUS — PO Box 30, Middlebury, VT, 05753-0030, USA; tel (802) 443-4827; fax (802) 443-2068; e-mail: campus@middlebury.edu; web site: www.middleburycampus.com
Zachary Karst
Brian Fung
Tess Russell
Format: Tabloid

NORWICH UNIV.: NORWICH GUIDON — 158 Harmon Dr, Northfield, VT, 05663-1097, USA; tel (802) 485-2763; fax (802) 485-2580; e-mail: syoungwo@norwich.edu
Susan Youngwood
Format: Broadsheet

SOUTHERN VERMONT COLLEGE: MOUNTAIN PRESS — 982 Mansion Dr, Bennington, VT, 05201-6002, USA; tel (802) 447-6347; fax (802) 447-4695; e-mail: mountainpress@svc.edu
Peter Seward
Format: Tabloid

ST. MICHAEL'S COLLEGE: DEFENDER — 1 Winooski Park, Colchester, VT, 05439-1000, USA; tel (802) 654-2421; e-mail: defender@smcvt.edu
Paul Beique
Andrew Dennett
Format: Tabloid

UNIVERSITY OF VERMONT: THE VERMONT CYNIC — UVM Student Life, Burlington, VT, 05405, USA; tel (802) 656-4412; fax (802) 656-8482; e-mail: crevans@uvm.edu; adv email: crevans@uvm.edu; ed email: crevans@uvm.edu; web site: https://vtcynic.com/Est. 1883
Adv. — Chris Evans
Published: WedCirc.(fr.) 5,000
Digital Edition Available?: Y
Digital Platform - Mobile: Apple, Android
Format: Tabloid

VERMONT LAW SCHOOL: FORUM — PO Box 96, South Royalton, VT, 05068-0096, USA; tel (802) 831-1299; fax (802) 763-7159; e-mail: forum@vermontlaw.edu; web site: www.vermontlaw.edu/students/x8685.xml
Sean Williams
Kevin Schrems
Format: Tabloid

VIRGINIA

BLUEFIELD COLLEGE: RAM PAGE — 3000 College Dr, Bluefield, VA, 24605-1799, USA; tel (276) 326-3682; fax (276) 326-4288; web site: www.bluefield.edu
Mimi Merritt
Format: Tabloid

BRIDGEWATER COLLEGE: VERITAS — PO Box 193, Bridgewater, VA, 22812-0193, USA; tel (540) 828-5329 ; fax (540) 828-5479; e-mail: veritas@bridgewater.edu; adv email: veritas@bridgewater.edu; ed email: veritas@bridgewater.edu; web site: http://veritas.bridgewater.edu/
Assistant Professor of Communication Studies — Bernardo Motta
Published: WedCirc.(fr.) 1,700
Digital Edition Available?: Y
Digital Platform - Mobile: Apple, Android, Windows, Blackberry
Digital Platform - Tablet: Apple iOS, Android, Windows 7, Blackberry Tablet OS, Kindle, Nook, Kindle Fire, Other
Price: Free
Format: 10 x 10.25

CHRISTOPHER NEWPORT UNIV.: THE CAPTAIN'S LOG — 1 University Pl, Newport News, VA, 23606-2949, USA; tel (757) 594-7196; e-mail: desk@thecaptainslog.org; web site: www.thecaptainslog.org
Terry Lee
Ed. in Chief — Ben Leistensnider
Faculty advisor — Nicole Emmelhainz
Published: Wed
Digital Edition Available?: Y
Format: Broadsheet

COLGATE DARDEN GRAD. SCHOOL OF BUS.: COLD CALL — 100 Darden Blvd, Charlottesville, VA, 22903-1760, USA; tel (434) 982-2395; e-mail: ccchronicle@darden.virginia.edu; web site: coldcallchronicle.com
Sarah Yoder
Laura Dart
Tyler Lifton

Format: Tabloid

COLLEGE OF WILLIAM AND MARY: FLAT HAT
— PO Box 8795, Williamsburg, VA, 23187-8795, USA; e-mail: flathat.editor@gmail.com; adv email: flathatads@gmail.com; ed email: fhnews@gmail.com; web site: www.flathatnews.comEst. 1911
Trici Fredrick
Editor-in-chief — Tucker Higgins
Published: Tues
Digital Edition Available?: Y
Price: Free
Format: Broadsheet
Note: Student newspaper

EMORY & HENRY COLLEGE: WHITETOPPER
— PO Box 947, Emory, VA, 24327-0947, USA; tel (276) 944-6870; e-mail: ehcwhitetopper@ehc.edu
Kathy Borterfield
Format: Broadsheet

FERRUM COLLEGE: IRON BLADE
— PO Box 1000, Ferrum, VA, 24088-9001, USA; tel (540) 365-4334; fax (540) 365-4203; web site: www.ferrum.edu/ironblade
Dr. Lana Whited
Format: Tabloid

GEORGE MASON UNIVERSITY: FOURTH ESTATE
— 4400 University Dr MS 2C5, Fairfax, VA, 22030-4444, USA; tel (703) 993-2947; fax (703) 993-2948; e-mail: cwilso12@gmu.edu; web site: gmufourthestate.com
Kathryn Mangus
Published: MonCirc.(fr.) 6,000
Digital Edition Available?: Y
Format: Broadsheet

HAMPDEN-SYDNEY COLLEGE: HAMPDEN-SYDNEY TIGER
— PO Box 127, Hampden Sydney, VA, 23943-0127, USA; tel (434) 223-6000; fax (434) 223-6345; e-mail: newspaper@hsc.eduEst. 1920
Editor-in-Chief — Max Dash
Published: Bi-Mthly

HOLLINS UNIV.: HOLLINS COLUMN
— PO Box 9707, Roanoke, VA, 24020-1707, USA; tel (540) 362-6000; fax (540) 362-6642; e-mail: hollinscolumns@hollins.edu; web site: www.columns.proboards.com
Emileigh Clare
Julie Abernethy
KaRenda J. LaPrade
Format: Tabloid

JAMES MADISON UNIVERSITY: THE BREEZE
— 1598 South Main Street, Harrisonburg, VA, 22807, USA; tel (540) 568-6127; fax (540) 568-6736; e-mail: breezeeditor@gmail.com; adv email: thebreezeads@gmail.com; ed email: breezeeditor@gmail.com; web site: www.breezejmu.orgEst. 1922
Advisor — Brad Jenkins
Advertising and Marketing Coordinator — Blake Shepherd
Published: ThurCirc. (pd.) 0 (fr.) 7,000
Digital Edition Available?: Y
Digital Platform - Mobile: Apple, Android
Digital Platform - Tablet: Apple iOS
Insert rate: $75/M
Price: Free
Format: Broadsheet, Tab Special Sections

LIBERTY UNIV.: LIBERTY CHAMPION
— 1971 University Blvd, Lynchburg, VA, 24515-0002, USA; tel (434) 582-2128; fax (434) 582-2420; e-mail: advertising@liberty.edu; web site: www.liberty.edu/championEst. 1971
Dean, School of Commun. — William Gribbin
Debra Huff
Jr. Assoc. Dean — Cecil V. Kramer
Benjamin Lesley
Chrmn. — William Mullen
Amanda Sullivan
Format: Broadsheet

LONGWOOD COLLEGE: ROTUNDA
— PO Box 2901, Farmville, VA, 23909-0001, USA; tel (434) 395-2120; fax (434) 395-2237; e-mail: rotunda@longwood.edu
Ramesh Rao
Emily Grove
Benjamin Byrnes
Format: Broadsheet

LYNCHBURG COLLEGE: CRITOGRAPH
— 1501 Lakeside Dr, Lynchburg, VA, 24501-3113, USA; tel (434) 544-8301; fax (804) 544-8661; e-mail: critograph@lynchburg.edu; adv email: critograph@lynchburg.edu; ed email: critograph@lynchburg.edu; web site: www.critograph.com
Editor-in-Chief — Rachad Davis
Dena/Prof., Journ. — Heywood Greenberg
Copy Desk Chief — Wayne Garret
Published: Tues
Digital Edition Available?: Y
Format: Tabloid

MARY BALDWIN COLLEGE: CAMPUS COMMENTS
— PO Box 1500, Staunton, VA, 24402-1500, USA; tel (540) 887-7112; fax (540) 887-7231; e-mail: campuscomments@mbc.edu
Bruce Dorries
Dawn Medley
Hannah Barrow
Format: Tabloid

MARYMOUNT UNIV.: THE BANNER
— 2807 N Glebe Rd, Arlington, VA, 22207-4299, USA; tel (703) 522-5600; fax (703) 284-3817; e-mail: banner@marymount.edu; web site: www.marymount.edu
Mass Commun. Coord. — Paul Byers
Vincent Stovall
Mass Commun. Coord. — Ralph Frasca
Format: Tabloid

NORFOLK STATE UNIVERSITY: SPARTAN ECHO
— 700 Park Ave., Norfolk, VA, 23504-8090, USA; tel (757) 823-8200; fax (757) 823-9119; e-mail: spartanecho@nsu.edu; adv email: spartanecho@nsu.edu; ed email: spartanecho@nsu.edu; web site: www.spartanecho.orgEst. 1952
Advisor — Steven E. Opfer
Published: Bi-MthlyCirc.(fr.) 1,000
Digital Edition Available?: Y
Digital Platform - Mobile: Apple, Android, Windows, Blackberry, Other
Digital Platform - Tablet: Apple iOS, Android, Windows 7, Blackberry Tablet OS, Kindle, Nook, Kindle Fire, Other
Format: Tabloid

OLD DOMINION UNIVERSITY: MACE & CROWN
— 1051 Webb Center, Norfolk, VA, 23529, USA; tel (757) 683-3452; e-mail: editorinchief@maceandcrown.com; adv email: advertising@maceandcrown.com; ed email: editorinchief@maceandcrown.com; web site: http://www.maceandcrown.comEst. 1930
Editor-in-Chief — Adam Flores
Advertising & Business Manager — Kavita Butani
Published: Wed
Digital Edition Available?: Y
Insert rate: $300
Format: Tabloid

RADFORD UNIV.: THE TARTAN
— PO Box 6985, Radford, VA, 24142-6985, USA; tel (540) 831-5474; fax (540) 831-6725; e-mail: tartan@radford.edu; web site: www.thetartan.com
Matt Labelle
Justin Ward
Colin Daileda
Format: Broadsheet

RANDOLPH-MACON COLLEGE: YELLOW JACKET WEEKLY
— PO Box 5005, Ashland, VA, 23005-5505, USA; tel (804) 752-7200; fax (804) 752-3748; e-mail: yellowjacket@rmc.edu; web site: www.rmc.edu
Robert Thomas
Derek Gayle
Lara O'Brien
Format: Tabloid

RANDOLPH-MACON WOMAN'S COLLEGE: SUNDIAL
— 2500 Rivermont Ave, Lynchburg, VA, 24503-1526, USA; tel (434) 947-8000; fax (434) 947-8298; web site: www.randolphcollege.edu
Dawn Linsner
Format: Broadsheet

ROANOKE COLLEGE: BRACKETY-ACK
— 221 College Ln Ofc Studentactivities, Salem, VA, 24153-3794, USA; tel (540) 375-2327; fax (540) 378-5129; e-mail: bracketyack@roanoke.edu; web site: www.roanoke.edu
Daniel Sarabia
Format: Tabloid

SOUTHWEST VIRGINIA CMTY. COLLEGE: CHARTER (OOB)
— PO Box SVCC, Richlands, VA, 24641, USA; tel (276) 964-2555; e-mail: pat.bussard@sw.edu
Pat Bussard
Format: Tabloid

SWEET BRIAR COLLEGE: SWEET BRIAR COLLEGE
— PO Box 1058, Sweet Briar, VA, 24595-1058, USA; tel (434) 381-6100; fax (434) 381-6132; e-mail: sbvoice@sbc.edu; web site: www.voice.sbc.edu
Katy Johnstone
Carinna Finn
Format: Tabloid

UNIV. OF RICHMOND: THE COLLEGIAN
— 40 W Hampton Way North Ct Rm B1, Richmond, VA, 23173-0001, USA; tel (804) 289-8483; fax (804) 287-6092; ed email: collegianstories@gmail.com; web site: www.thecollegianur.comEst. 1914
Editor in Chief — Claire Comey
Managing Editor — Liza David
Published: Mon, Tues, Wed, Thur, Fri, Sat, Sun
Digital Edition Available?: Y
Format: Online only

UNIV. OF VIRGINIA: THE CAVALIER DAILY
— PO Box 400703, Charlottesville, VA, 22904-4703, USA; fax (434) 924-7290; e-mail: editor@cavalierdaily.com; web site: www.cavalierdaily.comEst. 1890
Editor-in-chief — Karoline Komolafe
Published: Mon, ThurCirc.(fr.) 10,000
Digital Edition Available?: Y
Digital Platform - Mobile: Apple, Android, Windows, Blackberry
Digital Platform - Tablet: Apple iOS, Android
Format: Broadsheet

UNIV. OF VIRGINIA: HIGHLAND CAVALIER
— PO Box 3043, Wise, VA, 24293-3043, USA; fax (276) 328-0212; e-mail: info@uvawise.edu; web site: www.wise.virginia.edu
Michael McGill
Format: Tabloid

UNIV. OF VIRGINIA SCHOOL OF LAW: VIRGINIA LAW
— 580 Massie Rd, Charlottesville, VA, 22903-1789, USA; tel (434) 924-3070; fax (434) 924-7536; e-mail: editor@lawweekly.org; web site: www.lawweekly.orgEst. 1948
Editor-in-Chief — Jenna Goldman
Published: Wed
Digital Edition Available?: Y
Format: Tabloid

UNIVERSITY OF MARY WASHINGTON: THE BLUE & GREY PRESS
— 1301 College Ave, Fredericksburg, VA, 22401-5300, USA; tel (540) 654-1536; adv email: blueandgray.eic@gmail.com; web site: blueandgraypress.com
Advisor — Michael McCarthy
Digital Edition Available?: Y

VIRGINIA COMMONWEALTH UNIV.: THE COMMONWEALTH TIMES
— PO Box 842010, Richmond, VA, 23284-2010, USA; tel (804) 828-1058; fax (804) 828-9201; ed email: editor@commonwealthtimes.com; web site: www.commonwealthtimes.com
Greg Weatherford
Lauren Geerdes
Format: Tabloid

VIRGINIA MILITARY INSTITUTE: CADET
— PO Box 7, Lexington, VA, 24450-0007, USA; tel (540) 464-7326; fax (540) 463-5679; e-mail: vmicadet@vmi.edu; web site: www.vmicadetpublication.com
Captain Christopher Perry
Nick Weishar
Format: Broadsheet

VIRGINIA POLYTECHNIC INSTITUTE: COLLEGIATE TIMES
— 365 Squires Student Ctr, Blacksburg, VA, 24061-1000, USA; tel (540) 231-9870; fax (540) 231-9151; adv email: advertising@collegemedia.com; ed email: campuseditor@collegiatetimes.com; editor@collegiatetimes.com; web site: www.collegiatetimes.comEst. 1903
General Manager — Kiley Thompson
Published: Tues, Fri
Digital Edition Available?: Y
Digital Platform - Mobile: Apple, Android
Format: Broadsheet

VIRGINIA STATE UNIV.: VIRGINIA STATESMAN
— 402 Foster Hall # 9063, Petersburg, VA, 23806-0001, USA; tel (804) 524-5991; fax (804) 524-5406
Howard Hall
Thysha Shabazz
Format: Tabloid

VIRGINIA UNION UNIV.: VUU INFORMER
— 1500 N Lombardy St, Richmond, VA, 23220-1784, USA; tel (804) 257-5655; fax (804) 257-5818
Dept. Chair — Gloria D. Brogdon
Peter S. Tahsoh
Format: Tabloid

WASHINGTON AND LEE UNIV.: RING-TUM PHI
— 204 West Washington Street, Lexington, VA, 24450, USA; tel (540) 458-4060; fax (540) 458-4059; e-mail: phi-business@wlu.edu; phi@wlu.edu
David Seifert
Format: Broadsheet

WASHINGTON

BELLEVUE CMTY. COLLEGE: THE WATCHDOG
— 3000 Landerholm Cir SE, Bellevue, WA, 98007-6484, USA; tel (425) 564-2434; fax (425) 564-4152; e-mail: ataylor@bellevuecollege.edu; adv email: advertising@thejibsheet.com; web site: www.thejibsheet.com
Katherine Oleson
Janelle Gardener
Anne Taylor
Format: Tabloid

CENTRAL WASHINGTON UNIV.: THE OBSERVER
— 400 E University Way Rm 222, Ellensburg, WA, 98926-7502, USA; tel (509) 963-1026; fax (509) 963-1027; e-mail: cwuobserver@gmail.com; adv email: gaskillk@cwu.edu; ed email: cwuobserver@gmail.com; web site: www.cwuobserver.com
Published: ThurCirc.(fr.) 6,000
Digital Edition Available?: Y
Price: free
Format: Tabloid

CLARK COLLEGE: INDEPENDENT — 1933 Fort Vancouver Way # 124, Vancouver, WA, 98663-3598, USA; tel (360) 992-2159; fax (360) 992-2879; web site: clarkindependent.wordpress.com
Audrey McDougal
Nick Jensen
Daniel Hampton
Format: Tabloid

EDMONDS CMTY. COLLEGE: THE TRITON REVIEW — 20000 68th Ave W, Lynnwood, WA, 98036-5999, USA; tel (425) 640-1315; fax (425) 640-1191; e-mail: revedic@edcc.edu
Rob Harrill
Valerie Topacio
John Martin
Format: Broadsheet

EVERETT COMMUNITY COLLEGE: THE CLIPPER — 2000 Tower St., Everett, WA, 98201-1390, USA; tel (425) 388-9522; e-mail: clipper@everettcc.edu; web site: www.everettclipper.comEst. 1947
Adviser — T. Andrew Wahl
Editor-in-Chief — John Yeager
Business & Circulation Director — Terresa King
Published: Other Every three weeksCirc. (pd.) 0 (fr.) 2,500
Digital Edition Available?: Y
Digital Platform - Mobile: Other
Price: Free
Format: Magazine

GONZAGA UNIVERSITY: GONZAGA BULLETIN — Msc # 2477, Spokane, WA, 99258-0001, USA; tel (509) 313-6826; fax (509) 313-5848; e-mail: bulletin@zagmail.gonzaga.edu; adv email: adoffice@gonzaga.edu; ed email: bulletin@zagmail.gonzaga.edu; web site: www.gonzagabulletin.com
Advisor — Tom Miller
Adviser — Susan English
Adviser — John Kafentzis
Student Publications Manager — Joanne Shiosaki
Student Publications Assistant Manager — Chris Wheatley
Published: ThurCirc. (pd.) 0 (fr.) 3,000
Digital Edition Available?: Y
Digital Platform - Mobile: Apple, Android
Insert rate: $300.00 per 1,0000
Price: Free
Format: Broadsheet

GRAYS HARBOR COLLEGE — 1620 Edward P Smith Dr, Aberdeen, WA, 98520-7599, USA; tel (360) 532-9020; fax (360) 538-4299; web site: www.ghc.ctc.edu

GREEN RIVER COMMUNITY COLLEGE: THE CURRENT — 12401 SE 320th St, Auburn, WA, 98092-3699, USA; tel (253) 833-9111 x2375; fax (253) 288-3457; e-mail: thecurrent@greenriver.edu; web site: http://www.thecurrentonline.net
Adviser — Brian Schraum
Published: Every two weeks (approximately), excluding summerCirc.(fr.) 1,200
Digital Edition Available?: Y
Format: Tabloid

HIGHLINE COLLEGE: THUNDERWORD — PO Box 98000, Des Moines, WA, 98198-9800, USA; tel (206) 592-3291; fax (206) 870-3771; e-mail: tword@highline.edu; thunderword@highline.edu; adv email: thunderword@highline.edu; web site: https://thunderword.highline.edu/ Est. 1961
Advisor — T.M. Sell
Published: ThurCirc.(fr.) 2,000
Digital Edition Available?: Y
Insert rate: Do not accept inserts
Price: Free
Format: Tabloid

LOWER COLUMBIA COLLEGE: THE LOGOS — PO Box 3010, Longview, WA, 98632-0310, USA; tel (360) 442-2311; fax (360) 442-2120; web site: www.lowercolumbia.edu
Jill Homme
Format: Tabloid

OLYMPIC COLLEGE: OLYMPIAN — 1600 Chester Ave, Bremerton, WA, 98337-1699, USA; tel (360) 792-6050; fax (360) 475-7684; e-mail: olyeditor@olympic.edu; web site: www.ocolympian.com
Michael Prince
Jon Miller
Josh Nothnagle
Format: Broadsheet

PACIFIC LUTHERAN UNIV.: MOORING MAST — the Mooring Mast Pacific Lutheran University 1010 122nd Street S, Tacoma, WA, 98447-0001, USA; tel (253) 535-7492; fax (253) 536-5067; e-mail: mast@plu.edu; adv email: mastads@plu.edu; web site: www.plu.edu/~mastEst. 1924
Business and Ads Manager — Winston Alder
Editor-in-Chief — Jessica Trondsen
Published: FriCirc.(fr.) 3,500
Digital Edition Available?: Y
Insert rate: $400
Format: News Paper

PIERCE COLLEGE: THE PIONEER — 9401 Farwest Dr SW, Lakewood, WA, 98498-1999, USA; tel (253) 964-6604; fax (253) 964-6764; e-mail: pioneer@pierce.ctc.edu; web site: http://www.piercecollege.edu/
Michael Parks
Blake York
Format: Tabloid

SEATTLE CENTRAL CMTY. COLLEGE: CITY COLLEGIAN — 1701 Broadway # BE1145, Seattle, WA, 98122-2413, USA; tel (206) 587-6959; fax (206) 903-3235; e-mail: editor@thecitycollegian.com
Rachel Swedish
Format: Broadsheet

SEATTLE PACIFIC UNIV.: THE FALCON — 3307 3rd Ave W, Seattle, WA, 98119-1997, USA; tel (206) 281-2913; fax (206) 378-5003; e-mail: falcon-ads@spu.edu; ed email: falcon-online@spu.edu; falcon-news@spu.edu; falcon-sports@spu.edu; falcon-features@spu.edu; falcon-opinions@spu.edu; web site: www.thefalcononline.com
Katie-Joy Blanksma
Haley Libak
Madeline Tremain
Format: Tabloid

SEATTLE UNIVERSITY: THE SPECTATOR — PO Box 222000, Seattle, WA, 98122-1090, USA; tel (206) 296-6470; fax (206) 296-2163; ed email: editor@su-spectator.com; support@collegepublisher.com; web site: www.seattlespectator.comEst. 1933
Sonora Jha
Published: Wed
Digital Edition Available?: N
Format: Tabloid

SHORELINE CMTY. COLLEGE: THE EBBTIDE — 16101 Greenwood Ave N Rm 9101, Shoreline, WA, 98133-5667, USA; tel (206) 546-4730; fax (206) 546-5869; e-mail: webbtide@yahoo.com; web site: www.shoreline.edu/ebbtide/
Patti Jones
Amelia Rivera
Daniel Demay
Sean Sherman
Format: Tabloid

SKAGIT VALLEY CMTY. COLLEGE: THE CARDINAL — 2405 E College Way, Mount Vernon, WA, 98273-5899, USA; tel (360) 416-7710; fax (360) 416-7822; e-mail: cardinal.news@skagit.edu
Beverly Saxon
Format: Tabloid

SOUTH PUGET SOUND CMTY. COLLEGE: THE SOUNDS — 2011 Mottman Rd SW, Tumwater, WA, 98512-6218, USA; tel (360) 754-7711; fax (360) 596-5708; e-mail: soundsnewspaper@spscc.ctc.edu; web site: www.spscc.ctc.edu
Steve Valandra
Erin Landgraf
Format: Tabloid

SOUTH SEATTLE CMTY. COLLEGE: THE SENTINEL — 6000 16th Ave SW Jmb 135, Seattle, WA, 98106-1401, USA; tel (206) 764-5335; fax (206) 764-7936; e-mail: sentinelads@sccd.ctc.edu; ed email: sentineleditor@sccd.ctc.edu; web site: sites.southseattle.edu/thesentinel
Betsy Berger
Format: Tabloid

SPOKANE CMTY. COLLEGE: THE SASQUATCH TIMES — 1810 N Greene St, Spokane, WA, 99217-5399, USA; tel (509) 533-7000; fax (509) 533-8163; e-mail: reporter@scc.spokane.edu
Rob Vogel
Danie Elle
Format: Tabloid

SPOKANE FALLS CMTY. COLLEGE: THE COMMUNICATOR — 3410 W Fort George Wright Dr MS 3180, Spokane, WA, 99224-5204, USA; tel (509) 533-3246; fax (509) 533-3856; e-mail: communicator@spokanefalls.edu; web site: www.spokanefalls.edu/communicator
Jason Nix
Sarah Radmer
Madison Mccord
Wendy Gaskill
Format: Tabloid

TACOMA CMTY. COLLEGE — 6501 S 19th St Bldg 216, Tacoma, WA, 98466-6139, USA; tel (253) 566-6045; fax (253) 566-5384; web site: www.tacomachallenge.com
Serrell Collins
Kathy Tavia

THE EASTERNER: THE EASTERNER — 102 Isle Hall, Cheney, WA, 99004-2417, USA; tel (509) 359-6737; adv email: advertising@theeasterner.info; ed email: easterner.editor@gmail.com; web site: www.easterneronline.comEst. 1916
Published: WedCirc.(fr.) 3,000
Digital Edition Available?: Y
Format: Tabloid

THE EVERGREEN STATE COLLEGE: COOPER POINT — 2700 Evergreen Pkwy Cab 316, Olympia, WA, 98505-0005, USA; tel (360) 867-6213; fax (360) 867-6685; e-mail: cpj@evergreen.edu; web site: cpj.evergreen.edu
Dianne Conrad
Madeline Berman
Jason Slotkin
Format: Broadsheet

THE UNIVERSITY OF WASHINGTON TACOMA LEDGER STUDENT NEWSPAPER: LEDGER — 1900 Commerce St Mat 151, Tacoma, WA, 98402-3112, USA; tel (253) 692-4428; fax (253) 692-5602; e-mail: ledger@uw.edu; adv email: ledger@u.washington.edu; ed email: ledger@u.washington.edu; web site: www.thetacomaledger.com
Publications Manager — Daniel Nash
Editor-in-Chief — Kelsie Abram
Published: Mon
Digital Edition Available?: Y
Price: Free
Format: Tabloid

UNIV. OF PUGET SOUND: THE TRAIL — 1500 N Warner St Stop 1095, Tacoma, WA, 98416-1095, USA; tel (253) 879-3100; fax (253) 879-3645; e-mail: trail@pugetsound.edu; web site: www.pugetsound.edu
Anna Marie Ausnes
Format: Tabloid

UNIV. OF WASHINGTON: THE DAILY OF THE UNIVERSITY OF WASHINGTON — 132 Communications, Seattle, WA, 98195-0001, USA; tel (206) 543-2336; fax (206) 543-2345; adv email: ads@dailyuw.com; ed email: editor@dailyuw.com; web site: www.dailyuw.comEst. 1891
Dir., Student Publications — Diana Kramer
Editor-in-Chief — Rebecca Gross
Published: Mon, Tues, Wed, Thur, FriCirc.(fr.) 7,500
Digital Edition Available?: Y
Format: Tabloid

WALLA WALLA COLLEGE: COLLEGIAN — 204 S College Ave, College Place, WA, 99324-1198, USA; tel (509) 527-2971; fax (509) 527-2674; e-mail: comm@wwc.edu
Ross Brown
Chair — Pamela Harris
Format: Tabloid

WASHINGTON STATE UNIVERSITY, DAILY EVERGREEN: THE DAILY EVERGREEN — PO Box 642510, Pullman, WA, 99164-2510, USA; tel (509) 335-4573; fax (509) 335-7401; adv email: advertise@dailyevergreen.com; ed email: news@dailyevergreen.com; web site: www.dailyevergreen.comEst. 1895
Program Coord. — Tracy Milano
Dir of Student Media — Richard Miller
Fiscal Officer — K. Denise Boyd
Content Adviser — Jacob Jones
Published: Mon, Tues, Wed, Thur, FriCirc.(fr.) 5,945
Insert rate: $500 inserted in all papers
Format: Tabloid

WESTERN WASHINGTON UNIV.: THE WESTERN FRONT — 516 High St # CF230, Bellingham, WA, 98225-5946, USA; tel (360) 650-3160; fax (360) 650-7775; e-mail: editor@westernfrontonline.net; thewesternfronteditor@yahoo.com; web site: www.westernfrontonline.netEst. 1899
Carolyn Nielsen
Aletha Macomber
Michele Anderson
Nicholas Johnson
Managing Ed. — Katie
Online Ed. — Alex
Format: Tabloid

WHATCOM CMTY. COLLEGE: HORIZON — Syre Student Ctr. Rm. 202 237 W. Kellogg Rd., Bellingham, WA, 98226, USA; tel (360) 383-3101; fax (360) 676-2171; e-mail: horizonads@hotmail.com; admanager@whatcomhorizon.com; ed email: editor@whatcomhorizon.com; web site: www.whatcomhorizon.comEst. 1972
Toby Sonneman
Published: Bi-MthlyCirc.(fr.) 1,000
Digital Edition Available?: Y
Format: Tabloid

WHITWORTH UNIVERSITY: WHITWORTH UNIVERSITY — 300 W Hawthorne Rd, Spokane, WA, 99251-2515, USA; tel (509) 777-3248; fax (509) 777-3710; ed email: editor@whitworthian.com; web site: www.thewhitworthian.comEst. 1905
Jim McPherson
Editor-in-Chief — Rebekah Bresee
Published: Wed
Digital Edition Available?: Y
Price: Free
Format: Tabloid

YAKIMA VALLEY CMTY. COLLEGE — PO Box 22520, Yakima, WA, 98907-2520, USA; tel

(509) 574-4600; fax (509) 574-6860; adv email: nhopkins@yvcc.edu; web site: www.yvcc.eduEst. 1928
Ed. — Niki Hopkins

WEST VIRGINIA

ALDERSON-BROADDUS COLLEGE: BATTLER COLUMNS — 101 College Hill Dr, Philippi, WV, 26416, USA; tel (304) 457-6357; fax (304) 457-6239; web site: www.ab.edu/performing_arts/battler_columns
Jim Wilkie
Melissa Riffle
Format: Broadsheet

BETHANY COLLEGE: TOWER — 31 E Campus Dr, Bethany, WV, 26032-3002, USA; tel (304) 829-7951; fax (304) 829-7950; e-mail: tower@bethanywv.edu; web site: www2.bethanywv.edu/tower
Mike King
Format: Tabloid

CONCORD COLLEGE: CONCORDIAN — PO Box 1000, Athens, WV, 24712-1000, USA; tel (304) 384-5364; e-mail: concordian@concord.edu; web site: www.cunewspaper.com
Lindsey Mullins
Wendy Holdren
Format: Broadsheet

GLENVILLE STATE COLLEGE: THE PHOENIX — USA; tel (304) 462-4133; fax (304) 462-4407; e-mail: news.paper@glenville.edu; web site: www.glenville.edu/life/phoenix.php
Assistant Professor of English — Marjorie Stewart
Published: Thur Print edition twice a semester
Digital Edition Available?: Y
Format: online and tabloid

MARSHALL UNIVERSITY: THE PARTHENON — 109 Communications Building, Huntington, WV, 25755-0001, USA; tel (304) 696-6696; fax (304) 696-2732; e-mail: parthenon@marshall.edu; adv email: parthenon@marshall.edu; ed email: parthenon@marshall.edu; web site: www.marshallparthenon.comEst. 1898
Adviser — Sandy York
Published: Tues, Fri Print Tuesday and Friday, online 24-7. Circ.(fr.) 6,000
Digital Edition Available?: Y
Price: Free on campus
Format: Broadsheet

OHIO VALLEY UNIVERSITY: HIGHLANDER — 1 Campus View Dr, Vienna, WV, 26105-8000, USA; tel (304) 865-6151; web site: www.ovu.edu/site.cfm/newspaper.cfm
Philip Sturm
Format: Tabloid

SALEM INTERNATIONAL UNIV.: GREEN AND WHITE — 223 W Main St, Salem, WV, 26426-1227, USA; tel (304) 326-1538; fax (304) 782-1592
Nicole Michaelas
Format: Tabloid

SHEPHERD UNIVERSITY: SHEPHERD UNIVERSITY PICKET — PO Box 3210, Shepherdstown, WV, 25443-3210, USA; tel (304) 876-5100; fax (304) 876-5100; e-mail: pickweb@shepherd.edu; web site: www.picketonline.com
Jim Lewin
Jeb Inge
Format: Tabloid

UNIV. OF CHARLESTON: EAGLE — 2300 Maccorkle Ave SE, Charleston, WV, 25304-1099, USA; tel (304) 357-4716; fax (304) 357-4988
Andy Spradling
Ginny Bennett Helmick
Format: Broadsheet

WEST LIBERTY UNIVERSITY: TRUMPET — 208 Faculty Drive, West Liberty, WV, 26074, USA; tel (304) 336-8873; fax (304) 336-8323; e-mail: wltrumpet@wlsc.edu; web site: westlibertylive.com/thetrumpetEst. 1922
Tammie Beagle
Published: WedCirc.(fr.) 1,500
Digital Edition Available?: Y
Insert rate: $2.50/column inch
Price: Free
Format: Tabloid

WEST VIRGINIA STATE UNIV.: YELLOW JACKET — 214 Wilson Student Union, Institute, WV, 25112-1000, USA; tel (304) 766-3212; fax (304) 766-3309; web site: www.wvstateu.edu/~yellowjacket
Advisor — Robin Broughton
Mary Casto
Patrick Felton
Format: Magazine

WEST VIRGINIA UNIV.: DAILY ATHENAEUM — PO Box 6427, Morgantown, WV, 26506-6427, USA; tel (304) 293-2540; fax (304) 293-6857; e-mail: da-mail@mail.wvu.edu; web site: www.da.wvu.edu
Alan R. Waters
Format: Broadsheet

WEST VIRGINIA UNIV. INST. OF TECHNOLOGY: TECH COLLEGIAN — PO Box 1, Montgomery, WV, 25136-0001, USA; tel (304) 442-3180; fax (304) 442-3838; e-mail: collegianwv@hotmail.com; web site: collegian.wvutech.edu
Jim Kerrigan
Emily Wilkinson
Format: Tabloid

WEST VIRGINIA UNIV. PARKERSBURG: WVU-P CHRONICLE — 300 Campus Dr, Parkersburg, WV, 26104-8647, USA; tel (304) 424-8247; fax (304) 424-8315; e-mail: chronicle@wvup.edu; adv email: chronicle@wvup.edu; ed email: chronicle@wvup.edu; web site: http://issuu.com/wvuparkersburgchronicleEst. 1969
Torie Jackson
Published: ThurCirc.(fr.) 3,500
Digital Edition Available?: Y
Insert rate: Varies by size
Format: Tabloid

WHEELING JESUIT UNIV.: CARDINAL CONNECTION — 316 Washington Ave, Wheeling, WV, 26003-6295, USA; tel (304) 243-2250; ed email: news@wju.edu; web site: www.wju.edu/cardinal
Becky Forney
Format: Tabloid

WISCONSIN

BELOIT COLLEGE: ROUND TABLE — 700 College St, Beloit, WI, 53511-5595, USA; tel (608) 363-2000; fax (608) 363-2718; e-mail: admiss@beloit.edu; web site: www.beloit.edu
— India John
— Steven JacksonCo Editor-in-Chief s
Format: Tabloid

BLACKHAWK TECHNICAL COLLEGE: BLACKHAWK FLYER — PO Box 5009, Janesville, WI, 53547-5009, USA; tel (608) 757-7702; fax (608) 743-4407
Amber Feibel
Format: Magazine

CARDINAL STRITCH UNIV. — 6801 N Yates Rd, Milwaukee, WI, 53217-3985, USA; tel (414) 410-4173; fax (414) 410-4111
Mary Carson

CARTHAGE COLLEGE: THE CURRENT — 2001 Alford Park Dr, Kenosha, WI, 53140-1994, USA; tel (262) 551-5800; fax (262) 551-6629; web site: current.carthage.edu
Meg Durbin
Carmelo Chimera
Lauren Hansen
Format: Tabloid

CONCORDIA UNIV. OF WISCONSIN: BEACON — 12800 N Lake Shore Dr, Mequon, WI, 53097-2402, USA; tel (262) 243-5700; fax (262) 243-4351
Sarah Holtan
Alax Tomter
Format: Magazine

LAKELAND COLLEGE: THE MIRROR — PO Box 359, Sheboygan, WI, 53082-0359, USA; tel (920) 565-1316; fax (920) 565-1344; e-mail: mirror@lakeland.edu; web site: www.lakelandmirror.com
Becky Meyer
Ashley Paulson
Format: Tabloid

LAWRENCE UNIVERSITY: THE LAWRENTIAN — 711 E Boldt Way Spc 51, Appleton, WI, 54911-5699, USA; tel (920) 832-6768; fax (920) 832-7031; e-mail: lawrentian@lawrence.edu; web site: www.lawrentian.comEst. 1884
Editor-in-Chief — Emily Zawacki
Copy Chief — Nathan Lawrence
Published: FriCirc. (pd.) 250 (fr.) 1,000
Digital Edition Available?: Y
Format: Tabloid

MADISON AREA TECHNICAL COLLEGE: THE CLARION — 1701 Wright St, Madison, WI, 53704-2599, USA; tel (608) 243-4809; fax (608) 246-6488; e-mail: clarioned@matcmadison.edu; web site: www.matc-clarion.com
Doug Kirchberg
Vishmaa Ramsaroop Briggs
Format: Tabloid

MARIAN UNIVERSITY: THE SABRE — 45 S National Ave, Fond Du Lac, WI, 54935-4621, USA; tel (920) 923-8776; fax (920) 923-8158; web site: www.marianuniversitysabre.com
Vicky Hildebrandt
Katie Leist
Format: Tabloid

MARQUETTE UNIV.: MARQUETTE TRIBUNE — 1131 W Wisconsin Ave, Milwaukee, WI, 53233-2313, USA; tel (414) 288-1739; fax (414) 288-5896; e-mail: student.media@mu.edu; viewpoints@marquettetribune.org; web site: marquettetribune.org
Kim Zawada
Lauren Frey
Jim McLaughlin
Format: Tabloid

MILWAUKEE AREA TECH. COLLEGE: THE TIMES — 700 W State St Rm S220, Milwaukee, WI, 53233-1419, USA; tel (414) 297-6250; fax (414) 297-7925; e-mail: matctimes@gmail.com; web site: www.matctimes.comEst. 1959
Faculty Adviser — Bob Hanson
Published: bi-weeklyCirc.(fr.) 2,500
Digital Edition Available?: Y
Insert rate: $100 per 1000
Format: Tabloid

MILWAUKEE SCHOOL OF ENGINEERING — 1025 N. Milwaukee St., Milwaukee, WI, 53202-3109, USA; tel (414) 277-7255; fax (414) 277-7248
Nicholas Petrovits

MOUNT MARY COLLEGE: ARCHES — 2900 N Menomonee River Pkwy, Milwaukee, WI, 53222-4597, USA; tel (414) 258-4810; fax (414) 443-3602; web site: www.mtmary.edu
Heather Schroeder
Laura Otto
Elaina Meier
Format: Tabloid

RIPON COLLEGE: RIPON COLLEGE — PO Box 248, Ripon, WI, 54971-0248, USA; tel (920) 748-8126; fax (920) 748-9262; web site: www.riponcollegedays.com
Jonathan Bailey
John Bailey
Format: Tabloid

SOUTHWEST WISCONSIN TECH. COLLEGE — 1800 Bronson Blvd, Fennimore, WI, 53809-9778, USA; tel (608) 822-3262; fax (608) 822-6019; e-mail: jcullen@swtc.edu; web site: www.swtc.edu
Jackie Cullen

ST. NORBERT COLLEGE: ST. NORBERT TIMES — 100 Grant St Ste 320, De Pere, WI, 54115-2002, USA; tel (920) 403-3268; fax (920) 403-4092; e-mail: times@snc.edu
John Pennington
Samantha Christian
Insert rate: john.pennington@snc.edu
Format: Tabloid

THE NEW PERSPECTIVE: NEW PERSPECTIVE — 1111 Sentry Dr, Waukesha, WI, 53186-5965, USA; tel (262) 524-7351; e-mail: perspect@carrollu.edu; adv email: npadvertising@gmail.com; ed email: persepct@carrollu.edu; web site: www.thedigitalnp.comEst. 1874
Price: Free
Format: Tabloid

UNIV. OF WISCONSIN CENTER — 705 Viebahn St, Manitowoc, WI, 54220-6601, USA; tel (920) 683-4731; fax (920) 683-4776
Larry Desch
Format: Tabloid

UNIV. OF WISCONSIN CENTER MARATHON: UWMC FORUM — 518 S 7th Ave, Wausau, WI, 54401-5362, USA; tel (715) 261-6264; fax (715) 261-6333; e-mail: theforumuwmc@gmail.com; web site: www.uwmcforum.com
Mark Parman
Haley Zblewski
Format: Tabloid

UNIV. OF WISCONSIN EAU CLAIRE: THE SPECTATOR — 104B Hibbard Hall, 105 Garfield Ave, Eau Claire, WI, 54701, USA; tel (715) 836-5618; fax (715) 836-3829; e-mail: spectator@uwec.edu; web site: www.spectatornews.com
John Cayer
Scott Hansen
Breann Schossow
Frank Pellegrino
Format: Broadsheet

UNIV. OF WISCONSIN GREEN BAY: FOURTH ESTATE — 2420 Nicolet Dr, Green Bay, WI, 54311-7003, USA; tel (920) 465-2719; fax (920) 465-2895; e-mail: 4e@uwgb.edu; adv email: 4e@uwgb.edu; ed email: 4e@uwgb.edu; web site: www.fourthestatenewspaper.com
Victoria Goff
Nicole Angelucci
Maureen Malone
Published: ThurCirc.(fr.) 6,600
Digital Edition Available?: Y
Price: Free
Format: Tabloid

UNIV. OF WISCONSIN LA CROSSE: RACQUET — 1725 State St, La Crosse, WI, 54601-3788, USA; tel (608) 785-8378; fax

(608) 785-6575; e-mail: racquet@uwlax.edu; web site: www.theracquet.net
Chris Rochester
Mary Beth Valhalla
Format: Broadsheet

UNIV. OF WISCONSIN MARSHFIELD: INSIGHT — Marshfield, WI, 54449, USA; tel (715) 389-6545; fax (715) 389-6517; e-mail: msfur@uwc.edu; ed email: insight@uwc.edu; web site: www.marshfield.uwc.edu
Stacey Oelrich
Digital Edition Available?: Y
Format: Tabloid

UNIV. OF WISCONSIN MILWAUKEE: UWM POST — PO Box 413, Milwaukee, WI, 53201-0413, USA; tel (414) 229-4578; fax (414) 229-4579; e-mail: post@uwm.edu; post@uwmpost.com; web site: www.uwmpost.com
Simon Bouwman
Kurt Raether
Kevin Lessmiller
Format: Tabloid

UNIV. OF WISCONSIN OSHKOSH: ADVANCE-TITAN — 800 Algoma Blvd, Oshkosh, WI, 54901-8651, USA; tel (920) 424-3048; fax (920) 424-0866; web site: www.advancetitan.com
Vince Filak
Published: Thur
Format: Broadsheet

UNIV. OF WISCONSIN PARKSIDE: RANGER NEWS — PO Box 2000, Kenosha, WI, 53141-2000, USA; tel (262) 595-2287; fax (262) 595-2295; e-mail: rangernews@uwp.edu; adv email: advertising@therangernews.com; web site: www.therangernews.com
Jo Kirst
Format: Tabloid

UNIV. OF WISCONSIN PLATTEVILLE: EXPONENT — 1 University Plz Stop 1, Platteville, WI, 53818-3001, USA; tel (608) 342-1471; fax (608) 342-1671; e-mail: exponent@uwplatt.edu; web site: www.uwpexponent.orgEst. 1889
Administrative assistant — Becky Troy
Arthur Ranney
Published: ThurCirc.(fr.) 3,600
Format: Tabloid

UNIV. OF WISCONSIN SHEBOYGAN: THE VOICE — 1 University Dr, Sheboygan, WI, 53081-4789, USA; tel (920) 459-6600; fax (920) 459-6602; e-mail: shbinfo@uwc.edu; ed email: shbvoice@uwc.edu; web site: www.sheboygan.uwc.edu
Format: Tabloid

UNIV. OF WISCONSIN STEVENS POINT: THE POINTER — 1101 Reserve Street 104 CAC, Stevens Point, WI, 54481-3897, USA; tel (715) 346-3707; fax (715) 346-4712; e-mail: pointer@uwsp.edu; web site: http://pointer.uwsp.edu
Liz Fakazis
Steve Roeland
Format: Tabloid

UNIV. OF WISCONSIN SUPERIOR: THE STINGER — 1600 Catlin Ave, Superior, WI, 54880-2954, USA; tel (715) 394-8438; fax (715) 394-8454; e-mail: stinger@uwsuper.edu; web site: www.uwsuper-stinger.com
Joel Anderson
Format: Tabloid

UNIV. OF WISCONSIN WHITEWATER: ROYAL PURPLE — 66 University Ctr., Whitewater, WI, 53190, USA; tel (262) 472-5100; fax (262) 472-5101; adv email: rpads@uww.edu; ed email: rp@uww.edu; web site: www.royalpurplenews.comEst. 1901
Sam Martino
Adviser — Kyle Geissler
Format: Tabloid

UNIVERSITY OF WISCONSIN MADISON: BADGER HERALD — 152 West Johnson Street, Madison, WI, 53703-2017, USA; tel (608) 257-4712; fax (608) 258-3029; e-mail: publisher@badgerherald.com; adv email: addirector@badgerherald.com; ed email: editor@badgerherald.com; web site: www.badgerherald.comEst. 1969
Editor-in-Chief — Alice Vagun
Published: Tues
Digital Edition Available?: Y
Digital Platform - Mobile: Apple, Android, Windows, Blackberry
Digital Platform - Tablet: Apple iOS, Android, Windows 7
Format: Tabloid

UNIVERSITY OF WISCONSIN, FOX VALLEY: FOX JOURNAL — 1478 Midway Rd, Menasha, WI, 54952-1224, USA; tel (920) 832-2810; fax (920) 832-2674; e-mail: foxjournal@uwc.edu; web site: www.uwfox.uwc.edu/foxjournal
Paula Lovell
Format: Magazine

UNIVERSITY OF WISCONSIN-RIVER FALLS: STUDENT VOICE — 410 S. Third St., River Falls, WI, 54022, USA; tel (715) 425-3169; fax (715) 425-0658; e-mail: journalism@uwrf.edu; adv email: advertising@uwrfvoice.com; ed email: editor@uwrfvoice.com; web site: uwrfvoice.comEst. 1916
Advisor — Andris Straumanis
Chair — Sandra Ellis
Published: FriCirc.(fr.) 1,000
Digital Edition Available?: N
Price: 1
Format: Broadsheet

UNIVERSITY OF WISCONSIN-STOUT: STOUTONIA — 712 Broadway St S, Menomonie, WI, 54751, USA; tel (715) 232-1141; e-mail: stoutonia@uwstout.edu; adv email: stoutoniaads@uwstout.edu; ed email: stoutonia@uwstout.edu; web site: www.stoutonia.comEst. 1915
Advisor — Kate Edenborg
Shaun Dudek
Published: Every two weeks (7 issues per semester). Not
Published during the summer.Circ.(fr.) 2,700
Digital Edition Available?: Y
Format: mini-tab

VITERBO COLLEGE: LUMEN — 900 Viterbo Dr, La Crosse, WI, 54601-8804, USA; tel (608) 796-3046; fax (608) 796-3050; e-mail: communication@viterbo.edu; web site: www.viterbolumen.com
Pat Kerrigan
Jessica Weber
Format: Tabloid

WISCONSIN ENGINEER MAGAZINE — 1550 Engineering Dr., Madison, WI, 53706, USA; tel (608) 262-3494; fax (608) 262-3494; e-mail: wiscengr@cae.wisc.edu; web site: www.wisconsinengineer.comEst. 1912
Advisor — Steven Zwickel
Price: $12/yr mail subscriptions
Format: Magazine

WYOMING

CASPER COLLEGE: CHINOOK — 125 College Dr # CE-109, Casper, WY, 82601-4699, USA; tel (307) 268-2100; fax (307) 268-2203
Pete Vanhouten
Derek Schroder
Format: Tabloid

LARAMIE COUNTY CMTY. COLLEGE: WINGSPAN — 1400 E. College Dr., Cheyenne, WY, 82007-3204, USA; tel (307) 778-1304; e-mail: wingspan@lccc.wy.eduEst. 1976
Advisor — J.L. O'Brien
Adviser — Jake Sherlock
Published: MthlyCirc.(fr.) 1,000
Digital Edition Available?: Y
Insert rate: $200 per 1,000
Price: Free
Format: Tabloid

NORTHWEST COLLEGE: NORTHWEST TRAIL — 231 W 6th St Bldg 3, Powell, WY, 82435-1898, USA; tel (307) 754-6438; fax (307) 754-6700; web site: www.northwesttrail.org
Advisor — Rob Breeding
Kayla Dumas
Format: Tabloid

UNIV. OF WYOMING: BRANDING IRON — 1000 E University Ave Dept 3625, Laramie, WY, 82071-2000, USA; tel (307) 766-6190; fax (307) 766-4027; e-mail: bi@uwyo.edu; ed email: letters@brandingirononline.info; web site: www.brandingirononline.info
Carry Berry-Smith
Sasha Fahrenkops
Format: Tabloid

ETHNIC NEWSPAPERS IN THE UNITED STATES

AFGHAN

ALEXANDRIA

OMAID WEEKLY (EVERY OTHER MON)
PO Box 30818, Alexandria, VA, 22310-8818, Fairfax, USA; tel (703) 922-6321; fax (703) 922-6322; e-mail mail@omaid.com; web site www.omaid.com
Ethnicity: Afghan
Circulation: 1,600pd,; Sworn/Estimate/Non-Audited
Advertising: Open inch rate $4.00
Established: 1992
Adv. Mgr. .... Aseem Koshan
Ed. .... Mohammad Q. Koshan
Mechanical Specifications: Type page 10 x 15 1/2; E - 3 cols, 3 1/6, 3/16 between; A - 3 cols, 3 1/6, 3/16 between; C - 3 cols, 3 1/6, 3/16 between.

AFRICAN

HAWTHORNE

THE AFRICAN TIMES/USA
(Bi-Mthly)
5155 W Rosecrans Ave, Ste 213, Hawthorne, CA, 90250-6652, Los Angeles, USA; tel (213) 924-8166; adv tel (213) 924-8166; ed tel (213) 924-8166; fax (310) 644-5507; adv fax (310) 644-5507; ed fax (310) 644-5507; e-mail editor@theafricantimes.com; adv e-mail africantimes-usa@mindspring.com ; ed e-mail editor@theafricantimes.com; web site www.theafricantimes.com
Ethnicity: African
Circulation: 12,000pd, 48,000fr; Sworn/Estimate/Non-Audited
Advertising: Available on website
Established: 1989
Mktg. Dir. .... Ronald Mracky
Ed. .... Charles Anyiam
Mechanical Specifications: Available on website
Delivery Method: Mail, Newsstand, Carrier
Zip Codes Served: U.S. nation-wide
Note: Bi-monthly news journal serving the U.S. based Africa Emigre, African American, Afrophile and expatriate communities and those who need information on Africa issues in the U.S. and globally - investments, news, politics, art. Considered as "Africa's Influential Media Voice in America, Since 1989"

AMERICAN INDIAN (NATIVE AMERICAN)

FORT HALL

SHO-BAN NEWS
(Thur)
PO Box 900, Hrdc, Pima Drive, Fort Hall, ID, 83203-0900, Bingham, USA; tel (208) 478-3701; adv tel (208) 478-3810; ed tel (208) 478-3701; fax (208) 478-3702; adv fax (208) 478-3702; ed fax (208) 478-3702; e-mail shobnews@ida.net; adv e-mail brappenay@sbtribes.com; web site www.shobannews.com
Ethnicity: American Indian (Native American)
Circulation: 1,750pd, 50fr; Sworn/Estimate/Non-Audited
Advertising: Open inch rate $14.00
Established: 1970
Digital Platform - Mobile: Apple
Digital Platform - Tablet: Apple iOS
Ed. .... Lori Edmo-Suppah
Mechanical Specifications: Type page 9.889 x 21.5; E - 6 cols, 2, 1/8 between; A - 6 cols, 2, 1/8 between; C - 6 cols, 2, 1/8 between.
Equipment
: Hardware — APP/Mac; Software — Adobe Creative Suite 6, QPS/QuarkXPress 9.0.
Delivery Method: Mail
Zip Codes Served: 83203

ARABIC

JACKSONVILLE

THE SYRIAN-LEBANESE STAR
(Mthly)
4251 University Blvd S, Ste 201, Jacksonville, FL, 32216-4981, Duval, USA; tel (904) 737-6996; fax (904) 636-0150; web site www.syrianlebanesestar.com
Ethnicity: Arabic
Circulation: 22,000pd, 7,000fr; Sworn/Estimate/Non-Audited
Advertising: Open inch rate $15.00
Prodn. Mgr. .... Alvin M. Coplan

PASADENA

BEIRUT TIMES
(Thur) (Weekly)
PO Box 40277, Pasadena, CA, 91114-7277, Los Angeles, USA; tel (626) 844-7777; fax (626) 795-2222; e-mail 4beirut@gmail.com; adv e-mail beiruttimes@yahoo.com; ed e-mail beiruttimes@yahoo.com; web site www.beiruttimes.com
Ethnicity: Arabic
Circulation: 28,000fr; Sworn/Estimate/Non-Audited
Advertising: Open inch rate $25.00
Established: 1985
Digital Platform - Mobile: Apple, Android, Windows, Blackberry
Adv. Mgr. .... George Badir
Ed. .... Michel Abssi
Mechanical Specifications: Type page 9 3/4 x 15 1/2; E - 5 cols, 1 3/4, 1/6 between.
Delivery Method: Mail, Newsstand, Carrier, Racks

ARMENIAN

GLENDALE

CALIFORNIA COURIER
(Thur)
PO Box 5390, Glendale, CA, 91221-5390, Los Angeles, USA; tel (818) 424-9049; e-mail sassoun@pacbell.net
Ethnicity: Armenian
Circulation: 1,000pd, 200fr; Sworn/Estimate/Non-Audited
Advertising: Open inch rate $16
Established: 1958Editions: 1—
Pub. .... Harut Sassounian
Ed. .... Serge Samoniantz
Mechanical Specifications: Type page 10 x 13.75; E - 5 cols, 1 7/8, 1/6 between; A - 5 cols, 1 7/8, 1/6 between.
Equipment
: Hardware — PC; Software — Adobe/PageMaker 5.0, Microsoft/Office 6.0.
Delivery Method: Mail
Zip Codes Served: nationwide

LOS ANGELES

ASBAREZ DAILY (DAILY)
1203 N Vermont Ave, Los Angeles, CA, 90029-1703, Los Angeles, USA; tel (323) 284-0088; adv tel (818) 500-9555; ed tel (818) 500-0609; fax (323) 284-0080; ed fax (818) 956-1106; e-mail editor@asbarez.com; web site www.asbarez.com
Ethnicity: Armenian
Circulation: 12,000pd, 500fr; Sworn/Estimate/Non-Audited
Advertising: Open inch rate $2.80
Adv. Mgr. .... Armik Daghlian
Circ. Mgr. .... Sossi Atamian
Ed. .... Ara Khachatourian

PARAMUS

ARMENIAN REPORTER INTERNATIONAL, INC.
(Tues, Thur, Sat)
PO Box 129, Paramus, NJ, 07653-0129, Bergen, USA; tel (201) 226-1995; fax (201) 226-1660; e-mail armenianreporter@msn.com; web site www.armenianreporteronline.com
Ethnicity: Armenian
Circulation: 10,000pd, 100fr
Advertising: Open inch rate $10.00
Established: 1967
Ed. .... Vincent Lima
Prodn. Mgr. .... Sylva A. Boghossian
Equipment
: Hardware — IBM; Software — WordPerfect.

WATERTOWN

ARMENIAN MIRROR-SPECTATOR
(Wed)
755 Mount Auburn St, Watertown, MA, 02472-1509, Middlesex, USA; tel (617) 924-4420; fax (617) 924-2887; e-mail armenmirr@aol.com; web site www.mirrorspectator.com
Ethnicity: Armenian
Circulation: 2,600pd,; Sworn/Estimate/Non-Audited
Advertising: Open inch rate $6.00
Gen. Mgr. .... Kevork Marachlian
Ed. .... Alin Gregorian
Computer Designer .... Mark McKertich
Mechanical Specifications: Type page 10 x 15; E - 3 cols, 2 1/2, between; A - 4 cols, 2 1/2, 1/4 between.
Equipment
: Hardware — APP/Mac.

ARMENIAN WEEKLY
(Sat)
80 Bigelow Ave, Watertown, MA, 02472-2012, Middlesex, USA; tel (617) 926-3974; fax (617) 926-1750; e-mail manager@hairenik.com; web site www.hairenik.com
Ethnicity: Armenian
Circulation: 2,000pd, 550fr; Sworn/Estimate/Non-Audited
Advertising: Open inch rate $10.00
Adv. Mgr. .... Lala Emirdjiin
Ed. .... Khapchig Mouradian
Mechanical Specifications: Type page 10 x 16; E - 4 cols, 2, 1/4 between; A - 4 cols, 2, 1/4 between.
Equipment
: Hardware — IBM; Software — Adobe/PageMaker, Adobe/Photoshop, Microsoft/Word.

HAIRENIK WEEKLY
(Sat)
80 Bigelow Ave, Watertown, MA, 02472-2012, Middlesex, USA; tel (617) 926-3974; fax (617) 926-1750; e-mail manager@hairenik.com; web site www.hairenik.com
Ethnicity: Armenian
Circulation: 1,500pd, 200fr; Sworn/Estimate/Non-Audited
Advertising: Open inch rate $10.00
Adv. Mgr. .... Lala Emirdjiin
Ed. .... Khajag Mgrditchian
Equipment
: Hardware — IBM; Software — Microsoft/Word, Adobe/PageMaker, Adobe/Photoshop.

ASIAN

MESA

ASIAN AMERICAN TIMES
(Mthly) (Bi-Weekly)
2011 S Henkel, Mesa, AZ, 85202-6500, Maricopa, USA; tel (480) 839-5139; adv tel (480) 839-5139; fax (480) 247-3008; adv fax (480) 247-3008; e-mail ad@asianamericantimes.us; adv e-mail ad@asianamericantimes.us; ed e-mail news@asianamericantimes.us; web site www.asianamericantimes.us
Ethnicity: Asian
Advertising: Open inch rate $54.50
Established: 1990
Pub. .... Joseph Fu
Ed. .... Leung Eng
Delivery Method: Mail, Racks
Zip Codes Served: 85202

ASIAN AMERICANS

SEATTLE

NORTHWEST ASIAN WEEKLY
(Thur)
412 Maynard Ave S, Seattle, WA, 98104-2917, King, USA; tel (206) 223-5559; fax (206) 223-0626; e-mail info@nwasianweekly.com; web site www.nwasianweekly.com
Ethnicity: Asian Americans
Circulation: 2,000pd, 14,000fr; Sworn/Estimate/Non-Audited
Advertising: Open inch rate $30.00
Established: 1982
Pub. .... Assunta Ng
Adv. Mgr. .... Rebecca Yip
Circ. Mgr. .... George Liu
Mechanical Specifications: Type page 11 x 17; E - 4 cols, between; C - 5 cols, between.
Delivery Method: Mail, Newsstand, Carrier, Racks
Zip Codes Served: 981 - 985

BRITISH

LA MESA

UNION JACK
(Mthly)
8080 La Mesa Blvd, Ste 203, La Mesa, CA, 91942-0362, San Diego, USA; tel (619) 466-3129; fax (619) 337-1103; e-mail ujnews@ujnews.com; web site www.ujnews.com
Ethnicity: British
Circulation: 10,000pd, 100,000fr; Sworn/Estimate/Non-Audited
Advertising: Open inch rate $43.00
Established: 1982
Owners-Publishers .... Jeff & Ron Choularton
Ed. .... Ronald Choularton
Mechanical Specifications: Type page 10 1/4 x 15 1/2; E - 5 cols, 1 23/24, 1/6 between; A - 5 cols, 1 23/24, 1/6 between; C - 5 cols, 1 23/24, 1/6 between.
Equipment: Software — Ventura.
Delivery Method: Mail, Carrier, Racks
Zip Codes Served: all

BULGARIAN

FORT WAYNE

MACEDONIAN TRIBUNE
(Mthly)
124 W Wayne St, Fort Wayne, IN, 46802-2500, Allen, USA; tel (260) 422-5900; fax (260) 422-1348; e-mail mtfw@macedonian.org; web site www.macedonian.org
Ethnicity: Bulgarian
Circulation: 1,320pd, 64fr; Sworn/Estimate/Non-Audited
Advertising: Open inch rate $10.00
Established: 1927
Adv. Mgr. .... Lois Eubank
Circ. Mgr. .... Martha Haag
Ed. .... Virginia Surso
Mechanical Specifications: Type page 11 1/4 x 17; E - 4 cols, 2 3/8, 1/4 between.
Equipment
: Hardware — APP/Mac; Software — Corel/WordPerfect 4.0.

CARIBBEAN

BROOKLYN

CARIBBEAN LIFE
(Wed)
1 Metrotech Ctr, Ste 1001, Brooklyn, NY, 11201-3949, Kings, USA; tel (718) 260-2500; adv tel (718) 260-2500; ed tel (718) 260-8318; fax (718) 615-3828; e-mail CaribbeanLife@CNGLocal.com; adv e-mail JStern@CNGLocal.com; ed e-mail KKirby@CNGLocal.com; web site www.caribbeanlifenews.com
Ethnicity: Caribbean
Circulation: 125,000fr; Sworn/Estimate/Non-Audited
Advertising: Open inch rate $41.50
Vice Pres., Adv. .... Ralph D'onofrio
Circ. Mgr. .... Jennifer Stern
Ed. .... Kenton Kirby
Prodn. Mgr. .... Keith Oeschneo
Mechanical Specifications: Type page 10 x 14 1/4.

NEW YORK

CARIB NEWS
(Wed)
35 W 35th St, Ste 705, New York, NY, 10001-2205, New York, USA; tel (212) 944-1991; fax (212) 944-2089; e-mail info@nycaribnews.com; adv e-mail info@nycaribnews.com; web site www.nycaribnews.com
Ethnicity: Caribbean
Advertising: Open inch rate $45.00
Ed. .... Karlisa Rodney
Delivery Method: Mail, Racks
Zip Codes Served: New York

CHINESE

BOSTON

SAMPAN NEWSPAPER
(Bi-Mthly) (2 x Mthly)
87 Tyler St, Boston, MA, 02111-1833, Suffolk, USA; tel (617) 426-9492 x 208; adv tel (617) 426-9492 x 226; fax (617) 482-2316; e-mail editor@sampan.org; adv e-mail ads@sampan.org; ed e-mail editor@sampan.org; web site www.sampan.org

Ethnicity: Chinese
Circulation: 680pd, 10,000fr; Sworn/Estimate/Non-Audited
Advertising: Open inch rate $10.00
Established: 1972
Exec. Dir., AACA.......... Mary Chin
Ed. .... Ling-Mei Wong
Mechanical Specifications: Type page 11 x 17; E - 4 cols, 2 1/4, 1/4 between.
Equipment
: Hardware — Lenovo; Software — Adobe InDesign
Delivery Method: Mail, Racks

DENVER

COLORADO CHINESE NEWS
(Fri)
1548 W Alameda Ave, Ste A, Denver, CO, 80223-1973, Denver, USA; tel (303) 722-8268; fax (303) 722-7861; e-mail editor@cocnews.com; web site www.cocnews.com
Ethnicity: Chinese
Circulation: 913pd, 6,500fr; Sworn/Estimate/Non-Audited
Advertising: Open inch rate $28.00
Established: 1994
Digital Platform - Mobile: Windows
Mng. Ed.......... Wendy Y. Chao
Mechanical Specifications: Type page 16 x 22; C - 12 cols, between.
Equipment
: Hardware — PC 486, HP/LaserPrinter; Software — Shakespine/Chinese Desk Top Publishing System.
Delivery Method: Mail, Carrier, Racks
Zip Codes Served: 80223

FLUSHING

THE HERALD MONTHLY
(Mthly)
15603 Horace Harding Expy, Flushing, NY, 11367-1250, Queens, USA; tel (718) 359-2030; fax (718) 359-2130; e-mail herald@cchc.org; web site www.cchc.org
Ethnicity: Chinese
Circulation: 120,000pd, 120,000fr; Sworn/Estimate/Non-Audited
Advertising: Open inch rate $9.00
Adv. Mgr.......... Ruth Lee
Exec. Ed.......... Katie Chau
Mechanical Specifications: Type page 17 x 28.
Zip Codes Served: 10002

HOUSTON

SOUTHERN CHINESE DAILY NEWS
(Mon, Tues, Wed, Thur, Fri, Sat, Sun) (Daily)
11122 Bellaire Blvd, Houston, TX, 77072-2608, Harris, USA; tel (281) 498-4310; fax (281) 498-2728; web site www.scdaily.com
Ethnicity: Chinese
Circulation: 5,800fr; CVC
Advertising: Open inch rate $9.50
Established: 1979
Digital Platform - Mobile: Windows
Digital Platform - Tablet: Windows 7
Pub.......... Wea H. Lee
Adv. Mgr.......... Hilda Poon
Prodn. Mgr.......... Jean Lim
Mechanical Specifications: Type page 11.5 x 21.5, 4 cols.
Zip Codes Served: HOUSTON—GALVESTON—BRAZORIA, TX CMSA

U.S. ASIA NEWS
(Mthly)
11122 Bellaire Blvd, Houston, TX, 77072-2608, Harris, USA; tel (281) 498-4310; fax (281) 498-2724; e-mail wealee@scdaily.com; web site www.scdaily.com
Ethnicity: Chinese
Circulation: 25,000pd,; Sworn/Estimate/Non-Audited
Advertising: Open inch rate $10.00
Gen. Mgr.......... Emerson Chu
Mechanical Specifications: Type page 13 1/2 x 21; E - 6 cols, 2, 1/4 between; A - 6 cols, 2, 1/4 between.
Equipment
: Hardware — APP/Mac.

LOS ANGELES

TAIWAN JOURNAL
(Fri)
6300 Wilshire Blvd, Ste 1510A, Los Angeles, CA, 90048-5217, Los Angeles, USA; tel (323) 782-8770; fax (323) 782-8761; e-mail tj@mail.gio.gov.tw; web site www.taiwanjournal.nat.gov.tw
Ethnicity: Chinese
Pub.......... Pasuya Wen-Chih Yao
Ed. .... Steven Lai
Equipment
: Hardware — IBM; Software — Microsoft, Adobe/PageMaker.

NEW YORK

CHINA DAILY DISTRIBUTION CORP.
1500 Broadway, Ste 2800, New York, NY, 10036-4097, New York, USA; tel (212) 537-8888; adv tel (212) 537-8900; fax (212) 537-8898; e-mail readers@chinadailyusa.com; web site http://www.chinadaily.com.cn/cd/usa.html
Ethnicity: Chinese
Advertising: Open inch rate $102.00
Adv. Mgr.......... Lingling Sun
Ed. .... Yinghuang Zhu
Prodn. Mgr. .... Thomoson Chen

CHINESE CHRISTIAN HERALD CRUSADES, INC.
48 Allen St, New York, NY, 10002-5304, New York, USA; tel (212) 334-2033; ed fax (212) 334-2062; e-mail herald@cchc.org
Ethnicity: Chinese
Exec. Ed.......... Katie Chau

ROSEMEAD

PACIFIC TIMES
(Wed)
3001 Walnut Grove Ave, Ste 8, Rosemead, CA, 91770-2785, Los Angeles, USA; tel (626) 573-4831; fax (626) 573-4897; e-mail pacific@ix.netcom.com; web site www.pacific-times.com
Ethnicity: Chinese
Circulation: 15,000pd, 20,000fr; Sworn/Estimate/Non-Audited
Advertising: Open inch rate $40.00
Pres.......... Wencheng Lin
Mechanical Specifications: Type page 12 x 20.

SEATTLE

SEATTLE CHINESE POST
(Thur)
412 Maynard Ave S, Seattle, WA, 98104-2917, King, USA; tel (206) 223-0623; fax (206) 223-0626; e-mail info@nwasianweekly.com; web site www.nwasianweekly.com
Ethnicity: Chinese
Circulation: 5,000pd, 1,000fr; Sworn/Estimate/Non-Audited
Advertising: Open inch rate $20.00
Pub.......... Assunta Ng
Circ. Mgr.......... George Liu
Ed. .... Rebecca Yip
Mechanical Specifications: Type page 11 x 17.
Zip Codes Served: 98111, 98105, 98115, 98144, 98118, 98004

WHITESTONE

WORLD JOURNAL
(Mon, Tues, Wed, Thur, Fri, Sat, Sun) (Daily)
14107 20th Ave, Whitestone, NY, 11357-3062, Queens, USA; tel (718) 746-8889; fax (718) 445-5257; e-mail webmaster@worldjournal.com; adv e-mail nysales@worldjournal.com; ed e-mail citydesk@worldjournal.com; web site www.worldjournal.com
Ethnicity: Chinese
Circulation: 100,000pd, 2,500fr; Sworn/Estimate/Non-Audited
Established: 1976
Digital Platform - Mobile: Apple, Android, Windows, Blackberry
Digital Platform - Tablet: Apple iOS, Android, Windows 7
Ed. in Chief.......... Tyson Won
Prodn. Mgr. .... Wen-Te Ling
President .... James Yang
Mechanical Specifications: Type page W 12.5 x H 22.3
Equipment
: Hardware — PC, APP/Mac; Presses — G/Urbanite; Software — Adobe
Delivery Method: Mail, Newsstand, Carrier

CROATIAN

PITTSBURGH

ZAJEDNICAR
(Wed)
100 Delaney Dr, Pittsburgh, PA, 15235-5416, Allegheny, USA; tel (412) 351-3909; fax (412) 823-1594; ed e-mail editor@croatianfraternalunion.org; web site www.croatianfraternalunion.org
Ethnicity: Croatian
Circulation: 36,000fr; Sworn/Estimate/Non-Audited
Lauren Turkall
Ivan BeggProdn. Mgr.s
Mechanical Specifications: Type page 11 x 17.

DANISH

HOFFMAN ESTATES

THE DANISH PIONEER NEWSPAPER
(Mon) (Every other Monday)
1582 Glen Lake Rd, Hoffman Estates, IL, 60169-4023, Cook, USA; tel (847) 882-2552; fax (847) 882-7082; e-mail dpioneer@aol.com; web site www.thedanishpioneer.com
Ethnicity: Danish
Circulation: 3,200pd,; Sworn/Estimate/Non-Audited
Advertising: Open inch rate $8.00
Established: 1872
Ed.......... Linda Steffensen
Mechanical Specifications: Type page 10 x 13; A - 5 cols, 2, between.
Delivery Method: Mail

DUTCH

LYNDEN

THE WINDMILL HERALD (2 X MTHLY)
PO Box 313, Lynden, WA, 98264-0313, Whatcom, USA; tel (604) 532-1733; fax (604) 532-1734; e-mail windmill@godutch.com; web site www.godutch.com
Ethnicity: Dutch
Circulation: 10,400pd,; Sworn/Estimate/Non-AuditedEditions: 3— 3 total Windmill Herald-Central/Eastern Canada; Windmill Herald-U.S. Edition; Windmill Herald-Western Canada;
Mechanical Specifications: Type page 10 1/4 x 15 1/2; E - 6 cols, 1 7/12, 1/6 between; A - 6 cols, 1 7/12, 1/6 between; C - 6 cols, 1 7/12, 1/6 between.

ESTONIAN

NEW YORK

FREE ESTONIAN WORD
(Thur)
243 E 34th St, New York, NY, 10016-4852, New York, USA; tel (212) 686-3356; fax (212) 689-2939; e-mail talitus@vabaeestisona.com; web site www.vabaeestisona.com
Ethnicity: Estonian
Circulation: 1,400pd,; Sworn/Estimate/Non-Audited
Advertising: Open inch rate $14.00
Adv. Mgr.......... Reet Karu
Ed. .... Kart Ulmans
Mechanical Specifications: Type page 11 x 17; A - 5 cols, 1 4/5, 3/20 between.
Equipment
: Hardware — APP/Mac; Software — QPS/QuarkXPress.

VABA EESTI SONA
(Thur)
243 E 34th St, New York, NY, 10016-4852, New York, USA; tel (212) 686-3356; fax (212) 689-2939; e-mail talitus@vabaeestisona.com; ed e-mail toimetus@vabaeestisona.com; web site www.vabaeestisona.com
Ethnicity: Estonian
Circulation:; Sworn/Estimate/Non-Audited
Advertising: $14
Established: 1949
Group: The Nordic Press, Inc
Ed. .... Kart Ulman
Mechanical Specifications: Tabloid, 12 pages
Delivery Method: Mail

FILIPINO

BURLINGAME

PHILIPPINE NEWS
(Fri)
1818 Gilbreth Rd, Ste 240, Burlingame, CA, 94010-1217, San Mateo, USA; tel (650) 552-9775; fax (650) 552-9778; e-mail info@philippinenews.com; web site www.philippinenews.com
Ethnicity: Filipino
Circulation: 47,000pd, 2,000fr; Sworn/Estimate/Non-Audited
Advertising: Open inch rate $10.50
Chrmn.......... John B. Espiritu
Pub.......... Danilo Gozo
Exec. Vice Pres., Sales/Mktg.Margarita Argente
Ed. .... Christina Pastor

GLENDALE

ASIAN JOURNAL
(Wed, Sat)
1210 S Brand Blvd, Glendale, CA, 91204-2615, Los Angeles, USA; tel (213) 250-9797; fax (213) 481-0854; e-mail info@asianjournalinc.com; web site asianjournal.com
Ethnicity: Filipino
Circulation: 31,159fr; VAC
Ed. .... Stephen Padilla

Zip Codes Served: Los Angeles County

WEEKEND BALITA/MIDWEEK BALITA

(Wed, Sat)
520 E Wilson Ave, Ste 210, Glendale, CA, 91206-4374, Los Angeles, USA; tel (818) 552-4503; fax (818) 550-7635; e-mail communitynews@balita.com; ed e-mail editor@balita.com; web site www.balita.com
Ethnicity: Filipino
Circulation: 40,000fr; Sworn/Estimate/Non-Audited
Pub....Luchie Mendoza Allen
Office Mgr. ....Lyn Mendoza
Sales Mgr....Gary Escarilla
Adv. Coord. ....Carmen Vergara
Ed. in Chief....Rhony Laigo
Prodn. Mgr. ....Jojo Margen
Mechanical Specifications: Type page 10 1/2 x 15 1/2; E - 5 cols, 1 7/8, 3/16 between; A - 5 cols, 1 7/8, 3/16 between; C - 6 cols, 1 1/2, 3/16 between.
Equipment
: Hardware — Intel/Pentium; Software — Adobe/PageMaker, Archetype/Corel Draw, Archetype/Corel Scan, Adobe/Photoshop.

JERSEY CITY

FILIPINO EXPRESS

(Fri)
2711 John F Kennedy Blvd, Jersey City, NJ, 07306-5712, Hudson, USA; tel (201) 434-1114; fax (201) 434-0880; e-mail filexpress@aol.com; web site www.filipinoexpress.com
Ethnicity: Filipino
Circulation: 21,700pd, 3,000fr; Sworn/Estimate/Non-Audited
Advertising: Open inch rate $20.00
Adv. Mgr....Lito A. Gajilan

NEW YORK

THE FILIPINO REPORTER

(Fri)
350 5th Ave, Bldg 601, New York, NY, 10118-0110, New York, USA; tel (212) 967-5784; fax (212) 967-5848; e-mail info@filipinoreporter.com; web site www.filipinoreporter.us
Ethnicity: Filipino
Circulation: 47,000pd, 2,000fr; Sworn/Estimate/Non-Audited
Advertising: Open inch rate $11.00
Established: 1972
Mktg. Mgr....Tony Campo
Circ. Mgr....Albert Ignacio
Ed. ....Libertito Pelayo

FINNISH

FITCHBURG

RAIVAAJA (EVERY OTHER WED)

164 Elm St, Fitchburg, MA, 01420-3192, Worcester, USA; tel (978) 343-3822; fax (978) 343-8147; e-mail office@raivaaja.org; editor@raivaaja.org; web site www.raivaaja.org
Ethnicity: Finnish
Circulation: 2,000pd,; Sworn/Estimate/Non-Audited
Advertising: Open inch rate $7.00
Established: 1905
Bus. Mgr....Jonathan Ratila
Ed. ....Marita Cauthen
Mechanical Specifications: Type page 9 3/4 x 14; E - 5 cols, 1 3/4, between; A - 5 cols, 1 3/4, between.
Equipment
: Hardware — APP/Mac; Software — QPS/QuarkXPress.

FRENCH

BATH

FRANCE TODAY

(Bi-Mthly)
Cambridge House, 6 Gay Street, Bath, AL, BA1 2PH, Bath, UK; tel 0044 1225 463 752; adv tel 0044 1225 463 752; ed tel 0044 1225 463 752; e-mail info@francetoday.com; adv e-mail ben@francetoday.com; web site www.francetoday.com
Ethnicity: French
Circulation: 50,000pd, 20,000fr; Sworn/Estimate/Non-Audited
Advertising: Full Page
Established: 1985
Group: France Media Group
Digital Platform - Mobile: Apple, Blackberry
Digital Platform - Tablet: Apple iOS, Blackberry Tablet OS
Pub....Ben Stephens
Mechanical Specifications: Full Page: 220mm x 280mm
Equipment
: Hardware — IBM.
Delivery Method: Mail
Zip Codes Served: Worldwide

SAN FRANCISCO

JOURNAL FRANCAIS

(Mthly)
944 Market St, Ste 210, San Francisco, CA, 94102-4025, San Francisco, USA; tel (415) 981-9088; fax (415) 981-9177; e-mail info@francetoday.com; web site www.journalfrancais.com
Ethnicity: French
Pub....Louis Kyle
Office Mgr. ....Rovi Nett
Adv. Mgr. ....Vanessa Lotoux
Ed. ....Ame Senten
Prodn. Mgr. ....Linda Conner
Mechanical Specifications: Type page 11 x 14.
Equipment
: Hardware — IBM.

GERMAN

LOS ANGELES

CALIFORNIA-STAATS ZEITUNG

(Thur)
5750 Wilshire Blvd, Ste 100, Los Angeles, CA, 90036-3642, Los Angeles, USA; tel (213) 413-5500; fax (213) 413-5469; e-mail CaliforniaGermans@gmail.com; web site http://californiagermans.com/
Ethnicity: German
Advertising: Open inch rate $15.00
Pub....Stephanie Teichmann
Adv. Mgr. ....Erika Bartschat
Prodn. Mgr. ....Hans Reisch
Mechanical Specifications: Type page 15 1/2 x 21; E - 7 cols, 2 1/4, 1/4 between; A - 7 cols, between.

TROY

NORDAMERIKANICHE WOCHENPOST

(Sat)
1301 W Long Lake Rd, Ste 108, Troy, MI, 48098-6348, Oakland, USA; tel (248) 641-9944; fax (248) 641-9946; e-mail info@wochenpostusa.com; adv e-mail sales@wochenpostusa.com; ed e-mail ingrid@wochenpostusa.com; web site www.wochenpostusa.com
Ethnicity: German
Circulation: 30,000pd,; Sworn/Estimate/Non-Audited
Advertising: Open inch rate $21.50
Established: 1854
Pub....Kathrin Beth
Gen. Mgr. ....Ingrid Grotloh
Adv. Mgr. ....Ingrid Stein
Ed. ....Birgit Kroon
Sports Ed. ....Kenneth Burney
Mechanical Specifications: Type page 12 7/16 x 21; E - 6 cols, 1 7/8, 1/6 between; A - 6 cols, 1 7/8, 1/6 between; C - 6 cols, 1 7/8, 1/6 between.
Equipment
: Hardware — 7-APP/Mac; Software — InDesign
Delivery Method: Mail, Newsstand
Zip Codes Served: all US

GREEK

ASTORIA

GREEK NEWS

(Mon)
3507 23rd Ave, Astoria, NY, 11105-2204, Queens, USA; tel (718) 545-4888; adv tel (718) 545-4888; ed tel (718) 545-4888; fax (718) 545-4884; adv fax (718) 545-4884; ed fax (718) 545-4884; e-mail info@greeknewsonline.com; adv e-mail info@greeknewsonline.com; ed e-mail info@greeknewsonline.com; web site www.greeknewsonline.com
Ethnicity: Greek
Advertising: Open inch rate $8.00
Ed. ....Apostolos Zoupaniotis

CHICAGO

GREEK STAR

(Thur)
4159 N Western Ave, Fl 2, Chicago, IL, 60618-2813, Cook, USA; tel (773) 989-7211; fax (773) 313-2006; e-mail greek@britsys.net; web site www.thegreekstar.com
Ethnicity: Greek
Circulation: 2,000pd,; Sworn/Estimate/Non-Audited
Advertising: Open inch rate $12.00
Circ. Mgr....Maria Bappert
Prodn. Mgr. ....Diane Adam
Mechanical Specifications: Type page 13 x 21.
Equipment
: Hardware — APP/Mac; Software — Adobe/PageMaker.

LONG ISLAND CITY

THE NATIONAL HERALD

(Mon, Tues, Wed, Thur, Fri, Sat)
3710 30th St, Long Island City, NY, 11101-2614, Queens, USA; tel (718) 784-5255; fax (718) 472-0510; e-mail publisher@ekirikas.com; web site www.thenationalherald.com
Ethnicity: Greek
Circulation: 100,000pd,; Sworn/Estimate/Non-Audited
Advertising: Open inch rate $17.50
Asst. to Pub....Victoria Diamataris
Circ. Mgr....Demetrios Paregoris
Ed. ....Anthony H. Diamataris
Prodn. Mgr. ....Chrysoula Karametros
Mechanical Specifications: Type page 12 1/2 x 21; E - 6 cols, 1 15/16, between; A - 6 cols, 1 15/16, between; C - 6 cols, 1 15/16, between.

NEW YORK

HELLENIC TIMES

(Mthly)
823 11th Ave, New York, NY, 10019-3557, New York, USA; tel (212) 986-6881; fax (212) 977-3662; e-mail helnctimes@aol.com; web site www.thehellenictimes.com
Ethnicity: Greek
Circulation: 11,500pd, 2,000fr; Sworn/Estimate/Non-Audited
Advertising: Open inch rate $12.00
Pub....John Catsimatidis
Adv. Mgr. ....Margo Catsimatidis
Ed. ....Jimmy Kapsalis

HAITIAN

BROOKLYN

HAITI PROGRES

(Wed)
799 Crown St, Brooklyn, NY, 11213-5808, Kings, USA; tel (917) 484-6725; adv tel (917) 548-5568; fax (718) 284-6968; adv fax (718) 284-6968; e-mail editor@haiti-progres.com; adv e-mail sales@haitiprogres.com; web site www.haiti-progres.com
Ethnicity: Haitian
Circulation: 5,000pd,; Sworn/Estimate/Non-Audited
Advertising: Open inch rate $25.00
Established: 1983
Prodn. Mgr. ....Maude LeBlanc
Mechanical Specifications: Type page 10 x 12.75
Equipment
: Hardware — IBM; Software — Microsoft/Windows 3.1.
Delivery Method: Mail, Newsstand
Zip Codes Served: 11213
Note: Benjamin Dupuy is no longer with this company. Please remove his name

HELLENIC

CONCORDVILLE

HELLENIC NEWS OF AMERICA (BILINGUAL MONTHLY REVIEW)

780 Baltimore Pike #100, Concordville, PA, 19331, Delaware, USA; tel (610) 446-1463; fax (610) 356-4877; e-mail info@hellenicnews.com; adv e-mail paul@hellenicnews.com; ed e-mail aphrodite@hellenicnews.com; web site www.hellenicnews.com
Ethnicity: Hellenic
Circulation: 65pd, 35fr; Sworn/Estimate/Non-Audited
Advertising: Open inch rate $12.00
Established: 1987Editions: 28—
Digital Platform - Mobile: Apple, Android
Adv. Mgr. ....Paul Kotrotsios
Circ. Mgr....Linda Kotrotsios
Mechanical Specifications: Type page 11 x 17.
Equipment
: Hardware — APP/Mac, PC; Software — InDesign,
Adobe/PageMaker 6.5, Adobe/Photoshop 6.5.
Delivery Method: Mail, Newsstand, Racks
Zip Codes Served: all 190 , 191
19331, 194
PA, NJ, DE, NY, CT, MD, VA

INDIAN

NEW YORK

INDIA ABROAD

(Fri)
42 Broadway, Ste 1836, New York, NY, 10004-3855, New York, USA; tel (877) 463-4222; adv tel (877) 463-4222 ext. 2; ed tel (877) 463-4222 ext. 6045; fax (212) 627-9503; adv fax (212) 627-9503; ed fax (212) 627-9503; e-mail advertise@indiaabroad.com; adv e-mail classified@indiaabroad.com; ed e-mail editorial@indiaabroad.com; web site www.indiaabroad.com
Ethnicity: Indian
Circulation: 20,251pd, 720fr; AAM
Advertising: Open inch rate $34.00
Established: 1970
Digital Platform - Mobile: Apple, Android, Windows, Blackberry
Digital Platform - Tablet: Apple iOS, Android, Windows 7, Blackberry Tablet OS
Pub. Ajit Balakrishnan
Ed. Nikhil Laksham
Circ. Dir. Anjali Maniam
Adv. Dir. Anjali Subramaniam
COO - US Media Rajeev Bhambri
Delivery Method: Mail, Racks
Zip Codes Served: New York

INDIAN (ASIAN)

NEWS INDIA-TIMES

(Fri)
115 W 30th St, Rm 1206, New York, NY, 10001-4043, New York, USA; tel 212-675-7515; adv tel (212) 675-7515; fax (212) 675-7624; adv e-mail advertising@newsindia-times.com; ed e-mail editor@newsindia-times.com; web site www.newsindia-times.com
Ethnicity: Indian (Asian)
Circulation: 39,070pd,; AAM
Advertising: Open inch rate $45.00
COO Shomik Chodhuri
Pub. Sudhir Parikh
Sales Exec. Ilayas Quraishi
Mechanical Specifications: Type page 10 x 14; E - 4 cols, 2, between; A - 5 cols, 2, between; C - 5 cols, 2, between.
Equipment
: Hardware — Micron/Pentium 90mhz, PC; Software — Arclist 2.0, Adobe/PageMaker.

SAN LEANDRO

INDIA-WEST

(Fri)
933 MacArthur Blvd, San Leandro, CA, 94577-3062, Alameda, USA; tel (510) 383-1140; adv tel (510) 383-1147; ed tel (510) 383-1140; fax (510) 383-1154; adv fax (510) 383-1154; ed fax (510) 383-1154; e-mail editor@indiawest.com; adv e-mail dyana@indiawest.com; ed e-mail editor@indiawest.com; web site www.indiawest.com
Ethnicity: Indian (Asian)
Circulation: 24,000pd, 2,000fr; Sworn/Estimate/Non-Audited
Advertising: Open inch rate $20.00
Established: 1975
Digital Platform - Mobile: Apple, Android
Digital Platform - Tablet: Apple iOS
Pub. Ramesh P. Murarka
Circ. Mgr Rashmi Gupte
Ed. Bina A. Murarka
Dyana Bhandari
Mechanical Specifications: Type page 10 x 14; E - 5 cols, 2, 1/4 between; A - 5 cols, 2, 1/4 between; C - 5 cols, 2, 1/4 between.
Equipment
: Hardware — PC; Presses — Rotary web; Software — Adobe/Indesign
Delivery Method: Mail, Newsstand, Carrier, Racks
Zip Codes Served: ALL OVER USA

INDIAN (NATIVE AMERICAN)

ADA

CHICKASAW TIMES

(Mthly)
2612 Arlington St, Ste B, Ada, OK, 74820-2905, Pontotoc, USA; tel (580) 332-2977; fax (580) 332-3949; e-mail times.chickasaw@chickasaw.net; web site www.chickasaw.net
Ethnicity: Indian (Native American)
Circulation: 24,000fr; Sworn/Estimate/Non-Audited
Advertising: Open inch rate $10.00
Office Mgr. Vicky Gold
Ed. Tom Bolitho
Mechanical Specifications: Type page 10 x 13; E - 5 cols, 1 11/12, 1/6 between; A - 5 cols, 1 11/12, 1/6 between; C - 5 cols, 1 11/12, 1/6 between.
Equipment
: Hardware — APP/Power Mac 8100, 2-StarMax 3000/200, APP/Mac Performa 6320; Software — Adobe/PageMaker 6.5.
Zip Codes Served: 74820

CANASTOTA

INDIAN COUNTRY TODAY

(Wed)
3059 Seneca Tpke, Canastota, NY, 13032-3532, Madison, USA; tel (315) 829-8355; adv fax (315) 829-8028; ed fax (315) 829-8393; adv e-mail sales@indiancountry.com; ed e-mail editor@indiancountry.com; web site www.indiancountry.com
Ethnicity: Indian (Native American)
Circulation: 13,000pd,; Sworn/Estimate/Non-Audited
Advertising: Open inch rate $16.85
Pub. Ray Haldritter
Sales Mgr. Heather Donovan
Dir., Mktg. Pete Wiezalis
Circ. Mgr. Sabrina Sharkey
Mng. Ed. Ken Polisse
Mechanical Specifications: Type page ll 5/8 x 20; E - 6 cols, 1 13/16, between; A - 6 cols, 1 13/16, between; C - 8 cols, 1 1/6, between.

FLAGSTAFF

NAVAJO-HOPI OBSERVER

(Wed)
2717 N 4th St, Ste 110, Flagstaff, AZ, 86004-1813, Coconino, USA; tel (928) 635-4426; adv tel (928) 226-9696; ed tel (800) 408-4726; fax (928) 226-1115; adv fax (928) 226-1115; ed fax (928) 635-4887; e-mail rsmart@nhonews.com; adv e-mail nhographics@nhonews.com; ed e-mail nhoeditorial@nhonews.com; web site www.nhonews.com
Ethnicity: Indian (Native American)
Circulation: 25pd, 13,757fr; VAC
Advertising: Open inch rate $15.54
Established: 1981
Group: Western News&Info, Inc.
Pub. Debbie White-Hoel
Ed. Ryan Williams
Adv. Exec. Robb Smart
Prodn. Mgr. Mike Carroll
Connie Freson
Mechanical Specifications: SAU Broadsheet
Equipment
: Hardware — APP/Mac.
Delivery Method: Mail, Racks
Zip Codes Served: 86001

KESHENA

MENOMINEE NATION NEWS

(Bi-Mthly)
PO Box 910, Keshena, WI, 54135-0910, Menominee, USA; tel (715) 799-5167; fax (715) 799-5250; e-mail derdmann@mitw.org; adv e-mail mnnads@mitw.org; ed e-mail DErdmann@mitw.org; web site https://www.menominee-nsn.gov
Ethnicity: Indian (Native American)
Circulation: 1,300pd,; Sworn/Estimate/Non-Audited
Advertising: Open inch rate $5.50
Established: 1976
Group: Menominee Indian Tribe of Wisconsin
Ed. Devan Erdmann
Administrative/Design Assistant Melissa Wilber
Delivery Method: Mail, Newsstand
Zip Codes Served: Menominee Nation

LAC DU FLAMBEAU

OUR VOICE NEWSPAPER

(Mthly)
602 Peacepipe Rd, Lac Du Flambeau, WI, 54538, Vilas, USA; tel (715) 588-3303; fax (715) 588-7930; e-mail Info@ldftribe.com; web site www.ldftribe.com
Ethnicity: Indian (Native American)
Circulation: 300pd, 10,000fr; Sworn/Estimate/Non-Audited
Advertising: Open inch rate $8.25
Adv. Sales Abbey Thompson
Ed. Greg Johnson
Mechanical Specifications: Type page 10 1/2 x 15; E - 4 cols, 2 1/4, 1/5 between.

PABLO

CHAR-KOOSTA NEWS

(Thur)
51396 Hwy, 93 N, Pablo, MT, 59855, Lake, USA; tel (406) 275-2830; fax (406) 275-2831; e-mail news4u@charkoosta.com; charkoosta@cskt.org; web site www.charkoosta.com
Ethnicity: Indian (Native American)
Circulation: 4,000pd, 151fr; Sworn/Estimate/Non-Audited
Advertising: Open inch rate $5.00
Office/Dist. Mgr. Robert V. Fyant
Sales Rep. Leslie Camel
Ed. Kim Swaney
Asst. Ed. Sam Sandoval

WHITE EARTH

ANISHINAABEG TODAY

(Mthly)
PO Box 418, White Earth, MN, 56591-0418, Becker, USA; tel (218) 983-3285; fax (218) 983-3641; e-mail today@whiteearth.com; web site www.whiteearth.com
Ethnicity: Indian (Native American)
Circulation: 9,988fr; Sworn/Estimate/Non-Audited
Advertising: Open inch rate $5.50
Ed. Gary Padrta

WILMOT

SISSETON-WAHPETON SIOUX TRIBE

(Wed)
PO Box 5, Wilmot, SD, 57279-0005, Roberts, USA; tel (605) 938-4452; fax (605) 938-4676; e-mail earthskyweb@cs.com; web site www.earthskyweb.com/sota.html
Ethnicity: Indian (Native American)
Circulation: 4,088pd, 0fr; VAC
Advertising: Open inch rate $4.05
Established: 1968
Prodn. Mgr. Charles D. Floro
Mechanical Specifications: Type page 13 3/4 x 21 1/2; E - 6 cols, 2 1/6, 1/8 between; A - 6 cols, 2 1/6, 1/8 between.
Equipment
: Hardware — PC; Software — Adobe/PageMaker 6.5.

IRISH

NEW YORK

IRISH ECHO

(Wed)
165 Madison Ave, Rm 302, New York, NY, 10016-5431, New York, USA; tel (212) 482-4818; fax (212) 482-6569; ed e-mail letters@irishecho.com; web site www.irishecho.com
Ethnicity: Irish
Circulation: 60,000pd, 350fr; Sworn/Estimate/Non-Audited
Advertising: Open inch rate $32.76
Established: 1928
Pub. Mairtin O Muilleoir
Ed. Ray O'Hanlon
Prodn. Mgr. Eileen Murphy
Mechanical Specifications: Type page 9 5/6 x 13 5/6; E - 5 cols, 1 5/6, 1/6 between; A - 5 cols, 1 5/6, 1/6 between; C - 6 cols, 1 1/2, 1/6 between.
Equipment
: Hardware — APP/Power Mac 7300, APP/Power Mac G3; Software — QPS/QuarkXPress 3.32, Adobe/Photoshop 5.0.

IRISH VOICE

(Wed)
875 Avenue of the Americas, Rm 2100, New York, NY, 10001-3586, New York, USA; tel (212) 684-3366; adv tel (800) 582-6642; fax (212) 244-3344; e-mail irvce@aol.com; web site www.irishvoice.com
Ethnicity: Irish
Circulation: 65,000pd,; Sworn/Estimate/Non-Audited
Advertising: Open inch rate $32.75
Established: 1987
Pub. Niall O'Dowd
Adv. Dir. Robert Hogan
Adv. Mgr. Ronan Creaney
Classified Mgr. Naela El Assad
Circ. Mgr. Kevin Mangan
Ed. Debbie McGoldrick
Prodn. Mgr. Genevieve McCarthy
Mechanical Specifications: Type page 9 3/4 x 14; E - 6 cols, between; A - 6 cols, between; C - 7 cols, between.

ORELAND

IRISH EDITION, INC.

(Mthly)
1506 Walnut Ave, Oreland, PA, 19075-1714, Montgomery, USA; tel (215) 886-4900; adv tel (215) 886-4900; ed tel (215) 886-4900; e-mail info@irishedition.com; adv e-mail ads@irishedition.com; ed e-mail info@irishedition.com; web site www.irishedition.com
Ethnicity: Irish
Circulation: 15,000pd,; Sworn/Estimate/Non-Audited
Advertising: Open inch rate $10.00
Established: 1981
Pub. A.R. Byrne
Ed. Jane M. Duffin
Mechanical Specifications: Type page 10 x 15 7/8; E - 5 cols, 2, 1/8 between; A - 5 cols, 2, 1/8 between; C - 5 cols, 2, 1/8 between.
Delivery Method: Mail, Newsstand, Carrier, Racks
Zip Codes Served: PA, NJ & DE

ZION

IRISH AMERICAN NEWS
(Mthly)
PO Box 7, Zion, IL, 60099-0007, Lake, USA; tel (708) 445-0700; e-mail editor@irishamericannews.com; web site www.irishamericannews.com
Ethnicity: Irish
Circulation: 25,000fr; Sworn/Estimate/Non-Audited
Established: 1977
publisher.......................................Cliff Carlson
Mechanical Specifications: Type page 10 1/8 x 12 1/4; E - 5 cols, 1 15/16, 1/8 between; A - 4 cols, 2 3/8, 1/8 between; C - 5 cols, 1 15/16, 1/8 between.
Equipment
: Hardware — apple; Software — Adobe/PageMaker 5.0, QPS/QuarkXPress 3.32.
Delivery Method: Mail, Newsstand, Carrier, Racks
Zip Codes Served: all

ISRAELI

LAS VEGAS

LAS VEGAS ISRAELITE (2 X MTHLY)
PO Box 14096, Las Vegas, NV, 89114, Clark, USA; tel (702) 876-1255; fax (702) 364-1009; e-mail Lasvegasisraelite@cox.net; web site Lvisraelite.com
Ethnicity: Israeli
Circulation: 10,000pd, 33,000fr; Sworn/Estimate/Non-Audited
Advertising: Open inch rate $20.00
Established: 1964
Group: Joseph Jacobs Organization
Digital Platform - Mobile: Apple
Prodn. Mgr.....................................Michael Tell
Delivery Method: Mail, Newsstand, Racks

NEW YORK

THE JERUSALEM POST INTERNATIONAL EDITION
(Sun)
80 Wall St, Ste 715, New York, NY, 10005-3662, New York, USA; tel (212) 742-0505; fax (212) 742-0880; e-mail sigaln@jpost.com; web site www.jpost.com
Ethnicity: Israeli
Circulation: 50,000pd,; Sworn/Estimate/Non-Audited
Advertising: Open inch rate $45.35
Established: 1932
Pub..Mark Ziman
Ed. in Chief................................David Horovitz
Mng. Ed...Steve Linde
Mechanical Specifications: Type page 10 1/4 x 13 1/4; E - 5 cols, 1 3/16, between; A - 5 cols, 1 3/16, between; C - 5 cols, between.
Equipment
: Hardware — PC; Software — Microsoft/Word.

ITALIAN

MILWAUKEE

ITALIAN TIMES
631 E Chicago St, Milwaukee, WI, 53202-5914, Milwaukee, USA; tel (414) 223-2180; adv tel (414) 223-2189; ed tel (414) 223-2189; fax (414) 223-2187; adv fax (414) 223-2187; ed fax (414) 223-2187; e-mail themman@italiancc.org; adv e-mail themman@italiancc.org; ed e-mail themman@italiancc.org; web site www.ICCMilwaukee.com
Ethnicity: Italian
Circulation: 12,000pd,; Sworn/Estimate/Non-Audited
Advertising: Open inch rate $9.50
Established: 1979
Editor.................................Thomas Hemman
Gen. Mgr.................................Patrick Morgan
Mechanical Specifications: Type page 10 x 15; E - 4 cols, 2 1/4, 1/4 between; A - 4 cols, 2 1/4, 1/4 between; C - 4 cols, 2 1/4, 1/4 between.
Equipment
: Hardware — APP/Mac; Presses — WPC; Software — QPS/QuarkXPress 4.04, Microsoft/Word 98, Adobe/Photoshop 5.0, Adobe/Illustrator 8.0.
Delivery Method: Mail, Newsstand, Racks

MONTCLAIR

ITALIAN TRIBUNE
(Thur)
7 N Willow St, Ste 8C, Montclair, NJ, 07042-3591, Essex, USA; tel (973) 860-0101; fax (973) 860-0106; e-mail mail@italiantribune.com; web site www.italiantribune.com
Ethnicity: Italian
Circulation: 95,000pd,; Sworn/Estimate/Non-Audited
Advertising: Open inch rate $20.00
Established: 1931Editions: 52—
Digital Platform - Mobile: Windows
Digital Platform - Tablet: Windows 7
Pub.......................................Buddy Fortunato
Adv. Mgr.......................................Carl Houser
Ed.......................................Marion Fortunato
Managing Editor..........................Joan Alagna
Editor.......................................David Cavaliere
Circ. Mgr...................................Frank Carlone
Associate Editor................Annemarie Casella
Graphics Designer...............Pamela Davidson
Mechanical Specifications: Type page 10 x 12 - 5 cols, 2, 1/6 between; A - 5 cols, 2, 1/6 between; C - 6 cols, 1 7/12, 1/6 between.
Equipment
: Hardware — APP/Mac, PC, APP/Power Mac 7100; Software — In Design
Delivery Method: Mail, Newsstand
Zip Codes Served: 07042 10312 11229
Note: Printed entirely in English

NORWOOD

AMERICA OGGI
(Mon, Tues, Wed, Thur, Fri, Sat, Sun)
475 Walnut St, Norwood, NJ, 07648-1318, Bergen, USA; tel (201) 358-6697; adv tel (201)358-6692; ed tel 212-268-0250; fax (201) 358-9212; adv fax (201) 358-9212; ed fax (201) 358-9212; e-mail americoggi@aol.com; adv e-mail americoggi@aol.com; ed e-mail americoggi@aol.com; web site www.americaoggi.it
Ethnicity: Italian
Circulation: 19,750pd, 2,500fr; Sworn/Estimate/Non-Audited
Advertising: Open inch rate $25.00
Established: 1988
Group: JB Offset Printing Co.
President/Ed.........................Andrea Mantineo
Executive consultant.................Enzo De Blasio
Vice President ....Domenico Delli Carpini
Mechanical Specifications: Type page 11 x 14 1/2; A - 6 cols, 1 9/16, 3/16 between; C - 6 cols, 1 9/16, 3/16 between.
Delivery Method: Mail, Newsstand, Carrier, Racks
Zip Codes Served: national

PHILADELPHIA

THE TIMES
(Bi-Mthly)
170 S Independence Mall W, Ste 718E, Philadelphia, PA, 19106-3302, Philadelphia, USA; tel (215) 592-1713; fax (215) 592-9152; e-mail info@sonsofitalypa.org; web site www.sonsofitalypa.org
Ethnicity: Italian
Circulation: 15,000pd,; Sworn/Estimate/Non-Audited
Advertising: Open inch rate $600.00
Established: 1905
Digital Platform - Mobile: Apple, Android, Windows
Digital Platform - Tablet: Apple iOS
Executive Director.................Michael Paolucci
Mechanical Specifications: Type page 10 x 16.
Equipment; Software — QPS/QuarkXPress 5.0.

SAINT LOUIS

IL PENSIERO (2 X MTHLY)
10001 Stonell Dr, Saint Louis, MO, 63123-5213, Saint Louis, USA; tel (314) 638-3446; fax (314) 638-8222; e-mail ilpensiero@charter.net; web site www.ilpensierostl.com
Ethnicity: Italian
Circulation: 20,000pd, 5,000fr; Sworn/Estimate/Non-Audited
Advertising: Open inch rate $4.00
Pub.......................................Antonio Lombardo
Circ. Mgr.......................................Linda Marino
Ed...A. Gandolfo
Mng. Ed......................................Lina Lombardo

JAPANESE

CHICAGO

CHICAGO SHIMPO
(Fri)
4670 N Manor Ave, Chicago, IL, 60625-3718, Cook, USA; tel (773) 478-6170; fax (773) 478-9360; e-mail emailishimpo@mc.net
Ethnicity: Japanese
Circulation: 5,000pd,; Sworn/Estimate/Non-Audited
Advertising: Open inch rate $16.00
Established: 1945
Pub.......................................Yoshiko Urayama
Mechanical Specifications: Type page 10.125x15
Equipment
: Hardware — APP/Mac

HONOLULU

THE HAWAII HOCHI
(Mon, Tues, Wed, Thur, Fri) (Daily)
917 Kokea St, Honolulu, HI, 96817-4528, Honolulu, USA; tel (808) 845-2255; fax (808) 847-7215; ed e-mail kanaizumi@thehawaiihochi.com; web site www.thehawaiihochi.com
Ethnicity: Japanese
Circulation: 2,000pd,; Sworn/Estimate/Non-Audited
Advertising: Open inch rate $20.00
Established: 1912
Group: The Shizuoka Shimbun (Japan)
Editor, Hawaii Hochi .... Noriyoshi Kanaizumi
Production Manager, Vice President ...... Milton Yamamoto
President and Publisher ....Keiichi Tagata
Mechanical Specifications: Type page 13 3/4 x 21.
Equipment
: Hardware — APP/Mac.
Delivery Method: Mail, Racks
Zip Codes Served: all hawaii zip codes

LOS ANGELES

JAPANESE AMERICAN CITIZENS LEAGUE (EVERY OTHER FRI)
250 E 1st St, Ste 301, Los Angeles, CA, 90012-3819, Los Angeles, USA; tel (213) 620-1767; fax (213) 620-1768; e-mail pc@pacificcitizen.org; marketing @ pacificcitizen.org; adv e-mail busmgr@pacificcitizen.org; ed e-mail circulation @ pacificcitizen.org; web site www.pacificcitizen.org
Ethnicity: Japanese
Circulation: 23,946pd, 287fr; Sworn/Estimate/Non-Audited
Advertising: Open inch rate $30.00
Established: 1929
Circ. Dept..Eva Ting
Ed. ....Caroline Aoyagi Stom
Asst. Ed...Lynda Lin
Reporter ....Nalea Ko
Business Manager...................Staci Hisayasu
Mechanical Specifications: Type page 10 1/4 x 16.
Equipment
: Hardware — APP/Mac; Software — QPS/QuarkXPress.
Delivery Method: Mail

THE RAFU SHIMPO
(Mon, Tues, Wed, Thur, Fri, Sat) (Daily)
701 E 3rd St, Ste 130, Los Angeles, CA, 90013-1789, Los Angeles, USA; tel (213) 629-2231; adv tel (213) 453-9396; ed tel (213) 453-9396; fax (213) 687-0737; e-mail info@rafu.com; adv e-mail ads4rafu@earthlink.net; web site www.rafu.com
Ethnicity: Japanese
Circulation: 9,500pd,; Sworn/Estimate/Non-Audited
Established: 1903
Digital Platform - Mobile: Other
Digital Platform - Tablet: Other
Circ. Mgr.; advertising.................Gail Miyasaki
Ed., English ....Gwen Muranaka
Publisher.................................Michael Komai
Mechanical Specifications: Type page 16 x 21 1/2.
Equipment
: Hardware — APP/Mac; Software — InDesign CS2, CS3 & CS4, including Japanese versions
Delivery Method: Mail, Newsstand
Zip Codes Served: Mailed throughout United States.
Concentrated in Southern California and centered around Los Angeles

SAN DIEGO

SAN DIEGO YU YU
(Bi-Mthly)
4655 Ruffner St, Ste 290, San Diego, CA, 92111-2270, San Diego, USA; tel (858) 576-9016; adv tel (858) 576-9016 x110; ed tel (858) 576-9016 x116; fax (858) 576-7294; adv fax (858) 576-7294; ed fax (858) 576-7294; e-mail info@sandiegoyuyu.com; adv e-mail info@sandiegoyuyu.com; ed e-mail news@sandiegoyuyu.com; web site www.sandiegoyuyu.com
Ethnicity: Japanese
Circulation: 7,000fr; CVC
Established: 1987
Pres. ....Noriko Sato
Delivery Method: Mail, Racks
Zip Codes Served: 92111

SAN JOSE

NIKKEIWEST (BI-WKLY)
123 E San Carlos St, Ste 521, San Jose, CA, 95112-3680, Santa Clara, USA; tel (408) 998-0920; ed tel (916) 837-4178; e-mail questions@nikkeiwest.com; adv e-mail adsales@nikkeiwest.com; ed e-mail editor@nikkeiwest.com; web site www.nikkeiwest.com
Ethnicity: Japanese
Circulation: 3,800pd, 4,200fr; Sworn/Estimate/Non-Audited

Advertising: Open inch rate $7.25
Established: 1992
Group: OtomikMedia Corp.
Digital Platform - Mobile: Android, Windows
Digital Platform - Tablet: Android, Windows 7, Other
Adv. Mgr.. Ron Sakai
Ed...Jeffrey Kimoto
Reporter ....John Sammon
Mechanical Specifications: Type page 13 1/2 x 23; E - 6 cols, 1 9/10, 1/6 between; C - 6 cols, 1 9/10, 1/6 between.
Equipment
: Hardware — Windows 10Pro, AMD/3200, CPU; Software — Adobe/InDesign CS.
Delivery Method: Mail, Racks
Zip Codes Served: 95112, 95128, 94087, 95831, 95822

SEATTLE

THE NORTH AMERICAN POST (HOKUBEI HOCHI)
(Thur)
519 6th Ave S, Ste 200, Seattle, WA, 98104-2878, King, USA; tel (206) 623-0100; fax (206) 625-1424; e-mail info@napost.com; adv e-mail business@napost.com; ed e-mail editor@napost.com; web site www.napost.com
Ethnicity: Japanese
Circulation: 6,000pd,; Sworn/Estimate/Non-Audited
Established: 1902
Pub...Tomio Moriguchi
Editor .... Shihou Sasaki
General Manager........................ Shigeki Kajita
Designer .... Miwa Watanabe
Mechanical Specifications: Type page 10 x 16; E - 5 cols, 1 3/4, between; A - 5 cols, 1 3/4, between; C - 5 cols, 1 1/4, between.
Equipment
: Hardware — PC; Presses — Software; Adobe/PageMaker, Adobe/Photoshop, Adobe/Illustrator.; Software — Adobe/PageMaker, Adobe/Photoshop, Adobe/Illustrator.
Delivery Method: Mail, Racks

KOREAN

CHICAGO

DRAUGAS (DAILY)
4545 W 63rd St, Chicago, IL, 60629-5532, Cook, USA; tel (773) 585-9500; fax (773) 585-8284; e-mail administrator@draugas.org; web site www.draugas.org
Ethnicity: Korean
Circulation: 4,800pd, 100fr; Sworn/Estimate/Non-Audited
Advertising: Open inch rate $7.00
Adv. Mgr.........................Danga MacKericiene
Ed. in Chief.............................. Dalia Cidzikaite
Mechanical Specifications: Type page 15 x 20; E - 7 cols, 2, between; A - 7 cols, 2, between.
Equipment
: Hardware — APP/Mac, IBM; Presses — G, HI; Software — Microsoft/Office, Microsoft/Word.

LINCOLNWOOD

KOREA TIMES (DAILY)
3720 W Devon Ave, Lincolnwood, IL, 60712-1102, Cook, USA; tel (847) 626-0370; fax (847) 626-0351; e-mail koreatimes@irisnet.com; web site www.koreatimes.com
Ethnicity: Korean
Circulation: 50,000pd, 100fr; Sworn/Estimate/Non-Audited
Pres. .... Inkyu Kim
Ed. in Chief.......................................Tustin Lee
Mechanical Specifications: Type page 14 1/2 x 20 1/2.
Equipment
: Hardware — PC.

LONG ISLAND CITY

THE KOREA TIMES (DAILY)
4222 27th St, Long Island City, NY, 11101-4107, Queens, USA; tel (718) 482-1111; fax (718) 784-7381; e-mail hankuk97@aol.com; web site www.koreatimes.com
Ethnicity: Korean
Circulation: 30,000pd,; Sworn/Estimate/Non-Audited
Advertising: Open inch rate $30.00
Pres. .... Hak Y. Shin
Pub... Jaemin Chang

LOS ANGELES

KOREA TIMES (DAILY)
4525 Wilshire Blvd, Los Angeles, CA, 90010-3837, Los Angeles, USA; tel (323) 692-2000; fax (323) 692-2020; e-mail info@koreatimes.com; opinion@koreatimes.com; web site www.koreatimes.com
Ethnicity: Korean
Circulation: 75,000pd, 250fr; Sworn/Estimate/Non-Audited
Advertising: Open inch rate $10.50
Group: Admarket International (Div. of Marcom International, Inc.)
Pub..Jae Min Chang
Gen. Mgr. .... Grant Chang
Adv. Mgr..Michael Hon
Cir. Mgr..Brian Jan
Ed. ....Ki Kwon
Pdn. Mgr...Brian Jon
Equipment
: Hardware — APP/Mac; Software — Claris/FileMaker, Claris/Works, Microsoft/Excel.

LITHUANIAN

CLEVELAND

DIRVA
(Tues) (Every other Tues)
19807 Cherokee Ave, Cleveland, OH, 44119-2825, Cuyahoga, USA; tel (216) 531-8150; fax (216) 531-8428; e-mail dirva@ix.netcom.com; adv e-mail dirva@ix.netcom.com; ed e-mail dirva@ix.netcom.com
Ethnicity: Lithuanian
Circulation: 700pd, 65fr; Sworn/Estimate/Non-Audited
Advertising: Open inch rate $4.00
Established: 1915
Pres of Viltis Inc.
Pub of Dirva...............................A.V. Matulionis
Circ. Mgr.......................................G. Kijauskas
Delivery Method: Mail

NATIVE AMERICAN

WINDOW ROCK

NAVAJO TIMES PUBLISHING COMPANY, INC.
(Thur)
Jct of Hwy 264 & Navajo Rt 12, Window Rock, AZ, 86515, Apache, USA; tel (928) 871-1130; adv tel (928) 871-1145; ed tel (928) 871-1136; fax (928) 871-1159; adv fax (928) 871-1159; ed fax (928) 871-1159; e-mail tarviso@navajotimes.com; adv e-mail vernon@navajotimes.com; ed e-mail editor@navajotimes.com; web site www.navajotimes.com
Ethnicity: Native American
Circulation: 17,000pd,; USPS
Advertising: Open inch rate $14
Established: 1960Editions: 52— 52 per year
Digital Platform - Mobile: Apple
Digital Platform - Tablet: Apple iOS
CEO/ Pub .... Tom Arviso Jr.
Display Adv Mgr.........................Vernon Yazzie
Production Mgr ....Bobby Martin
Circulation Mgr ....Rhonda Joe
Controller.................................Olivia Benally
Class/Legals Mgr......................Josephine Carl
Editor .... Duane Beyal
Equipment: Presses — Heidelberg Harris V-30 6-unit press
Quad-Stack 4-over-4 1-unit; Software — Mac Computers software
Delivery Method: Mail, Newsstand, Carrier

NORWEGIAN-AMERICAN

SEATTLE

NORWEGIAN AMERICAN WEEKLY
(Fri)
7301 5th Ave NE, Ste A, Seattle, WA, 98115-8601, King, USA; tel (206) 784-4617; e-mail naw@na-weekly.com; adv e-mail evan@na-weekly.com; ed e-mail emily@na-weekly.com; web site www.na-weekly.com
Ethnicity: Norwegian-American
Circulation: 3,500pd,; Sworn/Estimate/Non-Audited
Advertising: Open inch rate $15.00
Established: 1889Editions: 47—
Editor-in-chief .... Emily Skaftun
Ed. Asst..Molly Jones
Adv. Mgr...Evan Deam
Mechanical Specifications: Type page 11 x 17.
Delivery Method: Mail
Zip Codes Served: all

PAN ASIAN

HAYMARKET

ASIAN FORTUNE
(Mthly)
PO Box 578, Haymarket, VA, 20168-0578, Prince William, USA; tel (703) 753-8295; e-mail info@asianfortune.com; web site www.asianfortunenews.com
Ethnicity: Pan Asian
Circulation: 1,000pd, 30,000fr; Sworn/Estimate/Non-Audited
Advertising: Open inch rate $85.00
Pres. ....Jay Chen
Adv. Mgr......................................Jizeng Chen
Ed. ....Jennie Ilustre

HOUSTON

INDO AMERICAN NEWS
(Thur)
7457 Harwin Dr, Ste 262, Houston, TX, 77036-2025, Harris, USA; web site www.indoamerican-news.com
Ethnicity: Pan Asian
Circulation: 0pd, 6,979fr; VAC
Established: 1982Jawahar Malhotra

VOICE OF ASIA
(Fri)
6200 Highway 6 S, Ste 225, Houston, TX, 77083-1539, Harris, USA; web site www.voiceofasiaonline.com
Ethnicity: Pan Asian
Circulation: 0pd, 9,900fr; VAC
Advertising: Open inch rate $25.00
Established: 1987
Publisher................................. Koshy Thomas

POLISH

CHICAGO

DZIENNIK ZWAIZKOWY
(Mon, Tues, Wed, Thur, Fri)
5711 N Milwaukee Ave, Chicago, IL, 60646-6215, Cook, USA; tel (773) 763-3343; fax (773) 763-3825; e-mail polish@popmailinsnet.com
Ethnicity: Polish
Circulation: 33,000pd, 1,110fr; Sworn/Estimate/Non-Audited
Advertising: Open inch rate $12.00
Pub..Frank Spula
Gen. Mgr. ....Emily Leszczynski
Adv. Mgr.....................................Bogdan Mazur
Circ. Mgr... Phil Chiaro
Ed. ....Wojciech Bialasiewicz
Mechanical Specifications: Type page 13 1/4 x 21; E - 6 cols, 2 1/8, 3/16 between; A - 6 cols, 2 1/8, 3/16 between; C - 6 cols, 2 1/8, 3/16 between.
Equipment
: Hardware — APP/Mac; Software — Adobe/PageMaker, QPS/QuarkXPress, Adobe/Photoshop.

POLONIA TODAY
(Mthly)
6348 N Milwaukee Ave, Ste 360, Chicago, IL, 60646-3728, Cook, USA; tel (773) 763-1646; fax (773) 763-1796; adv e-mail sales@poloniatoday.com; ed e-mail editor@poloniatoday.com; web site www.poloniatoday.com
Ethnicity: Polish
Circulation: 300,000fr; Sworn/Estimate/Non-Audited
Advertising: Website banners only
Established: 1911
Group: Ameripol Corporation
Ed. ....T. Ron Jasinski-Herbert
Mechanical Specifications: See Banners Page
Equipment
: Hardware — NEC/Pentium MMX; Software — Adobe Muse

ZGODA (2 X MTHLY)
6100 N Cicero Ave, Chicago, IL, 60646-4304, Cook, USA; tel (773) 286-0500; fax (773) 286-0842; e-mail pnazgoda@pna-znp.org; web site www.pna-znp.org
Ethnicity: Polish
Circulation: 65,847fr; Sworn/Estimate/Non-Audited
Pres. .... Frank J. Spula
Gen. Mgr. ....Emily Leszczyaski
Mechanical Specifications: Type page 15 x 11 1/2.

CLIFTON

THE POST EAGLE
(Wed)
800 Van Houten Ave, Clifton, NJ, 07013-2035, Passaic, USA; tel (973) 473-5414; fax (973) 473-3211; e-mail posteagle@aol.com; web site www.posteaglenewspaper.com
Ethnicity: Polish
Circulation: 14,000pd,; Sworn/Estimate/Non-Audited
Advertising: Open inch rate $15.00
Established: 1963
Group: Post Publishing Co.
Ed. ....Christine Witmyer
Mechanical Specifications: Type page 10 1/4 x 14; E - 5 cols, 2, 1/16 between; A - 5 cols, 2,

1/16 between; C - 5 cols, 2, 1/16 between.
Equipment
: Hardware — APP/Mac; Software — Quark Xpress 7.3, Adobe Photoshop CS3, Adobe Illustration, Filemaker Pro 9.0
Delivery Method: Mail

GARFIELD

NOWY DZIENNIK
(Wed) (Weekly)
70 Outwater Ln, Ste 402, Garfield, NJ, 07026-3867, Bergen, USA; tel (212) 594-2266; fax (212) 594-2383; e-mail listy@dziennik.com; web site www.dziennik.com
Ethnicity: Polish
Circulation: 7,650pd, 250fr; Sworn/Estimate/Non-Audited
Advertising: Open inch rate $18.00
Established: 1971
Group: Outwater Media Group, LLC
Commentator................................Tom Deptula
Tom Bagnowski
EIC/Partner................................Nick Sadowski
Mechanical Specifications: Type page 9 3/4 x 14 1/2; E - 5 cols, 1 3/4, between; A - 5 cols, 1 3/4, between; C - 5 cols, 1 3/4, between.
Equipment
: Hardware — APP/Mac Pro iMac; Presses — SLN; Software — QPS/QuarkXPress, Adobe/Photoshop.
Delivery Method: Mail, Newsstand

NORTH BOSTON

POLISH AMERICAN JOURNAL
(Mthly)
PO Box 271, North Boston, NY, 14110-0271, Erie, USA; tel (800) 422-1275; adv tel (800) 422-1275; ed tel (716) 312-8088; e-mail info@polamjournal.com; adv e-mail kbruno@polamjournal.com; ed e-mail editor@polamjournal.com; web site www.polamjournal.com
Ethnicity: Polish
Circulation: 10,100pd, 500fr; USPS
Advertising: Open inch rate $12.50
Established: 1911
Group: Panagraphics, Inc.
Digital Platform - Mobile: Other
Digital Platform - Tablet: Other
Ed.. Mark A. Kohan
Accounting.................................... Kathy Bruno
Assistant Editor....................Thomas Tarapacki
Mechanical Specifications: Type page 10 1/2 x 16; E - 2 cols, 2, 1/8 between; A - 2 cols, 2, 1/8 between; C - 2 cols, 2, 1/8 between.
Equipment; Software — Adobe CS
Delivery Method: Mail
Zip Codes Served: Nationally

ROCHESTER

ALTAD, INC.
(Wed) (bi weekly)
PO Box 80790, Rochester, MI, 48308-0790, Oakland, USA; tel (313) 365-1990; adv tel (313) 365 - 1990; e-mail polishweekly@comcast.net; adv e-mail alicjakarlic@gmail.com; ed e-mail alicjakarlic@gmail.com; web site www.polishweekly.com
Ethnicity: Polish
Circulation: 1,200pd, 200fr; Sworn/Estimate/Non-Audited
Advertising: Open inch rate $12.00
Established: 1904
Ed, in Chief
Publisher.. Alicja Karlic
Mechanical Specifications: Type page 11 x 17; E - 5 cols, 2, 1/2 between; A - 4 cols, 2 1/2, 1/2 between; C - 6 cols, 1 1/2, 1/2 between.
Equipment
: Hardware — APP/Mac; Software — Adobe/PageMaker, Microsoft/Word.

Delivery Method: Mail, Carrier
Zip Codes Served: 48309, 48306, 48212, 48135, 48095,48105, 48127, 48073, 48239, 48042, 48381, 48323, 48310, 48315, 30417, 28560,

SCRANTON

STRAZ
(Mthly)
1006 Pittston Ave, Scranton, PA, 18505-4109, Lackawanna, USA; tel (570) 344-1513; fax (570) 961-5961; e-mail straz@pnu.org; web site www.pnu.org
Ethnicity: Polish
Advertising: Open inch rate $5.50
Ed...Irene Jugan

STEVENS POINT

GWIAZDA POLARNA (EVERY OTHER SAT)
2804 Post Rd, Stevens Point, WI, 54481-6415, Portage, USA; tel (715) 345-0744; fax (715) 345-1913; e-mail pointpub@sbcglobal.net; web site www.gwiazda-polarna.com
Ethnicity: Polish
Circulation: 4,632pd,; Sworn/Estimate/Non-Audited
Advertising: Open inch rate $20.00
Pub.. Monica Pawlack
Ed. in Chief................................. Jacek Hilgier
Ed...Jerry Stolarek
Mechanical Specifications: Type page 10 x 13; E - 3 cols, 3 1/4, 3/16 between; A - 3 cols, 3 1/4, 3/16 between; C - 3 cols, 3 1/4, 3/16 between.
Equipment
: Hardware — APP/Mac; Software — Adobe/PageMaker 6.0.

PORTUGUESE

FALL RIVER

O JORNAL
(Fri)
10 Purchase St, Fall River, MA, 02720-3100, Bristol, USA; tel (508) 678-3844; fax (508) 678-1798; adv e-mail advertising@ojornal.com; ed e-mail editorial@ojornal.com; web site www.ojornal.com
Ethnicity: Portuguese
Circulation: 10,971pd, 51fr; CAC
Advertising: Open inch rate $14.50
Ed...Ric Oliveira
Mng. Ed.................................Lourdes DaSilva
Adv. Dir..Tom Talbot
Equipment; Software — QPS/QuarkXPress.

MIAMI

FLORIDA REVIEW
(Mthly)
905 Brickell Bay Dr, Ste 2CL23, Miami, FL, 33131-2935, Miami-Dade, USA; tel (305) 374-5235; fax (305) 358-9456; e-mail fr@floridareview.com; adv e-mail art@floridareview.com; ad@floridareview.com; web site floridareview.com
Ethnicity: Portuguese
Circulation: 32,000fr; Sworn/Estimate/Non-Audited
Advertising: Open inch rate $30.00
Established: 1985Editions: 2— 2 total Florida Review-Broward; Florida Review-Dade;
Ed. in Chief............................Marcos Ommati
Mng. Ed.................................Marco A. Laureti
Mechanical Specifications: Type page 10 x 12 3/4; E - 4 cols, between; A - 4 cols, between; C - 6 cols, between.

Equipment
: Hardware — PC; Software — Adobe/PageMaker 6.5, Archetype/Corel Draw.

NEWARK

24 HORAS
(Mon, Tues, Wed, Thur, Fri, Sat)
68 Madison St, Newark, NJ, 07105-7109, Essex, USA; tel (973) 817-7400; fax (973) 817-8383; adv e-mail advertising@24horasnewspaper.com; ed e-mail news@24horasnewspaper.com; web site www.24horasnewspaper.com
Ethnicity: Portuguese
Circulation: 12,000pd, 1,000fr; Sworn/Estimate/Non-Audited
Established: 1998Editions: 4,400—
Digital Platform - Mobile: Other
Digital Platform - Tablet: Other
News Ed. ....Joao Santos Matos
Ad. Director.........................Sonia Paula Alves
Marketing Director .... Igor M. Alves
Mechanical Specifications: 10" x 13" tabloid
Delivery Method: Mail, Newsstand, Racks

LUSO AMERICANO
(Wed, Fri)
88 Ferry St, Newark, NJ, 07105-1817, Essex, USA; tel (973) 589-4600; fax (973) 589-3848; e-mail lusoamerican@earthlink.net; web site www.lusoamericano.com
Ethnicity: Portuguese
Circulation: 33,460pd,; Sworn/Estimate/Non-Audited
Advertising: Open inch rate $6.50
Ed. in Chief..................................A.S. Matinho
Opns. Dir..................................... Paul Matinho

ROMANIAN

MIDDLE VILLAGE

NEW YORK MAGAZIN
(Wed)
6442 84th St, Middle Village, NY, 11379-2424, Queens, USA; tel (718) 896-8383; fax (718) 896-8383; e-mail nymagazin@aol.com; web site www.nymagazin.com
Ethnicity: Romanian
Circulation: 5,000fr; Sworn/Estimate/Non-Audited
Gen. Mgr. .... Andreea M. Culian
Ed. ....Grigore L. Culian
Mechanical Specifications: Type page 10 x 14; E - 3 cols, 2 3/4, 3/8 between; A - 3 cols, 2 3/4, 3/8 between; C - 4 cols, 2 1/8, 1/4 between.
Equipment
: Hardware — Corel/WordPerfect Suite 7; Software — Microsoft/Windows 95.

RUSSIAN

BROOKLYN

KURIER
(Fri)
145 Java St, Brooklyn, NY, 11222-1602, Kings, USA; tel (718) 389-3018; fax (718) 389-3140; e-mail kurier@kurierplus.com; web site http://kurierplus.com/
Ethnicity: Russian
Circulation: 30,000pd,; Sworn/Estimate/Non-Audited
Advertising: Open inch rate $10.00
Gen. Mgr. ....Michael Milochnikov
Mechanical Specifications: Type page 10 x 14; E - 4 cols, 2 1/8, 1/4 between; A - 4 cols, 2 1/8, 1/4 between; C - 6 cols, 1 5/8, 1/8 between.

RUSSIAN ADVERTISER
(Fri)
2699 Coney Island Ave, Brooklyn, NY, 11235-5004, Kings, USA; tel (718) 769-3000; fax (718) 769-4700; e-mail reklama2000@online.net; web site www.rusrek.com
Ethnicity: Russian
Circulation: 20,000pd,; Sworn/Estimate/Non-Audited
Advertising: Open inch rate $7.00
Ed. in Chief.........................Michael Trepolskey
Mechanical Specifications: Type page 10 x 14 1/4.

RUSSKAYA REKLAMA
(Fri)
2699 Coney Island Ave, Brooklyn, NY, 11235-5004, Kings, USA; tel (718) 769-3000; fax (718) 769-4700; e-mail reklama2000@yahoo.com; web site www.rronline.ws
Ethnicity: Russian
Circulation: 3,000pd,; Sworn/Estimate/Non-Audited
Advertising: Open inch rate $10.00
Adv. Mgr. .... Guily Gurevich
Ed. in Chief.........................Michael Trepolskey
Mechanical Specifications: Type page 10 x 14 1/4.

VECHERNIY NEW YORK
(Fri)
1529 Voorhies Ave, Brooklyn, NY, 11235-3912, Kings, USA; tel (718) 615-1210; fax (718) 615-1244; e-mail vechny@yahoo.com; web site www.vechny.com
Ethnicity: Russian
Circulation: 15,000pd, 5,000fr; Sworn/Estimate/Non-Audited
Advertising: Open inch rate $5.00
COO ....Irena Zolotora
Circ. Mgr...............................Boris Zaturenskiy
Entertainment Ed.............. Nargis Shekinskaya
News Ed. .... Vseslav Tkachenko
Mechanical Specifications: Type page 9 7/8 x 13 1/2; E - 4 cols, 2 5/16, 3/16 between; A - 4 cols, 2 5/6, 3/16 between.

NEW YORK

NOVOYE RUSSKOYE SLOVO
(Fri)
350 5th Ave, Ste 5301, New York, NY, 10118-0110, New York, USA; tel (646) 218-6900; fax (646) 218-6950; e-mail subscription@nrs.com; adv e-mail advertising@nrs.com; ed e-mail press@nrs.com
Ethnicity: Russian
Circulation: 40,000pd, 3,250fr; Sworn/Estimate/Non-Audited
Advertising: Open inch rate $15.00
Exec. Dir...................................Vladimir Sagal
Ed. ....Valery Weinsberg
Mechanical Specifications: Type page 14 x 20; E - 6 cols, 2 1/4, 1/6 between; A - 8 cols, 1/6 between; C - 8 cols, 1/6 between.
Equipment
: Hardware — PC, APP/Mac; Software — QPS/QuarkXPress, Microsoft/Word.

SAN FRANCISCO

RUSSIAN LIFE
(Sat)
2460 Sutter St, San Francisco, CA, 94115-3016, San Francisco, USA; tel (415) 921-5380; fax (415) 921-8726; e-mail russlife_news@yahoo.com
Ethnicity: Russian
Circulation: 600pd,; Sworn/Estimate/Non-Audited
Advertising: Open inch rate $12.00
Ed. ....George Avisov

SEMINOLE

HOLLYWOOD

THE SEMINOLE TRIBUNE

(Mthly)
3560 N State Road 7, Hollywood, FL, 33021-2105, Broward, USA; tel (954) 966-6300; fax (954) 965-2937; e-mail tribune@semtribe.com; adv e-mail tribune@semtribe.com; ed e-mail tribune@semtribe.com; web site www.seminoletribune.org
Ethnicity: Seminole
Circulation: 4,000pd, 2,000fr; Sworn/Estimate/Non-Audited
Group: The Seminole Tribe of Florida
Senior Ed. .... Kevin Johnson
Mechanical Specifications: Type page 12 1/2 x 20 1/2.
Delivery Method: Mail, Racks

SLOVAK

EAST ORANGE

SOKOL TIMES

(Mthly, Other) (every other month)
276 Prospect St, PO Box 189, East Orange, NJ, 07017-2889, Essex, USA; tel (973) 676-0281; e-mail sokolusahqs@aol.com; adv e-mail None Accepted
Ethnicity: Slovak
Circulation: 2,000fr; Sworn/Estimate/Non-Audited
Advertising: None Accepted
Established: 1905
Prodn. Mgr. .... Milan Kovac
Delivery Method: Mail
Zip Codes Served: All

IMPERIAL

PROSVETA (EVERY OTHER WED)

247 W Allegheny Rd, Imperial, PA, 15126-9786, Allegheny, USA; tel (724) 695-1100; fax (724) 695-1555; e-mail snpj@snpj.com; web site www.snpj.org
Ethnicity: Slovak
Circulation: 50,000pd,; Sworn/Estimate/Non-Audited
Advertising: Open inch rate $8.00
Prodn. Mgr. .... Jay Sedmak
Assoc. Ed. .... Kim Gonzalez
Mechanical Specifications: Type page 13 1/4 x 21 1/2.
Equipment: Software — Adobe/PageMaker 6.5.

JOLIET

KSKJ VOICE

2439 Glenwood Ave, Joliet, IL, 60435-5478, Will, USA; tel (800) 843-5755; fax (815) 741-2002; e-mail janice@kskjlife.com; news@kskjlife.com; web site www.kskjlife.org
Ethnicity: Slovak
Advertising: Open inch rate $9.00
Mng. Ed. .... Al Kath
Ed., English .... Janice Frantz
Mechanical Specifications: Type page 11 x 17; E - 5 cols, 1 1/2, 1/6 between.
Equipment
: Hardware — APP/Mac; Software — Microsoft, QPS/QuarkXPress.

MCMURRAY

NARODNE NOVINY

(Mthly)
351 Valley Brook Rd, McMurray, PA, 15317-3337, Washington, USA; tel (724) 731-0094; fax (724) 731-0145; e-mail info@nsslife.org; web site www.nsslife.org
Ethnicity: Slovak
Circulation: 12,000fr; Sworn/Estimate/Non-Audited
Circ. Mgr. .... David Blazek
Prodn. Mgr. .... Lori Crawley

MIDDLETOWN

JEDNOTA (EVERY OTHER WED)

1001 Rosedale Ave, Middletown, PA, 17057-4835, Dauphin, USA; tel (717) 944-0461; fax (717) 944-3107; ed e-mail editorjednota@yahoo.com; web site www.fcsu.com
Ethnicity: Slovak
Circulation: 500pd, 16,000fr; Sworn/Estimate/Non-Audited
Pub. .... Andrew Rajec
Ed. .... Anthony X. Sutherland

PASSAIC

SLOVAK CATHOLIC FALCON (EVERY OTHER WED)

205 Madison St, Passaic, NJ, 07055-5224, Passaic, USA; tel (973) 777-4010; fax (973) 779-8245; e-mail sokol205@aol.com; web site www.slovakcatholicsokol.org
Ethnicity: Slovak
Circulation: 11,200pd,; Sworn/Estimate/Non-Audited
Ed. .... Daniel F. Tanzone

SPANISH

PILGRIM GARDENS

EL HISPANO

(Thur)
PO Box 396, Pilgrim Gardens, PA, 19026-0396, Delaware, USA; tel (484) 472-6059; adv tel 484 4726059; ed tel 484 4726059; fax (484) 472-8153; adv fax 484 4728153; ed fax 484 4728153; e-mail hispads@aol.com; web site www.el-hispano.com
Ethnicity: Spanish
Circulation: 16,390fr; Sworn/Estimate/Non-Audited
Advertising: $31.00
Established: 1976
Co-pub. .... Sara Lopez
Ad. Director .... Madelyn Madary
Marketing Director .... Phillip Madary
Equipment
: Hardware — n/a; Presses — n/a; Software — Idesign
Delivery Method: Racks

SWEDISH

NEW CANAAN

NORDSTJERNAN (2 X MTHLY)

PO Box 1710, New Canaan, CT, 06840-1710, Fairfield, USA; tel (212) 490-3900; fax (203) 299-0381; e-mail info@nordstjernan.com; web site www.nordstjernan.com
Ethnicity: Swedish
Circulation: 19,000pd,; Sworn/Estimate/Non-Audited
Advertising: Open inch rate $21.00
Established: 1872
Circ. Mgr. .... Metta Barslund
Ed. .... Ulf E. Martensson
Prodn. Mgr. .... Eva Joenneo
Equipment
: Hardware — APP/Mac, PC; Software — Adobe/Illustrator, Adobe/PageMaker, Adobe/Photoshop.

UKRAINIAN

PARSIPPANY

SVOBODA

(Fri)
2200 State Rt 10, Parsippany, NJ, 07054-5304, Morris, USA; tel (973) 292-9800; adv tel (973) 292-9800 x3040; ed tel (973) 292-9800 x3049; fax (973) 644-9510; adv fax (973) 644-9510; ed fax (973) 644-9510; e-mail svoboda@svoboda-news.com; adv e-mail adukr@optonline.net; ed e-mail svoboda@svoboda-news.com; web site www.svoboda-news.com
Ethnicity: Ukrainian
Circulation: 7,524pd, 170fr; Sworn/Estimate/Non-Audited
Advertising: Open inch rate $10.00
Established: 1893
Group: Ukrainian National Association
Delivery Method: Mail, Newsstand

THE UKRAINIAN WEEKLY

(Sun)
2200 State Rt 10, Parsippany, NJ, 07054-5304, Morris, USA; tel (973) 292-9800; fax (973) 644-9510; e-mail staff@ukrweekly.com; adv e-mail adukr@optonline.net; ed e-mail staff@ukrweekly.com; web site www.ukrweekly.com
Ethnicity: Ukrainian
Circulation: 5,000pd,; Sworn/Estimate/Non-Audited
Advertising: Open inch rate $10.00
Established: 1933
Group: Ukrainian National Association
Adv./Circ. Mgr. .... Walter Honcharyk
Ed. in Chief .... Romana Hadzewycz
Mechanical Specifications: Type page 11 1/2 x 16; E - 4 cols, 2 1/3, 1/6 between; C - 4 cols, 2 1/3, 1/6 between.
Equipment
: Hardware — APP/Mac; Software — Microsoft/Word, QPS/QuarkXPress, Adobe/Photoshop, InDesign
Delivery Method: Mail, Newsstand, Carrier
Zip Codes Served: national and international

VIETNAMESE

SAN JOSE

VIET MERCURY

(Fri)
750 Ridder Park Dr, San Jose, CA, 95131-2432, Santa Clara, USA; tel (408) 920-5000; fax (408) 920-2748; e-mail letters@mercurynews.com; web site www.mercurynews.com/mld/vietmerc
Ethnicity: Vietnamese
Adv. Mgr. .... Ham Xuan Nguyen
Circ. Mgr. .... Terry Thompson
Ed. .... De Tren
Mng. Ed. .... Hoan Nguyen
Mechanical Specifications: Type page 10 13/16 x 12 3/4; E - 5 cols, 2 1/16, 1/16 between; A - 5 cols, 2 1/16, 1/16 between; C - 8 cols, 1 7/32, 1/17 between.
Equipment
: Hardware — APP/Mac; Presses — G; Software — QPS/QuarkXPress 2.3, Adobe/Illustrator 6.0, Adobe/Photoshop 4.0.

SEATTLE

NORTHWEST VIETNAMESE NEWS

6951 Martin Luther King Jr Way S, Ste 205, Seattle, WA, 98118-354, King, USA; tel (206) 722-6984; web site www.nvnorthwest.com
Ethnicity: Vietnamese

WESTMINSTER

NGUOI VIET NEWS

(Mon, Tues, Wed, Thur, Fri, Sat, Sun)
14771 Moran St, Westminster, CA, 92683-5553, Orange, USA; tel (714) 892-9414; fax (714) 894-1381; e-mail news@nguoi-viet.com; web site www.nguoi-viet.com
Ethnicity: Vietnamese
Circulation: 9,762pd, 0fr; VAC
Advertising: Open inch rate $6.50
Established: 1978
Pub. .... Do Baohanah
Pham Phu Thien Giao
Ed. in Chief .... Ngo Nhan Dung
Equipment
: Hardware — IBM, PC.

GAY AND LESBIAN NEWSPAPERS IN THE UNITED STATES

CALIFORNIA

LOS ANGELES

FRONTIERS IN LA
(Wed)
5657 Wilshire Blvd, Los Angeles, CA, 90036-3736, Los Angeles, USA; web site http://www.frontiersla.com
Circulation: 30pd, 27,888fr; VACDavid Stern

SAN DIEGO

GAY & LESBIAN TIMES
(Thur)
3433 Camino Del Rio S, Ste 300, San Diego, CA, 92108-3901, San Diego, USA; tel (619) 299-6397; fax (619) 299-3430; e-mail editor@uptownpub.com; ed e-mail editor@uptownpub.com; web site www.gaylesbiantimes.com
Circulation: 15,700fr; VAC
Publisher........................Michael G. Portantino
Art Dir...Sloan Gomez
Mechanical Specifications: Type page 10 1/2 x 13.
Equipment: Hardware — APP/Mac; Presses — WPC; Software — QPS/QuarkXPress, Adobe/PageMaker.

GAY SAN DIEGO
(Fri) (biweekly, every other Friday)
123 Camino De La Reina, Ste 202E, San Diego, CA, 92108-3006, San Diego, USA; tel (619) 519-7775; adv tel (619) 961-1951; ed tel (619) 961-1960; e-mail david@sdcnn.com; ed e-mail editor@sdcnn.com; web site http://gay-sd.com/
Circulation: 12,433fr; CVC
Advertising: $80 (smallest modular rate)
Established: 2009
Group: San Diego Community News Netwrok
Digital Platform - Mobile: Apple, Android, Windows, Blackberry
Digital Platform - Tablet: Apple iOS, Android, Windows 7, Blackberry Tablet OS, Kindle, Nook, Kindle Fire
Pub./Circ. Mgr............................David Mannis
Ed. ....Morgan Hurley
Adv. Mgr................................Mike Rosensteel
Mechanical Specifications: Type page 10" x 14.58"; 5 cols
Equipment: Hardware — Apple, PC; Software — Adobe Suite; Indesign
Delivery Method: Mail, Carrier, Racks
Zip Codes Served: San Diego County

SAN FRANCISCO

BAY AREA REPORTER
(Thur)
395 9th St, San Francisco, CA, 94103-3831, San Francisco, USA; tel (415) 861-5019; fax (415) 861-8144; e-mail information@ebar.com; web site www.ebar.com
Circulation: 47pd, 26,163fr; VAC
Advertising: Open inch rate $26.50
Established: 1971
Pub...Thomas E. Horn
Gen. Mgr...........................Michael Yamashita
Classified Adv. Mgr................David MacBrayer
Ed. ....Cynthia Laird
Mechanical Specifications: Type page 10 x 16; E - 5 cols, 1 7/8, 1/8 between; A - 5 cols, 1 7/8, 1/8 between; C - 5 cols, 1 7/8, 1/8 between.
Equipment: Hardware — 6-APP/Power Mac.

COLORADO

DENVER

OUT FRONT
(Wed) (First & Third Wednesdays)
3535 Walnut St, Denver, CO, 80205-2433, Denver, USA; tel (303) 477-4000; fax 303-325-2642; e-mail info@outfrontonline.com; adv e-mail advertising@outfrontonline.com; ed e-mail editorial@outfrontonline.com; web site http://www.outfrontonline.com/
Circulation: 1,000pd, 20,000fr; Sworn/Estimate/Non-Audited
Established: 1976
Pub...................................Jerry Cunningham
Ed. ....Berlin Sylvestre
Art Dir...Colby Brumit
Marketing ....Jay Duque
Sales..Dustin Krier
Sales...Jordan Jacobs
Associate Pub................................Ryan King
Equipment: Hardware — APP/Mac; Software — QPS/QuarkXPress, Microsoft/Word.
Delivery Method: Mail, Racks

DISTRICT OF COLUMBIA

WASHINGTON

WASHINGTON BLADE
1712 14th St NW, Washington, DC, 20009-5070, District Of Columbia, USA; tel (202) 747-2077; fax (202) 747-2070; e-mail info@washblade.com; adv e-mail lbrown@washblade.com; ed e-mail knaff@washblade.com; web site www.washblade.com
Circulation:; Sworn/Estimate/Non-Audited
Established: 1969
Circ. Mgr......................................Scott Gartey
Editor ....Kevin Naff
Art Dir...Rob Boeger
Michael Key
Publisher.......................................Lynn Brown
Sr. News Editor ....Lou Chibbaro
Dir Sales & Mktg...................Stephen Rutgers
Classified Advertising........Phillip G Rockstroh
Mechanical Specifications: Type page 9 3/4 x 11 1/2; E - 4 cols, 2 1/4, 1/6 between; A - 4 cols, 2 1/4, 1/6 between; C - 4 cols, 2 1/4, 1/6 between.

FLORIDA

ORLANDO

WATERMARK MEDIA
(Thur) (Every other Thur)
414 N Ferncreek Ave, Orlando, FL, 32803-5432, Orange, USA; tel (407) 481-2243; fax (407) 481-2246; e-mail editor@watermarkonline.com; sales@watermarkonline.com; web site www.watermarkonline.com
Circulation: 20,000fr; Sworn/Estimate/Non-Audited
Established: 1994
Pub...Tom Dyer
CFO..Rick Claggett
Sales Acct. Mgr...........................Don Williams
Ed. ....Steve Blanchard

WILTON MANORS

SOUTH FLORIDA GAY NEWS
(Wed)
2520 N Dixie Hwy, Wilton Manors, FL, 33305-1247, Broward, USA; tel 954-530-4970; fax 954-530-7943; web site www.southfloridagaynews.com
Circulation: 0pd, 10fr; Sworn/Estimate/Non-Audited
Established: 2010
Publisher..Norm Kent

ILLINOIS

CHICAGO

BLACK LINES
5315 N Clark St, Ste 192, Chicago, IL, 60640-2290, Cook, USA; tel (773) 871-7610; fax (773) 871-7609; ed e-mail editor@windycitymediagroup.com; web site www.windycitymediagroup.com
Circulation:; Sworn/Estimate/Non-Audited
Office Mgr. ....Rob Olson
Adv. Mgr.......................................Terri Klinsky
Ed. ....Tracy Baim
Mechanical Specifications: Type page 8 x 10 1/2.
Equipment: Hardware — APP/Mac.

EN LA VIDA
5443 N Broadway St, Ste 101, Chicago, IL, 60640-1703, Cook, USA; tel (773) 871-7610; fax (773) 871-7609; ed e-mail editor@windycitymediagroup.com; web site www.windycitymediagroup.com
Circulation:; Sworn/Estimate/Non-Audited
Ed. ....Tracy Baim
Mechanical Specifications: Type page 8 x 10 1/2.
Equipment: Hardware — APP/Mac.

NIGHTSPOTS
(Wed)
5315 N Clark St, Ste 192, Chicago, IL, 60640-2290, Cook, USA; tel (773) 871-7610; fax (773) 871-7609; e-mail nightspots@windycitymediagroup.com; adv e-mail advertising@windycitymediagroup.com; ed e-mail nightspots@windycitymediagroup.com; web site www.windycitymediagroup.com
Circulation: 5,000fr; Sworn/Estimate/Non-Audited
Established: 1990
Pub..Tracy Baim
Mng. Ed...................................Kirk Williamson
Mechanical Specifications: Type page 5 1/2 x 8.
Equipment: Hardware — APP/Mac.

WINDY CITY TIMES
(Wed) (Daily online)
5315 N Clark St, Ste 192, Chicago, IL, 60640-2290, Cook, USA; tel (773) 871-7610; fax (773) 871-7609; e-mail publisher@windycitymediagroup.com; adv e-mail advertising@windycitymediagroup.com; ed e-mail editor@windycitymediagroup.com; calendar@windycitymediagroup.com; theater@windycitymediagroup.com; graphics@windycitymediagroup.com; web site www.windycitymediagroup.com
Circulation: 0pd, 10,000fr; Sworn/Estimate/Non-Audited
Established: 1985
Digital Platform - Mobile: Apple
Digital Platform - Tablet: Apple iOS
Adv. Pub.......................................Terri Klinsky
Circ. Dir.....................................Jean Albright
Publisher, Exec. Ed.........................Tracy Baim
Mng. Ed ....Andrew Davis
Mechanical Specifications: Type page 10 inch x 10 inch full page
Delivery Method: Racks
Zip Codes Served: Chicago and Cook County, including 60640, 60613, 60660, 60614, 60616, etc.

INDIANA

INDIANAPOLIS

THE WORD
(Mthly) (Last Fri of the month)
110 E Washington St, Ste 1402, Indianapolis, IN, 46204-3727, Marion, USA; tel (317) 632-8840; e-mail ted@midwestword.com; adv e-mail ted@midwestword.com; web site www.thegayword.com
Circulation: 100pd, 13,900fr; Sworn/Estimate/Non-Audited
Advertising: Open inch rate $8.00
Established: 1990
Group: Word PublicationsEditions: 1—
Digital Platform - Mobile: Apple, Android, Windows
Digital Platform - Tablet: Apple iOS, Android
Publisher.................................Ted Fleischaker
Mechanical Specifications: Type page 10 1/4 x 13; E - 4 cols, 2 1/2, between; A - 4 cols, 2 1/2, between; C - 4 cols, 2 1/2, between.
Equipment: Hardware — 4-APP/Macs, Gateway/2000.
Delivery Method: Newsstand, Racks
Zip Codes Served: we go to 7 states

KANSAS

WICHITA

LIBERTY PRESS
(Mthly)
PO Box 16315, Wichita, KS, 67216-0315, Sedgwick, USA; tel (316) 652-7737; fax none; ed e-mail editor@libertypress.net; web site www.libertypress.net
Circulation: 150pd, 5,000fr; Sworn/Estimate/Non-Audited
Established: 1994
Ed. ....Kristi Parker
Mechanical Specifications: Type page 8 3/8 x 10 7/8.
Delivery Method: Mail, Racks
Zip Codes Served: all of KS

MASSACHUSETTS

BOSTON

BAY WINDOWS
(Thur)
28 Damrell St, Ste 204, Boston, MA, 02127-3077, Suffolk, USA; tel 617-464-7280; adv tel 617 464 7280 x202; ed tel 617 464 7280 x215; fax 617-464-7286; adv fax 617 464 7286; ed fax 617 464 7286; e-mail jcoakley@baywindows.com; adv e-mail jcoakley@baywindows.com; ed e-mail sue.baywindows@gmail.com; web site www.baywindows.com

Circulation: 125pd, 20,000fr; Sworn/Estimate/Non-Audited
Advertising: Open inch rate $14.75
Established: 1983
Jeff Coakley
Sue O'ConnellCo-Pub.s
Mechanical Specifications: Type page 10 x 12.75
Delivery Method: Mail, Racks
Zip Codes Served: New England

MICHIGAN

LIVONIA

BETWEEN THE LINES

(Thur)
11920 Farmington Rd, Livonia, MI, 48150-1724, Wayne, USA; tel (734) 293-7200; fax (734) 293-7201; e-mail info@pridesource.com; adv e-mail sales@pridesource.com; ed e-mail editor@pridesource.com; editor@pridesource.com; web site www.pridesource.com
Circulation: 17,000fr; Sworn/Estimate/Non-Audited
Advertising: Open inch rate $95.00
Established: 1993
Group: Pride Source Media Group
Digital Platform - Mobile: Apple, Android
Digital Platform - Tablet: Apple iOS, Android, Kindle Fire
Publisher/Editor in Chief.......... Susan Horowitz
Adv. Dir..................................... Jan Stevenson
Entertainment Ed.................... Chris Azzopardi
Webmaster/IT Mgr. .... Kevin Bryant
Delivery Method: Racks
Zip Codes Served: 48150

MINNESOTA

EDINA

LAVENDER

7701 York Ave S, Ste 225, Edina, MN, 55435-5884, Hennepin, USA; tel (612) 436-4660; fax (612) 436-4685; e-mail info@lavendermagazine.com; web site www.lavendermagazine.com
Circulation:; Sworn/Estimate/Non-Audited
Pub................................. Stephen J. Rocheford
Adv. Sales Dir............................... Barry Leavitt
Mng. Ed.............................. Stephen Boatner
Mechanical Specifications: Type page 8 1/16 x 10 5/16; E - 3 cols, 2 1/4, 1/8 between; A - 3 cols, 2 1/4, 1/8 between; C - 4 cols, 1 5/6, 1/8 between.

NEVADA

LAS VEGAS

QVEGAS

401 S Maryland Pkwy, Las Vegas, NV, 89101-7206, Clark, USA; tel 702-727-1800; fax (702) 650-0641; e-mail publisher@qvegas.com; web site www.qvegas.com
Circulation:; Sworn/Estimate/Non-Audited
Established: 1978
Group: QLV Holdings, Inc.
Publisher... Russ White
Mechanical Specifications: Type page 9 1/2 x 12 1/4; E - 4 cols, 2 3/16, 1/4 between; A - 4 cols, 2 3/16, 1/4 between; C - 4 cols, 2 3/16, 1/4 between.
Equipment: Hardware — Hardware PC, APP/Mac; Presses — Presses G/Community; Software — Software Adobe/InDesign, Webb Offset.

NEW YORK

NEW YORK

GAY CITY NEWS

(Thur)
515 Canal St, New York, NY, 10013-1330, New York, USA; tel 212-229-1890; fax 2152-229-2790; e-mail editor@gaycitynews.com; adv e-mail ads@communitymediallc.com; web site www.gaycitynews.com
Circulation: 47,000fr; Sworn/Estimate/Non-Audited
Established: 2002
Group: NYC Community Media, LLC
Publisher............................ Jennifer Goodstein
Assoc. Pub.................................. Troy Masters
Ed. in Chief............................... Paul Schindler
Mechanical Specifications: Type page 10 x 14; E - 4 cols, 2 1/4, between; A - 6 cols, 2 1/2, between; C - 6 cols, 1 1/2, between.
Delivery Method: Racks
Zip Codes Served: 10013, 10024, 10009, 10014

ROCHESTER

GAY ALLIANCE

(Mthly)
100 College Ave, Ste 100, Rochester, NY, 14607-1073, Monroe, United States; tel 5852448640; adv tel 5852448640; ed tel 5852448640; fax (585) 244-8246; e-mail jeffreym@gayalliance.org; adv e-mail jeffm@gayalliance.org; ed e-mail jeffm@gayalliance.org; web site www.gayalliance.org
Circulation: 680pd, 5,500fr; Sworn/Estimate/Non-Audited
Established: 1971
Group: Gay Alliance of the Genesee Valley
Digital Platform - Mobile: Android, Windows
Digital Platform - Tablet: Apple iOS, Android, Windows 7
Ed. .... Susan Jordan
Graphic Designer....................... Jim Anderson
Jeff Myers
Mechanical Specifications: Type page 10 x 15; E - 4 cols, 2 1/4, between; A - 4 cols, 2 1/4, between; C - 5 cols, 2, between.
Equipment: Hardware — Mac/G4 10.1; Software — Adobe/PageMaker, Microsoft/Word 6.0.
Delivery Method: Mail, Racks

NORTH CAROLINA

CHARLOTTE

Q NOTES

(Sat)
920 Central Ave, Charlotte, NC, 28204-2028, Mecklenburg, USA; tel (704) 531-9988; fax (704) 531-1361; e-mail info@goqnotes.com; ed e-mail editor@goqnotes.com; web site goqnotes.com
Circulation: 9,000fr; Sworn/Estimate/Non-Audited
Advertising: Open inch rate $7.00
Established: 1986
Pub.. Jim Yarbrough
Ed. .... Matt Comer
Prodn. Mgr. .... Lainey Millen
Mechanical Specifications: Type page 10 1/4 x 12 1/4; E - 4 cols, 2 3/8, 3/16 between; A - 4 cols, 2 3/8, 3/16 between; C - 4 cols, 2 3/8, 3/16 between.
Delivery Method: Mail, Newsstand, Carrier, Racks
Zip Codes Served: Most of NC & part of SC

OHIO

CLEVELAND

GAY PEOPLE'S CHRONICLE

(Fri) (Every Other Fri)
PO Box 391464, Cleveland, OH, 44139-8464, Cuyahoga, USA; tel (216) 769-4528; adv tel 216-769-4528; e-mail chronicle@chronohio.com; adv e-mail displayads@chronohio.com; ed e-mail editor@chronohio.com; web site www.gaypeopleschronicle.com
Circulation: 300pd, 11,500fr; Sworn/Estimate/Non-Audited
Established: 1985
Pub.. Patti Harris
Adv. Mgr.................................. David A. Ebbert
Circ. Mgr............................ Anthony Glassman
Ed./Mng. Ed.......................... Patricia G. Harris
Assoc. Ed.. Brian DeWitt
Mechanical Specifications: Type page 10 x 15 1/2.

COLUMBUS

STONEWALL COLUMBUS

(Tues)
1160 N High St, Columbus, OH, 43201-2411, Franklin, USA; tel (614) 299-7764; adv tel (614) 930-2262; ed tel (614) 930-2264; fax (614) 299-4408; adv fax (614) 299-4408; ed fax (614) 299-4408; e-mail info@stonewallcolumbus.org; adv e-mail info@lavenderlistings.com; ed e-mail info@stonewallcolumbus.org; web site www.stonewallcolumbus.org
Circulation: 0pd, 4,000fr; Sworn/Estimate/Non-AuditedEditions: 0—
Executive Director....................... Karla Rothan
Adv. Mgr............................. Michele Fregonas
Ed. .... Herman John
Equipment: Hardware — APP/Mac; Software — Indesign
Zip Codes Served: 43201-99 43001-99

PENNSYLVANIA

MIDDLETOWN

CENTRAL VOICE

(Bi-Mthly)
20 S Union St, Middletown, PA, 17057-1445, Dauphin, USA; tel (717) 944-4628; fax (717) 944-2083; e-mail fpizzoli@aol.com; adv e-mail Davebrown@pressandjournal.com; ed e-mail fpizzoli@aol.com; web site www.thecentralvoice.com
Circulation:; Sworn/Estimate/Non-Audited
Established: 2003Frank Pizzoli
Delivery Method: Mail

PHILADELPHIA

PHILADELPHIA GAY NEWS

(Fri)
505 S 4th St, Philadelphia, PA, 19147-1506, Philadelphia, USA; tel (215) 625-8501 ext 200; adv tel (215) 625-8501 ext 212; ed tel (215) 625-8501 ext 206; fax (215) 925-6437; adv fax (215) 925-6437; ed fax (215) 925-6437; e-mail pgn@epgn.com; adv e-mail prab@epgn.com; ed e-mail jen@epgn.com; web site www.epgn.com
Circulation: 17,000fr; Sworn/Estimate/Non-Audited
Advertising: NA
Established: 1976
Pub.. Mark Segal
Officer Manager........................... Don Pignolet
Advertising Manager.................... Prab Sandhu
Mechanical Specifications: 10.125x11.35
Equipment: Hardware — Hardware APP/Mac.
Delivery Method: Mail, Racks
Zip Codes Served: various

PITTSBURGH

OUT

(Mthly)
2366 Golden Mile Hwy, # 195, Pittsburgh, PA, 15239-2710, Allegheny, USA; tel (724) 733-0828; fax (412) 381-7989; e-mail out@outonline.com; web site www.outonline.com
Circulation: 2,000pd, 12,000fr; Sworn/Estimate/Non-Audited
Ed Molnar-Strejcek
Tony Molnar-StrejcekCo-Pub.s

TENNESSEE

NASHVILLE

OUT & ABOUT NASHVILLE

(Mthly)
3951 Moss Rose Dr, Nashville, TN, 37216-2925, Davidson, USA; tel (615) 596-6210; fax 615-246-2787; e-mail sales@outandaboutnashville.com; adv e-mail sales@outandaboutnashville.com; ed e-mail editor@outandaboutnashville.com; web site www.outandaboutnashville.com
Circulation: 15,000fr; Sworn/Estimate/Non-Audited
Established: 2002
Group: Out & About Nashville, Inc
Pub.. Jerry Jones
Managing Print Editor................. James Grady
Managing Digital Editor .... Joe Brant
Mechanical Specifications: Type page 10 x 11 1/4; E - 4 cols, 2 1/2, 1/4 between.
Delivery Method: Mail, Racks
Zip Codes Served: Nashville

TEXAS

DALLAS

DALLAS VOICE

(Fri)
4145 Travis St, Fl 3, Dallas, TX, 75204-1840, Dallas, USA; tel (214) 754-8710; fax (214) 969-7271; e-mail editor@dallasvoice.com; advertising@dallasvoice.com; adv e-mail advertising@dallasvoice.com; ed e-mail editor@dallasvoice.com; advertising@dallasvoice.com; web site www.dallasvoice.com
Circulation: 13,357fr; Sworn/Estimate/Non-Audited
Established: 1984
Pub.. Robert Moore
Adv. Dir....................................... Leo Cusimano
Ed. .... Tammey Nish
Circ. Mgr............................... Maryann Ramirez
Mechanical Specifications: Type page 10 3/8 x 12 1/2; E - 4 cols, between; A - 4 cols, between; C - 5 cols, between.
Equipment: Hardware — Hardware APP/Mac; Software — Software QPS/QuarkXPress.
Delivery Method: Mail, Newsstand

HOUSTON

HOUSTON VOICE

(Thur)
PO Box 540892, Houston, TX, 77254-0892, Harris, USA; tel (281) 410-8642; adv tel

(281) 410-8642; ed tel (281) 410-8642; e-mail media@houstonvoice.org; adv e-mail media@houstonvoice.org; ed e-mail steven@houstonvoice.org; web site www.houstonvoice.org
Circulation: 10,000fr; Sworn/Estimate/Non-Audited
Advertising: 15.00
Established: 1973
Group: Houston Voice Media
Digital Platform - Mobile: Apple, Android, Windows
Digital Platform - Tablet: Apple iOS, Android, Windows 7, Blackberry Tablet OS, Kindle
Publisher....Justin Galloway
Co-Publisher, Entertainment Editor....Steven Tillotta
Opinion Editor....Nikki Araguz
Political Editor....Jody Miller

VERMONT

BENSON

OUT IN THE MOUNTAINS
PO Box 287, Benson, VT, 05731-0287, Rutland, USA; tel (802) 275-5027; e-mail editor@oitm.org; web site www.oitm.org
Circulation:; Sworn/Estimate/Non-AuditedJohn Fedor-Cunningham
Gabe Christian
Equipment: Hardware — APP/Mac; Software — Microsoft/Word 98, QPS/QuarkXPress.

WASHINGTON

SEATTLE

SEATTLE GAY NEWS
(Fri)
1605 12th Ave, Ste 31, Seattle, WA, 98122-2487, King, USA; tel (206) 324-4297; fax (206) 322-7188; e-mail sgn2@sgn.org; web site www.sgn.org
Circulation: 13,500fr; Sworn/Estimate/Non-Audited
Advertising: Open inch rate $30.00
Pub....George Bakan
Circ. Mgr....Rick McKinnon
Mechanical Specifications: Type page 11 x 17.
Equipment: Hardware — IBM.
Delivery Method: Newsstand, Racks

HISPANIC NEWSPAPERS IN THE UNITED STATES

ARIZONA

PHOENIX

LA VOZ
(Wed)
7600 N 16th St, Ste 150, Phoenix, AZ, 85020-4487, Maricopa, USA; tel (602) 252-5331; adv tel (602) 444-3800; ed tel (602) 444-3800; fax (602) 444-3894; adv fax (602) 444-3999; ed fax (602) 444-3893; adv e-mail lisa.simpson@lavozarizona.com; web site www.lavozarizona.com
Circulation: 0pd, 58,277fr; VAC
Advertising: Open inch rate $27.00
Established: 2000
Publisher....Elvira Espinoza
Ed....Luis Manuel Ortiz
Delivery Method: Carrier, Racks

PRENSA HISPANA
(Wed)
809 E Washington St, Ste 209, Phoenix, AZ, 85034-1018, Maricopa, USA; tel (602) 256-2443; fax (602) 256-2644; e-mail prensahispana@qwest.net; web site www.prensahispanaaz.com
Circulation: 65,000fr; Sworn/Estimate/Non-Audited
Pres....Manny Garcia
Adv. Mgr., Classified....Lety Miranda-Garcia

YUMA

BAJO EL SOL
(Fri)
2055 S Arizona Ave, Yuma, AZ, 85364-6549, Yuma, USA; tel (928) 539-6800; adv tel (928) 539-6829; ed tel (928) 539-6850; fax (928) 343-1009; adv fax (928) 343-6928; ed fax (928) 782-7369; e-mail nationals@yumasun.com; adv e-mail nationals@yumasun.com; ed e-mail jvaughn@yumasun.com; web site www.bajoelsol.com
Circulation: 15,000fr; CAC
Advertising: Open inch rate $17.65 gross
Established: 1991
Group: Yuma Sun, Inc.Editions: 15,000-
Digital Platform - Mobile: Apple, Android, Windows, Blackberry
Digital Platform - Tablet: Apple iOS, Android, Windows 7, Blackberry Tablet OS, Kindle Fire
Ntl. Acct Mgr....Darlene Firestone
Mechanical Specifications: Type page 9.889 x 21
Equipment: Hardware — APP/Mac; Presses — 9-G/Urbanite; Software — DTI/AdSpeed 4.1, Adobe/Illustrator 7.0, Adobe/Photoshop 5.0.
Mechanical Specifications: Type page 9 3/4 x 11 1/2; E - 4 cols, between; A - 4 cols, between; C - 4 cols, between.
Equipment: Hardware — IBM, APP/Mac; Software — Adobe Indesign
Delivery Method: Racks
Zip Codes Served: 77008,77006,77254,77002
Delivery Method: Carrier, Racks
Zip Codes Served: 85364, 85365, 92283, 85367, 85356, 85352, 85350, 85336, 85349

ARKANSAS

FAYETTEVILLE

LA PRENSA LIBRE
(Thur)
212 N East Ave, Fayetteville, AR, 72701-5225, Washington, USA; tel (479) 530-9313; fax (479) 684-5570; adv fax (479) 251-8206; e-mail acueva@nwaonline.com; adv e-mail acueva@nwaonline.com; ed e-mail lpleditor@nwaonline.com; web site www.laprensanwa.com
Circulation: 15,000fr; Sworn/Estimate/Non-Audited
Advertising: Open inch rate $10.50
Established: 1996
Group: Northwest Arkansas Newspapers LLC WEHCO Media, Inc.
Digital Platform - Mobile: Apple
Ed....Jenser Morales
Acct. Exec....Alma Cueva
Delivery Method: Newsstand, Racks
Zip Codes Served: 72767, 72765, 72701, 72703, 72704, 72756, 72758, 72712

LITTLE ROCK

EL LATINO
(Thur)
201 E Markham St, Fl 2, Little Rock, AR, 72201-1627, Pulaski, USA; tel (501)-375-2985
Circulation: 7pd, 4,605fr; VAC
Group: Arkansas Times Limited Partnership

CALIFORNIA

ACTON

ACTON-AGUA DULCE NEWS
(Mon)
3413 Soledad Canyon Rd, Acton, CA, 93510-1974, Los Angeles, USA; tel (661) 269-1169; fax (661) 269-2139; e-mail aadnews@joycemediainc.com; help@joycemediainc.com; web site www.aadnews.com
Circulation: 1,000pd, 575fr; Sworn/Estimate/Non-Audited
Advertising: Open inch rate $10.97
Established: 1969
Pub....John Joyce
Ed....M. Gayle Joyce
Mng. Ed....Micah Joyce
Data Supvr....Jana Miranda
Mechanical Specifications: Type page 11 x 17.
Equipment: Hardware — APP/Mac, HP; Presses — RKW; Software — Adobe/PageMaker 6.5.

BAKERSFIELD

EL MEXICALO
931 Niles St, Bakersfield, CA, 93305-4535, Kern, USA; tel (661) 323-9334; fax (661) 323-6951; e-mail elmexicalonews@aol.com
Circulation:; Sworn/Estimate/Non-Audited
Advertising: Open inch rate $15.99
Pub....Esther H. Manzano
Gen. Mgr....Erlinda H. Manzano
Ed....Tony H. Manzano
Mechanical Specifications: Type page 12 3/4 x 21; E - 6 cols, 2, 1/6 between; A - 6 cols, 2, 1/6 between; C - 6 cols, 2, 1/6 between.
Equipment: Hardware — APP/Mac; Software — Adobe/PageMaker 4.0.

EL POPULAR
(Fri)
404 Truxtun Ave, Bakersfield, CA, 93301-5316, Kern, USA; tel (661) 325-7725; adv tel (661) 325-1351; ed tel (661) 325-1351; fax (661) 325-1351; adv fax (661) 325-1351; ed fax (661) 325-1351; e-mail pub@elpopularnews.com; adv e-mail ads@elpopularnews.com; ed e-mail news@elpopularnews.com; web site www.elpopularnews.com
Circulation: 100pd, 23,000fr; CVC
Advertising: Open inch rate $17.50
Established: 1983
Group: EL POPULAR, INC
Digital Platform - Mobile: Apple
Digital Platform - Tablet: Apple iOS
President/Publisher....George Camacho
Founding Publisher/Editor....Raul Camacho
Associate Editor....Lupe Medina
Mechanical Specifications: Six (6) columns x 21.50-inch column dept
Full page: 10.25" wide x 21.5" depth
Delivery Method: Carrier, Racks
Zip Codes Served: 93203, 93215, 93241, 93250, 93263, 93280, 93301, 93304, 93305, 93306, 93307, 93308, 93309,

CAMARILLO

SIGLO 21
(Wed)
550 Paseo Camarillo, Camarillo, CA, 93010-5900, Ventura, USA
Circulation: 16,361fr; VAC

CHULA VISTA

EL LATINO
(Fri)
1550 Broadway, Ste U, Chula Vista, CA, 91911-4091, San Diego, USA; tel (619) 426-1491; fax (619) 426-3206; e-mail fanny@ellatino.net; web site www.ellatinoonline.com
Circulation: 80,000fr; Sworn/Estimate/Non-Audited
Advertising: Open inch rate $53.50
Established: 1988
Pub./Pres....Fanny Miller

LA PRENSA SAN DIEGO
(Fri)
651 3rd Ave, Ste C, Chula Vista, CA, 91910-5720, San Diego, USA; tel (619) 425-7400; adv tel (619) 425-7401; adv fax (619) 425-7402; e-mail laprensa@ix.netcom.com; adv e-mail laprensa@ix.netcom.com; web site www.laprensa-sandiego.org
Circulation: 25,000fr; Sworn/Estimate/Non-Audited
Advertising: Open inch rate $28.00
Established: 1976
Publisher....Art Castanares
Mechanical Specifications: Type page 11 1/2 x 21; E - 6 cols, 1 13/16, 1/8 between; A - 6 cols, 1 13/16, 1/8 between; C - 8 cols, 1 1/3, 3/32 between.
Equipment: Hardware — IBM; Software — Adobe/PageMaker.
Delivery Method: Newsstand, Racks
Zip Codes Served: 91902; 91910; 91911; 91932; 91945; 91950; 91977; 91978; 92008; 92021; 92022; 92025; 92026; 92027; 92054; 92055; 92056; 92069; 92083; 92084; 92101; 92102; 92104; 92111; 92113; 92114; 92117; 92126; 92153; 92173

ESCONDIDO

HISPANOS UNIDOS
(Fri)
411 W 9th Ave, Escondido, CA, 92025-5034, San Diego, USA; tel (760) 740-9561; fax (760) 737-3035; e-mail info@hispanosnews.com; web site www.hispanosnews.com

Circulation: 26,000fr; Sworn/Estimate/Non-Audited
Advertising: Open inch rate $24.00
Pub. .... Ana Hannagan
Prodn. Mgr. .... Jaime A. Castaneda
Mechanical Specifications: Type page 11 3/4 x 21; E - 6 cols, 1.828, 0.1564 between; A - 6 cols, 1.828, 0.1564 between; C - 6 cols, 1.828, 0.1564 between.
Equipment: Hardware — PC; Software — QPS/QuarkXPress 4.2.

FRESNO

VIDA EN EL VALLE
(Wed)
1626 E St, Fresno, CA, 93706-2006, Fresno, USA; tel (559) 441-6780; adv tel (559) 441-6769; ed tel (559) 441-6781; fax (559) 441-6790; adv fax (559) 441-6790; ed fax (559) 441-6790; e-mail aguajardo@vidaenelvalle.com; adv e-mail bgutierrez@vidaenelvalle.com; ed e-mail jesparza@vidaenelvalle.com; web site www.vidaenelvalle.com
Circulation: 156,842fr; AAM
Advertising: 46.90 National/36.50 Local retail
Established: 1990
Group: The McClatchy Company
Pub. .... Valerie Bender
Office Mgr. .... Morgie Rice
Ed. .... Juan Esparza Loera
Prodn. Mgr. .... Anna Ramseier
Mechanical Specifications: Braodsheet
Delivery Method: Carrier, Racks

LOS ANGELES

BELL GARDENS SUN
(Thur)
111 S Avenue 59, Los Angeles, CA, 90042-4211, Los Angeles, USA; tel (323) 341-7970; fax (323) 341-7976; e-mail service@egpnews.com; adv e-mail advertise@egpnews.com; ed e-mail editorial@egpnews.com; web site www.egpnews.com
Circulation: 2pd, 6,973fr; CVC
Advertising: N/A
Established: 1945
Pub. .... Dolores Sanchez
Adv. Mgr. .... Jonathan M. Sanchez
Circ. Mgr. .... Bianca Sanchez
Mng. Ed. .... Gloria Alvarez
Prodn. Mgr. .... Elizabeth Chou
Mechanical Specifications: Type page 13 x 21; 6 cols
Equipment: Hardware — 3-Dell/Dell Dimension 2400 Series, 5-APP/IMac 24, 4-APP/MAC G5; Software — Adobe/Illustrator CS, Adobe/InDesign CS, Microsoft/Office 2008, 4-QPS/QuarkXPress 7.0, 6-Adobe/Photoshop CS, Adobe CS3.
Delivery Method: Mail, Carrier, Racks
Zip Codes Served: 90001, 90011, 90012, 90014, 90022, 90023, 90031, 90032, 90033, 90040, 90041, 90042, 90063, 90065, 91731, 91732, 91733, 91744, 91754, 91766, 91770, 91803, 91104

CITY TERRACE COMET
(Thur)
111 S Avenue 59, Los Angeles, CA, 90042-4211, Los Angeles, USA; tel (323) 341-7970; fax (323) 341-7976; e-mail service@egpnews.com; adv e-mail advertise@egpnews.com; ed e-mail editorial@egpnews.com; web site www.egpnews.com
Circulation: 4pd, 2,971fr; CVC
Advertising: N/A
Established: 1945
Pub. .... Dolores Sanchez
Adv. Mgr. .... Jonathan M. Sanchez
Circ. Mgr. .... Bianca Sanchez
Mng. Ed. .... Gloria Alvarez
Prodn. Mgr. .... Elizabeth Chou
Mechanical Specifications: Type page 13 x 21; 6 cols
Equipment: Hardware — 3-Dell/Dell Dimension 2400 Series, 5-APP/IMac 24, 4-APP/MAC G5; Software — Adobe/Illustrator CS, Adobe/InDesign CS, Microsoft/Office 2008, 4-QPS/QuarkXPress 7.0, 6-Adobe/Photoshop CS, Adobe CS3.
Delivery Method: Mail, Carrier, Racks
Zip Codes Served: 90001, 90011, 90012, 90014, 90022, 90023, 90031, 90032, 90033, 90040, 90041, 90042, 90063, 90065, 91731, 91732, 91733, 91744, 91754, 91766, 91770, 91803, 91104

COMMERCE COMET
(Thur)
111 S Avenue 59, Los Angeles, CA, 90042-4211, Los Angeles, USA; tel (323) 341-7970; fax (323) 341-7976; e-mail service@egpnews.com; adv e-mail advertise@egpnews.com; ed e-mail editorial@egpnews.com; web site www.egpnews.com
Circulation: 5pd, 6,475fr; CVC
Advertising: N/A
Established: 1945
Pub. .... Dolores Sanchez
Adv. Mgr. .... Jonathan M. Sanchez
Circ. Mgr. .... Bianca Sanchez
Mng. Ed. .... Gloria Alvarez
Prodn. Mgr. .... Elizabeth Chou
Mechanical Specifications: Type page 13 x 21; 6 cols
Equipment: Hardware — 3-Dell/Dell Dimension 2400 Series, 5-APP/IMac 24, 4-APP/MAC G5; Software — Adobe/Illustrator CS, Adobe/InDesign CS, Microsoft/Office 2008, 4-QPS/QuarkXPress 7.0, 6-Adobe/Photoshop CS, Adobe CS3.
Delivery Method: Carrier, Racks
Zip Codes Served: 90001, 90011, 90012, 90014, 90022, 90023, 90031, 90032, 90033, 90040, 90041, 90042, 90063, 90065, 91731, 91732, 91733, 91744, 91754, 91766, 91770, 91803, 91104

EASTSIDE SUN
(Thur)
161 S Avenue 24, Los Angeles, CA, 90031-2247, Los Angeles, USA; tel (323) 221-1092; adv tel (323) 221-1090; ed tel (323) 221-1092; fax (323) 221-1096; e-mail service@egpnews.com; adv e-mail advertise@egpnews.com; ed e-mail editorial@egpnews.com; web site www.egpnews.com
Circulation: 131pd, 43,944fr; CVC
Advertising: N/A
Established: 1945
Digital Platform - Mobile: Apple
Pub. .... Dolores Sanchez
Mng. Ed. .... Gloria Alvarez
Advertising/Office Manager .... Bianca Preciado
Mechanical Specifications: Type page 13 x 21; 6 cols
Equipment: Hardware — 3-Dell/Dell Dimension 2400 Series, 5-APP/IMac 24, 4-APP/MAC G5; Software — Adobe/Illustrator CS, Adobe/InDesign CS, Microsoft/Office 2008, 4-QPS/QuarkXPress 7.0, 6-Adobe/Photoshop CS, Adobe CS3.
Delivery Method: Carrier, Racks
Zip Codes Served: 90001, 90011, 90012, 90014, 90022, 90023, 90031, 90032, 90033, 90040, 90041, 90042, 90063, 90065, 91731, 91732, 91733, 91744, 91754, 91766, 91770, 91803, 91104

ELA BROOKLYN-BELVEDERE COMET
(Thur)
111 S Avenue 59, Los Angeles, CA, 90042-4211, Los Angeles, USA; tel (323) 341-7970; fax (323) 341-7976; e-mail service@egpnews.com; adv e-mail advertise@egpnews.com; ed e-mail editorial@egpnews.com; web site www.egpnews.com
Circulation: 4pd, 2,971fr; CVC
Advertising: N/A
Established: 1945
Pub. .... Dolores Sanchez
Adv. Mgr. .... Jonathan M. Sanchez
Circ. Mgr. .... Bianca Sanchez
Mng. Ed. .... Gloria Alvarez
Prodn. Mgr. .... Elizabeth Chou
Mechanical Specifications: Type page 13 x 21; 6 cols
Equipment: Hardware — 3-Dell/Dell Dimension 2400 Series, 5-APP/IMac 24, 4-APP/MAC G5; Software — Adobe/Illustrator CS, Adobe/InDesign CS, Microsoft/Office 2008, 4-QPS/QuarkXPress 7.0, 6-Adobe/Photoshop CS, Adobe CS3.
Delivery Method: Carrier, Racks
Zip Codes Served: 90001, 90011, 90012, 90014, 90022, 90023, 90031, 90032, 90033, 90040, 90041, 90042, 90063, 90065, 91731, 91732, 91733, 91744, 91754, 91766, 91770, 91803, 91104

EXCELSIOR LOS ANGELES
(Fri)
523 N Grand Ave, Los Angeles, CA, 90012-2149, Los Angeles, USA; tel (714) 796-4300; fax (714) 796-4316; adv fax (714) 796-4316; ed fax (714) 796-4319; e-mail adesantos@ocregister.com; adv e-mail excelsiorads@ocregister.com; web site www.ocexcelsior.com
Circulation: 52,529fr; Sworn/Estimate/Non-Audited
Advertising: Open inch rate $48.78
Group: Southern California News Group
Pub. .... Orlando Ramirez
Monette Ryan
Ed. .... Carlos Avilés
Zip Codes Served: Orange County

HOY FIN DE SEMANA
(Sat)
202 W 1st St, Los Angeles, CA, 90012-4299, Los Angeles, USA; adv tel (213) 237-3453; adv e-mail hcabral@hoyllc.com; web site www.vivalohoy.com
Circulation: 813,384fr; CAC
Group: Tronc, Inc.
Adv. Dir. .... Hector Cabral
Pub. .... Ronaldo Moran
Division Mgr. .... Deborah Albright

HOY LLC
(Mon, Fri, Sat) (weekly)
145 S Spring St, Fl 2, Los Angeles, CA, 90012-4053, Los Angeles, USA; tel (213) 237-4388; adv tel (213) 237-3453; ed tel (213) 237-3374; e-mail amaciel@hoyllc.com; adv e-mail hcabral@hoyllc.com; ed e-mail jmaciel@vivelohoy.com; web site www.hoylosangeles.com
Circulation: 1,000,400fr; Sworn/Estimate/Non-Audited
Established: 2004
Group: Tribune Media Group
Tronc, Inc.
Los Angeles Times Media GroupEditions: 5-Hoy (Mon and Fri) and 3 Hoy Fin de Semana (Weekend edition on Saturdays)
Digital Platform - Mobile: Apple, Android
Digital Platform - Tablet: Apple iOS
Gen. Mgr. .... John Trainor
Sales Director .... Michael Roenna
Managing Editor .... Fernando Diaz
Director of Sales Strategy .... Kim Benz
General Manager Hoy Los Angeles .... Roaldo Moran
Director Editorial Hoy/ Los Angeles ... Alejandro Maciel
Editor Adjunto Hoy/ Los Angeles Javier T. Calle
Delivery Method: Mail, Racks
Zip Codes Served: 90000
Note: Hoy is published Mo and Fr and Hoy Fin de Semana (weekend edition) is published on Saturday.

HOY LOS ANGELES
(Mon, Fri)
202 W 1st St, Los Angeles, CA, 90012-4299, Los Angeles, USA; adv tel (213) 237-3453; adv e-mail hcabral@hoyllc.com; web site http://www.hoylosangeles.com
Circulation: 135,361fr; CAC
Group: Tronc, Inc.
Adv. Dir. .... Hector Cabral
Division Mgr. .... Deborah Albright
Pub. .... Ronaldo Moran

LA OPINION - CONTIGO
(Mon, Wed, Thur, Fri, Sat, Sun)
700 S Flower St, Los Angeles, CA, 90017-4101, Los Angeles, USA
Circulation: 0pd, 581,129fr; AAM
Group: impreMedia LLC
Adv. Dir. .... Patricia Prieto
Gen. Mgr, ... Damian Mazzotta
Circ. Dir. .... Greg Hatch

LA PRENSA DE LOS ANGELES
(Sat) (once a month)
5554 Carlton Way, Apt 4, Los Angeles, CA, 90028-6847, Los Angeles, USA; tel (323) 572-0106; e-mail laprensa@laprensadelosangeles.com; adv e-mail sales@laprensadelosangeles.com; ed e-mail comentarios@laprensadelosangeles.com; web site www.laprensadelosangeles.com
Circulation: 10,000pd, 30,000fr; Sworn/Estimate/Non-Audited
Advertising: $75 1/4 page black and white (not sold by the inch)
Established: 1999
Ed. .... Carlos Groppa
Delivery Method: Newsstand, Racks

MEXICAN AMERICAN SUN
(Thur)
111 S Avenue 59, Los Angeles, CA, 90042-4211, Los Angeles, USA; tel (323) 341-7970; fax (323) 341-7976; e-mail service@egpnews.com; adv e-mail advertise@egpnews.com; ed e-mail editorial@egpnews.com; web site www.egpnews.com
Circulation: 186pd, 15,789fr; CVC
Advertising: N/A
Established: 1945
Pub. .... Dolores Sanchez
Adv. Mgr. .... Jonathan M. Sanchez
Circ. Mgr. .... Bianca Sanchez
Mng. Ed. .... Gloria Alvarez
Prodn. Mgr. .... Elizabeth Chou
Mechanical Specifications: Type page 13 x 21; 6 cols
Equipment: Hardware — 3-Dell/Dell Dimension 2400 Series, 5-APP/IMac 24, 4-APP/MAC G5; Software — Adobe/Illustrator CS, Adobe/InDesign CS, Microsoft/Office 2008, 4-QPS/QuarkXPress 7.0, 6-Adobe/Photoshop CS, Adobe CS3.
Delivery Method: Mail, Racks
Zip Codes Served: 90001, 90011, 90012, 90014, 90022, 90023, 90031, 90032, 90033, 90040, 90041, 90042, 90063, 90065, 91731, 91732, 91733, 91744, 91754, 91766, 91770, 91803, 91104

MONTEBELLO COMET
(Thur)
111 S Avenue 59, Los Angeles, CA, 90042-4211, Los Angeles, USA; tel (323) 341-7970; fax (323) 341-7976; e-mail service@egpnews.com; adv e-mail advertise@egpnews.com; ed e-mail editorial@egpnews.com; web site www.egpnews.com
Circulation: 4pd, 16,971fr; CVC
Advertising: N/A
Established: 1945
Pub. .... Dolores Sanchez
Adv. Mgr. .... Jonathan M. Sanchez
Circ. Mgr. .... Bianca Sanchez
Mng. Ed. .... Gloria Alvarez
Prodn. Mgr. .... Elizabeth Chou
Mechanical Specifications: Type page 13 x 21; 6 cols
Equipment: Hardware — 3-Dell/Dell Dimension 2400 Series, 5-APP/IMac 24, 4-APP/MAC G5; Software — Adobe/Illustrator CS, Adobe/InDesign CS, Microsoft/Office 2008, 4-QPS/QuarkXPress 7.0, 6-Adobe/Photoshop CS, Adobe CS3.
Delivery Method: Mail, Carrier, Racks
Zip Codes Served: 90001, 90011, 90012, 90014, 90022, 90023, 90031, 90032, 90033, 90040, 90041, 90042, 90063, 90065, 91731, 91732, 91733, 91744, 91754, 91766, 91770, 91803, 91104

MONTEREY PARK COMET
(Thur)
111 S Avenue 59, Los Angeles, CA, 90042-4211, Los Angeles, USA; tel (323) 341-7970; fax (323) 341-7976; e-mail service@egpnews.com; adv e-mail advertise@egpnews.com; ed e-mail editorial@egpnews.com; web site www.egpnews.com
Circulation: 4pd, 6,971fr; CVC
Advertising: N/A
Established: 1945
Pub....Dolores Sanchez
Adv. Mgr....Jonathan M. Sanchez
Circ. Mgr....Bianca Sanchez
Mng. Ed....Gloria Alvarez
Prodn. Mgr....Elizabeth Chou
Mechanical Specifications: Type page 13 x 21; 6 cols
Equipment: Hardware — 3-Dell/Dell Dimension 2400 Series, 5-APP/IMac 24, 4-APP/MAC G5; Software — Adobe/Illustrator CS, Adobe/InDesign CS, Microsoft/Office 2008, 4-QPS/QuarkXPress 7.0, 6-Adobe/Photoshop CS, Adobe CS3.
Delivery Method: Mail, Carrier, Racks
Zip Codes Served: 90001, 90011, 90012, 90014, 90022, 90023, 90031, 90032, 90033, 90040, 90041, 90042, 90063, 90065, 91731, 91732, 91733, 91744, 91754, 91766, 91770, 91803, 91104

NORTHEAST SUN
(Thur)
111 S Avenue 59, Los Angeles, CA, 90042-4211, Los Angeles, USA; tel (323) 341-7970; fax (323) 341-7976; e-mail service@egpnews.com; adv e-mail advertise@egpnews.com; ed e-mail editorial@egpnews.com; web site www.egpnews.com
Circulation: 10pd, 18,465fr; CVC
Advertising: N/A
Established: 1945
Group: Postmedia Network Inc.
Pub....Dolores Sanchez
Adv. Mgr....Jonathan M. Sanchez
Circ. Mgr....Bianca Sanchez
Mng. Ed....Gloria Alvarez
Prodn. Mgr....Elizabeth Chou
Mechanical Specifications: Type page 13 x 21; 6 cols
Equipment: Hardware — 3-Dell/Dell Dimension 2400 Series, 5-APP/IMac 24, 4-APP/MAC G5; Software — Adobe/Illustrator CS, Adobe/InDesign CS, Microsoft/Office 2008, 4-QPS/QuarkXPress 7.0, 6-Adobe/Photoshop CS, Adobe CS3.
Delivery Method: Mail, Carrier, Racks
Zip Codes Served: 90001, 90011, 90012, 90014, 90022, 90023, 90031, 90032, 90033, 90040, 90041, 90042, 90063, 90065, 91731, 91732, 91733, 91744, 91754, 91766, 91770, 91803, 91104

VERNON SUN
(Thur)
111 S Avenue 59, Los Angeles, CA, 90042-4211, Los Angeles, USA; tel (323) 341-7970; fax (323) 341-7976; e-mail service@egpnews.com; adv e-mail advertise@egpnews.com; ed e-mail editorial@egpnews.com; web site www.egpnews.com
Circulation: 4pd, 2,471fr; CVC
Advertising: N/A
Established: 1945
Pub....Dolores Sanchez
Adv. Mgr....Jonathan M. Sanchez
Circ. Mgr....Bianca Sanchez
Mng. Ed....Gloria Alvarez
Prodn. Mgr....Elizabeth Chou
Mechanical Specifications: Type page 13 x 21; 6 cols
Equipment: Hardware — 3-Dell/Dell Dimension 2400 Series, 5-APP/IMac 24, 4-APP/MAC G5; Software — Adobe/Illustrator CS, Adobe/InDesign CS, Microsoft/Office 2008, 4-QPS/QuarkXPress 7.0, 6-Adobe/Photoshop CS, Adobe CS3.
Delivery Method: Mail, Carrier, Racks
Zip Codes Served: 90001, 90011, 90012, 90014, 90022, 90023, 90031, 90032, 90033, 90040, 90041, 90042, 90063, 90065, 91731, 91732, 91733, 91744, 91754, 91766, 91770, 91803, 91104

WAVE PUBLICATIONS
(Thur)
3731 W Olympic Blvd, Ste 840, Los Angeles, CA, 90019-2030, Los Angeles, USA; tel (323) 556-5720; fax (213) 835-0584; e-mail newsroom@wavepublication.com; web site www.wavenewspapers.com
Circulation: 100,000fr; Sworn/Estimate/Non-Audited
Advertising: Open inch rate $70.00
Established: 1912
Pub....Pluria Marshall

WYVERNWOOD CHRONICLE
(Thur)
111 S Avenue 59, Los Angeles, CA, 90042-4211, Los Angeles, USA; tel (323) 341-7970; fax (323) 341-7976; e-mail service@egpnews.com; adv e-mail advertise@egpnews.com; ed e-mail editorial@egpnews.com; web site www.egpnews.com
Circulation: 1,975fr; CVC
Advertising: N/A
Established: 1945
Pub....Dolores Sanchez
Adv. Mgr....Jonathan M. Sanchez
Circ. Mgr....Bianca Sanchez
Mng. Ed....Gloria Alvarez
Prodn. Mgr....Elizabeth Chou
Mechanical Specifications: Type page 13 x 21; 6 cols
Equipment: Hardware — 3-Dell/Dell Dimension 2400 Series, 5-APP/IMac 24, 4-APP/MAC G5; Software — Adobe/Illustrator CS, Adobe/InDesign CS, Microsoft/Office 2008, 4-QPS/QuarkXPress 7.0, 6-Adobe/Photoshop CS, Adobe CS3.
Delivery Method: Mail, Carrier, Racks
Zip Codes Served: 90001, 90011, 90012, 90014, 90022, 90023, 90031, 90032, 90033, 90040, 90041, 90042, 90063, 90065, 91731, 91732, 91733, 91744, 91754, 91766, 91770, 91803, 91104

NORWALK

EL CLASIFICADO
(Tues, Wed)
11205 Imperial Hwy, Norwalk, CA, 90650-2229, Los Angeles, USA; tel 1800-242-2527; adv tel 866-893-0028; ed tel 888-261-9772; web site www.elclasificado.com
Circulation: 504,401fr; CVC
Established: 1988
Digital Platform - Mobile: Apple
Digital Platform - Tablet: Apple iOSMartha C. De la Torre
Delivery Method: Racks
Zip Codes Served: 92126, 92129, 92131, 92134, 92136, 92139, 92624, 92629, 92630, 92637, 92651, 92653, 92656, 92672, 92673, 92675, 92677, 92688, 92691, 92692, 92694, 93206, 93215, 93249, 93250, 93263, 93280, 93616, 93618, 93625, 93631, 93646, 93648, 93654, 93657, 93662, 93673, 93610, 93636, 93637, 93638, 92313, 92316, 92324, 92376, 92377, 92501, 92503, 92504, 92505, 92506, 92507, 92508, 92509, 92521, 92220, 92223, 92230, 92320, 92518, 92543, 92544, 92545, 92551, 92553, 92555, 92557, 92567, 92582, 92583, 90033, 90063, 90006, 90017, 90019, 90057, 93013, 93101, 93103, 93111, 93117, 93420, 93433, 93434, 93436, 93444, 93445, 93454, 93455, 93458

RIVERSIDE

LA PRENSA
(Fri)
3512 14th St, Riverside, CA, 92501-3841, Riverside, USA; tel (909) 806-3201; e-mail oramirez@pe.com; web site www.laprensaenlinea.com
Circulation: 95,478fr; VAC
Advertising: Open inch rate $35.70
Group: Southern California News Group
Ed....Orlando Ramirez
Deputy Ed....Enrique Carrion
Adv. Acc. Exec....Monette Ryan
Ed....Carlos Avilés

SACRAMENTO

EL HISPANO
(Wed)
1903 21st St, Sacramento, CA, 95811-6813, Sacramento, USA; tel (916) 442-0267; fax (916) 442-2818; e-mail plarenas2@yahoo.com
Circulation: 15,000fr; Sworn/Estimate/Non-Audited
Advertising: Open inch rate $15.29
Ed....Patrick Larenas
Mechanical Specifications: Type page 13 1/16 x 21; E - 6 cols, 2, between; A - 6 cols, 2, between.
Equipment: Hardware — APP/Mac; Software — Adobe/PageMaker, Adobe/Photoshop.

SALINAS

EL SOL
(Sat)
123 W Alisal St, Salinas, CA, 93901-2644, Monterey, USA; tel (831) 424-2221; ed tel (831) 754-4272; fax (831) 754-4286; e-mail ssancen@salinas.gannett.com; web site www.thecalifornian.com
Circulation: 29,940fr; CVC
Advertising: Open inch rate $21.68
Established: 1968
Gen. Mgr....Terry Feinberg
Ed....Silvia Sancen
Mechanical Specifications: Type page 11 5/8 x 21; E - 6 cols, 1 3/4, between; A - 6 cols, 1 3/4, between; C - 6 cols, 1 1/8, between.
Equipment: Hardware — PC; Presses — G/Urbanite; Software — QPS/QuarkXPress 4.1.
Delivery Method: Racks

SAN DIEGO

EL SOL DE SAN DIEGO
2629 National Ave, San Diego, CA, 92113-3617, San Diego, USA; tel (619) 233-8496; fax (619) 233-5017; e-mail elsolsd@aol.com; web site www.elsoldesandiego.com
Circulation:; Sworn/Estimate/Non-Audited
Advertising: Open inch rate $20.00
Adv. Mgr....Lynn Johansen
Ed....Julie J. Rocha
Mechanical Specifications: Type page 10 13/16 x 13; E - 5 cols, 2 1/16, 1/8 between; A - 5 cols, 2 1/16, 1/8 between; C - 5 cols, 2 1/16, 1/8 between.
Equipment: Hardware — PC.
Zip Codes Served: 92170

HOY SAN DIEGO - THE SAN DIEGO UNION TRIBUNE
(Sat)
600 B St, Ste 1201, San Diego, CA, 92101-4505, San Diego, USA; tel 619-299-4141; web site http://www.sandiegouniontribune.com/hoy-san-diego/
Circulation: 80,920pd,; AAM
Publisher and Editor....Jeff Light
President and General Manager Phyllis Pfeiffer
Managing Editor....Lora Cicalo

VIDA LATINA - THE SAN DIEGO UNION TRIBUNE
(Fri)
600 B St, Ste 1201, San Diego, CA, 92101-4505, San Diego, USA; tel (619)299-4141; web site http://www.sandiegouniontribune.com/hoy-san-diego/vida-latina/
Circulation: 30,500pd,; AAM
Pub. & Ed....Jeff Light
Pres. & Gen. Mgr....Phyllis Pfeiffer
V. Pres. Adv....Paul Ingegneri

SAN FRANCISCO

EL BOHEMIO NEWS
(Fri)
3288 21st St, # 116, San Francisco, CA, 94110-2423, San Francisco, USA; tel (415) 469-9579; fax (415) 970-8853; e-mail bohemio@ix.netcom.com; web site www.elbohemionews.info
Circulation: 22,472fr; CVC
Advertising: Open inch rate $30.00
Adv. Mgr....Rosalina Contreras
Circ. Mgr....Benny Velarde
Ed....Fernando Rosado
Mechanical Specifications: Type page 13 x 21; E - 6 cols, 2 1/4, 1/6 between.
Equipment: Hardware — APP/Mac; Software — Adobe/PageMaker, Great Works.

EL MENSAJERO
(Sun)
333 Valencia St, Ste. 410, San Francisco, CA, 94103-3500, San Francisco, USA; tel (415) 206-7230; adv tel (415) 206-7230; ed tel (415) 206-7230; fax (415) 206-7238; e-mail comentarios@elmensajero.com; adv e-mail michael.howard@elmensajero.com; ed e-mail comentarios@elmensajero.com; web site www.elmensajero.com
Circulation: 0pd, 103,800fr; CAC
Advertising: Open inch rate $58.79
Established: 1987
Group: impreMedia LLC
Digital Platform - Mobile: Apple, Android, Windows
Digital Platform - Tablet: Apple iOS, Android, Windows 7
Nat'l Sales Dir....Gabriel Guthellez
Ed....Madia Mejia
Gen. Mgr./West, IM Corp....Damian Mazzotta
Circ. Dir....Greg Hatch
Delivery Method: Carrier, Racks
Zip Codes Served: 95116, 95122, 95002, 95110, 95112.
95113, 95121, 95125, 95126, 95127, 95131, 95133, 94025, 94061, 94063, 94080, 94103, 94105, 94110, 94112, 94158, 94303, 94401, 94403, 94520, 94541, 94544, 94577, 94578, 94587, 94601, 94603, 94605, 94621, 94801, 94806

EL TECOLOTE (2 X MTHLY)
2958 24th St, San Francisco, CA, 94110-4132, San Francisco, USA; tel (415) 648-1045; fax (415) 648-1046; ed e-mail editor@accionlatina.org; web site www.eltecolote.org
Circulation: 250pd, 10,000fr; Sworn/Estimate/Non-Audited
Advertising: Open inch rate $16.25
Established: 1970
Ed....Roberto Daza
Mechanical Specifications: Type page 10 1/4 x 16; E - 4 cols, 2 1/4, 1/4 between; A - 4 cols, 2 1/4, 1/4 between; C - 4 cols, 2 1/4, 1/4 between.
Equipment: Hardware — APP/Mac LC II, APP/Mac II, APP/Mac 6200, APP/iMac, APP/Mac G3; Software — Microsoft/Word 5.0.

SAN JOSE

ALIANZA METROPOLITAN NEWS (EVERY OTHER THUR)
1090 Lincoln Ave, Ste 8, San Jose, CA, 95125-3156, Santa Clara, USA; tel (408) 272-9394; fax (408) 272-9395; web site www.alianzanews.com
Circulation: 40,000fr; Sworn/Estimate/Non-Audited
Advertising: Open inch rate $24.50
Pub....Rosana Drumond

Ed. .... Manuel Ortiz
Mechanical Specifications: Type page 13 x 21 1/2; E - 6 cols, 2 1/16, 1/8 between; A - 6 cols, 2 1/16, 1/8 between; C - 6 cols, 2 1/16, 1/8 between.
Equipment: Hardware — APP/Mac; Software — Adobe/PageMaker, Adobe/Photoshop.
Zip Codes Served: 95151

EL OBSERVADOR
(Fri)
1042 W Hedding St, Ste 250, San Jose, CA, 95126-1206, Santa Clara, USA; tel (408) 938-1700; fax (408) 938-1705; adv fax 408 938 1700; ed fax 408-938-1705; e-mail angelica@el-observador.com; adv e-mail angelica@el-observador.com; ed e-mail arturo@el-observador.com; web site www.el-observador.com
Circulation: 34,500fr; Sworn/Estimate/Non-Audited
Advertising: Open inch rate $30.00
Established: 1980
Digital Platform - Mobile: Apple, Android, Windows, Blackberry
Digital Platform - Tablet: Apple iOS, Android, Windows 7, Blackberry Tablet OS, Kindle, Nook, Kindle Fire
Pres./Pub. .... Angelica Rossi
Sales.. Justin Rossi
Ed. .... Arturo Hilario
Graphic Des.............................. Leila Velasco
Office Manager .... Erica Medrano
Managing Editor .... Arturo Hilario
Pub.. Hilbert Morales
Adv./Mktg. Dir.......................... Monica Amador
Acct. Rep.................................. Angelica Rossi
Graphics Design....................... Roberto Romo
Mechanical Specifications: Type page 13 x 21; E - 6 cols, 2 1/16, between; A - 6 cols, 2 1/16, between; C - 10 cols, 1 5/16, between.
Equipment: Hardware — IBM/486, APP/Power Mac 7100/66, APP/Mac IIcx, APP/Mac SE, APP/Mac Classic II, 4-APP/Mac Plus; Software — Microsoft/Word, Microsoft/Excel, QPS/QuarkXPress, Adobe/Photoshop.
Delivery Method: Mail, Newsstand, Carrier, Racks
Zip Codes Served: Santa Clara County
Note: El Observador is a multi-media service company offering advertising (print & digital) advertising and promotions via EO's social media platforms, legal notices, classifieds, jobs board, translations, graphic design, web development & motion graphics, photography, video production.

LA OFERTA REVIEW
(Fri)
90 S White Rd, Ste B, San Jose, CA, 95127-2944, Santa Clara, USA; tel (408) 436-7850; fax (408) 436-7861; e-mail info@laoferta.com; web site www.laoferta.com
Circulation: 21,000fr; Sworn/Estimate/Non-Audited
Advertising: Open inch rate $29.75
Established: 1978
Pub.............................. Franklin G. Andrade
Adv. Dir.............................. Veronica Andrade
Ed. .... Mary J. Andrade
Equipment: Hardware — Software Adobe/PageMaker 6.5, QPS/QuarkXPress 4.0, Microsoft/Word.
Zip Codes Served: 95002, 94086, 94089, 95035, 95036, 94059, 94061, 95065, 94301, 94310, 94546, 94039, 94560, 94560, 94536, 94555, 94587, 95050, 95110, 95112, 95113, 95114, 95116, 95118, 95120, 95121, 951232, 95132, 95132, 95125, 94605, 94112, 94114

NUEVO MUNDO
750 Ridder Park Dr, San Jose, CA, 95131-2432, Santa Clara, USA; tel (408) 920-5843; fax (408) 271-3732
Circulation:; Sworn/Estimate/Non-Audited
Advertising: Open inch rate $55.00
Adv. Mgr., Natl' Sales....... Rosaura Miramontes
Ed. .... Marina Hinestrosa

SAN YSIDRO

AHORA NOW
(Thur)
378 E San Ysidro Blvd, San Ysidro, CA, 92173-2722, San Diego, USA; tel (619) 428-2277; fax (619) 428-0871; e-mail ahoranow2008@hotmail.com
Circulation: 20,000fr; Sworn/Estimate/Non-Audited
Advertising: Open inch rate $19.00
Adv. Mgr........................... Juan Manuel Torres
Ed. .... Bertha Alicia Gonzalez

SANTA ANA

AZTECA NEWS
(Wed) (weekly)
1823 E 17th St, Ste 312, Santa Ana, CA, 92705-8630, Orange, USA; tel (714) 972-9912; adv tel (714) 760-4939; e-mail aztecanews@aol.com; adv e-mail fvelo@aztecanews.com; ed e-mail rromano@aztecanews.com; web site www.aztecanews.com
Circulation: 42fr; Sworn/Estimate/Non-Audited
Advertising: Net inch rate $21.50
Established: 1980
Pub.. Fernando Velo
Adv. Mgr...................... Alessandro Hernandez
Mng. Ed.............................. Rosanna Romano
Delivery Method: Racks

SANTA ROSA

LA PRENSA SONOMA
(Mthly)
427 Mendocino Ave, Santa Rosa, CA, 95401-6313, Sonoma, USA; tel (707) 526-8501; adv tel 707-521-5342; adv e-mail jose.delcastillo@pressdemocrat.com; ed e-mail ricardo.ibarra@pressdemocrat.com; web site http://www.laprensasonoma.com/
Circulation: 30,000fr; Sworn/Estimate/Non-Audited
Established: 2016
Group: Sonoma Media Investments
Digital Platform - Mobile: Apple, Android
Digital Platform - Tablet: Apple iOS, AndroidRicardo Ibarra

TORRANCE

IMPACTO USA
(Fri)
21250 Hawthorne Blvd, Torrance, CA, 90503-5506, Los Angeles, USA; tel (562) 499-1415; fax (562) 499-1484; web site www.impactousa.com
Circulation: 207,248pd,; AAM
Advertising: Open inch rate $62.00Editions: 250,000-
Dsgn. Mgr................................ Raúl Martínez
Ed. .... Carlos Avilés
Equipment: Hardware — APP/Mac; Software — QPS/QuarkXPress.
Zip Codes Served: 90650, 90723, 90280, 90222, 90201, 90716

TUSTIN

MINIONDAS
(Thur)
17291 Irvine Blvd, Ste 225, Tustin, CA, 92780-2941, Orange, USA; tel (714) 668-1010; web site www.miniondas.com
Advertising: Open inch rate $10.97
Established: 1975
Pub..................................... Sandra Cervantes

VAN NUYS

LA GUIA FAMILIAR
(Thur)
PO Box 9191, Van Nuys, CA, 91409, Los Angeles, USA; tel (818) 336-6617; fax (818) 336-6008; e-mail pr@latinpublications.com; adv e-mail ads@latinpublications.com
Circulation: 180,000fr; Sworn/Estimate/Non-Audited
Advertising: Open inch rate $67.37
Established: 1979
Jose M. Garcia
Diane LernerPub.s
Mechanical Specifications: Type page 7 1/2 x 10; E - 5 cols, 1 3/8, between; A - 5 cols, 1 3/8, between; C - 5 cols, 1 3/8, between.
Equipment: Hardware — APP/Mac; Software — Adobe/PageMaker, Microsoft.

VISALIA

EL SOL - VISALIA
(Fri)
PO Box 31, Visalia, CA, 93279-0031, Tulare, USA; web site www.elsolenlared.com
Circulation: 12,101fr; Sworn/Estimate/Non-AuditedPaula Goudreau

COLORADO

COLORADO SPRINGS

HISPANIA NEWS
(Thur)
1750 Monterey Rd, Ste 220, Colorado Springs, CO, 80910-1824, El Paso, USA; tel (719) 540-0220; fax (719) 540-0599; ed e-mail editor@hispanianews.com; web site www.hispania-news.com
Circulation: 155,000fr; Sworn/Estimate/Non-Audited
Advertising: Open inch rate $17.00
Established: 1987
Circ. Mgr.. Bill Green
Ed. .... R.L. Armendariz
Prodn. Mgr. .... Sami Armendariz
Mechanical Specifications: Type page 10 1/4 x 15; E - 5 cols, 2, 1/8 between; A - 5 cols, 2, 1/8 between; C - 5 cols, 2, 1/8 between.
Equipment: Hardware — APP/Mac; Software — Adobe/PageMaker.
Zip Codes Served: 80001, 80002, 80003, 80004, 80005, 80006, 80007, 80008, 80009, 80010, 80903, 80904, 80905, 80906, 80907, 80909, 80910, 80911, 80913, 80916, 80917, 80918, 80919, 80920, 80921, 80922

DENVER

LA VOZ NEWSPAPER
(Wed)
4047 Tejon St, # 202, Denver, CO, 80211-2214, Denver, USA; tel (303) 936-8556; fax (720) 889-2455; adv e-mail advertising@lavozcolorado.com; classifieds@lavozcolorado.com; ed e-mail news@lavozcolorado.com; web site www.lavozcolorado.com
Circulation: 596pd, 25,778fr; CAC
Advertising: Open inch rate $22.50
Established: 1974
Pub... Pauline Rivera
Sales Mgr............................... Romelia Ulibarri
Entertainment Ed......................... Emma Lynch
Prodn. Coord......................... Charles Corrales
Mechanical Specifications: Type page 10 1/3 x 14; E - 6 cols, 1 7/12, 1/6 between; A - 6 cols, 1 7/12, 1/6 between; C - 6 cols, 1 7/12, 1/6 between.
Equipment: Hardware — 4-MAC/G4; Software — Adobe/Acrobat 5.0, QPS/QuarkXPress 4.1.
Delivery Method: Mail, Newsstand, Racks
Zip Codes Served: 80002-800011, 80202-80236, 80621-80645

THORNTON

LA VOZ BILINGUE
(Wed)
12021 Pennsylvania St Ste 201, #201, Thornton, CO, 80241-3152, Adams, USA; tel (303) 936-8556; adv tel (303) 936-8556; fax (720) 889-2455; e-mail advertising@lavozcolorado.com; adv e-mail classsales@lavozcolorado. c om; ed e-mail news@lavozcolorado.com; web site www.lavozcolorado.com
Circulation: 31,729pd,; CAC
Advertising: Open inch rate $18.00
Pub./Adv. Dir. .... Pauline Rivera
Classified Mgr. .... Romelia Ulibarri
Circ. Mgr.. Jim Koucherik
Prod. Coord.......................... Charles Corrales
Delivery Method: Mail

CONNECTICUT

MERIDEN

TIEMPO
11 Crown St, Meriden, CT, 06450-5713, New Haven, USA; tel (203) 235-1661; adv tel (203) 317-2337; adv fax (203) 235-4048; e-mail tiempo@record-journal.com; web site www.tiempo.com
Circulation:; Sworn/Estimate/Non-Audited
Advertising: Open inch rate $15.50
Pub... Eliot C. White
Adv. Mgr......................... Leyda Ortiz-Sanchez
Ed. .... Elizabeth Tirado

DISTRICT OF COLUMBIA

WASHINGTON

EL TIEMPO LATINO
(Fri)
1150 15th St, Washington, DC, 20071-0001, District Of Columbia, USA; tel 202-334-9100; adv tel 202-334-9146; ed tel 202-334-9159; fax 202-496-3599; adv fax 202-496-3599; ed fax 202-496-3599; adv e-mail zulema@eltiempolatino.com; ed e-mail paula@eltiempolatino.com; web site www.eltiempolatino.com
Circulation: 50,000fr; AAM
Advertising: Open inch rate $38.00
Established: 1991
Group: The Washington Post
Director of Business Development .... Alberto Avendano
Office Mgr. .... Kris Holmes
Adv. Mgr..................................... Zulema Tijero
Mechanical Specifications: Type page 12 x 21; E - 6 cols, 1 43/50, 1/16 between; A - 6 cols, 1 43/50, 1/16 between; C - 6 cols, 1/16 between.
Equipment: Hardware — APP/Power Mac; Software — QPS/QuarkXPress 3.3, Adobe/Photoshop, Macromedia/Freehand, Adobe/Illustrator.
Delivery Method: Newsstand, Carrier, Racks

HISPANIC LINK WEEKLY REPORT
(Mon)
1420 N St NW, Washington, DC, 20005-2843, District Of Columbia, USA; tel (202)

234-0280; fax (202) 234-4090; ed e-mail charles1@hispaniclink.org; web site www.hispaniclink.org
Circulation: 3,000pd, 500fr; Sworn/Estimate/Non-Audited
Advertising: Open inch rate $45.00
Pub....................Charles Ericksen-Mendoza
Circ. Mgr...............Carlos Ericksen-Mendoza
Mechanical Specifications: Type page 7 x 9; E - 3 cols, 2 3/8, 3/16 between; A - 3 cols, 2 3/8, 3/16 between; C - 3 cols, 2 3/8, 3/16 between.
Zip Codes Served: 20005

FLORIDA

DORAL

EL NUEVO HERALD (DAILY)
3511 NW 91st Ave, Doral, FL, 33172-1216, Miami-Dade, USA; tel (305) 376-3535; fax (305) 376-2138; web site www.elnuevoherald.com
Circulation: 382,896pd,; Sworn/Estimate/Non-Audited
Advertising: Open inch rate $32.10
Group: McClatchy
Exec Ed ....Myriam Marquez
Dir of Strategic Advt.............Rick Banciella
Mechanical Specifications: Type page 13 x 22 1/4; E - 6 cols, 1/6 between; C - 10 cols, between.
Equipment: Hardware — APP/Mac, PC; Presses — Offset; Software — SII, QPS/QuarkXPress, Adobe/Photoshop, Microsoft/Windows 95, Microsoft/Windows NT.

FORT LAUDERDALE

EL HERALDO DE BROWARD
1975 E Sunrise Blvd, Ste 540, Fort Lauderdale, FL, 33304-1453, Broward, USA; tel (954) 527-0627; fax (954) 792-7402; e-mail elheralbroward@aol.com; web site www.elheraldo.com
Circulation:; Sworn/Estimate/Non-Audited
Advertising: Open inch rate $23.00
Pub..............................Elaine Vasquez
Ed. ....Elaine Miceli-Vasquez
Prodn. Mgr. ....Lisa Micelli
Mechanical Specifications: Type page 10 1/2 x 13; E - 5 cols, 2 1/16, 1/16 between; A - 5 cols, 2 1/16, 1/16 between; C - 5 cols, 2 1/16, 1/16 between.
Equipment: Hardware — APP/Power Mac 7200, APP/iMac; Software — QPS/QuarkXPress 3.2.

EL NOTICIERO (EVERY OTHER WEEK)
PO Box 480729, Fort Lauderdale, FL, 33348-0729, Broward, USA; tel (954) 766-4492; fax (954) 766-4492; e-mail elnoti2@aol.com
Circulation: 15,000fr; Sworn/Estimate/Non-Audited
Advertising: Open inch rate $12.00
Ed. ....Lilia Mantilla
Director ....Rodrigo Martinez
Mechanical Specifications: Type page 11 x 17; E - 5 cols, 2, 3/16 between; A - 5 cols, 2, 3/16 between; C - 5 cols, 2, 3/16 between.
Equipment: Hardware — 4-APP/Mac G4, APP/Mac 7500, APP/Mac Performa 6220; Software — Adobe/PageMaker 6.5, Adobe/Photoshop 5.0.
Delivery Method: Mail, Newsstand, Carrier, Racks

HIALEAH

LA VOZ DE LA CALLE
(Fri)
4696 E 10th Ct, Hialeah, FL, 33013-2108, Miami-Dade, USA; tel (305) 687-5555; fax (305) 681-0500; e-mail lavozdelacalle@bellsouth.net; web site www.lavozdelacalle.net
Circulation: 30,000fr; Sworn/Estimate/Non-Audited
Advertising: Open inch rate $25.00
Adv. Mgr. ....Vicente E. Rodriguez
Circ. Mgr.............................Juan M. Suarez
Ed. ....Vicente P. Rodriguez
Prodn. Mgr. ....Jose A. Marquez
Mechanical Specifications: Type page 10 1/4 x 12 1/2; E - 6 cols, 1 5/8, 3/8 between; A - 6 cols, 1 5/8, 3/8 between; C - 6 cols, 1 5/8, 3/8 between.
Equipment: Hardware — APP/Mac Performa 600, APP/Power Mac G3; Software — Adobe/PageMaker 5.0, 6-Canvas.

LONGWOOD

LA PRENSA
(Thur)
685 S Ronald Reagan Blvd, Ste 1001, Longwood, FL, 32750-6435, Seminole, USA; tel (407) 767-0070; adv tel (407) 767-0070; ed tel (407) 767-0070; fax (407) 767-5478; e-mail dora.toro@laprensaorlando.com; adv e-mail vicky.llevada@laprensaorlando.com; ed e-mail jesus.deltoro@impremedia.com; web site www.laprensafl.com
Circulation: 35,000pd,; CAC
Advertising: 1/8 Pg $287; 1/4 Pg $575.00; 1/2 pag. $1.167.; 1 page $2,334.
Established: 1981
Group: impreMedia LLC
Pub./CEO................Dora Casanova de Toro
Office Mgr. ....Julia Torres
Sales...................................Adalgiza Zouain
Sales...Milly Colon
Sales..Liza Ordonez
Calssified / Display Classifieds...Vicky Llevada
EIC......................................Jesus del Toro
Mechanical Specifications: Type page 10 1/16 x 13; E - 5 cols, 1 7/8, 1/10 between; A - 5 cols, 1 7/8, 1/10 between; C - 5 cols, 1 7/8, 1/10 between.
Equipment: Hardware — 6-APP/Mac; Software — QPS/QuarkXPress.
Delivery Method: Newsstand, Carrier, Racks
Zip Codes Served: Counties in Central Florida.

MIAMI

DIARIO LAS AMERICAS
(Sun)
888 Brickell Ave, Fl 5, Miami, FL, 33131-2913, Miami-Dade, USA; tel (305) 633-3341; adv tel (305) 633-3341; ed tel (305) 633-3341; fax (305) 635-7668; adv fax (305) 635-4002; ed fax (305) 635-7668; e-mail contacto@diariolasamericas.com; adv e-mail advertising@diariolasamericas.com; ed e-mail editorial@diariolasamericas.com; web site www.diariolasamericas.com
Circulation: 5,692pd, 30,453fr; VAC
Advertising: Open inch rate $32.25
Established: 1953
Asst. Pub...........................Maribel Suarez
Bus. Mgr./Controller..............Victor M. Vega
Prodn. Mgr. ....Ariel Martinez
Credit Mgr. ....Daniel Medina
Adv. Dir.............................Alejandro Aguirre
Adv. Mgr., Nat'l..................Bertha V. Enriquez
Adv. Mgr., Classified ....Jose A. Yuste
Ed. ....Horacio Aguirre
Deputy Ed......................Alejandro J. Aguirre
Food Ed. ....Virginia Godoy
News Ed. ....Gustavo Pena
Society Ed....................Luis David Rodriguez
Data Processing Mgr. ....Jesus Hernandez
Prod. Mgr. ....Gustavo De La Osa
Mechanical Specifications: Type page 13 x 21; E - 6 cols, 2 1/16, 1/8 between; A - 6 cols, 2 1/16, 1/8 between; C - 10 cols, 1/8 between.
Equipment: Hardware — Presses G/Urbanite.

EL ARGENTINO NEWSPAPER
PO Box 802133, Miami, FL, 33280-2133, Miami-Dade, USA; fax (305) 371-1656; e-mail showmgz@gate.net; info@elargentino.com; web site www.elargentino.com
Circulation:; Sworn/Estimate/Non-Audited
Adv. Mgr. ....Grace Micheli
Ed. ....Alberto Micheli

EL NUEVO HERALD
(Mon, Tues, Wed, Thur, Fri, Sun)
1 Herald Plz, Miami, FL, 33132-1609, Miami-Dade, USA; tel 1-800-843-4372; web site http://www.elnuevoherald.com/
Circulation: 53,356pd,; AAM
Group: The McClatchy Company

EL NUEVO PATRIA
(Wed)
425 NW 27th Ave Ste 2, Jose Marti Station, Miami, FL, 33135-4767, Miami-Dade, USA; tel (305) 530-8787; adv tel (786) 286-8787; adv fax (305) 698-8787; e-mail patrianews@aol.com; ed e-mail enpnews@aol.com
Circulation: 7,180pd, 22,820fr; Sworn/Estimate/Non-Audited
Advertising: Open inch rate $25.00
Established: 1959
Group: Patria Media Foundation, Inc.
Gen. Mgr. ....Maria Laura Figueroa
Ed. ....Dr. Carlos Diaz Lujan
Prodn. Mgr. ....Omar R. Rosa
Associate Ed.......................Sara P. Armesto
Publisher.........................Eladio Jose Armesto
Food & Wine Editor.................Sandra Baroja
Book Editor.............................Ralph Garcia
Feature Editor...................Madeline Sandoval
Mechanical Specifications: Type page 10 x 16; E - 6 cols, 1 3/5, 3/20 between; A - 6 cols, 1 3/5, 3/20 between; C - 6 cols, 1 3/5, 3/20 between.
Equipment: Hardware — 4-APP/Power Mac; Software — QPS/QuarkXPress, Adobe/Photoshop, Microsoft/Word.
Delivery Method: Mail, Newsstand, Racks

LIBRE
(Wed)
2700 SW 8th St, Miami, FL, 33135-4619, Miami-Dade, USA; tel (305) 643-2947; fax (305) 649-2767; e-mail main@libreonline.com; web site www.libreonline.com
Circulation: 1,100pd, 3,850fr; Sworn/Estimate/Non-Audited
Advertising: Open inch rate $21.00
Established: 1966
Pub......................................Demetrio Perez
Mechanical Specifications: Type page 10 x 12 1/4; E - 6 cols, 1 1/2, 1/8 between; A - 6 cols, 1 1/2, 1/8 between.
Equipment: Hardware — Software QPS/QuarkXPress 6.5, Adobe/Photoshop CS.

MIAMI BEACH

EL POPULAR
2955 N Bay Rd, Miami Beach, FL, 33140-3810, Miami-Dade, USA; tel (305) 677-2020; fax (305) 673-0507; e-mail info@elpopular.com; marco@laureti.com; web site www.elpopular.com
Circulation:; Sworn/Estimate/Non-Audited
Advertising: Open inch rate $50.00
Established: 1998
CEO/Pub............................Marco A. Laureti
Mechanical Specifications: Type page 10 x 12 3/4; E - 4 cols, 2 3/8, 1/25 between; A - 4 cols, 2 3/8, 1/25 between; C - 6 cols, 1 3/5, 1/25 between.
Equipment: Hardware — PC; Software — Adobe/PageMaker 6.5, Archetype/Corel Draw.

TAMPA

LA GACETA
(Fri)
3210 E 7th Ave, Tampa, FL, 33605-4302, Hillsborough, USA; tel (813) 248-3921; fax (813) 247-5357; e-mail lagaceta@tampabay.rr.com; adv e-mail lagaceta@tampabay.rr.com; ed e-mail lagaceta@tampabay.rr.com; web site www.lagacetanewspaper.com
Circulation: 18,000pd,; Sworn/Estimate/Non-Audited
Advertising: Open inch rate $11.00
Established: 1922
Adv. Mgr. ....Peggy Schmechel
Circ. Mgr.................................Gene Siudut
Ed. ....Patrick Manteiga
Mng. Ed..............................Angela Manteiga
Prodn. Mgr. ....Angie Manteiga
Mechanical Specifications: Type page 10 x 16 1/2; E - 5 cols, 1 3/4, 1/4 between; A - 5 cols, 1 3/4, 1/4 between; C - 5 cols, 1 3/4, 1/4 between.
Equipment: Hardware — Dell; Software — Adobe/Creative Suite.
Delivery Method: Mail, Newsstand, Racks

NUEVO SIGLO
(Thur)
7137 N Armenia Ave, Ste B, Tampa, FL, 33604-5263, Hillsborough, USA; tel (813) 932-7181; fax (813) 932-8202; e-mail n.siglo@verizon.net; web site www.nuevosiglotampa.com
Circulation: 3,000pd, 24,000fr; Sworn/Estimate/Non-Audited
Advertising: Open inch rate $16.00
Pub...........................Neris Ramon Palacios
Gen. Mgr. ....Rosmeli Palacios
Adv. Mgr. ....Griseldis Palacios
Mng. Ed.................................Ledis Palacios
Mechanical Specifications: Type page 10 1/4 x 16; E - 6 cols, 1 1/2, 1/4 between; A - 6 cols, 1 1/2, 1/4 between; C - 2 cols, 3 1/2, 1/4 between.
Equipment: Hardware — PC.

WEST PALM BEACH

EL LATINO NEWSPAPER
(Fri)
4404 Georgia Ave, West Palm Beach, FL, 33405-2500, Palm Beach, USA; tel (561) 835-4913; fax (561) 655-5059; e-mail ellatino@msn.com; web site www.ellatinosemanal.com
Circulation: 39,000fr; Sworn/Estimate/Non-Audited
Advertising: Open inch rate $16.00
Pub.....................................Miguel A. Lavin
Adv. Mgr. ....Eduardo Monzon
Ed. ....Jose Uzal

GEORGIA

ATLANTA

ATLANTA LATINO (EVERY OTHER THUR)
2865 Amwiler Rd, Ste 100, Atlanta, GA, 30360-2827, Gwinnett, USA; tel (770) 416-7570; fax (770) 416-7991; adv e-mail sales@atlantalatino.com; ed e-mail editor@atlantalatino.com; web site www.atlantalatino.com
Circulation: 20,000fr; Sworn/Estimate/Non-Audited
Advertising: Open inch rate $20.00
Adv. Mgr. ....Farid Sadri
Ed. in Chief ....Judith Martinez
Equipment: Hardware — APP/Power Mac G4; Software — Adobe/InDesign CS.
Zip Codes Served: 30338, 30339, 30340, 30341, 30341, 30342, 30344, 30345, 30360, 30501,

30504, 30507, 30518, 30519, 30001, 30004, 30005, 30008, 30022, 30024, 30030, 30032, 30033, 30035, 30039, 30040, 30043, 30044, 30045, 30047, 30059, 30060, 30062, 30064, 30066, 30071, 300

MUNDOHISPÁNICO NEWSPAPER

(Thur)
223 Perimeter Center Pkwy NE, Atlanta, GA, 30346-1301, Dekalb, USA; tel 404 881 0441; adv tel 404 982 5809; ed tel 404 982 5828; fax 404 881 6085; adv fax same as above; adv e-mail sales@mundohispanico.com; ed e-mail editorial@mundohispanico,com; web site www.mundohispanico.com
Circulation: 71,000fr; CVC
Advertising: CP
Established: 1979
Group: Cox Media Group
Digital Platform - Mobile: Apple, Android
Digital Platform - Tablet: Apple iOS, Android
General Manager.................... Mindy Buckalew
Delivery Method: Racks

ILLINOIS

ARLINGTON HEIGHTS

REFLEJOS BILINGUAL PUBLICATIONS

(Sun) (weekly)
155 E Algonquin Rd, , Arlington Heights, IL, 60005-4617, Cook, USA; tel (847) 806-1111; adv tel (847)806-1411; ed tel (847) 806-1171; fax (847) 806-1112; e-mail lsiete@reflejis.com; adv e-mail lsiete@reflejos.com; ed e-mail mortiz@reflejos.com; web site www.reflejos.com
Circulation: 4pd, 74,201fr; CVC
Advertising: N/A
Established: 1990
Group: Paddock Publications
Digital Platform - Mobile: Apple, Android
Digital Platform - Tablet: Apple iOS, Android
Gen. Mgr... Linda Siete
Asst. Mng. Ed................................ Marco Ortiz
Mechanical Specifications: Type page 9 x 11 1/4; E - 9 cols, 1 1/12, between; A - 9 cols, 11/12, between; C - 9 cols, 1 1/12, between.
Equipment: Hardware — APP/Mac; Software — Adobe/Acrobat, Adobe/Illustrator CS, Adobe/PageMaker, Adobe/Photoshop CS, Macromedia/Freehand, QPS/QuarkXPRess, Adobe/InDesign CS2.
Delivery Method: Mail, Newsstand, Racks
Zip Codes Served: 8 counties out side of Chicago

CHICAGO

EL HERALDO

(Bi-Mthly)
300 S Damen Ave, Apt 1508, Chicago, IL, 60612-3267, Cook, USA; tel (312) 666-3201; adv tel 312-217-6611; e-mail ehnews@aol.com; adv e-mail ehnews@aol.com; ed e-mail ehnews@aol.com
Circulation: 0pd, 1,000fr; Sworn/Estimate/Non-Audited
Advertising: Open inch rate $20.00
Established: 1989
Adv. Mgr....................................... Marta Foster
Ed.. Gonzalo Sanchez
Mechanical Specifications: Type page 10 1/4 x 16; E - 5 cols, 2 1/16, between; A - 5 cols, 2 1/16, between; C - 6 cols, 2 1/16, between.
Equipment: Hardware — Microsoft; Software — QPS/QuarkXPress./Microsoft edition
Delivery Method: Carrier, Racks
Zip Codes Served: 60612 - multiple zip codes

EXTRA BILINGUAL COMMUNITY NEWSPAPER

(Fri)
3906 W North Ave, Chicago, IL, 60647-4618, Cook, USA; tel (773) 252-3534; fax (773) 252-4073; adv e-mail sales@extranews.net; ed e-mail editor@extranews.net; web site www.extranews.net
Circulation: 66fr; CVC
Advertising: Open inch rate $46.15
Established: 1980
Pub... Mila Tellez
Assoc. Pub./Gen. Mgr. .... Nile Wendorf
Managing Editor Christina Elizabeth Rodriguez
Mechanical Specifications: Full Page: 10.375" by 10.5", HP 10.375" by 5.166", Quarter Page 5.104" by 5.166"
Equipment: Hardware — APP/Mac; Software — Adobe/Photoshop, Adobe/PageMaker, Microsoft/Excel, QPS/QuarkXPress.
Delivery Method: Newsstand, Racks
Zip Codes Served: 60804, 60632, 60623, 60647, 60639, 60629, 60608, 60618, 60625, 60609, 60641, 60617, 60622, 60402, 60651, 60601

LA RAZA NEWSPAPER

(Sun)
225 W Ohio St, Ste 300, Chicago, IL, 60654-7819, Cook, USA; tel (773) 273-2900; fax (312) 870-7030; ed e-mail agenda@laraza.com; web site www.laraza.com
Circulation: 153,620pd,; CAC
Advertising: Open inch rate $95.00
Established: 1970
Group: impreMedia LLC
Nat'l Acct. Exec............................ Brian Baase
Adv. Dir./Gen. Mgr.... Jimena Catarivas Corbett
Managing d......................... Fabiola Pomareda
Mktg. Mgr............................ Tatiana Canaval
Sr. Account Mgr., Local Sales...... Hugo Jordan
Nat'l Acct. Exec....................... Martha DeLuna
Mechanical Specifications: Display Advertising: 6 Col X 11"
Classified Advertising: 8 Col X 11"
Equipment: Hardware — APP/Mac; Software — Adobe/Photoshop, QPS/QuarkXPress.
Delivery Method: Mail, Newsstand, Carrier, Racks
Zip Codes Served: 26 Zip Codes: Chicago and Suburbs

CICERO

EL DIA

(Fri)
5718 W Cermak Rd, Cicero, IL, 60804-2128, Cook, USA; tel (708) 652-6397; fax (708) 652-8360; e-mail eldia@eldianews.com; web site www.eldianews.com
Circulation: 60,000pd,; Sworn/Estimate/Non-Audited
Advertising: Open inch rate $29.62
Pub................................ Jorge Montes De Oca
Ed.. Ana Maria Ugalde
Mechanical Specifications: Type page 10 1/4 x 14; E - 5 cols, 2, between; A - 5 cols, 2, between; C - 6 cols, 1 1/4, between.
Equipment: Hardware — PC, APP/Mac; Software — Adobe/PageMaker, QPS/QuarkXPress.

TELE GUIA DE CHICAGO

(Sun)
3116 S Austin Blvd, Cicero, IL, 60804-3729, Cook, USA; tel 708-656-6666; adv tel 708-656-6666 x1080; ed tel 708-656-6666 x1074; fax 866-4156776; adv fax 866-4156776; ed fax 866-4156776; adv e-mail rosemontes@aol.com; ed e-mail avazquez@teleguia.us; web site www.teleguia.us
Circulation: 7,481pd, 20,692fr; CVC
Advertising: 708-656-6666
Established: 1985
Digital Platform - Mobile: Apple, Android
Digital Platform - Tablet: Apple iOS, Android, Windows 7, Kindle FireZeke Montes
Delivery Method: Mail, Newsstand, Racks

THE LAWNDALE NEWS/SU NOTICIERO BILINGUE

(Thur, Sun) (Twice a month)
5533 W 25th St, Cicero, IL, 60804-3319, Cook, USA; tel (708) 656-6400; adv tel (708) 656-6400; fax (708) 656-2433; adv fax (708) 656-2433; e-mail printing@lawndalenews.com; adv e-mail pilar@lawndalenews.com; ed e-mail mandou@lawndalenews.com; web site www.lawndalenews.com
Circulation:; Sworn/Estimate/Non-Audited
Advertising: Open inch rate $55.00
Established: 1940
Digital Platform - Mobile: Android, Windows, Blackberry
Digital Platform - Tablet: Android, Windows 7, Kindle, Nook, Kindle Fire
VP.. JamesL. Nardini
Pub... Lynda Nardini
Adv. Mgr.. Gary Miller
Gen. Mgr.................................. Robert Nardini
Prodn. Mgr.................................... Pilar Merino
Ed... Ashmar Mandou
Mechanical Specifications: Type page 10"W x 10½" H; E - 6 cols, 1 1/2, between; A - 6 cols, 1 1/2, between; C - 6 cols, 1 1/2, between.
Equipment: Hardware — PC; Software — Adobe/PageMaker, Microsoft.
Delivery Method: Newsstand, Carrier, Racks
Zip Codes Served: ZIP CODES ATTACHED

PALATINE

NUEVA SEMANA

(Fri)
1180 E Dundee Rd, Palatine, IL, 60074-8305, Cook, USA; tel (847) 239-4815; fax (847) 890-6327; e-mail info@lanuevasemana.com; ed e-mail ealegria@lanuevasemana.com; web site www.lanuevasemana.com
Circulation:; Sworn/Estimate/Non-Audited
Established: 1999
Mechanical Specifications: Type page 10 1/4 x 12 3/4; E - 5 cols, 2 1/8, between; A - 5 cols, 2 1/8, between; C - 5 cols, 2 1/8, between.
Equipment: Hardware — PC
Delivery Method: Newsstand, Racks

INDIANA

GOSHEN

EL PUENTE

(Tues) (1st & 3rd Tuesday of the month (24 yearly issues))
1906 W Clinton St, Goshen, IN, 46526-1618, Elkhart, USA; tel (574) 533-9082; adv tel (574) 533-9082; ed tel (574) 533-9082; fax (574) 537-0552; e-mail mail@webelpuente.com; adv e-mail design@webelpuente.com; ed e-mail mail@webelpuente.com; web site www.webelpuente.com
Circulation: 9,000fr; Sworn/Estimate/Non-Audited
Advertising: Open inch rate $17.00
Established: 1992
Group: El Puente LLC
Production Director.
Marketing...................................... Yizzar Prieto
Editor .... Jimmer Prieto
Editor .... Zulma Prieto
Mechanical Specifications: Mini Tabloid format. Printable area is 9.88 W x 9.6 H.
Four-column format.
One-column ads are 2.35 inches wide Two-column ads are 4.85 inches wide. Three-column ads are 7.4 inches wide. Four-column ads are 9.88 inches wide.
Color costs an additional $100 for Full Color.
Equipment: Hardware — APP/Mac/PC; Software — Adobe/PageMaker 6.0, Adobe/Photoshop. Quarks.
Delivery Method: Newsstand, Racks
Zip Codes Served: 46563 - 46802 (34 Zip Codes total.)
Note: The First Hispanic Newspaper in Indiana.

KANSAS

GARDEN CITY

LA SEMANA EN EL SUROESTE DE KANSAS

(Fri)
310 N 7th St, Garden City, KS, 67846-5521, Finney, USA; tel (620) 275-8500; fax (620) 275-5165; e-mail lasemana@gctelegram.com; web site www.gctelegram.com
Circulation: 3,000fr; Sworn/Estimate/Non-Audited
Advertising: Open inch rate $5.28
Pub.. Dena Sattler
Adv. Mgr...................................... Charity Ochs
Circ. Mgr................................ Jeremy Banwell
Mng. Ed.. Brett Riggs
Equipment: Hardware — APP/Mac.

KANSAS CITY

DOS MUNDOS

(Thur)
1701 S 55th St, Kansas City, KS, 66106-2241, Wyandotte, USA; tel (816) 221-4747; adv tel (816)221-4747; fax (816) 221-4894; e-mail newstaff@dosmundos.com; ed e-mail CREYES@DOSMUNDOS.COM; web site www.dosmundos.com
Circulation: 20,000pd, 7,000fr; Sworn/Estimate/Non-Audited
Advertising: Open inch rate $14.00
Established: 1981
Digital Platform - Mobile: Apple
Pub... Manuel Reyes
Adv. Mgr..................................... Diana Raymer
Ed. .... Clara Reyes
Mechanical Specifications: Type page 13 x 21; E - 8 cols, 1 1/2, 1/4 between; A - 8 cols, 1 1/2, 1/4 between; C - 8 cols, 1 1/2, 1/4 between.
Equipment: Hardware — PC, APP/Mac; Software — QPS/QuarkXPress, Adobe/PageMaker.
Delivery Method: Newsstand, Carrier, Racks

LIBERAL

EL LIDER

16 S Kansas Ave, Liberal, KS, 67901-3732, Seward, USA; tel 620-629-0840; fax 620-624-2797; web site www.hpleader.com

MARYLAND

HYATTSVILLE

EL PREGONERO

(Thur)
5001 Eastern Ave, Hyattsville, MD, 20782-3447, Prince Georges, USA; tel (202) 281-2404; adv tel (202) 281-2406; ed tel (202) 281-2442; fax (202) 281-2448; e-mail rafael@elpreg.org; adv e-mail irieska@elpreg.org; ed e-mail rafael@elpreg.org; web site www.elpreg.org
Circulation: 25,167fr; CAC
Advertising: Open inch rate $19.00
Established: 1977
Ed. .... Rafael Roncal
Circ. Mgr............................. Irieska D. Caetano
Mechanical Specifications: Type page 10 1/4 x 13 1/2; E - 5 cols, 1 5/6, 1/6 between; A - 5 cols, 1/6 between; C - 7 cols, 1 1/3, 1/6 between.
Equipment: Hardware — 5-APP/Mac, 3-APP/Mac LaserPrinters; Software — QPS/QuarkXPress, Adobe/Photoshop, Adobe/Illustrator, Multi-Ad/Creator, Baseview/NewsEdit Pro, Class Manager/Plus.

Delivery Method: Newsstand, Carrier

SILVER SPRING

WASHINGTON HISPANIC
8455 Colesville Rd, Silver Spring, MD, 20910-7600, Montgomery, USA; tel (202) 667-8881; fax (202) 667-8902; e-mail info@washingtonhispanic.com; web site www.washingtonhispanic.com
Circulation:; Sworn/Estimate/Non-Audited
Advertising: Open inch rate $43.00
Adv. Mgr.......................................Johnny Yataco
Mechanical Specifications: Type page 13 x 21 1/10; E - 6 cols, 1 7/8, 1/6 between; A - 6 cols, 1 7/8, 1/6 between; C - 6 cols, 1 7/8, 1/6 between.
Equipment: Hardware — APP/Mac; Software — Adobe/Photoshop, QPS/QuarkXPress.

MASSACHUSETTS

BOSTON

EL MUNDO
(Thur)
408 S Huntington Ave, Boston, MA, 02130-4814, Suffolk, USA; tel (617) 522-5060; fax (617) 524-5886; adv e-mail sales@elmundoboston.com; ed e-mail editor@elmundoboston.com; web site www.elmundoboston.com
Circulation: 38,000pd,; Sworn/Estimate/Non-Audited
Advertising: Open inch rate $25.00
Established: 1972
Adv. Mgr.................................Jay Cosmopoulos
Ed...Alberto Vasallo
CMO...Elvis Jocol
Mechanical Specifications: Type page 9 3/4 x 16; E - 5 cols, 1 3/4, between; A - 5 cols, 1 3/4, between.
Equipment: Hardware — APP/Mac; Software — Adobe/PageMaker, QPS/QuarkXPress.
Delivery Method: Mail, Newsstand, Racks

EL PLANETA PUBLISHING
(Fri)
126 Brookline Ave, Ste 3, Boston, MA, 02215-3920, Suffolk, USA; tel (617) 937-5900; fax (617) 536-1463; adv e-mail sales@elplaneta.com; ed e-mail editor@elplaneta.com; web site www.tuboston.com
Circulation: 50,000fr; Sworn/Estimate/Non-Audited
Established: 2004
Ed..Marcela Garcia

LA SEMANA
(Thur)
903 Albany St, Boston, MA, 02119-2534, Suffolk, USA; tel (617) 541-2222; fax (617) 427-6227; e-mail wcea2000@aol.com; web site www.lasemanawceatv.com
Circulation: 10,000fr; Sworn/Estimate/Non-Audited
Advertising: Open inch rate $28.00 Classified, $24.00 Retail display
Established: 1978
Adv. Mgr....................................Nicolas Cuenca
Ed...Peter N. Cuenca
Equipment: Hardware — Pentium IV; Software — WordPerfect.
Delivery Method: Newsstand, Racks

MICHIGAN

DETROIT

EL CENTRAL
(Thur)
4124 W Vernor Hwy, Detroit, MI, 48209-2145, Wayne, USA; tel (313) 841-0100; fax (313) 841-0155; e-mail elcentral1@aol.com; adv e-mail elcentralads@aol.com
Circulation: 14,000fr; Sworn/Estimate/Non-Audited
Advertising: Open inch rate $16.00
Ed...Dolores Sanchez
Mechanical Specifications: Type page 10 x 16; E - 5 cols, 2, between; A - 5 cols, 2, between; C - 5 cols, 2, between.
Equipment: Hardware — IBM, PC.
Zip Codes Served: 48212

LATINO PRESS
(Thur)
6301 Michigan Ave, Detroit, MI, 48210-2954, Wayne, USA; tel (313) 361-3000; adv tel (313) 361-3000; ed tel (313) 361-3002; fax (313) 361-3001; e-mail hotline@latinodetroit.com; adv e-mail marketing@latinodetroit.com; ed e-mail editorial@latinodetroit.com; web site www.latinodetroit.com
Circulation: 1,500pd, 20,000fr; Sworn/Estimate/Non-Audited
Advertising: Open inch rate $25.00
Established: 1993
Digital Platform - Mobile: Apple, Android, Blackberry
Digital Platform - Tablet: Apple iOS, Android, Blackberry Tablet OS
President..............................Elias M. Gutierrez
Mechanical Specifications: AD DESIGN: Our creative staff is ready to design your ad. Basic ad design is $250 per ad which includes three proofs.
Additional proof will incur additional charges.
For custom design quotes, please consult your account representative.
LAYOUT SPECIFICATIONS: All digital art files must be sized to the dimensions listed at the top of this page. All colors must be converted to CMYK process.
IMAGES: Effective resolution for color and grayscale images must be at least 300 dpi. All color images must be sent to color mode of CMYK. All images must be embedded correctly into the PDF file or included with the page layout file.
TRANSFERRING FILES FOR PUBLICATION USE: File under 5 mb in size may be submitted via e-mail.
Submit materials to production@latinodetroit.com
Larger files sizes call for instructions.
Delivery Method: Mail, Newsstand, Racks
Zip Codes Served: 48209, 48210, 48216, 48342, 48101, 48108, 48238, 48146, 48185

MINNESOTA

MINNEAPOLIS

LA PRENSA DE MINNESOTA
(Thur)
1516 E Lake St, Ste 200, Minneapolis, MN, 55407-3579, Hennepin, USA; tel (612) 729-5900; fax (612) 729-5999; e-mail marian@lcnmedia.com; web site www.laprensademn.com
Circulation: 15,000fr; Sworn/Estimate/Non-Audited
Advertising: Open inch rate $25.00
Pub...Mario Duarte
Ed...Lorena Duarte

NEVADA

LAS VEGAS

BLOQUE LATINO AMERICANO DE PRENSA EL EXITO LATIN AMERICAN PRESS
(Fri)
PO Box 12599, Las Vegas, NV, 89112-0599, Clark, USA; tel (702) 431-1904; fax (702) 431-3339; e-mail elexito2@cox.net; adv e-mail elexito2@cox.net; web site www.elexitolasvegas.com
Circulation: 50,662fr; Sworn/Estimate/Non-Audited
Advertising: Open inch rate $18.00
Established: 1988
Adv. Mgr...Maggy Ruiz
Circ. Mgr.......................................Luz Delgado
Ed..Magaly Ruiz
Prodn. Mgr.................................Tirso Del Pozo
Mechanical Specifications: Page is 10"x16"; 5 cols. each col. 2" wide
Equipment: Hardware — APP/Mac; Software — Adobe/PageMaker.

EL MUNDO
(Fri)
760 N Eastern Ave, Ste 110, Las Vegas, NV, 89101-2888, Clark, USA; tel (702) 649-8553; fax (702) 649-7429; e-mail elchiefo@aol.com; adv e-mail ads@elmundo.net; web site www.elmundo.net
Circulation: 29,783fr; VAC
Advertising: Open inch rate $16.50
Established: 1980
Pub./Founder..........................Eddie Escobedo
Circ. Mgr.................................Nick Escobedo
Prodn. Mgr...............................Flora Hernandez
Mechanical Specifications: Type page 10 x 16; E - 6 cols, 1 3/4, between; A - 6 cols, 1 3/4, between.
Equipment: Hardware — APP/Mac.

EL TIEMPO
(Fri)
1111 W Bonanza Rd, Las Vegas, NV, 89106-3545, Clark, USA; tel 702-383-0300; adv tel (702) 477-3846; ed tel 702-387-2972; fax 702-383-0402; adv fax (702) 387-2981; ed fax 702-251-0736; adv e-mail gjurica@reviewjournal.com; ed e-mail hamaya@reviewjournal.com; web site www.eltiempolv.com
Circulation:; CAC
Advertising: $71.22
Established: 1994Editions: 50,000-
Editor....................................Hernando Amaya
Reporter............................Cristina Matta-Caro
Advertising Manager.....................Gaby Jurica
Art Director..........................Jorge Betancourt
Mechanical Specifications: 4col (10") x 20.50"
Equipment: Hardware — pc and mac; Presses — Goss Newsliner; Software — Atex, NewEngin, Indesign, CS5.5
Delivery Method: Carrier, Racks
Zip Codes Served: All

RENO

AHORA LATINO JOURNAL
(Tues, Wed, Other) (Bi-weekly)
605 S Wells Ave, Reno, NV, 89502-1825, Washoe, USA; tel (775) 677-9694; adv tel 775-378-7025; ed tel 775-378-7025; e-mail marioreno@live.com; adv e-mail marioreno@live.com; ed e-mail adelitazapata@live.com; web site www.ahoralatinojournal.com
Circulation: 8,000fr; Sworn/Estimate/Non-Audited
Advertising: Open inch rate $10.00
Established: 2010
Digital Platform - Mobile: Android
Digital Platform - Tablet: Other
Mechanical Specifications: Type page 10 x 14; E - 5 cols, 2, 1/6 between.
Equipment: Software — Adobe C4
Delivery Method: Racks
Zip Codes Served: 89501, 89502, 89503, 89506, 89423, 89721, etc

NEW JERSEY

CLIFTON

SU GUIA
1187 Main Ave, Ste 2D, Clifton, NJ, 07011-2252, Passaic, USA; tel (866) 784-8421; ed tel (973) 253-2707; ed fax (973) 478-9754
Circulation:; Sworn/Estimate/Non-Audited
Established: 2002Editions: 3- 3 total Su Guia - Bergen Edition; Su Guia - Bergen 2 Edition;
Pres...Stephen Borg
Vice Pres./Pub...........................Mike Lawson
Gen. Mgr......................................Jose Corban
Ed....................................... Daniel Santacruz
Vice Pres., Prodn.......................Glenn Garvie
Mechanical Specifications: Type page 9 1/2 x 11 11/16; E - 4 cols, 1 5/6, 1/4 between; A - 4 cols, 1 5/6, 1/4 between; C - 8 cols, 1 1/16, 1/8 between.
Zip Codes Served: 07055, 07501, 07502, 07503, 07504, 07505, 07011, 07012, 07013, 07014, 07508, 07621, 07603, 07010, 07631, 07022, 07026, 07601, 07602, 07643, 07644, 07074, 07650, 07663, 07666

ELIZABETH

LA VOZ (2 X MTHLY)
PO Box 899, Elizabeth, NJ, 07207-0899, Union, USA; tel (908) 352-6654; fax (908) 352-9735; e-mail lavoznj@aol.com; web site www.lavoznj.com
Circulation: 38,000fr; Sworn/Estimate/Non-Audited
Advertising: Open inch rate $12.40
Pub...Abel Berry
Adv. Mgr....................................Daniel Garcia
Mechanical Specifications: Type page 10 1/8 x 16; E - 7 cols, 1 3/8, 1/6 between; A - 7 cols, 1 3/8, 1/6 between; C - 7 cols, 1 3/8, 1/6 between.
Equipment: Hardware — APP/Mac; Software — Adobe/PageMaker, QPS/QuarkXPress.

TRENTON

EL LATINO EXPRESO
(Thur)
600 Perry St, Trenton, NJ, 08618-3934, Mercer, USA; tel (609) 989-7800; fax (609) 989-8758; e-mail cavila@trentonian.com; web site www.neexpreso.com
Circulation: 10,717fr; CAC
Advertising: Open inch rate $17.50
Pub..Bill Murray
Adv. Dir......................................Maggie Ashley
Ed...Carlos Avila
Mechanical Specifications: Type page 10 13/16 x 11 3/4.

UNION CITY

CONTINENTAL NEWSPAPER
(Fri)
212 48th St, Union City, NJ, 07087-6436, Hudson, USA; tel (201) 864-9505; fax (201) 864-9456; e-mail continews@aol.com
Circulation: 38,000pd,; Sworn/Estimate/Non-Audited
Advertising: Open inch rate $35.00Editions: 2- 2 total Continental Newspaper-New York (23,000);
Pres.......................................M. Ofelia Dones
Exec. Dir.......................................Mario Ciria

Mng. Ed................................ Veronica Romero
Mechanical Specifications: Type page 10 x 14; E - 5 cols, 2, between; A - 5 cols, 2, between.
Equipment: Hardware — APP/Mac; Software — Adobe/PageMaker, Microsoft/Word.

EL ESPECIALITO

(Fri) (Weekly)
3711 Hudson Ave, Union City, NJ, 07087-6015, Hudson, USA; tel (201) 348-1959; fax (201) 348-3385; e-mail anthony@elespecial.com; adv e-mail anthony@elespecial.com; ed e-mail jsibaja@elespecial.com; web site www.elespecial.com
Circulation: 0pd, 253,463fr; CAC
Advertising: Open inch rate $55.00
Established: 1985Editions: 13- El Especialito
Digital Platform - Mobile: Apple, Android, Windows, Blackberry
Digital Platform - Tablet: Apple iOS, Android, Windows 7, Blackberry Tablet OS, Nook
VP..John Ibarria
Adv. Mgr................................. Antonio Ibarria
Ed. Dir.. Jose Sibaja
Mechanical Specifications: Type page 10 x 11.25"; E - 4 cols, 2 3/8, between; A - 4 cols, between; C - 6 cols, between.
Equipment: Hardware — APP/Mac G3; Software — QPS/QuarkXPress, Adobe/Photoshop.
Delivery Method: Carrier, Racks
Zip Codes Served: New York and New Jersey

LA TRIBUNA PUBLICATION

300 36th St, Union City, NJ, 07087-4724, Hudson, USA; tel (201) 863-3310; fax (201) 617-0042; e-mail info@latribuna.com; web site www.latribuna.com
Circulation:; Sworn/Estimate/Non-Audited
Advertising: Open inch rate $19.80
Pub.. Ruth Molenaar
Adv. Mgr................................Soraya Molenaar
Circ. Mgr.....................................Rosario Tineo
Ed. ....Lionel Rodriquez
Mechanical Specifications: Type page 9 3/4 x 15; E - 6 cols, 1 1/2, 1/8 between; A - 6 cols, 1 1/2, 1/8 between; C - 6 cols, 1 1/2, 1/8 between.
Equipment: Hardware — PC; Software — Adobe/PageMaker, Microsoft/Excel, Microsoft/Word, Microsoft/Office, Quicker, Aldus.

NEW MEXICO

ESPANOLA

RIO GRANDE SUN

(Thur)
123 N Railroad Ave, Espanola, NM, 87532-2627, Rio Arriba, USA; tel (505) 753-2126; adv tel 505-753-2126; fax (505) 753-2140; adv fax 505-753-2140; e-mail rgsun@cybermesa.com; adv e-mail rgsunads@cybermesa.com; ed e-mail rgsun@cybermesa.com; web site www.riograndesun.com
Circulation: 10,000pd,; Sworn/Estimate/Non-Audited
Advertising: Open inch rate $10.80
Established: 1956
Digital Platform - Mobile: Apple
Digital Platform - Tablet: Apple iOS
General Manager.......................... Maria Garcia
Publisher.................................... Robert Trapp
Mechanical Specifications: SAU
Delivery Method: Mail, Newsstand, Racks
Zip Codes Served: 87532, 87520, 87567, 87528, 87575, 87501, 87505, 87544, 87510, 87511, 87515, 87518, 87522, 87012, 87527, 87530, 87531, 87533, 87537, 87539, 87549, 87521, 87551, 87553, 87566, 87578, 87579, 87581, 87582, 87577, 87017, 87029, 87046, 87064, 87548

NEW YORK

BROOKLYN

EL DIARIO LA PRENSA (DAILY)

1 Metrotech Ctr, Fl 18, Brooklyn, NY, 11201-3948, Kings, USA; tel (212) 807-4662; fax (212) 807-4746; e-mail editorial@eldiariolaprensa.com; adv e-mail communications@impremedia.com; web site www.eldiariony.com
Circulation: 134,696pd,; Sworn/Estimate/Non-Audited
Advertising: Open inch rate $52.08
Established: 1913
Group: Impremedia
Digital Platform - Mobile: Apple, Android
Digital Platform - Tablet: Apple iOS, Android, Windows 7
Circ. Dir. .... Denny Peña
CEO...............................Francisco Seghezzo
General Mgr Digital....................... Ivan Adaime
Content Dir.................................... Juan Varela
VP of Adv...................................... Jorge Ayala
Director, Ad Rev/Operations.....Fernando Lang
Angel Vazquez
Marketing Dir........................Lizbeth Rodriguez
Mechanical Specifications: Type page 9 13/16 x 13 1/2; E - 6 cols, 1 1/2, 1/6 between; A - 6 cols, 1 1/2, 1/6 between; C - 7 cols, 1 1/3, 1/6 between.
Equipment: Hardware — Dell/PC.
Apple
Delivery Method: Mail, Newsstand

HEMPSTEAD

LA TRIBUNA HISPANA-USA

(Wed)
48 Main St, Fl 2, Hempstead, NY, 11550-4052, Nassau, USA; tel (516) 486-6457; fax (866) 215-5982; e-mail editorial@tribunahispana.com; web site www.tribunahispanausa.com
Circulation: 49,000fr; Sworn/Estimate/Non-Audited
Advertising: Open inch rate $10.95Editions: 6- 6 total La Tribuna Hispana-Brooklyn Edition (10,000); La Tribuna Hispana-Nassau Edition (10,000); La Tribuna Hispana-New York Edition (10,000); La Tribuna Hispana-New Jersey Edition (10,000); La Tribuna Hispana-Queens Edition (10,000); La Tribuna Hispan
Digital Platform - Mobile: Apple, Android, Windows
Digital Platform - Tablet: Apple iOS, Android, Windows 7, Blackberry Tablet OS, Kindle, Nook, Kindle Fire
Gen. Mgr. .... Dora Escobar
Adv. Mgr....................................Emilio A. Ruiz
Ed. .... Luis Aguilar
Mechanical Specifications: Type page 13 3/4 x 13 3/4; E - 6 cols, 1 1/2, 1/4 between; A - 6 cols, 1 1/2, 1/4 between; C - 8 cols, between.
Delivery Method: Racks

JAMAICA

RESUMEN NEWSPAPER (DAILY)

13842 90th Ave, Apt F1, Jamaica, NY, 11435-4104, Queens, USA; tel (718) 899-8603; adv tel 718-424-7976; e-mail rojas123@aol.com; adv e-mail rojas123@aol.com; ed e-mail TRACEMYMOVES@GMAIL.COM; web site www.resumen.8m.net
Circulation: 8,000pd, 32,000fr; Sworn/Estimate/Non-Audited
Advertising: Open inch rate $14.00
Established: 1971
Pub.................................Fernando F. Rojas
Gen. Mgr. .... Jasmina Abril
Ed. ....Fernando J. Rojas
Mechanical Specifications: Type page 13 x 10 3/4; E - 4 cols, 2 1/8, 1/3 between; A - 4 cols, 2 1/8, 1/3 between; C - 4 cols, 2 1/8, 1/3 between.
Equipment: Hardware — APP/Power Mac; Software — Adobe/PageMaker 5.6, Adobe/Paint 2.1.
Delivery Method: Carrier
Zip Codes Served: 11102, 10034, 11201, 11201, 10451

KINGSTON

LAS NOTICIAS

(Wed)
79 Hurley Ave, Kingston, NY, 12401-2832, Ulster, USA; tel (845) 331-5000; fax (845) 338-0672; web site www.lasnoticiasny.com
Circulation: 5,000fr; CAC
Advertising: Open inch rate $7.90
Pub.. Ira Fusfeld
Adv. Dir...................................... Barber Norton
Ed. ....Antonio Flores-Lobos
Mechanical Specifications: Type page 10 1/8 x 15 7/5.

NEW YORK

DIARIO DE MEXICO EDICION USA

(Mon, Tues, Wed, Thur, Fri)
167 Madison Ave, Rm 401, New York, NY, 10016-5403, New York, USA; tel 646-285-3033; web site www.diariodemexicousa.com
Circulation: 12,181pd,; AAM

IMPACTO LATIN NEWS

(Wed)
225 W 35th St, Ste 1001, New York, NY, 10001-1949, New York, USA; tel (212) 807-0400; fax (212) 807-0408; e-mail media@impactony.com; adv e-mail vsmith@impactony.com; ed e-mail media@impactony.com; web site www.impactony.com
Circulation: 57,000fr; AAM
Advertising: Open inch rate $49.75
Established: 1967
Group: Impacto Latin News Publishing
Pub... Gail M Smith
Ed. .... Jason. K Smith
VP, Adv./Mktg...................... Vanessa. M Smith
Market Research Analyst ....Mar Verdugo
Delivery Method: Newsstand, Racks

LA VOZ HISPANA NEWSPAPER

(Thur)
159 E 116th St, New York, NY, 10029-1399, New York, USA; tel (212) 348-8270; adv tel (212) 348-8270; ed tel (917) 225-8576; fax (212) 348-4469; ed fax (212) 348-4469; e-mail discomund@aol.com; web site www.lavozhispanany.com
Circulation: 61,879pd, 9,200fr; Sworn/Estimate/Non-Audited
Advertising: Open inch rate $32.00
Established: 1970
Group: Casa Publications
Pub.. Nick Lugo
Mechanical Specifications: Type page 9 3/4 x 14.
Delivery Method: Mail, Racks

NUESTRO MUNDO

(Sat)
235 W 23rd St, New York, NY, 10011-2371, New York, USA; tel (212) 924-2523; fax (212) 229-1713; e-mail pww@pww.org; contact@peoplesworld.org; web site www.pww.org
Circulation: 15,000pd, 10,000fr; Sworn/Estimate/Non-Audited
Advertising: Open inch rate $20.00
Ed. ....Jose Cruz
Mechanical Specifications: Type page 11 x 17; E - 5 cols, between; A - 5 cols, between; C - 5 cols, between.
Equipment: Hardware — APP/Mac; Software — QPS/QuarkXPress.

NORTH CAROLINA

CHARLOTTE

HOLA NOTICIAS

(Tues)
4801 E Independence Blvd, Ste 815, Charlotte, NC, 28212-5490, Mecklenburg, USA; web site www.holanoticias.com
Circulation:; Sworn/Estimate/Non-AuditedJudy Galindo

LA NOTICIA

(Wed)
5936 Monroe Rd, Charlotte, NC, 28212-6106, Mecklenburg, USA; tel (704) 568-6966; fax (704) 568-8936; e-mail hgurdian@lanoticia.com; adv e-mail hgurdian@lanoticia.com; ed e-mail editor@lanoticia.com; web site www.lanoticia.com
Circulation: 26,000fr; Sworn/Estimate/Non-Audited
Advertising: N/A
Established: 1992
Digital Platform - Mobile: Apple
Digital Platform - Tablet: Apple iOS
Pub.. Hilda Gurdian
Mechanical Specifications: Type page 10 x 13 1/2.
Equipment: Hardware — APP/Mac.
Delivery Method: Racks

MI GENTE

(Tues)
4801 E Independence Blvd, Ste 800, Charlotte, NC, 28212-5408, Mecklenburg, USA; tel (704) 319-5044; adv tel (704) 449-0769; web site www.migenteweb.com
Circulation: 20,873fr; Sworn/Estimate/Non-AuditedRafael Prieto

WINSTON SALEM

QUE PASA - CHARLOTTE

(Wed)
3025 Waughtown St, Ste G, Winston Salem, NC, 27107-1679, Forsyth, USA; web site www.quepasamedia.com
Circulation: 0pd, 22,079fr; CVC
Advertising: Open inch rate $15.88
Established: 1994Jose Isasi
Mechanical Specifications: Type page: 9.889 x 12.85; 6 col

QUE PASA - PIEDMONT

(Thur)
3025 Waughtown St, Ste G, Winston Salem, NC, 27107-1679, Forsyth, USA; web site www.quepasamedia.com
Circulation: 0pd, 18,604fr; CVC
Advertising: Open inch rate $15.88
Established: 1994Jose Isasi
Mechanical Specifications: Type page: 10 x 21; 6 col

QUE PASA -TRIANGLE

(Thur)
3025 Waughtown St, Ste G, Winston Salem, NC, 27107-1679, Forsyth, USA; web site www.quepasamedia.com
Circulation: 0pd, 18,604fr; CVC
Advertising: Open inch rate $15.88
Established: 1994Jose Isasi
Mechanical Specifications: Type page: 10 x 21; 6 col

OHIO

BLUE ASH

LA JORNADA LATINA
(Fri)
4412 Carver Woods Dr, Ste 200, Blue Ash, OH, 45242-5539, Hamilton, USA; web site www.lajornadalatina.com
Circulation: 25pd, 8,933fr; Sworn/Estimate/Non-AuditedJason Riveiro
General Adv. ....Josh Guttman

LORAIN

EL LATINO EXPRESO
(Fri)
1657 Broadway, Lorain, OH, 44052-3439, Lorain, USA; tel (440) 245-6901; fax (440) 245-5637; web site www.morningjournal.com
Circulation: 8,322fr; CAC
Advertising: Open inch rate $15.95
Pub. ....Jeff Sudbrook
Mechanical Specifications: Type page 9 3/16 x 11.

OREGON

PORTLAND

EL HISPANIC NEWS
(Thur)
6700 N New York Ave, Ste 212, Portland, OR, 97203-2836, Multnomah, USA; tel (503) 228-3139; fax (503) 228-3384; e-mail info@elhispanicnews.com; web site www.elhispanicnews.com
Circulation: 20,000fr; CVC
Advertising: Open inch rate $22.00
Pub. ....Clara Padilla Andrews
Mng. Partner .... Melanie Davis
Adv. Mgr. ....Maria Perry Crawshaw
Ed. ....Julie Cortez
Prodn. Mgr. .... Christopher Alvarez
Equipment: Hardware — Software Adobe/PageMaker.
Zip Codes Served: 97214

PENNSYLVANIA

BOYERTOWN

LA VOZ
(Wed)
124 N Chestnut St, Boyertown, PA, 19512-1123, Berks, USA; tel (610) 367-6041; fax (610) 369-0233; web site www.digitallavoz.com
Circulation: 3,986fr; CAC
Advertising: Open inch rate $12.48
Pub. ....Patricia Paul
Mechanical Specifications: Type page 9 2/3 x 11 1/2.

GETTYSBURG

EL DAIRIO LATINO
1570 Fairfield Rd, Gettysburg, PA, 17325-7252, Adams, USA

PHILADELPHIA

AL DIA
(Sun)
1835 Market St, Fl 4, Philadelphia, PA, 19103-2968, Philadelphia, USA; tel (215) 569-4666; adv tel (215) 789-6975; ed tel (215) 789-6973; fax (215) 569-2721; adv fax (215) 569-2721; e-mail adsales@aldiainc.com; adv e-mail ads@aldiainc.com; ed e-mail editor@aldiainc.com; web site www.pontealdia.com
Circulation: 42,425fr; CAC
Advertising: Open inch rate $91.77
Established: 1992
Strategy & Operations ....Gaby Guaracao
Founder & CEO .... Hernan Guaracao
Managing Editor .... Sabrina Vourvoulias
Art Dir. .... Yesid Vargas
Mechanical Specifications: Type page 11 x 12; A - 5 cols, 2 1/16, 1/8 between.
Equipment: Hardware — APP/Mac; Software — InDesign, Adobe/Photoshop.
Delivery Method: Mail, Racks
Zip Codes Served: 19120, 08102

PILGRIM GARDENS

EL HISPANO
(Wed)
PO Box 396, Pilgrim Gardens, PA, 19026-0396, Delaware, USA; tel 484-472-6059; adv tel 484-472-6059; fax 484-472-8153; adv fax 474-472-8153; e-mail alopez5268@aol.com; adv e-mail hispads@aol.com; ed e-mail alopez5268@aol.com; web site www.el-hispano.com
Circulation: 500pd, 18,000fr; CVC
Advertising: $31 per CI
Group: Lopez Publicatons, Inc.Aaron G. Lopez
Madelyn Madary
Mechanical Specifications: 10" x 12" FP - Tabloid size
10" x 6" HP
Equipment: Hardware — Macs; Software — Indesign
Delivery Method: Mail, Racks
Zip Codes Served: 08101-5, 08608-29, 17101-05, 18015-18, 18101-04, 19601-19606, 19101-19152

READING

ACENTO HISPANO NEWS
1131 Butler St, Reading, PA, 19601-1911, Berks, USA; tel (610) 371-0137
Circulation:; Sworn/Estimate/Non-Audited
Advertising: Open inch rate $16.96
Circ. Mgr. .... Moises O. Manon
Ed. ....Moises O. Manon-Rossi
Mng. Ed. .... Binnelly A. Manon
Mechanical Specifications: Type page 10 1/2 x 13; E - 5 cols, 2, 1/8 between.
Equipment: Hardware — APP/Mac G3, IBM; Software — QPS/QuarkXPress 4.0, Adobe/Photoshop 5.0, Adobe/Illustrator 8.0, Adobe/PageMaker 6.5, Archetype/Corel Draw 8.0.

UPPER DARBY

EL HISPANO
(Wed)
8605 W Chester Pike, Upper Darby, PA, 19082-1101, Delaware, USA; tel (610) 789-5512; fax (610) 789-5524; e-mail alopez5268@aol.com; hispads@aol.com; web site www.el-hispano.com
Circulation: 100pd, 40,000fr; Sworn/Estimate/Non-Audited
Advertising: Open inch rate $41.00
Established: 1976
Adv. Mgr. .... Madelyn Madary
Circ. Mgr. .... Philip Madary
Mng. Ed. .... Aaron G. Lopez
Ed. ....Sara Lopez
Prodn. Mgr. .... Aaron Galicia
Mechanical Specifications: Type page 10 1/8 x 12; E - 5 cols, 1 7/8, 1/8 between; A - 5 cols, 1 7/8, 1/8 between; C - 7 cols, 1 3/8, 1/6 between.
Equipment: Hardware — 2-APP/Mac Quadra 650, 2-APP/Mac II, APP/Mac Power MC, 2-APP/Power Mac G3s, 2-Umax/PowerLook II Scanner, 2-Elite/XL808, 1-Epson/Stylus Color 1520, 2-APP/Mac G4; Presses — G; Software — Adobe/InDesign, Adobe/Photoshop 5.0, Microsoft/Word.
Zip Codes Served: 19102, 08101, 08625, 19601, 17101, 18015

WEST GROVE

UNIDAD LATINA
144 S Jennersville Rd, West Grove, PA, 19390-9430, Chester, USA; tel (610) 869-5553; fax (610) 869-9628; e-mail info@chestercounty.com; web site www.chestercounty.com/unidad/default.htm
Circulation:; Sworn/Estimate/Non-Audited
Advertising: Open inch rate $10.00
Established: 1995
Pub. ....Randall S. Lieberman
Adv. Mgr. .... Alan Turns
Mng. Ed. .... Steve Hoffman
Mechanical Specifications: Type page 10 x 15 1/2; E - 4 cols, 2 3/4, 1/4 between; A - 4 cols, 2 3/4, 1/4 between; C - 4 cols, 2 3/4, between.
Equipment: Hardware — PC; Software — Microsoft, Adobe/Photoshop.
Zip Codes Served: 19363

PUERTO RICO

CAGUAS

LA SEMANA
(Thur)
Calle Crista Bal Colafan, Esquina Ponce De Leafan, Caguas, PR, 725, Caguas, Puerto Rico; tel (787) 743-5606 ; fax (787) 743-5100; e-mail lasemanaelpionero@gmail.com; ed e-mail redaccion@periodicolasemana.net; web site www.lasemana.com
Circulation: 80,060fr; AAM

CAROLINA

PERIODICO PRESENCIA
(Wed)
PO Box 1928, Carolina, PR, 00984-1928, Carolina, USA; tel (787)-946-1391; fax (787)946-1342; web site presenciapr.com
Circulation: 49,975fr; VAC
Delivery Method: Newsstand

DORADO

EL EXPRESSO DE PUERTO RICO
(Thur)
PO Box 465, Dorado, PR, 00646-0465, Dorado, Puerto Rico; tel 787-794-2000; adv tel 787-794-2000; ed tel 787-794-2006; fax 787-794-2273; adv fax 787-794-2273; ed fax 787-794-2716; e-mail info@elexpresso.com; adv e-mail anuncios@elexpresso.com; ed e-mail redaccion@elexpresso.com; web site www.elexpresso.com
Circulation: 0pd, 74,900fr; VAC
Advertising: Open inch rate $35.00
Established: 1995
Digital Platform - Mobile: Android, Windows
Digital Platform - Tablet: Android, Windows 7
Publisher .... Angel Fret
Mechanical Specifications: 13" Heigh
10" widht
Equipment: Hardware — PC; Software — Photoshop
InDesign
Others
Delivery Method: Mail, Newsstand, Racks
Note: Delivered in 24 towns, North of Puerto Rico.

GUAYNABO

PERIODICO METRO PUERTO RICO
(Mon, Tues, Wed, Thur, Fri)
Carazo St, Guaynabo, PR, 969, Guaynabo, USA; tel (787)705-0920; fax (787)705-0926; adv e-mail multimedia@metro.pr; ed e-mail multimedia@metro.pr; web site www.metro.pr
Circulation: 102,832fr; CAC
Delivery Method: Newsstand, Racks

PRIMERA HORA
(Mon, Tues, Wed, Thur, Fri, Sat)
A 16 Genoa Street, Extension Villa Caparra, Guaynabo, PR, 965, Guaynabo, Puerto Rico; tel 787-641-4475; adv tel 787-641-4469; fax 787-641-4473; adv fax 787-641-4470; web site http://www.primerahora.com
Circulation: 68,746pd,; AAM

SAN JUAN

EL NUEVO DIA
(Mon, Tues, Wed, Thur, Fri, Sat, Sun)
Cond Almirante, San Juan, PR, 911, San Juan, Puerto Rico; tel 787-641-8000 ; web site www.elnuevodia.net
Circulation: 177,578pd,; AAM

RHODE ISLAND

NORTH PROVIDENCE

PROVIDENCE EN ESPANOL
(Mon, Tues, Wed, Thur, Fri, Sat, Sun) (daily updates)
45 Meadow View Blvd, North Providence, RI, 02904-2916, Providence, USA; tel 401.834.5552; fax 401.233.7500; adv e-mail ads@providenceenespanol.com; ed e-mail news@providenceenespanol.com; web site www.providenceenespanol.com
Established: 1999
Digital Platform - Mobile: Apple, Android, Windows
Digital Platform - Tablet: Apple iOS, Android, Windows 7
Ed. ....Arelis Pena
Vivian Cuenca
Victor Cuenca

SOUTH CAROLINA

MOUNT PLEASANT

EL INFORMADOR SPANISH LANGUAGE NEWSPAPER
(Wed) (Biweekly)
PO Box 2458, Mount Pleasant, SC, 29465-2458, Charleston, USA; tel 843-693-1116; adv tel 843-817-2896; ed tel 843-693-1116; fax 843-352-4506; adv fax 843-352-4506; ed fax 843-352-4506; e-mail lisa@elinformadornewspaper.com; adv e-mail sales@elinformadornewspaper.com; ed e-mail lisa@elinformadornewspaper.com; web site www.elinformador.us
Circulation: 10,000fr; Sworn/Estimate/Non-Audited

Established: 2008
Director.................................Lisa De Armas
Publisher................................Pedro De Armas
Delivery Method: Racks
Zip Codes Served: 29418, 29406, 29401,29403,29405,29407, 20410, 29420, 29445, 29455, 29456, 29461, 29464, 29483, 29485,29906, 29907, 29920, 29935, 29936, 29926,29928,29910,29927

TEXAS

ABILENE

ABILENE HISPANIC GUIDE
(Thur)
122 McGlothlin Campus Center, Acu Box 29004, Abilene, TX, 79699-0001, Taylor, USA; tel (325) 674-2067; fax (325) 674-6475; web site www.hispanicabilene.com
Circulation: 6,000fr; Sworn/Estimate/Non-Audited
Advertising: Open inch rate $8.00
Established: 1992
Owner.......................................Patricia Olvera
Mechanical Specifications: Type page 10 1/8 x 12 1/2; E - 5 cols, 1 3/4, 1/6 between.
Equipment: Hardware — Pentium/486; Software — Microsoft/Windows 98.
Zip Codes Served: 10003

AMARILLO

EL MENSAJERO
(Wed)
PO Box 895, Amarillo, TX, 79105-0895, Potter, USA; tel (806) 371-7084; fax (806) 371-7090; e-mail editor@elmensajero-ama.com
Circulation: 2,000pd, 960fr; CVC
Advertising: Open inch rate $31.50
Gen. Mgr.....................................David Godoy
Circ. Mgr...............................Enrique Gallardo
Ed.......................................Dr. Ramon Godoy
Mng. Ed.....................................Amada Isabel
Prodn. Mgr. ....Arturo Arevalo
Equipment: Hardware — APP/Mac; Software — Adobe/Photoshop, QPS/QuarkXPress.

AUSTIN

AHORA SI!
(Thur) (on web, daily)
305 S Congress Ave, Austin, TX, 78704-1200, Travis, USA; tel (512) 445-3500; adv tel (512) 912-2949; ed tel (512) 445-3500; fax n/a; e-mail eventos@ahorasi.com; adv e-mail Johnny.Flores@coxinc.com; ed e-mail jcasati@ahorasi.com; web site www.ahorasi.com
Circulation: 19,885fr; AAM
Advertising: Open inch rate $42.58
Established: 2004
Group: Austin American-Statesman
Ed. ....Josefina Villicana Casati
Equipment: Hardware — APP/Mac, Sim/Enterprise 4000; Presses — 9-G/Metroliner double width (5 half decks), KBA/Towers; Software — DTI/PageSpeed, DTI/SpeedPlanner.
Delivery Method: Carrier, Racks
Zip Codes Served: 78701-78705, 78708-78739, 78741-78742, 78744-78769

EL MUNDO - AUSTIN / SAN ANTONIO
(Thur)
2116 E Cesar Chavez St, Austin, TX, 78702-4514, Travis, USA; tel 512-476-8636; ed tel 512-474-8535; fax 512-476-6402; ed fax 512-476-6402; e-mail info@elmundonewspaper.com; adv e-mail angela@elmundonewspaper.com; ed e-mail jg@elmundonewspaper.com; web site www.elmundonewspaper.com
Circulation: 0pd, 45,000fr; CVC
Advertising: $28 Fc and $25 B&W
Established: 1989
Digital Platform - Mobile: Apple, Android
Digital Platform - Tablet: Apple iOS, Android
Publisher....................................Alba Angulo
Mechanical Specifications: 11.98 x 21.5
Equipment; Presses — Harris V15; Software — Indesign CS6
Delivery Method: Racks

PERIODICO BUENA SUERTE - AUSTIN
(Thur)
6901 N Lamar Blvd, Ste 139, Austin, TX, 78752-3532, Travis, USA; tel (512) 345-0101; web site www.austin.buenasuerte.com
Circulation: 0pd, 6,180fr; Sworn/Estimate/Non-Audited
Advertising: Open inch rate $13.00
Established: 1986
Digital Platform - Mobile: Apple, Android, Windows
Digital Platform - Tablet: Apple iOS, Android, Windows 7Emilio Martinez
Delivery Method: Newsstand, Racks
Zip Codes Served: 78701, 78702, 78703, 78704

BROWNSVILLE

EL NUEVO HERALDO
(Mon, Tues, Wed, Thur, Fri, Sat, Sun)
1135 E Van Buren St, Brownsville, TX, 78520-7055, Cameron, USA; tel (956) 542-4301; adv tel (956) 982-6636; ed tel (956) 982-6625; fax (956) 504-1119; adv fax (956) 982-4201; ed fax (956) 430-6233; e-mail tbhpress@brownsvilleherald.com; web site www.brownsvilleherald.com
Circulation: 2,612pd, 90fr; AAM
Advertising: Open inch rate $8.95
Pub.....................................R. Daniel Cavazos
Adv. Dir.............................Karen Ashanholtzer
Circ. Dir....................................Abe Gonzalez
Ed...Rachel Benavides
Ed. ....Marci Ponce
News Ed......................................Gary Long
Photo Ed....................................Brad Doherty
Prodn. Mgr., Systems ....Speedy Aldape
Mechanical Specifications: Type page 13 x 21 1/4; E - 6 cols, 2 1/4, 1/8 between; A - 6 cols, 2 1/16, 1/8 between; C - 10 cols, 1 1/4, 3/8 between.

CARRIZO SPRINGS

THE CARRIZO SPRINGS JAVELIN
(Thur)
610 N 1st St, Carrizo Springs, TX, 78834-2602, Dimmit, USA; tel (830) 876-2318; fax (830) 876-2620; e-mail csjaveline@yahoo.com; web site www.carrizospringsjavelin.com
Circulation: 2,000pd, 100fr; Sworn/Estimate/Non-Audited
Advertising: Open inch rate $4.00
Pub.......................................Howard McDaniel
Ed. ....Claudia McDaniel
Mechanical Specifications: Type page 13 x 21; E - 6 cols, 2 1/16, 1/6 between; A - 6 cols, 2 1/16, between; C - 6 cols, 2 1/16, between.
Equipment: Hardware — PC; Software — Adobe/PageMaker, Microsoft.

DALLAS

AL DIA
(Wed, Sat)
508 Young St, Fl 2, Dallas, TX, 75202-4808, Dallas, USA; tel (469) 977-3600; fax (469) 977-3601; e-mail preguntas@aldiatx.com; circulation@aldiatx.com; web site www.aldiatx.com
Circulation: 21,143fr; AAM
Advertising: Open inch rate $78.00
Gen. Mgr...................................Alex Sanchez
Exec. Asst......................................Yeradi Lara
Adv. Mgr., Nat'l Sales...................Becci Reyes
Mktg. Exec...Iris Diaz
Circ. Dir..................................Rosario Heredia
Cliente Serv. Coord................Yadira Gonzalez
Ed. in Chief.............................Alfredo Carbajal
Online Ed..................................Anthony Trejo
Sports Ed......................................Mauro Diaz
Delivery Method: Mail, Newsstand, Carrier, Racks

EL EXTRA NEWSPAPER
(Thur)
1214 Gardenview Dr, Dallas, TX, 75217-4311, Dallas, USA; tel 214-309-0990; adv tel 214-309-0990; ed tel 214-309-0990; fax 214-309-0204; adv fax 214-309-0204; e-mail pressrelease@elextranewspaper.com; adv e-mail clasificados@elextranewspaper.com; ed e-mail pressrelease@elextranewspaper.com; web site www.elextranewspaper.com
Circulation: 19,975fr; VAC
Advertising: Open inch rate $23.00
Established: 1987
Digital Platform - Mobile: Windows
Digital Platform - Tablet: Windows 7
Publisher/Editor
Advertising Manager.....................Emmy Silva
Mechanical Specifications: Offset - PDF - CMYK
Delivery Method: Newsstand, Racks

EL HERALDO NEWS
(Fri)
4532 Columbia Ave, Dallas, TX, 75226-1016, Dallas, USA; tel (214) 827-9700; fax (214) 827-8200; e-mail ellie@elheraldonews.com; web site www.elheraldonews.com
Circulation: 2pd, 17,998fr; CAC
Advertising: Open inch rate $25.00
Adv. Mgr...Ellie Byrd
Ed. ....Francisco Rayo
Mechanical Specifications: Type page 11.25 x 20.55; E - 6 cols, between; A - 6 cols, between.
Equipment: Hardware — PC, APP/Mac; Software — QPS/QuarkXPress, Adobe/Photoshop.

EL HISPANO NEWS
(Thur)
2102 Empire Central, Dallas, TX, 75235-4302, Dallas, USA; tel (214) 357-2186; adv tel (214) 357-2186 ext. 202; ed tel (214) 357-2186 ext. 225; fax (214) 357-2195; e-mail editor@elhispanonews.com; adv e-mail lupita@elhispanonews.com; ed e-mail reynaldo@elhispanonews.com; web site www.elhispanonews.com
Circulation: 20,390fr; CAC
Advertising: Open inch rate $26.00
Established: 1986
Group: RBLC, Inc
Digital Platform - Mobile: Apple, Android, Windows
Digital Platform - Tablet: Apple iOS, Android, Windows 7, Kindle, Nook
Adv. Mgr., Nat'l.....................Lupita Colmenero
Circ. Mgr..............................Ruben Colmenero
Office Mgr.............................Roxanna Lopez
Graphics ....Einer Agredo
Managing Ed ....Reynaldo Mena
Beana Ramirez
Marketing Mgr.......................Rodolfo Bustillos
Mechanical Specifications: File Format Specs
Web offset on 30 pound newsprint 50 lbs white stock
Composite PDF (Postscript): Files must be created carefully to ensure that they are properly optimized for hi-res
resolution output. Fonts need to be either outlined or properly embedded.
File must be process in CMYK mode, no fifth color will be accepted.
Trapping must be include in the file if is needed.
Standard trim; include bleed and center marks (cropping mark), no marks in the live or bleed image area.
Printing Specification
1 Column = 1.611
2 Column = 3.389
3 Column = 5.167
4 Column = 6.994
5 Column = 8.722
6 Column = 10.5
1/2 Page = 10.5 x 10.5
Full Page = 10.5 x 21
Unit Dimensions
Minimum depth in inches must be equal to/or greater than the number of columns used. Bleed pages are not available.
Equipment; Software — Microsoft/Windows 95, Adobe/PageMaker 6.5, Adobe/Photoshop.
Delivery Method: Mail, Newsstand, Carrier, Racks
Note: El Hispano News is the oldest Hispanic newspaper in North Texas, serving the Hispanic community since 1986. With a 20,000 copies verified distribution, and our active involvement with the community, especially with issues regarding education (including financial aspects), makes El Hispano News a prefer medium of information for the Dallas Fort Worth Hispanic community.

LA SUBASTA DE DALLAS
(Thur)
1555 W Mockingbird Ln, Ste 212, Dallas, TX, 75235-5080, Dallas, USA; tel (214) 951-9500; adv tel (713) 777-1010; fax (214) 951-9400; e-mail customerservice@lasubasta.com ; adv e-mail sales@lasubasta.com; web site www.lasubasta.com
Circulation: 57,137fr; VAC
Sales Manager ....Eduardo Perez

NOVEDADES NEWS
(Wed)
121 S Zang Blvd, P.O. Box# 4752, Dallas, TX, 75208-4530, Dallas, USA; tel (214) 943-2932; adv tel (214) 943-2932; ed tel (214) 943-2932; fax (214) 943-7352; adv fax (214) 943-7352; ed fax (214) 943-7352; e-mail editorial@novedadesnews.com; adv e-mail spuerto@novedadesnews.com; ed e-mail editorial@novedadesnews.com; web site www.novedadesnews.com
Circulation: 0pd, 37,800fr; CAC
Advertising: Open inch rate $26.00
Established: 1986Editions: 1,487-1,487-Circulation 38000
Digital Platform - Mobile: Android
Digital Platform - Tablet: Android
Mktg. Dir.................................Sergio Puerto
Pres./CEO ....Sergio Puerto Sr.
Mechanical Specifications: Web Offset Full Color Available
Delivery Method: Newsstand, Racks
Zip Codes Served: Dallas/Fort Worth Texas
Note: Largest and Oldest Newspaper in the Dallas/Fort Worth Texas Area.

PERIODICO BUENA SUERTE - DALLAS
(Wed, Thur)
1545 W Mockingbird Ln, Ste 1012, Dallas, TX, 75235-5014, Dallas, USA; tel (214) 575-4545; adv e-mail sales@buenasuerte.com; web site www.buenasuerte.com
Circulation: 0pd, 15,051fr; Sworn/Estimate/Non-Audited
Advertising: Open inch rate $13.00
Established: 2010
Digital Platform - Mobile: Apple, Android, Windows
Digital Platform - Tablet: Apple iOS, Android, Windows 7Emilio Martinez
Delivery Method: Newsstand, Racks
Zip Codes Served: 75235

EAGLE PASS

THE NEWS GRAM/THE GRAM
(Tues, Wed, Thur, Fri, Sun)
2543 Del Rio Blvd, Eagle Pass, TX, 78852-3627, Maverick, USA; tel (830) 773-8610; fax (830) 773-1641; e-mail elgram@hilconet.com; web site thenewsgramonline.net

Circulation: 23,000fr; Sworn/Estimate/Non-Audited
Advertising: Open inch rate $7.35
Pub.............................. Ruben Carrillo Mazuka
Adv. Mgr.................................... Celina Ramos
Ed...Jesus Maldonado
Delivery Method: Racks
Zip Codes Served: 78852, 78853, 78834, 78877

EL PASO

EL PASO Y MAS
(Sun)
500 W Overland Ave, Ste 150, El Paso, TX, 79901-1108, El Paso, USA; tel (915) 546-6300; adv tel (915) 542-6066 ; ed tel (915) 546-6149 ; fax (915) 546-6284; adv e-mail jmolina@elpasotimes.com; ed e-mail bmoore@elpasotimes.com; web site http://www.elpasotimes.com/
Circulation: 50,000fr; AAM
CEO/President & Publisher . Sergio H. Salinas
Dir., HR.. Malena Field
Senior VP of Advertising and Marketing Cecilia Uebel
VP of Online/Digital ....Jim Weddell
Mktg. Dir......................................Phillip Cortez
Circ. Dir...Jim Dove
Circ. Mgr., City Home Delivery................ Craig Pogorzelski
Circ. Mgr., Transportation......... Randy Waldrop
Bus. Ed........................... Ramon Bracamontes
City/Metro Ed..................... Armando V. Durazo
Design Ed.............................. Carlita Costello
Editorial Page Ed..................... Charlie Edgren
Features Ed...........................Melissa Martinez
Online Sales Mgr...................Mario Ontiveros
Information Technolgy Dir.............. Paz Garcia
VP of Production................. Patsy Hernandez
Sports Editor .... Margaret Gallardo
Ed...Robert Moore

FORT WORTH

LA ESTRELLA
(Sat)
400 W 7th St, Fort Worth, TX, 76102-4701, Tarrant, USA; tel (817) 390-7180; fax (817) 390-7280; e-mail jaramos@laestrelladigital.com; web site www.laestrelladigital.com
Circulation: 123,150fr; AAM
Advertising: Open inch rate $30.12
Adv. Mgr...................................... Baker Haymes
Ed...................................Juan Antonio Ramos
Mng. Ed...................................... Raul Caballero
Mechanical Specifications: Type page 13 1/2 x 22; E - 6 cols, 2, 1/6 between; A - 6 cols, 2, 1/6 between; C - 10 cols, 1 1/4, between.
Equipment: Hardware — PC; Presses — G/Metroliner; Software — QPS/QuarkXPress 3.32.
Zip Codes Served: 76102

PANORAMA DE NUEVOS HORIZONTES
(Sat)
3501 Williams Rd, Fort Worth, TX, 76116-7029, Tarrant, USA; web site www.panorama-news.com
Circulation: 0pd, 15,450fr; CVC
Advertising: N/A
Established: 2002Julia Martinez-Smit

HOUSTON

ENFOQUE DEPORTIVO
13227 Noblecrest Dr, Houston, TX, 77041-1871, Harris, USA; tel (713) 785-7191; fax (832) 467-9792; e-mail enfoque@sbcglobal.net; web site www.enfoquedeportivo.com
Circulation:; Sworn/Estimate/Non-Audited
Advertising: Open inch rate $17.00
Pub..................................William Jose Reyes
Adv. Mgr.......................................Juana Reyes
Ed...Maritza Reyes
Mechanical Specifications: Type page 10 1/2 x 14; E - 5 cols, 2, 1/8 between.
Zip Codes Served: 77057

LA SUBASTA
6120 Tarnef Dr, Ste 110, Houston, TX, 77074-3754, Harris, USA; tel (713) 772-8900; fax (713) 772-8999; web site www.eldiausa.com
Circulation:; Sworn/Estimate/Non-Audited
Advertising: Open inch rate $1.40
Pub... German Arango

LA VOZ DE HOUSTON
(Wed)
4747 Southwest Fwy, Houston, TX, 77027-6901, Harris, USA; tel (713) 362-8100; fax (713) 362-8630; e-mail aurora.losada@chron.com; web site www.chron.com
Circulation: 198,856fr; AAM
Advertising: Open inch rate $84.00
Mgr...Loida Ruiz
Adv. Sales Mgr............................Craig Hurluy
Ed.. Aurora Losada
Mechanical Specifications: Type page 12 x 21; E - 6 cols, 1 7/8, 1/8 between; A - 6 cols, 1 7/8, 1/8 between; C - 10 cols, 1 1/4, 1/16 between.
Equipment: Hardware — Software QPS/QuarkXPress 4.0.

MERCADO LATINO
(Tues)
5327 Aldine Mail Route Rd, Houston, TX, 77039-4919, Harris, USA; tel (281) 449-9945; fax (713) 977-1188; e-mail nenewsroom@aol.com; web site www.nenewsroom.com
Circulation: 30,000fr; Sworn/Estimate/Non-Audited
Advertising: Open inch rate $10.00
Group: Grafikpress Corp.
Editor/PUblisher............................Gil Hoffman
Mechanical Specifications: Type page 10 1/4 x 13; E - 6 cols, 2 1/8, 1/8 between; A - 7 cols, 1 3/4, 1/8 between; C - 9 cols, 1 1/8, 1/8 between.
Equipment: Hardware — APP/Mac/PC; Presses — 5 unit King web press
Two 4 color heidelberg sheet presses; Software — Adobe/PageMaker 6.5/photoshop/indesign
Delivery Method: Mail, Newsstand, Carrier, Racks
Zip Codes Served:
77039,77093,77060,77016,77336

PERIODICO BUENA SUERTE - HOUSTON
(Tues, Wed, Thur, Fri)
7324 Southwest Fwy, Ste 1720, Houston, TX, 77074-2058, Harris, USA; tel 713-272-0101; adv e-mail sales@buenasuerte.com; web site www.buenasuerte.com
Circulation: 84,918fr; Sworn/Estimate/Non-Audited
Advertising: Open inch rate $13.00
Established: 1986
Digital Platform - Mobile: Apple, Android, Windows
Digital Platform - Tablet: Apple iOS, Android, Windows 7, Kindle FireEmilio Martinez
Delivery Method: Newsstand, Racks
Zip Codes Served: 77002, 77036, 77055, 77074, 77036, 77055, 77478

SEMANA NEWS
(Sun)
10425 SW Plaza Dr, Houston, TX, 77074-1117, Harris, USA; tel (713) 774-4686; ed tel 832 431 5588; fax (713) 774-4666; e-mail info@semananews.com; ed e-mail editorial@semananews.com; web site www.semananews.com
Circulation: 134,240fr; AAM
Advertising: Open inch rate $47.94
Digital Platform - Mobile: Android
Pub..Mario G. Duenas
Circ. Mgr............................Armando Molinaris
Prodn. Mgr.................................. Raul Duenas
Felix Medina
Mechanical Specifications: Type page 11 x 13; E - 5 cols, 2, 1/6 between; A - 5 cols, 2, 1/6 between; C - 6 cols, 1 5/8, 1/6 between.
Equipment: Hardware — PC. MAC; Presses — Owned
Delivery Method: Racks

JACKSONVILLE

LA OPINION
(Other) (Bi-Weekly (Every Other Wednesday))
404 College Ave, Jacksonville, TX, 75766-2244, Cherokee, USA
Circulation: 0pd, 0fr; VAC
Advertising: Open inch rate $15.00
Established: 1989Judith Cantua

LAREDO

EL TIEMPQ DE LAREDO
111 Esperanza Dr, Laredo, TX, 78041-2607, Webb, USA; tel (956) 728-2500; fax (956) 724-3036; web site www.lmtonline.com
Circulation:; Sworn/Estimate/Non-Audited
Advertising: Open inch rate $30.50
Group: Hearst Communications, Inc.
Pub....................................... William B. Green
Gen. Mgr................................ Adriana DeVally
Circ. Mgr.................................. Christian Cruz
Ed..Melva Lavin
Ed..Diana Fuentes
Creative Dir..Raul Cruz
Mechanical Specifications: Type page 13 x 21; E - 6 cols, between; A - 6 cols, 2 1/16, between.
Equipment: Hardware — APP/Mac, IBM; Software — Adobe/Photoshop, QPS/QuarkXPress.

LUBBOCK

EL EDITOR-LUBBOCK
(Thur)
1502 Avenue M, Lubbock, TX, 79401-4950, Lubbock, USA; tel (806) 763-3841; fax (806) 741-1110; e-mail eleditor@sbcglobal.net; adv e-mail eleditorsales@sbcglobal.net; web site www.eleditor.com
Circulation: 0pd, 4,017fr; VAC
Advertising: Open inch rate $20.00
Established: 1977
Owner...............................Olga Riojas-Aguero
Mechanical Specifications: Type page 13 x 21; E - 6 cols, 2 1/4, 1/8 between; A - 6 cols, 2 1/4, 1/8 between; C - 6 cols, 2 1/2, 1/8 between.
Equipment: Hardware — APP/Power Mac; Software — Adobe/PageMaker 6.9, Adobe/Illustrator 5.0.
Delivery Method: Racks

EL EDITOR-PERMIAN BASIN
(Wed)
1502 Avenue M, Lubbock, TX, 79401-4950, Lubbock, USA; tel (806) 763-3841; fax (806) 741-1110; e-mail eleditor@sbcglobal.net; web site www.eleditor.com
Circulation: 15,000fr; Sworn/Estimate/Non-Audited
Advertising: Open inch rate $19.50
Circ. Mgr.....................................Gilbert Acuna
Ed.. Bidal Aguero
Prodn. Mgr....................................Olga Aguero
Mechanical Specifications: Type page 13 x 21 1/2; E - 6 cols, 2 1/16, 1/8 between; A - 6 cols, 2 1/16, 1/8 between; C - 6 cols, 2 1/16, 1/8 between.
Equipment: Hardware — CSI, APP/Mac.

EL SOL LATINO (2 X MTHLY)
1812 Texas Ave, Lubbock, TX, 79401-5145, Lubbock, USA; tel (806) 741-1956; fax (806) 740-0045; e-mail elsollatino@nts-online.net
Circulation: 59,975fr; Sworn/Estimate/Non-Audited
Advertising: Open inch rate $15.50
Ed.. Damian P. Morales
Mechanical Specifications: Type page 13 x 21; E - 6 cols, between.

MCALLEN

SPANISH PRINT MEDIA, INC
(Wed)
801 E Fir Ave, McAllen, TX, 78501-9320, Hidalgo, USA; tel (956) 631-5628; adv tel 956-631-5628; ed tel 956-631-5628; fax (956) 631-0832; adv fax 956-631-0832; ed fax 956-631-0832; e-mail jose@spanishprint.com; adv e-mail jose@spanishprint.com; ed e-mail jose@spanishprint.com; web site www.elperiodicousa.com
Circulation: 56,000pd,; CAC
Advertising: Open inch rate $25.00
Established: 1986
Editor/Director.......................... Jose B. Garza
Pub..Kathy Letelier
Mechanical Specifications: Type page 10.5 x 19 3/4; E - 6 cols, 1 3/4, 1/4 between; A - 6 cols, 1 3/4, 1/4 between; C - 6 cols, 1 3/4, 1/4 between.
Equipment: Hardware — APP/Mac; Software — In Design, Photoshop, Ilustrator, Office
Delivery Method: Carrier, Racks
Zip Codes Served: 78516, 78537, 78539, 78557, 78501, 785013, 78504, 78557, 78589, 78506, 78520, 78521

PRESIDIO

THE PRESIDIO INTERNATIONAL
(Thur)
Market @ Ralph England Streets, Presidio, TX, 79845, Presidio, USA; tel (432) 729-4342; e-mail editor@bigbendnow.com; web site www.bigbendnow.com
Circulation: 900pd, 100fr; USPS
Advertising: Open inch rate $9.50
Established: 1986
Digital Platform - Mobile: Apple
Digital Platform - Tablet: Apple iOS
Ed....................................... Robert L. Halpern
Mng. Ed................... Rosario Salgado-Halpern
Mechanical Specifications: Type page 13 x 21 1/2; E - 6 cols, 2 1/16, 1/8 between; A - 6 cols, 2 1/16, 1/8 between; C - 6 cols, 2 1/16, 1/8 between.
Equipment: Hardware — Mac; Presses — Monahans News, Monahans, Texas; Software — Adobe creative suite
Delivery Method: Mail, Newsstand, Racks

SAN ANTONIO

LA PRENSA DE SAN ANTONIO
(Wed, Sun)
230 N Medina St, San Antonio, TX, 78207-3022, Bexar, USA; tel (210) 242-7900; fax (210) 242-7901; adv e-mail tinoduran@laprensa.com; web site www.laprensa.com
Circulation: 10,640pd, 146,000fr; Sworn/Estimate/Non-Audited
Advertising: Open inch rate $30.59
Pub...Tino Duran
Ed....................................... Marinaelena Cruz

PERIODICO BUENA SUERTE - SAN ANTONIO
(Fri)
1804 NE Interstate 410 Loop, Suite #280A, San Antonio, TX, 78217, Bexar, USA; tel (210) 444-0001; adv e-mail sales@BuenaSuerte.com; web site www.buenasuerte.com
Circulation: 0pd, 14,004fr; Sworn/Estimate/Non-Audited
Advertising: Open inch rate $13.00
Established: 1986
Digital Platform - Mobile: Apple, Android, Windows
Digital Platform - Tablet: Apple iOS, Android,

Windows 7Emilio Martinez
Delivery Method: Newsstand, Racks

UTAH

OGDEN

EL ESTANDAR
(Wed)
332 Standard Way, Ogden, UT, 84404-1371, Weber, USA; web site www.standard.net
Circulation: 15,625fr; Sworn/Estimate/Non-AuditedLee Carter

WASHINGTON

KIRKLAND

EL MUNDO - WA
(Thur)
11410 NE 124th St, # 441, Kirkland, WA, 98034-4399, King, USA; web site www.elmundous.com
Circulation: 500pd, 14,113fr; CVC
Advertising: Open inch rate $18.00
Established: 1989Martha Montoya
Mechanical Specifications: Type page: 10.625 x 20; 6 columns

LAKEWOOD

FRONTERAS
8312 Custer Rd SW, Lakewood, WA, 98499-2526, Pierce, USA; tel (253) 584-1212; fax (253) 581-5962; e-mail swarnerkm@aol.com
Circulation:; Sworn/Estimate/Non-Audited
Advertising: Open inch rate $11.00
Established: 2007
Adv. Mgr. .... Bill White
Ed. .... Ken Swarner

WENATCHEE

EL MUNDO
(Thur)
10 N Mission St, Wenatchee, WA, 98801-2250, Chelan, USA; tel (509) 663-5737; fax (509) 663-6957; e-mail info@elmundous.com; web site www.elmundonews.net
Circulation: 20,000fr; Sworn/Estimate/Non-Audited
Advertising: Open inch rate $11.00
Adv. Mgr. .... Carlos Rossetti
Ed. .... Gustazo Montaya
Prod. Mgr. .... Luis Alvarz
Mechanical Specifications: Type page 12 1/2 x 22 1/2; E - 6 cols, 1 4/5, 3/16 between; A - 6 cols, 1 4/5, 3/16 between; C - 6 cols, 1 4/5, 3/16 between.
Equipment: Hardware — APP/Mac; Software — Adobe/PageMaker 6.5.
Zip Codes Served: 98004, 99301

JEWISH NEWSPAPERS IN THE UNITED STATES

ALABAMA

MOUNTAIN BRK

SOUTHERN JEWISH LIFE (Mthly)
14 Office Park Cir, Ste 104, Mountain Brk, AL, 35223-2792, Jefferson, USA; tel (205) 322-9002; adv tel (205) 870-7889; fax (866) 392-7750; e-mail connect@sjlmag.com; adv e-mail lee@sjlmag.com; ed e-mail editor@sjlmag.com; web site www.sjlmag.com
Circulation: 9,500fr; USPS
Advertising: Open inch rate $31.67
Established: 1990Editions: 2- Deep South, New Orleans
Adv. Mgr. .... Lee Green
Ed/Pub .... Larry Brook
Advertising .... Annetta Dolowitz
Mechanical Specifications: Glossy magazine, 8.5x11 finished. 7.75"x10" live area.
Equipment: Hardware — APP/Mac; Software — Adobe Creative Cloud, MS Office
Delivery Method: Mail
Zip Codes Served: 324-325, 350-368, 386-397, 700-714
Note: Formerly Deep South Jewish Voice, became Southern Jewish Life in August 2009. Official publication of the New Orleans Jewish community.

ARIZONA

PHOENIX

JEWISH NEWS (Fri) (annual Community Directory, annual Best of Jewish Phoenix magazine)
1430 E Missouri Ave, Ste B225, Phoenix, AZ, 85014-2489, Maricopa, USA; tel (602) 870-9470; fax (602) 870-0426; e-mail publisher@jewishaz.com; ed e-mail editor@jewishaz.com; web site www.jewishaz.com
Circulation: 0pd, 4,870fr; CVC
Advertising: N/A
Established: 1948
Group: Jewish Community FoundationEditions: 54-
Digital Platform - Mobile: Other
Digital Platform - Tablet: Other
Adv. Coord. .... Julie Goggin
Mng. Ed. .... Leisah Woldoff
Prodn. Mgr. .... Becky Globokar
Adv. Acc. Exec. .... Susan Breakstone
Adv. Acc. Exec. .... Susan Kabat
Mechanical Specifications: Type page 10" x 10.5"; 4 cols
Equipment: Hardware — PC, APP/Mac; Software — Adobe/PageMaker.
Delivery Method: Mail, Newsstand

TUCSON

ARIZONA JEWISH POST (Fri) (24x per year)
3822 E River Rd, Ste 300, Tucson, AZ, 85718-6635, Pima, USA; tel (520)319-1112; adv tel (520) 319-1112 ext. 136; ed tel (520) 319-1112 ext. 135; fax (520) 319-1118; e-mail office@azjewishpost.com; adv e-mail berti@azjewishpost.com; ed e-mail localnews@azjewishpost.com; web site www.azjewishpost.com
Circulation: 2,022pd, 4,038fr; CVC
Advertising: Open inch rate $20.00
Established: 1946
Group: Jewish Federation of Southern Arizona
Exec. Ed. .... Phyllis Braun
Account Executive .... Maris Finley
Mechanical Specifications: Six (6) columns x 12.75 inch column depth
Full page: 10.25" wide X 12.75 depth.
Delivery Method: Mail, Carrier, Racks
Zip Codes Served: 85614, 85641, 85653, 85658, 85701, 85702, 85704, 85705, 85706, 85576, 85710, 85711, 85712, 85713, 85715, 85716, 85718, 85719, 85730, 85737, 85739, 85741

CALIFORNIA

ENCINO

JEWISH NEWS (Mthly)
16501 Ventura Blvd, Ste 504, Encino, CA, 91436-2047, Los Angeles, USA; tel (818) 786-4000; fax (818) 380-9232; e-mail info@jewishlifetv.com; web site www.jewishlifetv.com
Circulation: 106,000pd,; Sworn/Estimate/Non-Audited
Advertising: Open inch rate $28.00
Ed. .... Phil Blazer

LA MESA

SAN DIEGO JEWISH TIMES
4731 Palm Ave, La Mesa, CA, 91941-5221, San Diego, USA; tel (619) 463-5515; fax (619) 463-1309; e-mail sdjt@sdjewishtimes.com; adv e-mail kgreen@sdjewishtimes.com; ed e-mail msirota@sdjewishtimes.com; web site www.sdjewishtimes.com
Advertising: Open inch rate $60.00
Established: 1980
Dir., Sales .... Michael Schwarz
Ed. .... Michael Sirota
Prodn. Mgr. .... Leslie Pebley
Mechanical Specifications: Type page 10 x 14.

LONG BEACH

JEWISH COMMUNITY CHRONICLE (Mthly)
3801 E Willow St, Long Beach, CA, 90815-1734, Los Angeles, USA; tel (562) 426-7601; fax (562) 424-3915; e-mail chronicle@jewishlongbeach.org; web site www.jewishlongbeach.org
Circulation: 6,300fr; Sworn/Estimate/Non-Audited
Advertising: Open inch rate $16.00
Established: 1947
Group: Jewish Federation of Greater Long Beach & West Orange CountyEditions: 12- Health, High Holy Days, Wedding/B'nai Mitzvah/Simchahs, Chanukah/Thanksgiving, Planned Giving, Seniors, Camp, Purim, Passover, Israel, Arts & Culture
Digital Platform - Mobile: Apple, Android, Windows, Blackberry, Other
Digital Platform - Tablet: Apple iOS, Android, Windows 7, Blackberry Tablet OS, Kindle, Nook, Kindle Fire, Other
CEO .... Deborah Goldfarb
Director of Development .... Danny Levy
Mechanical Specifications: Type page 9.5 x 12; E - 5 cols, 1 11/12, 1/6 between; A - 5 cols, 1 11/12, 1/6 between; C - 5 cols, 1 11/12, 1/6 between.
Equipment: Hardware — APP/Mac; Software — Adobe Creative Cloud
Delivery Method: Mail, Newsstand, Racks

LOS ANGELES

THE JEWISH JOURNAL OF GREATER LOS ANGELES (Fri)
3580 Wilshire Blvd, Ste 1510, Los Angeles, CA, 90010-2516, Los Angeles, USA; tel (213) 368-1661; fax (213) 368-1684; e-mail marketing@jewishjournal.com; adv e-mail advertising@jewishjournal.com; web site www.jewishjournal.com
Circulation: 0pd, 49,975fr; CVC
Advertising: N/A
Established: 1986
Circ. Mgr. .... Matthew Tenney
Ed. in Chief .... Rob Eshman
Sr. Ed. .... Adam Wills
Mng. Ed. .... Susan Freudenheim
Prodn. Dir. .... Lionel Ochoa
Mechanical Specifications: Type page 11 1/4 x 15; E - 5 cols, 1 11/12, 1/60 between; A - 5 cols, 1 11/12, 1/60 between; C - 6 cols, 1 3/5, 3/25 between.

LOS GATOS

JEWISH COMMUNITY NEWS
14855 Oka Rd, Ste 2, Los Gatos, CA, 95032-1957, Santa Clara, USA; tel (408) 358-3033; fax (408) 356-0733; e-mail jcn@jfgsj.org
Advertising: Open inch rate $14.00
Group: Joseph Jacobs Organization
Adv. Mgr. .... Lori Cinnamon
Ed. .... Amanda Glincher

SAN FRANCISCO

J. THE JEWISH NEWS WEEKLY OF NORTHERN CALIFONIA (Fri)
225 Bush St, Ste 1480, San Francisco, CA, 94104-4216, San Francisco, USA; tel (415) 263-7200; adv tel (415) 263-7200; fax (415) 263-7222; adv fax (415) 263-7222; e-mail info@jweekly.com; adv e-mail nora@jweekly.com; ed e-mail editors@jweekly.com; web site www.jweekly.com
Circulation: 17,000pd, 1,000fr; Sworn/Estimate/Non-Audited
Established: 1946
Publisher .... Nora Contini
Art Dir. .... Cathleen Maclearie
Editor .... Sue Fishkoff
Equipment: Hardware — APP/Mac; Software — Microsoft/Word 98, QPS/QuarkXPress 6.0.
Delivery Method: Mail
Zip Codes Served: SF Bay Area

COLORADO

DENVER

INTERMOUNTAIN JEWISH NEWS (Fri)
1177 N Grant St, Ste 200, Denver, CO, 80203-2362, Denver, USA; tel (303) 861-2234; fax (303) 832-6942; e-mail email@ijn.com; web site www.ijn.com
Circulation: 3,000pd, 287fr; Sworn/Estimate/Non-Audited
Advertising: Open inch rate $46.07

Group: Joseph Jacobs Organization
Gen. Mgr. .... Rabbi Hillel Goldberg
Adv. Mgr. .... Lori Aron
Ed. .... Miriam Goldberg
Mng. Ed. .... Larry Hankin
Prodn. Mgr. .... Judy Waldren
Mechanical Specifications: Type page 10 x 16; E - 4 cols, 2 1/4, 1/4 between; A - 5 cols, 2, 1/6 between.
Equipment: Hardware — APP/Mac; Software — QPS/QuarkXPress, Adobe/Illustrator.

CONNECTICUT

NEW LONDON

THE JEWISH LEADER (Other) (Twice a month on Fridays)
28 Channing St, New London, CT, 06320-5756, New London, USA; tel (860) 442-7395; fax (860) 443-4175; e-mail office.jfec@gmail.com; adv e-mail office.jfec@gmail.com; ed e-mail office.jfec@gmail.com; web site www.jfec.com
Circulation: 400pd, 1,075fr; Sworn/Estimate/Non-Audited
Advertising: Open inch rate $10.00
Established: 1970
Group: Jewish Federation of Eastern CT
Ed. .... Mimi Perl
Mechanical Specifications: Type page 10 x 12; E - 5 cols, 1 13/16, 3/16 between.
Equipment: Hardware — PC; Software — Adobe/InDesign2
Delivery Method: Mail
Zip Codes Served: 06320, 06360, 06385, 06333, 06357, 06340, 06415, 06226, 06260, 06475, 02891

WEST HARTFORD

CONNECTICUT JEWISH LEDGER (Fri)
740 N Main St, Ste W, West Hartford, CT, 06117-2403, Hartford, USA; tel (860) 231-2424; fax (860) 231-2485; ed fax (860) 231-2428; adv e-mail advertising@jewishledger.com; ed e-mail editorial@jewishledger.com; web site www.jewishledger.com
Circulation: 35,000pd,; Sworn/Estimate/Non-Audited
Advertising: Open inch rate $39.00
Group: Joseph Jacobs Organization
Pub. .... N. Richard Greenfield
Prodn. Mgr. .... Leslie Iarusso
Mng. Ed. .... Judie Jacobson
Mechanical Specifications: Type page 8 x 13; E - 5 cols, between; A - 5 cols, between.
Equipment: Hardware — IBM; Software — QPS/QuarkXPress, Adobe/PageMaker.

DELAWARE

WILMINGTON

THE JEWISH FEDERATION OF DELAWARE (Mthly)
101 Garden of Eden Rd, Wilmington, DE, 19803-1511, New Castle, USA; tel (302) 427-2100; fax (302) 427-2438; e-mail seth@shalomdel.org; adv e-mail kat@shalomdel.org; ed e-mail shoshana@shalomdel.org; web site www.shalomdelaware.org
Circulation: 3,000pd, 500fr; Sworn/Estimate/Non-Audited
Established: 1951
Editor .... Shoshana Martyniak
Delivery Method: Mail
Zip Codes Served: 19801, 19803, 19806, 19809, 19810

FLORIDA

CLEARWATER

JEWISH PRESS OF PINELLAS COUNTY
1101 S Belcher Rd, Ste H, Clearwater, FL, 33758, Pinellas, USA; tel (727) 535-4400; fax (727) 530-3039; e-mail jewishpress@aol.com
Advertising: Open inch rate $13.75
Established: 1985
Adv. Mgr. .... Jim Dawkins
Mng. Ed. .... Karen Dawkins
Mechanical Specifications: Type page 10 1/4 x 15 3/4; E - 5 cols, 2, 1/6 between; A - 5 cols, 2, 1/6 between.
Equipment: Hardware — APP/Mac; Software — Adobe/Pagemaker 6.0, Adobe/Photoshop 5.0, QPS/QuarkXPress.
Zip Codes Served: 34664, 34689, 33701, 33728, 33729, 33789

FERN PARK

HERITAGE FLORIDA JEWISH NEWS (Fri)
207 Obrien Rd, Ste 101, Fern Park, FL, 32730-2838, Seminole, USA; tel (407) 834-8787; fax (407) 831-0507; e-mail news@orlandoheritage.com; adv e-mail jeff@orlandoheritage.com; web site www.heritagefl.com
Circulation: 5,200pd,; Sworn/Estimate/Non-Audited
Advertising: Open inch rate $12.55
Established: 1976
Ed. .... Jeffrey Gaeser
Mechanical Specifications: Type page 10 5/16 x 16; E - 6 cols, 1/6 between; A - 6 cols, 1/6 between; C - 6 cols, 1/6 between.
Equipment: Hardware — APP/Mac; Software — Adobe/PageMaker, Adobe/Photoshop, Microsoft/Word.
Delivery Method: Mail, Newsstand, Racks

FORT LAUDERDALE

JEWISH JOURNAL - BROWARD CENTRAL (Thur)
500 E Broward Blvd, Fort Lauderdale, FL, 33394-3000, Broward, USA; tel (954) 698-6397; fax (954) 429-1207; e-mail jewishjournal@tribune.com; web site www.forumpubs.com
Circulation: 25,365fr; CVC
Advertising: Open inch rate $13.70
Gen. Mgr. .... Justo Rey
Adv. Mgr. .... Tom Adams
Circ. Mgr. .... Ed Wilder
Ed .... Allan Goch
Prodn. Mgr. .... Stewart Katy

JEWISH JOURNAL PALM BEACH SOUTH (Tues)
500 E Broward Blvd, Fort Lauderdale, FL, 33394-3000, Broward, USA; tel (954) 698-6397; fax (954) 429-1207; e-mail jewishjournal@tribune.com; web site www.forumpubs.com
Circulation: 27,798fr; CVC
Advertising: Open inch rate $13.70
Established: 1978
Adv. Mgr. .... Tom Adams
Adv. Mgr. .... Gregg Behar
Circ. Mgr. .... Ed Wilder
Ed. .... Alan Goch
Prodn. Mgr. .... Manny Rodriguez

SHALOM - BROWARD (Mthly)
500 E Broward Blvd, Fort Lauderdale, FL, 33394-3000, Broward, USA; tel (954) 536-4000; adv tel (954) 698-6397; ed tel (954) 698-6397; fax (954) 429-1207; adv fax (954) 429-1207; ed fax (954) 429-1207; e-mail rdaley@tribune.com; adv e-mail ewilder@tribune.com; ed e-mail ctouey@tribune.com; web site www.forumpubs.com
Circulation: 0pd, 25,448fr; CVC
Advertising: Open inch rate $21.00
Established: 1973
Group: Sun-Sentinel Co.
Digital Platform - Mobile: Apple, Android, Windows, Blackberry
Digital Platform - Tablet: Apple iOS, Android, Windows 7, Blackberry Tablet OS
Pub./Gen. Mgr. .... Tom Adams
Mng. Ed. .... Tracy Kolody
Circ. Mgr. .... Ed Wilder
Adv. Mgr. .... Ray Daley
Prodn. Mgr. .... Stewart Cady
Mechanical Specifications: Type page 10 3/8 x 16.
Delivery Method: Mail, Racks
Zip Codes Served: Broward County

SHALOM - PALM BEACH (Mthly)
500 E Broward Blvd, Fort Lauderdale, FL, 33394-3000, Broward, USA; tel (954) 356-4000; adv tel (954) 954-5341; ed tel (954) 698-6397; fax (954) 429-1207; adv fax (954) 429-1207; ed fax (954) 429-1207; e-mail rdaley@tribune.com; adv e-mail gbehar@tribune.com; ed e-mail ctouey@tribune.com; web site http://www.sun-sentinel.com/florida-jewish-journal/
Circulation: 0pd, 30,531fr; CVC
Advertising: Open inch rate $21.00
Established: 1973
Group: Sun-Sentinel Co.
Digital Platform - Mobile: Apple, Android, Windows, Blackberry
Digital Platform - Tablet: Apple iOS, Android, Windows 7, Blackberry Tablet OS
Pub./Gen. Mgr. .... Tom Adams
Mng. Ed. .... Tracy Kolody
Circ. Mgr. .... Ed Wilder
Adv. Mgr. .... Ray Daley
Prodn. Mgr. .... Stewart Cady
Mechanical Specifications: Type page 10 3/8 x 16.
Delivery Method: Mail, Racks
Zip Codes Served: Broward County

LARGO

JEWISH PRESS OF TAMPA (Bi-Mthly) (Every other Friday)
1101 Belcher Rd S, Ste H, Largo, FL, 33771-3356, Pinellas, USA; tel (727) 535-4400; fax (727) 530-3039; e-mail jewishpress@aol.com; adv e-mail jewishpressads@aol.com; ed e-mail Jewishpressnews@aol.com; web site www.jewishpresstampabay.com
Circulation: 11,500fr; Sworn/Estimate/Non-Audited
Advertising: Open inch rate $16.00
Established: 1988Editions: 2- Jewish Press of Tampa, Jewish Press of Pinellas Çounty
Pub. .... Jim Dawkins
Mng. Ed. .... Karen Dawkins
Prodn. Mgr. .... Harold Wolfson
Mechanical Specifications: Type page 10 1/4 x 15 3/4; E - 5 cols, 1/6 between; A - 5 cols, 2, 1/6 between.
Equipment: Hardware — APP/Mac; Software — Adobe CS5.5
Delivery Method: Mail
Zip Codes Served: 337s, 336s, 346s

POMPANO BEACH

JEWISH JOURNAL - BROWARD NORTH (Thur)
1701 Green Rd, Ste B, Pompano Beach, FL, 33064-1074, Broward, USA; tel (954) 698-6397; fax (954) 429-1207; e-mail jewishjournal@tribune.com; web site www.forumpubs.com
Circulation: 25,684fr; CVC
Advertising: Open inch rate $13.70
Group: Forum Publishing Group
Vice Pres. .... Justo Rey
Sr. Adv. Mgr. .... Tom Adams
Circ. Mgr. .... Ed Wilder
Ed. .... Sylvia Gurinski
Prodn. Mgr. .... Stuart Kety

JEWISH JOURNAL - BROWARD SOUTH (Thur)
1701 Green Rd, Ste B, Pompano Beach, FL, 33064-1074, Broward, USA; tel (954) 698-6397; fax (954) 429-1207; e-mail jewishjournal@tribune.com; web site www.forumpubs.com
Circulation: 33,604fr; CVC
Advertising: Open inch rate $13.70
Group: Forum Publishing Group
Gen. Mgr. .... Justo Rey
Sales Mgr. .... Tom Adams
Circ. Mgr. .... Ed Wilder
Prodn. Mgr. .... Stuart Cady
Ed. .... Alan Goch

JEWISH JOURNAL - MIAMI DADE (Thur)
1701 Green Rd, Ste B, Pompano Beach, FL, 33064-1074, Broward, USA; tel (954) 698-6397; fax (954) 429-1207; e-mail jewishjournal@tribune.com; web site www.forumpubs.com
Circulation: 16,915fr; CVC
Advertising: Open inch rate $13.70
Pres .... Lisa Goodlin
Adv. Mgr. .... Tom Adams
Circ. Mgr. .... Ed Wilder
Ed. .... Alan Goch
Prodn. Mgr. .... Stewart Cady

JEWISH JOURNAL - PALM BEACH CENTRAL (Tues)
1701 Green Rd, Ste B, Pompano Beach, FL, 33064-1074, Broward, USA; web site www.floridajewishjournal.com
Circulation: 28,056fr; CVCLisa Goodlin
Mechanical Specifications: Type page 9.667" x 10.5"; 5 cols
Delivery Method: Carrier, Racks

JEWISH JOURNAL - PALM BEACH NORTH (Tues)
1701 Green Rd, Ste B, Pompano Beach, FL, 33064-1074, Broward, USA; tel (954) 698-6397; fax (954) 429-1207; e-mail jrey@tribune.com; jewishjournal@tribune.com; web site www.forumpubs.com
Circulation: 17,031fr; CVC
Advertising: Open inch rate $13.70
Group: Forum Publishing Group
Pres. .... Justo Rey
Adv. Mgr. .... Tom Adams
Adv. Mgr. .... Gregg Behar
Circ. Mgr. .... Ed Wilder
Ed. .... Alan Goch
Mng. Ed. .... Joyce Moed
Prodn. Mgr. .... Stwart Cady

GEORGIA

ATLANTA

ATLANTA JEWISH TIMES (Fri) (weekly)
270 Carpenter Dr, Ste 320, Atlanta, GA, 30328-4933, Fulton, USA; tel (404) 883-2130; fax (404) 883-2136; e-mail kaylene@atljewishtimes.com; adv e-mail kaylene@atljewishtimes.com; ed e-mail mjacobs@atljewishtimes.com; web site www.atlantajewishtimes.com
Circulation: 3,500pd, 11,500fr; Sworn/Estimate/Non-Audited
Advertising: Open inch rate $24.80
Established: 1925
Group: Southern Israelite LLC
Digital Platform - Mobile: Apple, Android, Windows, Blackberry, Other
Digital Platform - Tablet: Apple iOS, Android, Windows 7, Blackberry Tablet OS, Kindle,

Nook, Kindle Fire, Other
Assoc. Pub. .... Kaylene Ladinsky
Pub. .... Michael Morris
Ed. .... Michael Jacobs
Mechanical Specifications: Type page 10 x 13;
Equipment: Hardware — APP/Mac
Delivery Method: Mail, Newsstand, Carrier, Racks

ILLINOIS

CHICAGO

JEWISH UNITED FUND
1 S Franklin St, Ste 701G, Chicago, IL, 60606-4611, Cook, USA; tel (312) 346-6700; fax (312) 855-2470; ed e-mail editorial@juf.org; web site www.juf.org
Advertising: Open inch rate $31.15
Gen. Mgr. .... Kathleen Evans-Mazur
Adv. Mgr. .... Robert Feiger
Ed. .... Aaron Cohen

SKOKIE

CHICAGO JEWISH NEWS (Fri)
5301 Dempster St, Ste 100, Skokie, IL, 60077-1800, Cook, USA; tel (847) 966-0606; fax (847) 966-1656; adv e-mail info@chicagojewishnews.com; web site www.chicagojewishnews.com
Circulation: 10,468pd, 2,422fr; Sworn/Estimate/Non-Audited
Advertising: Open inch rate $37.50
Established: 1994
Ed. and Pub. .... Joseph Aaron
Production Manager .... Denise Kus
Mechanical Specifications: Type page 9 3/4 x 14; E - 5 cols, 1 7/8, 1/6 between; A - 5 cols, 1 7/8, 1/6 between; C - 5 cols, 1 7/8, 1/6 between.
Equipment: Hardware — APP/Mac; Software — QPS/QuarkXPress 4.1, Adobe/Photoshop 3.0.5, Adobe/Illustrator 6.0.
Delivery Method: Mail, Racks

CHICAGO JEWISH STAR (2 x Mthly)
PO Box 268, Skokie, IL, 60076-0268, Cook, USA; tel (847) 674-7827; fax (847) 674-0014; e-mail chicagojewishstar@comcast.net
Circulation: 100pd, 17,500fr; Sworn/Estimate/Non-Audited
Advertising: Open inch rate $27.00
Ed./Pub. .... Doug Wertheimer
Mechanical Specifications: Type page 10 1/4 x 16; E - 6 cols, 1 5/8, 1/6 between; A - 6 cols, 1 5/8, 1/6 between; C - 6 cols, 1 5/8, 1/6 between.
Equipment: Hardware — PC; Software — QPS/QuarkXPress 3.32.

INDIANA

INDIANAPOLIS

NATIONAL JEWISH POST & OPINION (Monthly)
1427 W 86th St, # 228, Indianapolis, IN, 46260-2103, Marion, USA; tel (317) 405-8084; fax (317) 405-8084; e-mail jpostopinion@gmail.com; web site www.jewishpostopinion.com
Circulation: 10,000pd,; Sworn/Estimate/Non-Audited
Established: 1935
Ed. .... Jennie Cohen
Mechanical Specifications: Type page 8-1/2 x 11; E - 3 cols, 2, between; A - 3 cols, 2, between.
Equipment: Hardware — APP/Mac; Software — Adobe/PageMaker 5.0.
Delivery Method: Mail, Newsstand
Zip Codes Served: 46260, 46032, 46033, 47401,

THE INDIANA JEWISH POST & OPINION (Wed) (Every other Wed)
1427 W 86th St, # 228, Indianapolis, IN, 46260-2103, Marion, USA; tel (317) 405-8084; e-mail jpostopinion@gmail.com; web site www.jewishpostopinion.com
Circulation: 5,200pd,; Sworn/Estimate/Non-Audited
Advertising: Open inch rate $12.00
Established: 1935
Ed. .... Jennie Cohen
Mechanical Specifications: Type page 8-1/2 x 11; E - 3 cols, 2, between; A - 3 cols, 2, between.
Equipment: Hardware — APP/Mac; Software — Adobe/PageMaker 5.0.
Zip Codes Served: 46260, 46032, 46033, 46260, 46240, 46038, 46268, and others

KANSAS

FAIRWAY

THE KANSAS CITY JEWISH CHRONICLE (Fri)
4210 Shawnee Mission Pkwy, Ste 314A, Fairway, KS, 66205-2546, Johnson, USA; tel (913) 648-4620; fax (913) 381-1402; e-mail chronicle@sunpublications.com; web site www.kcjc.com
Circulation: 4,000pd,; Sworn/Estimate/Non-Audited
Advertising: Open inch rate $25.30
Established: 1920
Pub. .... David Small
Circ. Mgr. .... David Nevels
Ed. .... Rick Hellman
Mechanical Specifications: Type page 10 x 13 1/2; E - 6 cols, 1 1/2, between; A - 6 cols, 1 1/2, between.
Equipment: Hardware — APP/Mac; Software — QPS/QuarkXPress.

KENTUCKY

LOUISVILLE

JEWISH LOUISVILLE COMMUNITY (Mthly)
3600 Dutchmans Ln, Louisville, KY, 40205-3302, Jefferson, USA; tel (502) 459-0660; adv tel (502) 418-5845; fax (502) 238-2724; e-mail lchottiner@jewishlouisville.org; adv e-mail lsinger@jewishlouisville.org; web site www.jewishlouisville.org
Circulation: 6,472pd, 515fr; Sworn/Estimate/Non-Audited
Advertising: sold in increments from 1/16 pg at $70 to full page at $1000
Established: 1975
Group: Jewish Community of Louisville
Ed. .... Shiela Steinman Wallace
Adv Sales .... Larry Singer
Graphic Artist .... Misty Hamilton
Mechanical Specifications: Type page 10 x 13.75; E - 4 cols, 2 1/3, 1/4 between; A - 4 cols, 2 1/3, 1/4 between; C - 5 cols, 1 11/12, 1/6 between.
Equipment: Hardware — PC/Windows; Software — In Design CC, Adobe/Acrobat.
Delivery Method: Mail, Racks
Zip Codes Served: 40200-40299
Note: Community is published Monthly

LOUISIANA

METAIRIE

JEWISH NEWS (Mthly)
3747 W Esplanade Ave N, Metairie, LA, 70002-3145, Jefferson, USA; tel (504) 780-5600; fax (504) 780-5601; e-mail jewishnews@jewishnola.com; web site www.jewishnola.com
Circulation: 4,563fr; CVC
Established: 1995
Group: Joseph Jacobs Organization
Prodn. Mgr. .... Cait Muldoon
Mechanical Specifications: Type page 10 x 14.
Equipment: Hardware — APP/Mac; Software — QPS/QuarkXPress 4.1, Adobe/Photoshop 5.5, Adobe/Illustrator 7.0, Adobe/Acrobat.

MARYLAND

BALTIMORE

JEWISH TIMES (Fri)
1040 Park Ave, Ste 200, Baltimore, MD, 21201-5634, Baltimore City, USA; tel (410) 752-3504; e-mail information@jewishtimes.com; web site www.jewishtimes.com
Circulation: 35,000pd,; Sworn/Estimate/Non-Audited
Advertising: Open inch rate $39.06
Pub. .... Maayan Jaffe
Gen. Mgr. .... Claudia Meyers
Ed. .... Phil Jacobs
Prodn. Mgr. .... Erin Clare
Mechanical Specifications: Type page 9 13/16 x 12; E - 4 cols, 2 5/16, between; A - 4 cols, 2 5/16, between; C - 6 cols, 1 1/2, between.
Equipment: Hardware — APP/Mac.

ROCKVILLE

WASHINGTON JEWISH WEEK (Thur)
11426 Rockville Pike, Ste 236, Rockville, MD, 20852-3075, Montgomery, USA; tel 301-230-0474; fax (301) 881-6362; e-mail editorial@washingtonjewishweek.com; web site www.washingtonjewishweek.com
Circulation: 10,000pd,; Sworn/Estimate/Non-Audited
Advertising: Open inch rate $39.05
Established: 1965
Group: Joseph Jacobs Organization
Pub. .... Larry Fishbein
Ed. .... Debra Rubin
Prodn. Mgr. .... Patrick Fisher
Mechanical Specifications: Type page 9 3/4 x 13; A - 5 cols, 2, between; C - 8 cols, between.
Equipment: Hardware — APP/Mac; Software — QPS/QuarkXPress.

MASSACHUSETTS

BOSTON

THE JEWISH ADVOCATE (Fri)
15 School St, Boston, MA, 02108-4307, Suffolk, USA; tel (617) 367-9100; fax (617) 367-9310; e-mail sharonh@thejewishadvocate.com; adv e-mail business@thejewishadvocate.com; ed e-mail editorial@thejewishadvocate.com; web site www.thejewishadvocate.com
Circulation: 30,000pd,; Sworn/Estimate/Non-Audited
Advertising: Open inch rate $33.00
Established: 1902
Digital Platform - Mobile: Blackberry
Digital Platform - Tablet: Kindle, Kindle Fire
Pub. .... Grand Rabbi Y. A. Korff
Ed. .... Michael Whalen
Administrator .... Sharon Harrau Ian Thal
Mechanical Specifications: Type page 10 1/4 x 14 1/4; E - 5 cols, 1 15/16, 1/8 between; A - 5 cols, 1 15/16, 1/8 between; C - 10 cols, 1 3/16, 1/8 between.
Delivery Method: Mail, Newsstand

FRAMINGHAM

METROWEST JEWISH REPORTER (Mthly)
29 Upper Joclyn Ave, Framingham, MA, 01701-4400, Middlesex, USA; tel (508) 879-3300; fax (508) 879-5856; e-mail jewishreporter@aol.com
Circulation: 10,500fr; Sworn/Estimate/Non-Audited
Advertising: Open inch rate $25.00
Mng. Ed. .... Nancy Atlas
Asst. Mng. Ed. .... Wendy Davis

THE JEWISH REPORTER (Mthly)
29 Upper Joclyn Ave, Framingham, MA, 01701-4400, Middlesex, USA; tel (508) 872-4808; fax (508) 879-5856; e-mail jewishreporter@aol.com
Circulation: 6,500fr; Sworn/Estimate/Non-Audited
Advertising: Open inch rate $25.00
Group: Joseph Jacobs Organization
Ed. .... Nancy Atlas

PITTSFIELD

BERKSHIRE JEWISH VOICE (Mthly)
196 South St, Pittsfield, MA, 01201-6807, Berkshire, USA; tel (413) 442-4360; fax (413) 443-6070; e-mail jfb.berkshirevoice@verizon.net
Circulation: 3,000fr; Sworn/Estimate/Non-Audited
Advertising: Open inch rate $8.40
Group: Joseph Jacobs Organization
Pub. .... Arlene D. Schiff
Adv. Mgr. .... Jenny Greenfield
Ed. .... Albert Stern
Equipment: Hardware — Presses Web press; Software — Adobe/PageMaker 6.5.

SALEM

NORTH SHORE JEWISH PRESS (Thur)
27 Congress St, Ste 501, Salem, MA, 01970-5577, Essex, USA; tel (978) 745-4111; adv tel (978) 745-4111X114; ed tel (978) 745-4111X140; fax (978) 745-5333; e-mail business@jewishjournal.org; web site www.jewishjournal.org
Circulation: 16,000fr; Sworn/Estimate/Non-Audited
Advertising: Open inch rate $23.93
Established: 1976
Pub. .... Barbara Schneider
Editor .... Susan Jacobs
Ed. .... Bette Keva
Mechanical Specifications: Type page 9 3/4 x 15 3/4; E - 5 cols, 1 3/4, 1/4 between; A - 5 cols, 1 3/4, 1/4 between; C - 6 cols, 1 1/4, 1/4 between.
Equipment: Hardware — APP/Mac; Software — QPS/QuarkXPress 4.1.

WORCESTER

THE JEWISH CHRONICLE (Thur)
131 Lincoln St, Worcester, MA, 01605-2408, Worcester, USA; tel (508) 752-2512; fax

(508) 752-9057; e-mail chronicle.sales@verizon.net
Circulation: 1,000pd, 4,000fr; Sworn/Estimate/Non-Audited
Advertising: Open inch rate $12.00
Pub....................................... Sondra Shapiro
Adv. Mgr.................................. Reva Catellari
Ed.. Ellen Weingart
Mechanical Specifications: Type page 10 x 16; E - 4 cols, 2 1/2, between; A - 6 cols, 1 1/2, between.
Zip Codes Served: 1605

MICHIGAN

SOUTHFIELD

THE DETROIT JEWISH NEWS (Thur)
29200 Northwestern Hwy, Ste 110, Southfield, MI, 48034-1055, Oakland, USA; tel (248) 354-6060; ed fax (248) 304-0032; web site www.thejewishnews.com
Circulation: 17,134pd, 54fr; Sworn/Estimate/Non-Audited
Group: Joseph Jacobs Organization
Pub.. Arthur Horwitz
COO .... Kevin Browett
Adv. Mgr.................................... Keith Farber
Circ. Mgr.................................... Zina Davis
Ed.. Robert Sklar
Assoc. Ed.................................... Alan Hitsky
Mechanical Specifications: Type page 9 13/16 x 13; E - 4 cols, 1 9/16, between; A - 4 cols, 1 9/16, between; C - 6 cols, 1 7/16, between.
Equipment: Hardware — Software QPS/QuarkXPress 3.0, Adobe/Photoshop, Adobe/Illustrator 6.0.

MINNESOTA

MINNEAPOLIS

AMERICAN JEWISH WORLD (Bi-Mthly) (Every other Fri)
4820 Minnetonka Blvd, Ste 104, Minneapolis, MN, 55416-2278, Hennepin, USA; tel (952) 259-5237; adv tel (952) 259-5234; ed tel (952) 259-5239; fax (952) 920-6205; adv fax (952) 920-6205; ed fax (952) 920-6205; e-mail news@ajwnews.com; adv e-mail editor@ajwnews.com; ed e-mail community@ajwnews.com; web site www.ajwnews.com
Circulation: 3,500pd,; Sworn/Estimate/Non-Audited
Advertising: Open inch rate $15.00
Established: 1912
Group: Minnesota Jewish Media, LLC
Ed.................................... Mordecai Specktor
Mechanical Specifications: Type page 10 x 16; E - 5 cols, 1 7/8, 1/8 between; A - 5 cols, 1 7/8, 1/8 between; C - 5 cols, 1 7/8, 1/8 between.
Equipment: Hardware — APP/Mac; Software — Adobe CS, Microsoft/Word.
Delivery Method: Mail
Zip Codes Served: 55401, 55402, 55118, 55416, 55426, 55105, 55116

MISSOURI

SAINT LOUIS

SAINT LOUIS JEWISH LIGHT (Wed) (Quarterly Oy! Magazine, 24/7 website, weekly e-newsletter)
6 Millstone Campus Dr, Ste 3010, Saint Louis, MO, 63146-6603, Saint Louis, USA; tel (314) 743-3600; adv tel (314) 743-3677; ed tel (314) 743-3669; fax (314) 743-3690; adv fax (314) 743-3690; ed fax (314) 743-3690; e-mail office@thejewishlight.com; adv e-mail jschack@thejewishlight.com; ed e-mail msherwin@thejewishlight.com; web site www.stljewishlight.com
Circulation: 5,000pd, 4,000fr; Sworn/Estimate/Non-Audited
Advertising: Call 3147433663 for details
Established: 1947
Digital Platform - Mobile: Apple, Android, Blackberry
CEO/Pub...................................... Larry Levin
Mechanical Specifications: Call 3147433663 for details
Delivery Method: Mail, Racks

ST. LOUIS JEWISH LIGHT (Wed) (Quarterly magazine, 24/7 website, weekly email blast)
6 Millstone Campus Dr, Ste 3010, Saint Louis, MO, 63146-6603, Saint Louis, USA; tel (314) 743-3660; adv tel (314) 743-3677; ed tel (314) 743-3669; fax (314) 743-3690; adv fax (314) 743-3690; ed fax (314) 743-3690; e-mail office@thejewishlight.com; adv e-mail jschack@thejewishlight.com; ed e-mail news@thejewishlight.com; web site www.thejewishlight.com
Circulation: 4,813pd, 4,097fr; CVC
Advertising: contact for details
Established: 1963Editions: St. Louis Jewish Light; OY! Magazine
Digital Platform - Mobile: Apple, Android, Blackberry
Digital Platform - Tablet: Other
Publisher/CEO.............................. Larry Levin
Mechanical Specifications: Type page: 10.444 x 16; 6 col
Delivery Method: Mail, Racks
Zip Codes Served: 63xxx (St. Louis Metro)
Note: The Jewish Light is the nonprofit news organization of the St. Louis Jewish community.

NEBRASKA

OMAHA

JEWISH PRESS (Fri)
333 S 132nd St, Omaha, NE, 68154-2106, Douglas, USA; tel (402) 334-6448; fax (402) 334-5422; e-mail jpress@jewishomaha.org; web site www.jewishomaha.org
Circulation: 67,409pd, 1,875fr; Sworn/Estimate/Non-Audited
Advertising: Open inch rate $13.00
Established: 1920
Group: Joseph Jacobs Organization
Adv. Mgr................................ Allan Handleman
Ed.. Carol Katzman
Mng. Ed.................................... Richard Busse
Mechanical Specifications: Type page 10 5/16 x 16; E - 3 cols, 3 5/16, 1/6 between; A - 6 cols, 1 9/16, 1/6 between.
Equipment: Hardware — APP/Mac, PC, APP/Mac G4; Software — QPS/QuarkXPress 6.5, Adobe/Photoshop 7.0.

NEVADA

LAS VEGAS

JEWISH REPORTER
2317 Renaissance Dr, Las Vegas, NV, 89119-6191, Clark, USA; tel (702) 732-0556; fax (702) 732-3228; e-mail info@jewishlasvegas.com; adv e-mail ads@jewishlasvegas.com; ed e-mail editor@jewishlasvegas.com; web site www.jewishlasvegas.com
Group: Joseph Jacobs Organization
Adv. Sales Dir...................... Joanne Friedland
Ed.. Leah Brown
Ed.. Arthur Bloberger
Graphics/Layout Artist ....Andrew Bemson
Mechanical Specifications: Type page 10 3/4 x 13; E - 4 cols, 2 1/2, 1/4 between; A - 4 cols, 2 1/2, 1/4 between.
Equipment: Hardware — APP/Power Mac; Software — Adobe/PageMaker 5.1.
Zip Codes Served: 89119

NEW JERSEY

CHERRY HILL

JEWISH VOICE
1301 Springdale Rd, Ste 250, Cherry Hill, NJ, 08003-2763, Camden, USA; tel (856) 751-9500 x1217; ed tel 856-751-9500 x1237; fax (856) 489-8253; e-mail jvoice@jfedsnj.org; ed e-mail dportnoe@jfedsnj.org; web site http://www.jewishvoicesnj.org/
Advertising: Open inch rate $18.50
Group: Joseph Jacobs Organization
Pub....................................... Stuart Abraham
Pub....................................... Howard Gases
Adv. Mgr.............................. Judy Robinowitz
Ed... Lauren Silver
Prodn. Mgr............................ Oscar Trugler
Mechanical Specifications: Type page 10 x 14; E - 5 cols, 2, between.
Zip Codes Served: 7723

ENGLEWOOD

JEWISH VOICE AND OPINION (Mthly)
PO Box 8097, Englewood, NJ, 07631-8097, Bergen, USA; tel (201) 569-2845; adv tel (201) 569-2845; ed tel (201) 569-2845; e-mail susan@JewishVoiceAndOpinion.com; adv e-mail susan@JewishVoiceAndOpinion.com; ed e-mail susan@JewishVoiceAndOpinion.com; web site TheJewishVoiceAndOpinion.com
Circulation: 20,000pd, 18,000fr; Sworn/Estimate/Non-Audited
Advertising: Open inch rate $50.00
Established: 1987
Group: The Jewish Voice and Opinion
Editor .... Susan L. Rosenbluth
Mechanical Specifications: Type page 8 1/2 x 11; E - 4 cols, 1 1/2, 1/4 between.
Equipment: Hardware — APP/Mac; Software — Adobe/PageMaker.
Delivery Method: Mail, Racks
Zip Codes Served: 07010, 07011, 07012, 07013, 07014, 07024, 07036, 07039, 07047, 07052, 07055, 07078, 07079, 07081, 07087, 07094, 07202, 07205, 07208, 07302, 07304, 07305, 07306, 07307, 07410, 07470, 07605, 07621, 06531, 07632, 07646, 07652, 07666, 07670, 07726, 07747, 07866, 07960, 07962, 08002, 08003, 08034, 08402, 08406, 08816, 08817, 08820, 08901, 08902, 08904, 10461, 10463, 10467, 10471, 10475, 10901, 10952, 10956, 10977

HIGHLAND PARK

THE SPEAKER
320 Raritan Ave, Ste 203, Highland Park, NJ, 08904-2752, Middlesex, USA; tel (732) 393-0023
Advertising: Open inch rate $12.50
Group: Joseph Jacobs Organization
Ed.. Ron Ostroff
Mechanical Specifications: Type page 10 1/4 x 15 3/4; E - 5 cols, 1 7/8, between; A - 5 cols, 1 7/8, between.

JACKSON

JEWISH JOURNAL - OCEAN COUNTY (Mthly)
PO Box 1082, Jackson, NJ, 08527-1082, Ocean, USA; tel (732) 987-4783; adv tel (732) 987-4783; ed tel 732-987-4783; fax (732) 987-4677; e-mail ocjj@optonline.net; adv e-mail LUNJ@OPTONLINE.NET; ed e-mail LUNJ@OPTONLINE.NET
Circulation: 5,000fr; USPS
Ed.. Ron Ostroff
Delivery Method: Mail
Zip Codes Served: Ocean County

PLEASANTVILLE

JEWISH TIMES (Fri)
21 W Delilah Rd, Pleasantville, NJ, 08232-1403, Atlantic, USA; tel (609) 407-0909; fax (609) 407-0999; e-mail jwishtimes@aol.com; web site www.jewishtimes-sj.com
Circulation: 4,000pd, 1,000fr; Sworn/Estimate/Non-Audited
Advertising: Open inch rate $13.11
Group: Joseph Jacobs Organization
Pub.. Shy Kramer
Adv. Mgr.............................. Bonnie La Roche
Mng. Ed.................................... Gerald Etter
Mechanical Specifications: Type page 12 x 13; E - 5 cols, 2, between; A - 5 cols, 2, between.
Equipment: Hardware — APP/Mac.

TEANECK

JEWISH STANDARD (Fri)
1086 Teaneck Rd, Teaneck, NJ, 07666-4854, Bergen, USA; tel (201) 837-8818; fax (201) 833-4959; adv e-mail ads@jewishmediagroup.com; web site www.jstandard.com
Circulation: 24,000pd,; Sworn/Estimate/Non-Audited
Advertising: Open inch rate $42.95
Group: Joseph Jacobs Organization
Pub....................................... James Janoff
Ed.................................. Rebecca Boroson

WHIPPANY

NEW JERSEY JEWISH NEWS (Thur)
901 State Route 10, Whippany, NJ, 07981-1105, Morris, USA; tel (973) 887-8500; fax (973) 887-4152; ed fax (973) 887-5999; e-mail info@njjewishnews.com; web site www.njjewishnews.com
Circulation: 50,000pd,; Sworn/Estimate/Non-Audited
Advertising: Open inch rate $66.00Editions: 3- 3 total New Jersey Jewish News-MetroWest Edition (27,000);
Editor in Chief/CEO .... Andrew Silow-Carroll
Rick Kestenbaum
Mechanical Specifications: Type page 10 1/4 x 13 1/2; E - 5 cols, 1 7/8, 1/4 between; A - 5 cols, 1 7/8, 1/4 between; C - 6 cols, 1 9/16, 1/8 between.
Equipment: Hardware — APP/Mac; Software — QPS/QuarkXPress, Microsoft/Word.
Delivery Method: Mail

NEW MEXICO

ALBUQUERQUE

NEW MEXICO JEWISH LINK (Mthly)
5520 Wyoming Blvd NE, Albuquerque, NM, 87109-3238, Bernalillo, USA; tel (505) 821-3214; fax (505) 821-3351; e-mail news@

nmjlink.org; web site www.jewishnewmexico.org
Circulation: 6,500fr; Sworn/Estimate/Non-Audited
Pub. Sam Sokolove
Ed. Susan Abonyi
Israel Correspondent Mati Milstein
Mechanical Specifications: Type page 10 1/16 x 14 3/4; E - 5 cols, 1 7/8, 3/16 between; A - 5 cols, 1 7/8, 3/16 between.
Equipment: Hardware — APP/Mac IIci; Software — Microsoft/Word 7.0, Adobe/PageMaker.
Zip Codes Served: 87109

NEW YORK

BROOKLYN

ALGEMEINER JOURNAL (Wed)
508 Montgomery St, Brooklyn, NY, 11225-3023, Kings, USA; tel (347) 741-7830; fax (718) 771-0308; e-mail algemeiner@aol.com; web site www.algemeiner.com
Circulation: 30,000pd, 28,000fr; Sworn/Estimate/Non-Audited
Advertising: Open inch rate $31.50
Group: Joseph Jacobs Organization
Pub. Simon Jacobson
Dir. Dovid Efune
Adv. Mgr. Moshe Hecht
Ed. Yosef Jacobson

DER YID (Thur)
191 Rodney St, Brooklyn, NY, 11211-7787, Kings, USA; tel (718) 797-3900; fax (718) 797-1985; e-mail adv@deryid.org; web site deryid.org
Circulation:; Sworn/Estimate/Non-Audited
Advertising: Open inch rate $15.00
Group: Joseph Jacobs Organization
Gen. Mgr. Herman Friedman
Ed. Aron Friedman
Mechanical Specifications: Type page 10 x 15 1/2; E - 5 cols, 2, between.
Equipment: Hardware — APP/Mac.
Delivery Method: Mail, Newsstand, Racks

THE JEWISH PRESS (Fri)
338 3rd Ave, Brooklyn, NY, 11215-1816, Kings, USA; tel (718) 330-1100; fax (718) 935-1215; e-mail editor@jewishpress.com; web site www.jewishpress.com
Circulation: 67,409pd, 1,875fr; Sworn/Estimate/Non-Audited
Advertising: Open inch rate $77.00
Established: 1955
Pub. Irene Klass
Display Dept. Mgr. Heshy Kornblit
Circ. Mgr. Joseph Hochberg
Sr. Ed. Jason Maoz
Mng. Ed. Jerry Greenwald
Mechanical Specifications: Type page 10 1/4 x 14; E - 6 cols, 1 5/8, between; A - 6 cols, 1 5/8, between.
Equipment: Hardware — IBM; Software — Adobe/PageMaker 7.0, Microsoft/Word 2000, Adobe/Acrobat 6.0, Adobe/Illustrator 9.0.

BUFFALO

BUFFALO JEWISH REVIEW (Fri)
964 Kenmore Ave, Buffalo, NY, 14216-1450, Erie, USA; tel (716) 854-2192; fax (716) 854-2198; e-mail buffjewrev@aol.com; web site http://www.buffalojewishreview.com/
Circulation: 3,500pd,; Sworn/Estimate/Non-Audited
Advertising: Open inch rate $14.20
Group: Joseph Jacobs Organization
Pub. Arnold Weiss
Ed. Rita Weiss
Mechanical Specifications: Type page 10 1/2 x 15; E - 5 cols, 2, between; A - 5 cols, 2, between.
Equipment: Hardware — APP/Mac.

FAR ROCKAWAY

JEWISH TRIBUNE OF ROCKLAND COUNTY (Fri)
1525 Central Ave, Far Rockaway, NY, 11691-4019, Queens, USA; tel (516) 829-4000; fax (516) 594-4900; e-mail lijeworld@aol.com
Circulation: 7,541pd, 750fr; Sworn/Estimate/Non-Audited
Advertising: Open inch rate $19.00
Mng. Ed. Jerome W. Lippman
Mechanical Specifications: Type page 10 7/16 x 13; E - 5 cols, 2, 1/8 between; A - 5 cols, 2, 1/8 between; C - 7 cols, 1 7/16, between.

LONG ISLAND JEWISH WORLD (Fri)
1525 Central Ave, Far Rockaway, NY, 11691-4019, Queens, USA; tel (516) 829-4000; fax (516) 594-4900; e-mail lijeworld@aol.com
Circulation: 15,284pd, 1,159fr; Sworn/Estimate/Non-Audited
Advertising: Open inch rate $40.00
Mng. Ed. Jerome W. Lippman
Mechanical Specifications: Type page 10 7/16 x 13; E - 5 cols, 2, 1/8 between; A - 5 cols, 2, 1/8 between; C - 7 cols, 1 7/16, between.
Equipment: Hardware — IBM.

MANHATTAN JEWISH SENTINEL
1525 Central Ave, Far Rockaway, NY, 11691-4019, Queens, USA; tel (516) 829-4000; fax (516) 594-4900; e-mail lijeworld@aol.com
Advertising: Open inch rate $40.00
Group: Joseph Jacobs Organization
Ed. Jerome W. Lippman
Mechanical Specifications: Type page 10 7/16 x 13; E - 5 cols, 2, 1/8 between; A - 5 cols, 2, 1/8 between; C - 7 cols, 1 7/16, between.
Equipment: Hardware — IBM.

NEW YORK

JEWISH TELEGRAPHIC AGENCY DAILY NEWS BULLETIN (Daily)
330 7th Ave, Fl 17, New York, NY, 10001-5010, New York, USA; tel (212) 643-1890; fax (212) 643-8499; e-mail info@jta.org; web site www.jta.org
Circulation: 1,200pd, 50fr; Sworn/Estimate/Non-Audited
Pub. Mark J. Joffe
Gen. Mgr. Lenore A. Silverstein
Mng. Ed. Ami Eden
Mechanical Specifications: Type page 8 1/2 x 11; E - 2 cols, 3 5/8, 1/4 between.
Equipment: Hardware — PC; Software — WordPerfect 6.0.

JEWISH WEEK (Thur)
1501 Broadway, Ste 505, New York, NY, 10036-5501, New York, USA; tel (212) 921-7822; fax (212) 921-8420; web site www.thejewishweek.com
Circulation: 74,000pd,; Sworn/Estimate/Non-Audited
Advertising: Open inch rate $104.00
Group: Joseph Jacobs Organization
Assoc. Pub. Richard Waloff
Adv. Coord. Gershon Fastow
Sales Mgr. Ruth Rothseid
Circ. Mgr. Paul Bukzin
Ed. Gary Rosenblatt
Mng. Ed. Robert Goldblum
Mechanical Specifications: Type page 10 1/4 x 13; A - 6 cols, 1 2/3, 1/6 between; C - 7 cols, 1 5/12, 1/6 between.
Equipment: Hardware — APP/Mac, IBM; Software — Graphix/Adtaker, XYQUEST/XyWrite.

MANHATTAN/WESTCHESTER JEWISH WEEK (Fri)
1501 Broadway, Ste 505, New York, NY, 10036-5501, New York, USA; tel (212) 921-7822; adv tel (212) 921-7822 x254; ed tel (212) 921-7822 x213; fax (212) 921-8420; e-mail ruth@jewishweek.org; ed e-mail robert@jewishweek.org; web site www.thejewishweek.com
Advertising: (Modular Rates) 1/24 page, 2.833 x 1.5 - $252 1x
Managing Ed. Robert Goldblum
Sales Dir. Ruth Rothseid
Ed. & Pub. Gary Rosenblatt
Mechanical Specifications: Type page 8.75 x 11.75; 6 cols, 1.354, 0.125 between

THE FORWARD (Fri)
125 Maiden Ln, Fl 8, New York, NY, 10038-5015, New York, USA; tel (212) 889-8200; fax (212) 689-4255; adv e-mail advertising@forward.com; web site www.forward.com
Circulation: 14,222pd, 10,701fr; AAM
Advertising: Open inch rate $40.00
Adv. Mgr. Jerry Koenig
Ed. in Chief Jane Eisner
Mng. Ed. Lil Swanson
Mechanical Specifications: Type page 13 x 21; E - 6 cols, 2 1/16, between; A - 6 cols, 2 1/16, between; C - 6 cols, 2 1/16, between.
Equipment: Hardware — APP/Mac.

THE JEWISH WEEK (Fri)
1501 Broadway, Ste 505, New York, NY, 10036-5501, New York, USA; tel (212) 921-7822; adv tel (212) 997-2954; fax (212) 921-8420; e-mail editor@jewishweek.org; adv e-mail ruth@jewishweek.org; ed e-mail editor@jewishweek.org; web site www.thejewishweek.com
Circulation: 44,731pd, 6,289fr; AAM
Advertising: Open inch rate $101.00
Established: 1979
Digital Platform - Mobile: Apple
Digital Platform - Tablet: Apple iOS
Pub. Gary Rosenblatt
Assoc. Pub. Richard Waloff
Mng. Ed. Robert Goldblum
Sales Manager Ruth Rothseid
Mechanical Specifications: Live area, page size is 8.75 wide x 11. There ar 6 advertising columns per page and 3 or 4 editorial columns
Equipment: Hardware — PC and MAC; Software — InDesign, Photoshop, etc.
Delivery Method: Mail, Newsstand, Carrier
Zip Codes Served: 10001 through 11999, primarily

THE LONG ISLAND JEWISH WEEK (Fri)
1501 Broadway, Ste 505, New York, NY, 10036-5501, New York, USA; tel (212) 921-7822; fax (212) 921-8420; web site www.thejewishweek.com
Circulation: 90,000pd, 259fr; Sworn/Estimate/Non-Audited
Pub. Richard Waloff
Mng. Ed. Robert Goldblum
Ed. Gary Rosenblatt

THE QUEENS JEWISH WEEK (Fri)
1501 Broadway, Ste 505, New York, NY, 10036-5501, New York, USA; tel (212) 921-7822; fax (212) 921-8420; web site www.thejewishweek.com
Circulation: 14,500pd, 116fr; Sworn/Estimate/Non-Audited
Advertising: Open inch rate $92.00
Pub. Gary Rosenblatt
Adv. Mgr. Richard Waloff
Mng. Ed. Robert Goldblum

THE WESTCHESTER JEWISH WEEK (Fri)
1501 Broadway, Ste 505, New York, NY, 10036-5501, New York, USA; tel (212) 921-7822; fax (212) 921-8420; web site www.thejewishweek.com
Circulation: 15,661pd, 192fr; Sworn/Estimate/Non-Audited
Advertising: Open inch rate $92.00
Pub. Gary Rosenblatt
Adv. Mgr. Richard Waloff
Mng. Ed. Robert Goldblum

PELHAM

WESTCHESTER JEWISH LIFE (Mthly)
629 Fifth Ave, Pelham, NY, 10803-1251, Westchester, USA; tel (914) 738-7869; fax (914) 738-7876; e-mail hp@shorelinepub.com; adv e-mail hp@shorelinepub.com; ed e-mail hp@shorelinepub.com; web site www.shorelinepub.com
Circulation: 500pd, 24,000fr; Sworn/Estimate/Non-Audited
Advertising: Open inch rate $8.65
Established: 1996
Group: Shoreline Publishing
Digital Platform - Mobile: Windows
Adv. Mgr. Edward Shapiro
Editor and Publisher Helene Pollack
Mechanical Specifications: Type page 10 x 11; E - 4 cols, 2 1/4, between; A - 6 cols, 1 3/4, between; C - 6 cols, between.
Equipment: Hardware — IBM; Software — Adobe/PageMaker 6.0.
Delivery Method: Newsstand
Zip Codes Served: All Westchester County

ROCHESTER

THE JEWISH LEDGER (Thur) (Weekly)
2535 Brighton Henrietta Tl Rd, Rochester, NY, 14623-2711, Monroe, USA; tel (585) 427-2434; adv tel (585) 427-2468; ed tel 5854272434; fax (585) 427-8521; e-mail info@thejewishledger.com; adv e-mail info@the jewishledger.com; ed e-mail info@thejewishledger.com; web site www.thejewishledger.com
Circulation: 6,500pd, 1,000fr; USPS
Advertising: Open inch rate $35.00
Established: 1924
Digital Platform - Mobile: Apple
Digital Platform - Tablet: Apple iOS
Gen. Mgr. George Morgenstern
Ed. Barbara G. Morgenstern
Mechanical Specifications: Tabloid, five columns, 10.25"wide by 15"deep
Equipment: Hardware — APP/Mac; Software — InDesign
Delivery Method: Mail, Newsstand
Zip Codes Served: 14617,14618,14620,14623, 14534,14424

SCHENECTADY

THE JEWISH WORLD (Thur, Other) (twice a month)
1635 Eastern Pkwy, Schenectady, NY, 12309-6011, Schenectady, USA; tel (518) 344-7018; fax (518) 713-2137; e-mail news@jewishworldnews.org; web site www.jewishworldnews.org
Circulation: 8,500pd,; Sworn/Estimate/Non-Audited
Advertising: Open inch rate $13.50
Established: 1965
editor. Laurie Clevenson
Mechanical Specifications: Type page 10 x 15 3/4.
Equipment: Hardware — APP/Mac G3, GCC/Elite 1200; Software — QPS/QuarkXPress 4.0.
Word
Delivery Method: Mail, Newsstand
Note: serving Albany,Schenectady, Troy,all northeastern NY, western Mass, and south Vt

SYRACUSE

THE JEWISH OBSERVER (Thur) (bi-weekly)
5655 Thompson Rd, Syracuse, NY, 13214-1234, Onondaga, USA; tel (315) 445-0161; adv tel (800) 779-7896 ext 244; ed tel (315) 445-0161; fax (315) 445-1559; ed fax (315) 445-1559; e-mail jewishobservercny@gmail.com; adv e-mail jewishobserversyr@gmail.

com; ed e-mail jewishobservercny@gmail.com; web site www.jewishfederationcnyp.org
Circulation: 3,000pd,; Sworn/Estimate/Non-Audited
Established: 1976
Ed. .... Bette Siegel
Mechanical Specifications: Type page 10 3/8 x 16; E - 3 cols, 3 3/8, 1/6 between; A - 6 cols, 1 5/8, 1/6 between.
Delivery Method: Mail
Zip Codes Served: 01701-97201

VALLEY STREAM

JEWISH JOURNAL (Fri)
11 Sunrise Plz, Valley Stream, NY, 11580-6170, Nassau, USA; tel (516) 561-6900; fax (516) 561-3529
Circulation: 47,000pd, 33,000fr; Sworn/Estimate/Non-Audited
Advertising: Open inch rate $1.40
Group: Joseph Jacobs Organization
Ed. .... Paul Rubin
Equipment: Hardware — APP/Mac; Software — QPS/QuarkXPress.

VESTAL

THE REPORTER (Fri)
500 Clubhouse Rd, Vestal, NY, 13850-4700, Broome, USA; tel (607) 724-2360; fax (607) 724-2311; e-mail treporter@aol.com; web site www.thereportergroup.org
Circulation: 2,400pd,; Sworn/Estimate/Non-Audited
Advertising: Open inch rate $9.15
Established: 1971
Bus. Mgr. .... Dan Springer
Adv. Mgr. .... Bonnie Rosen
Circ. Mgr. .... Maria Kutz
Prodn. Coord. .... Jenn DePersis
Mechanical Specifications: Type page 10 3/8 x 16; E - 3 cols, 3 3/8, 1/6 between; A - 6 cols, 1 5/8, 1/6 between.

THE VOICE (Mthly)
500 Clubhouse Rd, Vestal, NY, 13850-4700, Broome, USA; tel (607) 724-2360; fax (607) 724-2311; e-mail treporter@aol.com; web site www.thereportergroup.org
Circulation: 3,000pd,; Sworn/Estimate/Non-Audited
Established: 1989
Bus. Mgr. .... Dan Springer
Prodn. Mgr. .... Jenn DePersis
Mechanical Specifications: Type page 10 3/8 x 16; E - 3 cols, 3 3/8, 1/6 between; A - 6 cols, 1 5/8, 1/6 between.

NORTH CAROLINA

CHARLOTTE

CHARLOTTE JEWISH NEWS (Mthly)
5007 Providence Rd, Charlotte, NC, 28226-5849, Mecklenburg, USA; tel (704) 944-6757; fax (704) 944-6766; e-mail info@jewishcharlotte.org; ed e-mail amontoni@shalomcharlotte.org; web site www.jewishcharlotte.org
Circulation: 4,200fr; Sworn/Estimate/Non-Audited
Advertising: Open inch rate $15.46
Established: 1979
Group: Joseph Jacobs Organization
Adv. Mgr. .... Rita Mond
Ed. .... Amy Montoni

OHIO

AKRON

AKRON JEWISH NEWS
750 White Pond Dr, Akron, OH, 44320-1128, Summit, USA; tel (330) 869-2424; fax (330) 867-8498; e-mail newspaper@jewishakron.org; web site www.akronjewishnews.com
Advertising: Open inch rate $8.00
Adv. Mgr. .... Lisa Hofmann
Circ. Mgr. .... Mary Herkimer
Ed. .... Paula Maggio
Mechanical Specifications: Type page 9 3/4 x 14.
Equipment: Hardware — APP/Mac; Software — Adobe/PageMaker 6.5, Adobe/Photoshop.

BEACHWOOD

CLEVELAND JEWISH NEWS (Fri)
23880 Commerce Park, Ste 1, Beachwood, OH, 44122-5830, Cuyahoga, USA; tel (216)454-8300; adv tel (216)342-5191; ed tel (216)342-5207; fax (216)454-8100; adv fax (216)454-8100; ed fax (216)454-8200; e-mail info@cjn.org; adv e-mail amandell@cjn.org; ed e-mail editorial@cjn.org; web site www.cjn.org
Circulation: 6,281pd, 400fr; USPS
Advertising: $330
Established: 1964
Group: Cleveland Jewish Publication Company
Pres., Pub. & CEO .... Kevin Adelstein
VP of Sales .... Adam Mandell
Mng. Ed. .... Bob Jacob
Controller .... Tracy DiDomenico
Delivery Method: Mail, Newsstand
Zip Codes Served: Cleveland and suburbs

CANTON

STARK JEWISH NEWS (Mthly)
2631 Harvard Ave NW, Canton, OH, 44709-3147, Stark, USA; tel (330) 452-6444; fax (330) 452-4487; e-mail starkjewishnews@aol.com; web site www.jewishcanton.org
Circulation: 500pd, 1,500fr; Sworn/Estimate/Non-Audited
Advertising: Open inch rate $7.00
Group: Joseph Jacobs Organization
Adv. Mgr. .... Bev Gross
Ed. .... Karen Phillipi
Mechanical Specifications: Type page 11 1/2 x 13 3/4.
Equipment: Hardware — APP/Mac; Software — Adobe/PageMaker 4.2.
Zip Codes Served: 44709

CINCINNATI

THE AMERICAN ISRAELITE (Thur)
18 W 9th St, Ste 2, Cincinnati, OH, 45202-2037, Hamilton, USA; tel (513) 621-3145; fax (513) 621-3744; e-mail publisher@americanisraelite.com; web site www.americanisraelite.com
Circulation: 6,522pd, 461fr; Sworn/Estimate/Non-Audited
Advertising: Open inch rate $20.30
Group: Joseph Jacobs Organization
Pub. .... Ted Deutsch
Mng. Ed. .... Sauni Lerner
Mechanical Specifications: Type page 10 x 13 1/4; E - 5 cols, between; A - 5 cols, between.
Equipment: Hardware — APP/Power Mac; Software — QPS/QuarkXPress.

COLUMBUS

OHIO JEWISH CHRONICLE (Thur)
2862 Johnstown Rd, Columbus, OH, 43219-1793, Franklin, USA; tel (614) 337-2055; fax (614) 337-2059; e-mail ojc@insight.rr.com
Circulation: 2,481pd, 322fr; Sworn/Estimate/Non-Audited
Advertising: Open inch rate $10.50
Group: Joseph Jacobs Organization
Adv. Mgr. .... Angela Miller
Mng. Ed. .... Stephen Pinsky
Mechanical Specifications: Type page 10 1/4 x 14; E - 6 cols, 1 5/8, 1/3 between; A - 6 cols, 1 5/8, 1/3 between.

DAYTON

THE DAYTON JEWISH OBSERVER (Mthly)
525 Versailles Dr, Dayton, OH, 45459-6074, Montgomery, USA; tel (937) 610-1555; fax (937) 853-0378; e-mail mweiss@jfgd.net; web site www.jewishdayton.org
Circulation: 3,232fr; Sworn/Estimate/Non-Audited
Advertising: Open inch rate $15.50
Established: 1996
Group: Jewish Federation of Greater Dayton
Digital Platform - Mobile: Other
Digital Platform - Tablet: Other
Ed./Pub. .... Marshall Weiss
Mechanical Specifications: Type page 10 3/16 x 12 1/4; E - 5 cols, 1 7/8, 1/8 between; A - 5 cols, 1 7/8, 1/8 between; C - 5 cols, 1 7/8, 1/8 between.
Equipment: Hardware — PC; PressesWeb press; Software — Adobe CS
Delivery Method: Mail, Newsstand, Racks
Zip Codes Served: Southwest Ohio

SYLVANIA

TOLEDO JEWISH NEWS (Mthly)
6465 Sylvania Ave, Sylvania, OH, 43560-3916, Lucas, USA; tel (419) 724-0318; fax (419) 885-3207; e-mail paul@jewishtoledo.org; web site www.jewishtoledo.org
Circulation: 2,000pd,; Sworn/Estimate/Non-Audited
Advertising: Open inch rate $13.25
Group: Jewish Federation of Greater Toledo
Marketing Manager and Editor . Paul Causman
Staff writer, Marketing Associate Emily Gordon
Delivery Method: Mail, Racks

PENNSYLVANIA

HARRISBURG

COMMUNITY REVIEW (Fri)
3301 N Front St, Harrisburg, PA, 17110-1436, Dauphin, USA; tel (717) 236-9555; fax (717) 236-8104; e-mail o.yagil@jewishfedhbg.org; adv e-mail o.yagil@jewishfedhbg.org; ed e-mail o.yagil@jewishfedhbg.org; web site www.jewishharrisburg.org
Circulation: 2,100pd,; Sworn/Estimate/Non-Audited
Advertising: Open inch rate $12.50
Established: 1925
Group: Jewish Federation of Greater HarrisburgOren Yagil
Mechanical Specifications: Type page 9 3/4 x 12 1/2; E - 5 cols, 7/8, 1/6 between; A - 5 cols, 1/6 between; C - 5 cols, 1/6 between.
Equipment: Hardware — APP/Mac; Software — InDesign
Zip Codes Served: 17013-17112

PHILADELPHIA

JEWISH EXPONENT (Thur)
2100 Arch St, Philadelphia, PA, 19103-1300, Philadelphia, USA; tel (215) 832-0700; fax (215) 832-0785; e-mail production@jewishexponent.com; web site www.jewishexponent.com
Circulation: 40,406pd, 4,460fr; Sworn/Estimate/Non-Audited
Advertising: Open inch rate $57.75
Established: 1887
Group: Joseph Jacobs Organization
Gen. Mgr. .... David Alpher
Circ. Mgr. .... Rose Houlne
Ed. .... Lisa Hostein
Prodn. Mgr. .... Josephine Kukuka
Mechanical Specifications: Type page 10 1/2 x 13; E - 5 cols, 2, between; A - 5 cols, 2, between; C - 7 cols, 1 3/8, between.
Equipment: Hardware — APP/Mac; Software — QPS/QuarkXPress, Adobe/Photoshop, Adobe/Illustrator.

PITTSBURGH

THE JEWISH CHRONICLE (Thur)
5915 Beacon St, Fl 3, Pittsburgh, PA, 15217-2005, Allegheny, USA; tel (412) 687-1000; fax (412) 521-0154; e-mail newsdesk@thejewishchronicle.net; adv e-mail advertising@thejewishchronicle.net; ed e-mail newsdesk@thejewishchronicle.net; web site www.thejewishchronicle.net
Circulation: 3,800pd, 300fr; Sworn/Estimate/Non-Audited
Advertising: Open inch rate $20.50
Established: 1962
Exec. Ed. .... Lee Chottiner
Prodn. Mgr. .... Dawn Wanninger
Interim CEO .... Jim Busis
Mechanical Specifications: Type page 10 1/4 x 14 1/2; E - 4 cols, 2 1/3, 3/8 between; A - 4 cols, 2 1/3, 3/8 between; C - 6 cols, 1 1/2, 1/4 between.
Equipment: Hardware — Macintosh, PC; Software — QPS/QuarkXPress 4.0, Adobe/Photoshop 6.0, Microsoft/Word 5.1A.
Delivery Method: Mail
Zip Codes Served: All

WYOMISSING

SHALOM NEWSPAPER (Mthly)
223 Hawthorne Ct N, Wyomissing, PA, 19610-1064, Berks, USA; tel (610) 921-0624; fax (610) 929-0886; e-mail joan@friedman.net; web site www.readingjewishcommunity.org
Circulation: 3,000pd,; Sworn/Estimate/Non-Audited
Advertising: Open inch rate $19.50

RHODE ISLAND

PROVIDENCE

JEWISH VOICE OF RHODE ISLAND (Other) (2 x Mthly)
130 Sessions St, Providence, RI, 02906-3444, Providence, USA; tel (401) 421-4111; fax (410) 331-7961; e-mail editor@jewishallianceri.org; ed e-mail editor@jewishallianceri.org; web site www.jvhri.org
Circulation: 10,000fr; Sworn/Estimate/Non-Audited
Advertising: Open inch rate $13.00
Digital Platform - Mobile: Apple
Digital Platform - Tablet: Apple iOS
Prodn. Mgr. .... Leah Camara
Mechanical Specifications: Type page 10 x 13;

E - 5 cols, 1 7/8, 1/4 between; A - 5 cols, 1 7/8, 1/4 between.
Equipment: Hardware — APP/Mac; Software — Adobe/InDesignCC
Delivery Method: Mail, Racks
Zip Codes Served: all Rhode Island and Southeastern Mass.

THE JEWISH VOICE (Every other Fri)
401 Elmgrove Ave, Providence, RI, 02906-3451, Providence, USA; tel (401) 421-4111; fax (401) 331-7961; e-mail editor@jewishallianceri.org; ed e-mail editor@jewishallianceri.org; web site www.jvhri.org
Circulation: 9,000fr; Sworn/Estimate/Non-Audited
Advertising: Open inch rate $18
Group: Jewish Alliance of Greater Rhode Island
Digital Platform - Mobile: Apple, Android, Windows, Blackberry
Digital Platform - Tablet: Apple iOS, Android, Windows 7, Blackberry Tablet OS, Kindle, Nook, Kindle Fire
Adv. Mgr. .... Chris Westerkamp
Exec. Ed .... Fran Ostendorf
Mechanical Specifications: Type page 10.25 x 13.5; C - 2 cols, 4, 1/2 between.
Equipment: Hardware — Mac; Software — Adobe

TENNESSEE

MEMPHIS

HEBREW WATCHMAN (Thur)
4646 Poplar Ave, Ste 232, Memphis, TN, 38117-4426, Shelby, USA; tel (901) 763-2215; fax (901) 763-2216; e-mail hebwat@bellsouth.net
Circulation: 3,000pd,; Sworn/Estimate/Non-Audited
Advertising: Open inch rate $9.00
Established: 1925
Ed. .... Herman I. Goldberger
Mechanical Specifications: Type page 10 3/4 x 13; E - 5 cols, 2 1/16, between; A - 5 cols, 2 1/16, between.
Equipment: Hardware — APP/Mac.
Delivery Method: Mail

NASHVILLE

THE JEWISH OBSERVER (Mthly)
801 Percy Warner Blvd, Ste 102, Nashville, TN, 37205-4128, Davidson, USA; tel (615) 354-1653; adv tel (615) 354-1699; ed tel (615) 354-1653; fax (615) 352-0056; e-mail info@jewishnashville.org; adv e-mail carrie@nashvillejcc.org; ed e-mail charles@jewishnashville.org; web site www.jewishobservernashville.org
Circulation: 4,000fr; Sworn/Estimate/Non-Audited
Advertising: Open inch rate $12.50
Established: 1937
Group: Jewish Federation of Nashville and Middle Tennessee
Adv. Mgr. .... Carrie Mills
Editor .... Charles Bernsen
Mechanical Specifications: Type page 10 x 14; E - 4 cols, 2 1/4, 1/4 between; A - 4 cols, 2 1/2, between.
Equipment: Hardware — Windows Desktop; PressesWeb; Software — InDesign and Quark
Delivery Method: Mail
Zip Codes Served: Nashville - Middle Tennessee

TEXAS

HOUSTON

JEWISH HERALD-VOICE (Thur)
3403 Audley St, Houston, TX, 77098-1923, Harris, USA; tel (713) 630-0391; adv tel (713) 630-0391; ed tel (713) 630-0391; fax (713) 630-0404; adv fax (713) 630-0404; ed fax (713) 630-0404; e-mail news@jhvonline.com; adv e-mail advertising@jhvonline.com; ed e-mail editor@jhvonline.com; web site www.jhvonline.com
Circulation: 5,000pd, 200fr; Sworn/Estimate/Non-Audited
Advertising: Open inch rate $40.00
Established: 1908
Advertising Manager .... Vicki Samuels
Editor .... Jeanne F. Samuels
Production Manager .... Aaron Poscovsky
Circulation .... Levy Lawrence
Mechanical Specifications: Type page 9 3/4 x 15 1/2; E - 4 cols, 2 1/4, 1/6 between; A - 4 cols, 2 1/4, 1/6 between.
Equipment: Hardware — MAC
Delivery Method: Mail
Zip Codes Served: All

SAN ANTONIO

THE JEWISH JOURNAL OF SAN ANTONIO (Mthly)
12500 NW Military Hwy, Ste 200, San Antonio, TX, 78231-1868, Bexar, USA; tel (210) 302-6960; fax (210) 408-2332; e-mail jewishj@jfsatx.org; adv e-mail advertising@jfsatx.org; web site www.jfsatx.org
Circulation: 4,000fr; Sworn/Estimate/Non-Audited
Group: Jewish Federation of San Antonio
Ed. .... Leslie Ausburn
Delivery Method: Mail, Racks

VIRGINIA

RICHMOND

VIRGINIA JEWISH LIFE
212 N Gaskins Rd, Richmond, VA, 23238-5526, Henrico, USA; tel (804) 740-2000; fax (804) 750-1341; ed e-mail editor@virginiajewishlife.com; web site www.virginiajewishlife.com
Established: 1977
Adv. Rep. .... Dana Zedd
Mng. Ed. .... Allie Vered

WISCONSIN

MILWAUKEE

THE WISCONSIN JEWISH CHRONICLE (Mthly)
1360 N Prospect Ave, Milwaukee, WI, 53202-3056, Milwaukee, USA; tel (414) 390-5770; adv tel (414) 390-5765; fax (414) 390-5766; e-mail chronicle@milwaukeejewish.org; web site www.jewishchronicle.org
Circulation: 8,000fr; Sworn/Estimate/Non-Audited
Advertising: Open inch rate $13.00
Established: 1921
Group: Milwaukee Jewish Federation
Production Manager .... Yvonne Chapman
Editor .... Leon Cohen
Mechanical Specifications: Type page 9 3/4 x 12 1/2; E - 5 cols, between; A - 5 cols, between.
Equipment: Hardware — APP/Mac; Software — QPS/QuarkXPress.

MILITARY NEWSPAPERS IN THE UNITED STATES

ALABAMA

FORT RUCKER

ARMY FLIER (Thur)
453 S Novasel St, Bldg 112, Fort Rucker, AL, 36362-5109, Dale, USA; tel (334) 255-2613; fax (334) 255-1004; web site www.armyflier.com
Circulation: 10,000fr; Sworn/Estimate/Non-Audited
Advertising: Open inch rate $10.00
Group: BH Media Group
Ed. .... Marty Gatlin
Mechanical Specifications: Type page 13 x 21 1/2; E - 6 cols, 2 1/8, between; A - 6 cols, 2 1/8, between; C - 9 cols, 1 9/20, between.

MAXWELL AFB

MAXWELL-GUNTER DISPATCH (Fri)
55 S Lemay Plz, Maxwell Afb, AL, 36112-5944, Montgomery, USA; tel (334) 953-2014; fax (334) 953-3379; e-mail maxwell.dispatch@maxwell.af.mil; web site www.maxwellgunterdispatch.com
Circulation: 12,000fr; Sworn/Estimate/Non-Audited
Advertising: Open inch rate $11.75
Ed. .... Christine Harrison
Mechanical Specifications: Type page 10 x 12 3/4; E - 5 cols, between; A - 5 cols, between; C - 5 cols, between.
Equipment: Hardware — APP/Mac; Software — QPS/QuarkXPress.

ARIZONA

YUMA

DESERT WARRIOR (Thur)
PO Box 99113, Yuma, AZ, 85369-9113, Yuma, USA; tel (928) 269-2275; e-mail shelby.shields@usmc.mil; web site www.yuma.usmc.mil
Circulation: 3,300fr; Sworn/Estimate/Non-Audited
Advertising: Open inch rate $15.47
Ed. .... Shelby Shields
Mechanical Specifications: Type page 11 13/16 x 21; E - 6 cols, 1 7/8, 1/16 between; A - 6 cols, 1 7/8, 1/16 between; C - 6 cols, 1 7/8, 1/16 between.
Equipment: Hardware — APP/Mac; Presses — G; Software — DTI/AdSpeed 4.1, Adobe/Illustrator 2.1.
Zip Codes Served: 85369

CALIFORNIA

BARSTOW

BARSTOW LOG (Thur)
Marine Corps Logistics Base, Bldg 204, Barstow, CA, 92311, San Bernardino, USA; tel (760) 577-6430; fax (760) 577-6350; e-mail robert.l.jackson@usmc.mil
Circulation: 3,700fr; Sworn/Estimate/Non-Audited
Advertising: Open inch rate $6.00
Group: Brehm Communications, Inc.
Pub. Affairs Officer .... Rob L. Jackson
Ed. .... Quentin Grogan
Mechanical Specifications: Type page 10 1/4 x 13; E - 5 cols, 1 11/12, 1/8 between; A - 5 cols, 1 11/12, 1/8 between; C - 5 cols, 1 11/12, 1/8 between.

EL CENTRO

SANDPAPER
1500 8th St, El Centro, CA, 92243-5041, Imperial, USA; tel (760) 339-2519; fax (760) 339-2699; e-mail elcnpao@navy.mil; web site www.nafec.navy.mil
Circulation:; Sworn/Estimate/Non-Audited
Ed. .... Michelle Dee

LANCASTER

AEROTECH NEWS & REVIEW (Fri)
456 E Avenue K4, Ste 8, Lancaster, CA, 93535-4642, Los Angeles, USA; tel (661) 945-5634; fax (661) 723-7757; e-mail aerotech@aerotechnews.com; web site www.aerotechnews.com
Circulation: 15,000fr; Sworn/Estimate/Non-Audited
Advertising: Open inch rate $15.70Editions: 2- 2 total Aerotech News & Review (35,000);
Pub. .... Paul J. Kinison
Adv. Mgr. .... Gail Ellis
Ed. .... Stewart Ibberson
Mechanical Specifications: Type page 10 1/4 x 13; E - 5 cols, 1 11/12, 1/8 between; A - 5 cols, 1 11/12, 1/8 between; C - 5 cols, 1 11/12, 1/8 between.
Equipment: Hardware — APP/Mac; Software — Adobe/PageMaker 6.5, Adobe/Photoshop 4.0, Microsoft/Word 6.0.

RIDGECREST

ON TARGET (EVERY OTHER THUR)
1 Administration Cir, Stop 1014, Ridgecrest, CA, 93555-6104, Kern, USA; tel (760) 939-3354; fax (760) 939-2796
Circulation: 5,000fr; Sworn/Estimate/Non-Audited
Advertising: Open inch rate $14.60
Ed. .... Dee Rorex

SAN DIEGO

COMPASS
(Thur)
937 N Harbor Dr, San Diego, CA, 92132-5001, San Diego, USA; tel (619) 532-1434; fax (619) 532-4537; e-mail johnb@navycompass.com; web site www.navycompass.com
Circulation: 43,000fr; Sworn/Estimate/Non-Audited
Advertising: Open inch rate $25.00
Adv. Mgr. .... Jim Missit
Ed. .... Jess Levens

YUCCA VALLEY

OBSERVATION POST
(Fri)
56445 29 Palms Hwy, Yucca Valley, CA, 92284-2861, San Bernardino, USA; tel (760) 365-3315; fax (760) 365-4181; adv e-mail advertising@hidesertstar.com; ed e-mail editor@hidesertstar.com; web site www.hidesertstar.com
Circulation: 6,500fr; Sworn/Estimate/Non-Audited
Advertising: Open inch rate $15.00
Group: Brehm Communications, Inc.
Hi-Desert Publishing Co., Inc.
Pub. .... Cindy Melland
Mechanical Specifications: Type page 10 x 21 ; E - 6 cols, 1 3/4, 1/8 between; A - 6 cols, 1 3/4, 1/8 between; C - 9 cols, 1 3/16, 1/8 between.
Equipment: Hardware — APP/Mac G4; Presses — G/Community; Software — In Design, Adobe/Photoshop 6.0, MultiAd 6.5.
Delivery Method: Carrier, Racks
Zip Codes Served: 92278 and 92277

COLORADO

COLORADO SPRINGS

MOUNTAINEER
(Fri)
31 E Platte Ave, Ste 300, Colorado Springs, CO, 80903-1246, El Paso, USA; tel (719) 634-1593; fax (719) 632-0265; e-mail advertising@gowdyprint.com
Circulation: 75,000fr; Sworn/Estimate/Non-Audited
Advertising: Open inch rate $13.00
Pub. .... Tex Stewart
Adv. Mgr. .... Barbara Hedges
Mechanical Specifications: Type page 10 7/8 x 15 5/8; E - 6 cols, 1 1/2, between; A - 6 cols, 1 1/2, between.
Equipment: Hardware — IBM, APP/Mac; Presses — Komori/M29, HI/25; Software — QPS/QuarkXPress, Adobe/Photoshop, Adobe/Illustrator.
Zip Codes Served: 80903

CONNECTICUT

GROTON

THE DOLPHIN
(Thur)
PO Box 44, Groton, CT, 06349-5044, New London, USA; tel (860) 694-3514; adv tel (203) 680-9935; fax (860) 694-5012; e-mail dolphin@ctcentral.com; adv e-mail blemkin@adtaxinetworks.com; ed e-mail dolphin@ctcentral.com; web site www.dolphin-news.com
Circulation: 8,000fr; Sworn/Estimate/Non-Audited
Advertising: Open inch rate $11.62
Established: 1918
Group: Hearst Communications, Inc.
Ed. .... Sheryl Walsh
Multi Media Sales Mgr. .... John Slater
Mechanical Specifications: Type page 12 x 21; E - 6 cols, 2, 1/6 between; A - 6 cols, 1 5/8, 1/6 between; C - 6 cols, 1 5/8, 1/6 between.
Equipment: Hardware — 2-APP/Mac G4, HP/Laserjet Scanner, HP/Laserjet 5100; Software — Multi-Ad/Creator, InDesign, Adobe/Photoshop 7.0, Microsoft/Word, Adobe/Acrobat.
Delivery Method: Racks
Zip Codes Served: 06340

FLORIDA

JACKSONVILLE

JAX AIR NEWS
(Thur)
PO Box 2, Jacksonville, FL, 32212-0002, Duval, USA; tel (904) 542-3531; adv tel (904) 359-4168; fax (904) 542-1534; e-mail jaxairnews@comcast.net; web site jaxairnews.com
Circulation: 10,000fr; Sworn/Estimate/Non-Audited
Advertising: Open inch rate $16.55
Established: 1940
Ed. .... Clark Pierce
Delivery Method: Newsstand, Racks
Zip Codes Served: 32202,32203,32204,32205,32207,32223,32218,32224,32217,32225

THE MIRROR
(Thur)
Massey Avenue, Jacksonville, FL, 32228, Duval, USA; tel (904) 270-7817; fax (904) 270-5329; e-mail mayportmirror@comcast.net; web site www.mayportmirror.com
Circulation: 10,000fr; Sworn/Estimate/Non-Audited
Advertising: Open inch rate $14.00
Pub. .... Ellen S. Rykert
Adv. Mgr. .... Paige Gnann
Zip Codes Served: 32228

MELBOURNE

MISSILEER
PO Box 419000, Melbourne, FL, 32941-9000, Brevard, USA; tel (321) 242-3500; fax (321) 242-6618; web site www.floridatoday.com
Circulation:; Sworn/Estimate/Non-Audited
Advertising: Open inch rate $11.91
Established: 1966
Pub. .... Mark Mikolajczyk
Opns. Dir. .... John Vizzini
Exec. Ed. .... Bob Stover
Mng. Ed. .... John Kelly
Adv. Dir. .... Chris Wood
Mechanical Specifications: Type page 9 2/3 x 11 1/2; E - 5 cols, 1 5/6, 1/8 between; A - 5 cols, 1 5/6, 1/8 between; C - 80 cols, 1 1/10, 1/16 between.
Equipment: Hardware — APP/Mac Platinum G3; Presses — Offset; Software — Multi-Ad/Creator 4.02, Adobe/Photoshop 5.0, Adobe/Illustrator 7.0.

MILTON

WHITING TOWER
(Wed)
Whiting Field, 7550 USS Essex St, Ste 109, Milton, FL, 32570, Santa Rosa, USA; tel (850) 665-6121; adv tel N/A; ed tel (850) 665-6121; fax (850) 623-7601; ed fax (850) 623-7601; e-mail jay.cope@navy.mil; adv e-mail N/A; ed e-mail jay.cope@navy.mil
Circulation: 3,000fr; Sworn/Estimate/Non-Audited
Established: 1943
Ed. .... Jay Cope

PANAMA CITY

GULF DEFENDER (2 X MTHLY)
501 W 11th St, Panama City, FL, 32401-2330, Bay, USA; tel (850) 747-5005; fax (850) 763-4636; e-mail phgregory@pcnh.com; web site www.newsherald.com
Circulation: 12,000fr; Sworn/Estimate/Non-Audited
Advertising: Open inch rate $18.00
Pub./Reg'l Vice Pres. .... Karen E. Hanes
Adv. Mgr. .... Wayne Kight
Adv. Dir. .... Pam Gregory
Reg'l Circ. Dir. .... Mike Miller
Opns. Dir. .... Ron Smith
Mechanical Specifications: Type page 10 1/4 x 11 1/4; E - 6 cols, 2 1/16, 1/8 between; A - 6 cols, 2 1/16, 1/8 between.
Equipment: Hardware — Advanced Publishing Technology; Presses — 6-G/Community; Software — Dewar Sys 4.
Zip Codes Served: 32403

PENSACOLA

GOSPORT
(Fri)
41 N Jefferson St, Pensacola, FL, 32502-5681, Escambia, USA; tel (850) 202-2242; adv tel (850) 433-1166; ed tel (850) 452-4466; fax (850) 202-2248; ed e-mail scott.hallford@navy.mil; web site www.ballingerpublishing.com
Circulation: 25,000fr; Sworn/Estimate/Non-Audited
Advertising: Open inch rate $20.30
Established: 1921
Group: U.S. Navy
Pub. .... Malcolm Ballinger
Ed. .... Scott Hallford
Assoc. Ed. .... Mike O'Connor
Simone Sands
Janet Thomas
Mechanical Specifications: Type page 10 x 16; E - 5 cols, 2, 1/4 between.
Equipment: Hardware — APP/Mac, PC; Presses — HI/M-1000; Software — QPS/QuarkXPress, Adobe/Photoshop.
Delivery Method: Mail, Racks
Zip Codes Served: 32501,02,03,04,05,06,07,08,09

TAMPA

THUNDERBOLT
(Fri)
8208 Hangar Loop Dr, Ste 14, Tampa, FL, 33621-5545, Hillsborough, USA; tel (813) 828-4586; fax (813) 828-3653; e-mail thunderbolt@macdill.af.mil; thunder- bolt@macdill.af.mil; web site www.macdillthunderbolt.com
Circulation: 8,456fr; CVC
Advertising: Open inch rate $20.65
Pub. .... Carla Floyd
Adv. Mgr. .... Annette Demask
Ed. .... Nick Stubbs
Mechanical Specifications: Type page 10 1/4 x 15; E - 5 cols, 2 1/16, between; A - 5 cols, 2 1/16, between; C - 8 cols, 1 5/16, between.
Zip Codes Served: 33621

GEORGIA

FORT BENNING

THE BAYONET
(Wed)
6460 Way Ave, Ste 102, Fort Benning, GA, 31905-3771, Chattahoochee, USA; tel (706) 545-4622; adv tel (706) 576-6239; web site www.thebayonet.com
Circulation: 22,000fr; Sworn/Estimate/Non-Audited
Advertising: Open inch rate $21.00
Ed. .... Lori Egan
Mechanical Specifications: Type page 13 x 20 1/2; E - 6 cols, 2 1/16, 1/6 between; A - 6 cols, 2 1/16, 1/6 between; C - 6 cols, 2 1/16, 1/6 between.
Equipment: Hardware — APP/Mac; Software — QPS/QuarkXPress 3.32.
Delivery Method: Mail, Newsstand, Carrier, Racks
Zip Codes Served: 31905

HINESVILLE

THE FRONTLINE
(Thur)
125 S Main St, Hinesville, GA, 31313-3217, Liberty, USA; tel (912) 368-0526; fax (912) 368-6329; web site www.coastalcourier.com
Circulation: 17,000fr; Sworn/Estimate/Non-Audited
Advertising: Open inch rate $11.10
Group: Morris Multimedia, Inc.
Pub. .... Mark Griffin
Mechanical Specifications: Type page 11 3/4 x 21 1/2; E - 6 cols, 2 1/16, between; A - 6 cols, 2 1/16, between; C - 6 cols, 2 1/16, between.

MACON

THE TELEGRAPH
(Mon, Tues, Wed, Thur, Fri, Sat, Sun)
487 Cherry St, Macon, GA, 31201-7972, Bibb, USA; tel (478) 744-4200; adv tel (478) 744-4245; ed tel (478) 744-4411; web site www.macon.com
Circulation: 18,000fr; AAM
Group: The McClatchy Company
Digital Platform - Mobile: Apple, Android
Digital Platform - Tablet: Apple iOS, Android, OtherJackie Middlemus
Equipment: Hardware — APP/Mac; Presses — G/Community (offset); Software — Baseview, QPS/QuarkXPress.
Delivery Method: Newsstand, Carrier, Racks

WAYNESBORO

THE SIGNAL
(Fri)
Nelson Hall Rm 215, Waynesboro, GA, 30830, Burke, USA; tel (706) 791-7069; fax (706) 791-5463; e-mail thesignal@conus.army.mil; web site www.fortgordonsignal.com
Circulation: 18,600fr; Sworn/Estimate/Non-Audited
Advertising: Open inch rate $11.97

Pub..Roy F. Chalker
Gen. Mgr.....................................Bonnie Taylor
Adv. Mgr..............................Deborah Kitchens
Prodn. Mgr.....................................Jill Dumars
Mechanical Specifications: Type page 13 x 21 1/2; E - 4 cols, 3 1/6, 1/6 between; A - 6 cols, 2 1/12, 1/6 between; C - 6 cols, 2 1/12, 1/6 between.
Equipment: Hardware — PC, APP/Mac; Presses — G/Community; Software — Adobe/PageMaker 6.5, QPS/QuarkXPress, Archetype/Corel Draw, Adobe/Photoshop.

HAWAII

MCBH KANEOHE BAY

MARINE STAR

(Fri)
PO Box 63062, McB Hawaii, Mcbh Kaneohe Bay, HI, 96863-3062, Honolulu, USA; tel (808) 257-8837; adv tel (808) 529-4700; ed tel (808) 257-8837; fax (808) 257-2511; adv fax (808) 529-4898; ed fax (808) 257-2511; e-mail HawaiiMarineEditor@gmail.com; adv e-mail displayads@staradvertiser.com; ed e-mail HawaiiMarineEditor@gmail.com; web site http://www.mcbhawaii.marines.mil
Circulation: 6,396fr; Sworn/Estimate/Non-Audited
Advertising: $28 pci (rates do not include Hawaii General Excise tax of 4.712%)
Group: Oahu Publications Inc.
Ed...Lynsey Beth Futa
Mechanical Specifications: 1/8 pg 4.787" x 5"
1/4 pg 4.787" x 10"
1/2 pg horizontal 9.7" x 10"
1/2 pg vertical 4.787" x 20"
Full pg 9.7" x 20"
Front pg banner 9.7" x 2"
Double truck 21" x 20"
Equipment: Hardware — Offset Presses; Black + 3 ROP Colors; Inserts Accepted (min size 3x4", max 10.5x11"); 70,000 CPM; Page Cutoff 21".; Presses — 6 Towers Man Roland Regioman 2004 (12 Towers in one press line; configured as two presses).; Software — PECOM
Delivery Method: Mail, Racks
Zip Codes Served: 96744, 96795, 96815, 96818, 96859, 96861, 96863

PEARL HARBOR

HO`OKELE (NAVY & AIR FORCE)

(Fri)
850 Ticonderoga St, Ste 110, Pearl Harbor, HI, 96860-5101, Honolulu, USA; tel (808) 473-2888; adv tel (808) 529-4700; fax (808) 473-2876; adv fax (808) 529-4898; e-mail editor@hookelenews.com; adv e-mail displayads@staradvertiser.com; ed e-mail editor@hookelenews.com; web site www.hookelenews.com
Circulation: 19,578fr; Sworn/Estimate/Non-Audited
Advertising: $28 pci (rates do not include Hawaii General Excise tax of 4.712%)
Established: 2010
Group: Oahu Publications Inc.
Managing Ed.............................Anna General
Ed..Don Robbins
Mechanical Specifications: 1/8 pg 4.787" x 5"
1/4 pg 4.787" x 10"
1/2 pg horizontal 9.7" x 10"
1/2 pg vertical 4.787" x 20"
Full pg 9.7" x 20"
Front pg banner 9.7" x 2"
Double truck 21" x 20"
Equipment: Hardware — Offset Presses; Black + 3 ROP Colors; Inserts Accepted (min size 3x4", max 10.5x11"); 70,000 CPM; Page Cutoff 21".; Presses — 6 Towers Man Roland Regioman 2004 (12 Towers in one press line; configured as two presses).; Software — PECOM
Delivery Method: Mail, Racks
Zip Codes Served: 96706, 96759, 96815, 96818, 96853, 96859, 96860, 96861, 96862,96863

SCHOFIELD BARRACKS

HAWAII ARMY WEEKLY

(Fri)
745 Wright Ave., Waaf, Building 107, Schofield Barracks, HI, 96857, Honolulu, USA; tel (808) 656-3155; adv tel (808) 529-4700; ed tel (808) 656-3155; fax (808) 656-3162; adv fax (808) 529-4898; ed fax (808) 656-3162; e-mail editor@hawaiiarmyweekly.com; adv e-mail displayads@staradvertiser.com; ed e-mail editor@hawaiiarmyweekly.com; web site www.hawaiiarmyweekly.com
Circulation: 13,093fr; AAM
Advertising: $28 pci (rates do not include Hawaii General Excise tax of 4.712%)
Group: Oahu Publications Inc.
Chief, Internal Communication.........Aiko Brum
Pau Hana Editor.............................Jack Wiers
Mechanical Specifications: 1/8 pg 4.787" x 5"
1/4 pg 4.787" x 10"
1/2 pg horizontal 9.7" x 10"
1/2 pg vertical 4.787" x 20"
Full pg 9.7" x 20"
Front pg banner 9.7" x 2"
Double truck 21" x 20"
Equipment: Hardware — Offset Presses; Black + 3 ROP Colors; Inserts Accepted (min size 3x4", max 10.5x11"); 70,000 CPM; Page Cutoff 21".; Presses — 6 Towers Man Roland Regioman 2004 (12 Towers in one press line; configured as two presses).; Software — PECOM
Delivery Method: Mail, Racks
Zip Codes Served: 96786, 96815, 96818, 96854, 96858, 96859, 96860, 96861

IDAHO

MOUNTAIN HOME

MOUNTAIN HOME PATRIOT

(Fri)
PO Box 1330, Mountain Home, ID, 83647-1330, Elmore, USA; tel (208) 587-3331; fax (208) 587-9205; e-mail bfincher@mountainhomenews.com; web site www.mountainhomenews.com
Circulation: 4,500fr; Sworn/Estimate/Non-Audited
Advertising: 10.55 thur 10/31/14 call for current pricing
Established: 1888
Business Manager..................Brenda Fincher
Ed..Kelly Everitt
Mechanical Specifications: 13x21.5
Equipment: Hardware — APP/Mac; Presses — WPC/Leader.
Delivery Method: Mail, Racks
Zip Codes Served: 83648/47

ILLINOIS

GRAYSLAKE

LAKE COUNTY SUBURBAN LIFE

(Fri)
1100 E Washington St, Ste 101, Grayslake, IL, 60030-7963, Lake, USA; tel (847) 223-8161; fax (847) 223-8810; e-mail edit@lakelandmedia.com; web site www.lakecountyjournals.com
Circulation: 22,000fr; Sworn/Estimate/Non-Audited
Advertising: Open inch rate $16.00
VP of Adv.................................Jill McDermott
Ed..Paul Engstrom
Ryan Wells
Mechanical Specifications: Type page 10 1/4 x 16; E - 5 cols, 1 11/12, 1/4 between; A - 5 cols, 1 11/12, 1/4 between; C - 7 cols, 1 1/3, 1/6 between.
Equipment: Hardware — 40-APP/Mac, Ethernet, 3-Flatbed Scanner, 2-Negative Scanner, CD-ROM 4x Burner, SyQuest/EZ135 drive, 2-1200 dpi Printer, 4-600 dpi Printer; Presses — G/Urbanite; Software — Adobe/Illustrator 6.0, QPS/QuarkXPress 3.32, Adobe/Photoshop 3.0.5, Micr

MASCOUTAH

SCOTT FLIER

(Thur)
314 E Church St, Mascoutah, IL, 62258-2100, Saint Clair, USA; tel (618) 566-8282; fax (618) 566-8283; e-mail heraldpubs@cbnstl.com; web site www.heraldpubs.com
Circulation: 8,000fr; Sworn/Estimate/Non-Audited
Advertising: Open inch rate $9.31
Pub...Greg Hoskins
Mng. Ed.......................................Keith Gillette

KANSAS

FORT LEAVENWORTH

FORT LEAVENWORTH LAMP

(Thur)
290 Grant Ave, Ste 6, Fort Leavenworth, KS, 66027-1292, Leavenworth, USA; tel (913) 682-0305; adv tel (913) 682-0305; ed tel (913) 684-1728; fax (913) 682-1089; adv fax (913) 682-1089; adv e-mail shattock@leavenworthtimes.com; ed e-mail editor@ftleavenworthlamp.com; web site www.ftleavenworthlamp.com
Circulation: 8,000fr; Sworn/Estimate/Non-Audited
Advertising: Open inch rate $9.70
Established: 1971
Group: GateHouse Media, Inc.
Public Affairs Officer..................Jeffery Wingo
Adv. Mgr..................................Sandy Hattock
Ed...Robert Kerr
Mechanical Specifications: Type page 10 x 16; E - 5 cols, 2, between; A - 5 cols, 2, between; C - 5 cols, 2, between.
Delivery Method: Newsstand, Carrier, Racks
Zip Codes Served: 66027, 66048, 66043

JUNCTION CITY

FORT RILEY POST

(Fri)
222 W 6th St, Junction City, KS, 66441-5500, Geary, USA; tel (785) 239-3410; fax (785) 762-8854; e-mail abb.mgr@dilyview.com; web site www.riley.army.mil
Circulation: 8,800fr; Sworn/Estimate/Non-Audited
Pub.............................John Grey Montgomery
Adv. Mgr.................................Patrick M. Keefe
Ed...Anna Morelock
Prodn. Mgr......................................Ron Maley
Mechanical Specifications: Type page 13 x 21 1/4; E - 6 cols, 2 1/16, 1/6 between; A - 6 cols, 2 1/16, 1/6 between; C - 6 cols, 2 1/16, 1/6 between.
Equipment: Hardware — APP/Mac; Presses — G/Community; Software — QPS/QuarkXPress, Adobe/Photoshop.
Zip Codes Served: 66442

WICHITA

TANKER TIMES

(Fri)
2918 E Douglas Ave, Wichita, KS, 67214-4709, Sedgwick, USA; tel (316) 681-1155; fax (316) 681-0360; e-mail ttimes@tcvpub.com
Circulation: 5,300fr; Sworn/Estimate/Non-Audited
Advertising: Open inch rate $16.00
Ed...Bonita Gooch

KENTUCKY

FORT KNOX

TURRET

(Thur)
Bldg 1109, Wing D, Sixth St, Fort Knox, KY, 40121-, Hardin, USA; tel (502) 624-6517; adv tel (270) 769-1200; fax (502) 624-2096; web site www.turret.com; www.newsenterpriseonline.com
Circulation: 20,896fr; Sworn/Estimate/Non-Audited
Advertising: Open inch rate $9.49
Ed...Larry Barnes
Assoc. Ed................................Maureen Rose
Leisure Ed...............................Kellie Etheridge
Sports Ed......................................Ally Rogers
Mechanical Specifications: Type page 13 1/2 x 21 1/2; E - 6 cols, 2 1/8, between; A - 6 cols, 2 1/8, between.

HOPKINSVILLE

FORT CAMPBELL COURIER

(Thur)
1618 E 9th St, Hopkinsville, KY, 42240-4430, Christian, USA; tel (270) 887-3220; adv tel (270) 887-3270; fax (270) 887-3222; e-mail editor@kentuckynewera.com; web site www.kentuckynewera.com
Circulation: 23,000fr; Sworn/Estimate/Non-Audited
Advertising: Open inch rate $15.20
Pub..................................Taylor Wood Hayes
Gen. Mgr........................Charles A. Henderson
Bus. Mgr..Sheryl Ellis
Classified Mgr...........................Nancy Reese
Sales/Mktg. Dir...............................Ted Jatczak
Circ. Mgr..............................George McCouch
Ed.......................................Jennifer Brown
Sports Ed......................................Joe Wilson
Prodn. Mgr....................................Chris Hollis
Mechanical Specifications: Type page 13 x 21 1/2; E - 6 cols, 2 1/30, 1/6 between; A - 6 cols, 2 1/30, 1/6 between; C - 8 cols, 1 1/3, 1/6 between.
Equipment: Hardware — 3-PC 486; Presses — G/Urbanite; Software — QPS/QuarkXPress, Microsoft/Word, Archetype/Corel Draw.

LOUISIANA

FORT POLK

GUARDIAN

(Fri)
7033 Magnolia Dr, Fort Polk, LA, 71459-3495, Vernon, USA; tel (337) 462-0616; adv tel (337) 462-0616; ed tel (337) 531-4033; adv fax (337) 463-5347; ed fax (337) 531-1401; e-mail guardian@wnonline.net; web site www.thefortpolkguardian.com
Circulation: 13,000fr; Sworn/Estimate/Non-Audited
Advertising: Open inch rate $15.05

Adv. Mgr. ....Beaux Victor

GRETNA

THE CURRENTS

359 Fairfield Ave, Gretna, LA, 70056-7004, Jefferson, USA; tel (504) 363-9010; fax (504) 366-4826; e-mail polov13@aol.com
Circulation:; Sworn/Estimate/Non-Audited
Advertising: Open inch rate $15.75
Established: 1989
Pres. .... Vicki A. Polo
Pub... Samuel F. Polo
Adv. Mgr. .... Gina D. Polo
Circ. Mgr.................................... David P. Leger
Ed. .... Donnie R. Ryan
Mng. Ed...................................... Roy P. Griggs
Prodn. Mgr. .... Carolyn R. Cuccia
Mechanical Specifications: Type page 10 1/4 x 13 3/8; E - 4 cols, between; A - 6 cols, between.
Equipment: Hardware — APP/Mac; Presses — WPC; Software — Adobe/PageMaker.

MAINE

BRUNSWICK

THE PATROLLER

(Thur)
3 Business Pkwy, Brunswick, ME, 04011-7390, Cumberland, USA; tel (207) 729-3311; fax (207) 729-5728; adv e-mail adsales@timesrecord.com; web site www.timesrecord.com
Circulation: 3,500fr; Sworn/Estimate/Non-Audited
Advertising: Open inch rate $6.95
Pub...Chris Miles
Adv. Dir.......................................John Bamford
Mechanical Specifications: Type page 10 1/8 x 15 1/4; E - 5 cols, between; A - 5 cols, between; C - 6 cols, between.
Equipment; Presses — G/Community.

MARYLAND

FORT MEADE

SOUNDOFF!

(Thur)
4409 Llewellyn Avenue, Fort Meade, MD, 20755, Anne Arundel, USA; tel (301) 677-5602; adv tel (410) 332-6300; ed tel (301) 677-6806; ed fax 301- 677-1305; e-mail soundoff@conus.army.mil; adv e-mail advertise@baltsun.com; ed e-mail rhirsch@tribune.com
Circulation: 267pd, 12,030fr; CAC
Group: Tribune Company
Editor ....Dijon Rolle
Delivery Method: Carrier, Racks

GAITHERSBURG

ANDREWS GAZETTE

(Wed, Thur, Fri)
9030 Comprint Ct, Gaithersburg, MD, 20877-1307, Montgomery, USA
Circulation: 14,350pd, 5,734fr; Sworn/Estimate/Non-Audited

CAPITAL FLYER

(Fri)
9030 Comprint Ct, Gaithersburg, MD, 20877-1307, Montgomery, USA; tel (301) 921-2800; fax (301) 948-2787; e-mail jrives@gazette.net
Circulation: 15,000fr; Sworn/Estimate/Non-Audited
Advertising: Open inch rate $18.20
Pub...John Rives
Adv. Mgr. ....Matt Dunigan
Mechanical Specifications: Type page 9 5/8 x 13 1/2; E - 6 cols, between; A - 6 cols, between; C - 7 cols, between.
Equipment: Hardware — APP/Mac; Presses — G/Urbanite, G/Community; Software — QPS/QuarkXPress.

FORT DETRICK STANDARD (EVERY OTHER THUR)

9030 Comprint Ct, Gaithersburg, MD, 20877-1307, Montgomery, USA; tel (301) 921-2800; fax (301) 948-2787; web site www.dcmilitary.com
Circulation: 4,100fr; Sworn/Estimate/Non-Audited
Advertising: Open inch rate $12.85
Adv. Mgr. ....John Rives
Circ. Mgr..Jean Casey
Ed. ....Ann Duble
Mechanical Specifications: Type page 9 5/8 x 13 1/2; E - 6 cols, between; A - 6 cols, between; C - 7 cols, between.
Equipment: Hardware — APP/Mac; Presses — G/Urbanite, G/Community; Software — QPS/QuarkXPress.

HENDERSON HALL NEWS

9030 Comprint Ct, Gaithersburg, MD, 20877-1307, Montgomery, USA; tel (301) 921-2800; fax (301) 948-2787; web site www.dcmilitary.com
Circulation:; Sworn/Estimate/Non-Audited
Advertising: Open inch rate $12.47
Adv. Mgr. ....John Rives
Mechanical Specifications: Type page 9 5/8 x 13 1/2; E - 6 cols, between; A - 6 cols, between; C - 7 cols, between.
Equipment: Hardware — APP/Mac; Presses — G/Urbanite, G/Community; Software — QPS/QuarkXPress.

JOINT BASE JOURNAL

(Wed, Thur)
9030 Comprint Ct, Gaithersburg, MD, 20877-1307, Montgomery, USA; tel (301) 921-2800; fax (301) 948-2787; web site www.dcmilitary.com
Circulation: 24,000fr; Sworn/Estimate/Non-Audited
Advertising: Open inch rate $29.62
Adv. Mgr. ....John Rives
Mechanical Specifications: Type page 9 5/8 x 13 1/2; E - 6 cols, between; A - 6 cols, between; C - 7 cols, between.
Equipment: Hardware — APP/Mac; Presses — G/Urbanite, G/Community; Software — QPS/QuarkXPress.

PENTAGRAM

(Wed, Thur)
9030 Comprint Ct, Gaithersburg, MD, 20877-1307, Montgomery, USA; tel (301) 921-2800; fax (301) 948-2787; web site www.dcmilitary.com
Circulation: 24,000fr; Sworn/Estimate/Non-Audited
Advertising: Open inch rate $29.62
Adv. Mgr. ....John Rives
Mechanical Specifications: Type page 9 5/8 x 13 1/2; E - 6 cols, between; A - 6 cols, between; C - 7 cols, between.
Equipment: Hardware — APP/Mac; Presses — G/Urbanite, G/Community; Software — QPS/QuarkXPress.

SOUTH POTOMAC PILOT

(Wed, Thur)
9030 Comprint Ct, Gaithersburg, MD, 20877-1307, Montgomery, USA; tel (301) 921-2800; fax (301) 948-2787; web site www.dcmilitary.com
Circulation: 24,000fr; Sworn/Estimate/Non-Audited
Advertising: Open inch rate $29.62
Adv. Mgr. ....John Rives
Mechanical Specifications: Type page 9 5/8 x 13 1/2; E - 6 cols, between; A - 6 cols, between; C - 7 cols, between.
Equipment: Hardware — APP/Mac; Presses — G/Urbanite, G/Community; Software — QPS/QuarkXPress.

STRIPE

(Fri)
9030 Comprint Ct, Gaithersburg, MD, 20877-1307, Montgomery, USA; tel (301) 921-2800; fax (301) 948-2787; web site www.dcmilitary.com
Circulation: 7,000fr; Sworn/Estimate/Non-Audited
Advertising: Open inch rate $15.85
Adv. Mgr. ....Matt Dunigan
Ed. ....John Rives
Mechanical Specifications: Type page 9 5/8 x 13 1/2; E - 6 cols, between; A - 6 cols, between; C - 7 cols, between.
Equipment: Hardware — APP/Mac; Presses — G/Urbanite, G/Community; Software — QPS/QuarkXPress.

TESTER

(Thur)
9030 Comprint Ct, Gaithersburg, MD, 20877-1307, Montgomery, USA; tel (301) 921-2800; fax (301) 948-2787; web site www.dcmilitary.com
Circulation: 15,000fr; Sworn/Estimate/Non-Audited
Advertising: Open inch rate $17.17
Adv. Mgr. ....Matt Dunigan
Ed. ....John Rives
Mechanical Specifications: Type page 13 1/4 x 21; E - 8 cols, between; A - 8 cols, between; C - 9 cols, between.
Equipment: Hardware — APP/Mac; Presses — G/Urbanite, G/Community; Software — QPS/QuarkXPress.

THE BOLLING AVIATOR

(Fri)
9030 Comprint Ct, Gaithersburg, MD, 20877-1307, Montgomery, USA; tel (301) 921-2800; fax (301) 948-2787; web site www.dcmilitary.com
Circulation: 15,000fr; Sworn/Estimate/Non-Audited
Advertising: Open inch rate $15.57
Pub...John Rives
Gen. Mgr. ....Matt Dunigan
Mechanical Specifications: Type page 9 5/8 x 13 1/2; E - 4 cols, between; A - 6 cols, between; C - 7 cols, between.
Equipment: Hardware — APP/Mac; Presses — G/Urbanite, G/Community; Software — QPS/QuarkXPress.

THE NNMC JOURNAL

(Thur)
9030 Comprint Ct, Gaithersburg, MD, 20877-1307, Montgomery, USA; tel (301) 921-2800; fax (301) 948-2787; web site www.dcmilitary.com
Circulation: 7,000fr; Sworn/Estimate/Non-Audited
Advertising: Open inch rate $14.37
Gen. Mgr. ....Matt Dunigan
Adv. Mgr. ....John Rives
Mechanical Specifications: Type page 9 5/8 x 13 1/2; E - 4 cols, between; A - 6 cols, between; C - 7 cols, between.
Equipment: Hardware — APP/Mac; Presses — G/Community, G/Urbanite; Software — QPS/QuarkXPress.

THE WATER LINE

(Thur)
9030 Comprint Ct, Gaithersburg, MD, 20877-1307, Montgomery, USA; tel (301) 921-2800; fax (301) 948-2787; web site www.dcmilitary.com
Circulation: 9,000fr; Sworn/Estimate/Non-Audited
Advertising: Open inch rate $15.85
Pub...John Rives
Adv. Mgr. ....Matt Dunigan
Ed. ....Jake Joy
Mechanical Specifications: Type page 9 5/8 x 13 1/2; E - 6 cols, between; A - 6 cols, between; C - 7 cols, between.
Equipment: Hardware — APP/Mac; Presses — G/Urbanite, G/Community; Software — QPS/QuarkXPress.

THE WATERLINE

9030 Comprint Ct, Gaithersburg, MD, 20877-1307, Montgomery, USA; tel 301-921-2800; fax (301) 948-2787; e-mail jrives@gazette.net; web site www.dcmilitary.com
Established: 1984
Publisher...John Rives

MASSACHUSETTS

COTUIT

OTIS NOTICE

(Mthly)
4507 Falmouth Rd, Cotuit, MA, 02635-2652, Barnstable, USA; tel (508) 428-8700; fax (508) 428-8524; e-mail L.printing@comcast.net; ed e-mail otis@lujeanprinting.com; web site www.lujeanprinting.com
Circulation: 5,000fr; Sworn/Estimate/Non-Audited
Established: 1963
Pub..Michael Lally
Graphic Manager..................Gerry Lynn Galati
Mechanical Specifications: Type page 10 1/4 x 16; E - 6 cols, 1 5/8, 1/8 between; A - 6 cols, 1 5/8, 1/8 between.
Equipment: Hardware — APP/Mac; Presses — HI/V-15A; Software — Adobe/InDesign
Delivery Method: Mail, Carrier, Racks
Zip Codes Served: 02536,02559,02532,02563

HANSCOM AFB

HANSCONIAN

(Fri)
20 Schilling Cir, Fl 2, Hanscom Afb, MA, 01731-2800, Middlesex, USA; tel (781) 377-5027; fax (781) 377-5077; e-mail hanscom.hansconian@hanscom.af.mil; hansconian@hanscom.af.mil; web site www.hanscom.af.mil
Circulation: 8,500fr; Sworn/Estimate/Non-Audited
Advertising: Open inch rate $14.50
Dir., Pub. Aff.............................Kevin Gilmartin
Mechanical Specifications: Type page 10 1/4 x 12 1/4; E - 5 cols, 1 7/8, 1/6 between; A - 5 cols, 1 7/8, 1/6 between.
Equipment: Hardware — Micron/Mellinia; Software — Adobe/Photoshop 5.5, QPS/QuarkXPress 4.1.

MISSISSIPPI

GULFPORT

KEESLER NEWS

(Thur)
205 Debuys Rd, Gulfport, MS, 39507-2838, Harrison, USA; tel (228) 896-2100; adv tel (228) 896-2463; ed tel (228) 377-3163; fax (228) 896-2362; adv fax (228) 896-0516; e-mail specialpublications@sunherald.com; adv e-mail cbiasi@sunherald.com; ed e-mail stephen.hoffmann.ctr@us.af.mil; web site www.sunherald.com
Circulation: 8,500fr; Sworn/Estimate/Non-Audited
Advertising: Open inch rate $14.69

Established: 1974
Group: The McClatchy Company
Adv. Mgr. .... Sandi Menendez
Publisher .... Glen Nardi
Ed. .... Susan Griggs
Special Publications Manager John McFarland
Editor .... Stephen Hoffmann
Mechanical Specifications: Type page 10 x 11; A - 5 cols,
Equipment: Hardware — APP/Mac, APP/Power Mac; Presses — 6-G/Headliner Offset; Software — InDesign v 4
Delivery Method: Mail, Newsstand, Carrier, Racks
Zip Codes Served: 39534 39531 39532 39535
Note: Published weekly by Sun Herald MultiMedia for Keesler Air Force Base under contract with the Department of the Air Force

MERIDIAN

SKYLINE
(Thur) (Every other Thur)
814 22nd Ave, Meridian, MS, 39301-5023, Lauderdale, USA; tel (601) 693-1551; fax (601) 485-1229; e-mail info@themeridianstar.com; adv e-mail eryan@themeridianstar.com; web site www.meridianstar.com
Circulation: 1,800fr; Sworn/Estimate/Non-Audited
Advertising: Open inch rate $9.18
Group: Community Newspaper Holdings, Inc.
Publisher .... Timothy Holder
Editor for The Meridian Star.... Michael Stewart
Skyline Advertising .... Elizabeth Ryan
Mechanical Specifications: Type page 9 11/16 x 11 3/4; E - 5 cols, 1 13/16, between; A - 5 cols, 1 11/16, between.
Equipment: Hardware — 1-Catra 46; Software — QPS/QuarkXPress 4.1.

MISSOURI

SAINT ROBERT

GUIDON
(Thur)
394 Old Route 66, Saint Robert, MO, 65584-3829, Pulaski, USA; tel (573) 336-0061; fax (573) 336-5487; e-mail guidon_staff@mygiidon.com; web site www.myguidon.com
Circulation: 10,000fr; Sworn/Estimate/Non-Audited
Advertising: Open inch rate $10.40
Adv. Mgr. .... Mike Bowers
Ed. .... Robert Johnson
Mechanical Specifications: Type page 13 1/2 x 21 1/2; E - 4 cols, 3 1/12, 1/6 between; A - 6 cols, 2 1/12, 1/6 between; C - 6 cols, 2 1/12, 1/6 between.
Equipment: Hardware — PC; Software — Adobe/PageMaker 5.0.

WHITEMAN AFB

WHITEMAN WARRIOR
(Fri)
1081 Arnold Ave, Whiteman Afb, MO, 65305-5108, Johnson, USA; tel (660) 826-1000; fax (660) 826-2413; adv e-mail advertising@sedaliademocrat.com
Circulation: 4,800fr; Sworn/Estimate/Non-Audited
Advertising: Open inch rate $8.75
Group: Phillips Media
Publisher .... Will Weibert
Mechanical Specifications: Type page 10 1/4 x 14; E - 6 cols, 1 7/12, between; A - 6 cols, 1 7/12, between; C - 7 cols, 1 1/3, 1/6 between.
Equipment: Hardware — APP/Mac; Presses — 10-G/Urbanite.
Delivery Method: Mail, Racks
Zip Codes Served: 65305

NEBRASKA

BELLEVUE

AIR PULSE
(Thur)
604 Fort Crook Rd N, Bellevue, NE, 68005-4557, Sarpy, USA; tel (402) 733-7300; fax (402) 733-9116; ed e-mail news@bellevueleader.com; web site www.omahanewsstand.com
Circulation: 9,500fr; Sworn/Estimate/Non-Audited
Advertising: Open inch rate $16.22
Established: 1946
Pub. .... Shon Barenklau
Adv. Mgr. .... Paul Swanson
Circ. Mgr. .... Mellissa Vanek
Prodn. Mgr. .... Amy Corrigan
Mechanical Specifications: Type page 9 3/4 x 11 1/2; E - 6 cols, 1 1/2, between; A - 6 cols, 1 1/2, between.
Equipment: Hardware — Apt, Dell.

NEW JERSEY

DENVILLE

VOICE
435 E Main St, # 53, Denville, NJ, 07834-2509, Morris, USA; tel (973) 586-3012
Circulation:; Sworn/Estimate/Non-Audited
Advertising: Open inch rate $10.00
Pub. .... Salvatore Paci
Adv. Mgr. .... Laurie Paci
Mechanical Specifications: Type page 10 x 13; E - 5 cols, 2, between; A - 5 cols, 2, between.

NEW MEXICO

CLOVIS

CANNON CONNECTION
(Fri)
521 Pile St, Clovis, NM, 88101-6637, Curry, USA; tel (575) 763-3431; fax (575) 762-3879; web site www.cnjonline.com
Circulation: 6,800fr; Sworn/Estimate/Non-Audited
Advertising: Open inch rate $6.70
Pub. .... Ray Sullivan
HR Dir. .... Joyce Cruce
Circ. Dir. .... Mike Grigg
Ed. .... David Stevens
Prodn. Mgr. .... Daryl Lee
Mechanical Specifications: Type page 10 1/4 x 12; A - 5 cols, 1 13/16, 1/6 between; C - 7 cols, 1 1/8, 1/6 between.

RIO RANCHO

KIRTLAND AFB NUCLEUS
(Fri)
409 NM 528 NE, Suite 101, Rio Rancho, NM, 87124, Sandoval, USA; tel (505) 892-8080; adv tel (505) 891-7168; adv fax (505) 892-5719; e-mail 377abw.nucleus@kirtland.af.mil; web site www.kirtland.af.mil
Circulation: 10,000fr; Sworn/Estimate/Non-Audited
Advertising: Open inch rate $10.55
Ed. .... Nancy Jones
Mechanical Specifications: Type page 10 1/8 x 16; A - 5 cols, 1 7/8, 3/16 between.
Equipment: Hardware — PC; Software — Adobe/Photoshop 7.0, PageMaker 7.0.
Zip Codes Served: 87117

WHITE SANDS MISSILE RANGE

WHITE SANDS MISSILE RANGER
(Thur)
Public Affairs Office, White Sands Missile Range, NM, 88002, Dona Ana, USA; tel (575) 678-2716; fax (575) 678-8814; e-mail wsmrranger@conus.army.mil; web site www.missileranger.com
Circulation: 6,000fr; Sworn/Estimate/Non-Audited
Advertising: Open inch rate $7.65
Ed. .... Miriam U. Rodriguez
Mechanical Specifications: Type page 11 x 11 3/4; E - 5 cols, 2 1/16, 1/8 between; A - 5 cols, 2 1/16, 1/8 between; C - 5 cols, 1/8 between.

NEW YORK

FORT DRUM

THE MOUNTAINEER
(Thur)
10012 S Riva Ridge Loop, Fort Drum, NY, 13602-5492, Jefferson, USA; tel (315) 772-5469; fax (315) 772-8295
Circulation: 10,000fr; Sworn/Estimate/Non-Audited
Managing editor .... Lisa Albrecht

NORTH CAROLINA

FAYETTEVILLE

CAROLINA FLYER
(Fri)
PO Box 849, Fayetteville, NC, 28302-0849, Cumberland, USA; tel (910) 323-4848; fax (910) 486-3544; web site www.fayobserver.com
Circulation: 4,019fr; Sworn/Estimate/Non-Audited
Advertising: Open inch rate $7.13
Pub. .... Charles W. Broadwell
Weekly Sales Mgr. .... Brad Parker
Circ. Dir. .... Jim Adkins
Exec. Ed. .... Brian Tolley
Mechanical Specifications: Type page 12 1/2 x 22; E - 6 cols, 1 5/6, 1/6 between; A - 6 cols, 1 5/6, 1/6 between; C - 10 cols, 1, 1/10 between.
Equipment: Hardware — Presses 24-KBA/Colora.

FORT BRAGG PARAGLIDE
(Thur)
458 Whitfield St, Fayetteville, NC, 28306-1614, Cumberland, USA; tel (910) 396-6817; adv tel (910) 323-4848; fax (910) 396-9629; e-mail paraglidebragg@gmail.com; web site www.paraglideonline.net
Circulation: 25,000fr; Sworn/Estimate/Non-Audited
Advertising: Open inch rate $25.00
Pub. .... Charles W. Broadwell
Mgr., Adv. Sales .... Brad Parker
Circ. Mgr. .... James Adkins
Mechanical Specifications: Type page 12 1/2 x 22; E - 6 cols, 1 5/6, 1/6 between; A - 6 cols, 1 5/6, 1/6 between; C - 10 cols, 1, 1/10 between.
Equipment; Presses — 24-KBA/Colora.
Zip Codes Served: 28307

HAVELOCK

WINDSOCK
(Thur)
230 Stonebridge Sq, Havelock, NC, 28532-9505, Craven, USA; tel (252) 444-1999; fax (252) 447-0897; web site www.havenews.com
Circulation: 11,500fr; Sworn/Estimate/Non-Audited
Advertising: Open inch rate $12.70
Adv. Dir. .... John Hetzler
Circ. Mgr. .... Roxanne Smith
Ed. .... Ken Buday
Mechanical Specifications: Type page 13 x 21 1/2; E - 6 cols, 2 1/16, 1/6 between; A - 6 cols, 2 1/16, 1/6 between; C - 9 cols, 1 5/16, between.
Equipment: Hardware — APP/Mac G3s; Software — QPS/QuarkXPress 4.0, Adobe/PageMaker.

JACKSONVILLE

ROTOVUE (EVERY OTHER WED)
149 Rea St, Ste 100, Jacksonville, NC, 28546-5717, Onslow, USA; tel (910) 347-9624; fax (910) 347-9628; web site www.newriverrotovue.com
Circulation: 8,600fr; Sworn/Estimate/Non-Audited
Advertising: Open inch rate $11.59
Pub. .... Jim Connors
Adv. Mgr. .... Heather Miller
Ed .... Ena Sellers
Mechanical Specifications: Type page 9 9/16 x 11 1/2; E - 5 cols, 1 25/32, between; A - 5 cols, 1 25/32, between; C - 5 cols, 1 25/32, between.
Equipment: Hardware — 9-APP/Mac G4, 1-Agfa/Jet Sherpa, Kayak, IBM/Pentium III, 2-Agfa/Avantra 25E, HP, XU, 4-Umax/Powerlook 1100 Scanners; Software — QPS/QuarkXPress 4.1, Adobe/Photoshop 5.5, Adobe/PageMaker 6.5, Adobe/Illustrator 9.0.

NORTH DAKOTA

MINOT

THE NORTHERN SENTRY
(Fri)
15-1 Ave SE, Minot, ND, 58701, Ward, USA; tel (701) 839-0946; fax (701) 839-1867; adv e-mail nsads@srt.com
Circulation: 6,000fr; Sworn/Estimate/Non-Audited
Advertising: Open inch rate $8.00
Group: BHG, Inc.
Pub. .... Michael W. Gackle
Adv. Mgr. .... Sharon Olson
Mechanical Specifications: Type page 10 x 16; E - 5 cols, 2, between; A - 5 cols, 2, between.

OKLAHOMA

FORT SILL

THE CANNONEER
(Thur)
455 McNair Hall, Ste 118, Fort Sill, OK, 73503, Comanche, USA; tel (580) 442-5150; fax (580) 585-5103; e-mail cannoneersill@conus.army.mil; web site www.woknews.com
Circulation: 12,000fr; Sworn/Estimate/Non-Audited
Advertising: Open inch rate $7.25James Brabanec
Jeff Crawley

Marie Berberea
Mechanical Specifications: Type page 13 x 21 1/6; E - 6 cols, 2 1/16, 1/8 between; A - 6 cols, 2 1/16, 1/8 between; C - 9 cols, 1 1/4, 1/8 between.
Equipment: Hardware — APP/Mac, PC; Presses — HI/1660; Software — Freedom System Integrators.

OKLAHOMA CITY

TINKER TAKE OFF
(Fri)
101 N Robinson Ave, Ste 101, Oklahoma City, OK, 73102-5500, Oklahoma, USA; tel (405) 278-6907; adv tel (405) 739-7626; fax (405) 278-6907; e-mail tinker.takeoff@tinker.af.mil; web site www.tinkertakeoff.com
Circulation: 21,820fr; Sworn/Estimate/Non-Audited
Advertising: Open inch rate $21.56
Chief of Pub. Aff. .... Ralph Monson
Ed. .... Micah Garbarino
Mechanical Specifications: Type page 10 7/16 x 16; E - 6 cols, 1 1/2, between; A - 6 cols, 1 1/2, between; C - 6 cols, 1 1/2, between.
Equipment: Hardware — PC; Software — QPS/QuarkXPress, Microsoft/Word.

RHODE ISLAND

NEWPORT

NEWPORT NAVALOG
(Fri)
101 Malbone Rd, Newport, RI, 02840-1340, Newport, USA; tel (401) 849-3300; fax (401) 849-3335; e-mail prepress@newportri.com; web site www.newportdailynews.com
Circulation: 4,400fr; Sworn/Estimate/Non-Audited
Advertising: Open inch rate $16.50
Pub. .... Albert K. Sherman
Gen. Mgr. .... William F. Lucey
Adv. Mgr. .... Ann Marie Brisson
Ed. .... Richard Alexander
Prodn. Mgr. .... Kevin Schoen

SOUTH CAROLINA

CAMDEN

FORT JACKSON LEADER
(Thur)
909 W Dekalb St, Camden, SC, 29020-4259, Kershaw, USA; tel (803) 432-6157; fax (803) 432-7609
Circulation: 15,000fr; Sworn/Estimate/Non-Audited
Advertising: Open inch rate $16.65
Established: 1960
Group: Morris Multimedia, Inc.
Pub. .... Michael Mischner
Adv. Mgr. .... Kathy Mccoy
Mechanical Specifications: Type page 10 x 13.

THE SHAW NEWS
(Fri)
909 W Dekalb St, Camden, SC, 29020-4259, Kershaw, USA; tel (803) 432-6157; adv tel (803) 432-6157; ed tel (803) 236-8425; adv fax (803) 432-7609; e-mail mmischner@ci-camden.com; web site www.ci-camden.com
Circulation: 7,200fr; Sworn/Estimate/Non-Audited
Advertising: Open inch rate $13.15
Group: Morris Multimedia, Inc.
Pub. .... Michael Mischner
Adv. Mgr. .... Betsy Greenway
Mechanical Specifications: Type page 10 x 14.
Equipment: Hardware — PC.

TENNESSEE

MILLINGTON

THE BLUEJACKET
(Thur)
5107 Easley Ave, Millington, TN, 38053-2107, Shelby, USA; tel (901) 872-2286; fax (901) 872-2965; e-mail mstar@bigriver.net; web site www.nsamidsouth.navy.mil/news-bj.htm
Circulation: 6,100fr; Sworn/Estimate/Non-Audited
Advertising: Open inch rate $8.40
Pub. .... John Fee
Ed. .... Julia A. Wallis
Mechanical Specifications: Type page 13 x 21 1/4; E - 6 cols, 2, between; A - 6 cols, 2, between; C - 9 cols, between.
Equipment: Hardware — APP/Power Mac; Software — Adobe/PageMaker 6.5, Adobe/Photoshop 4.0.

TEXAS

ABILENE

SOUND OF FREEDOM
(Fri)
101 Cypress St, Abilene, TX, 79601-5816, Taylor, USA; tel (325) 673-4271; fax (325) 670-5222; adv e-mail ads@reporternews.com; web site www.reporternews.com
Circulation: 7,500fr; Sworn/Estimate/Non-Audited
Advertising: Open inch rate $7.99
Established: 1984
Pub. .... Kim Nussbaum
Adv. Mgr. .... Stephanie Boggins
Ed. .... Barton Cromeens
Opns Dir. .... Mike Hall
Mechanical Specifications: Type page 9 5/8 x 11 5/8; E - 5 cols, 1 5/6, between; A - 5 cols, 1 5/6, between; C - 7 cols, 1 1/16, between.

EL PASO

FORT BLISS MONITOR
(Thur)
1420 Geronimo Dr, Bldg E, El Paso, TX, 79925-1855, El Paso, USA; tel (915) 772-0934; fax (915) 772-1594; e-mail sflav@whc.net; web site www.lavenpublishing.com
Circulation: 20,000fr; Sworn/Estimate/Non-Audited
Advertising: Open inch rate $13.60
Established: 1985
Vice Pres., Sales .... Mike Laven
Adv. Mgr. .... Skip Laven
Vice Pres., Prodn. .... Susan Laven
Mechanical Specifications: Type page 10 1/8 x 16; E - 4 cols, 2 1/4, 1/2 between; A - 4 cols, 2 1/4, 1/2 between; C - 7 cols, 1 1/4, 1/4 between.
Zip Codes Served: 79906, 79924, 79925, 79936, 79902

FORT HOOD

FORT HOOD SENTINEL
(Thur)
761 Tank Battalion, Bldg W105, Fort Hood, TX, 76544-4906, Bell, USA; tel (254) 287-9495; adv tel (254) 634-6666; ed tel (254) 287-9495; adv e-mail advertise@forthoodsentinel.com; ed e-mail todd.pruden@forthoodsentinel.com; web site www.forthoodsentinel.com
Circulation: 25,000fr; Sworn/Estimate/Non-Audited
Advertising: Open inch rate $12.50
Established: 1942
Group: Frank Mayborn Enterprises, Inc.
Pub. .... Sue Mayborn
Gen. Mgr. .... Ray Reed
Mechanical Specifications: Type page 12 x 21 1/2; E - 6 cols, 1 4/5, 1/8 between; A - 6 cols, 1 4/5, 1/8 between; C - 9 cols, 1 1/5, 1/16 between.
Equipment: Hardware — Dell; Presses — 10-G/Urbanite.; Software — InDesign
Delivery Method: Mail, Newsstand, Carrier, Racks
Zip Codes Served: 76541, 76544

SAN ANTONIO

LACKLAND TALESPINNER
(Fri)
301 Avenue E, San Antonio, TX, 78205-2006, Bexar, USA; tel (210) 250-3000; adv tel (210) 250-2500; ed tel (210) 250-3195; fax (210) 250-3715; adv fax (210) 250-2565; ed fax (210) 250-3105; e-mail communitysupport@express-news.net; adv e-mail communitysupport@express-news.net; ed e-mail editors@express-news.net; web site www.express-news.com
Circulation: 0pd, 0fr; VAC
Advertising: Open inch rate $346.77
Digital Platform - Mobile: Apple, Android
Digital Platform - Tablet: Apple iOS, Android, Windows 7
Pres./Pub. .... Thomas A. Stephenson
Vice Pres., Finance .... Fred Mergele
Vice Pres., HR .... Susan Ehrman
Vice Pres., Classified Adv. .... Charlotte Aaron
Sales Dir. ...... Rebecca Named Chavez-Becker
Adv. Mgr., Automotive .... Doug Bennight
Adv. Mgr., Telemktg./Classified .... Roxanne Beavers
Adv. Mgr., Telemktg./Retail .... Pat Harvey
Vice Pres., Mktg. .... Dean Aitken
Vice Pres., Mktg. .... Patrick Magallanes
Target Mktg. Mgr. .... Liz English
Circ. Sr. Vice Pres. .... Scott Frantzen
Circ. Dir., Admin. .... Paul Borrego
Dir., Metro Home Delivery .. Sammy Aburumuh
Ed. .... Robert Rivard
Mng. Ed. .... Brett Thacker
Asst. Mng. Ed., Features.... Terry Scott-Bertling
Asst. Mng. Ed., Graphics/Design/Photo... Hallie Paul
Asst. Mng. Ed., News .... Craig Thomason
Mechanical Specifications: Type page 11 5/8 x 21; E - 6 cols, 2 1/16, 1/8 between; A - 6 cols, 2 1/16, 1/8 between; C - 10 cols, 1 5/16, 1/16 between.
Delivery Method: Mail, Newsstand
Zip Codes Served: Bexar County

UTAH

OGDEN

HILLTOP TIMES
(Thur)
332 Standard Way, Ogden, UT, 84404-1371, Weber, USA; tel (801) 625-4310; adv tel (801) 625-4333; ed tel (801) 777-7322; fax (801) 625-4508; adv fax (801) 625-4508; ed fax (801) 625-4299; e-mail hilltoptimes@standard.net; adv e-mail advertise@standard.net; web site www.hilltoptimes.com
Circulation: 12,000fr; Sworn/Estimate/Non-Audited
Advertising: Open inch rate $18.36
Established: 1966
Group: Sandusky Newspapers, Inc.
Adv. Dir. .... Brad Roghaar
Circ. Mgr. .... Vaughn Jacobsen
Mechanical Specifications: 6 col. (11") x 20.5". One col. = 1.74"; gutter = .125"
Equipment; Presses — KBA/Comet.
Delivery Method: Newsstand, Carrier, Racks
Zip Codes Served: 84056, 84041, 84015, 84040, 84067

VIRGINIA

FORT BELVOIR

BELVOIR EAGLE
(Thur)
9820 Flagler Rd, Fort Belvoir, VA, 22060-5610, Fairfax, USA; tel (703) 805-3397; fax (703) 780-6145; e-mail eagle_editor@belvoir.army.mil; web site www.belvoireagle.com
Circulation: 19,500fr; Sworn/Estimate/Non-Audited
Advertising: Open inch rate $15.50
Group: Northern Virginia Media Services
Ed. .... Carl Previs
Sports Ed. .... Tamika Matthews

LEESBURG

QUANTICO SENTRY
(Thur)
19 N King St, Leesburg, VA, 20176-2819, Loudoun, USA; tel 703-771-8800; adv tel (703) 771-8800; fax (540) 659-0039; e-mail Jlesh@insidenova.com; adv e-mail bpowell@staffordcountysun.com; ed e-mail adolzenko@staffordcountysun.com ; web site http://www.quanticosentryonline.com/
Circulation: 8,500fr; Sworn/Estimate/Non-Audited
Advertising: Open inch rate $21.50
Group: Northern Virginia Media Services
GM/Sales mgr .... Tom Spargur
Mechanical Specifications: Type page 6 x 21; E - 6 cols, 2 1/16, 1/6 between; A - 6 cols, 2 1/16, 1/6 between.
Equipment: Hardware — 12-HP/PC; Software — QPS/QuarkXPress 4.1, Adobe/Illustrator 9.0, Adobe/Photoshop 6.0.
Delivery Method: Carrier

NORFOLK

FLAGSHIP
(Thur)
150 W Brambleton Ave, Norfolk, VA, 23510-2018, Norfolk City, USA; tel (757) 222-3990; fax (757) 622-6885; e-mail laura.baxter@militarynews.com; web site www.norfolknavyflagship.com
Circulation: 35,000fr; Sworn/Estimate/Non-Audited
Advertising: Open inch rate $20.50
Digital Platform - Mobile: Apple, Android, Windows, Blackberry
Digital Platform - Tablet: Apple iOS, Android, Windows 7, Blackberry Tablet OS, Kindle, Nook, Kindle Fire
Mechanical Specifications: Type page 11 1/2 x 21 1/2; E - 6 cols, 1 3/4, 1/8 between; A - 6 cols, 1 3/4, 1/8 between; C - 10 cols, 1 1/10, 1/16 between.
Equipment: Hardware — APP/Mac; Presses — Metro/Offset; Software — QPS/QuarkXPress.

PENINSULA WARRIOR- AIR FORCE
(Fri)
150 W Brambleton Ave, Norfolk, VA, 23510-2018, Norfolk City, USA; tel (757) 222-3990; fax (757) 622-6885; e-mail sales@militarynews.com; web site www.militarynews.com
Circulation: 14,000fr; Sworn/Estimate/Non-Audited
Advertising: Open rate $18.85

Digital Platform - Mobile: Apple, Android, Windows, Blackberry, Other
Digital Platform - Tablet: Apple iOS, Android, Windows 7, Blackberry Tablet OS, Kindle, Nook, Other
Pub.. Laura Baxter
Mechanical Specifications: Type page 9 7/8 x 14; E - 6 cols, 1 1/2, between; A - 6 cols, 1 1/2, between; C - 6 cols, 1 1/2, between.
Delivery Method: Racks

SOUNDINGS
10 W Brambleton Ave, Norfolk, VA, 23510, Norfolk City, USA; tel (757) 222-3990; fax (757) 853-1634; e-mail sales@militarynews.com; web site www.militarynews.com
Circulation:; Sworn/Estimate/Non-Audited
Advertising: Open inch rate $26.97
Pub.. Laura Baxter
Ed. ....Jim Van Slyke
Reagan Haynes
Mechanical Specifications: Type page 9 7/8 x 14; E - 6 cols, 1 1/2, between; A - 6 cols, 1 1/2, between; C - 6 cols, 1 1/2, between.
Equipment: Hardware — 9-APP/Mac G4, 2-AG/Avantra 25E, 1-AG/Jet Sherpa, HP, Kayak, XU, 1-Pentium III, 4-Umax/Powerlook 1100 Scanners; Presses — 8-Perfecting Units, 1-Quadra/Color Unit; Software — QPS/QuarkXPress 4.1, Adobe/PageMaker 6.5, Adobe/Photoshop 5.5, Adobe/Il

THE WHEEL
(Thur)
258 Granby St, Norfolk, VA, 23510-1812, Norfolk City, USA; tel (757) 222-3990; fax (757) 853-1634; web site www.militarynews.com
Circulation: 10,500fr; Sworn/Estimate/Non-Audited
Advertising: Open inch rate $15.98
Established: 1970
Adv. Mgr.. Laura Baxter
Ed. .... Zack Shelby
Mechanical Specifications: Type page 9 7/8 x 14; E - 6 cols, 1 1/2, between; A - 6 cols, 1 1/2, between; C - 6 cols, 1 1/2, between.
Equipment: Hardware — 9-APP/Mac G4, 2-AG/Avantra 25E, 1-AG/Jet Sherpa, HP, Kayak, XU, 1-Pentium III, 4-Umax/Powerlook 1100 Scanners; Presses — 8-Perfecting Units, 1-Quadra/Color Unit; Software — QPS/QuarkXPress 4.1, Adobe/Photoshop 5.5, Adobe/PageMaker 6.5, Adobe/Il

SPRINGFIELD

DEFENSE NEWS
(Mon)
6883 Commercial Dr, Springfield, VA, 22159-0002, Fairfax, USA; tel (703) 642-7330; fax (703) 642-7386; e-mail cust-svc@atpco.com; web site www.defensenews.com
Circulation: 7,319pd, 30,822fr; Sworn/Estimate/Non-Audited
Advertising: Open inch rate $200.00
Vice Pres., Adv......................... Donna Peterson
Ed. .... Vago Muradian

NAVY TIMES
(Mon)
6883 Commercial Dr, Springfield, VA, 22159-0002, Fairfax, USA; tel (703) 750-8636; fax (703) 750-8767; e-mail navylet@atpco.com; web site www.navytimes.com
Circulation: 79,500pd, 2,400fr; Sworn/Estimate/Non-Audited
Advertising: Open inch rate $25.96Editions: 1- 1 total Navy Times-Overseas Edition (3,304);
Pres./Pub..................................Elaine Howard
Circ. Mgr....................................... Dick Howlett
Ed. ....Christopher P. Cavas
Mng. Ed............................Christopher Lawson
Prodn. Mgr. ....Phil Rose
Mechanical Specifications: Type page 21 1/2 x 12 1/4.

WASHINGTON

LAKEWOOD

NORTHWEST AIRLIFTER
(Thur)
8312 Custer Rd SW, Lakewood, WA, 98499-2526, Pierce, USA; tel (253) 584-1212; fax (253) 581-5962; ed e-mail editor@ftlewisranger.com; web site www.ftlewisranger.com
Circulation: 8,200fr; Sworn/Estimate/Non-Audited
Pub.. Ken Swarner
Circ. Mgr.. Bill White
Mechanical Specifications: Type page 10 1/2 x 16; A - 7 cols, between; C - 8 cols, between.
Equipment: Hardware — APP/Mac; Software — Microsoft/Word, Multi-Ad/Creator, Adobe/PageMaker, QPS/QuarkXPress, Adobe/Illustrator, Microsoft/Excel, Adobe/Photoshop.

STEILACOOM

THE RANGER
(Thur)
218 Wilkes St, Steilacoom, WA, 98388-2122, Pierce, USA; tel (253) 584-1212; fax (253) 581-5962; adv e-mail sales@northwestmilitary.com; ed e-mail publisher@northwestmilitary.com; web site www.northwestmilitary.com
Circulation: 23,000fr; VAC
Advertising: $85 a unit
Established: 1951
Circ. Mgr.. Bill White
Ed. .... Ken Swarner
Prodn. Mgr. .... Diana Halstead
Mechanical Specifications: 24 units to the page. 4 units across by 6 units deep
Equipment: Hardware — APP/Mac; Software — Microsoft/Word, Multi-Ad/Creator, Adobe/PageMaker, QPS/QuarkXPress, Adobe/Illustrator, Microsoft/Excel, Adobe/Photoshop.
Delivery Method: Mail, Racks
Zip Codes Served: Pierce & Thurston counties

WYOMING

CHEYENNE

WARREN SENTINEL
(Fri)
307 E 20th St, Cheyenne, WY, 82001-3705, Laramie, USA; tel (307) 632-5666; fax (307) 632-1554; e-mail graphics@warrensentinel.com; adv e-mail ads@warrensentinel.com; web site www.warrensentinel.com
Circulation: 5,200fr; Sworn/Estimate/Non-Audited
Advertising: Open inch rate $9.00
Pub... Jim Wood
Sales Mgr................................ Kelly Sebastian
Inside Adv. Sales ....Barbara Coursey
Prodn. Mgr./Graphics..............Monica Valdez
Mechanical Specifications: Type page 9 3/4 x 13; E - 6 cols, 1 1/2, 1/6 between; A - 6 cols, 1 1/2, 1/6 between; C - 6 cols, 1 1/2, 1/6 between.
Equipment: Hardware — APP/Power Mac 7600-120; Presses — 5-G/Community; Software — Adobe/PageMaker 6.0, Adobe/Photoshop 3.0, Multi-Ad/Creator 3.8.

RELIGIOUS NEWSPAPERS IN THE UNITED STATES

ALABAMA

BIRMINGHAM

ONE VOICE (Fri)
2121 3rd Ave N, Birmingham, AL, 35203-3314, Jefferson, USA; tel (205) 838-8305; fax (205) 838-8319; e-mail onevoice@bhmdiocese.org; web site www.bhmdiocese.org
Circulation: 19,800pd, 293fr; Sworn/Estimate/Non-Audited
Advertising: Open inch rate $9.00
Pub...................................Bishop Robert Baker
Circ. Mgr... Ann Lanzi
Mng. Ed..............................Mary Alice Crockett

MOBILE

THE CATHOLIC WEEK (Fri)
356 Government St, Mobile, AL, 36602-2316, Mobile, USA; tel (251) 434-1544; adv tel (251) 434-1543; fax (251) 434-1547; e-mail thecatholicweek@bellsouth.net; adv e-mail cwadvertising@bellsouth.net; web site www.mobilearchdiocese.org/catholicweek
Circulation: 20,000pd, 362fr; Sworn/Estimate/Non-Audited
Advertising: Open inch rate $11.00
Established: 1934
Pub.. Thomas J. Rodi
Adv. Mgr...............................Mary Ann Stevens
Ed. .... Larry Wahl
Production Manager ....Pamela Wheeler
Mechanical Specifications: Type page 9 13/16 x 14 1/8.
Equipment: Hardware — Software InDesign
Delivery Method: Mail

ARKANSAS

LITTLE ROCK

ARKANSAS CATHOLIC (Sat)
2500 N Tyler St, Little Rock, AR, 72207-3743, Pulaski, USA; tel (501)664-0125; adv tel (501)664-0125; ed tel (501)664-0125; fax (501) 664-6572; e-mail mhargett@dolr.org; adv e-mail pstabnick@dolr.org; ed e-mail mhargett@dolr.org; web site www.arkansas-catholic.org
Circulation: 4,600pd, 500fr; Sworn/Estimate/Non-Audited
Advertising: Open inch rate $17.00
Established: 1911
Digital Platform - Mobile: Apple, Android, Windows, Blackberry
Digital Platform - Tablet: Apple iOS, Android, Windows 7, Blackberry Tablet OS, Kindle, Nook, Kindle Fire
Ed. .... Malea Hargett
Prodn. Mgr. .... Emily Roberts
advertising manager................. Pete Stabnick
associate editor .... Aprille Hanson
Mechanical Specifications: Type page 11 x 14; E - 4 cols, 2 2/5, 1/4 between; A - 4 cols, 2 2/5, 1/4 between.
Delivery Method: Mail
Zip Codes Served: All in Arkansas

BAPTIST TRUMPET (Wed)
10712 Interstate 30, Little Rock, AR, 72209-5835, Pulaski, USA; tel (501) 565-4601; fax (501) 565-6397; ed e-mail editor@baptisttrumpet.com; web site www.baptisttrumpet.com
Circulation: 9,250pd,; Sworn/Estimate/Non-Audited
Advertising: Open inch rate $15
Established: 1939
Circ. Mgr.. Joyce Lowe
Ed. .... Diane Spriggs
Mechanical Specifications: Type page 10 1/4 x 12 1/4; E - 5 cols, 1 4/5, 1/4 between; A - 5 cols, 1 4/5, 1/4 between.

CALIFORNIA

GARDEN GROVE

ORANGE COUNTY CATHOLIC (Fri)
13280 Chapman Ave, Garden Grove, CA, 92840-4414, Orange, USA; tel (714) 282-3075; adv tel (714) 881-1622; e-mail calmanza@rcbo.org; adv e-mail ads@occatholic.com; ed e-mail pmott@rcbo.org; web site http://occatholic.com/
Group: Times Media Group
Editor .... Patrick Mott
Delivery Method: Mail, Newsstand
Zip Codes Served: Orange County

LOS ANGELES

THE TIDINGS (Fri)
3424 Wilshire Blvd, Fl 3, Los Angeles, CA, 90010-2262, Los Angeles, USA; tel (213) 637-7360; adv tel (213) 637-7599; ed tel (213) 637-7543; fax (213) 637-6360; adv fax (213) 637-6599; ed fax (213) 637-6360; e-mail info@the-tidings.com; circlist@the-tidings.com; adv e-mail NJacob@the-tidings.com; ed e-mail Mnelson@the-tidings.com; web site www.the-tidings.com
Circulation: 88,000pd, 372fr; Sworn/Estimate/Non-Audited
Advertising: Open inch rate $72.00
Established: 1865
Group: Archdiocese of Los Angeles
Digital Platform - Mobile: Apple, Android
Digital Platform - Tablet: Apple iOS, Android, Kindle
Pub... David Mooree
Gen. Mgr. .... Natalie Jacob
Ed. .... Mike Nelson
Delivery Method: Mail
Zip Codes Served: 90001,90899, 91001,93599,93001-93009,93101-93109

SAN DIEGO

THE SOUTHERN CROSS (Mthly)
3888 Paducah Dr, San Diego, CA, 92117-5349, San Diego, USA; tel (858) 490-8266; fax (858) 490-8355; e-mail socross@sdcatholic.org; adv e-mail dlightsey@sdcatholic.org; ed e-mail cfuld@sdcatholic.org; web site www.thesoutherncross.org
Circulation: 34,800pd, 3,200fr; USPS
Advertising: Open inch rate $30.00
Established: 1912
Digital Platform - Mobile: Windows
Mng. Ed....Charles L. Fuld
Asst. Ed....Denis Grasska
Art Dir....Lucas Turnbloom
Advertising/Administrative Coordinator . Donna Lightsey
Bishop Robert McElroy
Staff Writer (Spanish)....Aida Bustos
Mechanical Specifications: Type page11.5 x 15; A - 4 cols, 2 1/3, between.
Equipment: Software — QPS/QuarkXPress 6.5
Delivery Method: Mail, Racks
Zip Codes Served: 91901-92299 (MAINLY)

VISTA

GOOD NEWS, ETC. (Mthly)
PO Box 2660, Vista, CA, 92085-2660, San Diego, USA; tel (760) 724-3075; e-mail goodnewseditor@cox.net; adv e-mail goodnewseditor@cox.net; ed e-mail goodnewseditor@cox.net; web site www.goodnewsetc.com
Circulation: 32,000pd, 32,000fr; Sworn/Estimate/Non-Audited
Advertising: Open inch rate $42
Established: 1984Editions: 2- 2 total; Good News Etc.-North County (20,000);
Adv. Mgr....Colleen Monroe
Ed....Rick Monroe
Mechanical Specifications: Type page 10x14 image area, 4 col.
Equipment: Hardware — APP/Mac.
Delivery Method: Racks

COLORADO

DENVER

DENVER CATHOLIC REGISTER (Wed)
1300 S Steele St, Denver, CO, 80210-2526, Denver, USA; tel (303) 722-4687; adv tel (303) 715-3212; fax (303) 715-2045; e-mail dcrads@archden.org; info@archden.org; web site www.archden.org
Circulation: 91,165pd, 379fr; Sworn/Estimate/Non-Audited
Advertising: Open inch rate $38.90
Established: 1900
Pub....Charles J. Chaput
Gen. Mgr....Jeanette DeMelo
Adv. Mgr....Chad Andrzejewski
Circ. Mgr....Karen Mendoza
Ed....Roxanne King
Mechanical Specifications: Type page 10 1/4 x 13 3/4; E - 3 cols, between; A - 6 cols, between.
Equipment: Hardware — IBM; Software — Adobe/PageMaker 5.0, Archetype/Corel Draw.

EL PUEBLO CATOLICO
1300 S Steele St, Denver, CO, 80210-2526, Denver, USA; tel (303) 715-3219; fax (303) 715-2045; e-mail elpueblo@archden.org; web site www.archden.org
Circulation:; Sworn/Estimate/Non-Audited
Advertising: Open inch rate $7.00
Pub....Archbishop Charles J. Chaput
Gen. Mgr....Jeanette DeMelo
Adv. Mgr....Ann Bush
Ed....Rosanna Goni
Prodn. Mgr....Filippo Piccone
Mechanical Specifications: Type page 10 1/4 x 12 1/2; E - 5 cols, 1 5/6, 1/8 between; A - 5 cols, 1 5/6, 1/8 between.
Equipment: Hardware — IBM; Software — Adobe/PageMaker 5.0, QPS/QuarkXPress 6.0.

CONNECTICUT

BLOOMFIELD

THE CATHOLIC TRANSCRIPT (Mthly)
467 Bloomfield Ave, Bloomfield, CT, 06002-2903, Hartford, USA; tel (860) 286-2828; adv tel (860) 286-2828 Ext 2; ed tel (860) 286-2828 Ext 1; fax (860) 726-0000; e-mail info@catholictranscript.org; adv e-mail jguerrette@catholictranscript.org; ed e-mail rtuttle@catholictranscript.org; web site www.catholictranscript.org
Circulation: 82,140pd, 1,472fr; USPS
Advertising: Open inch rate $30.00
Established: 1898
Pub....Archbishop Henry J. Mansell
Business Manager....Carole Cronsell
Adv. Rep....Jeff Guerette
Circ. Supvr....Joyce Boudreau
Exec. Ed....David Liptak
Mng. Ed....Roberta W. Tuttle
News Ed....Jack Sheedy
Graphic Designer....Leslie DiVenere
Graphic Designer....Joseph Brown
Mechanical Specifications: Tabloid format: 5 Columns X 16 inches. Full page 80 column inches 1 column 1.88 inches wide
Delivery Method: Mail
Zip Codes Served: Hartford and New Haven County

NORTH HAVEN

FAITH & FAMILY MAGAZINE
432 Washington Ave, North Haven, CT, 06473-1309, New Haven, USA; tel (203) 985-4450; fax (203) 230-3838; e-mail editor@faithandfamilylive.com; web site www.faithandfamilylive.com/magazine
Circulation:; Sworn/Estimate/Non-Audited
Pub....Father Owen Kearns
Circ. Mgr....Brendan McCaffrey
Ed....April Hoopes
Ed....Tom Hoopes
Prodn. Mgr....Joseph Hilliman
Equipment: Hardware — APP/Mac; Software — Microsoft/Word 6.0.
Zip Codes Served: 6514

DISTRICT OF COLUMBIA

WASHINGTON

CATHOLIC STANDARD (Thur)
145 Taylor St NE, Washington, DC, 20017-1008, District Of Columbia, USA; tel (202) 281-2410; fax (202) 281-2408; web site www.cathstan.org; www.catholicstandard.com
Circulation: 46,000pd, 368fr; Sworn/Estimate/Non-Audited
Advertising: Open inch rate $27.75
Gen. Mgr....Thomas H. Schmidt
Dir., Sales/Mktg....Alan Hay
Circ. Mgr....Irieska D. Caetano
Ed....Mark V. Zimmermann
Mechanical Specifications: Type page 10 1/4 x 13 1/2; E - 4 cols, 1 5/6, between; A - 5 cols, 1 5/6, 1/6 between; C - 7 cols, 1 1/3, 1/6 between.
Equipment: Hardware — APP/Mac Workstations; Software — QPS/QuarkXPress 3.32, Baseview/News Edit Pro 2.1.3, Baseview/Admanger Pro 2.0.6, Baseview/Circulation Pro 1.10.3.

FLORIDA

ORLANDO

FLORIDA CATHOLIC (Every other Fri)
50 E Robinson St, Orlando, FL, 32801-1619, Orange, USA; tel (407) 373-0075; fax (407) 373-0087; ed e-mail news@thefloridacatholic.org; web site www.thefloridacatholic.org
Circulation: 59,242pd, 250fr; Sworn/Estimate/Non-Audited
Advertising: Open inch rate $17.25
Pub....Gerald M. Barbarito
Serv. Mgr....Mary St. Pierre
Web Adv....Jane Radetsky
Circ. Mgr....Tammy Osborne
Equipment: Hardware — APP/Mac; Software — Microsoft/Word.

THE FLORIDA CATHOLIC (Every other Fri)
50 E Robinson St, Orlando, FL, 32801-1619, Orange, USA; tel (407) 373-0075; fax (407) 373-0087; e-mail info@thefloridacatholic.org; web site www.thefloridacatholic.org
Circulation: 59,000pd, 60,000fr; Sworn/Estimate/Non-Audited
Advertising: Open inch rate $21.03
Pub....Thomas G. Wenski
Adv. Sales Dir....Jane Radestsky
Circ. Mgr....Tammy Osburne
Ed....Mary St. Pierre

PENSACOLA

THE FLORIDA CATHOLIC
11 N B St, Pensacola, FL, 32502-4601, Escambia, USA; tel (850) 435-3500; fax (850) 436-6424; web site www.ptdiocese.org
Circulation:; Sworn/Estimate/Non-Audited
Advertising: Open inch rate $11.75
Assoc. Pub....Christopher Gunty
Adv. Sales Dir....David O'Leary
Circ. Mgr....Maureen Neder

VENICE

THE FLORIDA CATHOLIC (Fri)
1000 Pinebrook Rd, Venice, FL, 34285-6426, Sarasota, USA; tel (941) 484-9543; fax (941) 486-4763; e-mail peace&justice@dioceseofvenice.org; web site www.thefloridacatholic.org
Circulation: 16,250pd,; Sworn/Estimate/Non-Audited
Advertising: Open inch rate $14.25
Adv. Sales Mgr....Mark Caruso
Ed....Kristie Nguyen

GEORGIA

SAVANNAH

SOUTHERN CROSS (Thur) (Bi-weekly)
601 E Liberty St, Savannah, GA, 31401-5118, Chatham, USA; tel (912) 201-4100; fax (912) 201-4101; e-mail southerncross@diosav.org; adv e-mail 2cents@diosav.org; ed e-mail editor@diosav.org; web site www.diosav.org
Circulation: 27,600pd, 100fr; Sworn/Estimate/Non-Audited
Advertising: Open inch rate $12.00
Established: 1963
Publisher....Gregory J. Hartmayer
Editor....Michael J. Johnson
Mechanical Specifications: Type page 10 x 14; E - 3 cols, 1/8 between; A - 2 cols, 5, between; C - 3 cols, 5, between.
Delivery Method: Mail

SMYRNA

THE GEORGIA BULLETIN (Thur) (Bi-weekly)
2401 Lake Park Dr SE, Smyrna, GA, 30080-8862, Cobb, USA; tel (404) 920-7430; adv tel (404) 920-7441; ed tel (404) 920-7430; fax (404) 920-7431; adv fax (404) 920-7431; ed fax (404) 920-7431; e-mail editor@georgiabulletin.org; adv e-mail ads@georgiabulletin.org; ed e-mail editor@georgiabulletin.org; web site www.georgiabulletin.org
Circulation: 74,000pd,; Sworn/Estimate/Non-Audited
Advertising: Open inch rate $14.00
Established: 1963
Pub....Archbishop Wilton Gregory
Adv. Mgr....Tom Aisthorpe
Exec. Ed....Mary Anne Castranio
Ed....Gretchen R. Keiser
Graphic Artist....Tom Schulte
Mechanical Specifications: Type page 10 x 13 1/2; A - 5 cols, 2, between; C - 5 cols, 2, between.
Delivery Method: Mail
Zip Codes Served: 30002-33065

HAWAII

HONOLULU

HAWAII CATHOLIC HERALD
1184 Bishop St, Honolulu, HI, 96813-2859, Honolulu, USA; tel (808) 585-3300; ed tel (808) 585-3317; fax (808) 585-3381; ed e-mail herald@rcchawaii.org; web site www.hawaiicatholicherald.org
Circulation:; Sworn/Estimate/Non-Audited
Advertising: Open inch rate $48.00
Established: 1936
Group: Roman Catholic Church in the State of Hawaii
Pub....Clarence Silva
Circ. Mgr....Donna Aquino
Ed....Patrick Downes
Mechanical Specifications: Type page 10 1/4 x 15; E - 5 cols, 1 11/12, 1/6 between; A - 5 cols, 1 11/12, 1/6 between; C - 5 cols, 1 11/12, 1/6 between.
Delivery Method: Mail

IDAHO

BOISE

IDAHO CATHOLIC REGISTER (Every other Fri)
1501 S Federal Way, Boise, ID, 83705-2588, Ada, USA; tel (208) 342-1311; fax (208) 342-0224; e-mail idcathreg@rcdb.org; web site www.catholicidaho.org
Circulation: 16,700pd,; Sworn/Estimate/Non-Audited
Advertising: Open inch rate $9.95
Pub....Bishop Michael P. Driscoll
Adv. Mgr....Ann Bixby
Ed....Michael Brown
Mechanical Specifications: Type page 10 x 15; E - 5 cols, 1 7/8, 1/6 between; A - 5 cols, 1 7/8, 1/6 between; C - 5 cols, 1 7/8, 1/6 between.

ILLINOIS

BELLEVILLE

THE MESSENGER (2 x Mthly)
2620 Lebanon Ave, Belleville, IL, 62221-3002, Saint Clair, USA; tel (618) 235-9601; fax (618) 235-9605; e-mail cathnews@bellevillemessenger.org; web site www.bellevillemessenger.org
Circulation: 10,500pd,; Sworn/Estimate/Non-Audited
Advertising: Open inch rate $8.54
Established: 1808
Adv. Mgr.....Bernadette Middeke
Ed.....Liz Quirin

CHICAGO

THE CATHOLIC NEW WORLD (Every other Sat)
835 N Rush St, Chicago, IL, 60611-2030, Cook, USA; tel (312) 534-7777; fax (312) 534-7350; e-mail editorial@catholicnewworld.com; web site www.catholicnewworld.com
Circulation: 55,000pd,; Sworn/Estimate/Non-Audited
Established: 1892
Pub.....Cardinal Francis E. George
Adv. Mgr.....Dawn Vidmar
Ed.....Joyce Duriga
Prodn. Mgr.....Tony Rodriguez
Mechanical Specifications: Type page 10 1/4 x 14 5/8; A - 5 cols, 1 7/8, between; C - 5 cols, 1 7/8, between.
Equipment: Hardware — PC, APP/Mac; Software — QPS/QuarkXPress 4.0.
Delivery Method: Mail
Zip Codes Served: Cook and Lake counties

PEORIA

THE CATHOLIC POST (Other) (Bi-weekly)
419 NE Madison Ave, Peoria, IL, 61603-3719, Peoria, USA; tel (309) 671-1550; fax (309) 671-1579; e-mail cathpost@cdop.org; adv e-mail sknelson@cdop.org; web site www.thecatholicpost.com
Circulation: 16,000pd,; Sworn/Estimate/Non-Audited
Advertising: Open inch rate $14.50
Established: 1934
Pub.....Bishop Daniel R. Jenky
Adv. Mgr.....Sonia Nelson
Ed.....Tom Dermody
Jennifer Willems
Delivery Method: Mail
Zip Codes Served: Dozens throughout 26 counties in central Illinois

SPRINGFIELD

CATHOLIC TIMES (Sun) (bi-weekly)
1615 W Washington St, Springfield, IL, 62702-4757, Sangamon, USA; tel (217) 698-8500; fax (217) 698-0802; e-mail catholictimes@dio.org; web site www.dio.org
Circulation: 44,980pd, 115fr; USPS
Advertising: Open inch rate $18.73
Adv. Mgr.....Paula Ruot
Circ. Mgr.....Laura Weakley
Ed.....Kathie Sass
Reporter.....Cathy Locher
Reporter.....Diane Schlindwein
Mechanical Specifications: Type page 10 1/6 x 12 1/4; E - 4 cols, 2 1/3, 1/6 between; C - 4 cols, 2 1/3, 1/6 between.
Equipment: Software — Adobe Creative Suites
Delivery Method: Mail

INDIANA

EVANSVILLE

THE MESSAGE (Fri)
4200 N Kentucky Ave, Evansville, IN, 47711-2752, Vanderburgh, USA; tel (812) 424-5536; fax (812) 424-0972; e-mail message@evido.org; adv e-mail messagead@evdio.org; ed e-mail message@evdio.org; web site www.themessageonline.org
Circulation: 5,000pd,; Sworn/Estimate/Non-Audited
Advertising: Open inch rate $8.00
Established: 1970
Digital Platform - Mobile: Apple
Digital Platform - Tablet: Apple iOS
Ed.....Tim Lilley
Prod. Tech.....Sheila Barclay
Assist. Ed.....Trisha Smith
Mechanical Specifications: Type page 10 1/4 x 16; E - 5 cols, 1 11/12, 1/6 between; A - 5 cols, 1 11/12, 1/6 between.
Equipment: Hardware — APP/Mac; Software — QPS/QuarkXPress.
Delivery Method: Mail

FORT WAYNE

TODAYS CATHOLIC (Sun) (published 44 times per year)
915 S Clinton St, Fort Wayne, IN, 46802-2601, Allen, USA; tel (260) 456-2824; fax (260) 744-1473; adv e-mail jparker@diocesefwsb.org; ed e-mail editor@diocesefwsb.org; web site www.diocesefwsb.org; www.todayscatholicnews.org
Circulation: 207pd, 47,702fr; Sworn/Estimate/Non-Audited
Advertising: Open inch rate $15.85
Established: 1926
Digital Platform - Mobile: Apple, Android, Windows, Blackberry
Digital Platform - Tablet: Apple iOS, Android, Windows 7, Blackberry Tablet OS, Kindle, Nook, Kindle Fire
Pub.....Kevin Rhoades
Dir. of Comm.....Stephanie Patka
Ed.....Jodi Marlin
Mechanical Specifications: Type page 10 x 13; E - 5 cols, 1.875 inches, .167 between; A - 5 col, 2 inches.
Delivery Method: Mail, Racks
Zip Codes Served: 14 counties in northeastern Indiana

HUNTINGTON

OUR SUNDAY VISITOR (Sun)
200 Noll Plz, Huntington, IN, 46750-4310, Huntington, USA; tel (260) 356-8400; adv tel (260) 359-2578; ed tel (260) 359-2546; fax (260) 356-8472; adv fax (260) 359-2578; ed fax (260) 359-6446; e-mail oursunvis@osv.com; adv e-mail tcalouette@osv.com; ed e-mail gcrowe@osv.com; web site www.osv.com
Circulation: 43,000pd, 4,000fr; Sworn/Estimate/Non-Audited
Advertising: Open inch rate $90.00
Established: 1912Editions: Volume 103 - Our Sunday Visitor
Pres./Pub.....Greg R. Erlandson
Adv. Mgr.....Therese Calouette
Strategic Mktg. Dir.....John Christensen
Ed.....Gretchen Crowe
Prodn. Mgr.....Chris Rice
Mechanical Specifications: Type page 10 1/8 x 13; E - 5 cols, 1 7/8, 1/8 between; A - 5 cols, 2, 1/8 between; C - 1 cols, 1 7/8, 1/8 between.
Equipment: Hardware — 15-MAC; Software — QPS/QuarkXPress 4/5/6.
Delivery Method: Mail
Zip Codes Served: All/any

INDIANAPOLIS

THE CRITERION
1400 N Meridian St, Indianapolis, IN, 46202-2305, Marion, USA; tel (317) 236-7325; fax (317) 236-1593; e-mail criterion@archindy.org; web site www.archindy.org
Circulation:; Sworn/Estimate/Non-Audited
Pub.....Daniel Mark Buechlein
Asst. Pub.....Greg A. Otolski
Exec. Asst.....Ron Massey
Ed.....Mike Krokos
Asst. Ed.....John Shaughnessy
Online Ed.....Brandon A. Evans

LAFAYETTE

THE CATHOLIC MOMENT (Sun)
610 Lingle Ave, Lafayette, IN, 47901-1740, Tippecanoe, USA; tel (765) 742-2050; fax (765) 269-4615; e-mail moment@dol-in.org; web site www.thecatholicmoment.org
Circulation: 28,500pd, 264fr; USPS
Advertising: Open inch rate $13.00
Established: 1945
Pub.....Most Rev. Timothy L. Doherty
Circ. Mgr.....Carolyn McKinney
Mng. Ed.....Laurie Cullen
Ed.....Kevin Cullen
Mechanical Specifications: Type page 10 x 13; E - 5 cols, 1 7/8, 1/6 between; A - 5 cols, 1 7/8, 1/6 between.
Equipment: Hardware — 5-PC; Software — QPS/QuarkXPress 9.0, Adobe/Photoshop 7.0, Microsoft/Word, Adobe Acrobat Pro 9
Delivery Method: Mail
Zip Codes Served: Several

MERRILLVILLE

NORTHWEST INDIANA CATHOLIC (Sun)
9292 Broadway, Merrillville, IN, 46410-7047, Lake, USA; tel (219) 769-9292; fax (219) 736-6577; e-mail nwic@dcgary.org; web site www.nwicatholic.com
Circulation:; Sworn/Estimate/Non-Audited
Advertising: Open inch rate $10.75
Established: 1987
Group: Roman Catholic Diocese of Gary
Circulation/Administrative Assistant/Accounts Receivable.....Carol Macinga
Staff writer.....Marlene Zloza
Page and graphic designer.....Doris LaFauci
Photojournalist.....Anthony Alonzo
Advertising Representative.....Erin Ciszczon
????
Mechanical Specifications: Type page 10 1/2 x 16; E - 6 cols, 1 3/5, between; A - 6 cols, 1 3/5, between; C - 6 cols, 1 3/5, between.
Equipment: Hardware — PC; Presses — Web Offset; Software — QPS/QuarkXPress, Microsoft/Word InDesign
Delivery Method: Mail

IOWA

DAVENPORT

THE CATHOLIC MESSENGER (Thur)
780 W Central Park Ave, Davenport, IA, 52804-1901, Scott, USA; tel (563) 323-9959; adv tel (563) 323-9959; ed tel (563) 320-0551; fax (563) 323-6612; e-mail messenger@davenportdiocese.org; adv e-mail hart@davenportdiocese.org; ed e-mail arland-fye@davenportdiocese.org; web site www.catholicmessenger.net
Circulation: 18,000pd,; Sworn/Estimate/Non-Audited
Advertising: Open inch rate $10.00
Established: 1882
Digital Platform - Mobile: Windows
Digital Platform - Tablet: Windows 7
Circ. Mgr.....Nancy Hamerlinck
Mng. Ed.....Barb Arland-Fye
Asst. Ed.....Anne Marie Amacher
Equipment; Software — QPS/QuarkXPress.

DUBUQUE

THE WITNESS (Sun)
1229 Mount Loretta Ave, Dubuque, IA, 52003-7826, Dubuque, USA; tel (563) 588-0556; fax (563) 588-0557; e-mail dbqcwo@arch.pvt.k12.ia.us; web site www.arch.pvt.k12.ia.us/witness
Circulation: 14,000pd,; Sworn/Estimate/Non-Audited
Advertising: Open inch rate $12.10
Pub.....Jerome Hanus
Adv. Mgr.....Bret Fear
Circ. Mgr.....Catherine White
Ed.....Sister Carol Hoverman
Mechanical Specifications: Type page 13 1/4 x 21 1/2; E - 6 cols, 2, 3/16 between; A - 8 cols, 1 1/2, 3/16 between; C - 8 cols, 1 1/2, 3/16 between.
Equipment: Hardware — COM/MCS.

SIOUX CITY

THE GLOBE (Every Other Thur)
1825 Jackson St, Sioux City, IA, 51105-1055, Woodbury, USA; tel (712) 255-2550; fax (712) 255-4901; e-mail rwebb@catholicglobe.org; web site www.catholicglobe.org
Circulation: 25,268pd, 500fr; Sworn/Estimate/Non-Audited
Advertising: Open inch rate $12.50
Pub.....Bishop R. Walker Nickless
Ed.....Renee Webb

KANSAS

DODGE CITY

THE SOUTHWEST KANSAS CATHOLIC (Bi-Mthly, Other) (twice monthly)
910 Central Ave, Dodge City, KS, 67801-4905, Ford, USA; tel (620) 227-1519; adv tel (620) 227-1556; ed tel (620) 227-1519; fax (620) 227-1545; adv fax (620) 227-1545; ed fax (620) 227-1545; e-mail skregister@dcdiocese.org; adv e-mail twenzl@dcdiocese.org; ed e-mail skregister@dcdiocese.org; web site www.dcdiocese.org/swkscatholic
Circulation: 6,000fr; Sworn/Estimate/Non-Audited
Advertising: Open inch rate $15.00
Established: 1966
Group: Catholic Diocese of Dodge City
Digital Platform - Mobile: Windows
Ed.....David Myers
Adv Rep.....Tim Wenzl
Pub.....Brungardt Bishop John
Mechanical Specifications: 11x17 tabloid
Equipment; Software — InDesign, Photoshop, Microsoft Word
Delivery Method: Mail, Racks
Zip Codes Served: Southwest Quarter of Kansas

NEWTON

MENNONITE WEEKLY REVIEW (Mon)
129 W 6th St, Newton, KS, 67114-2117, Harvey, USA; tel (316) 283-3670; fax (316) 283-6502; ed e-mail editor@mennoweekly.org; web site www.mennoweekly.org

Circulation: 10,200pd, 751fr; Sworn/Estimate/Non-Audited
Advertising: Open inch rate $22.00
Pub.. Robert Schrag
Ed. .... Paul Schrag
Mechanical Specifications: Type page 10 1/4 x 16; E - 5 cols, 1 11/12, 1/6 between; A - 5 cols, 1 11/12, 1/6 between; C - 5 cols, 1 11/12, 1/6 between.
Equipment: Hardware — APP/Mac G3; Software — QPS/QuarkXPress 3.1.

WICHITA

THE CATHOLIC ADVANCE (Bi-Mthly)
424 N Broadway Ave, Wichita, KS, 67202-2310, Sedgwick, USA; tel (316) 269-3965; fax (316) 269-3902; e-mail advancenews@catholicdioceseofwichita.org; adv e-mail advanceads@cdowk.org; web site www.catholicadvance.org
Circulation: 37,500pd, 93fr; Sworn/Estimate/Non-Audited
Advertising: Open inch rate $12.75
Digital Platform - Mobile: Apple
Digital Platform - Tablet: Apple iOS
Ed. .... Christopher M. Riggs
Prodn. Mgr. .... Donald G. McClane
Mechanical Specifications: Type page 11 1/2 x 17; E - 5 cols, 1 7/8, between; A - 5 cols, 1 7/8, between; C - 5 cols, 1 7/8, between.
Delivery Method: Mail

KENTUCKY

COVINGTON

THE MESSENGER (Fri)
402 E 21st St, Covington, KY, 41014-1588, Kenton, USA; tel (859) 392-1500; e-mail mifcic@covingtondiocese.org; web site www.covingtondiocese.org
Circulation: 27,000pd, 75fr; Sworn/Estimate/Non-Audited
Advertising: Open inch rate $19.00
Pub.. Roger Foys
Adv. Mgr. .... Michael Ifcic
Circ. Mgr. .... Judy Russo
Ed. .... Tim Fitzgerald
Asst. Ed. .... Laura Keener
Equipment: Hardware — APP/Macs; Software — Adobe/PageMaker 6.5, Microsoft/Word 6.0, Macromedia/Freehand 5.5, Adobe/Photoshop 3.01.

LOUISVILLE

SOUTHEAST OUTLOOK (Thur)
920 Blankenbaker Pkwy, Louisville, KY, 40243-1845, Jefferson, USA; tel (502) 253-8650; fax (502) 499-6968; e-mail badams@secc.org; web site www.southeastoutlook.org
Digital Platform - Mobile: Apple, Android, Windows
Digital Platform - Tablet: Apple iOS, Android, Windows 7, Blackberry Tablet OS, Kindle, Nook, Kindle Fire, Other
Delivery Method: Mail, Racks

THE RECORD (Thur)
1200 S Shelby St, Louisville, KY, 40203-2627, Jefferson, USA; tel (502) 636-0296; fax (502) 636-2379; e-mail record@archlou.org; web site www.therecordnewspaper.org
Circulation: 61,000pd,; Sworn/Estimate/Non-Audited
Advertising: Open inch rate $34.00
Established: 1879
Group: Archdiocese of Louisville
Landmark Community Newspapers, LLC
Editor .... Marnie McAllister
Mechanical Specifications: Type page 10 x 21; E - 6 cols, 2 1/15, 1/10 between; A - 6 cols, 2 1/15, 1/10 between; C - 8 cols, 1 1/2, 1/6 between.
Delivery Method: Mail

WESTERN RECORDER (Tues)
13420 Eastpoint Centre Dr, Louisville, KY, 40223-4160, Jefferson, USA; tel (502) 489-3535; adv tel (502) 489-3428; ed tel (502) 489-3442; fax (502) 489-3565; adv fax (502) 489-3228; web site www.westernrecorder.org
Circulation: 24,000pd, 1,384fr; Sworn/Estimate/Non-Audited
Advertising: Open inch rate $30.00
Established: 1826
Mktg. Mgr. .... Tom Townsend
Mechanical Specifications: Type page 10 x 14.
Equipment: Hardware — PC network; Software — Microsoft/Word, Adobe/PageMaker 6.0.
Delivery Method: Mail
Zip Codes Served: Kentucky

LOUISIANA

ALEXANDRIA

BAPTIST MESSAGE
PO Box 311, Alexandria, LA, 71309-0311, Rapides, USA; tel (318) 442-7728; fax (318) 445-8328; e-mail info@baptistmessage.com; adv e-mail advertising@baptistmessage.com; ed e-mail editor@baptistmessage.com; web site www.baptistmessage.com
Established: 1886

BATON ROUGE

THE CATHOLIC COMMENTATOR (Mon)
1800 S Acadian Thruway, Baton Rouge, LA, 70808-1663, East Baton Rouge, USA; tel (225) 387-0983; fax (225) 336-8710; web site www.diobr.org
Circulation.................................. Lisa Disney

NEW ORLEANS

CLARION HERALD (Sat)
1000 Howard Ave, Ste 400, New Orleans, LA, 70113-1926, Orleans, USA; tel (504) 596-3035; adv tel (504) 524-1618; ed tel (504) 596-3030; fax (504) 596-3020; adv fax (504) 596-3039; ed fax (504) 596-3020; e-mail clarionherald@clarionherald.org; adv e-mail adsales@clarionherald.org; ed e-mail clarionherald@clarionherald.org; web site www.clarionherald.org
Circulation: 60,000pd, 400fr; Sworn/Estimate/Non-Audited
Advertising: Open inch rate $36.00 less 15% discount
Established: 1963Editions: Bridal Wedding Guide, High School Information, Elder Outlook, Good Business Matters, Mommy & Me, Lenten Recipe Guide (Holy Smoke), SUmmer Activities, Graduation, Catholic Schools Week
Adv. Dir. .... M.J. Cahill
Exec. Ed. .... Peter Finney
Mechanical Specifications: Type page 9 1/4 x 11 1/8; E - 5 cols, 1 3/4, 1/6 between; A - 5 cols, 1 3/4, 1/6 between.
Equipment: Hardware — PCs, APP/Mac; Presses — The Advocate, Baton Rouge; Software — Adobe/Photoshop, Adobe/InDesign 2.0.
Delivery Method: Carrier, Racks
Zip Codes Served: Southeast Louisiana

SCHRIEVER

THE BAYOU CATHOLIC (Thur)
2779 Highway 311, Schriever, LA, 70395-3273, Terrebonne, USA; tel (985) 850-3132; fax (985) 850-3232; e-mail bc@mobiletel.com; web site www.htdiocese.org
Circulation: 32,000pd,; Sworn/Estimate/Non-Audited
Advertising: Open inch rate $15.34
Sec. .... Pat Keese
Adv. Mgr. .... Peggy Adams
Ed. .... Louis G. Aguirre
Mechanical Specifications: Type page 9 13/16 x 13; E - 5 cols, 1 13/16, between.

MAINE

PORTLAND

CHURCH WORLD
510 Ocean Ave, Portland, ME, 04103-4936, Cumberland, USA; tel (207) 773-6471; fax (207) 773-0182; e-mail churchworld@portlanddiocese.net; web site www.portlanddiocese.org
Circulation:; Sworn/Estimate/Non-Audited
Advertising: Open inch rate $8.00
Established: 1930
Pub. .... Bishop Richard J. Malone
Adv. Mgr. .... Norman F. LeBlanc
Circ. Mgr. .... Rita Coulombe
Ed. .... Thomas J. Kardos
Mechanical Specifications: Type page 10 1/4 x 15 1/2; E - 5 cols, 1 7/8, 7/32 between; A - 5 cols, 1 7/8, 7/32 between.
Equipment: Hardware — APP/Mac; Software — QPS/QuarkXPress 4.1, Baseview/NewsEdit Pro, Adobe/Photoshop.
Zip Codes Served: 04001, 04999

MARYLAND

BALTIMORE

THE CATHOLIC REVIEW (Thur) (Biweekly, alternate Thursdays)
880 Park Ave, Baltimore, MD, 21201-4822, Baltimore City, USA; tel (443) 524-3150; adv tel (443) 263-0247; ed tel (443) 263-0259; fax (443) 524-3155; adv fax (443) 524-3155; ed fax (443) 524-3160; e-mail mail@catholicreview.org; adv e-mail mail@catholicreview.org; ed e-mail mail@catholicreview.org; web site www.catholicreview.org
Circulation: 47,843pd, 172fr; USPS
Advertising: Open rate per column inch is $97.28 (based on a 1-time, 1/8-page ad). Per page is $2,950
Established: 1914
Group: CR MediaEditions: 2- The Catholic Review, Review in the Pew
Digital Platform - Mobile: Blackberry
Managing Ed. .... Paul McMullen
Assoc. Pub./Editor .... Christopher Gunty
Advertising Mgr. .... Jeff Stintz
Mechanical Specifications: Type page 10 x 13; E - 4 cols x 11", 2.2475", .17" between; A - 4 cols x 11", 2.2475", .17" between; C - 4 cols x 11", 2.2475", .17" between.
Delivery Method: Mail, Racks
Zip Codes Served: 206XX-219XX

COLUMBIA

UNITED METHODIST CONNECTION (Every Other Wed)
7178 Columbia Gateway Dr, Ste D, Columbia, MD, 21046-2581, Howard, USA; tel (410) 309-3400; fax (410) 309-9794; e-mail connection@bwcumc.org; web site www.bwcumc.org
Circulation: 10,000pd,; Sworn/Estimate/Non-Audited
Advertising: Open inch rate $30.00
Ed. .... Melissa Lauber

HYATTSVILLE

EL PREGONERO (Thur)
5001 Eastern Ave, Hyattsville, MD, 20782-3447, Prince Georges, USA; tel (202) 281-2404; adv tel (202) 281-2406; ed tel (202) 281-2442; fax (202) 281-2448; e-mail rafael@elpreg.org; adv e-mail irieska@elpreg.org; ed e-mail rafael@elpreg.org; web site www.elpreg.org
Circulation: 25,167fr; CAC
Advertising: Open inch rate $19.00
Established: 1977
Ed. .... Rafael Roncal
Circ. Mgr. .... Irieska D. Caetano
Mechanical Specifications: Type page 10 1/4 x 13 1/2; E - 5 cols, 1 5/6, 1/6 between; A - 5 cols, 1/6 between; C - 7 cols, 1 1/3, 1/6 between.
Equipment: Hardware — 5-APP/Mac, 3-APP/Mac LaserPrinters; Software — QPS/QuarkXPress, Adobe/Photoshop, Adobe/Illustrator, Multi-Ad/Creator, Baseview/NewsEdit Pro, Class Manager/Plus.
Delivery Method: Newsstand, Carrier

SILVER SPRING

ADVENTIST REVIEW (Thur)
12501 Old Columbia Pike, Silver Spring, MD, 20904-6601, Montgomery, USA; tel (301) 680-6560; adv tel (301) 393-3054; fax (301) 680-6638; e-mail letters@adventistreview.com; web site www.adventistreview.org
Circulation: 23,500pd, 700fr; Sworn/Estimate/Non-Audited
Established: 1849
Ed. .... Bill Knott
Mng. Ed. .... Stephen Chavez
Tech. Pjcts. Coord. .... Merle Poirier
associate editor .... Lael Caesar
associate editor .... Gerald Klingbeil
assistant editor .... Wilona Karimabadi
Communication Director and News Editor........ Costin Jordache
Delivery Method: Mail
Zip Codes Served: all

MASSACHUSETTS

BRAINTREE

THE PILOT (Fri)
66 Brooks Dr, Braintree, MA, 02184-3839, Norfolk, USA; tel (617) 779-3780; adv tel (617) 779-3788; ed tel (617) 779-3782; fax (617) 779-4562; e-mail editorial@TheBostonPilot.com; adv e-mail advertising@TheBostonPilot.com; ed e-mail editorial@TheBostonPilot.com; web site www.TheBostonPilot.com.com
Circulation: 21,150pd, 300fr; USPS
Advertising: Open inch rate $25.00
Established: 1829
Group: iCatholic Media, Inc.
Digital Platform - Mobile: Apple, Android
Digital Platform - Tablet: Apple iOS, Android, Kindle, Kindle Fire
Adv. Mgr. .... Larry Ricardo
Ed. .... Antonio Enrique
Mng. Ed. .... Gregory Tracy
Prodn. Mgr. .... Nan Wilkins
Bus. Mgr. .... Ernesto Cuevas
Coord., Mktg./Circ. .... Jon Tan
Delivery Method: Mail, Racks

Zip Codes Served: 01462-02494

FALL RIVER

THE ANCHOR
887 Highland Ave, Fall River, MA, 02720-3820, Bristol, USA; tel (508) 675-7151; fax (508) 675-7048; e-mail theanchor@anchornews.org; web site www.anchornews.org
Circulation:; Sworn/Estimate/Non-Audited
Advertising: Open inch rate $13.75
Pub.................. Most Rev. George W. Coleman
Exec. Ed............................ Rev. Roger Landry
Mechanical Specifications: Type page 10 x 14; A - 5 cols, 2, between.
Equipment: Hardware — 3-HP/486; Software — Microsoft/Windows 95, Adobe/PageMaker 6.0, Microsoft/Works 3.0.

WORCESTER

THE CATHOLIC FREE PRESS (Fri)
49 Elm St, Worcester, MA, 01609-2514, Worcester, USA; tel (508) 757-6387; fax (508) 756-8315; e-mail cpfnews@catholicfreepress.org; adv e-mail advertising@catholicfreepress.org; ed e-mail editor@catholicfreepress.org; web site www.catholicfreepress.org
Circulation: 11,000pd, 660fr; Sworn/Estimate/Non-Audited
Advertising: Open inch rate $19.50
Established: 1951
Group: The Roman Catholic Diocese of Worcester
Digital Platform - Mobile: Apple
Digital Platform - Tablet: Apple iOS
Pub........................ Bishop Robert J. McManus
Adv. Mgr.......................... Robert C. Ballantine
Ed.................................. Margaret M. Russell
Mechanical Specifications: Type page 11 5/8 x 21; E - 6 cols, 1 4/5, 1/6 between; A - 6 cols, 1 4/5, 1/6 between.
Equipment: Hardware — APP/Mac; Software — Adobe Indesign
Delivery Method: Mail
Zip Codes Served: 01401-01790

MICHIGAN

DETROIT

THE MICHIGAN CATHOLIC (Fri) (Bi-weekly)
305 Michigan Ave, Detroit, MI, 48226-2631, Wayne, USA; tel (313) 224-8000; fax (313) 224-8009; web site www.themichigancatholic.com
Circulation: 25,000pd,; Sworn/Estimate/Non-Audited
Advertising: Open inch rate $21.00
Group: Archdiocese of Detroit
Managing Ed.................. Michael Stechschulte
Mechanical Specifications: Type page 10 1/3 x 13; E - 5 cols, 2, between; A - 5 cols, 2, between.
Equipment: Hardware — PC; Software — Microsoft, Adobe/Photoshop, Adobe/Illustrator, Adobe/PageMaker.

GRAND RAPIDS

THE BANNER (Mthly)
1700 28th St SE, Grand Rapids, MI, 49508-1414, Kent, USA; tel (616) 224-0732; adv tel (616) 224-5882; ed tel (616) 224-0824; fax (616) 224-0834; e-mail info@thebanner.org; adv e-mail ads@thebanner.org; web site www.thebanner.org
Circulation: 83,500fr; Sworn/Estimate/Non-Audited
Editor in chief............................. Shiao Chong
Mechanical Specifications: Type page 7 1/3 x 10; A - 3 cols, 2 1/3, 1/6 between; C - 3 cols, 2 1/3, 1/6 between.

SAGINAW

THE CATHOLIC TIMES (Fri)
PO Box 1405, Saginaw, MI, 48605-1405, Saginaw, USA; tel (989) 793-7661; fax (989) 793-7663; e-mail catholictimes@sbcglobal.net; catholicweekly@sbcglobal.net
Circulation: 8,660pd, 114fr; Sworn/Estimate/Non-Audited
Advertising: Open inch rate $7.25
Pub................................ Mark A. Myczkowiak
Adv. Mgr.. Julie Root
Circ. Mgr....................................... Chris Brass
Ed.. Mark Haney

THE CATHOLIC WEEKLY (Fri)
1520 Court St, Saginaw, MI, 48602-4067, Saginaw, USA; tel (989) 793-7661; fax (989) 793-7663; e-mail catholicweekly@sbcglobal.net; web site www.catholicweekly.org
Circulation: 13,173pd, 637fr; Sworn/Estimate/Non-Audited
Advertising: Open inch rate $7.75
Established: 1942
Group: G.L.S. Diocesan Reports, Inc.Editions: 2- 2 total Catholic Weekly-Gaylord (4,150); Catholic Weekly-Saginaw (7,700);
Gen. Mgr./Adv. Mgr.......... Mark A. Myczkowiak
Book Keeper................................ Chris Brass
Mng. Ed.. Mark Haney
Julie Root
Mechanical Specifications: Type page 10.25 x 16; E - 6 cols, 1 5/8, 1/8 between; A - 8 cols, 1 1/2, 1/8 between; C - 6 cols, 1 5/8, 1/8 between.
Equipment: Hardware — APP/Mac G3; Software — Adobe/PageMaker 6.5, Adobe/Photoshop 5.5, Microsoft/Word.

MINNESOTA

SAINT CLOUD

ST. CLOUD VISITOR (Every Other Thur)
305 7th Ave N, Ste 206, Saint Cloud, MN, 56303-3633, Stearns, USA; tel (320) 251-3022; fax (320) 251-0424; e-mail news@stcloudvisitor.org; web site www.stclouddiocese.org
Circulation: 45,000pd, 125fr; Sworn/Estimate/Non-Audited
Advertising: Open inch rate $17.00
Established: 1938
Pub.................................. Bishop John Kinney
Adv. Mgr........................... Rose Kruger Fuchs
Circ. Mgr....................................... Paula Lemke
Ed... Joe Towalski
Mechanical Specifications: Type page 10 x 15; A - 5 cols, 2, between.
Equipment: Hardware — QuarkXPress 4.1, Adobe/Photoshop 5.5.

SAINT PAUL

THE CATHOLIC SPIRIT (Thur)
244 Dayton Ave, Saint Paul, MN, 55102-1802, Ramsey, USA; tel (651) 291-4444; fax (651) 291-4460; e-mail catholicspirit@archspm.org; web site www.thecatholicspirit.com
Circulation: 85,000pd, 106fr; Sworn/Estimate/Non-Audited
Advertising: Open inch rate $43.00
Established: 1911
Pub.......................... Archbishop John Nienstedt
Assoc. Pub............................ Bob Zyskowski
Acct. Supvr............................ Martie McMahon
Ed... Joe Towalski
Mng. Ed... Pat Norby
Prodn. Mgr................................ John Wolszon
Mechanical Specifications: Type page 10 1/4 x 14; E - 4 cols, 2 1/3, 1/6 between; A - 4 cols, 2 1/3, 1/6 between; C - 5 cols, 1 5/6, 1/6 between.
Equipment: Hardware — APP/Mac; Software — QPS/QuarkXPress 4.11.
Zip Codes Served: 55100, 55400, 55300, 56000

MISSISSIPPI

BILOXI

GULF PINE CATHOLIC (Everyother Fri)
1790 Popps Ferry Rd, Biloxi, MS, 39532-2118, Harrison, USA; tel (228) 702-2126; fax (228) 702-2128; e-mail gulfpinecatholic&biloxidiocese.org; adv e-mail gulfpinecatholic@biloxidiocese.org; web site www.gulfpinecatholic.com
Circulation: 17,800pd,; Sworn/Estimate/Non-Audited
Advertising: Open inch rate $10.00
Established: 1983
Circ. Mgr.............................. Deborah Mowrey
Ed................................ Shirley M. Henderson
Reporter .... Terrance Dickson
Bishop of Biloxi .... Roger Morin
Pub.......................... Most Rev. Thomas J. Rodi
Mechanical Specifications: Type page 10 1/4 x 11 1/4; E - 3 cols, 3 1/6, 1/12 between; A - 6 cols, 1/12 between.
Equipment; Software — QPS/QuarkXPress.
Delivery Method: Mail

JACKSON

MISSISSIPPI CATHOLIC (Fri)
237 E Amite St, Jackson, MS, 39201-2405, Hinds, USA; tel (601) 969-3581; fax (601) 960-8455; e-mail editor@mississippicatholic.com; ed e-mail editor@mississippicatholic.com; web site www.mississippicatholic.com
Circulation: 13,112pd,; Sworn/Estimate/Non-Audited
Advertising: Open inch rate $10.50
Established: 1954
Pub....................................... Joseph N. Latino
Adv. Mgr................................. Elsa Baughman
Circ. Mgr.................................. Pamela Butler
Ed.. Janna Avalon
Prodn. Mgr. .... Tyna McNealy
Delivery Method: Mail

THE BAPTIST RECORD (Thur)
PO Box 530, Jackson, MS, 39205-0530, Hinds, USA; tel (601) 968-3800; fax (601) 292-3330; e-mail baptistrecord@mbcb.org; web site www.mbcb.org
Circulation: 92,000pd, 812fr; Sworn/Estimate/Non-Audited
Advertising: Open inch rate $36.04
Adv. Coord.......................... Dana Richardson
Circ. Mgr........................... Brenda Quattlebaum
Ed...................................... William H. Perkins
Assoc. Ed...................................... Tony Martin

MISSOURI

JEFFERSON CITY

THE CATHOLIC MISSOURIAN (Fri)
PO Box 104900, Jefferson City, MO, 65110-4900, Cole, USA; tel (573) 635-9127; fax (573) 635-2286; e-mail cathmo@diojeffcity.org; web site www.diojeffcity.org
Circulation: 20,578pd, 755fr; Sworn/Estimate/Non-Audited
Advertising: Open inch rate $8.03
Established: 1957
Pub............................ Bishop John R. Gaydos
Adv. Dir.. Kelly Martin
Ed.. Jay Nies
Mechanical Specifications: Type page 9 7/8 x 12 3/4.

THE PATHWAY (Other) (2 x Mthly)
400 E High St, Jefferson City, MO, 65101-3215, Cole, USA; tel (573) 636-0400; adv tel (573) 636-0400; fax (573) 635-5631; e-mail dhinkle@mobaptist.org; adv e-mail bpeeper@mobaptist.org; ed e-mail dhinkle@mobaptist.org; web site www.mbcpathway.com
Circulation: 25,050pd,; Sworn/Estimate/Non-Audited
Advertising: Open inch rate $15.00
Established: 2002
Group: Missouri Baptist Convention
Digital Platform - Mobile: Apple
Digital Platform - Tablet: Apple iOS
Editor .... Don Hinkle
News Writer............................... Brian Koonce
Ben Hawkins
Equipment: Hardware — APP/Mac; Software — indesign
Delivery Method: Mail
Zip Codes Served: All

KANSAS CITY

NATIONAL CATHOLIC REPORTER (Other) (Bi-Weekly)
115 E Armour Blvd, Kansas City, MO, 64111-1203, Jackson, USA; tel (816) 968-2202; adv tel (816) 968-2202; ed tel (816) 968-2202; fax (816) 968-2293; adv fax (816) 968-2268; e-mail mjudd@ncronline.org; adv e-mail mjudd@ncronline.org; ed e-mail mjudd@ncronline.org; web site www.ncronline.org
Circulation: 25,000pd, 150fr; Sworn/Estimate/Non-Audited
Advertising: Open inch rate $65.00
Established: 1964
Digital Platform - Mobile: Apple, Android, Windows, Blackberry
Digital Platform - Tablet: Apple iOS, Android, Windows 7, Blackberry Tablet OS, Kindle, Nook, Kindle Fire
CFO/Bus. Mgr............................... Wally Reiter
Art Dir.. Toni-Ann Ortiz
Editor .... Dennis Coday
Publisher/CEO............................ Caitlin Hendel
Adv Mgr .... Kim Rea
Aud Engagement Dir .... Sara Wiercinski
Circ Mgr...................................... Jo Schierhoff
Chief Advancement Officer........ Nancy Browne
Mechanical Specifications: Type page 10 7/16 x 14 1/2; E - 4 cols, 2 7/16, 1/6 between; A - 4 cols, 2 7/16, 1/6 between; C - 4 cols, 2 7/16, 1/6 between.
Delivery Method: Mail
Zip Codes Served: National and International

SAINT LOUIS

REPORTER (Mthly)
1333 S Kirkwood Rd, Saint Louis, MO, 63122-7226, Saint Louis, USA; tel (314) 996-1231; fax (314) 996-1126; e-mail adriane.dorr@lcms.org; adv e-mail kathryn.gritts@lcms.org; ed e-mail joe.isenhower@lcms.org; web site www.reporter.lcms.org
Circulation: 35,000fr; USPS
Established: 1974
Group: The Lutheran Church—Missouri SynodEditions: 39-
Executive Director....................... David Strand
Executive Editor, News & Information......... Joe Isenhower
Executive Editor........................... Adriane Dorr
Mechanical Specifications: Type page 11 x 17; E - 4 cols, 2 1/3, 1/6 between; A - 4 cols, 2 1/3, 1/6 between.
Equipment: Hardware — APP/Mac; Software —

Adobe/PageMaker 6.5.
Delivery Method: Mail

ST. LOUIS REVIEW (Fri)
20 Archbishop May Dr, Saint Louis, MO, 63119-5738, Saint Louis, USA; tel (314) 792-7500; fax (314) 792-7534; e-mail slreview@stlouisreview.com; web site www.stlouisreview.com
Circulation: 72,000pd,; Sworn/Estimate/Non-Audited
Advertising: Open inch rate $24.75
Ed. .... Teak Phillips
Mechanical Specifications: Type page 11 5/8 x 20 15/16; E - 6 cols, 1 5/6, 1/12 between; A - 6 cols, 1 5/6, 1/12 between; C - 8 cols, 1 1/3, 1/30 between.
Equipment: Hardware — APP/Mac; Software — QPS/QuarkXPress.

SPRINGFIELD

THE MIRROR (Fri)
601 S Jefferson Ave, Springfield, MO, 65806-3107, Greene, USA; tel (417) 866-0841; fax (417) 866-1140; web site www.the-mirror.org
Circulation: 17,000pd,; Sworn/Estimate/Non-Audited
Advertising: Open inch rate $13.50
Established: 1956
Administrative Assistant/Circulation Manager .. Angie Toben
Ed. .... Leslie Eidson
Production/Web .... Glenn Eckl
Mechanical Specifications: Type page 10 3/8 x 13; A - 4 cols, 2 3/8, 1/8 between.
Equipment: Hardware — APP/Power Mac G4; Software — QPS/QuarkXPress 4.1.
Delivery Method: Mail

NEBRASKA

GRAND ISLAND

WEST NEBRASKA REGISTER (Fri) (Twice monthly)
2708 Old Fair Rd, Grand Island, NE, 68803-5221, Hall, USA; tel (308) 382-4660; fax (308) 382-6569; web site www.gidiocese.org
Circulation: 17,153pd,; Sworn/Estimate/Non-Audited
Advertising: Open inch rate $8.56
Digital Platform - Tablet: Apple iOS
Ed. .... Mary Parlin
Assoc. Ed. .... Colleen Gallion
Delivery Method: Mail
Zip Codes Served: 688, 689, 691, 692, 693, 686,

LINCOLN

SOUTHERN NEBRASKA REGISTER (Fri)
3700 Sheridan Blvd, Lincoln, NE, 68506-6100, Lancaster, USA; tel (402) 488-0090; fax (402) 488-3569
Circulation: 25,000pd,; Sworn/Estimate/Non-Audited
Advertising: Open inch rate $20.00
Pub. .... James Conley
Circ. Mgr. .... Kim Breitfelder
Editor .... Nick Kipper
Mechanical Specifications: Type page 11 1/2 x 17 3/4; E - 5 cols, 2, 1/8 between; A - 5 cols, 2, 1/8 between.

OMAHA

THE CATHOLIC VOICE (Everyother Fri)
6060 NW Radial Hwy, Omaha, NE, 68104-3426, Douglas, USA; tel (402) 558-6611; fax (402) 558-6614; e-mail tcvomaha@archomaha.org; web site www.catholicvoiceomaha.com
Circulation: 48,000pd,; Sworn/Estimate/Non-Audited
Advertising: Open inch rate $29.95
Pub. .... Most Rev. Elden F. Curtiss
Adv. Mgr. .... Randy Grosse
Exec. Ed. .... Charlie Wieser
Equipment: Hardware — IBM; Software — Microsoft/Word '97, Adobe/PageMaker 6.5.

NEVADA

LAS VEGAS

THE BEEHIVE
7375 Peak Dr, Ste 220, Las Vegas, NV, 89128-9012, Clark, USA; tel (702) 255-6161; fax (702) 255-8383; e-mail info@beehivenewspaper.com
Circulation:; Sworn/Estimate/Non-Audited
Advertising: Open inch rate $6.00
Established: 1950
Pub. .... Robert Graham
Sales/Mktg. Mgr. .... Justin Evans
Circ. Mgr. .... Heather Payne
Prodn. Mgr. .... Stephanie Olsen
Mechanical Specifications: Type page 10 1/4 x 14; E - 4 cols, 2 1/4, 1/6 between; A - 4 cols, 2 1/4, 1/6 between.
Equipment: Hardware — APP/Power Mac; Software — Adobe/PageMaker 5.0.

NEW JERSEY

CAMDEN

CATHOLIC STAR HERALD (Bi-Mthly)
Pastoral Ctr 15 N Seventh St, Camden, NJ, 8102, Camden, USA; tel (856) 583-6142; adv tel (856) 583-6166; ed tel (856) 583-6147; fax (856) 756-7938; adv fax (856) 756-7938; adv e-mail pwothington@camdendiocese.org; ed e-mail cpeters@camdendiocese.org; web site www.catholicstarherald.org
Circulation:; Sworn/Estimate/Non-Audited
Advertising: Open inch rate $25.90
Established: 1951
Mechanical Specifications: Type page 9 3/8 x 13 1/4; E - 4 cols, 2 1/4, between; A - 4 cols, 2 1/4, between; C - 4 cols, 2 1/4, between.
Delivery Method: Mail

CLIFTON

THE BEACON (Thur)
775 Valley Rd, Clifton, NJ, 07013-2205, Passaic, USA; tel (973) 279-8845; fax (973) 279-2265; e-mail catholicbeacon@patersondiocese.org; msbeacon@optonline.net; web site www.patersondiocese.org
Circulation: 28,750pd, 200fr; Sworn/Estimate/Non-Audited
Advertising: Open inch rate $25.50
Established: 1967
Pub. .... Arthur Serratelli
Circ. Mgr. .... Joyce DeCeglie
Ed. .... Richard Sokerka
Mechanical Specifications: Type page 10 x 14; E - 4 cols, 2 1/3, 1/6 between; A - 6 cols, 1 5/8, 1/6 between; C - 6 cols, 1 5/8, 1/6 between.
Equipment: Hardware — APP/Power Mac G3; Software — QPS/QuarkXPress 4.04, Adobe/Photoshop 5.0, Microsoft/Word.
Delivery Method: Mail
Zip Codes Served: All of Passaic, Morris and Sussex Counties in Northern New Jersey

TRENTON

THE MONITOR (Thur, Other) (Bi-weekly)
701 Lawrence Rd, Trenton, NJ, 08648-4209, Mercer, USA; tel (609) 406-7404; adv tel (609) 403-7117; fax (609) 406-7423; e-mail monitor@dioceseoftrenton.org; info@dioceseoftrenton.org; adv e-mail monitor-advertising@dioceseoftrenton.org; ed e-mail monitor-news@dioceseoftrenton.org; web site www.TrentonMonitor.com
Circulation: 15,000pd,; Sworn/Estimate/Non-Audited
Advertising: Open inch rate $32.00
Established: 1953
Assoc. Pub. .... Rayanne Bennett
Bus. Dir. .... George Stevenson
Associate Ed. .... Mary Stadnyk
Bishop .... David M. O'Connell
Mng Ed. .... Mary Morrell
Mechanical Specifications: Type page 10 x 14; E - 4 cols, 2 1/4, between; A - 4 cols, 2 1/4, between; C - 6 cols, 1 1/2, between.
Equipment: Hardware — PCs; Software — InDesign
Delivery Method: Mail

NEW YORK

ALBANY

THE EVANGELIST (Thur)
40 N Main Ave, Albany, NY, 12203-1481, Albany, USA; tel (518) 453-6688; adv tel (518) 453-6696; ed tel (518) 453-6688; fax (518) 453-8448; adv fax (518) 453-8448; ed fax (518) 453-8448; e-mail christopher.ringwald@rcpa.org; adv e-mail john.salvione@rcda.org; web site www.evangelist.org
Circulation: 50,000pd, 280fr; Sworn/Estimate/Non-Audited
Advertising: Open inch rate $23.50
Established: 1926
Pub. .... Bishop Howard J. Hubbard
Mechanical Specifications: Type page 9 3/4 x 13 1/2.
Equipment; Software — QPS/QuarkXPress 5.0.

BROOKLYN

THE TABLET (Sat)
310 Prospect Park W, Brooklyn, NY, 11215-6214, Kings, USA; tel (718) 965-7333; fax (718) 965-7337; adv fax (718) 965-7338; e-mail jcaragiulo@desalesmedia.org; web site www.thetablet.org
Circulation: 41,806fr; CAC
Advertising: Open inch rate $33.13
Established: 1908
Pub. .... Bishop Nicholas DiMarzio
Assoc. Pub. .... Father Kieran E. Harrington
Ed. .... Ed Wilkinson
Adv. Sales Exec. .... Kimberly Benn
Circ. Mgr. .... James Caragiulo
Mechanical Specifications: Type page 10 1/4 x 14; E - 6 cols, 1 5/8, between; A - 6 cols, 1 5/8, between.
Equipment: Hardware — APP/Mac.

CONKLIN

THE WINDSOR STANDARD (Wed)
PO Box 208, Conklin, NY, 13748-0208, Broome, USA; tel (607) 775-0472; fax (607) 775-5863; e-mail deinstein@stny.rr.com; web site www.wecoverthetowns.com
Circulation: 1,315pd, 75fr; Sworn/Estimate/Non-Audited
Advertising: Open inch rate $4.50
Established: 1880
Group: Newspaper Publishers LLCEditions: 52-
Digital Platform - Mobile: Apple
Adv. Mgr. .... Donald Einstein
Ed. .... Elizabeth Einstein
Mechanical Specifications: PDF
Equipment: Hardware — Ma computers; Presses — none; Software — Adobe
Delivery Method: Mail
Zip Codes Served: Eastern Broome County

NEW YORK

AMERICA (Mon)
106 W 56th St, New York, NY, 10019-3866, New York, USA; tel (212) 581-4640; fax (212) 399-3596; e-mail america@americamagazine.org; web site www.americamagazine.org
Circulation: 46,000pd, 283fr; Sworn/Estimate/Non-Audited
Advertising: Open inch rate $43.00
Ed. .... Rew Christiansen
Mng. Ed. .... Robert C. Collins
Mechanical Specifications: Type page 8 1/8 x 10 1/2; E - 2 cols, 3 3/4, 1/4 between; A - 3 cols, 2 1/4, 1/4 between; C - 3 cols, 2 1/4, 1/4 between.
Equipment: Hardware — APP/Mac; Software — QPS/QuarkXPress 4.0.

CATHOLIC NEW YORK (Bi-Mthly) (Every Other Thursday, 26 issues per year.)
1011 1st Ave, Ste 1721, New York, NY, 10022-4112, New York, USA; tel (212) 688-2399; fax (212) 688-2642; e-mail cny@cny.org; adv e-mail ads@cny.org; ed e-mail cny@cny.org; web site www.cny.org
Circulation: 127,000pd,; AAM
Advertising: Open inch rate $60.60
Established: 1981
Digital Platform - Mobile: Apple, Android
Digital Platform - Tablet: Apple iOS, Android
Ed. .... John Woods
Mechanical Specifications: Type page 10.25x11; E - 6 cols; A - modular; C - 7 cols, 1 1/3, 1/12 between.
Equipment: Hardware — Mac; Software — Adobe CS InDesign
Delivery Method: Mail
Zip Codes Served: 10001-10276

THE FORWARD
45 E 33rd St, New York, NY, 10016-5336, New York, USA; tel (212) 889-8200; fax (212) 689-4255; e-mail newsdesk@forward.com; web site www.forward.com
Circulation:; Sworn/Estimate/Non-Audited
Advertising: Open inch rate $48.00
Group: Joseph Jacobs Organization
Adv. Mgr. .... Jerome Koenig
Circ. Mgr. .... Lori Weinberg
Ed. .... J.J. Goldberg
Mng. Ed. .... Wayne Hoffman
Prodn. Mgr. .... Kurt Hoffman
Mechanical Specifications: Type page 13 x 21; E - 6 cols, 2 1/16, between; A - 6 cols, 2 1/16, between; C - 6 cols, 2 1/16, between.

OGDENSBURG

NORTH COUNTRY CATHOLIC (Sun)
622 Washington St, Ogdensburg, NY, 13669-1724, Saint Lawrence, USA; tel (315) 608-7556; fax 866-314-7296; e-mail news@northcountrycatholic.org; web site www.northcountrycatholic.org
Circulation: 4,000pd, 25fr; Sworn/Estimate/Non-Audited
Advertising: $40.00/M.
Established: 1946Editions: 11-
Kilian Mary Lou
Mechanical Specifications: Type page 9 3/4 x 13; E - 5 cols, 1 7/8, between; A - 5 cols, 1 7/8, between.
Delivery Method: Mail
Zip Codes Served: 12883 through 13690

ROCHESTER

CATHOLIC COURIER (Mthly) (Weekly e-newsletter)
1150 Buffalo Rd, Rochester, NY, 14624-1823, Monroe, USA; tel (585) 529-9530; fax (585)529-9532; ed fax (585) 529-9509; e-mail info@catholiccourier.com; adv e-mail ads@catholiccourier.com; ed e-mail newsroom@catholiccourier.com; web site www.catholiccourier.com
Circulation: 104,812pd, 0fr; USPS
Advertising: Open inch rate $102.00
Established: 1889
Group: Rochester Catholic Press Association, IncEditions: 5- Monroe East, West and Central, Finger Lakes; Southern Tier
Digital Platform - Tablet: Apple iOS, Kindle Fire
GM/Editor .... Karen M. Franz
Asst. Ed................................ Jennifer Ficcaglia
Circ. Mgr................................ Donna Stubbings
President & Publisher....... Bishop Salvatore. R Matano
Graphics Mgr. .... Matt Saxon
Advertising................................ Angela Visconte
Mechanical Specifications: Type page 9.4"x 10; E - 4 cols, 2.16, 1/4 between.
Equipment: Hardware — Dell/Optiplex; Presses — MAN/Roland Geoman; Software — Adobe Creative Cloud, QuarkXPress 8-10, NewsEngin, AdWorks/AdForce, PICMan, MS Office
Delivery Method: Mail
Zip Codes Served: Generally 13021-14905 with some exceptions; specific circulation by zip code data available from circ. mgr.
Note: Issued in print first Wednesday of each month, except July and January; issued in digital form (digital.catholiccourier.com) 12x/yr.

ROOSEVELT

THE LONG ISLAND CATHOLIC (Wed)
200 W Centennial Ave, Ste 201, Roosevelt, NY, 11575-1937, Nassau, USA; tel (516) 594-1000; fax (516) 594-1092; ed e-mail editor@licatholic.org; web site www.licatholic.org
Circulation: 103,000pd, 899fr; Sworn/Estimate/Non-Audited
Advertising: Open inch rate $69.00
Established: 1962
Adv. Mgr.. Art O'Brien
Opns. Mgr. .... Mary Salegna
Mechanical Specifications: Type page 10 x 11 1/4; E - 5 cols, 2 3/8, 3/8 between; A - 5 cols, 2 3/8, 3/8 between; C - 8 cols, 1 1/8, between.
Equipment: Hardware — PCs; Presses — 3-G/486MFP; Software — Microsoft/Word, QPS/QuarkXPress 3.2, Novell.

SYRACUSE

CATHOLIC SUN (Thur)
420 Montgomery St, Syracuse, NY, 13202-2920, Onondaga, USA; tel (315) 422-8153; fax (315) 422-7549; e-mail catholicsun@yahoo.com; web site www.thecatholicsun.com
Circulation: 28,000pd, 348fr; Sworn/Estimate/Non-Audited
Advertising: Open inch rate $25.00
Pres. .... James Moynihan
Ed. in Chief................................ Katherine Long
Mechanical Specifications: Type page 10 x 14; E - 4 cols, 2 2/5, 1/8 between; A - 4 cols, 2 2/5, 1/8 between; C - 6 cols, 2, 1/8 between.
Equipment: Hardware — APP/Mac; Software — QPS/QuarkXPress.

THE CATHOLIC SUN (Thur)
424 Montgomery St, Syracuse, NY, 13202-2920, Onondaga, USA; tel (315) 422-8153; adv tel (315) 579-0001; fax (315) 422-7549; e-mail mklenz@syracusediocese.org; ed e-mail info@thecatholicsun.com; web site www.thecatholicsun.com
Circulation:; Sworn/Estimate/Non-Audited
Established: 1892
Ed. .... Katherine Long
Ad. Director................................ Mark Klenz
Mechanical Specifications: Type page 10 x 12.5
Delivery Method: Mail
Zip Codes Served: Broome, Cortland, Chenango, Madison, Oneida, Onondaga, Oswego Counties

NORTH CAROLINA

CARY

BIBLICAL RECORDER (Bi-Mthly) (Every Other Sat)
205 Convention Dr, Cary, NC, 27511-4257, Wake, USA; tel (919) 847-2127; fax (919) 467-6180; e-mail editor@BRnow.org; adv e-mail alison@BRnow.org; ed e-mail editor@brnow.org; web site www.BRnow.org
Circulation: 12,000pd, 5,000fr; Sworn/Estimate/Non-Audited
Advertising: Open inch rate $52.00
Established: 1833
Group: Baptist State Convention of North Carolina
Digital Platform - Mobile: Apple, Android, Windows
Digital Platform - Tablet: Apple iOS, Android, Windows 7
Bus. Mgr................................ Alison McKinney
Editor/President................................ Allan Blume
Mechanical Specifications: Type page 10 x 15; E - 4 cols, 2 1/3, 1/3 between; A - 4 cols, 2 1/3, 1/3 between.
Equipment: Hardware — APP/Mac Aldus; Software — Adobe/PageMaker InDesign
Delivery Method: Mail

GREENSBORO

NORTH CAROLINA CHRISTIAN ADVOCATE
PO Box 508, Greensboro, NC, 27402-0508, Guilford, USA; tel (336) 272-1196; fax (336) 271-6634; e-mail rippink@gborocollege.edu; web site www.ncadvocate.org
Circulation:; Sworn/Estimate/Non-Audited
Advertising: Open inch rate $18.75
Circ. Mgr................................ Darlene Stanley
Prodn. Mgr. .... Kevin Rippin

RALEIGH

THE NORTH CAROLINA CATHOLIC
715 Nazareth St, Raleigh, NC, 27606-2187, Wake, USA; tel (919) 821-9730; fax (919) 821-9705; ed e-mail reece@raldioc.org; web site www.nccatholics.org
Circulation:; Sworn/Estimate/Non-Audited
Established: 1946
Pub................................ Michael F. Burbidge
Adv. Mgr................................ Holly Stringer
Ed. .... Richard Reece

OHIO

CINCINNATI

CHRISTIAN STANDARD
8805 Governors Hill Dr, Ste 400, Cincinnati, OH, 45249-3319, Hamilton, USA; tel (513) 931-4050; fax (877) 867-5751; e-mail christianstd@standardpub.com; web site www.standardpub.com
Circulation:; Sworn/Estimate/Non-Audited
Established: 1866
Pub................................ Mark A. Taylor
Mng. Ed................................ Jim Nieman
Ed. .... Paul Williams
Delivery Method: Mail

THE CATHOLIC TELEGRAPH (Fri)
100 E 8th St, Cincinnati, OH, 45202-2129, Hamilton, USA; tel (513) 421-3131; fax (513) 381-2242; e-mail thempel@catholiccincinnati.org; web site www.catholiccincinnati.org/tct/curfeat1.htm
Circulation: 85,000pd, 400fr; Sworn/Estimate/Non-Audited
Advertising: Open inch rate $21.84
Pub................................ Daniel E. Pilarczyk
Adv. Mgr................................ Tim Mayer
Circ. Mgr................................ Greg Hartman
Ed. .... Tricia Hempel
Prodn. Mgr. .... Rick Barr
Steve Trosley

COLUMBUS

THE CATHOLIC TIMES (Sun)
197 E Gay St, Columbus, OH, 43215-3229, Franklin, USA; tel (614) 224-5195; fax (614) 241-2518; web site www.colsdioc.org
Circulation: 18,000pd,; Sworn/Estimate/Non-Audited
Advertising: Open inch rate $16.50
Pub................................ Frederick Campbell
Adv. Mgr................................ Deacon Steve Demers
Circ. Mgr................................ Jodie Shreddo
Ed. .... David Garick
Mechanical Specifications: Type page 10 1/3 x 12 1/2; E - 3 cols, between; A - 6 cols, between.
Equipment: Software — QPS/QuarkXPress 3.32.

TOLEDO

CATHOLIC CHRONICLE (Mthly)
1933 Spielbusch Ave, Toledo, OH, 43604-5360, Lucas, USA; tel (419) 244-6711; fax (419) 244-0468; e-mail ccnews@toledodiocese.org; adv e-mail ncooke@toledodiocese.org; web site www.catholicchronicle.org
Circulation: 500pd, 31,000fr; Sworn/Estimate/Non-Audited
Advertising: Open inch rate $64.00
Established: 1934
Adv. Sales Rep................................ Nancy Cooke
Commun. Dir................................ Sally Oberski
Ed. .... Angela Kessler
Circ. Coord................................ Rose Anne Conrad
Graphic Artist................................ Keith Tarjanyi
Staff Writer................................ Cherie Spino
Pub................................ Bishop Daniel Thomas
Mechanical Specifications: Type page 10 1/8 x 13 3/4; E - 4 cols, 2 7/16, 3/16 between; A - 6 cols, 1 9/16, 3/16 between; C - 6 cols, 1 9/16, 3/16 between.
Equipment: Hardware — APP/Mac; Software — Adobe/PageMaker, Microsoft/Word, Microsoft/Excel, Adobe/Photoshop.
Delivery Method: Mail, Racks
Zip Codes Served: 41017, 13316, 13402, 43410, 43420, 43430, 43431, 43435, 43440, 43449, 43445, 43450, 43452, 43456, 43460, 43465, 43502, 43506, 43511, 43512, 43516, 43517, 43521, 43522, 43524, 43526, 43527, 43528, 43537, 43543, 43545, 43548, 43551, 43552, 43558, 43560, 43566, 43567, 43571, 43602, 43604, 43605, 43606, 43607, 43608, 43609, 43610, 43611, 43612, 43613, 43614, 43615, 43616, 43620, 43623, 43624, 44089, 44807, 44809, 44811, 44820, 44827, 44830, 44833, 44839, 44846, 44847, 44851, 44853, 44854, 44857, 44865, 44870, 44875, 44882, 44883, 44889, 44890, 44902, 44904, 44905, 45699, 45801, 15805, 45817, 45827, 45830, 45833, 45840, 45844, 45848, 45853, 45856, 45864, 45872, 45875, 45876, 45879, 45887, 45891, 46225

OKLAHOMA

EDMOND

THE CHRISTIAN CHRONICLE (Mthly)
2801 E Memorial Rd, Edmond, OK, 73013-6474, Oklahoma, USA; tel (405) 425-5070; adv tel (405) 425-5071; ed tel (405) 425-5070; fax (405) 425-5076; adv fax (405) 425-5076; e-mail lynn.mcmillon@christianchronicle.org; adv e-mail tonya.patton@christianchronicle.org; ed e-mail erik@christianchronicle.org; web site www.christianchronicle.org.net
Circulation:; Sworn/Estimate/Non-Audited
Established: 1943
Group: Oklahoma Christian University
Delivery Method: Mail

OKLAHOMA CITY

BAPTIST MESSENGER (Thur)
3800 N May Ave, Oklahoma City, OK, 73112-6639, Oklahoma, USA; tel (405) 942-3800; adv tel (405) 942-3800 ext 4360; ed tel (405) 942-3800 ext 4361; fax (405) 942-3075; adv fax 405-942-3075; ed fax 405-942-3075; e-mail baptistmessenger@okbaptist.net; adv e-mail baptistmessenger@okbaptist.net; ed e-mail baptist messenger@okbaptist.net; web site www.baptistmessenger.com
Circulation: 55,670pd,; Sworn/Estimate/Non-Audited
Advertising: Open inch rate $63.00
Established: 1912Editions: 50-
Digital Platform - Mobile: Apple, Android
Digital Platform - Tablet: Apple iOS, Android
Assoc. Ed................................ Dana Williamson
Account Manager................................ Karen Kinnaird
Art Director................................ Ricardo Herrera
Editor................................ Brian Hobbs
Managing Editor................................ Bob Nigh
Mechanical Specifications: Type page 11 x 17.
Equipment: Hardware — APP/Mac, ECR; Presses — G/Web, G; Software — Adobe/Indesign/
Delivery Method: Mail, Racks
Zip Codes Served: 730-749; various other US zip codes

OREGON

PORTLAND

CATHOLIC SENTINEL (Tues, Other)
5536 NE Hassalo St, Portland, OR, 97213-3638, Multnomah, USA; tel (503) 281-1191; fax (503) 460-5496; e-mail sentinel@ocp.org; web site www.sentinel.org
Circulation: 3,000pd, 25,000fr; Sworn/Estimate/Non-Audited
Advertising: Open inch rate $35.00Editions: 1- 1 total El Centinela (Spanish) (7,500);
Digital Platform - Mobile: Apple, Android, Windows
Pub................................ John Limb
Managing editor................................ Ed Langlois
Mechanical Specifications: Type page 10 5/16 x 15.
Equipment: Hardware — Macbook Pro; Software — Indesign

PENNSYLVANIA

GREENSBURG

THE CATHOLIC ACCENT (Every Other Thur)
725 E Pittsburgh St, Greensburg, PA, 15601-2660, Westmoreland, USA; tel (724) 834-4010; fax (724) 836-5650; e-mail news@dioceseofgreensburg.org; web site www.dioceseofgreensburg.org
Circulation: 46,500pd, 924fr; Sworn/Estimate/Non-Audited
Advertising: Open inch rate $16.50
Established: 1961
Chief Executive Officer and PublisherLawrence E. Brandt
Adv. Mgr. .... Rose Govi
Circulation Coordinator .... Nancy Balfe
Editor, The Catholic Accent ... Jerome M. Zufelt
Assistant Editor, The Catholic Accent Elizabeth Fazzini
Production Coordinator .... Valerie Rodell
Mechanical Specifications: Type page 10 1/4 x 12 3/4; A - 5 cols, 1 7/8, 1/8 between.
Equipment: Hardware — PC; Presses — G; Software — InDesign CS4
Delivery Method: Mail
Zip Codes Served: 4 counties of the diocese (multiple)

PITTSBURGH

PITTSBURGH CATHOLIC (Fri)
135 1st Ave, Ste 200, Pittsburgh, PA, 15222-1529, Allegheny, USA; tel (412) 471-1252; fax (412) 471-4228; e-mail info@pittsburghcatholic.org; adv e-mail jconnolly@pittsburghcatholic.org; ed e-mail wcone@pittsburghcatholic.org; web site www.pittsburghcatholic.com
Circulation: 96,000pd, 7,687fr; Sworn/Estimate/Non-Audited
Advertising: Open inch rate $38.05
Established: 1844Editions: 52-
Dir. of Adv. .... John Connolly
Circ. Mgr. .... Peggy Zezza
Ed. .... William Cone
Prodn. Mgr. .... Carmella Weismantle
Mechanical Specifications: Type page 10.625 x 21; E - 5 cols, 2.025; A - 6 cols, 1.667; C -8 cols, 1.255.
Equipment: Hardware — APP/Mac; Software — Baseview.
Delivery Method: Mail

RHODE ISLAND

PROVIDENCE

RHODE ISLAND CATHOLIC (Thur)
1 Cathedral Sq, Providence, RI, 02903-3601, Providence, USA; tel (401) 272-1010; adv tel (401) 272-1010; ed tel (401) 272-1010; fax (401) 421-8418; adv fax (401) 421-8418; ed fax (401) 421-8418; e-mail editor@thericatholic.com; adv e-mail srichard@thericatholic.com; ed e-mail rsnizek@thericatholic.com; web site www.thericatholic.com
Circulation: 27,000pd, 422fr; Sworn/Estimate/Non-Audited
Advertising: Open inch rate $18.00
Established: 1875Editions: 2- 2 total Rhode Island Catholic (English); Rhode Island Catholic en Espanol (4,500);
Pub. .... Rev. Thomas J. Tobin
Executive Editor .... Rick Snizek
Display Advertising Manager.... Richard Lafond
Assistant Editor/Production Manager ...... Laura Kilgus
Mechanical Specifications: Type page 10 x 13; E - 5 cols, 1 11/12, 1/6 between; A - 5 cols, 1 11/12, 1/6 between; C - 5 cols, 1 11/12, 1/6 between.
Equipment: Hardware — APP/Mac; Software — Baseview/Ad Manager Pro.
Delivery Method: Mail, Newsstand
Zip Codes Served: Providence County

SOUTH CAROLINA

CHARLESTON

THE CATHOLIC MISCELLANY (Thur)
119 Broad St, Charleston, SC, 29401-2435, Charleston, USA; tel (843) 724-8375; fax (843) 724-8368; ed e-mail editor@catholic-doc.org; web site www.catholic-doc.org
Circulation: 29,000pd, 247fr; Sworn/Estimate/Non-Audited
Advertising: Open inch rate $10.00
Ed. .... Deirdre C. Mays
Circ./Adv. Coord. .... Karla Consroe
Mechanical Specifications: Type page 10 x 14.
Equipment; Software — QPS/QuarkXPress 4.0.

COLUMBIA

SOUTH CAROLINA UNITED METHODIST ADVOCATE (Mthly)
4908 Colonial Dr, Ste 207, Columbia, SC, 29203-6080, Richland, USA; tel (803) 786-9486; fax (803) 735-8168; e-mail advocate@umcsc.org; web site www.advocatesc.org
Circulation: 10,000pd, 1,000fr; Sworn/Estimate/Non-Audited
Advertising: Open inch rate $19.00
Established: 1836
Circ. Mgr. .... Allison Trussell
Editor .... Jessica Connor
Ed. .... Emily Cooper
Mechanical Specifications: Type page 11 1/2 x 17 1/2; C - 3 cols, 3 1/4, 1/6 between.
Equipment: Hardware — Pentium, APP/Mac; Software — QPS/QuarkXPress 4.11.

GREENVILLE

THE BAPTIST COURIER (Every Other Thur)
100 Manly St, Greenville, SC, 29601-3025, Greenville, USA; tel (864) 232-8736; fax (864) 232-8488; e-mail news@baptistcourier.com; web site www.baptistcourier.com
Circulation: 75,000pd, 2,000fr; Sworn/Estimate/Non-Audited
Advertising: Open inch rate $75.00
Bus. Mgr. .... Debbie Grooms
Mng. Ed. .... Butch Blame
Ed. .... Don Kirkland

TENNESSEE

MEMPHIS

THE WEST TENNESSEE CATHOLIC (Wed, Fri)
5825 Shelby Oaks Dr, Catholic Center, Memphis, TN, 38134-7316, Shelby, USA; tel (901) 373-1231; adv tel (901) 373-1209; fax (901) 373-1269; e-mail fwt.editor@cc.cdom.org; adv e-mail lorena.monge@cc.cdom.org; ed e-mail fwt.editor@cc.cdom.org; web site www.cdom.org
Circulation: 0pd, 1,000fr; Sworn/Estimate/Non-Audited
Established: 1972
Group: Catholic Diocese of Memphis
Digital Platform - Mobile: Apple, Android, Windows, Blackberry
Digital Platform - Tablet: Apple iOS, Android, Windows 7, Blackberry Tablet OS, Kindle, Nook, Kindle Fire
Pub. .... Martin D. Bishop Holley
Editor .... Suzanne Aviles
Ads and subscriptions .... Lorena Monge
Note: Electronic publication only

NASHVILLE

TENNESSEE REGISTER
2400 21st Ave S, Nashville, TN, 37212-5302, Davidson, USA; tel (615)783-0750; fax (615) 783-0285; e-mail tnregister@dioceseofnashville.com; web site www.dioceseofnashville.com
Circulation:; Sworn/Estimate/Non-Audited
Advertising: Open inch rate $8.75
Adv. Mgr. .... Byron Warner
Ed. in Chief .... Rick Musacchio
Mng. Ed. .... Andy Telli
Prodn. Mgr. .... Debbie Lane
Mechanical Specifications: Type page 10 x 14; E - 5 cols, 1 11/12, 1/6 between; A - 4 cols, 2 1/3, 1/6 between; C - 4 cols, 2 1/3, 1/6 between.
Equipment: Hardware — APP/Power Mac 7500/100, APP/Mac IIci, APP/Mac SE 30, APP/PowerBook 145B, LaserMaster 1200 dpi, Mk/Scanner 600zs, RasterOps/20; Software — QPS/QuarkXPress 4.04, Adobe/Photoshop 5.0.

THE UNITED METHODIST REPORTER (Online only...perpetually updated)
1300 Old Hickory Blvd, Nashville, TN, 37207-1417, Davidson, USA; tel (615) 673-4236; e-mail news@circuitwritermedia.com; adv e-mail cherrie@circuitwritermedia.com; ed e-mail news@circuitwritermedia.com; web site www.unitedmethodistreporter.org
Circulation:; Sworn/Estimate/Non-Audited
Established: 1847
Group: UMR Communications
CircuitWriter Media LLC
Digital Platform - Mobile: Apple, Android, Windows
Digital Platform - Tablet: Apple iOS, Android, Windows 7
Executive Editor .... Jay Vorhees
Zip Codes Served: Nationwide

TEXAS

CORPUS CHRISTI

SOUTH TEXAS CATHOLIC (2 x Mthly)
620 Lipan St, Corpus Christi, TX, 78401-2434, Nueces, USA; tel (361) 882-6191; adv tel (361) 693-6605; ed tel (361) 693-6609; fax (361) 693-6701; adv fax (361) 693-6701; ed fax (361) 693-6701; e-mail stc@dicesecc.org; web site www.southtexascatholic.com
Circulation: 43,000pd,; Sworn/Estimate/Non-Audited
Advertising: Varies
Associate Editor .... Mary Cottingham
Bishop .... Wm. Michael Mulvey
Editor .... Alfredo Cardenas
Administrative Assistant .... Adel Rivera
Theological Consultant... Father Joseph Lopez
Delivery Method: Mail

DALLAS

THE TEXAS CATHOLIC (Every other Fri)
3725 Blackburn St, Dallas, TX, 75219-4404, Dallas, USA; tel (214) 528-8792; fax (214) 528-3411; e-mail texascatholic@msn.com; web site www.texascatholic.com
Circulation: 54,000pd, 857fr; Sworn/Estimate/Non-Audited
Advertising: Open inch rate $37.00
Pub. .... Kevin Farrell
Adv. Mgr. .... Tony Ramirez
Circ. Mgr. .... Rosemary Allen
Exec. Ed. .... David Sedeno
Mechanical Specifications: Type page 10 1/4 x 14; E - 4 cols, 2 3/8, between; A - 5 cols, 1 7/8, between; C - 5 cols, 1 7/8, between.

FORT WORTH

NORTH TEXAS CATHOLIC (every other month)
800 W Loop 820 S, Fort Worth, TX, 76108-2936, Tarrant, USA; tel (817) 560-3300; fax (817) 244-8839; e-mail jrusseau@fwdioc.org; adv e-mail jrusseau@fwdioc.org; ed e-mail jhensley@fwdioc.org; web site www.fwdioc.org
Circulation: 27,000pd, 82,000fr; Sworn/Estimate/Non-Audited
Advertising: Open inch rate $48.00
Adv. Mgr. .... Judy Russeau
Ed .... Jeff Hensley
Mechanical Specifications: Type page 7.375 x 9.5; E - 4 cols, 1.625 1/6 between; A - 4 cols, 1.625, 1/6 between; C - 4 cols, 1.625, 1/6 between.
Equipment: Hardware — 4-APP/Mac G4; Software — Adobe/CS4 Indesign Adobe/Photoshop 6.0.
Delivery Method: Mail
Zip Codes Served: 76108

HOUSTON

THE TEXAS CATHOLIC HERALD (2 x Mthly)
1700 San Jacinto St, Houston, TX, 77002-8216, Harris, USA; tel (713) 659-5461; fax (713) 659-3444; e-mail tch@archgh.org; web site www.texascatholicherald.org
Circulation: 72,000pd, 1,680fr; Sworn/Estimate/Non-Audited
Advertising: Open inch rate $38.00
Pub. .... Daniel DiNardo
Mechanical Specifications: Type page 9 3/4 x 12.
Equipment: Hardware — APP/Mac; Software — Adobe/PageMaker 6.0.
Zip Codes Served: 77002

PLANO

BAPTIST STANDARD (Every other Mon)
7161 Bishop Rd, Ste 200, Plano, TX, 75024-3646, Collin, USA; tel (214) 630-4571; fax (214) 638-8535; e-mail bapstand@baptiststandard.com; web site www.baptiststandard.com
Circulation: 90,000pd, 2,104fr; Sworn/Estimate/Non-Audited
Advertising: Open inch rate $65.00
Established: 1888
Bus. Mgr. .... Kayla Andrews
Bus. Mgr. .... Lance Freeman
Ed. .... Marv Knox
Mng. Ed. .... Ken Camp
Mechanical Specifications: Type page 9 13/16 x 15; A - 5 cols, between; C - 2 cols, 1 7/8, 1/4 between.

SAN ANTONIO

TODAY'S CATHOLIC (Every other Fri)
2718 W Woodlawn Ave, San Antonio, TX, 78228-5124, Bexar, USA; tel (210) 734-2620; fax (210) 734-2939; e-mail tcpaper@archdiosa.org; web site www.satodayscatholic.org
Circulation: 26,000pd, 467fr; Sworn/Estimate/Non-Audited
Advertising: Open inch rate $15.00
Publisher .... Kevin Rhoades
Editor .... Jodi Martin

Page Designer ....Francis Hogan
News Specialist ....Mark Weber
Social Media Manager........Emily Mae Schmid
Advertising Sales ....Jackie Parker
Accounting/Circulation..................Geoff Frank
Business Mgr.................. Stephanie A. Patka
Mechanical Specifications: Type page 10 1/2 x 13; E - 5 cols, 2, 1/4 between; A - 5 cols, 2, 1/4 between.
Equipment: Hardware — APP/Mac, Optiplex; Presses — 5-HI; Software — Micro Photoeditor, Adobe/Acrobat 4.1, Windows/98, Microsoft Office/2001, Microsoft Word/2000, Adobe/PageMaker 6.5, Adobe/Illustrator 7.0, Adobe/Photoshop 5.0.

TYLER

CATHOLIC EAST TEXAS (Mthly) (online twice monthly)
1015 E Southeast Loop 323, Tyler, TX, 75701-9656, Smith, USA; tel (903) 534-1077; ed tel (903) 266-2144; fax (903) 534-1370; e-mail editorcet3@excite.com; ed e-mail editorcet3@excite.com; web site www.dioceseoftyler.org
Circulation: 17,000pd, 400fr; Sworn/Estimate/Non-Audited
Advertising: Open inch rate $10.00
Established: 1987Editions: 27-
Ed. ....Jim D'Avignon
Mechanical Specifications: Type page 10 x 14 1/4; E - 4 cols, 2 3/8, 1/6 between; A - 5 cols, 1 7/8, 1/6 between; C - 5 cols, 1 7/8, 1/6 between.
Equipment; Software — Adobe Creative Suite – indesign, photoshop, illustrator,
Delivery Method: Mail

UTAH

SALT LAKE CITY

INTERMOUNTAIN CATHOLIC (Fri)
27 C St, Salt Lake City, UT, 84103-2302, Salt Lake, USA; tel (801) 328-8641; fax (801) 537-1667; e-mail icnews@icnp.com; adv e-mail advertising@icatholic.org; web site www.icatholic.org
Circulation: 14,500pd, 24fr; Sworn/Estimate/Non-Audited
Advertising: Open inch rate $20.00
Pub....................Bishop John Charles Wester
Circ. Mgr.................... Arthur Heredia
Ed. ....Marie Mischel
Assoc. Ed....................Christine Young
Mechanical Specifications: Type page 10 1/4 x 14; E - 6 cols, 2 1/3, 1/6 between; A - 6 cols, 1 3/4, between; C - 6 cols, 1 5/8, 1/6 between.
Equipment: Hardware — 2-APP/Mac G4.
Zip Codes Served: All Utah Zip codes

VIRGINIA

ARLINGTON

ARLINGTON CATHOLIC HERALD (Thur)
200 N Glebe Rd, Ste 600, Arlington, VA, 22203-3763, Arlington, USA; tel (703) 841-2590; adv tel (703) 841-2598; fax (703) 524-2782; e-mail editorial@catholicherald.com; adv e-mail csalinas@catholicherald.com; web site www.catholicherald.com
Circulation: 66,500pd,; USPS
Advertising: Open inch rate $42.00
Established: 1976
Digital Platform - Mobile: Windows
Adv. Mgr....................Carlos Salinas
Circ. Mgr....................Joe Miller
Ed. ....Michael Flach
Mng. Ed....................Ann Augherton
Prodn. Coord....................Stacy Rausch
Rev. Michael F. Burbidge
Delivery Method: Mail, Racks

RICHMOND

THE PRESBYTERIAN OUTLOOK (Mon) (Published 26 times per year.)
1 N 5th St, Ste 500, Richmond, VA, 23219-2231, Richmond City, USA; tel (804) 359-8442; fax (804) 353-6369; adv fax (804) 353-6369; adv e-mail gwhipple@pres-outlook.org; ed e-mail jhaberer@pres-outlook.org; web site www.pres-outlook.org
Circulation: 7,434pd, 876fr; USPS
Advertising: Call for rates
Established: 1819Editions: The Presbyterian Outlook
Bus. Mgr.................... Patricia Gresham
Adv. Mgr.................... George Whipple
Prodn. Mgr. ....Stan Bailey
Editor/CEO ....Jack Haberer
Mechanical Specifications: Type page 7 x 9 3/4; E - 3 cols, 2, 1/4 between; A - 3 cols, 2, 1/4 between; C - 3 cols, 2, 1/4 between.
Equipment: Hardware — AG/Studio Scan IIsi, APP/Mac G3; Software — Adobe/Illustrator 8.0, Adobe/PageMaker 6.51, Adobe/Photoshop 5.5, QPS/QuarkXPress 4.1.
Delivery Method: Mail
Zip Codes Served: We serve the entire U.S., Canada, and clergy,missionary, chaplains, serving in foreign countries.

THE RELIGIOUS HERALD (Thur)
2828 Emerywood Pkwy, Richmond, VA, 23294-3718, Henrico, USA; tel (804) 672-1973; fax (804) 672-8323; e-mail rdilday@religiousherald.org; web site www.religiousherald.org
Circulation: 21,000pd,; Sworn/Estimate/Non-Audited
Advertising: Open inch rate $25.00
Established: 1808
Adv. Mgr....................Barbara Francis
Ed. .... James White

STAFFORD

ALL NEWS (Bi-Mthly)
1179 Courthouse Rd, Stafford, VA, 22554-7106, Stafford, USA
Group: American Life League
Editor .... Robert Gasper
Contributing Author....................Michael Hichborn
Delivery Method: Mail
Zip Codes Served: all

WISCONSIN

LA CROSSE

THE CATHOLIC TIMES (Every Other Thur)
3710 East Ave S, La Crosse, WI, 54601-7215, La Crosse, USA; tel (608) 788-1524; fax (608) 788-0932; e-mail catholictimes@dioceseoflacrosse.com
Circulation: 31,000pd, 193fr; Sworn/Estimate/Non-Audited
Circ. Mgr.................... Pamela Willer
Editor ....Stanton Gould
Associate Editor....................Denis Downey
Graphic Designer.................... Danelle Bjornson
Mechanical Specifications: Type page 10 x 13; E - 5 cols, 1 7/8, 1/6 between; A - 5 cols, 1 7/8, 1/6 between.
Equipment: Hardware — APP/Mac; Software — Adobe/Photoshop 6.0, QPS/QuarkXPress 4.1, Adobe/Acrobat 4.0.

MADISON

CATHOLIC HERALD NEWSPAPER (Thur)
702 S High Point Rd, Madison, WI, 53719-4925, Dane, USA; tel (608) 821-3070; fax (608) 821-3071; e-mail info@madisoncatholicherald.org; web site www.madisoncatholicherald.org
Circulation: 26,000pd,; Sworn/Estimate/Non-Audited
Advertising: Open inch rate $18.50
Established: 1948
Pub.................... Robert Morlino
Adv. Mgr. ....Steve Hefty
Ed. .... Mary Uhler
Assoc. Ed....................Pamela Payne
Equipment: Hardware — APP/Mac; Software — QPS/QuarkXPress 4.0, Adobe/Acrobat 4.0.

SAINT FRANCIS

CATHOLIC HERALD (Thur) (Weekly, 44 times per year)
3501 S Lake Dr, Saint Francis, WI, 53235-0900, Milwaukee, USA; tel (414) 769-3500; fax (414) 769-3468; e-mail chnonline@archmil.org; web site www.chnonline.org
Circulation: 15,000pd,; Sworn/Estimate/Non-Audited
Advertising: Open inch rate $33.10
Group: Milwaukee Catholic Press Apstolate
Gen. Mgr.................... Brian Olszewski
Maryangela Layman Roman
Mechanical Specifications: Type page 10 1/4 x 12 1/2; E - 5 cols, 1 7/8, between; A - 5 cols, 1 7/8, between; C - 7 cols, 1 7/16, between.
Equipment: Hardware — APP/Mac.
Delivery Method: Mail

SUPERIOR

CATHOLIC HERALD (Thur)
1201 Hughitt Ave, Superior, WI, 54880-1631, Douglas, USA; tel (715) 392-8268; fax (715) 392-8656; e-mail editor@catholicherald.org; web site www.catholicherald.org
Circulation: 18,000pd,; Sworn/Estimate/Non-Audited
Publisher....................Peter F. Christensen
Mechanical Specifications: Type page 10 1/4 x 12 1/2; E - 5 cols, 1 7/8, between; A - 5 cols, 1 7/8, between; C - 7 cols, 1 1/2, between.
Equipment: Hardware — APP/Mac.
Delivery Method: Mail

ALTERNATIVE NEWSPAPERS IN CANADA

ALBERTA

CALGARY

FAST FORWARD WEEKLY (Thur)
1204 20 Ave SE, Calgary, AB, T2G 1M8, Canada; tel (403) 244-2235; fax (403) 244-1431; e-mail info@ffwd.greatwest.ca; adv e-mail advertising@ffwd.greatwest.ca; web site www.ffwdweekly.com
Circulation: 23,049fr; Sworn/Estimate/Non-Audited
Established: 1995
Delivery Method: Racks
Postal Codes Served: T1L, T1W, T1Y, T2A, T2B, T2C, T2E, T2G, T2H, T2J, T2K, T2L, T2M, T2N, T2P, T2R, T2S, T2T, T2V, T2W, T2X, T2Y, T2Z, T3A, T3B, T3C, T3E, T3G, T3H, T3J, T3K, T4R, T5J, T5K, T6E

EDMONTON

VUE WEEKLY
Suite 200-11230 119 St NW, Edmonton, AB, T5G 2X3, Canada; tel (780) 426-1996; fax (780) 426-2889; web site www.vueweekly.com

BRITISH COLUMBIA

VICTORIA

MONDAY MAGAZINE (Mthly)
818 Broughton St., Victoria, BC, V8W 1E4, Canada, Canada; tel (250) 480-3251; ed tel (250) 480-3247; fax (250) 386-2624; adv e-mail janet@mondaymag.com; ed e-mail editorial@mondaymag.com; web site www.mondaymag.com
Circulation: 18,000fr; Sworn/Estimate/Non-Audited
Advertising: Open inch rate $16.00
Established: 1975
Group: Black Press Group Ltd.Kyle Slavin
Janet Gairdner
Ruby Della-Siega
Delivery Method: Racks
Postal Codes Served: V8V

NOVA SCOTIA

HALIFAX

THE COAST (Thur)
2309 Maynard Street, Halifax, NS, B3K 3T8, Nova Scotia (NS), Canada; tel (902) 422-6278; fax (902) 425-0013; e-mail audram@thecoast.ca; adv e-mail sales@thecoast.

ca; ed e-mail news@thecoast.ca; web site https://thecoast.ca
Circulation: 22,140fr; Sworn/Estimate/Non-Audited
Established: 1993
Group: Coast Publishing Ltd.
Ed .... Kyle Shaw
Delivery Method: Newsstand, Racks

ONTARIO

TORONTO

BAYVIEW POST
(Mthly)
30 Lesmill Road, Toronto, ON, M3B 2T6, Canada; tel (416) 250-7979; fax (416) 250-1737; adv e-mail advertising@postcity.com; ed e-mail concerns@postcity.com; web site www.postcity.com
Circulation: 24,516fr; VAC
Publisher....................................Lorne London

NORTH TORONTO POST
(Mthly)
30 Lesmill Road, Toronto, ON, M3B 2T6, Canada; tel (416) 250-7979; fax (416) 250-1737; adv e-mail advertising@postcity.com; ed e-mail concerns@postcity.com; web site www.postcity.com
Circulation: 29,392fr; VAC
Publisher....................................Lorne London

NORTH YORK POST
(Mthly)
30 Lesmill Road, Toronto, ON, M3B 2T6, Canada; tel (416) 250-7979; fax (416) 250-1737; adv e-mail advertising@postcity.com; ed e-mail concerns@postcity.com; web site www.postcity.com
Circulation: 24,491fr; VAC
Publisher....................................Lorne London

NOW
(Thur)
189 Church St., Toronto, ON, M5B 1Y7, Canada; tel (416) 364-1300; fax (416) 364-1166; e-mail news@nowtoronto.com; web site www.nowtoronto.com
Circulation: 7pd, 89,951fr; VAC
Established: 1981
Group: C-VILLE Holdings LLC
Pub... Michael Hollett
Ed. .... Alice Klein
Sr. News Ed. ....Ellie Kirzner
Prodn. Mgr. .... Greg Lockhart
Mechanical Specifications: Type page 9 13/16 x 11 1/4; E - 5 cols, 1 13/16, 3/16 between; A - 5 cols, 1 13/16, 3/16 between; C - 8 cols, 1 1/6, 1/8 between.

RICHMOND HILL POST
(Mthly)
30 Lesmill Road, Toronto, ON, M3B 2T6, Canada; tel (416) 250-7979; fax (416) 250-1737; adv e-mail advertising@postcity.com; ed e-mail concerns@postcity.com; web site www.postcity.com
Circulation: 24,970fr; VAC
Publisher....................................Lorne London

THORNHILL POST
(Mthly)
30 Lesmill Road, Toronto, ON, M3B 2T6, Canada; tel (416) 250-7979; fax (416) 250-1737; adv e-mail advertising@postcity.com; ed e-mail concerns@postcity.com; web site www.postcity.com
Circulation: 24,591fr; VAC
Publisher....................................Lorne London

VILLAGE POST
(Mthly)
30 Lesmill Road, Toronto, ON, M3B 2T6, Canada; tel (416) 250-7979; fax (416) 250-1737; adv e-mail advertising@postcity.com; ed e-mail concerns@postcity.com; web site www.postcity.com
Circulation: 24,620fr; VAC
Publisher....................................Lorne London

QUEBEC

MONTREAL

HOUR
(Thur)
355 St. Catherine W., 7th Fl., Montreal, QC, H3B 1A5, Canada; tel (514) 848-0777; fax (514) 848-9004; e-mail listings@hour.ca; web site www.hour.ca
Circulation: 6pd, 51,700fr; VAC
Pub... Pierre Paquet
Circ. Mgr.................................. Hugues Mailhot
Ed. in Chief ....Jamie O'Meara

LE JOURNAL VOIR
(Thur)
355 St. Catherine W., 7th Fl., Montreal, QC, H3B 1A5, Canada; tel (514) 848-0805; fax (514) 848-9004; e-mail courier@voir.ca; web site www.voir.ca
Circulation: 37,292fr; VAC
Advertising: Open inch rate $3.28
Adv. Mgr. .... Pierre Paquet

ETHNIC NEWSPAPERS IN CANADA

ARABIC

MONTREAL

L'AVENIR/AL-MOUSTAKBAL
(Tues)
1305 Rue Mazurette, Office Ste. 206, Montreal, QC, H4N 1G8, Canada; tel (514) 334-0909; fax (514) 332-5419; e-mail journal@almustakbal.com; web site www.almustakbal.com
Ethnicity: Arabic
Circulation: 27,875pd,; Sworn/Estimate/Non-Audited
Pub... Joseph Nakhle
Ed. .... Kamal Rib
Mng. Ed...Moe Attrach
Prodn. Mgr. .... Mary Bitar
Mechanical Specifications: Type page 17 x 11; E - 7 cols, 1 5/16, between.
Equipment: Hardware — PC.

TORONTO

AKBAR EL-ARAB EL-DAWLAH (2 x Mthly)
368 Queen St. E., Toronto, ON, M5A 1T1, Canada; tel (416) 362-0304; adv tel (416) 362-0307; fax (416) 861-0238; e-mail arabnews@yahoo.com; web site www.arabnews.ca
Ethnicity: Arabic
Circulation: 5,900fr; Sworn/Estimate/Non-Audited
Advertising: Open inch rate $1.35
Ed. ....Salah Allam
Ed. ....Ammar Shabban
Mng. Ed.. Emad Nafeh
Mechanical Specifications: Type page 14 1/2 x 15 1/2; E - 8 cols, 1 7/8, 1/4 between.

ARC ARABIC JOURNAL (2 x Mthly)
368 Queen St. E., Toronto, ON, M5A 1T1, Canada; tel (416) 362-0304; fax (416) 861-0238; e-mail allam@idirect.com
Ethnicity: Arabic
Circulation: 6,000fr; Sworn/Estimate/Non-Audited
Advertising: Open inch rate $1.20
Gen. Mgr. .... I. Salamah
Adv. Mgr... Sami Zubi
Ed. .... Emad Nafed

CANADA & ARAB WORLD (2 x Mthly)
368 Queen St. E., Toronto, ON, M5A 1T1, Canada; tel (416) 362-0304; fax (416) 861-0238; e-mail allam@idirect.com
Ethnicity: Arabic
Circulation: 6,000fr; Sworn/Estimate/Non-Audited
Advertising: Open inch rate $1.36
Pub...Salah Allam
Gen. Mgr. .... I. Salama

DALIL AL ARAB (2 x Mthly)
368 Queen St. E., Toronto, ON, M5A 1T1, Canada; tel (416) 362-0304; fax (416) 861-0238; e-mail info@arabnews.ca; ed e-mail arabnews@yahoo.com; web site www.arabnews.ca
Ethnicity: Arabic
Circulation: 6,000fr; Sworn/Estimate/Non-Audited
Advertising: Open inch rate $1.25
Co Pub... S. Allam
Adv. Mgr... Sami Zubi
Ed. .... F. Ahmed

WILLOWDALE

AL-HILAL (2 x Mthly)
338 Hollyberry Trail, Willowdale, ON, M2H 2P6, Canada; tel (416) 493-4374; fax (416) 493-4374; e-mail lowaisi@rogers.com
Ethnicity: Arabic
Circulation:; Sworn/Estimate/Non-Audited
Advertising: Open inch rate $1.00
Pub.. L. Owaisi
Adv. Mgr... A. Raza
Ed. ....Farida Abdullah
Mechanical Specifications: Type page 9 x 13; E - 5 cols, 1 7/8, between; A - 5 cols, 1 7/8, between.
Equipment: Hardware — IBM; Software — Adobe/PageMaker 4.0, Adobe/Illustrator, Microsoft.

BANGLADESHI

REGINA

THE WEEKLY JOGAJOG
(Thur)
109-2223 Victoria Ave., Regina, SK, S4N 7L2, Canada; tel (306) 999-3077; e-mail info@thejogajog.com; web site www.thejogajog.com
Ethnicity: Bangladeshi
Circulation: 9,267pd,; CMCA
Chief Editor.............................Rafique Bhuiyan

BLACK & CARIBBEAN

TORONTO

SHARE
(Thur)
658 Vaughan Rd., Toronto, ON, M6E 2Y5, Canada; tel (416) 656-3400; fax (416) 656-3711; e-mail share@interlog.com; web site www.sharenews.com
Ethnicity: Black & Caribbean
Circulation: 32,400fr; Sworn/Estimate/Non-Audited
Advertising: Open inch rate $2.58
Established: 1978
Pub.. Arnold Auguste
Delivery Method: Carrier, Racks

CANADIAN

SAINT CATHARINE'S

CHRISTIAN COURIER
(Mon, Bi-Mthly) (second and fourth Mondays of the month)
5 Joanna Dr., Saint Catharine's, ON, L2N 1V1, Niagara, Canada; tel (905) 937-3314; e-mail admin@christiancourier.ca; adv e-mail ads@christiancourier.ca; ed e-mail editor@christiancourier.ca; web site www.christiancourier.ca
Ethnicity: Canadian
Circulation: 2,100pd, 70fr; Sworn/Estimate/Non-Audited
Advertising: Open inch rate $8.00
Established: 1945
News Ed. ....Angela Reitsma-Bick
Mechanical Specifications: Type page 10 1/4 x 12 .
Delivery Method: Mail
Postal Codes Served: all

CHINESE

TORONTO

DA ZHONG BAO
(Tues, Fri, Sat)
50 Weybright Ct., Unit 11, Toronto, ON, M1S 5A8, Canada; tel (416) 504-0761; fax (416) 504-4928; e-mail cng@chinesenewsgroup.com; web site www.chinesenewsgroup.com
Ethnicity: Chinese
Circulation: 12,000fr; Sworn/Estimate/Non-Audited
Advertising: Open inch rate $1.68
Prodn. Mgr. .... Jack Jia
Mechanical Specifications: Type page 10 x 13 1/2.

SING TAO DAILY
(Mon, Tues, Wed, Thur, Fri, Sat, Sun)
417 Dundas St. W., Toronto, ON, M5T 1G6, Canada; tel (416) 861-8168; adv tel (416) 861-8168; ed tel (905) 754-1515; fax (416) 599-6668; adv fax (905) 752-3888; ed fax (905) 752-0133; e-mail admin@singtao.ca; adv e-mail jyuen@singtao.ca; ed e-mail tips@singtao.ca; web site www.singtao.ca
Ethnicity: Chinese
Established: 1978
Digital Platform - Mobile: Apple, Android, Windows
Digital Platform - Tablet: Apple iOS, Android, Windows 7
President and CEO.......................Louis Cheng
Delivery Method: Newsstand, Carrier

CZECH/SLOVAK

NOVY DOMOV (New Homeland)
(Other) (every 3 rd week)
450 Scarborough Golf Club Rd., Toronto, ON, M1G 1H1, Canada; tel (416) 439-4354; adv tel (416) 439-4354; ed tel (416) 439-4354; e-mail office@masaryktown.ca; adv e-mail vera.toronto@gmail.com; ed e-mail office@masaryktown.ca; web site www.masaryktown.ca
Ethnicity: Czech/Slovak
Circulation: 560pd, 200fr; Sworn/Estimate/Non-Audited
Advertising: Open inch rate $4.00
Established: 1946
Digital Platform - Mobile: Windows
Digital Platform - Tablet: Windows 7
Editor......................................Vera Kohoutova
Equipment: Hardware — PC; Software — Adobe/InDesign
Delivery Method: Mail, Racks
Postal Codes Served:
Canada, USA

SATELLITE 1416
(Thur) (One in month)
365 St. Clarence Ave., Toronto, ON, M6H 3W2, Ontario, Canada; tel (416) 530-4222; e-mail abe@satellite1-416.com; web site www.satellite1-416.com
Ethnicity: Czech/Slovak
Circulation: 300pd, 300fr; Sworn/Estimate/Non-Audited
Advertising: Open inch rate $1.65
Established: 1991
Digital Platform - Mobile: Apple
Pub...Ales Brezina
Equipment: Hardware — APP/Mac.; Software — Adobe InDesign
Delivery Method: Mail
Postal Codes Served: M6H 4E2

DUTCH

PENTICTON

MAANDBLAD DE KRANT
(Mthly)
457 Ellis Street, Penticton, BC, V2A 4M1, British Columbia, Canada; tel (250) 492-3002; e-mail info@mokeham.com; adv e-mail sales@mokeham.com; ed e-mail editor@dekrant.ca; web site www.mokeham.com
Ethnicity: Dutch
Circulation: 4,937pd, 186fr; CMCA
Advertising: Open inch rate $.85
Group: Mokeham Publishing
Digital Platform - Mobile: Apple, AndroidTom Bijvoet
Mechanical Specifications: Type page 10 1/4 x 15 1/2; E - 4 cols, 2 1/3, between.
Delivery Method: Mail, Newsstand
Postal Codes Served: All

FILIPINO

TORONTO

PHILIPPINE REPORTER (2 x Mthly)
807 Queen St. E., 1st Fl., Toronto, ON, M4M 1H8, Canada; tel (416) 461-8694; fax (416) 461-7399; e-mail editor@philreporter.com; web site www.philippinereporter.com
Ethnicity: Filipino
Circulation: 7,700pd, 300fr; Sworn/Estimate/Non-Audited
Advertising: Open inch rate $.52
Ed...Hermie Garcia
Mechanical Specifications: Type page 10 1/2 x 15 3/8; E - 5 cols, 2, between; A - 5 cols, 2, between.

GERMAN

STEINBACH

MENNONITISCHE POST
(Fri)
383 Main St., Steinbach, MB, R5G 1Z4, Canada; tel (204) 326-6790; fax (204) 326-6302; e-mail office@mennpost.org; ed e-mail editor@mennpost.org
Ethnicity: German
Circulation: 7,700pd, 300fr; Sworn/Estimate/Non-Audited
Advertising: Open inch rate $6.50
Adv. Mgr.......................................Anne Froese
Mng. Ed.............................Kennert Giesbrecht
Mechanical Specifications: Type page 10 1/4 x 15 1/2.
Equipment: Hardware — IBM; Software — WordPerfect, Adobe/PageMaker.

TORONTO

DEUTSCHE PRESSE
(Wed)
87 Judge Rd., Ste. 212, Toronto, ON, M8Z 5B3, Canada; tel (416) 595-9714; fax (416) 595-9716; e-mail design@austrianpublications.com
Ethnicity: German
Circulation: 27,500pd,; Sworn/Estimate/Non-Audited
Advertising: Open inch rate $21.00
Pub...Rolf G. Meyer
Adv. Mgr.....................................Gosta Kiobge
Ed...Christa Meevis
Mechanical Specifications: Type page 10 3/8 x 15 1/4; E - 5 cols, 2, 1/8 between.
Equipment: Hardware — APP/Mac; Software — QPS/QuarkXPress.

WINNIPEG

KANADA KURIER
(Sat)
955 Alexander Ave., Winnipeg, MB, R3C 2X8, Canada; tel (204) 774-1883; fax (204) 783-5740; e-mail kanadakurier@mb.sypatico.ca
Ethnicity: German
Circulation: 2,500pd, 100fr; Sworn/Estimate/Non-Audited
Advertising: Open inch rate $61.92
Pub...Renee Topham
Pub...Eva Rutzetter
Adv. Mgr.................................Christine Bogen
Ed.......................................Marion Schirrmann

GREEK

MONTREAL

GREEK CANADIAN TRIBUNE
(Sat)
7835 Wiseman Ave., Montreal, QC, H3N 2N8, Canada; tel (514) 272-6873; fax (514) 272-3157; e-mail info@bhma.net; web site www.bhma.net
Ethnicity: Greek
Circulation: 1,000pd, 13,200fr; Sworn/Estimate/Non-Audited
Advertising: Open inch rate $.86
Adv. Mgr.....................................Peter Manikis
Ed...Christos Manikis
Mechanical Specifications: Type page 10 x 13 3/4.
Equipment: Hardware — IBM.

HUNGARIAN

CLAREMONT

MAGYAR ELET
(Wed)
390 CONCESSION 7 R.R. 5, Claremont, ON, L1Y 1A2, Canada; tel (289) 200-6772; e-mail magyarelethetilap@gmail.com; web site www.magyarelet.ca
Ethnicity: Hungarian
Circulation:; Sworn/Estimate/Non-Audited
Advertising: Open inch rate $8.00
Established: 1948
Pub...Agnes Somorjai
Equipment: Hardware — IBM.
Delivery Method: Mail, Newsstand

TORONTO

KANADAI MAGYARSAG
(Tues)
747 St. Clair Ave. West #103, Toronto, ON, M6C 4A4, Ontario, Canada; tel (416) 656-8361; ed tel (416) 656-8361; fax (416) 651-2442; ed fax (416) 651-2442; e-mail info@kanadaimagyarsag.ca; adv e-mail info@kanadaimagyarsag.ca; ed e-mail info@kanadaimagyarsag.ca; web site kanadaimagyarsag.ca
Ethnicity: Hungarian
Circulation: 1,635pd, 166fr; CMCA
Advertising: Open inch rate $8.00
Established: 1949
Publisher/owner.........................William Aykler
Susan Papp-Aykler
Circ. Mgr..Judit Toth
Beata Reitner
Postal Codes Served: M6C 4A4

INDIAN - SOUTH ASIAN

MISSISSAUGA

CAN-INDIA NEWS
(Fri)
365 Watline Avenue, Unit# 3-4 , Mississauga, ON, L4Z 1P3, Canada; tel (905) 673-6625; adv tel (905) 673-6625; ed tel (905) 673-6625; fax (905) 673-6636; adv fax (905) 673-6636; ed fax (905) 673-6636; e-mail jazz@CanIndia.com; adv e-mail atul@CanIndia.com; ed e-mail editor@CanIndia.com; web site http://www.canindia.com/advertise-with-us-media-kit/
Ethnicity: Indian - South Asian
Circulation: 41,669fr; CMCA
Advertising: AGATE RATE: 4-COLOR $2.53
Established: 1999
Group: World Media Corp Inc
Digital Platform - Mobile: Apple, Android, Windows, Blackberry
Digital Platform - Tablet: Apple iOS, Android, Windows 7, Blackberry Tablet OS
Pres./Pub.............................Jaswinder Marjara
Mechanical Specifications: Tab Format - 1302 Agate Lines
Width 10" X Height 15.5" - 6 Columns X 217 lines
Col-width: 1 COL=1.5", 2 COL=3.2", 3 COL=4.9", 4 COL= 6.6", 5 COL= 8.3", 6 COL=10"
AGATE RATE: BLACK $2.07
AGATE RATE: 4-COLOR $2.53
Delivery Method: Mail, Newsstand, Racks

ITALIAN

MONTREAL

CORRIERE ITALIANO
(Wed)
1500 Jules-Poitras, Suite 203, Montreal, QC, H4N 1X7, Canada; tel (514) 855-1292; fax (514) 855-1855; e-mail corriereitaliano@transcontinental.ca; web site corriereitaliano.com
Ethnicity: Italian
Circulation: 5,642pd, 3,610fr; CCAB
Advertising: Open inch rate $1.50
Established: 1952
Adv. Mgr..........................Jimmy V. Campanelli
Mng. Ed.................................Fabrizio Intravaia
Editeur......................................Jean Touchette
Mechanical Specifications: Type page 10 x 14; E - 6 cols, 1 1/2, 1/4 between; C - 6 cols, 1 1/2, 1/4 between.
Equipment: Hardware — APP/Mac; Software — QPS/QuarkXPress 4.04, Adobe/Photoshop 5.0, Adobe/Illustrator 8.0.

IL CITTADINO CANADESE
(Wed)
5960 Jean Talon E., Ste. 209, Montreal, QC, H1S 1M2, Canada; tel (514) 253-2332; fax (514) 253-6574; e-mail journal@cittadinocanadese.com; web site www.cittadinocanadese.com
Ethnicity: Italian
Circulation: 20,000pd,; Sworn/Estimate/Non-Audited
Advertising: Open inch rate $1.55
Ed...Nina Mormina
Mechanical Specifications: Type page 11 1/4 x 15; E - 6 cols, 1 7/12, between; A - 6 cols, 1 7/12, between.

INSIEME
(Wed)
4358 Rue Charleroi, Montreal, QC, H1H 1T3, Canada; tel (514) 328-2062; fax (514) 328-6562; e-mail insieme@multimedianova.com
Ethnicity: Italian
Circulation: 12,000pd, 6,000fr; Sworn/Estimate/Non-Audited
Advertising: Open inch rate $2.00
Sec..Loretta Lombardi
Adv. Mgr.......................................Mimmo Forte
Circ. Mgr.................................Robert Brackett
Ed...Lori Abittan
Mechanical Specifications: Type page 10 1/4 x 14 1/4; C - 2 cols, 1 14/15, between.
Equipment: Hardware — APP/Mac; Software — QPS/QuarkXPress 4.1.

OTTAWA

L'ORA DI OTTAWA
(Mon)
203 Louisa St., Ottawa, ON, K1R 6Y9, Ottawa Carleton, Canada; tel (613) 232-5689; fax (855) 596 8522; e-mail info@loradiottawa.ca; adv e-mail info@loradiottawa.ca; ed e-mail info@loradiottawa.ca; web site loradiottawa.ca
Ethnicity: Italian
Circulation: 1,111pd, 242fr; AAM
Advertising: Open inch rate $.57
Established: 1968
Managing Editor .... Paolo Siraco
Assistant Editor .... Cynthia Nuzzi
Accounting .... Olita Schultz
Client Services .... AnnaMaria Morrone
Mechanical Specifications: Type page 11-1/4" x 16.5"; E - 8 cols, 1.5", 1/4 between.
Equipment: Hardware — APP/Mac; Software — Adobe Suite
Delivery Method: Mail
Postal Codes Served: Ottawa Carleton

JEWISH

CALGARY

JEWISH FREE PRESS
(Thur)
8411 Elbow Dr. SW, Calgary, AB, T2V 1K8, Canada; tel (403) 252-9423; fax (403) 255-5640; e-mail jewishfp@tellus.net; web site www.jewishfreepress.ca
Ethnicity: Jewish
Circulation: 50pd, 2,100fr; Sworn/Estimate/Non-Audited
Advertising: Open inch rate $50.00
Established: 1990
Pub .... Richard Bronstein
Adv. Mgr. .... Esther Migdal
Mechanical Specifications: Type page 10 1/8 x 15 1/4; E - 6 cols, 1 1/2, 1/8 between; A - 6 cols, 1 1/2, 1/8 between.
Equipment: Hardware — APP/Power Mac; Software — QPS/QuarkXPress 4.0, Adobe/Illustrator, Adobe/PageMaker, Adobe/Photoshop.

CONCORD

CANADIAN JEWISH NEWS
(Thur)
1750 Steeles Ave W, Concord, ON, L4K 2L7, Canada; tel (416) 391-1836; fax (416) 391-0849; e-mail adscjn@gmail.com ; adv e-mail adscjn@gmail.com; web site www.cjnews.com
Ethnicity: Jewish
Circulation: 25,011pd, 8,706fr; CMCA
Advertising: Open inch rate $3.89
Group: Joseph Jacobs OrganizationEditions: 2— Ontario Jewish News (30,000); Quebec Jewish News (17,500);
Circ. Mgr. .... David Collins
Ed. .... Yoni Goldstein
Managing Ed. .... Joe Serge
News Ed. .... Daniel Wolgelerenter
Ops. Mgr. .... Ella Burakwoski
Mechanical Specifications: Type page 11 1/2 x 15; E - 5 cols, 2, between; A - 5 cols, 2, between; C - 6 cols, between.
Equipment: Hardware — APP/Mac.
Delivery Method: Mail

DOWNSVIEW

TORONTO JEWISH PRESS
PO Box 142, Downsview, ON, M3M 3A3, Canada; tel (416) 633-0202
Ethnicity: Jewish
Advertising: Open inch rate $1.50
Pub .... M. Kissin
Ed. .... G. Kissin

EDMONTON

EDMONTON JEWISH LIFE
(Mthly)
7200 156th St. NE, Edmonton, AB, T5R 1X3, Canada; tel (780) 487-0585; fax (780) 484-4978; e-mail ejlife@shaw.ca; web site www.jewishedmonton.org
Ethnicity: Jewish
Circulation:; Sworn/Estimate/Non-Audited
Advertising: Open inch rate $1.42
Pub .... John Bresler
Ed. .... Neil Loomer
Mechanical Specifications: Type page 10 1/4 x 15; E - 6 cols, 1 9/16, between; A - 6 cols, 1 9/16, between.

VANCOUVER

JEWISH INDEPENDENT
(Fri)
PO Box 47100, RPO City Square, Vancouver, BC, V5Z 4L6, Canada, Canada; tel (604) 689-1520; adv e-mail sales@jewishindependent.ca; ed e-mail editor@jewishindependent.ca; web site www.jewishindependent.ca
Ethnicity: Jewish
Circulation:; Sworn/Estimate/Non-Audited
Advertising: Open inch rate $30.00
Established: 1930
Adv. Mgr. .... Leanne Jacobsen
publisher .... Cynthia Ramsay
Mechanical Specifications: Type page 9 13/16 x 13; E - 5 cols, 1 13/16, between; A - 5 cols, 1 13/16, between; C - 5 cols, 1 13/16, between.
Equipment: Hardware — Software QPS/QuarkXPress 4.0, Adobe/Photoshop 6.0, Adobe/Acrobat, Adobe/Illustrator.
Delivery Method: Mail, Newsstand, Carrier, Racks
Postal Codes Served: Any

WINNIPEG

JEWISH POST & NEWS
(Wed) (Every other Wed)
11-395 Berry St., Winnipeg, MB, R3J 1N6, Manitoba, Canada; tel (204) 694-3332; fax (204) 694-3916; e-mail jewishp@mymts.net; web site www.jewishpostandnews.com
Ethnicity: Jewish
Circulation: 2,300pd,; Sworn/Estimate/Non-Audited
Advertising: Open inch rate $1.30
Publisher/Editor .... Bernie Bellan
Mechanical Specifications: Type page 10 1/4 x 17; E - 6 cols, 1 1/2, 1/4 between; A - 6 cols, 1 1/2, 1/4 between; C - 6 cols, 1 1/2, 1/4 between.
Equipment: Hardware — APP/Mac; Software — Adobe/PageMaker 5.0, Macromedia/Freehand 5.0, Adobe/Photoshop 3.0. Quark 8.5
Delivery Method: Mail, Newsstand, Carrier
Postal Codes Served: All across Canada

LATVIAN

TORONTO

LATVIJA-AMERIKA
(Sat)
4 Credit Union Dr., Toronto, ON, M4A 2N8, Canada; tel (416) 466-1514; adv tel (416) 466-1514; ed tel (416) 465-7902; e-mail latvija.amerika@gmail.com
Ethnicity: Latvian
Circulation: 1,000pd,; Sworn/Estimate/Non-Audited
Advertising: Open inch rate $7.00
Established: 1951
Ed. .... Vita Gaike
admin .... Kristine Ludina
Delivery Method: Mail, Newsstand

LITHUANIAN

MISSISSAUGA

TEVISKES ZIBURIAI
(Tues)
2185 Stavebank Rd., Mississauga, ON, L5C 1T3, Halton-Peel, Canada; tel (905) 275-4672; fax (905) 275-4364; e-mail tevzib@rogers.com
Ethnicity: Lithuanian
Circulation: 1,266pd, 49fr; CMCA
Advertising: Open inch rate $8.50
Established: 1949
Office Manager .... Ausra Trussow
Mng. Ed. .... Ramune Jonaitis
Editor .... Ceslovas Senkevicius
Layout Designer .... Vida Tumosiene
Mechanical Specifications: Type page 17 x 22; E - 7 cols, 2, 1/4 between.
Equipment: Hardware — IBM; Software — Microsoft/Word 2000, Corel/Draw.
Delivery Method: Mail
Postal Codes Served: 9 provinces

THE LIGHTS OF HOMELAND
(Tues)
2185 Stavebank Rd, Mississauga, ON, L5C 1T3, Canada; tel (905) 275-4672; adv tel (905) 275-4672; ed tel (905) 275-4672; fax (905) 275-4364; adv fax (905) 275-4364; ed fax (905) 275-4364; e-mail tevzib@rogers.com; adv e-mail tevzib@rogers.com; web site www.tevzib.com
Ethnicity: Lithuanian
Circulation: 894pd, 46fr; CMCA
Digital Platform - Mobile: Apple, Android
Digital Platform - Tablet: Apple iOS, Android
Delivery Method: Mail, Racks
Postal Codes Served: L5C 1T3

MULTICULTURAL / FRENCH

N. VANCOUVER

COMMUNITY DIGEST
(Fri)
3707 Dollarton Hwy., N. Vancouver, BC, V7G 1A1, British Columbia, Canada; tel (604) 987-8313; e-mail mail@communitydigest.ca; ; adv e-mail adsales@communitydigest.ca; web site www.communitydigest.ca
Ethnicity: Multicultural / French
Circulation: 2,950pd, 25,000fr; Sworn/Estimate/Non-Audited
Advertising: Open inch rate $
Established: 1983Editions: 4— Community Digest-Alberta; Community Digest-British Columbia; Community Digest-Ontario;
Digital Platform - Mobile: Other
Digital Platform - Tablet: Windows 7
Adv. Mgr. .... Nick Ebrahim
Managing Editor .... Stephen Bowell
Mechanical Specifications: Type page 7 1/2 x 10; E - 5 cols, 1 3/8, 1/8 between; A - 5 cols, 1 3/8, 1/8 between.
Delivery Method: Mail, Newsstand, Carrier, Racks
Postal Codes Served: Alberta, BC , Ontario
Note: No phone calls will be attended. All should contact by e-mail only.

PAKISTANI

MISSISSAUGA

THE PAKISTAN POST
2386 Haines Rd. Suite #202, Mississauga, ON, L4Y 1Y6, Canada; tel (905) 272-3961; fax (905) 270-0046; e-mail pakistanpost2@bellnet.ca
Ethnicity: Pakistani
Circulation:; CCAB

POLISH

TORONTO

GLOS POLSKI
(Wed)
71 Judson St., Toronto, ON, M82-1A4, Canada; tel (416) 201-9601; fax (416) 201-9602; e-mail info@glospolski.com
Ethnicity: Polish
Circulation: 7,000pd, 1,000fr; Sworn/Estimate/Non-Audited
Advertising: Open inch rate $10.00
Ed. .... Wieslaw Magiera

ZWIAZKOWIEC
(Tues)
1586A Bloor St., Toronto, ON, M6P 1A7, Canada; tel (416) 531-2491; fax (416) 531-5153; e-mail redakcja@fakty.ca
Ethnicity: Polish
Circulation: 1,257pd, 192fr; CMCA
Advertising: Open inch rate $8.00
Ed. in Chief .... Stanislaw Stolarczyk

SERBIAN

HAMILTON

KANADSKI SRBROBAN
(Tues)
335 Brittania Ave., Hamilton, ON, L8H 1Y4, Canada; tel (905) 549-4079; fax (905) 549-8552; e-mail srbobran@excite.com
Ethnicity: Serbian
Circulation:; Sworn/Estimate/Non-Audited
Advertising: Open inch rate $2.00
Gen. Mgr. .... Cedo Asanin
Ed. .... Branka Popovic
Prodn. Mgr. .... Dragan Ciric
Mechanical Specifications: Type page 11 x 17; E - 4 cols, 2 11/16, 1/6 between; A - 4 cols, 2 11/16, 1/6 between; C - 4 cols, 2 11/16, 1/6 between.
Equipment: Hardware — PC; Software — QPS/QuarkXPress 4.0.

SIKH

BRAMPTON

DIVERSITY REPORTER
(Wed)
17 Schubert Cres, Brampton, ON, L6Y 2P9, Canada; tel (647) 800-0355; adv tel (647) 800-0355; ed tel (647) 800-0355; e-mail contact@diversityreporter.com; adv e-mail advertise@diversityreporter.com; ed e-mail

contact@diversityreporter.com; web site www.diversityreporter.com
Ethnicity: Sikh
Circulation: 1,539pd, 19,769fr; CMCA
Advertising: Text-Link ad rate $25.00 per month
Digital Platform - Mobile: Apple, Android, Windows, Blackberry
Digital Platform - Tablet: Apple iOS, Android, Windows 7, Blackberry Tablet OS
Pub.. Mohsin Abbas
Ed. .... Ahmed Humayun Khan

SLOVAK

MISSISSAUGA

KANADSKY SLOVAK / THE CANADIAN SLOVAK
(Sat)
259 Traders Bouleward East, Unit 6, Mississauga, ON, L4Z 2E5, Canada; tel (905) 507 8004; adv tel (403) 933 2741; e-mail editor@kanadskyslovak.ca; adv e-mail administrator@kanadskyslovak.ca; ed e-mail editor@kanadskyslovak.ca; web site www.kanadskyslovak.ca
Ethnicity: Slovak
Circulation: 900pd, 300fr; Sworn/Estimate/Non-Audited
Advertising: Open inch rate $2.00
Established: 194
Editor-in-Chief.............................. Julius Behul
Editorial Page .... George Frajkor
Chair, Business Committee .... Daniel Sulan
Webmaster, www.kanadskyslovak.ca........ Paul Carnogursky
President, Slovak Canadian Publishing Company....................... Mary Ann Doucette
Chair, Editorial Committe....... Stan Kirschbaum
Delivery Method: Mail, Racks
Postal Codes Served: Globally

SOUTH ASIAN

BRAMPTON

SOUTH ASIAN FOCUS
(Thur)
7700 Hurontario St., Brampton, ON, L6Y 4M3, Canada; tel (905) 454-1535; adv e-mail dchakroborty@southasianfocus.com; ed e-mail srao@southasianfocus.com; web site www.southasianfocus.ca
Ethnicity: South Asian
Circulation: 15,606fr; CCAB
Group: Metroland Media Group Ltd.
Publisher.............................. Gautam Sharma

MISSISSAUGA

THE WEEKLY VOICE
(Sat)
7015 Tranmere Dr. Suite #16, Mississauga, ON, L5S 1T7, Peel, Canada; tel (905) 795-8282; adv tel (647) 680 3228; fax (905) 795-9807; e-mail admin@weeklyvoice.com; adv e-mail dhruv@weeklyvoice.com; ed e-mail info@weeklyvoice.com; web site www.weeklyvoice.com
Ethnicity: South Asian
Circulation: 29,918fr; CMCA
Advertising: 2.25 per agate line
Established: 1998
Group: Voice Media Group
Digital Platform - Mobile: Apple, Android
Pub.. Sudhir Anand
Editor-in-Chief.......................... Binoy Thomas
Gen. Mgr..................................... Dhruv Ghosh
Mechanical Specifications: Media kit available on website
Delivery Method: Mail, Newsstand, Racks
Postal Codes Served: GTA

OAKVILLE

PAKEEZA INTERNATIONAL
(Wed)
1235 Trafalgar Rd., Oakville, ON, L6H 3J0, Canada; tel (905) 337-3030; fax (416) 352-1719; e-mail pakeeza@mansoor.com
Ethnicity: South Asian
Circulation: 6,000fr; Sworn/Estimate/Non-Audited
Advertising: Open inch rate $1.50
Prodn. Mgr.............................. Sabih Mansoor
Mechanical Specifications: Type page 10 1/3 x 15 1/2; E - 5 cols, 2, between; A - 5 cols, 2, between; C - 5 cols, 2, between.
Delivery Method: Carrier

THE SOUTH ASIAN VOICE
(Wed)
1235 Trafalgar Rd., Oakville, ON, L6H 3J0, Canada; tel (905) 337-3030; fax (416) 352-1719; e-mail southasianvoice@mansoor.com
Ethnicity: South Asian
Circulation: 6,000fr; Sworn/Estimate/Non-Audited
Advertising: Open inch rate $1.76
Mng. Ed..................................... Sabih Mansoor
Mechanical Specifications: Type page 10 3/5 x 15 1/2; E - 5 cols, 2, between; A - 5 cols, 2, between; C - 5 cols, 2, between.

TORONTO

NEW CANADA
(Fri)
120 Eglinton Ave. E., Ste. 500, Toronto, ON, M4P 1E2, Canada; tel (416) 481-7793; adv tel (416)481-7793; ed tel (416)481-7793; e-mail humanrights@sympatico.ca; adv e-mail humanrights@sympatico.ca
Ethnicity: South Asian
Circulation: 1,000pd, 9,000fr; Sworn/Estimate/Non-Audited
Advertising: $1.5 agateline,there are fifteen lines in a incha
Established: 1988
Mng. Ed......................... Hasanat Ahmad Syed
Ed. .... Shah Sahib
Mechanical Specifications: Type page 10 x 16; E - 4 cols, 5 x2+10 between; A - 4 cols, 2 1/4, 1/4 between; C - 4 cols, 2 1/4, 1/4 between.
Delivery Method: Mail, Carrier, Racks
Note: From pressroom to edition,we do not have any information

SPANISH

MONTREAL

LA VOZ DE MONTREAL
(Mthly)
5960 Jean Talon E., Ste. 209, Montreal, QC, H1S 1M2, Canada; tel (514) 253-2332; fax (514) 253-6574; e-mail journal@cittadinocanadese.com; web site www.cittadinocanadese.com
Ethnicity: Spanish
Circulation: 13,000pd,; Sworn/Estimate/Non-Audited
Advertising: Open inch rate $1.47
Ed. .... Vittorio Giordano
Prodn. Mgr............................. Basilio Giordano
Mechanical Specifications: Type page 11 1/4 x 15; E - 6 cols, 1 7/12, between; A - 6 cols, 1 7/12, between.

TORONTO

EL POPULAR
(Mon, Wed, Fri) (3 times per week)
2413 Dundas St. W., Toronto, ON, M6P 1X3, Canada, Canada; tel (416) 531-2495; fax (416) 531-7187; e-mail director@diarioelpopular.com; adv e-mail ads@diarioelpopular.com; ed e-mail nixa@diarioelpopular.com; web site www.diarioelpopular.com
Ethnicity: Spanish
Circulation: 11pd, 200fr; Sworn/Estimate/Non-Audited
Advertising: Open inch rate $.88
Established: 1970
Digital Platform - Mobile: Apple
Digital Platform - Tablet: Apple iOS
Mng. Ed................................ Eduardo Uruena
Mechanical Specifications: Type page 10 1/2 x 13.5; E - 6 cols, between; A - 6 cols, between; C - 6 cols, between.
Equipment: Hardware — APP/Mac; Software — Quark, Microsoft/Word,Indesign,adobe/phooshop
Delivery Method: Mail, Newsstand
Postal Codes Served: all GTA

SPANISH/ENGLISH

MISSISSAUGA

EL EXPRESO
(Fri) (weekly)
1233 Nigel Road Mississauga, Mississauga, ON, M6E 2G8, Canada, Canada; tel 647-642-3260; fax (416) 781-8420; e-mail expreso@interlog.com; adv e-mail expreso-inter@uniserve.com; web site www.elexpresocanada.com
Ethnicity: Spanish/English
Circulation: 55,000fr; Sworn/Estimate/Non-Audited
Advertising: Open inch rate $2.00/line/col
Established: 1992
Digital Platform - Mobile: Apple
Circ. Mgr..................................... George Baez
Mng. Ed... Nabil Saad
Mechanical Specifications: Type page 14 x 22 1/2; E - 6 cols, 2 1/3, between; A - 6 cols, 2 1/3, between.
Equipment: Hardware — mac; Software — Quarkxpress, inDesign
Delivery Method: Mail

UKRAINIAN

TORONTO

SVITLO
(Mthly)
265 Bering Ave., Toronto, ON, M8Z 3A5, Canada; tel (416) 234-1212; fax (416) 234-1213; e-mail baspress@pathcom.com
Ethnicity: Ukrainian
Circulation: 1,500pd, 25fr; Sworn/Estimate/Non-Audited
Ed. .... Vasil Cymbalisty
Mechanical Specifications: Type page 8 1/2 x 11; E - 2 cols, 2 1/2, between.
Equipment: Hardware — IBM, APP/Mac; Software — Archetype/Corel Draw, WordPerfect, QPS/QuarkXPress.

WINNIPEG

UKRAINSKY HOLOS
(Mon) (2 x Mthly)
842 Main St., Winnipeg, MB, R2W 3N8, MB, Canada; tel (204) 589-5871; adv tel (204) 589-5871; ed tel (204) 589-5871; fax (204) 586-3618; e-mail presstr@mts.net; adv e-mail presstr@mts.net; ed e-mail presstr@mts.net; web site ukrvoice.ca
Ethnicity: Ukrainian
Circulation: 1,890pd, 42fr; Sworn/Estimate/Non-Audited
Advertising: Open inch rate $.58
Established: 1910
Group: Trident Press Ltd
Ed. .... Maria Bosak
Mechanical Specifications: Type page 14 1/2 x 22 3/4; E - 6 cols, 2, 1/8 between; A - 6 cols, 2, 1/8 between; C - 6 cols, 2, 1/8 between.
Equipment: Hardware — IBM.
Delivery Method: Mail, Newsstand

PARENTING PUBLICATIONS IN THE UNITED STATES

ARIZONA

ARIZONA PARENTING
(Mthly)
4848 E Cactus Rd, Ste 110, Scottsdale, AZ, 85254-4127, Maricopa, USA; tel (602) 279-7977; fax (602) 279-7978; web site www.azparenting.com
Circulation:, 60,000fr; Sworn/Estimate/Non-Audited
Pub... Todd Fisher
Circ. Mgr.................................. Chris Neiman
Adv. Rep.......................... Kimberley Fischer
Ed. .... Todd Fischer
Mechanical Specifications: Type page 9 1/2 x 12 1/8.
Equipment: : Hardware — APP/Mac; Software — QPS/QuarkXPress.

ARKANSAS

LITTLE ROCK FAMILY
(Mthly)
114 Scott St, Little Rock, AR, 72201-1514, Pulaski, USA; tel (501) 372-1443; fax (501)

375-7933; adv e-mail rtucker@abpg.com; ed e-mail mbettis@abpg.com; web site www.littlerockfamily.com
Circulation:, 19,947fr; CVC
Advertising: N/A
Established: 1994
Parent Co.: Arkansas Business Publishing Group.
Sales Dir.................................... Robin Tucker
Pub.. Mitch Bettis
Delivery Method: Racks

CALIFORNIA

PARENTS' PRESS
(Mthly)
875A Island Dr, Ste 421, Alameda, CA, 94502-6751, Alameda, USA; tel (510)-748-9122; fax (510) 926-4131; e-mail sales@parentspress.com; web site www.parentspress.com
Circulation:, 62,000fr; Sworn/Estimate/Non-Audited
Established: 1980
Pub.. Tracy McKean
Equipment: : Hardware — APP/Macs; Software — InDesign
Delivery Method: Racks
Zip Codes Served: 94710; SAN FRANCISCO—OAKLAND—SAN JOSE, CA

SACRAMENTO PARENT
(Mthly)
457 Grass Valley Hwy, Ste 5, Auburn, CA, 95603-3725, Placer, USA; tel (530) 888-0573; fax (530) 888-1536; e-mail info@sacramentoparent.com; web site www.sacramentoparent.com
Circulation:, 44,975fr; CVC
Advertising: N/A
Established: 1992

KERN COUNTY FAMILY MAGAZINE
(Mthly)
1400 Easton Dr, Ste 112, Bakersfield, CA, 93309-9403, Kern, USA; tel (661) 861-4939; fax (661) 861-4930; e-mail kerncountyfamily@earthlink.net; web site www.kerncountyfamily.com
Circulation: 9pd,, 28,207fr; CVC
Advertising: N/A
Established: 1996
Ed.. L.J. Corby
Mechanical Specifications: Type page 10 1/4 x 12.
Equipment: : Hardware — APP/Mac; Presses — 4-WPC; Software — Adobe/PageMaker 6.5, Macromedia/Freehand 7.0, Adobe/Photoshop 5.0.

BAY AREA PARENT
(Mthly) (Five print special editions plus 16 special digital-only magazines
901 Campisi Way, Ste 300, Campbell, CA, 95008-2376, Santa Clara, USA; tel (408) 533-4413; adv tel (408) 533-4403; fax (408) 963-6124; e-mail dawn.hall@parenthood.com; adv e-mail dawn.hall@parenthood.com; ed e-mail jill.wolfson@parenthood.com; web site www.bayareaparent.com
Circulation: 0pd,, 122,000fr; CVC
Established: 1983Editions: 3— 3 total East Bay Edition; San Francisco City & Peninsula Edition; Silicon Valley Edition;
Digital Platform - Mobile: Apple, Android, Windows, Other
Digital Platform - Tablet: Apple iOS, Android
Editor.. Jill Wolfson
Group Publisher.................. Daniel Payomo Jr
Delivery Method: Newsstand, Racks
Zip Codes Served: 6 county bay area

PARENTING MAGAZINE OF ORANGE COUNTY
(Mthly)
172 N Tustin St, Ste 304, Orange, CA, 92867-7780, Orange, USA; tel (714) 771-7454; fax (714) 771-5852; web site www.parentingoc.com
Circulation: 108pd,, 80,000fr; Sworn/Estimate/Non-Audited
Advertising: Open inch rate $105
Ed. in Chief............................. Randall Tierney
Art Dir................................. Bahram Fattahinia
Mechanical Specifications: Type page 10 1/8 x 12; E - 4 cols, 2 1/4, 1/6 between; A - 4 cols, 2 1/4, 1/6 between; C - 5 cols, 1 3/4, 1/6 between.
Equipment: : Hardware — APP/Mac G3; Presses — WPC, G; Software — QPS/QuarkXPress 4.0.

SONOMA FAMILY-LIFE MAGAZINE
(Mthly)
100 Professional Center Dr, Ste 104, Rohnert Park, CA, 94928-2137, Sonoma, USA; tel (707) 586-9562; fax (707) 895-2154; e-mail info@family-life.us; web site www.sonomafamilylife.com
Circulation:, 23,000fr; Sworn/Estimate/Non-Audited
Advertising: Open inch rate $15.00
Ed.. Sharon Gowan

SAN DIEGO FAMILY MAGAZINE
(Mthly)
1475 6th Ave, Fl 5, San Diego, CA, 92101-3245, San Diego, USA; tel (619) 685-6970; fax (619) 685-6978; e-mail family@sandiegofamily.com; adv e-mail sharon@sandiegofamily.com; ed e-mail sharon@sandiegofamily.com; web site www.sandiegofamily.com
Circulation: 24pd,, 101,538fr; CVC
Advertising: N/A
Established: 1982
Publisher...................................... Sharon Bay
Mktg. Coord. .... Michele Hancock
Mechanical Specifications: Type page 8 x 10; E - 3 cols, 2 1/4, between; A - 3 cols, 2 1/4, between; C - 4 cols, 1 3/4, between.
Equipment: : Hardware — APP/Mac; Software — Adobe/Photoshop, Macromedia/Freehand.
Delivery Method: Carrier
Zip Codes Served: All of San Diego County

THE PARENT CONNECTION/SCRIPPS MEMORIAL HOSPITAL
(Mthly)
4275 Campus Point Ct # CP10, Scripps Memorial Hospital, San Diego, CA, 92121-1513, San Diego, USA; tel (858) 626-6944; e-mail info@sandiegoparent.com; adv e-mail info@sandiegoparent.com; web site www.sandiegoparent.com
Circulation: 1,500pd,, 1,000fr; Sworn/Estimate/Non-Audited
Established: 1980
Parent Co.: Parent Connection.
Digital Platform - Mobile: Apple, Android, Windows, Blackberry
Coord... Pam Nagata
Adv. Mgr. .... Martha Stillwell
Circ. Mgr... Alison Rob
Ed. .... Colleen McNatt
Prodn. Mgr. .... Angel Salazar
Equipment: : Hardware — APP/Mac G3; Presses — WPC, G; Software — QPS/QuarkXPress 4.0.
Delivery Method: Mail

FAMILY-LIFE MAGAZINE
(Mthly) (Weekly E-newsletters.
134 Lystra Ct, Santa Rosa, CA, 95403-8076, Sonoma, USA; tel (707) 305 1539; adv tel (707) 205-1539; ed tel (707) 205-1544; fax (707) 895-2154; adv fax (707) 586-9571; ed fax (707) 586-9571; e-mail info@family-life.us; adv e-mail Sales@family-life.us; ed e-mail Editor@family-life.us; web site www.sonomafamilylife.com
Circulation:, 46,000fr; VAC
Established: 1989Editions: 2— Sonoma Family Life Magazine & Mendo Lake Family Life Magazine
Digital Platform - Mobile: Apple
Digital Platform - Tablet: Apple iOS
Publisher/Editor .... Sharon Gowan
Delivery Method: Mail, Carrier, Racks

LA PARENT MAGAZINE
(Mthly)
5855 Topanga Canyon Blvd, Ste 210, Woodland Hills, CA, 91367-4671, Los Angeles, USA; tel (818) 264-2222; e-mail ron.epstein@laparent,com; adv e-mail ron.epstein@laparent,com; ed e-mail christina.elston@laparent,com; web site www.laparent.com
Circulation:, 70,000fr; Sworn/Estimate/Non-Audited
Established: 1980
Parent Co.: Epstein Custom Media Inc.. Editions: 2— City and Valley/Ventura County
Digital Platform - Mobile: Apple, Android, Windows, Blackberry
Digital Platform - Tablet: Apple iOS, Android, Windows 7, Blackberry Tablet OS, Kindle, Nook
Ed... Christina Elston
Mechanical Specifications: media kit is on our website
Equipment: : Hardware — Mac platform; Presses — 48-page; Software — Unsure
Delivery Method: Carrier, Racks
Zip Codes Served: All of LA County, and parts of Ventura County
Note: We have 2 annual editions: Inclusive L.A., which is published each April for families in LA who have children with learning differences, and our Education Guide that is published in October and addresses all things education — vital to parents in LA.

COLORADO

PIKES PEAK PARENT
(Mthly)
30 E Pikes Peak Ave, Ste 100, Colorado Springs, CO, 80903-1580, El Paso, USA; tel (719) 636-0306; fax (719) 636-0202; e-mail parent@gazette.com; web site www.pikespeakparent.com
Circulation:, 20,000fr; Sworn/Estimate/Non-Audited
Pub... Tom Mullen
Adv. Mgr. .... Renee Maisel
Ed. .... Lisa Carpenter

COLORADO PARENT
(Mthly)
1515 Wazee St Ste 400, Suite 400, Denver, CO, 80202-1672, Denver, USA; tel (303) 320-1000; fax (303) 265-9411; web site www.coloradoparent.com
Circulation:, 45,133fr; CVC
Advertising: N/A
Established: 1986
Parent Co.: 5280 Publishing, Inc..
Digital Platform - Mobile: Apple, Android, Windows
Digital Platform - Tablet: Apple iOS, Android
Ed.. Deborah Mock
Mechanical Specifications: Type page 8 3/8 x 11 1/8; E - 4 cols, 2 1/4, 1/4 between.
Equipment: : Hardware — APP/Macs; Software — QPS/QuarkXPress.
Delivery Method: Newsstand, Racks
Zip Codes Served: Greater Denver/Boulder Metro

DALLASCHILD
(Mthly)
825 Laporte Ave, STE 146, Fort Collins, CO, 80521-2520, Larimer, USA; tel (972) 447-9188; adv tel (972) 447-9188; ed tel (972) 447-9188; fax (972) 447-0633; e-mail Joy@dfwchild.com; adv e-mail advertising@dfwchild.com; ed e-mail editorial@dfwchild.com; web site www.dfwchild.com
Circulation:, 60,000fr; CAC
Advertising: N/A
Established: 1986
Parent Co.: Lauren Publications.
Digital Platform - Mobile: Apple, Android
Digital Platform - Tablet: Apple iOS, Android
Pub... Joylyn Niebes
Prodn. Mgr. .... Susan Horn
Sales Director .... Alison Davis
Creative Director...................... Lauren Niebes
Equipment: : Hardware — Apple
Delivery Method: Racks
Zip Codes Served: 75001, 75002, 75093, 75025, 75225, 75230, 75220, 75205, 75208, 75214, 75218, 75228, 75234, 75229, 75219, 7524
Note: Lauren Publications has 5 publications. DallasChild, FortWorthChild, NorthTexasChild, DFWBaby and DFWThrive magazines.

CONNECTICUT

CONNECTICUT PARENT MAGAZINE
(Mthly)
420 E Main St, Ste 18, Branford, CT, 06405-2942, New Haven, USA; tel (203) 483-1700; adv fax (203) 483-0522; e-mail joel.macclaren@ctparent.com; adv e-mail joel.macclaren@ctparent.com; ed e-mail editorial@ctparent.com; web site www.ctparent.com
Circulation: 0pd,, 47,239fr; Sworn/Estimate/Non-Audited
Advertising: N/A
Established: 1984
Parent Co.: Choice Media, LLC. Editions: 2— 2 total; Fairfield County (25,000); Hartford County (26,000);
Digital Platform - Mobile: Apple, Android
Digital Platform - Tablet: Apple iOS
Ed./Pub.................................. Joel MacClaren
Mechanical Specifications: call
Equipment: ; Software — QPS/QuarkXPress.
Delivery Method: Racks
Zip Codes Served: 06001-06999

FLORIDA

CINCINNATI PARENT
(Mthly)
1 Gannett Plaza, Melbourne, FL, 32940, Brevard, USA; tel (513) 444-2015; adv tel (317) 710-6622; ed tel (317) 722-8500, ext. 164; e-mail mary@cincinnatiparent.com; adv e-mail mary@cincinnatiparent.com; ed e-mail susan@cincinnatiparent.com; web site www.cincinnatiparent.com
Circulation:, 44,000fr; CVC
Established: 1986
Parent Co.: Midwest Parenting Publications.
Digital Platform - Mobile: Apple, Android, Windows, Blackberry
Digital Platform - Tablet: Apple iOS, Android, Windows 7, Blackberry Tablet OS, Kindle, Kindle Fire, Other
Publisher.............................. Mary Wynne Cox
Equipment: : Hardware — 4-APP/Mac, APP/Power Mac 7200-90; Software — QPS/QuarkXPress 3.1, Adobe/Photoshop 3.0.
Delivery Method: Mail, Newsstand, Carrier, Racks
Zip Codes Served: 46220-1039

FORT WORTH CHILD MAGAZINE
(Mthly) (monthly
6501 Nob Hill Rd, Tamarac, FL, 33321-6422, Broward, USA; tel (972) 447-9188; fax (972) 447-0633; e-mail support@dfwchild.com; adv e-mail advertising@dfwchild.com; ed e-mail editorial@dfwchild.com; web site www.dfwchild.com/fortworth
Circulation:, 40,000fr; CVC
Advertising: N/A
Established: 1992
Parent Co.: Lauren Publications.
Digital Platform - Mobile: Apple, Android
Digital Platform - Tablet: Apple iOS, Android
Pub.. Joylyn Niebes
Graphics Designer....................... Susan Horn
Delivery Method: Racks
Zip Codes Served: Fort Worth, Arlington, Hurst

Euless Bedford, Grapevine, Southlake, Colleyville, Keller

GEORGIA

ATLANTA PARENT
(Mthly)
2346 Perimeter Park Dr, Ste 101, Atlanta, GA, 30341-1319, Dekalb, USA; tel (770) 454-7599; fax (770) 454-7699; e-mail atlantaparent@atlantaparent.com; adv e-mail calendar@atlantaparent.com; advertising@atlantaparent.com; ed e-mail editor@atlantaparent.com; web site www.atlantaparent.com
Circulation:, 99,900fr; CVC
Advertising: N/A
Asst. Pub.......................... Michelle McGunagle
Bus. Devel. Mgr............................... Amy Smith
Adv. Sales Dir.................................... Liz White
Mng. Ed.. Kate Parrott
Prodn. Mgr.................................... Neal Wilkes
Mechanical Specifications: Type page 7 3/8 x 10; E - 3 cols, 2 1/4, 1/4 between; A - 3 cols, 2 1/4, 1/4 between; C - 3 cols, 2 1/4, 1/4 between.
Equipment: ; Software — Adobe/PageMaker 7.0.
Zip Codes Served: 30338

GEORGIA FAMILY MAGAZINE
(Mthly) (Monthly
523 Sioux Dr, Macon, GA, 31210-4217, Bibb, USA; tel (478) 471-7393; adv tel (478) 471-7393; ed tel 478 471-7393; e-mail publisher@georgiafamily.com; adv e-mail publisher@georgiafamily.com; ed e-mail editorial.gfm@gmail.com; web site www.GeorgiaFamily.com
Circulation: 105pd,, 55,000fr; CVC
Advertising: open full-page rate $1185.00
Established: 1992Editions: 2— Hard copy & digital
Ed. in Chief.................................. Olya Fessard
Mng. Ed................................. Veronique Saiya
Mechanical Specifications: Type page 7 1/4 x 10. 4/C/300dpi
Equipment: : Hardware — Computers
4C Laser printers; Software — Adobe Creative Suite 6
Quickbooks
TrendMicro
Delivery Method: Mail, Carrier, Racks
Zip Codes Served: Central Georgia too many to list

HAWAII

ISLAND FAMILY
(Mthly)
1000 Bishop St, Ste 405, Honolulu, HI, 96813-4204, Honolulu, USA; tel (808) 534-7544; adv tel (808) 534-7501; ed tel (808) 534-7105; fax (808) 537-6455; e-mail chuckt@pacificbasin.net; adv e-mail Donnaky@honolulumagazine.com; ed e-mail Christiy@honolulufamily.com; web site http://www.honolulufamily.com/
Circulation:, 40,000fr; Sworn/Estimate/Non-Audited
Adv. Mgr.................................... Lennie Omalza
Ed.. Helen McNeil

ILLINOIS

CHICAGO PARENT
(Mthly)
141 S Oak Park Ave, Oak Park, IL, 60302-2972, Cook, USA; tel (708) 386-5555; fax (708) 524-8360; e-mail chiparent@chicagoparent.com; web site www.chicagoparent.com
Circulation: 13pd,, 125,000fr; Sworn/Estimate/Non-Audited
Established: 1984Editions: 3— 3 total Chicago Parent Zone A (50,000);
Digital Platform - Mobile: Apple, Android, Blackberry
Digital Platform - Tablet: Apple iOS, Android, Kindle, Kindle Fire
Pub.. Dan Haley
Circ. Mgr.................................... Kathy Hansen
Ed. .... Tamara O'Shaughnessy
Mechanical Specifications: Type page 9 1/2 x 11 5/6; E - 3 cols, between; A - 4 cols, 2 3/16, 1/4 between; C - 6 cols, between.
Delivery Method: Mail, Carrier, Racks
Zip Codes Served: 60302

INDIANA

INDY'S CHILD
(Wed, Mthly)
6340 E Westfield Blvd, Ste 200, Indianapolis, IN, 46220-1746, Marion, USA; tel (317) 722-8500; fax (317) 722-8510; e-mail indyschild@indyschild.com; ed e-mail susan@indyschild.com; web site www.indyschild.com
Circulation: 0pd,, 45,278fr; Sworn/Estimate/Non-Audited
Advertising: Open inch rate $25.00
Established: 1984
Parent Co.: Midwest Parenting Publications.
Pub.. Mary Cox
Circ. Mgr.................................. Roxanne Burns
Adv. Mgr...................................... Mike Hussey
Ed. .... Lynette Rowland
Mechanical Specifications: Type page 10 x 13; E - 4 cols, 2 3/8, 1/8 between; A - 4 cols, 2 3/8, 1/8 between; C - 5 cols, 1 7/8, between.
Equipment: : Hardware — APP/Mac; Software — QPS/QuarkXPress 3.3, Adobe/Photoshop 3.0.
Zip Codes Served: 46240

KANSAS

NEW YORK FAMILY
(Mthly)
11936 W 119th St, Ste 335, Overland Park, KS, 66213-2216, Johnson, USA; tel (914) 381-7474; fax (914) 381-7672; e-mail mamaroneck.reception@parenthood.com; web site www.parenthood.com
Pub... Cate Sanderson
Adv. Coord. .... Sherine R. Chenault-Usher
Circ. Mgr................................ Thomas Butcher
Sr. Ed. .... Heather Hart
Ed. .... Larissa Phillips
Calendar Ed......................... Carolyn Rogalsky

KENTUCKY

LEXINGTON FAMILY MAGAZINE
(Mthly)
138 E Reynolds Rd, Ste 201, Lexington, KY, 40517-1259, Fayette, USA; tel (859) 223-1765; fax (859) 224-4270; web site www.lexingtonfamily.com
Circulation:, 28,539fr; CVC
Advertising: N/A
Established: 1996
Pub... Dana Tackett
Adv. Rep.. Karyn Potts
Ed. .... John Lynch
Mechanical Specifications: Type page 10 x 12 1/2; E - 4 cols, 2 23/60, 1/6 between; A - 4 cols, 2 23/60, 1/6 between.

TODAY'S FAMILY
(Bi-Mthly, Other) (Quarterly
9750 Ormsby Station Rd, Ste 307, Louisville, KY, 40223-4064, Jefferson, USA; tel (502) 327-8855; adv tel (502) 327-8855; ed tel (502) 327-8855; fax (502) 327-8861; adv fax (502) 327-8861; ed fax (502) 327-8861; e-mail info@todayspublications.com; adv e-mail advertising@todayspublications.com; ed e-mail editor@todayspublications.com; web site www.todaysfamilymag.com
Circulation:, 34,975fr; CVC
Established: 1982
Parent Co.: Zion Publications, LLC.
Owner/Publisher............................ Cathy Zion
Editor .... Anita Oldham
Delivery Method: Racks

LOUISIANA

BATON ROUGE PARENTS MAGAZINE
(Mthly)
11831 Wentling Ave, Baton Rouge, LA, 70816-6055, East Baton Rouge, USA; tel (225) 292-0032; fax (225) 292-0038; e-mail brpm@brparents.com; brpmcalendar@brparents.com; adv e-mail sales@brparents.com; web site www.brparents.com
Circulation: 31pd,, 14,776fr; CVC
Advertising: N/A
Established: 1990
Pub............................ Amy Foreman-Plaisance
Sales Mgr.................... Theresa Dold Payment

MARYLAND

CHESAPEAKE FAMILY LIFE
(Mthly)
121 Cathedral St, Fl 3, Annapolis, MD, 21401-2777, Anne Arundel, USA; tel (410) 263-1641; fax (410) 280-0255; e-mail dj@jecoannapolis.com; adv e-mail dj@jecoannapolis.com; ed e-mail editor@chesapeakefamily.com; web site www.chesapeakefamily.com
Circulation:, 34,641fr; Sworn/Estimate/Non-Audited
Advertising: N/A
Established: 1990
Parent Co.: Jefferson Communications.
Digital Platform - Mobile: Apple, Android, Windows
Digital Platform - Tablet: Apple iOS, Android
Adv. Mgr................................ Donna Jefferson
Mktg. Mgr............................ Jeanne Slaughter
Ed. .... Kristen Page-Kirby
Delivery Method: Newsstand, Racks
Zip Codes Served: 21401, 21061, 21146, 21403, 21062, 21012, 21666, 20715, 20678, 21114

BOSTON PARENT
11 Dutton Ct, Baltimore, MD, 21228-4922, Baltimore

WASHINGTON PARENT MAGAZINE
(Mthly)
4701 Sangamore Rd, Ste N270, Bethesda, MD, 20816-2528, Montgomery, USA; tel (301) 320-2321; fax (301) 229-9187; e-mail contactus@washingtonparent.net; web site www.washingtonparent.com
Circulation 36pd,, 66,939fr; CVC
Advertising: $295 (smallest modular rate)
Established: 1996
Pub... Deborah Benke
Adv. Mgr............................. Mary Fran Gildea
Circ. Mgr................................... George Benke
Ed. .... Margaret Hut
Prodn. Mgr. .... Jane MacNealy
Equipment: : Hardware — PC; Software — Adobe/PageMaker.

PARENT LINE
(Mthly)
11135 Beacon Way, Lusby, MD, 20657-2449, Calvert, USA; tel (410) 326-7030; fax (410) 326-0999; e-mail parentline@comcast.net; parentlinecalendar@comcast.net
Circulation:, 25,000fr; Sworn/Estimate/Non-Audited
Pub.. Kelly Wilder
Mechanical Specifications: Type page 10 13/16 x 13.

MARYLAND FAMILY MAGAZINE
(Bi-Mthly)
409 Washington Ave, Ste 400, Towson, MD, 21204-4919, Baltimore, USA; tel (410) 337-2400; fax (410) 296-2707; web site www.marylandfamilymagazine.com
Circulation: 0pd,, 43,645fr; CAC
Exec. Ed.. Paul Milton
Ed. .... Betsy Stein
Ed. .... Cheryl Clemens

MICHIGAN

METRO PARENT MAGAZINE
(Mthly)
22041 Woodward Ave, Ferndale, MI, 48220-2520, Oakland, USA; tel (248) 398-3400; fax (248) 399-4215; e-mail metroparent@metroparent.com; web site www.metroparent.com
Circulation:, 59,753fr; CVC
Advertising: N/A
Pub.. Alyssa Martina
Gen. Mgr. .... Alexis Bourkoulas
Office Mgr. .... Tracy Connelly
Assoc. Pub................................ Ruth Robbins
Ed. .... Julia Elliott
Mechanical Specifications: Type page 9 1/2 x 11 1/4; E - 4 cols, between; A - 4 cols, between.
Zip Codes Served: 48075

MISSOURI

SAVVY FAMILY
(Mthly)
14522 S Outer 40 Rd, Chesterfield, MO, 63017-5737, Saint Louis, USA; tel (314) 821-1110; fax (314) 821-3408; web site www.stltoday.com
Pub.................................. Mary Ann Wagner
Equipment: : Hardware — IBM, APP/Mac.

NEW HAMPSHIRE

PARENTING NEW HAMPSHIRE
(Mthly)
150 Dow St, Manchester, NH, 03101-1227, Hillsborough, USA; tel (603) 624-1310; adv tel (603) 624-1442; ed tel (603) 624-1442; fax (603) 624-1310; web site http://www.parentingnh.com/
Circulation:, 27,303fr; CVC
Advertising: Open inch rate $22.80
Established: 1993
Pub.................................... Sharron Mccarthy
Adv. Dir....................................... David Kruger
Circ. Mgr............................. Shannon Spiliotis
Ed. .... Melanie Hitchcock
Mechanical Specifications: Type page 9 1/2 x 11 5/8; E - 4 cols, 2 1/8, between; A - 4 cols, 2 1/8, between; C - 4 cols, 2 1/8, between.
Equipment: : Hardware — PC, APP/Mac; Software — QPS/QuarkXPress 4.0.

NEW JERSEY

KANSAS CITY PARENT
(Mthly)
1122 US Highway 22, Mountainside, NJ, 07092-2812, Union, USA; tel (913) 782-3238; fax (913) 681-5139; e-mail kcparent@mindspring.com; adv e-mail advertising@kcparent.com; ed e-mail editor@kcparent.com; web site www.kcparent.com
Circulation:, 26,200fr; CVC
Advertising: N/A
Established: 1985
Pub.................................. L. Richard Bruursema
Mechanical Specifications: Type page 10 1/2 x 12.

MORRIS COUNTY FAMILY
(Mthly)
1122 US Highway 22, Mountainside, NJ, 07092-2812, Union, USA; tel (908) 232-2913; fax (908) 317-9518; e-mail publisher@njfamily.com; ed e-mail editor@njfamily.com; web site www.njfamily.com
Circulation:, 30,000fr; Sworn/Estimate/Non-Audited
Pub. .... Cindy Mironovich
Assoc. Pub. .... Bonnie Vohden
Dir., Adv. .... Linda Galli
Ed. .... Farn Dupre
Mng. Ed. .... Lucy Banta
Mechanical Specifications: Type page 7 7/8 x 10 1/8.

UNION COUNTY FAMILY
(Mthly)
1122 Rt. 22 W., Mountainside, NJ, 07092-2812, USA; tel (908) 232-2913; fax (908) 317-9518; e-mail publisher@njfamily.com; ed e-mail editor@njfamily.com; web site www.njfamily.com
Circulation:, 126,000fr; Sworn/Estimate/Non-Audited
Established: 1991
Pub. .... Cindy Mironovich
Assoc. Pub. .... Bonnie Vohden
Dir., Adv. .... Linda Galli
Ed. .... Farn Dupre
Mng. Ed. .... Lucy Banta
Mechanical Specifications: Type page 7 7/8 x 10 1/8.

SUBURBAN PARENT
(Mthly)
850 Carolier Ln, North Brunswick, NJ, 08902-3312, Middlesex, USA; tel (732) 435-0005; fax (732) 435-0677; e-mail sales@njparentweb.com; web site www.njparentweb.com
Circulation:, 78,000fr; Sworn/Estimate/Non-AuditedEditions: 3— 3 total Suburban Parent-Zone 1 (30,000);
Pub. .... Mark Chelton
Adv. Mgr. .... Vern Boyer-Schwartz
Sr. Ed. .... Melodie Susan Dhondt
Prodn. Mgr. .... Matthew White
Mechanical Specifications: Type page 10 x 13 1/4; E - 4 cols, 2 3/8, 3/16 between; A - 4 cols, 2 3/8, 3/16 between; C - 4 cols, 2 3/8, 3/16 between.

NEW JERSEY FAMILY
(Mthly)
480 Morris Ave, Summit, NJ, 07901-1523, Union, USA; tel 9082771919; adv tel 9082771919x110; ed tel 9082771919; fax 9082771977; e-mail publisher@njfamily.com; adv e-mail sales@njfamily.com; ed e-mail dina@njfamily.com; web site www.njfamily.com
Circulation: 8pd,, 134,221fr; CVC
Advertising: N/A
Established: 1990Editions: 5— Central, Essex, Morris, North, Union
Digital Platform - Mobile: Apple
Digital Platform - Tablet: Apple iOS
Co-Pub. .... Cindy Mironovich
Bus. Mgr. .... Mary Lucid
Advertising Director .... Marcy Holeton
Editorial Director .... Dina El Nabli
Mechanical Specifications: Type page 7 7/8 x 10 1/8.
Delivery Method: Newsstand, Racks
Zip Codes Served: 07901

NEW YORK

WESTCHESTER FAMILY
(Mthly)
1872 Pleasantville Road, Suite 173, Braircliff Manor , NY, 10510, Westchester , USA; tel (914) 381-7474; fax (914) 462-3311; e-mail jean.sheff@westchesterfamily.com ; web site http://westchesterfamily.com/
Circulation: 0pd,, 35,000fr; Sworn/Estimate/Non-Audited
Advertising: N/A
Ed./Co-Pub .... Jean Sheff

WESTCHESTER PARENT
(Mthly)
1872 Pleasantville Rd, Ste 173, Briarcliff Manor, NY, 10510-1051, Westchester, USA; tel (914) 397-0200; fax (914) 397-1466; web site www.nymetroparents.com
Circulation:, 55,004fr; CVC
Advertising: N/A
Pub. .... David Miller
Ed. Dir. .... Phyllis Singer
Mng. Ed. .... Christine Tarulli

NEW YORK PARENTING - BROOKLYN FAMILY/MANHATTAN FAMILY/QUEENS FAMILY/BRONX-RIVERDALE FAMILY/ WESTCHESTER FAMILY
(Mthly) (Special Child magazines - Bi-Annual
1 Metrotech Ctr N, Fl 10, Brooklyn, NY, 11201-3875, Kings, USA; tel (718) 260-4554; adv tel (718) 260-4554; ed tel (718) 260-2587; fax (718) 260-2568; e-mail Susank@NYParenting.com; adv e-mail Family@NYParenting.com; ed e-mail Susan@NYParenting.com ; web site www.nyparenting.com
Circulation:, 167,500fr; CVC
Advertising: N/A
Established: 1999
Parent Co.: CNG.
Digital Platform - Mobile: Apple, Android, Windows, Blackberry
Digital Platform - Tablet: Apple iOS, Android, Windows 7, Blackberry Tablet OS, Kindle, Nook, Kindle Fire
Publisher/Exec. Editor .... Susan Weiss
Pub./Bus. Mgr. .... Clifford Luster
Ed. .... Vincent Dimecili
Delivery Method: Mail, Carrier, Racks
Zip Codes Served: New York City and Westchester

WESTERN NEW YORK FAMILY
(Mthly)
3147 Delaware Ave, Ste B, Buffalo, NY, 14217-2002, Erie, USA; tel (716) 836-3486; fax (716) 836-3680; e-mail feedback@wnyfamilymagazine.com; adv e-mail advertising@wnyfamilymagazine.com; ed e-mail michele@wnyfamilymagazine.com; web site www.wnyfamilymagazine.com
Circulation: 0pd,, 20,000fr; CVC
Advertising: Modular ad rates
Established: 1984
Digital Platform - Mobile: Apple, Android, Windows, Blackberry, Other
Digital Platform - Tablet: Apple iOS, Android, Windows 7, Kindle, Nook, Kindle Fire, Other
Editor & Publisher .... Michele Miller
Mechanical Specifications: Our complete media kit with specs can be downloaded from our website.
Equipment: : Hardware — Apple Computers Hewlett Packard Printers; Presses — NONE; Software — Adobe Creative Suite
Delivery Method: Racks
Zip Codes Served: We cover Erie and Niagara Counties of upstate New York. We are NOT a New York City publication. Call our office to receive a PDF of our complete audit report including zip codes.

CAPITAL DISTRICT PARENT
(Mthly)
595 New Loudon Rd, Ste 102, Latham, NY, 12110-4063, Albany, USA; tel (518) 862-2056; fax (845) 562-3681; e-mail publisher@excitingread.com; adv e-mail sales@excitingread.com; ed e-mail editor@excitingread.com; web site www.cdparent.com
Adv. Mgr. .... Terrie Goldstein
Ed. .... Leah Black
Art Dir. .... Lisa Jabbour

CONNECTICUT FAMILY
(Mthly)
141 Halstead Ave, Ste 3D, Mamaroneck, NY, 10543-2607, Westchester, USA; tel (203) 625-9825; fax (914) 381-7672; e-mail mamaroneckreception@unitedad.com; web site www.parenthood.com
Circ. Mgr. .... Thomas Butcher
Ed. .... Heather Hart

TULSA KIDS
(Mthly)
141 Halstead Ave, Ste 3D, Mamaroneck, NY, 10543-2607, Westchester, USA; tel (918) 582-8504; fax (918) 583-1366; e-mail publisher@tulsakids.com; adv e-mail publisher@tulsakids.com; ed e-mail editor@tulsakids.com; web site www.tulsakids.com
Circulation:, 20,000fr; CVC
Established: 1988
Digital Platform - Mobile: Blackberry
Mng. Ed. .... Betty Casey
Publisher, Designer .... Charles Foshee
Equipment: : Hardware — APP/Mac; Software — Adobe:Creative Suite 3 & 5, QPS/ QuarkXPress, Microsoft/Word.
Delivery Method: Racks
Note: Monthly parenting magazine with 12 issues per year plus 2 annual special editions.

NY METRO PARENTS
(Mthly)
498 Seventh Avenue, 10th Floor, New York, NY, 10018, New York, USA; tel (212) 315-0800; adv tel (212) 315-0800; ed tel (646) 652-7516; fax (212) 271-2239; ed fax (212) 271-2239; e-mail info@nymetroparents.com; adv e-mail info@nymetroparents.com; ed e-mail dskolnik@davlermedia.com; web site www.nymetroparents.com
Circulation: 0pd,, 335,000fr; CVC
Established: 1985
Parent Co.: Davler Media Group. Editions: 84— Big Apple Parent; Long Island Parent - Suffolk Edition; Long Island Parent - Nassau Edition; Westchester Parent; Queens Parent, Bergen / Rockland Parent; Brooklyn Parent
Digital Platform - Mobile: Apple, Android, Windows, Blackberry
Digital Platform - Tablet: Apple iOS, Android, Windows 7, Blackberry Tablet OS, Kindle, Nook, Kindle Fire, Other
CEO .... David Miller
Mechanical Specifications: Full page 7.3" W x 9.6" D
Full page bleed 8.9" W x 11.25" D
Junior page 5.4" W x 7.0" D
1.2 page (H) 7.3" W x 4.7" D
1.2 page (V) 3.55" W x 9.6" D
1.4 page (H) 7.3" W x 2.25" D
1.4 page (V) 3.55" W x 4.7" D
1.6 page (H) 3.55" W x 3.0" D
1.8 Page (H) 3.55" W x 2.25" D
Digital file of ads from advertisers or their ad agencies can be e-mailed as high resolution PDF, EPS (outlined), or TIFF file at least 300 dpi. Alternatively you can send your large materials via dropbox.yousendit.com/ Davler-Traffic.
Camera ready art should use an 85 line screen, which will be scanned and digitized by our production department.
Ads created in InDesign (Mac platform) should include: fonts (no stylized or TrueType fonts), artwork and photos (saved as TIFF or EPS files - CMYK - at least 300 dpi). INK DENSITIES FOR 3. COLOR IMAGES SHOULD NEVER EXCEED 220%.
Equipment: : Hardware — Mac; Presses — Outside printing companies; Software — InDesign CS6 Version 8.1
Delivery Method: Mail, Newsstand, Carrier, Racks
Zip Codes Served: All zip codes in Westchester, Rockland/Bergen, Suffolk, Nassau, Manhattan, Queens, and Brooklyn

SPACE COAST PARENT
(Mthly)
498 Seventh Ave, 10th Floor, New York, NY, 10018, New York, USA; tel (321) 242-3500; fax (321) 242-0760; e-mail brevardcounty@MomsLikeMe.com; web site brevardcounty.momslikeme.com
Circulation:, 29,950fr; Sworn/Estimate/Non-Audited
Adv. Mgr. .... Ann Greeville
Adv. Mgr. .... Kim Lyons
Ed. .... Sharon Kindred
Prodn. Mgr. .... Corinne Ishler
Mechanical Specifications: Type page 9 1/2 x 11.

HUDSON VALLEY PARENT
(Mthly)
174 South St, Newburgh, NY, 12550-4546, Orange, USA; tel (845) 562-3606; fax (845) 562-3681; e-mail publisher@excitingread.com; adv e-mail sales@excitingread.com; ed e-mail editor@excitingread.com; web site www.hvparent.com
Circulation:, 36,000fr; Sworn/Estimate/Non-Audited
Established: 1994
Pub. .... Terrie Goldstein
Editor .... Felicia Hodges
Delivery Method: Carrier

SYRACUSE PARENT
(Mthly)
5910 Firestone Dr, Syracuse, NY, 13206-1103, Onondaga, USA; tel (315) 434-8889; fax (315) 434-8883; e-mail syracuseparent@ yahoo.com; ed e-mail editor@syracuseparent.net; web site www.syracuseparent.net
Circulation:, 26,500fr; Sworn/Estimate/Non-Audited
Adv. Mgr. .... Linda Tocci
Adv. Sales .... Colleen Kompf
Prodn. Mgr. .... Rachel Gillette
Mechanical Specifications: Type page 10 x 13; E - 4 cols, 2 1/4, 1/4 between; A - 4 cols, 2 1/4, 1/4 between; C - 6 cols, 1 1/4, 1/8 between.
Equipment: : Hardware — PC; Presses — G/ Community; Software — Adobe/PageMaker.

CAROLINA PARENT
(Mthly)
901 N Broadway, Ste 21, White Plains, NY, 10603-2414, Westchester, USA; tel (919) 956-2430; fax (919) 956-2427; e-mail info@carolinaparent.com; adv e-mail cgriffin@carolinaparent.com; ed e-mail bshugg@carolinaparent.com; web site www.carolinaparent.com
Circulation:, 37,044fr; CVC
Advertising: N/A
Established: 1988
Parent Co.: Morris Media Network/Morris Visitor Publications.
Digital Platform - Mobile: Apple, Android, Windows, Blackberry
Digital Platform - Tablet: Apple iOS, Android, Windows 7, Blackberry Tablet OS, Kindle, Nook, Kindle Fire
Art Dir. .... Cheri Vigna
Editor .... Beth Shugg
Publisher .... Brenda Larson
Sales Team Leader .... Candi Griffin
General Manager .... Gail Harris
Ed. .... Crickett Gibbons
Circ. Mgr. .... Liz Sprague Holt
Mechanical Specifications: Page 7.125x9.25; 1/2 page (h) 7.125 x 4.5; 1/2 page (v) 3.475 x 9.25; 1/4 page 3.475 x 4.5; 1/8 page 3.475 x 2.187
Equipment: : Hardware — APP/Mac; Software — Adobe, CS6, Microsoft Office packages
Delivery Method: Carrier, Racks
Zip Codes Served: 27701

NORTH CAROLINA

CHARLOTTE PARENT
(Mthly)
214 W Tremont Ave, Ste 302, Charlotte, NC, 28203-5161, Mecklenburg, USA; tel

(704) 344-1980; adv tel (704) 248-5221; ed tel (704) 248-5225; fax (704) 344-1983; e-mail info@charlotteparent.com; promo@charlotteparent.com; adv e-mail advertising@charlotteparent.com; ed e-mail editor@charlotteparent.com; web site www.charlotteparent.com
Circulation: 0pd,, 39,900fr; CVC
Advertising: N/A
Established: 1987
Publisher.............................. Sharon Havranek
Ed. .... Eve White
Mechanical Specifications: Type page 9 1/2 x 11; E - 4 cols, 2 1/4, 1/4 between.
Equipment: : Hardware — APP/Mac; Presses — Offset; Software — QPS/QuarkXPress.
Delivery Method: Newsstand
Zip Codes Served: 28203

SOUTH FLORIDA PARENTING MAGAZINE
(Mthly)
5716 Fayetteville Rd, Ste 201, Durham, NC, 27713-9662, Durham, USA; tel (954) 747-3050; fax (954) 747-3055; e-mail parentingsubmissions@sfparenting.com; web site www.southflorida.com/sfparenting
Circulation:, 91,546fr; CVC
Parent Co.: Forum Publishing Group.
Pub.. Lisa Goodlin
Adv. Mgr.............................. Angela Bartolone
Equipment: ; Software — QPS/QuarkXPress, Multi-Ad/Creator, Adobe/Photoshop.
Zip Codes Served: 33146

PIEDMONT PARENT
(Mthly)
PO Box 530, King, NC, 27021-0530, Stokes, USA; tel (336) 983-4789; fax (336) 983-2378; e-mail info@piedmontparent.com; web site www.piedmontparent.com
Circulation: 1pd,, 30,766fr; CVC
Advertising: N/A
Pub...................................... Sharon Havranek
Ed. .... Myra Wrigh

OHIO

COLUMBUS PARENT
(Mthly)
7801 N Central Dr, Lewis Center, OH, 43035-9407, Delaware, USA; tel (740) 888-6000; adv tel (614) 883-1921; fax (740) 888-6001; e-mail columbusparent@thisweeknews.com; web site www.columbusparent.com; www.thisweeknews.com
Circulation:, 44,310fr; CAC
Established: 1990
Vice Pres., Sales .... Traci Hogue
Acct. Exec.................................. Karen Laney
Ed. .... Donna Willis
Mechanical Specifications: Type page 10 x 13; E - 4 cols, 2 1/4, 1/8 between; A - 4 cols, 2 1/4, 1/8 between; C - 6 cols, 1 1/2, 1/8 between.
Equipment: : Hardware — APP/Power Mac G3; Presses — Offset Color Press; Software — QPS/QuarkXPress 4.04.
Zip Codes Served: 43017, 43016, 43123, 43220, 43229, 43081, 43212, 43068, 43082, 43235, 43204, 43222, 43223, 43228, 43201, 43211, 43215, 43224, 43209, 43213, 43227, 43232

ANN ARBOR FAMILY PRESS
(Mthly)
1120 Adams St, Toledo, OH, 43604-5509, Lucas, USA; tel (419) 244-9859; fax (419) 244-9871; e-mail cjacobs@adamsstreetpublishing.com; adv e-mail sales@adamsstreetpublishing.com; ed e-mail editor@adamsstreetpublishing.com; web site www.annarborfamily.com
Circulation: 0pd,, 21,708fr; CVC
Advertising: N/A
Established: 1998
Parent Co.: Adams Street Publishing Co..
Accounting........................... Robin Armstrong
Ed. in Chief .... Collette Jacobs
Mechanical Specifications: Type page 9 1/2 x 11 7/8; E - 4 cols, 2 1/8, 1/4 between; A - 4 cols, 2 1/8, 1/8 between; C - 5 cols, 1 3/4, 3/16 between.
Equipment: : Hardware — APP/Mac; Software — QPS/QuarkXPress 3.30, Adobe/Photoshop 3.0, Adobe/Illustrator.
Delivery Method: Newsstand
Zip Codes Served: 48103, 48118, 48130, 48198, 43624, 48176

TOLEDO AREA PARENT NEWS
(Mthly)
1120 Adams St, Toledo, OH, 43604-5509, Lucas, USA; tel (419) 244-9859; fax (419) 244-9871; e-mail editor@toledocitypaper.com; web site www.toledocitypaper.com
Circulation:, 36,000fr; Sworn/Estimate/Non-Audited
Advertising: Open inch rate $60
Established: 1992
Pub... Collette Jacobs
Admin. Acct.......................... Robin Armstrong
Acct. Exec................................ Andrew Spahr
Mechanical Specifications: Type page 9 1/2 x 11 7/8; E - 4 cols, 2 1/8, 1/4 between; A - 4 cols, 2 1/8, 3/8 between; C - 5 cols, 1 3/4, 3/16 between.
Equipment: : Hardware — APP/Mac; Software — QPS/QuarkXPress 3.30, Adobe/Photoshop 3.0, Adobe/Illustrator.
Zip Codes Served: 43560, 43566, 43551, 43537, 48182, 48144, 48161, 48157, 43620, 43623, 43624, 43402, 43463, 43556, 43528, 43602, 43604, 43605, 43606, 43607, 43608, 43609, 43610, 43611, 43612, 43613, 43614, 43615, 43616, 43617, 43618, 43619

ROCKY MOUNTAIN PARENT MAGAZINE
(Mthly)
224 S Market St, Troy, OH, 45373-3327, Miami, USA; tel (970) 221-9210; fax (970) 221-8556; e-mail editor@rockymountainpub.com; web site www.rmparentmagazine.com
Circulation:, 20,000fr; Sworn/Estimate/Non-Audited
Advertising: Open inch rate $28.00
Pub...................................... Scott Titterington
Adv. Mgr.................................. Greg Hoffman
Ed. .... Kristin Titterington

MAHONING VALLEY PARENT MAGAZINE
(Mthly)
240 Franklin St SE, Warren, OH, 44483-5711, Trumbull, USA; tel (330) 629-6229; adv tel (330) 651-5411; e-mail editor@mvparentmagazine.com; adv e-mail advertising@forparentsonline.com; ed e-mail editor@mvparentmagazine.com; web site www.forparentsonline.com
Circulation:, 36,830fr; CVC
Established: 1989
Parent Co.: Ogden Newspapers Inc.. Editions: Trumbull County Parent Magazine
Adv. Sales.................................. Robert Kurtz
Ed. .... Amy Leigh Wilson
Mechanical Specifications: Type page 7 1/4 x 9 1/2; E - 5 cols, 2 5/16, 1/12 between; A - 5 cols, 2 5/16, 1/12 between; C - 5 cols, 2 5/16, 1/12 between.
Delivery Method: Carrier
Zip Codes Served: 44512, 44514, 44515, 44484, 44408

LAKE COUNTY KIDS
(Mthly)
7085 Mentor Ave, Willoughby, OH, 44094-7948, Lake, USA; tel (440) 951-0000; adv tel 440-951-7653; fax (440) 951-0917; e-mail countykids@news-herald.com; ed e-mail tambrose@news-herald.com; web site www.news-herald.com
Circulation:, 13,000fr; Sworn/Estimate/Non-Audited
Pub..................................... Steve Roszczyk
Gen. Mgr................................ Rachel DiBiasio
Ed. .... Tricia Ambrose

OKLAHOMA

METROFAMILY MAGAZINE
(Mthly)
318 NW 13th St, Ste 101, Oklahoma City, OK, 73103-3709, Oklahoma, USA; tel (405) 601-2081; fax (405) 445-7509; e-mail sarah@metrofamilymagazine.com; adv e-mail sarah@metrofamilymagazine.com; ed e-mail hannah@metrofamilymagazine.com; web site www.metrofamilymagazine.com
Circulation: 20pd,, 32,000fr; CVC
Advertising: full page open rate: $2024
Established: 1998Editions: 12—
Dist. Mgr.................................. Kathy Alberty
Publisher.................................... Sarah Taylor
Editor .... Hannah Schmitt
Delivery Method: Racks
Zip Codes Served: 73034, 73013, 73120, 73116, 73112, 73069

PARENTS
(Mthly)
1622 S Denver Ave, Tulsa, OK, 74119-4233, Tulsa, USA; tel (937) 335-5634; fax (937) 335-3552; web site www.troydailynews.com
Pub.. Frank Beeson

OREGON

OREGON FAMILY MAGAZINE
(Mthly)
PO Box 21732, Eugene, OR, 97402-0411, Lane, USA; tel (541) 683-7452; adv tel (541) 683-7452; e-mail info@oregonfamily.com; adv e-mail sandy@oregonfamily.com; ed e-mail info@oregonfamily.com; web site www.oregonfamily.com
Circulation:, 20,000fr; Sworn/Estimate/Non-Audited
Established: 1994
Parent Co.: Pacific Parents Publishing. Editions: 264— month/year
Digital Platform - Mobile: Apple, Android, Windows, Blackberry
Digital Platform - Tablet: Apple iOS, Android, Blackberry Tablet OS
Owner/Pub.............................. Sandra Kauten
Advt Acct Mgr .... Christi Kessler
Mechanical Specifications: Type page 10x12
Equipment: : Hardware — PC, APP/Mac; Presses — web, cold, UV; Software — Adobe InDesign
Delivery Method: Newsstand, Carrier, Racks
Zip Codes Served: 97401, 97402, 97477, 97405, 97478, 97404, 97403

PENNSYLVANIA

PARENTS' EXPRESS
(Mthly)
290 Commerce Dr, Fort Washington, PA, 19034-2400, Montgomery, USA; tel (215) 542-0200; fax (215) 645-9495; web site www.parents-express.net
Circulation: 25pd,, 45,248fr; Sworn/Estimate/Non-Audited
Adv. Mgr.. John Bell
Ed. .... Daniel Sean Kaye
Zip Codes Served: 19147

SOUTH JERSEY PARENTS EXPRESS
(Mthly)
290 Commerce Dr, Fort Washington, PA, 19034-2400, Montgomery, USA; tel (215) 542-0200; fax (215) 629-4853; ed e-mail dkaye@montgomerynews.com; web site www.parents-express.net
Adv. Mgr.. John Bell
Ed. .... Daniel Kaye
Mechanical Specifications: Type page 9 1/2 x 12 1/4; E - 3 cols, 1 7/8, between; A - 4 cols, 1 7/8, 1/8 between.
Equipment: : Hardware — Software QPS/QuarkXPress 4.11, Adobe/Photoshop 5.5.

CENTRAL PENN PARENT
(Mthly)
1500 Paxton St, Harrisburg, PA, 17104-2615, Dauphin, USA; tel (717) 236-4300; fax (717) 236-6803; ed fax (717) 909-0538; e-mail annas@journalpub.com; web site www.centralpennparent.com
Circulation: 0pd,, 40,325fr; CVC
Established: 1996
Pub............................. David A. Schankweiler
Assoc. Pub.................................. Cathy Ashby
Adv. Mgr.............................. Sherry Kleinklaus
Circ. Dir.................................. Criss Kirkendall
Ed. .... Nikki M. Merry
Act. Exec...................................... Anna Seipe
Prodn. Mgr. .... Chad Pickard
Assoc. Pub.............................. Richard Cochran
Mechanical Specifications: Type page 10 1/8 x 13; E - 4 cols, 2 3/8, 3/16 between; C - 4 cols, 2 3/8, 3/16 between.
Equipment: : Hardware — APP/Power Mac; Software — QPS/QuarkXPress 4.1, Adobe/Photoshop 4.0, Adobe/Illustrator 6.0.

ABOUT FAMILIES PARENTING NEWSPAPER
(Mthly)
100 E Cumberland St, Lebanon, PA, 17042-5400, Lebanon, USA; tel (717) 273-8127; fax (717) 273-0420; ed e-mail editor@aboutfamiliespa.com; web site www.aboutfamiliespa.com
Circulation:, 42,390fr; CVC
Advertising: N/A
Established: 1995
Publication Coord. .... Judy Fetterolf
Adv. Mgr.................................. James Snyder
Ed. .... Susan Zeller
Mechanical Specifications: Type page 10 1/2 x 13; E - 4 cols, 2 1/2, 1/4 between; A - 4 cols, 2 1/2, 1/4 between; C - 4 cols, 2 1/2, 1/4 between.
Equipment: : Hardware — APP/Mac; Software — Microsoft/Word `97, QPS/QuarkXPress 4.0.

BALTIMORE'S CHILD
(Mthly)
1414 Pine St, Philadelphia, PA, 19102-4603, Philadelphia, USA; tel (410) 542-4166; fax 443-697-0212; e-mail info@baltimoreschild.com; web site www.baltimoreschild.com
Circulation:, 45,000fr; Sworn/Estimate/Non-Audited
Advertising: Open inch rate $40.40
Established: 1983
Digital Platform - Mobile: Apple, Android
Digital Platform - Tablet: Apple iOS, Android, Kindle
Pub... Joanne Giza
Mng. Ed.................................... Sharon Keech
Prodn. Mgr. .... Jen Perkins Frantz
Mechanical Specifications: Full page:7.125 x 9.4375, 1/2 page: 3.5 x 9.4375, 1/3 page: 2.25 x 9.4375, 1/4 page: 3.5 x 4.625. Other sizes available.
Delivery Method: Racks
Zip Codes Served: 20707, 20708, 20723, 20724, 20759, 20763, 20777, 20794, 21001, 21005, 21009, 21014, 21015, 21017, 21017, 21022, 21028, 21029, 21030, 21030, 21031, 21040, 21042, 21043, 21044, 21045, 21046, 21047, 21048, 21050, 21051, 21057, 21061, 21071, 21074, 21075, 21076, 21078, 21084, 21085, 21087, 21090, 21093, 21093, 21102, 21104, 21108, 21111, 21113, 21117, 21120, 21122, 21128, 21131, 21136, 21146, 21153, 21156, 21157, 21158, 21162, 21163, 21201, 21202, 21203, 21204, 21205, 21206, 21207, 21208, 21209, 21210, 21211, 21212, 21213, 21214, 21215, 21216, 21217, 21218, 21219, 21220, 21221, 21221, 21222, 21223, 21224, 21225, 21225, 21226, 21226, 21227, 21228, 21229, 21230, 21231, 21234, 21234, 21235, 21236, 21237, 21239, 21244, 21252, 21285, 21286, 21287, 21401, 21723, 21771, 21771, 21776, 21784, 21784, 21797, 21901, 21903, 21904,

21911, 21914, 21915, 21915, 21919, 21921, 21930, 21102-0408, 21229-5299

METROKIDS DELAWARE
(Mthly)
1412-1414 Pine St, Philadelphia, PA, 19102, Philadelphia, USA; tel (856) 667-3555; fax (215) 291-5563; e-mail info@metrokids.com; adv e-mail sales@metrokids.com; ed e-mail editor@metrokids.com; web site www.metrokids.com
Established: 1990
Adv. Mgr. .... Darlene Weinmann
Circ. Mgr. .... Andrea Spiegel
Ed. in Chief .... Nancy Lisagor
Exec. Ed. .... Tom Livingston
Prod. Mgr. .... Tracie Rucker
Mechanical Specifications: Type page 10 x 12 3/8; E - 4 cols, 2 3/8, 1/6 between; A - 4 cols, 2 3/8, 1/6 between; C - 4 cols, 2 3/8, 1/6 between.
Equipment: : Hardware — APP/Macs.
Zip Codes Served: 19701, 19973, 21901, 21921

METROKIDS SOUTH JERSEY
(Mthly)
1412-1414 Pine St, Philadelphia, PA, 19102, Philadelphia, USA; tel (215) 291-5560; fax (215) 291-5563; e-mail info@metrokids.com; adv e-mail sales@metrokids.com; ed e-mail editor@metrokids.com; web site www.metrokids.com
Adv. Mgr. .... Darlene Weinmann
Circ. Mgr. .... Andrea Miller
Ed. in Chief .... Nancy Lisagor
Exec. Ed. .... Tom Livingston
Prod. Mgr. .... Tracie Rucker
Mechanical Specifications: Type page 10 x 11 1/4; E - 4 cols, 2 3/8, between; A - 4 cols, 2 3/8, between; C - 5 cols, 1 5/8, between.
Equipment: : Hardware — APP/Mac; Software — QPS/QuarkXPress.
Zip Codes Served: 08002, 08691

PITTSBURGH PARENT
(Mthly)
1126 Pittsburgh Rd, # RT8, Valencia, PA, 16059-1930, Butler, USA; tel (724) 898-1898; fax (724) 898-1877; e-mail manager@pittsburghparent.com; adv e-mail manager@pittsburghparent.com; ed e-mail editor@pittsburghparent.com; web site www.pittsburghparent.com
Circulation: 32pd,, 45,728fr; VAC
Established: 1988
Parent Co.: Honey Hill Publishing.
Digital Platform - Mobile: Apple
Digital Platform - Tablet: Apple iOS
Circ. Mgr. .... Lynn Honeywill
Delivery Method: Mail, Racks
Zip Codes Served: ti-state area of western PA

SOUTH CAROLINA

LOWCOUNTRY PARENT MAGAZINE
(Mthly)
134 Columbus St, Charleston, SC, 29403-4809, Charleston, USA; tel (843) 577-7111; adv tel (843) 958-7394; ed tel (843) 958-7393; fax (843) 937-5579; adv fax (843) 937-5579; ed fax (843) 937-5579; e-mail info@lowcountryparent.com; adv e-mail dkifer@postandcourier.com; ed e-mail editor@lowcountryparent.com; web site www.lowcountryparent.com
Circulation:, 41,000fr; Sworn/Estimate/Non-Audited
Established: 1997
Parent Co.: The Post and Courier.
Adv. Sales Mgr. .... Doug Kifer
Ed. .... Shannon Brigham

TENNESSEE

MEMPHIS PARENT
(Mthly)
460 Tennessee St, Ste 200, Memphis, TN, 38103-4486, Shelby, USA; tel (901) 521-9000; fax (901) 521-0129; e-mail mphsparent@contemporary-media.com; web site www.memphisparent.com
Circulation:, 34,975fr; CVC
Advertising: N/A
Pub. .... Kenneth Neill
Adv. Mgr. .... Sheryl Butler
Ed. .... Jane Schneider
Mechanical Specifications: Type page 9 3/4 x 12 1/2; E - 4 cols, 2 5/16, 1/4 between; A - 4 cols, 2 5/16, between; C - 4 cols, 2 5/16, between.

NASHVILLE PARENT MAGAZINE
(Mthly)
2200 Rosa L Parks Blvd, Nashville, TN, 37228-1306, Davidson, USA; tel (615) 256-2158; fax (615) 256-2114; e-mail stewart@daycommedia.com; web site www.parentworld.com
Circulation: 10pd,, 36,191fr; CVC
Advertising: N/A
Established: 1993
Parent Co.: Day Communications Inc.
Pub. .... Stewart Day
Ed. .... Susan Day
Mng. Ed. .... Chad Young
Prodn. Mgr. .... Tim Henard
Mechanical Specifications: Type page 9 1/2 x 11.

RUTHERFORD PARENT
(Mthly)
2200 Rosa L Parks Blvd, Nashville, TN, 37228-1306, Davidson, USA; tel (615) 256-2158; fax (615) 256-2114; e-mail stewart@daycommedia.com; web site www.parentworld.com
Circulation:, 13,111fr; CVC
Advertising: N/A
Established: 1993
Adv. Mgr. .... Stewart Day
Circ. Mgr. .... Tom Guardino
Ed. in Chief .... Susan Day
Mng. Ed. .... Chad Young
Prodn. Mgr. .... Tim Henard

TEXAS

DALLASCHILD
(Mthly)
4275 Kellway Cir, Ste 146, Addison, TX, 75001-5731, Dallas, USA; tel (972) 447-9188; adv tel (214) 707-6174; ed tel (214) 707-6174; e-mail publishing@dfwchild.com; adv e-mail advertising@dfwchild.com; ed e-mail editorial@dfwchild.com; web site dfwchild.com
Circulation:, 55,000fr; CVC
Established: 1984
Parent Co.: Lauren Publications.
Digital Platform - Mobile: Apple, Android
Digital Platform - Tablet: Apple iOS, Android
Publisher .... Joylyn Niebes
Creative & Content Director .... Lauren Niebes-Piccirillo
Equipment: : Hardware — APP/Mac; Software — QPS/QuarkXPress, Adobe/Photoshop, Adobe/Illustrator.
Delivery Method: Racks
Zip Codes Served: 75001, 75002, 75019, 75006, 75007, 75010, 75023, 75024, 75093, 75204, 75205, 75209, 75219, 75220, 75225, 75218, 75214, 75243, 75248, 75252,75033, 75034, 75035, 75068, 75078, 75070. 75002, 75013, 75025.

METROKIDS MAGAZINE
(Mthly) (Special Editions Annually, Bi Annually
4275 Kellway Cir, Ste 146, Addison, TX, 75001-5731, Dallas, USA; tel (215) 291-5560; fax (215) 291-5565; e-mail info@metrokids.com; adv e-mail sales@metrokids.com; ed e-mail editor@metrokids.com; web site www.metrokids.com
Circulation:, 90fr; Sworn/Estimate/Non-Audited
Established: 1991Editions: 3— Pennsylvania, South Jersey and Delaware
Digital Platform - Mobile: Apple, Android, Windows, Blackberry, Other
Digital Platform - Tablet: Apple iOS, Android, Windows 7, Blackberry Tablet OS, Kindle, Nook, Kindle Fire, Other
Publisher .... Darlene Weinmann
Ed. in Chief .... Nancy Lisagor
Managing Editor .... Sara Murphy
Delivery Method: Racks
Zip Codes Served: Greater Philadelphia MetroMarket
5 County Southeastern PA, Southern New Jersey and Delaware

QUEENS PARENT
(Mthly)
4275 Kellway Cir, Ste 146, Addison, TX, 75001-5731, Dallas, USA; tel (212) 315-0800; web site www.nymetroparents.com
Circulation:, 54,910fr; CVC
Advertising: N/A
Established: 1985

HOUSTON FAMILY MAGAZINE
(Mthly)
5131 Braesvalley Dr, Houston, TX, 77096-2609, Harris, USA; tel (713) 266-1885; fax (713) 266-1915; e-mail dana@houstonfamilymagazine.com; adv e-mail kim@houstonfamilymagazine.com; ed e-mail dana@houstonfamilymagazine.com; web site www.houstonfamilymagazine.com
Circulation:, 60,000fr; Sworn/Estimate/Non-Audited
Advertising: Open inch rate $51.00
Publisher .... Kimberly Davis-Guerra
Adv. Mgr. .... Dana Donovan

AUSTIN FAMILY
(Mthly)
PO Box 7559, Round Rock, TX, 78683-7559, Williamson, USA; tel (512) 733-0038; adv e-mail kaye2003@austinfamily.com; ed e-mail editor2003@austinfamily.com; web site www.austinfamily.com
Circulation:, 35,000fr; Sworn/Estimate/Non-Audited
Established: 1991
Pub. .... Kaye Kemper
Ed. .... Melanie Dunham
Advising Ed. .... Dr. Betty Kehl Richardson
Art Dir. .... John Faranzetti
Calendar Ed. .... Betty Kemper
Mechanical Specifications: Type page 10 x 13.

OUR KIDS SAN ANTONIO
(Wed)
8400 Blanco Rd, Ste 300, San Antonio, TX, 78216-3055, Bexar, USA; tel (210) 349-6667; adv tel (210) 305-4181 Ext. 101; fax (210) 349-5618; e-mail sanantonio.parenting@parenthood.com; adv e-mail pat@ourkidsmagazine.com; web site http://www.ourkidsmagazine.com/
Circulation:, 50,000fr; Sworn/Estimate/Non-Audited
Pub. .... Rudy Riojas
Ed. .... Cynthia Ladson
Zip Codes Served: 78216

VIRGINIA

RICHMOND PARENTS MONTHLY
(Mthly)
1506 Staples Mill Rd, Ste 102, Richmond, VA, 23230-3631, Richmond City, USA; tel (804) 673-5203; fax (804) 673-5308; e-mail rpmag@aol.com; web site www.richmondparents.com
Circulation:, 35,000fr; Sworn/Estimate/Non-Audited
Ed. .... Mark E. Fetter
Mng. Ed. .... Angela Lehman-Rios

WASHINGTON FAMILY MAGAZINE
(Mthly)
1372 Old Bridge Rd, Ste 101, Woodbridge, VA, 22192-2755, Prince William, USA; tel (703) 318-1385; fax (703) 318-5509; e-mail publisher@thefamilymagazine.com; adv e-mail sales@thefamilymagazine.com; ed e-mail editor@thefamilymagazine.com; web site www.washingtonfamily.com
Circulation: 7pd,, 53,500fr; CVC
Advertising: N/A
Established: 1992
Parent Co.: Northern Virginia Media Services.
Digital Platform - Mobile: Apple, Android, Windows, Blackberry
Digital Platform - Tablet: Apple iOS, Android, Windows 7, Blackberry Tablet OS, Kindle, Kindle Fire
Chief Operating Officer .... Bruce Potter
Associate Publisher .... Sylvia Witaschek
Mechanical Specifications: Type page 8 x 11; E - 3 cols, 1 11/16, 1/2 between; A - 3 cols, 1 11/16, 1/2 between; C - 3 cols, 1 11/16, 1/2 between.
Equipment: : Hardware — APP/Mac; Software — Adobe/InDesign
Delivery Method: Racks

WASHINGTON

SEATTLE'S CHILD
(Mthly)
4303 198th St SW, Lynnwood, WA, 98036-6777, Snohomish, USA; tel (206) 441-0191; fax (425) 774-8622; ed e-mail editor@seattleschild.com; web site www.seattleschild.com
Circulation:, 80,000fr; Sworn/Estimate/Non-AuditedEditions: 1— 1 total Snohomish Co. (28,000);
Pub. Asst. .... Mary Armstrong
Ed. .... Ann Bergman
Mechanical Specifications: Type page 10 3/16 x 13 1/4.
Zip Codes Served: 98121

PARENTMAP
(Mthly)
7683 SE 27th St, Mercer Island, WA, 98040-2804, King, USA; tel (206) 709-9026; adv tel (206) 709-9026; fax (206) 455-7984; e-mail admin@parentmap.com; adv e-mail jess@parentmap.com; ed e-mail jody@parentmap.com; web site https://www.parentmap.com/
Circulation: 120pd,, 45,000fr; Sworn/Estimate/Non-Audited
Established: 2003
Digital Platform - Mobile: Apple, Android
Advertising & Partnerships, Manager .... Ida Wicklund
Circ. Mgr. .... Danielle Sackett
Ed. .... Karen Matthee
Prodn. Mgr. .... Anton Hafele
Mechanical Specifications: Type page 10 3/16 x 13 1/4.
Delivery Method: Mail, Carrier, Racks
Zip Codes Served: Over 140 zip codes
Note: ParentMap is a free monthly news magazine for parents in the Puget Sound area of the Pacific Northwest.
ParentMap also offers a web site with searchable online events calendar for family-related activities, as well as a family directory, where parents can search for local businesses and classes that cater to families.

WISCONSIN

DANE COUNTY KIDS
(Mthly)
2420 Evans Rd, Mc Farland, WI, 53558-9043, Dane, USA; tel (608) 444-0654; adv tel (608) 444-0654; ed tel same; e-mail kerickson@ericksonpublishing.com; adv e-mail same; ed e-mail same; web site tbd... revising
Circulation:, 50,000fr; Sworn/Estimate/Non-Audited
Advertising: $1200. per full page 7.5"H x 9.75"V
Established: 1992Editions: 1— tbd
Digital Platform - Mobile: Apple
Digital Platform - Tablet: Apple iOS, Android, Other
Pres./Pub. .... Kristin Erickson
Assoc. Editor .... Lynn Wittsell
Mechanical Specifications: full color available; send PDFs; inquire about full-page bleed ads and special placement and four-color vs. black and white.
Equipment: : Hardware — Macintosh; Presses — Web Press; Software — Quark, Illustrator, Photoshop
Delivery Method: Mail, Racks
Zip Codes Served: throughout southcentral Wisconsin and nationwide with our special family tourism guide
Note: We need the latest, most interesting info.about parenting kids birth-18. Also info. pertaining to women 25-54. We are also in need of info.re: new books, CDs, toys, parenting equip. of all kinds, education-related materials, pampering products for mom, pregnancy products, gifts, the best the women's and parenting industries have to offer. We want to share the news. Send product samples to Kristin Erickson, Publisher, Dane County Kids, 2420 Evans Road, McFarland, WI 53558.

METROPARENT
(Mthly)
333 W State St, Milwaukee, WI, 53203-1305, Milwaukee, USA; tel (414) 647-2478; adv tel 414-647-4734; fax (414) 224-7690; adv fax 414-224-7690; e-mail info@metroparentmagazine.com; adv e-mail bsteimle@journalsentinel.com; ed e-mail rchristman@metroparentmagazine.com; web site www.metroparentmagazine.com
Circulation:, 42,233fr; CVC
Advertising: Open inch rate $39.00
Established: 1986
Parent Co.: Journal Media Group.
Milwaukee Journal Sentinel.
General Manager .... Becky Steimle
Ed. .... Amanda Robison
Editor .... Rebecca Christman
Mechanical Specifications: Type page 9 x 11; E - 4 cols, 2 1/4, between; A - 4 cols, 2 1/4, between; C - 4 cols, 2 1/4, between.
Equipment: : Hardware — APP/Power Mac 8500, APP/Mac Performa 600, APP/Mac Performa 638, APP/Mac Laserwriter 360/6cc, Elite XI 616, SyQuest 200mb; Presses — G/Community, G/Urbanite; Software — QPS/QuarkXPress 3.32.
Delivery Method: Newsstand, Racks

REAL ESTATE PUBLICATIONS IN THE UNITED STATES

CALIFORNIA

ALTA LOMA

THE HOMES MAGAZINE (Mthly)
6683 Capitol Pl, Alta Loma, CA, 91701-7784, San Bernardino, USA; tel (909) 948-7255; fax (909) 948-7258; e-mail homemag@earthlink.net; web site www.thehomesmagazine.com
Circulation:, 25,500fr; Sworn/Estimate/Non-Audited
Pub .... Connie Endter
Gen. Mgr. .... Dave Endter
Equipment: Hardware — APP/Mac G3; Software — QPS/QuarkXPress 3.3.

ATASCADERO

CENTRAL COAST HOMES MAGAZINE
(Mthly)
7544 Morro Rd, Atascadero, CA, 93422-4404, San Luis Obispo, USA; tel (805) 461-7898; fax (805) 466-8359; e-mail mraike@homesmagazine.com; sales@globalhomes.com; web site www.globalhomes.com
Circulation:, 30,000fr; Sworn/Estimate/Non-Audited
Pub .... Mike Raike

NAPA

DISTINCTIVE PROPERTIES (Mthly)
1615 2nd St, Napa, CA, 94559-2818, Napa, USA; tel (707) 256-2244; adv tel (707) 256-2244; ed tel (707) 256-2244; fax (707) 252-6047; e-mail jfawkes@napanews.com; adv e-mail jfawkes@napanews.com; ed e-mail jfawkes@napanews.com; web site www.distinctiveproperties.com
Circulation:, 5,000fr; Sworn/Estimate/Non-Audited
Advertising: Open inch rate $11.15
Group: Lee Enterprises, Inc.
Pub .... Brenda Speth
Circulation & Classified Advertising Director .... Jennifer Fawkes
Mechanical Specifications: Type page 7 1/2 x 9 3/4.
Delivery Method: Racks
Zip Codes Served: 94559, 94558, 94574, 94515, 94508, 94503, 94562, 94567, 94573, 94576, 94599

WINE COUNTRY WEEKLY REAL ESTATE READER (Fri)
1436 2nd St, Unit 182, Napa, CA, 94559-5005, Napa, USA; tel (707) 258-6150; adv tel (707) 258-6150; fax (707) 258-6152; e-mail publisher@rereader.com; adv e-mail support@rereader.com; web site www.rereader.com
Circulation: 9,500pd, 57,000fr; Sworn/Estimate/Non-Audited
Advertising: Open inch rate $30.00
Established: 1987.
Pub .... Teresa M. Galligan
Mng. Ed. .... Charles Kamins
Prodn. Mgr. .... Heather N. Hayne
Mechanical Specifications: Type page 10 1/4 x 13; E - 5 cols, 2, 1/8 between; C - 6 cols, 1 1/4, 1/8 between.
Equipment: Hardware — APP/Mac.
Zip Codes Served: 94558

PALM SPRINGS

HOMEFINDER (Sat)
750 N Gene Autry Trl, Palm Springs, CA, 92262-5463, Riverside, USA; tel (760) 322-8889; fax (760) 778-4560; adv fax (760) 778-4528; ed fax (760) 778-4654; e-mail mwinkler@gannet.com; adv e-mail sbweaver@gannett.com; ed e-mail grburton@gannett.com; web site www.mydesert.com
Circulation: 52,213pd, 50,000fr; Sworn/Estimate/Non-Audited
Advertising: Open inch rate $46.00
Established: 1927.
Circ. Mgr. .... Greg Castro
Equipment; Presses — 6-G; Software — QPS/QuarkXPress 3.2, Adobe/Photoshop 6.0.
Delivery Method: Carrier, Racks
Zip Codes Served: 92262, 92234, 92240, 92264, 92210, 92211, 92260, 92270, 92276, 92236, 92201, 92203, 92253

COLORADO

COLORADO SPRINGS

COLSOUTHERN COLORADO HOMES ILLUSTRATED (Other) (Every two weeks)
660 Southpointe Ct, Ste 200, Colorado Springs, CO, 80906-3874, El Paso, USA; tel (719) 785-4172; fax (719) 576-2918; e-mail info@homes-illustrated.com; web site www.homesillustrated.com
Circulation:; Sworn/Estimate/Non-Audited
Pub .... Hal Douthit
Delivery Method: Mail, Carrier, Racks

SOUTHERN COLORADO HOMES ILLUSTRATED (Bi-Weekly)
660 Southpointe Ct, Ste 200, Colorado Springs, CO, 80906-3874, El Paso, USA; tel (800) 876-5777; fax (719) 785-4172; e-mail info@homes-Illustrated.com; web site www.homesillustrated.com
Circulation:, 4,500fr; Sworn/Estimate/Non-Audited
Pub .... Hal Douthit
Editor .... Nina Halloran

CONNECTICUT

BETHLEHEM

TOWN & COUNTRY HOMES (Mthly)
70 Main St S, Bethlehem, CT, 06751-2001, Litchfield, USA; tel (860) 583-5363; fax (203) 266-5364
Circulation:; Sworn/Estimate/Non-Audited
Pub .... Edward Mergenthaler
Ed. .... Jennifer Goewy

CANTON

FOR SALE BY OWNER CONNECTION
(Mthly)
PO Box 602, Canton, CT, 06019-0602, Hartford, USA; tel (860) 659-3726; fax (860) 633-1850; e-mail info@cutthecommission.com; web site www.cutthecommission.com
Circulation:, 60,000fr; Sworn/Estimate/Non-Audited
Ed. .... Carol York
Zip Codes Served: 6019

NORWICH

HALLMARK HOMES (Every other Wed)
PO Box 626, Norwich, CT, 06360-0626, New London, USA; tel (860) 886-5245; fax (860) 886-5244; adv e-mail hhhomesmag@aol.com; web site http://www.hallmarkct.com/
Circulation:, 23,000fr; Sworn/Estimate/Non-Audited
Pub .... Mike Connell
Delivery Method: Carrier

FLORIDA

KISSIMMEE

OSCEOLA HOMEFINDER (Mthly)
108 Church St, Kissimmee, FL, 34741-5055, Osceola, USA; tel (407) 846-7600; adv tel (321) 402-0413; ed tel (321) 402-0436; fax (321) 402-2946; adv e-mail BBerry@osceolanewsgazette.com; ed e-mail bmcbride@osceolanewsgazette.com; web site www.aroundosceola.com
Circulation:; Sworn/Estimate/Non-Audited
Advertising: Open inch rate $12.95
Pub .... Paula Stark
Circ. Mgr. .... Kathy Beckham
Ed. .... Marvin Cortner
Asst. Ed. .... Rick Madewell
Prodn. Mgr. .... Ellen Johnston
Mechanical Specifications: Type page 9 3/4 x 12 1/2; E - 6 cols, 1 3/8, 3/8 between; A - 6 cols, 1 3/8, 3/8 between; C - 6 cols, 1 3/8, 3/8 between.
Equipment: Hardware — APP/Macs; Software — QPS/QuarkXPress 4.1, Adobe/Photoshop 6.0, Adobe/Illustrator 9.0.
Zip Codes Served: 34741, 34743, 34744, 34746, 34747, 34758, 34759, 34769, 34771, 34772

NORTH PORT

FLORIDA MARINER/GULF MARINER
(Every other Sun)
PO Box 8070, North Port, FL, 34290-8070, Sarasota, USA; tel (941) 488-9307; fax (941) 488-9309; e-mail flmariner@floridamariner.com; ed e-mail cjones@floridamariner.com; web site www.floridamariner.com
Circulation:, 23,500fr; Sworn/Estimate/Non-Audited
Advertising: Open inch rate $39.95
Publisher .... Michael Jones
Ed. .... Stacey Fulgieri

OKEECHOBEE

REAL ESTATE PREVIEW (Mthly)
106 SE 5th St, Okeechobee, FL, 34974-4320, Okeechobee, USA; tel (863) 763-2205; fax (863) 467-1674
Circulation:; Sworn/Estimate/Non-Audited
Ed. .... J.W. Owens
Mechanical Specifications: Type page 7 3/4 x 10; E - 4 cols, between; A - 4 cols, between.
Equipment: Hardware — IBM; Presses — HI;

Software — Adobe/PageMaker.

GEORGIA

MARTINEZ

HOME GUIDE (Mthly)
109 Camilla Ave, Martinez, GA, 30907-3406, Columbia, USA; tel (706) 868-8544; fax (706) 868-8381; e-mail handl@augustashomes.com; web site www.augustashomes.com
Circulation:; Sworn/Estimate/Non-Audited
Ed.............Larry Boerckel

HOMES & LAND OF AUGUSTA (Mthly)
109 Camilla Ave, Martinez, GA, 30907-3406, Columbia, USA; tel (706) 868-8544; fax (706) 868-8381; e-mail handl@augustashomes.com; web site www.augustashomes.com
Circulation:, 22,000fr; Sworn/Estimate/Non-Audited
Ed.............Larry Boerckel
Zip Codes Served: 30907

KANSAS

KANSAS CITY

JACKSON-CASS HOMES (Every other Thur)
130 Abbie Ave, Kansas City, KS, 66103-1304, Wyandotte, USA; tel (913) 621-4663; fax (913) 621-6470; e-mail jackson@kchomes.com; web site www.kchomes.com
Circulation:, 10,000fr; Sworn/Estimate/Non-Audited
Pub.............Bonnie Boyles

KANSAS HOMES (Every other Thur)
130 Abbie Ave, Kansas City, KS, 66103-1304, Wyandotte, USA; tel (913) 621-4663; fax (913) 621-6470; web site www.kchomes.com
Circulation:, 15,000fr; Sworn/Estimate/Non-Audited
Pub.............Bonnie Boyles
Zip Codes Served: 64103

SUBURBAN NORTH HOMES BUYER'S GUIDE (Every other Week)
130 Abbie Ave, Kansas City, KS, 66103-1304, Wyandotte, USA; tel (913) 621-4663; fax (913) 621-6470; e-mail north@kchomes.com; web site www.kchomes.com
Circulation:, 13,000fr; Sworn/Estimate/Non-Audited
Pub.............Bonnie Boyles
Zip Codes Served: 64103

WICHITA

REAL ESTATE BOOK (Mthly)
PO Box 1897, Wichita, KS, 67201-1897, Sedgwick, USA; tel (316) 788-0191; fax (316) 794-8767; e-mail jstebens@aol.com
Circulation:; Sworn/Estimate/Non-Audited
Jim Stebens
Nikki StebensEd.s

KENTUCKY

ELIZABETHTOWN

CENTRAL KENTUCKY HOMES REAL ESTATE (Mthly)
408 W Dixie Ave, Elizabethtown, KY, 42701-2455, Hardin, USA; tel (270) 769-1200; fax (270) 765-7318; adv e-mail Ljobe@thenewsenterprise.com; web site www.newsenterpriseonline.com
Circulation:, 10,000fr; Sworn/Estimate/Non-Audited
Pub.............Chris Ordway
Ed.............Ben Sheroan
Circ. Mgr.............Portia Oldham
Advertising Director............Larry Jobe
Delivery Method: Racks
Zip Codes Served: 42701

MASSACHUSETTS

BOSTON

BANKER & TRADESMAN (Mon)
280 Summer St, Fl 8, Boston, MA, 02210-1131, Suffolk, USA; tel (617) 428-5100; adv tel (617) 896-5357; ed tel (617) 896-5313; e-mail editorial@thewarrengroup.com; adv e-mail gchateauneuf@thewarrengroup.com; ed e-mail editorial@thewarrengroup.com; web site www.bankerandtradesman.com
Established: 1872.
Group: The Warren Group
Pres./COO............David Lovins
Ed Dir............Cassidy Murphy
CEO............Timothy Warren
Delivery Method: Mail

FALL RIVER

REAL ESTATE GUIDE (Fri)
207 Pocasset St, Fall River, MA, 02721-1532, Bristol, USA; tel (508) 676-8211; fax (508) 676-2588; e-mail news@heraldnews.com; web site www.heraldnews.com
Circulation: 32,173pd; Sworn/Estimate/Non-Audited
Advertising: Open inch rate $17.50
Pub.............Sean Burke
Adv. Dir.............Tom Booth
Circ. Dir.............Tom Amato
Mng. Ed.............Linda Murphy
Mng. Ed.............Jon Root
Prodn. Mgr.............Mike Niland
Mechanical Specifications: Type page 10 1/2 x 12; E - 7 cols, 1 7/16, between; C - 7 cols, 1 7/16, between.
Equipment: Hardware — IBM, APP/Macs, MON; Presses — 9-G/Urbanite; Software — Dewar, Multi-Ad/Creator.

NEEDHAM

BOSTON HOMES
254 2nd Ave, Needham, MA, 02494-2829, Norfolk, USA; tel (617) 262-0444; adv tel (888) 828-1515; ed tel (781) 433-8323; fax (617) 266-7333; web site http://www.linkbostonhomes.com
Pub. David Petruska
Ed. Marilyn Jackson

SPRINGFIELD

APARTMENTS (Mthly)
525 Belmont Ave, Springfield, MA, 01108-1789, Hampden, USA; tel (413) 734-3411; fax (413) 734-0099; e-mail tomgreen@apt-4-rent.com, info@apt-4-rent.com; web site www.apt-4-rent.com
Circulation:, 30,000fr; Sworn/Estimate/Non-Audited
Pub.............Tom Green
Dir., Mktg.............Tom Savoy
Zip Codes Served: 1108

MICHIGAN

MOUNT PLEASANT

NORTHERN MICHIGAN REAL ESTATE MARKETPLACE (Mthly)
711 W Pickard St, Mount Pleasant, MI, 48858-1585, Isabella, USA; tel (989) 779-6000; fax (989) 779-6162; e-mail news@michigannewspapers.com; web site www.themorningsun.com
Circulation:, 25,000fr; Sworn/Estimate/Non-Audited
Pub.............Al Frattura
Adv. Dir.............Don Negus
Adv. Mgr.............Donna Pung
Exec. Ed.............Rick Mills

THE REAL ESTATE REVIEW (Mthly)
711 W Pickard St, Mount Pleasant, MI, 48858-1585, Isabella, USA; tel (800) 616-6397; fax (989) 779-6009; web site http://www.myhomemi.com/
Circulation:, 15,000fr; Sworn/Estimate/Non-Audited
Circ. Mgr.............Christine Fox
Mktg. Cood.............Angel Norbury
Mechanical Specifications: Type page 7 1/4 x 9 1/2; A - 4 cols, 1 5/8, 1/8 between.

PONTIAC

HOMES FOR SALE (Thur)
48 W Huron St, Pontiac, MI, 48342-2101, Oakland, USA; tel (248) 745-4794; fax (248) 332-3003; web site www.theoaklandpress.com
Circulation:, 17,000fr; Sworn/Estimate/Non-Audited
Pub.............Jeannie Parent

NEW JERSEY

COLTS NECK

HOME IMPROVEMENT GUIDE (Mthly)
440 State Route 34, Colts Neck, NJ, 07722-2525, Monmouth, USA; tel (732) 780-7474; fax (732) 414-1736; e-mail info@homeimprovementguides.com; web site www.homeimprovementguides.com
Circulation:, 95,000fr; Sworn/Estimate/Non-Audited
Advertising: see website
Established: 2003.
Circ. Mgr.............Nick Montalbano
Mechanical Specifications: see website
Delivery Method: Mail, Racks

MORRISTOWN

HOMES & ESTATES MAGAZINE (Wed)
173 Morris St, Morristown, NJ, 07960-4332, Morris, USA; tel (201) 394-3084; fax (973) 264-1153; e-mail gene@homesandestatesonline.com; web site http://www.homesandestatesonline.com/skins/housemagazine/
Circulation:, 35,000fr; Sworn/Estimate/Non-Audited
Peter Best
Gene PetragliaPub.s
Mechanical Specifications: Type page 6 3/4 x 9 3/8.

NEW MEXICO

LAS CRUCES

REAL ESTATE PRESS OF LAS CRUCES (Mthly)
256 W Las Cruces Ave, Las Cruces, NM, 88005-1804, Dona Ana, USA; tel (575) 541-5467; fax (575) 541-5499; e-mail mderk@lcsun-news.com; web site www.repress.comMaria Derk
Delivery Method: Racks
Zip Codes Served: 88001, 88005, 88007, 88011, 88012

SANTA FE

HOME/SANTA FE REAL ESTATE GUIDE (Sun, Mthly)
202 E Marcy St, Santa Fe, NM, 87501-2021, Santa Fe, USA; tel (505) 983-3303; adv tel (505) 986-3007; ed tel (505) 986-3043; fax (505) 995-3875; adv fax (505) 984-1785; ed fax (505) 995-3875; e-mail reguide@sfnewmexican.com; adv e-mail wortega@sfnewmexican.com; ed e-mail pweideman@sfnewmexican.com; web site www.santafenewmexican.com
Circulation: 18,000pd; Sworn/Estimate/Non-Audited
Established: 1997.
Group: The New Mexican, Inc.
Digital Platform - Mobile: Apple, Android, Windows, Blackberry, Other
Digital Platform - Tablet: Apple iOS, Android, Windows 7, Blackberry Tablet OS, Kindle, Nook, Kindle Fire, Other
Ed.............Paul Weideman
Advertising AE............Wendy Ortega
Mechanical Specifications: Type page 9 3/4 x 11 1/2; E - 4 cols, 1 1/5, between; A - 4 cols, 1 1/5, between.
Equipment: Hardware — APP/Macs, PCs; Presses — 9-G/Urbanite; Software — NewsEditPro/IQue 3.5.1, Adobe/InDesign 2.0.
Delivery Method: Mail, Newsstand, Carrier, Racks
Zip Codes Served: 87501, 87502, 87504, 87505, 87508, 87544, 87532, 87507, 87010

NEW YORK

BOHEMIA

FSBO (17 x a year)
3140 Veterans Memorial Hwy, Bohemia, NY, 11716-1039, Suffolk, USA; tel (800) 584-3726; fax (631) 928-1755; e-mail info@lifsbo.com
Circulation:, 50,000fr; Sworn/Estimate/Non-Audited
Established: 1988.
Pub.............Kevin C. Wood
Adv. Mgr.............Craig Martin
Prodn. Mgr.............Renee Alborelli
Mechanical Specifications: Type page 7 x 10.
Equipment; Software — QPS/QuarkXPress 3.30.

PLATTSBURGH

ADIRONDACK PROPERTIES (Mthly)
177 Margaret St, Plattsburgh, NY, 12901-1837, Clinton, USA; tel (518) 563-0100; fax (518) 562-0303; e-mail pennysaver@westelcom.com; web site www.adkpennysaver.com
Advertising: Open inch rate $15.00

Pub. .... Mark Rigby
Adv. Mgr. .... Carol VanHise
Prodn. Mgr. .... John Bruno

REAL ESTATE ADVERTISER (4 x a year)
177 Margaret St, Plattsburgh, NY, 12901-1837, Clinton, USA; tel (518) 563-0100; fax (518) 562-0303; e-mail mail@adkpennysaver.com; web site www.adkpennysaver.com
Circulation:, 18,000fr; Sworn/Estimate/Non-Audited
Advertising: Open inch rate $15.00
Pub. .... Mark Rigby
Adv. Mgr. .... Carol VanHise
Prodn. Mgr. .... John Bruno

TROY

CAPITAL REGION REAL ESTATE GUIDE (2 x Mthly)
501 Broadway, Troy, NY, 12180-3324, Rensselaer, USA; tel (518) 270-1200; fax (518) 270-1251; e-mail newsroom@troyrecord.com; web site www.troyrecord.com
Circulation: 25,946pd; Sworn/Estimate/Non-Audited
Pub .... Jim Murphy
Ed .... Lisa Robert Lewis
Mechanical Specifications: Type page 5 1/4 x 9 1/2; E - 4 cols, 1 3/16, 1/8 between; A - 4 cols, 1 3/16, 1/8 between; C - 4 cols, 1 3/16, 1/8 between.
Equipment: Hardware — ACI; Presses — G; Software — Dewar.

NORTH CAROLINA

CHARLOTTE

HOMES & LAND OF METRO CHARLOTTE (Mthly)
4525 Park Rd, Ste B202, Charlotte, NC, 28209-3704, Mecklenburg, USA; tel (704) 527-6553; fax (704) 527-6118; e-mail clthomes@attglobal.net; web site www.homesandland.com
Circulation:, 40,000fr; Sworn/Estimate/Non-Audited
Pub. .... Jeff P. Cathey

OHIO

HOLMESVILLE

HOMESELLER MAGAZINE (Mthly)
8068 Township Road 574, Holmesville, OH, 44633-9751, Holmes, USA; tel (330) 674-7653; fax (330) 674-7653; ed e-mail editor@homesellermagazine.com
Circulation:, 9,000fr; Sworn/Estimate/Non-Audited
Established: 1988.
Ed. .... Joe Waitkunas
Zip Codes Served: 44691, 44654, 44256

OREGON

MEDFORD

PROFESSIONAL IMAGE PUBLISHING (Mthly)
3350 1/2 W Main St, Medford, OR, 97501-2132, Jackson, USA; tel (541) 773-5744; fax (541) 776-0445; e-mail office@move2oregon.com; web site www.move2oregon.com
Circulation:; Sworn/Estimate/Non-Audited
Advertising: Open inch rate $12.50
Pub. .... Cynthia Rucklos

PENNSYLVANIA

HAZLE TOWNSHIP

REAL ESTATE JOURNAL (Mthly)
425 Jaycee Dr, Hazle Township, PA, 18202-1151, Luzerne, USA; tel (866) 401-5023; fax (570) 371-4433; e-mail rej1@ptd.net; web site www.therealestatejournal.com
Circulation:, 15,000fr; Sworn/Estimate/Non-AuditedEditions: 2— 2 total Real Estate Journal Schuylkill County;
Nick Walser
Steve WalserCo-Pub.s
Equipment: Hardware — APP/Mac; Presses — Software QPS/QuarkXPress.

WEST CHESTER

HOMES MAGAZINE (Mthly)
250 N Bradford Ave, West Chester, PA, 19382-1912, Chester, USA; tel (610) 430-6961; ed tel (610) 430-1116; fax (610) 430-1190; e-mail advertising@dailylocal.com; web site www.dailylocal.com
Circulation:; Sworn/Estimate/Non-Audited
Advertising: Open inch rate $2.75
Pub. .... Shelly Meenan
Ed. .... Andy Hachadorian
Mechanical Specifications: Type page 6 x 10.
Equipment: Hardware — Pentium/PC 200; Presses — G/Urbanite; Software — CNI.
Zip Codes Served: 19382

TENNESSEE

CHATTANOOGA

BUY A HOME (Mthly)
3407 Fleeta Ln, Chattanooga, TN, 37416-2802, Hamilton, USA; tel (423) 855-1831; fax (423) 499-8543
Circulation:, 18,000fr; Sworn/Estimate/Non-Audited
Pub. .... Randy Harden
Adv. Mgr. .... Tammy Harden

REAL ESTATE GUIDE (Mthly)
3407 Fleeta Ln, Chattanooga, TN, 37416-2802, Hamilton, USA; tel (423) 855-1831; fax (423) 499-8543
Circulation:, 15,000fr; Sworn/Estimate/Non-Audited
Adv. Mgr. .... Tammy Harden
Prodn. Mgr. .... Randy Harden

REAL ESTATE REVIEW (Mthly)
3415 Fleeta Ln, Chattanooga, TN, 37416-2802, Hamilton, USA; tel (423) 855-1831; fax (423) 499-8543; e-mail r4rrpub@aol.com; web site www.rivercountiesrealestatereview.com
Circulation:, 15,000fr; Sworn/Estimate/Non-Audited
Adv. Mgr. .... Tammy Harden
Prodn. Mgr. .... Randy Harden

TEXAS

EL PASO

REAL ESTATE WEEKLY (Thur)
6006 N Mesa St, Ste 600, El Paso, TX, 79912-4655, El Paso, USA; tel (915) 585-1000; fax (915) 261-0234; e-mail sandy@mesapub.com; web site www.mesapublishing.com
Circulation:, 10,000fr; Sworn/Estimate/Non-Audited
Established: 1988.
Group: Mesa Publishing Corp.
Ed. .... Riley R. Stephens
Mng. Ed. .... Ceci Marquez
Prodn. Mgr. .... Nancy Wiseman
Mechanical Specifications: Type page 9 3/4 x 11 3/4.
Equipment: Hardware — APP/Macs; Software — QPS/QuarkXPress
Zip Codes Served: 79901, 79999

TYLER

HOMES & LAND OF TYLER & EAST TEXAS (Mthly)
5604 Old Bullard Rd, Ste 101, Tyler, TX, 75703-4359, Smith, USA; tel (903) 509-2339; adv tel (903) 509-2339; fax (903) 509-2326; adv fax (903) 509-2326; e-mail psager@tyler.net; adv e-mail psager@tyler.net; ed e-mail psager&tyler.net; web site www.tyleretex.com
Circulation:, 20,000fr; Sworn/Estimate/Non-Audited
Established: 1977.
Digital Platform - Mobile: Apple
Digital Platform - Tablet: Apple iOS
OWNER/PUBLISHER .... Pat Sager
Pub. .... Tom Sager

VERMONT

BRATTLEBORO

NEW ENGLAND SHOWCASE (3 x Mthly)
14 Noahs Ln, Brattleboro, VT, 05301-4463, Windham, USA; tel (802) 254-3550; fax (802) 257-1453; e-mail info@newenglandshowcase.com; ed e-mail editor@newenglandshowcase.com; web site www.newenglandshowcase.com
Circulation:, 20,000fr; Sworn/Estimate/Non-AuditedEditions: 2— 2 total New England Showcase-Central and N. Vermont/W. New Hampshire;
Marketing Mgr. .... Donna McElligott
Zip Codes Served: 5303

MANCHESTER CENTER

ROUTE 2 TRAVEL, DINING AND SHOPPING GUIDE (Mon) (annual)
PO Box 1880, Manchester Center, VT, 05255-1880, Bennington, USA; tel (802) 362-3149; e-mail route2@sover.net; adv e-mail route2@sover.net; ed e-mail route2@sover.net; web site www.route2touristguide.com
Circulation: 0pd, 0fr; Sworn/Estimate/Non-Audited
Established: 1998.
Group: STMLLC
Pub. .... Robert H. Smith
Ed. .... Patti Smith
Delivery Method: Racks

RUTLAND

PREFERRED PROPERTIES REAL ESTATE GUIDE (Mthly)
27 Wales St, Rutland, VT, 05701-4027, Rutland, USA; tel (800) 776-5512; fax (802) 775-2423; e-mail glenda.hawley@aol.com; web site www.vermontclassifieds.com; www.rutlandherald.com
Circulation:, 22,500fr; Sworn/Estimate/Non-Audited
Advertising: Open inch rate $17.61
Pub. .... R. John Mitchell
Gen. Mgr. .... Catherine Nelson
Adv. Mgr. .... Sean Bruke
Adv. Design Mgr. .... Christina Mahoney
Mechanical Specifications: Type page 9 11/16 x 12; E - 5 cols, 1 13/16, 1/4 between; A - 5 cols, 1 13/16, 1/4 between.
Zip Codes Served: 5701

WISCONSIN

APPLETON

HOME SHOWCASE (Mthly)
306 W Washington St, Appleton, WI, 54911-5452, Outagamie, USA; tel (920) 733-4411; fax (920) 954-1945; e-mail pcnews@athenet.net
Circulation:, 15,000fr; Sworn/Estimate/Non-Audited
Circ. Mgr. .... Bruce Tischer
Ed. .... Dan Flannery
Prodn. Dir. .... Greg Fiorito
Mechanical Specifications: Type page 5 3/4 x 10; A - 3 cols, 2, between.
Equipment: Hardware — APP/Mac; Presses — 7-G/Metro; Software — Multi-Ad, QPS/QuarkXPress 3.32, Adobe/Photoshop 4.0, Adobe/Illustrator 6.0.

GREEN BAY

GREEN BAY REAL ESTATE GUIDE (Mthly)
PO Box 2467, Green Bay, WI, 54306-2467, Brown, USA; tel (920) 432-2941; fax (920) 432-8581; e-mail chronicle@gogreenbay.com; web site www.greenbaynewschronicle.com
Circulation:; Sworn/Estimate/Non-Audited
Advertising: Open inch rate $17.00
Established: 1990.
Gen. Mgr. .... Al Rasmussen
Mechanical Specifications: Type page 7 1/4 x 9 3/4.
Equipment: Hardware — APP/Macs.
Zip Codes Served: 54301, 54302, 54303, 54304, 54311, 54115

WEEKEND OPEN HOUSE MAGAZINE (Mthly)
435 E Walnut St, Green Bay, WI, 54301-5001, Brown, USA; tel (920) 432-2941; fax (920) 432-8581; e-mail chronicle@gogreenbay.com
Circulation:; Sworn/Estimate/Non-Audited
Advertising: Open inch rate $20.00
Established: 1995.
Pub. .... Frank Wood
Adv. Mgr. .... Al Rasmussen
Mechanical Specifications: Type page 8 x 10.
Equipment: Hardware — APP/Macs.
Zip Codes Served: 54306, 54301, 54302, 54303, 54311, 54313, 54115

MADISON

START RENTING MAGAZINE (Mthly)
102 N Franklin St, Madison, WI, 53703-2376, Dane, USA; tel (608) 257-4990; fax (608)

257-6896; e-mail info@startrenting.com; web site www.startrenting.com
Circulation:; Sworn/Estimate/Non-AuditedEditions: 3— 3 total Start Renting-Green Bay/Fox Cities (15,000); Start Renting Magazine-Madison (15,000);
Adv.Mgr .... Dennis Barber
Acct. Exec. .... Shawn Bacon
Acct. Exec. .... Melissa Schwefel

STURGEON BAY

DOOR COUNTY REAL ESTATE GUIDE (Mthly)
235 N 3rd Ave, Sturgeon Bay, WI, 54235-2417, Door, USA; tel (920) 743-3321; fax (920) 743-5817; ed fax (920)743-8908; e-mail khenz@doorcountyadvocate.com; adv e-mail lineads@doorcountyadvocate.com; ed e-mail advocate@doorcountyadvocate.com; web site www.doorcountyadvocate.com
Circulation:, 14,000fr; Sworn/Estimate/Non-Audited
Advertising: $195
Group: Gannett
General Manager / Ad Director.. Scott Schmeltzer
Account Executive .... Katie Henz
Mechanical Specifications: Type page 8 x 10.
Equipment: Hardware — APP/Macs.
Delivery Method: Racks
Zip Codes Served: 54235

WYOMING

CHEYENNE

PREVIEW REAL ESTATE GUIDE (Mthly)
2021 Warren Ave, Cheyenne, WY, 82001-3725, Laramie, USA; tel (307) 634-8895; fax (307) 634-8530; e-mail publisher@wyopreview.com; web site www.wyopreview.com
Circulation:, 8,000fr; Sworn/Estimate/Non-Audited
Established: 1984.
Pub. .... Patrick Rice
Gen. Mgr. .... Bob Johnigan
Circ. Mgr. .... Jeff Hite
Ed. .... Will Perrell
Mechanical Specifications: Type page 7 x 9 3/4.
Equipment: Hardware — APP/Macs; Software — Multi-Ad/Creator.

SENIOR PUBLICATIONS IN THE UNITED STATES

ALASKA

SENIOR VOICE
(Mthly)
3340 Arctic Blvd, Ste 106, Anchorage, AK, 99503-4550, Anchorage, USA; tel (907) 276-1059; adv tel (907) 276-1059; ed tel (907) 276-1059; fax (907) 278-6724; adv fax (907) 278-6724; ed fax (907) 278-6724; e-mail info@seniorvoicealaska.com; adv e-mail execdiropag@gci.net; ed e-mail seniorvoice@gci.net; web site www.seniorvoicealaska.com
Circulation: 1,300pd, 11,500fr; Sworn/Estimate/Non-Audited
Advertising: Open inch rate $22.00
Established: 1969
Mng Ed .... David Washburn
Execu Dir .... James Bailey
Delivery Method: Mail, Newsstand, Carrier, Racks

ARIZONA

LOVIN' LIFE AFTER 50
(Mthly) (Monthly)
3200 N Hayden Rd, Ste 210, Scottsdale, AZ, 85251-6654, Maricopa, USA; tel (480) 348-0343; fax (480) 348-2109; e-mail info@lovinlifeafter50.com; adv e-mail fishs@seniormedia.com; ed e-mail christina@timespublications.com; web site lovinlife.com
Circulation: 0pd, 105,283fr; CVC
Advertising: N/A
Established: 1979
Parent Co.: EOS Publishing, LLCEditions: 6— East Valley, Southeast Valley, West Valley, Scottsdale, Phoenix, Tucson
Pub .... Steve H. Fish
Mechanical Specifications: Full page 10"X11"
Delivery Method: Carrier, Racks

LOVIN' LIFE AFTER 50
(Mthly)
1620 W Fountainhead Pkwy Ste 219, Suite # 210, Tempe, AZ, 85282-1848, Maricopa, USA; tel (480) 898-5612; adv tel (480) 898-5612; ed tel (480) 898-5612; fax (480) 348-2109; e-mail ndandrea@timespublications.com; adv e-mail ndandrea@timespublications.com; ed e-mail ndandrea@timespublications.com; web site www.lovinlifeafter50.com
Circulation:; Sworn/Estimate/Non-Audited
Established: 1979
Parent Co.: Times Media Group
Executive Editor .... Niki D'Andrea
Publisher .... Steve Strickbine
Calendar Editor...... Christina Fuoco-Karasinski
Designer .... Tonya Mildenberg
Travel Editor .... Ed Boitano
Senior Account Executive .... Lou Lagrave
Senior Account Executive .... Gordon Wood
Pub .... Steve H. Fish
Nat'l/Regl. Sales .... Tony Erickson
Ed. .... Mary Fish
Prodn. Mgr. .... Patrice Derbas
Mechanical Specifications: Type page 9 7/8 x 11 3/8.

CALIFORNIA

JOURNAL PLUS MAGAZINE
(Mthly)
654 Osos St, San Luis Obispo, CA, 93401-2713, San Luis Obispo, USA; tel (805) 546-0609; fax (805) 546-8827; e-mail slojournal@fix.net; web site www.slojournal.com
Circulation: 25,000fr; Sworn/Estimate/Non-Audited
Pub .... Steve Owens
Adv. Mgr. .... Jan Owens
Ed. .... Erin Mott
Mechanical Specifications: Type page 7 1/2 x 10; E - 3 cols, 2 1/2, between; A - 3 cols, 2 1/2, between.
Delivery Method: Mail, Newsstand, Racks

COLORADO

SENIOR VOICE
(Mthly)
1471 Front Nine Dr, Fort Collins, CO, 80525-9459, Larimer, USA; tel (970) 223-9271; fax (970) 223-9271; e-mail thevoice@frii.com; web site www.theseniorvoice.net
Circulation: 42,000fr; Sworn/Estimate/Non-Audited
Advertising: Open inch rate $36.80
Established: 1980
Pub .... William Lambdin
Adv. Mgr. .... Wolfgang Lambdin
Prodn. Mgr. .... Peggy Hunt
Mechanical Specifications: Type page 10 x 12 3/4; E - 4 cols, 2 1/3, 1/4 between; A - 4 cols, 2 1/3, 1/4 between.

BEACON SENIOR NEWSPAPER
(Mthly)
524 30 Rd, Ste 4, Grand Junction, CO, 81504-4437, Mesa, USA; tel (970) 243-8829; adv tel (970) 243-8829; ed tel (970) 243-8829; fax (800) 536-7516; adv fax (800) 536-7516; ed fax (800) 536-7516; e-mail beacon@pendantpublishing.com; adv e-mail kevin@pendantpublishing.com; ed e-mail cloie@pendantpublishing.com; web site www.beaconseniornews.com
Circulation: 1,200pd, 20,000fr; CVC
Advertising: Open inch rate $28.44
Established: 1987
Parent Co.: Pendant Publishing, Inc.
Digital Platform - Mobile: Apple, Android, Windows, Blackberry, Other
Digital Platform - Tablet: Apple iOS, Android, Windows 7, Blackberry Tablet OS, Kindle, Nook, Kindle Fire, Other
Pub .... Kevin VanGundy
Acct Exec .... Sue Bowen
Graphic Arts .... Karen Jones
Mgr Ed .... Cloie Sandlin
Acct Exec .... Sidney Jayne
Graphic Artist .... Melissa Trottier
Mechanical Specifications: Type page 10.37" x 10.98"; 4 cols
Equipment: Hardware — APP/Macs Windows; Presses — The BIG kind.; Software — Adobe InDesign
Delivery Method: Mail, Newsstand, Carrier, Racks
Zip Codes Served: 81501, 81502, 81503, 81504, 81505, 81506, 81507, 81520, 81521, 81526, 81527, 81401, 81403, 81413, 81416, 81425, 81432

LIFE AFTER 50
(Mthly)
329 Manitou Ave, Ste 103, Manitou Springs, CO, 80829-2590, El Paso, USA; tel (719) 685-9690; fax (719) 685-9705; e-mail dennis@pikespeakpublishing.com; adv e-mail sales@pikespeakpublishing.com; web site www.pikespeakpublishing.com
Circulation: 20,000fr; Sworn/Estimate/Non-Audited
Pub .... Dennis Ingmire
Adv. Mgr. .... Stephanie Stanford
Sales Mgr. .... Bruce Schlabough
Ed. .... Jeanne Davant
Prodn. Mgr. .... Don Bouchard
Mechanical Specifications: Type page 10 x 13 3/4; E - 4 cols, 2 5/16, 1/4 between; A - 4 cols, 2 5/16, 1/4 between; C - 4 cols, 2 5/16, 1/4 between.
Equipment: Hardware — Pentium/PC, 2-PC Celeron, PC 586, Pentium/PC II; Software — Adobe/PageMaker 6.5, Adobe/Photoshop 4.0.

FLORIDA

BOOMER TIMES AND SENIOR LIFE
(Mthly)
1515 N Federal Hwy, Ste 300, Boca Raton, FL, 33432-1994, Palm Beach, USA; tel (561) 736-8925; fax (561) 369-1476; e-mail srlife@gate.net; web site www.babyboomers-seniors.com
Circulation: 19,199pd, 41,000fr; Sworn/Estimate/Non-Audited
Established: 1990
Digital Platform - Mobile: Windows
Digital Platform - Tablet: Windows 7
Vice Pres., Admin. .... Marilyn Weiss
Adv. Mgr. .... Anita R. Finley
Mktg. Mgr. .... Leoni Kendall
Mng. Ed./Travel Ed. .... Bill Finley
Prodn. Mgr. .... Connie Crimi
Mechanical Specifications: 8-1/2 x 11
Delivery Method: Mail, Carrier, Racks
Note: 19,000 of the 41,000 are inserted monthly in The Miami Herald for their subscribers.

GEORGIA

SENIOR NEWS
(Mthly)
115 Bigham Dr, Warner Robins, GA, 31088-3749, Houston, USA; tel (478) 929-3636; fax (478) 929-4258; e-mail seniornewsga@aol.com; adv e-mail seniornewsga@cox.net; ed e-mail seniornewsga@cox.net; web site www.seniornewsgeorgia.com
Circulation: 50pd, 38,000fr; Sworn/Estimate/Non-Audited
Advertising: Open inch rate $26.00
Established: 1987
Parent Co.: Byron Publishing Corp., Inc.
President/Publisher .... Billy R. Tucker
Mechanical Specifications: Type page 10 x 14; E - 4 cols, 2 5/16, 1/4 between; A - 4 cols, 2 5/16, 1/4 between.
Equipment: Hardware — eMac; Software — QuarkXPress 4.1
Adobe Photoshop 5.0
Adobe Acrobat 5.0
AppleWorks6
Delivery Method: Mail, Newsstand, Carrier, Racks
Zip Codes Served: 30001, 30002, 30004, 30005, 30012, 30013, 30014, 30019, 30024, 30025, 30030, 30032, 30033, 30034, 30035, 30038, 30040, 30041, 30042, 30043, 30044, 30045, 30047, 30054, 30057, 30058, 30059, 30060, 30062, 30064, 30067, 30068, 30071, 30073, 30075, 30076, 30078, 30080, 30082, 30083, 30084, 30087, 30088, 30092, 30093, 30094, 30096, 30097, 30101, 30102, 30106, 30110, 30114, 30115, 30116, 30117, 30120, 30121, 30122, 30126, 30127, 30132, 30134, 30135, 30136, 30141, 30144, 30152, 30168, 30176, 30188, 30189, 30201, 30213, 30214, 30215, 30224, 30236, 30252, 30253, 30260, 30263, 30265, 30268, 30269, 30274, 30281, 30291, 30297, 30303, 30305, 30306, 30307, 30308, 30309, 30310, 30311, 30312, 30314, 30315, 30316, 30317, 30318, 30319, 30324, 30327, 30328, 30329, 30331, 30334, 30337, 30338, 30339, 30341, 30342, 30344, 30345, 30346, 30349, 30350, 30354, 30360, 30501, 30503, 30506, 30507, 30518, 30519, 30566, 30601, 30605, 30606, 30622, 30655, 30656, 30666, 3068029801, 29803, 29841, 29860, 30809, 30813, 30814, 30824, 30901, 30904, 30906, 30907, 30909, 31008, 31030, 31052, 31069, 31088, 31093, 31201, 31204, 31206, 31210, 31211, 31216, 31217, 31220
Note: Senior News is delivered in the Atlanta, Augusta, and Macon, Georgia Metro Areas.

Individual market information available.

IDAHO

IDAHO SENIOR NEWS
(Mthly)
233 W State St, Ste E, Eagle, ID, 83616-4982, Ada, USA; tel (208) 336-6707; adv tel (800) 657-6470; fax (208) 336-6752; e-mail editor@idahoseniornews.com; adv e-mail advertising@idahoseniornews.som; ed e-mail editor@idahoseniornews.com; web site www.idahoseniornews.com
Circulation: 3,500pd, 22,000fr; Sworn/Estimate/Non-Audited
Established: 1978
Parent Co.: Graphic Arts Publishing, Inc.
Publisher/Owner .... Jane Seil
Mechanical Specifications: Type page 10 3/8 x 15; E - 5 cols, 2, 1/16 between; A - 5 cols, 2, 1/16 between; C - 5 cols, 2, 1/16 between.
Delivery Method: Mail, Carrier, Racks

ILLINOIS

DENBAR PUBLISHING, INC
(Mthly)
PO Box 478, Dundee, IL, 60118-0478, Kane, USA; tel (847) 931-0234; adv tel (847) 567-0234; ed tel (630) 531-1670; fax (847) 697-6817; e-mail sn50andbetter@yahoo.com; info@sn50andbetter.com; adv e-mail chisrnews@aol.com; ed e-mail chgoseniornews@yahoo.com; web site www.sn50andbetter.com
Circulation:; Sworn/Estimate/Non-Audited
Established: 1986Editions: 10— 10 total; Senior News-City (Chicago) (15,000); Senior News-Cook North (20,000); Senior News-Cook South (15,000); Senior News-Cook West (15,000); Senior News-Dupage (20,000); Senior News-Kane (10,000); Senior News-Lake (8,000); Senior News-McHenry (4,000)
Circ. Mgr. .... Jim Thomas
Ed. .... Barbara Simonini
Mng. Ed. .... Dennis Simonini
Managing Editor .... Dawn Williams
Prodn. Mgr. .... Jeff Busse
Mechanical Specifications: Type page 10 x 15 1/2; E - 4 cols, 2 1/2, between; A - 4 cols, 2 1/2, between.
Equipment: Hardware — HP; Presses — WPC; Software — Microsoft/Windows.
Delivery Method: Mail, Racks
Zip Codes Served: chicaogland 5 counties

SENIOR COURIER
(Mthly)
11512 N 2nd St, Machesney Park, IL, 61115-1101, Winnebago, USA; tel (815) 877-4044; fax (815) 654-4857; e-mail info@rvpublishing.com; web site www.rockvalleypublishing.com
Circulation: 20,000fr; Sworn/Estimate/Non-Audited
Advertising: Open inch rate $10.00
Pub. .... Randy Johnson
Adv. Mgr. .... Maxine Bayer
Circ. Mgr. .... Melinda Sweet
Ed. .... Amy Kennedy
Prodn. Mgr. .... Linda Lano
Mechanical Specifications: Type page 10 1/4 x 16; E - 4 cols, between; A - 4 cols, between; C - 6 cols, between.
Equipment; Presses — WPC/Web Leader.
Zip Codes Served: 61132, 61101, 61111, 61115, 61072, 61063

KANSAS

KEYNOTES NEWS FOR OLDER KANSANS
401 Houston St, Manhattan, KS, 66502-6135, Riley, USA; tel 785-776-9294; fax 785-776-9479; web site www.ncfhaaa.com

THE BEST TIMES
(Bi-Mthly) (Bimonthly (first of month))
111 S Cherry St, Ste 3300, Olathe, KS, 66061-3487, Johnson, USA; tel (913) 715-8930; adv tel (913) 715-8920; ed tel (913) 715-0736; fax (913) 715-0440; adv fax (913) 715-0440; ed fax (913) 715-0440; e-mail gerald.hay@jocogov.org; adv e-mail cherell.bilquist@jocogov.org; ed e-mail gerald.hay@jocogov.org; web site www.jocogov.org/thebesttimes
Circulation: 300pd, 68,000fr; Sworn/Estimate/Non-Audited
Advertising: Variable; contact us for rate card.
Established: 1982
Parent Co.: Johnson County (Kansas) Government
Director of Public Affairs and Communications Sharon Watson
Editor .... Gerald Hay
Advertising Manager .... Che'rell Bilquist
Delivery Method: Mail, Racks
Zip Codes Served: Most, if not all, Zip Codes in Johnson County, KS

THE ACTIVE AGE
(Mthly)
125 S West St, Ste 105, Wichita, KS, 67213-2114, Sedgwick, USA; tel (316) 942-5385; fax (316) 946-9180; e-mail editor@theactiveage.com; adv e-mail teresa@theactiveage.com; ed e-mail fran@theactiveage.com; web site www.theactiveage.com
Circulation: 58,000fr; Sworn/Estimate/Non-Audited
Advertising: Open inch rate $45.70
Established: 1979
Digital Platform - Mobile: Apple
Digital Platform - Tablet: Apple iOS, Other
Editor/Publisher .... Fran Kentling
Advertising Manager .... Teresa Schmeid
Business and media manager. Tammara Fogel
Mechanical Specifications: Type page 10 x 14; E - 4 cols, 2 1/3, 4/15 between; A - 4 cols, 2 1/3, 4/15 between; C - 4 cols, 2 1/3, 4/15 between.
Equipment; Software — Adobe/InDesign, Adobe/Photoshop.
Delivery Method: Mail, Racks
Zip Codes Served: Three counties — Butler, Harvey and Sedgwick in Kansas
Note: 'Active aging' was re-named 'the active age' and was re-designed. Both debuted in May 2015. The editorial content, when possible, is now based on current events with an emphasis on news.

LOUISIANA

THE BEST OF TIMES
(Mthly)
PO Box 19510, Shreveport, LA, 71149-0510, Caddo, USA; tel (318) 636-5510; e-mail gary.calligas@gmail.com; adv e-mail gary.calligas@gmail.com; ed e-mail gary.calligas@gmail.com; web site www.thebestoftimesnews.com
Circulation: 250pd, 20,000fr; CVC
Advertising: $71.79 per inch column (column width is 3.67 inches)
Established: 1993
Parent Co.: TBT Multimedia, LLCEditions: 1— 1
Digital Platform - Mobile: Apple, Android
Digital Platform - Tablet: Apple iOS, Android
Publisher .... Gary Calligas
Mechanical Specifications: Quarter page vertical ad = 3.6 inches by 4.75 inches height
Half page horizontal ad = 7.5 inches by 4.75 inches
Full page ad = 7.5 inches wide by 9.75 inches height.
Delivery Method: Mail, Racks
Zip Codes Served: Caddo Parish, Louisiana
Bossier Parish, Louisiana
Shreveport, Louisiana
Bossier City, Louisiana
Note: Monthly glossy magazine for readers who are 50 and older in age residing in Northwest Louisiana to help them celebrate age and maturity. Also, TBT Multimedia hosts a weekly one hour radio talk show at 9 am every Saturday morning on NEWSRADIO 710 KEEL in Shreveport, Louisiana and is also streaming live at www.710KEEL.COM and streaming via the RADIOPUP app on apple and android phones and tablets.

MARYLAND

THE BEACON
(Mthly)
3720 Farragut Ave, Ste 105, Kensington, MD, 20895-2110, Montgomery, USA; tel (301) 949-9766; adv tel 301-949-9766; ed tel (301) 949-9766; fax (301) 949-8966; adv fax (301) 949-8966; ed fax 301-949-8966; e-mail info@thebeaconnewspapers.com; adv e-mail alan@thebeaconnewspapers.com; ed e-mail barbara@thebeaconnewspapers.com; web site www.thebeaconnewspapers.com
Circulation: 230,000fr; CVC
Advertising: Open inch rate $96.00
Established: 1989Editions: 4— The Beacon - Baltimore (68,000); The Beacon - DC (110,000); The Beacon - Howard County (17,000); Fifty Plus Richmond, VA (35,000)
Vice President Sales & Marketing Alan Spiegel
Ed. .... Stuart Rosenthal
Mng. Ed. .... Barbara Ruben
Sales Dir. .... Alan Spiegel
Mechanical Specifications: Type page 10 x 13 1/2; E - 4 cols, 2 1/2, 1/6 between; A - 4 cols, 2 1/2, 1/6 between; C - 4 cols, 2 1/2, 1/6 between.
Delivery Method: Racks

MASSACHUSETTS

PRIME TIMES
(Mthly)
280 N Main St, East Longmeadow, MA, 01028-1868, Hampden, USA; tel (413) 525-6661; fax (413) 525-5882; e-mail news@thereminder.com; web site www.thereminder.com
Circulation: 3pd, 16,826fr; CVC
Advertising: Open inch rate $17.00
Pub. .... Daniel J. Buendo
Gen. Mgr. .... Christopher Buendo
Adv. Mgr. .... Barbarra Terry
Mng. Ed. .... G.Michael Dobbs
Mechanical Specifications: Type page 10 x 16; E - 4 cols, 2 3/8, 1/8 between; A - 4 cols, 2 3/8, 1/8 between; C - 5 cols, 2, 1/8 between.
Equipment: Hardware — APP/Mac; Software — QPS/QuarkXPress, Adobe/Photoshop.
Zip Codes Served: 01001, 01002, 01013, 01020, 01027, 01028, 01033, 01036, 01038, 01040, 01056, 01060, 01075, 01089, 01095, 01101, 01105, 01106, 01108, 01109, 01118, 01119, 01128, 01129, 01301, 01337, 01338, 01342, 01375

FIFTY PLUS ADVOCATE
(Mthly)
131 Lincoln St, Worcester, MA, 01605-2408, Worcester, USA; tel (508) 752-2512; adv tel (508) 752-2512 x128; fax (508) 752-9057; adv e-mail rcapellari@fiftyplusadvocate.com; web site www.fiftyplusadvocate.com
Circulation: 50,000fr; CVC
Advertising: B+W Full Page $1700.00; 4-Color Full Page $1900.00
Established: 1975
Parent Co.: FiftyPlus MediaEditions: 2— FiftyPlus Adovocate Central MA, Fiftyplus Advocate Eastern MA
Pub. .... Philip Davis
Circ. Mgr. .... Stacy Lemay
Exec. Ed. .... Sondra Shapiro
Sales Coord. .... Reva Capellari
Art Dir. .... Sue Clapham
Mechanical Specifications: Type page 10 x 12.75; E - 4 cols, 2 1/2, between; A - 6 cols, 1 1/2, between.
Delivery Method: Mail, Racks
Zip Codes Served: Central or Eastern MA

MICHIGAN

SENIOR TIMES
(Mthly)
595 Jenner Dr, Allegan, MI, 49010-1516, Allegan, USA; tel (269) 673-1720; fax (269) 673-4761; e-mail debra.sloan@flashespublishers.com; adv e-mail debra.sloan@flashespublishers.com; web site flashpublishers.com
Circulation: 18pd, 16,500fr; Sworn/Estimate/Non-Audited
Advertising: full page = 1050; quarter page = $320
Mgr. .... Debbie Sloan
Mechanical Specifications:

SENIOR TIMES SOUTH CENTRAL MICHIGAN
(Mthly)
4642 Capital Ave SW, Battle Creek, MI, 49015-9305, Calhoun, USA; tel (269) 979-1411; adv tel (269) 979-1479 x106; ed tel (269) 979-1412 x102; fax (269) 979-3474; e-mail sherii@wwthayne.com; adv e-mail sheriis@wwthayne.com; ed e-mail sheriis@wwthayne.com; web site www.scenepub.com/seniortimes
Circulation: 100pd, 15,850fr; Sworn/Estimate/Non-Audited
Established: 1971
Asst. Pub. .... Shirley DeRuiter
Gen. Mgr. .... Keith Sherban
Adv. Mgr. .... Leslie Hole
Circ. Mgr. .... Shelii Penny
Publisher / Exec. Ed. .... Sherii Sherban
Mechanical Specifications: Type page 10 1/4 x 16; E - 4 cols, 2 3/8, 1/4 between; A - 6 cols, 1 1/2, 1/4 between; C - 6 cols, 1 1/2, 1/4 between.
Equipment: Hardware — APP/Mac, Microsoft/WordPerfect; Software — QPS/QuarkXPress 4.0.
Zip Codes Served: 49017, 49015, 49016, 49068, 49245, 49092, 49224, 49021, 49011, 48813

WEST MICHIGAN SENIOR TIMES
(Mthly) (2nd Friday of each month)
54 W 8th St, Holland, MI, 49423-3104, Ottawa, USA; tel ; adv tel (269) 673-1701; ed tel (269) 673-1720; fax ; adv e-mail tiffany.andrus@flashespublishers.com; ed e-mail debra.sloan@flashespublishers.com; web site flashespublishers.com
Circulation: 50pd, 18,000fr; Sworn/Estimate/Non-Audited
Advertising: Open inch rate $16.00
Established: 1984
Parent Co.: GateHouse Media, Inc.
Editorial .... Debbie Sloan
Sales .... Tiffany Andrus
Publisher .... Tricia Johnston
Mechanical Specifications: Type page 9.375" x 14.5"; E - 4 cols, 1 col = 2.25", 1/8 between;
Equipment: Hardware — APP/Mac; Presses — G/Community; Software — QPS/QuarkXPress.
Delivery Method: Racks
Zip Codes Served: 49001, 49002, 49004, 49006, 49007, 49008, 49009, 49010, 49012, 49013, 49024, 49048, 49053, 49055, 49056, 49062, 49065, 49067, 49071, 49073, 49078, 49079, 49080, 49083, 49087, 49090, 49093, 49097, 49306, 49315, 49321

MINNESOTA

THE SENIOR REPORTER
(Mthly)
PO Box 161318, Duluth, MN, 55816-1318, Saint Louis, USA; tel (218) 624-

4949; fax (218) 624-1541; e-mail info@theseniorreporter.com; ed e-mail editor@theseniorreporter.com; web site www.theseniorreporter.com
Circulation: 2,100pd, 100fr; Sworn/Estimate/Non-Audited
Established: 1988
Ed. .... Burton Laine
Mechanical Specifications: Type page 8 1/2 x 11; E - 3 cols, 2 1/3, 1/6 between; A - 3 cols, 2 1/3, 1/6 between.
Equipment: Hardware — APP/Macs; Software — QPS/QuarkXPress 5.0.

GOOD AGE
(Mthly)
1115 Hennepin Ave, Minneapolis, MN, 55403-1705, Hennepin, USA; tel (612) 825-9205; fax (612) 825-0929; web site www.mngoodage.com
Circulation: 78pd, 49,892fr; CVC
Established: 1981Editions: 2— 2 total; Good Age-East Metro (29,000); Good Age-West Metro (43,500);
Pub. .... Janis Hall
Co-Pub. .... Terry Gahan
Adv. Sales Mgr. .... Mellisa Ungerman Levy
Ed. .... Tricia Cornell
Asst. Ed. .... Jake Weyer
Dist. Mgr. .... Marlo Johnson
Mechanical Specifications: Type page 7 3/4 x 10 7/8; E - 4 cols, 2 1/4, 1/4 between; A - 6 cols, 1 5/12, between; C - 3 cols, 3 1/6, between.
Equipment: Hardware — APP/Power Mac G4; Software — Adobe/Photoshop 7.0, QPS/QuarkXPress 4.0.

NEW JERSEY

SENIOR SCOOP (4X YR)
3600 Highway 66, Neptune, NJ, 7754, Monmouth, USA; tel 732-922-6000; fax (732) 557-5659; e-mail senscoop@app.com; web site www.app.com
Circulation: 80,000fr; Sworn/Estimate/Non-Audited
Advertising: Open inch rate $40.23Editions: 2— 2 total Monmouth County Senior Scoop (35,000); Ocean County Senior Scoop (45,000);
Adv. Mgr. .... Bonnie Russell
Mechanical Specifications: Type page 9 x 11 5/8; E - 5 cols, 1 4/5, between; A - 5 cols, 1 4/5, between.
Equipment; Presses — G/Urbanite.

THE GOLDEN TIMES
(Mthly)
PO Box 134, Pitman, NJ, 08071-0134, Gloucester, USA; tel (856) 582-3940; fax (801) 720-9176; web site www.thegoldentimes.com
Circulation: 47,000fr; Sworn/Estimate/Non-Audited
Advertising: Open inch rate $35.00Editions: 3— 3 total The Golden Times-Camden County Edition (12,000); The Golden Times-Delaware Valley Edition (25,000); The Golden Times-Gloucester County Edition (10,000);
Adv. Mgr. .... Alex Augunas
Ed. .... Harry G. Armstrong
Mng. Ed. .... Barbara Murphy
Prodn. Mgr. .... Ryan Armstrong
Mechanical Specifications: Type page 10 x 13; E - 5 cols, 1 9/10, 1/10 between.
Equipment: Hardware — IBM; Software — Microsoft/Windows 95, QPS/QuarkXPress.

NEW MEXICO

PRIME TIME
(Mthly)
6300 Montano Rd NW, Ste G3, Albuquerque, NM, 87120-1826, Bernalillo, USA; tel (505) 888-0470; e-mail primetime@swcp.com; ed e-mail primeedit@swcp.com; web site www.ptpubco.com
Circulation:; Sworn/Estimate/Non-Audited
Advertising: Open inch rate $40.00
Established: 1991
Adv. Mgr. .... Sydney Dickinson
Editor .... David Rivord
Prodn. Mgr. .... Christine Carter
Mechanical Specifications: Type page 10 1/4 x 15 3/4; E - 4 cols, 2 5/16, 3/8 between; A - 4 cols, 2 5/16, 3/8 between.
Equipment: Hardware — APP/Mac.
Zip Codes Served: 87191

NEW YORK

50+ LIFESTYLES
(Mthly)
146 S Country Rd, Ste 4, Bellport, NY, 11713-2530, Suffolk, USA; tel (631) 286-0058; adv tel (877) 677-6397; fax (631) 286-6866; e-mail tim@50plusny.com; ed e-mail editor@50plusny.com; web site www.50plusny.com
Circulation: 5,000pd, 100,000fr; Sworn/Estimate/Non-Audited
Established: 1975Editions: 2— Long Island and Metro NY
Digital Platform - Tablet: Other
Pres./Pub. .... Frank C. Trotta
Ed. .... Gary P. Joyce
Exec. Ed. .... Tim Edwards
Art Dir. .... Suzanne DeLuca
Mechanical Specifications: Type page 10 x 12 1/2.
Delivery Method: Mail, Newsstand, Racks
Zip Codes Served:

FOREVER YOUNG
(Mthly)
1738 Elmwood Ave, Ste 103, Buffalo, NY, 14207-2465, Erie, USA; tel (716) 783-9119; fax (716) 783-9983; e-mail calarlev@aol.com; circulation@buffalospree.com; web site www.foreveryoungwny.com
Circulation: 36,153fr; CVC
Established: 1988
Pub. .... Laurence A. Levite
Dir., Sales .... Barbara E. Macks
Dir., Circ. .... Robin M. Lenhard
Ed. in Chief .... Elizabeth Licata
Prod. Dir. .... Jade Z. Chen
Prod. Mgr. .... Jennifer Ellis
Mechanical Specifications: Type page 9.75 x 11.25.
Delivery Method: Newsstand, Racks
Zip Codes Served: 14043

WSN2DAY.COM
(Mthly)
629 Fifth Ave, Ste 213, Pelham, NY, 10803-3708, Westchester, USA; tel (914) 738-7869; fax (914) 738-7876; e-mail shorelineproduction@gmail.com; adv e-mail hp@shorelinepub.com; ed e-mail hp@shorelinepub.com; web site www.shorelinepub.com
Circulation: 500pd, 24,000fr; Sworn/Estimate/Non-Audited
Established: 1992
Parent Co.: Shoreline Publishing
CEO/Pub. .... Edward Shapiro
Ed. in Chief .... Helene Pollack
Mechanical Specifications: Type page 10 x 13; E - 4 cols, 2 1/4, between; A - 6 cols, 1 3/4, between.
Equipment: Hardware — IBM; Software — Adobe/PageMaker 6.0.
Delivery Method: Carrier, Racks

NORTH CAROLINA

LIVIN' OUT LOUD
(Mthly) (Weekly email blast)
PO Box 15944, Wilmington, NC, 28408-5944, New Hanover, USA; tel (910) 338-1205; adv tel (910) 338-1205; ed tel (910) 338-1205; e-mail info@livinoutloudmag.com; adv e-mail todd@nancyhall.net; ed e-mail editor@livinoutloudmag.com; web site www.livinoutloudmag.com
Circulation: 10,976fr; CVC
Established: 2010
Parent Co.: Nancy Hall Publications
Digital Platform - Mobile: Apple, Android
Digital Platform - Tablet: Apple iOS, Android, Windows 7, Kindle, Nook, Kindle Fire
Pub./Adv. Mgr. .... Todd Godbey
Mechanical Specifications: Type page: 9.75 x 11.5; 3 col
Delivery Method: Mail, Racks
Zip Codes Served: 28401, 28402, 28403, 28404, 28405, 28406, 28407, 28408, 28409, 28411, 28412, 28451, 28465

OHIO

SENIOR TIMES
(Mthly)
PO Box 623, New Albany, OH, 43054-0623, Franklin, USA; tel (614) 337-2055; fax (614) 337-2059; e-mail seniortimes@insight.rr.com
Circulation: 60,000fr; Sworn/Estimate/Non-Audited
Established: 1983
Pub. .... Stephen Pinsky
Adv. Mgr. .... Angela Miller
Circ. Mgr. .... Lee Pinsky
Mechanical Specifications: Type page 10 1/4 x 14; E - 6 cols, 1 5/8, between.
Delivery Method: Mail, Racks

PENNSYLVANIA

ICON MAGAZINE
(Mthly)
PO Box 120, New Hope, PA, 18938-0120, Bucks, USA; tel (215) 862-9558; fax (215) 862-9845; e-mail trobba@comcast.net; web site www.icondv.com
Circulation:; Sworn/Estimate/Non-Audited
Advertising: Open inch rate $38.00Editions: 2— 2 total Prime Time Monthly-Bucks County (PA) (26,500); Prime Time Monthly-S. Jersey (40,000);
Ed. .... Trina McKenna
Mechanical Specifications: Type page 10 x 14; A - 6 cols, 1 1/2, 1/5 between; C - 6 cols, 1 1/2, 1/5 between.
Equipment: Hardware — 3-APP/Mac 8500/150, 2-HP/Laserjet 4mv; Software — QPS/QuarkXPress 3.32.

MILESTONES
(Mthly)
642 N Broad St, Philadelphia, PA, 19130-3424, Philadelphia, USA; tel (215) 765-9000; adv tel (215) 765-9000 ext. 5051; ed tel (215) 765-9000 ext 5080; fax (215) 765-9066; e-mail milestonesnews@pcaphl.org; adv e-mail milestones@pcaphl.org; ed e-mail milestonesnews@pcaphl.org; web site http://www.pcacares.org/default.aspx
Circulation: 25pd, 67,325fr; CVC
Advertising: full page, one-time b&w inside page: $1980
Established: 1987
Parent Co.: Philadelphia Corporation for AgingEditions: 1—
Editor .... Linda Riley
Director, Marketing and Corporate Relations ... Joan Zaremba
Mechanical Specifications: see website
Equipment: Hardware — APP/Mac; Software — QPS/QuarkXPress 3.3.
Delivery Method: Mail, Racks
Zip Codes Served: All 191xxx
Note: Digital version, Milestones e-news is weekly, published on Wednesdays and has some identical, some different content. Available on web or via email subscription.

TENNESSEE

MATURE LIFESTYLES OF TENNESSEE
(Mthly)
PO Box 857, Lebanon, TN, 37088-0857, Wilson, USA; tel (615) 444-6008; adv tel (615) 444-6008; ed tel (615) 444-6008; fax (615) 444-6818; e-mail bharville@mainstreetmediatn.com; adv e-mail dgould@mainstreetmediatn.com; ed e-mail bharville@mainstreetmediatn.com
Circulation: 13,000fr; Sworn/Estimate/Non-Audited
Advertising: 15/inch
Parent Co.: Main Street Media of Tennessee
Ed .... Brian Harville
Mechanical Specifications: 10" x 14"
Delivery Method: Racks
Zip Codes Served: Davidson, Williamson, Rutherford, Wilson and Sumner counties

THE BEST TIMES
(Mthly)
3100 Walnut Grove Rd, Ste 404, Memphis, TN, 38111-3530, Shelby, USA; tel (901) 458-2911; adv tel 901-505=0945; ed tel (901) 458-2911 ext. 2; fax (901) 207-2448; e-mail admin@thebesttimes.com; adv e-mail jgrubbs@thebesttimes.com; ed e-mail tjordan@thebesttimes.com; web site thebesttimes.com
Circulation: 25,500fr; Sworn/Estimate/Non-Audited
Advertising: modular
Established: 1982
Parent Co.: The Best Times presented by Jimmy GrubbsEditions: 1— The Best Times
Digital Platform - Mobile: Windows
Digital Platform - Tablet: Windows 7, Other
Publisher .... Jimmy Grubbs
managing editor .... Tom Jordan
Assistant Publisher .... Sherry Greene
advertising manager .... Jim Moffatt
Publisher's representative .... Jeff Martin
Social Media Specialist .... William Mitchum
Graphics Designer .... Mindy Fulcher
Online Manager .... Paul Rhodes
publisher emeritus .... Lester Gingold
Mechanical Specifications: modular tab
Equipment: Hardware — ; Presses — web offset; Software — Adobe In Design
Delivery Method: Racks
Zip Codes Served: Shelby, Tipton, Fayette, Lauderdale, Dyer and Haywood Counties. TN - Desoto County, Marshall and Lafayette Counties MS and West Memphis, Arkansas
Note: Printing is contracted out

FORWARD FOCUS
(Mthly)
174 Rains Ave, Nashville, TN, 37203-5319, Davidson, USA; tel (615) 743-3400; fax (615) 743-3480; e-mail info@fiftyforward.org; web site www.fiftyforward.org
Circulation: 8,000fr; Sworn/Estimate/Non-Audited
Advertising: Open inch rate $20.00
Established: 1956
Pub. .... Janet Jernigan
Adv. Mgr. .... Bob Newman
Ed. .... Paul Carlton
Mechanical Specifications: Type page 9 3/4 x 11 1/2; E - 4 cols, 2 3/8, between.
Equipment: Hardware — 3-APP/Mac Power Mac 6500/300, 5-APP/Mac 8.6; Software — QPS/QuarkXPress 5.0.

TEXAS

SENIORIFIC NEWS
(Mthly) (n/a)
PO Box 23307, Waco, TX, 76702-3307, McLennan, USA; tel (800) 736-7350; adv tel (800) 736-7350; fax (877) 736-7350; e-mail ads@seniorific.com; adv e-mail Ads@Seniorific.com; ed e-mail editor@Seniorific.com.

com; web site seniorific.com
Circulation: 520,000fr; CVC
Advertising: N/A
Established: 1988Editions: 28— 28 total covering DFW, Houston, Austin, San Antonio and many mid-size Texas markets
Digital Platform - Mobile: Apple, Android, Windows
Digital Platform - Tablet: Apple iOS, Android, Windows 7
Pub.. Dan McNeil
Editor.................................... Michael Bracken
COO .... Donovan McNeil
Mechanical Specifications: Type page 10 x 13; E - 4 cols, 2 3/8, 1/8 between; A - 4 cols, 2 3/8, between; C - 4 cols, 2 3/8, between.
Delivery Method: Racks
Zip Codes Served: Texas

UTAH

PRIMETIMES

(Mthly)
PO Box 651663, Salt Lake City, UT, 84165-1663, Salt Lake, USA; tel (916) 877-4638; fax (801) 263-1170; e-mail primet@xmission.com; adv e-mail frred@primetimesonline.com; ed e-mail frred@primetimesonline.com; web site www.primetimesonline.com
Circulation: 39,000fr; CVC
Advertising: Open inch rate $23.50
Established: 1999
Digital Platform - Mobile: Windows
Asoc. Ed....................................... Job Matusow
Ed.. Fred Henkel
Graphic Design........................ Shannon Smith
Mechanical Specifications: Type page 10 3/8 x 16; E - 6 cols, 1 5/8, 1/6 between; A - 6 cols, 1 5/8, 1/6 between.
Delivery Method: Mail, Carrier, Racks
Zip Codes Served: 84115

VERMONT

VERMONT MATURITY MAGAZINE

(Mthly, Other) (Spring, Summer, Fall, Winter, EXPO Guide issue)
PO Box 1158, Williston, VT, 05495-1158, Chittenden, USA; tel (802) 872-9000; adv tel (802) 872-9000 x118; fax (802) 872-0151; e-mail vermontmaturity@aol.com; adv e-mail vermontmaturity@aol.com; ed e-mail vermontmaturity@aol.com; web site www.vermontmaturity.com
Circulation: 10,000fr; Sworn/Estimate/Non-Audited
Established: 1993
Parent Co.: Williston Publishing & Promotions
Digital Platform - Mobile: Apple, Android, Windows, Blackberry, Other
Digital Platform - Tablet: Apple iOS, Android, Windows 7, Blackberry Tablet OS, Kindle, Nook, Kindle Fire, Other
Ed & Pub .... Marianne Apfelbaum
Pub.. Paul Apfelbaum
Mechanical Specifications: Type page 7 1/4 x 9 3/4; E - 3 cols, 2 1/4, 1/4 between; A - 3 cols, 2 1/4, 1/4 between.
Equipment; Software — InDesign
Delivery Method: Mail, Racks

VIRGINIA

FIFTY PLUS

(Mthly)
1506 Staples Mill Rd, Ste 102, Richmond, VA, 23230-3631, Richmond City, USA; tel (804) 673-5203; ed tel (804) 673-4966; fax (804) 673-5308; e-mail mail@richmondpublishing.com; web site www.fiftyplusrichmond.com
Circulation: 35,000fr; Sworn/Estimate/Non-Audited
Pub...Mark Fetter
Office Mgr. .... Lisa Fracker
Ed .... Lisa Crutchfield

WASHINGTON

SENIOR SCENE

(Mthly)
223 N Yakima Ave, Tacoma, WA, 98403-2230, Pierce, USA; tel (253) 722-5687; adv tel (253) 722-5687; fax (253) 597-6456; adv fax (253) 597-6456; e-mail seniormedia@lcsnw.org; ed e-mail bdicskon@lcsnw.org; web site www.seniorscene.org
Circulation:; Sworn/Estimate/Non-Audited
Established: 1975
Ed... Bonnie Dickson
Gen. Mgr.................................. Christine Nagy
Circ. Mgr...Jacky Lee
Office Mgr.......................................Judith Silva
Adv. Sales Supvr................. George Kenworthy
Mechanical Specifications: Type page 11 x 17; E - 3 cols, 3 1/8, 1/4 between; A - 3 cols, 3 1/8, 1/4 between; C - 3 cols, 3 1/8, 1/4 between.
Equipment: Hardware — PC; Software — Adobe Creative Suite, Microsoft Office
Delivery Method: Mail, Racks

SENIOR MESSENGER

(Mthly)
400 E Evergreen Blvd, Ste 111, Vancouver, WA, 98660-3263, Clark, USA; tel (360) 750-9900; fax (360) 750-9907; e-mail circulation@seniormessenger.org; adv e-mail ads@seniormessenger.org; ed e-mail news@seniormessenger.org; web site www.vanmessenger.org
Circulation: 15,000fr; Sworn/Estimate/Non-Audited
Advertising: Open inch rate $14.00
Digital Platform - Mobile: AppleMarita Sempio
Mechanical Specifications: Type page 10 1/4 x 16; E - 4 cols, 2 5/12, 1/5 between; A - 4 cols, 2 5/12, 1/5 between.
Equipment: Hardware — PC ad MAC; Software — QuarkExpress, Photoshop, Acrobat

WISCONSIN

MATURITY TIMES

(Mthly)
PO Box 1955, Fond Du Lac, WI, 54936-1955, Fond Du Lac, USA; tel (920) 922-8640; fax (920) 922-0125; adv e-mail classified@actionadvertiser.com; ed e-mail scottw@actionprinting.com; web site www.actiononline.net
Circulation: 11,000fr; Sworn/Estimate/Non-Audited
Established: 1987
Adv. Mgr.................................. Gloria Krueger
Mng. Ed.................................... Scott Wittchow
Mechanical Specifications: Type page 9 x 16; E - 4 cols, 2 1/2, between; A - 4 cols, 2 1/2, between.
Equipment: Hardware — APP/Mac; Software — QPS/QuarkXPress, Adobe/Photoshop.
Zip Codes Served: 54936

50 PLUS

(Mthly)
PO Box 230, Hartland, WI, 53029-0230, Waukesha, USA; tel (262) 367-5303; fax (262) 367-9517; e-mail editorial@50plusnewsmag.com; adv e-mail saran@50plusnewsmag.com; ed e-mail editorial@50plusnewsmag.com; web site mymilwaukeelife.com
Circulation: 6,000pd, 50,000fr; Sworn/Estimate/Non-Audited
Advertising: Open inch rate $38.95Editions: 4— 50Plus News Magazine
Adv. Mgr.. Saran Piehl
Circ. Mgr..Tom Slattery
Ed. ....Jim McLoone
Mng. Ed................................ Maureen Slattery
Mechanical Specifications: Type page 10 x 15; E - 4 cols, 2 1/4, between; A - 4 cols, 2 1/4, between; C - 4 cols, 2 1/4, between.
Equipment: Hardware — APP/Mac; Software — InDesign, Photoshop, Claris/Works.
Zip Codes Served: 53029

JOURNEY OF AGING (ANNUALLY)

PO Box 930156, Verona, WI, 53593-0156, Dane, USA; tel (608) 274-5200; fax (608) 848-5474; e-mail mary@ogarapub.com; adv e-mail mary@ogarapub.com; ed e-mail mary@ogarapub.com; web site www.JourneyofAging.com
Circulation: 20,000fr; Sworn/Estimate/Non-Audited
Advertising: Call for rates
Established: 1994
Parent Co.: O'Gara PublishingEditions: 20,000— Journey of Aging
Owner.. Mary O'Gara
Mechanical Specifications: Type page 10 x 16; E - 4 cols, 2 1/4, 3/16 between; A - 3 cols, 2 1/4, 3/16 between.
Equipment; Presses — Sheet-fed offset press, Heat-Set Web; Software — In Design Photoshop
Delivery Method: Mail, Racks
Zip Codes Served: 53744, 53704, 53705, 53711, 53713, 53714, 53715, 53716, 53717, 53719
Note: Since 1994, OGara Publishing has been producing niche publications for readers in the Greater Madison area. We are a locally owned and family-operated business focused exclusively on the community here in Dane County, WI.
We currently produce the Journey of Aging Guide annually each September. This publication is a valuable and practical reference tool for information regarding aging resources, services and products in this area. Our target market is aging adults, disabled adults, adult children of parents,caregivers, social workers, case managers and discharge nurses.
In September 2014, we will distribute 20,000 glossy, 4-color copies at over 150 locations throughout Dane County. We provide restocking throughout the year. We printed 17,500 copies in 2013 and our stock was depleted as of early May 2014.

Section IV

Weekly Newspaper Groups and Other Organizations, Industry Services

Weekly Newspaper and Shopper Publication Groups in the U.S. 2

Weekly Newspaper and Shopper Publication Groups in Canada ... 21

Alternative Delivery Services 24

Associations and Clubs - National and International..............26

Associations and Clubs - City State and Regional 30

Newspaper Brokers and Appraisers 33

Newspaper Representatives - National..............................35

Newspaper Representatives - State 37

Newspaper Distributed Magazines and TMC Publications 38

WEEKLY NEWSPAPER AND SHOPPER PUBLICATION GROUPS IN THE U.S

ADAMS PUBLISHING GROUP, LLC — 704 S 7th Ave, Virginia, MN, 55792-3086, USA; tel (218) 750-2615; fax (419) 782-2944; e-mail crescent@crescent-news.com; web site www.adamspg.com
Est.: 1887
Ed. — Peter Bodley
Mktg. Dir. — Bob Cole
Reg. Pres. — Christopher Knight
Reg. Pub. — Sam Gett
Pres. & Pub. — David Fike
Reg. Pub. — Chad Hjellming
Reg. Pub. — Julie Frazier
Pub. — John D. Worthington
Adv. Mgr. — Mary Anne Pfeiffer
Adv. Mgr. — Mark Ryan
Ed. — Debbie Horne
Circ. Mgr. — Betty Lentz
Ed. — Dennis Van Scoder
Sports Ed. — Bruce Hefflinger
Prepress Mgr. — Beverly Stahl
Gen. Mgr. — Steve VanDemark
I.T. Director — Adam Breckler
Pres. — Carl Esposito
Newspapers: APG Media of Tennessee/North Carolina, TN
The Avery Journal-Times, NC
The Blowing Rocket, NC
The Pilot, NC
Anacortes American, WA
Belgrade News, MT
Bozeman Daily Chronicle, MT
Cecil Whig, MD
Daily Record, WA
Eastern Shore Bargaineer, MD
Eau Claire Press Co., WI
Herald and News, OR
Idaho State Journal, ID
Kuna Melba News, ID
Lake County Examiner, OR
News-Herald, TN
Preston Citizen, ID
Skagit Valley Herald, WA
Stanwood Camano News, WA
Teton Valley News, ID
The Advocate & Democrat, TN
The Ashe Mountain Times, NC
The Daily Post-Athenian, TN
The Daily Times, TN
The Greeneville Sun, TN
The Herald-News, TN
The Maryland Independent, MD
The Nickel, OR
The Rogersville Review, TN
The Watauga Mountain Times, NC
Watauga Democrat, NC
Aitkin Independent Age, MN
Mille Lacs Messenger, MN
Faribault Daily News, MN
Bargain Hunter, MN
The Ashland Daily Press, WI
The Newport Plain Talk, TN
The Bay Times, MD
Gladwin County Record, MI
The Times Record, MD
Hibbing Daily Tribune, MN
Mesabi Daily News, MN
Andrews Gazette, MD
Wyoming Business Report, WY
Rawlins Daily Times, WY
Bayfield County Journal, WI
Post Register, ID
Kenyon Leader, MN
Rock Springs Rocket Miner, WY
The Chisholm Tribune Press, MN
Anoka County Shopper, MN
Kent County News, MD
Laramie Boomerang, WY
The Enterprise, MD
Wyoming Tribune-Eagle, WY
Brooklyn Center/Brooklyn Park Sun-Post, MN
Co-pilot, MN
Blaine-Spring Lake Park Life, MN
Minnetonka/Deephaven/Hopkins Sun Sailor, MN
Le Sueur News-Herald, MN
St. Louis Park Sun Sailor, MN
Logan Daily News, OH
Richfield Sun-Current, MN
Anoka County Union Herald, MN
Bloomington Sun-Current, MN
Crescent Extra, OH
Minnesota River Valley Shopper, MN
The Caledonia Argus, MN
Carver County News, MN
Champlin-Dayton Press, MN
Lonsdale News - Review, MN
Columbia Heights/Fridley Sun Focus, MN
Northfield Weekender, MN
North Crow River News, MN
Northfield News, MN
South Crow River News, MN
Robbinsdale/Crystal/New Hope/Golden Valley Sun-Post, MN
Sawyer County Record, WI
Dairyland Peach, MN
Owatonna People's Press, MN
Dakota County Tribune, MN
The Avenue News, MD
St. Peter Herald, MN
The Post Review, MN
Eden Prairie Sun-Current, MN
The Challis Messenger, ID
Edina Sun-Current, MN
Park Falls Herald, WI
The Le Center Leader, MN
Excelsior/Shorewood/Chanhassen Sun Sailor, MN
Forest Lake Times, MN
Isanti County News, MN
Waseca Area Shopper, MN
The Laker, MN
The Vinton County Courier, OH
Mille Lacs County Times, MN
Waseca County News, MN
Monticello Times, MN
Morrison County Record, MN
Perry County Tribune, OH
Mounds View/New Brighton Sun Focus, MN
Owatonna Area Shopper, MN
Norwood Young America Times, MN
Price County Review, WI
Lonsdale Area News-Review, MN
Osseo-Maple Grove Press, MN
The Calvert Recorder, MD
The Pioneer, MN
The Crescent-News, OH
Wayzata/Orono/Plymouth/Long Lake Sun Sailor, MN
Princeton Union-Eagle, MN
The Leader, MN
Faribault Area Shopper, MN
Scotsman, MN
St. Croix Valley Peach, MN
The Early Bird, WI
Star News, MN
Stillwater Gazette, MN
The Circleville Herald, OH
Sun Thisweek Apple Valley, MN
The Dorchester Star, MD
Thisweek Burnsville-Eagan Sun, MN
Queen Anne's Record Observer, MD
Sun Thisweek Lakeville, MN
Rice Lake Chronotype, WI
Town & Country Shopper, GA
The Waconia Patriot, MN
Rocket-Miner, WY
Spooner Advocate, WI
Star Democrat, MD
Newark Post, DE
The Enterprise, MD
Dundalk Eagle, MD
Enquirer Gazette, MD
Pentagram, VA
Tester, MD
The Journal, MD
Quarterdeck, DC
Joint Base Journal, DC
Southern Maryland Advertiser, MD
South Potomac Pilot, VA
The Bargainer, MD
The Standard, MD

ADVANCE PUBLICATIONS, INC. — 950 W Fingerboard Rd, Staten Island, NY, 10305-1453, USA; tel (718) 981-1234; fax (718) 981-1456; web site www.advance.net
Chrmn. of the Bd. — S.I. Newhouse
Pres. — Donald E. Newhouse
Pub., Staten Island Advance — Caroline Diamond Harrison
Executive VP — Mark Newhouse
Newspapers: The Patriot-News, PA
The Warren Reporter, NJ
South Advance, MI
Beaverton Leader, OR
Sun News, OH
Forest Grove Leader, OR
The US, PA
The Ann Arbor News, MI
The Kalamazoo Gazette, MI
Advantage, GA
Bayonne Journal (OOB) , NJ
Cadence, MI
Chronicle Shopping Guide (OOB), MI
Cranford Chronicle, NJ
Davison Flagstaff, MI
Duncannon Record, PA
Grand Blanc News, MI
Grand Valley Advance, MI
Hillsboro Argus, OR
Hunterdon County Democrat, NJ
Independent Press, NJ
Juniata Sentinel, PA
Kearny Weekly, NJ
Southeast Advance, MI
Metuchen/Edison Review, NJ
Northwest Advance, MI
Northeast Advance, MI
Penasee Globe, MI
Perry County Times, PA
Press-Register, AL
Record Press, NJ
Secaucus Journal (OOB) , NJ
Ledger Somerset Observer, NJ
South Plainfield Reporter, NJ
Southwest Advance, MI
Staten Island Advance, NY
Suburban News, NJ
Sun Scoop Journal, OH
The Advance, GA
The Bay City Times, MI
The Birmingham News, AL
The Burton News, MI
The Community Journal, MI
The Express-Times, PA
The Fenton Press, MI
The Flint Journal, MI
The Flint Township News, MI
The Flushing Observer, MI
The Gloucester County Times, NJ
The Grand Rapids Press, MI
The Huntsville Times, AL
The Jackson Citizen Patriot, MI
The Jersey Journal, NJ
The Mississippi Press, MS
The Muskegon Chronicle, MI
The News of Cumberland County, NJ
The News-Sun, PA
The Oregonian, OR
The Post-Standard, NY
The Reporter, NJ
The Republican, MA
The Saginaw News, MI
Star-Gazette, NJ
The Swartz Creek News, MI
The Times, NJ
The Times-Picayune, LA
South Jersey Times , NJ
Waterfront Journal, NJ
The Plain Dealer, OH
The Star-Ledger, NJ

AIM MEDIA INDIANA — 2980 N National Rd, Ste A, Columbus, IN, 47201-3234, USA; tel (812) 372-7811; web site www.therepublic.com
Est.: 1872
CFO — Jeff Rogers
Dir., Info. Servs. and human resources — Karen Fox Thompson
Publisher — Chuck Wells
Newspapers: Amherst News-Times, OH
Bellville Star & Tri-Forks Press, OH
Daily Advocate, OH
Daily Reporter, IN
Englewood Independent, OH
Fairborn Daily Herald, OH
Galion Inquirer, OH
Gallipolis Daily Tribune, OH
Hillsboro Times-Gazette, OH
Huber Heights Courier, OH
Macon County Times, TN
Miami County Advocate, OH
Sentinel-Tribune, OH
The Lima News, OH
The Register-Herald, OH
News Journal Star, OH
Republic Extra, IN
The Portsmouth Daily Times, OH
Daily Journal, IN
The Republic, IN
Pendleton Times-Post, IN
Brown County Democrat, IN
The Jackson County Banner, IN
The (Columbus) Republic, IN
Daily Journal, IN
The (Seymour) Tribune, IN
The Jackson County Banner, IN

AIM MEDIA TEXAS LLC — 1400 E Nolana Ave, McAllen, TX, 78504-6111, USA; tel (956) 683-4060; e-mail manager@aimmediatx.com; web site www.aimmediatexas.com
Newspapers: The Brownsville Herald, TX
Valley Morning Star, TX
The Monitor, TX
Odessa American, TX

AMERICAN CLASSIFIEDS - FARMINGTON - FOUR CORNERS — 928 E Main St, Ste C, Farmington, NM, 87401-2700, USA; tel (505) 564-2535; e-mail 4corners@AmClass.us; web site www.AmClass.us
Group: Want Ads of Farmington, Inc.
Est.: 1985
Pres. — Robert Elmore
Sales Mgr. — Allen Elmore

AMERICAN COMMUNITY NEWSPAPERS LLC — 33 2nd St NE, # 280, Osseo, MN, 55369-1252, USA; tel (763) 425-3323; fax 763-425-2945; web site www.americancommunitynewspapers.com
Est.: 1998
CEO — Gene Carr
CFO — David Kosofsky
Cor. Controller — Richard D. Hendrickson
Newspapers: Osseo-Maple Grove Press, MN
Champlin-Dayton Press, MN
North Crow River News, MN
Eden Prairie Sun-Current, MN
Sunnyvale View, TX
Columbia Heights/Fridley Sun Focus, MN
Eagan/Apple Valley/Rosemount Sun Thisweek, MN
Edina Sun-Current, MN
Excelsior/Shorewood/Chanhassen Sun Sailor, MN
Lakeville Sun-Current, MN
Monticello Shopper, MN
Monticello Times, MN

Northwest Columbus News, OH
Ramsey County Sun Focus (OOB), MN
Robbinsdale/Crystal/New Hope/Golden Valley Sun-Post, MN
Suburban News Publications, OH
The Big Walnut News, OH
The Times, OH
Wayzata/Orono/Plymouth/Long Lake Sun Sailor, MN

AMERICAN HOMETOWN PUBLISHING — 110 3rd Ave N, Franklin, TN, 37064-2506, USA; tel (615) 599-8751; fax (615) 599-8752; e-mail bsmith@americanhometownpublishing.com; web site www.americanhometownpublishing.com
Vice President HR — Stephanie L. Jameson
President & COO — Brian Smith
Newspapers: Blackwell Journal-Tribune, OK
Brownsville States-Graphic, TN
Chester County Independent, TN
Guthrie News Leader, OK
The Collierville Herald, TN
The Dickenson Star, VA
The Tri-City Reporter, TN

ANAMOSA PUBLICATIONS — PO Box 108, P.O. Box 108, Anamosa, IA, 52205-0108, USA; tel (319) 462-3511; fax (319) 462-4540; e-mail admin@journal-eureka.com; web site www.Journal-Eureka.com
Group: Anamosa Publications
Est.: 1856
Pub — W. James Johnson
Newspapers: The Kalona News, IA
Journal-Eureka, IA

ANTON COMMUNITY NEWSPAPERS — 132 E 2nd St, Mineola, NY, 11501-3522, USA; tel (516) 747-8282; fax (516) 742-5867; e-mail info@antonnews.com; web site www.antonnews.com
Pub. — Angela Susan Anton
Gen. Mgr. — William Delventhal
Managing Editor — Cary Seaman
Newspapers: Garden City Life, NY
Glen Cove Record-Pilot, NY
Hicksville Illustrated News, NY
Levittown Tribune, NY
Manhasset Press, NY
Massapequan Observer, NY
Mineola American, NY
Oyster Bay Enterprise Pilot, NY
Plainview/Old Bethpage Herald, NY
Port Washington News, NY
Syosset/Jericho Tribune, NY
Floral Park Dispatch, NY
New Hyde Park Illustrated, NY
Roslyn News, NY
Westbury Times, NY
Farmingdale Observer, NY
Great Neck Record, NY

APG MEDIA OF TENNESSEE/NORTH CAROLINA — 103 W Summer St, Greeneville, TN, 37743-4923, USA; tel (423) 638-4181; fax (423) 639-9701; web site www.greenevillesun.com
Group: Adams Publishing Group, LLC
President of APG East and Publisher of The Greeneville Sun — Gregg K. Jones
VP of Human Resources of Adams Publishing Group — Jo Ann Hopson
Chief Revenue Officer of APG Media of TN/NC, and General Manager of The Greeneville Sun. — John E. Cash
President of APG Media of TN/NC and Publisher of The Daily Times — Carl Esposito
Newspapers: The Connection, TN
Note: APG Media of TN/NC publishes three daily and eleven non-daily general circulation newspapers in East Tennessee and the High Country of Western North Carolina. The company also publishes tourism publications in the Great Smoky Mountains region, operates a brochure distribution company, and publishes monthly hotel/motel travel guides and websites throughout the southeastern United States. The company also owns and operates The High Road Agency, a full service marketing solutions firm based out of Tri-Cities TN/VA.

ASSOCIATED NEWSPAPERS OF MICHIGAN — 35540 W Michigan Ave, Wayne, MI, 48184-1626, USA; tel (734) 467-1900; fax (734) 729-1840; web site www.associatednewspapers.net
Pub. — Susan Willett
Gen. Mgr. — Sean Rhaesa
Newspapers: The Wayne Eagle, MI
The Romulus Roman, MI
Canton Eagle, MI
The Westland Eagle, MI
Plymouth Eagle, MI
Northville Eagle, MI
The Inkster Ledger Star, MI
The Belleville Enterprise, MI

BATTLE BORN MEDIA LLC — 297 11th St E, Ely, NV, 89301-2300, USA; tel (775) 289-4491
Est.: 2011
— Tim Dahlberg
— Tom SmithFounders
Newspapers: Ely Times, NV
Mesquite Local News, NV
Mineral County Independent News, NV
The Eureka Sentinel, NV
Lincoln County Record, NV

BEE GROUP NEWSPAPERS — 5564 Main St, Williamsville, NY, 14221-5410, USA; tel (716) 632-4700; fax (716) 633-8601; e-mail tmeaser@beenews.com; web site www.beenews.com
Group: Bee Group Newspapers
Est.: 1879
Pres./Pub. — Trey Measer
David Sherman
Newspapers: Amherst Bee, NY
Clarence Bee, NY
Ken-Ton Bee, NY
Lancaster Bee, NY
Depew Bee, NY
Cheektowaga Bee, NY
West Seneca Bee, NY
Orchard Park Bee, NY
East Aurora Bee, NY

BERKS-MONT NEWSPAPERS, INC. — 124 N Chestnut St, Boyertown, PA, 19512-1123, USA; tel (610) 367-6041; fax (610) 369-0233; web site www.berksmontnews.com
Est.: 1968
Pub. — Patti Paul
Newspapers: The Boyertown Area Times, PA
The Kutztown Area Patriot, PA
The Hamburg Area Item, PA
Berksmont News, PA
Tri-County Record, PA
The Community Connection, PA

BH MEDIA GROUP — 1314 Douglas St, Ste 1500, Omaha, NE, 68102-1848, USA; e-mail berkshire@berkshirehathaway.com; web site www.berkshirehathaway.comScott Searl

THOMAS KASTRUP
Corporate Director — Jeffrey Carney
SR. VICE PRESIDENT, COO — Doug Hiemstra
VICE PRESIDENT, BH MEDIA MIDWEST GROUP — Alex Skovgaard
Regional Sales Director, NC Group of BH Media — Jason Propst
Vice President — Dale Lachniet
Sr. Vice President, COO — Hiemstra Doug
Newspapers: Bellevue Leader, NE
Advantage, NE
The Free Lance-Star, VA
Kearney Hub, NE
Star-Herald, NE
The Grand Island Independent, NE
The North Platte Telegraph, NE
Tulsa Business & Legal News, OK
Valley News Today, IA
Waco Tribune-Herald, TX
Market Weekly, NE
Smyth County News & Messenger, VA
Lexington Clipper-Herald, NE
Tulsa World, OK
Midlands Newspapers, Inc., NE
News & Record, NC
Powhatan Today, VA
Richlands News-Press, VA
Rockingham Now, NC
The Waverly News, NE
Gering Courier, NE
Shore News Today, NJ
Culpeper Star-Exponent, VA
The Burg, VA
Lake City News & Post, SC
Pow, NC
The Eagle, TX
The Enterprise Ledger, AL
The Eden News, NC
The Press of Atlantic City, NJ
The Messenger, NC
Wahoo Newspaper, NE
The Buffalo News, NY
The Roanoke Times, VA
Morning News, SC
The News & Advance, VA
Omaha World-Herald, NE
Bristol Herald Courier, VA
The Dothan Eagle, AL
News & Messenger, VA
Independent Tribune, NC
Jackson County Floridan, FL
The News Herald, NC
The Daily Progress, VA
The Hickory Daily Record, NC
The McDowell News, NC
Winston-Salem Journal, NC
Hernando Today (OOB), FL
Statesville Record & Landmark, NC
Opelika-Auburn News, AL
Richmond Times-Dispatch, VA
The News Virginian, VA
Dothan Progress, AL
Atlantic City Weekly, NJ
Mechanicsville Local, VA
Goochland Gazette, VA
The Greene County Record, VA
Madison Eagle, NJ
Orange County Review, VA
Danville Register & Bee, VA
The Floyd Press, VA
Bland County Messenger, VA
Wytheville Enterprise, VA
Martinsville Bulletin, VA
The Franklin News-Post, VA
Mooresville Tribune, NC
Army Flier, AL
Eufaula Tribune, AL
The Hartsville Messenger, SC
Gretna Breeze, NE
Papillion Times, NE
Ralston Recorder, NE
The Ashland Gazette, NE
The Clarinda Herald-Journal, IA
The Daily Nonpareil, IA
York News-Times, NE
The Eden Daily News, NC
The Reidsville Review, NC
The Suncoast News, FL

BHG, INC. — 91 N Main St, Garrison, ND, 58540-7166, USA; tel (701) 463-2201; fax (701) 463-2201; web site www.nd-bhginc.com
Pres. — Michael W. Gackle
Adv. Dir. — Angela Kolden
Newspapers: Beulah Beacon, ND
Center Republican, ND
The Hazen Star, ND
Leader-News, ND
McLean County Independent, ND
McLean County Journal, ND
McClusky Gazette, ND
Mountrail County Record, ND
New Town News, ND
The Northern Sentry, ND
Underwood News, ND
Velva Area Voice, ND

BLUFF COUNTRY NEWSPAPER GROUP — 112 N Broadway St, Spring Valley, MN, 55975-1224, USA; tel (507) 346-7365; fax (507) 346-7366; e-mail info@bluffcountrynews.com; web site www.bluffcountrynews.com
Est.: 1974
Pres. — Dave Phillips
Newspapers: The Chatfield News, MN
Bluff Country Reader, MN
Spring Grove Herald, MN
Spring Valley Tribune, MN
Tri-County Record, MN
Fillmore County News Leader, MN
Note: Group includes: Bluff Country Reader, Chatfield News, Fillmore County News Leader, Spring Grove Herald, Spring Valley Tribune, Tri-County Record of Rushford.

BOONE NEWSPAPERS, INC. — 15222 Freemans Bend Rd, Northport, AL, 35475-3800, USA; tel (205) 330-4100; fax (205) 330-4140; e-mail bni@boonenewspapers.com; web site www.boonenewspapers.com
Chrmn. of the Bd./CEO/Dir. — James B. Boone
Pres./COO — Todd H. Carpenter
Sr. Vice Pres. — William T. Beckner
Sr. Vice Pres. — David D. Churchill
Vice Pres. — Jason Cannon
Vice Pres. — Joseph C. Davis
Vice Pres. — Michele Cox Gerlach
Vice Pres. — Michael R. Kelley
Vice Pres. — Dennis M. Palmer
Vice Pres. — Joseph C. Davis
VP — Kevin Cooper
Vice Pres. — Tim Prince
Newspapers: Americus Times-Recorder, GA
Claiborne Progress, TN
LaGrange Daily News, GA
The Advocate-Messenger, KY
The Interior Journal, KY
The Jessamine Journal, KY
The Stanly News & Press, NC
The Winchester Sun, KY
Cordele Dispatch, GA
Daily Leader, MS
Dowagiac Daily News, MI
The Farmville Herald, VA
The State Journal, KY
Washington Daily News, NC
Pelham Reporter, AL
The Madison Record, AL
Albert Lea Tribune, MN
Alabaster Reporter, AL
Alexander City Outlook, AL
Andalusia Star-News, AL
Atmore Advance, AL
Austin Daily Herald, MN
Butler County News, AL
Cassopolis Vigilant, MI
Dadeville Record, AL
Demopolis Times, AL
Eclectic Observer, AL
Edwardsburg Argus, MI
The Fergus Falls Daily Journal, MN
Franklin County Times, AL
Freeborn County Shopper, MN
Gates County Index, NC
Hartselle Enquirer, AL
Lowndes Signal, AL
Miss-lou Buyers Guide, MS
Mower County Shopper, MN
Natchez Newspapers, Inc., MS
Post-searchlight Extra, GA
Roanoke-Chowan News-Herald, NC
Shelby County Reporter, AL
Suffolk News-Herald, VA
The Brewton Standard, AL
The Clanton Advertiser, AL
The Greenville Advocate, AL
The Ironton Tribune, OH
The Leader, MI
The Luverne Journal, AL
The Troy Messenger, AL
The Natchez Democrat, MS
The Post-Searchlight, GA
The Roanoke-chowan's Shopper Weekly, NC
The Tidewater News, VA
Tribune Shopping News, MN
Weekender, MN
The Selma Times-Journal, AL
The Tallassee Tribune, AL
Blackbelt Gazette, AL
The Wetumpka Herald, AL
Elizabethton Star, TN
The Madison County Record, AR

Bogalusa Daily News, LA
L'Observateur, LA
Port Arthur News, TX
Tryon Daily Bulletin, NC
Salisbury Post, NC
The Vicksburg Post, MS
Picayune Item, MS
The Oxford Eagle, MS
Niles Daily Star, MI

BQE PUBLISHING INC. — 45-23 47 St, Woodside, NY, 11377, USA; tel (718) 639-7000; fax (718) 429-1234; e-mail news@queensledger.com; web site www.queensledger.com
Group: BQE Publishing Inc
Est.: 1873
Pub. — Walter H. Sanchez
Newspapers: Queens Ledger, NY
Forest Hills/Rego Park Times, NY
Glendale Register, NY
The Leader-Observer of Woodhaven, NY
Long Island City/Astoria/Jackson Heights Journal, NY
The Queens Examiner, NY
Greenpoint Star & Northside Weekly News, NY
Brooklyn Downtown Star, NY
Note: Queens Ledger Weekly Newspaper Group:
The Queens Ledger bought the Newtown Register in 1935, which was a continually published weekly since 1873.

BREHM COMMUNICATIONS, INC. — 16644 W Bernardo Dr, Ste 300, San Diego, CA, 92127-1901, USA; tel (858) 451-6200; fax (858) 451-3814; e-mail debbiel@brehmmail.com; web site www.brehmcommunications.com
Est.: 1919
Pres — William Brehm
Controller — Jeff Johnson
Execu Asst — Debbie Lindsay
VP-Sales and Mktg — Thomas Kirk
Dir, Human Resources — Sara Salinas
Interactive Media & Technology Mgr — Ryan Schuyler
Real Estate Mgr — Barbara Schuyler
Newspapers: Auburn Journal, CA
Big Bear Grizzly, CA
Wine Country This Week, CA
Laughlin Entertainer, AZ
Wabash And Edwards Today, IN
Desert Entertainer, CA
Big Bear Shopper, CA
Bullhead City Booster, AZ
Desert Trail, CA
Emery County Progress, UT
Grizzly Weekender, CA
Hi-Desert Star, CA
Mohave Valley Daily News, AZ
Mountain News & Crestline Courier-News, CA
Needles Desert Star, CA
Warrick County Today, IN
Oakland City Journal, IN
Auburn Trader, CA
Gibson County Today, IN
Loomis News, CA
Richfield Reaper, UT
Wickenburg Sun, AZ
Sun Advocate, UT
Vernal Express, UT
Uintah Basin Standard, UT
Placer Herald, CA
Colfax Record, CA
Observation Post, CA
Barstow Log, CA
Laughlin Nevada Times, AZ
Folsom Telegraph, CA
Lincoln News Messenger, CA
El Dorado Hills Telegraph, CA
Note: Subsidiaries: The Democrat Co.; Gull Communications, Inc.; Hi-Desert Publishing Co., Inc.; News West Publishing Company Inc.; Gold Country Media, Inc.; Wine Country Publications, Inc.; Princeton Publishing, Inc.; Mt. Carmel Register Co.; Warrick Publishing Co., Inc.

BUCHHEIT NEWS MANAGEMENT, INC. — 364 S Pine St, Ste B230, Spartanburg, SC, 29302-2664, USA; tel (864) 573-8706; fax (864) 573-8710
Est.: 1993
Pres. — Mellnee G. Buchheit
Exec. Vice Pres./Treasurer — Vickie G. Myers
Newspapers: Goldsboro News-Argus, NC
Chesnee Tribune, SC
Spartanburg County News, SC

BYRD NEWSPAPERS — 2 N Kent St, Winchester, VA, 22601-5038, USA; tel (540) 667-3200
Group: Ogden Newspapers Inc.
Newspapers: Daily News-Record, VA

C & G NEWSPAPERS — 13650 E 11 Mile Rd, Warren, MI, 48089-1422, USA; tel (586) 498-8000; fax (586) 498-9631; web site www.candgnews.com
Adv. Mgr. — Elaine Myers
Ed. — John Carlisle
Editorial Dir. — Gregg Demers
Adv. Dir. — Jeff Demers
Newspapers: The Eastsider, MI
Fraser-Clinton Chronicle, MI
Journal, MI
Macomb Chronicle, MI
Shelby-Utica News, MI
St. Clair Shores Sentinel, MI
Sterling Heights Sentry, MI
Warren Weekly, MI
Birmingham-Bloomfield Eagle, MI
Farmington Press, MI
Madison-Park News, MI
Rochester Post, MI
Royal Oak Review, MI
Southfield Sun, MI
Troy Times, MI
West Bloomfield Beacon, MI
Woodward Talk, MI
Advertiser Times, MI
Grosse Pointe Times, MI

CAMPBELL PUBLISHING CO., INC. — 832 S State St, Jerseyville, IL, 62052-2343, USA; tel (618) 498-1234; fax 630-206-0320; e-mail jcjnews@campbellpublications.net
Publisher — Julie Boren
Newspapers: Jesey County Journal, IL
Calhoun News-Herald, IL
Greene Prairie Press, IL
Scott County Times, IL
The Weekly Messenger, IL
Pike Press

CAPITAL NEWSPAPERS — 1901 Fish Hatchery Rd, Madison, WI, 53713-1248, USA; tel (608) 252-6200; fax (608) 252-6028; e-mail customerservice@madison.com; web site www.capitalnewspapers.com
Pres./Pub. — Clayton Frink
CFO — Pam Wells
Chrmn., Board — John H. Lussier
Treasurer — Philip Blake
Ed. — Paul Fanlund
Production Dir. — Robert Strabala
Julie Belschner
VP of Advertising, Sales & Marketing — Joe Allen
Newspapers: Columbus Journal, WI
Juneau County Star-Times, WI
Monday-mini, WI
Reedsburg Times-Press, WI
Sauk Prairie Eagle, WI
Shopper Stopper, WI
Shopping Reminder, WI
Tri-county, WI
Wisconsin Dells Events, WI
Baraboo News Republic, WI
Daily Citizen, Beaver Dam, WI
Wisconsin State Journal, Madison, WI
Note: Capital Newspapers is partially owned by Lee Enterprises Inc. Capital Newspapers owns five daily newspapers and 16 non-daily publications.

CASA GRANDE VALLEY NEWSPAPERS INC. — 200 W 2nd St, Casa Grande, AZ, 85122-4409, USA; tel (520) 836-7461; fax (520) 836-0343; e-mail ads@pinalcentral.com; web site www.pinalcentral.com
Est.: 1912
Pres. — Ruth A. Kramer
Co-Pub., Mng. Ed. — Donovan Kramer Jr.
Sr. Adv. Consultant — Jenny Scharf
Circulation Manager — Kris Finke
Co-publisher, Adv. Dir. — Kara K. Cooper
Newspapers: Casa Grande Dispatch, AZ
Coolidge Examiner, AZ
Florence Reminder & Blade-Tribune, AZ
Maricopa Monitor, AZ
Eloy Enterprise, AZ
Note: Casa Grande Valley Newspapers Inc. owns the daily Casa Grande Dispatch. Casa Grande Valley Newspapers Inc. is owned by Kramer Publications.

CENTURY GROUP NEWSPAPERS — 35154 Yucaipa Blvd, Yucaipa, CA, 92399-4339, USA; tel (909) 797-9101; fax (909) 797-0502; e-mail tbush@centurygroup.com; web site www.centurygroup.com
President / CEO / Pub. — Toebe Bush
Owner — Gerald A. Bean
Newspapers: Fontana Herald News, CA
Highland Community News, CA
Yucaipa & Calimesa News-Mirror, CA
Yucaipa / Calimesa News Mirror, CA
Record Gazette, CA

CLAYTON COUNTY REGISTER — 106 Cedar St NW, Elkader, IA, 52043, USA; tel (563) 245-1311; fax (563) 245-1312; e-mail ccrnews@alpinecom.net; web site www.claytoncountyregister.com
Newspapers: The Clayton County Register, IA
Courier-Press, WI
Guttenberg Press, IA
Note: News Publishing Co., Inc. (IA) is owned by News Publishing, Inc. which owns 10 non-daily publications.

CNHI, LLC — 445 Dexter Ave, Montgomery, AL, 36104-3775, USA; tel (334) 293-5800; web site www.cnhi.com
Sr. VP — Mike Beatty
Newspapers: Crossroads Supersaver, IL
North Coast, MI
The Madison County Advertiser, KY

COLORADO COMMUNITY MEDIA — 9137 Ridgeline Blvd, Ste 210, Highlands Ranch, CO, 80129-2752, USA; tel (303) 566-4100; fax (303) 566-4098; web site www.coloradocommunitymedia.com
Est.: 2000
Pub. — Gerard Healey
John Tracy
Newspapers: Wheat Ridge Transcript, CO
Douglas County News Press, CO
Northglenn-Thornton Sentinel, CO
Castle Rock News Press, CO
Centennial Citizen, CO
Elbert County News, CO
The Englewood Herald, CO
Lone Tree Voice, CO
Highlands Ranch Herald, CO
Parker Chronicle, CO
Littleton Independent, MA
South Platte Independent, CO
Arvada Press, CO
Lakewood Sentinel, CO
Golden Transcript, CO
Westminster Window, CO
Northglenn-Thornton Sentinel, CO
Castle Pines News Press, CO

COMMUNITY MEDIA GROUP — 805 S Logan St, West Frankfort, IL, 62896-2637, USA; tel (618) 937-6412; fax (618) 932-3848; web site www.communitymediagroup.com
Chrmn./Pres./CEO — Larry J. Perrotto
Vice Chrmn. — John H. Satterwhite
Exec. Vice Pres. — John D. Perrotto
Exec. Vice Pres. — Mark J. Perrotto
Exec. Vice Pres. — Joan R. Williams
Vice Pres. — Paul Barrett
VP Accounting — Kristen Ahlberg
Newspapers: Barr's Post Card News, IA
Bonny Buyer, IA
Daily Gate City, IA
Fort Madison Daily Democrat, IA
Hancock County Journal-Pilot, IL
The Progress, PA
Ludington Daily News, MI
Ludington Shopper's Edition, MI
Cedar Falls Times (OOB), IA
The Star-News, CA
The Hoopeston Chronicle, IL
Ossian Bee, IA
Fayette Leader, IA
Colonie/Loudonville Spotlight, NY
Fayette County Union, IA
The Leader-Vindicator, PA
Neoga News (OOB), IL
The Spotlight, NY
The Elgin Echo, IA
Oblong Gem (OOB), IL
Bremer County Independent, IA
Tri-County Sunday, PA
Atlantic News Telegraph, IA
Audubon County Advocate Journal, IA
Bremer-butler Super Shopper, IA
Finger Lakes Times, NY
Fountain County Neighbor, IN
Free Press-Courier, PA
Indiana Spirit, IN
Iosco County News Herald, MI
Lafayette Leader, IN
Messenger, IN
News Times, IN
Oceana's Herald-Journal, MI
Port Allegany Reporter-Argus, PA
Rensselaer Republican, IN
Shopper's Reminder, IA
The Chronicle, IL
The Extra, IL
The News-Gazette, IN
The Newton County Enterprise, IN
The Oelwein Daily Register, IA
The News Reminder, IN
The Reporter (OOB), IL
The Wellsboro Gazette, PA
Times-Republic, IL
White Lake Beacon, MI
Oscoda Press, MI
Vinton Livewire, IA
Kankakee Valley Post-News, IN
The Review-Republican, IN
Olean Times Herald, NY
Independence Bulletin Journal, IA
The Courier Express, PA
Jeffersonian Democrat, PA
Bradford Era, PA
Note: Community Media Group owns ten daily newspapers, 23 weekly and 18 shopper publications.

COMMUNITY NEWSPAPER CO. - SOUTH — 165 Enterprise Dr, Marshfield, MA, 02050-2132, USA; tel (781) 837-4500; fax (781) 837-4543; e-mail molivieri@cnc.com; web site www.wickedlocal.com
Group: GateHouse Media, Inc.
Chief Operating Officer — Richard J. Daniels
Adv. Mgr. — Mark Olivieri
Pres./CEO/Pub. — Kirk Davis
Newspapers: Braintree Forum, MA
Bridgewater Independent, MA
Carver Reporter, MA
Cohasset Mariner, MA
Duxbury Reporter, MA
East Bridgewater Star, MA
Halifax-Plympton Reporter, MA
Hanover Mariner, MA
Hanson Town Crier, MA
Hingham Journal, MA
Holbrook Sun, MA
Kingston Reporter, MA
The Lakeville Call, MA
Marshfield Mariner, MA
Norwell Mariner, MA
Old Colony Memorial, MA
Pembroke Reporter, MA
Pembroke Mariner & Express, MA
Randolph Herald, MA
The Raynham Call, MA
Rockland Standard, MA
Scituate Mariner, MA
Wareham Courier, MA
West Bridgewater Times, MA

Weymouth News, MA
Whitman Times, MA
Bourne Courier, MA
Harwich Oracle, MA
The Register, MA
Sandwich Broadsider, MA
Upper Cape Codder, MA

COMMUNITY NEWSPAPER CO.-METRO — 254 2nd Ave, Needham, MA, 02494-2829, USA; tel (781) 433-8200; fax (781) 453-6650; web site www.wickedlocal.com
CEO — Kirk Davis
Adv. Dir. — Chris Warren
Mktg. Mgr. — Robin Lorenzen
Newspapers: Allston-Brighton TAB, MA
Brookline TAB, MA
Cambridge Chronicle & TAB, MA
Dover-Sherborn Press, MA
Roslindale Transcript, MA
Somerville Journal, MA
Needham Times, MA
Newton Tab, MA
Watertown TAB, MA
Wellesley Townsman, MA
West Roxbury Transcript, MA

COMMUNITY NEWSPAPER CO.-NORTH — 72 Cherry Hill Dr, Ste 1001, Beverly, MA, 01915-1030, USA; tel (978) 739-1300; fax (978) 739-1392; web site www.heraldmedia.com
Pres./CEO/Pub. — Kirk Davis
Assoc. Pub. — Rick Daniels
Adv. Dir. — Fred Splaine
Newspapers: Amesbury News, MA
Beverly Citizen, MA
Danvers Herald, MA
Cape Ann Beacon, MA
Georgetown Record, MA
Hamilton-Wenham Chronicle, MA
Ipswich Chronicle, MA
Malden Observer, MA
Marblehead Reporter, MA
Medford Transcript, MA
Melrose Free Press, MA
Newburyport Current, MA
North Andover Citizen, MA
North Shore Sunday, MA
Salem Gazette, MA
Saugus Advertiser, MA
Stoneham Sun, MA
Swampscott Reporter, MA
Tri-Town Transcript, MA
Wakefield Observer, MA

COMMUNITY NEWSPAPER CO.-WEST — 33 New York Ave, Framingham, MA, 01701-8857, USA; tel (508) 626-3800; fax (508) 626-3810; web site www.wickedlocal.com
Pres./CEO/Pub. — Kirk Davis
Newspapers: Ashland TAB, MA
Canton Journal, MA
The Country Gazette, MA
Easton Journal, MA
Framingham TAB, MA
Holliston TAB, MA
Hopkinton Crier, MA
Hudson Sun, MA
Mansfield News, MA
Marlborough Enterprise, MA
Medfield Press, MA
Norton Mirror, MA
Norwood Transcript & Bulletin, MA
Sharon Advocate, MA
Shrewsbury Chronicle, MA
Southborough Villager, MA
Stoughton Journal, MA
The Westborough News, MA
Westborough News, MA
Weston Town Crier, MA
Westwood Press, MA

COMMUNITY NEWSPAPER HOLDINGS, INC. — 445 Dexter Ave, Ste 7000, Montgomery, AL, 36104-3892, USA; tel (334) 293-5800; fax (334) 293-5913; web site www.cnhi.com
Pres./CEO — Donna Barrett
Executive VP/COO — F. Steve McPhaul
Senior VP, Revenue — Jack Robb
Senior VP, Audience Development — Linwood Pride
Executive VP/COO — Keith Blevins
Chief Digital Officer/VP — Matthew Ipsan
Chief Financial Officer — Jennifer Pustaver
Vice Pres., Digital Sales — Dee Dee Mathis
Regional Executive — Henry Bird
Director, Internal Audit — Nick Stanfill
Senior Vice President — Robyn McCloskey
Senior Vice President & Senior Controller — Chris Cato
Newspapers: Laurel Leader-Call, MS
Herald-Banner, TX
Royse City Herald Banner, TX
Cooperstown Crier, NY
Rockwall County Herald Banner, TX
Chickasha News, OK
The Herald-Tribune, IN
Herald Journal, IN
Pharos-Tribune, IN
The Goshen News, IN
Tribune-Star Publishing Co., Inc., IN
Marion County Reminder, IA
Oskaloosa Shopper, IA
Princeton Times, WV
Skyline, MS
The Free Press, MN
Ad Express, IA
Rutherford Weekly, NC
Enid News & Eagle, OK
The Randolph Guide, NC
Glasgow Daily Times, KY
Gloucester Daily Times, MA
Suwannee Democrat, FL
Pauls Valley Democrat, OK
Ad-Express & Daily Iowegian, IA
The Salem News, MA
The Ada News , OK
Albion Advertiser, NY
Allied News, PA
Woodward News, OK
Andover Townsman, MA
The Eagle-Tribune, MA
Athens Daily Review, TX
Bluefield Daily Telegraph, WV
Branford News, FL
Bravo Extra, PA
Carriage Towne News, NH
Cleburne Times-Review, TX
Clinton Herald, IA
Coffee County News (OOB), GA
Commerce Journal, TX
Commercial News, IL
Corsicana Daily Sun, TX
Crossville Chronicle, TN
Daily Union, IL
Effingham Daily News, IL
Gainesville Daily Register, TX
Greensburg Daily News, IN
Greenup County News-Times, KY
Hartshorne Sun, OK
Hendricks County Flyer, IN
Hometown, IN
Image, IN
Jasper News, FL
Kokomo Tribune, IN
Madison County Direct, IN
McAlester News-Capital, OK
Mineral Wells Index, TX
Montgomery Herald, WV
Moore American, OK
Muskogee Phoenix, OK
New Castle News, PA
Niagara Gazette, NY
Norman Transcript, OK
North Jefferson News, AL
Oskaloosa Herald, IA
Palestine Herald-Press, TX
Mineral Wells Index, TX
Parker County Shopper, TX
Pella Chronicle, IA
Press-Republican, NY
Traverse City Record-Eagle, MI
Register-News, IL
Route 66, OK
Rushville Republican, IN
Sapulpa Daily Herald, OK
Shopper's Edge, OK
St. Clair News-Aegis, AL
Star Beacon, OH
Star Shopper, TX
Stilwell Democrat Journal, OK
Tahlequah Daily Press, OK
The Claremore Daily Progress, OK
The Commonwealth-Journal, KY
The Cullman Times, AL
The Cumberland Times-News, MD
The Daily Citizen, GA
The Daily Independent, KY
The Daily Item, PA
The Daily News, MA
The Daily Star, NY
The Pryor Times, OK
The Danville News, PA
The Duncan Banner, OK
The Eastern Oklahoma County News, OK
The Edmond Sun, OK
News and Tribune, IN
The Express-Star, OK
The Fayette Tribune, WV
The Greensburg Times, IN
The Herald, PA
The Herald Bulletin, IN
The Huntsville Item, TX
The Joplin Globe, MO
The Knoxville Journal-Express, IA
The Meadville Tribune, PA
The Meridian Star, MS
The Moultrie Observer, GA
Stillwater News Press, OK
The News-Courier, AL
The Poplarville Democrat, MS
The Register Herald, WV
The Reporter, IN
The Richmond Register, KY
The Sentinel-Echo, KY
The Star, TX
The Sun/Sunday Sun, OK
The Tifton Gazette, GA
The Tribune Star, IN
The Tribune-Democrat, PA
The Tuttle Times, OK
The Union-Recorder, GA
The Washington Times, DC
The Wayne County Outlook, KY
The Weatherford Democrat, TX
The Weekend Flyer, IN
Thomasville Times-Enterprise, GA
Times West Virginian, WV
Times-Tribune, KY
Tribune, IN
Lockport Union-Sun & Journal, NY
Valdosta Daily Times, GA
Westville Reporter, OK
Zionsville Times Sentinel, IN
Jacksonville Daily Progress, TX
The Haverhill Gazette, MA
Derry News, NH
Olive Hill Times, KY
Grayson Journal-Enquirer, KY
The Daily Southerner, NC
The Morehead News, KY
The Ottumwa Courier, IA
Mayo Free Press, FL
The Times-Leader, NC
The Times Tribune, TX

COMMUNITY NEWSPAPERS, INC. — PO Box 792, Athens, GA, 30606-6003, USA; tel (706) 548-0010; fax (706) 548-0808; web site www.cninewspapers.com
Est.: 1967
Chrmn. — Tom Wood
Pres. — William H. Dink NeSmith
CFO — Mark Major
Corporate Marketing Director / Major Account Manager — Joel Jenkins
Eric NeSmith
Newspapers: Andrews Journal, NC
Cherokee Scout, NC
The Elberton Star, GA
Bay View NOW, WI
Clay County Progress, NC
North Shore NOW, WI
Brookfield-Elm Grove NOW, WI
Crossroads Chronicle, NC
Dawson News & Advertiser (OOB), GA
Lake City Reporter, FL
Cudahy NOW, WI
News-Leader, FL
Elm Grove NOW, WI
Palatka Daily News, FL
Fox Point NOW, WI
The Clayton Tribune, GA
Franklin NOW, WI
The Dahlonega Nugget, GA
Germantown NOW, WI
Glendale NOW, WI
The Franklin Press, NC
Oak Creek-Franklin-Greendale-Hales Corners NOW, WI
The Graham Star, NC
Greenfield-West Allis NOW, WI
The Hartwell Sun, GA
Hales Corners NOW, WI
The Highlander, NC
Menomonee Falls-Germantown NOW, WI
The News Leader, GA
Mequon NOW, WI
The Northeast Georgian, GA
Mitchell News-Journal, NC
Muskego-New Berlin NOW, WI
The Telfair Enterprise, GA
New Berlin NOW, WI
The Toccoa Record, GA
Oak Creek NOW, WI
Tribune & Georgian, GA
Nassau County Record, FL
South Milwaukee NOW, WI
St. Francis NOW, WI
White County News, GA
The Smoky Mountain Times, NC
Wauwatosa NOW, WI
West Allis NOW, WI
Note: Community Newspapers Inc. maintains 28 subscriber newspapers and affliates in Georgia, Florida and North Carolina. Also, select non-duplicating TMC's are available.

COMMUNITY PUBLISHERS, INC. — 900 SE 5th St, Ste 22, Bentonville, AR, 72712-6090, USA; tel (479) 271-3782; fax (479) 271-3788; e-mail commpub.com; web site www.commpub.com
Group: Phillips Media Group LLC
Est.: 1982
Pres. — Steve Trolinger
Exec. Vice Pres. — Michael Brown
Vice Pres. — Dave Berry
CFO — Tom Bruns
Prodn. Mgr. — Charles Heidelberg
Ronnie Bell
Roger Frye
David Guay
Newspapers: Harrison Daily Times, AR
Community Publishers, Inc./Neighbor News, AR
Bolivar Herald-Free Press, MO
Cedar County Republican/Stockton Journal, MO
Collinsville News, OK
Coweta American (OOB), OK
Owasso Reporter, OK
Sand Springs Leader, OK
Skiatook Journal, OK
South County Mail, MO
The Newton County Times, AR
The Republic Monitor, MO
Wagoner Tribune, OK
South County Leader - (OOB), OK
Broken Arrow Ledger, OK
Tulsa Business Journal, OK
Note: Community Publishers Inc. owns the Harrison Daily Times in Harrison, AR and one daily business newspaper plus 20 weekly and semi-weekly community newspapers as well as three commercial printing plants.

CONLEY MEDIA LLC — 115 Monroe St, Beaver Dam, WI, 53916-2436, USA; tel (920) 885-7800; fax (920) 887-2779; e-mail hrd@conleynet.com; web site www.gmtoday.com
Est.: 1970
Pres./CEO — James E. Conley
Newspapers: Milwaukee Post, WI
Washington County Post, WI
The Daily News, WI
Greater Milwaukee Jobs, WI
The Freeman, WI
The Hartford Times Press, WI
Oconomowoc Enterprise, WI
Ozaukee County Guide, WI
News Graphic, WI

Note: Conley Publishing Group Ltd. is a printing and publishing corporation with locations throughout Wisconsin, Colorado and Arizona. Conley Publishing publishes nine non-daily publications along with two daily newspapers in WI. Conley also publishes lifestyle magazines.

CONNECTION PUBLISHING, INC. — 1606 King St, Alexandria, VA, 22314-2719, USA; tel (703) 821-5050; fax (703) 778-9445; web site www.connectionnewspapers.com
Est.: 1987
Founder/Prinicpal/Pres./CEO — Peter C. Labovitz
Vice Pres. — Mary Kimm
Vice Pres. — Jerry Vernon
Dir., Cor. — Deborah Funk
Theismann Jeanne
Newspapers: Alexandria Gazette Packet, VA
Arlington Connection, VA
Burke Connection, VA
Centre View, VA
Fairfax Connection, VA
Fairfax Station/Clifton/Lorton Connection, VA
Great Falls Connection, VA
McLean Connection, VA
Mount Vernon Gazette, VA
Oak Hill/Herndon Connection, VA
Potomac Almanac, VA
Reston Connection, VA
Springfield Connection, VA
Vienna/Oakton Connection, VA

CONSOLIDATED PUBLISHING CO. — PO Box 189, Anniston, AL, 36202-0189, USA; tel (256) 235-9200; fax (256) 241-1980; web site www.annistonstar.com
Chrmn. — H. Brandt Ayers
Pres. — Phillip A. Sanguinetti
Vice Pres. — Chris Waddle
Controller/Treasurer — Scott Calhoun
Multimedia Advertising Director — David Bragg
Social Media Consultant — Chris Pittman
Newspapers: The Anniston Star, AL
Piedmont Journal, AL
The Cleburne News, AL
The Daily Home, AL
The Jacksonville News, AL
The Saint Clair Times, AL
Note: Consolidated Publishing Co. also owns three weekly publications: the Jacksonville (AL) News, Heflin (AL) The Cleburne News and Pell (AL) The Saint Clair Times.

CONSUMER NEWS SERVICE INC. — 7801 N Central Dr, Lewis Center, OH, 43035-9407, USA; tel (740) 888-6000; fax (740) 888-6001; web site www.thisweeknews.com
Est.: 1989
Dir., Sales — Earl Smith
Sales Mgr. — Doug Dixon
Classified Mgr. — Doug Abdelnour
Exec. Ed. — Ben Cason
Asst. Mng. Ed. — Lee Cochran
Newspapers: ThisWeek Bexley News, OH
ThisWeek The Canal Winchester Times, OH
ThisWeek Clintonville Booster, OH
ThisWeek Delaware News, OH
ThisWeek Dublin Villager, OH
ThisWeek German Village Gazette, OH
ThisWeek Grove City Record, OH
ThisWeek Hilliard Northwest News, OH
ThisWeek Johnstown Independent, OH
ThisWeek Licking County News, OH
ThisWeek Marysville News, OH
ThisWeek New Albany News, OH
ThisWeek Northland News, OH
ThisWeek Northwest News, OH
ThisWeek Olentangy Valley News, OH
ThisWeek Pickerington Times-Sun, OH
ThisWeek Reynoldsburg News, OH
ThisWeek Rocky Fork Enterprise, OH
ThisWeek Tri-Village News, OH
ThisWeek Upper Arlington News, OH
ThisWeek Westerville News & Public Opinion, OH
ThisWeek Whitehall News, OH
ThisWeek Worthington News, OH
ThisWeek West Side News, OH

COOKE COMMUNICATIONS NORTH CAROLINA, LLC — 1150 Sugg Pkwy, Greenville, NC, 27834-9077, USA; tel (252) 329-9500; fax (252) 752-8181; web site www.reflector.com
Publisher, Rocky Mount Telegram — Mark Wilson
Chief Operating Officer — Tim Holt
President and Publisher — John Kent Cooke, Jr.
HR Director — Donna Allen
Publisher, The Daily Advance — Mike Goodman
CFO — Mariann McQueen
Circulation Director, The Daily Reflector — David Adams
Production Director — Regina Lytle
Director of Information Systems — Gary Lytle
Director of Sales & Marketing — Elizabeth Semple
Editor — Bobby Burns
Newspapers: Duplin Times, NC
Rocky Mount Telegram, NC
The Daily Advance, NC
The Daily Reflector, NC
Bertie Ledger-Advance, NC
The Chowan Herald, NC
The Farmville Enterprise, NC
Perquimans Weekly, NC
The Standard Laconic, NC
The Times-Leader, NC
Enterprise & Weekly Herald, NC
The Tarboro Weekly, NC

CORNERSTONE MEDIA — 120 W North St, Peotone, IL, 60468-9226, USA; tel (708) 258-3473; fax (708) 258-6295; e-mail info@russell-publications.com; web site www.russell-publications.com
Pub. — Chris Russell
Treasurer — Sharon Russell
Newspapers: New Lenox Community Reporter, IL
The Vedette, IL
Beecher Herald, IL

COUNTRY MEDIA INC. — 1515 SW 5th Ave, Ste 640, Portland, OR, 97201-5445, USA; tel (503) 444-7924; fax (503) 444-7926
Est.: 2000
Pres. — Steve Hungerford
Dir., Admin. — Carol Hungerford
Newspapers: The Herald, ND
Fallon County Times, MT
Bowman County Pioneer, ND
Cavalier County Republican, ND
Adams County Record, ND
Dunn County Herald, ND
The News Guard, OR
North Coast Citizen, OR
The Chief, OR

COURIER LIFE PUBLICATIONS, INC. — 1 Metrotech Ctr N, Brooklyn, NY, 11201-3832, USA; tel (718) 229-0300; fax (718) 615-3828; e-mail info@courierlife.com; web site www.yournabe.com
Grp. Co-Pub. — Dan Holt
Grp. Co-Pub. — Clifford Luster
Ralph D Onofrio-e
Newspapers: Brooklyn Graphic, NY
Mill-Marine Courier & Canarsie Digest, NY
Kings Courier (OOB), NY
Bay News, NY
Bay Ridge Courier, NY
Brooklyn Courier, NY

COURIER PUBLICATIONS, LLC — 301 Park St, Rockland, ME, 04841-2124, USA; tel (207) 594-4401; fax (207) 594-6981; e-mail cgnews@courierpub.com; web site www.courierpub.com
Controller — Janice Katz
Newspapers: The Camden Herald, ME
The Republican Journal, ME

COX MEDIA GROUP — 6205 Peachtree Dunwoody Rd, Fl 9, Atlanta, GA, 30328-4524, USA; tel (678) 645-0000; fax (678) 645-5002; web site www.coxnewspapers.com
Est.: 1898
Chrmn./CEO, Cox Enterprises Inc. — James C. Kennedy
Pres./COO, Cox Enterprises Inc. — Jimmy Hayes
Pres. — Sandy Schwartz
Exec. Vice Pres./CFO, Cox Enterprises Inc. — John Dyer
Exec. Vice. Pres. — Douglas Franklin
Vice Pres./CFO — Melody Darch
Vice Pres./CIO — Christopher Caneles
Vice Pres./HR — Susan S. Davidson
Vice Pres., Adv. — Cathy B. Coffey
Vice Pres., Circ. — Al Smith
Vice Pres., Mktg./Grp. Vice Pres., Community Newspapers — Caroline C. John
Vice Pres., Newsprint Supply — Mark Mansfield
Vice Pres., Digital Media — Leon Levitt
Gen. Mgr., COXnet — John Reetz
Dir., Classified/Internet Adv. — Dean Welch
Dir., Newsprint Supply — Greg Tant
Nat'l Online Sales Mgr. — Bill Sullivan
Vice Pres., Opns. — Stanley P. Richmond
Newspapers: MundoHispánico Newspaper, GA
Westlake Picayune, TX
Florida Pennysaver, FL
Lake Travis View, TX
Marshall News Messenger, TX
The Bastrop Advertiser, TX
The Daily Advance, NC
The Daily Sentinel, CO
The Nickel, CO
The Pflugerville Pflag, TX
The Smithville Times, TX
Note: Cox Newspapers Inc. also owns Valpak; Cox Custom Media, and PAGAS. Cox Newspapers also has 50% ownership of Trader Publishing Co. and 33% of SP Newsprint. Cox Newspapers is a subsidiary of Cox Enterprises, Inc. and owns Austin Community Newspapers Gro

COX MEDIA GROUP — 6205 Peachtree Dunwoody Rd, Atlanta, GA, 30328-4524, USA; tel (678) 645-0000; fax (678) 645-5002Bruce Karlson
Sr. Mgr. — Michael Zuniga
Pres. — Mark Mansfield
Director of Online Strategy — Doug Franklin
Newspapers: JournalNews, OH
Middletown Journal, OH
Springfield News-Sun, OH
Atlanta Journal-Constitution, GA
Dayton Daily News, OH

CRESCENT PUBLISHING COMPANY LLC — 109 Laurens Rd, Ste 4C, Greenville, SC, 29607-1860, USA; tel (864) 250-4446; fax (864) 240-7408
Pres./CEO — William deBerniere Mebane
Newspapers: Bar Harbor Times, ME
The Independent (OOB) , AL
The Bulletin, AL
The Republican Journal, ME

DELPHOS HERALD, INC. — 405 N Main St, Delphos, OH, 45833-1577, USA; tel (419) 695-0015; fax (419) 695-7602; e-mail murray@delphosherald.com; web site www.delphosherald.com
Pres. — Murray Cohen
Bus. Mgr. — Ray Geary
VP — Roberta Cohen
Adv. Mgr. — Doug Nutter
Newspapers: Bolivar Bulletin-Times, TN
The Ada Herald, OH
Bulletin-Times, TN
The Dearborn County Register, IN
Delphos Daily Herald, OH
Falmouth Outlook, KY
Monroe County Beacon, OH
The Ohio County Times, KY
The Paulding Progress, OH
Putnam County Sentinel, OH
The Ohio County News/Rising Sun Recorder, IN
Star-gazette Extra, IL
Three Lakes News, WI
The Times Bulletin, OH
Putnam County Vidette, OH
West Central Ohio Shopping Guide, OH
Weekly Reminder, OH
Waushara Argus, WI
North Woods Trader, WI
Sylvania Herald, OH
The Market Place, IN
The Shopper's Outlook (free Shopper), KY
Hardeman County Shopper (OOB), TN
Monroe County Sentinel, OH
Note: Delphos Herald Inc. also publishes the Delphos Daily Herald in Delphos, Ohio.

DIGITAL FIRST MEDIA — 101 W. Colfax Ave, Fl 11, Denver, CO, 80202-5177, USA; tel (215) 504-4200; fax (215) 867-2174; e-mail rvenengas@journalregister.com; web site www.digitalfirstmedia.com
CFO — Michael J. Koren
Pub — Sharon Ryan
CEO — Steven B. Rossi
EVP Sales & Digital — Chris Loretto
EVP, Operations — Bill Higginson
VP., Prodn. — William J. Higginson
EVP & Chief Human Resources Officer — Robert Monteleone
Newspapers: Boston Herald, MA
Mid Michigan Buyer's Guide, MI
Press-Telegram, CA
Southern California News Group, CA
The Orange County Register, CA
The Press-Enterprise, CA
The Detroit News, MI
Advance of Bucks County, PA
Clear Lake Observer-American, CA
Grunion Gazette, CA
The Leader and The Kalkaskian, MI
The Willits News, CA
Tri-City Weekly, CA
Lake County's Penny Saver, CA
Oneida-madison Pennysaver, NY
South County News, CA
The Jack County Herald (OOB), TX
The Ukiah Daily Journal, CA
Ambler Gazette, PA
Prairie Mountain Publishing, CO
Bristol Pilot, PA
The Mendocino Beacon, CA
County Press, PA
The Advisor & Source, MI
Fort Bragg Advocate-News, CA
Garnet Valley Press, PA
The Canon City Daily Record, CO
Glenside News, PA
The Foothills Trader, CT
Montgomery Life, PA
News of Delaware County, Town Talk, Garnet Valley Press, Springfield Press, County PRess, PA
Montgomery Media, PA
Newtown Advance, PA
North Penn Life, PA
Perkasie News-Herald, PA
Public Spirit, PA
Piedmonter, CA
Souderton Independent, PA
Springfield Sun, PA
The Berkeley Voice, CA
The Boyertown Area Times, PA
Marin Independent Journal, CA
The Community Connection, PA
The Denver Post, CO
The Globe, PA
The Montclarion, CA
News-Herald, MI
Los Angeles Daily News, CA
The Hamburg Area Item, PA
The Review, PA
The Star Group, Inc., TX
Akron News-Reporter, CO
Times Chronicle, PA
Willow Grove Guide, PA
The Bay Voice, MI
Alameda Journal, CA
The Chelsea Standard, MI
Colorado Daily, CO
The Macomb Daily, MI
East Bay Times, CA
The Oakland Press, MI
Daily Camera, CO

The Reporter, PA
Loveland Reporter-Herald, CO
West Hartford News, CT
Alpena Star, MI
Blue Water Voice, MI
Longmont Times-Call, CO
Community News, NY
Daily Local News, PA
Fairfield Minuteman, CT
Ile Camera, MI
Burlington Record, CO
The Macomb Voice, MI
Main Line Suburban Life, PA
Chico Enterprise-Record, CA
Main Line Times, PA
Press & Guide, MI
Estes Park Trail-Gazette, CO
Shoreline Times, CT
Fort Morgan Times, CO
Southern Chester County Times Record, PA
Fremont Bulletin, CA
The Central Record, NJ
The Litchfield County Times, CT
Hometown Shopper, CA
The North Macomb Voice, MI
Julesburg Advocate, CO
The Recorder, PA
Berksmont News, PA
The Phoenix Reporter & Item, PA
The View, MI
Lake County Record-Bee, CA
Tri-County Record, PA
The Lamar Ledger, CO
Marin Independent Journal, CA
Palo Alto Daily News, CA
The Middletown Press, CT
Bellows Falls Town Crier, VT
Royal Oak Daily Tribune (OOB), MI
Morning Sun, MI
Heritage Newspapers, Inc., MI
The Oneida Daily Dispatch, NY
The Mercury News, CA
The Saratogian, NY
San Mateo County Times (OOB), CA
The Record, NY
Daily Freeman, NY
Santa Cruz Sentinel, CA
Sentinel & Enterprise, MA
The News-Herald, OH
St. Paul Pioneer Press, MN
The Morning Journal, OH
Delaware County Daily Times, PA
The Mercury, PA
The Brush News-Tribune, CO
The Times Herald, PA
The Daily Democrat, CA
The Trentonian, NJ
Main Line Media News, PA
The Monterey County Herald, CA
The Reporter, CA
Journal-Advocate, CO
The Sun, MA
Times-Standard , CA
Tri-Valley Herald/San Ramon Valley Herald (OOB), CA
Vallejo Times-Herald, CA
The Journal - Albany, El Cerrito, Kensington, CA
Press-Telegram (Long Beach), CA
Longmont Weekly (OOB), CO
Palos Verdes Peninsula News, CA
Ft Bragg Advocate-News, CA
Broomfield Enterprise, CO
Willits News, CA
Redwood Times, CA
Impacto, CA
Valley Journal, CA
Tri-City Weekly, CA
The Penny Slaver, CA
Clear Lake Ovserver, CA
Salinas Weekly, CA
Royal George Shopping News, CO
Rome Observer (OOB), NY
Morning Star Publishing Company, MI
Freedom Communications, Inc., CA

Note: Journal Register Company is a newspaper company that owns 22daily newspapers, including the New Haven Register, and 346 non-daily publications. All of the company's operations in six geographic areas: Connecticut, Greater Philadelphia, Greater Cleveland,

DOUTHIT COMMUNICATIONS, INC. — 520 Warren St, Sandusky, OH, 44870-2958, USA; tel (419) 625-5825; fax (419) 625-2834
Est.: 1957
Pres. — H. Kenneth Douthit
Newspapers: Chagrin Valley Times, OH
Geauga Courier, OH
North Ridgeville Press, OH
Solon Times, OH
The Press, OH
The Press, OH
Vermilion Photojournal, OH
West Life, OH

DOW JONES & COMPANY — 1211 Avenue of the Americas, New York, NY, 10036-8701, USA; tel (212) 416-2000; web site www.dowjones.com
Est.: 1882
CEO — Leslie Hinton
Pres., Dow Jones Online — Gordon McLeod
Exec. Vice Pres./CFO — Stephen Daintith
Exec. Vice Pres., Enterprise Media Grp. — Clare Hart
Exec. Vice Pres./Gen. Counsel — Mark H. Jackson
Sr. Vice Pres., Local Media Grp. — John N. Wilcox
Sr. Vice Pres./Chief HR Officer — Greg Giangrande
Sr. Vice Pres., Special Projects — Ian Weston
Vice Pres., Commun. — Linda E. Dunbar
Vice Pres., Security — Joseph J. Cantamessa
Ed. in Chief — Robert Thomson
Newspapers: The Wall Street Journal, NY
Dow Jones Local Media Group, NY
Note: Dow Jones is the world's premier publisher of business news and information in every form of media

DOW JONES LOCAL MEDIA GROUP — 40 Mulberry St, Middletown, NY, 10940-6302, USA; tel (845) 341-1100; web site www.dowjoneslmg.com
Group: Dow Jones & Company
Est.: 1936
CFO — Jonathan Kahan
Chief Operating Officer — William T. Kennedy
Senior Vice President, Advertising Sales — Molly Evans
Senior Vice President, Printing & Distribution — Don Waterman
Senior Vice President, Product Marketing — Kurt Lozier
Senior VP, Advertising Sales — Molly Evans
Vice Pres., Human Resources — Patricia Gatto
Treasurer — Chet D. Krinsky
Ed. — Ken Hall
Vice Pres., Information Servs. — John Treglia
Vice Pres., Opns./Adv. — Zeke Fleet
Circulation Director — Kelvin Parker
National & Major Accounts Manager — Gregory Appel
Newspapers: Medford Nickel, OR
Nantucket Today, MA
Barnstable Patriot, MA
The Inquirer and Mirror, MA
Exeter News-Letter, NH
The Hampton Union, NH
The York Weekly, NH
York County Coast Star, NH
The Advocate, MA
Middleboro Gazette, MA
The Chronicle, MA
The Spectator, MA

E. W. SCRIPPS CO. — 312 Walnut St, Ste 2800, Cincinnati, OH, 45202-4019, USA; tel (513) 977-3000; fax (513) 977-3090; e-mail michele.roberts@scripps.com; web site www.scripps.com
COO — Richard A. Boehne
Sr. Vice Pres./Newspapers — Timothy E. Stautberg
Sr. VP/CFO/Treasurer — Tim Wesolowski
Pres. & CEO — Adam Symson
Board Member — Roger Ogden
Chief Administrative Officer — Lisa Knutson
Director of Digital Sales, Newspapers — Jay Horton
Senior Director, Digital Revenue — Tom Sly
VP, Strategic Planning & Development — Robin Davis
VP, Finance & Administration — Mike Hales
VP/Content, Newspapers — Mizell Stewart
Michele Roberts
Sr. Analyst/Systems Engineer — Donald Murray
Sr. Systems Analyst — Todd Nakamura
Newspapers: Metro Pulse, TN
Anderson Valley Post, CA
Jupiter Courier, FL
Note: The E. W. Scripps Company is a diverse media concern with interests in newspaper publishing, broadcast television, cable television programming and interactive media.

EAGLE MEDIA — 114 W Diamond St, Butler, PA, 16001-5747, USA; tel (724) 282-8000; fax (724) 282-1280; e-mail news@butlereagle.com; web site www.butlereagle.com
Mng. Ed. — Chris Morelli
Newspapers: Butler Eagle, PA
Pittsburgh City Paper, PA

EAGLE NEWSPAPERS, INC. — 4901 Indian School Rd NE, Salem, OR, 97305-1128, USA; web site www.eaglenewspapers.com
Newspapers: Daily Sun News, WA
The Dalles Daily Chronicle, OR
Hood River News, OR
Idaho County Free Press, ID
Omak-Okanogan County Chronicle, WA
The Polk County Itemizer-Observer, OR
The Enterprise, WA
Moneysaver-lewis Clark Edition, ID
Moneysaver-palouse Edition, ID

EAST BAY NEWSPAPERS — 1 Bradford St, Bristol, RI, 02809-1906, USA; tel (401) 253-6000; fax (401) 253-6055; e-mail bristol@eastbaynewspapers.com; web site www.eastbayri.com
Est.: 1837
Pub./ Adv. Mgr. — Matthew D. Hayes
Gen. Mgr. — Lisa Carro
Advertising Dir. — Toni Nuttall
Ed. — Jim McGaw
Mng. Ed. — Scott Pickering
Prodn. Mgr. — Jock Hayes
MANAGING DIRECTOR, ONE BRADFORD — Dichiappari Kirsten
Newspapers: Barrington Times, RI
Bristol Phoenix, RI
The Post, RI
Sakonnet Times, RI
Portsmouth Times, RI
Warren Times-Gazette, RI
Westport Shorelines, RI

EASTLAND COUNTY NEWSPAPERS — 215 S Seaman St, Eastland, TX, 76448-2745, USA; tel (254) 629-1707; fax (254) 629-2092; e-mail ecn@att.net; web site www.eastlandcountytoday.com
Pres./Co-Pub. — Houston V. O'Brien
Gen. Mgr. — Amy O'Brien-Glenn
Newspapers: Eastland Telegram, TX
Rising Star, TX
Cisco Press, TX
Ranger Times, TX
Gorman Progress, TX

ELLIOTT PUBLISHING, INC. — 202 E State St, Camp Point, IL, 62320-1114, USA; tel (217) 593-6515; fax (217) 593-7720; e-mail cpjournal@adams.net; web site http://elliott-publishing.com/
Pres. — James W. Elliott
Adv. Mgr. — Marcia Elliott
Newspapers: The Liberty Bee-Times, IL
Camp Point Journal, IL
Mendon Dispatch-Times, IL
Golden-Clayton New Era, IL

EMMERICH NEWSPAPERS, INC. — PO Box 16709, Jackson, MS, 39236-6709, USA; tel (601) 957-1122; fax (601) 957-1533; e-mail wyatt@northsidesun.com; web site www.northsidesun.com
Pres./CEO — J. Wyatt Emmerich
Newspapers: Charleston Sun Sentinel, MS
The Choctaw Plaindealer, MS
The Hattiesburg Post, MS
The Petal News, MS
The Star-Herald, MS
Clarke County Tribune, MS
Delta Democrat Times, MS
Dumas Clarion, AR
Enterprise-Journal, MS
Madison Journal, LA
Northside Sun, MS
Scott County Times, MS
Simpson County News, MS
Southwest Sun, MS
The Charleston Sun-Sentinel, MS
The Clarksdale Press Register, MS
The Columbian-Progress, MS
The Conservative, MS
The Enterprise-Tocsin, MS
The Era-Leader, LA
The Greenwood Commonwealth, MS
The Magee Courier, MS
The Winona Times, MS
The Yazoo Herald, MS
The Laurel Chronicle, MS
Carrollton Conservative, MS
The Newton County Appeal, MS
Newto County Appeal, MS
Kosciusko Star-Herald, MS
Winston County Journal, MS
Note: Emmerich Newspapers Inc. also owns 26 community newspapers primarily in Mississippi.

ENGLE PRINTING & PUBLISHING CO., INC. — 1425 W Main St, Mount Joy, PA, 17552-9589, USA; tel (717) 492-2514; fax (717) 492-2584; e-mail jhemperly@engleonline.com; web site www.engleonline.com
Est.: 1955
Adv. Mgr. — John Hemperly
Newspapers: Advertiser, PA
Engle - West Chester Community Courier, PA
Engle - Columbia / Wrightsville Merchandiser, PA
Engle - Conestoga Valley / Pequea Valley Penny Saver, PA
Engle - Downingtown / Exton / Community Courier, PA
Engle - Elizabethtown / Mount Joy Merchandiser, PA
Engle - Gap / Oxford Community Courier, PA
Engle - Hempfield / Mountville Merchandiser, PA
Engle - Hershey / Hummelstown / Palmyra Community Courier, PA
Engle - Manheim / Lititz Merchandiser, PA
Engle - Manheim Township Merchandiser, PA
Engle - Middletown Shopper, PA
Engle - Millersville Advertiser, PA
Engle - Morgantown / Honey Brook Community Courier, PA
Engle - New Holland Pennysaver, PA
Engle - Quarryville Advertiser, PA
Engle - Willow Street Strasburg Advertiser, PA
Engle - York Community Courier East Edition, PA
Engle - York Community Courier South Edition, PA
Pennysaver, PA
Hershey Community Courier, PA
Engle - York Community Courier West Edition, PA
Merchandiser-lancaster County, PA
Chester County Community Courier, PA
Note: Local Weekly Free Saturation Distribution. 28 Editions reaching over 438,000 Homes. Delivered each week(100% by the US Post Office)
30% local editorial.
Competitive Preprint rates. Sub-Zip Code distribution available

ENTERPRISE — 50 Depot Ave, Falmouth, MA, 02540-2302, USA; tel (508) 548-4700; fax

(508) 540-8407; e-mail enterprise@cape.com; web site www.capenews.net
Est.: 1895
Pub. — William Henry Hough
Circ. Mgr. — Tracey Moniz
Mng Ed — John Paradis
Newspapers: The Bourne Enterprise, MA
The Falmouth Enterprise, MA
The Mashpee Enterprise, MA
The Sandwich Enterprise, MA

ENTERPRISE PUBLISHING CO. — 138 N 16th St, Blair, NE, 68008-1633, USA; tel (402) 426-2121; fax (402) 426-2227; e-mail mrhoades@enterprisepub.com
Group: Enterprise Publishing Co.
Pres. — Mark Rhoades
Ed. — Katie Rohman
Newspapers: Arlington Citizen, NE
Friend Sentinel, NE
Lyons Mirror-Sun, NE
Mapleton Press, IA
Oakland Independent, NE
Wilber Republican, NE
The Clipper, NE
Seward County Connection, NE
Seward County Independent, NE
Washington County Enterprise, NE
The Pilot Tribune / Enterprise, NE
Missouri Valley Times-News, IA
Milford Times, NE

EO MEDIA GROUP — 1400 Broadway St NE, Salem, OR, 97301-0504, US; tel (503) 364-4431; e-mail hwright@eomediagroup.com; web site www.eomediagroup.com
Group: EO Media Group
Est.: 1875
COO — Heidi Wright
Newspapers: Hermiston Herald, OR
Capital Press, OR
Chinook Observer, WA
Oregon Coast Today, OR
East Oregonian, OR
The Daily Astorian, OR
Seaside Signal, OR
Cannon Beach Gazette, OR
Coast River Business Journal, OR
Blue Mountain Eagle, OR
Wallowa County Chieftain, OR

EVENING POST PUBLISHING NEWSPAPER GROUP — 134 Columbus St, Charleston, SC, 29403-4809, USA; tel (843) 577-7111; fax (843) 937-5788; e-mail dherres@postandcourier.com; web site www.charleston.net
Pres., Evening Post Community Publications Grp. — Dan Herres
Vice Pres., Evening Post Community Publications Grp. — Kathy Wilkinson
Newspapers: Evening Post Industries' Aiken Communications, SC
Waccamaw Times, SC
Berkeley Independent, SC
Summerville Journal-Scene, SC
The Clemmons Courier, NC
The Georgetown Times, SC
The News, SC
The Post and Courier, SC
The Star, SC
Moultrie News, SC
The Gazette, SC
Note: Evening Post Community Publications Group, Inc. also owns the Buenos Aires (Argentina) Herald (mS) and operates 11 television stations as well as Solo Syndicate, LTD. in London. The company also owns and manages timberland in Soth Carolina through White

EXAMINER PUBLICATIONS, INC. — 4N781 Gerber Rd, Bartlett, IL, 60103-2021, USA; tel (630) 830-4145; e-mail randy@examinerpublications.com; web site www.examinerpublications.com
Est.: 1978Randall Petrik
Newspapers: Examiner Publications, Inc., IL
The Examiner of Wayne, IL
The Examiner of Carol Stream, IL
The Examiner of Streamwood, IL
The Examiner of South Elgin, IL
The Examiner of Hanover Park, IL

FAYETTEVILLE PUBLISHING CO. — 458 Whitfield St, Fayetteville, NC, 28306-1614, USA; tel (910) 323-4848; fax (910) 433-3431; e-mail customerservice@fayobserver.com; news@fayobserver.com; web site www.fayobserver.com
Est.: 1816
Pres./Pub. — Charles W. Broadwell
Operations Director — Eric Schult
Chief Financial Officer — Rhonda Graham
Newspapers: Iwanna, SC
Carolina Trader Autos, NC
Note: Fayetteville Publishing Co. also owns the The Fayetteville Observer, a daily newspaper in Fayetteville, NC.

FEATHER PUBLISHING CO., INC. — 287 Lawrence St, Quincy, CA, 95971-9477, USA; tel (530) 283-0800; fax (530) 283-3952; e-mail mail@plumasnews.com; web site plumasnews.com
Est.: 1866
Pub. — Michael Taborski
Mng Ed — Debra Moore
VP/operations — Cobey Brown
HR Dir/Office Mgr — Mary Newhouse
Advertising Director — Holly Buus
Newspapers: Chester Progressive, CA
Feather River Bulletin, CA
Lassen County Times, CA
Portola Reporter, CA
Westwood Pinepress, CA
Indian Valley Record, CA
Note: Feather Publishing Co. Inc. publishes six weeklies in Plumas and Lassen County. Also publishes a telephone directory.

FENICE COMMUNITY MEDIA — 211 W 3rd St, Taylor, TX, 76574-3518, USA; tel (512) 352-8285; fax (512) 352-8295; e-mail granite@granitepub.com; web site www.granitepub.com
Est.: 1978
Founder — Jim Chionsini
CEO — Brandi Chionsini
Newspapers: Madisonville Meteor, TX
Bandera Bulletin, TX
Boerne Star, TX
Elgin Courier, TX
The Light & Champion, TX
The Gonzales Inquirer, TX
The Colorado County Citizen, TX
The Hutto News, TX
The Fort Stockton Pioneer, TX
The Vindicator, TX
Hill Country News, TX
Mount Pleasant Daily Tribune, TX
The Sealy News, TX
The Navasota Examiner, TX
Taylor Press, TX
Note: Granite Publications also owns the Mount Pleasant Daily Tribune, a 5-day daily in Mount Pleasant, Texas.

FINGER LAKES COMMUNITY NEWSPAPERS — 109 Cayuga St, Ithaca, NY, 67665-, USA; tel (607) 277-7000; fax (607) 387-9421; e-mail jbilinski@ithacatimes.com; web site www.ithaca.com
Est.: 1865
Pub. — James Bilinski
Newspapers: Spencer Random Harvest Weekely, NY
The Candor Chronicle, NY
The Dryden Courier, NY
The Lansing Ledger, NY
Newfield News, NY
Groton Independent, SD
Ovid Gazette, NY
The Trumansburg Free Press, NY
The Interlaken Review, NY

FORUM COMMUNICATIONS CO. — 101 5th St N, Fargo, ND, 58102-4826, USA; tel (701) 235-7311; fax (701) 241-5406; e-mail wmarcil@forumcomm.com; web site www.forumcomm.com
CFO — John Hajostek
Pub. — William C. Marcil
President & CEO — Bill Marcil Jr.
Director of Circulation — Christopher Berdahl
Jill Colosky
Dir. of Finance — Jon Buller
Pres./CEO — Lloyd Case
Frederick Greer
Dennis Doeden
Newspapers: Echoland - Piper Shopper, MN
Perham Focus, MN
Farmington Rosemount Independent Town Pages, MN
Echo Journal, MN
Agweek, ND
The Bulletin, MN
Lake Area Press, MN
Advertizer, ND
Sunday Reminder, MN
River Falls Journal, WI
Intercom, MN
Park Rapids Enterprise Express, MN
Duluth News Tribune, MN
Echo-Press, MN
Enterprise Bulletin, MN
Hastings Star Gazette, MN
InForum, ND
Lake County News-Chronicle, MN
Lakeland Shopping Guide, MN
Morris Sun Tribune, MN
New Richmond News, WI
New York Mills Herald, MN
Osakis Review, MN
Park Rapids Enterprise, MN
Pierce County Herald, WI
Republican Eagle, MN
South Washington County Bulletin, MN
The American, MN
Detroit Lakes Tribune, MN
Worthington Daily Globe, MN
The Daily Republic, SD
Superior Telegram, WI
The Detroit Lakes Tribune, MN
The Farmington Independent, MN
The Hancock Record, MN
The Jamestown Sun, ND
The Pine Journal, MN
The Bemidji Pioneer, MN
The Rosemount Town Pages, MN
The Metro Weekly, ND
Wadena Pioneer Journal, MN
West Central Tribune, MN
West Fargo Pioneer, ND
Woodbury Bulletin, MN
Grand Forks Herald, ND
Duluth Budgeteer News, MN
Brainard Dispatch, MN
Brainerd Dispatch, MN
The Forum, LA
The Hudson Star-Observer, WI
Note: Forum Communications Co. owns eleven daily newspapers and 28 non-daily publications. Forum Communications also owns several television and radio stations, a commerical printing division and a new media division.

FORUM PUBLISHING GROUP — 1701 Green Rd, Ste B, Deerfield Beach, FL, 33443, USA; tel (954) 698-6397; fax (954) 698-9062; web site www.forumpubs.com
VP/Editorial — Pamela Doto
Newspapers: Delray Beach Forum, FL
West Boca Forum, FL
Boca Raton Forum, FL
East Side Forum, FL
Boynton Forum, FL
Lake Worth Forum, FL
Margate / Coconut Creek Forum, FL
South Florida Parenting Magazine, NC
Live Wellington, FL
Jewish Journal - Palm Beach North, FL
Jewish Journal - Broward North, FL
Jewish Journal - Broward South, FL

GANNETT — 7950 Jones Branch Dr, Mc Lean, VA, 22107-0002, USA; tel (703) 854-6000; fax (703) 854-2001; e-mail gcishare@gannett.com; web site www.gannett.com
Est.: 1906
President and CEO, Gannett — Robert J. Dickey
Chief Revenue Officer — Kevin Gentzel
Chief Product Officer — David Payne
Chief Strategy Officer — Maribel Wadsworth
Chief Financial Officer — Alison Engel
Chief Legal Officer — Barbara Wall
President of Domestic Publishing — John Zidich
Chief Technology Officer — Jamshid Khazenie
Chief Marketing Officer — Andy Yost
CEO Newsquest — Henry Faure Walker
Chief People Officer — David Harmon
Newspapers: Detroit Free Press, MI
Evansville Courier & Press, IN
Lehigh Acres News-Star, FL
Record Searchlight, CA
The Daily Times, NM
The Gleaner, KY
The Journal News, NY
The Lebanon Daily News, PA
The Record, NJ
The Tennessean, TN
Ventura County Star, CA
Wilmington News Journal, OH
Media Network of Central Ohio, OH
Las Cruces Sun-News, NM
Action Advertiser, WI
Action Sunday, WI
Ross County Advertiser, OH
Best - Central, FL
Door County Real Estate Guide, WI
Best - North, FL
Visalia Times-Delta, CA
Eastern Shore News, VA
Tri-County Press, OH
Loveland Herald, OH
Indian Hill Journal, OH
Forest Hills Journal, OH
Eastern Hills Journal, OH
St. John's Recorder, FL
Best - South, FL
Living - Kettle Moraine Sunday, WI
Bethel Journal, OH
Asbury Park Press, NJ
News-Record, WI
Lakeshore Chronicle, WI
Newark-licking Advertiser, OH
Milford-Miami Advertiser, OH
Pickaway County Advertiser, OH
Wausau Buyers Guide, WI
Delhi Press, OH
Lancaster/fairfield Advertiser, OH
Hilltop Press, OH
Hocking Valley Advertiser, OH
Price Hill Press, OH
Rockland County Express, NY
Coshocton County Advertiser, OH
Local Living, IN
South Lyon Herald, MI
The Cincinnati Enquirer, OH
Northwest Press, OH
The Antigo Area Shopper, WI
Maryland Beachcomber, MD
Mukwonago Publications, WI
Appeal Tribune, OR
Tribune-Gazette, WI
Reno Gazette-Journal, NV
The Baxter Bulletin, AR
Times Press, WI
Baltic Beacon, SD
Gallatin News Examiner, TN
Home News Tribune, NJ
Pelican Press, FL
Williamston Enterprise, MI
Toms River Observer-Reporter, NJ
Daily World, LA
Add Sheet, IA
The Daily Journal, NJ
Campbell County Recorder, KY
Great Falls Tribune, MT
North English Record, IA
Atlantic County Record, NJ
The Commercial Appeal, TN
Star Press Union, IA
Outlook, OH
The Greenville News, SC
Marengo Pioneer-Republican, IA
Pensacola News Journal, FL
The Livingston County Daily Press & Argus, MI
Topics North Central, IN

Towne Courier, MI
Iowa City Press-Citizen, IA
The Jackson Sun, TN
Fairview Observer, TN
The Wausau Daily Herald, WI
Beacon Mailbag (OOB) , NJ
Forest County Beacon, WI
Nashville Record, TN
The Source Sampler, MI
Journal and Courier, IN
Western Hills Press, OH
Ottawa County Outlook, OH
The Erlanger Recorder, KY
Courier News, NJ
Ankeny Register & Press Citizen, IA
Wright Way Shopper, MN
Delta-Waverly Community News, MI
Oconto County Reporter, WI
Blue Water Shopper, MI
Ocean Pines Independent, MD
The Salinas Californian, CA
Mainland Journal, NJ
Stewart-Houston Times, TN
Stayton Mail, OR
Pennysaver, HI
Chillicothe Gazette, OH
The Des Moines Register, IA
The Spectrum, UT
Robertson County Times, TN
The Times, NY
Springfield News-Leader, MO
The Advocate, OH
Portland Review & Observer, MI
Palladium-Item, IN
The News Leader, VA
The Courier-Journal, KY
The Sumner County Shopper, TN
The Marion Star, OH
USA TODAY, VA
The Pataskala Standard, OH
Madison County Herald, MS
Beachcomber, DE
Tuckerton Beacon, NJ
Grinnell Pennysaver, IA
The Daily Advertiser, LA
Fort Thomas Recorder, KY
Chincoteague Beacon, VA
San Juan Sun, NM
Lake Orion Eccentric, MI
The Daily News Journal, TN
Colorado Connection, CO
The Patent Trader, NY
Review Press (OOB), NY
Community Journal Clermont, OH
News Journal, OH
The Delaware Wave, DE
Democrat and Chronicle, NY
Lamoille County Advertiser, VT
Extra, IA
Montezuma Republican, IA
Eagle-Gazette Media, OH
Oconto County Beacon, WI
TN Media, TN
The Courier-Post, NJ
Poughkeepsie Journal, NY
Air Force Times, VA
The Coloradoan, CO
The Noblesville Ledger, IN
Green Bay Press-Gazette, WI
The Green Bay News-Chronicle, WI
West Bloomfield Eccentric, MI
Northeast Suburban Life, OH
Lansing State Journal, MI
Windsor Beacon, CO
The Hendersonville Star News, TN
Times Herald, MI
The News-Star, LA
Delaware Coast Press, DE
Community Snapshot, WI
Tribune-Times, SC
Door County Advocate, WI
The Shopping News, MN
The Fond du Lac Reporter, WI
Stevens Point Journal, WI
Garden City Observer, MI
The News-Messenger, OH
The Leaf-Chronicle, TN
Times Recorder, OH
Daily Record, NJ
Topics Northeast, IN
The Granville Sentinel, OH
Buyers' Digest, VT
The Coshocton Tribune, OH
Chittenden County Advertiser, VT
Bulletin Board, AL
Record-Herald and Indianola Tribune, IA
Beach Haven Times, NJ
The Burlington Free Press, VT
Ashland City Times, TN
Brandon Valley Challenger, SD
The Asheville Citizen-Times, NC
The Indianapolis Star, IN
Pennypower Shopping News, MO
The Desert Sun, CA
Novi News, MI
The Lacey Beacon, NJ
Post-Crescent, WI
Oshkosh Northwestern, WI
Franklin-grand Isle County Advertiser, VT
Mason Valley News/The Leader-Courier, NV
The News Journal, DE
Somerset Herald, MD
Sunday Kewaunee County Chronicle (OOB), WI
Island Weekly, HI
Dickson Shopper, TN
Florence Recorder, KY
Poweshiek County CR, IA
The Southwest Copper Shopper, NM
Desert Valley Times, NV
Dell Rapids Tribune, SD
St. Cloud Times, MN
The Star Press, IN
Egg Harbor News, NJ
Black Mountain News, NC
Consumers Press, MT
Daily Tribune, WI
Telegraph-Forum, OH
Star Advocate, FL
Clinton News, MS
The Dickson Herald, TN
Prattville Progress, AL
The Sheboygan Press, WI
Weekly Item, IN
Record Journal, NJ
Carencro News, LA
News-Record and Sentinel, NC
The Beacon, NJ
Hammonton News, NJ
Hattiesburg American, MS
Argus Leader, SD
USA WEEKEND - New York, NY (OOB), NY
Florida Today, FL
The Times, LA
Press & Sun-Bulletin, NY
The Ithaca Journal, NY
The Arizona Republic, AZ
Tucson Citizen (OOB), AZ
Star-Gazette, NY
Tulare Advance-Register, CA
Federal Times, VA
Arizona Business Gazette, AZ
Army Times, VA
Battle Creek Enquirer, MI
Montgomery Advertiser, AL
De Pere Journal, WI
Marine Corps Times, VA
Journal Tribune, IA
Poweshiek County Chronicle-Republican, IA
Boone Community Recorder, KY
News Herald, OH
Birmingham Eccentric, MI
South Kenton Recorder, KY
Redford Observer, MI
The Clarion-Ledger, MS
Farmington Observer, MI
Northville Record, MI
Herald Times Reporter, WI
Lakes/forest Beacon, WI
Marshfield News-Herald Media, WI
The Town Talk, LA
Canton Observer, MI
Livonia Observer, MI
Milford Times, MI
Westland Observer, MI
Cheatham County Money Saver, TN
Statesman Journal, OR
Kewaunee County Star-News, WI
Observer & Eccentric Media, MI
Plymouth Observer, MI
South Oakland Eccentric, MI
Tallahassee Democrat, FL
The Daily Times, MD
Alamogordo Daily News, NM
Current-Argus, NM
Deming Headlight, NM
Silver City Sun-News, NM
The Evening Sun, PA
York Daily Record/York Sunday News, PA
El Paso Times, TX
Public Opinion, PA

Note: Gannett Co. Inc.'s portfolio includes 92 daily local market newspapers, USA TODAY, and their related digital platforms and non-daily publications, and Newsquest, a leading U.K. regional news provider.

GATEHOUSE MEDIA, INC. — 175 Sully's Trail #3, Corporate Crossings Office Park, Pittsford, NY, 14534-4560, USA; tel (585) 598-0030; fax (585) 248-2631; web site www.gatehousemedia.com
Group: New Media Investment Group
Est.: 1997
CEO — Michael E. Reed
Pres./COO — Kirk Davis
Sr. Vice Pres./CFO — Melinda A. Janik
CIO — Paul Ameden
Vice Pres., Sales & Marketing — Brad Harmon
Senior Vice Pres., Content/News Opns. — Brad Dennison
Regional VP - Midwest — Gloria Fletcher
Regional VP - Atlantic — James O'Rourke
Regional VP - Western — Nick Monico
Regional VP - New England — Rick Daniels
Regional VP - Great Lakes — Kevin Kampman
Reg. Pub. — Scott Harrell
Vice President, Content and Audience — Arkin David
Crystal Barrett
Director, Major & National Accounts — Anna St. Charles
VP Circulation/Consumer Marketing — Paul Felicissimo
VP of Sales and Digital Services — Michael Petrak
VP of Sales Productivity — Rebecca Capparelli
VP Publishing - Community East — Brad Harmon
Alice Coyle
Charles Goodrich
Jesse Floyd
National Acct. Sales Mgr. — Eliot Putnam
William Down
Megan Reynolds
VP, Adv. — John Bordeleau
Director of National Sales — Gregory Appel
SR Director of Digital Strategy — Rich Hoover
New England Reg. Pub. — Peter D. Meyer
Newspapers: Calkins Media, PA
The Newport Daily News, RI
The Register-Guard, OR
Alice Echo-News Journal, TX
The Helena Arkansas Daily World, AR
Lehigh Valley Business, PA
The Bee, KS
The Hays Daily News Extra, KS
Beaver County Times, PA
Miami News-record, OK
Times2, AL
Long Island Business News, NY
Beauregard Daily News, LA
Burlington County Times, NJ
Bluffton Today, SC
Amarillo Globe-News, TX
The Wayne Independent, PA
Ashland Times-Gazette, OH
Athens Banner-Herald, GA
Aurora Advocate, OH
Cuyahoga Falls News-Press, OH
Hudson Hub-Times, OH
Juneau Empire, AK
Log Cabin Democrat, AR
Lubbock Avalanche-Journal, TX
Peninsula Clarion, AK
Savannah Morning News, GA
The Augusta Chronicle, GA
The Fayetteville Observer, NC
The Florida Times-Union, FL
The Leesville Daily Leader, LA
The St. Augustine Record, FL
The Topeka Capital-Journal, KS
homer News, AK
The Hawk Eye, IA
Cherokee County News-Advocate, KS
Record-Courier, OH
StarNews, NC
The Alliance Review, OH
Ad Sack, TX
The Daily Jeffersonian, OH
The Columbus Dispatch, OH
Eldorado Daily Journal, IL
Stow Sentry, OH
Arizona Capitol Times, AZ
The Daily Record, OH
Columbia Daily Tribune, MO
The Journal Record, OK
The Apalachicola Carrabelle Times, FL
The Salina Journal, KS
St. Charles County Business Record, MO
St. Louis Daily Record, MO
The Garden City Telegram, KS
The Hays Daily News, KS
The Hutchinson News, KS
The Ottawa Herald, KS
Crestview News Bulletin, FL
Pocono Record Plus, PA
Alma Journal, AR
The Daily Record, MO
Freer Press, TX
Missouri Lawyers Media, MO
Nueces County Record-Star, TX
Perry Chief, IA
Ellis County Trading Post, TX
Hockessin Community News, DE
Tonopah Times-Bonanza and Goldfield News, NV
Bent County Democrat, CO
Argus-Sentinel, IL
Penny Press 1, NE
Abington Mariner, MA
Access Shoppers' Guide, MI
Allston-Brighton TAB, MA
Amesbury News, MA
Easton Journal, MA
Framingham TAB, MA
Hopkinton Crier, MA
Kingston Reporter, MA
Medfield Press, MA
Natick Bulletin & TAB, MA
Nebraska City News-Press, NE
Needham Times, MA
Newburyport Current, MA
Newton Tab, MA
North Shore Sunday, MA
Norwood Transcript & Bulletin, MA
Rockland Standard, MA
Salem Gazette, MA
Saugus Advertiser, MA
Scituate Mariner, MA
West Michigan Senior Times, MI
Sharon Advocate, MA
Shrewsbury Chronicle, MA
Somerville Journal, MA
Stoneham Sun, MA
Sudbury Town Crier, MA
The Dedham Transcript, MA
The Harvard Post, MA
The Sentinel, MA
The Villager, MA
The Westborough News, MA
Tri-Town Transcript, MA
Wakefield Observer, MA
Watertown TAB, MA
Wayland Town Crier, MA
Wellesley Townsman, MA
West Roxbury Transcript, MA
Weston Town Crier, MA
Westwood Press, MA
Weymouth News, MA
Wilmington Advocate, MA
Winchester Star, MA
Woburn Advocate, MA
Bridgewater Independent, MA
Catskill Shopper - Eastern Sullivan County, NY
Catskill Shopper - Ulster County, NY
Fort Leavenworth Lamp, KS
Horseheads Shopper, NY
Milford Beacon, DE
Provincetown Banner, MA
Sandwich Broadsider, MA
Stoughton Journal, MA

Swampscott Reporter, MA
The Bulletin, MA
Town & Country Shopper, MN
Victor Post, NY
Wareham Courier, MA
Wayne Post, NY
Your Valley, NY
Andover American, KS
Sunflower Shopper's Guide, KS
Times & Courier, MA
Allegany County Pennysaver, NY
Arlington Advocate, MA
Ashland TAB, MA
Ashley News, IL
Bargain Hunter, CA
Belmont Citizen-Herald, MA
Big Nickel, MO
Billerica Minuteman, MA
Braintree Forum, MA
Brookline TAB, MA
Brown County Reminder, MN
Burlington Union, MA
Cajun Gazette, LA
Cambridge Chronicle & TAB, MA
Cambridge Chronicle IN ILLINOIS, IL
Chelmsford Independent, MA
Chilli Corthe Cho Cho Advertiser, IL
Chronicle Ad-viser, NY
Chronicle Shopper, KS
Classified Plus, MA
Cohasset Mariner, MA
Community News, NY
Corning Leader, NY
Courier-Gazette, NY
Courier-Journal, NY
Daily Midway Driller, CA
Danvers Herald, MA
Dover Post, DE
Dover-Sherborn Press, MA
Dunsmuir News, CA
East Peoria Times-Courier, IL
Fort Folk Guardian, LA
Fulton County Shopper, IL
Gardner Chronicle, IL
Gateway Shoppers Guide, MI
Genesee Country Express, NY
Geneseeway Shopper, NY
Geneseo Republic, IL
Gentry County Shopper, MO
Georgetown Record, MA
Gonzales Weekly Citizen, LA
Granite Falls-Clarkfield Advocate-Tribune, MN
Hamburg Reporter, IA
Hamilton-Wenham Chronicle, MA
Harwich Oracle, MA
Hingham Journal, MA
Hockessin Community News, DE
Holbrook Sun, MA
Holliston TAB, MA
Pennesaverplus, NY
Hudson Sun, MA
Images of Herkimer County (OOB), NY
Ipswich Chronicle, MA
Kansas City Kansan (OOB), KS
Lexington Minuteman, MA
Lincoln Journal, MA
Linn County Leader, MO
Littleton Independent, MA
Logan County Shopper, IL
McDonough County Voice, IL
Malden Observer, MA
Marblehead Reporter, MA
Marlborough Enterprise, MA
Marshfield Mariner, MA
Maryville Penny Press, MO
Medford Transcript, MA
Money Stretcher, IL
Montevideo American-News, MN
Mt. Shasta Herald, CA
Nevada County Picayune, AR
Newport Independent, AR
Newton Press-Mentor, IL
Newton TAB, MA
North Andover Citizen, MA
Old Colony Memorial, MA
Pembroke Mariner & Express, MA
Pennysaver, IL
PeoriaTimes-Observer, IL
Post South, LA
Raynham Journal, MA
Reading Advocate, MA
Redwood Falls Livewire, MN
Roselle Itasca Press, IL
Roseville Independent, IL
Si Trader, IL
Shoppers Fair, MI
Sleepy Eye Herald-Dispatch, MN
Smyrna/Clayton Sun-Times, DE
Springfield Shopper, IL
St. James Leader-Journal OOB, MO
St James Plaindealer, MN
Steuben Courier-Advocate, NY
Syracuse Journal-Democrat, NE
Tazewell County Shopper, IL
Tewksbury Advocate, MA
The Advantage, IL
The Beacon-Villager, MA
The Blade, IL
The Bolton Common, MA
The Cape Codder, MA
The Chronicle-Express, NY
The Clay County Advocate-Press, IL
The Commercial Express, MI
The Concord Journal, MA
The Country Gazette, MA
The Derby Reporter, KS
The Donaldsonville Chief, LA
The Extra, IA
The Fowler Tribune, CO
The Gurdon Times, AR
The Jackson Star News, WV
The Marceline Press, MO
The Middletown Transcript, DE
The Progress, IL
The Redwood Falls Gazette, MN
The Register, MA
Gallatin Democrat, IL
The Shopper, NY
The Shopper, MN
The Star Shopper, IL
The Star-herald, WV
The Sussex Countian, DE
The Times Record, IL
The Moscow Villager, PA
The Walpole Times, MA
The Weekly, MO
Timesaver Shopping Guide, NY
Today's Shopper, WV
Tri-county Buyer's Guide, MI
Weed Press, CA
Wellington Daily News, KS
Westborough News, MA
Westford Eagle, MA
The Money Stretcher White County, IL
White Hall Journal, AR
Whitman Times, MA
Wyandotte County Shopper, KS
The Suburbanite, OH
Carbondale News, PA
Livingston Shopping News, IL
Bedford Minuteman, MA
Canton Journal, MA
Halifax-Plympton Reporter, MA
Hanover Mariner, MA
Duxbury Reporter, MA
Norton Mirror, MA
Mansfield News, MA
Melrose Free Press, MA
Carver Reporter, MA
Norwell Mariner, MA
Randolph Herald, MA
The Gridley Herald, CA
Waltham News Tribune, MA
Kiowa County Signal, KS
Beverly Citizen, MA
The Sun-Times, AR
Woodford Times, IL
Brockport Post, NY
Mackinaw Journal, MI
Weekly Mail, IL
Eldora Herald-Ledger, IA
The Gridley Shopping News, CA
Suburban Life Publications, IL
The Fairbury Blade, IL
The News Eagle, PA
Aurora Advertiser, MO
Vicksburg Commercial-Express, MI
Oquawka Current, IL
Jackson Herald, WV
Norris City Banner, IL
Community Newspaper Co. - South, MA
The Spokesman, IL
Morton Times-News, IL
Washington Times Reporter, IL
The McDonough County Voice, IL
Penny Press, NE
Big Aa Shopper, MO
Chillicothe Times-Bulletin, IL
Messenger Post Media, NY
Times News Group, IL
Flashes Publishers, MI
Springfield Advertiser, IL
Tip-off Shopping Guide, MI
St. John News, KS
The Echo-Pilot, PA
Glen Rose Reporter, TX
Edinburg Review, TX
Valley Town Crier, TX

Note: GateHouse Media Inc. is owned by Fortress Investment Group LLC.

GAZETTE NEWSPAPERS, INC. — 46 W Jefferson St, Jefferson, OH, 44047-1028, USA; tel (440) 576-9125; fax (440) 576-2778; e-mail gazette@gazettenews.com; web site www.gazettenews.com
Est.: 1876
Pres./Pub. — William Creed
Newspapers: Lake County Tribune, OH
The Albion News (OOB), PA
The Courier, OH
The Gazette, OH
The News, OH
The Shores News, OH

GOLD NUGGET PUBLICATIONS, INC. — 169 W Jackson St, Virden, IL, 62690-1269, USA; tel (217) 965-3355; fax (217) 965-4512; e-mail editor@gnnews.net
Est.: 1982
Gen. Mgr. — Nathan Jones

GOLDEN PLAINS PUBLISHING — 101 S Main St, Cimarron, KS, 67835-8856, USA; tel (620) 855-3902; fax (620) 855-2489; e-mail jacksoniannews@me.com
Group: Golden Plains Publishing
Pub. — Mark Anderson
Ed — Kirk Anderson
Newspapers: Jacksonian, KS
Harper County Leader, OK
The Leoti Standard, KS
The Oakley Graphic, KS
Jetmore Republican, KS
Dighton Herald, KS
Bucklin Banner, KS
Haskell County Monitor Chief, KS

GREEN BANNER PUBLICATIONS, INC. — 490 E State Road 60, Pekin, IN, 47165-7928, USA; tel (812) 967-3176; fax (812) 967-3194; e-mail sales@gbpnews.com; web site www.gbpnews.com
Est.: 1933
Pub. — Joe Green
Newspapers: The Banner-Gazette, IN
The Giveaway, IN
The Leader, IN
The Washington County Edition, IN

Note: Green Banner Publications owns five community newspapers and they also provide complete distribution and printing services.

GULF COAST NEWSPAPERS — 325 Fairhope Ave, Fairhope, AL, 36532-2317, USA; tel (251) 928-2321; fax (251) 928-9963; e-mail courier@gulfcoastnewspapers.com; web site www.baldwincountynow.comSudie Gambrell
Newspapers: The Onlooker, AL
The Baldwin Times Independent, AL
The Fairhope Courier, AL
The Islander, AL

HAGADONE CORPORATION — 111 S 1st St, Coeur D Alene, ID, 83814-2794, USA; tel (208) 667-3431; fax (208) 664-7206; e-mail info@hagadone.com; web site www.hagadone.com
Est.: 1966
Chrmn. of the Bd. — Duane B. Hagadone
President — Bradley D. Hagadone
CFO — Mont Garman
Mgr., MIS Dept. — Judd Jones
Newspapers: Advertiser, MT
Daily Inter Lake, MT
Hungry Horse News, MT
Basin Business Journal Farm News, WA
The Sun Tribune, WA
Mineral Independent, MT
Beloit Daily News, WI
Bonner County Daily Bee, ID
Clark Fork Valley Press, MT
Coeur d'Alene Press, ID
Columbia Basin Herald, WA
Lake County Leader, MT
Priest River Times, ID
Shoshone News-Press, ID
The Western News, MT
West Shore News, ID
My Stateline Shopper, WI
The Whitefish Pilot, MT
Bonners Ferry Herald, ID

Note: Hagadone Corp., also owns a Printing, Hospitality and Real Estate Division.

HALIFAX MEDIA — 2339 Beville Rd, Daytona Beach, FL, 32119-8720, USA; tel 386-265-6700; fax 386-265-6750; e-mail info@halifaxmediagroup.com; web site www.halifaxmediagroup.comThomas Boni
Rgl. Controller
— Robert Delaney
Newspapers: The Destin Log, FL
Santa Rosa Press Gazette, FL
The Havelock News, NC
The Star, FL
The Walton Sun, FL
West Volusia Pennysaver, FL
Holmes County Times-Advertiser, FL
South Lake Press, FL

HAN NETWORK — 16 Bailey Ave, Ridgefield, CT, 06877-4512, USA; tel (800) 372-2790; web site www.HAN.Network
CEO & Publisher — Martin V. Hersam
Director of Sales & Marketing — Jessica Murren
Newspapers: Darien Times, CT
Easton Courier, CT
Milford Mirror, CT
Monroe Courier, CT
New Canaan Advertiser, CT
Redding Pilot, CT
Ridgefield Press, CT
Shelton Herald, CT
Stratford Star, CT
Trumbull Times, CT
Weston Forum, CT
Wilton Bulletin, CT

HARTMAN NEWSPAPERS LP — 1914 4th St, Rosenberg, TX, 77471-5140, USA; tel (281) 342-8691; fax (281) 342-6968
Group: Hartman Newspapers, L.P.
Est.: 1974Bill Hartman
Pres. — Clyde C. King
Vice Chairman — Fred B. Hartman
Controller — Mark Thormaehlen
Newspapers: Brenham Banner-Press, TX
Fort Bend Herald, TX
Henderson Daily News, TX
The Katy Times, TX
The Kaufman Herald, TX
El Campo Leader-News, TX
Wharton Journal-Spectator, TX
East Bernard Express, TX
The Rockport Pilot, TX
Port Lavaca Wave, TX
Alvin Advertiser, TX

HAYNES PUBLISHING CO. — 170 S Penn Ave, Oberlin, KS, 67749-2243, USA; tel (785) 475-2206; fax (785) 475-2800; e-mail obherald@nwkansas.com; web site www.nwkansas.com
Est.: 1879
Pres. — Stephen C. Haynes
CFO — Cynthia A. Haynes
Newspapers: Country Advocate, KS
St. Francis Herald, KS
Goodland Star-News, KS
The Norton Telegram, KS
Oberlin Herald, The, KS

Bird City Times, KS
Colby Free Press, KS
Note: Company publishes six newspapers and two shoppers in Northwest Kansas.

HEARST COMMUNICATIONS, INC. — 300 W 57th St, New York, NY, 10019-3741, USA; tel (212) 649-2000; fax (806) 296-1315; web site www.hearst.com
Est.: 1887
Vice Chrmn./CEO — Frank Bennack
Pres., Hearst Newspapers — Steven R. Swartz
Sr. Vice Pres., Finance — John M. Condon
Vice Pres., Digital Media — Neeraj Khemlani
Sr. Vice Pres. — Mark E. Aldam
Newspapers: Atascocita Observer, TX
New Haven Register, CT
The Register Citizen, CT
The Dolphin, CT
Times Union, NY
Connecticut Post, CT
Darien News, CT
Deer Park Broadcaster, TX
Eastex Advocate, TX
The Advocate, CT
Bellaire Examiner, TX
The Daily Commercial Recorder, TX
The Courier of Montgomery County, TX
The Hour, CT
Cypress Creek Mirror, TX
El Tiempo de Laredo, TX
New Canaan News, CT
East Montgomery County Observer, TX
Laredo Morning Times, TX
Fairfield Citizen, CT
Fort Bend Sun, TX
Friendswood Journal, TX
Westport News, CT
Humble Observer, TX
Huron Daily Tribune, MI
Kingwood Observer, TX
Lake Houston Observer, TX
The Beaumont Enterprise, TX
Magnolia Potpourri, TX
Memorial Examiner, TX
The Canyon News, TX
River Oaks Examiner, TX
New Milford Spectrum, CT
Sugar Land Sun, TX
Bay Area Citizen, TX
The Hardin County News, TX
The Examiners, TX
The Pennysaver, NY
Pasadena Citizen, TX
The Vassar Pioneer Times, MI
Midland Daily News, MI
The Rancher, TX
Midland Reporter-Telegram, TX
Tomball Potpourri, TX
Norwalk Citizen (OOB), CT
Tribune Recorder Leader, MI
Edwardsville Intelligencer, IL
Muleshoe Journal, TX
Houston Chronicle, TX
San Francisco Chronicle, CA
The News-Times, CT
Plainview Herald, TX
Greenwich Time, CT
Note: The Hearst Corporation is a diversified communications company, with interests in magazine, newspaper and business publishing; television and radio stations; newspaper comics and features syndication; cable TV networks; television production and syndicati

HELMER PRINTING, INC. — N6402 790th St, Beldenville, WI, 54003-4704, USA; tel (715) 273-4601; fax (715) 273-4769; e-mail info@helmerprinting.com; web site www.helmerprinting.com
Co-Pub. — Scott A. Helmer
Adv. Mgr. — Mark Helmer
Circ. Mgr. — Steve Block
Newspapers: Baldwin Shopper, WI
Free Press, WI
Hiawatha Valley Shopper, WI
Hiawatha Valley Shopper, MN
Shopper, WI

HERBURGER PUBLICATIONS, INC. — 604 N Lincoln Way, Galt, CA, 95632-8601, USA; tel (209) 745-1551; fax (209) 745-4492; e-mail rherburger@herburger.net.; web site http://www.herburger.net/
Pres./CEO — Roy Herburger
Grp. Pub./Gen. Mgr. — David Herburger
Newspapers: Elk Grove Citizen, CA
Laguna Citizen, CA
The Galt Herald, CA
Galt Shopper, CA
River Valley Times, CA

HERITAGE NEWSPAPERS, INC. — 1 Heritage Dr, Ste 100, Southgate, MI, 48195-3047, USA; tel (734) 246-0800; fax (734) 282-7942; e-mail info@heritage.com; web site www.heritagenews.com
Group: Digital First Media
Pres. — Jim Williams
Circ. Dir. — Robert Riddell
Adv. Dir. — Carol Kruemmer
Newspapers: The Manchester Enterprise-OOB, MI
The Dexter Leader-OOB, MI
The Chelsea Standard, MI
The Milan News-Leader-OOB, MI

HI-DESERT PUBLISHING CO., INC. — 56445 29 Palms Hwy, Yucca Valley, CA, 92284-2861, USA; tel (760) 365-3315; fax (760) 365-8686; e-mail cmelland@hidesertstar.com; web site www.hidesertstar.com
Pub. — Cindy Melland
Jerry Simpkins
Newspapers: Hi-Desert Star, CA
Desert Trail, CA
Observation Post, CA
Desert Entertainer, CA
Note: Hi-Desert Publishing Co., Inc. also owns the Observation Post, a weekly military publication located in Yucca Valley, CA.

HOCKESSIN COMMUNITY NEWS — 24 W Main St, Middletown, DE, 19709-1039, USA; tel (302) 239-4644; web site www.hockessincommunitynews.com
Group: GateHouse Media, Inc.
Est.: 1966
Pres./Pub. — Keven Todd
Newspapers: Dover Post, DE
Kent County SUNDAY, DE
Middletown Transcript, DE
Smyrna/Clayton Sun Times, DE
Sussex Countian, DE
Note: Hockessin Community News is a part of GateHouse Media Delaware Group which also publishes 6 other non-daily papers across the state.

HORIZON PUBLICATIONS INC. — 1120 N Carbon St, Ste 100, Marion, IL, 62959-1055, USA; tel (618) 993-1711; fax (618) 997-4018; web site www.horizonpublicationsinc.com
Est.: 1999
Exec. Vice Pres./CFO — Roland McBride
Newspapers: Big Spring Herald, TX
Poteau Daily News, OK
The Chronicle-Journal, ON
The Shoppers Guide, OK
Mammoth Times, CA
Auglaize Merchandiser, OH
Berne Shopping News, IN
Bulldog Beat, MS
Deer Park Tribune, WA
Malvern Daily Record, AR
Post And Mail Shopping News, IN
Statesman Examiner, WA
The Post and Mail (Tuesday), IN
The Saline Courier TMC
Daily Times Leader, MS
Inyo Register, CA
Malvern Daily TMC
Morning News, ID
Bingham County Bargains, ID
Starkville Daily News, MS
The Community Post, OH
The Evening Leader, OH
The Monroeville News, IN
The Newport Daily Express, VT
The Observer News Enterprise, NC
The Post & Mail, IN
Valley City Times-Record, ND
Wapakoneta Daily News, OH
The Saline Courier, AR
Decatur Daily Democrat, IN
Custer County Chief, NE
Antlers American, OK
Guymon Daily Herald, OK
The Kane Republican, PA
The Punxsutawney Spirit, PA
The Ridgway Record, PA
The Daily Press, PA
Borger News-Herald, TX
Sweetwater Reporter, TX
Penticton Herald, BC
The Lethbridge Herald, AB
Medicine Hat News, AB

HUDSON REPORTER ASSOCIATES, LP — 447 Broadway, 447 Broadway, Bayonne, NJ, 07002-3623, USA; tel (201) 798-7800; fax (201) 798-0018; e-mail dunger@hudsonreporter.com; web site 447 Broadway
Est.: 1983
Co-Pub./Gen. Mgr. — Lucha Malato
Co-Pub./Adv. Dir. — David S. Unger
Newspapers: The Hoboken Reporter, NJ
The Weehawken Reporter, NJ
Secaucus Reporter, NJ
Bayonne Community News, NJ
The North Bergen Reporter, NJ
West New York/Union City Reporter, NJ
Note: Hudson Reporter Inc. also publishes five speacialty publications; the Secaucus Guidebook, Phone Hoboken, Phone Med, All About Horses and the Gateway Guide.

INDEPENDENT NEWSMEDIA INC. USA — 110 Galaxy Dr, Dover, DE, 19901-9262, USA; tel (302) 674-3600; fax (877) 377-2424; e-mail newsroom@newszap.com; web site www.newszap.com
Est.: 1953
Chrmn. of the Bd./CEO — Joe Smyth
Corp. Pres. — Tamra Brittingham
Pres., Opns. — Ed Dulin
Vice Pres., Adv. — Darel LaPrade
Dir., Research/Devel. — Chris Engel
Exec. Asst. — Sheila Clendaniel
Pub. — Greg Tock
Newspapers: Daily News-Sun, AZ
Surprise Today, AZ
Glendale Today, AZ
Glendale-peoria Today, AZ
Caloosa Belle, FL
Dorchester Banner, MD
Immokalee Bulletin, FL
Salisbury Independent, MD
Biltmore Independent (OOB), AZ
The Clewiston News, FL
Crisfield-Somerset County Times, MD
Delaware State News, DE
East Mesa Independent (OOB), AZ
Glades County Democrat, FL
Apache Junction/Gold Canyon Independent, AZ
Milford Chronicle, DE
Okeechobee News, FL
Peoria Independent, AZ
Queen Creek Independent, AZ
Scottsdale Independent, AZ
Sun City Independent, AZ
Surprise Independent, AZ
Sussex Post, DE
Town of Paradise Valley Independent, AZ
The Harrington Journal, DE
Note: Independent Newspapers Inc. owns three daily newspapers and 25 weekly publications.

INDEPENDENT NEWSPAPER GROUP — 385 Broadway, Ste 105, Revere, MA, 02151-3049, USA; tel (781) 284-2400; fax (781) 485-1403; e-mail editor@reverejournal.com; web site www.reverejournal.com
Pres. — Stephen Quigley
Vice Pres. — Joshua Resnek
Joshua
Newspapers: Chelsea Record, MA
Everett Independent, MA
The Lynn Journal, MA
The Revere Journal, MA
Winthrop Sun-Transcript, MA
East Boston Times, MA
The Back Bay Sun, MA
The Beacon Hill Times, MA
The Charlestown Patriot-Bridge, MA
Jamaica Plain Citizen, MA

INDEPENDENT NEWSPAPERS, INC. (ARIZONA) — 23043 N 16th Ln, Phoenix, AZ, 85027-1331, USA; tel (623) 445-2800; fax (623) 445-2740; e-mail valleyoffc@aol.com
Pres. — Ed Dulin
Printing Contact — Steve Steinke
Terrance Thornton
Bret McKeand
Newspapers: Peoria Independent, AZ
Sun City West Independent, AZ
Arrowhead Ranch Independent (OOB), AZ
Surprise Independent, AZ

INDEPENDENT NEWSPAPERS, INC. (FLORIDA) — 3109 Old State Road 8, Lake Placid, FL, 33852-5551, USA; tel (863) 465-7300; fax (863) 465-4046
Pres. — Ed Dulin
Newspapers: The Clewiston News, FL
Glades County Democrat, FL
Caloosa Belle, FL
Okeechobee News, FL

INDEPENDENT PUBLICATIONS INC — 945 E Haverford Rd, Bryn Mawr, PA, 19010-3814, USA; tel (610) 527-6330; fax (610) 527-9733; web site www.independentpublicationsinc.com
Pres./CEO — Andrew T. Bickford
Sr. Vice Pres./Treasurer — Charles E. Catherwood
President — William McLean
Newspapers: Hollis Brookline Journal, NH
The News Leader, FL
Osceola News-Gazette, FL
Pasco Shopper, FL
Sumter Shopper, FL
Triangle News Leader, FL

IOWA NEWSPAPERS, INC. — 317 5th St, Ames, IA, 50010-6101, USA; tel (515) 232-2160; fax (515) 232-2364; e-mail news@amestrib.com; web site www.amestrib.com
Chrmn. — Verle Burgason
Pres. — John Goossen
Vice Pres./Controller — Pat Snyder
Circ. Dir. — Daniel Cronin
Newspapers: Northeast Dallas County Record (OOB), IA
Story County Advertiser, IA
The Tri-County Times, IA

J-AD GRAPHICS — 1351 N M-43 Hwy, Hastings, MI, 49058, USA; tel (269) 945-9554; fax (269) 945-5192; e-mail fred@j-adgraphics.com; web site www.Hasatingsreminder.com
Est.: 1945
CEO — Fred Jacobs
Newspapers: Reminder, MI
Battle Creek Shopper News, MI
Ad-Visor and Chronicle, MI
Sun & News, MI
Maple Valley News, MI
The Hastings Banner, MI
Kidsworld, MI
Lowell Ledger, MI
Lowell Buyers Guide, MI

JACKALOPE PUBLISHING — 8710 Grant St, Thornton, CO, 80229-4716, USA; tel (303) 426-6000
Owner/Pres./Pub. — Scott D. Perriman
CFO — Kimberly Carmichael
Newspapers: Thornton Frontier (OOB), CO
Westsider (OOB), CO

JOHNSON NEWSPAPER CORP. — 260 Washington St, Watertown, NY, 13601-4669, USA; tel (315) 782-1000; fax (315) 661-2520; e-mail news@wdt.net; web site www.watertowndailytimes.com
Est.: 1861

Chrmn. of the Bd./CEO — John B. Johnson
Pres./COO — Harold B. Johnson
CFO — Ray Weston
Jill Van Hoesen
Editor, VP of News Operations — Tim Farkas
Newspapers: Carthage Republican Tribune, NY
Ogdensburg Journal/Advance News, NY
The Daily Mail, NY
The Daily News, NY
Chatham Courier, NY
The Ravena News-Herald, NY
The Drummer Pennysaver, NY
Jefferson County Pennysaver, NY
Journal and Republican, NY
Register-Star, NY
The Malone Telegram, NY
Watertown Daily Times, NY
Ogdensburg Journal, NY
Daily Courier-Observer

JOURNAL PUBLISHING COMPANY — 1242 S Green St, Tupelo, MS, 38804-6301, USA; tel (662) 842-2611; fax (662) 842-2233; e-mail clay.foster@journalinc.com; web site www.djournal.com
Group: Journal, Inc.
Est.: 1870
CEO/Publisher/President — Clay Foster
Newspapers: Northeast Mississippi Daily Journal, MS
Southern Advocate, MS
Monroe County Journal, MS
Southern Sentinel, MS
Pontotoc Progress, MS
Chickasaw Journal, MS
The Itawamba County Times, MS
Note: Journal Publishing Company owns these weekly publications: Pontotoc Progress, Monroe Journal, Chickasaw Journal, Southern Sentinel, Southern Advocate, Itawamba County Times

KPC MEDIA GROUP, INC. — 102 N Main St, Kendallville, IN, 46755-1714, USA; tel (260) 347-0400; fax (260) 347-7281; e-mail helpdesk@kpcmedia.com; web site www.kpcnews.com
Group: KPC Media Inc.
Est.: 1911
Principal Owner — George O. Witwer
President — Terry Housholder
CEO — Randy Mitchell
Grace Householder
CFO — Rick Mitchell
IT Manager — Brent Folkner
Production Manager — Gary Craiger
Regional Advertising Director — Joy Newman
Newspapers: The Advance Leader, IN
Greater Fort Wayne Business Weekly, IN
Churubusco News, IN
The Butler Bulletin, IN
The Herald Republican, IN
The Star, IN
Smart Shopper, IN
Smart Shopper, IN
The News Sun, IN
The Garrett Clipper, IN
Albion New Era, IN
Northwest News, IN
INIWhitley County, IN
INIFort Wayne Publications (5 zones), IN
Note: KPC Media Group publishes: 3 dailies - The News Sun, The Star and The Herald Republican. 6 paid weeklies - The Albion New Era, Churubusco News, Northwest News, The Garrett Clipper, Butler Bulletin and Advance-Leader. Fort Wayne Business Weekly, INIFort Wayne Publications (5 publications direct mailed to 90,000 residence in Fort Wayne). One free direct mail weekly in Whitley County (13,000), one Northeast Regional Shopper (42,000), Three phone books covering 4 north east Indiana counties. Commercial printing and mailing operation.

LAKE COUNTY PUBLICATIONS — 810 Cardinal Ln, Hartland, WI, 53029-2390, USA; tel (262) 367-3272; fax (262) 367-7414; e-mail lakenews@jcpgroup.com; web site www.livinglakecountry.com
Pub. — Steve Lyles
Newspapers: Lake Country Reporter, WI
Oconomowoc Focus, WI
Kettle Moraine Index, WI
Living - Kettle Moraine Sunday, WI

LAKEWAY PUBLISHERS, INC. — 1609 W 1st North St, Morristown, TN, 37814-3724, USA; tel (423) 581-5630; fax (423) 581-3061; e-mail copyboy@lcs.net; web site www.lakewaypublishersinc.com
Group: Lakeway Publishers, Inc.
Est.: 1966
Pub. — R. Michael Fishman
Vice Pres., Middle TN/Cor. Sec./Treasurer — Jeffrey Fishman
President — R. Jack Fishman
Newspapers: Citizen Tribune, TN
The Tullahoma News, TN
The Elk Valley Times, TN
Grundy County Herald, TN
Manchester Times, TN
Moore County News, TN
Bowling Green Times, MO
The Elsberry Democrat, MO
The Hermann Advertiser-Courier, MO
The Lincoln County Journal, MO
Louisiana Press Journal, MO
The Centralia Fireside Guard, MO
The Vandalia Leader, MO
Northern Neck News, VA
The Caroline Progress, VA
Westmoreland News, VA
Northumberland Echo, VA
Herald-Progress, VA
The Central Virginian, VA
Osceola News-Gazette, FL
Clermont News Leader, FL
The News Leader, FL
Triangle News Leader, FL
The Civil War Courier, TN
Newstime, MO
Note: Lakeway Publishers Inc. also own the Morristown (TN) Citizen Tribune, a daily publication.

LANCASTER MANAGEMENT, INC. — 645 Walnut St, Gadsden, AL, 35901-7102, USA; tel (256) 543-3417; fax (256) 543-3548; e-mail mschuver@lminews.com; web site www.lminews.com
Pres. — Charles W. Lancaster
Vice Pres. — Michael F. Schuver
Vice Pres. — Jeff R. Selsor
John Lancaster
Ben Lancaster
Newspapers: Ashley News Observer, AR
Floyd County Times, KY
The Hazard Herald, KY
DeQueen Bee, AR
Eudora Enterprise, AR
Chicot Spectator, AR
The Mena Star, AR
The Waldron News, AR
The McDuffie Progress, GA
Monroe County News, IA
Albia Union-Republican, IA
The Chariton Leader, IA
Chariton Herald-Patriot, IA
The Humeston News Era, IA
Moravia Union, IA
Georgetown News-Graphic, KY
The Murray Ledger & Times, KY
The Paintsville Herald, KY
The Appalachian News-Express, KY
Sea Coast Echo, MS
Stone County Enterprise, MS
Branson Tri-Lakes News, MO
The Moore County News-Press, TX
The Hopewell News, VA
Note: Lancaster Management Inc. owns one daily newspapers and more than 30 weekly and shopper publications.

LANDMARK COMMUNICATIONS, INC. — 150 W Brambleton Ave, Norfolk, VA, 23510-2018, USA; tel (757) 446-2010; fax (757) 446-2004; e-mail info@landmarkinteractive.com; web site www.landmarkinteractive.com; www.landmarkinteractive.com
Chrmn. of the Bd./CEO — Frank Batten
Vice Chrmn. — Richard F. Barry
Pres./COO — Decker Anstrom
Exec. Vice Pres./Sec./Gen. Counsel — Guy Friddell
Exec. Vice Pres./Pres., Landmark Publishing Grp. — R. Bruce Bradley
Exec. Vice Pres., HR — Charlie W. Hill
Vice Pres., Finance — Colleen Pittman
Operations Director — David Reno
Newspapers: Bedford Bullet, VA
The Virginian-Pilot, VA
The Sentinel-News, KY
Brighton Standard Blade, CO
Casey County News, KY
Central Kentucky News-Journal, KY
Citrus County Chronicle, FL
Columbine Courier, CO
Commerce City Express, CO
Cynthiana Democrat, KY
Fort Lupton Press, CO
Grant County News and Express, KY
Harriman Record, TN
La Salle Leader (OOB), CO
LaRue County Herald News, KY
Lancaster News, SC
Lebanon Enterprise, KY
Lincoln's Country Shopper, IN
Lincolnland Shopping Guide, IN
Los Alamos Monitor, NM
Marketplace, KY
Mason-dixon Marketplace, MD
Morgan County News, TN
Chester News & Reporter, SC
Carrollton News-Democrat, KY
Owenton News-Herald, KY
Oldham Era, KY
Opinion-Tribune, IA
Pageland Progressive-Journal, SC
Pioneer News, KY
Red Oak Express, IA
River City Trading Post, KY
Riverland News, FL
Rockwood Times, TN
Sentinel News Plus, KY
Spencer County Journal-Democrat, IN
Spencer Magnet, KY
Sumter County Times, FL
The Anderson News, KY
The Brunswick Beacon, NC
The Leader-union Publishing Co., IL
The News-Enterprise, KY
The Shopper, TN
Trimble Banner, KY
Williston Pioneer Sun News, FL
Note: Landmark Communications Inc. has a 49.9% interest in Capital-Gazette Communications Inc. in Annapolis, MD. Landmark owns and operates two CBS affiliated television stations and cable channel networks. Landmark is also 50% owner, with Cox Communications,

LANDMARK COMMUNITY NEWSPAPERS, LLC — 601 Taylorsville Rd, Shelbyville, KY, 40065-9125, USA; tel (502) 633-4334; fax (502) 633-4447; web site www.lcni.com
Group: Landmark Media Enterprises, LLC
Est.: 1973
Pres. — Michael G. Abernathy
Adv. Dir. — Tony Martinette
Exec. VP. — Daniel Sykes
Editorial Director — John Nelson
Newspapers: Galax Gazette, VA
The Anderson News, KY
Bedford Bulletin, VA
Brighton Standard Blade, CO
The Brunswick Beacon, NC
The Canyon Courier, CO
Carrollton News-Democrat, KY
Casey County News, KY
Cedar Key Beacon, FL
Central Kentucky News-Journal, KY
Chester News & Reporter, SC
Chiefland Citizen, FL
Clear Creek Courant, CO
Commerce City Sentinel Express, CO
Cynthiana Democrat, KY
Declaration, VA
Fort Lupton Press, CO
Gadsden County Times, FL
Grant County News and Express, KY
Henry County Local, KY
Kentucky Standard, KY
La Follette Press, TN
Lancaster News, SC
LaRue County Herald News, KY
Lebanon Enterprise, KY
Morgan County News, TN
Mount Vernon Democrat, IN
Oldham Era, KY
Opinion-Tribune, IA
Owenton News-Herald, KY
Pageland Progressive-Journal, SC
Perry County News, IN
Pioneer News, KY
The Record, KY
Red Oak Express, IA
Riverland News, FL
Roane County News, TN
The Sentinel-News, KY
Spencer County Journal-Democrat, IN
Spencer Magnet, KY
Springfield Sun, KY
Sumter County Times, FL
Trimble Banner, KY
The Leader-Union, IL
The Wakulla News, FL
Williston Pioneer Sun News, FL
Gazette Plus, VA
Sentinel News Plus, KY

LEBANON PUBLISHING CO. — 100 E Commercial St, Lebanon, MO, 65536-3257, USA; tel (417) 532-9131; fax (417) 532-8140; e-mail dwright@lebanondailyrecord.com; web site www.lebanondailyrecord.com
Est.: 1934
Pres. — Dalton Wright
Newspapers: Mountain Grove News-Journal, MO
The Lebanon Daily Record, MO
Mansfield Mirror, MO
Note: Lebanon Publishing Co. also owns the Lebanon Daily Record, in Lebanon, Missouri.

LEE ENTERPRISES, INC. — 201 N Harrison St, Ste 600, Davenport, IA, 52801-1918, USA; tel (563) 383-2100; fax (563) 328-4319; e-mail information@lee.net; web site www.lee.net
Est.: 1890
Chairman/Pres./CEO — Kevin Mowbray
Exec. Chairman — Mary Junck
VP/CFO/Treasurer — Ronald Mayo
VP, Publishing — Michael R. Gulledge
VP, Commun. — Daniel K. Hayes
VP, Publishing — Greg R. Veon
VP, Strategy — Greg P. Schermer
VP, IT — Michele White
VP, Audience — Suzanna Frank
VP, Digital — James Green
VP, Digital Sales — Paul Farrell
VP, HR — Astrid Garcia
Charles Arms
Newspapers: Ad Extra, IL
Moline Dispatch Publishing Company, L.L.C, IL
Arizona Daily Sun, Flagstaff, AZ
The Dispatch-Argus, IL
Fremont Area Shopper, NE
The Philomath Express, OR
Missoula Independent, MT
Dunn County Big Buck, WI
Flagstaff Live!, AZ
Badgerland Values Columbia County, WI
Country Folks - East Zone, NY
The Post-Star, NY
Hot Springs Star, SD
The World, OR
Quad-City Times, IA
The Dunn County News, WI
Arizona Daily Star, AZ
Democrat News, MO
Santa Maria Times, CA
The Lompoc Record, CA
The Sentinel, CA
Napa Valley Register, CA
The Times-News, ID
Elko Daily Free Press, NV
The Pantagraph, IL
The Southern Illinoisan, IL
Herald & Review, Decatur, IL

Journal Gazette & Times-Courier, IL
The Times of Northwest Indiana, IN
Globe Gazette, Mason City, IA
Muscatine Journal, IA
Sioux City Journal, IA
The Courier, IA
The Ledger Independent, KY
Daily Journal, Park Hills, MO
St. Louis Post-Dispatch, MO
Billings Gazette, MT
The Montana Standard, MT
Helena Independent Record, MT
Missoulian, MT
Ravalli Republic, MT
The Bismarck Tribune, ND
Lincoln Journal Star, NE
Beatrice Daily Sun, NE
The Columbus Telegram, NE
Fremont Tribune, NE
The Citizen, Auburn, NY
Albany Democrat-Herald, OR
Corvallis Gazette-Times, OR
The Sentinel, PA
The Times and Democrat, SC
Rapid City Journal, SD
The Daily News, WA
Wisconsin State Journal, Madison, WI
Daily Citizen, Beaver Dam, WI
Baraboo News Republic, WI
Daily Register, WI
The Journal Times, WI
La Crosse Tribune, WI
Winona Daily News, MN
The Chippewa Herald, WI
Casper Star-Tribune, WY
Meade County Times-Tribune, SD
Mitchell County Press-News, IA
Pennysaver, ND
Jackson County Chronicle, WI
Five Cities Times Press Recorder (OOB), CA
Times-Press-Recorder (OOB), CA
Bettendorf News, IA
Lee Agri-Media, Bismarck, ND
The Kingsburg Recorder, CA
La Crosse Foxxy Shopper, WI
Midwest Messenger, NE
Burt County Plaindealer, NE
Coulee News, WI
Suburban Journals of Greater St. Louis, MO
Lebanon Express, OR
Forest City Summit, IA
The Plattsmouth Journal, NE
Neighborhood Extra, NE
Illinois Suburban Journals, IL
Mandan News, ND
The Chadron Record, NE
The Banner-Press, NE
Mini Nickel Classifieds, MT
The Schuyler Sun, NE
The Garden Island, Lihue, HI
The Weekly Calistogan, CA
Tri-county Foxxy Shopper, WI
Casper Journal, WY
Distinctive Properties, CA
Onalaska Holmen Courier-Life, WI

Note: Lee Enterprises is a leading provider of local news and information and advertising in 50 markets, with 46 daily newspapers and a joint interest in four others, rapidly growing digital products and nearly 300 specialty publications in 22 states. Lee's markets include St. Louis, MO; Lincoln, NE; Madison, WI; Davenport, IA; Billings, MT; Bloomington, IL; and Tucson, AZ. Lee Common Stock is traded on the New York Stock Exchange under the symbol LEE.

LILLIE SUBURBAN NEWSPAPERS — 2515 7th Ave E, North Saint Paul, MN, 55109-3004, USA; tel (651) 777-8800; fax (651) 777-8288; e-mail tlillie@lillienews.com; web site www.lillienews.com
Est.: 1938
— Jeff R. Enright
— Ted H. LillieCo-Pub.s
Newspapers: South St. Paul - South West Review, MN
South-West Review, MN
East Side Review, MN
Roseville Review, MN
Shoreview Bulletin, MN
Shoreview Arden Hills Bulletin, MN
New Brighton Bulletin, MN
New Brighton-Mounds View Bulletin, MN
St. Anthony Bulletin, MN
Oakdale Lake Elmo Review, MN
Ramsey County Review, MN
Maplewood Review, MN
Review Perspectives, MN
Woodbury-South Maplewood Review, MN

LITMOR PUBLISHING — 821 Franklin Ave, Ste 208, Garden City, NY, 11530-4519, USA; tel (516) 931-0012; fax (516) 931-0027; e-mail editor@gcnews.com; web site www.gcnews.com
Group: Litmor Publishing Corp.
Est.: 1953
Pres./Pub. — Margaret Norris
Newspapers: Garden City News, NY
Hicksville Mid-Island Times, NY
Jericho News Journal, NY
Syosset Advance, NY
Bethpage Newsgram, NY

LNP MEDIA GROUP, INC. — 8 W King St, Lancaster, PA, 17603-3824, USA; tel (717) 291-8811; e-mail lnp@lnpnews.com; web site www.lancasteronline.com
Group: LNP Media Group
Est.: 1764
Community Liaison — Barbara Hough Roda
Publisher and Chairman — Robert Krasne
Client Solutions Operations Manager — Michelle Fisher
Managing Editor — Tom Murse
IT Manager — Vic Nigro
Sr. Client Solutions Manager — Amanda Janaszek
Production Manager — Connie Solon
VP of Client Solutions — John Derr
Sr. Vice President of Administration — Shane Zimmerman
Chief Information Officer — Caroline Muraro
Managing Editor — Ted Sickler
Executive Vice President — Ralph Martin
Newspapers: Lititz Record Express, PA
The Ephrata Review, PA
Lancaster Farming, PA
Note: No new titles

LOUISA PUBLISHING CO. LTD. — 301 Highway 61 N, Wapello, IA, 52653-1242, USA; tel (319) 523-4631; fax (319) 523-8167; e-mail lpc@louisescomm.net
Est.: 1954
Pres./Pub. — Michael A. Hodges
Newspapers: Des Moines County News, IA
New London Journal, IA
Van Buren County Register, IA
Wapello Republican, IA

LSN PUBLISHING COMPANY LLC — 600 Jefferson St, Ste 913, Lafayette, LA, 70508, USA; tel (337) 266-2154; fax (337) 266-2127; web site www.louisianastatenewspapers.com
Chairman — B.I. Moody III
Pres. — Kevin Moody
COO — Darrell Guillory
Newspapers: Abbeville Meridional, LA
Avoyelles Journal, LA
Franklin Banner-Tribune, LA
The Basile Weekly, LA
The Bayou Journal, LA
Bunkie Record, LA
Caldwell Watchman, LA
Church Point News, LA
The Crowley Post-Signal, LA
The Daily Review, LA
The Delhi Dispatch, LA
The Eunice News, LA
Gueydan Journal, LA
The Kaplan Herald, LA
Kinder Courier News, LA
The Mamou Acadian Press, LA
The Marksville Weekly News, LA
The Oakdale Journal, LA
The Rayne-Acadian Tribune, LA
Richland Beacon-News, LA
Teche News, LA
Tensas Gazette, LA
Ville Platte Gazette, LA
The West Carroll Gazette, LA
Note: Louisiana State Newspapers owns four daily newspapers and 19 weekly publications.

MAIN STREET MEDIA, INC. — 102 E Benton St, Carrollton, MO, 64633-1609, USA; tel (660) 542-0881; fax (660) 542-2580; e-mail democrat@carolnet.com
Group: Main Street Media, Inc.
Est.: 1800
Pres. — Jack Krier
Pub. — Frank W. Mercer
Ed. — Elaine Mercer
Newspapers: Glasgow Missourian, MO
Norborne Democrat-Leader, MO
The Santa Fe Times, MO
Carrollton Democrat, MO
Higginsville Advance, MO
Lexington News, MO
The Lafayette County Shopper, MO

MAIN STREET MEDIA, INC. — 958 E Wichita Ave, Russell, KS, 67665-2445, USA; tel (785) 483-2116; fax (785) 483-4012; e-mail russel@mainstreetmedia.us; web site http://www.mainstreetmedia.us/
Pub. — Chuck Krier
Chrmn. — Jack Krier
Newspapers: The Russell County News, KS
Downs News and Times, KS
The Ellis Review, KS
Franklin County Chronicle, NE
Harlan County Journal, NE
Natoma Luray Independent, KS
Osborne County Farmer, KS
Phillips County Review, KS
Plainville Times, KS
The Red Cloud Chief, NE
Smith County Pioneer, KS
Blue Hill Leader, NE
The Lindsborg News-Record, KS
The Phillips County News, MT
Appleton City Journal, MO
Carrollton News-Democrat, KY
Glasgow Missourian, MO
Humansville Star-Leader, MO
The Lexington News, MO
Rich Hill Mining Review, MO
St. Clair Co. Courier, MO
The Windsor Review, MO
The Santa Fe Times, MO
Norborne Democrat-Leader, MO

MAIN STREET NEWSPAPERS, INC. — PO Box 1125, Salem, VA, 24153-1125, USA; tel (540) 389-9355; fax (540) 382-3009; e-mail nrv@ourvalley.org; web site www.ourvalley.org
Est.: 2000
Pres. — E. Wilson Koeppel
Vice Pres. — Jeff Stumb

MAINLINE NEWSPAPERS — 975 Rowena Dr, Ebensburg, PA, 15931-2077, USA; tel (814) 472-4110; fax (814) 472-2275; e-mail mainlinenews@verizon.net; web site http://www.mainline-news.com/
Pub. — Bill Anderson
Office Mgr. — Joyce Keith
Newspapers: Mainline Extra, PA
The Dispatch, PA
The Journal, PA
The Star-Courier, PA
The Mountaineer-Herald, PA
The Mainliner, PA

MAINSTREET MEDIA GROUP, LLC — 6400 Monterey Rd, Gilroy, CA, 95020-6628, USA; tel (408) 842-6400; fax (408) 842-7105; e-mail clake@mainstreetmg.com
Group: Mainstreet Media Group Holdings, LLC
Est.: 2003
COO, CFO & General Counsel — Chris Lake
Newspapers: Amador Ledger-Dispatch, CA
The Gilroy Dispatch, CA
The Pinnacle (OOB), CA
La Jolla Light, CA
Santa Cruz Good Times, CA
San Diego Suburban News (OOB), CA
Solana Beach Sun, CA
Del Mar Times, CA
Rancho Bernardo News-Journal, CA
Rancho Santa Fe Review, CA
Carmel Valley News, CA
Poway News Chieftan, CA
Note: Mainstreet Media Group owns 12 weekly newspapers, clustered in San Diego and south of San Jose.

MANCHESTER NEWSPAPERS, INC. — 14 E Main St, Granville, NY, 12832-1334, USA; tel (518) 642-1234; fax (518) 642-1344; e-mail publisher@manchesternewspapers.com; web site www.manchesternewspapers.com
Est.: 1875
Pres. — John MacArthur Manchester
Exec. Vice Pres. — Lisa Manchester
Newspapers: The Lakes Region Free Press, NY
The North Country Free Press, NY
The Granville Sentinel, NY
The Whitehall Times, NY
Northshire Free Press, NY
The Weekender, NY

MARINSCOPE COMMUNITY NEWSPAPERS — 1301 Grant Ave, # B, Novato, CA, 94945-3143, USA; tel (415) 892-1516; fax (415) 897-0940; e-mail mscope@marinscope.com; web site www.marinscope.com
Group: Battle Born Media — Marin
Est.: 1922
Owner/Publisher — Sherman Frederick
Newspapers: Mill Valley Herald, CA
Novato Advance, CA
Ross Valley Reporter, CA
San Rafael News Pointer, CA
Sausalito Marinscope, CA
Twin Cities Times, CA
Pacifica Tribune, CA
Note: 7 weekly newspapers in the Bay Area, the Novato Advance, the San Rafael News Pointer, the Mill Valley Herald, the Twin City Times, the Ross Valley Reporter, the Sausalito Marinscope and the Pacifica Tribune.

MCNAUGHTON NEWSPAPERS — 1250 Texas St, Fairfield, CA, 94533-5748, USA; tel (707) 425-4646; fax (707) 425-5924; web site www.dailyrepublic.com
Pres./CEO — Foy McNaughton
Vice Pres. — R. McNaughton
Adv. Dir. — Sharon Guy
Ed. — Debra DeAngelo
Newspapers: Daily Republic, CA
The Davis Enterprise, CA
Village Life, CA
Winters Express, CA
Mountain Democrat, CA
Note: McNaughton also owns the El Dorado Gazette, Georgetown Gazette & Town Crier, Folsom Life Folsom, the Village Life and the Winters Express all weekly publications located in California.

MID VALLEY PUBLISHING — 6950 Gerard Ave, Winton, CA, 95388, USA; tel (209) 358-5311; fax (209) 358-7108; e-mail midvalleypub@aol.com; web site www.midvalleypublications.com
CEO — Fran Sodini
Newspapers: Hilmar Times, CA
Hughson Chronicle-Denair Dispatch, CA
Merced County Times, CA
The Dinuba Sentinel, CA
Waterford News, CA
Winton Times, CA
Note: Mid-Valley Publications also owns El Tiempo, a spanish weekly newspaper in Merced, California.

MILEHIGH NEWSPAPERS — 110 N Rubey Dr, Unit 120, Golden, CO, 80403-3219, USA; tel (303) 279-5541; e-mail scottp@milehighnews.com; web site www.milehighnews.com
Pub. — Scott Perriman
Gen. Mgr. — Tom Lucas
Acct. Mgr. — Carla Bethke
Newspapers: Wheat Ridge Transcript, CO

Castle Rock News Press, CO
Golden Transcript, CO
Lakewood Sentinel, CO
Northglenn-Thornton Sentinel, CO
The Englewood Herald, CO
Wheat Ridge Transcript, CO

MILLER PUBLISHING — 6796 SW 62nd Ave, South Miami, FL, 33143-3306, USA; tel (305) 669-7355; fax (305) 662-6980; e-mail cneditor@gate.net; web site www.communitynewspapers.com
Pres./Pub — Grant Miller
Ed. — Michael Miller
Newspapers: Palmetto Bay News, FL
South Miami News, FL
Kendall Gazette, FL

MONTGOMERY NEWSPAPERS — 290 Commerce Dr, Fort Washington, PA, 19034-2400, USA; tel (215) 542-0200; fax (215) 643-9475; web site www.montgomerynews.com
Est.: 1896
Pub. — Elizabeth Wilson
Circ. Mgr. — John Maguire
Newspapers: Ambler Gazette, PA
Glenside News, PA
North Penn Life, PA
Perkasie News-Herald, PA
Souderton Independent, PA
Springfield Sun, PA
Note: Montgomery Newspapers also owns one twice-yearly, two quarterly and seven monthly publications.

MORNING STAR — 711 W Pickard St, Mount Pleasant, MI, 48858-1585, USA; tel (989) 779-6000; fax (989) 779-6009; e-mail news@themorningsun.com; web site www.morningstarpublishing.com
Est.: 1950
Administrative Asst. — Linda Kunkel
Newspapers: Grand Traverse Insider, MI
The Leader and The Kalkaskian, MI

MORRIS COMMUNICATIONS CO. LLC — 725 Broad St, Augusta, GA, 30901-1336, USA; tel (888) 622-6358; fax (706) 722-7125; e-mail morrismarketing@morris.com; web site www.morris.com
Group: Morris Communications Company, LLC
CEO — William S. Morris III
Sr. Vice Pres., Finance/Sec./Treasurer — Craig S. Mitchell
Newspapers: The Alaska Star, AK
Note: Morris Communications Company, LLC is part of a privately held media company with diversified holdings that include newspaper, magazine, and cable television. Morris' holdings numerous magazines and specialized publications, visitor (travel and tourism) publications, including Where Magazine, Wheretraveler.com, and Where Guestbooks and provides cable television, internet, broadband, and telephone services.

MORRIS MULTIMEDIA, INC. — 27 Abercorn St, Savannah, GA, 31401-2715, USA; tel (912) 233-1281; fax (912) 238-4639; e-mail info@morrismultimedia.com; web site www.morrismultimedia.com
Est.: 1970
Chrmn./CEO — Charles H. Morris
Vice Pres./CFO — Jeffrey Samuels
Asst. to President — Kathy Kurazawa
Regional Vice President - SE Georgia Newspapers — Joe McGlamery
COO - Morris Network — Bobby Berry
Newspapers: Bryan County News, GA
Great Bend Tribune, KS
Lanier Life, GA
The Boscobel Dial, WI
Chronicle-Independent, SC
The Coastal Courier, GA
The Country Chronicle, SC
The Covington News, GA
Crawford County Independent & Kickapoo Scout, WI
Effingham Herald, GA
The Ellsworth County Independent-Reporter, KS
Fennimore Times, WI
Escalon Times, CA
The Frontline, GA
The Times, GA
Fort Jackson Leader, SC
The Fort Jackson Leader, SC
Grant County Herald Independent (Lancaster), WI
Great Bend Tribune, KS
Hillsboro Sentry-Enterprise, WI
Lee County Observer, SC
The Marquette Tribune, KS
Muscoda Progressive, WI
Marquette Tribune, KS
The Platteville Journal, WI
Republican Journal, WI
Platteville Journal, WI
Richland Observer, WI
The Richland Observer, WI
The Shaw News, SC
Smithville Review , TN
Southern Standard, TN
Statesboro Herald, GA
The Times, GA
Tri-County Press, WI
Connect Savannah, GA
Connect Statesboro, GA
Tri-County Press (Cuba City), WI
Reminder Shopper, WI
Round-up Shopper, WI
Darlington Republican, WI
Savannah Pennysaver, GA
Statesboro Pennysaver, GA
Tri-county Pennysaver, GA
The Connection, SC
Lake Wateree News, SC
Poultry & Egg News (Gainesville), GA
Manteca Bulletin, CA
The Ceres Courier, CA
Oakdale Leader, CA
The Riverbank News, CA
Turlock Journal, CA
The Forsyth County News, GA
Barrow County News, GA
Dawson County News, GA
South Forsyth News, GA
Liberty County Pennysaver, GA
Hinesville Area Real Estate Today, GA
Statesboro Area Real Estate Today, GA
The Connection, SC
Monroe Times, WI
Note: Morris Multimedia, Inc. is the parent company of Morris Newspapers Corp. which owns and publishes more than 65 daily and non daily newspapers, shoppers and niche publications in nine states and the Caribbean, as well as seventeen television stations in six southeastern U.S. markets.

NASSAU COUNTY PUBLICATIONS — 5 Centre St, Hempstead, NY, 11550-2422, USA; tel (516) 481-5400; e-mail thebeaconnews5@aol.com
Pub. — Kathleen Hoegl
Newspapers: East Meadow Beacon, NY
The Hempstead Beacon, NY
The Merrick Beacon, NY
The Uniondale Beacon, NY
West Hempstead Beacon, NY

NATCHITOCHES TIMES NEWSPAPERS — PO Box 448, 904 Hwy. 1 S., Natchitoches, LA, 71458-0448, USA; tel (318) 352-3618; fax (318) 352-7842; e-mail news@natchitochestimes.com; web site www.natchitochestimes.com
Group: NTN Media
Pres./Pub. — Lovan Thomas
Newspapers: Advertiser, LA
Bienville Democrat, LA
Coushatta Citizen Shopper, LA
Springhill Press & News-Journal, LA
The Enterprise & Interstate Progress, LA
The Progress, LA
Winn Parish Enterprise-News American, LA

NEIGHBOR NEWSPAPERS — 524 S Main St, Broken Arrow, OK, 74012-4331, USA; tel (918) 663-1414; web site www.neighbor-newspapers.com
Pub. — Mike Brown
Opns. Dir. — Bill Robert
Newspapers: Cherokee Tribune, GA
Alpharetta Neighbor, GA
The Clayton Neighbor (OOB), GA
Bartow Neighbor, GA
Mid DeKalb Neighbor (OOB), GA
DeKalb Neighbor, GA
The Douglas Neighbor, GA
Henry Neighbor, GA
Johns Creek Neighbor (OOB), GA
Milton Neighbor, GA
Paulding Neighbor, GA
Roswell Neighbor, GA
Northside Neighbor, GA

NEW CENTURY PRESS — 310 1st Ave, Rock Rapids, IA, 51246-1506, USA; tel (712) 472-2525; fax (712) 472-3414; e-mail jhensley@ncppub.com; web site www.ncppub.com
Est.: 1884
Chief Operating Officer — James (Jim) Hensley
General Manager — Lisa Miller
Newspapers: The (Moorhead, MN) Extra, SD
Westbrook Sentinel Tribune, MN
West Lyon Herald, IA
Griggs County Courier, ND
Lyon County Reporter, IA
Steele County Press, ND
The Northwest Iowa Extra, IA
The (Moorhead) Extra, MN
River Valley Woman (Mankato), MN

NEW ENGLAND NEWSPAPERS INC — 75 S Church St, Pittsfield, MA, 01201-6157, USA; tel (413) 447-7311; fax (413) 499-3419; e-mail news@berkshireeagle.com
Group: Birdland Acquisition LLC.
Est.: Roots dating back to 1789
Asst. Editor-Berkshire Eagle — Jennifer Huberdeau
CCSEO — Warren C. Dews Jr.
Page Des./Copy Ed. — Mitchell Chapman
Newspapers: Berkshire Eagle, MA
Bennington Banner, VT
Manchester Journal, VT
Brattleboro Reformer, VT
UpCountry Magazine, MA

NEW JERSEY HILLS MEDIA GROUP — 100 S Jefferson Rd, Ste 104, Whippany, NJ, 07981-1009, USA; tel (908) 766-3900; fax (908) 766-6365; web site www.newjerseyhills.com
Co-Pub./Bus. Mgr. — Stephen W. Parker
Co-Pub./Exec Editor — Elizabeth K. Parker
Gen. Office Mgr. — Diane Howard
Rita Annan-Brady
Vice President, Sales and Marketing — Jerry O'Donnell Jr.
Advertising Sales Representative — Peter Farrell
Advert. Sales Rep. — Brian Johnson
Newspapers: Today in Hunterdon (OOB), NJ
The Citizen, NJ
Hunterdon Review, NJ
Hanover Eagle, NJ
Roxbury Register, NJ
Madison Eagle, NJ
Morris News-Bee, NJ
Mount Olive Chronicle, NJ
Florham Park Eagle, NJ
Chatham Courier, NJ
The Progress, NJ
Observer Tribune, NJ
Bernardsville News, NJ
The Randolph Reporter, NJ
Echoes-Sentinel, NJ

NEW MEDIA INVESTMENT GROUP — 1345 Avenue of the Americas, Fl 46, New York, NY, 10105-4302, USA; tel (212) 479-3160; e-mail ir@newmediainv.com
Newspapers: Akron Beacon Journal, OH
Austin American-Statesman, TX
GateHouse Media, Inc., NY
Palm Beach Daily News, FL
The Palm Beach Post, FL
Alive, OH
Bedford Now, MI
Columbia Daily Tribune, MO
Rochester Business Journal, NY
Times Record, AR
McPherson Sentinel, KS
Dodge City Daily Globe, KS
The Newton Kansan, KS
The Morning Sun, KS
The Pratt Tribune, KS
Bastrop Daily Enterprise, LA
Cheboygan Daily Tribune, MI
Ames Tribune, IA
Crookston Daily Times, MN
Taunton Daily Gazette, MA
The Courier, LA
The Daily Reporter, MI
Hillsdale Daily News, MI
Cape Cod Times, MA
The Leavenworth Times, KS
Ionia Sentinel-Standard, MI
Sault Ste. Marie Evening News, MI
The Enterprise, MA
Rolla Daily News, MO
The Monroe News, MI
Milford Daily News, MA
The Daily Register, IL
Benton Evening News, IL
The Journal-Standard, IL
Olney Daily Mail, IL
The Daily Leader, IL
The Herald News, MA
The Standard-Times, MA
Hannibal Courier-Post, MO
Daily Guide, MO
Stuttgart Daily Leader, AR
The Evening Tribune, NY
The Carmi Times, IL
The Observer-Dispatch, NY
Times-News, NC
Daily Review Atlas, IL
The State Journal-Register, IL
The Daily American, IL
Devils Lake Journal, ND
The Repository, OH
Telegram & Gazette, MA
Pekin Daily Times, IL
Journal Star, IL
The Holland Sentinel, MI
Sturgis Journal, MI
The Oak Ridger, TN
The Courier-Tribune, NC
The Progress-Index, VA
The Moberly Monitor-Index, MO
The Star, NC
Neosho Daily News, MO
La Junta Tribune-Democrat, CO
The Ledger, FL
The Daily Commercial, FL
Daily Messenger, NY
Ocala Star-Banner, FL
Sarasota Herald-Tribune, FL
Lake Sun Leader, MO
Daily Comet, LA
Foster's Daily Democrat, NH
Hope Star, AR
The Record Herald, PA
Metrowest Daily News, MA
The Patriot Ledger, MA
The Gadsden Times, AL
The Daily Telegram, MI
Mineral Daily News-Tribune, WV
The Ardmoreite, OK
Mail Tribune, OR
The Kinston Free Press, NC
The Sun Journal, NC
The Times Herald-Record, NY
Wellsville Daily Reporter, NY
The Gaston Gazette, NC
Siskiyou Daily News, CA
The Bulletin, CT
Pocono Record, PA
Columbia Daily Herald, TN
Herald-Journal, SC
Daily Press, CA
The Butler County Times-Gazette, KS
The Daily News, NC
The Dispatch, NC
Miami News-Record, OK
Daytona Beach News-Journal, FL
The News Herald, FL
News Chief, FL
Northwest Florida Daily News, FL
The Gainesville Sun, FL
The Examiner / Examiner Weekend, MO

Kirksville Daily Express, MO
Mexico Ledger, MO
Pine Bluff Commercial, AR
Star-Courier, IL
Lincoln Courier, IL
The Marion Daily Republican, IL
Brownwood Bulletin, TX
Waxahachie Daily Light, TX
Shawnee News-Star, OK
Du Quoin Evening Call, IL
The Register-Mail, IL
Erie Times-News, PA
The Herkimer Telegram, NY
Daily Ledger, IL
Times-News, NC
Rockford Register Star, IL
The Times-Reporter, OH
The Independent, OH
The Carthage Press, MO
Examiner-Enterprise, OK
The Ashland Daily Tidings, OR
The Tuscaloosa News, AL
Portsmouth Herald, NH
Arkadelphia Siftings Herald, AR
Herald Democrat, TX
Boonville Daily News, MO
Constitution-Tribune, MO
The Daily Independent, CA
The Leader, NY
The Providence Journal, RI
The Record, CA
Stephenville Empire-Tribune, TX
Thisweek Newspapers, MN

NEWS GAZETTE COMMUNITY NEWS — 1332 Harmon Dr, Rantoul, IL, 61866-3310, USA; tel (217) 892-9613; fax (217) 892-9451; e-mail news@rantoulpress.com
Gen. Mgr. — Tim Evans
Newspapers: Piatt County Journal-Republican, IL
Mahomet Citizen, IL
Ford County Record, IL
Rantoul Press, IL
Independent News, IL
The Leader, IL
Note: East Central Communications is owned by News-Gazette Inc. which also own The News-Gazette a daily newspapers located in Champaign, IL.

NEWS MEDIA CORP. — 211 E II Route 38, Rochelle, IL, 61068-2303, USA; tel (815) 562-2061; fax (815) 562-2161; web site www.newsmediacorporation.com
Est.: 1975
Pres. — John C. Tompkins
Vice Pres. — Michael Tompkins
Gen. Mgr. — John Shank
Controller — Michael Rand
Newspapers: Arizona Silver Belt, AZ
Ashton Gazette, IL
Center Post-Dispatch, CO
Ogle County Life, IL
The Lingle Guide, WY
Copper Country News, AZ
Lake Powell Chronicle, AZ
Register-Pajaronian, CA
The Rustler, CA
Gonzales Tribune, CA
Soledad Bee, CA
Greenfield News, CA
Paso Robles Press, CA
Atascadero News, CA
Valley Courier, CO
The Monte Vista Journal, CO
The Mineral County Miner, CO
The South Fork Tines, CO
The Del Norte Prospector, CO
The Conejos County Citizen, CO
The Rochelle News Leader, IL
Clinton Journal, IL
The Amboy News, IL
Mendota Reporter, IL
News-Times, OR
Siuslaw News, OR
Cottage Grove Sentinel, OR
Brookings Register, SD
Moody County Enterprise, SD
The Daily Plainsman, SD
The Redfield Press, SD
The Record Delta, WV
Mountain Statesman, WV
Taylor County Value Guide, WV
The Torrington Telegram, WY
The Lusk Herald, WY
The Platte County Record-Times, WY
Guernsey Gazette, WY
The Business Farmer, NE
Sublette Examiner, WY
The Pinedale Roundup, WY
Uinta County Herald, WY
Bridger Valley Pioneer, WY
The Kemmerer Gazette, WY

NEWS PUBLISHING, CO., INC. — 1126 Mills St, Black Earth, WI, 53515-9419, USA; tel (608) 767-3655; fax (608) 767-2222; web site www.newspubinc.com
Pub. — Daniel Witte
Pub. — Mark Witte
Controller/CFO — Tom Finger
Newspapers: Post Messenger Recorder, WI
Middleton Times-Tribune, WI
News-Sickle-Arrow, WI
Sauk Prairie Star, WI
Spring Green Home News, WI

NEWS-JOURNAL CORP. — 901 6th St, Daytona Beach, FL, 32117-3352, USA; tel (386) 252-1511; fax (386) 258-8465; web site www.news-jrnlonline.com
Newspapers: West Volusia Pennysaver, FL
Daytona Pennysaver, FL
Flagler Pennysaver, FL

NEWS-PRESS & GAZETTE CO. — 825 Edmond St, , Saint Joseph, MO, 64501-2737, USA; tel (816) 271-8500; fax (816) 271-8695; e-mail dennis.ellsworth@npgco.com; web site www.newspressnow.com
Group: NPG Newspapers Inc.
Est.: 1918
Chief Executive Officer — David R. Bradley
President — Brian Bradley
Exec. Vice-President, COO- Newspapers — Stacey Hill
Newspapers: Atchison Globe, KS
The Daily Star Journal - Warrensburg
Hiawatha World, KS
The Miami County Republic, KS
St. Joseph News-Press, MO
Courier Tribune, MO
Note: News-Press & Gazette Co. also owns the newspapers in Atchison, Hiawatha, Louisburg, Osawatomie, Paola, Kansas and Missouri newspapers in St. Joseph, Smithville, Liberty, Kearney, & Warrensburg.

NEWSPAPER MEDIA GROUP — 2 Executive Campus, Ste 400, Cherry Hill, NJ, 08002-4102, USA; tel (856) 779-3800; fax (609) 921-2714; e-mail feedback@centraljerseycom; web site www.newspapermediagroup.com
Est.: 1786
Ed. — Aubrey Huston
Exec. Ed. — Donna Kenyon
Newspapers: Atlanticville, NJ
Burlington Township Sun, NJ
Cherry Hill Sun, NJ
Cinnaminson Sun, NJ
Haddonfield Sun, NJ
Marlton Sun, NJ
Medford Sun, NJ
Moorestown Sun, NJ
Mt. Laurel Sun, NJ
Palmyra Sun, NJ
Shamong Sun, NJ
Sicklerville Sun, NJ
Tabernacle Sun, NJ
The Berlin Sun, NJ
Voorhees Sun, NJ
Hillsborough Beacon, NJ
South Brunswick Post, NJ
The Register News (OOB), NJ
Hopewell Valley News, NJ
The HUB, NJ
Examiner, NJ
The Manville News (OOB), NJ
The Beacon, NJ
The Independent, NJ
News Transcript, NJ
The Lawrence Ledger, NJ
Tri-Town News, NJ
Windsor-Hights Herald, NJ
Metuchen/Edison Review, NJ
North/South Brunswick Sentinel, NJ
Suburban, NJ
East Brunswick Sentinel, NJ

NORDMARK PUBLISHING — 11 1st Ave NE, Rolla, ND, 58367-7125, USA; tel (701) 477-6495; fax (701) 477-3182
Pub. — Jason Nordmark
Newspapers: Billings County Pioneer, ND
Dickey County Leader, ND
The Golden Valley News, ND
The Mouse River Journal, ND
The Oakes Times, ND
The Walsh County Press, ND
Towner County Record-Herald, ND
Turtle Mountain Star, ND

NORTH JERSEY COMMUNITY NEWSPAPERS — 1 Garret Mountain Plz, Woodland Park, NJ, 07424-3320, USA; tel (973) 569-7000; fax (973) 569-7129; web site www.northjersey.com
Group: North Jersey Media Group Inc.
Est.: 2003
VP/Pub. — Janice Friedman
VP/Pub. — Michael Lawson
Pres. — Stephen A Borg
Newspapers: Aim Jefferson
Aim Vernon, NJ
Aim West Milford, NJ
Argus, NJ
Belleville Times, NJ
Bloomfield Life, NJ
Bogota Bulletin, NJ
Cliffside Park Citizen, NJ
Clifton Journal, NJ
Community News, NJ
Edgewater View, NJ
Fort Lee Suburbanite, NJ
Franklin Lakes/Oakland Suburban News, NJ
The Gazette, NJ
Glen Ridge Voice, NJ
Glen Rock Gazette, NJ
Hackensack Chronicle, NJ
The Item of Millburn and Short Hills, NJ
Leonia Life, NJ
Little Ferry Local, NJ
Mahwah Suburban News, NJ
Midland Park Suburban News, NJ
The Montclair Times, NJ
Neighbor News, NJ
Northern Valley Suburbanite, NJ
Nutley Sun, NJ
Parsippany Life, NJ
Pascack Valley Community Life, NJ
Passaic Valley Today, NJ
Ramsey Suburban News, NJ
Ridgefield Park Patriot, NJ
The Ridgewood News, NJ
South Bergenite, NJ
Suburban News, NJ
Suburban Trends, NJ
Teaneck Suburbanite, NJ
Town Journal, NJ
Town News, NJ
Twin-Boro News, NJ
Verona-Cedar Grove Times, NJ
Waldwick Suburban News, NJ
Wayne Today, NJ
Wyckoff Suburban News, NJ
Englewood Suburbanite, NJ
Tenafly Suburbanite, NJ

NORTHEAST NEBRASKA NEWS CO. — 102 W Main St, Hartington, NE, 68739-3005, USA; tel (402) 254-3997; fax (402) 254-3999; e-mail ccnews@hartel.net
Pub. — Rob Dump
Pub. — Peggy Year
Office Mgr. — Lori Liese
Newspapers: Coleridge Blade, NE
Cedar County News, NE
Laurel Advocate, NE
The Osmond Republican, NE
The Randolph Times, NE
The Wausa Gazette, NE
Times, NE

NORTHERN VIRGINIA MEDIA SERVICES — 19 N King St, Leesburg, VA, 20176-2819, USA; tel (703) 771-8800; e-mail bpotter@insidenova.com; web site insidenova.com
COO — Bruce Potter
Sales Mgr. — Connie Fields
Class. Sales Mgr. — Tonya Fields
Sr. Ed. — Kari Pugh
Newspapers: Sun Gazette, VA
Belvoir Eagle, VA
Quantico Sentry, VA
Washington FAMILY Magazine, VA

NYC COMMUNITY MEDIA, LLC — 515 Canal St, Unit 1C, New York, NY, 10013-1330, USA; tel (212) 229-1890; fax (212) 229-2790; e-mail francesco@communitymediallc.com; web site www.communitymediallc.com
Newspapers: Gay City News, NY
The Downtown Express, NY
East Villager and Lower East Sider, NY
Chelsea Now, NY
The Villager, NY

OAHU PUBLICATIONS INC. — 500 Ala Moana Blvd, Ste 7-500, Honolulu, HI, 96813-4930, USA; tel 808) 529-4818; web site www.oahupublications.com
Group: Black Press Group Ltd.
Newspapers: Honolulu Star-Advertiser, HI
MidWeek Oahu, HI
Metro HNL (OOB), HI
USA Today Hawaii Edition , HI
Street Pulse, HI
The Garden Island, Kauai, HI
Kauai Midweek, HI
Hawaii Tribune-Herald, HI
West Hawaii Today, HI
North Hawaii News, HI
Hawaii Army Weekly, HI
Marine Star, HI
Ho`okele (Navy & Air Force), HI

OGDEN NEWSPAPERS INC. — 1500 Main St, Wheeling, WV, 26003-2826, USA; tel (304) 233-0100; fax (304) 233-9397; e-mail myer@news-register.net; web site www.oweb.com
Est.: 1800
Publisher — G. Ogden Nutting
Pres./CEO — Robert M. Nutting
Vice Pres. — William O. Nutting
Vice Pres. — William C. Nutting
Treasurer/CFO — Duane D. Wittman
Newspapers: Adirondack Daily Enterprise, NY
Byrd Newspapers, VA
Page News & Courier, VA
The Shenandoah Valley-Herald, VA
The Warren Sentinel, VA
The Winchester Star, VA
Daily Herald, UT
Herald-Standard, PA
The Frederick News-Post, MD
Independent, MN
Independent Shopper's Review, MN
Lawrence Journal-World, KS
Northern Virginia Daily, VA
Cape Coral Breeze, FL
The Lake Placid News, NY
The Leader-Herald, NY
The Maui Bulletin, HI
Lee County Shopper, FL
Island Reporter, FL
Sanibel-Captiva Islander, FL
Sanibel - Captiva Shopper's Guide, FL
Captiva Current, FL
The Pine Island Eagle, FL
Fort Myers Beach Observer, FL
Fort Myers Beach Bulletin, FL
The Maui News, HI
The News-Sentinel, IN
The Messenger, IA
Times-Republican, IA
Consumer News, IA
The Daily Freeman-Journal, IA
The Dysart Reporter, IA
Estherville News, IA
Reporter-Democrat, IA

Tama County Shopper, IA
The Tama News-Herald, IA
Toledo Chronicle, IA
The Traer Star-Clipper, IA
Reinbeck Courier, IA
Northern-Sun Print, IA
Pennysaver, IA
The Alpena News, MI
The Daily Mining Gazette, MI
The Daily News, MI
Daily Press, MI
The Mining Journal, MI
Up Action News, MI
Action Shopper, MI
Advertiser, MI
Sentinel, MN
The Journal, MN
Faribault County Register, MN
New Ulm Shopper/post Review, MN
Minot Daily News, ND
Pierce County Tribune, ND
The Post-Journal, NY
The Observer, NY
The Westfield Republican, NY
Sentinel-News, NY
The Advertiser-Tribune, OH
Herald-Star, OH
The Marietta Times, OH
Morning Journal, OH
The Review, OH
The Times Leader, OH
The Tribune Chronicle, OH
Salem News, OH
Boardman Town Crier, OH
Williamsport Sun-Gazette/Lock Haven Express, PA
Times Observer, PA
The Express, PA
The Sentinel, PA
Altoona Mirror, PA
County Observer, PA
East Lycoming Shopper, PA
The Luminary, PA
The Intelligencer, WV
The Inter-Mountain, WV
The Journal, WV
Parkersburg News & Sentinel, WV
Wetzel Chronicle, WV
Tyler Star News, WV
Weirton Daily Times, OH
The Shepherdstown Chronicle, WV
Green Tab, WV
Bedford Journal, NH
Mahoning Valley Parent Magazine, OH
Poland Town Crier, OH
The Milford Cabinet, NH
The Trading Post, ND
Merrimack Journal, NH
Austintown Town Crier, OH
Gasparilla Gazette (OOB), FL
Westfield Republican, NY
Canfield Town Crier, OH
The Emmetsburg Reporter, IA
Town Crier Shopper, MN
Quality Guide, NY

Note: Nutting Newspapers also publishes the Capper's, Grit, Mother Earth News, Brave Hearts, The Herb Companion, Herbs for Health, Farm Collector, Gas Engine Magazine, and Steam Traction.

OMAHA WORLD-HERALD — 1314 Douglas St, Ste 1500, Omaha, NE, 68102-1848, USA; tel (402) 444-1000; fax (402) 444-1231; e-mail phil.taylor@owh.com; web site www.omaha.com
Group: BH Media Group
Est.: 1885
Pres. & CEO, Pub. — Terry J. Kroeger
Dir., Digital Development — Jeff Carney
Dir., Production — Kristy Gerry
CFO/Sr. Vice Pres. — Duane Polodna
Sr. VP/Gen. Counsel — Scott Searl
Exec VP — Doug Hiemstra
Finance Dir./Controller — Mike Kirk
Chief Revenue Officer — Thom Kastrup
Director of Local Sales — Brett Snead
Adv. Mgr., Custom Publishing/Events — Tam Webb
Classified Employment Manager — Aaron Consalvi
Director of Classified Advertising — Deb McChesney
Mgr., Suburban Newspapers — Paul Swanson
VP of Advertising — Keely Byars
Dir Community Relations — Susan Violi
Executive Editor — Melissa Matczak
General Manager — Phil Taylor

PAGE-SHENANDOAH NEWSPAPER CORP. — 231 S Liberty St, Harrisonburg, VA, 22801-3621, USA; tel (540) 574-6200; fax (540) 574-6299; web site www.shenvalleynow.com
Group: Page Shenandoah Newspaper Corporation
Est.: 1896
Pub. — Thomas T. Byrd
Pres — Peter S. Yates
Ed and Gen Mgr — Randy Arrington
Note: Byrd Newspapers owns Rockingham Publishing Co. , publisher of the Daily News-Record and The Winchester Evening Star. Inc, publisher of The Winchester (VA) Star. Several weekly newspapers are also included in the group.

PAMPLIN MEDIA GROUP — 6605 SE Lake Rd, Portland, OR, 97222-2161, USA; tel (503) 684-0360; fax (503) 620-3433; e-mail email@commnewspapers.com; web site www.commnewspapers.net
Pres./Pub. — Steve Clark
Pres./Pub. — Mark Garber
Gen. Mgr. — Brian Monihan
Retail Adv Dir — Christine Moore
Newspapers: The Beaverton Valley Times, OR
The Bee, OR
The Canby Herald, OR
Central Oregonian, OR
The Clackamas Review, OR
Estacada News, OR
Forest Grove News-Times, OR
The Hillsboro Tribune, OR
The Lake Oswego Review, OR
The Times (Tigard/Tualatin Times), OR
The Madras Pioneer, OR
Molalla Pioneer, OR
The Newberg Graphic, OR
Oregon City News, OR
The Portland Tribune, OR
Sandy Post, OR
The South County Spotlight, OR
Southwest Community Connection, OR
West Linn Tidings, OR
Wilsonville Spokesman, OR
Woodburn Independent, OR
Note: Community Newspapers is a subsidiary of Oregon Newspapers Publications Corp.

PARK RAPIDS ENTERPRISE EXPRESS — 203 Henrietta Ave N, Park Rapids, MN, 56470-2617, USA; tel (218) 732-3364; fax (218) 732-8757; e-mail aerickson@parkrapidsenterprise.com; web site www.parkrapidsenterprise.com
Group: Forum Communications Co.
Publisher — Rory Palm
Adv. Mgr. — Candy Parks
Sports Editor — Vance Carlson
Editor — Anna Erickson

PAXTON MEDIA GROUP, LLC — 201 S 4th St, Paducah, KY, 42003-1524, USA; tel (270) 575-8600; fax (270) 442-8188; e-mail classified@sanfordherald.com; web site www.sanfordherald.com
Est.: 1896
Pres./CEO — David M. Paxton
VP/CFO — Richard E. Paxton
Asst. — Milinda Harnice
Newspapers: Daily Herald, NC
Grayson County News-Gazette, KY
The Current Bargain, IN
The Villa Rican, GA
The Standard, IN
West Georgia Weekly, GA
Princeton Daily Clarion, IN
Chronicle-Tribune, IN
Elkhart Truth, IN
Mount Carmel Register, IL
The Mayfield Messenger, KY
Metropolis Planet, IL
Paragould Daily Press, AR
Peru Tribune, IN
South Haven Tribune, MI
Harbor Country News, MI
Douglas County Sentinel, GA
The Courier, AR
The Daily Citizen, AR
The Daily Corinthian, MS
The Daily Courier, NC
Daily Dispatch, NC
Griffin Daily News, GA
Paragould Daily Press, AR
The Daily Star, LA
The Enquirer-Journal, NC
High Point Enterprise, NC
The Herald-Palladium, MI
Herald-Sanford, NC
Herald-Argus, IN
The Messenger, KY
Messenger-Inquirer, KY
The Mountain Press, TN
The Shelbyville News, IN
News Dispatch, IN
Connersville News-Examiner, IN
News-Topic, NC
Wabash Plain Dealer, IN
The Paducah Sun, KY
The Jonesboro Sun, AR
Vincennes Sun-Commercial, IN
The Times, IN
Times-Georgian, GA
Huntington Herald-Press, IN
The Courier-Times, IN
Thomasville Times, NC
Marshall County Tribune-Courier, KY
Archdale-Trinity News, NC
McLean County News, KY
Franklin Favorite, KY
Metropolis Planet, IL
Portland Leader, TN
The Mayfield Messenger, KY
Gateway Beacon, GA
The Cadiz Record, KY
Note: Paxton Media Group LLC owns 31 daily newspapers and 13 paid non-daily publications. Paxton Media also owns and operates an NBC-affiliated television station in Paducah, KY.

PIKES PEAK NEWSPAPERS, INC. — 153 Washington St, Monument, CO, 80132-9181, USA
Newspapers: The Pikes Peak Courier, CO
The Tribune, CO

PIONEER GROUP — 115 N Michigan Ave, Big Rapids, MI, 49307-1401, USA; tel (231) 796-4831; fax (231) 796-1152; e-mail pioneer@pionneergroup.net; info@pioneergroup.com; web site www.pioneergroup.net
Chrmn. — John (Jack) A. Batdorff
Pres./CEO — John Batdorff
Pub. — John Norton
Adv. Dir. — Sharon Frederick
Candy Allan
Newspapers: Herald Review, MI
Lake County Star, MI
River Valley News Shopper, MI
The Benzie County Record-Patriot, MI
Tri-county Shoppers Guide, MI
West Shore Shopper's Guide, MI
Manistee News Advocate, MI

PIONEER NEWSPAPERS INC — 221 1st Ave W, Ste 405, Seattle, WA, 98119-4238, USA; tel (206) 284-4424; fax (206) 282-2143; e-mail jwampler@pioneernewsgroup.com; web site www.pioneernewsgroup.com
Est.: 1976
Pres. — Mike Gugliotto
CFO — Jeffrey Hood
Corp. Controller — Fred Eberlein
Internal Auditor & Advertising Systems Support — Larry Wells
Information & Circulation Systems Mgr. — Julie Hughes
Payroll & Finance Analyst — Sue Persh
Jeff Wampler
Human Resources Director — Megan Berg
Eric Johnston
Jeff Avgeris
Newspapers: Messenger-Index, ID
Idaho Press, ID
Stanwood Camano Advertiser, WA
The Argus, WA
The Herald Journal, UT
Idaho Press-Tribune, ID
The Leader, UT
Lone Peak Lookout OOB, MT
The News-Examiner, ID
The Standard-Journal, ID
The West Yellowstone News OOB*, MT
Note: Pioneer News Group owns eight daily newspapers and 15 publications throughout the northwestern United States.

POLK COUNTY PUBLISHING CO. — 100 E Calhoun St, Livingston, TX, 77351-2908, USA; tel (936) 327-4357; fax (936) 327-7156; e-mail polknews@livingston.net; web site www.easttexasnews.com
Pres./Pub. — Alvin Holley
Newspapers: Corrigan Times, TX
Groveton News, TX
Houston County Courier, TX
Lake Livingston Progress (OOB), TX
Polk County Enterprise, TX
San Jacinto News-Times, TX
The Trinity Standard, TX
Tyler County Booster, TX
Note: Polk County Publishing Co. also owns and operates three commercial printing shops.

PRESS AND NEWS PUBLICATIONS — 33 2nd St NE, Osseo, MN, 55369-1252, USA; tel (763) 425-3323; fax (763) 425-2945; e-mail jeremy.bradfield@ecm-inc.com; web site www.pressnews.com
Est.: 1924
COO — Dick Hendrickson
Circ. Mgr — Sylvia Fitzsimmons
Adv. Dir. — Jeremy Bradfield
Newspapers: South Crow River News, MN
Rockford Area News Leader, MN

PRESS PUBLICATIONS, INC. — 4779 Bloom Ave, White Bear Lake, MN, 55110-2764, USA; tel (651) 407-1200; fax (651) 429-1242; e-mail ppinfo@presspubs.com; web site www.presspubs.com
Est.: 1896
Adv. Consultant — Patty Steele
Adv. Consultant — Patti Carlson
Mng. Ed. — Debra Neutkens
News Clerk — Amy Johnson
Newspapers: Forest Lake Lowdown, MN
The Lowdown - St. Croix Valley Area, MN
White Bear Press, MN
Quad Community Press, MN
The Lowdown - Forest Lake Area, MN
Vadnais Heights Press, MN
Hugo Citizen
The Hugo Citizen, MN

PRINCETON PUBLISHING CO., INC. — 100 N Gibson St, Princeton, IN, 47670-1855, USA; tel (812) 385-2525; fax (812) 386-6199; e-mail lrembee@pdclarion.com; web site www.pdclarion.com
Est.: 1846
Pub./CEO — Jeff Schumacher
Ed. — Andrea Howe
Newspapers: Oakland City Journal, IN
Weekender, IN
Note: Princeton Publishing Co., Inc. is owned by Brehm Communications Inc.

RECORD PUBLISHING COMPANY, LLC — 1050 W Main St, Kent, OH, 44240-2006, USA; tel (330) 541-9400; fax (330) 296-2698; e-mail rwaite@dixcom.com; web site www.recordpub.com
Est.: 1832
General Manager — Waite Ron
Pub. — David Dix
Newspapers: Streetsboro Gateway News (OOB), OH
Nordonia Hills News Leader, OH
Tallmadge Express, OH
Twinsburg Bulletin, OH
Record-Courier, OH

Note: Record Publishing Co. is part of Dix Communications which is owned by the Wooster Republican Printing Co. Through it's subsidiaries, Alliance Publishing Co. LLC, Ashland Publishing Co. LLC, Defiance Publishing LLC, Frankfort Publishing Co., Jeffersonian C

RED WING PUBLISHING CO. — 433 W 3rd St, Ste 200, Red Wing, MN, 55066-2344, USA; tel (651) 388-5000; fax (651) 388-7973
Chrmn. — Arlin Albrecht
COO — Mark Poss
CFO — James Becker
Ops. Dir. — Laurie Hartmann
CFO — Becker Jim
Newspapers: The Journal, MN
Hutchinson Leader And Leader Shopper, MN
Jordan Independent, MN
Savage Pacer, MN
Chaska Herald, MN
Hutchinson Leader, MN
Chanhassen Villager, MN
Eden Prairie News, MN
Prior Lake American, MN
Shakopee Valley News, MN
Note: Red Wing Publishing Co. owns seven non-daily publications through it's subsidiary Southwest Suburban Publishing and also owns the International Falls (MN) Daily Journal.

RICHNER COMMUNICATIONS, INC. — 2 Endo Blvd, Garden City, NY, 11530-6707, USA; tel (516) 569-4000; fax (516) 569-4942; e-mail sales@liherald.com; web site www.liherald.com
Pub. — Clifford Richner
President — Stuart Richner
Vice Pres., Sales — Rhonda Glickman
Vice Pres., Opns. — Michael Bologna
Circulation Director — Dianne Ramdass
Kevin Plaut
New Media Director — Lori Berger
Newspapers: Baldwin Herald, NY
Gold Coast Gazette, NY
Nassau Herald, NY
Oyster Bay Guardian, NY
Lynbrook/East Rockaway Herald, NY
South Shore Record (OOB) , NY
Franklin Square/Elmont Herald, NY
Primetime, NY
Merrick Herald, NY
Malverne/West Hempstead Herald, NY
The Riverdale Press, NY
Rockville Centre Herald, NY
Bellmore Herald, NY
East Meadow Herald, NY
Long Beach Herald, NY
Herald Community Newspapers (OOB) , NY
Oceanside-Island Park Herald, NY

RISN OPERATIONS INC. — 508 Main St, Wilmington, DE, 19804-3911, USA
Newspapers: Chariho Times, RI
Coventry Courier, RI
East Greenwich Pendulum, RI
Kent County Daily Times, RI
Narragansett Times, RI
Standard-Times, RI
The Call, RI
The Porterville Recorder, CA
The Times, RI
Yuma Sun, AZ

ROCK VALLEY PUBLISHING LLC — 11512 N 2nd St, Machesney Park, IL, 61115-1101, USA; tel (815) 877-4044; fax (815) 654-4857; web site www.rvpublishing.com
Pub. — Pete Cruger
Gen. Mgr. — Randy Johnson
Newspapers: The Herald, IL
Post Journal, IL
The Belvidere Daily Republican, IL
The Clinton Topper, WI
The Herald, IL
The Sharon Reporter (OOB), WI
Note: Rock Valley Publishing LLC also publishes the Belvidere Republican in Belvidere, Illinois.

ROCKINGHAM PUBLISHING CO. — 231 S Liberty St, Harrisonburg, VA, 22801-3621, USA; tel (540) 574-6200; fax (540) 574-6299; e-mail business@dnronline.com; web site www.dnronline.com
Est.: 1913
Pres. — Thomas T. Byrd
Gen. Mgr. — Peter S. Yates
Newspapers: The Valley Banner, VA
Rocktown Weekly, VA
Note: Rockingham Publishing Co. is owned by Byrd Newspapers which also owns one daily and three weekly newspapers.

RUST COMMUNICATIONS — 301 Broadway St, Cape Girardeau, MO, 63701-7330, USA; tel (573) 335-6611; fax (573) 334-9258; e-mail editor@mccookgazette.com; web site www.mccookgazette.com
Est.: 1883
Chrmn. — Gary W. Rust
Co-Pres./Pub. — Jon K. Rust
Co-Pres. — Rex D. Rust
Vice Pres./COO — Wally Lage
Vice Pres., Opns. — Jim Maxwell
Vice President of Production — David Guay
Newspapers: Big Nickel, NE
The Fort Scott Tribune, KS
Remsen Bell-Enterprise, IA
Southeast Missourian, MO
Southeast Missourian Plus, MO
The Daily Statesman, MO
The Daily Dunklin Democrat, MO
Daily Dunklin Democrat Extra, MO
The Marshall Democrat-News, MO
The Monett Times, MO
The Nevada Daily Mail, MO
Daily American Republic, MO
Standard Democrat, MO
The Democrat Argus, MO
Cassville Democrat, MO
Scott County Signal, MO
The Concordian, MO
Delta News Citizen, MO
Missourian-News, MO
The Steele Enterprise, MO
South Missourian-News, MO
The Banner-Press, MO
Puxico Press, MO
Blytheville Courier News, AR
Lovely County Citizen, AR
Carroll County News, AR
The Town Crier, AR
The Osceola Times, AR
Clay County Times-Democrat, AR
The News, AR
Poinsett County Democrat, AR
State Gazette, TN
Marshall County Tribune, TN
Shelbyville Times-Gazette, TN
The Brazil Times, IN
Banner-Graphic, IN
Greene County Daily World, IN
Cherokee Chronicle Times, IA
Le Mars Daily Sentinel, IA
The Daily Reporter, IA
Pilot Tribune, IA
Dickinson County News, IA
McCook Daily Gazette, NE
Shoppers Guide, IA

SALMON PRESS — 5 Water St, Meredith, NH, 03253-6233, USA; tel (603) 279-4516; fax (603) 279-6677; e-mail publisher@salmonpress.com; web site www.newhampshirelakesandmountains.com; www.salmonpress.com
Est.: 1999
Pub. — Rich Piatt
Circ. Mgr. — Nancy Turner
Acct. Mgr. — Wendy Couto-Herne
Prodn. Mgr. — Marcy Stanek
Newspapers: Carroll County Independent, NH
Granite State News, NH
Littleton Courier, NH
Meredith News, NH
The Baysider, NH
The Berlin Reporter, NH
The Gilford Steamer, NH
The Record-Enterprise (OOB), NH
Winnisquam Echo, NH
The Coos County Democrat, NH

SAMPLE NEWS GROUP LLC — 28 W South St, Corry, PA, 16407-1810, USA; tel (814) 665-8291
CEO — George Sample
Graphics/I.T. Manager — David Coyle
Newspapers: Citizen (OOB), NH
Morning Times, PA
The Huntingdon Daily News, PA
The Palladium-Times, NY
The Standard-Journal, PA
The Times Record, ME
The Latrobe Bulletin, PA
The Daily Herald, PA
Journal-Tribune, ME
The Bedford Gazette, PA
Corry Journal, PA
Ocean City Sentinel, NJ
Gettysburg Times, PA
The Shippensburg News-Chronicle, PA
The Mountaineer-Herald, PA
The Portage Dispatch, PA
The Star-Courier, PA

SAN PATRICIO PUBLISHING CO., INC. — PO Box B, Sinton, TX, 78387-0167, USA; tel (361) 364-1270; fax (361) 364-3833; web site www.sanpatpublishing.com
— James F. Tracy
— John H. TracyCo-Pub.s
Newspapers: Mathis News, TX
Portland News, TX
San Patricio County News, TX

SANDUSKY NEWSPAPERS, INC. — 17 Executive Park Rd, Ste 3A, Hilton Head Island, SC, 29928-4738, USA; tel (843) 842-9162; fax (843) 842-9617
Chrmn/CEO — David Rau
Vice Pres./Gen. Counsel/CFO — Peter Vogt
President and COO — Doug Phares
Newspapers: Sandusky Register, OH
Norwalk Reflector, OH
Hilltop Times, UT
Grand Haven Tribune, MI
The Lebanon Democrat, TN
Mt. Juliet News, TN
The Hartsville Vidette, TN
Herald & Tribune, TN
The Erwin Record, TN
Kingsport Times-News, TN
Johnson City Press, TN
The Tomahawk, TN

SCHURZ COMMUNICATIONS INC — 1301 E Douglas Rd, Mishawaka, IN, 46545-1732, USA; tel (574) 247-7237; fax (574) 247-7238; web site www.schurz.com
Est.: 1872
Sr VP and CFO — Gesumino A. Agostino
President and CEO — Todd F. Schurz
VP Digital Media — J.B. Ozuna
VP of Human Resources and Corporate Development — Scott Schurz
VP of Publishing — Cory Bollinger
Director of Strategic Planning and Corporate Development — Chris Dautel
Newspapers: Farm Forum, SD
Watertown Public Opinion, SD
The Times-Mail, IN
The Herald-Mail, MD
The Herald Times, IN
Charlevoix Courier, MI
The Reporter Times, IN
Gaylord Herald Times, MI
The Mooresville-Decatur Times, IN
Petoskey News-Review, MI
South Bend Tribune, IN
Daily American, PA
Aberdeen American News, SD
Northern Michigan Review, Inc., MI
Herald-mail Express, MD
The Public Opinion, SD

SHAW MEDIA — 3200 E Lincolnway, Sterling, IL, 61081-1773, USA; tel (815) 284-4000; fax (815) 301-1727; e-mail tshaw@shawmedia.com; web site www.shawmedia.com
Est.: 1851
Pres. and COO
— John Rung
CFO
Treasurer — Terri Swegle
Chairman — Ryan McKibben
Secretary/Admin. Asst. — Peggy Campbell
Corp Strategy Coor — Peter Shaw
CEO — John Rung
Newspapers: The Times, IL
Berwyn Suburban Life, IL
Jasper County Tribune, IA
The Telegraph, IL
West Chicago Suburban Life, IL
Bureau County Republican, IL
Downers Grove Suburban Life, IL
Geneva Chronicle, IL
Glen Ellyn Suburban Life, IL
St. Charles Chronicle, IL
Hinsdale Suburban Life, IL
Villa Park Suburban Life, IL
Westmont Suburban Life, IL
Addison Suburban Life, IL
Elmhurst Suburban Life, IL
Carol Stream Suburban Life, IL
LaGrange Suburban Life, IL
Tonica News, IL
Creston News Advertiser, IA
Daily Chronicle, IL
The Midweek, IL
Forreston Journal, IL
Kane County Chronicle, IL
Morris Herald-News, IL
Mt. Morris Times, IL
Newton Daily News, IA
Oregon Republican Reporter, IL
Osceola Sentinel-Tribune, IA
Lake County Journal, IL
Southwest Iowa Advertiser, IA
Tri-County Press, IL
Northwest Herald, IL
Daily Gazette, IL
McHenry County Magazine, IL
Kane County Magazine, IL
Valley Life, IL
SV Weekend, IL
The Review, IL
The Advertiser, IA
Jasper County Advertiser, IA
Sunrise Edition, IA
Batavia Chronicle, IL
Herald Life, IL
Putnam County Record, IL
Wheaton Suburban Life, IL
Lombard Suburban Life, IL
Lemont Suburban Life, IL
Woodridge Suburban Life, IL
The Herald-News, IL
The Prairie Advocate News, IL
Jasper County Tribune, IA
Illinois Valley Scene, IL
Kendall County Record, ID
Oswego Ledger, IL
Plano Record, IL
Sandwich Record, IL
Elburn Herald
Sugar Grove Herald
Note: Brand Promise: Relevant Information, Marketing Solutions, Community Advocates.

SHERMAN PUBLICATIONS, INC. — 666 S Lapeer Rd, Oxford, MI, 48371-5034, USA; tel (248) 628-4801; fax (248) 628-9750; e-mail shermanpub@aol.com; web site www.oxfordleader.com
CEO/Pub. — James A. Sherman
Newspapers: Penny Stretcher, MI
The Lake Orion Review, MI
Ad-vertiser, MI
Oxford Leader, MI
Citizen, MI
Clarkston News, MI

SMITH NEWSPAPERS — PO Box 680027, Fort Payne, AL, 35968-1600, USA; tel (256) 845-5512; fax (256) 845-5509
Newspapers: Advance-Monticellonian, AR
The Wayne Herald, NE

SNYDER COMMUNICATIONS — 18-20 Mechanic St, Norwich, NY, 13815-1437, USA;

tel (607) 334-4714; fax (607) 334-8273; e-mail info@pennysaveronline.com; web site www.pennysaveronline.com
Pub. — Richard Snyder
Newspapers: Hall Of Fame Pennysaver, NY
My Shopper, NY
Sidney Pennysaver, NY
The Evening Sun, NY
The New Berlin Gazette, NY
Wharton Valley Pennysaver, NY
Note: Snyder Communications owns the Evening Sun, a daily newspapers in Norwich, NY.

SOUND PUBLISHING, INC. — 19351 8th Ave NE, Ste 106, Poulsbo, WA, 98370-8710, USA; tel (360) 394-5800; fax (360) 394-5841; e-mail marketing@soundpublishing.com; web site www.soundpublishing.com; www.bainbridgereview.com
Est.: 1988
Vice Pres. — Lori Maxim
CFO — David Theobald
Pub. — Chris Allen-Hoch
President — Gloria Fletcher
Director, National and Regional Sales — Barrett Stephen
Kurt Ploudre
Newspapers: Snoqualmie Valley Record, WA
The Whidbey Examiner, WA
Kent Reporter, WA
Tukwila Reporter, WA
Bainbridge Island Review, WA
Bellevue Reporter, WA
The Courier-Herald, WA
Bothell/Kenmore Reporter, WA
Covington-Maple Valley-Black Diamond Reporter, WA
Kingston Community News, WA
Veterans' Life-OOB, WA
Mercer Island Reporter, WA
South Whidbey Record, WA
The Enumclaw Courier-Herald, WA
The Islands' Sounder, WA
Federal Way Mirror, WA
Forks Forum, WA
Central Kitsap Reporter, WA
Port Orchard Independent, WA
The Islands' Weekly, WA
The Arlington Times, WA
The Journal of the San Juan Islands, WA
Vashon-Maury Island Beachcomber, WA
The Sequim Gazette, WA
Bremerton Patriot-OOB, WA
Issaquah/Sammamish Reporter, WA
Kirkland Reporter, WA
The Marysville Globe, WA
Redmond Reporter, WA
Renton Reporter, WA
Whidbey News Times, WA
Bellingham Business Journal, WA
Okanogan Valley Gazette-Tribune, WA
North Kitsap Herald, WA
Note: Sound Publishing Inc. is Printing, Publishing and Distribution Company. Sound Publishing is a division of Canadian-based Black Press Ltd.

SOUTH COUNTY PUBLICATIONS — 110 N 5th St, Auburn, IL, 62615-1449, USA; tel (217) 438-6155; fax (217) 438-6156; e-mail southco@royell.org; web site southcountypublications.net
Group: South County Publications
Pub. — Joseph M. Michelich
Adv. Mgr. — Connie Michelich
Newspapers: Chatham Clarion, IL
Divernon News (OOB), IL
New Berlin Bee, IL
Pawnee Post, IL
Pleasant Plains Press, IL
Riverton Register, IL
Rochester Times, IL
Tri-City Register, IL
Auburn Citizen, IL
Sun-Times (serving Williamsville and Sherman), IL
South County Express, IL
The Jersey County Star (OOB), IL

SOUTHERN CALIFORNIA NEWS GROUP — 21860 Burbank Blvd, Ste 200, Woodland Hills, CA, 91367-7439, USA; tel (818) 713-3883; web site www.socalnewsgroup.com
Group: Digital First Media
Est.: 1878
Pres. & Pub. — Ron Hasse
SVP & Exec Ed — Frank Pine
Chief Revenue Officer — Tom Kelly
VP, Mktg — Bill VanLaningham
CFO — Dan Scofield
Sr. Dir HR — Rosemaria Altieri
VP Operations — Jon Merendino
Newspapers: Excelsior Los Angeles, CA
Daily Breeze, CA
La Prensa, CA
The Whittier Daily News, CA
Pasadena Star-News, CA
The Facts (Redlands), CA
San Gabriel Valley Tribune, CA
The Sun, CA
Press-Telegram, CA
Los Angeles Daily News, CA
Inland Valley Daily Bulletin, CA
Excelsior Orange County, CA
Note: Two reputable and trusted news sources, Los Angeles News Group and Freedom Communications have united to establish Southern California News Group (SCNG), the largest local news provider in the five-county Los Angeles metropolitan area. With 11 daily local newspapers and more than two dozen community weeklies, the SCNG is a leader in circulation among top news publications nationwide.

SOUTHERN COMMUNITY NEWSPAPERS, INC. — PO Box 603, Lawrenceville, GA, 30046-0603, USA; tel (770) 963-9205; fax (770) 277-5277; web site www.southerncommunitynewspapers.com/
Newspapers: Clayton News Daily, GA
Henry Daily Herald, GA
The Rockdale Citizen, GA
The Albany Herald, GA
Gwinnett Daily Post, GA

SOUTHERN LAKES NEWSPAPERS LLC — 700 Pine St, Burlington, WI, 53105-, USA; tel (262) 763-3330; fax (262) 763-2238; e-mail sln@StandardPress.com; web site Southern Lakes Newspapers
Est.: 1863
Pres./COO — John Cruger
Pub. — Peter Cruger
Adv. Dir. — Rory Farley
Annette Newcomb
Newspapers: Waterford Post, WI
The Delavan Enterprise, WI
Lake Geneva Times, WI
Paddock Lake Report, WI
Burlington Standard Press, WI
Westosha Report, WI
The Elkhorn Independent, WI
Palmyra Enterprise, WI
The Delavan Times (OOB), WI

SOUTHERN NEWSPAPERS INC. — 5701 Woodway Dr, Ste 131, Houston, TX, 77057-1589, USA; tel (713) 266-5481; e-mail lwalls@sninews.com; web site www.sninews.com
Est.: 1951
Treasurer — Ruby Barrow
CEO — Lissa Walls
Pres.
— Dolph Tillotson
Newspapers: Sand Mountain Shopper's Guide, AL
The Lawton Constitution, OK
The Bay City Tribune, TX
The Baytown Sun, TX
Del Rio News-Herald, TX
The Facts, TX
The Times-Journal, AL
The Galveston County Daily News, TX
Kerrville Daily Times, TX
The Lufkin Daily News, TX
New Braunfels Herald-Zeitung, TX
The Paris News, TX
Sand Mountain Reporter, AL
The Seguin Gazette, TX
The Daily Sentinel, AL
The Daily Sentinel, TX
The Independent, TN
News Telegram, TX

SOUTHERN RHODE ISLAND NEWSPAPERS — 187 Main St, Wakefield, RI, 02879-3504, USA; tel (401) 789-9744; fax (401) 789-1550; web site www.ricentral.com
Publisher — Nanci Batson
Newspapers: Kent County Daily Times, RI
Chariho Times, RI
Coventry Courier, RI
Narragansett Times, RI
East Greenwich Pendulum, RI
Standard-Times, RI
Note: Southern Rhode Island Newspapers is owned by RISN (Rhode Island Suburban Newspapers) Operations.

SOUTHWEST MESSENGER PRESS, INC. — 3840 147th St, Midlothian, IL, 60445-3452, USA; tel (708) 388-2425; fax (708) 385-7811; e-mail spressnews@aol.com
Pub. — Margaret Lysen
Newspapers: Beverly News, IL
Evergreen Park Courier, IL
Mount Greenwood Express - Alsip Edition, IL
Worth Citizen, IL
Bridgeview Independent, IL
Burbank-Stickney Independent, IL
Chicago Ridge Citizen, IL
Evergreen Park Courier, IL
Hickory Hills Citizen, IL
Midlothian-Bremen Messenger, IL
Mount Greenwood Express, IL
Oak Lawn Independent, IL
Orland Township Messenger, IL
Palos Citizen, IL
Burbank-Stickney Independent - Scottsdale Edition, IL
Worth Citizen, IL

STAR COMMUNITY NEWSPAPERS — 624 Krona Dr, Ste 170, Plano, TX, 75074-8304, USA; tel (972) 424-6565; fax (972) 398-4470; web site www.starlocalnews.com
Group: Times Media Group
Est.: 1901
Publisher — Roger Will
Newspapers: Colony-Courier Leader, TX
The Leader, Flower Mound, Highland Village, Lewisville, TX
Note: Owned by 1013 Communication, Star Community Newspapers are sister papers of Houston Community Newspapers.

STAR PUBLISHING CO. — 11 N Third St, Beresford, SD, 57004, USA; tel (605) 763-2006; fax (605) 763-5503; e-mail republic@bmtc.net
Pub. — Shane Hill
Newspapers: Centerville Journal, SD
Lake Andes Wave, SD
Beresford Republic, SD
Viborg Enterprise/Hurley Leader, SD

STAR-MERCURY PUBLISHING CO. — 3051 Roosevelt Hwy, Manchester, GA, 31816-6406, USA; tel (706) 846-3188; fax (706) 846-2206; e-mail starmercury@earthlink.net; web site www.starmercury.com
Est.: 1999
Owner/CEO — Millard Grimes
Newspapers: Hogansville Home News, GA
Manchester Star-Mercury, GA
Meriwether Vindicator, GA
The Harris County Journal, GA

STRAUS NEWS — 20 West Ave, Chester, NY, 10918-1032, USA; tel (845) 469-9000; fax (845) 469-9001; e-mail nyoffice@strausnews.com; web site www.strausnews.com
Pres & Pub — Jeanne Straus
Vincent Gardino
Newspapers: West Side Spirit, NY
Our Town Eastside, NY
Sparta Independent, NJ
The Advertiser-News (North), NY
Township Journal, NJ
Photo News, NY
Warwick Advertiser, NY
Dirt Magazine, NY
Chelsea News/Chelsea Clinton News
Our Town Downtown
The Advertiser-News (South)
Chronicle
West Milford Messenger
Pike County Courier

STUMPF PUBLISHING CO., INC. — 409 W Broadway, Plainview, MN, 55964-1257, USA; tel (507) 534-3121; fax (507) 534-3920; e-mail plainnew@mywdo.com
Owner — Daniel Stumpf
Newspapers: Lewiston Journal, MN
Plainview News, MN
Rochester Buyers' Guide, MN
St. Charles Press, MN
Wabasha County Herald, MN

SUN COMMUNITY NEWS, PUBLISHED BY:DENTON PUBLICATIONS, INC. — 14 Hand Ave, Elizabethtown, NY, 12932, USA; tel (518) 873-6368; fax (518) 873-6360; e-mail denpubs@denpubs.com; web site www.suncommunitynews.com
Group: Denton Publications, Inc.
Est.: 1948
Pub/Pres — Daniel E. Alexander
Gen Mgr — Daniel Alexander
Plant Operations Mgr — William Coats
Deputy Mng Ed — Pete DeMola
Post Press Produ Mgr — Jeff Davey
Southern Adirondacks Publishing Group Mgr — Scarlette Merfeld
Northern Adirondacks Publishing Group Mgr — Ashley Alexander
Financial controller — Gayle Alexander
Newspapers: The News Enterprise Sun, NY
The Eagle, VT
The North Countryman Sun, NY
The Times of Ti Sun, NY
The Adirondack Journal Sun, NY
The Valley News Sun, NY
The Burgh Sun, NY

SUN MEDIA GROUP — 104 Park St, Lewiston, ME, 04240-7202, USA; tel (207) 784-5411; fax (207) 777-3436; web site www.sunjournal.com
Pres. — James R. Costello
Vice Pres./Bus. Mgr. — Jim Thorton
Vice Pres., HR — Maureen Wedge
Vice Pres., Adv./Mktg. — Steve Costello
Dir., Finance — Karen Nyberg
Newspapers: Advertiser Democrat, ME
The Forecaster, ME
Franklin Journal, ME
Livermore Falls Advertiser, ME
Penobscot Times, ME
Sun Journal, ME
The Bethel Citizen, ME

SUN NEWSPAPERS — 5510 Cloverleaf Pkwy, Cleveland, OH, 44125-4815, USA; tel (216) 986-2600; fax (216) 986-2401; e-mail sun@sunnews.com; web site www.sunnews.com
Pres./CEO — Keith Mathis
Classified Mgr. — Donna Krause
Circ. Mgr. — Cathy McBride
Exec. Ed. — Linda Kinsey
Mgr. Online News — Bob Palmer
Newspapers: Bloomington Sun-Current, MN
Brooklyn Center/Brooklyn Park Sun-Post, MN
Minnetonka/Deephaven/Hopkins Sun Sailor, MN

SUN PUBLICATIONS OF FLA. — 7060 Havertys Way, Lakeland, FL, 33805-1413, USA; tel (863) 583-1202; fax (863) 583-1212; e-mail rmiller@sunpubfla.com; web site www.sunpubfla.com
Commercial Print Manager — Robin Miller
Newspapers: Clermont News Leader, FL
The News Leader, FL
Pasco Shopper, FL
Sumter Shopper, FL
Triangle News Leader, FL
Osceola News-Gazette, FL

SUN-SENTINEL CO. — 200 E Las Olas Blvd, Fort Lauderdale, FL, 33301-2299, USA; tel (954) 356-4000; fax (954) 356-4555; web site www.sun-sentinel.com
Est.: 1910
Pres. — Robert Gremillion
Sr. Vice Pres. — Earl Maucker
Commun. Mgr. — Kevin Courtney
Janis Rogers
Manager of Preprints
— Bill Ritchie
Pub. & Editor in Chief — Howard Saltz
Newspapers: Shalom - Palm Beach, FL
Deerfield and Pompano Forum, FL
Hi-Riser - Broward, FL
Coral Springs Focus (OOB), FL
Oakland Park Gazette (OOB), FL
South Woodham Focus (OOB), FL
Weston Gazette, FL
Shalom - Broward, FL
Lake Worth Forum, FL
West Boca Forum, FL
Boca Raton Forum, FL
Plantation/Davie Forum, FL
The Forum - Sunrise & Tamarac, FL
Note: Sun-Sentinel Co. is owned by the Tribune Co.

SUN-TIMES MEDIA GROUP INC. — 30 N Racine Ave, Chicago, IL, 60607-2183, USA; tel (312) 321-3000; fax (312) 321-6426; e-mail metro@suntimes.com; web site www.suntimes.com
CEO
— Edwin Eisendrath
Editor-in-Chief — Chris Fusco
SVP, Digital News Products — Carol Fowler
Chief Digital Strategist — Matthew Watson
SVP, Advertising — Alison Laffe
Chief Operating Officer — Nykia Wright
Newspapers: Chicago Sun-Times, IL
The Straight Dope (website only), IL

SUPERIOR PUBLISHING COMPANY — PO Box 408, 148 East Third Street, Superior, NE, 68978-0408, USA; tel (402) 879-3291; fax (402) 879-3463; e-mail tse@superiorne.com; web site www.superiorne.com
Est.: 1900
Pub — BILL Blauvelt
Newspapers: The Superior Express, NE
Jewell County Record, KS
Nuckolls County Locomotive-Gazette, NE
Note: Superior Publishing Company owns 3 weekly newspapers and one newsletter.

SWIFT COMMUNICATIONS, INC. — 580 Mallory Way, Carson City, NV, 89701-5360, USA; tel (775) 850-7676; fax (775) 850-7677; e-mail info@swiftcom.com; web site www.swiftcom.com
Chrmn., Bd. — Richard K. Larson
Pres./CEO — Arne L. Hoel
President & COO — Robert L. Brown
Cor. Controller — Bill J. Waters
Cor. Dir. — Debbie Spieker-Martin
AUDIENCE DEVELOPMENT DIRECTOR — Trisha Woodside
James Morgan
Valerie Richardson
Newspapers: Craig Daily Press, CO
Steamboat Pilot, CO
Steamboat Today, CO
Sierra Sun, CA
Tahoe Daily Tribune, CA
The Union, CA
Nevada Appeal, NV
North Lake Tahoe Bonanza, NV
The Record-Courier, NV
The News-Review, OR
The Eagle Valley Enterprise, CO
Glenwood Springs Post Independent, CO
Grand Junction Free Press, CO
Greeley Daily Tribune, CO
Sky-Hi News, CO
Snowmass Sun, CO
Summit Daily News, CO
The Aspen Times, CO
Citizen Telegram, CO
Vail Daily, CO
Windsor Now, CO
Valley Journal, CO
Lahontan Valley News & Fallon Eagle Standard, NV
Note: Swift Newspapers Inc. also publishes two farm and ranch magazines as well as Northern Nevada Business Weekly.

TALLAPOOSA PUBLISHERS, INC. — 548 Cherokee Rd, Tallapoosa County, Alexander City, AL, 35010-2503, USA; tel (256) 234-4281; fax (256) 234-6550; web site www.boonenewspapers.com
Group: Tallapoosa Publishers Inc.
Bus. Mgr. — Angela Mullins
Editor — Mitch Sneed
Pres./Pub. — Steve Baker
Advertising Director — Tippy Hunter
Newspapers: Tallassee Tribune, AL

TAMPA BAY NEWSPAPERS, INC. — 9911 Seminole Blvd, Seminole, FL, 33772-2536, USA; tel (727) 397-5563; fax (727) 399-5900; e-mail dautrey@tbnweekly.com; web site www.tbnweekly.com / www.suncoastnews.com
Group: Times Publishing Company
Est.: 1975
Pres./Pub. — Dan L. Autrey
Adv. Dir. — Jay Rey
Executive Editor — Tom Germond
Newspapers: Belleair Bee, FL
Clearwater Beacon, FL
Largo Leader, FL
Pinellas Park Beacon, FL
Seminole Beacon, FL
Dunedin Beacon, FL
Palm Harbor Beacon, FL
Suncoast News - Pasco South, FL
Suncoast News - Pasco Central, FL
Suncoast News - Pinellas North
Suncoast News - Pinellas North, FL
Beach Beacon, FL
Spring Hill Beacon
Note: Tampa Bay Newspapers, Inc. (TBNI) publishes nine weekly and four monthly community newspapers in Pinellas, Pasco and Hernando Counties. TBNI is owned by Times Publishing Company, which also produces the Tampa Bay Times and tbt*.

THE ANSCHUTZ CO. — 555 17th St, Ste 2400, Denver, CO, 80202-3941, USA; tel (303) 298-1000; fax (303) 298-8881
Chrmn./CEO — Philip F. Anschutz
Pres./CEO — Cannon Y. Harvey
CEO, Clarity Media Grp. — Ryan McKibben
CFO — Wayne A. Barnes
Exec. Vice Pres./CFO, Clarity Media Grp. — Frederick Anderson
Newspapers: The Washington Examiner (OOB, now a magazine), VA

THE DOLAN COMPANY — 222 S 9th St, Ste 2300, Minneapolis, MN, 55402-3363, USA; tel (612) 317-9420; web site www.thedolancompany.com
Newspapers: Daily Journal of Commerce, OR
The Daily Record, MD
North Carolina Lawyers Weekly, NC
The Mecklenburg Times, NC
Daily Journal of Commerce, OR

THE EDWARD A. SHERMAN PUBLISHING CO. — 101 Malbone Rd, Newport, RI, 02840-1340, USA; tel (401) 849-3300; fax (401) 849-3306; e-mail circDept@newportRI.com; web site www.newportdailynews.com
Est.: 1846
Mng Ed — Jonathan Zins
Newspapers: The Independent, RI
Newport Mercury, RI

THE GAZETTE - GAZETTEXTRA.COM — 1 S Parker Dr, Janesville, WI, 53545-3928, USA; tel (608) 754-3311; fax (608) 754-8038; e-mail sbliss@gazettextra.com; web site www.gazettextra.com
Group: Bliss Communications, Inc
Est.: 1845
Pres./Chrmn./CEO — Sidney H. Bliss
VP Strategic Operations. — Mary Jo Villa
VP Financial Operations — Pam Schmoldt
Director of Technical Services & Facilities — Chad Lette
Ed. — Sid Schwartz
Vice President Printing Operations — Tony Smithson
Director of Advertising Operations — Tom Bradley
Director of Circulation — Rudy Frank
Director of Digital Advertising — Laura Feit
Vice President & General Manager-EagleHerald — Kathy Springberg
Newspapers: EagleHerald - ehextra.com, WI
Walworth County Shopper Advertiser, WI
Stateline News, WI
Messenger, WI

THE MCCLATCHY COMPANY — 2100 Q St, Sacramento, CA, 95816-6816, USA; tel (916) 321-1855; fax (916) 321-1869; web site www.mcclatchy.com
Est.: 1857
VP/Sec./Gen. Counsel — Karole Morgan-Prager
VP, Interactive Media — Chris Hendricks
VP, News and Washington Ed. — Anders Gyllenhaal
Controller — Hai Nguyen
Nat. Digital Sales Mgr. — Monica Woodworth
National Sales Mgr. — Julie Lambert
VP of Adv. — Kim Nussbaum
Pres./CEO — Craig Forman
Newspapers: The Fresno Bee, CA
The Herald-Sun, NC
Merced Sun-Star, CA
The Modesto Bee, CA
The Sacramento Bee, CA
The Tribune, CA
Bradenton Herald, FL
Miami Herald, FL
El Nuevo Herald, FL
Columbus Ledger-Enquirer, GA
The Telegraph, GA
Idaho Statesman, ID
The Wichita Eagle, KS
The Sun Herald, MS
The Kansas City Star, MO
The Charlotte Observer, NC
The News & Observer, NC
Centre Daily Times, PA
The Beaufort Gazette, SC
The Herald, SC
The Island Packet, SC
The State, SC
The Sun News, SC
Fort Worth Star-Telegram, TX
The Bellingham Herald, WA
The Olympian, WA
The News Tribune, WA
Mansfield News-Mirror, TX
The Peninsula Gateway, WA
Lee's Summit Journal, MO
Livingston Chronicle, CA
Bee Niche Products, CA
Keesler News, MS
Vida en el Valle, CA
Herald Values, FL
Almaden Resident, CA
Atwater Signal, CA
Berkeley Voice (duplicate), CA
Campbell Reporter, CA
Cass County Democrat-Missourian, MO
El Cerrito Albany Journal, CA
Florida Keys Keynoter, FL
Fort Mill Times, SC
Lamorinda Sun, CA
Los Banos Enterprise, CA
O'Fallon Progress, IL
Pinckneyville Democrat, IL
Rose Garden Resident, CA
Salinas Valley Weekly, CA
Saratoga News, CA
Sierra Star, CA
Sparta News-Plaindealer, IL
Sun-Bulletin, CA
The Cambrian, CA
The Cary News, NC
The Chowchilla News, CA
The Clovis Independent, CA
The Cupertino Courier, CA
The Keller Citizen, TX
The Olathe News, MO
The Puyallup Herald, WA
The Reporter, FL
The Sunnyvale Sun, CA
Valley Times (OOB), CA
The Enquirer-Herald, SC
The Telegraph, GA
Note: The McClatchy Company is a leading news and information provider, offering a wide array of print and digital products in each of the markets it serves. As the third largest newspaper company in the United States, McClatchy's operations include 30 daily newspapers, community newspapers, websites, mobile news and advertising, niche publications, direct marketing and direct mail services. McClatchy's largest newspapers include The Miami Herald, The Sacramento Bee, the Fort Worth Star-Telegram, The Kansas City Star, The Charlotte Observer and The News & Observer in Raleigh, N.C. McClatchy is listed on the New York Stock Exchange under the symbol MNI.

THE NEWS-GAZETTE — 15 E Main St, Champaign, IL, 61820-3625, USA; tel (217) 351-5252; fax (217) 351-5291; e-mail advertising@news-gazette.com; web site www.news-gazette.com
Est.: 1852
Pres. — John Foreman
Columnist — Tom Kacich
Librarian — Carolyn Vance
Photo Ed. — Darrell Hoemann
Ed. — Jim Rossow
Circ. Dir. — Pete Jones
CEO/Pub. — John Reed
VP/Dir. HR — Tracy Nally
VP/Gen. Mgr. Radio — Mike Haile
Adv. Dir. — Tom Zalabak
Adv. Sales Mgr. & National Sales — Jackie Martin
Customer Care Center Manager — Denny Santarelli
Opinions Page Ed. — Jim Dey
Features Ed. — Tony Mancuso
Dir. of Market Dev. — Amy George
Adv. Services Mgr. — Alice Vaughan
Online Ed. — Niko Dugan
Newspapers: Independent News, IL
The Leader, IL
Leroy Farmer City Press, IL
Mahomet Citizen, IL
Ford County Record, IL
Piatt County Journal-Republican, IL
Rantoul Press, IL
The Regional, IL

THE PENNYSAVER GROUP — 510 Fifth Ave, Pelham, NY, 10803-1206, USA; web site www.nysaver.comLarry Ross Weinberger

THE RECORD-JOURNAL PUBLISHING CO. — 500 S Broad St, 2nd Floor, Meriden, CT, 06450-6643, USA; tel (203) 235-1661; fax (203) 235-6345; e-mail newsroom@record-journal.com; web site www.myrecordjournal.com
Est.: 1867
Pres./Pub. — Eliot C. White
Executive VP and Assistant Publisher — Liz White
Sr. Vice President & Editor — Ralph Tomaselli
Senior VP and CRO — Shawn Palmer
Newspapers: Record-Journal, CT
Berlin Citizen, CT
The Plainville Citizen, CT
The Southington Citizen, CT
Town Times, CT
The North Haven Citizen
The Cheshire Citizen
The Westerly Sun, RI
The Mystic River Press, CT
Note: The Record-Journal Publishing Co. also owns The Westerly Sun and eight weekly newspapers.

THE SEATTLE TIMES — 1000 Denny Way, Ste 501, Seattle, WA, 98109-5323, USA; tel (206) 464-2988; fax (206) 464-2239; e-mail

advertising@seattletimes.com; web site www.seattletimes.com
Group: The Seattle Times
Est.: 1896
Mng Ed — Michele Matassa Flores
Sr. VP, Finance — Buster Brown
Managing Ed. — Jim Simon
Managing Ed. — Michele Matassa Flores
Assistant Managing Ed., Visuals — Leon Espinoza
Deputy Mng. Ed. — Lynn Jacobson
Exec. Ed. — Don Shelton
Newspapers: Newcastle News, WA
The Seattle Times, WA
Sammamish Review, WA
Walla Walla Union-Bulletin, WA
The Issaquah Press, WA
Yakima Herald-Republic, WA
SnoValley Star, WA

THE SHEBOYGAN SUN — 708 Erie Ave, # A, Sheboygan, WI, 53081-4060, USA; tel (920) 803-9945; fax (920) 803-9946; e-mail thesun@sheboygansun.com; web site www.sheboygansun.com
Group: Walton Publishing, LLC
Est.: 1999
Publisher — Greg Dillon
Mike Walton
Note: 100% direct mail distribution.

THE WESTFIELD NEWS GROUP LLC — 62 School St, Westfield, MA, 01085-2835, USA; tel (413) 562-4181; web site www.thewestfieldnews.com
Newspapers: Pennysaver, MA
The Westfield News , MA

THUNDER PRAIRIE PUBLISHING — 161 Main St, Deport, TX, 75435, USA; tel (903) 652-4205; fax (903) 652-6041; e-mail tppub@1starnet.com
Est.: 1908
Owner/Pub. — Nanalee Nichols
Newspapers: Deport Times-Blossom Times, TX
Detroit Weekly, TX
Bogata News-Talco Times, TX
Note: no web page at this time

TIMES COMMUNITY NEWS (TCN) — 202 W 1st St, Los Angeles, CA, 90012-4299, USA; tel (818) 637-3200; fax (818) 241-1975; e-mail gnp@latimes.com; web site www.glendalenewspress.com
Editor — Dan Evans
CFO — Gordon Tomaske
Gen. Mgr. — Tom Johnson
Bus. Mgr. — Debbie Feyerabend
Opns. Mgr. — Neil McAnally
Exec. Ed. — John Canalis
Newspapers: Burbank Leader, CA
Park Labrea News & Beverly Press, CA
La Canada Valley Sun, CA
Huntington Beach Independent (OOB), CA
Note: Times Community News (TCN) is owned by the Los Angeles Times.

TIMES MEDIA GROUP — PO Box 10528, Reno, NV, 89510-0528, USA; tel (775) 333-0004; e-mail info@freedom.com; web site www.freedom.com
Est.: 1955
Pres. — Randy Miller
Owner, President — Eric Spitz
Owner, Publisher — Aaron Kushner
Dir., Strategy and Development — Emily Martin
Newspapers: Capistrano Valley News, CA
Deer Park Broadcaster, TX
Orange County Catholic, CA
Fountain Valley View, CA
Huntington Beach Wave, CA
West University Examiner, TX
Colony-Courier Leader, TX
Irvine World News, CA
San Clemente Sun Post, CA
Spring Observer, TX
Aliso Viejo News, CA
The Woodlands Villager, TX
Anaheim Bulletin, CA
East Valley Tribune, AZ
Dana Point News, CA
Eastex Advocate, TX
Fullerton News-Tribune, CA
Brea-La Habra Star-Progress, CA
Star Community Newspapers, TX
Laguna News-Post, CA
Ahwatukee Foothills News, AZ
Laguna Niguel News, CA
Laguna Woods Globe, CA
Orange City News, CA
Placentia News Times, CA
Saddleback Valley News, CA
Sun-Post News, CA
The Tustin News, CA
Yorba Linda Star, CA
Santa Ana Register (OOB), CA
Rancho Canyon News (OOB), CA
Plano Star-Courier, TX
Saddleback Valley News
Humble Observer, TX
Atascocita Observer, TX
Kingwood Observer, TX
Los Angeles Register (OOB)
East Montgomery County Observer, TX
Garden Grove Journal
Lake Houston Observer, TX
Long Beach Register
Cleveland Advocate, TX
The Current (Newport Beach & Costa Mesa)
Dayton News, TX
The Long Beach Register (OOB), CA
Tomball Potpourri, TX
Magnolia Potpourri, TX
Cypress Creek Mirror, TX
Ladera Post (OOB), CA
Pasadena Citizen, TX
Mojave Desert News, CA
Bay Area Citizen, TX
Saddleback Valley News - Mission Viejo, CA
Hesperia Star, CA
Pearland Journal, TX
Friendswood Journal, TX
Rancho Santa Margarita News (OOB), CA
River Oaks Examiner, TX
Bellaire Examiner, TX
Colusa County Sun-Herald, CA
Memorial Examiner, TX
Corning Observer, CA
The Rancher, TX
Sugar Land Sun, TX
Willows Journal (OOB), CA
Scuppernong Reminder, NC
The Hickory News, NC
The Mid-Valley Town Crier, TX
The Shopper, NC
Note: Freedom Communications is headquartered in Santa Ana, Calif.

TIMES NEWS GROUP — 306 Court St, Pekin, IL, 61554-3104, USA; tel (309) 692-6600; fax (309) 686-3122; e-mail lsmithbrown@timestoday.com; web site mortontimesnews.com
Group: GateHouse Media, Inc.
Est.: 1840
Gen. Sales Mgr. — Linda Smith Brown
Pub. — Ken Mauser
Exec. Ed. — Jeanette Kendall
Office Mgr. — Donna Reaska

TIMES-SHAMROCK COMMUNICATIONS — 149 Penn Ave, Scranton, PA, 18503-2055, USA; tel (570) 348-9100; fax (570) 348-9149; web site www.thetimes-tribune.com
Est.: 1895
Pub. — William R. Lynett
COO — Don Farley
CEO — George Lynett Jr
CEO — Bobby Lynett
CEO — Matthew Haggerty
Pub. — Edward Lynett
Pub. — George Lynett
Newspapers: The Times-Tribune, PA
The Citizens' Voice, PA
The Republican-Herald, PA
Wyoming County Press Examiner, PA
The Valley Advantage, PA
The Pocono Shopper, PA
Hazleton Standard-Speaker, PA

TIOGA PUBLISHING COMPANY — 25 East Ave, Wellsboro, PA, 16901-1618, USA; tel 570-724-2287; web site www.tiogapublishing.com
Newspapers: The Wellsboro Gazette, PA
Free Press-Courier, PA

TN MEDIA — 1100 Broadway, Nashville, TN, 37203-3116, USA; tel (615) 259-8000; fax (615) 259-8875; e-mail rateinfo@tennessean.com; web site www.tennessean.com
Group: Gannett
Est.: 1812
VP, Finance — Bob Engel
Gen. Mgr. GPS Production Nashville — Thom Gregory
Pres./Pub. — Laura Hollingsworth
Vice Pres., Circ. — Jay Winkler
Key Accounts Mgr. — Kimberly Hood
Consumer Exper. Dir. — Lance Williams
Director of News & Editor — Maria De Varenne
VP, Sales — John Ward
Sr. HR Business Partner — Helen Jacobs
Music Writer — Peter Cooper
Frank Sutherland
Manager, National/Major Accounts — Sean Lupton
Consumer Experience Director — David Anesta
Content Strategist — Duane Gang
Daphne Lowell
Music Reporter — Juli Thanki
Peter Antone
Photographer — Shelley Mays
Director of Sales — Shelley Davis
Newspapers: Ashland City Times, TN
Cheatham County Money Saver, TN
The Dickson Herald, TN
Dickson Shopper, TN
Fairview Observer, TN
The Hendersonville Star News, TN
Gallatin News Examiner, TN
Robertson County Times, TN
Stewart-Houston Times, TN
Nashville Record, TN
The Sumner County Shopper, TN
Note: The Tennessean is owned by Gannett Co., Inc. which owns more than 90 daily newspapers.

TRIB PUBLICATIONS — PO Box 127, Centreville, AL, 35042-0127, USA; tel (205) 926-9769; fax (205) 926-9760
Pres. — Robert E. Tribble
Newspapers: Polk County News Journal OOB, NC
Talbotton New Era, GA
Yancey Common Times Journal, NC
The Sandersville Progress, GA
The Centreville Press, AL
The Pelham Journal, GA
Camilla Enterprise, GA
Marion Times-Standard, AL
The Westminster News, SC
The Wrightsville Headlight, GA

TRIB TOTAL MEDIA, INC. — 503 Martindale St, DI Clark Building, Suite 250, Pittsburgh, PA, 15212-5746, USA; tel (412) 321-6460; web site www.tribtotalmedia.com/
Est.: 1889
Pub. — Richard M. Scaife
Pres./CEO — Ralph Martin
Exec. Dir. Sales — William M. Cotter
Pres/CEO — Jennifer Bertetto
CFO — Jennifer Walters
Gary Mazzotta
Janet Corrinne-Harvey
Lindsay Berdell
Exec. Dir. Prodn. — Keith Bertetto
Prodn. Dir. — Shawn Callahan
Board Chairman — H. Yale Gutnick
Newspapers: Pittsburgh Tribune-Review, PA
Tribune-Review, PA
Valley News Dispatch, PA
Buttermilk Falls, PA
The Times Express, PA
Murrysville Star, PA
Norwin Star, PA
Penn-Trafford Star, PA
Pine Creek Journal, PA
Plum Advance Leader, PA
Sewickley Herald, PA
South Hills Record, PA
The Dispatch, PA
The Herald, PA
The Jeannette Spirit, PA
The Times-Sun, PA
The Independent-Observer, PA
The Ligonier Echo, PA
The Mount Pleasant Journal, PA
The Signal Item, PA
McKnight Journal, PA
North Journal, PA
Cranberry Journal, PA
Bridgeville Area News, PA
Shaler Journal, PA
Hampton Journal, PA
Penn Hills Progress, PA

TRIBCO LLC — 150-50 14 Rd, Whitestone, NY, 11357, USA; tel (718) 357-7400; fax (718) 357-0079; e-mail news@queenstribune.com; web site www.queenstribune.com
Est.: 1970
Pres./Pub. — Michael Schenkler
Assoc. Pub. — Peter Sloggatt
Newspapers: The Record, NY
The Northport Journal, NY
The Press of Southeast Queens, NY
Queens Tribune, NY
The Long-Islander News, NY

TRIBUNE-REVIEW PUBLISHING CO. — 622 Cabin Hill Dr, Greensburg, PA, 15601-1657, USA; tel (724) 838-5124; fax (724) 834-1151; e-mail info@tribweb.com; web site www.tribLIVE.com
Chrmn./Pres. — Ralph Martin
Sr. Vice. Pres./CFO — Raymond Hartung
COO — Nickolas F. Monico
COO — Trish Hooper
Newspapers: Penn State New Kensington:Communications Dept, PA
The Daily News (OOB), PA
The Valley Independent (OOB), PA
Valley News Dispatch, PA

TRONC, INC. — 435 N Michigan Ave, Chicago, IL, 60611-4066, USA; tel (312) 222-9100; fax (208) 746-7341; web site www.tribpub.com
Est.: 1892
CEO & Dir. — Justin Dearborn
Newspapers: Baltimore Messenger-OOB, MD
News-Press, CA
St. Louis/Southern Illinois Labor Tribune, MO
Milton Record-Transcript, MA
Hoy Los Angeles, CA
Hoy Fin de Semana, CA
Dorchester Argus-Citizen, MA
Arbutus Times, MD
Jamaica Plain Citizen, MA
Hyde Park Tribune, MA
South Boston Tribune, MA
Crown Point Star, IL
Los Angeles Times, CA
Chicago Tribune, IL
The Baltimore Sun, MD
Orlando Sentinel, FL
The Morning Call, PA
Daily Press, VA
Hoy LLC, CA
Howard County Times, MD
Jeffersonian, MD
Northeast Booster Reporter-OOB, MD
The Aegis, MD
The Weekender, MD

TURLEY PUBLICATIONS, INC. — 24 Water St, Palmer, MA, 01069-1885, USA; tel (413) 283-8393; fax (413) 289-1977; web site www.turley.com
Est.: 1962
Pres. — Patrick H. Turley
Mng Ed — Michael Ballaway
Newspapers: Agawam Advertiser News, MA
Barre Gazette, MA
Country Journal, MA
Shopping Guide, MA
Southwick Suffield News, MA

The Chicopee Register, MA
The Holyoke Sun, MA
The Journal Register, MA
The Register, MA
The Sentinel, MA
Town Reminder, MA
Ware River News, MA
Wilbraham-Hampden Times, MA
Quaboag Current, MA
Town Common, MA
New England Antiques Journal, MA

ULSTER PUBLISHING — 322 Wall St, Kingston, NY, 12401-3820, USA; tel (845) 334-8200; fax (845) 334-8202; web site www.ulsterpublishing.com
Pub. — Geddy Sveikauskas
Newspapers: Kingston Times, NY
New Paltz Times, NY
Saugerties Times, NY
Woodstock Times, NY
Almanac Weekly, NY

VAN ZANDT NEWSPAPERS LLC — 103 E Tyler St, Canton, TX, 75103-1413, USA; tel (903) 873-2525; fax (903) 873-4321; e-mail vznews@aol.com; web site www.vanzandtnews.com
Group: Van Zandt Newspapers, LLC
Pub. — Brad Blakemore
Donnita Fisher
Newspapers: Canton Herald, TX
Wills Point Chronicle, TX
Van Banner, TX
Van Zandt News, TX
Quinlan-Tawakoni News, TX
Mabank Monitor, TX
The News (Athens / Malakoff), TX
Kerens Tribune, TX
Lake Area Leader, TX
Shoppers Edge, TX
DollarSaver Shopper, TX
Van Zandt News, TX
Lake Area Leader, TX
Note: John Buzzetta owns Van Zandt Newspapers LLC which consists of the following weekly newspapers and shoppers: Canton Herald, Van Banner, Wills Point Chronicle, Quinlan-Tawakoni News, Van Zandt News, Canton Guide, Mabank Monitor, The News (Athens & Malakoff,) Kerens Tribune, Lake Area Leader, Shoppers Edge and DollarSaver

VILLAGE NETMEDIA, INC. — 301 Park St, Rockland, ME, 04841-2124, USA; tel (207) 594-4401; fax (207) 594-6981; web site http://knox.villagesoup.com
CEO — Richard Anderson
COO — Ron Belyea
Newspapers: Bar Harbor Times, ME
The Republican Journal, ME
The Waldo Independent, ME
Capital Weekly, ME

VIRGINIA NEW GROUP — 602 Village Market Blvd Ste 360, Leesburg, VA, 20175, USA; tel (703) 777-1111; fax (703) 771-0036; web site www.com
Chairman/CEO — Peter W. Arundel
Vice Pres., Sales/Mktg. — Angus Twombly
Mgr., Free Publications — Ron Sauer
Bus. Mng. — Agnes Osborne
Ray Finefrock

HD MEDIA COMPANY LLC — 946 5th Ave, Huntington, WV, 25701-2004, USA; tel (304) 526-2798; fax (304) 526-2857; e-mail ruth@waynecountynews.com; web site http://www.herald-dispatch.com
Est.: 1874
Consultant — Tom George
Mng. Ed. — Rob Robinson
Adv. Dir. — Ruth Adkins
Newspapers: The Independent Herald, WV
Williamson Daily News, WV
The Charleston Gazette-Mail, WV
Coal Valley News, WV
The Logan Banner, WV
The Herald-Dispatch, WV
Putnam Herald, WV

WESTERN NEWS&INFO, INC. — 1748 S Arizona Ave, Yuma, AZ, 85364-5727, USA; tel (928) 783-3311; fax (928) 783-3313; e-mail urnumber1@westernnews.com; web site www.westernnews.com
Est.: 1958
Pres./CEO — Joseph E. Soldwedel
Sr. Vice Pres. — Blake DeWitt
Vice Pres./CFO — David Montgomery
Vice Pres./Dir., HR — D.J. Johnson
Vice Pres./CEO, Prescott Newspapers Inc. — Kit Atwell
Newspapers: Desert Shopper, CA
Kudos, AZ
Navajo-Hopi Observer, AZ
Palo Verde Valley Times, CA
Quartzsite Times, CA
Smart Shopper, AZ
Camp Verde Bugle, AZ
The Daily Courier, AZ
The Verde Independent, AZ
Prescott Valley Tribune, AZ
Chino Valley Review, AZ
Big Bug News (OOB), AZ
Kingman Daily Miner, AZ
Williams-Grand Canyon News, AZ
The Parker Pioneer, AZ
Today's News-Herald, AZ
Smart Buyer, AZ
Smart Shopper Ash Fork, AZ
Smart Shopper, AZ
River Extra, AZ
Note: Western Newspapers Inc. shares 50% ownership of the Lake Havasu City (AZ) Today's News Herald (mS), and the weekly Parker (AZ) Parker Pioneer (w) with Wick Communicatons.

WICK COMMUNICATIONS — 333 W Wilcox Dr, Ste 302, Sierra Vista, AZ, 85635-1791, USA; tel (520) 458-0200; fax (520) 458-6166; web site www.wickcommunications.com
Est.: 1984
Sec./Treasurer — Robert J. Wick
Pres. / CEO — Francis Wick
Dig. Media Mgr. — Alessia Alaimo
CFO — Ron Parra
COO — Nickolas Monico
Newspapers: The Wenatchee World, WA
Today's News-Herald, AZ
Frontiersman, AK
Anchorage Press, AK
Arizona Range News, AZ
The Copper Era, AZ
The Daily Territorial, AZ
The Douglas Dispatch, AZ
Eastern Arizona Courier, AZ
Green Valley News & Sahuarita Sn, AZ
Nogales International, AZ
The Parker Pioneer, AZ
San Pedro Valley News-Sun, AZ
Sahuarita Sun, AZ
Wick Communications - Herald/Review, AZ
Sierra Vista Herald - Sunday Bravo Shopper, AZ
Half Moon Bay Review, CA
The Montrose Daily Press, CO
Independent-Enterprise, ID
The Daily Iberian, LA
Sidney Herald, MT
News-Monitor, ND
The Daily News, ND
Williston Daily Herald, ND
Argus Observer, OR
Treasure Valley Reminder, OR
Capital Journal, SD
Reminder Plus, SD
Note: Wick Communications shares 50% ownership of the Lake Havasu City (AZ) Today's News-Herald (mS), and the weekly Parker (AZ) Pioneer with Western Newspapers Inc.

WOMACK PUBLISHING CO. — 30 N Main St, Lynchburg, VA, 24513-0001, USA; tel (434) 432-1654; fax (434) 432-1005; web site www.womackpublishing.com
Chrmn. — Charles Zan Womack
Pres./COO — Diane C. White
HR Mgr. — Ron Cox
Accounting Mgr. — Jim Glidewell
Circ. Mgr. — Shirley Adkins
Editorial Dir. — Tim Davis
Press Opns. Mgr. — Randy Velvin
Newspapers: Altavista Journal, VA
Brunswick Times-Gazette, VA
Caswell Messenger, NC
Independent Messenger, VA
Lake Gaston Gazette-Observer, NC
The Mebane Enterprise, NC
Montgomery Herald, NC
The News of Orange County, NC
The News Progress, VA
Smith Mountain Eagle, VA
South Hill Enterprise, VA
Star-Tribune, VA
Times-Virginian, VA
The Union Star, VA
Warren Record, NC

WOODWARD COMMUNICATIONS, INC. — 801 Bluff St, Dubuque, IA, 52001-4661, USA; tel (563) 588-5685; e-mail tom.woodward@wcinet.com; web site www.wcinet.com
CEO/Pres. — Tom Woodward
Newspapers: Cascade Pioneer, IA
Dyersville Commercial, IA
Oregon Observer, WI
Grant, Iowa, Lafayette Shopping News, WI
Telegraph Herald, IA
The Verona Press, WI
Eastern Iowa Shopping News, IA
Great Dane Shopping News, WI
Richland Center Shopping News, WI
Wisconsin-Iowa Shopping News, WI
Stoughton Courier Hub, WI
Unified Newspaper Group, WI
Manchester Press, IA
Fitchburg Star, WI
Mount Vernon-Lisbon Sun, IA
Solon Economist, IA
West Liberty Index, IA
West Branch Times, IA
North Liberty Leader, IA
Marion Times, IA
Linn News-Letter, IA
Note: WCI is a diversified, employee-owned company, composed of community media, agency and targeted business trade services. The corporation has seven operating divisions: TH Media, Woodward Community Media, Woodward Radio Group, Woodward Printing Services, Two Rivers Marketing, ON Communication, and WoodwardBizMedia.

WORRALL COMMUNITY NEWSPAPERS, INC. — 1291 Stuyvesant Ave, Union, NJ, 07083-3854, USA; tel (908) 686-7700; fax (908) 686-4169; web site www.localsource.com
Est.: 1968
Pres./Pub. — David Worrall
Vice Pres. — Peter W. Worrall
Vice Pres., Bookkeeping/Circ./Accts. Payable — Nancy Worrall
Vice Pres., Editorial/Composing — Raymond Worrall
Newspapers: Belleville Post, NJ
Irvington Herald, NJ
News-Record of Maplewood & South Orange, NJ
Nutley Journal, NJ
Record-Transcript of east orange and orange, NJ
The Glen Ridge Paper, NJ
The Independent Press of Bloomfield, NJ
Union County Local Source, NJ
Vailsburg Leader, NJ
West Orange Chronicle, NJ

YELLOWSTONE COMMUNICATIONS — 401 S Main St, Livingston, MT, 59047-3418, USA; tel (406) 222-2000; fax (406) 222-8580; e-mail enterprise@livent.net; web site www.livingstonenterprise.com
Pres. — John Sullivan
Comptroller — Scott Squillace
Mktg. Dir. — Jim Durfey
Newspapers: Big Horn County News, MT
The Big Timber Pioneer, MT
Carbon County News, MT
Dillon Tribune, MT
The Independent Press, MT
Glendive Ranger-Review, MT
Judith Basin Press, MT
Laurel Outlook, MT
Lewistown News-Argus, MT
The Livingston Enterprise, MT
Miles City Star, MT
The Stillwater County News, MT
The Terry Tribune, MT
Park County Super Shopper, MT
Note: Yellowstone Newspapers owns two daily newspapers, two twice weeklies and seven weekly newspapers. Yellowstone also owns KATL, an AM radio station in Miles City, Montana Best Times, a monthly senior publication and two commerical job and web printing plan

WEEKLY NEWSPAPER AND SHOPPER PUBLICATION GROUPS IN CANADA

A

ALTA. NEWSPAPER GROUP, LTD — 504 Seventh St. S., Lethbridge, AB, T1J 2H1, Canada; tel (403) 328-4411; fax (403) 328-4536
Vice Pres./Gen. Mgr. — Bob Carey
Circ. Dir. — Tony LeBlancNewspapers:The 40-mile County Commentator, AB
The Lethbridge Herald, AB
The Southern Sun Times, AB
Medicine Hat News, AB
The Sunny South News, AB
The Taber Times, AB
Vauxhall Advance, AB

The Maple Creek News, SK
Maple Creek & Southwest Advance Times, SK
The Lethbridge Shopper, AB
The Medicine Hat Shopper, AB
The Shaunavon Standard, SK
Brome County News, QC
The Record, QC
Note: Southern Alberta Newspaper Group owns two daily newspapers, four weekly newspapers and three shopper publication.

B

BLACK PRESS GROUP LTD. — #310-5460 152nd St., Surrey, BC, V3S 5J9, Canada; tel (604) 575-2744; fax (604) 575-5329; web site www.blackpress.ca
Est.: 1975
Chair/Founder — David Black
Pres. and CEO — Rick O'Connor
Pres., Group Ops — Randy Blair
VP Finance — Frank HansonNewspapers:100 Mile House Free Press, BC
Alberni Valley News, BC
Shuswap Market News, BC
The Abbotsford News, BC
The Agassiz-harrison Observer, BC
Alberni Valley Times, BC
The Aldergrove Star, BC
Arrow Lakes News, BC
The Ashcroft-cache Creek Journal, BC
Barriere Star Journal, BC
The Boundary Creek Times, BC
Burns Lakes District News, BC
Caledonia Courier, BC
The Campbell River Mirror, BC
The Castlegar News, BC
The Chilliwack Progress, BC
North Thompson Times, BC
Cloverdale Reporter, BC
Comox Valley Record, BC
Cranbrook Daily Townsman, BC
Eagle Valley News, BC
Golden Star, BC
Goldstream Gazette, BC
The Grand Forks Gazette, BC
The Kimberley Daily Bulletin, BC
Northern Sentinel - Kitimat, BC
Kootenay Advertiser, BC
The Ladysmith Chronicle, BC
The Lake Cowichan Gazette, BC
Lakeshore News, BC
Langley Advance, BC
Langley Times, BC
The Maple Ridge News, BC
Maple Ridge & Pitt Meadow Times, BC
Mission City Record, BC
Monday Magazine, BC
Nanaimo News Bulletin, BC
Nelson Star, BC
North Island Gazette, BC
North Island Midweek, BC
Oak Bay News, BC
Parksville Qualicum Beach News, BC
The Peace Arch News, BC
The Peninsula News Review, BC
Penticton Western News, BC
Quesnel Cariboo Observer, BC
Revelstoke Review, BC
Rossland News, BC
Saanich News, BC
Salmon Arm Observer, BC
Princeton Similkameen Spotlight, BC
The Smithers Interior News, BC
The Sooke News Mirror, BC
Summerland Review, BC
Surrey Now-leader, BC
The Terrace Standard, BC
The Free Press, BC
Tri-city News, BC
Westerly News, BC
Trail Daily Times, BC
Vanderhoof Omineca Express, BC
Victoria News, BC
The Williams Lake Tribune, BC
The Yukon Review, OK
The Bashaw Star, AB
Castor Advance, AB
Eckville Echo, AB
Ponoka News, AB
Red Deer Advocate, AB
Red Deer Express, AB
Rimbey Review, AB
Stettler Independent, AB
Sylvan Lake News, AB
Leduc-wetaskiwin Pipestone Flyer, AB
The Arlington Times, WA
Kent Reporter, WA
Bainbridge Island Review, WA
Bellevue Reporter, WA
Bellingham Business Journal, WA
Bothell/Kenmore Reporter, WA
Bremerton Patriot-OOB, WA
Central Kitsap Reporter, WA
Covington-Maple Valley-Black Diamond Reporter, WA
The Enumclaw Courier-Herald, WA
Federal Way Mirror, WA
Forks Forum, WA
The Islands' Sounder, WA
The Islands' Weekly, WA
Issaquah/Sammamish Reporter, WA
The Journal of the San Juan Islands, WA
Kirkland Reporter, WA
The Marysville Globe, WA
Mercer Island Reporter, WA
Okanogan Valley Gazette-Tribune, WA
Peninsula Daily News, WA
Port Orchard Independent, WA
Redmond Reporter, WA
Renton Reporter, WA
The Sequim Gazette, WA
Snoqualmie Valley Record, WA
South Whidbey Record, WA
Tacoma Daily Index, WA
Tukwila Reporter, WA
Vashon-Maury Island Beachcomber, WA
Veterans' Life-OOB, WA
The Whidbey Examiner, WA
Whidbey News Times, WA
Friday Forward, AB
Honolulu Star-Advertiser, HI
Oahu Publications Inc., HI
The Daily World, WA
The Herald, WA
BOnny Lake Sumner Courier, WA
Boulevard Chinese, BC
Chemainus Valley, BC
Clearwater Times, BC
Coast Mountian News, BC
Cowichan Valley News, BC
Creston Valley Advance, BC
Haida Gwaii Observer, BC
Hawaii Tribune-Herald, HI
Hope Standard, BC
Houston Today, BC
Kaua'i Midweek, HI
Keremeos Review, BC
Kingston Community , WA
Lacombe Express, AB
Lake Country Calendar, WA
Metro HNL, HI
Midweek, HI
North Delta Reporter, BC
North Kitsap Herald, WA
SF Weekly, CA
Street Pulse, HI
Garden ISland, HI
The Northern View, BC
San Francisco Examiner, CA
Vernon Morning Star, BC
West Hawaii Today, HI
Note: In the U.S., Black Press owns Sound Publishing Inc. and Oahu Publications, publishers of the Honolulu Star Advertiser as well as the Akron Beacon Journal and San Francisco Examiner and SF Weekly newspapers.

C

CANORA COURIER — 123 First Ave. E., Canora, SK, S0A 0L0, Canada; tel (306) 563-5131; fax (306) 563-6144; e-mail canoracourier@sasktel.net; web site canoracourier.com
Group: Glacier Media Group
Pub — Ken LewchukNewspapers:The Kamsack Times, SK
Preeceville Progress, SK

CARIBOO PRESS — 188 N. 1st Ave., Williams Lake, BC, V2G 1Y8, Canada; tel (250) 392-2331; fax (250) 392-7253; web site www.wltribune.com
Pres. — Lorie Williston
Lisa Bowering

CIE D'EDITION ANDRE PAQUETTE, INC. — 1100 Aberdeen St., Hawkesbury, ON, K6A 1K7, Canada; tel (613) 632-4155; fax (613) 632-6383; e-mail bertrand.castonguay@eap.on.ca; web site www.editionap.ca
Est.: 1947
Pres — Bertrand CastonguayNewspapers:L'argenteuil, QC
Le Carillon, ON
Tribune Express, ON
Vision, ON
Le Reflet/News, ON

G

GLACIER MEDIA GROUP — 2188 Yukon Street, Vancouver, BC, V5Y 3P1, Canada; tel (604) 872-8565; fax (604) 638-2453; e-mail info@glaciermedia.ca; web site www.glaciermedia.ca
Est.: 1999
Chairman — Sam Grippo
Pres./CEO — Jonathan J.L. Kennedy
Dir. — Bruce W. Aunger
Pres., Comm. Media — Peter Kvarnstrom
CFO — Orest SmysnuikNewspapers:New Westminster Record, BC
The Northern Horizon, BC
The Westender, BC
Alaska Highway News, BC
Assiniboia Times, SK
Barrhead Leader, AB
Bonnyville Nouvelle, AB
Bowen Island Undercurrent, BC
Bridge River Lillooet News, BC
Burnaby Now, BC
Canora Courier, SK
Carlyle Observer, SK
Carstairs Courier, AB
Coast Reporter, BC
The Deloraine Times And Star, MB
Delta Optimist, BC
The Didsbury Review (OOB), AB
Elk Point Review, AB
Southeast Lifestyles, SK
Estevan Mercury, SK
Flin Flon Reminder, MB
The Humboldt Journal, SK
Innisfail Province, AB
The Kamsack Times, SK
Lac La Biche Post, AB
Melita New Era, MB
North Shore News, BC
Okotoks Western Wheel, AB
Olds Albertan, AB
Pique Newsmagazine, BC
Powell River Peak, BC
Preeceville Progress, SK
The Prince George Citizen, BC
Redvers Optimist (OOB), SK
The Reston Recorder, MB
Richmond News, BC
Rocky Mountain Outlook, AB
Rocky View Weekly, AB
Souris Plaindealer, MB
Squamish Chief, BC
St. Albert Gazette, AB
St. Paul Journal, AB
Sundre Round-up, AB
Battlefords News-optimist, SK
Kipling Citizen, SK
Dawson Creek Mirror, BC
Yorkton News Review, SK
The Outlook, SK
The Tisdale Recorder, SK
Parkland Review, SK
Thompson Citizen/nickel Belt News, MB
Victoria Times Colonist, BC
Tri-city News, BC
The Vancouver Courier, BC
Virden Empire-advance, MB
The Westlock News, AB
Westman Journal, MB
Weyburn Review, SK
Weyburn This Week, SK
The Whistler Question, BC
Yorkton This Week, SK

GREAT WEST NEWSPAPERS LP — 340 Carleton Dr., St. Albert, AB, T8N 7L3, Canada; tel (780) 460-5500; fax (780) 460-8220; e-mail gazette@stalbert.greatwest.ca; web site www.greatwest.ca
Est.: 1966
Pres. — Duff Jamison
Senior Advisor — Paul Rockley
Vice President, Publishing — Brian Bachynski
Plant Mgr. — Evan Jamison
Senior Group Publisher — Murray ElliottNewspapers:Airdrie City View, AB
Sundre Round-up, AB
Barrhead Leader, AB
Bonnyville Nouvelle, AB
Carstairs Courier, AB
Elk Point Review, AB
Innisfail Province, AB
Okotoks Western Wheel, AB
Olds Albertan, AB
Rocky View Weekly, AB
St. Albert Gazette, AB
St. Paul Journal, AB
The Athabasca Advocate, AB
The Didsbury Review (OOB), AB
Lac La Biche Post, AB
Sundre Roundup, AB
Mountain View Gazette, AB
Rocky Mountain Outlook, AB
Cochrane Eagle, AB
Edmonton Senior, AB
FFWD Weekly, AB
Calgary Senior, AB
Edmonton Woman, AB
Central Alberta Adviser (OOB), AB
Wheel & Deal, AB

H

HAYTER WALDEN PUBLICATIONS INC. — 1 King St., W., Forrest, ON, N0N 1J0, Canada; tel (519) 786-5242; fax (519) 786-4884; e-mail guideadvocate@execulink.com
Pub. — Dale Hayter

HOLMES PUBLISHING CO. LTD. — 1577 Dunmore Rd. SE, Medicine Hat, AB, T1A 1Z8, Canada; tel (403) 526-5937; fax (403) 526-5678; e-mail holmesprinting@inter.ab.ca; web site www.holmesprinting.com
Est.: 1920
Pres. — Ron HolmesNewspapers:Oyen Echo, AB
The Provost News, AB

J

JAMAC PUBLISHING — 919 Main St., Kindersley, SK, S0L 1S0, Canada; tel (306) 463-4611; fax (306) 463-6505; e-mail ads_jamac@sasktel.net
Pub. — Stewart Crump
Adv. Sales Mgr. — Barry MalindineNewspapers:Eston-elrose Press Review, SK
Kindersley Clarion, SK
Leader News, SK
Macklin Mirror, SK
The Kerrobert Citizen Dispatch (OOB), SK
West Central Crossroads, SK

L

LES HEBDOS MONTEREGIENS — 184 de Normandie, Boucherville, QC, J4B 5S7,

Canada; tel (450) 655-5556; fax (450) 655-9951; e-mail hm@hebdos.net; web site www.hebdos.net
Dir. — Phillippe Auclair
Controller — Lise DiotteNewspapers:L'oeil Regional, QC
Le Journal De St-bruno, QC
Le Soleil Du Mercredi, QC
Le Journal Saint-francois, QC
Journal De Chambly, QC
L'Information Regionale, QC
Le Soleil Du St-laurent, QC
Les 2 Rives, QC
Journal La Voix, QC
Le Reflet, QC
Le Soleil Du St-laurent, QC

M

METROLAND MEDIA GROUP LTD. — 3125 Wolfedale Rd., Mississauga, ON, L5C 1W1, Canada; tel (905) 281-5656; fax (905) 279-5103; e-mail result@metroland.com; web site www.metroland.com
Pres. — Ian Oliver
Vice Pres. — Kathie Bride
Sr. Vice Pres. — Tim Whittaker
Sr. Vice Pres. — Ian McLeod
Vice Pres. — Ian Proudfoot
Vice Pres., HR — Brenda Biller
Vice Pres. — Joe Anderson
Vice Pres. — Bruce Danford
Vice Pres. — Ron Lenyk
Vice Pres. — Ken Nugent
Vice Pres. — Carol Peddie
Gordon Paolucci
Vice President — Kukle Terry
Ed-In-Chief — Lois Tuffin
John Willems
Scott Miller Cressman
Tracy Magee-Graham
Editor-In-Chief — Haggert Peter
VP, Business Development & Acquisitions — Terry KukleNewspapers:Belleville News, ON
Fort Erie Post, ON
Independent & Free Press, ON
Ajax-pickering News Advertiser, ON
The Alliston Herald, ON
Almaguin News, ON
Ancaster News, ON
Arnprior Chronicle-Guide, ON
Arthur Enterprise News, ON
The Aurora Banner, ON
The Barrie Advance, ON
Beach-Riverdale Mirror, ON
Belleville News Emc, ON
Bloor West Villager, ON
Bracebridge Examiner, ON
Bradford & West Gwillimbury Topic, ON
Brampton Guardian, ON
Brant News, ON
The Brighton Independent, ON
Brock Citizen, ON
The Burlington Post, ON
Caledon Enterprise, ON
Cambridge Times, ON
The Carleton Place-almonte Canadian Gazette Emc, ON
City Centre Mirror, ON
Clarington This Week, ON
Dundas Star News, ON
Express, ON
The East York Mirror, ON
The Elmira Independent, ON
The Erin Advocate, ON
Etobicoke Guardian, ON
Times Advocate, ON
The Fergus-elora News Express, ON
The Flamborough Review, ON
The Frontenac Gazette, ON
The Georgina Advocate, ON
Glanbrook Gazette, ON
The Gravenhurst Banner, ON
The Grimsby Lincoln News, ON
The Guelph Mercury Tribune, ON
Guelph Tribune, ON
Hamilton Mountain News, ON
The Hamilton Spectator, ON
Huntsville Forester, ON
Innisfil Journal, ON
Kanata Kourier-standard Emc, ON
Kawartha Lakes This Week, ON
Kemptville Advance Emc, ON
Kingston Heritage Emc, ON
Kitchener Post, ON
The Listowel Banner, ON
Manotick News Emc, ON
Markham Economist & Sun, ON
The Mirror, ON
The Milton Canadian Champion, ON
Minto Express, ON
Mississauga News, ON
The Mount Forest Confederate, ON
The Muskokan, ON
Nepean-barrhaven News Emc, ON
New Hamburg Independent, ON
The Newmarket Era-banner, ON
North York Mirror, ON
Northumberland News, ON
Niagara This Week, ON
Oakville Beaver, ON
The Orangeville Banner, ON
Orillia Today, ON
Orleans News Emc, ON
Oshawa-whitby This Week, ON
Ottawa East Emc, ON
Ottawa South Emc, ON
Ottawa West Emc, ON
The Parkdale Villager, ON
Parry Sound Beacon Star, ON
Parry Sound North Star, ON
The Perth Courier Emc, ON
Peterborough This Week, ON
The Port Perry Star, ON
Quinte West Emc, ON
The Renfrew Mercury Emc, ON
The Richmond Hill Liberal, ON
The Grand River Sachem, ON
The Scarborough Mirror, ON
Smiths Falls Record News Emc, ON
South Asian Focus, ON
St. Lawrence News, ON
St. Mary's Journal Argus, ON
St. Thomas/elgin Weekly News, ON
The Stayner Sun, ON
The Stittsville News, ON
Stoney Creek News, ON
Stratford Gazette, ON
Collingwood Connection, ON
Uxbridge Times-journal, ON
Vaughan Citizen, ON
Walkerton Herald-times, ON
Waterloo Chronicle, ON
The Record, ON
West Carleton Review, ON
The Wingham Advance-times, ON
The York Guardian, ON

MOUNTAIN VIEW PUBLISHING — PO Box 3910, Olds, AB, T4H 1P6, Canada; tel (403) 556-7510; e-mail melliott@olds.greatwest.ca
Grp. Pub./Gen. Mgr. — Murray Elliott

O

OPTIPRESS PRINT — 140 Joseph Zatzman Dr., Dartmouth, NS, B3B 1M4, Canada; tel (902) 457-7468; fax (902) 468-7366; web site www.transcontinental.com
Gen. Mgr. — Mark Lancaster

Q

QUEBECOR COMMUNICATIONS, INC. — 999 De Maisonneuve Blvd. W, Ste. 1100, Montreal, QC, H3A 3L4, Canada; tel (514) 877-5334; fax (514) 954-3624; e-mail serge.sasseville@quebecor.com; web site www.quebecor.com
Vice Pres. — Tony RossNewspapers:Le Journal De Joliette, QC
The Observer, ON
The Edmonton Sun, AB
The Mitchell Advocate, ON
The Weekender, ON
Shoreline Beacon, ON
The Valley Leader, MB
Le Pharillon, QC
Dunnville Chronicle, ON
Le Saint-laurent Portage, QC
Le Point, QC
L'avant-poste Gaspesien, QC
The Enterprise-bulletin, ON
Times-reformer, ON
The Barrie Examiner, ON
The Brockville Recorder and Times, ON
The Timmins Daily Press, ON
Northern News, ON
Le Reveil, QC
Le Citoyen De La Vallee De L'or, QC
Niagara Falls Review, ON
The Daily Observer, ON
St. Catherines Shopping News, ON
Pincher Creek Echo, AB
Le Journal Des Pays D'en Haut Le Vallee, QC
Oxford Shopping News/review, ON
Cochrane Times, AB
L'eclaireur-progres/beauce Nouvelles, QC
The Melfort Journal, SK
Le Reveil, QC
Winkler Times, MB
Kingston This Week, ON
Daily Herald-Tribune, AB
The Markdale Standard, ON
The Calgary Sun, AB
The Spirit of Bothwell, ON
Information Du Nord L'annonciation, QC
Plein Jour Sur Manicouagan, QC
Chronicle, ON
The Chatham Daily News, ON
Lloydminster Meridian Booster, AB
The Petrolia Topic, ON
The Huron Expositor, ON
Information Du Nord Mont Tremblant, QC
The Post, ON
The Peterborough Examiner, ON
The Examiner, ON
Information Du Nord Sainte-agathe, QC
Niagara Shopping News, ON
Airdrie Echo, AB
L'echo Du Nord, QC
Le Courrier Du Sud/south Shore Courier, QC
Sarnia This Week, ON
Lindsay Post (OOB), ON
Bow Valley Crag & Canyon, AB
Napanee Guide, ON
West Niagara News, ON
Le Rimouskois, QC
Age Dispatch Focus, ON
St. Catharines Standard, ON
Welland Tribune, ON
Nipawin Journal, SK
The Tillsonburg News, ON
Strathmore Standard, AB
Banff Crag & Canyon OOB* (2013), AB
The Strathroy Age Dispatch, ON
Nugget, ON
Fort Erie Shopping Times, ON
Objectif Plein Jour, QC
Woodstock Sentinel-Review, ON
Morden Times, MB
Meadow Lake Progress, SK
Crowsnest Pass Promoter (OOB), AB
The Kinistino Birch Hills Post Gazette (OOB), SK
Colborne Chronicle, ON
Northumberland Today, ON
Le Journal de Saint-Hubert (OOB), QC
Drayton Valley Western Review, AB
Le Mirabel, QC
Plein Jour De Charlevoix, QC
Owensound Sun Times, ON
Leamington Post, ON
The Interlake Spectator, MB
Peuple De Lotbiniere, QC
Central Plains Herald Leader, MB
Trentonian, ON
Brandtford Expositor, ON
The Kingston Whig-Standard, ON
Selkirk Journal, MB
The Mayerthorpe Freelancer, AB
The Red River Valley Echo, MB
La Sentinelle de Chibougamau, QC
Les Actualites, QC
Le Port Cartois, QC
Paris Star, ON
The Wiarton Echo, ON
Intelligencer, ON
Brossard Eclair, QC
Edmonton Examiner, AB
The Stratford Beacon Herald, ON
The Niagara Advance, ON
Journal Le Peuple, QC
L'information, QC
Fairview Post, AB
Hanna Herald, AB
Edson Leader, AB
The Stonewall Argus & Teulon Times, MB
Clinton News-record, ON
Barry's Bay This Week, ON
Le Journal de Montreal, QC
The Sault Star, ON
The Beausejour Review, MB
The Ingersoll Times, ON
St. Thomas Times-Journal, ON
The Simcoe Reformer, ON
Le Journal de Quebec, QC
The London Free Press, ON
Timmins Times, ON
The Lucknow Sentinel, ON
What's Up Muskoka, ON
L'echo De La Baie, QC
Fort McMurray Today, AB
Le Progres-echo, QC
The Fort Erie Times, ON
Beauce Media, QC
La Voix Gaspesienne, QC
Lac du Bonnet Leader, MB
Delhi News-record, ON
The Winnipeg Sun, MB
Le Peuple Cote-sud, QC
Lake Shore Shopper, ON
Welland Shopping News, ON
Amherstburg Echo (OOB), ON
The Northern Times, ON
The Ottawa Sun, ON
The Reporter, ON
Sault Ste. Marie This Week, ON
Leduc Representative, AB
Standard-freeholder Complimentary, ON
Lacombe Globe, AB

R

ROCKY VIEW PUBLISHING — #403-2903 Kingsview Blvd, Airdrie, AB, T4A 0C4, Canada; tel (403) 948-1885; fax (403) 948-2554; web site rockyviewweekly.com
Group: Greatwest Publishing
Publisher — Cameron ChristiansonNewspapers:Rocky View Weekly, AB
Note: Rocky View Publishing is owned by Great West Newspaper Group Ltd. which owns various non-daily publications.

RUNGE NEWSPAPERS, INC. — 35 Opeongo Rd. W., Renfrew, ON, K7V 2T2, Canada; tel (613) 432-3655; fax (613) 432-6689; web site www.runge.net
Regl. Pub. — Chris McWebbNewspapers:Arnprior Chronicle-Guide, ON
Kanata Kourier-standard Emc, ON
The Renfrew Mercury Emc, ON
The Stittsville News, ON

S

SHIELD MEDIA — 20 Hanna Ct., Belleville, ON, K8P 5J2, Canada; tel (613) 962-3294; fax (613) 962-0234; e-mail e.jones@shieldmedia.com; web site www.shieldmedia.com
Est.: 1995
Exec. Pub. — Harold JonesNewspapers:Havelock Citizen, ON
Marmora Edition (OOB), ON
Stirling Edition (OOB), ON

SIMCOE-YORK GROUP — 34 Main St. W., Beeton, ON, L0G 1A0, Canada; tel (905) 729-2287; fax (905) 729-2541; e-mail admin.syp@rogers.com; web site www.simcoeyorkprinting.com
Group: London Publishing Corp

Est.: 1974
Publisher — John Archibald
Co-Pub. — Bruce R.
HaireNewspapers:Caledon Citizen, ON
The Scope Of Innisfil, ON
The Times Of New Tecumseth, ON
Tottenham Times, ON
Note: Simcoe-York Group also owns The Tapestry, a quarterly publication published in King Twp. Ontario.

T

TORSTAR — One Yonge St., Toronto, ON, M5E 1P9, Canada; tel (416) 869-4010; fax (416) 869-4183; e-mail torstar@torstar.ca; web site www.torstar.ca
Chrmn. of the Bd. — Frank Ialobucci
Pres./CEO — Dr. Robert Prichard
Exec. Vice Pres./CFO — David P.
HollandNewspapers:Ajax-pickering News Advertiser, ON
Cowichan Valley Citizen, BC
Creston Valley Advance, BC
Hope Standard, BC
Houston Today, BC
Invermere Valley Echo, BC
Kelowna Capital News, BC
Keremeos Review, BC
Lake Country Calendar, BC
The Morning Star, BC
Ancaster News, ON
Annex Guardian, ON
Arthur Enterprise News, ON
Beach-Riverdale Mirror, ON
Bloor West Villager, ON
Bracebridge Examiner, ON
Brampton Guardian, ON
Brock Citizen, ON
Caledon Enterprise, ON
Cambridge Times, ON
Clarington This Week, ON
Collingwood Connection, ON
Dresden-Bothwell Leader-Spirit (OOB), ON
Dundas Star News, ON
Etobicoke Guardian, ON
Guelph Tribune, ON
Huntsville Forester, ON
Independent & Free Press, ON
Kawartha Lakes This Week, ON
Markham Economist & Sun, ON
Minto Express, ON
New Hamburg Independent, ON
Niagara This Week, ON
North York Mirror, ON
Northumberland News, ON
Oakville Beaver, ON
Orillia Today, ON
Oshawa-whitby This Week, ON
Peterborough This Week, ON
Shopping News, ON
St. Mary's Journal Argus, ON
Stoney Creek News, ON
The Barrie Advance, ON
The Burlington Post, ON
The East York Mirror, ON
The Elmira Independent, ON
The Erin Advocate, ON
The Fergus-elora News Express, ON
The Flamborough Review, ON
The Georgina Advocate, ON
The Gravenhurst Banner, ON
The Grimsby Lincoln News, ON
The Listowel Banner, ON
The Milton Canadian Champion, ON
The Mirror, ON
The Muskokan, ON
The Newmarket Era-banner, ON
The Orangeville Banner, ON
The Port Perry Star, ON
The Richmond Hill Liberal, ON
The Scarborough Mirror, ON
The Stayner Sun, ON
The Wasaga Sun, ON
The Wingham Advance-times, ON
The York Guardian, ON
Times Advocate, ON
Toronto Star, ON
Uxbridge Times-journal, ON
Walkerton Herald-times, ON
Waterloo Chronicle, ON
Note: Torstar owns Metroland Media Group, which owns three daily newspapers.

TRANSCONTINENTAL MEDIA — 1 Place Ville Marie, Ste. 3315, Montreal, ON, H3B 3N2, Canada; tel (514) 954-4000; fax (514) 954-4016; e-mail info@transcontinental.ca; web site www.transcontinental.com
Est.: 1976
Exec. Chrmn. of the Bd. — Remi Marcoux
Pres./CEO — Francois Olivier
CFO — Benoit Huard
Pres., Trancontinental Media Inc. — Natalie Larivi
Vice Pres./Chief Legal Officer/Cor. Sec. — Christine Desaulniers
Vice Pres. Corp. Devel. — Isabelle Marcoux
Sr. Vice Pres., Transcontinental Media Inc./ Newspapaper Grp. — Marc N. Ouellette
Media Relations Dir. — Nessa
BrendergastNewspapers:Amherst Daily News, NS
Broadview Express, SK
Charlesbourg Express, QC
Cites Nouvelles, QC
Courrier-ahuntsic, QC
Courrier-laval, QC
Courrier-sud, QC
Grenfell Sun, SK
Hants Journal, NS
Harbour Breton Coaster, NL
Hebdo Rive Nord, QC
Hebdo Du St. Maurice, QC
Journal L'actuel, QC
L'action, QC
L'artisan, QC
L'avenir De L'erable, QC
L'echo De La Tuque, QC
L'echo De Maskinonge, QC
L'express, QC
L'hebdo Journal, QC
L'hebdo Mekinac/des Chenaux, QC
La Nouvelle, QC
La Petite Nation, QC
La Revue De Gatineau, QC
La Voix Populaire, QC
La Voix Du Sud, QC
Le Courrier Bordeaux/cartierville, QC
Le Lac St. Jean, QC
Northern Pen, NL
Prince Albert Daily Herald, SK
Progres Saint-leonard, QC
Radville Deep South Star, SK
Register, NS
Saint-laurent News, QC
The Advance, NS
The Advertiser, NS
The Advertiser, NL
The Aurora, NL
The Cape Breton Post, NS
The Citizen-record, NS
The Coast Guard, NS
The Compass, NL
The Daily News, NS
The Daily News, NS
The Gander Beacon, NL
The Gulf News, NL
The Labradorian, NL
The Moose Jaw Times-Herald, SK
The News, NS
The Nor'wester, NL
The Packet, NL
The Pilot, NL
The Sackville Tribune-post, NB
The Southern Gazette, NL
The Southwest Booster, SK
The Spectator, NS
The Star, ON
The Telegram, NL
The Vanguard, NS
The Western Star, NL
The Westmount Examiner, QC
Transcontinental Medias, QC
The Digby County Courier, NS
The Chronicle, QC
L'etoile Du Lac, QC
The Oxbow Herald, SK
The Georgian, NL
The Journal Pioneer, PE
Seaway News, ON
The Guardian, PE

ALTERNATIVE DELIVERY SERVICES

A

A & A Distribution, Inc. — 1780 Rogers Ave, San Jose, CA, 95112-1109, USA; tel (408) 436-2300; fax (408) 436-0844; e-mail aadist@aol.com; web site www.aa-distribution.net
Pres. — Manuel Austin
Adco Marketing — 5580 Power Inn Rd, Sacramento, CA, 95820-6748, USA; tel (916) 388-1101; fax (916) 388-1040
Pres. — Dick Avery
Addresses Unlimited — 3600 Hwy 66, Neptune, NJ, 7754, USA; tel (732) 922-6000; fax (732) 643-3719; e-mail editors@app.com; web site www.app.com
Vice Pres. — Sam Sicliano
ADS Delivery, Inc. — 236 W II Route 173, Antioch, IL, 60002-1834, USA; tel (847) 395-7500; fax (847) 395-2814; e-mail advertising@advertisernetwork.com; web site www.advertisernetwork.com
Administrative Dir. — Kris Shepard
Advertisers PS/LLC — 1584 Dickerson Rd, Gaylord, MI, 49735-9206, USA; tel (989) 732-1797; fax (989) 732-8300
Gen. Mgr. — Mel Ihnatenko
Alexandria Daily Town Talk — 1201 3rd St, Alexandria, LA, 71301-8246, USA; tel (318) 487-6409; fax (318) 487-2952; web site www.thetowntalk.com
Pub. — Ed. Humphrey
Alternate Marketing Networks — 4675 32nd Ave, Hudsonville, MI, 49426-8012, USA; tel (616) 662-6420; fax (616) 662-6422; e-mail pmiller@altmarknet.com; web site www.altmarknet.com
Pres./Vice Pres., Sales — Frank O'Connell
Atlanta Journal-Constitution — 223 Perimeter Center Pkwy NE, Atlanta, GA, 30346-1301, USA; tel (404) 526-7003; fax (404) 526-5746; e-mail allen.dunstan@coxinc.com; web site www.ajc.com
Group: Cox Media Group
VP, Marketing — Amy Chown
Dir., Mktg. Devel. — Laura Inman
Mktg. Mgr., Classified/Territory — Chris Hood
Pub. — Amy Glennon
Ed. — Kevin Riley
VP, Adv. Sales — Eric Myers
Sr. Dir., Nat'l Accts. — Allen Dunstan
Sr. VP, Finance & Business Op. — Brian Cooper
Sr. VP, Audience & Group Lead for CMG Newspapers — Mark Medici
VP, Fulfillment — Joe McKinnon

B

Bee Niche Products — 2100 Q St, Sacramento, CA, 95816-6816, USA; tel (916) 321-1000; fax (916) 326-5578; e-mail jpaquette@sacbee.com; web site www.sacbee.com
Group: The McClatchy Company
Vice-President, Human Resources — Linda Brooks

C

Carrigan Advertising Carriers, Inc. — 40 Walnut St, Hyde Park, MA, 02136-2732, USA; tel (617) 361-1950; fax (617) 361-1995
Pres. — James Carrigan
Cba Industries — 669 River Dr, Ste 404, Elmwood Park, NJ, 07407-1361, USA; tel (201) 587-1717; fax (201) 414-5201; e-mail tjcastello@cbaol.com
Chrmn. — Harold Matzner
Pres. — Barry Schiro
Market Mapping Specialist — Tom Castello
Executive VP — Eva Kohn
Midwest Regional Sales Representative — Nikki Schultz
Senior VP, Marketing — Nick Passariello
Senior VP, Sales — John Durante
VP, Sales — Tim Brahney
CeCe's Postal Service — 6344 University Ave, San Diego, CA, 92115-5813, USA; tel (619) 283-7157
Pres. — Margaret Lindahl
Cie d'Edition Andre Paquette, Inc. — 1100 Aberdeen St., Hawkesbury, ON, K6A 1K7, Canada; tel (613) 632-4155; fax (613) 632-6383; e-mail bertrand.castonguay@eap.on.ca; web site www.editionap.ca
Pres — Bertrand Castonguay
Cips Marketing Group, Inc. — 13110 Avalon Blvd, Los Angeles, CA, 90061-2738, USA; tel (310) 769-6900; fax (310) 538-1170; web site www.cipsmarketing.comJennifer Fawkes
President & CEO — Manuel Collazo
City Pages — 800 N 1st St, Ste 300, Minneapolis, MN, 55401-1387, USA; tel (612) 372-3700; fax (612) 372-3737; e-mail adinfo@citypages.com; web site www.citypages.com
Circ. Mgr. — Tom Imberston
Ed. in Chief — Kevin Hoffman
Mng. Ed. — Matt Smith
Prodn. Mgr. — Doug Snow
Editor — Mary Erickson
Community Delivery Service — 1010 E New Circle Rd, Lexington, KY, 40505-4117, USA; tel (859) 231-3382; fax (859) 231-3450
Community News Advertiser — 201 S Clinton St, Ste 200, Iowa City, IA, 52240-4011, USA; tel (319) 339-3100; fax (319) 339-3112; web site www.iccommunitynews.com
Gen. Mgr. — Robb Rood
Connecticut Post — 410 State St, Bridgeport, CT, 06604-4501, USA; tel (203) 333-0161; fax (203) 367-8158; e-mail edit@ctpost.com; web site www.connpost.com
Pub. — John DeAugusgine
Ed. — Tom Baden
Prodn. Mgr. — George Onze

D

Daily Press — 13891 Park Ave, Victorville, CA, 92392-2435, USA; tel (760) 241-7744; fax (760) 241-7145; e-mail rlipscomb@vvdailypress.com; web site www.vvdailypress.com
Group: New Media Investment Group
Nat'l/Majors., Adv. — Leslie Poe
Online Coordinator — Bryan Kawasaki
Ed. — Steve Hunt
Adv. Director — Angie Callahan

Classified Supervisor — Janet Baldwin
Pub. — Donnie Welch

Daily Press Porch Plus — 7505 Warwick Blvd, Newport News, VA, 23607-1517, USA; tel (757) 247-4600; fax (757) 245-7113; web site www.dailypress.com
Pres./CEO/Pub. — Timothy Ryan

Dayton City Paper — 126 N Main St, Ste 240, Dayton, OH, 45402-1766, USA; tel (937) 222-8855; e-mail contactus@daytoncitypaper.com; web site www.daytoncitypaper.com
Group: Dayton City Media
CEO, Dayton City Media — Paul Noah
Publisher — Wanda Esken

DHL Smart & Global Mail — 21240 Ridgetop Cir, Ste 160, Sterling, VA, 20166-6560, USA; tel (703) 463-2200; fax (800) 455-6615; web site www.globalmail.com

Direct Marketing Distribution — 101 N 6th St, Allentown, PA, 18101-1403, USA; tel 610-841-2301; fax 610-841-2306; web site www.mcall.com
Sales Manager — Todd Wendling
Vice Pres. — James Feher

Distribution Unlimited, Inc. — PO Box 315, Springfield, OH, 45501-0315, USA; tel (937) 325-5300; fax (937) 289-0172
Pres. — Wayne E. Pullins

E

Easy Reader — PO Box 427, 832 Hermosa Ave, Hermosa Beach, CA, 90254-0427, USA; tel (310) 372-4611; fax (424) 212-6708; e-mail easyreader@easyreader.info; web site http://www.easyreadernews.com/
Group: C-VILLE Holdings LLC
Adv. Mgr. — Kevin Cody
Dispaly Sales — Amy Berg
Display Sales — Erin McCoy
Classifieds — Tami Quattrone
Arts/Entertainment Ed. — Bondo Wyszpolski
News Ed. — Mark McDermott
Prodn. Dir. — Graciela Huerta
Richard Budman

El Paso Times — 500 W Overland Ave, Ste 150, El Paso, TX, 79901-1108, USA; tel (915) 546-6100; fax (915) 546-6284; e-mail advertising@elpasotimes.com; web site www.elpasotimes.com
Group: Gannett
Dir., HR — Malena Field
Circ. Mgr., Transportation — Randy Waldrop
VP of Production — Patsy Hernandez
Executive Editor — Robert Moore
Victor Kolenc
President — Lilia Jones
Sales Director — Salvador Hernandez

F

Fort Worth Weekly — 3311 Hamilton Ave, Fort Worth, TX, 76107-1877, USA; tel (817) 321-9700; fax (817) 321-9733; e-mail Michael.Newquist@fwweekly.com; web site www.fwweekly.com
Ed. — Gayle Reaves
Adv. Dir. — Michael Newquist
Classified Adv. Dir. — Brian Martin
Eric Griffey

Freedom Marketing Corporation — 2522 W Geneva Dr, Tempe, AZ, 85282-3128, USA; tel (602) 258-6400; fax (602) 258-9700; e-mail brandy@freedomdelivers.com; web site www.freedomdelivers.com
Sr. Sales Coord. — Brandy Jenkins

G

Green Bay Community News (East/West) — 133 S Monroe Ave, Green Bay, WI, 54301-4056, USA; tel (920) 432-2941; fax (920) 432-8581; e-mail chronicle@itol.com; web site www.greenbaynewschronicle.com
Vice Pres. — Al Rasmussen
Circ. Mgr. — Keith Davis

H

Harte-Hanks — 4545 Annapolis Rd, Baltimore, MD, 21227-4817, USA; tel (410) 636-6660; fax (410) 636-2567; web site www.harte-hanks.com
Gen. Mgr. — Tom Ugast

Heartland Delivery, Inc. — 3420 E Hwy 30, Columbus, NE, 68601, USA; tel (402) 564-1025; fax (402) 562-6480
Gen. Mgr. — Dan Thomas

Home Express — 5457 Greenwich Rd, Virginia Beach, VA, 23462-6539, USA; tel (757) 446-2890; fax (757) 499-1966

J

Journal/Sentinel, Inc. — 333 W State St, Milwaukee, WI, 53203-1305, USA; tel (414) 224-2000; fax (414) 224-2485; web site www.jsonline.com
Vice Pres., Adv. — Margie Cochrane
Vice Pres., Mktg. — David Wiese
Dir., Adv. Classified — Daryl Hively

K

Kapp Advertising Service, Inc. — 100 E Cumberland St, Lebanon, PA, 17042-5400, USA; tel (717) 273-8127; fax (717) 273-0420; e-mail sales@themerchandiser.com; web site www.themerchandiser.com
Gen. Mgr. — Valerie Stokes
Circ. Mgr. — Joanne Walkinshaw
General Sales Manager — Randy Miller

M

Marketing Information Distribution Service — 18 E Vine St, Mount Vernon, OH, 43050-3226, USA; tel (740) 397-5333; fax (740) 397-1321; e-mail csplain@mountvernonnews.com; web site www.mountvernonnews.com
Pub. — Kay H. Culbertson
MIDS Mgr. — Michael P. McNichols

Media One of Utah — 4770 S 5600 W, West Valley City, UT, 84118-7400, USA; tel (801) 204-6151; fax 801-204-6399; web site www.mediaoneutah.com
Vice President Circulation Operations — Hal Mortensen

Messenger Consumer Services — 9300 Johnson Hollow Rd, Athens, OH, 45701-9028, USA; tel (740) 592-6612; fax (740) 592-4647; e-mail sbossart@athensmessenger.com; web site www.athensmessenger.com
Adv. Mgr. — Sherrie Bossart
Pub. — Monica Nieporte

Metro Group, Inc. — 75 Boxwood Ln, Cheektowaga, NY, 14227-2707, USA; tel (716) 668-5223; fax (716) 668-4526; e-mail edit@metrowny.com; web site www.metrowny.com
Ed. — Lorne Marshall

Midwest Independent Postal — 595 Jenner Dr, Allegan, MI, 49010-1516, USA; tel (269) 673-2141; fax (269) 673-6768; e-mail gerald.raab@flashespublishers.com; web site www.flashespublishers.com
Prodn. Mgr. — Gerald Raab

Missoula Independent — 317 S Orange St, Missoula, MT, 59801-1810, USA; tel (406) 543-6609; fax (406) 543-4367; e-mail indy@missoulanews.com; web site www.missoulanews.com
Group: Lee Enterprises, Inc.
Prodn. Dir. — Joe Weston
Editor — Brad Tyer
General Manager — Andy Sutcliffe

N

New Media Venture — 999 W Riverside Ave, Spokane, WA, 99201-1005, USA
CEO — Shaun Higgins

Northeastern Shopper — 129 North St E, Tawas City, MI, 48763-9294, USA; tel (989) 362-3495; fax (989) 362-0057
Gen. Mgr. — Tom Greene

O

Oklahoma Gazette — 3701 N Shartel Ave, Oklahoma City, OK, 73118-7102, USA; tel (405 605-6789; fax (405) 528-4600; web site www.okgazette.com
Group: Tierra Media Group
Pub — Bill Bleakley
Associate Pub — James Bengfort

On Target Marketing, The Bag — 7801 N Central Dr, Lewis Center, OH, 43035-9407, USA; tel (740) 548-2100; fax (740) 888-6006; e-mail szonars@the.dispatch.com; web site www.thebag.com
Vice Pres. — Stephen C. Zonars

P

Pinpoint Target Marketing — 201 Campbell Ave SW, Roanoke, VA, 24011-1105, USA; tel (540) 981-3307; fax (540) 981-3177; web site www.roanoke.com
Mktg. Mgr. — Libba Wolfe

Publishers Circulation Fulfillment Inc. — 303 Smith St, Ste 1, Farmingdale, NY, 11735-1110, USA; tel (631) 2703133; e-mail sales@pcfcorp.com; web site www.pcfcorp.com
Pres./CEO — Jerry Giordana
VP of Growth and Development — Tom Dressler
James Cunningham

Q

Quicksaver — 1950 S State St, Tacoma, WA, 98405-2817, USA; tel (253) 597-8742; fax (253) 552-7054; web site www.thenewstribune.com

R

R-J Delivery Systems, Inc. — 490 E State Road 60, Pekin, IN, 47165-7928, USA; tel (812) 967-3176; fax (812) 967-3194; web site www.gbpnews.com
Pub. — Joe Green

Richmond Delivery Service — 7500 Ranco Rd, Richmond, VA, 23228-3750, USA; tel (804) 775-2723; fax (804) 775-2801; e-mail rneely@timesdispatch.com; web site www.timesdispatch.com
Sales Mgr. — Richard Neeley
Metro Home Delivery Mgr. — Tom Smith
Circ. Dir. — Raymond Bruett

Road Runner Ad Delivery — 1760 Ulster St, Denver, CO, 80220-2053, USA; tel (303) 758-5096
Pres. — Arnold Rundiks

Roberson Advertising Service, Inc. — 3010 Lausat St, Metairie, LA, 70001-5924, USA; tel (504) 832-1481; fax (504) 837-5923
Pres. — Michael Roberson
Ed. — Joe Chambers

S

Sacramento News & Review — 1124 Del Paso Blvd, Sacramento, CA, 95815-3607, USA; tel (916) 498-1234; fax (916) 498-7910; e-mail sacdofi@newsreview.com; web site https://www.newsreview.com/sacramento
Group: Chico Community Publishing, Inc.
Distribution Mgr — Greg Erwin
President — Jeff von Kaenel
Chief Operating Officer — Deborah Redmond
Sales Manager — Michael Gelbman
Design Manager — Chris Terrazas

San Antonio Current — 915 Dallas St, San Antonio, TX, 78215-1433, USA; tel (210) 227-0044; fax (210) 227-7755; web site www.sacurrent.com
Publisher — Michael Wagner
Advertising Director — Greg Harman

Specialized Marketing Services — 3421 W Segerstrom Ave, Santa Ana, CA, 92704-6404, USA; tel (949) 553-0890; fax (949) 553-0891; web site www.teamsms.com

Stanley Advertising & Distributing Co. — 1947 W Fort St, Detroit, MI, 48216-1817, USA; tel (313) 961-7177; fax (734) 525-2340; e-mail stanleysadvertising@gmail.com; web site www.stanleysadvertising.com
Pres. — Stanley Wojtalik

STL Distributor — 5025 Pattison Ave, Saint Louis, MO, 63110-2037, USA; tel (314) 664-2700; fax (314) 772-7063
Vice Pres./Gen. Mgr. — Tom Livingston

T

The Advocate Newspaper — 7290 Bluebonnet Blvd, Baton Rouge, LA, 70810-1611, USA; tel (225) 383-1111; fax (225) 388-0348; e-mail lruth@theadvocate.com; web site www.2theadvocate.com
Mgr., Customer Sales — Larry Ruth
Distr. Mgr. — Paul Fugarino

The Cincinnati Enquirer — 312 Elm St, Cincinnati, OH, 45202-2739, USA; tel (513) 721-2700; e-mail abaston@enquirer.com; web site www.cincinnati.com; www.enquirermedia.com
Group: Gannett
Interim Editor — Michael McCarter
Group Dir/Home Delivery — Denette Pfaffenberger
Dir of News Content — Kate McGinty
Dir. of Print Prod — Joe Powell
VP of Sales — Chris Strong
Ed. & VP of Audience Engagement — Peter Bhatia
Market Sales & Distribution Director — Jeff Lawson
Client Strategy Director — Libby Korosec
Major Sales & Marketing Manager — John Berry

The Columbian Alternate Delivery Service — 701 W 8th St, Vancouver, WA, 98660-3008, USA; tel (360) 694-3391; fax (360) 735-4605; web site www.columbian.com
Circ. Dir. — Marc Dailey
Circ. Mgr., Promo./Sales — Rachel Rose

The Daily News — 193 Jefferson Ave, Memphis, TN, 38103-2322, USA; tel (901) 523-1561; fax (901) 526-5813; e-mail advertising@memphisdailynews.com; web site www.memphisdailynews.com
Group: The Daily News Publishing Co.
Publisher — Eric Barnes
Marketing Director — Leah Sansing
Associate Publisher/Exec. Ed. — James Overstreet

The Door Store — 2950 Robertson Ave, Cincinnati, OH, 45209-1268, USA; tel (513) 731-1200; fax (859) 283-1809
Regl. Vice Pres. — Roger Saunders
Customer Serv. Rep. — Diane Re

The Gazette Company — 501 2nd Ave SE, Cedar Rapids, IA, 52401-1303, USA; tel (319) 398-8422; fax (319) 368-8505; e-mail customercare@thegazettecompany.com; web site www.thegazettecompany.com
Chrmn. — Joe Hadky
President and CEO — Chuck Peters
VP Sales & Marketing — Chris Edwards

The Penny Saver — 100 E Cumberland St, Cedar Rapids, IA, 52401, USA; tel (319) 398-8222; fax (319) 398-5846; web site pennysaverguide.com
Adv. Dir. — Ron Bode

The Riverfront Times — 308 N 21st St, Saint Louis, MO, 63103-1642, USA; tel (314) 754-5966; fax (314) 754-5955; e-mail Letters@riverfronttimes.com; web site www.riverfronttimes.com
Group: Euclid Media Group
Circ. Mgr. — Kevin Powers
Editor in Chief — Sarah Fenske
Publisher — Chris Keating

The Telegraph Publishing Co. — 17 Executive Dr, Hudson, NH, 03051-4903, USA; tel (603) 882-2741; fax (603) 882-5138; e-mail btyers@nashuatelegraph.com; web site www.nashuatelegraph.com
Prodn. Mgr. — William Tyers

Tucson Newspapers/TMC — 4850 S Park Ave, Tucson, AZ, 85714-1637, USA; tel (520) 573-4167; fax (520) 807-8418; e-mail adserv@azstarnet.com; web site www.azstarnet.com
Pub. — John Humenik
VP of Advertising — Chase Rankin

V

Valassis — 19975 Victor Pkwy, Livonia, MI, 48152-7001, USA; tel (734) 591-3000; web site www.valassis.com
Pres. & CEO — Rob Mason
VP of ROP Sales — Larry Berg
Chief Operating Officer — Ron Goolsby
President and CEO, NCH Marketing Services, Inc. — Brian

Husselbee
Donna Schelby
FSI Project Mgr.
— Jeff Price
Sales Exec. — Dave Safford
Senior Buyer
— Laura Narbut
Senior Buyer
— Bridget Rabel
Senior Buyer
— Ruth Williams
Senior Client Marketing Mgr.
— Tracie Pollet
Senior Newspaper Specialist
— Janene Graham
Senior VP of Digital Media
— Greg Bogich
VP Media Services
— Barry Haselden
VP, Integrated Media Sales
— Tim Garvey
Debbie Gauthier
Client Liason Manager — Lisa Kershaw
Sales Director — Lesa Kirkman
Manager, Media Services — Kathy Trumbo

W

Willow Bend Communications, Inc. — 18333 Preston Rd, 250, Dallas, TX, 75252-5466, USA; tel (972) 553-3600; fax (972) 732-8807; e-mail info@willowbend.com; support@willowbend.com; web site www.willowbend.com
Pres — Steve Thompson
Cust Sup Mgr — Layton Kolb
CFO — Diane Thompson
Chief Software Engineer — Steven Lerch
VP Bus Development — Jim Schell

Woodward Printing Services — 11 Means Dr, Platteville, WI, 53818-3829, USA; tel (608) 348-2817; fax (608) 348-2816; e-mail woodwardprint@wcinet.com; web site http://www.woodwardprinting.com/
Gen. Mgr. — Marty Tloessl

Y

Yankee Peddler Postal Service — 3375 S Bannock St, Englewood, CO, 80110-2404, USA; tel (303) 761-4200; fax (303) 761-4291; e-mail addenver@aol.com; web site http://www.yankeepeddlerpostal.com/
Treasurer — John Minger

ASSOCIATIONS AND CLUBS - NATIONAL AND INTERNATIONAL

A

AAF COLLEGE CHAPTERS — 1101 Vermont Ave NW, Ste 500, Washington, DC, 20005-3521, USA (202) 898-0089; fax (202) 898-0159; e-mail education@aaf.org; aaf@aaf.org; web site www.aaf.org
Pres./CEO .... James Datri
Sr. Vice Pres. .... Joanne Schecter
Note: Elections held in June

ACCREDITING COUNCIL ON EDUCATION IN JOURNALISM AND MASS COMMUNICATIONS — University of Kansas, 1435 Jayhawk Blvd., Lawrence, KS, 66045-0001, USA (785) 864-3973; fax (785)864-5225; e-mail sshaw@ku.edu; web site www.acejmc.org
Pres .... Peter Bhatia
Exec. Dir. .... Susanne Shaw
Vice President .... Paul Parsons

ADVERTISING MEDIA CREDIT EXECUTIVES ASSOCIATION INTERNATIONAL — PO Box 43514, Louisville, KY, 40253-0514, USA N/A; web site www.amcea.org
President .... Vickie Bolinger
Note: Elections held in May

AIGA, THE PROFESSIONAL ASSOCIATION FOR DESIGN — 233 Broadway, Rm 1740, New York, NY, 10279-1803, USA (212) 807-1990; e-mail general@aiga.org; web site www.aiga.org
Exec. Dir. .... Julie Anixter
CEO/CFO .... Hezron Gurley
Chief of Staff .... Amy Chapman
Note: AIGA is the professional association for design, a nonprofit organization dedicated to advancing design as a professional craft, strategic tool and vital cultural force. Founded in 1914, AIGA today serves more than 22,000 members through 66 chapters and 200 student groups across the United States. AIGA stimulates thinking about design, demonstrates the value of design and empowers the success of designers at each stage of their careers.

ALLIANCE FOR AUDITED MEDIA (AAM) — 48 W Seegers Rd, Arlington Heights, IL, 60005-3900, USA (224) 366-6939; fax (224) 366-6949; web site www.auditedmedia.com
VP, Product Leadership .... Joe Hardin
EVP, Com. Dev. .... Brian Condon
Dir., Client Dev. .... Kevin Rehberg

AMERICAN ADVERTISING FEDERATION — 1101 Vermont Ave NW, Ste 500, Washington, DC, 20005-3521, USA (202) 898-0089; fax (202) 898-0159; e-mail aaf@aaf.org; web site www.aaf.org

AMERICAN ASSOCIATION OF INDEPENDENT NEWS DISTRIBUTORS — PO Box 70244, Washington, DC, 20024-0244, USA (202)678-8350; fax (202)889-9209; e-mail cnnorthrop@southwestdistribution.com; web site www.aaind.org
Pres. .... Cary Northrop

AMERICAN BUSINESS MEDIA — 201 E 42nd St Fl 7, Suite 2200, New York, NY, 10017-5704, USA (212) 661-6360; fax (212) 370-0736; e-mail info@abmmail.com; web site www.abmassociation.com
Note: Elections held in May

AMERICAN BUSINESS MEDIA AGRICULTURAL COUNCIL — 201 E 42nd St, Rm 2200, New York, NY, 10017-5714, USA (212) 661-6360; fax (212) 370-0736; e-mail info@abmmail.com; web site www.americanbusinessmedia.com
Exec. Dir. .... Todd Hittle

AMERICAN FOREST & PAPER ASSOCIATION, INC. — 1111 19th St NW, Ste 800, Washington, DC, 20036-3652, USA (202) 463-2700; fax (202) 463-2040; e-mail info@afandpa.org; membership@afandpa.org; web site www.afandpa.org
Pres./CEO .... Donna Harman

AMERICAN JEWISH PRESS ASSOCIATION — C/O Kca Association Management, 107 S. Southgate Dr., Washington, DC, 20036, USA 480-403-4602; fax 480-893-7775; e-mail info@aipa.org; web site www.ajpa.org
Pres .... Elana Kahn-Oren
Assoc. Dir. .... Natasha Nadel
Exec. Dir. .... Toby Dershowitz
Note: Elections held in June

AMERICAN MARKETING ASSOCIATION — 311 S Wacker Dr, Ste 5800, Chicago, IL, 60606-6629, USA (312) 542-9000; fax (312) 542-9001; e-mail info@ama.org; web site www.marketingpower.com
Note: Elections held in spring

AMERICAN NEWS WOMEN'S CLUB, INC. — 1607 22nd St NW, Washington, DC, 20008-1921, USA (202) 332-6770; fax (202) 265-6092; e-mail anwclub@comcast.net; web site www.anwc.org
Pres. .... Pam Ginsbach
Note: Elections held in May.

AMERICAN NEWSPAPER LAYOUT MANAGERS ASSOCIATION (ANLOMA) — 2442 Dr Martin Luther King Blvd, Fort Myers, FL, 33901-3904, USA (239) 335-0340; fax (239) 335-0205
Vice Pres. .... Jonathan Tolton
Pres. .... Robert Hammond
Note: Yearly Conference - March/April

AMERICAN PRESS INSTITUTE — 4401 Wilson Blvd, Ste 900, Arlington, VA, 22203-4195, USA (571) 366-1200; e-mail hello@pressinstitute.org; web site www.americanpressinstitute.org
Exec. Dir./Pres. .... Andrew B. Davis
Vice Pres., Programming/Personnel .... Carol Ann Riordan
Dir., Tailored Solutions .... Elaine Clisham
Assoc. Dir. .... Mary Peskin
Deputy Director .... Jeff Sonderman
Editorial Coordinator .... Millie Tran
Executive Director .... Thomas Rosenstiel
Program Coordinator .... Kevin Loker
Tonda Rush
Content Strategy Program Manager .... Liz Worthington
Senior Research Project Manager .... Jane Elizabeth

AMERICAN SOCIETY OF JOURNALISTS AND AUTHORS — 1501 Broadway, Ste 302, New York, NY, 10036-5501, USA (212) 997-0947; fax (212) 937-2315; e-mail staff@asja.org; web site www.asja.org
Exec. Dir. .... Alexandra Owens
Pres. .... Salley Shannon

AMERICAN SOCIETY OF NEWS EDITORS — 209 Reynolds Journalism Institute, Missouri School of Journalism, Columbia, MO, 65211-0001, USA (573)884-2405; fax (573)884-3824; e-mail asne@asne.org; web site www.asne.org
Exec. Dir. .... Teri Hayt
Comm. Mgr. .... Jiyoung Won
Sr. Info. Specialist .... Megan Schumacher
Note: Elections held in June

ANGLO-AMERICAN PRESS ASSOCIATION OF PARIS — 67 Rue Halle, Paris, 75014, France; tel (33) 1 4545 7400; e-mail axelkrause@wanadoo.fr; web site www.aapafrance.com
Sec. Gen. .... Axel Krause
British Co-Pres. .... Georgina Oliver
American Co-Pres. .... Gregory Viscusi

ASIAN AMERICAN JOURNALISTS ASSOCIATION — 5 3rd St, Ste 1108, San Francisco, CA, 94103-3212, USA (415) 346-2051; fax (415) 346-6343; e-mail national@aaja.org; web site www.aaja.org
Contact .... Annabelle Udo-O'Malley

ASSOCIATED PRESS MANAGING EDITORS ASSOCIATION — 450 W 33rd St, New York, NY, 10001-2603, USA (212) 621-1838; fax (212) 506-6102; e-mail apme@ap.org; web site www.apme.com
Gen. Mgr. .... Sally Jacobsen
Note: Elections held in Oct

ASSOCIATION FOR EDUCATION IN JOURNALISM AND MASS COMMUNICATION — 234 Outlet Pointe Blvd, Ste A, Columbia, SC, 29210-5667, USA (803) 798-0271; fax (803) 772-3509; e-mail aejmchq@aol.com; web site www.aejmc.org
Exec. Dir. .... Jennifer McGill
Note: Elections held in March; conventions in early August.

ASSOCIATION FOR WOMEN IN COMMUNICATIONS — 3337 Duke St, Alexandria, VA, 22314-5219, USA (703) 370-7436; fax (703) 342-4311; e-mail info@womcom.org; web site www.womcom.org
Exec. Dir. .... Pamela Valenzuela
Note: Group and individual memberships only from all communications disciplines

ASSOCIATION OF ALTERNATE POSTAL SYSTEMS — 1725 Oaks Way, Oklahoma City, OK, 73131-1220, USA (405) 478-0006; e-mail aaps@cox.net; web site www.aapsinc.org
Exec. Dir. .... John White
Pres. .... Michael Lynch
Note: Elections held at annual conference

ASSOCIATION OF ALTERNATIVE NEWSMEDIA — 1156 15th St NW, Ste 1005, Washington, DC, 20005-1722, USA 289-8484; fax (202) 289-2004; e-mail web@aan.org; web site www.altweeklies.com
Dir. of Meetings .... Debra Silvestrin
Int. Exec. Dir. .... Jason Zaragoza
Note: Annual convention held in summer.

ASSOCIATION OF AMERICAN EDITORIAL CARTOONISTS — 3899 N Front St, Harrisburg, PA, 17110-1583, USA (717) 703-3003; fax (717) 703-3008; e-mail info@pa-news.org; aaec@pa-news.org; web site www.editorialcartoonists.com
Manager .... Teresa Shaak
Note: Elections held each year at the annual convention.

ASSOCIATION OF CANADIAN ADVERTISERS — 95 St Clair Ave. W., Ste. 1103, Toronto, ON, M4V 1N6, Canada (416) 964-3805; fax (416) 964-0771; web site www.acaweb.ca

ASSOCIATION OF FOOD JOURNALISTS, INC. — 7 Avenida Vista Grande, Ste B7 # 467, Santa Fe, NM, 87508-9207, USA 505-466-4742; e-mail caroldemasters@yahoo.com; web site www.afjonline.com
Exec. Dir. .... Carol DeMasters

Note: Election held in summer of even years

ASSOCIATION OF FREE COMMUNITY PAPERS — 7445 Morgan Rd, Ste 203, Liverpool, NY, 13090-3990, USA 877-203-2327; fax 781-859-7770; e-mail loren@afcp.org; web site www.afcp.org
Executive Director .... Loren Colburn
Administrative Assistant .... Alix Browne
Administrative Assistant .... Cassey Recore
Editor .... Dave Neuharth
Production Manager .... Barbara Holmes
Marketing Representative Wendy MacDonald

ASSOCIATION OF NATIONAL ADVERTISERS, INC. — 708 3rd Ave, 33rd Flr., New York, NY, 10017-4201, USA (212) 697-5950; fax (212) 687-7310; web site www.ana.net

ASSOCIATION OF NATIONAL ADVERTISERS, INC. — 2020 K St NW, Ste 660, Washington, DC, 20006-1900, USA (202) 296-1883; fax (202) 296-1430; web site www.ana.net

ASSOCIATION OF OPINION JOURNALISTS (FORMERLY THE NATIONAL CONFERENCE OF EDITORIAL WRITERS) — 801 3rd St S, Saint Petersburg, FL, 33701-4920, USA 727-821-9494; e-mail david.haynes@jrn.com; web site aoj.wildapricot.org

ASSOCIATION OF SCHOOLS OF JOURNALISM AND MASS COMMUNICATION — 234 Outlet Pointe Blvd, Ste A, Columbia, SC, 29210-5667, USA (803) 798-0271; fax (803) 772-3509; e-mail aejmchq@aol.com; web site www.asjmc.org
Exec. Dir. .... Jennifer McGill
Note: Elections held in April

B

BASEBALL WRITERS ASSOCIATION OF AMERICA — PO Box 610611, Bayside, NY, 11361-0611, USA (718) 767-2582; fax (718) 767-2583; e-mail bbwaa@aol.com; web site http://bbwaa.com
Secretary-Treasurer .... Jack O'Connell
Note: Elections held in Oct

BBM CANADA — 1500 Don Mills Rd., 3rd Fl., Toronto, ON, M3B 3L7, Canada (416) 445-9800; fax (416) 445-8644; e-mail info@bbm.ca; web site www.bbm.ca
Vice Pres., Western Servs..... Catherine Kelly
Corp. Scrvs. .... Dorena Noce
Exec. Vice Pres./CFO .... Glen Shipp
Exec. Asst. .... Heather Gillis
Pres./CEO .... Jim Mac Leod
Vice Pres., Meter Servs........... Randy Missen
Vice Pres., Quebec Servs.... Robert Langlois

BPA WORLDWIDE — 100 Beard Sawmill Rd, Fl 6, Shelton, CT, 06484-6156, USA (203) 447-2800; fax (203) 447-2900; web site www.bpaww.com
Chairman .... Carole A. Walker
Pres./CEO .... Glenn Hansen
Vice Pres., Commun.......... Karlene Lukeovitz
Sr. Vice Pres., Auditing .... Richard Murphy
Sr. Vice Pres., Mktg. Servs. .... Peter Black
Note: Elections held in May

CANADIAN PRESS, THE - TORONTO, ON — 36 King St. E., Toronto, ON, M5C 2L9, Canada (416) 364-0321; fax (416) 364-0207; e-mail info@thecanadianpress.com; web site www.thecanadianpress.com
Chrmn.................................. John Honderich
News Editor .... Ellen Huebert
Legislature Correspondent .... Keith Leslie
Pres. .... Eric Morrison
CFO .... David Ross
Chief, Ontario Servs. .... Wendy McCann
Vice Pres., Broadcasting .... Terry Scott
Vice Pres., French Servs................ Jean Roy
Dir., HR .... Paul Woods
Office Mgr. .... Sharon Hockin
Exec. Dir. .... Philipe Mercure
Note: Elections held in April

BUSINESS MARKETING ASSOCIATION — 1833 Centre Point Cir, Ste 123, Naperville, IL, 60563-4848, USA (630) 544-5054; fax (630) 544-5055; e-mail info@marketing.org; web site www.marketing.org
Membership Mgr. .... Kelly Staley
Exec. Dir. .... Patrick Farrey
Note: Elections held in June

C

CANADIAN BUSINESS PRESS — 2100 Banbury Cresent, Oakville, ON, L6H 5P6, Canada 905-844-6822; e-mail torrance@cbp.ca; web site www.cbp.ca
Executive Director .... Trish Torrance

CANADIAN CIRCULATIONS AUDIT BOARD (CCAB, INC.) — 1 Concorde Gate Suite 800, SUITE 800, Toronto, ON, M3C 3N6, Canada (416) 487-2418; fax (416) 487-6405; e-mail info@bpaww.com; web site www.bpaww.com
Mktg. Mgr. .... Neil Ta
Note: Elections held in April

CANADIAN NEWS MEDIA ASSOCITION — 37 Front Street East Suite 200, Toronto, ON, M5E 1B3, Canada; tel (1) 416 (416) 923-3567; fax (416) 923-7206; e-mail info@newsmediacanada.ca; web site www.https://nmc-mic.ca
Chairman .... Bob Cox
Vice-Chairmain .... Craig Bernard
Note: News Media Canada was formed by the merger of the Canadian Newspaper Association and the Canadian Community Newspapers Association in 2017

CANADIAN PRINTING INK MANUFACTURERS ASSOCIATION — 52 Palmer Rd., Grimby, ON, L3M 5L4, Canada (905) 309-5883; fax (905) 309-5838; e-mail cpima@sympatico.ca; web site www.cpima.org
Exec. Dir./Sec./Treasurer....... Dorothea Nace
Pres. .... Neil Marshall
Vice Pres. .... Vivy da Costa
Note: Elections held in Aug. for a two year term

CATHOLIC PRESS ASSOCIATION — 205 W Monroe St, Ste 470, Chicago, IL, 60606-5011, USA (312) 380-6789; fax (312) 361-0256; e-mail cathjourn@catholicpress.org; web site www.catholicpress.org
Exec. Dir .... Timothy Walter
Note: Elections held in Feb

COLLEGE MEDIA ASSOCIATION — 355 Lexington Ave, Fl 15, New York, NY, 10017-6603, USA 212-297-2195; e-mail info@collegemedia.org; web site www.collegemedia.org
Executive Director .... Meredith Taylor
Note: Elections held in Oct every two years.

COUNCIL FOR ADVANCEMENT AND SUPPORT OF EDUCATION — 1307 New York Ave NW, Ste 1000, Washington, DC, 20005-4726, USA (202) 328-2273; fax (202) 387-4973; e-mail memberservicecenter@case.org; web site www.case.org
Exec. Dir. .... Ben Patrusky
Pres. .... Cristine Russell
Admin. .... Diane McGurgan
Pres. .... John Lippincott
Note: Elections held in July.

COUNCIL FOR THE ADVANCEMENT OF SCIENCE WRITING, INC. — PO Box 910, Hedgesville, WV, 25427-0910, USA (304) 754-6786; e-mail info@casw.org; web site www.casw.org
Admin. .... Diane McGurgan
Pres. .... Alan Boyle
Exec. Dir. .... Rosalind Reid
Note: Elections held in April. Not a membership organization.

D

DIGITAL CONTENT NEXT — 1350 Broadway, Rm 606, New York, NY, 10018-7205, USA (646) 473-1000; fax (646) 473-0200; e-mail info@online-publishers.org; web site www.online-publishers.org

DOG WRITERS' ASSOCIATION OF AMERICA — 173 Union Rd, Coatesville, PA, 19320-1326, USA (610) 384-2436; fax (610) 384-2471; e-mail dwaa@dwaa.org; web site www.dwaa.org
Sec. .... Pat Santi
Pres. .... Dr. Carmen Battaglia
Pres. .... Carmen Battaglia
Note: Elections held in Feb. Writers contest closes Sept. 1 each year

E

EPICOMM — 1800 Diagonal Rd, Ste 320, Alexandria, VA, 22314-2862, USA 703-836-9200; fax 703-548-8204; e-mail info@epicomm.org; web site www.epicomm.org
President & CEO .... J. Ken Garner

EUROPEAN NEWSPAPER PUBLISHERS' ASSOCIATION — Square du Bastion 1A, Bte 3, 1050 Bruxelles, Belgium; tel (32) 2 551 0190; fax 551 0199; e-mail enpa@enpa.be; web site www.enpa.be
Dir. .... Valtteri Niiranen
Office Mgr. .... Viviane Garceau
Note: The ENPA is an association of European daily newspaper publishers organizations

F

FOREIGN PRESS ASSOCIATION — 333 E 46th St, Apt 1K, New York, NY, 10017-7426, USA (212) 370-1054; fax (212) 370-1058; e-mail fpanewyork@aol.com
Member .... Agnes Niemetz
Pres. .... Alan Capper
Vice Pres. .... David Michaels
Asst. Gen. Sec. .... Hadar Harel
Treasurer .... Jan Latus
Asst. Treasurer .... Roberto Socas
Note: Elections held in Dec

FREEDOM FORUM — 555 Pennsylvania Ave NW, Washington, DC, 20001-2114, USA (202) 292-6100; e-mail news@freedomforum.org; info@newseum.org; web site www.freedomforum.org
Chrmn./CEO .... Charles L. Overby
Sr. Vice Pres., Int'l Programs .... Chris Wells
Vice Pres., Opns. .... James Thompson
Sr. Vice Pres., Devel. .... Mary Kay Blake
Sr. Vice Pres., Finance ...... Nicole Mandeville
Vice Pres., Mktg. .... Susan Bennett
Note: Not a membership organization

G

GRAPHIC COMMUNICATIONS CONFERENCE/INTERNATIONAL BROTHERHOOD OF TEAMSTERS — 25 Louisiana Ave NW, Washington, DC, 20001-2130, USA (202) 508-6800; fax (202) 508-6661; web site www.gciu.org
Secretary-Treasurer/Vice President .... Robert Lacey
Note: Elections held quadrennially.

GRAPHIC COMMUNICATIONS COUNCIL — 1899 Preston White Dr, Reston, VA, 20191-5458, USA (703) 264-7200; fax (703) 620-0994; e-mail npes@npes.org; web site www.npes.org
Administrator .... Carol J. Hurlburt
Asst. Dir., Membership .... Carol Lee Hawkins

GRAVURE ASSOCIATION OF AMERICA — 8281 Pine Lake Rd, Denver, NC, 28037-8812, USA (201) 523-6042; fax (201) 523-6048; e-mail gaa@gaa.org; web site www.gaa.org
Pres./CEO .... Bill Martin
Exec. Dir. .... Bernadette Carlson
Dir. .... Michelle Jones Aronowitz
Ed. .... Roger Ynosroza
Note: Elections held in April

H

HEBDOS QUEBEC — 2550 Daniel-Johnson,, Bureau 345, Laval, QC, H7T 2L1, Canada 514 (514) 861-2088; fax (514) 861-1966; e-mail communications@hebdos.com; web site hebdos.com
Exec. Dir. .... Gilber Paquette

I

IDEALLIANCE — 1600 Duke St, Ste 420, Alexandria, VA, 22314-3421, USA (703)837-1070; e-mail http://idealliance.org; web site www.ipa.org
Exec. Asst. .... Donna McDevitt
Pres. .... Steven Bonoff
Note: Elections held in Oct.

INDEPENDENT FREE PAPERS OF AMERICA — 107 Hemlock Dr, Rio Grande, NJ, 08242-1731, USA (609) 408-8000; fax (609) 889-0141; web site www.ifpa.com
Exec. Dir. .... Gary Rudy
Note: Elections held in Sept

INTER AMERICAN PRESS ASSOCIATION — 1801 SW 3rd Ave, Fl 7, Miami, FL, 33129-1500, USA (305) 634-2465; fax (305)635-2272; e-mail info@sipiapa.org; web site www.sipiapa.org
Librarian .... Alfonso Juarez
Exec. Dir. .... Julio Munoz
Editor .... Horacio Ruiz
Note: Elections held in Nov

INTERMARKET AGENCY NETWORK — 5307 S 92nd St, Hales Corners, WI, 53130-1681, USA (414) 425-8800; fax (414) 425-0021; web site www.intermarketnetwork.com
Exec. Dir. .... Bill Eisner

INTERNATIONAL ADVERTISING ASSOCIATION, INC. — 747 3rd Ave, Fl 2, New York, NY, 10017-2878, USA 646-722-2612; fax 646 722 2501; e-mail iaa@iaaglobal.org; membership@iaaglobal.org; web site www.iaaglobal.org
Mgr. IT. .... Karl Kam
Exec. Dir. .... Michael Lee
Note: Elections held every two years at the IAA World-Advertising Congress. The IAA is a global partnership of advertisers, agencies, and media. The Association has 3,700 members in 95 countries, 105 corporate members, 65 organizational members and 61 chapters

INTERNATIONAL ASSOCIATION OF BUSINESS COMMUNICATORS (IABC) — 601 Montgomery St, Ste 1900, San Francisco,

CA, 94111-2690, USA (415) 544-4700; fax (415) 544-4747; e-mail service_centre@iabc.com; web site www.iabc.com
Pres./CEO .... Julie Freeman
Note: Elections held at international conference

INTERNATIONAL ASSOCIATION OF SPORTS NEWSPAPERS (IASN) — 7 rue Geoffroy Saint Hilaire, Paris, 75005, France; tel (33) 1 47 42 85 29; fax 47 42 49 48; e-mail rcuccoli@press-iasn.org; web site www.press-iasn.org
Sec. Gen. .... Rosarita Cuccoli

INTERNATIONAL CENTER FOR JOURNALISTS — 1616 H St NW, Fl 3, Washington, DC, 20006-4903, USA (202) 737-3700; fax (202) 737-0530; e-mail editor@icfj.org; web site www.icfj.org
Pres. .... Joyce Barnathan
Vice Pres., Finance .... Nancy Frye
Vice Pres., Programs .... Patrick Butler
Vice Pres., Development .... Vjollca Shtylla
Vice Pres., New Initiatives ... Sharon Moshavi
Note: International Center for Journalists is not a membership organization.

INTERNATIONAL LABOR COMMUNICATIONS ASSOCIATION AFL/CIO/CLC — 815 16th St NW, Washington, DC, 20006-4101, USA (202) 637-5068; fax (202) 637-5069; e-mail ilca@aflcio.org; web site www.ilcaonline.org
Pres. .... Steve Stallone
Note: Elections held biennially.

INTERNATIONAL NEWSPAPER MARKETING ASSOCIATION, INC. — PO Box 740186, Dallas, TX, 75374-0186, USA (214) 373-9111; fax (214) 373-9112; e-mail inma@inma.org; web site www.inma.org
Exec. Dir. .... Earl J. Wilkinson
Note: Elections held in May

INTERNATIONAL PRESS CLUB OF CHICAGO (IPCC) — PO Box 2498, Chicago, IL, 60690-2498, USA; tel (312-834-7728) Chicago 312-834-7228; e-mail info@ipcc.org; web site www.internationalpressclubofchicago.org
President .... Wayne Toberman
Note: Lunch meetings every Thursday monthly at Union League Club Chicago

INTERNATIONAL PRESS INSTITUTE — Spiegelgasse 2, Vienna, A-1010, Austria; tel (43) 1 512 9011; fax 512 9014; e-mail ipi@freemedia.at; web site www.freemedia.at
Dir. .... David Dadge
Note: Elections held annually on a rotation basis

INTERNATIONAL SOCIETY OF WEEKLY NEWSPAPER EDITORS — 3950 Newman Rd, Joplin, MO, 64801-1512, USA (417) 625-9736; fax (417) 659-4445; e-mail stebbins-c@mssu.edu; web site www.iswne.org
Exec. Dir. .... Chad Stebbins
Note: Elections held in June or July at the annual conference.

INVESTIGATIVE REPORTERS AND EDITORS (IRE) — 141 Neff Annex, Columbia, MO, 65211-0001, USA (573) 882-2042; fax (573) 882-5431; e-mail info@ire.org; web site www.ire.org
Exec. Dir. .... Mark Horvit
Note: Elections held in June

J

JAPAN NEWSPAPER PUBLISHERS & EDITORS ASSOCIATION — Nippon Press Center Bldg., 2-2-1 Uchisaiwai-cho, Chiyoda-ku, Tokyo, 100-8543, Japan; tel (+81) 3-3591-3462; fax -9743; e-mail editor@pressnet.or.jp; web site www.pressnet.or.jp/english/index.htm
North American Rep. .... Ryuta Araki

K

KAPPA ALPHA MU HONORARY SOCIETY IN PHOTO JOURNALISM — 316F Lee Hills Hall, Columbia, MO, 65211-1370, USA 573-882-4821; fax 573-884-5400; e-mail kratzerb@missouri.edu; web site www.photojournalism.missouri.edu
Chrmn. .... David Rees
Director of Photography, Assistant Professor. Brian Kratzer
Note: An affiliate of the National Press Photographers Association. Elections held in the fall.

KAPPA TAU ALPHA NATIONAL HONOR SOCIETY FOR JOURNALISM & MASS COMMUNICATION — University of Missouri, 76 Gannett Hall, Columbia, MO, 65211-0001, USA (573) 882-7685; fax (573) 884-1720; e-mail umcjourkta@missouri.edu; web site www.kappataualpha.org
P, Kent State University .... Jeff Fruit
VP, Arkansas State .... Holly Hunt
Exec. Dir./Treasurer .... Beverly Horvit
Note: Elections held every two years

L

LEAGUE OF ADVERTISING AGENCIES, INC. — 65 Reade St, Apt 3A, New York, NY, 10007-1841, USA (212) 528-0364; fax (212) 766-1181; web site www.adagencies.org
Exec. Dir. .... Deana Boles
Pres. .... Lori Fabisiak
Treasurer .... Mark Levit
Sec. .... Mindy Gale
Vice Pres. .... Richard Harrow
Note: Elections held in May

LOCAL MEDIA ASSOCIATION — PO Box 450, Lake City, MI, 49651-0450, USA (888) 486-2466; fax (888) 317-0856; e-mail hq@localmedia.org; web site www.localmedia.org
Vice President - Director of R & D ServicesAl Cupo
President .... Nancy Lane
Sales and Marketing Director .... Conti Peter
Sales & Marketing Manager
.... Lindsey Estes
Classified Avenue Director of Sales .. Deanna Lewis
Marketing Technology Manager .. Abdul Khan
Local Media Today Editor .... Deb Shaw
Accounting & Finance Director .... Janice Norman
Director of Broadcast Services .. Jack Zavoral
Note: Elections held in the fall

M

MARKETING ADVERTISING GLOBAL NETWORK — 1017 Perry Hwy, Ste 5, Pittsburgh, PA, 15237-2173, USA (412) 366-6850; fax (412) 366-6840; e-mail cheri@magnetglobal.org; web site www.magnetglobal.org
Executive Director .... Cheri Gmiter
Note: Elections held in Oct

MEDIA ALLIANCE — 2830 20th St Ste 102, Pacific Felt Factory, San Francisco, CA, 94110-2825, USA; tel (01) 415 746-9475; fax N/A; e-mail tracy@media-alliance.org; web site www.media-alliance.org
Exec. Dir. .... Tracy Rosenberg

MEDIA FINANCIAL MANAGEMENT ASSOCIATION — 550 W Frontage Rd, Ste 3600, Northfield, IL, 60093-1243, USA 847-716-7000; fax 847-716-7004; e-mail info@mediafinance.org; web site www.mediafinance.org
President & CEO .... Mary Collins
Director of Operations .... Jamie Smith

MEDIA HUMAN RESOURCES ASSOCIATION — 1800 Duke St, Alexandria, VA, 22314-3494, USA (800) 283-7476; fax (703) 535-6490; e-mail shrm@shrm.org; web site www.shrm.org
Pres. .... Laurence O'Neil
Note: Elections held in June

N

NATIONAL ASSOCIATION OF BLACK JOURNALISTS — 1100 Knight Hall, Suite 3100, College Park, MD, 20742-0001, USA (301) 405-0248; fax (301) 314-1714; e-mail nabj@nabj.org; web site www.nabj.org
Exec. Dir. .... Karen Wynn Freeman
Pres. .... Kathy Times
Note: Elections held every two years

NATIONAL ASSOCIATION OF BROADCASTERS — 1771 N St NW, Washington, DC, 20036-2800, USA (202) 429-5300; fax (202) 429-4199; e-mail nab@nab.org; web site www.nab.org
Joint Board Chrmn. .... Bruce T. Reese
COO/CFO .... Janet McGregor
Note: Elections held once in two years.

NATIONAL ASSOCIATION OF CREDIT MANAGEMENT — 8840 Columbia 100 Pkwy, Columbia, MD, 21045-2100, USA (410) 740-5560; fax (410) 740-5574; e-mail info@nacm.org; web site www.nacm.org
Dir., Commun. .... Caroline Zimmerman
Treasurer .... James E. Vanghel
Pres. .... Robin D. Schauseil
Note: Elections held in May

NATIONAL ASSOCIATION OF HISPANIC JOURNALISTS — 1050 Connecticut Ave NW, Fl 10, Washington, DC, 20036-5334, USA (202) 662-7145; fax (202) 662-7144; e-mail nahj@nahj.org; web site www.nahj.org
Interim Executive Director ...... Anna M. Lopez Buck

NATIONAL ASSOCIATION OF HISPANIC PUBLICATIONS — 529 14th St NW, Ste 1126, Washington, DC, 20045-2120, USA (202) 662-7250; e-mail directory@nahp.org; web site www.nahp.org
Exec. Dir. .... Kerry Stackpole
Note: Elections held every two years

NATIONAL ASSOCIATION OF REAL ESTATE EDITORS (NAREE) — 1003 NW 6th Ter, Boca Raton, FL, 33486-3455, USA (561) 391-3599; fax (561) 391-0099; e-mail madkimba@aol.com; web site www.naree.org
Executive Director .... Mary Doyle-Kimball
Note: 63rd Annual Journalism Competition - Entry Deadline March 1, 2013 for work published in 2012. Platinum, Gold, Silver and Bronze Awards, plus awards for Best Freelance Collection and Best Young Journalist. 25 categories for journalists specializing in residential and commercial real estate, mortgage finance, green building, home design and urban planning. New category this year: "Best Breaking News Report."

NATIONAL ASSOCIATION OF REAL ESTATE PUBLISHERS — PO Box 5292, Florence, SC, 29502-5292, USA N/A; e-mail narep2014@gmail.com; web site www.narep.org
Secretary/Treasurer .... Sheila Stepp
Note: Elections held in May

NATIONAL ASSOCIATION OF SCIENCE WRITERS — PO Box 7905, Berkeley, CA, 94707-0905, USA 510-647-9500; e-mail director@nasw.org; web site www.nasw.org

NATIONAL CARTOONISTS SOCIETY — 341 N Maitland Ave, Ste 130, Maitland, FL, 32751-4761, USA (407) 647-8839; fax (407) 629-2502; e-mail crowsegal@crowsegal.com; web site www.reuben.org
Pres. .... Jeff Keane
Note: Elections held annually

NATIONAL FEDERATION OF PRESS WOMEN — 200 Little Falls St, Ste 405, Falls Church, VA, 22046-4302, USA 800-780-2715; fax (703) 237-9808; e-mail presswomen@aol.com; web site www.nfpw.org
Executive Director .... Carol Pierce
Note: Elections held odd years in June

NATIONAL LESBIAN AND GAY JOURNALISTS ASSOCIATION — 2120 L St NW, Ste 850, Washington, DC, 20037-1550, USA (202) 588-9888; fax (202) 588-1818; e-mail info@nlgja.org; web site www.nlgja.org
Pres. .... David Barrie
Note: Elections held annually

NATIONAL NEWSPAPER ASSOCIATION — 900 Community Drive, Springfield, IL, 62703, USA (217)241-1400; fax (217) 241-1301; e-mail lynne@nna.org; web site www.nna.org
Comm. Dir. .... Stan Schwartz
Chief Operating Officer .... Lynne Lance
CEO .... Sam Fisher
Note: Officer elections held in Sept/Oct during Annual Convention; annual Leadership Conference in March; annual Better Newspaper Contest entry deadline Spring

NATIONAL NEWSPAPER PUBLISHERS ASSOCIATION BLACK PRESS OF AMERICA — 1816 12th St NW, Washington, DC, 20009-4422, USA 202-588-8764; fax 202-588-8960; e-mail nnpadc@nnpa.org; web site www.nnpa.org
Interim Exec. Ed. .... Hazel Trice Edney
Note: Elections held every two years in June.

NATIONAL PAPER TRADE ASSOCIATION, INC. — 330 N Wabash Ave, Ste 2000, Chicago, IL, 60611-7621, USA (312) 321-4092; fax (312) 673-6736; e-mail npta@gonpta.com; web site www.gonpta.com
Pres. .... Newell Holt
Note: Elections held in Oct

NATIONAL PRESS CLUB — 529 14th St NW, Washington, DC, 20045-1217, USA (202) 662-7500; fax (202) 662-7569; web site www.press.org
Exec. Dir. .... William McCarren
Note: Elections held in Nov

NATIONAL PRESS FOUNDATION — 1211 Connecticut Ave NW, Ste 310, Washington, DC, 20036-2709, USA (202) 663-7280; fax (202) 530-2855; e-mail npf@nationalpress.org; web site www.nationalpress.org
President and COO .... Bob Meyers

NATIONAL PRESS PHOTOGRAPHERS ASSOCIATION, INC. — 3200 Croasdaile Dr, Ste 306, Durham, NC, 27705-2588, USA (919) 383-7246; fax (919) 383-7261; e-mail info@nppa.org; web site www.nppa.org
Exec. Dir. .... Jim Straight
Membership Dir. .... Mindy Hutchison
Note: Elections held in June

NATIONAL RETAIL FEDERATION — 325 7th St Nw, Liberty Pl, Ste 1100, Washington, DC, 20004, USA (202) 783-7971; fax (202) 737-2849; web site www.nrf.com
CFO .... Carleen C. Kohut

Pres. ....Tracy Mullin
Note: Elections held in Jan

NATIONAL SCHOLASTIC PRESS ASSOCIATION
— 2221 University Ave SE, Ste 121, Minneapolis, MN, 55414-3074, USA (612) 625-8335; fax 612-605-0072; e-mail info@studentpress.org; web site www.studentpress.org
Exec. Dir. .... Logan Aimone

NATIONAL WRITERS ASSOCIATION
— 10940 S Parker Rd, Ste 508, Parker, CO, 80134-7440, USA (303) 841-0246; e-mail natlwritersassn@hotmail.com; web site www.nationalwriters.com
Exec. Dir. ....Sandy Whelchel

NATIVE AMERICAN JOURNALISTS ASSOCIATION
— 395 W Lindsey St, Norman, OK, 73019-4201, USA (405) 325-1649; fax (405) 325-6945; e-mail info@naja.com; web site www.naja.com
Pres. .... Cristina Azocar
Interim. Dir. ....Jeff Harjo
Note: Elections held in August

NEW YORK MEDIA CREDIT GROUP
— 1100 Main St, Buffalo, NY, 14209-2308, USA 716-887-9547; fax 716-878-0479; e-mail robert.gagliardi@abc-amega.com
Regional Account Manager. Robert Gagliardi
Pres. ....Nina Link
Dir. .... Vaughn P. Benjamin
Note: Elections held in March

NEWS MEDIA ALLIANCE
— 4401 Wilson Blvd, Ste 900, Arlington, VA, 22203-4195, USA (571) 366-1000; fax (571) 366-1195; e-mail sheila.owens@naa.org; web site www.naa.org
Pres. & CEO ....David Chavern
CFO.......................................Robert Walden
VP of HRO.......................... Sarah Burkman
SVP Bus. Dev. .... Rich Schiekofer
VP of Audience Dev. ....John Murray
Comm. Mgr. .... LIndsey Loving
SVP of Public Policy......................Paul Boyle
VP of Public Policy .... Danielle Coffey
VP, Research & Industry Analysis...........Jim Conaghan
Public Policy Mgr. ....Kristina Zaumseil
Note: Elections held in April/May

NEWS MEDIA CANADA
— 37 Front Street East Suite 200, Toronto, ON, M5E 1B3, Canada (416) 923-3567; fax (416) 923-7206; e-mail info@newspaperscanada.ca; web site www.ccna.ca
Pres. ....John Hinds

NEWSPAPER ASSOCIATION MANAGERS, INC.
— 32 Dunham Rd, Beverly, MA, 01915-1844, USA 978-338-2555; e-mail mlpiper52@cmcast.net; web site www.nammanagers.com
Exec. Dir. .... Morley Piper
Finance Officer......................... Susan Daigle
Note: Elections held in Aug

NEWSPAPER CANADA
— 890 Yonge Street Ste 200, Toronto, ON, M4W 3P4, Canada (416) 923-3567; fax (416) 923-7206; e-mail info@newspapercanada.ca; web site www.newspapercanada.ca

NORTH AMERICAN AGRICULTURAL JOURNALISTS
— 6434 Hurta Ln, Bryan, TX, 77808-9283, USA (979) 845-2872; fax (979) 862-1202; e-mail ka-phillips@tamu.edu; web site www.naaj.net
Exec. Sec./Treasurer ....Kathleen Phillips
Note: Elections held in April

NORTH AMERICAN MATURE PUBLISHERS ASSOCIATION
— 1140 Jupiter Rd, Camdenton, MO, 65020-4403, USA (877) 466-2672; fax (573) 873-9993; e-mail kzarky@maturepublishers.com; web site www.maturepublishers.com
Exec. Dir. ....Karen Zarky
Note: Election held in Nov

NPES
— 1899 Preston White Dr, Reston, VA, 20191-5458, USA (703) 264-7200; fax (703) 620-0994; e-mail npes@npes.org; web site www.npes.org
Dir., Commun............................ Judy Durham
Pres. ....Ralph Nappi
Chrmn....................................Tom Saggiomo
Note: NPES is the association for suppliers of printing, publishing and converting technologies. Elections held at fall meeting

O

ORGANIZATION OF NEWS OMBUDSMEN
— 6336 Hawthorn Lane, Vancouver, BC, V6T 2J6, Canada (604) 353-6228; e-mail klapointe@newsombudsmen.org; web site www.newsombudsmen.org
Executive Director .... Kirk LaPointe

OUTDOOR ADVERTISING ASSOCIATION OF AMERICA (OAAA)
— 1850 M St NW, Ste 1040, Washington, DC, 20036-5821, USA (202) 833-5566; fax (202) 833-1522; e-mail info@oaaa.org; web site www.oaaa.org
Pres. & CEO .... Nancy Fletcher

OUTDOOR WRITERS ASSOCIATION OF AMERICA, INC.
— 615 Oak St, Ste 201, Missoula, MT, 59801-2469, USA (406) 728-7434; fax (406) 728-7445; e-mail info@owaa.org; web site www.owaa.org
Executive Director ....Brandon Shuler
Note: Elections held in Spring

OVERSEAS PRESS CLUB OF AMERICA
— 40 West 45 Street, New York, NY, 10036, USA (212) 626-9220; fax (212) 626-9210; e-mail info@opcofamerica.org; web site www.opcofamerica.org
Exec. Dir. .... Patricia Kranz
Note: Elections held in late summer

P

PRINTING INDUSTRIES OF AMERICA
— 200 Deer Run Rd, Sewickley, PA, 15143-2324, USA (412) 741-6860; fax (412) 741-2311; e-mail printing@printing.org; web site www.printing.org
Mktg. Mgr. .... Lisa Erdner
VP.. Gary Jones

PRINTING, PUBLISHING & MEDIA WORKERS SECTOR-CWA
— 501 3rd St NW, Ste 950, Washington, DC, 20001-2760, USA (202) 434-1106; fax (202) 434-1482; e-mail bshippe@cwa-union.org; web site www.cwa-union.org
Pres. ....Larry Cohen
Note: Elections to be held at CWA convention in August 2008.

PROFESSIONAL FOOTBALL WRITERS OF AMERICA (PFWA)
— 11345 Frontage Ave, Maryland Heights, MO, 63043-5000, USA (314) 298-2681; e-mail hbalzer@aol.com; web site www.pfwa.org
Secretary...............................Howard Balzer
Note: Elections held in Jan

PROMOTION MARKETING ASSOCIATION, INC.
— 650 1st Ave, Ste 2-SW, New York, NY, 10016-3240, USA (212) 420-1100; fax (212) 533-7622; e-mail pma@pmalink.org; web site www.pmalink.org
Note: Elections held in June

PROMOTIONAL PRODUCTS ASSOCIATION INTERNATIONAL
— 3125 Skyway Cir N, Irving, TX, 75038-3526, USA 972-252-0404; fax (972) 258-3004; e-mail pr@ppai.org; web site www.ppai.org
Vice Pres., Mktg./Commun... Paul Bellantone
Pres./CEO ....Steve Slagle

PUBLIC RELATIONS SOCIETY OF AMERICA, INC.
— 33 Maiden Ln, Fl 11, New York, NY, 10038-5149, USA (212) 460-1400; fax (212) 995-0757; e-mail hq@prsa.org; web site www.prsa.org
Pres. ....Willam Murray
Note: Elections held in October

Q

QUILL AND SCROLL SOCIETY
— 100 Adler Journalism Bldg Ste W111, Univ. of Iowa School of Journalism and Mass Comm., Iowa City, IA, 52242-2004, USA (319) 335-3457; fax (319) 335-3989; e-mail quill-scroll@uiowa.edu; web site www.uiowa.edu

R

RADIO TELEVISION DIGITAL NEWS ASSOCIATION
— 529 14th St NW, Ste 1240, Washington, DC, 20045-2520, USA (770) 622-7011; fax (202) 223-4007; e-mail mikec@rtdna.org; web site www.rtdna.org
Exec. Dir. ....Mike Cavender
Awards, Membership and Programs Manager Katie Switchenko
Digital, Communications and Marketing Manager ....Derrick Hinds
Manager of Membership and ProgramsKaren Hansen
Meetings and Events Manager. Noukla Ruble

REGIONAL REPORTERS ASSOCIATION
— 1575 Eye St NW Suite 350, Washington, DC, 20005, USA (202) 408-2705; e-mail president@rra.org; web site www.rra.org
Sec. .... Adrianne Flynn
Pres. ....Suzanne Struglinski

RELIGION NEWS ASSOCIATION
— University of Missouri, 30 Neff Annex, Columbia, MO, 65211-0001, USA (740)263-7875; e-mail McCallen@RNA.org; web site www.RNA.org
Chief Ops. Officer...............Tiffany McCallen
Business Mgr..........................Amy Schiska

REPORTERS COMMITTEE FOR FREEDOM OF THE PRESS
— 1101 Wilson Blvd, Ste 1100, Arlington, VA, 22209-2275, USA (703) 807-2100; fax (703) 807-2109; e-mail rcfp@rcfp.org; web site www.rcfp.org
Exec. Committee ....Dahlia Lithwick
Exec. Dir. ....Lucy A. Dalglish
Exec. Committee .... Neil Lewis
Exec. Committee ....Tony Mauro

RTDNA - CANADA (RADIO TELEVISION DIGITAL NEWS ASSOCIATION)
— 2800 - 14th Ave., Ste. 210, Markham, ON, L3R 0E4, Canada (416) 756 2213; fax (416) 491-1670; e-mail sherry@associationconcepts.ca; info@rtdnacanada.com; web site www.rtdnacanada.com
Operations Manager........... Sherry Denesha
Note: Elections held in June

S

SALES AND MARKETING EXECUTIVES INTERNATIONAL
— PO Box 1390, Sumas, WA, 98295-1390, USA (312) 893-0751; fax (604) 855-0165; e-mail willis.turner@smei.org; web site www.smei.org
Pres./CEO .... Willis Turner
Note: Elections held on a rolling basis

SOCIETY FOR FEATURES JOURNALISM
— 1100 Knight Hall, College Park, MD, 20742-0001, USA (301) 314-2631; fax (301) 314-9166; e-mail aasfe@jmail.umd.edu; web site www.aasfe.org
Pres. .... Denise Joyce
Exec. Dir. .... Kalyani Chadda
Note: Elections held in Sept./Oct

SOCIETY FOR NEWS DESIGN, INC.
— 424 E Central Blvd, Ste 406, Orlando, FL, 32801-1923, USA (407) 420-7748; fax (407) 420-7697; e-mail snd@snd.org; web site www.snd.org
Exec. Dir. ....Stephen Komives
Note: Annual competition deadline is mid-January. Officer elections held in fall prior to annual workshop exhibition.

SOCIETY OF AMERICAN BUSINESS EDITORS AND WRITERS, INC.
— 555 N Central Ave, Ste 302, Phoenix, AZ, 85004-1248, USA (602) 496-7862; fax (602) 496-7041; e-mail sabew@sabew.org; web site www.sabew.org
Note: Elections held in April

SOCIETY OF AMERICAN TRAVEL WRITERS, INC.
— 7044 S 13th St, Oak Creek, WI, 53154-1429, USA (414) 908-4949; fax (414) 768-8001; e-mail satw@satw.org; web site www.satw.org
Exec. Dir. ....Nancy Short

SOCIETY OF ENVIRONMENTAL JOURNALISTS (SEJ)
— PO Box 2492, Suite 301, Jenkintown, PA, 19046-8492, USA (215) 884-8174; fax (215) 884-8175; e-mail sej@sej.org; web site www.sej.org
Exec. Dir. ....Beth Parke
Note: Board elections held each fall

SOCIETY OF PROFESSIONAL JOURNALISTS
— 3909 N Meridian St, Ste 200, Indianapolis, IN, 46208-4011, USA (317) 927-8000; fax (317) 920-4789; e-mail spj@spj.org; web site www.spj.org
Interim Executive Director ....Tara Puckey

SOCIETY OF THE SILURIANS
— PO Box 1195, Madison Square Station, New York, NY, 10159-1195, USA (212) 532-0887; e-mail silurians@aol.com; web site www.silurians.org
Membership Chairman..........Mort Sheinman
Editor, Silurian News ....Bernard Kirsch
Note: Elections of officers and board members held in May

SPECIAL LIBRARIES ASSOCIATION, NEWS DIVISION
— 331 S Patrick St, Alexandria, VA, 22314-3501, USA (703) 647-4900; fax (703) 647-4901; e-mail sla@sla.org; web site www.sla.org
CEO................................. Janice R. Lachance
COO/CFO...................... Nancy A. Sansalone
Dir., Exec. Office Relations...Natasha Kenner
Note: Elections held in May

T

TECHNICAL ASSOCIATION OF THE GRAPHIC ARTS
— 200 Deer Run Rd, Sewickley, PA, 15143-2324, USA (412) 259-1706; fax (412) 741-2311; e-mail taga@printing.org; web site www.taga.org
Managing Director......................Mark Bohan
Note: Elections held in February

THE 4 A'S
— 1065 Avenue of the Americas, Fl 16, New York, NY, 10018-0174, USA (212) 682-2500; fax (212) 682-8391; e-mail info@aaaa.com; web site www.aaaa.org
Pres. & CEO .... Nancy Fletcher
Note: Election held in April

THE ADVERTISING COUNCIL, INC. — 815 2nd Ave, Fl 9, New York, NY, 10017-4500, USA (212) 922-1500; fax (212) 922-1676; e-mail info@adcouncil.org; web site www.adcouncil.org
Pres. & Chief Exec. Officer...... Lisa Sherman

THE ADVERTISING RESEARCH FOUNDATION (ARF) — 432 Park Ave S, Fl 6, New York, NY, 10016-8013, USA (212) 751-5656; fax (212) 319-5265; e-mail info@thearf.org; web site www.thearf.org
CEO & Pres............................. Gayle Fuguitt
Note: Elections held in March

THE DIRECT MARKETING ASSOCIATION, INC. — 1120 Avenue of the Americas, New York, NY, 10036-6700, USA (212) 768-7277; fax (212) 302-6714; web site www.the-dma.org
CEO .... Lawrence M. Kimmel
Note: Elections held in Oct

THE NATIONAL SOCIETY OF NEWSPAPER COLUMNISTS, INC. — 205 Gun Hill St, Milton, MA, 02186-4026, USA 617 322-1420; e-mail director@columnists.com; web site www.columnists.com
Executive Director (as of January 2017) .... Suzette Standring
Note: Annual conference held in June.

THE NEWSGUILD-CWA — 501 3rd St NW Fl 6, Fl 6, Washington, DC, 20001-2760, USA (202) 434-7177; fax (202) 434-1472; e-mail guild@newsguild.org; web site www.newsguild.org
President ....Bernard Lunzer
International Chairperson..Martha Waggoner
Exec. VP ....Marian Needham

TRANS-CANADA ADVERTISING AGENCY NETWORK — 25 Sheppard Ave. West, Suite 300, Toronto, ON, M2N 6S6, Canada 416-221-8883; e-mail mabill@waginc.ca; web site www.tcaan.ca
Exec. Dir. ....Alice Zaharchuk
Mng. Dir./Treasurer ....Bill Whitehead

U

UNITED NATIONS CORRESPONDENTS ASSOCIATION — United Nations, Room S-308, New York, NY, 10017, USA (212) 963-7137; e-mail contactus@unca.com; web site www.unca.com
Pres. .... Giam Paolo Pioli
1st Vice Pres.................. Louis Charbonneau
2nd Vice Pres. .... Masood Haider
Note: Elections held in Dec

W

WINNIPEG PRESS CLUB — C/O St. James Legion Branch #4, 1755 Portage Avenue, Winnipeg, MB, R3J 0E6, Canada (204) 800-1887; e-mail winnipegpressclub@outlook.com
VP.. Wendy Hart
Pres. .... Dwight MacAulay
Note: Since 2011, we have made our home at a local Royal Canadian Legion branch in Winnipeg, which has allowed us gracious use of their facilities. (Bar, meeting rooms, games room, food services).
We welcome visitors from press clubs and media organizations around the world. If you are planning to be in Winnipeg, please email winnipegpressclub@outlook.com, or call (204) 800-1887.

WORLD ASSOCIATION OF NEWSPAPERS AND NEWS PUBLISHERS (WAN-IFRA) — Rotfeder-Ring 11, Frankfurt am Main, 60327, Germany; tel (49) 69 240063-0; fax 240063-300; e-mail info@wan-ifra.org; web site www.wan-ifra.org
WAN-IFRA President.............Michael Golden
WAN-IFRA CEO .... Vincent Peyrègne
Note: Elections held every two years in June.

WORLD ASSOCIATION OF NEWSPAPERS AND NEWS PUBLISHERS (WAN-IFRA) — Rotfeder-Ring 11, Frankfurt, 60327, Germany; tel (49) 69 240063-0; fax 240063-300; e-mail info@wan-ifra.org; web site www.wan-ifra.org
.... Vincent Peyrègne
.... Christoph RiessCEOs

WORLD PRESS INSTITUTE — 3415 University Ave W, Saint Paul, MN, 55114-1019, USA 612-205-7582; e-mail info@worldpressinstitute.org; web site www.worldpressinstitute.org
Exec. Dir. .... David McDonald

Y

YOUTH EDITORIAL ASSOCIATION — 4401 Wilson Blvd, Ste 900, Arlington, VA, 22203-4195, USA 571-366-1000; e-mail sandy.woodcock@naa.org; web site www.naafoundation.org
Director- NAA Foundation ..Sandy Woodcock

ASSOCIATIONS AND CLUBS - CITY STATE AND REGIONAL

A

ADVERTISING CLUB OF GREATER NEW YORK — 989 Avenue of the Americas, 7th floor, New York, NY, 10018, USA; tel (212) 533-8080; fax (212) 533-1929; e-mail memberships@theadvertisingclub.org; web site www.theadvertisingclub.org
Exec. Dir. .... Gina Grillo
Note: Elections held in July

ALBERTA WEEKLY NEWSPAPERS ASSOCIATION — 3228 Parsons Rd, Edmonton, AB, T6N 1M2, Canada; tel (780) 434-8746; fax (780) 438-8356; e-mail info@awna.com; web site www.awna.com
Exec. Dir. .... Dennis Merrell

ALLIED DAILY NEWSPAPERS OF WASHINGTON — 1110 Capitol Way S, Olympia, WA, 98501-2251, USA; tel (360) 943-9960; fax (360) 943-9962; e-mail anewspaper@aol.com
Exec. Dir. ....Rowland Thompson

ARIZONA ASSOCIATED PRESS MANAGING EDITORS ASSOCIATION — 1850 N. Central Ave., Ste. 640, Phoenix, AZ, 85004, USA; tel (602) 258-8934; fax (602) 254-9573; e-mail aparizona@ap.org; web site www.ap.org/arizona
Bureau Chief .... Michelle Williams
Note: Elections held in the summer

ARKANSAS PRESS WOMEN ASSOCIATION, INC. — 1301 Golden Pond Rd, Little Rock, AR, 72223-9549, USA; tel 501-671-2126; fax 501-671-2121; e-mail arkpresswomen@yahoo.com; web site arkpresswomen.wordpress.com
President .... Mary Hightower
Treasurer .... Terry Hawkins
Note: Elections held in the fall of spring odd numbered years

ASSOCIATED COLLEGIATE PRESS — 2221 University Ave. SE, Ste. 121, Minneapolis, MN, 55414, USA; tel (612) 625-8335; fax (612) 626-0720; e-mail info@studentpress.org; web site www.studentpress.org
Exec. Dir. .... Logan Aimone

ASSOCIATED PRESS — 184 High St #3, Boston, MA, 02110, USA; tel (617) 357-8100; fax (617) 338-8125; e-mail apboston@ap.org; web site www.ap.org/boston
News Ed. .... William Kole
Dir., Local Media...........Dwayne Desaulniers
Pres. & CEO .... Gary Pruitt

ASSOCIATED PRESS/CALIFORNIA-NEVADA NEWS EXECUTIVES — 221 S. Figueroa St., Ste. 300, Los Angeles, CA, 90012, USA; tel (213) 626-5833; e-mail losangeles@ap.org; web site www.ap.org/losangeles
Bureau Chief, Los Angeles Anthony Marquez
Bureau Chief, San Francisco.......John Raess
Reg'l Vice Pres. Newyork ....Sue Cross
Note: Elections held in May

ASSOCIATED PRESS/OKLAHOMA NEWS EXECUTIVES — 525 Central Park Dr., Ste. 202, Oklahoma City, OK, 73105, USA; tel (405) 525-2121; fax (405) 524-7465; e-mail apoklahoma@ap.org; web site www.ap.org/oklahoma
Bureau Chief .... Dale Leach

ATLANTIC COMMUNITY NEWSPAPERS ASSOCIATION — 7075 Bayers Rd., Ste. 216, Halifax, NS, B3L 2C2, Canada; tel (902) 832-4480; fax (902) 832-4484; e-mail info@newspapersatlantic.ca; web site www.acna.com
Exec. Dir. ....Mike Kierstead

B

BRITISH COLUMBIA/YUKON COMMUNITY NEWSPAPERS ASSOCIATION — #9 West Broadway, Vancouver, BC, V5Y 1P1, Canada; tel (604) 669-9222; fax (604) 684-4713; e-mail info@bccommunitynews.com; web site www.bccommunitynews.com
Gen. Mgr.................................George Affleck
Note: Elections held in May

C

CAL WESTERN CIRCULATION MANAGERS' ASSOCIATION — 123 Sequoia Glen Ln, Novato, CA, 94947, USA; tel (415) 297-8836; e-mail cwcma@imblake.com; web site www.cwcma.org
Executive Director .... Blake Webber
Pres. ....Aaron Kotarek
Note: Election of officers is held during the annual meeting. Annual meeting is in June every year.

CALIFORNIA PRESS ASSOCIATION — Cal. Newspr. Publs. Assoc., 2000 O St., Suite 120, Sacramento, CA, 95811, USA; tel (916) 288-6000; web site www.cnpa.com
Exec. Dir. .... Thomas Newton
Note: Elections held in Dec

CAPITOL PRESS ASSOCIATION — PO Box 191, Raleigh, NC, 27602, USA; tel (919) 836-2858; e-mail smooneyh@ncinsider.com
Mgr....................................Scott Mooneyham
Note: Elections held in Jan

CCNMA: LATINO JOURNALISTS OF CALIFORNIA — ASU Walter Cronkite School of Journalism, 725 Arizona Ave. Ste. 404, Santa Monica, CA, 90401-1723, USA; tel (424) 229-9482; fax (424) 238-0271; e-mail ccnmainfo@ccnma.org; web site www.ccnma.org
Executive Director .... Julio Moran

CENTRAL STATES CIRCULATION MANAGERS ASSOCIATION — 562 54th Street A, Moline, IL, 61265, USA; tel N/A; e-mail cscma@aol.com; web site www.cscma.com
Board Chair
.... Angie Lyons
President ....Scott Kinter
Secretary/Treasurer.................Jill Henderson
Note: Elections held in April

COLORADO ASSOCIATED PRESS EDITORS AND REPORTERS — 1444 Wazee St., Ste. 130, Denver, CO, 80202-1395, USA; tel (303) 825-0123; fax (303) 892-5927; e-mail apdenver@ap.org; web site www.ap.org/colorado
Bureau Chief ....Jim Clarke
Note: Elections held in Feb

COMMUNITY PAPERS OF INDIANA — PO Box 1004, Crown Point, IN, 46308, USA; tel (219) 689-6262; fax (219) 374-7558
Pub./Owner ....Shari Foreman
Note: Elections held in April

COMMUNITY PAPERS OF MICHIGAN — 5000 Northwind Dr., Ste. 240, East Lansing, MI, 48823, USA; tel (517) 333-3355; fax (517) 333-3322; e-mail jackguza@cpapersmi.com;slkotecki@cpapersmi.com; web site www.communitypapersofmichigan.com
Exec. Dir. ....Jack Guza

CONNECTICUT ASSOCIATED PRESS MANAGING EDITORS ASSOCIATION — 10 Columbus Blvd., Hartford, CT, 06106, USA; tel (860) 246-6876; fax (860) 727-4003; e-mail aphartford@ap.org; web site www.ap.org
Bureau Chief ....William Kole

CONSEIL DE PRESSE DU QUEBEC — 1000, rue Fullum, Ste. A.208, Montreal, QC, H2K 3L7, Canada; tel (514) 529-2818; fax (514) 873-4434; e-mail info@conseildepresse.qc.ca; web site www.conseildepresse.qc.ca
Contact...Guy Amyot
Director of communication........ Julien Acosta

CUSTOMIZED NEWSPAPER

ADVERTISING (IOWA) — 319 E 5th St, Des Moines, IA, 50309-1927, USA; tel (515) 244-2145; fax (515) 244-4855; web site www.cnaads.com; www.inanews.com
Exec. Dir. .... Chris Mudge
Acct. Exec. .... Bryan Rohe
Sales Dir. .... Ron Bode
Sales Rep. .... Bruce Adams
Note: Represents 302 daily and weekly newspapers in Iowa and can place advertising in any newspaper in the country.

F

FLORIDA NEWSPAPER ADVERTISING & MARKETING EXECUTIVES — 610 Crescent Executive Court, Suite 112, Lake Mary, FL, 32746, USA; tel (321) 283-5273; e-mail hello@fname.org; web site www.fname.org
Exec. Dir. .... Sandy Osteen

FLORIDA SOCIETY OF NEWSPAPER EDITORS — 336 E. College Ave. Suite 203, Tallahassee, FL, 32301, USA; tel (850) 222-5790; fax 850-224-6012; e-mail fpa-info@flpress.com; web site www.fsne.org
Membership Coordinator .... Marcia Cyr
Note: Elections held at June convention

FREE COMMUNITY PAPERS OF NEW ENGLAND — 100-1 Domino Drive, Concord, CT, 01742, USA; tel 877-423-6399; e-mail bne@fcpne.com; web site www.communitypapersne.com
Admin. .... Lynn Duval

FREE COMMUNITY PAPERS OF NEW YORK — 750 W. Genesee St., Syracuse, NY, 13204, USA; tel (315) 472-6007; fax (315) 472-5919; e-mail ads@fcpny.com; web site www.fcpny.org
Executive Director .... Dan Holmes
Sales & Training .... Tom Cuskey

FREE LANCE JOURNALIST/BLOGGER — 121 South Street, 121 South Street, Churubusco, IN, 46723, USA; tel (260) 241-7737; e-mail vsade8@gmail.com
Freelance writer/blogger
2017-18 WPCI President; WPCI Communications Contest co-chair .... Vivian Sade

FREEDOM OF INFORMATION FOUNDATION OF TEXAS — 3001 N Lamar Blvd., Ste. 302, Austin, TX, 78705, USA; tel (512) 377 1575; fax (512) 377 1578; e-mail kelley.shannon@foift.org; web site www.foift.org
Executive Director .... Kelley Shannon
Note: Elections held in Dec

G

GREAT LAKES/MIDSTATES NEWSPAPER CONFERENCE, INC. — 1335 Dublin Rd., Suite 216-B, Colombus, OH, 43215, USA; tel (614) 486-6677; fax (614) 486-4940; e-mail glmsconf@comcast.net; web site www.ohionews.org
Bus. Mgr./Sec./Treasurer .... Jack Gahagan
Note: Elections held in Feb

H

HOLLYWOOD FOREIGN PRESS ASSOCIATION — 646 N. Robertson Blvd., West Hollywood, CA, 90069-5078, USA; tel (310) 657-1731; fax (310) 657-5576; e-mail info@hfpa.org; web site www.hfpa.org
Head, Mktg. .... Michael Russell
Pres. .... Philip Berk

HOOSIER STATE PRESS ASSOCIATION — 41 E Washington St, Ste 101, Indianapolis, IN, 46204-3560, USA; tel (317) 803-4772; fax (317) 624-4428; web site www.hspa.com
Exec. Dir./Gen. Counsel .... Stephen Key
Adv. Dir. .... Pamela Lego
Communications Specialist .... Milissa Tuley
HSPA Foundation Dir. .... Karen Braeckel
Office Mgr. .... Yvonne Yeadon
Adv. Coord. .... Shawn Goldsby
Note: Represents daily and weekly newspapers in Indiana

I

IDAHO PRESS CLUB — PO Box 2221, Boise, ID, 83701-2221, USA; tel (208) 389-2879; e-mail email@idahopressclub.org; web site www.idahopressclub.org
Exec. Dir. .... Martha Borchers
Note: IPC accepts individual memberships for reporters and public information officers in several areas. Elections and awards ceremony held in the spring. One annual seminars held in spring and fall

ILLINOIS ASSOCIATED PRESS MANAGING EDITORS — 10 S. Wacker Drive, Suite 2500, Chicago, IL, 60606, USA; tel (312) 781-0500; e-mail chifax@ap.org; web site www.ap.org
Note: Elections held in Sept

ILLINOIS WOMAN'S PRESS ASSOCIATION, INC. — PO Box 180150, Chicago, IL, 60618-9997, USA; tel (708) 296-8669; e-mail iwpa@gmail.com; web site www.iwpa.org
Pres. .... Cora Weisenberger

INDIANA ASSOCIATED PRESS MANAGING EDITORS — 251 N. Illinois St., Ste. 1600, Indianapolis, IN, 46204, USA; tel (317) 639-5501; e-mail indy@ap.org

INDIANAPOLIS PRESS CLUB FOUNDATION — PO Box 40923, Indianapolis, IN, 46240, USA; tel (317) 701-1130; e-mail jlabalme@indypress@att.net; web site www.indypressfoundation.org
Executive Director .... Jenny Labalme
Note: Elections held in January

INLAND PRESS ASSOCIATION — 701 Lee St., Ste. 925, Des Plaines, IL, 60016, USA; tel (847) 795-0380; fax (847) 795-0385; e-mail inland@inlandpress.org; web site www.inlandpress.org
Mgr. of Research & Member Services... Karla Zander
Dir. of Membership and Programming... Patty Slusher
Exec. Dir. .... Tom Slaughter
Ed. .... Mark Fitzgerald
Accounting Mgr. .... Steve Hoffman
Note: Elections held in Oct

IOWA ASSOCIATED PRESS MEDIA EDITORS ASSOCIATION — 505 Fifth Ave., Ste. 1000, Des Moines, IA, 50309, USA; tel (515) 243-3281; fax (515) 243-3884; e-mail apdesmoines@ap.org; web site www.apiowa.org
Reg. Dir. .... Kia Breaux
Note: Elections held in June

IOWA NEWSPAPER ASSOCIATION, INC. — 319 E 5th St, Fl 2, Des Moines, IA, 50309-1927, USA; tel (515) 244-2145; fax (515) 244-4855; e-mail ina@inanews.com; web site www.inanews.com
Sales & Mktg. Dir. ...... Susan Patterson Plank
Business Mgr. .... Brent Steemken
Comm. Dir. .... Jodi Hulbert
Dev. Dir .... Geof Fischer
Inside Sales Mgr. .... Samantha Fett
Media Dir. .... Heidi Geisler
Program Dir. .... Jana Shepherd
Tech. & Digital Dev. Mgr. .... Susan James
Pres. .... Ryan Harvey
Sales & Mktg. Assist. .... Kaitlyn Van Patten
Note: Elections held in May

K

KANSAS ASSOCIATED PRESS MANAGING EDITORS ASSOCIATION — Associated Press, 215 W. Pershing St., Ste. 221, Kansas City, MO, 64108, USA; tel (816) 421-4844; fax (816) 421-3590; e-mail apkansascity@ap.org; web site www.ap.org/kansas
Bureau Chief .... Randy Picht
Note: Elections held in Oct

KANSAS ASSOCIATED PRESS PUBLISHERS AND EDITORS — Associated Press, 215 W. Pershing, Ste. 221, Kansas City, MO, 64108, USA; tel (816) 421-4844; fax (816) 421-3590
Bureau Chief .... Paul Stevens
Bd. Chrmn. .... Tom Bell
Note: Elections held in Dec

KANSAS PROFESSIONAL COMMUNICATORS — 2369 Road J5, Americus, KS, 66835, USA; tel 620-227-1807; fax 620 227-1806; e-mail kansasprocom@gmail.com; web site www.kansasprofessionalcommunicators.org
Pres. .... Jennifer Latzke
Professor, WSU Elliott School of Communication .... Les Anderson
Becky Funke
Wilma Moore-Black
Miller Jill
Note: We are the Kansas affiliate of the National Federation of Press Women.

KENTUCKY ASSOCIATED PRESS EDITORS ASSOCIATION — 525 W. Broadway, Louisville, KY, 40202, USA; tel (502) 583-7718; fax (502) 589-4831; e-mail ayeomans@ap.org; web site www.ap.org/kentucky
Note: Elections held in Nov

L

LEGISLATIVE CORRESPONDENTS ASSOCIATION OF NYS — 25 Eagle St., NYS Capital, Albany, NY, 12224, USA; tel (518) 455-2388; web site www.lcapressroom.com
President .... Matthew Hamilton

LOS ANGELES PRESS CLUB — 4773 Hollywood Blvd., Los Angeles, CA, 90027, USA; tel (323) 669-8081; fax (323) 669-8069; e-mail info@lapressclub.org; web site www.lapressclub.org
Exec. Dir. .... Diana Ljungaeus
Note: Elections held in Nov

LOUISIANA PRESS WOMEN, INC. — The Advocate, 7290 Blue Bonnet Rd., Baton Rouge, LA, 70810, USA; tel (225) 383-1111; fax (225) 388-0323; e-mail mshuler@theadvocate.com; web site www.theadvocate.com
Pres. .... David Manship
Note: Elections held even years

LOUISIANA-MISSISSIPPI ASSOCIATED PRESS MANAGING EDITORS ASSOCIATION — 125 south congress st. suite 1330, Jackson, MS, 39201, USA; tel 601-948-5897; fax 601-948-7975; e-mail jkme@ap.org ; web site www.ap.org
News Ed. .... Brian Schwaner

M

MAINE DAILY NEWSPAPER PUBLISHERS ASSOCIATION — 26 Elmwood Road, Cape Elizabeth, ME, 04107, USA; tel 207-799-2996; e-mail scostello@sunjournal.com; web site www.mainepressassociation.orgGary Gagne
Note: Elections held in June

MANITOBA COMMUNITY NEWSPAPER ASSOCIATION — 943 McPhillips Street, Winnipeg, MB, R2X 2J9, Canada; tel (204) 947-1691; fax (204) 947-1919; web site www.mcna.com

NOTE: ELECTIONS HELD AT ANNUAL APRIL CONVENTION

MARYLAND-DELAWARE-DC PRESS ASSOCIATION — 60 West St., Ste. 107, Annapolis, MD, 21401-2479, USA; tel (855) 721-6332; fax (855) 721-6332; e-mail rsnyder@mddc.com; web site www.mddcpress.com
Exec. Dir. .... Rebecca Snyder

MASSACHUSETTS NEWSPAPER PUBLISHERS ASSOCIATION — 7 S Street Ct., Rockport, MA, 01966, USA; tel (978) 546-3400; fax (978) 418-9161; e-mail info@masspublishers.org; web site www.masspublishers.org
Exec. Dir. .... Robert J. Ambrogi

METROPOLITAN NEW YORK FOOTBALL WRITERS ASSOCIATION — American Football Networks, Inc., P.O. Box 477, Roseland, NJ, 07068-0477, USA; tel (973) 364-0605; fax (973) 364-0425; e-mail americanfootballnetworks@gmail.com; web site www.mnyfwa.com
Pres. .... Dennis Wilson

MICHIGAN ASSOCIATED PRESS EDITORIAL ASSOCIATION — 300 River Pl., Ste. 2400, Detroit, MI, 48207, USA; tel (313) 259-0650; fax (313) 259-4966; e-mail apmichigan@ap.org; web site www.ap.org
Regional Director - East .... Eva Parziale

MICHIGAN PRESS ASSOCIATION — 827 N Washington Ave, Lansing, MI, 48906-5135, USA; tel (517) 372-2424; fax (517) 372-2429; e-mail mpa@michiganpress.org; web site www.michiganpress.org
Growth & Operations Manager Roselie Lucus
Public Affairs Manager .... Lisa McGraw
Design & Communications Specialist.... Sean Wickham
Mgr. .... Janet Mendler
Exec. Dir. .... James Tarrant
Adv. Dir. .... Paul Biondi
Note: Elections held in Jan

MID-ATLANTIC CIRCULATION MANAGERS ASSOCIATION — Daily Herald, PO Box 520, Roanoke Rapids, NC, 27870-0520, USA; tel (252) 537-2505; fax (252) 537-1887; web site www.midatlanticcma.org
Sec./Treasurer .... Carol Moseley
President .... Robyn Ashley
First Vice President .... Keven Zepezauer
Second Vice President .... David Adams
Representative .... Kevin Craig
Representative ..... Patricia Speziale Edwards
Representative .... Sean Torain
Representative .... Clayton Hall
Note: Elections held in May

MID-ATLANTIC COMMUNITY PAPERS ASSOCIATION — 375 Jalappa Road, Hamburg, PA, 19526, USA; tel 800-450-7227; e-mail info@macpa.net; web site www.macpa.net
Exec. Dir. .... Alyse Mitten
Note: Elections Held in April for both Boards

MID-ATLANTIC NEWSPAPER ADVERTISING & MARKETING EXECUTIVES — 359-C Wando Place Drive, Mt. Pleasant, SC, 29464, USA; tel (509)540-1534; e-mail edwardrbryant@yahoo.com; web site www.midatlanticname.com
Exec. Dir. .... Terri Saylor
Note: Elections held in March

MIDWEST FREE COMMUNITY PAPERS — PO Box 1350, Iowa City, IA, 52244-1350, USA; tel (319) 341-4352; fax (319) 341-4358; e-mail mfcp@mchsi.com; web site www.mfcp.org
Office Mgr. .... Jori Hendon
Note: Classified advertising for 124 publications

MIDWEST TRAVEL WRITERS ASSOCIATION — 902 S. Randall Road, Suite C311, St. Charles, IL, 60174, USA; tel 888-551-8184; e-mail sylvia@forbesfreelance.com; web site www.mtwa.org
Active Dir. .... Carla Waldemar
Treasurer .... Rich Warren
Active Dir. .... Susan Pollack
Administrative Assistant .... Sylvia Forbes
Note: Elections held in Mar or April

MINNESOTA ASSOCIATED PRESS ASSOCIATION — 425 Portland Ave, Third Floor, Minneapolis, MN, 55488, USA; tel (612) 332-2727; fax (612) 342-5299; e-mail apminneapolis@ap.org; web site www.ap.org
News Ed. .... Doug Glass

MINNESOTA FREE PAPER ASSOCIATION — 21998 Hwy. 27, Little Falls, MN, 56345, USA; tel 320-630-5312; fax (320) 632-2348; e-mail terry@littlefalls.net; web site www.mfpa.com
Asst. Sec./Treasurer .... Terry Lehrke
Pres. .... Trevor Slette
Note: Elections held in Feb

MISSOURI ASSOCIATED PRESS MANAGING EDITORS — Associated Press, 215 W. Pershing, Ste. 221, Kansas City, MO, 64108, USA; tel (816) 421-4844; fax (816) 421-3590; e-mail apkansascity@ap.org; web site www.ap.org
Bureau Chief .... Randy Picht
Note: Elections held in April

MISSOURI PRESS WOMEN — 528 Pamela Ln., Kirkwood, MO, 63122-1138, USA; tel N/A; e-mail MPCNFPW@gmail.com; web site www.mpc-nfpw.org
treasurer .... Janice Denham
Deborah Reinhardt

MONTANA ASSOCIATED PRESS ASSOCIATION — 321 Fuller Ave. #2, Helena, MT, 59601, USA; tel (406) 442-7440; fax (406) 442-5162; e-mail apmontana@ap.org; web site www.ap.org/montana
Bureau Chief .... Jim Clark
Note: Elections held in June every two years

N

NASJA EAST — 22 Cavalier Way, Latham, NY, 12110, USA; tel 518 339-5334; e-mail nasjaeast@nasja.org; web site http://www.nasja.org/east/index.cfm
Pres. .... Peter Hines

NATIONAL NEWSPAPER ASSOCIATION — 900 Community Drive, Springfield, IL, 62703, USA; tel (217)241-1400; fax (217) 241-1301; e-mail lynne@nna.org; web site www.nna.org
Comm. Dir. .... Stan Schwartz
Chief Operating Officer .... Lynne Lance
CEO .... Sam Fisher
Note: Officer elections held in Sept/Oct during Annual Convention; annual Leadership Conference in March; annual Better Newspaper Contest entry deadline Spring

NEBRASKA ASSOCIATED PRESS ASSOCIATION — 845 "S" Street, Lincoln, NE, 68508, USA; tel (402)476-2851; fax (402)476-2942; e-mail nebpress@nebpress.com; web site www.ap.org/nebraska
Bureau Chief .... Tina Heraldson
Note: Elections held in Sept

NENPA MARKETING & ADVERTISING COUNCIL — 370 Common St., Dedham, MA, 02026, USA; tel (781) 320-8050; fax (781) 320-8055; e-mail info@nenpa.com; web site www.nenpa.com
Exec. Dir. NENPA .... Dan Cotter
Note: Elections held in Oct

NEW ENGLAND ASSOCIATION OF CIRCULATION EXECUTIVES — 4 Trotting Rd., Chelmsford, MA, 1824, USA; tel (978) 256-0691; fax (978) 256-4873; e-mail neace@neace.com; web site www.neace.com
Sec. .... William H. Hoar
Note: Elections held in May

NEW ENGLAND NEWSPAPER & PRESS ASSOCIATION — 1 Arrow Drive, Suite 6, Woburn, MA, 01801, USA; tel (781) 281-2053; fax (339) 999-2174; e-mail info@nenpa.com; web site www.nenpa.com
Note: Elections held in March

NEW ENGLAND SOCIETY OF NEWSPAPER EDITORS — 370 Common Street, 3rd Floor Ste 319, Barletta Hall, Dedham, MA, 02026, USA; tel 781-320-8050; fax 781-320-8055; e-mail info@nenpa.com; web site www.nesne.org
Ed. .... George Geers
Note: Elections held in Nov

NEW JERSEY ASSOCIATED PRESS MANAGING EDITORS ASSOCIATION — 50 W. State St., Ste. 1114, Trenton, NJ, 8608, USA; tel (609) 392-3622; fax (609) 392-3525; e-mail aptrenton@ap.org; web site www.ap.org/nj
BC .... Sally Hale

NEW JERSEY LEGISLATIVE CORRESPONDENTS CLUB — Hackensack Record, Trenton, NJ, 8625, USA; tel (609) 292-5159; fax (609) 984-1888
Pres. .... Jim Hooker
Note: This group accepts news organizations with correspondents based in Trenton, N.J

NEW MEXICO PRESS WOMEN — 256 DP Rd., Los Alamos, NM, 87544, USA; tel (505) 662-4185; fax (505) 827-6496; e-mail lanews@lamonitor.com; web site www.newmexicopresswomen.org
Pres. .... Carol Clark
Note: Elections held May 1st of even numbered years

NEW ORLEANS PRESS CLUB — 846 Howard Avenue, New Orleans, LA, 70113, USA; tel 504-259-4687; e-mail info@pressclubneworleans.org; web site www.pressclubneworleans.org
Exec. Dir. .... Bill Langkopp
Note: Elections held in July

NEW YORK FINANCIAL WRITERS ASSOCIATION, INC. — PO Box 338, Ridgewood, NJ, 07451-0338, USA; tel (201) 612-0100; fax (201) 612-9915; e-mail nyfwa@aol.com; web site www.nyfwa.org
Exec. Mgr. .... Jane Reilly
Note: Elections held on fourth Wed. of Jan. Members are journalists in the business or financial media

NEW YORK NEWS PUBLISHERS ASSOCIATION — 252 Hudson Ave, Albany, NY, 12210, USA; tel (518) 449-1667; web site www.nynpa.com
Pres. .... Diane Kennedy

NEW YORK PRESS PHOTOGRAPHERS ASSOCIATION, INC. — PO Box 3346, New York, NY, 10008-3346, USA; tel (212) 889-6633; e-mail office@nyppa.org; web site www.nyppa.org
Trustee .... Ray Stubblebine
Secretary - Historian .... Marc Hermann
President .... Bruce Cotler
Vice President .... Todd Maisel
Note: Elections held every other year

NEW YORK SOCIETY OF NEWSPAPER EDITORS — 222 Waverly Avenue, Syracuse, NY, 13244, USA; tel (315) 443-2305; fax (315) 443-3946
Pres. .... Joann M. Crupi

NEW YORK STATE ASSOCIATED PRESS ASSOCIATION — 450 W. 33rd St., Albany, NY, 10001, USA; tel 212-621-1670; fax 212-621-1679; e-mail info@ap.org; web site www.ap.org
Bureau Chief .... Howard Goldberg
Note: Elections held in Sept

NEW YORK STATE CIRCULATION MANAGERS ASSOCIATION — 85 Civic Center Plz., Poughkeepsie, NY, 12601, USA; tel (845) 437-4738; fax (845) 437-4902; e-mail farrellb@poughkee.gannett.com; web site www.poughkeepsiejournal.com
Board Member .... Bill Farrell
Note: Elections held in May

NORTH CAROLINA PRESS CLUB — 200 Countryside Rd, Harmony, NC, 28634-9420, USA; tel (704)546-7900; e-mail suzyb3@gmail.com; web site www.nfpw.org
Past President .... Suzy Barile
Note: Elections held in March

NORTH DAKOTA ASSOCIATED PRESS — PO Box 1018, Bismarck, ND, 58502-5646, USA; tel (701) 223-8450; fax (701) 224-0158; e-mail apbismarck@ap.orgBlake Nicholson

NORTHERN ILLINOIS NEWSPAPER ASSOCIATION — Campus Life Building, Suite 130, DeKalb, IL, 60115, USA; tel (815) 753-4239; fax (815) 753-0708; web site www.ninaonline.org
Communications Coordinator .... Shelley Hendricks

NORTHERN STATES CIRCULATION MANAGERS ASSOCIATION — PO Box 220, Grand Rapids, MN, 55744, USA; tel (218) 326-6623; fax (218) 326-6627; e-mail ron.oleheiser@grandrapidsmn.com; web site www.grandrapidsmn.com
Pub. .... Ron Oleheiser
Note: Elections held in Sept

NORTHWEST INTERNATIONAL CIRCULATION EXECUTIVES — PO Box 778, La Conner, WA, 98257, USA; tel (360) 466-2006; fax (360) 466-2006; e-mail nice@galaxynet.com; web site www.nicex.org
Sec./Treasurer .... Dale Irvine
Note: Management seminars sponsored in Oct. (non-dailies welcome). Elections held at annual conference in May

O

OHIO CIRCULATION MANAGERS ASSOCIATION — 1335 Dublin Rd., Suite 216-B, Columbus, OH, 43215, USA; tel (614) 486-6677; fax (614) 486-4940; e-mail bbarker@plaind.com; web site www.ohiocirculation.com
Committee Chair .... Kim Wilhelm
Note: Elections held in Oct

OHIO NEWSPAPER ADVERTISING EXECUTIVES — 1335 Dublin Rd. S., Ste. 216-B, Columbus, OH, 43215, USA; tel (614) 486-6677; fax (614) 486-6373; e-mail mhenry@adohio.net; web site www.adohio.net
Mgr. .... Mark Henry
Note: Elections held in Feb.

ONTARIO COMMUNITY NEWSPAPERS ASSOCIATION — 3228 South Service Rd. Ste 116, Burlington, ON, L7N 3H8, Canada; tel (905) 639-8720; fax (905) 639-6962; e-mail info@ocna.org; web site www.ocna.org
Executive Director .... Anne Lannan

ORANGE COUNTY PRESS CLUB — 1835 Newport Blvd., #A-109-538, Costa Mesa, CA, 92627, USA; tel (714) 564-1052; fax (714) 564-1047; e-mail OCPressClub@orangecountypressclub.com; web site www.ocpressclub.org
Sec./Treasurer .... Jean O. Pasco
Note: Elections held in July

OVERSEAS PRESS CLUB OF AMERICA — 40 West 45 Street, New York, NY, 10036, USA; tel (212) 626-9220; fax (212) 626-9210; e-mail info@opcofamerica.org; web site www.opcofamerica.org
Exec. Dir. .... Patricia Kranz
Note: Elections held in late summer

OVERSEAS PRESS CLUB OF PUERTO RICO (ESTABLISHED 1968) — 1399 Ave. Ana G. M?ndez, San Juan, PR, 00928-1345, Puerto Rico; tel (787) 525-8901; fax N/A; e-mail opcpr@yahoo.com; web site www.opcpr.wordpress.com
Pres. .... Ángel Rodríguez
Note: Martha Alonso - 787-408-3033

P

PACIFIC NORTHWEST ASSOCIATION OF WANT AD NEWSPAPERS (PNAWAN) & WESTERN REGIONAL ADVERTISING PROGRAM (WRAP) — 304 W 3rd Ave, C/O Exchange Publishing, Spokane, WA, 99201-4314, USA; tel (509) 922-3456; fax (509) 455-7940; e-mail Ads@PNAWAN.org; web site www.RegionalAds.org
Executive Director of the Pacific Northwest Association of Want Ad Newspapers (PNAWAN) & Western Regional Advertising Program (WRAP) .... Kylah Strohte PNAWAN Office
Note: We are audited and verified by the Circulation Verification Council annually. PNAWAN headquarters are located at the offices of hosting member publication, Exchange Publishing, in Spokane, WA.

PACIFIC NORTHWEST NEWSPAPER ASSOCIATION — 708 Tenth St., Sacramento, CA, 95814, USA; tel (888) 344-7662; fax (916) 288-6002; e-mail tom@cnpa.com; web site www.pnna.com
Exec. Dir. .... Jack Bates
Note: Elections held in the July

PENNSYLVANIA SOCIETY OF NEWS EDITORS — 3899 N. Front St., Harrisburg, PA, 17110, USA; tel (717) 703-3000; fax (717) 703-3001; e-mail teresas@pa-news.org; web site www.panewsmedia.org
President, PA Newspaper Association ..... Teri Henning
Note: Elections held in May

PENNSYLVANIA WOMEN'S PRESS ASSOCIATION — 511 Lenox St., Stroudsburg, PA, 18360, USA; tel (717) 295-7869; e-mail pwpa@lancasteronline.com; web site www.

pwpa.us
Note: Elections held in May. Organization accepts freelancers

Q

QUEBEC COMMUNITY NEWSPAPERS ASSOCIATION — 189 Hymus Blvd., Suite 207, Pointe-Claire, QC, H9R 1E9, Canada; tel (514) 697-6330; fax (514) 697-6331; e-mail execdir@qcna.qc.ca; web site www.qcna.org
Executive Director ....Richard Tardif

S

SASKATCHEWAN WEEKLY NEWSPAPERS ASSOCIATION — 14-401 45th St. W., Saskatoon, SK, S7L 5Z9, Canada; tel (306) 382-9683; fax (306) 382-9421; e-mail swna@swna.com; web site www.swna.com
Tech. Officer ....Cameron Just
Commun.Coord...........................Julie Schau
Office Mgr............................Louise Simpson
Adv. Coord., Classified ....Nicole Nater
Exec. Dir. ....Steve Nixon

SOCIETY OF CLASSIFIED ADVERTISING MANAGERS OF AMERICA, INC. — PO Box 531335, Mountain Brook, AL, 352530-1335, USA; tel (205) 592-0389; fax (205)599-5598; e-mail hrushing@usit.net; web site www.scama.com
Exec. Officer........................Hugh J. Rushing
Note: Elections held in Feb

SOUTH CAROLINA ASSOCIATED PRESS — 1401 Shop Road, Suite B, Columbia, SC, 29201, USA; tel (803) 799-5510; fax (803) 252-2913; e-mail apcolumbia@ap.org
Bureau Chief.......................Maryann Mrowca

SOUTHEASTERN ADVERTISING PUBLISHERS ASSOCIATION — 104 Westland Dr, Columbia, TN, 38401-6522, USA; tel (931) 223-5708; fax (888) 450-8329; e-mail info@sapatoday.com; web site www.sapatoday.com
Exec. Dir. ....Douglas Fry
Note: Classified advertising for 75 publications in 10 Southeastern states. Display Network also available.

SOUTHERN CIRCULATION MANAGERS ASSOCIATION — P.O. Box 1163, Kingsport, TN, 37662, USA; tel N/A; e-mail info@scmaonline.net; web site www.scmaonline.net
Sec. ....Debra Casciano
Treasurer ....Glen Tabor
Note: Elections held in April. Organization accepts shoppers as Associate Members

SOUTHERN NEWSPAPER PUBLISHERS ASSOCIATION — 3680 N. Peachtree Rd., Ste. 300, Atlanta, GA, 30341, USA; tel (404) 256-0444; fax (404) 252-9135; e-mail edward@snpa.org; web site www.snpa.org
Asst ED ....Cindy Durham
Exec. Dir. ....Edward VanHorn
Office Mgr......................... Paulette Sheffield
Charles H. Morris
Thomas A. Silvestri
David Dunn-Rankin
Note: Elections held at the annual convention in Oct.

SOUTHWEST CLASSIFIED ADVERTISING MANAGERS ASSOCIATION — Dallas Morning News, 508 Young St., Dallas, TX, 75265-5237, USA; tel 214-977-8222; e-mail jmckeon@dallasnews.com; web site www.dallasnews.com
President and General Manager ....John Mckeon
General Manager, Recruitment, Real Estate, General Classifieds .... Michael Mayer

STATE HISTORICAL SOCIETY OF WISCONSIN — 816 State St., Madison, WI, 53706, USA; tel (608) 264-6534; fax (608) 264-6520; web site www.wisconsinhistory.org
Administrative Asst. ....Margaret T. Dwyer

T

TENNESSEE ASSOCIATED PRESS MANAGING EDITORS — John Siegenthaler Center, 1207 18th Avenue South, Suite 261-A, Nashville, TN, 37212, USA; tel (615) 373-9988; fax (615) 376-0947; e-mail apnashville@ap.org; web site www.ap.org/states/tennessee
Bureau Chief ....Adam Yeomans

TENNESSEE PRESS SERVICE, INC. — 625 Market St, Ste 1100, Knoxville, TN, 37902-2219, USA; tel (865) 584-5761; fax (865) 558-8687; e-mail info@tnpress.com; web site www.tnadvertising.biz
Exec. Dir. .... Greg Sherrill
Director of Advertising.................David Wells
Note: Elections held in June

TEXAS ASSOCIATED PRESS MANAGING EDITORS — The Dallas Morning News, 508 Young St., Dallas, TX, 75202, USA; tel (214) 977-8222; web site www.txapme.org
Deputy Mng. Ed..........................Leona Allen
Note: Elections held in March

TEXAS CIRCULATION MANAGEMENT ASSOCIATION — c/o PO Box 9577, The Woodlands, TX, 77387, USA; tel N/A; e-mail tcma@texascma.org; web site www.texascma.org
Secretary/Treasurer...................... J W Smith
Note: America's First Circulation Sectional Founded September 18, 1913

TEXAS COMMUNITY MEDIA LLC — 1226 Newberry Drive, Allen, TX, 75013, USA; tel 972-741-6258; e-mail jack@tcnatoday.com; web site www.tcnatoday.com
Exec. Dir. ....Dick Colvin

THE AD CLUB — 9 Hamilton Pl., Boston, MA, 02108-3210, USA; tel (617) 262-1100; fax (617) 456-1772; e-mail newsfeed@adclub.org; web site www.adclub.org

THE AD CLUB — 22 Batterymarch Street, 1st Floor, Boston, MA, 02109, USA; tel 617-262-1100; web site www.adclub.org
Pres. ....Kathy Kiely

THE PRESS CLUB OF CLEVELAND — 28022 Osborn Road, Cleveland, OH, 44140, USA; tel 440-899-1222; e-mail pressclubcleveland@oh.rr.com; web site pressclubcleveland.com
President, Trustee .... Ed Byers
Executive Administrator.............Lynn Bracic

U

UNIVERSITY PRESS OF KENTUCKY — 663 S. Limestone St., Lexington, KY, 40508-4008, USA; tel (859) 257-8419; fax (859) 323-1873; e-mail smwrin2@uky.edu; web site www.kentuckypress.com
Mktg. Dir....................................John Hussey
Dir. ....Stephen Wrinn
Note: Elections held in spring/fall of odd numbered years

UTAH-IDAHO-SPOKANE ASSOCIATED PRESS ASSOCIATION — 30 E. 100 South St., Ste. 200, Salt Lake City, UT, 84111, USA; tel (801) 322-3405; fax (801) 322-0051; e-mail apsaltlake@ap.org
Bureau Chief ....Jim Clarke
Note: Elections held in June

V

VALLEY PRESS CLUB, INC. — PO Box 5475, Springfield, MA, 01101-5475, USA; tel (413) 682-0007; e-mail info@valleypressclub.com; web site www.valleypressclub.com
Pres. ....Charlie Bennett
Note: Elections held in March

W

WASHINGTON ASSOCIATED PRESS NEWSPAPER EXECUTIVES ASSOCIATION — 3131 Elliott Ave., Ste. 750, Seattle, WA, 98121, USA; tel (206) 682-1812; fax (206) 621-1948; e-mail apseattle@ap.org; web site www.ap.org
Bureau Chief ....Nancy Trott
Note: Elections held in Oct./Nov

WASHINGTON PRESS ASSOCIATION — c/o 15642 129th Court SE, Renton, WA, 98058, USA; tel N/A; web site www.washingtonpressassociation.com
President ....Bill Virgin
Vice President ....Mike Maltais
Secretary ....Sarah Smith

WEST TEXAS PRESS ASSOCIATION — 706 SW 10th St., Perryton, TX, 79070, USA; tel (806) 435-3631; fax (806) 435-2420; e-mail secretary@wtpa.org; web site www.wtpa.org
Secretary-Treasurer .... Mary Dudley
Note: Elections held at annual convention in July

WHITE HOUSE CORRESPONDENTS ASSOCIATION — 600 New Hampshire Ave., Ste. 800, Washington, DC, 20037, USA; tel 202-266-7453; fax (202) 266-7454; e-mail director@whca.net; web site www.whca.net
Executive Director .... Steven Thomma
Note: Elections held in July

WHITE HOUSE NEWS PHOTOGRAPHERS ASSOCIATION, INC. — PO Box 7119, Washington, DC, 20044-7119, USA; tel (202) 785-5230; e-mail info@whnpa.org; web site www.whnpa.org
Treasurer ....Jon Elswick
President .... Whitney Shefte
Vice President .... Jim Bourg
Note: Elections held in Mar.

WISCONSIN ASSOCIATED PRESS ASSOCIATION — 111 E. Wisconsin Ave., Ste.1925, Milwaukee, WI, 53202, USA; tel (414) 225-3580; e-mail apmlw@ap.org; web site www.ap.org
News Ed. ....Roger Schneider
Note: Elections held in May

WISCONSIN FREE COMMUNITY PAPERS — 101 S. Main St., Fond Du Lac, WI, 54935, USA; tel 800-727-8745; fax 920-922-0861; e-mail wcp@wisad.com; web site www.wisad.com
Exec. Dir. ....Janelle Anderson

WYOMING ASSOCIATED PRESS — 320 W. 25th St., Ste. 310, Cheyenne, WY, 82001, USA; tel (307) 632-9351; fax (307) 637-8538; web site www.ap.org
Bureau Chief .... Jim Clark

NEWSPAPER BROKERS AND APPRAISERS

ADMEDIA PARTNERS, INC. — 3 Park Ave, Fl 31, New York, NY, 10016-5902, USA; tel (212) 759-1870; fax (212) 888-4960; e-mail info@admediapartners.com; web site www.admediapartners.com; Established 1990
Mgr. Dir. — Seth R. Alpert
Principal — Oliver Schweitzer
Managing Dir. — Greg Smith
Managing Dir. — Andy Schoder
Managing Dir. — Adam Birnbaum
Managing Dir. — Mike Mortell

ASSOCIATED TEXAS NEWSPAPERS, INC. — 4100 Jackson Ave, Apt 460, Austin, TX, 78731-6067, USA; tel (512) 407-8283; fax (512) 407-8289; e-mail Billberger@austin.rr.com; web site www.hondoanvilherald.com; Established 1886
Pres. — Bill Berger
Vice Pres. — Jeff Berger

CAPITAL ENDEAVORS, INC. — 232 W Crogan St, Ste C, Lawrenceville, GA, 30046-4853, USA; tel (770) 962-8399; fax (770) 962-8640; e-mail davidstill@capitalendeavors.com; web site www.capitalendeavors.com
Pres. — David R. Still

CBS ASSOCIATES — 423 Sutton Cir, Danville, CA, 94506-1154, USA; tel (925) 736-6350; fax (925) 736-3034
Contact — Carl B. Shaver

CRIBB, GREENE & COPE LLC — 825 Great Northern Blvd, Ste 202, Helena, MT, 59601-3340, USA; tel (406) 579-2925; fax (866) 776-8010; e-mail jcribb@cribb.com; web site www.cribb.com; Established 1923
Managing Dir. — John Cribb
Managing Dir. — Gary Greene
Dir. — Randy Cope
Assoc. — John Thomas Cribb

DIRKS, VAN ESSEN & MURRAY — 119 E Marcy St, Ste 100, Santa Fe, NM, 87501-2092, USA; tel (505) 820-2700; fax (505) 820-2900; web site www.dirksvanessen.com; Established

1980
Pres. — Owen D. Van Essen
Exec. Vice Pres. — Philip W. Murray
Vice Pres. — Sara April
Analyst — Holly Myers

FOURNIER MEDIA SERVICES, INC. — 613 7th St, Prosser, WA, 99350-1459, USA; tel (206) 409-9216; fax (509) 786-1779; e-mail mutinybaydad@aol.com; web site www.recordbulletin.com; Established 1982
Pres. — John L. Fournier

FRENCH, BARRY — 3 Ashlawn Rd, Assonet, MA, 02702-1105, USA; tel (508) 644-5772; e-mail barryfrench@yahoo.com; Established 1986
Pres. — Barry French

GAUGER MEDIA SERVICE, INC. — PO Box 627, Raymond, WA, 98577-0627, USA; tel (360) 942-3560; e-mail dave@gaugermedia.com; web site www.gaugermedia.com; Established 1987
Pres/Broker — Dave Gauger

GOLD COUNTY ADVISORS, INC. — 604 Sutter St, Ste 394, Folsom, CA, 95630-2698, USA; tel (916) 673-9778; fax (888) 933-0807; e-mail jeff@goldcountryadvisors.com; web site www.goldcountryadvisors.com; Established 2003
Principal — Jeffrey Potts

GRIMES, MCGOVERN & ASSOCIATES — 10 W 15th St, Apt 903, New York, NY, 10011-6823, USA; tel (917) 881—6563; e-mail lgrimes@mediamergers.com; web site www.mediamergers.com; Established 1959
Chmn. — Larry Grimes
V.P., Head of Newspaper Division — Julie Bergman
Senior Associate-Northeast/New England — John Szefc
Senior Associate- Southeast/South — David Slavin
Owner, CEO — John McGovern
Senior Associate-Southern States — Lewis Floyd
Founder — Walter Grimes
Sr. Assoc.-SW/Plains — Gary Borders
Sr. Assoc.-CANADA-Mag. & Newspapers — Gord Carley
Sr. Advisor-Newspapers — Joe Bella
Sr. Assoc.-Western/Mtn. States — Ken Amundson
Senior Associate-Sales Nationwide — Ken Blum

GRIMES, W.B. & CO. — 59 Manor Sq, Sparta, NJ, 07871-2731, USA; tel (201) 230-0848; fax (973) 729-0648; e-mail dslavin@mediamergers.com; web site www.mediamergers.com; Established 1959
Senior Associate
— David Slavin

GRIMES, W.B. & CO. — 59 Manor Sq, Sparta, NJ, 07871-2731, USA; tel (201) 230-0848; fax (973) 729-0648; e-mail dslavin@mediamergers.com; web site www.mediamergers.com; Established 1959
Southeast/South/Mid-Atlantic Assoc. — David Slavin

GRIMES, W.B. & CO. — 699 Channing Way, Camden, TN, 38320-5277, USA; tel (731) 694-2149; fax (731) 584-4943; e-mail drichardson@mediamergers.com; web site www.mediamergers.com
South/Southwest Assoc. — Dennis Richardson

GRIMES, W.B. & CO. — 24212 Muscari Ct, Gaithersburg, MD, 20882-3804, USA; tel (301) 253-5016; e-mail lgrimes@mediamergers.com; web site www.mediamergers.com

GRIMES, W.B. & CO. — 35 Ridge Rd, Goshen, NY, 10924-5300, USA; tel (845) 291-7367; fax (845) 291-7367; e-mail jszefc@mediamergers.com; web site www.mediamergers.com
Northeast/New England Regl. Mgr. — John Szefc

HARRIS WILLIAMS & CO. — 575 Market St, Fl 31, San Francisco, CA, 94105-2854, USA; tel (415) 288-4260; fax (415) 288-4269; e-mail tarmstrong@harriswilliams.com; web site www.harriswilliams.com
Mng. Dir. — Tiff B. Armstrong

HARRIS WILLIAMS & CO. — 1001 Haxall Pt, Fl 9, Richmond, VA, 23219-3944, USA; tel (804) 648-0072; fax (804) 648-0073; e-mail kbaker@harriswilliams.com; web site www.harriswilliams.com; Established 1999
Marketing Director — Kimberly Baker

HARVEY, FAYE — PO Box 1410, Lebanon, MO, 65536-1410, USA; tel (417) 532-4809; e-mail f_harvey@hotmail.com
Broker — Faye Harvey

HEMPSTEAD & CO., INC. — 807 N Haddon Ave, Haddonfield, NJ, 08033-1749, USA; tel (856) 795-6026; fax (856) 795-4911; e-mail jeh@hempsteadco.com; web site www.hempsteadco.com
Mng. Dir. — Mark Penny

JORDAN, EDMISTON GROUP, INC. — 150 E 52nd St, Fl 18, New York, NY, 10022-6260, USA; tel (212) 754-0710; fax (212) 754-0337; e-mail adamg@jegi.com; web site www.jegi.com
CEO — Wilma Jordan
COO — Bill Hitzig
Mng. Dir. — Tolman Geffs
Mng. Dir. — Michael Marchesano
Mng. Dir. — Richard Mead
Mng. Dir. — Scott Peters
Vice Pres., Mktg. — Adam Gross

KAMEN & CO. GROUP SERVICES — 626 Rxr Plz, Uniondale, NY, 11556-0626, USA; tel (516) 379-2797; fax (516) 379-3812; e-mail info@kamengroup.com; web site www.kamengroup.com; Established 1981
Pres./CEO — Kevin Brian Kamen
Vice Pres. — Celeste Myers

KEVIN BRIAN KAMEN & CO. (KAMEN & CO. GROUP SERVICES) — 626 Rxr Plz, Uniondale, NY, 11556-0626, USA; tel (516) 379-2797; fax (516) 379-3812; e-mail info@KamenGroup.com; web site www.KamenGroup.com; Established 1981
Pres./CEO — Kevin Brian Kamen
Vice Pres., New York — Gary R. Kamen
Vice Pres., Tampa — Rosalyn Kamen
Gen. Mgr., Los Angeles — Mathew Kamen
Office Mgr. — Mary Hiscock
Office Mgr. — Tom Horowitz

KNOWLES MEDIA BROKERAGE SERVICES — PO Box 910, Carroll, IA, 51401-0910, USA; tel (712) 792-2179; fax (712) 792-2309; e-mail gregg.knowles@netzero.com; web site www.media-broker.com; Established 1987
Owner — Gregg Knowles

LEWIS FLOYD- GRIMES, W.B. & CO. — 20050 Oak Rd E, Unit 1814, Gulf Shores, AL, 36542-5739, USA; tel (850) 532-9466; fax (850) 290-5535; e-mail lfloydmedia@gmail.com; web site www.mediamergers.com; Established 1959
President — Larry Grimes
Senior Associate-Northeast — John Szefc
Senior Associate-Mid-Atlantic/Southeast — David Slavin
Senior Associate-Southeast — Mark Laskowski
Senior Associate-Midwest — Julie Bergman
Consulting Services — Lewis Floyd
Senior Associate-South — Dennis Richardson
Senior Associate-Southwest/Plains/West — Rollie Hyde
Senior Associate-Western States — Jay Harn

MANAGEMENT PLANNING, INC. — 5401 S Kirkman Rd, Ste 310, Orlando, FL, 32819-7937, USA; tel (407) 599-0060; fax (407) 641-8778; e-mail jgitto@mpival.com; web site www.mpival.com
Vice Pres. — Joseph A. Gitto

MANAGEMENT PLANNING, INC. — 70 W Madison St, Ste 1400, Chicago, IL, 60602-4267, USA; tel (312) 214-6141; fax (312) 214-3110; e-mail sroberts@mpival.com; web site www.mpival.com
Vice Pres. — Stephen J. Roberts

MANAGEMENT PLANNING, INC. — 300 Park Ave, Ste 1700, New York, NY, 10022-7402, USA; tel (212) 572-6291; fax (212) 572-6499; e-mail jhardwick@mpival.com; web site www.mpival.com
Reg'l Dir. — John H. Hardwick

MANAGEMENT PLANNING, INC. — 10 Station St, Ste 3, Simsbury, CT, 06070-2258, USA; tel (860) 651-8185; fax (860) 651-0032; e-mail bcranshaw@mpival.com; web site www.mpival.com
Vice Pres. — William O. Cranshaw
Gen. Mgr. — Harry.L Curtis

MANAGEMENT PLANNING, INC. — 101 Poor Farm Rd, Princeton, NJ, 08540-1941, USA; tel (609) 924-4200; fax (609) 924-4573; e-mail mpival.com; web site www.mpival.com
Pres. — Harry L. Curtis
Sr. Vice Pres. — Thomas A. Egan
Sr. Vice Pres. — Frank E. Koehl
Sr. Vice Pres. — Roy H. Meyers
Vice Pres. — Gerald P. Valentine

MANAGEMENT PLANNING, INC. — 77 Franklin St, Fl 5, Boston, MA, 02110-1510, USA; tel (617) 482-6462; fax (617) 482-2515; e-mail jweir@mpival.com; web site www.mpival.com
Reg'l Dir. — Jeremy Weir

MAYO COMMUNICATIONS — 7248 Bernadine Ave, Fl 2, West Hills, CA, 91307-1410, USA; tel (818) 340-5300; fax ; e-mail Publicity@mayocommunications.com; web site www.MAYOCommunications.com; Established 1995
CEO & President — Aida Mayo

MEDIA AMERICA BROKERS — 1130 Piedmont Ave NE, Apt 912, Atlanta, GA, 30309-3783, USA; tel (404) 875-8787; e-mail lonwwilliams@aol.com; Established 1989
Owner — Lon W Williams

MEDIA SERVICES GROUP, INC. — 149 S Roscoe Blvd, Ponte Vedra, FL, 32082-4127, USA; tel (904) 285-3239; fax (904) 285-5618; e-mail george@mediaservicesgroup.com; web site www.mediaservicesgroup.com
Mng. Dir. — George R. Reed
Dir. — William H. Lytle
Dir. — Robert J. Maccini
Dir. — Thomas McKinley
Dir. — Gregory Merrill
Dir. — William L. Whitley
Dir. — Jody McCoy
Assoc. — Eddie Esserman
Assoc. — Stephan Sloan

NATIONAL MEDIA ASSOCIATES — PO Box 849, Ada, OK, 74821-0849, USA; tel (580) 421-9600; fax (580) 272-5070; e-mail bolitho@nationalmediasales.com; web site www.nationalmediasales.com; Established 1995
— Thomas Bolitho
— Edward AndersonPres.s

NATIONAL MEDIA ASSOCIATES — PO Box 2001, Branson, MO, 65615-2001, USA; tel (417) 338-6397; fax (417) 338-6510; e-mail Brokered1@gmail.com; web site www.nationalmediasales.com; Established 1997
Owner — Edward M. Anderson

PHELPS, CUTLER & ASSOCIATES — 35 Barnard St, Ste 300, Savannah, GA, 31401-2515, USA; tel (912) 351-9122; fax (678) 826-4708; e-mail phelpscutler@aol.com; web site www.phelpscutler.com; Established 1991
Pres. — Louise D. Phelps

RICKENBACHER MEDIA — 6731 Desco Dr, Dallas, TX, 75225-2704, USA; tel (214) 384 2779; e-mail rmedia@msn.com; web site www.rickenbachermedia.com; Established 1985
Pres./Exec. Dir. — Ted Rickenbacher
Western States Dir. — Jim Afinowich

VERONIS SUHLER STEVENSON — 55 E 52nd St, Fl 33, New York, NY, 10055-0007, USA; tel (212) 935-4990; fax (212) 381-8168; e-mail stevensonj@vss.com; web site www.vss.com
Co-Founder/Mng. Partner/Chrmn./Co-CEO — John J. Veronis
Co-Founder/Mng. Partner — John S. Suhler
Mng. Partner/Co-CEO — Jeffrey T. Stevenson

W.B. GRIMES & COMPANY — 24212 Muscari Ct, Gaithersburg, MD, 20882-3804, USA; tel (301) 253-5016; e-mail lgrimes@mediamergers.com; web site www.mediamergers.com; Established 1959
Sr. Associate-South/Southwest — Lewis Floyd
Sr. Associate-Midwest/Plains States — Julie Bergman
Sr. Associate-Northeast/News England — John Szefc
David Slavin
Sr. Associate-West- Mtn. States — Ken Amundson
Pres. — Larry Grimes

NEWSPAPER REPRESENTATIVES - NATIONAL

A

AD REPS
51 Church St, Boston, MA, 02116-5417, USA; tel (617) 542-6913; fax (617) 542-7227; e-mail adreps1@yahoo.com
Pres. — Steve Ganak

ADVANTAGE NEWSPAPER CONSULTANTS
2850 Village Dr, Ste 102, Fayetteville, NC, 28304-3864, USA; tel (910) 323-0349; fax (910) 323-9280; e-mail info@newspaperconsultants.com; web site www.newspaperconsultants.comEstablished 1996
President — Timothy O. Dellinger
General Mgr. — Susan M. Jolley
Exec. Dir. of Sales — Marie Smith
Advantage Newspaper Consultants (ANC) is recognized as the leader in TV Magazine advertising sales in the United States. ANC works with both independent publishers and major newspaper chains to increase their core product ad revenue using innovative campaigns and creative, seasoned sales professionals that produce quantifiable results. Our sales manager's work with newspaper management to set goals and create an incentive plan which accelerates a TV Magazine sales campaign targeted towards finding key hidden revenue in their market in two weeks or less.
Using the same proven formula of enthusiastic joint sales calls and dedicated management support that has lead to thousands of successful TV magazine sales campaigns, ANC also offers a cross-platform advertising sales program - Total Market Reach (TMR) - which includes print, mobile and digital ad combo sales.

ADVERTISING MEDIA PLUS, INC.
5397 Twin Knolls Rd, Ste 17, Columbia, MD, 21045-3256, USA; tel (410) 740-5077; fax (410) 740-5888; e-mail info@ampsinc.net; web site www.ampsinc.net
Group: Medinger Media LLC Established 2001
Owner and President — Daniel Medinger

AMERICAN NEWSPAPER REPRESENTATIVES, INC.
2075 W Big Beaver Rd, Ste 310, Troy, MI, 48084-3439, USA; tel (248) 643-9910; fax (248) 643-9914; web site www.gotoanr.comEstablished 1943
Pres. — John Jepsen
Exec. Vice Pres./COO — Robert Sontag
ANR represents over 9,000 daily and weekly community newspapers nationwide

AMERICAN NEWSPAPER REPRESENTATIVES, INC.
940 County Road B W, Roseville, MN, 55113-4405, USA; tel (651) 487-5778; e-mail mcox@anrinc.net; web site www.anrinc.net
Sales Mgr. — Melanie Cox

C

C-VILLE HOLDINGS LLC
308 E Main St, Charlottesville, VA, 22902-5234, USA; tel 434/817-2749; fax 434/817-2758; e-mail aimee@c-ville.com; web site www.c-ville.comEstablished 1995
Ed — Jessica Luck

CALIFORNIA NEWSPAPER SERVICE BUREAU (CNSB)
915 E 1st St, Los Angeles, CA, 90012-4050, USA; tel (213) 229-5500; fax (213) 229-5481; e-mail ari_gutierrez@dailyjournal.com; web site www.legaladstore.comEstablished 1888
Division Director
Government Advertising Division
Daily Journal Corporation and California Newspaper Service Bureau — Ari Gutierrez
The Daily Journal Corporation is a publisher of legal and business publications, including the Los Angeles and San Francisco Daily Journals, distributed in major California cities. Additionally, its in-house clearinghouse service provides ad placement services to government agencies, attorney's and other advertisers for legally mandated and outreach advertising including class action notices in any daily, community and/or ethnic publication and/or websites.

CAMPUS MEDIA GROUP
7760 France Ave S, Ste 800, Bloomington, MN, 55435-5929, USA; tel (952) 854-3100; e-mail info@campusmediagroup.com; web site www.campusmediagroup.comEstablished 2002
COO — Jason Bakker
Pres./CEO — Tom Borgerding
College marketing agency.

CENTRO INC.
11 E Madison St, 6th Fl., Chicago, IL, 60602-4574, USA; tel (312) 423-1565; e-mail socialmedia@centro.net; web site www.centro.netEstablished 2001
EVP, Customer Experience — Katie Risch
VP, Pub. Solutions — John Hyland

H

HARTE-HANKS COMMUNICATIONS, INC.
9601 McAllister Fwy, Ste 610, San Antonio, TX, 78216-4632, USA; tel (210) 829-9000; fax (210) 829-9101; web site www.harte-hanks.com
Pres., Direct Mktg. — Gary Skidmore
Represents shopper publications

I

INTERSECT MEDIA SOLUTIONS
610 Crescent Executive Ct, Ste 112, Lake Mary, FL, 32746-2111, USA; tel (321) 283-5255; e-mail info@intersectmediasolutions.com; web site www.intersectmediasolutions.com
Group: Florida Press Association Established 1959
Pres./CEO — Dean Ridings
VP/CSO — Melanie Mathewson
Acct. Mgr. — Carolyn Klinger
Media Mgr. — Jessica Pitts
CFO — Mark Burger
General Counsel — Sam Morley

J

JOSEPH JACOBS ORGANIZATION
349 W 87th St, Ste 1, New York, NY, 10024-2662, USA; tel (212) 787-9400; fax (212) 787-8080; e-mail erosenfeld@josephjacobs.org; web site www.josephjacobs.orgEstablished 1919
Pres. — David Koch
Represents Jewish publications

L

LATINO 247 MEDIA GROUP
3445 Catalina Dr, Carlsbad, CA, 92010-2856, USA; tel (760) 434-1223; fax (760) 434-7476; e-mail kirk@whisler.com; web site www.latino247.newsEstablished 1996
Pres. — Kirk Whisler
General Manager — Ana Patiño
Accounting Manager — Ericka Benitez

M

MCNAUGHTON NEWSPAPERS
424 E State Pkwy, Ste 228, Schaumburg, IL, 60173-6406, USA; tel (847) 490-6000; fax (847) 843-9058; e-mail rickb@usspi.com; web site www.usspi.com
Vice President Media Relations — Rick Baranski
CEO — Philip Miller
Vice President Sales — Barbara Ancona
Executive Vice President — Michelle Hammons
Designs cost effective print and digital solutions for national/regional/local advertisers.

MEDIASPACE SOLUTIONS
904 Mainstreet, Hopkins, MN, 55343-7529, USA; tel (612) 253-3900; fax (612) 454-2848; e-mail bstcyr@mediaspace.com; web site www.mediaspacesolutions.comEstablished 1999
Chief Operating Officer — Randy Grunow
VP of Business Development & Marketing — Brian St. Cyr
Dir., Account Development — Tony Buesing
Sr. Med. Supervisor — Brian Kieser
Director of Media Development — Colin May
Buying Manager — Carol Wagner
Buying Supervisor — Jason Armstrong
Director Media Planning — Tom Johnson

METRO NEWSPAPER ADVERTISING SERVICES, INC.
8 W 38th St, 8 W. 38th St., 4th Fl., New York, NY, 10018-6229, USA; tel (212) 576-9510; fax (212) 576-9526; e-mail billh@metrosn.com; web site www.metrosn.comEstablished 1932
Chairperson & CEO — Phyllis Cavaliere
SVP Client Services — Tack Prashad
President/COO — Michael Baratoff
Sr. Vice Pres./Midwest Sales Dir. — Carl Berg
Exec. Dir. — Tom Vorel
Sr. Vice Pres., Eastern Adv. — Bill Huck
Sr. Vice Pres., Finance — Nili DeBono
Sr. Vice Pres./Eastern Region — William Huck
New Ventures Development — Frank Grasso
Senior VP, Operations — Kim Viggiano
Metro has been creating networks for national advertisers since 1932. It places advertising for represented newspapers through its Sunday Magazine, Metro-Puck Comics and Metro ROP Networks. Please see these entries in Section V of the Year Book.

METRO NEWSPAPER ADVERTISING SERVICES, INC.
160 Spear St, Ste 1875, San Francisco, CA, 94105-5146, USA; tel (310) 798-4986; fax (310) 564-7633; e-mail kathy@metrosn.com; web site www.metrosn.com
Mgr. — Kathy Jahns
Sr. Vice Pres. — Ali Nazem

METRO SUBURBIA, INC./NEWHOUSE NEWSPAPERS
711 3rd Ave, Fl 6, New York, NY, 10017-4029, USA; tel (212) 697-8020; fax (212) 972-3146; e-mail johnt@metrosuburbia.com; web site www.metrosuburbia.com
Adv. Sales Mgr. — Kevin Drolet
Adv. Sales Mgr. — John Tingwall
Adv. Sales Mgr. — Chad Johnson
Pres. — Robert N. Schoenbacher
New York Sales Mgr. — John A. Colombo
Adv. Sales Mgr. — Jon Gold
Adv. Sales Mgr. — Brenda Goodwin-Garcia

METROLAND MEDIA GROUP LTD.
3125 Wolfedale Rd., Mississauga, ON, L5C 1W1, Canada; tel (905) 281-5656; fax (905) 279-5103; e-mail result@metroland.com; web site www.metroland.com
Pres. — Ian Oliver
Vice Pres. — Kathie Bride
Sr. Vice Pres. — Tim Whittaker
Sr. Vice Pres. — Ian McLeod
Vice Pres. — Ian Proudfoot
Vice Pres., HR — Brenda Biller
Vice Pres. — Joe Anderson
Vice Pres. — Bruce Danford
Vice Pres. — Ron Lenyk
Vice Pres. — Ken Nugent
Vice Pres. — Carol Peddie
Gordon Paolucci
Vice President — Kukle Terry
Ed-In-Chief — Lois Tuffin
John Willems
Scott Miller Cressman
Tracy Magee-Graham
Editor-In-Chief — Haggert Peter
VP, Business Development & Acquisitions — Terry Kukle

MOTIVATE, INC.
4141 Jutland Dr Ste 300, Suite 300, San Diego, CA, 92117-3658, USA; tel (866) 664-4432; e-mail marcia@MotivateROI.com; web site www.motivateROI.comEstablished 1977
Prtnr. — Marcia A. Hansen
CEO — Trevor Hansen
Motivate, Inc. represents the following target markets: Multicultural (Hispanic, African American, Asian); Youth, LGBTQ, Senior, Military.

N

NEWSPAPER NATIONAL NETWORK
41899 Waterfall Rd, Northville, MI, 48168-3267, USA; tel (248) 680-4676; fax (248) 680-4667
Sales Exec. — Larry Doyle

NEWSPAPER NATIONAL NETWORK LP
20 W 33rd St, Fl 7, New York, NY, 10001-3305, USA; tel 212-856-6300; fax 212-856-6343; e-mail rchelstowski@nnnlp.com; web site www.nnnlp.comEstablished 1994
President & CEO — Jason E. Klein
Sr. Vice Pres., Bus. Devel. — Paul C. Atkinson
CEO — Ray Chelstowski
SVP, Sales — Lynn Lehmkuhl
Vice Pres., Newspaper Rel. — Frank P. Grasso
Sr. Vice Pres., Sales — Lynn A. Lehmkuhl
Sr. Vice Pres., Mktg. — Mary Ellen Holden
Doug MacDonald
Sales Dir. — Jack Grandcolas

Sales Dir. — Mary Dowling
Sr. Vice Pres., Media/Opns. — Jerry Fragetti
Anthony Moreno
Marshall Genger

NEWSPAPERS FIRST, INC
4601 Sheridan St, Ste 317, Hollywood, FL, 33021-3433, USA; tel (954) 987-8666; fax (954) 963-0921
Vice Pres./Sales Mgr. — Lawrence J. Malloy

NEWSPAPERS FIRST, INC.
330 Madison Ave, Fl 11, New York, NY, 10017-5001, USA; tel (212) 692-7100; fax (212) 286-9004; web site www.newspapersfirst.comEstablished 1960
Pres./CEO — Bob Termotto
Sr. Vice Pres./CFO — Robert Termotto
Vice Pres., Southern Reg. — Darren Larson
Vice Pres., Eastern Reg. — Allen Dunstan

NEWSPAPERS FIRST, INC.
5757 Wilshire Blvd, Ste 570, Los Angeles, CA, 90036-3683, USA; tel (323) 549-9144; fax (323) 459-0944
Vice Pres./Sales Mgr. — Richard Riegle

NEWSPAPERS FIRST, INC.
8115 Preston Rd, Ste 640, Dallas, TX, 75225-6319, USA; tel (214) 696-8666; fax (214) 696-3416; web site www.newspapersfirst.com
Vice Pres./Sales Mgr. — Darren Larson

P

PHILADELPHIA AREA NEWSPAPERS
580 W Germantown Pike Ste 108, Plymouth Plz., Plymouth Meeting, PA, 19462-1370, USA; tel (610) 941-3555; fax (610) 941-1289; e-mail brian@phillyareapapers.com; web site www.phillyareapapers.comEstablished 1929
Pres. — R. Brian Hitchings
Acct. Supvr. — Donna DeFrangesco

PUBLICITAS MCGOWN INC.
8250 Boul Decarie Bureau 205, Montreal, QC, H4P 2P5, Canada; tel (514) 735-5191; fax (514) 342-9406; e-mail cynthia.jollymore@publicitas.com; web site www.publicitas.com
Mng. Dir. — Wayne Faint John
Vice Pres., Sales — Cynthia Jollymore
McGown/Intermac represents 25 U.S. daily newspapers

PUBLICITAS NORTH AMERICA, INC.
2701 Troy Center Dr, Ste 250, Continental Plz, Troy, MI, 48084, USA; tel (248) 720-2456; fax (248) 404-9609
Branch Dir. — Michael May

PUBLICITAS NORTH AMERICA, INC.
330 7th Ave, Fl 5, New York, NY, 10001-5443, USA; tel (212)330-0720; fax (212) 599-8298; e-mail newyork@publicitas.com; web site www.publicitas.com
CFO — Joseph DeFalco

PUBLICITAS NORTH AMERICA, INC.
330 7th Ave, Fl 18, New York, NY, 10001-5010, USA; tel (310) 601-7618; e-mail newyork@publicitas.com; web site www.publicitas.com
Senior Account Director — Francisca Hoogeveen

PUBLICITAS NORTH AMERICA, INC.
3400 Peachtree Rd NE, Ste 1700, Atlanta, GA, 30326-1187, USA; tel (404) 467-8783; fax (404) 262-3746; e-mail ppn-atlanta@publicitas.com
Branch Dir. — Sal Zammuto

PUBLICITAS NORTH AMERICA, INC.
26234 N 72nd Dr, Peoria, AZ, 85383-7331, USA; tel (623) 561-5692; fax (623) 561-5539; web site www.publicitas.com
Contact — Lisa Richmeier

PUBLICITAS NORTH AMERICA, INC.
970 N Kalaheo Ave Ste C107, Pali Palms Plaza, Kailua, HI, 96734-1871, USA; tel (808) 587-8300; fax (808) 587-8307; e-mail ppn-honolulu@publicitas.com; honolulu@publicitas.com; web site www.publicitas.com
Director Hawaii/Pacific — G. Robert Wiegand

PUBLICITAS NORTH AMERICA, INC.
13355 Noel Rd, Ste 1030, Dallas, TX, 75240-6602, USA; tel (972) 386-6187; e-mail ppn-dallas@publicitas.com
Branch Dir. — Jo Neese

PUBLICITAS NORTH AMERICA, INC.
1401 E Broward Blvd, Ste 204, Fort Lauderdale, FL, 33301-2116, USA; tel (954) 768-9992; fax (954) 768-9013
Branch Dir. — Brad Ames

PUBLICITAS NORTH AMERICA, INC.
32 Lincoln Park, San Anselmo, CA, 94960-2561, USA; tel 415-464-6899; e-mail sanfrancisco@publicitas.com ; web site www.publicitas.com
Mgr. — Humberto Najar

PUBLISHERS REPRESENTATIVES OF FLORIDA, INC.
4601 W Kennedy Blvd, Ste 227, Tampa, FL, 33609-2519, USA; tel (813) 286-8299; fax (813) 287-0651; e-mail proftampa@aol.com
Mgr. — Rick Cammack
Pres. — Jim Gundry
Mgr. — Lee Knox

R

RE:FUEL
151 W 26th St, 12th Fl., New York, NY, 10001-6810, USA; tel 866-360-9688; e-mail info@refuelnow.com; web site www.refuelnow.comEstablished 1968
President/CEO — Andrew T. Sawyer
SVP, Sales — Greg Anthony
Director, Sales Strategy — Andrew O'Dell
re:fuel specializes in the military, college, Hispanic, African-American, ethnic and senior markets.

RIVENDELL MEDIA, INC.
1248 US Highway 22, Mountainside, NJ, 07092-2692, USA; tel (908) 232-2021 EXT 200; fax (908) 232-0521; e-mail info@rivendellmedia.com; sales@rivendellmedia.com; web site www.rivendellmedia.comEstablished 1979
Pres. — Todd Evans
Represents LGBT publications and digital properties.

RUXTON GROUP/VMG ADVERTISING
1201 E Jefferson St, Phoenix, AZ, 85034-2300, USA; tel 1800-278-9866; fax 602.238-4805; e-mail ads@voicemediagroup.com; web site www.vmgadvertising.com
Group: Voice Media Group Established 1983
SVP Sale & Operations — Joe Larkin
SVP Sales — Susan Belair
Business Manager — Veronica Villela

S

SHELBY PUBLISHING CO. INC.
517 Green St NW, Gainesville, GA, 30501-3313, USA; tel (770) 534-8380; fax (678) 343-2197; web site www.theshelbyreport.comEstablished 1967
VP/Sales Mgr. Midwest — Geoffrey Welch
C. Ronald Johnston

T

THE NEWSPAPER NETWORK (TNN)
400 Interstate North Pkwy SE, Ste 1050, Atlanta, GA, 30339-5054, USA; tel (770) 988-1750; fax (770) 988-1756
Vice Pres., Sales (Southern Reg.) — Ann Robb
Vice Pres., Automotive Sales — June Holmes

THE NEWSPAPER NETWORK (TNN)
106 Outlet Pointe Blvd, Columbia, SC, 29210-5669, USA; tel 888-727-7377; fax 803-551-0903
Regl. Sales Mgr. — Cynthia Miller
Regl. Sales Exec. — LaTrecia Hopson
Regl. Sales Exec. — Stephanie Stanton

THE NEWSPAPER NETWORK (TNN)
350 5th Ave, Rm 1802, New York, NY, 10118-0110, USA; tel (212) 268-1540; fax (212) 268-1541
Regl. Sales Mgr. — Rita Jurczyk

TOWMAR REPRESENTACIONES S.A.
Presa Endho # 11, Col. Irrigacion, M.H., Mexico City, FL, 11500, Mexico; tel (55) 5395-5888; fax (55) 5395-4985; e-mail INFO@towmar.net; web site www.towmar.netEstablished 1967
Pres. — Juan Martinez Dugay
Pres. — Juan Martinez Dugay
VP, Sales — Cesar Quijas
New address

TRIBUNE 365
2839 Paces Ferry Rd SE, Ste 1105, Atlanta, GA, 30339-5770, USA; tel (770) 433-9554; fax (770) 433-1927; web site www.ctmgadvertise.com
Atlanta Mgr. — Gail Brinkman

TRIBUNE 365
19500 Victor Pkwy, Ste 100, Livonia, MI, 48152-7012, USA; tel (734) 464-6500; fax (734) 464-7188; web site www.ctmgadvertise.com
Detroit Mgr. — Mark Barrons

TRIBUNE 365
220 E 42nd St, Rm 400, New York, NY, 10017-5833, USA; tel 212-448-2620; e-mail kvansaun@tribune.com; web site www.tribune.com
Dir., Mktg. — Irina David
Account Director — Kimberly Michaud

TRIBUNE 365
3107 Stirling Rd, Ste 205, Fort Lauderdale, FL, 33312-8502, USA; tel (954) 989-8833; fax (954) 963-3395; web site www.ctmgadvertise.com
Florida Mgr. — Berry Werblow

TRIBUNE MEDIA NETWORK
12900 Preston Rd, Ste 615, Dallas, TX, 75230-1322, USA; tel (972) 789-6920; fax (972) 239-2737; web site www.tribunemediagroup.com
Southwestern Regl. Sales Dir. — Grant Moise

TRIBUNE MEDIA NETWORK
100 Bush St, Ste 925, San Francisco, CA, 94104-3920, USA; tel (415) 693-5600; fax (415) 391-4992; web site www.tribunemediagroup.com
Mgr. — Neal Zimmerman

TRIBUNE MEDIA NETWORK
202 W 1st St, Los Angeles, CA, 90012-4299, USA; tel (213) 237-2135; fax (213) 237-2007
Pres./CEO — Peter Liguori
Dir., Western Reg. — Richard Jones

V

VOICE MEDIA GROUP
969 N Broadway, Denver, CO, 80203-2705, USA; tel (602) 271-0040; e-mail joe.larkin@voicemediagroup.com; web site www.voicemediagroup.com
Sr. Vice Pres. Sales — Joe Larkin
Vice Pres., Sales — Susan Belair
Newspaper represents for 50 alternative newsweeklies

W

WIDE AREA CLASSIFIED
113 N Minnesota St, New Ulm, MN, 56073-1729, USA; tel 800-324-8236; fax 866-822-5487; e-mail info@wideareaclassifieds.com; web site www.wideareaclassifieds.comEstablished 1986
Exec. Dir. — Shannon Reinhart
Represents shopper publications in 50 states

NEWSPAPER REPRESENTATIVES - STATE

ADNETWORKNY — 109 Twin Oaks Dr, Ste D, Syracuse, NY, 13206-1204, USA; tel (315) 472-6007; fax (877) 790-1976; e-mail ads@fcpny.com; web site www.fcpny.comEst.: 1950
Exec. Dir. — Dan Holmes
Sales & Training Director — Tom Cuskey
AdNetworkNY is the advertising arm of Free Community Papers of NY (FCPNY), an association of free distribution publishers delivering to more than 3.2 million homes across the Empire State.
AdNetworkNY enables advertisers to reach all or parts of New York through classified, display and insert advertising. Low CPM's and high readership brings great value for your ad dollar.
Classified and display advertising

ALABAMA NEWSPAPER ADVERTISING SERVICE, INC. — 3324 Independence Dr, Ste 200, Birmingham, AL, 35209-5602, USA; tel (205) 871-7737; fax (205) 871-7740; e-mail mail@alabamapress.org; web site www.alabamapress.org
Exec. Dir. — Felicia Mason
Adv. Mgr. — Brad English

ALLIED DAILY NEWSPAPERS OF WASHINGTON — 1110 Capitol Way S, Olympia, WA, 98501-2251, USA; tel (360) 943-9960; fax (360) 943-9962; e-mail anewspaper@aol.com
Exec. Dir. — Rowland Thompson

ANA ADVERTISING SERVICES, INC. (ARIZONA NEWSPAPER ASSOCIATION) — 1001 N Central Ave, Ste 670, Phoenix, AZ, 85004-1947, USA; tel (602) 261-7655; fax (602) 261-7525; e-mail office@ananews.com; web site www.ananews.comEst.: 1931
Exec. Dir. — Paula Casey
Media Buyer — Cindy London
Communications Manager — Julie O'Keefe
Represents daily and weekly newspapers in Arizona

ARKANSAS PRESS SERVICES — 411 S Victory St, Little Rock, AR, 72201-2933, USA; tel (501) 374-1500; fax (501) 374-7509; e-mail info@arkansaspress.org; web site www.arkansaspress.orgEst.: 1873
Exec. Dir. — Tom Larimer
Adv. & Mktg. Dir. — Ashley Wimberley
The Arkansas Press Association is the trade association for the newspapers of Arkansas. We represent Arkansas newspapers will national advertisers and hand advertising placement for a broad spectrum of advertisers, including political and advocacy advertisers.
Represents daily and weekly newspapers in Arkansas

CNPA ADVERTISING SERVICES — 2000 O St, Ste 120, Sacramento, CA, 95811-5299, USA; tel (916) 288-6000; fax (916) 288-6003; e-mail bryan@cnpa.com; web site www.cnpa.com
Exec. Dir. — Jack Bates
Dir. — Sharla Trillo
Client Rel./Sales Mgr. — Patrice Bayard-Miller

COMMUNITY PAPERS OF FLORIDA — 12601 SE 53rd Terrace Rd, Belleview, FL, 34420-5106, USA; tel (352) 237-3409; fax (352) 347-3384; e-mail djneuharth@aol.com; web site www.communitypapersofflorida.comEst.: 1960
Executve Director — Dave Neuharth
Administrative Asst. — Barbara Holmes
Florida statewide association for free papers Classified advertising in 82 community news and shopper publications in Florida.

COMMUNITY PAPERS OF MICHIGAN, INC. — 5000 Northwind Dr, Ste 240, East Lansing, MI, 48823-5032, USA; tel (800) 783-0267; fax (517) 333-3322; e-mail jackguza@cpapersmi.com; web site www.communitypapersofmichigan.com
Pres. — Terry Roby
Exec.Dir. — Jack Guza
Office Mgr. — Stacy Kotecki
Display advertising for 90 publications in Michigan that in cooperation with Community Papers of Michigan reaches more than 2.5 million Michigan households. Classifed advertising reaches 1.7 million Michigan households

CUSTOMIZED NEWSPAPER ADVERTISING (IOWA) — 319 E 5th St, Des Moines, IA, 50309-1927, USA; tel (515) 244-2145; fax (515) 244-4855; web site www.cnaads.com; www.inanews.com
Exec. Dir. — Chris Mudge
Acct. Exec. — Bryan Rohe
Sales Dir. — Ron Bode
Sales Rep. — Bruce Adams
Represents 302 daily and weekly newspapers in Iowa and can place advertising in any newspaper in the country.

FLORIDA PRESS SERVICE, INC. — 336 E College Ave, Ste 203, Tallahassee, FL, 32301-1559, USA; tel (850) 222-5790; fax (850) 222-4498; e-mail fps-info@flpress.com; web site www.flpress.com
Pres./CEO — Dean Riddings
Florida Press is an intergrated, full service placement, research invoicing and verification firm owned and operated by all of Florida's newspapers. Our mission is to help our client advertisors coordinate multi-market newspaper campaigns quickly, effecie
Represents 42 daily and 135 weekly newspapers in Florida

GEORGIA NEWSPAPER SERVICE, INC. — 3066 Mercer University Dr, Ste 200, Atlanta, GA, 30341-4137, USA; tel (770) 454-6776; fax (770) 454-6778; e-mail mail@gapress.org; web site www.gapress.org
Exec. Dir. — Robin Rhodes
Represents daily and weekly newspapers in Georgia

GREAT NORTHERN CONNECTION — 8703 Midway Rd, Lena, WI, 54139-9769, USA; tel (920) 829-5145; e-mail classifieds@greatnorthernconn.com; web site www.greatnorthernconn.comEst.: 1985
Adv. Contact — Char Meier
Represents 35 publications in northeastern Wisconsin and upper peninsula Michigan

HITCHINGS & CO. — 580 W Germantown Pike, Ste 108, Plymouth Meeting, PA, 19462-1370, USA; tel (610) 941-3555; fax (610) 941-1289; e-mail brian@phillyareapapers.com; web site www.phillyareapapers.com
Pres. — Brian Hitchings
Acct. Supvr. — Donna DeFrangesco

INTERSECT MEDIA SOLUTIONS — 610 Crescent Executive Ct, Ste 112, Lake Mary, FL, 32746-2111, USA; tel (321) 283-5255; e-mail info@intersectmediasolutions.com; web site www.intersectmediasolutions.comEst.: 1959
Pres./CEO — Dean Ridings
VP/CSO — Melanie Mathewson
Acct. Mgr. — Carolyn Klinger
Media Mgr. — Jessica Pitts
CFO — Mark Burger
General Counsel — Sam Morley
Intersect Media Solutions is the advertising agency of the Florida Press Association. Our mission is to provide outstanding client services with innovative media solutions that reach relevant and prospective audiences, to promote our relationships with our media partners, and to be profitable in the pursuit.

KENTUCKY PRESS SERVICE, INC. — 101 Consumer Ln, Frankfort, KY, 40601-8489, USA; tel (502) 223-8821; fax (502) 875-2624; e-mail dthompson@kypress.com; web site www.kypress.comEst.: 1959
Exec. Dir. — David Thompson
Controller — Bonnie Howard
Membership organization of all Kentucky newspapers
Represents daily and weekly newspapers in Kentucky

LOUISIANA PRESS ASSOCIATION — 404 Europe St, Baton Rouge, LA, 70802-6403, USA; tel (225) 344-9309; fax (225) 344-9344; e-mail pam@lapress.com; web site www.lapress.comEst.: 1880
Communications Dir. — Mike Rood
Exec. Dir. — Pamela Mitchell
Dir. of Ops. — Mitchell-Ann Droge
Adv. Dir. — Erin Palmintier
State Newspaper Trade Association

MACNET — PO Box 408, Hamburg, PA, 19526-0408, USA; tel (800) 450-7227; fax (610) 743-8500; e-mail info@macpa.net; web site www.macpa.net; www.macnetonline.com
Exec. Dir. — Alyse Mitten
Classified advertising for 360 publications in PA, OH, NY, NJ, DE, MD, WV, VA, Washington DC.

MANSI MEDIA — 3899 N Front St, Harrisburg, PA, 17110-1583, USA; tel (717) 703-3030; fax (717) 703-3033; e-mail sales@mansimedia.com; web site www.mansimedia.com
VP/Adv. — Lisa Knight
Chris Kazlauskas
Dir. Client Solutions — Wes Snider
Sr. Media Buyer — Ronaldo Davis
Dir., Interactive Media — Matthew Caylor
Account Manager — Lindsey Artz
Account Manager — Shannon Mohar
Director, Client Solutions — Brian Hitchings
Represents daily and weekly newspapers and their digital products anywhere in the U.S. and beyond.

MIDWEST FREE COMMUNITY PAPERS — PO Box 1350, Iowa City, IA, 52244-1350, USA; tel (319) 341-4352; fax (319) 341-4358; e-mail mfcp@mchsi.com; web site www.mfcp.orgEst.: 1955
Office Mgr. — Jori Hendon
Classified advertising for 124 publications

MISSISSIPPI PRESS SERVICES, INC. — 371 Edgewood Terrace Dr, Jackson, MS, 39206-6217, USA; tel (601) 981-3060; fax (601) 981-3676; e-mail mspress@mspress.org; web site www.mspress.orgEst.: 1866
Exec. Dir. — Layne Bruce
Member Services Manager — Monica Gilmer
Business Development Manager — Sue Hicks
Media Director — Andrea Ross
Represents daily and weekly newspapers in Mississippi

MNI — 827 N Washington Ave, Lansing, MI, 48906-5135, USA; tel (517) 372-2424; fax (517) 372-2429; e-mail mpa@michiganpress.org; web site www.michiganpress.orgEst.: 1868
Executive Director — Mike MacLaren
Growth & Operations Manager — Rose Lucas
Public Affairs Manager — Lisa McGraw
Represents print and digital media in Michigan

MONTANA NEWSPAPER ADVERTISING SERVICE, INC. — 825 Great Northern Blvd, Ste 202, Helena, MT, 59601-3340, USA; tel (406) 443-2850; fax (406) 443-2860; e-mail randy@mtnewspapers.com; web site www.mtnewspapers.comEst.: 1955
Accounting Specialist — Randy Schmoldt
Represents daily and weekly newspapers in Montana.

NEBRASKA PRESS ADVERTISING SERVICE — 845 S St, Lincoln, NE, 68508-1226, USA; tel (402) 476-2851; fax (402) 476-2942; e-mail nebpress@nebpress.com; web site www.nebpress.comEst.: 1879
Adv. Sales Dir. — Rob James
Exec. Dir., Nebraska Press Assoc. — Allen Beermann
Professional trade association that represents the daily and weekly newspapers in Nebraska.

NENPA AD NETWORK (NEW ENGLAND NEWSPAPER AND PRESS ASSOCIATION) — 1 Arrow Dr, Ste 6, Woburn, MA, 01801-2039, USA; tel (781) 281-2053; fax (339) 999-2174; e-mail info@nenpa.com; web site www.nenpa.comEst.: 1930
Executive Director — Linda Conway
Represents daily, weekly and specialty newspapers in the six New England states

NEW JERSEY NEWSMEDIA NETWORK (NJNN) — 810 Bear Tavern Rd, Ste 307, Ewing, NJ, 08628-1022, USA; tel (609) 406-0600; fax (609) 406-0399; e-mail njnn@njpa.org; web site www.njpa.org/njnnEst.: 1991
Adv. Dir. — Amy Lear
NJPA Exec Dir — George White
NJNN Networks Mgr — Diane Trent
Media planning and placement service for print and digital campaigns. Specializing in daily, weekly, ethnic and specialty pubs reaching New Jersey.

NEW MEXICO PRESS ASSOCIATION — 700 Silver Ave SW, Albuquerque, NM, 87102-3019, USA; tel (505) 275-1241; fax (505) 275-1449; e-mail info@nmpress.org; web site www.nmpress.org
Office Mgr. — Holly Aguilar
Elections held in Oct

NEW YORK NEWS PUBLISHERS ASSOCIATION — 252 Hudson Ave, Albany, NY, 12210-1802, USA; tel (518) 449-1667; fax (518) 449-1667; web site www.nynpa.comEst.: 1927
Pres. — Diane Kennedy
Education Services Dir. — Mary H. Miller
Dir. of Adv. & Event Mgmt. — Don Ferlazzo
NYNPA is the non-profit trade association representing the daily, weekly, and online newspapers of New York State. NYNPA monitors the New York State Legislature on behalf of the newspaper industry, opposing unfavorable legislation and working to craft new laws to open up government activities to public scrutiny. The Association also provides training and professional networking opportunities to its member publishers, advertising and marketing, and circulation

staff. It organizes an annual contest to recognize excellence in journalism, provides curriculum guides and support to Newspaper in Education programs, and assists advertisers in placing advertising in member newspapers. Additionally, the association manages the New York Newspapers Foundation, which provides grants to literacy-oriented community organizations.
Represents daily newspapers in New York State. Offers statewide and regional newspaper advertising solutions to general public at discounted rates.

NEW YORK PRESS SERVICE — 1681 Western Ave, Albany, NY, 12203-4305, USA; tel (518) 464-6483; fax (518) 464-6489; e-mail nypa@nynewspapers.com; web site www.nynewspapers.comEst.: 1853
Adv. Rep., Classified Sales — Phil Anthony
Mktg. Dir. — Jill Van Dusen
New York Press Service is a nationwide newspaper advertising, buying and placement service. Market analysis, rate/coverage spreadsheets. Nine publications, ethnic, senior family, alternative and mainstream community newspapers. Target marketing solutions
Represents weekly newspapers in New York

NORTH CAROLINA PRESS SERVICE, INC. — 5171 Glenwood Ave, Ste 364, Raleigh, NC, 27612-3266, USA; tel (919) 787-7443; fax (919) 787-5302; web site www.ncpress.comEst.: 1985
Exec. Dir. — Beth Grace
Member Services Director — Laura Nakoneczny
Director of Sales — Mark Holmes
Represents all daily and weekly newspapers in North Carolina

NORTH DAKOTA NEWSPAPER ASSOCIATION — 1435 Interstate Loop, Bismarck, ND, 58503-0567, USA; tel (701) 223-6397; fax (701) 223-8185; e-mail info@ndna.com; web site www.ndna.comEst.: 1885
Mktg. Dir. — Kelli Richey
Exec. Dir. — Steve Andrist
Adv. Dir. — Mike Casey
Adv./Public Notice Coord. — Colleen Park
Office Coord./Adv. Assist. — Shari Peterson
Pres., NDNA Ed. Foundation — Aaron Becher
Past President — Sara J. Plum
President — Harvey Brock
Second Vice President — Jill Denning Gackle
NDNA Director — Paul Erdelt
NDNA Director — Leah Burke
NDNA Director — Matt McMillan
Director — Frank Perea
Director — Karen Speidel
Advertising placed in 89 North Dakota newspapers and related publications.
Statewide classified advertising and small space advertising programs.
Represents daily and weekly newspapers in North Dakota

OHIAD — PO Box 69, Covington, OH, 45318-0069, USA; tel (937) 473-2028; fax (937) 473-2500; e-mail dselanders@woh.rr.com; web site www.arenspub.com
Secreatary/Treasurer — Gary Godfrey
Classified advertising for 16 publications. In cooperation with Community Papers of Ohio.

OHIO NEWSPAPER SERVICES, INC. — 1335 Dublin Rd, Ste 216B, Columbus, OH, 43215-1000, USA; tel (614) 486-6677; fax (614) 486-4940; web site www.ohionews.org; www.adohio.netEst.: 1933
Executive Director
Ohio Newspaper Association — Dennis Hetzel
Acting Director of Advertising — Walt Dozier
Manager, Administrative Services — Sue Bazzoli
Manager of Communications & Content — Jason Sanford
Receptionist and Secretary — Ann Riggs
Advertising Coordinator — Patricia Conkle
Network Account Executive — Kathy McCutcheon
Advertising Account Executive — Casey Null
Represents all 81 daily and 154 weekly Ohio newspaper and affiliated websites.

OKLAHOMA PRESS SERVICE — 3601 N Lincoln Blvd, Oklahoma City, OK, 73105-5411, USA; tel (405) 524-4421; fax (405) 499-0048; e-mail sysop@okpress.com; web site www.okpress.com
Exec. Vice Pres. — Mark Thomas
Represents daily and weekly newspapers in Oklahoma

PACIFIC NORTHWEST ASSOCIATION OF WANT AD NEWSPAPERS (PNAWAN) & WESTERN REGIONAL ADVERTISING PROGRAM (WRAP) — 304 W 3rd Ave, C/O Exchange Publishing, Spokane, WA, 99201-4314, USA; tel (509) 922-3456; fax (509) 455-7940; e-mail Ads@PNAWAN.org; web site www.RegionalAds.orgEst.: 1977
Executive Director of the Pacific Northwest Association of Want Ad Newspapers (PNAWAN) & Western Regional Advertising Program (WRAP) — Kylah Strohte
PNAWAN Office
PNAWAN is an association of 30 different publications throughout the greater Pacific Northwest region: Washington, Oregon, Idaho, Montana, Alberta & British Columbia. The combined total distribution is approximately 600,000 per week.
Reach a bigger audience & Advertise in local community papers throughout the Pacific Northwest region!
PNAWAN (Pacific NW Assoc. of Want Ad Newspapers) makes advertising on a regional scale easy and affordable.
Prices start at just $50 per Regional Ad!
Place both classified & display ads in up to 30 different publications throughout Washington, Oregon, Idaho, Montana, Alberta & British Columbia in just 1 easy phone call.
Our publications believe in high standards of quality and ethics in advertising. PNAWAN publications are well-known in their communities and have very loyal readerships.
Total weekly distribution: 537,006
We are audited and verified by the Circulation Verification Council annually.
Classified Ad Rates:
$6.25 per edition, minimum 8 editions required
(Note: Editions are calculated as number of weeks x number of running publications)
Examples:
8 publications x 1 week = $50
4 publications x 2 weeks = $50
12 publications x 1 week = $75
6 publications x 2 weeks = $75
16 publications x 1 week = $100
8 publications x 2 weeks = $100
....etc.
Maximum USA coverage: 23 pubs x 1 week = $143.75
Maximum coverage incl. Canada: 30 pubs x 1 week = $187.50
25 word max. Extra words = 10 cents per word per edition
Call today to place your Pacific Northwest Regional Ads! 509-922-3456 or 1-800-326-2223 (toll-free). Note: PNAWAN is hosted by member company, Exchange Publishing, so be sure to ask for PNAWAN Regional Ads when calling.
You may also email ads@pnawan.org for any inquiries, or contact the Executive Director of PNAWAN, Kylah Strohte, directly at Kylah@ExchangePublishing.com
More information about the Pacific Northwest Association of Want Ad Newspapers (PNAWAN) online at www.RegionalAds.org
Mission:
To unite, promote, and facilitate advertising between the free community newspaper publications of the Pacific Northwest so that our advertisers can easily reach a bigger audience.
We are audited and verified by the Circulation Verification Council annually.
PNAWAN headquarters are located at the offices of hosting member publication, Exchange Publishing, in Spokane, WA.

PUBLISHERS DEVELOPMENT SERVICE — PO Box 1256, Fond Du Lac, WI, 54936-1256, USA; tel (920) 922-4864; fax (920) 922-0861; e-mail janelle@pdsadnet.com; web site www.pdsadnet.comEst.: 1978
CEO — Janelle Anderson
Gen. Mgr. — Jeanne Schmal
Classified Sales Mgr. — Kathy Braun
Media placement firm specializing in print media in particular community papers.
Display advertising for 122 publications. In cooperation with Wisconsin Free Community Papers

RESEAU SELECT/SELECT NETWORK — 25 Sheppard Ave W, Suite 500, Toronto, ON, M2N 6S7, Canada; tel (416) 733-7600; fax (416) 726-8519; e-mail inforeseauselect@tc.tc; web site www.reseauselect.com

RESEAU SELECT/SELECT NETWORK — 8000 Av Blaise-Pascal, Montreal, QC, H1E 2S7, Canada; tel (514) 643-2300; fax (514) 866-3030; e-mail inforeseauselect@tc.tc; web site www.reseauselect.comEst.: 1976
General Manager — François Laferriére
Represents more than 148 weekly French-language newspapers in Quebec, Ontario, Manitoba and New Brunswick

SOUTH CAROLINA PRESS SERVICES, INC. — 106 Outlet Pointe Blvd, Columbia, SC, 29210-5669, USA; tel (803) 750-9561; fax (803) 551-0903; e-mail rsavely@scpress.org; web site http://www.scnewspapernetwork.com/ Est.: 1985
Director of Opertions — Randall Savely
Represents all South Carolina newspapers in placement of classified and display advertising

SOUTHEASTERN ADVERTISING PUBLISHERS ASSOCIATION — 104 Westland Dr, Columbia, TN, 38401-6522, USA; tel (931) 223-5708; fax (888) 450-8329; e-mail info@sapatoday.com; web site www.sapatoday.comEst.: 1979
Exec. Dir. — Douglas Fry
Classified advertising for 75 publications in 10 Southeastern states. Display Network also available.

SYNC2 MEDIA — 1120 N Lincoln St, Ste 912, Denver, CO, 80203-2138, USA; tel (303) 571-5117; fax (303) 571-1803; e-mail info@sync2media.com; web site www.sync2media.com
CEO — Jerry Raehal
Account Executive — Judy Quelch
Account Executive — Peyton Jacobson
Represents daily and weekly newspapers in Colorado

TEXCAP — 1226 Newberry Dr, Allen, TX, 75013-3669, USA; tel (972) 741-6258; fax (866) 822-4920; e-mail jack@tcnatoday.com; web site www.tcnatoday.comEst.: 1964
Exec. Dir. — Dick Colvin
Classified advertising for 109 publications. In cooperation with Texas Community Newspapers Assoc

WISCONSIN NEWSPAPER ASSOCIATION — 34 Schroeder Ct, Ste 220, Madison, WI, 53711-2528, USA; tel (608) 283-7620; fax (608) 283-7631; e-mail wna@wnanews.com; web site www.wnanews.comEst.: 1853
Exec. Dir. — Beth Bennett
Media Services Dir. — Denise Guttery
Communications Dir. — James Debilzen
Member Services Dir. — Julia Hunter
Represents 34 daily and over 225 weekly and specialty newspapers

NEWSPAPER DISTRIBUTED MAGAZINES AND TMC PUBLICATIONS

AMERICAN PROFILE - CHICAGO, IL — 500 N Michigan Ave, Ste 910, Chicago, 60611-3741, USA; tel (312) 948-0333; fax (312) 948-0555; web site www.americanprofile.com
Group: Publishing Group of America
Executive Director, Integrated Media — Nanci Davidson
Circ. 10,000,000; Sworn/Estimate/Non-Audited September 30, 2017

AMERICAN PROFILE - FRANKLIN, TN — 341 Cool Springs Blvd, Ste 400, Franklin, 37067-7224, USA; tel (615) 468-6021; web site www.americanpub.com
Nashville/West Coast Assoc. Pub. — Frank Zier
Circ. ; Sworn/Estimate/Non-Audited September 30, 2017

AMERICAN PROFILE - LOS ANGELES, CA — 6255 W Sunset Blvd, Ste 705, Los Angeles, 90028-7408, USA; tel (323) 467-5906; fax (323) 467-7180; web site www.americanprofile.com
Adv Sales Rep. — Debbie Siegel
Circ. ; Sworn/Estimate/Non-Audited September 30, 2017

AMERICAN PROFILE - NEW YORK, NY — 60 E 42nd St, Ste 1111, New York, 10165-1111, USA; tel (212) 478-1900; fax (646) 865-1921; web site www.americanprofile.com
Sr. Vice Pres./Grp. Pub. — Amy Chernoff
Adv. Dir. — Shannon Hay
Assoc. Ed., Direct Response — Linda Rich
Circ. 9,801,887; BPA June 30, 2008

AMERICAN PROFILE - NORTHVILLE, MI — 22185 Heatheridge Ln, Northville, 48167-9300, USA; tel (248) 991-1810; web site www.

americanprofile.com
Auto Adv. Mgr. — Jim Main
Circ. ; Sworn/Estimate/Non-Audited September 30, 2017

L'ORA DI OTTAWA — 203 Louisa St., Ottawa, ON, K1R 6Y9, Canada; tel (613) 232-5689; fax (855) 596 8522; e-mail info@loradiottawa.ca; web site loradiottawa.ca
Managing Editor — Paolo Siraco
Assistant Editor — Cynthia Nuzzi
Accounting — Olita Schultz
Client Services — AnnaMaria Morrone
Circ. ; AAM December 31, 2017

LUXURY LAS VEGAS MAGAZINE — 1111 W Bonanza Rd, Las Vegas, NV, 89106-3545, USA; tel (415) 519-8758; e-mail bash@luxurylv.com; web site www.luxurylv.com
Group: Sands Corporation
Pub. — Blue Ash
Ed. — Leslie Frisbee
Anastasia Hendrix
Circ. September 1, 2017

METRO NEWSPAPER ADVERTISING SERVICES, INC. — 160 Spear St, Ste 1875, San Francisco, CA, 94105-5146, USA; tel (310) 798-4986; fax (310) 564-7633; e-mail kathy@metrosn.com; web site www.metrosn.com
Mgr. — Kathy Jahns
Sr. Vice Pres. — Ali Nazem
Circ. ; Sworn/Estimate/Non-Audited September 30, 2017

METRO NEWSPAPER ADVERTISING SERVICES, INC. — 8 W 38th St, 8 W. 38th St., 4th Fl., New York, NY, 10018-6229, USA; tel (212) 576-9510; fax (212) 576-9526; e-mail billh@metrosn.com; web site www.metrosn.com
Chairperson & CEO — Phyllis Cavaliere
SVP Client Services — Tack Prashad
President/COO — Michael Baratoff
Sr. Vice Pres./Midwest Sales Dir. — Carl Berg
Exec. Dir. — Tom Vorel
Sr. Vice Pres., Eastern Adv. — Bill Huck
Sr. Vice Pres., Finance — Nili DeBono
Sr. Vice Pres./Eastern Region — William Huck
New Ventures Development — Frank Grasso
Senior VP, Operations — Kim Viggiano
Circ. 8,237,412; Sworn/Estimate/Non-Audited March 31, 2007
Note: Metro has been creating networks for national advertisers since 1932. It places advertising for represented newspapers through its Sunday Magazine, Metro-Puck Comics and Metro ROP Networks. Please see these entries in Section V of the Year Book.

MIRAMICHI LEADER — 175 General Manson Way, Miramichi, NB, E1N 6K7, Canada; tel (506) 622-2600; fax (506) 622-6506; e-mail news@miramichileader.com; web site https://www.telegraphjournal.com/miramichi-leader/
Group: Brunswick News, Inc.
Pub. — Nancy Cook
Circ. Mgr. — Christine Savoy
Circ. ; AAM December 31, 2013

MOLINE/ROCK ISLAND/QUAD CITY METRO UNIT — 1720 5th Ave, Moline, 61265-7907, USA; tel (309) 764-4344; e-mail advertising@qconline.com; web site www.qconline.com
Group: Small Newspaper Group
CRO — Val Yazbec
Ed. — Jerry Taylor
Adv. Dir. — Kelly Johannes
Circ. 39,625; CAC March 31, 2015

PARADE — 60 E 42nd St, Ste 820, New York, 10165-0820, USA; tel (212) 478-1910; e-mail sales@amgparade.com; web site www.parade.com
Group: AMG/Parade
Athlon Media Group
Sr. Vice Pres., Newspaper Rel. — David Barber
Vice Chrmn./COO — John L. Beni
Chrmn./CEO — Jack Haire
Pres. — Randy Siegel
Exec. Vice Pres., Adv. — Mike DeBartolo
Sr. Vice Pres., Mktg. — Jim Hackett
Pub. — Brett Wilson
Editor — Maggie Murphy
Vice Pres., Commun. — Christie Emden
Executive Editor — Brad Dunn
Social Media Editor — Jessica Wozinsky
VP of Newspaper Relations Group — Scot Dalquist
Circ. 22,000,000; GfK MRI September 1, 2017

PARADE PUBLICATIONS, INC. - BLOOMFIELD HILLS, MI — 100 W Long Lake Rd, Bloomfield Hills, 48304-2773, USA; tel (248) 540-9820; fax (248) 540-9891; e-mail det_sales@parade.com; web site www.parade.com
Vice Pres., Adv. — Mike DeBartolo
Circ. ; Sworn/Estimate/Non-Audited September 30, 2017

PARADE PUBLICATIONS, INC. - CHICAGO, IL — 500 N Michigan Ave, Ste 910, Chicago, 60611-3741, USA; tel (312) 661-1620; fax (312) 661-0776; e-mail chi_sales@parade.com; web site www.parade.com
Vice Pres./Mid-Western Mgr. — Eric Karaffa
Circ. ; Sworn/Estimate/Non-Audited September 30, 2017

PARADE PUBLICATIONS, INC. - LOS ANGELES, CA — 6300 Wilshire Blvd, Los Angeles, 90048-5204, USA; tel (323) 965-3649; fax (323) 965-4971; web site www.parade.com
Acct. Dir. — Greg Hancock
Circ. ; Sworn/Estimate/Non-Audited September 30, 2017

PARADE PUBLICATIONS, INC. - SAN FRANCISCO, CA — 50 Francisco St, Ste 400, San Francisco, 94133-2114, USA; tel (415) 955-8222; fax (415) 397-0562; e-mail sf_sales@parade.com; web site www.parade.com
Adv. Contact — Bill Murray
Circ. ; Sworn/Estimate/Non-Audited September 30, 2017

RELISH - CHICAGO, IL — 500 N Michigan Ave, Ste 910, Chicago, 60611-3741, USA; tel (312) 948-0333; fax (312) 948-0555; web site www.pubgroup.com
Adv. Coord. — Andrea Blank
Circ. ; Sworn/Estimate/Non-Audited September 30, 2017

RELISH - FRANKLIN, TN — 341 Cool Springs Blvd, Ste 400, Franklin, 37067-7224, USA; tel (615) 468-6000; fax (615) 468-6100; web site www.pubgroup.com
Nashville/West Coast Assoc. Pub. — Frank Zier
Circ. ; Sworn/Estimate/Non-Audited September 30, 2017

RELISH - LOS ANGELES, CA — 300 Corporate Pointe, Ste 340, Culver City, 90230-8713, USA; tel (310) 216-7270; fax (310) 216-7212; web site www.relishmag.com
Acct. Mgr. — Jamie Relis
Circ. ; Sworn/Estimate/Non-Audited September 30, 2017

RELISH - NEW YORK, NY — 60 E 42nd St, Ste 1115, New York, 10165-1115, USA; tel (212) 478-1900; fax (646) 865-1921; web site www.relishmag.com
Sr. Vice Pres./Grp. Pub. — Amy Chernoff
Adv. Dir. — Shannon Hay
Assoc. Ed., Direct Response — Linda Rich
Circ. 12,005,646; BPA June 30, 2008

SEQUATCHIE VALLEY SHOPPER — 399 Spring Street, Pikeville, TN, 37367, USA; tel (423) 447-2996; fax (423) 447-2997; e-mail valleypubinc@bledsoe.net; web site www.thebledsonian-banner.com
Group: Valley Publishing Company, Inc
— Amy Sue Hale
— Sandy DodsonPublishers
Circ. ; manager December 15, 2017

SPOTLIGHT — 250 Yonge St, Winston Salem, 27101, USA; tel (800) 457-1156; fax (336) 727-7461; web site www.starwatch.com
Bus. Mgr. — Alan Cronk
Sales Agent — Jody Stephenson Sarver
Circ. ; Sworn/Estimate/Non-Audited September 30, 2017

STAR WATCH — 418 N Marshall St, Winston Salem, 27101-2815, USA; tel (336) 727-7406; fax (800) 430-0532; web site www.starwatch.com
Sales Agent — Jody Stephenson Sarver
Exec. Ed. — Alan Cronk
Circ. ; Sworn/Estimate/Non-Audited September 30, 2017

THE AEGIS — 501 North Calvert Street, Baltimore, MD, 21278, USA; tel (410) 838-4400; fax (410) 638-0357; e-mail news@theaegis.com; web site www.theaegis.com
Group: Tronc, Inc.
Pub. — John D. Worthington
Mktg. Dir. — Mary Anne Pfeiffer
Exec. Ed. — Ted Hendricks
Sr VP Sales & Mkting — Judith Berman
Dir, Nat'l Adv & Majors — Susan Duchin
Circ. 14,084; AAM September 30, 2017

THE BILTMORE BEACON — 220 N. Main St., Waynesille, NC, 28786, U.S.; tel 8284520661; e-mail sdufour@themountaineer.com; web site themountaineer.com

THE NEWSLEADERS — 32 1ST AVE NW, SAINT JOSEPH, MN, 56374-4524, USA; tel (320) 363-7741; fax (320) 363-4195; e-mail sales@thenewsleaders.com; web site www.thenewsleaders.com
Group: Von Meyer Publishing Inc.
Ops. Mgr/Assg. Ed. — Frank Lee
CEO/Owner/Pub. — Janelle Von Pinnon
Prod. Mgr/Designer — Tara Wiese
Ed.-in-Chief — Dennis Dalman
Circ. September 30, 2016

THE REPUBLICAN — 108 S 2ND ST, OAKLAND, MD, 21550-1520, USA; tel (301) 334-3963; fax (301) 334-5904; e-mail advertising@therepublicannews.com; web site www.therepublicannews.com
Group: Sincell Publishing Co. Inc.
Pub. — Donald Sincell
Adv. Mgr. — Lisa Rook
Circ. Mgr. — Paula Glotfelty
Circ. ; AAM September 30, 2016

TMS SPECIALTY PRODUCTS — 435 N Michigan Ave, Ste 1400, Chicago, IL, 60611-7551, USA; tel (800) 637-4082; fax (312) 527-8256; e-mail ctrammell@tribune.com; web site www.tmsspecialtyproducts.com
Gen. Mgr. — Marco Buscaglia
Sales manager — Curtis Trammell
Mng. Ed. — Mary Elson
Art Dir. — Todd Rector
Circ. ; Sworn/Estimate/Non-Audited September 30, 2017
Note: TMS Specialty Products provides articles and images suitable for use in advertorial sections, niche publications and other targeted media, as well as custom ordered content, including local and paginated products.

TRIBUNE MEDIA SERVICES TV LOG — 435 N. Michigan Ave., Ste. 1500, Chicago, IL, 60611-4012; tel (312) 222-3394; web site Mail, Newsstand.David D.

TRIBUNE MEDIA SERVICES TV LOG - LOS ANGELES, CA — 5800 W Sunset Blvd, Los Angeles, 90028-6607, USA; tel (310) 581-5011; fax (310) 581-8025; web site www.tribunemediaservices.com
Circ. ; Sworn/Estimate/Non-Audited September 30, 2017

TRIBUNE MEDIA SERVICES TV LOG - QUEENSBURY, NY — 40 Media Dr, Queensbury, 12804-4086, USA; tel (518) 792-9914; fax (212) 210-2863; web site www.tribunemediaservices.com
Circ. ; Sworn/Estimate/Non-Audited September 30, 2017

TVTIMES — 250 Yonge St., Toronto, ON, M5B 2L7, Canada; tel (416) 593-6556; fax (416) 593-7329; e-mail tvtimes3@canwest.com; web site www.canwest.com
Dir., Newspaper Sales — Quin Millar
Circ. 1,124,839; ABC September 30, 2007

WEEKLY NEWS JOURNAL — 221 West Main Street, Burley, ID, 83318, USA; tel 208-678-6643; fax 208-678-6375; e-mail jay@theweeklymailer.com; web site minicassia.com
Group: Sierra Marketing
Circ. June 21, 2013
Note: We also have a companion publication delivered via direct mail in Cassia and Minidoka Counties, Idaho